Who's Who
Among American
High School Students®
Honoring Tomorrow's Leaders Today®

1984-85
Nineteenth Annual Edition
Volume I

WHO'S WHO AMONG AMERICAN HIGH SCHOOL STUDENTS® is a publication of Educational Communications, Inc. of Lake Forest, Illinois and has no connection with "Who's Who In America" and its publisher, Marquis — Who's Who, Inc. Students featured in this volume attended school in the following states: Connecticut, Foreign, Maine, Massachusetts, New Hampshire, New York, Puerto Rico, Rhode Island, Vermont and the Virgin Islands.

Compilation of the copyright matter published in this volume has been accomplished only through the expenditure of considerable time, a monumental effort and at a great cost, and is intended for the exclusive use of our subscribers. Such information may not be key punched, entered into a computer or photocopied in any manner for any purpose whatsoever. Its use as a mailing list, either in whole or in part, is strictly forbidden. The contents have been coded and cannot be copied without detection; infringements will be prosecuted.

©Copyright 1985
Educational Communciations, Inc.
721 N. McKinley Road
Lake Forest, Illinois 60045
Printed in U.S.A.
ISBN 0-930315-02-2
ISBN 0-930315-01-4 (10 Volume Set)
Library of Congress Catalog Card Number 68-43796

WHO'S WHO AMONG AMERICAN HIGH SCHOOL STUDENTS® is a registered trademark owned by Educational Communications, Inc.

TABLE OF CONTENTS

Publisher's Corner V

Who's Who Review VI

College-Bound Digest®.. XIII

Scholarship Award Winners XXXI

Glossary of Abbreviations XXXIV

Sample Biography XXXV

*Biographical Sketches Listed Alphabetically by State 1

Students' Photographs Listed Alphabetically by State P-1

*Wherever students attend school out of state they will be listed in
the state where they attend school.

PUBLISHER'S CORNER:

People ask, "What's the matter with kids today?"

In case no one has told you this lately, you're very special. All of you. And one of the major purposes of this publication is to tell as many people as possible who you are, what you have accomplished and what you plan to achieve in the future.

Each year, for the past nineteen years, we have published WHO'S WHO AMONG AMERICAN HIGH SCHOOL STUDENTS® so students like yourself will realize that many people care about good students, doing good work at good schools. We know it hasn't always been easy for most of you — sometimes it seems as if the only way to get recognition is to do something bad. Other times, it probably appears as if your parents or teachers pushed too hard for you to do better even when you thought you were doing rather well. Maybe the pressure was excessive at times, but nevertheless, you managed to perform and this book says, "We see you."

Colleagues and friends often ask me what I think about today's teens. Frequently the question is rhetorical because they're all set to unleash a ten minute monolog about how standards, values and morals have deteriorated and "kids just aren't the same as when we were growing up." (They usually don't comment much on how different they are from their parents.)

My answer usually surprises them. Admittedly, I see the teen world through rose colored glasses. Our organization works with most of the major youth organizations in the country and we attend many of their national conventions where thousands of high achieving students congregate and participate in competitive events, display their skills and communicate their concerns. Anyone who has been as fortunate as we have to be exposed to large and small groups of you and your peers could not possibly be negative about the future.

From my limited and highly selective perspective, I see a generation of highly motivated, well skilled and well schooled young adults eager to contribute to their communities and their nation. I hear concerns voiced that assure me that you are a sensitive, caring group of individuals committed to making the world a better place to live for yourselves, for your families and all of your fellowmen.

In spite of the impressive achievements and goals of most of you listed in this book, there will be skeptics — people who are convinced your generation is determined to ruin the world. They'll point to drugs, sexual promiscuity, teen-age abortions, etc. as if you invented all of these maladies. So you're going to have to keep performing, growing, maturing, developing your skills, talents and ideas. It will take a little more time and a lot more effort. But, before you know it, you will have earned the right to lead, be listened to and be respected. That's just the way things work.

In the meantime, if anyone asks you, "what's the matter with kids today," show them this book or tell them to call me. Nobody's ever asked me twice.

Who's Who Review

A Summary of the Objectives, Programs, Policies for
WHO'S WHO AMONG AMERICAN HIGH SCHOOL STUDENTS®

Since 1967, WHO'S WHO AMONG AMERICAN HIGH SCHOOL STUDENTS® has been committed to celebrating outstanding students for their positive achievements in academics, athletics, school and community service. Our first edition recognized 13,000 students from 4,000 high schools; the current, 19th edition, published in ten regional volumes honors over 423,000 junior and senior class high school students representing 18,000 public, private, and parochial high schools nationwide.

As our publication has grown and matured over the years, we have expanded the scope and depth of the services and benefits provided for listed students and refined our policies and procedures in response to the needs of the schools and youth organizations who share our objectives. Hopefully, this review will properly define and explain the substance and significance of our total program.

In our view, the growth, acceptance, and preeminence of WHO'S WHO AMONG AMERICAN HIGH SCHOOL STUDENTS as the leading student recognition publication in the nation, can be attributed to the involvement of educators in the policy-making areas of our programs. We routinely receive valuable input from counselors, principals, and other school faculty members when we correspond with their institutions during the academic year. Additionally, during the past several years, we have hosted over 90 day-long reviews with key educational association executives to exchange ideas and perspectives regarding our standards, criteria, and services.

Most importantly, however, we must acknowledge the contributions of our Committee on Ethics, Standards and Practices. This committee consists of distinguished educators representing relevant areas in secondary and post-secondary education. The committee was first created in 1979 and was charged with the responsibility of formalizing demanding standards for our program which could be used as a guide for all student recognition programs. These standards are routinely distributed to 80,000 high school principals, guidance counselors, and other faculty members each year.

It is a tribute to the committee that the standards they developed have been used as a model by several educational associations who have created their own guidelines for evaluating student recognition programs on a uniform basis. WHO'S WHO is proud of its well documented leadership role in promoting standards and ethics for all student recognition programs.

The committee meets each year and reviews literature, policies, programs, and services. They bring a perspective to the company which assures students and school administrators that WHO'S WHO policies and programs are in compliance and compatible with the standards and objectives of the educational community.

Major Policies and Procedures

Free Book Program—*Guarantees extensive recognition through wide circulation*

WHO'S WHO sponsors the largest Free Book Program of any publisher in any field. The book is automatically sent free to all participating high schools and youth organizations and offered free to all 7,500 libraries and 3,000 colleges and universities. Up to 15,000 complimentary copies are distributed each year.

The major purposes of this extensive free distribution system are to provide meaningful, national recognition for listed students among insitutions traditionally concerned with student achievement, and to make it convenient and easy for these students to view their published biography without purchasing the book.

For students who cannot locate an inspection copy of the book in their community, a listing of libraries within their state which received the most current edition is available upon request.

The recognition and reference purpose(s) of WHO'S WHO AMONG AMERICAN HIGH SCHOOL STUDENTS® have been acknowledged in the favorable review of the publication by the Reference and Subscription Books Reviews Committee of the American Library Association (*Booklist*, 3/1/82).

Financial Policies—*Legitimate honors do not cost the recipient money*

There are no financial requirements whatsoever contingent upon recognition in WHO'S WHO AMONG AMERICAN HIGH SCHOOL STUDENTS. The vast majority of students featured in all past editions have not purchased the book, but have received the recognition they have earned and deserve.

For those students who do purchase the publication or any related award insignia, satisfaction is guaranteed. Refunds are always issued on request.

Nominating Procedures— *Representation from all areas of student achievement*

Each year all 22,000 public, private, and parochial high schools are invited to nominate junior and senior class students who have achieved a "B" grade point average or better and demonstrated leadership in academics, athletics, or extracurricular activities. On rare occasions, students with slightly under a "B" average have been included when their achievements in non-academic areas were extraordinary. Nominators are requested to limit selections to 15% of their eligible students. Most nominate less.

Approximately 13,500 high schools participate in our program by nominating students. An additional 5,000-7,500 schools are represented by their outstanding students as a result of nominations received from bona fide youth organizations, churches with organized youth activities, scholarship agencies, civic and service groups. Most of our nation's major youth groups participate in our program by nominating their meritorious student leaders.

Editing—*Maintains the integrity of the honor*

Occasionally, nominators recommend students who are not qualified for recognition. When these students receive our literature and forms, there may be confusion concerning our standards and criteria. When biography forms are submitted for publication, they are all reviewed and edited to monitor compliance with our high standards. In the past nine years, approximately 163,000 students were disqualified by our editors because they did not meet our standards, including several thousand who ordered the publication. More than $980,000 in orders were returned to these students. Our standards are never compromised by the profit motive. (Auditor's verification available upon request.)

Verification of Data—*A continuous safety check on the effectiveness of our procedures*

To monitor the accuracy and integrity of data submitted by students, a nationally respected accounting firm conducts annual, independent audits of published biographical data. Previous audits reveal that up to 97.2% of the data published was substantially accurate. (Complete studies available upon request.)

Educational Communications Scholarship Foundation Committee members meet to select 50 scholarship winners for the 1983-84 academic year. Each winner receives a $1,000 award. Left: Dr. Norman Feingold, President, National Career & Counseling Services; Morton Temsky, Educator; Lester Benz, Executive Secretary Emeritus, Quill & Scroll Society; Wally Wikoff, Former Director, National Scholastic Press Association; Lily Rose, Scholarship Committee Chairperson and Director of Admissions, Roosevelt University; Fred Brooks, Asst. VP for Enrollment Services & Management, SUNY at Binghamton; Aline Rivers, 1979-80 Executive Board, National Association of College Admissions Counselors, Robert MacVicar, President Emeritus, Oregon State University; and Dr. James Schelhammer, Dean of Admissions, Austin Peay State University. Committee members not shown: Neill Sanders, Associate Director of Admissions, Washington State University and Dr. Hilda Minkoff, 1983-84 President, American School Counselor's Association.

Programs, Services and Benefits for Students

Scholarship Awards—From $4,000 in 1968 to $100,000 annually since 1982

The Educational Communications Scholarship Foundation®, a not-for-profit organization which is funded by the publishing company, now sponsors three separate scholarship award programs, which award over $100,000 in college scholarships each year. Over $700,000 has been funded to date.

Through the general high school program, 50 awards of $1,000 each are awarded to students by a committee of knowledgeable educators on the basis of grade point average, class rank, test scores, activities, an essay and financial need. An additional $30,000 in scholarships is funded through grants to youth organizations where we sponsor awards for their officers or contest winners. For students already in college, $25,000 in scholarships is awarded through THE NATIONAL DEAN'S LIST® Program.

Our research indicates that the Educational Communications Scholarship Foundation's programs represent one of the 10 largest scholarship programs in the nation funded by a single private sector organization. The Foundation is listed in numerous government and commercial directories on financial aid and scholarships.

Grants-In-Aid—Financial support for organizations who work with or for students

Since 1975, we have funded grants to youth and educational organizations to support their programs and/or services on behalf of high school students. The stipends fund scholarships or subsidize research, educational publications or competitive events, and programs. A brief summary of grants issued or committed to date, totaling approximately $330,000 appears in this review.

The College Referral Service (CRS)® — Links students with colleges

WHO'S WHO students receive a catalog listing all 3,000 colleges and universities. They complete a form indicating which institutions they wish us to notify of their honorary award. This service links interested students with colleges and universities and serves as a "third party" reference.

Certainly, listing in WHO'S WHO will not assure a student of admission into the college of his or her choice any more than any other award or honor society. Most selective colleges rely almost exclusively on grade point average, class rank, and test scores. Nevertheless, several hundred colleges have indicated that the CRS and/or the publication is a valuable reference source in their recruitment programs. (Letters from colleges available for inspection.)

16th Annual Survey of High Achievers™ —The views of student leaders are as important as their achievements

Since 1969, we have polled the attitudes and opinions of WHO'S WHO students on timely issues of interest. This study provides students with a collective voice otherwise not available to them. As young voters and future leaders, their views are important. Therefore, survey results are sent to the President, all members of Congress, state Governors, educational agencies, high school administrators, and the press.

Each year, survey results are widely reported in the press and have been utilized in academic studies and research indicating the educational value of this program.

WHO'S WHO Spokesteen Panel™— Another voice for student leaders and a service for media

Because WHO'S WHO has become an authoritative source on high school students, we receive frequent inquiries from reporters when they are preparing special features on teen views, lifestyles, etc. To assist reporters and to assure teens of appropriate representation of their views, we have created a network of articulate and well-informed students, nationwide, who are made available to the press for interviews of local and national coverage. WHO'S WHO Spokesteens have appeared on the "CBS Morning News," NBC "Today Show," "Merv Griffin Show," "Hour Magazine," and numerous other broadcasts, newspaper and magazine stories.

College-Bound Digest®—What students need to know

A compilation of articles written by prominent educators covering the various opportunities available to college-bound students, i.e., financial aid opportunities, the advantages of large schools, small schools, research universities, achievement test usage, and preparation and numerous other topics of similar relevancy. The Digest appears in the introductory section of this publication and is offered as a separate publication, free of charge, to 20,000 high school guidance offices, 20,000 principals, and 3,000 college admissions offices.

Local Newspaper Publicity—Additional recognition for honored students

Consistent with our primary purpose of providing recognition for meritorious students, we routinely provide over 2,000 newspapers nationwide with rosters of their local students featured in the publication with appropriate background information. (Students must authorize this release.)

Other Publications

Who's Who Among Black Americans®

The fourth edition of WHO'S WHO AMONG BLACK AMERICANS® was published by our organization in November of 1985. The book contains biographical sketches of over 15,000 high achieving black adults from all fields of endeavor.

This publication has been extremely well received by librarians, government agencies, educational institutions, and major corporations. All four major library trade journals reviewed and recommended earlier editions for their subscribers. The book was selected by the American Library Association as one of the "Outstanding Reference Books of the Year" and by *Black Scholar* as "A Notable Book," one of only 19 publications to receive this distinction.

WHO'S WHO AMONG BLACK AMERICANS was one of 380 titles chosen by the Library of Congress to be exhibited at The White House Conference on Library & Information Services held in November, 1979 and was selected for inclusion in the Presidential Library at Camp David.

William C. Matney, Editor of WHO'S WHO AMONG BLACK AMERICANS, was introduced on the "Today Show" by book and theatre critic Gene Shalit. The publication has received numerous awards and honors.

The National Dean's List®

The eighth edition of THE NATIONAL DEAN'S LIST® recognizes 90,000 outstanding students representing 2,500 colleges and universities. All students were selected by their respective deans or registrars because of their academic achievements. This year, $25,000 in scholarships were distributed to twenty-five students. For 1985-86, a minimum of $25,000 in scholarships will again be awarded.

In a 1980 survey of deans and registrars, 90% indicated there is a need to provide more recognition for high achieving students and 95% stated that positive recognition provides additional motivation for students. More than 86% acknowledged that THE NATIONAL DEAN'S LIST represents a meaningful program of educational value for listed students.

Memberships

Educational Communications, Inc. or its publisher is a member of the following organizations:
American Association for Counseling & Development
American Association of Higher Education
American Association of School Administrators
Chicago Metropolitan Better Business Bureau
Distributive Education Clubs of America,
  National Advisory Board
Educational Press Association
Future Farmers of America, Executive Sponsor
National Association of Financial Aid Administrators
National School Public Relations Association
Office Education Association,
  National Business Advisory Council

Profile of Who's Who Student

(Statistics From 1985 Edition)

General Listing
Total number of Students	423,993
WHO'S WHO Students as Percentage of 6,500,000 Juniors and Seniors Enrolled Nationwide	6½%
Females (%)	62%
Males (%)	38%

Academics
Grade Point Average (%)
"A"	69%
"B"	30%
"C"	6%
Local Honor Roll	194,607
National Honor Society	131,186
Valedictorian/Salutatorian	9,955

Leadership Activities/Clubs
Student Council	79,666
Boys State/Girls State	36,980
Senior Class Officers	29,840
Junior Class Officers	47,840
Key Club	24,708

Major Vocational Organizations
Future Homemakers of America	30,535
4-H	30,356
Junior Achievement	23,327
Future Farmers of America	15,491
Distributive Education Clubs of America	9,556
Office Education Association	6,513

Varsity Athletics
Basketball	76,107
Track	62,739
Cheerleading/Pom Pon	47,806
Football	44,678
Volleyball	32,664
Baseball	26,763
Tennis	25,319
Soccer	22,461
Cross Country	21,043
Wrestling	11,508

Music/Performing Arts
Orchestra/Band	88,882
Chorus	65,628
Drama	42,085

Miscellaneous
Church/Temple Activities	155,864
Yearbook	87,256
School Paper	66,633
Community Worker	28,926
Fellowship of Christian Athletes	26,596

Grants to Youth and Educational Organizations

American Association for Gifted Children
$2,000, 1 Grant
To sponsor a conference for educators concerning "The Gifted Child, the Family and the Community."

American Children's Television Festival
$2,000, 1 Grant
To promote excellence in television programming for our nation's youth. Founded by the Central Educational Network.

American Council on the Teaching of Foreign Language
$500, 1 Grant
To support the general goals and objectives in the field of foreign language.

American Legion Auxiliary Girls Nation
$17,500, 7 Grants
Scholarships for Vice President and Outstanding Senator of program where students participate in mock government structure.

American Legion Boys Nation
$18,500, 8 Grants
Scholarships for President and Vice President of program where students learn about government through participation.

Animal Welfare Institute
$1,582, 2 Grants
For biology textbook on experiments which do not involve cruelty towards animals. Second grant to fund convention booth equipment.

Black United Fund
$5,000, 1 Grant
Scholarships for Black students selected by BUF Committee.

Colorado Forum of Educational Leaders
$1,000, 1 Grant
To fund a series of quarterly activities regarding the educational successes of Colorado Schools.

Contemporary-Family Life Curriculum
$1,500, 1 Grant
Funded formal grant request, resulting in $100,000 grant from government to test this contemporary curriculum.

Distributive Education Clubs of America (DECA)
$37,800, 11 Grants
ECI serves on the National Advisory Board for this major vocational/educational organization and sponsors scholarships for national officers.

Earthwatch
$3,000, 3 Grants
Scholarships for students conducting scientific expeditions with scientists, researchers.

Education Roundtable
$5,000, 1 Grant
To fund the creation of a committee of representatives from government, education, private industry, and the general public to support and improve education in America.

Fellowship of Christian Athletes
$12,800, 5 Grants
Original stipend funded seminar of athletic directors. Subsequent grants for scholarships for coaches' conferences concerning spiritual, professional and family growth.

Joint Council on Economic Education
$11,000, 4 Grants
Funds ongoing economic education program for students and educators from elementary school to college level.

Junior Achievement
$12,000, 6 Grants
Grants will be used for scholarship for the winner of the WHO'S WHO Essay Contest.

Junior Classical League
$5,000, 5 Grants
Funds a scholarship to the outstanding member selected by an educational committee for this organization whose members study the civilizations of Greece and Rome to provide a better understanding of our culture, literature, language and arts.

Junior Engineering Technical Society
$6,000, 2 Grants
Stipends were used to help revise the National Engineering Aptitude Search Test.

Law & Economic Center, University of Miami Law School
$4,500, 1 Grant
Funded study on use of media to effectively communicate economic issues and policies to general public.

Miss Teenage America Scholarship Program
$33,000, 8 Grants
Currently funds a $5,000 scholarship for student selected as Miss Teenage America; previously funded four $1,000 awards for each of the semifinalists.

Modern Music Masters
$4,500, 2 Grants
For chapter expansion program of this national music honor society, high school level.

Mr. U.S.A. Teen Program
$5,500, 4 Grants
Scholarship for outstanding student selected on basis of leadership, citizenship, academics, and community involvement.

National Cheerleaders Association
$7,100, 7 Grants
Scholarships for winners of state drill team contests.

National Federation for Catholic Youth Ministry
$3,000, 2 Grants
Funds a scholarship of $1,000 for the student elected President of the National Youth Council and a $500 scholarship for another Catholic Teen Leader selected by the National organization.

National Forensic League
$8,000, 4 Grants
For two scholarships of $1,000 each to the members of the first place National Debate Team.

National Foundation for Advancement in the Arts
$2,000, 2 Grants
For general support for the Arts, Recognition, and Talent Search Program of this Foundation.

National 4-H Council
$18,500, 7 Grants
Grants will be used for scholarship for outstanding 4-H students.

National Future Farmers of America (FFA)
$27,000, 9 Grants
Grants will be used for scholarship for outstanding FFA students.

Office Education Association (OEA)
$39,000, 10 Grants
ECI serves on the National Business Advisory Council and sponsors scholarship program for national officers.

Performing & Visual Arts Society (PAVAS)
$4,000, 2 Grants
To conduct expansion program for high school chapters.

The President's Committee on the Employment of the Handicapped
$4,000, 4 Grants
Scholarship for the winner of the President's Committee National Poster contest, high school division.

Quill & Scroll Society
$8,000, 4 Grants
For two scholarships of $1,000 each to students who apply as contestants in Quill & Scroll's Current Events Quiz and National Writing/Photography Contest.

Soroptimist International of the Americas, Inc.
$4,000, 4 Grants
Scholarship for organization's Youth Citizenship Award Winner.

Special Olympics, Inc.
$1,000, 1 Grant
Scholarship for outstanding student volunteer and direct mail promotion to high school athletic directors requesting volunteers to work with handicapped children.

Standards for
Who's Who Among American High School Students and Other Recognition Programs and Societies

1. Nominations will be from established organizations that work with and for the benefit of high school aged youth. Under no circumstances will recommendations be accepted from students, their parents or solicited from standard commercial lists.

2. Criteria for students to be selected will be clearly defined and reflect high personal achievement.

3. Listing in "Who's Who" will not require purchase of any items or payments of any fees.

4. Additional programs and services which are available to those listed in "Who's Who" at cost to the students, will be clearly described in the literature provided.

5. A refund policy will be clearly stated in all literature.

6. Nominators will be able to recommend students without releasing confidential data or fear of having confidential data released by program sponsors.

7. Student information will be confidential and will not be released except where authorized by the student.

8. Home addresses will not be published in the book or made public in any way.

9. Under no circumstances will "Who's Who" sell student information or lists.

10. The publisher will describe, disseminate and verify the methods employed to assure national/regional recognition to students listed.

11. The publisher will respond to all inquiries, complaints and requests for relevant background information.

12. The basis for the scholarship program competition will be defined. Number and amount of awards will be stated, lists of previous winners will be available. Finalist selection process and funding method will be clearly defined. Employees or their relatives will not be eligible for scholarships.

13. There will be an advisory council (external to the organization) to review and make recommendations regarding the policies, procedures, and evaluation process of the "Who's Who" programs.

14. The publisher will set forth in writing and make publicly known the policies and procedures it follows in the implementation of these standards.

Our company's adherence to the above standards has been attested to by an independent public accounting firm. A copy of their report is available upon request.

Members of the Committee on Ethics, Standards and Practices:

Dr. Wesley Apker
*Executive Director
Association of California
School Administrators
Sacramento, CA*

James T. Barry
*Assoc. Vice President
for College Relations
St. Ambrose College
Davenport, IA*

Phyllis Blaunstein
*Executive Director
National Association of State
Boards of Education
Alexandria, VA*

Dr. Harold Crosby
*Regents Professor
University of West Florida
Pensacola, FL*

Dr. S. Norman Feingold
*President
National Career &
Counseling Services
Washington, DC*

Dr. Betty James
*Assoc. Dean for
Academic Affairs
Livingstone College
Salisbury, NC*

Dr. John Lucy
*Principal
Ft. Campbell Jr. High School
Ft. Campbell, KY*

Paul Masem
*Superintendent
Ames Community
School Dist.
Ames, IA*

Dr. Edward J. Rachford
*Superintendent
Homewood-Flossmoor
Community High School
Flossmoor, IL*

Dr. Vincent Reed
*Vice President for
Communications
The Washington Post
Washington, DC*

Salvatore Salato
*Principal
Thornridge High School
Dolton, IL*

David Hartman, host of ABC's "Good Morning America" (right), interviewed WHO'S WHO Spokesteen Shannin Mealiffe from LaCanada High School, LaCanada, CA (second from left), with two authorities on teen suicide.

On the NBC "Today Show," host Tom Brokow (center) interviews WHO'S WHO Spokesteens (left) Burnell Newsome, Hazelhurst, Mississippi, Amy Krentzman, Deerfield Beach, Florida, Tari Marshall, ECI Representative, and Mike McGriff, Chicago, Illinois.

Merv Griffin interviews WHO'S WHO Spokesteen Steven Silver from South Shore High School, Brooklyn, New York on the nationally televised talk show.

WHO'S WHO sponsors $1,000 scholarships for each member of the winning Debate Team in the National Forensic League's annual competition. The 1985 winners were David Bearce and Jeff Grizzel.

For the Office Education Association (OEA), WHO'S WHO sponsors scholarships for its National Officers and is a member of the National Business Advisory Council. Shown above are the 1985-86 National OEA Officers at the Secondary level: (front row) Tod Stapleton, Eastern Region Vice President; Keli Kite, Treasurer; Lisa Clifton, Western Region Vice President; Tammy L. Maloy, Parliamentarian; Kim Owen, Vice President; (back row) Janice McEndarfer, Historian; Todd Whan, President; and Lynn Krebs, Secretary.

President Reagan greets Miss Teenage America, Amy Sue Brenkacz in the Oval Office. WHO'S WHO sponsors a $5,000 scholarship for Miss Teenage America and listed Amy Sue in the publication.

Bill Kurtis, host of the "CBS Morning News," interviews WHO'S WHO Spokesteens Stephanie Woolwich, Long Beach, New Jersey and Alex Tachmes, Miami Beach, Florida.

For the Distributive Educational Clubs of America (DECA), WHO'S WHO serves on the National Advisory Board and sponsors scholarships for DECA National Officers. Shown (above) are 1985-86 National Officers from left to right: Robert J. Smith, III, Southern Region Vice President; Michael A. Nass, Central Region Vice President; Casey Corcoran, North Atlantic Region Vice President; Michael A. Ellenhorn, Western Region Vice President and Zachary L. Rhodes, President.

WHO'S WHO sponsors $1,500 and $1,000 scholarships for the president and vice-president of the American Legion Boy's Nation program. (Left to right) Dale L. Renaud, Chairman, National Americanism Commission; Michael L. Diggs, 1984 Boy's Nation Vice-President; Jackie McGuinn, Assistant to the Publisher, WHO'S WHO AMONG AMERICAN HIGH SCHOOL STUDENTS; J. Michael Verde, II, 1984 Boy's Nation President and Mike Ayers, Director, Americanism and Children & Youth Division.

Penni Ann McClean, right, Congress delegate advisor from North Carolina, presents a citation to Mrs. Jackie McGuinn, assistant to the publisher of WHO'S WHO, for five years support of the 4-H Citizenship-Washington Focus program.

Right to left: Debbie Moyer from Allentown, PA pointing to her prize winning poster in the high school category with Harold Russell, Chairman, President's Committee on Employment of the Handicapped. WHO'S WHO sponsors a $1,000 college scholarship for this annual contest.

College-Bound Digest®

As a public service to the 96% of WHO'S WHO students who will continue their education after graduation from high school, we have invited a group of distinguished educators to use our publication as a forum to inform and assist students through the articles in this section.

While we do not presume that these articles contain "everything you need to know" about preparing for college, we believe you will find they will be helpful in learning "some of the things you need to know."

We wish to acknowledge the special contribution of Robert McLendon, Vice President For Enrollment Planning & Dean of Admissions and Financial Aid at Lambuth College, Jackson, Tennessee who was instrumental in selecting appropriate topics and authors for this section.

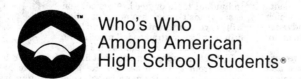

Who's Who
Among American
High School Students®

Getting the most from your high school counselor

By James Warfield

A high school counselor, helping you apply to college, is able to provide a wide variety of services tailored to your needs. The nature of this assistance will depend upon your abilities and achievement as well as the nature and quality of the colleges to which you apply. Effective use of the counselor's services will require you to have frequent discussions. Although your ideas about which colleges to apply to will change often, the more closely you work with your counselor the more valuable he/she will be to you.

Finding, selecting and applying to the colleges that are right for you is a long and studied process. It involves a lot of letter-writing, telephoning, research, weighing alternatives, and just plain old thinking. It's a decision-making process.

Your counselor makes recommendations as to which courses you should be taking in high school. These recommendations should be based upon your academic abilities and goals. This is a critical issue because the appropriateness of this advice is determined by the consistency between your aspirations and aptitudes. Verifying the accuracy of your self-perceptions is important in order to avoid sudden surprises caused by false hopes or unrealistic expectations. The reason why your counselor exists, is to help you become everything you are capable of within a realistic framework.

For many students, the college selection process begins with the PSAT, taken in the fall of the junior year. Your counselor should advise you which of the college entrance tests to take, SAT, ACT, ACH and AP, and when to take them. The type of college you apply to will determine which tests to take. The quality of the college, or the quality of your own academic program, and whether or not you plan to apply Early Decision, will determine when you should take such tests. Many students don't know in their junior year to which schools they'd like to apply, so advance planning is necessary in order to maintain open options.

Finding the right college will require you to know yourself, your likes and dislikes. In what kind of environment do you see yourself being most comfortable? Can you picture yourself at a small college or a mid-size or large university setting? Do you want a school to be in a rural community, a suburb or to be in an urban environment? Do you want to be in a different geographic part

of the country or is being close to home important to you? What are some of your academic areas of interest? What kind of extra curricular offering do you want to participate in? As you answer these questions the attributes of your ideal college will become more clear. Through discussion with your counselor you'll be able to assess your needs, and more clearly focus your perceptions of yourself and of the schools you will be researching.

Your counselor should help generate a list of colleges that meet your requirements by drawing upon his/her own wealth of knowledge or utilizing the many reference materials available.

Many counselors have access to computers that will provide a list of colleges for you to investigate, once you have determined the characteristics you are looking for. If the guidance office does not have a computer, the same information can be obtained, with a little effort, from the commercially published reference books that are available through your counselor. After generating a list of perhaps twelve to twenty schools, your research really begins.

Resource books provide a wealth of statistical and narrative descriptions on virtually every college. The counseling office is likely to have college catalogs as well as files on each college containing brochures, view books and leaflets of the various academic and extracurricular offerings available at that particular school. Although college catalogs are boring reading material, information relating to admission procedures and requirements, course offerings and requirements for each of the academic majors are outlined. In addition, course prerequisites and methods of exempting yourself from some prerequisites are also indicated. As your research continues, you'll be able to eliminate schools and determine some colleges in which you are seriously interested.

Many high schools set up procedures whereby students may meet with representatives from colleges to obtain more information or answer individual questions. These representatives may be the Director of Admission, Admissions officers, or personnel hired to represent the college. Of course, the more you know about the college, before talking with the college representative, the more value they will be to you. Some colleges require an interview either by the representative, an alumni, or by an admissions officer. Your counselor should help you determine if an interview is necessary in your situation.

Campus visits are the most effective means to determine if the college is right for you. When to visit is a matter of individual taste or need. A school you casually visit during a summer vacation will serve a different purpose, and have different flavor, than a visit made in the fall after you have applied. It is also difficult to compare schools that are on break from those in session. Keep in mind that as you visit more schools your observational skills will become more sophisticated and your reflections of each will be altered. It may be more prudent to visit only those schools to which you have been accepted, after you have received all your admissions decisions.

As you narrow your choice of colleges, your counselor should review with you the possibilities of acceptance or rejection at each. At least one of your choices should be a safety choice, one in which you are almost guaranteed of being admitted.

After the list of colleges to which you are going to apply has been determined, it is your responsibility to obtain the application and meet deadline dates. Many colleges require a counselor's recommendation or a Secondary School Reference. Some require additional recommendations from specific teachers. Establish application procedures with your counselor so that he/she, the teacher, and school have adequate time to do their part in order to meet your deadline dates. If you are required to write an essay, or personal statement, discuss this with your counselor. These discussions serve several purposes: help you generate ideas and narrow topics that you wish to write about; provide you with suggestions that will enhance your applications; and provide the counselor with insights that will compliment your application.

It is your responsibility to file your applications on time, see that your test scores are sent to the admissions office, and file the financial aid applications. Your counselor will help you determine which scores to send, which financial aid form is required and how to fulfill these requirements.

Selecting and applying to a college is a decision-making process. The truly wise decision maker knows that he must clarify questions, obtain the most information possible, and probe until no new information becomes evident. Generally, the more information obtained, the better the decision, and the happier the college experience.

Jim Warfield is Director of Guidance at Lake Forest High School, Lake Forest, Illinois. Jim is currently involved and active in a number of professional organizations, and presently serving on the National Advisory Council for The Educational Records Bureau, Wellesley, Massachusetts.

The use of the SAT at selective colleges

By Dr. Judith Gatlin

For many students the numbers — from 200 to 800 on the verbal and on the quantitative sections of the College Board examination — seem to be the voice of doom; for others, they announce the possibility of admission into the nation's most selective colleges. But just how important, really, are those scores, and how will college admissions committees interpret them?

It is important to remember that the SAT (or ACT) is only one part of your total record. Your rank in your high school class, your grades, extracurricular activities which show leadership potential, and your recommendations are all extremely important. In addition, some colleges will consider your geographic location (it may be easier for the valedictorian of a South Dakota high school to enter Harvard than for the top student in a Connecticut prep school), your relationship with alumni, your religious preference at some denominational colleges, and the success of other graduates from your school at the institution.

Colleges treat scores, grades, rank, activities and recommendations in a variety of ways, but very few use arbitrary cut-off scores to determine acceptance. Every selective college or university attempts to select a class which will be successful (they don't want you to flunk out after your first year). Students who are admitted are those who they can predict will do well; and admissions staff experience with standardized tests suggests that certain levels of achievement, can be predicted with a fair degree of accuracy when used in conjunction with the high school record.

Often the total score on the SAT is less important than the individual score on either the verbal or the quantitative aptitude section. While colleges and universities may publish their average SAT as a combination, many liberal arts colleges believe that the verbal score is a particularly good indicator of ability, and many technically oriented engineering programs will be impressed with a very good quantitative score. A pre-engineering student with an 1150 SAT may be a very good candidate if his scores are 450 on the verbal section and 700 in the quantitative area; he might be substantially less impressive with 650/500.

One of the problems that many students confront when they first look at their scores is a sinking feeling that their numbers do not match their high school achievement level. The 'A' student who is third in her class and barely makes a 450/450 on the SAT is disappointed for days afterwards. It is important, however, to understand what your scores mean. The national average on the verbal section of the SAT is 427; on the mathematics section it is 467. Clearly, many college bound students will have a total score under 900. Many colleges and most state universities have average scores at this level or below it; more selective institutions will generally have average scores that are substantially higher, but even among these colleges there will be a number of students whose scores are at this level if their grades and rank indicate a strong chance of success.

But how can you explain or understand an average score when you have been an excellent student? It may be that you had a bad day (or a bad night before); a headache, too little sleep, a testing environment that is too hot or too cold may cause your scores to be less than your best. It may be that the scores are an accurate indicator of your aptitude and that you are a high achiever. Or it may mean that your grades have

been inflated and that you have not been challenged by teachers or peers. One way that you can determine if it was just the specific test day is to compare your scores on the SAT with your PSAT. If you scored, for example, 48/50 on the PSAT and have a combined total on the SAT of from 970 to 1020 your test is probably valid. If, on the other hand, your PSAT was 55/58 and you scored 1020 on the SAT, you probably should plan to retake the examination to see if the second time might show real improvement.

In addition to the "bad day" low score there are other reasons that good students do not do well on standardized tests. It may be that they panic under time pressure, that they are unfamiliar with national tests and the testing environment, or that their skills and abilities cannot be shown on such tests. Really creative students, those with talents in the arts, and those who work very slowly through a problem, analyzing as they go, are sometimes at a disadvantage. If you fall in one of these categories, it is especially useful for a teacher whose recommendation you have requested be asked to discuss your other strengths in an admissions letter.

Some students retake the SAT two or three times to see if they can improve their overall scores, and it is important to realize that scores will vary slightly every time you take a Scholastic Aptitude Test. A variation of 30 points in either direction is normal; more than 50 points, unusual. How worthwhile is it to retake the SAT if your scores are under the average published by the college of your choice? Some schools, like Furman, accept your best scores from each test. Others may average your test results. It is probably true that you can improve your quantitative score with tutoring over several months; improving verbal scores is far more difficult. You should remember, however, that while selective colleges have many high-scoring students, their *average* SAT is just that: there have been many others whose scores are under the average but who have the proven achievement to be admitted.

Suppose, however, that you are very interested in an institution which indicates an average SAT of 1275; your score is 1050, but your parents are alumni, you graduated in the top 20% of your class, and you have been an outstanding high school leader. Academically you would be in the bottom quarter of your class, yet you may well be admitted because of your parents and your activities. Should you attend such a college? Will you be able to compete at a level comfortable for you with students whose high school backgrounds may be substantially superior? Are you ready to make a number of "C's" or to study harder and longer than your roommates?

You should consider, too, that very high scores do not necessarily mean admission to the college of your choice. Several years ago a young man with an SAT score of 1440 applied to a selective Southeastern liberal arts college. He had graduated in the lower half of his high school class and although he had been involved in some extracurricular activities, he also had been a discipline problem in high school. After substan-

tial discussion, he was not admitted, but the college admissions office was interested enough to trace his career several years later. He had flunked out of two other colleges. SAT scores indicate aptitude — the ability to learn — not achievement. They do not show the desire to learn, the ambition to succeed or the perserverance necessary for academic excellence. College admissions officers are aware of these facts and they will read your entire application with an awareness that you are more than a score on a computer printout.

Dr. Judith Gatlin is the Director of Educational Services and Assistant Professor of English at Furman University, Greenville, South Carolina. She has authored various articles for the *Journal of College Placement* and is a former columnist for the *Charlotte Observer*.

Tips on taking the SAT

By Dr. Ernest W. Beals

If you are college-bound or plan to be, chances are that you will be required to take a college admissions test such as the Scholastic Aptitude Test (SAT) of The College Board or the American College Testing Program's assessment test (ACT).

The SAT's format and content have changed enormously over its 55 years of existence, and is now designed to measure the extent to which your reasoning abilities, that is skill with verbal expressions and mathematical concepts, have been developed up to the time you take the test.

It is important to realize that students are neither accepted nor denied admission to an institution solely on the basis of SAT or other test scores. When looking at prospective students, institutions of higher learning also stress to varying degrees such factors as your high school record (including courses taken, grade patterns, and class rank or high school average) and extracurricular activities. Other factors may be the outcome of personal interviews and teacher or counselor recommendations, as well as the student body needs of the college or university itself.

Students frequently ask: What can I do about raising my SAT scores or about making them better than they would be otherwise? The answer is: Quickly and immediately, probably not much. Over longer periods it depends on how much time, effort and concentration goes into the preparation. The abilities measured by the test are related to academic success in college. These abilities grow over a period of time through learning experiences such as those encountered in the family, in the classroom, with your friends and associates, and in reading and independent study.

The best preparation for the SAT is to have had varied opportunities of this kind and to have made the most of them. The contents of the tests cover such a broad area that trying to "cram" for it has never been found to yield validly measurable results. You may, however, find it useful to review some of the fundamental principles of algebra and geometry in order to refresh your memory for the mathematical section of the test.

In order to reduce anxiety and increase confidence when test time arrives, here are some valuable tips: First, become familiar with the format of the test. Obtain a copy of the informative booklet, *Taking the SAT*, from your guidance counselor. This free booklet describes the nature and components of the SAT and, provides a full sample SAT which you can administer and score yourself. By taking this sample test, you will familiarize yourself with the directions and the format of the questions. You will also gain valuable practice in allocating your time to each item.

You will also learn that, as a rule, the easier questions of each section come at the beginning of that section, with the questions growing progressively more difficult to the end of the section. Use your time wisely. If you find the individual items of a particular section are extremely difficult for you, read quickly through the remaining questions in the group, answering only those that you feel you know. You should then begin work on the next set of questions, returning to the omitted questions in that section if you have time. You receive as much credit for answering correctly the questions you find easy as you get for answering the hard ones. Above all, don't panic. You receive one point for each question correctly answered; you lose a fraction of a point for each item incorrectly answered. You neither gain nor lose points for omitted questions. Therefore, keep in mind that random guessing on questions will rarely increase your scores, and might even have the effect of reducing your raw score. However, some selective guessing can pay off for you: If you can confidently eliminate as incorrect at least two of the possible four or five answers to a question, then it would be to your advantage to take a stab at one of the remaining answers to that question.

Your raw score on the SAT is determined by adding up all correct answers and subtracting from that total the sum of the fractions for all incorrect answers. The raw score is then converted to the College Board scale ranging from a low of 200 to a high of 800 on the verbal and mathematics sections of the SAT.

The Test of Standard Written English (TSWE) is a 30-minute multiple-choice test administered with the SAT. The questions evaluate your ability to recognize standard written English, the language of most college textbooks and the English you will be expected to use in the papers you write for college courses. The scores may be used to place you in a freshman English course that is appropriate for you.

Contrary to the anxiety-ridden expectations of students taking the SAT and TSWE for the first time, these tests do not require specialized knowledge in science, social sciences, literature, or any other field.

In brief summary, the best strategies to follow in order to prepare yourself for taking the SAT include: enroll in college preparatory courses that your school offers, maintain good solid and consistent effort in your everyday classroom work and classroom tests, force yourself to read as many and varied outside readings as possible, brush up on your algebra and geometry lessons, become familiar with the SAT format, content, directions, etc. (obtain a copy of *Taking the SAT* booklet from your counselor and take the sample SAT test, score it yourself, and read the suggestions and explanations included with it), get a good night's sleep the night before the examination and take a positive attitude with you to the test center. If you do all of the above, you will be putting your best foot forward and enhancing your chances of obtaining good test scores. Good luck to you.

Dr. Ernest W. Beals is Association Director of the Southern Regional Office of The College Board. Dr. Beals has worked in the field of education for the past 26 years at the high school and college level including 13 years in college admissions.

Can you prepare for the SAT?

By Stanley H. Kaplan

The discussion of the issue of preparation for the SAT has come full circle since the 1950's. In the 1957 Bulletin, issued to the students, the College Board stated, "Coaching may be a sound and rewarding method. If coaching means an honest effort, under the guidance of a good teacher, over an extended period of time, to improve those skills in which you are weak, then it can be recommended as effective study." In the 1960's, the statement about the possible positive effects of coaching was withdrawn. The reason, I was told, was the proliferation of cram schools that preyed on students' (and parents') anxieties and offered little of educational value and little possibility of an improvement on the SAT. And now in the 1980's, the College Board and ETS which constructs the SAT, once again are distinguishing between cramming and long-term coaching which is now looked upon as "supplementary education."

Can one be prepared for the SAT? My answer is an emphatic yes. Some students can prepare by self-study. There are many materials, including tests released by the College Board and SAT review books available at bookstores.

My organization has been preparing students for the SAT for more than thirty years. Actually — and this is important — we are not preparing for the SAT per se. Rather, we are working to improve a student's basic math, verbal, and reasoning skills. The SAT does not measure a scholastic aptitude — if by aptitude we mean an innate, unchangeable indication of academic potential. The SAT measures the level of verbal and mathematical achievement, including the ability to handle innovative, non-routine approaches in these areas. The SAT evaluates the learning experiences of students in and out of school. The more the experience, the higher the level of achievement and therefore the higher the SAT score. Only an improved student can achieve an improved score. It seems that many students and parents still believe that all a test preparation program has to do is teach a few test techniques and strategies, wave a magic wand, and presto — a higher score. The goal of an SAT preparation program should go beyond that of improved SAT scores. It should provide improved skills to insure better performance at the college level. In fact, parents are beginning to realize the valuable long-range effects of SAT preparation. When reports of declining SAT scores made a big splash in the press, several years ago, the enrollments in our programs increased dramatically, despite the decreasing importance of SAT scores in the college admissions process. Declining SAT scores indicate a deficiency in basic skills which in turn could mean a poorer performance at the college level. Years of experience have convinced me that the "specter" of the SAT is an excellent device in motivating students toward working and improving these skills necessary for success at the college level.

Unfortunately, too many students memorize facts that teachers and textbooks provide, regurgitate this information on a test, and then promptly proceed to forget. A review can be of immense value in "bringing it all back," in making what one has learned more meaningful, and in giving the student an opportunity to think more creatively. This does not mean that every student should enroll in an SAT preparation program. Certainly, you should take at least one of the released exams to become familiar with the instructions, format, content, and time pressures of the test. If you feel, however, that you would like to enroll in a structured program of preparation, here are some tips you might follow in choosing a legitimate program that could give you the maximum benefit:

1) The program should be a long-range one — extending over a period of at least several months. Cram courses are of little value. The lessons should be held weekly with home-study assignments in between to reinforce what has been taught in class.

2) The classes should be small — not seminars of 100 or so. A class size should not exceed 25.

3) There should be an opportunity to make up missed lessons. Very frequently, you might miss a lesson because of illness or other commitments. Certainly,

you should not give up studying for an important school exam in order to attend a class session.

4) The program should offer you the option of continuing your study for the SAT if you choose to take the exam for a second time.

5) Most important, the school should have a *permanent* location where you might look at the materials and be able to talk in depth with a person in charge. Beware of fly-by-night programs that advertise by box numbers, have telephone answering services, hold classes in hotels or other meeting rooms, and silently steal away when the course is over.

6) The better programs offer scholarship assistance if you cannot afford to pay for the program.

7) You should check a program out with others who have taken it previously. Their experiences as to the quality of the teaching, the adequacy of the materials, and most important, the improvement they have achieved, can be most helpful in making your decision.

Be suspicious of high pressure tactics designed to corral you as a student — such as statements that the SAT is the most important exam you will ever take, claims of fantastic improvements, and guarantees of improved scores. Avoid correspondence courses. They are often expensive — almost as much as a course with live class programs. Usually the purchase of an SAT review book and use of materials supplied by the College Board itself is just as helpful.

Remember, the SAT is *not* the most important exam you'll ever be taking. It is only one of many criteria used by admissions officers to make a decision. Certainly your high school record is more important than the SAT score you will get.

Perhaps one of the best reasons for some kind of preparation is to make sure that the SAT score evaluates your achievement as reliably as possible. After all, you wouldn't enter a tennis tournament cold. I've seen hundreds of cases of underachievers or poor "test-takers" whose self-images have been enhanced by improved scores that more accurately evaluated this academic achievement.

Remember, there is much you can do on your own long before you take a preprartion course or even decide to do so. You can start reading — newspapers, magazines, best-sellers, — read something that interests you, but read! At the same time, you'll be improving your vocabulary and the ability to integrate ideas. In math, as well as in science, don't just memorize rules and standard ways of attacking problems. Try to reason things through and find out the why as well as the how as well as the what. Then, when the time comes to review for the SAT, you will have done most of your preparation already. Good luck!

Stanley H. Kaplan is Executive Director of the Stanley H. Kaplan Educational Center, Ltd., New York, New York with offices nationwide and abroad. Kaplan has been featured in numerous articles including *Time*, *Newsweek*, and the *New York Times*. He has also appeared on numerous public radio and television programs as an authority on test preparation.

Searching for student financial aids

By S. Norman Feingold
and Marie Feingold

The purpose of this article is to suggest practical techniques and pathways for gathering accurate information about financial aids that are available and to indicate time frames within which it is advisable to initiate financial aid seeking efforts.

1. Start Early

The high school student should begin not later than the beginning of the junior year of high school. Many scholarships require that the student have taken the Scholastic Aptitude Test or the Preliminary SAT. The National Merit Scholarship competitions start the beginning of the junior year in high school. Many organizations use the results of this exam for the selection of their recipients; and this includes some companies which provide scholarships for the children of its employees. Some colleges select student aid recipients from National Merit competitors. Some competitions for research fellowships, overseas grants may close a year before recipients are announced.

2. Federal Publications

A. The U.S. Department of Education publishes two helpful pamphlets, that are revised annually. They are *Five Federal Financial Aid Programs: A Student Consumer's Guide* and *Federal Financial Aid for Men and Women Resuming Their Education or Training*. They are both available without cost from Federal Financial Aid, Box 84, Washington, DC 20044.

B. Veterans Administration each January publishes *Federal Benefits for Veterans and Dependents*. It contains details of educational assistance and is available from the Superintendent of Documents, U.S. Printing Office, Washington, DC 20402. Cost $1.50.

C. The Department of Defense. Each of the armed forces has ROTC programs and annually revises its pamphlets about programs.

Achievement through Education, Air Force ROTC is obtained from the Department of the Air Force, Air Force Reserve Officers Training Corps, Maxwell Air Force Base, AL 36112.

Navy-Marine Corps Scholarship Programs. U.S. Department of the Navy, Navy Recruiting Command, 4015 Wilson Boulevard, Arlington, VA 22203.

Information about Army ROTC scholarships can be obtained by writing to:

Army ROTC, P.O. Box 7000
Larchmont, NY 10538.

D. The U.S. Department of Health and Human Services, Washington, DC 20201 maintains up-to-date publications about social security benefits. Details should be obtained from the local Social Security office. Generally dependents of deceased or disabled contributors to Social Security are eligible for benefits while they are full-time elementary or high school students under the age of 19. Until April, 1985, there is a phasing out of the benefits as they existed until August, 1981.

Information about financial aid for students in the health and allied health professions is available from the U.S. Public Health Service, Bureau of Health Manpower, Student Assistance Branch, Center Building, Room G-23, 3700 East-West Highway, Hyattsville, MD 20782.

E. The U.S. Department of the Interior, Bureau of Indian Affairs, Washington, DC 20245 publishes pamphlets about educational assistance for native Americans.

If you are having difficulty locating information about Federal financial assistance for training and education, write to your Congressman or Senator at either his local office or at his Washington, DC office in the House of Representatives of the Senate.

3. State Publications

Most if not all states publish booklets or flyers about the student financial aid programs they administer. *Five Federal Financial Aid Programs: A Student Consumer's Guide* lists the names, addresses and telephone numbers of every state agency that provides information on the Guaranteed Student Loan Program and *Federal Financial Aid for Men and Women Resuming Their Education or Training* lists the names and addresses of each state scholarship agency. For details write to the state scholarship agency of the state in which you are a resident.

States also publish material on scholarships for special groups within the state such as veterans and their dependents, policemen, prison guards and firemen. It is likely that the state scholarship agency can give you the name and address you need.

Your state Senator can help you locate state aids.

4. Local Publications
(City and County)

Many communities have a printed or typed listing of student aids available to their residents. Your counselor may be helpful in directing you to these sources.

5. Know the ethnic, religious, and place origins of your family.

A fairly large amount of student financial aid is awarded by private organizations to persons of specific origin. Consult *Scholarships, Fellowships and Loans, Volumes VI and VII*, by S. Norman Feingold and Marie Feingold, and the *Scholarships, Fellowships, and Loans News Service and Counselors Information Services*, Bellman Publishing Company, P.O. Box 164, Arlington, MA 02174-0164.

6. Know for whom your parents or guardian work.

Some corporations and labor unions provide awards for their employees and members respectively. Have your parents speak to the personnel department of the company and the steward of the labor union for details. Company and union newspapers/magazines are good sources of keeping abreast of these financial aids.

7. As soon as practical for you, try to determine a **field of interest and hobby.** Some aids are given for majoring or studying certain subjects or having engaged in specific activities.

8. Enter Contests.

There are many different kinds of contests. The National Federation of Music Clubs, 310 South Michigan Ave., Suite 1936, Chicago, IL 60604 publishes scholarships and awards charts for two-year periods.

9. Get your own work experience.

Students who have been caddies or delivered newspapers or worked in other capacities are often eligible for scholarship competitions. Tuition refunds from the company for which you work cover a part or all of the fees for courses. Generally, the course must be related to your work and permission must be obtained.

10. Attend free post-secondary institutions of education and training.

The military academies and the Webb Institute of Naval Architecture are schools for which there are no tuition or room and board fees.

11. Consider scholarship loans.

In areas of work in which there are manpower shortages, it is possible to convert a loan to a scholarship by working in a given geographical area or in a specific subject matter field. Teaching the handicapped and working in rural poverty areas where there are shortages of specific personnel are two ways. Generally these programs are federally or state sponsored.

12. Loans to parents, to children of employees, to residents of service areas.

Such loans may be administered and awarded by business, foundations, banks, non-profit corporations. Two programs for which you should write for information are those of the United Student Aid Funds, Inc., 200 East 42nd St., New York, NY 10017 and Richard C. Knight Insurance Agency, Inc., 53 Beacon St., Boston, MA 02108.

13. Attend Cooperative or Work-Study Schools.

Your earnings will cover much if not all of your tuition and living expenses. More than 200,000 college students are enrolled in cooperative education programs. In the "typical" co-op program, students alternate semesters of study and supervised paid work. More than 1,000 colleges now offer co-op programs. Request *Undergraduate Programs of Cooperative Programs in the United States and Canada* which is available at no cost from the National Commission for Cooperative Education, 360 Huntington Ave., Boston, MA 02115.

14. Apprenticeship Training

In the skilled trades this is a way to learn and earn. Details are available from the following four sources: State Bureau of Apprenticeship and Training

(one office is located in each state capital); a network of approximately 2,300 local and state employment offices; in a number of states there is a state apprenticeship council; U.S. Department of Labor, Bureau of Apprenticeship and Training, 601 D St., N.W., Washington, DC 20213.

15. Teachers, principals, ministers, lawyers, bankers, business people, counselors may know of individuals who anonymously assist deserving individuals to obtain the training and education they are seeking.

16. How do you locate the donors and administrators of financial aid programs?

There are a number of publications that should either be in the public library, school library, or college library. If not, request the library to order them. Some are:

Need a Lift, American Legion, P.O. Box 1055, Indianapolis, IN 46206. Revised every fall.

Scholarships, Fellowships and Loans, Volumes VI and VII, S. Norman Feingold and Marie Feingold. Bellman Publishing Company, P.O. Box 164, Arlington, MA 02174-0164, 1977 and 1982 respectively.

Scholarships, Fellowships and Loans News Service and Counselors Information Services, quarterly newsletter. Bellman Publishing Company, P.O. Box 164, Arlington, MA 02174-0164.

Don't Miss Out. The Ambitious Student's Guide to Scholarships and Loans, 5th ed., 1980/82, Robert Leider, Octameron Associates, Alexandria, VA. Published biennially.

Financial Aids for Higher Education 1980-81 Catalog, 9th ed., 1980, Wm. Brown Publisher, Dubuque, IA.

AFL-CIO Guide to Union Sponsored Scholarships, Awards, and Student Financial Aid, 1981. AFL-CIO Department of Education, 815 16th St., N.W., Washington, DC 20006.

Additionally, there are local newspapers, particularly suburban ones. They generally announce who won what and provide a name or address you can contact.

Local banks, community foundations, and social service agencies are aware of funds about which there is little or no publicity.

Usually there is less competition for local student aid funds in comparison with those available to candidates on a national level.

Many states publish directories of local aids. Your guidance counselor or public librarian will know how to obtain a copy or will have a copy for you to read.

17. The financial aid office of the institution you wish to attend or are attending.

Many funds are administered by the schools themselves, and you must let the financial aids officer know of your need for assistance. Many schools and colleges and universities publish a directory of their aids; they are usually free.

18. Answer all letters and application forms with great care.

Be certain that you have answered *every* question; for those not applicable, write N/A. If at all possible, type; be certain of accuracy and neatness. Meet all deadline dates. Deadline dates may change from those listed in directories. You need enough time to edit your answers several times. The quality of essays when they are required with the application blank is an important screening device. Be certain you remind your references and schools you've attended to submit requested material on time.

19. If you try each one of the methods described above and have ability and potential, you have a good chance of getting student aid. A study by the authors showed that with students of equal ability, the ones who applied to more resources were more successful in obtaining assistance. You may get a scholarship on your second try from the same fund.

Good luck. Don't let the lack of money deter you from seeking further education and training. Your post-secondary education can open up rewarding careers to which you otherwise would not have access.

Dr. S. Norman Feingold is President, National Career and Counseling Services, Washington, DC; Honorary National Director of B'nai B'rith Career and Conseling Services; Past-President of the American Personnel and Guidance Association and the author of several publications including seven volumes of *Scholarships, Fellowships and Loans.* Marie Feingold is a Rehabilitation Counselor, Washington, DC and co-author of volumes six and seven of *Scholarships, Fellowships and Loans.*

Tough questions to ask any admissions officer

By Robert G. McLendon

As a college admissions officer for the past fourteen years, it is clear to me that today's prospective students are carefully comparing colleges and striving to learn all they can about the colleges to which they apply. The age group of 18 to 24 year olds is declining in the United States, and this is creating a type of "buyer's market" in the market place of higher education.

In order to assure yourself that your expectations of a college are met, you, the student consumer, need not hesitate to ask admissions officers some "tough questions." This article will offer you a few suggestions of some tough questions that I hope will help you make the right choice when selecting a college.

Academic Questions

1. How many students in last year's

freshman class returned for their sophomore year?

2. What percent of the freshman class obtained a 2.00 (C) average or above last year?

3. If accepted, will you tell me my predicted freshman grade-point average?

Many colleges use a mathematical formula based on studies of currently enrolled students to predict an applicant's freshman grade average.

4. What is the college's procedure for class placement?

This is especially important in the areas of English and mathematics because freshmen often vary significantly in their ability to handle these important academic skills.

5. What procedure is used to assign a faculty advisor when the student is undecided as to the major area of study?

6. What type of additional academic services does your college offer at no additional cost to the student (e.g., tutoring, career or personal counseling, study-skills workshops, improving reading speed, etc.)?

7. How effective is your college's honor code? What is the penalty for cheating?

Social Questions

1. What is the average age of your student body and what percent resides on campus?

Many colleges today have a large and increasing population of commuting part-time adult students and a dwindling enrollment of 17 to 18 year old full-time, degree-seeking students residing on campus.

2. Is your college a "suitcase college" on the weekends? If not, what are some typical weekend activities for students on your campus?

3. What procedure is used to select roommates if no preference is listed?

4. What are some of the causes of students being suspended or dismissed from your college? Is there a system of appeal for those who have been dismissed?

5. How can a prospective student arrange a campus visit?

Clearly the best possible way to evaluate a college socially is to plan a visit to the campus. When you visit, try not to be shy. After your talk and tour with the admissions officer, walk around by yourself and informally ask students their opinions. A good place to chat with students is in the college's student center or at the dining hall.

6. What are some of the rules and regulations that govern residence hall life? Are there coeducational residence halls?

Financial Questions

1. What percent of your students received financial aid based on financial need?

2. What percent of your students received scholarships based on academic ability?

3. What percent of a typical financial aid offer is in the form of a loan?

4. How much did your college increase cost (room, board, tuition, and fees)

from last year to current year?

5. If an accepted student must submit a room deposit, when is the deposit due, and when is it refundable?

The deposit should be refundable in full up to May 1, if the college or university is a member of the National Association of College Admissions Counselors.

6. If my family demonstrates a financial need on the FAF or FFS forms; what percent of the established need will typically be awarded? When can I expect to receive an official financial aid award letter?

The distinguishing quality of any person is the quality of the mind, and the college you select will have a long-lasting impact on your career and life. I realize that you are painfully aware of the need to make the right college choice because most high school students realize that the college years are often the most productive stage of life. Knowing what questions to ask an admissions officer is an important part of this decision-making process. Most admissions officers want you to ask "tough questions" because if you make the wrong choice we, too, have failed in our job.

Bob McLendon is Vice President for Enrollment Planning, Dean of Admissions, and Financial Aid at Lambeth College, Jackson, Tennessee. He served on the Admissions Practices Committee of the National Associaton of College Admissions Counselors and has been Chairman of the Admissions Practices Committee of the Southern Association of College Admissions Counselors. He is a member of the Executive Board of SACAC and President-Elect of the Carolinas Association of Collegiate Registrars and Admissions Officers.

Common mistakes students make in selecting a college

By William B. Stephens, Jr.

The process of choosing a college can be a rewarding, worthwhile experience or it can be an endless, frustrating series of mistakes. Those mistakes are common and are usually the result of inadequate research and preparation — both characteristics you will need as a successful college student. The selection of a college is a good place to begin developing those virtues.

Begin the process with a series of questions. Am I most interested in a small, medium, or large college? Do I want to stay close to home or go away? What will be my major? Does the college have a broad curriculum if my major is undecided? How academically competi-

tive do I want my college to be? What are the costs? Is financial aid available? Which extracurricular activities are the most importhant to me? When these questions are satisfactorily answered, it is time to begin the next stage.

Research is of primary importance in selecting a college. Do not make the mistake of choosing a college simply because your friends go there. List priorities. Be willing to invest time and effort in investigating colleges which share these priorities.

In writing to colleges for information, be neat, concise, and accurate in providing information about yourself. Many students forget to include the address to which the college should send material. Also include your high school graduation date, the high school you attend, your anticipated major (if that has been decided), and any pertinent information regarding grades and test scores. Decisions are made about students on the basis of their initial contact with the college. Do not be careless in this important decision.

There are numerous publications which are helpful in gathering information. These publications may be located in school and public libraries, bookstores, and guidance offices. Many are cross-referenced according to majors offered, geographic locations, costs, and sizes. Once familiar with college publications, the task of choosing a college becomes an easier one. Do not make the mistake of floundering with too many college options.

Your school guidance office can offer an abundance of information. Among the many contributions of guidance counselors is the provision of data concerning financial aid, college representatives scheduled to visit the school and/or vicinity, College Fairs, and testing for college entrance. In addition, most schools provide counseling to help students choose colleges compatible with their scholastic aptitudes, personality, financial means, and extracurricular interests. Often these guidance resources are not tapped, yet they can be among the most beneficial that you could explore.

Do not neglect the value of contacting alumni, college representatives, and currently enrolled students. Alumni can provide firsthand accounts of life at college while representatives will have the current facts about admissions requirements, new majors offered, scholarships, sports, and campus activities. Students who are currently enrolled in a particular college can provide additional insight into the actual experiences you can expect at the institution.

It is important that you visit the colleges which are your first preferences. Never will catalogs, counseling, or recommendations from alumni replace an actual visit to the campus. Much can be learned from sitting in on a few classes, walking through dormitories, and talking to faculty and staff. It is extremely risky to choose a college without personal observation.

Many colleges have orientation programs to acquaint students and their parents with the facilities and various aspects of student and faculty involvement. Investigate the colleges being considered to discover their plans for orientation programs. Do not fail to be present at the programs in which you are most interested.

Since the cost of attending college can be one of the greatest factors determining your choice, the possibility of obtaining financial aid is to be taken into careful consideration. Watch for the deadlines in applying for financial assistance, and have the appropriate forms completed well in advance. If financial aid is offered, be certain to compare the amount of aid offered and the total cost of attending that particular college. Remember that the matter of final importance is in determining the amount which has to be paid by you and your family.

College preparations should begin in the ninth grade. Solid academic courses (usually beyond the minimum required for high school graduation) should be completed each year. Four years of English is normally expected. Most colleges expect a student to complete at least three years of math, including two years of algebra and one of geometry. Although requirements vary from college to college, it is generally advantageous to have a sound background in biology, chemistry, physics, history, and a foreign language.

High schools administer PSAT, SAT, and ACT exams to juniors and seniors. It is wise to plan to take a College Board exam more than once. As these exams take four to six weeks to be graded, you should allow plenty of time so as not to delay the application process. Your score on a college board exam will further indicate the type of college to attend. Colleges vary considerably in their College Board score requirements.

By October of your senior year, choices should be narrowed to two or three prospective colleges. You should be aware of all admission requirements for each institution considered. Do not delay the application process until after Christmas. Many colleges begin waiting lists very soon after the beginning of each new year. Your application and all required documents should be on file by November 1 at each college considered. Do not expect high schools to send transcripts or teachers to send recommendations the day the request is made. Allow a couple of weeks for these items to be completed and mailed to the college.

Incomplete or illegible applications will greatly diminish the opportunity for rapid processing. These types of delays can mean the difference between being able to attend your first choice of colleges and having to wait another full academic year to enroll.

College-bound students should never hesitate to ask questions. Begin early and be organized. Parental involvement is essential in choosing a college that will meet the need of you and your family. Diligent research and careful planning are the keys to the prevention of the most common mistakes made by college applicants today.

Bill Stephens is Director of Admissions at Florida Southern College, Lakeland, Florida and has worked in the Admissions field for ten years. Stephens is a member of the National Association of Admissions Counselors, the Southern Association of Admissions Counselors, the American Association of Collegiate Admissions and Registrar Officers, and the Southern and Florida Associations of Collegiate Admissions and Registrars Officers.

The advantages and pitfalls of advanced placement and credit by examination for the freshman year of college

By Carl D. Lockman

I think we all agree that gifted young people need help in order to recognize their potential role in society. Through advanced placement and credit by examination programs, secondary school systems and universities alike are making a bona fide effort to encourage the development of academic talent, thus helping students to better understand their contributions to society and self.

Perhaps an explanation of the main difference between advanced placement and credit by examination is appropriate at this point. Both programs serve the purpose of awarding the student college course credit for acceptable scores on examinations. However, the Advanced Placement Program is a function of the College Entrance Examination Board. It is a formally structured program of instruction culminating with an examination. Institutions also may give departmental examinations which may be referred to as advanced placement. Credit by examination may or may not be a formally structured program. The College Level Examination Program (CLEP) is an example of the former, through which a student can receive credit for non-traditional (learning outside the classroom) educational experiences by presenting satisfactory scores on examinations.

All programs designed to award credit at the university level have advantages that are worth the student's consideration. Credit programs complement conventional instruction by allowing students to begin academic study at a level appropriate to their experience. They require students to demonstrate that they have achieved at a level equal to college experience. By being given this opportunity, the student can save both time and money.

A second advantage is that studies indicate that advanced placement continues throughout the undergraduate years. Quantitatively and qualitatively the student benefits. Course credit granted through advanced placement generally allows for increased hours to be completed in a four-year program, much of which may be completed at the junior level and above. This certainly allows for greater flexibility and versatility in designing one's curriculum. Somewhat the opposite has shown up in early studies of CLEP credit. Students with CLEP credit tend to graduate earlier. However, this still permits the student the advantages of having saved money and time and allows the opportunity to move into graduate studies at an earlier date. The challenge for the student is brought to the front when he/she is placed into courses recognizing achievement when his/her ability surpasses basic proficiency level courses.

Another advantage to the participation in and the receiving of credit through these programs is the quality of instruction associated with advanced placement. Generally speaking, it is safe to say that some of the best secondary instructors are asked to conduct the advanced courses. These instructors will stretch to stay ahead of these bright students who comprise the classes. Also, students in these programs not only benefit from the quality of instruction, but from the fact that most schools set up programs by drawing on the experiences of other school systems. In effect, students are being exposed to highly researched programs that have been trial tested for years by many systems.

A closer look at these programs reveals additional advantages. Many advanced placement programs borrow lectures, lab facilities, and equipment from local businesses and universities to accelerate their programs. Schools sometimes pool courses to give a wider curriculum offering. Credit programs allow secondary schools and colleges to articulate their programs, thus helping to bridge the curriculum gap that has been prevalent for years. In bridging this gap the student with an outstanding background can be recognized.

The advantages far outweigh the disadvantages when studying advanced placement and credit by examination programs. Two negative comments might be made at this point. There is always the possibility that students entering these programs do not have a thorough understanding of the extra demands that will be placed on them. Remember that the courses offered in the secondary schools are rigorous college-level courses. College credit granted may result in the student being placed in upper-level courses, which in turn will demand more effort on the student's part. It is not a bad idea either that parents be made aware of what is to be expected of students involved in advanced placement programs and of those having received credit by examination.

Secondly, uninformed secondary and college personnel cause very definite problems. After a student has participated in an advanced placement program or has the experience to achieve credit through examination, it is imperative that the secondary counselors advise students and their parents of colleges that have established policies that would meet the needs of the student. I can think of few things more disappointing than for a student to miss the opportunity to have more flexibility in his courses and to avoid repetition. The other fears are that the college officials may not have required faculty members in the subject areas covered by the tests to review the examinations and that the procedures and practices of the college regarding credit have not been carefully studied. As you can see, such omissions by the institution in establishing policies could lead to improper credit and, even worse, improper placement in courses "over the head" of the student.

In conclusion, whether a student goes through the CEEB Advanced Placement Program, participates in the institution's own advanced placement program by taking departmental examinations, or receives credit for life experiences, the importance of the programs is that they are attempts to equate classroom and/or non-classroom experience to college-level learning. The programs are models of learning closely conforming with college courses. Placement and credit programs are relatively new opportunities which each year seem to become more and more accepted by the academic communities. These are ways to recognize the individual differences in students, an attempt to confront the age-long problems of recognizing the variety of experiences students bring to college, and a breaking from the tradition that all students need to enroll in core curricula.

For students with exceptional learning experiences and/or intellectual talents, advanced placement and credit by examination programs are recommended. The rewards for such accomplishments are great.

Carl D. Lockman is Assistant Director of Admissions at Georgia Institute of Technology, Atlanta, Georgia. Lockman serves on the Admissions Practices Committee of the Southern Association for College Admissions Counselors and is a member of the American and Georgia Associations of Collegiate Registrars and Admissions Officers. He was appointed to the Governor's Committee to study recruitment techniques and is a board member of the Middle Georgia Drug Council.

The academic and social benefits of large American universities

By James C. Blackburn

There is no type of collegiate experience which is most appropriate for all students. The purpose(s) of this essay are to identify and discuss the academic and social benefits of large universities.

In almost every state in the union, there is at least one large university whose enrollment exceeds 10,000 persons. More than a score of states have within their borders, universities enrolling more than 30,000 students. There are several community colleges whose enrollments meet the criterion of having 10,000+ enrollments. Those institutions are not included within the scope of this essay.

A substantial number of large universities are state-supported. However, more than a few large universities are private institutions of higher education. Such universities are more common in the more populous regions of the nation, e.g. the East Coast and upper Midwest. The tuition prices of large universities vary from nominal charges to $10,000 per year. It is, therefore, possible to select a large university from any price range. Some of America's most expensive and least costly institutions can be classified as large universities.

Large universities are located in large cities such as New York, Boston, and Los Angeles, as well as in small towns, e.g. Bloomington, Indiana and Tuscaloosa, Alabama. The selectivity of admission to large universities is also quite varied. Some universities admit as few as one in five of its applicants. Other moderately large institutions offer admission to more than 90% of their applicant pools.

In short, the diversity between and among large universities makes it possible for almost every student who desires to attend such an institution. Enrollment at a large university is not the private privilege of any socio-economic or intellectual sub-segment of American society. That being the case, there must be some good reasons for matriculation at and graduation from a large university.

There are academic benefits which apply to each size and type of college or university. The academic benefits of enrolling at a large university are especially striking.

Few freshmen actually complete the academic major which they begin. At a large university, the available academic majors often number in the hundreds, not dozens. If a student changes his or her major or career choice, the large university is most likely to be able to accommodate that change.

As a result of the "knowledge explosion," many undergraduate *curricula* now require extensive equipment and large library resources. Because of their graduate and professional schools, large universities tend to offer more sophisticated laboratory equipment and libraries of considerable size. So called "economies of scale" seem likely to perpetuate this circumstance. At a large university, undergraduates often compete with others for these resources. The point is that the equipment and libraries are available.

For most students, post-graduate employment is a major reason for college enrollment. Large universities typically offer a multiplicity of services designed to help students in the identification and pursuit of career options. Selecting a career and finding a job are not often easy; it may be well to get as much help as possible.

There is an additional "job search" benefit to holding a degree from a large university. Most such institutions are well known on at least a regional basis. Assuming the reputation of a given institution is good, the employer or graduate school may be more impressed if they are familiar with an applicant's university.

Each type and size of college and university has academic benefits to offer. Ony a few of the academic benefits of the large university have been addressed here. There are other benefits related to the academic learning environment of each large university. Academic learning is clearly the primary reason for the existence of colleges and universities. It would be foolish to suggest that all of the benefits of college attendance happen inside the classroom, laboratory, and library. Many of the non-academic benefits of college attendance are social in nature. It is well that those benefits be discussed.

The typical ages of college attendance (18-22) constitute an important period of intellectual and social development. It is important that these changes take place in the most nearly appropriate environment possible. Intellectual development is obviously an academic enterprise. Social development, which means more than just dating, parties, and football games, happens throughout the campus environment. As with the academic areas, each type of college or university has social benefits to offer prospective students. The social benefits of large universities are significant; those benefits should be considered carefully by aspiring freshmen.

It is reasonable to state that larger universities offer more student activities and more varied opportunities to associate with other students. In fact, many freshmen who enroll at the largest university find themselves inundated with opportunities for social involvement, community service, etc. It may be difficult to select the activities, clubs, and personal associations which are most appropriate for individual students.

The variety of opportunities for student involvement at a large university are often more impressive than the sheer number of such involvements, activities, clubs, etc. Many larger universities offer organizations which cater to a plethora of interests ranging from handicrafts to hang gliding. There are often religious organizations for many faiths and denominations. The opportunities for political involvement are often wide ranging. From the most serious of religious or political convictions to the desire for big or small parties, large universities can frequently provide activities which meet the needs of all their students.

As universities grow, the size of the student services staffs also grow. With regard to academics, this growth in student services results in improved opportunities for career identification and job seeking. In the arena of social development, this growth means more opportunities for personal counseling and other activities which are designed to help a person to improve their social awareness and skills.

A final social benefit of large universities has to do with one's classmates.

Because of their size, large universities often enroll students whose backgrounds present a wide variety of experiences, values, and perspectives. Exceptions to this rule do exist, but is is generally true that one's classmates at a large university will be less homogeneous than might be the case at smaller colleges and universities.

There is an important social benefit in this lack of sameness among a student's classmates. Most students will study, work, and live out their lives in a world composed of a huge variety of persons. Our society has become more pluralistic in recent years. It seems, therefore, likely that there is a good in being able to live and work with a wide variety of persons. College is an excellent place to gain experience in dealing with people whose backgrounds and perspectives may be different from your own. Large universities offer many opportunities for such experiences.

By way of the above, it is hoped the nature(s) and benefits of large universities may be better understood by qualified prospective students. The more important points of this essay are that American higher education is quite varied and that no type of colleges or universities is inherently superior to any other type or types. Each student must make his or her own decisions about the appropriateness of small colleges, community colleges, church affiliated colleges, and large universities.

This writer's bias for large universities should be obvious. Huge varieties of academic and social opportunities are available at large universities. Those varieties serve to make such institutions an excellent choice for many aspiring freshmen. Large universities, although varied themselves, are not for everyone. They do present very appropriate choices for many prospective students.

Jim Blackburn is Director of Admissions at the University of Northern Colorado, Greeley, Colorado and has been involved in the college admissions process for over ten years. He has conducted a number of conference presentations for admissions personnel at various association meetings.

The academic and social advantages of a private church-related college or university

By A. Mitchell Faulkner

Many educators in recent days are concerned that moral and ethical matters have been so largely excluded from the educational experience. Under the influence of a technology expanding beyond all expectations, the demands placed upon most professions, including the social and natural sciences, have worked to exclude serious consideration of moral and ethical concerns inseparably bound up in that expanding technology.

But the assumption that our complex society can be safely led by technicians untrained in the making of serious ethical decisions affecting our corporate well being is totally unacceptable to any thinking person.

As Bruce Haywood has written in *The Chronicle of Higher Education,* "too many of our colleges and universities have become vocational schools... Whereas once they offered our children avenues to a larger sense of their humanity, they now direct them to the market place. Instead of seeing themselves enlarged under the influence of great minds and grand ideas, students find themselves shrunken to fit the narrowing door of the graduate school or tailored to a job description. It is time for our colleges and universities to talk again about the worth of a free life, time while we are still able to distinguish between the *training* of young people and their *education.*" (1/8/79)

Young people are not born with moral and ethical convictions. They are learned in the educational process, if learned at all, by precept and by example, by being in the presence of people with convictions. Healthy self identity, says Lloyd Averill, emerges out of an environment which has convictional distinctiveness, in which the maturing self has access to a range of clear and competing values where the competition serves to sharpen and enliven the options rather than to subjugate or obliterate them.

A subtle but pervasive element emerging in our day is what Archibald MacLeish has called the diminution of man, the "long diminishment of value put upon the idea of man" in our society. Why has this happened now at the moment of our greatest intellectual triumphs, our never equalled technological mastery, our electronic miracles? "Man was a wonder to Sophocles when he could only sail and ride horseback and plow; now that he knows the whole of modern science he is a wonder to no one," says MacLeish.

At least part of this loss of the humane is caused by the knowledge explosion, the sheer weight of information in the print and electronic media, so that man despairs of any cognitive wholeness and surrenders ever increasing areas of knowledge to a vast array of experts.

Earl McGrath, former Commissioner of Education, says on the other hand, that this vast array of facts and theories needs to be collated and evaluated within the framework of philosophic convictions and religious beliefs in order for the wisdom of the ages to again invest dehumanizing facts with meaning for man.

One further point of definition needs stating. Our sense of community has well nigh been lost, and every social philosopher recognizes the need to restore it. What is at stake here, says John Gardner, is the individual's sense of responsibility for something beyond the self. The "me" generation threatens the cohesiveness of our social fabric, and a spirit of concern and caring is virtually impossible to sustain in a vast, impersonal society.

All of the above points directly to the purpose of the church-related liberal arts college. The essence of the liberal arts is the passion for man, the development of the humane values in literature, philosophy, history, and religion; and the great ideas of the race, such as truth, justice, love, beauty, honor, and wisdom are precisely the vehicles through which the deepest purposes of religion are served. Religion is only secondarily a matter of creeds and rituals. At its heart it is a matter of meaning, and this meaning is conveyed most effectively through the wisdom of the ages, the liberal arts.

Education is more than a learned set of mental exercises, the ability to respond properly to fixed mental inquiries. A computer does this admirably. To be fully human is to add to this a capacity for imagination, the ability to feel reverence and awe in the presence of mystery, a capacity for caring and compassion, and appreciation for the mixed grandeur and misery of the human experience. These represent the uniquely human accomplishment and point the direction for the church-related liberal arts college.

Further, the church-related college, usually smaller, offers a community in which students have more opportunity to learn through experience the interpersonal skills so necessary to effective participation in today's society. The development of the whole person involves taking responsibility for the care of the community, its governance, its social life, its ethical and moral tone, its operative effectiveness. A broad participation in all aspects of the campus community should mark the church-related college.

Students are not uniformly at the same place in their development, and ought not to be coerced to march lock step through some standardized program. The undergraduate program, through flexibility made possible by forms of governance and individual care, ought to allow as much as possible for diversity of interest and differences in development as the student progresses. A college ought to find ways to encourage each student to develop to the fullest potential his individual gifts and educational aspirations. A student's goals ought to be headed by the desire not only to master the curriculum but to develop himself. The church-related college will seek to aid this through the total experience, intellectual, social, cultural and religious.

The church-related college, if dedicated to the fully human development of its students, will retain a healthy respect for the vocational skills. In order to fully *be*, a person must be able to *do*. Life cannot be divorced from work, and a healthy self identity depends in part upon the ability to make some significant contribution to society. Thus the great truths of the liberal arts must be brought to focus and a point of service through competency in a chosen area of the world's work, where one may serve and fully live.

After all, as Montaigne said a long time ago, the purpose of education is not to make a scholar but a man.

A. Mitchell Faulkner is the former Executive Director, Council for Higher Education, Western North Carolina Conference, The United Methodist Church. He is on the Board of Trustees for Pfeiffer, Greensboro, High Point and Brevard Colleges, and is a member of many educational associations including the North Carolina Association of Independent Colleges and Universities, Secretary, S.E. Jurisdictional Commission on Higher Education.

Advantage of attending a state university

By Stanley Z. Koplik

For most students and their families, the cost of a four-year college education is an important consideration, and for this reason alone, many choose state colleges and universities. These institutions are usually considerably less expensive than private institutions and in many cases provide students with the option of living at home while pursuing a degree.

State scholarship programs are frequently available providing monetary incentives even to those who attend state institutions. Some families appreciate the opportunity of utilizing a system they continue to support with their tax dollars. But state universities are a wise choice for the college bound for many reasons other than simply economics. For young people growing toward independence, the proximity of the state college or university to parents, friends and home community can provide the firm base of support students need as they adjust to the academic, social and emotional pressures of a more demanding way of life.

High school graduates seeking to continue their education in an atmosphere of intellectual challenge and academic diversity should also look to the state universities and colleges. With a wide range of courses and curricula from which to choose, state institutions of higher education provide a solid grounding in most fields from vocational and technical training to liberal arts education. No longer stereotyped as teacher training schools, state colleges and universities now emphasize engineering, computer technology, business, and science as well as teacher education and the humanities.

As a first step for those seeking professional careers, state institutions offer programs in such fields as medicine, dentistry, law and architecture. Virtually, any area of academic interest can be satisfied through state college programs. At the University of Kansas, for example, there are 112 degree programs offered; the University of Missouri offers approximately 125. Other states offer an equally broad array of programs. With outstanding faculties in many disciplines, and national reputations in many areas, state institutions have developed into comprehensive universities where intellectual inquiry and academic excellence flourish.

A large number of state colleges and universities are equipped with fine research facilities and outstanding libraries providing unlimited opportunities for questioning and stimulating creative minds. In some areas the most complete and comprehensive library in the state thrives on the campus of the state university, while inter-library loan systems enhance access of all state residents to study and research materials.

For those who are concerned about "being lost in the crowd," state higher education systems usually provide a variety of campus sizes ranging from the very samll school with 1-2,000 students to the "mega-campus" with a student population of 25,000 or more. Attendance at a smaller campus does not imply inferior educational quality or diminished services. Excellent instruction, stimulating classroom discussion and challenging extracurricular activities can be found on all state college campuses regardless of size.

Providing an integrated educational program with a maximum of flexibility is the goal of many state systems. To facilitate student choice, states such as Kansas and Missouri have developed clear articulation or transfer agreements with junior college for a senior institution. Many junior college graduates enter four-year institutions as juniors with legitimate standing.

Continuous attendance at college or university is ideal for those pursuing a degree but it is not always possible. When attendance must be interrupted, many state universities provide cooperative extension programs and programs of continuing education for those who cannot attend classes full-time on campus. State higher education institutions also use sophisticated telecommunications systems to bring the university and its courses to the most outlying areas of the state.

The college years are, for many, a time to develop relationships which will provide a source of friendships and professional contacts for a lifetime. Attending college in one's home state increases opportunities to establish such long-lasting relationships and to be woven more fully into the fabric of state life.

Young people are increasingly aware of significant roles they will play in the social, political and economic life of this country. A college education in the state in which they are most likely to live can provide students with early involvement in the complexities of state activity. Increasingly, states are encouraging participation by student government groups in legislative activities. Some states, including Kansas, have authorized the appointment of a Student Advisory Committee to the Board of Regents, thus ensuring direct student participation in the decision making process.

State universities have long been known for athletic as well as academic excellence, and this continues to be true. On many campuses, intramural sports along with intercollegiate sports, enable large numbers of students to develop athletic prowess. As early responders to the growing need for quality in women's athletics, state universities provide equal opportunity in such sports as basketball, volleyball, swimming and tennis. Large multipurpose buildings springing up on many campuses indicate a dedication of state institutions to physical development and the cultural development of both campus and community. In some areas, the state college campus is the site of important cultural events, bringing lecturers, exhibits and the performing arts to an entire region. Attention must be given to the academic interest, the scholastic ability and the social and emotional maturity of the student as well as to the range of curricula, quality of instruction and extracurricular activities of the institution. A close examination of state university systems in the United States will indicate that there is virtually around every corner a quality institution of higher education solidly grounded in academics and attuned to the social and cultural needs of both students and community. State colleges and universities are a vital link in the network of public educational services and as such, merit serious consideration by the college bound.

Stanley Z. Koplik is Executive Officer of the Kansas Board of Regents, the governing body of public higher education in Kansas. Prior to assuming his current duties, Koplik served as Commissioner of Higher Education for the State of Missouri, where he directed activities of the Coordinating Board for Higher Education.

Advantages of a women's college

By Dr. Julia McNamara

Women's colleges are alive and well, even in 1982's all-too-realistic environment which predicts financial aid cuts, decreasing numbers of traditional college-age students, and a tight job market. Today, the mission and goals of 117 women's colleges in the United States matches neatly and clearly those of thousands of young women precisely because of these realities which they must face.

Women's colleges affirm and strengthen a woman's talent and ability; they exist specifically to develop the potential of their students; they demand and expect student participation and involvement. Women's colleges implant in women an attitude that is invaluable for success and achievement: "I can accomplish this task *and* I am a woman," not "even though" or "because" one is a woman. Rather the emphasis is on the fact that being a woman *and* accomplishing the task are quite compatible. Women's colleges instill in students the attitude that there is no sex-based limit to their potential for success. "I've lost that 'If-you're-a-woman-maybe-you-can't' attitude," said a 1982 women's college graduate who was also a student governor.

At a women's college, women learn that they can handle things because they have to handle them. They run the show; they exert influence; they wield power in student organizations which are exclusively their own. No one ever tells them that a particular leadership role is inappropriate for a woman. They can become properly aggressive and assertive without fear of seeming unattractive to men.

They learn to compete intellectually in an environment that consciously prepares them to realize that, if they seek it, the opportunity is there to excel. Their femininity will not be a deterrent at a women's college. Thus, women in leadership roles are not conspicuous at a women's college. Theirs is the only leadership that will occur, and they become comfortable with it. Women have to be in front of and behind all campus activities and events through which they learn to expect the best of themselves and of one another.

One woman, slightly overwhelmed by the extent of her responsibilities as student government treasurer, a task which involved budgets and planning, told me that she learned more from that experience than from some of her accounting classes, because she had final responsibility, and she had to make hard and unpopular decisions. She also said that her shyness and timidity would, in another setting, have prevented her from running for that office. "I would have thought some sharp guy could do it better."

When considering a women's college, it is important to understand several facts: First, women's colleges are not havens for people who could not survive elsewhere. Challenges and difficulties are just as much a part of this educational scene as any other, but there is emphasis on assisting women to meet the challenges which are special to them. Second, traditional views of women's colleges as protective shelters for innocent girls just do not pertain in 1982. Women's colleges are usually exciting places where learning and living mesh to create a viable educational and human experience. Third, women's colleges are not islands or ivory towers which exist by themselves, tiny spheres of influence which no other form of life can touch. Today, women's colleges often share facilities, faculty, and activities with neighboring schools so that students do participate in other educational environments. Thus, women's colleges can and do enjoy the benefits of co-education while maintaining their basic identity. This identity distinguishes her college and gives the young woman a chance to

become a competitor, an achiever, a doer in an environment that is specifically concerned with her own development as a woman.

If women's colleges do not apologize for their *raison d'etre* of being for and about women's education, neither do they ignore men. Quite the contrary: women at a college for women, know well that this environment is only a temporary one, a step on the way to fuller participation in the human, common endeavor. If the college does its job well, the woman will realize that this environment prepares her for the next move and, indeed, sets the pace for it.

"You probably won't find your husband at a women's college," said one admissions counselor to a roomful of high school juniors, "but you will find out a lot about yourself, and about the kind of man you may want to marry." In considering a college, a woman needs to be clear about the reason for attendance at *any* college. Social life and experience are part of the rationale, but her intellectual development, the best and most comprehensive of which she is capable, is the key factor. To honor a woman's desire for quality education and self-development is the mission of a college which proclaims that it is *for* women.

Both academic and student services programs at women's colleges are consciously designed to achieve this mission. The opportunity to be leaders increases a student's self-awareness and inculcates a sense of feminine identity, preparing women for participation in every area of endeavor. No matter how secure or talented they are, young women do need affirmation and assistance in developing self-confidence. For example, two young women on my campus participated recently in the management of a political campaign. They were hired as business manager and associate to the candidate who was a woman. Because of specific communication skills that they had learned while working in a college office where the woman supervisor constantly exemplified a serious professional relationship with them, they succeeded admirably in a tough task. Of course, such training could occur on any college campus, but the point is that on a women's college campus specific efforts to develop a young woman's potential are a priority in all aspects of campus life from residence hall to classroom.

At women's colleges, career development offices train women for the competitive environment of the job market. Internship programs established in cooperation with local business and professional offices give students initial experience in administration or management or one of the professions, and provides a bridge between the world of academe and the business scene. When academic credit is linked with direct work experience a student's incentive increases; so does her personal satisfaction. And before she started out for the office, the student learned in a seminar room or through directed role-play what would be expected of her as a woman in the internship environment.

Faculties and administrative staffs at women's colleges are aware of their

responsibility to develop young women's awareness of problems which she may face because she is a woman in a particular environment. The realities of discrimination and sexual harassment, can be a shock for the individual who needs to learn to deal with them effectively and, above all, to move beyond them.

When considering a women's college, these are questions which an applicant may want to ask during interviews:

1. Do the college's representatives seem to value their institution's specific identity as a women's college?
2. Does the college offer career guidance and advice for women?
3. Does the college have an internship program for its women?
4. What rapport has this institution established with neighboring universities and colleges?
5. What do students there say about their experience at a women's college?
6. Does the social life there give them a chance to meet men?

Responses to such questions give the prospective student a clear picture of the institution's commitment to the specific and unique character of a women's college. Certainly, a women's college is not for every woman. But equally as certain is the fact that these colleges continue to be extremely advantageous to the women who choose them.

Note: For more information on women's colleges, see: "A Profile of Women's Colleges" Women's College Coalition, Suite 1003, 1725 K St. N.W. Washington, DC 20006.

Dr. Julia McNamara is President of Albertus Magnus College in New Haven, Connecticut where she is also adjunct assistant professor of French literature. Dr. McNamara has also served as Dean of Students at this women's college. As an undergraduate she attended two women's colleges, Marymount Manhattan in New York City and St. Mary of the Springs, now Ohio Dominican, Columbus, Ohio and holds a Master's degree from Middlebury College and a Ph.D. from Yale University. She has been a Fulbright scholar and has studied for two years in Paris.

Opportunities at independent research universities

By F. Gregory Campbell

The diversity in American higher education is one of the greatest glories of our culture. No where else in the world does a prospective student enjoy such a wide range of choice. Public or private, large or small, urban or rural, secular or religiously oriented — American universities and colleges vary so greatly that any student should be able to find an institution seemingly tailor-made for that individual.

The major independent research universities constitute an important segment of American higher education. Frequently, they are considered primarily graduate or professional centers, and it is true that many students would be well advised to spend their undergraduate years elsewhere. But those universities typically possess vital undergraduate colleges offering a highly stimulating intellectual and extracurricular environment. For the right kind of student there is no better place.

In academic circles, the independent research universities enjoy an extraordinary reputation. That image depends on the quality of the faculty, and research is normally the means by which a scholar is evaluated. No one has yet devised a reliable method of measuring, comparing, and publicizing good teachers across the country. Good researchers are easy to spot, however, for they publish their discoveries for their colleagues around the world to evaluate. The research universities boast outstanding faculties containing highly innovative scholars with worldwide reputations.

But do they — or can they — teach? In ideal circumstances, the answer is yes. A standard view is that teachers are best when they continue to discover knowledge in their respective fields of scholarship. Conversely, the challenge of sharing their discoveries with critical young minds makes researchers better as a result of their also being teachers. Clearly, this ideal is not always realized. No university can guarantee that its most recent Nobel-prize winner will be teaching freshman chemistry, but such does happen.

The hope of learning from such scholars lures top-notch students to the research universities. Indeed, those institutions would have to do very little in order to produce outstanding graduates. Most college students quickly discover that they learn as much, or more, from their fellow students as from their professors. Inasmuch as the research universities serve as a meeting point for many bright young people, much of the intellectual stimulation on the campuses is provided by the students themselves. Compatibility with others who take their studies seriously is an essential prerequisite for prospective students.

But college life cannot be all work and pressure. There have been persistent efforts over the past fifteen years or so to reduce intellectual competition among students. Professorial complaints about "grade inflation" reflect the fact that it is much easier for a student to stay in the universities than to get into them to begin with. The drop-out rate is low, the failure rate even lower.

The learning experience extends beyond classrooms, libraries, and laboratories, and cannot be measured by grades alone. Extracurricular opportunities for learning and growth are central to a college experience. Most of the independent research universities seek to encourage informal association between professors and students. Professors may be encouraged to eat meals regularly with students in the dining halls. Leaders in public affairs or the arts and sciences may be invited to the campuses in order to engage in informal meetings with students. How does one measure the worth to a pre-law student of a breakfast conversation with a Supreme Court justice?

The independent research universities almost never appear on the list of major NCAA powers in football or basketball. Their teams normally compete at a lower level. But their programs do offer opportunities to participate in intercollegiate athletics to many young men and women who could not make the teams of the major powers. In addition, the intra-mural programs typically attract the vast majority of students on campus. The schools do not figure prominently in the sports pages, but the student communities are active and vigorous.

The undergraduate colleges within the independent research universities are normally quite small. Whereas they enroll more students than a typical liberal arts college, they have many fewer students than the state universities. That size both provides a critical mass for a wide variety of activities and allows for a sense of community and personal identity in a manageable environment.

The student bodies themselves are quite diverse. Admissions officers try hard to insure a nationally representative student body — including students from various regions of the country, diverse ethnic groups, and economic levels. There is also a significant number of foreign students. This intimate exposure to differences among people is a key element in the growth to adulthood.

The kind of education that is offered in the independent research universities is expensive, and tuition levels are high. Yet, since the 1960's, those institutions have tried to provide sufficient amounts of aid to enable students to matriculate regardless of financial need. It is an open question whether that policy can be maintained, even formally, in a more difficult economic environment.

The concept of a "University College" is the most apt way of thinking about undergraduate programs in an independent research university. Students find a relatively small college with a distinct identity of its own. Yet that college lives within a much larger institution possessing resources available for undergraduates to exploit. Those "University Colleges" are not appropriate for everyone, and there are many other excellent institutions from which to choose. But, when the match is right, a "University College" can offer gifted and serious young people opportunities seldom found elsewhere.

F. Gregory Campbell is Secretary of the Board of Trustees and Special Assistant to the President at The University of Chicago. He is a historian specializing in the history of international relations and Central and Eastern European history. In addition to administrative duties, he teaches in the college and the Graduate Divisions at Chicago.

Choosing the right college major

By James E. Moore

Implicit in this analysis is the assumption that there are some important decisions to make before choosing a major. A brief look at these is in order. First is the decision to enroll in a college or university. There is much rewarding and lucrative work in the world which does not require a college education. Furthermore, a wealth of adult programs have sprung up in the last decade, making the college education readily available later on to those who for a variety of reasons do not attend on a full-time basis immediately after high school. While there is immense peer and parental pressure in favor of college directly after grade twelve, there are many fascinating people who can attest to the value of travel or work after twelve years of formal schooling; these experiences shape and enrich the college experience when it is finally pursued.

Once the decision to go to college is made, one must choose the right college in order to be able to choose the right major. Not all schools teach everything, nor do they all teach as well as one another in a particular area. Obviously, the school should offer a program in what is the applicant's current major interest. Then, with some agressive questioning of students, faculty, and admissions personnel, the applicant can get a sense of how well the school does in that area and what, if any, particular perspective on the discipline is represented by that department.

The choosing of the major — in educational parlance, it is called "declaring the major" — is something which usually occurs toward the end of the sophomore year. While colleges and universities are interested in knowing what a prospective student intends to study and generally solicit that information on the application, that designation is neither binding nor necessary. Admissions officers and academic advisors are understanding of the many freshmen who simply do not know in what field they will concentrate, and it is not uncommon for a person to change directions a number of times during the first two years of college. It is, however, difficult to change majors as a junior or senior and still complete degree requirements in four years.

How does one determine what should be the major area of interest? A critical look at the high school record and aptitude and preference tests is a good way to start. What were the courses that proved exciting? In what did the student excel? Are the verbal or the quantitative skills more highly developed? The Kuder Preference Test asks the taker to respond to a variety of hypothetical situations and, by patterns that emerge from the responses, is a decent indicator of the general kind of work that will be congruent with the sense of self and others that is reflected in a person's answers.

Most colleges and universities require all students to complete course work in a variety of broad areas regardless of the intended major. This work commences during the freshman year and can be a useful way to further define the primary interest. Colleges offer courses in subjects that most high schools cannot or do not. In the process of meeting course requirements in the humanities, social sciences, and natural sciences or math, students expose themselves to new disciplines, one of which might well become the major.

In recent years, along with curricular development, there has been much interest and innovation in the issue of modes of learning. While the conventional classroom-lecture-textbook-test method of teaching and learning remains prevalent, the opportunity of "learning by doing" has become a widespread option. Some high schools offer their seniors the opportunity to do volunteer work for a variety of agencies, businesses, and charities. This work often evolves into summer employment for high school students. At the college level, the programs are more comprehensive, often involving both college credit and remuneration. Internships and cooperative education placements are an excellent way for students to discover exactly what a particular workplace is like and to determine just how suitable their preparation for that career is.

In addition to faculty, libraries, and laboratories, one of the most important resources for the undergraduate is the student who lives two doors down the hall. He or she probably studies in an area far removed from one's own or comes to the same interests for entirely different reasons. That person has parents who may well have had professional experiences and can share a sense of that professionalism from a perspective more personal than one that is offered in the classroom. The "bull session" is both misnamed and underestimated; these hours of informal exchange are often fundamental in shaping the direction and quality of life for many college students.

These are times when choosing the right major entails a gamble, regardless of how one sees it. The numbers of options are mind-boggling. The lack of certainty about the usefulness of a particular degree is a reality which should not be ignored, given rapid and constant change in the nature and needs of the workplace. Perhaps more than ever there is a case to be made for seeing the undergraduate years as ones for refining skills in reading, writing, and reasoning well, whichever department serves as the context for such endeavors. The risks are substantially reduced if the student is realistic about his or her capabilities and commitments, and thorough in exposure to the wealth of opportunity and resources colleges and universities offer. Above all, choosing the right major is cast in an appropriate light when seen as but one milestone of many in the process of learning, a venture which lasts a lifetime.

Jim Moore is an Admissions Officer at The American University in Washington, DC and previously worked in admissions at Aurora College, Aurora, Illinois; Goddard College, Plainfield, Vermont; and The New England Graduate Center of Antioch College, Keene, New Hampshire.

A yearn to earn

By Lawrence B. Durham

Throughout the 1970's much was made over the fact that the earnings differential between those with college degrees and those with only high school diplomas had shrunk. Many sought to interpret this statistical fact as evidence of the lessened worth of a college education. In the latter part of the decade, spiraling inflation and unemployment rates combined to produce a generation of college-bound young people more dedicated than ever to securing degrees which would assure them of employment upon graduation.

High school graduates of the early 1980's have thus been conditioned towards a very pragmatic view of the value of a college education. Yet, while post-college employment should be enhanced by this credentialing process, there is a real danger of overlooking the far more important and life-spanning aspects of the collegiate experience. Indeed, many college faculties have contributed to this trend since the Russians launched their first Sputnik in 1957. Now, increasing numbers of these unwitting advocates of vocationalism are breathing fresh life into time-proven concepts such as core curricula and general education programs. Thus, the student entering college in the early 1980's faces the perplexing efforts of college faculties and our national economy as both seek to regain lost equilibrium through seemingly contradictory means.

In order to plot a realistic and rewarding course through the uncharted waters of higher education in this decade, students should be careful to expect neither too much nor too little from their collegiate experience. In an era where many college graduates may have to accept employment in jobs which had typically been filled by persons without degrees, certainly one would be unwise to expect a guaranteed position upon graduation. On the other hand, the rate of change in our society and in technological development is so rapid that a significant portion of the jobs in the next decade are non-existent at the present time. Consequently, one must seek to attain preparation for the unknown.

Education at its best results in the participant learning *how to learn* and *how to cope with change.* Given these two skills, the future can be faced with confidence. "Educational experiences" not producing these skills would better be labeled "training." And, it is crucial to note that such skills cannot be *taught,* they must be *learned.* As a result, the burden is on the student, not the teacher!

How then should one pursue such lofty goals? First, and foremost, there should be a commitment made to be an active participant in the educational process rather than to be satisfied as a passive subject. Then, a process of exploration should ensue during which the fear of the unknown is overcome by the excitement of discovery. In short, courage will lead to adventure!

Perhaps it would be useful at this point to emphasize the scope of these considerations. During the course of a life's work, a person may well change jobs eight to ten times. While several jobs may be in the same field, such as engineering, others may be in another field altogether, such as education. Generally, the different jobs are referred to as vocations, while the different fields are spoken of as careers. Thus an engineer might have several jobs within the field of engineering and then change careers to education where his vocation might be teaching in a particular college. In today's world and even more so in the future, students can ill afford to prepare for only a single career, let alone for a single vocation!

In this context, this author submits that the academic debate between specialized curricula and liberal arts programs is little more than a semantic exercise if the importance of developing both useful skills and broad perspectives is recognized. Just as an engineering program can include courses in the humanities, so can a liberal arts program include basic business courses. Studies continue to show that those who communicate effectively (orally as well as in writing), reason analytically, work well with others, and understand basic business principles find their respective pursuits far more rewarding.

A word of caution is in order, too, lest the reader fail to acknowledge consciously that the most important "rewards" are not financial. Over the years, studies of worker attitudes and values have increasingly revealed that pay ranks below other aspects of work such as the nature of the job environment the degree of individual autonomy, and the self-esteem derived from performing the work. Therefore, students should be careful not to choose a career path for purely financial reasons.

The process of choosing a course of study is no mean feat! Unless one has a burning desire to qualify for a particular profession, it is quite likely that several fields are of interest. Naturally, in the former case, the student would follow that academic track leading to certification in the chosen field. However, even in such cases, sampling courses in other fields and apprenticeships in the field of primary interest will often pay unexpected dividends. A person who is undecided should not develop an inferiority complex and go through senior high school and college apologizing! Rather, that individual should seek counsel and work experiences in areas of interest and engage in a sound, broadly-based course of study up to the point where declaration of a major field is required.

As of this writing, energy and computer science head the list of promising fields with other engineering and business areas and health services close behind. As we become more and more dependent on information exchange, related vocations in that field will increase in their attractiveness. And who knows where we are headed in the fields of microelectronics and genetic engineering. Yet, the reader who selected a course of collegiate study based solely on this or any similar listing would have missed the real point of this article. The true value of a college education cannot be quantified. To the contrary, its qualitative dimensions transcend the relatively narrow considerations of vocation and career to affect our entire lives.

Yearn to learn and you will learn to live. Live to learn and you will learn to earn.

Dr. Lawrence B. Durham is Dean of Admission Services, The University of Alabama. He holds memberships in many associations including the American, Southeastern and Alabama Associations of Collegiate Registrars and Admissions Officers. He has published numerous articles in the field of education.

The two-year experience

By Dr. Jacob C. Martinson, Jr.

It is a difficult adjustment for a student to go from a high school, sometimes a small high school at that, directly into a multi-complex university often with thousands and thousands of other students. Are the majority of high school graduates equipped for this kind of transition? The answer, of course, is that some are, and some are not. There is an alternative approach.

There is a wide range of academic programs available among two-year colleges today. There are many accredited institutions which offer outstanding two-year terminal programs in areas such as business arts, computer science, and medical arts. This article, however, will focus on the two-year colleges that are designed to prepare the students for continuation at a four-year college or university. It will address the belief that, in many cases, the pursuit of the baccalaureate degree is greatly enhanced by "The Two-Year Experience."

When it comes to the role of a college

education in career performance, an academically recognized two-year college can provide the essential foundations of undergraduate training often better than the best universities. After all, it doesn't take an expert to see that faculty qualifications are not that different from one center of learning to another. For example, a survey of the educational credentials of faculty members at good two-year colleges reveals that they have received their graduate training at the finest colleges and universities in the country.

The advantages of getting a good start at a two-year college are numerous. I will cite some reasons why a two-year college program should be considered.

1. Access to the Faculty

A faculty member ordinarily does not choose to teach at a two-year college unless he/she is specifically dedicated to teaching. Those faculty members who are interested in publishing or research usually go to the multi-complex universities where much of their undergraduate teaching responsibilities are delegated to graduate assistants. Classes in two-year colleges are generally taught by first-line faculty members.

Students have a right to expect some time with their professors who have spent many hours embodying much of the knowledge in which the students are interested. In the smaller two-year colleges, the opportunity is provided to know professors on a one-to-one basis. It is not uncommon to observe ballgames between faculty and students, or for faculty to invite students to their homes for refreshments.

2. A Good Beginning

The first two years of college are probably the most important of a student's college career. With the exception of kindergarten and first grade, they are all-important to the pursuance of formal education. Statistics show that when a students does well in an academically sound two-year college, he/she seldom does poorly academically anywhere else. A good start can make the difference.

3. Budget Appropriations

Many multi-complex universities give the "lion's share" of the funds to the upper-level undergraduate courses and to the graduate programs. Two-year colleges, on the other hand, give their entire budget to those critical first two undergraduate years.

4. Less Expense to the Student

One can attend a fine two-year college with a superb academic reputation for less than one can attend most universities. The community colleges are less expensive to the student, but even the private residential two-year colleges are relatively inexpensive. Of course, if commuting is possible, the expense is even less. Since the private college also wants to serve the surrounding community, special scholarships to commuting area residents are offered by some colleges.

5. Opportunities for Leadership and Participation

The freshmen and sophomores at a two-year college will have no juniors and seniors to compete with in extra-

curricular activites for campus leadership roles, team sport participation, and faculty time. The individual has an opportunity to become involved more quickly and more deeply in the total life of the college. Where else could a student be a representative to the college committees and the Board of Trustees at the age of 18? In short, there is no "sophomore slump" in the two-year college.

6. Vocational Future

The two-year college can enrich one's vocational future. The fact is that too many college graduates today are ignorant of the English language, history, science, and math. Many are deficient in their ability to get along with others and in that all-important skill of communication. One need only watch a nationally televised athletic event to observe the inability of some students from the so-called "prestigious" centers of learning to speak proper English. This is not to imply that the two-year college student will consistently perform any better; however, at good two-year colleges, there is a concerted effort to start wherever a student is academically and teach him/her to read and write effectively. For example, some of the better two-year colleges have 3 or 4 different levels of beginning English. The same is true of math. These schools place great emphasis on English and math with the conviction that if one can read and write and add and subtract, one has the educational foundation to function in the world. The hallmark of the best two-year colleges is that of toughness with caring. Such colleges encourage the formulation of long-range educational goals and positive views on how education can assist one in meeting vocational objectives. Obviously, there are some limitations to the depth to which one can pursue objectives in a two-year setting, but the seeds are planted and the incentives aroused.

7. The Best of Both Worlds

A student can have the best of the two-year and the four-year educational systems. During those critical first two years of college, a fine two-year school can provide an excellent academic program and curriculum, caring faculty members, and a concerned college community, all of which prepare the student to transfer to the larger college or university.

There are those in educational circles who would have one believe that transferring is dangerous to one's educational future. In most cases this belief is unfounded. On the contrary, it is sometimes easier to get into the best four-year schools after a two-year Associate of Arts/Science/Fine Arts degree than to apply right out of high school. Academic credits from a good, academically sound, two-year college are accepted by most of the finest universities. In fact, transfer students are not only accepted, they are actively recruited because of the natural attrition in the senior colleges and universities after the first and second years. Also, some students perform better in a two-year college than they did in high school; therefore, these students are more likely to have their application accepted when they leave the two-year college than when they graduated from high school. Further, there are certain rights and responsibilities which are uniquely applicable to the transferring student. A statement of these rights and responsibilities has been approved by the NACAC (National Association of College Admissions Counselors) in 1980 and revised in 1982.

In conclusion, today's two-year college generally offers a university-parallel curriculum. It is nearly always designed for the brilliant as well as the average student. The task is to successfully meet and challenge each student where he/she is academically despite varying aptitudes, dispositions, and outlooks.

The two-year college experience is not for everyone, but it certainly fills a need. It is a good place to start in higher educational pursuits — a good place to begin on the way toward the baccalaureate degree.

Jake Martinson is President of Brevard College, Brevard, North Carolina. Before going to Brevard in 1976, he was President of Andrew College in Cuthbert, Georgia. Dr. Martinson holds degrees from Huntingdon College, Duke University, and Vanderbilt University. Beyond serving Brevard College, he has been President of the Brevard Chamber of Commerce and Secretary of the Independent College Fund of North Carolina and is an elected Board member of the National Association of Schools and Colleges of the United Methodist Church. Born of Norwegian-American lineage, he is an honorary member of the American-Scandinavian Foundation.

The value of a liberal arts education

By Dr. David Maxwell

We are in the midst of a crisis that threatens the very fabric of higher education in America today, and that endangers the quality of education that we all desire for our children. The crisis centers on the relationship between undergraduate education and the so-called "real world": What are we preparing our students for? The resolution of this crisis has serious implications for the undergraduate curriculum, for the nature of the demands placed on our students by the institutions, by their parents and by themselves — and profound consequences for the continuing health and vitality of our nation.

A liberal education has always been measured in terms of its relevance to society's needs, and there is no reason that it should not continue to be; the notion of utility is firmly ingrained in our national character. The crisis to which I refer lies in the determination of precisely what those needs are, for it is in those "needs" that we express the relationship between education and the "real world."

I have witnessed a trend in American

College students that I find particularly disturbing. An increasingly large number of students are demanding what they term "relevance" in their studies. Clearly, I feel that liberal education has profound relevance to the "real world," but these students have a definition of that term that is different from mine. By "relevance," they often mean professional training; training not for the future, but for jobs. With an entirely justifiable concern for their future economic well-being, they are making — I am afraid — a terrible and potentially devastating error of logic.

Although few of our students would accept the state of our "reality" as ideal, many are allowing the priorities of that reality — as expressed in economic terms — to dictate the priorities of their education. They are mistaking financial reward, prestige, and excitement for genuine intellectual interest. Many, I fear, view the undergraduate experience as a "credentialling" process, rather than as an education that will make them productive, fulfilled adults. I am not suggesting that our students do have neither genuine intellectual curiosity nor the thirst for pure knowledge, for they have ample supplies of both. But they are subjected to enormous pressures from the outside: the fear that the field in which they are truly interested will not provide them with a comfortable income; the fear that their parents (often professionals themselves) will not approve of their interests; the fear that their ambitions are not sufficiently "prestigious" in the eyes of their peers. These are all very real fears and pressures that must be recognized as valid, but they have two important — and destructive — consequences. It is my sense that many of our students go on to careers in the so-called "professions" with very little idea of what these professions entail and, what is worse, they have tailored their entire undergraduate education to fit what they feel is appropriate preparation for those professions.

We are engaging in the process of creating many unhappy adults as such students grow up to find that they have no real intellectual investment in the occupation toward which they have aspired since they were teenagers. Having focused their education at an early stage, with the mistaken impression that you have to major in economics to go into business, in political science to enter law school, or in biology to be a physician, they will be plagued with the gnawing feeling that they have missed something — but without knowing quite what it was that they have missed.

Furthermore, the misplaced emphasis on grades caused by the intense competition for professional schools discourages many students from their natural inclination to question, to challenge, to experiment, to take risks. Rather than risk the uncharted waters of their own ideas and their own imagination, many students choose the safe route of repeating what they've heard and read as they write their examinations and papers.

Clearly, it is our responsibility to find ways to encourage our students to follow their natural inclinations, to resist the pressures — we must make it clear to them that, as teachers, we will reward initiative, originality, and risk-taking. Perhaps most important is that we must convince them that it is precisely these skills that are the most "pre-professional," that no business ever grew without developing original ideas, that every physician must take calculated risks daily, and that the practice of law rests on the principle of challenge to ideas.

Most people with professional aspirations hope to advance beyond entry-level positions into managerial or executive roles; positions in which they can assume responsibility, control, and authority and positions in which they can implement their own visions. It is precisely these roles that demand breadth of education — not only in subject matter, but breadth in the range of personal and intellectual skills that the student acquires in his/her studies.

There is growing evidence that the "real world" is taking notice of the correlation between liberal arts skills at the professions. For the past twenty-nine years, AT&T has been conducting longitudinal studies of its managers, correlating field of undergraduate major to career advancement and managerial skills. The AT&T study showed clearly that those with nontechnical majors (humanities and the social sciences) were "clearly superior in administrative and interpersonal skills." (Robert E. Beck, *The Liberal Arts Major in Bell System Management*, [Washington, D.C.: 1981], pp. 6, 8). Significantly, "Nearly half of the humanities and social science majors were considered to have potential for middle management, compared to only thirty-one percent of the business majors . . ." (p. 12) Within eight years of employment, the average management level of humanities and social science majors was significantly higher than that of other groups. As the author of the Bell report states: "One overall conclusion from these data is that there is no need for liberal arts majors to lack confidence in approaching business careers." (p. 13) It is interesting to note that this affirmation of the professional value of a liberal education comes from the experience of one of the world's largest high-tech corporations!

I am not presenting this evidence to argue that those who genuinely love engineering and the sciences should not pursue them, for their love is the best reason to enter those fields. Rather, the evidence presents a powerful argument for those whose interests lie elsewhere to *follow* their interests without fearing that their skills and knowledge will not be needed.

Not long ago, I had a meeting with several people who work in admissions at the Harvard Business School. We discussed the criteria for evaluating applicants, and they stressed that the single most important criterion was academic excellence at a respected, selective institution. Certainly, a few courses in economics and a familiarity with mathematics were an advantage, but the field of undergraduate major was not significant. As do the law and medical schools, they stress breadth of excellence and potential ability as reflected in the quality of the student's educational experience. It is significant that at Harvard, like many of the nation's best business schools, ninety-seven percent of their admitted applicants have had at least one year of full-time work experience before applying.

It should be clear from what I've said that liberal education *is* valued in certain segments of the "real world," and that there is often no correlation between choice of major and choice of career. Therefore we must encourage our students to spend their first year or more exploring, taking courses in a broad range of fields; courses in which they suspect they might be interested because of previous experience, courses in which they might be interested because they sound fascinating, courses in subjects that they know nothing about.

They should talk with their teachers, their advisors, their deans, their fellow students, with their parents, with other adults. In this process of exploration —if they are allowed to explore without pressure — they will find something in which they are genuinely fascinated. Pursuit of that fascination will lead them not only to sophisticated knowledge of a particular field, but to the development of intellectual and personal skills that will enable them to survive, happily and productively, as adults. The fascination will lead them to accept challenges, exercise their creativity, to take risks in the name of learning, to find out what they are good at and what to avoid, to be critical rather than accepting, and to be pathfinders rather than followers. It will also lead them, the evidence suggests, to a career that will allow them to use what they've learned in the broadest sense; one which they will find rewarding, interesting and challenging. To put it simply, they should decide *who* they want to be when they grow up, not just *what* they want to be.

David Maxwell has been the Dean of Undergraduate Studies at Tufts University since 1981. Formerly the Director of the Program in Russian at Tufts, he has been teaching Russian language and literature nearly fifteen years, and in 1979 was the recipient of the Lillian Leibner Award for Distinguished Teaching and Advising. A Fulbright Fellow in Moscow in 1970-71, Dean Maxwell is the author of numerous scholarly articles on Russian literature. He is active in a number of organizations concerned with liberal arts education, and is a charter member of the Council on Liberal Learning.

Preparing for a career in the arts

By Gene C. Wenner

Although the notion that there is no future in a career in the arts is still espoused by many, the number and quality of opportunities in the arts has dramatically increased in the past ten years. Not every vocational opportunity is with the Metropolitan Opera, Carnegie Hall or on Broadway but nationally the growth of the arts organization and career opportunities is much improved.

Many colleges and universities are responding to this trend, by greatly expanding their programs in the arts (music, dance, theater, visual arts and writing) that develop performers, creative artists, arts educators and arts administrators. In addition, there are many course offerings in the arts for those students less determined to pursue a career in the arts, but who also desire further training and experience in the arts.

Many young people are able to combine their artistic and academic skills in preparation for the demands of being an artist. Combination of skills are also necessary for careers in the management of artists or arts organizations.

If you are seriously considering further training and education in either music, dance, theater, visual arts or writing, you should be aware of a program designed to assist young artists.

The Arts Recognition and Talent Search (ARTS) program of the National Foundation for Advancement in the Arts is a national program to recognize and support excellence in the arts. Over 5,000 high school seniors from every state participate in ARTS nationally every year.

The Educational Testing Service (ETS) of Princeton, N.J. administers the screening and adjudication activities of ARTS for the Foundation. Applications received from aspiring young artists include; a video tape of performance in dance and theater, an audio tape of solo music performance, a slide portfolio for visual artists and a portfolio of compositions by writers.

Each year, students with ability in the arts who will be high school seniors register for the ARTS program by these two dates: a regular registration deadline, May 15, (as a junior) and a late registration deadline, October 15 (as a senior).

The decisions made by panels of expert judges in each art field made solely on the basis of the artistic content of the student's performances as submitted. No other criteria, such as grades or academic standing have any bearing on their decisions.

As the result of these judgements four categories are selected: Finalists, awarded $3,000 in cash, Semifinalists, awarded $1,500, Merits, awarded $500 and Honorable Mention, a non-cash award. In addition, the registrants and award winners are recruited by leading colleges, universities and professional arts organizations who offer over 3 million dollars in scholarships and internships.

The Foundation recommends their top artistically talented students to the Presidential Commission on Scholars each year and twenty are selected as Presidential Scholars in the Arts. These young artists are presented in concert at the John F. Kennedy Center for the Performing Arts in Washington, D.C.

If you aspire to a creative career, you need to be realistic about your talent, for that is what is most important in getting a job in the arts or establishing a reputation. Practical experience outside of the school environment — with local theaters, music and dance groups, galleries and community newspapers — can give you an extra edge. Even the most talented artist must be willing to spend years of their lives mastering their skills so it is not too early to develop that necessary sense of dedication.

A life in the arts can be very rewarding because you give of yourself to others and what you get in return makes it more than worth the hard work and dedication.

Gene Wenner is the Vice President of Programs for the National Foundation for the Advancement in the Arts.

College-bound — a reciprocal experience

(Continued next column)

By Dr. Sheila Pickard

While there is nothing mysterious about "leaving for college," it is a time of great excitement involving a major transition for the family. This article will address issues concerning parents and college bound students engaged in this transactional separation process.

Parents and young adults may be anticipating their first significant separation, an event embracing both parties. This process can be a gradual unfolding of individuality and differentiation that will optimally result in independence for all participants.

Any transitional phase requires loosening and letting go of old demands and comfortable, sometimes unproductive ways. Simultaneously we come to terms with new demands and bring forth what we can for the future. What results is often varying degrees of pain and confusion along with joy, new awarenesses and growth.

A key ingredient in a successful transition requires open communication. Truly listening to, and hearing, the younger generation may facilitate comfort and conversation. Because both generations are coming to this transitional phase with different perspectives, careful listening can increase comprehension and decrease stress.

Respecting each other's privacy frequently perpetuates sharing and closeness. Whether discussing social situations, academic issues or feelings, confidentiality is an integral part of communication illustrating respect. However, despite extending opportunities for open discussion, young adults may shy away from topics that are emotionally sensitive to them. Sharing concerns about school pressures, personal relationships, or leaving the family nest may be too uncomfortable, or private, to verbalize. Sometimes these subjects are easier for young adults to "talk over" with friends. Respecting one another's privacy can nurture a smoother transition.

During this transaction separation process a mental "shifting of gears" accompanies some role changes. The college age group is moving from dependency to independence, perhaps looking towards their peers rather than their parents for modeling. Moms and dads need to confront their lessening influence while recognizing their offspring's emerging independence. This is sometimes a tricky and high hurdle for the older generation to leap over, but repeated efforts often ease the task. Parental availability may be more appreciated than parental advice.

In "shifting gears," the attitudes involved in the mental machinery may need some realigning. Balancing all the feelings involved in this growth process may necessitate some rocky stretches on the journey. One of the most common complaints from college freshmen is "parental interference," while the parents of freshmen often register "student irresponsibility" as their primary annoyance. The young adult may be experimenting with his/her independence; simultaneously parents might be trying to protect their child from misusing the independence.

Projecting the issues of independence and interference a step further, we may consider a picture of the first trip home from college. As one freshman said;

"Going home was strange. I felt out of place, alienated. Here the family function had kept on going without me, you know, and it hadn't changed because I'd left. The first time home it kind of hurt."

The separation process includes many feelings and changes. While the college age person may respond negatively to interference, the response to involvement may indeed be positive.

Both generations bring different issues to the transaction separation process. The parents are concerned with midlife tasks, while the young adults are focused on their identity as independent adults. This transitional phase, like all others, is predictable and necessary for growth to occur. Moving forward demands that former positions are replaced with new, more appropriate ones. In this way the taut ties of the child/parent bond acquires some elasticity and affords both groups more freedom, flexibility, and space.

Sheila Pickard received her doctorate in Counseling Psychology from Northwestern University. She has a private practice in Highland Park, Illinois, and is a psychology lecturer in the adult continuing education department of Truman College. Dr. Pickard has served on the faculty of Lake Forest College as a member of the counseling department and works in an inpatient facility of a substance abuse center.

Learning a new role

By Paul and Ann Krouse

Most literature directed to parents of college-bound students focuses on financial matters, an area of great interest and concern to most of us. Yet there are other roles besides bankrolls which require attention and involvement. Some are obvious and others more subtle. Having just completed the college admissions process with our eldest daughter, my wife and I would like to share our experiences and views.

Be involved.

Selecting a college is just one more experience in the parenting process with the usual mixture of risks, rewards, joys, and uncertainties. You will find yourself pouring over directories, college catalogs, counselor recommendations, applications, and financial aid forms. The more you do together, the less tedious the tasks and the more enlightening the process becomes. We found ourselves engaged in a very productive cycle which started with counselor/student meetings. From this counselor-to-parent shuttle which was repeated several times over a period of a few weeks, our daughter developed a list of six or seven college choices. We visited several of her college choices on a 4-day car trip and ultimately she selected a college which happily accepted her. Waiting for the acceptance letter was agonizing, receiving it was joyous. The family celebration which followed was memorable.

Our experiences were undoubtedly quite common. The subtleties merit equal awareness.

Listen to your child.

Most of us have our own preferences of where we would like our children to go to school, but we've had our chance(s) and now it's their turn. Certainly your guidance, opinions, and views are important. You may have some inflexible requirements which your child must be responsive to such as financial limitations. Nevertheless, it is imperative that you listen to your child's preferences and to the best of your ability and with your best judgement encourage your child to fulfill his or her dreams, not yours.

Be patient and "tune-in."

The separation between child and family is beginning and it impacts on everyone involved in different ways and at different times. So much of the college admissions process requires that the children initiate action which will cause separation that there is frequently a reluctance to complete a task which can easily be misinterpreted as laziness or irresponsibility. An application may remain untouched, an essay delayed, a conference postponed. You must "tune-in" to your child's emotions and try to determine when he or she is being lax and when normal anxieties are rising to the surface, slowing down progress. Try to be patient, guide instead of push and acknowledge your mutual feelings instead of hiding them. The closer the family is, the more pronounced these experiences may be.

Respect your child's privacy.

Social gatherings will undoubtedly bring you into contact with other parents of college-bound students and the plans and experiences of your children will become timely topics of conversation. Sharing experiences with other parents can be mutually beneficial.

But, revealing your child's exact SAT scores, GPA, class rank and similar information is an invasion of privacy. If your child wants to announce this information to friends, relatives or other parents, that's his or her business and choice — not yours. Certainly you wouldn't want your child publicizing your income or other personal information to outsiders. Similarly, your child probably would prefer that some aspects of this process remain within the family. You will be amazed at what remarkably bad taste some parents exhibit in discussing their children's experiences.

Shop carefully.

As adults, you are undoubtedly a more experienced and sophisticated shopper than your child and your experience can be significant as your child shops for a college. Most colleges are very ethical and professional in their recruitment practices, but remember they are "selling." At college fairs, admissions officers can be persuasive which is not to their discredit. College catalogs can be slick and attractive which is also understandable and acceptable. But remember, most colleges are selling a package that can cost $5,000 to $15,000 per year or $20,000 to $60,000 over four years. They need from 100 to 10,000 new students each year to keep their doors open. That's not an indictment of their motives, but simply a representation of their realities. Read between the lines and beyond the pretty pictures. Don't hesitate to confer with your child's counselors about the choices and options available — counselors are generally objective and committed to serving the student, not a particular institution. When you visit campuses allow enough time to wander on your own *after* your formal tour, usually conducted by the admissions office. Walk into the library, dormitories, student union and even classrooms, if possible. Talk to students around the campus and observe as much as you can. Virtually all college admissions officials will encourage such "investigations" on your part since they don't want your child to make a mistake and stay for one year or less anymore than you do.

Naturally, each family's experiences will be a little different. The process is not very scientific yet, inspite of computerbanks, search services, video presentations, etc. Like looking for a house, there is more emotion in the process than some are ready to acknowledge. Nevertheless, as we look back, it was another enjoyable family experience where the rewards far outweigh the risks.

Paul and Ann Krouse are the publishers of WHO'S WHO AMONG AMERICAN HIGH SCHOOL STUDENTS and the parents of four delightful children. This article was written shortly after they completed the college selection/admissions process for the first time with their eldest daughter Amy who entered the freshman class at Tufts University, Medford, Massachusetts in the fall of 1983. WHEW!

THE EDUCATIONAL COMMUNICATIONS
SCHOLARSHIP FOUNDATION®

During the 1984-85 academic year, approximately 20,000 students competed for scholarship awards sponsored by the Educational Communications Scholarship Foundation® which is funded by the publishing company. Students competed by completing an application which requested data regarding aptitude test scores, grade point average, extracurricular activities, work experience and general background information. Semifinalists were selected based on careful examination of all this information and were then requested to provide information regarding financial need. In addition, semifinalists were asked to write an essay from which the Scholarship Awards Committee attempted to evaluate the overall maturity of the students.

Fifty winners were selected and a total of $50,000 was awarded. Over $700,000 has been distributed through the Scholarship Foundation to date.

1984-85 SCHOLARSHIP WINNERS

John M. Abele
Archbishop Alter H.S.
Kettering, OH
University of
Notre Dame
Notre Dame, IN

Angela D. Burgstahler
St. Hubert Catholic
High School
Philadelphia, PA
Yale University
New Haven, CT

Brent E. Crowther
Grantsville High School
Grantsville, UT
Utah State University
Logan, UT

Todd S. Anderson
Portage Northern
Portage, MI
Michigan State
University
East Lansing, MI

Westley Chapman
Chamberlain High
School
Tampa, Fl
Harvard University
Cambridge, MA

Bernadette Donohue
Saratoga Central
Catholic High School
Chesapeake, VA
Cornell University
Ithica, NY

Louis J. Bajuk
Lorain Catholic
High School
Lorain, OH
Oberlin College
Oberlin, OH

Michael Ming-Hui Cho
Avon Grove High
School
West Grove, PA
Northwestern University
Evanston, IL

Julie M. Fessel
Marian Hts. Academy
Floyds Knobs, IN
University of
Notre Dame
Notre Dame, IN

Ellen Bales
Savannah High School
Savannah, MO
University of Chicago
Chicago, IL

David A. Clepley
Central High School
Evansville, IN
Princeton University
Princeton, NJ

Michele Filoramo
Hoffman Estates
High School
Hoffman Estates, IL
University of Illinois
Urbana, IL

LeAnne G. Bischoff
Hibbing High School
Hibbing, MN
University of Minnesota
at Minneapolis
Minneapolis, MN

Wendell M. Clough
Chelmsford High School
Chelmsford, MA
Brown University
Providence, RI

Todd E. Francis
Lincoln Southeast
High School
Lincoln, NE
Grinnell College
Grinnell, IA

1984-85 SCHOLARSHIP WINNERS

Kelly A. Franklin
Manatee High School
Bradenton, FL
Northwestern University
Evanston, IL

Dean Hoornaert
Concord High School
Concord, CA
University of California
at Berkeley
Berkeley, CA

Diana Laulainen
Lincoln Sr. High School
Sioux Falls, SD
Washington University
St. Louis, MO

Kristine L. Franklin
Manatee High School
Bradenton, FL
Yale University
New Haven, CT

Jessica Siao-Hui Huang
Schurr High School
Montebello, CA
University of California
at Berkeley
Berkeley, CA

Abel M. Lezcano
Wilson High School
Portland, OR
Northwestern University
Evanston, IL

Craig Gill
Russellville High School
Russellville, AR
The University of Texas
Austin, TX

Jonathan E. Jacobson
Indian Hills
  High School
Oakland, NJ
Princeton University
Princeton, NJ

Todd O. Litfin
Laguna Hills
  High School
Laguna Hills, CA
Harvard University
Cambridge, MA

Rod M. Goncalves
Susan E. Wagner
  High School
Staten Island, NY
Northwestern University
Evanston, IL

Hannah R. Joyner
Coastal Academy
Myrtle Beach, SC
Harvard University
Cambridge, MA

Deborah E. Lynn
Carmel High School
Carmel, IN
Northwestern University
Evanston, IL

Camille D. Holmes
Central High School
Memphis, TN
Harvard University
Cambridge, MA

Katharine M. Keough
W. T. Woodson
  High School
Fairfax, VA
Duke University
Durham, NC

Dean A. Manson
St. Francis DeSales
  High School
Toledo, OH
Princeton University
Princeton, NJ

Deanne J. Holmes
Nokomis Regional
  High School
Detroit, ME
University of Vermont
Burlington, VT

Traci L. King
West Jordan
  High School
West Jordan, UT
University of Utah
Salt Lake City, UT

Sandra Ann Murray
Coventry High School
Coventry, RI
Massachusetts Institute
  of Technology
Cambridge, MA

1984-85 SCHOLARSHIP WINNERS

Ruth A. Nicholson
Hempstead Sr.
  High School
Dubuque, IA
University of Iowa
Iowa City, IA

Susan K. Snyder
Somerset Area H.S.
Somerset, PA
Carnegie-Mellon
  University
Pittsburgh, PA

Marlo Van Slate-Teves
Placer High School
Newcastle, CA
Stanford University
Stanford, CA

Carmyn G. Priewe
Central Cass H.S.
Amenia, ND
Gustavus Adolphus
  College
St. Peter, MN

Edwin A. Sosa
Colegio San Antonio
Quebradillas, PR
Recinto Universitario
  de Mayaguez
Mayaguez, PR

Gregory M. Vydra
Notre Dame High
  School for Boys
Chicago, IL
University of Illinois
Champaign, IL

Karen Regelman
Breck School
Burnsville, MN
Princeton University
Princeton, NJ

Nicholas D. Stamos
Westhill High School
Syracuse, NY
Massachusetts Institute
  of Technology
Cambridge, MA

Karen A. Weber
Clarence Senior H.S.
Williamsville, NY
State University of NY
  at Buffalo
Buffalo, NY

Paul J. Roback
Anoka Senior
  High School
Anoka, MN
Swarthmore College
Swarthmore, PA

Kathryn Sylvester
Dos Pueblos
  High School
Goleta, CA
Stanford University
Stanford, CA

Christina C. M. Wee
St. Elizabeth High
  School
Wilmington, DE
Ursinus College
Collegeville, PA

Andrew C. Rudalevige
Watertown High School
Watertown, MA
The University of
  Chicago
Chicago, IL

Julie Tarara
St. Mary's High School
Bradford, MA
Colby College
Waterville, ME

David M. Wisniewski
Southwestern H.S.
Vinton, OH
Shawnee State
  Community College
Portsmouth, OH

Dawn Schultz
Cobleskill Central
  High School
Cobleskill, NY
University of Rochester
Rochester, NY

Brian L. Tunis
Mariner High School
Edmonds, WA
University of
  Washington
Seattle, WA

GLOSSARY OF ABBREVIATIONS

Acpl Chr	Acappella Choir
AFS	American Field Service
Am Leg Boys St	American Legion Boys State
Am Leg Aux Girls St	American Legion Auxiliary Girls State
Aud/Vis	Audio-Visual
Awd	Award
Badmtn	Badminton
Bsbl	Baseball
Basktbl	Basketball
Btty Crckr Awd	Betty Crocker Award
Bus	Business
Bwlng	Bowling
C of C Awd	Chamber of Commerce Award
Camp Fr Inc	Camp Fire, Inc.
CAP	Civil Air Patrol
Capt	Captain
Cit Awd	Citizenship Award
Clb	Club
Cmnty Wkr	Community Worker
Coach Actv	Coaching Activities
Crs Cntry	Cross Country
DAR Awd	Daughters of the American Revolution Award
DECA	Distributive Education Clubs of America
Dnfth Awd	Danforth (I Dare You) Award
Drm & Bgl	Drum & Bugle Corps
Drm Mjr(t)	Drum Major(ette)
Ed-Chief	Editor-In-Chief
FBLA	Future Business Leaders of America
FCA	Fellowship of Christian Athletes
FFA	Future Farmers of America
FHA	Future Homemakers of America
Fld Hcky	Field Hockey
FNA	Future Nurses of America
FTA	Future Teachers of America
Ftbl	Football
GAA	Girls Athletic Association
Gov Hon Prg Awd	Governors Honor Program Award
Gym	Gymnastics
Hist	Historian
Hon	Honor
Hosp Aide	Hospital Aide
Ice Hcky	Ice Hockey
Intnl Clb	International Club
JA	Junior Achievement
JC Awd	Jaycees Award
JCL	Junior Classical League
JETS Awd	Junior Engineering Technical Society Award
JP Sousa Awd	John Philip Sousa Award
Jr NHS	Junior National Honor Society
JV	Junior Varsity
L	Letter
Lcrss	Lacross
Lion Award	Lions Club Award
Lit Mag	Literary Magazine
Mgr(s)	Manager(s)
MMM	Modern Music Masters
Mrchg Band	Marching Band
NCTE Awd	National Council of Teachers of English Award
NEDT Awd	National Educational Development Test Award
NFL	National Forensic League
NHS	National Honor Society
Ntl	National
Nwsp	Newspaper
OEA	Office Education Association
Opt Clb Awd	Optimist Club Award
Orch	Orchestra
PAVAS	Performing & Visual Arts Society
Phtg	Photographer
Pres	President
Prfct Atten Awd	Perfect Attendance Award
Rep	Representative
Rptr	Reporter
ROTC	Reserve Officer Training Corps

Sal	Salutatorian	**Trea**	Treasurer
SAR Awd	Sons of the American Revolution Award	**Trk**	Track
Schol	Scholarship	**Twrlr**	Twirler
Sec	Secretary		
SF	Semifinalist	**V**	Varsity
Sftbl	Softball	**Val**	Valedictorian
Socr	Soccer	**VICA**	Vocational Industrial Clubs of America
Sprt Ed	Sports Editor	**Vllybl**	Volleyball
St Schlr	State Scholar	**Voice Dem Awd**	Voice of Democracy Award
Stf	Staff	**VP**	Vice President
Stu Cncl	Student Council		
Swmmng	Swimming		
Symp Band	Symphonic Band	**Wrstlng**	Wrestling
		Wt Lftg	Weight Lifting
Tm	Team		
Thesps	Thespians	**Yrbk**	Yearbook

Sample Biography

This sample is presented to familiarize the reader with the format of the biographical listings. Students are identified by name, school, home, city and state. In order to protect the privacy and integrity of all students, home addresses are not published.

KEY
1 Name
2 High School
3 Home, City and State
4 Nomination Source*
5 Class Rank (when given)
6 Accomplishments
7 Future Plans

*(S) = School Nomination
 (Y) = Youth Organization Nomination

1 Wolk, Sheffield L.; **2** Normandy Isle H.S.; **3** Miami, FL; **4** (S); **5** 10-350; **6** Pres Stu Cncl; VP Sr Cls; Ftbl; 4-H; NHS; Cit Awd; Am Leg Awd; **7** Harvard University; Biochemist

STUDENT BIOGRAPHIES

CONNECTICUT

AAFEDT, DANIEL R; Windsor HS; Windsor, CT; (S); DECA; Schlrshp To HH Ellis Tech-From Windsr Mfg Co 85; Dist/ST Wnr-Careen Dev Conf Of DECA ST Of CT 85; H H Ellis Vo Tech; Aviatn Mech.

ABBOT, JESSE; Bloomfield HS; Bloomfield, CT; (Y); 13/231; Pres French Clb; Rep Model UN; Nwsp Rptr; Nwsp Stf; Ed Lit Mag; French Hon Soc; High Hon Roll; Hon Roll; NHS; Ctr For Creative Yth Schlrshp 83-85; COLT Frgn Lang Poetry Rectn Cont Frnch 4 85; Brown U Bk Awd 85; Wrtng.

ABBOTT, SHERYL; Daniel HS; Madison, CT; (Y); 55/236; Church Yth Grp; Drama Clb; GAA; Chorus; Church Choir; Madrigals; School Musical; L Var Trk; Hon Roll; All-Sthrn & ST Chrs 84; Music Thrpy.

ABBRUZZO, CRAIG; Farmington HS; Farmington, CT; (Y); 10/209; Am Leg Boys St; Drama Clb; School Play; Lit Mag; High Hon Roll; NHS; Ntl Merit Ltr; Intershp WA 85; 1st Pl Ntl Math Comptn 85; Chem Olymp 84-85.

ABDULLOVSKI, DOREEN; Killingly HS; Danielson, CT; (Y); Yrbk Stf; Rep Stu Cncl; Var Capt Crs Cntry; Trk; French Hon Soc; High Hon Roll; Hon Roll; NHS; Yrbk Sprt Ed; Jr NHS; Alumni Assc Schlrshp 85; Brd Of Educ Nathan Prince Schlrshp 85; Assumption Col6; Librl Arts.

ABELARDO, ANABELA; Stamford Catholic HS; Stamford, CT; (Y); 23/145; JA; Chorus; Church Choir; School Musical; School Play; NHS; Acad Excllnce Frnch III, Conscience & Moralty John Carroll Awd 85; Soc Stud Faculty Awds 83-84; Lib Arts.

ABELE, JOSEPH P; East Catholic HS; Bolton, CT; (Y); Exploring; Ski Clb; Stage Crew; Ice Hcky; Score Keeper; Socr; Tennis; Wt Lftg; U Of Bridgeport; Engrng.

ABITZ, DEREK; Ansonia HS; Ansonia, CT; (Y); 5/130; Am Leg Boys St; Church Yth Grp; Cmnty Wkr; Spanish Clb; Yrbk Stf; Capt Bsbl; Capt Ftbl; High Hon Roll; Jr NHS; NHS; Schlr-Athl Awd New Haven Ftbl Fndtn 85; All Vly Awd 85; Coaches All St Awd 85; U PA; Math.

ABRAHAMIAN, DAVID J; New Britain HS; New Britain, CT; (Y); 68/388; Office Aide; Yrbk Stf; Ftbl; Wt Lftg; Hon Roll; Acctg.

ABRINES, LINDA GARCIA; Saint Marys HS; New Haven, CT; (Y); Church Yth Grp; Ski Clb; Spanish Clb; School Musical; Nwsp Stf; Sec Jr Cls; Pres Sr Cls; French Hon Soc; Hon Roll; Spanish NHS; CT Fr Poet Recitatn Awd 85; Frgn Affrs.

ABRIOLA, NICOLE; Stratford HS; Stratford, CT; (Y); 24/241; FBLA; Hon Roll; Sacred Heart U.

ACAMPORA, MARY; Bristol Central HS; Britol, CT; (Y); 2/325; Latin Clb; Sec Frsh Cls; Pres Soph Cls; Sec Jr Cls; Var L Swmmng; Var L Tennis; High Hon Roll; NHS; Ski Clb; Var L Trk; Yale Bk Prz 85; JR Marshal 85.

ACCURSO, ANN MARIE; Saint Mary HS; Greenwich, CT; (Y); 3/69; Drama Clb; Latin Clb; Math Tm; Pep Clb; Spanish Clb; School Play; Rep Stu Cncl; Var Fld Hcky; Var Powder Puff Ftbl; 4-H Awd; Ntl Essay Cntst 2nd Pl 84; Jrnlst.

ACHANE, RONA; Wilbur Cross HS; New Haven, CT; (S); Cmnty Wkr; Nwsp Rptr; Yrbk Stf; Off Soph Cls; Sec Jr Cls; Off Sr Cls; Sftbl; Cit Awd; Miss SR 84-85; Comp Sci.

ACHILLE, ALAN; Naugatguck HS; Naugatuck, CT; (Y); Am Leg Boys St; Ski Clb; Var L Bsbl; Var Capt Bsktbl; Hon Roll; HS Rep Middle Schl Grad 85; Pilot.

ADAIR, JOHN; Fairfield College Prep; Newhyde Park, NY; (Y); Church Yth Grp; Key Clb; Q&S; Spanish Clb; Nwsp Bus Mgr; JV Crs Cntry; High Hon Roll; NHS; Spanish NHS; Rensselaer Polytech Inst Math & Sci Awd 85; Georgetwn U; Fin.

ADAM, DANIEL; William H Hall HS; W Hartford, CT; (Y); 67/324; Political Wkr; Mgr(s); Score Keeper; High Hon Roll; NHS; Spanish NHS; Voice Dem Awd; JA; Timer; Mrt Awd From The Jewish Fmly Svc Fo Greater Hartford 83; Vol Svc Awd For Wrk Done At A Hm/Elderly 83; Frgn Lang.

ADAM, LISA; Trumbull HS; Trumbull, CT; (Y); Church Yth Grp; Drama Clb; Chorus; Church Choir; Bsktbl; Sftbl; Trk; Hon Roll; Exc & Achvt In Art 84-85; Art.

ADAMO, M LISS; Saint Bernard HS; Westerly, RI; (S); Library Aide; Yrbk Stf; Sec Frsh Cls; Stu Cncl; JV Cheerleading; Mgr(s); High Hon Roll; Acad Lttr Hgh Hnrs 84; JR Sen 84; Harvard; Pre-Med.

ADAMS, ADRIANNE; Stratford HS; Stratford, CT; (Y); 78/240; Church Yth Grp; FBLA; Variety Show; Rep Soph Cls; Sec Jr Cls; Sec Sr Cls; Rep Stu Cncl; Hon Roll; Prfct Atten Awd; Psych.

ADAMS, CINDY; Farmington HS; Unionville, CT; (Y); 32/206; Drama Clb; Girl Scts; Chorus; Nwsp Rptr; Cheerleading; Deans Schlrshp 85; Educ Assoc Schlrshp 85; U Of Hartford; Elem Educ.

ADAMS, JEFF; New London HS; New London, CT; (Y); 9/200; Am Leg Boys St; Key Clb; Ski Clb; Variety Show; Capt Golf; Var Socr; High Hon Roll; Hon Roll; NHS; Outstndng Sprtsmnshp & Skll In Glf 84-85; Duke U; Pre-Med.

ADAMS, KIMBERLY; Lyman Hall HS; Wallingford, CT; (Y); 1/235; JA; Sec Key Clb; Rep Stu Cncl; Powder Puff Ftbl; High Hon Roll; Pres NHS; Prfct Atten Awd; Pres Schlr; Val; Yale Bk Awd 84; Renssalear Polytech Inst Mdl 84; Citatn Soc Of Womn Engrs 84; Brown U; Mth.

ADAMS, PAULENE; Warren F Kaynor Tech Schl; Waterbury, CT; (Y); Church Yth Grp; Hosp Aide; Pep Clb; VICA; Yrbk Stf; Rep Stu Cncl; Hon Roll; Jr NHS; NHS; Prfct Atten Awd; Med.

ADAMS, TIMOTHY G; Ellington HS; Ellington, CT; (Y); 14/142; Aud/Vis; Latin Clb; Acpl Chr; Band; VP Concert Band; Jazz Band; Mrchg Band; Variety Show; Nwsp Stf; Yrbk Stf; All Nw Englnd Chrs 84-85; All ST Chrs 85; Music Engr.

ADELBERG, MARC E; Enfield HS; Enfield, CT; (Y); 5/240; Am Leg Boys St; Computer Clb; Concert Band; Jazz Band; Mrchg Band; Rep Stu Cncl; Im Tennis; High Hon Roll; NHS; Mth Comp Awd 85; Aerontcl Engrng.

ADELMAN, WILLIAM; Stamford HS; Stamford, CT; (Y); 1/457; Var Capt Socr; Var Capt Wrstlng; Elks Awd; High Hon Roll; NHS; St Schlr; Val; JA; Scholastic Bowl; Temple Yth Grp; Nalt Cncl Merit Schlar 85; PTO Cncl Merit Scsholar 85; Mens Clb Scholar 85; Princeton; Eng.

ADKINS, SCOTT; Horace C Wilcox R V T S; Cheshire, CT; (Y); High Hon Roll; Hon Roll; Air Cndtng.

ADLER, MARCI; North Haven SR HS; North Haven, CT; (Y); 44/295; Computer Clb; Girl Scts; Spanish Clb; Band; Chorus; Flag Corp; School Musical; Yrbk Stf; Stat Bsbl; Socr; Hartford U; Comp Engr.

ADSHADE, GORDON; Southington HS; Milldale, CT; (Y); DECA; JV Bsbl; Hon Roll; Med.

AGUIAR, LAUREN; Newington HS; Newington, CT; (Y); 43/368; Sec Drama Clb; Pep Clb; Drill Tm; Madrigals; School Musical; Ed Yrbk Stf; Chrmn Sr Cls; Mgr Lcrss; Hon Roll; NHS; Englsh.

AGUIRRE, DOROTHY; New London HS; New London, CT; (Y); Hon Roll; Intl Frgn Lang Awds 83-84; Natl Ldrshp & Svc Awds 84-85; Acadmc All-Amer At Large Div 83-84.

AGULAY, FELITA; Stamford HS; Stamford, CT; (Y); Dance Clb; DECA; Lit Mag; Var Cheerleading; Hon Roll; Lewis Prsnnl Inc Steno I Awd 85; DECA 84 Drunk Drvng Awrnss Campgn Fnlst 84; Sacred Heart U; Sec Studies.

AHERN, CARLEEN; St Marys HS; New Haven, CT; (Y); 18/115; Hosp Aide; Service Clb; Ski Clb; Spanish Clb; School Musical; School Play; Var Capt Sftbl; Var L Vllybl; Hon Roll; Spanish NHS; Mst Vlble Plyr Awd Sftbll 84 & 85; Hlth Fld.

AHN, MINA; East Catholic HS; Manchester, CT; (Y); 14/300; Sec Sr Cls; Stu Cncl; High Hon Roll; Hnrs E Awd 84-85; Bus.

AIMONE, MARK; Fairfield Prep; Huntington, CT; (Y); Computer Clb; Quiz Bowl; Bsktbl; JV Socr; Sftbl; High Hon Roll; VP NHS; 1st Schl Sci Fair Adv Bio 85; Law.

AIRES, IRENE; Danbury HS; Danbury, CT; (Y); 37/625; Exploring; JA; Varsity Clb; Variety Show; Yrbk Stf; Rep Frsh Cls; Sec Soph Cls; Sec Jr Cls; Sec Sr Cls; Rep Stu Cncl; Princeton Bk Awd 8k; Publ Rel.

AKERSON, VALERIE; Bethel HS; Bethel, CT; (Y); 11/260; AFS; Variety Show; Yrbk Stf; Var L Crs Cntry; JV Mgr(s); JV Trk; High Hon Roll; Hon Roll; NHS; JR Marshal 85; Wellesley Bk Awd 85; Lawyer.

AKOURY, LISA; Masuk HS; Monroe, CT; (Y); JA; Spanish Clb; Hon Roll; Engrng.

AKOWITZ, DANIEL; Notre Dame HS; W Haven, CT; (Y); 22/250; Am Leg Boys St; Church Yth Grp; Pres Debate Tm; Scholastic Bowl; Lit Mag; High Hon Roll; NHS; Ntl Merit SF; 1st Pl Vrsty Team & 2nd Pl Vrsty Speaker-CT Debate Assn Champnshp 85; Corp Law.

AKSEN, LYNN S; Greenwich HS; Stamford, CT; (Y); Service Clb; Nwsp Rptr; Lit Mag; Pres Frsh Cls; Rep Soph Cls; Rep Jr Cls; Rep Sr Cls; Hon Roll; Saferids Treas 83-84; Hotln Volntr 84; Franklin & Marshall; Pre-Law.

ALBERT, LAURIE; Southington HS; Southington, CT; (Y); Church Yth Grp; Cmnty Wkr; Library Aide; Color Guard; Flag Corp; Hon Roll; Fred J Miller Otstndng Indvdl 85; Nrsng.

ALBERT, SUSAN K; St Paul HS; Forrestville, CT; (Y); 64/320; Drama Clb; French Clb; Hosp Aide; Band; School Musical; Stu Cncl; Hghst Avg Nrsng Asstnt Prog 85; Cert Nrs Aid & CPR 85; Russell Sage; Nrsng.

ALBERTI, SUSAN; Holy Cross HS; Oxford, CT; (Y); 68/352; Church Yth Grp; Spanish Clb; High Hon Roll; Hon Roll; Spanish NHS; Spnsh Achv Awd 83-84; Lwyr.

ALDSWORTH, SCOTT; Notre Dame HS; Hamden, CT; (Y); 35/274; Pep Clb; Political Wkr; Ski Clb; Spanish Clb; Yrbk Rptr; Yrbk Stf; Lit Mag; High Hon Roll; Hon Roll; Spanish NHS; Babson Coll; Invstmnts.

ALEJANDRO, MARTHA; Bassick HS; Bridgeport, CT; (S); Exploring; Hosp Aide; Pep Clb; Band; Drm Mjr(t); Yrbk Phtg; Lit Mag; Stu Cncl; Bsktbl; Sftbl; Nurse.

ALESSANDRO, JOSEPH; New Fairfield HS; New Fairfld, CT; (Y); 45/265; Cmnty Wkr; JA; Latin Clb; Yrbk Stf; JV Bsbl; Var L Ftbl; Im Wt Lftg; Var Wrstlng; Hon Roll; Psych.

ALEXANDER JR, JOSEPH; Shelton HS; Shelton, CT; (Y); Boys Clb Am; JA; Chorus; Nwsp Stf; Bsbl; Var Bsktbl; Var Socr; Hon Roll; Nwsp Rptr; Im Vllybl; Tutr Math Awd; Cert Awd Bus Ed; U Of Tampa; Comp Sci.

ALEXOPOULOS, EVELYN S; New Britain SR HS; New Britain, CT; (Y); 2/385; Math Tm; Church Choir; Madrigals; VP Jr Cls; French Hon Soc; High Hon Roll; NHS; Voice Dem Awd; Drama Clb; French Clb; Wellesley & Brwn Bk Awds 85; Biochmstry.

ALFORD, DAN; Norwalk HS; Norwalk, CT; (Y); Computer Clb; Pep Clb; Spanish Clb; Yrbk Stf; Hon Roll; Bus.

ALGIERE, MICHELE; St Bernard HS; Bradford, RI; (S); 90/290; Cmnty Wkr; Exploring; GAA; Hosp Aide; Teachers Aide; Sec Varsity Clb; Yrbk Stf; Sec Frsh Cls; Sec Soph Cls; Sec Jr Cls; Phys Ther.

ALIX, CHRISTYANN; East Catholic HS; Marlborough, CT; (Y); 58/296; Church Yth Grp; Band; High Hon Roll; Hon Roll; Elem Educ.

ALLAIN, RODNEY; Trumbull HS; Stratford, CT; (Y); FFA; Ski Clb; Variety Show; Hofstra U; Elect Engr.

ALLAN, KATHARINE; Shelton HS; Shelton, CT; (Y); 10/425; Am Leg Aux Girls St; Nwsp Rptr; Yrbk Ed-Chief; Sec Jr Cls; Sec Stu Cncl; Crs Cntry; Trk; VP French Hon Soc; Hon Roll; NHS; Wellesly Bk Awd; Shelton Ed Assn Scholar; Shelton Permanent War Mem Scholar; Boston Coll; Eng.

ALLARD, KELLY; Montville HS; Oakdale, CT; (Y); 13/175; Church Yth Grp; Office Aide; Rep Soph Cls; Sec Jr Cls; Pres Sr Cls; Rep Stu Cncl; Score Keeper; French Hon Soc; Hon Roll; NHS; Creatv Wrtng Awd 85; Law.

ALLEN, EDWIN V; Bloomfield HS; Bloomfield, CT; (Y); 4/245; Civic Clb; Math Clb; Math Tm; Model UN; VP Sr Cls; Var L Bsbl; Var L Wrstlng; High Hon Roll; NHS; Ntl Merit Ltr; U S Military Acad; Ofcr.

ALLEN, JULIE M; Terryville HS; Plymouth, CT; (Y); 4/130; Am Leg Aux Girls St; Acpl Chr; Church Choir; Mrchg Band; School Play; Yrbk Phtg; Var Bsktbl; JP Sousa Awd; NHS; Talcott Mtn Sci Ctr Stu; Frgn Lang Clb Sec; Stu For Europe Clb France & Spain; U MA; Intl Tourism Mgt.

ALLEN, LACHELLE; Weaver HS; Hartford, CT; (Y); Dance Clb; Gym; Hon Roll; Prfct Atten Awd; Drama Clb; School Musical; School Play; Trk; Excptnl Perfrmnc Fine Art & Frnch III 85; Cmmnctns.

ALLEN, SANDRA; Fitch SR HS; Groton, CT; (Y); 39/410; Sec Intnl Clb; Nwsp Ed-Chief; Nwsp Rptr; Lit Mag; High Hon Roll; Hon Roll; Sec JA; Science Clb; P Crawfrd/R Cook Acadmc Schlrshps Kings Coll; 2nd Prz Potry Litry Mag; Pfizer Inc Schlrshp Chem Div; Kings Coll; Emen Schl Tchr.

ALLEN, SUSAN; Brookfield HS; Brookfield, CT; (Y); Camp Fr Inc; Church Yth Grp; Dance Clb; Drama Clb; Library Aide; Chorus; School Play; Stage Crew; Yrbk Ed-Chief; Hgh Hnrs-1st Smstr 84-85; Hnrs-2nd Smstr 84-85; Bay Path JC; Fshn Mrchndsng.

ALLEN, TRACY; George J Penney HS; E Hartford, CT; (Y); Hon Roll; Soc Wrk.

ALLER, BENJAMIN; Conard HS; W Hartford, CT; (Y); 1/322; Church Yth Grp; Debate Tm; Sec French Clb; Math Tm; VP Model UN; Ed Yrbk Phtg; Wrstlng; Pres French Hon Soc; High Hon Roll; NHS; 2nd ST Chemathon 85; Harvard Radcliffe, Alliance Francaise Bk Prz 85; Intl Rel.

ALLES, LUCIA; Bassick HS; Bridgeport, CT; (S); Yrbk Rptr; Yrbk Stf; Hon Roll; Bus.

ALLING, R DOUGLAS; The Gilbert Schl; Torrington, CT; (Y); Am Leg Boys St; VP Key Clb; Science Clb; Ski Clb; Spanish Clb; Band; Concert Band; Jazz Band; Mrchg Band; Pep Band; Harvard Radcliffe Book Awd 84-85; Michaels Jewelers Awd 84-85; Summr Sci Sem 85; Engrng.

ALLINSON, DEIRDRE; East Catholic HS; Coventry, CT; (Y); 21/275; VP French Clb; Math Tm; Church Choir; Lit Mag; High Hon Roll; Hon Roll; NHS; Hnrbl Mntn Schl Sci Fair 84; Semi Fnlst US Japan Snt Schlrshp Prog 85.

ALLISON, BEN; Wilbur Cross HS; New Haven, CT; (S); 5/252; PAVAS; Chorus; Jazz Band; French Hon Soc; High Hon Roll; NHS; NYU; Music.

ALPERT, LAUREN; Amity Regional SR HS; Woodbridge, CT; (S); 78/376; Hosp Aide; Latin Clb; Pep Clb; Stu Cncl; Var L Cheerleading; Var Trk; NHS; Nwsp Stf; Yrbk Stf; High Hon Roll; Natl Art Hnr Soc; Peer Tutor & Counsel; Amity Volunteers; Art.

ALSTON, LINDA; James Hillhouse HS; New Haven, CT; (S); High Hon Roll; Hon Roll; NHS; W Babbitt Awd, 1st PSC Geo 84; Hgh Rnk Awd 83; Acctng.

ALTAMIRANO, TANIA L; Shelton HS; Shelton, CT; (Y); 35/416; Drama Clb; Exploring; French Clb; Key Clb; Color Guard; School Play; Nwsp Bus Mgr; High Hon Roll; NHS; Richardson Vicks Sci Scholar 85; Wesleyan U; Bio-Chem.

ALTMAN, ELIZABETH A; William H Hall HS; W Hartford, CT; (Y); 6/324; Church Yth Grp; Chorus; Rep Soph Cls; Rep Jr Cls; Lcrss; Swmmng; Pres French Hon Soc; High Hon Roll; Pres NHS; Wesleyan Coll Bk Awd 85; Mth.

AMAKER, KAREN; Richard C Lee HS; New Haven, CT; (Y); Nwsp Stf; Yrbk Ed-Chief; Rep Frsh Cls; Rep Soph Cls; Rep Jr Cls; Sec Stu Cncl; Trk; High Hon Roll; Hon Roll; VP NHS; Briarwood, Harvard Bk Awds Mst Outstndng Stu 85; Chem, Bio Awds 84-85; Yale U; Pre-Med.

AMANN, DAN; East Lyme HS; E Lyme, CT; (Y); Boy Scts; Church Yth Grp; Band; Concert Band; Mrchg Band; Hon Roll; NHS.

AMANN, TOM; East Lyme HS; E Lyme, CT; (Y); Boy Scts; Band; Hon Roll.

AMARAL, CRAIG; Notre Dame Catholic HS; Bpt, CT; (Y); Church Yth Grp; Var VP Bowling; Var VP Golf; Incentive Schlrshp Meth Coll 85; Gus Lindmark YMCA Golf Awd 85; Meth Coll.

AMBRUSCO, JOHN; Notre Dame HS; W Haven, CT; (Y); 81/260; L Socr; High Hon Roll; Hon Roll; Prfct Atten Awd; Hnr Rl 82-85; UNH; Engrng.

AMELLIN, KAREN; North Haven HS; North Haven, CT; (Y); Church Yth Grp; Latin Clb; Model UN; Ski Clb; Spanish Clb; Stage Crew; Yrbk Stf; Stu Cncl; Hon Roll; Pre Med.

AMENDOLA, SCOTT; Danbury HS; Danbury, CT; (Y); Boy Scts; ROTC; Color Guard; Drill Tm; JV Crs Cntry; Var Diving; Trk; Vllybl; Hon Roll; ROTC Perry Awd 84; Kitty Hawk Air Soc 84-85; U CT; Drftsmn.

AMICUCCI, MARY; Stamford Catholic HS; Stamford, CT; (Y); 21/166; GAA; Varsity Clb; Var Bsktbl; JV Sftbl; Capt Var Vllybl; High Hon Roll; Hon Roll; NHS; MVP U Mass V Ball Camp 84; All Cty,St Vlybl 85; Psych.

AMILL, SALLY; Weston HS; Weston, CT; (Y); 61/147; Intnl Clb; Key Clb; Latin Clb; Pep Clb; Spanish Clb; Yrbk Stf; Stat Bsktbl; Var Mgr(s); JV Var Powder Puff Ftbl; JV Vllybl; Lang.

AMODEI, VICTOR; North Haven HS; N Haven, CT; (Y); 60/281; Church Yth Grp; Var L Trk; Hon Roll; Art.

ANASTASI, LEAH; Windham HS; Willimantic, CT; (Y); 49/285; Hosp Aide; Sec Stu Cncl; Capt L Vllybl; Elks Awd; High Hon Roll; Hon Roll; Lawrence King Schlrshp Fund 85; St Josephs Coll; Nrsng.

ANDERSEN, GLENN; Bethel HS; Bethel, CT; (Y); Band; Concert Band; Jazz Band; Variety Show; High Hon Roll; Hon Roll; NHS; Engr.

ANDERSON, ERIK; East Lyme HS; East Lyme, CT; (Y); 29/271; Am Leg Boys St; Band; Concert Band; Jazz Band; Mrchg Band; Trs Sec Jr Cls; Bsbl; Bsktbl; Hon Roll; Bst Frshmn Band Stu 83; Law.

ANDERSON, ERIKA; Lee HS; New Haven, CT; (Y); VP Church Yth Grp; VP Stu Cncl; Cheerleading; Vllybl; Cit Awd; Hon Roll; Sal; Med.

ANDERSON, JO ELLE; Southington HS; Southington, CT; (Y); Sec Church Yth Grp; Pep Clb; Ski Clb; Jazz Band; Variety Show; Yrbk Stf; High Hon Roll; Hon Roll; Cmnty Wkr; Band; Lewis Alumni Alg Awd 83; Southington Arts Cncl Exhbt 83; Discover III-ARTS, Music, & Acad 84; Int Design.

ANDERSON, JODI; Robert E Fitch SR HS; Groton, CT; (Y); 20/410; Church Yth Grp; Drama Clb; Thesps; Jazz Band; School Musical; Yrbk Ed-Chief; Var L Swmmng; NHS; Ntl Merit SF; Intnl Clb; Svc Awd Intl Order Rainbow Girls 83; Rensselaer Polytech Inst; Arch.

ANDERSON, JOHN; Bethel HS; Bethel, CT; (Y); AFS; Boy Scts; Computer Clb; Band; Chorus; Concert Band; Mrchg Band; Symp Band; Hon Roll; NHS; Engr.

ANDERSON, JOHN; Coventry HS; Coventry, CT; (Y); Church Yth Grp; Concert Band; Jazz Band; Golf; Hon Roll; NHS.

ANDERSON, KAREN; Newington HS; Newington, CT; (Y); Church Yth Grp; Trs Civic Clb; Dance Clb; Acpl Chr; Chorus; Church Choir; Jazz Band; School Musical; Yrbk Stf; Trk.

ANDERSON, KELLIE; Litchfield HS; Litchfield, CT; (Y); 3/97; Am Leg Aux Girls St; Pres Chorus; School Play; Pres Sr Cls; Sec Stu Cncl; Var L Golf; DAR Awd; French Hon Soc; High Hon Roll; NHS; Hugh O Brien Yth Ldrshp Smnr 83; Ntl Ltn Cntst Cum Laude 85; Tufts U; Intnl Bus.

ANDERSON, ROSEMERI; Norwalk HS; E Norwalk, CT; (Y); Church Yth Grp; English Clb; GAA; Church Choir; Off Jr Cls; JV Capt Bsktbl; Mgr(s); Trk; Vllybl; Hon Roll; 2nd Runner-Up Cndrlla Ball 85; Accntng.

ANDERSON, RUDD; Weston HS; Weston, CT; (Y); Dance Clb; Drama Clb; Chorus; Concert Band; Jazz Band; School Musical; School Play; Stage Crew; Pres Frsh Cls; Rep Stu Cncl; Ballet Schlrshp Frm Amer Ballet Acad 85; Prfrmng Arts.

ANDRADE, EDMOND; Notre Dame HS; New Haven, CT; (Y); Var Crs Cntry; JV Trk; Hon Roll; Ltrs Trk 84-85; Peer Cnslr 85-86; Engrng.

ANDRE, CHRIS; Weston HS; Weston, CT; (Y); 10/155; Var Capt Crs Cntry; JV Lcrss; Var Swmmng; Var Tennis; Var Trk; High Hon Roll; NHS; Ntl Merit SF; Brown U Bk Awd 85; CT All ST Swim Tm 84-85.

ANDREAS, ELISE; Farmington HS; Farmington, CT; (Y); 12/215; Acpl Chr; Band; Pres Chorus; Madrigals; Pres Frsh Cls; Rep Soph Cls; Rep Jr Cls; French Hon Soc; High Hon Roll; NHS; Michaels Jwrlrs Ldrshp Awd 85; Cmmnctns.

ANDREWS, CHRISTINE; Greenwich HS; Riverside, CT; (Y); Church Yth Grp; JA; Teachers Aide; Chorus; Church Choir; School Musical; JV Var Bsbl; Mgr(s); Score Keeper; Hon Roll; Smith; Econ.

ANDREWS, SHERRI; St Marys HS; New Haven, CT; (Y); Church Yth Grp; Cmnty Wkr; Office Aide; Political Wkr; Spanish Clb; Rep Stu Cncl; Tennis; High Hon Roll; Hon Roll; Albertus Magnus Coll; Law.

ANDRYCHOWSKI, SUSAN; Windham HS; Columbia, CT; (Y); 7/285; Math Tm; Red Cross Aide; JV Fld Hcky; Var L Swmmng; High Hon Roll; Mu Alp Tht; NHS; Ntl Merit Ltr; Pres Schlr; U CT; Chem.

ANGELILLO JR, RONALD R; Southington HS; Marion, CT; (Y); Key Clb; Ftbl; Golf; Trk; Wt Lftg; Hon Roll; Second Hnrs 82-84; Tax Lawyr.

ANGELO, THOMAS; Toutelotte Memorial HS; Quinebaug, CT; (Y); Am Leg Boys St; Boy Scts; Ski Clb; Var Band; Concert Band; Mrchg Band; Pep Band; Symp Band; Bsbl; Bsktbl; Serra Essay Cntst 83; Anna Maria Coll; Bus Mgmt.

ANGERS, GLEN; Bristol Central HS; Bristol, CT; (Y); 22/274; Ski Clb; Var Socr; Var Wrstlng; Hon Roll; Wrstlng Schlr Awd 82; UCONN; Pharmcy.

ANGLEMYER, CRAIG; Pomperaug HS; Southbury, CT; (Y); Boy Scts; Band; Pep Band; Art Clb; JV Bsbl; Im Bsktbl; Bus.

ANNICK, JENNIFER; Trumbull HS; Trumbull, CT; (Y); Math Tm; Mrchg Band; Trs Frsh Cls; Rep Stu Cncl; Var L Bsktbl; Var L Tennis; JV Co-Capt Vllybl; French Hon Soc; NHS; Ntl Merit Ltr; Hugh O Brian Yth Fndtn; Excllnc Engl Awd By PTA; Amer H S Athl Vllybl & Bsktbl; Engrng.

ANNUNZIATA, BETH ANN; Sacred Heart Acad; West Haven, CT; (Y); Church Yth Grp; FBLA; Pep Clb; Political Wkr; Stage Crew; Variety Show; Rep Soph Cls; Rep Jr Cls; Stu Cncl; Var Sftbl; Top Athltc Cls; Bus.

ANNUNZIATA, CHRISTINA M; Cheshire Acad; Cheshire, CT; (Y); 10/54; Key Clb; VP Jr Cls; VP Stu Cncl; Stat Bsktbl; Stat Socr; Var Sftbl; Var Vllybl; High Hon Roll; Jr NHS; NHS; Cheshire Twn Schlrshp-4 Yr-Cheshire Acad 82; Proctorshp 83; Educ.

ANNUNZIATA, CHRISTOPHER; East Haven HS; E Haven, CT; (Y); 10/280; Am Leg Boys St; Varsity Clb; Pres Frsh Cls; Pres Soph Cls; Pres Jr Cls; Pres Sr Cls; L Ice Hcky; High Hon Roll; NHS; Hugh O Brian Yth Fndtn 84; CT JR Sci & Humnts Sympsm 85; Med.

ANSALDO, JAMES; Guilford HS; Guilford, CT; (Y); Boy Scts; Church Yth Grp; Cmnty Wkr; Hon Roll; Emerson Coll; Jrnlsm.

ANSEVIN, RENE; Bethel HS; Bethel, CT; (Y); AFS; Drama Clb; French Clb; Variety Show; JV Trk; Var L Vllybl; NHS; Pittsburg U; Art.

ANTONOWICZ, MIKE; Ledyard HS; Ledyard, CT; (Y); Ftbl; Wt Lftg; Hon Roll; Clemson.

ANZALONE, DEBORAH; Stanford Catholic HS; Stamford, CT; (Y); 25/146; Red Cross Aide; Nwsp Stf; Ed Yrbk Stf; Ed Lit Mag; Var JV Sftbl; Var Tennis; High Hon Roll; Hon Roll; NHS; Cmnty Wkr; John Carroll Awd Outstndng Hist 84; Syracuse U; Comm.

ANZIVINE, DEANNA; Crosby HS; Waterbury, CT; (Y); Church Yth Grp; FHA; Hosp Aide; Key Clb; Stage Crew; Rep Stu Cncl; Hon Roll; Briarwood; Exec Sec.

APONTE, LISA; O H Platt HS; Meriden, CT; (Y); Cmnty Wkr; Key Clb; Latin Clb; Yrbk Stf; Powder Puff Ftbl; Socr; Hon Roll; Wesleyan U; Pre-Med.

APPERT, DAVID; Ridgefield HS; Ridgefield, CT; (Y); 29/364; Debate Tm; Pres German Clb; Library Aide; Var L Golf; Hon Roll; NHS; Ntl Merit Ltr; Nt Germn Exm Hgh Scr 80-81; Presidntl Acadmc Ftns Awd 85; Specl Cmndtn Excllnc Socl Sci 85; U Of VA; Law.

APPLEBY, JACKIE; St Bernard HS; Old Lyme, CT; (Y); 49/305; Yrbk Stf; Tennis; Hon Roll; Acad Awds 82-85fSF CT Modern Miss 85; Frnch.

APUZZO, MIKE J; East Haven HS; E Haven, CT; (Y); CT Schl Elec; Elec Tech.

AQUARO, FRANCINE; East Haven HS; E Haven, CT; (Y); 46/250; Spanish Clb; Varsity Clb; Yrbk Stf; Sec Stu Cncl; Var L Bsktbl; Var Mgr(s); Sec Sftbl; Jr NHS; US Stu Cncl Awd; Legal Asst.

AQUINO, JOHN; Kolbe Cathedral HS; Bridgeport, CT; (Y); 8/103; Bsbl; Bowling; Var Wt Lftg; Hon Roll; NHS; Schlstc Awd, Hghst Avr Basc Geo, Spnsh II 84; U Bridgeport; Law.

ARAYA, JOHN RICHARD; Immaculate HS; New Milford, CT; (Y); 15/202; Yrbk Stf; Rep Stu Cncl; Var Bsktbl; High Hon Roll; NHS; Spanish NHS; Natl Hspnc Schlr Awd 85; Pre-Law.

ARBACHOUSKAS, TERI; Kolbe-Cathedral HS; Ansonia, CT; (Y); Art Clb; Church Yth Grp; Dance Clb; Math Clb; Spanish Clb; Variety Show; Nwsp Stf; Stu Cncl; Crs Cntry; Spanish NHS; 2nd Pl Overal Avg Math Comp 85; Awd Modern Jazz 84; V Ltr Awd Cross Cty 83; Bus.

ARBOUR, WILLIAM; New Britain HS; New Britain, CT; (Y); 22/357; Church Yth Grp; Computer Clb; JA; Wt Lftg; Hon Roll; NCTE Awd; Cert Accmplshmt Proj Bus JR Achvt 81; U Of CT; Bus Adm.

ARCERI, GERALDINE; Bethel HS; Bethel, CT; (Y); 49/280; Camp Fr Inc; Church Yth Grp; Cmnty Wkr; FBLA; FNA; Hosp Aide; JA; Yrbk Stf; Stu Cncl; Tennis; Contsnt In Miss Teen Ct Pngt 84; Fin In The Western Ct Conf Tourn 84; Fin In WCC 3rd Sngls Tnns 85; Occptnl Thrpy.

ARCHAMBAULT, DANIELLE; St Bernard HS; Lisbon, CT; (S); 53/290; Ski Clb; Rep Jr Cls; Rep Sr Cls; Chrmn Stu Cncl; Mgr(s); Score Keeper; Stat Socr; Var Trk; Hon Roll; All ST Trk Tm 84; Bio.

ARCHAMBAULT, MARIANNE; Tourtellotte Memorial HS; N Grosvenordale, CT; (Y); 3/97; Am Leg Aux Girls St; Pres Jr Cls; Co-Capt Bsktbl; Stat Score Keeper; Capt Capt Sftbl; VP NHS; Rep Frsh Cls; Rep Stu Cncl; U Of CT Hnrs Seminar 85; Med Tech.

ARENTZEN, RICHARD W; Guilford SR HS; Guilford, CT; (Y); 13/266; Church Yth Grp; Pres German Clb; Model UN; Stu Cncl; L Bsbl; Capt Var Bsktbl; NHS; Schlr Athl Awd 85; German Hnr Scty 83-85; Physics Olympiad Awd 85; Bucknell U; Mech Engr.

ARIAS, TATIANA; Ansonia HS; Ansonia, CT; (Y); Computer Clb; Debate Tm; FBLA; Latin Clb; Political Wkr; Yrbk Phtg; Yrbk Stf; Var Tennis; Lobbyst YMCA 84; Tnns WVL 85; Law.

ARIETTI, RICARDO J; Enrico Fermi HS; Enfield, CT; (Y); 25/377; Am Leg Boys St; Model UN; Quiz Bowl; Variety Show; High Hon Roll; NHS; Pres Schlr; Grnd Marshal Cls Grad 84; Co-Fndr SR Intrmrl Flr Hcky Lg 85; Bates Coll; Psych.

ARKILANDER, ALISON; Lauralton Hall HS; Stratford, CT; (Y); Church Yth Grp; GAA; Hosp Aide; Math Tm; Service Clb; Yrbk Stf; Lit Mag; Rep Frsh Cls; Rep Stu Cncl; Co-Capt Cheerleading; Boston Coll; Comm.

ARLE, CARRIE ANN; Lyman Hall HS; Wallingford, CT; (Y); FBLA; FHA; JA; Library Aide; Teachers Aide; Powder Puff Ftbl; High Hon Roll; Hon Roll; Cert Of Hnr Earth Sci 83; Hayward U CA; Radio/TV Comm.

ARMATA, RAEGAN; Torrington HS; Torrington, CT; (Y); 17/330; Pres French Clb; Band; Stage Crew; JV Var Bsktbl; JV Sftbl; High Hon Roll; NHS; NEDT Awd; :; Arch.

ARMOUR, ALLISON R; Darien HS; Darien, CT; (Y); Hst MMM; Church Choir; School Play; Ed Nwsp Stf; Pres Frsh Cls; Sec Stu Cncl; High Hon Roll; NHS; Ntl Merit SF; Cit Awd; Rickover Sci Inst Inaug Sessn 84; Lib Arts.

ARMSTRONG, CHRISTOPHER L; Taft Schl; Unityville, PA; (Y); Art Clb; Drama Clb; PAVAS; Acpl Chr; Chorus; School Musical; School Play; Yrbk Stf; Socr.

ARMSTRONG, JACQUELINE; Staples HS; Westport, CT; (Y); Cmnty Wkr; Dance Clb; Cheerleading; Hon Roll; Jr NHS; 1st 2nd Pl Rbbns Horseback Ridng Jumpng 79-81; Math.

ARMSTRONG, JULIE; Trumbull HS; Trumbull, CT; (Y); French Clb; Pep Clb; Ski Clb; Chorus; Stu Cncl; JV Cheerleading; High Hon Roll; Hon Roll; Jr NHS; NHS; Coll; Pltcl Sci.

ARMSTRONG, MARIA; North West Catholic HS; Windsor, CT; (Y); JV L Bsktbl; Var L Sftbl; Hon Roll; Bio Awd 83-84; All HCC Conf Sftbl 83-84; MVP Sftbl 83-84; Chld Psychlgy.

ARNHOLD, KIRSTEN S; Valley Regional HS; Centerbrook, CT; (Y); 9/140; Am Leg Aux Girls St; Band; Yrbk Stf; Lit Mag; Rep Stu Cncl; Var Sftbl; Hon Roll; NHS; Pres Schlr; Essex Rotary Clb Schlrshp 85; Union Coll.

ARNOLD, HEATHER; Rockville HS; Vernon, CT; (Y); 3/360; VP Church Yth Grp; Quiz Bowl; Sec Trs Stu Cncl; Var Stat Bsktbl; Mgr(s); Var L Socr; Var L Tennis; High Hon Roll; NHS; Ntl Merit Schol; Harvard Radcliffe Book Awd 85; Soc Wmn Engrs Cert Merit 85.

ARNOLD, STEFAN; Amity Regional SR HS; Woodbridge, CT; (Y); Science Clb; Hon Roll; Cls 2 Awd-Rcvng Hnrs 2 Yrs In Row; Comp Sci.

ARNOW, BRETT; Hall HS; Cincinnati, OH; (Y); Spanish Clb; Sec Temple Yth Grp; Band; Concert Band; Jazz Band; Pep Band; Nwsp Phtg; Nwsp Stf; JV Bsktbl; JV Socr; IN ST U; Bus Adm.

ARONSON, TRACI D; Cheshire HS; Cheshire, CT; (Y); 46/319; Art Clb; Dance Clb; Key Clb; Ski Clb; Yrbk Stf; Im Badmtn; JV Capt Lcrss; Cit Awd; French Hon Soc; High Hon Roll; Certificate Of Schltc Achvt 82-84; Outstndng Student Certificate 82-83; Parsons Schl Of Design; Illust.

ARROYO, ARMANDO; New Britain HS; New Britain, CT; (Y); MMM; Chorus; Bsbl; Ftbl; Wt Lftg; Var Wrstlng; Hon Roll; JETS Awd; Prfct Atten Awd; Thames Vly ST Tech; Nuclr Engr.

ARSENAULT, MICHAEL R; Woodstock Acad; Woodstock, CT; (Y); Am Leg Boys St; JCL; Latin Clb; Chorus; Crs Cntry; Socr; Trk; Hon Roll; Tm Co-Capt Trk 85; Hawthorne; Aero.

ARTERS, HARRY; Killingly HS; Danielson, CT; (Y); 8/250; Church Yth Grp; Ski Clb; JV Bsktbl; JV Var Ftbl; Var Tennis; Med.

ARTESE, MARY; Joseph A Foran HS; Milford, CT; (Y); #69 In Class; Drama Clb; JCL; Keywanettes; Latin Clb; Varsity Clb; Chorus; Swmmng; Hon Roll; Prfct Atten Awd.

ASBJORNSEN, HEIDI; Pomperaug HS; Southbury, CT; (Y); 2/185; Pres AFS; Church Yth Grp; Math Tm; Model UN; Ski Clb; Off Stu Cncl; Tennis; High Hon Roll; VP NHS; Sal; Eng Achvt Awd; Career Intrnshp Vet Hosp; Yr Abroad Norway; Carleton Coll; Biol.

ASCIONE, DONNA; Southington HS; Plantsville, CT; (Y); 61/550; Dance Clb; Girl Scts; Latin Clb; Pep Clb; Band; Concert Band; School Musical; School Play; Variety Show; Sec Soph Cls; Textron Div Schlrshp 85; U Of CT; Phy Thrpy.

ASHBY, KAREN; The Masters Schl; West Hartford, CT; (S); Drama Clb; FCA; Model UN; Ski Clb; Chorus; School Play; Var Capt Socr; Var Sftbl; High Hon Roll; Yrbk Stf; US Achvmnt Acad 83-84.

ASHE, JULIA; Holy Cross HS; Waterbury, CT; (Y); 117/344; Service Clb; Stage Crew; Yrbk Stf; Rep Stu Cncl; Hon Roll; Most Artstc & Creatv Of Cls JR; Most Artstc Clss SR; U Of CT-STORRS; Graphc Dsgn.

ASHE, LORRAINE; Holy Cross HS; Waterbury, CT; (Y); 23/352; Cmnty Wkr; Teachers Aide; Stage Crew; Lit Mag; French Hon Soc; Hon Roll; NHS; Mst Artstc 84; Easter Seals Day Cmp Bst Feml Vlntr 83; Ltn I Lvl Awd 83; U Of CT; Art.

ASHE, SUSAN M; Newington HS; Newington, CT; (Y); Am Leg Aux Girls St; Drama Clb; Pep Clb; Band; Chorus; Church Choir; Madrigals; Mrchg Band; Orch; School Musical.

ATWOOD, DAWN; Torrington HS; Torrington, CT; (Y); 42/271; 4-H; Varsity Clb; Concert Band; Drm & Bgl; School Musical; Var Capt Crs Cntry; Var Trk; 4-H Awd; JP Sousa Awd; Prfct Atten Awd; Mst Outstndng Sr In Band Awd; Unico Music Awd; Thesbian Hnr Awd; Johnson & Wales Coll; Clnry Art.

ATWOOD, GLENN; Northwestern Regional No 7 HS; New Hartford, CT; (Y); Church Yth Grp; Rep FFA; Hon Roll; Star Greenhand FFA Awd 85.

AUCLAIR, DOUGLAS M; Nathan Hale-Ray HS; Moodus, CT; (Y); 2/55; Am Leg Boys St; CAP; Capt Math Tm; Capt L Crs Cntry; High Hon Roll; Hon Roll; Trs NHS; Ntl Merit SF; Sal; Im Mgr Tennis; All Leag Hghst Scorer Math Tm 84; Air Force Acad; Aero Engr.

AUGER, ALLISON; Killingly HS; Danielson, CT; (Y); 30/270; Latin Clb; Ski Clb; Spanish Clb; Cheerleading; Trk; Hon Roll; NHS; Ntl Merit Ltr; Spanish NHS; Acdmc All Amer 84; Intl Brthd Of Plc Ofcrs Law Enfrcmnt Schlrshp 85; U Of Miami; Pltcl Sci.

AUGUSTINE, GREGORY J; R Rham HS; Marlborough, CT; (Y); 2/174; Am Leg Boys St; Boy Scts; Var L Golf; Var L Socr; Bausch & Lomb Sci Awd; High Hon Roll; NHS; Sal; Church Yth Grp; French Clb; Harvard Bk Awd 84; SF Japan Senate Schlrshp Pgm 84; Cornell U; Elect Engr.

AUGUSTYN, BEATA; Saint Joseph HS; Stratford, CT; (Y); Chorus; Rep Frsh Cls; Rep Jr Cls; Art Clb; Church Yth Grp; Yrbk Stf; Rep Soph Cls; Stu Cncl; JV Var Bowling; 2nd Pl Trophy Yamaha Elect Organ Comptn 84; 3rd Pl Miss Polonia Comptn 85; Trinity Coll.

AUSTIN, SHERRAL; William H Hall HS; W Hartford, CT; (Y); 50/342; Service Clb; Lcrss; JV Capt Socr; NHS; Church Yth Grp; Girl Scts; Hosp Aide; Stu Cncl; Med.

AVERY, HOLLI D; East Hampton HS; E Hampton, CT; (Y); French Clb; Library Aide; Office Aide; Drill Tm; Variety Show; Yth Svc Pgm 84-85; Cntrl CT ST U; Lbrl Arts.

AVERY, JANA D; East Lyme HS; E Lyme, CT; (Y); Trs AFS; Church Yth Grp; Key Clb; Capt Color Guard; Mrchg Band; Stage Crew; Hon Roll; Mst Outstndng Clr Grd Awd 84-85; Bst Techncn Clrgrd Awd 84-85; Bst Techncn New Cmr Clrgrd Awd 81-82; Hofstra U; Mktg.

AVERY, REED; Northwest Catholic HS; Windsor, CT; (Y); Cmnty Wkr; Service Clb; Hon Roll; Church Yth Grp; Model UN; Acpl Chr; Chorus; Stage Crew; Vllybl; Wt Lftg; Elec Engr.

AVERY, ROBERT; Central Catholic HS; Norwalk, CT; (Y); 21/78; French Clb; Jazz Band; Variety Show; JV Bsktbl; JV Var Golf; Wt Lftg; High Hon Roll; Hon Roll; Prfct Atten Awd; CT Hstry Day 2nd Pl Lcl Essay; Syracuse; Arch.

AVERY, WILLIAM BRADFORD; Jonathan Law HS; Milford, CT; (Y); 23/260; Am Leg Boys St; Church Yth Grp; Cmnty Wkr; Key Clb; Church Choir; School Play; Yrbk Stf; Stu Cncl; Hon Roll; Spnsh & Bio Awds 83; U Of CT; Gntc Engrng.

AVILA, PAUL; Cooperative HS; New Haven, CT; (Y); Nwsp Rptr; Rep Jr Cls; Sr Cls; Rep Stu Cncl.

AYLES, MIKE; Guilford HS; Guilford, CT; (Y); 39/315; Teachers Aide; JV Bsbl; High Hon Roll; Hon Roll; Schlstc Achvt Awd Drftng 84; Arch.

AZEVEDO, PAULA; Holy Cross HS; Naugatuck, CT; (Y); Pres Church Yth Grp; Cmnty Wkr; English Clb; French Clb; JA; Library Aide; Nwsp Rptr; Nwsp Sprt Ed; Lit Mag; Sec Frsh Cls; NY U; Law.

BABINET, ERIC; Greenwich HS; Greenwich, CT; (Y); Cmnty Wkr; Math Tm; Chorus; Nwsp Rptr; French Hon Soc; High Hon Roll; Hon Roll; NHS; Ntl Merit Ltr; Physics, Chmstry & Cntntl Calculus Leag Awds 84-85; Stanford U; Comp Sci.

BABOFF, AMY; Amity Regional SR HS; Bethany, CT; (S); 24/376; Am Leg Aux Girls St; Drama Clb; Temple Yth Grp; Chorus; Capt Flag Corp; Yrbk Stf; Lit Mag; Stu Cncl; Var Cheerleading; NHS; Natl Latn Exm Awd 83; Poetry Publ Natl Teen Mag 84; Hlth Fld.

BACCHIOCCHI, NANCY; Sacred Heart Acad; West Haven, CT; (Y); 8/114; Church Yth Grp; FBLA; Math Tm; Quiz Bowl; Im Vllybl; High Hon Roll; NHS; NEDT Awd; Prfct Atten Awd; WHAIIA Schlrshp 85; Cert Merit Energy Cmmrcl 84; Fairfield U; Accntnt.

BAGNALL, PAMELA; Coventry HS; Coventry, CT; (Y); Band; Yrbk Phtg; Yrbk Stf; JV Var Bsktbl; Trk; Hon Roll; NHS; Natl Sci Olympd Awd 84; Vet Sci.

BAI, MATT; Trumbull HS; Trumbull, CT; (Y); Band; Drm Mjr(t); Mrchg Band; Symp Band; Nwsp Ed-Chief; Hon Roll; Stu Ldrshp Comm 84-85; Pol Sci.

BAILEY, MONTE; James Hillhouse HS; New Haven, CT; (S); Model UN; Var Bsbl; Var Bsktbl; Cit Awd; High Hon Roll; Hon Roll; NHS; Prfct Atten Awd; Spanish NHS; St Schlr; Thurgood Marshall Awd 84; Coll; Law.

BAILEY, SUSAN L; Southington HS; Southington, CT; (Y); 9/550; Hosp Aide; Key Clb; Ski Clb; Spanish Clb; Yrbk Stf; High Hon Roll; Lion Awd; NHS; St Schlr; Spnsh Awd Schlrshp 85; U Connecticut; Pre-Vet.

BAKER, BECKIE J; New Britain HS; New Britain, CT; (Y); 32/385; Church Yth Grp; Hosp Aide; Office Aide; Nwsp Rptr; Nwsp Stf; Hon Roll; Pepperdine U Malibu CA; Jrnlsm.

BAKER, BRIAN; Crosby HS; Waterbury, CT; (Y); Boys Clb Am; Band; Mrchg Band; Ftbl; Mgr(s); Hon Roll; Acctng.

BAKER, DAWN R; Newington HS; Newington, CT; (Y); Hosp Aide; Spanish Clb; High Hon Roll; Hon Roll; Graphc Dsgn.

BAKER, STUART; Avon Old Farms Schl; West Simsbury, CT; (S); 23/102; Chrmn Church Yth Grp; Pep Clb; Radio Clb; Chorus; School Play; Stage Crew; Hon Roll; Schl Radio Stn Mgr 84-85; Stu Swtchbrd Superv 84-85; St Lawrence U.

BAKER, SUSAN; Manchester HS; Manchester, CT; (Y); Art Clb; Aud/Vis; Aud/Vis; Nwsp Rptr; Ed Nwsp Stf; Lit Mag; Hon Roll; NHS; Brown U Bk Awd 85.

BALBONI, IMELDA; Manchester HS; Manchester, CT; (Y); AFS; Drama Clb; Spanish Clb; High Hon Roll; Hon Roll; NHS; Anmls.

BALCH, WILLIAM; Cheshire HS; Cheshire, CT; (Y); 53/303; Red Cross Aide; Pres Frsh Cls; Pres Soph Cls; Rep Sr Cls; JV Golf; Var L Socr; Var Capt Trk; High Hon Roll; Hon Roll; Cum Laude Natl Latin Exam 83.

BALDO, RENEE; North Haven HS; N Haven, CT; (Y); 70/286; Aud/Vis; Drama Clb; PAVAS; Yrbk Stf; French Hon Soc; Hon Roll; Prfct Atten Awd; ECA Theatre Dept 83-84; Pre-Med.

BALDWIN, LISA; Kaynor Regional Voc Tech; Wolcott, CT; (Y); VICA; Var Capt Bsktbl; Score Keeper; Var Capt Sftbl.

BALDWIN, SHEREE LENORE; Stratford HS; Stratford, CT; (Y); 31/241; Cmnty Wkr; Drama Clb; Hosp Aide; Q&S; Spanish Clb; Band; Concert Band; School Play; Rep Frsh Cls; Pres Soph Cls; Outstndg Svc Awd Stu Cncl 82-85; Outstndg Svc Awd 82-83; Ped.

BALDWIN, STEVEN; Robert E Fitch SR HS; Groton, CT; (Y); 32/410; Pres Church Yth Grp; Dance Clb; Speech Tm; Church Choir; School Musical; School Play; VP Soph Cls; Var L Trk; High Hon Roll; NHS; Gordon Coll; Theolgy.

BALET, STEVEN; Penney HS; E Hartford, CT; (Y); Trs VP Church Yth Grp; Spanish Clb; Nwsp Phtg; Ed Yrbk Phtg; Frsh Cls; Jr Cls; Var Tennis; High Hon Roll; Hon Roll; NHS; Union Carbide WA Wrkshps Schlrshp 85; Schduler ST Rides 85-86; George Washington U; Bus.

BALINSKAS, BETH; Southington HS; Southington, CT; (Y); Hosp Aide; Key Clb; Ski Clb; Variety Show; Var L Tennis; High Hon Roll; Hon Roll; Acctg.

BALINSKAS, CINDY; St Thomas Aquinas HS; E Berlin, CT; (Y); French Clb; Pep Clb; School Musical; Stage Crew; Rep Soph Cls; Sls.

BALLARO, CHARLES; Shelton HS; Shelton, CT; (Y); 140/325; Drama Clb; School Play; Ftbl; Jrnlsm.

BALLESTAS, PATRICIA; Bulkeley HS; Hartford, CT; (Y); Camera Clb; FHA; JA; Yrbk Stf; Rep Jr Cls; Capt Vllybl; Cit Awd; Hon Roll; Nrsng.

BALOG, MADELYN; Masuk HS; Monroe, CT; (Y); 36/266; VP AFS; French Clb; Ski Clb; Swmmng; JA; Bsktbl; Sftbl; U Denver; Bus Mngmnt.

BALZANO, DONNA; Branford HS; Branford, CT; (Y); DECA; Paralegal.

BANACH, SHARON; Danbury HS; Danbury, CT; (Y); German Clb; Key Clb; ROTC; Variety Show; Sftbl; Mgr Vllybl; Western CT; Educ.

BANDZES, JULIE; Berlin HS; Kensington, CT; (Y); 13/244; Rep Jr Cls; Rep Stu Cncl; Powder Puff Ftbl; High Hon Roll; Hon Roll; U MA Essay Cont Wnnr; Poltcl Sci.

BANSAK II, RONALD R; Avon Old Farms Schl; Norwalk, CT; (S); 8/110; Art Clb; Cmnty Wkr; Pep Clb; Radio Clb; Var Capt Lcrss; Var Socr; Var Trk; Hon Roll; Ski Clb; Nwsp Stf; All State Lacrosse Player 84; Natl SR N S All Star Game Player 84; Natl Scholastic Art Comp 85; Architecture.

BARAKA-BRIDGFORTH, JAMES; Choate Rosemary Hall HS; Kalamazoo, MI; (Y); Off Computer Clb; Ntl Merit SF; Morehouse Coll; Comp Sci.

BARAN, H ELIZABETH; Platt HS; Meriden, CT; (Y); 44/190; Church Yth Grp; Hosp Aide; Key Clb; Latin Clb; Chorus; Variety Show; L Crs Cntry; Elks Awd; Post Step Schlrshp 85; Meridens Jr Miss 85; Eastern CT ST U; Bio.

BARBEE JR, DONALD C; Brien Mc Mahon HS; Norwalk, CT; (Y); 42/420; Computer Clb; JA; Frsh Cls; Trs Soph Cls; Jr Cls; Rep Sr Cls; Rep Stu Cncl; JV Capt Bsbl; JV Socr; Wt Lftg; St Rnnr Up Comp Sci Comp 85; Fordham U; Bus.

BARBER, DIANE; Manchester HS; Manchester, CT; (Y); Hon Roll.

BARBER, JACQUELINE; Academy Of Our Lady Of Mercy; Stratford, CT; (Y); Cmnty Wkr; Hosp Aide; Latin Clb; Math Clb; Service Clb; Spanish Clb; Chorus; Variety Show; Yrbk Phtg; Im Vllybl; Awd For Outstndng NEDT Tst Scrs 83; Bus Admnstrtn.

BARBER, KAREN; Seymour HS; Seymour, CT; (Y); 93/215; Girl Scts; Band; Concert Band; Mrchg Band; Swmmng; Central CT ST U; Accntng.

BARBER, SCOTT; Westhill HS; Stamford, CT; (Y); Boy Scts; Computer Clb; German Clb; JA; Latin Clb; Math Clb; Science Clb; GA Tech; Aerontcl Engrng.

BARBOZA, ROBERT; Guilford SR HS; Guilford, CT; (Y); 79/350; Church Yth Grp; Science Clb; Spanish Clb; Chorus; High Hon Roll; Hon Roll; Ntl Merit Ltr; Spanish NHS; Acad Achvt African Studies 85; Bus.

BARBUTI, LISA; New Fairfield HS; New Fairfld, CT; (Y); Yrbk Stf; Chem.

BARD, DAWNE; Vinal Regional Vo-Tech; Middletown, CT; (Y); Keywanettes; Ski Clb; VICA; Rep Soph Cls; Voc Ind Clbs Am Model 2nd Pl 84; Electrncs.

BARDELL, KRISTIN; Griswold HS; Griswold, CT; (Y); GAA; Varsity Clb; Yrbk Stf; Vllybl; High Hon Roll; Hon Roll; Untd Nations Pilgrimage For Yth Jurisdctnl Delg 85; Optmtry.

BARKER, JOHN; Tourtellotte Memorial HS; Thompson, CT; (Y); 5/98; Drama Clb; Chorus; Yrbk Stf; High Hon Roll; NHS; Church Yth Grp; Church Choir; Hon Roll; Excllnce Amer Studs 84; Natl Merit Commended Stu 84; Church Life Essay Cont 1st Prize Wnnr 85; Yale; Theolgn.

BARMMER, SCOTT; Westbrook JR SR HS; Westbrook, CT; (Y); 7/60; Church Yth Grp; Political Wkr; School Play; Nwsp Ed-Chief; Yrbk Ed-Chief; Lit Mag; Pres Stu Cncl; Capt Var Tennis; DAR Awd; NHS; Exchng Clb Yth Yr 85; Congrssnl Cert Mert 85; Centry III Ldrs ST Alt 85; Boston Coll; Law.

BARNETT, DEBBIE; Norwalk HS; E Norwalk, CT; (Y); 16/472; Spanish Clb; Color Guard; Mrchg Band; Stage Crew; Soph Cls; Rep Jr Cls; High Hon Roll; Ntl Merit Ltr; Intl Law.

BARNETT, PETER; St Bernard HS; Plainfield, CT; (S); 14/289; Drama Clb; Exploring; School Play; Wrstlng; High Hon Roll; NHS; Library Aide; Office Aide; Academic Letter & Chevron 83; Social Studies Awd 82; Projct AIM Particpant 84; Chem.

BARNOLA, MARK; Bethel HS; Bethel, CT; (Y); Church Yth Grp; Computer Clb; JV Bsktbl; Var Trk; Bethel Exchng Clb Schlrshp 85; U Of CT; Bus.

BARON, RON; Staples HS; Westport, CT; (Y); German Clb; Band; Im Bsbl; Im Bsktbl; Var Socr; JV Sftbl; Wrstlng; Brandeis; Bus.

BARONE, DONALD J; Amity Regional HS; Bethany, CT; (Y); 71/376; Am Leg Boys St; Church Yth Grp; Stu Cncl; Ice Hcky; Cit Awd; Hon Roll; Pres Schlr; James Dunleavy Awd Sprtsmnshp 84; Betheny Orange Woodbridge Yth Hcky Awd 85; U Connecticut; Bus.

BARONE, NATALIE; Holy Cross HS; Prospect, CT; (Y); 99/344; Church Yth Grp; Pres Frsh Cls; Sec Soph Cls; Cheerleading; Score Keeper; Hon Roll; NHS; Ldrshp Awd 81; Jazz Schlrshp,CT Acad Of Perfrmng Arts 81-84; Yth Cncl Awd,Awd Of Merit 85; U Of Connecticut; Sprts.

BARONI, LISA; St Thomas Aquinas HS; New Britain, CT; (Y); 5/150; Library Aide; Political Wkr; Trs Spanish Clb; Yrbk Stf; Rep Soph Cls; Rep Jr Cls; Rep Sr Cls; Elks Awd; Hon Roll; Pres NHS; Ella Grasso Fndtn Schlrshp 85; UNICO Schlrshp 85; Barnard Coll; Pre-Law.

BARRE, LISA; Nonnewage HS; Wdby, CT; (Y); 4-H; FFA; High Hon Roll; Hon Roll; Outstndng Achvt Comp Pgmmng 83; Horticulture.

BARRETT, DEBBIE; Thomaston HS; Thomaston, CT; (Y); Church Yth Grp; French Clb; GAA; Chorus; Church Choir; Sec Frsh Cls; Sec Rep Jr Cls; Sec Sr Cls; Stu Cncl; Bsktbl; Var Ltr Fld Hcky, Bsktbll & Sftbll 82-85; Elem Educ.

BARRETT, JOHN; Danbury HS; Danbury, CT; (Y); Drama Clb; Key Clb; Madrigals; School Musical; School Play; Stage Crew; Variety Show; Bus.

BARRS, KEVIN C; Waterford HS; Waterford, CT; (Y); 10/220; Am Leg Boys St; Church Yth Grp; Nwsp Stf; Pres Frsh Cls; Rep Stu Cncl; Var Bsktbl; JV Trk; High Hon Roll; Hon Roll; NHS.

BARRY, KATHLEEN; East Catholic HS; E Hartford, CT; (Y); 68/294; French Clb; Rep Soph Cls; Rep Jr Cls; JV Var Cheerleading; Hon Roll; NHS; Stonehill Coll; Hosp Adm.

BARRY, SEAN; Stamford Catholic HS; Stamford, CT; (Y); 7/160; Math Tm; Ski Clb; Stage Crew; Pres Stu Cncl; Var Crs Cntry; Var Ftbl; High Hon Roll; NHS; Ntl Merit SF; NEDT Awd; ST Stu Advsry Cncl Ed 84-85; Bio.

BARRY, WILLIAM; Daniel Hand HS; Madison, CT; (Y); 45/286; Church Yth Grp; Model UN; Ski Clb; Concert Band; Jazz Band; Mrchg Band; Var Socr; JV Var Trk; High Hon Roll; Pltcl Sci.

BARRY, WILLIAM; Southington HS; Southington, CT; (Y); Church Yth Grp; Pres German Clb; VP Concert Band; Jazz Band; Rep Stu Cncl; Capt L Bsbl; Var L Bsktbl; Im Cook Actv; Im Golf; Im Ice Hcky; Mst Imprvd Jr Bsbll 85; All Conf Bsbll 85; US Nvl Acad; Educ.

BARTIS, CHRIS; Orville H Platt HS; Meriden, CT; (Y); Key Clb; Band; Jazz Band; Mrchg Band; Rep Stu Cncl; Ftbl; High Hon Roll; Hon Roll; Bsktbl; Yth In Govt Rep In The House 85; Outstndng JR Boy 84-85.

BARTNER, NICOLE; Brookfield HS; Brookfield, CT; (Y); Varsity Clb; Capt Crs Cntry; Trk; Wt Lftg; High Hon Roll; VP NHS; Boy Scts; Church Yth Grp; French Clb; FBLA; Bst Stdnt Frnch II 83; Bst Stdnt Creatv Wrtg 85; VP Safe Rides 84; Tufts; Vet.

BARTOLOTTA, LISA; St Joseph HS; Ansonia, CT; (Y); 24/218; Dance Clb; Drama Clb; Girl Scts; Political Wkr; Spanish Clb; Stage Crew; Yrbk Stf; Lit Mag; High Hon Roll; NEDT Awd; Lib Arts.

BARTON, LORI; Conard HS; West Hartford, CT; (Y); 38/322; Church Yth Grp; Pep Clb; School Play; Var L Cheerleading; Var L Gym; JV Trk; High Hon Roll; Hon Roll; Accntnt.

BARTONE, LISA; Shelton HS; Shelton, CT; (Y); Art Clb; Gym; Hon Roll; Excptnl Frnch Wrk Merit Cert 82-83.

BARTYZEL, HELEN B; Newington HS; Newington, CT; (Y); Intnl Clb; High Hon Roll; Hon Roll; JV Bsktbl; Var Tennis; Magna Cum Laude Ntl Latin Bd 84; Bio.

BASCETTA, SUSAN; Torrington HS; Torrington, CT; (Y); 11/279; Cmnty Wkr; Dance Clb; FBLA; Key Clb; Math Clb; Math Tm; Ski Clb; Yrbk Stf; JV Cheerleading; High Hon Roll; Northeastern U; Bus Admin.

BASCH, RICHARD; Wilton HS; Wilton, CT; (Y); 15/300; Hosp Aide; Math Tm; Y-Teens; High Hon Roll; Hon Roll; NHS; Math Assn Of Amer Outstdng Profcncy Awd 84; Accptd In Gftd Prog 84; Comp Engrng.

BASCHE, DAVID; William H Hall HS; W Hartford, CT; (Y); Cmnty Wkr; Drama Clb; School Play; Trs Soph Cls; Rep Jr Cls; Rep Stu Cncl; Bsbl; JV Capt Socr; Cit Awd; Hon Roll; Flagg Hse Stu Of Mnth 85; Cert Of Apprectn Community Corps 85; Bus.

BASSETT, TODD; North Haven HS; N Haven, CT; (Y); Aud/Vis; Boy Scts; Church Yth Grp; Cmnty Wkr; Computer Clb; Band; Chorus; Church Choir; Concert Band; Jazz Band; Eagl Sct 85; Asbury Coll; Comp Sci.

BASSOS, KIM; William H Hall HS; W Hartford, CT; (Y); 79/356; Church Yth Grp; Rep Jr Cls; JV Var Bsktbl; Var Tennis; JV Trk; Hon Roll; U CA Santa Cruz; Zoo.

BASTA, MICHAEL; West Haven HS; W Haven, CT; (Y); Am Leg Boys St; Rep Frsh Cls; Rep Soph Cls; Rep Jr Cls; Rep Stu Cncl; JV Ftbl; Law.

BASTRZYCKI, STEPHAN; Northwestern Reginal No 7; Collinsville, CT; (Y); Church Yth Grp; German Clb; Red Cross Aide; Ski Clb; Var Tennis; High Hon Roll; Hon Roll; NHS; Hugh O Brian Ldrshp Sem 84; Exclnce Geom 83; Exclnce German 83-85; U CT; Comp Sci.

BATES, STACIA; Coventry HS; Coventry, CT; (Y); Church Yth Grp; French Clb; Hosp Aide; Teachers Aide; Var Capt Cheerleading; Hon Roll; Peer Grp Cnslr 84-85; Occptnl Thrpy.

BATES, SUSAN M; Lyman Hall HS; Wallingford, CT; (Y); Trs FBLA; JA; Office Aide; Political Wkr; Teachers Aide; Stu Cncl; 4-H Awd; Hon Roll; FBLA 83; JR Achvt 83; Spnsh 84; U Of CT; Fin.

BATTAGLINO, ANNETTE C; Shelton HS; Shelton, CT; (Y); 7/438; Rep Stu Cncl; Pom Pon; High Hon Roll; Hon Roll; NHS; Itln Cert Merit; Itln Ntl Hnr Soc; Itln Clb; Sons Itly Schlrshp; U Of CT; Chld Psychlgy.

BAUM JR, HENRY T; Daniel Hand HS; Madison, CT; (Y); 52/259; Am Leg Boys St; Spanish Clb; Band; Drm Mjr(t); Mrchg Band; Cit Awd; JP Sousa Awd; Lion Awd; Rotary Awd; Ski Clb; CBT Schlrshp; De Vry; Comp Sci.

BAVEDAS, FRANK; Notre Dame HS; Milford, CT; (Y); Debate Tm; Ski Clb; DAR Awd; Hon Roll; Ntl Merit Ltr; Comm.

BAZAKAS, TODD; Westhill HS; Stamford, CT; (Y); German Clb; JA; Ski Clb; Socr; Hon Roll; NHS.

BEARDSLEY JR, KENNETH P; Naugatuck HS; Naugatuck, CT; (Y); 15/329; Am Leg Boys St; Computer Clb; Library Aide; Bsbl; Bsktbl; Var L Trk; Hon Roll; NHS; Prfct Atten Awd; Naugatuck Rtry Clb Schlrshp 85; U CT; Comp Sci.

BEAUDOIN, LISA; St Bernard HS; Lebanon, CT; (Y); 53/297; Church Yth Grp; Exploring; FNA; Hosp Aide; Red Cross Aide; Yrbk Stf; Stu Cncl; Stat Sftbl; Hon Roll; Cert Merit JR Volntr Prog 83; Visl Arts Awd Art 83; Acadmc Exclinc Awd 84; Surgcl Nrsg.

BEAUDREAULT, LEE ANN C; Killingly HS; Dayville, CT; (Y); 15/280; Church Yth Grp; Band; Concert Band; Mrchg Band; Symp Band; Fld Hcky; Hon Roll; Spanish NHS; Schlrshp Eastrn CT ST U 85-86; Yth Volntr Assn Awd 85; Top Spnsh Grds Awd 84; Eastern CT ST U; Bus Admin.

BEAULAC, BETH ANN; Tolland HS; Tolland, CT; (Y); Camera Clb; Church Yth Grp; French Clb; Yrbk Stf; Hon Roll; Outstdng Schlstc Achv In Englsh 84; Art.

BEAUPRE, KIM; East Granby HS; East Granby, CT; (Y); 32/50; Stat JV Socr; Var Tennis; Hon Roll; Briarwood Coll; Travel.

BECCONSALL, KEITH; Roger Ludlowe HS; Fairfield, CT; (Y); Am Leg Boys St; Latin Clb; Pep Clb; Thesps; School Musical; School Play; Stage Crew; Nwsp Rptr; Ftbl; Trk; Awd Theatr Lghtg Dsgn 85; Hstry.

BECHARD, KEVIN D; Bristol Eastern HS; Bristol, CT; (Y); Am Leg Boys St; Art Clb; Rptr FBLA; Ski Clb; Spanish Clb; Yrbk Stf; Hon Roll; Frontier Appld Sci Yale U 84; FBLA Awd 85; Clark U.

BECHER, THOMAS; Greenwich HS; Greenwich, CT; (Y); Pres JA; Pres Radio Clb; Nwsp Ed-Chief; Nwsp Rptr; Nwsp Sprt Ed; Nwsp Stf; JV Socr; Hon Roll; Jrnlsm.

BECK, DAVID; Naugatuck HS; Naugatuck, CT; (Y); Trs Drama Clb; Chorus; Drm & Bgl; Drm Mjr(t); Jazz Band; Orch; Sec Symp Band; Variety Show; Var Tennis; Hon Roll; Genl Fdrtn Wmns Clbs Of CT Inc Awd 85; Naugtck Band Parents Assn-Laurel Music Cmp Schlr 83-85; Music Ed.

BECK, KIRSTEN; Masukk HS; Monroe, CT; (Y); Church Yth Grp; Capt Bsktbl; JV Fld Hcky; JV Sftbl; Var Trk; Hon Roll; U CT; Nrsng.

BECKENSTEIN, MICHELE; Guilford HS; Guilford, CT; (Y); Dance Clb; Exploring; FFA; Girl Scts; Office Aide; Teachers Aide; Temple Yth Grp; Orch; Badmtn; Bsbl.

BECKER, KAREN E; Newington HS; Newington, CT; (Y); Math Clb; High Hon Roll; U Of Bridgeport; Arch Engrng.

BECKER, LIBBE; Brien Mc Mahon HS; Norwalk, CT; (Y); Silvermine Guild Artists Smmr Schlrshp 85; Hickry Hl Figure Sktng Clb Achvt Cert 83-84.

BECKER, RAY; Vinal Tech HS; Durham, CT; (Y); ROTC; Diving.

BECOTTE, DONNA; St Bernard; Fitchville, CT; (S); Boy Scts; Flag Corp; Jr Cls; Hon Roll; Safe Rides; Math.

BEDARD, DONNA; East Catholic HS; E Hartford, CT; (Y); French Clb; Vllybl; Hon Roll; FUTURE Sec Of Amer; Manchester CC; Accntng.

BEELER, JEFFREY; Watertown HS; Watertown, CT; (Y); 3/238; Computer Clb; Chorus; Rep Frsh Cls; Rep Soph Cls; Rep Jr Cls; Rep Sr Cls; Rep Stu Cncl; Socr; High Hon Roll; NHS; CIAC-CASS Schlr Athl Awd 85; Outstndg Schlr Athlete 84; Ntl Merit Lttr 85; Boston U; Pol Sci.

BEESLEY JR, NEIL; Notre Dame HS; W Haven, CT; (Y); 88/266; Aud/Vis; Church Yth Grp; Cmnty Wkr; Exploring; Latin Clb; Teachers Aide; Band; Concert Band; Jazz Band; Mrchg Band; Pre-Med.

BEEZEL, CHARLES M; Shelton HS; Huntington, CT; (Y); Am Leg Boys St; VP Latin Clb; Scholastic Bowl; Yrbk Sprt Ed; Sec Jr Cls; Sec Sr Cls; Mgr(s); Cit Awd; High Hon Roll; NHS; Pres SADD 84-85; Harvard Bk Awd 84-85; Latn Ntl Hnr Soc 83-86; Law.

BEGG, MICHAEL; Holy Cross HS; Waterbury, CT; (Y); 110/352; Boys Clb Am; Red Cross Aide; Varsity Clb; Rep Soph Cls; Trs Jr Cls; Sec Sr Cls; Stu Cncl; Bsbl; Capt Var Ftbl; Var Lcrss; All Conf Defns-Ftbl 85; All City Offns & Defns 85; All Northern CT-LACROSS 85; Pre-Law.

BEGIN, MIMI M; Crosby HS; Waterbury, CT; (Y); French Clb; FNA; Hosp Aide; VICA; Stu Cncl; Cit Awd; DAR Awd; High Hon Roll; Hon Roll; NHS; Svc Awd Crosby Cuisine Clb 84; Mattatuck Coll; RN.

BEGIN, RENEE; Holy Cross HS; Waterbury, CT; (Y); 19/352; Church Yth Grp; Hosp Aide; Yrbk Stf; Rep Jr Cls; Rep Stu Cncl; French Hon Soc; High Hon Roll; VP NHS; Fine Arts Clb 84-85.

BEHNKEN, KARIN; Nonnewaug HS; Woodbury, CT; (Y); GAA; Band; School Musical; Yrbk Sprt Ed; Trs Frsh Cls; Var Fld Hcky; JV Var Sftbl; Cit Awd; Hon Roll; Amer Musicl Fndtn Band Hnrs 83; Bst All Arnd Plyr Fld Hcky 82-83; Sprts Med.

BELANGER, MIKE; Rockville HS; Vernon, CT; (S); 8/369; Am Leg Boys St; Pres FFA; Stu Cncl; High Hon Roll; JETS Awd; NHS; ROTC Schlrshp 85-89; Top Physics Stu 84; Top Bio Stu 82; Elec Engrng.

BELCHER, DANA; Norwalk HS; Norwalk, CT; (Y); Ski Clb; Acpl Chr; Symp Band; Yrbk Stf; Rep Jr Cls; Stu Cncl; Var Swmmng; Var Tennis; Var Trk; High Hon Roll; Cum Laude Latin Awd 85.

BELCHER, LIAMA; Thomas Snell Weaver HS; Hartford, CT; (Y); 50/400; Camera Clb; Church Yth Grp; Cmnty Wkr; 4-H; Church Choir; School Musical; Jr Cls; Crs Cntry; Trk; Hon Roll; Scientist Of Tomorrow Cmpltn Awd-Greater Hartford Coll 83; Psych.

BELIASOV, PAUL J; Hartford Christian Acad; Manchester, CT; (S); 1/5; Church Yth Grp; Acpl Chr; Chorus; Church Choir; School Musical; School Play; Yrbk Ed-Chief; Pres Jr Cls; Var Bsktbl; High Hon Roll.

BELL, KENNETH; Southington HS; Plantsville, CT; (Y); 2/526; Church Yth Grp; Am Leg Aux Girls St; Pres Band; Concert Band; Jazz Band; Mrchg Band; Orch; Pep Band; JV Bsktbl; JV Ftbl; All-Eastern Band 85; All-State Band & Orchestra 83-85; Music.

BELL, KEVIN; Fitch SR HS; Groton, CT; (Y); Boy Scts; Latin Clb; Letterman Clb; Science Clb; Bsktbl; Ftbl; Golf; Trk; Wt Lftg; Hon Roll; Bible Awd Church Atten 83; U Of VA; Polit Sci.

BELL, LAWRENCE M; Wethersfield HS; Wethersfield, CT; (Y); 50/350; Am Leg Boys St; VP Pres Key Clb; Var L Bsktbl; Var L Socr; MVP Chmpnshp Socr Game 85; Temple U; Bus Mgmt.

BELL, STEVEN; Guilford HS; Guilford, CT; (Y); 20/350; Chess Clb; Cmnty Wkr; French Clb; German Clb; Latin Clb; Letterman Clb; Ski Clb; Band; Concert Band; Jazz Band; Intl Rel.

BELLEROSE, BARRY CHARLES; Putnam HS; Putnam, CT; (Y); 7/140; Chrmn Church Yth Grp; School Play; Yrbk Ed-Chief; Var Bsktbl; Var Trk; Bausch & Lomb Sci Awd; High Hon Roll; NHS; Ntl Merit Ltr; MI ST U; Pre-Med.

BELLITTO, ROBERT; Fairfield College Prep School; Fairfield, CT; (Y); Church Yth Grp; Q&S; Nwsp Rptr; Nwsp Stf; JV Crs Cntry; JV Trk; Spanish NHS; Chaplaincy Tm 84-85; Engl.

BELLIZZI, ELIZABETH A; Farmington HS; Farmington, CT; (Y); 94/210; Church Yth Grp; Chorus; JV Fld Hcky; Hon Roll; Rotary Awd; UNICO Intl Frmngtn Chap 84-85; Graham Found 84-85; Frmngtn Comm Chest 84-85; U Bridgeport; Intr Dsgn.

BELLO, KATHLEEN; Norwalk HS; Norwalk, CT; (Y); 9/400; VP Key Clb; Ski Clb; Color Guard; Stage Crew; Rep Frsh Cls; Sec Soph Cls; Rep Jr Cls; Powder Puff Ftbl; High Hon Roll; Pres NHS.

BELLOCK, SANDY; Brookfield HS; Brookfield, CT; (Y); 5/220; Church Yth Grp; Pres Girl Scts; Math Clb; Speech Tm; Boys Clb Am; Church Choir; Lit Mag; Trk; High Hon Roll; Pres NHS; Grl Sct Slvr Awd 83; Gld Awd 85; U Of CT; Pupptry.

BELOIN, GARY; New Britain HS; New Britain, CT; (Y); Church Yth Grp; Tennis; Wrstlng; French Hon Soc; Jr NHS; NHS; Vrsty Wrstlng 82-83; U Of CT; Elec Engr.

BELSITO, KARIN; Tolland HS; Tolland, CT; (Y); Sec Cmnty Wkr; Band; Jazz Band; School Musical; JV Var Vllybl; High Hon Roll; NHS; Madrigals; Schlrshp-Cntr For Crtv Yth-Wesleyan U 84; Hnrs Piano Rctl,U Of Hrtfrd 85; NCCC Chrous & Band 84 & 85; Sci.

BELVEDERE JR, DANIEL; Crosby HS; Waterbury, CT; (Y); JA; Key Clb; NHS; US Hstry Clb 84-85; Cert CT ST Energy Audtr 83-84; Yale; Tchr.

BEMIS, JAMES S; Enfield HS; Enfield, CT; (Y); Variety Show; Wrstlng; Hon Roll; Rotary Awd; Ind Ed Awd 85; German II Awd 85; Cabinetmaker.

BENDER, ERIK; Ledyard HS; Gales Ferry, CT; (Y); 38/225; AFS; Var JV Socr; Var Wrstlng; Band; Wt Lftg; Hon Roll; Plaque-Class M Champ At 105 Lb 84; Med.

BENDER, SHELLY; North Haven HS; N Haven, CT; (Y); Church Yth Grp; JV Trk; High Hon Roll.

BENEDETTO, CHRISTINE; Sacred Heart Acad; Redding, CT; (Y); Sec Church Yth Grp; Drama Clb; School Play; Lit Mag; VP Frsh Cls; VP Soph Cls; Cheerleading; French Hon Soc; High Hon Roll; Hon Roll; Bus Mgmt.

BENEDICT, MARK; St Bernard HS; Groton, CT; (S); Church Yth Grp; Hosp Aide; Band; Mrchg Band; JV Tennis; Med.

BENEDICT, SALLY; Northwestern Regional No 7 HS; Norfolk, CT; (Y); Drama Clb; Key Clb; Chorus; School Musical; School Play; Stage Crew; Variety Show; Yrbk Stf; Stu Cncl; Hon Roll; Dramtcs Cert For Actng 85; Music Cert 85; Anna-Maria Coll; Music Thrpst.

BENNETT, DEREK; New Canaan HS; New Canaan, CT; (Y); JA; Office Aide; Band; Chorus; Concert Band; Drm & Bgl; Jazz Band; Mrchg Band; JV Trk; Hon Roll; Gifted Stu 83; Econ.

BENNETT, JEFFREY L; Branford HS; Branford, CT; (Y); Yrbk Sprt Ed; Rep Stu Cncl; JV Bsktbl; JV Golf; Var Socr; JV Trk; MVP Soccer 84-85; Bus.

BENNETT, JOSEPH; Enrico Fermi HS; Enfield, CT; (Y); 39/350; Am Leg Boys St; Drama Clb; School Musical; School Play; Stu Cncl; High Hon Roll; NHS.

BENNETTA, JOLENE; Shelton HS; Shelton, CT; (Y); Church Yth Grp; Hosp Aide; Ski Clb; Spanish Clb; Stu Cncl; Bus.

BENOIT, KENNETH; Warren F Kaynor Regnl Voc Tech Schl; Watertown, CT; (Y); #21 In Class; JV Bsbl; JV Var Socr; High Hon Roll; NHS; Machn Excllnc 85; Waterbury ST Tech; Mech Engrng.

BENSON, HEATHER; Staples HS; Westport, CT; (Y); Church Yth Grp; Pep Clb; Chorus; Orch; Pep Band; Im Powder Puff Ftbl; Score Keeper; Var L Trk; JV Vllybl; High Hon Roll; Meritorious Awd From Natl Cncl On Alchlsm Inc 85; Boston Coll; Lbrl Arts.

BENSON, VERONICA; Hillhouse HS; New Haven, CT; (S); 6/272; High Hon Roll; Hon Roll; NHS; Prfct Atten Awd; Spnsh & Sci Awd 82; Albertus Magnus; Art Thrpy.

BENSTEIN, PETER; Guilford HS; Guilford, CT; (Y); 24/315; Model UN; JV Bsktbl; JV Crs Cntry; JV Wrstlng; Hon Roll; Spanish NHS; Schlr Athl Awd 83; Safe Rds Vlntr 85; Aerosp Engrng.

BENTON, KATHLEEN A; Glastonbury HS; S Glastonbury, CT; (Y); 4/393; Trs Church Yth Grp; Cmnty Wkr; Co-Capt Math Tm; Political Wkr; Chorus; High Hon Roll; NHS; Ntl Merit SF; Yale Bk Awd 84; Russn.

BEQUARY, CHRISTINE; Litchfield HS; Northfield, CT; (Y); AFS; Art Clb; Church Yth Grp; Girl Scts; ROTC; Stage Crew; Variety Show; Nwsp Stf; Yrbk Stf; Capt Fld Hcky; 1st Art Clb Awds 84-85; Outstndng Hnrs 85; Vrsty Ltrs 83-85; Comm.

BERARDI, LYNN; Kaynor Vo Tech; Waterbury, CT; (Y); Yrbk Stf; Hon Roll; Pres Peer Cnlsng 85; Waterbury ST Tech Coll; El Eng.

BERG, KARI; Tolland HS; Tolland, CT; (Y); Church Yth Grp; Band; Mrchg Band; Pep Band; School Musical; Hon Roll; All State Orch 83-85; New Englnd Fiddle Champ 84; All Eastrn US Orch 85.

BERG, SCOTT M; Southington HS; Southington, CT; (Y); Am Leg Boys St; Key Clb; Variety Show; Pres Sr Cls; Rep Stu Cncl; Bsbl; Capt Var Socr; Trk; Hon Roll; NHS; Sr Clss Pres 85-86; Natl Hnr Soc 85-86; Co Capt Sccr Tm 85-86; Med.

BERGER, KARIN; Berlin HS; Berlin, CT; (Y); 15/200; Hosp Aide; JA; Band; Color Guard; Concert Band; Mrchg Band; Trs Frsh Cls; Trs Soph Cls; Trs Jr Cls; Sec Sr Cls; U CT; Physcl Thrpst.

BERGERON, PAUL; St Bernard HS; Norwich, CT; (Y); 37/312; Service Clb; JV Bsbl; Capt Var Bsktbl; High Hon Roll; Hon Roll; Phelps Dodge Bus Stu Awd 85; Bus Admin.

BERGERON, PETER; Bristol Central HS; Bristol, CT; (Y); Art Clb; Boy Scts; JA; Math Tm; Hon Roll; Ntl Merit Ltr; Amer Chem Soc Cert 85; Hnrbl Men Art Shw 84; Boston Coll; Comp Sci.

BERISTAIN, SUZANNE; Conard HS; W Hartford, CT; (Y); 27/297; Chorus; School Musical; Capt L Cheerleading; JV Diving; Var L Trk; High Hon Roll; NHS; Spanish NHS; Rensselaer Polytchnc Inst; Arch.

BERKOVITZ, REED; Tolland HS; Tolland, CT; (Y); Debate Tm; VP JA; Temple Yth Grp; Chorus; Madrigals; School Play; Lit Mag; Crs Cntry; Dale Carnegie Crs 85-86; Bio.

BERLIN, KAREN; Wilton HS; Wilton, CT; (Y); 1/327; Chorus; Yrbk Bus Mgr; Yrbk Stf; Capt Powder Puff Ftbl; L Socr; High Hon Roll; NHS; Ntl Merit SF; Val; Church Yth Grp; Recog Fairfld Cnty Med Assn 85; Citatn Soc Wmn Engrs 84; Princeton Bk Awd 84; Dartmouth Coll; Psych.

BERLINER, ERIC; Rockville HS; Vernon, CT; (Y); 17/357; Yrbk Phtg; Trs Stu Cncl; L Badmtn; L Cheerleading; L Capt Tennis; High Hon Roll; NHS; Lucille Koehnley Awd Chem 85; Rockvl Schlr 85; Bates Coll; Math.

BERMAN, LISA; Hall HS; West Hartford, CT; (Y); 116/341; Pep Clb; Ski Clb; Yrbk Stf; VP L Cheerleading; Hon Roll.

BERMAN, MARK; Trumbull HS; Trumbull, CT; (Y); Chrmn Temple Yth Grp; Nwsp Ed-Chief; Nwsp Sprt Ed; High Hon Roll; Hon Roll; NCTE Awd; NHS; Ntl Merit Schol; Best Hist Stu 81-82; Trumull Arts Fest Essay Cont 83; Syracuse U; Brcst Jrnlsm.

BERNADINO, TOM; Southington HS; Southington, CT; (Y); Computer Clb; JV Var Trk; Wt Lftg; High Hon Roll; Hon Roll; Lawyer.

BERNARD, DAVID; Fairfield College Prep Schl; Bridgeport, CT; (Y); Cmnty Wkr; Capt L Trk; Ntl Merit Schol; Pres Intrcl Yth Cncl 84-85; Schl Stu Cncl 82-83; All-Leag Trck 83-84; Columbia U; Elec Engrng.

BERNARD, MARCEL; Weaver HS; Hartford, CT; (Y); 1/360; JA; High Hon Roll; Hon Roll; NHS; Trvl Scholar Isidore & Selma Wise Fndtn 85; Toastmstr Awd Cert Excllnce 85; Brown U Bk Awd 85; Comp Pgmmg.

BERNARDI, VALERIE; Windsor Locks HS; Windsor Locks, CT; (Y); 9/171; Civic Clb; Cmnty Wkr; Chorus; Concert Band; Mrchg Band; School Musical; NHS; Nova Suprnova Sci Prog Talcot Mt Sci Ctr 84; Frntrs Appld Sci Yale U 85; Bio.

BERNIER, LEIGH; Killingly HS; Brooklyn, CT; (Y); 8/300; Am Leg Aux Girls St; Var Capt Cheerleading; French Hon Soc; High Hon Roll; Hon Roll; Jr NHS; NHS; Phscl Thrpy.

BERNSTEIN, ANYA; Guilford HS; Guilford, CT; (Y); 18/315; Pres Boy Scts; Model UN; Quiz Bowl; Chorus; VP Stu Cncl; NHS; Ntl Merit Ltr; Church Yth Grp; Drama Clb; Hosp Aide; Colby Bk Awd, Womens Stds Awd 85; Bd Ed Stu 84-86; Hist.

BERRY, DAWN MARIE; St Bernard HS; Norwich, CT; (S); Pres French Clb; Hosp Aide; Yrbk Stf; Off Jr Cls; Stu Cncl; Var Tennis; Hon Roll; Acad Achvt Lttr Hnrs 83-84; Bio Sci.

BERTORELLI, ANN-MARIE; Killingly HS; Danielson, CT; (Y); 86/245; Drama Clb; French Clb; School Play; Stage Crew; Yrbk Stf; Hon Roll; Home Ec Awd 81; Becker JC; Mktg.

BERUBE, CAROL A; Watertown HS; Watertown, CT; (Y); Variety Show; Frsh Cls; JV Cheerleading; Hon Roll; NHS; Brdcstng.

BETZ, KAREN; Sacred Heart Acad; Stamford, CT; (Y); Art Clb; GAA; Varsity Clb; Yrbk Stf; Var L Sftbl; Var Trk; Hnrbl Ment Poster, All Leag Sftbl, Schl Excel Awd Adv Art 85; Grphc Dsgnr.

BEZIO, TWILA; Bristol Central HS; Bristol, CT; (Y); Hosp Aide; Ski Clb; Teachers Aide; Band; Concert Band; Mrchg Band; Socr; Prfct Atten Awd; U Of CT-STORRS; Vet.

BIANCHI, MARK; Amity Regional SR HS; Woodbridge, CT; (Y); Boy Scts; Band; Mrchg Band; Math.

BIASI, FRANCIS B; Danbury HS; Danbury, CT; (Y); Art Clb; Latin Clb; Yrbk Stf; Lit Mag; Stu Cncl; JV Socr; Im Vllybl; Hon Roll; Jr NHS; Nghbrhds Wrk Art Cont 82; Wslyn U Cntr Crtv Yth 83; Artwrk Displyd Equitable Life Bldg 82; Studio Art.

BIBEAU, PAULA; Windham Regional-Voc Tech; Willimantic, CT; (Y); Church Yth Grp; Hosp Aide; Library Aide; VICA; Church Choir; Yrbk Stf; High Hon Roll; Hon Roll; Prfct Atten Awd; Arch.

BICKFORD, SAMANTHA; Danbury HS; North Branford, CT; (Y); German Clb; Hosp Aide; JA; Pres VP Key Clb; Office Aide; Red Cross Aide; Variety Show; Rep Stu Cncl; Im Fld Hcky; Im Gym; Danbury Grdn Clb Schlrshp 85; Key Clubber Of The Schl 85; Southern CT ST U; Earth Sci.

BIDWELL, LYNNEA; Daniel Hand HS; Madison, CT; (Y); 9/236; Church Yth Grp; Pres Exploring; French Clb; JCL; Model UN; School Musical; Mgr Ed Nwsp Rptr; High Hon Roll; Hon Roll; NHS; Danc Schlrshp 80-85; Schlrshp Visit Japn Exch Stdnt YFU 84; Schlrshp Ctr Creatv Yth Wesleyan U 85; Creatv Wrtg.

BILL, CYNTHIA; Southington HS; Southington, CT; (Y); FBLA; Ski Clb; Variety Show; Co-Capt Gym; Powder Puff Ftbl; Hon Roll; Quinnipiac Coll; Occptnl Thrpy.

BILLINGHAM, KELLY; Bethel HS; Bethel, CT; (Y); FBLA; Variety Show; Rep Stu Cncl; JV Var Cheerleading; JV Trk; High Hon Roll; Hon Roll.

BILLINGS, KEVIN; Danburg HS; Danbury, CT; (Y); 26/600; French Clb; Nwsp Sprt Ed; Yrbk Stf; Rep Jr Cls; Pres Stu Cncl; Bsbl; Bsktbl; High Hon Roll; NHS; Prfct Atten Awd; Harvard Bk Awd 85; Elctrcl Engrng.

BILLINGS, TIMOTHY; Farmington HS; Farmington, CT; (Y); Boy Scts; Ski Clb; JV Trk; Eagl Sct; Ordr Arrw; Forstry Engr.

BILLINGSLEY, DAVID; Amity Regional SR HS; Orange, CT; (Y); Aud/Vis; Boy Scts; Ski Clb; Off Soph Cls; JV Bsktbl; Var L Golf; Hon Roll; PA Gvrnrs Intl Stud Schl 84; Agrnmy.

BILLUS, KATHLEEN M; Watertown HS; Watertown, CT; (Y); 15/241; AFS; Church Yth Grp; Cmnty Wkr; Pres French Clb; Variety Show; High Hon Roll; NHS; Pres Schlr; Awd Excllnc Fr V 85; Watertwn Fndtn Schlrshp 85; 34th Annl Untd Natns Pilgrmag For Yth 83; Smith Coll; Librl Arts.

BINDER, DARREN TODD; Avon HS; Avon, CT; (Y); JA; Political Wkr; Ski Clb; Temple Yth Grp; Nwsp Ed-Chief; High Hon Roll; NHS; Hon Roll; Safe Rides 84-86; Excllnc Anlytcl Geom Cert Merit 85; Excllnc Hnrs Shrt Stry Cert Merit 85; Bus.

BINGELL, CARYN; Griswold HS; Jewett City, CT; (Y); VP Frsh Cls; Sec Soph Cls; VP Jr Cls; JV Var Cheerleading; JV Trk; Hon Roll; Bio Awd 84; Northeastern U; Nrsng.

BIRCHENOUGH, PAM; Farmington HS; Farmington, CT; (Y); 35/206; Church Yth Grp; Ski Clb; Band; Concert Band; Var Crs Cntry; JV Sftbl; Var Trk; Im Vllybl; Im Wt Lftg; High Hon Roll; Mst Imprvd Cross Cnty 84; Physcl Thrpst.

BIRDEN, LISA; Torrington HS; Torrington, CT; (Y); 10/271; Church Yth Grp; Drama Clb; Latin Clb; Stage Crew; Var Tennis; Var Capt Vllybl; NEDT Awd; U Of Hartford; Med Tech.

BIRMINGHAM, SUSAN; Pomperaug HS; Southbury, CT; (Y); Sec Church Yth Grp; Library Aide; Concert Band; Mrchg Band; Orch; JV Socr; L Trk; Bausch & Lomb Sci Awd; NHS; Aud/Vis; Audubon Awd 85; Envrnmntl Sci.

BISAILLON, RICHARD D; Holy Cross HS; Southbury, CT; (Y); 17/344; Science Clb; Ski Clb; Lit Mag; Rep Stu Cncl; High Hon Roll; NHS; Pres Schlr; Math Tm; Quiz Bowl; Hon Roll; Highest Distnctn Grad85; Cert Of Merit-Social Studies Hnr Soc 84; Hnr Carrier Of Yr-Dist 83-84; Fairfield U; Bio.

BISHOP, STEVE; Lyman Hall HS; Wallingford, CT; (Y); 50/280; JV Socr; Hon Roll; Prfct Atten Awd; Outstdng Achv In Power III 84-85; Outstdng Achv In Arch Drftng I 83-84; Auto Mech.

BITEL, KEVIN; Ellington HS; Ellington, CT; (Y); 26/144; Am Leg Boys St; Yrbk Bus Mgr; Pres NHS; Computer Clb; Chorus; Nwsp Stf; Hon Roll; Ct Am Ind Arts Stu Asscn VP 84-85; St Treas 85-86; Ellingtun Chptr Pres 84-85; Keene ST Coll; Ind Arts.

BITTNER, KATHY; Berlin HS; Kensington, CT; (Y); Science Clb; Pres Service Clb; Chorus; Color Guard; Mrchg Band; Variety Show; High Hon Roll; Hon Roll; Spnsh Awds 83 & 84; Psych.

BLACK, ANDREA; Stratford HS; Stratford, CT; (Y); 34/241; Var Bsktbl; Var Sftbl; Engrng.

BLACK, CAROLYN; East Catholic HS; Marlborough, CT; (Y); 20/380; Chess Clb; Church Yth Grp; Computer Clb; Math Tm; Church Choir; Rep Soph Cls; Rep Jr Cls; Rep Sr Cls; High Hon Roll; Hon Roll; 1st Pl Regnl Dressage Champ Awd 82; Abrabian Horse Clb Of CT 82; Comp Sci.

BLACKWOOD IV, ANDREW W; Amity Regional HS; Orange, CT; (Y); Orch; School Musical; Symp Band; Ntl Merit Ltr; All St Bnd 83-85; CT Vly Yth Wind Ensmbl 83-85; Prmr Brss Ensmble 82-85; Music.

BLACKWOOD, KIMBERLY ANN; Ansonia HS; Ansonia, CT; (Y); 6/135; Girl Scts; Hosp Aide; Latin Clb; Science Clb; Nwsp Rptr; Yrbk Stf; High Hon Roll; NHS; Voice Dem Awd; 2nd Pl Amvets Drvng Exc Comp 85; Vicks Schlrshp Sci 85; Mattatuck Comm Coll; Radiolgc.

BLAIR, DANIELLE; St Paul Catholic HS; Burlington, CT; (Y); 81/331; Cmnty Wkr; Girl Scts; JA; Science Clb; School Musical; Variety Show; Yrbk Stf; Lit Mag; Pres Frsh Cls; Pres Soph Cls; 3rd Pl Inschl Acad Excllnc Food Ntrtn 83; Kathren King Ebersold Memrl Schlrshp Awd 85; St Joseph Coll; Dietetics.

BLAKE, DIANE; Seymour HS; Oxford, CT; (Y); Trs Church Yth Grp; Drama Clb; Hosp Aide; Office Aide; Band; Concert Band; Mrchg Band; Orch; School Play; Stage Crew; Nrsng.

BLAKE, ROBERT; Westhill HS; Stamford, CT; (Y); 39/460; Church Yth Grp; Computer Clb; Service Clb; High Hon Roll; Hon Roll; NHS; Rotary Awd; Presdntl Acadmc Ftnss Awd 85; Alph Phi Bet Lambda Chap 85; Fairfield U; Bio.

BLAKE, SUSAN; Southington HS; Southington, CT; (Y); Church Yth Grp; Key Clb; Stage Crew; Variety Show; Yrbk Stf; Mgr Bsbl; Var Cheerleading; Var Powder Puff Ftbl; Mgr Trk; High Hon Roll; Ne Britain Hosp; X-Ray Tech.

BLAKEMORE, WHITNEY W; Choate Rosemary Hall; Columbia, MO; (S); Math Clb; Acpl Chr; Chorus; School Musical; School Play; Sec Stu Cncl; High Hon Roll; Hon Roll; Drama Clb; French Clb; WIMOWEH Singers; Math Tutor; Drama.

BLANCHARD, BRUCE; Tourtellotte Memorial HS; N Grosenordale, CT; (Y); 2/100; Am Leg Boys St; Trs Frsh Cls; Trs Soph Cls; Trs Jr Cls; JV Var Bsbl; JV Var Bsktbl; High Hon Roll; Hon Roll; Pres NHS; Prfct Atten Awd; Delg Catholic Org 83-84; Med Tech.

BLANCHETTE, JOHN; Bristol Eastern HS; Bristol, CT; (Y); 5/270; VP French Clb; Pres Ski Clb; Im Vllybl; DAR Awd; High Hon Roll; CT Schlr 84; Worcester Polytechnc Inst; Bio.

BLANCHFIELD, MARCIA; Brookfield HS; Brookfield Ctr, CT; (Y); 49/224; VP Church Yth Grp; FBLA; Orch; Var Cheerleading; Hon Roll; Bus Admin.

BLANK, RANDALL; Cheshire HS; Cheshire, CT; (Y); Debate Tm; Science Clb; Ed Nwsp Stf; Stu Cncl; Hon Roll; Sec NHS; Magna Cum Laude Natl Latn Exm Amer Clsscl Leag 83 & 85.

BLANKSTEEN, SCOTT; William H Hall HS; W Hartford, CT; (Y); 118/324; Math Clb; Math Tm; Hon Roll; Ntl Merit SF; CT ST Chemathon 4th Pl 84; New Englnd Math Leag 3rd Pl 85; Law.

BLEIFELD, BECKY; Weston HS; Weston, CT; (Y); French Clb; JA; Latin Clb; Chorus; Nwsp Ed-Chief; Off Soph Cls; Off Jr Cls; Sec Stu Cncl; JV Capt Fld Hcky; Var Tennis; Le Grand Concours 1st In CT 1st In New Englnd 2nd In USA 83; Intl Rel.

BLINSTURBAS, THOMAS; Holy Cross HS; Waterbury, CT; (Y); 29/352; Bsbl; JV Bsktbl; Hon Roll; NHS.

BLODGET, HUGH; Manchester HS; Manchester, CT; (Y); Am Leg Boys St; Drama Clb; German Clb; Nwsp Stf; Var Crs Cntry; Var Ice Hcky; Var Trk; NHS; Congrss-Bundestag Schlr 85; Navl Acad Smmr Semnr 85; Engrng.

BLOOD, CHRISTOPHER J; Avon HS; Avon, CT; (Y); Boy Scts; Church Yth Grp; Quiz Bowl; Ski Clb; Nwsp Bus Mgr; Crs Cntry; Trk; Bus Mngmnt.

BLOUIN, BRUCE; Oliver Wolcott Tech; Torrington, CT; (Y); 5/142; Math Clb; Tennis; High Hon Roll; Hon Roll; Rotary Awd; Brian A Peck Awd 85; Waterbury ST Tech; Elec Engrng.

BLOUNT, ROBERT; Notre Dame HS; New Haven, CT; (Y); Church Yth Grp; Church Choir; Concert Band; Im Bsktbl; Hon Roll; Recvd 3rd Hnrs 83-85; Acctg.

BLOY, GREGORY J; Taft Schl; Watertown, CT; (Y); Latin Clb; Church Choir; Concert Band; Jazz Band; Var L Socr; Var L Tennis; Var L Trk; Var L Wrstlng; Hon Roll; Ntl Merit SF; Music.

BLUM, DENA; Amity SR HS; Orange, CT; (Y); Latin Clb; Pep Clb; Temple Yth Grp; Band; Concert Band; Mrchg Band; Pep Band; School Musical; Symp Band; Lit Mag; Natl Latin Exm-Cum Laude 83-85.

BLUM, ROBIN S; Bloomfield HS; Bloomfield, CT; (Y); 16/231; Nwsp Rptr; Nwsp Stf; Lit Mag; JV Var Sftbl; Var L Vllybl; Hon Roll; NHS; Civic Clb; JA; CT Mock Trail Comp 85; Indpndnt Study & Smnr Pgm; Vol Tutoring Pgm.

BLUMBERG, PETER; Kingswood-Oxford HS; W Hartford, CT; (Y); Drama Clb; Intnl Clb; Math Tm; Model UN; Q&S; School Play; Nwsp Ed-Chief; Im Bsktbl; L Crs Cntry; JV Golf; Trinity Clb Hartford Prz 85; Bus.

BLUNDO, SCOTT; Holy Cross HS; Woodbury, CT; (Y); 37/359; Ski Clb; Varsity Clb; JV Bsbl; Var Ftbl; High Hon Roll; NHS; Peer Ministry; Engrng.

BOBINSKI, LEONARD; Southington HS; Southington, CT; (Y); Key Clb; Latin Clb; Ski Clb; Band; Concert Band; Drm Mjr(t); Jazz Band; Mrchg Band; Tennis; Discover III 83-84; Southern Regnl All ST Bands 84-85; Psych.

BOCCUZZI, CARMINE; Westhill HS; Stamford, CT; (Y); VP JA; Latin Clb; Capt Quiz Bowl; Ed Yrbk Stf; Rep Frsh Cls; VP Soph Cls; Trs Jr Cls; High Hon Roll; NCTE Awd; NHS; Yale Bk Awd; Excell Latin II & III.

BOCHNIAK, LAUREN; Brien Mc Mahon HS; Norwalk, CT; (Y); 4/356; French Clb; Key Clb; Latin Clb; Symp Band; Nwsp Stf; Rep Sr Cls; NHS; Sal; Band; Concert Band; Wstrn Regnl All ST Band; Slvr Mdl Ntl Ltn Exam; Norwalk Evenng Wmns Clb Schlrshp; Bucknell U.

BOCK, MICHELLE; Naugatuck HS; Naugatuck, CT; (Y); Church Yth Grp; Latin Clb; Chorus; Church Choir; Hon Roll; Sec.

BODLEY, GARY T; Oliver Wolcott Tech Schl; Torrington, CT; (Y); 3/143; Math Clb; Yrbk Stf; High Hon Roll; NHS; Moonie Conti Awd; Quota Clb; Waterbury ST Tech Schl; Engrng.

BODY, STEPHEN; Holy Cross HS; Oakville, CT; (Y); 121/352; L Var Ftbl; JV Wrstlng; Var Hon Roll; Creatv Wrtng Cntst Wnnr-1st Pl 80; Royl Arcanum Soc Schlrshp 81; Pre-Med.

BOEHME, ANDREW; Fairfield Prep; New Canaan, CT; (Y); Church Yth Grp; Drama Clb; JA; Key Clb; Letterman Clb; Pep Clb; Service Clb; Varsity Clb; Band; Mrchg Band.

BOGANSKI, CHRISTINE; Wilcox Technical Schl; Meriden, CT; (Y); Art Clb; Church Yth Grp; Computer Clb; Variety Show; Yrbk Bus Mgr; Yrbk Ed-Chief; Yrbk Rptr; Yrbk Sprt Ed; Yrbk Stf; Soph Cls; Intr Dsgn.

BOGER, VERONICA; James Hillhaise HS; New Haven, CT; (S); 9/226; Cmnty Wkr; Model UN; Quiz Bowl; Band; Sec Jr Cls; Mgr(s); High Hon Roll; Hon Roll; NHS; Prfct Atten Awd; Spnsh 3 Prz Exam Awd 83; Frshmn Engl Prz Exam 82; Pscyh Awd 83; Emory U; Pre Med.

BOGERTY, ADRIENNE; St Marys HS; E Haven, CT; (Y); 41/115; Church Yth Grp; Cmnty Wkr; Pep Clb; VP Spanish Clb; VP Church Choir; Yrbk Stf; Rep Soph Cls; Rep Jr Cls; Im Tennis; Hon Roll; St Elizabeth Seton Fund Scholar 82-85; Princeton; Law.

BOGUE, JAMES M; Robert E Fitch HS; Mystic, CT; (Y); Drama Clb; Stage Crew; Trk.

BOGUES, SHARON; Danbury HS; Danbury, CT; (Y); 61/612; Variety Show; Rep Soph Cls; Rep Stu Cncl; Var L Bsktbl; JV L Sftbl; Bus Mgmt.

BOGUS, SHANON M; Stamford Catholic HS; Pound Ridge, NY; (Y); Girl Scts; JA; Concert Band; Flag Corp; Mrchg Band; Lit Mag; Mgr Bsktbl; Mgr(s); Score Keeper; Sftbl; Miss Polonia 85-86; Libry Aid Awd 83-86; Katheryn Gibbs Sec; Exec Sec.

BOHANNON, BOBBY; New Canaan HS; New Canaan, CT; (Y); Boy Scts; Church Yth Grp; Y-Teens; JV Lcrss; Hon Roll; Aud/Vis; Ski Clb; Yrbk Phtg; Engrng.

BOIANO, DANIEL; Holy Cross HS; Waterbury, CT; (Y); 15/352; Church Yth Grp; Varsity Clb; School Play; Var JV Bsbl; High Hon Roll; Envrnmntl Protect.

BOKINE, MICHELE LEA; St Joseph HS; Trumbull, CT; (Y); 25/216; Exploring; Hosp Aide; Spanish Clb; Yrbk Stf; High Hon Roll; Kiwanis Awd; NHS; Pres Schlr; Spanish NHS; SR Seminar 84-85; Scranton U; Nrsng.

BOLDUC, JOEL; Windham HS; Willimantic, CT; (Y); Am Leg Boys St; High Hon Roll; Hon Roll.

BOLDUC, JOHN; Windham HS; Willimantic, CT; (Y); Am Leg Boys St; High Hon Roll; Hon Roll.

BOLES, MATTHEW; Trumbull HS; Trumbull, CT; (Y); AFS; Boy Scts; Natl Beta Clb; Mrchg Band; Yrbk Phtg; Yrbk Stf; Var L Ftbl; High Hon Roll; Hon Roll.

BOLGER, JANET; Lauralton Hall HS; Ffld, CT; (Y); Cmnty Wkr; French Clb; Library Aide; Chorus; Church Choir; Stage Crew; Fairfield U; Educ.

BOMBERY, MICHELE; Andrew Warde HS; Fairfield, CT; (Y); VP Church Yth Grp; Church Choir; Hon Roll; Westbrook Coll; Nrsng.

BOMBINO, DONNA; Stamford Catholic HS; Stamford, CT; (Y); 28/160; Ski Clb; Nwsp Stf; Sec Jr Cls; VP Stu Cncl; Var Cheerleading; Capt Var Fld Hcky; Var Swmmng; Var Tennis; High Hon Roll; NHS; Knights Of Columbus Schlrshp 81; Natl Merit Awd 82; Roger Williams Coll Awd 85; Roger Williams Coll; Arch.

BONADIES, TRACEY; Farmington HS; Unionville, CT; (Y); 30/210; Cmnty Wkr; Yrbk Stf; Hon Roll; Accntng.

BONNELL, BRYON; Guilford HS; Guilford, CT; (Y); Boy Scts; Intnl Clb; Letterman Clb; Model UN; Science Clb; Varsity Clb; Var Ftbl; Var Wrstlng; Cit Awd; God Cntry Awd; Hnr Roll; US Mil Acad OH ST; Sci.

BONNETT, CRAIG; Trumbull HS; Trumbull, CT; (Y); Church Yth Grp; Ski Clb; Capt Var Socr; JV Trk; High Hon Roll; Hon Roll; Pre-Med.

BONTATIBUS, DONNA; Branford HS; Branford, CT; (Y); High Hon Roll; Hon Roll; Acadmc Excllnc 84-85.

BONTEMPO, PAM; Daniel Hand HS; Madison, CT; (Y); 15/200; French Clb; Nwsp Stf; High Hon Roll; Hon Roll; Psych.

BOOTH, ROONEY; Litchfield HS; Litchfield, CT; (Y); Civic Clb; Cmnty Wkr; 4-H; Political Wkr; Red Cross Aide; Variety Show; Stu Cncl; Trk; 4-H Awd; Hon Roll; SADD Treas 85-86; Stu Spkr Assmbly -Pres 84; 4-H Excllnc Horse Proj; Lawyr.

BORDEN, THOMAS M; William H Hall HS; W Hartford, CT; (Y); 37/343; Jazz Band; Var L Bsbl; Var L Ftbl; French Hon Soc; NHS; Ski Clb; Concert Band; High Hon Roll.

BORODIN, MARC; William Hall HS; W Hartford, CT; (Y); 49/342; Political Wkr; Temple Yth Grp; Chorus; Ed Yrbk Phtg; JV Socr; French Hon Soc; High Hon Roll; NHS.

BOSAK, ANNE; Sacred Heart Acad; Stamford, CT; (Y); 8/52; Church Yth Grp; Cmnty Wkr; JA; Nwsp Rptr; Yrbk Rptr; Lit Mag; Cheerleading; Hon Roll; NHS; Spanish NHS.

BOSAK, WILLIAM S; Fairfield College Pre Schl; Stamford, CT; (Y); Church Yth Grp; Key Clb; Pep Clb; Q&S; Ski Clb; Var Trk; High Hon Roll; Pres Schlr; Grad Party Awd 85; Good Luck Awd At Cornell Engnr 85; Cornell U; Engnrng.

BOSCO, ALLENE; Naugatuck HS; Prospect, CT; (Y); Dance Clb; Chorus; Variety Show; Cheerleading; Swmmng; Wt Lftg; Hon Roll; Off Frsh Cls; Rep Jr Cls; Southern CT; Dent.

BOTTICELLO, JULIE; Penney HS; E Hartford, CT; (Y); Cmnty Wkr; Spanish Clb; Nwsp Stf; Yrbk Stf; Diving; High Hon Roll; NHS; Spnsh Spkng Cntst Awd 1st Pl 85.

BOUCHER, GREGORY; Rham HS; Andover, CT; (Y); 4/177; AFS; Math Tm; Ski Clb; Capt Crs Cntry; Trk; High Hon Roll; NHS; Engrng.

BOUDREAU, JACQUELYN; North Haven HS; N Haven, CT; (Y); 105/281; Yrbk Stf; Hon Roll; Schlrshp To Ed Ctnr For Arts In New Haven For Dance 83-84; Dance Instrct.

BOULANGER, EDWARD; Holy Cross HS; Waterbury, CT; (Y); 45/365; Var Crs Cntry; Var Trk; Hon Roll; NHS; Comp Excell Awd 85; Bunker Hill Sprts Assoc Civic Schlrshp 82; Pharm.

BOULEY, LORI; Bulkeley HS; Hartford, CT; (Y); JA; Band; Concert Band; Mrchg Band; Rep Stu Cncl; Var Diving; Var Capt Gym; Var Swmmng; Hon Roll; Prfct Atten Awd; U Of CT; Bio.

BOURGAULT, FRANCELLE; East Lyme HS; Niantic, CT; (Y); Church Yth Grp; Drama Clb; Intnl Clb; Key Clb; School Musical; School Play; Stage Crew; Variety Show; Nwsp Ed-Chief; Yrbk Stf; Anthrplgy.

BOURNIVAL, ROBIN; Litchfield HS; Litchfield, CT; (Y); Trs FHA; Sec Speech Tm; Variety Show; Yrbk Stf; Capt Cheerleading; Hon Roll; Briarwood Coll Awd 85; Stu Cncl Awd For Chrldng 84; 3rd Yr Varsity Awd Bsktbl Chrldng 84-85; Exec Sec.

BOUSQUET, JIM; Holy Cross HS; Beacon Falls, CT; (Y); 59/352; Church Yth Grp; French Clb; Ed Nwsp Stf; Lit Mag; Im Tennis; High Hon Roll; NHS; 1st Pl Lit Mag Schl-Wde Shrt Stry Cont 84; Creatve Wrtg.

BOUTHILLIER, KRIS; Killingly HS; Danielson, CT; (Y); Church Yth Grp; Drama Clb; FCA; FHA; Pep Clb; Tennis; Trk; Vllybl; Gregg Accntng Awd 85; Gregg Typng Awd 84-85; Eastern Nazarene Coll; Bus Law.

BOUTOT, MICHELLE; Southington HS; Southington, CT; (Y); 29/550; FBLA; Key Clb; High Hon Roll; NHS; U Of CT; Acctg.

BOWEN, MELISSA; Seymour HS; Seymour, CT; (Y); Church Choir; High Hon Roll; Hon Roll; Outstndng JR Bus Stu Awd 85; Brianwood Book Awd 85; Briarwood Coll; Wrd Prcsng.

BOWER, JAY; Weston HS; Weston, CT; (Y); Boy Scts; Cmnty Wkr; Key Clb; Red Cross Aide; Service Clb; JV Capt Ftbl; Var Ice Hcky; Capt Var Tennis; Wt Lftg; JV Wrstlng; WHS Act Awd 85; Colgate; Psych.

BOWERS, RAY; Derby HS; Derby, CT; (Y); Am Leg Boys St; Church Yth Grp; Computer Clb; JA; VP Jr Cls; Var Bsbl; Ftbl; Hon Roll; JA Scholar Dale Carnegie Course Publc Spkng & Human Rltns 84-85; Bus Admin.

BOWLER, JACQUELINE; St Marys HS; W Haven, CT; (Y); 11/110; French Clb; Sec Frsh Cls; Rep Stu Cncl; L Sftbl; French Hon Soc; High Hon Roll; Hon Roll; Jr NHS; U Of MA; Pre-Law.

BOWMAN, SALLY A; Holy Cross HS; Cheshire, CT; (Y); 241/352; Sec Soph Cls; VP Jr Cls; Pres Sr Cls; JV Var Bsktbl; Var Capt Sftbl; All Cty, All ST, All Naugatuck Vly Sftbl 85; Rl Est.

BOYCE, KRISTEN; Watertown HS; Watertown, CT; (Y); 19/257; AFS; Trs Church Yth Grp; School Play; Sec Frsh Cls; Trs Sr Cls; Capt Swmmng; High Hon Roll; Hon Roll; NHS; Pres Schlr; Cls 1916 Schlrshp 85; Coaches Awd Tnns 85, Swmmng 83; Northeastern U; Intl Bus.

BOYNTON, TIMOTHY; St Joseph HS; Derby, CT; (Y); 22/227; Spanish Clb; Rep Soph Cls; JV Ftbl; High Hon Roll; Hon Roll; Prfct Atten Awd; Spn Hnr Soc 84; Mech Engrng.

BOZIKIS, GERASIMOS; Westhill HS; Stamford, CT; (Y); German Clb; NHS; U Of CT; Aerodyn.

BRACCIA, RICHARD; Avon Old Farms Schl; Boxford, MA; (S); 6/103; Art Clb; Yrbk Stf; Ice Hcky; Trk; Wt Lftg; High Hon Roll; Hon Roll; Ntl Art Awd 85; Hockey Schlrshp To Boston Coll 85; Boston Coll.

BRACKETT, JENNIFER; Pomperaug HS; Southbury, CT; (Y); AFS; Church Yth Grp; French Clb; FBLA; Hosp Aide; Red Cross Aide; Ski Clb; Band; Chorus; Yrbk Stf.

BRACNARO, ROBERT; Shelton HS; Shelton, CT; (Y); Am Leg Boys St; Pres Sr Cls; Off Stu Cncl; Ftbl; JV Sftbl; JV Tennis; High Hon Roll; Hon Roll; NHS; Prfct Atten Awd; Fathers Clb Awd 85; Temple U; Pre-Med.

BRADFORD, KRISTEN; Guilford HS; Guilford, CT; (Y); 60/320; Church Yth Grp; Cmnty Wkr; Model UN; Political Wkr; Red Cross Aide; Chorus; Madrigals; School Musical; Rep Frsh Cls; Rep Soph Cls; Hnr Rll 83-85.

BRADLEY, MARK; Central HS; Bridgeport, CT; (Y); JA; Pres Latin Clb; Y-Teens; Stage Crew; VP Sr Cls; Rep Stu Cncl; Phrmcy.

BRADLEY, SHARI; Sacred Heart Acad; West Haven, CT; (Y); 6/115; Capt Quiz Bowl; CC Awd; Elks Awd; Pres French Hon Soc; Pres NHS; Ntl Merit Ltr; NEDT Awd; Church Yth Grp; French Clb; School Musical; 3rd Pl Natl Fr Exam; 1st Pl Natl Fr Creative Wrtg Comp; James L Turrentine Scholar; Providence Coll; Lib Art.

BRADLEY, TRISH; Danbury HS; Danbury, CT; (Y); 155/600; Hosp Aide; Varsity Clb; Madrigals; Off Frsh Cls; Off Jr Cls; Off Sr Cls; Cheerleading; Gym; Trk; Hon Roll; Southern C T; Comp Sci.

BRADY, JAMES; Wilbur Cross HS; New Haven, CT; (Y); 18/280; Band; Mrchg Band; Yrbk Stf; Comp Prgrm.

BRAGA, KERRY; Ellington HS; Ellington, CT; (Y); Exploring; FBLA; Hosp Aide; Latin Clb; Hon Roll; Mst Dedctd Svc Awd 85; 100 Hrs Hosp Aide 83; Nrsg.

BRAGG, DAVID C; Choate Rosemary Hall HS; Elon College, NC; (S); Church Yth Grp; French Clb; Acpl Chr; Chorus; Church Choir; School Musical; Variety Show; Nwsp Stf; Yrbk Stf; French Hon Soc; Peer Counselg Tm 84-85; Psychtry.

BRAND, MICHAEL E; East Lyme HS; E Lyme, CT; (Y); 18/300; Quiz Bowl; Scholastic Bowl; Band; Concert Band; Mrchg Band; Stu Cncl; Hon Roll; Ntl Merit Ltr; Brd Of Ed Rep 84-85; New England Ambassdr Music 83; PA U.

BRANDER, SCOTT; Amity HS; Woodbridge, CT; (S); 155/376; Cmnty Wkr; FBLA; Latin Clb; Spanish Clb; Nwsp Rptr; Nwsp Stf; Yrbk Stf; Capt L Bsktbl; Business.

BRANDI, ROBIN P; St Paul Catholic HS; Bristol, CT; (Y); Boy Scts; Camera Clb; Drama Clb; Math Clb; Science Clb; Chorus; School Musical; School Play; Stage Crew; Variety Show; Music Awd 85; Pres Glee Clb 84-85; Orgnzr Schl Folk Grp 84-85; Southern CT ST U; Psych.

BRANDON, CYNTHIA; Thomas Snell Weaver HS; Hartford, CT; (Y); Drama Clb; JA; Library Aide; Teachers Aide; Hon Roll; Hghst Avg Erth Sci 82-83; Acadmc Art Achvt Awd 83-84; Achvt Awd Crtcl Thnkng II 84-85; Elem Educ.

BRANNELLY, COLLEEN; Notre Dame Cathlic HS; Bridgeport, CT; (Y); Church Yth Grp; Chorus; School Musical; School Play; JV Var Bsktbl; Var Sftbl; Hon Roll; Awd Geomtry & Engl Outstndng Imprvmnt 83; Fordham U; Pre Law.

BRAVO, MICHELLE; Lauralton Hall HS; Fairfield, CT; (Y); Church Yth Grp; Hosp Aide; Science Clb; Service Clb; Spanish Clb; Lit Mag; Amnesty Intl 85; Advrtsng.

BRAYFIELD, ROBYN; Southington HS; Southington, CT; (Y); Art Clb; Cmnty Wkr; Hosp Aide; Key Clb; Library Aide; Band; Rep Frsh Cls; Rep Stu Cncl; Hon Roll; Central CT ST U; CPA.

BRAZELL, DAVID L; Conard HS; W Hartford, CT; (Y); 50/295; Red Cross Aide; Spanish Clb; Rep Stu Cncl; Var L Ftbl; JV Socr; Hon Roll; NHS; Spanish NHS; New Englnd Inst Tech Bk Awd 85; Pres Outstndg Acad Achvt Fit Awds Pgm 84-85; Cert Awd Ftbl 85; Worcester Polytech Inst; Engrng.

BREADING, SANDRA; Naugatuck HS; Naugatuck, CT; (Y); Pres VP Church Yth Grp; Ski Clb; Jazz Band; Madrigals; Mrchg Band; Orch; Stage Crew; Symp Band; Rep Soph Cls; JV Sftbl.

BREAULT, DAVID; Putham HS; Putnam, CT; (Y); 6/145; Boy Scts; Drama Clb; Math Clb; Band; Chorus; Church Choir; Concert Band; Drm Mjr(t); Mrchg Band; Pep Band; Trinity Coll; Allied Hlth.

BREAULT, MICHAEL; Coventry HS; Coventry, CT; (Y); 4-H; Concert Band; Jazz Band; Yrbk Stf; JV Crs Cntry; Var Crs Cntry; Var Trk; Hon Roll; Arabian Horse Clb Champ 79-84; Canadian Natl Res Champ Hunter 83; Top 10 Canadian Natl Arabian 83; Landscapng.

BREAULT, MICHELLE A; Tourtellotte Memorial HS; Putnam, CT; (Y); Am Leg Aux Girls St; Pep Clb; Nwsp Stf; Yrbk Stf; Rep Jr Cls; Dnfth Awd; Hon Roll; NHS; Ed.

BREAULT, VANESSA; Norwalk HS; Norwalk, CT; (Y); Key Clb; Band; Concert Band; Mrchg Band; Orch; Pep Band; School Musical; Symp Band; All-ST Band 85; Otstndg Jr Musician 85; Music Educ.

BREINAN, DEBORAH R; Glastonbury HS; Glastonbury, CT; (Y); 5/393; AFS; Pres Temple Yth Grp; Yrbk Bus Mgr; Yrbk Sprt Ed; Var L Crs Cntry; Im Socr; Var Trk; High Hon Roll; NHS; Ntl Merit SF; Frdom Shrine Hist Cont 84; Graphic Art 83; Ntl Piano Plyng 82-83; Advertsng.

BREINAN, HOWARD; Glastonbury HS; Glastonbury, CT; (Y); 1/426; Am Leg Boys St; Capt Math Tm; Trs Temple Yth Grp; Var Capt Crs Cntry; Var L Wrstlng; Cit Awd; NHS; SAR Awd; Quiz Bowl; Scholastic Bowl; Stu Space Shuttle Invlvmnt Pgm Natl Wnnr 85; CT Frgn Lang Poetry Cntst 1st Span 83; Harvard Bk Awd 85; Engrng.

BRENCHAK, KRISTEN; Shelton HS; Huntington, CT; (Y); Math Tm; Concert Band; Jazz Band; Mrchg Band; Stage Crew; Yrbk Stf; Hon Roll; Central Connecticut; Mktg.

BRENNAN, ALLISON A; Naugatuck HS; Beacon Fls, CT; (Y); Church Yth Grp; Sec GAA; Sec Ski Clb; Chorus; Sec Jr Cls; JV Bsktbl; Mgr(s); JV Sftbl; Var L Swmmng; L Capt Tennis.

BRENNAN, CATHERINE M; St Mary HS; Greenwich, CT; (Y); 1/72; Drama Clb; Hosp Aide; Math Tm; School Play; Yrbk Bus Mgr; Yrbk Stf; High Hon Roll; NHS; NEDT Awd; Holy Crss Bk Prz 85; Engrng.

BRENNAN, DAVID J; Windsor Locks HS; Windsor Locks, CT; (Y); 15/179; Boy Scts; Pres Computer Clb; VP JA; Math Tm; School Play; Nwsp Ed-Chief; High Hon Roll; Hon Roll; U Hartford Sat Schlr 84; Stu Cncl Schlrshp 85; Renssaelaer Polytech; Comp Sci.

BRENNAN, KARA; Bristol Central HS; Bristol, CT; (Y); Yrbk Stf; Var Co-Capt Cheerleading; GAA.

BRENNAN, NOREEN; Sacred Heart Acad; Stamford, CT; (Y); 4/54; Drama Clb; FBLA; Girl Scts; Hosp Aide; JA; Latin Clb; Red Cross Aide; Spanish Clb; School Musical; School Play; Magna Cum Laude Natl Latn Exm 84; Pres Of Yr 84-85; Med.

BRESNAHAN, KELLY; Southington HS; Southington, CT; (Y); Church Yth Grp; FBLA; Girl Scts; JA; Key Clb; Library Aide; Stage Crew; Variety Show; Yrbk Stf; Cheerleading; Bus.

BRETON, CHRISTINE; Stratford HS; Stratford, CT; (Y); 32/285; Drama Clb; French Clb; Drill Tm; Rep Soph Cls; Rep Jr Cls; Rep Sr Cls; JV Var Pom Pon; French Hon Soc; High Hon Roll; Hon Roll; Comp Sci.

BRETON, STEVEN; St Paul Catholic HS; Bristol, CT; (Y); 4/258; Am Leg Boys St; Boy Scts; VP Exploring; Var Trk; VP French Hon Soc; High Hon Roll; VP NHS; French Clb; Math Tm; Ski Clb; Order Arrow-Section Vice Chf NE-1E 85-86; Ntl Frnch Cont-1st Pl In CT & New England 83; Public Adm.

BREWSTER, MAYA; Putnam HS; Putnam, CT; (Y); 10/135; Band; Chorus; Concert Band; Variety Show; Yrbk Rptr; Trs Jr Cls; Var Cheerleading; Var Golf; Var Trk; Hon Roll; All Eastrn Band Connecticut; Bio.

BREWSTER, STEPHANIE; Putnam HS; Putnam, CT; (Y); Concert Band; Drm Mjr(t); Mrchg Band; Stage Crew; Elks Awd; High Hon Roll; Hon Roll; SAR Awd; NHS; All Eastern Band 83-85; Syracuse U; Zoolgy.

BREYAN, KIM E; Notre Dame Catholic HS; Easton, CT; (Y); 73/284; Church Yth Grp; Ski Clb; Rep Jr Cls; Rep Stu Cncl; Var Swmmng; Hon Roll; Hnr Roll; Skidmore Coll; Bus Mgmt.

BRIDGES, GINA; Orville H Platt HS; So Meriden, CT; (Y); French Clb; Yrbk Stf; VP Frsh Cls; Crs Cntry; High Hon Roll; Hon Roll; NHS; Yth Govt Prog Press Corps Stff 85; Prom Cmmttee 85; U Of CT; Phy Thrpy.

BRIGANTI, MARIA; St Joseph HS; Trumbull, CT; (Y); 69/227; Church Yth Grp; Drama Clb; JA; School Play; Stage Crew; Trk; High Hon Roll; Hon Roll; Law.

BRIGHT, RENEE; The Cheshire Acad; Cheshire, CT; (Y); Computer Clb; French Clb; Intnl Clb; Key Clb; Church Choir; Stage Crew; Stu Cncl; JV Badmtn; Var Bsktbl; Var Fld Hcky; Awd Hgst Acad Avg 82; Awd Ct Womens Dean 85; Optmtry.

BRINIUS, LORI A; Newington HS; Newington, CT; (S); Cmnty Wkr; DECA; Hosp Aide; Hon Roll; U Of CT; Bnkng.

BRIODY, PATRICIA; Ridgefield HS; Ridgefield, CT; (Y); 12/370; Service Clb; School Musical; Off Soph Cls; Off Jr Cls; Off Sr Cls; Var Bsktbl; Pres NHS; Ntl Merit Ltr; Pres Schlr; IBM Thomas J Watson Mem Scholar 85; PTSA Scholar Awd 85; Wellesley Bk Awd 84; U Notre Dame.

BRISTOL, LORENA SUE; Nonnewaug HS; Seymour, CT; (Y); Church Yth Grp; Drama Clb; FFA; Chorus; Church Choir; Color Guard; Nrse Ade.

BRKIC, CHRISTINE; Acad Of Our Lady Of Mercy; Bridgeport, CT; (Y); Pres Drama Clb; French Clb; Math Clb; Model UN; Service Clb; School Play; Lit Mag; Rep Stu Cncl; Mu Alp Tht; NHS; Schls Mst Effcnt Typst 83-84; Bus.

BRODER, KENNETH N; Bloomfield HS; Bloomfield, CT; (Y); 15/235; Civic Clb; JA; Model UN; Yrbk Stf; Off Soph Cls; Off Jr Cls; Var Lcrss; Var Socr; High Hon Roll; Hon Roll; Med Tech.

BRODER, LISA N; Central HS; Bridgeport, CT; (Y); 8/320; Office Aide; Service Clb; Pres Stu Cncl; JV Vllybl; Cit Awd; High Hon Roll; NHS; NEDT Awd; Pres Schlr; St Schlr; Isadore L Kotler Meml Schlrshp 85; Edward J Caldwell Meml Schlrshp 85; Florence Fream Btchldr Schlrshp; Post Clg; Parlgl.

BRODEUR, MICHELLE; Putnam HS; Putnam, CT; (Y); 8/145; Service Clb; School Play; Off Soph Cls; Off Jr Cls; Off Sr Cls; Stat Bsktbl; Mgr Crs Cntry; Tennis; Vllybl; Cit Awd; U Of CT; Educ.

BRODEUR, RICHARD A; Emmett O Brien RVTS HS; Naugatuck, CT; (Y); Boy Scts.

BRODT, SONJA; Amity Regional SR HS; Woodbridge, CT; (Y); VP German Clb; Service Clb; High Hon Roll; NHS; Prfct Atten Awd; Amer Assoc Tchrs Frnch Awd 83,German Awd 84; Cngrss-Bndstg Yth Exch Pgm 84-85; Grmn Frng Lang Ptry 84; Bio Sci.

BRODY, BRIDGET; Thomaston HS; Thomaston, CT; (Y); Am Leg Aux Girls St; Church Yth Grp; Teachers Aide; Mrchg Band; Frsh Cls; Soph Cls; Jr Cls; Sr Cls; Var Bsktbl; Var Fld Hcky; Presdntl Physical Fitness Awd 83-85; Elem Educ.

BRODY, JOE; Naugatuck HS; Naugatuck, CT; (Y); Am Leg Boys St; VP JA; Concert Band; Jazz Band; Mrchg Band; Hon Roll; U PA; Pre-Med.

BRODY, LINDA; Shelton HS; Shelton, CT; (Y); Drama Clb; Hosp Aide; Spanish Clb; Teachers Aide; Temple Yth Grp; Band; Concert Band; Mrchg Band; Pep Band; Hon Roll; Nrsng.

BROESCH, KATHRYN; Andrew Warde HS; Fairfield, CT; (Y); Church Yth Grp; German Clb; JA; Office Aide; Church Choir; Hon Roll; Daisy Chain Grad Cermny 85.

BROMILEY, TIM; Bethel HS; Bethel, CT; (Y); 11/280; Am Leg Boys St; Variety Show; Nwsp Rptr; Nwsp Stf; Off Sr Cls; Capt Crs Cntry; Capt Trk; NHS; Cert Apprctn Support Spec Olympcs 85; Multiple Schlerosis Awareness Mtng 83; L Div Crs Cntry 84-85; Arch.

BRONKE, PATTI; Rham SR HS; Andover, CT; (Y); 10/150; Sec Church Yth Grp; Chorus; School Play; JV Bsktbl; Var Capt Cheerleading; Gym; Mgr(s); Score Keeper; High Hon Roll; Kiwanis Awd; Achvt Hnrs 6 Qtrs 84; Am Leg St Ofcr 81-85; Sang-Audition 8 Person Singing Grp 82-85.

BRONSON, NANCY; Torrington HS; Torrington, CT; (Y); Sec French Clb; Hosp Aide; Chorus; School Musical; Stu Cncl; Score Keeper; High Hon Roll; Hon Roll; Certificat De Merite Frnch III Awd 83-84.

BROOKES, SEAN; Haddam-Killingworth HS; Haddam, CT; (Y); 26/126; Teachers Aide; Pres Frsh Cls; VP Soph Cls; VP Jr Cls; Stu Cncl; Var L Bsbl; Var L Bsktbl; Hon Roll; All Cty Bsbl Plyr 85; New Haven Regstr Plyr Wk 85; Lawyer.

BROOKS, KAREN L; Plainfield HS; Jewett City, CT; (Y); GAA; Girl Scts; Red Cross Aide; Varsity Clb; VP Jr Cls; Rep Stu Cncl; Bsktbl; Trk; Hon Roll; Voice Dem Awd; Mc Hegan Coll; ER RN.

BROOKS, RUTH MARGUERITE; Amity Regional HS; Orange, CT; (Y); 84/376; Trs German Clb; Hosp Aide; Orch; School Musical; JV Var Fld Hcky; Var Capt Tennis; Amity Eductnl Fund Schlrshp 85; Manhattanville Coll; Psych.

BROOKS, TRACY; Windham HS; N Windham, CT; (Y); 5/285; Concert Band; Var Capt Trk; Elks Awd; High Hon Roll; Lion Awd; Pres NHS; Pres Schlr; U CT Co Op Prog Sup Acad Achvt 85; 4 Yrs Excll Sci 85; Republic Oil Awd 85; U CT; Math.

BROUGHTON, JACQUELYN; Francis T Maloney HS; Meriden, CT; (Y); VP DECA; JA; Latin Clb; Teachers Aide; Rep Stu Cncl; JV Var Cheerleading; Cit Awd; 4-H Awd; Hon Roll; NHS; Schlrshp-Wll Strt Smnr-WA Wrkshps 85; 3rd &6 Frshmn Cls Am HS Math Exam 83; Bus.

BROVERO, MICHAEL; Griswold HS; Norwich, CT; (Y); Boy Scts; Varsity Clb; Var L Ftbl; JV Var Trk; Hon Roll; Prfct Atten Awd; Cong Cert Merit 83; Bio Hnrs Awd 84; VFW Patrtsm 3rd Pl Local Awd BSA Cert Merit 85; Phys Ther.

BROWDER, DEENA; Andrew Warde HS; Fairfield, CT; (Y); Band; Concert Band; Mrchg Band; Bsktbl; Score Keeper; Sftbl; Cit Awd; Hon Roll; Spanish NHS; Pltcl Sci.

BROWN, CARYN; St Bernards HS; Lisbon, CT; (Y); Red Cross Aide; Science Clb; Ski Clb; Chorus; Variety Show; Yrbk Stf; Stu Cncl; Stat Ftbl; Hon Roll; Vet.

BROWN, CHRISTOPHER; Crosby HS; Waterbury, CT; (Y); 3/350; Church Yth Grp; Exploring; Key Clb; Latin Clb; Ski Clb; Var Bsbl; Var Bsktbl; High Hon Roll; NHS; Prjct SAGE 84-85; SR Cls Rep 85-86; Med.

BROWN, CRYSTAL; Wilbur Cross HS; New Haven, CT; (Y); French Clb; Band; Concert Band; Mrchg Band; Var Trk; Cit Awd; Hon Roll; Frnch & Steno Awds 86; Spn & Engl Awds 83; Gym Awd 83; BCI; Crt Steno.

BROWN, DANIEL; Cheshire HS; Cheshire, CT; (Y); Boy Scts; Church Yth Grp; Computer Clb; Ski Clb; Band; Church Choir; Jazz Band; School Musical; Variety Show; Bsbl; Aerosp Engrng.

BROWN, DAVID; Haddam-Killingworth HS; Cromwell, CT; (Y); Metal Shop 84; Welding 85.

BROWN, DOUGLAS; Robert E Fitch SR HS; Mystic, CT; (Y); 3/410; Am Leg Boys St; Pres Exploring; VP Key Clb; Ski Clb; Yrbk Sprt Ed; Capt Socr; NHS; Ntl Merit SF; Nwsp Rptr; JV Tennis; Harvard Bk Prz; CT Hnrs Sem; Indoor Soccer Capt; Sci.

BROWN, KIM; Rockville HS; Manchester, CT; (S); Sec Church Yth Grp; 4-H; Sec FFA; High Hon Roll; Hon Roll; ST FFA Publ Spkng 84; ST FFA Cred Cntst 83; Str Greenhd 83; Cobleskill U; Dairy Mgmt.

BROWN, MARJORIE; Stamford Catholic HS; Stamford, CT; (Y); Ski Clb; Yrbk Stf; Var Capt Bsktbl; Var Swmmng; Var L Vllybl; Hon Roll; Bus.

BROWN, MATTHEW H; Loomis Chaffee Schl; West Hartford, CT; (Y); Pres Exploring; Rptr Nwsp Sprt Ed; Quiz Bowl; Im Bsbl; Im Ice Hcky; Im Socr; Ntl Merit SF; Jrnlsm.

BROWN, MELISSA; Berlin HS; Kensington, CT; (Y); 17/200; Church Yth Grp; Key Clb; Service Clb; Nwsp Stf; Var Tennis; Hon Roll; Art Achv Awd 83; Nwspapr Achv Awd 85.

BROWN, MELISSA; Hamden-New Haven Coop HS; New Haven, CT; (Y); 1/65; Cmnty Wkr; Office Aide; Yrbk Ed-Chief; High Hon Roll; Hon Roll; Prfct Atten Awd; St Schlr; Val; Jr Cls Steering Comm 84-85; Choate Summer Pgm 84-85; Yale Intershp 85-86; Med.

BROWN, MICHAEL; Trumball HS; Trumbull, CT; (Y); Teachers Aide; Variety Show; Bsbl; Var Capt Bsktbl; Var Capt Ftbl; JV Tennis; Var L Trk; French Hon Soc; High Hon Roll; Cntrbtn Schl Spirit Awd PTA 83; Hartford Courant All St Ftbl Tm 85; All Fairfield Co 1st Dfnsve Tm 85; Engrng.

BROWN, ROBERT C; East Haven HS; East Haven, CT; (Y); 6/300; Church Yth Grp; Latin Clb; Pres Math Clb; Capt Math Tm; Model UN; Co-Capt Quiz Bowl; JETS Awd; NHS; Ntl Merit Ltr; Rotary Awd; Rensselaer Medal Excel Math,Sci 84; Harvard Bk Awd 84; Perf Score Math SAT 84; Rensselaer Polytech Inst; Comp.

BROWN, YVONNE; Richard C Lee HS; New Haven, CT; (Y); Hosp Aide; Variety Show; Yrbk Stf; JV Var Socr; Var L Trk; NHS; Ntl Merit Schol; Martin Luther King Essy Cntst 2nd; Brown U Bk Awd; NY U; Med.

BROWNE, BETH A; Low-Heywood Thomas HS; Stamford, CT; (Y); 10/29; Model UN; Yrbk Phtg; Lit Mag; Var Stu Cncl; Var Bsktbl; Var Fld Hcky; Var Lcrss; JCL; Pep Clb.

BROWNE, HEATHER; Low Heywood Thomas HS; Stamford, CT; (Y); Art Clb; JA; Pep Clb; Rep Frsh Cls; Rep Soph Cls; Var Bsktbl; Fld Hcky; Lcrss; Mgr(s); Timer.

BROWNING, CATHERINE; Guilford HS; Guilford, CT; (Y); 40/318; Church Yth Grp; Rep Stu Cncl; Stat Bsktbl; JV Trk; Hon Roll; NHS; Acad Achvt For Excllnc In Lang Arts 85; Schl Spirit Clb 82-83; Political Sci.

BRUCE, TODD A; Wethersfield HS; Wethersfield, CT; (Y); 7/275; Am Leg Boys St; Boy Scts; Math Tm; Quiz Bowl; VP Sr Cls; Socr; High Hon Roll; Hon Roll; NHS; NEDT Awd; Aid Assoc Luth All Coll Scholar 85; Marjorie S Carter Boy Sct Scholar 85; Pres Acad Fitnss Awd 85; Dartmouth Coll; Elec Engrng.

BRUCHAC, TORI; Joel Barlow HS; W Redding, CT; (Y); 60/227; Library Aide; PAVAS; Teachers Aide; Symp Band; Yrbk Stf; High Hon Roll; Joel Barlow Scshlrshp Fund 85; U Miami; Dsgn & Motion Picture.

BRUHO, CAROL; St Marys HS; New Haven, CT; (Y); Hosp Aide; Math Clb; Ski Clb; Spanish Clb; Stage Crew; Nwsp Stf; Sftbl; Hon Roll; NHS; Spanish NHS; Quinnipiac Coll; Hlth.

BRUNELLE, MARGOT; Daniel Hand HS; Madison, CT; (Y); Church Yth Grp; FCA; GAA; Red Cross Aide; School Play; Ed Yrbk Stf; Rep Soph Cls; Sec Sr Cls; Stu Cncl; Var Fld Hcky; Laurel Grls ST, Smnr Crtv Yuth 84-85; Visual Arts.

BRUNNER JR, KENNETH H; North Haven HS; N Haven, CT; (Y); 39/255; Aud/Vis; Computer Clb; Mgr Bsbl; Golf; Hon Roll; HS Rep Quinnipac Coll Comp Olympcs 84; Comp Sci.

BRUNO, CAROL; St Marys HS; New Haven, CT; (Y); 10/125; Hosp Aide; Math Clb; Spanish Clb; Sftbl; Hon Roll; Jr NHS; NHS; Spanish NHS; Med.

BRUNO, KIMBERLY; Bunnell HS; Stratford, CT; (Y); Drama Clb; Office Aide; Ski Clb; Swmmng; High Hon Roll; Hon Roll; Spanish NHS; Arista Schlrshp; Stratford Educ Assn Schlrshp; Southern CT ST U; Spcl Educ.

BRUSH, SAMANTHA; Lauralton Hall HS; Bridgeport, CT; (Y); Sec Latin Clb; Science Clb; Service Clb; Spanish Clb; Chorus; Rep Stu Cncl; Capt Cheerleading; Hon Roll; Pres NHS; Spanish NHS.

BRUYNS, PAMELA; Trumbull HS; Trumbull, CT; (Y); Church Yth Grp; Girl Scts; Color Guard; High Hon Roll; U Of CT; Accntnt.

BRYAN, AMY E; Wilton HS; Wilton, CT; (Y); Pres VP Drama Clb; Pres French Clb; School Musical; School Play; Lit Mag; NHS; Church Yth Grp; Model UN; Acpl Chr; Chorus; Welton Arts Cncl Awd Frmtc Arts 84-85; Model US Senate 82-84; Psychlgy.

BRYAN, JO ANN; Brien Mc Mahon HS; Darien, CT; (Y); 17/342; Church Yth Grp; Latin Clb; Ski Clb; Rep Jr Cls; JV Bsktbl; JV Var Fld Hcky; Var Powder Puff Ftbl; High Hon Roll; Hon Roll; Cum Laude Natl Lat Exam 85; Aero Engrng.

BRYK, BARBARA; St Bernard HS; Uncasville, CT; (Y); Camera Clb; Camp Fr Inc; Church Yth Grp; Cmnty Wkr; FBLA; FNA; Girl Scts; Library Aide; Office Aide; Red Cross Aide; Central CT ST U; Accntng.

BRZENCZEK, MARY-LOUISE; New Britain HS; New Britain, CT; (Y); 51/367; Church Yth Grp; FBLA; Acpl Chr; Chorus; Church Choir; Madrigals; Swing Chorus; Hon Roll; Mayor Day Pgm; U CT Syracuse; Nrsng.

BUCHER, OLIVIA; Shelton HS; Shelton, CT; (Y); Mgr(s); Socr; Elem Tchr.

BUCK, KATHLEEN S; The Morgan HS; Clinton, CT; (Y); Drama Clb; French Clb; Hosp Aide; Chorus; Capt Color Guard; Hon Roll; NHS; Ord Rainbow, H J, M Munger Schlrshps 85; Souterhn CT ST U; Nrsg.

BUCKLEY, JONATHAN; The Morgan Schl; Clinton, CT; (Y); 17/185; Am Leg Boys St; Political Wkr; VP Spanish Clb; Chorus; School Musical; Var Socr; Hon Roll; Quiz Bowl; Ski Clb; Tennis; Ct Summr Intrn Pgm Senator Weicker 85; Liason ST Rep Sidney Holbrk 85; Polit Sci.

BUCKLEY, PATRICK; Berlin HS; Kensington, CT; (Y); 16/280; Am Leg Boys St; Aud/Vis; Boy Scts; Exploring; Pres Radio Clb; Ski Clb; NHS; Cmnty Wkr; Stage Crew; Var Crs Cntry; CT ST Crtfd Emrgncy Medcl Techncn 85; Egl Sct 82; Lcl EMS; U Of MD; Emrgncy Hlth Svcs.

BUCZAK, MARY; Holy Cross HS; Prospect, CT; (Y); 42/352; Church Yth Grp; Stat Wrstlng; Hon Roll; NHS; Soc Stud Hnr Soc 84.

BUDNY, KRISTEN L; Litchfield HS; Litchfield, CT; (Y); 5/100; Pres Church Yth Grp; French Clb; Teachers Aide; Chorus; Concert Band; Variety Show; Yrbk Stf; VP Frsh Cls; VP Soph Cls; Pres Jr Cls; Hugh Obrien Yth Fdnt Ldrshp Awd 84.

BUDZYN, EDWARD G; Oliver Wolcott Technical Schl; Torrington, CT; (Y); 4/142; Math Clb; Yrbk Stf; Stu Cncl; High Hon Roll; NHS; OWTS Cert For Schlrshp 82-85; Cert Of Rcgntn From Talcott Mntn Sci Prog 83; Waterbury ST Tech Coll; Elc En.

BUECHLER, COLIN; East Catholic HS; East Hartford, CT; (Y); 3/337; Church Yth Grp; Civic Clb; Teachers Aide; Im Bsktbl; Crs Cntry; High Hon Roll; Hon Roll; Kiwanis Awd; NHS; Partcpnt US JR Sci Sympsm 85.

BUEHLER, MICHAEL L; Stamford HS; Stamford, CT; (Y); 1/400; Cmnty Wkr; Debate Tm; Temple Yth Grp; High Hon Roll; NCTE Awd; NHS; Ntl Merit SF; Ski Clb; Nwsp Stf; JV Socr; Harvard Bk Awd Engl 84; Engl.

BUGL, LYNN; Granby Memorial HS; Granby, CT; (Y); AFS; Drama Clb; French Clb; JA; Model UN; Office Aide; Ski Clb; Drill Tm; Am Leg Aux Girls St; French Hon Soc; Frgn Lang.

BUISMATO, LISA MICHELLE; Nonnewaug HS; Woodbury, CT; (Y); Dance Clb; JV Fld Hcky; Lion Awd; Most Clssrm Effort 83-84; Dean JC; Dance.

BULSON, SEAN W; Daniel Hand HS; Madison, CT; (Y); 23/218; AFS; Am Leg Boys St; Boy Scts; Ski Clb; Band; Concert Band; Drm & Bgl; Mrchg Band; Stage Crew; Im Vllybl.

BURACESKI, SUSAN; Amity Regional SR HS; Orange, CT; (Y); Nwsp Phtg; Bio.

BURGER, DOUG; Staples HS; Westport, CT; (Y); Debate Tm; JA; L Socr; Spllng Cont Wnnr; Ski Team Ltr; Law.

BURGESS, LAWRENCE; Sheehan HS; Wallingford, CT; (Y); 53/236; Church Yth Grp; Hosp Aide; Band; Mrchg Band; JV Var Socr; Var L Swmmng; Var L Trk; High Hon Roll; Hon Roll; Engrng.

BURGESS, LYNN; Miss Porters Schl; Somerville, NJ; (Y); Computer Clb; French Clb; Model UN; Band; Concert Band; Mrchg Band; High Hon Roll; Hon Roll; LEAD Pgm In Busnss 85; ABC Student 83-86; U Of PA; Intl Finance.

BURKE, CATHERINE; East Catholic HS; Manchester, CT; (Y); 49/320; Am Leg Aux Girls St; Yrbk Stf; Pres Frsh Cls; Pres Sr Cls; Trs Stu Cncl; Var Bsktbl; Capt Crs Cntry; Capt Trk; High Hon Roll; JC Awd; Hugh O Brien Leadershp Awd 84; Girls ST Awd 85.

BURKE, EDMUND J; Xavier HS; Wethersfield, CT; (Y); 37/188; Cmnty Wkr; Stage Crew; Nwsp Stf; Im Var Golf; Hon Roll; Arthur Donofrio Memrl Schlrshp 85; Middletown Prss Cert Of Jrnlstc Merit 85; Fairfield U; Eng.

BURKE, ELIZABETH; East Lyme HS; Salem, CT; (Y); Church Yth Grp; Key Clb; Library Aide; Teachers Aide; Nwsp Rptr; JV Fld Hcky; Powder Puff Ftbl; JV Var Trk; High Hon Roll; NHS; Engr.

BURKOWSKY, SUSAN; Nonnewaug HS; Ansonia, CT; (Y); Pres Church Yth Grp; VP FFA; Pep Clb; Yrbk Bus Mgr; Off Frsh Cls; VP Jr Cls; Var Trk; Intl Ordr Of Rainbow Girls Wrthy Advsr 85; Bio.

BURKSA, DAWN; Wilby HS; Wtby, CT; (Y); Hosp Aide; Chorus; Hon Roll; NHS.

BURLINGAME, DARLENE M; Plainfield HS; Plainfield, CT; (Y); Drama Clb; VP Exploring; Red Cross Aide; Service Clb; School Play; Nwsp Rptr; Yrbk Rptr; Hon Roll; Stage Crew; Nwsp Stf; Svc Awd 85; Democrat Twn Cmmttee Awd 85; Isacc Cat Awd 85; Wells Coll; Intl Govt.

BURMAN, RONA; William H Hall HS; Lafayette, IN; (Y); 198/324; Dance Clb; Drama Clb; Pres JA; Pres VP Temple Yth Grp; Chorus; School Play; Nwsp Ed-Chief; JV Trk; High Hon Roll; Hon Roll; Merit Scholar Hartford Ballet Co 82-83; Rep Pres Srch Outstndng Secn Schls 84-85; Mdrn Miss CT 84-85; Purdue U; Spch Pthly.

BURNAT, MICHELE; George J Penney HS; East Hartford, CT; (Y); 10/251; Church Yth Grp; VP Spanish Clb; Yrbk Stf; Var Capt Bsktbl; Var Sftbl; Var Swmmng; High Hon Roll; Hon Roll; NHS; Rotary Awd; Rotary Clb Schlrshp 85; ROTC 4-Yr Schlrshp 85; Presdntl Acadmc Ftns Awd 85; Pennsylvania ST U; Engrng.

BURNS, BONNIE; Plainville HS; Plainville, CT; (Y); Hosp Aide; Ski Clb; Nwsp Rptr; Yrbk Phtg; Yrbk Stf; Capt L Bsktbl; Var L Sftbl; Var L Vllybl; Hon Roll; NHS; All Cnfrnc In Bsktbl & Sftbl 85; Schlrshp To Ntl Comp Camp 85; Sprngfld Coll; Physcl Thrpy.

BURNS, JOEL; Seymour HS; Seymour, CT; (Y); VP JA; Stage Crew; Variety Show; Yrbk Rptr; Yrbk Sprt Ed; Yrbk Stf; Rep Soph Cls; Rep Jr Cls; Rep Sr Cls; Stu Cncl; Outstnd Achvmt Spanish III, Typng Awd 85; Anml Sci.

BURNS, PAMELA; Shelton HS; Shelton, CT; (Y); Spanish Clb; Stu Cncl; Capt Crs Cntry; Capt Trk; NHS; Vitramon Awd 85; All New Haven Cnty Tm Crss Cntry 83; All Vlly Tm Crss Cntry All Housatonc Tm 83.

BURR, JAMES D; Rockville HS; Vernon, CT; (Y); 14/365; Am Leg Boys St; Chess Clb; Concert Band; Mrchg Band; Rep Stu Cncl; Golf; High Hon Roll; Ntl Merit SF.

BURROUGHS, KELVIN; Hillhouse HS; New Haven, CT; (S); Church Yth Grp; Computer Clb; Math Clb; Science Clb; Spanish Clb; Chorus; Church Choir; Mrchg Band; Variety Show; Soph Cls; Hnr, Music Awd 80-82; Lab Tech.

BURROWS, CHUCK; Suffield Acad; Hilltown, PA; (Y); 30/103; AFS; Boy Scts; Hosp Aide; Spanish Clb; Yrbk Stf; Var Ftbl; Var Lcrss; Hon Roll; Ntl Merit Ltr; Hnr Cncl 83; U CA Santa Cruz; Pre Med.

BURT, DEBRA; Sacred Heart Academy; North Haven, CT; (Y); Art Clb; French Clb; Variety Show; Gym; Sport Clb 82-83; Boston U; Med.

BURWELL, HEATHER ALLISON; The Masters Schl; Winsted, CT; (Y); Ski Clb; Stage Crew; Co-Capt Bsktbl; Socr; High Hon Roll; Hon Roll; NHS; Gordon Clg Pres Schlrshp 85; Gordon Clg; Marn Bio.

BUSCH, GWENDOLYN; Acad Of Our Lady Of Mercy; W Haven, CT; (Y); Church Yth Grp; Math Clb; Math Tm; Science Clb; Spanish Clb; Church Choir; Rep Frsh Cls; Pres Soph Cls; VP Sr Cls; Mu Alp Tht; Accntng.

BUSH, STEPHANIE; East Lyme HS; E Lyme, CT; (Y); 11/280; AFS; Key Clb; Yrbk Stf; Var Tennis; Var Trk; High Hon Roll; Hon Roll.

BUSH, WILLIAM; St Bernard HS; Bozvah, CT; (S); 45/295; Exploring; Science Clb; Yrbk Stf; Stu Cncl; Var Crs Cntry; Var Tennis; Var Trk; Hon Roll; All Amer Cls L Champ Tm 83; Pol Sci.

BUSHNELL, MICHAEL; Orville H Platt HS; Meriden, CT; (Y); Boy Scts; Pres Chess Clb; Pres Church Yth Grp; Pres Computer Clb; Drama Clb; French Clb; German Clb; Church Choir; Yrbk Phtg; Yrbk Rptr; Comp Sci.

BUTCHER, MICHELE; Bassick HS; Bridgeport, CT; (S); Church Yth Grp; English Clb; Exploring; Hosp Aide; Yrbk Stf; Lit Mag; VP Rep Jr Cls; Hon Roll; Corp Law.

BUTEAU, LORI; East Catholic HS; Coventry, CT; (Y); 75/300; Girl Scts; Teachers Aide; Yrbk Stf; Sec Soph Cls; Coach Actv; Hon Roll; Human Svcs.

BUTERA, SUSAN; Stamford HS; Stamford, CT; (Y); Drama Clb; Exploring; Hosp Aide; Thesps; School Musical; School Play; Stage Crew; Rep Soph Cls; Rep Sr Cls; Diving; Bst Actrss Schl Muscl 82; Entrtnmt.

BUTKIEWICZ, KRISTIN; West Haven HS; W Haven, CT; (Y); DECA; Stu Cncl; Schltc Excllnc In U S Hist 84-85; U Of Boca Raton; Bus Admin.

BUTLER, ADRIENNE; James Hillhouse HS; New Haven, CT; (S); 5/227; Debate Tm; Pres JA; Red Cross Aide; Church Choir; Capt Trk; High Hon Roll; Hon Roll; NHS; Ntl Merit Ltr; Prfct Atten Awd; Stpehen Marcucci Mem Awd 83; E Crowley Mem Awd 82; Ldrshp Trng Conf 83; Wesleyan; Med.

BUTLER, DAVID; Windham HS; Willimantic, CT; (Y); 90/285; Am Leg Boys St; Boy Scts; Church Yth Grp; Var Capt Swmmng; Var L Trk; Hon Roll; Southern CT ST U; Comp Sci.

BUTLER, MARI; Robert E Fitch SR HS; Groton, CT; (Y); 4/401; Girl Scts; Varsity Clb; Mrchg Band; Lit Mag; Var Capt Swmmng; Var Capt Tennis; Var L Trk; High Hon Roll; Hon Roll; NHS; ECC Schlr/Athl Awd 85; Groton Schlrshp Fnd 85; Elec Boat Mgmt Clb Schlrshp 85; Coast Guard Acad; Bio.

BUTVILAS, LAURIE A; Windsor Locks HS; Windsor Locks, CT; (Y); 16/165; Band; Chorus; Concert Band; Jazz Band; Mrchg Band; School Musical; Swing Chorus; Nwsp Stf; Yrbk Stf; Sec Frsh Cls; Berklee Coll Music Smmr Pgm Schlrshp 85; Music.

BYCK, HOWARD; Ridgefield HS; Ridgefield, CT; (S); 56/361; Orch; Pres Frsh Cls; Pres Soph Cls; Pres Stu Cncl; Capt Bsktbl; DAR Awd; High Hon Roll; NHS; Centry III Ldr 85; Hugh O Brien Found CT Yth Ldrshp Semnr 83; Cornell U; Law.

BYRD, ANTHONY A; William H Hall HS; W Hartford, CT; (Y); 57/301; Aud/Vis; Cmnty Wkr; Pep Clb; Nwsp Stf; Rep Stu Cncl; JV Bsktbl; Var Golf; Cit Awd; High Hon Roll; Hon Roll; Sprt Of Hall Awd 85; Bucknell U.

BYRD, DAVID D; W F Kaynor R V T S HS; Waterbury, CT; (Y); Boy Scts; Pep Clb; VICA; Nwsp Stf; Yrbk Sprt Ed; Yrbk Stf; Rep Jr Cls; Rep Stu Cncl; Bsktbl; Trk; Wstbry ST Tech; Engrng.

BYRD, MARGIE; Hall HS; W Hartford, CT; (Y); 22/350; JA; Yrbk Stf; Lcrss; French Hon Soc; High Hon Roll; Hon Roll; NHS.

BYRD, SHAHEENA; Richard C Lee HS; New Haven, CT; (Y); Drama Clb; 4-H; Math Tm; Drill Tm; School Play; Nwsp Rptr; Yrbk Stf; Rep Frsh Cls; Rep Soph Cls; Rep Jr Cls; Howard U; Med.

CACACE, CHRISTINA; East Catholic HS; Coventry, CT; (Y); Church Yth Grp; English Clb; Service Clb; Band; Church Choir; Lit Mag; Off Jr Cls; Off Sr Cls; Stu Cncl; High Hon Roll; Holy Cross; Law.

CADELLA, MARY ANN; North Haven HS; N Haven, CT; (Y); Church Yth Grp; Science Clb; Hon Roll; Accntng.

CADIEUX, ELISE; Seymour HS; Oxford, CT; (Y); AFS; Yrbk Stf; U MA; Psych.

CAFIERO, ANTHONY; Notre Dame HS; W Haven, CT; (Y); 57/250; Cmnty Wkr; Ski Clb; Var Crs Cntry; Var Golf; Im Ice Hcky; Tennis; Hon Roll; Var Ltr Crs Cntry, Golf 85; Providence Coll; Comp Sci.

CAGGIANO, JEFFREY J; Bristol Eastern HS; Bristol, CT; (Y); Am Leg Boys St; Boys Clb Am; VP Jr Cls; Var Capt Socr; Cit Awd; High Hon Roll; NHS.

CAHILL, CARI; Daniel Hand HS; Madison, CT; (Y); Cmnty Wkr; GAA; Red Cross Aide; Yrbk Stf; Cheerleading; Capt Gym; High Hon Roll; Hon Roll; Outstndng Chrldr & Gymnst Awd 85; U Of Sthrn CA; Sprts Med.

CAIAZE, ROBERT; Plainville HS; Plainville, CT; (Y); Band; Concert Band; Drm & Bgl; Jazz Band; Mrchg Band; Pep Band; Var Swmmng; Cntrl CT ST U; Bus.

CAIN, KIMBERLEY; Danbury HS; Danbury, CT; (Y); Camp Fr Inc; Church Yth Grp; Trs Girl Scts; Hosp Aide; Office Aide; Acpl Chr; Yrbk Phtg; Yrbk Stf; Stu Cncl; Hon Roll; Acadmc Achvt Awds 82-85; Cmmnty Svc Awd 82-85; Eastern CT ST U; Anml Med.

CAIN, MONIQUE RENEE; James Hillhouse HS; New Haven, CT; (Y); 21/236; JV Bsktbl; Var Capt Sftbl; Hon Roll; New Haven Schlrshp Fnd 85; Sci Mert Awd 85; Ph Delt Kapp Inc Ntl Schlrshp 85; Douglass Coll; Med.

CALDERA, MARIAN; Bassick HS; Bridgeport, CT; (S); Drama Clb; English Clb; Lit Mag; High Hon Roll; Hon Roll; Ntl Merit Ltr.

CALDWELL, DALE; Windham Techinical Schl; Tolland, CT; (Y); Var L Bsbl; Hon Roll; USC.

CALHOUN, ALLISON; Granby Memorial HS; Granby, CT; (Y); AFS; Church Yth Grp; JA; Stu Cncl; Var L Bsktbl; Var L Fld Hcky; Var L Sftbl; Hon Roll; N Centrl CT Conf Bsktbl 84-85; Most Imprvd Bsktbl Awd 84-85; Am HS Athlete Awd 84-85.

CALLAHAN, DEBBIE; Jonathan Law HS; Milford, CT; (Y); 50/240; Hosp Aide; Keywanettes; Color Guard; Yrbk Stf; Tennis; Hon Roll.

CALLAHAN, PATTI; Danbury HS; Danbury, CT; (Y); 160/600; Dance Clb; Exploring; Acpl Chr; Color Guard; School Musical; Variety Show; Nwsp Rptr; JV Fld Hcky; Hon Roll; Occuptnl Thrpst.

CALLAN, ELIZABETH; Weston HS; Weston, CT; (Y); Drama Clb; Key Clb; Acpl Chr; Chorus; Madrigals; School Musical; Nwsp Stf; High Hon Roll; Hon Roll; Ntl Merit SF; Interntl Rltns.

CALLEGARI, ERNESTO; Torrington HS; Torrington, CT; (Y); 32/280; Boy Scts; Math Tm; VP Band; Concert Band; Orch; Pep Band; School Musical; Bowling; High Hon Roll; NHS; U Connecticut; Phrmcy.

CALVI, DONNA; Platt HS; Meriden, CT; (Y); Socr; Swmmng; State Chmpn In Karate 81-83; Sclgst.

CALVO, LINDA; Rham HS; Hebron, CT; (Y); #8 In Class; Am Leg Aux Girls St; Sec FBLA; Acpl Chr; Chorus; High Hon Roll; Hon Roll; Sec NHS; Amer Achvmnt Awds 84-85; Bus.

CAMARRO, THOMAS; Fairfield Prep; Fairfield, CT; (Y); Aud/Vis; Computer Clb; High Hon Roll; NHS; JA; Science Clb; Chorus; Swmmng; Engrng.

CAMBO, MARY H; Canton HS; Canton, CT; (Y); 13/107; Model UN; Political Wkr; School Play; Yrbk Phtg; VP Frsh Cls; VP Soph Cls; Rep Stu Cncl; JV Capt Fld Hcky; NHS; Hnrs Englsh Awd 84; Ldrshp Schlrshp 85; Manhattanville Coll; Pre-Law.

CAMERA, NEISHA; Northbranford HS; Northford, CT; (Y); Variety Show; Nwsp Rptr; Yrbk Stf; Stu Cncl; Cheerleading; Mgr(s); Powder Puff Ftbl; Nrsng.

CAMPAGNA, JOSEPH; Berlin HS; Kensington, CT; (Y); Am Leg Boys St; VP Soph Cls; VP Jr Cls; VP Sr Cls; L Bsktbl; L Ftbl; Var Capt Socr; L Var Trk; Hon Roll.

CAMPAIGNE, CATHERINE; Gilford HS; Guilford, CT; (Y); AFS; Church Yth Grp; Drama Clb; Political Wkr; Trs Band; Chorus; Church Choir; Trs Concert Band; Jazz Band; Mrchg Band; Awd For Excell In Lang Arts 83-85; Var Lttr In Bnd 85; Ind Law.

CAMPANELLI, CHRISTINE; William Hall HS; W Hartford, CT; (Y); Church Yth Grp; Hosp Aide; Pep Clb; Sec Sr Cls; Off Stu Cncl; Var Capt Bsktbl; Var Socr; Var Capt Tennis; Bus.

CAMPANELLI, RICK; Oliver Wolcott Vo-Tech; Torrington, CT; (S); 4/180; VICA; Nwsp Rptr; Pres VP Stu Cncl; Var JV Bsbl; Var Golf; Var Capt Socr; High Hon Roll; Hon Roll; NHS; Waterbury ST; Elec Engr.

CAMPBELL, CAROLYN; Bethel HS; Bethel, CT; (Y); Camp Fr Inc; Church Yth Grp; PAVAS; Band; Concert Band; Variety Show; JV Bsktbl; Juvenile Law.

CAMPBELL, SEAN MICHAEL; Avon Old Farms HS; Avon, CT; (S); 1/100; Sec French Clb; Radio Clb; JV Crs Cntry; Var L Golf; Ice Hcky; High Hon Roll; Bronze Medl Excllnce Fr I 83; Silvr Medl Excllnce Fr II 84; Colgate; Engrng.

CAMPBELL, WAYNE; East Hartford HS; E Hartford, CT; (Y).

CAMPOLI, DEBBIE; Amity SR HS; Woodbridge, CT; (Y); Drama Clb; Latin Clb; Spanish Clb; Chorus; Color Guard; School Musical; School Play; Bsktbl; Cit Awd; High Hon Roll; Natl Art Hnr Scty Awd 83-84; Natl Art Hnr Scty Club 83-85; Gourmet Club 84-85; Law.

CAMPOS, JOSE; Naugatuck HS; Naugatuck, CT; (Y); Church Yth Grp; DECA; JV Crs Cntry; Var L Socr; Commnctns.

CANAL, JANEEN; Tolland HS; Tolland, CT; (Y); 23/173; Am Leg Aux Girls St; Church Yth Grp; VP Frsh Cls; VP Soph Cls; VP Jr Cls; VP Sr Cls; Trs Stu Cncl; Var Capt Cheerleading; Coach Actv; Hon Roll; N Centrl CT Ldrshp Conf 84-85; Reprsntv.

CANALIA, PAULA; Orville H Platt HS; Meriden, CT; (Y); Boys Clb Am; Church Yth Grp; Hon Roll; Bus.

CANAVAN, KAREN; Lyman Hall HS; Wallingford, CT; (Y); 9/220; Spanish Clb; Sec Soph Cls; VP Jr Cls; VP Sr Cls; Var Capt Bsktbl; Var Sftbl; High Hon Roll; Hon Roll; NHS.

CANE, LISA; St Thomas Aquinas HS; New Britain, CT; (Y); 12/150; Cmnty Wkr; Yrbk Rptr; Yrbk Stf; Rep Soph Cls; Rep Jr Cls; Hon Roll; Briarwood Bk Awd Excel Bus 84; J Mangan Mem, Cntrl Labr Cncl Schlrshps, Outstndng Bus Awd 85; Boston U; Psyc.

CANELLI, JANINE; Sacred Heart Acad; Hamden, CT; (Y); Cmnty Wkr; Computer Clb; Hosp Aide; Orch; School Musical; Im Vllybl; Hon Roll; Merit Awd Excllnc Pian 85; Hnr Rll Awd 85; Comp Sci.

CANESTRINI, GINA; Centrl Catholic HS; Norwalk, CT; (Y); Girl Scts; Ski Clb; Bsktbl; Tennis; Hon Roll.

CANEVARI, TYSEN; Norwalk HS; Norwalk, CT; (Y); Letterman Clb; Var Bsbl; Var Capt Bsktbl; Hon Roll.

CANEY, LESLIE; Stamford HS; Stamford, CT; (S); #1 In Class; Dance Clb; Drama Clb; Ski Clb; Temple Yth Grp; School Musical; Rep Frsh Cls; Sec Soph Cls; Sec Jr Cls; Rep Stu Cncl; Var L Gym; Hnrd At C T Hnrs Semnr 85; Advrtsng.

CANNAVERDE, ALEXA; Amity SR HS; Bethany, CT; (Y); 4-H; GAA; Pep Clb; Spanish Clb; Stage Crew; Crs Cntry; Mgr(s); Trk; CHSA Lcl Pony Hntr ST Chmpn 82; U Of CT; Bus Mngmnt.

CANNON, GARRETT; Stamford Catholic HS; Stamford, CT; (Y); 40/160; Aud/Vis; JV Bsbl; Im Vllybl; Im Wt Lftg; Spanish NHS; Im Bsktbl; Spnsh Excel Awd 83.

CANTIN, MARK; East Catholic HS; Manchester, CT; (Y); Boy Scts; Church Yth Grp; Ski Clb; Band; Pep Band; School Musical; School Play; Ftbl; Var Wrstlng; God Cntry Awd; Bronze Palm Eagle Awd 85; CT U; Law.

CANTOR, SHARON; Cheshire HS; Cheshire, CT; (Y); Debate Tm; Ski Clb; Var L Fld Hcky; Var Sftbl; High Hon Roll; NHS; Teachers Aide; Socr; Hon Roll; Prfct Atten Awd; Ist Tm In Housatonic Leag Fld Hcky 84; Mst Imprvd Midfldr Fld Hcky 84.

CAPASSO, MARIA; St Marys HS; New Haven, CT; (Y); Church Yth Grp; Cmnty Wkr; FBLA; Office Aide; Ski Clb; Church Choir; Yrbk Bus Mgr; Lit Mag; Rep Sr Cls; Hon Roll; Hostss On Recptn Committee Drng Orientatn Wk 83; Religious Instrctr Drng Smmr Schl 83-85; The Acad; Exec Sec.

CAPITANI, DINA R; Old Saybrook HS; Old Saybrook, CT; (Y); Drama Clb; Key Clb; Chorus; School Musical; Lit Mag; Hon Roll; Nationally Rankd Elite Gym 83-84; Music.

CAPLE, MARCELLA; Wilbur Cross HS; New Haven, CT; (Y); French Clb; Pep Clb; Acpl Chr; Chorus; Church Choir; Drill Tm; School Play; Cit Awd; DAR Awd; SAR Awd; Hal Jacksons Tlnts Tns 83; Adrian & Alice Redmond Schlrshp Tlnt Shw 83; Ms Frshmn 82-83; Ms Soph 83-84; Lwyr.

CAPOBIANCO, THOMAS; Plainfield HS; Sterling, CT; (Y); 5/160; Stat Bsktbl; High Hon Roll; Hon Roll; Jr NHS; Elec Engr.

CAPONI, ROBERT; Saint Josephs HS; Shelton, CT; (Y); 120/240; Camera Clb; Nwsp Phtg; JV Bowling; JV Socr; NEDT Awd; Culnry Arts.

CAPPELLINA, DAVID; Avon Old Farms HS; Torrington, CT; (S); 5/110; Aud/Vis; Computer Clb; Service Clb; Varsity Clb; Nwsp Rptr; Jr Cls; Trs Stu Cncl; Capt Var Bsktbl; Var Crs Cntry; Var Tennis; Dartmouth Bk Prize Acad Achvt 84; Jennings Cup Ahtl & Acadmc Achvt 84; Alt CT Boys ST 83; Ec.

CAPPUCCIA, LAURA; Central Catholic HS; Norwalk, CT; (Y).

CAPRON, PATRICIA ANN; Central HS; Bridgeport, CT; (S); 7/330; Spanish Clb; Nwsp Ed-Chief; Jr Cls; Stu Cncl; Sftbl; High Hon Roll; NHS; Computer Clb; Vllybl; Jr NHS; CT Schlrs Prog; Schlrshp & Ldrshp Awd; NY U; Ed.

CARANFA, ANNA MARIA; George J Penney HS; E Hartford, CT; (Y); High Hon Roll; NHS; Spn I Spkg Cont 1st Pl 82-83; Spn II Spkg Cont 2nd Pl 83-84; Bus Adm.

CARAVELLO, VINCENT J; Choate Rosemary Hall HS; Rome, NY; (Y); Boy Scts; Stage Crew; Wt Lftg; High Hon Roll; Ntl Merit SF; Amer Assn Teachrs Of Ger Awd Natl Exam 82; MA Inst Of Tech; Theor Math.

CARBONE, MARIO; Windham HS; Willimantic, CT; (Y); 42/285; Camera Clb; FBLA; Hon Roll; 4th Pl FBLA ST Ldrshp Conf Econ Exam 85; FBLA Scholar Awd 85; U CT; Mgr.

CARBONE, ROBIN; Jonathan Law HS; Stratford, CT; (Y); 40/247; Civic Clb; Drama Clb; Teachers Aide; School Musical; School Play; VP Jr Cls; VP Sr Cls; Stu Cncl; Gym; Suprntndts Acadmc Achvt Awd 85; Frnch II Spkng Awd 81; Athony C Mirmina Mem Awd 85; American Intl Coll; Intl Bus.

CARDONE, KELLIE; Notre Dame Acad; Bethlehem, CT; (Y); 17/62; Church Yth Grp; Drama Clb; School Play; Stage Crew; Variety Show; Nwsp Bus Mgr; Sec Frsh Cls; VP Soph Cls; Pres Jr Cls; Pres Sr Cls; Bus.

CARDUCCI, LUCY; Newington HS; Newington, CT; (Y); Pep Clb; Rep Stu Cncl; High Hon Roll; Hon Roll; Prfct Atten Awd; Frgn Lang Awds-Itln I & III 82-85; Yth Cncl Stu 83-85; Central CT ST U; Bus Adm.

CAREY, JILL; Danbury HS; Danbury, CT; (Y); 57/600; JA; Ski Clb; Variety Show; Yrbk Phtg; Yrbk Stf; Off Frsh Cls; Off Soph Cls; Off Civic Clb; NHS; Prfct Atten Awd; Bio Awd; Schlrshp Awd; Presndtl Acadmc Ftns Awd; CT U; Comp Engr.

CARLSON, DEBORAH; Branford HS; Branford, CT; (Y); 12/300; Church Yth Grp; Dance Clb; Latin Clb; Nwsp Rptr; Yrbk Stf; Stat Socr; Twrlr; Hon Roll; Bus.

CARLSON, LISA; Amity Regional SR HS; Orange, CT; (Y); Church Yth Grp; Drama Clb; Girl Scts; Math Tm; Chorus; Church Choir; School Musical; Hon Roll; Clss I, II Awd 83-84; Grl Sct Slvr Awd 84; Librn Cncrt Choir 84-85; Math.

CARLSON, MARY; Guilford HS; Guilford, CT; (Y); Hon Roll; NHS; 2nd Pl USFSA Comp 83; 3rd Nassau Cnty Free Skatng Champ 83; Schltc Achvt Awd As Engl Aide 85.

CARMON, SHEILA; Wilbur Cross HS; New Haven, CT; (S); 77/243; Church Yth Grp; FBLA; Pep Clb; Political Wkr; Church Choir; Sec Frsh Cls; Pres Soph Cls; Rep Jr Cls; Rep Sr Cls; Rep Stu Cncl; Pauline Davis Awd 83; Elks Oratrcl Cntst Schlrshp 83; Engl TN Awd 82 & 85; Howard U; Law.

CARNEGLIA, LAURA; Norwalk HS; Norwalk, CT; (Y); Cmnty Wkr; Red Cross Aide; Acpl Chr; Church Choir; High Hon Roll; Hon Roll; Pres Acad Fit Awd 85; Elms Coll Chicopee; Socl Wrk.

CARO, JANECE; Francis T Maloney HS; Meriden, CT; (Y); 10/292; VICA; School Play; Lit Mag; Powder Puff Ftbl; Hon Roll; NHS; Ntl Hispanic Schlr Awd 85; U CT; RN.

CARON, DALE; Middletown HS; Middletown, CT; (Y); 75/300; Am Leg Boys St; Ski Clb; School Play; Nwsp Rptr; Trs Sr Cls; Ftbl; Trk; Hon Roll; Alpha Omega Theta Frat Pres 84; New England Coll; Psych.

CARON, DAVID M; Killingly HS; Dayville, CT; (Y); 1/295; Off Jr Cls; DAR Awd; Elks Awd; French Hon Soc; Hon Roll; NHS; Val; Voice Dem Awd; Fairfield U; Med.

CARON, SONIA; Plainfiled HS; Plainfield, CT; (Y); 11/138; Hon Roll; Jr NHS; Voice Dem Awd; Natl JHS Awd 83; Fr II Awd 84; Fr III Awd 85; U Of CT; Dietics.

CARPENTIERE, BARBARA ANN; Holy Cross HS; Middlebury, CT; (Y); 185/352; Girl Scts; Hosp Aide; Chorus; Cncrt Choir Nmbrs JV & V 83-85; St Marys Schl Nursng; Nursng.

CARPIO, CARLOS; Windham HS; Willimantic, CT; (Y); JV Ftbl; U Conn; Engrng.

CARR, THOMAS; Oliver Wolcott Vo Tech; Torrington, CT; (S); 32/153; Aud/Vis; Drama Clb; Yrbk Ed-Chief; Hon Roll; Top Hnrs Earth Sci & Env Conf 84; Michaels Tchrs Schlrshp $500 85; U Hartford; Comp Sci.

CARRERA, FRANCISCO; Avon Old Farms Schl; Bahamas; (S); 15/100; Math Clb; Pep Clb; Off Sr Cls; Off Stu Cncl; JV Ftbl; Var Swmmng; Var Trk; Hon Roll; Geometry And Algebra Award; Business Administration.

CARRERAS, ISMAEL E; William H Hall HS; W Hartford, CT; (Y); 34/326; Church Yth Grp; Rep Sr Cls; Var L Socr; High Hon Roll; NHS; Pres Spanish NHS; Symp Band; Scrkpr Bsbl.

CARRIERE, KYLE; The Gilbert Schl; Winsted, CT; (Y); Am Leg Boys St; Pres Key Clb; Variety Show; VP Sr Cls; Capt Bsbl; Capt Ftbl; Var Swmmng; Var Wrstlng; Prfct Atten Awd.

CARRINGTON, ELIZABETH; Holy Cross HS; Waterbury, CT; (Y); 72/358; Cmnty Wkr; GAA; Latin Clb; Trs Band; Concert Band; Mrchg Band; Variety Show; Var Mgr(s); Var Score Keeper; Swmmng; Eductn.

CARRINGTON III, HIRAM; Amity Regional HS; Bethany, CT; (Y); Am Leg Boys St; Boy Scts; Trs Church Yth Grp; Rep Drama Clb; VP Chorus; Var Crs Cntry; JV Socr; Var Trk; Cit Awd; NHS; USMA.

CARROLL, SEAN; Central Catholic HS; Norwalk, CT; (Y); Nwsp Ed-Chief; Sec Sr Cls; Capt Golf; Var Socr; French Hon Soc; High Hon Roll; NHS; Ntl Merit Ltr; NEDT Awd; Rotary Awd; Boston Coll; Engr.

CARROLL, SEAN; Stratford HS; Stratford, CT; (Y); 8/244; JA; Variety Show; Nwsp Rptr; Rep Soph Cls; Rep Jr Cls; Var L Bsbl; Var L Bsktbl; Var L Crs Cntry; High Hon Roll; NHS; Columbia U Bk Awd 85.

CARROZZO, CHRIS; Northwestern Regional No 7 HS; Winsted, CT; (Y); JV Sftbl; Hon Roll; Bus.

CARSON, GREGORY; Fairfield Prep; Bridgeport, CT; (Y); Chess Clb; Nwsp Stf; Trk; Engl Hnrs Adv Plcmnt 85-86; Jrnlsm.

CARTER, JOAN; Weaver HS; Hartford, CT; (Y); 5/625; Church Yth Grp; Dance Clb; 4-H; JA; Pres Jr Cls; JV Gym; JV Sftbl; Cit Awd; Stat 4-H Awd; High Hon Roll; Schlr Of Monts Bright Light 83; Mst Outstndng Stu Of Soph Cls 84; Dartmouth Bk Schlrshp Awd 85; Emerson Coll; Mass Comm.

CARTER, RICHARD; Brookfield HS; Brookfield, CT; (Y); JV Trk; High Hon Roll; Hon Roll; Chrch Fllwshp-VP; Comp.

CARTER, STEPHEN; Jonathan Law HS; Milford, CT; (Y); #1 In Class; Am Leg Boys St; Sec Key Clb; Band; Jazz Band; Yrbk Stf; Off Sr Cls; VP Stu Cncl; High Hon Roll; Sec NHS; Computer Clb; Yale Bk Awd 85; Brown U Bk Awd 85; Elec Engrng.

CARUSO, KIMBERLY ANN; Newtown HS; Newtown, CT; (Y); 41/300; Church Yth Grp; Hosp Aide; Spanish Clb; Band; Concert Band; Mrchg Band; Symp Band; Yrbk Phtg; Mgr(s); Powder Puff Ftbl; Boston Coll; Elem Ed.

CARVER, RICK; Herigage Christian Acad; Beacon Falls, CT; (S); 1/7; Chess Clb; Church Yth Grp; Political Wkr; Chorus; School Musical; School Play; Stu Cncl; Var Bsbl; Var Bsktbl; Var L Socr; Highest Gd Pt Avg 83-84; Athletic Exclnce V Bsktbl 83; Pensacola Christian Coll; Theol.

CARY, LYNDA; Rockville HS; Vernon, CT; (Y); 49/365; Drama Clb; Chorus; Jazz Band; Mrchg Band; School Musical; Symp Band; High Hon Roll; Hon Roll; NHS; Ntl Merit Ltr; Schlrshps-Vrnon Frnds Music & Margrt Rusks Grffths 85; Pres Acadmc Ftns Awd 85; All ST Band 85; Bladwin-Wallace Coll; Music.

CASCIANO, SCOTT; Mark T Sheehan HS; Wallingford, CT; (Y); Church Yth Grp; Cmnty Wkr; JV Bsbl; Var Capt Ftbl; Var Capt Tennis; Home Ec Awd 85; Pub Rel.

CASE, ANISA L; Rockville HS; Vernon, CT; (Y); 2/335; VP Chess Clb; Computer Clb; Math Tm; Mrchg Band; Pep Band; School Musical; Symp Band; Stu Cncl; High Hon Roll; NHS; U Of CT; Mech Engrng.

CASEY, CHRIS; South Kent Schl; Houston, TX; (Y); 2/31; Boy Scts; Key Clb; Political Wkr; School Play; Nwsp Ed-Chief; Yrbk Ed-Chief; Var L Cheerleading; Var L Swmmng; Var L Wrstlng; Hon Roll; Washington & Lee U; Rl Est Devl.

CASEY, EILEEN; East Haven HS; E Haven, CT; (Y); 14/260; Spanish Clb; Varsity Clb; Yrbk Stf; Pom Pon; Hon Roll; Jr NHS; NHS; 5 Yr Awd Swmmng; Bus.

CASSATA, ANTONIETTA G; Stonington HS; Pawcatuck, CT; (Y); 1/217; Am Leg Aux Girls St; Nwsp Rptr; Yrbk Rptr; VP Stu Cncl; JV Var Cheerleading; Cit Awd; DAR Awd; Pres NHS; Pres Schlr; Val; Yale U; Med.

CASSELLA, JENNIFER; North Bradford HS; North Branford, CT; (Y); 34/160; Chorus; Madrigals; JV Bsktbl; Capt Sftbl; High Hon Roll; Hon Roll; Outstndng Musicansp Chorus 84-85; Music.

CASSIDY, JOHN; Daniel Hard HS; Madison, CT; (Y); JV Bsktbl; Var Socr; Bus Adm.

CASSIDY, KEVIN; Lyman Hall HS; Wallingford, CT; (Y); 12/250; Church Yth Grp; JA; Spanish Clb; Stu Cncl; Var Socr; Dnfth Awd; High Hon Roll; Prfct Atten Awd; VFW Awd; Voice Dem Awd; Outstndg Achvt Spn I & II Hnrs Awd 83 & 84; JA Co Of Yr 85; Comp Sci.

CASSIDY, ROBERT; Cheshire HS; Cheshire, CT; (Y); Band; Concert Band; Mrchg Band; Orch; Ntl Merit Ltr; Med.

CASTEL, NICOLE; St Mary HS; Stamford, CT; (Y); 12/74; Cmnty Wkr; Dance Clb; Drama Clb; Red Cross Aide; Thesps; Varsity Clb; School Play; JV Var Cheerleading; Hon Roll; NHS; Merchndsng.

CASTELLANO, LISA; Norwalk HS; Norwalk, CT; (Y); Cmnty Wkr; Dance Clb; JA; Ski Clb; Speech Tm; Rep Frsh Cls; Rep Soph Cls; Rep Jr Cls; Stat Bsbl; Powder Puff Ftbl; Educ.

CASTELLON, ELIZABETH; East Haven HS; North Haven, CT; (Y); 42/300; DECA; Yrbk Stf; Pom Pon; Central CT ST U; Bus Adm.

CASTILLO, NESTOR; Koble/Cathedral HS; Bridgeport, CT; (Y); Art Clb; Computer Clb; Math Clb; Ski Clb; Bsbl; Socr; Wt Lftg; Prfct Atten Awd; U Of Bridgeport; Elec Engrng.

CASTONGUAY, LISA; New Milford HS; New Milford, CT; (Y); 7/301; Girl Scts; School Musical; School Play; Yrbk Phtg; Yrbk Rptr; Yrbk Stf; Ftbl; Hon Roll; Masonic Awd; VP NHS; Crtv Wrtng Awd 85; New Milford Ed Assc Schlrshp 85; New Milford PTO Schlrshp 85; Manhattanville Coll; Englsh.

CATERSON, SUZANNE; Danbury HS; Danbury, CT; (Y); 86/613; French Clb; Hosp Aide; Varsity Clb; Band; Mrchg Band; Symp Band; Variety Show; Var Cheerleading; Var Tennis; Hon Roll; Brokers Flr Rep.

CAVALLARO, MARK; Notre Dame HS; West Haven, CT; (Y); 105/255; Church Yth Grp; Band; Concert Band; Hon Roll; U Of New Haven; Comptr Sci.

CAWOOD, KEVIN R; Cheshire HS; Cheshire, CT; (Y); 16/324; Aud/Vis; Boy Scts; Computer Clb; Exploring; School Play; Var Socr; High Hon Roll; NHS; Pres Schlr; Magna Cum Laude Awds; Schlstc Achvt Awds; Outstndng Stu Cert; CT U; Pathlgy.

CELENTANO, MICHAEL; Notre Dame HS; New Haven, CT; (Y); Boy Scts; Church Yth Grp; Var L Trk; Hon Roll; Bernard Pellegrino Schlrshp 85; 1200 SAT Score 8th Clss 85; Ltr Cmmndtn Schl Prncpl SAT Scores 85; U Of CT; Bus Ec.

CELESTE, LAUREL M; Cheshire HS; Cheshire, CT; (Y); Chorus; School Musical; Var L Swmmng; French Hon Soc; Hon Roll; Ntl Merit Ltr; Schlrshp-Ctr Creative Yth Wesleyan U 83; Law.

CELLA, TRACY; Lyman Hall HS; Wallingford, CT; (Y); FHA; Spanish Clb; Stat Bsktbl; Stat Ftbl; Fshn Mrchndsng.

CELLURA, JEFFREY; Bethel HS; Bethel, CT; (Y); 68/265; Church Yth Grp; Computer Clb; Ski Clb; Variety Show; Golf; Tennis; Hon Roll; Cornell; Chem Engr.

CELONE, DIANE; Crosby HS; Waterbury, CT; (Y); Hosp Aide; Latin Clb; Chorus; NHS; Prfct Atten Awd; Ltn Awd 85; U Of CT.

CELTRUDA, CHRIS; St Bernard HS; Mystic, CT; (Y); 34/300; Boy Scts; Ski Clb; Var L Crs Cntry; Trk; Hon Roll; Visl Arts Awd-Ntabl Achvt 83; Engrng.

CENCE, SANDRA; Southington HS; Southington, CT; (Y); 25/550; Am Leg Aux Girls St; Nwsp Ed-Chief; Nwsp Rptr; Nwsp Sprt Ed; L JV Bsktbl; L Var Swmmng; L Var Tennis; High Hon Roll; Hon Roll; NHS; Jrnlsm.

CENKUS, TARA; Cheshire HS; Cheshire, CT; (Y); Church Yth Grp; Pep Clb; Teachers Aide; Var Capt Cheerleading; Var Diving; Var Gym; JV Score Keeper; Hon Roll; Wheaton IL; Scl Wrk.

CEPPETELLI, JILL; Tolland HS; Tolland, CT; (Y); Am Leg Aux Girls St; Yrbk Stf; Var Cheerleading; Trk; Psych.

CERINO, SCOTT; Trumbull HS; Trumbull, CT; (Y); Boy Scts; Church Yth Grp; Teachers Aide; Nwsp Ed-Chief; Nwsp Rptr; Yrbk Stf; Hon Roll; Rotary Awd; Outstndng Svc Awd Rtry 83; Italian Clb Treas 83-84; Bus Admn.

CERNIAUSKAS, CHRISTOPHER; East Hartford HS; E Hartford, CT; (Y); Boy Scts; CAP; Model UN; Chorus; Rep Frsh Cls; Rep Soph Cls; Rep Jr Cls; JV Crs Cntry; JV L Ftbl; JV Trk; Elctd Attnd CT Bus Ind Assc Bus Wk U Hrtfrd 84; Boston Coll; Comp Sci.

CESARINI, DORIAN; North Haven HS; N Haven, CT; (Y); 92/281; Yrbk Stf; Off Jr Cls; Socr; Trk; Hon Roll; Fidle Socty 83-85; Crfts Acadmc Excllnc 83; Fshn Dsgn.

CHABINA, IRENE; Brookfield HS; Brookfield Cntr, CT; (Y); Varsity Clb; Chorus; Concert Band; Mrchg Band; Rep Jr Cls; Var Capt Cheerleading; Var Tennis; High Hon Roll; Hon Roll; U Of AZ; Arch.

CHADZIEWICZ, THERESA; Plainville HS; Plainville, CT; (Y); 32/205; Church Yth Grp; Band; Drm Mjr(t); Mrchg Band; Yrbk Stf; Trs Sr Cls; High Hon Roll; Hon Roll; NHS; Outstndg Home Econ Stdnt 85; Tunxis CC; Exec Sec.

CHAFFEE JR, DON J; Newington HS; Newington, CT; (Y); 85/375; Church Yth Grp; Spanish Clb; Jazz Band; School Musical; Symp Band; Variety Show; Var Crs Cntry; Var Trk; Hon Roll; Pres Symph Band 85-86; Vol Newington Chldrns Hosp 83; Yth Cncl 84-86; Math.

CHAKMAKJIAN, CARMEN; Notre Dame Catholic HS; Bridgeport, CT; (Y); 27/284; Drama Clb; Hosp Aide; JA; Keywanettes; Pep Clb; Teachers Aide; Chorus; Church Choir; School Musical; School Play; Dale Carnegie Schlrshp 85; Pres Acad Fitnss Awd 85; Roxanne Garguilo Mem Schlrshp 85; Art Awd 85; Paier Coll Art; Illstrtn.

CHAMBERLAIN, LOUISE; Coventry HS; Coventry, CT; (S); Var Capt Bsktbl; Var Capt Sftbl; JV Var Vllybl; Hon Roll; NHS; Acctng Aide 84; Bus Clb 82; Math,Acctng Hnr Awd 82-83; FL Southern; Bus.

CHAMBERS, DEIRDRE; Weaver HS; Hartford, CT; (Y); Hosp Aide; JA; Office Aide; Red Cross Aide; Rep Jr Cls; Rep Stu Cncl; Gym; Cit Awd; High Hon Roll; Hon Roll; Harvard Radcliffe Bk Awd 85; Schl Wd Hnr Rll 84; Maintaining An Avg Grd Of 89 For 3 Mk Pds 85; Pre-Med.

CHAMBERS, KELLY ANN; J M Writht Technical HS; Stamford, CT; (Y); JA; Var Sftbl; Bst Dfnsv Sftbl 84-85; Athl Of Yr 82-83; Fairchester All Leag Awd 84-85.

CHAMBLIN, BETH; East Lyme HS; E Lyme, CT; (Y); Church Yth Grp; Key Clb; Band; Var L Crs Cntry; Var L Trk; High Hon Roll; Hon Roll; Socl Sci.

CHAN, MAY C; Norwalk HS; Norwalk, CT; (Y); 39/450; Concert Band; Mrchg Band; Orch; Yrbk Stf; Stat Trk; High Hon Roll; NCTE Awd; NHS; Nominee All-Amer Hall Of Fame Hnrs 85; Liberal Arts.

CHANG, PANG-YUAN NICOLE; Hamden HS; Hamden, CT; (Y); 2/451; Math Clb; Math Tm; Orch; School Musical; Rep Sr Cls; High Hon Roll; NHS; Sal; Tlnt Srch Hnrs Grp 85; Math & Sci Awd 84; Semi-Fnlst Arts Recogntn & Tlnt Srch Wrtr 85; Vet Med.

CHANG, PAUL; Windham HS; Columbia, CT; (Y); 36/280; Am Leg Boys St; Crs Cntry; Capt Trk; Hon Roll; Beckish Memrl Awd 85; U Of CT; Cvl Engrng.

CHANG, ROBERT; Manchester HS; Manchester, CT; (Y); Var Bsbl; Var Bsktbl; Var Socr; Hon Roll; Athlts Awd 84; Engrng.

CHAPMAN, KENNETH D; Simsbury HS; W Sims, CT; (Y); JV Ftbl; Var Lcrss; Var Capt Wrstlng; Wrstlng-LL ST Champ 85.

CHAPMAN, ROGER L; Guilford HS; Guilford, CT; (Y); 68/266; Pres Church Yth Grp; Chorus; Var VP Socr; Var Trk; Hon Roll; Steven Looney Schlrshp 84-85; Jackson Nwspr All-State 84; Coaches All-State Soccr 84.

CHARBONEAU, QYNNE; Sacred Heart Acad; West Haven, CT; (Y); Church Yth Grp; Chorus; Church Choir; Stage Crew; Vllybl; Pro Life Clb 83-85; VP Pro Life Exec Bd 85-86; Oral Roberts U; Med.

CHAREST, WILLIAM H; Conard HS; West Hartford, CT; (Y); 8/300; Math Tm; Spanish Clb; Concert Band; Jazz Band; Pep Band; High Hon Roll; NHS; Ntl Merit Ltr; Pres Schlr; Spanish NHS; Gradtd Hgh Hnrs 85; Trinity Coll; Math.

CHARTIER, ALAN; W F Kaynor RTVS HS; Waterbury, CT; (Y); Boy Scts; High Hon Roll; Hon Roll; NHS; Ordr Ot Arrw; Electrncs Engr.

CHARTIER, VERONICA; Ellington HS; Ellington, CT; (Y); 34/140; Boy Scts; Drama Clb; Exploring; Hosp Aide; Latin Clb; Chorus; School Play; Bsktbl; Mgr(s); Score Keeper; Emergency Med Svc Med Response Tech 83; Emrgcy Med Tech EMT 85; Mus Hnr Awd 84; Manchester Hnr Awd 84; Manchester CC; Resp Ther.

CHARY, KASTHURY; Stamford HS; Stamford, CT; (S); Debate Tm; JA; Trk; NHS; Chess Tm 83-85; U Of CT; Bus Adm.

CHASE, KELLY MARIE; Lyman Hall HS; Greensboro, NC; (Y); Pres Variety Show; Yrbk Phtg; Yrbk Rptr; Pres Sr Cls; Rep Stu Cncl; High Hon Roll; Band; Concert Band; Mrchg Band; Fld Hcky; US Hstry Merit Awd 84; Stu Asmbly Srv Awd 85; Pres Ftns & Acdmc Achvt Awd 85; Glfrn Coll; Sprts Med.

CHAU, ANDREW; St Bernard HS; Stonington, CT; (S); 72/290; JV Bsktbl; Capt Ftbl; JV Trk; Bio-Med.

CHAUVIN, RONALD; Griswold HS; Jewett City, CT; (Y); Boy Scts; FFA; School Play; Stage Crew; Polish Bicentnl Awd 85; Elec.

CHE, FLORA; Staples HS; Westport, CT; (Y); Hosp Aide; Library Aide; Model UN; Acpl Chr; Mgr(s); Hon Roll; Ntl Merit SF; Day Of Pride Top 15 SR 84; 3rd Yr Frnch Awd 83; Matrls Sci.

CHEN, ELEANOR; Amity Regional HS; Orange, CT; (S); French Clb; Latin Clb; Concert Band; Mrchg Band; Symp Band; Nwsp Stf; Rep Stu Cncl; Var Fld Hcky; Var L Swmmng; High Hon Roll; Cls I & II Acad Awd 83 & 84; All-Hstnc Leag Swm Team Hnrs 83 & 84; Med.

CHENG, CHARLES S; North Haven HS; N Haven, CT; (Y); AFS; Am Leg Boys St; Art Clb; Aud/Vis; Ski Clb; Nwsp Rptr; Rep Stu Cncl; JV Trk; Union Carbide/WA Wrkshps Congrsnl Semnr 85; US Cost Gurd MITE 85; ST Fnlst Futr Prob Solvrs CT 84.

CHEPUL, AMY B; John F Kennedy HS; Waterbury, CT; (S); Pres Key Clb; Science Clb; Spanish Clb; Sec Trs Band; Yrbk Stf; Pres Sec Stu Cncl; High Hon Roll; NHS; UN Pilgrimage For Yth 83; Psych.

CHERIAN, BEENA; Sacred Heart Acad; Old Greenwich, CT; (Y); Sec Service Clb; Nwsp Rptr; Lit Mag; NHS; Sci Educ Ctr Awd Sci 85; :Med.

CHERNICK, KATHLEEN; Windsor HS; Windsor, CT; (Y); Church Yth Grp; Pres Jr Cls; Pres Sr Cls; Rep Stu Cncl; Var Cheerleading; Var Gym; Var Socr; Hon Roll; Ldrshp Conf JR & SR Yrs; Comp Sci.

CHERNIK, KATHLEEN; Windsor HS; Windsor, CT; (Y); 81/349; Band; Chorus; Nwsp Stf; Pres Jr Cls; Pres Sr Cls; Rep Stu Cncl; L Var Cheerleading; L Var Gym; Var Mgr(s); Hon Roll; Stu Ldrshp Training Pgm 83-85; Keene ST Coll; Radlgy.

CHERNOVETZ, JOSEPH; Ansonia HS; Ansonia, CT; (Y); Computer Clb; Varsity Clb; Yrbk Stf; JV Bsktbl; Var Ftbl; Var Trk; Comp Sci.

CHETCUTI, MARGARET; Brien Mc Mahon HS; Norwalk, CT; (Y); #26 In Class; Church Yth Grp; Band; Concert Band; Mrchg Band; Orch; Symp Band; High Hon Roll; Citatn Merit Symp Womens Assoc 85; Music.

CHEVALIER, JUDITH A; Hamden HS; Hamden, CT; (Y); 6/451; Church Yth Grp; Hosp Aide; Pres Math Clb; Capt Math Tm; Mrchg Band; Orch; School Play; Nwsp Rptr; Ntl Merit SF; Soc Of Wmn Engrns Awd 84; Engrng.

CHHABRA, SANDIP SINGH; Stamford HS; Stamford, CT; (S); 32/406; Sec L Debate Tm; Hosp Aide; Jazz Band; Rep Stu Cncl; Var Socr; High Hon Roll; NHS; JA; Pres Science Clb; Spanish Clb; Top 15 Minority Stu In CT 84-85; Awded 4 Yr Schlrshp To U Of CT 84-85; JR Sci & Humanities 84-85; U Of CT; Medicine.

CHIAPPETTA, MARK; Trumbull HS; Trumbull, CT; (Y); Hon Roll; Electrnc Engrng.

CHIAPPINELLI, JOHN P; Central Catholic HS; S Norwalk, CT; (Y); Cmnty Wkr; Var L Bsbl; High Hon Roll; NHS; Prfct Atten Awd; Bst Itln Stu 84-85; Excllnc Ltn & Engl III 82-85; Stu Of Itln Clb.

CHIARIZIO, TAMMY; Torrington HS; Torrington, CT; (Y); 115/286; Hosp Aide; Chorus; Rep Soph Cls; Hon Roll; Hartford Hospital; X-Ray Tech.

CHIAT, JONATHAN; Trumbull HS; Trumbull, CT; (Y); AFS; Trs Drama Clb; Political Wkr; Temple Yth Grp; Pres Thesps; Acpl Chr; Chorus; School Musical; School Play; Rep Frsh Cls; Lib Art.

CHICHESTER, ALICE; Conard HS; W Hartford, CT; (Y); 40/314; Spanish Clb; Acpl Chr; School Musical; Mgr(s); Socr; Sftbl; Trk; High Hon Roll; Spanish NHS; Chorus; Sgt Police Explr 82-85; Lang.

CHICKNEAS, JASON; Roger Ludlowe HS; Fairfield, CT; (Y); Am Leg Boys St; Boy Scts; Computer Clb; Math Tm; Variety Show; Rep Frsh Cls; L Crs Cntry; L Ftbl; L Lcrss; Capt Wrstlng; PA ST; Naval Offcr.

CHICOINE, DENISE; East Catholic HS; E Hartford, CT; (Y); 6/297; Art Clb; Church Yth Grp; Drama Clb; Ski Clb; Yrbk Stf; Lit Mag; Rep Frsh Cls; Rep Soph Cls; Rep Jr Cls; JV Trk; Amherst; Law.

CHICOINE, ROSEMARY; Guilford HS; Guilford, CT; (Y); 15/315; Sec 4-H; Latin Clb; Spanish Clb; Teachers Aide; 4-H Awd; High Hon Roll; NHS; Spanish NHS; Guilford H S Ldrshp Tm 84-85; Lang Arts Awd 83 & 85; Med.

CHIN, CAMILLE A; The Gunnery HS; Brooklyn, NY; (Y); Church Yth Grp; Cmnty Wkr; Dance Clb; Debate Tm; English Clb; Hosp Aide; Letterman Clb; Mathletes; Office Aide; Service Clb; Hazell Golembeske Mem Scshlrshp Awd 83; Norman R Lemke Mem Schlrshp Awd 84; Movie Club TV Host 82; Econ.

CHIN, STEFAN; Cheshire HS; Cheshire, CT; (Y); 14/324; German Clb; Concert Band; Mrchg Band; Stage Crew; Bausch & Lomb Sci Awd; High Hon Roll; NHS; Pres Schlr; Fred Willets Chem Awd 84; Credit Hrs Yale U 82-84; Greenhouse Mgr & Cheshire Gdn Clb Scholar 85; U Of Rochester; Dr.

CHIOFFI, VANESSA; Sacred Heart Acad; Branford, CT; (Y); Hosp Aide; Orch; Rep Frsh Cls; Rep Soph Cls; Rep Jr Cls; Rep Stu Cncl; Capt Crs Cntry; Econmcs.

CHMIELECKI, SANDRA; St Bernard HS; Taftville, CT; (Y); 53/300; Jr Cls; Hon Roll; Acdmc Excllnce Awd 83.

CHO, ME YOUNG; The Hotchkiss Schl; Voorhees, NJ; (Y); Church Yth Grp; French Clb; Band; School Musical; Symp Band; Lit Mag; Ntl Merit Ltr; Bus.

CHOINERE, JAMES E; Southington HS; Southington, CT; (Y); 76/550; Ski Clb; Var JV Bsktbl; Var Golf; Im Sftbl; High Hon Roll; Hon Roll; U Of CT; Civil Engr.

CHORDAS, CHRISTINE; Sacred Heart Acad; Wallingford, CT; (Y); Church Yth Grp; Cmnty Wkr; Hosp Aide; Ski Clb; Band; Stage Crew; Yrbk Rptr; Yrbk Stf; Lit Mag; Var Crs Cntry; Latn Hnrb Mntn 83; Future Dirctn Clb 84-85; Scungilli Schlrshp 85-86; Phys Thrpy.

CHORDAS, JOSEPH S; Mark T Sheehan HS; Wallingford, CT; (Y); 50/250; German Clb; Pres Soph Cls; VP Jr Cls; Stu Cncl; Var Swmmng; Hon Roll; SR Cls Pres 85-86; Treas Stu Cncl 83-84; Exec Bd Stu Cncl 84-85; Pol Sci.

CHRISTIAN, KAREN; Windham HS; Willimantic, CT; (Y); Latin Clb; Var Capt Bsktbl; Var Sftbl; Var Vllybl; Hon Roll; Psych.

CHRISTIAN, MELISSA; T Orrington HS; Torrington, CT; (Y); 34/330; Church Yth Grp; Sec French Clb; Girl Scts; Library Aide; Trs Service Clb; Band; Concert Band; Mrchg Band; Orch; High Hon Roll; Law.

CHRISTIE, JEFFREY; Holy Cross HS; Watertown, CT; (Y); 12/358; Boy Scts; Ski Clb; Yrbk Stf; Rep Stu Cncl; Var Socr; Var Tennis; French Hon Soc; Hon Roll; NHS; Ntl Merit Ltr; Awd For Hghst Avg In Frnch 83-84; Soc Stds Hnr Scty-VP 84; Pre-Dnstry.

CHRISTOFORO, ALICE; North Haven HS; North Haven, CT; (Y); 3/294; Chorus; Concert Band; School Musical; Nwsp Stf; Off Jr Cls; Off Sr Cls; Var Capt Swmmng; French Hon Soc; Pres French Hon Soc; AFS; Fencing-Capt, Varsty 83-85; NE Conf Awd-Frnch 85; Yale U.

CHRISTOPHER, ROBIN L; Litchfield HS; Litchfield, CT; (Y); 13/86; VP Art Clb; French Clb; PAVAS; Var Tennis; French Hon Soc; High Hon Roll; NHS; Center For Creative Yth 85; Art.

CHROSTOWSKI, CHERYL; Holy Cross HS; Waterbury, CT; (Y); 101/367; Church Yth Grp; Hon Roll; Acctng.

CHRZAN, DONALD; Putnam HS; Putnam, CT; (Y); Chess Clb; Band; Concert Band; Mrchg Band; Stage Crew; Var Crs Cntry; Var Trk; Elec.

CHUNG, DAVID; Amity Regional HS; Woodbridge, CT; (Y); Am Leg Boys St; Pres Latin Clb; VP Science Clb; Band; Concert Band; Mrchg Band; School Musical; School Play; Nwsp Stf; Capt Crs Cntry.

CHUPKA, LEE; Torrington HS; Torrington, CT; (Y); 25/271; Sec Drama Clb; Thesps; Varsity Clb; VICA; School Play; Stage Crew; Yrbk Stf; Rep Stu Cncl; Cheerleading; High Hon Roll; Fnlst OWE/DO Stu Of Yr Awd 85; 4th Pl Fnlst VICA Conf Job Intrvw 85; CT Schltc Achvt Grnt Pgm 85; U Of Hartford; Physcns Asst.

CHUPKA, WENDY; Torrington HS; Torrington, CT; (Y); 46/271; Cmnty Wkr; Trs Drama Clb; FHA; Girl Scts; Key Clb; Latin Clb; Ski Clb; Thesps; Stage Crew; High Hon Roll; Charlotte Hungerford Hosp Aux Schlrshp 85; Regina Tate Balfe Mem Schlrshp 85; Mass Coll; Radiothrpy.

CIANCIOLO, THERESA; Holy Cross HS; Waterbury, CT; (Y); 46/352; Art Clb; Latin Clb; Hon Roll; Nrsg.

CIARLEGLIO, STEVEN; Branford HS; Branford, CT; (Y); 36/280; Am Leg Boys St; Latin Clb; Science Clb; Yrbk Stf; Rep Frsh Cls; Rep Soph Cls; Var JV Bsbl; Var JV Ftbl; High Hon Roll; Hon Roll; Hnrb Mntn All Housatonic Lg Var Bsbl 84; Acctng.

CIBROWSKI, TOM; Danbury HS; Danbury, CT; (Y); Boy Scts; Cmnty Wkr; French Clb; Variety Show; Nwsp Ed-Chief; Nwsp Phtg; Nwsp Rptr; Yrbk Phtg; Yrbk Stf; Rep Frsh Cls; Washington Wrkshps Cngrssnl Smnr; Stu Rep Brd Educ; George W Perry Awdd Scl Stds; Brdcst Jrnlsm.

CICCARELLO, MATTHEW; Norwalk HS; Norwalk, CT; (Y); Cmnty Wkr; Political Wkr; Var Ice Hcky; Attorney.

CICE, JOSEPH HENRY; Ridgefield HS; Ridgefield, CT; (Y); 2/365; Cmnty Wkr; Political Wkr; VP Civic Clb; VP Sr Cls; JV Bsbl; Dnfth Awd; NHS; Aud/Vis; Service Clb; Jazz Band; Ridgefield Lttle Leg Bsbl Tms Coach; WA Wrkshps Congrssnl Sem; Elizabeth Ballard PTSA Paul Scholar; Harvard; Govt.

CIOTTI, MICHAEL; Daniel Hand HS; Madison, CT; (Y); 28/238; Am Leg Boys St; FCA; JV Var Bsbl; JV Var Ftbl; JV Var Wrstlng.

CIPRIANO, JOHN; Holy Cross HS; Waterbury, CT; (Y); 1/344; Debate Tm; Math Tm; Pres Trs Science Clb; High Hon Roll; NHS; Ntl Merit Ltr; Val; Greenblatt Schlrshp 85; Prfssnl Estmtrs Schlrshp 85; Itln Clb Treas; U PA; Engrng.

CIPRIANO, MELISSA; Crosby HS; Waterbury, CT; (Y); Cmnty Wkr; Letterman Clb; Office Aide; Varsity Clb; Sec Jr Cls; Sec Sr Cls; Var Capt Swmmng; Hon Roll; Mt St Mary Coll; Rn.

CIRIE, ANDREA; Gailford HS; Guilford, CT; (Y); Drama Clb; Acpl Chr; Chorus; Madrigals; School Musical; School Play; Stage Crew; Lit Mag; Outstndng Actrss CT Drama Assn 85; Cmmnctns.

CISZEWSKI, JOEL; East Catholic HS; E Hartford, CT; (Y); 1/270; Teachers Aide; Rep Stu Cncl; Var L Golf; Var L Socr; High Hon Roll; Pres NHS; Rennselaer Medl Excllnc Math; CT Hnrs Semnr; Chem Olympiad; Biogcl Sci.

CIUFFO, LUCI ANNE; Sacred Heart Acad; Stamford, CT; (Y); 20/44; Church Yth Grp; Drama Clb; Ski Clb; Variety Show; Yrbk Stf; Pres Jr Cls; Rep Stu Cncl; Dnfth Awd; Excell In Music 82; Salve-Regena Coll.

CIUFFREDA, MICHAEL; St Joseph HS; Bridgeport, CT; (Y); 54/227; Hon Roll; Aerontcl Engr.

CIVITELLO, LAURA; Sacred Heart Acad; Hamden, CT; (Y); Art Clb; FBLA; Teachers Aide; Mrchg Band; Stage Crew; Vllybl; FBLA Chrprsn Ad Cmpgn 85; Notre Dame Mrchng Band Awds 82-83; Bus.

CLANCY, RACHEL; Shelton HS; Shelton, CT; (S); DECA; Drama Clb; Office Aide; Ski Clb; Hon Roll; Jr DECA Tres 83-84; Spcl Olympc Vlntr 81-84.

CLARK, ADRIAN; St Bernard HS; Uncasville, CT; (Y); 127/298; Var Bsbl; JV Bsktbl; Var Capt Ftbl; Var L Trk; Hon Roll; Engrng.

CLARK, ALLISON KEARNS; George J Penney HS; East Hartford, CT; (S); Church Yth Grp; DECA; Drill Tm; Hon Roll; Dist CDC 85; Vtng Delg DECA Natls 85; Manchester CC; Bus Mgmt.

CLARK, FREDERICK; Cheshire Acad; Meriden, CT; (Y); 4/54; Key Clb; Var Capt Lcrss; Var Socr; High Hon Roll; NHS; NEDT Awd; Camera Clb; Church Yth Grp; Amer Clsscl Lg Cum Laude Awd Natl Lat Exm 85; Yth Undrstndg Stu Exch Hllnd 84; Im Flr Hcky Lg Chmps 85; Pre-Med.

CLARK, JANICE; East Hartford HS; East Hartford, CT; (Y); 15/230; Church Yth Grp; Lit Mag; Off Sr Cls; Hon Roll; NHS; Crossroads Poetry Awd 85; Christ Natns Inst; Theology.

CLARK, KEVIN; Simsbury HS; W Simsbury, CT; (Y); Am Leg Boys St; Church Yth Grp; FBLA; JA; Yrbk Phtg; Bsbl; Bsktbl; Socr; Cit Awd; DAR Awd; Simsbury Educ Assoc Schlrshp 85; Humphrey Schlrshp 85; CT St Emplys Union Schlrshp 85; Fairfield U; Elect Engnr.

CLARK, KRISTEN LEIGH; St Bernard HS; Ledyard, CT; (Y); Cmnty Wkr; Drama Clb; Hosp Aide; Church Choir; Madrigals; School Musical; School Play; Yrbk Stf; Chrmn Stu Cncl; Diving; Excllnc Awd All New England Chorus 85; Bethany Coll; Comm.

CLARK, MELANIE; Northwet Regional 7 HS; New Hartford, CT; (Y); French Clb; Science Clb; Band; Concert Band; Mrchg Band; School Musical; Tennis; High Hon Roll; NHS; Brown U Smmr Acad 85; Soc Stud Excllnc Awd 81-84; Advncd Math Excllnc Awd 85.

CLARK, SHELBY L; Wooster Schl; Newtown, CT; (Y); Boy Scts; Ski Clb; Chorus; Church Choir; School Play; Nwsp Stf; Ed Lit Mag; Var Socr; Var Wrstlng; Ntl Merit SF.

CLARK, STEPHEN; Norwalk HS; Norwalk, CT; (Y); 13/450; Ski Clb; Yrbk Sprt Ed; Rep Frsh Cls; Rep Soph Cls; Rep Jr Cls; JV Ftbl; JV Tennis; Pres NHS; Mayors Proclmtn Prtcptn Big Bros Pgm 85; Arch.

CLAR !, TANYA F; Stamford HS; Stamford, CT; (Y); 82/406; Color Guard; Stu Cncl; Var Trk; Hon Roll; NHS; Stark Schlrshp 85; American U; Brdcstng.

CLARK, TODD; Putnam HS; Putnam, CT; (Y); 40/145; Chess Clb; Church Yth Grp; Band; Chorus; Concert Band; Jazz Band; Mrchg Band; School Play; L Ftbl; L Trk; Music Awds 83-85; Javln ST Fnls 85; Clss S ST Fnls Ftbl 84; Liberty Baptist U; Music.

CLARKE, AUDREY R; Weaver HS; Hartford, CT; (Y); Art Clb; Church Yth Grp; Cmnty Wkr; Computer Clb; FBLA; Girl Scts; JA; Office Aide; Church Choir; School Play; Hghst Avg Engl, Accntng & Typng 85; Manchester CC; Accntnt.

CLAUDIO, RAYNAE; Stratford HS; Stratford, CT; (Y); Spanish Clb; Drill Tm; Yrbk Stf; Pom Pon; Hon Roll; Sherwood Beauty Schl; Sec.

CLAYPOOLE, JOHN; Central Catholic HS; Norwalk, CT; (Y); Boy Scts; Pres Math Tm; Spanish Clb; Yrbk Stf; Lit Mag; Stu Cncl; Ftbl; Score Keeper; Hon Roll; Boston; Acctnt.

CLEARY, ANNIE; Trumbull HS; Trumbull, CT; (Y); Band; Concert Band; Mrchg Band; Symp Band; Var Mgr(s); High Hon Roll; NHS; Spanish NHS; Bus.

CLEVELAND, KAREN; East Catholic HS; Bolton, CT; (Y); Elem Ed.

CLINCH, LYNN; East Catholic HS; E Hartford, CT; (Y); 77/300; Drill Tm; High Hon Roll; Hon Roll; Biotech.

CLOHERTY, MICHAEL; Conard HS; W Hartford, CT; (Y); 9/314; Model UN; JV Bsbl; Capt Swmmng; High Hon Roll; NHS; Ntl Merit Ltr; Spanish NHS; Wesleyan U Bk Awd 85; 6th St Chemathon 85.

CLOSE, GLEN S; Guilford HS; Guilford, CT; (Y); 1/266; Orch; NHS; Ntl Merit SF; Pres Spanish NHS; Harvard Book Awd 84; AATSP Medal Awd 84.

CLOSE, KEN; Guilford HS; Guilford, CT; (Y); 1/300; Math Tm; Capt Quiz Bowl; Pres Spanish Clb; Yrbk Phtg; Golf; Elks Awd; JETS Awd; NCTE Awd; NHS; Spanish NHS; Rensselaer Mdl 85; Hrvard Bk Awd 85; Engrng.

COATES, WILLIAM; Canton HS; Canton, CT; (Y); 10/90; Ski Clb; Band; Concert Band; Jazz Band; School Musical; Yrbk Stf; Sec Sr Cls; Var Golf; Var Wrstlng; Hon Roll; Law.

COBB, MICHELLE; Farmington HS; Farmington, CT; (Y); 25/210; Am Leg Aux Girls St; Pres Drama Clb; Hosp Aide; Model UN; Political Wkr; Ski Clb; School Play; Nwsp Stf; Yrbk Stf; Hon Roll.

COBBOL, SUZANNE; Westover Schl; Naugatuck, CT; (Y); Latin Clb; Ski Clb; Spanish Clb; Teachers Aide; Madrigals; Nwsp Stf; Var Sftbl; Var Vllybl; Chorus; Lit Mag; Math Dept Rep 83-84; Magna Cum Laude Ntl Latin Exam 81-85; Schlrhsp Colonial Bnk 85; Gordon Coll; Accntng.

CODEANNE, CHRIS; Xavier HS; Guilford, CT; (Y); Rep Soph Cls; JV Bsktbl; Var JV Ftbl; JV Golf; Hon Roll; Trs NHS; JR Volunteer 85.

CODEANNE, SHARON L; Joseph A Foran HS; Milford, CT; (Y); 9/273; Cmnty Wkr; Hosp Aide; JCL; Keywanettes; Latin Clb; Varsity Clb; Yrbk Stf; Stu Cncl; Var L Tennis; Cit Awd; Adv Stdy Prog Europn 85; Cvlztn Trnty Coll Suprntndt Acadmc Awd 85; Trinity Coll; Pol Sci.

CODIANNI JR, DANIEL V; Crosby HS; Waterbury, CT; (Y); 3/350; Latin Clb; High Hon Roll; Hon Roll; NHS; St Schlr; Waterbury ST Tech Coll; Data.

CODY, ALISA; Farmington HS; Farmington, CT; (S); Church Yth Grp; DECA; Girl Scts; Ski Clb; Rep Stu Cncl; Var Cheerleading; JV Fld Hcky; Var Pom Pon.

COE, PEGGY; Trumball HS; Trumbull, CT; (Y); AFS; Latin Clb; Ski Clb; Chorus; URI; Dntl Hygntst.

COGGINS, MATTHEW; St Bernard HS; N Stonington, CT; (S); 120/300; Pres Aud/Vis; Church Yth Grp; Drama Clb; Ski Clb; Yrbk Stf; Rep Frsh Cls; Rep Soph Cls; Rep Jr Cls; Rep Sr Cls; VP Stu Cncl.

COHAN, JEFFREY A; Hall HS; W Hartford, CT; (Y); 60/324; Cmnty Wkr; Hosp Aide; Temple Yth Grp; Chorus; Var Tennis; High Hon Roll; NHS; Spanish NHS; Orthodntst.

COHEN, CYNTHIA; The Williams Schl; Clinton, CT; (Y); 13/36; VP Thesps; Varsity Clb; Chorus; Madrigals; School Musical; School Play; Stage Crew; Lit Mag; VP Sr Cls; Var Fld Hcky; Alg II & Chem Dprtmntl Hnrs 83-84; Emory U; Psych.

COHEN, KENNETH; Conard HS; W Hartford, CT; (Y); 2/315; Math Tm; Model UN; Trs Temple Yth Grp; Band; Jazz Band; Orch; Lit Mag; High Hon Roll; Pres NHS; Spanish NHS; Yale Bk Prz 85; CT JR Sci & Humnts Sympsm Awd 85; ST Chmthn 1st Pl 85.

COHEN, SHARON; Cooperative HS; New Haven, CT; (Y); 3/60; Nwsp Ed-Chief; Nwsp Rptr; Nwsp Stf; Yrbk Phtg; Yrbk Stf; Lit Mag; Var Tennis; High Hon Roll; Hon Roll; Prfct Atten Awd; Rookie Yr Ten 85; Albertus Magnus; Child Psych.

COHEN, SHELLEY H; William H Hall HS; W Hartford, CT; (Y); 113/324; Aud/Vis; Dance Clb; Political Wkr; Chorus; School Musical; Variety Show; Var Cheerleading; Var L Pom Pon; Var L Twrlr; JV Vllybl; New Englnd Music Fstvl Mdl Awd 84-85.

COLANGELO, LISA M; Putnam HS; Putnam, CT; (Y); 40/148; Drama Clb; School Play; Var Capt Bsktbl; Var Capt Socr; Sftbl; Var Trk; High Hon Roll; Jr NHS; NHS; Old Dominion U; Polit Sci.

COLANGELO, THOMAS; Bristol Central HS; Bristol, CT; (Y); 36/274; Church Yth Grp; Hon Roll; Fred S Fletcher/Mary A Callen Schlrshp 85; Lawrence Barett Math Schlrshp 85; Western New England Coll; Bus.

COLANINNO, JOSEPH; Crosby HS; Waterbury, CT; (Y); Church Yth Grp; FCA; Hon Roll.

COLBERT, BRIAN L; Immaculate HS; Bethel, CT; (Y); Boy Scts; VP Pres JA; Rep Jr Cls; Crs Cntry; Trk; NHS; Cmmnty & Acad Awds 84; Pre-Law.

COLBURN, KRISTYN; Branford HS; Branford, CT; (Y); DECA; Variety Show; Rep Frsh Cls; Hon Roll; Stetson U; Bus Admin.

COLE, LAURA; East Lyme HS; E Lyme, CT; (Y); Church Yth Grp; Key Clb; Pep Clb; Var Bsktbl; Vllybl; Hon Roll; Music Tchr CA Awd-Piano 82-84; Bus.

COLE, MARLANA; New Fairfield HS; New Fairfield, CT; (Y); Stat Bsbl; Stat Bsktbl; Stat Fld Hcky; JV Var Mgr(s); JV Var Score Keeper; JV Var Timer; Hon Roll; New England Schl; Grphc Desgn.

COLE, STEPHANIE; Nonnewaug HS; Woodbury, CT; (Y); 4-H; Pres FFA; Chorus; Church Choir; Vllybl; Hon Roll; Ldrshp Awd FFA 84-85; Cvl Engrng.

COLELLO, DAVID J; Joseph A Foran HS; Milford, CT; (Y); 2/290; Chess Clb; Computer Clb; Trs Key Clb; Math Tm; Stu Cncl; Bausch & Lomb Sci Awd; NHS; Ntl Merit SF; NEDT Awd; Pres Schlr; CA Inst Tech; Elctrcl Engrng.

COLEMAN, JULIA HEATH; Amity Regional HS; Orange, CT; (S); Trs Church Yth Grp; French Clb; Model UN; Nwsp Rptr; Yrbk Stf; Rep Stu Cncl; Var Sftbl; Var L Vllybl; High Hon Roll; Hosp Aide.

COLEMAN, MELISSA; Robert E Fitch SR HS; Mystic, CT; (Y); 12/300; Intnl Clb; Nwsp Phtg; Nwsp Rptr; Lit Mag; High Hon Roll; Hon Roll; Ntl Merit SF; John E & Noreen Mc Keen Schlrshp 85-86; U Of IA; Engl.

COLEMAN, RONALD; Notre Dame HS; New Haven, CT; (Y); Hon Roll; Bus.

COLETTI, CHRISTIE; The Morgan Schl; Clinton, CT; (Y); 12/170; AFS; Church Yth Grp; Sec Spanish Clb; Band; Chorus; School Musical; Yrbk Stf; JV Fld Hcky; Score Keeper; NHS; Bus.

COLKER, ELIZABETH; Loomis Chaffee Schl; Pittsfield, MA; (Y); Drama Clb; Chorus; School Musical; School Play; Stage Crew; Ed Lit Mag; NCTE Awd; Ntl Merit Ltr; Yale U; Psych.

COLLEN, KEVIN; Oliver Wolcott RVTS HS; Harwinton, CT; (Y); 1/150; Am Leg Boys St; Math Clb; VICA; Yrbk Stf; High Hon Roll; NHS; 2nd Pl Job Skill Demonstrtn VICA ST Competitn 85; Elec Engrng.

COLLINGS, ABIGAIL; Trumbull HS; Trumbull, CT; (Y); Pres French Clb; Latin Clb; Nwsp Rptr; Cheerleading; JV Trk; French Hon Soc; Pres Frnch Clb 85-86; Peer Tutors 84-85; Matrls Sci.

COLLINS, AMANDA C; Saint Mary HS; Greenwich, CT; (Y); 6/72; Math Tm; Red Cross Aide; Rep Stu Cncl; Capt Cheerleading; JV Fld Hcky; Im Powder Puff Ftbl; JV Socr; High Hon Roll; Hon Roll; NHS; 1st Pl Essay ST-ANCIENT Ordr Hibernians 84; Psych.

COLLINS, CHERYL; Daniel Hand HS; Madison, CT; (Y); Hon Roll; Art Dsgn Awd 85; Enrgy Cnsrvtn Cntst 3rd Pl Regnl 85; Intr Dsgn.

COLLINS, DONNA; Shelton HS; Shelton, CT; (Y); French Clb; FHA; JA; Office Aide; Mgr(s); Score Keeper; Trk; Hon Roll; Southern CT ST U; Crimnl Just.

COLLINS, JENNINGS; The Hotch Kiss Schl; Brooklyn, NY; (Y); Drama Clb; French Clb; Acpl Chr; Chorus; School Musical; School Play; Stage Crew; JV Var Crs Cntry; Hon Roll; Ntl Merit Ltr; 5 Faculty Commendations 83-85; Music Awd For Chorus 85; Brown U; Math.

COLLINS, LYNN; East Catholic HS; E Hartford, CT; (Y); Cmnty Wkr; Dance Clb; Hosp Aide; Math Tm; Band; Concert Band; Drm & Bgl; School Musical; JV Crs Cntry; Var L Golf; Outstndng Vlntr Awd YWCA 85; Dance Ed.

COLLINS, PAULINE; St Bernard HS; Jewett City, CT; (Y); 107/309; Cmnty Wkr; FBLA; Girl Scts; Ski Clb; Yrbk Phtg; Rep Soph Cls; Rep Jr Cls; Sec Jr Cls; Rep Stu Cncl; Var Golf; Jr Clb Champ Hay Harbor Golf Clb 82-84; Yales Frontiers Applied Sci 85; Peer Mnstr HS 85-86; Bus.

COLLINS, STACEY LYNN; James Hillhouse HS; New Haven, CT; (Y); GAA; Chorus; Score Keeper; Var Capt Vllybl; High Hon Roll; Hon Roll; NHS; Excel Bio Awd; Human Phys Prz Ex Awd; Law.

COLSON, SUSAN; Cheshire HS; Cheshire, CT; (Y); Pres Church Yth Grp; Dance Clb; Variety Show; High Hon Roll; Hon Roll; Hnrd 3 Yr Hgh Schlstc Recrd 85; Persnl Progrss Ad 83-85; Hnrd Bllt Dancng 85; Brigham Yng U; Hlth & Nutrtn.

COLTHUP, BRUCE; Stamford HS; Stamford, CT; (S); 35/406; Church Yth Grp; Latin Clb; Ski Clb; Trk; Hon Roll; Jr NHS; NHS; CT ST Schlstc Achvt Schlrshp 85; Bates Coll; Chem.

COLUCCI, ANTHONY R; St Joseph HS; Ansonia, CT; (Y); 49/227; Boy Scts; Spanish Clb; L Var Ftbl; NEDT Awd.

COLVIN, VALERIE; East Catholic HS; Manchester, CT; (Y); Sec Trs Cmnty Wkr; French Clb; Pres Girl Scts; Library Aide; Hon Roll; Am Red Cross Ldrshp Awd 83; Girl Scout Gold Awd 85; Ed.

COMMANDER, JANE; Old Saybrook SR HS; Old Saybrook, CT; (Y); Art Clb; Varsity Clb; Stage Crew; Ed Yrbk Stf; Crs Cntry; Gym; Trk; Hon Roll; Cert Achvmnt Most Prmsng Fresh In Art 83; U Of CT; Engr.

COMSTOCK, KRISTIN; Guilford HS; Guilford, CT; (Y); 20/315; Church Yth Grp; Cmnty Wkr; Hosp Aide; Latin Clb; Orch; Ed Yrbk Bus Mgr; Trk; French Hon Soc; High Hon Roll; NHS; Yale Series Of Appld Sci 85.

CONANT, EILEEN; Sacred Heart Acad; Stamford, CT; (Y); 2/60; Nwsp Stf; Yrbk Stf; Lit Mag; High Hon Roll; NHS; Spanish NHS; Prfct Atten Awd; Yale Bk Awd 85; Gen Excllnce Awd 85; Fairfld Cnty Med Assn Biolgcl Sci Awd 84; Mth Ed.

CONCILIO, JON; Holy Cross HS; Beacon Falls, CT; (Y); 109/352; Trs Church Yth Grp; Exploring; Im Tennis; High Hon Roll; Hon Roll; Rev John S Soloeleski Scholar 82; Bus.

CONDON, MARC R; Newington HS; Newington, CT; (Y); Church Yth Grp; Concert Band; Mrchg Band; Symp Band; Variety Show; JV Bsbl; Bsktbl; Hon Roll; NHS; Engr.

CONDROW III, JAMES P; Notre Dame HS; Hamden, CT; (Y); Ski Clb; Outdr Clb, Racqtbll Clb.

CONELLI, FRANCINE; Sacred Heart Acad; Branford, CT; (Y); Hosp Aide; Nwsp Stf; Rep Frsh Cls; Pres Soph Cls; Sec Trs Jr Cls; Sec Pres Sr Cls; Stu Cncl; NHS; Prfct Atten Awd; Spanish NHS; Michael Jewelers Clss Ldrshp Awd 85; Svc Awd 85; 3 Yr Hnrs Awd 85; Mgr Awd For Bsktbl & Sftbl 85; Med.

CONFALONE, STACEY; Bethel HS; Bethel, CT; (Y); 60/268; Church Yth Grp; Jazz Band; Madrigals; Ed Lit Mag; Sec Stu Cncl; JV Cheerleading; High Hon Roll; Church Choir; CCY Wesleyan U Piano 84; All ST Chrs CT 85; Self Comp Bethel High Chrs 85; Music.

CONLEY, BRIAN; New London HS; New London, CT; (Y); 9/183; Am Leg Boys St; FBLA; Spanish Clb; Nwsp Rptr; Var Capt Bsbl; JV Bsktbl; Im Ftbl; Var Capt Socr; High Hon Roll; Hon Roll; New London Booster Clb Schlrshp Awd 85; Paul K Scrigan Mem Awd 85; Pres Ftns Awd 85; U MA; Accntng.

CONLIN, MARY BETH; Trumbull HS; Trumbull, CT; (Y); French Clb; Ski Clb; School Play; Variety Show; Yrbk Stf; Cheerleading; Coach Actv; Trk; High Hon Roll; Hon Roll.

CONNELL, KIM O; Trumbull HS; Trumbull, CT; (Y); Color Guard; Mrchg Band; Socr; Trk; High Hon Roll; Hon Roll; Hotel Mgmt.

CONNELLY, LISA; East Lyme HS; East Lyme, CT; (Y); Drama Clb; Chorus; Church Choir; Jazz Band; Yrbk Stf; Im Fld Hcky; Im Powder Puff Ftbl; Hon Roll; Finance.

CONNOLLY, DESMOND M; Newington HS; Newington, CT; (Y); 79/357; VP Pres JA; Rep Stu Cncl; Var Ftbl; Var Trk; Ntl Merit Ltr; NROTC Schlrhsp 85; JA VP Prsnl Fnlst & Dlgt Ntl Convtn 84; Villanova U; Accntng.

CONNOLLY, PATRICIA; Amity Regional SR HS; Orange, CT; (Y); Drama Clb; French Clb; Band; Concert Band; Mrchg Band; Symp Band; Lit Mag; Church Yth Grp; Pep Clb; Stage Crew; Ntl Art Hnr Soc Scrtry 84-85; Ntl Art Hnr Soc VP 85-86.

CONNOR, MARGOT; Newtown HS; Newtown, CT; (Y); 12/350; Debate Tm; GAA; NFL; Speech Tm; Var Bsktbl; Trk; Var Capt Vllybl; High Hon Roll; NHS; Cntry 21 Accntng Mst Accmplshd JR 85.

CONNORS, TAMARA; Northwestern Reg No 7; New Hartford, CT; (Y); Pres Pep Clb; Spanish Clb; Varsity Clb; Band; Concert Band; Mrchg Band; Orch; School Musical; Variety Show; Nwsp Rptr; Occidental Coll:Wrtng.

CONROY, CONSTANCE; Holy Cross HS; Naugatuck, CT; (Y); 21/352; Concert Band; Mrchg Band; Orch; School Musical; Swing Chorus; Variety Show; Ntl Merit Ltr; Spanish NHS; U S Hstry Hnr Soc 84; Psych.

CONROY, TIMOTHY; Xavier HS; Meriden, CT; (Y); Am Leg Boys St; Boy Scts; School Musical; Rep Soph Cls; Pres Jr Cls; Im Bsktbl; Im Ice Hcky; JV Trk; Hon Roll; Middletown Yth Assn Retrd Ctzns 84-85; Spec Olympcs 83-85; Dntstry.

CONSIGLI, JOSEPH; Bethel HS; Bethel, CT; (Y); Computer Clb; JA; Ski Clb; School Play; Var Capt Bsbl; Stat Socr; Var Trk; Hon Roll; CPA.

CONSLINI, DEBORAH M; St Paul Catholic HS; Meriden, CT; (Y); 1/305; Lib Yrbk Rptr; Sftbl; Bausch & Lomb Sci Awd; High Hon Roll; NHS; Ntl Merit SF; Harvard Bk Awd 84; Mission Clb 81-85; Bio Sci.

CONTE, MARILENA; Stamford Catholic HS; Stamford, CT; (Y); #78 In Class; Hon Roll; Intr Dsgnr.

CONTE, MEAGHAN; Branford HS; Branford, CT; (Y); 1/268; Latin Clb; Yrbk Stf; Stu Cncl; Fld Hcky; Tennis.

CONTI, YVONNE M; Frank Scott Bunnell HS; Stratford, CT; (Y); 63/257; Ski Clb; Band; Concert Band; Mrchg Band; Yrbk Stf; Trs Frsh Cls; Sec Soph Cls; Rep Jr Cls; Rep Sr Cls; High Hon Roll; Chem Sci Fair 3rd Bst In Shw, 2nd Mst Original; Arista; Music Hon Awd; Salve Regina; Politics.

CONTRASTANO, EMILY; Bristol Central HS; Bristol, CT; (Y); 14/320; Church Yth Grp; VP Intnl Clb; VP JA; Latin Clb; Yrbk Ed-Chief; Yrbk Rptr; Yrbk Sprt Ed; Yrbk Stf; Elks Awd; High Hon Roll; Doris Lazorik Scholar 85; Grace Atkins Scholar 85; Latin Awds 84-85; Fordham U; Lib Arts.

CONWAY, ROSEMARY; St Bernard HS; Noank, CT; (Y); 91/297; Church Yth Grp; Girl Scts; Chorus; Church Choir; Var Diving; Hon Roll; Sci.

COOK, JENNIFER M; Newington HS; Newington, CT; (Y); DECA; Spanish Clb; JV Bsktbl; Capt Var Tennis; High Hon Roll; Hon Roll; Gregg Typng Awd 83; CCC Tennis Champ Awd 85; Bus.

COOK, PAUL W; Simsbury HS; W Simsbury, CT; (Y); 19/360; Am Leg Boys St; Church Yth Grp; Concert Band; Jazz Band; Orch; School Musical; Symp Band; Wt Lftg; Hon Roll; Pres NHS; NROTC Schlrshp 85; Natl Ski Patrl 85; Untd Tech Schlrshp 85; Annapolis Appt 85; US Navl Acad; Polit Sci.

COOKE, JAMES; Ledyhard HS; Ledyard, CT; (Y); ROTC; JV Score Keeper; JV Var Socr; L Swmmng; JV Tennis; Stat Timer; Ofcr NJROTC; Soccer Clb Referee; NROTC; Engrng.

COOPER, CLIFTON J; Weaver HS; Hartford, CT; (Y); 14/365; Am Leg Boys St; FBLA; Rep Stu Cncl; Var Bsktbl; Var JV Ftbl; Hon Roll; Wise Trvl Awd Tour Europe 84; Pres Acad Fit Awd 85; Derrick Ma Horn Scholar 85; U CT; Elec Engrng.

COOPER, JONATHAN; Northwest Catholic HS; Hartford, CT; (Y); Stu Cncl; High Hon Roll; Hon Roll; NHS; Nuclear Engrng.

COOPER, MARY CATHERINE; Daniel Hand HS; Madison, CT; (Y); Church Yth Grp; GAA; Nwsp Rptr; Nwsp Rptr; Nwsp Stf; VP Frsh Cls; Rep Soph Cls; Rep Jr Cls; Bsktbl; Fld Hcky; Providence Coll; Bus Adm.

COPLEY, ROBERT; Pomperoug HS; Middlebury, CT; (Y); Drama Clb; French Clb; Chorus; School Play; Stage Crew; Variety Show; Yrbk Stf; JV Tennis; Ntl Sci Olympd Gio Cntst 84; PHS Tnns Boys Divsnl Chmpns 83; Fshn Mrchndsng.

COPPOLA, MICHELE; Daniel Hand HS; Madison, CT; (Y); 12/463; Church Yth Grp; FCA; Speech Tm; School Play; Cheerleading; High Hon Roll; NHS; Voice Dem Awd; Drama Clb; German Clb; Ger Natl Hon Soc 84; Schl Declmtn Cont Fin 85; Mary E Coughlin Mem Awd 85; Wellesley Coll; Intl Reltns.

COPPOLA, PATRICIA; H C Wilcox Tech Schl; Wallingford, CT; (Y); Computer Clb; Debate Tm; English Clb; FBLA; Political Wkr; Service Clb; Cit Awd; Pres Schlr; Awd Profssnl VICA 84-85; Acad Of Bus; Csmtlgst.

COPPOLA, SUZANNE; Holy Cross HS; Naugatuck, CT; (Y); 50/352; JA; Var Cheerleading; Hon Roll; NHS; Italn Natl Hnr Soc 84; CYO 82-83; Italn Clb Sec 82-85; Phrmcy.

COPPOLA, TAMMY; Lauralton Hall HS; W Haven, CT; (Y); Cmnty Wkr; Latin Clb; Science Clb; Service Clb; Spanish Clb; Nwsp Stf; Yrbk Stf; Lit Mag; High Hon Roll; NHS; 3 Awds Outstndg Wrk In Lat 82; Lat Tstng 83; Phrmcst.

CORATOLA, JOHN A; Lewis S Mills HS; Harwinton, CT; (Y); 15/159; Am Leg Boys St; Jazz Band; Mrchg Band; Stu Cncl; JV Bsbl; Var Capt Socr; Capt Tennis; High Hon Roll; NHS; Pres Schlr; Stu Faculty Rep 84-85; MVP Socr & Ten 85; Excllnce Latin Awd 84; Lewis Mills Scholar 85; Catholic U Amer; Med.

CORBETT, CHERYL ANN; Lyman Hall HS; Wallingford, CT; (Y); 20/240; Spanish Clb; Yrbk Phtg; Yrbk Rptr; Yrbk Stf; Var Powder Puff Ftbl; Hon Roll; Cert Hnr Earth Sci 83; Fash Merch.

CORCORAN, JEFFREY M; New Fairfield HS; New Fairfield, CT; (Y); 21/237; Camera Clb; Var Chess Clb; CAP; Computer Clb; Mathletes; Nwsp Phtg; Nwsp Rptr; Var Trk; High Hon Roll; Ntl Merit Ltr; Math, French Excllnc Awd 85; Ldrshp Awd 84; Air Force Acad; Aerosp.

CORCORAN, NORA; Notre Dame Acad; Waterbury, CT; (Y); 9/54; Hosp Aide; Nwsp Stf; Yrbk Stf; Bsktbl; Mgr(s); Capt Socr; Hon Roll; VP NHS; Galvin Schlrshp 85; Smplcty Swng Schlrshp 83; Villanova U; Engrng.

CORDANI, JOE; Simsbury HS; Weatogue, CT; (Y); 136/352; Var L Golf; Hon Roll; Cnrl CT Intrschlstc League Golf 83-84; Simsbur Hgh Athltc Awd 83-85; PGA JR Tm Champ Capt Golf 84; Bus Mgmt.

CORDANI, NICOLE; Oliver Wolcott RVTS; Torrington, CT; (Y); 30/150; Am Leg Aux Girls St; Art Clb; Drama Clb; Girl Scts; VICA; Chorus; School Play; Yrbk Stf; Rep Stu Cncl; JV Cheerleading; Hstry.

CORDNER, DELLA; Rockville HS; Vernon, CT; (Y); 13/357; Church Yth Grp; Color Guard; Mrchg Band; NHS; Ntl Merit Ltr; Boston Coll; Econ.

CORDONE, LAURA; Notre Dame Acad; Wolcott, CT; (Y); 2/65; Dance Clb; Girl Scts; Library Aide; Red Cross Aide; Nwsp Stf; Yrbk Stf; Pres Soph Cls; High Hon Roll; NHS; Ntl Merit Ltr; Brownell; Law.

CORMIER, ERIC J; Wilcox Tech HS; Southington, CT; (Y); 6/196; High Hon Roll; Wtby Tech; Elec Engr.

CORNIELLO, JOHN; North Haven HS; N Haven, CT; (Y); 31/286; Church Yth Grp; Nwsp Rptr; Yrbk Stf; Swmmng; Hon Roll; FIDLE Awd 84; U CT; Comp Bus.

COROLLA, MIKE; East Haven HS; E Haven, CT; (Y); 62/320; Ftbl; Wt Lftg; Hon Roll; Ftbl Ltr 84-85; U Of New Haven; Elec Engr.

CORREARD, GREG; Bethel HS; Bethel, CT; (Y); 58/268; Computer Clb; Ski Clb; School Play; Yrbk Stf; Var Capt Socr; Var Trk; Chem Engr.

CORRENTY, LISA; Brien Mc Mahon HS; Norwalk, CT; (Y); 13/350; School Musical; School Play; French Clb; Band; Chorus; Concert Band; Mrchg Band; Score Keeper; High Hon Roll; NHS; Iona Coll Frnch Awd-2nd Hnrs 85; U CT; Phys Thrpy.

CORRIS, TRACEY; Stratford HS; Stratford, CT; (Y); 51/271; Drama Clb; Office Aide; Chorus; School Musical; Rep Frsh Cls; Rep Stu Cncl; Hon Roll; Madrigals; School Play; Rep Soph Cls; Accntnt.

CORRIVEAU, KAREN; Killingly HS; Danielson, CT; (Y); Office Aide; Cheerleading; Sftbl; Social Wrk.

CORSON, GINA; New Milford HS; Gaylordsville, CT; (Y); 93/301; School Play; Stage Crew; Stu Cncl; Swmmng; Tennis; Trk; Hon Roll; Girl Scts; Acad All Amer Schlr 85; Exec Comm 84-85; Johnson & Wales Coll; Mngmnt.

CORVINO, CHRISTIAN; Shelton HS; Huntington, CT; (Y); Drama Clb; School Musical; School Play; Stage Crew; Nwsp Stf; VP Stu Cncl; Arch.

COSCIO, DEBORAH; Lauralton Hall HS; Trumbull, CT; (Y); French Clb; Hosp Aide; Library Aide; Model UN; Science Clb; Spanish Clb; Chorus; School Musical; Rep Frsh Cls; Rep Soph Cls; Wlk A Thon, Comm Mssn Day 83-85; Intl Mgmnt.

COSENTINO, SUSAN; Farmington HS; Farmington, CT; (Y); 1/200; Church Yth Grp; Ski Clb; Concert Band; VP Jr Cls; Var Socr; Var Tennis; High Hon Roll; NHS; Spanish NHS; Math Tm; Harvard-Radcliffe Bk Awd 85; NW Conf Ten Champ 85.

COSGRIFF, CATHERINE A; Daniel Hand HS; Madison, CT; (Y); Church Yth Grp; GAA; School Musical; Rep Stu Cncl; JV Cheerleading; JV Fld Hcky; Hon Roll; Peer Advct Prgm 85; Hnrs Hstry Symposm 85; Psych.

COSGROVE, JOHN; H C Wilcox R V T S HS; Wallingford, CT; (Y); Am Leg Boys St; Drama Clb; Pres JA; VICA; Yrbk Ed-Chief; Yrbk Phtg; Rep Stu Cncl; Var Trk; High Hon Roll; Pres NHS; JR Achvt Pres Yr, Co Chrprsn Sfty Cncl 84-85; RPI; Elec Engrng.

COSKER, EDWARD; East Windsor HS; E Windsor, CT; (Y); 7/100; Computer Clb; Drama Clb; Intnl Clb; Spanish Clb; Varsity Clb; School Musical; School Play; JV Socr; JV Trk; Var L Wrstlng; Comp Sci Awds 83-85; CA U Berkeley; Comp Pgm.

COSTELLO, ERIC; Choate Rosemary Hall HS; Old Saybrook, CT; (Y); Chrmn Model UN; Political Wkr; Nwsp Stf; L Socr; High Hon Roll; Ntl Merit SF; Computer Clb; Trs Frsh Cls; Swmmng; Cert Excl Soc Studies 82; Sntr Mc Millan Lewis Awd Am Hist 84; WA Wkshps Smnr Forgn Rel Ctee 84; Hist.

COSTELLO, GREGORY; Southington HS; Plantsville, CT; (Y); Church Yth Grp; Var Bsbl; L Socr; High Hon Roll; Hon Roll; Hlth.

COTE, NANCY J; Watertown HS; Oakville, CT; (Y); 7/250; Ski Clb; Spanish Clb; Chorus; Variety Show; Yrbk Stf; High Hon Roll; NHS; Pres Acad Fitness Awd 85; Spanish Awd; Trinity Coll.

COTT, ALLISON; Amity Regional HS; Woodbridge, CT; (Y); Key Clb; Latin Clb; Pep Clb; Spanish Clb; Yrbk Stf; Sec Soph Cls; Cit Awd; High Hon Roll; Engl Stdtn Awd 84; Bus.

COTT, PATRICK L; Choate Rosemary Hall HS; New York, NY; (S); Computer Clb; JA; Radio Clb; Acpl Chr; Chorus; Madrigals; Rep Jr Cls; Im Socr; Watson Bradley Dickerman Cup Hlpfl Ctzn 83; Samuel Gates Bowl Debt 83; Pal Rotella Cup 83.

COUGHLIN, WENDY; St Joseph HS; Huntington, CT; (Y); 13/240; Debate Tm; Drama Clb; Hosp Aide; Spanish Clb; Thesps; School Musical; School Play; Yrbk Ed-Chief; Trk; High Hon Roll; Psych.

COUTINHO, DEDE M; Newington HS; Newington, CT; (Y); Hon Roll; Bus.

COUTTS, CYNTHIA; Shelton HS; Shelton, CT; (Y); Drama Clb; Latin Clb; Nwsp Rptr; Nwsp Stf; Stu Cncl; Bsktbl; Gym; Pom Pon; Trk; Hon Roll; ST Fin Gymn Assn 84; ST Fin Miss Teenager Amer Pgnt 85; Bus.

COUTU, BONNIE; Windham HS; Willimantic, CT; (Y); 12/290; Concert Band; Orch; Var Capt Bsktbl; Var L Sftbl; Var Capt Vllybl; Mu Alp Tht; NHS; High Hon Roll; Natl Ldrs & Svc Awd 84-85; All-ST Sftbl 85; Acadmc All-Amer 84; Bio.

COWGILL, KAREN D; Hamden HS; Hamden, CT; (Y); 3/451; Cmnty Wkr; Math Clb; Math Tm; Political Wkr; Nwsp Ed-Chief; Nwsp Rptr; Lit Mag; High Hon Roll; Ntl Merit SF; Harvard Bk Awd 84; Bio Sci.

COX, CATHERINE MARY; Daniel Hand HS; Madison, CT; (Y); 165/205; Church Yth Grp; Cmnty Wkr; Hosp Aide; Red Cross Aide; Color Guard; Flag Corp; Twrlr; Exec Sec.

COYNE, DAVID; The Morgan Schl; Clinton, CT; (Y); AFS; French Clb; Scholastic Bowl; Band; Chorus; Orch; School Musical; JV Socr; L Trk; High Hon Roll; Acad Distnctn Awd Art 85; Ntl Merit Comp 85; Telluride Assoc 85; Georgetown U; Intl Sales.

COYNE, KERRY; Norwalk HS; E Norwalk, CT; (Y); 77/472; Church Yth Grp; Cmnty Wkr; Letterman Clb; Ski Clb; Rep Stu Cncl; JV Sftbl; Var Swmmng; Hon Roll; Med.

COZZOLINO, SUSAN; Saint Bernard HS; Westerly, RI; (Y); 53/297; Yrbk Stf; Off Jr Cls; Hon Roll; Art Awd 83; USAA Ntl Math Awd 83; Ntl Ldrshp & Svc Awd 84; Fashn Merchnd.

CRAIG, JOSEPH; Bethel HS; Bethel, CT; (Y); 3/237; Am Leg Boys St; Boy Scts; Trs JA; Quiz Bowl; Band; Nwsp Rptr; High Hon Roll; NHS; Lib Arts.

CRAIN, W ERIC; William H Hall HS; W Hartford, CT; (Y); 69/324; Im Badmtn; Ftbl; Im Vllybl; High Hon Roll; Hon Roll; NHS.

CRAMER, SETH; Litchfield HS; Litchfield, CT; (Y); Yrbk Stf; Tennis; French Hon Soc; OH ST U; Acctng.

CRAMERI, DANIEL; Torrington HS; Torrington, CT; (Y); 38/271; Boy Scts; Math Tm; Thesps; Band; Concert Band; Jazz Band; Mrchg Band; Orch; School Musical; Var Socr; Litchfield Cnty U Clb Schlrshp 85; Torrington Womans Clb Schlrshp 85; Syracuse U; Arch.

CRANE, RICHARD; Lyman Hall HS; Wallingford, CT; (Y); 30/150; Am Leg Boys St; Boys Clb Am; JA; Key Clb; Varsity Clb; VICA; Variety Show; Stu Cncl; L Socr; Hon Roll; Arch.

CRAVEN, SANDRA; Killingly HS; Danielson, CT; (Y); JA; Key Clb; Teachers Aide; Hon Roll.

CRAWFORD, KEITH; East Lyme HS; East Lyme, CT; (Y); 71/283; Cmnty Wkr; Band; Concert Band; Mrchg Band; Pep Band; Symp Band; Sec Sr Cls; Var Bsbl; Var Bsktbl; JV Ftbl; U Of CT; Acctg.

CRAWFORD, MICHAEL; Guilford HS; Guilford, CT; (Y); Church Yth Grp; Hosp Aide; Var Capt Bsktbl; Var Capt Tennis; High Hon Roll; Hon Roll; NHS; Schl Ldrshp Team 84-85; Conf Dbls Champ Tennis 85; Treas Natl Hnr Scty 85.

CREBASE, CHERYL A; Choate Rosemary Hall HS; Wallingford, CT; (Y); Cmnty Wkr; Girl Scts; Key Clb; Spanish Clb; Band; JV Socr; Im Tennis; JV Vllybl; Natl Merit Commded Schlr 85; Gettysburg Coll.

CREDIT, KIMBERLY; Plainfield HS; Moosup, CT; (Y); 2/157; Am Leg Aux Girls St; GAA; Varsity Clb; Yrbk Stf; Chrmn Soph Cls; Chrmn Jr Cls; Chrmn Sr Cls; Cheerleading; Mgr(s); Score Keeper; NE Utilities Schlrshp 85; Thomas Valley ST; Nuclr Engrg.

CRESPO, LUZ; Richard C L HS; New Haven, CT; (Y); FNA; FTA; Girl Scts; Latin Clb; Red Cross Aide; Teachers Aide; Gym; Sftbl; Trk; Spanish NHS.

CREW, TOBY WILLIAM; Pomperaug Regional HS; Southbury, CT; (Y); Boy Scts; Chess Clb; Math Tm; Model UN; Capt Scholastic Bowl; Teachers Aide; High Hon Roll; NHS; Ntl Merit Ltr; Chess Tm Champs W CT 84-85; Chess Tm Ind Wnnr 85; CT Law Soc Mock Trial 83-85; CT Bus Wk 84; MIT; Transprtatn Engrng.

CRIBBINS, JENNIFER L; Lyman Hall HS; Wallingford, CT; (S); Art Clb; DECA; JA; Key Clb; JV Bsktbl; Var Powder Puff Ftbl; Trk; Wt Lftg; Hon Roll; Outstndng Excel Rcrd Jrnl Schlrshp, 1st ST Apprel, Accessrs Distbutv Ed; Ntl Fnlsh SF 84; Endicott Coll; Fash Merch.

CRIPPEN, CARA; Daniel HS; Madison, CT; (Y); 6/296; Church Yth Grp; Drama Clb; Office Aide; Spanish Clb; Teachers Aide; School Musical; School Play; Yrbk Stf; Cit Awd; DAR Awd; Delta Kappa Gamma Ed Awd 85; Princpl Schlr 85; Dar Good Citzn Awd 85; Gordon Coll; Elem Ed.

CRISCUOLO, PAUL; Amity SR HS; Woodbridge, CT; (Y); Church Yth Grp; Ski Clb; Yrbk Phtg; Yrbk Stf; Capt Socr; L Trk; Cit Awd; High Hon Roll; Hon Roll; Pres Athl Fit & Sprtsmnshp Awds; Bus.

CROCE, BILL; Bethel HS; Bethel, CT; (Y); 62/268; High Hon Roll; Hon Roll; JV Bsktbl; Var Ice Hcky; Var Tennis; U Of CT; Bus.

CROCKER, DIANNE; Joseph A Foran HS; Milford, CT; (Y); 7/250; Church Yth Grp; JCL; Yrbk Stf; Stu Cncl; Mgr(s); Trk; High Hon Roll; NHS; NEDT Awd; Pres Schlr; Newrk Of Exec Wmn Schlrshp 85; Grmn Awd 85; Gchr Coll Bltmr MD; Intl Bus.

CROMBIE, KAREN; East Catholic HS; Manchester, CT; (Y); Church Yth Grp; Yrbk Stf; Var Swmmng; High Hon Roll; Hon Roll.

CROMBIE, MARK; Ellington HS; Ellington, CT; (Y); Capt Bsktbl; Crs Cntry; Co-Capt Golf; Hon Roll; MVP Golf 83-84; Thomas W Hartmann Ath Yr Awd 84; Boston U; Elec Engrng.

CRONIN, SEAN; Rocky Hill HS; Rocky Hill, CT; (Y); 1/129; Am Leg Boys St; Church Yth Grp; Teachers Aide; Pres Jr Cls; Pres Sr Cls; Var Bsbl; Var Capt Socr; High Hon Roll; NHS; MVP Socr 84-85; Brown U Book Awd 84-85; CT Sci & Humanities Sympsm 84-85.

CROOT, ANDREA; Westhill HS; Stamford, CT; (Y); Church Yth Grp; French Clb; JA; Service Clb; Fld Hcky; Mgr(s); Hon Roll; Ntl Merit Ltr.

CROUSE, STEVE; Naugatuck HS; Naugatuck, CT; (Y); Crpntry.

CROW, GREGORY; St Thomas More Schl; Gales Ferry, CT; (Y); Chess Clb; Ftbl; TX Med Schl; Dntl Lab Tech.

CROWE, KATHLEEN; Sacred Heart Acad; Hamden, CT; (Y); Aud/Vis; Computer Clb; Chorus; School Musical; Nwsp Phtg; French Hon Soc; High Hon Roll; Hon Roll; NHS; 1st Pl Essy Cntst 83; 3rd Hnrs ST Sci Fair 84; Peabody Sci Awd 82; Zoolgy.

CROWLEY, DEIRDRE; St Bernard HS; Westerly, RI; (S); Library Aide; Pep Clb; Political Wkr; Teachers Aide; Chorus; Yrbk Stf; Jr Cls; Stat Bsbl; Var Cheerleading; Hon Roll; Acad Excel Awd 84; Amherst Coll.

CRUZ, EDNA; Richard C Lee HS; New Haven, CT; (Y); Chorus; Spanish NHS; Sci Awd 83-84.

CSUKA, STEPHEN; Holy Cross HS; Beacon Fls, CT; (Y); 14/344; Science Clb; Service Clb; Pres Concert Band; Pres Jazz Band; Pres Mrchg Band; Stage Crew; French Hon Soc; JP Sousa Awd; Lion Awd; NHS; CT ST Schltc Achvt Grnt 85; Western CT ST U; Comp Sci.

CUBETA, KAREN L; Newington HS; Newington, CT; (Y); Church Yth Grp; Key Clb; Office Aide; JV Socr; High Hon Roll; NHS; Schlr Awd-Outstndng Acadmc Achvt 84; Outstndng Achvt-US Hstry 85; Outstndng Achvt-Coll Compstn 85; Elem Eductn.

CUBETA JR, ROBERT B; The Williams Schl; Haddam, CT; (Y); Pres Aud/Vis; Chess Clb; Church Yth Grp; Computer Clb; Drama Clb; Letterman Clb; Bsbl; Comp Dept Hnrs; Clarkson U; Aerontcl Engrng.

CUDDEBACK, BRIAN P; Ridgefield HS; Ridgefield, CT; (Y); 100/420; Computer Clb; French Clb; Letterman Clb; Ski Clb; Varsity Clb; Yrbk Stf; Socr; Tennis; High Hon Roll; Hon Roll; U VT; Bus.

CUFFEE, JAUMARRO A; Central HS; Bridgeport, CT; (Y); Pres Jr Cls; VP Sr Cls; Capt Var Cheerleading; L Var Sftbl; GAA; Hosp Aide; DAR Awd; Day Of Pride U CT 84; Ntl Achvt Schlrshp Prog 83; Athl Acad Awd Xerox 84; Pre-Med.

CULMONE, JEFFREY; Notre Dame HS; Milford, CT; (Y); Library Aide; Political Wkr; Y-Teens; Bsktbl; DAR Awd; Hon Roll; Sr Lge Bsbll Sprtmnshp & All-Star Awd 83; Fairfield U; Bus Mgmt.

CUMMINGS, ALISON; Trumbull HS; Trumbull, CT; (Y); AFS; Church Yth Grp; Church Choir; Mrchg Band; Var Bsktbl; JV Fld Hcky; Var Trk; Hon Roll; Amer H S Athlte Fld Hockey & Bsktbl.

CUMMINGS, CHRISTINE; Sacred Heart Acad; Hamden, CT; (Y); Pres French Clb; Stage Crew; Yrbk Stf; Lit Mag; French Hon Soc; High Hon Roll; NEDT Awd; Hosp Aide; Vllybl; Yale Frntrs App Sci Pgm, 3rd Ntl Crtv Wrtng, Jap, US Sen Schlrshp Pgm; Lang.

CUMMINGS, SUSAN C; Acad/Of Our Ldy Of Mcy Lauralt Hall; Stamford, CT; (Y); Dance Clb; Drama Clb; French Clb; Chorus; Variety Show; Nwsp Stf; Yrbk Stf; Lit Mag; Var Capt Crs Cntry; IN U Bloomington; Acctng.

CURI, ANNE; The Hotchkiss Schl; Goshen, CT; (Y); Chrmn Civic Clb; Girl Scts; Science Clb; Spanish Clb; Chorus; Var Bsktbl; Var Crs Cntry; Var Trk; High Hon Roll; Ntl Merit Ltr; Ntl Hstry Day Essay Awd 84; Chrlt Mungerford Schlr 85; Cum Laude & Bio Prz 85; Yale; Molecular Bio.

CURLEY, SUSAN L; South Catholic HS; Weth, CT; (Y); 2/227; Nwsp Rptr; Yrbk Stf; Lit Mag; High Hon Roll; Sec Pres NHS; Ntl Merit SF; St Schlr; Hosp Aide; Quiz Bowl; Trinity Book Awd; Acad Letter; Schlr Of Mnth; Amherst Coll; Med.

CURRIE, MARY; Granby Memorial HS; W Granby, CT; (Y); Trs 4-H; Hosp Aide; Chorus; School Musical; JV Bsktbl; Var Tennis; 4-H Awd; Hon Roll; Johnson & Wales; Crt Rprtng.

CURTISS, MARK; Lyme-Old Lyme HS; Old Lyme, CT; (Y); AFS; Church Yth Grp; Ski Clb; Stu Cncl; JV Var Socr; Hon Roll; 2nd Prz Photo Hartfrd Covrnts Cntst; Astrophyscs.

CUSANELLI, DIANE LYNN; West Haven HS; W Haven, CT; (Y); 9/350; Nwsp Stf; High Hon Roll; Hon Roll; NHS; Pres Schlr; Frgn Lng Schlrshp/Ialian 85; Exc Awds In Bkpng I & II & Italian I, II & III 83-85; U Of New Haven; Bus.

CUTHBERTSON, BETH; Norwalk HS; Norwalk, CT; (Y); 27/384; Latin Clb; School Musical; Stage Crew; Mgr(s); L Stat Trk; High Hon Roll; Hon Roll; Lwyr.

CUTLER, DAWN; Tourtellotte Memorial HS; N Grosvenordale, CT; (Y); 4-H; Pep Clb; Capt Drill Tm; Yrbk Stf; Rep Stu Cncl; Cit Awd; Dnfth Awd; 4-H Awd; Jr NHS; NHS; 4-H Ctznshp Week WA DC 84; Arch.

CWEKLINSKY, CHRISTINE; Seymour HS; Seymour, CT; (Y); Nwsp Rptr; Nwsp Sprt Ed; Rep Frsh Cls; Rep Soph Cls; Rep Jr Cls; Rep Stu Cncl; Var Bsktbl; Var Sftbl; Hon Roll; Drftng I II III Cmpttn 1st & 2nd 83-85.

CYBUL, ELLEN; Ledyard HS; Gales Ferry, CT; (Y); 55/250; Nwsp Sprt Ed; Nwsp Stf; Trs Frsh Cls; Soph Cls; Pres Soph Cls; Sr Cls; Var Socr; Var Sftbl; AFS; Nwsp Phtg; Soccer All-Area Awd 83-84; Cmmnctns.

CYPRES, TONY; Central Catholic HS; Norwalk, CT; (Y); 25/80; Drama Clb; Trs Ski Clb; Pres Spanish Clb; School Musical; School Play; Stage Crew; Yrbk Stf; Hon Roll; NEDT Awd.

CYR, DENISE; East Catholic HS; E Hartford, CT; (Y); French Clb; Pep Clb; Ski Clb; Nwsp Stf; Rep Stu Cncl; Hon Roll; Dntl Hytgnst.

CZECZOTKO, ALBERTO CARLOS; Bullard Havens RVTS; Bridgeport, CT; (Y); 2/230; Aud/Vis; Computer Clb; Exploring; Library Aide; Orch; Cit Awd; DAR Awd; High Hon Roll; NHS; Prfct Atten Awd; Guild Polka Dot Theatr Mdlln Awd 85; 1st Elect Dept Awd 85; NHS Of Scndry Schls Awd 85; US Air Force; Elect Engnrng.

CZERWINSKI, CHRISTOPHER; Shelton HS; Shelton, CT; (Y); Am Leg Boys St; JA; Mrchg Band; Cit Awd; High Hon Roll; Hon Roll; NHS; Spanish NHS; Elec Engrng.

CZESZEL, MICHAEL; Shelton HS; Shelton, CT; (Y); Boys Clb Am; Church Yth Grp; Exploring; Band; Concert Band; Mrchg Band; Pep Band; Hon Roll.

CZYZ, MICHAEL E; Ellington HS; Ellington, CT; (Y); 13/114; Aud/Vis; Drama Clb; Concert Band; Jazz Band; Mrchg Band; Stage Crew; Hon Roll; NHS; Ldrshp Awd-CT Assc Of Scndry Schls 85; Wilfred Lutz Schlrshp 85; Cmnty Schlrshp 85; U Of CT; Bus.

CZYZEWSKI, KASIA; St Bernard HS; Norwich, CT; (Y); Cmnty Wkr; Pep Clb; Var Capt Cheerleading; Bus.

D ABATE, GAYLE; Farmington HS; Farmington, CT; (Y); 21/204; Drama Clb; Chorus; Church Choir; Concert Band; Drm Mjr(t); Mrchg Band; School Play; JV Trk; French Hon Soc; High Hon Roll; Engrng.

D ADDABBO, TIMOTHY; Berlin HS; Kensington, CT; (Y); 32/195; Am Leg Boys St; Church Yth Grp; Yrbk Stf; Var Golf; Var Capt Socr; Var Wrstlng; Lion Awd; Pol Sci.

D ADDIO, GINA; St Marys HS; New Haven, CT; (Y); Hon Roll; Score Keeper; Awd Bus Excel 85; Typng Awd Excel 85; Exec Sec.

D ADDONA III, SALVATORE; Jonathan Law HS; Milford, CT; (Y); Pumpkin Dlght Grammar Schl Awd 85; Nrwlk ST Tech Schl; Comp Sci.

D AGOSTINI, LISA; Stamford HS; Stamford, CT; (S); Cmnty Wkr; DECA; JA; Office Aide; Yrbk Ed-Chief; Yrbk Stf; Rotary Awd; Schlrshp Bus Wk U Of Hartford 84; Intrct Clb Vice Pres; Commnty Wrk 83-85; Bus Admn.

D AGOSTINO, GEORGE V; North Haven HS; N Haven, CT; (Y); L Ice Hcky; JV Ftbl; Hon Roll.

D AGOSTINO, VINCENZA; Sacred Heart Acad; Stamford, CT; (Y); Church Yth Grp; Chorus; School Musical; Yrbk Stf; VP Frsh Cls; U New Haven; Bus.

D AMARO, MICHAEL; Shelton HS; Shelton, CT; (Y); Boys Clb Am; Im Ftbl; Var L Wrstlng; Hon Roll; Bus.

D ANGELO, WILLIAM; Newington HS; Newington, CT; (Y); 30/368; Am Leg Boys St; Church Yth Grp; Math Tm; Yrbk Stf; JV Ftbl; JV Lcrss; Var Trk; Hon Roll; NHS; Yale U Frontiers Engr,Math,Sci Pgm 85; Engr.

D ANIELLO, RALPH; Ansonia HS; Ansonia, CT; (Y); 51/272; Computer Clb; Letterman Clb; Pep Clb; Ski Clb; Varsity Clb; Yrbk Stf; Bsktbl; Ftbl; Golf; Valdctrn 81; U CT; Bus.

D EMIDIO, PATRIZIA; Brien Mc Mahon HS; Norwalk, CT; (Y); Rep Jr Cls; High Hon Roll; Hon Roll; Recgntn Typng II 85; Hnrb Mntn Ldrhsp Future Sec 85; Katharine Gibbs Schl; Sec.

D ONOFRIO, DINA; Joseph A Foran HS; Milford, CT; (Y); 50/250; Civic Clb; Dance Clb; VP Pres Keywanettes; Red Cross Aide; Yrbk Stf; NEDT Awd; Michaels Jewelers Awd Schlstc Achvt, Comm Svc 85; Intl Bus.

D ORLANDO, DAWN; Guilford HS; Guilford, CT; (Y); 68/315; 4-H; Hosp Aide; Ski Clb; Band; Concert Band; Mrchg Band; Var Trk; Hon Roll; Geriatrc Nrsg.

DABKOWSKI, CYNTHIA; Bristol Central HS; Bristol, CT; (Y); 3/275; Office Aide; Trs Frsh Cls; Capt Var Diving; Var Mgr(s); High Hon Roll; NHS; Trinity Bk Awd 85; Hgh Pt Dvng Awd 83-85.

DADDIO, KAREN; Seymour HS; Seymour, CT; (S); 13/224; Pres AFS; Church Yth Grp; Church Choir; Camp Fr Inc; Rep Frsh Cls; Rep Soph Cls; Stu Cncl; Co-Capt Crs Cntry; Pom Pon; Score Keeper; Messiah Coll; Dietetics.

DAHILL, BRIDGET; Branford HS; Branford, CT; (Y); 7/284; Latin Clb; Rep Frsh Cls; Rep Jr Cls; Rep Sr Cls; Rep Stu Cncl; JV Bsktbl; JV Fld Hcky; JV Sftbl; Var Swmmng; High Hon Roll; Natl Latn Cntst Hnbl Mntn; Stdnt Mnth March; Engrng.

DALEK, JOSEPH; St Thomas Aquinas HS; New Britain, CT; (Y); Latin Clb; Teachers Aide; Yrbk Stf; High Hon Roll; Hon Roll; NHS; Prfct Atten Awd; U Of CT Hnrs Semnr 84; Roman Kazmierczak Schlrshp 85; Schl Svc Awd 85; U Of CT; Mech Engrng.

DALEY, BRIAN C; Fredrick J Conard HS; W Hartford, CT; (Y); 10/322; Madrigals; School Musical; Yrbk Sprt Ed; Rep Stu Cncl; Lcrss; Wrstlng; NHS; Spanish NHS; Church Yth Grp; Hosp Aide; 1st Pl ST AATSP Spnsh Tst 83; Trinity Coll Bk Prz 85; Engrng.

DALEY, CHERYL A; Conard HS; W Hartford, CT; (Y); 44/291; Madrigals; School Musical; Yrbk Sprt Ed; Rep Sr Cls; Sec Stu Cncl; Gym; Im Lcrss; Hon Roll; NHS; Spanish NHS; Boston Coll.

DALTON, JOHN; Shelton HS; Shelton, CT; (Y); Bsbl; High Hon Roll; Hon Roll; Spanish NHS; Math Awd 83-85; Connecticut Comp Olym Tm 84; Comp Sci.

DALY, CATHERINE; E Catholic HS; S Windsor, CT; (Y); Trs Sec 4-H; Bay Path Jr Coll Awd 85; Hartfrd Cty Horse Jdgng Tm 84; 4 H Altn Exh 84-85; Acctng.

DALY, ELIZABETH; Farmington HS; Farmington, CT; (Y); Church Yth Grp; Ski Clb; Band; Concert Band; Mrchg Band; Var Trk; Var Vllybl; Hon Roll; Coaches Awd Vlybl 84; Bus Adm.

DAMAMIAN, BETH M; The Morgan Schl; Clinton, CT; (Y); Am Leg Aux Girls St; Pres Spanish Clb; Band; Rep Stu Cncl; Var Capt Bsktbl; Var L Sftbl; Var L Tennis; Var L Vllybl; High Hon Roll; Trs NHS; V Sftbl MVP 1st Tm All Shoreline; Cert Acad Dist Soc Studies; Stu SADD.

DAMARJIAN, BETH; The Morgan Schl; Clinton, CT; (Y); Off Am Leg Aux Girls St; Pres Spanish Clb; Band; Rep Stu Cncl; Co-Capt VP Bsktbl; Powder Puff Ftbl; Var L Sftbl; Var L Tennis; High Hon Roll; Trs NHS; MVP Morgan Grls Sftbl 85; Acadmc Distnctn Soc Stds Cert; SADD Prog.

DAMIA, FULVIO WILLIAM; Danbury HS; Danbury, CT; (Y); 84/615; Cmnty Wkr; Acpl Chr; Chorus; Madrigals; Variety Show; Rep Stu Cncl; Var L Tennis; Hon Roll; Jr NHS; George W Perry Awd Music 84; Ctr Creatv Yth Wesleyan U Visl Arts 85-86; Gld Music Awd 83; Phtgrphy.

DANCE, HOLLY; Sacred Heart Acad; Stamford, CT; (Y); 4/44; Variety Show; Yrbk Stf; Pres Sr Cls; Co-Capt Cheerleading; DAR Awd; Hon Roll; NHS; Spanish NHS; Excllnce Spn Iv 85; Police Anchr Clb Awd 85; NE Conf Tchg Frgn Land Spn Awd; Marymount Coll; Fshn Mrch.

DANDENEAU, SCOTT; Holy Cross HS; Waterbury, CT; (Y); Computer Clb; Var Crs Cntry; JV Trk; Hon Roll; Blck Belt 82; Quinnipiac Coll; Rdlgy.

DANESI, JENNIFER; Saint Bernard HS; W Mystic, CT; (Y); 49/310; Church Yth Grp; Ski Clb; Chorus; Swing Chorus; Swmmng; Trk; High Hon Roll; Hon Roll; Phys Thrpy.

DANG, LOAN PHUONG; Kinswood-Oxford HS; E Hartford, CT; (Y); Art Clb; Intnl Clb; Math Tm; Chrmn Model UN; Service Clb; Yrbk Stf; Rep Jr Cls; Hon Roll; Voice Dem Awd; Tennis; Inter Racl Schlrshp 85; Wellesley Coll; Chem.

DANIEL, SANDRA; Brien Mc Mahon HS; Norwalk, CT; (Y); Hon Roll; Jr NHS; U Southern CA; Lawyer.

DANIEL, SHERRY C; Choate Rosemary Hall HS; Poughkeepsie, NY; (Y); French Clb; Math Clb; Yrbk Ed-Chief; Swmmng; Tennis; Vllybl; High Hon Roll; Ntl Merit Ltr; Ayres Mem Schlrshp 83-85; Lowndes Prz 84; Spencer Awd 85; Fall Term Abroad France 84; Chem.

DANIELE, FRANK; Stamford HS; Stamford, CT; (Y); Computer Clb; Var Capt Socr; High Hon Roll; Hon Roll; NHS; Coachs Awd For V Sccr 84-85; 3 Ltrs Sccr; U CT; Engrng.

DANIELS, LIANNE; East Catholic HS; Vernon, CT; (Y); Church Yth Grp; Hosp Aide; Pep Clb; Rep Jr Cls; Rep Stu Cncl; Gym; Hon Roll; Hnrs E 85; Schlrshp Sprng 84; Dntl Hygien.

DANIELS, SHAUNDA M; James Hillhouse HS; New Haven, CT; (Y); 19/227; Church Yth Grp; Model UN; Sec Stu Cncl; NHS; Acad All-Amer 84.

DANIELS, TAMMY; Bloomfield HS; Bloomfield, CT; (Y); 33/235; VP FBLA; Nwsp Stf; Rep Soph Cls; Rep Jr Cls; Hon Roll; Accntng.

DANNAHER, MARK; Holy Cross HS; Prospect, CT; (Y); Var L Trk; Sprg Trck-Most Dedctd 85; Bus Admin.

DANNENFELS, LUIS; New Canaan HS; Hackettstown, NJ; (Y); AFS; Intnl Clb; Library Aide; Political Wkr; Trs Spanish Clb; Chorus; Lit Mag; JV Crs Cntry; Var Trk; Var L Wrstlng; ABC Pgm 82-85; Union Coll; Elec Engrng.

DARCY, CAREY-ANNE; Cheshire HS; Cheshire, CT; (Y); Pep Clb; Yrbk Stf; High Hon Roll; Hon Roll; Johnson & Wales; Trvl.

DARCY, CHRISTOPHER; Northwest Catholic HS; Hartford, CT; (Y); Drama Clb; French Clb; Acpl Chr; Chorus; School Musical; School Play; CT All ST Music Fest 84; All Estrn & CT All ST Music Fests 85; Hstry.

DARLING, MELANIE; Brookfield HS; Brookfield Ctr, CT; (Y); 45/177; Pres AFS; Pres Trs Girl Scts; Band; Drm Mjr(t); VP Stu Cncl; Swmmng; High Hon Roll; Church Yth Grp; GAA; Concert Band; Ctr Creatv Yth 84-85; Amer Music Abroad 82 & 83; AFS Awd 85; Janet E Davidson Scholar Awd 85; MD Inst; Graphic Desgn.

DARNELL, STEPHEN R; Danbury HS; Danbury, CT; (Y); 7/524; Pres Computer Clb; Key Clb; VP Math Tm; Spanish Clb; High Hon Roll; JETS Awd; Jr NHS; NHS; Ntl Merit SF; IBM Watson Mem Scholar 85; Distingshd Schlr Sci 84-85; Tufts U; Engrng.

DATE, HARI; Trumbull HS; Trumbull, CT; (Y); Band; Chorus; Concert Band; Jazz Band; Orch; Symp Band; Hon Roll; Vet.

DAUDELIN, MICHELLE P; Windsor Locks HS; Windsor Locks, CT; (Y); 8/167; Drama Clb; Band; Chorus; Concert Band; Jazz Band; Mrchg Band; Orch; Church Yth Grp; French Clb; Nwsp Stf; Psych.

DAUPHINAIS, DEBBY; Killingly HS; Brooklyn, CT; (Y); Hosp Aide; Office Aide; Yrbk Stf; Stu Cncl; Capt Cheerleading; Cit Awd; Hon Roll; Ldrshp Awd 82; Stone Schl New Haven; Exec Sec.

DAVELUY, BARB; Naugatuck HS; Naugatuck, CT; (Y); VP JA; Office Aide; Teachers Aide; Nwsp Stf; Lit Mag; Rep Soph Cls; High Hon Roll; Hon Roll; JA 100 & 1000 Dllr Sls Clbs & Co Of The Yr 84; Exec Sec.

DAVIDSON, KRISTEN; George J Penny HS; E Hartford, CT; (Y); Am Leg Aux Girls St; Trs Church Yth Grp; Scholastic Bowl; Lib Concert Band; Lib Mrchg Band; Nwsp Stf; Var L Trk; High Hon Roll; NHS; French Clb; Yth Rep On Brd Of Educ At Cntrl Baptst Church Hartford 84-85; Math.

DAVIDSON, SUSANNE A; Northwest Catholic HS; Hartford, CT; (Y); #3 In Class; Church Yth Grp; Dance Clb; Hosp Aide; JA; Library Aide; Office Aide; Church Choir; Nrsng.

DAVIDSON III, WILLIAM F; Fairfield Prep; Stratford, CT; (Y); 15/240; Rep Jr Cls; Rep Sr Cls; JV Ftbl; JV Var Trk; Im Wt Lftg; High Hon Roll; Jr NHS; NHS; VP Spanish NHS; Bst Ancient Western Cvlztn Stu 83; Bst Human Rel Stu 83; Aeronautical Engrng.

DAVIES, WILLIAM; East Lyme HS; Niantic, CT; (Y); Church Yth Grp; Im Bsktbl; Var L Ftbl; JV L Trk; Im Wt Lftg; Hon Roll; Northeastern; Elec Engrng.

DAVINO, CHRISTINA; Seymour HS; Oxford, CT; (S); 5/224; Church Yth Grp; Ed Yrbk Stf; Rep Frsh Cls; Rep Soph Cls; Rep Jr Cls; Trs Sr Cls; Cmnty Wkr; Var Capt Tennis; High Hon Roll; Prfct Atten Awd; Music Awd 83-84; Spnsh IV Awd 83-84; Kings Coll; Accntnt.

DAVIS, ANGELA; Lauralton Hall HS; Brdgeport, CT; (Y); Church Yth Grp; Hosp Aide; Math Clb; Spanish Clb; Church Choir; Im Vllybl; Upward Bound 83-86; Typng Awd 84-85; Pres Tbrncl Jr Choir 80-83; Grtr Lov Choir 82-85; Cls Pres 84-85; Bus.

DAVIS, ANTHONY DONNELL; Hartford Public HS; Hartford, CT; (S); Church Yth Grp; DECA; FBLA; JA; Ski Clb; Church Choir; Yrbk Ed-Chief; Jr Cls; Sr Cls; Socr; Johnson & Wales; Bus Mgmt.

DAVIS, BETH ANN; Manchester HS; Manchester, CT; (Y); 30/541; Art Clb; Hon Roll; Acad Excell Awd 83; Art.

DAVIS, CARLA ANN; Sacred Heart Acad; New Haven, CT; (Y); Computer Clb; Dance Clb; Pep Clb; Political Wkr; School Musical; Variety Show; Im Vllybl; High Hon Roll; NHS; Spanish NHS; Spnsh III Outstndng Achvt Awd 84-85; 3 Yr High Hnr Awd 84-85; Scrd Hrt Acad Advsry Brd Schlrshp 82-84; Bio.

DAVIS, CATHERINE; Stamford HS; Stamford, CT; (S); Drama Clb; German Clb; JA; Service Clb; School Musical; Off Soph Cls; Stu Cncl; High Hon Roll; NHS; Ntl Merit Ltr; Iona Coll Lang Comp 85; Sci Olympiad Bio Team 83; Telluride Assoc 84-85; Bio Sci.

DAVIS, EMILY; Coventry HS; Coventry, CT; (S); 10/120; Jazz Band; Yrbk Bus Mgr; NHS; Church Yth Grp; Band; Chorus; School Musical; High Hon Roll; Hon Roll; Excel Frnch 83; U CT; Math.

DAVIS, ERIC R; Canton HS; Canton, CT; (Y); 15/108; Am Leg Boys St; Math Clb; Science Clb; Speech Tm; JV Bsktbl; Var L Golf; Im Swmmng; Im Vllybl; MVP Golf Tm Vrsty 85; Certifd Lifeguard 83; Canton Volnteer Fire Cadet 84 & 85; US Military Acad; Mech Engrng.

DAVIS, KIMBERLY; Weaver HS; Hartford, CT; (Y); Gym; Trk; High Hon Roll; Hon Roll; NHS; Prfct Atten Awd; Trnty Club Awd Outstndg JR 85; Comp Sci.

DAVIS, MARY-BETH; Bulkeley HS; Hartford, CT; (Y); 5/375; Sec Church Yth Grp; Pres Computer Clb; Trs Ski Clb; Yrbk Ed-Chief; Var L Mgr(s); Var L Socr; Var L Sftbl; High Hon Roll; NHS; Stu Of Month 85; Eastrn CT ST U; Educ.

DAVIS, TANYA; Low-Heywood Thomas Schl; Norwalk, CT; (Y); 2/36; Drama Clb; Model UN; Pres Thesps; Chorus; School Musical; School Play; Variety Show; Nwsp Rptr; Frsh Cls; Hon Roll; Class Prz 83; Acad Schlrshp 83-85; Amherst; Law.

DAWN, KOLDRAS; Shelton HS; Shelton, CT; (S); VP DECA; Drama Clb; French Clb; Library Aide; Rep Frsh Cls; Rep Soph Cls; Rep Jr Cls; Spcl Ccommendtn Civics,Play Prod I,II; Am Acad Of Dramatic; Theatre.

DAY, JONATHAN; Oliver Wolcott Rgnl Vo-Tech Schl; New Hartford, CT; (Y); 10/160; Boy Scts; 4-H; Math Clb; Nwsp Stf; Yrbk Stf; JV Socr; Hon Roll; NHS; VT ST Tech; Elec Engr.

DAYMONDE, LISA; Bassick HS; Bridgeport, CT; (S); 1/250; VP Exploring; Sec Key Clb; Yrbk Stf; High Hon Roll; NHS; Val; Schlrshp Ldrshp Pin 84; Harvard Bk Prz 84; Pre-Med.

DE BONEE, JEFFREY; Avon Old Farms Schl; Hampden, MA; (S); 9/102; Pep Clb; Yrbk Stf; Im Bsbl; JV Ice Hcky; Im Wt Lftg; Hon Roll; Head Dorm Mntr; Boston Coll; Med.

DE BRIGITA, RHONDA; St Marys HS; W Haven, CT; (Y); 7/86; Church Yth Grp; Ski Clb; Pres Jr Cls; VP Rep Stu Cncl; Hon Roll; NHS; Pres Schlr; Spanish NHS; St Marys Of The Springs Scholar 81-85; U New Haven; Acctng.

DE CAPUA, SARAH; Shelton HS; Shelton, CT; (Y); Drama Clb; Exploring; Ski Clb; Spanish Clb; School Play; Yrbk Bus Mgr; Yrbk Stf; Pom Pon; Hon Roll; Spanish NHS; Mass Cmmnctns.

DE CHELLO, GEORGE; Notre Dame HS; W Haven, CT; (Y); Ski Clb; JV Crs Cntry; Math Hnr Socty.

DE COSTA, DAWN; Ledyard HS; Galesferry, CT; (Y); 80/250; Church Yth Grp; GAA; JV Var Bsktbl; Im Powder Puff Ftbl; Var Sftbl; Im Vllybl; Im Wt Lftg; Hon Roll; Vrsty Sftbl MIP Awd 84; Psych.

DE FAZIO, RICHARD; Weston HS; Weston, CT; (Y); 2/174; FBLA; Spanish Clb; Var Ftbl; JV Lcrss; Wt Lftg; JV Wrstlng; Hon Roll; NHS; Pres Safe Rides 81-85; Acctg Awd Outstndng Achvt 84-85; Stasia Cina Memrl Awd 85; Syracuse U; Acctg.

DE FRANCISCO, JOY E; Southington HS; Southington, CT; (Y); 211/550; Church Yth Grp; Cmnty Wkr; Hosp Aide; Key Clb; Pep Clb; Teachers Aide; Rep Frsh Cls; Pin & Cert Awd Hosp Volntr 83; Woodmere Hlth Care Ctr Cert Volntr Wrk 82; Southern CT ST U; Social Wrk.

DE GASPERIS, CHRISTINE M; Berlin HS; Kensington, CT; (Y); Office Aide; Offc Aid Awd; Comp Prog.

DE GENNARO, PATRICIA; Mark T Sheehan HS; Wallingford, CT; (Y); 54/212; Trs Church Yth Grp; Hosp Aide; Sec Key Clb; Pep Clb; Political Wkr; Spanish Clb; VP Frsh Cls; VP Soph Cls; Rep Stu Cncl; Var JV Fld Hcky; Stu Council Schlrshp 85; Quinnipiac Coll; Paralegal.

DE GRAY, ANN; East Lyme HS; Niantic, CT; (Y); Church Yth Grp; Key Clb; Band; Church Choir; Concert Band; Mrchg Band; Pep Band; JV Fld Hcky; Powder Puff Ftbl; Hon Roll; USCGA Air Force Acad; Intl Law.

DE GROOT, MARY; St Bernard HS; Norwich, CT; (Y); Girl Scts; Varsity Clb; Nwsp Stf; Yrbk Stf; Rep Frsh Cls; Rep Soph Cls; Rep Jr Cls; Rep Sr Cls; Rep Stu Cncl; Stat Bsktbl; Villanova; Pre-Med.

DE JOHN, MICHELE; Southington HS; Southington, CT; (Y); 80/550; Church Yth Grp; Cmnty Wkr; FBLA; Key Clb; Office Aide; Pep Clb; Ski Clb; Chorus; Powder Puff Ftbl; High Hon Roll; Awd In Read-Athn Disbld Chldrn 82; U Of CT; Bus Adm.

DE JONGH, MATTHEW; Daniel Hand HS; Madison, CT; (Y); 83/238; Church Yth Grp; FCA; ROTC; Var Bsktbl; JV Socr; Pol Union 84-85; Syracuse U; Engrng.

DE LILLO, DENA; St Bernard HS; Waterford, CT; (S); Off Jr Cls; Var Sftbl; Acctng.

DE LUCA, ANNEMARIE; North Branford HS; Northford, CT; (Y); 11/155; Church Yth Grp; Cmnty Wkr; Dance Clb; Stu Cncl; Fld Hcky; Powder Puff Ftbl; Sftbl; High Hon Roll; Hon Roll; Jr NHS; Med.

DE LUCA, KATHLEEN; Stamford HS; Stamford, CT; (Y); Dance Clb; Ski Clb; Band; Yrbk Ed-Chief; Stu Cncl; Var Capt Cheerleading; Fld Hcky; Score Keeper; Hon Roll; NHS.

DE LUCA, LAURA; Brien Mc Mahon HS; Norwalk, CT; (Y); 6/342; Church Yth Grp; Key Clb; Ski Clb; Var L Tennis; High Hon Roll; NHS; Smith Clg Bk Awd 85; Iona Clg Lang Cntst 1st Hon Lvl 3 85; Chldhd Educ.

DE LUCA, SUSAN; Pomperaug Regional HS; Middlebury, CT; (Y); AFS; Cmnty Wkr; Acpl Chr; Concert Band; Jazz Band; Mrchg Band; Hon Roll; Band; Chorus; Pep Band; All New Englnd Chrs; All-ST Chrs; Band & Chrs Rgnl Music Fstvl; Sthrn CT ST U; Grntlgy.

DE LUCIA, FRANK; Notre Dame HS; New Haven, CT; (Y); 50/254; Church Yth Grp; Pep Clb; Ski Clb; Jazz Band; JV Ftbl; Hon Roll; NHS; Spanish NHS; Natl Hnr Rll 84-85; Boston U; Engrng.

DE MAIO, THEODORE A; Wilbur L Cross HS; New Haven, CT; (Y); Aud/Vis; French Clb; School Play; Hon Roll; Video Awd 83-84; Adv Art Awd 84-85; Film Schl; Movie Makng.

DE MARKEY, KIRSTEN; Brien Mc Mahon HS; Rowayton, CT; (Y); 15/342; Key Clb; Ski Clb; Spanish Clb; Band; Yrbk Stf; Powder Puff Ftbl; Swmmng; High Hon Roll; Hon Roll; Comp Sci.

DE ROCCO, NORINE; Kaynor Tech HS; Waterbury, CT; (Y); Nwsp Rptr; Nwsp Stf; Yrbk Stf; VP Jr Cls; Rep Stu Cncl; JV Bsktbl; Stat Sftbl; High Hon Roll; Hon Roll; Csmtlgy.

DE ROSIMO, JOHN F; Taft HS; Waterbury, CT; (Y); Boy Scts; Yrbk Phtg; Im Bsktbl; JV Crs Cntry; Var Trk; Hon Roll; Pre-Med.

DE VENY, CHRISTINE M; Academy Of Our Lady Of Mercy; Bridgeport, CT; (Y); Church Yth Grp; Political Wkr; Church Choir; Ntl Merit Ltr; NEDT Awd; Bd Trustees Schlrshp 81-85; Ursinus Coll.

DE VITO, JEFF; Oliver Wolcott Tech; Torrington, CT; (Y); Math Clb; VICA; Off Soph Cls; Off Jr Cls; Off Sr Cls; ROTC; NHS; Elec.

DEAN, ALAN; Daniel Hand HS; Madison, CT; (Y); 68/236; Church Yth Grp; Cmnty Wkr; Political Wkr; Red Cross Aide; Spanish Clb; Nwsp Rptr; Nwsp Stf; Stu Cncl; Lcrss; Hon Roll; Meteorlgy.

DEAN, SHARON A; Plainville HS; Plainville, CT; (Y); 33/213; Ski Clb; Diving; Swmmng; Trk; Hon Roll; All Conf, All ST Diver 84; Keene ST Coll; Sci.

DEANGELIS, SUSAN; Holy Cross HS; Watertown, CT; (Y); 77/352; Chorus; Yrbk Stf; JV Trk; High Hon Roll; Mktg.

DEARBORN, LESLEY; Staples HS; Westport, CT; (Y); 3/450; Church Yth Grp; French Clb; Chorus; Hon Roll; Ntl Merit Ltr.

DEARY, KRISTINA M; Conard HS; W Hartford, CT; (Y); 25/291; Church Yth Grp; Chorus; School Musical; Yrbk Ed-Chief; Yrbk Stf; Stat Lcrss; JV Socr; High Hon Roll; NHS; Spanish NHS; U Of VT; Bus.

DEAVENPORT, JOSEPH; East Lyme HS; E Lyme, CT; (Y); 38/271; Church Yth Grp; Stat Bsbl; Mgr Bsktbl; Mgr Ftbl; Mth.

DEBERNARDO, CAREN; Trumball HS; Trumbull, CT; (Y); AFS; Church Yth Grp; Office Aide; Ski Clb; Varsity Clb; Yrbk Stf; Tennis; High Hon Roll; NHS; Commrcl Art.

DEBIASE, SABRINA; Norwalk HS; Norwalk, CT; (Y); Sftbl; High Hon Roll; IONA Lang Cont Italian II First Hnrs 83-84; IONA Lang Cont Italian III Secnd Hnrs 84-85; Fashn Desgn.

DEBO, SYLVIA; Mary Immaculate Acad; New Britain, CT; (S); VP Drama Clb; Teachers Aide; Chorus; School Musical; Rep Frsh Cls; Pres Stu Cncl; Var Cheerleading; Hon Roll; Ntl Merit SF; Prfct Atten Awd; Med.

DECAPRIO, MARY EVELYN; Sacred Heart Acad; Hamden, CT; (Y); Church Yth Grp; FBLA; Hosp Aide; Stage Crew; Nwsp Stf; Yrbk Stf; Hon Roll; NHS; Pres Yth Hrtbd Chptr Pro Life Cncl Of CT 85-86; Stu Sptlght 85; Nrsng.

DECKER, JOYCE; Torrington HS; Torrington, CT; (Y); DECA; Library Aide; Hon Roll; Dist Hnr Awd 6th Pl Restrnt Mrktng 85; Stu Lbrarn Cert 85; Northwestern; Erly Chldhd Educ.

DEEN, FEROZE; Bolton HS; Bolton, CT; (Y); 1/75; Am Leg Boys St; Boy Scts; Computer Clb; Intnl Clb; Model UN; Spanish Clb; School Musical; Rep Soph Cls; Pres Jr Cls; Trs Stu Cncl; Rensselaer Math & Sci Mdl 85; Yale Book Clb Awd 85; Scientsts Of Tmrrw Cert 83; MIT; Aerosp Engrg.

DEFELICE, MARTIN J; East Haven HS; E Haven, CT; (Y); Am Leg Boys St; Spanish Clb; Yrbk Stf; Sec Sr Cls; Stu Cncl; Var L Bsbl; Var Ftbl; Cit Awd; Hon Roll; VP Pres NHS; Rtry Youth Awd 85; Law.

DEFEO, RENEE; Windham HS; W Willington, CT; (Y); Im Socr; Trk; High Hon Roll; Hon Roll; Rnkd 3rd HS Ntl Math Exm 85; Spnsh Cls Estrn CT ST U 84; Multiply Optns Conf Math & Sci 85; Med.

DEFLIPPO, PAUL F; Morgan HS; Clinton, CT; (Y); JV Bsbl; Var Capt Bsktbl; Landscape Arch.

DEGRAY, DIANE; Ellington HS; Ellington, CT; (Y); 9/146; Band; Concert Band; Mrchg Band; Yrbk Stf; High Hon Roll; Hon Roll; Ski Clb; School Musical; School Play; Outstndng Achvt French III 85; Math.

DEHNEL, LAURA J; New Britain HS; New Britain, CT; (Y); 25/300; German Clb; Hosp Aide; Nrsng.

DEKUTOWSKI, LAURA; Southington HS; Southington, CT; (Y); 59/550; Band; Concert Band; Mrchg Band; High Hon Roll; Hon Roll; NHS; Angelo Fusco Sr Schlrshp 85; Southington Apple Hrvst Fest Hstss 84; Its Poetry Any Lang Cntst 84; Tunxis CC.

DEL PRIORE, NICOLE; Holycross HS; Prospect, CT; (Y); Art Clb; Math Tm; Spanish Clb; Chrmn Stu Cncl; High Hon Roll; NHS; Spanish NHS; St Schlr; Soc Stud Natl Hnr Soc 84; Bryant Coll RI; Acctg.

DELIO, KARLA; Central Catholic HS; Norwalk, CT; (Y); 12/94; Church Yth Grp; Spanish Clb; Yrbk Stf; JV Vllybl; High Hon Roll; Hon Roll; NHS; Bronze, Silver Ice Skating Medal; Law.

DELLERT, KAREN; Sacred Heart Acad; N Branford, CT; (Y); Computer Clb; FBLA; Stage Crew; Nwsp Ed-Chief; JV Bsktbl; Im Vllybl; High Hon Roll; NHS; NEDT Awd; Prfct Atten Awd.

DELLIO, DENA; St Bernard HS; Waterford, CT; (Y); Var L Sftbl; Hon Roll.

DELO, DIRK A; Greenwich HS; Riverside, CT; (Y); Am Leg Boys St; VP Key Clb; Band; Mrchg Band; Var Tennis; Cit Awd; JC Awd; Kiwanis Awd; NHS; Woodrow Wilson Yth Svc Awd 85; Amer Legn Yng Persn Of Yr 84; Yth Ctzn Of Yr; Amherst Coll; Ed.

DELOGE, STEPHEN; Cheshire HS; Cheshire, CT; (Y); Church Yth Grp; Science Clb; Bsktbl; Var Socr; High Hon Roll; Hon Roll; Jr NHS; NHS; Engrng.

DELOHERY, DIANNA; New Fairfield HS; New Fairfield, CT; (Y); 25/252; Church Yth Grp; Cmnty Wkr; Hosp Aide; Latin Clb; School Musical; Im Bsktbl; JV Fld Hcky; Var Socr; Hon Roll; Natl Latn Exm Hnrbl Mntn 83; Phy Ther.

DELUCA, SUSIE; Sacred Heart Acad; Stamford, CT; (Y); #8 In Class; Variety Show; Lit Mag; Trs Frsh Cls; Trs Soph Cls; Pres Jr Cls; Pres Stu Cncl; Var L Bsktbl; JV Vllybl; Dnfth Awd; Hon Roll; Acctng.

DELUCIA, JOANNA; Ellington HS; Ellington, CT; (Y); 8/141; FBLA; Ski Clb; Yrbk Stf; Var Crs Cntry; Var Trk; High Hon Roll; Hon Roll; Ntl Merit Ltr; 2nd Pl FBLA ST Ldrshp Conf 84; Outstndg Achvt Wrtng Awd 85; Jrnlsm.

DEMAINE, MICHAEL; Fairfield College Prep; Bridgeport, CT; (Y); Boy Scts; Church Yth Grp; Drama Clb; JA; PAVAS; Thesps; Chorus; School Play; Lit Mag; Hon Roll; Actg.

DEMARS, ELIZABETH; St Bernard HS; Norwich, CT; (S); Church Yth Grp; FNA; Hosp Aide; Office Aide; Nwsp Rptr; VP Frsh Cls; VP Soph Cls; VP Jr Cls; Rep Stu Cncl; Stat Bsbl; Hugh OBRIAN Yth Ldrshp Awd 84.

DEMARTINI, DINA; Low-Heywood Thomas HS; Stamford, CT; (Y); Aud/Vis; Camera Clb; Drama Clb; Model UN; School Musical; Stage Crew; Variety Show; JV Sftbl; Var Vllybl; Hon Roll; Boston U; Comm.

DEMETER, ANNA; Bassick HS; Bridgeport, CT; (S); Drama Clb; VP Sec JA; Key Clb; Radio Clb; Yrbk Stf; Lit Mag; Rep Stu Cncl; Capt JV Bsktbl; Var Capt Sftbl; Var Capt Vllybl; Mst Imprvd Plyr Sftbl 84; Choate Rsmry Hall Schlrshp 84; Yale U Of CT; Comp Engrng.

DEMILO, JUSTINE; Sacred Heart Acad; New Haven, CT; (Y); Pep Clb; Spanish Clb; Im Vllybl; Hon Roll; Spanish NHS; Vlybl Sportsmnshp 82; Endowmnmt Schlrhsp 83; Yale Frontier Of Sci 85; Syracuse; Med Tech.

DEMJAN, TABITHA; Notre Dame Catholic HS; Bridgeprort, CT; (Y); 8/284; VP JA; Pres Latin Clb; Library Aide; DAR Awd; High Hon Roll; NHS; Fordham U; Law.

DEMPSEY, KATHLEEN L; The Morgan School; Clinton, CT; (Y); Band; Chorus; Concert Band; Mrchg Band; School Musical; Nwsp Phtg; Yrbk Phtg; Rep Stu Cncl; Var L Fld Hcky; Capt Powder Puff Ftbl; Psych.

DEMPSKY, MICHAEL DAVID; Montville HS; Uncasville, CT; (Y); 14/170; Boy Scts; Elks Awd; NHS; Pres Schlr; Voice Dem Awd; Sen Eric Bensons Yng Ctzn Schlrshp Awd 85; Hugh Obrien Yth Ldrshp Sem 83; U CT Coop Pgm Supr HS Stu; U CT; Pol Sci.

DEMSEY, SCOTT; Holy Cross HS; Watertown, CT; (Y); 16/344; Church Yth Grp; Math Tm; Trs Science Clb; Chorus; JV Var Socr; NHS; Spanish NHS; Pres Acad Fit Awd 84-85; Soc Stud Hon Soc 84-85; U CT; Mech Engrng.

DENIEGA, THERESA; Brookfield HS; Brookfield, CT; (Y); Concert Band; Mrchg Band; Pep Band; Yrbk Stf; High Hon Roll; Sec NHS; Crtv Yth Pgm Wesleyan U 84; Odyssy Mind Wrld Fnls U Of MD 85.

DENIS, KAREN; Joseph A Foran HS; Milford, CT; (Y); 5/275; Spanish Clb; High Hon Roll; NHS; Ntl Merit Ltr; NEDT Awd; Pres Schlr; Pres Acad Ftnss Awd 85; Suprntndnts Acad Awd 85; Wesleyan U; Comp Sci.

DENISEVICH, LISA; Pomperaug HS; Southbury, CT; (Y); 35/200; French Clb; Yrbk Phtg; Yrbk Stf; Rep Jr Cls; Var Cheerleading; Var Swmmng; Var Tennis; JV Trk; Bio.

DENNIN, AMY P; Brien Mc Mahon HS; Norwalk, CT; (Y); #1 In Class; Church Yth Grp; Hosp Aide; JCL; Key Clb; Sec Spanish Clb; Nwsp Ed-Chief; Rep Soph Cls; Rep Jr Cls; Rep Sr Cls; Capt Tennis; CT Schlr 84-85; Rensselaer Medal 85; Iona Lang Cont Spnsh 1st Hnrs 84-85; Biophy.

DENNIS, NANCY; St Bernard HS; Quaker Hill, CT; (Y); 17/297; Pres Sec Dance Clb; Hon Roll; NHS; USNMA Awd 83-84; Cert Merit Concours Ntl De Francais 83; Dance.

DENNIS, RONALD; Central HS; Bridgeport, CT; (S); 29/320; Church Yth Grp; JA; Yrbk Stf; VP Jr Cls; Pres Sr Cls; Rep Stu Cncl; Var L Ftbl; JV Trk; Schlrshp Ldrshp Awd; Dale Carnegie Schlrshp; 1st Tm All MBIAC Ftbl; Virginia Tech; Acctng.

DENTE, MARCELLO; East Haven HS; East Haven, CT; (Y); Art Clb; Concert Band; JV Socr; Prfct Atten Awd.

DEONARINE, BARRY; Westminster Schl; Hempstead, NY; (Y); 1/98; Debate Tm; Nwsp Ed-Chief; Bsbl; Bsktbl; Mgr(s); High Hon Roll; Harvard Bk Awd 85; Exclnce Chem Awd 85; Elem Enrng.

DEPALMA, DAVID; W F Kaynor Technical Voc HS; Waterbury, CT; (Y); 25/190; JA; Hon Roll; Prfct Atten Awd; Waterbury ST Tech; Elctrcl Eng.

DEROSA, MARY; St Marys HS; W Haven, CT; (Y); 30/115; Church Yth Grp; Hosp Aide; Stu Cncl; JV Bsktbl; Var Sftbl; High Hon Roll; Ply Violin 79-84; Providence Coll; Pre Med.

DEROSIER, LISA; Southington HS; Southington, CT; (Y); 60/550; Key Clb; Latin Clb; Ski Clb; Yrbk Stf; Rep Stu Cncl; Mgr(s); Score Keeper; Timer; High Hon Roll; Hon Roll; Accntng.

DERVIN, KAREN; Pomperaug HS; Southbury, CT; (Y); 33/206; Drama Clb; Math Tm; Chorus; Concert Band; Madrigals; Rep Soph Cls; Var Capt Socr; Church Yth Grp; School Musical; All New England Chorus 84-85; All State Chorus 85; Mt Holyoke Coll; Psych.

DERWIN, WILLIAM; Holy Cross HS; Waterbury, CT; (Y); 1/352; Ski Clb; Band; Mrchg Band; JV Bsbl; Capt L Socr; Capt L Tennis; French Hon Soc; High Hon Roll; Pres NHS; Val; Frnch Lvl I & III Awds; Harvard Bk Club Awd; Vrsty Ski Team Capt & MVP; Elec Engr.

DERY, LISA; Putnam HS; Putnam, CT; (Y); Girl Scts; Hosp Aide; Band; Chorus; Madrigals; Mrchg Band; Yrbk Stf; Sec Frsh Cls; Sec Soph Cls; Sec Sr Cls; Exec Sec.

DES JARDINS, LORI; Manchester HS; Manchester, CT; (Y); Debate Tm; French Clb; Yrbk Stf; Hon Roll; French Awd 85; Bus Mgmt.

DESCOTEAUX, RICHARD; Avon Old Farms HS; Watertown, CT; (S); 32/110; Art Clb; Pep Clb; Yrbk Rptr; Golf; Ice Hcky; Hon Roll; Yale; Bus.

DESJARDINS JR, THOMAS; Holy Cross HS; Watertown, CT; (Y); 20/400; Im Bsbl; Capt Crs Cntry; Var Trk; Jr NHS; NHS; Spanish NHS; St Schlr; All ST Tm-Trck 84; Babson Coll; Acctg.

DESPER, RICHARD M; William H Hall HS; W Hartford, CT; (Y); 2/324; Math Tm; Model UN; Jazz Band; Orch; Symp Band; French Hon Soc; High Hon Roll; NHS; Berklee H S Jazz Ensmbl Fstvl Cert Of Mrt.

DESROCHERS, KIM; Stratford HS; Stratford, CT; (Y); Swmmng; Hon Roll; Cosmetlgy.

DESROSIERS, JEANETTE; Naugatuck HS; Naugatuck, CT; (Y); 15/340; Office Aide; Ski Clb; Mrchg Band; Symp Band; Yrbk Stf; Rep Soph Cls; Jr Cls; Var Crs Cntry; Var Trk; Rep Sr Cls; CT Sthrn Regnl Mus Fest 85; Bus Mgmt.

DESRUISSEAUX, CHERYL; Rham HS; Hebron, CT; (Y); Trs FBLA; Teachers Aide; Yrbk Stf; Lrgst Singl Fund Rsr Leukemia Type Thn 85; Becker JC; Travl.

DESRVISSEAUX, CORINNE; Windham Technical Schl; Tolland, CT; (Y); Yrbk Stf; Hon Roll; Jr NHS; NHS; Electrncs.

DEVANEY, KATHLEEN; Guilford HS; Guilford, CT; (Y); 17/315; Band; Concert Band; Drm Mjr(t); Mrchg Band; Var Bsktbl; Var Capt Socr; Var Trk; French Hon Soc; Hon Roll; NHS; Natl Latin Exam Magna Cum Laude 83; Gen Exclnce Eng Awd 83; CT ST Select Soccr Tm 85; Hstry.

DEVINE, MICHAEL; Daniel Hand HS; Madison, CT; (Y); 11/267; Boy Scts; Church Yth Grp; Model UN; Ski Clb; JV Trk; Hon Roll; NHS; Eagle Sct Brnz Palm 83.

DEVINO, SARA; Holy Cross HS; Oxford, CT; (Y); 99/365; Church Yth Grp; Acpl Chr; Chorus; Church Choir; Swing Chorus; Yrbk Rptr; Yrbk Stf; Rep Frsh Cls; Rep Soph Cls; Rep Stu Cncl; Am Leg Awd 82; JR Vrsty Ltrs Sftbl & Singng 83-84; Numrls & Pin Stu Cncl 83-84; U CT; Phys Ther.

DEVIVO, JOSEPH M; King Schl; Wilton, CT; (S); 10/32; Drama Clb; VP JA; Model UN; School Musical; Nwsp Stf; Yrbk Stf; Sec Pres Stu Cncl; Capt Var Bsktbl; Var L Ftbl; Tennis; Bantram Mem Awd Extracurrclr 85; U Richmond.

DEWALT, SHERYL; Trumbull HS; Trumbull, CT; (Y); AFS; Church Yth Grp; Church Choir; Score Keeper; Mgr Trk; High Hon Roll; Hon Roll; Achvmnts Home Ec Awd 83-85; Hosp Admin.

DEWEY, INGER C; Choate Rosemary Hall HS; Greenwich, CT; (S); Art Clb; Key Clb; Acpl Chr; Pres Chorus; Madrigals; School Musical; Nwsp Rptr; VP Soph Cls; Var Fld Hcky; Var Vllybl; Marion M Kinglsey Awd; Sr Hse Counslr Dorm; Stu Adm Offcr; Hist.

DI BUCCIO, ANTHONY V; Notre Dame HS; Branford, CT; (Y); Church Yth Grp; FCA; Hosp Aide; Political Wkr; Varsity Clb; Im Bsktbl; Var Ftbl; Var Wt Lftg; Hon Roll; Peer Cnclng 84-85; Johnson Whales Coll; Fin.

DI CAMILLO, STEPHEN R; Loomfield HS; Bloomfield, CT; (Y); 3/231; French Clb; JA; Capt Math Tm; Science Clb; Concert Band; Jazz Band; Mrchg Band; Var Golf; French Hon Soc; NHS; Yale Bk Awd 85; MVP Math Team Awd 85; Top Pre-Calculus Stu 85; MA Inst Of Tech; Elec Engrng.

DI CECCO, ADRIANA; Litchfield HS; Litchfield, CT; (Y); 1/97; VP AFS; MMM; Chorus; Madrigals; Yrbk Ed-Chief; Sec Sr Cls; Bausch & Lomb Sci Awd; French Hon Soc; Ntl Merit Ltr; Val; Latin Hnr Scty; NMSC Spec Schlrshp 85; Princeton U.

DI DOMINIC JR, DOMINIC; J A Foran HS; Milford, CT; (Y); Chess Clb; Drama Clb; French Clb; JCL; Latin Clb; Letterman Clb; Math Clb; Math Tm; Ski Clb; Teachers Aide; Sportsmnshp Awd 81 & 83; Bus.

DI DONNO, LAURA; Southington HS; Southington, CT; (Y); FBLA; Math Tm; High Hon Roll; Sec Jr NHS; Sec NHS; Hnr Awd Notetkg I FBLA Comp 84-85; Achvt Awd Home Ec 83; Bus Mgmt.

DI ELSI, DAWN MARIE; St Marys HS; New Haven, CT; (Y); 4/86; Am Leg Aux Girls St; Cmnty Wkr; Hosp Aide; JA; Pres Math Clb; Service Clb; School Play; Stage Crew; Yrbk Stf; Hon Roll; Math Awd 85; Schlstc Achvt Awd 85; CT ST Achvt Schlrshp 85; Lynchburg Coll; Med Tech.

DI LUNGO, ANTHONY; East Haven HS; E Haven, CT; (Y); Yrbk Rptr; Yrbk Stf; Ice Hcky; Hon Roll; Athlt Of Wk 85; Scrd 100th Career Pt 85; All Housatnc 1st Tm & All ST Hcky 2nd Tm 85; Top Screr ST 85; Accntng.

DI MAIO, KAREN; Ansonia HS; Ansonia, CT; (Y); Computer Clb; French Clb; Spanish Clb; Pom Pon; Hon Roll.

DI MAURO, DINA; Coginchaug Regional HS; Middlefield, CT; (Y); Ski Clb; Varsity Clb; School Musical; Swing Chorus; Sec Soph Cls; Var Sftbl; Capt Tennis; Hon Roll; Drama Clb; Chorus; ST Tnns Trnmnt 82-84; Mst Valbl Plyr Tnns 82 & 84; Spnsh I Awd & Drma Awd 84; DDM.

DI MAURO, VANESSA JUSTINE; South Catholic HS; Rocky Hill, CT; (Y); VP Church Yth Grp; Thesps; Madrigals; School Musical; Ed Nwsp Rptr; Yrbk Ed-Chief; Ed Lit Mag; VP Stu Cncl; Var Tennis; Hon Roll; Century III Ldrshp Awd 85; St Anselm; Engl.

DI NOIA, CHRISTINE; Lyman Hall HS; Wallingford, CT; (Y); Sec VP AFS; Pres Aud/Vis; Church Yth Grp; JA; Band; Concert Band; Mrchg Band; Swmmng; Trk; Hon Roll; Outstndg Svc To Schl 84; Outstndg Svc To Schl Lightg 85; Apprec & Svc AFS 85; Nrsg.

DI PIETRO, DAWN; Holy Cross HS; Prospect, CT; (Y); PAVAS; Band; Concert Band; Jazz Band; Mrchg Band; Symp Band; Psychlgy.

DI PIETRO, DONNA; St Thomas Aquinas HS; New Britain, CT; (Y); 34/160; Rep Spanish Clb; Rep Soph Cls; Rep Jr Cls; Hon Roll; Excll Accntng II 85; Central CT ST U; Accntng.

DI PIETRO, LISA; Southington HS; Southington, CT; (Y); Cmnty Wkr; Hosp Aide; Latin Clb; Capt Quiz Bowl; Powder Puff Ftbl; High Hon Roll; Hon Roll; Jr NHS; NHS; Home Ec-Highest Avrge Awd; Latin-Highest Avrge Awd; Lewis Alumni Latin Prize Exam Awd; Nrsng.

DIAZ, ANGEL; Buckeley HS; Hartford, CT; (Y); 25/298; Church Yth Grp; Letterman Clb; Rep Stu Cncl; Var Capt Bsbl; JV Crs Cntry; Eastern CT ST U; Bus Admin.

DIAZ, EFRAIN; Richard C Lee HS; New Haven, CT; (Y); Chess Clb; Var Bsbl; Hon Roll; Spanish NHS; Chrstphr Clmbs Essay Cntst 84; Acad Of Bus Careers; Bus Adm.

DIBBLE, PAIGE; Farmington HS; Farmington, CT; (Y); DECA; Chorus; Var Capt Cheerleading; High Hon Roll; Bus Mgmt.

DICKEY, ELEANOR; Andrew Warde HS; Westport, CT; (Y); Art Clb; French Clb; JCL; Orch; Lit Mag; Rep Stu Cncl; French Hon Soc; High Hon Roll; NHS; German Clb; Gold & Slvr Mdls For Ntl Latin Exam 83-84; Byrn Mawr Coll; Archaeology.

DICKINSON, CHRIS; East Catholic HS; Vernon, CT; (Y); 8/330; Computer Clb; Math Tm; Service Clb; Ski Clb; Nwsp Stf; Var Tennis; JV Wrstlng; High Hon Roll; Hon Roll; NHS; Schlr Athl, Big Bros 85; Hnr E Awd 83-85; Trinity Coll; Math.

DICKSON, SEAN; Tolland HS; Tolland, CT; (Y); JV Socr; Hon Roll; Yale U Appld Sci & Physcs Lectrs 84; Arch Engrng.

DICKSON, SHAWN; Coventry HS; Coventry, CT; (Y); Spanish Clb; Teachers Aide; Band; Concert Band; Mrchg Band; Pep Band; Lit Mag; VP Frsh Cls; Sec Jr Cls; Sec Sr Cls; Geomtry Excllnc Awd 83-84.

DIDIER, ELLEN; Saint Bernard HS; Gales Ferry, CT; (S); Church Yth Grp; Exploring; Girl Scts; School Play; Yrbk Stf; VP Mgr(s); Hon Roll; Ancilla Domini Awd 81; Slvr Awd 2nd Hghst GS Awd 84; Arch.

DIDIER, JOHN; St Bernard HS; Gales Ferry, CT; (S); 62/295; Spanish Clb; Band; Concert Band; Jazz Band; Mrchg Band; Pep Band; JV Socr; Hon Roll; Schlstc Awd Band; Elec Engrng.

DIGLIO, JEFFERY; Lyman Hall HS; Wallingford, CT; (Y); Bsbl; Bsktbl; Hon Roll; Prfct Atten Awd; Elec Engrng.

DIKEGOROS, PERSEFONE; Conard HS; W Hartford, CT; (Y); 22/291; VP Pres FBLA; Chorus; School Musical; Yrbk Stf; Rep Jr Cls; Rep Sr Cls; Stu Cncl; French Hon Soc; High Hon Roll; NHS; Gerald Hague Awd 85; Conard Retirees Awd 85; Briarwd Bk Prz 84; Bentley Coll; Bus.

DILETTUSO, MELISSA; Greens Farms Acad; Weston, CT; (Y); 9/40; AFS; Drama Clb; Ski Clb; Spanish Clb; School Play; Yrbk Phtg; Yrbk Stf; Capt Sftbl; Capt Vllybl; Hon Roll; Davidson Coll.

DILLANE, TIM; Central Catholic HS; Norwalk, CT; (Y); 1/80; Math Tm; VP Frsh Cls; VP Soph Cls; Pres Jr Cls; Pres Sr Cls; JV Var Bsbl; JV Bsktbl; JV Ftbl; High Hon Roll; NHS.

DILLMAN, TRACY; Cheshire HS; Cheshire, CT; (Y); 4/317; School Play; Rep Frsh Cls; Rep Jr Cls; Mgr Bsbl; Mgr Fld Hcky; Mgr Socr; High Hon Roll; Hon Roll; NHS; Mgr(s); Schlstc Achvt Awds 84-85; Magna Cum Laude Latin Awd 83; St Grant Schlrshp 85; Boston Coll; Psych.

DILLON, BEVIN C; Guilford HS; Guilford, CT; (Y); Cmnty Wkr; Model UN; Teachers Aide; Concert Band; Mrchg Band; Rep Stu Cncl; JV Fld Hcky; Hon Roll; Guilford Hand Crft Ctr Chrmns Schlrshp 84-85; Ctr Creatv Yth Wesleyan U 84; Fashn Desgn.

DILLON, JOHN; Thomaston HS; Thomaston, CT; (Y); 6/66; Am Leg Boys St; Spanish Clb; Church Choir; Concert Band; School Play; Var Crs Cntry; Var Trk; High Hon Roll; NHS; Aud/Vis; Rensselaer Math & Sci Awd 84-85; Comp Engr.

DIMARTINO, KRISTINE; Daniel Hand HS; Madison, CT; (Y); 23/247; High Hon Roll; Hon Roll; NHS; Church Yth Grp; Stage Crew; Jr Sci & Humanities Symposium 85; Ctr Creative Yth Wesleyan U 85; Pres A Better Chance Clb 85-86; Psych.

DIMOPLON, STEPHEN; Trumbull HS; Trumbull, CT; (Y); AFS; Var Crs Cntry; Var Trk; High Hon Roll; NHS; Ntl Merit Ltr; Ntl Merit Cmmnded Schlr 85; Bst Sci 83; Bio.

DINENNO, DENISE; Sacred Heart Acad; West Haven, CT; (Y); Church Yth Grp; Computer Clb; FBLA; Pep Clb; Nwsp Rptr; High Hon Roll; NHS; Prfct Atten Awd; Spanish NHS; Mothers Clb Schlrshp 82-83; Louis A Sidoli Schlrshp 85-86; FBLA Hstrn 85-86; Bus.

DINHO, ALAN; Danbury HS; Danbury, CT; (Y); 180/700; Church Yth Grp; Office Aide; Rep Frsh Cls; Soph Cls; JV Bsbl; Hon Roll; City Bsebl & All Star Games 82-84; Lndscpng.

DINSMORE, ALLISON; Southington HS; Southington, CT; (Y); Ski Clb; Variety Show; Bsktbl; Capt Socr; Sftbl; Trk; Hon Roll; NHS; Proj Discover 82-86.

DION, TERRANCE; Crosby HS; Waterbury, CT; (Y); Boy Scts; French Clb; Key Clb; Hon Roll; Arch.

DIONE, MICHELLE; The Morgan Schl; Clinton, CT; (Y); 11/160; Sec Church Yth Grp; Chorus; School Musical; Stage Crew; Yrbk Bus Mgr; Var L Tennis; Hon Roll; NHS; Acad Achv Awd In Soc Stds 85; Bentley Coll; Gen Bus.

DIORIO, GERI A; Notre Dame Catholic HS; Bridgeport, CT; (Y); 34/285; Keywanettes; Pres Library Aide; JV Trk; High Hon Roll; NHS; Ntl Merit Ltr; ALSMA Schlrshp 85; Pres Awd Acdmc Ftns 85; Bridgeport U; Marine Bio.

DISTASIO, KAREN; Brandford HS; Branford, CT; (Y); Am Leg Aux Girls St; Cmnty Wkr; Rep Frsh Cls; VP Soph Cls; Rep Jr Cls; Sec Stu Cncl; Cheerleading; Fld Hcky; Powder Puff Ftbl; God Cntry Awd; Lib Arts.

DIVITTIS, JENNIE; Holy Cross HS; Wolcott, CT; (Y); 126/352; German Clb; Library Aide; Nwsp Rptr; Nwsp Stf; VP Frsh Cls; Trs Jr Cls; Rep Stu Cncl; High Hon Roll; Hon Roll; Stat Bsbl; Nrs.

DIXON, KERRY; Tolland HS; Tolland, CT; (Y); Band; Jazz Band; Pep Band; Var L Socr; Var Trk; High Hon Roll; NHS.

DIXON, MARK; Trumbull HS; Trumbull, CT; (Y); Concert Band; Mrchg Band; JV Bsbl; Hon Roll; NCTE Achve Awds-Wrtg 84-85.

DIXON, SANDRA; New Milford HS; New Milford, CT; (Y); 2/303; JA; Math Tm; Ed Yrbk Stf; Lit Mag; Capt Crs Cntry; Trk; High Hon Roll; NHS; Ntl Merit Ltr; Hnrs Grp Westinghouses Sci Talent Srch 84; Renssalaer Mdl 84; Harvard Bk Awd 84; Engrng.

DIZES, KRISTINA; Berlin HS; Berlin, CT; (Y); 26/290; Church Yth Grp; Chorus; JV Fld Hcky; JV Vllybl; Hon Roll; Bus.

DIZIGAN, MARK; St Bernard HS; Waterford, CT; (S); Chess Clb; Computer Clb; Hon Roll; Top Clss Math Awd 83-84; Yale; Sci.

DOBERMAN, JENNIFER; William H Hall HS; W Hartford, CT; (Y); 45/322; FBLA; Pep Clb; Trs Sr Cls; Stu Cncl; Var Cheerleading; Var Fld Hcky; JV Gym; High Hon Roll; Hon Roll; NHS; Pre Dent.

DOBIE, STEPHEN; Notre Dame HS; Hamden, CT; (Y); 15/248; Am Leg Boys St; Boy Scts; Church Yth Grp; Cmnty Wkr; Ski Clb; High Hon Roll; Jr NHS; NHS; Racqutbl Clb 82-85; Math Hnr Soc 84-85; Outdr Clb 82-83.

DOBKINS, DAVID; Watertown HS; Oakville, CT; (Y); Am Leg Boys St; Var Ftbl; JV Trk; Wt Lftg; High Hon Roll; Awd Seal Exclince Chem 84-85; Sci.

DOBRINDT, RHONDA; Francis T Maloney HS; Meriden, CT; (Y); Art Clb; Aud/Vis; DECA; Drama Clb; JA; School Play; Stage Crew; Yrbk Phtg; Yrbk Rptr; Yrbk Stf; Busn Ownr.

DOCKUS, LISA; Daniel Hand HS; Madison, CT; (Y); Art Clb; Church Yth Grp; GAA; Pep Clb; Chorus; Nwsp Rptr; Nwsp Stf; Yrbk Rptr; Yrbk Stf; Rep Frsh Cls; Art.

DOCTOROFF, JEFFREY; Kingswood-Oxford Schl; W Hartford, CT; (Y); Hosp Aide; Math Tm; Q&S; Quiz Bowl; Scholastic Bowl; School Musical; School Play; Nwsp Ed-Chief; Rep Frsh Cls; Rep Soph Cls; Harvard-Radcliffe Clb Nrthn CT Prz 85; Director Of Sevrl Plays 84-85; Pre-Med.

DODGE, CAROL A; Danbury HS; Danbury, CT; (Y); 64/600; Key Clb; Variety Show; Yrbk Stf; High Hon Roll; Hon Roll; NHS; Tap-N-Jazz Schlrshp 83-84; Stu Wstchstr Theatre Dnc Acads 80-86; Trvlng Troupe-Bnft Prfrmncs; Dean JC; Dance.

DODGE, MICHAEL A; Oliver Wolcott Tech; Litchfield, CT; (S); 3/180; Rep Stu Cncl; Var Socr; Var Tennis; High Hon Roll; Hon Roll; NHS; Engrng.

DOERING, BRETT; Portland HS; Portland, CT; (Y); 7/90; Am Leg Boys St; Camera Clb; French Clb; Yrbk Ed-Chief; Yrbk Phtg; Var Capt Trk; NHS; Intnl Clb; Ski Clb; Rep Stu Cncl; Rochester Inst Tech; Photo.

DOERR, JENNIFER; The Morgan Schl; Clinton, CT; (Y); Library Aide; Spanish Clb; School Musical; Stage Crew; Variety Show; Nwsp Rptr; Yrbk Rptr; JV Fld Hcky; Hon Roll; Ntl Merit SF; Engl Achvt Awd 84.

DOLAN, PETER; Ridgefield HS; Ridgefield, CT; (Y); 95/450; DECA; Ski Clb; Varsity Clb; Nwsp Stf; Golf; Socr; High Hon Roll; Hon Roll; Value Awd 84; Div Stu Affairs Awd 84; Boston U; Bus Adm.

DOLAN, WALTER; North Haven SR HS; North Haven, CT; (Y); 49/330; FBLA; Letterman Clb; Science Clb; Ski Clb; Spanish Clb; Varsity Clb; Concert Band; Jazz Band; Mrchg Band; School Musical; Ftbl All Housatonic Leag 2nd Tm; Trck All Leag Champ Tm; Schlstc Hnr Rl; Western New England Coll; Acctg.

DOLLAK, MELISSA; Wm H Hall HS; W Hartford, CT; (Y); 145/324; High Hon Roll; Hon Roll; Bay Path JC Bus Awd 84-85; Chld Dev.

DOLNIER, KATHLEEN M; Trumbull HS; Trumbull, CT; (Y); Key Clb; Ski Clb; Yrbk Stf; Var Stu Cncl; JV Var Cheerleading; High Hon Roll; Gregg Typg Awd 84; Ballet, Jazz Dncg Awd 83; Mktg.

DOLYAK, DANIEL; Shelton HS; Shelton, CT; (Y); Spanish Clb; Hon Roll.

DOMBEK, SUSAN; Seymour HS; Oxford, CT; (S); 17/224; Teachers Aide; Mrchg Band; Pom Pon; High Hon Roll; NHS; Mst Acad Achvt Alg II 84; Gregg Typng Awd 84; U CT; Bus Mrktng.

DOMBROWSKI, WALTER; St Bernard HS; Jewett City, CT; (S).

DOMKOWSKI, PATRICK; Notre Dame HS; Bridgeport, CT; (Y); Am Leg Boys St; Pep Clb; Chorus; School Musical; School Play; Stage Crew; VP Frsh Cls; VP Jr Cls; Pres Stu Cncl; Wt Lftg; Foundr Notre Dame Care Clb 84-85; Awd Exclince Relign 85; Awd Ldrshp & Charactr 85; Fordham U; Chem.

DONAHUE, HEIDI; East Haven HS; E Haven, CT; (Y); 2/250; Hosp Aide; Trs Frsh Cls; Trs Soph Cls; Var L Swmmng; Var L Trk; NHS; Rotary Awd; Yrbk Stf; High Hon Roll.

DONALD, KAREN M; Farmington HS; Hartford, CT; (Y); Sec Church Yth Grp; Hosp Aide; Lib Teachers Aide; Chorus; Church Choir; Accntnt.

DONALDSON, MEG; Holy Cross HS; Woodbury, CT; (Y); 172/352; Hosp Aide; Hst Service Clb; Chorus; Nwsp Rptr; Nwsp Sprt Ed; Lit Mag; Mgr(s); Score Keeper; Cmnctns.

DONALDSON, MICHELLE; St Marys HS; W Haven, CT; (Y); 62/115; Sec Church Yth Grp; Pres Civic Clb; Cmnty Wkr; Intnl Clb; Service Clb; Spanish Clb; Variety Show; Sec Stu Cncl; Hon Roll; Prfct Atten Awd; Sclgy.

DONATO, DAVID; Bassick HS; Bpt, CT; (Y); Band; Concert Band; Mrchg Band; Orch; Pep Band; Arch.

DONOFRIO, DEBBY; Stratford HS; Stratford, CT; (Y); 13/241; Teachers Aide; High Hon Roll; Hon Roll; Outstndng Future Bus Women 85; Word Processing Awd 85; Math Tutor 83-84; Sacred Heart U; Bus.

DONOHUE, LIAM S; Wethersfield HS; Wethersfield, CT; (Y); 5/275; Am Leg Boys St; Scholastic Bowl; Ski Clb; VP Jr Cls; Pres Sr Cls; Var Socr; Sec NHS; Ntl Merit Ltr; NEDT Awd; Pres Schlr; Mst Prmsng Sci Stu 83; Chem.

DONOVAN, KELLEY; North Branford HS; North Branford, CT; (Y); Cmnty Wkr; School Play; JV Crs Cntry; JV Vllybl; Hon Roll; Ntl Merit Ltr; Voice Dem Awd; AFS; Church Yth Grp; Drama Clb; Bio Cert Achv 83; Sales Awd 84 & 85; Bus.

DONOVAN, LAUREN ANNE; Our Lady Of The Angels Acad; Somers, CT; (Y); 3/21; Math Tm; Model UN; Yrbk Stf; VP Sr Cls; High Hon Roll; Lion Awd; Pres Scholar Bay Path 85; Pres Acad Fit Awd 85; Awd Exclince Spn IV 85; Bay Path JC; Comp.

DOOHAN, JOSEPH; Fairfield College Prep; Stratford, CT; (Y); Political Wkr; Ntl Merit Ltr; U Of CO; Business.

DOOLEY, PATRICK J; Shelton HS; Shelton, CT; (Y); Boy Scts; Drama Clb; Exploring; Band; Mrchg Band; School Play; Stage Crew; Hon Roll; Ntl Hnr Rl 85; Sacred Heart U; Med Tech.

DORMAN, DEBORAH A; Killingly HS; Brooklyn, CT; (Y); 4/279; Varsity Clb; VP Stu Cncl; Var Bsktbl; Var L Tennis; Var Trk; Bausch & Lomb Sci Awd; French Hon Soc; Pres Jr NHS; Pres NHS; CT Coll; Math.

DORMAN, TAMMY; Seymour HS; Seymour, CT; (S); 10/215; AFS; Yrbk Stf; High Hon Roll; NHS; Voice Dem Awd; Prncpls Awd Of Merit 85; Parsons Schl Of Dsgn; Fshn Dsgn.

DORNFRIED, JAMES; St Thomas Aquinas HS; Kensington, CT; (Y); 3/143; Quiz Bowl; Red Cross Aide; Capt L Socr; Elks Awd; NHS; Rensselaer Medal; Rensselaer Polytech Inst; Chem.

DORSEY, JENNIFER; Sacred Heart Acad; New Haven, CT; (Y); Art Clb; Church Yth Grp; Computer Clb; Debate Tm; Ed Lit Mag; French Hon Soc; High Hon Roll.

DORSEY, SARAH; Guilford HS; Guilford, CT; (Y); 10/300; Church Yth Grp; Mgr Bsktbl; Mgr Sftbl; French Hon Soc; High Hon Roll; NHS; Ntl Merit Ltr; French Clb; German Clb; Girl Scts; German & Latin Hnr Soc; Am Assoc Trchrs Of German; 1st Prz Ntl Exam & Trip To Germany; Brown U; Lingustcs.

DOUGHERTY III, JAMES H; Ledyard HS; Ledyard, CT; (Y); 9/268; AFS; Am Leg Boys St; Church Yth Grp; Yrbk Sprt Ed; Var Capt Bsktbl; JV Socr; Var L Tennis; Hon Roll; NHS; Ntl Merit Ltr; Dartmouth Bk Clb Awd 84; U S Army Rsrve Natl Schlr/Ath Awd 85; Booster Clb Bsktbl Awd 84; U VA.

DOUGHTY, BONNIE; Plainville HS; Plainville, CT; (Y); 40/213; Church Yth Grp; Cmnty Wkr; Teachers Aide; Variety Show; Yrbk Stf; Stu Cncl; Var Capt Twrlr; Hon Roll; NHS; Stu Cncl Svc Awd 84 & 85; EAP Scholar 85; Plainville Fire Dept Scholar Geo & Ridabel Seymour Mem 85; St Joseph Coll; Spec Ed.

DOUGLAS, KATHY; Westhill HS; Stamford, CT; (Y); Gov Hon Prg Awd; High Hon Roll; Hon Roll; Jr NHS; NHS; Ntl Merit Schol; NEDT Awd; St Schlr; Outstndng JR Bus Dept 85; Ldrshp Awd Future Sec In Recgntn Outstndng Ldrshp Ablty 85; Ka Marine Gibbs Schl; Bus.

DOUGLAS, VERONICA ANN; Richard C Lee HS; New Haven, CT; (Y); 29/202; Hosp Aide; Pep Clb; Teachers Aide; Drill Tm; Stage Crew; Variety Show; Nwsp Ed-Chief; Nwsp Rptr; Nwsp Stf; Yrbk Rptr; NAACP Scholar 85; Mst Cls Spirit Awd 85fstar Reprtr Awd 85; Northeastern U; Mass Media.

DOUGLASS, RHONDA; Saint Marys HS; New Haven, CT; (Y); 15/115; Math Clb; Service Clb; Spanish Clb; Stage Crew; Variety Show; Yrbk Stf; High Hon Roll; Hon Roll; Soc Stud Awd, Am Hist Awd Hnrs Convocation 85; Merch.

DOUKAS, DAVID; Mark T Sheehan HS; Wallingford, CT; (Y); 72/236; Boys Clb Am; Var L Bsbl; Var L Bsktbl; Var L Ftbl; Hon Roll; Ind Psychlgst.

DOUTON JR, BERNARD; St Bernard HS; Waterford, CT; (S); 1/284; Church Yth Grp; Exploring; French Clb; Hosp Aide; Intnl Clb; Library Aide; Model UN; Office Aide; Ski Clb; Rep Jr Cls.

DOWD, DAVID; Enrico Fermi HS; Enfield, CT; (Y); 1/397; Am Leg Boys St; Model UN; Lit Mag; Var JV Bsbl; Var Capt Socr; High Hon Roll; NCTE Awd; NHS; Church Yth Grp; Cmnty Wkr; Schl Engl Litry Awds 81-84; Chrstn Yth Organ Bsktbl Chrstn Awd 84; Georgetown U; Hist.

DOWD, JENNIFER; Torrington HS; Torrington, CT; (Y); 4/330; Am Leg Aux Girls St; Rep Frsh Cls; Rep Soph Cls; Trs Jr Cls; Trs Stu Cncl; Var Crs Cntry; Capt Var Trk; High Hon Roll; VP NHS; French Clb; Delg Hugh O Brien Ldrshp Smnr 84; Harvard Bk Awd 85; Ex-Officio Mbr Bd Educ 85-86.

DOWLING, MARY PATRICIA; St Bernard; N Stonington, CT; (S); 22/289; Pres Dance Clb; Office Aide; School Play; Stat Bsbl; JV Cheerleading; JV Crs Cntry; Hon Roll; NHS; U CT.

DOWNING, THOMAS; North Haven HS; North Haven, CT; (Y); 18/294; Trs Band; Var Capt Golf; Church Yth Grp; Computer Clb; Quiz Bowl; Ski Clb; Spanish Clb; Concert Band; Jazz Band; School Musical; Amer Assn Physcs Tchrs Outstndng Stu Of Yr 85; U Of CT; Engrng.

DOYLE, JONATHAN; Fairfield Prep; Fairfield, CT; (Y); Im Bsktbl; Var Golf; JV Socr; Im Sftbl; Church Yth Grp; Drama Clb; Ski Clb; Church Choir; Stage Crew; Yrbk Phtg; Spcl Essay Awd 84; Yale; Bio.

DOYLE, LAURA; Trumbull HS; Trumbull, CT; (Y); Church Yth Grp; Chorus; Church Choir; Trs Stu Cncl; Swmmng; French Hon Soc; High Hon Roll; Jr NHS; NHS; Most Likely To Succeed 83; Intl Busnss.

DOYLE, SEAN; Notre Dame HS; N Haven, CT; (Y); Varsity Clb; Im Bsktbl; Var Capt Ftbl; Var L Trk; Im Wt Lftg; West Point; Pre-Law.

DOYLE, TIMOTHY; Danbury HS; Danbury, CT; (Y); Band; Concert Band; Mrchg Band; School Play; JV Tennis; Emerson Coll; Cmnctns.

DRAKE, CHRIS; Staples HS; Westport, CT; (Y); Cmnty Wkr; JA; Radio Clb; Ski Clb; Yrbk Phtg; Var L Golf; Advrtsng.

DRAKE, KARIN; Plainville HS; Plainville, CT; (Y); Cmnty Wkr; Political Wkr; Service Clb; Trs Ski Clb; Sec Jr Cls; Rep Stu Cncl; Var L Cheerleading; Var Trk; High Hon Roll; Hon Roll; Peer Education 83-84; Zoology.

DREW, CHRISTINE; Amity Regional SR HS; Orange, CT; (Y); Art Clb; French Clb; Latin Clb; Spanish Clb; Yrbk Stf; Hon Roll; Hnrb Mntn Natl Frnch Exam 83; Cls I & II Awds 84-85.

DREW, CHRISTOPHER SMITH; Avon Old Farms Schl; Avon, CT; (S); 3/100; Trs Model UN; Nwsp Ed-Chief; Var L Bsbl; Var L Socr; High Hon Roll; NHS; Duke U; Law.

DREWS, DENA A; Glastonbury HS; Glastonbury, CT; (Y); 17/393; French Clb; GAA; Red Cross Aide; Ski Clb; Jazz Band; Symp Band; Yrbk Stf; Lcrss; NHS; Ntl Merit SF; Hopwood Schlrshp 84; Arch.

DREZEK, DAWN; Windsor Locks HS; Windsor Locks, CT; (Y); 12/167; Church Yth Grp; Band; Concert Band; Mrchg Band; Hon Roll; Miss Teen CT Scholar & Rcgntn Pgnt 84; Colby-Sawyer Coll; Bus Admin.

DRIPCHAK, PETER; Southington HS; Southington, CT; (Y); Church Yth Grp; French Clb; Library Aide; Teachers Aide; Nwsp Ed-Chief; Hon Roll; Tchr.

DRISCOLL, KATHLEEN; Hall HS; W Hartford, CT; (Y); 39/324; Ski Clb; High Hon Roll; NHS; Engrng.

DRISCOLL, KEVIN; Danbury HS; Danbury, CT; (Y); 5/560; Variety Show; Yrbk Stf; VP Soph Cls; VP Jr Cls; VP Sr Cls; Stu Cncl; Crs Cntry; Elks Awd; High Hon Roll; Jr NHS; Harvard Bk Awd 84; Perkin Elmer Schlrshp 85; Exch Clb Stu Of Month 85; U Of PA; Civil Engr.

DROBISH, DIANA; Amity SR HS; Orange, CT; (Y); Drama Clb; Spanish Clb; Chorus; School Musical; School Play; Variety Show; Yrbk Stf; Stu Cncl; Var L Cheerleading; Hon Roll; Lead Roles Community Plays; Won Vanes Talnt Cont.

DRUGAN, DANIELLE ELIZABETH; Lyme Old Lyme HS; Old Lyme, CT; (Y); 25/125; Art Clb; Cmnty Wkr; Service Clb; Nwsp Stf; Yrbk Stf; Trs Jr Cls; JR Prom Queen; Drawng & Paintng Awd; Engl Awd; Capt Crew Tm; U CT; Clinicl Dietcn.

DSUPIN, SHELLY; Guilford HS; Guilford, CT; (Y); Church Yth Grp; Diving; GAA; Latin Clb; Pep Clb; Spanish Clb; Chorus; Rep Frsh Cls; Rep Soph Cls; Sec Jr Cls; Dr.

DU BAC, BRYAN DAVID; Trumbull HS; Trumbull, CT; (Y); Trs JA; Trs Key Clb; Office Aide; Trs Spanish Clb; Yrbk Stf; High Hon Roll; VP Fin JA 84 & 85; Natl JA Conf Del 85; Bryant Coll; Accntng.

DUBAIL, MICHELLE; Waterford HS; Waterford, CT; (Y); 32/205; AFS; Band; Mrchg Band; Sftbl; Hon Roll; Ruth Looby Awd 85; U Of CT; Acctnt.

DUBAUSKAS, LEIGH ANN; Holy Cross HS; Waterbury, CT; (Y); 34/352; GAA; Trs Service Clb; Var Capt Crs Cntry; Var Trk; High Hon Roll; NHS; Spanish NHS; Bus.

DUBE, JENNIFER; Tolland HS; Tolland, CT; (Y); 4-H; Library Aide; Office Aide; Chorus; Cit Awd; 4-H Awd; Hon Roll; Ctznshp WA Fcs 84; WA Conf 85; Natl 4-H Cngrss 85; Nrsng.

DUBE, PETER; Fairfield College Prep; Fairfield, CT; (Y); Am Leg Boys St; Civic Clb; Key Clb; Yrbk Stf; Lcrss.

DUBIK, ANNA LESIA; New Britain HS; New Britain, CT; (Y); Church Yth Grp; Dance Clb; Church Choir; Vllybl; Ukrainian Schl 73-84; Vet Med.

DUBNICKA, PAUL; West Haven HS; W Haven, CT; (Y); Computer Clb; Var L Tennis; High Hon Roll; Jr NHS.

DUCHARME, LORI; Marianapolis Prep; Douglas, MA; (Y); 2/49; Nwsp Ed-Chief; Nwsp Rptr; Yrbk Stf; Sec Stu Cncl; Cheerleading; High Hon Roll; NHS; Sal; Englsh Awd, US Hstry & Scl Stds Medal 85; CT Coll; Pltcl Sci.

DUDA, WENDY; Notre Dame Catholic HS; Easton, CT; (Y); 27/254; Art Clb; French Clb; Trs Key Clb; Library Aide; Pep Clb; Yrbk Stf; NHS; Social Judgs Awd Most Cratv Art Show Notre Dame 85; Fairfield U; Psychlgy.

DUER, KELLY; Holy Cross HS; Wolcott, CT; (Y); 116/352; Cmnty Wkr; Teachers Aide; Var Cheerleading; Hon Roll; Spanish NHS; Elem Ed.

DUFFANY, REBECCA; Thomaston HS; Thomaston, CT; (Y); #4 In Class; Spanish Clb; School Play; Trs Frsh Cls; VP Soph Cls; Pres Jr Cls; Pres Stu Cncl; Var L Cheerleading; Var Trk; NHS; Marguerite Magraw Scholar 85; Stu Cncl Scholar 85; Spn Awd 85; Western CT ST U; Bus Admin.

DUHL, ADAM J; Newington HS; Newington, CT; (Y); 1/340; Am Leg Boys St; Sec Key Clb; Math Clb; Scholastic Bowl; Nwsp Sprt Ed; Rep Stu Cncl; High Hon Roll; NHS; Ntl Merit Schol; Val; Harvard Bk Awd, Ntl Hnr Society 83-84; Ntl Hnr Society Schlrsph, Premier Math Stu Awd 84-85; U Of PA.

DUMAS, MARCO; Windham Reg Voc Tech Schl; Stafford Spgs, CT; (Y); Computer Clb; VICA; Yrbk Stf; Rep Stu Cncl; High Hon Roll; Hon Roll; NHS; Elec Engrng.

DUNBAR, SUSAN ALEXANDRA; South Windsor HS; S Windsor, CT; (Y); 57/328; Drama Clb; 4-H; Thesps; Acpl Chr; School Musical; Swing Chorus; Mgr Stat Ftbl; Church Yth Grp; Cmnty Wkr; Dance Clb; All ST Chrl Grp 85; 1st Pl Awds Chrl Grps 85; Cmmnctns.

DUNCAN, TRINITY BROOKE; Central HS; Bridgeport, CT; (Y); English Clb; Library Aide; Teachers Aide; Church Choir; Wt Lftg; Hon Roll; Proj Bus 82-83; Peer Proj 82-83; Schlrshp & Diploma Billard Havens Tech 82-86; U Of Bridgeport; Vet.

DUNN JR, JAMES; Staples HS; Westport, CT; (Y); Boy Scts; Ski Clb; Varsity Clb; Bsbl; Var L Bsktbl; Var L Ftbl; Ice Hcky; Lcrss; Var Socr; Wt Lftg; U Of CO; Econ.

DUNN, RICHARD; Windsor HS; Windsor, CT; (Y); 43/310; Am Leg Boys St; Crs Cntry; Diving; Golf; Swmmng; Tennis; Wt Lftg; Hon Roll; U Of RI; Poli Sci.

DUNNACK, KERRY; R H A M HS; Andover, CT; (Y); Art Clb; Dance Clb; English Clb; French Clb; Soroptimist; Drill Tm; Mrchg Band; Nwsp Rptr; Nwsp Stf; Yrbk Rptr; 1st Pl Soroptimist Art Shw 84; 1st Pl Desgn Art Shw 85; Fine Art.

DUPRE, MICHAEL; Notre Dame HS; W Haven, CT; (Y); 7/254; Boy Scts; Church Yth Grp; French Clb; Band; Concert Band; Mrchg Band; Pep Band; School Musical; French Hon Soc; High Hon Roll; Math Hnr Scty 83-85; Frnch Awd & Schlrshp 85-86; Mrching Band 84-85; Engrng.

DURKIN, IAN; Brookfield HS; Brookfield, CT; (Y); 14/203; Pres Trs AFS; Political Wkr; Q&S; Nwsp Stf; Trs Frsh Cls; Pres Stu Cncl; JV Capt Socr; High Hon Roll; NHS; Rotary Awd; WA Wrkshp Congrssnl Semnrs Part 85; Exchng Stu To Brazil 83-84; Rcvd Undergrad Awds Am-Govt 85; Intl Rel.

DURWIN, KAREN; Trumbull HS; Trumbull, CT; (S); DECA; FBLA; Rep Stu Cncl; High Hon Roll; Finance & Credit Wrtn Event ST CDC 2nd Pl 85; Typng Awd 84; U CT; Bus.

DUTERTRE, ALBERT; Stamford HS; Stamford, CT; (S); Drama Clb; Stage Crew; Hon Roll; NHS; Aviation.

DUTKO, JILL; Lyman Hall HS; Wallingford, CT; (Y); 8/250; JA; Off Stu Cncl; Diving; Capt Twrlr; Vllybl; High Hon Roll; Hon Roll; Accntng I Awd 85; Outstndng Achvr Awd 85; Bus Adm.

DUTTA, RAJAT; Stamford HS; Stamford, CT; (S); Boy Scts; Debate Tm; Pres JA; Swmmng; Hon Roll; Hon Roll; NHS; AFS; Ski Clb; Mgr(s); Outstndg Yng Bus Man 85; 1st Spkr CT Debtng Assn 84; NAJAC, ROJAC Awds 85; Bio.

DUVALL, SUE; East Hampton HS; Cobalt, CT; (Y); 1/93; Am Leg Aux Girls St; Drama Clb; Model UN; School Musical; Pres Jr Cls; Pres Pres Stu Cncl; Var L Socr; Var L Trk; NHS; Pres Schlr; Harvard Bk Awd 84; United Technlgs Schlrshp 85; Century III Ldrs Schlrshp-St Fnlst 85; Brown U; Social Stds.

DUWAN, PAUL; Avon Old Farms Schl; Avon, CT; (S); 1/100; Church Yth Grp; Model UN; Quiz Bowl; Yrbk Ed-Chief; JV Bsbl; Var L Socr; Ntl Merit Ltr; Val; Harvard Book Prize 84; Cum Laude Soc 84-85; Princeton U; Biol.

DUZY, GLENN; St Bernard HS; Gales Ferry, CT; (Y); 127/300; Art Clb; Computer Clb; Science Clb; Crs Cntry; Aerosp Engr.

DWELLY, STEPHEN T; Tolland HS; Tolland, CT; (Y); Boy Scts; Rep Sr Cls; Var Capt Crs Cntry; Var Trk; Hon Roll; Pres Schlr; Eagl Sct 84; Ordr Arrw 82; U Of Hartford; Mech Engrng.

DWYER, MICHELE M; East Lyme HS; Niantic, CT; (Y); Church Yth Grp; Girl Scts; Mrchg Band; Var Capt Tennis; L Capt Twrlr; Hon Roll; 1st Cls Girl Scts 81; All ECC Ten 84; Outstndng Auxlry 84; Worcester Polytech; Comp Sci.

DYER, LINDA; Griswold HS; Jewett City, CT; (Y); 2/100; Church Yth Grp; 4-H; GAA; Girl Scts; Hosp Aide; Varsity Clb; Chorus; Church Choir; Variety Show; Rep Jr Cls; Hrtfrd Schl Of Musci Schlrshp 83; Music Awd 84; U Of CT; Physcl Thrpy.

DYKEMA, ERIK P; New Canaan HS; New Canaan, CT; (Y); Cmnty Wkr; JA; Math Tm; L Crs Cntry; High Hon Roll; Ntl Merit SF; Bus.

DZIENNIS, SUZAN; Canton HS; Collinsville, CT; (Y); 1/80; Church Yth Grp; Thesps; Band; Jazz Band; School Musical; Lit Mag; Im Vllybl; High Hon Roll; NHS; Trinity Coll Book Awd 85; Outstndng Achvt Awds In Psychlgy, Frnch II, Hmn Bdy, & Frnch I 83-84.

EARL, JENNIFER A; Crosby HS; Waterbury, CT; (Y); Hosp Aide; Key Clb; Latin Clb; Trs Jr Cls; Trs Sr Cls; Stu Cncl; Hon Roll; NHS.

EARLY, MICHAEL; Southington HS; Southington, CT; (Y); FCA; Variety Show; Nwsp Stf; Capt Crs Cntry; Capt Trk; All ST & All Conf Cross Cntry & Trk 83-85; Accntng.

EARLY, RENEE; Shelton HS; Shelton, CT; (Y); Am Leg Aux Girls St; Drama Clb; Rep Frsh Cls; Trs Soph Cls; Rep Jr Cls; Rep Stu Cncl; French Hon Soc; High Hon Roll; NHS; Exploring; Frnch Awd; Intl Rltns.

EARNEST, MELISSA; New Fairfield HS; New Fairfield, CT; (Y); 50/237; Rptr DECA; Variety Show; JV Var Cheerleading; Hon Roll; Phy Thrpy.

ECABERT, FRANCINE; Manchester HS; Manchester, CT; (Y); Debate Tm; French Clb; Stu Cncl; Crs Cntry; Hon Roll; Fshn Shw Displyd Drss 83; Tufts; Vet.

ECKBRETH, KELLY ANNE; Glastonbury HS; Glastonbury, CT; (Y); 25/393; Cmnty Wkr; Ski Clb; Concert Band; Mrchg Band; Orch; Symp Band; Nwsp Rptr; JV Var Cheerleading; Var Trk; High Hon Roll; Outstndng Vlntr Wrk Music, Art Camp 84; Cert Recgntn NASA 84; Comp Sci Engrng.

EDELSON, SHARON; Norwalk HS; Norwalk, CT; (Y); French Clb; High Hon Roll; Hon Roll; Parsons Schl Design; Fash Desgn.

EDER, KATRINA; Sacred Hearth Acad; Darien, CT; (Y); Church Yth Grp; Drama Clb; French Clb; JCL; School Musical; School Play; Sftbl; Vllybl; Hon Roll; Slvr Mdl-Ntl Latn Exm 83; Oratrcl Awd-Amer Lgn 85; U Of CT; Vet Med.

EDGECOMB, TODD; Southington HS; Southington, CT; (Y); JV Bsbl; Var JV Ftbl; Hon Roll; Law Enfrcmt.

EDSON, SALLY ANN; Cheshire HS; Cheshire, CT; (Y); Yrbk Stf; Sec Frsh Cls; Sec Soph Cls; Var L Bsktbl; Var L Fld Hcky; Var L Trk; Hon Roll; Cit Awd; All Housatonic Lg Tm Trk 83, Field Hockey 84; All ST Field Hockey 84; Bio.

EDWARDS, BECKY; East Hartford HS; E Hartford, CT; (Y); French Clb; JA; Ski Clb; Band; Concert Band; Jazz Band; Mrchg Band; Pep Band; Symp Band; Tennis.

EDWARDS, BRIAN; Greenwich HS; Cos Cob, CT; (Y); Am Leg Boys St; Pres JA; Jazz Band; Nwsp Ed-Chief; Pres Frsh Cls; JV Bsbl; Jr NHS; Ntl Merit Ltr; Spanish NHS; Coll Of Holy Cross Bk Prz 85.

EDWARDS, JENINE; Hillhouse HS; New Haven, CT; (Y); Church Yth Grp; Church Choir; Yrbk Stf; Rep Stu Cncl; Sftbl; High Hon Roll; Hon Roll; NHS; 1st Pl Frnch II Prz Exam 85; 2nd Pl Frnch I Prz Exam 84; 2nd Pl Frnc II COLT Poetry Cont 85; Frnch.

EDWARDS, LISA; Thomaston HS; Thomaston, CT; (Y); 1/75; Church Yth Grp; French Clb; Teachers Aide; Church Choir; Yrbk Stf; Rep Stu Cncl; JV Stat Ftbl; Mgr(s); Score Keeper; JV Stat Sftbl; Typng Awd 83; Frnch Awd 84; Engl Awd 85; Clark U; Math.

EDWARDS, LYNETTE; Richard C Lee HS; New Haven, CT; (Y); 19/202; Library Aide; Math Clb; Rep Frsh Cls; Rep Soph Cls; Vllybl; Hon Roll; NHS; Pres Schlr; St Schlr; Cty Schlr Awd 85; Richard Clee Endwmnt Awd Outstndng SR 85; Greatest Effrt Ed Pursuit Awd 85; Central CT ST U; Acctnt.

EDWARDS, TRACY; Branford HS; Branford, CT; (Y); Church Yth Grp; Dance Clb; Library Aide; PAVAS; Teachers Aide; Chorus; School Play; Variety Show; Yrbk Stf; Off Jr Cls; Music.

EGAN, MARTY; Oliver Wolcott Tech; Thomaston, CT; (S); 3/160; Rep Jr Cls; L Bsbl; L Bsktbl; High Hon Roll; Hon Roll; Jr NHS; NHS; MVP Bsktbl & Bsebl 83-85; Waterbury ST Tech; Electrncs.

EGAN, MARY; Sacred Heart Acad; Stamford, CT; (Y); Drama Clb; Hosp Aide; Lit Mag; Rep Frsh Cls; Rep Jr Cls; JV Capt Bsktbl; Var Cheerleading; Var JV Vllybl; French Hon Soc; Hon Roll; Mst Imprvd Bsktbl Plyr 82-83; USCAA Chrldng Awd 84-85; Bates; Bio.

EISMAN, HANNAH; West Haven HS; W Haven, CT; (Y); 12/341; Pres Soph Cls; Rep Stu Cncl; Var Crs Cntry; Var L Tennis; Hon Roll; Jr NHS; Sec NHS; Hugh O Brien Yth Found Ldrshp Sem; Rec Womans Clb Awd; Awd W H Tennis Assoc; U Vermont; Bus Adm.

EKROTH, MATT; Ellington HS; Ellington, CT; (Y); 39/172; Yrbk Phtg; Yrbk Stf; Trk; Engrng.

ELDREDGE, JOHN; East Lyne HS; E Lyme, CT; (Y); Boy Scts; JV Bsbl; Capt Var Ice Hcky; Hon Roll; New London Emblem Clb Schlrshp 85; Joseph L De Lura Schlrshp 85; Niantic Rotary Clb Schlrshp 85; Quinnipiac Coll; Comp Info Syst.

ELDRIDGE, TRICIA; Killingly HS; Danielson, CT; (Y); Church Yth Grp; Dance Clb; Teachers Aide; Band; Concert Band; Mrchg Band; Pep Band; Symp Band; Hon Roll; QVCC; Bus Mgmt.

ELKOW, CHRISTOPHER; Ridgefield HS; Ridgefield, CT; (S); 101/375; Church Yth Grp; Church Choir; Drm Mjr(t); Mrchg Band; Orch; School Musical; Symp Band; Variety Show; High Hon Roll; Ithaca Coll; Music Ed.

ELLINGTON, DAVID; Saint Bernard HS; Stonington, CT; (S); 71/300; Boy Scts; Band; Rep Jr Cls; Var Stat Bsktbl; Score Keeper; Trk; Hon Roll; Elec Engrng.

ELLIOTT, LAURA E; Southington HS; Southington, CT; (Y); Pep Clb; Camp Fr Inc; Var L Swmmng; High Hon Roll; Hon Roll; NHS; Fnncl Advsr.

ELLIOTT, MICHAEL J; Windham HS; Canterbury, CT; (Y); 30/285; Am Leg Boys St; Jr Cls; Sr Cls; Var Capt Bsbl; JV Bsktbl; Var L Ftbl; Hon Roll; Pres Schlr; St Schlr; Am Stu Athlt 84; Brandeis U; Comp Sci.

ELLIOTT, THOMAS; Canton HS; Collinsville, CT; (Y); 11/100; Model UN; Band; Jazz Band; School Musical; Stu Cncl; JV Var Bsbl; JV Var Bsktbl; JV Var Socr; Hotel Mgmt.

ELLIS, KIM; Amity Regional HS; Woodbridge, CT; (Y); Church Yth Grp; Yrbk Sprt Ed; Yrbk Stf; Pres Rep Stu Cncl; Var JV Bsktbl; JV Var Vllybl; Hon Roll; NHS; Mgr(s); Sftbl.

ELOVICH, JENNIFER; Trumbull HS; Trumbull, CT; (Y); Ski Clb; Band; Color Guard; Yrbk Stf; Rep Jr Cls; High Hon Roll; Hon Roll; Van Duren Awd Engl Excllnc 85; U NH; Lbrl Arts.

ELVERSKOG, CARL; Wilton HS; Wilton, CT; (Y); Ski Clb; Varsity Clb; Band; Nwsp Bus Mgr; Nwsp Ed-Chief; High Hon Roll; Acctng.

EMBARDO, LISA; Holy Cross HS; Waterbury, CT; (Y); 4/352; Am Leg Aux Girls St; Pres Service Clb; High Hon Roll; NHS; Italian Hnr Soc 84-85; Italian II SR Awd 84-85; Acad All-Amer.

EMELKO, MARK; Farmington HS; Farmington, CT; (Y); Boy Scts; Cmnty Wkr; Ski Clb; Nwsp Sprt Ed; JV Trk; Var Wrstlng; Hon Roll; Eagle Scout With Gld Palm 84-85; Ad Altaire Dei 84; Ordr Of Arrow-Chptr VP 84-85; Arch.

EMOUS, J DEREK; Brunswick HS; Greenwich, CT; (Y); Var L Socr; Ntl Merit Ltr; Pres Schlr; Church Yth Grp; Stage Crew; JV Bsbl; JV Tennis; Cert Hnr 82-84; Hgh Hnrs Cert 84-85; Cum Laude Socty 84-85; Dartmouth Coll; Comp Sci.

ENGEL, SAMANTHA E; Naugatuck HS; Naugatuck, CT; (Y); Debate Tm; French Clb; Sec Stu Cncl; Var Sftbl; High Hon Roll; NHS; Polit Sci.

ENGELBRECHTSEN, CLAUS; Fairfield Prep; Stamford, CT; (Y); Bus.

ENGLAND JR, JOHN F; Southington HS; Southington, CT; (Y); 30/560; Aud/Vis; Church Yth Grp; Key Clb; Ski Clb; Concert Band; Mrchg Band; Yrbk Sprt Ed; Stu Cncl; High Hon Roll; NHS; Hon Men Colt Frgn Lang Poetry Cont 84; U CT; Civl Engrng.

ENGLISH, GAIL L; Granby Memorial HS; Granby, CT; (Y); 3/108; AFS; Drama Clb; Library Aide; Nwsp Stf; Yrbk Stf; Rep Frsh Cls; JV Bsktbl; JV Var Fld Hcky; JV Var Sftbl; High Hon Roll; Am Leg Sprtmnshp Awd; 3rd Grad Cls; Granby Cmnty Scholar; Fairfield U; Bio.

ENGLISH, SUSAN; Bethel HS; Bethel, CT; (Y); 7/265; Ski Clb; Variety Show; Nwsp Stf; Sec Soph Cls; Trs Jr Cls; Rep Stu Cncl; Tennis; High Hon Roll; NHS.

EPPINGER, ERIC; Rham HS; Marlborough, CT; (Y); Am Leg Boys St; Church Yth Grp; Yrbk Phtg; JV Bsktbl; Var Socr; Var Tennis; Hon Roll; Ski Clb; Band; Jazz Band; WA DC Smr Intrnshp 85; Cliff Martinez Schlrshp 85; Peter Crawford Schlrshp 84; Bus Ecnmcs.

EPSTEIN, LAURIE; Cheshire HS; Cheshire, CT; (Y); 1/319; French Clb; Red Cross Aide; Teachers Aide; Band; Concert Band; School Play; Yrbk Stf; CC Awd; French Hon Soc; High Hon Roll; PTO Orgnztn Memrl Schlrshp 85; DKG Schlrshp 85; Nrthestrn U; Physcl Thrpy.

EPSTEIN, STEVEN; Conard HS; West Hartford, CT; (Y); 13/314; Am Leg Boys St; Cmnty Wkr; Drama Clb; Chorus; School Musical; School Play; NHS; Spanish NHS; Psych.

ERICKSON, AMY; Berlin HS; Kensington, CT; (Y); 42/180; Church Yth Grp; Drama Clb; FHA; Color Guard; School Musical; Powder Puff Ftbl; Socr; Engl.

ERICKSON, TROY; Wethersfield HS; Wethersfield, CT; (Y); 32/315; Am Leg Boys St; Church Yth Grp; Ski Clb; Yrbk Sprt Ed; VP Stu Cncl; Var L Socr; Var L Tennis; NHS; Cmnty Wkr; Dance Clb; All Conf,All ST Soccer 83-84; Bus.

ERLENHEIM, JUDITH; Trumbull HS; Trumbull, CT; (Y); Chorus; Madrigals; Lit Mag; High Hon Roll; NHS; Vassar Bk Awd 85; Most Outstndng Eng 83; Italian Clb Pres 85; Brdcstng.

ESHOO, MARLENE; Berlin HS; Kensington, CT; (Y); Church Yth Grp; Hosp Aide; Church Choir; Concert Band; Trs Mrchg Band; Pep Band; Yrbk Stf; Stu Cncl; JV Cheerleading; Var Socr; Oil Pntng Awd 83-84; Physcl Ed Awd 83-85; Outstndng Sop & JR Music Awd 83-85; Graphic Design.

ESPINOZA, SHEILA JEANETTE; New Britain HS; New Britain, CT; (Y); Camera Clb; Cmnty Wkr; JA; Key Clb; Office Aide; Spanish Clb; Rep Stu Cncl; CC Awd; Hon Roll; SR Ctr Dir For Day 85; Rep Stu Cncl 85-86; JA 85; Bus Law.

ESPINOZA, YVONNE; Northwest Catholic HS; Hartford, CT; (Y); Church Yth Grp; Dance Clb; Hosp Aide; Spanish Clb; Nwsp Stf; Lit Mag; High Hon Roll; Hon Roll; Spansh Awd 82-83; Comm Art.

ESPOSITO, DAVID; Joseph A Foran HS; Milford, CT; (Y); 1/260; Am Leg Boys St; Key Clb; VP Latin Clb; Pres Soph Cls; Pres Jr Cls; Pres Sr Cls; Var L Bsbl; Var L Ftbl; Capt L Wrstlng; Pres NHS; Harvard Bk Awd 85; Excell Chem 84; Excell Latin I,II & III 83-85; Med.

ESPOSITO, LIA; East Haven HS; East Haven, CT; (Y); 23/300; Church Yth Grp; Teachers Aide; Hon Roll; Pres Schlr; Jan Stopka Italian Schlrshp Awd 85; Italian Clb Tres 81-85; Southern CT ST U; Tchng.

ESPOSITO, LISA; Trumbull HS; Trumbull, CT; (Y); Sec Jr Cls; Fld Hcky; High Hon Roll; NHS; Cert Prof Awd Acctng 85; Acctng.

ESPOSITO, MICHELE; North Branford HS; Northford, CT; (Y); 15/187; Nwsp Ed-Chief; VP Frsh Cls; Pres Soph Cls; Pres Jr Cls; DAR Awd; Hon Roll; NHS; St Monicas Rosary Scty Schlrshp 85; Exc In Frgn Lng 85; Bryant Coll; Mrktng.

ESPOSITO, TONI LYNN; St Paul Catholic HS; Southington, CT; (Y); French Clb; Chorus; School Play; Rep Soph Cls; Rep Jr Cls; Rep Sr Cls; Stu Cncl; French Hon Soc; Anna Tedesco Mem Schlrshp 84; Music Awd 82; Med.

ESTELLE, DIANE; St Bernard HS; Groton Long Point, CT; (S); Church Yth Grp; Chorus; Church Choir; Off Stu Cncl; Var Diving; Hon Roll.

ESTEVES, ANTONIO; Naugatuck HS; Naugatuck, CT; (Y); Hon Roll; U Of CT; Elec Engr.

ESTONY, JENNIFER; Staples HS; Westport, CT; (Y); Pep Clb; Band; Chorus; School Musical; Yrbk Stf; Off Sr Cls; Var L Cheerleading; Powder Puff Ftbl; Var L Vllybl; Hon Roll; High 2nd Hnrs 81-85; Ntl Chrldrs Assn Spirit Awd 84; Retl Sls & Mktg.

ETERGINIO, CARLA M; Crosby HS; Waterbury, CT; (Y); Office Aide; School Musical; School Play; Mgr(s); Hon Roll; St Schlr; Wtrbury ST Tech Coll; Elec Eng.

EVANS, BRETT; Guilford HS; Guilford, CT; (Y); 22/308; Latin Clb; Yrbk Stf; Trs Frsh Cls; Pres Soph Cls; Rep Stu Cncl; JV Bsktbl; JV Crs Cntry; JV Trk; Hon Roll; NHS; Schlr Athl Awd 84; Engrng.

EVANS, DAVID B; Bloomfield HS; Bloomfield, CT; (Y); 10/254; Yrbk Ed-Chief; Lit Mag; Rep Jr Cls; Var Capt Trk; High Hon Roll; NHS; Ntl Merit Ltr; Spanish NHS; Civic Clb; Letterman Clb; Full Schlrshp Wnnr; U Of CT Day Of Pride Awd 84-85; Engrng.

EVANS, JAMES; Stamford Catholic HS; Stamford, CT; (Y); 57/148; Boy Scts; FBLA; JA; Nwsp Rptr; Nwsp Sprt Ed; Lit Mag; Rep Sr Cls; Stu Cncl; JV Var Bsbl; JV Stat Bsktbl; RI U; Accntng.

EVANS, MARK; Farmington HS; Farmington, CT; (Y); 52/230; Aud/Vis; Camera Clb; Church Yth Grp; Cmnty Wkr; Stage Crew; JV Ftbl; Im Golf; Var L Wrstlng; Bus.

EVANS, MELINDA; Danbury HS; Danbury, CT; (Y); 77/612; Church Yth Grp; Exploring; Hosp Aide; Key Clb; High Hon Roll; Hon Roll; Engrng.

EVANS, NANCY; Rockville HS; Vernon, CT; (Y); 60/367; Girl Scts; Hosp Aide; Ski Clb; Band; Yrbk Sprt Ed; Stu Cncl; Var Cheerleading; Powder Puff Ftbl; Hon Roll; Spcl Schlstc Merit Awd Steamftng 85; Ind Imprvmnt Fund; Gettysburg Coll.

EVANS, THOMAS; St Bernard HS; Willimantic, CT; (Y); Var L Ftbl.

EVELAND, JEFFREY; Greenwich HS; Riverside, CT; (Y); Am Leg Boys St; Bsktbl; Coach Actv; JV Var Socr; Var Trk; High Hon Roll; NHS; Ntl Merit Ltr; Church Yth Grp; Band; CT Hnrs Sem Excptnl Stu 85; Church Play 85; Summr Yth Fest 85.

EVON JR, FRANCIS J; Naugatuck HS; Naugatuck, CT; (Y); 5/322; Am Leg Boys St; Boy Scts; Red Cross Aide; VP Spanish Clb; Band; Pres Jr Cls; Pres Sr Cls; VP Stu Cncl; JV Bsktbl; Cit Awd; Regstr Yth Yr; U Of CT; Bus.

EVON, SCOTT J; Naugatuck HS; Naugatuck, CT; (Y); 13/340; Am Leg Boys St; Boy Scts; Var L Bsbl; High Hon Roll; U Of CT Hnrs Semnr 85; Proj Sage Post Coll 85.

EWAN, TODD; Choate Rosemary Hall HS; Katonah, NY; (Y); French Clb; Pres JA; Letterman Clb; Model UN; Varsity Clb; Var L Bsktbl; Var L Ftbl; Var L Lcrss; Im Wt Lftg; High Hon Roll; SR Stu Advsr 85-86; Mth.

FABRYCKI JR, EDWARD; Bulkeley HS; Hartford, CT; (Y); Computer Clb; Civil Engr.

FAGAN, DAWN; Jonathan Law HS; Milford, CT; (Y); Color Guard; Ed Yrbk Stf; Hon Roll; NHS; Pres Schlr; Rotary Awd; Trs Computer Clb; Sprntndnts Schlstc Awd; Ntl Merit Hnr Roll; Drexel U; Comp Sci.

FALES, EMERSON; Pomfret Schl; Miami, FL; (Y); Church Yth Grp; JV Ice Hcky; JV Socr; Capt Tennis; Tour Guide; Press Club.

FALLIS, BARBARA; Southington HS; Southington, CT; (Y); Key Clb; Library Aide; Chorus; Hon Roll; Central CT ST U; Accntnt.

FALLON, FRANCES; Manchester HS; Manchester, CT; (Y); Church Yth Grp; French Clb; Sec JA; Hon Roll; Post JC; Fash Mech.

FALLON, SCOTT; Bristol Central HS; Bristol, CT; (Y); #30 In Class; Am Leg Boys St; Cmnty Wkr; Ski Clb; Spanish Clb; Band; Jazz Band; Orch; Stu Cncl; Var L Golf; JV Socr; CT Prncpls Awd 85; U Of CT; Bus.

FANNING, SERENA; Lewis S Mills HS; Harwinton, CT; (Y); 12/156; Church Yth Grp; VP FHA; Hosp Aide; Office Aide; VP Frsh Cls; Soph Cls; Cheerleading; Hon Roll; NHS; Pres Schlr; 4th Crochet, 2000 Clb, Bible Achvt 83; Consumer Tm Awd 84; U Denver; Bus Mgt.

FAPPIANO, MARIA LISA; Sacred Heart Acad; North Haven, CT; (Y); Hosp Aide; School Musical; Med Tech.

FARGEORGE, CAROLINE; Sacred Heart Acad; New Haven, CT; (Y); Church Yth Grp; Cmnty Wkr; Sec French Clb; Hosp Aide; Pep Clb; School Musical; Off Jr Cls; Im Vllybl; High Hon Roll; Ntl Merit SF; Pre-Law.

FARLEY, MARY SUE; Convent Of The Sacred Heart; Bedford, NY; (Y); 1/40; Pres Model UN; Nwsp Stf; Rep Stu Cncl; High Hon Roll; NHS; Ntl Merit SF; Natl Sci Merit Awd 84; Harvard Book Awd 83; Intl Banker.

FARNHAM, LUCINDA MAE; Windham Regional Vo-Tech HS; Ashford, CT; (Y); Camera Clb; Var Cheerleading; Hon Roll; NHS; Prfct Atten Awd; Mach Drftng.

FASCIANO, CLAUDIA; Lyme-Old Lyme HS; Old Lyme, CT; (Y); 18/125; Ski Clb; JV Crs Cntry; JV Var Tennis; Var JV Trk; High Hon Roll; Hon Roll; 4th Pl ST Champ Trck Race 4x100 Relay 85; 2nd Pl Shoreline Champ Trck Race 4x400 Relay 85; Htl/Rest Mgmt.

FASOLD, KIMBERLY A; Academy Of Our Lady Of Mercy HS; Milford, CT; (Y); 74/111; Church Yth Grp; Cmnty Wkr; Dance Clb; Hosp Aide; Service Clb; Spanish Clb; Chorus; Nwsp Rptr; Yrbk Stf; Rep Stu Cncl; 300-Hr Awd Mlfd Hosptl 85; Outstndng Svc Awd St Marys Chrch 85; Hofstra U; Poli Sci.

FAUCETTE, HENRY; Hartford Public HS; Hartford, CT; (Y); Nwsp Rptr; Nwsp Stf; Lit Mag; JV Var Wrstlng; Cit Awd; High Hon Roll; Hon Roll; NHS; Prfct Atten Awd; St Schlr; Summr Sessn Chote Rosemary Hall Scholar 84-85; Acturial Sci.

FAUCI, TRACY C; Westhill HS; Stamford, CT; (Y); 115/460; Drama Clb; Hosp Aide; Pres JA; School Play; Stage Crew; Var L Sftbl; Var L Trk; Hon Roll; JR Achvt Schlrshp 85; MVP Indr Trk Trphy 85; SR Awd-Trk & Sftbl 85; U Of CT; Intl Accntng.

FAUGNO, DUILIO; Stamford Catholic HS; Stamford, CT; (Y); Computer Clb; JA; Hon Roll; Arch.

FAULKNER, PRESCOTT; Simsbury HS; W Simsbury, CT; (Y); Am Leg Boys St; Pres Church Yth Grp; Drama Clb; VP JA; School Play; Stage Crew; Yrbk Phtg; Hon Roll; Biolgcl.

FAUSEY, JOY; Windham HS; Willimantic, CT; (Y); Am Leg Aux Girls St; Cmnty Wkr; Ski Clb; Var Capt Cheerleading; Var L Tennis; High Hon Roll; Mu Alp Tht; NHS; Outstndng Achvt Alg II, Trig HH, Engl 11 HH, U S Hstry HH 85.

FAY, JODY A; Tolland HS; Tolland, CT; (Y); 24/171; 4-H; Mrchg Band; Var Capt Cheerleading; Coach Actv; 4-H Awd; Hon Roll; NHS; Prfct Atten Awd; Rep Frsh Cls; Rep Soph Cls; Tolland Newcomers Schlrshp 85; Springfield Coll; Pol Sci.

FAZIO, PATTI; Cheshire HS; Cheshire, CT; (Y); French Clb; JA; Pep Clb; Color Guard; Yrbk Stf; French Hon Soc; High Hon Roll; Intl Bus.

FAZIO, ROSINA; Conard HS; W Hartford, CT; (Y); 43/295; Church Yth Grp; Service Clb; Spanish Clb; School Musical; Pres Jr Cls; Trs Stu Cncl; Socr; Hon Roll; NHS; Spanish NHS; Harry & Ruth Kleinman Schlrshp Awd 85; St Joseph Coll.

FEDAK, KIMBERLY; Stamford Catholic HS; Stamford, CT; (Y); Church Yth Grp; Ski Clb; Varsity Clb; Rep Sr Cls; Cheerleading; Psych.

FEDAK, MARY; Shelton HS; Shelton, CT; (Y); GAA; JCL; Latin Clb; Spanish Clb; Var L Bsktbl; Var L Sftbl; Hon Roll; Latn Natl Hnr Socty; Natl Phy Ed Awd; Comp Sci.

FEDIRKO, JOHN; West Haven HS; West Haven, CT; (Y); Am Leg Boys St; Hosp Aide; Math Tm; Nwsp Sprt Ed; Pres Soph Cls; Var L Tennis; High Hon Roll; Hon Roll; Jr NHS; NHS; W Haven Rotry Schlr Athlt 85; Treas Natl Hnr Soc 85-86; Engrng.

FEDUCIA, SHARON; Ansonia HS; Ansonia, CT; (Y); Hosp Aide; Library Aide; Yrbk Stf; Trs Jr Cls; Trs Sr Cls; Trs Stu Cncl; Pom Pon; High Hon Roll; NHS; Spanish NHS; 2nd-Spanish III 85; LPN.

FEENEY, JOSEPH; St Bernard HS; New London, CT; (S); Bsbl; Ftbl; Hon Roll; Cert Of Awd Acad Excllnc 83.

FEENEY, KATHLEEN; East Catholic HS; Coventry, CT; (Y); 116/300; Rep Stu Cncl; JV Bsktbl; JV Sftbl; Hgh Hnr Rl 83-84; Spec Ed.

FEERO, STEVEN; Kaynor Tech; Prospect, CT; (Y); Ski Clb; Stage Crew; Pres Soph Cls; Pres Jr Cls; Pres Sr Cls; Stu Cncl; High Hon Roll; Hon Roll; Jr NHS; NHS; Waterbury ST Ech; Electnc Engr.

FELICE, MARK; Coventry HS; Coventry, CT; (Y); Band; Concert Band; Jazz Band; Yrbk Sprt Ed; Stu Cncl; JV Bsbl; JV Bsktbl; JV Capt Socr; Hon Roll; NHS.

FERGUSON, BRIAN; Fairfield Coll Prep Schl; Fairfield, CT; (Y); Boy Scts; Church Yth Grp; Cmnty Wkr; Ski Clb; JV Capt Socr; Hon Roll; Spanish NHS; Math & Art Achvt Awds 83; Math.

FERGUSON, BRIAN; St Mary HS; Greenwich, CT; (Y); 17/80; Exploring; Band; Jazz Band; Variety Show; Rep Stu Cncl; Var Ftbl; Var Lcrss; Capt Wrstlng; NHS; NEDT Awd; Rev James Gay Mem Schlrshp 85; Spnsh Hnrs Awd 85; MV Defnsv Linemn 83; Bus.

FERGUSON, CHERYL; Sacred Heart Acad; Northford, CT; (Y); Aud/Vis; FBLA; Hosp Aide; Chorus; School Musical; Var L Crs Cntry; Im Vllybl; Yales Frontiers Applied Sci Pgm; CPR Cert Course; Pre-Med.

FERGUSON, KELLY J; Bloomfield HS; Bloomfield, CT; (Y); 1/235; Band; Concert Band; Jazz Band; Mrchg Band; Orch; School Musical; Yrbk Stf; Lit Mag; French Hon Soc; High Hon Roll; Creative Arts Pgm Scholar 83 & 84; ST Wide Energy Cont 84; Harvard Bk Awd 85; Yale; Engl.

FERGUSON, KIRK; Guilford HS; Guilford, CT; (Y); 6/300; AFS; Stu Cncl; Var L Socr; Var L Tennis; VP NHS; CT JR Sci & Humnts Sympsm 85; Sci.

FERGUSON, LAURA; Coventry HS; Coventry, CT; (S); Teachers Aide; Band; Concert Band; Mrchg Band; Symp Band; Rep Frsh Cls; Rep Soph Cls; VP Jr Cls; Hon Roll; E CT ST U; Bus.

FERRACCI, THOMAS; Southington HS; Southington, CT; (Y); 110/580; Bsbl; Ftbl; Bentley; CPA.

FERRARA, MICHELLE; Brookfield HS; Brookfield Ctr, CT; (Y); Pres Trs Drama Clb; Varsity Clb; Chorus; Orch; School Play; Sec Sr Cls; VP Sec Stu Cncl; High Hon Roll; NHS; Var L Fld Hcky; Merill Lynch Inc Schlrhsp 85; Drama Clb Awd 84-85; Presdntl Acadmc Ftns Awd 85; NY U; Actng.

FERRARO, ROSANNA; St Mary HS; New Haven, CT; (Y); Chorus; Church Choir; School Musical; School Play; Lit Mag; Sec Soph Cls; Hon Roll; Prfct Atten Awd; JV Vllybl; Foreign Lang Poetry Cont 85; Typing & Bus Awd 85; CPI; Comp.

FERRERI, MICHAEL; Southington HS; Southington, CT; (Y); Church Yth Grp; U CT; Engrng.

FERRI, JEFFREY; Amity Regional HS; W Haven, CT; (Y); Ski Clb; Band; Concert Band; Jazz Band; Camera Clb; School Musical; Symp Band; Var Capt Socr; Hon Roll; Ed Ctr Arts Yth Orch 83-84; Recrdng.

FERRUCCI, ANGELA L; North Haven HS; N Haven, CT; (Y); VP Church Yth Grp; Hosp Aide; Pep Clb; Yrbk Stf; Hon Roll; Fgn Lang Hon Soc 84; Phys Ther.

FERSZT, ELIZABETH; Trumbull HS; Trumbull, CT; (Y); JA; Concert Band; French Hon Soc; High Hon Roll; Hon Roll; Psych.

FETZER, DANIEL; Trumbull HS; Trumbull, CT; (Y); AFS; Aud/Vis; Boy Scts; Cmnty Wkr; Band; Concert Band; Jazz Band; Mrchg Band; Pep Band; Stage Crew; Bus.

FICHTENKORT, JANE; Staples HS; Westport, CT; (Y); Boys Clb Am; Dance Clb; Band; Orch; School Musical; Var L Cheerleading; Stat Sftbl; Syracuse; Accntnt.

FICKS, PAUL J; Berlin HS; Kensington, CT; (Y); 24/225; Am Leg Boys St; Church Yth Grp; Civic Clb; Cmnty Wkr; Service Clb; Yrbk Stf; JV Bsbl; JV Bsktbl; JV Ftbl; JV Golf; Excll Spnsh Citation.

FIELD, BRIAN; Coginchaug Regional HS; Durham, CT; (Y); 51/125; AFS; Cmnty Wkr; Exploring; FBLA; Rep Frsh Cls; Rep Soph Cls; JV Im Bsktbl; Im Vllybl; Perf Attndnc JR Yr 84-85; Bus.

FIELDMAN, KATHY; Oliver Wolcott Reg Voc Tech Schl; Torrington, CT; (Y); VICA; Crs Cntry; Socr; Sftbl; Trk; Hon Roll; Nrsng.

FIELITZ, ELLEN; Trumbull HS; Greenville, DE; (Y); Cmnty Wkr; Dance Clb; Ski Clb; Variety Show; Rep Jr Cls; High Hon Roll; Hon Roll; Mech Engrng.

FIERTEK, CHRIS; Newington HS; Newington, CT; (Y); Math Clb.

FIGLIOLI, THOMAS; Maloney HS; Meriden, CT; (Y); Hon Roll; Chemcl Engrng.

FIGLIOMENI, CARLA; Orville H Platt HS; Meriden, CT; (Y); Hon Roll; Italian II & III Awd.

FILINGERI, DEBORAH-LEE; St Joseph HS; Huntington, CT; (Y); 76/240; VP Church Yth Grp; Drama Clb; Hosp Aide; Spanish Clb; Nwsp Stf; Yrbk Bus Mgr; Yrbk Stf; JV L Swmmng; JV L Trk; Hon Roll; Med.

FILIPPONE, MICHAEL; Holy Cross HS; Waterbury, CT; (Y); 7/352; Church Yth Grp; High Hon Roll; NHS; Ntl Merit Ltr; Soc Stds Hnr Soc 84-85; Chem Engrng.

FILLION, MICHAEL R; St Bernard HS; Noank, CT; (S); Am Leg Boys St; Church Yth Grp; Cmnty Wkr; Exploring; Red Cross Aide; Var Bsbl; Var Ftbl; Hon Roll; Phys Thrpy.

FINKE, STACY; Holy Cross HS; Watertown, CT; (Y); Teachers Aide; Varsity Clb; Acpl Chr; Chorus; Swing Chorus; Stu Cncl; Hon Roll; Mck Trl ST Chmpn Awd 85; Vocal Jazz Ensmbl 85; Law.

FINKEL, MIKE; Westhill HS; Stamford, CT; (Y); Ski Clb; Temple Yth Grp; Nwsp Sprt Ed; Capt JV Crs Cntry; JV Var Trk; High Hon Roll; Hon Roll; NCTE Awd; NHS; Oberlin Coll Bk Awd 85; Bus.

FINN JR, THOMAS J; Stamford Catholic HS; Stamford, CT; (Y); 35/160; Boy Scts; Chess Clb; JA; Spanish Clb; Nwsp Rptr; Capt Bowling; Socr; Hon Roll; Algbr I Hnrs Awd 83; Connecticut U; Pre-Dentl.

FINNEGAN, BRETT WILLIAM; Branford HS; Brandord, CT; (Y); Rep Stu Cncl; Bsktbl; JV Capt Ftbl; Trk; Wt Lftg; Hon Roll; Stu Ldr; Boxy Socl Chrprsn 85-86.

FINNEGAN, MICHAEL; Canterbury HS; Dallas, TX; (Y); 38/80; Dance Clb; Debate Tm; Spanish Clb; School Play; Nwsp Rptr; Bsbl; Bsktbl; Ftbl; Hon Roll.

FINNEMORE, MICHELLE; Plainfield HS; Dayville, CT; (Y); 4/157; GAA; Varsity Clb; Mrchg Band; Trs Jr Cls; Trs Sr Cls; Crs Cntry; Var Trk; Elks Awd; Trs NHS; Am Leg Aux Girls St; Schlrs Pgm 81-85; Svc Awd 85; Bd Ed Plaque 85; Quinebaug Vly Comm Coll.

FIORE, APRIL; Southington HS; Milldale, CT; (Y); Dance Clb; Variety Show; Powder Puff Ftbl; Mgr Score Keeper; JV Sftbl; Psych.

FIORE, CAROLYN; Sacred Heart Acad; North Haven, CT; (Y); Art Clb; Church Yth Grp; French Clb; GAA; Variety Show; Gym; Hon Roll; Regnl Cls II USGF Beam Chmpn Rgn VI 84; Rgn VI USGF Cls II 6th AA 84; Polit Sci.

FIRGELESKI, MICHELE LEE; Trumbull HS; Trumbull, CT; (Y); Cmnty Wkr; Library Aide; Band; Concert Band; Mrchg Band; Symp Band; High Hon Roll; NHS; Jr Mrshl 84-85 Sr Grad Cls 85; Natl PTA Rflctns Proj 85; U CT; Ansthslgst.

FISHBERG, MITCHELL; Newington HS; Newington, CT; (Y); 40/380; Cmnty Wkr; Pep Clb; Tennis; Hon Roll; Sprtsmnshp Awd 84; All Conf Tnns Tm 85; Pol Sci.

FISHER, GRETCHEN; Windham HS; Willimantic, CT; (Y); 4-H; Intnl Clb; Off Concert Band; Off Orch; Nwsp Phtg; 4-H Awd; Hon Roll; HS Msc Awd 85; Acdmc All Amer 85; Zoology.

FISHER, JEANNETTE D; The Gilbert Schl; Winsted, CT; (Y); 45/110; Chess Clb; Chorus; Stat Bsktbl; Score Keeper; Var L Tennis; Choir-2 Yr Awd 83; Choir-3 Yr Awd 84; Choir-4 Yr Sr Awd 85; Comp.

FITZ, JEFF W; Masuk HS; Monroe, CT; (Y); 85/290; Spanish Clb; Yrbk Stf; JV Var Bsbl; JV Var Bsktbl; JV Var Ftbl; Freshmn & Vrsty Bsktbl Tm Cptn; JV Bsbl Tm Cptn; Crmnl Jstc.

FITZ GERALD, ANGELA; East Catholic HS; Manchester, CT; (Y); 49/365; Church Yth Grp; Lit Mag; Im Coach Actv; Var L Swmmng; Im Wt Lftg; High Hon Roll; Hon Roll; Raymond & Fitzpatrick Mem Fund Schlrshp 85; Adv Lfsvng Cert 82; Multimedia First-Aid Cert 85; Villanova U; Pre-Law.

FITZGERALD, BETH; Sacred Heart Acad; Hamden, CT; (Y); French Clb; FBLA; Pep Clb; Stage Crew; Var JV Crs Cntry; Im Vllybl; Michaels Jewelers Educ Schlrshp 85.

FITZGERALD, GEOFF; Holy Cross HS; Waterbury, CT; (Y); Band; Concert Band; Jazz Band; Mrchg Band; Pep Band; School Musical; Variety Show; Hon Roll; Ocean Engr.

FLANAGAN, CLARE; St Bernard HS; Norwich, CT; (Y); Chorus; Church Choir; Mrchg Band; School Musical; Rep Jr Cls; Rep Stu Cncl; Tennis; Hon Roll; Musical Achvt Awd 83-85; New England Achvt Awd 85; Music Educ.

FLATHERS, SCOTT; Guilford HS; Guilford, CT; (Y); 70/330; Church Yth Grp; Cmnty Wkr; Math Tm; Band; Mrchg Band; Pres Stu Cncl; Var Crs Cntry; Var Swmmng; Hon Roll; Symp Band; Arch.

FLAVIN, CATHERINE; Sacred Heart Acad; Ridgefield, CT; (Y); Service Clb; Chorus; Nwsp Rptr; Lit Mag; Pres Soph Cls; VP Jr Cls; Vllybl; French Hon Soc; Hon Roll; NHS; Ntl Latin Exam 85; Pol Sci.

FLEEZER, MARIA; Thomaston HS; Thomaston, CT; (Y); 8/74; Cmnty Wkr; Dance Clb; Trs Spanish Clb; Teachers Aide; Yrbk Stf; Bausch & Lomb Sci Awd; High Hon Roll; NHS; Rotary Stu Mnth 85; Span Exch Stu 84-85; Hesser Coll; Dgtl Elctrncs.

FLEMING, KIMBERLY; Daniel Hand HS; Madison, CT; (Y); 61/265; FCA; Pres GAA; Band; Mrchg Band; Trs Frsh Cls; Bsktbl; Var Cheerleading; Fld Hcky; Var Sftbl; Hon Roll.

FLEMMING, AGATHE; The Morgan Schl; Clinton, CT; (Y); 24/160; 4-H; FBLA; Spanish Clb; Nwsp Stf; Yrbk Stf; 4-H Awd; Hon Roll; CT Hrse Show Accoc Champ 84; Phys Ther.

FLETCHER, DIANE; Plainville HS; Plainville, CT; (Y); 13/213; Drama Clb; Girl Scts; School Musical; School Play; Swing Chorus; Var Capt Swmmng; DAR Awd; Hon Roll; Lion Awd; NHS; Grl Scout Gold Awd 85; Emily Chaison Scholar Grl Scouts 85; Exch Clb Scholar 85; U VT; Animal Sci.

FLETCHER JR, RICHARD P; Nathan Hale Ray HS; Moodus, CT; (Y); 3/51; Trs Am Leg Boys St; VP Jr Cls; Pres Sr Cls; Rep Stu Cncl; Var Bsbl; Var Capt Bsktbl; Var Socr; DAR Awd; NHS; Model UN; CIAC-CASS Schlr Athlte 85; Boston U; Physlgy.

FLOREK, JOHN; Naugatock HS; Naugatuck, CT; (Y); Boy Scts; Ski Clb; Variety Show; Var Co-Capt Crs Cntry; Var Trk; Hon Roll; Engrng.

FLOYD, MARK BENEDICT; Kent Schl; Wellesley, MA; (Y); 3/193; Concert Band; Jazz Band; Var L Bsbl; Var L Ftbl; Var Capt Wrstlng; High Hon Roll; Ntl Merit Ltr; Trnty Clb Bk Awd 84; Cum Laude Soc 85; Latin Prze 85; Stanford U; Engrg.

FOBERG, HEATHER; St Bernard HS; Westerly, RI; (Y); #152 In Class; Art Clb; Dance Clb; Exploring; Hosp Aide; Library Aide; Stage Crew; Yrbk Phtg; Yrbk Stf; Margret D Donahue Awd 85; Intrior Dsgn.

FOEHRENBACH, LAURA; Trumbull HS; Trumbull, CT; (Y); Chorus; Capt Var Fld Hcky; High Hon Roll; Hon Roll; Cert Dstngshd Svc Music 82; Leukemia Type A Thon 3rd 85; CBI Typng SF 84-85; Katharine Gibbs Schl; Exec Secr.

FOELLMER, OLIVER; Guilford HS; Guilford, CT; (Y); Boy Scts; German Clb; JV Socr; Hon Roll; Peabody Sci Awd 81-82; Chemathon Awd 84-85; Fncng Capt MVP 81-85; Sci.

FOGELBERG, CAMILLA; Notre Dame Central HS; Bridgeport, CT; (Y); 56/284; Key Clb; Swmmng; High Hon Roll; NHS; Spanish NHS; U CT; Cmmnctns.

FOLCIK, MELISSA; Southington HS; Southington, CT; (Y); 56/550; Church Yth Grp; Pres Key Clb; Vllybl; High Hon Roll; Hon Roll; NHS; All Conf 1st Tm Vllybl 84-85; Fairfield U.

FOLEY, JENNIFER; Mancheter HS; Manchester, CT; (Y); AFS; French Clb; Hosp Aide; Band; Tennis; Hon Roll; NHS; Awd Outstndng Bnd 83-84; Awd Outstndng Acadmc Achv 82-83; Tnns Magzns Awd Outstndng Sprtsmnshp 85; Hotl Mgmt.

FOLEY, JOHN B; St Thomas More HS; Plan Dome, NY; (Y); Boy Scts; Trs Frsh Cls; Off Soph Cls; Rep Stu Cncl; JV Ftbl; Capt Var Lcrss; JV Var Wrstlng; High Hon Roll.

FOLEY, NEAL; East Catholic HS; Glastonbury, CT; (Y); Boy Scts; School Musical; School Play; Stage Crew; Hon Roll; Vetrnrn.

FOLEY, SEAN T; New Fairfield HS; New Fairfield, CT; (Y); 1/218; Church Yth Grp; Math Tm; School Musical; Lit Mag; Trs Stu Cncl; High Hon Roll; NHS; Ntl Merit SF; Val; JA; Amer Chem Soc Awd; Engrng.

FOLSOM, ELIZABETH; Joseph A Foran HS; Milford, CT; (Y); 15/385; Varsity Clb; Rep Stu Cncl; Var L Swmmng; Var L Trk; DAR Awd; Elks Awd; High Hon Roll; NHS; Ntl Merit Ltr; SAR Awd; WPIX-TV Editrl Cntst-Tri St Fnlst 83; Chldrn Of American Revltn-Ntl Librrn/Curator 85-86; Lehigh U; Bus Mgmt.

FONICELLO, SUSAN P; Guilford HS; Guilford, CT; (Y); Church Yth Grp; Cmnty Wkr; Drama Clb; Chorus; Stage Crew; Lit Mag; Var Socr; Var Trk; Boy Scts; Ski Clb; Creative Yth Wesleyan U 84; Arts Recgntn & Tlnt Srch 84; Paralgl Stds.

FONOVIC, LISA; Masuk HS; Monroe, CT; (Y); 65/266; AFS; Cmnty Wkr; JA; Spanish Clb; Stage Crew; Coach Actv; Mgr(s); Pom Pon; Hon Roll; Cert Outstndg Achvt Hm Ec, Swng & Chld Dev 83-84; Cert Outstndg Achvt Spn Ii Hnrs 83-84; Nrsg.

FONSECA, SANDI; Kolbe Cathedral HS; Bridgeport, CT; (Y); Camera Clb; Church Yth Grp; Teachers Aide; Hon Roll.

FORAND, PETER A; Hall HS; W Hartford, CT; (Y); 9/324; Pres VP JA; Model UN; Symp Band; L Capt Crs Cntry; L Capt Trk; Dnfth Awd; High Hon Roll; Sec NHS.

FORCIER, LYNNE; St Bernard HS; Groton, CT; (S); 4/350; Chrmn Cmnty Wkr; Ski Clb; Teachers Aide; Varsity Clb; Lit Mag; Off Jr Cls; Chrmn Stu Cncl; Var Tennis; Pres NHS; Acad Awd Excllnc Engl.

FOREMAN, LESA; Bethel HS; Bethel, CT; (Y); 9/265; JA; Spanish Clb; Varsity Clb; Coach Actv; Diving; Gym; Var L Trk; High Hon Roll; NHS; USGF Gym ST Chmpnshps 82-84; WCC Trck Chmpnshps 83-85; CIAC Trck Chmpnshps 83-85; Sports Med.

FORGIONE, MAUREEN; Southington HS; Southington, CT; (Y); 68/580; Church Yth Grp; Cmnty Wkr; Pep Clb; Ski Clb; Band; Variety Show; Stu Cncl; Var L Bsktbl; Powder Puff Ftbl; Score Keeper.

FORMICA, STEVEN; Vinal RVTS; Middletown, CT; (Y); VICA; Capt Socr; Hon Roll; NHS; U CT; Engrng.

FORSYTH, KARA; Seymour HS; Seymour, CT; (Y); Church Yth Grp; Hon Roll; Var Cheerleading; Para-Legal.

FORTE, FRANCIS; Notre Dame HS; Hamden, CT; (Y); 1/250; Sec Rep Am Leg Boys St; Varsity Clb; Nwsp Phtg; Nwsp Rptr; Nwsp Sprt Ed; Nwsp Stf; JV Ftbl; JV Var Trk; High Hon Roll; NHS; Italn Clb Pres; Harvard; Med.

FOSS, SARA; Danbury HS; Danbury, CT; (Y); DECA; Exploring; Chorus; Hon Roll; Hrn Crncrt Chr 83; Good Attndnce Awd 83; Berkeley Bus Schl; Acctg.

FOSTER, EDWARD; Bulkeley HS; Hartford, CT; (Y); Comp Sci.

FOSTER, KIMBERLY; Manchester HS; Manchester, CT; (Y); Church Yth Grp; Library Aide; Church Choir; Hon Roll; Prfct Atten Awd; Int Des.

FOSTER, RENEE; New Britain SR HS; New Britain, CT; (Y); Capt Debate Tm; Acctg.

FOTI, JOANNA; Branford HS; Branford, CT; (Y); 22/280; Drama Clb; Latin Clb; Teachers Aide; School Play; Yrbk Stf; Rep Frsh Cls; Rep Soph Cls; VP Jr Cls; VP Sr Cls; Rep Stu Cncl.

FOURNIER, NICOLE; Lymi-Old Lyme HS; Old Lyme, CT; (Y); French Clb; Intnl Clb; Pres Key Clb; Band; Jazz Band; Nwsp Rptr; Yrbk Stf; Sec Sr Cls; Stu Cncl; Socr; 2nd Pl Medl Natl Womns Rowg Champ JR Lghtwt 85; Regnl Brd Ed Distngshd Ctzn Awd 85; Phy Thrpy.

FOWLER, COLLEEN; Windsor HS; Windsor, CT; (Y); 27/329; Girl Scts; Intnl Clb; Drm & Bgl; Rep Stu Cncl; Stat Bsbl; Capt Cheerleading; Hon Roll; Spanish NHS; Physical Therapy.

FOWLER, DONETTE D; Stratford HS; Stratford, CT; (Y); 22/241; Church Yth Grp; French Clb; Office Aide; Red Cross Aide; Stu Cncl; French Hon Soc; Ntl Merit Ltr; Pres Schlr; Rotary Awd; Hon Roll; U OK; Intl Law.

FOWLER, KIMBERLY; Southington HS; Plantsville, CT; (Y); 36/580; Pep Clb; Concert Band; Mrchg Band; Nwsp Rptr; Nwsp Stf; Stat Bsktbl; Cheerleading; Stat Socr; High Hon Roll; NHS; Fundraisng Coordntr Natl Hnr Soc 85; Toys For Tots 82.

FOWLER, KRISTY; Holy Cross HS; Cheshire, CT; (Y); 237/352; Yrbk Stf; Rep Frsh Cls; JV Trk; Hon Roll; Exec Secy.

FOX, CHRISTOPHER M; Pomperaug Regional HS; Middlebury, CT; (Y); 32/203; Acpl Chr; Band; Chorus; Concert Band; Jazz Band; Mrchg Band; Pep Band; Symp Band; Louis Armstrong Jazz Awd 85; Uconn; Elec Engnrng.

FOX, LE ANNE; Guilford SR HS; Guilford, CT; (Y); Church Yth Grp; Sec Band; Concert Band; Mrchg Band; Orch; French Hon Soc; High Hon Roll; NHS; Cmnty Wkr; French Clb; Latin I Awd 84; Latin II Awd & Lang Arts Awd 85; Sec Latin Hnr Soc 84-85; Sunday Schl Tchr 82-85; Premed.

FOX, MICHAEL; Plainville SR HS; Plainville, CT; (Y); 33/213; Boy Scts; Pres Church Yth Grp; Drama Clb; Acpl Chr; Chorus; Madrigals; School Musical; School Play; Stage Crew; Swing Chorus; Tunxis CC; Crmnl Jstc.

FOX, MICHAEL; St Bernard HS; Westerly, RI; (Y); 108/312; Art Clb; Church Yth Grp; Cmnty Wkr; Debate Tm; Drama Clb; PAVAS; Political Wkr; Thesps; Chorus; School Musical; Fshn Inst.

FOX, PETER; Guilford HS; Guilford, CT; (Y); 83/250; Key Clb; Ski Clb; Var L Ftbl; Var L Trk; All Shoveline Ftbl 84; All ST Indr Trk 84-85; All ST Sprng Trk & Fld 84; Bus.

FRANCESCHET, JOHN; North Haven HS; N Haven, CT; (Y); 51/281; Radio Clb; Teachers Aide; Hon Roll; Prfct Atten Awd; Mech Engrng.

FRANCISCO, CIDALIA; Danbury HS; Danbury, CT; (Y); Church Yth Grp; Girl Scts; Church Choir; Yrbk Stf; Im Bsktbl; Im Capt Fld Hcky; Im Gym; Im Capt Sftbl; Hon Roll; Prfct Atten Awd; Perry Awd Alg II 84; U Connecticut; Pre-Med.

FRANCO, DIANA; Holy Cross HS; Waterbury, CT; (Y); 36/354; Spanish Clb; JV Crs Cntry; Var Swmmng; JV Trk; High Hon Roll; Spanish NHS; V Ltr Swmmng 82; Sci.

FRANCO, JAMES; Notre Dame HS; Orange, CT; (Y); Cmnty Wkr; Political Wkr; Teachers Aide; Cit Awd; Hon Roll; Tchr.

FRANK, BILLY; East Haven HS; E Haven, CT; (Y); 25/250; Cmnty Wkr; Var JV Bsbl; JV Ice Hcky; High Hon Roll; Hon Roll; Jr NHS; Bobby Orr AHA Pgm Plyr Sprtsmnshp Awd 80-81; Law.

FRANKES, DEBORAH E; Amity Regional HS; Woodbridge, CT; (Y); 6/376; Debate Tm; VP Drama Clb; Model UN; Temple Yth Grp; Pres Chorus; Color Guard; Madrigals; School Musical; School Play; Stage Crew; Cornell Book Awd; Natl Merit Schlrshp Semifinalist; Brown U; Law.

FRANKIEWICZ, THERESA; Ansonia HS; Ansonia, CT; (Y); Art Clb; Computer Clb; Girl Scts; Spanish Clb; Yrbk Stf; Hon Roll; Spanish NHS; Paier Coll Art; Comm Art.

FRASCARELLI, KIM; Manchester HS; Manchester, CT; (Y); AFS; Ed Art Clb; Drama Clb; School Musical; School Play; Socr; Trk; High Hon Roll; Hon Roll; NHS; MIP Trophy 83; Amer HS Athl Awd 85; Bost U; Psych.

FRATARCANGELI, KENNETH; Jonathan Law HS; Milford, CT; (Y); 2/270; Am Leg Boys St; Key Clb; Yrbk Sprt Ed; Var L Socr; JV Trk; High Hon Roll; Trs NHS; Harvard Bk Awd 85; Hon Guard 85; Frnch I, II, III Awds; Pre-Med.

FRATONI, DEBRA; St Bernard HS; Preston, CT; (S); 103/289; Cmnty Wkr; Dance Clb; Exploring; Church Choir; Nwsp Stf; Yrbk Phtg; Yrbk Stf; Capt Var Cheerleading; JV Crs Cntry; Var JV Score Keeper; Mst Outstanding Chrldr In SE CT 84-85; Hmcmng Queen 84-85; Miss NECA 84-85; Lib Arts.

FRATTAROLA, MARK W; Greenwich HS; Greenwich, CT; (Y); AFS; Am Leg Boys St; Hst Key Clb; Nwsp Rptr; Im Tennis; High Hon Roll; NHS; Ntl Merit Ltr; Spanish NHS; Olympics Mind Town & St Wnnr, Compete Wrld Fnls 83; Natl Sci Olympiad Bio 83.

FRAY, CHRISTOPHER; Thomaston HS; Thomaston, CT; (Y); 3/68; Am Leg Boys St; Aud/Vis; Rep Stu Cncl; High Hon Roll; NHS; Acadmc All Amer 84; U CT; Engrng.

FREDERICK, SHEILA; East Haven HS; E Haven, CT; (Y); Exploring; Pres Girl Scts; VP Latin Clb; Trs Band; Yrbk Stf; Var Capt Bsktbl; Var L Sftbl; High Hon Roll; Jr NHS; NHS; Grl Scout Slvr Awd 83; Grl Scout Gld Ldrshp Awd 84; 10 Yr Grl Scout Pin 85; Nrsng.

FREED, PETER; Wilbur Cross HS; New Haven, CT; (Y); 2/315; Art Clb; PAVAS; Political Wkr; Quiz Bowl; Teachers Aide; School Play; Nwsp Stf; Lit Mag; Rep Soph Cls; JV Crs Cntry; Hist Prz Ex Awd 83; Eng Awd 84-85; Eng.

FREEDMAN, MICHAEL B; Greenwich HS; Greenwich, CT; (Y); Am Leg Boys St; Key Clb; VP Science Clb; Nwsp Stf; Lit Mag; VP Frsh Cls; Stu Cncl; L Ftbl; L Capt Ice Hcky; JV Trk; Dartmouth Coll.

FREEMAN JR, JEFFREY; Windham Tech; Baltic, CT; (Y); Am Leg Boys St; Boy Scts; Chess Clb; VICA; JV Trk; High Hon Roll; Hon Roll; NHS; Worcester Poly Tech; Engrng.

FREEMAN, RONNIE; Richard C Lee HS; New Haven, CT; (Y); Art Clb; Boys Clb Am; Boy Scts; Camera Clb; Chess Clb; Church Yth Grp; Cmnty Wkr; Computer Clb; FCA; School Play; Syracuse U; Physcl Ed.

FREIBOTT, PAUL; St Joseph HS; Stratford, CT; (Y); 42/227; Art Clb; Drama Clb; Hon Roll; Ntl Merit Ltr; NEDT Awd.

FRIEDMAN, DANIEL; Stamford HS; Stamford, CT; (S); Trs Key Clb; Capt Swmmng; Hon Roll; NHS; Ntl Merit Ltr.

FRIEDMANN, KRISTIN; New Britain SR HS; New Britain, CT; (Y); 35/350; Band; Color Guard; Clss 46 Schlrshp; Rita Ciccarillo Schlrshp; Secy Schlrshp; Bay Path JC; Prof Secy.

FRIEND, JENNIFER; Sacred Heart Acad; Stamford, CT; (Y); Cmnty Wkr; Yrbk Stf; Im Cheerleading; Mktng.

FRISBIE, ELIZABETH; Miss Porters Schl; Edwardsville, IL; (Y); Sec Church Yth Grp; Drama Clb; Girl Scts; School Play; Stage Crew; Nwsp Rptr; Stat Ftbl; JV Mgr Vllybl; Wellesley Coll Bk Awd 85; Clare Prentice Neilson Schlrshp 83-86; Val Svc Awd Girl Scouts 85.

FRITH, DAVID E; William H Hall HS; W Hartford, CT; (Y); 162/324; Ski Clb; Hon Roll; Vocational.

FRITSCHE, WAYNE R; Danbury HS; Danbury, CT; (Y); 10/585; Church Yth Grp; Nwsp Stf; Yrbk Stf; High Hon Roll; Hon Roll; Ntl Merit SF; CA Schlrshp Federtn 82-84; Expository Wrtng Awd 81-82; Creative Wrtng Awd 82-83; Liberal Arts.

FRITZ, CHUCK; The Morgan Schl; Clinton, CT; (Y); Boy Scts; Church Yth Grp; Drm & Bgl; Capt Var Ftbl; Wt Lftg; US Marine Corp; Peace Corp.

FROLIGER, JO ANN; Naugatuck HS; Naugatuck, CT; (Y); Office Aide; Rep Soph Cls; Rep Jr Cls; Rep Stu Cncl; Hon Roll; Psych.

FROMER, DEBRA LEIGH; Pomperaug HS; Middlebury, CT; (Y); 7/280; FHA; Math Tm; Model UN; Rep Sr Cls; Trs Stu Cncl; Var Capt Crs Cntry; Var Capt Trk; High Hon Roll; Lion Awd; NHS; Knights Of Columbus, Tribury Rotary Schlrshps, Mock Trial Awd 85; Mt Hmt Holyoke Coll; Econ.

FROMHEIN, DEREK P; East Lyme HS; Niantic, CT; (Y); Socr; Hon Roll; Silver Cup Chinese Form New Haven Tourn 85; Nrtheastrn U; Archit.

FROST, MICHAEL; Fairfield College Preparatory Schl; Fairfield, CT; (Y); NHS; Ntl Merit Ltr; Spanish NHS; Var Swmmng.

FU, DANIEL D; Newington HS; Newington, CT; (Y); Aud/Vis; Library Aide; Math Tm; Yrbk Stf; Lit Mag; JV Crs Cntry; Hon Roll; Debate Tm; Cornell U; Elec Engr.

FUCHS, DOUGLAS; Stamford HS; Stamford, CT; (S); 18/406; Pres German Clb; JA; Key Clb; Political Wkr; Radio Clb; Chrmn Red Cross Aide; Teachers Aide; Temple Yth Grp; Nwsp Ed-Chief; Ftbl; Comm.

FUELLHART, KURT; Rockville HS; Vernon, CT; (Y); 50/362; Computer Clb; Capt Tennis; High Hon Roll; Hon Roll; Cntrl CT Conf All-Conf Tennis Tm 85; Boys Tennis Coachs Awd 85; Med.

FULLER, JEAN; Vinal Regional Vo-Tech HS; Middletown, CT; (Y); 6/142; Girl Scts; Hosp Aide; Library Aide; Office Aide; Ski Clb; VICA; Nwsp Stf; Yrbk Stf; Rep Chess Clb; Rep Soph Cls.

FULLER, KATRINA; Bassick HS; Bridgeport, CT; (S); Drama Clb; VP JA; Science Clb; Sec Spanish Clb; School Play; Nwsp Stf; Lit Mag; Stu Cncl; Var Cheerleading; JV Vllybl; Dael Carneige Schlrshp For Pub Speaking & Human Reltaions 85; UCLA; Law.

FULLWOOD, SUSAN; Grandy Memorial HS; Granby, CT; (Y); 7/105; AFS; Band; Concert Band; Mrchg Band; Rep Stu Cncl; Var Capt Bsktbl; Var Capt Fld Hcky; Var Capt Trk; NHS; Ntl Merit Ltr; CT Schlr/Athl Awd 85; US Army Rsrv Natl Schlr/Athl Awd 85; Coaches All-ST Athl Awd 85; Fairfield U; Accntnt.

FULTON, STEVEN W; Stamford HS; Stamford, CT; (Y); 21/406; Ski Clb; Rep Jr Cls; Rep Sr Cls; JV Tennis; High Hon Roll; Hon Roll; NHS; Ntl Merit SF; Comp Sci.

FURBERT, TRACI A; Wilbur Cross HS; New Haven, CT; (S); 22/425; Dance Clb; French Clb; Y-Teens; School Play; Stage Crew; Stu Cncl; JV Sftbl; High Hon Roll; Hon Roll; Excel Awd In Frnch; Black Achvt Awd; Doctor.

FUSARIS, KIM W; Hamden HS; Hamden, CT; (Y); Chorus; School Musical; Stage Crew; Swing Chorus; Stu Cncl; High Hon Roll; JETS Awd; 3rd Pl 3rd Yr Spnsh All CT Poetry Cntst 84; Cert Merit ST Latn Tst 85; Chem.

FUSCO, JOHN; George J Penney HS; E Hartford, CT; (Y); Rep Frsh Cls; Rep Soph Cls; Rep Jr Cls; Var Crs Cntry; Var Trk; Hon Roll; Aerntc Engrng.

FUTTNER, JEFF; East Hartford HS; E Hartford, CT; (Y); Sec Trs Am Leg Boys St; Nwsp Sprt Ed; Yrbk Phtg; Pres Sr Cls; Pres Stu Cncl; Capt Bsbl; Var Capt Ftbl; Pres NHS; Church Yth Grp; Cmnty Wkr; Trinity Clb Htfd Awd-Outstndg Clss Mbr 84-85; Guidnc Dept Awd-Outstndg Schl Svc 84-85; Hon Roll 84-85; Cmmnctns.

GABRIEL, LISA M; Nortre Dame Central HS; Bridgeport, CT; (Y); 50/284; Keywanettes; Spanish Clb; Yrbk Stf; High Hon Roll; Hon Roll; NHS; Pres Schlr; Spanish NHS; Sacred Heart U; Med Tech.

GABRIELSON, KATHARINE; Naugatuck HS; Naugatuck, CT; (Y); Church Yth Grp; Drama Clb; Girl Scts; Ski Clb; Chorus; School Play; Yrbk Stf; Rep Soph Cls; Stu Cncl.

GADE, ROBERT; Northwestern Regioanl No 7; Barkhamsted, CT; (Y); Boy Scts; Church Yth Grp; Cmnty Wkr; 4-H; Ski Clb; Bsktbl; Socr; Hon Roll; Arntcs.

GADOMSKI, ROBERT; Holy Cross HS; Watertown, CT; (Y); 48/380; High Hon Roll; Hon Roll; Spanish NHS; Champ Bwlg Troph 82; Spnsh Hnr Socty 84; Bus.

GADUE, LYNN M; William H Hall HS; West Hartford, CT; (Y); 70/342; Swmmng; Trk; High Hon Roll; Hon Roll; NHS; Spanish NHS; Safe Rides 82-85; Yth Advsry Brd 84-85; Psych.

GAETANO, CAROL; West Haven HS; W Haven, CT; (Y); Church Yth Grp; Band; Concert Band; Mrchg Band; Yrbk Stf; Hon Roll; NHS; Phys Ftnss Awd 83; Frnch 83.

GAFFNEY, ELIZABETH; Sacred Heart Acad; Hamden, CT; (Y); Church Yth Grp; FBLA; Pep Clb; Teachers Aide; Var L Crs Cntry; Providence Coll; Law.

GAGAIN, RUSSELL; O H Platt HS; Meriden, CT; (Y); Church Yth Grp; Key Clb; Pres Soph Cls; Pres Jr Cls; Capt L Wrstlng; High Hon Roll; Hon Roll; Crs Cntry; Ftbl; Trk; HOBY Ambssdr 84; Yth & Govt Senator, Attnd Natl Affairs NC 85; USAF Acad Co; Aeron Engrng.

GAGLIARDI, DAWN M; Southington HS; Southington, CT; (Y); Capt Color Guard; Flag Corp; Mrchg Band; Hon Roll; Sec.

GAGLIARDI, DENISE MARIE; Lyman Hall HS; Wlfd, CT; (Y); Yrbk Stf; Pres Stu Cncl; Capt L Socr; High Hon Roll; NHS; Pres Schlr; Fordham U; Psychlogy.

GAGLIARDI, GERARD; Notre Dame HS; Hamden, CT; (Y); NHS; Spanish NHS; Math Hnr Scty 84-85; Quinnipiac Schlrshp 85; Quinnipiac Coll; Accntng.

GAGLIO, SUZANNE M; Bunnell HS; Stratford, CT; (Y); 23/258; Pres Sec FBLA; Stage Crew; Yrbk Stf; Rep Soph Cls; Mgr Swmmng; High Hon Roll; NHS; Pres Schlr; Arista SR Hnr Soc 84-85; 4th FBLA Natl Ldrshp Conf 85; Sacred Heart U; Legl Asst.

GAGNE, BERNADETTE; Jonathan Law HS; Milford, CT; (Y); Keywanettes; JV Bsktbl; Var Swmmng; JV Trk; Hon Roll; Rotary Exch Stu 84-85; 1st Pl Art Cont City Nwsp 83-84; 3rd Art Cont Yth Booklet 82-83; Art.

GAGNON, TIMOTHY; Farmington HS; Farmington, CT; (Y); Band; Church Choir; Concert Band; Bsbl; Golf; Socr; Wt Lftg; Hon Roll; Arch.

GAISFORD, IAN; Avon Old Farms Schl; Avon, CT; (S); 1/102; Yrbk Ed-Chief; Yrbk Stf; Var Bsbl; Var Socr.

GAJDA, NANCY; Berlin HS; Kensington, CT; (Y); 35/200; Band; Concert Band; Jazz Band; Mrchg Band; Pep Band; School Musical; Yrbk Stf; Hon Roll; Bus Clb Secy 84-85; Outstndng Achvt Awd Hist 84; Fash Dsgn.

GALER, CHRISTOPHER; Christian Heritage HS; Ansonia, CT; (Y); Drama Clb; School Play; Bsktbl; Socr; Trk; High Hon Roll; Hon Roll; Pres Fit Awd; Coaches Awd Socr & Bsktbl; All Star Socr Tm; Messiah Coll PA; Pre-Law.

GALLAGHER, ADRIENNE C; Greenwich HS; Cos Cob, CT; (Y); 2/719; Off Church Yth Grp; Service Clb; Concert Band; Madrigals; Mrchg Band; Orch; School Musical; NHS; Drama Clb; Chorus; CT Western Regnl Orch Princpl Bassoon 84-85; CT All ST Bank 83-84; Talented & Giftd Prog GHS 85; Business.

GALLAGHER, GREGORY; Simsbury HS; Simsbury, CT; (Y); Church Yth Grp; JA; Hon Roll; Prfct Atten Awd; Arch.

GALLAGHER, REGINA R; Academy Of Our Lady Of Mercy Lauraltn; W Haven, CT; (Y); Church Yth Grp; Mktng.

GALLERY, DANIELLE; George J Penney HS; E Hartford, CT; (Y); JA; Spanish Clb; Rep Jr Cls; High Hon Roll; Hon Roll; NHS; Cert Mert Typthn Leukmia 83-84; Comp Sci.

GALLO, CHRISTOPHER M; St Mary HS; Greenwich, CT; (Y); Variety Show; Sr Cls; Bsbl; Ftbl; Capt Lcrss; Socr; Greenwich Cncl Cath Women Awd Rlgn Stud 85; Athl Mdl Outstndng Cntrbtn Sr 85; St U NY Cortland.

GALUSHKO, ANDY; East Haven HS; E Haven, CT; (Y); Boy Scts; Church Yth Grp; Spanish Clb; Varsity Clb; Band; Concert Band; Drm & Bgl; Mrchg Band; Capt L Bsktbl; JP Sousa Awd.

GAMACHE, ERIC; Windham HS; Willimantic, CT; (Y); Camera Clb; Cmnty Wkr; Ski Clb; Trk; Hon Roll; CT U.

GAMAGE, KIMBERLY; Enfield HS; Enfield, CT; (Y); 27/241; Art Clb; VP Sec 4-H; FBLA; JA; Office Aide; Spanish Clb; VP Soph Cls; Pres Sr Cls; 4-H Awd; High Hon Roll; Outstndng Art Stu Soph & Jr Yrs 84 & 85; Law.

GAMBARDELLA, LYNN; Hamden HS; Hamden, CT; (Y); Cheerleading; Bus.

GAMBER, KIM; Southington HS; Southington, CT; (Y); FBLA; Variety Show; Rep Stu Cncl; Var Bsktbl; Capt Socr; Hon Roll; Jr NHS; Advertsng Mktg.

GANDINI, LORI; Norwalk HS; Norwalk, CT; (Y); FBLA; GAA; Soph Cls; Jr Cls; Stu Cncl; Sftbl; Vllybl; High Hon Roll; Hon Roll; Westchester Bus Inst 85; Bus Admin.

GANNON, PATRICK M; Danbury HS; Danbury, CT; (Y); 160/585; Art Clb; DECA; Drama Clb; French Clb; JA; Key Clb; Color Guard; School Musical; Lit Mag; Crs Cntry; Ctr Creative Yth, Wesleyan U, Intnsv Study Theatre 84; Theatre.

GANS, JENNIFER; Weston HS; Weston, CT; (Y); AFS; Church Yth Grp; Cmnty Wkr; Drama Clb; JA; Key Clb; Spanish Clb; Temple Yth Grp; Acpl Chr; Chorus; Pres Acad Ftnss Awd 85; Lehigh U; Bus.

GARAFANO, GLENN; Naugatuck HS; Naugatuck, CT; (Y); 22/360; Am Leg Boys St; Boy Scts; Church Yth Grp; Computer Clb; Drama Clb; JA; Science Clb; Mrchg Band; Pep Band; School Play; Rose-Hulman Inst Tech; Elec Eng.

GARAFOLA, LISA; Holy Cross HS; Watertown, CT; (Y); 17/349; High Hon Roll; Hon Roll; NHS; Pres Schlr; Spanish NHS; St Schlr; Spnsh Ntl Hnr Soc 85; U Of CT; Mrktng.

GARBER, ROSS; St Bernard HS; Uncasville, CT; (S); Political Wkr; Nwsp Ed-Chief; Nwsp Rptr; Nwsp Stf; Rep Frsh Cls; Rep Soph Cls; Rep Jr Cls; Rep Sr Cls; Chrmn Stu Cncl; Wrstlng; Law.

GARBUKAS, MELISSA; Holy Cross HS; Waterbury, CT; (Y); 35/352; Cmnty Wkr; Hosp Aide; Service Clb; Varsity Clb; JV L Tennis; JV Var Trk; JV Var Vllybl; High Hon Roll; Jr NHS; NHS; JR H Vldctrn Awd; Psych.

GARCEAU, ROBERTA J; Naugatuck HS; Naugatuck, CT; (Y); 1/350; Am Leg Aux Girls St; Acpl Chr; Madrigals; Swing Chorus; Variety Show; VP Stu Cncl; Capt Cheerleading; High Hon Roll; Church Yth Grp; Drama Clb; CT All-St Chorus 84; All Eastern Div Chorus 85; Bio.

GARCIA, GRACIELLA; Saint Marys HS; Hamden, CT; (Y); 10/115; Drama Clb; Girl Scts; Pep Clb; Spanish Clb; Variety Show; JV Bsktbl; Var Sftbl; Hon Roll; NHS; Minority Stu Union 82; Pre-Med.

GARCIA, RENEE; Seymour HS; Seymour, CT; (Y); Drama Clb; Hosp Aide; Pep Clb; JV Var Cheerleading; Hon Roll; Dntl Hyg.

GARCIA, SANTOS H; Kolbe-Cathedral HS; Bridgeport, CT; (Y); 31/101; JA; Rep Soph Cls; Trs Sr Cls; Var Bsbl; Wt Lftg; Hon Roll; Math Awd 83-84; Cert Prfct Attndnc 84-85; Rochester Inst Tech; Comp Engr.

GARCIA-ABRINES, ALICIA; St Marys HS; New Haven, CT; (Y); Spanish Clb; Nwsp Stf; Rep Frsh Cls; Trs Jr Cls; VP Sr Cls; French Hon Soc; High Hon Roll; Hon Roll; NHS; Spanish NHS; Dsgn.

GARDEN, CAROLINE; Miss Porters Schl; Lexington, KY; (Y); Dance Clb; GAA; Pep Clb; School Musical; School Play; JV Fld Hcky; Dance Wrkshp; Athltc Assn; Pep Clb; Sch Musical; Sch Play; JV Field Hockey; Dorm Rep; 1st Hd Stu Guides.

GARGAN, DAVID; Wamoga Regional HS; New Preston, CT; (Y); AFS; Am Leg Boys St; Camera Clb; Pep Clb; Ski Clb; Yrbk Phtg; Trs Stu Cncl; Var L Socr; Var L Tennis; High Hon Roll; Pres Physcl Ftns Awd 85.

GARIBALDI, SUSANNE; William H Hall HS; W Hartford, CT; (Y); Am Leg Aux Girls St; VP Frsh Cls; Sec Soph Cls; Pres Jr Cls; VP Stu Cncl; Var L Socr; Var L Tennis; High Hon Roll; NHS; Spanish NHS; Smith Clg Bk Awd 85; Lawrence Goldstein Memrl Awd 83.

GARLAND, KELLY A; Crosby HS; Waterbury, CT; (Y); 20/347; Latin Clb; Ski Clb; Chorus; Hon Roll; Sec NHS; Ntl Merit Ltr; St Schlr; U Of CT; Bus.

GARLITZ, KEITH; Naugatuck HS; Naugatuck, CT; (Y); VP Band; Concert Band; Jazz Band; Mrchg Band; Pep Band; Symp Band; Music.

GAROFALO, DAVID; Tolland HS; Tolland, CT; (Y); 24/180; Am Leg Boys St; Acpl Chr; Band; Chorus; Concert Band; Jazz Band; Madrigals; Mrchg Band; School Musical; Yrbk Rptr; Hugh O Brien Yth Ldrshp ST Rnnr-Up 84; Intl Affairs.

GARRETT, KEVIN; Stamford HS; Stamford, CT; (S); 51/461; Drama Clb; JA; Thesps; Band; Concert Band; Drm Mjr(t); Jazz Band; Mrchg Band; School Musical; School Play; U CT; Psych.

GARRISON, STACEY; Immaculate HS; Danbury, CT; (Y); 5/192; Trs Church Yth Grp; Soc Sr Cls; Rep Stu Cncl; Var L Fld Hcky; Lion Awd; NHS; Pres Schlr; Sec Pres Spanish NHS; Cmnty Wkr; Hosp Aide; Exchnge Clb Yth Of Mnth Awd 85; Outstndng Sr Awd 85; Washington Workshop & Hugh O Brian Awd Fnlst 84; Catholic U Of Amer; Intl Rltns.

GARRITY, KATE; Masuk HS; Monroe, CT; (Y); 17/300; Nwsp Rptr; Var Capt Bsktbl; Var Capt Crs Cntry; Var Capt Trk; High Hon Roll; NHS; Natl Schlr Ath Awd 85; Outstng Frgn Lang Stdt 83; UNH; Sprts Med.

GASPAR, ISABEL; Naugatuck HS; Naugatuck, CT; (Y); High Hon Roll; Mattatuck CC; Lgl Sec.

GATELY, GAIL L; Avon HS; Avon, CT; (Y); 56/172; Acpl Chr; Band; Chorus; Madrigals; School Musical; Stu Cncl; Var Capt Crs Cntry; Var Capt Trk; Hon Roll.

GATHY, ELIZABETH; St Bernard HS; Waterford, CT; (S); Dance Clb; School Musical; Rep Jr Cls; Var Cheerleading; JV Trk; Acctng.

GAUDIO, CRAIG T; Stamford HS; Stamford, CT; (Y); Church Yth Grp; JA; Var Bsbl; JV Ftbl; Hon Roll; Bus.

GAUDIO, JIM; Shelton HS; Shelton, CT; (S); DECA; JA; Vet.

GAUSS, MICHAEL H; The Robert Fitch HS; Gales Ferry, CT; (Y); 83/401; Church Yth Grp; Cmnty Wkr; Band; Drm Mjr(t); Jazz Band; Mrchg Band; Orch; School Musical; JV Var Trk; JV Var Wrstlng; Nutmeg Fife & Drum Corp Music Schlrshp 85; Fitch Hs Hm Schl Assoc Schlrshp 85; Berklee Col; Music.

GAUTHIER, LISA; St Bernard HS; Groton, CT; (S); Library Aide; Chorus; Lit Mag; Off Jr Cls; Sftbl; Swmmng; High Hon Roll; Vrsty Ltr Swmmng 83-84; USC; Psych.

GAUTHIER, MARNI; East Hampton HS; East Hampton, CT; (Y); 3/96; Church Yth Grp; Cmnty Wkr; Drama Clb; French Clb; Math Tm; Model UN; Political Wkr; Ski Clb; Yrbk Stf; Lit Mag; Ella Grasso Fndtn Schlrshp 85; Bishop Mc Farland Awd Excllnc Socl Studies 84; CT Rep Natl Flag Day 84; Boston U; Intl Rel.

GAUTRAU, JUDITH; Low-Heywood Thomas HS; Stamford, CT; (Y); 5/36; VP JA; Teachers Aide; Band; Yrbk Ed-Chief; Trs Soph Cls; Trs Jr Cls; Var Fld Hcky; Var Lcrss; Hon Roll; Stat Bsktbl; Wnnr Best Sales Rep Awd.

GAVRI, LULE; Pamperaug HS; Middlebury, CT; (Y); AFS; Drama Clb; Math Tm; Model UN; Stage Crew; Var Cheerleading; JV Trk; Hon Roll; Lion Awd; Rotary Awd; CT Schltc Achvt 85; N Amer Philip Corp 85; Middlebury Knights Columbus 85; U CT; Biomed Engr.

GAWE, MICHELLE R; Housatonic Valley Regional HS; Kent, CT; (Y); 1/127; Yrbk Stf; Lit Mag; High Hon Roll; Ntl Merit SF; Val; AFS; Art Clb; Chess Clb; French Clb; Nwsp Stf; Creative Yth Prog 81; Harvard-Radcliffe Clb Of Nrthrn Conn Bk Prz 84.

GAY, SUSAN; Norwalk HS; Norwalk, CT; (Y); Exploring; Letterman Clb; Spanish Clb; Chorus; Lit Mag; Co-Capt Jr Cls; Co-Capt Trk; High Hon Roll; Hon Roll; Rutgers NJ; Comm.

GAZDIK, RONALD J; Joel Barlow HS; Redding, CT; (Y); Church Yth Grp; Cmnty Wkr; Vllybl; High Hon Roll; Pres Schlr; Stop & Shop Co Schlrshp 85; Shaker Family Schlrshp 85; Cert Merit Frnch V 85; Fairfield U; Accntnt.

GEADRITIES, MICHELE; Masuk HS; Monroe, CT; (Y); Dance Clb; Exploring; Mgr(s); Score Keeper; Trk; Wt Lftg; Hon Roll; JC Awd; Sthrn CT; Bus.

GEARY, BARBARA; Cheshire HS; Cheshire, CT; (Y); FCA; FHA; Spanish Clb; School Play; Nwsp Rptr; Bsktbl; Sftbl; Tennis; Hon Roll; Church Yth Grp; U CT; Fash Merch.

GEARY, NANCY; Sacred Heart HS; Prospect, CT; (Y); Church Yth Grp; Var Bsktbl; Bowling; Sftbl; High Hon Roll; Hon Roll; Summer Sftbl Bst Pitcher, MVP 83; Summer Sftbl Pitching Awd 84; CPA.

GEDANSKY, BETH; Amity Regional HS; Woodbridge, CT; (Y); Spanish Clb; Yrbk Stf; JV Var Cheerleading; Mgr(s); Score Keeper; Hon Roll; Peer Tutr Counslr; Socl Wrk.

GEFFERT, JAMES; Shelton HS; Shelton, CT; (Y); Am Leg Boys St; Ski Clb; Spanish Clb; Stu Cncl; Capt Bsbl; Ftbl; Hon Roll; NHS; Spanish NHS; Engrng.

GELBACH, SARAH; Conrad HS; W Hartford, CT; (Y); 14/322; Pres Church Yth Grp; Hosp Aide; Sec Concert Band; Mrchg Band; Orch; School Musical; Yrbk Ed-Chief; NHS; Cmnty Wkr; Sec Band; Psych.

GELEZUNAS, LINDA S; Pomperaug Regional HS; Middlebury, CT; (Y); 6/206; VP AFS; Drama Clb; Math Tm; Chorus; School Musical; School Play; Stu Cncl; Var Vllybl; High Hon Roll; NHS; Hnrbl Mntn CT ST Drama I Act Ply Fstvl 83; Cert Hghst Avg/All Arnd Excel Spnsh II 84; Lib Arts.

GELINAS, LYNETTE; St Bernard HS; Jewett City, CT; (Y); 69/289; Computer Clb; French Clb; Church Choir; Yrbk Stf; High Hon Roll; Hon Roll; Ntl Merit Ltr; Pres Schlr; Rensselaer Polytech; Physics.

GELO JR, LARRY; Guilford HS; Guilford, CT; (Y); Ski Clb; Coach Actv; Ftbl; Wrstlng; Susquehanna U; Biochem.

GEMMA, MICHELLE; Robert E Fitch SR HS; Groton, CT; (Y); 8/410; Church Yth Grp; Key Clb; Varsity Clb; Yrbk Stf; Rep Stu Cncl; Capt Crs Cntry; Mgr(s); Var Trk; High Hon Roll; NHS; UCONN Bk Awd 85; Chemathon 84; Dept Hnrs Hstry & Chem 85; U Of CT; Bus Admin.

GENDREAU, ROBERT; Coventry HS; Coventry, CT; (S); Concert Band; Jazz Band; Pep Band; Symp Band; VP Soph Cls; VP Jr Cls; JV Socr; Hon Roll; NHS.

GENOVESE, LAURIE; New Fairfield HS; New Fairfield, CT; (Y); 31/237; Cmnty Wkr; Hosp Aide; Math Clb; Rptr Nwsp Stf; Lit Mag; Off Stu Cncl; Var Fld Hcky; Science Clb; Acad Excllnce Frnch III, Engl, Soc Stud 84; Psych.

GENTILE, KATHY; North Haven HS; N Haven, CT; (Y); Church Yth Grp; Pep Clb; Yrbk Stf; Stu Cncl; Var Cheerleading; Hon Roll; Prfct Atten Awd; Grad Usherette; Bus.

GEOGHEGAN, NOREEN; Northwest Catholic HS; West Hartford, CT; (Y); Church Yth Grp; Church Choir; School Musical; School Play; Nwsp Rptr; Yrbk Rptr; Hon Roll; Ntl Merit Ltr; Amer HS Math Assn Top Hnrs 85.

GEORGE, KIM; West Haven HS; W Haven, CT; (Y); Pep Clb; Hon Roll; Masonic Awd; Intl Order Of Rainbow; Past Worthy Advsr; Past Grand Rep To Germany; Past Grand Keeper Of Jewels; Medcl Technlgy.

GEORGE, KIMBERLY; Southington HS; Woodbury, CT; (Y); 12/550; Drama Clb; Key Clb; Yrbk Stf; French Hon Soc; High Hon Roll; NHS; U CT; Nrsng.

GERSZ, DONNA; Mark T Sheehan HS; Wallingford, CT; (Y); Spanish Clb; Sec Stu Cncl; Var Cheerleading; Corrspndg Secr Stu Cncl 83-85.

GERTNER, ABIGAIL; Guilford HS; Guilford, CT; (Y); Temple Yth Grp; Band; Concert Band; Mrchg Band; Orch; School Musical; School Play; Yrbk Stf; High Hon Roll; Hon Roll; Cornell Bk Awd 85; Grmn Hnr Soc 84; Wesleyan Sci Symp; Med.

GESSECK, STEFANIE LYNN; Saint Margarets-Mc Ternan HS; Cheshire, CT; (Y); Girl Scts; Spanish Clb; Chorus; School Musical; Nwsp Rptr; Sec Trs Stu Cncl; Var L Crs Cntry; Var L Sftbl; Var L Vllybl; Hon Roll.

GETTLES, SHANNON; Wilby HS; Waterbury, CT; (Y); Boy Scts; Eagle Sct 85; TX Tech; Arch.

GHATT, KIM E; Pomfret Schl; Brooklyn, NY; (Y); Key Clb; Acpl Chr; School Musical; School Play; Mgr(s); Socr; Tennis; Hon Roll; Ntl Merit Ltr; JV Citation Crew 84; Barnard Coll; Novelist.

GHERLONE, ELIZABETH R; North Haven HS; North Haven, CT; (Y); 1/294; Church Yth Grp; Scholastic Bowl; Band; School Musical; Yrbk Stf; Var Swmmng; Twrlr; JV Im Vllybl; NHS; Val; The Rensselaer Mdl 84; New Haven Rgstr Yth Yr 85; PA ST U; Meteorology.

GHIO, BRYAN J; Crosby HS; Waterbury, CT; (Y); Church Yth Grp; Bsbl; Capt Crs Cntry; Trk; Hon Roll; NHS; Prfct Atten Awd; Mth.

GIACHINO, WENDI; East Lyme HS; E Lyme, CT; (Y); Hosp Aide; Teachers Aide; Band; Concert Band; Mrchg Band; Pep Band; School Musical; Hon Roll; E Lyme/Waterford Welcme Wagn Bst New Stu; Bnd Awd; CT Coll; Mth.

GIAIMO JR, EDWARD M; North Haven HS; North Haven, CT; (Y); 60/350; Chess Clb; Band; Concert Band; Jazz Band; Mrchg Band; Variety Show; Hon Roll; Outstndng Elec Achvt Awd 83; Outstndng Musicl Drums Achvt Awd 83; CPR Sci Pgm Cert 84; Elec Engrng.

GIANNINI, STEPHEN J; New Britain HS; New Britain, CT; (Y); Boy Scts; Church Yth Grp; JA; Im Bsbl; Im Ftbl; Comp.

GIANONI, JEANETTE T; Saint Paul Catholic HS; Bristol, CT; (Y); 89/321; Cmnty Wkr; JA; Math Tm; Chorus; Trs Frsh Cls; Trs Soph Cls; Trs Jr Cls; Stu Cncl; Capt Var Cheerleading; High Hon Roll; U Of CT; Jrnlsm.

GIAVARA, STEPHEN; Tourtellotte Memorial HS; Quinebaug, CT; (Y); 10/98; Am Leg Boys St; Ski Clb; JV Bsktbl; Var L Crs Cntry; Hon Roll; Ntl Merit SF; U CT; Comp Sci.

GIBBONS, KRISTINE; Immaculate HS; Brookfield, CT; (Y); 90/202; Church Yth Grp; JV Bsktbl; Var Capt Fld Hcky; JV Var Sftbl; Im Vllybl; S Casey Memrl Awd 84; Daubury Bar Assc J Deakin Schlrshp 85; Emmaus; Salve Regina Clg; Admin Jstc.

GIBBS, SHEILAH G; Our Lady Of Angels Acad; Somers, CT; (Y); 2/21; Girl Scts; Hosp Aide; Math Tm; Band; Nwsp Rptr; Yrbk Stf; Lit Mag; High Hon Roll; Hon Roll; Schl Match Wits Team; Boston Coll; Spec Educ.

GIBIAN, ROGER; Greenwich HS; Greenwich, CT; (Y); Computer Clb; Debate Tm; Drama Clb; Orch; Nwsp Rptr; Yrbk Stf; Lit Mag; JV Ice Hcky; JV Trk.

GIBSON, ERIC; Windham HS; Willimantic, CT; (Y); Am Leg Boys St; Ski Clb; JV Var Socr; Var Capt Swmmng; Var Capt Tennis; High Hon Roll; Hon Roll; VP NHS; Pre Dntstry.

GIBSON, LISA; Central HS; Bristol, CT; (Y); Church Yth Grp; FNA; Hosp Aide; JA; Library Aide; Office Aide; Color Guard; Hon Roll; Ona M Wilcox Schl Nrsng; Nrsng.

GIELLA, SUSAN; Griswold HS; Voluntown, CT; (Y); 1/94; GAA; High Hon Roll; Hon Roll; NHS; Prz Bk Harvard Clb Southern Ct 85; Cert Merit Phys 85; Cert Awd Microbio 84; U Connecticut; Pre-Med.

GIFFORD, ANDREW; Manchester HS; Manchester, CT; (Y); Trs Church Yth Grp; Drama Clb; Library Aide; Math Tm; School Play; NHS; Ntl Merit Ltr; Comp Sci.

GIGUERE, AMY; Manchester HS; Manchester, CT; (Y); 71/586; Church Yth Grp; VP Drama Clb; Girl Scts; Hosp Aide; Thesps; Band; Chorus; Church Choir; Concert Band; Mrchg Band; Outstndng Acad Achvt 83; Cap & Pin Manchester Mem Hosp 250 Vol Hrs 84.

GILBERT, DEAN; E Lyme HS; E Lyme, CT; (Y); 50/244; Acpl Chr; Band; Chorus; Church Choir; Concert Band; Mrchg Band; School Musical; Stu Cncl; Hon Roll; HS Schlrshp 85; Nw Englnd Music Fstvl Sol Awd Grad VI Ratng II 85; Ithaca Coll; Music.

GILBERT II, GREGORY; Greenwich HS; Old Greenwich, CT; (Y); Am Leg Boys St; Boy Scts; Church Yth Grp; Exploring; Scholastic Bowl; Swmmng; High Hon Roll; NHS; SAR Awd; Schltc Achvt Awd 83; CT Hnrs Smnr Dstngshd JR 85; Delg To 15th Intl Jambre Boys Scts 83; Law.

GILBERT, LISA; Killingly HS; Danielson, CT; (Y); 32/297; French Clb; Band; Concert Band; Mrchg Band; Symp Band; Score Keeper; Sftbl; French Hon Soc; High Hon Roll; Nathan Prince Scholar 85-86; Almond M Payne Scholar 85-86; Dixon-Putnam Scholar 85-86; Becker JC; Admin Asst.

GILCHRIST, TERRIANN; Danbury HS; Danbury, CT; (S); DECA; FBLA; Trs German Clb; Chorus; Mrchg Band; Symp Band; Stu Cncl; Mgr(s); Var Socr; Hon Roll; Central CT ST U; Accntng.

GILGER, GARY; Robert E Fitch SR HS; Bremerton, WA; (Y); Boy Scts; Church Yth Grp; Key Clb; High Hon Roll; Hon Roll; Jr NHS; Eagle Scout 83; U WA; Hist.

GILL, MOIRA; Greenwich HS; Greenwich, CT; (Y); Church Yth Grp; Drama Clb; Pep Clb; Service Clb; Chorus; Church Choir; School Musical; School Play; JV Mgr Lcrss; JV Trk; PTA Schlrshp 85; Greenwich Assn Of Schlrshp Funds 85; The Linda Hoenig Schlrshp Awd 85; Tufts U.

GILL, ROBERT; Robert E Fitch SR HS; Noank, CT; (Y); 2/401; Sec Trs Drama Clb; VP Intnl Clb; Thesps; Band; Mrchg Band; Stage Crew; Ed Lit Mag; NCTE Awd; NHS; Key Clb; Schlstc Press Assoc Wrtng Awd 1st Pl Short Story 84; Cong Cert Merit 85; Model Cong 84; Brown U; Pol Sci.

GILLAM, THERESE; Miss Porters Schl; Pasadena, CA; (Y); Cmnty Wkr; Dance Clb; Drama Clb; Hosp Aide; Varsity Clb; School Musical; School Play; Stage Crew; Variety Show; Lit Mag; CA Schltc Merit Awd 82; Head Dance Clb 85-86; Head Drama Clb 85-86; Psych.

GILLAND, BRENDA; Holy Cross HS; Southbury, CT; (Y); 10/352; Hosp Aide; Red Cross Aide; Service Clb; School Musical; Trk; High Hon Roll; NHS; Spanish NHS.

GILLEN, PETER; Cheshire HS; Cheshire, CT; (Y); Math Clb; Quiz Bowl; Scholastic Bowl; Pres Science Clb; Band; Concert Band; Nwsp Rptr; Nwsp Sprt Ed; JV Crs Cntry; JV Ftbl; Hist.

GILLIAMS, TERESA; St Marys HS; New Haven, CT; (Y); Church Yth Grp; Intnl Clb; Spanish Clb; School Musical; School Play; Sec Sr Cls; Rep Stu Cncl; Var Sftbl; Var Vllybl; Hon Roll; Vllybl Tm Spirit Awd 84; Law.

GILLIS, LA CHALE; New London HS; New London, CT; (Y); 37/160; DECA; Key Clb; Spanish Clb; Sec Jr Cls; Capt Cheerleading.

GILLIS, MICHAEL; Holy Cross HS; Oakville, CT; (Y); 22/352; JV Bsbl; Var Bsktbl; Var High Hon Roll; Hon Roll; Jr NHS; NHS.

GILLOREN, KIMBERLY; St Marys HS; Derby, CT; (Y); Church Yth Grp; Computer Clb; Hosp Aide; Spanish Clb; Church Choir; Stage Crew; Nrsng.

GILLOTTI, DONALD A; Danbury HS; Danbury, CT; (Y); 23/613; Ski Clb; Band; Concert Band; Jazz Band; Mrchg Band; Variety Show; Jr Cls; Wrstlng; NHS; George W Perry Awd Frnch 83-84; Darbury Yth Cmsn; Bus.

GILMAN, STEVE A; R E Fitch SR HS; Mystic, CT; (Y); Computer Clb; Band; Concert Band; Jazz Band; Mrchg Band; Pep Band; School Musical; Hon Roll; Rep Frsh Cls; Rep Jr Cls; Music.

GILMORE, DIANE; East Lyme HS; Niantic, CT; (Y); Am Leg Aux Girls St; Key Clb; Flag Corp; Mrchg Band; Rep Soph Cls; Trs Jr Cls; Trs Sr Cls; Stu Cncl; JV Bsktbl; Var Fld Hcky; Bus Mngmnt.

GILSTAD, PAUL; Est Lyme HS; Niantic, CT; (Y); Boy Scts; Band; Church Choir; Concert Band; Jazz Band; Mrchg Band; Orch; High Hon Roll; Hon Roll; Ntl Merit Ltr; Chem Awd; Am HS Math Exm 1st; Chem Engr.

GINCH, BARRY; Bethel HS; Bethel, CT; (Y); Chorus; Madrigals; Variety Show; Bsbl; Ftbl; Wt Lftg; High Hon Roll; NHS; Am HS Athl Awd 85; New Englnd Rgnl Babe Ruth Bsbl Pnnant Awd 82; Engrng.

GINSBURG, CANDICE; Amity Regionai SR HS; Woodbridge, CT; (S); 4/376; Spanish Clb; Temple Yth Grp; Nwsp Rptr; Ed Yrbk Stf; Trs Soph Cls; Trs Jr Cls; Pres Stu Cncl; High Hon Roll; NHS; Ntl Merit Ltr; National Art Honor Society.

GINSBURG, MITCHELL; Bloomfield HS; Bloomfield, CT; (Y); 5/230; VP JA; Model UN; Ski Clb; Stu Cncl; Var Socr; Var Tennis; Trs French Hon Soc; NHS; Intl Stds.

GINZ, BETSEY; Cheshire HS; Cheshire, CT; (Y); Band; Mrchg Band; Yrbk Stf; Rep Frsh Cls; Rep Soph Cls; Rep Jr Cls; Rep Sr Cls; Var L Bsktbl; Var L Sftbl; Hon Roll.

GIONTA, ELLEN; Bristol Central HS; Bristol, CT; (Y); 15/300; Trs Intnl Clb; Office Aide; Ed Yrbk Ed-Chief; High Hon Roll; NHS; Cathlc Wmns Asssn Schlrshp 85; Ntl Hnr Soc Ldrshp Awd 85; Fordham U; Lbrl Arts.

GISLE, KIRSTEN; Wilton HS; Wilton, CT; (Y); 35/325; AFS; Cmnty Wkr; Key Clb; Pep Clb; School Musical; Rep Soph Cls; VP Jr Cls; Rep Sr Cls; High Hon Roll; Hon Roll; U Of CA Boulder; Intl Bus.

GISSELBRECHT, STEPHEN; Torrington HS; Torrington, CT; (Y); 3/330; Am Leg Boys St; Drama Clb; Ed Latin Clb; Math Tm; School Musical; Mrchg Band; School Play; Stage Crew; NHS; Ntl Merit Ltr; Amer Invivatnl Math Exam 85; Cum Laude Natl Latin Exam 85; Magna Cum Laude Natl Latin Exam 84; Med.

GIUSTI, CHRIS; Westhill HS; Stamford, CT; (Y); Boy Scts; Church Yth Grp; Stage Crew; Nwsp Bus Mgr; Nwsp Ed-Chief; Nwsp Stf; Var Socr; High Hon Roll; Hon Roll; NHS.

GLASS, SHARON; Wilton HS; Wilton, CT; (Y); 49/327; Varsity Clb; JV Var Vllybl; High Hon Roll; Hon Roll; Drew U.

GLAZIER, JASON S; William H Hall HS; West Hartford, CT; (Y); 62/324; Concert Band; Jazz Band; Orch; Yrbk Phtg; Lit Mag; Wt Lftg; JV Wrstlng; High Hon Roll; NHS; Sci.

GLENN, BETSY; Rockville HS; Vernon, CT; (Y); 28/358; Drama Clb; Sec 4-H; Band; Var Crs Cntry; Var Trk; 4-H Awd; High Hon Roll; Hon Roll; NHS; 4-H Citznshp WA Focus CT Delegte 84; Cntrl CT Conf East Crss Cntry Rnr 84; Biol.

GLENN, LINDSAY; Norwalk HS; Norwalk, CT; (Y); Art Clb; Drama Clb; German Clb; Chorus; Madrigals; Yrbk Phtg; High Hon Roll; Hon Roll; 2nd 3rd Prize & Hon Mntn In ACN Photogrphy Cntst 85; 2nd Prize In CIAA Graphic Arts Cntst 85; Sarah Lawrence Coll; Comm Art.

GLENN, LISA; Holy Cross HS; Waterbury, CT; (Y); Church Yth Grp; Chorus; Business Admin.

GLENNON, MATTHEW; Berlin HS; Berlin, CT; (Y); Boy Scts; Church Yth Grp; Debate Tm; Y-Teens; JV Bsktbl; Var Socr; Var L Tennis; JV Trk; Hon Roll; Law.

GLOVER, AMY; East Catholic HS; Manchester, CT; (Y); Church Yth Grp; Cmnty Wkr; French Clb; Drm Mjr(t); Yrbk Stf; Socr; Swmmng; Tennis; Bus.

GLUCH, ANNA; South Catholic HS; Hartford, CT; (Y); 11/224; Church Yth Grp; Ski Clb; Spanish Clb; Yrbk Stf; Var Crs Cntry; Trk; JC Awd; NHS; Pres Schlr; St Schlr.

GOBBEE, FLORENCE; Holy Cross HS; Cheshire, CT; (Y); 9/352; Sec Frsh Cls; VP Soph Cls; Var Trk; Var Vllybl; Hon Roll; Jr NHS; NHS; Spanish NHS; Bus.

GOBELI, CHARLENE; East Lyme HS; E Lyme, CT; (Y); AFS; Key Clb; Var Trk; Hon Roll; All St Trk Tm 84; Bio.

GOIJBURG, SANDY; Trumbull HS; Trumbull, CT; (Y); Exploring; Spanish Clb; Chorus; Stage Crew; Yrbk Stf; High Hon Roll; NHS; Spanish NHS; Excllnc In Art Prsntd By Hillcrest PTA 83; Illstrtn.

GOLBA, CATHLEEN; John F Kennedy HS; Waterbury, CT; (Y); JA; Key Clb; Red Cross Aide; Band; Chorus; Concert Band; Mrchg Band; Cheerleading; Swmmng; Hon Roll; Rtry Intl Exh Stu Prog; Comp Sci.

GOLDBERG, ANDREA; Stamford HS; Stamford, CT; (Y); Drama Clb; Sec French Clb; VP JA; Pres Temple Yth Grp; School Musical; School Play; Off Stu Cncl; Bsktbl; Hon Roll; NHS; Outstndng Yng Buswmn JA 85; ROJAC Offcr 85; Bus.

GOLDBERG, ANDREW; Stamford HS; Stamford, CT; (Y); VP Civic Clb; Cmnty Wkr; Service Clb; Rep Stu Cncl; JV Bsktbl; High Hon Roll; NHS; Ntl Merit Ltr; Spanish NHS; Bus.

GOLDIN, JOSHUA; Jonathan Law HS; Milford, CT; (Y); 46/248; Pres VP Computer Clb; Key Clb; Red Cross Aide; Temple Yth Grp; Trs Concert Band; Jazz Band; Yrbk Phtg; Crs Cntry; Trk; Mayors Yth Advsry Cncl; U Bridgeport; Comp Engr.

GOLDSMITH, WENDY; Branford HS; Branford, CT; (Y); 30/300; Capt Color Guard; Yrbk Ed-Chief; Capt Ice Hcky; Hon Roll; MVP Wmns Hcky Tm 84 & 85; Supr Rtng Fred J Miller Clrgrd Camp 85.

GOLDSTEIN, BRYAN; Rockville HS; Vernon, CT; (Y); Boy Scts; Computer Clb; Concert Band; Symp Band; Rep Stu Cncl; Northeastern U; Elec Eng.

GOLUB, NEIL; Norwalk HS; Norwalk, CT; (Y); 47/492; Cmnty Wkr; Temple Yth Grp; Orch; School Musical; High Hon Roll; Hon Roll; Commnty Cittn-Life Svng 84; Comp Sci.

GOMES, CHRISTINA; Koibe Cathedral HS; Bridgeport, CT; (Y); Bst Atten 82; Svc Awd 82; Fairfield U; Nrsng.

GONSALVES, GREGG A; Saint Bernard HS; Norwich, CT; (Y); 14/300; Computer Clb; Math Clb; Im JV Bsktbl; High Hon Roll; Hon Roll; NHS; Math Awd 83-84; Elec Engr.

GONSLAVES, GREGG A; Saint Bernard HS; Norwich, CT; (Y); 11/293; Cmnty Wkr; Computer Clb; Office Aide; Bsktbl; Wt Lftg; High Hon Roll; NHS; Ntl Merit Ltr; Excel Math 83-84; Spec Olympic Vltnr 82-84; Engrng.

GONTARZ, PATTI E; Berlin HS; Berlin, CT; (Y); 2/188; Math Tm; Sec Pres Service Clb; Co-Capt Flag Corp; JV Var Trk; High Hon Roll; Lion Awd; NHS; Ntl Merit Ltr; Pres Schlr; Sal; U Of Notre Dame; Chem.

GONTARZ, PAULA; Berlin HS; Berlin, CT; (Y); 1/188; Math Tm; Trs VP Service Clb; Flag Corp; Yrbk Stf; Capt Crs Cntry; Var Trk; High Hon Roll; Pres NHS; Pres Schlr; Pres Clssrm For Yng Amer Stu 85; Georgetown U; Rsrch Chem.

GONYEA, TINA; Orville H Platt HS; Meriden, CT; (Y); Rep Frsh Cls; VP Soph Cls; Rep Jr Cls; Var Bsktbl; Var Capt Socr; Var Sftbl; Hon Roll; MVP In Soccer Awd 85fhnrb Mntn All-ST Soccer All ST 1st Team In Bsktbl & Sftbl 84-85; Guidance Cnslr.

GONZALEZ, ALEXANDER; Brien Mc Mahon HS; Norwalk, CT; (Y); Hosp Aide; Hon Roll; Norwalk Hosp Awd In Rcngntn For Vlntrng 81-83; U Of CT Hlth Sci Duster Prog & Day Of Pride 82-84; U Of CT; Bio.

GOODE, JOEL; Avon Old Farms Schl; Middleton, WI; (S); 3/105; Pep Clb; Nwsp Rptr; Yrbk Bus Mgr; Rep Soph Cls; Rep Jr Cls; Rep Stu Cncl; Var Golf; JV Ice Hcky; High Hon Roll; Pre Med.

GOODMAN, LORI; New Fairfield HS; New Fairfld, CT; (Y); Drama Clb; Latin Clb; Chorus; Color Guard; Drm & Bgl; Drm Mjr(t); Mrchg Band; School Musical; JV Fld Hcky; Hon Roll; Excel Frnch 83; Music Achvt Awd 84; Western CT ST U; Comm.

GOODWIN, ED; East Lyme HS; Niantic, CT; (Y); Key Clb; Yrbk Stf; Var JV Socr; Var Trk; Elec Engrng.

GOODWIN, ROBERT; Wamogo Regional HS; Thomaston, CT; (Y); 4/74; Stat Boy Scts; Pres Chess Clb; FFA; Drm & Bgl; JV Var Bsktbl; Var L Crs Cntry; High Hon Roll; Hon Roll; NHS; Mngmnt.

GOOLEY, MARK; Shelton HS; Shelton, CT; (Y); Ski Clb; Spanish Clb; Tennis; Hon Roll; Spanish NHS; Bus Mngmnt.

GORDISKI, PATRICIA; Sacred Heart Acad; Ansonia, CT; (Y); Aud/Vis; VP Church Yth Grp; Hosp Aide; Stage Crew; Im Vllybl; High Hon Roll; NHS.

GORDON, JULIE; Bethel HS; Bethel, CT; (Y); 5/264; Am Leg Aux Girls St; Math Tm; Quiz Bowl; Nwsp Ed-Chief; Nwsp Sprt Ed; Yrbk Stf; Var Capt Crs Cntry; JV Trk; NHS; Ntl Merit SF; Hugh O Brian Ytn Fndtn Ldrshp Awd 84; Lbrl Arts.

GORMAN, DEBBIE; Suffield Acad; Suffield, CT; (Y); 15/100; Chorus; School Play; Nwsp Rptr; Var L Bsktbl; JV Socr; Var L Sftbl; High Hon Roll; Hon Roll; Jr NHS; Readrs Digst Schlr 82-85; Wake Forost U; Poli Sci.

GORMLEY, CHRISTOPHER; Southington HS; Southington, CT; (Y); 19/600; Am Leg Boys St; FCA; Key Clb; Scholastic Bowl; Variety Show; Rep Stu Cncl; Var L Socr; Var L Trk; NHS; Political Wkr; Am Leg Boys ST 85; CT Chemathon 85; Morning Anncr 85.

GORNISH, ALANNA E; William Hall HS; W Hartford, CT; (Y); 81/324; Debate Tm; Temple Yth Grp; Ed Yrbk Stf; High Hon Roll; Hon Roll; Spanish NHS; Cls II CT Gymstcs Vltng Champ 83; CT Rep Amer Athltc Union Ntls Gymstcs Rep 83; Fgr Sktng Excllnc; Comp Engr.

GOSHGARIAN, MARK; Danbury HS; Danbury, CT; (Y); Rep Frsh Cls; Rep Soph Cls; Trs Jr Cls; Trs Sr Cls; Rep Stu Cncl; JV Trk; Cmnty Wkr; Office Aide; Ski Clb; Variety Show; Hnry Mntn Awd Sci Fair At WCONN & Edtrl Wrtg Danbury News Times 84-85; Perry Awd Frnch 84-85; Syracuse U; Mass Cmmnctns.

GOSLEE II, JAMES C; Litchfield HS; W Bantam, CT; (Y); 9/95; Quiz Bowl; Scholastic Bowl; Variety Show; Nwsp Stf; Var JV Bsbl; Hon Roll; NHS; CT Cngrsnl Intrnshp 85; US Air Force Acad; Aero Engrng.

GOSTYLA, JEFFREY; Berlin HS; Berlin, CT; (Y); Am Leg Boys St; Church Yth Grp; Stu Cncl; Im Bsktbl; Var Ftbl; Var Capt Golf; Berlin H S Redcoat Awd Glf 84.

GOTKIN, ALISON; Corentry HS; Coventry, CT; (Y); 2/108; Am Leg Aux Girls St; Pres 4-H; Concert Band; Jazz Band; Chrmn Stu Cncl; Capt Socr; Trk; NHS; Sal; Elks Clb Schlrshp 85; Cmnty Schlrshp 85; Helen Monza Sci Schlrshp 85; Worcester Polytech Inst.

GOULET, CHRISTINE M; Masuk HS; Stevenson, CT; (Y); Camp Fr Inc; Cmnty Wkr; French Clb; Chorus; Hon Roll; Ed.

GOUTHIER, JONATHAN J; The Gilbert Schl; Winsted, CT; (Y); 22/110; Art Clb; Church Yth Grp; Drama Clb; Spanish Clb; Acpl Chr; Chorus; Church Choir; Stage Crew; Hon Roll; Prfct Atten Awd; Schlrshp G Awd 83; Soc Distngshd Amer HS Stu 84-85; Chrl Awds 83-85; U Of Hartford; Grphc Dsgn.

GRABARZ, LESTER E; Stratford HS; Stratford, CT; (Y); 31/257; High Hon Roll; Hon Roll; NHS; Comp Prcssng Inst; Comp Oper.

GRABARZ, RICHARD; Shelton HS; Shelton, CT; (Y); Am Leg Boys St; French Clb; Ski Clb; French Hon Soc; Hon Roll; French Cert Of Merit 83 & 84; Electrncs Engr.

GRABOSKI, PAUL; Oliver Wolcott Technical Schl; Torrington, CT; (S); 2/143; VICA; Rep Stu Cncl; Capt Bowling; High Hon Roll; Hon Roll; Sal; Pitney Bowes Schlrshp; Wentworth Inst Tech; Comp Engrn.

GRACE JR, EDMUND M; Holy Cross HS; Beacon Falls, CT; (Y); 25/352; Boy Scts; French Clb; Science Clb; Service Clb; Stage Crew; Lit Mag; High Hon Roll; NHS; 1st-SS Comptn Comp Applctns 85; Comp Sci.

GRADY, AMY; New Fairfield HS; New Fairfld, CT; (Y); 53/237; AFS; Pres JA; Latin Clb; Political Wkr; Chorus; School Musical; Mgr(s); Awd Exclnc Spnsh I 85; Danbury Area JR Achvt Pres Of Yr 85; Dale Carnegie Crse Schlrshp 85; Bus Mgmt.

GRAHAM, DARCY; Lauralton Hall HS; Fairfield, CT; (Y); Latin Clb; VP Science Clb; Spanish Clb; Yrbk Stf; Lit Mag; NHS; Spanish NHS; Stndrzd Ltn Exam Awd 83-84.

GRAHAM, DREW; Avon Old Farms Schl; Avon, CT; (S); 2/100; Cmnty Wkr; Radio Clb; Pres Band; Yrbk Bus Mgr; Off Sr Cls; Var Lcrss; VP Capt Swmmng; High Hon Roll; Socr; Yale Bk Awd 84; CT Intrnshp WA DC Essy Wnnr 84; Hstry Clb Pres 84-85; Govt.

GRAHAM, KELLY; West Haven HS; W Haven, CT; (Y); 34/428; Church Yth Grp; DECA; JA; Pep Clb; Nwsp Rptr; Nwsp Stf; Var Swmmng; High Hon Roll; Hon Roll; Jr NHS; Accntng.

GRAJALES, ISRAEL; Hartford Public HS; Hartford, CT; (Y); 24/404; FBLA; Band; Socr; Tennis; Wrstlng; Hon Roll; Anml Doc.

GRANDE, ELIZABETH; Newington HS; Newington, CT; (Y); Church Yth Grp; Ski Clb; Var Gym; Var Socr; Var Trk; Hon Roll; NHS; CVC Conf Rnnr 4 X 400 Relay 84; CCC Conf Rnnr 100 Hurdles 85; Math.

GRANDE, MICHAEL; Conard HS; W Hartford, CT; (Y); FBLA; Yrbk Stf; Var L Bsbl; Var L Bsktbl; Var L Trk; Im Vllybl; Im Wt Lftg; Hon Roll; UCONN; Mgmt.

GRANFORS, GAIL; Masuk HS; Monroe, CT; (Y); 49/266; VP Church Yth Grp; Drama Clb; Hosp Aide; JA; Spanish Clb; Stage Crew; Nwsp Rptr; Stat Trk; Var Vllybl; High Hon Roll; Jrnlsm Cert Outstndg Achvt 85; Mgmt.

GRANGER, KELLI D; Central HS; Bridgeport, CT; (Y); Church Yth Grp; DECA; FNA; Hosp Aide; JA; Chorus; Church Choir; Sec Jr Cls; Sec Sr Cls; Stu Cncl; E Carolina U; Nrsg.

GRANSKOG, CINDY; Stamford HS; Stamford, CT; (S); Church Yth Grp; JA; Ski Clb; Nwsp Rptr; Nwsp Stf; Stu Cncl; JV Gym; Mgr(s); JV Trk; Hon Roll; Intl Bus.

GRANT, CASSANDRA; New Britain SR HS; New Britain, CT; (Y); 170/330; Dance Clb; Var Badmtn; Endicott JC; Phtgrphy.

GRANT, CYNTHIA; Avon HS; Avon, CT; (Y); Church Yth Grp; Cmnty Wkr; Chorus; Madrigals; School Play; Ed Lit Mag; High Hon Roll; Hon Roll; NHS; Recpnt Of Franklin & Marshall Bk Prz 85; Soclgy.

GRANVILLE, CHRISSIE; Weston HS; Weston, CT; (Y); 2/160; Debate Tm; Key Clb; Latin Clb; Political Wkr; Lit Mag; Polit Sci.

GRASSO, BRADLY; Crosby HS; Waterbury, CT; (Y); Var L Bsbl; Hon Roll.

GRASSO, LISA M; Penney HS; E Hartford, CT; (Y); Spanish Clb; Rep Jr Cls; Accntg.

GRATT, DAVID; Stamford HS; Stamford, CT; (S); 1/700; Computer Clb; JA; Latin Clb; Science Clb; Stu Cncl; High Hon Roll; NCTE Awd; Pres NHS; Ntl Merit Ltr; Latn Awd Societatis Classicae Nova Engl 83; Univ CT Hnrs Prog 85.

GRAVELINE, MICHELLE; Southington HS; Marion, CT; (Y); Church Yth Grp; Pep Clb; Ski Clb; Variety Show; Nwsp Stf; JV Co-Capt Cheerleading; L Capt Gym; High Hon Roll; Scndry Ed.

GRAVES, SHELLEY; St Bernard HS; Norwich, CT; (Y); 43/300; Library Aide; Off Jr Cls; Hon Roll; Acad All Amer 84-85; Acad Excllnc Awds 82-85; Ntbl Achvt Visual Arts Awd 82-83.

GRAY, CHRISTOPHER E; Cheshire HS; Cheshire, CT; (Y); Boy Scts; Var L Ftbl; Im Wt Lftg; God Cntry Awd; High Hon Roll; Hon Roll; Ntl Merit SF; Voice Dem Awd; Eagle Scout 84; Order Arrow 82; Magne Cum Laude 82; US Naval Acad; Engr.

GRAY, DIAN; Gullford HS; Guilford, CT; (Y); 6/250; Key Clb; Office Aide; High Hon Roll; NHS; Spanish NHS; Val; Latin Hnr Soc 84; Charles Raskin Mem Awd 83; Gen Excllnce In Schlrshp Awd 83; U Of Rochester; Bio.

GRAY, GARY S; Notre Dame Catholic HS; Bpt, CT; (Y); 129/284; Boys Clb Am; FTA; JA; MMM; Yrbk Stf; Sthrn CT ST U; Scndry Ed.

GRAY, KIM; Lyme Old Lyme HS; Old Lyme, CT; (Y); 14/125; VP AFS; Drama Clb; Latin Clb; Chorus; School Musical; Stage Crew; Rep Soph Cls; Var Cheerleading; High Hon Roll; Hon Roll; Albegra II Awd 85; U Of CT; Nrs.

GRAZIANO, ALISON; Southington HS; Plantsville, CT; (Y); 37/530; Band; Rep Concert Band; Gym; Mgr(s); Powder Puff Ftbl; High Hon Roll; Jr NHS; NHS; Western CT ST U; Bus.

GRECO, JAY; Notre Dame HS; New Haven, CT; (Y); 73/254; Ski Clb; Var Trk.

GREEN, DAVINA; Rivhard C Lee HS; New Haven, CT; (Y); FNA; Pep Clb; Chorus; Off Jr Cls; Acad Achvt Awd 84; Art Awd; Nrsng.

GREEN, ELISSA; Norwalk HS; Norwalk, CT; (Y); French Clb; Key Clb; Latin Clb; Teachers Aide; Temple Yth Grp; Nwsp Rptr; Stu Cncl; Crs Cntry; Powder Puff Ftbl; Ntl Latin Exam 83 & 84; Ntl Frnch Exam 83.

GREEN, KELLY; Choate Rosemary Hall Prep Schl; Wallingford, CT; (Y); JA; Latin Clb; Pep Clb; Yrbk Stf; Var Fld Hcky; Var Ice Hcky; Var Lcrss; Julie M Case Prize 83; Hnrbl Mntn Perg Modo Awd 85; Outstndng Prfrmnc Fld Hcky 83; Pediatrician.

GREEN, MARTIN; Shelton HS; Shelton, CT; (S); Pres DECA; VP JA; Hon Roll; $20 Award For Work In Carreers Club 83; Biological Studies.

GREEN, TRACY; Staples HS; Westport, CT; (Y); Swmmng; Bio.

GREENBERG, ANNA; Wilbur Cross HS; New Haven, CT; (Y); Church Yth Grp; Cmnty Wkr; Debate Tm; Political Wkr; Nwsp Bus Mgr; Nwsp Ed-Chief; Yrbk Stf; Lit Mag; VP Stu Cncl; Diving; Prz Exm Hstry I 2nd & Hstry II 3rd 84-85; 1st Pl Regl Hstry Day Cntst 85; Red Crss Cmmnty Svc Awd 85; Pol Sci.

GREENBERG, KATHRYN; Wilbur Cross HS; New Haven, CT; (Y); Church Yth Grp; Cmnty Wkr; Drama Clb; Political Wkr; Spanish Clb; Nwsp Rptr; Nwsp Stf; Yrbk Stf; Lit Mag; Off Stu Cncl; Spnsh Awd 83; Psych Awd 84-85; Psych.

GREENE, BELINDA; Bassick HS; Bridgeport, CT; (Y); Hosp Aide; Band; Color Guard; Drm Mjr(t); Mrchg Band; Nwsp Rptr; Nwsp Stf; VP Rep Jr Cls; Rep Stu Cncl; Homecmg Qn Of Bassick Awd 85; Amer Homecmg Qn Fnlst 85; Chld Dev Compltn 84; Nrsg.

GREENE, JULIE CANDICE; Amity Regional SR HS; Woodbridge, CT; (Y); Art Clb; Boy Scts; Drama Clb; Trs Pres French Clb; Latin Clb; Band; Chorus; Concert Band; Mrchg Band; School Musical; Arch.

GREENIA, LAURIE; Amity Regional HS; New Haven, CT; (Y); Church Yth Grp; Cmnty Wkr; Hosp Aide; Library Aide; Office Aide; Spanish Clb; Varsity Clb; Y-Teens; Concert Band; Stu Cncl; Med.

GREENLAW, CHRISTOPHER; St Paul Catholic HS; Bristol, CT; (Y); Science Clb; Bowling; JV Socr; Hon Roll; GM Schlrshp Pgm Co-Op Stu 85-86; 2nd Pl Swmmg Awd 80-82; 3rd Pl Cyclng Awd 80-81; U CT; Bio-Engr.

GREENSPOON, DAVID H; William H Hall HS; W Hartford, CT; (Y); 40/330; Debate Tm; Math Tm; Model UN; Concert Band; Mrchg Band; Orch; Capt Stu Cncl; Var L Swmmng; French Hon Soc; High Hon Roll; Engl.

GREINEDER, PAUL; Waterford HS; Waterford, CT; (Y); Am Leg Boys St; Key Clb; Ski Clb; Rep Stu Cncl; JV Bsktbl; JV Var Golf; High Hon Roll; Hon Roll; NHS; Elctrcl Engrng.

GREY, LISA; Guilford HS; Guilford, CT; (Y); 71/315; Ski Clb; Tennis; Hon Roll; Hnrb Mntn-Shoreline Allnc For Arts Schlrshp 85; Advrtsng.

GREY, LISA; West Haven HS; W Haven, CT; (Y); 49/340; Intnl Clb; Band; Mrchg Band; Yrbk Stf; Stu Cncl; Spanish NHS; NH Coll; Fash Merch.

GRIDLEY, DENISE; Plainville HS; Plainville, CT; (Y); 24/213; Girl Scts; Band; Concert Band; Mrchg Band; Pep Band; Yrbk Stf; Swmmng; Hon Roll; Lion Awd; NHS; Band Awd, CT ST Achvt Grnt 85; U CT; Nrsg.

GRIECO, LYNNE; Daniel Hand HS; Madison, CT; (Y); Art Clb; FCA; French Clb; GAA; Math Tm; Pep Clb; Stu Cncl; Var Bsktbl; JV Var Fld Hcky; Var Sftbl; Phys Fit Awd 83 & 84; Med.

GRIFFIN, CARRIE A; Laurakon Hall HS; Milford, CT; (Y); Hosp Aide; Science Clb; Stu Cncl; Brd Of Cndystrpng Sec 83; Salve Regina Coll; Bio.

GRIFFIN, LAURA; Southington HS; Southington, CT; (Y); 45/550; Key Clb; Pep Clb; Ski Clb; Color Guard; High Hon Roll; NHS; Southern CT ST U; Elem Educ.

GRIFFIN, LYNNE; St Bernards HS; Norwich, CT; (Y); 69/289; Church Yth Grp; Cmnty Wkr; Varsity Clb; Stu Cncl; Score Keeper; Tennis; Trk; Hon Roll; Frgn Crrspndnt.

GRIFFIN, WENDY; Nonnewaug HS; Woodbury, CT; (Y); 11/119; Stu Cncl; Hon Roll; Lion Awd; Woodbury Womans Clb Schrlshp 85; Woodbury Hmmkrs Awd 85; Briarwood Coll; Exec Sec.

GRIFFITH, THOMAS; St Bernard HS; N Stonington, CT; (Y); 120/300; Church Yth Grp; Cmnty Wkr; Computer Clb; JV Bsktbl; JV Var Socr; JV Tennis; Hon Roll; Pre Law.

GRIGEREK, GLEN; Farmington HS; Farmington, CT; (Y); Church Yth Grp; Science Clb; Var Wrstlng; Hon Roll; 4th ST 83-85; Outstndng Perfrmnc 84-85.

GRILLO, ANTHONY; Naugatuck HS; Naugatuck, CT; (Y); Am Leg Boys St; Var L Bsbl; Var Capt Ftbl; Hon Roll; Ftbl Plyr Wk 84; Outstndng Pitcher 85.

GRIMES, KELLY MICHELE; Heritage Christian Acad; Meriden, CT; (Y); Church Yth Grp; Civic Clb; Library Aide; Office Aide; Church Choir; School Play; Yrbk Stf; Golf; Score Keeper; Vllybl; Lbry Sci.

GRIMES, LEONA; Wilbur Cross HS; New Haven, CT; (S); 24/242; Red Cross Aide; Yrbk Rptr; Pres Frsh Cls; Trs Soph Cls; VP Jr Cls; Rep Sr Cls; VP Stu Cncl; Var Pom Pon; Capt Vllybl; DAR Awd; Duke U; Real Est.

GRINDLE, DAVID; East Haven HS; E Haven, CT; (Y); Spanish Clb; Nwsp Stf; Acctg.

GROCHOWSKI JR, RONALD; Oliver Wolcott Tech Schl; Torrington, CT; (Y); 93/157; VICA; Im Bsktbl; Mgr(s); JV Socr; U New Haven; Elect Engr.

GROHOSKI, WENDY HAMLIN; Litchfield HS; Litchfield, CT; (Y); 23/90; AFS; Cmnty Wkr; English Clb; French Clb; Red Cross Aide; Ski Clb; Variety Show; Nwsp Stf; Yrbk Sprt Ed; Yrbk Stf; Vrsty Ltr Crew 83-85; U Of RI; Anml Sci.

GROMKO, WENDY; Farmington HS; Unionville, CT; (Y); Church Yth Grp; Drama Clb; Ski Clb; Yrbk Stf.

GROPPO, LISA; The Gilbert HS; Winsted, CT; (Y); 27/108; FHA; Hosp Aide; Hon Roll; G Lttr Hnr Roll 82-83; Endicott Coll; Htl Mgmt.

GROSKY, JENNIFER; Trumbull HS; Trumbull, CT; (Y); AFS; Chrmn French Clb; Key Clb; VP Sec Temple Yth Grp; Chorus; Rep Frsh Cls; Stu Cncl; High Hon Roll; Hon Roll; Ldrshp Awd 83; Music Excllnc 83; Librl Arts.

GROSNER, JENNIFER; Lauralton Hall HS; Stratford, CT; (Y); French Clb; Girl Scts; Latin Clb; VP Model UN; Science Clb; NEDT Awd; 3rd Hnrs CT Sci Fair 84, 2nd Hnrs 85; Magna Cum Laude Natl Latin Exam 84; Spc Shttl Stu Proj 84; Cazenovia Coll; Fashn Desgn.

GROSSE, LARA; Farmington HS; Farmington, CT; (Y); Off Church Yth Grp; French Clb; Ski Clb; Drill Tm; School Musical; Hon Roll; Bus.

GROSSHART, ROB; Bethel HS; Bethel, CT; (Y); 1/264; AFS; Am Leg Boys St; Church Yth Grp; Math Tm; Variety Show; Yrbk Stf; High Hon Roll; NHS; Spnsh Stu Of Mnth; Grnd Marshall Grad 85; Connecticut Chemathon 85; Pre-Med.

GROSZMANN, YVETTE; Amity SR HS; Woodbridge, CT; (Y); 7/370; Political Wkr; Pres Spanish Clb; Nwsp Rptr; Rep Stu Cncl; JV Var Cheerleading; Hon Roll; Ntl Art Hnr Soc 83-85; Smifnlst Ntl Hspnc Schlrshp 84-85; Bio.

GROTE, WALTER E; Simsbury HS; Simsbury, CT; (Y); 102/356; Church Yth Grp; Yrbk Stf; Pres Jr Cls; Pres Stu Cncl; Var L Ice Hcky; Var L Lcrss; Hon Roll; Rotary Awd; U Of Richmond; Bus Law.

GROTH, KATHLEEN; O H Platt HS; Meriden, CT; (Y); Civic Clb; French Clb; Chorus; Variety Show; High Hon Roll; Central CT St U; Sci.

GROZINGER, THOMAS; Ridgefield HS; Ridgefield, CT; (Y); 17/364; Debate Tm; Nwsp Stf; Off Sr Cls; High Hon Roll; NHS; Quiz Bowl; Off Jr Cls; Pres Schlr; CT Debate Assn St Chmpn Tm 82-83; CT Debate Assn St Chmpn Spkr 82-84; Mc Gill U; Poltcl Sci.

GRUENDEL, DAVID; Bradford HS; Branford, CT; (Y); 32/260; Pres Rep Stu Cncl; Bsktbl; Var JV Socr; Var Tennis; Hon Roll; Student Senate; Princpls Advisory Committee; Student Rep To Board Of Eductn; History.

GRUNBECK, ALICE; North Branford HS; Northford, CT; (Y); 15/150; Church Yth Grp; Dance Clb; Latin Clb; Math Tm; JV Bsktbl; JV Var Fld Hcky; High Hon Roll; Hon Roll; Sftbl; Latin, Comp Sci Awd 84-85; Comp Engrng.

GRYK, MICHAEL; St Thomas Aquinas HS; New Britain, CT; (Y); 3/154; Chess Clb; Drama Clb; Spanish Clb; Chorus; School Musical; School Play; High Hon Roll; NHS; Hon Roll; Rensselear Polytech Inst Exclnce Math & Sci 85; Chemathon 85; NMSQT Hi Scorer 85; Bio Sci.

GUARDIANI, DANIELLE; St Joseph HS; Ansonia, CT; (Y); #28 In Class; Spanish Clb; JV Bsktbl; JV Sftbl; JV Trk; Var Vllybl; Hon Roll; Spanish NHS; Pre-Med.

GUCCIONE, GLADYS; Notre Dame Catholic HS; Bridgeport, CT; (Y); 58/284; 4-H; Keywanettes; High Hon Roll; Spanish NHS; Pres Acad Fit Awd 85; Southern CT ST U; Vet.

GUDZ, ROBERT; St Bernard HS; Gales Ferry, CT; (Y); 30/310; Boy Scts; Off Jr Cls; Off Stu Cncl; JV Ftbl; JV Trk; JV Wrstlng; Hon Roll; NHS; Church Yth Grp; Mech Engrng.

GUERETTE, STEPHEN; Rockville HS; Vernon, CT; (Y); 30/362; Am Leg Boys St; Church Yth Grp; Quiz Bowl; Concert Band; Mrchg Band; Symp Band; JV Capt Bsktbl; Var L Crs Cntry; Var L Trk; High Hon Roll; David Hull Memrl Awd Percssn 85.

GUERREIRO, SANDRA; Holy Cross HS; Prospect, CT; (Y); 108/344; Teachers Aide; High Hon Roll; Hon Roll; Vrsty Lttr & Pin 85; Mattatuck CC; Exec Sec.

GUERRERA, JOE; W F Kaynor Rvts HS; Watertown, CT; (Y); 9/205; Aud/Vis; Rep Stu Cncl; CC Awd; High Hon Roll; NHS; ARCO Metals Schlrshp 85; Society Of Mfg Engrs Awd 85; U CT; Mech Engr.

GUERRERA, MICHELLE M; Watertown HS; Oakville, CT; (Y); 32/250; Computer Clb; Band; Variety Show; Sec Sr Cls; Co-Capt Cheerleading; Mgr Ice Hcky; NHS; Concert Band; Mrchg Band; Rep Frsh Cls; Polk Schl Schlrshp 85; St Josephs Coll; Nrs.

GUERRERA, SANDRA LYNN; Holy Cross HS; Waterbury, CT; (Y); 63/344; Band; Concert Band; Mrchg Band; High Hon Roll; Bro Francis Leary Mem Scholar 81; Natl Ldrshp Orgnztn 84; U Of CT; Phrmcy.

GUERRERA, SERGIO; Holy Cross HS; Oakville, CT; (Y); 26/352; High Hon Roll; Hon Roll; NHS; Spanish NHS; Acctg.

GUERRERO, SUSAN; Northwest Catholic HS; W Hartford, CT; (Y); Church Yth Grp; Hosp Aide; VP Spanish Clb; Band; Concert Band; Yrbk Phtg; Yrbk Stf; Hon Roll; U Of CT; Med.

GUERTIN, MARGARET H; Northwest Catholic HS; W Hartford, CT; (Y); Pres Church Yth Grp; Drama Clb; School Play; Stage Crew; Hon Roll; NHS; Ntl Merit Ltr; Fairfield U; Bus.

GUETZLOFF, TOM; Trumbull HS; Trumbull, CT; (Y); Church Yth Grp; Var L Ftbl; Var L Trk; High Hon Roll; Hon Roll; Sprtsmnshp Awd 83; Chem.

GUEVIN, ANN L; Shelton HS; Shelton, CT; (Y); Drama Clb; Exploring; JA; Thesps; Church Choir; School Musical; High Hon Roll; NHS; Ntl Merit Schol; Pres Schlr; Canisius Coll; Vet Med.

GUGLIETTA, LISA; Trumbull HS; Trumbull, CT; (Y); French Clb; VP JA; Nwsp Stf; JV Bsktbl; VP Socr; VP Sftbl; French Hon Soc; High Hon Roll; Hon Roll; Sftbl Gldn Glve, Bst Defnsv Plyr, 2nd Tm All Str Greatr Bostn Lg 83-84, Mst Dedctd Plyr Yr 82-83; Psych.

GUIDA, KIMBERLEY; St Bernard HS; E Lyme, CT; (S); Dance Clb; Drama Clb; Hosp Aide; Library Aide; Church Choir; Orch; School Musical; School Play; Stu Cncl; High Hon Roll; New Eng Music Fstvl Orch 84; Bio Sci.

GUIEL, MINDY; Enrico Fermi HS; Enfield, CT; (Y); Church Yth Grp; Drama Clb; Latin Clb; Spanish Clb; Chorus; Color Guard; Drm & Bgl; Drm Mjr(t); School Musical; Variety Show; U CT; Med Tech.

GUILBEAULT, MARYBETH; Windham HS; Willimantic, CT; (Y); 65/300; FBLA; Swmmng; Hon Roll; U S Air Force.

GUINER, STEPHANIE; Sacred Heart Acad; E Norwalk, CT; (Y); Aud/Vis; Cmnty Wkr; Spanish Clb; School Musical; Bsktbl; High Hon Roll; Ntl Merit SF; Sprntndnts Cncl 82-84; CT Chem Assn Chem Awd 85; Outstndng Sci Stu 84-85; Pre-Med.

GUISTO, RANDY M; Holy Cross HS; Waterbury, CT; (Y); 202/344; American Inst Of Bankers; Acctg.

GULIUZZA, DAVID; Seymour HS; Seymour, CT; (Y); Boy Scts; Cmnty Wkr; Hosp Aide; JA; Culinary.

GUMAN, MARK D; Fairfield College Preparatory Schl; Bridgeport, CT; (Y); Im Bsktbl; Im Ice Hcky; Im Sftbl; High Hon Roll; NHS; Aerosp.

GUNNING, KELLY A; Sacred Heart Acad; W Haven, CT; (Y); Hosp Aide; Pep Clb; NHS; CPR Cert; Comp Club; Sacred Heart Acad Endowmnt Schlrshp; Nrs.

GUNTHER, BRENDAN; Jonathan Law HS; Milford, CT; (Y); Boy Scts; Computer Clb; Intnl Clb; Latin Clb; Capt L Diving; Var JV Socr; Var L Swmmng; Latin Natl Hon Soc.

GUPTA, ANUJ; Glastonbury HS; Glastonbury, CT; (Y); Pres Computer Clb; VP Debate Tm; Var Math Tm; Lit Mag; High Hon Roll; NHS; Latin Ntl Hnr Soc Cncl; Peer Tutrng Coordntr; Med.

GUPTA, APARNA; The Hotchkiss Schl; Releigh, NC; (Y); Cmnty Wkr; French Clb; Orch; Lit Mag; JV Fld Hcky; Chorus; Nwsp Stf; Yrbk Stf; Mgr(s); Var Trk; Math Awd 83; Head Lang Lab 86; Math Tutor 83-86; Comp Engr.

GURKA, JON; New London HS; New London, CT; (Y); 20/180; Am Leg Boys St; Var Bsbl; Var Ftbl; Hon Roll; Yth/Gvrnmnt Cty Mgr 85; Alg II Excllnc Awd 83; U Of CT; Elec Engr.

GURSKY, KIM; Naugatuck HS; Naugatuck, CT; (Y); Rep Frsh Cls; Rep Soph Cls; Hon Roll; Mattatuck CC; Med Tech.

GUSTAVSON, CHARISSA; North Haven HS; North Haven, CT; (Y); 10/294; AFS; Pres Church Yth Grp; School Play; Yrbk Stf; Ed Lit Mag; Rep Stu Cncl; NHS; JA; Latin Clb; JV Sftbl; Frgn Lang Hnr Soc 84-85; Top Acctng Stu 85; Top Econ Stu 85; Kings Coll; Accntnt.

GUTHRIE, EMILY; Nonnewaug HS; Woodbury, CT; (Y); AFS; Drama Clb; Pep Clb; Ski Clb; Chorus; Drm & Bgl; School Play; Rep Civic Clb; Rep Stu Cncl; JV Var Sftbl; Awd Dancing 84; Northeastern U; Nrsng.

GUTKNECHT, MELISSA; Griswold HS; Griswold, CT; (Y); 12/90; French Clb; GAA; VP Soph Cls; Pres Jr Cls; JV Var Bsktbl; L Cheerleading; Var L Trk; Hon Roll.

GWIAZDA, STEPHANIE; Griswold HS; Norwich, CT; (Y); French Clb; GAA; High Hon Roll; Hon Roll; Lib Sci.

GWIAZDOWSKI, CAROL B; Southington HS; Marion, CT; (Y); Church Yth Grp; Key Clb; Pep Clb; Ski Clb; Nwsp Stf; Bowling; High Hon Roll; Bus.

HAAF, DONNA; North Haven HS; N Haven, CT; (Y); 94/294; AFS; Latin Clb; Twrlr; Ntl Merit Ltr; 2nd Pl ST Latin Exam 85; Maxima Cum Laude Natl Latin Exam 85; SCSU; Math.

HAASE, DONNA; Windsor HS; Windsor, CT; (S); 54/318; Cmnty Wkr; VP DECA; Band; Concert Band; Rep Sr Cls; Rep Stu Cncl; Cheerleading; Pom Pon; High Hon Roll; Stu Of Yr-Busnss, Srvc & Leadrshp 85; 2nd Pl Dist Conf-Mrktng 85; 3rd Pl ST Conf-Mrktng 85; Southeastern Acad; Travl Agnt.

HABER, BETH; Orville H Platt HS; S Meriden, CT; (Y); Trs Drama Clb; Rptr FBLA; School Play; Stage Crew; High Hon Roll; Frnch I Awd Excllnce 82-83; Yth & Govt Pgm 84-85; Typng I Awd Excllnce 82-83; Bus Admin.

HABER, PAMELA H; Bloomfield HS; Bloomfield, CT; (Y); 28/234; Office Aide; Spanish Clb; Teachers Aide; Temple Yth Grp; Nwsp Rptr; Rep Soph Cls; Hon Roll; NHS; Spanish NHS; Union; Math.

HACKETT, ELLEN; Sacred Heart Acad; West Haven, CT; (Y); Pres Church Yth Grp; FBLA; Office Aide; Acctg.

HACKETT, SUSAN; Cheshire HS; Cheshire, CT; (Y); 9/319; Mrchg Band; DAR Awd; High Hon Roll; NHS; Ntl Merit Ltr; Pres Schlr; Balso Fndtn Schlrshp $750 85; Cheshire H S Bnd Parent Schlrshp $200 85; CT Schlstc Achvmnt Grnt $500; U Of PA; RN.

HAERTEL, HEIDI; Rham HS; Marlborough, CT; (Y); Church Yth Grp; Ski Clb; Band; Concert Band; Drm & Bgl; Mrchg Band; Pep Band; JV Socr; Hon Roll; NHS; Dntl Hygnst.

HAGAN, ROSE; Stamford Catholic HS; Stamford, CT; (Y); 1/148; Red Cross Aide; School Musical; Nwsp Ed-Chief; Var Capt Crs Cntry; Var Capt Trk; Ntl Merit SF; Val; Church Yth Grp; Cmnty Wkr; Drama Clb; ST CT Feml Yth Yr Exch Clb 85; CIAC Schlr Athl & N Stamford Exch Clb Schlr-Athl 85; Stanford U.

HAGEN, PATRICIA; Shelton HS; Huntington, CT; (Y); Spanish Clb; Ed Nwsp Rptr; Yrbk Bus Mgr; Hon Roll; Spanish NHS.

HAGER, JENNIFER B; Bloomfield HS; Bloomfield, CT; (Y); 7/231; Church Yth Grp; Civic Clb; JA; Model UN; Red Cross Aide; Spanish Clb; Variety Show; Nwsp Ed-Chief; Yrbk Stf; Pres Soph Cls; Socl Sci.

HAGERTY, SKIP; Central Catholic HS; Norwalk, CT; (Y); 3/100; Letterman Clb; Math Tm; Ski Clb; Spanish Clb; Varsity Clb; Yrbk Bus Mgr; Pres Frsh Cls; Pres Soph Cls; Sec Jr Cls; Sec Sr Cls; Francis X Sullivan Schlr/Athl Schlrshp; Hugh O Brian Ldrshp Schlrshp; All Schl Adv Cncl Schlrshp; Econ.

HAITHWAITE, SHARON; Danbury HS; Danbury, CT; (Y); 45/615; Exploring; Hosp Aide; Library Aide; Band; Concert Band; Drm & Bgl; Mrchg Band; JV Tennis; Hon Roll; Jr NHS; Pharm.

HALBERT, LARA; Stratford HS; Stratford, CT; (Y); 7/241; Drama Clb; Concert Band; School Musical; School Play; Variety Show; Nwsp Stf; Yrbk Stf; Capt Pom Pon; High Hon Roll; NHS.

HALIM, ERNESTO; Choate Rosemary Hall HS; Stamford, CT; (Y); Model UN; Pres Frsh Cls; Rep Stu Cncl; High Hon Roll; Hon Roll; Ntl Merit Ltr; JV Socr; Var Tennis; House Cnslr 85-86; Math Tutor 85-86; Martial Arts Clb 85-86.

HALL, BETH; Cheshire HS; Cheshire, CT; (Y); Church Yth Grp; Trs Sec 4-H; Pep Clb; Concert Band; Mrchg Band; Yrbk Stf; JV Sftbl; Cum Laude Natl Nat Exam; Give A Damn Clb; Yth & Govt; Soc Wrk.

HALL, DARLENE; Griswold HS; Jewett City, CT; (Y); Varsity Clb; Hon Roll; FFA; Trk; Comp.

HALL, EDWARD; Danbury HS; Danbury, CT; (Y); Cmnty Wkr; Spanish Clb; Variety Show; Stat Bsktbl; Im Vllybl; Hon Roll; Spanish NHS; Outstndng Achvt Spnsh Awd 83; CIAC Awd 84; G W Perry Awd Phy Ed 85; Jrnlsm.

HALL, MATTHEW; Torrington HS; Torrington, CT; (Y); Art Clb; JV Bsbl; De Vry Inst Of Tech; Elec Engrg.

HALL, SUSAN E; Andrew Warde HS; Fairfield, CT; (Y); Trs Dance Clb; VP MMM; Pres Red Cross Aide; Teachers Aide; Orch; School Musical; Var Swmmng; French Hon Soc; NHS; Westrn Regnl Fest Orch Violn 83-85; Hgh Hnr Rll 82-85; Pre-Vet.

HALLBROK, SUSAN; Holy Cross HS; Cheshire, CT; (Y); 5/352; JCL; Concert Band; Mrchg Band; School Musical; Stage Crew; Lit Mag; High Hon Roll; NHS; Latin Hnr Soc 84; Vetrnrn.

HALPIN, ELIZABETH; Greenwich HS; Greenwich, CT; (Y); Dance Clb; JA; Band; Badmtn; High Hon Roll; NHS; MVP-VRSTY Badmntn 81-83; Pipe Sgt-Greenwich Celtic Pipes & Drums 85; Partl Schlrshp-Irish Way Trip 85; Accntng.

HAMAN, LYNN; Southington HS; Southington, CT; (S); 300/550; Aud/Vis; Hst DECA; FBLA; Library Aide; Chorus; Variety Show; Nwsp Stf; Rep Stu Cncl; DECA Schlrshp Awd 84-85; Htl Admin.

HAMANN, JAMES B; Hatchkiss Schl; Hummelstown, PA; (Y); Stu Cncl; Var L Ftbl; Var L Ice Hcky; Var L Trk; High Hon Roll; Ntl Merit Ltr; Edwards Prz 83; Probasco Awd 84; Cornell U; Engrng.

HAMELIN, WENDY; Kaynor Regional Vo-Tech HS; Wolcott, CT; (Y); Dance Clb; Girl Scts; VICA; Church Choir; Hon Roll; Peer Cnslr 84-85; Jr Prom Committee 85; Johnson & Whales; Culnry Art.

HAMILTON, DENNIS; Avon Old Farms Schl; New Britain, CT; (S); 8/100; Art Clb; Yrbk Stf; Var Diving; JV Socr; JV Swmmng; Hon Roll; Mdrn Eurpn Hstry Awd 83-84; Rnnr Up Engl & Over All Acdmc Awds 83-84.

HAMILTON, GINA; Bullard-Havens Technical Schl; Bridgeport, CT; (Y); 11/230; Church Yth Grp; Church Choir; Yrbk Stf; Stu Cncl; Trs Stu Cncl; Vllybl; Elks Awd; High Hon Roll; Hon Roll; NHS; Rhinehart Buckley Awd 85; Waterbury; Acctg.

HAMILTON, JENNIFER; Wilton HS; Wilton, CT; (Y); AFS; Church Yth Grp; Sec French Clb; Natl Beta Clb; Pep Clb; Service Clb; Chorus; Church Choir; Madrigals; Yrbk Stf; Outstndg Civcs Awd 82-83; Awd Acad Excllnce 84-85.

HAMILTON, KAREN R; Conard HS; W Hartford, CT; (Y); 20/280; Church Yth Grp; Trs Cmnty Wkr; Chorus; Church Choir; School Musical; NHS; Pres Schlr; Spanish NHS; Smith Coll.

HAMMEL, DOUGLAS J; New London HS; New London, CT; (Y); 18/200; Band; Drm Mjr(t); Orch; School Play; Nwsp Stf; Sr Cls; Bsbl; Golf; Hon Roll; NHS; U CT; Engr.

HAMMERMANN, HOWARD; Pomperaug Regional HS; Southbury, CT; (Y); 16/215; Math Tm; Model UN; Yrbk Phtg; Stat Ftbl; JV Golf; Ntl Merit Ltr; George Washington U; Intl Affrs.

HAMMIE, SHEILA; Wilbur Cross HS; New Haven, CT; (S); 33/242; Dance Clb; Red Cross Aide; Cheerleading; Gym; Hon Roll; Acad All-Amer Schlr 84; Military; Allied Hlth.

HAMMOND, DARRELL; Naugatuck HS; Naugatuck, CT; (Y); Church Yth Grp; Drama Clb; JA; PAVAS; Variety Show; Hon Roll; Ringlg Bros Barnum-Bailey Coll.

HANDRINOS, PETER; Fairfield College Prep Schl; Norwalk, CT; (Y); Computer Clb; JV Socr; Hon Roll; NHS; 1st Bio Awd In Schl Sci Fair 84; Hnrb Mntn Chem 85.

HANJIAN, CAROLYN E; Conard HS; W Hartford, CT; (Y); 11/291; Acpl Chr; Jazz Band; Var Tennis; High Hon Roll; NHS; Pres Schlr; Spanish NHS; Spanish Clb; Band; Chorus; Yale Bk Awd 84; Louis Armstrong Jazz Awd 85; Wendy Womick Music Awd 85; U Of CT; Comm.

HANLEY, JAMES; Stamford Catholic HS; Stamford, CT; (Y); 41/205; Boy Scts; JA; Ski Clb; Nwsp Stf; Off Sr Cls; Bsktbl; Ftbl; Golf; Wt Lftg; Spanish NHS; Southern CT ST U; Bus.

HANNA, JOHN; Staples HS; Westport, CT; (Y); 3/450; Church Yth Grp; Cmnty Wkr; Golf; Trk; High Hon Roll; Hon Roll; Art Awd 83; Bus.

HANNA, MARION; Mark T Sheehan HS; Wallingford, CT; (Y); JV Var Bsktbl; Var Ftbl; Var L Trk; Most Outstndng Defensive Plyr-Ftbll 84; Southern CT ST U; Athltc Trnr.

HANNAH, PAMELA S; Glastonbury HS; S Glastonbury, CT; (Y); 27/393; Church Yth Grp; Drama Clb; French Clb; School Musical; School Play; Trs Frsh Cls; Trs Soph Cls; Trs Jr Cls; Trs Sr Cls; Trs Stu Cncl; Wellesley Bk Awd 84; Faculty Hnrs 85; Michael Jones Schlrshp 85; Babson Coll; Bus.

HANNAN JR, RAYMOND T; Notre Dame HS; W Haven, CT; (Y); 33/248; Church Yth Grp; Lib Concert Band; Jazz Band; Lib Mrchg Band; Orch; School Musical; Ed Lit Mag; High Hon Roll; NHS; Ntl Merit Ltr; Amer Mscl Fndtn Bnd Hnrs 83; Hstry.

HANNIGAN, SUSAN; Southington HS; Southington, CT; (Y); Am Leg Aux Girls St; Variety Show; Sec Jr Cls; Stat Bsbl; JV Var Cheerleading; Powder Puff Ftbl; High Hon Roll; Hon Roll; NHS; Prfct Atten Awd; Socl Sci.

HANRATTY, MARK G; Greenwich HS; Greenwich, CT; (Y); 81/763; Am Leg Boys St; Radio Clb; Y-Teens; Nwsp Rptr; Yrbk Stf; Hon Roll; NHS.

HANSCHKA, DORETTA M; Bloomfield HS; Bloomfield, CT; (Y); 14/254; Church Yth Grp; Dance Clb; Library Aide; Church Choir; Nwsp Stf; Yrbk Stf; Mgr(s); High Hon Roll; NHS; NE Baptist Conf Womns Scholar 85; Bloomfield Ctzn Scholar 85; Gordon Coll; Bus Admin.

HANSEN, HEIDI J; Shelton HS; Shelton, CT; (Y); Ski Clb; Spanish Clb; Band; NHS; Spanish NHS; Natl Hnr Rl 84-85; Pres Acadmc Ftns Awd 85; U Of RI; Elem Educ.

HANSEN, KAREN; Southington HS; Southington, CT; (Y); 147/550; Ski Clb; Capt Color Guard; Hon Roll; Briarwood Coll; Exec Sec.

HANSEN, KENNETH; Staples HS; Westport, CT; (Y); 280/848; Boy Scts; Key Clb; Jazz Band; Im Crs Cntry; Var L Swmmng; JV Trk; Sci.

HANSEN, MARK; Shelton HS; Shelton, CT; (Y); Church Yth Grp; Civic Clb; Debate Tm; Ski Clb; Band; Concert Band; Drm Mjr(t); Mrchg Band; Orch; Hon Roll; 1st Rnnr Mr Stu Body 84; Law.

HANSON, EDWARD; Jonathan Law HS; Milford, CT; (Y); 2/270; JV Boy Scts; Pres Church Yth Grp; Trs Exploring; Key Clb; Trs Soph Cls; Mgr Ftbl; Hon Roll; NHS; NEDT Awd; Hugh O Brian Yth Rep 84; Natl Latin Hnr Soc 83-85.

HANZEL, SUSAN; Norwalk HS; Norwalk, CT; (Y); 4/375; Hosp Aide; Key Clb; Orch; Yrbk Bus Mgr; Rep Soph Cls; Rep Jr Cls; Mgr(s); Mgr Vllybl; High Hon Roll; NHS; Med.

HAPPY, SUSAN ELIZABETH; Joseph A Foran HS; Milford, CT; (Y); 31/285; Church Yth Grp; Keywanettes; Cmnty Wkr; High Hon Roll; Hon Roll; Jr NHS; NHS; Ntl Merit Ltr; Supt Acad Awd 85; MAES De Gray Mem Awd 85; Pres Acad Fit Awd 85; U Of CT; Fitness.

HARDER, ROBERT; Emmett Obrien RUTS; Ansonia, CT; (Y); Boy Scts; Church Yth Grp; Ski Clb; Var Bsbl; Hon Roll; Star Supply Co Awd 84; Ralph Mann & Sons Awd Air Condtn & Refrg 85; Refrigrtn Bus.

HARDIMAN, EILEEN; Shelton HS; Shelton, CT; (Y); FHA; Prfct Atten Awd; Chef.

HARDIN, CLEVELAND; Avon Old Farms Schl; Chicago, IL; (S); 4/180; JV Crs Cntry; JV Trk; Hon Roll; Ntl Merit Schol; Purdue U; Aerospc Engr.

HARDING, KEVIN; Roger Ludlowe HS; Fairfield, CT; (Y); 38/320; Im L Lcrss; Im Capt Socr; U Of CT; Bus.

HARDING, TODD; Guilford SR HS; Guilford, CT; (Y); 91/320; CAP; Exploring; Im Ftbl; Hon Roll; Quinlan Awd 83; Arch.

HARGREAVES, BETH; Trumbull HS; Trumbull, CT; (S); DECA; Drama Clb; FTA; JA; Spanish Clb; Teachers Aide; School Play; Sec Frsh Cls; Cheerleading; Acad Achvt Awd 83-84; Mst Lkly/Sccd-Mktg 85; E CT ST U; Erly Chldhd Educ.

HARLAN, WENDY; Daniel Hand HS; Madison, CT; (Y); 2/236; Church Yth Grp; JCL; Model UN; Band; Nwsp Ed-Chief; High Hon Roll; NHS; Ntl Merit SF; French Clb; Latin Clb.

HARMON, WARREN; Manchester HS; Manchester, CT; (Y); Church Yth Grp; Drama Clb; Sec Thesps; Acpl Chr; Band; Chorus; Mrchg Band; School Musical; Aud/Vis; Math Tm; Hghst Scor Amer HS Math Exm; 2nd Pl CT Chemathon; Sem Fnlst, Chem Olympiad.

HAROVAS, ANNE; Wethersfield HS; Wethersfield, CT; (Y); Yrbk Stf; Cheerleading; Hon Roll; Boston U; Accntnt.

HARPER, ELIZABETH; Francis T Maloney HS; Meriden, CT; (Y); Church Yth Grp; Hosp Aide; High Hon Roll; Hon Roll; Wall St Sem 85.

HARPER, KIM; Naugatuck HS; Naugatuck, CT; (Y); Chorus; JV Sftbl; Var Trk; Hon Roll; Med Asst.

HARRINGTON, MARIE; Staples HS; Westport, CT; (Y); JA; Latin Clb; Radio Clb; Powder Puff Ftbl; Hon Roll.

HARRIS, ANDREW; New Canaan HS; New Canaan, CT; (Y); Ski Clb; JV Lcrss; JV Socr; Hon Roll; Co-Fondr & Pres HS Astrnmy Clb 85; Stu HS Astrnmcl Soc 85; U S Sccr Fed Refre-Cls 2 84-85; Physcs.

HARRIS, BRIAN; Windham Regional Vo-Tech Schl; Willimantic, CT; (Y); Boy Scts; Chess Clb; Library Aide; Teachers Aide; Hon Roll; Draftmn.

HARRIS, DONNA; Kolbe-Cathedral HS; Bridgeport, CT; (Y); 23/100; JA; Pep Clb; Bsktbl; Sftbl; Vllybl; High Hon Roll; Hon Roll; Hghst Avg Chem 85; Alg Excllnce Acad 85; Quinnipiac; Comp Sci.

HARRIS, ERICKA; James Hillhouse HS; New Haven, CT; (Y); Band; Concert Band; Flag Corp; Mrchg Band; Variety Show; Pres Stu Cncl; DAR Awd; Hon Roll; Busnss Admin.

HARRIS, HENRY P; William Hall HS; W Hartford, CT; (Y); 39/324; Pres Debate Tm; Temple Yth Grp; School Play; Symp Band; Rep Stu Cncl; NHS; Spanish NHS.

HARRIS, LEIGH; The Hutchkiss Schl; Lexington, KY; (Y); Drama Clb; Chorus; School Musical; School Play; Stage Crew; JV Fld Hcky; Mgr(s); High Hon Roll; Hon Roll.

HARRIS, LORINA M; Bloomfield HS; Bloomfield, CT; (Y); Pres Art Clb; Sec Church Yth Grp; Pres Civic Clb; Church Choir; Yrbk Stf; Lit Mag; Stu Cncl; Trk; Hon Roll; Best In Show-Drawing-Watkinson Invtnl 85; Rotary Cl Stu Of Mnth 84; U Hartford; Cmrcl Art.

HARRIS, TIA; Suffield HS; West Suffield, CT; (Y); 53/157; Church Yth Grp; Library Aide; Chorus; School Musical; Yrbk Stf; JV Var Cheerleading; Hon Roll; Accntnt.

HARRISON, DEANNA; Rham HS; Marlborough, CT; (Y); 6/155; Church Yth Grp; Pep Clb; Sec Band; Chorus; Church Choir; Mrchg Band; Pep Band; Hon Roll; NHS; Bus Admin.

HARRISON, PAUL; F Scott Bunnell HS; Stratford, CT; (Y); 2/268; French Clb; Yrbk Stf; Var L Crs Cntry; Var L Trk; French Hon Soc; High Hon Roll; JETS Awd; NHS; New England Math League Cntst 84 & 85; Chemathon 84; Applied Sci Series Yale U 85; Math.

HARROP, JAMES; Avon Old Farms Schl; Avon, CT; (S); 2/106; Boy Scts; Church Yth Grp; Ski Clb; School Play; Variety Show; Yrbk Stf; Ftbl; Lcrss; L Socr; High Hon Roll.

HART, DANIEL F; Southington HS; Southington, CT; (Y); 34/550; Church Yth Grp; Dance Clb; JV Golf; High Hon Roll; Hon Roll; NHS; CT ST & Fuller Schlrshp Grant Awds 85; Bentley Coll; Comp Inf Sys.

HART, DAVID; Manchester HS; Manchester, CT; (Y); French Clb; Var Socr; High Hon Roll; Hon Roll; Ntl Merit Ltr; Acad Excllnce Plaque; 1st Pl Socr Tm Trophy; Arch.

HART, KRIS; Stratford HS; Stratford, CT; (Y); 3/241; JA; Rep Soph Cls; Rep Jr Cls; Rep Sr Cls; High Hon Roll; NHS; Outstndng Physics Stu Awd 85; Outstndng Svc Cls Cncl 84 & 85; Early Chldhd Ed.

HART, ROBERT; Daniel Hand HS; Madison, CT; (Y); 40/270; JCL; Latin Clb; Varsity Clb; Var L Golf; Socr; Hon Roll; Physcs Olympd 85; Golf Trphy MIP 85; Law.

HARTMANN, CATHERINE; Daniel Hand HS; Madison, CT; (Y); 26/249; Hosp Aide; Political Wkr; Spanish Clb; Chorus; Nwsp Phtg; Nwsp Stf; Yrbk Phtg; Yrbk Stf; High Hon Roll; Hon Roll; Barnard Coll NY; Hstry.

HARTUNG, NANCY; Notre Dame Catholic HS; Trumbull, CT; (Y); 15/284; Pres Church Yth Grp; French Clb; Girl Scts; JA; Swmmng; French Hon Soc; High Hon Roll; NHS; Latin Clb; Church Choir; Alliance Francaise Awd 85; Hon For Top 20 Of Clss 85; Pres Acad Ftnss Awd 85; U Of CT; Lang.

HARTWELL, ROBERT; Plainfield HS; Sterling, CT; (Y); 18/138; Am Leg Boys St; Mrchg Band; JV Ftbl; Score Keeper; Var Wt Lftg; Hon Roll.

HARVEY, CATHERINE; Trumbull HS; Trumbull, CT; (Y); Art Clb; Cmnty Wkr; Drama Clb; Office Aide; Ski Clb; Color Guard; Mrchg Band; Score Keeper; JV Trk; Hon Roll; Outstndg Achvt Art 85; Comm Art.

HARVEY, ELIZABETH; Manchester HS; Manchester, CT; (Y); 1/500; AFS; VP Church Yth Grp; German Clb; Math Tm; Spanish Clb; Orch; Crs Cntry; High Hon Roll; VP NHS; Rensselaer Math & Sci Awd 85; Math.

HARVEY, RACHAEL; West Haven HS; W Haven, CT; (Y); Stage Crew; Nwsp Rptr; Outstndng Achvt Awd Alge I 83; Chsn Mass Prodc Wdn Toys 83; Acctg.

HASKEDAKES, LISA E; Academy Of Our Lady Of Mercy; W Haven, CT; (Y); 43/112; Drama Clb; French Clb; Chorus; School Musical; Lit Mag; Stu Cncl; U Of RI; Spch Comm.

HASSELBERG, KATE; Orville H Platt HS; Meriden, CT; (Y); Pres Drama Clb; Hosp Aide; Chorus; Variety Show; Yrbk Stf; Crs Cntry; Trk; Hon Roll; Ntl Merit Ltr; Music.

HATCH, AARON; Windham HS; Willimantic, CT; (Y); Church Yth Grp; JV Socr; Var Wrstlng; Hon Roll; Arch.

HATCHER, JENNIFER; Miss Porters Schl; Maumee, OH; (Y); Varsity Clb; Mgr Var Bsktbl; Var JV Fld Hcky; JV Capt Lcrss; Hd Of Angelettes 85-86; Tour Guide 83-86; Usher Alumni Fnctns & Spcl Prog 85-86.

HATHAWAY, JOHN; Windham Reg Vo-Tec Schl; Lebanon, CT; (Y); 1/120; VP Exploring; VP VICA; Yrbk Stf; Stu Cncl; JV Socr; JV Var Trk; God Cntry Awd; High Hon Roll; Hon Roll; NHS; CT Bus & Indus Assn-1st 85; JR R Danc Of CT-1ST 84; VICA ST Skll Olympcs-Arch Drftg 2nd 85; U Of UT; Theatre.

HATTIER, TOM; Masok HS; Monroe, CT; (Y); 90/266; Cmnty Wkr; Crs Cntry; Wrstlng.

HATZINIKOLAS, CHRISTINA; East Hartford HS; E Hartford, CT; (Y); Church Yth Grp; Color Guard; Off Frsh Cls; Off Soph Cls; Off Jr Cls; Briarwood Bk Awd 85.

HAUSER, BRIAN J; The Morgan Schl; Clinton, CT; (Y); 16/166; Chorus; Church Choir; Stage Crew; Var L Bsbl; Capt L Bsktbl; Capt L Socr; Hon Roll; NHS; Prncpls Cup Awd 85; Schlr/Athlte Awd 85; All ST, All Cnty & All Shrlne Sccr Tm 83-84; U Of CT; Sprt Med.

HAVEY, KATHLEEN; Bethel HS; Bethel, CT; (Y); 2/280; Am Leg Aux Girls St; Church Yth Grp; Hosp Aide; Yrbk Ed-Chief; Im JV Sftbl; High Hon Roll; NHS; Ntl Merit Ltr; AFS; Chorus; Bus Mgr JR Shw 85; CT Hnrs Sem 85.

HAVOURD, VICTORIA L; Shelton HS; Shelton, CT; (Y); 38/417; Church Yth Grp; French Clb; Var Bsktbl; Var Capt Socr; JV Trk; Hon Roll; La Salle U; Spec Elem Ed.

HAVRILKO, JOHANNA; Shelton HS; Shelton, CT; (S); 283/416; VP DECA; Hosp Aide; Hon Roll; Distbtv Educ Clb Of Amer Won 1st Pl At ST Conf In The Apprl & Accssns Wrttn Evnt 85; ST Acad Of Hairdrssng; Cosmtlg.

HAVUNEN, SANDEE; Northwestern Regional No 7 HS; Winsted, CT; (Y); Dance Clb; Varsity Clb; School Musical; School Play; Variety Show; Lit Mag; Var Cheerleading; High Hon Roll; Hon Roll; Drwng Awd 1st Pl 85; Creatv Wrtng 85; Tlnt Awd Miss Amer Co-Ed Bllt 84; Northwestern CC; Grphc Dsgn.

HAWK, MARY ELLEN; Stamford Catholic HS; Stamford, CT; (Y); 37/160; High Hon Roll; Hon Roll; Fash Merch.

HAX, COLLEEN; Lyman Hall HS; Wallingford, CT; (Y); Varsity Clb; Sec Band; Mrchg Band; Off Stu Cncl; Var L Bsktbl; Var L Fld Hcky; Var L Trk; High Hon Roll; Hon Roll; NHS; Bio Cert Of Hnr 84; Earth Sci Cert Of Hnr 85; Highest Female Rcgntn Monogram In Phys Ftns 85.

HAYDEN, VANESSA; Windham HS; Coventry, CT; (Y); 3/285; Drama Clb; Math Tm; Acpl Chr; Madrigals; School Musical; Swing Chorus; Elks Awd; High Hon Roll; Mu Alp Tht; Ntl Merit SF; Willimantic Womens Club Schlrshp 84-85; Best Sr Frnch & Engl Awds 84-85; Stu Yr Awd Fnlst 84-85; U Of CT; Comp.

HAYES, MARK; Bloomfield HS; Bloomfield, CT; (Y); 20/230; Church Yth Grp; Exploring; Model UN; Ski Clb; Nwsp Rptr; Capt Lcrss; Socr; Hon Roll; NHS; Miltry Acad; Engrng.

HAYES, MICHAEL; St Bernard HS; Ledyard, CT; (Y); 26/300; Church Yth Grp; JV Crs Cntry; Ftbl; High Hon Roll; Hon Roll; Ntl Merit Ltr; Art Awd 84; Cvl Engrng.

HAYNOS, JUDITH ELLEN; Newtown HS; Newtown, CT; (Y); 89/290; Yrbk Ed-Chief; Sec Jr Cls; Sec Sr Cls; Rep Stu Cncl; DAR Awd; High Hon Roll; VFW Awd; Voice Dem Awd; Pres Office Aide; Concert Band; Quota Clb Schlrshp 85; Wellesley Coll Bk Awd/Ctznshp-Acadmc Excllnc 84; Guidnc Hnr Assn Awd 85; Nazareth Coll; Spch Pathlgy.

HEAD, LISA; Saint Marys HS; New Haven, CT; (Y); 11/115; Church Yth Grp; Ski Clb; Nwsp Stf; VP Jr Cls; Trk; French Hon Soc; Mu Alp Tht; Pep Clb; Stage Crew; Yrbk Stf; Polit Sci.

HEAP, SHANNON MICHAEL; New London HS; New London, CT; (S); 33/200; DECA; Trs Key Clb; VP Jr Cls; VP Sr Cls; Rep Stu Cncl; Capt Ftbl; Golf; High Hon Roll; Hon Roll; Bus.

HEARD, BRIAN; Ledyard HS; Leyard, CT; (Y); Var Bsbl; Var Bsktbl; Hon Roll.

HEATH, RANDALL; Southington HS; Southington, CT; (Y); Pres Church Yth Grp; Computer Clb; Nwsp Rptr; Nwsp Stf; Rep Soph Cls; Var L Bsktbl; DAR Awd; Hon Roll; Comp Sci.

HEATH, RICHARD ANDREWS; Bristol Eastern HS; Bristol, CT; (Y); 26/271; Rep Jr Cls; Rep Stu Cncl; Var L Socr; Trk; Hon Roll; NHS; Am Leg Boys St; Cmnty Wkr; Spanish Clb; Thesps; Stu Cncl Schlrshp 85; Norwich U; Engr.

HEAVREN, BRIAN; St Thomas Aquinas HS; Berlin, CT; (Y); VP Art Clb; Boy Scts; Exploring; Stage Crew; Yrbk Phtg; Hon Roll; Prfct Atten Awd; Fndr & Pst Pres Explrer Post 911 82-85; Lng Rvrs Cncls Explrer Ldrshp Awd 85; Egl Sct 83; U Of MD; Emrgncy Hlth Svc.

HEBB, LESLIE; Conard HS; W Hartford, CT; (Y); 14/314; Var Capt Bsktbl; Var Capt Sftbl; Var Vllybl; High Hon Roll; NHS; Spanish NHS; ST Latn Awd; Bio.

HEBERT, DENNIS; Norwich Free Acad; Norwich, CT; (Y); Am Leg Boys St; Boy Scts; Church Yth Grp; Varsity Clb; Nwsp Rptr; JV Var Wrstlng; High Hon Roll; Russian Club Pres 83-85; Order Of Arrow-BSA Chptr Chief 84-85; Industrl Design.

HEENIE, CHERYL L; West Haven HS; W Haven, CT; (Y); 21/355; Church Yth Grp; Intnl Clb; Yrbk Stf; High Hon Roll; Jr NHS; NHS; Spanish NHS; CT Schltc Achvt Grnt Pgm 84-85; Fin Aid Awd Messiah Coll 84-85; Messiah Coll; Acctg.

HEFFLON, CINDY; Suffield HS; West Suffield, CT; (Y); 5/156; Church Yth Grp; Church Choir; Concert Band; Madrigals; School Musical; Symp Band; Gym; High Hon Roll; Hon Roll; NHS; Natl Merit Ltr Of Commndtn 84-85; Hghst Verbal PSAT Score 84; Eng Awd 85; Tufts U; Mth.

HEINE, KEVIN; East Catholic HS; Manchester, CT; (Y); 90/300; CAP; Computer Clb; Ski Clb; Off Frsh Cls; L Crs Cntry; L Trk; Prfct Atten Awd; Air Force ROTC.

HEINE, SUSAN; Derby HS; Waterbury, CT; (Y); 1/126; Church Yth Grp; Hosp Aide; Math Tm; Nwsp Stf; High Hon Roll; NHS; VP Spanish NHS; Val; Acadmc Hnrs Schlrshp; New Hvn Cnty Shrffs Assn Schlrshp; Dr M A Parlato Schlrshp; Harvard Bk Awd; Pensacola Chrstn Coll; Math.

HEINZMANN, MIRIAM V; Cromwell HS; Cromwell, CT; (Y); 5/117; Am Leg Aux Girls St; School Play; Yrbk Ed-Chief; Trs Sr Cls; Rep Trs Stu Cncl; Var Capt Socr; Var Capt Sftbl; DAR Awd; Lion Awd; Pres NHS; CT Assn Of Sec Schl Schlr-Athlt 85; Kiwanis Clb Hnry Lifetm Mbrshp In Cromwell Hstrcl Scty 84; Simmons Coll; Phy Thrpy.

HELLER, STEVE; Weston HS; Weston, CT; (Y); 32/200; Debate Tm; Band; Ftbl; Swmmng; Hon Roll; CT U; Physics.

HELLER, SUSAN; New Britain HS; New Britain, CT; (Y); 35/389; Rep Sr Cls; Rep Stu Cncl; Var Capt Crs Cntry; Hon Roll; Elem Ed.

HELT, DAVID; New Fairfield HS; New Fairfield, CT; (Y); 18/205; Ski Clb; Band; Chorus; Concert Band; Jazz Band; Mrchg Band; Orch; School Musical; School Play; Symp Band; SR Band Awd 85; Rchster Tech; Mcro Elec Engrng.

HENCLEWSKI, MICHAEL; Saint Thomas Aquinas HS; New Britain, CT; (Y); Chess Clb; Church Yth Grp; French Clb; Teachers Aide; Hon Roll; NHS; Ntl Merit Ltr; Prfct Atten Awd; Wstrn Cvlztn Schlrshp Awd 83; 7th Annl Chemathn Comptn 85; Engrng.

HENDERSON, AMELIA; Richard C Lee HS; New Haven, CT; (Y); Cmnty Wkr; Computer Clb; FBLA; JA; Red Cross Aide; Yrbk Stf; VP Sr Cls; Cit Awd; High Hon Roll; Ntl Merit Schol; Acad Achvt Hill SDA Church 84; Oakwood Coll; Bus Admin.

HENDERSON, CINDY; Stratford HS; Stratford, CT; (Y); 25/241; French Clb; JA; Pres Chorus; Capt Drill Tm; Yrbk Stf; Rep Frsh Cls; Rep Soph Cls; VP Jr Cls; VP Sr Cls; French Hon Soc; Engnr.

HENNESSEY, KEITH; Weston HS; Weston, CT; (Y); 7/160; Church Yth Grp; French Clb; Latin Clb; School Musical; Lit Mag; Trs Stu Cncl; High Hon Roll; Hon Roll; NHS; Hugh O Brian Yth Fndtn Ldrshp Semr 83-84; Calculus Tchng Asst 83-85; Rickover Sci Inst 85; Stanford; Bus.

HENNESSY, MICHAEL S; Shepaug Valley HS; Bridgewater, CT; (Y); 4/83; VP Frsh Cls; Pres Soph Cls; Sec Pres Stu Cncl; Capt L Crs Cntry; Co-Capt L Swmmng; L Trk; NHS; Ntl Merit SF; Boy Scts; Church Yth Grp; Harvard Club Sthrn CT Awd 84; Co-Cptn Track Tm; Scholar Athlete Awd.

HENRICKS, SARAH; Farmington HS; Farmington, CT; (Y); 2/206; Math Tm; Band; VP Soph Cls; Sec Jr Cls; Sec Sr Cls; Var Capt Fld Hcky; NHS; Ntl Merit Ltr; Spanish NHS; Rep Frsh Cls; Yale Bk Awd 85; Wesleyan Sci Symosium Dlegt 85; Big Sister/Big Brother Prog 84-86; Med.

HENRY, LOREL; Shelton HS; Shelton, CT; (Y); Trs Exploring; Sec 4-H; FFA; JCL; Sec Latin Clb; 4-H Awd; High Hon Roll; Hon Roll; NHS; Adelaide Coombs Awd 85; Achvt Awd 83; Summa Cum Laude 85; Wldlf.

HENRY, MARLA JALENE; William H Hall HS; Hartford, CT; (Y); 212/324; Church Yth Grp; Church Choir; Stage Crew; Hon Roll; Briarwood Clg Bk Awd; Bus.

HENRY, SUSAN; East Hartford HS; E Hartford, CT; (Y); VP Church Yth Grp; Drama Clb; VP French Clb; Stage Crew; Hon Roll; NHS; Outstndng Art Awd 85; Art Thrpy.

HENSEL, PATRICIA A; Newtown HS; Sandy Hook, CT; (Y); Varsity Clb; VP Jr Cls; VP Sr Cls; Rep Stu Cncl; Capt Bsktbl; Capt Socr; Var Sftbl; Hon Roll; MBP Soccr 83; Outstndng JR Athlt 85; Red Cross Blood Mobl Recog 85; Commctns.

HERBERT, STACY; East Lyme HS; Salem, CT; (Y); Key Clb; Ed Yrbk Stf; High Hon Roll; Hon Roll; Grls Vrsty Crew Tm 85; Grls ST Awd 85; Law.

HERLIHY, MARLA J; Putnam HS; Putnam, CT; (Y); 1/145; Stage Crew; Pres Frsh Cls; VP Rep Stu Cncl; Capt Var Cheerleading; Var Trk; High Hon Roll; NHS; Val; Harvard-Radcliff Bk Awd 84; U Of CT; Bus.

HERMAN, MARIANNE C; Trumbull HS; Trumbull, CT; (Y); Church Yth Grp; French Clb; Ski Clb; Yrbk Stf; JV Trk; French Hon Soc; High Hon Roll; VP NHS; Excllnc Frnch Awd 84; Trumbull Ed Assoc Schlrhsp 85; Georgetown U.

HERMSEN, MATTHEW R; William H Hall HS; W Hartford, CT; (Y); #86 In Class; Church Yth Grp; JA; Q&S; Yrbk Sprt Ed; Var L Ftbl; Var L Trk; Hon Roll; Stu Mth 85; Alfred U; Bus Adm.

HERRERA, CYNTHIA; Ledyard HS; Gales Ferry, CT; (Y); Nwsp Stf; Yrbk Stf; Stu Cncl; Mgr(s); Var Sftbl; Var Trk; Stat Wrstlng; Church Yth Grp; Science Clb; Nwsp Rptr; Pres Phys Ftns Awd 82; Sci Fair 2nd 82; Elem Educ.

HERRING, LORRI; Platt HS; Meriden, CT; (Y); Boys Clb Am; Girl Scts; Key Clb; Latin Clb; Band; Chorus; Drm & Bgl; Mrchg Band; Swing Chorus; Hon Roll; Teen Of Mnth 84; Briarwood Coll Sptlght Pgm 85; Tchg.

HERSKIND, MARK; Cheshire HS; Cheshire, CT; (Y); 24/319; Am Leg Boys St; Church Yth Grp; School Play; Rep Frsh Cls; Rep Soph Cls; Rep Jr Cls; Rep Sr Cls; Socr; Tennis; French Hon Soc; Rotary, PTO & ROTC Schlrshp 85; Wheaton Coll; Phys Sci.

HERVEY, SUSAN; Trumbull HS; Trumbull, CT; (Y); Church Yth Grp; Trs Key Clb; JV Trk; Hon Roll; Accntnt.

HERZOG, MARC; North Haven HS; N Haven, CT; (Y); 118/281; French Clb; Latin Clb; Med.

HEWITT, SPENCER; Holy Cross HS; Prospect, CT; (Y); 117/352; Boy Scts; Band; Concert Band; Mrchg Band; Pep Band; Hon Roll; Nrsg.

HIBBARD, SALLY; Oliver Wolcott Tech HS; Goshen, CT; (Y); Boy Scts; Drama Clb; Pres 4-H; VICA; 4-H Awd; Hon Roll; Sec NHS; Aviatn.

HICKCOX, KATHARINE J; William H Hall HS; W Hartford, CT; (Y); Church Yth Grp; Acpl Chr; Chorus; Church Choir; Madrigals; School Musical; Swing Chorus; Yrbk Phtg; Cit Awd; Art Clb; Jr St Cecelia Music Awd Hghst Awd/Royl Schl Chrch Music Amer 85; Archry Awd Abv Avg Skl 82 & 83; Cmnctns.

HICKEY, SEAN; Wethersfiled HS; Wethersfield, CT; (Y); 17/315; Am Leg Boys St; Church Yth Grp; Nwsp Ed-Chief; VP Stu Cncl; JV Var Socr; High Hon Roll; NHS; Model UN; Spanish Clb; Nwsp Rptr; CT Ind Art Assn Drftg Awd 83-85; Archit & Mech Drftg Cont Awd 85; CT Bus Week CBIA 84; Engrng.

HICKMAN, SEAN; Penney HS; E Hartford, CT; (Y); Computer Clb; Science Clb; Var Ftbl; Im Wt Lftg; JV Wrstlng; Bio.

HICKS, DAVID; Greenwich HS; Old Greenwich, CT; (Y); Am Leg Boys St; Key Clb; Jazz Band; Pres Frsh Cls; Pres Soph Cls; Pres Sr Cls; NHS; Math Tm; Band; Mrchg Band; Natl Merit Spec Scholar 85; Am Leg Boys Nation 84; Fr Alliance Greenwich Fr Awd 85; Harvard U; Med.

HIGGINS, MARY ELLEN; Saint Bernard HS; Pawcatuck, CT; (Y); 24/290; Dance Clb; Ski Clb; Teachers Aide; School Play; Lit Mag; Var Cheerleading; Chess Clb; High Hon Roll; Hon Roll; NHS; Providence Coll; Psych.

HILDRETH, SCOTT; Ste Bernard HS; Norwich, CT; (S); Church Yth Grp; Cmnty Wkr; Computer Clb; Ski Clb; Church Choir; Im Bsktbl; L Var Ftbl; Var Wt Lftg; Var L Wrstlng; Hon Roll; Comp Engr.

HILL, CHRISTINE E; Haddam Killingworth HS; Killingworth, CT; (Y); #11 In Class; Band; Concert Band; Mrchg Band; School Musical; Nwsp Stf; Stu Cncl; Stat Vllybl; Debate Tm; L Pep Band; Nwsp Rptr; Schlrshp Clinton Killingworth Assoc U Women 85; Shoreline Allnc Arts Schlrshp 85; Pres Acad Ftns Awd; Syracuse U; Jrnlsm.

HILL, ELIZABETH; William Hall HS; W Hartford, CT; (Y); Church Yth Grp; French Clb; Girl Scts; JA; Band; Mrchg Band; Pep Band; Var Capt Fld Hcky; Var JV Gym; Var JV Trk; Lang.

HILL, PAMELA; Trumbull HS; Trumbull, CT; (Y); Church Yth Grp; Hosp Aide; Political Wkr; Chorus; Color Guard; Flag Corp; Mrchg Band; High Hon Roll; NHS; Prfct Atten Awd; Ntl Hstry Day-2nd Pl 85; Peer Tutrng Awd 85; Jrnlsm.

HILLBURN, ROBERT A; St Paul Catholic HS; Meriden, CT; (Y); 29/258; Drama Clb; French Clb; Chorus; School Play; Crs Cntry; French Hon Soc; Hon Roll; NHS; Math.

HILLMAN, MARGARET; Ridgefield HS; Ridgefield, CT; (S); 34/365; Church Yth Grp; Orch; School Musical; High Hon Roll; Hon Roll; CT Western Reg Orch 84-85; All CT Orch 84-85; Music Ed Ntl Conf 85; Chem.

HINES, ERIC; Hadam Killingworth HS; Higganum, CT; (Y); 37/134; Trk; Hon Roll; Cls S Champ & ST Champ-Outdr Pole Vaultng 1st Pl 85; Cls M ST Open-Indoor Pole Vaultng 3rd Pl 85; Hawthorne Coll; Avionics.

HINKLEY, JAMES; Conard HS; W Hartford, CT; (Y); JA; Lit Mag; Northeastern; Bus Admin.

HIRBOUR, SUZANNE MARIE; Pomeraug Regional HS; Middlebury, CT; (Y); 43/206; French Clb; German Clb; Spanish Clb; High Hon Roll; Lion Awd; Excllnce In Study Of Spnsh 83-85; Excllnce In Study Of Frnch 84-85; Outstndng Effrt In Peer Tutrng 85; Assumption Coll; Frgn Lang.

HIRE, MARGARET; Killingly HS; Dayville, CT; (Y); Mrchg Band; Symp Band; Var Fld Hcky; Hon Roll; Jr NHS; NHS; Spanish NHS; Outstndng Wrtg Skill Prep Engl 85; U Of Connecticut; Pre Bus.

HLOZEK, LAURA; Trumbull HS; Trumbull, CT; (Y); AFS; Church Yth Grp; Concert Band; Mrchg Band; Rep Frsh Cls; High Hon Roll; Hon Roll; Prfct Atten Awd; 2nd Dst Ntl Hist Day; Acctng.

HO, JOHN; Stamford HS; Stamford, CT; (S); 2/408; Debate Tm; Off Key Clb; Pres Math Clb; Chrmn Red Cross Aide; Pres Science Clb; Ski Clb; VP Frsh Cls; Rep Soph Cls; Rep Jr Cls; Rep Sr Cls; Chem Olympd Awd 82-83; All Cnty Javeln Thrwr 83-84 Top 6 83-84; Outstndng Acadmc Achvt Awd 84-85; Brown U; Med.

HO, MARIE XUAN HUONG; Northwestern Regional No 7; New Hartford, CT; (Y); 10/170; French Clb; Hon Roll; NHS; Explrng Frontiers Of Sci At Yale 84; Sci For The Gftd 84; U Of CT.

HOAG, ALEXANDREA; Shelton HS; Huntington, CT; (Y); Dance Clb; Drama Clb; FNA; Pep Clb; Spanish Clb; Yrbk Stf; Rep Frsh Cls; Rep Soph Cls; Rep Jr Cls; Rep Sr Cls; Psych.

HOAGLAND, JAMES; Manchester HS; Manchester, CT; (Y); Trs Church Yth Grp; Ski Clb; Band; Concert Band; Mrchg Band; JV Var Socr; Hon Roll; Arch.

HOANG, DANH; Wilbur Cross HS; New Haven, CT; (S); FBLA; Office Aide; Stu Cncl; Hon Roll; Rotary Awd; St Schlr; New Haven Schlrshp Fnd Inc Schltc Achvt Grnt 85; Hnr Dnnr 81-85; SR Awd 85; Quinnipiac Coll; Accntng.

HOBERMAN, JENNIFER; William H Hall HS; West Hartford, CT; (Y); 52/342; FBLA; Pep Clb; Stu Cncl; Var Cheerleading; Var Fld Hcky; JV Gym; High Hon Roll; Hon Roll; Med Careers Club 83-85; Dartmouth; Dnstry.

HODER IV, STEPHEN M; Stamford Catholic HS; Stamford, CT; (Y); JV Bsktbl; JV Ftbl; Hlth.

HODGE, TRACEY; Daniel Hand HS; Madison, CT; (Y); Office Aide; Teachers Aide; Sec Frsh Cls; Rep Soph Cls; Var Capt Bsktbl; Var L Sftbl; Var L Trk; Hon Roll; Prncpls Brd Panl 83-84; Elem Ed.

HOEING, MICHELLE; Pomperaug HS; Southbury, CT; (Y); Chorus; JV Var Sftbl; JV Swmmng; JV Vllybl; High Hon Roll; Hon Roll; U Of CT; Bus Mngmnt.

HOEY, KELLEY; Stamford Catholic HS; Stamford, CT; (Y); 41/160; Cmnty Wkr; 4-H; Red Cross Aide; Nwsp Stf; AFS; Church Yth Grp; Exploring; JA; Band; Crs Cntry; Citznshp WA Focus; Bio.

HOFFA, MARK; Windsor Locks HS; Windsor Locks, CT; (Y); 5/175; Am Leg Boys St; Boy Scts; Church Yth Grp; Math Tm; Concert Band; Orch; Nwsp Ed-Chief; Var L Tennis; Hon Roll; NHS; Yale U Frontiers Appld Sci 85; Talcott Mts Nova III & Super Nova Sci Pgm 84; Engrng.

HOFFMAN, CHRISTINE; Kingswood-Oxford Schl; Bloomfield, CT; (Y); Spanish Clb; Concert Band; Ed Yrbk Ed-Chief; Ed Lit Mag; JV Lcrss; JV Capt Socr; Hon Roll; U Of TX At Austin; Brdcst Jrnl.

HOFFMAN, M; Hall HS; W Hartford, CT; (Y); 51/360; Pres Camera Clb; Debate Tm; Radio Clb; Ed Yrbk Phtg; Var Crs Cntry; Trk; Vllybl; High Hon Roll; NHS; Ntl Merit Ltr; Comm Svc Awd 83; 3rd Pl Milestones Of Freedm Awd 85; Crss-Cntry Athltc Awd 84; Pol Sci.

HOHNKE, MICHELLE; Hall HS; W Hartford, CT; (Y); 6/324; Church Yth Grp; Ski Clb; VP Soph Cls; Var L Crs Cntry; Trk; High Hon Roll; Trs NHS; Spanish NHS; Schlstc Art Awd 85; Charles & Helen Keller Awd Excel Humnts 85.

HOJNOWSKI, MARK W; William Hall HS; W Hartford, CT; (Y); 56/324; Aud/Vis; Church Yth Grp; Band; Jazz Band; Symp Band; Im Badmtn; Im Vllybl; High Hon Roll; NHS; Spanish NHS; Bus.

HOKENSON, JACKIE; William H Hall HS; W Hartford, CT; (Y); 45/321; Cmnty Wkr; Sec Debate Tm; VP Pres JA; Pep Clb; Service Clb; Ski Clb; Ed Yrbk Rptr; Off Frsh Cls; Off Soph Cls; Off Jr Cls; Frgn Lang Poetry Cntst; Pre Law Study 84; Howard U Smmr Sessn 85; Intl Law.

HOLBROOK, WENDY; Lyman Hall HS; Wallingford, CT; (Y); 1/227; JV Var Fld Hcky; High Hon Roll; NHS; VP Scl Sci Forum; Yale Bk Awd 85; Rennsselaer Polytechnic Inst Mdl 85; Pres SADD; Med.

HOLDEN, SCOTT N; Glastonbury HS; South Glastonbury, CT; (Y); 115/384; Boy Scts; Church Yth Grp; Drama Clb; Acpl Chr; Chorus; Madrigals; School Play; Stage Crew; Variety Show; Nwsp Rptr; All ST Chrs; Cls Actor; Psych.

HOLLAND, ELLEN; Wilton HS; Wilton, CT; (Y); 117/330; Key Clb; Pep Clb; Varsity Clb; Yrbk Sprt Ed; Yrbk Stf; Rep Stu Cncl; Powder Puff Ftbl; Trk; Hon Roll; Gettysburg Coll; Engl.

HOLLENBECK, JON; W F Kaynor Tech Schl; Oakville, CT; (Y); VICA; Hon Roll; Pep Clb; Nwsp Stf; Mgr Bsbl; Mgr Bsktbl; Bus.

HOLLENBERG, MELISSA; Masuk HS; Monroe, CT; (Y); 11/280; Cmnty Wkr; Spanish Clb; Temple Yth Grp; Tennis; High Hon Roll; NHS; Acctg Awd 84.

HOLMES, HEATHER; East Hartford HS; E Hartford, CT; (Y); Church Yth Grp; Drama Clb; Pres French Clb; Ski Clb; Church Choir; Drill Tm; Nwsp Rptr; JV Trk; High Hon Roll; NHS; Engrng.

HOLMWOOD, SCOTT; East Lyme HS; Salem, CT; (Y); Temple Yth Grp; Yrbk Phtg; Yrbk Stf; JV Bsbl; JV Ftbl; Var Wrstlng; Cit Awd; Hon Roll.

HOLNESS, CHRISTOPHER; Daniel Hand HS; Madison, CT; (Y); Boy Scts; Church Yth Grp; Model UN; Band; Concert Band; Mrchg Band; Orch; JV Bsktbl; JV Trk; JV Crs Cntry; Dstnctn Awd Ntl Scl Stds Olympiad 85.

HOLNESS, DANIELLE; Richard C Lee HS; New Haven, CT; (Y); Pep Clb; Chorus; Nwsp Rptr; Nwsp Stf; Yrbk Stf; Hon Roll; Jrnlsm.

HOLT, CAMMY; Penney HS; E Hartford, CT; (Y); High Hon Roll; Hon Roll; NHS; Optomtrst.

HOLT, JOHN; Hotchkiss Schl; St Albans, VT; (Y); Church Yth Grp; Cmnty Wkr; Political Wkr; Band; Concert Band; Lit Mag; Var L Crs Cntry; Var L Ice Hcky; High Hon Roll; NHS; Intl Reltns.

HOLYST, JODY; Southington HS; Plantsville, CT; (Y); Am Leg Aux Girls St; Chess Clb; FBLA; Key Clb; Ski Clb; Band; Concert Band; Mrchg Band; Hon Roll; Wesleyan U; Law.

HOLYST, KURT JOHN; Southington HS; Plantsville, CT; (S); 72/550; Capt Chess Clb; Church Yth Grp; FFA; Var L Bsktbl; Im Bowling; Var L Ftbl; Var L Tennis; Var L Wrstlng; Hon Roll; JR Chess Team MVP 80; ST Schlstc Chess Champ; Natl FFA Fndtn Awd Turf & Lndscp Mgmt 85; Marietta Coll; Ntrl Rsrcs.

HOLZMAN, JONATHAN; Stamford HS; Stamford, CT; (S); 38/408; Pres Computer Clb; French Clb; JA; Key Clb; Science Clb; Temple Yth Grp; Var L Tennis; Hon Roll; NHS; Frontiers Of Applied Sci Yale 84; Sci Symposium Yale U 84; John Hopkins U; Elect Engrng.

HOMAN, DONNA; Tolland HS; Tolland, CT; (Y); Camera Clb; French Clb; Band; Mrchg Band; Yrbk Stf; High Hon Roll; Hon Roll; VA Tech; Forgn Bus.

HOMER, AMY; Guilford HS; Guilford, CT; (Y); Church Yth Grp; 4-H; Hosp Aide; Political Wkr; Chorus; Yrbk Bus Mgr; Yrbk Stf; Lit Mag; Hon Roll; Connecticut Intern Prog US Congress 85; Phys Ther.

HONG, L; Cheshire HS; Cheshire, CT; (Y); 5/350; Am Leg Aux Girls St; Scholastic Bowl; Sec Science Clb; Chorus; School Musical; Variety Show; Nwsp Rptr; Sec Jr Cls; Sec Sr Cls; Cit Awd; CCY Prog At Wesleyan U CT 84; Alliance Franc Awd Excllnc 84-85; Harvrd Bk Awd 85; Obstrcn.

HOODBHOY, MEHLIKA; Pomeraug HS; Southbury, CT; (Y); Model UN; Yrbk Ed-Chief; Sec Soph Cls; JV Var Fld Hcky; High Hon Roll; NHS; Pres Pomperaug Chptr SADD.

HOPKINS, MEGHAN; Canton HS; Canton, CT; (Y); 7/90; Cmnty Wkr; JA; Model UN; Quiz Bowl; JV Var Fld Hcky; High Hon Roll; NHS; Debate Tm; Red Cross Aide; Band; CT Assoc Of Secndry Schls 85; Hartford Wellesley Clb Awd 85; Vet.

HOPKINS, ROBERT; Daniel Hand HS; Madison, CT; (Y); Church Yth Grp; Im Bsktbl; JV Crs Cntry; JV Trk; Hon Roll; Bus.

HOPKINSON, DOLLY ANN; East Haven HS; E Haven, CT; (Y); 41/300; Library Aide; Office Aide; Spanish Clb; Band; Chorus; Bsktbl; Hon Roll; JP Sousa Awd; Austin N TX ST; Bus Mgmt.

HORENSAVITZ, TAMMY ANNE; West Haven HS; Hamden, CT; (Y); Church Yth Grp; Cmnty Wkr; Drama Clb; Library Aide; Church Choir; Stage Crew; Variety Show; Mgr(s); Vllybl; Schlrshp Parents Clb 85; Personal Id Human Reltnshp Awd 85; S Central CC; Psych.

HORRIGAN, CHERYL M; Saint Joseph HS; Shelton, CT; (Y); 11/221; Spanish Clb; Nwsp Rptr; Var Capt Crs Cntry; Capt Trk; High Hon Roll; NHS; Spanish NHS; NEDT Awd 82; St Anselm Coll; Psych.

HOSKING, SUSAN E; Conard HS; W Hartford, CT; (Y); 64/322; Church Yth Grp; Cmnty Wkr; Spanish Clb; Chorus; School Musical; School Play; Yrbk Phtg; Capt Swmmng; Tennis; Hon Roll; Bus.

HOSTETLER, NAN; Westhill HS; Stamford, CT; (Y); Latin Clb; Math Clb; Pep Clb; Science Clb; VP Service Clb; Diving; Capt Fld Hcky; Tennis; Hon Roll; NHS; Ntl Stndt Athl Awd 84-85; Sci.

HOTCHKISS, JOHN; Notre Dame HS; W Haven, CT; (Y); Boy Scts; Church Yth Grp; Dance Clb; Band; Concert Band; Jazz Band; Mrchg Band; Trk; Hon Roll; U Of CT; Med.

HOWARD, CARL; Richard C Lee HS; New Haven, CT; (Y); Cmnty Wkr; Math Clb; Pep Clb; Quiz Bowl; Band; Syracuse U; Elect Engr.

HOWARD, SAMANTHA; Kaynor Technical Schl; Waterbury, CT; (Y); Church Yth Grp; Acpl Chr; Band; Church Choir; Variety Show; High Hon Roll; Hrdrssng/Cosmtlgy-Licns, Cert For Prfcncy & 3rd Pl Cntst 83-85; Word Proc.

HOWE, ALBERTO; New London HS; New London, CT; (S); DECA; Spanish Clb; Y-Teens; Pres Jr Cls; Im Bsktbl; JV Ftbl; Var Capt Trk; Hon Roll; IFLA Span; Bus.

HOWE, ALISON; Lyman Hall HS; Wallingford, CT; (Y); Dance Clb; Spanish Clb; Sec Varsity Clb; Band; Concert Band; Mrchg Band; Variety Show; Rep Stu Cncl; Var Capt Cheerleading; Hon Roll; Elem Ed.

HOWE, KIM; Thomaston HS; Thomaston, CT; (Y); 7/73; Hosp Aide; Spanish Clb; Band; Concert Band; Mrchg Band; Rptr Yrbk Stf; L Tennis; High Hon Roll; Hon Roll; NHS; Rotary Club Schlrshp 85; Henry & Nellie Blakeslee Schlrshp 85; Thmstn Educ Svgs Bond & Awd; U Of CT; Pharm.

HOYT, LISA M; Enfield HS; Enfield, CT; (Y); VP JA; Mgr Band; Concert Band; Mrchg Band; Orch; Pep Band; School Musical; School Play; Nwsp Stf; Trs Church Yth Grp; Outstndng Earth Sci Awd 82-83; Outstndng Bio Awd 83-84; Embry-Riddle U; Aviator.

HOYT, SHERI; Norwalk HS; Norwalk, CT; (Y); Art Clb; Office Aide; High Hon Roll; Hon Roll; Pres Schlr; Central CT ST U; Lib Arts.

HRIBKO, RICHARD A; Notre Dame HS; East Haven, CT; (Y); Spanish Clb; Thesps; Chorus; School Musical; School Play; Stage Crew; Variety Show; Nwsp Rptr; High Hon Roll; Hon Roll; Natl Drama & Speech Awd 84-85; Writer.

HRISTOV JR, PETER; Notre Dame Catholic HS; Bridgeport, CT; (Y); 22/285; Church Yth Grp; Ski Clb; Band; Hon Roll; Presdntl Acad Ftns Awd 85; Alfred F Doty Awd 85; Aviation.

HRYB, SUZANNE H; East Hampton HS; East Hampton, CT; (Y); 4/106; Am Leg Aux Girls St; Pres Church Yth Grp; Pres Model UN; School Musical; Nwsp Ed-Chief; Sec Stu Cncl; VP L Socr; VP L Trk; NHS; Ntl Merit SF; George Wash U; Jrnlsm.

HUBBARD, ARTHUR; Oliver Wolcott Tech; Winsted, CT; (Y); Computer Clb; Hon Roll; Cert Of Awd Scholar 85; Elect Engrng.

HUBBARD, CHRISTINA; Guilford SR HS; Guilford, CT; (Y); Pres Sec Key Clb; Sec Band; Timer; Var L Trk; Art.

HUBBARD, LINDA; Guilford HS; Guilford, CT; (Y); 35/264; Church Yth Grp; Dance Clb; Chorus; School Musical; VP French Hon Soc; High Hon Roll; NHS; Drama Clb; Variety Show; Hon Roll; Miss CT Natl Teenager Pgnt Fnlst 84-85; Chematon 84; Clark U; Frgn Lang.

HUBENY, SHARON A; Southington HS; Plantsville, CT; (Y); 31/550; Key Clb; High Hon Roll; NHS; Southern CT ST U; Librl Art.

HUBER, JEANNE; Southington HS; Southington, CT; (Y); 84/550; Church Yth Grp; JA; Key Clb; Variety Show; Yrbk Stf; Hon Roll; Artist Mnth; Southington Ed Assoc Schlrshp; U CT; Spcl Ed.

HUBERT, KIMBERLY; Farmington HS; Farmington, CT; (Y); 3/204; Church Yth Grp; Cmnty Wkr; Ski Clb; Yrbk Stf; Rep Frsh Cls; Sec Soph Cls; Rep Jr Cls; Rep Stu Cncl; Mgr Bsktbl; JV Socr; Wlsly Coll Bk Awd 85; Cngrsnl Schlr 85; Hugh O Brian Ldrshp Smnr 84; Law.

HUBON, COLLEEN R; Sacred Heart Acad; West Haven, CT; (Y); Church Yth Grp; Computer Clb; Spanish Clb; Art Clb; Swmmng; Bus Admin.

HUDOCK, NORA A; Rockville HS; Rockville, CT; (Y); 1/354; Am Leg Aux Girls St; Capt Math Tm; Model UN; Rep Stu Cncl; High Hon Roll; NHS; Ntl Merit SF.

HUDSON, DANNY; Canton HS; Canton, CT; (Y); Art Clb; Chorus; Church Choir; L Crs Cntry; L Trk; L Wrstlng; High Hon Roll; Hon Roll; Elctrnc Engr.

HUERTA, ANNA; Stamford HS; Stamford, CT; (S); Cmnty Wkr; DECA; Key Clb; Spanish Clb; Vllybl; Hon Roll; District IV CDC General Marketing 1st 85; Sacraed Heart U; Chld Psychtrst.

HUESTIS, CHRISTOPHER; Manchester HS; Manchester, CT; (Y); French Clb; Band; Concert Band; Jazz Band; Mrchg Band; Pep Band; School Musical; High Hon Roll; Hon Roll; NHS.

HUGHES, ANDREA; New Fairfield HS; New Fairfld, CT; (Y); Church Yth Grp; JA; Church Choir; Stage Crew; Tennis; Hon Roll; Awd Of Bst Costumes In Drama Clss 82; Fshn Merch.

HUGHES, ANDREA; Sacred Heart Acad; Derby, CT; (Y); Art Clb; Church Yth Grp; Dance Clb; Hosp Aide; Teachers Aide; Nwsp Rptr; Im Vllybl; High Hon Roll; Hon Roll; NHS; Two Yr Hnr Awd 85; Physcl Thrpst.

HUGHES, BRENDA J; Southington HS; Southington, CT; (Y); 28/550; Key Clb; Concert Band; Mrchg Band; Nwsp Rptr; Yrbk Ed-Chief; Lit Mag; Hon Roll; NCTE Awd; NHS; Reuben E Thalberg Schlrshp 85; Bentley Coll; Bus Cmmnctns.

HUGHES, JOAN; Christian Heritage Schl; Trumbull, CT; (S); Church Yth Grp; Teachers Aide; Band; Chorus; School Play; Yrbk Stf; Pres Sr Cls; High Hon Roll; Ntl Merit Ltr; Bsktbl; Outstndg Christian HS Stu 83-84; Math.

HUGO, MARK; Mark T Sheehan HS; Wallingford, CT; (Y); German Clb; VP JA; L Swmmng; Hon Roll; Chem.

HUGO, RUSSELL; Canterbury Schl; Apo New York, NY; (Y); French Clb; Latin Clb; Pep Clb; ROTC; Varsity Clb; Drill Tm; Var L Crs Cntry; Var L Ice Hcky; Var L Lcrss; JV Socr; Red & Slvr Star Hnrs 81-83.

HULL, HAROLD; Plainfield HS; Moosup, CT; (Y); 7/155; Am Leg Boys St; Model UN; Yrbk Stf; Stat Bsktbl; Capt Crs Cntry; Var Trk; Cit Awd; High Hon Roll; Hon Roll; Jr NHS; Hgh Hnr Roll 83; Vrsty Clb 85; CT Bus Wk 85; Bus Admin.

HULSTRUNK, GEOFFREY; W F Kaynor Tech; Naugatuck, CT; (Y); 20/205; Pres VICA; Var L Crs Cntry; Var L Golf; Mgr(s); Var L Trk; High Hon Roll; Hon Roll; NHS; Aud/Vis; Yrbk Stf; Schi Fair Chem Div-1st Pl 83; Ambassador Awd VICA Skill Olymp 85; Wtby ST Tech; Engr.

HULTMAN, TRACY LYNN; New Milford HS; New Milford, CT; (Y); Cmnty Wkr; Dance Clb; Hosp Aide; Rep Stu Cncl; Fld Hcky; Swmmng; Tennis; High Hon Roll; Hon Roll; Camp Fr Inc; Fnlst Miss Natl Teenage CT 85; Hnr Awd 84-85; Med.

HUMMEL, MARTIN; Notre Dame HS; New Haven, CT; (Y); Pres Concert Band; Mrchg Band; School Musical; JV Crs Cntry; JV Trk; High Hon Roll; Hon Roll; Amer Musical Fndtn Band Hnrs 83-85; CT Hnrs Smnr 84-85; Elec Engr.

HUNT JR, BUELL H; Choate Rosemary Hall HS; Wallingford, CT; (S); Drama Clb; Spanish Clb; Thesps; Acpl Chr; Chorus; Madrigals; School Musical; School Play; Stage Crew; JV Vllybl; Edward Tallmagde Schlrshp 81-85; Drama.

HUNT, IRIS; Kolbe Cathedral HS; Bridgeport, CT; (Y); Computer Clb; Math Clb; Teachers Aide; Drill Tm; School Play; Variety Show; Vllybl; Cit Awd; Ntl Merit Ltr; Prfct Atten Awd; Trk Awd 81-83; Gymnastics Awd 81-84; Spellng Bee Awd 82; Let For Acad Achvt 84; Valedictorian 82; Spelman Coll; Comp Tech.

HUNT, MICHAEL; Northwest Catholic HS; Avon, CT; (Y); Church Yth Grp; Cmnty Wkr; Church Choir; JV Ftbl; Im Vllybl; U Hartford.

HUNTE, CLAIRE; Guilford HS; Guilford, CT; (Y); AFS; Cmnty Wkr; Math Tm; Office Aide; Nwsp Ed-Chief; Rep Stu Cncl; Crs Cntry; Hon Roll; NHS; Arista Hnr Soc 82-83.

HUNTER, MAUREEN; R H A M HS; Amston, CT; (Y); AFS; Church Yth Grp; Cmnty Wkr; Pres 4-H; FBLA; Spanish Clb; Church Choir; Variety Show; 4-H Awd; Hon Roll; CCSU; Comm.

HUNTER, YOLANDA; Hillhouse HS; Hamden, CT; (Y); Cmnty Wkr; Debate Tm; Hosp Aide; ROTC; Speech Tm; Drill Tm; Yrbk Stf; High Hon Roll; Hon Roll; NHS; Acctd Yale Mdcl Smmr Apprntcshp Prog 85; Cert Of Merit From Howard Cnty Brd Of Eductn 83; Corp Law.

HUOT, STEPHANIE; Suffield HS; West Suffield, CT; (Y); 5/154; Teachers Aide; Church Choir; Yrbk Stf; Capt Bsktbl; Capt Trk; Lion Awd; NHS; Pres Schlr; Rotary Awd; ELEET Schlrshp 85; Prof Secy Intl Schlrshp 85; CT ST Pstl Wrks Union Schlrshp 85; Grand Rapids Baptist Coll; Bus.

HURDLE, DAMMEIN LA ROY; Warren Fox Regional Vo Tech Schl; Waterbury, CT; (Y); Am Leg Boys St; Church Yth Grp; VICA; Church Choir; Drill Tm; Sec Stu Cncl; JV Bsktbl; JV Var Mgr(s); JV Var Trk; Hon Roll; Waterbury ST Tech; Mach Drftg.

HURLBERT, DANIEL; Coginchaug Regional HS; Durham, CT; (Y); Am Leg Boys St; Chess Clb; Rep JCL; Math Tm; Chorus; Var Bsktbl; Var Tennis; Var Trk; Hon Roll; CT Intern Prog Wash DC 85; U Hartford; Comp Prog.

HURLBURT, DAWN; Vinal Reg Tech; Middletown, CT; (Y); 26/180; Cmnty Wkr; English Clb; Variety Show; Yrbk Stf; Rep Frsh Cls; VP Rep Soph Cls; VP Rep Jr Cls; VP Sr Cls; Rep Stu Cncl; JV Cheerleading; Fshn Merch.

HURLBURT, EDWARD; H C Wilcox RVTS; Wallingford, CT; (Y); 8/200; Boy Scts; VP JA; Hst Stu Cncl; High Hon Roll; Hon Roll; Envrnmtl Sci; Envrn Sci.

HURLEY, BRIDGET; Academy Of The Holy Family; Mankato, MN; (Y); Drama Clb; Acpl Chr; Chorus; School Musical; School Play; Stage Crew; Crs Cntry; Score Keeper; Spnsh.

HURST IV, VICTOR W; Amity Regional HS; Woodbridge, CT; (S); 56/376; Am Leg Boys St; Spanish Clb; Variety Show; Nwsp Rptr; Nwsp Stf; Stu Cncl; Var L Bsktbl; Var Tennis; Hon Roll; NHS; Aerosp Clb Pres; 1st Pl Lab Skls Olympd; Frntrs Of Appld Sci; Aerontcl Engrng.

HUSSEY III, RICHARD; Trumbull HS; Trumbull, CT; (Y); Boy Scts; Church Yth Grp; Cmnty Wkr; JV Golf; High Hon Roll; Hon Roll; NHS; Prfct Atten Awd; Eagle Sct 83; Pilot.

HUTCHINSON, SCOTT; Windham HS; Columbia, CT; (Y); Computer Clb; Band; Concert Band; Mrchg Band; Orch; Pep Band; High Hon Roll; Hon Roll; Worchester Polytech Inst; Elec.

HUTTON, JIM; Tolland HS; Tolland, CT; (Y); Boy Scts; Ski Clb; L Socr; L Tennis; Var Trk; Hon Roll; NHS; Eagle Scout 84.

HUYDIC, PAM; Stratford HS; Stratford, CT; (Y); 29/241; Ski Clb; Temple Yth Grp; Capt Drill Tm; Mrchg Band; Nwsp Rptr; Sec Stu Cncl; Capt Cheerleading; Hon Roll; Ntl Merit Ltr; Busn Mngmnt.

HUYNH, P HONG; Avon Old Farms HS; Hartford, CT; (S); 4/100; Computer Clb; FNA; Socr; JV Swmmng; High Hon Roll; Hon Roll; Outstndng Math, Sci 83; Achvt Awd Englsh 83; Outstndng Awd Bio, Geom, Histy 84; Physican.

HWANG, HELEN; Glastonbury HS; Glastonbury, CT; (Y); 76/450; Chorus; Cheerleading; Hon Roll; Fash Inst Of Tech; Fash Design.

HYLAND, LYNN E; Killingly HS; Dayville, CT; (Y); 3/271; Band; Mrchg Band; Yrbk Stf; Rep Stu Cncl; JV Capt Fld Hcky; Stat Trk; High Hon Roll; NHS; Spanish NHS; Church Yth Grp; Outstndng Achvt Englsh 83; CT Elks Shclrshp 85; Ruth Fiske Mrl Schlrshp 85; Bryant Coll; Accntnt.

HYLAND, MICHAEL; Ridgefield HS; Boca Raton, FL; (Y); 21/375; Aud/Vis; Scholastic Bowl; Varsity Clb; Nwsp Rptr; Rep Jr Cls; Capt JV Lcrss; Hon Roll; Bsktbl; Var Ftbl; Ftbl Dfnsv Bach Of Yr 83; Excllnc Chem II 85; Pres Acadmc Ftnss Awds Pgm 85; Colgate U; Math Eco.

HYLTON, MICHELE; Weaver HS; Hartford, CT; (Y); Dance Clb; Hosp Aide; MMM; School Musical; School Play; Nwsp Ed-Chief; Yrbk Stf; Sr Cls; Gym; Sftbl; Cert Awd Recog Exclint Achvt & Excllnt Readg & Excllnc Thru Out Schl Yr 85; American Coll Of Fashion; Merch.

IANELLO, LOUIS; Morgan HS; Clinton, CT; (Y); 25/160; Band; Chorus; Concert Band; Jazz Band; Mrchg Band; Orch; Pep Band; School Musical; L Socr; Hon Roll; Sthrn Regnl Al-ST Band 85; Scor 83/100 Al-ST Band Cmptn 84; Comp Sci.

IANNONE, ARIANNE; Amity SR HS; Orange, CT; (Y); Cmnty Wkr; French Clb; Pep Clb; Spanish Clb; Chorus; School Musical; Variety Show; VP Frsh Cls; Rep Stu Cncl; Im Trk; Bio Sci.

IANNONE, JONATHAN THERON; North Haven HS; N Haven, CT; (Y); 98/281; Aud/Vis; Stage Crew; Lit Mag; Hon Roll; Natl Champ At Camp Perry; CT ST Assn Rifle Tm 84-85; Schlrshp To Ctr For Creative Yth 85-86; Engl Lit.

IANNUCCI, SHERRY; Sacred Heart Acad; W Haven, CT; (Y); Church Yth Grp; FBLA; Office Aide; Band; School Musical; School Play; Stage Crew; Variety Show; Rep Frsh Cls; Im Bowling; CYO Chrldr 82-85; Hnr Court 83; Pro-Life 84; Bus Adm.

IASSOGNA, KAREN; St Joseph HS; Bridgeport, CT; (Y); 14/216; Drama Clb; Spanish Clb; Stage Crew; Variety Show; Yrbk Sprt Ed; Capt Cheerleading; Mgr(s); Hon Roll; NHS; Spanish NHS; Father Gloucester Schlrhsp 81; CT ST Schlrshp 85; St Joseph U Schlrshp 85; St Josephs U; Psychlgy.

IDEROSA, CATHERINE S; Morgan Schl; Clinton, CT; (Y); 11/160; Trs French Clb; FBLA; Hosp Aide; Hon Roll; NHS; Frnch Awd 83 & 85; Engl Dept Awd 85; Italian Awd 84.

IFFLAND, MELODY CAROL; Torrington HS; Torrington, CT; (Y); 6/271; Drama Clb; Math Tm; Pres Thesps; School Musical; School Play; High Hon Roll; NHS; Ntl Merit Ltr; VP Church Yth Grp; Cmnty Wkr; Torrington JR Civic Thtr Schlrshp 85; Bst Thspn 85; Rensselaer Polytch Inst; Law.

ILES, SCOTT; Naugatuck HS; Naugatuck, CT; (Y); Hon Roll; U CT; Finance.

INFANTE, MIKE; Trumbull HS; Trumbull, CT; (Y); Trs JA; Chorus; Nwsp Stf; Im Bowling; Im Golf; Im Wt Lftg; High Hon Roll; Excllnce Bus Awd; Bryant Coll; Acctg.

INGALLS, KELLY; Berlin HS; Kensington, CT; (Y); 1/190; Am Leg Aux Girls St; Math Tm; Var JV Bsktbl; Var JV Sftbl; Var JV Vllybl; High Hon Roll; NHS; Harvard Bk Awd, Dr R P Long Awd 85; All Conf Bsktbll 84-85.

INGENITO, JOSEPH A; New Britain SR HS; New Britain, CT; (Y); 35/330; Art Clb; Camera Clb; JA; Ski Clb; Yrbk Phtg; Var L Crs Cntry; JV Golf; Trk; Pres Acadmc Fit Awd 85; Arrw Drg Schlrshp 85; Rutgers U; Lndscp Arch.

INGER, MARC; Lewis S Mills HS; Harwinton, CT; (Y); Am Leg Boys St; Nwsp Sprt Ed; Pres Jr Cls; Var Bsbl; JV Bsktbl; Hon Roll; Chris Smith Outstndng Dedication Awd Bsbl 85; Hamilton Coll; Lib Arts.

INNAMORATO, ANNMARIE; West Haven HS; W Haven, CT; (Y); 100/352; Pres DECA; Ed Yrbk Stf; Stu Cncl; Jr NHS; Briarwood Bk Awd 84; DECA Pres 84-85; DECA Natl Comp Fnlst Mrktng & Mgmt 84-85; U Of New Haven; Bus Mgmt.

IORLI, DALE; Bristol,Central HS; Bristol, CT; (Y); Church Yth Grp; Cmnty Wkr; GAA; Office Aide; Teachers Aide; Coach Actv; Gym; Var Trk; Var Vllybl; Wt Lftg; Bristol Fed Of Tchrs 85; Delta Kappa Gamma 85; AZ ST U; Math Ed.

IOVANNE, JENNIFER; Sacred Heart Acad; East Haven, CT; (Y); Art Clb; Computer Clb; Pep Clb; High Hon Roll; Jr NHS; Spanish NHS; Wrtng Awd 83; Quinnipiac Coll; Chld Day Care.

IOVANNE, RICHARD; Notre Dame HS; New Haven, CT; (Y); 23/250; Boy Scts; Im Bsktbl; Var L Golf; High Hon Roll; Pre-Med.

IRVING, JUDY; St Bernard HS; Norwich, CT; (Y); Exploring; Amer Horse Show Assoc 85; Peer Ministry 85; Amimal Tech.

ISAAC, PAUL; Shelton HS; Huntington, CT; (Y); Church Yth Grp; Hon Roll; Comp.

ISAACS, MEREDITH; Trumbull HS; Trumbull, CT; (Y); VP Temple Yth Grp; Concert Band; Mrchg Band; Symp Band; Trs Frsh Cls; Trs Soph Cls; Trs Jr Cls; Trs Sr Cls; Stat Trk; High Hon Roll; Advrtsng.

ISENHOUR, STEVEN L; Ledyard HS; Gales Ferry, CT; (Y); 36/287; JV Bsktbl; Var Coach Actv; Var Mgr(s); Var Sftbl; Hon Roll; Jr NHS; Mech Engr.

ITZO, DOREEN L; Crosby HS; Waterbury, CT; (Y); Trs French Clb; Trs Library Aide; Hon Roll; Waterbury ST Tech; Data Proc.

IZZO, MARCELLA; Branford HS; Branford, CT; (Y); Art Clb; Drama Clb; Thesps; Chorus; Lit Mag; Bsktbl; Cheerleading; Lbrl Arts.

JACHIMIEC, HALINA; Bulkeley HS; Hartford, CT; (S); Church Yth Grp; DECA; FBLA; Library Aide; Teachers Aide; Stu Cncl; 1st Pl ST & Dist 6 DECA Conf 85; 2nd Pl ST DECA Conf 84; 4th Pl ST FBLA Conf 84; Johnson & Wales Coll; Bus Adm.

JACKSON, AMY; Newtown HS; Newtown, CT; (Y); 51/298; Camp Fr Inc; Acpl Chr; Pres Chorus; Church Choir; School Musical; School Play; Pom Pon; High Hon Roll; Church Yth Grp; Drama Clb; Occdntl Schlrshp Awd 85; Ted Carling Newtown Schlrshp Awd 85; Dir Awd Chorus Svc 85; Occidental Coll; Music.

JACKSON, CRYSTAL; Academy Of Our Lady Of Mercy; Bridgeport, CT; (Y); Church Yth Grp; Exploring; Math Clb; Math Tm; Spanish Clb; Pres Jr Cls; Pres Sr Cls; Pre-Med.

JACKSON, DIONNE; Stratford HS; Stratford, CT; (Y); FBLA; FNA; Girl Scts; JA; Spanish Clb; Teachers Aide; Color Guard; Concert Band; Variety Show; Southern CT ST Coll; Pre-Med.

JACKSON, EDWARD C; Shelton HS; Shelton, CT; (Y); 95/423; Spanish Clb; High Hon Roll; Hon Roll; NHS; Fairfield U; Bio.

JACKSON, LOREN H; Farmington HS; Hartford, CT; (Y); Am Leg Boys St; Aud/Vis; Pres Civic Clb; DECA; JA; Political Wkr; Stu Cncl; Hon Roll; O Meara Fndtn & Intrracl Schlrshps 85; Beta Sigma Lamboa Chptr Schl 85; Syracuse U; Acctg.

JACKSON, TAMIKO; Sacred Heart Acad; New Haven, CT; (Y); 55/119; Church Yth Grp; Cmnty Wkr; Hosp Aide; Chorus; School Musical; Variety Show; Bsktbl; Cheerleading; Tennis; Vllybl; Camp Cnslr 85; Confmtn Inst Local Parish 85; Mgmt Expltn Babson Coll 85; Pre-Med.

JACKSON, TAMMY; Central HS; Bridgeport, CT; (Y); FHA; FNA; FTA; Hosp Aide; Office Aide; Teachers Aide; Chorus; Drill Tm; Stu Cncl; Prfct Atten Awd; Nrs Aide Cert 85; Sacred Heart; Nrsg.

JACOBY, RACHEL; Guilford HS; Guilford, CT; (Y); Teachers Aide; Temple Yth Grp; Band; Orch; High Hon Roll; Hon Roll; NCTE Awd; NHS; Gen Excllnc Lang Arts 83&85; Psych.

JACQUES, ERIN; Coventry HS; Coventry, CT; (Y); Dance Clb; Spanish Clb; Band; Concert Band; Mrchg Band; Trs Frsh Cls; Trs Soph Cls; Trs Jr Cls; Hon Roll; NHS; U Of CT; Psych.

JADACH, MICHAEL; Derby HS; Derby, CT; (Y); 8/125; Rep Am Leg Boys St; Boys Clb Am; Boy Scts; Pres Church Yth Grp; Computer Clb; Varsity Clb; Hon Roll; Rep Frsh Cls; VP Soph Cls; Rep Jr Cls.

JAGOE, SUZANNE; Joseph A Foran HS; Milford, CT; (Y); Keywanettes; Pres Frsh Cls; Capt Cheerleading; Mgr(s); Hon Roll; Jr NHS; Law.

JAHNE, DEBRA; Northwestern Regional No 7 HS; New Hartford, CT; (Y); 3/180; Cmnty Wkr; Science Clb; Spanish Clb; Lit Mag; Var Score Keeper; Var Tennis; High Hon Roll; NHS; English Clb; Rep Stu Cncl; Bd Educ Sci Awd 85; Mt Holyoke Coll.

JAKONCZUK, JEFF; Bethel HS; Bethel, CT; (Y); 54/268; Var Bsbl; Var Bsktbl; Hon Roll; Chem Engr.

JAMHARIAN, DAVID; Southington HS; Southington, CT; (Y); Boy Scts; High Hon Roll; Hon Roll; Ordr Arrow Hnr Cmprs BSA 83-85; BSA Jr Ldrs Trng Crse 83; Qurtrmstr Troop 85 Natl Jambree 85; Elec Engnrng.

JAMROG, STANLEY; Avon Old Farms Schl; Turners Falls, MA; (S); 18/100; Church Yth Grp; Drama Clb; Radio Clb; School Musical; School Play; Stage Crew; Hon Roll; Psychlgy.

JANCIS, ERIK; Naugatuck HS; Naugatuck, CT; (Y); Am Leg Boys St; Library Aide; Political Wkr; Red Cross Aide; Ski Clb; Var Bsktbl; High Hon Roll; Med.

JANKOWSKI, CHRISTA; East Catholic HS; Bristol, CT; (Y); 32/300; Cmnty Wkr; Sec Trs Band; Concert Band; Orch; Pep Band; Frsh Cls; Var L Ftbl; High Hon Roll; Hon Roll; NHS; John Brahams Mem Schlrshp 84-85; Prncpls Awd 85; Congrss-Bundestag Yth Exch Pgm 84-85; Intl Bus Admin.

JANNETTY, DAVID; Holy Cross HS; Waterbury, CT; (Y); 109/344; Church Yth Grp; Spanish Clb; Var L Bsbl; JV Crs Cntry; JV Wrstlng; NHS; Spanish NHS; St Schlr; Pres Acad Ftnss Awd 84; U Of CT; Pre-Med.

JANSEN, JOHN M; Joseph A Foran HS; Milford, CT; (Y); 3/270; Rep Am Leg Boys St; Sec Pres Key Clb; Stu Cncl; Var L Wrstlng; Cit Awd; Dnfth Awd; High Hon Roll; Kiwanis Awd; NHS; Pres Schlr; CT U Almn Bk Awd 85; Excllnc Trig 84; CT U; Elec Engr.

JARONCZYK, JENNIFER; Holy Cross HS; Ansonia, CT; (Y); Pres Church Yth Grp; Hosp Aide; Spanish Clb; Church Choir; Stage Crew; Hon Roll; Prom Comm; Med.

JARVIS, KIMBERLY; Trumbull HS; Trumbull, CT; (Y); Church Yth Grp; French Clb; Band; Concert Band; Mrchg Band; Symp Band; Nwsp Rptr; Mgr Bsktbl; Mgr(s); Mgr Sftbl; Hon Mntn Litry Fstvl Awd 82-84; Nwspr Staff Awd 84-85; Jrnlsm.

JASSO-AGUILAR, CRISTINA; Wilbur L Cross HS; New Haven, CT; (Y); Dance Clb; Spanish Clb; School Musical; Variety Show; Nwsp Rptr; ESOL US Hist & US Hist 1 85; ESOL B & C Engl 85; Hnr Diploma 85; S CT ST Coll; Frgn Lang.

JAWORSKI, JENNIFER; St Bernard HS; East Lyme, CT; (Y); 91/297; Church Yth Grp; Dance Clb; Hosp Aide; Stage Crew; Yrbk Stf; Stat Diving; Score Keeper; Stat Swmmng; Chiroprctr.

JEANNIN, JEFFREY; Warren F Kaynor Vo Tech; Oakville, CT; (Y); 5/203; Cmnty Wkr; Red Cross Aide; NHS; NH Vo Tech Coll; Auto Tech.

JEANS, KATHY; Ellington HS; Rockville, CT; (Y); Church Yth Grp; Cmnty Wkr; Exploring; Latin Clb; Acpl Chr; Hon Roll.

JEDOW, MARK; Pomperaug HS; Southbury, CT; (Y); Church Yth Grp; Cmnty Wkr; Band; Chorus; Concert Band; Jazz Band; Pep Band; JV Bsbl; Var Capt Swmmng; Hon Roll; Bio.

JEFFERSON, FRANK; Bassick HS; Bridgeport, CT; (S); Yrbk Stf; Lit Mag; Pres Jr Cls; Hon Roll; NHS; Fairfield U Upward Bnd Prog 83-86; MA Inst Of Tech; Engrng.

JEFFKO, KEVIN; Bristol Eastern HS; Bristol, CT; (Y); 55/345; Aud/Vis; JA; Ski Clb; Stage Crew; Bowling; JV Socr; Var L Tennis; Hon Roll; U Of AZ; Cmmnctns.

JEFFRIES, LYNNE; Rham HS; Marlborough, CT; (Y); AFS; Church Yth Grp; Latin Clb; Ski Clb; Chorus; Yrbk Stf; Stu Cncl; Var Crs Cntry; Var Trk; Hon Roll; Northeastern U; Langg.

JELLIFFE, MARIE LOUISE; West Haven HS; W Haven, CT; (Y); Cmnty Wkr; Hosp Aide; Chorus; Coach Actv; Mgr(s); Score Keeper; Swmmng; High Hon Roll; Hon Roll; Jr NHS; Kids Invstgtng Careers 82-83; Southern CT; Spcl Ed.

JENACARO, DIANA; Shelton HS; Shelton, CT; (Y); Boy Scts; Drama Clb; JA; Ski Clb; Spanish Clb; Ed Nwsp Rptr; Rep Stu Cncl; Capt Pom Pon; L Trk; Hon Roll; Cmmnctns.

JENKINS, GAIL; Pomperaug Regional HS; Southbury, CT; (Y); Yrbk Stf; Mgr(s); Var Vllybl; High Hon Roll; Law.

JENNINGS, ANGELA; Thomas Snell Weaver HS; Hartford, CT; (Y); 17/365; Cmnty Wkr; Library Aide; Stu Cncl; Mgr(s); Dnfth Awd; Hon Roll; NHS; Rotary Awd; Prfct Atten Awd; H Burlow Bk Awd; B C Jones, Hartford Comm Schlrshps; Boston Coll; Bus Admn.

JENNINGS, JAMES; Oliver Wokott Rvts HS; Kent, CT; (Y); 33/176; Boy Scts; Church Yth Grp; Red Cross Aide; Hon Roll; JR Intrn Congrss 85; Electrnc Tech.

JEPSON, JENNIFER; Daniel Hand HS; Madison, CT; (Y); Church Yth Grp; Chorus; School Musical; Yrbk Stf; Rep Stu Cncl; Bsktbl; Mgr(s); Hon Roll; Ntl Socl Studs Olympd Fnshd Distnctn 85; Madison Saf Rides Outstndng Svc 85; Tchng.

JERRELL, JENNIFER; Acad Of Our Lady Of Mercy; W Haven, CT; (Y); Church Yth Grp; Debate Tm; Girl Scts; Latin Clb; Model UN; Science Clb; Spanish Clb; Church Choir; Lit Mag; Natl Latin Exam 83-85; Girl Scout Silver Awd 83; Bus Adm.

JEZIERNY, NICHOLAS; Stratford HS; Stratford, CT; (Y); 25/250; Am Leg Boys St; Camera Clb; Computer Clb; Ski Clb; Varsity Clb; Nwsp Phtg; Nwsp Rptr; Nwsp Sprt Ed; Nwsp Stf; Yrbk Phtg; 11th All Lg Crs Cntry Chmpshps 84-85; Jrnlsm.

JIMENEZ, MARISOL; W F Kaynor R V T S HS; Waterbury, CT; (Y); High Hon Roll; NHS; CT Schltc Achvt Grant 85-86; Outstndg Achvt-Math 85; New Waves Bty Saln Awd-Excllnc Csmtlgy & Hair; Central CT ST U; Comp Sci.

JOHANNSSEN, BRIAN; Danbury HS; Danbury, CT; (Y); 112/614; German Clb; Varsity Clb; Var L Ftbl; Var L Trk; Ntl Merit SF; U S Nvl Acad Smmr Smnr 85; U S Naval Acad; Engrng.

JOHN, JERRY L; Newington HS; Newington, CT; (Y); Intnl Clb; Yrbk Phtg; JV Golf; Hon Roll; Accntng.

JOHNDROW, KIMBERLY; Ellington HS; Ellington, CT; (Y); 19/145; Am Leg Aux Girls St; Cmnty Wkr; Latin Clb; Ski Clb; Varsity Clb; Band; Concert Band; Mrchg Band; Yrbk Sprt Ed; Yrbk Stf; N Cntrl CT Conf Al-Star Tm-Sccr/Sftbl 84-85; MVP Vrsty Sccr Tm 84-85; Poli Sci.

JOHNSON, ANDREW B; West Haven HS; W Haven, CT; (Y); Scholastic Bowl; Nwsp Rptr; Nwsp Stf; Stu Cncl; Im Bsbl; Outstndng Achvt Alg I, Kids Invstgtng Carers 82-83; Cert Of Achvt & Mst Outstndng Hlth Sci Prog 83-85; U Of CT; Pharmacy.

JOHNSON, ARTEMUS; Weaver HS; Hartford, CT; (Y); Prfct Atten Awd; SAR Awd; Acctng & Typng Awds 84-85; Y Hghst Achv Hstry; Comp Pgm.

JOHNSON, BRAD A; Bunnell HS; Stratford, CT; (Y); 68/264; Church Yth Grp; FBLA; Var Capt Crs Cntry; Ftbl; Var Trk; Hon Roll; All Leag Crss Cntry & Trck; Med Fld Schlrshp; Schl Crss Cntry Cours Rcrd Hldr; U Of CT; Pharm.

JOHNSON, CHRISTINE; Manchester HS; Manchester, CT; (Y); Church Yth Grp; Cmnty Wkr; Girl Scts; Office Aide; School Play; Variety Show; Yrbk Stf; Rep Stu Cncl; Var Capt Cheerleading; Var Capt Twrlr; Stephen Dunfield Mem Schlrhsp 85; Albert & Jane De Wey Mem 85; Emanuel Lutheian Schlrshp 85; Bus.

JOHNSON, DALE; Branford HS; Branford, CT; (Y); 40/250; Church Yth Grp; Civic Clb; Computer Clb; Drama Clb; French Clb; Hosp Aide; Office Aide; School Play; Nwsp Stf; Stu Cncl; Vet Schl Awd, Rotary Intract Schlrshp 85; U WI Madison; Comp Sci.

JOHNSON, ERIK; The Hotchkiss Schl; Madison, WI; (Y); Ski Clb; Chorus; VP Soph Cls; Im Bsbl; Var L Ftbl; Im Golf; Var L Ice Hcky; Im Wt Lftg; Most Impvd Hockey Play 84; Elec Engrng.

JOHNSON JR, HARLEY; Southington HS; Southington, CT; (Y); Boy Scts; Church Yth Grp; VP JA; Math Tm; Nwsp Rptr; JV Tennis; JV L Wrstlng; Ntl Merit Ltr; Engrng.

JOHNSON, JAMES M; St Bernard HS; New London, CT; (Y); 66/290; Church Yth Grp; Band; Church Choir; Capt L Ftbl; Var Trk; Var Wt Lftg; Hon Roll; Ntl Merit Schol; Robt B Demars Bk Awd Outstndng Acad Achvmnt; Busi Mgmt.

JOHNSON, JENNIFER; Southington HS; New Britain, CT; (Y); 19/586; Church Yth Grp; Trs FFA; Pres Girl Scts; Band; Concert Band; High Hon Roll; NHS; Wind Ensmbl 83-84; Natrl Resrcs.

JOHNSON, JENNIFER; St Bernard HS; Groton, CT; (Y); 111/320; Church Yth Grp; Ski Clb; Stage Crew; Yrbk Stf; Rep Stu Cncl; Var Swmmng; JV Trk; Math.

JOHNSON, JORY K; The Hotchkiss Schl; Weatogue, CT; (Y); 4/158; Debate Tm; Varsity Clb; Nwsp Rptr; JV Lcrss; Var Socr; Ntl Merit SF; Eng Bk Prz 82-83; Dartmouth Coll; Geo.

JOHNSON, LESLIE; Manchester HS; Manchester, CT; (Y); 18/541; AFS; FBLA; VP German Clb; Hosp Aide; Var L Tennis; NHS; Russell Wright Acctng Awd Acct I Stu 85; Intl Bus.

JOHNSON, MARK; Stamford HS; Stamford, CT; (S); 21/402; Cmnty Wkr; Ski Clb; Spanish Clb; Lit Mag; Stu Cncl; DAR Awd; Hon Roll; NHS; Ntl Merit Ltr; Tufts U; Corporate Lwyr.

JOHNSON, SUSAN; Canton HS; Canton, CT; (Y); Aud/Vis; Library Aide; Ski Clb; Teachers Aide; Lit Mag; Var Bsktbl; Var Fld Hcky; Var Sftbl; High Hon Roll; Hon Roll; Awd Compltn Trng Peer Cnslng 84; Awd Excllnce Phy Educ 83; Sci.

JOHNSON, SYDNEY; Trumbull HS; Salt Lake City, UT; (Y); Pres Church Yth Grp; Ski Clb; Chorus; School Musical; Rep Frsh Cls; Pres Rep Stu Cncl; Var JV Cheerleading; French Hon Soc; High Hon Roll; Piano Natl Guild Audtns 83-85; Drama Awd Outstndng Wrk 85; Bsktbl Awd All Star Regnl Trvlng Tm 84; U UT Salt Lake City.

JOHNSSON, MARIE; Lyman Hall HS; Wallingford, CT; (Y); AFS; Art Clb; French Clb; Fld Hcky; Powder Puff Ftbl; Tennis; Hon Roll; Lttr In Tnns 85; Natl Hnr Scty 85; Lttr In Fld Hcky 84; Fyris.

JOHNSTON, JAMES; Tolland HS; Tolland, CT; (Y); School Play; Rep Soph Cls; Hon Roll; Engrng.

JOLY, BRETT; William Hall HS; W Hartford, CT; (Y); Boy Scts; Church Yth Grp; JA; Boy Scts; JV Var Crs Cntry; JV Var Lcrss; High Hon Roll; Hon Roll.

JONES, BEVERLY; Hartford Christian Acad; W Hartford, CT; (S); 1/2; Cmnty Wkr; Teachers Aide; Chorus; School Musical; School Play; VP Soph Cls; VP Jr Cls; Sec VP Sr Cls; Var Bsktbl; Var Capt Cheerleading; Bob Jones U; Elem Educ.

JONES, CAROLINE; Weaver HS; Hartford, CT; (Y); Crs Cntry; Var Trk; Prfct Atten Awd; Mst Imprvd Rnnr Crss Cntry 83-84; Mktng Mgt.

JONES, DANNY C; Wilby HS; Waterbury, CT; (Y); FBLA; Office Aide; Red Cross Aide; Band; Concert Band; Rep Frsh Cls; Rep Soph Cls; Rep Jr Cls; Var Trk; Hon Roll; Bus Mgmt.

JONES, DENISE B; Thomas Snell Weaver HS; Hartford, CT; (Y); Church Yth Grp; Drama Clb; Church Choir; Crs Cntry; Trk; Hon Roll; Exc In Intrdctn To Algebra 85; Comp Engrng.

JONES, GAIL; Ansonia HS; Ansonia, CT; (Y); Computer Clb; French Clb; GAA; Latin Clb; Ski Clb; Yrbk Stf; Var L Bsktbl; Var L Sftbl; Capt Awd & MVP-BSKTBL 85; Derby All Tourny Tm-Bsktbl; 2nd Tm NVL, 1st Tm All Vly-Sftbl & Bsktbl 85; U CT; Specl Eductn.

JONES, HOWARD; West Haven HS; W Haven, CT; (Y); Political Wkr; Chorus; VP Frsh Cls; Var JV Bsbl; Bsbl Awd 83-84; Southern CT; Bus.

JONES, JOHN; Danbury HS; Danbury, CT; (Y); 90/613; JA; Varsity Clb; Chorus; Variety Show; Rep Soph Cls; Golf; JV Socr; Hon Roll; Jr NHS; Ntl Merit SF; Regnl Chr Fstvl; Sci Hrzns 85; Attnry.

JONES, JOHN; East Haven HS; E Haven, CT; (Y); 13/270; Am Leg Boys St; Church Yth Grp; Spanish Clb; Bsktbl; Coach Actv; Capt Swmmng; High Hon Roll; Jr NHS; NHS; Algbr II Hgh GPA Awd 85; Swmmng Lttr 83-85; Pre-Med.

JONES, KAREN M; St Bernard HS; Norwich, CT; (Y); 99/290; Art Clb; Red Cross Aide; Band; Church Choir; Jazz Band; Mrchg Band; School Musical; Yrbk Stf; Chrmn Stu Cncl; Hon Roll; Art Awds; St Bernard Sci Awd Cthlc Wmn; Clb Awd Congrsnl Merit Of Svc 85; Southern CT ST U; Spcl Ed.

JONES, KIMBERLY; Naugatuck HS; Naugatuck, CT; (Y); 20/340; Rep Soph Cls; Trs Jr Cls; Var L Sftbl; Var L Vllybl; High Hon Roll; All Naugatuck Vlly League Ptchr 85; Nrsng.

JONES, KIMBERLY F; South Windsor HS; S Windsor, CT; (Y); 15/337; Trs FBLA; Hosp Aide; Chorus; Yrbk Stf; Stu Cncl; Hon Roll; Stu Tnl Schlrshp Outstndng Negro Stu 84.

JONES, LISA; New Britain HS; New Britain, CT; (Y); Church Yth Grp; Dance Clb; Exploring; French Clb; Variety Show; U Of CT; Psych.

JONES, MARITZKA A; James Hillhouse HS; New Haven, CT; (Y); Art Clb; Church Yth Grp; Mathletes; Red Cross Aide; Science Clb; Acpl Chr; Chorus; Church Choir; Color Guard; Drm Mjr(t); Comp.

JONES, MICHELE D; Choate Rosemary Hall HS; Queens Village, NY; (Y); Church Yth Grp; Computer Clb; Girl Scts; Math Clb; Church Choir; Im Fld Hcky; Im Tennis; Var VP Trk; Honorable Mention 82-83; Flora Mc Donald Bonney Schlrshp 82-84; Med.

JONES, RHONDA; New London HS; New London, CT; (S); Church Yth Grp; DECA; Office Aide; Spanish Clb; Nwsp Rptr; Nwsp Stf; Capt Cheerleading; JV Trk; High Hon Roll; Hon Roll; Commentary Editor For School Paper 84-85; Johnson & Wales; Business Admin.

JONES, SAM; Weston HS; Weston, CT; (Y); Church Yth Grp; Latin Clb; Capt L Swmmng; Hon Roll; Cls S Outstndg Swmmr 85; Biol.

JONES, SHARON; Berlin HS; Berlin, CT; (Y); Am Leg Aux Girls St; Yrbk Stf; Sec Frsh Cls; Sec Soph Cls; Pres Jr Cls; Pres Sr Cls; VP Stu Cncl; High Hon Roll; Hon Roll; Jr NHS; Pul Rel.

JONES, SHERI; Newfairfield HS; New Fairfld, CT; (Y); 23/242; Trs Church Yth Grp; Band; Concert Band; Jazz Band; Mrchg Band; Orch; School Musical; JV Bsktbl; Var Mgr(s); Tennis; Music Achvt Awd 82-85; Ntl Hnr Ntl Fed Fest 78-85; Music.

JORDAN, CHARLES; Loomis Chaffer HS; Charlotte, NC; (Y); Boy Scts; Church Yth Grp; VP Radio Clb; VP Jr Cls; Pres Stu Cncl; Ftbl; God Cntry Awd; Ntl Merit Ltr; Band; Chorus; Russian Clb Pres 83-86; Tilney-Taylor Amer Hstry Essay Cont 85; Hstry.

JORDAN, DEBORAH; William H Hall HS; W Hartford, CT; (Y); 84/324; Pep Clb; Yrbk Stf; Cheerleading; Hon Roll; Psych.

JOSEF, JOHN; Holy Cross HS; Middlebury, CT; (Y); 107/352; Hosp Aide; Im Ftbl; JV Var Golf; Var L Socr; Hon Roll; Boston Coll; Pre Med.

JOSEPH, PAUL R; William H Hall HS; W Hartford, CT; (Y); 27/325; Band; JV Bsbl; French Hon Soc; High Hon Roll; NCTE Awd.

JOSEPHY, ANNE DEBORAH; Hamden Hall Country Day Schl; W Haven, CT; (Y); 4/73; Drama Clb; Key Clb; Office Aide; PAVAS; Teachers Aide; Thesps; School Play; Nwsp Rptr; Cheerleading; Cit Awd; Tufts U.

JOSLIN, ELIZABETH S; Frederick V Conrad HS; W Hartford, CT; (Y); 3/322; Latin Clb; Math Tm; Church Choir; NHS; Ntl Merit SF; Church Yth Grp; Jazz Band; Mrchg Band; Pep Band; School Musical; Rensselaer Polytech Inst Mth & Sci Mdl 85; Brown U Bk Prize 85; Silver Mdl Natl JR Clsscl Lg 83; Sci.

JOYCE, JOE; Central Catholic HS; Norwalk, CT; (Y); Ski Clb; JV Var Bsbl; Var Ftbl.

JUERGENS, MARIE; George J Penney HS; E Hartford, CT; (Y); Cmnty Wkr; Spanish Clb; Stage Crew; Yrbk Stf; Soph Cls; Trk; Hon Roll; NHS; 9th Girls Shotput Outdr Trck 85; CCC All Conf Tm Girls Outdr Trck 85; New England Clg; Dietcs.

JUHASZ, SUSAN; Sacred Heart Acad; N Haven, CT; (Y); 6/114; Scholastic Bowl; Nwsp Ed-Chief; Lit Mag; Rep Frsh Cls; Rep Jr Cls; Var Crs Cntry; Bausch & Lomb Sci Awd; French Hon Soc; High Hon Roll; NHS; Cane ST Latn Awd 82; CT Womn Engrs Awd Merit 84; 4 Yr Hnrs Awd 85; George Washington U; Ststcs.

JULESON, RAYMOND; Manchester HS; Manchester, CT; (Y); #87 In Class; Cmnty Wkr; JV Socr; Hon Roll; Arch.

JULIAN, TRACY; Wetherfield HS; Wethersfield, CT; (Y); 31/319; Chorus; Capt JV Cheerleading; High Hon Roll; Hon Roll; Syracuse U; Arts.

JUNG, MARLENE DORIS; Granby Memorial HS; Granby, CT; (Y); 18/102; Church Yth Grp; German Clb; Library Aide; Concert Band; Mrchg Band; Pep Band; Stage Crew; Symp Band; High Hon Roll; Hon Roll; Chem Awd 85; Problty & Statstcs Awd 84; Typ I Awd 85; U Of CT; Vet Tech.

KACZKA, KIMBERLY A; Enfield HS; Enfield, CT; (Y); Church Yth Grp; Civic Clb; Dance Clb; Office Aide; Ski Clb; Varsity Clb; Variety Show; Trk; High Hon Roll; Hon Roll; U Of CT; Med.

KACZOR, CHARLES; Berlin HS; Kensington, CT; (Y); 3/191; Church Yth Grp; Math Tm; Science Clb; Band; Concert Band; Mrchg Band; JV Var Trk; High Hon Roll; NHS; JR Sci Humanties Symp Awd 85; Chemathon Tm Awd 84; HS Achvt Awds Bio,Chem,Spnsh Sci 83-85; Chem.

KACZOWKA, ROBERT; Saint Thomas Aquinas HS; New Britain, CT; (Y); 8/150; Chess Clb; JA; Spanish Clb; Var Trk; High Hon Roll; Hon Roll; NHS; Prfct Atten Awd; Comp Prog.

KACZYNSKI, PATRICIA; Beryn HS; Kensington, CT; (Y); Church Yth Grp; Drama Clb; Band; Sec Trs Chorus; Concert Band; Drm Mjr(t); Jazz Band; Mrchg Band; Pep Band; School Musical; Outstndng Frshmn In Band & Chorus 81-82; Center For Creative Yth At Wesleyan 82-83; Cntrl CT ST U; Spch Path.

KAHN, LEWIS; Andrew Warde HS; Fairfield, CT; (Y); VP Church Yth Grp; Pres Debate Tm; Hon Roll; NHS; VFW Awd; Dora Wheeler Schlrshp-Fairfield PTA Cncl 85; U Of CT; Accntng.

KAIKO, TINA; Griswold HS; Jewett City, CT; (Y); GAA; JV Var Cheerleading; Hon Roll; Spanish Clb.

KALAMA, LUANA; Windham Regnl Voc Tech Schl; Amston Lake, CT; (Y); VP Pres VICA; Yrbk Ed-Chief; Trs Stu Cncl; Var Trk; NHS; Am Leg Aux Girls St; Yrbk Stf; Cit Awd; Hon Roll; Prfct Atten Awd; MVP Trck 84-85; QVC All-Star In 100m Dash & 200m Dash 84-85; Fin In VICA Skll Olympcs Arch Dftng 85; Intr Dsgn.

KALANDYK, KATHLEEN M; Lyman Hall HS; Wallingford, CT; (Y); 21/250; Key Clb; Spanish Clb; Varsity Clb; Trs Frsh Cls; Trs Soph Cls; Trs Jr Cls; Trs Sr Cls; Stu Cncl; Capt Var Cheerleading; Powder Puff Ftbl; Bus.

KALJULAID, KAREN; William H Hall HS; W Hartford, CT; (Y); 21/324; Church Yth Grp; Pres Concert Band; Jazz Band; Mrchg Band; Orch; Pep Band; Crs Cntry; French Hon Soc; High Hon Roll; NHS; Bio.

KANDSCHUR, HEIDE ERIKA; Bloomfield HS; Bloomfield, CT; (Y); 4/231; Church Yth Grp; Model UN; Var Capt Tennis; Var JV Vllybl; VP French Hon Soc; NHS; Boy Scts; French Clb; Ski Clb; Wellesley Bk Awd 85; Ltn Achvt Awd 85; Intl Affrs.

KANE, GARY; W F Kaynor R V T S HS; Waterbury, CT; (Y); VICA; Yrbk Stf; Stu Cncl; Var Golf; High Hon Roll; Hon Roll; Trs NHS; Stu Cong Of Conn Voc Tech Schls VP 85-86; Arch.

KANE, KATHERINE M; Staples HS; Westport, CT; (Y); Acpl Chr; Chorus; School Musical; School Play; Sr Cls; Powder Puff Ftbl; Tennis; Trk; Vllybl; Hon Roll; Bus.

KANOS, CHARLES; Stamford HS; Stamford, CT; (S); 30/407; Pres Church Yth Grp; Pres Latin Clb; Rep Stu Cncl; JV Bsktbl; JV Ftbl; JV Socr; Co-Capt Trk; High Hon Roll; Hon Roll; NHS; Vanderbilt U; Chemistry.

KAPLAN, ADENA; Hall HS; W Hartford, CT; (Y); 121/345; Aud/Vis; Teachers Aide; Temple Yth Grp; Concert Band; Mrchg Band; Symp Band; L Cheerleading; Swmmng; French Hon Soc; High Hon Roll; Hlth.

KAPOUCH, JOSEPH; Northwest Catholic HS; W Hartford, CT; (Y); French Clb; Model UN; Band; Nwsp Rptr; Yrbk Stf; Lit Mag; JV Trk; Hon Roll; Engl.

KAPPES, ROBERT; Northwest Catholic HS; W Hartford, CT; (Y); Latin Clb; Ski Clb; Band; Concert Band; Jazz Band; Mrchg Band; JV Bsbl; JV Ftbl; Socr.

KARAGIANNIS, OURANIA; East Hartford HS; East Hartford, CT; (Y); 41/260; Church Yth Grp; Dance Clb; Drill Tm; High Hon Roll; Hon Roll; Prncpls Achvt Awd 81-85; Drill Team Awd 85; U Of CT; Elem Ed.

KARAS, JUDITH ANNE; Westhill HS; Stamford, CT; (Y); Church Yth Grp; JA; Stage Crew; Fld Hcky; Tennis; FL ST U; Intl Affrs.

KARCHER, BETH; Trumbull HS; Trumbull, CT; (Y); AFS; French Clb; Ski Clb; Sec Frsh Cls; Capt Fld Hcky; Hon Roll; Intl Bus.

KARCHER, COLLEEN; Shelton HS; Shelton, CT; (Y); Cmnty Wkr; Hosp Aide; Ski Clb; Spanish Clb; Cheerleading; Hon Roll.

KARDAMIS, LISA; Frank Scott Bunnell HS; Stratford, CT; (Y); 7/250; Band; Mrchg Band; Yrbk Ed-Chief; Rep Frsh Cls; Rep Soph Cls; Rep Stu Cncl; Var Mgr(s); Var Capt Swmmng; High Hon Roll; NHS; Stratford Rotary Clb Schrlsh P85; Easter Seals Rehab Schrshp 85; Hnr Soc 85; Quinnipiac Coll; Occup Thrpy.

KARDYS, DAVID; Windsor Locks HS; Windsor Locks, CT; (Y); 36/160; Var Ftbl; High Hon Roll; Hon Roll; UCONN; Engrng.

KARL, PAUL; New Canaan HS; New Canaan, CT; (Y); Boy Scts; Church Yth Grp; Cmnty Wkr; High Hon Roll; Hon Roll; Jr NHS; Knights Of Columbus Schlrshp 85; Rotary Clb Exchnge 85; Eagle Scout 83; U Of CT; Pol Sci.

KAROLL, MARYBETH; Amity Regional SR HS; Bethany, CT; (Y); 16/470; Nwsp Ed-Chief; Nwsp Rptr; Ed Nwsp Sprt Ed; Lit Mag; NHS; Ntl Merit SF; French Clb; Latin Clb; Brown Bk Awd 84; Holy Cross Bk Awd 84; Jrnslm.

KARSZES, JASON; Rockville HS; Somers, CT; (S); 22/352; FFA; Stu Cncl; Socr; High Hon Roll; NHS; Ag.

KASPERSKI, JENNIFER; Holy Cross HS; Prospect, CT; (Y); 27/362; Art Clb; Mgr(s); Hon Roll; Jr NHS; NHS; Soc Stud Hnr Soc 84-86; Syracuse; Bio.

KATAN, JOSHUA; Lyme-Oldlyme HS; South Lyme, CT; (Y); Am Leg Boys St; Cmnty Wkr; Ski Clb; Off Soph Cls; Off Sr Cls; Var Socr; Var Tennis; Pres Yth Advsry Comm 85-86; Ctzn Yr SADD 84; Recgntn Awd Outstndng Achvt Ldrshp 85; St Michaels; Comp Sci.

KATZ, DEBBIE; William Hall HS; West Hartford, CT; (Y); 90/324; Church Yth Grp; Hosp Aide; VP Y-Teens; L Vllybl; High Hon Roll; Hon Roll; Spanish NHS; Bently Coll; Law.

KATZ, DEBORAH; William Hall HS; W Hartford, CT; (Y); 96/342; Cmnty Wkr; JV Var Vllybl; High Hon Roll; Hon Roll; Safe Rides Of W Hartford VP 84-85; Yth Advsry Brd W Hartford 84-85; Paralgl.

KATZ, RACHEL A; Avon HS; Avon, CT; (Y); 11/198; Cmnty Wkr; Drama Clb; Band; Chorus; Im Socr; Trk; Mgr Hon Roll; NHS; Pres Schlr; Spn Awd Of Excllnce 85; U Of DE; Bus Adm.

KATZ, SAMUEL H; Newington HS; Newington, CT; (Y); 14/360; Boy Scts; Temple Yth Grp; Concert Band; Mrchg Band; Symp Band; Variety Show; Rep Jr Cls; High Hon Roll; Hon Roll; NHS; Med.

KATZMAN, DAVID D; Newington HS; Newington, CT; (Y); 2/377; Pres Math Tm; Quiz Bowl; Teachers Aide; Ed Lit Mag; High Hon Roll; NHS; Ntl Merit SF; Yrbk Stf; Rensselaer Polytech Inst Math & Sci Mdl 84; Brown U Bk Awd Engl 84; Chem, Physics,Lat I & II Awds; Bio Med.

KAUER, JOSH; Wilbur Cross HS; New Haven, CT; (S); 15/320; Spanish Clb; Socr; Tennis; Hon Roll; 1st Ntl Hist Day Cntst; Tafts UPSYCHLGY.

KAUFMANN, KRISTINE; Daniel Hand HS; Madison, CT; (Y); 54/236; Civic Clb; Hosp Aide; Office Aide; Band; Concert Band; Mrchg Band; Yrbk Phtg; Yrbk Sprt Ed; Hon Roll; Psych.

KAVALEK, LAURA JEAN; Brookfiield HS; Brookfield, CT; (Y); 15/180; Red Cross Aide; NHS; Pres Schlr; Rssn Hstry Awd 85; Shrt Stry Awd 85; Music Apprctn 85; Muhlenberg Coll; Pre Med.

KAWESA, ANNE; Academy Of The Holy Family; Taylor, MI; (Y); Art Clb; Red Cross Aide; Chorus; Stage Crew; Var Crs Cntry; Hon Roll; MVP Rnnr Crss Cntry 83; Vet.

KAY, TERRIANN; Platt HS; Meriden, CT; (Y); Church Yth Grp; Cmnty Wkr; Hosp Aide; Yrbk Stf; Rep Jr Cls; Swmmng; Hon Roll; Athltc Lttr In Swmmng 82-83; Var Time Awds For Candystriping 82; Mrktng.

KAZLAUSKAS, MICHELLE; Crosby HS; Oakville, CT; (Y); Art Clb; DECA; Office Aide; Lit Mag; JV Sftbl; Hon Roll; Distrbutv Educ Mrchndsng Awd 85; Distrbutv Ed Awd Genrl Mktng 85-Mastr Emplyee; Morse Schl Bus; Medcl Adm Asst.

KEARNEY, KEVIN; Trumbull HS; Trumbull, CT; (Y); Scrd Heart U Pres Schlrshp 85; Sacred Heart U; Accntng.

KEEFE, KELLEY MARIE; Glastonbury HS; Glastonbury, CT; (Y); 33/430; Church Yth Grp; Cmnty Wkr; Dance Clb; Key Clb; Ski Clb; Y-Teens; Yrbk Stf; Lcrss; Mgr(s); Hon Roll; ST Frgn Lang Poetry Cntst Awd 83; 1st Pl All Wrld Dance Drm Comtn 83; Rgnl & Ntl Irish Step Dnc Champ.

KEEFE, KEVIN; Holy Cross HS; Watertwn, CT; (Y); 44/344; Band; Concert Band; Pres Stu Cncl; French Hon Soc; Hon Roll; NHS; Ntl Merit Ltr; Pres Schlr; Amer Legion Awd 85; Fathers Club Holy Cross Svc 85; SADD 85; U Of CT; Bus.

KEEGAN, ERIC; George J Penney HS; E Hartford, CT; (Y); Rep Frsh Cls; Rep Soph Cls; JV Golf; JV Score Keeper; Hon Roll; Comm.

KEEGAN, THOMAS; Notre Dame HS; E Haven, CT; (Y); Cmnty Wkr; Ski Clb; Ftbl; Ice Hcky; JV Trk; Hon Roll; Brown U; Engr.

KEELER, KATHY; Manchester HS; Manchester, CT; (Y); AFS; Nwsp Ed-Chief; Yrbk Ed-Chief; Yrbk Phtg; Yrbk Stf; VP Stu Cncl; Var Cheerleading; Hon Roll; Jrnslm.

KEEN, BETH; East Hartford HS; E Hartford, CT; (Y); Drama Clb; Spanish Clb; Chorus; School Musical; School Play; Yrbk Stf; High Hon Roll; Hon Roll; NHS; Ntrl Sci.

KEENE, GRETCHEN M; Trumbull HS; Trumbull, CT; (Y); Chorus; Nwsp Rptr; Nwsp Stf; Syracuse U; Eng.

KEENEY, WILLIAM; William Hall HS; W Hartford, CT; (Y); 7/342; Var Socr; Red Cross Aide; NHS; Ntl Merit Ltr; Sec Spanish NHS; Psychtry.

KEESHAN, RALPH TIMOTHY; The Forman Schl; Litchfield, CT; (Y); 8/63; Art Clb; Aud/Vis; Drama Clb; Key Clb; School Play; Stage Crew; Nwsp Stf; Yrbk Stf; JV Crs Cntry; Im Socr; Hdmstrs Awd 84; Sci Fair Prjct 1st Pl 84; Monitrl Soc 83-85; San Jose ST U; Art.

KEILHAUER, CATALINA; Miss Porters Schl; Hingham, MA; (Y); Art Clb; French Clb; Service Clb; Spanish Clb; School Musical; Off Sr Cls; Var Sftbl; Var Vllybl; French Hon Soc; Hon Roll.

KEINARD, CHRISTINE; Farminton HS; Unionville, CT; (Y); Sec Church Yth Grp; Acpl Chr; Band; Chorus; Concert Band; Jazz Band; Mrchg Band; Orch; JV Var Fld Hcky; High Hon Roll; Julius Hartt Schl Of Music Schlrshp 84; Bus.

KEISH, BRIAN F; Glastonbury HS; Glastonbury, CT; (Y); 10/393; Church Yth Grp; 4-H; Math Tm; Symp Band; JV Capt Wrstlng; NHS; Ntl Merit SF; Computer Clb; 4-H Awd; High Hon Roll; Rensselaer Medal Math/Sci; Naval Acad Engr/Sci Smnr; 4-H Delg Ctznshp-Wash Focus; Elec Engr.

KEISS, AIJA; Manchester HS; Manchester, CT; (Y); High Hon Roll; Hon Roll; UCONN; Vet.

KELLER, JENNIFER; Maloney HS; Meriden, CT; (Y); Church Yth Grp; Drama Clb; Hon Roll.

KELLETT, MARY JANE; Shelton HS; Shelton, CT; (Y); Sec Exploring; Mgr(s); Hon Roll; Explorer Of The Yr 85; Grand Rep To NV For Rainbow 85; Best Sustain Avrge In Bus 85; Cazenovia; Bus Mgt.

KELLEY, CHRISTINE A; Watkinson HS; Bloomfield, CT; (Y); 10/49; Art Clb; Girl Scts; PAVAS; Teachers Aide; High Hon Roll; Hon Roll; Creative Arts Pgm Diploma Stu; U Of Hartford Coll NOW Pgm; Visual Arts.

KELLEY, COURTNEY; Masuk HS; Monroe, CT; (Y); 55/300; AFS; French Clb; JCL; Latin Clb; Var Swmmng; Var Tennis; JV Trk; Hon Roll; Outstndng Swmrs Awd 84; Ntl Latin Exam Slvr Mdl 85.

KELLEY, EDWARD; Ridgefield HS; Ridgefield, CT; (Y); 17/350; Rep Am Leg Boys St; Church Yth Grp; Civic Clb; Nwsp Bus Mgr; Nwsp Ed-Chief; JV Var Socr; Capt Var Trk; High Hon Roll; NHS; Princeton Book Awd Excllnce Humants 85; Gold Medl Yale Invtnl 84; Outstndng Svc & Ldrshp Cls 83 & 85; Humanities.

KELLEY, TIM; East Catholic HS; Manchester, CT; (Y); 31/300; Church Yth Grp; Cmnty Wkr; Drama Clb; Chorus; School Musical; Variety Show; Nwsp Stf; Pres Soph Cls; High Hon Roll; Hon Roll; Parnts Clb Schlrshp; Entrtnmt.

KELLOGG, ELIZABETH; Brien Mc Mahon HS; Rowayton, CT; (Y); #26 In Class; Church Yth Grp; French Clb; Key Clb; Yrbk Stf; Sec Sr Cls; Powder Puff Ftbl; Tennis; High Hon Roll; Hon Roll.

KELLOGG, TODD T; Notre Dame Catholic HS; Easton, CT; (Y); Church Yth Grp; Drama Clb; Sec Key Clb; Pep Clb; Pres Ski Clb; School Play; Stage Crew; Rep Soph Cls; Rep Jr Cls; Trs Stu Cncl; Awd Excllnc Chem 84; Awd Excllnc Afro Asian Hstry 83; Providence Coll; Math.

KELLY, BRIAN; Trumbull HS; Trumbull, CT; (Y); Concert Band; Mrchg Band; Symp Band; Variety Show; Lit Mag; JV Bsktbl; Var Ftbl; Var Trk; High Hon Roll; NHS; Music Hnr Awd 83.

KELLY, KATHLEEN A; Naugatuck HS; Union City, CT; (Y); Chorus; Var L Crs Cntry; JV Sftbl; Var L Trk; Hon Roll; Amer H S Ath Crs Cntry 84-85; Crim Just.

KELLY, LARA; St Thomas Aquinas HS; New Britain, CT; (Y); Pres Church Yth Grp; Spanish Clb; Var L Bsktbl; Var Capt Crs Cntry; Var Capt Trk; DAR Awd; Hon Roll; NHS; Harvard-Radcliffe Bk Awd Acadmc Achv 84; CIAC Schlr-Athlt Awd 85; St Thms Aquinas Fem Athlt Yr Awd 85; U Of VT; Math.

KELLY, LYNN; Sacred Heart Acad; New Haven, CT; (Y); Church Yth Grp; School Musical; Cheerleading; Im Vllybl; NEDT Awd; Bus.

KELSEY, JOHN; Staples HS; Westport, CT; (Y); Drama Clb; School Play; Var Crs Cntry; Var Swmmng; Var Trk; Natl Cncl Alchlsm Meritorious Awd 85; All ST Swmmr 85; Eductr.

KENDALL, LEIGH; William H Hall HS; W Hartford, CT; (Y); JA; Ski Clb; Jazz Band; Mrchg Band; Orch; Pep Band; School Musical; Symp Band; JV Var Ftbl; Hon Roll; Berklee Schl Of Music Schlrshp 85; Law.

KENDALL, RICHARD; St Bernard HS; Lebanon, CT; (S); 123/290; Boy Scts; Ski Clb; Band; Var Capt Socr; Trk; Hon Roll; Tm Ldrshp Awd Var Soccer 84-85; Keene ST Coll; Athltc.

KENDRICK, LINDA; George J Penney HS; E Hartford, CT; (Y); Sec Church Yth Grp; Drama Clb; School Musical; School Play; Stage Crew; Rep Soph Cls; Rep Jr Cls; Hon Roll; NHS; Dntl Asst.

KENNEDY, DENNIS; Killingly HS; Wauregan, CT; (Y); Art Clb; Aud/Vis; Church Yth Grp; Cmnty Wkr; Computer Clb; Library Aide; Band; Hon Roll; Outstndng Asstnc Awd In Comp Course 84-85; Hall Inst; Comp Prgmr.

KENNEDY, KEVIN; Putnam HS; Putnam, CT; (Y); 5/145; Am Leg Boys St; Boy Scts; Ski Clb; School Play; Yrbk Ed-Chief; VP Frsh Cls; Var Socr; Var Capt Trk; Pres NHS; Ntl Merit Ltr; Aerosp Engrng.

KENNEDY, ROBERT H; Danbury HS; Danbury, CT; (Y); 2/538; Exploring; Stu Cncl; Var Capt Ftbl; Capt Trk; Jr NHS; NHS; Sal; Cmnty Wkr; Varsity Clb; Variety Show; CT Schlr 84; Danbury Exchng Clb Stu/Yr 85; IBM Watson Schlrshp 85; Brown U-Providence; Math.

KENNEY, KRISTEN A; Choate Rosemary Hall; Wallingford, CT; (S); Latin Clb; Pep Clb; Chorus; Im Socr; JV Vllybl; Hon Roll; Jr NHS.

KENNEY JR, THOMAS J; Holy Cross HS; Waterbury, CT; (Y); 207/352; Church Yth Grp; Cmnty Wkr; Office Aide; Political Wkr; Service Clb; Sec VP Stu Cncl; JV Bsktbl; JV Var Ftbl; Sftbl; Peer Mnstry 84-86; Holy Cross Stu Agnst Drvng Drnk 84-85; Accntng.

KENT, CHARLES; Mark T Sheehan HS; Wallingford, CT; (Y); Boy Scts; Church Yth Grp; Hon Roll.

KEOGH, MAUREEN; Brien Mc Mahon HS; Norwalk, CT; (Y); 1/337; Am Leg Aux Girls St; Church Yth Grp; Debate Tm; Hosp Aide; Band; NHS; Ntl Merit Ltr; Spanish Clb; Concert Band; Mrchg Band; Havard U Bk Awd 85; Oberlin Coll Bk Awd 85; CT Western Rgnl Bnd 85; Med.

KEOGH, PATRICIA; Brien Mc Mahon HS; Norwalk, CT; (Y); 1/337; Am Leg Aux Girls St; Church Yth Grp; Debate Tm; Hosp Aide; Band; NHS; Ntl Merit Ltr; Spanish Clb; Concert Band; Mrchg Band; Harvard U Bk Awd, Coll Holy Cross Bk Awd, CT Wstrn Regn Band 85; Med.

KEOVILAY, VICHITPHANH; Manchester HS; Manchester, CT; (Y); French Clb; Band; Concert Band; JV Vllybl; High Hon Roll; Hon Roll; Manchester CC; Lang.

KERN, BARBARA JANE; Lauralton Hall HS; Milford, CT; (Y); Church Yth Grp; Cmnty Wkr; Service Clb; Lit Mag; Southern CT ST U; Law.

KERNS, KATHLEEN; Southington HS; Marion, CT; (Y); Spanish Clb; High Hon Roll; Hon Roll; Exec Sec.

KERRIGAN, RICHARD K; Montville HS; Chicago, IL; (Y); 1/168; Math Tm; High Hon Roll; Hon Roll; NHS; Spanish NHS; Val; Harvard Prz-Outstndng Stu 84; Readrs Digst Prz-Outstndng Stu 85; Pres Acadmc Ftnss Awd 85; IL Inst Of Tech; Cvl Engrng.

KERSEY, ALEXANDRA; Trumbull HS; Trumbull, CT; (Y); AFS; Ski Clb; Concert Band; Mrchg Band; Symp Band; Timer; French Hon Soc; Hon Roll; NHS; Ntl Merit Ltr; Intntl Studies.

KERTESZ, KAREN; Masuk HS; Monroe, CT; (Y); 47/285; JCL; Pep Clb; Spanish Clb; Capt Cheerleading; High Hon Roll; Hon Roll; Bus.

KERTESZ, LYNN; Ridgefield HS; Ridgefield, CT; (S); 51/343; Church Yth Grp; DECA; Church Choir; Variety Show; Var Gym; Powder Puff Ftbl; Hon Roll; NHS; Mrktng.

KETT, DENISE; Lauralton Hall HS; Stratford, CT; (Y); Math Clb; Math Tm; Service Clb; Spanish Clb; Teachers Aide; Chorus; Mu Alp Tht; NHS; Spanish NHS; 10th Pl Ntl Spanish Ex CT 83; Med.

KHAN, TARA E; Staples HS; Westport, CT; (Y); Camera Clb; Church Yth Grp; French Clb; Girl Scts; Ski Clb; Variety Show; Tennis; Hon Roll; Principal Awd 85; Culinary Inst Of Am; Restrt Mgt.

KICZYINSKI, MATT; Branford HS; Branford, CT; (Y); Ski Clb; JV Socr; Hon Roll; Speed Wrtng 85; Bicycle Motocrs Racng 83-84; Quinnipiac Coll; Physcl Thrpy.

KIDD, DEBORAH; Stamford HS; Stamford, CT; (S); 19/406; JA; Office Aide; Spanish Clb; Hon Roll; NHS; Lehigh U; Liberal Arts.

KIDDER, DAVID; Wilton HS; Wilton, CT; (Y); 11/349; Varsity Clb; Pres Frsh Cls; Pres Soph Cls; Trs Sr Cls; Stu Cncl; Lcrss; Socr; High Hon Roll; NHS; Hugh O Brien Awd 83; Notre Dame U; Bus.

KIEFER, KATHERYN; Mercy HS; S Glastonbury, CT; (Y); 100/200; Cmnty Wkr; Political Wkr; School Musical; School Play; Rep Frsh Cls; Rep Jr Cls; Rep Sr Cls; Rep Stu Cncl; Var Cheerleading; Var Sftbl; Poetry Cntst 3rd Pl 85; Fash Dsgn.

KIEFER, MARK; The Morgan Schl; Clinton, CT; (Y); Quiz Bowl; Scholastic Bowl; Jazz Band; Orch; Pep Band; School Musical; School Play; High Hon Roll; Hon Roll; Aerospace Engrng.

KIERNAN, BRIAN; Torrington HS; Torrington, CT; (Y); 31/320; Aud/Vis; Library Aide; High Hon Roll; Hon Roll; NHS; Elctrnc Dsgn Engr.

KIGANDA, MARY EDNA; Academy Of The Holy Family; Silver Spring, MD; (Y); 2/29; Girl Scts; Chorus; Bsktbl; Crs Cntry; Sftbl; Hon Roll; Rookie Yr 82-83; Sftbll 83; MIP Bsktbll 84; MVP & MIP Sftbll 85.

KIJANKA, KIM; Plainville HS; Plainville, CT; (S); Dance Clb; Pres DECA; Girl Scts; Hosp Aide; PAVAS; Color Guard; Var Crs Cntry; Trk; NHS; Voice Dem Awd; Deca Ntl Nomntng Comm 85; Pres Physcl Ftns Awd 83-85; Peer Ed Cnslng Cert 84; Central CT ST U; Comm.

KILLEEN, MARY ELIZABETH; Holy Cross HS; Waterbury, CT; (Y); 11/344; Hosp Aide; Service Clb; High Hon Roll; Spanish NHS; St Schlr; Earth Sci Awd 85; Prov Coll Acad Schlrshp 85; Stonehill Coll Hnrs & Fairfield U Schlrshp 85; Providence Coll; Pre Med.

KILLIAN, JEFFREY G; Trumbull HS; Trumbull, CT; (Y); 2/510; Stu Cncl; Co-Capt Var Swmmng; Bausch & Lomb Sci Awd; DAR Awd; NHS; Ntl Merit SF; Sal; Naval ROTC Scholar 85; MA Inst Tech; Aerontcs.

KILLINGBECK, KELLI; Torrington HS; Torrington, CT; (Y); 5/330; Am Leg Aux Girls St; Pres Key Clb; Math Tm; Chorus; Stage Crew; JV Trk; High Hon Roll; Pres NHS; NEDT Awd; New England Mth Lg Cert Of Merit; Cert Merit Soc Of Women Engrs; Ltr & Cert Outstndg Soph Chrs; Acctg.

KIM, MATTHEW; Manchester HS; Manchester, CT; (Y); 3/570; Am Leg Boys St; Art Clb; French Clb; Quiz Bowl; Concert Band; Jazz Band; JV Socr; High Hon Roll; NHS; AFS; Acadmc Ftns Awd 83; Trnty Clb Bk Awd 85; Bus Admin.

KIM, NOEL M; Saint Thomas Aquinas HS; New Britain, CT; (Y); 1/155; Church Yth Grp; Library Aide; Chorus; Yrbk Stf; Stu Cncl; Stat Bsktbl; Hon Roll; Val; Spanish Clb; Rep Soph Cls; Yale Bk Awd 84; 8th Poltcl Ward Schlrshp 85; Colgate U; Math.

KIMBALL, JAMES; Naugatuck HS; Naugatuck, CT; (Y); Boy Scts; Church Yth Grp; Library Aide; Yrbk Sprt Ed; Var L Crs Cntry; Var L Trk; Hon Roll.

KIMBLETON, KERN; Trumbull HS; Trumbull, CT; (Y); Debate Tm; JA; Chorus; JV Crs Cntry; High Hon Roll; NHS; Elec Engr.

KINDLUND, ERIKA PAIGE; Choate Rosemary Hall HS; Syracuse, NY; (S); Drama Clb; Ski Clb; Acpl Chr; Sec Chorus; Madrigals; Orch; School Musical; School Play; Hon Roll; John Edwards Engl Awd Manlius Pebble Hill Schl 82; Lawrence Brown Awd Music 83-84; Cornell U.

KING, JONATHAN; William H HS; W Hartford, CT; (Y); 62/342; Cit Awd; French Hon Soc; High Hon Roll; Hon Roll; US Naval Acad Annapolis; Mltry.

KING, KIMBERLY; Cheshire HS; Cheshire, CT; (Y); 34/320; Drama Clb; Nwsp Ed-Chief; Yrbk Ed-Chief; Rep Soph Cls; Rep Jr Cls; Rep Sr Cls; Cit Awd; French Hon Soc; Rep Frsh Cls; Hon Roll; Engl Achvt Awds 85; Sftbl Coach Pk & Recrtn Dept; Colby Coll ME; Lib Arts.

KING, RONALD; Windsor Locks HS; Windsor Locks, CT; (Y); 14/160; Am Leg Boys St; Boy Scts; Church Yth Grp; Chorus; Concert Band; Mrchg Band; Var Swmmng; Var Tennis; Hon Roll; NHS; Comp Sci.

KINSELLA, BARBARA C; Norwalk HS; Norwalk, CT; (Y); 9/459; Aud/Vis; Church Yth Grp; Cmnty Wkr; French Clb; Ski Clb; Yrbk Stf; Trs Sr Cls; Powder Puff Ftbl; Sftbl; Swmmng; Mst Outstndng Thesis Ppr In Cls 84; CT Brdcstrs Asn Schlrshp 85; Mrchnts Bk Schlrshp 85; UCLA; Cmnctns.

KINSELLA, LEANNE; Brookfield HS; Brookfield, CT; (Y); Church Yth Grp; Cmnty Wkr; FBLA; Girl Scts; Hosp Aide; Math Clb; Math Tm; Spanish Clb; Chorus; Lit Mag; Alg IA, Music Apprctn, Spnsh IV Hnrs Aachvt, Hnrs Engl III Achvt Awd 83-85; Psych.

KINTZLER, SASHA K; Shelton HS; Shelton, CT; (Y); Spanish Clb; Nwsp Rptr; Nwsp Stf; Yrbk Stf; Hon Roll; NHS; Spanish NHS.

KIRBY, CAROLYN; Conard HS; W Hartford, CT; (Y); 90/291; Cmnty Wkr; Hosp Aide; Red Cross Aide; Service Clb; School Play; Yrbk Stf; Hon Roll; NHS; Salve Regina The Newport Coll Schlrshp 85-86; W Hartford Womens Clb Schlrshp 85-86; Salve Regina/Newport Coll; Nrsg.

KIRCH, SUSAN ANN; Stafford HS; Stafford Sprgs, CT; (Y); 7/109; Am Leg Aux Girls St; Hosp Aide; Chorus; Variety Show; Sec Frsh Cls; VP Stu Cncl; JV Fld Hcky; DAR Awd; High Hon Roll; NHS; Mt Holyoke Coll.

KIRWAN, ELIZABETH A; Avon HS; Avon, CT; (Y); FCA; German Clb; Chorus; Church Choir; Crs Cntry; Swmmng; Trk; Hon Roll; NHS; Merit Excel Art 85; All St Cross Cty 85; MV Rnning Swmmng 83.

KISSANE, JAMES; Pomperaug HS; Middlebury, CT; (Y); Math Tm; Yrbk Stf; JV Bsbl; JV Var Bsktbl; JV Var Socr; Var Tennis; Hon Roll; Engrng.

KLARIDES, NICOLE; Seymour HS; Seymour, CT; (Y); Varsity Clb; Rep Frsh Cls; Rep Soph Cls; Pres VP Jr Cls; VP Pres Sr Cls; VP Trs Stu Cncl; Var Cheerleading; Capt Swmmng; Hon Roll; Trinity Coll; Econ.

KLIMAS, NANCY; Branford HS; Branford, CT; (Y); 20/250; Church Yth Grp; Latin Clb; Rep Stu Cncl; Var Capt Bsktbl; Var Capt Fld Hcky; Trk; Hon Roll; NHS; U Of CT Bk Awd 85; VA Moessmang Sprtsmnshp Bsktbl Awd 85; CIAC & New Haven Tap Off Clb Schlr/Athlte; U Of CT; Frgn Lang.

KLIMEK, CHRISTINE; Central Catholic HS; Norwalk, CT; (Y); Drama Clb; French Clb; Math Tm; School Musical; School Play; Stage Crew; Lit Mag; JV Capt Sftbl; NHS; NEDT Awd; High Hnr Roll 82-84; Hnr Rl 84-85; Awd Achvt Hist 85; Cmnctns.

KLIMKIEWICZ, AIMEE; Bristol Central HS; Bristol, CT; (Y); JV Bsktbl; Hon Roll; U Hartford; Cmmnctns.

KLIMKOWSKY, CHERYL; Seymour HS; Seymour, CT; (Y); Church Yth Grp; Hosp Aide; JA; Sec Frsh Cls; Sec Soph Cls; Sec Jr Cls; Sec Stu Cncl; Hon Roll; Hnr Roll 2nd Hnrs; Secretary Church Youth Group 83-85; Nursing.

KLIPSTEN, WILLIAM; Kingswood Oxfod HS; Manchester, CT; (Y); Chess Clb; Math Tm; Model UN; Q&S; Quiz Bowl; School Play; Stage Crew; Nwsp Stf; Wrstlng; Hon Roll; Pre-Med.

KLOPP, CARYN; New Britain HS; New Britain, CT; (Y); 25/350; Office Aide; Capt Cheerleading; Hon Roll; Rotary Awd; Rotry Clb Schlrshp 85; Central CT ST U; Secdry Bio.

KLOSS, MICHAEL; Pomperang HS; Middlebury, CT; (Y); Boy Scts; Church Yth Grp; JV Bsbl; JV Bsktbl; Hon Roll; Prfct Atten Awd; U CT; Urban Studies.

KLUESS, COURTNEY R; Ridgefield HS; Ridgefield, CT; (Y); 4/400; Band; French Hon Soc; High Hon Roll; Ntl Merit Ltr; Pres Schlr; Wheeler-Ellison Scholar 85; Schlumberger-Doll Fr Awd 82 & 85; Natl Fr Awd 83; Fordham U; Comm.

KMETZ, JANICE; The Morgan HS; Clinton, CT; (Y); 40/180; Pres AFS; Stage Crew; Nwsp Stf; Var Crs Cntry; Var Powder Puff Ftbl; Var Trk; Var Vllybl; Crimnlgy.

KMETZ, JOY M; Morgan HS; Clinton, CT; (Y); 44/180; FBLA; Hosp Aide; Pep Clb; Powder Puff Ftbl; Hon Roll; Prfct Atten Awd; Hm Ec Awd 82-83; Becker-Junior; Travl.

KNIGHT, CHRISTINE; Torrington HS; Torrington, CT; (Y); Aud/Vis; Drama Clb; Library Aide; Stage Crew; Yrbk Stf; Mnstr.

KNIGHT, CYNTHIA; Conard HS; W Hartford, CT; (Y); 12/314; Concert Band; Yrbk Stf; Var Capt Bsktbl; Var L Socr; Var Capt Sftbl; High Hon Roll; NHS; Spanish NHS; All Conf Sftbl 84-85; Bsktbl 85.

KNIGHT, ERICA; St Bernard HS; Westerly, RI; (S); Aud/Vis; Church Yth Grp; Hosp Aide; Var Swmmng; High Hon Roll; Hon Roll; 1st Hnrs 83-84; Vet Med.

KNIGHT, PAM; Danbury HS; Danbury, CT; (Y); Hosp Aide; JA; Varsity Clb; Acpl Chr; Yrbk Phtg; Var Cheerleading; Coach Actv; Jr NHS; Concert Choir; Pop Choir; Fashion Buyer.

KNOWLES, NIGEL; Daniel Hand HS; Madison, CT; (Y); 40/235; Band; Im Bsktbl; JV Ftbl; Var Trk; Im Wt Lftg; Var Wrstlng; Hon Roll; Engrng.

KNOWLES, SCOTT; Stonington HS; Pawcatuck, CT; (Y); Varsity Clb; Bsbl; Eastern CT ST U; Bio.

KNOX, DAREN; Oliver Wolcott Reg Vo Tech; Torrington, CT; (Y); 11/142; Math Clb; Ski Clb; Yrbk Stf; VP Jr Cls; Hon Roll; Rotary Awd; Camel Greens Inc Schlrshp 85-86; Wm C Nicholas C E Nejaime Mem Schlrshp 85-86; Wtrbry ST Tech Coll; Elec Engr.

KNOX, KAREN; Pomperaug Regional HS; Southbury, CT; (Y); Drama Clb; French Clb; Girl Scts; Acpl Chr; Band; Chorus; Church Choir; Concert Band; Jazz Band; Madrigals; Med.

KNYBEL, DONALD; Rockville HS; Vernon, CT; (Y); 152/372; High Hon Roll; Hon Roll; Hgh Hnr Roll; Central CT ST U; Accntng.

KOCHANEK, KATHRYN; Tolland HS; Tolland, CT; (Y); 7/160; Debate Tm; Hosp Aide; Rep Frsh Cls; Rep Soph Cls; Rep Jr Cls; JV Bsktbl; Var L Crs Cntry; High Hon Roll; Hon Roll; NHS; Math.

KOENIG, LISA; North Haven HS; N Haven, CT; (Y); 62/187; Yrbk Stf; L Fld Hcky; Trk; Hon Roll; Bus.

KOENIG, MICHAEL; Trumbull HS; Trumbull, CT; (Y); Temple Yth Grp; JV Bsktbl; JV Crs Cntry; JV Trk; High Hon Roll; NHS; Yale U Frontiers Appld Sci Series 85; Med.

KOHL, MICHELLE; Manchester HS; Manchester, CT; (Y); Cmnty Wkr; Hosp Aide; Color Guard; Yrbk Stf; Sftbl; Hon Roll; AZ ST U; Accntng.

KOHLER, KRISTEN L; Pomperaug HS; Southbury, CT; (Y); Church Yth Grp; Hon Roll.

KOHLER, MARGARET; East Catholic HS; Manchester, CT; (Y); 37/350; Church Yth Grp; Hon Roll; Spnsh.

KOHLI, ANUJ; Danbury HS; Danbury, CT; (Y); Intnl Clb; Math Clb; Math Tm; Variety Show; Hon Roll; Clarkson Schl Schlrshp 84-85; Math Tm Awd Ltr Beta 83; Clarkson U; Elec Engrng.

KOIVA, ERIC; Windham HS; Andover, CT; (Y); 69/275; Boy Scts; Nwsp Rptr; Nwsp Sprt Ed; Var Bsktbl; Im Vllybl; U Of CT; Engr.

KOLPAK, DOUG; Southington HS; Southington, CT; (Y); Am Leg Boys St; Trs Church Yth Grp; FBLA; Key Clb; School Musical; Variety Show; Trs Sr Cls; Var Bsktbl; Var L Socr; Bus Adm.

KOMARENKO, PAUL; East Haven HS; E Haven, CT; (Y); Am Leg Boys St; Debate Tm; French Clb; Library Aide; Math Clb; Quiz Bowl; Science Clb; Yrbk Stf; L Swmmng; NHS; Yale Bk Awd 85; Rensselaer Mdl 85; MA Inst Tech; Physcs.

KOMAROWSKA, AGNES; Norwalk HS; Norwalk, CT; (Y); Art Clb; Cmnty Wkr; German Clb; Hosp Aide; Teachers Aide; High Hon Roll; Math Achvt Awd 85; Grmn Goethe Inst Awd 85; Comp Learning Ctr Awd 82.

KONNIK, LAURA; Seymour HS; Seymour, CT; (Y); Yrbk Sprt Ed; Stu Cncl; Var Bsktbl; Var Sftbl; Var Swmmng; DAR Awd; Hon Roll; All Vly Sftbl; Med.

KONTRAKOS, JOSEPH; Masuk HS; Monroe, CT; (Y); 123/266; German Clb; Trk.

KOPCHA, CHERYL L; Crosby HS; Waterbury, CT; (Y); Key Clb; Var Sftbl; Var Vllybl; NHS; Comp Tech.

KOPERWHATS, KATHY; Stratford HS; Stratford, CT; (Y); Ski Clb; Teachers Aide; School Musical; Nwsp Rptr; Yrbk Stf; Cheerleading; Coach Actv; Gym; Hon Roll.

KORDYS, CYNTHIA; Southington HS; Southington, CT; (Y); Pres Debate Tm; French Clb; Key Clb; JV Tennis; High Hon Roll; NHS; Italian Club VP 84-85; Giftd & Talntd Discvr III Pgm 83-84; Smith Coll; Librl Arts.

KOREN, EDNA; Ledyard HS; Ledyard, CT; (Y); Hosp Aide; Band; Chorus; Concert Band; Mrchg Band; Symp Band; 1st Prz Estrn CT Yth Symph Cmptn 84; Ntl Hnr Ntl Fdrtn Music Clbs Festivls 84-853rd Prz Pian Cmptn; Julliard Schl Music; Muscn.

KOSAKONSKI, SHARON; Avon HS; Avon, CT; (Y); 6/198; Cmnty Wkr; VP FCA; Chorus; Rep Stu Cncl; Bsktbl; Capt Fld Hcky; Capt Tennis; Hon Roll; NHS; Dartmouth Bk Awd 84; Prep All Amer Girl Ath 85; TAG; Harvard U.

KOSHA, KELLY A; Ellington HS; Ellington, CT; (Y); 10/117; VP FBLA; Varsity Clb; Yrbk Bus Mgr; Im Bsktbl; Var Capt Vllybl; Hon Roll; Trs NHS; Lutz Schlrshp; Womns Forum Schlrshp; Bryant Coll; Accntng.

KOSHA, TODD; Holy Cross HS; Watertown, CT; (Y); 73/352; Concert Band; Mrchg Band; Swmmng; Hon Roll; Jr NHS.

KOSLOWSKI, BRIAN; Emmett O Brien Regnl Vo Tech Schl; Ansonia, CT; (Y); Carpntry.

KOST, CAROLYN; Trumbull HS; Trumbull, CT; (Y); Computer Clb; FTA; JA; Sec Math Clb; Chorus; Lit Mag; High Hon Roll; NCTE Awd; NHS; Spanish NHS; Excell Spnsh 85; Peer Tutor 85; Outstndg Svc Choir 83; Educ.

KOUTROUBIS, CHRISTINA; Norwalk HS; Norwalk, CT; (Y); 87/450; Trs Church Yth Grp; Latin Clb; School Musical; Stage Crew; Var Mgr(s); Var Trk; Hon Roll; Awds V Trk 82-85; Hlth.

KOWACK, ERIC; St Bernard HS; N Stonington, CT; (S); Computer Clb; Rep Jr Cls; Stat Bsktbl; Im Fld Hcky; Im Pom Pon; JV Score Keeper; Var Socr; Var Tennis; Im Wt Lftg; High Hon Roll; Frntrs Appl Sci Yale U 84; Med.

KOWALCZYK, JANET; Branford HS; Branford, CT; (Y); 40/249; Cmnty Wkr; Dance Clb; Chorus; School Musical; Variety Show; Var Trk; Hon Roll; Prfct Atten Awd; Schlrshp Branford PTA Cncl 85; Southern CT ST U; Nrsng.

KOZLOWSKI, LISA; Southington HS; Southington, CT; (Y); Am Leg Aux Girls St; Church Yth Grp; Key Clb; Pres Latin Clb; Variety Show; Nwsp Stf; High Hon Roll; NHS; Cmnty Wkr; Red Cross Aide; CT Jr Sci & Hmnty Symposium 85; CT St Latin Test-Hnrb Mntn 84; Southington Gftd & Tlntd Prgm 83-85; Med Tech.

KRAFT, SHARON; Joseph A Foran HS; Milford, CT; (Y); 6/270; Church Yth Grp; Hosp Aide; JCL; Sec Keywanettes; Latin Clb; Political Wkr; Spanish Clb; Co-Capt Color Guard; High Hon Roll; NHS; Milford Safe Rides; Peer Cnslng; Trinity Coll; Psych.

KRAJACK, TRACY; Pomperaug HS; Southbury, CT; (Y); AFS; Math Tm; Trs Jr Cls; JV Cheerleading; Var Capt Swmmng; JV Trk; Hon Roll; Mrktng.

KRALIK, STEPHEN; New Britain HS; New Britain, CT; (Y); Boy Scts; High Hon Roll; Hon Roll; Central CT ST U; Comp.

KRALL, CAREN; Amity Regional HS; Woodbridge, CT; (Y); Cmnty Wkr; Spanish Clb; Varsity Clb; Yrbk Stf; Cheerleading; Tennis; Cit Awd; Hon Roll; Acad Hnr Awds 82-85; Peer Tutoring/Cnclng 84-85.

KRALL, MAGGIE; William H Hall HS; W Hartford, CT; (Y); 19/342; Service Clb; Var Capt Bsktbl; Var Sftbl; High Hon Roll; NHS; Ntl Merit SF; Centrl Connecticut Conf All Conf Tm Sftbl 85; Psych.

KRAMER, MARC; Andrew Warde HS; Fairfield, CT; (Y); Am Leg Boys St; Key Clb; VP Stu Cncl; JV Var Ftbl; Var L Trk; Var Wt Lftg; DAR Awd; High Hon Roll; Hon Roll; Lt Gov Boys ST 85.

KRASSOWSKI, ALAN; Rockville HS; Vernon, CT; (Y); 26/400; Boy Scts; Chess Clb; Computer Clb; Jazz Band; Variety Show; Lit Mag; Wt Lftg; Capt Wrstlng; High Hon Roll; NHS; Pro Drmmr.

KRAUS, GREGORY J; Wilbur Cross HS; New Haven, CT; (S); PAVAS; Political Wkr; Spanish Clb; Lit Mag; Rep Jr Cls; Rep Stu Cncl; Crs Cntry; Swmmng; Trk; Hon Roll; Exchng Stu-Exprmnt In Intl Lvng 83; Acadmc Hgh Achvt-Law Smnr 84; Acadmc High Achvt-Psych 85.

KRAUSE, DAWN; St Bernard HS; Ledyard, CT; (S); Dance Clb; Red Cross Aide; Ski Clb; Varsity Clb; Stat Ftbl; Timer; Trk; Hon Roll.

KRAUSE, JESSICA L; R E Fitch HS; Mystic, CT; (Y); 7/369; Church Yth Grp; Varsity Clb; Swing Chorus; Lit Mag; Trs Soph Cls; Var L Gym; L Mgr(s); High Hon Roll; Hon Roll; NHS; Phy Thrpy.

KRAYESKI, SUSAN; Holy Cross HS; Naugatuck, CT; (Y); Church Yth Grp; Civic Clb; Dance Clb; JV L Crs Cntry; Hon Roll; Bus Admin.

KREITNER, HILARY; Shelton HS; Shelton, CT; (Y); Church Yth Grp; JA; Ski Clb; Band; Concert Band; Drm & Bgl; Mrchg Band; High Hon Roll; Hon Roll; U Of CT; Arch.

KREONIDES, NICK C; Litchfield HS; Litchfield, CT; (Y); Trs Sec AFS; Sec Am Leg Boys St; Trs Sec 4-H; Rep Frsh Cls; Rep Soph Cls; Rep Jr Cls; Rep Sr Cls; Rep Stu Cncl; Cit Awd; 4-H Awd; Clncl Psych.

KRISHNAN, MAHESH; Trumbull HS; Trumbull, CT; (Y); Off Exploring; Trs JA; VP Math Clb; Capt Math Tm; Im Bsktbl; Var Trk; Im Vllybl; High Hon Roll; Hon Roll; NHS; U Of FL; Med.

KRIZ, JOHN E; Trumbull HS; Trumbull, CT; (Y); Aud/Vis; Boy Scts; Church Yth Grp; German Clb; Concert Band; Stage Crew; High Hon Roll; Hon Roll; Sci Dept Svc Awd 84; Elec Engr.

KROCHTA, STEPHEN; Stratford HS; Stratford, CT; (Y); 10/241; Pres Church Yth Grp; Math Clb; Rep Jr Cls; Rep Stu Cncl; JV Crs Cntry; JV Trk; Hon Roll; Trs NHS; Coast Guard Acad; Aerontcl Engr.

KROESE, MICHAEL; Southington HS; Southington, CT; (Y); 1/560; Latin Clb; Math Tm; Quiz Bowl; Ski Clb; JV Socr; High Hon Roll; Pres NHS; Geomtry Prz 83; Gftd & Tlntd Prog 83-86; Engrng.

KROIS, KEVIN; Greenwich HS; Greenwich, CT; (Y); Am Leg Boys St; Aud/Vis; Boy Scts; Church Yth Grp; Exploring; JA; Key Clb; Quiz Bowl; Var Ftbl; Var L Trk; Aero Engr.

KRONEN, BRADLEY; St Josephs HS; Huntington, CT; (Y); 28/250; Drama Clb; Scholastic Bowl; Spanish Clb; Chorus; School Musical; JV Crs Cntry; JV Trk; High Hon Roll; Hon Roll; Spanish NHS; Coll Of The Holy Cross.

KRUPNIKOFF, HENRY; Avon Old Farms Schl; W Hartford, CT; (S); Yrbk Stf; L Bsbl; Stat Bsktbl; L Ice Hcky; L Socr; Im Tennis; Hon Roll; Accntng.

KRUSINSKI, DONNA M; Frank Scott Bunnell HS; Stratford, CT; (Y); 72/250; Drama Clb; GAA; Ski Clb; Chorus; Color Guard; Drm Mjr(t); Mrchg Band; Pres Frsh Cls; Pres Soph Cls; Pres Jr Cls; Marist Coll; Cmnctns.

KRVIATKOWSKI, TOM; Norwalk HS; Norwalk, CT; (Y); Computer Clb; German Clb; ROTC; JV Socr; Amer Lgn Mlrty Excllnc Awd 85; :Writer.

KUBECK, MICHAEL; O H Platt HS; S Meriden, CT; (Y); Math Clb; Stu Cncl; High Hon Roll; Hon Roll; Engnr.

KUBIS, JOHN; Stafford HS; Stafford Springs, CT; (Y); 12/124; Am Leg Boys St; Madrigals; Yrbk Stf; Pres Soph Cls; Pres Jr Cls; Pres Sr Cls; Rep Stu Cncl; Var Capt Socr; High Hon Roll; Hon Roll.

KUEN, ANDREA; Lauralton Hall HS; New Haven, CT; (Y); Drama Clb; Service Clb; Spanish Clb; School Play; Variety Show; Lit Mag; JV Crs Cntry; Hon Roll.

KUHN, SUSAN; Rockville HS; Vernon, CT; (Y); 10/362; Church Yth Grp; VP Exploring; Math Tm; Office Aide; JV Var Sftbl; High Hon Roll; NHS; Ntl Merit Ltr; Aerosp Engrng.

KULAS, DONALD; Granby Memorial HS; Granby, CT; (Y); Aud/Vis; Drama Clb; Exploring; Library Aide; Quiz Bowl; Nwsp Stf; Trs Jr Cls; High Hon Roll; NHS; Havard Bk Awd 85; The Rensselaer Mdl 85; Awd For Exemplry Achv In Sci 85; Biochem.

KUMIEGA, JOELL; Joseph A Foran HS; Milford, CT; (S); Art Clb; DECA; Stage Crew; Cit Awd; Hon Roll; Bus.

KUNG, TERESE; Stamford Catholic HS; Stamford, CT; (Y); 5/160; Girl Scts; JA; Office Aide; Variety Show; Ed Nwsp Stf; High Hon Roll; NHS; Chopn Awd 1st Pl Jr Div; 1st Pl Sr Div 84 & 85; Baldwin ST Cmptn 2nd Pl Jr Kybrd Awd 82.

KUPSON, JONATHAN; Amity Regional SR HS; Orange, CT; (Y); Am Leg Boys St; Hst Latin Clb; Chorus; Lit Mag; Var Crs Cntry; Var Trk; Hon Roll; NHS; Ntl Merit Ltr; Church Yth Grp; Ntl Latn I Exm Awd 85; Peer Tutrng Prog 85; Bio.

KURTZ, STEPHEN; Norwalk HS; Norwalk, CT; (Y); Cmnty Wkr; Computer Clb; Political Wkr; Pres Temple Yth Grp; Yrbk Stf; Rep Stu Cncl; JV Var Tennis; High Hon Roll; NHS; Ntl Merit Ltr; Bruce Newman Humntrn Yth Awd 85; Norwalk Sci Fair Hnrbl Mntn 85; Louis Olanoff Meml Schlrshp Awd 85; Tufts U; Engrng.

KUSNITZ, ABBY; Masuk HS; Monroe, CT; (Y); 29/255; Church Yth Grp; Pres Spanish Clb; Stat Bsbl; JV Fld Hcky; Var L Vllybl; High Hon Roll; NHS; Gregg Typng Awds 84-85; Outstndng Achvt-Eng Awd 83-84; Outstndng Achvt-Spansh Awd 83-84.

KUZIAK, PAUL; Southington HS; Plantsville, CT; (Y); Concert Band; Mrchg Band; Yrbk Phtg; JV Crs Cntry; Im Sftbl; JV Trk; Elec Engrng.

KYROPOULOS, ADRIANE; Westhill HS; Stamford, CT; (Y); 25/463; Church Yth Grp; Drama Clb; French Clb; Hosp Aide; Nwsp Ed-Chief; Nwsp Rptr; Hst Frsh Cls; Rep Soph Cls; JV Fld Hcky; High Hon Roll; 1st Hnrs Frnch III, IV Iona Lang Cont 82-83; Oberlin Bk Awd 84; Frnch Awd 83 & 85; Jrnlst Of Yr 85; Duke U; Econ.

KYROPOULOS, LAURA; Westhill HS; Stamford, CT; (Y); Drama Clb; French Clb; School Play; Stage Crew; Nwsp Rptr; Rep Jr Cls; Var Capt Fld Hcky; Hon Roll; NHS; Iona Coll Lang Cntst 1st Hnrs Frnch III & 2nd Hrns Frnch IV 83-84; Wellesley Bk Awd 85.

L HEUREUX, KIMBERLY; Southington HS; Southington, CT; (Y); Pres Church Yth Grp; FTA; Key Clb; Latin Clb; Trs Chorus; Variety Show; Hon Roll; Prfct Atten Awd; 2nd Kelloggs Art Awd 82; Elem Ed.

LA BARRE, BRENDA JEAN; Griswold HS; Jewett City, CT; (Y); 10/86; Cmnty Wkr; Hosp Aide; School Play; Var L Tennis; Hon Roll; VFW Awd; Voice Dem Awd.

LA BELLE, JOANNE; Putnam HS; Putnam, CT; (Y); 6/140; Hosp Aide; Concert Band; Jazz Band; Mrchg Band; School Play; Ed Yrbk Ed-Chief; Trs Sr Cls; Rep Stu Cncl; Score Keeper; Sec NHS; MI Band Awd 84.

LA CAVA, LAURA; Amity SR HS; Bethany, CT; (Y); 26/376; French Clb; Latin Clb; Political Wkr; Var Socr; Var Sftbl; French Hon Soc; Hon Roll; JCL; Varsity Clb; Latin Clb Schlrshp; Magna Cum Laude Natl Latin Exam; French AAIF Exam Hnrbl Mntn; Wesleyan U; Film.

LA CLAIR, KIRSTEN; Brien Mc Mahon HS; Rowayton, CT; (Y); Church Yth Grp; Cmnty Wkr; Key Clb; Teachers Aide; Church Choir; Rep Jr Cls; Coach Actv; Powder Puff Ftbl; Socr; Swmmng.

LA FEMINA, PATRICIA; Holy Cross HS; Cheshire, CT; (Y); 148/356; Church Yth Grp; Service Clb; Ski Clb; Rep Soph Cls; Var Swmmng; JV Trk; Hon Roll; Dental Hygnst.

LA FOREST, BRAD; Putnam HS; Putnam, CT; (Y); 35/140; Ski Clb; Band; Concert Band; Mrchg Band; Bsbl; Bsktbl; Tennis; Jr NHS; Physcs.

LA FRANCE, CASSANDRA JOYCE; Terryville HS; Terryville, CT; (Y); 20/135; Pep Clb; Yrbk Stf; Var Cheerleading; Var Fld Hcky; Hon Roll; Art Clb; French Clb; Library Aide; Spanish Clb; Bsktbl; Trip To Europe 84 & 85; Terryvl Schlrshp 85; Central CT ST U; Acctng.

LA VECCHIA, ANTOINETTE; Darien HS; Darien, CT; (Y); Church Yth Grp; Pres Drama Clb; MMM; School Musical; School Play; Yrbk Ed-Chief; Cit Awd; NHS; Spanish NHS; Dance Clb; Best Actress 84; Vassar Bk Awd Humanities 84; Outstndng Svc To Schl 84.

LACHAPELLE, JOLIE; Southington HS; Southington, CT; (Y); 16/502; Sec FBLA; Ski Clb; Capt Color Guard; School Play; Mgr(s); Stat Tennis; Capt Twrlr; High Hon Roll; Chsn Go To WA DC Attnd Tax Smnr 85; Bentley Coll; Bus Admin.

LACOBELLE, JAMES V; Notre Dame HS; W Haven, CT; (Y); Church Yth Grp; Cmnty Wkr; Political Wkr; Ski Clb; Trk; Hon Roll; Georgetown U; Pre-Med.

LACOMBE, JEFFREY; Windham HS; Willimantic, CT; (Y); Computer Clb; Yrbk Phtg; Yrbk Stf; Timer; Hon Roll; U MIAMI; Mech Engrng.

LACOMBE, JENNIFER; New Britain HS; New Britain, CT; (Y); JA; Hon Roll; Stone Schl; Acctng.

LADOTA, KIM; Stamford HS; Stamford, CT; (S); 82/406; Cmnty Wkr; German Clb; Girl Scts; Political Wkr; Red Cross Aide; Ski Clb; Rptr Frsh Cls; Rptr Soph Cls; Rptr Jr Cls; Rptr Sr Cls; Local UNICO Schlrshp 85; Lehigh U; Bus.

LADYKA, MELISSA; Tourtellotte Memorial HS; N Grosvenbrdale, CT; (Y); Church Yth Grp; Computer Clb; Drama Clb; Chorus; School Musical; School Play; Hon Roll; Acct.

LAFLUUR, SUZANNE; Ledyard HS; Ledyard, CT; (Y); AFS; Church Yth Grp; Drama Clb; Concert Band; Mrchg Band; School Play; Symp Band; Var Crs Cntry; Var Trk; Hon Roll; Psychlgy.

LAHMAN, SCOTT; Loomis Chaffee Schl; Tolland, CT; (Y); Library Aide; Temple Yth Grp; Ed Nwsp Ed-Chief; Im Lcrss; Ntl Merit Ltr; Natl Merit Leter.

LAHOSKI, ALEX; Windham HS; Windham Ctr, CT; (Y); Boy Scts; Chess Clb; Computer Clb; Hosp Aide; JV Stu Cncl; Hon Roll; U Miami; Comp Sci.

LAI, EUNICE WAN-YIN; Choate Rosemary Hall; Wallingford, CT; (S); Math Tm; Science Clb; Acpl Chr; Chorus; Orch; School Musical; Nwsp Ed-Chief; Var Swmmng; High Hon Roll; Mu Alp Tht; Cornell Clb Prz 84; Caroline Route Rees Prz 84; Harvard U.

LALIBERTE, JOHN; Southington HS; Southington, CT; (Y); 17/580; Chess Clb; Key Clb; Math Tm; Variety Show; Rep Stu Cncl; Var L Tennis; High Hon Roll; NHS; Boy Scts; Cmnty Wkr; NEML Awd 83-85; CAML Awd 84; Discvr III Gftd & Talntd Grp 84-85; RIT; Physcn.

LAMAR, RODNEY; Weaver HS; Hartford, CT; (Y); Am Leg Boys St; DECA; Yrbk Phtg; Crs Cntry; Var Ftbl; Var Trk; Var Wrstlng; Hon Roll; CT Bus Wk Schlrshp 85; Inner City Striders Truck Clb 85; Bus Admin.

LAMARINE, NICOLE M; Hononapolis Prep; Southbridge, MA; (Y); 7/47; Drama Clb; Ski Clb; Nwsp Ed-Chief; Sec Trs Soph Cls; Sec Jr Cls; Pres Stu Cncl; Var L Cheerleading; Var L Socr; High Hon Roll; NHS; Providence Coll.

LAMARRE, MICHAEL; Southington HS; Southington, CT; (Y); 112/560; Bsbl; Bsktbl; Hon Roll; Civil Engrng.

LAMB, SCOTT D; Naugatuck HS; Naugatuck, CT; (Y); Am Leg Boys St; Library Aide; Capt L Crs Cntry; Var Diving; Capt L Swmmng; Elks Awd; U CT; Bus Adm.

LAMB, SUSANNE K; Rockville HS; Vernon, CT; (Y); 85/337; Church Yth Grp; Drama Clb; Girl Scts; Band; Color Guard; Pres Concert Band; Drill Tm; Flag Corp; School Play; Trk; U Of RI; Chld Dvlpmnt.

LAMBERT, ELIZABETH; Waterford HS; Waterford, CT; (Y); 40/203; Sec Church Yth Grp; Pres 4-H; Hosp Aide; Y-Teens; Church Choir; Yrbk Phtg; Yrbk Stf; Swmmng; Spec Ed.

LAMBERT, HUGH; St Thomas Aquinas HS; Southington, CT; (Y); 8/130; Debate Tm; Latin Clb; Political Wkr; Ski Clb; Nwsp Stf; Yrbk Stf; Stu Cncl; Socr; Hon Roll; Prfct Atten Awd; Excel Vlvs Hum Survl, Cert Rcgntn Svc Schl 85; Fairfield U; Acctng.

LAMBERTO, KATRINA; Danbury HS; Danbury, CT; (Y); 124/650; Ski Clb; Jazz Band; Orch; Symp Band; Variety Show; Yrbk Stf; Rep Stu Cncl; Var JV Socr; JV Vllybl; Hon Roll; Perry Awd Schl Achvt Awd Engl 85; Cmmnctns.

LAMMIE, MARCIA A; Danbury HS; Danbury, CT; (Y); 249/612; Church Yth Grp; Cmnty Wkr; JA; Library Aide; Office Aide; Chorus; Variety Show; Yrbk Stf; Pres Frsh Cls; Rep Soph Cls; George W Perry Awd Engl 85; Math Awd 84; Phy Ed & Fit Awd 83; Johnson & Wales Fashn Inst Tec.

LAMOUREUX, MICHAEL; Berlin HS; Berlin, CT; (Y); Aud/Vis; Var Golf; Var Socr; Var Tnk; Sccr Redcoat Awd 84; Bus.

LAMPADARIOS, EVANGELINE; Bullard-Havens Tech; Bridgeport, CT; (Y); 4/190; English Clb; Math Clb; Yrbk Phtg; Yrbk Rptr; Yrbk Stf; High Hon Roll; Hon Roll; Rotary Awd; Eng Bond; Five Hndred Dllr Scholar; Pre Natl Hnr Soc; Norwalk ST Tech Coll; Civ Engr.

LAMSON, JUDY; Shelton HS; Shelton, CT; (Y); 72/343; Cmnty Wkr; Ski Clb; Spanish Clb; Mrchg Band; Nwsp Rptr; Stu Cncl; Trk; Capt Twrlr; Hon Roll; Trs Spanish NHS; Spansh Awd 85; Natl Hnr Roll 85; FL ST U; Fashn Merch.

LAMY, DAVID; East Catholic HS; Vernon, CT; (Y); Political Wkr; Off Ski Clb; Rep Frsh Cls; Rep Soph Cls; Rep Jr Cls; Rep Sr Cls; Rep Stu Cncl; JV Var Crs Cntry; Var Tennis; CT JR Intrn Pgm 85; Gvrnmnt.

LANDINO, DAWN; Southington HS; Southington, CT; (Y); Church Yth Grp; Cmnty Wkr; DECA; FCA; JA; Pep Clb; Ski Clb; Band; Variety Show; Bsktbl; 1st Pl Mrktng Dist 85; All ST All Conf Soccer 84-85; ST Select Tm Reg I Camp Soccer 85; Psych.

LANDINO, PHILIP G; Southington HS; Southington, CT; (Y); 150/550; Am Leg Boys St; Church Yth Grp; Ski Clb; School Musical; School Play; Stage Crew; Variety Show; Stu Cncl; Bsbl; Bsktbl; Brian Blanchard Schlrshp 85; Bette Lundino Schlr 85; S Vlly Mdgt Ftbl Leag Schlrshp 85; U Of CT; Pre-Law.

LANDINO, SANDRA; Sacred Heart Acad; New Haven, CT; (Y); Dance Clb; Pep Clb; Variety Show; High Hon Roll; Spanish NHS; Law.

LANDON, WILLIAM; East Hampton HS; East Hampton, CT; (Y); 3/87; Am Leg Boys St; Boy Scts; Trs Model UN; Band; Yrbk Stf; Var L Crs Cntry; Var L Trk; High Hon Roll; Trs NHS; JV Socr; Harvard Clb Southern CT Awd 85; Biol Sci.

LANDQUIST, THOMAS BRENT; Watertown HS; Oakville, CT; (Y); 45/250; Boy Scts; Church Yth Grp; Cmnty Wkr; FBLA; Teachers Aide; Variety Show; Trs Frsh Cls; Stu Cncl; God Cntry Awd; High Hon Roll; Ldrshp Dvlpmnt Awd 81; ST Treas FBLA 83-85; Best Bus Stu 85; Munson Fund Schlrshp 85; Mattatuck CC; Bus Mgmt.

LANDRY, DEBRA; Francis T Maloney HS; Meriden, CT; (Y); Hosp Aide; VP JA; VICA; JV Bsktbl; Hon Roll; Physcl Thprst.

LANG, MARCIA; St Bernard HS; Lebanon, CT; (S); Cmnty Wkr; Girl Scts; Hosp Aide; Radio Clb; Concert Band; Hst Mrchg Band; Ed Yrbk Phtg; Stu Cncl; Stat Sftbl; Camera Clb; Musical Achvt Awd 83-84; Grl Scts 1st Clss Awd 82; All-Estrn Regnl Band Fest 83-84; Pre-Med.

LANGE, SCOTT; Danbury HS; Danbury, CT; (Y); 300/640; ROTC; Ski Clb; Varsity Clb; Color Guard; Variety Show; Var Cheerleading; Var Capt Trk; ROTC Airman Yr 84; Pre-Law.

LANGE, SHELLEY; Cheshire Acad; Wallingford, CT; (Y); 19/56; Church Yth Grp; Key Clb; Yrbk Ed-Chief; Lit Mag; Off Stu Cncl; Hon Roll; Tele-Cmnctns.

LANGELAND, ERIK H; Conard HS; W Hartford, CT; (Y); 13/295; Spanish Clb; Var Socr; High Hon Roll; VP NHS; Sec Trs Spanish NHS; Dartmouth Clb Bk Awd 84; NE Conf Awd Spnsh 85; Boudoin Coll; Biochem.

LANGLOIS JR, DONALD F; Branford HS; Branford, CT; (Y); 25/250; Boy Scts; Yrbk Phtg; Yrbk Stf; Im Bsbl; Coach Actv; Hon Roll; Prfct Attndnc 82-85; Roanoke Coll; Poli Sci.

LANGOU, VIVIANA; Amity Regional HS; Woodbridge, CT; (Y); Church Yth Grp; Cmnty Wkr; Latin Clb; Spanish Clb; Chorus; Church Choir; Variety Show; Hon Roll; NHS; Cit Awd; Yale Frontiers Of Appld Sci 85; Cert Of Recgntn-Math Fair 83; Frgn Langs.

LANNI, DAVID; West Haven HS; W Haven, CT; (Y); Var L Bsbl; Var Capt Ftbl; Dnfth Awd; High Hon Roll; NHS; Trs Frsh Cls; JV Bsktbl; God Cntry Awd; Jr NHS; Spanish NHS; West Haven Rotry Clb Schlr Athl 85; Engrng.

LANO, SUSAN; Holy Cross HS; Waterbury, CT; (Y); 132/349; Political Wkr; VP Service Clb; Spanish Clb; Rep Stu Cncl; Crs Cntry; Hon Roll; Natl Mrt Sci Awd 84; Western CT ST U; Cmrnl Jstc.

LANOSA, CHRISTEN; Bristol Eastern HS; Bristol, CT; (Y); 8/272; Cmnty Wkr; Drama Clb; GAA; Political Wkr; Spanish Clb; Thesps; Chorus; Madrigals; School Musical; Yrbk Stf; Michaels Jr Marshal Awd-Acad Achvt 84; Quota Clb Good Ctznshp Awd 85; Stu Cncl Awd 84-85; Fairfield U; Math.

LANTERI, VINCENT; St Thomas Aquinas HS; New Britain, CT; (Y); 7/148; Latin Clb; Yrbk Stf; Bausch & Lomb Sci Awd; High Hon Roll; Hon Roll; NHS; Prfct Atten Awd; Itln JR League Schlrshp 85; Chmthn 84 CT ST Grnt 84; U Of CT; Engrng.

LANTIERI, PAUL; East Catholic HS; Manchester, CT; (Y); 57/301; Bsbl; Ski Clb; NHS; Pre-Law.

LANZA, JOHN; East Lyme HS; Niantic, CT; (Y); Church Yth Grp; CAP; Key Clb; Ski Clb; Yrbk Stf; Im Bsbl; Im Coach Actv; JV Ftbl; Var Trk; Im Wt Lftg; Outstndng Achvt For Excllnc In Bio 83-84; Lbrl Arts.

LAPREAY, JOHN; Southington HS; Plantsville, CT; (Y); Am Leg Boys St; Ski Clb; Nwsp Rptr; Nwsp Sprt Ed; Rep Stu Cncl; Var Ftbl; Var Trk; High Hon Roll; NHS; Prfct Atten Awd; Amer Legn Boys ST; Hgh Hon Roll; Ntl Hon Soc; Law.

LARESE, JACK P; Mark T Sheehan HS; Wallingford, CT; (Y); Boys Clb Am; Yrbk Phtg; Yrbk Stf; Var Capt Bsktbl; Var Golf; Hon Roll; U RI; Bus.

LARKHAM, ROBERT; Norwich Free Acad; Baltic, CT; (Y); Church Yth Grp; 4-H; Letterman Clb; Pres Soph Cls; Pres Stu Cncl; Var Capt Wrstlng; Cit Awd; 4-H Awd; Springfield Coll; B A.

LARKIN, HOLLY; Notre Dame Acad; Oakville, CT; (Y); 11/63; Dance Clb; Sec Frsh Cls; Sec Soph Cls; VP Jr Cls; Rep Stu Cncl; Socr; High Hon Roll; Hon Roll; Jr NHS; NHS; Psych.

LARKIN, PAULA; Manchester HS; Manchester, CT; (Y); Hosp Aide; Nrsng.

LARKIN, RICHARD H; Morgan Schl; Clinton, CT; (Y); 60/200; Var Bsbl; Var Wrstlng; Lbrl Arts.

LARSON, HOLLY; Southington HS; Southington, CT; (Y); 101/580; Church Yth Grp; Cmnty Wkr; Hosp Aide; Key Clb; Latin Clb; Sec Chorus; Mgr Bsktbl; Mgr(s); Sftbl; Hon Roll; Hnrbl Ment Latin Ex 84; Elem Ed.

LASBURY, MARY BETH; Holy Cross HS; Waterbury, CT; (Y); 30/400; Yrbk Stf; Var Capt Bsktbl; Var Capt Crs Cntry; Var Sftbl; Hon Roll; NHS; CT Grls JR Olympcs Bsktbl Tm 85; Bsktbl & Sftbl All Naugatuck Vlly Leag 85-86; Athltcs.

LASHER, JENNIFER; Tolland HS; Tolland, CT; (Y); 13/180; Church Yth Grp; Ski Clb; Band; Color Guard; Mrchg Band; School Play; Yrbk Stf; Sec Jr Cls; Var L Crs Cntry; Swmmng; Frnch.

LASKOS, PETER; Derby HS; Derby, CT; (Y); 16/130; Varsity Clb; Var Capt Crs Cntry; Var L Trk; Comp Drftng.

LASKOS, STEVEN; Trumbull HS; Trumbull, CT; (Y); Office Aide; Trk; Hon Roll; Comp Engrng.

LATHAM, TERRY LYN; Vinal Technical Schl; Middletown, CT; (Y); Camera Clb; Scholastic Bowl; Pres Sr Cls; Sec Stu Cncl; High Hon Roll; Hon Roll; Top Sls Awd Cls Fndrsr 84-85; Wesleyan Humanities Pgm 84-85; Western CT ST U; Elec Engr.

LATHROP, PAMELA; Saint Bernard HS; Bozrah, CT; (Y); 96/253; Sec Church Yth Grp; Civic Clb; Pres Trs 4-H; Lib Band; Lib Concert Band; Drm Mjr(t); Off Jr Cls; Cit Awd; 4-H Awd; Teachers Aide; Instrumentalist Magazine Merit Awd 84; Pol Sci.

LAUF, TIMOTHY; Immaculate HS; Danbury, CT; (Y); 11/202; School Musical; Pres Jr Cls; Pres Sr Cls; Co-Capt Bsbl; JV Bsktbl; DAR Awd; High Hon Roll; Lion Awd; NHS; Spanish NHS; Exchange Club Yth Of Mnth; Exchange Club Little Leag Schlrshp; Outstndng SR Awd; Bucknell U; Librl Arts.

LAURANT, PHILLIP; Kolbe Cathedral HS; Bridgeport, CT; (Y); Computer Clb; Teachers Aide; Socr; Hon Roll; Prfct Atten Awd; Mech Engr.

LAUSTEN, KAREN; Central Catholic HS; Norwalk, CT; (Y); French Clb; Yrbk Stf; Stu Cncl; Cheerleading; French Hon Soc; High Hon Roll; Hon Roll; NHS; Jr Prom Chrprsn 85.

LAVALLEE, EDWARD J; Wilby HS; Waterbury, CT; (Y); Boy Scts; CAP; High Hon Roll; Hon Roll; Soc Stud Awd 85; Mltry.

LAVANGA, DANIEL A; New Fairfield HS; New Fairfield, CT; (Y); 3/220; Model UN; School Musical; Nwsp Ed-Chief; Off Frsh Cls; Off Soph Cls; Pres French Hon Soc; NHS; JA; Math Tm; Variety Show; Soc Women Eng Awd 84; Talented Writers Prog 81; Ntl Hist Cont 82; Engrng.

LAVIGNE, DOREEN; Academy Of The Holy Family; Taftville, CT; (Y); 4/29; Church Yth Grp; GAA; Chorus; Var Capt Bsktbl; Var Crs Cntry; Var Sftbl; Hon Roll; Prfct Atten Awd; MVP Bsktbl Plyr 83-85; QVC Bsktbl All Star 85.

LAVOIE, LISA; Canton HS; Canton, CT; (Y); Girl Scts; JA; Model UN; Band; School Musical; Nwsp Ed-Chief; Ed Yrbk Phtg; Stu Cncl; JV Bsktbl; JV Capt Fld Hcky; Nomnee For The Hartford Courant Carrier Of The Mnth 85; Hnrbl Mntn Schl Nwspr Spon By Hart Courant 85; Bus.

LAWLER, AMANDA; Suffield HS; Enfield, CT; (Y); 24/154; FFA; Cit Awd; High Hon Roll; Hon Roll; Lion Awd; NHS; De Kalb Ag Awd 85; Star Ag Persn 85; Outstndng Stu Eng Wrtng 84; U Conn; Vet-Med.

LAWLOR IV, JAMES R; Holy Cross HS; Waterbury, CT; (Y); 102/352; Church Yth Grp; Political Wkr; Var JV Crs Cntry; JV Golf; Hon Roll; NHS; Accntnt.

LAWRENCE, TONYA; Pomfret School; Pomfret Center, CT; (Y); Chrmn 4-H; Ed Key Clb; Rep Frsh Cls; Rep Soph Cls; Var L Bsktbl; Var L Lcrss; Var L Socr; High Hon Roll; Hon Roll; Jr NHS; Excllnce Hstry 1st Acad Awd 83; 2nd Acad Awd 84; Pomfret Comm Schl Scholar 83-86; Genetcs.

LAWTON, NOEL; Holy Cross HS; Middlebury, CT; (Y); Band; Concert Band; Jazz Band; Mrchg Band; School Musical; School Play; Stage Crew.

LAYTON, CHRISTINE; Newington HS; Newington, CT; (Y); Church Yth Grp; DECA; English Clb; GAA; Math Clb; Teachers Aide; Varsity Clb; JV Var Bsktbl; Mgr Tennis; JV Var Vllybl; Homcmng Attndnt 82 & 83; Hollyhp Attndnt 85; Travl Svcs.

LAZEV, AMY; East Lyme HS; E Lyme, CT; (Y); Temple Yth Grp; Color Guard; Frsh Cls; AFS; Hosp Aide; Mrchg Band; JV Fld Hcky; Hon Roll.

LAZU, CAROLYN; Hartford HS; Hartford, CT; (Y); Bsbl; Bsktbl; Socr; Swmmng; Tennis; Trk; Vllybl; Wt Lftg; Hon Roll; Accntng.

LE, TRANG; Central HS; Bridgeport, CT; (Y); Church Yth Grp; Library Aide; Office Aide; Band; Concert Band; Mrchg Band; Hon Roll; NHS; 2nd Pl Awd Visual Ed; Cons Inc Madison Wi 81; Jr All Am Hall Fame Band Hnrs 84; U BPT; Bus.

LE BLANC, CATHERINE; Putnam HS; Putnam, CT; (Y); Am Leg Aux Girls St; Band; Chorus; Church Choir; Color Guard; Concert Band; Jazz Band; Mrchg Band; School Play; Yrbk Stf; Pro-Chrl Dir.

LE CLERC, GINA; Stamford HS; Stamford, CT; (S); Dance Clb; VP French Clb; Hosp Aide; Church Yth Grp; Jr Cls; Stu Cncl; Hon Roll; 1st Hnrs Cert Iona Coll Lang Cont 85; Merit Awd Stuart Hall Schlstc Awds Comp; Boston Coll; Pre-Med.

LE CLERC, MARJORIE S; Stamford HS; Stamford, CT; (Y); Church Yth Grp; Cmnty Wkr; Drama Clb; Exploring; Chorus; Variety Show; Var Vllybl; Stmfrd Wmns Clb 85; Delta Sgma Theta Srty 85; U Of CT; Drama.

LE CUYER, PENNY A; Frank Scott Bunnell HS; Stratford, CT; (Y); 22/252; Drama Clb; Ski Clb; School Play; Yrbk Stf; Stu Cncl; Vllybl; High Hon Roll; Advrtsng Art Awd Scholar 85; Hood Intermdte Schl Tchrs Ass Scholar Awd 85; CT Ind Arts Awd 85; Schl Museum Fine Arts; Grphc Ds.

LE FORT, BRIAN T; Southington HS; Southington, CT; (Y); 187/550; L Socr; Hon Roll; Indstrl Arts Awd 83; U S Army; Acctg.

LE FORT, JAMES D; Southington HS; Southington, CT; (Y); 24/550; Church Yth Grp; Ski Clb; Stu Cncl; JV Bsbl; Im Bsktbl; Mgr(s); Im Vllybl; High Hon Roll; Hon Roll; Top 25 Stu 84-85; Air Force; Med Trng.

LE PAGE, JOSEPH F; Watertown HS; Oakville, CT; (Y); 1/247; Boy Scts; Yrbk Ed-Chief; Pres Stu Cncl; Bausch & Lomb Sci Awd; DAR Awd; High Hon Roll; NHS; Val; Chorus; Pres Frsh Cls; Most Outstndng Sr 85; Rennselaer Medal 84; US Naval Acdmy; Elec Engr.

LEACH, JORDAN; Danbury HS; Danbury, CT; (Y); 82/612; Aud/Vis; Church Yth Grp; Computer Clb; Radio Clb; Orch; Rep Frsh Cls; Rep Soph Cls; Rep Jr Cls; JV Crs Cntry; Hon Roll; Bus.

LEACH, SUE; Southington HS; Southington, CT; (Y); 109/600; Drama Clb; Chorus; Concert Band; Mrchg Band; Variety Show; Yrbk Stf; L Cheerleading; Var Capt Fld Hcky; Var L Trk; Hon Roll; Psych.

LEAHAN, JOHN J M; Suffield HS; Suffield, CT; (Y); Church Yth Grp; JA; Ski Clb; Church Choir; Crs Cntry; Socr; Trk; Drama Clb; Hon Roll; Schlrshp Wesleyan U CCY 84; Poetry Cont Europe 82; Arts Council Schlrshp 85; The New Schl NYC; Music.

LEANDER, KRISTEN C; Conard HS; W Hartford, CT; (Y); 31/290; Church Yth Grp; Chorus; Yrbk Stf; Rep Jr Cls; Var L Fld Hcky; Var L Gym; Mgr(s); High Hon Roll; NHS; Spanish NHS; La Fayette Coll.

LECLAIR, CHRISTINE; St Bernard HS; N Stonington, CT; (S); Hon Roll.

LECLAIR, DAVID; Lyman Hall HS; Wallingford, CT; (Y); 12/200; JA; Socr; Tennis; Hon Roll; Mth Acctg Awd 85; Engrng.

LECLAIR, DENISE; St Bernard HS; Colchester, CT; (Y); 89/297; Cmnty Wkr; Hosp Aide; Teachers Aide; Band; Concert Band; Mrchg Band; Hon Roll; Emergency Med Svc Pgm 85; Psych.

LEDYARD, TOM; Guilford HS; Guilford, CT; (Y); Boy Scts; Camera Clb; Chess Clb; Church Yth Grp; JV Bsbl; God Cntry Awd; Hon Roll; Ordr Arrw Chptr Chf 84-85; Ordr St Vincents Membr 84-85; Co Pres Audubon Clb H S 84-85.

LEE, JEROME PETER; Haddam Killingworth HS; Killingworth, CT; (Y); 53/239; Church Yth Grp; French Clb; Science Clb; Band; Concert Band; Jazz Band; Mrchg Band; Pep Band; Var L Ftbl; High Hon Roll; Awd Excllnc Stdy Amer Revltn 85; Citadel; Bus Adm.

LEE, JOSEPH; Windham HS; Willimantic, CT; (Y); 1/333; Am Leg Boys St; Camera Clb; Hosp Aide; Varsity Clb; Pres Soph Cls; Golf; High Hon Roll; Hon Roll; Mu Alp Tht; NHS; CT Hugh O Brien Ldrshp Conf 84; Natl H S Math Exam 5 Times 80-84; Harvard-Radcliffe Bk Clb 85; U Of PA; Arch.

LEE, KENNETH E; Hopkins Grammar Schl; Woodbridge, CT; (Y); Math Tm; Model UN; Scholastic Bowl; School Musical; Nwsp Ed-Chief; Rep Frsh Cls; Rep Soph Cls; Pres Jr Cls; Rep Sr Cls; VP Stu Cncl; Yale Bk Awd 84; Donald Ferguson Awd Svc Above Self 85; Yth Of Yr New Haven Regstr 85; Harvard U; Med.

LEE, LISA; Southington HS; Southington, CT; (Y); Church Yth Grp; Hosp Aide; JA; Trs Key Clb; Pres Pep Clb; Stat Bsktbl; Jr NHS; NHS; Finc.

LEE, LORI; Danbury HS; Danbury, CT; (Y); Bus.

LEE, PATRICIA; Norwalk HS; Norwalk, CT; (Y); Rep Frsh Cls; High Hon Roll; Hon Roll; Katharine Gibbs Ldrshp Awd 85; Bk Awd Briarwood Coll Bus 85; Katharine Gibbs; Secy.

LEE, STANLEY S; Amity Regional HS; Orange, CT; (Y); 9/376; Trs VP French Clb; Capt Math Tm; Nwsp Stf; Var L Socr; VP NHS; Ntl Merit SF; Yale Frtrs Of Appld Sci 83; Dntstry.

LEE, SUYIN; Amity Regional SR HS; Orange, CT; (S); Drama Clb; Latin Clb; Model UN; Chorus; Color Guard; Madrigals; Nwsp Rptr; Lit Mag; Rep Stu Cncl; Hon Roll; Iole V Ackley Awd 83; Stanley HS Ctznshp Awd 83; Law.

LEEMAN, KYLE; Putnam HS; Pomfret Center, CT; (Y); 5/145; Am Leg Boys St; Church Yth Grp; School Play; Yrbk Sprt Ed; JV Var Bsktbl; Var Socr; Hon Roll; Jr NHS; NHS; Prfct Atten Awd; All St Bsktbl Plyr 85; Quinebaug Vly Conf N Bsktbl Plyr Yr 85; Engrng.

LEFEBVRE, TIMOTHY; Oliver Wolcott Vo-Tech; Winsted, CT; (S); 6/176; Rep VICA; Rep Stu Cncl; Hon Roll; 2nd Music Clb Comp 85; ST Stdnt Advsry Cncl Educ 84-86; CT Cncl Voc Stdnt Org 84-86; Prof Sngr.

LEFORT, RENEE L; Southington HS; Southington, CT; (Y); Ski Clb; Chorus; Yrbk Stf; Cheerleading; Sftbl.

LEGATO, MIKE; St Bernard HS; Salem, CT; (Y); 5/297; Boy Scts; Rep Stu Cncl; Wrstlng; High Hon Roll; Hon Roll; NHS; Ntl Merit Schol; Natl Eng Merit Awd; Am HS Ath Wrstlng; Acad All Am; Engrng.

LEHMANN, STEVEN; Oliver Wolcott Tech Schl; Winsted, CT; (Y); 6/142; Cmnty Wkr; Computer Clb; Drama Clb; Ski Clb; VICA; Trs Jr Cls; Golf; Socr; Hon Roll; Hnr-Washington DC Summer Intern Pgm 84; PFC; Electronics.

LEMANSKI, STEVE A; Windsor Locks HS; Suffield, CT; (Y); 1/181; Am Leg Boys St; VP JA; Capt Math Tm; Jazz Band; Orch; Ed Nwsp Stf; Var L Tennis; Bausch & Lomb Sci Awd; Ntl Merit SF; Val; Amer Legn Schl Awd 84-85; Harvard Bk Awd 84; Natl Merit Fnlst 85; Drew U; Ec.

LEMEK, CYNTHIA R; Tolland HS; Tolland, CT; (Y); 3/167; Church Yth Grp; Trs Girl Scts; School Musical; Yrbk Ed-Chief; Yrbk Stf; Lit Mag; Rep Frsh Cls; High Hon Roll; NHS; E H Cooper Mem, Tolland HS Schlrshps, Prsdntl Acad Ftnss Awd 85; Marist Coll; Comm.

LENGYEL, LISA; Saint Marys HS; E Haven, CT; (Y); Ski Clb; Nwsp Stf; Yrbk Stf; Mu Alp Tht; North Eastern U.

LENIHAN, LINDA; New Canaan HS; New Canaan, CT; (Y); Church Yth Grp; Cmnty Wkr; French Clb; GAA; JA; Pep Clb; Varsity Clb; Y-Teens; Var Capt Cheerleading; Score Keeper; ST Finlst 4 Tn Pgnts 84; Rgnl Fnlst Tn Pgnt 84; U Of CT; Engl.

LENSIS, PATRICIA; St Bernard HS; Stonington, CT; (Y); 30/300; Cmnty Wkr; Drama Clb; Intnl Clb; Library Aide; Red Cross Aide; Teachers Aide; School Play; Stage Crew; High Hon Roll; Hon Roll; Bus Mgmt.

LENT, NANCY; Brien Mc Mahon HS; Norwalk, CT; (Y); 13/340; Church Yth Grp; Hosp Aide; Key Clb; Red Cross Aide; Ski Clb; Concert Band; Mrchg Band; Symp Band; Yrbk Stf; Powder Puff Ftbl; Vassar Bk Awd Excllnc Humnits 85; P.

LEO, PATRICIA M; Plainfield HS; Moosup, CT; (Y); 9/140; Am Leg Aux Girls St; GAA; Varsity Clb; Pres Soph Cls; Pres Jr Cls; Var Cheerleading; CC Awd; Cit Awd; DAR Awd; High Hon Roll; QVCC; Acctg.

LEONARDI, LINDA; Hamden HS; Hamden, CT; (Y); Ski Clb.

LESCHINSKI, SUSAN; Plainville HS; Plainville, CT; (Y); 2/188; Pep Clb; Varsity Clb; Band; Concert Band; Jazz Band; Mrchg Band; Pep Band; Var Capt Crs Cntry; Var Capt Trk; High Hon Roll; Yale Book Awd 85; Springfield Coll; Phys Ther.

LESPERANCE, LORI; East Catholic HS; Manchester, CT; (Y); Cmnty Wkr; French Clb.

LESSNER, JILLIAN; Farmington SR HS; Farmington, CT; (Y); 23/210; Church Yth Grp; Cmnty Wkr; Ski Clb; Band; Concert Band; Mrchg Band; JV Var Fld Hcky; Var Mgr(s); High Hon Roll; Hon Roll; MVP Awd Fld Hcky 82; MIP Awd JV Fld Hcky 83; Bus.

LEUNG, JANET; Westhill HS; Stamford, CT; (Y); French Clb; Sec Math Clb; Sec Science Clb; Stu Cncl; Crs Cntry; Hon Roll; NHS; Pre-Law.

LEUTERITZ, ERIC; Simsbury HS; Simsbury, CT; (Y); 46/352; Am Leg Boys St; Pres VP Church Yth Grp; Var L Lcrss; JV Socr; Hon Roll; NHS; Book Awd 85.

LEVENBAUM, SHARI; Simsbury HS; Simsbury, CT; (Y); 100/352; Teachers Aide; Temple Yth Grp; Yrbk Stf; Rep Jr Cls; Rep Sr Cls; Var Mgr(s); Powder Puff Ftbl; JV Sftbl; Hon Roll; Psych.

LEVESQUE, DON; Bristol Eastern HS; Bristol, CT; (Y); 19/271; French Clb; Ski Clb; Socr; High Hon Roll; NHS; Pres Schlr; Pace Acadmc Schlrshp 85; Pace U; Comp Sci.

LEVI, ROSS D; Jonathan Law HS; Milford, CT; (Y); 17/235; Am Leg Boys St; Pres Exploring; Sec VP Key Clb; Yrbk Ed-Chief; Elks Awd; Trs NHS; St Schlr; Church Yth Grp; Computer Clb; Trs Drama Clb; Hugh O Brian Yth Fndtn 83; Milford High Mem Scholar 85; Area Rep CT ST Stu Advsry Cncl On Ed 84-85; Boston U; Cmmnctn Arts.

LEVIN, DAVID M; William Hall HS; W Hartford, CT; (Y); 100/324; Cmnty Wkr; Yrbk Stf; Var Trk; Hon Roll; Frnch Merit Cert.

LEVIN, JAYME; Westhill HS; Stamford, CT; (Y); Drama Clb; Girl Scts; JA; Rep Jr Cls; Mgr Tennis; Hon Roll; NHS; Law.

LEWANDOWSKI, ROBERT; Southington HS; Southington, CT; (Y); Ski Clb; Stage Crew; JV Golf; Var Capt Socr; Var High Hon Roll; NHS; All Conf Soccer Tm 84; 4th Hghst Scorer In MEML Test In Schl 84-85; Chemathon 85.

LEWIS, ANN; James Hillhouse HS; New Haven, CT; (Y); 125/300; FBLA; Pep Clb; Church Choir; Yrbk Stf; Pom Pon; Prfct Atten Awd; Typng Awd 84-85; CPA.

LEWIS, DAWN; East Hartford HS; E Hartford, CT; (Y); Church Yth Grp; Drama Clb; Spanish Clb; Chorus; Church Choir; School Musical; School Play; JV Socr; Fnnc.

LEWIS, JENNIFER; Mark T Sheehan HS; Wallingford, CT; (Y); 40/236; GAA; Letterman Clb; Varsity Clb; Var Bsktbl; Var L Sftbl; Var L Vllybl; Hon Roll; Outstndng Bus Ed 85.

LEWIS, JOLIE; Maloney HS; Meriden, CT; (Y); Art Clb; Band; Concert Band; Mrchg Band; Pep Band; Yrbk Stf; Var Capt Bsktbl; Var Sftbl; Var Capt Vllybl; Hon Roll; Jacket Awd 85; All Conf Vlybl Tm 84-85; Vlybl All ST Hnrbl Mntn Tm 84-85; Art.

LEWIS, KIMBERLY; Baptist Bible Acad; Waterford, CT; (Y); Church Yth Grp; Variety Show; Yrbk Ed-Chief; Var Bsbl; Var Trk; Var Vllybl; High Hon Roll; Prfct Atten Awd; Val; Cert Merit Compltng Coll Prep 85; Treas & Pres Bible Club 83-84; Success Seminai; Bob Jones U; Offc Admin.

LEWIS, MAURA L; Hall HS; W Hartford, CT; (Y); Chorus; Jazz Band; School Musical; School Play; Stage Crew; Swing Chorus; Lit Mag; Hon Roll; Aud/Vis; Drama Clb; All ST Chrus 84; All New Engl Chrus 85; Prof Actng, Mdlng 83-85; DRAMTC Arts.

LEWIS, MICHELE; Ellington HS; Ellington, CT; (Y); 10/145; FBLA; Latin Clb; Ski Clb; Capt Drill Tm; Yrbk Stf; Twrlr; High Hon Roll; Hon Roll; Nrsng.

LEWIS, PATRICIA K; Pomperaug Regional 16 HS; Middlebury, CT; (Y); Band; Chorus; Mrchg Band; JV Bsktbl; Var Sftbl; Var Vllybl; Hon Roll; Bryant U; Hotel Mgmt.

LEWIS, RON; New London HS; New London, CT; (Y); FCA; Concert Band; Stage Crew; Bsbl; Ftbl; Ice Hcky; Wt Lftg; Rames Valley Tech Schl; Draftng.

LEYTON, KAREN A; Trumbull HS; Bridgeport, CT; (Y); Spanish Clb; Band; Lit Mag; Hon Roll; U Of CT.

LHEREUX, KIMBERLY; Southington HS; Southington, CT; (Y); Pres Church Yth Grp; FTA; Key Clb; Latin Clb; Trs Chorus; Hon Roll; Prfct Atten Awd; ST Latin I Awd 84; De Paolo Yth Actn 82-83; Elem Eductn.

LI, GEORGE; William A Hall HS; W Hartford, CT; (Y); Computer Clb; Im Socr; Hon Roll; Engrng.

LIBANO, CELESTE ANN; Coginchaug Regional HS; Durham, CT; (Y); 2/95; Math Tm; Concert Band; Jazz Band; Pep Band; Yrbk Stf; VP Frsh Cls; VP Soph Cls; High Hon Roll; NHS; Sal; U Of CT; Phrmcy.

LICARE, MARIANNE; St Mary HS; Greenwich, CT; (Y); 18/70; Drama Clb; Hosp Aide; Thesps; School Play; Mgr Bsktbl; Mgr(s); Powder Puff Ftbl; Score Keeper; Sftbl; Timer; Lyndonville VT; Eng Lit.

LIEB, JAMES R; Fairfield College Prep; Huntington, CT; (Y); Cmnty Wkr; Debate Tm; Sec Key Clb; Church Choir; Var Socr; High Hon Roll; NHS; Pre-Med.

LIEBL, SANDRA; Guilford HS; Guilford, CT; (Y); Cmnty Wkr; French Clb; GAA; Library Aide; Pep Clb; Political Wkr; Ski Clb; Varsity Clb; Chorus; Yrbk Stf; Bus Mngmnt.

LIGHT, ALLEN; Danbury HS; Danbury, CT; (Y); Boy Scts; Pres Trs JA; VP Mfg Yr 84; Cngrssnl Awd Distngshd Svc Cmmnty 84; Selectn Natl Conf JA IN ST U 85; Bus.

LIGHT, ALLISON; Guilford HS; Guilford, CT; (Y); AFS; Trs Band; Concert Band; Mrchg Band; Orch; School Musical; Stage Crew; High Hon Roll; Hon Roll; NHS; Gen Exclinc Englsh 84.

LIGOURI, TINA; Masuk HS; Monroe, CT; (S); 131/263; DECA; JA; Var Capt Fld Hcky; Var Trk; Nwsp Phtg; Nwsp Rptr; Nwsp Sprt Ed; Nwsp Stf; Rep Sftbl; Cert Of Outstndng Achvt For DECA 85; Hnr Cert In DECA ST Sec 85; Elctd ST Sec In DECA 85-86, Johnson & Whales; Culnry Arts.

LILLIS, GERALDINE; St Marys HS; Hamden, CT; (Y); Rep Church Yth Grp; Girl Scts; Service Clb; Pres Service Clb; Spanish Clb; School Musical; Trs Soph Cls; Rep Sr Cls; Rep Stu Cncl; L Var Cheerleading; Dentl Hyg.

LIM, NATHAN L; East Lyme HS; E Lyme, CT; (Y); Church Yth Grp; Concert Band; Mrchg Band; Pep Band; Ntl Merit Schol; Band Ltr 84; Rensselaer Poly Tech Inst; Engr.

LIMBACHER JR, RICHARD B; Greenwich HS; Greenwich, CT; (Y); Am Leg Boys St; Church Yth Grp; Chorus; Capt Var Bsbl; Bsktbl; Ftbl; High Hon Roll; Hon Roll; Boys Clb Am; Boy Scts; Bus.

LINBLAD, ELENA; West Haven HS; Westhaven, CT; (Y); Hosp Aide; Band; Concert Band; Jazz Band; Mrchg Band; JV Var Bsktbl; Var Sftbl; JV Vllybl; High Hon Roll; Hon Roll.

LINDEN, JULIE A; Plainfield HS; Plainfield, CT; (Y); 2/196; Chorus; Yrbk Stf; Stu Cncl; High Hon Roll; Hon Roll; Jr NHS; NHS; Ntl Merit Ltr; Comm.

LINDEN, POLLY; Low-Heywood Thomas HS; Stamford, CT; (Y); 8/36; Cmnty Wkr; Pep Clb; Yrbk Phtg; Bsktbl; Fld Hcky; Var Capt Sftbl; Swmmng; Hon Roll; Commend Ltr Comm Svcs 83-84; Schlrshp Outstndng Partcptn & Wrk 85.

LINDQUIST, LORYN; Southington HS; Southington, CT; (Y); 10/560; Hosp Aide; Key Clb; Rep Frsh Cls; Rep Soph Cls; Trs Jr Cls; Trs Sr Cls; Rep Stu Cncl; Var L Mgr(s); High Hon Roll; NHS; Joseph P Knapp Awd Ldrshp,Citznsp,Humnty; Jr Womens Clb Awd Hgst Acad Avg; Med.

LINDSAY, LISA; Berlin HS; Kensington, CT; (Y); Am Leg Aux Girls St; Chorus; School Play; Yrbk Stf; Trs Jr Cls; Co-Capt Socr; Co-Capt Trk; Hon Roll; Trs NHS; Pres Acad Fitnss Awd 85; Coachs Soccr Awd 84; 1st Pl Trphy Trck 83; U Of CT-HARTFORD; Cmmnctns.

LINDSEY, ETHEL; Hotchkiss Schl; Palm Beach, FL; (Y); Church Choir; Var Socr; Var Sftbl; Capt Swmmng; JV Tennis; Hon Roll; NHS; Ntl Merit Ltr; TX A&M; Vet.

LINDSEY, LETA; Weaver HS; Hartford, CT; (Y); 2/500; FBLA; Yrbk Stf; Rep Soph Cls; Rep Jr Cls; Sec Sr Cls; Crs Cntry; Trk; Vllybl; Cit Awd; French Hon Soc; Dr Martin Lthr King Book Awd 85; Schlr Of Mnth Awd 84; Hghst Hnr Awd 85; Howard U; Bus Mngmnt.

LINDSTROM, ALISSA; Masuk HS; Monroe, CT; (Y); 9/288; VP JA; JCL; Spanish Clb; Band; Nwsp Stf; Rep Stu Cncl; Stat Socr; JV Var Sftbl; High Hon Roll; NHS; Outstndng Frgn Lang Stu 85; Frgn Lang.

LINGENFELTER, DIANNE; Suffield HS; West Suffield, CT; (Y); 12/154; Am Leg Aux Girls St; Church Yth Grp; Yrbk Stf; Rep Soph Cls; Rep Jr Cls; Rep Sr Cls; VP Stu Cncl; Var Socr; Capt Tennis; Hon Roll; Hugh O Brian Yth Ldrshp Semnr Awd 83; 1st Chch Christ Congrgtnl & Suffield Womns Clb Schlrshp 85; U Of RI; Elem Ed.

LINGENFELTER, SUZANNE; Suffield HS; West Suffield, CT; (Y); 15/156; Am Leg Aux Girls St; Pres Church Yth Grp; VP Frsh Cls; VP Soph Cls; VP Jr Cls; VP Sr Cls; Rep Stu Cncl; Var Capt Tennis; Cit Awd; Hon Roll; Pres Acad Awds 85; 1st Church Christ Cong Scholar 85; Am Leg Aux Mem Awd 85; U RI; Elem Ed.

LINN, HERB; Stratford HS; Stratford, CT; (Y); 37/250; Trs Ski Clb; Band; Jazz Band; Trs Frsh Cls; Rep Soph Cls; Rep Jr Cls; Rep Sr Cls; Rep Stu Cncl; Var Capt Crs Cntry; Var Trk; Athl Assoc Treas 85-86; All CCIAC X-Cntry & Trk 83-84 & 84-85; St Open 84-85 45th Pl; Chef.

LINSLEY, NANCY; Branford HS; Branford, CT; (Y); DECA; Latin Clb; Rep Frsh Cls; Capt L Bsktbl; Sftbl; Capt L Vllybl; Hon Roll; Prfct Atten Awd; Amer H S Ath 85; 2nd Tm All Housy Vllybl 84; Acctng.

LIONETTI, MELISSA; St Joseph HS; Ansonia, CT; (Y); 46/227; Drama Clb; Hosp Aide; Spanish Clb; Stage Crew; Nwsp Rptr; Yrbk Stf; Lit Mag; Mgr Socr; Hon Roll; NEDT Awd; Tchr.

LIPIN, NANCY; Wilbur Cross HS; New Haven, CT; (S); 10/300; Drama Clb; Pres French Clb; Political Wkr; Ski Clb; School Play; Stage Crew; Nwsp Rptr; Nwsp Stf; Ed Lit Mag; Rep Frsh Cls; Schlrshp Ctr Creat Yth Wesleyan U 83; Ind Psych Awd 84; Tufts U; Law.

LISKOV, DONALD; Trumbull HS; Trumbull, CT; (Y); AFS; Temple Yth Grp; JV Bsbl; Hon Roll; Bus.

LISMAN, DEBORAH; Lauralton Hall HS; Milford, CT; (Y); Church Yth Grp; Hosp Aide; Science Clb; Service Clb; Spanish Clb; Nwsp Stf; Yrbk Phtg; Mgr(s); Jr NHS; Phys Ther.

LITTEL, AMY; Guilford HS; Guilford, CT; (Y); Church Yth Grp; Hosp Aide; Band; Jazz Band; Mrchg Band; Stage Crew; Yrbk Stf; Lit Mag; Hon Roll; NHS; Safe Rides Secy-Treas 85-86; Yale U Frntrs Appld Sci 85.

LITVINOFF, DAVID L; Jonathan Law HS; Milford, CT; (Y); Intnl Clb; Key Clb; Library Aide; VP Temple Yth Grp; Hon Roll; U Of Miami; Bus.

LIU, ROBERT; Trumbull HS; Trumbull, CT; (Y); Boys Clb Am; Chess Clb; Computer Clb; Exploring; Science Clb; Socr; High Hon Roll; Hon Roll; Comp Pgmmng Awd 84; Comp.

LJUNGAREN, DEBORAH; St Marys HS; N Haven, CT; (Y); Church Yth Grp; Girl Scts; Hosp Aide; Spanish Clb; Drm & Bgl; Drm Mjr(t); School Play; Rep Sr Cls; Cheerleading; Nrsg.

LLOYD, ANDREA H; William H Hall HS; W Hartford, CT; (Y); 15/301; Ski Clb; Im Lcrss; French Hon Soc; High Hon Roll; NHS; Ntl Merit SF; Pres Acdmc Ftns Awd 85; Ntl Hnr Scty Srv Awd 85; Dartmouth Coll.

LLOYD, TANYA; Kolbe Cathedral HS; Bridgeport, CT; (Y); Cmnty Wkr; VP Stu Cncl; Hon Roll; NHS; Spanish NHS; Yale Book Awd 85.

LO BIANCO, DEBRA; Rockville HS; Somers, CT; (S); FFA; Girl Scts; Hosp Aide; Library Aide; Natl Beta Clb; Bsktbl; Fld Hcky; Sftbl; Hon Roll; Prfct Atten Awd; Slvr Awd Girl Scouts 83; Cableskill; Plant Sci.

LOALBO, MICHAEL; East Hartford HS; E Hartford, CT; (Y); Off Jr Cls; Hnr Roll; Bus.

LOBASZ, KRISTEN; North Haven HS; N Haven, CT; (Y); Yrbk Stf; JV Bsktbl; Var L Trk; Hon Roll; 2nd Pl Housatonic Leag Trck Champ Hgh Jmp 85; Bus.

LOBO, JENNIFER; Canterbury Schl; New York, NY; (Y); 29/80; Var Bsktbl; Var Socr; Var Sftbl; Var Tennis; Var Vllybl; High Hon Roll; Hon Roll; Hosp Aide; Ski Clb; Chorus; MVP Vlybl Cty Trnmnt 83; Mst Enthstc Tnns Plyr Awd 83; 1st Pl Tnns Womns Dbls Trnmnt 82; Spnsh.

LOCKE, ILENE; Low-Heywood Thomas Schl; Norwalk, CT; (Y); 12/36; AFS; Aud/Vis; Hosp Aide; Model UN; Pep Clb; Pres Temple Yth Grp; Chorus; School Play; Nwsp Phtg; Yrbk Stf; Fnlst Local Congrsnl Art Comptn 85; Stu Art Exb 84; Ilver Star Deborah Bnai Brith 85; Bus.

LOCKER, MICHAEL C; Westhill HS; Stamford, CT; (Y); 1/460; Pres Computer Clb; Math Clb; Concert Band; Jazz Band; Mrchg Band; Orch; High Hon Roll; NHS; Ntl Merit Schol; Val; Soc Of Women Engrs Awd 84; Wellesley Bk Awd 84; Hnrble Mention Latin I, II New England Clss Soc 82-83; Pre Med.

LOCKROW, MICHAEL E; Middletown HS; Middletown, CT; (Y); 4/300; Capt Math Tm; Drm Mjr(t); Trs Stu Cncl; Var Capt Trk; High Hon Roll; JP Sousa Awd; Pres NHS; AFS; Am Leg Aux Girls St; French Clb; Athlt Schlr 85; Music Schlrshp 85; Wesleyan U Hnrs Prog 85; Boston U; Econmcs.

LODA, MARIA; Sacred Heart Acad; Ansonia, CT; (Y); Hosp Aide; Intnl Clb; Chorus; School Musical; Variety Show; Cheerleading; High Hon Roll; Math.

LOERCH, WENDY; New Fairfield HS; New Fairfld, CT; (Y); 55/253; VP Church Yth Grp; Cmnty Wkr; Drama Clb; Office Aide; Church Choir; School Musical; School Play; Sec Soph Cls; Sec Jr Cls; Hon Roll; Cmnctns.

LOEWY, RAYMOND M; Avon Old Farms Schl; Loudonville, NY; (Y); 11/111; Radio Clb; Band; Orch; Nwsp Stf; Im Ice Hcky; Var L Trk; High Hon Roll; Hon Roll; Awd For Acad Achvt 84; Bar Assn Prsctng Atty 85; Schlrshps Obrian Van Cliburn 83 & 82; Law.

LOFERSKI, KATHRYN A; Conventry HS; Coventry, CT; (Y); 5/106; Drama Clb; Sftbl; Vllybl; DAR Awd; High Hon Roll; Hon Roll; Sec NHS; Achv In Frnch 82-84; Achv In Uconn Co-Op Prog 84; Willimantic Cntry Clb Schlrshp85; U Of IL; Acctng.

LOGALBO, SHERYL; Saint Joseph HS; Trumbull, CT; (Y); 86/227; Drama Clb; Hosp Aide; Nwsp Sprt Ed; Nwsp Stf; Yrbk Stf; JV Cheerleading; Mgr(s); Hon Roll; Natl Merit Fndtn Natl Hnr Rl 85; Eng.

LOGLISCI, KARIN; Stamford HS; Stamford, CT; (Y); Art Clb; School Musical; Lit Mag; Sec Frsh Cls; Hon Roll; Church Yth Grp; Drama Clb; French Clb; Ski Clb; Chorus; Schlstc Art Assoc Awd 84; Stamford H Art Fair 2nd Pl 84-85; Art.

LOJKO, KEITH; Joseph A Foran HS; Milford, CT; (Y); Rep Am Leg Boys St; JCL; Latin Clb; Spanish Clb; Bsktbl; Var Capt Tennis; Cit Awd; Hon Roll; Safe Rides 83-85; SADD 85; U CT; Pre Med.

LOJZIM, AMY; St Bernard HS; Stonington, CT; (S); 54/300; Church Yth Grp; Hosp Aide; Ski Clb; Yrbk Stf; Rep Jr Cls; Rep Sr Cls; Trk; Hon Roll; U Of NH; Occputnl Therpy.

LOMAX, EDWARD; Bullard-Havens R V T S HS; Bridgeport, CT; (Y); 3/210; Hosp Aide; Rep Frsh Cls; Rep Soph Cls; Sec Trs Sr Cls; Var L Bsbl; Im Bsktbl; Var L Ftbl; Im Socr; Im Tennis; High Hon Roll; Penn ST U; Arch.

LOMBARDI, MARIA; Sacred Heart Acad; Stamford, CT; (S); JA; Chorus; School Musical; Variety Show; Yrbk Stf; Sec Jr Cls; Sec Stu Cncl; Bsktbl; Cheerleading; Vllybl; Fairchester Athltc Assn Al-Leag Vllybl; Bus Adm.

LOMBARDIA, DEVEN; Stamford HS; Stamford, CT; (S); Church Yth Grp; Hosp Aide; Latin Clb; Red Cross Aide; Rep Stu Cncl; Var Capt Crs Cntry; Capt Var Trk; High Hon Roll; Hon Roll; NHS; Crs Cntry Champ 84; All Cnty Crs Cntry 2nd Tm 84; Bonne Bell Cir Of Excel 85; Pre Med.

LOMBARDO, GARY; Nathan Hale-Ray HS; East Haddam, CT; (Y); Am Leg Boys St; Drama Clb; Stage Crew; Nwsp Rptr; Nwsp Stf; Yrbk Ed-Chief; Yrbk Phtg; VP Stu Cncl; Im Tennis; Hon Roll; 2nd Pl Rotary Essay Cont; Cert Jrnlstc Merit Middletown Press; Reprtg Contrib Schl Papr; CPA.

LONG, MARYBETH; Edwin O Smith HS; Storrs, CT; (Y); 4/188; Dance Clb; Drama Clb; VP Chorus; Madrigals; School Musical; School Play; Mu Alp Tht; Pres NHS; Ger Awd 85; Frederic Chopin Piano Awd 85; Goethe Inst Awd Exclince Ger 83; U Of CT; Engrng.

LONGO, PAUL; Holy Cross HS; Watertown, CT; (Y); 81/352; Var Capt Socr; High Hon Roll; Hon Roll; Mattatuck Scl Sci Fair 2nd Pl 83-84; Aviation.

LOPEZ, RAFAEL; Daniel Hand HS; Jamaica, NY; (Y); 13/270; Debate Tm; Drama Clb; Spanish Clb; School Play; Off Frsh Cls; Crs Cntry; Trk; High Hon Roll; Hon Roll; NHS; Clemente Bilingl Awd; 2nd Pl Bilingl Spllg Bee NY; Bus.

LOPEZ GARCIA, FERNANDO; Avon Old Farms HS; Avon, CT; (S); 17/100; Aud/Vis; Radio Clb; Ski Clb; Im Socr; Bar Assn 84; Econ.

LOPIANO, JOANN; Southington HS; Southington, CT; (Y); Cmnty Wkr; Hosp Aide; Latin Clb; Nwsp Rptr; Yrbk Stf; Sec Stu Cncl; Var L Fld Hcky; Hon Roll; NHS; Fairfield U; Lawyer.

LOPREIATO, ANTHONY; Berlin HS; Berlin, CT; (Y); 26/200; Am Leg Boys St; Hon Roll; Presdntl Acadmc Ftns Awd 85; U Of CT; Mech Engr.

LORENCE, CHRISTOPHER B; Hall HS; W Hartford, CT; (Y); 27/324; Orch; JV Golf; High Hon Roll; NHS; Ntl Merit Ltr; Stu Mnth 85; Trinity Clb Hartford Bk Prz 85; Princpl Bass All St Orch 85; Comp Sci.

LORKING, JACQUELINE; New London HS; New London, CT; (S); 28/184; DECA; French Clb; Pres FBLA; Band; Color Guard; Mrchg Band; Ed Lit Mag; 2nd Dist Typng Comptn 84; 2nd Gnrl Mrchndsng Tst 85; U Of CT-AVERY Point; Bus Admin.

LORUSSO, KAREN; Mark T Sheehan HS; Wallingford, CT; (Y); 10/210; Trs Pres Church Yth Grp; Cmnty Wkr; FBLA; Key Clb; Band; Rep Stu Cncl; High Hon Roll; Hon Roll; NHS; Pep Clb; Outstndng Accntng I & II Stu 84-85; Out Stndng Four Yr Bus Stu 85; JR & SR Prom Chrpsn 84-85; Quinnipiac Coll; Accntng.

LOUM, JEANNINE; Seymour HS; Seymour, CT; (Y); 12/197; Church Yth Grp; Chorus; Church Choir; Orch; School Musical; Hon Roll; NHS; Milligan Coll; Elem Educ.

LOVEJOY, TODD; Danbury HS; Danbury, CT; (Y); 125/525; Church Yth Grp; Key Clb; Church Choir; Hon Roll; Cedarville Coll; Engnrng.

LOVETERE, LISSA; Holy Cross HS; Woodbury, CT; (Y); 141/352; Hosp Aide; Yrbk Stf; Off Soph Cls; Off Jr Cls; Off Sr Cls; Stu Cncl; Gym; Hon Roll; Bus.

LOW, ALLISON; Farmington HS; Unionville, CT; (Y); Church Yth Grp; Drama Clb; Ski Clb; Chorus; School Play; Rep Frsh Cls; Rep Soph Cls; Rep Jr Cls; Trk; High Hon Roll; Intl Bus.

LOWE, HOPE ELAINE; Penney HS; E Hartford, CT; (Y); Church Yth Grp; Drama Clb; Church Choir; School Play; Stage Crew; Tennis; Hon Roll; NHS; TX Christian U; Nrsng.

LOWE, T DOUGLAS; Bistol Central HS; Birstol, CT; (Y); Latin Clb; Pep Clb; Teachers Aide; JV Bowling; High Hon Roll; Hon Roll; NHS; Prfct Atten Awd.

LOWNEY, MARK; Amity Regional HS; Orange, CT; (Y); Am Leg Boys St; French Clb; Chorus; Nwsp Stf; Swmmng; Hon Roll; NHS; Harry Barlett Awd 85; Capt Swim Team 85; All Hstnc 1st Team Swmmng 84-85; Top 10 CT Swmmng 84; Pre-Law.

LOZADA, STEPHANIE; Central HS; Bridgeport, CT; (S); 47/328; Church Yth Grp; Computer Clb; Church Choir; Rep Frsh Cls; VP Soph Cls; Rep Jr Cls; Rep Sr Cls; Hon Roll; Fairfield U; Med.

LUBAS, MARK; Wethersfield HS; Wethersfield, CT; (Y); 10/313; Am Leg Boys St; French Clb; Model UN; Acpl Chr; Madrigals; School Musical; Sec Rep Soph Cls; Var Crs Cntry; NHS; Ntl Merit SF; Town Party Ldr & Senator CT Boys ST 85; Regnl Chorus 84-86; Natl Hon Rl 83-85; Psych.

LUBLIN, LAUREN; Joseph A Foran HS; Milford, CT; (Y); 1/300; Am Leg Aux Girls St; Drama Clb; French Clb; JCL; Keywanettes; Political Wkr; Ski Clb; Stage Crew; Stu Cncl; Crs Cntry; Harvard Book Prz; Soc Of Women Engnrs Cert; Eng I, II, III, IV; Radcliffe-Harvard Coll; Law.

LUCAS, KEVIN; Shelton HS; Shelton, CT; (Y); DECA; Spanish Clb; Hon Roll; NHS.

LUCASIEWICZ, AMY; Wamogo Regional HS; Morris, CT; (Y); AFS; FBLA; Ski Clb; Chorus; Nwsp Stf; Hon Roll; FBLA Hnr Awd-In Note Tkng 85; Acadmc Awd-Shrthnd 85; Northwestern CT CC; Bus.

LUCITTI, JENNIFER L; Southington HS; Plantsville, CT; (Y); 35/600; Pep Clb; Ski Clb; Rep Stu Cncl; High Hon Roll; NHS; Gifted & Talented Pgm 82-85; Vet Sci.

LUCKY, ONDRIA LYNN; West Haven HS; W Haven, CT; (Y); Girl Scts; Intnl Clb; Spanish Clb; Varsity Clb; Yrbk Stf; Trs Frsh Cls; Tennis; High Hon Roll; Natl JHS 82; Cornell U; Intl Bus.

LUDWIG, DEBORAH A; Brien Mc Mahon HS; Norwalk, CT; (Y); Church Yth Grp; Latin Clb; Color Guard; Orch; Rep Frsh Cls; Rep Soph Cls; Rep Jr Cls; Rep Sr Cls; Var Capt Crs Cntry; Capt L Trk; Silvr Mdlst Natl Latn Exam 83-84; Lehigh U.

LUEDEE, PHIL; Fairfiel Prep; New Haven, CT; (Y); Boy Scts; Rep Soph Cls; Im Bsktbl; JV Var Ftbl; Im Sftbl.

LUGO, MARIA; Kolbe-Cathedral HS; Bridgeport, CT; (Y); Church Yth Grp; Church Choir; Bsktbl; Norwalk Tech Coll; Comp.

LUNING, JONATHON T; New Milford HS; Sherman, CT; (Y); 25/301; Pres Computer Clb; Math Tm; Scholastic Bowl; School Play; Nwsp Stf; Bausch & Lomb Sci Awd; High Hon Roll; Hon Roll; NHS; Ntl Merit SF; ST JR Sci & Hum Sympsm Wnnr 84; Reg Sci & Env Conf Wnnr 83-84; Comp Sci.

LUNT, REBECCA; East Catholic HS; Hebron, CT; (Y); Gym; Lwyr.

LUPARIA, KATHLEEN; Guilford HS; Guilford, CT; (Y); Acpl Chr; Chorus; Madrigals; Rep Stu Cncl; Hon Roll; Psych.

LURIE, STEPHEN M; W H Hall HS; W Hartford, CT; (Y); Concert Band; Jazz Band; Mrchg Band; Orch; Pep Band; Symp Band.

LUSSIER, CHRISTINE; Newington HS; Newington, CT; (Y); 5/360; Cmnty Wkr; Key Clb; Political Wkr; Capt Flag Corp; School Musical; Symp Band; Yrbk Ed-Chief; High Hon Roll; NHS; Pres Schlr; Schlr Awd Hghst Girl Avg 83; NE Divsnl Music Hnrs 84 & 85; Dirctrs Awd 85; Boston Coll; Bus Admin.

LUSSIER, JO ANNE; Windham HS; Willimantic, CT; (Y); 64/285; Drama Clb; Office Aide; School Musical; School Play; Nwsp Rptr; Nwsp Stf; Yrbk Rptr; Yrbk Stf; Hon Roll; Otstndng SR Crmcs 85; Otstndng SR Stngrphy II 85; Acad Business Careers; Trvl.

LUTZ, MARK; Notre Dame HS; Milford, CT; (Y); Chess Clb; Church Yth Grp; Ski Clb; Spanish Clb; Im Bsktbl; JV Var Ftbl; Golf; Psych.

LYDIKSEN, JENNIFER; Trumball HS; Trumbull, CT; (Y); AFS; French Clb; JA; Ski Clb; Chorus; JV Fld Hcky; Trk; ASP 84-85; Church Yth Group 84-85; Colinary Art.

LYGA, DANIEL; Terryville HS; Terryville, CT; (Y); Var Tennis; JV Wrstlng; Elec Tech.

LYNCH, DIANE; Saint Marys Catholic HS; No Haven, CT; (Y); Church Yth Grp; School Musical; Nwsp Rptr; Yrbk Stf; JV Vllybl; High Hon Roll; Mu Alp Tht; NHS; Ntl Merit SF; French Clb; Natl Sci Olympiad Merit Awd 83; Soph Eng Awd 84; St Marys Of Springs Scholar 84 & 85; Acctg.

LYNCH, KAREN; St Bernard HS; Norwich, CT; (Y); 57/290; Church Yth Grp; Chorus; Off Jr Cls; Off Sr Cls; Var Capt Gym; Var Trk; Hon Roll; St Anseims Clg; Crmnl Just.

LYNCH, KEANE; South Kent Schl; Brookfield, CT; (Y); 10/40; Var Socr; JV Tennis; Hon Roll; Latin Awd 82-84; Law.

LYNCH, MICHELLE; Plainville HS; Plainville, CT; (Y); 17/213; Trs Church Yth Grp; Cmnty Wkr; Color Guard; Yrbk Stf; Hon Roll; NHS; Pensacola Christian Coll Schlrshp 85-86; Pensacola Chrstn Coll; Hme Econ.

LYNCH, PATRICK; N Haven HS; N Haven, CT; (Y); Bsbl; Bsktbl; Hon Roll; Sprtsmnshp Awd 83; Phy Ed Acad Excell 83; Bus.

LYNOTT, ROBERT; Pomperaug HS; Southbury, CT; (Y); 7/200; Church Yth Grp; Yrbk Stf; Off Jr Cls; Var Bsktbl; Var Capt Socr; Var Trk; High Hon Roll; NHS; Rep Frsh Cls; 1st Tm All Wild Div Socr 84; All WCC Hnrb Mntn Bsktbl 84-85; Exclince Acctng Awd 85; Bus.

LYON, REBECCA; Staples HS; Westport, CT; (Y); Drama Clb; Library Aide; Chorus; School Musical; School Play; Stage Crew; Tennis; Hartwick Coll; Theatre.

LYONS, EILEEN; Danbury HS; Danbury, CT; (Y); 4/612; Science Clb; Orch; Yrbk Stf; High Hon Roll; NHS; Outstndng Schlr & Femle Stu 82-85; Excel In Orchstr 82-83; Pre Med.

LYONS, KAREN; Central Catholic HS; East Norwalk, CT; (Y); Office Aide; Red Cross Aide; Ski Clb; Yrbk Stf; Sec Frsh Cls; Sec Soph Cls; Trs Jr Cls; Trs Sr Cls; Rep Stu Cncl; Capt Var Tennis; Walter J Mc Carthy Schlrshp By Ancinet Order Hibernians 85.

MAC DONALD, ALAN; St Bernards HS; Mystic, CT; (Y); 162/301; Boy Scts; Church Yth Grp; JV Ftbl; Golf; Wt Lftg; Cntrl CT; Bus Admin.

MAC DONALD, ERIN; Sacred Heart Acad; Hamden, CT; (Y); Trs Church Yth Grp; Computer Clb; Var Bowling; Vllybl; Hon Roll; Soc Wrk.

MAC DONALD, SARAH; William H Hall HS; W Hartford, CT; (Y); 50/300; Am Leg Aux Girls St; Church Yth Grp; Cmnty Wkr; Hosp Aide; Pep Clb; Red Cross Aide; Chorus; Church Choir; Madrigals; Mgr Trk; Stu Mnth 83; Bk Awd 85; Boston Coll; PN.

MAC DONALD, SEAN; Wilbur L Cross HS; Birmingham, AL; (S); Computer Clb; Math Clb; Math Tm; School Play; Lit Mag; Jr NHS; NHS; Harvard Book Awd 84-85; Chem.

MAC DOWELL, MELISSA; Southington HS; Southington, CT; (Y); 14/502; FTA; Pres Pep Clb; Band; Chorus; Concert Band; Jazz Band; Mrchg Band; Nwsp Stf; High Hon Roll; NHS; All Southern Div Band 83; Hartl Schl Music; Music Educ.

MAC DOWELL, SCOTT; Southington HS; Southington, CT; (Y); Rptr FBLA; VP Key Clb; Nwsp Rptr; Rep Soph Cls; High Hon Roll; NHS.

MAC EWEN, BONNIE; Wilton HS; Wilton, CT; (Y); 15/328; AFS; Church Yth Grp; Chorus; Madrigals; School Musical; Swing Chorus; Tennis; Rep Frsh Cls; Fld Hcky; Varsity Clb; Gold Key Schltc Art Awds Comp Pottery 85; Natl Chrl Awd 85; Faclty-Stu Bk Awd Ceram & Sculpt 85; CT Coll; Art.

MAC KENZIE, CAMERON; Killingly HS; Brooklyn, CT; (Y); 9/250; Hosp Aide; Political Wkr; Acpl Chr; Chorus; Color Guard; Nwsp Stf; French Hon Soc; High Hon Roll; Voice Dem Awd; Home Econ Awd; Outstndng Effort In Chorus Awd; Hnrs Engl Achvt Awd; CT Coll; Engl.

MAC LEOD, KRISTIN; East Lyme HS; Niantic, CT; (Y); 48/247; AFS; Church Yth Grp; Cmnty Wkr; VP Exploring; Pres Key Clb; Red Cross Aide; Teachers Aide; Rep Stu Cncl; Trk; Cit Awd; Outstndng Citzn Awd 83; Recog Peer Cnslng 85; Awd Schl Serv & Vlntrng 85; Phys Thrpy.

MAC MATH, TRACY A; Trumbull HS; Trumbull, CT; (Y); Concert Band; Drm & Bgl; Jazz Band; Mrchg Band; Symp Band; Nwsp Rptr; High Hon Roll; Hon Roll; NHS; Natl Assn Jazz Edctrs Schlrshp Smmr Stdy U Of MA 84; Music.

MAC NEAL, DEBORAH; Tolland HS; Tolland, CT; (Y); Church Yth Grp; Teachers Aide; Chorus; Church Choir; Madrigals; Mrchg Band; Yrbk Bus Mgr; Hon Roll; Awd Fr Exllnc In Vcl Music 85; CT All-SST Chr 85.

MAC SAVENY, BETH A; Morgan HS; Clinton, CT; (Y); 29/170; Hosp Aide; Red Cross Aide; Chorus; School Musical; School Play; Stage Crew; Yrbk Stf; Hon Roll; Prfct Atten Awd; Southern CT ST U; Comp Sci.

MACAULEY JR, ARTHUR P; St Bernard HS; Westerly, RI; (S); JV Bsbl; JV Socr; Var Swmmng.

MACBRIEN, NATHAN; Pomperaug HS; Southbury, CT; (Y); 1/216; Church Yth Grp; Math Tm; Chorus; Jazz Band; Madrigals; School Musical; Symp Band; NHS; Cmnty Wkr; Drama Clb; Eastern US Music Fest 85; Music.

MACCIO, STEPHANIE; Southington HS; Southington, CT; (Y); 32/580; Latin Clb; Library Aide; Ski Clb; Concert Band; Mrchg Band; Yrbk Stf; Rep Stu Cncl; Mgr Sftbl; High Hon Roll; NHS; Clscl Soc NEW England St Latin Test Hnry Ment 84-85; Town Southington Apple Harvst Fest Hostes 85; Law.

MACDONALD, STEPHEN; Manchester HS; Manchester, CT; (Y); High Hon Roll; Hon Roll; Civl Engrng.

MACISCO, BETH; Foran HS; Milford, CT; (Y); Dance Clb; Hosp Aide; Hon Roll; RN.

MACK, JOSEPH; Rockville HS; Vernon, CT; (Y); 21/362; Am Leg Boys St; Church Yth Grp; Pres Latin Clb; Jazz Band; Lit Mag; Var L Socr; Var Trk; High Hon Roll; NHS; Yth Evangelizer Diocese Norwich 83-85; Biomed Engrng.

MACKAY, BRYAN; Holy Cross HS; Waterbury, CT; (Y); 180/352; Boys Clb Am; Letterman Clb; Chorus; School Musical; Var Swmmng; Prfct Atten Awd; The Amer Lgn 82; Psych.

MACKEY, FIONNUALA; St Marys HS; New Haven, CT; (Y); 22/115; Church Yth Grp; Dance Clb; Drama Clb; French Clb; Ski Clb; Chorus; School Musical; Var Cheerleading; French Hon Soc; Hon Roll; Bus.

MACKLE, JULIE M; New Canaan HS; New Canaan, CT; (Y); 1/336; Church Yth Grp; Orch; Yrbk Sprt Ed; Var Fld Hcky; JV Capt Tennis; Pres NHS; French Clb; Letterman Clb; High Hon Roll; Mst Distingshd Cls Female Schlr 85; All ST & All County Tms Field Hockey 84; Excllnce AP Frnch 85; Duke U; Finance.

MADAR III, LAWRENCE; Trumbull HS; Trumbull, CT; (Y); AFS; Exploring; Pres JA; Rep Stu Cncl; Var Trk; High Hon Roll; NHS; Computer Clb; Math Clb; Science Clb; Outstndg Acad Achvt 83; Excllnce Biol 84; Excllnce Chem, Outstndg JR Mth 85; Am Chem Soc Scholar 85; Comp Engrng.

MADDEN, KEVIN; East Catholic HS; Vernon, CT; (Y); 2/350; Church Yth Grp; Cmnty Wkr; Service Clb; Teachers Aide; Rep Stu Cncl; Capt Bsbl; Var L Church Yth Grp; Var L Socr; High Hon Roll; NHS; Yale Book Awd 85; CT Hnr Sem 85; Sci Fld.

MADDEN, NORA; Brookfield HS; Brookfield, CT; (Y); 9/216; Drama Clb; JCL; Chorus; High Hon Roll; Trs NHS; Pres Acdmc Ftns Awd 85; Wstrn CT ST U; Elem Ed.

MADERA, LYDIA; Crosby HS; Waterbury, CT; (S); Art Clb; Pres Church Yth Grp; Spanish Clb; Chorus; School Musical; Rep Frsh Cls; Rep Soph Cls; Rep Jr Cls; JV Vllybl; Hon Roll; CT ST Schlr 85; Miss PR Of CT 84-85; Storrs U CT; Accntng.

MADEUX, MARTIN; Torrington HS; Torrington, CT; (Y); 37/271; Pres Varsity Clb; Stat Bsktbl; Score Keeper; Mgr Vllybl; Hon Roll; Nrthwstrn CT CC; Graphic Arts.

MADISON, DANA; Plainville HS; Plainville, CT; (Y); Pres Science Clb; Yrbk Sprt Ed; Capt Ftbl; Capt Golf; DAR Awd; High Hon Roll; NHS; All Conf Ftbll 84; Pre Med.

MAGAC, NADINE J; Naugatuck HS; Naugatuck, CT; (Y); Church Yth Grp; Orch; Rep Frsh Cls; Rep Soph Cls; Rep Jr Cls; Var Capt Crs Cntry; Var L Trk; Hon Roll; Engrng.

MAGALHAES, JOSE PAUL; Warren F Kaynor HS; Waterbury, CT; (Y); 5/200; Computer Clb; Stage Crew; Stu Cncl; Im Bsbl; Im Bsktbl; Var Capt Socr; Im Vllybl; High Hon Roll; NHS; UT CT; Elec Engr.

MAGALIS, MARY BETH; Tourtellotte Memorial HS; Thompson, CT; (Y); Var Bsktbl; JV Cheerleading; Im Gym; Var Socr; Capt Var Trk; MIP Sccr 1st Yr 82-83; 1st Plyr Awd Trck 83-84; 2nd Pl Medl Lng Jmp 84-85; Norwich Military Acad; Crmnl Js.

MAGAN, LEA; Shelton HS; Shelton, CT; (Y); VP Key Clb; Drill Tm; Pom Pon; Trk; Hon Roll; Bus.

MAGDON, CHRISTINE; Lauralton Hall HS; Milford, CT; (Y); Latin Clb; Science Clb; Spanish Clb; Yrbk Stf; NHS; Amer Clsscl Leag Latin Exam Cum Laude 84; CT Clsscl Soc Latin Exam Cum Dignitate 83; Poltcl Sci.

MAGGI, LEA; Shelton HS; Shelton, CT; (Y); Bus.

MAGISH, IRENE; Windsor Locks HS; Windsor Locks, CT; (Y); Am Leg Aux Girls St; Church Yth Grp; Cmnty Wkr; French Clb; JA; Model UN; Political Wkr; Acpl Chr; Chorus; JV Bsktbl.

MAGNO, CATHRYN; Bloomfield HS; Bloomfield, CT; (Y); 18/231; Church Yth Grp; Model UN; Concert Band; Mrchg Band; Stu Cncl; Var Socr; JV Sftbl; Var Tennis; French Hon Soc; NHS; Schlrshp Friends Music 83; Schlrshp Creative Arts Prog 84-85; Awds All New Engl Music Assn 85; Frgn Lang.

MAGRI, JENNIFER MARIE; Southington HS; Southington, CT; (Y); 27/50; High Hon Roll; NHS; Span Schlrshp & Awd 82; Italian Clb & Sec & Actvts Dir 83-85; CT U; Civil Engr.

MAGUDER, JILL; Berlin HS; Kensington, CT; (Y); JA; Band; Mrchg Band; Trs Stu Cncl; Var Powder Puff Ftbl; Stu Cncl Awd 84-85; Hmcmng Quen Alt 82.

MAGYAR, BRUCE; Oliver Wolcott Technical Schl; Torrington, CT; (Y); Hon Roll; NHS; Crpntry.

MAHALSKI, JOANNE; Enfield HS; Enfield, CT; (S); VP DECA; Spanish Clb; Chorus; Variety Show; Mgr(s); Hon Roll; DECA Outstndng Stu Awd 85; 1st & 2nd Pl Shplftng & Apprl ST Of CT 84-85; STCC; Law.

MAHON, JENNIFER; Hotchkiss Schl; Sharon, CT; (Y); Art Clb; French Clb; Chorus; Nwsp Stf; Yrbk Stf; Lit Mag; L Capt Crs Cntry; L Trk; Hon Roll; NHS; Capt & Mgr Cyclng Tm; Barnard Coll; Psych.

MAHON, PAMELA; East Lyme HS; Niantic, CT; (Y); Chorus; Church Choir; Flag Corp; Madrigals; Mrchg Band; School Musical; School Play; Yrbk Rptr; Yrbk Stf; High Hon Roll; Wellesly Bk Awd 85; Frgn Lang Spnsh 84; Prfmng Arts.

MAHONEY, CATHLEEN; Saint Joseph HS; Stratford, CT; (Y); 35/227; French Clb; Nwsp Rptr; JV Bsktbl; Var Sftbl; Var Capt Vllybl; French Hon Soc; Hon Roll.

MAIGNAN, JASMINE; Valley Regional HS; Essex, CT; (Y); 66/137; French Clb; Mgr(s); Score Keeper; Var Trk; Var Capt Vllybl; Hon Roll; Acad, Frgn Lang Schlrshp 85; Phy Ed Awd 85; Northeastern U; Lang.

MAIKOWSKI, JAMES; St Thomas Aquinas HS; New Britain, CT; (Y); 11/153; High Hon Roll; Hon Roll; NHS; Spanish Clb; U Of CT; Elec Engrng.

MAIN, KEVIN; Oliver Wolcott Tech; Litchfield, CT; (Y); Yrbk Rptr; Yrbk Stf; Golf; Hon Roll; Waterbury ST Tech; Carpntr.

MAINA, MARINA; O H Platt HS; Meriden, CT; (Y); Art Clb; Church Yth Grp; French Clb; Key Clb; Chorus; Yrbk Phtg; Yrbk Rptr; Yrbk Stf; Rep Jr Cls; JV Var Cheerleading; 1st Pl Tlnt Show Key Clb Conv 85; Vrsty Chrldng Ltr 83-84; Art Merits & Outstndng Contrbtns In Art; RI U; Art.

MAINI, ENZO; Trumbull HS; Trumbull, CT; (Y); Var Capt Socr; AYSO Vol Effort Awd 84; Engr.

MAIORANO, RACHEL A; North Branford HS; N Branford, CT; (Y); 1/188; Hosp Aide; Yrbk Ed-Chief; Var L Crs Cntry; Var L Trk; NCTE Awd; Pres NHS; Ntl Merit SF; Val; Capt Scholastic Bowl; Variety Show; Bio Hnrs Awd,World Hist Awd,Spanish II Awd 82; Human Antomy Awd, Amer Lit Awd Gnlr Art Awd 83; Child Psychology.

MAISANO, LISA; Bethel HS; Bethel, CT; (Y); AFS; Boy Scts; Church Yth Grp; Hosp Aide; Political Wkr; Varsity Clb; Variety Show; Var L Crs Cntry; Var Trk; Hon Roll; Explrs Clb Volnteer Danbury Hosp 83-84; Volnteer Spec Olympcs 85; Phys Ther.

MAISANO, MARY; North Haven HS; N Haven, CT; (Y); 89/386; Model UN; Yrbk Stf; Rep Frsh Cls; Rep Soph Cls; Rep Jr Cls; Rep Stu Cncl; JV Var Cheerleading; French Hon Soc; Hon Roll; Outstndng Achvt Engl Cert 83-84; Intl Stds.

MAISTERRA, AMY; Westover Schl; Middlebury, CT; (Y); 2/60; Dance Clb; Pres Spanish Clb; Acpl Chr; VP Chorus; Madrigals; School Musical; Yrbk Stf; Lit Mag; High Hon Roll; Lang.

MAJCHROWSKI, EWA JOANNA; Bristol Central HS; Bristol, CT; (Y); Church Yth Grp; Dance Clb; German Clb; Science Clb; Ski Clb; Yrbk Stf; Hon Roll; Schlrshp JR Polish Leag 85; U Of CT; Phy Thrpy.

MAJESKI, MICHAEL P; Southington HS; Plantsville, CT; (Y); 6/550; Am Leg Boys St; Latin Clb; Concert Band; Stu Cncl; Var L Bsbl; Var L Bsktbl; Bausch & Lomb Sci Awd; Elks Awd; High Hon Roll; NHS; U S Naval Acad Appt 85; Alumni Spkg Prz 84; All Conf Sel Cntrl CT Conf S Div Bsbl 84 & 85; Yale U; Chem.

MAJOWICZ, ADAM; East Hartford HS; E Hartford, CT; (Y); Boy Scts; Computer Clb; French Clb; JA; Library Aide; Science Clb; Ski Clb; Spanish Clb; Band; Concert Band; Natl Egl Sct Assc 85; U Of CT; Comp Sci.

MAKOS, KARI; Brookfield HS; Brookfield, CT; (Y); 39/245; Varsity Clb; Rep Jr Cls; JV Var Bsktbl; Var Trk; Hon Roll; Fshn Dsgng.

MAKOS, MICHELE; Brookfield HS; Brookfield Ctr, CT; (Y); 3/220; Varsity Clb; Chorus; Yrbk Stf; Var Capt Bsktbl; Var Capt Trk; Var Vllybl; High Hon Roll; NHS; Pres Schlr; Rotary Awd; U Of CT Alumni Awd 85; Fairfield Cnty Bio Awd 85; Brookfields Rotary Schlrshp 85; U Of CT; Bio-Tech.

MAKOWICZ, DAVID; Ellington HS; Rockville, CT; (Y); 1/151; Rep Am Leg Boys St; Aud/Vis; Yrbk Ed-Chief; High Hon Roll; VP NHS; CAP; Latin Clb; Red Cross Aide; Bsbl; Math & Bio Awd Peer Tutor 84; Hnrs Prog Roject Spotlght 85; Holy Crss Bk Awd Peer Tutor 85; Engrng.

MALARIO, MATTHEW; Holy Cross HS; Waterbury, CT; (Y); 120/400; Var Capt Bsbl; JV L Bsktbl; Var L Ftbl; Hon Roll; Mst Athltc Boy Clss Of 86; Dartmouth; Bus.

MALAY, SUSAN; Shelton HS; Shelton, CT; (Y); Am Leg Aux Girls St; Nwsp Rptr; Yrbk Stf; VP Frsh Cls; VP Soph Cls; Rep Jr Cls; Rep Sr Cls; Var Capt Sftbl; VFW Awd; Voice Dem Awd; Hotl Mgmt.

MALDONADO, NELSON E; Kolbe Cathedral HS; Bridgeport, CT; (Y); 17/104; Yrbk Stf; NHS; Stdnts Schl Unity 84-85; Outstndng Achvmnt Spanish 85; Outstndng Serv SSU 85; Archt.

MALEC, KIMBERLY; Sacred Heart Acad; Orange, CT; (Y); Church Yth Grp; Pres FBLA; Pep Clb; Chorus; School Musical; JV Crs Cntry; NHS; Spanish NHS; Hosp Aide; Im Vllybl; Briarwood Bk Awd 85; Entrprnshp II 1st Pl ST FBLA Conv 85; Bus.

MALERBA, KRIS; Joseph A Foran HS; Milford, CT; (Y); DECA; Hosp Aide; Jr NHS; Nrsg Arts 85; Bus Admin.

MALHAME, MELISSA; Canterbury Schl; Milford, PA; (Y); 8/85; Band; Concert Band; Nwsp Phtg; Nwsp Rptr; VP Frsh Cls; Pres Soph Cls; Rep Stu Cncl; Im Bowling; Var Diving; Var Capt Fld Hcky; Hugh O Brien Ldrshp Smnr 83; Brody Awd 85; Ldrshp Awd For Athltcs 85; Lafayette Coll; Bus Admin.

MALLANE, DARREN; Naugatuck HS; Naugatuck, CT; (Y); 67/325; Am Leg Boys St; Acpl Chr; Chorus; Stage Crew; Variety Show; Hon Roll; Hon Nwsp Carrier 84; Johnson & Wales; Htl Mngmnt.

MALLETTE, YVONNE; Shelton HS; Shelton, CT; (Y); Art Clb; FHA; Girl Scts; JA; Office Aide; Hon Roll; Legl Secy.

MALLICK, CAROLINE; Academy Of Our Lady Of Mercy; Trumbull, CT; (Y); Church Yth Grp; Latin Clb; Math Clb; Science Clb; Service Clb; Spanish Clb; Chorus; Yrbk Phtg; Var Cheerleading; NHS; Magna Cum Lauda Awd Natl Latn Exm 84; Bio.

MALONEY, DARBY; Greenwich HS; Riverside, CT; (Y); Cmnty Wkr; Pres Rep Service Clb; Chorus; Variety Show; JV Socr; Var Sftbl; Var Tennis; Var Vllybl; High Hon Roll; Liberal Arts.

MALTBY, PETE; Amity Regional SR HS; Bethany, CT; (Y); Church Yth Grp; Computer Clb; Teachers Aide; Cit Awd; Hon Roll; Prfct Atten Awd; Acad Achvt Awd 84; CT Comp Olympics Awd 84; Bus Admin.

MANCHUCK, AMY MARIE; Sacred Heart Acad; Stamford, CT; (Y); 1/57; Madrigals; Var Bsktbl; Var Sftbl; Var Vllybl; French Hon Soc; High Hon Roll; NHS; Church Yth Grp; GAA; JA; Holy Cross Book Awd 85; Hugh O Brian Yth Ldrshp Awd 84; CT Dstngshd Stu Awd 85; Med.

MANCINI, FRANK; Holy Cross HS; Waterbury, CT; (Y); 37/350; Trk; High Hon Roll; NHS; Prfct Atten Awd; Mc Donalds & Royal Arcanum Scholars 85; CT ST Awd 85; U CT; Bio.

MANCINI, LAUREN; St Marys HS; New Haven, CT; (Y); Church Yth Grp; Exploring; Girl Scts; Quiz Bowl; Service Clb; Chorus; Church Choir; School Musical; Var Capt Vllybl; Rep Jr Cls; Outstndng Svc & Wmn Ldrshp Awds 85; Elms Coll; Ed.

MANCINI, STEVEN; Berlin HS; Berlin, CT; (Y); 6/210; Am Leg Boys St; Church Yth Grp; JA; Band; Concert Band; Mrchg Band; Tennis; High Hon Roll; Jr NHS; NHS; Talcott Mtn Sci Cmp 83-85; Colgate; Pre-Med.

MANCINI, TONY; Warren F Kaynor Regional Vo Tech; Watertown, CT; (Y); Socr; High Hon Roll; Hon Roll; NHS.

MANCOLL, REBECCA; Loomis Chaffee HS; W Hartford, CT; (Y); Library Aide; Math Tm; Nwsp Stf; Israel Quiz Bowl 1st & 2nd Prz 84-85.

MANCUSO, MICHAEL; Masuk HS; Monroe, CT; (Y); 70/280; Church Yth Grp; Drama Clb; JA; School Play; VP Frsh Cls; VP Soph Cls; Trs Jr Cls; Rep Stu Cncl; Var Bsktbl; JV Lcrss; Hugh O Brien Ldrshp Awd 83-84; Sibleys Art Awd Hnrbl Ment 82-83; Pol Sci.

MANGIAFICO, TODD A; Bristol Eastern HS; Bristol, CT; (Y); Art Clb; Spanish Clb; High Hon Roll; Natl Schltc Art Awd 85; Northwestern CT CC; Graph Dsn.

MANGIAGLI, SUSAN ANN; Southington HS; Southington, CT; (Y); 23/580; Hosp Aide; Key Clb; Nwsp Stf; Ed Yrbk Bus Mgr; Rep Frsh Cls; Rep Soph Cls; Rep Jr Cls; Rep Sr Cls; Rep Stu Cncl; Powder Puff Ftbl; Hghst Frnch Avg; Dscvr III Gftd & Tlntd; Hghst Cvcs Avg; Math.

MANGINI, KYLE; Bulkeley HS; Hartford, CT; (Y); 3/381; Am Leg Boys St; Drama Clb; Political Wkr; Ski Clb; Nwsp Phtg; Yrbk Ed-Chief; Pres Stu Cncl; Var L Ftbl; High Hon Roll; NHS; MVP Ftbl 84-85; Fox Schlr; Holy Cross Bk Prz 84; Wesleyan U; Econ.

MANN, VINCENT E; Wind Ham Regional Vo-Tech; Tolland, CT; (Y); JV Bsbl; Hon Roll; Rookie Yr Ftbl 83; Def Plyr Yr Ftbl 84; Co Capt Ftbl 85; Autobody Tech.

MANNEL, BETHALEE LYNN; Rockville HS; Rockville, CT; (Y); 33/357; FBLA; JCL; High Hon Roll; Hon Roll; Bus Soph 82-83; Pres Acad Ftns Awd 84-85; Becker Jr Coll; Exec Sec.

MANSFIELD, CHRISTOPHER S; Hopkins Grammar Day Prosp Hill Schl; New Haven, CT; (Y); 37/110; Cmnty Wkr; Letterman Clb; Varsity Clb; Pep Band; Stage Crew; Nwsp Stf; Yrbk Stf; Rep Frsh Cls; Rep Soph Cls; Rep Jr Cls; Ftbl Hnrs Tacklng, Sprtsmnsp Ldrshp & Dedctn 83-84; Mech Engr.

MANSY, JACQUELINE A; Norwalk HS; Norwalk, CT; (Y); 30/493; Church Yth Grp; Orch; Nwsp Rptr; Yrbk Stf; Rep Frsh Cls; Rep Soph Cls; Rep Jr Cls; Rep Sr Cls; Rep Stu Cncl; High Hon Roll; Pres Amer Fit Awd 84-85; Natl Spn Cont Awd 4th Pl 82-83; Post Coll Acad Scholar 85; Cert Excllnce Bus; Post Coll; Bus Mngmnt.

MANWARE, MICHELLE; The Morgan Schl; Clinton, CT; (Y); 13/180; Church Yth Grp; Chorus; Concert Band; School Musical; Nwsp Stf; Yrbk Phtg; Yrbk Rptr; Stat Bsktbl; Hon Roll; NHS; Mrktng.

MANWARE, PAUL; Southington HS; Southington, CT; (Y); #155 In Class; FBLA; Ski Clb; School Play; Variety Show; Ftbl; Hon Roll; Joseph A Depaolo Schlrshp 85; CT U; Acctng.

MAPES, SHANNON L; Acad Of The Holy Family; Brooklyn, CT; (Y); JA; Library Aide; Office Aide; Red Cross Aide; Teachers Aide; Chorus; Yrbk Stf; Fld Hcky; Lcrss; Socr; Mst Imprvd Stu 84-85; Pre-Dntl.

MARAFINO, ANDREW R; Northwest Catholic HS; W Hartford, CT; (Y); JA; Chorus; School Musical; School Play; Rep Stu Cncl; Var L Golf; Pol Sci.

MARATEA, KIMBERLY; Amity Regional SR HS; Orange, CT; (Y); Art Clb; Pep Clb; Ski Clb; Cit Awd; Hon Roll; Natl Art Hnr Soc Treas; Artstic Achvt Awd; Vis Art.

MARC AURELE, MICHAEL; Holy Cross HS; Thomaston, CT; (Y); 188/352; Cmnty Wkr; Band; JV Socr; High Hon Roll; Hon Roll; MA Coll Pharm; Nuclr Med.

MARCEY, DIANA; Holy Cross HS; Waterbury, CT; (Y); 174/352; JV Crs Cntry; JV Capt Sftbl; JV Trk; Mgmnt.

MARCH, CHRISTINE; Newington HS; Newington, CT; (Y); Church Yth Grp; Hosp Aide; Sec Ed.

MARCH, SCOTT; Danbury HS; Danbury, CT; (Y); Civic Clb; Drama Clb; Key Clb; PAVAS; Acpl Chr; Chorus; Stage Crew; Variety Show; Hon Roll; Jessie Owens Gms Trk 83; Cntr Crtv Yths Wesleyan U 85; Tech Thtr.

MARCHESSEAULT, DONALD; South Windsor HS; S Windsor, CT; (Y); Boy Scts; VP Exploring; Yrbk Phtg; High Hon Roll; Hon Roll; Architect.

MARCIANO, PATTY; Notre Dame Acad; Prospect, CT; (Y); 1/53; Chorus; VP Stu Cncl; Elks Awd; High Hon Roll; NHS; St Schlr; Val; Church Yth Grp; Cmnty Wkr; Dance Clb; CT Miss TEEN 84; Natl Miss TEEN 85; Unico John S Cappelo Mem Music Awd For Prof In Piano 85; Trinity Coll Hartford CT; Trtr.

MARCICZKIEWICZ, MONICA; Berlin HS; Kensington, CT; (Y); 9/180; Drill Tm; Ed Yrbk Rptr; Stu Cncl; Gym; Powder Puff Ftbl; Hon Roll; NHS; Trk; High Hon Roll; Pres Acadmc Fit Awd 85; C G Jeffrey Swanson Arts & Humnties Awd 85; U CT Engl Achvt Awd 85; Central CT ST U; Engl.

MARCIL, JOSEPH; Holy Cross HS; Watertown, CT; (Y); 148/352; Boy Scts; Band; Concert Band; JV Bsbl; Var Ftbl; Var L Trk; Var JV Wrstlng; High Hon Roll; Hon Roll; Trk Mdl ST Comp & Naugahick Vly Lg 85; Shot Put & Javln Awds 85; Syracuse; Pre-Med.

MARCOTTE, ANDREA; Trumbull HS; Trumbull, CT; (Y); Church Yth Grp; Letterman Clb; Ski Clb; Band; Concert Band; Drm Mjr(t); Mrchg Band; Symp Band; Mgr(s); High Hon Roll.

MARCUCCI, JENNIFER; St Marys HS; E Haven, CT; (Y); 25/115; Hosp Aide; Math Clb; Math Tm; Service Clb; Yrbk Stf; Hon Roll; Jr NHS; Mu Alp Tht; Med Asst.

MARCUS, BRIAN; George J Penney HS; E Hartford, CT; (Y); Am Leg Boys St; Quiz Bowl; Temple Yth Grp; Drm Mjr(t); Jazz Band; Mrchg Band; Yrbk Stf; Stu Cncl; Var Tennis; NHS; Med.

MARCUS, DANIEL; Amity Regional HS; Bethany, CT; (Y); Am Leg Boys St; Pres Drama Clb; Acpl Chr; Sec Chorus; Tennis; Trk; Im Vllybl; NHS; Schl Plcy Comm 83-84; Peer Tutor 84-85.

MARGELOT, GARY; Watertown HS; Watertown, CT; (Y); 66/275; Ski Clb; Band; Drm Mjr(t); Mrchg Band; Hon Roll; Ski Tm Ltr 84; Pro Ski Instrctrs Amer Registrd 84-85; Otis Ridge Ski Area Instrctr Cnslr 82-85; Bentley Coll; Comp Sci.

MARGIOTTA, JESSICA; Crosby HS; Waterbury, CT; (Y); 19/347; Latin Clb; Ski Clb; School Musical; School Play; Tennis; High Hon Roll; Hon Roll; NHS; Ntl Merit Ltr; Prfct Atten Awd; U CT; Engl.

MARIANO, CHERYL; Holy Cross HS; Naugatuck, CT; (Y); 80/360; Civic Clb; JA; Spanish Clb; Crs Cntry; Sftbl; Hon Roll; NHS; Spanish NHS; Phy Thrpy.

MARINO, JODI ANN; Frank Scott Bunnell HS; Stratford, CT; (Y); 85/250; Church Yth Grp; FBLA; Hosp Aide; Ski Clb; School Musical; Var Cheerleading; Swmmng; Cit Awd; Hon Roll; JC Awd; Future Bus Ldrs Of Amer Bus Grphcs Awd 84; Vetrns Of War Memrl Awd 85; Southern CT ST U; Grphc Dsgn.

MARKHAM, ROBERT; Pomperaug HS; Southbury, CT; (Y); JV Bsbl; JV Trk; Hon Roll; CT U; Med.

MARKIE, KAREN; East Catholic HS; E Hartford, CT; (Y); Cmnty Wkr; Band; Nwsp Stf; Volunteer Awd YWCA 85; Volunteer Awd-Manchester Cmnty Svcs Cncl 85; Elem Educ.

MARKIN, OMELAN; Notre Dame HS; New Haven, CT; (Y); Chess Clb; JV Ftbl; Hon Roll; 1st Pl Dcthln Ukrnn Sprts Camp NY 85; 1st Pl Ukrnn Chess Trnmnt NY 85; Cert Of Merit Frnch Cntst 83; New Haven U; Engr.

MARKIW, OMELAN; Notre Dame HS; New Haven, CT; (Y); Chess Clb; Church Yth Grp; JV Ftbl; Hon Roll; Prfct Atten Awd; Cert Merit Frnch Lang 83; 2nd Pl Chess 83; 3rd Pl Smmr Swim Comp 82; U Of New Haven; Engrng.

MARKS, LAURA C; St Thomas Aquinas HS; New Britain, CT; (Y); 8/154; Church Yth Grp; Cmnty Wkr; French Clb; Church Choir; School Musical; Yrbk Stf; Lit Mag; High Hon Roll; Hon Roll; 1st Rgnl, ST Ntl Hist Day 84; Outstndngn Perf US Hist Svc Schl 85; U CT; Jrnlsm.

MARKS, LINDA; Wilbur Cross HS; New Haven, CT; (Y); Church Choir; JV Bsktbl; Outstndng Achvt Chem, Spnsh 85; Excel Achvt Spnsh 85; Oral Roberts U; Bibcl Thlgy.

MARKUS, REBECCA; The Hotchkiss Schl; Wayne, PA; (Y); Pres Dance Clb; Hosp Aide; Nwsp Rptr; Off Frsh Cls; Var L Fld Hcky; Var L Lcrss; Hon Roll; Church Yth Grp; Lit Mag; Hnrs In Latin 83; The Neil H Scott Field Hcky Awd Mst Imprvmnt 84; Accmmndtn For Acad Excell 85.

MARMORA, STACEY; Shelton HS; Shelton, CT; (Y); Crs Cntry; Socr; Hon Roll; Law Enforcmnt.

MARONE, MATTHEW J; St Bernard HS; N Franklin, CT; (Y); 53/304; Boy Scts; Science Clb; Var Swmmng; Elks Awd; Hon Roll; SAR Awd; Genl Exclnce Art 85; Aerospace Engrng.

MARONEY, DENNY; Danbury HS; Danbury, CT; (Y); 30/600; Chess Clb; Church Yth Grp; Computer Clb; Drama Clb; FCA; Science Clb; Spanish Clb; Varsity Clb; School Play; Variety Show; U Of CT; Chem.

MARRANO, LYNN; St Mary HS; Rye Brook, NY; (Y); 5/70; Pep Clb; Var Capt Bsktbl; Crs Cntry; Sftbl; Vllybl; High Hon Roll; NHS; Schlr-Ath Awd U S Army Res 85; Fairchester Ath Assn All Lg Bsktbl & MVP 85, All ST Tm 85; Manhatanville Coll; Ed.

MARRON, DAWN; Bethel HS; Bethel, CT; (Y); DECA; Bnkng.

MARRONE, DAVID; Xavier HS; Killingworth, CT; (Y); Boy Scts; Rep Frsh Cls; Rep Soph Cls; Rep Jr Cls; JV Bsbl; JV Socr; Var Trk; Var Wt Lftg; High Hon Roll; Hon Roll; Eagle Scout Awd 85; Envrnmntl.

MARSH, BRIDGET; The Hotchkiss Schl; Rhinebeck, NY; (Y); French Clb; Acpl Chr; Chorus; Orch; Nwsp Sprt Ed; Var Bsktbl; Var Fld Hcky; Var Lcrss; High Hon Roll; Hon Roll; Proctor Dormitry 84-85; NY ST Regnts Schlrshp 85; Georgetown U; Intl Law.

MARSHALL, JOHN; Rockville HS; Vernon, CT; (Y); Cmnty Wkr; Ski Clb; Hon Roll; Eastern CT ST U; Lbrl Arts.

MARSHALL, JOSH; North Haven HS; N Haven, CT; (Y); Aud/Vis; Camera Clb; Nwsp Phtg.

MARSLAND, CATHERINE KATY; Westover Schl; Baton Rouge, LA; (Y); Church Yth Grp; French Clb; Spanish Clb; Chorus; Yrbk Stf; Hon Roll; Emory U; Intl Affrs.

MARTIN, BONNIE; Danbury HS; Danbury, CT; (Y); 88/500; Drama Clb; Exploring; Hosp Aide; Excllnc Art Awd 83-84; Perry Phy Educ Awd 84; Wesleyan U Ctr-Crtv Yth 85-86; Studio Art.

MARTIN, DALE; East Lyme HS; E Lyme, CT; (Y); 50/280; Boy Scts; L Crs Cntry; Im Ftbl; Im Ice Hcky; U Of CT; Elctrncs.

MARTIN, ELAINE; Bristol Eastern HS; Bristol, CT; (Y); French Clb; FBLA; Capt Cheerleading; Powder Puff Ftbl; Hon Roll; NHS; Briarwood Bk Prz 83-84; A Joyce Martin Meml Bus Awd 84-85; Briarwood Schlrshp 84-85; Briarwood Coll; Exec Sec.

MARTIN, KIMBERLY; Central Catholic HS; Wesport, CT; (Y); Church Yth Grp; Drama Clb; Chorus; Stage Crew; Lit Mag; Sftbl; Trk; Hon Roll; Cthlc Schls Dsgn Awd 84; 1st Pl Norwalk Schls Essay Cntst 85.

MARTIN, MARY-JO; Jonathan Law HS; Millford, CT; (Y); Library Aide; Var Cheerleading; Gym; Exc Design I 84; Math.

MARTIN, ROBERT A; Tolland HS; Tolland, CT; (Y); Trs Church Yth Grp; Exploring; Band; Concert Band; Mrchg Band; School Musical; School Play; Stage Crew; Ntl Merit SF; Auditrm Tech Staff 84-86; U CT; Med.

MARTIN, SHARON; Wilbur Cross HS; New Haven, CT; (Y); Church Yth Grp; French Clb; Ski Clb; Church Choir; Yrbk Stf; Lit Mag; Var Sftbl; Chem.

MARTIN, SUSAN; Southington HS; Southington, CT; (Y); 124/550; VP JA; Hon Roll; Library Aide; Chorus; CCSU; Psych.

MARTIN, SUSAN BETH; St Joseph HS; Trumbull, CT; (Y); 29/216; Camera Clb; Drama Clb; English Clb; Spanish Clb; Thesps; Chorus; School Musical; School Play; Stage Crew; Variety Show; Coll Holy Cross; Arts.

MARTINDALE, CHARLES; Notre Dame HS; New Haven, CT; (Y); JV Ftbl; Athltc Trnr.

MARTINEZ, DAISY; West Hill HS; Stamford, CT; (Y); Church Yth Grp; Computer Clb; Drama Clb; Spanish Clb; Chorus; Church Choir; Madrigals; School Musical; Stu Cncl; High Hon Roll; Miss Stamford Schlrshp 85; Katherine Gibbs Future Sec Awd 85; Bus.

MARTINEZ, ERIC; Daniel Hand HS; Madison, CT; (Y); 100/236; Church Yth Grp; VP FCA; JCL; Latin Clb; Var L Bsktbl; Var L Golf; Var L Socr; MIP Vrsty Bsktbl 84-85; Cum Digntat ST Ltn Tst 84-85; Marquette; Engrng.

MARTINEZ, JOSE RENE; St Bernard HS; New London, CT; (S); 148/290; Boy Scts; Drama Clb; NFL; Spanish Clb; Speech Tm; School Play; Bsbl; Spanish NHS; U Of CT; Elec Engrng.

MARTINI, MICHAEL; Trumbull HS; Trumbull, CT; (Y); JA; Band; Jazz Band; Mrchg Band; Symp Band; Nwsp Rptr; JV Trk; High Hon Roll.

MARTINO, SUSAN; North Branford HS; Northford, CT; (Y); 19/162; Trs AFS; Church Yth Grp; Cmnty Wkr; FBLA; Chorus; Stage Crew; Yrbk Stf; JV Sftbl; High Hon Roll; NHS; Fnlst In Michaels Jewelers Schlrshp 85; Educ.

MARTINOLI, ANNE; St Bernard HS; Oakdale, CT; (Y); 26/297; Drama Clb; Band; Church Choir; Concert Band; Mrchg Band; Pep Band; School Musical; Stu Cncl; Hon Roll; NHS; Music Excell Awd 83-85; Music.

MARTINS, DEBORA; Central HS; Bridgeport, CT; (Y); Hon Roll; U Of CT; Doctor.

MARY, CHERYL; Windsor HS; Windsor, CT; (Y); French Clb; Band; Chorus; Swing Chorus; Var L Cheerleading; Im Socr; Var Tennis; Bryant Coll; Bus Mgmt.

MARZI, ALAN; Farmington HS; Farmington, CT; (Y); 39/207; Church Yth Grp; Ski Clb; Jazz Band; Madrigals; School Play; Trs Frsh Cls; JV Socr; Hon Roll; Ntl Merit Ltr; All ST Chorus 85.

MARZULLO, SCOTT; St Mary HS; Stamford, CT; (Y); 26/68; Pres VP Exploring; Spanish Clb; Stage Crew; Im Lcrss; Im Socr; Var Tennis; Amer U; Audio Tech.

MASCARO, MARISA LYNN; Simsb Ury HS; W Simsbury, CT; (Y); 3/352; Concert Band; Yrbk Stf; Stu Cncl; Var L Bsktbl; Var JV Fld Hcky; High Hon Roll; NHS; Ntl Merit Ltr; Band; Mrchg Band; Harvrd Bk Awd 84; UNICO Schlrshp 85; Tp 10 Cls Schlr 81-85; Princeton U.

MASCHIO, KAREN; Sacred Heart Acad; Wallingford, CT; (Y); Hosp Aide; School Play; Nwsp Rptr; Sec Soph Cls; Sec Jr Cls; VP Stu Cncl; NHS; Spanish NHS; Variety Show; Rep Frsh Cls; Del Of Sacred Hrt Acad, Sent To Mt W/Pope At Intl Yth Gathrng In Rome Italy 85; Stdy Piano 10 Yrs; Pre-Law.

MASCOLI, JEFFREY W; Holy Cross HS; Middlebury, CT; (Y); 85/352; Var Socr; High Hon Roll; Hon Roll; NHS.

MASLOW, LAURA; Masuk HS; Monroe, CT; (Y); 7/275; Math Tm; Ski Clb; Spanish Clb; VP Concert Band; Mrchg Band; School Musical; Stage Crew; Nwsp Ed-Chief; High Hon Roll; NHS; Outstndng JR Math Stu 85; 3 Yr Bnd Awd 85; Spnsh Class Awd 83-85; Coll; Sci.

MASON, BETH; Suffield HS; West Suffield, CT; (Y); 6/154; Band; Concert Band; Madrigals; School Musical; Symp Band; Var JV Fld Hcky; Var Mgr(s); High Hon Roll; Hon Roll; NHS; Excel In Alg I; Cls Of 76 Bicentnl Awd; Pres Acad Awd; Dickinson Coll; Sci.

MASONE, BRYAN; Daniel Havel HS; Madison, CT; (Y); 100/250; Model UN; Spanish Clb; Nwsp Phtg; Nwsp Rptr; Nwsp Stf; Coach Actv; CC Awd; Natl Soc Stud Olmpd Awd 85; Hstry.

MASOTTI, JOHN; Bristol Central HS; Bristol, CT; (Y); Church Yth Grp; Ski Clb; Varsity Clb; Tennis; U Of CT; Engrng.

MASSEY, MIKE; Norwalk HS; Norwalk, CT; (Y); #26 In Class; Cmnty Wkr; Ski Clb; Spanish Clb; Yrbk Stf; Rep Soph Cls; Rep Jr Cls; Var Capt Tennis; Hon Roll; Natl Sci Olympiad Merit 85; Bus.

MASSI, MARIA; St Thomas Aquinas HS; New Britain, CT; (Y); 1/154; Church Yth Grp; Cmnty Wkr; Debate Tm; French Clb; Hosp Aide; JA; Latin Clb; Political Wkr; Y-Teens; Yrbk Ed-Chief; Fres Engl Awd 83; JR Engl Awd 85; Trignmntry Awd 85; Jrnlsm.

MASSICOTT, RICKY J; H C Wilcox Regional Voc Tech Schl; Meriden, CT; (Y); 1/200; Am Leg Boys St; Ski Clb; VICA; High Hon Roll; NHS; Val; U Of CT; Elctrcl Engrng.

MASSICOTTE, MICHAEL; Northwest Catholic HS; W Simsbury, CT; (Y); French Clb; Ski Clb; Yrbk Stf; Var Socr; Var Tennis; Var Trk; Hon Roll; Prfct Atten Awd; St Michaels; Bus.

MASTERS, KAREN E; Farmington HS; Hartford, CT; (Y); 73/220; Church Yth Grp; Dance Clb; Chorus; Church Choir; Engl.

MASTO, CHRISTOPHER; Amity Regional HS; Orange, CT; (S); 3/376; Boy Scts; Church Yth Grp; Drama Clb; Spanish Clb; Nwsp Rptr; Yrbk Stf; VP Stu Cncl; VP Capt Swmmng; Hon Roll; NHS; Eagle Scout 84; Engr.

MASTO, STEPHEN; Notre Dame HS; Orange, CT; (Y); Sec Boy Scts; Church Yth Grp; Nwsp Stf; Im Bsktbl; JV Crs Cntry; Var L Trk; High Hon Roll; NHS; Mth Hnr Soc; Bus.

MASTRODIMOS, ZOE; Stratford HS; Stratford, CT; (Y); 1/247; Off Sr Cls; Bausch & Lomb Sci Awd; DAR Awd; High Hon Roll; Trs NHS; Pres Schlr; Val; Harvard Bk Awd 85; Rensselaer Medal 84; Full Paid Tuitn Fairfld U 85; Fairfield U; Politcs.

MASTROGIOVANNI, WILLIAM; Torrington HS; Torrington, CT; (Y); 16/320; French Clb; Model UN; Bsktbl; JV Ftbl; High Hon Roll; NHS; NEDT Awd; Prfct Atten Awd; Publ Artcle Wrtng Wrld Afrs 85; Pre Med.

MASTROIANNI, MICHAEL; Pomperaug HS; Middlebury, CT; (Y); 97/226; Im Bsbl; Im Bsktbl; Im Socr; Im Sftbl; Im Swmmng; Im Vllybl; Lion Awd; Middlebury Lions Clb Schlrshp Awd 85; U Connecticut; Phrmcy.

MATIAS, LISA; Farmington HS; Farmington, CT; (Y); 13/204; Acpl Chr; Chorus; Var Gym; High Hon Roll; Hon Roll; NHS; Spanish NHS; Dance.

MATIC, JANETTE; Westhill HS; Stamford, CT; (Y); Church Yth Grp; French Clb; Hon Roll; Bus Educ Awd 82-83; Spnsh Awd 84-85; U Of Bridgeport; Elec Engrng.

MATOS, EVELINDA; Crosby HS; Waterbury, CT; (Y); Art Clb; Pres Church Yth Grp; Latin Clb; Spanish Clb; Hon Roll; Prfct Atten Awd; Law.

MATOS, LAUREN; Naugatuck HS; Naugatuck, CT; (Y); Office Aide; Spanish Clb; Chorus; Pres Frsh Cls; Pres Soph Cls; Pres Jr Cls; Var Capt Badmtn; L Tennis; High Hon Roll; Hstry Clb Secy 84-85; Funeral Director.

MATT, THOMAS J; Valley Regional HS; Chester, CT; (Y); 10/145; Church Yth Grp; School Musical; Yrbk Stf; Var L Socr; Var L Tennis; NHS; SAR Awd; Chorus; Variety Show; Lit Mag; Ponds Famly Theme Awd 82; CT Schltc Art Awd 85; Hallmark Hnr Prize 85; Boston U; Art.

MATTHEWS, TANYA; Bloomfield HS; Bloomfield, CT; (Y); 39/289; Hosp Aide; Pep Clb; Color Guard; Hon Roll; Spanish NHS; Bst Spnsh II Stdnt 84; Briarwd Bk & Bst Shrthd Stdnt Awds 85; Secy.

MATTIE, JEAN; Oliver Wolcott RVTS HS; Torrington, CT; (S); Art Clb; VICA; Yrbk Ed-Chief; Rep Stu Cncl; Sftbl; Psychlgy.

MATTISON, KAREN; Ridgefield HS; Ridgefield, CT; (Y); 5/380; Art Clb; Lit Mag; Var L Cheerleading; Var L Lcrss; Var L Trk; Var L Vllybl; Cit Awd; High Hon Roll; Ntl Merit Ltr; Pres Schlr; Exclinc In Cermc Sclptr 85; Engl Awd/USC Trste Schlrshp 83-85; Acad Excllnc & Presdtl 81-85; U South CA; Arch.

MATTO, JEFF; Joseph A Foren HS; Milford, CT; (Y); 15/250; Am Leg Boys St; FBLA; Key Clb; Rep Stu Cncl; Var Bsbl; JV Bsktbl; Var Socr; Hon Roll; NHS; Ntl Merit Ltr; Finance.

MATTSON, JOHN; East Haven HS; East Haven, CT; (Y); 18/300; Am Leg Boys St; Spanish Clb; Band; Concert Band; Jazz Band; Mrchg Band; High Hon Roll; Hon Roll; NHS; N Haven Model Congrss 85; Musician.

MATURO III, ALFRED; Xavier HS; Middletown, CT; (Y); 30/222; Am Leg Boys St; VP Soph Cls; VP Jr Cls; VP Sr Cls; VP Stu Cncl; JV Var Ftbl; JV Var Trk; High Hon Roll; Hon Roll; NHS; Brother Celesine Awd 83; Ssgt Thomas Smith Scholar 85.

MATURO, AMEDEO; Hamden HS; Hamden, CT; (Y); Hon Roll; TCI; Elec Engr.

MATUSOVICH, WENDY; Pomperaug HS; Southbury, CT; (Y); 25/220; Cmnty Wkr; Model UN; Yrbk Stf; Pres Soph Cls; Pres Jr Cls; Rep Stu Cncl; VP Capt Fld Hcky; Var Capt Sftbl; CC Awd; Hon Roll; Conf 2nd Tm Sftbl Ptchr 84-85; Hnrbl Mntn Conf Goalie-Fld Hcky 84-85; Educ.

MAULTSBY, KIMBERLY; West Haven HS; W Haven, CT; (Y); Computer Clb; Exploring; Intnl Clb; Pep Clb; Color Guard; Madrigals; Off Frsh Cls; Off Soph Cls; Rep Jr Cls; Off Stu Cncl; Amer Indstrl Arts Stu Assn 83-85; Schlstc Excllnc Bnd 85; Schlstc Excllnc Mdrgls 83; Busn.

MAURICE, MEG; Norwich Free Acad; Baltic, CT; (Y); Art Clb; Sec 4-H; Quiz Bowl; Spanish Clb; JV Gym; JV Trk; 4-H Awd; Hon Roll; Estrn CT Coll; Chldhd Dev.

MAUTTEIII, SIDNEY DOUGLAS; West Woods Christian Acad; Meriden, CT; (Y); 1/8; Teachers Aide; Yrbk Ed-Chief; Pres Sr Cls; Pres Stu Cncl; Capt Socr; Val; Pres Chess Clb; Computer Clb; Acad All-Amer 84-85; Natl Sci Olympiad-Phy Sci 82-83; Acad Excell Awd By Schl; Kings Coll; Math.

MAVOR, JASON H; Killingly HS; Ballouville, CT; (Y); 25/270; 4-H; Ski Clb; Pres Temple Yth Grp; Stu Cncl; Ftbl; Hon Roll; St Schlr; Ed Loans Encrg Excel Tchng 85; U CT; Engrng.

MAXWELL, KATHLEEN; Watertown HS; Watertown, CT; (Y); 64/247; Pres Church Yth Grp; Trs French Clb; Sec Trs Band; Church Choir; Yrbk Bus Mgr; Sec Soph Cls; Mgr(s); Vllybl; Hon Roll; Yrbk Awd, Siemon Co Schlrshp Awd 85; Mattatuck Coll; Librl Arts.

MAYER, LORRAINE; East Lyme HS; E Lyme, CT; (Y); 2/271; Art Clb; JV Sftbl; High Hon Roll; Hon Roll; Owens Art Awd 85; Vconn Hnrs Smnr 85; Art.

MAYER, LYNN; Trumbull HS; Trumbull, CT; (Y); AFS; Church Yth Grp; Computer Clb; Drama Clb; Pres Key Clb; Mrchg Band; Stage Crew; Lit Mag; High Hon Roll; Cmnty Wkr; Stu Ldr 84-85; U Of Bridgeport; Pol Sci.

MAYHEW, CINDY; Hartford Public HS; Hartford, CT; (Y); Var Tennis; Hon Roll; Bus.

MAZZUCCO, BENJAMIN; Notre Dame HS; E Haven, CT; (Y); Computer Clb; Hosp Aide; Hon Roll; Comp Pgmr.

MC BRIDE, SHELLEY; Saint Bernard HS; Lisbon, CT; (S); 32/290; Church Yth Grp; Nwsp Rptr; Pres Soph Cls; Pres Jr Cls; Chrmn Stu Cncl; Stat JV Bsbl; JV Stat Sftbl; L Capt Tennis; DAR Awd; SR Class Rep Parents Cncl 84-85; ST Bernard Rep Japan 82; Bio.

MC BRIDE, SHIRLEY; West Haven HS; New Haven, CT; (Y); Church Yth Grp; Debate Tm; Band; Chorus; Church Choir; Rep Jr Cls; Mgr(s); JV Sftbl; Mgr Swmmng; Var Tennis; Norwalk CC; Liberal Arts.

MC CANN, DAVID; Tortellotte Memorial HS; N Grosvenordale, CT; (Y); 1/97; Am Leg Boys St; Pres Frsh Cls; Pres Soph Cls; Stu Cncl; High Hon Roll; Hon Roll; Jr NHS; NHS; Ski Clb; Yrbk Stf; Rensselaer Awd Math & Sci 85; Awd Excll Amer Stud & US Hstry 85; West Point; Aero Engnrng.

MC CARLEY, KRISTIE; Danbury HS; Danbury, CT; (Y); 181/612; Drama Clb; Church Choir; School Musical; Nwsp Rptr; Nwsp Stf; Yrbk Stf; Rep Jr Cls; Hon Roll; Prfct Atten Awd; George Perry Awd Phy Ed 83-84; Hnbl Mntn Wrtg Ptry 82-83; Theatr Arts.

MC CARTHY, CRAIG; Bristol Central HS; Bristol, CT; (Y); 45/340; Am Leg Boys St; Boys Clb Am; Stu Cncl; Capt Var Bsbl; Capt Var Bsktbl; Cit Awd; Yth Yr Bys Clbs Amer; Bentley Coll; Accntng.

MC CARTHY, KARA BETH; West Haven HS; W Haven, CT; (Y); Church Yth Grp; Civic Clb; Cmnty Wkr; Political Wkr; High Hon Roll; Hon Roll; Jr NHS; NHS; Knights Columbus Exclnce Awd Religion 82; Med.

MC CARTHY, KELLY; Shelton HS; Shelton, CT; (Y); Cmnty Wkr; Hosp Aide; Office Aide; Ski Clb; Spanish Clb; Rep Frsh Cls; Rep Soph Cls; Rep Jr Cls; Cheerleading; Gym; Nrsg.

MC CARTHY, KRISTIN; Farmington HS; Farmington, CT; (Y); Ski Clb; Nwsp Sprt Ed; VP Frsh Cls; Var Capt Socr; Var Tennis; Var Trk; Exploring; Chorus; Rep Soph Cls; Rep Jr Cls; CT Sccr Coaches Assn All-St 83 & 84; Hearld Bk Awd-Jrnlsm Excllnc 85; Hartford Courant All-St Sccr 84.

MC CARTHY, PATRICIA; Lauralton Hall HS; Trumbull, CT; (Y); French Clb; Science Clb; Service Clb; School Play; Nwsp Stf; Ed Yrbk Phtg; Lit Mag; Im Vllybl; Amer Legn Schl Awd 82; 2nd Pl Sci Fair 82; Hnbl Mntn ST Sci Fair 82; Sci.

MC CARTHY, SUSAN M; Convent Of The Sacred Heart; Stamford, CT; (Y); Aud/Vis; Library Aide; Chorus; Stage Crew; Nwsp Ed-Chief; Rep Sr Cls; Achvt For Art & Comm Svc 84; Personal Exhibition Of Work 84; Illustration.

MC CAULEY, KERRY; Bethel HS; Bethel, CT; (Y); 36/268; Exploring; Chorus; School Musical; Variety Show; High Hon Roll; Hon Roll; Jr NHS; NHS; Pre-Vet.

MC CLOSKEY, SEAN; Killingly HS; Danielson, CT; (Y); 1/300; Am Leg Boys St; VP Soph Cls; VP Jr Cls; Var Bsbl; Var Socr; NHS; Val; Church Yth Grp; Band; Mrchg Band; Amer Legn Boys Nation 85; Eastern CT Conf All Star Soccer Tm 84; Brown U Book Awd 85; Latin Hnr Soc 84; Lawyer.

MC CORD, SAMANTHA A; Granby HS; N Granby, CT; (Y); Concert Band; Var Fld Hcky; Var Sftbl; Hon Roll; Cornell; Vetrnrn Med.

MC CORMACK, KELLY; Berlin HS; Kensington, CT; (Y); 33/183; Am Leg Aux Girls St; Teachers Aide; Capt Color Guard; Nwsp Stf; Ed Lit Mag; Hon Roll; NHS; Service Clb; Art & Calligraphy Awds 84; Art & Colby Coll Bk Awd 85; Wesleyan U Ctr Creative Yth Vis Arts 85; Grphc Art.

MC CORMACK, MAUREEN; Trumbull HS; Trumbull, CT; (Y); AFS; Church Yth Grp; Girl Scts; Hosp Aide; Spanish Clb; Chorus; Color Guard; Mrchg Band; High Hon Roll; NHS; 1st Clss Awd In Grl Scouting 81; Silver Awd In Grl Scouting 83; Med.

MC CORMICK, TERESA A; East Windsor HS; Broad Brook, CT; (Y); Band; Chorus; Church Choir; Madrigals; Rep Jr Cls; Cheerleading; Trk; Hon Roll.

MC CREARY, KERRIE; The Morgan Schl; Clinton, CT; (Y); Sec 4-H; Hosp Aide; Spanish Clb; Hon Roll; Marine Bio.

MC CULLAGH, JEANNE; Stamford Catholic HS; Stamford, CT; (Y); 22/156; Yrbk Stf; High Hon Roll; Hon Roll; NHS; Prtcptd In Chemathon 85; Vet.

MC CULLOUGH, LOUISE; Newtown HS; Newtown, CT; (Y); 29/293; Pres AFS; Hosp Aide; Spanish Clb; Var Socr; Var Tennis; High Hon Roll; Hon Roll; Spanish NHS; French Clb; Key Clb; Spnsh Hnr Tutr 84.

MC DONAGH, CHRISTOPHER S; The Hotchkiss Schl; Wilton, CT; (Y); Nwsp Rptr; Yrbk Stf; Im Ice Hcky; Var JV Lcrss; Im Socr; Hon Roll; Ntl Merit SF; Economics.

MC DONALD, DEBORAH; Farmington HS; Farmington, CT; (Y); Church Yth Grp; Drama Clb; Chorus; Madrigals; School Play; JV Trk; Hon Roll; Psych.

MC DONALD, DINA; Lauralton Hall HS; Fairfield, CT; (Y); 15/117; French Clb; GAA; Hosp Aide; Latin Clb; Math Clb; Math Tm; Model UN; Service Clb; Orch; Yrbk Stf; Math Exam Awd 85; Civc Ldrshp Awd Blackrck Cmnty 1st Pl 84; Cm Laud Awd Ntl Latn Exm 84; Bus Adm.

MC DONALD III, JOHN W; Bethel HS; Bethel, CT; (Y); 120/250; Pres DECA; Radio Clb; School Play; Stage Crew; Rep Frsh Cls; Rep Soph Cls; JV Ice Hcky; Hon Roll; DECA Dist 3rd Pl, ST 1st-Natl CDC 83-84; DECA Dist 4th Pl, ST 2nd Pl-Natl CDC 84-85; Waterbury ST Tech; Elec Engrng.

MC DOUGALL, BRIAN; Coventry HS; Coventry, CT; (Y); 4/108; Boy Scts; Trs Drama Clb; Yrbk Sprt Ed; JV Trk; Bausch & Lomb Sci Awd; High Hon Roll; NHS; Ntl Merit SF; Colgate U; Econ.

MC DOWELL, BILL; Bethel HS; Bethel, CT; (Y); Church Yth Grp; DECA; JA; Stage Crew; Variety Show; JV Var Socr; High Hon Roll; NHS; JR Mrshl Gradtn; Bus Admin.

MC FADDEN, MARK; Avon Old Farms HS; Madison, CT; (S); 12/110; Church Yth Grp; Cmnty Wkr; Pep Clb; Radio Clb; Yrbk Rptr; JV Lcrss; Socr; Cit Awd; Hon Roll; Jrnlsm.

MC FARLAND, ROBERT; Simsbury HS; Simsbury, CT; (Y); 6/352; Am Leg Boys St; Church Yth Grp; JA; Church Choir; School Musical; School Play; Yrbk Bus Mgr; Cit Awd; High Hon Roll; NHS; Best Actr-One Act Play Cls Comptn 84; Engrng.

MC FARLANE, GERALDINE; Masuk HS; Monroe, CT; (Y); 4/270; Math Tm; Nwsp Stf; Yrbk Stf; Crs Cntry; Trk; High Hon Roll; NHS; JA; Outstndng Achvt Frgn Lang 84; Outstndng Achvt German 85; Outstndng Achvt Soc Stu 85; Chem Engrng.

MC GARRITY, HEATHER; Torrington HS; Torrington, CT; (Y); English Clb; Ski Clb; Nwsp Rptr; Nwsp Stf; JV Trk; High Hon Roll; Hon Roll; NHS; Drama Clb; Thesps; CT Math Leag Hnrbl Mntn; Pre-Law.

MC GARRY, EDWARD; Ansonia HS; Ansonia, CT; (Y); 20/169; Cmnty Wkr; Computer Clb; Nwsp Rptr; Nwsp Stf; Yrbk Stf; Var L Bsbl; Var L Ftbl; Wt Lftg; Hon Roll; Prfct Atten Awd; Outstndng JV Awd Bsbl 85; Le High Coll; Cmnctns.

MC GILL, LYNN; Ansonia HS; Ansonia, CT; (Y); Computer Clb; Spanish Clb; Varsity Clb; Yrbk Stf; JV Var Bsktbl; Var Cheerleading; Indctd In Spnsh Natl Hnr Soc 85; Rcvd Hnrs 83-85; Mth Tchr.

MC GLASSON, LAURA; Tolland HS; Tolland, CT; (Y); Cmnty Wkr; Debate Tm; Hosp Aide; Yrbk Ed-Chief; Hon Roll; Hist.

MC GLYNN, JULIE; Brookfield HS; Brookfield, CT; (Y); 18/240; Band; Mrchg Band; Var Bsktbl; Var Fld Hcky; Var Sftbl; NHS.

MC GOLDRICK, AMY; Wolcott HS; Marion, CT; (Y); 42/397; Spanish Clb; Yrbk Ed-Chief; Trs Frsh Cls; Stu Cncl; Var Cheerleading; Hon Roll.

MC GOVERN, BARBARA; Hamden HS; Hamden, CT; (Y); 108/451; Sec Frsh Cls; Rep Soph Cls; Hst Jr Cls; Hst Sr Cls; Hon Roll; Amity Charitable Schlrshp 85; Hammerman-Moody Schlrshp 85; Edward Lent Mem Schlrshp 85; Cookng Achvt 85; U Of MA Amherst; Htl Adm.

MC GOVERN, GEORGE; Masuk HS; Monroe, CT; (Y); 70/320; Church Yth Grp; JCL; Latin Clb; Letterman Clb; Spanish Clb; Varsity Clb; JV Var Bsbl; Var Capt Ice Hcky; Spanish NHS; Hocky Coaches Awd 84-85; Clarkson U; Civl Engr.

MC GRATH, PATRICIA; Kolbe-Cathedral HS; Bridgeport, CT; (Y); Camera Clb; Computer Clb; Hosp Aide; Hon Roll; U S Hstry & Govt Awd 85; Law.

MC GUINNESS, KATHERINE A; Central Catholic HS; Norwalk, CT; (Y); 6/96; Am Leg Aux Girls St; Drama Clb; French Clb; Ski Clb; Mgr Stage Crew; Ed Yrbk Ed-Chief; French Hon Soc; NHS; NEDT Awd; Knghts Of Clmbs Annual Schlrshp 83 & 85.

MC GUIRE, BRIDGET; St Bernard HS; Norwich, CT; (Y); 120/300; Church Yth Grp; JA; Red Cross Aide; Rep Jr Cls; Rep Stu Cncl; Ftbl; Robert Demars Awd Hnr Achvt & Christn Ldrshp 83; Pre-Med.

MC GUIRE, KARA; Central Catholic HS; Norwalk, CT; (Y); French Clb; Office Aide; Stu Cncl; Var Cheerleading; Var Trk; Hon Roll; Psych.

MC GUIRE, LAURA; St Bernard HS; Noank, CT; (S); Library Aide; Chorus; Church Choir; Swing Chorus; Gym; High Hon Roll; Hon Roll; Music.

MC GUIRE, MEGAN; Guilford HS; Guilford, CT; (Y); Church Yth Grp; Cmnty Wkr; GAA; Mrchg Band; Sec Soph Cls; Pres Jr Cls; Pres Sr Cls; Rep Stu Cncl; Capt Fld Hcky; Hon Roll; Field Hocky MVP 84.

MC GURK, JAMIE A; Litchfield HS; Litchfield, CT; (Y); 25/100; AFS; Boy Scts; Camera Clb; Church Yth Grp; FCA; Quiz Bowl; Radio Clb; Scholastic Bowl; Variety Show; Var Socr; Coach/Capt Swmmg Awd 83; Swmmng Rcd Awds 400 Relay & Brstrke 83; Cinema.

MC INTYRE, TIMOTHY; Rockville HS; Vernon, CT; (Y); 9/360; Church Yth Grp; Jazz Band; Pep Band; Var L Cheerleading; Var L Socr; High Hon Roll; NHS.

MC KAIGE, WENDY; Sacred Heart Acad HS; Stamford, CT; (Y); Art Clb; Hosp Aide; Hon Roll; NHS; Spanish NHS; Magna Cum Laude Awd; Excllnc In Spnsh Awd; Safe Rds Of Stamford.

MC KEEVER, KEVIN; Stamford Catholic HS; Stamford, CT; (Y); 1/141; Aud/Vis; Math Tm; Capt Quiz Bowl; Nwsp Ed-Chief; Nwsp Rptr; Nwsp Stf; Lit Mag; Var Bsbl; Mgr(s); Stat Vllybl; Harvard Bk Awd 84-85; Jrnlsn.

MC KENNA, JENNIFER; East Catholic HS; S Windsor, CT; (Y); 4-H; French Clb; Pep Clb; Chorus; Drm Mjr(t); Rep Soph Cls; Rep Jr Cls; Rep Stu Cncl; Twrlr; 4-H Awd; Majrtte Awd 85; Archry Cert For Achvt 85; Elem Ed.

MC KENNA, JOHN; St Bernard HS; Oakdale, CT; (S); Stu Cncl; JV Bsbl; JV Crs Cntry; JV Socr; Hon Roll; Gen Art Excllnce Awd 82-83; MIT; Chem.

MC KENNA III, JOSEPH; Windsor Locks HS; Windsor Locks, CT; (Y); 12/170; Am Leg Boys St; Boy Scts; Ftbl; Capt Golf; Hon Roll; NHS; Talcott Mtn Sci Ctr Nova I & II 84; Natl Chemathon 85; All Conf Glf Tm 85.

MC KENNA, KRISTEN; St Bernard HS; Gales Ferry, CT; (S); Dance Clb; Library Aide; Chorus; Hon Roll; Med.

MC KEON, MICHAEL; Saint Barnard HS; Niantic, CT; (Y); 70/305; Cmnty Wkr; Computer Clb; Drama Clb; School Play; Yrbk Stf; VP Sr Cls; Stu Cncl; Crs Cntry; Socr; Trk; Peer Ldrshp 85.

MC KEON, RICHARD; Amity Regional SR HS; Woodbridge, CT; (Y); 148/376; Church Yth Grp; Cmnty Wkr; FBLA; Latin Clb; Yrbk Stf; Lion Awd; Am Leg Post 127 85; Amity Ed Fund Scholar Grnt 85; Fairfield U; Bus.

MC KERNAN, CHRIS; Notre Dame HS; W Haven, CT; (Y); 18/248; Church Yth Grp; L Var Crs Cntry; L Var Trk; Cit Awd; High Hon Roll; NHS; W Haven Rotry Clb Schlr Athlt 85; U Of Charleston WV; Bus Mgmt.

MC KEW, TIMOTHY; East Lyme HS; E Lyme, CT; (Y); 90/260; Stat Bsktbl; Mgr(s); Hon Roll; U CT; Eng.

MC KINNEY II, THOMAS EARL; Fairfield Preparatory College; Stamford, CT; (Y); Boy Scts; Debate Tm; JA; Library Aide; Model UN; Im Bsktbl; JV Socr; Var L Trk; Jr NHS; Prfct Atten Awd; 3rd CT Ortrcl 84; Bst 1st Yr Achvr 85; Law.

MC KNERNEY, KEVIN; Southington HS; Plantsville, CT; (Y); Cmnty Wkr; Ski Clb; Var L Wrstlng; Hon Roll.

MC KNIGHT, WHITNEY; Glastonbury HS; Apalachin, NY; (Y); 76/393; Dance Clb; Pres Sec French Clb; Intnl Clb; Chrmn Model UN; Political Wkr; School Play; Capt Cheerleading; Mgr(s); Var Trk; Hon Roll; Miss New England Amer Co-Ed 84; Rotary Clb Prod Shw Qn Fnlst 84; Mary Washington Coll; Frnch.

MC LAUGHLIN, DIANE; Coginchaug Regional HS; Durham, CT; (Y); AFS; Varsity Clb; Concert Band; Off Frsh Cls; Off Soph Cls; Off Jr Cls; Off Sr Cls; Var Co-Capt Cheerleading; Socr; Vllybl; Quinnipiac; Phys Thrpy.

MC LAUGHLIN, SUE; Wilton HS; Wilton, CT; (Y); 5/300; Hosp Aide; Band; Nwsp Stf; Sec Frsh Cls; Trs Sr Cls; Var Socr; JV Capt Sftbl; JV Trk; High Hon Roll; NHS; Dartmouth Alumni Bk Awd 85; CT Jr Intershp Pgm.

MC LEES, MELISSA A; Daniel Hand HS; Madison, CT; (Y); 4-H; Hon Roll; TSGA Yth Tm Good Sportsmnshp Awd 83; Amer Assn U Womn Awd Merit 85; Hlth.

MC LELLAN, DELISA; Westhill HS; Stamford, CT; (Y); Church Yth Grp; DECA; Girl Scts; OEA; Chorus; Church Choir; Color Guard; Rep Frsh Cls; Rep Soph Cls; Hon Roll; Bus.

MC LEOD, DIONNE; Norwalk HS; E Norwalk, CT; (Y).

MC MAHON, KATHLEEN; Amity Regional HS; Orange, CT; (Y); Drama Clb; FHA; FNA; Hosp Aide; Ski Clb; Spanish Clb; Chorus; Yrbk Stf; Stu Cncl; Swmmng; Nrsng.

MC MAHON, LORA; Crosby HS; Waterbury, CT; (Y); Art Clb; Church Yth Grp; Hosp Aide; Swmmng; Hon Roll; Nursng.

MC MILLAN, DARYL; Notre Dame HS; New Haven, CT; (Y); Church Yth Grp; Church Choir; Variety Show; Assumption Coll; Accntnt.

MC NAMARA, LAURA; St Joseph HS; Trumbull, CT; (Y); 24/240; JA; Spanish Clb; Stage Crew; Nwsp Sprt Ed; Yrbk Stf; JV Vllybl; NHS; Spanish NHS; Cmmnctns.

MC NAMARA, PAUL; Masuk HS; Monroe, CT; (Y); 2/278; Math Tm; Spanish Clb; Stu Cncl; High Hon Roll; NHS; Ntl Merit Ltr; Outstndg Eng Stu 85; Outstndg Soc Stud Stu 84; CT Hnrs Sem U Of CT; Vet Med.

MC NAMARA, TERRY; Ansonia HS; Ansonia, CT; (Y); Am Leg Boys St; Computer Clb; English Clb; French Clb; Latin Clb; Yrbk Stf; Var L Bsbl; Var Capt Bsktbl; Var L Ftbl; Var L Golf; Trinity; Librl Arts.

MC NEILL, YVONNE; Sacred Heart Acad; West Haven, CT; (Y); High Hon Roll; Prfct Atten Awd; Spanish NHS.

MC QUEEN, WENDY; Tolland HS; Tolland, CT; (Y); Office Aide; Var Gym; Trk; Hon Roll; Lab Tech.

MC QUOWN, CHRISTY; Montville HS; Uncasville, CT; (Y); Cmnty Wkr; Office Aide; Hon Roll; Bus.

MC WILLIAMS, WILLIAM A; New Fairfield HS; New Fairfield, CT; (Y); 11/226; JA; Latin Clb; Math Clb; Model UN; Var L Socr; High Hon Roll; NHS; Ntl Merit SF; Church Yth Grp; Hon Roll; Erth Sci & Bio Hnrs 82 & 83; U Of CT; Physics.

MEADDOUGH, ERIKA L; Amity Regional SR HS; Bethany, CT; (Y); 17/376; Church Yth Grp; Hosp Aide; Spanish Clb; Chorus; Church Choir; Concert Band; Jazz Band; Orch; Tennis; Hon Roll; Ntl Spnsh Exam Cert 83; Acad Chair Achvt 84; Bio Sci.

MEADE, SHARON; Ansonia HS; Ansonia, CT; (Y); 8/135; Teachers Aide; Nwsp Stf; Yrbk Stf; CC Awd; High Hon Roll; NHS; Spanish NHS; VFW Awd; Voice Dem Awd; Womens Clb Scholar 85; George Hegyi Scholar 85; Gerard Ryan Scholar 85; U Of ME Farmington; Spec Ed.

MEADOWS, KATHY N; Westminster Schl; Henderson, NC; (Y); French Clb; Mrchg Band; School Play; Symp Band; JV Capt Socr; Var Sftbl; Capt JV Vllybl; High Hon Roll; Hon Roll; Jr NHS; Awd Outstndng Gr Pt 82; Awd Excel Frnch 1 82; Cmmndtn Frnch II Hnrs; Studio Art.

MEASER, CARL; Hall HS; W Hartford, CT; (Y); 177/324; Temple Yth Grp; Chorus; School Musical; Symp Band; Var L Lcrss; Var L Socr; Var Capt Swmmng; Hon Roll; Mst Vlbl Swmmr 85.

MEDINA, DANIELLE; Notre Dame C HS; Bpt, CT; (Y); 94/284; Church Yth Grp; Pep Clb; Spanish Clb; Chorus; School Musical; School Play; Stage Crew; Rep Frsh Cls; Rep Soph Cls; High Hon Roll; Pace U; Lit.

MEDINA, NORA; Bassick HS; Bpt, CT; (Y); Band; Mrchg Band; High Hon Roll; NHS; Musician.

MEDINA, NYDIA; Kolbe-Cathedral HS; Bridgeport, CT; (Y); Church Yth Grp; JA; Church Choir; Nwsp Stf; Trs Frsh Cls; Rep Jr Cls; Bsktbl; Score Keeper; Sftbl; Vllybl.

MEHTA, BEJUN; Guilford HS; Ann Arbor, MI; (Y); Chorus; Church Choir; Madrigals; Orch; High Hon Roll; Rotary Awd; Solo Vcl Albm Wth LA Chmbr Orch 85; NY Dbt Vcl 82; NY Tms & NY Mag; Amer Music Tchrs Strng Comp 82; Yale U.

MEIMAN, MARGARET; Andrew Warde HS; Fairfield, CT; (Y); Aud/Vis; Cmnty Wkr; Drama Clb; Political Wkr; Chorus; Orch; School Play; Mgr Stage Crew; Thesps; Hon Roll; Schl Dramatic Awd 84-85; SOCL Work.

MELE, DONNA; New Britain SR HS; New Britain, CT; (Y); Sec Church Yth Grp; JA; Key Clb; Office Aide; Red Cross Aide; Color Guard; Yrbk Stf; Rep Jr Cls; Sftbl; Hon Roll; Psych.

MELENDEZ, DEAN; Hartford Public HS; Hartford, CT; (Y); Am Leg Boys St; Church Yth Grp; Pres Computer Clb; Soroptimist; Ed Lit Mag; Pres Frsh Cls; Trs Jr Cls; Rep Stu Cncl; Crs Cntry; Hon Roll; U Of CT Connpep Incntv Awds 83-84; Boys ST Mst Vol Del Awd 85; Hghr Horizon Hghst-Englsh/Math/Sci Aw; Med.

MELENDEZ, KRISTEN; Guilford HS; Guilford, CT; (Y); 37/266; Church Yth Grp; Hon Roll; Natl Hspnc Schlr Awds Semi-Fin 8k; U Of CT; Bio.

MELLO, LISA; Lyman Memorial HS; Lebanon, CT; (Y); 2/81; Am Leg Aux Girls St; Trs FBLA; Girl Scts; Var Capt Bsktbl; Var Capt Socr; Elks Awd; Lion Awd; NHS; Sal; Schlr Athlete Awd 85; Wheaton Coll; Ed.

MELO, VERA; Hartford Public HS; Hartford, CT; (S); Cmnty Wkr; DECA; Drama Clb; JA; Model UN; Swmmng; Tennis; Hon Roll; UCLA; Bus.

MELOTTO, ALBERT; Notre Dame HS; W Haven, CT; (Y); Church Yth Grp; Im Tennis; Engrng.

MELTON, WILHELMINA; Hopkins Grmmr Day Prospect Hll HS; West Haven, CT; (Y); JV Socr; Var Capt Vllybl; ISIS Scholar 81-85; Med Tech.

MELVIN, MICHAEL; Avon Old Farms Schl; Avon, CT; (S); 7/110; Church Yth Grp; Radio Clb; Var Crs Cntry; Var Trk; Capt Wrstlng; Hon Roll; Elec Engr.

MENDEZ, REBECCA; Wilbur Cross HS; New Haven, CT; (Y); Church Yth Grp; Hosp Aide; JA; Office Aide; Red Cross Aide; Spanish Clb; Band; Mrchg Band; School Play; Stage Crew.

MENDOZA, PAULA; Brien Mc Mahon HS; Norwalk, CT; (Y); GAA; JA; Stage Crew; Rep Soph Cls; JV Crs Cntry; Trk; Hon Roll; U Of CT; Math.

MENKEN, MERIDETH E; New Fairfield HS; New Fairfield, CT; (Y); 31/218; Pres Latin Clb; Political Wkr; Lit Mag; Off Jr Cls; Off Stu Cncl; NHS; Ntl Merit SF; Office Aide; Hon Roll; Achvt Awd Wrtng 84; 6th Pl ST Latin Exm 83; Fnlst Union Carbide Wrkshp Prog 84.

MENNA, JULIE; Brien Mc Mahon HS; Norwalk, CT; (Y); Band; Concert Band; Jazz Band; Mrchg Band; Symp Band; Rep Jr Cls; Rep Sr Cls; High Hon Roll; Hon Roll; JR Ldrshp Awd Bus Katherine Gibbs 85; Typg II Awd 85; Hon Men Norwalk Sci Fair 84; Katherine Gibbs; Sec.

MENO, CAROLYN; Wilton HS; Wilton, CT; (Y); 69/335; Hosp Aide; Pep Clb; Acpl Chr; Chorus; Madrigals; Swing Chorus; L Fld Hcky; JV Tennis; Hon Roll; Dickinson Coll.

MENZEL, SALLY; Daniel Hand HS; Madison, CT; (Y); Drama Clb; Ski Clb; Thesps; Band; Yrbk Rptr; Yrbk Stf; Mgr(s); U Of Denver; Chld Psychlgy.

MERCED, ELIZABETH; Bassick HS; Bridgeport, CT; (S); 6/200; NHS; Church Yth Grp; JA; Key Clb; Office Aide; Spanish Clb; Teachers Aide; Yrbk Stf; Hon Roll; Futuro Schlrshp 2nd Pl 85; U CT; Elem Ed.

MERCUGLIANO, LISA A; Hmden Hall Country Day HS; Hamden, CT; (Y); 9/66; Hosp Aide; Key Clb; Nwsp Ed-Chief; Nwsp Rptr; Lit Mag; Cheerleading; JV Fld Hcky; JV Sftbl; High Hon Roll; Hon Roll; Cum Laude Soc; Union Coll; Bio.

MERISOTIS, EMANUEL; Manchester HS; Manchester, CT; (Y); AFS; Am Leg Boys St; Church Yth Grp; French Clb; Math Tm; JV Bsktbl; JV Crs Cntry; High Hon Roll; Hon Roll; NHS; Math.

MERO, ROXANA; New Haven Cooperative HS; New Haven, CT; (Y); 10/51; Church Yth Grp; Nwsp Stf; Lit Mag; Stu Cncl; Tennis; Hon Roll; Prfct Atten Awd; Acdmc All Amer Schlr 85; Englsh Awd 84; Hstry Awd & Yth Intvs For Peace Awd 85; Prnctn U; Bus.

MERRILL, DIANNE M; Griswold HS; Jewett City, CT; (Y); 1/100; Band; Co-Capt Tennis; Trk; High Hon Roll; NHS; Ntl Merit SF; U N Pilgrimage For Yth; Drew U; Pol Sci.

MERRILL, JEAN MARIE; Ella T Graso-Southeastern Rvt; New London, CT; (Y); 2/140; Cmnty Wkr; Hosp Aide; Sec JA; Red Cross Aide; Yrbk Stf; Rep Pres Stu Cncl; High Hon Roll; NHS; Prfct Atten Awd; Sal; St Jospeh Coll; Bus Adm.

MERRILL, JENNIFER; Cheshire HS; Cheshire, CT; (Y); Var Swmmng; Var Trk; Drama Clb; Acctng.

MERROW, KYLE; Brookfield HS; Wayne, PA; (Y); 5/267; Civic Clb; Drama Clb; Math Clb; Math Tm; Stage Crew; Trs Sr Cls; Stat Bsktbl; Var Tennis; High Hon Roll; Achvt Awd Outstndg Achvt Humn Anat 85; Pre-Med.

MESSIER, ROBERT; Bristol Central HS; Bristol, CT; (Y); Am Leg Boys St; Boy Scts; Latin Clb; Library Aide; Ski Clb; Stu Cncl; Var Capt Golf; Var Capt Socr; Hon Roll; NHS; All Conf Golf Tm 83-85; All Conf Soccer Tm 83-85; 2nd Pl ST Schlstc Golf Tour; Tennis Rnnr Up; Bus Adm.

MESSINGER, RICHARD A; William H Hall HS; W Hartford, CT; (Y); 169/330; Cmnty Wkr; Office Aide; Teachers Aide; Temple Yth Grp; Concert Band; Mrchg Band; Hon Roll; Syracuse U; Comp Sci.

METRO, KATHY A; Shelton HS; Shelton, CT; (Y); 16/438; Ski Clb; Nwsp Stf; Jr Cls; Sr Cls; Rep Stu Cncl; Var L Gym; Var L Trk; Hon Roll; NHS; Spanish NHS; John West Memrl Schlrshp Acadmc Achv 85; Spnsh Mert Awd 82-83; Stu Cncl Svc Awd 83; U Of CT; Phy Thrpy.

MEYER, MICHAEL; Masuk HS; Monroe, CT; (Y); Chess Clb; Trs Pres Church Yth Grp; Band; Concert Band; Jazz Band; Mrchg Band; Orch; Pep Band; Symp Band; Hon Roll; Penn ST; Aerontcl Engr.

MEYERS, BILL; Masuk HS; Monroe, CT; (Y); 21/285; Library Aide; Math Tm; Rep Stu Cncl; Var L Ftbl; High Hon Roll; NHS; Prfct Atten Awd; Spanish NHS; U CT; Acctg.

MEYERS, MICHELE; Plainville HS; Plainville, CT; (Y); 24/213; Church Yth Grp; Hosp Aide; Teachers Aide; Swing Chorus; Yrbk Stf; Stu Cncl; High Hon Roll; NHS; CT Schlstc Achvt 85; U Of Hartford; Comp Engrng.

MEYERS, STEVEN; Guilford HS; Guilford, CT; (Y); Model UN; Political Wkr; Red Cross Aide; Science Clb; Spanish Clb; Temple Yth Grp; Pres Orch; School Musical; Symp Band; Nwsp Rptr; Outstndg Achvt Comp Sci 83; Clark U; Pre-Med.

MEZZAPELLE, DAVID; Stamford Catholic HS; Stamford, CT; (Y); Cmnty Wkr; FBLA; JA; Pep Clb; Variety Show; Rep Jr Cls; Pres Sr Cls; Stu Cncl; Crs Cntry; High Hon Roll; Outstdng Soph Awd 8; Mayors Advsry Panel For Yth City Of Stamford 85; Law.

MEZZATESTA, BARBARA; St Joseph HS; Ansonia, CT; (Y); 56/227; Dance Clb; Drama Clb; Yrbk Stf; Hon Roll; Bus.

MICACCI, ANNMARIE; Southington HS; Southington, CT; (Y); Color Guard; Concert Band; Mrchg Band; Variety Show; Rep Soph Cls; Stat Sftbl; Capt Twrlr; NHS; Hgh Hnrs 83.

MICELI, GINA; St Bernard HS; New London, CT; (Y); 86/200; Awd Acad Excll 82 & 83; Mdl Excll Italian 83; New London Schl Bus; Med Asst.

MICHAEL, CHRISTOPHER S; St Paul Catholic HS; Meriden, CT; (Y); 3/321; JA; Spanish Clb; Bowling; Socr; Trk; NHS; Rev James E Noonah Awd 84; NHS Awd 85; 3rd Awd Religion 85; Boston Coll; Pre-Med.

MICHAELS, LYNNE; Pomperaug HS; Southbury, CT; (Y); 8/200; Church Yth Grp; Cmnty Wkr; Political Wkr; Band; Chorus; Madrigals; Mrchg Band; Pep Band; School Musical; Yrbk Stf.

MICHALAK, LISA; Berlin HS; Kensington, CT; (Y); 35/200; Church Yth Grp; Girl Scts; Band; Concert Band; Mrchg Band; Lit Mag; Jean Bertagna GSA Awd 85; U CT; Pol Sci.

MICHALKA, WAYNE; Trumbull HS; Trumbull, CT; (Y); Key Clb; Latin Clb; Ski Clb; Var Ftbl; JV Golf; Var Trk; Var Wrstlng; Hon Roll; Med.

MICHAUD, GARY P; Putnam HS; Putnam, CT; (Y); Chess Clb; Office Aide; Capt Bsktbl; Capt Ftbl; Vllybl; Nichols Coll; Bus.

MICHAUD, LIZ A; Lyme-Old Lyme HS; Old Lyme, CT; (Y); 30/110; Pres Art Clb; Computer Clb; French Clb; Girl Scts; Service Clb; Stage Crew; Ed Nwsp Stf; High Hon Roll; Hon Roll; Agl I Achvt 81-82; Art Achvt 83-84; Poster Cont Emplymnt Hndcppd Cont 2nd Pl 85; Adv.

MICHAUD, LOUISE; Manchester HS; Manchester, CT; (Y); 49/525; AFS; French Clb; Hosp Aide; JA; Var Bsktbl; High Hon Roll; Hon Roll; NH U; Ed.

MICHAUD, PAUL; East Catholic HS; E Hartford, CT; (Y); Pres Chess Clb; CAP; Yrbk Phtg; Ntl Archery Assoc Awd 82; USAF Cert Traing 85; Civil Airpatrol Cert 85; Air Trf.

MICHAUD, PAULA; Enfield HS; Enfield, CT; (Y); 6/257; Church Yth Grp; Cmnty Wkr; Yrbk Stf; Stu Cncl; High Hon Roll; NHS; Pres Schlr; Girl Scts; JA; Chorus; Calcls Awd 85; Acctg II Awd 85; Comptrs Awd 84; Bentley Coll; Acctg.

MICINITIO, ROBIN; Framk Scott Bunnell HS; Stratford, CT; (Y); 25/250; Church Yth Grp; Sec FBLA; School Musical; Ed Yrbk Sprt Ed; Rep Stu Cncl; NHS; Pres Schlr; Spanish NHS; Outstndng Svc Stdnt Cncl Awd 85; Bryant Coll; Mktg.

MICKENBERG, JULIA; Pomperaug HS; Southbury, CT; (Y); 1/215; Cmnty Wkr; Model UN; Yrbk Stf; Rep Frsh Cls; Rep Soph Cls; Rep Jr Cls; JV Var Cheerleading; High Hon Roll; Trs NHS; French Clb; Frnch Exc Awd 84-85; Math,Sci Medal 85.

MICLETTE JR, RICHARD; Crosby HS; Waterbury, CT; (Y); Latin Clb; School Play; Stage Crew; Stu Cncl; Tennis; Hon Roll; Jr NHS; NHS; U CT; Acctng.

MIDDLETON, JEANINE; West Haven HS; W Haven, CT; (Y); Band; Concert Band; Mrchg Band; Variety Show; Rep Stu Cncl; L Bsktbl; L Sftbl; Var Trk; L Vllybl; 2nd All Dist Tm Vlybl 83; All Dist Hnrb Mntn Sftbl 85; Class Athlt & Musician 83; Bio Sci.

MIEDZINSKI, IRENE; St Marys HS; New Haven, CT; (Y); 20/115; French Clb; Ski Clb; Chorus; School Musical; Lit Mag; Sftbl; French Hon Soc; Hon Roll; RI Schl Design; Advrtsng Des.

MIGLIARESE, DOLORES J; Sacred Heart HS; Waterbury, CT; (Y); Church Yth Grp; Drama Clb; Hosp Aide; Pep Clb; Chorus; School Musical; School Play; Variety Show; Cheerleading; High Hon Roll; Am Bus Womens Schlrshp 85; Marquerite Magraw Schlrshp 85; U Southern ME; Acctng.

MIHALEK, MICHAEL; Mark T Sheehan HS; Wallingford, CT; (Y); Am Leg Boys St; Key Clb; Spanish Clb; Nwsp Rptr; Yrbk Phtg; Yrbk Sprt Ed; Rep Stu Cncl; Var L Bsbl; Var L Bsktbl; Var L Crs Cntry; Bio Bwl Mbr 84; Chem Bwl Mbr 85; Pre-Law.

MIHALY, MATTHEW; Trumbull HS; Trumbull, CT; (Y); Boy Scts; Trs Church Yth Grp; Band; Jazz Band; Ftbl; Trk; Cit Awd; High Hon Roll; NHS; VFW Awd; PSAT NMSQT Selection Index High Scorer 84; FBI.

MIKULAK, JASON; Windham HS; Stafford Spgs, CT; (Y); JV Capt Socr; Hon Roll; Embry-Riddle Aeronatical U.

MIKUTAJTIS, IRENE M; Newington HS; Newington, CT; (Y); Var Capt Diving; Var Capt Swmmng; High Hon Roll; Hon Roll; Gftd & Tlntd Prog Schl 82-86; U Of CT; Comp Sci.

MILANO, DENISE; Daniel Hand HS; Madison, CT; (Y); 63/236; Church Yth Grp; Drama Clb; FCA; GAA; Chorus; Church Choir; Madrigals; School Musical; School Play; JV Sftbl; Hist Hnrs Symposium Medical Ethics 85; Bus.

MILAZZO, LAURA L; Bunnell HS; Stratford, CT; (Y); 12/250; Cit Awd; Ctznshp Awd Schlrshp; Shrthnd Awd.

MILDREN, KEITH; Cromwell HS; Cromwell, CT; (Y); Am Leg Boys St; Rep Frsh Cls; Rep Soph Cls; Rep Jr Cls; Rep Sr Cls; VP Stu Cncl; Bsktbl; Trk; Gov Hon Prg Awd; NHS; Comp Sci.

MILES, JULIE E; William H Hall HS; W Hartford, CT; (Y); GAA; Pep Clb; Ski Clb; Temple Yth Grp; Chorus; Yrbk Bus Mgr; Stu Cncl; Capt Cheerleading; Hon Roll; Bus.

MILEWSKI, YVONNE; Stamford Catholic HS; Stamford, CT; (Y); 10/170; Church Yth Grp; FBLA; Library Aide; Red Cross Aide; School Play; Ed Nwsp Stf; Yrbk Stf; Rep Frsh Cls; High Hon Roll; NHS; U NEW England; Marine Bio.

MILLER JR, DANIEL J; Ellington HS; Ellington, CT; (Y); 2/148; Am Leg Boys St; Aud/Vis; Trs Stu Cncl; Var L Bsktbl; Var L Socr; High Hon Roll; NHS; Church Yth Grp; Computer Clb; French Clb; Math Awd 83-85; Sci Awd 83-85; Harvard Bk Awd 85; Elect Engr.

MILLER, DAWN; Seymour HS; Seymour, CT; (S); 14/224; High Hon Roll; NHS; Stone Schl; Acctng.

MILLER, MARK G; St Mary HS; Pt Chester, NY; (Y); 19/68; Boy Scts; Tennis; Hon Roll; 1st Hnrs Europn Hstry 83-84; 1st Hnrs Frnch 84-85; Manhattan; Finc.

MILLER, MICHELLE; Stamford Catholic HS; Stamford, CT; (Y); Art Clb; Cmnty Wkr; Dance Clb; French Clb; Hosp Aide; Pep Clb; Red Cross Aide; Nwsp Stf; Yrbk Stf; Rep Frsh Cls; Semifnlst-Young Miss 84; Cmmrcl Art.

MILLER, STACEY; Manchester HS; Hartford, CT; (Y); AFS; Girl Scts; VP Intnl Clb; JA; Library Aide; Nwsp Stf; Sec Sr Cls; JV Capt Bsktbl; Hampton U; Sociolgy.

MILLER, SUSAN; Central Catholci HS; S Norwalk, CT; (Y); Dance Clb; Drama Clb; School Musical; School Play; Stage Crew; Variety Show; Yrbk Stf; Lit Mag; Hon Roll; Laux-Lajoie Schlrshp 82-83; Home Schl Assoc Schlrshps 83-85.

MILLERICK, RICHARD G; Bristol Central HS; Bristol, CT; (Y); Ski Clb; Band; Concert Band; Jazz Band; Mrchg Band; Symp Band; Capt Tennis; Amer Musical Fndtn Band Hnrs 83; CT Valley Yth Wind Ensmble 82-86.

MILLIKAN, AINO; Edwin O Smith HS; Mansfield Ctr, CT; (Y); 25/178; Art Clb; Band; Concert Band; Mrchg Band; JV Bsktbl; Var L Fld Hcky; JV Tennis; JV Trk; Ntl Merit SF; 1st Congressional Arts Contest Painting Category 83-84.

MILLS, ALLISON B; New Canaan HS; New Canaan, CT; (Y); Church Yth Grp; Acpl Chr; Band; Madrigals; Mrchg Band; Orch; School Musical; Yrbk Ed-Chief; Hon Roll; Pro Arte Chambr Singrs CT 84-85; Ithaca Coll; Music.

MILLS, COLE ADON; Holy Cross HS; Naugatuck, CT; (Y); Pres Chess Clb; Pres JA; Model UN; Political Wkr; Radio Clb; Pres Frsh Cls; Rep Soph Cls; Rep Stu Cncl; Hon Roll; CT ST Chmps Mock Trl Tm 85; Pre Med.

MILLS, GLORIA; James Hillhouse HS; New Haven, CT; (Y); Band; Concert Band; Ftbl; Mgr(s); Hon Roll; NHS; U Of New Haven; Medcn.

MILLS, MICHAEL; Bristol Eastern HS; Bristol, CT; (Y); Am Leg Boys St; JCL; Stat Bsktbl; Var L Crs Cntry; Stat Ftbl; Var L Trk; NHS; U S Senate Repblcn Page 84-85; Yale Bk Awd 85; Schlrshp George Washington U 85; Intl Stud.

MILLSTEIN, RUTH E; East Catholic HS; E Hartford, CT; (Y); 8/340; Capt Drill Tm; Ed Nwsp Rptr; Pres Jr Cls; Pres Stu Cncl; Capt Golf; Vllybl; Cit Awd; Elks Awd; High Hon Roll; Lion Awd; Principals Awd Scholar & Ctznshp 85; Womns Bus & Prof Card Hartford 85; Exch Clb Stu Of Mnth 85; Brandeis U; Bus.

MILNE, G TODD; East Lyme HS; Niantic, CT; (Y); 1/254; Am Leg Boys St; Bausch & Lomb Sci Awd; Elks Awd; Pres NHS; Ntl Merit Ltr; Val; Natl Hnr Soc Balfar Scholar 85; Fnlst CT JR Sci & Humnities Symp 84-85; 2nd Pl CT Sci Fair 84; Biochem.

MILOT, CHARLENE; Holy Cross HS; Waterbury, CT; (Y); 48/352; JV Capt Cheerleading; French Hon Soc; Hon Roll; NHS; Frnch I Hghst Avg In All Frnch I Clss Awd 83; Bus.

MINAR, MARK; New London HS; New London, CT; (Y); Concert Band; Drm Mjr(t); Jazz Band; Mrchg Band; Nwsp Stf; Yrbk Stf; Var Tennis; Hon Roll; German Clb; Band; CT Eastern Rgnl Cncrt Fstvl 85; Vrsty Rifle Tm 83-85.

MINELLA, CHRISTOPHER G; Bristol Central HS; Bristol, CT; (Y); 18/276; Am Leg Boys St; Boys Clb Am; Var Bsbl; Stat Bsktbl; Var L Ftbl; Hon Roll; NHS; Grace Atkins Mem Schrlshp 85; All Conf Linebckr 84; All City Linebacker 84; U Connecticut; Bus.

MINER, LORI; Trumbull HS; Trumbull, CT; (Y); 13/154; Drama Clb; Hosp Aide; Intnl Clb; Library Aide; Model UN; School Play; Variety Show; Nwsp Stf; High Hon Roll; Albright Coll; Genetic Engrng.

MINICHINO, DONNA; Guilford HS; Guilford, CT; (Y); 21/315; Hosp Aide; Red Cross Aide; Teachers Aide; Var Trk; Spanish NHS; VP Key Clb; Latn Hon Soc 84-85; Phys Ther.

MINNICK, BETH; East Hartford HS; E Hartford, CT; (Y); #21 In Class; FNA; Political Wkr; Yrbk Stf; Off Frsh Cls; Off Soph Cls; Off Jr Cls; Var Stu Cncl; Hon Roll; Prncpls Achvt Awd 83-84; Anatomy & Physclgy Sci Achvt Awd 84-85; Prncpls Achvt Awd 84-85; U Of CT; Nrsng.

MINNICK, SCOTT; East Hampton HS; East Hampton, CT; (Y); 11/90; Am Leg Boys St; Church Yth Grp; Drama Clb; Model UN; School Musical; Yrbk Bus Mgr; Yrbk Ed-Chief; Yrbk Stf; Trs Jr Cls; Stu Cncl; Bio.

MIRANDO, RICHARD; H C Wilcox Technical Schl; Plantsville, CT; (Y); Boy Scts; Church Yth Grp; Ski Clb; JV Wt Lftg; Cit Awd; High Hon Roll; Hon Roll; NHS; Prfct Atten Awd; Elect Engr.

MIRMINA, CHRISTINE; Jonathan Law HS; Milford, CT; (Y); GAA; Girl Scts; Rep Frsh Cls; Var Capt Bsktbl; L Sftbl; Var L Vllybl; Hon Roll; Jr NHS; Betty Anderson Awd; Milford Emblem Clb Awd; James Foster Mem Trphy Outstndng Athletic Ability; Southern CT ST U; Bus Fin.

MIRMINA, STEVEN A; Jonathan Law HS; Milford, CT; (Y); 3/256; Pres Intnl Clb; Pres Key Clb; Pres Latin Clb; Capt Scholastic Bowl; Pres Stu Cncl; High Hon Roll; Pres NHS; Pres Schlr; Am Leg Boys St; Band; Organizing Pres-SADD 84-85; VP Safe Rides 84-85; Brandeis U; Pre-Law.

MISHRA, VIBHA R; Newington HS; Newington, CT; (Y); Pres JA; Model UN; Office Aide; Yrbk Stf; Rep Frsh Cls; Rep Soph Cls; High Hon Roll; Ntl Merit SF; Greggs Typing Awd 83; Spn II Awd 84; Jr Achvr Pin 84; Schlrs Brkfst 83-85; Spn III Awd 85; Frn I Awd 85; Librl Arts.

MISIORSKI, DEBRA; Berlin HS; Kensington, CT; (Y); 10/188; Cmnty Wkr; High Hon Roll; Hon Roll; NHS; Art Achvt Awd 84; Tunxis CC; Cmmrcl Art.

MISKA, LORI A; Notre Dame Catholic HS; Stratford, CT; (Y); Keywanettes; Library Aide; Var Tennis; Stonehill Coll; Bio.

MITCHELL, CAROLE D; Bloomfield HS; Bloomfield, CT; (Y); 40/236; Yrbk Stf; Rep Jr Cls; Bsktbl; Socr; Trk; Hon Roll; Conserv Enrgy Awds Rsrch Ppr 85; Cert Awd Amer Hstry, Frnch II, Grls Trck, Bsktbl, Sccr, Sftbl 84-85; U Of CT; Pre-Med.

MITTENDORFF, LISA; Trumbull HS; Trumbull, CT; (Y); VP Drama Clb; Girl Scts; Library Aide; Church Choir; Madrigals; School Musical; Swmmng; High Hon Roll; NHS; Music Awd 83; Bus.

MIZESKI, SUZANNE; Naugatuck HS; Union City, CT; (Y); Church Yth Grp; Teachers Aide; Church Choir; Var L Swmmng; Var Tennis; Elks Awd; High Hon Roll; Hon Roll; Prfct Atten Awd; SAGE Proj; Acctnt.

MLOGANOSKI, SUSAN; Tolland HS; Tolland, CT; (Y); 20/180; Sec Soph Cls; Var JV Socr; Var Capt Trk; Hon Roll; NHS; North Central Ct Conf Soccr 84; Physcl Therp.

MOCARSKI, NORA; Westhill HS; Stamford, CT; (Y); Church Yth Grp; Cmnty Wkr; Ski Clb; Teachers Aide; Var L Sftbl; Var L Trk; Var L Vllybl; Hon Roll.

MODUGNO, MARCY; Holy Cross HS; Seymour, CT; (Y); Nwsp Bus Mgr; Nwsp Rptr; Nwsp Stf; Yrbk Bus Mgr; Yrbk Rptr; Yrbk Stf; Hon Roll; Cert Of Achvt For Holy Cross 85; Katherine Gibbs; Exec Sec.

MODZELEWSKI, FRANCIS MARK; Naugatuck HS; Naugatuck, CT; (Y); Art Clb; Aud/Vis; Computer Clb; DECA; Rep Science Clb; Nwsp Rptr; Yrbk Stf; Ftbl; L Trk; Hon Roll; US Senate Intern Prog 85; Mus Of Cartn Art Awd 84; JR Wmns Clb Mary Teeple Art Awe 85; Boston U; Comm Art.

MOEWS, DAVID J; E O Smith HS; Willimantic, CT; (Y); Computer Clb; Math Tm; Band; NHS; Ntl Merit SF; USA Math Olympd Wnnr 84; Intl Math Olympd 1st Prz 84; Math.

MOFFA, MICHELLE E; Danbury HS; Danbury, CT; (Y); 16/600; Band; Concert Band; Drm Mjr(t); Jazz Band; Mrchg Band; Orch; School Musical; Symp Band; Variety Show; Jr NHS; Westrn CT ST Band 82-85; Boston U; Music Ed.

MOFFITT, JIM; Newtown HS; Newtown, CT; (Y); 21/295; Varsity Clb; Var Ftbl; High Hon Roll; NHS; Ntl Merit Ltr; Pres Schlr; Western New England Coll; Comp.

MOHYDE, TIM; Shelton HS; Shelton, CT; (Y); Spanish NHS; Spnsh Awd 82; Comp Sci.

MOKULIS, LINDA; Southington HS; Southington, CT; (Y); 39/550; Library Aide; Math Clb; Ski Clb; School Musical; School Play; Variety Show; Capt Powder Puff Ftbl; Wt Lftg; High Hon Roll; Hon Roll; U Of CT Storrs; Chem.

MOLDER, SONJA; Orville H Platt HS; Meriden, CT; (Y); German Clb; Sec Key Clb; Latin Clb; Ski Clb; Nwsp Rptr; Lit Mag; Rep Frsh Cls; VP Soph Cls; Rep Jr Cls; VP Sr Cls; Key Clb Advsrs Awd 84-85; Key Clb Outstndng Sctry Awd 84-85; 2nd Pl Key Clb Intl Key Clb Essay 85; Jrnlsm.

MOLINELLI, LUCIA H; Norwalk HS; Norwalk, CT; (Y); Chorus; Madrigals; Rep Frsh Cls; Crs Cntry; JV Socr; Trk; Hon Roll; Church Yth Grp; Powder Puff Ftbl; Sftbll All Stars 83-84.

MOLLER, KRIS HEMINGWAY; Miss Porters Schl; Weston, CT; (Y); Cmnty Wkr; Drama Clb; Spanish Clb; Concert Band; School Musical; School Play; Yrbk Rptr; High Hon Roll; Hon Roll; Ntl Merit SF; Brown U Alumni Awd 84; Dartmouth Coll.

MOLLICA, FRANK; St Mary HS; Pt Chester, NY; (Y); Cmnty Wkr; Exploring; Math Tm; Quiz Bowl; JV Var Bsbl; Hon Roll.

MOLLICA, KRISTEN; Pomperaug HS; Middlebury, CT; (Y); Var L Fld Hcky; Var L Trk; Hon Roll; Var Fld Hockey Awds 83-85; Var Track Awds 82-85; Art.

MOLYET, REBECCA L; Naugatuck HS; Naugatuck, CT; (Y); Office Aide; Variety Show; Rep Frsh Cls; Rep Soph Cls; Rep Jr Cls; JV Bsktbl; Cheerleading; Var L Gym; Var Sftbl; Capt L Tennis; JR Hnr Grd; Pltcl Sci.

MONAGHAN, ELIZABETH; Trumbull HS; Trumbull, CT; (Y); Church Yth Grp; Service Clb; Teachers Aide; Chorus; Var L Bsktbl; Var L CAP; Capt Vllybl; High Hon Roll; NHS; Prfct Atten Awd; RPI Mdl Excll Math & Sci 85; Stu Cncl Awd Mst Outstndng Physcsw Stu 85; Bio Med.

MONAHAN, ANN; Notre Dame Catholic HS; Fairfield, CT; (Y); 4/284; Hosp Aide; Keywanettes; Math Clb; Scholastic Bowl; VP Trs Spanish Clb; Nwsp Stf; High Hon Roll; Kiwanis Awd; Pres NHS; Spanish NHS; Holy Cross Bk Awd 84; Awd Excllnc Hstry 85; Pres Acad Ftnss Awd 85; Fairfield U; Comp Sci.

MONARCA, SUSAN; Seymour HS; Seymour, CT; (S); 20/224; Church Yth Grp; JV Crs Cntry; Var High Hon Roll; Var Hon Roll; Awd Outstndng Achvt Algebra II 83; Paralegal Studies.

MONARCHIE, CHRIS; Norwalk HS; Norwalk, CT; (Y); #150 In Class; Church Yth Grp; Spanish Clb; Chorus; Orch; Stage Crew; Yrbk Stf; Rep Jr Cls; JV Vllybl; Hnr Awds 82; High Hnrs Awd 83; Hnrs Eng 81.

MONDO, PATRICIA; George J Penney HS; E Hartford, CT; (Y); DECA; Latin Clb; Rep Frsh Cls; Rep Soph Cls; Sec Jr Cls; JV Trk; Merch.

MONGILLO, MICHAEL; Orvil H Platt HS; Meriden, CT; (Y); Jazz Band; Stage Crew; Variety Show; Swmmng; Art Rcgntn Awd; Variety Show Awd; Boston Art Inst; Graphic Dsgn.

MONNIER, MELISSA; Masuk HS; Monroe, CT; (Y); 14/259; JA; Spanish Clb; High Hon Roll; NHS; Med Tech.

MONOCCHI, VICTORIA M; Lauralton Hall HS; New Haven, CT; (Y); French Clb; Sec Science Clb; Rep Stu Cncl; U RI; Zoology.

MONTALTO, DEAN; Central Catholic HS; Norwalk, CT; (Y); Drama Clb; French Clb; School Play; Nwsp Stf; Lit Mag; French Hon Soc; High Hon Roll; Hon Roll; Kiwanis Awd; NHS; Pres Schlr; St Anns Schlrshp 85; Rita Cocchia Mem Schlrshp 85; Emerson Coll; Comm.

MONTALTO, DOM; Cheshire HS; Cheshire, CT; (Y); Hon Roll; Central CT; Comp Engr.

MONTANARO, KAREN; Trumbull HS; Trumbull, CT; (S); Trs DECA; Fshn Merch.

MONTANARO, NICHOLAS; Trumbull HS; Trumbull, CT; (S); Pres DECA; Hon Roll; Sacred Hrt U; Insrnc Salsmn.

MONTAVON, VINNIE; Naugatuck HS; Naugatuck, CT; (Y); DECA; High Hon Roll; Prfct Atten Awd.

MONTELEONE, MARIA; Brien Mc Mahon HS; Norwalk, CT; (Y); 10/200; High Hon Roll; Hon Roll; Nursng.

MONTELLO, TODD M; Holy Cross HS; Waterbury, CT; (Y); 52/352; Church Yth Grp; Cmnty Wkr; Spanish Clb; Bsbl; Var Golf; JV Swmmng; JV Wrstlng; High Hon Roll; NHS; Spanish NHS; Holy Cross; Chem Engrg.

MONTGOMERY, JASON; Heritage Christian Acad; Cheshire, CT; (Y); Church Yth Grp; School Play; Stu Cncl; Var L Socr; Hon Roll; Heritage Chrstn Acad Spirit Awd; US Army; Spcl Forces.

MONTI JR, DAVID A; Southington HS; Plantsville, CT; (Y); Latin Clb; Var L Ftbl; Var L Ftbl; High Hon Roll; NHS; Church Yth Grp; Jr NHS; St Ftbl Schlr Athl Awd 84; Schl Schlr Athl Awd 85; Ntl Schlr Athl Awd 85.

MONTI, ROBERT; Southington HS; Plantsville, CT; (Y); Church Yth Grp; JA; Letterman Clb; Coach Actv; L Ftbl; JV Golf.

MONTOVANI, KENDA M; William H Hall HS; W Hartford, CT; (Y); 24/301; Church Yth Grp; Var L Crs Cntry; Var L Trk; French Hon Soc; High Hon Roll; NHS; Grad Comm 85; Suburban Womens Clb Schlrshp 85; Providence Coll; Bus.

MOODY, BILL; Bethel HS; Bethel, CT; (Y); Cmnty Wkr; High Hon Roll; Hon Roll; VFW Awd; Voice Dem Awd; Rcktbl Clb; Boston Coll; Arlne Plt.

MOODY, ROBIN L; Wilbur Cross HS; New Haven, CT; (S); 21/242; Church Yth Grp; VP Spanish Clb; Chorus; Church Choir; School Musical; Nwsp Rptr; Frsh Cls; Jr Cls; Hon Roll; Yale Shafer Smmr Schlrshp 84; Htl Mgmt.

MOORE III, ALEXANDER; Fairfield Prep; Redding, CT; (Y); Debate Tm; Key Clb; Yrbk Stf; Var Crs Cntry; JV Swmmng; JV Twrlr; High Hon Roll; NHS; Aviatn.

MOORE, CHERYL; Penney HS; E Hartford, CT; (Y); French Clb; Spanish Clb; Swmmng; Trk; Hon Roll.

MOORE, DEBORAH; O H Platt HS; Meriden, CT; (Y); Key Clb; Capt Tennis; French Hon Soc; High Hon Roll; NHS; Rotary Awd; Sec French Clb; Pres Latin Clb; Pres Math Clb; Band; Interact Clb-Brazil 83-84; Brown U Bk Awd 83; Harvard U Bk Awd 85.

MOORE, DENNIS; St Bernard HS; Waterford, CT; (S); Library Aide; Stu Cncl; JV Golf; JV Socr; Hon Roll; Acad Ltr 84; Jr Sen 84; Peer Tutor 84; Statiscs.

MOORE, ELIZABETH; Amity Regional HS; Bethany, CT; (S); 90/376; Capt Bsktbl; Fld Hcky; Mgr(s); Capt Sftbl; Vllybl; Cit Awd; Hon Roll; NHS; Ldrshp Council 84-85; English Recognition Awd 83-84; Nursing.

MOORE, KIMBERLY; Brien Mc Mahon HS; Norwalk, CT; (Y); JCL; Latin Clb; High Hon Roll; Hon Roll; Natl Latin Exam Slvr Mdlst 84-85; Fash Dsgn.

MOORE, KIMBERLY; The Hotchkiss Schl; Newburgh, IN; (Y); French Clb; Chorus; JV Mgr(s); Var Capt Swmmng; VA U.

MOORE, MICHELLE; Jonathan Law HS; Milford, CT; (Y); 32/250; Church Yth Grp; Capt Dance Clb; Drama Clb; Intnl Clb; School Musical; Capt Cheerleading; Gym; Hon Roll; Dean JC; Danc.

MOORE, TIMOTHY; Joseph A Foran HS; Milford, CT; (Y); Am Leg Boys St; VP Pres Drama Clb; Spanish Clb; Varsity Clb; School Play; Stage Crew; Yrbk Stf; Var L Socr; Var L Tennis; Ntl Merit SF; Lib Arts.

MOQUIN, KAREN; Jonathan Law HS; Milford, CT; (Y); 4/238; Sec Drama Clb; Keywanettes; Band; Ed Yrbk Stf; Off Jr Cls; Off Sr Cls; Mgr(s); High Hon Roll; NHS; Pres Schlr; Superintendents Acad Awd 85; Stu Ldrshp 85; Accntng II 85; S CT ST U; Elem Educ.

MORA, JOSEPH; Berlin HS; Berlin, CT; (Y); 24/191; Civic Clb; JA; Band; Jazz Band; Mrchg Band; Pep Band; School Musical; School Play; Ftbl; Socr; Outstndg Muscn 84-85; All ST Band Stu; Med.

MORABITO, BRIAN; Bethel HS; Bethel, CT; (Y); Wrstlng; High Hon Roll; Hon Roll; Sci.

MORALES, ELAINE; Joseph A Foran HS; Milford, CT; (Y); 3/233; Cmnty Wkr; Dance Clb; Drama Clb; JCL; Keywanettes; Spanish Clb; School Play; Yrbk Stf; High Hon Roll; Jr NHS; Yale Bk Awd; Exclnce Spn I & II; Intl Bus.

MORALES, RAQUEL; Canton HS; Canton, CT; (Y); 8/95; Chorus; Madrigals; School Musical; Yrbk Sprt Ed; VP Soph Cls; Stu Cncl; Var Bsktbl; Var Cheerleading; Mgr(s); Var Sftbl; Canton Safe Rides 84-86; Close-Up Acad Trip WA DC 85; Greater Hartford Yth 85; U Of CT; Pre-Med.

MORAN, DEBORAH; Holy Cross HS; Watertown, CT; (Y); 41/352; Chrmn Church Yth Grp; Library Aide; Office Aide; Chorus; Yrbk Stf; High Hon Roll; Hon Roll; Jr NHS; NHS; Spanish NHS; Offla-Chrty Fnd Rsng Clb 85-86; Fine Arts Clb-Apprctn Of Fine Arts 84-86; Peer Mnstry Pgm 85-86; Educ.

MORAN, KELLY; Shelton HS; Shelton, CT; (Y); Pres Exploring; FHA; Hosp Aide; JA; Spanish Clb; Mgr(s); Trk; Hon Roll; NHS; Spanish NHS.

MORAN, LISA; Sacred Heart Academy; Hamden, CT; (Y); English Clb; Hosp Aide; Stage Crew; Nwsp Ed-Chief; Lit Mag; High Hon Roll; Ntl Merit Ltr; Speech Tm; Nwsp Rptr; NEDT Awd 82; De Witt Wallace Schlr 85; Yth Rep 82-85; Macalester Coll; Lib Arts.

MORAN, MOIRA; Branford HS; Branford, CT; (Y); 68/246; Latin Clb; Chorus; School Musical; Var Capt Crs Cntry; Var Trk; JC Awd.

MORAN, PATRICK; The Hotchkiss Schl; Lakeville, CT; (Y); Nwsp Rptr; Lcrss; Socr; Ntl Merit Schol; Upson Prz-Outstndng Frshmn Acadmc & Sprts 83; Ltn Prz 83 & 84; Bio Prz 83; Nvl Offcr.

MORDARSKI, TERESA I; Lyman Hall HS; Wallingford, CT; (Y); Church Yth Grp; Church Choir; L Trk; JV Vllybl; Hon Roll; Prfct Atten Awd; Hnr Awd Erth Sci & Drftng I; Pre Med.

MOREA, JENNIFER; Holy Cross HS; Waterbury, CT; (Y); 73/386; Hosp Aide; Teachers Aide; Concert Band; Hon Roll; NHS; Latin Clb; Pres Band; Mrchg Band; Orch; Stage Crew; Phy Thrpy.

MOREIRA, KATHY R; Danbury HS; Danbury, CT; (Y); JA; Chorus; School Musical; Yrbk Stf; NHS; Engl Hnrs 84-85; Ger Awd 83-84; U CT Waterbury; Bus.

MORENO, HERIBERTO; Orville H Platt HS; Meriden, CT; (Y); Am Leg Boys St; Computer Clb; Sec Key Clb; Math Clb; Rep Jr Cls; Stu Cncl; Var Capt Crs Cntry; Var Capt Trk; High Hon Roll; Track All St & All Conf 85; X-Cntry Cnty & All Conf 84; Pre-Law.

MORGAN, EDWARD; Canterbury Schl; Huntington, NY; (Y); 5/85; Cmnty Wkr; Ski Clb; Rep Soph Cls; Rep Jr Cls; Rep Sr Cls; Trs Pres Stu Cncl; Var Lcrss; Var Socr; High Hon Roll; Edward Mack Awd Outstndg Contrib Stu Govt 85; Dorm Proctor 85; Georgetown U; Comp Sci.

MORGAN, LEE A; Saint Mary HS; Bethel, CT; (Y); Church Yth Grp; Cmnty Wkr; Stage Crew; Variety Show; VP Jr Cls; Var JV Cheerleading; Var Socr; Hon Roll; Adv.

MORGAN, MICHELLE; The Morgan Schl; Clinton, CT; (Y); 10/164; French Clb; Chorus; School Musical; Sec Frsh Cls; Sec Soph Cls; Sec Jr Cls; Sec Sr Cls; Rep Stu Cncl; Var L Fld Hcky; Var Capt Trk; Grls Trk Outstndng Ahtl Awd 85; Schlr/Athl Awds-Morgn Schl & CASS & CIAC 85; Smith Coll; Math.

MORGILLO, ANTHONY; West Haven HS; W Haven, CT; (Y); French Clb; Band; Var Capt Bsbl; Var Capt Ftbl; Hon Roll; Jr NHS; 2nd Tm All Leag Slctn Bsball 85; CT 5 Star Bsball Acad 85; Outstndng Acad Awd French 82-83.

MORIN, CAROLE; Farmington HS; Farmington, CT; (Y); Church Yth Grp; Ski Clb; Rep Soph Cls; Var Bsktbl; Var Fld Hcky; Hon Roll; Ntl Merit Ltr; Physcl Thrpy.

MORIN, JOHN; Joseph A Foran HS; Milford, CT; (Y); 40/272; JCL; Key Clb; Spanish Clb; Yrbk Stf; Stu Cncl; Crs Cntry; Trk; Cit Awd; High Hon Roll; Hon Roll; U Of CT; Pre-Med.

MORIN, KELLY A; Litchfield HS; Litchfield, CT; (Y); 2/86; AFS; Am Leg Aux Girls St; MMM; Band; Concert Band; Yrbk Stf; Var L Crs Cntry; Var L Trk; French Hon Soc; High Hon Roll; All ST Athlte In X-Cntry & Trck 83-84; Soclgy.

MORIN, ROBIN; Tolland HS; Tolland, CT; (Y); 20/150; Hosp Aide; Ski Clb; Band; Mrchg Band; School Musical; Rep Frsh Cls; Rep Jr Cls; Var Crs Cntry; Var Tennis; Hon Roll; Nacel Cultrl Exchng Stu 84; Intl Bus.

MORKAN, THOMAS S; Simsbury HS; Simsbury, CT; (Y); Church Yth Grp; Pres VP FBLA; Chorus; Swing Chorus; CYO 76-85; Swing Choir 82-83; FBLA Schl Chptr Pres 82-83; FBLA St VP 83-84; YMCA Bsktbl Lgue 76-84.

MOROCHNIK, PAUL J; Newington HS; Newington, CT; (Y); Boy Scts; Temple Yth Grp; Band; Chorus; Jazz Band; Mrchg Band; School Musical; Symp Band; Variety Show; Socr.

MORREY, GARY; Windsor Locks HS; Windsor Locks, CT; (Y); 9/160; Am Leg Boys St; Boy Scts; Ed Nwsp Ed-Chief; Hon Roll; Wrcstr Poly Inst; Comp Engrng.

MORRIS, CYNTHIA; Southington HS; Southington, CT; (Y); Ski Clb; Band; Chorus; Drill Tm; Drm Mjr(t); Flag Corp; Mrchg Band; School Musical; Variety Show; Twrlr; Bentley Coll; Law.

MORRIS II, FREDDIE; Windsor HS; Windsor, CT; (Y); Var Bsbl; Bsktbl; Var Ftbl; Var Mgr(s); Wt Lftg; Hon Roll; JC Awd; Civitan Clb Of Windsor Ldrshp & Ctznshp Prog 84; U Of Hartford; Bus Admin.

MORRIS, JENNIFER; Danbury HS; Danbury, CT; (Y); 29/613; Church Yth Grp; Off Cmnty Wkr; Hosp Aide; School Musical; School Play; Variety Show; Hon Roll; Sec Stu Cncl; Stat Bsktbl; Var Capt Fld Hcky; Honorary Bus Stu Awd 85; Fld Hockey Sprtsmnshp Awd 84; Chrprsn Jr Prom & Hmcmng Dance 84-85; Accntng.

MORRIS, MELINDA; St Marys HS; New Haven, CT; (Y); Church Yth Grp; Math Clb; Natl Beta Clb; Teachers Aide; Hon Roll; Mu Alp Tht; NHS; Spanish NHS; Spnsh IV-III Awds 83-85.

MORRIS, PATIRCIA; Notre Dame Catholic HS; Redding, CT; (Y); 16/284; Sec Church Yth Grp; Keywanettes; Library Aide; Math Clb; Political Wkr; Scholastic Bowl; High Hon Roll; VP NHS; Tennis; Baccalaureate Awd; Rhodes Coll; Intl Rltns.

MORRIS, VICTORIA; Sacred Heart Acad; Guilford, CT; (Y); French Clb; FBLA; Thesps; Chorus; School Musical; School Play; Swing Chorus; Im Vllybl; Engl.

MORRISON, ALWYN RAY; Kolbe Cathedral HS; Bridgeport, CT; (Y); Boy Scts; Camera Clb; Church Yth Grp; Computer Clb; Math Clb; Science Clb; Nwsp Stf; Yrbk Stf; Wt Lftg; Boy Sct Yr 84; Wrkg On Eagl Sct; Comp Sci.

MORROW, SUZANNE; Granby Memorial HS; Granby, CT; (Y); Church Yth Grp; JV Var Cheerleading; JV Var Fld Hcky; Var Sftbl; Var Hon Roll; Psych.

MOSELY, LESLIE; Central HS; Bridgeport, CT; (Y); Camera Clb; Girl Scts; Hosp Aide; JA; Chorus; Drill Tm; Swing Chorus; JV Bsktbl; Mgr(s); Capt Pom Pon; Nrsng.

MOSES, KAREN A; St Paul Catholic HS; Bristol, CT; (Y); 51/321; Cmnty Wkr; Drama Clb; Hosp Aide; Chorus; School Play; Twrlr; Capt Of Majorettes 84-85; 3rd Pl Latin Awd 82; Becker JC; Occuptnl Thrpst.

MOSHKA, WILLIAM; Bristol Central HS; Bristol, CT; (Y); Hon Roll; Electrcn.

MOSIMANN, KRISTIN; Thomaston HS; Thomaston, CT; (Y); Spanish Clb; Band; Concert Band; Mrchg Band; Off Stu Cncl; Var Cheerleading; Mgr(s); Trk; High Hon Roll; Hon Roll.

MOTLEY, THOMAS; Avon Old Farms Schl; Nahant, MA; (S); 4/100; ROTC; JV Bsktbl; Var Lcrss; JV Socr; JV Tennis; Hon Roll; Tennis Champ Windridge Tennis Camp 83; Harvard; Sociology.

MOTTER, LESLIE; Masuk HS; Monroe, CT; (Y); 31/300; JCL; Latin Clb; Pep Clb; Thesps; School Musical; School Play; Stage Crew; Trs Jr Cls; Var Cheerleading; JV Swmmng.

MOUNTSIER, JANE; Daniel Hand HS; Madison, CT; (Y); #79 In Class; Church Yth Grp; VP FCA; GAA; Ski Clb; Yrbk Stf; Trs Sr Cls; Cheerleading; JV Tennis; Lib Arts.

MOURA, MARIA; Kolbe-Cathedral HS; Bridgeport, CT; (Y); 1/103; JA; Math Clb; Nwsp Stf; Yrbk Ed-Chief; Rep Soph Cls; Rep Soph Cls; Pres Jr Cls; High Hon Roll; JC Awd; NHS; Harvard Bk Clb Awd 85; Fairfield U; Psych.

MOWAD, GEORGE; Holy Cross HS; Prospect, CT; (Y); 179/352; Church Yth Grp; Ftbl; Trk; Hon Roll; Accntnt.

MOY, WAYNE; Danbury HS; Danbury, CT; (Y); 73/612; Boy Scts; Computer Clb; Nwsp Rptr; Lit Mag; Mgr(s); Score Keeper; Timer; Var L Trk; High Hon Roll; Hon Roll; Sci And Envrmntl Conf 84; Var Athltc Awd 85; Cornell U; Arch.

MOYHER, JEFFREY; Trumbull HS; Trumbull, CT; (Y); Cmnty Wkr; Key Clb; Chorus; JV Bsktbl; Ftbl; Var Golf; Hon Roll; Bus Mgmt.

MOYLETT, DIANNE; Immaculate HS; Danbury, CT; (Y); French Clb; Office Aide; Pep Clb; Teachers Aide; Yrbk Stf; Im Bsktbl; Im Score Keeper; Var Swmmng; Var Timer; Im Vllybl; Pres Phy Fit Awd 82-84; Lib Arts.

MOYNIHAN, MAURA; Conard HS; W Hartford, CT; (Y); 35/315; Girl Scts; Service Clb; Var Fld Hcky; High Hon Roll; NHS; Ntl Merit Ltr; Spanish NHS; Math Tm; Yrbk Stf; Rep Frsh Cls; Jr Cititan Clb Pres 84-85; Colby Coll Book Prz 85; Hugh O Brian Yth Ldrshp Conf Ambssdr 84.

MUCCIACCIARO, DONNA; St Joseph HS; Stratford, CT; (Y); 10/227; Spanish Clb; High Hon Roll; NHS; Spanish NHS; Cert Of Merit Spn 84 & 85; Ed.

MUELLER, KAREN; East Catholic HS; Tolland, CT; (Y); Church Yth Grp; Cmnty Wkr; JV Socr; Var Trk; Hon Roll; Law.

MUELLER, MARIA; Bristol Central HS; Bristol, CT; (Y); Sec JA; Sec Teachers Aide; High Hon Roll; Hon Roll; V Ltr Athl Assoc 84-85; Junior Coll; Bus.

MUHL, ADEL-MARIE; The Morgan Schl; Clinton, CT; (Y); AFS; Chorus; Var L Cheerleading; Powder Puff Ftbl; High Hon Roll; Hon Roll; Acadmc Distnctn Math 84-85; Acctng.

MULDOON, DAVID; St Joseph HS; Shelton, CT; (Y); 59/250; Letterman Clb; Spanish Clb; Varsity Clb; Nwsp Stf; Crs Cntry; Ftbl; Trk; Hon Roll; Law.

MULHALL, BILL; Trumbull HS; Trumbull, CT; (Y); Pres Aud/Vis; Cmnty Wkr; JA; Chorus; Madrigals; Mgr Stage Crew; Variety Show; Cit Awd; Hon Roll; JR Of Yr Audio-Vis 84-85; Med Tech.

MULHERN, SERENA A; Stamford HS; Stamford, CT; (Y); 1/406; Pres Church Yth Grp; French Clb; Math Clb; Math Tm; Pres Science Clb; Church Choir; Var Capt Swmmng; Var L Trk; French Hon Soc; NHS; Rensselaer Medl Math, Sci 84; Soc Women Engrs Awd 84; 1st Pl HS Sci Olympd-Bio 84; Coachs Awd 84-85.

MULINSKI, CYNTHIA; Holy Cross HS; Beacon Fls, CT; (Y); 21/344; French Hon Soc; High Hon Roll; Lion Awd; Ntl Merit Ltr; CT Schlstc Achv Awd 85; Brianwd Bk Awd 84; Jr Wmns Clb Schlrshp 85; Post Coll; Bus Adm.

MULLANE, KARIN A; St Joseph HS; Bridgeport, CT; (Y); 46/221; Spanish Clb; Yrbk Bus Mgr; Yrbk Rptr; Yrbk Stf; Var L Bsktbl; L Capt Sftbl; L Capt Vllybl; Hon Roll; All St & Conf Vllybl 84-85; All St All Conf Stftbl 85; Schlrshp Holy Cross, Bryant, Franklin Pierce; US Naval Acad; Comp Sci.

MULLIGAN, ELIZABETH; Tolland HS; Tolland, CT; (Y); Lit Mag; Chrmn Stu Cncl; L Cheerleading; L Socr; L Trk; 4-H Awd; High Hon Roll; Hon Roll; NHS; Prfct Atten Awd; Outstndng Eng Stu Soph; Elem Ed.

MULLIN, JEFFERY; Woodstock Acad; Woodstock Valley, CT; (Y); 8/92; Am Leg Boys St; JCL; Model UN; School Play; Rep Frsh Cls; Rep Soph Cls; Rep Jr Cls; Rep Sr Cls; Var Socr; Var Trk; 1st Pl ST CT Future Problm Slvg 85; 1st Pl ST CT Div S Chemathn 85; MIT; Engrng.

MULREADY, CANDACE; Conard HS; W Hartford, CT; (Y); 43/314; Chorus; VP Jr Cls; Rep Stu Cncl; Var Socr; Var Trk; Hon Roll; Spanish NHS; CCIL Trck Team Hnrbl Mntn, All-Star Trck Team.

MUNROE, GARRETT; Richerd C Lee HS; New Haven, CT; (Y); Pep Clb; Red Cross Aide; ROTC; Scholastic Bowl; Chorus; Rep Soph Cls; Var L Ftbl; Trk; Sci Olympd & Lab Tech Awd For Excel 85; Ahltcs Ftbl & Trck Ltrs 84; Radlgy.

MURACH, BRYAN; Southington HS; Southington, CT; (Y); 102/600; Math Clb; Band; Concert Band; Jazz Band; Mrchg Band; Talcott Mt Sci Pgms 78-85; Briarwood Coll Sptlght Pgm 84-85; Dis I & II 78-83; Frntrs Appl Sci 85; AEROSPACE Engrng.

MURDOCK, JEANNE; Litchfield HS; Northfield, CT; (Y); Am Leg Aux Girls St; Cmnty Wkr; Band; Chorus; Church Choir; Concert Band; French Hon Soc; NHS; NEDT Awd; Church Yth Grp; St Pauls Lodge AFM Awdd 85; Chem.

MURDY, DAVID; Maloney HS; Meriden, CT; (Y); Boy Scts; Cmnty Wkr; Math Clb; Math Tm; Ski Clb; Teachers Aide; Nwsp Stf; Ice Hcky; Powder Puff Ftbl; Exploring; Ind Mgmt.

MURE, VINCENT; Berlin HS; Kensington, CT; (Y); Band; Concert Band; Jazz Band; Mrchg Band; Pep Band; School Musical; Variety Show; Arch Engr.

MURKETT, JEFFREY; St Bernard HS; Norwich, CT; (Y); Aud/Vis; Church Yth Grp; English Clb; French Clb; JA; Political Wkr; Science Clb; Var Crs Cntry; Var Trk; Im Vllybl; Ntbl Achvt-Vsl Arts Awd 84-85; Nat Sci.

MURKETT, TIMOTHY; St Bernard HS; Norwich, CT; (S); 88/300; Aud/Vis; Church Yth Grp; Cmnty Wkr; Stage Crew; Stu Cncl; Var Bsbl; JV Ftbl; JV Wrstlng; Hon Roll; Im Bsktbl; Frontiers Appld Sci At Yale 84; Bus.

MURPHY, DARREN J; Killingly HS; Brooklyn, CT; (Y); 71/236; Letterman Clb; Yrbk Stf; Var Bsktbl; Var Ice Hcky; Var L Socr; High Hon Roll; Supr Efft Eng Comp Awd 85; W CT ST U; Bus Admin.

MURPHY, ELIZABETH; East Catholic HS; Ellington, CT; (Y); 32/316; Var Trk; High Hon Roll; Hon Roll; NHS; Hnrs E Clb Acad Ltr 83-85; Law.

MURPHY, JENNIFER; Bethel HS; Bethel, CT; (Y); 43/270; AFS; Key Clb; Stat Socr; Stat Sftbl; Hon Roll; Law.

MURPHY, JERRY; East Catholic HS; Bolton, CT; (Y); 8/318; Boy Scts; Band; Pep Band; School Play; Rep Stu Cncl; Var L Socr; Var L Trk; High Hon Roll; NHS; Eagl Sct.

MURPHY, JOHN; Danbury HS; Danbury, CT; (Y); 50/620; Boy Scts; Varsity Clb; Band; Nwsp Sprt Ed; JV Bsbl; Crs Cntry; Var Trk; High Hon Roll; NHS; Concert Band; Math.

MURPHY, LAUREN; East Lyme HS; Niantic, CT; (Y); 1/271; Am Leg Aux Girls St; Yrbk Rptr; Off Soph Cls; Off Jr Cls; Off Sr Cls; Var Capt Tennis; High Hon Roll; Pres NHS; All Conf Ten Tm; Congressnl Internshp WA DC; Harvard Prize Bk; Frgn Diplomacy.

MURPHY, TODD B; Shelton HS; Huntington, CT; (Y); Boy Scts; Ski Clb; Crs Cntry; Trk; Hon Roll; Unity Coll; Forstry.

MURRAY, LEE ANN; Northwest Catholic HS; Bloomfield, CT; (Y); Drama Clb; French Clb; Chorus; Hon Roll; Psych.

MURZYNSKA, MONIKA; Crosby HS; Waterbury, CT; (Y); Art Clb; French Clb; Vllybl; Hon Roll; Intl Rel.

MUSACCHIO, JACQUELINE M; Bethel HS; Bethel, CT; (Y); 39/270; JA; Nwsp Rptr; Yrbk Stf; VP Sr Cls; Var Crs Cntry; Trk; NHS; Ntl Merit Ltr; Bethel Exch Clb Stdnt Schlrshp; Creative Wrtng Awd; Creative Wrtr.

MUSCHINSKY, BODIN; East Lyme HS; E Lyme, CT; (Y); 12/270; Orch; School Musical; Variety Show; JV Bsbl; Hon Roll; CT All ST Orch 84 & 85; All New Engl Orch 85; 2nd Pl E CT Symp Yth Orch Prfrmcne Awd 85; Hstry.

MUSSHORN, PAM; Southington HS; Southington, CT; (Y); 193/550; French Hon Soc; Hon Roll; Tunxis CC; Comp Sci.

MYERS, KRISTIN; Roger Ludlowe HS; Fairfield, CT; (Y); 1/320; Trs Key Clb; Stage Crew; Yrbk Sprt Ed; Yrbk Stf; L Trk; High Hon Roll; NHS; Ntl Merit Ltr; Spanish NHS; Val; 4.0 Avg Plaque; Mth & Sci Awds; Fairfield U; Mth.

MYOTT, TRACY L; Ellington HS; Ellington, CT; (Y); Pres Trs Church Yth Grp; Cmnty Wkr; Variety Show; Yrbk Stf; Sec Sr Cls; Stu Cncl; JV Var Cheerleading; Var Capt Sftbl; Hon Roll; NHS; Intl Corp Law.

NACHAZEL, BOB; Stamford Catholic HS; Stamford, CT; (Y); #20 In Class; JA; Ftbl; Swmmng; Hon Roll; U Of CT-STORES; Engrng.

NADEAU, LAUREN J; Plainfield HS; Plainfield, CT; (Y); 16/157; Drama Clb; Band; Mrchg Band; Yrbk Stf; Trk; High Hon Roll; Hon Roll; Prfct Atten Awd; Voice Dem Awd; Masonic Lodge Scholar 85; Mohegan CC; Acctng.

NAGARDEOLEKAR, VIKAS; Tolland HS; Tolland, CT; (Y); Am Leg Boys St; CAP; Rep Jr Cls; JV Socr; High Hon Roll; NHS; Acad Excell Sci Awd 85; Acad Excell Engl Awd 85; Syracuse U; Arch.

NAGLE, MARTIN; St Bernard HS; East Lyme, CT; (Y); 70/302; Cmnty Wkr; Hosp Aide; Letterman Clb; Varsity Clb; Pres Frsh Cls; Var L Bsbl; Bsktbl; Var L Ftbl; Var L Trk; Wt Lftg; Peer Ldrshp 85-86; Art Awd; Acad Awd; Pre Med.

NAHMANSON, LISA; Guilford HS; Guilford, CT; (Y); Pres Temple Yth Grp; Chorus; Orch; School Musical; Var Mgr(s); JV Socr; High Hon Roll; NHS; Ntl Merit SF; Spanish NHS; Gen Exclince Engl 84-85; Ger Hon Soc 84-85; NE Fed Temple Yth Brd 85-86; Law.

NAIMO, PETER; Morgan HS; Clinton, CT; (Y); JV Bsbl; JV Ftbl; Hon Roll; Cert Acad Distnctn Home Ec & Sci 84, Phys Ed 83.

NAJJAR, MICHELE; Holy Cross HS; Seymar, CT; (Y); 18/352; Spanish Clb; School Musical; Stage Crew; High Hon Roll; Hon Roll; NHS; Spanish NHS; Brother Francis Leary Schlrshp Awd 82; U Connecticut; Bus Adm.

NAKIAN, ELIZABETH; Stanford HS; Stanford, CT; (S); Church Yth Grp; Cmnty Wkr; JA; Ski Clb; Yrbk Stf; Stu Cncl; Var L Trk; Hon Roll; Sec NHS; Track Coaches Awd 83; 1st Pl Art Awd 83; Law.

NAPOLI, MICHAEL; Guilford HS; Guilford, CT; (Y); 20/315; Church Yth Grp; Cmnty Wkr; Political Wkr; Var Ftbl; Wrstlng; High Hon Roll; Hon Roll; NHS; Prfct Atten Awd; Spanish NHS; Princeton; Med.

NARANG, PRIYA; Staples HS; Westport, CT; (Y); 5/400; Dance Clb; French Clb; JA; Model UN; Chorus; Orch; School Musical; School Play; JV Bsktbl; Var Fld Hcky; Field Hockey; Hnr Roll.

NARANJO, JACKIE; Southington HS; Southington, CT; (Y); 142/550; Church Yth Grp; Varsity Clb; Band; Variety Show; Nwsp Sprt Ed; Trs Frsh Cls; VP Jr Cls; VP Sr Cls; Stu Cncl; Cheerleading; Hugh O Brian Ldrshp Awd 83-84; Vrsty Ltrs In Sprts 84-85; U Of CT; Cmmnctns.

NARCISSE, PAUL; Westhill HS; Stamford, CT; (Y); Boy Scts; French Clb; JA; Ftbl.

NARDELLO, CATHERINE; Crosby HS; Waterbury, CT; (Y); Latin Clb; Varsity Clb; Chorus; School Musical; Vllybl; High Hon Roll; Hon Roll; Awd Rifle Team 85; Cert Apprctn Piano 85; Ntl Hnr Scty 85; Chem.

NARDI, RENEE; Wilcox Tech HS; Meriden, CT; (Y); Drama Clb; Variety Show; Yrbk Stf; Rep Stu Cncl; Var Capt Cheerleading; Hon Roll; Fash Merch.

NARRACCI, ROBERT; East Haven HS; E Haven, CT; (Y); 3/300; Am Leg Boys St; Church Yth Grp; Latin Clb; Math Tm; Model UN; L Capt Swmmng; High Hon Roll; NHS; Rotary Awd; CT Hnrs Smnr-Delg Cnvctn Distngshd Stu At U CT 85; Arch.

NARUS, LISA; Stratford HS; Stratford, CT; (Y); 1/241; Trs Church Yth Grp; JA; Pres VP Concert Band; Rep Frsh Cls; Rep Soph Cls; High Hon Roll; Pres NHS; Rensselaer Math & Sci Awd 85; Yalt U Bk Awd 85; Vassar Clb Fairfld Cnty Bk Awd 85; Resrch Sci.

NASH, ALLISON; The Ethel Walker Schl; Newton, MA; (Y); Pres Math Tm; Pep Clb; Political Wkr; Q&S; Service Clb; Nwsp Rptr; Sec Frsh Cls; JV Capt Bsktbl; High Hon Roll; Caroline Walker Hnr Soc 85; Cummngs Prz 85; Acerone Awd 85; Wellesley Coll; Law.

NASH, BILL; Edwin O Smith HS; Storrs, CT; (Y); 24/188; Boy Scts; Ski Clb; Yrbk Stf; Var JV Bsbl; Bowling; Var L Crs Cntry; Golf; Im Bsktbl; Coach Actv; Sperry Hutchinson Merchant Scholar 85; Hgh Avg Southeastern CT JR Bowlng Assn 84; U CT; Chem.

NASSA, CATHERINE F; Daniel Hand HS; Medford, NJ; (Y); 120/556; Debate Tm; Political Wkr; Spanish Clb; Yrbk Stf; Stu Cncl; Powder Puff Ftbl; Hon Roll; Jr NHS; St Schlr; Principals Seminars For Outstndng Srs 84-85; Brandeis U; Pol Sci.

NATALE, JENNIFER; Holy Cross HS; Waterbury, CT; (Y); 133/364; Art Clb; Service Clb; Hon Roll.

NAUGHTON, THOMAS; Suffield HS; Suffield, CT; (Y); 2/150; Am Leg Boys St; Trs Sr Cls; Trs Stu Cncl; Var L Bsktbl; Var L Socr; Var L Tennis; NHS; Ntl Merit SF; Pres Schlr; Sal; Dartmouth Coll; Pre Med.

NAVICKAS, JOHN; RHAM HS; Marlborough, CT; (Y); 42/167; Am Leg Boys St; Ski Clb; VP Jr Cls; Pres Sr Cls; JV Bsbl; Var L Stu Cncl; Hon Roll; Bus.

NEARY, DARLENE; East Lyme HS; Niantic, CT; (Y); 12/280; Key Clb; Pep Clb; Red Cross Aide; Yrbk Stf; Sec Stu Cncl; Var Capt Cheerleading; Powder Puff Ftbl; Hon Roll; Outstndg Senat Awd 84-85; Engrng.

NEDJOIKA, KATHERINE; Southington HS; Southington, CT; (Y); 85/550; Aud/Vis; JV Sftbl; Hon Roll; Waterbury ST Tech; Data Proc.

NEFF, DEBBIE; Harvard H Ellis Reg Vo Tech Schl; N Windham, CT; (Y); 5/128; Pres Church Yth Grp; VP Pres 4-H; Sec Sr Cls; Sec Stu Cncl; JV Bsktbl; Var Score Keeper; DAR Awd; Elks Awd; Sec NHS; U CT; Therptc Recrtn.

NEILL, SONJA T; The Ethel Walker Schl; Oxon Hill, MD; (Y); Dance Clb; Girl Scts; Math Clb; Teachers Aide; Chorus; Church Choir; Yrbk Bus Mgr; Pres Frsh Cls; Stu Cncl; Bsktbl; Child Psychlgy.

NELSON, BRIAN; Regional No 7 HS; New Hartford, CT; (Y); Computer Clb; Band; Concert Band; Mrchg Band; VP Sr Cls; Rep Stu Cncl; High Hon Roll; Hon Roll; Teachers Aide; JV L Bsktbl; Fronteers Of Applied Sci At Yale 84-85; Gifted Sci Prog 84-85; U CT; Engnrng.

NELSON III, JOHN D; Joseph A Foran HS; Milford, CT; (Y); 5/200; Am Leg Boys St; Key Clb; VP Soph Cls; VP Jr Cls; VP Sr Cls; Var L Socr; Var L Trk; NHS; Ntl Merit SF; Voice Dem Awd; Yale Book Awd 84; Brown Book Awd 84; Telluride Schlrshp Semi Fnlst 84; Williams Coll; Arch.

NELSON, MARK; East Lyme HS; Niantic, CT; (Y); Band; Concert Band; Jazz Band; Mrchg Band; Engrng.

NELSON, MELISSA; Litchfield HS; Litchfield, CT; (Y); Var L Trk; Hon Roll; NEDT Awd; AFS; Latin Clb; Math Tm; Spanish Clb; Sec Frsh Cls; Sec Soph Cls; JV Var Bsktbl; SADD Sec 83-85.

NELSON, RICHARD; Avon Old Farms/East Haven HS; East Haven, CT; (Y); 32/92; Cmnty Wkr; Nwsp Phtg; Nwsp Rptr; Ftbl; Lcrss; Wrstlng; U CT; Real Est.

NELSON, STEPHEN; Pomperaug HS; Southbury, CT; (Y); Boy Scts; Church Yth Grp; Drama Clb; Stage Crew; JV Trk; Var Wrstlng; Hon Roll; OH ST; Arch.

NEMEC, MARIANNE; Stratford HS; Stratford, CT; (Y); 2/240; Church Yth Grp; JA; Sec Soph Cls; Pres Jr Cls; Pres Sr Cls; Rep Stu Cncl; Var Cheerleading; JV Swmmng; Cit Awd; High Hon Roll.

NEMETZ, DAVID; Brookfield HS; Brookfield, CT; (Y); 1/208; Church Yth Grp; Math Tm; Spanish Clb; Lit Mag; Rep Stu Cncl; High Hon Roll; NHS; Ntl Merit Ltr; Sal; Amer Assoc Rtrd Prsns Acad Achvt & Svc Awd 85; Cath War Vets Essay Awd 85; Brkfld Wmns Clb Acad Schlrs; Beloit Coll; Geology.

NESBIT, ROBERT; New Canaan HS; New Canaan, CT; (Y); Pres Spanish Clb; Bsbl; JV Capt Ice Hcky; JV Lcrss; JV Tennis; High Hon Roll; Hon Roll; NHS.

NESCI, LAURA; Orville H Platt HS; Meriden, CT; (Y); Church Yth Grp; French Clb; Letterman Clb; Var L Sftbl; Hon Roll; Italian Clb 82-85; Pre-Med.

NESSON, ERIC; Amity Regional HS; Bethany, CT; (S); 104/376; FBLA; Model UN; Ski Clb; Var L Socr; Cit Awd; Class I Awd 82; Inter Comm.

NEUMAN, SANDY; Watertown HS; Oakville, CT; (Y); Chorus; Hon Roll; Reading Excllnc Awd 82; Vet.

NEWELL, TAMMY; Rockville HS; Vernon, CT; (Y); FBLA; Hosp Aide; Band; Mrchg Band; Yrbk Stf; Rep Frsh Cls; Rep Soph Cls; Rep Jr Cls; Hon Roll; Bay Path FBLA Awd 85; Bay Path Outstndng Achvt Awd 85; Manchester CC; CPA.

NEWSOM, SUSAN J; The Morgan Schl; Clinton, CT; (Y); 77/167; AFS; Ski Clb; Band; Concert Band; Mrchg Band; Var Capt Cheerleading; Var Trk; Hon Roll; Outstndng Chrldr 84; Keene ST Coll; Bus Mgmt.

NEWTON, HEATHER; Cheshire HS; Cheshire, CT; (Y); 40/319; School Play; Stage Crew; Yrbk Stf; Rep Jr Cls; Rep Sr Cls; High Hon Roll; Pres Schlr; Natl Latn Awd Cum Laude 82-85; U Of Connecticut; Bus Admin.

NEWTON, NANCY; New Britain HS; East Hartford, CT; (Y); Hon Roll; Manchester CC; Soc Serv.

NG, JESSICA; Stamford HS; Stamford, CT; (S); 40/406; Drama Clb; JA; Spanish Clb; High Hon Roll; Hon Roll; NHS; U CT, Stamford Brd Ed Cert Of Achvt, Apprctn 84; U Of CT; Comp.

NGUYEN, MAI; East Hartford HS; East Hartford, CT; (Y); 2/235; Math Clb; Science Clb; DAR Awd; French Hon Soc; High Hon Roll; Hon Roll; Jr NHS; NHS; Pres Schlr; Rotary Awd; Benjamin Bates Schlrshp 85; Daughters Of Amer Women Rvltn 85; Rotary Club Schlrshp 85; Bates Coll; Bio.

NGUYEN, TUAN; Windham HS; Willimantic, CT; (Y); Im Badmtn; Im Socr; Im Sftbl; Im Swmmng; Im Tennis; Im Trk; Im Vllybl; High Hon Roll; Hon Roll; Cert Spec Awd In Math & Typing 84; U Of CT; Elec Engnrng.

NICHOLS, SUE; Pomperaug HS; Southbury, CT; (Y); 18/200; Jr Cls; JV Bsktbl; JV Sftbl; Var Vllybl; Hon Roll; NHS; Acae All Amer Awd 85; Elem Schl Tchr.

NICHOLS, TIMOTHY; Fairfield Prep; Fairfield, CT; (Y); 97/233; Key Clb; Spanish Clb; Im Bsktbl; Var Capt Socr; Var Capt Tennis.

NICKERSON, SARAH; Miss Porters Schl; Greenwich, CT; (Y); 1/92; Debate Tm; French Clb; Hosp Aide; Political Wkr; Nwsp Rptr; Nwsp Stf; Rep Frsh Cls; JV Fld Hcky; Var Sftbl; JV Vllybl; Debating Awd 83; Fin In Soph Spch Cont 84; Elec To Cum Laude Scty Inc 84-85.

NICOL, KIM; Torrington HS; Torrington, CT; (Y); 80/320; Hon Roll.

NICOLELLI, ALLISON; St Marys HS; W Haven, CT; (Y); 21/120; Cmnty Wkr; Intnl Clb; Ski Clb; Sftbl; High Hon Roll; Hon Roll; Spanish NHS; Awd Excllnc 83; Italn Awd Excllnc 84; Italn Dept Awd 85; U Of CT; Italn.

NIELSEN, ARLA; Amity Regional HS; Orange, CT; (Y); Church Yth Grp; Drama Clb; Key Clb; Thesps; Church Choir; School Musical; Ricks Coll; Math.

NIGAM, VIVEK; Southington HS; Southington, CT; (Y); Am Leg Boys St; Latin Clb; Concert Band; Jazz Band; Lit Mag; Rep Stu Cncl; Trk; Elks Awd; High Hon Roll; Prfct Atten Awd; Elks Clb Stu Of Mnth 85; Ctr Creatve Yth Wesleyan U 83; Pre-Med.

NIRMAL, MARY; Mark T Sheehan HS; Wallingford, CT; (Y); 3/250; Hosp Aide; Sec Spanish Clb; Variety Show; VP Powder Puff Ftbl; Sec Stu Cncl; Var L Fld Hcky; High Hon Roll; NHS; Am Leg Aux Girls St; Hghst Acad Achvmnt Spnsh Awd; Comp Sci.

NISKI, KAREN E; Naugatuck HS; Naugatuck, CT; (Y); 54/350; Am Leg Aux Girls St; Church Yth Grp; Yrbk Stf; Pres Stu Cncl; JV Bsktbl; Var Mgr(s); Var Score Keeper; Var L Sftbl; Var Timer; Var L Vllybl; Psych.

NISKI, SHARON; Notre Dame Acad; Naugatuck, CT; (Y); Church Yth Grp; Cmnty Wkr; GAA; Variety Show; Yrbk Stf; Off Sr Cls; Stu Cncl; Crs Cntry; Sftbl; Swmmng; Boston U; Bus.

NOBLES, KYLE; Danbury HS; Danbury, CT; (Y); 9/612; Church Yth Grp; Drama Clb; Jazz Band; Madrigals; Mrchg Band; Orch; Yrbk Phtg; Rep Jr Cls; High Hon Roll; NHS; Asstnc Strtng Prfsnl Theatre Co Danbury 85; Perry Awd Spnsh 84; Drama.

NOBLES, TERRY; Platt HS; Meriden, CT; (Y); Var L Bsktbl; Var L Sftbl; Var L Vllybl; Hon Roll; Sftbl & Bsktbl Ltrd 83-85; Vllybl Ltrd 82-85; Bus Mgmt.

NOBREGA, EDWARD; Masuk HS; Monroe, CT; (Y); 6/365; AFS; Band; Socr; Trk; High Hon Roll; Jr NHS; NHS; Mst Imprvd Plyr Soccer & Band 83-85; Oustndng Achvt Creative Writing 84-85; Biolgcl Engnrng.

NOCERA, JODI; Briston Central HS; Bristol, CT; (Y); 16/300; Latin Clb; Sec Soph Cls; Trs Jr Cls; Cheerleading; Swmmng; Cheerleading; Swmmng; Tennis; High Hon Roll; NHS; Cum Laude In Natl Latin Exam & Cum Dignitate In CT Latin Exam 84-85.

NOGA, JILL; Shelton HS; Shelton, CT; (Y); Church Yth Grp; Exploring; French Clb; Sec FHA; Office Aide; JV Bsktbl; JV Crs Cntry; JV Trk; Hon Roll; Spec Ed.

NOLAN, KATHLEEN; East Catholic HS; Glastonbury, CT; (Y); 86/318; Cmnty Wkr; Service Clb; Yrbk Stf; Jr Cls; Sr Cls; Trk; High Hon Roll; CPA.

NOLAN, PATRICK; Joseph A Foran HS; Milford, CT; (Y); 4/270; Drama Clb; School Play; Nwsp Rptr; Lit Mag; High Hon Roll; NHS; Ntl Merit Ltr; NEDT Awd; Pres Schlr; St Schlr; Emerson Elec Co Schlrshp; Polka Dot Theatre Awd; Pace U; Engl.

NOLTE, MICHELLE; New Fairfield HS; New Fairfld, CT; (Y); 20/239; Drama Clb; Chorus; School Musical; School Play; Variety Show; High Hon Roll; NHS; All St Chrs 83, 84 & 85; Outstndng Musicianshp Chrs 84-85; Prof Dncr.

NOOME, MARK; Staples HS; Westport, CT; (Y); French Clb; Im Bsbl; Im Bsktbl; JV Var Ftbl; JV Var Wt Lftg; Im Wrstlng; Staples Superstar 83-84; US Navy; Aviation.

NOONAN, MARK; Old Saybrook SR HS; Old Saybrook, CT; (Y); 3/150; Latin Clb; Band; Nwsp Stf; VP Frsh Cls; Rep Soph Cls; Rep Stu Cncl; Var Bsbl; Var Socr; High Hon Roll; Hghst Hstry Avg 85.

NORELLI, NANCY ANN; Nonnewaug HS; Bethlehem, CT; (Y); 4-H; Hosp Aide; Pep Clb; Band; Concert Band; Jazz Band; Yrbk Ed-Chief; Yrbk Stf; Pres Frsh Cls; Rep Soph Cls; FBL Typng Stengrphy Awd 83-84; Fairfield U; Pre-Med.

NORKO, MELANIE J; Kolbe Cathedral HS; Bridgeport, CT; (Y); Hosp Aide; Office Aide; Capt Cheerleading.

NORMAN, KEVIN; Ledyard HS; Ledyard, CT; (Y); 55/250; Boy Scts; Church Yth Grp; Band; Concert Band; Mrchg Band; Var Ftbl; Wt Lftg; JV Wrstlng; Hon Roll; Springfield Coll; Hlth.

NORMAN, MARIA; Enfield HS; Enfield, CT; (Y); 7/257; Sec Trs Spanish Clb; Yrbk Stf; Stu Cncl; CC Awd; High Hon Roll; NHS; Bus Dept Awd 85; Frgn Lang Awd 85; Spn Awd 85; Providence Coll; Accntng.

NORMAN, SHERRY L; Southington HS; Plantsville, CT; (Y); 36/550; Church Yth Grp; Pres FBLA; Hosp Aide; Latin Clb; Nwsp Rptr; High Hon Roll; NHS; Pep Clb; Pres Church Choir; Variety Show; Anne M Fontana FBLA Awd 85; Am Leg Aux Kiltnc Scholar 85; U CT; Bus Adm.

NORMANDY, LISA; Maloney HS; Meriden, CT; (Y); Key Clb; VICA; High Hon Roll; Hon Roll; NHS; Certif Professionalism VICA 85; Phys Ther.

NORRIS, AMY; Academy Of The Holy Family; Norwich, CT; (Y); 13/27; Church Yth Grp; Drama Clb; Acpl Chr; Band; Concert Band; Orch; Sftbl; Swmmng; VP Soph Cls; Rep Stu Cncl; Dghtrs Of The Amer Revltn 82; Outstdng Part Orch & Bnd 81-83; Hnrs Rdng; Phy Ed.

NORTON, KATHRYN A; Newton HS; Newtown, CT; (Y); 2/294; Trs AFS; French Clb; Key Clb; Capt Quiz Bowl; VP Spanish Clb; French Hon Soc; Ntl Merit SF; Sal; Spanish NHS; Hosp Aide; Michaels Jewelers Good Citizens Awd 84; Intl Business.

NORTON, KELLY; Maloney HS; Meriden, CT; (Y); Cmnty Wkr; FNA; Teachers Aide; VICA; Hon Roll; Occuptnl Thrpst.

NOSAL, MICHAEL; Westhill HS; Stamford, CT; (Y); Chess Clb; Computer Clb; Math Clb; Science Clb; Var Capt Crs Cntry; Var L Trk; Hon Roll; NHS; Ntl Merit Ltr; Cntr Fo Advncd Of Acdmcly Tlntd Yth Awd Wnr 82-83; Comp Sci.

NOTARINO, CONNIE A; East Haven HS; E Haven, CT; (Y); Church Yth Grp; Cmnty Wkr; Girl Scts; Hosp Aide; Latin Clb; Office Aide; Political Wkr; Stu Cncl; Hon Roll; St Josephs Coll; Pre Med.

NOTMAN JR, CHARLIE LEE; Weaver HS; Hartford, CT; (Y); Am Leg Boys St; Boy Scts; Letterman Clb; Varsity Clb; Yrbk Stf; Lit Mag; Capt Crs Cntry; Var Ftbl; Capt Trk; High Hon Roll, All Amer 84-85; All ST 83-85; Law.

NOURIZADEH, KAREN; St Thomas Aquiras HS; New Britain, CT; (Y); Teachers Aide; Trk; Vllybl; NHS.

NUCIFORA, SALVATORE; Vinal Regional Vocational Tech Schl; East Hampton, CT; (Y); Am Leg Boys St; Aud/Vis; Camera Clb; VICA; Yrbk Stf; Pres Stu Cncl; Trk; High Hon Roll; 4R Cls Exec Brd 84-85; Ntl Freestyle Rllrsktng Comptr 84.

NUGENT, SCOTT; Amity Regional SR HS; Woodbridge, CT; (Y); Am Leg Boys St; Church Yth Grp; Drama Clb; Jazz Band; Mrchg Band; School Musical; School Play; Ftbl; Hon Roll; NHS; Boys ST Awds Mst Religious & Mst Outstndg 85; Mst Imprvd Musicn; Music Ed.

NUNES, HELEN; Conard HS; Pine Meadow, CT; (Y); 31/297; Service Clb; Yrbk Stf; Off Stu Cncl; Fld Hcky; Sftbl; High Hon Roll; Hon Roll; NHS; Frank Schechl Schlrshp Fund 85; CT Schlrshp Achvt Grnt 85.

NUNZIANTE, FERDINANDO; Bristol Central HS; Bristol, CT; (Y); Library Aide; Var Socr; Var Capt Trk; Hon Roll; Am Chem Soc CT Vly Sect Chem Olympiad 85; Frgn Culture Clb 85; Chem Engrng.

NUNZIANTE, RICHARD; Notre Dame Of West Haven HS; West Haven, CT; (Y); 10/300; Rep Church Yth Grp; Spanish Clb; Teachers Aide; School Musical; Nwsp Rptr; Lit Mag; High Hon Roll; NHS; Ntl Merit SF; ND Spn Clb Schlrshp-Excllnc 85; Spn Lang.

NYREN, RONALD; Southington HS; Southington, CT; (Y); Church Yth Grp; Latin Clb; Nwsp Stf; Lit Mag; High Hon Roll; NHS; Ntl Merit Ltr; Harvard Bk Prz 85; Creatv Yth Ctr Wesleyan U 85; New Eng Yng Writrs Conf Breadloaf 85; Writr.

O BRIEN, COLLEEN; Guilford SR HS; Guilford, CT; (Y); Church Yth Grp; Drama Clb; Acpl Chr; Madrigals; School Musical; School Play; Stage Crew; Symp Band; Coach Actv; Socr; All ST Choir 83-85; All Eastern Choir 84-85; Music.

O BRIEN, JOHN; Xavier HS; Wallingford, CT; (Y); 50/200; Hosp Aide; Ski Clb; JV Var Ftbl; Hon Roll; Phrmcy.

O BRIEN, LAURA; St Joseph HS; Stratford, CT; (Y); 130/225; Art Clb; Drama Clb; Girl Scts; Ski Clb; Stage Crew; Crs Cntry; Mgr(s); Tennis; Fshn Merch.

O BRIEN, MARY BETH; New Milford HS; New Milford, CT; (Y); 3/285; Trs AFS; Math Tm; Concert Band; Mrchg Band; School Musical; School Play; Yrbk Ed-Chief; Rep Stu Cncl; Cit Awd; High Hon Roll; Am Legn Schl Awd 85; DAR Hstry Awd 85; PTA Schlrshp 85; U Of Notre Dame; Bus Admin.

O BRIEN, RICH; Granby Memorial HS; Granby, CT; (Y); VP Church Yth Grp; Yrbk Stf; Var Crs Cntry; Var Trk.

O CONNELL, DANIEL; Shelton HS; Shelton, CT; (Y); Am Leg Boys St; Spanish Clb; Trs Jr Cls; Trs Sr Cls; High Hon Roll; Hon Roll; NHS; Spanish NHS; Black Belt Karate 84; Accntnt.

O CONNOR, ANDREA E; Northwestern Regional H S No 7; Norfolk, CT; (Y); French Clb; Cheerleading; Sftbl; U CT; Legl Sec.

O CONNOR, CAROLYN; Trumbull HS; Trumbull, CT; (Y); Ski Clb; Rep Stu Cncl; Var Swmmng; Hon Roll; Excell Home Ec 83; Pre-Law.

O CONNOR, CRISTY; Holy Cross HS; Watertown, CT; (Y); 70/352; Art Clb; Concert Band; Jazz Band; Mrchg Band; Orch; School Musical; Stage Crew; Hon Roll; Frnch Merit Awd Ntl Cntst 83; Med.

O CONNOR, ELISE; Northwest Catholic HS; West Hartford, CT; (Y); Church Yth Grp; Drama Clb; Spanish Clb; Acpl Chr; Chorus; Church Choir; School Musical; School Play; Yrbk Stf; Lit Mag; Cert For Excllnce In Engl 84; Hnrs Engl Prgrms 82-86; Engl Comm.

O CONNOR, KEVIN J; William H Hall HS; W Hartford, CT; (Y); 46/317; Spanish Clb; Pres Sr Cls; Rep Stu Cncl; Im Capt Bsktbl; Var L Ftbl; Var L Lcrss; Wt Lftg; High Hon Roll; Kiwanis Awd; Spanish NHS; Stanley Fisher Scholar; U Notre Dame; Intl Reltns.

O CONNOR, LAURA A; Stamford Catholic HS; Stamford, CT; (Y); 22/160; Church Yth Grp; Civic Clb; Cmnty Wkr; Computer Clb; English Clb; FBLA; Pep Clb; Red Cross Aide; Yrbk Stf; Bowling; Westchester Bus Inst Educ Awd 85; Teen Life Ctr-Fin Dir Dist II 85-86; Acad Awds Acctg & Engl 84-85; Boston Coll; Comp Sci.

O CONNOR, MAIREAD; Glastonbury HS; S Glastonbury, CT; (Y); 171/393; Civic Clb; Drama Clb; Yrbk Ed-Chief; Hon Roll; Dance Clb; School Play; Variety Show; Yrbk Stf; Rep Stu Cncl; Irish Step Dncng Champ; Miss CT Untd Teenager 83-84; ARTS Recgntn, Tlnt Hnrbl Ment Dance 84-85; Skidmore Coll; Dance Thrpy.

O CONNOR, PHILIP X; Wilbur L Cross HS; New Haven, CT; (Y); 57/315; Boy Scts; Church Yth Grp; Pres Debate Tm; Latin Clb; Political Wkr; Red Cross Aide; Sec Ski Clb; Teachers Aide; Pres Varsity Clb; Yrbk Stf; Athltc Awds 84; Hstry Priz Exm 84; ST Law Cmptn 2nd Pl 85; Philsphy.

O CONNOR, RICHARD; Torrington HS; Torrington, CT; (Y); 6/320; Math Tm; VP Sr Cls; Bsktbl; Socr; Tennis; High Hon Roll; Trs NHS; NEDT Awd; Engrng.

O CONNOR, TRACY; St Paul Catholic HS; Bristol, CT; (Y); Chorus; Variety Show; Lit Mag; Hon Roll; U Connecticut; Phrmcy.

O DAY, KATHLEEN; Daniel Hand HS; Madison, CT; (Y); 14/287; Church Yth Grp; FCA; GAA; JCL; Spanish Clb; Yrbk Stf; Trs Sr Cls; Fld Hcky; Trk; Hon Roll; Henry J & Marie Munger Schlrshp 85; U Of CT; Bus.

O FARRELL, SUZANNE; St Bernard HS; Niantic, CT; (S); Church Yth Grp; Drama Clb; Girl Scts; Hosp Aide; Library Aide; Band; Concert Band; Mrchg Band; School Play; Rep Stu Cncl; Marian Awd 83; Bio.

O HAGAN, PATRICIA; Sacred Heart Acad; New Haven, CT; (Y); Art Clb; Dance Clb; Drama Clb; English Clb; School Musical; School Play; Variety Show; Var Cheerleading; Trk; Hon Roll; Clelian Scholar 83-84.

O HANLON, TRACEY E; Daniel Hand HS; Madison, CT; (Y); 83/235; Church Yth Grp; Cmnty Wkr; GAA; Pep Clb; Red Cross Aide; Chorus; School Musical; Stage Crew; Yrbk Stf; Trs Soph Cls; CT Shorelnd Ldrshp Conf 84-85; CT JR Intrn Prog 85.

O HARA, BRYAN M; Tolland HS; Tolland, CT; (Y); Var Crs Cntry; Var Trk; U CT; Lib Arts.

O HARA, SEAN W; Tolland HS; Tolland, CT; (Y); U Of CT; Engrng.

O HARE, KIM R; Coate Rosemary Hall HS; Guilford, CT; (Y); German Clb; JA; Pep Clb; Var Capt Tennis; USSRA 84-85; Math.

O NEILL, DARREN; Holy Cross HS; Watebury, CT; (Y); 95/352; Church Yth Grp; Nwsp Rptr; JV Bsbl; Im Bsktbl; Hon Roll; Co-Capt St Champ Mock Trial Tm; Asst Spec Olym Bsktbl Tm; Mickey Mantle Bsbl Wrld Series; Pre-Med.

O NEILL, SCOTT; East Catholic HS; S Windsor, CT; (Y); CAP; French Clb; Ski Clb; Band; Score Keeper; Wrstlng; U Of CT Citadale; Law.

O NEILL, STEPHEN; East Catholic HS; Manchester, CT; (Y); 150/300; Crs Cntry; Trk; Hon Roll; Cvl Engrng.

O REGAN, RICHARD; Enfield HS; Enfield, CT; (Y); Ski Clb; Band; Concert Band; Mrchg Band; Pep Band; Bowling; Var Wrstlng; Hon Roll; Cert Awd Mst Imprvd Musicn 83.

O SHEA, SHERYL; Sacred Heart Acad; N Branford, CT; (Y); Spanish Clb; Crs Cntry; Cert Hon Latin Natl Tst 83; Hnrs Cert 85; Psych.

OBER, PETER; Branford HS; Branford, CT; (Y); Capt Bsbl; Capt Ftbl; Hon Roll; Bus Mgmt.

OGORODNIK, CLAUDINE; Joseph A Foran HS; Milford, CT; (Y); 6/230; Cmnty Wkr; French Clb; Keywanettes; Spanish Clb; Yrbk Rptr; Var Trk; JV Vllybl; Hon Roll; NHS; NEDT Awd; Frnch Awd 85; Sci Awd 83; Cert Of Mrt Mock Trial Part 85; Sci.

OGUSCHEWITZ, MARK; Tolland HS; Tolland, CT; (Y); Wrtr.

OIEN, JAMES M; St Bernards HS; Stonington, CT; (Y); 138/290; Chess Clb; Computer Clb; Drama Clb; School Musical; School Play; Stage Crew; Yrbk Stf; John J Pescettello Chractr Awd 85; Northeastern; Elec Engrng.

OLCESE, LISA M; Litchfield HS; Northfield, CT; (Y); VP Art Clb; Cmnty Wkr; Latin Clb; Math Tm; Chorus; Nwsp Rptr; Yrbk Stf; Cheerleading; Sec French Hon Soc; Senators Intrnshp 84; Smith Coll; Intl Corp Law.

OLDAKOWSKI, ANNA; Sacred Heart HS; Naugatuck, CT; (Y); 9/187; Computer Clb; JV Var Bsktbl; High Hon Roll; Hon Roll; Trs NHS; U Of CT.

OLEARCZYK, LISA; Pomperaug Regional HS; Southbury, CT; (Y); Church Yth Grp; Library Aide; Red Cross Aide; Teachers Aide; High Hon Roll; Hst NHS; Yng Volntrs Action Awd 85; Phrmclgy.

OLENIK, PETER C; Stonington HS; Pawcatuck, CT; (Y); 11/192; Am Leg Boys St; Ed Nwsp Stf; Ed Yrbk Stf; Im Badmtn; Stat Trk; High Hon Roll; NHS; Prfct Atten Awd; Yale Frontiers Appld Sci; Worcester Poly-Tech Frontiers Sci & Mth; Hghst Schl Score ASME Tst; Wesleyan U; Astrophyscs.

OLIN, DOUG; Amity Regional HS; Woodbridge, CT; (Y); Latin Clb; Model UN; Temple Yth Grp; Var Capt Swmmng; High Hon Roll; All Housatonic League Swmng 1st Team 84 & 85; Bus.

OLIVA, KEVIN CHARLES; Windsor Locks HS; Windsor Locks, CT; (Y); Am Leg Boys St; Church Yth Grp; Trs Jr Cls; Pres Sr Cls; Stu Cncl; Ftbl; Voice Dem Awd; Ella T Grasso Pltcl Sci Awd For Srv 85; Windsor Locks Tchrs Assn Schlrshp 85; Sprngfld Tech CC; Bus Adm.

OLSCHEFSKI, DIANA; Newington HS; Newington, CT; (Y); Civic Clb; Stu Cncl; Var Cheerleading; High Hon Roll; Hon Roll; Schlrshp Bus Wk 84; Bus.

OLSEN, WILLIAM T; Foundation HS; East Haven, CT; (Y); Computer Clb; French Clb; Pres Ski Clb; Stage Crew; Im Bsktbl; Im Bowling; Im Sftbl; Hon Roll; Dir Awd 83-84; Arch.

OLSON, JANICE; Bristol Central HS; Bristol, CT; (Y); 13/276; Church Yth Grp; GAA; Intnl Clb; Latin Clb; Ski Clb; Variety Show; Off Jr Cls; Off Sr Cls; Stu Cncl; JV Bsktbl; Italian Achvt Awd 85; Mary A Callen Schlrshp 85; Tufts U; Librl Arts.

ONEIL, TOM; Ansonia HS; Ansonia, CT; (Y); Boy Scts; Rep Frsh Cls; Rep Soph Cls; Var Ftbl.

ONEILL, NED; Tolland HS; Tolland, CT; (Y); Rep Stu Cncl; JV Bsbl; Var Bsktbl; Ftbl; Hon Roll; NHS; Boston Coll; Busnss Admin.

ONNEN, DOUGLAS; Coventry HS; Coventry, CT; (S); Chess Clb; High Hon Roll; Hon Roll; NHS; Amer HS Math Exam Awd 84; Math.

ONTRA, ALEX ANNDRA; Lauralton Hall HS; Bridgeport, CT; (Y); French Clb; Hosp Aide; Latin Clb; Library Aide; Yrbk Bus Mgr; Hon Roll; NHS; Amer Clscl League 84; Clscl Scty New Englnd Cum Dignitate 84; U Of TX Austin; Bus.

OPATKIEWICZ, NEAL; Canterbury HS; Schenectady, NY; (Y); 20/84; Camera Clb; German Clb; Key Clb; Letterman Clb; Varsity Clb; Band; Concert Band; Orch; Symp Band; Lit Mag; Slvr Mdl Ice Hcky 84; Brckprt ST U; Pre-Law.

ORR, MATTHEW; Danbury HS; Danbury, CT; (Y); 7/612; Computer Clb; German Clb; Math Tm; Band; Concert Band; Mrchg Band; School Musical; Variety Show; Rep Jr Cls; Hon Roll; Chem.

ORR, TIMOTHY C; Avon Old Farms Schl; Plano, TX; (S); 18/100; Cmnty Wkr; Radio Clb; Pres Band; Pres Jazz Band; Nwsp Phtg; Yrbk Phtg; Yrbk Stf; Swmmng; Hon Roll; Acad All-Amer Citation 85; Wesleyan U; Photo Journ.

ORZECHOWSKI, CINDY; Ansonia HS; Ansonia, CT; (Y); 17/130; JA; Spanish Clb; Church Choir; Bsktbl; Hon Roll; Spanish NHS; Briarwood Book Awd 83-84; Briarwood Schlrshp 84-85; Briarwood Coll; Exec Secretary.

OSBORNE, EDWARD; Glastonbury HS; Glastonbury, CT; (Y); 100/399; Church Yth Grp; Hosp Aide; Varsity Clb; Band; L Ftbl; JV Socr; Var Trk; Cit Awd; Hon Roll; Jr NHS; Tufts; Bus.

OSHEA, PETER; Fairfield Prep; Fairfield, CT; (Y); Boy Scts; Camera Clb; Spanish Clb; Jazz Band; Pep Band; Im Bsktbl; JV Crs Cntry; Trk; Spanish NHS; Ortho.

OSOWIECKI, BRIGITTE K; Thomaston HS; Thomaston, CT; (Y); 1/68; Church Yth Grp; Cmnty Wkr; French Clb; Variety Show; Fld Hcky; High Hon Roll; NHS; Natl Ldrshp & Svc Awd 84-85; Acadmc All Amer Stdnt Awd 83-84; Harvard Bk Clb Awd 84-85; Bus.

OSOWIECKI JR, CHETTE; Oliver Wolcott Technical Schl; Thomaston, CT; (Y); 9/143; Am Leg Boys St; Church Yth Grp; Variety Show; Rep Soph Cls; Pres Jr Cls; Rep Sr Cls; Var Tennis; Hon Roll; NHS; Fel-Rpo Auto Tech Schlrshp 85; UNICO Natl Auto Grant 85; W C Nicholas-C E Nejaime Mem Schlrshp 85; NH Vo Tech Coll; Auto Mech.

OSTENDORF, TIMOTHY ROSS; East Granby HS; East Granby, CT; (Y); AFS; Cmnty Wkr; Drama Clb; Thesps; Chorus; School Musical; School Play; Stage Crew; Hon Roll; CT All-State Chorus 85; Grtr Hartford Acad Prfrmng Arts 85; Musical Theatre.

OTTALAGANA, FRED; Southington HS; Southington, CT; (Y); 257/550; Socr; Hon Roll; Indstrl Arts Awd 82; VP Itln Clb 83-85; Wtrbry ST Tech Coll; Mfg Engrn.

OUIMET, ARTHUR; Suffield HS; Enfield, CT; (Y); 10/153; Am Leg Boys St; VP FFA; JV Bsbl; JV Var Bsktbl; Var Crs Cntry; Var Trk; High Hon Roll; Hon Roll; NHS; Civl Engrng.

OWENS, DOUGLAS; Oliver Wolcott Technical Schl; Torrington, CT; (Y); 6/175; Bsbl; Bsktbl; Wt Lftg; Jr NHS; Waterbury ST Schl; Elec Engr.

OWENS, EVELYN; Wilbur Cross HS; New Haven, CT; (Y); Office Aide; Pep Clb; Teachers Aide; Church Choir; Drill Tm; School Play; Rep Frsh Cls; Rep Soph Cls; Rep Jr Cls; High Hon Roll; Hnrs 85; Rep Schl Clss 82-85; Rep Schl Clss 83-85; Nrsng.

OWENS, MICHELE; West Haven HS; W Haven, CT; (Y); Church Yth Grp; Office Aide; Yrbk Stf; Cit Awd; Hon Roll; Secy.

PABILONIA, CHRISTOPHER; Windham HS; Willimantic, CT; (Y); 51/320; Am Leg Boys St; DECA; Political Wkr; Nwsp Rptr; Rep Stu Cncl; JV Var Ftbl; Var Capt Trk; High Hon Roll; Hon Roll; 1942 Schlrp Mem Awd 85; Avery Point; Finance.

PACE, ANGELA; Saint Thomas Aquinas HS; New Britain, CT; (Y); Cmnty Wkr; JA; Latin Clb; Yrbk Bus Mgr; Stat Socr; Hon Roll; Jr NHS; NHS; Prfct Atten Awd; Briarwood Coll Bk Awd 85; Accntnt.

PACE, MICHAEL; North Haven HS; N Haven, CT; (Y); 15/290; Cmnty Wkr; Science Clb; Service Clb; Band; Nwsp Phtg; Nwsp Rptr; Stu Cncl; NHS; Spanish NHS; Hosp Aide; Fire Prtctn Engr.

PACKMAN, CHERYL; William H Hall HS; West Hartford, CT; (Y); 64/342; Chorus; Trs Frsh Cls; Off Soph Cls; Trs Jr Cls; VP Capt Gym; Var Socr; Var Tennis; French Hon Soc; High Hon Roll; NHS; CCC Hon Men All Lg Socr 85; MVP Ten Tm 85; CT ST Select Socr & Regnl Trnng Cmp 84-85; Psych.

PAE, ROBERT; Newington HS; Newington, CT; (Y); 3/379; Am Leg Boys St; Hosp Aide; Key Clb; Math Tm; Scholastic Bowl; Nwsp Ed-Chief; Yrbk Bus Mgr; High Hon Roll; NHS; Ntl Merit SF; Spnsh Awd 83-84; Chem Engrng.

PAGE, SANDY; Guilford SR HS; Guilford, CT; (Y); Cmnty Wkr; Teachers Aide; Hon Roll; Briarwood Book Awd 85; Busnss.

PAGEAU, MICHELE; Hamden HS; Hamden, CT; (Y); Band; Cheerleading; Gym; Sftbl.

PAINTER, ROBERT; Amity Regional SR HS; Bethany, CT; (Y); 14/367; Am Leg Boys St; Rep Drama Clb; Pres Latin Clb; Acpl Chr; Band; Chorus; Madrigals; School Musical; School Play; Yrbk Stf; Yale Bk Awd 84; U CT Sem Outstndng Jrs 84; Haverford Coll.

PALAIA, THOMAS; Farmington HS; Farmington, CT; (Y); 26/220; Church Yth Grp; Math Clb; Var Crs Cntry; JV Tennis; Var Trk; High Hon Roll; Hon Roll; Michaels Jwlrs Awd 85; Civil Engnrng.

PALESE, DANIEL R; Danbury HS; Danbury, CT; (Y); JA; Ski Clb; Yrbk Stf; JV Socr; Vllybl.

PALICKI, LISA; Manchester HS; Manchester, CT; (Y); Hosp Aide; Red Cross Aide; Yrbk Stf; Crs Cntry; Trk; Vllybl; High Hon Roll; Hon Roll; Grtr Hrtfrd Area Awd 85; Manchester Schlrshp Fndtn 85; Manchester Meml Hosp Awd 85; St Joseph Coll; Nrsg.

PALLATTO, ELIZABETH; Windham HS; Columbia, CT; (Y); Am Leg Aux Girls St; VP Frsh Cls; Stu Cncl; JV Tennis; NHS; Ntl Merit Ltr; Close-Up Fndtn 85; YDLC Ldrshp Red Cross Camp 85; Bk Awd Outstng Jr Hist 85; Polt Sci.

PALLOF, CAROLYN; St Bernard HS; New London, CT; (Y); #12 In Class; Cmnty Wkr; Library Aide; Capt Crs Cntry; Capt Trk; High Hon Roll; Hon Roll; NHS; Ntl Merit SF; All ST Crs Cntry 83 & 84; Cls L Chmp Crs Cntry 83 & 84; Chem Tutor; Excllnce Art Awd; Peer Ldrshp 85-86; Ocnolgy.

PALMER, NANCY I; Greenwich HS; Cos Cob, CT; (Y); Church Yth Grp; Exploring; Chorus; Mgr Sftbl; Var L Vllybl; Hon Roll; Linda Wachnicki Schlrshp 85; GASFA Schlrshp 85; Cos Cob Schl Bk Awd 85; St Joseph Coll; Hmn Dvlp.

PALMER, SHAWN; Rocky Hill HS; Rocky Hill, CT; (Y); 32/128; Rep Am Leg Boys St; Church Yth Grp; Drama Clb; Ski Clb; Teachers Aide; Concert Band; Mrchg Band; School Play; Yrbk Bus Mgr; Hon Roll; Med.

PALMESE, LISA; Southington HS; Southington, CT; (Y); JA; Pep Clb; Sec Frsh Cls; Capt Var Cheerleading; Var L Gym; High Hon Roll; Hon Roll; Jr NHS.

PALMIERI, KIM TRACY; Southington HS; Plantsville, CT; (Y); 85/600; Sec VP Church Yth Grp; Pep Clb; PAVAS; Ski Clb; Chorus; Concert Band; Mrchg Band; Variety Show; Yrbk Stf; Sec Sr Cls; 1st Pl Tlnt Shw 83; Gftd/Tlntd Prog 82-85; Frgn Lang.

PALMIERI, LUCIA; East Haven HS; North Haven, CT; (Y); 16/300; Spanish Clb; Church Choir; Stage Crew; Hon Roll; Jr NHS; NHS; Schlrshp 82; Ldrshp Pin 82; Quinipiac Coll; Accntnt.

PALUMBO, MARGARET; Branford HS; Branford, CT; (Y); 15/270; Band; Chorus; Church Choir; Concert Band; Jazz Band; Mrchg Band; Variety Show; Lit Mag; Rep Frsh Cls; High Hon Roll; Prof Wrtng.

PALUMBO, TRACEY; St Thomas Aquinas HS; New Britain, CT; (Y); 5/178; Church Yth Grp; Computer Clb; Drama Clb; Trs Latin Clb; Chorus; School Musical; Lit Mag; Rep Frsh Cls; Rep Soph Cls; Trs Stu Cncl; Natl Hnr Soc Schlrshp 84-85; Svc Awd 84-5; Rlgn Awd 82-83; Med Tech.

PANARONI, DONNA; Seymour HS; Seymour, CT; (Y); 2/210; AFS; Am Leg Aux Girls St; Hosp Aide; JV Crs Cntry; Mgr(s); High Hon Roll; NHS; Hugh O Brien Yth Awd ST Semnr Rep 84; Erly Chldhd Ed.

PANDISCIA, CHRISTOPHER; Newington HS; Newington, CT; (Y); Am Leg Boys St; Drama Clb; Ski Clb; Acpl Chr; Pres Chorus; Madrigals; School Musical; Variety Show; Bsbl; Socr; All ST Choir 84; Accptnc Into Hartford Acad For Perf Arts 85; Natl Hnr Scty 85; Msc.

PANICO, KRISTIE; Lauralton Hall HS; Orange, CT; (Y); Church Yth Grp; French Clb; Science Clb; Service Clb; Chorus; Yrbk Phtg; Yrbk Stf; Bus.

PANKEY, NANCY; Newton HS; Hawleyville, CT; (Y); 66/298; AFS; French Clb; Pres Girl Scts; Spanish Clb; Nwsp Phtg; Nwsp Rptr; Yrbk Ed-Chief; Lit Mag; Swmmng; High Hon Roll; American U; Intl Rltns.

PANKIEWICZ, PHILIP; St Bernard HS; Lebanon, CT; (S); Library Aide; Teachers Aide; Var Tennis; Hon Roll; Optics.

PANNONE, ROBERT; St Bernard HS; N Franklin, CT; (S); 88/279; Cmnty Wkr; JV Bsktbl; JV Ftbl; Var L Golf; Hon Roll; U CT; Phrmcy.

PANNULLO, MARYFRANCES; Holy Cross HS; Waterbury, CT; (Y); 65/362; Yrbk Rptr; Ntl Merit SF; Bio Sci.

PANOS, ANASTASIA JOY; Berlin HS; Berlin, CT; (Y); Art Clb; Drama Clb; School Play; Stage Crew; Lit Mag; High Hon Roll; Hon Roll; NHS; Pres Schlr; Hnry Art Awd 84; Art Achvmnt Awd 83; Carnegie-Mellon U; Arch.

PAPALLO, ANNE; Platt HS; Meriden, CT; (Y); Key Clb; Swmmng; Hon Roll; Yth Gov Lbbyst 85; Stu Senate Bd Rep 85-86; Pre Cnselrs Pgm 85-86; Pre-Med.

PAPILE, JOHN; Bristol Central HS; Bristol, CT; (Y); Latin Clb; Ski Clb; Spanish Clb; Bsbl; Golf; Score Keeper; Trk; Hon Roll; UCLA; Soc Sci.

PAPP, JENNIFER E; Plainfield HS; Moosup, CT; (Y); 1/180; GAA; Varsity Clb; Concert Band; Jazz Band; Mrchg Band; Var Capt Crs Cntry; Var Capt Trk; High Hon Roll; NHS; Voice Dem Awd; Rensselaer Medal 85; Harvard Prz Bk Awd 85; Schlrs Grp 82-85; Chem Engr.

PAPP, JILL DENISE; Lyman Hall HS; Wallingford, CT; (Y); Key Clb; Pres Spanish Clb; Varsity Clb; Stat Ftbl; Var Tennis; NHS; AFS; FHA; Mgr(s); Score Keeper; Medals Earth Sci Chem 85; Cert Spansh IIIII 83-85; Wnnr Town Splng Bee 80; Chem.

PAPPADIA, JOSEPH F; St Bernard HS; Westerly, RI; (Y); 20/292; Band; Var L Swmmng; Hon Roll; NHS; SR Swin Tm Awd, J W Horton Sci Awd 85; Worcester Polytech; Elec Engr.

PAQUIN, TODD; J M Wright Tech; Stamford, CT; (Y); Socr; Hon Roll; Elec Fld.

PARADIS, ERIC; Shelton HS; Shelton, CT; (Y); Boy Scts; Drama Clb; Exploring; JA; Drm & Bgl; Trk; Hon Roll; U Of Bridgeport; Pedtrcs.

PARADIS, HEATHER; Orville H Platt HS; Meriden, CT; (Y); Church Yth Grp; French Clb; Latin Clb; Yrbk Stf; VP Sr Cls; Powder Puff Ftbl; Var Swmmng; CPA.

PARDUS, MARY LOU A; Farmington HS; Unionville, CT; (Y); 18/219; VP JA; Sftbl; Hon Roll; NHS; Outstndng Bus Stu Awd 85; Presdntl Acadmc Ftnss Awd 85; Athltc Awd 82 & 83; Quinnipiac Coll; Mgr Mrktng Div.

PARENTE, CIRO; Oliver Wolcott Technical Schl; Torrington, CT; (Y); Var Capt Socr; Elec.

PARHAM, DEANIA; Masuk HS; Monroe, CT; (Y); Church Yth Grp; Chorus; School Musical; Nwsp Rptr; Var L Cheerleading; Hon Roll; Outstndng Achvt Hm Ec & Pwr & Spd Rdng 85; Hm Ec Tchr.

PARIKH, NIMMI C; Hopkins Grmr Day Prospect Hill Schl; North Haven, CT; (Y); 4/109; Dance Clb; Model UN; Church Choir; Lit Mag; Im Capt Socr; JV Tennis; Ntl Merit SF; Key Clb; School Play; Natl Frnch Cntst 6th In Ct, 7th In N E; Cum Laude Soc 83-85; Natl Ptry Prss Publ 83; Phsics.

PARILLO, AUDREY; North Haven HS; N Haven, CT; (Y); 72/300; Church Yth Grp; Nwsp Rptr; Stu Cncl; Hon Roll; 6th Gup Awd Tang Soo Doo Karate 85; 1st Prz Paintng Fair 83; Stu Cncl Awd Outstndng Perfmnce 83; Arch.

PARILLO, WILLIAM; Amity HS; Orange, CT; (Y); Church Yth Grp; Band; Concert Band; Drm Mjr(t); Jazz Band; Mrchg Band; Symp Band; Var Ftbl; Trk; Cert Achvt Mus 85; Acad Chair Achvt 84; Jazz & Cncrt Bnd Awds 83-85; Astromy Engrng.

PARISI, GLENN C; North Haven HS; North Haven, CT; (Y); JA; Latin Clb; Spanish Clb; VP Band; Concert Band; Mrchg Band; Stu Cncl; Var L Crs Cntry; Var L Swmmng; JV Trk.

PARISI, RITA; Plainfield HS; Plainfield, CT; (Y); 10/157; Drama Clb; Chorus; School Play; Swing Chorus; Stu Cncl; Hon Roll; VFW Awd; S&M Corp Awd Scholar 85; Boston U; Bio-Med.

PARK, ALYCE; Francis T Maloney HS; Meriden, CT; (Y); 1/292; Am Leg Aux Girls St; Hosp Aide; Key Clb; Yrbk Stf; VP Frsh Cls; Pres Soph Cls; Sec Stu Cncl; Pres NHS; Pres Schlr; Val; Military Ordr Wrld Wars Merit Awd 85; United Technlgs Scholar 85; Pres Clsrm Yng Amercns Awd 84; Fairfield U; Comp Sci.

PARK, BERNARD; The Hotchkiss Schl; Glendale, CA; (Y); Library Aide; Spanish Clb; Orch; Bsbl; Ice Hcky; High Hon Roll; Ntl Merit SF; Math Bk Prz 83; Princeton U.

PARK, JOHN; Choate Rosemary Hall HS; Vienna, VA; (Y); Church Yth Grp; JA; Key Clb; Teachers Aide; Nwsp Stf; JV Bsktbl; Var L Tennis; Var L Vllybl; Hon Roll; NHS; Bus.

PARKER, CRAIG; Masuk HS; Monroe, CT; (Y); 8/200; German Clb; Band; Jazz Band; Var Capt Golf; Var Capt Socr; High Hon Roll; NHS; Outstndg Achvt Sci Awd Plq 83; Golf Tm Outstndg Prfrmr Plq 84; Harvard Bk Awd 85.

PARKER, HEATHER A; St Bernard HS; Mystic, CT; (S); 42/298; Civic Clb; Sec French Clb; Sec Science Clb; Chorus; School Musical; School Play; Stage Crew; Swing Chorus; Nwsp Stf; Yrbk Stf; U Of CT; Bio.

PARKER, KIRSTEN; East Lyme HS; Niantic, CT; (Y); Concert Band; Mrchg Band; School Play; Mgr(s); Powder Puff Ftbl; Score Keeper; Stat Socr; Hon Roll; Ntl Merit Ltr; Dartmouth Coll; Comp.

PARKER, SUSAN; Trumbull HS; Trumbull, CT; (Y); AFS; Church Yth Grp; French Clb; Concert Band; Yrbk Stf; Var Capt Fld Hcky; Var Trk; Hon Roll; Outstndng Athltc Achvt 83; FCIAC Fld Hockey Champs 84; Physio Ther.

PARKER, TARA; New London HS; New London, CT; (Y); Cmnty Wkr; Debate Tm; FBLA; JA; Key Clb; Library Aide; Spanish Clb; Nwsp Stf; Yrbk Stf; Church Yth Grp; Med Secy.

PARYLOVICH, KIM; St Paul Catholic HS; Terryville, CT; (Y); 24/304; Drama Clb; Hosp Aide; Science Clb; Spanish Clb; Chorus; Church Choir; School Play; Variety Show; Nwsp Ed-Chief; Off Stu Cncl; Acad Scholar Salve Regina Coll; Hghst Music Awd; Ldrshp Awd; Salve Regina; Nrsg.

PASCALE, MICHAEL; North Haven HS; N Haven, CT; (Y); 30/300; AFS; Church Yth Grp; Computer Clb; Ski Clb; Band; Lit Mag; Var Swmmng; JV Trk; French Hon Soc; Hon Roll; Acctng.

PASCENTE, ANN; Granby Memorial HS; Granby, CT; (Y); JA; Nwsp Rptr; JV Sftbl; Hon Roll.

PASS, MONICA; Norwalk HS; Norwalk, CT; (Y); Church Yth Grp; Cmnty Wkr; Chorus; Church Choir; Var Crs Cntry; Var Trk; Var Hon Roll; Norwalk CC; RN.

PASTOR, SUSAN; Stratford HS; Stratford, CT; (Y); JA; Chorus; Church Choir; School Musical; Rep Jr Cls; Rep Stu Cncl; Var Sftbl; Var Vllybl; Astrnmy.

PASZCZUK, ELIZABETH; New Britain HS; New Britain, CT; (Y); 54/332; Var L Bsktbl; Capt L Sftbl; Hon Roll; Lt George C Sulliman Mem Scholar 85; Pres Acad Fit Awd 85; Central CT ST U; Acctg.

PATACCA JR, ANGELO M; Glastonbury HS; Glastonbury, CT; (Y); Am Leg Boys St; Boy Scts; Sec Sr Cls; Pres Stu Cncl; Var Capt Lcrss; Var L Wrstlng; NHS; Intnl Clb; Band; Yrbk Stf; Eagle Scout Awd 83; Yale Clb Awd 85; Trinty Bk Awd 84; West Point Acad; Military.

PATCHKOFSKY, DEBORAH A; Seymour HS; Oxford, CT; (S); 2/224; Church Yth Grp; Yrbk Stf; Rep Stu Cncl; Swmmng; High Hon Roll; NHS; Sal; Northeastern U; Engrng.

PATEL, AAKAR; Southington HS; Southington, CT; (Y); Computer Clb; Math Clb; Math Tm; Variety Show; JV Bsktbl; JV Socr; Var Trk; JV Wrstlng; High Hon Roll; Hon Roll; Carnegie-Mellen U; Elec Engrng.

PATEL, HINA; North Haven HS; N Haven, CT; (Y); 43/250; Art Clb; Drama Clb; Science Clb; Concert Band; Crs Cntry; Hon Roll; Comp Prgrmr.

PATEL, KEYURI M; Stamford HS; Norwalk, CT; (Y); Church Yth Grp; Computer Clb; JA; VP Spanish Clb; School Play; Hon Roll; NHS; Top 100 Minority Stu CT UCONN 84-85; U CT; Biomed Engrng.

PATERNOSTRO, GINA; Holy Cross HS; Waterbury, CT; (Y); 65/360; Hosp Aide; Yrbk Stf; Stat Ftbl; High Hon Roll; Presdntl Acadmc Ftns Awd 85; Miss Amer Photgnc 84-85; Miss Intl Radiance 84-85; CT U; Corp Law.

PATERNOSTRO, PATRICK; Watertown HS; Watertown, CT; (Y); 19/250; Church Yth Grp; Yrbk Stf; Bowling; Crs Cntry; Ftbl; Trk; High Hon Roll; NHS; Pres Schlr; Pres Acad Fitnss Awd 85; Trck MVP Rnnr 85; Cls 1916 HS Schlrshp 85; Bentley Coll; Acctng.

PATTERSON, DEIRDRE; Crosby HS; Waterbury, CT; (Y); Soph Cls; Orch; Symp Band; Hon Roll; Afro Amer Clb Membr 83; Comp Oper.

PATTERSON, JENNIFER B; Norwalk HS; Norwalk, CT; (Y); 6/460; Church Yth Grp; Ski Clb; Jazz Band; Mrchg Band; School Musical; Yrbk Stf; NHS; Trs German Clb; Key Clb; Band; Outstndg Jr Engl Stu 84; U Of VA; Intl Reltns.

PAUCIELLO, JANET; Trumbull HS; Trumbull, CT; (Y); Art Clb; Stu Cncl; Trk; Hon Roll; Rotary Awd; Rtry Clb-Outstndng Bus 83; Art.

PAULSON, PETRICE; Weston HS; Weston, CT; (Y); 20/167; Intnl Clb; Pep Clb; JV Socr; Var Swmmng; JV Trk; Psychlgy.

PAVELO, MARLENE; Shelton HS; Shelton, CT; (S); 240/438; Church Yth Grp; Dance Clb; DECA; Drama Clb; Hosp Aide; Ski Clb; Hon Roll; Pres Of Dstrbtve Educ Clb Of Amer 84-85; Trvl.

PAVELO, WENDY; Stratford HS; Stratford, CT; (Y); 33/241; Hosp Aide; Hon Roll; Accntng.

PAWLAK, JENNIFER; Holy Cross HS; Watertown, CT; (Y); 113/352; Service Clb; Chorus; Rep Stu Cncl; JV Trk; JV Vllybl; Hon Roll; Human Svcs.

PAWLICH, SCOTT; East Hampton HS; E Hampton, CT; (Y); Boy Scts; Var L Bsbl; Var L Bsktbl; Hon Roll; Coachs Awd Bsktbl 84-85; Chrtr Oak Conf Bsktbl All Strs Tm 84-85.

PAWLIK, MARIA VERONIKA R; Stamford Catholic HS; Stamford, CT; (Y); 27/147; Church Yth Grp; FBLA; Library Aide; Red Cross Aide; Yrbk Stf; Hon Roll; NHS; Polsh Natl Merit Schlrshp 85; Legato Mem Schlrshp Awd 85; Polsh Amer Cultrl Soc Stamford Schlrshp 85; Alliance Coll; Intl Bus.

PAWLOSKI, SCOTT A; Lymon Hall HS; Wallingford, CT; (Y); Am Leg Boys St; Boys Clb Am; Boy Scts; Church Yth Grp; Varsity Clb; Stu Cncl; Var L Bsbl; Var L Socr; Hon Roll; Aeros Engrng.

PAWLOWSKI JR, HENRY J; East Catholic HS; Manchester, CT; (Y); Am Leg Boys St; Political Wkr; Nwsp Stf; Lit Mag; Trs Sr Cls; Rep Stu Cncl; Var Trk; Hon Roll; Ntl Merit Ltr; US Senat Yth Pgm 85; Catholic U Amer; Poli Sci.

PAYNE, LARIAYN; Low Heywood Thomas Schl; Stamford, CT; (Y); 3/36; Pres Band; Yrbk Bus Mgr; Var Bsktbl; Var Sftbl; Var Tennis; Var Vllybl; High Hon Roll; Hon Roll; Chem Awd 84; Yale Bk Awd 85; Lou Heywood Thomas Schl Commdtn 84; Engrng.

PAYNE, ROBIN; James Hillhouse HS; New Haven, CT; (Y); Camera Clb; Hon Roll; Med.

PEACOCK, CYNTHIA; Ellington HS; Ellington, CT; (Y); 27/117; Sec Computer Clb; FBLA; Sec Chorus; Co-Capt Color Guard; Co-Capt Flag Corp; Yrbk Stf; Hon Roll; Bentley Coll; Acctng.

PEARCE, KERRY A; Traumbull HS; Trumbull, CT; (Y); French Clb; VP JA; Math Clb; Office Aide; Var L Bsktbl; Var Capt Vllybl; French Hon Soc; High Hon Roll; NHS; Ntl Merit Ltr; Math.

PEARLMAN, LAWRENCE; Hotchkiss HS; Cambridge, MA; (Y); Debate Tm; Model UN; School Play; Yrbk Rptr; Swmmng; High Hon Roll; Hon Roll; Prfct Atten Awd; Harvard; Wrtr.

PECCERILLO, TERESA; Sacred Heart Acad; New Haven, CT; (Y); Aud/Vis; Church Yth Grp; Computer Clb; Spanish Clb; Church Choir; Southern CT ST U; Comp Sci.

PECK, TERRIE; Danbury HS; Danbury, CT; (Y); 184/600; Varsity Clb; Chorus; Yrbk Stf; Var Bsktbl; Var Socr; Capt Var Sftbl; JV Capt Vllybl; Jr NHS; All Cnty FCIAC & Gldn Glv Sftbl 85; Sprtsmnshp-Bsktbl 83; Phy Educ.

PEGEAS, GEORGE; Buckeley HS; Hartford, CT; (Y); Am Leg Boys St; Computer Clb; Math Tm; Red Cross Aide; Var Capt Ftbl; Stat Mgr(s); Howard U; Medcl Tech.

PEKARSKI, NARDA; Parish Hill HS; Hampton, CT; (Y); Yrbk Stf; High Hon Roll; Hon Roll; Sec NHS.

PELCHAR, JAY; Terryville HS; Terryville, CT; (Y); Am Leg Boys St; Trs Jr Cls; Bsbl; Bsktbl; Hon Roll; NHS; U CT; Engrng.

PELCHAT, SHERRI; Simsbury HS; Simsbury, CT; (Y); 128/352; Ski Clb; Bsktbl; Lcrss; Vllybl; High Hon Roll; Hon Roll; Vrsty Lttr Bsktbl,Vlybl & La Crosse 84-85; Math.

PELLEI, DAVID D; Fairfield College Preparatory Schl; Trumbull, CT; (Y); 18/226; Church Yth Grp; Drama Clb; Key Clb; Church Choir; Stage Crew; Mgr(s); High Hon Roll; NHS; Ntl Merit SF; Spanish NHS; Princeton U; Engr.

PELLETIER, GARY; St Bernard HS; Ashaway, RI; (S); 2/290; Exploring; French Clb; Library Aide; Office Aide; High Hon Roll; Sec NHS; Dartmouth Bk Awd 84; Engl.

PELLETIER, LISA; Farmington HS; Farmington, CT; (Y); 14/205; Church Yth Grp; Ski Clb; Band; Rep Frsh Cls; Rep Soph Cls; Rep Jr Cls; JV Var Socr; Tennis; French Hon Soc; High Hon Roll; Boston Coll; Bus.

PELLO, WILLIAM J; Lyman Hall HS; Wallingford, CT; (Y); 15/243; Cmnty Wkr; Varsity Clb; Variety Show; Var Capt Ftbl; Var Capt Trk; Im Wt Lftg; High Hon Roll; Natl Ftbly Fndtn Schlr Athlt 85; Pres Acad Fitnss Awd 85; Anna M Fredericks Med Bus Schlrshp 85; WCSU; Finance.

PELOSI, NICKIE; Watertown HS; Oakville, CT; (Y); AFS; Ski Clb; Band; Mrchg Band; Dentl Hyg.

PELRIN, JILL; Southington HS; Plantsville, CT; (Y); 58/550; FTA; Capt GAA; Variety Show; Trs Rep Soph Cls; Sec Stu Cncl; Var L Bsktbl; Var L Sftbl; Hon Roll; Jr NHS; Pres Schlr; Frosh Athlete Yr 82-83; All ST All Conf Sftbll 85; JR Prom Coord 84; Phys Ed.

PENSIERO, FRANK; Notre Dame Catholic HS; Bridgeport, CT; (Y); 9/285; Pres Latin Clb; Ed Nwsp Ed-Chief; High Hon Roll; NHS; Itln Hnr Soc 84-85; 3rd Prz CT ST Ltn Cntst; Pres Acad Fitnss Awd; Fairfield U; Acctng.

PEPE, MARA D; Danbury HS; Danbury, CT; (Y); 15/585; Art Clb; Hosp Aide; Nwsp Rptr; Yrbk Ed-Chief; Lit Mag; Stu Cncl; Jr NHS; NHS; Schlrshp Silvermine Guild Artst Paintg 84; Perry Awd Math 83; Hnbl Mntn City Wide Poetry Cntst 84; Studio Art.

PEPIN, KARL; Griswold HS; Jewett City, CT; (Y); Varsity Clb; Var Bsktbl; JV Civic Clb; Var Golf; Var Tennis; Hon Roll.

PEPLAU, JAMES; Saint Thomas Aquinas HS; New Britain, CT; (Y); 4/153; Boy Scts; CAP; Sec Exploring; Yrbk Ed-Chief; Elks Awd; Hon Roll; NHS; Natl Elks Fdn Schlrshp 85; Unico Natl Schlrshp 85; Rev Thomas P Quinn Awd For Outstdng Schlrsp 85; Rensselaer Polytechnic Inst; Ae.

PERCIVAL, PATRICIA; Granby Memorial HS; Granby, CT; (Y); 2/102; AFS; Sec Drama Clb; Yrbk Stf; Lit Mag; VP Sec Stu Cncl; Var Capt Fld Hcky; Var Capt Sftbl; DAR Awd; NHS; Sal; Scholar Comm Scholar Assn Granby Inc 85; Scholar Granby C Of C Inc 85; CT Coll; Eng.

PEREIRA, ANTHONY; West Haven HS; West Haven, CT; (Y); Am Leg Boys St; Intnl Clb; Spanish Clb; Capt Ftbl; Capt Lcrss; High Hon Roll; Jr NHS; NHS; Rotary Awd; Spanish NHS; Rotry Clb Schlr Athl 84-85; Duke U; Cvl Engr.

PEREZ, DAMARIS L; Hartford Public HS; Hartford, CT; (Y); 16/404; Computer Clb; Debate Tm; Exploring; Hon Roll; NHS; Prfct Atten Awd; Pease Latn Prz 84; MA Coll; Anthro.

PERILLO, SANDRA; Crosby HS; Waterbury, CT; (Y); 1/300; Key Clb; Rep Stu Cncl; High Hon Roll; NHS; Ntl Merit SF; Voice Dem Awd; Vrsty Stu Rfl Tm; 1st Pl Alg II Exam; Med Tech.

PERINGER, JENNIFER; Bethel HS; Bethel, CT; (Y); Church Yth Grp; FBLA; Var Capt Crs Cntry; Var Capt Trk; High Hon Roll; Hon Roll; NHS; All-Area X-Cntry 83; All Leag WCC X-Cntry 83-84.

PERITO, CHRISTINE; St Mary HS; Greenwich, CT; (Y); French Clb; Varsity Clb; Variety Show; Stu Cncl; Cheerleading; Fld Hcky; Powder Puff Ftbl; Socr; Wt Lftg; Hon Roll; Natl Fedrtn Of Music Clbs JR Fstvls 82-85; JR Shubert Clb 82-85; Med.

PERLOT, DAVID; Southington HS; Southington, CT; (Y); 56/600; Church Yth Grp; FBLA; Key Clb; Nwsp Stf; Yrbk Stf; JV Trk; High Hon Roll; New England Math Leag 84-85; Comp Sci.

PERNA, RICHARD; St Mary HS; Cos Cob, CT; (Y); Boys Clb Am; JA; Jr Cls; Bsbl; Ftbl; Mgr(s); Hon Roll; Hugh O Brien Yth Fndtn 84; Comp Litrcy Awd 84; JR Cls Tres Postn 85; Acctg.

PERNAL, JANICE; East Haven HS; E Haven, CT; (Y); 6/300; Math Clb; Math Tm; Sec Spanish Clb; JV Var Bsktbl; JV Var Sftbl; High Hon Roll; Jr NHS; NHS; Rotary Awd; JV Var Diving; Weselyan U Sci & Humnts Sympsm 85; Hnrbl Mntn Grls Sftbl 85; All Appont Tm Sftbl 84-85; Comp Sci.

PERRETTA, DANIEL; South Catholic HS; W Hartford, CT; (Y); Chess Clb; French Clb; Quiz Bowl; Nwsp Rptr; Lit Mag; Im Bsktbl; Im Var Ftbl; Hon Roll; Lib Arts.

PERRI, KEVIN; Bristol Central HS; Bristol, CT; (Y); Crs Cntry; Trk; Church Yth Grp; Hartford ST Tech; Draftng.

PERRINA, EVA; Tolland HS; Tolland, CT; (Y); Church Yth Grp; Lit Mag; Hmmkr.

PERRON, DIANE; John F Kennedy HS; Waterbury, CT; (Y); Stat Swmmng; Hon Roll; Hist & Italn Clbs; Bus Adm.

PERROTT, STEPHANIE; Nonnewaug HS; Seymour, CT; (Y); FBLA; Rptr FFA; Red Cross Aide; Hon Roll; Florclture.

PERROTTI, MARY KAY; Amity SR HS; Woodbridge, CT; (Y); Church Yth Grp; Dance Clb; Drama Clb; French Clb; Latin Clb; Model UN; Ski Clb; Spanish Clb; School Play; Nwsp Bus Mgr; Hnrbl Ment Ntl Frnch Ex; CT Yth Gov Pgm Hse Rep; Columbia; Bus.

PERROTTI, MAUREEN; Academy Of Our Lady Of Mercy; New Haven, CT; (Y); Drama Clb; French Clb; Chorus; School Play; Nwsp Stf; Yrbk Ed-Chief; Yrbk Stf; RI Schl Dsgn; Arch.

PERRY, EDWARD ALLEN; Notre Dame Catholic HS; Bridgeport, CT; (Y); 13/284; Sec Exploring; Pres JA; Latin Clb; Sec Spanish Clb; Nwsp Rptr; NHS; Spanish NHS; Sumner Simpson Scholar Awd 85; Dale Carnegie Scholar Awd 85; Mst Outstndg Male SR Achvr JA 85; Schiller Intl U; Intl Rel.

PERRY, KEITH; W H Hall HS; W Hartford, CT; (Y); 81/324; Model UN; NHS; Natl Affrs Yth Conf 85; Yth & Govt 84 & 85.

PERRY, KRISTINA; Weaver HS; West Hartford, CT; (Y); JA; Obstrcn.

PERRY, LAURA; North Haven HS; North Haven, CT; (Y); 16/296; AFS; Drama Clb; Latin Clb; Chorus; School Musical; Rep Sr Cls; Stu Cncl; JV Var Swmmng; High Hon Roll; Trs NHS; Fnlst Mis Ntl Teenager 85; Jr Hnr Guard 85; Yrbk Staff 85; Fairfield U; Acctng.

PERUGINI, MARIA A; Sacrd Heart HS; Prospect, CT; (Y); 5/224; Church Yth Grp; Off Stu Cncl; Var L Swmmng; L Trk; High Hon Roll; NHS; Ntl Merit Ltr; Intl Stud.

PERUZZI, MICHELE; Jonathon Law HS; Milford, CT; (Y); Church Yth Grp; Band; Concert Band; Drm Mjr(t); Jazz Band; Mrchg Band; Pep Band; Yrbk Stf; Rep Jr Cls; Rep Sr Cls.

PESANELLI, LEIGH; Naugatuck HS; Naugatuck, CT; (Y); 35/340; Dance Clb; GAA; Ski Clb; Yrbk Stf; Rep Frsh Cls; Rep Soph Cls; Rep Jr Cls; Var L Badmtn; JV Sftbl; JV Vllybl; Bus.

PESCE, LINDA R; Roger Ludlowe HS; Fairfield, CT; (Y); 11/360; Crs Cntry; Tennis; French Hon Soc; Ntl Merit SF; NELTA Ranked Jr Plyr 81-82; Ntl Assn Of Frnch Tchrs 81-82; Ntl Merit Semi-Fnl 84.

PETAJASOJA, NANCY; Putnam HS; Putnam, CT; (Y); 3/150; Band; Chorus; Trs Frsh Cls; Trs Soph Cls; Trs Stu Cncl; Cheerleading; Hon Roll; Jr NHS; Med.

PETER, ANN MARIE; St Bernard HS; Waterford, CT; (Y); 72/290; Art Clb; Trs Girl Scts; Hosp Aide; Ski Clb; Rep Stu Cncl; Hon Roll; Church Yth Grp; Drama Clb; Spanish Clb; Excell Bus 85; Champmn Fndtn Schlrshp 85; Acad Excell 82; Niagra U; Trvl Mgmt.

PETERS, ALISON; East Haven HS; E Haven, CT; (Y); Church Yth Grp; Spanish Clb; Stu Cncl; High Hon Roll; Hon Roll; NHS; Quinipiac Coll; Comp Pgrmr.

PETERS, HEATHER; Guilford HS; Guilford, CT; (Y); Church Yth Grp; Ski Clb; Rep Frsh Cls; Rep Soph Cls; Rep Stu Cncl; Stat Sftbl; Hon Roll; Lang Arts Dept Gen Excllnc 84-85; Chld Psych.

PETERS, MAUREEN; Stratford HS; Stratford, CT; (Y); Church Yth Grp; Ski Clb; Rep Jr Cls; Mgr(s); Pom Pon; Hon Roll; Bus Mngmnt.

PETERS, TRACY; Cheshire HS; Cheshire, CT; (Y); 20/324; Hosp Aide; Red Cross Aide; Pres Chorus; School Musical; Yrbk Stf; French Hon Soc; High Hon Roll; JC Awd; NHS; Franklin & Marshall Coll; Med.

PETERSON II, B DOUGLAS; Fairfield College Prepatory Schl; Shelton, CT; (Y); 27/226; Boy Scts; Church Yth Grp; Yrbk Phtg; JV L Ftbl; JV L Trk; High Hon Roll; Hon Roll; NHS; Spanish NHS; Church Choir; Commended Stu Of Ntl Achvt Schlrshp Pgm 84; Engrng.

PETERSON, JONATHAN; New London HS; New London, CT; (Y); 10/180; Church Yth Grp; Boy Scts; Drama Clb; Scholastic Bowl; School Musical; Yrbk Stf; Nwsp Ed-Chief; Nwsp Phtg; Hon Roll; Sec NHS; Schl Hlth Cncl; Var Rifle Tm; Eagle Scout W/ Palm.

PETERSON, LAURA; Guilford HS; Guilford, CT; (Y); Church Yth Grp; Var L Socr; Var L Sftbl.

PETERSON, REBECCA; Ledyard HS; Ledyard, CT; (Y); Art Clb; Church Yth Grp; Pep Clb; School Play; Trk; Hon Roll; SE CT Comm Emplymnt Handicp 85; N Eng S Shore Artists Inc 85; Art Show 84; Comm Desgn.

PETERSON, RON; Pomperaug Regional HS; Southbury, CT; (Y); 40/225; Mgr Chess Clb; Math Tm; Model UN; Office Aide; Varsity Clb; JV Var Crs Cntry; JV Trk; Var Wrstlng; Outstndng Volntrsm 84; US Hstry Golden Shvl Awd 85.

PETIT, LOU-ANNE E; Northwestern Regional #7 HS; New Hartford, CT; (Y); PAVAS; Chorus; Smmr Schlrshp Awd Intrn Prog At Sentr Lowell Weikers Offc; Endicott MA; Bus Adm.

PETRASY, ELAINE; Pomperaug HS; Southbury, CT; (Y); 34/240; Cmnty Wkr; Drama Clb; Ski Clb; Band; Concert Band; School Play; Yrbk Stf; Sftbl; Vllybl; NHS; Early Childhd Ed.

PETRAZZUOLI, MARCO; Norte Dame HS; E Haven, CT; (Y); 2/754; Drama Clb; School Musical; School Play; Stage Crew; Nwsp Stf; High Hon Roll; NHS; Sal; Itln Awd Itln Clb VP 84-85; Poet Cont Wnr COLT 83-85; Yale U; Pre-Med.

PETRICONE, STEPHEN; Litchfield HS; Litchfield, CT; (Y); 1/90; Am Leg Boys St; Political Wkr; Capt Scholastic Bowl; VP Stu Cncl; Crs Cntry; Trk; NHS; Spanish NHS; High Hon Roll; Off Soph Cls; WA DC JR Intrnshp 85; Renssaler Polytcnc Inst Sci & Math Achvt Mtl 85; Zymlgy.

PETRILLO, JENNIFER ARLENE; North Haven HS; North Haven, CT; (Y); 65/281; Church Yth Grp; Hosp Aide; Hon Roll; Theater Clb 82-83; Fidle Soc 83-84; Nrsng.

PETRINI, JOANN; Danbury HS; Danbury, CT; (Y); Ski Clb; Varsity Clb; Band; Concert Band; Variety Show; Var Cheerleading; JV Stat Trk; NCTE Awd.

PETRINI, LORI; Danbury HS; Danbury, CT; (Y); Ski Clb; Band; Concert Band; Mrchg Band; Symp Band; Variety Show; Var Crs Cntry; JV Trk; Hon Roll; Fshn Dsgn.

PETRINO, LAURIE; St Joseph HS; Trumbull, CT; (Y); 9/240; Church Yth Grp; Hosp Aide; Spanish Clb; Yrbk Stf; Var JV Crs Cntry; Var JV Trk; Hon Roll; NHS; Spanish NHS; Bus.

PETRISKO, KIMBERLY; New Britain HS; New Britain, CT; (Y); 143/354; Church Yth Grp; Dance Clb; GAA; Girl Scts; Hosp Aide; Office Aide; Band; Chorus; Church Choir; Capt Color Guard; Rewinkle Sheldon Schrlshp 85; Briarwood Coll; Med Assist.

PETROKAITIS, ELIZABETH; Holy Cross HS; Waterbury, CT; (Y); 60/352; Art Clb; Service Clb; Hon Roll; NHS.

PETROLITO, ANTHONY; Southington HS; Southington, CT; (Y); 105/600; Ski Clb; Band; Concert Band; Jazz Band; Mrchg Band; Pep Band; Symp Band; Socr; Hon Roll; Coast Guardd Acad; Meterology.

PETRONE, JAMES MICHAEL; William H Hall HS; Wethersfield, CT; (Y); 17/346; Pres Stu Cncl; Var L Bsbl; Var L Ftbl; Var L Wrstlng; Hon Roll; NHS; VP Spanish NHS; W Hartford Spec Olympics Vol 84-85; Yale; Econ.

PETRONI, KAREN; Stamford HS; Stamford, CT; (S); Church Yth Grp; Cmnty Wkr; Band; Concert Band; Jazz Band; Mrchg Band; High Hon Roll; Hon Roll; NHS; Ntl Merit Ltr; Comp Sci.

PETRUCCI, JON; Holycross HS; Waterbury, CT; (Y); 180/330; Church Yth Grp; Yrbk Stf; Stu Cncl; Crs Cntry; Tennis; All Nul Freshmn X Cntry 83; Accntng.

PETRUZZI, DONALD; Kennedy HS; Waterbury, CT; (S); Hosp Aide; Key Clb; Band; Concert Band; Jazz Band; Mrchg Band; Jr Cls; Hon Roll; Choate Rosemary Hall Summer Schlrshp 84-85; Key Clb Awd 84-85; Proj SAGE Tlnted & Gftd 84-85.

PETTEWAY, TONYA; Crosby HS; Waterbury, CT; (Y); 15/350; JA; Latin Clb; Chorus; Church Choir; School Play; Hon Roll; NHS; Ntl Merit Ltr; St Schlr; Delta Sigma Theta Schlrshp 85; Debutante Ball Schlrshp 84; James Doran Alg II Awd 83; Howard U; Math.

PETTINICO JR, GEORGE; Holy Cross HS; Waterbury, CT; (Y); 14/352; Boy Scts; Concert Band; Jazz Band; Mrchg Band; Variety Show; High Hon Roll; NHS; Bio Achvt Awd 84; Chem Achvt Awd 85.

PETTWAY, ANITA; Notre Dame Catholic HS; Bridgeport, CT; (Y); 5/284; Nwsp Stf; Lit Mag; Ntl Merit Ltr; Spanish NHS; Ntl Achvt Schlrshp; Yale U; Wrtng.

PFAHLER, KRISTIN; Berlin HS; Kensington, CT; (Y); 11/180; Am Leg Aux Girls St; Drama Clb; Service Clb; VP Band; School Musical; Yrbk Stf; Stu Cncl; JV Capt Cheerleading; Hon Roll; VP NHS.

PFEIFFER, JULIE KRISTINE; Farmington HS; Farmington, CT; (Y); Church Choir; Symp Band; High Hon Roll; Ntl Merit Schol; Band; Concert Band; Mrchg Band; Symp Band; Lit Mag; Hon Roll; U Ct Physcis Awd 85; Ntl German Tchrs Asoc Awd 85; Ctr Cretv Yth Wesleyan U 83; Carleton Coll; Philsphy.

PHAIAH, CAROL ANNE; Killingly HS; Danielson, CT; (Y); Cmnty Wkr; Drama Clb; French Clb; Hosp Aide; Band; Color Guard; Mrchg Band; Yrbk Stf; Frsh Cls; Soph Cls; Marchng Band Bst Flag 84; Yng Volntrs Action 85; Becker JC; Travel.

PHAN, NANCY; Maloney HS; Meriden, CT; (Y); Church Yth Grp; JA; Office Aide; Service Clb; Church Choir; Hon Roll.

PHELAN, TRACEY; Academy Of Our Lady Of Mercy; Milford, CT; (Y); Hosp Aide; Spanish Clb; JV Sftbl; JV Vllybl.

PHIDD, BRIDGETTE; Bassick HS; Bridgeport, CT; (S); FBLA; Church Choir; Nwsp Rptr; Nwsp Stf; High Hon Roll; Hon Roll; Katharine Gibbs; Exec Sec.

PHILLIPS, DEIDRE; Sacred Heart Acad; Seymour, CT; (Y); Computer Clb; French Clb; FBLA; Hosp Aide; Hon Roll; Endowmnt Scholar 84-85 & 85-86; Wrk Study Scholar 83-84 & 84-85; Music.

PHILLIPS, JEDAN; Pomfret HS; Queens, NY; (Y); Boy Scts; Teachers Aide; School Play; Stage Crew; Nwsp Rptr; Nwsp Stf; Var Bsktbl; Var Ftbl; Var Tennis; Dollars Schlrs Schrshp 83; Schlrshp Astoria Civic Assoc 85; Schlrshp Ntl Jr Tennis Leag 82; Johns Hopkins U; Med.

PHILLIPS, KAREN; Pomperaug HS; Southbury, CT; (Y); 22/206; French Clb; FBLA; Office Aide; Ski Clb; Yrbk Stf; Stu Cncl; Var Capt Tennis; Hon Roll; US Bus Ed Awd 83-84; Ntl Hnr Rll 84-85; Providence Coll; Bus Mgt.

PIASECKI, GLENN; Southington HS; Southington, CT; (Y); CAP; DECA; German Clb; JA; JV Bsbl; Var Trk; High Hon Roll; Hon Roll; Mrktng Mgr.

PICARD, DANIEL J; St Paul Catholic HS; Bristol, CT; (Y); Aud/Vis; Variety Show; Yrbk Stf; JV Socr; JV Wrstlng; High Hon Roll; Hon Roll; Hnrb Mntn-Ntl Frnch Tst 81-82; U Of CT; Comp Sci.

PICARD, KRISTEN; Holy Cross HS; Waterbury, CT; (Y); Church Yth Grp; Varsity Clb; Var Diving; Var Gym; Var Mgr(s); Var Score Keeper; Var Timer; High Hon Roll; Chesire YMCA Swim Team Coaches Awd 83; Acctnt.

PICCIONE, CHRISTA; Daniel Hand HS; Madison, CT; (Y); 18/236; Church Yth Grp; Cmnty Wkr; Chorus; Madrigals; School Musical; Swmmng; Hon Roll; NHS; All Southern Chorus 85; Spnsh.

PICCOLO, ALAN; Crosby HS; Waterbury, CT; (Y); Art Clb; Spanish Clb; Var Capt Bsktbl; Hon Roll; Engrng.

PICKERING, JOHN; New London HS; New London, CT; (Y); Am Leg Boys St; Bsktbl; Var Capt Ftbl; High Hon Roll; NHS; St Schlr; Rotary Schlr 84-85; Chem, Algbr II, Spnsh II & III, Columbia Bk Awds 84-85.

PICZKO, PAMELA; Kolbe Cathedral HS; Bridgeport, CT; (Y); JA; Drm & Bgl; Rep Soph Cls; Hon Roll; Outstndg Improvemnt In Religion I 83; Excellence In Math 84; Outstndg Stu In Recordkeeping 85; Bus Schl; Secr.

PIERCE, LENORE; Weaver HS; Hartford, CT; (Y); Cmnty Wkr; Girl Scts; Red Cross Aide; Teachers Aide; Y-Teens; School Musical; Hon Roll; Prfct Atten Awd; Hghst Avg-Gen Math 81-82; Hghst Avg-Intro Algbra 82-83; Hghst Avg-US Hist Acadmc 83-84; Naval Acad; Bus.

PIERCE, TODD; Brunswick Schl; Old Greenwich, CT; (Y); Ed Am Leg Boys St; Cmnty Wkr; Service Clb; School Play; Ed Nwsp Ed-Chief; Ed Yrbk Ed-Chief; Var Crs Cntry; High Hon Roll; Ntl Merit Ltr; Vassar Bk Awd Ovrll Excllnc Humnties 85; Holy Crss Bk Awd Excllnc Wrtg 85; Law.

PIERNE, CHERYL; Shelton HS; Shelton, CT; (Y); 27/413; Pep Clb; Spanish Clb; Nwsp Rptr; Nwsp Stf; Rep Frsh Cls; Rep Soph Cls; Rep Jr Cls; Rep Sr Cls; Var Cheerleading; Var Trk; Excel Phy Ed, Acad Excel Citznshp, Sacred Heart U Prsdntl Schlrshp 85; Sacred Heart U; Bus Admn.

PIERSON, RUSS; Guilford HS; Guilford, CT; (Y); 101/315; Boy Scts; Church Yth Grp; Exploring; Band; Concert Band; Mrchg Band; VP Orch; School Musical; JV Bsktbl; Sthrn Regnl Music Fstvl 83-85; Shoreline Yth Symph 83-84; New Haven Yth Orch 84-85; SCI.

PIETRA, LYNN DELLA; Guilford HS; Guilford, CT; (Y); 8/266; Chorus; Madrigals; School Musical; School Play; Stage Crew; Cheerleading; Vllybl; High Hon Roll; NHS; Sec Spanish NHS; Knghts Of Columbus Schlrshp 85; E Haven Tchrs Schlrshp 85; Guilfrd Schlrshp Assn Awd 85; Boston Coll; Dntstry.

PIETRORAZIO, DEAN; Holy Cross HS; Middlebury, CT; (Y); Boy Scts; VP Band; VP Concert Band; Mrchg Band; Hon Roll; NHS; Spanish NHS; U Hartford; Psych.

PIKUL, JO ANNE; East Windsor HS; East Windsor, CT; (Y); Ski Clb; Chorus; Rep Soph Cls; Rep Jr Cls; Var Cheerleading; Trk; Hon Roll; NHS; Cls Marshall 85; Personnel Mgmt.

PILLA, TONY; Lyman Hall HS; Wallingford, CT; (Y); 50/250; Boys Clb Am; Yrbk Phtg; Yrbk Rptr; Yrbk Stf; Socr; Comp Sci.

PIMENTEL, FRANCIE; Sacred Heart Acad; Wallingford, CT; (Y); FBLA; Hosp Aide; Orch; Lit Mag; Sec Jr Cls; High Hon Roll; NHS; Ski Clb; Chorus; School Musical; Yale Frontiers-Appld Sci Prgm 85; Cert Duracell Sci Cmptn 83; Miss Teen New Englnd Wnnr 83; Weslyan U; Nuclear Engr.

PIMER, LAURA; Platt Regional Vo Tech; West Haven, CT; (Y); Rep Jr Cls; Var Cheerleading; JV Sftbl; Swmmng; Hon Roll; Grtr New Haven Tech; Auto Mech.

PINTO, KIM; Stamford HS; Stamford, CT; (S); Church Yth Grp; Cmnty Wkr; Pres DECA; VP JA; Mgr(s); Sftbl; Vllybl; Hon Roll; Rotary Awd; Art Clb; Interact Club VP 84-85; DECA 84-85; Johnson & Whales Coll; Mgmnt.

PIRIGYI JR, ALBERT J; Windsor HS; Windsor, CT; (Y); 6/341; Model UN; Scholastic Bowl; School Musical; French Hon Soc; Hon Roll; Masonic Awd; NHS; Am Leg Boys St; Math Tm; Trk; Indiv Achvt Awd 84; Combustion Engnrng Chem/Physics Schlrshp 85; Hnr Prog 85; U Of DE; Chmcl Engnrng.

PISACICH, KAREN; St Bernards HS; Waterford, CT; (S); Church Yth Grp; Band; Concert Band; Mrchg Band; Bsktbl; Sftbl.

PISANI, CRAIG; Naugatuck HS; Beacon Fls, CT; (Y); 74/340; Church Yth Grp; DECA; Ski Clb; JV Var Ftbl; Hon Roll; Aerontcl Engrng.

PISANI, MARIA; Richard C Lee HS; New Haven, CT; (Y); 12/202; JA; Office Aide; Spanish Clb; Yrbk Stf; Rep Frsh Cls; High Hon Roll; Hon Roll; NHS; Ntl Merit SF; Pres Schlr; Acad Achvt Eng; Ntl Merit Sci Awd; Outstndng Bus Stu; Corp Law.

PISCIOTTA, WAYNE C; Stafford HS; Stafford Spgs, CT; (Y); 3/111; French Clb; Var Capt Bsktbl; High Hon Roll; NHS; Schlr Athl Awds-U S Army Ntl & CT HS; NCCC All Conf Bsktbl Tm; Schls Bsktbl Scrng Rcrd; Bentley Coll; Bus.

PITBLADO, BONNIE; Farmington HS; Farmington, CT; (Y); 4/208; AFS; VP Cmnty Wkr; Hosp Aide; Model UN; Nwsp Rptr; Nwsp Stf; JV Sftbl; JV Vllybl; High Hon Roll; NHS.

PITT, RONALD; Southington HS; Southington, CT; (Y); Boy Scts; Pres Church Yth Grp; Ski Clb; Variety Show; Ed Nwsp Stf; JV Socr; Hon Roll.

PITTS, STEVEN J; Hamden HS; Hamden, CT; (Y); 1/451; VP Church Yth Grp; Math Clb; Math Tm; Jazz Band; Mrchg Band; Orch; School Play; High Hon Roll; Ntl Merit SF; Val; CT JR Sci & Humnities Symp 84; Biochem.

PITTU, DAVID J; Andrew Warde HS; Fairfield, CT; (Y); Drama Clb; Key Clb; Thesps; School Musical; School Play; Lit Mag; Rep Frsh Cls; Rep Soph Cls; Rep Jr Cls; Trk; Darien Dinner Theatre Bst Spprtng Actor Awd 83; Audition Miami FL Arts Recognition Talent Srch 85; Theatre.

PIVER, JON; Stonington HS; Stonington, CT; (Y); 24/220; Boy Scts; Church Yth Grp; Chorus; Drm Mjr(t); Jazz Band; Mrchg Band; Pep Band; Symp Band; Lit Mag; Rep Stu Cncl; Eagle Boy Scout 85; All Eastern CT Regnl Choir 84-85; U CT; Bus Admin.

PIZZI, LAUREN A; Sacred Heart Acad; Ansonia, CT; (Y); 16/114; Cmnty Wkr; Dance Clb; Teachers Aide; Stage Crew; Yrbk Stf; Lit Mag; Capt Var Cheerleading; Im Vllybl; High Hon Roll; NHS; Svc Awd; Pro-Lif Awd; Duquesne U; Spcl, Elem Ed.

PLACZEK, GARY; Windsor Locks HS; Windsor Locks, CT; (Y); 12/179; Boy Scts; Stage Crew; Var Golf; Hon Roll; NHS; Pres Schlr; Worcester Poly Inst; Elect Engr.

PLASKY, RONALD C; Naugatuck HS; Naugatuck, CT; (Y); Am Leg Boys St; DECA; Ski Clb; Yrbk Stf; Var L Bsbl; Var JV Bsktbl; Coach Actv; Im Fld Hcky; Im Ftbl; Hon Roll; U Of RI; Phy Ed.

PLEASENT-ROMAN, GERARDO O; South Catholic HS; E Hartford, CT; (Y); Cmnty Wkr; Quiz Bowl; Crs Cntry; Trk; Ntl Merit Ltr; Ntl Merit Hspnc Schlr 85fCT ST Schlr; US Naval Acad.

PLEVAN, JILL; New Fairfield HS; New Fairfld, CT; (Y); 20/240; French Clb; Pres Temple Yth Grp; VP Soph Cls; Pres Jr Cls; Pres Sr Cls; JV Crs Cntry; French Hon Soc; Hon Roll; NHS.

PLOSZAY, PETER J; Windsor Locks HS; Windsor Locks, CT; (Y); 15/179; Boy Scts; Var Bsbl; Trk; Ski Clb; School Musical; Trs Soph Cls; St Anselm; Mth.

PLUMLEY, KAREN; Simsbury HS; Weatogue, CT; (Y); 72/352; Church Yth Grp; Drama Clb; School Play; Yrbk Stf; Mgr(s); Score Keeper; Hon Roll.

PLUNKETT, COLLEEN; Southington HS; Plantsville, CT; (Y); Trs Church Yth Grp; Hosp Aide; Band; Church Choir; Concert Band; Mrchg Band; Symp Band; Hon Roll; Schlrshp Phillips Acad Music 85; Schlrshp U Of Hartford Music 85; Perfrmnc.

PODLAHA, FRANK; New Fairfield HS; New Fairfld, CT; (Y); 7/242; Camera Clb; Computer Clb; Mathletes; Math Tm; Drm & Bgl; High Hon Roll; Hon Roll; NHS; NE Drum Crps Chmpn 84; 1st Pl ST Indvdl Drm Solo 84; Aerosp Engrng.

POHLMANN, CHRISTINE; Berlin HS; Kensington, CT; (Y); #9 In Class; Am Leg Aux Girls St; Drama Clb; Pres Service Clb; Drill Tm; Nwsp Stf; Yrbk Stf; Var Socr; Var Tennis; Hon Roll; NHS; Eng Achvt Awd 83-85; Biol.

POHORYLO, BRIAN; Windsor Locks HS; Windsor Locks, CT; (Y); 7/161; Am Leg Boys St; Church Yth Grp; Math Tm; Hon Roll; Ntl Merit Ltr; Comp Engrng.

POIRIER, RYAN; Killingly HS; Brooklyn, CT; (Y); Varsity Clb; Pres Stu Cncl; Var Capt Bsbl; Var L Ftbl; S CT ST U; Accntnt.

POITRAS, GREGORY; Francis T Maloney HS; Meriden, CT; (Y); Am Leg Boys St; Key Clb; Yrbk Stf; Rep Sr Cls; Pres Stu Cncl; Var L Socr; Var Capt Tennis; High Hon Roll; NHS; Pres Schlr; Corp Law.

POKRAS, KAREN; Amity Regional HS; Orange, CT; (Y); FBLA; Key Clb; Pep Clb; Ski Clb; Temple Yth Grp; Yrbk Stf; Hon Roll; NHS; French Clb; Ctznshp Hnr; Class Hnrs Awd; Busn Admin.

POLGAR, DAVID S; Newtown HS; Newtown, CT; (Y); 7/340; Sec Exploring; Quiz Bowl; Ski Clb; Sec VICA; Var Capt Diving; Var Socr; Var Capt Trk; JETS Awd; Coach Actv; Pres Spanish NHS; Span Nhs; Youth Serv In Newtown-Board Member 85-86; Rensselaer Medal For Excel In Math And Science 85; Science.

POLICASTRO, MARIANNE; Manchester HS; Manchester, CT; (Y); Drama Clb; Trs Spanish Clb; Thesps; Stage Crew; Soph Cls; Var Sftbl; Hon Roll; Lynchburg Coll-Hopwood Schlrshp 84; Marist Coll; Nrsng.

POLIDORO, DANIEL; Granby Memorial HS; Granby, CT; (Y); AFS; Am Leg Boys St; Pres Drama Clb; Yrbk Ed-Chief; JV Bsktbl; High Hon Roll; Hon Roll; Ski Clb; Spanish Clb; School Play; Outstndng Achvt Awd Spn II 83-84; Meritorious Achvt Awd Bio I 83-84; Am Leg Cert Schl Awd 84-85; Bio.

POLTRACK, ANDREW F; Westhill HS; Stamford, CT; (Y); 30/427; Key Clb; Var Ftbl; Var Trk; Hon Roll; NHS; Ntl Merit Ltr; Dartmouth Coll.

POMERLEAU, JULIE; Miss Porters Schl; Ann Arbor, MI; (Y); Debate Tm; English Clb; Intnl Clb; Orch; Lit Mag; High Hon Roll; Hon Roll; 4th Pl Natl Schltc Wrtng Cont; CT All ST Orch; All East Orch.

POMERLEAU, JULIE; Miss Porters Schl; W Hartford, CT; (Y); Debate Tm; Model UN; Orch; School Musical; Lit Mag; High Hon Roll; Hon Roll; Ntl Schlstc Wrtng Awd-4th Pl.

POON, THOMAS; Holy Cross HS; Wolcott, CT; (Y); 31/352; Hon Roll; 2nd Pl Awd Law Day Essay Cont 85; Med.

POPE, CHRISTOPHER CHARLES; Ridgefield HS; Ridgefield, CT; (Y); 46/331; Am Leg Boys St; Computer Clb; Chorus; Variety Show; High Hon Roll; Hon Roll; NHS; Aud/Vis; Church Yth Grp; Library Aide; Ridgefield Yth Orch Tour 5 Cntrs 84; Thtrcl Lghtng Clb Pres 84-86; Amer Airlns Sabre Comp Schl Grad 85; Bus.

POPOLIZIO, MARK; Notre Dame HS; Wallingford, CT; (Y); Hon Roll.

PORRAZZO, SANDRA; West Haven HS; W Haven, CT; (Y); Pres Frsh Cls; Var JV Bsktbl; Var Sftbl; Elks Awd; High Hon Roll; NHS; North Eastern; Acctng.

PORRICELLI, MICHAEL; St Mary HS; Old Greenwich, CT; (Y); 40/74; Varsity Clb; Stage Crew; Bsbl; Ftbl; Art Clb; Exploring; School Play; Bsktbl; Coach Actv; Score Keeper.

PORTER, BRIAN; Tolland HS; Tolland, CT; (Y); Boy Scts; Ski Clb; Var Crs Cntry; Var Trk; Hon Roll; Jr NHS; NHS; Acad Excllnc Awd 86; Ntl Hnr Soc Hstrn 85-86; Elec Engrng.

PORTER, RICHARD; Bethel HS; Bethel, CT; (Y); 9/268; Drama Clb; Math Tm; Quiz Bowl; School Play; Nwsp Ed-Chief; Yrbk Stf; Trs Stu Cncl; High Hon Roll; Ntl Merit Ltr; Harvard Bk Awd 85; Med.

PORTNOV, BETSY; Wilbur Cross HS; New Haven, CT; (S); 18/250; Ski Clb; Spanish Clb; Temple Yth Grp; Nwsp Ed-Chief; Nwsp Stf; Yrbk Bus Mgr; Hon Roll; Yrbk Layout Edtr 85; Brandeis U; Intl Bus.

PORTO, GINO; Bassick HS; Bridgpt, CT; (Y); Bowling; Coach Actv; Crs Cntry; Trk; Hon Roll; Ntl Merit Ltr; Prfct Atten Awd; Ag.

PORTO, PATTY; East Haven HS; E Haven, CT; (Y); #10 In Class; Spanish Clb; Yrbk Stf; Stu Cncl; High Hon Roll; Hon Roll; Jr NHS; NHS; Ntl Ldrshp & Svc Awds 83.

PORYDZY, LAURA; Southington HS; Southington, CT; (Y); Dance Clb; Girl Scts; Pep Clb; Ski Clb; Spanish Clb; Rep Stu Cncl; JV Cheerleading; JV Powder Puff Ftbl; DAR Awd; Hon Roll; Disc III Gft & Tlntd Awds 83-85; Chld Psych.

POTTER, BONNIE; Housatonic Valley Regional HS; W Cornwall, CT; (S); French Clb; Ski Clb; Band; Concert Band; Pep Band; Nwsp Rptr; VP Soph Cls; Sec Jr Cls; Rep Stu Cncl; Var Fld Hcky; Jrnlsm.

POTTER, JAMES W; St Bernard HS; Mystic, CT; (Y); 4/289; Pres Computer Clb; Drama Clb; School Musical; School Play; Lit Mag; Stu Cncl; Bausch & Lomb Sci Awd; High Hon Roll; NHS; Tufts U; Engrng.

POTTER, JAY; Torrington HS; Torrington, CT; (Y); Aud/Vis; Debate Tm; Latin Clb; Model UN; Quiz Bowl; Trs Thesps; Ntl Merit Ltr; NEDT Awd; Trs Church Yth Grp; Drama Clb; Video Clb Treas Cum Laude Natl Latn Exm 82-84; Harvard U Smmr Schl Secdry Schl Stdnts 85.

POTTS, AMY; Trumbull HS; Trumbull, CT; (Y); Hosp Aide; Office Aide; Ski Clb; Variety Show; Yrbk Stf; Stu Cncl; Mgr Bsbl; Im Gym; High Hon Roll; Hon Roll; Psych.

POULOS, LESLIE E; The Taft Schl; Wethersfield, CT; (Y); Drama Clb; Acpl Chr; School Musical; School Play; Rep Sr Cls; Var Capt Socr; Hon Roll; MVP Grls V Scr 84-85; ST Drma Fstvl Cast 83-84; Theatre.

POVINELLI, MICHAEL; East Catholic HS; E Hartford, CT; (Y); 70/285; Church Yth Grp; High Hon Roll; Hon Roll; Bus.

POWELL, NADINE; Stratford HS; Stratford, CT; (Y); Art Clb; Church Yth Grp; Computer Clb; Quiz Bowl; Spanish Clb; Chorus; Church Choir; Variety Show; Golf; Gym; Comp Pgrmr.

POWELL, SIMONE; Weaver HS; Hartford, CT; (Y); Church Yth Grp; Cmnty Wkr; Drama Clb; FBLA; Hosp Aide; Intnl Clb; JA; Model UN; Red Cross Aide; Band; Stu Of Mnth 85; Soph Poetry Cont 84; Hghst Avg Soph Acad Eng 84; Polit Sci.

POZARLIK, SHERRI; Shelton HS; Shelton, CT; (Y); Drama Clb; French Clb; Spanish Clb; Rep Stu Cncl; Spanish NHS; Lope De Vega Spnsh Acad Schlrshp 85; Frnch Cert Merit 85; Psych.

PRAJER, STEPHEN; Seymour HS; Oxford, CT; (Y); School Play; JV Bsktbl; Var Capt Ftbl; Var Capt Trk; Var Wt Lftg; Trck Pole Vlt Clss M 1st Pl Brk Schl Rcrd & CIAC ST 3rd Pl Nw Schl Rcrd 85.

PRATT, JOHN; Watkinson Schl; Glastonbury, CT; (Y); Am Leg Boys St; Yrbk Bus Mgr; Bsbl; JV Var Socr; High Hon Roll; Hon Roll; Bsktbl; Ftbl; Ice Hcky; Sftbl; Henry A Gleason III Bio Prz 83-84; Dwyer Memrl Sci Awd 84-85; West Point; Mltry.

PREFONTAINE, KAREN; Berlin HS; Berlin, CT; (Y); Trs Service Clb; Band; Concert Band; Drm Mjr(t); Mrchg Band; Yrbk Stf; Sec Stu Cncl; Hon Roll; Del Govs Yth Conf 85; Animal Sci.

PRENDERGAST, LYNN AMES; Daniel Hand HS; Madison, CT; (Y); Church Yth Grp; Cmnty Wkr; Band; Concert Band; Yrbk Stf; Stu Cncl; Im Lcrss; Cit Awd; SAR Awd; CT Chldrn Of Am Revltn-St Offcr 80-84; Bus.

PRESPARE, SUZANNE; Simsbury HS; Simsbury, CT; (Y); 78/356; Am Leg Aux Girls St; Church Yth Grp; Hosp Aide; Varsity Clb; Rep Frsh Cls; Trs Soph Cls; Rep Jr Cls; VP Stu Cncl; Stat Bsbl; Stat Bsktbl; Boston Coll Fairfield; Nrs.

PRESS, RANDI; Amity Regional HS; Orange, CT; (Y); Drama Clb; French Clb; Pep Clb; Chorus; School Musical; School Play; Variety Show; Yrbk Stf; Cit Awd; Ntl Art Hnrs Soc Pres 84-86; Art.

PREST, SUE; Tolland HS; Tolland, CT; (Y); Madrigals; Stu Cncl; JV Var Socr; Trk; NHS; Chorus; Rep Frsh Cls; Rep Soph Cls; Rep Jr Cls; Stat Bsktbl; All Conf & All ST 83; Charles H Leonard Awd Schl Schlrshp 85; Central CT ST U; Elem Ed.

PRESTON, ELIZABETH; St Bernards HS; Charlestown, RI; (Y); Church Yth Grp; Cmnty Wkr; Stage Crew; Yrbk Stf; Rep Jr Cls; JV Trk; CC Awd; Hon Roll; NE & RI Hrsmn Assoc Champ Jr Exhbtr Hack 84; Jr Rep Wide Cmnty Invlvmnt Mdl & Lcl Plnng 81-82; Sci.

PRESTON, MICHAEL; St Bernards HS; Colchester, CT; (Y); Boy Scts; Hosp Aide; Band; Tennis; Eagle Scout 82; Chrprtc Sci.

PRIOLEAU, CASSANDRA; Stratford HS; Stratford, CT; (Y); 14/244; Library Aide; Chorus; Variety Show; Trk; High Hon Roll; Hon Roll; Cert Of Proficiency 82-83; Med.

PRIOR, DAWN; Southington HS; Southington, CT; (Y); Pep Clb; Ski Clb; High Hon Roll; Hon Roll; Pres Phy Fitnss Awd 83.

PROCHNOW, THOMAS H; The Hotchkiss Schl; Lake Forest, IL; (Y); Nwsp Bus Mgr; Nwsp Ed-Chief; Nwsp Rptr; JV Crs Cntry; JV Trk; High Hon Roll; Ntl Merit SF; Top Scholar.

PRODAN, ANGELA JEAN; Shelton HS; Shelton, CT; (Y); Am Leg Aux Girls St; Nwsp Sprt Ed; Yrbk Sprt Ed; Pres Frsh Cls; Pres Sr Cls; Capt Var Sftbl; Hon Roll; NHS; Nwsp Stf; Rep Soph Cls; Itln Clb Pres; Italian Ntl Hnr Soc & Treas; Holy Cross Bk Prz Awd; Intl Affairs.

PROTSKO, DEANNA; Masuk HS; Monroe, CT; (Y); #20 In Class; Drama Clb; Spanish Clb; Pres Chorus; Madrigals; School Musical; Coach Actv; Var JV Mgr(s); Stat Socr; High Hon Roll; Sec NHS; Mst Outstndng Chrs Stu 84 & 85; Wesrn CT ST Chr 83; 3 Yr Chrs Awd & Ltr 85; Bio.

PROULX, JOHN DANIEL; Mark T Sheehan HS; Wallingford, CT; (Y); Math Tm; Quiz Bowl; Nwsp Stf; VP Jr Cls; High Hon Roll; Ntl Merit SF; Computer Clb; Hon Roll; Sci Olympiad 2nd Pl 84; Winning Team Intra Schl Math Competion 84; Pres Dungeons, Dragons Clb 83-84; Astronomy.

PRUCHNICKI, JOHN; Holy Cross HS; Naugatuck, CT; (Y); #127 In Class; Church Yth Grp; JV Bsktbl; JV Golf; Hon Roll; Providence Coll; Bus.

PRUKALSKI, JENNIFER; Danbury HS; Danbury, CT; (Y); Variety Show; Hon Roll; Medcl.

PRZYBYLSKI, BRUNO; Southington HS; Plantsville, CT; (Y); Pres Ski Clb; Ftbl; JV Golf; Hon Roll; Bus Mgmt.

PUESCHEL, DEBBIE; Pomperaug HS; Southbury, CT; (Y); Sec Church Yth Grp; Cmnty Wkr; Girl Scts; Church Choir; JV Var Cheerleading; Swmmng; JV Trk.

PUIG, MURPHY; Lyman Hall HS; Wallingford, CT; (Y); 18/230; Key Clb; Spanish Clb; Varsity Clb; School Play; Trs Frsh Cls; Stu Cncl; Powder Puff Ftbl; JV Sftbl; Var Tennis; Elks Awd; Providence Coll; Bus Mgmnt.

PURDY, CHRISTINE; Masuk HS; Monroe, CT; (Y); Sec AFS; Hosp Aide; JA; Spanish Clb; Chorus; Swmmng; Hon Roll; Accntnt.

PUSKAR, JACKIE; Trumbull HS; Trumbull, CT; (Y); Aud/Vis; FNA; Hosp Aide; Library Aide; PAVAS; Ski Clb; Band; Concert Band; Mrchg Band; Pep Band; Med.

PUSSINEN, CINDY E; Plainfield HS; Plainfield, CT; (Y); 4/146; Am Leg Aux Girls St; Quiz Bowl; Yrbk Stf; Lit Mag; Rep Stu Cncl; Tennis; High Hon Roll; Hon Roll; Sec Trs Jr NHS; NHS; Aerosp Engrng.

PYCH, JOE T; Enfield HS; Enfield, CT; (Y); 11/245; Church Yth Grp; Ski Clb; Band; Concert Band; Jazz Band; Mrchg Band; Var Ftbl; Var Trk; High Hon Roll; Hon Roll; Earth Sci Awd 83; Amrcn Musicl Fndtn Band Hnrs 83; Comp Sci Awd 85; Comp Sci.

PYE, JENNIFER; Choate Rosemary Hall HS; Norwalk, CT; (S); Art Clb; Church Yth Grp; Pres Dance Clb; French Clb; Chorus; Church Choir; School Musical; School Play; Stage Crew; Nwsp Phtg; Commdtn Drama, Art & Music 82.

QUADRATO, LORI; Holy Cross HS; Middlebury, CT; (Y); 62/352; Church Yth Grp; Girl Scts; Spanish Clb; Hon Roll; NHS; Spanish NHS; Fullbright Germn Amer Exch Prgm 84; Girl Scout Svc Recog Awd 82-84; U Of RI; Chld Educ.

QUAGLIAROLI, JODI ANN M; Lyman Hall HS; Wallingford, CT; (Y); AFS; Drama Clb; FHA; FTA; Key Clb; Rep Stu Cncl; Mgr Bsktbl; JV Fld Hcky; Hon Roll; Italian Clb; Frgn Lang.

QUARATELLA, KRISTEN; St Bernard HS; Pawcatuck, CT; (S); Dance Clb; Hosp Aide; Library Aide; Stage Crew; Yrbk Stf; Sec Soph Cls; Stu Cncl; Cheerleading; High Hon Roll; Spnsh Awd 83-84.

QUEEN, JAMES; Rham HS; Hebron, CT; (Y); AFS; French Clb; FBLA; Ski Clb; Band; Hon Roll; CBIA Scholar U Of Hftd 85; Bryant Coll; Acctg.

QUENTAL, CESAR; W F Kaynor Technical HS; Naugatuck, CT; (Y); Aud/Vis; Ski Clb; Rep Jr Cls; Diving; Var Socr; Swmmng; Wt Lftg; High Hon Roll; Jr NHS; NHS; Mech Engrng.

QUERIJERO, MICHELLE; Notre Dame Acad; Woodbury, CT; (Y); 9/64; Hosp Aide; Nwsp Phtg; Hon Roll; NHS; NEDT Awd; Chorus; Stage Crew; Variety Show; 1st Essay Cntst Awd 85; Nwspapr Awd 85; Pre Law.

QUESNEL, NANCY; St Marys HS; W Haven, CT; (Y); Church Yth Grp; Nwsp Rptr; Nwsp Stf; Lit Mag; Stu Cncl; Hon Roll; Southern CT ST Coll; Sci.

QUICQUARO, RONALD; Kaynor Vo Tech; Middlebury, CT; (Y); 12/205; VICA; High Hon Roll; Hon Roll; NHS; Hartford ST Tech Coll; Arch.

QUINLEY, MATTHEW; Coginchaug Regional HS; Durham, CT; (Y); 7/128; Am Leg Boys St; Math Tm; Concert Band; Jazz Band; Mrchg Band; Pep Band; School Musical; Variety Show; High Hon Roll; Hon Roll; Comp Sci.

QUINN, KELLEY; Joseph A Foran HS; Milford, CT; (Y); Girl Scts; Capt Color Guard; Lit Mag; High Hon Roll; Hon Roll; NHS; Pres Schlr; Excllnce Bio 83; Suprntndnts Awd 85; Excllnce Adv Bio 85; Southern CT ST U; Bio.

QUINN, LORI; North Branford HS; Northford, CT; (Y); 16/176; Dance Clb; Hosp Aide; Yrbk Stf; Lit Mag; Sec Rep Stu Cncl; JV Var Cheerleading; High Hon Roll; NHS; Spnsh II/III Cert; Typing I Awd; U S Stu Cncl Awd Wnnr; Phys Thrpy.

QUINN, MARIBETH; William H Hall HS; W Hartford, CT; (Y); 31/324; Church Yth Grp; Var L Bsktbl; Capt Var Sftbl; NHS; Spanish NHS; Educ.

QUINN, PAMELA MICHELE; Ridgefield HS; Ridgefield, CT; (Y); 1/350; Trs Stu Cncl; Var L Crs Cntry; Var L Trk; Dnfth Awd; High Hon Roll; NHS; Val; Band; Mrchg Band; Orch; Fairfield Cnty Med Assn Awd 85; PTSA Awd Excllnce Frgn Lang 85; Zeoli ST Invitnl 3rd Pl 85; Biochem.

QUINONES, LUZ; Richard C Lee HS; New Haven, CT; (Y); Cmnty Wkr; Var Sftbl; High Hon Roll; Hon Roll; NHS; Headmasters Awd 83; Natl Latin II Exam Summa Cum Laude 83; 2nd Pl New Haven Fair Housing Essay 84.

QUINT, SUSAN; Naugatuck HS; Naugatuck, CT; (Y); Hon Roll; Pharmcst.

QUIRKE, JEFFREY; Pomperaug HS; Southbury, CT; (Y); 5/200; Chess Clb; Cmnty Wkr; Math Tm; Model UN; Quiz Bowl; Scholastic Bowl; Stat Bsktbl; Var Golf; JV Swmmng; High Hon Roll; Chematon 84; Mock Trial Comp 83-85; Rbtcs.

RABENOLD, CHRISTA; Brien Mc Mahon HS; Darien, CT; (Y); 1/342; Trs Key Clb; Spanish Clb; Yrbk Stf; Trs Jr Cls; Trs Sr Cls; Crs Cntry; Powder Puff Ftbl; Trk; High Hon Roll; Yale Clb Awd 85.

RABIN, BRADFORD; Choate Rosemary Hall HS; Short Hills, NJ; (Y); Debate Tm; Natl Beta Clb; Band; Ed Nwsp Sprt Ed; Rep Frsh Cls; Var Tennis; Hon Roll; Ntl Merit SF; Pres Of Stu Hlpng Stu 84-85; VP Of Corp Clb 84-85; Bus Admin.

RABIS, SANDRA; Coginchaug Regioanl HS; Middlefield, CT; (Y); Cmnty Wkr; GAA; Ski Clb; Varsity Clb; School Play; Off Soph Cls; Off Jr Cls; Socr; Sftbl; Hon Roll; Vol Awd Lcl Hosp 84; Law.

RABITAILLE, ANDREA; New London HS; New London, CT; (Y); Girl Scts; Sec JA; Orch; Yrbk Stf; Lit Mag; Hon Roll; Orchestra Vrsty Let & Numerls 84-85; Girl Scout Slvr Awd 85; Jr Achvt Salesmnshp & 100% Attendn Awd 84; U Of CT; Busnss Admin.

RACCAGNI, DAVID; Rockville HS; Vernon, CT; (Y); 27/369; Boy Scts; Band; Concert Band; Mrchg Band; Pep Band; School Musical; Symp Band; High Hon Roll; NHS; Ntl Merit Ltr; Eagle Sct 84; Sct Hnr Soc 82; Jrnl Inqrer Crrier/Mnth 84; Holy Cross Coll; Law.

RACINE, MICHELLE; Suffield HS; Suffield, CT; (Y); Girl Scts; Library Aide; Office Aide; Chorus; Yrbk Stf; Cheerleading; Vllybl; Hon Roll; Alg I Hnrs 83; U Of CT; Bus Mgt.

RADEMACHER, LARRY; Bristol Eastern HS; Bristol, CT; (Y); Exploring; Pres French Clb; Political Wkr; Nwsp Phtg; VP Stu Cncl; NHS; JA; Ruth Crockett Soc Studies Awd 85; Rep Page US Hse Rep 85; Georgetown U; Pol Sci.

RADER, KATIE; Daniel Hand HS; Madison, CT; (Y); 65/280; Art Clb; Church Yth Grp; Dance Clb; Office Aide; Chorus; Madrigals; School Musical; Rep Stu Cncl; Var Capt Cheerleading; St Poster Cont Reg Rnnr Up 85; All Southern All St Chorus 84-85; Annual Art Dept Awd 85; Comm Art.

RADOLOVIC, KRISTIAN; Cheshire HS; Cheshire, CT; (Y); Science Clb; Renssalear Poly Tech; Elec Engr.

RADZEVICH, DEIRDRE ANN; Canton HS; Canton, CT; (Y); 21/105; Camera Clb; Church Yth Grp; Model UN; Ski Clb; Varsity Clb; Variety Show; Nwsp Ed-Chief; Nwsp Phtg; Nwsp Rptr; Nwsp Stf; Sociolgy Awd; Frnch IV Awd; Zoolgy Awd; U VT; Intl Bus.

RAFFIN, CHRISTINE; East Catholic HS; Marlborough, CT; (Y); Church Yth Grp; Band; Var Bsktbl; Co-Capt Socr; Var Sftbl; Hon Roll; Hnrbl Mntn All HCC Girls Bsktbl 85; Most Imprvd Plyr Girls Bsktbl 84; Coaches Awd Girls Bsktbl 83; Bet Ast.

RAFFONE IV, EUGENE; Notre Dame HS; Orange, CT; (Y); 5/260; Science Clb; Ski Clb; Teachers Aide; Lit Mag; Golf; Socr; High Hon Roll; John Auditore Schlrshp 85; HS Chematon Part 85; Hi Hnrs 83-85; Yale U; Bus Admin.

RAFIEYAN, KAMRAN L; William H Hall HS; W Hartford, CT; (Y); 2/300; Math Tm; Ed Yrbk Ed-Chief; Wrstlng; French Hon Soc; High Hon Roll; NHS; Ntl Merit Ltr; Pres Schlr; Sal; All Conf Wrstlng Tm 1st Pl 83-85; Princeton U; Engrng.

RAGOZZINO, DEANNA; Sacred Heart Acad; New Haven, CT; (Y); Wt Lftg; Rep Pep Clb; School Play; Stage Crew; Variety Show; Ed Yrbk Stf; Cheerleading; Coach Actv; Im Vllybl; Hon Roll; Med.

RAGOZZINO, MICHELLE; West Haven HS; W Haven, CT; (Y); 20/341; French Clb; Nwsp Stf; Ed Yrbk Phtg; Lit Mag; Rep Stu Cncl; French Hon Soc; High Hon Roll; Hon Roll; Jr NHS; NHS; U CT Book Awd 85; U Of CT; Pltcl Sci.

RAINIS, KIMBERLY; Acad Of Our Lady Of Mercy; Southport, CT; (Y); Pres Debate Tm; Pres Model UN; Political Wkr; Ed Nwsp Stf; Off Frsh Cls; Var JV Vllybl; Poltcl Sci.

RAK, ROBERT; New Britain HS; New Britain, CT; (Y); #8 In Class; High Hon Roll; Hon Roll; NEDT Awd; Pres Schlr; Voice Dem Awd; Michaels Jwlrs Awd84; C J Parker Prz For Ctznshp 85; C J P Schlrshp 85; Cntrl CT ST U; Comp Sci.

RAMETTA, DAWN; Platt HS; Meriden, CT; (Y); Sec German Clb; Hosp Aide; Trk; Hon Roll; Acad Bus Careers; Acctng.

RAMETTA, FRANCES RITA; S Catholic HS; Hartford, CT; (Y); 8/225; Hosp Aide; JA; Ski Clb; Nwsp Stf; Yrbk Stf; Im Vllybl; High Hon Roll; NHS; Pres Schlr; St Schlr; Outstndng Serv As Cathlc Tutr Awd 84; Outstndng Perfrmnce Spnsh III 84; CT Audubn Soc Fnlst Sci Fair; Trinity Coll.

RAMOS, EDWARD; Simsbury HS; Jersey City, NJ; (Y); 61/356; Boy Scts; VP FBLA; Math Tm; Trs Radio Clb; Spanish Clb; Chorus; Rep Frsh Cls; Im Bsbl; Im Bsktbl; High Hon Roll; Selectd To ABC Progrm 82-85; Selectd LEAD Bus Progrm Northwestern U 84; Natl Hispnc Schlr Awd 84; U Of PA; Acctg.

RAMSON, RICHARD; Hartford Public HS; Hartford, CT; (Y); 79/220; Church Yth Grp; FBLA; JA; Yrbk Phtg; Yrbk Stf; Lit Mag; Trk; VA ST U; Acctg.

RANANDO, LYNNE; Holy Cross HS; Waterbury, CT; (Y); 32/352; Spanish Clb; Co-Capt Bsktbl; High Hon Roll; NHS; Spanish NHS; Bio.

RANDALL, BRIAN M; St Paul Catholic HS; Southington, CT; (Y); NHS; Prvidence Coll Grant 85-86; Providence Coll.

RANDALL, DAVID A; St Paul Catholic HS; Southington, CT; (Y); NHS; Providence Coll Grant 85-86; Providence Coll.

RANDALL, KARL; Cheshire HS; Cheshire, CT; (Y); Church Yth Grp; Var JV Lcrss; Hon Roll; Archlgy.

RANDAZZO, MATTHEW; Cromwell HS; Cromwell, CT; (Y); Am Leg Boys St; Spanish Clb; Chorus; School Musical; Variety Show; Yrbk Stf; Var Bsbl; Var Bsktbl; Var Capt Socr; Var Trk; All Cnty & All Star Tm Sccr 84-85; Mtlwrkng Awd 84-85; Music.

RANIS, BETTINA; Amity Regional HS; Woodbridge, CT; (S); 150/376; Drama Clb; Model UN; Spanish Clb; Stu Cncl; Cit Awd; Sec NHS; Hosp Vol 84; Recgnt Eng III 84.

RANNO, CHRISTINE; Ansonia HS; Ansonia, CT; (Y); Hosp Aide; Latin Clb; Nwsp Stf; Yrbk Stf; Hon Roll; NHS; Vet.

RANNO, MICHELE; Ansonia HS; Ansonia, CT; (Y); 2/130; Church Yth Grp; Hosp Aide; Nwsp Rptr; Yrbk Stf; Bausch & Lomb Sci Awd; Elks Awd; High Hon Roll; NHS; Sal; Voice Dem Awd; Mst Outstndg Physcs Stu 85; Naugatuck Vly Med Soc Prz 85; Alcine Webstr Hotchkiss Prz; Fairfield U; Physcn.

RAPOPORT, KAREN A; Trumbull HS; Trumbull, CT; (Y); Aud/Vis; FBLA; Office Aide; Ski Clb; Yrbk Stf; Stu Cncl; High Hon Roll; Hon Roll; Sacred Heart U; Accntng.

RAPSON, LISA; Griswold HS; Jewett City, CT; (Y); 15/94; GAA; Varsity Clb; Band; Chorus; School Musical; School Play; Variety Show; Trk; High Hon Roll; Girl Scts; Micro Bio Cert High Hnrs 83-84; CT U; Doctor.

RASCATI JR, RONALD R; Notre Dame Of West Haven HS; West Haven, CT; (Y); 126/260; Concert Band; Hon Roll; Ntl Merit Ltr; Schlrshp Grnt Frm HS 82-85; S CT; Accntng.

RASHBA, GARY; Amity Regional SR HS; Orange, CT; (Y); Am Leg Boys St; Political Wkr; Quiz Bowl; Pres Temple Yth Grp; Nwsp Bus Mgr; Nwsp Phtg; Pres Soph Cls; Hon Roll; Ntl Merit Ltr; Merit Awd-Stuart Hall Schltc Awds Cmptitn 85; Hnrb Mntn-CT Essay Cntst Selctn Pgs Repblcn Ntl Cnv 84; Intl Rltns.

RAWSON, GERALD K; Putnam HS; Putnam, CT; (Y); 8/130; Am Leg Boys St; Concert Band; Mrchg Band; School Play; Pres Frsh Cls; Pres Soph Cls; Socr; High Hon Roll; Hon Roll; Voice Dem Awd; Pol Sci.

RAY JR, PAUL W; East Catholic HS; Tolland, CT; (Y); 3/350; Boy Scts; Varsity Clb; Var Capt Crs Cntry; Var L Trk; Hon Roll; NHS; Dartmouth Clb Bk Awd 85; U S Naval Acad Smmr Smnr 85; U Of Notre Dame; Aerontcl Engr.

RAYNE, DAVID T; Southington HS; Southington, CT; (Y); 13/550; Hosp Aide; Latin Clb; Jazz Band; Mrchg Band; Symp Band; NHS; Ntl Merit Ltr; Rotary Awd; Eagle Scout 85; Exc In Music Awd 81-82; Bcknl U; Bio Med.

RAZZA, CARLA; Holy Cross HS; Oakville, CT; (Y); 100/345; Cmnty Wkr; Var Capt Cheerleading; Var Capt Trk; Hon Roll; Springfield Coll; Bus.

RE PASS, KENDALL; E O Smith HS; Storrs, CT; (Y); 15/188; Exploring; Scholastic Bowl; Var Capt Crs Cntry; Var Trk; Ntl Merit SF; Carleton; Eng.

READ, KAREN; St Bernard HS; Stonington, CT; (S); 10/290; Sec Church Yth Grp; VP Sec Computer Clb; Band; Chrmn Stu Cncl; L Diving; Mgr(s); NHS; Muscl Achvt 82; Acad Excllnc 82-84; Soc Distngshd Amer H S Stu 84; Pharm.

REAMS, MARK; East Lynne HS; Niantic, CT; (Y); Boy Scts; Band; Concert Band; Jazz Band; Mrchg Band; Pep Band; School Musical; Hon Roll; Ntl Rifle Assn Dstngshd Expert Awd 85; Fbi.

RECCE, JEAN; Shelton HS; Shelton, CT; (Y); Drama Clb; Spanish Clb; Stu Cncl; Pom Pon; Hon Roll; Italian Natl Hnr Soc 85; Italian Clb 82-85; Flight Attndnt.

REDDEN, DENISE N; Naugatick HS; Naugatuck, CT; (Y); Church Yth Grp; Spanish Clb; Chorus; Church Choir; Hon Roll; Schltc Achvt Awd S NE Amer Coed Pgnt 85; S NE Amer Coed Pagnt 85; Comm.

REDEN, ROBERT; Jonathan Law HS; Milford, CT; (Y); Intnl Clb; Ski Clb; Band; Chorus; Concert Band; Jazz Band; Mrchg Band; Swmmng; Hon Roll; Span Educ.

REDINGER, PAULA; Rockville HS; Vernon, CT; (Y); 5/365; Church Yth Grp; Jazz Band; Mrchg Band; Symp Band; Var Trk; High Hon Roll; NHS; All New England Music Fest 83-85; Eastern Regn Music Fest 84-85; Outstndng Cls Musician 83-85; Vet Med.

REDMAN, JENNIFER; George J Penny HS; E Hartford, CT; (Y); Am Leg Aux Girls St; French Clb; Band; Mrchg Band; Orch; School Musical; Yrbk Stf; Rep Frsh Cls; Rep Soph Cls; Rep Jr Cls; Harvard Clb Bk Awd 85; Soc Women Engrns Merit Awd 85; Frnch Spkng Cntst 1st 85; Sci.

REECE, PAULA; Jonathan Lw HS; Milford, CT; (Y); 10/231; Band; Color Guard; Yrbk Stf; Mgr(s); Hon Roll; NHS; Rotary Awd; Pres Schlrshp; Excllnc Awd IPS & Bio & Certo & Humn Bio; Coll Of New Rochelle; Nrsg.

REED, APRIL; Trumbull HS; Trumbull, CT; (Y); AFS; Church Yth Grp; Drama Clb; Chorus; High Hon Roll; Hon Roll; Ntl Merit Ltr; Chld Psych.

REED, DANIEL; Southington HS; Southington, CT; (Y); JA; Ski Clb; Concert Band; Hon Roll; Prfct Atten Awd; U Of VT; Envrnmntl Sci.

REED, ERIC; Berlin HS; Berlin, CT; (Y); 3/200; Am Leg Boys St; Science Clb; VP Service Clb; Var Trk; Pres NHS; Math Tm; Ophelia Clup Distngshd Svc Awd; Elec Engr.

REED, JOHN; Central HS; Bridgeport, CT; (Y); Hon Roll.

REED, JOHN EDGAR; The Hammonasett Schl; New London, CT; (Y); French Clb; Speech Tm; Concert Band; School Play; Nwsp Rptr; Lit Mag; Hon Roll; Adv Bio Awd 83; Pfizer Marine Resrch Pgm 83; Wesleyan Coll/U S Army Jr Sci Sympsm 84; Commrcl Arts Illustrtr.

REED, KEVIN; The College Preparatory Schl; Stratford, CT; (Y); Spanish Clb; Variety Show; Im Bsktbl; JV Var Ftbl; JV Var Trk; Var Wt Lftg; Hon Roll; Spanish NHS; Magna Cum Laude 83-84; Bus.

REED, KIMBERLY; Trumbull HS; Trumbull, CT; (Y); Church Yth Grp; JA; Chorus; Church Choir; Color Guard; High Hon Roll; NHS.

REELITZ, KATHRYN; St Bernard HS; Gales Ferry, CT; (S); Church Yth Grp; Computer Clb; Trs 4-H; Yrbk Stf; Stu Cncl; Diving; Mgr(s); 4-H Awd; High Hon Roll; Bus Fin.

REELITZ, KATHY; St Bernard HS; Gales Ferry, CT; (Y); Church Yth Grp; Trs Sec 4-H; Nwsp Stf; Yrbk Stf; Rep Stu Cncl; Diving; Mgr(s); 4-H Awd; High Hon Roll; Bankng Fin.

REES, ELIZABETH; Brien Mcmahon HS; Norwalk, CT; (Y); 1/297; Pres Spanish Clb; Band; Nwsp Ed-Chief; Val; Yrbk Ed-Chief; Rep Frsh Cls; Rep Soph Cls; Rep Jr Cls; Rep Sr Cls; High Hon Roll; CT Schlr Math & Sci Schlrhsp 84; Harvard Clb Bk Awd 84; Yale Clb Awd 84; Yale U.

REESE, DAVID; Pomperaug HS; Middlebury, CT; (Y); Debate Tm; Exploring; Hon Roll; Natl Sci Olympd Bio; CT ST Leg Cert; Crmnl Jstc.

REESER, CHRISTINE; Naugatuck HS; Naugatuck, CT; (Y); 24/340; Color Guard; Drm & Bgl; Frsh Cls; Rep Soph Cls; Im Badmtn; JV Bsktbl; Mgr(s); Score Keeper; Vllybl; High Hon Roll; Dietn.

REGAL, JOSEPH; Fairfield Prep; Fairfield, CT; (Y); Chess Clb; Church Yth Grp; Drama Clb; Spanish Clb; Chorus; Church Choir; Jazz Band; Orch; School Musical; Nwsp Rptr.

REGAN, MEREDITH; Tolland HS; Tolland, CT; (Y); 16/180; Church Yth Grp; Ski Clb; Band; Rep Frsh Cls; Rep Jr Cls; Var Cheerleading; JV Trk; High Hon Roll; Hon Roll; NHS; Math.

REGER, ROBERT; Avon Old Farms Schl; New Vernon, NJ; (S); 12/102; Yrbk Stf; Crs Cntry; Trk; JV Wrstlng; High Hon Roll; Hist Awd; Awd Ernst & Perstnt Effort Acad Area.

REID, MARK; Rockville HS; Manchester, CT; (S); 86/375; FFA; High Hon Roll; Hon Roll; Dairy Prods U Of Conn 83; Cornell; Vet.

REILING, MARK; The Hotchkiss Schl; Litchfield, CT; (Y); Capt Aud/Vis; Drama Clb; Co-Capt Stu Cncl; Var L Lcrss; Var L Socr; Var L Swmmng; Nwsp Rptr; School Play; Stage Crew; Pres Of Schl 85-86; Edwards Cup-Outstndg Achvt 84; Talbott Cup-Swmmg 83.

REILLY, SARAH E; New Britain SR HS; New Britain, CT; (Y); 122/450; Office Aide; Cheerleading; Gym; Central Conn ST Coll; Law.

REILLY, SEAN; Holy Cross HS; Waterbury, CT; (Y); Im Bsktbl; JV Wrstlng.

REILLY, STACEY; Canton HS; Canton, CT; (Y); Model UN; Chorus; Yrbk Bus Mgr; High Hon Roll; Hon Roll; World Affairs Sem 84-85; Mth.

REIMER, LISA; Manchester HS; Manchester, CT; (Y); Trs AFS; Math Tm; Service Clb; JV Socr; High Hon Roll; Hon Roll; Trs NHS; Nwsp Stf; Yrbk Stf; Yale Bk Awd 85; Bus.

REINHARDT, MARY E; East Haven HS; E Haven, CT; (Y); #35 In Class; Girl Scts; Band; Concert Band; Mrchg Band; Symp Band; Hon Roll; Jr NHS; Partcptn Southern Regnl Band 84-85; Partcptn Lourel Music Camp By Conn Music Ed 84-85; Psychlgy.

REINKOBER, ERIC; St Joseph HS; Shelton, CT; (Y); 12/227; Church Yth Grp; French Clb; JA; Key Clb; Quiz Bowl; JV Bsbl; French Hon Soc; Hon Roll; NHS; Notre Dame U.

REINOEHL, LISA; Stratford HS; Stratford, CT; (Y); Rep Frsh Cls; Rep Soph Cls; Rep Jr Cls; Var Mgr(s); Capt Var Tennis; Hon Roll; Fairfield U; Busn Mngmnt.

REISCHERL, PAMELA; E Catholic HS; Manchester, CT; (Y); 22/298; GAA; JV Sftbl; Var Capt Swmmng; Hon Roll; Mst Imprvd Swmmr 84-85; Mrktng.

REISER, PETER J; St Thomas More HS; New Canaan, CT; (Y); Art Clb; Computer Clb; Exploring; French Clb; Pres JA; Letterman Clb; Math Clb; Band; Pres Yrbk Stf; JV Var Bsbl; New London Day Awd Outstndng Achvt 84-85; Soccer, Bskl & Ftbl Awds 83, 84-85; Acdmc Hnrs; Aviation.

REISNER, MARC; Bloomfield HS; Bloomfield, CT; (Y); 6/233; Model UN; Ski Clb; Temple Yth Grp; Rep Frsh Cls; Rep Soph Cls; Rep Jr Cls; Var Bsbl; Var Socr; French Hon Soc; High Hon Roll; Bus.

REK, LAURA; Naugatuck HS; Naugatuck, CT; (Y); Dance Clb; Chorus; Jazz Band; Mrchg Band; Pep Band; Symp Band; Variety Show; Var L Gym; Var Trk; Hon Roll; CT Souther Regional Band 84; CT Southern Regional Band 85; Nrsng.

REK, TRISHA A; Naugatuek HS; Prospect, CT; (Y); Office Aide; Pep Clb; Yrbk Stf; Rep Frsh Cls; Rep Soph Cls; Rep Sr Cls; JV L Badmtn; Hon Roll; Prfct Atten Awd; Roger Williams Coll.

RELIC, REBECCA; Conard HS; West Hartford, CT; (Y); 71/298; Pres Pep Clb; Chorus; School Musical; Yrbk Bus Mgr; Stu Cncl; Var L Cheerleading; Var L Gym; Capt Lcrss; Conard Prid Awd 85; De Pauw U; Cmnctns.

RELUGA, ERIC; Granby HS; W Granby, CT; (Y); Drama Clb; Jazz Band; Mrchg Band; School Play; Symp Band; Crs Cntry; Tennis; Trk; High Hon Roll; NHS; Meritorious Awd Bio 84; Exemplary Achvt Band 83; Outstndng Achvt Chem 85; Bst Suppt Actor 83.

RELVA, MICHAEL; Oliver Wolcott Technical Schl; Torrington, CT; (Y); 5/152; Pres VICA; Pres Jr NHS; Pres NHS; Church Yth Grp; Yrbk Stf; JV Tennis; Hon Roll; MA Inst Of Technlgy; Gen Engrg.

REMLIN, LISA; Staples HS; Westport, CT; (Y); VP Church Yth Grp; Radio Clb; Acpl Chr; Chorus; Church Choir; Hon Roll.

RENDA, CRAIG; Danburg HS; Danbury, CT; (Y); Chorus; School Play; Swing Chorus; Variety Show; Yrbk Stf; Var Bsbl; Var Ftbl; Hon Roll; Bus.

RENDA JR, FRANK; Wilcox Tech HS; Wallingford, CT; (Y); Boy Scts; Exploring; Red Cross Aide; Hon Roll; Prfct Atten Awd; Biochem.

RENEY, KRISTEN; Saint Thomas Aquinas HS; New Britain, CT; (Y); 20/180; Church Yth Grp; Rep Frsh Cls; Rep Soph Cls; Rep Jr Cls; Rep Sr Cls; VP Stu Cncl; JV Var Cheerleading; Coach Actv; JV Var Vllybl; Hon Roll; Hgst Awd Schlstc Achvt, Ldrshp & Svc 82; ST Sci Fair Audubn Socty Awd 82; Bus.

RENZULLI, DAVID; Fairfield College Preparartory Schl; Southport, CT; (Y); Key Clb; Spanish Clb; Yrbk Stf; Var Capt Bsktbl; Var Capt Golf; Hon Roll; NHS; Wakeman Boys Clb Boy Yr 85; CT ST Glf Assoc Jr Champ 84; Accntng.

RESTIVO, NANCY; Robert E Fitch SR HS; Groton, CT; (Y); 35/300; VP Intnl Clb; VP Capt JA; Band; Score Keeper; Trk; High Hon Roll; Hon Roll; Hnrs Distinction Schlrshp From Ball ST U; Art Awd 82; Schlr Awd 82; Ball ST U; Arch.

RESTREPO, INGRID; Brien Mc Mahon HS; Norwalk, CT; (Y); Sec Spanish Clb; 2nd Hnrs In The Iona Lang Cont 85; Southern CT ST U; Spec Ed.

RETAMAR, MICHELLE; Bassick HS; Bridgeport, CT; (S); #15 In Class; Church Yth Grp; Cmnty Wkr; FNA; Girl Scts; JA; Key Clb; Political Wkr; Teachers Aide; Church Choir; School Play; Miss PR Of CT 83; Intl Mayor Councl Awd 83; Key Clb Kiwanis Scholar Awd 85; Baptist Liberty; Educ.

REUTER, DEBORAH; Bethal HS; Bethel, CT; (Y); 19/268; AFS; Variety Show; Nwsp Rptr; Nwsp Stf; Yrbk Stf; JV Crs Cntry; JV Trk; High Hon Roll; NHS; Jrnlsm.

REY, LISA; Central Catholic HS; Norwalk, CT; (Y); Math Tm; Ski Clb; Nwsp Stf; Yrbk Stf; Pres Soph Cls; Trs Sr Cls; Var JV Cheerleading; Powder Puff Ftbl; Hon Roll; VP NHS; Cntry III Ldrshp Schl Wnnr 84-85; CA ST Schlr 84-85; Law.

REYES, ELIZABETH; Stratford HS; Stratford, CT; (Y); 23/241; Sec FBLA; Girl Scts; Hosp Aide; Hon Roll; Physcl Thrpy.

REYES, MARIBEL; Hartford HS; Hartford, CT; (Y); 14/408; FNA; JA; Var Capt Gym; Var Sftbl; Hon Roll; Sec NHS; Med.

REYNOLDS, GLENN; Notre Dame HS; Milford, CT; (Y); Ski Clb; Wt Lftg; Hon Roll; St Mary Schlrshp 82-86.

REYNOLDS, JENNIFER; Bethel HS; Bethel, CT; (Y); 34/268; AFS; Computer Clb; JA; Political Wkr; Ski Clb; Varsity Clb; School Play; Variety Show; Yrbk Stf; JV Tennis; Engrng.

REYNOLDS, KAREN; Canton HS; Collinsville, CT; (Y); 20/90; Teachers Aide; Var Capt Cheerleading; High Hon Roll; Hon Roll; Cert Awd Typng 85; Bus.

REYNOLDS, KARI; Danbury HS; Danbury, CT; (Y); 57/612; Rep Jr Cls; Cit Awd; Hon Roll; Jr NHS; Bus.

REYNOLDS, KELLY; Sacred Heart Acad; West Haven, CT; (Y); FBLA; Spanish Clb; Teachers Aide; Vllybl; Martl Arts Clb 82-83; Math.

REYNOLDS, PAULA; Sacred Heart Acad; Hamden, CT; (Y); Church Yth Grp; Cmnty Wkr; Drama Clb; FBLA; School Musical; Nwsp Rptr; JV Crs Cntry; High Hon Roll; Art Clb; Chorus; Stdnt Cncl Rep Pro Lf Chptr 85-86; WA Wrkshp Congrssnl Fndtn 85; Pre-Law.

REYNOLDS, THOMAS; Ledyard HS; Gales Ferry, CT; (Y); 42/280; Am Leg Boys St; Thesps; School Play; Nwsp Ed-Chief; Nwsp Phtg; Nwsp Rptr; Yrbk Phtg; VP Jr Cls; Pres Sr Cls; Var Swmmng; Schlstc Jrnlst Awdd 84; Cngrssnl Medal Merit 85; U Of New Haven; Crmnl Jstc.

REZOSKI, LISA; East Catholic HS; Marlborough, CT; (Y); Art Clb; Church Yth Grp; Civic Clb; Yrbk Stf; Lit Mag; Sftbl; Hon Roll; Advrtsg.

RHEA, SAKSA; Stratford HS; Stratford, CT; (Y); 16/265; Var Cheerleading; Hon Roll; Word Prsccng 85; Bus Educ II 84; U Of CT; Bus.

RHOADS, KERRY; Bethel HS; Bethel, CT; (Y); 58/264; Church Yth Grp; FBLA; Ski Clb; Variety Show; Stu Cncl; Var JV Cheerleading; Hon Roll; Yrbk Editor 85; Emmaus Relgs Weekend 84-85; Sci.

RHODES, JULIA A; Central HS; Bridgeport, CT; (Y); AFS; JA; Spanish Clb; Color Guard; VP Jr Cls; Cit Awd; Hon Roll; NHS; Phillips Acad Ms2 Pgm; Michaels Jewelers Awd 85; Harvard Bk Awd 85; Amherst Coll; Lwyr.

RHYNHART, ERICH; Woodstock Acad; Woodstock, CT; (Y); 15/100; Am Leg Boys St; Drama Clb; Latin Clb; Pres Model UN; Madrigals; Pres Stu Cncl; Hon Roll; NHS; Chorus; Variety Show; 3rd Pl ST Ftr Prblm Slvng Cmptn 85.

RICCI, MELISSA E; Sacred Heart Acad; New Haven, CT; (Y); Dance Clb; School Musical; Rep Stu Cncl; Capt Cheerleading; High Hon Roll; NHS; Church Yth Grp; Cmnty Wkr; Pep Clb; Chorus; Sacred Heart Acad Schlrshp; Conn Ballet Schlrshp; Var ST & Natl Dance Tlnt Awds 84; NY U; Dance.

RICCIO, ANGELA; Portland SR HS; Portland, CT; (Y); CAP; FBLA; Lit Mag; Hon Roll; NHS; Loyola U.

RICCITELLI JR, JOSEPH; East Haven HS; East Haven, CT; (Y); CAP; Comp Sci.

RICCITELLI, TROY; Hamden HS; Hamden, CT; (Y); Boy Scts; Var Ice Hcky.

RICE, BRENT; Masuk HS; Monroe, CT; (Y); 25/276; JV Score Keeper; Var Tennis; Hon Roll; NHS; Vrsty Tnns Chmpn Wstrn CT Conf 85.

RICHARD, TAMMY; Torrington HS; Torrington, CT; (Y); 12/271; Am Leg Aux Girls St; Aud/Vis; Variety Show; High Hon Roll; Rory Hatch Mem Fund Engrng Scholar 85; Friends Natrl Envrnmnt Inc Scholar 85; Womans Clb Scholar 85; U Of CT; Elec Engrng.

RICHARDS, DIANE; Stratford HS; Stratford, CT; (Y).

RICHARDSON, LARRY DARNELL; Central HS; Bridgeport, CT; (Y); 69/320; School Play; Rep Frsh Cls; Rep Soph Cls; Rep Sr Cls; Rep Stu Cncl; Hon Roll; Headmasters Awd Ldrshp 82; Ctrl Svc Awd 85; St Josephs Coll; Mkt Resrch.

RICHMAN, STACY E; William H Hall HS; W Hartford, CT; (Y); 21/305; Pep Clb; Jazz Band; Symp Band; Var Cheerleading; Im Lcrss; Var Capt Pom Pon; Var Capt Twrlr; French Hon Soc; NHS; U Of CT.

RIDENHOUR, PATRICK; Holy Cross HS; Waterbury, CT; (Y); JA; Hon Roll; NHS; Spanish NHS; U Of CT; Pol Sci.

RIEGEL, BRAD; Brookfield HS; Brookfield, CT; (Y); Church Yth Grp; Math Tm; Concert Band; Jazz Band; Mrchg Band; Var Tennis; High Hon Roll; NHS; Aerontcl Engrng.

RIKER, KATHERINE; Westhill HS; Stamford, CT; (Y); JA; Pep Clb; Soroptimist; Temple Yth Grp; Varsity Clb; Off Jr Cls; Pres Stu Cncl; Var Fld Hcky; Hon Roll.

RILEY, MARY CHRISTINE; Miss Porters Schl; Larchmont, NY; (Y); Chess Clb; Church Yth Grp; Computer Clb; Hosp Aide; Golf; Tennis; Jr NHS; 2nd Hnr Roll 84-85; Magna Cum Laude 83; Afro Asian Stds Cert Excell 83.

RIMMER, VALERIE; Stamford HS; Stamford, CT; (S); Cmnty Wkr; Hosp Aide; JA; Office Aide; VP Spanish Clb; Ed Nwsp Ed-Chief; Stu Cncl; Hon Roll; NHS; 1st Pl Feat Wrtng Awd Columbia Schltc Assn 84.

RINALDI, FILOMENA; Holy Cross HS; Oakville, CT; (Y); 28/352; Art Clb; Drama Clb; Intnl Clb; School Musical; School Play; Stage Crew; Hon Roll; Itln Hnr Soc; Bus.

RINOSKI, TY WILLIAM; East Lyme HS; Niantic, CT; (Y); 15/290; Var Bsbl; Var Bsktbl; Var Ftbl; Hon Roll; Pres Schlr; Rotary Awd; MVP Var Bsbl 85; U S Army Res Schlr Ath 85; U CT H S Coop Pgm 85; U S Coast Guard Acad; Comp Sci.

RIORDAN, ROBERT; Fairfield College Preparatory School; Fairfield, CT; (Y); 32/237; Trs Art Clb; Cmnty Wkr; Key Clb; Political Wkr; Q&S; Sec Spanish Clb; Teachers Aide; School Play; Nwsp Bus Mgr; Yrbk Ed-Chief; Pres-Drug & Alcohol Council 84-85; Pre-Law.

RISH, MICHELLE; Amity Regional HS; Woodbridge, CT; (Y); Church Yth Grp; French Clb; School Musical; School Play; Variety Show; Sec Frsh Cls; Rep Stu Cncl; Var Cheerleading; Var Trk; Hon Roll; Natl Art Hon Soc 83-85; Psych.

RISHI, ARTHUR; Amity Regional HS; Woodbridge, CT; (S); Church Yth Grp; Model UN; High Hon Roll; Natl Franch Contest; CT Composers Festival.

RITCH, WENDY; Greenwich HS; Cos Cob, CT; (Y); Church Yth Grp; Cmnty Wkr; Swing Chorus; Nwsp Rptr; Nwsp Stf; Lit Mag; JV Bsktbl; JV Sftbl; NHS; Library Aide; Yale U Frontiers Applied Sci Symposm 84-85; Ldrshp Ability VP Bk Selectn Comm 85; Dartmouth; Pre-Law.

RITCHIE, WAYNE; East Lyme HS; E Lyme, CT; (Y); 8/280; Church Yth Grp; Yrbk Rptr; Pres Soph Cls; Pres Jr Cls; Stu Cncl; Ftbl; Elks Awd; Hon Roll; Jr NHS; NHS; George Wash U; Librl Arts.

RITTER, JEFFREY; Heritage Christian Acad; Seymour, CT; (Y); Camera Clb; Chess Clb; Church Yth Grp; Computer Clb; School Play; Var Bsktbl; Var Socr; High Hon Roll; Extraordinary Chrstn Stu Awd 85; Air Force CC.

RITTER, KAREN A; Amity Regional SR HS; Woodbridge, CT; (Y); 51/376; VP Drama Clb; Band; VP Chorus; Capt Color Guard; Madrigals; School Musical; School Play; Variety Show; Lit Mag; NHS; Academic Award Class I 82-83; Music.

RIVARD, RAYMOND; Ansonia HS; Ansonia, CT; (Y); 8/250; Am Leg Boys St; Computer Clb; Varsity Clb; Y-Teens; Nwsp Rptr; Ftbl; Golf; Im Wt Lftg; DAR Awd; Hon Roll; Yth Understndng 85; Harvard Clb Bk Awd 85; JR Sci Humntes Symp 85; Pol.

RIVERA, CARMEN LETICIA; Hartford Public HS; Hartford, CT; (Y); 31/200; Office Aide; Sr Cls; Sftbl; Cit Awd; Hon Roll; Judith Ann Margel Schlrshp 85; CT Achvt Grant 85; Merit Schlrshp 85; Hartford Coll Women; Educ.

RIVERA, RAQUEL L; New Fairfield HS; New Fairfield, CT; (Y); 23/243; Natl Beta Clb; Variety Show; Co-Capt Var Cheerleading; Var Trk; Hon Roll; NHS; All Amer Chrldr Natl Assc 84-85.

RIZZI, CHERYL; Westhill HS; Stamford, CT; (Y); Church Yth Grp; DECA; French Clb; Girl Scts; Hosp Aide; Y-Teens; Frsh Cls; Soph Cls; Bsktbl; Sftbl; Atten Awd 80-82; Dance Marathon 84-85; Pres Physcl Ftns Awd 82; Beautcn.

RIZZO, LOUIS; St Joseph HS; Shelton, CT; (Y); Church Yth Grp; Cmnty Wkr; Drama Clb; Band; Chorus; Church Choir; Orch; School Musical; School Play; Stage Crew; Sci.

ROATH, DALE; St Bernard HS; Norwich, CT; (Y); 142/300; JV Crs Cntry; Var L Trk; Bus Adm.

ROBBINS, ALLISON M; Our Lady Of Mercy Acad; Milford, CT; (Y); Varsity Clb; Nwsp Rptr; Lit Mag; Var L Bsktbl; NHS; Spanish NHS; Church Yth Grp; GAA; Political Wkr; Science Clb; Knight Columbus Schlrshp 85; Most Improved Plyr Bsktbl 85; Marist Coll.

ROBBINS, NICHOLAS; Avon Old Farms Schl; Avon, CT; (S); 17/112; Intnl Clb; Model UN; Political Wkr; Nwsp Ed-Chief; Lit Mag; Im Ice Hcky; Im Lcrss; Im Socr; Im Tennis; Hon Roll; Biol Awd 83; 2nd Pl Columbia Schltc Press Assn Cont 84; Alt Page Repub Natl Conv 84; Intl Law.

ROBBINS, TARA E; Lyman Hall HS; Wallingford, CT; (Y); 15/218; FFA; Mgr JA; Pep Clb; Band; Concert Band; Mrchg Band; Sec Jr Cls; Sec Sr Cls; Stu Cncl; Var Capt Socr.

ROBELLA, SUSAN; Saint Bernard HS; Jewett City, CT; (Y); #22 In Class; Church Yth Grp; VP Dance Clb; Exploring; Yrbk Stf; Trk; Drama Clb; Fine Arts I & II Awds; Tchr.

ROBERTS, ADRIENE; Cooperative HS; New Haven, CT; (Y); 21/71; Church Choir; Yrbk Stf; Hon Roll; Acadmc All Amer 84-85.

ROBERTS, DEBORAH; Trumbull HS; Trumbull, CT; (Y); Boy Scts; Cmnty Wkr; Office Aide; Red Cross Aide; Color Guard; Drm & Bgl; Yrbk Phtg; Bsktbl; JV Sftbl; Var Vllybl; Trumbull Safe Rides; Cert Apprectn 85; Girls V Bsktbl Partcptn Awd 85; Sftbl Awd 83-84; Med Tech.

ROBERTS, JENNIFER; Lyman Hall HS; Wallingford, CT; (Y); 9/247; AFS; PAVAS; Spanish Clb; Rep Frsh Cls; Rep Sec Soph Cls; Rep Jr Cls; Rep Stu Cncl; Var Fld Hcky; Var Tennis; High Hon Roll; MVP Tnns 84; Bus Admin.

ROBERTS, MARILYN JOYCE; Haddam-Killingworth HS; Killingworth, CT; (Y); 21/88; Church Yth Grp; Drama Clb; Key Clb; School Play; Sec Soph Cls; Sec Jr Cls; Stu Cncl; Hon Roll; Mst Outstndng Stu 82; JR Beta Clb 80-82; Arch.

ROBERTS, RONALD; Windham Regional Tech Schl; Storrs, CT; (Y); Hon Roll; NHS.

ROBERTS, SANDRA J; Morgan Schl; Clinton, CT; (Y); Chorus; Rep Soph Cls; Rep Jr Cls; NHS; Soclgy.

ROBERTSON, THOMAS; Avon Old Farms Schl; Glastonbury, CT; (S); 5/110; Nwsp Rptr; Nwsp Stf; Lit Mag; Im Lcrss; JV Wrstlng; High Hon Roll; Hon Roll; Im Socr; Acad Hnrs Awd 84; Engl Awd 84; Co Capt Var Riflery Team 85; GA Tech; Engrng.

ROBICHAND, MICHELLE; West Haven HS; W Haven, CT; (Y); Tennis; Recog Awd Outstndng Effrt 83; Bus.

ROBIN, ANDREW; Westhill HS; Stamford, CT; (Y); Drama Clb; Science Clb; Thesps; Acpl Chr; Chorus; Madrigals; School Musical; School Play; Hst Frsh Cls; Var Trk; Retird Ofcrs Assc Yng Amer Awd 85; Hnbl Mntn Phy Chem Sci Fair 85; Stamford Hlth Dept Awd Merit 85; Natrl Sci.

ROBINSON, BRETT S; Norwich Free Acad; Lisbon, CT; (Y); Am Leg Boys St; Im Ice Hcky; Marion R Quinlan Memrl Awd 85; C P Hamblen Awd 85; U Of CT; Comp Engr.

ROBINSON, GEORGE; Hillhouse HS; New Haven, CT; (Y); Church Yth Grp; Cmnty Wkr; Drama Clb; Model UN; School Play; Rep Stu Cncl; Tennis; High Hon Roll; NHS; Slvr Mdl Wnnr Rgnl Columbus Day Essay 84; Outstndng Achvt Bio 82-83; Engrng.

ROBINSON, MICHAEL; Bassick HS; Bridgeport, CT; (S); 13/200; Key Clb; Socr; Hon Roll; Cert From U CT Day Of Pride; Cert Engrng For Disadvantaged Yth; U Of CT; Engrng.

ROBINSON, OPAL; Bassick HS; Bridgeport, CT; (S); Drama Clb; JA; Science Clb; Lit Mag; Stu Cncl; Hon Roll; Ntl Merit Ltr.

ROBINSON, PUTRINA; Wilbur Cross HS; New Haven, CT; (Y); DECA; Girl Scts; Drill Tm; Stu Cncl; Hon Roll; CPR Red Cross Badge & Dash Meter Run; Advanced 1st Aide Awd; Freddy Fixer Beauty Pageant Awd; Plaza Three Acad; Fash.

ROBINSON, SHAWN; Holy Cross HS; Waterbury, CT; (Y); Boys Clb Am; Church Yth Grp; Capt Ftbl; Pre-Med.

ROBINSON, SHEILA M; James Hillhouse HS; New Haven, CT; (Y); 120/253; JA; Science Clb; Band; Bsktbl; Vllybl; Space Shuttle Stu Awd Sci Superstar Awd 84; Hnrb Mntn Awd 85; Human Physlgy Awd 84; Tuskeger Inst; Hlth Care.

ROBINSON, STACY; Haddam-Killingworth HS; Killingworth, CT; (Y); 4-H; Teachers Aide; Chorus; Swing Chorus; Engl Tchr.

ROBLES, SARA; St Bernard HS; Griswold, CT; (Y); 41/297; Church Yth Grp; Dance Clb; Drama Clb; Chorus; School Musical; School Play; Stu Cncl; Hon Roll; Music Achvt Awds 83 & 85; Archtctr.

ROCHE, KELLY; Maloney HS; Meriden, CT; (Y); Hon Roll.

ROCHEFORT, ELIZABETH; Manchester HS; Manchester, CT; (Y); Library Aide; Teachers Aide; Hon Roll; Hnbl Mntn Natl Frnch Cntst 83; Awd Outstndng Achvt Frnch I 83; Comp Sci.

ROCHELEAU, TOM; Newington HS; Newington, CT; (S); Boy Scts; Church Yth Grp; Pres DECA; Chorus; Church Choir; Rep Soph Cls; Rep Stu Cncl; Ftbl; Wrstlng; Hon Roll; Cert Merit Saving Life 82; Boy Sct Medl; Tunxis CC; Bus Mgmnt.

ROCHESTER, GARY; Weaver HS; Hartford, CT; (Y); Math Clb; Math Tm; Golf; High Hon Roll; Hon Roll; NHS; Spnsh, Frnch & Engl Awds 83-85; Chem & Phy Ed Awds 83-85; Edward Bode Mem Schlrshp 83-85; U Of New Haven; Aviation.

ROCHETTE, KIMBERLY A; Stafford HS; Somers, CT; (Y); 7/109; Art Clb; Drama Clb; French Clb; Thesps; Band; Chorus; Madrigals; Yrbk Stf; Rep Stu Cncl; JV Fld Hcky; U Of CT; Educ Psych.

ROCHLIS, DAN; Stamford HS; Stamford, CT; (Y); Jazz Band; Drama Clb; PAVAS; Jazz Band; Orch; School Musical; Arts Recgntn & Tlnt Srch 85; Musician.

RODICK, KIRALY; Lauralton Hall HS; Milfort, CT; (Y); French Clb; GAA; Latin Clb; Model UN; Yrbk Ed-Chief; Swmmng.

RODRIGUE, SUSAN; George J Penney HS; E Hartford, CT; (Y); French Clb; Office Aide; Ski Clb; Yrbk Stf; Cheerleading; Sftbl; Swmmng; High Hon Roll; NHS; Rep Frsh Cls; Gary M Blount 3 Yr Sci Awd 85; Frshmn Soc Stds Awd 83; Coll; Sci.

RODRIGUEZ, MARYBELLE; Richard C Lee HS; New Haven, CT; (Y); Sec Church Yth Grp; Chorus; Church Choir; Hon Roll; NHS; New Haven Hosp Hlth Intrnshp Awd 85; Hlth.

RODRIGUEZ, PAUL; Parish Hill HS; Hampton, CT; (Y); Band; Rep Frsh Cls; Rep Soph Cls; Rep Jr Cls; Var L Bsbl; Var L Socr; Hon Roll; U Of CT.

RODRIQUEZ, DAVID; Bassick HS; Bridgpt, CT; (Y); Var Ftbl; Var Trk; All ST Outdr Trck Tm 85; 1st Tm 84-85; Arch.

RODRIQUEZ, ELIZABETH; Saint Mary HS; Greenwich, CT; (Y); Varsity Clb; Var Bsktbl; Hon Roll; Briarwood Bk Awd 85; Med.

RODRIQUEZ, MARYBELLE; Richard C Lee HS; New Haven, CT; (Y); Sec Church Yth Grp; Chorus; Church Choir; NHS; Yale-Nw Hvn Hosp Hlth Intrnshp Awd 85; Hlth.

ROELOFSEN, LORI; Haddam-Killingworth HS; Killingworth, CT; (Y); 9/114; Pres Church Yth Grp; Band; Rep Soph Cls; Rep Jr Cls; Rep Sr Cls; Stu Cncl; Var Capt Fld Hcky; High Hon Roll; NHS.

ROGERS, JOANNA; Danbury HS; Danbury, CT; (Y); Dance Clb; JA; Office Aide; Varsity Clb; School Musical; Variety Show; Rep Stu Cncl; Var Crs Cntry; Var Trk; Psych.

ROGERS, JULIA; Bethel HS; Woodbury, CT; (Y); AFS; Church Choir; Nwsp Rptr; Var Mgr(s); JV Tennis; Mgr Trk; Mgr Vllybl; Hon Roll; Eng.

ROGERS, PATRICIA; Holy Cross HS; Wolcott, CT; (Y); 158/352; FNA; Hosp Aide; VP Latin Clb; Trs Spanish Clb; Varsity Clb; Crs Cntry; Trk; Hon Roll; Rtrt Leag Schlrshp 83-86; Nursng.

ROGERS, RAINER; Trumbull HS; East Brunswick, NJ; (Y); Aud/Vis; Church Yth Grp; Sec Trs Exploring; Im Lcrss; JV Trk; JV Wrstlng; Hon Roll; Law.

ROGERS, STACEY; St Bernard HS; Stonington, CT; (S); 4/290; Cmnty Wkr; Computer Clb; Library Aide; Band; Trs Stu Cncl; Swmmng; High Hon Roll; NHS; Ntl Frnch Tst Awd 82; Engrng.

ROGOZINSKI, KEITH; St Thomas More HS; Thomaston, CT; (Y); ROTC; Trk; High Hon Roll; Hon Roll; Grnd Marshl Hghst Rnkg JR 85; Boston U; Bus.

ROJAS, ERIC; East Hartford HS; East Hartford, CT; (Y); Boy Scts; Ski Clb; Varsity Clb; Variety Show; Pres Sr Cls; JV Var Socr; Hon Roll; Penn ST U; Engrng.

ROJAS, RENATA; Sacred Heart Acad; Stamford, CT; (Y); Church Yth Grp; Church Choir; School Play; Variety Show; Lit Mag; NHS; Ocngrphy.

ROLAND, RENEE L; Miss Porters Schl; Rocky Hill, CT; (Y); Dance Clb; Debate Tm; French Clb; Acpl Chr; Chorus; Off Soph Cls; Off Sr Cls; Surgn.

ROLAND, WILLIAM; East Haven HS; East Haven, CT; (Y); 12/280; Am Leg Boys St; Pres Chess Clb; Capt Scholastic Bowl; Nwsp Ed-Chief; Pres Frsh Cls; Rep Stu Cncl; Mgr(s); Hon Roll; NHS; Rotary Awd; Yale Bk Awd; Am Leg Scholar; Southern CT ST U; Engl.

ROLFE, JOHN J; Torrington HS; Torrington, CT; (Y); Church Yth Grp; Key Clb; Ski Clb; Band; Drm & Bgl; Bowling; Var L Crs Cntry; Var Trk; Hon Roll; 2 Merit Awds-New England Math League 84-85; Syracuse U; Arch.

ROLLBERG, KATHLEEN MARIE; Low-Heywood Thomas HS; Ridgefield, CT; (Y); 21/36; Church Yth Grp; Cmnty Wkr; Drama Clb; Girl Scts; Model UN; Service Clb; Mrchg Band; Orch; School Musical; Yrbk Stf; Ntl German Test Awd 83; Acdmc Schlrshp 85; Music Awd 83; Lib Arts.

ROMAJAS, LISA; Southington HS; Marion, CT; (Y); Art Clb; Church Yth Grp; Boy Scts; Ski Clb; Church Choir; Color Guard; Concert Band; Flag Corp; Mrchg Band; Cheerleading.

ROMAN, IVAN; Francis T Maloney HS; Meriden, CT; (Y); 11/254; High Hon Roll; Hon Roll; NHS; Pres Schlr; CT Assn Bilingl Stu & Eagl Clb Schlrshps 85; 3rd Pl ST Outstndng Stu Yr 85; Occup Job Manl ST 1st; CT Coll; Comp Sci.

ROMAN, PATTY; Masuk HS; Stevenson, CT; (Y); 115/300; Church Yth Grp; DECA; Chorus; High Hon Roll; Hon Roll; DECA Awd 84-85; Pwr & Spd Rdng Awd 84-85; Mtl Acad Of Hairdrssng; Csmtlgy.

ROMANIELLO, JOSEPH; Holy Cross HS; Waterbury, CT; (Y); Church Yth Grp; Band; Concert Band; Mrchg Band; Bsktbl; Capt Ftbl; Mgr(s); Swmmng; Hon Roll; Natl Hnr Rl 85; Tuit Remsn Grnt 85; U Of Dayton; Commctns.

ROMANIELLO, SUSAN; Crosby HS; Waterbury, CT; (S); Latin Clb; Library Aide; Ski Clb; Chorus; Hon Roll; NHS; Choral Achvt Awd 84; U Of CT; Elem Educ.

RONAN IV, JOHN T; Weston HS; Weston, CT; (Y); Hosp Aide; Latin Clb; Ski Clb; Var L Socr; Hon Roll.

RONDEAU, DENISE; Killingly HS; Lowell, MA; (Y); Yrbk Stf; Hst Sr Cls; French Hon Soc; High Hon Roll; Hon Roll; Art Achv Awd 82-84; Supr Art Achv Paintng 84-85; MA Coll Art; Comrcl Artst.

RONDOMANSKI, JODY; East Lyme HS; Niantic, CT; (Y); AFS; Stage Crew; Stat Bsktbl; Powder Puff Ftbl; Var Trk; Hon Roll; Rotary Awd; Rensselaer Polytech Inst; Arch.

ROPA, CHRISTINE; Stratford HS; Stratford, CT; (Y); #39 In Class; Church Yth Grp; Girl Scts; Hosp Aide; Ski Clb; Chorus; Cheerleading; Hon Roll.

ROPER, GREGORY B; Weaver HS; Hartford, CT; (Y); Comp Prgmr.

RORRIO, JOHN H; George J Penney HS; East Hartford, CT; (Y); #2 In Class; JA; Quiz Bowl; Spanish Clb; Band; Concert Band; Drm Mjr(t); Mrchg Band; High Hon Roll; NHS; Pres Schlr; USAF ROTC 85; Penn St Schlr 84; Outstndng Instrmntl Awd 85; Worcester Polytech Inst; Comp.

ROSA, FAITH; Cooperative HS; New Haven, CT; (Y); 17/71; Church Yth Grp; Church Choir; Yrbk Stf; Rep Jr Cls; Rep Stu Cncl; Hon Roll; Nrsg.

ROSADINI, MICHELLE; Taft Schl; Thomaston, CT; (Y); FTA; JV Bsktbl; Var Sftbl; Im Tennis; Cit Awd; High Hon Roll; Hon Roll; Math.

ROSADINO, MICHAEL; Notre Ame HS; Hamden, CT; (Y); Office Aide; Political Wkr; ROTC; Ski Clb; Rep Stu Cncl; JV Bsbl; Var Ftbl; Wt Lftg; Hon Roll; Wake Forest U; Bio.

ROSARBO, LOUISE; Sacred Heart Acad; New Haven, CT; (Y); Pep Clb; Chorus; Church Choir; School Musical; High Hon Roll; Svc Awd 85; Pol Sci.

ROSE, DOUGLAS; Southington HS; Southington, CT; (Y); Church Yth Grp; Crs Cntry; Swmmng.

ROSE, ELLEN; Griswold HS; Jewett City, CT; (Y); Girl Scts; Varsity Clb; Band; Concert Band; Mrchg Band; Orch; Pep Band; School Musical; Pstry Arts.

ROSE, STEVEN; Branford HS; Branford, CT; (Y); 21/251; Am Leg Boys St; Computer Clb; Teachers Aide; Yrbk Ed-Chief; Rep Stu Cncl; Stat Bsktbl; Hon Roll; VP Chess Clb; Cmnty Wkr; Political Wkr; Yale Peabody Museum Assocs Sci Awd 83; Pres Interact Clb 85-86; Stu Rep Branford Brd Ed 85-86; Comp Sci.

ROSEFF, SHERYL; Trumbull HS; Trumbull, CT; (Y); Cmnty Wkr; Key Clb; Ski Clb; Spanish Clb; Temple Yth Grp; Yrbk Stf; Rep Frsh Cls; Rep Soph Cls; Rep Jr Cls; Var Capt Cheerleading; Peer Tutr 84-85; Bus Law.

ROSEFSKY, DOUGLAS; The Taft Schl; Binghamton, NY; (Y); 6/125; Computer Clb; Key Clb; Temple Yth Grp; Nwsp Stf; Var L Tennis; High Hon Roll; Chess Clb; Mathletes; Math Clb; Mensa Mental Olympics Champ 82-83; Sthrn Tier Athl Conf Tnns Champ 83; 1st Pl U Of NY Tnns Tourn 84; Engr.

ROSELLE, JENNIFER; East Lyme HS; Salem, CT; (Y); 45/291; Key Clb; Pep Clb; Yrbk Stf; Var Gym; Powder Puff Ftbl; Var Trk; Hon Roll; San Diego ST U; Psych.

ROSEN, MICHAEL; Trumbull HS; Trumbull, CT; (Y); Church Yth Grp; Latin Clb; Science Clb; Ski Clb; Var Bsktbl; JV Socr; JV Trk; Yng Ldrshp Schlrshp Masada Israel 84; U CT; Med.

ROSEN, SHERYL; Windham HS; S Windham, CT; (Y); Temple Yth Grp; Var Sftbl; Var Vllybl; Med.

ROSENBERG, ANDREW; Rockville HS; Vernon, CT; (Y); Pres Computer Clb; Math Tm; Band; Mrchg Band; Pep Band; Capt Stu Cncl; Hon Roll; U PA; Bio Rsrch.

ROSENBERG, MICHAEL; Hall HS; W Hartford, CT; (Y); Hosp Aide; Political Wkr; Red Cross Aide; Service Clb; Spanish Clb; Chorus; Rep Stu Cncl; Crs Cntry; High Hon Roll; Hon Roll; Bus.

ROSENBERG, SHARON; Trumbull HS; Trumbull, CT; (Y); Computer Clb; JA; Trs Math Clb; Bsktbl; Trk; High Hon Roll; NHS; Spanish NHS; Yale Bk Awd 85; CT U Hnrs Sem 85; Excllnc In Sci 83; Engrng.

ROSENBLATT, SARAH; William Hall HS; W Hartford, CT; (Y); 108/344; GAA; Hosp Aide; Chorus; Var Cheerleading; JV Fld Hcky; Var Lcrss; Var Capt Swmmng; Cit Awd; High Hon Roll; Hon Roll; Psych.

ROSENBLUM, ELISE; Danbury HS; Danbury, CT; (Y); French Clb; Ski Clb; Trs Temple Yth Grp; Variety Show; Nwsp Stf; Yrbk Phtg; Stu Cncl; Tennis; Hon Roll; George Perry Awd 85; Photogrphy Hnrs 85.

ROSENGRANT, KENNETH; Southington HS; Southington, CT; (Y); 287/555; Boy Scts; Exploring; Ski Clb; Nwsp Stf; Art Stu Mnth 85; Midgt Ftbl Lg 85; Tunkis CC; Fine Art.

ROSENTHAL, JENNIFER; William H Hall HS; W Hartford, CT; (Y); 64/324; Pres Pep Clb; Temple Yth Grp; Yrbk Bus Mgr; Yrbk Stf; Trk; Vllybl; High Hon Roll; Ntl Merit Ltr; Intl Bus.

ROSIN, ROY M; William H Hall HS; W Hartford, CT; (Y); 1/350; Debate Tm; Capt Math Tm; Quiz Bowl; Nwsp Ed-Chief; Var L Crs Cntry; Var L Tennis; VP French Hon Soc; High Hon Roll; NHS; Cmnty Wkr; Harvard Bk Awd 85.

ROSIOS, PETROULA; Andrew Warde HS; Fairfield, CT; (Y); Church Yth Grp; Dance Clb; Hon Roll; U Of Bridgeport; Elec Engr.

ROSS, BETSY; Danbury HS; Danbury, CT; (Y); 47/612; Office Aide; Varsity Clb; Orch; Variety Show; Yrbk Stf; Var L Cheerleading; Hon Roll; Jr NHS; Med.

ROSS, CHERYL; Rockville HS; Vernon, CT; (Y); 3/350; Hosp Aide; Math Tm; Band; Drill Tm; JV Badmtn; JV Trk; DAR Awd; High Hon Roll; NHS; Ntl Merit Ltr; Harvard Bk Awd 84; Rensselaer Sci & Math Awd 84; Boston Coll; Pre-Med.

ROSS JR, JONATHAN WOODMAN; Daniel Hand HS; Madison, CT; (Y); Am Leg Boys St; FCA; Var L Crs Cntry; JV Socr; Var Tennis; Var L Trk; High Hon Roll; Church Yth Grp; Ski Clb; Hon Roll; HS Art Show 1st Pl Mixed Media 85; Hugh O Brien Fndtn Awd 84; Hns Symposium 84; Cornell; Arch.

ROSSI, KIMBERLY; Naugatuck HS; Naugatuck, CT; (Y); Church Yth Grp; Dance Clb; GAA; Girl Scts; Chorus; Variety Show; Rep Frsh Cls; Rep Soph Cls; Var L Gym; Var L Trk; FIT; Fash Merch.

ROSSINI, NADINE; Lauralton Hall HS; Orange, CT; (Y); Hosp Aide; Stage Crew; Nwsp Stf; Yrbk Stf; High Hon Roll; NHS; Comm Art.

ROTH, AMY; Bethel HS; Bethel, CT; (Y); 6/280; Church Yth Grp; Computer Clb; Hosp Aide; Chorus; Church Choir; School Musical; Variety Show; JV Crs Cntry; High Hon Roll; NHS; Genetics.

ROTH, MICHAEL SVEN; Manchester HS; Coventry, CT; (Y); 61/502; German Clb; Hon Roll; Hnrs Grad 85; U Of CT; Bio.

ROTH, SVEN; Manchester HS; Coventry, CT; (Y); 61/501; German Clb; Bsbl; High Hon Roll; Hon Roll; NEDT Awd; Natl Ger Tst Top 90 Pcnt 82-85; U CT; Bio.

ROTHSCHILD, J DAVID; Brookfield HS; Brookfield, CT; (Y); Math Tm; Socr; High Hon Roll; NHS; Cmmssnr Brookfield Yth Cmmssn; VP & Treas Brookfield Safe Rides; Comp Sci.

ROURKE, REBECCA; St Bernard HS; Lisbon, CT; (S); Y-Teens; Church Choir; School Play; Nwsp Rptr; Nwsp Sprt Ed; Rep Stu Cncl; Stat Ftbl; Drama Clb; French Clb; Hgst Avr Soc Stu 83; Pol Sci.

ROUSSEAU, MICHAEL; Lewis S Mills HS; Burlington, CT; (Y); 3/158; Rep Am Leg Boys St; Chess Clb; Math Tm; Ed Lit Mag; High Hon Roll; Hon Roll; NHS; NEDT Awd; Michls Jwlrs Awd Outstndng Soph 84; Frnk Hays Hstry Achvt Awd 85; Sci.

ROVERO, DIANNE J; East Lyme HS; Oakdale, CT; (Y); 4/243; Church Yth Grp; Nwsp Phtg; Var Crs Cntry; Var Capt Trk; High Hon Roll; Lion Awd; Sec NHS; Yrbk Phtg; JV Bsktbl; Powder Puff Ftbl; Outstndng Physcs Stu Of Yr Awd 85; Outstndng Achvt Mth, Calculus Awd 85; John Broughton Mem Awd 85; Rensselaer Polytech; Envr Engr.

ROWLAND, WENDY; Bethel HS; Southbury, CT; (Y); AFS; VP Church Yth Grp; DECA; Ski Clb; Church Choir; Variety Show; Yrbk Stf; High Hon Roll; Hon Roll; Med Tech.

ROWLEY, MARK; Xavier HS; Killingworth, CT; (Y); Boy Scts; Var Math Tm; Var Crs Cntry; Var Trk; High Hon Roll; NHS; Ntl Merit Ltr; Engrng.

ROY, BRIAN; Masuk HS; Monroe, CT; (Y); Church Yth Grp; Hon Roll; Comp.

ROY, JEFF; Danburg HS; Danbury, CT; (Y); 198/615; French Clb; Varsity Clb; Wrstlng; Mrktng.

RUA, CHARLES; Jonathan Law HS; Milford, CT; (Y); Drama Clb; Acpl Chr; Band; Chorus; Concert Band; Jazz Band; Mrchg Band; School Musical; School Play; Stage Crew; Solo Concert Choir; Band Ltr & Sweater; Hartt Schl Music; Music.

RUBANO, MICHELE; Southgington HS; Southington, CT; (Y); 26/600; Cmnty Wkr; Key Clb; Latin Clb; Ski Clb; Flag Corp; Variety Show; Nwsp Stf; Im Mgr Bsktbl; High Hon Roll; NHS; Spec Awd Excllnc Latn 82-83; Paramed.

RUBENSTEIN, SAM; Avbon Old Farms Schl; Shreveport, LA; (S); 10/110; Pep Clb; Red Cross Aide; Ed Nwsp Phtg; JV Yrbk Phtg; Hon Roll; Earnest & Persistnt Effort Awd; Chem Awd; U S Hist Awd; Dorm Monitor; Stu Trainer; U Of Richmond; Busi.

RUBINO, STACEY; Branford HS; Branford, CT; (Y); Nwsp Stf; Yrbk Stf; Lit Mag; Stu Cncl; High Hon Roll; Hon Roll; Eng.

RUCK, CINDY PATRICIA; Holy Cross HS; Canada; (Y); 53/352; Service Clb; JV Trk; JV Var Vllybl; Hon Roll; NHS; Soc Stud Hnr Soc Co-Treas 84-85; JR Apprectn Night Comm Pgm Coordntr 84-85.

RUDCAVICE, KIM; Nonnewaug HS; Bethlehem, CT; (Y); Church Yth Grp; Cmnty Wkr; 4-H; FFA; Chorus; School Musical; School Play; Rep Jr Cls; 4-H Awd; Litchfield Pony Clb Awds The Dains Awd 84; Most Imprvd Pony Clbbr 83; Most Imprvd Ride & Horse 84; Forensic Sci.

RUDZAVICE, KIM; Nonnewaug HS; Bethlehem, CT; (Y); Church Yth Grp; Civic Clb; Cmnty Wkr; 4-H; FFA; Pep Clb; Political Wkr; Chorus; School Musical; Rep Jr Cls; Litchfield Pony Clb Imprvd Rider Awd 84, Daines Awd 84; Regnl Conf Riders Awd 85; Criminl Justc.

RUFFINO JR, SEBASTIAN J; Portland HS; Portland, CT; (Y); 14/115; Band; School Play; Wrstlng; High Hon Roll; Hon Roll; Coaches Awd & MIP Wresling 85; Portland Volunteer Fire Dept 84-85; Middlesex CC; Ag.

RUGGIERO, JOANNE; Central Catholic HS; Darien, CT; (Y); 3/81; Math Tm; Ski Clb; Nwsp Ed-Chief; VP Soph Cls; VP Jr Cls; Sec Stu Cncl; Var Cheerleading; Im Powder Puff Ftbl; High Hon Roll; Pres NHS; Soc Women Engrs Awd 84-85; Theology Awd 84; CT St Schlr 84-85; Engrng.

RUIZ, VINCENT; Naugatuck HS; Naugatuck, CT; (Y); Church Yth Grp; JV Bsbl; Socr; Hon Roll; Sccr Ltr Vrsty 82-84; Hmrm Rep 82-84; Air Force CC; Optmtry.

RURAN, DANI N; William H Ahll HS; West Hartford, CT; (Y); 12/316; Cmnty Wkr; JA; Orch; Bsbl; High Hon Roll; NHS; Spanish NHS; Cncrtmstr Soloist Grtr Hartford Yth Orch & I Giovani Solisti Chmbr Grp 83-85; Ntl Schl Orch Assn Awd; Bus Law.

RUSSACK, LEAH; St Bernard HS; Groton, CT; (Y); 85/303; Drama Clb; French Clb; Girl Scts; Hosp Aide; Pep Clb; Red Cross Aide; Teachers Aide; Varsity Clb; School Play; Yrbk Stf; Yale Frntrs Sci Pgm 84-85; Cls Pres 85; Trk Tm Capt 85; Pre-Med.

RUSSELL, DIANE; Branford HS; Branford, CT; (Y); 2/247; Am Leg Aux Girls St; Cmnty Wkr; Quiz Bowl; Yrbk Stf; Trs Frsh Cls; Sec Soph Cls; Pres Jr Cls; Pres Sr Cls; Stu Cncl; Hugh Obrien Outstndng Soph Awd; Yale Frontiers Of Applied Sci Prog; Boston Coll.

RUSSELL, KEVIN; Danbury HS; Danbury, CT; (Y); Church Yth Grp; French Clb; Rep Soph Cls; JV Ftbl; Hon Roll.

RUSSELL, KIRSTEN VON SEEBECK; Miss Porters Schl; Farmington, CT; (Y); Dance Clb; English Clb; German Clb; Bus.

RUSSELL, MIDDLETON; Shelton HS; Shelton, CT; (Y); Rep Am Leg Boys St; Var Capt Socr; French Hon Soc; Treas SADD 85; Trvlg Sccr Tm 84; Fairfield U; Bus.

RUSSMAN, DAVID; O H Platt HS; Meriden, CT; (Y); Trs Key Clb; Math Clb; Teachers Aide; Temple Yth Grp; Rep Frsh Cls; Rep Jr Cls; Capt Crs Cntry; L Trk; JV Wrstlng; High Hon Roll; Rensselaer Medal & H S Ntl Chemathn 85; CT Hnr Smnr & Am H S Athlt 85; CT Schlr 84-85.

RUSSO, DEBY; Holy Cross HS; Naugatuck, CT; (Y); 51/360; Red Cross Aide; Service Clb; Spanish Clb; Chorus; Hon Roll; Pres Schlr; St Schlr; Naugatuck SR Wmns Clb Schlrhsp 85; St Joseph Coll Grant 85; St Joseph Coll; Bio.

RUSSO, GINA; St Bernards HS; Franklin, CT; (Y); 85/297; Hon Roll; Art Awd Genl Excllnc 83; Bus Mgmt.

RUSSO, JON M; Tolland HS; Tolland, CT; (Y); 18/170; Ski Clb; Band; Pep Band; Rep Sr Cls; JV Var Golf; Var L Tennis; Hon Roll; Trs NHS; Concert Band; Scientsts Of Tmrrw Pgm 82; Tri Twn Cmnty Bnd 83-85; Crew Chf Mc Donald Corp; U Of CT; Bus.

RUSSO, MICHELE; Sacred Heart Acad; Hamden, CT; (Y); Dance Clb; Pep Clb; School Musical; Vllybl; High Hon Roll; Spanish NHS; Dance.

RUSSO, MONICA; Masuk HS; Monroe, CT; (Y); 9/238; Math Tm; Spanish Clb; Drm Mjr(t); Mrchg Band; School Musical; Symp Band; Variety Show; Dnfth Awd; High Hon Roll; NHS; Outstdng Achv In Bnd 82-85; Outstdng Achv In Phy Ed 82-83; Pre-Med.

RUSSO, ROBERT; St Benard HS; Lisbon, CT; (Y); 100/204; Wrstlng; Embry; Flght.

RUSSOTTO, DARCY; Enrico Fermi HS; Enfield, CT; (Y); 74/378; Sec Drama Clb; Chorus; School Musical; Stage Crew; Variety Show; Yrbk Ed-Chief; JV Fld Hcky; Var Trk; High Hon Roll; Drama Clb Schlrshp 85; Florence Gross Meml Schlrshp 85; Enfield Wmns Clb Schlrshp Perfm Arts 85; Fordham U; Mass Cmmnctns.

RUSZKOWSKI, ANDREW; Holy Cross HS; Middlebury, CT; (Y); Boy Scts; Church Yth Grp; Band; Church Choir; Concert Band; Jazz Band; Mrchg Band; Var Socr; Hon Roll; Ltrs & Pins Sccr & Band 82-85; Hnrs Hstry 84-85; Intl Stds.

RUTHENY, GREG; Westhill HS; Stamford, CT; (Y); Art Clb; Church Yth Grp; JA; Nwsp Stf; Lit Mag; Stamford Art Assn Drwng 2nd Pl 84, 1st Pl 85; Natl Art Cont Drwng Hnrbl Mntn 84; Illus.

RUTKIS, SIG; Bethel HS; Bethel, CT; (Y); 18/286; Letterman Clb; Jazz Band; Variety Show; Rep Stu Cncl; JV Ftbl; Var L Tennis; High Hon Roll; NHS; Ntl Hnr Soc 85; PA ST; Engrng.

RUTTY, MICHAEL; Vinal Technical Schl; Haddam, CT; (Y); Am Leg Boys St; Boy Scts; VP Stu Cncl; L Trk; God Cntry Awd; High Hon Roll; NHS; Camera Clb; Rep Soph Cls; Mgr Bsktbl; Elec Engr.

RYAN, ANDREA; East Catholic HS; Manchester, CT; (Y); 20/300; French Clb; GAA; Yrbk Stf; Rep Jr Cls; Rep Sr Cls; Rep Stu Cncl; Bsktbl; Sftbl; Hon Roll; NHS.

RYAN, DENISE; Cheshire HS; Cheshire, CT; (Y); Church Yth Grp; Cmnty Wkr; GAA; Rep Sr Cls; Var Capt Bsktbl; Var Mgr(s); Trk; Cit Awd; High Hon Roll; Hon Roll; Schltc Achvt Awds Banqt 85; JR Wmns Bsktbl Awd 85; Capt Vrsty Bsktbl 85-86.

RYAN, SEAN; Enfield HS; Enfield, CT; (Y); #94 In Class; Quiz Bowl; Ski Clb; Nwsp Phtg.

RYBCZYK, JEAN ANNE; Cheshire HS; Cheshire, CT; (Y); 32/324; Latin Clb; Red Cross Aide; Chorus; School Musical; School Play; Nwsp Stf; Trk; Vllybl; DAR Awd; Hon Roll; Amer U Of Wmn Ctznshp Awd 85; U Of CT; Cmnctns.

RYBICKI, ALISSA; Robert E Fitch SR HS; Groton, CT; (Y); Drama Clb; Office Aide; Chorus; School Musical; Nwsp Rptr; Rep Frsh Cls; High Hon Roll; Hon Roll; Trphy Mst Outstndng Stu Engl 83; Acctng.

RYE, ROBERT; Branford HS; Branford, CT; (Y); 1/267; Pres Chess Clb; Var Bsbl; High Hon Roll; NHS; Ntl Merit Ltr; 1st Pl-Shoreline Physcs Assn-Physcs Olympiad 85; CT JR Sci & Humnties Sympsm 85.

SABATINI, MARY; Wethersfield HS; Wethersfield, CT; (Y); 6/275; Church Yth Grp; Spanish Clb; Nwsp Ed-Chief; Rptr Yrbk Stf; Var Capt Cheerleading; High Hon Roll; NHS; NEDT Awd; Pres Schlr; Clifford Barnes Mem Sci Awd 82; U CT Cooprtv Spnsh Awd 84; Awd Excllnc Spnsh 85; Trinity Coll; Psych.

SABIA, HEATHER; Stamford HS; Stamford, CT; (S); 5/406; Ski Clb; JV Sftbl; JV Vllybl; High Hon Roll; Hon Roll; NHS; Pace U; Acctng.

SABIA, SHARON; Westhill HS; Stamford, CT; (Y); JA; Latin Clb; Math Clb; Science Clb; Orch; Rep Stu Cncl; JV Bsktbl; JV Sftbl; Hon Roll; Sec NHS; Med.

SABIN, HEIDI; Acad Of The Holy Family; Taftville, CT; (Y); 3/27; Chorus; Hon Roll; Histry Excllnc Awd 85; Bus.

SABIO, LORI; Holy Cross HS; Naugatuck, CT; (Y); 114/352; Dance Clb; Band; Concert Band; Mrchg Band; Hon Roll; Vrsty Ltr & Pin 85; Mrch Band Pin 84-85; Hlth Thrpst.

SABNIS, SUSHIL; Amity Regional District No 5 HS; Orange, CT; (S); 1/376; Am Leg Boys St; VP French Clb; Off Quiz Bowl; Ed Yrbk Stf; Rep Stu Cncl; High Hon Roll; NCTE Awd; NHS; Ntl Merit Ltr; CT Jr Sci/Hmnts Symp 84; Yale Frontiers Appld Sci Prg 84; Harvard Bk Awd Rensselaer Mdl Awd 84; HPME Northwestern; Med.

SACCHETTA, MARIA L; Bristol Central HS; Bristol, CT; (Y); Church Yth Grp; Office Aide; Teachers Aide; Yrbk Stf; Stu Cncl; Vllybl; Hon Roll; NHS.

SACCHI, CHERYL; John F Kennedy HS; Waterbury, CT; (Y); 31/177; FBLA; Yrbk Stf; Pres Jr Cls; High Hon Roll; Hon Roll; NHS; Miss Gtr Waterbury Scshlrshp Pgnt Miss Congeniality 84; Miss Jr Kennedy 83-84; CT Schlstc Achvt Pgm; Mattatuck CC; Bus Admin.

SACCONE, KRISTINE; St Joseph HS; Monroe, CT; (Y); 100/250; Cmnty Wkr; Drama Clb; Hosp Aide; Stage Crew; Hon Roll; Bryant Coll; Bus.

SACHS, RACHEL; North Haven HS; North Haven, CT; (Y); 15/288; Model UN; Ski Clb; Off Jr Cls; Trs Sr Cls; Capt Diving; Capt Swmmng; Capt Tennis; Hon Roll; NHS; Dental Hygiene.

SACK, MICHAEL K; William H Hall HS; W Hartford, CT; (Y); Boy Scts; School Play; Stage Crew; Stu Cncl; JV Socr; God Cntry Awd; W H Hall Stu Of Mnth 83; Brd Dir GHJCC 84-85; Thtr Arts.

SACOUTO, SUSANA; Staples HS; Westport, CT; (Y); 1/486; Debate Tm; JA; Spanish Clb; Acpl Chr; Chorus; Stu Cncl; Cheerleading; Gym; High Hon Roll; Block S For Staples Gymnastics Tm 85; Acad Excllnc Awd 83; Economics.

SADLOWSKI, MICHAEL; Fairfield Prep; Fairfield, CT; (Y); Boy Scts; Church Yth Grp; Debate Tm; JA; Model UN; JV Crs Cntry; JV Golf; High Hon Roll; NHS; Eagle Sct 85; Elec Engnrng.

SAGE, MECHELLE; Valley Regional HS; Chester, CT; (S); 5/150; VP Frsh Cls; VP Soph Cls; VP Jr Cls; Pres Stu Cncl; High Hon Roll; Sec NHS; Am Leg Aux Girls St; Pres French Clb; Ski Clb; Intern W/Senator Lowell Weicker In Wash DC; U Of VA.

SAINSBURY, PAUL; St Bernard HS; Pawcatuck, CT; (S); 32/300; Cmnty Wkr; Drama Clb; Office Aide; Teachers Aide; School Play; Stu Cncl; JV Bsbl; Bsktbl; Hon Roll; NHS; Coast Guard Acad; Engr.

SALEMI, JAMES; Holy Cross HS; Waterbury, CT; (Y); 106/352; Hon Roll; Briarwood Bk Awd 85; 2nd Pl Colt Poetry Cont 85; Acctng.

SALERNO, TAMMY; Southington HS; Southington, CT; (Y); Art Clb; Chorus; Yrbk Stf; High Hon Roll; Hon Roll; Art Cncl Yth Awd 83-85; Art.

SALLEY, SHARON; Warren Harding HS; Bridgeport, CT; (Y); FBLA; Hosp Aide; Special H Awd-Natl Honor Soc 85; Western CT ST U; Busnss.

SALLVIK, ANNIKA; Danbury HS; Danbury, CT; (Y); 37/538; Math Tm; High Hon Roll; Vet Med.

SALOMON, DEIRDRE; Staples HS; Westport, CT; (Y); Debate Tm; French Clb; Intnl Clb; Latin Clb; Ski Clb; Temple Yth Grp; Hon Roll; Intl Bus.

SALTZMAN, JENNIFER; Amity Regional SR HS; Woodbridge, CT; (S); 41/376; Am Leg Aux Girls St; Yrbk Ed-Chief; VP Soph Cls; Pres Jr Cls; Rep Stu Cncl; Var L Fld Hcky; Var L Tennis; DAR Awd; Hon Roll; NHS; U S Ntl Ldrshp Merit Awd.

SALVATORE, CATHERINE; Shelton HS; Shelton, CT; (S); 98/348; Trs DECA; Hon Roll; Bnk Mgmt.

SALVIN, AMY; The Morgan HS; Clinton, CT; (Y); 2/160; Art Clb; Cmnty Wkr; Spanish Clb; Chorus; Nwsp Ed-Chief; Sec Soph Cls; Sec Jr Cls; JV Var Cheerleading; NHS; Hist,Spnsh,Comp Awd 83-85; Intl Rel.

SALZER, DANIELLE; Southington HS; Plantsville, CT; (Y); French Clb; Intnl Clb; Chorus; Church Choir; School Play; Sec Soph Cls; JV Swmmng; High Hon Roll; Hon Roll; Photo.

SAMELE, SCOTT; Bristol Central HS; Bristol, CT; (Y); Boys Clb Am; Latin Clb; Var L Bsbl; JV L Bsktbl; High Hon Roll; NHS; Var L Socr.

SAMMATARO, MICHAEL; Ledyard HS; Gales Ferry, CT; (Y); Socr; Wrstlng; Engrng.

SAMOJEDNY, NANCY A; Southington HS; Southington, CT; (Y); 71/550; Hosp Aide; Key Clb; Spanish Clb; Band; Concert Band; Mrchg Band; Cmnty Wkr; High Hon Roll; Hon Roll; Vlntr Spcl Olympcs; Quinnipiac Coll; Occptnl Thrpy.

SAMOKAR, ROBERT; Notre Dame HS; W Haven, CT; (Y); 40/250; Boy Scts; Church Yth Grp; Math Clb; Math Hnr Scty 85; Providence; Math.

SAMPIERI, CLAIRE; Amithy Regional Dist No 5 HS; Orange, CT; (S); 18/376; Am Leg Aux Girls St; Church Yth Grp; Exploring; Hosp Aide; Trs Latin Clb; School Play; Stage Crew; Ed Yrbk Stf; Sec Stu Cncl; NHS; Stu Cncl Awd 84; Bio.

SAMPSON, CHRISTOPHER; Stratford HS; Stratford, CT; (Y); 4/250; JV Golf; Mgr(s); High Hon Roll; NHS; Radio Brdcstng.

SANCHEZ, MAX ARTHUR; William H Hall HS; W Hartford, CT; (Y); 210/324; JA; JV Bsbl; JV Im Ftbl; JV Socr; Army.

SANCHEZ, STEPHANIE JAE; Hartford Public HS; Hartford, CT; (S); Art Clb; Pres Camera Clb; Pres DECA; FBLA; School Musical; Mgr Stage Crew; Capt Socr; Trk; Vet.

SANDERS, BRIAN T; Hopkins Grammar Day; West Haven, CT; (Y); Boy Scts; Red Cross Aide; School Play; Variety Show; Lit Mag; JV Var Bsktbl; JV Socr; Trk; Jr NHS; Ntl Merit SF; Pre-Dent.

SANDERSON, DIANE L; Morgan HS; Clinton, CT; (Y); French Clb; JV Var Fld Hcky; Mgr(s); Sftbl; Hon Roll; Physical Educ Awd 82-83; Child Care.

SANFORD, LYNNE; East Lyme HS; E Lyme, CT; (Y); 32/259; Church Yth Grp; Cmnty Wkr; Library Aide; Pep Clb; Teachers Aide; Band; Concert Band; Mrchg Band; Pep Band; School Musical; NY U; Grphc Dsgn.

SANTA LUCIA JR, JOSEPH; Windham HS; Willimantic, CT; (Y); Ski Clb; Ice Hcky; Trk; Hon Roll; Acad Awds Woods 85; Aviatn.

SANTAIGO, HIRAM; Kolbe-Cathedral HS; Bridgeport, CT; (Y); Church Choir; Nwsp Rptr; Nwsp Stf; Rep Soph Cls; Hon Roll; NHS; VP Spanish NHS; Spanish Clb; Myr Renaissance Intrshp Awd 85; Trl Rngr Spnsh Estrn Dstrct Sctnl 85; Gld Mdl Of Achvt Ryl Rngrs 84; Pre-Med.

SANTANA, LISSETTE; Bassick HS; Bridgeport, CT; (S); Drama Clb; Latin Clb; Office Aide; Yrbk Stf; Lit Mag; Sec Jr Cls; Stu Cncl; High Hon Roll; Hon Roll; Sacred Heart U; Bus Adm.

SANTANELLO, MARIBETH; Branford HS; Branford, CT; (Y); Church Yth Grp; Hosp Aide; Rep Frsh Cls; Rep Soph Cls; Rep Jr Cls; Rep Stu Cncl; Var Capt Cheerleading; JV Fld Hcky; Var Powder Puff Ftbl; Var Trk; Nrsng.

SANTANGELO, MELISSA; Sacred Heart Acad; Ansonia, CT; (Y); Hosp Aide; Chorus; Nwsp Rptr; Lit Mag; High Hon Roll; NHS; NEDT Awd; Spanish NHS; Im Vllybl; Voice Dem Awd; Appld Sci Yale Frntrs 84-85; SAT Tst Hgh Screr Lttr Snt 84-85.

SANTARELLA, DANA A; Norwalk HS; Norwalk, CT; (Y); Letterman Clb; Varsity Clb; Nwsp Stf; Yrbk Rptr; Yrbk Sprt Ed; Yrbk Stf; Stu Cncl; Var Capt Bsktbl; Var Powder Puff Ftbl; Sftbl.

SANTARSIERO, GINA; Holy Cross HS; Waterbury, CT; (Y); Cmnty Wkr; Rep Frsh Cls; Rep Soph Cls; Psych.

SANTIAGO, REYNALDO; Guilford HS; Guilford, CT; (Y); AFS; Church Yth Grp; Var Ftbl; Wrstlng; Hon Roll; Prfct Atten Awd; Wrstlng 1st Tourn, Shoreline Champ 84-85; 2nd Ward Melville Tourn Long Islnd 84-85; Boston Coll; Cvl Engr.

SANTINO, MICHELE; West Haven HS; W Haven, CT; (Y); Var High Hon Roll; Hon Roll; Var NHS; Church Yth Grp; GAA; Eng I II III, Frnch II III, Soclgy II, Bio I, Foods Awds 83-85; Sthrn CT ST U; Early Chld Ed.

SANTO, RONALD J; Notre Dame HS; Milford, CT; (Y); Boy Scts; Church Yth Grp; Bsktbl; Ftbl; Cit Awd; Hon Roll; U CT; Bus.

SANTOS, CATHY; Naugatuck HS; Middlebury, CT; (Y); Dance Clb; GAA; Mrchg Band; Orch; Trs Symp Band; Off Frsh Cls; Off Soph Cls; JV Var Crs Cntry; High Hon Roll; Band Dirctrs Awd 83; Med.

SANTOS, MARIA; Naugatuck HS; Naugatuck, CT; (Y); Dance Clb; GAA; Library Aide; Chorus; Yrbk Stf; Crs Cntry; Trk; Nrsng.

SANTOS, MARIO; Kaynor Tchnical HS; Naugatuck, CT; (Y); 15/205; Aud/Vis; Church Yth Grp; Debate Tm; Letterman Clb; Teachers Aide; Varsity Clb; Chorus; Stu Cncl; Var Bsktbl; Var Socr; Waterbury Sportsmens Schlrshp Awd 85; Morrison Schlrshp Fund 85; U New Haven; Mech Engrng.

SAPPO, KERRY; Shelton HS; Huntington, CT; (Y); Am Leg Aux Girls St; Cmnty Wkr; Drama Clb; Off FHA; Nwsp Ed-Chief; High Hon Roll; Sec NHS; U Of Hrtfrd Schlrshp To Bus Wk 84; Intl Soc Of Wmn Edctrs Cert Of Merit 84; SADD VP 84-85; Princeton; Bus Mgmt.

SARANTOPOULOS, CHRISTIAN; Killingly HS; Danielson, CT; (Y); 4/289; Am Leg Boys St; Band; Pres Frsh Cls; Pres Jr Cls; Pres Stu Cncl; Var Golf; Dnfth Awd; DAR Awd; Hon Roll; Sec Trs NHS; All New Englnd Adjdctn Div I Hnrs-Piano Solo; Ltn Hnrs; Med.

SARAPA, GEORGE; Valley Regional HS; Deep River, CT; (Y); 13/155; Am Leg Boys St; Band; Lit Mag; JV Trk; High Hon Roll; Hon Roll; NHS; Intro Phys Sci Awd 82-83; Amer Lg Good Ctznshp Awd 84-85; Engrng.

SARGENT, HEATHER; The Loomis Chaffee Schl; W Hartford, CT; (Y); Acpl Chr; Chorus; Church Choir; School Musical; School Play; Stage Crew; Rep Stu Cncl; JV Bsktbl; Var Socr; Sftbl; Tour Guide Coordinator 85-86; Richmond Fund Schlrshp Wnnr 85; Teatre Assocs 85-86; Southern Methodist; Cmnctns.

SARGIS, RHONDA; Southington HS; Plantsville, CT; (Y); 117/540; Chorus; School Play; Variety Show; Nwsp Stf; Pres Soph Cls; Pres Jr Cls; Powder Puff Ftbl; Score Keeper; High Hon Roll; Hon Roll; Discvry III 82-83; Western CT ST U; Finance.

SARNO, GLENN; Joel Barlow HS; Easton, CT; (Y); 27/250; Am Leg Boys St; Church Yth Grp; Computer Clb; Debate Tm; Scholastic Bowl; Var Ftbl; Var Trk; Var Wt Lftg; High Hon Roll; NHS; Harold F Schweede 84; Russell Eewi Schlrshp Ldrshp Awd 85; Fairfield Cnty Schlr Athlt Awd 85; UCONN; Bus.

SARNO, MARINO ROSARIO; Brien Mc Mahon HS; Norwalk, CT; (Y); JV Var Socr; Trk; High Hon Roll; Hon Roll; Rotary Awd; Amer Assn Italn Tchrs Hnrb Mntn Level III 85; UW Whitewater World Affairs Sem 85; Corp Law.

SARNO, TRACY; Notre Dame Catholic HS; Fairfield, CT; (Y); Rep Jr Cls; Katharine Gibbs Schlrshp 85; Katharine Gibbs; Exec Sec.

SARTRYS, SCOTT DAVID; South Kent Schl; Bristol, RI; (Y); 9/33; Ice Hcky; Socr; Tennis; CT Coll; Marin Bio.

SASKAL, RICHARD; Branford HS; Branford, CT; (Y); 15/260; JV Socr; High Hon Roll; Hon Roll; Prfct Atten Awd; Cmpltd Grmn Crs U Of Vienna Austria 84.

SASTRAM, CARL M; Shelton HS; Shelton, CT; (Y); 102/438; Boys Clb Am; Church Yth Grp; Spanish Clb; Rep Stu Cncl; JV Bsbl; Var L Ftbl; Var L Trk; Hon Roll; Spcl Commndtn Physics; MIP Ftbl; Central Comm ST U; Comm Art.

SASZIK, ERIK; New London HS; New London, CT; (Y); 3/180; Am Leg Boys St; Quiz Bowl; Scholastic Bowl; Spanish Clb; Var L Golf; Var L Swmmng; Var L Tennis; High Hon Roll; NHS; Harvard Bk Awd 85; Pre Calcls Awd 85; Outstndng Swmg Awd 85; Cornell U; Ag.

SAUCIER, JANET; Bristol Central HS; Bristol, CT; (Y); Hosp Aide; JA; Band; Concert Band; Mrchg Band; Symp Band; Yrbk Stf; Hon Roll.

SAUNDERS, DREW W; F V Conard HS; W Hartford, CT; (Y); 6/297; Debate Tm; Drama Clb; French Clb; German Clb; Intnl Clb; Model UN; Teachers Aide; School Play; Lit Mag; High Hon Roll; Scientist Of Tommrrw Internshp Pgm 83 & 84; Stanford U; Bio.

SAVAGE, ANNE M; Greenwich HS; Old Greenwich, CT; (Y); Camera Clb; Church Yth Grp; Service Clb; Chorus; Mgr(s); Socr; Hon Roll; GASFA Scholar 85; Pine Manor Coll; Comm.

SAVAGE, MARK; Bristol Eastern HS; Unionville, CT; (Y); Thesps; Stage Crew; High Hon Roll; High Hon Roll; Hon Roll; U CT; Math.

SAVINO, DENISE; East Haven HS; E Haven, CT; (Y); Spanish Clb; Pom Pon; Hon Roll; Jr NHS; NHS; Northeastern.

SAVINO, PHILLIP; Saint Paul HS; Forestville, CT; (Y); 2/650; Computer Clb; English Clb; FBLA; JA; Latin Clb; Math Tm; NFL; Band; Nwsp Ed-Chief; Yrbk Ed-Chief; Math Leag Awd; Latn Clb Awd; Dist Hnry Stdnt Awd; Princeton; Med.

SAVOIE, LISA; Bassick HS; Bridgpt, CT; (Y); Hosp Aide; Red Cross Aide; Sftbl; Black Hist Awd 85; Crim Just.

SAVULAK, SUSAN T; St Paul Catholic HS; Unionville, CT; (Y); 1/258; French Clb; Band; Rep Frsh Cls; Rep Soph Cls; Rep Jr Cls; Rep Stu Cncl; Trs French Hon Soc; High Hon Roll; Sec NHS; Highest Dept Awds Eng, Hist, Frnch IV, Latin, Theo, Frnch 3 & Math 84 & 85; Slvr Mdl Natl Latin Exam; Surgeon.

SAVVAIDES, ANDY; Norwalk HS; Norwalk, CT; (Y); 69/450; Church Yth Grp; Socr; Hon Roll.

SAWYER, TIMOTHY; Windsor Locks HS; Windsor Locks, CT; (Y); 28/162; Boy Scts; Church Yth Grp; JV Bsbl; Hon Roll; Accntng.

SAWYER, TINA; George J Penney HS; E Hartford, CT; (Y); Trk; High Hon Roll; Hon Roll; Busn.

SAYDAM, NEJDET; New Britain HS; New Britain, CT; (Y); Aud/Vis; Computer Clb; Debate Tm; German Clb; Varsity Clb; Socr; Hon Roll; U Rochester; Space.

SAYERS, COLLEEN M; Windham HS; Willimantic, CT; (Y); 55/390; Drama Clb; Acpl Chr; Chorus; Madrigals; School Musical; School Play; Variety Show; Yrbk Rptr; Pres Frsh Cls; Rep Soph Cls; U Of CT Music Schlrshp 85-86; U Of CT; Music Thrphy.

SAYERS, KEVIN; Windham HS; Willmantic, CT; (Y); Am Leg Boys St; Var JV Bsbl; Var JV Bsktbl; Bus Mgmt.

SBARDELLATI, LISA; St Joseph HS; Ansonia, CT; (Y); Drama Clb; Girl Scts; Political Wkr; Spanish Clb; Teachers Aide; Stage Crew; Hon Roll; Pre-Med.

SCANLON, ANNEMARIE; Conard HS; West Hartford, CT; (Y); 16/295; VP Jr Cls; VP Sr Cls; Rep Stu Cncl; Capt Cheerleading; Capt Gym; Capt Trk; High Hon Roll; NHS; Spanish NHS; Willms Clg Books Prz 84; Janice Aaron Awd 85; Dale Harper Awd 85; Schlr Athl Awd; Boston Clg; Law.

SCARANO, JANET; North Haven HS; N Haven, CT; (Y); 70/281; Trs Church Yth Grp; Pep Clb; Rep Frsh Cls; Rep Soph Cls; Rep Jr Cls; Rep Sr Cls; Sec Stu Cncl; Var L Cheerleading; JV Fld Hcky; Var L Gym; Fiddl Soc-Spnsh 84-85; Bus.

SCARINGE, LORI; Southington HS; Southington, CT; (Y); 16/600; Am Leg Aux Girls St; FTA; Key Clb; Var L Bsktbl; Var Co-Capt Vllybl; VP NHS; Elem Ed.

SCARPETTI, MARIA; Notre Dame Catholic HS; Easton, CT; (Y); JA; Keywanettes; Spanish Clb; Nwsp Rptr; Rep Frsh Cls; Rep Soph Cls; Rep Jr Cls; Rep Sr Cls; Fairheld U; Bus Mgmt.

SCARRITT, JENNIFER; Terryville HS; Terryville, CT; (Y); JV Bsktbl; C W F Corp Wk Ed 84-85; Drftng Clb 84-85; Drftng.

SCEBELO, STEVE; Newfairfield HS; New Fairfield, CT; (S); 18/215; DECA; Variety Show; Lit Mag; Pres Sr Cls; Im Badmtn; JV Bsbl; Var Ftbl; Wt Lftg; NHS; Western CT ST U; Bus Adm.

SCHAUB, MARIA; Holy Cross HS; Oxford, CT; (Y); 48/344; Church Yth Grp; PAVAS; Stage Crew; Lit Mag; High Hon Roll; Hon Roll; NHS; Cume Laude Cert Ntl Ltn Exm 83-84; Mary Washington Coll; Bio.

SCHEIPS, DEREK K; William H Hall HS; West Hartford, CT; (Y); 23/316; Yrbk Rptr; Yrbk Sprt Ed; Ed Yrbk Stf; L Tennis; NHS; Magna Cum Laude Ntl Latn 83; New Englnd Rnkd Jr Tenns Plyr; Humnts.

SCHEMPP, PATTY; Vinal Reg Voc Tech; Middletown, CT; (Y); Art Clb; Church Yth Grp; Keywanettes; Library Aide; Ski Clb; VICA; Yrbk Stf; VP Frsh Cls; Pres Soph Cls; Sec Jr Cls; Inter Design.

SCHENKEL, LISSA; Oliver Wolcott Technical Schl; Thomaston, CT; (S); 11/156; Art Clb; Math Clb; Ski Clb; Yrbk Stf; Trs Jr Cls; Tennis; Hon Roll; NHS; Comp Aided Drftg.

SCHICK, KIM; Ellington HS; Ellington, CT; (Y); 3/143; Church Yth Grp; Cmnty Wkr; French Clb; Flag Corp; Yrbk Stf; VP Rep Stu Cncl; Var Socr; Twrlr; Hon Roll; NHS; Cert Awd Cmmnty Svc 84; Bus Adm.

SCHIFF, ERIC T; William H Hall HS; W Hartford, CT; (Y); 34/324; Math Tm; Q&S; Yrbk Stf; Lit Mag; Im Socr; Capt L Trk; NHS; Ntl Merit SF; Latin Medal 85; Engrng.

SCHIFF, KAREN L; Hamden HS; Hamden, CT; (Y); 5/451; Temple Yth Grp; Nwsp Ed-Chief; Lit Mag; Cit Awd; Hon Roll; NHS; Ntl Merit Ltr; English Hnrs 84; Math Hnrs 84; Spanish Hnrs 83; Brown U; Humanities.

SCHLAEFER, DAVID; East Catholic HS; Bolton, CT; (Y); 129/418; Boy Scts; Cmnty Wkr; Ski Clb; Crs Cntry; Trk; High Hon Roll; Lion Awd; Prfct Atten Awd; Awd For Hlpng At Lions Chicken BBQ 83; Automtv Dsgn.

SCHLESS, GARY; Trumbull HS; Trumbull, CT; (Y); JV Bsbl; High Hon Roll; Acctg.

SCHLICHTING, DOUG; Granby HS; N Granby, CT; (Y); Exploring; Band; Concert Band; Jazz Band; Mrchg Band; Stage Crew; Symp Band; Law.

SCHLUTER, KIM; Academy Of Our Lady Of Mercy; Fairfield, CT; (Y); French Clb; GAA; VP JA; Varsity Clb; School Musical; Yrbk Stf; Rep Stu Cncl; NHS; Drama Clb; Girl Scts; Pre Law.

SCHMIDT JR, KURT M; Killingly HS; Dayville, CT; (Y); 31/271; Letterman Clb; Ski Clb; Varsity Clb; L Ftbl; Ice Hcky; JV Tennis; Im Wt Lftg; Hon Roll; Norwich U Schlrshp 85; Almni Assn Schlrshp 85; Norwich Ufcrmnl Justc.

SCHMUS, BOB W; Danbur HS; Danbury, CT; (Y); Art Clb; Camera Clb; Chess Clb; Computer Clb; German Clb; JA; Math Clb; Math Tm; Science Clb; Ski Clb; A Hnrs In Math 83; B Hnrs In German 83; MVP On Soccer Tm 83-84; Mech Engnr.

SCHNEIDER, CHRISTINE; Danbury HS; Danbury, CT; (Y); 70/615; Girl Scts; Ski Clb; Varsity Clb; Concert Band; Mrchg Band; JV Sftbl; JV Trk; Var Vllybl; Hon Roll; NHS; Slvr Awd Grl Scouts 83; Grmn Cultrl Soc Awd 84; Sprts Med.

SCHNEIDER, KARL; Trumbull HS; Trumbull, CT; (Y); Trs AFS; Debate Tm; Science Clb; Mrchg Band; Var JV Ice Hcky; Ind Engrng.

SCHNEIDER, KURT; Canterbury HS; Sea Girt, NJ; (Y); 10/84; Church Yth Grp; Cmnty Wkr; Ski Clb; Teachers Aide; Yrbk Sprt Ed; JV Lcrss; JV Socr; Capt Wrstlng; High Hon Roll; Boston Coll; Pre-Med.

SCHOFIELD, BRADY; Avon Old Farms Schl; Stafford Springs, CT; (S); 12/115; JV Golf; Im Ice Hcky; Im Lcrss; Hon Roll; Outstndng Achvt Comp Sci 83; U VT; Comp Sci.

SCHONDELMAYER, TAMMY; St Bernard HS; New London, CT; (Y); 121/289; Ski Clb; Chorus; VP Stu Cncl; Var Sftbl; Hon Roll; Jr NHS; Eastern CT ST U; Psych.

SCHOR, PAUL; William Hall HS; W Hartford, CT; (Y); 124/324; Boy Scts; JA; Ski Clb.

SCHOWALTER, BETHANY L; Hopkins Grammar Dy Prospect Hl HS; New Haven, CT; (Y); Key Clb; Radio Clb; Band; Chorus; Variety Show; Rep Frsh Cls; Rep Soph Cls; Rep Jr Cls; Rep Stu Cncl; JV Socr; Cum Laude; Mary Brewster Thompson Awd Otstndg Acad Achiev; Child Psych.

SCHRAMM, MARK; Fairfield Prep; Westport, CT; (Y); Art Clb; Church Yth Grp; Computer Clb; Drama Clb; Band; Nwsp Rptr; Yrbk Stf; Swmmng; Georgetown; Bus.

SCHREIBER, CHRIS; Danbury HS; Danbury, CT; (Y); Varsity Clb; Chorus; Yrbk Stf; Var L Socr; Var L Trk; Hon Roll; Schl Rcrd 300m Dash Relay 85; Jrnlsm.

SCHREIBER, REBECCA; Wilbur Cross HS; New Haven, CT; (S); 5/242; Cmnty Wkr; French Clb; PAVAS; Political Wkr; Teachers Aide; Lit Mag; Var Swmmng; Hon Roll; NHS; U S Sen Schlrshp Fnlst Alt 84; Indep Study Psych Awd 82-83; Flm Mkng.

SCHREIBER, STEPHANIE; Danbury HS; Danbury, CT; (Y); 142/615; Math Tm; JV Bsktbl; JV Sftbl; Perry Italn Awd 85; Comm.

SCHUBERT, CLAUDINE; Shelton HS; Shelton, CT; (Y); German Clb; Spanish Clb; Stu Cncl; Pom Pon; Hon Roll; NHS; Librl Arts.

SCHUBERT, RICHARD; Holy Cross HS; Bedford, CT; (Y); 6/352; Art Clb; Trs Church Yth Grp; French Clb; Lit Mag; French Hon Soc; U Of CT; Thelgy.

SCHUELE, JOCHEN; William H Hall HS; W Hartford, CT; (Y); 60/399; JA; Model UN; Boston U; Intl Rel.

SCHUHL, MARK W; Manchester HS; Manchester, CT; (Y); AFS; Cmnty Wkr; German Clb; Pres Spanish Clb; Nwsp Ed-Chief; High Hon Roll; NHS; 90 Pct AATG German Test Awd 84; Bk Awd 85; Harvard Radcliffe Bk Awd 85; Spnsh.

SCHULTZ, DEBRA; Ridgefield HS; Ridgefield, CT; (Y); 26/363; Church Yth Grp; Red Cross Aide; Service Clb; Mrchg Band; Lit Mag; High Hon Roll; Hon Roll; Ntl Merit Ltr; Pres Schlr; Spnsh Bk Awd; Serv Awd Vlntr Grp; Serv Awd Inst CPR; Holy Cross Clg; Ecnmcs.

SCHULTZ, KIM; Southington HS; Plantsville, CT; (Y); Hosp Aide; Key Clb; Band; Concert Band; Mrchg Band; Yrbk Stf; Im Bowling; Powder Puff Ftbl; Var Trk; Hon Roll; CT U; Physcl Thrpy.

SCHULZ, PAUL; Guilford HS; Guilford, CT; (Y); Pres Ski Clb; Variety Show; Yrbk Stf; JV Crs Cntry; Var Tennis.

SCHUM, MICHAEL; Wolcott HS; Wolcott, CT; (Y); 6/250; Am Leg Boys St; Var Bsbl; JV Bsktbl; Var Socr; High Hon Roll; Hon Roll; NHS; Atten Proj Sage Pgm Giftd Talntd 84-85; Acad Excel Elect 83; MVP Bsbl 83; MIT; Engr.

SCHWAB, JULIE A; East Haven HS; E Haven, CT; (Y); #12 In Class; Pres French Clb; Var Bsktbl; Cheerleading; Var Capt Crs Cntry; Var Capt Trk; High Hon Roll; Trs NHS; Rotary Yth Awd 84; Boston Coll; Sci.

SCHWARTZ, THEA; Amity Regional HS; Woodbridge, CT; (S); German Clb; Off Latin Clb; Model UN; Red Cross Aide; Concert Band; Lit Mag; L Crs Cntry; L Trk; Cit Awd; High Hon Roll; All-State Cross Country Tm 84; Natl French Consest 7th In New Engl 83; Peabody Sci Awd.

SCHWARZ, GARY J; Stratford HS; Stratford, CT; (Y); Art Clb; Letterman Clb; Spanish Clb; Varsity Clb; Rep Frsh Cls; Rep Soph Cls; Rep Jr Cls; JV Var Ftbl; Var Wt Lftg; Hon Roll; Spnsh Spkg Awd 82-83; Athl Sell-A-Thon 84; Rensellaer Cath U; Arch.

SCHWEIGHOFER, PETER; Ridgefield HS; Ridgefield, CT; (S); 14/315; Church Yth Grp; Orch; School Musical; High Hon Roll; Hon Roll; Wstrn CT Rgnl Orch 83-84; CT All-ST Orch 85; Outstndng Achvt Music Awd 83-84; Grmn Consulate Bk Awd; Crtv Wrtng.

SCIANNA, STEPHEN; Portland HS; Portland, CT; (Y); 4/100; Am Leg Boys St; Cmnty Wkr; Trs Stu Cncl; JV Golf; Var Socr; High Hon Roll; NHS; Math Tm; Ski Clb; Bsktbl; U CT JR Hnrs Schlr 85; K Of C Awd Hghst Avg U S Hstry 85; Peer Ldrshp Pgm 85; Lib Art.

SCICCHITANO, CATERINA L; Stamford HS; Stamford, CT; (Y); Var L Sftbl; Var L Vllybl; High Hon Roll; Stamford Coaches Awd Vlybl 84-85; Girls Sftbl Awd; ST Champshp 84; Miss Sftbl Am.

SCIME, DESIREE; Central HS; Bridgeport, CT; (S); 28/302; Church Yth Grp; Intnl Clb; Office Aide; Ski Clb; School Musical; School Play; High Hon Roll; Hon Roll; Rep Jr Cls; Rep Sr Cls; Schlrshp Ldrshp Ablty; Housatonic Comm; Psych.

SCIORTINO, MICHAEL J; Trumbull HS; Trumbull, CT; (Y); Var Bsbl; JV Ftbl; Var Wt Lftg; Vrsty Let Awd Baseball 84-85; All FCIAC Tm Baseball 85; Bus.

SCOTT, JENNIFER; Mark T Sheehan HS; Wallingford, CT; (Y); 13/230; German Clb; Hosp Aide; JA; Key Clb; Chorus; Nwsp Ed-Chief; High Hon Roll; Hon Roll; Bio.

SCOTT, SPENCER; Staples HS; Westport, CT; (Y); Boy Scts; Rep Church Yth Grp; German Clb; Math Tm; Im Mgr Badmtn; JV Var Ftbl; L Socr; Var Trk; Im Mgr Wt Lftg; Var Hon Roll; Brigham Young U.

SCOVILLE, EDWARD; Pomperaug HS; Southbury, CT; (Y); Exploring; Math Tm; Rep Jr Cls; Ftbl; Trk; Wt Lftg; Engrng.

SCRUTON, GREGORY R; Southington HS; Southington, CT; (Y); 4/502; Math Tm; Quiz Bowl; Scholastic Bowl; JV Var Socr; High Hon Roll; Ntl Merit Ltr; Rensselaer Polytech Inst; Mth.

SCULLY, DEIRDRE; Windham HS; Willimantic, CT; (Y); Rep Soph Cls; Rep Jr Cls; Trs Stu Cncl; JV Bsktbl; Var Capt Fld Hcky; JV Sftbl; JV Trk; High Hon Roll; NHS; Comm.

SCULLY, JACQUELYN; Holy Cross HS; Waterbury, CT; (Y); Var Bsktbl; Hon Roll; Phys Thrpy.

SCULLY, JANICE; Frank Scott Bunnell HS; Stratford, CT; (Y); 51/250; Drama Clb; Sec JA; Library Aide; Pres Chorus; Ed Nwsp Stf; Lit Mag; Rep Jr Cls; Rep Stu Cncl; Hon Roll; Excllnc In Jrnlsm 85; Southern CT ST U.

SEAFORT, JAMES; Brookfield HS; Brookfield, CT; (Y); Var Ftbl; Var Lcrss; Var Trk; U Of UT; Elec Engr.

SEARLES, DEBRA; Naugatuck HS; Naugatuck, CT; (Y); Girl Scts; VP Pres JA; Office Aide; Pep Clb; Hon Roll; Pre Med.

SEARS, MAYRA; Norwich Free Acad; Franklin, CT; (Y); Sec Letterman Clb; Spanish Clb; Teachers Aide; Varsity Clb; Variety Show; Rep Stu Cncl; Var Capt Cheerleading; JV Trk; High Hon Roll; Hon Roll; Vrsty N-Club Awd 85; Sears Ctznshp Awd 85; U Of CT; Liberal Arts.

SEAVER, SHANNON; Bristol Eastern HS; Bristol, CT; (S); Camera Clb; DECA; FHA; GAA; Pep Clb; Thesps; Stage Crew; Gym; Powder Puff Ftbl; Hon Roll; 1st Regnl & 2nd ST Public Speaking 85; DECA Outstndng Femal Achvt Awd 85; Mitchell JC; Early Child Devlp.

SECONDO, SEAN; Southington HS; Southington, CT; (Y); JA; Ski Clb; Nwsp Stf; Hon Roll; U Hartford; Comp Tech.

SEEBAUER, DAVE; Central HS; Bristol, CT; (Y); 66/276; Trs Computer Clb; Var L Crs Cntry; Socr; Capt Trk; Hon Roll; Grace Atkins & Forstvl Lttl Leag Schlrshps 85; Rogr Wliams Coll; Comp Engrng.

SEEGER, MICHAEL; East Catholic HS; Glastonbury, CT; (Y); Boy Scts; Yrbk Stf; Rep Jr Cls; VP Sr Cls; Rep Stu Cncl; JV Ftbl; Var L Trk; Hon Roll; Ntl Merit Ltr; Acad All-Amer Schlr Prog.

SEELEY, WENDY; Vinal Regional Tech Schl; Killingworth, CT; (Y); Church Yth Grp; VICA; Yrbk Stf; High Hon Roll; VICA 2nd Pl Awd, Fnlst Hrdrssng 84 & 85; Prnt Fclty Orgnztn Schlrshp 85; Secy.

SEGRETARIO, KRISTEN; Bristol Central HS; Bristol, CT; (Y); 51/289; Church Yth Grp; Cmnty Wkr; Intnl Clb; Spanish Clb; Teachers Aide; Sec Frsh Cls; VP Soph Cls; Rep Stu Cncl; Twrlr; Hon Roll; St Joseph Coll; Spcl Eductn.

SEIFERT, JOHN; Trumbull HS; Trumbull, CT; (Y); Wrstlng; High Hon Roll; Hon Roll; Tool & Die.

SELBY, STEPHEN; Nonnewang HS; Bethlehem, CT; (Y); Am Leg Boys St; Var Bsbl; Bsktbl; JV Wrstlng; High Hon Roll; Hon Roll; Chem Engrng.

SELMONT, LINDA; North Haven HS; N Haven, CT; (Y); 50/218; Girl Scts; Flag Corp; Stage Crew; Yrbk Stf; Hon Roll.

SEMENTINI, NANCY; Stamford HS; Stamford, CT; (Y); Dance Clb; JA; Key Clb; Lit Mag; High Hon Roll; Hon Roll; NHS; Jr Achvt Superior Slsmnshp 84.

SEMMELROCK, ARNAULD; Saint Bernard HS; Fitchville, CT; (Y); Band; Concert Band; Mrchg Band; Pep Band; Ftbl.

SEMMELROCK, MARY A; Putnam HS; Pomfret Ctr, CT; (Y); Drama Clb; 4-H; Girl Scts; Flag Corp; Mrchg Band; School Play; Variety Show; 4-H Awd; Southern Conn ST U; Eng.

SEMON, SUZANNE; Saint Josephs HS; Ansonia, CT; (Y); 7/227; Nwsp Stf; Var Capt Sftbl; Var Capt Vllybl; High Hon Roll; NHS; Spanish NHS; Spanish Clb; JV Bsktbl; Hon Roll; Bus Admin.

SENAY, CHERYL; Killingly HS; Danielson, CT; (Y); Church Yth Grp; GAA; MMM; Office Aide; Band; Concert Band; Mrchg Band; Cheerleading; Gym; Mgr(s); Airline Stwrdss.

SENESAC, ROBERT J; St Paul Catholic HS; Bristol, CT; (Y); Church Yth Grp; JV Bsbl; Var L Bsktbl; Coach Actv; Var L Ftbl; Var L Golf; Hon Roll; Untd Auto Wrkrs Schlrshp Awd 85; St Bonaventure U; Bus Adm.

SENGSTOCK, MICHAEL; H C Wilcox Tech HS; Meriden, CT; (Y); Hon Roll; Top Shp Awd 84-85.

SENTEIO, CHARLES; Manchester HS; Manchester, CT; (Y); AFS; L Var Bsktbl; JV Socr; Hon Roll; Elec Engnrng.

SERIMONKON, SUSAN; Ellington HS; Ellington, CT; (Y); Exploring; Sec Chorus; Hon Roll; Solo, Ensmb Fstvl Awd 84; Gld Music Awd 84-85.

SERRAMBANA JR, VICTOR; East Catholic HS; Vernon, CT; (Y); 7/318; Lit Mag; Rep Soph Cls; Pres Jr Cls; Trs Rep Stu Cncl; Var Ice Hcky; JV Socr; Cit Awd; High Hon Roll; Hon Roll; NHS; Prncpls Awd 85; Law.

SERRANO, DAISY; Academy Of The Holy Family; Willimantic, CT; (Y); 7/27; Acpl Chr; Chorus; Church Choir; School Musical; VP Frsh Cls; VP Soph Cls; VP Jr Cls; Var Bsktbl; Crs Cntry; Sftbl; Rookie Yr Bsktbl 83-84; MI Bsktbl 84-85; Arch.

SERRANO, LISSETTE; East Catholic HS; Manchester, CT; (Y); Church Yth Grp; Ped Nurse.

SESTO, VINCENZO; Bristol Central HS; Bristol, CT; (Y); Am Leg Boys St; Boys Clb Am; Church Yth Grp; Cmnty Wkr; Library Aide; Rptr VICA; Nwsp Stf; High Hon Roll; NHS; Carnegie Smnr 84-85; Awd High Sci MA Inst Tech 85; Elec Engr.

SETARO, NANCY; Holy Cross HS; Waterbury, CT; (Y); 55/352; Church Yth Grp; Cmnty Wkr; Hon Roll; NHS; Natl Italian Hnr Soc 84; CYO - St Lucy Chrldr Tm Won New England Title 84; Italian III Awd 85; Bus.

SEUFERT, PETER; Notre Dame HS; Ansonia, CT; (Y); 27/254; Boy Scts; CAP; Exploring; Radio Clb; Rep Sr Cls; Rep Stu Cncl; JV Crs Cntry; French Hon Soc; Hon Roll; Math Hnr Socty 83-85; Mitchell Awd Cvl Air Patrl 85; Embry-Riddle Aero U; Aerontcl.

SEVENOFF, KAREN S; Windsor HS; Windsor, CT; (Y); 10/341; Am Leg Aux Girls St; Dance Clb; Drama Clb; Pres Intnl Clb; Model UN; VP Spanish Clb; Pres Thesps; Band; Chorus; Concert Band; Exch Clb Awd 85; All ST Choir 84; All Eastern Choir 85; NY U; Drama.

SEVIGNY, CHRISTINE M; Haddam-Killingworth HS; Haddam Neck, CT; (Y); 10/128; Teachers Aide; Sec Soph Cls; Sec Jr Cls; Sec Sr Cls; VP Stu Cncl; Var Powder Puff Ftbl; JV Var Vllybl; High Hon Roll; Hon Roll; NHS; Excell In Phy Ed 85; Excell In Acctng I 85; Haddam Schlrshp Awd 85; Dean JR Coll; Bus Mgmt.

SEYMOUR, PETER DU BOIS; Kent School; Belgium; (Y); 1/170; Chess Clb; Nwsp Sprt Ed; Yrbk Stf; Crs Cntry; Swmmng; High Hon Roll; Ntl Merit SF; Horace Scheidt Chem Prz 84; Thomas Talbot Seeley Greek Prz 84; Clifton K Loomis Engl Prz 84.

SGRILLO, LORI; Southington HS; Southington, CT; (Y); Pep Clb; Ski Clb; Rep Soph Cls; Stat Bsbl; Stat Bsktbl; Var Capt Cheerleading; Im Gym; Powder Puff Ftbl; Hon Roll.

SHACKETT, HEATHER; Windosr Locks HS; Windsor Locks, CT; (Y); 4/175; Church Yth Grp; Trs Civic Clb; Trs Cmnty Wkr; NHS; Talcott Mntn Nova & Super Nova Prgms 84; Bio.

SHAGORY, PETER; Fairfield College Prep HS; Ridgefield, CT; (Y); Trs Pres Church Yth Grp; Model UN; JV Ftbl; JV Var Lcrss; Hon Roll; Arch.

SHAKER, JOSEPH; Holy Cross HS; Waterbury, CT; (Y); 135/352; Boys Clb Am; Church Yth Grp; Bsktbl; Golf; Hon Roll; Bus Admin.

SHALLIS, RENEE; Jonathan Law HS; Milford, CT; (Y); 19/237; Intnl Clb; Keywanettes; Spanish Clb; Band; Concert Band; Jazz Band; Mrchg Band; Trk; Prfct Atten Awd; Excllnce Spn III Awd 85.

SHANLEY, JUSTIN M; Amity Regional HS; Woodbridge, CT; (Y); 40/376; Am Leg Boys St; Yrbk Sprt Ed; Var L Ftbl; Var Capt Golf; Hon Roll; NHS; Pres Schlr; French Clb; Nwsp Rptr; Ftbl Al-Leag, Tm MVP 84; Glf Al-Leag 83-85; Glf Tm MVP 84; Schlr-Athlt Awds 85; Yale U.

SHAPRIO, DAVID E; Pomperaug HS; Middlebury, CT; (Y); Var Chess Clb; Math Tm; Model UN; Scholastic Bowl; High Hon Roll; Hon Roll; Outdr Clb; Mock Trl Ldr; Peer Tutrng Prgm Ldr.

SHARP, CHRISTOPHER; Westhill HS; Stamford, CT; (Y); FFA; VP JA; Science Clb; Swmmng; High Hon Roll; NHS; Ntl Merit Ltr; NAJAC Del Reg Wnnr VP Prod 85; CHEMATHON Cert 84; Yale Sci & Free Enter Sympsm 84 & 85; Physics.

SHAW, CRAIG M; Rockville HS; Vernon, CT; (Y); 20/369; Art Clb; Aud/Vis; Chess Clb; Drama Clb; Political Wkr; School Play; Variety Show; Nwsp Stf; Lit Mag; Stu Cncl.

SHAW, IVAN; Westhill HS; Stamford, CT; (Y); JA; Key Clb; Teachers Aide; Nwsp Rptr; Rep Soph Cls; Rep Jr Cls; Tennis; Hon Roll; Lbrl Arts.

SHAW, ROSEMARY J; St Joseph HS; Lighthouse Point, FL; (Y); 35/221; Church Yth Grp; English Clb; Latin Clb; Nwsp Stf; Lit Mag; High Hon Roll; Ntl Latn Exam Silver Mdl 82-83; Margaret Mc Padden Awd 85; FL Atlantic U; Bus Mgmt.

SHEA, ELIZABETH; Southington HS; Southington, CT; (Y); 13/600; German Clb; Key Clb; Trs Pep Clb; Bsktbl; Mgr(s); Var Vllybl; High Hon Roll; Jr NHS; NHS; Sal; German Awd 84-85; Latin Awd 84-85; Lt Sci Fair Awd 83; Med.

SHEA, KYLA; Holy Cross HS; Middlebury, CT; (Y); 36/352; Swmmng; Trk; Spanish NHS; Villanova; Bio.

SHEA, NANCY; North Haven HS; N Haven, CT; (Y); 44/300; Church Yth Grp; Dance Clb; Model UN; Spanish Clb; Rep Frsh Cls; Trs Church Yth Grp; Trs Jr Cls; Stu Cncl; JV Bsktbl; Var Socr; JR Hnr Gurd 85; Psychlgy.

SHEA JR, WALTER; Wethersfield HS; Wethersfield, CT; (Y); 1/325; Am Leg Boys St; VP Sr Cls; Capt Bsktbl; High Hon Roll; NHS; Boys Clb Am; Math Tm; Spanish Clb; Rep Frsh Cls; Rep Soph Cls; Harvard Bk Awd Rensselaer Mdl & Cmmnded ST Natl Merit 84-85; Beatrice Day Geom Awd 83-84; Bus.

SHEA, WILLIAM; Ansonia HS; Ansonia, CT; (Y); VP Church Yth Grp; Cmnty Wkr; Computer Clb; French Clb; Intnl Clb; VP JA; Variety Show; Yrbk Phtg; Rep Frsh Cls; JV Ftbl; Hghst Ovral Mrk Hstry; Wnnr Bus Mgmt Cours JA; Mass Cmnctns.

SHEEHAN, EILEEN; East Lyme HS; E Lyme, CT; (Y); 16/280; Am Leg Aux Girls St; Off Frsh Cls; Off Soph Cls; Off Jr Cls; Off Sr Cls; Var Capt Tennis; Church Yth Grp; Key Clb; Band; Yrbk Stf; Amer Lgn Aux Girls ST Awd 85; Pre-Law.

SHEEHAN, PATRICIA; Farmington HS; Farmington, CT; (Y); 6/215; Chorus; Church Choir; Concert Band; Jazz Band; Madrigals; Mrchg Band; Var JV Fld Hcky; High Hon Roll; NHS; Spanish NHS; Trinity Clb Book Awd 83-84; Daughters Of The American Revolution 84-85.

SHEFTEL, STEPHEN; O H Platt HS; Meriden, CT; (Y); VP Key Clb; Ftbl; High Hon Roll; Hon Roll; Pol Sci.

SHEK, KAREN E; Academy Of Our Lady Of Mercy HS; Milford, CT; (Y); Cmnty Wkr; Drama Clb; Service Clb; Spanish Clb; Variety Show; Nwsp Stf; Yrbk Phtg; Yrbk Stf; Lit Mag; Im Vllybl; Central CT ST U; Accntng.

SHELBURNE, PETER D; Choate Rosemary Hall HS; Greensboro, NC; (S); Pres Chess Clb; Computer Clb; Chorus; School Musical; School Play; Stage Crew; Lit Mag; Hon Roll; Ntl Merit Ltr; Sci.

SHELDON, CHESCA; East Lyme HS; E Lyme, CT; (Y); 47/274; Yrbk Ed-Chief; High Hon Roll; CT Coll.

SHELDON, JOSLYN; Putnam HS; Putnam, CT; (Y); 2/140; Sec Church Yth Grp; Sec Band; Concert Band; Jazz Band; Mrchg Band; School Play; Ed Yrbk Stf; Var Sftbl; High Hon Roll; VP NHS; Awds-Hghst Avg Crtv Wrtng & Beng In 4 Ctgrs In Band 84-85; Phys Thrpy.

SHELTON, CAREY; Ansonia HS; Ansonia, CT; (Y); 4/130; Computer Clb; Spanish Clb; Yrbk Stf; Capt Var Cheerleading; High Hon Roll; NHS; Spanish NHS; Yale Bk Awd 84; Acctng.

SHELTON, DANA; Notre Dame Acad; Waterbury, CT; (Y); 4/53; Stage Crew; Nwsp Ed-Chief; Yrbk Stf; Pres Frsh Cls; Pres Jr Cls; Pres Stu Cncl; Var L Bsktbl; Var L Socr; Var L Sftbl; Cit Awd; Harvard Bk Awd 84; Western CT ST Sccr All Star 85; CT ST Schlr Athl 85; Boston Coll; Psych.

SHERAMY, RONA; Amity Regional SR HS; Orange, CT; (S); Model UN; Pep Clb; Spanish Clb; Temple Yth Grp; Nwsp Bus Mgr; Nwsp Rptr; Rep Sec Stu Cncl; Capt JV Cheerleading; Hon Roll; Regnl Rep CT Fed Of Stu Cncls 83-84; Bus.

SHERMAN, MIA E; William H Hall HS; West Hartford, CT; (Y); 128/316; Rptr FBLA; VP PAVAS; Acpl Chr; School Musical; School Play; Swing Chorus; Yrbk Stf; Hon Roll; Drama Clb; Q&S; 3rd Pl German Poetry Cntst 83; U Of NY; Theatre.

SHERRINGTON, ZANDRA; Low-Heywood Thomas HS; Stamford, CT; (Y); 3/36; Church Yth Grp; JA; School Play; Off Soph Cls; Off Jr Cls; Pres Sr Cls; Var Fld Hcky; Var Lcrss; High Hon Roll; Vassar Awd 84-85; Soc Wmn Engrs Awd 84-85; Bus.

SHERWILL, BARBARA; Mark T Sheehan HS; Yalesville, CT; (Y); 25/210; Spanish Clb; Teachers Aide; High Hon Roll; Hon Roll; Excllne Spnsh II 84; Tchng.

SHERWOOD, KATHRYN; Lauralton Hall HS; Fairfield, CT; (Y); French Clb; Chorus; Nwsp Phtg; Yrbk Phtg; JV Swmmng; Im Vllybl; Chem Engr.

SHILBERG, NATHAN; Bristol Center HS; Bristol, CT; (Y); 1/200; Drama Clb; Math Tm; School Play; Nwsp Rptr; Im Trk; High Hon Roll; NHS; Harvard Bk Prz 85; Michaels Jewlrs Awd 85; Tufts U; Jrnlsm.

SHINN, WENDY; Hartford Christian Acad; Ellington, CT; (S); 2/5; Church Yth Grp; Yrbk Ed-Chief; Sec Frsh Cls; Pres VP Soph Cls; VP Jr Cls; Var Cheerleading; Var Sftbl; Var Vllybl; Hon Roll; NHS.

SHIPLETT, STUART; Westhill HS; Bedford, NH; (Y); Intnl Clb; Latin Clb; Science Clb; Nwsp Stf; Im Bsbl; JV Ftbl; Wt Lftg; Ntl Hnr Soc Diner Prespctv 82-83; U VA; Bus Adm.

SHORT, INGRID; Northwestern Regional #7 HS; New Hartford, CT; (Y); 16/170; German Clb; Political Wkr; Varsity Clb; Mgr Band; Color Guard; Mgr Concert Band; Mgr Mrchg Band; Yrbk Stf; Rep Stu Cncl; Badmtn; Excllnc Germn 81; Union Coll; Pre-Med.

SIBILLA, ANGELA; Stamford HS; Stamford, CT; (S); Dance Clb; DECA; Girl Scts; Office Aide; Red Cross Aide; Drm & Bgl; Stage Crew; Hon Roll; NHS; Gold Awd Sct 84; CT Bus Wk Schlrshp 84; Pres Interact Clb 84; Bus Schl; Merchndsng.

SIBLEY, STACY; Conard HS; West Hartford, CT; (Y); 48/291; Pep Clb; Chorus; School Musical; Yrbk Stf; Rep Jr Cls; Rep Sr Cls; Stu Cncl; Var Cheerleading; High Hon Roll; Hon Roll; Ntl Schl Choral Awd 85; Conn Coll; Eng.

SICIGNANO, GERALYN; East Haven HS; E Haven, CT; (Y); 9/300; Church Yth Grp; Cmnty Wkr; Spanish Clb; Lit Mag; Capt Pom Pon; High Hon Roll; Hon Roll; NHS; Pres Schlr; Amer Lgn Auxlry Schlrhsp 85; CT U; Comm Sci.

SICKLER, STACEY; Daniel Hand HS; Madison, CT; (Y); AZ ST U; Bus.

SIDAT, SUSAN; Windham HS; Willimantic, CT; (Y); 17/289; Pres Jr Cls; Mgr Swmmng; Vllybl; High Hon Roll; Hon Roll; NHS; John D Welch Awd 85; U Of CT; Phrmcy.

SIEFERT, SUSANNE; Andrew Warde HS; Fairfield, CT; (Y); Church Yth Grp; JA; JCL; Latin Clb; Red Cross Aide; Hon Roll; Cum Laude Ltn Exam 85; Hnrb Mntn Ntl Latin Exam 85; Liberal Arts.

SIEKIERSKI, EVA M; Acad Of Our Lady Of Mercy; Milford, CT; (Y); 3/111; Service Clb; Spanish Clb; Yrbk Stf; High Hon Roll; NHS; Spanish NHS; Boston U; Bus Admin.

SIGHINOLFI, LIZA A; St Paul Catholic HS; Forestville, CT; (Y); 15/304; Pres French Clb; Mgr Stage Crew; Mgr Variety Show; Stu Cncl; High Hon Roll; NHS; Elks Tngr Mnth, Bristol Wmn Coll Clb Schlrshp, 3rd Hgh Math Awd 85; Worcester Polytech; Elec Engrng.

SIGNOROVICH, ALEXANDER; Holy Cross HS; Beacon Fl, CT; (Y); 157/400; Cmmnty Svc 85; Acctg.

SIHGEWALD, ROB; Fairfield Prep; Redding, CT; (Y); Church Yth Grp; Cmnty Wkr; Debate Tm; JA; Keywanettes; Model UN; Nwsp Ed-Chief; JV Ice Hcky; Im Lcrss; Var Socr; Scala Awd; Colgate; Bus Mgmt.

SIKORSKI, PATRICK; Norwich Regional Vo Tech; Norwich, CT; (Y); 1/142; Am Leg Boys St; Chess Clb; High Hon Roll; NHS; Prfct Atten Awd; Sal; Val; Comp.

SILKOFF, SHARI; James Hillhouse HS; New Haven, CT; (Y); 11/240; Cmnty Wkr; Pres JA; Rep Model UN; Temple Yth Grp; VP Pres Stu Cncl; Hon Roll; NHS; Ntl Merit Ltr; YWCA Wmn Ldrshp Honoree 85; Greater New Haven Jaycees 1st Scholar 85; U MA; Psych.

SILVA, ANTONIO M; Hartford HS; Hartford, CT; (Y); Ftbl; Socr; Strght A In Algebra.

SILVA, BILL; St Joseph HS; Shelton, CT; (Y); 71/250; Off Frsh Cls; Stu Cncl; Bsbl; Ftbl; Wt Lftg; Hon Roll; Bus Mktng.

SILVA, DAYLE; Danbury HS; Danbury, CT; (Y); Art Clb; Dance Clb; Ski Clb; Acpl Chr; Chorus; Hon Roll; Presdntl Acadmc Fitness Awd 85; Concordia Soc Schlrshp 85; Western CT ST U; Graphc Desgn.

SILVA, JESSICA; Ansonia HS; Ansonia, CT; (Y); Computer Clb; Dance Clb; Drama Clb; FBLA; Stu Cncl; Cit Awd; Hon Roll; NHS; Sal; Val; NY Inst Of Tech; H/R Admin.

SILVA, LAURA A; Andrew Ward HS; Fairfield, CT; (Y); Sec Band; Orch; Lit Mag; Rep Stu Cncl; Cit Awd; High Hon Roll; VP NHS; Ntl Merit Ltr; CT Reg Music Fest 83-85; All St Reg Music Fest 84-85; U Notre Dame; Engrng.

SILVA, LEON; Kaynor Tech Schl; Naugatuck, CT; (Y); Rep Jr Cls; Socr; High Hon Roll; Hon Roll; NHS; Pres Of Hnr Soc For Schl 85; New Haven U; Elect Engr.

SILVA, LUCY; Kolbe Cathedral HS; Bridgeport, CT; (Y); 4/100; VP Camera Clb; Cmnty Wkr; Math Clb; Nwsp Phtg; Yrbk Phtg; Yrbk Stf, Rep Soph Cls; DAR Awd; 4-H Awd; High Hon Roll; Harvard Bk Awd 84; Portugse Scholar 85; U Of Bridgeport; Dntl Hyg.

SILVERGLADE, DAVID; Joel Barlow HS; Redding, CT; (Y); Chorus; Trs Frsh Cls; Rep Stu Cncl; Church Yth Grp; Exploring; Latin Clb; CT ST Latin Day 1st 85; Wldrns Schl Pgm 85; Outing Clb Pres 84-85; Beloit; Anthrplgy.

SILVERMAN, HOWARD; Danbury HS; Danbury, CT; (Y); 135/612; Varsity Clb; Var L Ftbl; Wt Lftg; High Hon Roll; Hon Roll; Jr NHS; Geo W Perry Awd Eng 85; Bus Mktg.

SILVERSTEIN, AMY; East Catholic HS; Bolton, CT; (Y); 39/298; Sec Trs French Clb; Ski Clb; Nwsp Rptr; Nwsp Stf; Yrbk Rptr; Yrbk Stf; Off Soph Cls; Sec Jr Cls; Off Sr Cls; Rep Stu Cncl; WA Intrnshp Awd 85; Nacel Cultrl Exch Prog France 85; Psych.

SILVERTON, WILLIAM J; William Hall HS; W Hartford, CT; (Y); 33/342; Drama Clb; Ski Clb; Concert Band; Mrchg Band; Pep Band; School Play; Symp Band; High Hon Roll; Hon Roll; NHS; Mech Engrng.

SILVESTER III, THEODORE; Avon Old Farms Schl; Rye, NH; (Y); 38/120; Cmnty Wkr; Pres Stu Cncl; Capt Var Ftbl; Var Lcrss; Var Capt Wrstlng; Cit Awd; High Hon Roll; Rnkd 9th Cls/Dean Lst 84; Louis B Adams Ctznshp Awd 85; Pres Elect-Wardn Cls 86.

SIMARD, STEPHANIE; St Paul Catholic HS; Burlington, CT; (Y); 55/300; Concert Band; Variety Show; Yrbk Stf; Rep Soph Cls; Rep Stu Cncl; Capt JV Cheerleading; Var Trk; Hon Roll; Russell Sage Coll; Bus.

SIMIONE III, WILLIAM J; Notre Dame HS; Orange, CT; (Y); 79/248; French Clb; Ski Clb; Varsity Clb; Sec Frsh Cls; Sec Soph Cls; VP Jr Cls; Var Ftbl; Capt Golf; Wt Lftg; Peer Counselor 85; CPA.

SIMMONS, DENNIS; Daniel Hand HS; Madison, CT; (Y); 33/270; Am Leg Boys St; Church Yth Grp; Ski Clb; Orch; School Musical; VP Pres Stu Cncl; Var Capt Ftbl; Var Capt Lcrss; Im Wt Lftg; High Hon Roll; Outstndng Jr Awd 85; CT All ST Lacrosse Tm 85; CT All ST Orchstra 85.

SIMMONS, WILLIAM A; Putnam HS; Putnam, CT; (Y); Boy Scts; Chess Clb; Cmnty Wkr; Political Wkr; School Play; Hon Roll; U CT.

SIMOES, LINDA C; Naugatuck HS; Naugatuck, CT; (Y); Church Yth Grp; Library Aide; Spanish Clb; Teachers Aide; High Hon Roll; Hstry Clb-Pblcty Offcr 84-85; Law.

SIMPSON, ELIZABETH; Granby Memorial HS; Granby, CT; (Y); 21/107; Pres AFS; Nwsp Stf; Yrbk Bus Mgr; Trs Rep Frsh Cls; Trs Stu Cncl; Mgr Fld Hcky; Cit Awd; Hon Roll; Ntl Merit Schol; Boys Clb Am; Natl Hnr Soc Good Ctznshp Awd 85; Granby Educ Schlrshp 85; Thomas Horton Good Ctznshp Awd 85; Southern CT ST U; Educ.

SINA, MERMISA; Nonnewaug HS; Woodbury, CT; (Y); AFS; Camera Clb; Pep Clb; Band; Concert Band; Pep Band; School Play; Yrbk Stf; Sr Cls; Gym; Law.

SINACORI, MICHAEL; Simsbury HS; W Simsbury, CT; (Y); VP Church Yth Grp; Cmnty Wkr; Varsity Clb; Var Bsbl; Var Ice Hcky; Hon Roll; Prfct Atten Awd; Legn Bsbk Tri-Town 85; Capt JC Courant Bsbl Tm ST Title 84; MVP, ST Bsbl Tm Wnr 84; Syracuse U; Comm.

SINGER, DEBORAH; Ledyard SR HS; Norwich, CT; (Y); Aud/Vis; Church Yth Grp; Cmnty Wkr; Latin Clb; Library Aide; Pep Clb; Yrbk Stf; JV Mgr Bsbl; Var JV Mgr(s); Var JV Score Keeper; Nrs.

SINGH, SURVEEN; Shelton HS; Shelton, CT; (Y); Drama Clb; French Clb; Yrbk Stf; Trk; French Hon Soc; High Hon Roll; Hon Roll; NHS; Med.

SINOPOLI, LISA; Fitch SR HS; Groton, CT; (Y); Mitchell Coll; Bus Mgmt.

SIPPLES, TIMOTHY F; Morgan HS; Clinton, CT; (Y); 1/175; Quiz Bowl; Spanish Clb; Band; Chorus; Jazz Band; School Musical; High Hon Roll; Pres NHS; Ntl Merit SF; Am Leg Boys St; Yale Bk Awd 85; Comp Sci.

SIRICO, ANITA; Danbury HS; Danbury, CT; (Y); French Clb; PAVAS; Tennis; Hon Roll; Visual Arts.

SIROIS, KIM; George J Penney HS; E Hartford, CT; (Y); Sec French Clb; Nwsp Stf; Rep Soph Cls; Trs Jr Cls; Rep Stu Cncl; JV Cheerleading; Var Crs Cntry; Var Trk; Hon Roll; NHS; Eastern CT ST U; Cmmnctns.

SIROIS, TINA; Haddam-Killingworth HS; Higganum, CT; (Y); 14/128; Trs Church Yth Grp; Rep Band; Trs Sr Cls; Capt Bsktbl; Powder Puff Ftbl; Sftbl; Capt Swmmng; High Hon Roll; JP Sousa Awd; Trs NHS; William Watrous Mem Athltc Scholar 85; Carl J Anderson Athltc Awd 85; UCONN Alumni Assn Bk Awd 85; U CT; Lib Arts.

SIROWICH, MICHAEL; Seymour HS; Oxford, CT; (S); 19/224; Church Yth Grp; Variety Show; Nwsp Rptr; VP Jr Cls; Bsbl; Capt L Ftbl; Var L Trk; Var Wt Lftg; Hon Roll; NHS; Michaels Jewelers Awd 84; Engrng.

SISK, BRIAN; East Hartford HS; E Hartford, CT; (Y); Var Bsbl; Var Ftbl; Hon Roll; George J Clark Awd Ftbl 84; RI U; Bus.

SISK, KAREN N; Stonington HS; Pawcatuck, CT; (Y); 10/212; Church Yth Grp; Drama Clb; Pres FNA; Model UN; Pep Clb; School Play; Nwsp Rptr; Yrbk Stf; Var Capt Cheerleading; Im Wt Lftg; Achvt & Ldrshp Cup 85; Southern CT ST U; Nrsng.

SISK, MICHELLE E; East Lyme HS; Niantic, CT; (Y); 135/260; Boys Clb Am; Cmnty Wkr; Dance Clb; Office Aide; Yrbk Ed-Chief; Yrbk Rptr; Yrbk Stf; Powder Puff Ftbl; Hon Roll; Ms Tn CT Partcpnt 85; Avery Point U Of CT; Bus.

SISKO, CHERYL; Pomperaug HS; Southbury, CT; (Y); Rep Frsh Cls; Rep Soph Cls; JV Trk; High Hon Roll; Hon Roll; Kathryn Gibbs Ldrshp Awd 85; Briarwood Bk Awd 85; Typng, Accntg I Awds 84-85; Bus Adm.

SIVJEE, KHALIL; Rham HS; Andover, CT; (Y); 1/184; Am Leg Boys St; Cmnty Wkr; Math Tm; Pres Science Clb; Capt JV Bsbl; Var Tennis; Chrmn NHS; Ntl Merit Ltr; Harvard-Radcliff Awd 84-85; Annl MAA Test Hgh Scr 84-85; Talcott Mtn Sci Cntr Pgm Gifted Chldrn 82-85; Pre-Med.

SIZEMORE, DAVID; Xavier HS; Northford, CT; (Y); Rep Stu Cncl; Capt Bsktbl; Capt Socr; DAR Awd.

SKELLY, SUZANNE; South Catholic HS; Wethersfield, CT; (Y); 22/223; Church Yth Grp; Cmnty Wkr; Quiz Bowl; VP Sec Spanish Clb; Variety Show; Nwsp Rptr; Lit Mag; Rep Stu Cncl; Vllybl; Pres Schlr; Michaels Jewelers Scholar Cont Fin 85; CT ST Schlr 85; Acad Awd 83 & 85; U Of CT; Engl.

SKINNER, CAROL; East Lyme HS; E Lyme, CT; (Y); 45/250; Trs Church Yth Grp; Hosp Aide; Key Clb; Band; Concert Band; Mrchg Band; School Musical; Nwsp Stf; Yrbk Stf; AFS; Psych.

SKRIPOL, LORI; Colchester Christian Acad; Marlborough, CT; (Y); Church Yth Grp; Chorus; Var Bsktbl; Var Vllybl; Hon Roll; Bus Adm.

SLADE, LISA; Kolbe Cathedral HS; Bridgeport, CT; (Y); Church Yth Grp; FHA; Girl Scts; JA; Chorus; Church Choir; Concert Band; Hon Roll; Hoysatonic CC; Psych.

SLAY, TONIA; Guilford HS; Guilford, CT; (Y); Girl Scts; Teachers Aide; Band; Chorus; Sec Sr Cls; Rep Stu Cncl; Hon Roll; NHS; Gen Excell Lang Arts 83-85; New Horizon Schlrshp 85; Acad Achvt Awd 85; U Of PA; Bio.

SLIBY, MATTHEW; West Haven HS; W Haven, CT; (Y); DECA; JA; Rep Stu Cncl; Hon Roll; Jr NHS; NHS; Outstndng Stu Recog Awd 82-83; Culinary Inst; Culinary Arts.

SLOAT, DAVID; William H Hall HS; W Hartford, CT; (Y); Cmnty Wkr; Ski Clb; Pep Band; Symp Band; High Hon Roll; Hon Roll; Spanish NHS; Comp Sci.

SLOWIK, CHRIS; Shelton HS; Shelton, CT; (Y); Cmnty Wkr; Hon Roll; Woodworking Awd 85; Law Enfrcmnt.

SLOWITSKY, KERA J; New Canaan HS; New Canaan, CT; (Y); 2/350; Dance Clb; Pep Clb; Spanish Clb; Yrbk Phtg; Var Capt Cheerleading; Var Diving; Var Powder Puff Ftbl; CC Awd; High Hon Roll; Ntl Merit Ltr; U Of MI; Psych.

SMALLWOOD, BRADFORD; Simsbury HS; W Simsbury, CT; (Y); Am Leg Boys St; Boy Scts; Exploring; Hosp Aide; VP JA; ROTC; Yrbk Stf; JV Crs Cntry; JV Gym; JV Var Trk; Med.

SMART, JAMES R; Wethersfield HS; Wethersfield, CT; (Y); 1/279; Am Leg Boys St; Socr; Trk; Bausch & Lomb Sci Awd; Pres NHS; Ntl Merit Ltr; Val; Intnl Clb; Quiz Bowl; Ski Clb; JR Wmns Clb 85; John Willard Hstry Awd 85; H S Physcs Awd 85; Princeton U.

SMARZ, ANDREA; Brien Mc Mahon HS; S Norwalk, CT; (Y); #8 In Class; French Clb.

SMIAROWSKI, DONALD; St Thomas Aquinas HS; New Britain, CT; (Y); 17/154; Boy Scts; French Clb; JA; Im Bsktbl; Var L Crs Cntry; Var L Trk; Hon Roll; Prfct Atten Awd; Coachs Awd Trck 85; Pre-Med.

SMILANCSKY, DIANE; Brien Mc Mahon HS; S Norwalk, CT; (Y); Key Clb; Spanish Clb; Chorus; Church Choir; School Play; Chrmn Sr Cls; Rep Stu Cncl; Var Fld Hcky; Var Tennis; High Hon Roll; Engl.

SMITH, ALLISON; Choate Rosemary Hall HS; Brecksville, OH; (Y); Cmnty Wkr; Dance Clb; French Clb; Intnl Clb; Key Clb; Pep Clb; School Play; Stage Crew; High Hon Roll; NHS; Intl Rltns.

SMITH, ANDREW; Tolland HS; Tolland, CT; (Y); Camera Clb; Church Yth Grp; JA; JV Golf; Hon Roll; U Of CT; Bus.

SMITH, CHARMAINE; Weaver HS; Hartford, CT; (Y); Var L Tennis; Comp Pgmmr.

SMITH, CHRIS W; Naugatuck HS; Naugatuck, CT; (Y); Hon Roll; Auto Elec.

SMITH, DARYL R; Greenwich HS; Old Greenwich, CT; (Y); Am Leg Boys St; Boy Scts; Church Yth Grp; Exploring; Quiz Bowl; Var L Swmmng; High Hon Roll; NHS; Schlstc Achv Awd 83; Mst Imprvd Smn 84; Mst Imprvd Watr Pol 84.

SMITH, DJUANA; Wilbur Cross HS; New Haven, CT; (S); 29/286; Church Yth Grp; FBLA; Hosp Aide; Church Choir; Variety Show; Rep Jr Cls; Hon Roll; Ntl All Am Schlr Awd 84; Schlrshp Acad Bus Careers 84; VA ST U; Bus.

SMITH, JEFFREY; Northwestern Regional Hs; New Hartford, CT; (Y); Am Leg Boys St; VP Church Yth Grp; Band; Jazz Band; JV Bsbl; Var Crs Cntry; Hon Roll; Awd For Exclnc Soc Stud & Alg II 85; Bio.

SMITH, JILL; East Lyme HS; Salem, CT; (Y); 4-H; Pep Clb; Science Clb; Trs Frsh Cls; Trk; High Hon Roll; Hon Roll.

SMITH, KIMBERLY J; Brien Mc Mahon HS; S Norwalk, CT; (Y); 85/350; GAA; Color Guard; Nwsp Stf; JV Sftbl; Trk; Hon Roll; Engl.

SMITH, KRISTINA R; Southington HS; Southington, CT; (Y); French Clb; Girl Scts; JA; Latin Clb; Pep Clb; Ski Clb; Rep Soph Cls; Cheerleading; Swmmng; DAR Awd; Mod Lang.

SMITH, LARA; Shelton HS; Huntington, CT; (Y); Spanish Clb; High Hon Roll; Hon Roll; NHS; Spanish NHS; Italian Natl Honor Society; Engineering.

SMITH, LISA YVETTE; James Hillhouse HS; New Haven, CT; (Y); 54/321; Spanish Clb; JA; Red Cross Aide; Science Clb; Chorus; Mrchg Band; Rep Frsh Cls; High Hon Roll; Hon Roll; NHS; Irving Mitchell Weiss Awd, Most Studious Stu Libr Awd 85; U DC; Chld Psych.

SMITH, MARY ANN; St Bernard HS; Old Lyme, CT; (S); Drama Clb; FNA; Library Aide; School Play; Stage Crew; Yrbk Stf; Stu Cncl; JV Crs Cntry; High Hon Roll; Bio Sci.

SMITH, MATTHEW; Griswold HS; Danielson, CT; (Y); 12/100; Chess Clb; CAP; Spanish Clb; Nwsp Stf; Ftbl; High Hon Roll; NHS; Ntl Merit SF; Prfct Atten Awd; Pres Schlr; Stevens Inst Of Tech; Comp Pgmr.

SMITH, MICHAEL; Suffield HS; Suffield, CT; (Y); Sec Am Leg Boys St; Trs Church Yth Grp; Ski Clb; Rep Soph Cls; VP Jr Cls; Sec Sr Cls; Pres Stu Cncl; Bsktbl; JV Socr; Var Tennis; Ldrshp Awd; Colgate; Bus Adm.

SMITH, MONICA; James Hillhouse HS; New Haven, CT; (Y); Library Aide; School Play; Yrbk Stf; Pres Jr Cls; Sec Stu Cncl; Cit Awd; Hon Roll; NHS; Prfct Atten Awd; 1st Poetry Spnsh VI, Yale New Haven Hosp Apprentcshp Pgm 85; Vltnr Spec Olymp Pgm 84; Bio.

SMITH, PAMELA; St Bernard HS; Taftville, CT; (Y); 63/279; Art Clb; Hosp Aide; Stage Crew; Yrbk Stf; Off Jr Cls; Pres Stu Cncl; Gnrl Excel Fine Arts I 83; Acad Excel 83.

SMITH, PATRICIA; Sacred Heart Acad; N Branford, CT; (Y); FBLA; Hosp Aide; Pep Clb; Chorus; School Musical; Nwsp Stf; Yrbk Stf; Lit Mag; Drama Clb; Spanish Clb; Connecticut Bus Wk Stu Schlrshp 85; Intl Rel.

SMITH, REGINA; Putnam HS; Putnam, CT; (Y); 5/140; Spanish Clb; VP Pres Band; Chorus; Concert Band; Jazz Band; Mrchg Band; Yrbk Stf; High Hon Roll; Jr NHS; All Estrn Band.

SMITH, SHARON; East Hartford HS; E Hartford, CT; (Y); Boy Scts; Library Aide; Spanish Clb; Rep Jr Cls; High Hon Roll; Hon Roll; NHS; Spch Path.

SMITH III, SIDNEY S; New Canaan HS; New Canaan, CT; (Y); Church Yth Grp; Computer Clb; Latin Clb; PAVAS; Radio Clb; Band; Concert Band; Jazz Band; Mrchg Band; School Musical.

SMITH, SOPHIA; Thomas Snell Weaver HS; Hartford, CT; (Y); 7/500; Am Leg Aux Girls St; Dance Clb; Red Cross Aide; School Play; Rep Soph Cls; Rep Jr Cls; Rep Stu Cncl; Cit Awd; High Hon Roll; Hon Roll; Otstndng Female Technlgy 83-84; Stu Of Month 84; Bright Light Of The Day; Cornell U; Archtctrl Engnrng.

SMITH, TERYL ANN; North Branford HS; Northford, CT; (Y); 10/175; AFS; Church Yth Grp; 4-H; Yrbk Bus Mgr; Lit Mag; Pres Frsh Cls; Stu Cncl; Fld Hcky; Mgr(s); 4-H Awd; WA Smr Intrnshp Prg 84; Schl Achvt Awd Hstry/Engl 83; Jr Cert Merit Am Leg Post 85; Law.

SMITH, TONI MERCEDITA; Bulkeley HS; Hartford, CT; (Y); 1/300; Drama Clb; Soroptimist; Yrbk Bus Mgr; VP Sr Cls; Var Socr; DAR Awd; Elks Awd; High Hon Roll; NHS; Rotary Awd; Harvard; Psychlgy.

SMOLEN, ELIZABETH; Seymour HS; Seymour, CT; (Y); Yrbk Stf; Trs Soph Cls; Rep Stu Cncl; Hon Roll; U CT; Pre-Med.

SMOLEN, PETER; Farmington HS; Unionville, CT; (Y); JV Var Ftbl; JV Wrstlng; Ftbl Awds 78-79; Bicycle Moto-Crs Awds 81-82; Engr.

SMUTS, MARIA; Old Saybrook HS; Old Saybrook, CT; (Y); VP Sec AFS; Church Yth Grp; Cmnty Wkr; Pres VP Service Clb; Teachers Aide; Chorus; Concert Band; Mrchg Band; School Play; Yrbk Stf; Cert Awd Hartford Symphny Master Cls 84; Cert Recgntn Guidnc Dept Tutrng 85; Educ.

SNYDER, ANDREW; Amity Regional SR HS; Woodbridge, CT; (S); 52/376; Boy Scts; Drama Clb; Acpl Chr; Yrbk Phtg; Var Diving; Var Capt Swmmng; High Hon Roll; NHS; Uth & Gov ST LT Gov Schlrshp Natl Affrs Cncl 83-85; U Of MI; Pre Med.

SOBIERAJ, RICHARD; Saint Joseph HS; Stratford, CT; (Y); 64/227; Chess Clb; Cmnty Wkr; Spanish Clb; Varsity Clb; Nwsp Rptr; Var L Bsbl; JV Bsktbl; Stat Ftbl; Im Wt Lftg; Hon Roll.

SOBOL, PATRICIA; Bolton HS; Bolton, CT; (Y); 2/69; VP Intnl Clb; Pres Ski Clb; Pres Sr Cls; Var Capt Cheerleading; Var Capt Socr; Var Sftbl; DAR Awd; NHS; Sal; Pres Church Yth Grp; ST Schlr/Athlte 85; Yale Bk Clb Of Hartford Awd 84; Army Ntl Schlr/Athlte 85; Yale U; Ec.

SODERBERG, ROBERT; Rham HS; Hebron, CT; (Y); 45/160; Am Leg Boys St; JV Var Bsbl; JV Var Socr; Hon Roll; Justice Enfrcmnt.

SODLOSKY, LEE-ANN; Sacred Heart Acad; West Haven, CT; (Y); Church Yth Grp; Pres 4-H; Sec FBLA; Office Aide; Service Clb; Teachers Aide; Band; Orch; School Musical; Rep Frsh Cls; Bus.

SOHN, ROBERT; Newington HS; Newington, CT; (Y); 1/368; Am Leg Boys St; Civic Clb; Cmnty Wkr; Latin Clb; Var Ftbl; High Hon Roll; Amer Lgn Boys ST 85; Top Schlr For Boys 83; Magna Cum Laude Latin 83; U CT; Med.

SOKOLIK, LORI; Torrington HS; Torrington, CT; (Y); 51/271; Art Clb; Varsity Clb; Rep Stu Cncl; JV Var Cheerleading; Var Trk; High Hon Roll; Hon Roll; Prfct Atten Awd; Lizotte Art Awd 85; Cntrl CT ST U; Grphc Dsgn.

SOKOLOV, AMY L; E Lyme HS; Niantic, CT; (Y); 6/244; Drama Clb; Stage Crew; Nwsp Rptr; Yrbk Stf; High Hon Roll; Ntl Merit Ltr; Rotary Awd; East Lyme Schlrshp 85; U Of CA Brkly; Psychology.

SOLANO, LAURA; Central Catholic HS; Norwalk, CT; (Y); Yrbk Stf; Trs Soph Cls; VP Jr Cls; VP CAP; Stu Cncl; Powder Puff Ftbl; Var Capt Vllybl; Hon Roll; NHS; Yrbk Phtg; Exc In Italian I 84; Accntnt.

SOLAZ, RODNEY; Trumbull HS; Trumbull, CT; (Y); Hgh Hnr Rll 83-85; Northeastern U; Elec Engr.

SOLER, WILFREDO; Bullard-Havens RVTS; Bridgeport, CT; (Y); Chess Clb; Church Yth Grp; JA; Library Aide; Church Choir; Hon Roll; Prfct Atten Awd; Lucille Warber Awd Culinary Arts Excllnc 85; Chefs Awd 85; Culinary Arts.

SOLESKI, LYNN MARIE; St Joseph HS; Ansonia, CT; (Y); 54/221; English Clb; French Clb; JA; Political Wkr; Yrbk Bus Mgr; Lit Mag; French Hon Soc; Hon Roll; Cert Awd NEDT Tsts 82; Syracuse U; Arch.

SOLLA, MELISSA; Bulkeley HS; Hartford, CT; (Y); VP Church Yth Grp; French Clb; Hosp Aide; JA; Ski Clb; Band; Concert Band; Mrchg Band; Rep Stu Cncl; Robt T Daly Frnch Awd 85; Eckerd Coll; Bio.

SOLOMON, DONALD; Windham Regional Vocation Tech HS; Willimantic, CT; (Y); Computer Clb; Church Choir; Stage Crew; Socr; Robotc Engr.

SOLOWAY, BRETT; Amity Regional SR HS; Woodbridge, CT; (Y); Model UN; VP Temple Yth Grp; Ed Yrbk Phtg; Rep Frsh Cls; Var L Swmmng; Cit Awd; High Hon Roll; NHS; Clss III Awd Sustnd Excllnc 85; Awd Excllnc CT ST Latn Exm 82-83; Law.

SOLTESZ, ANDREA; Masuk HS; Monroe, CT; (Y); 50/325; Girl Scts; JA; JV Var Sftbl; Var Swmmng; High Hon Roll; Hon Roll; Outstndng Achvt Bus Ed 82-85; E F Moore Awd 84-85; Briarwood Bk Awd 84-85; Sacred Heart U; Bus Admn.

SOMODY, MICHELLE; Westhill HS; Stamford, CT; (Y); JA; Stu Cncl; Var Gym; Var Vllybl; Hon Roll; NHS; Busnss.

SON, CHENDA; Central HS; Bridgeport, CT; (Y); Camera Clb; FCA; FHA; Band; Church Choir; Comp Sci.

SORACCHI, CHRISTINE; Tolland HS; Tolland, CT; (Y); 20/160; Church Yth Grp; Cmnty Wkr; FBLA; Office Aide; Teachers Aide; Trk; Wt Lftg; Hon Roll; Hghst Avr Art Cls; Bus Mgmnt.

SORBO, MICHELE; Holy Cross HS; Waterbury, CT; (Y); 12/352; Church Yth Grp; VP Service Clb; High Hon Roll; NHS; Acadmc All Amer 85; Med Tech.

SORDI, MARY; Guilford HS; Guilford, CT; (Y); Chrmn AFS; Church Yth Grp; Key Clb; Red Cross Aide; Spanish Clb; Teachers Aide; Hon Roll; NHS; Spanish NHS; St Schlr; Sci Serv Awd 85; Westfield ST; Polit Sci.

SORENSEN, ERIC D; Bloomfield HS; Bloomfield, CT; (Y); 54/236; VP Church Yth Grp; Civic Clb; Var JV Bsbl; Im Bsktbl; Var JV Socr; Cit Awd; Hon Roll; Bloomfield Ctzn Schlrshp 85; U CT; Bus.

SORENSEN, HOLLY; Shelton HS; Shelton, CT; (Y); 25/400; Hosp Aide; JA; Pres Spanish Clb; Cheerleading; Mgr(s); High Hon Roll; Hon Roll; NHS; Spanish NHS; Spnsh Awd 85.

SORENSEN, LEE; Manchester HS; Manchester, CT; (Y); AFS; 4-H; JA; High Hon Roll; Hon Roll; Arch.

SORGE, MARIANNE; Trumbull HS; Trumbull, CT; (Y); Ski Clb; Spanish Clb; JV Swmmng; JV Trk; High Hon Roll; Hon Roll; Spanish NHS; Loyola Mrymnt U; Doctor.

SOSNOWSKI, DONALD; Danbury HS; Danbury, CT; (Y); 51/612; AFS; Boy Scts; VP Church Yth Grp; VP JA; Rep Stu Cncl; French Hon Soc; Hon Roll; Ftbl; Var Trk; Star Scout Awd, Life Scout Awd 83-84; Scouting Merit Badges 81-85; Theology.

SOTO, NATALIE; Bethel HS; Bethel, CT; (Y); 73/268; Chorus; JV Bsktbl; JV Var Tennis; High Hon Roll; Hon Roll; Engrng.

SOUSA, CHERYL ANN; East Haven HS; E Haven, CT; (Y); 8/215; Am Leg Aux Girls St; Church Yth Grp; Model UN; High Hon Roll; Hon Roll; Jr NHS; NHS; Rotary Awd.

SOUSA, NORMAN; Robert E Fitch SR HS; Groton, CT; (Y); 15/410; Debate Tm; Intnl Clb; VP JA; Varsity Clb; Yrbk Phtg; Yrbk Rptr; Yrbk Sprt Ed; Yrbk Stf; Trs Sr Cls; Rep Stu Cncl; Excell Frnch I & 22 Trphy 82; Outstndg VP Fin JA 84; Ftbl Unsung Hero Awd Trphy 84; U Of CT; Bus.

SOUZA, JOHN; St Bernard HS; Gales Ferry, CT; (S); 6/290; Library Aide; Rep Band; Mrchg Band; JV Socr; JV Tennis; High Hon Roll; NHS; Spnsh & Sci Awd; Chem.

SPADA, JOELE; Marianapolis Prep HS; Brooklyn, CT; (Y); 5/47; Sec Frsh Cls; Pres Soph Cls; Pres Jr Cls; Pres Sr Cls; Capt Cheerleading; Capt Socr; CT Intrschlstcc Athl Conf Schlr Athl 85; Sccr MVP 85; Bentley Coll; Bus.

SPADJINSKE, SUE; Southington HS; Southington, CT; (Y); VP Church Yth Grp; Cmnty Wkr; Hosp Aide; Band; Concert Band; Drm Mjr(t); Mrchg Band; Music E.

SPAGNOLETTI, JOSEPH J; Watertown HS; Oakville, CT; (Y); 66/250; Computer Clb; Variety Show; L Ftbl; Mgr Ice Hcky; Capt L Trk; High Hon Roll; Bst Prsnlty Cls 85; Unsung Hero Cls 85; Cntrl CT ST U; Accntng.

SPANO, STEVEN; New Britain HS; New Britain, CT; (Y); Band; Mrchg Band; US Air Force; Comp Oprtns.

SPELL, MIA; James Hillhouse HS; New Haven, CT; (Y); Yrbk Stf; High Hon Roll; Hon Roll; Jr NHS; NHS; Indend Stdy Semnr Prog 84-85; Yale U Schl Med Smmr Rsrch Apprntcshp Prog 85; Chld Psych.

SPENCE, CARLINE; Bassick HS; Bridgeport, CT; (S); 5/200; JA; VP Key Clb; Yrbk Stf; Sec Jr Cls; Trs Stu Cncl; High Hon Roll; Hon Roll; NHS; Prfct Atten Awd; Acad Awd 84; Fairfield U; Bio.

SPENCER, CATHERINE; Miss Porters Schl; Annapolis, MD; (Y); GAA; Teachers Aide; Ed Lit Mag; Fld Hcky; Lcrss; JV Mgr(s); Hon Roll; Var Trk; Engl.

SPENCER, JEB; Fairfield College Preparatory Schl; Fairfield, CT; (Y); 31/236; Pres Drama Clb; School Musical; School Play; Nwsp Ed-Chief; Im Lcrss; Socr; High Hon Roll; Hon Roll; NHS; Spanish NHS.

SPENCER, JOANNE; Southington HS; Meriden, CT; (Y); Art Clb; Band; Concert Band; Jazz Band; Mrchg Band; Bsktbl; Powder Puff Ftbl; Sftbl; Hon Roll; Librarian Schl Band 83; Stu Schlr 84-85; Franklin Pierce; Advrtsng.

SPEZIALI, CHRISTINE; St Bernard HS; Stonington, CT; (S); Hosp Aide; Teachers Aide; Rep Yrbk Stf; Off Frsh Cls; Rep Stu Cncl; Var Cheerleading; Trk; High Hon Roll; Hon Roll; GAA; Hnrs With Dstncton; Awd Hghst Acad Grd Frnch; Holy Cross; Pre Dntl.

SPIELMAN, JOHN; Crosby HS; Waterbury, CT; (Y); Church Yth Grp; ROTC; Swmmng; Hon Roll; U Of CT.

SPIES, STACY; Weston HS; Weston, CT; (Y); 17/170; Church Yth Grp; Ski Clb; Chorus; Yrbk Ed-Chief; Lit Mag; Socr; Hon Roll; NHS; Pres Schlr; Mem Yrbk Awd Outstndng Svc 85; Meritorious Svc Yrbk 85; Georgetown U; Psych.

SPILECKI, SUSAN; Sacred Heart Acad; Hamden, CT; (Y); 11/114; Cmnty Wkr; Concert Band; School Musical; Stage Crew; Nwsp Stf; Yrbk Stf; Ed Lit Mag; Rep Stu Cncl; Im Vllybl; French Hon Soc; Assoc Am Des Prof De Francais Cert Hnr; Sacred Heart Acad Excel Eng Awd; Ntl Rifle Assoc Awd; Middlebury Coll; Eng.

SPILLANE, ERIN; Bethel HS; Bethel, CT; (Y); 36/264; Sec AFS; Computer Clb; Ski Clb; Variety Show; Yrbk Stf; Tennis; Stat Vllybl; High Hon Roll; Hon Roll; NHS; Pre-Law.

SPINELLA, SUZANNE; Stamford HS; Stamford, CT; (Y); FHA; Spanish Clb; JV Fld Hcky; JV Sftbl; Hon Roll; Lib Arts.

SPINELLI, VITO; Kolbe-Cathedral HS; Bridgeport, CT; (Y); Sec Camera Clb; Math Clb; Nwsp Phtg; Nwsp Stf; Yrbk Phtg; Pres Stu Cncl; Hon Roll; Prfct Atten Awd; Am Chem Soc Outstndng Achvt,Chem Reasng & Comprhns 84-85; SR Jacqueln Robllrd Schlrshp 84-85.

SPINKS, WENDY; Bassick HS; Bridgeport, CT; (S); 4/200; Drama Clb; Office Aide; Chorus; School Musical; Pres Jr Cls; Stu Cncl; Jr NHS; Fairfield U; Bus Adm.

SPIVACK, MARGERY; Trumbull HS; Trumbull, CT; (Y); Key Clb; Ski Clb; Spanish Clb; Yrbk Stf; Rep Chess Clb; Rep Soph Cls; Rep Jr Cls; Var Cheerleading; High Hon Roll; Hon Roll; Dntstry.

SPIVAK, JAY; Simsbury HS; Simsbury, CT; (Y); 7/356; VP JA; Math Tm; Pres Temple Yth Grp; Ed Yrbk Stf; Socr; High Hon Roll; Hon Roll; NHS; Math Dept Awd 85; JA Ofcr Of Yr 85; Soccr Awd 84; U Of PA; Mngmnt.

SPONZO, SARAH J; Newington HS; Newington, CT; (Y); Drama Clb; Office Aide; Chorus; Capt Drill Tm; School Musical; Variety Show; Yrbk Stf; Rep Soph Cls; Rep Jr Cls; Hon Roll; CT JR Intern Pgm 85; Engl.

SPOONER, SANDRA; Seymour HS; Seymour, CT; (S); 22/224; Church Yth Grp; Debate Tm; High Hon Roll; Criminal Just.

SPRAGUE, JODIE L; Southington HS; Southington, CT; (Y); 39/550; Pres Concert Band; Jazz Band; Mrchg Band; Symp Band; Yrbk Sprt Ed; Var Capt Fld Hcky; Var L Trk; High Hon Roll; NHS; Ntl Merit Ltr; Band Backees Music Awd 85; Stu Of The Mnth Elks Clb 85; U Of CT; Vet.

SPREDA, TAMMY; Southington HS; Plantsville, CT; (Y); 8/560; Am Leg Aux Girls St; Computer Clb; French Clb; Key Clb; Math Tm; Flag Corp; Yrbk Stf; Twrlr; High Hon Roll; NHS; Jr Womens Highest Avg Achiev Awd 83; Pre Med.

SPRINGER, STEPHNEY; Weaver HS; Hartford, CT; (Y); Hosp Aide; Letterman Clb; Nwsp Rptr; Nwsp Stf; Lit Mag; Sec Jr Cls; Crs Cntry; Trk; Hon Roll; Debate Tm; Cert Sci Of Tomrw 83; Essy Cntst Awd 84; Weaver H S Brght Lght 84; Chld Psych.

SQUEO, CHRISTINE; Oliver Wolcott Tech; Sharon, CT; (S); 12/147; Trs Rptr VICA; Yrbk Bus Mgr; Sec Stu Cncl; NHS; Yrbk Stf; Var Capt Bsktbl; Hon Roll; Sharon Womns Clb Schlrshp 85; CBIA Indstry Awd 85; Champlain Coll; Elctrncs Engrng.

SRITHARAN, KUMUDESH; Amity SR HS; Orange, CT; (Y); Model UN; Concert Band; Mrchg Band; Trk; Med.

ST GEORGES III, GEORGE W; East Catholic HS; Broad Brook, CT; (Y); 21/294; Boy Scts; Drama Clb; Church Choir; School Musical; Yrbk Stf; Rep Jr Cls; Hon Roll; JP Sousa Awd; NHS; Holy Cross Bk Awd 85; Engrng.

ST HILAIRE II, GENE; Norwich Free Acad; Taftville, CT; (Y); Am Leg Boys St; Math Tm; Trk; High Hon Roll; Hon Roll; Newton Perkins Outstndng Soc Studs Stu; Norwich Soc NY Current Events Prize; Proj Outreach Vlntr; Pol Sci.

ST JEAN, MICHAEL; Woodstock Acad; Woodstock, CT; (Y); 5/70; Am Leg Boys St; Chess Clb; Var Capt Bsbl; Var L Bsktbl; Bausch & Lomb Sci Awd; Hon Roll; NHS; Bostr Clb Athltc Schlrshp 85; Woodstck Acad Yale Hnr Cup 85; CT Stu/Athl Awd 85; U CT Schl Engrng; Mech Engrng.

STAATERMAN, STACEY; Ridgefield HS; Ridgefield, CT; (Y); 160/386; AFS; Art Clb; Church Yth Grp; Dance Clb; Drama Clb; Ski Clb; Church Choir; Color Guard; School Musical; School Play; Natl Hnr Rll 84-85; Svc AFS 84-85; Svc Clss 85 84-85; Syracuse U; Psych.

STABACK, TRACEY; Cheshire Acad; Meriden, CT; (Y); Computer Clb; Drama Clb; Library Aide; School Musical; School Play; Nwsp Rptr; Yrbk Stf; Hon Roll; Culnry Arts.

STABILE, DENISE M; Danbury HS; Danbury, CT; (S); 39/565; Church Yth Grp; Pres DECA; Drama Clb; FBLA; Trs JA; PAVAS; Ski Clb; School Play; Variety Show; Yrbk Bus Mgr; Lcl, ST, Ntl Awd Medal Wnnrs 84-85; U CT; Pre Law.

STACHELCZYK, SUSAN; Sacred Heart Acad; Ansonia, CT; (Y); Trs Church Yth Grp; Trs FBLA; Hosp Aide; School Musical; Nwsp Ed-Chief; Nwsp Stf; JV Cheerleading; High Hon Roll; NHS; Computer Clb; FBLA Entrepreneurship II 1st Dist/St 85; Rensaeller Purdue; Bio-Med.

STACK, MAUREEN; Holy Cross HS; Oakville, CT; (Y); 92/300; Church Yth Grp; Cmnty Wkr; Concert Band; Mrchg Band; Dance.

STAHL, TIMOTHY; Manchester HS; Manchester, CT; (Y); 9/550; Drama Clb; French Clb; JA; PAVAS; Scholastic Bowl; Thesps; Chorus; School Play; Crs Cntry; Golf; Engrng.

STANFIELD, BRIDGETTE; St Marys Catholic HS; New Haven, CT; (Y); #36 In Class; Pep Clb; Spanish Clb; School Play; Variety Show; Cheerleading; Hon Roll; NHS; Duquesne U; Fornsc Pathlgst.

STANIAR, LAUREN; Greenwich HS; Cos Cob, CT; (Y); Chorus; Stu Cncl; Cheerleading; Im Powder Puff Ftbl; JV Socr; JV Sftbl; Hon Roll; Prncpls Brd 82-83.

STANKEWICH, PAUL; Robert E Fitch SR HS; Groton, CT; (Y); 1/360; Drama Clb; Trs Intnl Clb; Key Clb; Science Clb; Stage Crew; JV Tennis; High Hon Roll, Jr NHS; CT Hnrs Soc For Distngshd HS Stu 85; CT JR Sci & Humnts Sympsm 85; Boys ST 85; Bus Law.

STANOWSKI, KIM A; Berlin HS; Kensington, CT; (Y); Am Leg Aux Girls St; Bsktbl; Powder Puff Ftbl; Socr; Sftbl; High Hon Roll; Jr NHS; Lion Awd; NHS; Pres Schlr.

STANULONIS, ANDREW Q; Windham Reg Technical HS; Colchester, CT; (Y); 8/138; Am Leg Boys St; Church Yth Grp; Pres Soph Cls; Var Capt Bsbl; Hon Roll; Carpentry.

STARGAARD, TOM; Westhill HS; Stamford, CT; (Y); Computer Clb; German Clb; Excllnc Germn 4 84; 1st Pl Phy Sr Div Stmaford Sci Fair 85; CBS Technlgy Ctr Awd Stamfrd Sci Fair 85; U CT; Comp Sci.

STARKEY, JIM; Holy Cross HS; Ansonia, CT; (Y); 39/344; Concert Band; Mrchg Band; Stu Cncl; Var Capt Ftbl; NHS; Ntl Merit Ltr; Boy Scts; Presdtnl Acadmc Ftns Awd 85; Brennan Ftbl Mem Schlrshp 85; Army 4 Yr ROTC Schlrshp 85; MI ST U; Sci.

STARZISKI, JANICE; Naugatuck HS; Naugatuck, CT; (Y); Trs Church Yth Grp; Yrbk Stf; Var Capt Bsktbl; Var Capt Vllybl; High Hon Roll; JR Hon Grd; All-NVL 1st Tm Vlybl, 2nd Tm B Sktbl; Bio.

STASIUK, CHRISTINA; Southington HS; Southington, CT; (Y); 51/600; German Clb; Key Clb; Ski Clb; Symp Band; Ed Yrbk Stf; High Hon Roll; NHS; Church Choir; Trk; Kiwanis Awd; 1st In Cls Grad At Ukranian Schl 85; 1st Pl Flute Schlrshp 85; High GPA Awd 85; Med.

STATKEVICH, PETER; Shelton HS; Shelton, CT; (Y); Am Leg Boys St; Trs Sec Spanish Clb; VP Jr Cls; VP Sr Cls; Rep Stu Cncl; JV Bsbl; Var L Golf; High Hon Roll; NHS; Spanish NHS; Pre-Law.

STAVE, LORI; Mark T Sheehan HS; Wallingford, CT; (Y); 21/225; Art Clb; Spanish Clb; Yrbk Rptr; Yrbk Stf; Trs Soph Cls; Co-Capt Bsktbl; Gym; Powder Puff Ftbl; Socr; Tennis; Plaq Hartford Courant Drwg Publ 83-84; Fine Arts Ed.

STEADMAN, TIM S; Robert E Fitch SR HS; Mystic, CT; (Y); 78/400; Boy Scts; Drama Clb; Varsity Clb; Band; Chorus; Concert Band; Drm Mjr(t); Mrchg Band; School Musical; Swing Chorus; U S Naval Acad; U Of CT.

STEARNS, CINDY; South Windsor HS; S Windsor, CT; (Y); Exploring; Science Clb; Ski Clb; Teachers Aide; Chorus; High Hon Roll; Hon Roll; Sec.

STEARNS, DAVID L; Xavier HS; Wallingford, CT; (Y); 16/199; Boys Clb Am; Church Yth Grp; Cmnty Wkr; Teachers Aide; Stu Cncl; Im Bsbl; Im Bsktbl; Im Ftbl; Im Vllybl; High Hon Roll; Bro Celestine Awd 81-82; Natl Hnr Soc VP 83-85; 1st Cong Chrch Schlrshp 85; Bryant Coll; Acturial Sci.

STEELE, DOUG; Daniel Hand HS; Madison, CT; (Y); Band; Concert Band; Mrchg Band; Pep Band; Symp Band; Clark U; Psych.

STEELMAN, JAMES; St Bernards HS; Mystic, CT; (Y); 95/330; Stat Boy Scts; Computer Clb; Trs Jr Cls; JV Gym; JV Trk; JV Wrstlng; Elctrcl Engrng.

STEEVES, CHRISTINE; West Haven HS; W Haven, CT; (Y); Sec Trs DECA; Yrbk Stf; Rep Soph Cls; Rep Jr Cls; Rep Stu Cncl; JR Prom Qn 85; CT Post Mall Swthrt MDA Fndrsr 85; JR Prom Comm 85.

STEEVES, MARSHALL; Avon HS; Avon, CT; (Y); 16/170; JA; Office Aide; Political Wkr; Nwsp Rptr; High Hon Roll; Hon Roll; Jr NHS; Ntl Merit Ltr; Civic Clb; Nwsp Stf; Cert Merit Frnch IV 85; Cert Merit Media & Cmmctns 85; Bus Admin.

STEFANIK, TRACY A; St Paul Catholic HS; Bristol, CT; (Y); 38/258; Drama Clb; Chorus; School Play; Variety Show; Var Tennis; Hon Roll; Med.

STEFANSKI, LORI; Bristol Central HS; Bristol, CT; (Y); Cmnty Wkr; Drama Clb; Hosp Aide; Stage Crew; High Hon Roll; Hon Roll; NHS; Comm.

STEFFANCI, TOM; Southington HS; Plantsville, CT; (Y); Rep Am Leg Boys St; Church Yth Grp; Ski Clb; Variety Show; Sec Sr Cls; Stu Cncl; L Wrstlng; Hon Roll; Boys ST Rep 85; UCSB; Econ.

STEGINA, LAUREL; Guilford HS; Guilford, CT; (Y); 7/250; Concert Band; Chrmn Mrchg Band; Var L Fld Hcky; Var L Sftbl; High Hon Roll; NHS; Sec Spanish NHS; Excllnce U S Hstry Awd 85; CT Assn Wmn Deans, Admin, Cnslrs Awd 85; Ldrshp Tm 85.

STEIGERWALD, JESSICA; Westhill HS; Stamford, CT; (Y); Cmnty Wkr; German Clb; Sec Math Clb; Sec Science Clb; Chorus; Madrigals; Orch; Orch; Hon Roll; NHS; Excell In Grmn II 84; Pol Sci.

STEIZ, CHARLES T; Jonathan Law HS; Milford, CT; (Y); 21/253; Am Leg Boys St; Key Clb; School Play; Yrbk Sprt Ed; Rep Sr Cls; Rep Stu Cncl; Capt L Crs Cntry; Capt L Trk; Ntl Merit Ltr; Intnl Clb; Pres Acad Fit Awd 85; Class M All ST Relay 85; Rochester Natl Scholar 85; U Of Rochester; Engrng.

STELLA, LOUISE; Southington HS; Southington, CT; (Y); 18/550; Ski Clb; Spanish Clb; School Musical; School Play; Variety Show; Nwsp Stf; High Hon Roll; Hon Roll; VP NHS; Spnsh Schlrshp Acadmc 85; Cmmnty Actvty Tchg Comp Course Deaf Prsns 85; U Of CT; Chem.

STEPHAN, SHARI L; Newington HS; Newington, CT; (Y); Church Yth Grp; Hosp Aide; Key Clb; Library Aide; Teachers Aide; Chorus; Church Choir; Var Fld Hcky; Var Trk; Hon Roll; Nrsg.

STEPHENSON, GEORGIA; Westhill HS; Stamford, CT; (Y); JA; Chorus; JV Mgr(s); Nrses Aide 84-85; Bus.

STERLING, MARIE; East Hartford HS; E Hartford, CT; (Y); Am Leg Aux Girls St; Hosp Aide; Off Jr Cls; JV Bsktbl; Var Swmmng; Hon Roll; NHS; Principals Achvt Awd 83-84; 100 Hr Awd Vol Hartford Hosp 84; Med.

STEWART, JOHN; Torrington HS; Torrington, CT; (Y); 24/320; French Clb; Drm & Bgl; High Hon Roll; Hon Roll; NHS; NEDT Awd.

STEWART, JOSEPH SHANE; Danbury HS; Danbury, CT; (Y); 31/612; Am Leg Boys St; Boy Scts; Nwsp Sprt Ed; Yrbk Stf; Rep Stu Cncl; Var Capt Ftbl; Var Capt Trk; High Hon Roll; NHS; Church Yth Grp; JV Sprtsmnshp Awd Ftbl 84; Hon Mntn All FCIAC Ftbl 85; Perry Awd Outstndng Achvt Engl 85; Aerntcl Engrng.

STEWART, LISA; New London HS; New London, CT; (S); DECA; Girl Scts; Key Clb; Pep Clb; Spanish Clb; Chorus; Cheerleading; Mgr(s); Pom Pon; Trk; DECA Schlrshp 85; ECC Medal Track 84; Bst Jumper Awd Chrldng Camp 84; Johnson & Wales Coll; Fash Mer.

STEWART, WILLIAM M; Northwestern Regional #7 HS; Gloucester, MA; (Y); Ski Clb; Trs Soph Cls; Bsktbl; Capt Socr; Tennis; Yrbk Phtg; Hugh O Brian Yth Ldrshp Fndtn 83; Wshngtn DC Twn Rep Intrnshp 84; Boston U; Bio Sci.

STICCO, DEBORAH; Crosby HS; Waterbury, CT; (Y); Church Yth Grp; Hosp Aide; Key Clb; Latin Clb; Library Aide; Office Aide; Red Cross Aide; Variety Show; High Hon Roll; NHS; Awd For Volntrng At St Mary Hosp 82-84; Med Tech.

STICKEL, SUE; Danbury HS; Danbury, CT; (Y); 72/585; Hosp Aide; Varsity Clb; Chorus; Variety Show; Rep Stu Cncl; Var Capt Cheerleading; Gym; Trk; Jr NHS; NHS; Hnr Rl 81-85.

STILES, KATHLEEN J; Orville H Platt HS; Meriden, CT; (Y); 1/300; French Clb; Key Clb; Yrbk Stf; Rep Jr Cls; Rep Stu Cncl; Var Socr; Var L Tennis; French Hon Soc; High Hon Roll; NHS; Yale Bk Awd 85; Prom Cmmtte 85; Yth In Gvrnmnt Pgm 85; Bio.

STIMSON, NANCY; Eat Hartford HS; E Hartford, CT; (Y); 40/350; Yrbk Stf; Var Diving; Var Gym; Var Sftbl; Var Swmmng; Hon Roll; Mst Imprvd Gymnst 84-85; Mst Outstndng-Dvng 83; All Conf Tm-Sftbl.

STIRLING, DAVID; Thomaston HS; Thomaston, CT; (Y); Camera Clb; French Clb; Band; Yrbk Phtg; High Hon Roll; NHS; L Tennis; Pres Campus Life/Yth Christ Clb 84-85; Fr Exch Rotary Intl 85-86; Vlnteer Tutor, Elem Schl Comp Lab 85; Gordon Coll; Comp Sci.

STITTS, KATHY; Edwin O Smith HS; Mansfield Cte, CT; (Y); 35/188; Church Yth Grp; Chorus; Stage Crew; Yrbk Stf; U Fo CT; Pysch.

STOCKEY, ANDREW; Simsbury HS; W Simsbury, CT; (Y); 87/352; Am Leg Boys St; FBLA; VP JA; Yrbk Sprt Ed; Trs Stu Cncl; JV Bsbl; Coach Actv; Var Ftbl; Wt Lftg; Hon Roll; CT Bus-Indstry Awd 85; Connell Awd-Amer Lgn Bys ST 85; YMCA Bsktbl, Co-MVP Awd 84-85; Radio-TV.

STOCKMAL, GREGORY; Jonathan Law HS; Milford, CT; (Y); 51/250; Am Leg Boys St; Boy Scts; Cmnty Wkr; Drama Clb; Pres Key Clb; Red Cross Aide; VP Band; VP Concert Band; VP Jazz Band; VP Mrchg Band; Milford Yth & Fmly Svcs HRD Mayors Yth Sub Comm Awd 84-85; Music.

STOCKMAN, DEBORA; Bristol Central HS; Britol, CT; (Y); Office Aide; Yrbk Stf; Hon Roll; NHS.

STOCKWELL, TODD; West Haven HS; W Haven, CT; (Y); Yrbk Stf; High Hon Roll; Hon Roll; Jr NHS; NHS; SAR Awd; Mech Engrng.

STODDARD, ANDREW; St Bernard HS; N Stoninston, CT; (Y); Exploring; Rep Jr Cls; JV Socr; JV Trk; Aerosp Engrng.

STOLFI, DAWN; Holy Cross HS; Waterbury, CT; (Y); Service Clb; Speech Tm; Chorus; Church Choir; Yrbk Stf; Lit Mag; Rep Stu Cncl; JV Var Cheerleading; VFW Awd; Voice Dem Awd; Am Leg Schl Awd 84; Pol Sci.

STOLFI, STEPHEN M; Crosby HS; Waterbury, CT; (Y); 56/360; Church Yth Grp; Nwsp Sprt Ed; VP Jr Cls; Pres Sr Cls; L Capt Bsbl; L Bsktbl; L Ftbl; Hon Roll; Key Clb; Latin Clb; Olympn Clb Scholar 84-85; Amer Nwsp Publshrs Assn Awd 84-85; Prncpls Awd 84-85; Hartwick Coll.

STONE, ILENE; Cheshire HS; Cheshire, CT; (Y); Co-Capt Flag Corp; Mrchg Band; School Play; Yrbk Stf; Rep Soph Cls; French Hon Soc; High Hon Roll; Jr NHS; NHS; Outstndng Frnch Stu 82-83; Flg Tm Cmp Supr Rbbn 84.

STONWOOD, NANCY; Bloomfield HS; Bloomfield, CT; (Y); 2/234; Model UN; Ed Lit Mag; Rep Stu Cncl; Var Socr; Var Tennis; Sec French Hon Soc; High Hon Roll; NHS; Trinity Bk Awd 85; Bst U S Hstry Stdnt 85.

STOPPER, BETH; Seymour HS; Oxford, CT; (Y); 41/224; Church Yth Grp; Dance Clb; Girl Scts; Teachers Aide; Variety Show; Rep Soph Cls; JV Var Cheerleading; Hon Roll; GNH Danc Assn Comptn 1st Pl 83; GNH Danc Assn Comptn Brnz Medl 85; Hghst Achvt Spnsh IV 84; W CT ST U; Crim Jstc.

STOPPER, MARK; Naugatuck HS; Naugatuck, CT; (Y); 68/312; Am Leg Boys St; Boy Scts; Church Yth Grp; Ski Clb; Acpl Chr; Chorus; Church Choir; Madrigals; Swing Chorus; Variety Show; Music Scholar 85; CT Essay Awd 84; Waterbury ST Tech Coll; Comp.

STOTLER, KRIS; Bethal HS; Bethel, CT; (Y); 20/246; Church Yth Grp; Chorus; Church Choir; Variety Show; Rep Stu Cncl; JV Cheerleading; Tennis; Wt Lftg; High Hon Roll; NHS; MVP Tnns 81-83; Wstrn CT Tnns Chmpn 83-85; CT ST Tnns Sngls Chmpn 83-84; All-ST Tnns Tm 84-85; Sprts Med.

STRAIN, LINDA P; Choate Rosemary Hall; Poughkeepsie, NY; (Y); French Clb; Nwsp Stf; Yrbk Stf; Ice Hcky; Capt Socr; Capt Sftbl; Hon Roll; Coaches Sccr Awd 82 & 84; All St Sccr 82-84; Sftbl Coaches Awd 84; Sftbl Excllnc Awd 85; Stanford; Poltcl Sci.

STRANG, JOHN; Ansonia HS; Ansonia, CT; (Y); Church Yth Grp; Computer Clb; Political Wkr; Spanish Clb; Var Capt Bsbl; Var Capt Ftbl; Spanish NHS; Heffernon Mem Awd Spirit & Dedication 85; Sports Med.

STRANGE, GERALD; Bristol Central HS; Bristol, CT; (Y); Boys Clb Am; Church Yth Grp; Computer Clb; French Clb; Ski Clb; Rep Stu Cncl; JV Socr; High Hon Roll; NHS; Ntl Merit Ltr; Chem Awd 84; Comp Sci.

STRELOW, TIFFANY; Weston HS; Weston, CT; (Y); Dance Clb; French Clb; Chorus; School Musical; Yrbk Rptr; High Hon Roll; NHS; Art Clb; JA; Pep Clb; Vassar Humnts Awd 85; Varsty Danc Ltr 83 & 84; Lawyr.

STRINGER IV, EDWARD F; Middletown HS; Middletown, CT; (Y); Am Leg Boys St; Var Socr; Var L Swmmng; U GA; Physcn.

STROINEY, ANNE MARIE; Enrico Fermi HS; Enfield, CT; (Y); 33/386; Church Yth Grp; French Clb; Office Aide; Band; Variety Show; Ed Yrbk Ed-Chief; Yrbk Stf; High Hon Roll; Hon Roll; NHS; Bay Path JC Almn Awd 84; Bus Stdnt Mnth 85; Typg Awd 84; Bentley Coll; Acctg.

STROM, KATHLEEN; Ansonia HS; Ansonia, CT; (Y); Church Yth Grp; Computer Clb; Pres Soph Cls; Pres Jr Cls; Stu Cncl; Var Cheerleading; Var Tennis; Hon Roll; NHS; Hugh Obrian Soph Ambssdr 84.

STROUSE, SUSAN; Ridgefield HS; Ridgefield, CT; (S); 121/384; Drm Mjr(t); Mrchg Band; Orch; School Musical; Yrbk Ed-Chief; Hon Roll; Regnl Band 2 Yrs 84-85; All ST Band 84-85; Ridgefield Yth Orch 4 Yrs 81-85; Slippery Rock U; Music Ther.

STRUBELL, MARYANNE; Stafford HS; Stafford Spg, CT; (Y); 14/108; Spanish Clb; Fld Hcky; High Hon Roll; Lion Awd; VP NHS; Outstndg Achvt Spnsh; Var Lcl Schlrshps; Merrimack Coll; Educ.

STUPAK, DONNA; Trumbull HS; Trumbull, CT; (Y); VP Girl Scts; Latin Clb; Drm Mjr(t); Mrchg Band; Symp Band; Nwsp Stf; Vllybl; High Hon Roll; Hon Roll; Bio.

STUPIC, JOSEPH; Seymour HS; Seymour, CT; (S); 6/224; VP AFS; Am Leg Boys St; Drm Mjr(t); Nwsp Stf; Pres Stu Cncl; Var Crs Cntry; Cit Awd; NHS; Harvard Book Prz 84; Elec Engr.

STURGES, CORBY; Lyme-Old Lyme HS; Old Lyme, CT; (Y); 7/110; Pres MMM; Capt Scholastic Bowl; Symp Band; Rep Stu Cncl; Var Crs Cntry; Trs NHS; Ntl Merit SF; Church Yth Grp; Concert Band; Jazz Band; Dartmouth Bk Awd Intellctl Ldrshp 84; Varsity Crew; Russian Studies.

SUAREZ, MANUEL A; Wilton HS; Wilton, CT; (Y); 95/330; Cmnty Wkr; Pres Varsity Clb; Rep Stu Cncl; Ftbl; Capt Lcrss; Cit Awd; Boy Scts; Church Yth Grp; Spanish Clb; Nwsp Rptr; Outstndng Sr Awd 84-85; John Corr Awd 85; Outstndng La Crosse Plyr 85; Brown U; Frgn Svc.

SUH, HYEJONG; Trumbull HS; Trumbull, CT; (Y); AFS; Church Yth Grp; DECA; FNA; Library Aide; Perfct Attndnc Awd 85; Nurse.

SULAM, GREG; Rockville HS; Vernon, CT; (Y); 44/363; Computer Clb; Temple Yth Grp; Band; Concert Band; L Tennis; High Hon Roll; Hon Roll; NHS; Ntl Merit Ltr; Bus.

SULLIVAN, ANDREW D; Tourtelotte HS; N Grosvenordale, CT; (Y); Ski Clb; Golf; Ice Hcky; Prfct Atten Awd; Sci.

SULLIVAN, BRIAN; Holy Cross HS; Waterbury, CT; (Y); 135/355; JA; Political Wkr; Yrbk Stf; Trs Soph Cls; Trs Jr Cls; Trs Sr Cls; Var Lcrss; Var Wrstlng; Cit Awd; Hon Roll; Jr Glf Clb Chmpn-Cntry Clb Of Waterbury 85; Bus.

SULLIVAN, BRIDGET THERESA; Simsbury HS; W Simsbury, CT; (Y); 85/356; Church Yth Grp; Cmnty Wkr; Pres Girl Scts; Varsity Clb; Chorus; Madrigals; School Play; Bsktbl; Hon Roll; Irl Sct Gld Awd Recip 85; Humphrey Awd 85; Music Awd 85; Smith Coll; Edit.

SULLIVAN JR, CHARLES H; St Paul Catholic HS; Southington, CT; (Y); 21/258; Boy Scts; French Clb; VP Ski Clb; Lit Mag; Rep Soph Cls; Rep Jr Cls; Rep Stu Cncl; JV Socr; NHS; Yale Frontiers Sci 85; Math.

SULLIVAN, JOHN; Berlin HS; Kensington, CT; (Y); Drama Clb; JA; Radio Clb; Band; Concert Band; Mrchg Band; JV Golf; Jr NHS; U S Army; Pol Sci.

SULLIVAN, JOHN M; Notre Dame HS; N Branford, CT; (Y); 56/240; Cmnty Wkr; Ski Clb; Stu Cncl; Hon Roll; Peer Cnslng 85-86; Mgmt.

SULLIVAN, MOLLY; Conard HS; W Hartford, CT; (Y); 12/279; Church Yth Grp; Hosp Aide; Chorus; Yrbk Stf; Sec Jr Cls; Rep Sr Cls; Rep Stu Cncl; Var Fld Hcky; Stat Gym; Mgr(s); Marion Jones Bk Prz 84; U Of VT; Nrsng.

SUMMER, IRENE A; Notre Dame Catholic HS; Easton, CT; (Y); 87/284; Pres Girl Scts; Rep Keywanettes; Stage Crew; Nwsp Ed-Chief; Capt Swmmng; Grl Sct Gld Awd 85; Grl Sct Slvr Awd 83; Ithaca Coll.

SUNEGA, WENDY; East Catholic HS; E Windsor, CT; (Y); Church Yth Grp; Church Choir; Off Jr Cls; Off Sr Cls; Off Stu Cncl; Gym; High Hon Roll; Hon Roll; Bus.

SUNSERI, MARK; Danbury HS; Danbury, CT; (Y); Varsity Clb; Variety Show; Nwsp Rptr; Nwsp Stf; Rep Stu Cncl; Var Trk; Comp.

SUPPLE, CHRISTOPHER SCOTT; Masuk HS; Monroe, CT; (Y); Hosp Aide; Var Wrstlng; Var High Hon Roll; Var Hon Roll; Spanish NHS; Ceart Outstndng Achvt French II Hnrs 85; Schlrshp Monroe Schlrshp Fndtn 85; Pres Acad Ftns Awd 85; Franklin Pierie Coll; Mass Medi.

SURGEON, KIRK; Westhill HS; Stamford, CT; (Y); Drama Clb; Acpl Chr; Chorus; Variety Show; Tennis; Hon Roll; Schl Ltr Musicl Achvt 85; Boston Col6; Bus Mgmnt.

SURI, ASHU; Canterbury HS; Danbury, CT; (Y); 2/80; Camera Clb; Pres Computer Clb; Debate Tm; Ski Clb; Teachers Aide; Ed Nwsp Stf; Ed Yrbk Stf; JV Lcrss; JV Socr; Var Capt Wrstlng; Genetic Inst Scholar 84; James A Farrel Awd Mth Excllnce 85; John S Burke Awd Oper Rsrch Proj 85; Princeton U; Pre-Med.

SUROWIEC, CINDY; Berlin HS; Berlin, CT; (Y); Church Yth Grp; Cmnty Wkr; Dance Clb; Girl Scts; Hosp Aide; Service Clb; Drill Tm; School Musical; School Play; Yrbk Stf; Bsktbl & Ftbl 83-85; Drill Team; Mrktng.

SUTTON, ANDREA; Holy Cross HS; Waterbury, CT; (Y); French Hon Soc; Hon Roll.

SUTTON, FRANK; Southeastern Tech; Lyme, CT; (S); 34/163; Church Yth Grp; Cmnty Wkr; Library Aide; Political Wkr; VICA; Cit Awd; Hon Roll; Govrnrs Awd Outstndg Svc To Yth 84; Pres SADD Schl & ST 82-85; Pres Yth Orgnzatn United 84-85; Johnson; Culinary Art.

SVEHLAK, STEVEN; Seymour HS; Oxford, CT; (S); Var L Swmmng; High Hon Roll; NHS; Outstndng Achvt Alg II 83, Spnsh II 84; Hnrbl Ment Drftng I 82; Pre Med.

SWAGERTY, MARK R; Newington HS; Newington, CT; (Y); Boys Clb Am; Church Yth Grp; Cmnty Wkr; FCA; Teachers Aide; Pres Frsh Cls; Capt Bsktbl; Capt Ftbl; Hon Roll; Ntl Merit Ltr; Wesleyan; Corp Law.

SWANBERY, BETH; Andrew Warde HS; Fairfield, CT; (Y); GAA; Var L Fld Hcky; Var Score Keeper; Im Vllybl; Hon Roll; Bus Curriculum Achvt 85; Fash Merch.

SWANSON, KERRY D; Naugatuck HS; Naugatuck, CT; (Y); 7/323; Am Leg Boys St; Trs Computer Clb; DECA; VP Library Aide; VP Science Clb; Im Fld Hcky; Var L Ftbl; Var Capt Trk; Bausch & Lomb Sci Awd; High Hon Roll; ROTC Scholar; AARP Scholar 85; PA ST U; Aerospc Engrng.

SWANSON, PAUL; Glastonbury HS; Glastonbury, CT; (Y); 2/428; Am Leg Boys St; French Clb; Ski Clb; Jazz Band; Yrbk Sprt Ed; Capt Socr; Tennis; French Hon Soc; NHS; Sal; Chemathn Cntrl CT ST U Top Chem Stu 84; Brown; Chem.

SWANSON, SCOTT; Bristol Central HS; Bristol, CT; (Y); Latin Clb; Ski Clb; Jazz Band; Mrchg Band; Pep Band; Symp Band; Off Stu Cncl; Crs Cntry; Trk; Hon Roll; JV Lttr 84; Athl Number 84; All City Wind Ensmbl 84-85.

SWEATT, ELLEN; Bristol Central HS; Bristol, CT; (Y); Drama Clb; Chorus; School Play; Stage Crew; High Hon Roll; Hon Roll; NHS; ACL/NYCL Natl Latin Exam Cum Laude 83-84; CT Latin Exam Cum Dignitate 84-85; Psych.

SWEENEY, JANET MARIE; Sacred Heart Acad; New Haven, CT; (Y); 31/114; 4-H; Service Clb; Spanish Clb; School Play; Variety Show; Nwsp Rptr; 4-H Awd; High Hon Roll; NHS; Spanish NHS; Yale U Frntrs Appld Sci 83; U Of New Havn Sci Smnr Series 84; Per Cnslng Prgm 84-85; U Of CT; Psych.

SWEENEY, PATRICK T; Southington HS; Southington, CT; (Y); 204/550; Pres Aud/Vis; Camp Fr Inc; Church Yth Grp; Cmnty Wkr; Pres Radio Clb; Drm & Bgl; Variety Show; Bsktbl; Hon Roll; Barry U-Miami FL; Commnctn Art.

SWEET, ERIC; Brien Mc Matton HS; Norwalk, CT; (Y); 46/348; Key Clb; Band; Concert Band; Jazz Band; Mrchg Band; Orch; Pep Band; Symp Band; Yrbk Stf; Tennis.

SWEETING, ANDREW; Avon Old Farms HS; Avon, CT; (S); 26/120; Jr Cls; JV Crs Cntry; JV Lcrss; JV Swmmng; Trk; JV Wrstlng; MIP Swmmng 84.

SWEETLAND, ANNE-MARIE; Edwin O Smith HS; W Willington, CT; (Y); Am Leg Aux Girls St; Debate Tm; French Clb; Intnl Clb; Pep Clb; Band; Drm & Bgl; Mrchg Band; Pep Band; VP Stu Cncl; Natl Frnch Awds 82-84; Amer Intl Coll; Intl Bus.

SWENSON, DANA; Daniel Hand HS; Madison, CT; (Y); 19/270; FCA; GAA; Pep Clb; Ski Clb; Band; Concert Band; Yrbk Stf; Var Cheerleading; Coach Actv; JV Gym; Schlrshp Bus Wk Pgm 85; Boston Coll; Bus Adm.

SWIFT, KATHLEEN; Academy Of Our Lady Of Mercy; Milford, CT; (Y); Latin Clb; Sec Math Clb; Math Tm; Service Clb; Spanish Clb; Jr NHS; NHS; Spanish NHS; Cert Hnrb Mntn Maxima Cum Laude Natl Latin Exam 83-84 & 84-85; Cert Ed Develpmnt Natl NEDT 83-84; Engrng.

SWINDLE, HONEY; New London HS; New London, CT; (Y); Church Yth Grp; Band; Chorus; Church Choir; Mrchg Band; School Musical; Hon Roll; 1st Pl Batton Twrlng 81; Mitchell Coll; Elem Ed.

SYMANSKI, TRACY; Jonathan Law HS; Milford, CT; (Y); Cmnty Wkr; Keywanettes; Pep Clb; Var Cheerleading; Acctng.

SYNNOTT, MAURA; Holy Cross HS; Waterbury, CT; (Y); 79/360; Art Clb; French Clb; Hosp Aide; Service Clb; JV L Crs Cntry; JV L Trk; NHS; Pre-Law.

SYPNIEWSKI, ELLEN; Holy Cross HS; Seymour, CT; (Y); 36/344; Church Yth Grp; Ed Yrbk Stf; Hon Roll; NHS; Spanish NHS; Var Capt Sftbl; Sftbl Schlrshp Becker JC 85; Joyce Stochmal Schlrshp 85; Becker JC; Trvl Mgt.

SZARKA, ROBERT; Norwich Free Acad; Norwich, CT; (Y); Am Leg Boys St; Church Yth Grp; Chorus; Church Choir; Jazz Band; Ntl Merit Ltr; Sec VP Computer Clb; Math Tm; Service Clb; High Hon Roll; Chrstn Music.

SZATKOWSKI, PAUL; Manchester HS; Manchester, CT; (Y); JV Crs Cntry; Var L Trk; Hon Roll; Nrthestrn U; Phrmcy.

SZATKOWSKI, SUSAN; Bethel HS; Bethel, CT; (Y); 27/264; AFS; Church Yth Grp; Sec Concert Band; Mrchg Band; School Play; Nwsp Stf; Fld Hcky; Tennis; High Hon Roll; NHS; Chem.

SZPAK, KAREN M; Southington HS; Southington, CT; (Y); 10/550; Key Clb; Math Clb; Math Tm; Yrbk Stf; Elks Awd; High Hon Roll; Jr NHS; NHS; Citzns Ntl Bk Schlrshp 85; Frnch Awd 82; U Hartford; Acctng.

SZYMANSKI, JANE; Shelton HS; Shelton, CT; (Y); Girl Scts; Hosp Aide; Latin Clb; Sec Frsh Cls; Sec Soph Cls; Rep Stu Cncl; Cheerleading; Hon Roll; Nrsng Awd 85; St Vincent Schl Nrsg; Nrsg.

SZYMBORSKI, ALEXANDRA; Greenwich HS; Old Greenwich, CT; (Y); Drama Clb; Chorus; School Musical; School Play; Lit Mag; Hon Roll; Library Aide; Service Clb; Stage Crew; Parish Schrlshp Awd 82-83; Eng Spkng Un 85; Bella Hse Poetry Awds 84-85; Eng.

TABER, MATTHEW; The Hotchkiss HS; Salisbury, CT; (Y); Church Yth Grp; Drama Clb; Concert Band; School Play; Nwsp Stf; Yrbk Stf; Bsbl; JV Ftbl; Capt-Nordic Ski Tm 84-85; Wnnr Nordic Ski Awd 84-85.

TADDEI, CHRIS; Notre Dame Of West Haven HS; N Haven, CT; (Y); 11/254; Latin Clb; Pep Clb; Quiz Bowl; Capt Scholastic Bowl; Yrbk Ed-Chief; Lit Mag; High Hon Roll; NHS.

TAGLIATELA, WILLIAM P; Mark T Sheehan HS; Wallingford, CT; (Y); 34/250; Hon Roll; Pol Sci.

TAIT, ANDREW; Masuk HS; Monroe, CT; (Y); 26/280; Trs Church Yth Grp; French Clb; JCL; Latin Clb; Math Tm; Var L Ice Hcky; Var L Socr; High Hon Roll; NHS; Ntl Merit Ltr.

TALBOT, GLEN; Oliver Wolcott Tech Schl; Winsted, CT; (Y); Art Clb; Drama Clb; VICA; Nwsp Ed-Chief; Nwsp Stf; Yrbk Stf; Stu Cncl; Golf; Hon Roll; VICA Comp Top 6 CT 85; NW CT Coll; Fine Arts.

TALBOT, JULIA; Wilbur L Cross HS; New Haven, CT; (S); 11/189; French Clb; Chorus; Yrbk Stf; Lit Mag; JV Fld Hcky; JV Lcrss; Im Swmmng; Hon Roll; Hist Awd 84; Lit Mag Ed 84-85; Yth Grp Sec 84-85.

TALBOT, KENNETH; Southington HS; Southington, CT; (Y); Ski Clb; Band; Concert Band; Hon Roll.

TALLEY, MICHELLE; Killingly HS; Danielson, CT; (Y); 20/330; Chorus; Concert Band; Mrchg Band; Pep Band; Symp Band; JV Mgr(s); JV Score Keeper; Hon Roll; Psych.

TAMULEVICH, DAVID; Vinal RVTS HS; Northford, CT; (Y); ROTC; VICA; High Hon Roll; Hon Roll; Engr.

TANGNEY, LISA; Southington HS; Southington, CT; (Y); Aud/Vis; Hosp Aide; Key Clb; Pep Clb; Ski Clb; Hon Roll; Apple Harvst Festvl Hosts 85; Goethe-Inst Bostn Awd Excllnc Grmn 86.

TAPLEY, ELLEN; Housatonic Valley Regional HS; Lakeville, CT; (S); Band; Nwsp Stf; Lit Mag; Sec Soph Cls; VP Jr Cls; Var Bsktbl; Var Capt Fld Hcky; Var Sftbl; High Hon Roll; NHS; Scndry Ed.

TAPPIN, LOLANDA; James Hillhouse HS; New Haven, CT; (Y); Rep Jr Cls; JV Sftbl; Capt Vllybl; Elks Awd; High Hon Roll; NHS; Prfct Atten Awd; Church Yth Grp; 4-H; Church Choir; Crimnlgy Rsrch Awd; Thurgood Marshall Awd; Coll Biol I Awd; Hampton Inst; Nrsg.

TAR, EVA MARIE; Valley Regional HS; Chester, CT; (Y); 7/138; Chess Clb; Church Yth Grp; Civic Clb; Cmnty Wkr; Computer Clb; Drama Clb; English Clb; 4-H; French Clb; Rptr FBLA; Ntl Hnr Soc Schlrshp 85; Bruse Waterman Mem Schlrshp 85; Wellesley Coll; Microbio.

TARADINA, JOSEPH S; New Britain HS; New Britain, CT; (Y); 39/367; French Clb; FBLA; FTA; Math Tm; Quiz Bowl; Bsbl; Bsktbl; Crs Cntry; Socr; Tennis; Central CT ST U; Bus.

TARASKA, WALTER; St Thomas Aquinas HS; New Britain, CT; (Y); 9/152; CAP; Debate Tm; French Clb; Scholastic Bowl; Drill Tm; Var Crs Cntry; Var Trk; Hon Roll; NHS; Chem-A-Thon Tm 85; US Miltry Acad; Aerontcl Engnr.

TARINI, LISA A; Seymour HS; E Seymour, CT; (Y); Girl Scts; Sec JA; Church Choir; Yrbk Stf; Rep Frsh Cls; Rep Soph Cls; Rep Jr Cls; Pom Pon; Hon Roll; Law.

TART, BEVERLY; East Haven HS; E Haven, CT; (Y); #24 In Class; Church Yth Grp; Latin Clb; Library Aide; Nwsp Stf; Yrbk Stf; Rep Stu Cncl; Hon Roll; NHS; Med.

TARTAGLIA, DONNA; Masuk HS; Monroe, CT; (Y); Var L Cheerleading; Hmcmng Queen 83-84; Bus.

TASHJIAN, MATT; Hall HS; W Hartford, CT; (Y); Art Clb; Ski Clb; Band; Concert Band; Jazz Band; Mrchg Band; Orch; Pep Band; School Musical; Stage Crew; Bus Adm.

TATE, KEVIN; Hartford HS; Hartford, CT; (Y); JA; Chorus; Concert Band; Ftbl; Trk; Wt Lftg; Wrstlng; Elec.

TAUBER, DAN; Westhill HS; Stamford, CT; (Y); Math Clb; Chorus; Jazz Band; Crs Cntry; Trk; VP NHS; Ntl Merit SF; Science Clb; Acpl Chr; School Play; CT Chemathn Awd 84; Amer Chem Socty Outstndng 1st Yr Chem Stdnt 84.

TAVANO, THERESA; East Catholic HS; E Hartford, CT; (Y); 74/294; Cmnty Wkr; Var Cheerleading; Hon Roll; Miss Sweetland Schlrhsp 83-84; Ed.

TAVARES, AMERICO; Naugatuck HS; Naugatuck, CT; (Y); L Bsbl; L Bsktbl; L Socr; U Of CT; Elctrcl Engrng.

TAVARES, LISA; Joseph A Foran HS; Milford, CT; (Y); Church Yth Grp; Dance Clb; JCL; Key Clb; Latin Clb; Color Guard; Sec Jr Cls; Stu Cncl; Var Cheerleading; Hon Roll; Spelman Coll; Comm.

TAYLOR, ANDREA; Richard C Lee HS; Hamden, CT; (Y); 8/202; Pep Clb; Yrbk Stf; Var Cheerleading; Hon Roll; NHS; Ntl Merit Schol; Rotary Awd; St Schlr; Greatst Achvt Chem 83; Rotry Clb & Mc Kuster Trstee Schlrshps 85; CT Coll; Chld Psych.

TAYLOR, DAWN; Holy Cross HS; Semour, CT; (Y); Hosp Aide; Science Clb; Soc Studs Hon Soc 84-85; Salve Regina; Med Tech.

TAYLOR, MICHAEL; Manchester HS; Manchester, CT; (Y); Boy Scts; Debate Tm; Band; Chorus; Mrchg Band; JV Ftbl; Capt L Wrstlng; High Hon Roll; Hon Roll; Ntl Merit Ltr; Comp Engrng.

TAYLOR, NELL; Simsbury HS; Weatogue, CT; (Y); Rep Stu Cncl; JV Var Fld Hcky; Hon Roll; Intr Dsgn.

TAYLOR, SHARON; Kaynor Tech; Waterbury, CT; (Y); VP VICA; Yrbk Stf; Sec Stu Cncl; Hon Roll; Hosp Aide; Nwsp Stf; Cheerleading; Drftg.

TAYLOR, UNA; Weaver HS; Hartford, CT; (Y); Computer Clb; Office Aide; Teachers Aide; Trk; Hon Roll; NHS; Prfct Atten Awd; Oberlin Book Awd Hghst Avg Pre-Calculus 85; Cert Merit Soc Wmn Engrs Excllnce Mth & Sci 85; Howard U; Accntnt.

TE HENNEPE, LAURA K; New London HS; New London, CT; (Y); 3/168; Am Leg Aux Girls St; Drama Clb; VP Soph Cls; Mgr(s); Var Capt Tennis; High Hon Roll; Jr NHS; Sec NHS; Pres Schlr; Rotary Awd; Pre-Calculus Awd; Natl Merit PSAT Scores; Kaplan Mem Awd; Carleton Coll.

TEAGUE, MATTHEW; St Bernard HS; Bradford, RI; (S); 25/295; Cmnty Wkr; Library Aide; Office Aide; Stu Cncl; 4-H Awd; High Hon Roll; Hon Roll; Jr NHS; NHS; Acad Excel 81-83; Art Awd 84; Worcester Polytech Inst; Engrng.

TELFORD JR, BOB; Daniel Hand HS; Madison, CT; (Y); Boy Scts; Church Yth Grp; Cmnty Wkr; Ski Clb; Im Badmtn; Bowling; Im Lcrss; Im Sftbl; Im Tennis; Im Vllybl; Paul Smith Coll; Forstry.

TEMPLE, KRISTIN; Tourtellotle HS; Quinebaug, CT; (Y); Hosp Aide; Ski Clb; Capt Flag Corp; Yrbk Stf; Pres Stu Cncl; Stat Bsbl; Stat Bsktbl; Var L Crs Cntry; Jr NHS; Physcl Thrpy.

TEMPLETON, LAURIE-ANN; Conrad HS; W Hartford, CT; (Y); 4/291; Church Yth Grp; Latin Clb; Q&S; Chorus; Church Choir; School Musical; Kiwanis Awd; NHS; Pres Schlr; Wesleyan Bk Awd 84; NE Conf Latin Awd 85; PTO Acad Excllnce Awd 85; St Joseph Coll; Nrsng.

TENCELLENT JR, DONALD J; East Catholic HS; Manchester, CT; (Y); Church Yth Grp; Cmnty Wkr; Rep Frsh Cls; Rep Soph Cls; Rep Jr Cls; Rep Sr Cls; JV Stat Bsktbl; JV Mgr(s); JV Var Socr; Hon Roll; Bus Mngmnt.

TEODOSIO, MARGARET; Sacred Heart Acad; Ansonia, CT; (Y); Art Clb; Church Yth Grp; Stage Crew; High Hon Roll; Spanish NHS; Ten Clb 82-83; Cooking Clb 83-84; Pro Life Clb 84-85; Spch Thrpy.

TEPPER, ALISON; Hall HS; W Hartford, CT; (Y); Sec Stu Cncl; Var L Lcrss; Var L Socr; Mgr Tennis; 2nd Annl Schl Art Exhbt 85; Al-Conf Sccr 85.

TERBAN, SCOTT A; Tolland HS; Tolland, CT; (Y); Camera Clb; Madrigals; School Musical; School Play; Trk; Ctr Creative Yth 83-84; Schlrshp Attend CCY 84; RI Schl Design; Comm Art.

TERKELSEN, SANDRA; Greenwich HS; Greenwich, CT; (Y); Church Yth Grp; Band; Church Choir; Concert Band; Mrchg Band; Rep Stu Cncl; High Hon Roll; Hon Roll; Music Eductn.

TERWILLIGER, KIM; Wm H Hall HS; W Hartford, CT; (Y); Band; Yrbk Stf; Rep Sr Cls; Var Lcrss; JV Socr; Hon Roll.

TETREAULT, MONIQUE; Staples HS; Westport, CT; (Y); 4/200; Cmnty Wkr; Girl Scts; Spanish Clb; Acpl Chr; Band; Chorus; Church Choir; Powder Puff Ftbl; JV Trk; Var Vllybl; U Of Bridgeport; Art.

THALBERG, DEBRA A; Amity SR HS; Woodbridge, CT; (Y); 111/376; Drama Clb; Chorus; Madrigals; Orch; School Musical; Hon Roll; 1st Pl CT Chptr Amer Harp Soc Comp 82-83; Harpst Sec Co Govrnr Footguard Recep 85; Prof Harpst.

THAYER, JENNIFER; Guilford HS; Guilford, CT; (Y); 37/264; Trs Church Yth Grp; Teachers Aide; Chorus; Yrbk Bus Mgr; NHS; 1st Pl CT Gov Commttn; Emplymnt Handicpped Jrnlsm Cont 85; Congrssmns Mdl Merit 85; Delta Kappa Gamma; James Madison U; Spec Ed.

THAYER, REBEKAH; Holy Cross HS; Propect, CT; (Y); 52/354; Cmnty Wkr; Service Clb; Acpl Chr; Stage Crew; Variety Show; JV Var Sftbl; High Hon Roll; Hon Roll; NHS; Varsity Clb; Peer Minister; Civil Engnrng.

THERIAULT, NICOLE; Old Saybrook SR HS; Old Saybrook, CT; (Y); Am Leg Aux Girls St; Cmnty Wkr; French Clb; Ski Clb; Chorus; Flag Corp; Nwsp Rptr; Rep Stu Cncl; Var Cheerleading; JV Crs Cntry; Stu Pilot Licns; Flight Schl; Engr.

THERMENOS, NICK; Cheshire HS; Cheshire, CT; (Y); Church Yth Grp; CAP; Teachers Aide; Nwsp Phtg; Yrbk Phtg; Rep Jr Cls; Rep Sr Cls; Lcrss; Socr; Hon Roll; Bus.

THIBODROW, LISA A; East Hartford HS; E Hartford, CT; (Y); 32/260; Sec FBLA; Trs Frsh Cls; Sec Soph Cls; Rep Jr Cls; Rep Sr Cls; Trs Stu Cncl; Capt Cheerleading; High Hon Roll; St Schlr; Office Aide; Prncpls Achvt Awd 83-85; FBLA Jb Intrvw 3rd Pl ST Awd 85; Natl Hnr Roll 85; FBLA Accntng & Dist Awd; Briarwood Coll; Accntng.

THOMAS, AGLAEEZAHIRA; Bloomfield HS; Bloomfield, CT; (Y); Computer Clb; French Clb; FBLA; FHA; Spanish Clb; Chorus; School Musical; Mgr(s); Hon Roll; Yale U; Ob/Gyn.

THOMAS, CHRISTIAN; Avon Old Farms Schl; Cairo, NY; (S); 10/100; Cmnty Wkr; Computer Clb; Dance Clb; Ski Clb; Varsity Clb; Nwsp Stf; Bsbl; Bsktbl; Im Socr; Im Tennis; Chem Engrng.

THOMPSON, CRYSTAL; Kolbe-Cathedral HS; Bridgeport, CT; (Y); 7/99; Dance Clb; Drama Clb; Math Clb; Spanish Clb; Speech Tm; Drill Tm; School Musical; School Play; Variety Show; Sr Cls; Acad Awd Wnnr 85; Trinity Coll; Bio.

THOMPSON, DUSHAWN; Stratford HS; Stratford, CT; (Y); Church Yth Grp; JA; Pep Clb; Variety Show; JV Bsbl; JV Var Bsktbl; Var Crs Cntry; JV Ftbl; Hon Roll; Cert Achvt Fairfield U Upwrd Bnd Pgm 84 & 85; Engrng.

THOMPSON, ELIZABETH; St Bernards HS; Gales Ferry, CT; (S); Church Yth Grp; Hosp Aide; Library Aide; Chorus; Stu Cncl; Hon Roll.

THOMPSON, JENNIFER; St Bernard HS; Gales Ferry, CT; (S); 14/290; VP Church Yth Grp; Hosp Aide; Office Aide; Service Clb; Ski Clb; Band; Orch; Stu Cncl; High Hon Roll; NHS; Pre Med.

THOMPSON, KIM; North Bradford HS; Northford, CT; (Y); 17/157; Drama Clb; Chorus; Church Choir; School Play; Variety Show; Var Cheerleading; Gym; High Hon Roll; Hon Roll; Cert Of Excl In Spanish I & II 82-83; Sthrn CT ST U; Erly Chldhd Ed.

THOMPSON, MICHAEL; Crosby HS; Waterbury, CT; (Y); Boys Clb Am; JV Bsbl; Gym; Hon Roll; Gymnstcs Schl Schlrshp 81; Bsebl; Wtby ST Tech; Elec Engr.

THOMPSON, MICHELLE; Guilford SR HS; Guilford, CT; (Y); 25/266; Trs German Clb; Pres Sec Key Clb; Model UN; Pres Soph Cls; Pres Stu Cncl; JV Bsktbl; Var L Trk; French Hon Soc; NHS; MENSA Awd Exc Wrtng 85; George Washngton U; Intl Law.

THOMPSON, MICHELLE A; Danbury HS; Danbury, CT; (S); 100/525; Trs DECA; Color Guard; Hon Roll; DECA Natl Career Devlpmt Confrnce 85; Fnlst In DECA St Comp 85; 1st Pl In DECA Dstrct Comp 84; Post Coll; Mrktng.

THOMPSON, TAMMY L; Crosby HS; Waterbury, CT; (Y); Latin Clb; VP Library Aide; Ski Clb; Chorus; School Play; Sftbl; Vllybl; High Hon Roll; NHS; Pres Schlr; James & Phyllis Tracy Fndtn Scholar 85; CT Schltc Achvt Grant 85; U CT; Pre-Med.

THOMPSON, TIMOTHY TRENT; Windham HS; W Willington, CT; (Y); 12/310; Am Leg Boys St; Ski Clb; Sr Cls; Var L Bsbl; Var L Bsktbl; Var L Ftbl; High Hon Roll; Hon Roll; Mu Alp Tht; NHS; Natl Ftbll Found & Hll Fme Schlr Athl 85; Schlr Athl Awd 85; Thomas Meikle Awd 85; USMA West Point; Elec Engnrng.

THOMSON, ROBERT; Hall HS; Hartford, CT; (Y); Crs Cntry; Socr; Trk; French Hon Soc; U Of CT Storres; Engrng.

THOMSON, ROBERT M; Southington HS; Southington, CT; (Y); Var L Bsktbl; L Capt Ftbl; Var L Trk; High Hon Roll; NHS; All Conf Def Bck Ftbl 85; Hnrbl Mntn All-ST Db Ftbl 85; Bus.

THORBURN, LINDA; Danbury HS; Danbury, CT; (Y); 129/612; Church Yth Grp; VP Exploring; Hosp Aide; Acpl Chr; Nwsp Rptr; Im Bsbl; Gym; Hon Roll; Perry Awd Frnch 84; Stu Quater Hm Ec 83; Physcl Thrpy.

THOROUGHGOOD, DAISY L; Choate Rosemary Hall HS; Carpinteria, CA; (Y); French Clb; Teachers Aide; Stage Crew; Var Fld Hcky; Var Lcrss; Hon Roll; Coachs Awd Vrsty La Crosse 85; Peer Counslr 85; Stu Life Commt 83.

THORP, HOWARD; St Bernard HS; Westerly, RI; (Y); CAP; JV Var Ftbl; Peer Ldrshp Pgm; Citadel.

THURZ, MICHAEL; East Catholic HS; Glastonbury, CT; (Y); 156/319; Boy Scts; Church Yth Grp; Capt Exploring; Ski Clb; Hon Roll; Pre-Law.

TIBERIO, ROGER; Stratford HS; Stratford, CT; (Y); 79/241; Ski Clb; Nwsp Phtg; Nwsp Rptr; Off Sr Cls; Stu Cncl; Var Crs Cntry; Hon Roll; Accntng.

TICHY, KURT; Seymour HS; Oxford, CT; (S); 3/224; Church Yth Grp; Variety Show; Im Bsbl; L Trk; High Hon Roll; Trs NHS; PA ST U; Pre Med.

TICKNER, JOEL A; Avon HS; Avon, CT; (Y); 20/200; Drama Clb; Math Tm; Ski Clb; Madrigals; School Musical; Symp Band; Var Capt Crs Cntry; Var Trk; NHS; CT Div Chorus 85; Colby Coll; Med.

TIEMANN, JENNIFER; Danbury HS; Westlake Village, CA; (Y); 6/618; Church Yth Grp; Varsity Clb; Variety Show; Mgr(s); Var Trk; Hon Roll; NHS; Sprtsmnshp Awd Trck 84-85; Perry Awd Hist 84-85.

TIENKEN, KIRSTEN; Southington HS; Southington, CT; (Y); 24/570; Sec Church Yth Grp; German Clb; Hosp Aide; Trs Pres Key Clb; Yrbk Stf; Mgr(s); High Hon Roll; NHS; Elem Educ.

TIERNAN, EDWARD; St Thomas More Schl; Brentwood, NY; (Y); Var Trk; Var Wt Lftg; Hon Roll; Boston U; Film.

TILKI, JOHN; Derby HS; Derby, CT; (Y); 2/100; Am Leg Boys St; Computer Clb; Math Tm; Nwsp Ed-Chief; Pres Frsh Cls; Pres Soph Cls; Pres Jr Cls; Pres Stu Cncl; JV Bsbl; Var Ftbl; Math Team Hgh Scr 84-85; MIT; Engrng.

TILLEY, ANGELA; Miss Porters Schl; Ft Worth, TX; (Y); Debate Tm; GAA; Model UN; Varsity Clb; Yrbk Stf; Rep Soph Cls; Capt Socr; Var Vllybl; High Hon Roll; Church Yth Grp; 2nd Nead New Girls 85-86; Lang.

TILLSON, KAREN; Trumbull HS; Solon, OH; (Y); Concert Band; Mrchg Band; Symp Band; High Hon Roll; NHS; Comm.

TILTON, JEFF; Daniel Hand HS; Madison, CT; (Y); Art Clb; Boy Scts; Church Yth Grp; Computer Clb; Debate Tm; German Clb; Science Clb; Hon Roll; Sci Fair Wnnr; Social Stds Fair Wnnr; Aerospc.

TIMKO, KAREN; East Hartford HS; E Hartford, CT; (Y); 1/260; JA; Yrbk Stf; Rep Frsh Cls; Trs Soph Cls; Sec Jr Cls; Sec Sr Cls; Stu Cncl; Var Capt Tennis; High Hon Roll; Pres NHS; Harvard-Radcliffe Clb Bk Awd; Hartford-Wellesley Clb Bk Awd; Exchng Clb Stu Of Mnth; Fairfield U; Bio.

TINO, CHRISTOPHER R; East Granby HS; East Granby, CT; (Y); 9/60; Boy Scts; Church Yth Grp; Stage Crew; Yrbk Phtg; JV Bsbl; JV Bsktbl; JV Crs Cntry; JV Trk; High Hon Roll; Hon Roll; Life Sct BSA 85; Cmmndtn Supt Prfct Atten 85; Mst Imprvd Plyr JV Bsbl 85; IL Inst Tech; Aero Engrng.

TINYSZIN, KATERYNA; New Britain HS; New Britain, CT; (Y); 32/385; Church Yth Grp; Pres German Clb; JA; Key Clb; Office Aide; Orch; Grmn Hnrs Soc 83-84; Phys Thrpy.

TITUS, AMY; Guilford HS; Guilford, CT; (Y); 16/315; Pres Cmnty Wkr; French Clb; Hosp Aide; Latin Clb; Rep Stu Cncl; Capt Var Tennis; French Hon Soc; NHS; Ntl Merit Ltr; Excllnc Lang Arts Awd 84 & 85; Hon Awd Natl Latn Exm 84 & 85; Econ.

TOBIN, DEBRA SARAH; Trumbull HS; Trumbull, CT; (Y); Cmnty Wkr; Teachers Aide; Temple Yth Grp; Nwsp Rptr; Nwsp Stf; Yrbk Stf; High Hon Roll; AFS; Drama Clb; Cit Awd; Cert Peer Tutorng 84-85; Art Awd Calligrphy 83; Dieticn.

TOBIN, POLLY; Bristol Central HS; Forestville, CT; (Y); Church Yth Grp; Hosp Aide; Office Aide; Ski Clb; Bus.

TOCE, NICOLE; East Hartford HS; East Hartford, CT; (Y); Girl Scts; Band; Concert Band; Mrchg Band; Yrbk Stf; Var Badmtn; JV Var Tennis; High Hon Roll; Hon Roll; NHS; Gregg Typg Awd 83-84; LPN.

TODD, ERICA; Holy Cross HS; Beacon Falls, CT; (Y); 131/344; French Clb; Teachers Aide; High Hon Roll; ST Camps Mock Trial Comp 85; CT Glas Dealrs Assoc Schlrshp 85; U Of Bridgeport; Pre Law.

TOEDT, JOHN; Windham HS; Columbia, CT; (Y); Am Leg Boys St; JV Bsbl; Var Ftbl; JV Wrstlng; Hon Roll; ST Chemathon 84; Biochem.

TOFFOLON, CAROL; Southington HS; Southington, CT; (Y); 120/600; Cmnty Wkr; Key Clb; Ski Clb; Variety Show; Yrbk Stf; VP Frsh Cls; VP Soph Cls; VP Jr Cls; Powder Puff Ftbl; Hon Roll; Hnr Rl; Tnns Tm; U Southern CA; Htl Mgt.

TOGNERI, JANICE E; Ledyard HS; Gales Ferry, CT; (Y); 6/272; Church Yth Grp; Hosp Aide; Acpl Chr; Pres Chorus; Church Choir; Yrbk Stf; Rep Sr Cls; High Hon Roll; Hon Roll; NHS; Jennie D Miller Mem Awd 85; Edward C Farrell Mem Schlrshp 85; Cert Of Mrt A Avg In Frnch IV 85; Providence Coll; Chld Psych.

TOKARZ, CHRISTOPHER; Notre Dame HS; Seymour, CT; (Y); French Clb; Political Wkr; French Hon Soc; Hon Roll; U CT; Pre-Law.

TOLCHINSKY, YELENA; East Lyme HS; Niantic, CT; (Y); High Hon Roll; Hon Roll.

TOLO, PAUL C; William H Hall HS; W Hartford, CT; (Y); 43/342; Am Leg Boys St; VP Pres Church Yth Grp; Orch; Trs Jr Cls; Capt Var Crs Cntry; Trs French Hon Soc; High Hon Roll; NHS.

TOLOMEO, CONCETTINA; East Haven HS; North Haven, CT; (Y); 5/280; Am Leg Aux Girls St; Church Yth Grp; Office Aide; Yrbk Stf; High Hon Roll; JC Awd; Rotary Awd; Italian Clb Pres; Ct Miss TEEN Pageant; N Haven Model Congres; Southern CT ST U; Nursing.

TOMAN, LORI L; Enrico Fermi HS; Enfield, CT; (Y); 2/387; Cit Awd; NHS; Ntl Merit Schol; Pres Schlr; Sal; Cmnty Wkr; Chorus; Rep Stu Cncl; Awds In Spanish, Hist, Geom, Bio & Chem 82-85; Hugh O Brian Ledrshp Awd 83; PA ST Schlr 84; Quinnipiac Coll; Phys Therapy.

TOMKO, JEROME; East Catholic HS; E Hartford, CT; (Y); 29/350; Hon Roll; Law.

TOMLINSON, RICHARD; Pomperaug HS; Southbury, CT; (Y); 113/250; FBLA; Drm & Bgl; Tourism.

TOMOLONIS, PAUL; East Windsor HS; Broad Brook, CT; (Y); 2/92; Church Yth Grp; Computer Clb; Office Aide; Var Crs Cntry; Var Trk; High Hon Roll; NHS; Outstndg Acad Achvt 84-85; CT Comp Olympics 84; Elec Engr.

TONER, CHRISTINE; St Bernard HS; Preston, CT; (Y); 111/300; Church Yth Grp; Cmnty Wkr; Hosp Aide; Stage Crew; Off Jr Cls; Hon Roll; Bus.

TORELLI, STACY; Sacred Heart Acad; Branford, CT; (Y); Im Vllybl; High Hon Roll; Hon Roll; NHS; Sacred Heard Endwmnt Scholar 83; Vet Med.

TORNILLO, PENNI DIANE; Stratford HS; Stratford, CT; (Y); 26/246; Hosp Aide; Teachers Aide; JA; Trs Chorus; Off Frsh Cls; Off Soph Cls; Off Sr Cls; Hon Roll; Outstndng Svc Awd Ushers Guld 83-85, Nurses Aid 84-85; Amer Intl Coll; Spec Ed.

TORRE, JOHN DAVID; Notre Dame HS; E Haven, CT; (Y); Cmnty Wkr; Library Aide; Political Wkr; Spanish Clb; Nwsp Rptr; Nwsp Stf; Hon Roll; Englsh.

TORREGIANI, SETH; Staples HS; Westport, CT; (Y); VP JA; Radio Clb; School Play; Nwsp Rptr; Bsbl; Coach Actv; Ftbl; Powder Puff Ftbl; Youth Adult Cncl Teen Grp Pres 84.

TORRENTI, MATTHEW; Lyne-Old Lyme HS; Old Lyme, CT; (Y); Am Leg Boys St; Var Bsbl; Var Bsktbl; Var Socr; High Hon Roll; Hon Roll; NHS; Acadmc Awd-Intro To Busnss 82-83; Acadmc Awd-Modrn European Hstry 83-84; Schl Senate/Hs Commtt 82-86.

TORTORA, KERRI; Glastonbury HS; Glastonbury, CT; (Y); 59/430; Drama Clb; French Clb; Chorus; Yrbk Stf; VP Soph Cls; VP Jr Cls; Stu Cncl; Var Cheerleading; Var Tennis; High Hon Roll; ST Of CT Stu Advsry Cncl Altnt 84-85; 3rd Rnnr Up CT Miss Untd Tngr Pgnt 84; 1st Rnnr Up Essy 84; American U; Lang.

TOSADO, DAVID; Stratford HS; Stratford, CT; (Y); 55/241; Cmnty Wkr; Rep Frsh Cls; JV Wrstlng; CT Indstrl Arts Assn Achvt Cert 85; Hnr Cert 83-85.

TOTH, ALISON; New Fairfield HS; New Fairfld, CT; (Y); 1/243; Latin Clb; Pres Frsh Cls; Var Bsktbl; Var Socr; Var Trk; JV Vllybl; French Hon Soc; High Hon Roll; NHS; Ntl Merit Ltr; Harvard Bk Awd 84-85; All Conf Socr Tm 84-85; All Div Bsktbl Tm 84-85; Pre-Med.

TOTH, CHERYL ANN; New Britain HS; New Britain, CT; (Y); Church Yth Grp; Sec Trs Exploring; Chorus; Nwsp Rptr; Nwsp Stf; Rep Jr Cls; JV L Vllybl; Boy Scts; Cmnty Wkr; Drama Clb; Fin Dept Dir For Day 85; Natl Hstry Day Locl 1st, ST 2nd, Natl Supr Ratg 85; Gftd & Talntd 84-85; Chld Psych.

TOTTEN, DARREN; Masuk HS; Monroe, CT; (Y); 70/360; Boys Clb Am; Boy Scts; Radio Clb; Hon Roll; Masonic Awd; Demolay Souhegan Vly Chaptr 83; Comp Sci.

TOTTENHAM, TERESA; Ansonia HS; Ansonia, CT; (Y); #1 In Class; Computer Clb; Spanish Clb; High Hon Roll; NHS; Mth Hghst 83-84; RN.

TOUSSAINT, MICHAEL; Guilford HS; Guilford, CT; (Y); AFS; Variety Show; Yrbk Stf; Bsbl; JV Ftbl; Im Vllybl; Hon Roll; Accntng.

TOWNSEND, KENYA; Brien Mc Mahon HS; Norwalk, CT; (Y); JCL; Latin Clb; Stu Cncl; Bsktbl; Trk; Vllybl; Hon Roll; Ntl Latin Hr Soc Cum Laudi 83-84; 2nd Pl Sci Fair 83-84; Boston U; Psych.

TOWNSEND, STEVE; Kaynor RVTS HS; Waterbury, CT; (Y); 80/205; Art Clb; Stage Crew; Yrbk Stf; High Hon Roll; Hon Roll; SMA Awd Excel Mach Trde 81-82; Ball & Sckt Mfg Co Awd 84-85.

TRACEY, COLLEEN; Sacred Heart Acad; Hamden, CT; (Y); Office Aide; Scholastic Bowl; Nwsp Rptr; Trs Soph Cls; Pres Jr Cls; Var L Bsktbl; Var Capt Sftbl; NHS; NEDT Awd; Spanish NHS; Hly Cross Bk Awd & Hnr Awd 85; Mchls Jewlers Awd 85; Srv Awd 85; Pre-Med.

TRACEY, THERESA D; Enrico Fermi HS; Enfield, CT; (Y); 41/398; Cmnty Wkr; Variety Show; Yrbk Stf; Stu Cncl; Cheerleading; Hon Roll; NHS; CT ST Schlrshp 85; Knights Of Columbus Schlrshp 85; CT Bowling Congress Schlrshp 85; Northeastern U; Phys Thrpy.

TRAILOR, SUZANNE; St Bernard HS; Norwich, CT; (Y); FNA; GAA; Hosp Aide; Ski Clb; Stu Cncl; JV Tennis; Peer Minstry Prog 85-86; Spec Olympcs Vol 85; JR Senate Prog 84-85; Nrsng.

TRAISCI, LEIGH; New Fairfield HS; New Fairfield, CT; (Y); Church Yth Grp; Hosp Aide; Teachers Aide; Chorus; School Play; VP Frsh Cls; Sr Cls; JV Socr; French Hon Soc; Hon Roll; Chld Psych.

TRAMONTANO, MARIE; Cooperative HS; New Haven, CT; (Y); Office Aide; Political Wkr; Teachers Aide; Lit Mag; Hon Roll; Prfct Atten Awd; Outstndng Schl Svc Awd 85; Mst Imprvd Stu In Jr Engl 85; Outstndng Schl Voltr 84; Achvt In Gen Sci 84; Chldhd Educ.

TRAN, BEN; Middletown HS; Middletown, CT; (Y); Trk; High Hon Roll; Hon Roll; Prfct Atten Awd; Engl 12 Awds 85; Hon Rl Dinner Awd 85; Med Sci.

TRAN, PHU MINH; Danbury HS; Danbury, CT; (Y); 6/650; Art Clb; Computer Clb; Exploring; French Clb; Hosp Aide; Math Clb; Math Tm; Orch; Yrbk Rptr; High Hon Roll; Perry Awd; Bst Math & Hlth Stu; Yale; Psych.

TREMONTE, EDWARD; Brookfield HS; Brookfield, CT; (Y); Var Ftbl; Var Golf; U Of CT; Bus.

TRIANO, PAULA; Holy Cross HS; Waterbury, CT; (Y); Hosp Aide; Volntr Wrk Awd 83-84; March Of Dimes Wlk Amer Wlkthn Awd 85; Lgl Asstnt.

TRINH, CHU; Bassick HS; Bridgeport, CT; (S); Hon Roll; Comp Engrng.

TRIOMPO, DAVID; Terryville HS; Terryville, CT; (Y); Am Leg Boys St; Band; Concert Band; Jazz Band; Mrchg Band; Pep Band; Variety Show; Rep Frsh Cls; Rep Soph Cls; Rep Jr Cls; Michaels Jewlers Outstndng Stu Awd 84-85; Am Leg Boys ST 84-85.

TRIPP, MICHELLE D; Naugatuck HS; Naugatuck, CT; (Y); Art Clb; Drama Clb; German Clb; Teachers Aide; Thesps; Rep Jr Cls; Sftbl; Vllybl; Hon Roll; Parsons Of NY; Illustrator.

TROCCHI, MIRIAM; Notre Dame Acad; Waterbury, CT; (Y); Nwsp Stf; Trs Frsh Cls; Trs Soph Cls; Trs Jr Cls; Trs Stu Cncl; Jr NHS; NHS; Frnch Acad Awd; Acctng.

TROCCIOLA, LYNNE B; East Catholic HS; Glastonbury, CT; (Y); 14/348; Church Yth Grp; Pres JA; Math Clb; Band; Nwsp Stf; Crs Cntry; Var L Tennis; Cit Awd; High Hon Roll; NHS; Prncpls Awd Schlrshp/Ctznshp 84; Mst Imprvd Plyr Tnns Tm 84; JA Conf-Delgtn Bst Delgtn Awd 84; Fairfield U; Math.

TROJAN, HEATHER; Low Heywood Thomas HS; Rowayton, CT; (Y); 15/36; Art Clb; Pep Clb; Ed Yrbk Stf; VP Rep Frsh Cls; Rep Soph Cls; Rep Stu Cncl; Capt JV Bsktbl; Capt JV Fld Hcky; Capt JV Lcrss; Hon Roll; JV Fld Hcky MVP 82-85; Volntr Wrk Admssns Tsts 82-85; Psychlgy.

TROJANOWSKI, LORI; Southington HS; Southington, CT; (Y); Sec Key Clb; Ski Clb; Yrbk Stf; Mgr Trk; Hon Roll; Acctg.

TROSUK, LORI; West Haven HS; W Haven, CT; (Y); Girl Scts; Chorus; Church Choir; School Musical; School Play; Sec Frsh Cls; Rep Jr Cls; Rep Stu Cncl; Hon Roll; Sec Jr NHS; Prom Cmmtte 84-85; Art Cnvntn Hstss 85; Art Excllnc Spec Awd 85; Paier Coll Of Art; Intr Dsgn.

TROTTA, RON; Ledyard HS; Gales Ferry, CT; (Y); 15/270; Hon Roll; U CT; Phrmcy.

TRUDEL, CHRISTINE; Danbury HS; Danbury, CT; (Y); Exploring; Ski Clb; Varsity Clb; Yrbk Stf; VP Soph Cls; VP Jr Cls; VP Sr Cls; Stu Cncl; Var Fld Hcky; JV Sftbl; CT Bus Week 85; Sec.

TRUONG, TRANG; Hartford Public HS; Hartford, CT; (Y); Computer Clb; Exploring; Math Clb; Math Tm; Science Clb; Socr; Var Trk; French Hon Soc; Hon Roll; NHS; MIT; Elec Engr.

TSARFATY, VERED; Hall HS; W Hartford, CT; (Y); 33/342; Church Yth Grp; Concert Band; Orch; Lit Mag; NHS; Symp Band; Mgr(s); Stat Vllybl; Jr NHS; All ST Band 84, All Estrn Band, All ST Orch 85.

TUAZON, NORA MARIE; Ledyard SR HS; Gales Ferry, CT; (Y); Art Clb; Pres Sec 4-H; Chorus; Color Guard; Yrbk Ed-Chief; Yrbk Stf; Off Jr Cls; Off Sr Cls; JV Var Trk; 4-H Awd; Nrsng.

TUBRIDY, BOB; East Lyme HS; Niantic, CT; (Y); Rep Jr Cls; Bsktbl; Capt Var Tennis; All Conf Tnns Tm 85; Bus.

TUCCI, MARY FRANCES; Brookfield HS; Brookfield Ctr, CT; (Y); Pres Church Yth Grp; Cmnty Wkr; Chorus; High Hon Roll; JC Awd; NHS; Cls Scholar 85; Brookfield Ed Assn Scholar 85; Pres Acad Fitnss Awd 85; Boston Coll; Soclgy.

TUCCIARONE, THOMAS; Lyme Old Lyme HS; Old Lyme, CT; (Y); 23/110; Computer Clb; Pres Latin Clb; Ski Clb; Lit Mag; Bsbl; Vllybl; High Hon Roll; Hon Roll; Ntl Merit Ltr; CT All ST Rifl Tm 82; Excllnc Humnts Awd 82-83; Excllnc Engl Awd 81-85; U Of VT; Engl.

TUCKER, KRISTEN; Wilton HS; Wilton, CT; (Y); Key Clb; Bsktbl; Tennis; Vllybl; Hon Roll; Ldrshp Awd In Tnns 83-84; Var Lttr 84-8k; Acctng.

TULLOCH-REID, DHANA; The Maskis Schl; Hartford, CT; (Y); 1/19; Church Yth Grp; Drama Clb; Hosp Aide; Model UN; Yrbk Ed-Chief; Var Capt Bsktbl; Var Capt Socr; Var L Sftbl; High Hon Roll; NHS; Day Of Pride Scholar Recip; U CT; Hematlgy.

TUPPONCE, DAVID; Rockville HS; Rockville, CT; (Y); 9/362; Am Leg Boys St; Church Yth Grp; Hosp Aide; Concert Band; Jazz Band; Mrchg Band; Var L Crs Cntry; Var L Trk; NHS; Bio.

TURANO, SARAH; East Lyme HS; E Lyme, CT; (Y); AFS; Cmnty Wkr; Hosp Aide; Key Clb; Capt Flag Corp; Nwsp Stf; Yrbk Ed-Chief; JV Fld Hcky; Powder Puff Ftbl; High Hon Roll; Pre-Med.

TURCI, PATRICIA A; Southington HS; Southington, CT; (Y); 8/550; Key Clb; Pep Clb; Rep Stu Cncl; High Hon Roll; Hon Roll; NHS; CT Schlstc Achvt Grant 85; Unico Clb Schlrshp 85; Southington Women Moose Schlrshp 85; U CT; Nrsng.

TURECHEK, DAVID; Trumbull HS; Trumbull, CT; (Y); Boy Scts; Band; Drm & Bgl; Jazz Band; Mrchg Band; Symp Band; Trk; Hon Roll; Vigl Hnr Ordr Of Arrw 84; Music.

TURIANO, MICHAEL; Trumball HS; Trumbull, CT; (Y); Boy Scts; Yrbk Stf; High Hon Roll; Hon Roll; Fairfield U; Pre-Med.

TURKO, MICHELLE; St Joseph HS; Monroe, CT; (Y); 59/227; Cmnty Wkr; Dance Clb; Variety Show; Acctg.

TURNER, AMY L; The Ethel Walker Schl HS; Highlands Ranch, CO; (Y); Art Clb; Drama Clb; Hosp Aide; Ski Clb; Thesps; Acpl Chr; Chorus; Orch; School Musical; School Play.

TURNER, CHRISTIAN; Shelton HS; Shelton, CT; (Y); Boy Scts; Debate Tm; JA; JV Var Bsktbl; JV Crs Cntry; U Of WI-MADISON; Law.

TUTINO, STACY RUTH; Lauralton Hall HS; Milford, CT; (Y); Church Yth Grp; Drama Clb; Latin Clb; Science Clb; Spanish Clb; Nwsp Ed-Chief; Nwsp Rptr; Nwsp Stf; Yrbk Stf; Lit Mag; Stu Cncl VP, Pres; Natl Latin Awd; Law.

TUTTLE, DONNA; East Catholic HS; Manchester, CT; (Y); 1/339; Math Tm; VP Science Clb; Teachers Aide; Church Choir; Lit Mag; High Hon Roll; NHS; Val; Rensselaer Mdl 84; O Brien Schlr, 1TC Schlrshp 85; RPI; Pre Med.

TWILLEY, SUE M; Robert E Fitch SR HS; Mystic, CT; (Y); 47/323; Intnl Clb; Pres Key Clb; VP Science Clb; Service Clb; Chorus; Nwsp Stf; Rep Stu Cncl; Powder Puff Ftbl; Hon Roll; Bio.

TYCZ, PAUL B; Tourlellotte Memorial HS; Thompson, CT; (Y); 12/97; Chess Clb; Var L Bsbl; Var L Bskthl; Var L Crs Cntry; High Hon Roll; Hon Roll; Prfct Atten Awd; Phrmctcl.

TYRANSKI, CHAD; Newtown HS; Newtown, CT; (Y); 1/310; Sec French Clb; Trs VICA; French Hon Soc; High Hon Roll; VP NHS; Ntl Merit Ltr; Pres Schlr; Val; Racqtbl, CT ST AARA Chmpshps 85; Spec Timex Corp & Ntl Merit Comm Schlrshps 85; Dartmouth Coll; Engrng.

TZEPOS, GEORGE; Seymour HS; Oxford, CT; (S); 15/224; Church Yth Grp; Nwsp Stf; Rep Stu Cncl; Swmmng; High Hon Roll; NHS; Bio.

ULINSKAS, ALGERD M; Terryville HS; Terryville, CT; (Y); Am Leg Boys St; Boy Scts; Computer Clb; Radio Clb; Science Clb; Yrbk Stf; Var Crs Cntry; Var Trk; Engr.

UNDERHILL, DOUG; Jonathan Law HS; Milford, CT; (Y); 35/250; Boy Scts; Computer Clb; Drama Clb; Intnl Clb; School Musical; School Play; Stage Crew; Kiwanis Awd; Pres Schlr; VFW Awd; Suprntndnts Awd Of Achvt; Rebekah Assmbly Schlrshp; U Of WI-EAU Claire; Hlth Care.

UNGARO, SAVIN JOHN; Granby Memorial HS; Granby, CT; (Y); 5/104; Pres FBLA; Trs Spanish Clb; Rep Stu Cncl; Bsbl; Bsktbl; Crs Cntry; Trk; Pres NHS; Granby Lions Clb & Ed Assoc & Cmmnty Assoc Schlrshps 85; Engl Dept Schlr & Exempl Achvt Math 85; U Of CT; Actrl Sci.

UNVALA, SHEILA; Brein Mc Mahon HS; Norwalk, CT; (Y); Orch; Var Tennis; High Hon Roll; Trs NHS; Ntl Merit Ltr; Pres Schlr; 2nd Hnrs Frnch Iona Coll Frgn Lang Cont 85; Excllnt Ratng JR Schubert Clb 84 & 85.

UPENDER, BHARGAV; East Lyme HS; Niantic, CT; (Y); 6/271; Boy Scts; Computer Clb; Key Clb; Mathletes; Nwsp Ed-Chief; Yrbk Ed-Chief; Crs Cntry; Hon Roll; NHS; U CT Biomdcl Rsrch Prog 85; Frntrs Appld Sci Yale U 85; MIT; Elec Engr.

URBAN, DANNA; Ellington HS; Vernon, CT; (Y); 10/143; FBLA; Hosp Aide; Concert Band; Mrchg Band; Rep Stu Cncl; Stat Bsktbl; Mgr(s); Stat Sftbl; High Hon Roll; Hon Roll; Bus.

URSO, SALVATORE; Berlin HS; Kensington, CT; (Y); 48/191; Am Leg Boys St; Concert Band; Jazz Band; Mrchg Band; Pep Band; School Musical; JV Bsbl; Wt Lftg; Var Wrstlng; Nichols Coll; Bus Mgmt.

USMAN, SAJID; Westhill HS; Stamford, CT; (Y); Church Yth Grp; VP Computer Clb; Pres JA; Key Clb; Latin Clb; Math Clb; Rep Frsh Cls; Rep Soph Cls; JV Bsbl; Hon Roll; Omega Engrng 3rd Pl Comp Cntst 85; Bio.

VAICIULIS, AMY; St Bernard HS; Mystic, CT; (S); Cmnty Wkr; Exploring; FNA; Hosp Aide; Library Aide; Science Clb; Ski Clb; Sec Jr Cls; Var Gym; High Hon Roll; Med.

VAITHEESWARAN, VIJAY; Cheshire HS; Cheshire, CT; (Y); 1/353; Am Leg Boys St; Capt Debate Tm; Math Clb; Capt Scholastic Bowl; Nwsp Ed-Chief; VP Jr Cls; VP Sr Cls; NCTE Awd; NHS; Political Wkr; ST Chmp Spnsh Cmptn; Schl Spllng Chmp; JR Prom King; Bus.

VALENTE, MICHAEL; Notre Dame HS; New Haven, CT; (Y); Church Yth Grp; Pep Clb; Rep Frsh Cls; Rep Soph Cls; JV Var Crs Cntry; JV Var Trk; High Hon Roll; Hon Roll; U Of CT; Engrng.

VALENTI, PAUL; Waterttown HS; Oakville, CT; (Y); 50/230; Rep Am Leg Boys St; Var Trk; Mattatuck Coll Masterqz 4th Of 150 85; H S Schltc Tm 85-86; Law.

VALERIO, ALISON; Danbury HS; Danbury, CT; (Y); 121/628; Church Yth Grp; Yrbk Stf; Var L Tennis; Im Vllybl; Hon Roll; Jr NHS; Schlrshp Silvermine Guild Art Schl Smmr Prog 85; Art.

VALERIO, JOSEPH; Notre Dame HS; Milford, CT; (Y); Boy Scts; Computer Clb; Pep Clb; Tennis; Hon Roll.

VALINHO, SUZANNE; Naugatuck HS; Naugatuck, CT; (Y); Hosp Aide; Band; Mrchg Band; Symp Band; Hon Roll; Southern CT; Fine Arts.

VALLIERE, ERIC; Tolland HS; Tolland, CT; (Y); Band; Chorus; Jazz Band; Madrigals; Pep Band; School Musical; Hon Roll; NHS; All ST Chrs CT 85; Al NCCC Band 82; All NCCC Chrs 83-84; Music Thetr.

VALUCKAS, LAUREN; Farmington HS; Farmington, CT; (Y); 32/206; Church Yth Grp; Hosp Aide; Ski Clb; Nwsp Phtg; JV Bsktbl; Var JV Socr; Var JV Tennis; Im Wt Lftg; High Hon Roll; Hon Roll; Nrsng.

VAN DINE, HEATHER; East Catholic HS; Bolton, CT; (Y); 99/300; Hosp Aide; Yrbk Stf; Rep Jr Cls; JV Trk; IOH Treas,Pres 84-86; Chrch Choir 82-84; Comp Sci.

VAN DYKES, CYNTHIA; East Catholic HS; Manchester, CT; (Y); French Clb; Girl Scts.

VAN NESS, RONALD R; Southington HS; Southington, CT; (Y); 65/550; Am Leg Boys St; Band; Chorus; Concert Band; Jazz Band; Mrchg Band; School Play; Variety Show; Nwsp Rptr; Ed Yrbk Stf; Sthngtn Arts Cncl Awd Artstc Excllnc 85; Wesleyan Univ CCY Pgm 82; All St Chorus 85; Law.

VAN NGUYEN, TAM; Richard C Lee HS; New Haven, CT; (Y); Socr; Sftbl; Wt Lftg; Sci Drftng 83-84; Comp Rpr.

VAN SCHELT, SHEILA C; Windsor Locks HS; Windsor Locks, CT; (Y); 23/170; Am Leg Aux Girls St; Cmnty Wkr; GAA; Band; Chorus; Concert Band; Mrchg Band; School Musical; Swing Chorus; Hon Roll; CASS Awd Ldrshp 85; Am Leg Aux Awd Outstndng Stu 85; VP NHS 85; Rochester Inst Tech; Med Tech.

VAN VALKENBURG, KAREN; Windsor Locks HS; Windsor Locks, CT; (Y); 26/162; Church Yth Grp; Mrchg Band; School Musical; Nwsp Stf; Trs Jr Cls; Sec Sr Cls; Stu Cncl; Var Fld Hcky; Var Trk; Hon Roll; Freshmn Hmcmng Queen 82; Lib Arts.

VAN VOORHIS, KRISTIN; Trumbull HS; Trumbull, CT; (Y); Key Clb; Pep Clb; Ski Clb; Nwsp Stf; VP Soph Cls; VP Jr Cls; Stat Bsktbl; Var Sftbl; Var Capt Tennis; High Hon Roll; Student Rep-Brd Of Eductn 84-85; Student Leadrs Commtt; U Of Richmond.

VANCINI, FABIUS W; Stamford HS; Stamford, CT; (Y); 9/430; Bio Clb Pres & Fndr; Italian Clb Pres; German Clb; Stu Cncl; Cap Cross-Cntry Team; Most Intelligent; Cornell U; Med.

VANLEUWEN, ELIZABETH; Trumball HS; Trumbull, CT; (Y); Ski Clb; Teachers Aide; Acpl Chr; Chorus; Rep Frsh Cls; Rep Soph Cls; Rep Jr Cls; Var Diving; Var Sftbl; High Hon Roll; Ldrshp & Ctznshp Awd 85; Physcl Thrpy.

VANOUREK, SCOTT; New Canaan HS; New Canaan, CT; (Y); 7/140; Hosp Aide; NFL; JV Var Socr; Var Trk; NHS; Ntl Merit Ltr.

VARDON, KELLY; Naugatuck HS; Naugatuck, CT; (Y); Church Yth Grp; Hosp Aide; Nwsp Rptr; Var Bsktbl; L Trk; Hon Roll; Prfct Atten Awd; Comm.

VARVISIOTIS, TOULA; Sacred Heart Acad; Stamford, CT; (Y); Nwsp Rptr; Sec Frsh Cls; Sec Soph Cls; Jrnlsm.

VAUGHN, TRACEY; James Hill House HS; New Haven, CT; (Y); English Clb; Hosp Aide; JA; Red Cross Aide; Nwsp Stf; Off Soph Cls; Sftbl; Wt Lftg; NCTE Awd.

VECE, PEGGY J; The Morgan Schl; Clinton, CT; (Y); Hosp Aide; Spanish Clb; Nwsp Stf; Yrbk Stf; JV Var Sftbl; Hon Roll; Engl Awd 82-83; Mngmnt.

VECKERELLI, MARK J; St Bernard HS; Norwich, CT; (Y); 49/289; Cmnty Wkr; Drama Clb; Pres Ski Clb; Y-Teens; School Musical; School Play; Nwsp Rptr; VP Frsh Cls; VP Soph Cls; VP Jr Cls; Hugh O Brian Yth Ldr Outstndg Soph 83; Top Century III Ldr 85; Parents Cncl Awd Svc Schl 85; SUNY-COBLESKILL; Lndscp Arch.

VEGIARD, ROLAND LEE; East Catholic HS; E Hartford, CT; (Y); 53/298; CAP; Cmnty Wkr; School Play; JV Socr; High Hon Roll; Teachers Aide; Drill Tm; JC Awd; Billy Mitchell Awd 85; Cdt Comm Compst Squdrn Civil Air Ptrl; Amer Lgn Cert 84; Chem Olympd 85; Airline Pilot.

VELKY, COLLEEN; Nonnewaug HS; Woodbury, CT; (Y); 4-H; FFA; GAA; Yrbk Stf; Bsktbl; Fld Hcky; Sftbl; Vllybl; Hon Roll; Mattatuck CC.

VELLA, ANDREA; Bethel HS; Bethel, CT; (Y); 38/265; AFS; Church Yth Grp; Acpl Chr; Chorus; Church Choir; Var L Socr; High Hon Roll; NHS; Vet.

VELLONE, KARRIE; Brien Mc Mahon HS; Norwalk, CT; (Y); 83/372; Girl Scts; JA; Key Clb; Teachers Aide; Band; Concert Band; Mrchg Band; Pep Band; Symp Band; Powder Puff Ftbl; EDY Scholar U Bridgeport 85; Archit.

VELORIA, AGNES; St Bernard HS; Waterford, CT; (S); Camera Clb; Library Aide; Yrbk Phtg; Jr Cls; Stu Cncl; JV Bsktbl; Sftbl; Hon Roll; Amer HS Ath 84; Vsul Arts Awd 83; Dds.

VELTRI, LOUIE; St Joseph HS; Trumbull, CT; (Y); 115/229; Boy Scts; Church Yth Grp; Spanish Clb; Varsity Clb; Var Capt Tennis; Mst Imprvd Stu Outstndng Svc 81-82.

VENDITTO, DEE ANN; East Haven HS; E Haven, CT; (Y); 50/300; Library Aide; Trs Spanish Clb; Var Crs Cntry; Var L Trk; East Haven Yellow Jckt Var Clb 83-85; Rec Aide 84; Miss TEEN CT Pgnt 84; Surgeon.

VENDOLA, ARTHUR R; St Pual HS; Farmington, CT; (Y); Church Yth Grp; Math Tm; Science Clb; Ski Clb; Concert Band; Stu Cncl; Var Tennis; JV Wrstlng; High Hon Roll; Jr NHS; Med.

VENICE, ROBERT; Emmett O Brien RVTS; Ansonia, CT; (Y); 11/165; Boys Clb Am; Boy Scts; Camera Clb; Chess Clb; Debate Tm; Stage Crew; Yrbk Stf; Stu Cncl; High Hon Roll; NHS; Natl Hnr Soc Treas 85-86; Elec Engrng.

VENICE, STEPHEN V; East Haven HS; East Haven, CT; (Y); 16/268; Am Leg Boys St; Chess Clb; Ski Clb; Teachers Aide; Capt L Crs Cntry; Hon Roll; NHS; Pres Schlr; NHCYABA Schlrshp 85; Foxon Recrtn Leag Schlrshp 85; Deer Run Schlrshp 85; U Of New Haven; Comp Sci.

VENTRESCA, MICHAEL; W F Kaynor R V T S HS; Waterbury, CT; (Y); 40/240; Church Yth Grp; Pres Computer Clb; VICA; Stage Crew; VP Jr Cls; Golf; Vllybl; Hon Roll; Most Deservng JR Awd, CBIA Schlrshp Bus Wk 85; Elect Engr.

VENTRESCA, PATRICIA; St Joseph HS; Monroe, CT; (Y); 13/240; Yrbk Bus Mgr; Yrbk Stf; Var Cheerleading; High Hon Roll; Jr NHS; NHS; Bus Mgmt.

VENTRESCA, PAULA M; St Paul Catholic HS; Thomaston, CT; (Y); Drama Clb; Sec French Clb; School Musical; School Play; Variety Show; Lit Mag; Hon Roll; JA; Color Guard; Drm & Bgl; Dance Certs & Awds Teaching 81-85; 4th Rnnr Up Miss CT U S Teen Pageant 84; Mission Clb VP 84-85; Southern CT ST U; Psych.

VERDONE, CHERYL; Granby Memorial HS; Granby, CT; (Y); Church Yth Grp; Nwsp Rptr; Hon Roll; Outstndng Achvt Bsc Dsgn,Paintng 84-85; Art Dir.

VERMONT, SANDRA; Wearer HS; Hartford, CT; (Y); FBLA; JA; Church Choir; Hon Roll; Hnr Roll Hon Men 83; Hon Men 84; Chld Psych.

VERNICK, RUSSELL; Staples HS; Westport, CT; (Y); Math Tm; Ski Clb; Tennis; Engrng.

VERNIK, AARON S; Trumbull HS; Trumbull, CT; (Y); Boy Scts; Library Aide; Capt JV Socr; Trk; High Hon Roll; JV Lttrs Sccr 84-85; La Salle; Geolgy.

VERRILLI, DANIELLE; Joseph A Foran HS; Milford, CT; (Y); 32/250; Camera Clb; Drama Clb; JCL; Keywanettes; Ski Clb; Band; Chorus; VP Soph Cls; Var Cheerleading; High Hon Roll; Frntr Applied Sci 85; Comm.

VERSLUIS, ROLF D; Hall HS; W Hartford, CT; (Y); 48/300; Pres Church Yth Grp; Computer Clb; VP JA; Yrbk Stf; JV Var Socr; Trk; High Hon Roll; Hon Roll; NHS; Ntl Merit SF; Naval Acad Engr & Sci Smnr 84; Yale Frntrs Sci 84; Elec Engr.

VERTULI, PAULA L; Pomperaug HS; Middlebury, CT; (Y); Mattatuck CC; Rdlgy Tchnlgst.

VESSICHIO, LAURA; Lyman Hall HS; Wallingford, CT; (Y); 5/240; AFS; Lit Mag; High Hon Roll; Hon Roll; Cert Of Prfncy In Frnch & Englsh 84 & Bkkpng/Accntng 85; Accntng.

VESTUTI, GARY M; East Haven HS; E Haven, CT; (Y); 50/300; Cmnty Wkr; Math Clb; JV Bsktbl; JV Ftbl; Comp Engrng.

VETRO, DONNA; Hamden HS; Hamden, CT; (Y); High Hon Roll; Hon Roll; Outstndng Achvt Spn 84; Hgh Hnrs 85; Sthrn CT ST U; Chld Devlpmnt.

VICINUS, KAREN E; Plainville HS; Plainville, CT; (Y); 1/213; Red Cross Aide; Yrbk Stf; Var Capt Bsktbl; Var Sftbl; Hon Roll; Trs NHS; Harvard Bk Awd 84.

VIEIRA, CATHERINE J; Holy Cross HS; Naugatuck, CT; (Y); Pres Latin Clb; Service Clb; Spanish Clb; Variety Show; VP Frsh Cls; Var Crs Cntry; Var Swmmng; Var Trk; Hon Roll; Prfct Atten Awd; Most Imprvd Cross Cty Rnnr 84-85; Bus Adm.

VIEIRA, DAVID; Danbury HS; Danbury, CT; (Y); Chess Clb; Color Guard; Drill Tm; JV Wrstlng; Hon Roll; Jr NHS; NHS; Excllnc Germn Awd 82-83; USAF JROTC Medl & Rbbn Achvt 85; Perry Awd In Aerosp 84-85; Engrng.

VIEIRA, HELENA S; Naugatuck HS; Naugatuck, CT; (Y); 4/323; Church Yth Grp; Office Aide; Spanish Clb; Off Frsh Cls; Off Jr Cls; High Hon Roll; JC Awd; NHS; William H Dyer Schlrshp 85; Maruerite Mograw Schlrshp 85; Naugatuck Vol Amb Corp Schlrshp 85; St Joseph Coll; Pre-Med.

VIEIRA, ROBERT; Ansonia HS; Ansonia, CT; (Y); Am Leg Boys St; Computer Clb; Latin Clb; Spanish Clb; Yrbk Stf; Var L Bsktbl; Var L Ftbl; Hon Roll; Engr.

VIELE, ARMAND; Wheeler HS; N Stonington, CT; (Y); Am Leg Boys St; Letterman Clb; Spanish Clb; Varsity Clb; Yrbk Stf; VP Jr Cls; VP Sr Cls; Var Capt Bsbl; JV Var Bsktbl; Var Crs Cntry; Bus.

VIETZKE, GAY; Branford HS; Branford, CT; (Y); 10/270; Am Leg Aux Girls St; Band; Chorus; Ed Yrbk Stf; Lit Mag; Rep Stu Cncl; High Hon Roll; Outstndng Band Trphy 83; Stu Of Mnth 85; Art.

VIGGIANO, JOHN; Ridgefield HS; Ridgefield, CT; (Y); Church Yth Grp; Varsity Clb; Variety Show; Bsbl; Ftbl; Wrstlng; High Hon Roll; Hon Roll; Lion Awd; Willson Hiller Awd & Schlrshp & Tiger Touchdown 85; Edw Ballard & Anne Richardson Schlrshp 85; West Point Mltry Acad.

VIGURS, LISA MARIE; Conard HS; West Hartford, CT; (Y); 61/275; Rep Am Leg Aux Girls St; Pres Am Leg Aux Girls St; Service Clb; School Musical; Chrmn Jr Cls; Sec Stu Cncl; Var Capt Bsktbl; Var Capt Socr; Cit Awd; DAR Awd; Vanderbilt U; Nrsng.

VILLARA, LISA; Berlin HS; Berlin, CT; (Y); Band; Flag Corp; Mrchg Band; School Musical; Yrbk Stf; Twrlr; Lamp Awd 85; Central CT ST U; Psych.

VINCENT, JAMES; Notre Dame HS; N Branford, CT; (Y); 7/254; Math Clb; Capt Scholastic Bowl; Science Clb; Pres Frsh Cls; Pres Stu Cncl; Var L Ftbl; High Hon Roll; NHS; Ntl Merit SF; Political Wkr; Natl Ftbl Fdn Hall Fame Schlr Athlete 85; A&r Harry Zilber Awd 85; Wesleyan U; Astron.

VIRELLI, JASON; Jonathan Law HS; Milford, CT; (Y); 8/273; Rep Am Leg Boys St; Boy Scts; Computer Clb; Key Clb; High Hon Roll; Hon Roll; NHS; Prfct Atten Awd; Exclnc In US Hstry Hnr Lvl 84; Engrng.

VIRGULTO, SUSAN; Sacred Heart Acad; E Haven, CT; (Y); 6/123; Am Leg Aux Girls St; Drama Clb; Scholastic Bowl; School Musical; Nwsp Rptr; Var Capt Crs Cntry; High Hon Roll; Jr NHS; NHS; Voice Dem Awd; Yale Bk Awd; Hugh O Brien Yuth Ldrshp 84; ALA Grls Ntn Wnnr 85; Amer HS Math Exam Wnnr 84; Yale U; Law.

VITALE, ROSEMARIE; Sacred Heart Acad; East Haven, CT; (Y); FBLA; Chorus; School Musical; Bus.

VITELLI, WILLIAM; Joseph A Foran HS; Milford, CT; (Y); 20/275; Am Leg Boys St; Key Clb; Letterman Clb; Varsity Clb; Ftbl; Trk; Hon Roll; Ntl Merit Ltr; NEDT Awd; Pres Schlr; Hugh O Brien Awd 83; John D Silvay Awd Bys ST 85; Amer Lgn Essyst 84; Law.

VOBORIL, SCOTT; Tolland HS; Tolland, CT; (Y); Camera Clb; Church Yth Grp; Exploring; Ski Clb; School Musical; VP Sr Cls; Stu Cncl; Cheerleading; JV Var Socr; Var Trk; FL Inst Tech; Mrn Bio.

VOGEL, ALON; Hall HS; West Hartford, CT; (Y); Debate Tm; Yrbk Sprt Ed; Rep Stu Cncl; Trs Tennis; Hon Roll; U Of Rochester; Bio Med.

VOGT, COLLEEN; West Haven HS; W Haven, CT; (Y); Hosp Aide; Intnl Clb; Nwsp Stf; Jr NHS; Spanish NHS; S CT ST ; Tchg.

VOGT, ERIK N; Hammonasset School; Guilford, CT; (Y); School Play; Stage Crew; Var Socr; Ntl Merit SF; Scuba Dvng Cert 83; NY U; Film.

VOGT, JOHN; Staples HS; Westport, CT; (Y); Art Clb; Church Yth Grp; Computer Clb; French Clb; Latin Clb; Ski Clb; Varsity Clb; Im Var Bsktbl; Var Capt Crs Cntry; Var Capt Trk; L Almond Awd, Hnr Rl Awd 83; Indstrl.

VOISINE, JANICE L; St Paul Catholic HS; Bristol, CT; (Y); 97/304; Church Yth Grp; French Clb; Library Aide; Yrbk Stf; JV Var Cheerleading; Im Vllybl; High Hon Roll; Hon Roll; Natl Frnch Exam Merit Cert 82-83; Salve Regina; Bio.

VOLPE, MATT; Guilford HS; Guilford, CT; (Y); Drama Clb; English Clb; Ski Clb; Concert Band; Jazz Band; School Musical; School Play; Lit Mag; NHS; Ntl Merit Ltr.

VON JAKO, CHRISTOPHER RICHARD; Avon Old Farms Schl; Melrose, MA; (S); 7/97; Pep Clb; Nwsp Stf; Stu Cncl; JV Capt Swmmng; Var JV Tennis; High Hon Roll; Hon Roll; Computer Clb; Red Cross Aide; SPHERE; Alg II Hon Mntn; Dartmouth Coll; Med.

VOORHEES, CYNTHIA; Southington HS; Southington, CT; (Y); Key Clb; Ski Clb; Yrbk Stf; Capt Var Swmmng; L Var Trk; Hon Roll; Travl/Toursm.

VOORHEES, JOE; Guilford HS; Guilford, CT; (Y); Church Yth Grp; Computer Clb; FBLA; Spanish Clb; Teachers Aide; Varsity Clb; Var Golf; Var Socr; Hon Roll; Bus Comp.

VORBACH, EMILY; St Bernard HS; New London, CT; (S); Off Jr Cls; Rep Stu Cncl; Var Swmmng; JV Trk; Hon Roll; Psych.

VOSE, JESSE; Canton HS; Canton, CT; (Y); 3/86; Math Tm; Model UN; Quiz Bowl; Ski Clb; Concert Band; Yrbk Ed-Chief; Ed Lit Mag; Var L Crs Cntry; High Hon Roll; NHS; Outstndng Achvt In Geo, Bio, Math, Engl, & Adv Chmstry; Engrng.

VOSS, DOUG; Fairfield College Prep Schl; Trumbull, CT; (Y); Key Clb; Var Capt Swmmng; Hon Roll; NHS; Polit Sci.

VUJS, MARY L; Newington HS; Newington, CT; (Y); 50/347; Hosp Aide; JA; Hon Roll; Yth Cncl; Aide Jefferson Home; Becker JC; Acctng.

VUONG, KIM DIEN; Bassick HS; Bridgeport, CT; (Y); Art Clb; NHS; Natl Art Hon Soc 85; Norwalk ST Tech Coll; Data Pro.

WADE, KIMBERLY; Amity Regional District No 5 HS; Orange, CT; (S); 15/376; Chorus; Nwsp Stf; Yrbk Bus Mgr; Trs Stu Cncl; Var L Cheerleading; Var L Crs Cntry; Var L Trk; High Hon Roll; NHS; Soc Of Wmn Engrns Citatn; Biomed Engrng.

WADE, LADORA; Sacred Heart Acad; Hamden, CT; (Y); Dance Clb; Hosp Aide; Variety Show; Sftbl; Hon Roll; Bowling Hnrs-Awds 78; YMCA Dance Troop Swd 82; Princeton; Med.

WADSWORTH, ELIZABETH; Loomis Chaffee Schl; Vernon, CT; (Y); Hosp Aide; Math Tm; Band; Orch; School Musical; Ntl Merit SF; Cardiologist.

WAGENSEIL, PAUL V; Kent HS; Brookfield Ctr, CT; (Y); Debate Tm; Drama Clb; French Clb; School Play; Nwsp Rptr; Lit Mag; Ice Hcky; Socr; Tennis; Hon Roll.

WAGER, JAY; Brien Mc Mahon HS; Norwalk, CT; (Y); Boy Scts; Key Clb; Ski Clb; Jazz Band; Mrchg Band; Rep Jr Cls; Var Capt Crs Cntry; Var Capt Golf; Var Capt Swmmng; Hon Roll; Hnrs & Hgh Hnrs; Bio Sci.

WAGNBLAS, ADAM; Notre Dame HS; Ffld, CT; (Y); JA; Swmmng; Trk; Hon Roll; NHS; Elec Engrng Scholar 85; U Bridgeport; Elec Engr.

WAGNER, LAURIE LYNN; Acad Of Our Lady Of Mercy; Milford, CT; (Y); Church Yth Grp; Hosp Aide; Service Clb; Spanish Clb; Chorus; Yrbk Stf; Hon Roll; Jr NHS; NHS; Spanish NHS; Lauralettes 84-85; TN; Zoology.

WAGNER, MARY; St Bernard HS; Colchester, CT; (Y); Band; Concert Band; Drm Mjr(t); Mrchg Band; Off Jr Cls.

WAGNER, MICHELE; Cheshire HS; Cheshire, CT; (Y); 23/319; Cmnty Wkr; Hosp Aide; French Hon Soc; High Hon Roll; NHS; Dance Clb; French Clb; Hon Roll; Schlstc Achv Awd 84 & 85; Schlstc Achv Awd Frnch 82-85; U CT; Bus Adm.

WAGNER, PAULINE; Holy Cross HS; Waterbury, CT; (Y); 152/392; Church Yth Grp; Stage Crew; Natl Sci Mrt Schlr; Aerospc Engr.

WAGNER, ROBERT; Tolland HS; Tolland, CT; (Y); Rep Am Leg Boys St; Lit Mag; Rep Jr Cls; Rep Sr Cls; Crs Cntry; Capt Trk; High Hon Roll; Trs NHS; Russian Club 85; Holy Cross Bk Prz 85; Biochem.

WAKELEY, AARON JAKAB; Milford Acad; Huntington, CT; (Y); 1/25; Cmnty Wkr; Math Tm; Jazz Band; Orch; NHS; Val; Church Choir; Variety Show; Nwsp Stf; Wt Lftg; Harvard Bk Awd 84; Rensselaer Polytchnc Math & Sci Mdl 84; Thrtcl Astrphyscs.

WALDRON, DALE; St Bernard HS; Preston, CT; (S); Art Clb; Teachers Aide; JV Socr; High Hon Roll; Hon Roll; Art Hnr 84; Acad Hnr 83-84; Eng.

WALENDA, GRACE; Newtown HS; Sandy Hook, CT; (Y); 35/296; AFS; Cmnty Wkr; Hosp Aide; Yrbk Ed-Chief; Yrbk Phtg; Yrbk Stf; Cit Awd; High Hon Roll; NHS; Pres Schlr; Fairfield U; PHD In Psych.

WALKA, MCHELE; O H Platt HS; Meriden, CT; (Y); Art Clb; Church Yth Grp; Cmnty Wkr; Dance Clb; GAA; Girl Scts; Hosp Aide; JA; Pep Clb; Varsity Clb; Schlstc Art Awd 85; Cert Merit SR Pl Awd Wtr Clrs 85; Intr Dsgn.

WALKER, EVAN HUDSON; Hopkins HS; Hamden, CT; (Y); Boy Scts; Church Yth Grp; Cmnty Wkr; Chorus; School Play; Nwsp Stf; Lit Mag; Rep Stu Cncl; Var L Ftbl; Ntl Merit Ltr; Ntl Poetry Press Awd 83; NE Bk Rvw Cntst Prz 84; Collegian Schlrshp Lamboth Coll 84; Psych.

WALKER, JONATHAN; Cooperative HS; New Haven, CT; (Y); Boy Scts; Drama Clb; Political Wkr; Thesps; School Play; Nwsp Rptr; Lit Mag; Hon Roll; Dr Alice Hamltn Peace & Frdm Awd 85; Drama.

WALKER, NANCY; George J Penney HS; E Hartford, CT; (S); DECA; 4-H; Office Aide; 4-H Awd; Hon Roll; DECA ST Awd 85; Manchester CC; Bus Mgmt.

WALKER, TIFFANY; Weaver HS; Hartford, CT; (Y); VP Church Yth Grp; Drama Clb; JA; School Play; High Hon Roll; Hon Roll; Excell Push For Excell Commtt 83; Outstndg Female Talntd & Gftd Pgm 84; Outstndg Achvt Amer Hist 85; Psych.

WALLACE, FRANCIS; W F Raynor Tech; Waterbury, CT; (Y); Boy Scts; High Hon Roll; Hon Roll; NHS; U Hartford; Elec Engrng.

WALLIN, EVA KRISTINA; Bethel HS; Bethel, CT; (Y); 4/260; Variety Show; Nwsp Rptr; Yrbk Ed-Chief; JV Tennis; French Hon Soc; High Hon Roll; NHS; Civic Clb; Band; WA Wrkshp Congres Sem 85; CT Hnrs Semnr UCONN 85; Amer Scandinavian Stu Exch 85.

WALLNER, ABBIE; Guilford HS; Guilford, CT; (Y); VP Church Yth Grp; FCA; Model UN; Chorus; Church Choir; Var Capt Socr; Var L Trk; Hon Roll; Soccr, Trck Awds 83-85; ST Selct Tms 82-85; Lbrl Arts.

WALSER, SUSAN; Masuk HS; Monroe, CT; (Y); 5/280; JA; JCL; Math Tm; Stage Crew; Nwsp Sprt Ed; Yrbk Sprt Ed; Var JV Bsktbl; Var Vllybl; High Hon Roll; NHS; Outstndng JR Girl 85; Outstndng Engl 83, 84, Frgn Lang 84; Intl Rel.

WALSH, AMY; Southington HS; Southington, CT; (Y); 5/580; Sec German Clb; Key Clb; Rep PAVAS; Chorus; Flag Corp; Ed Nwsp Stf; Stat Bsktbl; High Hon Roll; NHS; Ntl Merit Ltr; Art Stu Mnth 84; 1st Pl Meriden Ct Arts Crfts Soc Annual Exh 84; Ctr Cretv Yth 84; Art.

WALSH, ERIN; Sacred Heart Acad; Stamford, CT; (Y); Drama Clb; JA; Service Clb; Variety Show; Lit Mag; Stat Bsktbl; Score Keeper; Var Sftbl; Hon Roll; Jr NHS; Cmmnctns.

WALSH, GARY; North Haven HS; N Haven, CT; (Y); 35/281; Boy Scts; Pres Church Yth Grp; Var Ftbl; Var Trk; Var Hon Roll; Math.

WALSH, JEANNA; The Williams Schl; Killingworth, CT; (Y); Band; Jazz Band; Variety Show; Var Bsktbl; Score Keeper; Sftbl; Hon Roll; Ntl Merit Ltr; Pfizer Schlrshp 85-89; Wellesley Coll.

WALSH, JOSEPH; Notre Dame HS; Seymour, CT; (Y); 100/250; Boys Clb Am; Boy Scts; Church Yth Grp; Computer Clb; Teachers Aide; Hon Roll.

WALSH, SUSAN J; Guilford HS; Guilford, CT; (Y); 38/315; Church Yth Grp; Trs Girl Scts; Hosp Aide; Sec Band; Jazz Band; Mrchg Band; Orch; School Musical; Hon Roll; Am Musical Fndtn Outstndng Musical Tlnt, Dedication & Svc 85; St Joseph Coll; Nrsng.

WALTERS, DEBBIE; Westhill HS; Stamford, CT; (Y); Mgr Crs Cntry; Capt Trk; Hon Roll; Cert Of Achvt From Board Of Ed For Track 85; Dvsnl & Cty Chmpns In Relay 85; Bus Adm.

WALTHER, PAM; Westhill HS; Stamford, CT; (Y); Church Yth Grp; Hosp Aide; Ed Yrbk Stf; JV Fld Hcky; Hon Roll; Lbrl Arts.

WALTS, ALAN; Guilford HS; Guilford, CT; (Y); Band; Orch; Bsbl; JV Ftbl; High Hon Roll; Hon Roll; Ntl Merit SF; Ftbl-Most Impvd Plyr; Engl-Genl Exclnc Awd; Wrtr.

WAN-WAH LAI, CHRISTINE; Choate Rosemary Hall HS; Wallingford, CT; (S); Acpl Chr; Chorus; School Musical; Nwsp Stf; Swmmng; High Hon Roll; Mu Alp Tht; 5th Frms All Round Awd; 5th Frms Math Awd; Harvard U; Lib Arts.

WANCIAK, MELANIE; Seymour HS; Seymour, CT; (Y); 58/224; Church Yth Grp; JA; Church Choir; Hon Roll; Intrdctn Bus Awd 82; Typing I Timing Awd 83; Med.

WANKERL, THOMAS; Newington HS; Newington, CT; (Y); 20/375; Am Leg Boys St; Church Yth Grp; VP JA; Nwsp Ed-Chief; Nwsp Rptr; Yrbk Ed-Chief; Yrbk Stf; Off Stu Cncl; Hon Roll; NHS; Ecnmcs.

WARD, BRENNA L; East Lyme HS; East Lyme, CT; (Y); 47/280; Hosp Aide; Key Clb; Office Aide; Teachers Aide; Chorus; Hon Roll; Awd For Volunteer Svc Peer Tutering 85; Hofstra U; Pre Law.

WARNE, KATE; Notre Dame C H S; Fairfield, CT; (Y); 5/284; Church Yth Grp; Sec French Clb; Library Aide; School Musical; Ed Nwsp Ed-Chief; JV Trk; Pres French Hon Soc; High Hon Roll; NHS; Ntl Merit Ltr; Alliances Francaises Awd Exclnce French 82-83 & 83-84; Wesleyan U.

WARREN, RANDOLPH; Notre Dame HS; New Haven, CT; (Y); Varsity Clb; Variety Show; Var Ftbl; Co-Capt Trk; Wt Lftg; Hon Roll; Hnrbl Mntn Trck-All Amer 84; All-CT Trck 84 & 85; U Of RI; Chem.

WARYCH, ELIZABETH; New Britain HS; New Britain, CT; (Y); Church Yth Grp; Red Cross Aide; High Hon Roll; Hon Roll; Jr NHS; NHS; Pres Acadmc Ftnss Awd; Andrew House Hlth Care Schlrshp; New Britain Genrl Hosp Aux Schlrshp; U Of CT; Nrsng.

WASFEY, SHEILA; Trumbull HS; Trumbull, CT; (Y); JA; Pres Spanish Clb; JV Bsktbl; Var Sftbl; Im Vllybl; High Hon Roll; NHS; Prfct Atten Awd; Bus.

WASHINGTON, DANIEL; Oliver Wolcot Vo-Tech; Torrington, CT; (Y); 42/146; Am Leg Boys St; Nwsp Sprt Ed; VP Jr Cls; Rep Stu Cncl; Var Capt Bsbl; Var Capt Bsktbl; Elec Engr.

WASILEWSKI, MARK; Norwich Reg Tech; Taftville, CT; (Y); 6/140; Am Leg Boys St; Yrbk Sprt Ed; Yrbk Stf; Var Bsbl; Var Socr; Hon Roll; Var NHS; Thams Vly ST; Elec Engrng.

WATERMAN, JANEL; James Hillhouse HS; New Haven, CT; (Y); Church Yth Grp; Math Clb; Nwsp Stf; Sec Stu Cncl; Stat Bsktbl; High Hon Roll; Jr NHS; NHS; St Schlr; Yale Bk Awd 85; Smith Clg Bk Awd 85; Bus Adm.

WATERMAN, TAMMY; Farmington HS; Farmington, CT; (Y); 21/204; Church Yth Grp; Var Fld Hcky; High Hon Roll; Vrsty Fld Hcky Coaches Awd 84; Katherine Gibbs Schl Ldrshp Awd 85; Bus.

WATERS, ANTHONY; Avon Old Farms Schl; Darien, CT; (S); 6/97; Orch; School Musical; Rep Frsh Cls; Rep Stu Cncl; Lcrss; Hon Roll; Pep Clb; Chorus; Ftbl; Sphere Pgm 84-85; Mbr Vrsty Ski Team 84-85; Outstndng Musician Awd 82-83; Cornell; Intl Bus.

WATKINS, AMY; Greenwich HS; Greenwich, CT; (Y); Drama Clb; Chorus; School Musical; Variety Show; Lit Mag; Rep Frsh Cls; Rep Stu Cncl; JV Trk; JV Vllybl; Royal Shkspr Co Wrkshps 84; Stu Human Rltns Proj 83; Law.

WATKINS, JOHN F; Fairfield Prep; Fairfield, CT; (Y); Model UN; Quiz Bowl; Nwsp Bus Mgr; Jr Cls; Var Crs Cntry; JV Var Socr; Var Tennis; High Hon Roll; Hon Roll; Ntl Merit SF; Fr Drama 1st Pl Poetry 2nd Spllng 3rd 83; Fr & Eng Bk Awd 82; Hnrs Scholar U Of TX Austin; Pol Sci.

WATSON, MICHAEL; Coventry HS; Coventry, CT; (Y); Church Yth Grp; Cmnty Wkr; Band; Concert Band; Mrchg Band; School Musical; Symp Band; Stu Cncl; Crs Cntry; Wt Lftg; Engl.

WATSON, THOMAS; Holy Cross HS; Waterbury, CT; (Y); Band; Rep Stu Cncl; JV Var Ftbl; JV Lcrss; Ntl Ldrshp & Serv Awds 83; FL A&M U; Rdio & TV Comm.

WATTERWORTH, CARLA; Crosby HS; Waterbury, CT; (Y); Church Yth Grp; Exploring; Chrmn FHA; Variety Show; Hon Roll; Pres Schlr; St Schlr; U Of CT; Phrmcy.

WATTS, ALFRED; Wilbur Cross HS; New Haven, CT; (Y); Capt Band; Capt Concert Band; Capt Mrchg Band; Capt Pep Band; School Play; Var Bsktbl; Hon Roll; Busn Admin.

WATTS, LAURA; St Bernard HS; Mystic, CT; (S); 12/289; Drama Clb; FNA; Band; Chorus; Church Choir; School Musical; Stage Crew; Yrbk Stf; Crs Cntry; High Hon Roll; Nrsg.

WEATHERBEE, NANCY; Windsor Locks HS; Windsor Locks, CT; (Y); 2/160; Am Leg Aux Girls St; Church Yth Grp; Math Tm; Band; Chorus; Church Choir; Concert Band; Jazz Band; Mrchg Band; Orch; Natl Math Tst; U Of CT Hnrs Semnr; Yale Bk Awd.

WEBBER, ELIZABETH; Bristol Central HS; Bristol, CT; (Y); Capt Drm Mjr(t); Var Swmmng; JV Trk; Hon Roll; Central CT; Acctng.

WEBSTER, ANDREW; Fitch SR HS; Mystic, CT; (Y); 2/411; VP Drama Clb; Pres Intnl Clb; Thesps; School Play; Mgr Stage Crew; Nwsp Rptr; Yrbk Ed-Chief; French Hon Soc; Columbia; Engl.

WEBSTER, DYANE L; Shelton HS; Shelton, CT; (Y); 32/438; Cmnty Wkr; Spanish Clb; Church Choir; Variety Show; Rep Stu Cncl; Hon Roll; NHS; Spanish NHS; Southern CT ST U; Spcl Ed.

WEEKS, STEPHANIE; St Bernard HS; Waterford, CT; (Y); 91/298; Spanish Clb; Band; Concert Band; Mrchg Band; Hon Roll; Pre-Law.

WEILAND, JAMES; Wilton HS; Wilton, CT; (Y); Rep Church Yth Grp; Letterman Clb; Varsity Clb; Mrchg Band; Stage Crew; Symp Band; JV Lcrss; Var L Socr; Hon Roll; Acton-Boxboro JV Lacrosse-Unsung Hero Awd 83; U Of MA-AMHERST; Botany.

WEINBERG, SCOTT; Waterford HS; Waterford, CT; (Y); 2/200; Key Clb; Ski Clb; Temple Yth Grp; Var Crs Cntry; Var Trk; High Hon Roll; NHS; Rotary Awd; Am Leg Boys St; Rep Jr Cls; U CT Hnrs Semnr 85; Dartmouth Bk Clb Awd 85; Comp.

WEINSTEIN, JEFFREY P; Trumbull HS; Trumbull, CT; (Y); 1/515; Science Clb; Jazz Band; Mrchg Band; Symp Band; Trs Soph Cls; Rep Stu Cncl; NHS; Ntl Merit SF; Spanish NHS; Val; Outstndng Soph Hnrs Math 83; Exclnce Chemistry, Rep CT Hnrs Sem 84; Dartmouth Coll; Phys Sci.

WEINSTOCK, MATT; Trumball HS; Trumbull, CT; (Y); Cmnty Wkr; JA; Temple Yth Grp; JV Socr; Hon Roll; Sci.

WEISBLATT, JONATHAN; Danbury HS; Danbury, CT; (Y); 80/615; Political Wkr; Temple Yth Grp; Var Crs Cntry; Var Trk; Hon Roll; JV Sprtsmnshp Indoor Trck 83-84; Med.

WEISENBERG, MICHAEL A; William H Hull HS; W Hartford, CT; (Y); 130/310; VP Frsh Cls; Trs Soph Cls; Pres Jr Cls; Pres Sr Cls; Pres Stu Cncl; Var L Bsbl; Var L Bsktbl; Var L Ftbl; Var Golf; Var L Socr; U Of CT; Accntnt.

WEISS, JEFF; Holy Cross HS; Oakville, CT; (Y); 51/352; Computer Clb; Drama Clb; Pres Science Clb; School Play; Stage Crew; French Hon Soc; High Hon Roll; Comp Engr.

WEISS, KATY; Rham HS; Marlborough, CT; (Y); FBLA; Chorus; Church Choir; Mgr(s); Art.

WEISS, LARA M; Robert E Fitch HS; Mystic, CT; (Y); Drama Clb; Intnl Clb; Key Clb; Thesps; Chorus; Color Guard; School Musical; School Play; Stage Crew; Nwsp Stf.

WEISS, MIKE; Trumbull HS; Trumbull, CT; (Y); Key Clb; Temple Yth Grp; Varsity Clb; Im Lcrss; JV Tennis; JV Trk; Var Wrstlng; Hon Roll; One Of The Bst Acctng Stu To Attnd Semnr At Quinnipiac Coll Hamnden CT 84-85; Bryant Coll; Acctng.

WEISSENBURGER, MICHAEL; Bloomfield HS; Bloomfield, CT; (Y); 23/231; Church Yth Grp; Debate Tm; VP JA; Model UN; Ski Clb; Pres Thesps; Yrbk Phtg; Stu Cncl; Var Bsbl; Intl Bus.

WELLINGTON, KATHERINE M; Stratford HS; Stratford, CT; (Y); 23/235; Cmnty Wkr; Yrbk Stf; Rep Frsh Cls; Rep Soph Cls; VP Jr Cls; VP Sr Cls; Rep Stu Cncl; High Hon Roll; Hon Roll; JC Awd; Wilton Ed Assoc Schlrshp; Cncl Awd; Patricia E Wynne Mem Schlrshp; U Conn; Bio.

WELLS, ALLISON; Shelton HS; Shelton, CT; (Y); Pom Pon; High Hon Roll; Hon Roll; Spanish NHS.

WELLS, GARNET; Cooperative HS; Hamden, CT; (Y); Church Yth Grp; Ski Clb; Spanish Clb; Dnfth Awd; Hon Roll; Ntl Merit Ltr; Prfct Atten Awd; Holy Crs Bk Awd 85; Acad All Amer Wnr 85; Pre-Med.

WELLS, HANNAH; Avon HS; Avon, CT; (Y); 9/150; Teachers Aide; Ed Yrbk Phtg; Yrbk Stf; Mgr(s); High Hon Roll; Hon Roll; Sec NHS; Cert Mert Brit Lit, Fr IV 84-85; Diploma Merit Spn II 84-85; Vet Med.

WELLS, SKIP; Portland HS; Portland, CT; (Y); 9/90; Am Leg Boys St; Trs Band; Nwsp Rptr; Yrbk Ed-Chief; Var JV Bsktbl; Var JV Golf; High Hon Roll; Hon Roll; NHS; NEDT Awd; Gildersleeve Schlrshp 85; Hgst Avg 85; Sprtsmnshp Awd Bsktbl 85; U Connecticut; Bus.

WELSH, MARK; Amity Regional SR HS; Orange, CT; (Y); French Clb; FBLA; Latin Clb; Quiz Bowl; Ski Clb; Band; Rep Stu Cncl; JV Socr; High Hon Roll; Class I & II Awds; Bus.

WELZ, LISA; Berlin HS; Kensington, CT; (Y); 42/200; Service Clb; School Play; Nwsp Stf; Yrbk Stf; Conversatnl German Awd 83-84; CT U; Bio.

WENDT, SARAH; Low-Heywood Thomas Schl; Stamford, CT; (Y); Pres Church Yth Grp; Hosp Aide; Model UN; Service Clb; Chorus; Lit Mag; Sec Frsh Cls; Hst Soph Cls; Rep Jr Cls; Var Swmmng; Pre-Med.

WERKHEISER, LORA; Shelton HS; Shelton, CT; (Y); Cmnty Wkr; Hosp Aide; VP JA; Ski Clb; Spanish Clb; Yrbk Stf; Rep Jr Cls; Rep Sr Cls; Mgr(s); Hon Roll; Bus Mgmt.

WERNER, SUSAN; Simsbury HS; Simsbury, CT; (Y); 155/357; Pres JA; Rep Stu Cncl; JV Cheerleading; Diving; JV Socr; George Washington U; Fin.

WERTZ, HEATHER; Trumbull HS; Trumbull, CT; (Y); Cmnty Wkr; Trs German Clb; Library Aide; Office Aide; Teachers Aide; Chorus; Cheerleading; Golf; Sftbl; Ger Clb Awd 85; Eastern Ct ST U; Comm.

WERTZ, INGRID M; William H Hall HS; W Hartford, CT; (Y); 11/300; Spanish Clb; Nwsp Rptr; Yrbk Sprt Ed; Stu Cncl; Var Im Lcrss; Capt L Swmmng; JV Trk; High Hon Roll; NHS; Spanish NHS; Wellesley Bk Awd 85; Math.

WEST, DOREEN; St Bernard HS; Uncasville, CT; (S); 35/289; Red Cross Aide; Chorus; Church Choir; School Musical; Pres VP Stu Cncl; High Hon Roll; Hon Roll; USAA Math Awd 82.

WEST, LISA; Branford HS; Garland, TX; (Y); Church Yth Grp; Office Aide; Acpl Chr; Chorus; Drill Tm; Rep Stu Cncl; Hon Roll; ST Choir 84-85.

WEST, TONYA A; Southington HS; Southington, CT; (Y); Sec Church Yth Grp; Computer Clb; FBLA; Girl Scts; JA; Key Clb; Library Aide; Pep Clb; Ski Clb; Church Choir; U Of Houston; Bus Admin.

WESTBY, STEPHANIE; Trumbull HS; Trumbull, CT; (Y); Church Yth Grp; Church Choir; Sec Frsh Cls; Rep Soph Cls; Sec Stu Cncl; High Hon Roll; NHS; Sal; Socty Womn Engr Awd Hghst Combnd Ave Math & Sci 84; Awds Outstndng Achvt Engl, Math, Frnch 83; Fairfield U; Bus.

WESTENHOER, WILLIAM; Brookfield HS; Brookfield, CT; (Y); 3/210; Boy Scts; Drama Clb; Math Tm; Varsity Clb; Stage Crew; Yrbk Stf; JV Golf; High Hon Roll; Hon Roll; Art Portflo Awd 84-85; Comp Grphcs.

WEYANT II, JAMES; Mark T Sheehan HS; Wallingford, CT; (Y); 98/205; Church Yth Grp; FBLA; JA; Varsity Clb; JV Ftbl; Ice Hcky; Wt Lftg; Amer Stu Stdy Grp Frgn Cntries 84; Middlesex CC; Comp Sci.

WHALEN, A J; Southington HS; Southington, CT; (Y); 60/550; VP Church Yth Grp; Nwsp Ed-Chief; Nwsp Sprt Ed; Nwsp Stf; Rep Frsh Cls; Pres Stu Cncl; Stat Sftbl; Alumni Spkng Awd 85; Jrnlsm.

WHEATLEY, DIONNE; James Hillhouse HS; New Haven, CT; (Y); Sec Church Yth Grp; Scholastic Bowl; Variety Show; Lit Mag; JV Crs Cntry; JV Trk; Elks Awd; High Hon Roll; NHS; Spanish NHS; Yale Peabody Museum Sci Awd 83; Hugh O Brien Yth Semnr 84; Yale Shafer Fmly Schlr 85; Pol Sci.

WHEATON, NEIL D; Haddam-Killingworth HS; Killingworth, CT; (Y); 1/130; Math Tm; Scholastic Bowl; Pres Jr Cls; Pres Sr Cls; Pres Stu Cncl; Var Capt Crs Cntry; JV L Trk; DAR Awd; Ntl Merit SF; Val; Havard Book Awd 84; Rensselaer Medal Math & Sci 84; Penn Scholar 84; MIT; Engrng.

WHEELER JR, FREDERICK W; Jonathan Law HS; Milford, CT; (Y); 14/273; Am Leg Boys St; Trs Key Clb; Rep Soph Cls; Var Tennis; L Wrstlng; Hon Roll; Prfct Atten Awd; Excllnce Pgmmg I; Excllnce Acctg I; NEDT Awd; Comp Engrng.

WHITE, BRIAN; Vinal Regional Tech/Voch HS; Middletown, CT; (Y); 22/147; Ski Clb; VICA; Yrbk Stf; Hon Roll; NHS; Rep Stu Cncl; Excel Adv Math, Excel Engl, Hnr Rl 4 Trms 81; Machnst.

WHITE, BRID M; Saint Mary HS; Greenwich, CT; (Y); Art Clb; Drama Clb; Intnl Clb; Math Tm; Pep Clb; School Play; Ed Yrbk Phtg; JV Cheerleading; Var Fld Hcky; Im Socr; Trinity Coll; Law.

WHITE, CAROLYN; Amity Reginal HS; Orange, CT; (Y); Church Yth Grp; French Clb; Ski Clb; Trk; JV Vllybl; Cit Awd; Hon Roll; Pres Jr NHS; NHS; Natl Art Hon Soc 85.

WHITE, CAROLYN; Bristol Eastern HS; Bristol, CT; (Y); 12/271; Sec Church Yth Grp; Spanish Clb; Rep Stu Cncl; Var L Bsktbl; Var Capt Socr; Var L Trk; High Hon Roll; VP NHS; Holy Cross Coll; Ec.

WHITE, MEGEEN; Simsbury HS; W Simsbury, CT; (Y); 64/356; Church Yth Grp; Cmnty Wkr; FBLA; Band; Concert Band; Mrchg Band; Pep Band; Stage Crew; Symp Band; Socr; Vrsty Lttr & Plq-Vllybl 84-85; Lions Clb Schlrshp 85; Humphrey Awd 85; U Of Scranton; Pre-Med.

WHITE, MICHAEL; St Bernard HS; N Franklin, CT; (S); 78/300; Exploring; Var Bsbl; Var Ftbl; Var Wrstlng; Hon Roll; All HCC Ftbl Conf 2nd Tm 84; Chem Engr.

WHITE, TRACY; North Haven HS; N Haven, CT; (Y); 28/298; Civic Clb; Debate Tm; Drama Clb; Science Clb; Yrbk Stf; Hon Roll; Vet Med.

WHITEFORD, VICTORIA; Staples HS; Westport, CT; (Y); Drama Clb; Acpl Chr; Band; Church Choir; Flag Corp; Jazz Band; Mrchg Band; Orch; School Musical; School Play; Music.

WHITEHEAD, LAUREN J; Daniel Hand HS; Madison, CT; (Y); 69/236; French Clb; GAA; JCL; Band; Pres Frsh Cls; Rep Stu Cncl; Capt JV Sftbl; Var Capt Swmmng; Hon Roll; Intl Rel.

WHITMAN, MILES; Miles Whitman HS; W Hartford, CT; (Y); Boy Scts; Cmnty Wkr; Hosp Aide; Ski Clb; Band; Chorus; Off Frsh Cls; Off Soph Cls; Stu Cncl; Mgr(s); HS Live Hero Awd 85; Article Mag 83.

WHITMORE, EMILY; Choate Rosemary Hall; Craftsbury Common, VT; (Y); Cmnty Wkr; Chrmn Latin Clb; Math Clb; Concert Band; School Musical; Im Socr; Hon Roll; Latin.

WHITMORE, SUSAN; St Paul HS; Plantsville, CT; (Y); 32/257; Cmnty Wkr; Drama Clb; Exploring; Hosp Aide; Office Aide; Teachers Aide; Band; Church Choir; Rep Stu Cncl; Hon Roll; Concours Natl De Francais Certificat De Merite 83; Med.

WHITNEY, AUTUMN; Windham Tech; Andover, CT; (Y); Camera Clb; Yrbk Stf; Stu Cncl; Var Trk; High Hon Roll; Hon Roll; NHS; VICA Most Likely To Succeed; Arch.

WHITTABY, VERONICA; Cooperative HS; New Haven, CT; (Y); Church Yth Grp; Teachers Aide; Band; Chorus; Church Choir; Variety Show; Lit Mag; Off Jr Cls; DAR Awd; Hon Roll; Charles Twyan Schlrshp 85; Hal Jacckson Tlntd Teens Schlrshp 83; New Haven Chptr Jack & Jill 83; Music.

WHITTAKER, CAMI; Griswold HS; Lisbon, CT; (Y); 9/100; GAA; Spanish Clb; Varsity Clb; School Play; Yrbk Stf; Sec Jr Cls; VP Sr Cls; Var Capt Cheerleading; JV Trk; High Hon Roll; Arremonys Bkry Awd 85; U Connecticut; Chld Psych.

WHYTE, JEFFREY R; East Hartford HS; E Hartford, CT; (Y); Am Leg Boys St; High Hon Roll; Hon Roll; CT Congrssnl JR Intern 85; Tchr.

WICKLUND, DESIREE; Kolbe-Catherdral HS; Bridgeport, CT; (Y); JA; Score Keeper; High Hon Roll; Acad All Amer 86.

WIELOCH, CHRISTINE; Orville H Platt HS; Meriden, CT; (Y); Church Yth Grp; Key Clb; Political Wkr; Yrbk Stf; Rep Soph Cls; Pres Stu Cncl; JV Vllybl; High Hon Roll; Hon Roll; Rotary Awd; Intl Econs.

WILBER, VANCE; Shelton HS; Shelton, CT; (Y); 18/437; Am Leg Boys St; Chess Clb; Drama Clb; Exploring; School Musical; Socr; Trk; NHS; Prfct Atten Awd; Spanish NHS; Colgate U; Math.

WILCOX, LORI A; Southington HS; Southington, CT; (Y); Key Clb; Math Tm; Teachers Aide; Rep Frsh Cls; Rep Soph Cls; Rep Stu Cncl; Var L Bsktbl; Var L Sftbl; Var Capt Vllybl; High Hon Roll; Engl Writing Awd; Lewis Alumni Algebra Awd; Discover III; Chemathon CT Hnrs Day; U Of CT; Engrng.

WILKES, CYNTHIA; Shelton HS; Shelton, CT; (S); Church Yth Grp; DECA; German Clb; Ski Clb; Spanish Clb; Stu Cncl; Hon Roll; Grmn Natl Hnr Soc 83-84.

WILLIAMS, CHERIE; East Catholic HS; S Windsor, CT; (Y); 86/294; Church Yth Grp; French Clb; Yrbk Stf; Wt Lftg; Hon Roll; Hon Roll; St Josephs Coll; Comm.

WILLIAMS, DANIELLE; Wilbur Lee Cross HS; New Haven, CT; (Y); Church Yth Grp; Spanish Clb; Church Choir; Variety Show; Rep Jr Cls; Var Trk; Var JV Vllybl; Hon Roll; Hlth Sci Cluster Pgm U CT Summr Pgm 85; Howard U; Microbio.

WILLIAMS III, FLOYD L; Manchester HS; Manchester, CT; (Y); 68/468; Church Yth Grp; French Clb; FBLA; Acpl Chr; Chorus; Church Choir; JV Swmmng; JV Trk; Hon Roll; Bus Admin.

WILLIAMS, HEBERTON; Roger Ludlowe HS; Fairfield, CT; (Y); 25/320; Lcrss; Socr; Wt Lftg; NHS; OH Wesleyan U; Math.

WILLIAMS, JANICE; Sacred Heart Acad; New Haven, CT; (Y); Church Yth Grp; FBLA; Hosp Aide; Chorus; Church Choir; School Musical; Stage Crew; Mgr(s); High Hon Roll; NHS; Duke U; Math.

WILLIAMS, PAUL; East Lyme HS; East Lyme, CT; (Y); Am Leg Boys St; Concert Band; Mrchg Band; VP Stu Cncl; JV Bsktbl; Hon Roll; Attnd CT Fedrtn Of Stu Govts 84; Attd Gov Yth Action Conf 84; Toured Europe W/New Englsh Ambssdrs/Msc; Bus Adm.

WILLIAMS, RONALD; Cheshire HS; Cheshire, CT; (Y); Rep Frsh Cls; Rep Soph Cls; Rep Jr Cls; Rep Sr Cls; Im Bsktbl; Bowling; Hon Roll; Jr NHS; Boy Scts; Im Socr; JR Prom King 1st Rnnr Up 85; Vrsty Bsktbl Partcptn 82; Engrng.

WILLIAMS, SHANNON; William H Hall HS; W Hartford, CT; (Y); Pep Clb; Ski Clb; Yrbk Stf; Cheerleading; Fld Hcky; Hon Roll.

WILLIAMS, TONYA; Wilbur Cross HS; New Haven, CT; (S); Church Yth Grp; Cmnty Wkr; FBLA; Hosp Aide; JA; Band; Church Choir; Concert Band; Orch; Stu Cncl; Algb, Typng II Awds; Central CT ST U; Comp Sci.

WILLS, NANCY; Masuk HS; Monroe, CT; (Y); 77/324; Church Yth Grp; Hon Roll; Elem Ed.

WILMOT, BRIAN; Norwalk HS; Norwalk, CT; (Y); FBLA; Letterman Clb; Var Bsbl; Var Crs Cntry; Var Trk; Hon Roll; NHS; Ntl Merit Schol; St Schlr; Bsebl All-City Pick 85; City Batting Title 85; Accntnt.

WILSON, AARON; Stamford HS; Stamford, CT; (Y); Trs Computer Clb; VP JA; Concert Band; Jazz Band; Orch; Pep Band; High Hon Roll; Hon Roll; Ntl Merit Ltr; Phyllis Layton Wrtng Awd; Engrng.

WILSON, DONALD; Fairfield Prep; Shelton, CT; (Y); VP Church Yth Grp; VP JA; Key Clb; Yrbk Stf; Var Crs Cntry; Var Trk; High Hon Roll; NHS; Ntl Merit Ltr; Hnrbl Mntn-Sci Fair 83 & 84; Aeronaut Engrng.

WILSON, JAMES; Notre Dame HS; W Haven, CT; (Y); Church Yth Grp; Lit Mag; Hon Roll; Bus.

WILSON, KAREN; Jonathan Law HS; Milford, CT; (Y); 39/247; Intnl Clb; Sec Keywanettes; Library Aide; Color Guard; Rep Jr Cls; Hon Roll; Eng.

WILSON, KIMBERLY A C; Westhill HS; Stamford, CT; (Y); Chrmn Latin Clb; Lit Mag; Rep Stu Cncl; Var Bsktbl; Capt Fld Hcky; Var Sftbl; Ntl Merit Schol; French Clb; Ski Clb; Pres Mnrty Stu Un 84-85; Am Lgn Oratry Cont 2nd Pl 82-83; Asst Dir Amen Crnr 84-85; Hampton U; Law.

WILSON, MARGARET YVETTE; Brien Mc Mahon HS; Norwalk, CT; (Y); 13/271; Cmnty Wkr; Yrbk Stf; Elks Awd; High Hon Roll; Jr NHS; Sec NHS; Stu Of Yr George Washington Carver Ctr 83-85; Pres Acad Fit Awds Pgm 85; Georgetown U; Acctg.

WILSON, SAMUEL VINCENT; Notre Dame HS; W Haven, CT; (Y); Spanish Clb; Concert Band; Jazz Band; Mrchg Band; Hosp Aide; School Musical; Rep Stu Cncl; Im Bsktbl; Hon Roll; ND Cncrt Mrchg Bnd JV/V Ltrs & VP 83-85; Spn Tutor 84-85; Frgn Lang Poet Cont 85; Host & Exch Stu 85; Southern CT ST U; Frgn Lang.

WILTON, AMY A; Litchfield HS; Litchfield, CT; (Y); AFS; Art Clb; Church Yth Grp; Cmnty Wkr; School Musical; Yrbk Phtg; Trs Jr Cls; L Var Crs Cntry; Drama Clb; Math Tm.

WILUSZ, TINA; Litchfield HS; Litchfield, CT; (Y); 17/91; Chorus; Concert Band; Var L Crs Cntry; Var L Trk; High Hon Roll; Hon Roll; Spanish NHS; Church Yth Grp; Band; Jazz Band; Mabry Music Awd 85; Latin Hnr Soc & Cert Hnrbl Merit NL Exam 82; All New Englnd Awd Solo Perfmnc 84; Bio.

WINANS, KATHARINE A; Glastonbury HS; S Glastonbury, CT; (Y); 3/393; Math Tm; Political Wkr; Ntl Merit SF; Bio.

WINANS, KEITH M; Enfield HS; Enfield, CT; (Y); Bsbl; Bsktbl; Socr; High Hon Roll; Hon Roll; Phy Ther.

WINARSKI, ROBERT; Southington HS; Plantsville, CT; (Y); JA; Ftbl; Wrstlng; U Of CT; Law.

WINKLEBLACK, GRANT; Farmington HS; Unionville, CT; (Y); Pres Church Yth Grp; Chorus; School Musical; Var L Bsktbl; Var L Trk; CT Clss M All St Trck 85; All Northwest Conf Trck 84 & 85; Mgmt.

WISHART, DANIEL L; St Paul Catholic HS; Bristol, CT; (Y); 120/298; Church Yth Grp; Political Wkr; Im Bsktbl; JV Var Ftbl; Hon Roll; Western CT ST U; Comp Engrng.

WISNIESKI, JENNIFER A; St Marys HS; Cos Cob, CT; (Y); 2/68; Hosp Aide; Latin Clb; Spanish Clb; Var Capt Bsktbl; Var Sftbl; Var Vllybl; Hon Roll; NHS; Scndry Chem Comp-Chemathon 85; CT Hnrs Sem- U Of CT 85.

WITHINGTON, LORETTA; St Marys HS; Northford, CT; (Y); 33/115; Nwsp Rptr; Lit Mag; Rep Stu Cncl; Hon Roll; U Of NH; Med Tech.

WITT, PENNY; Naugatuck HS; Naugatuck, CT; (Y); Church Yth Grp; Trs Library Aide; Orch; Rep Frsh Cls; Rep Soph Cls; Rep Jr Cls; Var L Trk; Hon Roll; Hugh O Brian Ldrshp Awd 84; Wmn Engrng Sem MI Technlgcl U 85.

WIVAGG, DEBORAH; Tolland HS; Tolland, CT; (Y); Rep Church Yth Grp; Dance Clb; 4-H; Band; Concert Band; Drm Mjr(t); Mrchg Band; Rep Sr Cls; 4-H Awd; Cmnty Wkr; Compete Miss TEEN Crt 85; Rep Crt 4-H Fshn Revw 83-84; Marist Coll; Fshn Dsgn.

WLOCHOWSKI, AARON M; Manchester HS; Manchester, CT; (Y); DECA; FBLA; JA; Letterman Clb; Trs Frsh Cls; Off Stu Cncl; Tennis; Hon Roll; Bentley; Fincl Mgmt.

WOHLEVER, RUSSELL; Brookfield HS; Brookfield Ctr, CT; (Y); Latin Clb; Stage Crew; Stat Bsktbl; Var L Trk; High Hon Roll; NHS; Ldrshp Awd CT Assoc Scndry Schls 85; Paul Mc Padden Schlrshp 85; Pres Acad Ftns Awdd 85; Penn ST; Meteorolgy.

WOJTOWICZ, LISA; Northweste Catholic HS; Hartford, CT; (Y); Pres Sec Church Yth Grp; Spanish Clb; Chorus; Yrbk Ed-Chief; Yrbk Stf; High Hon Roll; Hon Roll; Natl Hnr Soc 84-85; Spnsh Awd 83; Grmmr Schl Tchr.

WOJTUSIK, WENDY; Newington HS; Newington, CT; (Y); Civic Clb; Pep Clb; Cheerleading; Socr; Hon Roll.

WOLF, SANDRA; Guilford HS; Guilford, CT; (Y); 24/268; Pres Church Yth Grp; Latin Clb; Chorus; Church Choir; Ed Yrbk Stf; Rep Frsh Cls; Rep Stu Cncl; NHS; VP Spanish NHS; Munger Schlrshp Nrsg 85; U CT; Nrsg.

WOLF, WENDY D; William H Hall HS; W Hartford, CT; (Y); 138/324; Band; Concert Band; Jazz Band; Mrchg Band; Orch; Stage Crew; Symp Band; JV Var Mgr(s); JV Var Score Keeper; L Vllybl; Comp Inf Sys.

WOLINSKI, ROBERT; Norwich Reg Vo Tech Schl; Norwich, CT; (Y); Am Leg Boys St; Pres VICA; High Hon Roll; Hon Roll; NHS; Prfct Atten Awd; Hghst Avg Gen & Related Ed; Outstndng Svc & Ldrshp 84-85; Elec.

WOLL, LARA; The Masters Schl; Simsbury, CT; (S); 1/19; Church Yth Grp; Drama Clb; Chorus; School Play; Stage Crew; Yrbk Stf; Var Bsktbl; Var Socr; Var Sftbl; High Hon Roll.

WOMACK, PAUL; Thomas Snell Weaver HS; Hartford, CT; (Y); 6/300; Var Wrstlng; Hon Roll; Prfct Atten Awd; Hghst Avg Acad Cvcs 83; Hghst Avg Acad Eng II 84-85; Mst Imprvd Wrstlr 84-85; Howard; Comp Engnr.

WOOD, ROXANNE; Daniel Hand HS; Madison, CT; (Y); 102/270; Art Clb; Church Yth Grp; Cmnty Wkr; JA; Pep Clb; Red Cross Aide; Spanish Clb; Yrbk Stf; Safe Ride/Kids Agnst Drnk Drvng 84-86; Art Prntmkng Awd 1st Pl 85; Babson; Bus Cmnctns.

WOODARD, PAULETTE R; Thomas Snell Weaver HS; Hartford, CT; (Y); 22/345; Pres Dance Clb; Pep Clb; Nwsp Phtg; Rep Jr Cls; Hon Roll; Prfct Atten Awd; Typing Awd 84; Most Casual SR 85; Cheyney ST Coll; Earth Sci.

WOODBERRY, ROGER; Avon Old Farms HS; Reading, MA; (Y); 38/92; Aud/Vis; Camera Clb; Cmnty Wkr; Chorus; School Musical; School Play; Yrbk Phtg; Golf; Socr; Hon Roll; Drama Awd 83; Faculty Awd 83; Formed Glee Club 84; Dorm Monitor Designate 85; Hstry.

WOODBRIDGE, RUSSELL S; The Morgan Schl; Clinton, CT; (Y); 8/170; Church Yth Grp; Chorus; School Musical; Ed Yrbk Stf; Trs Stu Cncl; Swmmng; Pres NHS; AFS; All Eastrn Chrs 85; ST Stdnt Advsry Cncl Ed 84-85; Redfield Schlrshp 85; Rensselaer Polytechnic Inst.

WOODEN, JASON MARK; Manchester HS; Hartford, CT; (Y); Church Yth Grp; Cmnty Wkr; Intnl Clb; Science Clb; Band; Church Choir; Concert Band; Mrchg Band; High Hon Roll; Hon Roll; Top 100 Acad Minrty Stu CT, Outstndg Svc Co-Pres Schls Human Rel Clb 84; Cert CT JR Sci & Human 85; Setav Hll U; Bio.

WOODHALL, DAVID; Baptist Bible Acad; Waterford, CT; (Y); 2/3; Church Yth Grp; Drama Clb; FCA; Pep Clb; Y-Teens; Church Choir; School Play; Stage Crew; JV Socr; Sftbl; Perf Atndnc Awd 81, 82, 84 & 85.

WOODMAN, DAVID; North Branford HS; North Branford, CT; (Y); 3/153; Rep Am Leg Boys St; Church Yth Grp; VP Soph Cls; Var Socr; High Hon Roll; Hon Roll; VP NHS; Scholastic Bowl; JV Crs Cntry; JV Trk; CT Hnrs Sem Pgm 84-85; Algebra I & Hlth Awds 82-83; Phys Ed Awd 84-85; Aerospc.

WOODMANSEE, DONALD; St Bernard HS; Uncasville, CT; (S); Library Aide; JV Bsbl; Var Capt Gym; High Hon Roll; Frnch, Sci, Engl Awd Top Soph 83-84; Med.

WOODS, SARA; Stratford HS; Stratford, CT; (Y); 37/300; VP FBLA; Nwsp Rptr; Nwsp Stf; Rep Jr Cls; Hon Roll; Engl.

WOODS, WENDY L; Ledyard HS; Ledyard, CT; (Y); 1/275; Yrbk Stf; Var Capt Crs Cntry; Var Capt Trk; Hon Roll; Trs NHS; Ntl Merit SF; Rensselaer Mth & Sci Awd 84.

WORFOLK, GAIL; Greenwich HS; Riverside, CT; (Y); Service Clb; Color Guard; Nwsp Rptr; Ed Lit Mag; Badmtn; High Hon Roll; Hon Roll; NHS; Ntl Merit Ltr; Pres Of Folsom House Actn Brd 85-86.

WORKINGER, KEN; Guilford HS; Guilford, CT; (Y); Pres Orch; Rptr Yrbk Phtg; High Hon Roll; Hon Roll; NHS; Fencng Var Ltr 84-85; Mech Engr.

WOROZILCAK, KRISTEN; Jonathan Law HS; Milford, CT; (Y); Keywanettes; Ed Nwsp Stf; Ed Yrbk Stf; Bsktbl; Hon Roll; NEDT Awd; Comm Arts.

WOSLEGER, JEFF; Stamford Catholic HS; Stamford, CT; (Y); 70/149; Yrbk Stf; Var Capt Ice Hcky; Hon Roll; Donald Rafferty Mem Schlrshp Awd 84-85; St Anselms Coll; Bus.

WOUNDY, RICHARD M; St Margarets-Mc Ternan HS; Prospect, CT; (Y); Capt Church Yth Grp; JA; Ed Nwsp Stf; Pres Stu Cncl; L Bsktbl; L Socr; Ntl Merit SF; Harvard Bk Clb Southern CT Awd 84; Cum Laude Soc 84; Awd Achvt Hnrs Chem 83.

WOUNDY, THOMAS; Kaynor Technical Schl; Prospect, CT; (Y); Church Yth Grp; Computer Clb; VICA; Band; Vllybl; Hon Roll; NHS; Electrn Engr.

WRIGHT, HEATHER; Sacred Heart Acad; New Haven, CT; (Y); Trs French Clb; Hosp Aide; Nwsp Rptr; Nwsp Stf; French Hon Soc; High Hon Roll; NHS; Ntl Merit Ltr; NEDT Awd; FBLA; 2nd Pl Frnch Poetry Recitation Cont; Engl.

WRIGHT, JOAN; Enrico Fermi HS; Enfield, CT; (Y); Church Yth Grp; Cmnty Wkr; Drama Clb; Ski Clb; Capt Color Guard; Capt Mrchg Band; Stage Crew; Variety Show; Becker JC; Occptnl Thrpy.

WRIGHT, MATTIE; James Hillhouse HS; New Haven, CT; (Y); 4-H; FNA; Girl Scts; Pep Clb; Drill Tm; Gym; Score Keeper; Hon Roll; Nrs.

WRIGHT, SAMONE T; Kolbe-Cathedral HS; Bridgeport, CT; (Y); 2/95; Church Yth Grp; Cmnty Wkr; Hosp Aide; Library Aide; Office Aide; Chorus; Church Choir; Hon Roll; Yrbk Stf; Bus Awd Typng 84; St Vincents Hosp Pin 84; Hnr Rl Awd 85; Sacrew Heart U; Pre-Nrsng.

WRIGHT, THOMAS; Oldsaybrook SR HS; Old Saybrook, CT; (Y); Leo Clb; Var Capt Crs Cntry; Var Capt Trk; Var Twrlr; Shoreline Champ 200 M 85; 2nd Cls S Div 200 M Schl Rec 85; St Open CIAC 85; Bus Mgt.

WRIGHT, TRACY; Southington HS; Southington, CT; (Y); 100/580; Library Aide; Ski Clb; School Play; Variety Show; Sec Frsh Cls; Sec Stu Cncl; Var Trk; High Hon Roll; Hon Roll; Chld Psych.

WYNN, CHARLES; Windham HS; Colmbia, CT; (Y); 2/300; Stu Cncl; Var Wrstlng; Bausch & Lomb Sci Awd; High Hon Roll; Mu Alp Tht; NHS; Ntl Merit Ltr; Sal; Outstndng Physics Stu 84; U Of CT; Physics.

WYSHNER, DAVID BRENDAN; The Hotchkiss HS; Canaan, CT; (Y); Pres Intnl Clb; Service Clb; Teachers Aide; Nwsp Stf; JV Golf; Bausch & Lomb Sci Awd; High Hon Roll; Frst Schlr; Cum Laude Socty; A Wm Olsen Prz; Yale U; Math.

XAVIER, MARIA; Bassick HS; Bridgeport, CT; (S); Teachers Aide; School Play; Nwsp Stf.

YACHTIS, DAVE; Holy Cross HS; Naugatuck, CT; (Y); 20/352; JV Bsktbl; JV Trk; High Hon Roll; NHS; Rensselaer Poly-Tech Inst Mth & Sci Awd 85; Brother Francis Leary Scholar Awd 83; Engrng.

YAGGI, MAUREEN; Stamfofd HS; Stamford, CT; (S); Church Yth Grp; DECA; Teachers Aide; Color Guard; Bus.

YAMAMOTO, MARIE A; East Hartford HS; E Hartford, CT; (Y); Girl Scts; Political Wkr; Red Cross Aide; Nwsp Bus Mgr; Nwsp Ed-Chief; Yrbk Bus Mgr; Rep Stu Cncl; NHS; High Hon Roll; Hon Roll; Grl Sct Slvr Awd 84; Grl Sct Ntl Brd Of Dirctrs Cmmttee 85-87; Govt Serv.

YAZMER, AMY; Shelton HS; Huntington, CT; (Y); Hosp Aide; Spanish Clb; Sec Temple Yth Grp; Band; Concert Band; Mrchg Band; Pep Band; Rep Jr Cls; Hon Roll; Prfct Atten Awd; Cert Of Merit Imprvmnt Stud 82; Oscar Robul Awd; U Of CT; Elem Ed.

YEE, WYATT; Rockville HS; Vernon, CT; (Y); 4/370; Am Leg Boys St; Cmnty Wkr; Math Tm; Quiz Bowl; Spanish Clb; Nwsp Stf; High Hon Roll; NHS; Political Wkr; Trk; Yale Bk Awd 85.

YEPES, DIANA; Brien Mc Mahon HS; Rowayton, CT; (Y); 23/342; French Clb; GAA; JCL; Latin Clb; Yrbk Stf; Chrmn Sr Cls; Im Powder Puff Ftbl; Var Tennis; High Hon Roll; Jr NHS; Brien Mc Mahon Mixed Dbls Tennis 83; Uconn Spnsh Crse 83; Med.

YERKES, ANDREW; Guilford HS; Guilford, CT; (Y); Drama Clb; Thesps; Acpl Chr; Chorus; Camera Clb; School Musical; School Play; Swing Chorus; CT Drama Assn, All CT Cst, CT Rgnl Choir 85; Brigham Young U.

YERXA, DANIEL; Joseph A Foran HS; Milford, CT; (Y); 11/245; Am Leg Boys St; Exploring; Trs JCL; Key Clb; Latin Clb; Ski Clb; Spanish Clb; Varsity Clb; Var L Ftbl; Var L Trk; Jimmy Brennan Mem Scholar Awd 80; Excllnce Geom & Bio Awd 83-84; Pre-Med.

YESCOTT, EDWARD; Farmington HS; Farmington, CT; (Y); Aud/Vis; Church Yth Grp; Exploring; FCA; Ski Clb; Stage Crew; Rep Stu Cncl; JV Lcrss; Var Swmmng; Im Wt Lftg; USCG Acad; Aviatn Tech.

YEVICH, MIKE A; Shelton HS; Shelton, CT; (Y); 173/415; Band; Concert Band; Mrchg Band; Orch; Pep Band; School Musical; Stage Crew; Hon Roll; NY Inst Of Tech; Arch.

YOCIS, KAREN; Notre Dame HS; Fairfield, CT; (Y); 9/290; Church Yth Grp; Spanish Clb; Nwsp Sprt Ed; Var Capt Bsktbl; JV Trk; High Hon Roll; Pres Schlr; Rotary Awd; US Army Resrv Ntl Schlr/Athlt Awd 85; ALSMA Schlrshp Awd 85; Presdntl Hnr Schlrshp 85; ND Schl 85; Marietta Coll.

YOON, SEIHEE; Miss Porters Chl; Southington, CT; (Y); Church Yth Grp; Computer Clb; English Clb; Intnl Clb; Math Tm; Model UN; Science Clb; Var Badmtn; JV Lcrss; Hon Roll; Ec.

YORZINSKI, DEBBIE; Guilford HS; Guilford, CT; (Y); Church Yth Grp; Red Cross Aide; Sec Frsh Cls; Stu Cncl; JV Tennis; Hon Roll; Bus.

YOUNG, DEBORAH; Trumbull HS; Trumbull, CT; (Y); Color Guard; Concert Band; Mrchg Band; High Hon Roll; NHS; U New Hampshire.

YOUNG, JANET; Loomis-Chaffee Schl; Windsor Locks, CT; (Y); Model UN; Ntl Merit SF; Commttee Jr Imfrmt; Peer Suppt; Dntl Asst; Sr Prom Comm; Russn Clb; Hrsebck Rdng; Stu Tour Guid; Pre Med.

YOUNG, LISA; Staples HS; Westport, CT; (Y); Church Yth Grp; Drama Clb; JA; PAVAS; Chorus; School Musical; School Play; Stage Crew; Nwsp Sprt Ed; Fshn Merch.

YOUNG, SHARON L; East Hampton HS; East Hampton, CT; (Y); 15/98; Am Leg Aux Girls St; Drama Clb; Yrbk Ed-Chief; Trs Stu Cncl; Cheerleading; Trk; Hon Roll; NHS; Belfry Clb East Hampton Awd 85; U Of CT; Indus Psych.

YOUNG, TED; Brunswick Schl; Greenwich, CT; (Y); 11/41; Cmnty Wkr; Varsity Clb; Nwsp Sprt Ed; Rep Soph Cls; Var Crs Cntry; Wrstlng; Hon Roll; Pres Schlr; CT ST Wrstlng Rnr Up 85; Schl Rcrd Season Pins 85; Sec Pol Discussion Grp FORUM 85; Dartmouth Coll; Hstry.

YOUNGREN, DAVID M; Choate Rosemary Hall HS; Wallingford, CT; (S); Church Yth Grp; Computer Clb; Acpl Chr; Chorus; Church Choir; School Musical; JV Wrstlng; High Hon Roll; Stus Hlpng Stus Schlrshp 84; Systms Anlyst.

YOUNGS, JILL; Tolland HS; Tolland, CT; (Y); 3/180; Ski Clb; Band; Mrchg Band; School Musical; Rep Jr Cls; Var L Crs Cntry; Var L Trk; High Hon Roll; NHS; Prfct Atten Awd; High Average In Frgn Lang, Pre Calculus, Typing I & Engl 82-85; Math.

YUM, DAVID; O H Platt HS; Meriden, CT; (Y); Math Clb; Bsbl; Bsktbl; Ftbl; Trk; Wt Lftg; Hon Roll; Mech Engr.

YUSKO, MICHELE; Notre Dame Catholic HS; Bridgeport, CT; (Y); 12/284; Hosp Aide; JA; Pres Latin Clb; High Hon Roll; NHS; Presdntl Acadmc Ftnss Awd 85; John A & Mary Behunick Heritg Awd 85; St U Of NY-ONEONTA.

YWANCIOW, JOSEPH D; Plainfield HS; Moosup, CT; (Y); 34/158; Varsity Clb; Var Bsktbl; Im Tennis; Var Trk; Voice Dem Awd; Thames Valley Tech Inst; Comp.

ZABLAN, GABRIELLA; Wilbur Cross HS; New Haven, CT; (Y); French Clb; Yrbk Stf; Lit Mag; Pom Pon; High Hon Roll; Outstndng Achvt Frnch I II,Geo 83-84; Acad Excel Physcl Ed 83-84; Engrng.

ZACK, HENRY J; St Joseph HS; Trumbull, CT; (Y); 19/216; Debate Tm; Scholastic Bowl; Ed Yrbk Sprt Ed; Var L Trk; Cit Awd; High Hon Roll; Spanish NHS; Cmnty Wkr; Exploring; Political Wkr; All-MBIAC & 1st Pl Inct M Div Trck Champ 85; Asst Fin Sec For St Joseph Slovak Scty 84-85; Boston Coll; Pre-Law.

ZACKERY, DIONE; The Cooperative HS; New Haven, CT; (Y); Chorus; Drill Tm; School Musical; Rep Jr Cls; Stu Cncl; Vllybl; High Hon Roll; Hon Roll; Prfct Atten Awd; Law.

ZACKIN, PAUL; Pomperaug HS; Middlebury, CT; (Y); 3/200; Math Tm; Ed Yrbk Stf; JV Socr; High Hon Roll; NHS; Ntl Merit Ltr; Outstndg Physics Stu Yr 85; Scty Women Engrs Awd 85; Natl Sci Olympd Chem Wnnr 85; Engr.

ZAGORA, LYNN; East Catholic HS; Tolland, CT; (Y); 68/296; Hon Roll; Bus.

ZAIK, DIANNA M; Tolland HS; Tolland, CT; (Y); 39/169; Yrbk Stf; Rep Frsh Cls; Rep Soph Cls; Rep Jr Cls; Hon Roll; Sec NHS; Rockville Exchng Clb Schlrshp 85; Rotary Clb Schlrshp 85; Bay Path JC; Fshn Mrchndsng.

ZAIK, EDWARD; Tolland HS; Tolland, CT; (Y); 34/170; Am Leg Boys St; Aud/Vis; School Musical; Stage Crew; Pres Soph Cls; Pres Jr Cls; Pres Sr Cls; Off Stu Cncl; JV Socr; Hon Roll; Bus.

ZAK, REBECCA; Southington HS; Southington, CT; (Y); 22/630; Church Yth Grp; Cmnty Wkr; FTA; Hosp Aide; Key Clb; Latin Clb; Variety Show; High Hon Roll; Hon Roll; Jr NHS; NHS; CT Latn Cntst Hnrbl Mntn 83-84; CT ST U; Elem Ed.

ZALONSKI, DEBBIE; Mark T Sheehan HS; Wallingford, CT; (Y); 17/210; Powder Puff Ftbl; Wrd Prcssng.

ZAREBSKI, CHRISTINE A; New Britain HS; New Britan, CT; (Y); High Hon Roll; Hon Roll; Rgstrd Nrs.

ZARET, ADAM; Amity Regional SR HS; Woodbridge, CT; (Y); Boy Scts; Rep Drama Clb; Model UN; Political Wkr; Capt Quiz Bowl; Capt Varsity Clb; Acpl Chr; Band; Chorus; School Musical; Chrmn Of Amity Chptr Of The Teenage Republcns 84-85; Sci Olympiad Of The U Of CT 85; Aerospce Engrng.

ZARS, ERIK; Bloomfield HS; Bloomfield, CT; (Y); 19/231; Boy Scts; Church Yth Grp; Model UN; Thesps; Yrbk Stf; Trs Soph Cls; Trs Jr Cls; Trs Sr Cls; Var L Tennis; Hon Roll; Ntl Rifle Assn 3 Hghst Awds In Shrpshtr 83-84; Bio Chmstry.

ZAVAGLIA, ANTOINETTE; Branford HS; Branford, CT; (Y); Am Leg Aux Girls St; GAA; Pep Band; Ed Yrbk Bus Mgr; Yrbk Stf; Sec Frsh Cls; Sec Soph Cls; Sec Jr Cls; Pres Sr Cls; JV Sftbl; Fnlst Sen Yth Prog 84-85; Prom Queen 84-85; Pol Sci.

ZAWACKI, KAREN MARIE; Danbury HS; Danbury, CT; (Y); 110/642; Hosp Aide; Key Clb; Math Tm; Acpl Chr; Church Choir; Capt Color Guard; School Musical; Yrbk Ed-Chief; Stu Cncl; Jr NHS; Miss CT Natl Teen-Ager 82-83; Miss CT All-Amer Teen Girl 85; Co-Hosts TV Chldrns Show 82-84; Boston U; Vclsm.

ZAWILINSKI, BRIAN; Vinal Reg Voc Tech HS; Middletown, CT; (Y); 5/143; Stage Crew; Trs Stu Cncl; Var Bsktbl; Crs Cntry; Var Trk; High Hon Roll; Hon Roll; VP NHS; Rnr-Up DAR Coed Awd 84; CT Bus & Ind Awd Recip 85; Hartford ST Tech; Elec Engrng.

ZEITLIN, LARRY; Cheshire HS; Cheshire, CT; (Y); 1/320; Am Leg Boys St; Hosp Aide; Scholastic Bowl; Pres Science Clb; Teachers Aide; Ed Nwsp Stf; Im Vllybl; High Hon Roll; NHS; Yales Frontiers Sci 84; Achvt Awd Wrtng 85; Team Sci Olymp 85; Med.

ZELINSKI, CHRISTINE; Seymour HS; Seymour, CT; (Y); JV Sftbl; High Hon Roll; Hon Roll; Prm Comte 84-85; U Of RI; Physcl Thrpy.

ZEMAITIS, AL; W F Kaynor Techical Schl; Oakville, CT; (Y); Hon Roll; NHS; Elec Engr.

ZEMBROSKI, LAURA ANN; Stamford HS; Stamford, CT; (Y); Latin Clb; Sftbl; High Hon Roll; Hon Roll; Jr NHS; NHS; U Of MD; Zoolgy.

ZEMKE, SUSANNAH L; Branford HS; Branford, CT; (Y); 1/250; French Clb; Key Clb; Math Tm; Band; Orch; Var L Crs Cntry; Var L Trk; High Hon Roll; NHS; Ntl Merit Schol; Rice U; Econmcs.

ZERING, FREDERICK A; Southington HS; Southington, CT; (Y); 168/550; Boys Clb Am; Church Yth Grp; Cmnty Wkr; Bsbl; Bsktbl; Hon Roll; Sir Thomas Lipton Sprtsmnshp Awd 85; Boys Club Lds Aux Schlrshp 85; U Of CT; Engr.

ZIBAITIS, ELIZABETH; St Thomas Aquinas HS; Newington, CT; (Y); Spanish Clb; Hon Roll; Ski Clb; Speech Tm; Peer Tutor; Central CT ST U; Acctng.

ZIEHL, MATTHEW; Greens Farms Acad; Greens Farms, CT; (Y); 4/39; Political Wkr; Chorus; School Play; Variety Show; Nwsp Ed-Chief; Crs Cntry; Hon Roll; Ntl Merit SF; Gld Medal Ntl Ltn II Exm; Nwsp Awd; Hstry Awd; Cum Laude Soc; Mst Imprvd Crs Cntry Rnnr; Yale U; Hstry.

ZIGMOND, GARY; Norwalk HS; Norwalk, CT; (Y); 42/486; Church Yth Grp; Computer Clb; Service Clb; Yrbk Stf; Im Bsktbl; Var Crs Cntry; Var Trk; High Hon Roll; Hon Roll; 2nd Pl Norwalk Sci Fair 84; Ntl Sci Olympiad 85; Finance.

ZILVITIS, BRIAN; Wilton HS; Wilton, CT; (Y); 9/245; Rep Stu Cncl; L Bsktbl; L Tennis; High Hon Roll; Ntl Merit Ltr; CT Schlr Athl Awd 85; Trnty Coll Outstndng JR Awd 84; Boston Coll; Pre-Med.

ZIMMER, H JUSTIN; Greenwich HS; Cos Cob, CT; (Y); Am Leg Boys St; Boy Scts; Exploring; High Hon Roll; NHS; Hdmstrs Awd Acad Excel 85; Eagle Sct 82; Outstndng 1st Yr Physc Stu 84; Cornell U.

ZIMMERMANN, ELOISE; H C Wilcox Technical Schl; Middletown, CT; (Y); Dance Clb; Drama Clb; Library Aide; Red Cross Aide; VICA; Yrbk Stf; VP Stu Cncl; Var Cheerleading; High Hon Roll; Hon Roll; Von Lee; Hairdressing.

ZINGO, GINA; Masuk HS; Monroe, CT; (Y); AFS; Church Yth Grp; Drama Clb; Trs Frsh Cls; Hon Roll; Ec.

ZINYCH, MARK; Amity Regional SR HS; Bethany, CT; (Y); Boy Scts; Library Aide; Ski Clb; Spanish Clb; Yrbk Stf; Lit Mag; JV Var Socr; Cit Awd; Prfct Atten Awd; Spnsh Awd 83; Sccr Leadg Asst 83; Boy Scts Patrl Ldr; Pre-Law.

ZISTERER, UTE; Lyman HS; West Germany; (Y); AFS; School Musical; Var Powder Puff Ftbl; Var Tennis; Hon Roll; NHS; Lang.

ZITNAY, JEFFREY S; Shelton HS; Shelton, CT; (Y); Am Leg Boys St; Boy Scts; French Clb; Quiz Bowl; Scholastic Bowl; Hon Roll; Ntl Cncl Tchrs Engl Achvt Awds Wrtng 85; Fairfield U; Accntng.

ZOLLA, PHILLIP; Notre Dame HS; Ansonia, CT; (Y); Am Leg Boys St; Lit Mag; High Hon Roll; NHS; 9th Grd Sci Awd 1st Pl 83; Math/Sci Awd 85; CT ST Sci Fair 5th Plant Tissu Cult 85; Worcester Polytech; Biotech.

ZUCCARO, TIA MARI; Southington HS; Southington, CT; (S); DECA; Pep Clb; Band; Chorus; Mrchg Band; Off Frsh Cls; Rep Stu Cncl; Hon Roll; 1st Pl ST Wnnr DECA 85; DECA Ntl Comptn SF 85; Johnson & Wales; Comp Prog.

ZUCKER, AMY I; Hamden HS; Hamden, CT; (Y); Cmnty Wkr; Political Wkr; VP Temple Yth Grp; School Musical; School Play; Nwsp Rptr; High Hon Roll; Ntl Merit Ltr; Ed Ctr Arts 83-85; Capt H S Bowl Tm 84-85; CT Chem-A-Thon 84-85; Frnch Ptry Cntst 1st Pl 84-85; Humnities.

ZUELLA, TODD; Fairfield College Prep Schl; Oxford, CT; (Y); Cmnty Wkr; Ski Clb; Rep Frsh Cls; Rep Soph Cls; Rep Stu Cncl; Socr; JV Wrstlng; High Hon Roll; Hon Roll; NHS; Bio.

ZUROLO, MARY; Sacred Heart Acad; Hamden, CT; (Y); Nwsp Rptr; High Hon Roll; Church Yth Grp; Cmnty Wkr; English Clb; Red Cross Aide; Chorus; School Musical; Mgr(s); $50 Awd For Being 1 Of Top Sellers In Champaign Of The Schl 83; Writer.

ZYMBA, PAUL F; Enfield HS; Enfield, CT; (Y); JV Var Socr; High Hon Roll; Hon Roll; NHS; Comp Sci.

MAINE

ABBOTT, MIKE; Fort Kent Community HS; St Francis, ME; (Y); Cmnty Wkr; Varsity Clb; Var Socr; Var Trk; Var Wrstlng; High Hon Roll; Hon Roll; Aroostook Leag Wrstlng Champ Awd 85; Math, Sci Outstndng Achvt Awd 83; Alg, Bio Outstndng Achvt Awd 84; Wldlf.

ADAMS, DANA; Bangor HS; Bangor, ME; (Y); English Clb; FTA; Math Tm; Church Choir; Yrbk Stf; Lit Mag; Rep Jr Cls; Var Mgr(s); Var Swmmng; Hon Roll; FL A&M; Cmmnctns.

ADELMAN, BETH; Bangor HS; Bangor, ME; (Y); Variety Show; Yrbk Stf; Trs Frsh Cls; Off Soph Cls; Off Jr Cls; Off Sr Cls; Pres Stu Cncl; Fld Hcky; Swmmng; NHS; Arch.

AHERN, HEATHER; Mt Abram Regional HS; Strong, ME; (Y); Drama Clb; Intnl Clb; Yrbk Stf; VP Frsh Cls; Trs Jr Cls; Var L Cheerleading; JV Crs Cntry; UVM; Lang Arts.

AINAIRE, BETH; Gray-New Cloucester HS; New Gloucester, ME; (Y); 12/160; French Clb; Band; Concert Band; Crs Cntry; Var Socr; Trk; Hon Roll; Athl Awds Sccr & Trk 81 & 85; Mid State Bus Coll; Lgl Secry.

ALBERI, MICHELE; Oxford Hils HS; S Paris, ME; (Y); 32/234; Cmnty Wkr; Key Clb; Pres Latin Clb; VP Frsh Cls; Rep Soph Cls; Pres Jr Cls; Pres Stu Cncl; Var Fld Hcky; DAR Awd; NHS; Norway Paris Fish Game Schlrshp 85; Northeastern U; Psych.

ALBERT, LISA; Van Buren District Secondary Schl; Van Buren, ME; (Y); Pres Church Yth Grp; VP DECA; Rep Model UN; Teachers Aide; School Play; JV Var Bsktbl; High Hon Roll; Hon Roll; Pres Schlr; Voice Dem Awd; Bus.

ALBERT, MICHELLE; Fort Kent Community HS; Eagle Lake, ME; (Y); 12/180; Church Yth Grp; Var Trk; Im Vllybl; Hon Roll; Hgh Achvt Awd Civics 82-83; Cert Excllnce 82-85; Var Ltr Trk 85; Real Est.

ALEX, ANDREA L; Camden-Rockport HS; Camden, ME; (Y); 13/128; Pres Church Yth Grp; Library Aide; Teachers Aide; Lit Mag; JV Mgr(s); High Hon Roll; Hon Roll; Charles Marstaller Scholar; Libr Clb Scholar; Robert Babb Scholar; Eastern Coll; Early Chldhd.

ALEXANDER, JAMES; Deering HS; Portland, ME; (Y); Library Aide; Crs Cntry; Hon Roll; Air Force CC; Comp.

ALEXANDRE, MICHAEL; Sanford HS; Sanford, ME; (Y); Church Yth Grp; Diving; Hon Roll; Jr NHS; 1st Pl Trophy Ping Pong 85; Elect.

ALLAIN, BARBARA; Cony HS; Augusta, ME; (Y); Church Yth Grp; Hon Roll; Dent Asst.

ALLAIN, CHRISTOPHER; Yarmouth HS; Yarmouth, ME; (Y); Church Yth Grp; Ski Clb; Im Bsktbl; Im Golf; Hon Roll; Arch.

ALLARD, NANCY ANNE; Noble HS; N Berwick, ME; (Y); Rptr Am Leg Aux Girls St; Key Clb; Band; Jazz Band; Var Mgr Bsktbl; Mgr Socr; Var Sftbl; NHS; Hon Roll; Prfct Atten Awd; Svc Pin For Being Peer Counslr,Trombone Back Up Show Choir,Schl Muscl Orchstra; Pre Med.

ALLEN, DEBORAH; Westbrook HS; Westbrook, ME; (Y); French Clb; Keywanettes; Yrbk Bus Mgr; Yrbk Sprt Ed; Yrbk Stf; Socr; Psych.

ALLEN, SUSAN; Robert W Traip Acad; Kittery, ME; (Y); Am Leg Aux Girls St; Drama Clb; French Clb; Thesps; Chorus; School Musical; School Play; Yrbk Stf; Capt Var Bsktbl; Hon Roll; ME All-ST Acting Awd At A Rgnl Drama Comp 85; UMO; Thtr.

ALLEY, DOUGLAS; Jonesport-Beals HS; Beals, ME; (Y); 2/28; Am Leg Boys St; Pres Jr Cls; Pres Sr Cls; Dnfth Awd; High Hon Roll; NHS; Sal; Church Yth Grp; Drama Clb; Am Govt Awd, Pol Sci Schlrshp 85; ME Dsblty Essay, Chem Awds 84; Johnson Wales Coll; Bus Mgmnt.

ALLEY, SCOTT; Jonesport Beals HS; Jonesport, ME; (Y); Am Leg Boys St; School Play; Yrbk Bus Mgr; Stu Cncl; Var Bsbl; JV Bsktbl; Golf; Var Socr; Hon Roll; NHS; Comp Tech.

ALLEY, TINA; Vinalhaven HS; Vinalhaven, ME; (Y); Am Leg Aux Girls St; French Clb; Nwsp Bus Mgr; VP Frsh Cls; VP Jr Cls; VP Sr Cls; Var Capt Bsktbl; Var Cheerleading; Hon Roll; Bus.

ALLISON, SCOTT; Gorham HS; Gorham, ME; (Y); Am Leg Boys St; Drama Clb; Pres Latin Clb; School Play; Yrbk Bus Mgr; Rep Stu Cncl; JV Bsbl; Var Socr; High Hon Roll; VP NHS; Harvard Bk Awd 84-85; Bus Adm.

ALLOCCA, GINA; Catherine Mc Auley HS; Westbrook, ME; (Y); 19/61; Drama Clb; Exploring; Key Clb; School Musical; Yrbk Stf; Stat Bsktbl; Cheerleading; Hon Roll; NHS; NEDT Awd; Am Leg Scholar 85; U NH; Pol Sci.

ALWARD, JEANNE; Caribou HS; New Sweden, ME; (Y); 27/197; Church Yth Grp; Church Choir; High Hon Roll; Hon Roll; Prsdntl Acad Ftnss Awd 85; Nrs Aide.

AMES, CRYSTAL; Morse HS; Wiscasset, ME; (Y); French Clb; FBLA; Library Aide; Varsity Clb; School Play; Variety Show; Var Crs Cntry; Var L Trk; Grls ST 85; Cheesebrough Arts Competitn 1st Pl 84; Engl.

ANCTIL, SUZANNE; Lewiston HS; Lewiston, ME; (Y); Lit Mag; VP Frsh Cls; Hon Roll; Comm Arts.

ANDERSON, JENNIFER; Caribou HS; Caribou, ME; (S); 8/245; Am Leg Aux Girls St; Drama Clb; Capt Mrchg Band; School Musical; Trs Jr Cls; Rep Sr Cls; Vllybl; High Hon Roll; NHS; Artcle Natl Magz Enthusiast 85; U Sthrn ME; Comm.

ANDERSON, RENEE; Brunswick HS; Brunswick, ME; (Y); Church Yth Grp; Drama Clb; Pep Clb; School Musical; Cheerleading; Gym; Hon Roll; Davis Awd 83; Brunswick Hnr Soc 85.

ANDREWS, JEAN; Vinalhaven HS; Vinalhaven, ME; (Y); 2/15; French Clb; Hosp Aide; Yrbk Stf; Pres Frsh Cls; Cheerleading; Socr; Sftbl; Vllybl; Hon Roll; NEDT Awd; ME Smmr Inst USM 85.

ANDREWS, MARJORIE; Deering HS; Portland, ME; (Y); Color Guard; Mrchg Band; Stage Crew; Lit Mag; Hon Roll; Chnse.

ANGELLO, JENNIFER; Leavitt Area HS; Turner, ME; (Y); Dance Clb; Thesps; School Play; Cheerleading; Var Mgr(s); Var Score Keeper; Hon Roll; Nrsng.

ANTHOINE, SCOTT; Lewiston HS; Lewiston, ME; (Y); Am Leg Boys St; Church Yth Grp; VP Key Clb; Letterman Clb; Political Wkr; Varsity Clb; Pres Frsh Cls; VP Jr Cls; JV Var Bsbl; Var Bsktbl; ST Of ME Champ Foul Shtr 80; Hist.

ANTHONY, ELLEN; Lincoln HS; Vinalhaven, ME; (Y); Am Leg Aux Girls St; Art Clb; Church Yth Grp; Computer Clb; French Clb; Girl Scts; Band; Mrchg Band; Hon Roll; U Of ME Machias; Elem Educ.

ARNEAULT, STACY; Lewiston HS; Lewiston, ME; (Y); Church Yth Grp; Letterman Clb; Varsity Clb; Off Frsh Cls; Off Soph Cls; Off Jr Cls; Sec Sr Cls; Var Capt Cheerleading; JV Fld Hcky; Var Capt Tennis; U Of New England; Phy Thrpy.

ARSENAULT, KERRI LYNN; Mexico HS; Mexico, ME; (Y); 10/69; Am Leg Aux Girls St; Pres Rep Stu Cncl; Var Capt Bsktbl; Var Capt Fld Hcky; Var Capt Sftbl; Kiwanis Awd; Lion Awd; NHS; Math Tm; Pep Clb; US Army Rsrv Natl Schl/Athlt Awd 85; Natl Hnr Soc Ldrshp Awd 84; Eng Mdl 85; U Of Southern ME; Cmmnctns.

ARSENAULT, MIKE; Westbrook HS; Westbrook, ME; (Y); French Clb; Chrmn Key Clb; Math Tm; Rep Frsh Cls; Rep Soph Cls; Rep Jr Cls; Rep Stu Cncl; Var Capt Crs Cntry; Var L Trk; Boston Coll; Educ.

ARSENAULT, WENDY L; Cape Elizabeth HS; Cape Elizabeth, ME; (Y); Intnl Clb; JA; Math Tm; Pep Clb; U Of Southern ME; Accntng.

ASHLEY, KAY; Deering HS; Portland, ME; (Y); French Clb; Variety Show; Yrbk Stf; Lit Mag; French Hon Soc; High Hon Roll; NHS; Colby Coll Bk Awd 84-85; 2nd Pl St MS Soc Essy Cntst 82-83; Music.

ASKUE, DIANE ELISE; Camden-Rockport HS; Camden, ME; (Y); JCL; Latin Clb; Math Tm; Thesps; Nwsp Bus Mgr; Lit Mag; Hon Roll; NHS; Church Yth Grp; Drama Clb; Dimgo Grls ST Delg 85; Slvr & Gld Mtl-Ntl Ltn Exam 84-85; Ltn.

ATKINSON, IDA; Bonny Eagle HS; Hollis, ME; (Y); 3/245; Am Leg Aux Girls St; Drama Clb; Trs 4-H; Chorus; VP Sr Cls; Trs Stu Cncl; Var Mgr(s); DAR Awd; Pres NHS; Natl 4-H Congrss 84; Prncpl Awd Acadmc Excllnc & Ctznshp 85; Pres Acadmc Fit Awd 85; U Of ME Farmington; Hm Ec Bus.

ATKINSON, MARY; Bonny Eagle HS; Hollis, ME; (Y); 4-H; Key Clb; Chorus; Swing Chorus; Trs Jr Cls; Stu Cncl; Var JV Bsktbl; Var JV Sftbl; 4-H Awd; Hon Roll; Natl 4-H Congress Trip Wnnr 85; JR Res Bar Mills 85; Med.

AYER, DEREK L; Mattanawcook Acad; Lincoln, ME; (Y); Am Leg Boys St; Letterman Clb; Ski Clb; Band; Jazz Band; Golf; Tennis; Hon Roll; Prsdntl Schlrshp Acad Achvmt 85; Music Boosters Schlrshp 85; U ME Augusta; Music.

AZEVEDO, CHERYLE; Oak Hill HS; Sabattus, ME; (Y); 10/88; Girl Scts; Math Tm; Chorus; Yrbk Stf; Cheerleading; Fld Hcky; Sftbl; Hon Roll; Math/Alg Awd; US Hist Mst Imprvd Awd; Thomas Coll; Accntng.

BABB, KELLY; Gray New Gloucester HS; Gray, ME; (Y); Church Yth Grp; French Clb; Pep Clb; Teachers Aide; Cheerleading; Crs Cntry; Mgr(s); Score Keeper; Socr; Hon Roll; Bus.

BACHELDER, BRENT ALAN; Telstar Regional HS; Newry, ME; (Y); #18 In Class; Am Leg Boys St; Drama Clb; Ski Clb; Teachers Aide; School Musical; School Play; Stage Crew; Nwsp Rptr; Nwsp Stf; Yrbk Stf; Art Summer Sch 81-84; Outstndng Art Awd 83; RI Schl Of Design; Art.

BACHELDER, CAROLYN; Leavitt Area HS; Leeds, ME; (Y); 3/140; Pres VP Church Yth Grp; Math Tm; Band; School Play; Pres Sr Cls; Rep Stu Cncl; Var L Fld Hcky; L Trk; High Hon Roll; NHS; William J Irish Awd 85; Ranatra Fusca Cretvty Tm Awd 85; 3rd Pl Mdl ST II-CONE Met 84; Sci.

BACKER, AMY; Central HS; Kenduskeag, ME; (Y); Yrbk Ed-Chief; Sec Stu Cncl; Var Cheerleading; Im JV Fld Hcky; Var High Hon Roll; Pres NHS; St Schlr; French Clb; Math Tm; Pep Clb; Acdmc Achvt Awd 83-84; Acdmc Achvt Awd 84-85; ST Champ Typng I 83-84; Pre-Med.

BADGER, SHERI; Edward Little HS; Mechanic Falls, ME; (Y); Trs AFS; Sec Debate Tm; Sec Speech Tm; JV Diving; High Hon Roll; Hon Roll; ME Schlrs Day 85; Law.

BAEZA, RAFAEL; Camden Rockport HS; Camden, ME; (Y); 13/130; Am Leg Boys St; Latin Clb; Thesps; Jazz Band; Sec Jr Cls; High Hon Roll; NHS; Church Yth Grp; Civic Clb; Drama Clb; MVP Schl Band 84-85; All ST Clarinet 85; Lead In Schl Musical 84-85.

BAGLEY, ANNE; Lewiston HS; Lewiston, ME; (Y); Am Leg Aux Girls St; 4-H; Speech Tm; Varsity Clb; Lit Mag; L Crs Cntry; NHS; 1/4 Annl Tuition Schlrshp-U Of ME Orono-85; Dirigo Girls ST 85; Vet Med.

BAGLEY, JENNIFER; Deering HS; Portland, ME; (Y); Exploring; French Clb; Letterman Clb; Yrbk Stf; Var L Fld Hcky; Var L Swmmng; High Hon Roll; Hon Roll.

BAGSHAW, BARBARA; Gorham HS; Gorham, ME; (Y); Church Yth Grp; Drama Clb; Intnl Clb; Var Bsktbl; Im Swmmng; Hon Roll; Lion Awd; 1 Yr Schlrshp-Swedish Exchng Student; Priv Audience-King & Qn Of Sweden; Nobel Prz Ceremny-Invittn Awd; Bennington Coll; Intl Studies.

BAILEY, AMY; Erskine Acad; Windsor, ME; (Y); Letterman Clb; Office Aide; Mgr(s); Sftbl; Hon Roll; NHS.

BAILEY, DALE; Biddeford HS; Biddeford, ME; (Y); FCA; Teachers Aide; Varsity Clb; Bsbl; Ftbl; Trk; Wt Lftg; Wrstlng; Postal Clerk.

BAILEY, MARK; Mt Blue HS; Farmington, ME; (Y); Am Leg Boys St; Var L Bsktbl; Var L Golf; High Hon Roll; NHS; MI Glfr 84-85; U Of ME Orono; Elctrcl Engr.

BAILEY, PATRICIA; Lee Acad; Topsfield, ME; (Y); 5/48; Letterman Clb; Math Tm; Red Cross Aide; Trs Jr Cls; Bsktbl; Socr; Capt Sftbl; High Hon Roll; NHS; Fernald K Linscott Awd For Sprtsmnshp; Rdrs Dgst Schlrshp; Stu Cncl Sclhrshp; U Of New Englnd; Physcl Thrpy.

BAILOW, ROBERT; Yarmouth JR SR HS; Yarmouth, ME; (Y); Boy Scts; VP Trs Church Yth Grp; Off Drama Clb; Var French Clb; School Play; Crs Cntry; Swmmng; Hon Roll; Spanish Clb; Stage Crew; Ntl Sci Bio Awd 84; Cert Merit Frnch 84; Bio.

BAKER, DEBBIE; Westbrook HS; Westbrook, ME; (Y); 32/193; Yrbk Stf; Hon Roll; Warren Memrl Nrsng Fndtn Schlrshp 85; Pine Tre Grnt 85; St Josphs Coll Schlrshp 85; St Jsphs Coll; Nrsng.

BAKER, MILTON; Valley HS; Bingham, ME; (Y); Am Leg Boys St; Computer Clb; French Clb; Math Tm; Ski Clb; School Play; Stage Crew; Var Bsbl; JV Bsktbl; NHS; Hi-Q Tm; Ltr & Numrls Ski Tm; Amer H S Mth Exam Awd Wnnr.

BALL, CHRISTOPHER; Lake Region HS; North Bridgton, ME; (Y); Varsity Clb; JV Var Bsbl; JV Capt Bsktbl; Wt Lftg; High Hon Roll; Hon Roll; Jr NHS; NEDT Awd; Air Force Acad; Engrng.

BALSAMO, PAUL; Jay HS; Jay, ME; (Y); 13/84; Aud/Vis; Boy Scts; Church Yth Grp; Service Clb; Teachers Aide; Crs Cntry; Var L Mgr(s); Var Trk; Hon Roll; Prfct Atten Awd; Sportsmnshp Awd 85; Franklin Pierce Coll; Comm Art.

BANTOS, MELISSA A; Edward Little HS; Auburn, ME; (Y); Pres Church Yth Grp; JA; Office Aide; Pep Clb; Spanish Clb; Hon Roll; Chld Care.

BARD, KIMBERLY; Caribou HS; Caribou, ME; (Y).

BARD, RYAN; Van Buren Dist Secondary Schl; Van Buren, ME; (Y); 8/85; Am Leg Boys St; Computer Clb; Math Clb; Variety Show; High Hon Roll; Hon Roll; NHS; Prfct Atten Awd; 1st Pl Indvdl Progrming 84; Presdntl Acadmc Ftns Awd 85; Thomas Coll ME; Comp.

BARKER, ANGELA M; Massabesic HS; Waterboro, ME; (Y); 9/144; Church Yth Grp; French Clb; Girl Scts; Chorus; Pres Jr Cls; Var Mgr Wrstlng; Elks Awd; Hon Roll; NHS; Massabesic Lions Clb Schlrshp 85; Highest Sci Av Awd 81; Gordon Coll; Bus Admin.

BARNES, LAUREL; Jonesport-Beals HS; Jonesport, ME; (Y); 1/28; Pres Sec Church Yth Grp; Sec French Clb; Math Tm; Church Choir; Yrbk Ed-Chief; Dnfth Awd; High Hon Roll; NHS; Val; Gordon Coll; Psych.

BARNEZ, MARGARET; Fort Fairfield HS; Ft Fairfield, ME; (Y); 3/30; Hon Roll; Chef.

BARTER, ELIZABETH; Deering HS; Portland, ME; (Y); Church Yth Grp; Letterman Clb; Spanish Clb; Varsity Clb; Stage Crew; Variety Show; Yrbk Stf; Rep Soph Cls; Var Fld Hcky; Var Swmmng.

BARTER, JODY M; Gardiner HS; Gardiner, ME; (Y); French Clb; FBLA; Office Aide; Political Wkr; Chorus; Hon Roll; Svc Awd.

BARTER, KIM; Jonesport-Beals HS; Isle Au Haut, ME; (Y); 4-H; French Clb; Yrbk Stf; Stat Var Bsktbl; Var Sftbl; Stat Var Vllybl; Hon Roll; Randy Frnch Awd 85; Mansfield Beauty Acad; Cosmtlgy.

BASSETT, MARIA; Fryeburg Acad; Brownfield, ME; (S); Church Yth Grp; French Clb; Band; Chorus; Yrbk Bus Mgr; Var Fld Hcky; Var Trk; High Hon Roll; NHS; St Schlr; Eva L Mulford Music Schlrshp 83; New Engl Sci & Hum Sympsm 84; Rensellaer Mdl 84; Grphc Dsgn.

BATES, KEVIN S; Leavitt Area HS; Greene, ME; (Y); 4/180; Church Yth Grp; French Clb; Math Tm; Quiz Bowl; School Play; Stage Crew; Variety Show; Yrbk Phtg; Rep Stu Cncl; JV Bsbl; Olympics Of Mind 84-85; ME Schlrs Day Pgm 85; New England Mth Lg 85; Arch.

BEAL, CHRISOPHER; Jonesport-Beals HS; Beals, ME; (Y); Pres Church Yth Grp; Yrbk Bus Mgr; Trs Frsh Cls; Trs Soph Cls; VP Jr Cls; Var Bsbl; Var Bsktbl; Var Golf; Var Socr; Hon Roll; Pres Physcl Ftnss Awd 85; EMVTI; Elec.

BEAL, GAYLE; Belfast Area HS; Belfast, ME; (Y); Church Yth Grp; Spanish Clb; Teachers Aide; Prfct Atten Awd; Scndry Educ.

BEAL, GLENACE; Jonesport-Beals HS; Beals, ME; (Y); Am Leg Aux Girls St; Church Yth Grp; Cmnty Wkr; 4-H; French Clb; Band; Chorus; Church Choir; School Play; Stage Crew; Nnrb Nmtn Bangor Daily News Artcl 85; U Of ME; Elem Ed.

BEAL, JANNELL; Jonesport-Beals HS; Beals, ME; (Y); 4-H; Varsity Clb; School Play; Var Bsktbl; JV Var Cheerleading; Var Sftbl; JV Var Vllybl; 4-H Awd; NHS; Natl Bus Hnr Soc 84-85; Cmrcl Arts.

BEAL JR, LEWIS; Jonesport-Beals HS; Beals, ME; (Y); Rep Am Leg Boys St; Chess Clb; Pres Church Yth Grp; FBLA; Var Bsbl; JV Bsktbl; Hon Roll; NHS; Natl Bus Hon Soc 85; U OF ME Machias; Acctg.

BEAULIEU, KIM; Van Buren District Secondary Schl; Grand Isle, ME; (Y); Yrbk Stf; Trs Frsh Cls; Trs Jr Cls; Trs Sr Cls; JV Capt Cheerleading; High Hon Roll; Voice Dem Awd; Church Yth Grp; Variety Show; Fld Hcky; John J Vollmann Mem Scholar; Wmns Aux Scholar; Dollars For Schlrs Scholar; Casco Bay Coll; Sec Sci.

BECHARD, ANNE-MARIE; Lewiston HS; Lewiston, ME; (Y); 26/411; Rep Sec Keywanettes; Political Wkr; Q&S; Yrbk Stf; Rep Soph Cls; Hon Roll; NHS; Johnson & Wales Coll; Chef.

BECHARD, MICHAEL GUY; Lisbon HS; Lisbon, ME; (Y); Rep Sr Cls; Var Ice Hcky; Var Socr; Hon Roll.

BECHARD, PHILLIP; Lewiston HS; Lewiston, ME; (Y); Trs Computer Clb; Key Clb; Letterman Clb; Varsity Clb; Yrbk Sprt Ed; Yrbk Stf; Rep Frsh Cls; Tennis; Mech Engr.

BECKWITH, AMY; Caribou HS; Caribou, ME; (S); Ski Clb; Varsity Clb; Concert Band; Mrchg Band; School Musical; Rep Jr Cls; Trk; Hosp Aide; Music Honor Awd 83-84; Outstndg Studnt Awd 82-83; Distngshd Performanc Awd 82-84; Chef.

BECKWITH, CHRISTIAN; Medomak Valley HS; Warren, ME; (Y); AFS; French Clb; Ski Clb; Nwsp Rptr; Rep Stu Cncl; Var Wrstlng; Hon Roll; 1st Pl Annl TDS Ctznshp Essy Cntst 85.

BEHR, CHRISTIAN; Oak Hill HS; Sabattus, ME; (Y); 24/60; Drama Clb; Speech Tm; Jazz Band; Variety Show; Sec Jr Cls; Var Ftbl; Im Ice Hcky; Var Lcrss; Lion Awd; Ski Clb; Actng Awd 83-84; Boston Coll; Drama.

BELANGER, DEBRA A; Fort Kent Community HS; Soldier Pond, ME; (Y); 20/170; Red Cross Aide; Im Vllybl; Hon Roll; Hgh Achvt Psych II; Upward Bound Pgm; Hgh Achvt Alg II; Outstndng Achvt Intro Comp; Norwich U; Crimnl Justc.

BELANGER, RENEE; Ashland Community HS; Ashland, ME; (Y); Band; Pres Soph Cls; Pres Jr Cls; Stu Cncl; Bsktbl; L Socr; L Sftbl; L Vllybl; High Hon Roll; NHS; USM; Nrsng.

BELL, ALAN E; Edward Little HS; Auburn, ME; (S); Boy Scts; VP Bowling; Capt Math Tm; School Play; JV Bsbl; Var Bsktbl; Var Golf; Tennis; High Hon Roll; NHS; US Air Force Acad.

BELL, GREG; Hodgdon HS; Houlton, ME; (Y); Church Yth Grp; Varsity Clb; Crs Cntry; Socr; Soccer Awds 82, 83 & 84.

BELL, HELEN; Caribou HS; Caribou, ME; (S); 26/215; Church Yth Grp; Drama Clb; Letterman Clb; Rep Band; Chorus; Concert Band; Jazz Band; Mrchg Band; School Musical; Swing Chorus; UNSLMA 84; Natl Hnr Soc 84; Optomtry.

BELLIVEAU, STEPHANIE; Skowhegan Area HS; Skowhegan, ME; (Y); German Clb; JCL; Latin Clb; Varsity Clb; Stu Cncl; Capt L Cheerleading; High Hon Roll; Hon Roll; Geom Awd 83-84; Latn Awd I & II 82-84; U Of ME; Elem Ed.

BENNETT, RICHARD; Presque Isle HS; Presque Isle, ME; (Y); 20/216; Boy Scts; Church Yth Grp; Hon Roll; NHS; SAR Awd; Schlstc Achvt Awd 83-84; Bronze Palm Eagle Scout 84; Order Arrow 83; Northern ME Vo Tech; Cmnty Dev.

BENOIT, JUANITA; Gray-New Gloucester HS; Gray, ME; (Y); 13/125; Sec Church Yth Grp; Band; Concert Band; Hon Roll; Wrd Of Lfe Bible Inst; Elem Ed.

BENTO, BARBARA; Portland HS; Portland, ME; (Y); Church Yth Grp; French Clb; JA; Nwsp Stf; Yrbk Stf; Off Frsh Cls; Off Soph Cls; Off Jr Cls; Off Sr Cls; Var Bsktbl; 6th Plyr Awd Bsktbl 85.

BERGERON, DONNA; St Dominic Regional HS; Lewiston, ME; (Y); Sec French Clb; French Hon Soc; High Hon Roll; Hon Roll; NHS; Art Exhibit St Doms 85; U ME Farmington; Elem Ed.

BERGERON, NICOLE; St Dominic Regional HS; Lewiston, ME; (Y); Drama Clb; Var Tennis; High Hon Roll; Hon Roll; NHS; Fitns Exprt.

BERGNER, CARLA; Leavitt Area HS; Turner, ME; (Y); 29/142; Band; Variety Show; JV Score Keeper; Socr; Stat Sftbl; Trk; Hon Roll; Lavr Leavitt Awd Mst Imprvd 84; Mid Maine Coll; Accntng.

BERNARD, BUDDY; Penobscot Valley HS; Howland, ME; (Y); Var Golf; Var Wrstlng; Elec.

BERNIER, DEBBIE; Windham HS; S Windham, ME; (Y); French Clb; Math Tm; Rep Jr Cls; French Hon Soc; High Hon Roll; Hon Roll; NHS; Chorus; Prfct Atten Awd; Biol 84; Chem Fr & Lat 85; Biol.

BERRY, GREGORY; Belfast Area HS; Belfast, ME; (Y); Rep Am Leg Boys St; Letterman Clb; Band; Concert Band; Mrchg Band; Socr; Hon Roll; Variety Show; Rotary Awd; Mdl ST Legsltr 83; KVC Music Fstvl 83-86; Solo & Ensmbl Music Fstvl 84-86; Law Enfrcmnt.

BERRY, RON; Gray-New Gloucester HS; Nw Gloucstr, ME; (Y); 4/110; Am Leg Boys St; Church Yth Grp; Math Tm; Concert Band; School Play; Var Capt Crs Cntry; Var Capt Trk; Im Vllybl; VP NHS; French Clb; Daniel Webster Coll; Avatn Sci.

BERUBE, MICHAEL R; St Dominic Regional HS; Lewiston, ME; (Y); 1/73; Drama Clb; Key Clb; Math Tm; Trs Sr Cls; Stu Cncl; High Hon Roll; Ntl Merit SF; Church Yth Grp; Math Clb; School Play; Robert F Lucas Oustndng Lt Govnr Awd 84; WCSH Amer Future Awd 84; ME ST Smmr Inst For Gftd HS Stu; Mtrls Engrng.

BERV, DAVID; Cheverus HS; Yarmouth, ME; (Y); 10/95; French Clb; Ski Clb; Rep Frsh Cls; Bsktbl; Socr; Sftbl; Swmmng; Wt Lftg; French Hon Soc; High Hon Roll; Boston Coll; Soc Sci.

BEVIN, MATTHEW; Gould Acad; Gorham, NH; (Y); 2/56; Debate Tm; 4-H; School Play; Rep Stu Cncl; 4-H Awd; High Hon Roll; NHS; Church Yth Grp; Stage Crew; JV Bsktbl; Charles Merrill Schlrshp 82-85; Hghst Avg In Engl & Spnsh I & II 83-84; Washington & Lee U; Bus Admin.

BICHREST, MEREDITH E; Mt Ararat HS; Brunswick, ME; (Y); Camp Fr Inc; Office Aide; Ski Clb; Teachers Aide; Varsity Clb; Off Soph Cls; Off Jr Cls; Off Sr Cls; Stu Cncl; JV Gym; Bangor CC; Trvl Agnt.

BICKFORD, BETH ANN; Foxcroft Acad; Monson, ME; (Y); Am Leg Aux Girls St; Pres VP Girl Scts; Hosp Aide; Letterman Clb; Tennis; Silver Ldrshp Awd 85; Husson Coll; Nrs.

BICKMORE, ELIZABETH; Central HS; E Corinth, ME; (Y); Church Yth Grp; Math Tm; Quiz Bowl; Spanish Clb; Varsity Clb; Band; Chorus; Mrchg Band; Pep Band; School Musical; Phy Thrpy.

BICKNELL, CHRISTINE; Yarmouth HS; Yarmouth, ME; (Y); Drama Clb; Band; Nwsp Rptr; VP Frsh Cls; VP Soph Cls; VP Stu Cncl; JV Var Fld Hcky; NHS; Ntl Merit Ltr; Am Leg Aux Girls St; Smith Coll Book Awd 84-85; Alg Awd 82-83; Spn Awd 83-84; Theatr Art.

BIGGIE, THERESE; Bucksport HS; Castine, ME; (Y); French Clb; Varsity Clb; School Musical; Nwsp Stf; Var Capt Bsktbl; Trk; Hon Roll; NHS; VFW Awd; Voice Dem Awd; Hugh O Brien Yth Ldrshp Conf 84; Nat Tn Agr Pgnt Mss Hosp ME & Ust Rnr Up 85; Amer H S Athl Bsktbl 85.

BILLINGS, STACI; Brunswick HS; Brunswick, ME; (Y); Church Yth Grp; Drama Clb; School Musical; JV L Cheerleading; Hon Roll.

BILLINGS, STEFANIE ANNE; Sumner Memorial HS; Ellsworth, ME; (Y); 6/96; Am Leg Aux Girls St; Dance Clb; Chorus; School Play; Variety Show; Trs Frsh Cls; VP Soph Cls; Rep Jr Cls; Off Stu Cncl; Cheerleading; Natl Hnr Rl 85; Dirigo Grls ST Govt Senate Awd 84; Early Admissns Pgm UMM 84-85; Thomas Coll; Bus Admin.

BILODEAU, NOEL; Fryeburg Acad; Fryeburg, ME; (S); Varsity Clb; Chorus; School Musical; Lit Mag; Pres Frsh Cls; Var L Crs Cntry; High Hon Roll; NHS; Art Clb; Church Yth Grp; Newspaper Asst Ed 84-85; Creative Writing Prog Gifted Stu 82-84; Sanford U; Lib Arts.

BINETTE, DOREEN; Lewiston HS; Lewiston, ME; (Y); Rep Frsh Cls; Rep Soph Cls; JV Fld Hcky; Hon Roll; Jr NHS.

BIRCH, JENNIFER; Marshwood HS; S Berwick, ME; (Y); Latin Clb; Var JV Fld Hcky; Hon Roll; Latn Clb Schlrshp 85; Ntl Latn Exm Awds 83-84; Husson Coll; Bus Admn.

BISBEE, SUSAN W; Berwick Acad; Rochester, NH; (Y); 12/38; Camera Clb; Camp Fr Inc; Chorus; School Musical; School Play; Stage Crew; Var L Socr; Var Tennis; Hon Roll; Spnsh Hnr Awd 85; Spnsh Tchr.

BLACK, VALERIE; Presque Isle HS; Mapleton, ME; (Y); Church Yth Grp; Band; Sec Chorus; Concert Band; Mrchg Band; Hon Roll; Jr NHS; Beulah Turner Schlrshp 85; All Aroostook Chrs & Band 83-84; U Of ME; Elem Educ.

BLACK, VALERIE L; Winslow HS; Winslow, ME; (Y); AFS; Am Leg Aux Girls St; Art Clb; Church Yth Grp; School Play; Yrbk Stf; Rep Jr Cls; Var Cheerleading; Var Fld Hcky; Jr NHS; Cmmrcl Art.

BLACKETT, DEBORAH; Winthrop HS; Winthrop, ME; (Y); AFS; Church Yth Grp; JCL; Latin Clb; School Play; Variety Show; Yrbk Stf; Vllybl; Hon Roll; Hon Men Sci Fair 85; Magna Cum Laude Natl Lat Exam 83; Cum Laude Natl Lat Exam 84; Nrsg.

BLACKMORE, REBECCAH; Presque Isle HS; Presque Isle, ME; (Y); Am Leg Aux Girls St; Church Yth Grp; Drama Clb; Church Choir; Drill Tm; School Musical; Stage Crew; Yrbk Stf; Stu Cncl; Pom Pon; Bryant Coll; Accntng.

BLAIR, SARAH; George Stevens Acad; Brooklin, ME; (Y); Am Leg Aux Girls St; French Clb; Chorus; Yrbk Ed-Chief; Trs Soph Cls; Var JV Cheerleading; Hon Roll; NHS; Val; Williams Coll Bk Awd 85; ME Summr Arts Pgm 85; Cmmnctns.

BLAIS, RONALD; Lewiston HS; Lewiston, ME; (Y); VP Computer Clb; High Hon Roll; Hon Roll; Jr NHS; LHS Comp Clb Pgmr Awd 83-84; Outstndng Devotn Awd 83; Comp Sci.

BLAISDELL, GREGORY; Westbrook HS; Westbrook, ME; (Y); Church Yth Grp; Drama Clb; Math Tm; Spanish Clb; School Musical; School Play; Stage Crew; JV Crs Cntry; JV Trk; Math.

BLAKE, LINCOLN; Belfast Area HS; Belfast, ME; (Y); Boy Scts; Drama Clb; German Clb; Band; Concert Band; Jazz Band; Mrchg Band; Pep Band; School Musical; School Play; Mltry Sci.

BLAKE, LISA; Fryeburg Acad; Brownfield, ME; (S); Camera Clb; French Clb; Pres Latin Clb; Varsity Clb; Nwsp Stf; Ed Yrbk Ed-Chief; Var Fld Hcky; Sftbl; Hon Roll; NHS; Girls St Dlgt 84; Psych.

BLAKE, SCOTT; Medomak Valley HS; Waldoboro, ME; (Y); 10/150; Drama Clb; Thesps; Chorus; Swing Chorus; Yrbk Ed-Chief; Hon Roll; NHS; Band; JCL; Latin Clb; Pres Acad Ftnss Awd 85; Stu Of Mnth 85; Ithaca Coll; Brdcstg.

BLAKEMAN, CARRIE; Yarmouth HS; Yarmouth, ME; (Y); 14/85; Latin Clb; Ski Clb; Yrbk Stf; Fld Hcky; Swmmng; Tennis; High Hon Roll; Hon Roll; NHS; Spanish NHS; MVP Tnns Plyr 82-85; Dollars For Schlrs 85; Louisa T York Schlrshp 85; Hofstra U; Math.

BLANCHARD, JOCELYNN; Brewer HS; Brewer, ME; (Y); Key Clb; Varsity Clb; Band; Chorus; Yrbk Stf; Capt Var Cheerleading; JV Fld Hcky; Hon Roll; Letterman Clb; Pep Clb; Chrldng Excllnc Awd 84-85; Sub Deb Sorority 84-85; U Of ME-OROM; Psych.

BLANCHARD, MELISSA; Deering HS; Portland, ME; (Y); Church Yth Grp; JA; Key Clb; Variety Show; Coach Actv; Fld Hcky; Sftbl; Tennis; Trk; Hon Roll.

BLEASE, KIMBERLEE; Orono HS; Orono, ME; (Y); Camera Clb; Yrbk Stf; Lit Mag; Coach Actv; Var Capt Ice Hcky; Trk; Cit Awd; 4-H Awd; Hon Roll; Expns Pd Trp Natl 4-H Congrss Chgo ST Rep 83; Mary Ann Hillson Awd Schlrshp 85; U Of Southern ME; Bus Adm.

BLIER, BEVERLY; Fort Kent Community HS; Ft Kent, ME; (Y); VP DECA; Chorus; Hon Roll; Church Yth Grp; 2nd Pl ST Cmptn Gnrl Mrchndsng 85; Awd For Outstndng Wrk In Dstrbtn Ed 85; Cert In Phy Ed 83; Bus.

BLISH, TORI; Lee Acad; Springfield, ME; (Y); Am Leg Aux Girls St; Letterman Clb; Office Aide; Pep Clb; Varsity Clb; Chorus; Yrbk Stf; Bsktbl; High Hon Roll; Hon Roll; 3rd Pl Advanced Typing Reg 85; U MA Orono; Bus Admin.

BLOOD, KYLE; Skowhegan Area HS; Skowhegan, ME; (Y); 1/179; Am Leg Boys St; Mgr Drama Clb; VP French Clb; Band; Nwsp Ed-Chief; Yrbk Ed-Chief; Pres Stu Cncl; L Tennis; High Hon Roll; Pres NHS; R B Shepherd Prz Hghst Rnkg Frsh 82-83; Dely ME Hugh O Brien Yth Ldrshp Sem 83-84; Stu Of Mnth 84-85; Dartmouth; Lang.

BLUE, ANDREA; Leavitt Area HS; Turner, ME; (Y); Pres Church Yth Grp; Band; Chorus; Concert Band; Jazz Band; Sec Jr Cls; Sec Sr Cls; Var Capt Cheerleading; Var L Trk; Hon Roll; Outstndng Tlnt Area Dirigo Girls ST 85; Ranatra Fusca Creat Awd Olympcs Mnd Assn 85; Natl Chrldg Comp; Bus Adm.

BOARDMAN, STEPHANIE; Lawrence HS; Fairfield, ME; (Y); French Clb; Ski Clb; Rep Frsh Cls; Sec Soph Cls; Var Capt Cheerleading; JV Sftbl; Hon Roll; Cosmetologst.

BOBIER, KIMBERLY; Bonny Eagle HS; Gorham, ME; (Y); Office Aide; Stat Var Bsktbl; Hon Roll; Jr NHS; Bus Admin.

BOISSE, DEBBY; Lewiston HS; Lewiston, ME; (Y); Drama Clb; Hosp Aide; Letterman Clb; School Play; Yrbk Stf; VP Soph Cls; Stat Var Bsktbl; Var L Cheerleading; JV Fld Hcky; Hon Roll; Johnson & Wales; Travel.

BOLDUC, DEBBIE; Lewiston HS; Lewiston, ME; (Y); Intnl Clb; Pep Clb; Yrbk Stf; Hon Roll; Prfct Atten Awd; Outstndg Achvt Adv Math 85; Acctg.

BOLDUC, LISA; Lewiston HS; Lewiston, ME; (Y); Exploring; Fld Hcky; JV Sftbl; Sci.

BOLICK, CATHERINE; Oxford Hills HS; Harrison, ME; (Y); 37/238; Pres DECA; VP FBLA; Band; Chorus; Church Choir; Yrbk Ed-Chief; Yrbk Phtg; Yrbk Stf; Cheerleading; Powder Puff Ftbl; Vo Ed Scholar 85; ST DECA 2nd Pl Overall Advrtsng 85; FBLA Spec Recogntn 85; U Southern ME; Bus.

BONARRIGO, JOSEPH; Georges Valley HS; Thomaston, ME; (Y); 10/78; Intnl Clb; Math Tm; Radio Clb; VP Science Clb; Trs Sr Cls; Var Capt Crs Cntry; Var Trk; Hon Roll; NHS; Coaches Awd Track 84; MVP Cross Cntry 85; Enrichment Smnr Awd 85; U Of ME-ORONO; Engr.

BONNER, LYN; Lewiston HS; Lewiston, ME; (Y); VP Sec JA; L Crs Cntry; Hon Roll; Var Trk; Gym Awd 84; U Of ME Farmington; Secy.

BONVIE, ARTHUR; Windham HS; Windham, ME; (Y); Boy Scts; Exploring; Crs Cntry; Trk; Vllybl; Hon Roll; CC Of Air Frc; Elec Comm Engr.

BOODY, KEVIN; Deering HS; Portland, ME; (Y); Church Yth Grp; Debate Tm; Intnl Clb; JA; Ski Clb; Color Guard; Stage Crew; Nwsp Phtg; Yrbk Ed-Chief; VP Jr Cls; Cook.

BOOMER, LISA; Woodland HS; Woodland, ME; (S); 25/65; Computer Clb; Drama Clb; French Clb; FBLA; Hosp Aide; Thesps; Varsity Clb; Band; Yrbk Stf; Lit Mag; Consistent Effort Sci; Husson Coll; Nurse.

BORNSTEIN, STACY; Edward Little HS; Auburn, ME; (Y); AFS; GAA; Latin Clb; Letterman Clb; Pep Clb; Ski Clb; Temple Yth Grp; Varsity Clb; Sec Jr Cls; Stu Cncl; Poli Sci.

BOSSIE, REGINALD; Caribon HS; Caribon, ME; (S); 9/240; Am Leg Boys St; Church Yth Grp; Exploring; ROTC; Band; Concert Band; JV Var Bsbl; JV Var Socr; High Hon Roll; Hon Roll; C H S Var Ski Tm Qulfd ST Meet 83-85; Henry Anderson Ski Race 1st JR Div 84; Caribon Winter Triathln.

BOSTON JR, ROBERT C; Wells HS; Wells, ME; (Y); Am Leg Boys St; Church Yth Grp; Drama Clb; Math Tm; Chorus; School Musical; School Play; Cit Awd; Hon Roll; NHS; VFW Awd 84-85; Schl Play 85; Math Tm 85; Bus Mngmnt.

BOUCHARD, JENNIFER; Edward Little HS; Auburn, ME; (S); Am Leg Aux Girls St; JCL; Trs VP Latin Clb; Math Tm; Pep Clb; Sftbl; High Hon Roll; Pres NHS; Prfct Atten Awd; Williams Coll Book Awd 84; U Of CT; Pharmacy.

BOUCHARD, KIM; Wisdom HS; Madawaska, ME; (Y); Church Yth Grp; Pres DECA; French Clb; Variety Show; Rep Stu Cncl; Hon Roll; 3rd Pl Restrnt, Mktg DECA 85; Ms TEEN 82; Wilma Boyd Schl; Trvl.

BOUCHIER, PAULA; Presque Isle HS; Mapleton, ME; (Y); FNA; Hosp Aide; Red Cross Aide; Cit Awd; Hon Roll; Yrbk Photo 81-82; Lib Aide 80-82; Outstdng Schl Ctznshp 81-82; Owno U; Nrsng.

BOUFFARD, MARY; Maine Central Inst; Pittsfield, ME; (Y); Am Leg Aux Girls St; Sec Pres Key Clb; Band; Yrbk Stf; Pres Soph Cls; Var L Bsktbl; Var Capt Fld Hcky; High Hon Roll; Prfct Atten Awd; VFW Awd.

BOULRISSE, RICHARD C; Lee Acad; Lee, ME; (Y); 3/54; Am Leg Boys St; Cmnty Wkr; Letterman Clb; Math Tm; Varsity Clb; Capt Bsbl; Capt Bsktbl; Capt Socr; High Hon Roll; NHS; Rdrs Digest Schlrshp Awd 85; Roger Lowell Math Awd 85; U Of ME Orono; Pre Law.

BOURASSA, JENNIFER; Winslow HS; Winslow, ME; (Y); 3/205; Sec VP Church Yth Grp; Sec Math Tm; Quiz Bowl; Color Guard; Mrchg Band; Rep Frsh Cls; Rep Soph Cls; Rep Jr Cls; Stat Bsktbl; Hon Roll; Winslows Stu Rep To The Waterville Rotary Clb 85; Elks Teenager Of The Mnth 85; Blaine Hse Schlr 85; U Of ME; Eng.

BOURASSA, LUCIE M; Cony HS; Augusta, ME; (Y); 6/278; Am Leg Aux Girls St; Church Yth Grp; French Clb; Band; Chorus; Variety Show; Nwsp Bus Mgr; Nwsp Ed-Chief; Nwsp Rptr; Sec Jr Cls; Schl Fnlst-Cntry III Ldrshp Pgm 84; 4th Pl Ntl Frnch Tchrs Cntst 84; Schlr 82-85; Colby Coll; Pre Dntstry.

BOURGOINE, RENEE JEAN; Oxford Hills HS; Norway, ME; (Y); 10/240; Am Leg Aux Girls St; Church Yth Grp; Debate Tm; NFL; Varsity Clb; Trs Sr Cls; Var L Trk; High Hon Roll; NHS; Hosp Aide; Hugh O Brian Ledrshp Semnr For Outstndng Soph 84; Hmcmng Queen 84; Law.

BOUSQUET, WENDY; Monmouth Acad; North Monmouth, ME; (Y); 6/52; Drama Clb; Library Aide; Math Tm; Speech Tm; Chorus; School Musical; JV Score Keeper; Hon Roll; NHS; 4th In ST Of ME In Spch Tm For Orgnl Oration 84; Sec Ed Math.

BOUTIN, MICHAEL; Freeport HS; Freeport, ME; (Y); Pres JA; Pres Ski Clb; Rep Soph Cls; Rep Stu Cncl; Var Im Socr; JV Bsktbl; Im Vllybl; ME U Oromd.

BOWIE, CHRISTOPHER; Deering HS; Portland, ME; (Y); 42/265; Church Yth Grp; JA; Band; Church Choir; Concert Band; Mrchg Band; Trk; Southern Technel Inst; Archtctr.

BOWMAN, MONICA; Skowhegan Area HS; Skowhegan, ME; (Y); Sec Church Yth Grp; German Clb; Pep Clb; Varsity Clb; Band; Chorus; Concert Band; Mrchg Band; Pep Band; Yrbk Stf; Excel Band Awd 83-84; Mst Imprvd Chrs Awd 84-85; Psych.

BOWMAN, TANYA; East Corinth Central HS; E Corinth, ME; (Y); FHA; Library Aide; Teachers Aide; Chorus; Yrbk Stf; Hon Roll; Acad Achvmnt Awd 84; Bus Devlpmnt.

BOWMAN, VICKI L; Skowhegan Area HS; Athens, ME; (Y); 27/223; Varsity Clb; Band; Chorus; Concert Band; Mrchg Band; JV Crs Cntry; JV Fld Hcky; NHS; N Cornville Ladies Aid Awd 85; NHS Awd 85; Pres Acd Fit Awd 85; Hawthorne Coll; Flight Training.

BOYINGTON, BENJAMIN J; Freeport HS; Freeport, ME; (Y); 5/80; Aud/Vis; Drama Clb; Math Tm; School Musical; School Play; Stage Crew; Yrbk Stf; Sec Frsh Cls; Hon Roll; Drama.

BOYINGTON, SUSAN L; Dexter Regional HS; Dexter, ME; (Y); 12/104; French Clb; Ed Yrbk Ed-Chief; Sec Frsh Cls; Sec Soph Cls; Sec Jr Cls; Sec Sr Cls; Stu Cncl; Capt Socr; Hon Roll; NHS; U ME Farmington; Spec Educ.

BOZENHARD, DAVID; Bonny Eagle HS; Limerick, ME; (Y); Var L Bsbl; Var L Bsktbl; JV Var Socr; Jr NHS; Ntl Merit Ltr; St Schlr; Coach Actv; Arch.

BRACK, KRISTEN; Skowhegan Area HS; Skowhegan, ME; (Y); 10/180; German Clb; Varsity Clb; Band; Concert Band; Mrchg Band; Var Capt Bsktbl; Var Capt Sftbl; High Hon Roll; Hon Roll; NHS; Spec Educ.

BRADLEY, FAITH L; Skowhegan Area HS; Norridgewock, ME; (Y); 30/216; Am Leg Aux Girls St; Girl Scts; Ski Clb; Varsity Clb; Band; Drill Tm; Mrchg Band; Yrbk Phtg; Fld Hcky; Mgr(s); OH ST U; Physcl Thrpy.

BRADLEY, MARYKATE; Medomak Vly HS; Waldoboro, ME; (Y); Am Leg Aux Girls St; Church Yth Grp; Office Aide; Variety Show; Var Bsktbl; Var Sftbl; Im Vllybl; Early Ed.

BRAGG, RANDI A; Skowhegan Area HS; Canaan, ME; (Y); 35/216; Am Leg Aux Girls St; German Clb; Varsity Clb; Yrbk Ed-Chief; VP Jr Cls; Tennis; Hon Roll; Prfct Atten Awd; Pres Schlr; Voice Dem Awd; Ctzns Schlrshp Fndtn Awd 85; Franklin Svngs Bnk Schlrshp Awd 85; Dllrs-Schlrs Awd 85; U Of S ME.

BRANCELY, MELISSA LOUISE; Thornton Acad; Saco, ME; (Y); Am Leg Aux Girls St; Church Yth Grp; Latin Clb; Rep Soph Cls; Rep Sr Cls; Var Capt Bsktbl; Var Capt Trk; Hon Roll; NHS.

BRESSETTE, STEPHEN D; Edward Little HS; Lisbon, ME; (Y); Var Trk; Hon Roll; Engrng.

BRIDGES, VIVIAN; Woodland HS; Princeton, ME; (Y); 6/64; Drama Clb; Thesps; Varsity Clb; School Play; Yrbk Stf; Score Keeper; Hon Roll; Pres NHS; St Schlr; Woodlnd Rotary Schlrshp, Ntl Hnr Society Schlrshp, SR Class Schlrshp 85; Bowdoin; Engl.

BRIER, MARCI LOREN; Belfast Area HS; Belfast, ME; (Y); Letterman Clb; Ski Clb; Y-Teens; Band; Mrchg Band; Yrbk Stf; Bowling; Coach Actv; Diving; Var Capt Fld Hcky; F H 2nd Tm All ST; 1st Tm KUAC 84-85; Gymnstcs 8th ST Vajlt 2 Yrs 83-85; Trk Schl Rcrd 440 Rly 83-84; Fash Merch.

BRILTON, MICHELLE RENE; South Portland HS; South Portland, ME; (Y); 7/300; Am Leg Aux Girls St; Hosp Aide; JCL; Pres Leo Clb; Capt Math Tm; Nwsp Rptr; Hon Roll; Sec NHS; Ntl Merit Ltr; Cum Laude Natl Latin Exam 83; Hnrs Part 85; Hnrs Assmbly 82-85; Graceland Coll; Bio.

BRISKEY, HEATHER; Windham HS; South Windham, ME; (S); Hon Roll; Academic All-Am 84.

BROOKS, CHERYL; Georges Valley HS; Cushing, ME; (Y); 13/85; Am Leg Aux Girls St; Teachers Aide; Yrbk Phtg; Pres Jr Cls; Sec Rep Stu Cncl; DAR Awd; NHS; FBLA; FHA; Trs GAA; Pratt Ntl Tlnt Srch Fnlst 85; ME Smmr Photo Wrkshp Schlrshp 84; 2nd, 3rd, & 4th Pl Lcl Phto Cntst 84; OH U; Phtogrphy.

BROOKS, WENDY; William W Traip Acad; Kittery Pt, ME; (Y); Church Yth Grp; Band; Concert Band; Jazz Band; Pep Band; Yrbk Stf; Stat Bsktbl; Mgr(s); Hon Roll; VP NHS; Clarinet Music Fest 83-85; Med Outstndng Achvt Band 85; Music.

BROPHY II, RICHARD A; Livermore Falls HS; Livermore Falls, ME; (Y); Am Leg Boys St; Church Yth Grp; Yrbk Sprt Ed; VP Jr Cls; Var Bsbl; Var Bsktbl; Var Ftbl; Varsity Clb; Band; Yrbk Stf.

BROWN, CHERYL; Westbrook HS; Westbrook, ME; (Y); Church Yth Grp; Exploring; Red Cross Aide; Yrbk Stf; Swmmng; Hon Roll; Ad Dsgn.

BROWN, DELMONT; Jonesport-Beals HS; Jonesport, ME; (Y); Church Yth Grp; French Clb; Stage Crew; Yrbk Stf; Rep Jr Cls; Rep Stu Cncl; Mgr Bsbl; Mgr Bsktbl; Mgr(s); Score Keeper; Comp Sci.

BROWN, JOANN; Calais HS; Perry, ME; (Y); 1/52; Drama Clb; Sec Leo Clb; Yrbk Ed-Chief; Yrbk Stf; Sec VP Stu Cncl; Capt Cheerleading; Mgr(s); Sftbl; DAR Awd; High Hon Roll; Pulpand Paper Schlrshp 86; Pgm Gifted Sci,Engrng 84; Yr Bk Awd 85; U ME; Chem Engrng.

BROWN, JODIE L; Wells HS; Wells, ME; (Y); Girl Scts; Letterman Clb; Ski Clb; Concert Band; Yrbk Sprt Ed; Sec Sr Cls; Var Capt Bsktbl; Var Capt Fld Hcky; Var L Sftbl; Hon Roll; All ST Field Hockey Tm Cls B 84; Colby Coll; Bus.

BROWN, KENNETH P; Camden-Rockport HS; Appleton, ME; (Y); 3/125; Am Leg Boys St; VP 4-H; JCL; Math Tm; Stage Crew; Lit Mag; 4-H Awd; High Hon Roll; NHS; Ntl Merit SF; Schlrshp To U Of ME 84; Env Engrng.

BROWN, LORI; Belfast Area HS; Belfast, ME; (Y); 4/115; Am Leg Aux Girls St; Math Tm; Band; School Musical; Stage Crew; VP Soph Cls; Var L Crs Cntry; Var L Swmmng; High Hon Roll; NHS; ME Schlrs Day 85; Schl Svc Awd 85; Interact Clb 83-85; Engrng.

BROWN, STACEY; Belfast Area HS; Belfast, ME; (Y); Y-Teens; Chorus; Variety Show; Yrbk Phtg; Yrbk Stf; Badmtn; Bowling; Sftbl; Wt Lftg; Hon Roll; Intrr Desgn.

BROWN, TAMMY; Central HS; Stetson, ME; (Y); Office Aide; JV Bsktbl; Hon Roll; Hstry, Math, Sci, & Typng Acad Achvt Awds 84-85; Bangor CC; Law Enfrcmnt.

BROWN, TODD DAVID; Mt Abram HS; Strong, ME; (Y); 4/80; Am Leg Boys St; Church Yth Grp; Computer Clb; Drama Clb; Intnl Clb; Teachers Aide; School Play; Stage Crew; Yrbk Bus Mgr; Yrbk Stf; Comp Excllnce Awd 85; RI Coll; Filmmkng.

BROWNSBERGER, TERRY; Traip Acad; Rochester, NH; (Y); Aud/Vis; Boy Scts; Church Yth Grp; Drama Clb; Nwsp Rptr; Nwsp Sprt Ed; JV Bsbl; Brdcstng.

BRULE, MICHELLE L; Edward Little HS; Auburn, ME; (S); Church Yth Grp; Latin Clb; Sec Band; Concert Band; Mrchg Band; Cheerleading; High Hon Roll; Hon Roll; NHS; Prfct Atten Awd; All-ST Band Mbr 83-84; Comp Sci.

BRYAN, JAROD; Cony HS; Augusta, ME; (Y); 2/300; Chess Clb; Civic Clb; German Clb; Math Tm; Science Clb; Im Mgr Bsktbl; Im Mgr Vllybl; High Hon Roll; Hon Roll; St Schlr; Rensselaer Medl Excllnc Math & Sci 85; La Verdieres Essy Cntst Wnnr 83; Math.

BRYER, VALERIE; Mattanawcook Acad; Lincoln, ME; (Y); Am Leg Aux Girls St; Letterman Clb; Band; School Musical; Yrbk Stf; Rep Stu Cncl; Cheerleading; Score Keeper; NHS; Colby Coll Bk Awd 85; Soc Wrk.

BUBIER, KIMBERLY A; Leavitt Area HS; Greene, ME; (Y); Yrbk Stf; JV Bsktbl; Var L Sftbl; High Hon Roll; Hon Roll; Cosmtlgst.

BUCK, DAVID; Mt Blue HS; Weld, ME; (Y); Church Yth Grp; Cmnty Wkr; Y-Teens; Stage Crew; Variety Show; Bsktbl; Capt Socr; Trk; Im Vllybl; Mst Imprvd Socr Plyr 83; Ath Cncl 84-85; Jrnlsm.

BUCKLEY, JULIE; Lewiston HS; Lewiston, ME; (Y); Letterman Clb; Capt Ski Clb; Varsity Clb; Yrbk Rptr; Yrbk Stf; L Capt Fld Hcky; JV Tennis; Ski Tm Capt 84; Sorority Pres 85; Bus Admin.

BUCKMAN, SARAH; Telstar Regional HS; Bethel, ME; (Y); 1/70; Drama Clb; French Clb; Pres Library Aide; Pres Sr Cls; High Hon Roll; NHS; St Schlr; Math Tm; School Play; Hghst Acad Achvt Hist Hnr 83-85; Moses Mason Essay Cont Wnnr 85; Stdy Abrd France Schlrshp 85; Bowdoin; Hist.

BULL, LARRY; Old Town HS; Old Town, ME; (Y); Chorus; Church Choir; Swing Chorus; Variety Show; Spnsh Awd 85; Outstndng Contrbtns Drama Awd 85; Rotry Clb Schlrshp 85; Boston U; Theatr Arts.

BURBANK, CRAIG; Carrabec HS; N Anson, ME; (Y); French Clb; Math Tm; Band; Concert Band; Jazz Band; Pep Band; Tennis; High Hon Roll; Hon Roll; NHS; Peer Tutor; Scott High Q; U ME Orono; Chem Engr.

BUREAU, DANA D; Edward Little HS; Auburn, ME; (S); Key Clb; Varsity Clb; VP Jr Cls; VP Stu Cncl; Bsbl; Capt Ice Hcky; Capt Socr; Hon Roll; NHS; ME H S Ice Hockey All ST Hnrb Recog 82-83; ME H S Ice Hockey All ST Select 83-84; Bowdoin Coll Brunswick ME; Med.

BURKE, DIANNA; Woodland HS; Princeton, ME; (Y); Church Yth Grp; Hon Roll; Pre-Law.

BURNHAM, JEFF; Oxford Hills HS; Norway, ME; (Y); AFS; Key Clb; Math Tm; Rep Frsh Cls; VP Jr Cls; Rep Sr Cls; Hon Roll; St Schlr; Comp Sci.

BURNS, ERIC; Community HS; Ft Kent, ME; (Y); Boy Scts; Computer Clb; Dance Clb; Drama Clb; Pep Clb; PAVAS; Thesps; Acpl Chr; Band; Chorus; All Aroostook Chorus 83-85; Nrthrn ME Wrtg Inst Wnnr 83; ME Smmr Humnties Prgm 85; Engl.

BURNS, LAURA; Cony HS; Augusta, ME; (Y); JCL; Latin Clb; Pep Clb; Spanish Clb; Magna Cum Laude Ntl J C L Ex 83-84; Cum Laude Ntl JCL Ex 85; Archlgy.

BURWELL, BASHA; Portland HS; Cumberland Cent, ME; (Y); Ed Yrbk Stf; Trs Frsh Cls; Trs Soph Cls; Rep Jr Cls; Rep Stu Cncl; Var Fld Hcky; Var Trk; NHS; Am Leg Aux Girls St; Art Clb; ME Schlr 85; Merc Marne Essay Wnnr 85; Gifted Ldrshp Bk Awd 83; Fine Arts.

BUSHEY, PAUL; Freeport HS; Freeport, ME; (Y); JA; Appl Tech.

BUSWELL, ROBIN; Buckfield JR SR HS; Buckfield, ME; (Y); School Play; Hon Roll.

BUTLER, DOUGLAS; Banger HS; Bangor, ME; (Y); Chess Clb; Im Bsktbl; Ftbl; Var Trk; Im Vllybl; Im Wt Lftg; High Hon Roll; Hon Roll; Ntl Merit SF; YMCA Ldrs Clb-Pres 84-86; ME Ldrshp Trainng Schl-Fellwshp Cup-Outstndng Ldr 84; Brown U; Elec Engr.

BUTLER, RANDY; Nokomis Reginal HS; Hartland, ME; (Y); 1/154; Math Tm; Var L Bsbl; Var Capt Socr; High Hon Roll; NHS; Prfct Atten Awd; Val; U Of ME-ORANO; Civl Engrng.

BUTTERFIELD, BARRY; Jay HS; Jay, ME; (Y); Boy Scts; Ski Clb; Var L Crs Cntry; Im Mgr(s); Var L Trk; Var Vllybl; Hon Roll; NHS; Prfct Atten Awd; Central ME; Carpntry.

BUXTON, RONALD; Windham HS; Windham, ME; (Y); CAP; Color Guard; Drill Tm; Var Crs Cntry; Var Trk; Hon Roll; Outstndg Cadet Ofcr Of Yr 84.

BYRON, BETH; Hodgdon Hodgdon HS; Houlton, ME; (Y); 4-H; Varsity Clb; Chorus; Var Bsktbl; Var Crs Cntry; Var Socr; Var Vllybl; 4-H Awd; School Musical; ME Potato Growers Awd 84; Northen ME Fair Art Judges Awd Excllnce 84; UMF; Bio.

BYRON, KEVEN; Hodgdon HS; Houlton, ME; (Y); 1/50; Chess Clb; Church Yth Grp; French Clb; Math Tm; High Hon Roll; NHS; St Schlr; Teleqz Tm 83-85; ME H S Indiv Champ 82-84; Intl Rel.

CABRAL, SUE; Nokomis Regional HS; Newport, ME; (Y); Am Leg Aux Girls St; French Clb; Var Fld Hcky; Mgr(s); Var Sftbl; Hon Roll; Shorthand Awd-1st Pl 85; Shorthand Regnl Competn Awd-3rd Pl 85; Sec.

CADMAN, DAWN; Gray New Gloucester HS; Mcfalls, ME; (Y); Girl Scts; Mgr(s); Twrlr; Vllybl; Accntng.

CAGLEY, DAWN M; Brunswick HS; Brunswick, ME; (Y); Church Yth Grp; Latin Clb; Math Tm; School Play; Variety Show; Trs Soph Cls; Var Cheerleading; Mgr(s); Vllybl; Hon Roll; Brnswck Hnr Soc; Georgetown; Intl Bus.

CAIRNIE, MELISSA; Lawrence HS; Waterville, ME; (Y); Hosp Aide; Spanish Clb; Pres Frsh Cls; Pres Soph Cls; Var Capt Cheerleading; Coach Actv; Pom Pon; Score Keeper; Hon Roll; NCA Awd Of Excllnce 84; 1st Pl Downeast Cheering Comp 83.

CALDWELL, CYNTHIA; Mt Blue HS; New Sharon, ME; (Y); 11/230; Am Leg Aux Girls St; Church Yth Grp; Pres Girl Scts; Stu Cncl; Capt Bsktbl; Capt Fld Hcky; Capt Sftbl; High Hon Roll; Jr NHS; NHS; Farmington Oil Co Female Athl Yr 84-85; Harry F Smith Awd Best All-Arnd Athl 84-85; U Of NH; Phy Ed.

CALDWELL, DEIDRA; Leavitt Area HS; Turner, ME; (Y); 22/141; School Play; Nwsp Phtg; Yrbk Bus Mgr; Yrbk Phtg; Sec Frsh Cls; JV Fld Hcky; JV Sftbl; Hon Roll; Jr NHS; NHS.

CAMAGE, HOLLY; Greely HS; Yarmouth, ME; (Y); 26/146; Church Yth Grp; Hosp Aide; JA; Band; Concert Band; Crs Cntry; Trk; Hon Roll; NHS; U Of S ME; Bio.

CAMIRE, DIANE; Sanford HS; Sanford, ME; (Y); 107/245; Church Yth Grp; French Clb; Office Aide; Red Cross Aide; Hon Roll; Sanford Regnl Vo Tech Schlrshp 85; SMVTI; Radlgy.

CAMPBELL, JOAN; Fort Fairfield HS; Ft Fairfield, ME; (Y); Am Leg Aux Girls St; Church Yth Grp; Drama Clb; Varsity Clb; Band; Jazz Band; Yrbk Stf; Var Capt Bsktbl; Var L Sftbl; High Hon Roll.

CAMPBELL, ROBIN; Windham HS; Windham, ME; (Y); Pres Chorus; Yrbk Stf; VP Soph Cls; VP Jr Cls; VP Sr Cls; Rep Stu Cncl; L Var Bsktbl; L Var Socr; Jr NHS; NHS; Hnr Roll 83-85; Recog Schl Comm Socr & Sftbl 83-85; U South ME; Sprts Med.

CAMPEAU, LISA; Lewiston HS; Lewiston, ME; (Y); Office Aide; Stat Ice Hcky; Stat Socr; High Hon Roll; Hon Roll; NHS; Accntnt.

CANADY, JOHN; George Stevens Acad; Penobscot, ME; (Y); Rep Am Leg Boys St; Boy Scts; Church Yth Grp; JV Mgr(s); Score Keeper; Hon Roll; NHS; Trs Frsh Cls; St Josephs Coll ME; Nrsng.

CARBONE, BETSY A; Massabesic HS; Waterboro, ME; (Y); 6/147; Church Yth Grp; French Clb; Girl Scts; Math Clb; Math Tm; Spanish Clb; Trs Jr Cls; Trs Sr Cls; L Crs Cntry; L Mgr(s); Colby Coll Bk Awd Eng 84; Gordon Coll; Marine Bio.

CARBONNEAU, SUZANNE M; Lewiston HS; Lewiston, ME; (Y); Church Yth Grp; Drama Clb; French Clb; Pres Pep Clb; Yrbk Stf; Stu Cncl; Hon Roll; Brdcstng.

CARD, CHARYL; Fryeburg Acad; Fryeburg, ME; (Y); French Clb; Varsity Clb; Stage Crew; Yrbk Stf; JV Var Cheerleading; JV Var Mgr(s); Hm-Cmng Queen 83-84; Bsktbll Medal 81; SMUTI; X-Ray Tech.

CARL, JASON; Lawrence HS; Albion, ME; (Y); Am Leg Boys St; Debate Tm; Drama Clb; NFL; Speech Tm; Rep Stu Cncl; L Ftbl; NHS; Ntl Merit Ltr; Pres Schlr; U Of Puget Sound; Hstry.

CARLSTROM, CHRISTINA; Jay HS; Jay, ME; (Y); 16/85; Drama Clb; Chorus; School Musical; School Play; Nwsp Stf; Yrbk Stf; Mgr Crs Cntry; Mgr(s); Hon Roll; Poland Sullivan Comm Schlrshp 85; U Southern ME; Lib Arts.

CARON, APRIL; Fort Kent Comm HS; Fort Kent Mills, ME; (S); Church Yth Grp; DECA; Yrbk Stf; Vllybl; Sellng Adds Yrbk 85; 2nd St Comp Deca 85; Pierres Schl Cosmotology; Cosmt.

CARON, MARTY; Washburn District HS; Washburn, ME; (Y); 1/52; Am Leg Boys St; Drama Clb; French Clb; Pep Clb; Band; School Play; Yrbk Bus Mgr; High Hon Roll; NHS; NEDT Awd; Exchng Stu Sweden 84-85; St Josephs Coll; Pre-Med.

CARON, MICHAEL R; Lewiston HS; Lewiston, ME; (Y); JV Bsbl; JV Var Socr; Hon Roll; Excllnce Phys Ed 82-83; Law.

CARON, RONALD; Community HS; Ft Kent, ME; (Y); Am Leg Boys St; Church Yth Grp; Band; Pep Band; Nwsp Stf; High Hon Roll; Hon Roll; NHS; St Schlr; Voice Dem Awd; Cert Of Merit For Tutoring 85; Outstndng Sphmr 84; St Anslems; Phlsphy.

CARPENTER, GEORGE; Fort Kent Community HS; Ft Kent, ME; (Y); Am Leg Boys St; Sec Boy Scts; Band; Concert Band; Pep Band; Hon Roll; All ST Band 85; All Aroostook County Band 84-85; U ME Orono; Psych.

CARPENTER, KAREN; Lewiston HS; Lewiston, ME; (Y); Letterman Clb; Var Capt Bsktbl; Var L Crs Cntry; Var Fld Hcky; Var L Sftbl; Hon Roll; Sports Med.

CARPENTER, LONNIE LANDRY; Limestone HS; Loring Afb, ME; (Y); 14/80; Debate Tm; Drama Clb; Exploring; French Clb; Library Aide; NFL; Speech Tm; Thesps; School Play; Hon Roll; Limestone Rotry Clb Schrlshp 85; Purdue U; Hist.

CARVER, JEAN DENISE; Narraguagus HS; Addison, ME; (Y); Am Leg Aux Girls St; Dance Clb; Drama Clb; Pres French Clb; Yrbk Stf; Var Capt Cheerleading; JV Vllybl; Hon Roll; Outstndng Schl Sprt Awd 85; Constnt A Avg Art Hstry Hnr 85; A Avg Clthng & Txtils Hnr 85.

CARVER, MIKE; Dering HS; Portland, ME; (Y); VP JA; Varsity Clb; JV Bsbl; JV Bsktbl; Var L Ftbl; Var L Trk; Im Wt Lftg; Hon Roll.

CASALE, CHRIS; Deering HS; Portland, ME; (Y); Exploring; French Clb; VP Trs Key Clb; Math Tm; Varsity Clb; Nwsp Stf; Yrbk Ed-Chief; JV Var Golf; Vllybl; Hon Roll; Pre-Med.

CASTNER, SHAWN; Leavitt Area HS; Greene, ME; (Y); 30/145; Church Yth Grp; Cmnty Wkr; JA; Letterman Clb; Science Clb; Varsity Clb; School Play; Stage Crew; Variety Show; Capts Awd 84-85; Cochs Awd 83-84; Army; Electrncs.

CHABOT, JEFF; Sumner Mem HS; Prospect Harbor, ME; (Y); 13/97; Am Leg Boys St; Band; Jazz Band; Variety Show; Hon Roll; NHS; Boy Scts; Mrchg Band; Pep Band; School Musical; Louis Armstrong Jazz Awd 85; U ME-ORONO; Engrng.

CHABOT, JOSEPH; Liu Falls HS; Livermore Fls, ME; (Y); High Hon Roll; Hon Roll; NHS; Eng Awd 83-84; Indstrl Arts Awd 83-84 & 84-85; CMUTI; Electrncs.

CHABOT, SHELLEY; Lewiston HS; Lewiston, ME; (Y); 122/450; Library Aide; Stat Bsbl; Stat Score Keeper; NHS; Cert Of Recogntn Intermrls 81; Cert Of Awd Excllnc Math 81; Beal Coll; Paralegal.

CHADBOURNE, LISA M; Portland HS; Portland, ME; (Y); Computer Clb; French Clb; JA; Rep Frsh Cls; JV Fld Hcky; Hon Roll; Lab Tech.

CHAMBERLAIN, ANNE; Camden Rockport HS; Camden, ME; (Y); 10/130; Am Leg Aux Girls St; Church Yth Grp; Latin Clb; Band; Chorus; Church Choir; Concert Band; Jazz Band; Madrigals; Mrchg Band; All ST Band & Orch-1st Chr Flute 85; MVP Band 85; MIP-BAND 82; U Of Southern ME; Music Educ.

CHAMBERLAIN, DANNY; Erskine Acad; S China, ME; (Y); Am Leg Boys St; French Clb; Speech Tm; Yrbk Stf; Stu Cncl; Hon Roll; Prfct Atten Awd; Kennebec Cnty Soil & Wtr Conservtn Essy Wnnr 84; Fshn Mrchndsng.

CHAMBERLAND, GREGORY; Wisdom HS; St Agatha, ME; (Y); 1/65; Am Leg Boys St; Church Yth Grp; Drama Clb; Yrbk Stf; Cit Awd; High Hon Roll; Trs VP NHS; Pres Schlr; Val; Pres Soph Cls; Am Legn Of Schl Awd; U Of ME-ORONO; Elec Engrng.

CHAMBERLAND, SANDRA; Wisdom HS; Decatur, GA; (Y); 3/65; VP Church Yth Grp; Drama Clb; Yrbk Stf; Var L Cheerleading; High Hon Roll; Hon Roll; Pres Schlr; Rotary Awd; Hnr Essay 85; Engl Awd 85; GA Tech; Chem.

CHAMBERLAND, SHELLY; Wisdom HS; St Agatha, ME; (Y); 3/50; Church Yth Grp; Cmnty Wkr; French Clb; Band; Church Choir; Yrbk Stf; Cheerleading; Hon Roll; VP NHS; St Schlr; Mdcl Fld.

CHAMPAGNE, CAROLYN; Lewiston HS; Lewiston, ME; (Y); Hosp Aide; Letterman Clb; Var Crs Cntry; Var Trk; High Hon Roll; Hon Roll; Bus.

CHAMPLIN, MATHEW; Van Buren District Secondary School; Van Bur, ME; (Y); Am Leg Boys St; Band; Yrbk Phtg; Pres Jr Cls; Var L Bsbl; JV Bsktbl; Var L Socr; Hon Roll; Comp Prog.

CHANDLER, SUSAN; Fryeburg Acad; Fryeburg, ME; (S); Latin Clb; School Play; Sec Frsh Cls; Rep Soph Cls; Rep Jr Cls; VP Stu Cncl; Cheerleading; NHS; Varsity Clb; Chorus; Walter A Robinson Ltn Awd 83-84; Ntl Hnr Soc Awd 83; Rep FA For Nrthrn Nw Englnd JR Sci 84-85; Bowdoin Coll; Psych.

CHAPMAN, SHELDON; Hampden Acad; Hampden, ME; (Y); 30/174; Church Yth Grp; Band; Concert Band; Mrchg Band; Var Ftbl; Var Trk; Wt Lftg; Hon Roll; Polytech Inst NY; Aerosp Engr.

CHAREST, DONNA; Lewiston HS; Lewiston, ME; (Y); Hon Roll; Nrsng.

CHAREST, KELLY JEAN; South Portland HS; S Portland, ME; (Y); 32/300; Key Clb; Nwsp Rptr; Yrbk Stf; Trs Soph Cls; Trs Jr Cls; Trs Sr Cls; Var Bsktbl; Var Fld Hcky; Capt Sftbl; NHS; Wmn Rotary Scholar 85; Wheaton Coll; Med.

CHAREST, WENDY; Cony HS; Augusta, ME; (Y); Am Leg Aux Girls St; Church Yth Grp; Sec French Clb; Pres JCL; Variety Show; Yrbk Sprt Ed; JV Sftbl; Im Vllybl; High Hon Roll; Wellesley Bk Awd 85; Natl Latin Exam Gold Mdl 85; AATF Frnch Cont 2nd Pl In ST 83; Chapel Hill NC; Latin.

CHARETTE JR, GERARD; Ashland Community HS; Portage, ME; (Y); 7/48; School Play; Pres Frsh Cls; Trs Soph Cls; Off Jr Cls; Off Sr Cls; Trs Stu Cncl; Var Bsbl; Var Socr; Var Vllybl; Hon Roll; J Paul Levesque Schlrshp 85; St Cncl 85; NMUTI; Elec Maint.

CHARLEBOIS, JULIE; Portland HS; S Portland, ME; (Y); Nwsp Stf; High Hon Roll; Hon Roll; Gold Key Awd 85; Rufus Cutler Cushman Scholar 85; Andover Coll; Comp Sci.

CHASE, LINDA M; Lincon Acad; Pemaquid Beach, ME; (Y); AFS; Am Leg Aux Girls St; JCL; Math Tm; Ski Clb; Band; Capt Gym; Var Tennis; High Hon Roll; Pres NHS; Cornell U; Metorlgy.

CHASSE, DANIEL; St Dominics R HS; Lewiston, ME; (Y); Lcrss; Socr; Tennis; Hon Roll; 3 Times Slctd ME All Star 83; Hcky Tm 84-85; Bus.

CHENEY, ANDREA L; Morse HS; Bath, ME; (Y); 10/190; Rep Am Leg Aux Girls St; Thesps; Stage Crew; Yrbk Ed-Chief; Yrbk Sprt Ed; Pres NHS; Pres Acdmc Ftns Awd 85; John Carey Pltcl Sci Schlrshp 85; Outstndng Glbl Issues Stu 85; Bates Coll; Hstry.

CHESLEY, JANET; Buckfield JR SR HS; Buckfield, ME; (Y); 6/45; Church Yth Grp; French Clb; Letterman Clb; Library Aide; Math Tm; Varsity Clb; Chorus; Yrbk Stf; Var L Cheerleading; Var L Crs Cntry; Coaches Awd-Vrsty Chrldng 83; Coaches Awd-Math Tm 85; Prncpls Awd-MSSPA 84; Bates Coll-Lewiston; Chld Psych.

CHIARAMONTE, JOHN F; Caribou HS; Caribou, ME; (Y); 30/190; Hon Roll; U Of ME-ORONO; Engrng.

CHILDRESS, DEBRA L; Livermore Falls HS; Livermore Falls, ME; (Y); 3/97; Am Leg Aux Girls St; Yrbk Stf; VP Frsh Cls; VP Soph Cls; Stu Cncl; JV Bsktbl; Var L Fld Hcky; High Hon Roll; NHS; Church Yth Grp; VP Wstrn Reg Stu Clnls; U NH; Lib Arts.

CHILDS, SHERRY; Traip Acad; Kittery, ME; (Y); Hon Roll; NHS; Awd Adv Bus 85; Awd Eng 85; Awd Alg 83; Acctg.

CHIPMAN, REBECCA; Mt Blue HS; Weld, ME; (Y); Trs 4-H; Var L Trk; Hon Roll; NHS; Crmnl Jstc.

CHIPMAN, SONJA; Windham HS; S Windham, ME; (Y); Sec Spanish Clb; Yrbk Stf; Jr NHS; Outstndng Achvt Typng 84; Outstndng Achvt Infrmtn Procssng III 85; Accntng.

CHISSLER, STEPHANIE; Mt Ararat HS; Orrs Island, ME; (Y); VP Pres AFS; Drama Clb; School Play; NHS; Lit Mag; Rep Frsh Cls; Rep Soph Cls; Rep Jr Cls; Var Fld Hcky; DAR Awd; Exch Stu Sweden AFS 83; U MS Amherst; Psych.

CHOMAS, MARY K; Edward Little HS; Auburn, ME; (Y); 67/360; Latin Clb; Political Wkr; Ski Clb; Varsity Clb; Yrbk Stf; Cheerleading; Trk; Wt Lftg; Hon Roll; Prfct Atten Awd; Bentley Coll; Intl Mrkdtn.

CHRISTAKOS, PETER; High School HS; Bangor, ME; (Y); Church Yth Grp; Rep Frsh Cls; Rep Soph Cls; Rep Jr Cls; Rep Sr Cls; VP Stu Cncl; Var Bsbl; Var Socr; High Hon Roll; NHS; JR Sci & Holy Crs Bk Awds 85; ST Sci Fair 82-83; Pre Med.

CHURCHILL, CAROLYN; Fort Fairfield HS; Ft Fairfield, ME; (Y); 4/70; Am Leg Aux Girls St; Trs Church Yth Grp; Orch; High Hon Roll; Top Ten Cls Awd 83-85; Chrch Cert Awd 85; Husson Coll; Bus.

CHURCHILL, LESLEY A; Showhegan Area HS; Norridgewock, ME; (Y); 26/214; Pep Clb; Band; Concert Band; Mrchg Band; Pep Band; High Hon Roll; Hon Roll; Higgins Fund 85; Madison Paper Schlrshp 85; Outstndng Band Mbr Awd 85; ME ST Acad Hair Dsgn; Beautcn.

CIALINI-CHARLES, MELISSA; Windham HS; S Windham, ME; (Y); Hosp Aide; Spanish Clb; Chorus; Nwsp Ed-Chief; Mgr(s); Hon Roll; U Of ME Farmington; Spec Educ.

CLAPP, JAC; Skowhegan Area HS; Skowhegan, ME; (Y); 3/250; Am Leg Boys St; German Clb; Letterman Clb; Ed Yrbk Stf; JV L Bsktbl; Var Tennis; High Hon Roll; NHS; Ntl Merit Ltr; Shepherd Awd 84; Maine Schlrs Day 85; Comp Sci.

CLARK, CHRIS; Caribou HS; Caribou, ME; (S); Boy Scts; Chess Clb; Exploring; Math Clb; Math Tm; Science Clb; Ntl Merit Ltr.

CLARK, DAVID; Sanford HS; Springvale, ME; (Y); Hon Roll.

CLARK, GORDON; Wisdom HS; Madawaska, ME; (Y); Badmtn; Hon Roll; U Of Southern ME; Comptr Sci.

CLARK, MELISSA CHAISSON; Gorham HS; Gorham, ME; (Y); 20/115; Am Leg Aux Girls St; Spanish Clb; School Play; Pres Jr Cls; Stu Cncl; Hon Roll; NHS; Spanish NHS; Drama Clb; School Musical; Hugh O Brien Ldrshp Awd; Outstndng Spnsh Stu; CARES Tm; Wheaton Coll; Ec.

CLARK, PEGGY; Carrabec HS; Anson, ME; (Y); Am Leg Aux Girls St; Band; Trs Jr Cls; Bsktbl; Crs Cntry; Fld Hcky; Trk; Hon Roll; Prfct Atten Awd.

CLARK, TANIS; Penquis Valley HS; Milo, ME; (Y); Am Leg Aux Girls St; Church Yth Grp; Drama Clb; Band; Concert Band; Mrchg Band; Pep Band; School Musical; Variety Show; Yrbk Stf; Elem Tchr.

CLARK, TOM; Cony HS; Gardiner, ME; (Y); Aud/Vis; Library Aide; Bsbl; Hon Roll; US Air Force; Pilot.

CLARKE, ELLEN; Edward Little HS; Auburn, ME; (Y); 154/338; Church Yth Grp; Cmnty Wkr; Exploring; Pep Clb; Teachers Aide; Varsity Clb; Variety Show; Var Cheerleading; Hon Roll; New Englnd Schlr Fnd 85; U Of ME Farmington; Spec Ed.

CLEALE, LEWIS; Houlton HS; Houlton, ME; (Y); 6/106; Am Leg Boys St; Spanish Clb; Acpl Chr; Concert Band; School Musical; Swing Chorus; High Hon Roll; NHS; Ntl Merit Ltr; Church Yth Grp; James B Ashe Schlrshp 85.

CLEVENGER, ROBERT; Deering HS; Portland, ME; (Y); JV Socr; Var Wrstlng; Hon Roll; Engr.

CLIFFORD, KAREN L; Oxford HS; Norway, ME; (Y); Am Leg Aux Girls St; Cmnty Wkr; Debate Tm; Drama Clb; English Clb; Latin Clb; High Hon Roll; Hon Roll; Bryn Mawr; Arch.

CLINE, LISA J; Calais HS; Calais, ME; (Y); 4/55; Am Leg Aux Girls St; Concert Band; Mrchg Band; Pep Band; Yrbk Stf; JV Var Bowling; Var L Sftbl; High Hon Roll; NHS; Stu Corrspndnt-Locl Papr; U Of ME-ORONO; Jrnlsm.

CLOUTIER, CLAUDE M; Leavitt Area HS; Greene, ME; (Y); 15/111; Math Tm; Im Bsbl; Hon Roll; NHS; Embry-Riddle Aerontcl U; Engrng.

CLOUTIER, KEVIN; Portland HS; Portland, ME; (Y); Var Bsbl; Var Ftbl; Var Capt Ice Hcky; Im Vllybl; High Hon Roll; Sec NHS; Dartmouth Clb Bk Awd; Merchnt Marine Essay Cntest Wnnr; Antmy Of Ldrshp.

CLOUTIER, LISE; Saint Dominic Regional HS; Lewiston, ME; (Y); School Play; Variety Show; Rep Frsh Cls; VP Soph Cls; VP Jr Cls; VP Sr Cls; Sec VP Stu Cncl; Var Cheerleading; Var Capt Fld Hcky; Var Sftbl; Physcn Asst.

CLUFF, KELLY; Kennebunk Christian Acad; Kennebunk, ME; (S); 2/5; Church Yth Grp; Chorus; Church Choir; School Musical; School Play; Yrbk Ed-Chief; Yrbk Stf; Cheerleading; Score Keeper; Sftbl; High GPA Geometry 84; Word Of Life Bible Inst; Music.

COBB, CASEY; Orono HS; Orono, ME; (S); 8/105; Am Leg Boys St; Math Tm; Nwsp Stf; Yrbk Rptr; Pres Frsh Cls; Pres Church Yth Grp; VP Jr Cls; Pres Sr Cls; Rep Stu Cncl; Var Capt Bsbl; MVP Vrsty Football 84; DAR Good Ctznshp Awd 84; Allstate Qrtbk 84.

COBB, JANET S; Greenville HS; Greenville, ME; (Y); 4/28; Am Leg Aux Girls St; Drama Clb; Key Clb; Band; School Musical; Yrbk Bus Mgr; Stu Cncl; DAR Awd; Hon Roll; Kiwanis Awd; Mc Iver Awd 83-84; Hist Awd 83-84; U ME Farmington; Hist Tchr.

COCHRAN, MICHELE; Woodland HS; Princeton, ME; (S); 13/65; Church Yth Grp; French Clb; Thesps; Yrbk Stf; Var L Bsktbl; Var L Sftbl; L Capt Vllybl; Hon Roll; NHS; U Of ME; Elem Educ.

COCKS, CATHERINE C; Waterville HS; Waterville, ME; (Y); 2/200; Am Leg Aux Girls St; Sec Spanish Clb; Stage Crew; Nwsp Stf; Capt Crs Cntry; Trk; High Hon Roll; NHS; Ntl Merit SF; Sal; Excellence In Spanish Awd 82-84; Excellence In French Awd 83-84.

COFFIN, BEVERLY; Bonny Eagle HS; N Windham, ME; (Y); Church Yth Grp; Latin Clb; Math Tm; Band; Church Choir; Symp Band; Stat Gym; Mgr(s); Kiwanis Awd; NHS; U Of ME Orono.

COHEN, HALLEY; Deering HS; Portland, ME; (Y); Drama Clb; French Clb; Latin Clb; Chorus; School Play; Ed Lit Mag; Stu Cncl; Trk; French Hon Soc; Hon Roll; Merit Awd Lalliance Francaise 85facad Cont St Latin Conv 85.

COLE, KATHRINE A; Freeport HS; Freeport, ME; (Y); 3/100; Am Leg Aux Girls St; Drama Clb; Band; School Musical; School Play; Yrbk Stf; Sec Soph Cls; Sec Jr Cls; Hon Roll; Sec Jr NHS; Nw Englnd Wrtrs Conf 85; Engl.

COLELLO, PAULA; Deering HS; Portland, ME; (Y); Im Cheerleading.

COLLINS, CAROLINE R; Lake Region HS; Bridgton, ME; (Y); 10/150; AFS; French Clb; Varsity Clb; Nwsp Phtg; Yrbk Rptr; Var Cheerleading; NHS; Ntl Merit SF; NEDT Awd; Williams Coll Bk Awd 84; Natl JR Clsscl Leag Latin Awd; Lib Arts.

COLLINS, SCOTT; Caribou HS; Caribou, ME; (S); 40/213; Am Leg Boys St; Var L Bsbl; Var L Bsktbl; Var L Socr; NHS; U Of Southern ME; Bus.

COLON, MARY ELLEN; Lewiston HS; Lewiston, ME; (Y); Church Yth Grp; Chorus; Church Choir; Hon Roll; Johnson Wales Coll; Hotel Mgr.

COLUCCI, ANGELA; Westbrook HS; Westbrook, ME; (Y); Bsktbl; Fld Hcky; U Of Orono.

COMPTON, MARY; Mt Blue HS; East Wilton, ME; (Y); Am Leg Aux Girls St; 4-H; JA; Chorus; Var Capt Cheerleading; 4-H Awd; High Hon Roll; Jr NHS; NHS; Ntl Merit SF; ME 4-H Eastern St Horse Tm 82, 83 & 84; Bowdoin Coll; Lobbying.

CONANT, HEATHER; Fort Fairfield HS; Ft Fairfield, ME; (Y); 2/78; Am Leg Aux Girls St; Trs Pres Church Yth Grp; Varsity Clb; Band; Chorus; Pres Frsh Cls; Trs Stu Cncl; High Hon Roll; NHS; Drama Clb; Top 10 Pct Cls 82-85; All Aroostook Chorus 82-83 & 84-85; Outstndng Stu US Hist 84-85; U RI; Pharm.

CONANT, RHONDA L; Leavitt Area HS; Turner, ME; (Y); 19/112; Dance Clb; Drama Clb; 4-H; Yrbk Rptr; Pres Frsh Cls; Pres Soph Cls; Pres Jr Cls; Pres Sr Cls; Cheerleading; Fld Hcky; ST Drss Revue Wnnr 4-H Awd 83; U Of Southern ME; Bus Adm.

CONDON, ANGELA; Belfast Area HS; Belfast, ME; (Y); 7/140; Church Yth Grp; VP FHA; Cheerleading; Socr; Hon Roll; Jr NHS; NHS; Blaine Hse Schlrs Pgm 85; U ME Orono; Elem Ed.

CONDON, MANNY; Gorham HS; Gorham, ME; (Y); VP Spanish Clb; Rep Frsh Cls; Rep Soph Cls; Rep Stu Cncl; Var Bsbl; Var Bsktbl; Var Crs Cntry; Var Golf; Var Trk; Spanish NHS.

CONLEY, PATRICIA; Westbrook HS; Westbrook, ME; (Y); Art Clb; French Clb; Yrbk Stf; Socr; Archtctr.

CONLEY, PETER; Cape Elizabeth HS; Cape Elizabeth, ME; (Y); JV Bsbl; JV Bsktbl; Var Golf; JV Socr; JV Tennis; Hon Roll; Hnr Rll Socty 85; Acctg.

CONLOGUE, MELISSA J; Maine Central Inst; Pittsfield, ME; (Y); Sec French Clb; Yrbk Stf; Bsktbl; Mgr(s); Sftbl; High Hon Roll; Hon Roll; NHS; Prfct Atten Awd; Bus.

CONNORS, GAIL; Wiscasset HS; Wiscasset, ME; (Y); Am Leg Aux Girls St; Latin Clb; Band; Rep Stu Cncl; Var JV Socr; Sftbl; High Hon Roll; NHS; St Schlr; Top 10 Pct Soph Clss 83-84; U Of VT; Doc.

CONWAY, LAMONT M; Vinalhaven HS; Vinalhaven, ME; (Y); 2/15; Boy Scts; Computer Clb; French Clb; Math Clb; Var Capt Bsbl; Var Capt Bsktbl; Var Coach Actv; Var Golf; Var Capt Socr; Var Vllybl; MVP Vrsty Bsktbl & Sccr 84 & 85; Am Leg Schlrshp 85; U Of ME Farmington; Math.

COOK, LYNN; Caribou HS; Caribou, ME; (S); 13/215; Church Yth Grp; Key Clb; Sec Trs Band; Chorus; Jazz Band; Mrchg Band; Yrbk Ed-Chief; High Hon Roll; Hon Roll; NHS; Houghton Coll; Psych.

COOKSON, LYLA; Westbrook HS; Westbrook, ME; (Y); Camp Fr Inc; French Clb; Keywanettes; Concert Band; Drm & Bgl; Drm Mjr(t); Mrchg Band; Yrbk Stf; Hon Roll; NHS; Nominated Mc Donalds Band 85; Engrng.

COOLEY, NANCY; Washington District HS; Washburn, ME; (Y); 26/50; Pep Clb; Band; Hon Roll; U ME-BANGOR:Dental Hyg.

COOPER, MARIANNE; Edward Little HS; Auburn, ME; (S); JA; High Hon Roll; Hon Roll.

CORBIN, DAVID; Cony HS; Augusta, ME; (Y); FBLA; Varsity Clb; Variety Show; Var L Golf; Mgr L Ice Hcky; Var L Tennis; Vllybl; Hon Roll; Court Clrk.

COREAU, MICHELLE M; South Portland HS; South Portland, ME; (Y); 5/300; Am Leg Aux Girls St; Intnl Clb; JA; Math Tm; Yrbk Stf; Trk; High Hon Roll; Hon Roll; NHS; Intrntl Rltns.

CORNELIO, ANN; Jay HS; Jay, ME; (Y); Drama Clb; Chorus; Concert Band; Mrchg Band; Pep Band; Hon Roll; Band; Stage Crew; JV Bsktbl; All State Music Fest; All Estrn Music Fes; Americans Yth Concert; Music.

CORTEZ, DAMIAN P; Biddeford HS; Biddeford, ME; (Y); 32/295; Church Yth Grp; Leo Clb; Library Aide; Band; Concert Band; Mrchg Band; Hon Roll; St Josephs CYO Treas & Pres 84-85; SMSU; Pltcl Sci.

COSSETTE, ANNETTE; Fryeburg Acad; Fryeburg, ME; (Y); Pres Church Yth Grp; Radio Clb; Chorus; School Play; Yrbk Phtg; Lit Mag; VP Frsh Cls; Var Socr; Hon Roll; NHS; Natl Engl Merit Awd 85; Intr Decrtg.

COTE, KERRI; Learitt Area HS; Turner, ME; (Y); 20/140; Dance Clb; Color Guard; Drill Tm; Drm & Bgl; Flag Corp; Variety Show; Stu Cncl; Var Cheerleading; Fld Hcky; JV Sftbl; Vrsty Ftbl Squad Won Excllnce Awd At Chrldng Camp 84; Andover; Bus.

COTE, MIKE; Edward Little HS; Auburn, ME; (Y); Boy Scts; Church Yth Grp; JV Socr; Var Capt Trk; Hon Roll; Prfct Atten Awd; 11th ME ST Adv Typng 85; Air Force; Comp Engr.

COTE, STEVEN; Fryeburg Acad; Fryeburg, ME; (S); 1/150; Rep Am Leg Boys St; Latin Clb; VP Varsity Clb; Nwsp Sprt Ed; Yrbk Sprt Ed; Var L Bsbl; Var L Bsktbl; DAR Awd; High Hon Roll; Pres NHS; Pre-Law.

COUGHLIN, CHRIS; Portland HS; Portland, ME; (Y); Church Yth Grp; Latin Clb; Math Clb; Math Tm; Spanish Clb; Var Bsbl; High Hon Roll; Hon Roll; Prfct Atten Awd; Undergrad Awd Bst Stu Geom 83; Undergrad Awd Bst Stu Bio 83; Undergrad Awds Bst Stu Alg II & Chem 84; Math.

COURANT, JAY; Leavitt Area HS; Greene, ME; (Y); 5/141; Band; High Hon Roll; NHS; Natl Ski Patrol 85; Capt, 3 Ltrs, Alpine X-Cntry Ski 82-85; Elec Engrng.

COURTEMANCHE, MARK; Lewiston HS; Lewiston, ME; (Y); Letterman Clb; Varsity Clb; Bsbl; DECA; Ftbl; Hon Roll; U Sthrn ME; Bus Admin.

COWPERTHWAITE, BRUCE; Ellsworth Christian HS; Ellsworth, ME; (S); 1/2; Math Tm; Band; Chorus; Church Choir; School Play; VP Bsktbl; Var Socr; High Hon Roll; Hon Roll; Elec.

COX, DANIEL; Monmouth Acad; North Monmouth, ME; (Y); Am Leg Boys St; Drama Clb; French Clb; Math Tm; Speech Tm; Yrbk Stf; Rep Soph Cls; Var Crs Cntry; High Hon Roll; NHS; Pre-Med.

COX, LLOYD; Woodland HS; Woodland, ME; (S); Camera Clb; Trs Computer Clb; Drama Clb; French Clb; School Play; Stage Crew; Lit Mag; High Hon Roll; NHS; Prfct Atten Awd; Comp Pgrmr.

CRAGIN, CHRISTINE; Falmouth HS; Falmouth, ME; (S); 7/110; French Clb; JA; Leo Clb; Math Tm; Yrbk Stf; Var JV Fld Hcky; JV Tennis; Dnfth Awd; High Hon Roll; Jr NHS; US Senate Page 85; Engr.

CRISTINA, SCOTT; Jay HS; Jay, ME; (Y); 38/90; JV Bsbl; JV Bsktbl; Var L Ftbl; Var Trk; High Hon Roll; Hon Roll; Ntl Merit Ltr; David True Scholar; MCVTI; Building Tech.

CROCKETT, KAREN JOAN; Cony HS; Augusta, ME; (Y); 6/285; Am Leg Aux Girls St; Am Leg Boys St; Pep Clb; Band; Mrchg Band; Pep Band; Yrbk Sprt Ed; Yrbk Stf; Rep Soph Cls; Rep Jr Cls; Tp 10 Per Cnt Cls 82-85; Lillian Sherbourne Dtr Schlrshp 85; Knghts Columbus Patritc Awd 85; U Of ME Orone; Bus Adm.

CRONKHITE, TRACY; Jay HS; Livermore Falls, ME; (Y); Am Leg Aux Girls St; Church Yth Grp; Drama Clb; Ski Clb; Rep Soph Cls; Var Capt Crs Cntry; JV Fld Hcky; Var Trk; Hon Roll; Legsltr Awd Odyssey Mind 85; Nrsg.

CROOK, KELLY; Hampden Acad; Hampden, ME; (Y); Dance Clb; French Clb; Yrbk Stf; Cheerleading; Vllybl; High Hon Roll; Hon Roll; Lab Tech.

CROOKER, TAMMY; Hampden Acad; Hampden, ME; (Y); Band; Concert Band; Jazz Band; Mrchg Band; Yrbk Stf; Var Bsktbl; Im Coach Actv; Var Socr; Var Trk; Hon Roll; Tchng.

CROPLEY II, ROGER L; Mattanawcook Acad; Lincoln, ME; (Y); 2/114; Am Leg Boys St; Cmnty Wkr; School Play; Bsbl; Bowling; Vllybl; High Hon Roll; Ntl Merit Schol; Pres Schlr; Sal; Colby Coll Awd Outstndng Acadmc Achvmnt 84; St Joseph Coll; Brdcstng.

CROSSLEY, ELIZABETH L; Edward Little HS; Auburn, ME; (S); AFS; JCL; Latin Clb; Pep Clb; Varsity Clb; Yrbk Stf; Trk; Hon Roll; U Of NH.

CROTEAU, KAREN A; Biddeford HS; Biddeford, ME; (Y); 11/320; Am Leg Aux Girls St; Church Yth Grp; Leo Clb; Nwsp Stf; Yrbk Stf; Cheerleading; Hon Roll; Jr NHS; NHS.

CROTEAU, TAMI; Madison HS; Skowhegan, ME; (Y); 7/100; Ski Clb; Band; Yrbk Stf; Cheerleading; Radiologcl Tech.

CROTEOU, GERRI; Deering HS; Portland, ME; (Y); FTA; Sec JA; Office Aide; Pep Clb; Hon Roll; Top Seller JA 82-83; Bsktbl Mgr Plaque 82-83; Human Svcs.

CROWE, SHARON J; Mt Ararat Schl; Bailey Island, ME; (Y); Chorus; Church Choir; Nwsp Rptr; Nwsp Stf; Hon Roll; Mansfield; Beautician.

CRUMLEY, JOYCE A; Hall-Dale HS; Hallowell, ME; (Y); 20/84; Drama Clb; GAA; Red Cross Aide; Band; Chorus; Yrbk Stf; Stu Cncl; Jr NHS; NHS; Val; Excell Phy Ed 84-85, Engl IV 85,Co-Op Educ 85; U Of ME-AUGUSTA; Liberal Arts.

CRUZ, MARIO; Fryeburg Acad; Chicago, IL; (Y); Church Yth Grp; Radio Clb; Spanish Clb; Orch; Yrbk Stf; High Hon Roll; Hon Roll; NHS; St Alphonsus Fathers Clb Scholar 82; Scholl Fndtn Scholar 84.

CUMMINGS, LAURA; Fryeburg Acad; Fryeburg, ME; (S); 3/150; Sec Trs French Clb; Varsity Clb; Nwsp Rptr; Yrbk Phtg; Lit Mag; Var L Fld Hcky; Var L Sftbl; High Hon Roll; Jr NHS; Ntl Merit SF.

CUMMINGS, PATRICIA A; Penquis Valley HS; La Grange, ME; (Y); 2/65; Am Leg Aux Girls St; Pres Drama Clb; Science Clb; Varsity Clb; Nwsp Stf; Stu Cncl; DAR Awd; High Hon Roll; NHS; Sal; MSSPA Principls Awd 85; MSAD Edctrs Assn Scholar 85; Milo H S Alumni Assn Scholar 85; U Of ME Orono; Brdcst Jrnlsm.

CURRIER, KRISTIN; Mount Blue HS; Farmington, ME; (Y); Chorus; Color Guard; Mrchg Band; School Musical; School Play; Var L Cheerleading; Var JV Mgr(s); Church Yth Grp; Grmn Awd 83-84; Forster Fndtn Schlrshp 85; U Of ME; Psych.

CURRY, DAVID M; South Portland HS; South Portland, ME; (Y); Am Leg Boys St; Computer Clb; Drama Clb; Church Choir; School Play; Crs Cntry; Trk; High Hon Roll; Hon Roll; NCTE Awd; Dartmouth Book Awd 84; Frgn Lang Day German II & III Ptary Rec Awd 83-84; Worcester Polytech Inst; Engrng.

CURTIS, ANNETTE; Erskine Academy; Weeks Mills, ME; (Y); Math Tm; Yrbk Stf; Hon Roll; Svc Awd For Tutering 85; Typng 50 Wrds A Min Awd 84; Bus Clb 83-85; Lgl Sec.

CURTIS, DEBORAH; Livermore Falls HS; Fayette, ME; (Y); Am Leg Aux Girls St; Church Yth Grp; Drama Clb; Math Tm; Yrbk Stf; Trs Frsh Cls; NHS; St Schlr; Portland Yth Symph Orch 83-85; ME Smmr Hmnts Pgm 85; Liberal Arts.

CURTIS, NORMAN; Belfast Area HS; Belfast, ME; (Y); Rep Am Leg Boys St; Cmnty Wkr; French Clb; Political Wkr; Yrbk Ed-Chief; Hon Roll; Jr NHS; NHS; Yrbk Stf; HOBY Sem Delg 84; Model ST Legisltr 82 & 83; Pol Sci.

CUSHMAN, DAPHNE; Hodgdon HS; Houlton, ME; (Y); Am Leg Aux Girls St; Pres Church Yth Grp; Chorus; School Musical; Sec Soph Cls; Sec Jr Cls; Dnfth Awd; High Hon Roll; Hon Roll; All Aroostook Chrs 83-85; Elem Ed.

CYR, DAVID; Kennebunk HS; Kennebunk, ME; (Y); Boy Scts; Math Tm; Var Capt Ftbl; Wt Lftg; Hon Roll; Most Dedctd Ftbl Plyr 84.

CYR, DOUGLAS; Winslow HS; Winslow, ME; (Y); Boy Scts; Church Yth Grp; Band; Chorus; Church Choir; Concert Band; School Play; Yrbk Stf; Soph Cls; NHS; Driver Educ Awd 84-85; Stetson U; Soc Sci.

CYR, ERIC; Van Buren District Secondary Schl; Van Buren, ME; (Y); 15/90; Cmnty Wkr; JV Var Bsktbl; Var Capt Tennis; Acctng.

CYR, MARK; Fort Kent Community HS; Ft Kent, ME; (Y); 1/165; Am Leg Boys St; Boys Clb Am; Yrbk Phtg; Pres Frsh Cls; Rep Sr Cls; VP Stu Cncl; Trk; Im Vllybl; Hon Roll; Class Ctznshp Awd 83; Hlth Sci.

CYR, SHELLY; Caribou Caribou; Caribou, ME; (S); 6/230; Chrmn Church Yth Grp; VP Key Clb; School Play; Stage Crew; Rep Sr Cls; Rep Stu Cncl; Tennis; Vllybl; NHS; Bio Sci.

D AUTEUIL JR, DANIEL; St Dominics Regional HS; Lewiston, ME; (Y); Key Clb; Varsity Clb; Var Ice Hcky; Var Socr; Hon Roll; NHS; NEDT 83; Law.

DAIGLE, BETH V; Fort Kent Community HS; Ft Kent, ME; (Y); Band; Yrbk Ed-Chief; Yrbk Phtg; Var Capt Bsktbl; Var Cheerleading; Var Socr; Var Capt Tennis; Capt Vllybl; High Hon Roll; Hon Roll; Blaine House Loan 85; Outstndng SR Feml Athlete 85; Outstndng Underclssmn Feml Athlete 84; U Of ME-FORT Kent; Publc Reltn.

DAIGLE, DEAN; Wisdom HS; Frenchville, ME; (Y); 6/60; Drama Clb; French Clb; Varsity Clb; Var L Socr; Var L Vllybl; High Hon Roll; Hon Roll; NHS; Var Bsbl; NHS & Tchrs Assn Schlrshps; Union Of St Jean Baptiste Schlrshp; U Of ME-ORONO; Elec Engr.

DAIGLE, FRED; Gorham HS; Goulds, FL; (Y); 56/280; JV Bsbl; Var Capt Crs Cntry; Var Socr; Var Capt Trk; High Hon Roll; Hon Roll; NHS; Agri.

DAIGLE, PAUL; Fort Kent Community HS; Ft Kent, ME; (Y); 9/145; Church Yth Grp; Civic Clb; Ski Clb; Var Socr; Var Tennis; Var Vllybl; Cit Awd; High Hon Roll; Pres NHS; St Schlr; Elec Engr.

DALRYMPLE, SUSAN; Mt Blue HS; Farmington, ME; (Y); Am Leg Aux Girls St; Rep Jr Cls; Var Capt Cheerleading; Score Keeper; High Hon Roll; Jr NHS; NHS; Cert Of Hnr 83-85; BEAM Rgn Cntst 85; Acctg.

DAVENPORT, NICOLA; Fort Fairfield HS; Ft Fairfield, ME; (Y); Cmnty Wkr; Drama Clb; Speech Tm; Chorus; School Musical; School Play; Cheerleading; Crs Cntry; Hon Roll; Miss ME Teen USA 1st Rnnr Up 84; Balgn Schl Of Mdlng Schlrshp; ME U Orano; Pblc Rltns.

DAVIS, EDWARD; Freeport HS; Freeport, ME; (Y); Am Leg Boys St; Latin Clb; Band; Chorus; School Musical; School Play; Stage Crew; VP Stu Cncl; Var Bsktbl; Var Socr; BYU.

DAVIS, GRETCHEN; Marshwood HS; Eliot, ME; (Y); 7/100; Concert Band; Jazz Band; Mrchg Band; Orch; Symp Band; Rep Frsh Cls; NHS; Band Dir Awd 85; Outstndg Soloist 84-85; Distngsd Perfrmnc 83-85; S ME U; Music.

DAVIS, KELLY; Mattanawcook Acad; Lincoln, ME; (Y); Church Yth Grp; Leo Clb; Chorus; Church Choir; JV Var Bsktbl; Var Crs Cntry; High Hon Roll; Hon Roll; Prfct Atten Awd; Cert Of 1st Blood Dontn-Red Cross 85; Cert Of Compltn Of Voctnl Eductn-Regn 3-Comp 85; Sectrl Wrk.

DAWSON, DANIELLE ERIN; Mt Blue HS; Farmington, ME; (Y); Am Leg Aux Girls St; Chorus; Concert Band; Jazz Band; School Musical; Rep Stu Cncl; Var Capt Cheerleading; High Hon Roll; NHS; Church Yth Grp; Acad Awds 90 Plus Avg 83-85; Pres Acad Fit Awd 85; Helen True Scholar 85; J A Green Faclty Scholar 85; Mt Holyoke Coll; Eng.

DAY, TERI; Fryeburg Acad; Fryeburg, ME; (Y); Drama Clb; Chorus; School Musical; School Play; Bsktbl; Trk; Wt Lftg; Hon Roll; Auto Mech.

DAY, TODD; Gorham HS; Gorham, ME; (Y); Boy Scts; Spanish Clb; Var L Bsbl; Var L Bsktbl; Var L Crs Cntry; Var L Golf; FL ST; Bus Adm.

DE BECK, MARLISA; Maine Central Inst; Pittsfield, ME; (Y); Am Leg Aux Girls St; Trs Key Clb; Yrbk Ed-Chief; Sec Jr Cls; VP Sr Cls; Fld Hcky; Cit Awd; High Hon Roll; NHS; VFW Awd; Ed.

DE GIOSAFATTO, JOANN; Ellsworth HS; Ellsworth, ME; (Y); 40/115; French Clb; Girl Scts; Band; Yrbk Stf; Var L Bsktbl; Var L Socr; Hon Roll; Recgntn Awd-Soccer Imprvmnt 84; Natl Athletic Plcmnt Serv Recruitng Guide 85; Librl Arts.

DE LISLE, MATT W; Lewiston HS; Lewiston, ME; (Y); 42/446; Im Bsbl; High Hon Roll; U Of ME; Mech Engrng.

DE RAAT, MAIA; George Stevens Acad; Castine, ME; (Y); Church Yth Grp; Stage Crew; Nwsp Stf; Yrbk Stf; JV Bsktbl; JV Fld Hcky; ME Smr Art Pgm Gftd-Tlntd Stu 85; Locl Nwspr Illstrtr-Castine Patriot 84-85.

DEBLOIS, PAM; Lewiston HS; Lewiston, ME; (Y); 13/350; Letterman Clb; Varsity Clb; Rep Soph Cls; JV Fld Hcky; Var L Sftbl; High Hon Roll; NHS; Outstndg Prfmnce Eng 83.

DECKER, CHRIS; Orono HS; Orono, ME; (S); 7/105; Am Leg Boys St; Chess Clb; Nwsp Stf; Yrbk Stf; Trk; High Hon Roll; Hon Roll.

DEGRINNEY, JOSEPH; St Dominic Regional HS; Livermore Falls, ME; (Y); Key Clb; Math Clb; Math Tm; Stu Cncl; JV Bsbl; Var Bsktbl; JV Socr; Tennis; Hon Roll; St Schlr; Pre-Med.

DELISLE, BRENDA; Livermore Falls HS; Livermore Falls, ME; (Y); Varsity Clb; Band; Mrchg Band; Rep Stu Cncl; Var Bsktbl; Var Fld Hcky; Var Sftbl; Var Trk; Hon Roll; German Clb; AF Acad; Env Bio.

DELLAIRE, TERESA; Penquis Valley HS; Milo, ME; (Y); 4/86; Am Leg Aux Girls St; Church Choir; Concert Band; Yrbk Ed-Chief; Lit Mag; VP Jr Cls; Var Socr; High Hon Roll; NHS; Teachers Aide; Sunday Schl Supt 84-85; ST Sci Fair 1st Pl Wnr 2 Times 83 & 84; U ME Orono; Elem Ed.

DELMONACO, JOHN P; Calais HS; Calais, ME; (Y); 2/70; Am Leg Boys St; Chess Clb; Jazz Band; Yrbk Phtg; Pres Stu Cncl; Var Bsktbl; Var Socr; High Hon Roll; Pres NHS; St Schlr; Outstndng Citizen, Boys State 85; Magna Cum Laude Latin 83-85; Page Hse Rep Augusta ME 83-84.

DEMASO, LISA; Orono HS; Bangor, ME; (S); 4/105; Church Yth Grp; Yrbk Stf; Trs Soph Cls; Trs Jr Cls; Stu Cncl; JV Var Bsktbl; VP Socr; VP Trk; French Hon Soc; High Hon Roll; U MO.

DEMERS, DAWN; Bonny Eagle HS; W Buxton, ME; (Y); Church Yth Grp; Drama Clb; Latin Clb; Chorus; Variety Show; Yrbk Phtg; Stu Cncl; Fld Hcky; Mgr(s); Wt Lftg; Psychlgy.

DENISON, DAVID; Telstar Regional HS; Bethel, ME; (Y); Am Leg Boys St; Church Yth Grp; Jazz Band; Trk.

DEPUIS, CINDY; Fryeburg Acad; Fryeburg, ME; (Y); FHA; Library Aide; Spanish Clb; School Play; Hon Roll.

DERESZEWSKI, LISA; Woodland HS; Princeton, ME; (S); 2/66; Am Leg Aux Girls St; VP Varsity Clb; Yrbk Stf; Pres Sr Cls; Stu Cncl; Capt Cheerleading; Mgr(s); Score Keeper; NHS; Computer Clb; All Cmptn Sqd Chrldng 82; Hghst Avg Sci 82-83; Hghst Hnrs 82-85; U Of ME; Med Tech.

DESCHAINE, DONNA J; Messalonskee HS; Belgrade Lakes, ME; (Y); 1/145; Church Yth Grp; Drama Clb; Math Tm; Band; Chorus; School Play; Bausch & Lomb Sci Awd; Elks Awd; NHS; Am Leg Aux Girls St; Soc Wmn Engrs Hon Awd 85; Physcs Awd 85; U Of CT; Phrmcy.

DESCHENE, PAUL; Jay HS; Jay, ME; (Y); Am Leg Boys St; Boy Scts; Computer Clb; Var L Bsktbl; Var L Ftbl; L Trk; Hon Roll; Exch Stu Sweden 84; Elec Engr.

DESCHENES, SUZANNE M; St Dominic Regional HS; Lewiston, ME; (Y); 1/80; VP Pres French Clb; Math Tm; Pres NHS; NEDT Awd; High Hon Roll; Queen Of Franco-Am Fstvl In Lewiston 84; Holy Cross Bk Prz 85; Minor Schltc/Extrcrrclar Trphy 84; Pre Med.

DESGROSSEILLIERS, SUSAN; Gould Acad; Auburn, ME; (Y); 24/81; Church Yth Grp; Cmnty Wkr; Dance Clb; GAA; Key Clb; Office Aide; Political Wkr; Varsity Clb; Orch; Var L Bsktbl; Bently Coll MA; Intl Trade.

DESJARDINS, JUDY; Livermore Falls HS; Livermore Falls, ME; (Y); Am Leg Aux Girls St; Pres Varsity Clb; Pres Frsh Cls; Rep Stu Cncl; Var Capt Bsktbl; Var Capt Fld Hcky; Var Sftbl; Hon Roll; NHS; Prfct Atten Awd; Vrsty L Schlrshp 85; Pres Acadmc Ftns Awd 85; US Army Rsrv Ntl Schlr/Athlt Awd 85; Hesser Coll; Comp.

DESJARDINS, RACHEL; Fort Kent CHS HS; Ft Kent, ME; (Y); Mrt Awd For Clthng 85-86; Hnr Awd For Civics 82-83; U Of ME; Early Chldhd Educ.

DESPRES, SCOTT; Livermore Falls HS; Livermore Falls, ME; (Y); Am Leg Boys St; Church Yth Grp; English Clb; Letterman Clb; Varsity Clb; Yrbk Sprt Ed; JV Bsbl; Var Capt Bsktbl; Var Capt Crs Cntry; Trk; Comp Sci.

DESROCHERS, JOLINE D; Edward Little HS; Auburn, ME; (S); Church Yth Grp; Pep Clb; Band; Concert Band; Mrchg Band; JV Sftbl; Hon Roll; NHS; Prfct Atten Awd; Home Ec Awd 82; Ntl Frnch Fnlst 83; Westbrook Coll; Dntl Hyg.

DESROCHERS, JOSEPH; Oak Hill HS; Sabattus, ME; (Y); Political Wkr; Speech Tm; Stage Crew; Rep Frsh Cls; Rep Soph Cls; Pres Jr Cls; Pres Sr Cls; Sec Rep Stu Cncl; Hon Roll; NHS; Hugh O Brian Ldrshp Smnr 84; Lions Club Spkout 2nd Pl 85; Model ST Legsltr 84-85; Polt Sci.

DEVOID, MARC A; Sanford HS; Sanford, ME; (Y); Church Yth Grp; Cmnty Wkr; Political Wkr; Var Coach Actv; Score Keeper; Timer; Concours Francais Cooperants 84; New Englnd Cath Coll; Lbrl Arts.

DI BIASE, CRAIG; Westbrook SR HS; Westbrook, ME; (Y); Math Clb; Math Tm; Spanish Clb; JV Ftbl; Var L Wrstlng; Hon Roll; Ntl Merit SF; St Schlr; Most Points Takedowns Wrstlng 84-85; Tm Awd 84-85; Boys ST Delg 85; Hlth.

DI BIASE JR, DANA; Erskine Acad; Palermo, ME; (Y); Am Leg Boys St; Mathletes; Math Clb; Math Tm; Teachers Aide; Varsity Clb; Rep Stu Cncl; Socr; French Clb; Letterman Clb; Comm Scuba Diving.

DI FILIPPO, SUSAN; Mc Auyle HS; Portland, ME; (Y); 2/61; VP French Clb; Science Clb; Yrbk Stf; Rep Stu Cncl; Fld Hcky; Tennis; High Hon Roll; NHS; Sal; Wellesley Bk Awd; Itln Hrtge Schlrshp; ME Schlrs Day; Holy Cross.

DINSMORE, LISA; Tralp Acad; Kittery, ME; (Y); 5/70; Rep Am Leg Aux Girls St; Band; VP Jr Cls; VP Sr Cls; Var L Cheerleading; Var L Fld Hcky; Var L Sftbl; Hon Roll; Sec NHS; Yrbk Stf; Hnr Roll Pin 83-85; Chem & US Histry Achvt Pin 85; Dietetics.

DINSMORE, STEPHEN; Medomak Valley HS; Friendship, ME; (Y); 1/100; Orch; Variety Show; Lit Mag; Pres Sr Cls; JV Var Socr; Bausch & Lomb Sci Awd; NHS; VFW Awd; Boy Scts; Drama Clb; Bowdoin Smmr Humanities Prog 85; VFW Essay Cont Wnnr 83; Outstdng Frnch Stu Awd 84-85; Wesleyan U Middletown CT.

DOAK, GREGORY PHILIP; Caribou HS; Caribou, ME; (Y); 40/225; Am Leg Boys St; Yrbk Stf; Trk; U Of SO Maine; Ocptnl Thrpy.

DOBBIN, KATHRYN; Jonesport Beals HS; Jonesport, ME; (Y); Am Leg Aux Girls St; Church Yth Grp; Trs French Clb; School Play; Yrbk Sprt Ed; Yrbk Stf; Off Stu Cncl; Var L Bsktbl; JV Cheerleading; Var L Sftbl.

DOBBINS, JENNIFER; Lisbon HS; Lisbon Falls, ME; (Y); French Clb; VP Latin Clb; Ski Clb; Yrbk Stf; JV Cheerleading; Var Fld Hcky; Cit Awd; Hon Roll; VP Frsh Cls; Ntl Latn Clb Awd 85; Pres Stus Agnst Hngr 85; Johnson & Wales Coll; Htl Mgt.

DODGE, MICHELLE; Medomak Valley HS; Union, ME; (Y); 10/131; AFS; Pep Clb; VP Soph Cls; JV Var Cheerleading; Var Crs Cntry; Var Trk; Hon Roll; Ctznshp Essy Awd-Annl TDS Ctznshp Essy Cntst 85; Hlth Educ.

DOHERTY, GAYLE J; Lawrence HS; Fairfield, ME; (Y); 10/200; Am Leg Aux Girls St; Key Clb; Yrbk Ed-Chief; Yrbk Stf; VP Jr Cls; Var Cheerleading; High Hon Roll; Hon Roll; Prfct Atten Awd; Grwth Engl; Acctg Achvt; Johnson & Wales; Fashn Merch.

DOIRON, MARC; Lewiston HS; Lewiston, ME; (Y); 50/411; Letterman Clb; Rep Frsh Cls; Rep Soph Cls; Stu Cncl; JV Bsbl; L Golf; Hon Roll; NHS; U Of ME; Chem Engrng.

DONNELL, KIMBERLY O; Houlton HS; Houlton, ME; (Y); Camera Clb; Math Clb; Var L Bsktbl; Var L Socr; Var L Sftbl; Var Vllybl; Hon Roll; NHS; Nrsng.

DONNELL, PAUL; Medomak Valley HS; Rockland, ME; (Y); Art Clb; Stage Crew; Farnsworth Art Museum Art Awds 85; Portland Schl Of Art; Art Thrpy.

DORREGO, ANA; Winslow HS; Spain; (Y); AFS; Church Yth Grp; Math Tm; Ski Clb; Var Swmmng; Var High Hon Roll; Med.

DOUGHTY, PATRICIA; Woodland HS; Baileyville, ME; (Y); Am Leg Aux Girls St; FBLA; Yrbk Ed-Chief; Yrbk Phtg; VP Sr Cls; High Hon Roll; Hon Roll; 1st Cnty Typng 84; 1st Cnty Adv Typng, Acctng I 85; U ME Machias; Secrtl Sci.

DOUGLAS, LEON; Medomak Valley HS; Warren, ME; (Y); Computer Clb; Drama Clb; Latin Clb; Science Clb; School Musical; School Play; Stage Crew; High Hon Roll; Hon Roll; Upward Bound Bowdoin Coll 85; Rest Mgmt.

DOW, ROBERT; Sanford HS; Sanford, ME; (Y); Key Clb; Ski Clb; Bsbl; Var L Socr; Trk; Hon Roll; Prfct Atten Awd.

DOW, TASHA A; Leavitt Area HS; Turner, ME; (Y); 23/120; Am Leg Aux Girls St; Hosp Aide; Yrbk Stf; Sec Frsh Cls; Sec Soph Cls; Mgr Bsbl; JV Var Fld Hcky; Score Keeper; High Hon Roll; Hon Roll; Pell Grant 85; Westbrook Coll Grnt 85; Clifford & Laverna Newell Schlrshp Fnd 85; Westbrook Coll; Med Tech.

DOWNEY, LAURA; Orono HS; Orono, ME; (S); Drama Clb; Speech Tm; Chorus; School Musical; School Play; Nwsp Ed-Chief; Nwsp Rptr; Lit Mag; High Hon Roll; NFL; YMCA Modl ST Legis 84.

DOWNEY, PATRICK; Freeport HS; Freeport, ME; (Y); 1/50; French Clb; Math Tm; Yrbk Phtg; VP Frsh Cls; Pres Soph Cls; Sec Sr Cls; JV Bsktbl; Var Mgr(s); Score Keeper; JV Socr; ME Schlrs Day 85; Plummr Awd Tp Stu 83-85; Northestrn; Engrng.

DOYLE, LAURIE; Leavitt Area HS; Greene, ME; (Y); 2/100; Am Leg Aux Girls St; School Play; VP Jr Cls; VP Sr Cls; Var Capt Cheerleading; French Hon Soc; High Hon Roll; NHS; Sal; Nwsp Sprt Ed; ME Schlrs Day; Auburn Lewiston Rotry Schlrshp; U ME; Soc Sci.

DOYON, AMY L; Edward Little HS; Auburn, ME; (Y); 6/386; Spanish Clb; Yrbk Ed-Chief; Rep Frsh Cls; High Hon Roll; Hon Roll; Jr NHS; NHS; ELHS Alumni, Roger Williams Coll Schlrshp 85; Top 10 Stu Awd 85; Roger Williams Coll; Acctng.

DOYON, ANN; Cony HS; Augusta, ME; (Y); Spanish Clb; Nwsp Phtg; Nwsp Stf; Cheerleading; Score Keeper; Tennis; FBLA; Pep Clb; Chorus; Madrigals; Mid-ST Bus Coll; Trvl/Trsm.

DOYON, LISA; Cony HS; Augusta, ME; (Y); AFS; Church Yth Grp; Dance Clb; Hosp Aide; Spanish Clb; Variety Show; Im Socr; Hon Roll; Nrsg.

DRAPEAU, MICHAEL; Lewiston HS; Lewiston, ME; (Y); Boy Scts; Cmnty Wkr; Key Clb; Red Cross Aide; JV Socr; Tennis; Hon Roll; Eagle Scout Awd 83; U Sthrn ME; Acctg.

DRAPEAU, MONIQUE MICHELLE; Edward Little HS; Auburn, ME; (Y); 69/329; Trs JA; JV Sftbl; Hon Roll; Ntl Merit Schol; Outstndng Stu Hlth Ocptnl Stus Of Amer 85; Crtfd Nrs Asstnt 85; Mid-State Coll; Med Scrtry.

DRAPER, NANCY; Gray-New Gloucester HS; New Gloucester, ME; (Y); 10/120; French Clb; Socr; High Hon Roll; Hon Roll; Med Tech.

DRUMMOND, CHRISTOPHER; Dirigo HS; Dixfield, ME; (Y); 1/60; Am Leg Boys St; Math Tm; Ski Clb; Var JV Bsbl; Var JV Ftbl; Var Tennis; Bausch & Lomb Sci Awd; High Hon Roll; NHS; MVP Footbll 84; All-St Footbll Tm-Class C 84; ME All Star Math Tm 85; Rensselaer Poly Inst; Engr.

DU LONG, CAROLE; Wells HS; Moody, ME; (Y); Math Tm; Political Wkr; Nwsp Rptr; Nwsp Stf; NHS; Engl.

DUBE, DENISE; Lewiston HS; Lewiston, ME; (Y); Library Aide; Office Aide; Hon Roll; Typng I Awd 83-84; Clrcl Sec.

DUBOIS, BEVERLY; Fort Kent Community HS; Ft Kent, ME; (Y); 15/160; Am Leg Aux Girls St; VP Church Yth Grp; Concert Band; Pep Band; JV Cheerleading; Im Vllybl; High Hon Roll; Hon Roll; NHS; Voice Dem Awd; Schlrshp Cert Of Hnr 83 & 85; Cert Of Hnr-Outstndng Achvt Algbr I 83; Athltc Awd-Sftbl 84 & 85; U Of ME-ORONO; Lab Tech.

DUBOIS, YVONNE; Lewiston HS; Lewiston, ME; (Y); French Clb; Varsity Clb; Yrbk Stf; L Bsktbl; L Crs Cntry; L Swmmng; L Trk; Athltc Achvmnt 7th Pl Benenor Cross Cntry Chmpnshps Awd 82; 7th Pl ST In Concours Ntl De Francais; Frgn Lang.

DUBORD, GINA; Livermore Falls HS; East Livermore, ME; (Y); Varsity Clb; Color Guard; Yrbk Stf; Var Cheerleading; Var Trk; Hon Roll; NHS.

DUCHESNEAU, SHARON; Bangor HS; Bangor, ME; (Y); Church Yth Grp; Orch; Yrbk Stf; Var Fld Hcky; Var Trk; High Hon Roll; Hon Roll; NHS; Ntl Merit Ltr; St Schlr; Half Tuitn Scholar Awd U Of ME 85; ME Comm Women Hstry Wk Essay Comp 1st Hon Men 85.

DUCHETTE, MARC; St Dominic Regional HS; Lewiston, ME; (Y); Pres Jr Cls; Pres Sr Cls; Var Capt Bsbl; Var L Ice Hcky; Var Capt Socr; Hon Roll; Trs NHS; NEDT Awd; Hcky Rgnl Dvlpmnt Camp CO Sprgns 85; Med.

DUDLEY, DENA; Gorham HS; Gorham, ME; (Y); Am Leg Aux Girls St; German Clb; Trs Leo Clb; Trs Jr Cls; Var Cheerleading; High Hon Roll; Debate Tm; Drama Clb; Hosp Aide; Latin Clb; Chld Psych.

DUDLEY, JULI-ANN; Cony HS; Augusta, ME; (Y); Am Leg Aux Girls St; French Clb; Pep Clb; Spanish Clb; JV Var Fld Hcky; JV Sftbl; High Hon Roll; Hon Roll; Prfct Atten Awd; St Schlr; Cony Schlr; Boston Coll; Psych.

DUFF, PAUL B; Greely HS; Cumberland Ctr, ME; (Y); 5/147; Drama Clb; Band; Chorus; Nwsp Sprt Ed; Lit Mag; Socr; High Hon Roll; Jr NHS; NHS; Ntl Merit SF; Bio.

DUGUAY, LAURA; Rumford HS; Rumford, ME; (Y); Cmnty Wkr; Drama Clb; French Clb; Office Aide; Hon Roll; St Schlr; Voice Dem Awd; ME Schlrs Day Awd 85; ME Plng & Advsry Cnsl On Dvlpmnt Dsblts Awd 84; Paralegal-Law.

DUGUAY, MICHAEL A; Lawrence HS; Fairfield, ME; (Y); Service Clb; Spanish Clb; Pres Stu Cncl; JV Bsktbl; Im Vllybl; Im Wt Lftg; High Hon Roll; Hon Roll; Prfct Atten Awd; Prom Chrmn; Sci Achv Awd; Clss Ldr Awd; U Of NH; Bio-Chem.

DUMOND, MARK J; Fort Kent HS; Ft Kent, ME; (Y); 20/170; Chess Clb; Ski Clb; Mgr Socr; Ntl Merit Ltr; Exclc Schlrshp Awd 82-85; Hnr Stu 85; U Of ME Arono; Elec Engnrng.

DUMONT, BRIAN; Sanford HS; Sanford, ME; (Y); Am Leg Aux Girls St; Boy Scts; Ski Clb; Acpl Chr; Chorus; Church Choir; School Musical; School Play; Rep Stu Cncl; Cit Awd; ME All ST Chr 84-85; Lbrl Arts.

DUMONT, LUCINDA L; Gasliner Area HS; Litchfield, ME; (Y); 2/234; Pres Church Yth Grp; VP French Clb; Band; Chorus; Church Choir; Jazz Band; Mrchg Band; Pep Band; School Musical; Yrbk Ed-Chief; Bangor CC; Dental Hyg.

DUMONT, RHONDA; St Dominic R HS; Auburn, ME; (Y); Pep Clb; Var L Fld Hcky; Capt L Sftbl; Hon Roll; Holy Cross Schlrshp 85; Tmstrs Loc 340 85; Notre Dame Clg; Phrmcy.

DUNLOP, LISA; Hodgdon HS; Houlton, ME; (Y); Church Yth Grp; Varsity Clb; Chorus; Yrbk Stf; Trs Jr Cls; Bsktbl; Crs Cntry; Socr; Sftbl; Vllybl; Hnr Ltr Mkg Hnr 3 Consec Times 84-85; MVP Bsktbl & Sccr 84-85.

DUNN, MARY; Houlton HS; Houlton, ME; (Y); 13/150; Camera Clb; Church Yth Grp; Cmnty Wkr; Math Clb; Political Wkr; Spanish Clb; Yrbk Phtg; Bowling; Var Tennis; Im Vllybl; Cls Rcqutbl Cptn; Vlybl Tm Schl Champs Cptn; Tennis Rgnls; Hnr Roll; Physcl Thrpy.

DUNTON, RANDALL; Gorham HS; Gorham, ME; (Y); 9/110; Chess Clb; Latin Clb; Science Clb; Jr Cls; JV Trk; High Hon Roll; Hon Roll; NHS.

DUPLESSIE, PATRICIA ANN; Winslow SR HS; Winslow, ME; (Y); 1/205; AFS; Am Leg Aux Girls St; Math Clb; Band; Capt Color Guard; Concert Band; Drm & Bgl; Drm Mjr(t); Mrchg Band; Pep Band; Englsh, Calculus, Physcs Awds 85; Cora & Everett Harris Fund Schlrshp 85; Pres Shclrshp Westbrook Coll; Westbrook Coll; Med Tech.

DUPREY, JANEL L; Caribou HS; Caribou, ME; (S); Am Leg Aux Girls St; Key Clb; Sec Varsity Clb; Var L Fld Hcky; Var Capt Gym; Var L Trk; Jr NHS; NHS; Rep Frsh Cls; Rep Soph Cls; U Of Farmington; Dietic Tech.

DURANEAU, PATRICIA; Marshwood HS; S Berwick, ME; (Y); 11/99; Church Yth Grp; Latin Clb; Band; Color Guard; Mrchg Band; Off Jr Cls; Hon Roll; Westbrook Coll; Med Tchnlgst.

DURGIN, WENDY; Windham HS; S Casco, ME; (Y); Church Yth Grp; Rep Frsh Cls; Rep Soph Cls; Rep Jr Cls; Var L Bsktbl; Var L Fld Hcky; JV Var Trk; Jr NHS; NHS; Yrbk Sprt Ed; Lylty Awd Bsktbll Var 84-85; Accntng.

DUROCHER, KRISTEN; York HS; York, ME; (Y); German Clb; Key Clb; Math Clb; Math Tm; Yrbk Ed-Chief; Yrbk Rptr; Yrbk Stf; Stat Bsktbl; JV Fld Hcky; Var Mgr(s); Math Excllnc 85; Grmn I, III, & IV Excllnc 83-85; Alg I & II Awds 83-84; Colby Coll Bk Awd 85; Law.

DURRELL, ANGI; Westbrook HS; Westbrook, ME; (Y); Drama Clb; Library Aide; Band; Chorus; Nwsp Rptr; Hon Roll; NHS; School Musical; School Play; Lit Mag; Russel Square Smmr Theatre Schlrshp 85; Jap-Amer Exchg Schlrshp 85; 3rd Pl Poem 84; Engl.

DUSSAULT, SCOTT; Biddeford HS; Biddeford, ME; (Y); Chess Clb; Mechnc.

EARLE, JOYCE; Robert W Traip Acad; Kittery, ME; (Y); Art Clb; Spanish Clb; Band; Concert Band; JV Bsktbl; JV Sftbl; Var Trk; Hon Roll; Drwng, Pntng, & Grphcs Awd 84-85; Newbury JC; Canine Sci.

EASTMAN, LORRINA; Jay HS; Livermore Falls, ME; (Y); Am Leg Aux Girls St; Church Yth Grp; Cmnty Wkr; Ski Clb; Yrbk Ed-Chief; Pres Stu Cncl; Fld Hcky; Hon Roll; NHS; Stdnt Cncl Awd & Schlrshp, Pres Fit Awd & Cmmnty Schlrshp & Top Ten 85; Mary Washington Coll; Psych.

EASTMAN, MARIANNE; Fryeburg Acad; Fryeburg, ME; (Y); Church Yth Grp; Girl Scts; Library Aide; JV Var Socr.

EASTMAN, RUSELL; Fryeburg Acad; Center Conway, NH; (Y); Hon Roll; Engrng.

ECKENROAD, KIMBERLEY ANNE; Sumner Memorial HS; W Gouldsboro, ME; (Y); Am Leg Aux Girls St; Pres 4-H; Pres Jr Cls; Sec Sr Cls; Stu Cncl; Bsktbl; Socr; Sftbl; Cit Awd; 4-H Awd; Sthrn ME; Accntng.

EDGECOMB, ANGIE A; Caribou HS; Caribou, ME; (Y); 42/213; Sec French Clb; Varsity Clb; Yrbk Stf; Rep Frsh Cls; Rep Soph Cls; Rep Jr Cls; Var Socr; Var Sftbl; High Hon Roll; Hon Roll; Phys Ed.

EDMONDS, DONNA; Jonesport-Beals HS; Jonesport, ME; (Y); Church Yth Grp; 4-H; School Play; Yrbk Stf; Var Bsktbl; Var Cheerleading; Var Sftbl; Var Vllybl; Hon Roll; NHS; Natl Bus Hnr Soc 84-85.

EDSTRAND, NANCY; Caribou HS; Caribou, ME; (Y); 41/235; Rep Am Leg Aux Girls St; Church Yth Grp; Library Aide; Office Aide; Band; Chorus; School Play; Scl Wrkr.

EHRENFRIED, SALLY J; Lewiston HS; Lewiston, ME; (Y); 14/398; Rep Am Leg Aux Girls St; Yrbk Ed-Chief; Yrbk Stf; Stat Ftbl; Stat Ice Hcky; NHS; Drama Clb; Pep Clb; Q&S; Lewiston Tchrs Assn Schlrshp 85; Bates Coll; Poli Sci.

ELLIOTT, LORI; Bangor HS; Bangor, ME; (Y); Stage Crew; Variety Show; Yrbk Stf; VP Soph Cls; Rep Jr Cls; Rep Stu Cncl; Var L Cheerleading; Var L Diving; Hon Roll; Ntl Merit Ltr; Fll Schlrshp To Univ Of ME At Orono 85; Pol Sci.

ELLIS, KRISTI L; Ashland Community HS; Ashland, ME; (Y); 3/44; Am Leg Aux Girls St; Pres Church Yth Grp; Band; VP Church Choir; Yrbk Phtg; Trs Sr Cls; Var L Bsktbl; Trs NHS; Voice Dem Awd; French Clb; Miss Ashland 85; St Marys Hosp Schl Nrsng; RN.

ELLIS, WENDY; Marshwood HS; Eliot, ME; (Y); Rep Frsh Cls; Rep Sr Cls; Rep Stu Cncl; JV Bsktbl; JV Var Sftbl; Travel.

ELLSMORE, TRACY C; Machias Memorial HS; Machias, ME; (Y); Math Tm; Trs Frsh Cls; Trs Soph Cls; Pres Jr Cls; High Hon Roll; Hon Roll; NHS; Exclnc Algeb II & Trig 84; Exclnc Fr III 85.

ELOWITCH, LEANNE; Deering HS; Portland, ME; (Y); Key Clb; Math Tm; Spanish Clb; Temple Yth Grp; Varsity Clb; Church Choir; Var Diving; Var Mgr(s); Var Swmmng.

EMERY, KATHLEEN; South Portland HS; S Portland, ME; (Y); 2/310; JCL; Trs Latin Clb; Math Tm; Mgr School Play; Stage Crew; High Hon Roll; Hon Roll; Sal; K J Higgins Mem Schlrshp, Histrcl Soc, Boston U Schlrshp 85; U ME Orono; Comm.

ERB, STEPHANIE; Orono HS; Stockton Springs, ME; (Y); AFS; Drama Clb; Math Clb; Spanish Clb; Chorus; School Musical; School Play; Nwsp Stf; Yrbk Rptr; Yrbk Stf; Coordntr Red Crss Blood Dr 85; Excllnc Jazz Awd Deneen Danc Stdo 83; Emerson Coll; Perf Arts.

ERCK, DEAN; Traip Acad; Kittery, ME; (Y); 10/100; Church Yth Grp; Cmnty Wkr; Science Clb; Chorus; Yrbk Stf; Ftbl; Golf; Wt Lftg; Wrstlng; Hon Roll.

ERICKSON, KIRSTEN; Lisbon Falls Christian Acad; Lisbon Falls, ME; (Y); Church Yth Grp; Chorus; Church Choir; School Play; Score Keeper; Vllybl; Honor Schlrshp-Central Coll 85; Christian Brothers 85; Central Coll-Mc Pherson; Bio.

ERICKSON, MITZI; Bangor HS; Bangor, ME; (Y); Political Wkr; Nwsp Rptr; Yrbk Rptr; JV Swmmng; Hon Roll; ME Schlrs Day 85; U Of Chicago; Lingusts.

ERICKSON, STASIA W; Caribou HS; Caribou, ME; (Y); French Clb; Yrbk Stf; JV Bsktbl; Var Socr; Var Sftbl; Var Im Vllybl; Hon Roll.

ERICKSON, TROY S W; Caribou HS; Caribou, ME; (Y); Key Clb; Office Aide; Yrbk Stf; Bsktbl; Mgr(s); Hon Roll; Prfct Atten Awd; SADD 85; U Of Southern ME; Crmnl Jstc.

ESPOSITO, LISA; Deering HS; Portland, ME; (Y); VP Latin Clb; Bsktbl; Fld Hcky; High Hon Roll; Hon Roll; St Schlr; Med.

ESTES, WILLIAM JOSEPH; Westbrook HS; Westbrook, ME; (Y); 17/211; Pres English Clb; Key Clb; Math Tm; Pres Stu Cncl; Bsktbl; Var L Ftbl; Var L Trk; DAR Awd; NHS; Pres Schlr; Cls AA All Acad Ftbl Tm 84; SR Cls Marshal 85; Syracuse U; Chem Engrng.

ESTY, MELISSA; Westbrook HS; Westbrook, ME; (Y); French Clb; Keywanettes; Spanish Clb; Variety Show; Var Capt Socr; Var Sftbl; Var Trk; French Hon Soc; Pres Schlr; Spanish NHS.

EVANS, JILL; Fort Fairfield HS; Ft Fairfield, ME; (Y); 3/73; Am Leg Aux Girls St; French Clb; Ski Clb; Varsity Clb; Band; Jazz Band; Trs Soph Cls; Trs Jr Cls; JV Bsktbl; High Hon Roll; Top 10 Of Cls Awd; Englsh & Hstry Awds; Outstndng Mscn Awd; Spch Thrpy.

EVERLITH, WENDY; Lawrence HS; Fairfield, ME; (Y); Art Clb; Exploring; Socr; Trk; NHS; Bst Grl Ath Awd; Art.

EZZY, RICHARD J; Van Buren District Secondary HS; Van Buren, ME; (Y); 1/86; Quiz Bowl; Capt Bsbl; JV Bsktbl; Socr; High Hon Roll; NHS; Pres Schlr; Val; Am Leg Boys St; Computer Clb; Princpls Awd Schlrshp 85; U Of ME-ORONO; Bus Adm.

FARAGHER, EMILY WEIR; Narraguagus HS; Addison, ME; (Y); 5/60; Drama Clb; Math Tm; Nwsp Rptr; High Hon Roll; NHS; Ntl Merit Schol; Early Admitnce U ME 84; U ME-ORONO; Fash Desgnr.

FARRAR, CHRISTINE; Windham HS; S Windham, ME; (Y); Church Yth Grp; Keywanettes; Teachers Aide; Trs Jr Cls; Trs Sr Cls; Rep Stu Cncl; Var Capt Bsktbl; Var Coach Actv; Var JV Fld Hcky; JV Socr; Acctg.

FARRAR, TRACY L; Edward Little HS; Poland Spring, ME; (S); VP AFS; Drama Clb; Intnl Clb; Latin Clb; Pep Clb; Varsity Clb; Chorus; School Play; Variety Show; Nwsp Phtg; ASSE To Sweden 83-84; Interact Clb; Comp Sci.

FARRINGTON, DAVID; Greater Portland Christian Schl; Gray, ME; (Y); 1/21; Church Yth Grp; Drama Clb; Chorus; School Play; VP Sr Cls; L Bsbl; Capt L Bsktbl; L Socr; Dnfth Awd; NHS; Messiah Coll; Relgn.

FARRINGTON, MELANIE; Jay HS; Dryden, ME; (Y); Am Leg Aux Girls St; Math Tm; Varsity Clb; Sec Stu Cncl; Var Capt Bsktbl; Var Capt Fld Hcky; Var Sftbl; High Hon Roll; Hon Roll; NHS; Bio.

FAUNCE, KAREN ANGELA; Gardiner Area HS; Gardiner, ME; (Y); #2 In Class; Am Leg Aux Girls St; Dance Clb; JCL; Latin Clb; Pep Clb; Variety Show; Pres Frsh Cls; Cheerleading; Fld Hcky; Cit Awd; ME Schlrs Day 85; Soph Hnr Awd 84; Colby Coll; Pre-Law.

FAVREAU, DEBORAH; Morse HS; Bath, ME; (Y); 3/193; VP French Clb; Math Tm; Sec Science Clb; Variety Show; L Crs Cntry; Var L Trk; Elks Awd; High Hon Roll; NHS; St Schlr; Brandeis U; Biochem.

FAVREAU, SUZANNE; Morse HS; Bath, ME; (Y); Stage Crew; Variety Show; Mgr Bsktbl; Mgr Socr; Mgr Sftbl; Trk; Sci Fair Awd; Hmcmng Prncs; Nrsng.

FAY, REGINA; Easton HS; Easton, ME; (Y); French Clb; Library Aide; Varsity Clb; Yrbk Ed-Chief; Nwsp Rptr; Nwsp Stf; Yrbk Rptr; Yrbk Stf; Lit Mag; Var Cheerleading; Litry Gld 83-84; Actng.

FECTEAU, CHRISTOPHER M; Bangor HS; Bangor, ME; (Y); 16/321; Chorus; Church Choir; Orch; School Musical; High Hon Roll; Hon Roll; NHS; Ntl Merit SF; Math Tm; School Play; All ST Orch ME; All Eastrn Orch 12 States; New England Music Cmp Phi Mu Alpha Sinfonia Outstndg Male; Music Perfrmr.

FELTON, RITA C; Robert W Traip Acad; Kittery, ME; (Y); 3/90; Am Leg Aux Girls St; Band; Yrbk Stf; Cit Awd; Hon Roll; VP NHS; Church Yth Grp; Spanish Clb; Jazz Band; Rep Frsh Cls; Kwanza Scholar 85; Mark M Paul Scholar 85; Proj Grad Staff 85; Tuskegee Inst; Chem Engrng.

FERGUSON, KACY L; Brunswick HS; Brunswick, ME; (Y); 4/235; Church Yth Grp; Dance Clb; Drama Clb; Chorus; Drill Tm; School Musical; Yrbk Sprt Ed; Diving; Socr; Swmmng; Sci.

FERRANTE, MILVA; Deering HS; Portland, ME; (Y); Sec FTA; VP Spanish Clb; Nwsp Rptr; Yrbk Stf; Sftbl; Hon Roll; Ntl Spnsh Exm 11th Pl In ST 85; Bus Adm.

FIDRYCH, JOHN; Cheverus HS; Portland, ME; (Y); Pres Church Yth Grp; Key Clb; Bsbl; Diving; Socr; Swmmng; Hon Roll.

FILLIETTAZ III, CHARLES M; Lewiston HS; Lewiston, ME; (Y); 55/405; Am Leg Boys St; Camera Clb; Computer Clb; Drama Clb; Pres JA; Rep Key Clb; Letterman Clb; Q&S; Ski Clb; School Play; Boston U; Telecomm.

FINKELMAN, LISA; Deering HS; Portland, ME; (Y); VP FBLA; FTA; VP JA; Key Clb; Yrbk Stf; Var Swmmng; JV Trk; High Hon Roll; Hon Roll; Spanish NHS; Grls ST Cls A Swm Meet Outstndng Perfmr 84; ME All Star-Zone Swm Tms 83-85.

FINLEY, LYNN; Belfast Area HS; Belfast, ME; (Y); Church Yth Grp; Pres FBLA; Office Aide; Teachers Aide; Chorus; Church Choir; Yrbk Stf; Mgr Sftbl; Hon Roll; Prfct Atten Awd; Cert Profcncy Bus Flng 85; Cert Achvt ME Consrvtn Corps 84; Cert Achvt 84; Husson Coll; Bus Tchr.

FINN, DANIEL F; Fryeburg Acad; Fryeburg, ME; (Y); 56/139; Ski Clb; Varsity Clb; Stage Crew; Lit Mag; JV Bsbl; Var Ftbl; Var Golf; JV Lcrss; Var Wrstlng.

FINN, HOPE C; Bangor HS; Bangor, ME; (Y); Cmnty Wkr; Hosp Aide; Sec Temple Yth Grp; Band; Orch; Ed Nwsp Stf; Yrbk Stf; High Hon Roll; Hon Roll; Lib Arts.

FISHER, CATHERINE; Windham HS; S Windham, ME; (Y); St Josephs Coll; Math.

FISKE, JAMES; Telstar Regional HS; Bethel, ME; (Y); 4/70; Am Leg Boys St; Var Bsbl; Var Bsktbl; Var Crs Cntry; Var Socr; High Hon Roll; NHS; Outstndng Achvt Chem Stud 84-85; Outstndng JR Hstry Stu 84-85; Pres NHS 85; Engrng.

FITZPATRICK, KELLEY; Houlton HS; Houlton, ME; (Y); 3/135; Pres Trs Church Yth Grp; Church Choir; Hon Roll; NHS; St Schlr; Engl.

FLANDERS, LORRI; Piscataquis Community HS; Guilford, ME; (Y); #6 In Class; Am Leg Aux Girls St; Cmnty Wkr; School Play; Yrbk Stf; JV Var Bsktbl; JV Var Fld Hcky; Mgr(s); Hon Roll; Hnrs Fstvl -Band 84-85; Mdl ST Govt 84-85.

FLANNERY, JEANNIE; Fort Fairfield HS; Ft Fairfield, ME; (Y); Capt Pres FFA; Varsity Clb; Chorus; L Crs Cntry; Hon Roll; ST FFA Farmer 85; FFA Diversifd Livestck Prodctn Awd ST 85; Hstry.

FLETCHER, MARIANNE LEE; Belfast Area HS; Belfast, ME; (Y); 15/140; Art Clb; Drama Clb; Chorus; School Musical; School Play; Stage Crew; Hon Roll; Pres Schlr; FBLA; Color Guard; Schlrshp Art Awd; Caroline F Dutton Schlrshp; Southern ME U.

FLEWELLING, BRENT; Easton HS; Easton, ME; (Y); FFA; Varsity Clb; Pres Soph Cls; L Var Bsktbl; L Var Socr; Var L Vllybl; JR X Spkng Cntst 84; U Of ME-ORONO ME; Frmng.

FLEWELLING, PAMELA; Easton HS; Easton, ME; (Y); 1/23; Trs Church Yth Grp; French Clb; Math Tm; Yrbk Bus Mgr; Pres Sr Cls; Bausch & Lomb Sci Awd; JP Sousa Awd; Pres NHS; Val; ME Scndry Schl Principals Assoc Awd 85; ME Smmr Inst Gifted & Talented HS Stus 84; All-ST Band 85; U Of ME-MACHIAS; Bus Admin.

FLOOD, STACY; Nokomis Regional HS; Hartland, ME; (Y); 15/208; French Clb; Varsity Clb; Band; Concert Band; Mrchg Band; Symp Band; Var Trk; Var L Wrstlng; High Hon Roll; Hon Roll; Syracuse U; Arch.

FLOYD, RYAN; Belfast Area HS; Belfast, ME; (Y); Am Leg Boys St; Var Diving; Var Capt Socr; Hon Roll; Bates; Psychlgy.

FLYNN, KATHLEEN A; Edward Little HS; Auburn, ME; (S); Girl Scts; Latin Clb; Var Ski Clb; Varsity Clb; Band; Concert Band; Mrchg Band; Yrbk Stf; Var L Cheerleading; L Capt Crs Cntry; Cum Laude Awd Ntl Latin Ex82; Magna Cum Laude Ntl Latin Ex 83; Bus.

FLYNN, KELLY; Lee Acad; Carroll, ME; (Y); Camera Clb; Church Yth Grp; Cmnty Wkr; Drama Clb; Ski Clb; School Play; Sec Soph Cls; Trs Jr Cls; Hon Roll; Own Bus.

FOLEY, JONATHAN; Nokomis Regional HS; Dixmont, ME; (Y); 6/161; Math Tm; Pres Science Clb; High Hon Roll; Chess Clb; Computer Clb; Drama Clb; Ski Clb; Chorus; School Musical; School Play; Math & Sci Dept Awd 85; Lab Physcs Awd 85; Calculus Awd 85; MIT; Physcs.

FOLEY, PATRICK; Westbrook HS; Westbrook, ME; (Y); Church Yth Grp; Cmnty Wkr; Dance Clb; DECA; Drama Clb; English Clb; FBLA; JA; Pep Clb; Political Wkr; Retlng.

FOLSOM, KRISTEN; Bonny Eagle HS; Sebago Lake, ME; (Y); Key Clb; Spanish Clb; Sec Frsh Cls; Sec Soph Cls; Sec Jr Cls; Rep Stu Cncl; Var Bsktbl; Var Capt Crs Cntry; Var Trk; Hon Roll; Class Marshall; Mv Cross Cty; Most Imprvd Bsktbl; Hotel Adm.

FOLSTER, MICHELLE A; Mattanowcook Acad; Lincoln, ME; (Y); #20 In Class; Am Leg Aux Girls St; Church Yth Grp; Drama Clb; FHA; Girl Scts; Letterman Clb; Thesps; Varsity Clb; Band; Chorus; ME All ST Chorus 83-85; Lioness Clb Schlrshp 85; Stu Cncl Schlrshp 85; U Of ME; Chld Devlpmnt.

FORD, TERRY A; Wells HS; N Berwick, ME; (Y); Bsbl; Bsktbl; Ftbl; Hon Roll; Jr NHS; Acctng.

FOREMAN, ROGER; Gardiner Area HS; Gardiner, ME; (Y); 32/240; Church Yth Grp; French Clb; Latin Clb; Chorus; School Musical; Variety Show; Yrbk Stf; L Socr; L Tennis; NHS; Blaine Schlrshp 85; Presdntl Awd-Cedarville Coll 85; Kennebec Vly Chorus 85; Cedarville Coll; Eductn.

FORTIN, BRENDA; Van Buren District HS; Lille, ME; (Y); 5/92; Rep Am Leg Aux Girls St; Rep Math Clb; Nwsp Bus Mgr; Ed Yrbk Stf; Rep Stu Cncl; Gym; Tennis; High Hon Roll; NHS; Prfct Atten Awd; French Diplma 85; Va Buren Bty Pgnt 1st Rnr Up 84; Lector Chrch 84-85; Colby-Sawyer Coll; Med Tech.

FORTIN, JANE; Yarmouth HS; Yarmouth, ME; (Y); Pres Trs Church Yth Grp; French Clb; Chorus; Church Choir; School Musical; School Play; French Hon Soc; High Hon Roll; Hon Roll; Elem Educ.

FORTUNA, RICHARD; Medomak Valley HS; Union, ME; (Y); Boy Scts; JCL; Latin Clb; Library Aide; Hon Roll; Ntl Merit Ltr; Nuclr Physcs.

FOSS, JOHN; East Grand HS; Danforth, ME; (Y); 1/20; Am Leg Boys St; French Clb; School Play; Stage Crew; Pres Soph Cls; Pres Jr Cls; Rep Stu Cncl; Var Bsbl; Var JV Bsktbl; Hon Roll.

FOSS, LYNDA; Woodland HS; Grove, ME; (Y); Art Clb; Math Tm; Office Aide; Band; Yrbk Phtg; JV Var Cheerleading; Hon Roll; Yrbk Stf; High Eng,Math Avg 84; Best Avg Art 83; Nrs.

FOSTER, JOAN; Lisbon HS; Lisbon Falls, ME; (Y); 8/120; Am Leg Aux Girls St; Pres Sec Stu Cncl; Var Socr; Latin Clb; Yrbk Stf; Var Bsktbl; Trk; Glenys Thompson Awd 85; Mst Outstndg JR Girl 85; Mst Outstndg Soph Girl 84.

FOSTER, KAYE L; Skowhegan Area HS; Skowhegan, ME; (Y); 9/225; Am Leg Aux Girls St; Drama Clb; Pres French Clb; Band; Chorus; Drill Tm; Orch; High Hon Roll; NHS; Pres Schlr; Blaine House Schlrshp 85; Pres Acadmc Fit Awd 85; U Sthrn ME; Mus Ed.

FOURNIER, DOREEN; Jay HS; Jay, ME; (Y); Am Leg Aux Girls St; Ski Clb; Band; Concert Band; Yrbk Ed-Chief; Ed Yrbk Stf; Trs Stu Cncl; JV Var Fld Hcky; Hon Roll; VP NHS; YMCA Model ST Legislature 84-85; Delg ME Teens Against Drunk Driving Seminar 84; Teaching.

FOURNIER, GLEN; Lisbon HS; Lisbon Falls, ME; (Y); 4/130; Latin Clb; Math Tm; Band; Jazz Band; Var L Bsbl; High Hon Roll; Hon Roll; NHS; Silver Medal Natl Latin Exam 85; NEML Schl Hghst Scorer 84-85; Engrng.

FOWLEY, LISSA; Windham HS; Poland Spg, ME; (Y); Band; Concert Band; Jazz Band; Mrchg Band; Pep Band; Hon Roll; Jr NHS; St Schlr; Church Yth Grp; Pep Clb; Natl Cultural Arts Proj-Natl Level 85; Vet Med.

FOX, CHERYL; Lewiston HS; Lewiston, ME; (Y); Pep Clb; Teachers Aide; School Play; Yrbk Stf; Rep Frsh Cls; Stat Socr; Trk; Outstndng Stu Child Care Aide 85; U NH; Elem Ed.

FOX, WENDY; Fryeburg Acad; Stoneham, ME; (Y); Church Yth Grp; Chorus; Church Choir; Var L Sftbl; Hon Roll; St Josephs Coll; Nrsg.

FRAHM, TIMOTHY; Lewiston HS; Lewiston, ME; (Y); 4/411; VP French Clb; Capt Math Tm; Tennis; High Hon Roll; NHS; Natl Hon Rl 85; WA Wrkshps I 84; ME All ST Mth Tm 85; Abilene Christian U; Mth.

FRANCIS, CHERYL LAURALYN; Searsport District HS; Searsport, ME; (Y); Drama Clb; Pres Frsh Cls; Rep Soph Cls; Rep Jr Cls; Stu Cncl; JV Capt Bsktbl; JV Capt Fld Hcky; Var Score Keeper; Var Sftbl; Jr NHS; Girls ST 85; ME Schlr Day 85; Frgn Lang Clb 85; Bangor Comm Coll; Dental Hygn.

FRANKENFIELD, JOHN; Mt Blue HS; E Wilton, ME; (Y); Am Leg Boys St; Band; Chorus; Jazz Band; Mrchg Band; JV Bsktbl; Var Crs Cntry; Var Trk; High Hon Roll; VP Jr NHS; ME Schlrs Day 85; U ME Farmington; Lib Arts.

FRANSON, JOHN; Mt Blue HS; Farmington, ME; (Y); 5/230; Am Leg Boys St; Boy Scts; Church Yth Grp; Debate Tm; Hosp Aide; Crs Cntry; Trk; High Hon Roll; Jr NHS; NHS; Humanties Prog 84; J Arthur Green Faclty Schlrshp 85; Schlrshp Brigham Yng U; Brigham Young U; Pre Med.

FRASER, SUE; Telstar Regional HS; Bethel, ME; (Y); 24/65; Cmnty Wkr; Dance Clb; French Clb; Political Wkr; Ski Clb; Teachers Aide; Variety Show; Capt Cheerleading; Hon Roll; Outstndng Achvt-Voctnl Hm Ec I 83; Lbrl Arts.

FRASIER, TODD; Fort Fairfield HS; Ft Fairfield, ME; (Y); Yrbk Phtg; Hon Roll; Acctg.

FRECHETTE, RUTH G; Biddeford HS; Biddeford, ME; (Y); Political Wkr; Band; Concert Band; Mrchg Band; Pep Band; AATF Cntst Lvl IB 1st Pl Frnch Awd 83; Acctng.

FRECHETTE, SUSAN; Lewiston HS; Lewiston, ME; (Y); Letterman Clb; Ski Clb; Varsity Clb; Yrbk Stf; JV Fld Hcky; JV Tennis; Ntl Merit Ltr; Med.

FREEMAN, MICHAEL; Gardiner Area HS; Gardiner, ME; (Y); Latin Clb; Spanish Clb; Coach Actv; Var Ftbl; Var L Socr; High Hon Roll; Hon Roll.

FRENCH, LAURA; Gorham HS; Gorham, ME; (Y); 3/115; Church Yth Grp; GAA; Science Clb; Var L Bsktbl; Var L Crs Cntry; Capt L Sftbl; High Hon Roll; Hon Roll; Prfct Atten Awd; Spnsh I Awd 84; Chem & Coll Rvw Math Awds 85; Hlth.

FRITH, KELLY; Madison Area HS; Athens, ME; (Y); 2/96; Cmnty Wkr; Var Capt Bsktbl; Var Capt Socr; Var Capt Sftbl; Elks Awd; NHS; Sal; Pres 4-H; Math Tm; Quiz Bowl; ME Prncpls Awd Acad Excell & Ctznshp 85; US Army Natl Schlr/Athl Awd 85; 7E Bsktbl All-Star 85; U Of VT; Anml Sci.

FRIZZELL, BEVERLY A; Edward Little HS; Auburn, ME; (Y); Pep Clb; Spanish Clb; Band; Color Guard; Lit Mag; Pom Pon; Church Yth Grp; Concert Band; Jazz Band; Fresh Cls Music Awd 83; Schl Let Pom-Pon Squad 85; Bus Mngmnt.

FROHLICH, AMY C; Edward Little HS; Auburn, ME; (S); Am Leg Aux Girls St; French Clb; JA; Rep Pres Pep Clb; Variety Show; High Hon Roll; Hon Roll; NHS; Prfct Atten Awd; Life Sci.

FULLER, DONETTA; Penquis Valley HS; Brownsville, ME; (Y); VP Drama Clb; French Clb; Hon Roll.

FULTON, LESLIE; George Stevens Acad; Blue Hill, ME; (Y); French Clb; Math Tm; School Musical; School Play; Yrbk Ed-Chief; Stu Cncl; Co-Capt Bsktbl; High Hon Roll; Hon Roll; NHS; Frnch.

FURLONG, TERRY; York HS; York, ME; (Y); German Clb; Hosp Aide; Math Tm; Yrbk Rptr; Yrbk Stf; Stat Bsktbl; JV Capt Fld Hcky; Stat Trk; High Hon Roll; Hon Roll; German Awd; Am Hist Awd.

GAGNON, DANA; Van Buron Dist Secondary HS; Van Buren, ME; (Y); 8/86; Church Yth Grp; Math Clb; Math Tm; Science Clb; Stu Cncl; Bsbl; Bsktbl; Socr; Tennis; Vllybl.

GAGNON, GREGORY; Lewiston HS; Lewiston, ME; (Y); 10/411; VP Letterman Clb; Bsbl; Co-Capt Bsktbl; Socr; Hon Roll; NHS; Acad All ST Bsktbl 84-85; Randall Awd Bsktbl 84-85; Norman Dion Awd 84-85; U S Army Schlr Athlt Awd; Bentley Coll; Bus Mgmt.

GALLANT, MICHELLE; Rumford HS; Rumford, ME; (Y); Am Leg Aux Girls St; Latin Clb; Office Aide; Red Cross Aide; Ski Clb; Stage Crew; Im Mgr Bsktbl; Im Mgr Coach Actv; Var JV Fld Hcky; Var Tennis; Regnl Wnr Just Like Me Essy Cntst 84; NH Tech Ins; Paramed Tech.

GALLETTA, MATTHEW; Cariboy HS; Caribou, ME; (Y); 37/255; Model UN; Hon Roll; Bio-Chem.

GANNON, ANNE ARLENE; Falmouth HS; Falmouth, ME; (Y); 2/98; French Clb; Political Wkr; Nwsp Rptr; Yrbk Bus Mgr; Var L Fld Hcky; Sec NHS; Sal; Voice Dem Awd; Leo Clb; Century III Ldrs Awd 85; Pres Acadmc Fit Awd 85; Wmns Litry Union Delg 84; ME At Statehd Delg 84; Bowdoin Coll; Poltcl Sci.

GANNON, NANCY; Nokomis Regional HS; Pittsfield, ME; (Y); 13/180; Drama Clb; French Clb; Mrchg Band; School Musical; School Play; Symp Band; High Hon Roll; NHS; Ntl Merit SF; Band; Gifted & Talented Music & Writing 82-85; Roger Williams Coll; Jrnlsm.

GARCEAU, DAVID; Madison HS; Madison, ME; (Y); 5/96; Am Leg Boys St; Math Tm; Ski Clb; Var JV Bsbl; Var JV Ftbl; Var Golf; Hon Roll; St Schlr; St Josephs; Pre-Dntl.

GARDNER, DOUGLAS; Sanford HS; Sanford, ME; (Y); Sec Pres Key Clb; Ski Clb; Ftbl; Trk; Wrstlng; Hon Roll; Pre-Med.

GARDNER, SHELLI; Lewiston HS; Lewiston, ME; (Y); Church Yth Grp; Dance Clb; Debate Tm; DECA; Drama Clb; 4-H; Hosp Aide; Pep Clb; Ski Clb; Yrbk Stf; U Southern ME; Bio.

GARLAND, BILL; Westbrook HS; Westbrook, ME; (Y); Church Yth Grp; English Clb; Spanish Clb; Nwsp Phtg; Yrbk Phtg; JV Bsbl; Im Bsktbl; JV Ftbl; Hon Roll; Summer Humanities Inst; Brdcstng.

GARRIS, JANIE B; Cony HS; Augusta, ME; (Y); 2/293; Pres Science Clb; Sec Spanish Clb; Math Tm; Yrbk Ed-Chief; Ntl Merit SF; Sal; St Schlr; Am Leg Aux Girls St; Church Yth Grp; Cmnty Wkr; U ME At Orono Math, Sci & Engr Prog 84; U Southrn ME Smmr Human Prog Gftd & Talntd HS Stu 83-84; U ME Orono; Bio.

GARRISON, MICHELLE; Cony HS; Augusta, ME; (Y); Church Yth Grp; French Clb; FBLA; Spanish Clb; Church Choir; Yrbk Bus Mgr; Yrbk Stf; Im Tennis; Im Vllybl; Hon Roll; Bus Admin.

GARRITY, MARY; Deering HS; Portland, ME; (Y); JA; Key Clb; Hon Roll; Comp Sci.

GAUDET, TERESA; Deering HS; Portland, ME; (Y); French Clb; FTA; Key Clb; Political Wkr; Band; Concert Band; Mrchg Band; French Hon Soc; Church Yth Grp; Teachers Aide; Pres Forum Clb 84-85; Chinese Clb 85; Intl Law.

GAUDIN, SHARON K; Rumford HS; Rumford, ME; (Y); 11/160; Math Tm; Thesps; Band; School Play; Yrbk Bus Mgr; Yrbk Stf; JV Var Bsktbl; Var Tennis; High Hon Roll; NHS; Jr Prize Spkng 84; Big Bros Big Sister 84-85; St Michaels Coll; Jrnlsm.

GAUTHIER, JODELLE; Saint Dominic Regional HS; Lewiston, ME; (Y); Keywanettes; Var Bsktbl; Var Fld Hcky; Var Sftbl; Var Tennis; Hon Roll; Bsktbl Vrsty Pins & Ltr Awd 82-85; Fldhcky Vrst Pins Awd 83-85; Sftbl Ltr 82-84; Air Force; Accntng.

GAVIN III, MARTIN F; Windham HS; W Windham, ME; (Y); Am Leg Boys St; Church Yth Grp; Sec Pres Key Clb; Pres Latin Clb; Political Wkr; Variety Show; Pres Stu Cncl; Badmtn; Cit Awd; Trs Jr NHS; Amer Future Awd Outstndng Pblc Svc 85; Pschlgy.

GEBHARDT, THOMAS; Skowhegan Area HS; Norridgewock, ME; (Y); 56/185; Church Yth Grp; JCL; VP Latin Clb; Varsity Clb; Band; Concert Band; Jazz Band; Mrchg Band; Yrbk Phtg; JV Ftbl; Lehigh U, Engrng.

GELLER, DAVID S; Edward Little HS; Auburn, ME; (S); Am Leg Boys St; Debate Tm; Latin Clb; Math Tm; Pres Temple Yth Grp; Nwsp Phtg; Tennis; Bausch & Lomb Sci Awd; High Hon Roll; NHS; Most Improved Player Athletic Awd Soccer 84-85; Med.

GEMME, TAMMI I; Mt Ararat HS; Brunswick, ME; (Y); Chorus; Madrigals; JV Var Bsktbl; Mgr(s); Score Keeper; Hon Roll.

GENDRON, BONNIE; Robert W Traip Acad; Kittery, ME; (Y); Acctng.

GEORGE, APRIL; Bangor HS; Bangor, ME; (Y); Cmnty Wkr; Sec Key Clb; Nwsp Stf; Yrbk Stf; Rep Soph Cls; Rep Jr Cls; Rep Stu Cncl; Cheerleading; Socr; Hon Roll; Pres Phy Fit Awd 82; Cert Acadmc Excllnc 82-83; Cert Achvt Engl 85; Pol Sci.

GEROW, ALERTA-ANGELINA; Oxford Hills HS; Salem, MA; (Y); 17/239; Art Clb; Drama Clb; Chorus; School Musical; Yrbk Ed-Chief; Lit Mag; Gym; Hon Roll; NHS; Pres Schlr; Goddard Coll; Art.

GIBBS, HEIDI; Belfast Area HS; Belfast, ME; (Y); Variety Show; JV Bsktbl; Var Cheerleading; JV Mgr(s); JV Sftbl; Tennis; Mngr Bsktbl 83-84; Chrldr Vrsty Capt 85-86; CA; Fshn Merch.

GIBSON, CINDY; Van Buren District Secondary Schl; Van Buren, ME; (Y); Hosp Aide; Yrbk Stf; High Hon Roll; Hon Roll; Tutrl Svcs Undrclss Stu 84-85; Top Accntng I Stu 84-85; 2nd Eng Stu 84-85.

GIFFORD, MICHELE; Acadia Christian Acad; Gouldsboro, ME; (Y); 1/3; School Play; Yrbk Ed-Chief; Sec Trs Frsh Cls; Sec Soph Cls; Rep Jr Cls; Rep Sr Cls; Var L Bsktbl; Var Capt Cheerleading; Hon Roll; Most Schl Spirit; Best Chrstn; Hgst Eng Avg; Gordon Coll; Child Psych.

GIFTOS, ALEXANDER; Cape Elizabeth HS; Cape Elizabeth, ME; (Y); 45/128; Drama Clb; Spanish Clb; School Play; Variety Show; Var Capt Lcrss; Pres Schlr; Vrsty La Crosse MVP Awds 84-85; Drama Awds Partcptn 85; U Of NH.

GIGUERE, STEVEN; Lewiston HS; Lewiston, ME; (Y); 10/422; Church Yth Grp; Letterman Clb; Varsity Clb; Var L Diving; Var L Swmmng; Messiah Coll; Art.

GILBERT, STEVEN; Lewiston HS; Lewiston, ME; (Y); Boy Scts; Cmnty Wkr; Exploring; Political Wkr; Ftbl; Hon Roll; Boston U; Rsrch Sci.

GILLMAN, KIRSTEN; Waterville HS; Waterville, ME; (Y); 9/200; Am Leg Aux Girls St; Key Clb; Letterman Clb; Sec Spanish Clb; Rep Jr Cls; L Trk; High Hon Roll; Ntl Merit Ltr; Spanish NHS; GAA; Tp Latn I Stu 84; Tp Spnsh III IV Stu 84 & 85; Recgntn Peer Tutr 84; Anml Behvr.

GILPIN, MARGARET; Houlton HS; Houlton, ME; (Y); Church Yth Grp; Math Clb; Band; Chorus; Madrigals; School Musical; JV Bsktbl; Var Socr; Var Sftbl; Im Swmmng; 1st Pl ST Jaxx Perf Comp 84; CYO Yth Grp Treas 83.

GIRARDIN, LAURIE; Leavitt Area HS; Greene, ME; (Y); 18/142; Church Yth Grp; Cmnty Wkr; Hon Roll; Cntrl ME Vo-Tech; Graph Arts.

GIROUX, FREDERICK P; Kennebec Valley Christian HS; Fairfield, ME; (Y); 1/2; Rep Band; Bsktbl; Jazz Band; Pep Band; O Berlin; Music.

GLEASON, BRETT; Medomak Valley HS; Union, ME; (Y); Nwsp Stf; Pres Jr Cls; JV Var Bsktbl; Hon Roll; Publshd Schl News Papr Courier Gazet 83-84; Target Prog Enlg,Poetry & Philsphy 84-85; U CA Berkeley; Phlsphy.

GLEESON, LAWRENCE; Belfast Area HS; Belfast, ME; (Y); 2/120; Boy Scts; Band; Concert Band; Jazz Band; School Musical; Var L Socr; Var L Swmmng; Dnfth Awd; High Hon Roll; NHS; KVAC Band 85; Humanties Prog 85.

GLIDDEN, BRUCE; Erskine Acad; Palermo, ME; (Y); French Clb; Science Clb; Teachers Aide; Stu Cncl; Bsktbl; Pres SADD Chptr 84-85; Bus Adm.

GLIDDEN, TORI; Ashaldn Community HS; Ashland, ME; (Y); 5/46; Am Leg Aux Girls St; Trs Sec Band; School Musical; School Play; Yrbk Ed-Chief; Sec Stu Cncl; Sftbl; Vllybl; NHS; All Aroostook Band 84-85; U Of ME-ORONO; Art.

GOFF, TANYA; Monmouth Acad; Monmouth, ME; (Y); 2/52; Am Leg Aux Girls St; Letterman Clb; Speech Tm; Teachers Aide; Varsity Clb; Bsktbl; Crs Cntry; Sftbl; DAR Awd; High Hon Roll; Coly Coll; Bio.

GOODALE, KAREN; Greely HS; Cumberlnd Fsde, ME; (Y); 16/147; Church Yth Grp; Hosp Aide; Math Tm; Band; Swmmng; Hon Roll; Greely HS Schlrshp 85; Latin Awd 85; Presdntl Acad Ftns Awd 85; U Of VT; Physical Therapy.

GOODINE, AMY; Penquis Valley HS; Dover Foxcroft, ME; (Y); Teachers Aide; Pres Frsh Cls; Rep Stu Cncl; Var JV Bsktbl; Var Socr; Var Sftbl; High Hon Roll; Hon Roll; Typng Cntst; Bus Machine Cntst 1st Pl 83-84; Sec.

GOODRIDGE, KRISTEN; Skowhegan Area HS; Canaan, ME; (Y); 9/214; Church Yth Grp; Sec Frsh Cls; Rep Stu Cncl; Var Cheerleading; Var Vllybl; High Hon Roll; Typng II Awd 84; Eagles Schrlsh Pawd 85; Lancater Bible Coll.

GOODWIN, THERESA LYNN; Deering HS; Portland, ME; (Y); Hosp Aide; Band; Concert Band; Mrchg Band; Pep Band; Comprehnsv Math 80, 81, 84 & 85; Inst Ply Flute 78-85; Air Trffc Control.

GOODY, KELLY; Lisbon HS; Lisbon Falls, ME; (Y); Latin Clb; L Cheerleading; Var JV Mgr(s); Silver Medal Ntl Latin Exam 83; Physcl Thrpy.

GOOLDRUP, THERESA; Erskine Acad; Weeks Mills, ME; (Y); Am Leg Aux Girls St; Drama Clb; FBLA; Office Aide; School Play; Stage Crew; Yrbk Stf; High Hon Roll; Hon Roll; Dorris L Young Schlrshp 85; Mid-ST Coll; Legal Secy.

GORAJ, KATHERINE J; Cony HS; Augusta, ME; (Y); Am Leg Aux Girls St; Church Yth Grp; Computer Clb; Nwsp Rptr; Nwsp Stf; Hon Roll; Maxima Cumm Laude (JCL Exam) 83; Magna Cum Laude 84; Comptr Sci.

GORDON, LISA BETH; Marshwood HS; Eliot, ME; (Y); 3/123; French Clb; Math Tm; Color Guard; Mrchg Band; School Musical; Nwsp Ed-Chief; Pres Sr Cls; Stu Cncl; Sec NHS; Am Leg Aux Girls St; Louis Armstrong Jazz Awd; Pres Acad Ftns Awd; SADD Sec; Coll Of New Rochelle; Cmmnctn.

GORDON, SHERRY; Mt Blue HS; Farmington, ME; (Y); Off Intnl Clb; Ski Clb; Chorus; Mgr Color Guard; Mgr Mrchg Band; High Hon Roll; Hon Roll; German Awd Goethe Inst Boston 85; U Of ME Farmington; Comp Arts.

GORMAN, PATRICIA; Fort Fairfield HS; Ft Fairfield, ME; (Y); 7/78; Varsity Clb; Band; Chorus; School Musical; Pres Soph Cls; Pres Jr Cls; High Hon Roll; NHS; Church Yth Grp; Cmnty Wkr; All St Choir 84-85; Comp Highlnd Dancer 82-84; Top Ten Pct 83-85; U RI; Pharmcy.

GOSNELL, JESSICA ERIN; Mt View HS; Thorndike, ME; (Y); Letterman Clb; Political Wkr; VP Soph Cls; Pres Jr Cls; Var Bsktbl; Var Fld Hcky; Var Trk; Cit Awd; NHS; Voice Dem Awd; Prfct Attndnce 83 & 84; Pres Phys Ftns Awd 83, 84 & 85; Bst Undergrad Athl 85; Dartmouth/Smith; Pre-Med.

GOSSELIN, DENISE P; Lewiston HS; Lewiston, ME; (Y); Church Yth Grp; Hosp Aide; Pep Clb; Drm Mjr(t); Variety Show; Rep Jr Cls; VP Sr Cls; Twrlr; Jr NHS; NHS; ME Miss Teen Pageant Schltc Wnnr 82-85; Outstndng Achvt Algebra II Awd 85; Awd Outstndng Part Yth; Tele Broadcasting.

GOULD, WILLIAM T; Edward Little HS; Minot, ME; (Y); Chess Clb; Drama Clb; School Play; Var Capt Swmmng; Cit Awd; Hon Roll; Prfct Atten Awd; Bio.

GOVE, MAURA; York HS; York, ME; (Y); Church Yth Grp; Yrbk Stf; Mgr L Bsktbl; JV Fld Hcky; Mgr L Trk; High Hon Roll; Hon Roll; NHS; Psychgy,Soclgy Awd 85; Houghton Clg; Commctn.

GOWER, LISA; Wiscasset HS; Dresden, ME; (Y); Trs Sr Cls; Mgr(s); Score Keeper; JV Socr; Var JV Sftbl; Hon Roll; Clss Svc Awd 85; Top 10 Pct Clss 82-85; Bay ST JC; Trvl.

GRAHAM, HEATHER; Bonny Eagle HS; Saco, ME; (Y); Church Yth Grp; Hosp Aide; JA; Math Tm; Ski Clb; Im Bsktbl; Var Fld Hcky; JV Gym; Var Mgr(s); Var Trk; U ME Schlrs Day 84; Data Gen Cls 85; Recgnzd Exc Comp Cls 85; Mt Holyoke; Econ.

GRANT, DEBORAH M; Matanawcook Acad; Lincoln Center, ME; (Y); 7/112; Am Leg Aux Girls St; Sec French Clb; Girl Scts; Letterman Clb; Chorus; Stat Bsbl; JV Bowling; Im Gym; High Hon Roll; NHS; Eastern ME Vo Tech; Med Lab.

GRANT, G ALFRED; Cape Elizabeth HS; Cape Elizabeth, ME; (Y); Debate Tm; Political Wkr; Varsity Clb; School Play; Variety Show; Yrbk Rptr; Var Bsbl; Var Bsktbl; Coach Actv; Var Socr; Class Bearor Grad-Jr Rep 85; Day Of Dialogue Host 85; Bus.

GRASS, SANDRA; Belfast Area HS; Belfast, ME; (Y); 21/141; Girl Scts; School Musical; Variety Show; Hon Roll; Jr NHS; Prfct Atten Awd; Outstndng Student Awd-Food Serv Vac Schl 85; Presdntl Acadmc Fitness Awd 85.

GRAY, MICHELLE; Gardiner Area HS; Gardiner, ME; (Y); 10/225; Pres AFS; Trs Church Yth Grp; Pres French Clb; Band; Mrchg Band; School Musical; French Hon Soc; High Hon Roll; NHS; Rotary Awd; Richard Simms Schrshp 85; Frnch Clb Schlrshp 85; Robinson Fund 85; Frgn Lang.

GRAY, TAMATHA; Penquis Valley HS; Milo, ME; (Y); Drama Clb; Girl Scts; Varsity Clb; Band; Concert Band; Pep Band; Variety Show; Yrbk Stf; Lit Mag; Var L Crs Cntry; Hon Rl 82-85; UMO; Vet Asst.

GREELEY, CINDY; Windham HS; Raymond, ME; (Y); Yrbk Stf; JV Bsktbl; Westbrook Coll; Chldhd Educ.

GREENE, AMY; Hermon HS; Carmel, ME; (S); Pres French Clb; Pres FHA; Hosp Aide; School Play; Yrbk Stf; Jr Cls; Bsktbl; Fld Hcky; Score Keeper; Dnfth Awd; Dirigos Girls ST 84; U Of ME-ORONO; Jrnlsm.

GREENLEAF, CYNTHIA; Gardner HS; Litchfield, ME; (Y); Church Yth Grp; Dance Clb; French Clb; FNA; Girl Scts; Q&S; Yrbk Stf; Var Cheerleading; Mat Maids; Trk; U Of Sthrn ME; Nrsng.

GREENLEAF, MICHELE; Gardiner Area HS; Gardiner, ME; (Y); Am Leg Aux Girls St; French Clb; Letterman Clb; Varsity Clb; Variety Show; Rep Frsh Cls; Rep Soph Cls; Rep Jr Cls; Rep Sr Cls; Rep Trs Stu Cncl; Florida C Lewin Mem Schlrshp 85; Chrldng Awd-Outstdng Chrldr 85; MVP Tnns 83-85; U Of Southern ME; Nrsng.

GREENWOOD, SARAH; Jay HS; Jay, ME; (Y); Church Yth Grp; Cmnty Wkr; Y-Teens; Color Guard; Yrbk Stf; JV Bsktbl; Hon Roll; Med Asst.

GREGOR, KATHY; Yarmouth HS; Yarmouth, ME; (Y); Drama Clb; Rep French Clb; Latin Clb; Office Aide; School Play; Stage Crew; Variety Show; Yrbk Stf; Var Mgr(s); Hon Roll.

GRENIER, MARTIN; Forest Hills HS; Jackman, ME; (Y); 5/17; Drama Clb; Stage Crew; Yrbk Stf; Hon Roll; USM Smmr Inst Gftd & Tlntd Stdnts 84; Bishops U; Comp Sci.

GRIFFETH, HEIDI J; Caribou HS; Caribou, ME; (Y); 26/237; Rep Frsh Cls; Rep Soph Cls; Rep Jr Cls; Var Bsktbl; Var Socr; Var Sftbl; High Hon Roll; Hon Roll; U ME Presque Isle.

GRINDLE, YVETTE; George Stevens Acad; Blue Hill Falls, ME; (Y); Aud/Vis; Church Yth Grp; Cmnty Wkr; Drama Clb; 4-H; French Clb; FHA; Library Aide; Science Clb; Thesps; Sci Olymp Bronze Art 85; Bangor CC; Svcs.

GRONDIN, RONALD; Livermore Falls HS; Livermore Falls, ME; (Y); Letterman Clb; Varsity Clb; Stu Cncl; Var L Bsbl; JV Capt Bsktbl; Var L Ftbl; Hon Roll; NHS; UMF Upward Bound; Physical Therapy.

GROSS, CAROLYN MARIE; Stearns HS; Millinocket, ME; (Y); Pres Church Yth Grp; Drama Clb; Acpl Chr; Band; Chorus; Jazz Band; School Musical; School Play; Crs Cntry; Trk; MVP-X Cntry 84; Team Contribtn-Track 85; Most Imprvd Plyr-X Cntry 82; U Of ME-ORONO; Art Eductn.

GROSS, JAYE; George Stevens Acad; Penobscot, ME; (Y); Aud/Vis; Church Yth Grp; Cmnty Wkr; Pres FBLA; Library Aide; Bowling; Hon Roll; Bus Admin.

GUAY, SCOTT; Lisbon HS; Lisbon Falls, ME; (Y); Am Leg Boys St; Trs Band; Drm Mjr(t); Jazz Band; Stage Crew; High Hon Roll; NHS; Ntl Merit SF; St Schlr; Optmtry.

GUERRETTE, REBECCA; Wisdom HS; St Agatha, ME; (Y); 2/45; Church Yth Grp; Drama Clb; 4-H; Pres French Clb; Quiz Bowl; Varsity Clb; Pres Band; Church Choir; Concert Band; Mrchg Band; ST Hugh O Brian Ldrshp Conf 83-84; ST Schlrs Day U Of ME 84-85; ST VP Natl Hnr Socty 84-85; Pre-Med.

GUNTY, MURRY; Deering HS; Portland, ME; (Y); 6/295; Am Leg Boys St; VP JA; Nwsp Sprt Ed; Yrbk Rptr; L Golf; L Capt Tennis; High Hon Roll; Ntl Merit Ltr; Spanish NHS; Hugh O Brien Yth Ldrshp Fndtn 83; U Of PA.

GWARJANSKI, THERESE; Lewiston HS; Lewiston, ME; (Y); Am Leg Aux Girls St; Yrbk Stf; Rep Soph Cls; Rep Sr Cls; JV Fld Hcky; Var Trk; High Hon Roll; Hon Roll; Jr NHS; NHS; Hugh O Brian Yth Ldrshp Smnr 84; Mdcl.

HAGAN, BRENDA; Catherine Mc Auley HS; Topsham, ME; (Y); 3/63; Church Yth Grp; Drama Clb; Keywanettes; Ski Clb; Yrbk Stf; Rep Sr Cls; Stu Cncl; Bsktbl; Socr; DAR Awd; Blaine Hse & Randl Mc Allstr Schlrshps 85; Dghtrs Of Cinn Schlrshp Fnlst 85; Bowdoin Coll; Pre Law.

HAINES, TAMMY; Fort Fairfield HS; Ft Fairfield, ME; (Y); 1/73; Trs Church Yth Grp; Red Cross Aide; Chorus; Sec Stu Cncl; Cheerleading; Trk; Twrlr; High Hon Roll; NHS; Voice Dem Awd; Eng Awd 83-85; Mth Awd 83 & 85; Fr Awd 83 & 84; Acctg.

HALACY, CHRISTINA; Rumford HS; Rumford Center, ME; (Y); Sec Church Yth Grp; Drama Clb; Pres FHA; Varsity Clb; Band; Concert Band; Jazz Band; Mrchg Band; Pep Band; Var Sftbl; Lgl Sec Sci.

HALE, CARLEEN; Catherine Mc Auley HS; N Windham, ME; (Y); 5/61; Drama Clb; French Clb; Science Clb; Band; Chorus; Yrbk Phtg; Yrbk Stf; Im Vllybl; Hon Roll; Prfct Atten Awd; Schlrshp 85; Latin Awd 84; Frnch & Math Awd 82; U Of NH; Lbrl Arts.

HALL, WANDA N; Leavitt Area HS; Greene, ME; (Y); 5/110; Church Yth Grp; French Clb; FHA; Fld Hcky; French Hon Soc; High Hon Roll; Hon Roll; Pian 83; Greene Baptst Chrch Schlrshp 85; Travl-Toursm.

HALLETT, CHERYL; Caribou HS; Caribou, ME; (Y); 51/300; Cmnty Wkr; French Clb; Band; Concert Band; Mrchg Band; Rep Frsh Cls; Rep Soph Cls; Trs Jr Cls; Rep Stu Cncl; Var Cheerleading; NH Coll; Accntnt.

HALLOWELL, FRANI; Bucksport HS; Bucksport, ME; (Y); Am Leg Aux Girls St; Art Clb; Computer Clb; Pres Drama Clb; GAA; Girl Scts; Spanish Clb; Thesps; Varsity Clb; Band; Dirctrs Cup Drama 84-85; Marn Bio.

HAM, HEATHER; Leavitt Area HS; Greene, ME; (Y); Church Yth Grp; 4-H; Band; Chorus; Church Choir; Concert Band; Mrchg Band; Variety Show; Nwsp Rptr; Nwsp Stf; Miss Cngnlty-Auburn Chptr Demday Swthrt Pgnt 85; U Of ME-FARMINGTON; Psych.

HAM, SHEILA L; Wells HS; E Lebanon, ME; (Y); 2/120; Nwsp Rptr; Nwsp Stf; Yrbk Stf; High Hon Roll; NHS; Hstry Fair Awd 83; Highest Grade Avrg In Latin Ii Awd 84; Highest Grade In Gvrnmt Awd 85; MI ST U; Physcs.

HAM, WENDI S; Leavitt Area HS; Greene, ME; (Y); 15/109; Am Leg Aux Girls St; Church Yth Grp; Cmnty Wkr; 4-H; Intnl Clb; Band; Chorus; Church Choir; Jazz Band; Variety Show; Mabel J Deshon Rainbow Schlrshp 85; Natl Choral Awd 82-85; Cleo Laire Schlrshp 85; Berklee Coll; Perf Arts.

HAMALAINEN, BETH; Yarmouth JR SR HS; Yarmouth, ME; (Y); Church Yth Grp; Drama Clb; Girl Scts; Trs Spanish Clb; Band; Chorus; Church Choir; Concert Band; Jazz Band; Mrchg Band; Gould Music Awd 85; ST Solo/Ensmble Comptn 83-84; U Of Amer; Intr Dsgn.

HAMANN, JACQUELINE MARIE; Lewiston HS; Lewiston, ME; (Y); 18/404; French Clb; VP Keywanettes; Q&S; Nwsp Ed-Chief; Nwsp Rptr; Nwsp Stf; Hon Roll; NHS; Spcl Fr Advnc Plcmnt Imprv Awd 85; Hstry 4 Yr A Avg Awd 85; Johny Robinson Most Imprtnt Staffer Awd 85; Lesley Coll; Elem Educ.

HAMEL, BRENT; Lewiston HS; Lewiston, ME; (Y); Im Bsbl; Air Force.

HAMILTON, DALE; Brewer HS; East Holden, ME; (Y); Rep Am Leg Boys St; Teachers Aide; Rep Frsh Cls; Rep Soph Cls; JV Capt Bsktbl; Coachs Awd 82-84; U ME Onono; Pre Med.

HAMILTON, LORI LYNN; Yarmouth JR SR HS; Yarmouth, ME; (Y); 7/90; Am Leg Aux Girls St; Church Yth Grp; Cmnty Wkr; Drama Clb; French Clb; Girl Scts; Latin Clb; Political Wkr; Science Clb; Teachers Aide; Ntl Sci Olympd 84; Hugh O Brian Yth Ldrshp 83 & 85; WA Wrkshps 84 & 85; George Washington U; Pol Sci.

HAMM, PAUL; Bangor HS; Bangor, ME; (Y); Capt Chess Clb; Prfct Atten Awd; ME Chess Cert; Cert Of Merit-Bangor Dialy News Art Cntst; Air Force Acad.

HAMMOND, GWEN; Westbrook HS; Westbrook, ME; (Y); Pres Keywanettes; Latin Clb; Spanish Clb; Chorus; Concert Band; Mrchg Band; Yrbk Stf; JV Sftbl; Trsm Bus Adm.

HANDLEY, ERIC; Skowhegan Area HS; Harrison, ME; (Y); Boy Scts; Church Yth Grp; Drama Clb; German Clb; Letterman Clb; Varsity Clb; Sec Band; Chorus; Sec Concert Band; Jazz Band; Best Linmn Ftrbl; All ST Ftbl; ME Maritime Acad; Marine Engr.

HANDLEY, JOSEPH; Lawrence HS; Madison, ME; (Y); English Clb; French Clb; Office Aide; Spanish Clb; Yrbk Stf; High Hon Roll; Hon Roll; Prfct Atten Awd; Frnch Awd 85; Svc Awd 85; Comp Sci.

HANKARD, HEIDI; Machias Memorial HS; Machias, ME; (Y); Church Yth Grp; Drama Clb; FBLA; Hosp Aide; Chorus; Church Choir; School Musical; School Play; Cheerleading; U Of ME; Bus Tchr.

HANNA, SARAH; Westbrook HS; Westbrook, ME; (Y); Sec Spanish Clb; JV Var Bsktbl; JV Var Fld Hcky; JV Var Sftbl; FBI Agnt.

HANNON, TERI M; Leavitt Area HS; Turner, ME; (Y); 15/100; Church Yth Grp; Dance Clb; FHA; Letterman Clb; Ski Clb; Teachers Aide; Varsity Clb; Band; School Play; Variety Show; U Of New England; Occup Thrpy.

HANSCOM, ERIC; Hodgdon HS; Haynesville, ME; (Y); 2/50; Am Leg Boys St; French Clb; Pres Jr Cls; Dnfth Awd; French Hon Soc; High Hon Roll; NHS; Yth Understndng Smmr Pgm 85; ME Schlrs Day 85; Stu Mnth 84-85.

HARDING, MICHAEL; Jay HS; N Jay, ME; (Y); Teachers Aide; Ftbl; US Army.

HARMON, SUZANNE; Caribou HS; Caribou, ME; (S); 3/215; Am Leg Aux Girls St; Model UN; Capt Ski Clb; Varsity Clb; Band; VP Jr Cls; Rep Stu Cncl; High Hon Roll; Pres NHS; Ntl Hnr Soc Pres; Model UN; Varsity Clb; Chem Engr.

HARRIMAN, MARK; Deering HS; Portland, ME; (Y); French Clb; JV Bsbl; Mgr(s); Hon Roll; Ntl Merit Ltr; St Schlr; Anatmy Of Leadrshp Pgm 84-85; Engrng.

HART, MARCELLA A; Lawrence HS; Fairfield, ME; (Y); 51/210; FCA; Key Clb; Band; Concert Band; Mrchg Band; Yrbk Stf; Lit Mag; JV Bsktbl; Var Score Keeper; Hon Roll; ME ST Acad Of Hair Design.

HARTFORD, KIM; Hodgdon HS; Houlton, ME; (Y); Art Clb; Church Yth Grp; Dance Clb; French Clb; Girl Scts; Library Aide; Office Aide; Pep Clb; Ski Clb; Teachers Aide; Typng Awd 83-85; VA Schlrshp 85; Beal Coll Bangor; Trvl.

HARTFORD, MICHELE; Leavitt Area HS; Leeds, ME; (Y); Speech Tm; Stu Cncl; JV Var Fld Hcky; Var JV Trk; Hon Roll; Coop Prog 85-86; Lwyr.

HARTFORD, TAMMY L; Leavitt Area HS; Leeds, ME; (Y); Am Leg Aux Girls St; French Clb; VP Y-Teens; School Play; Nwsp Ed-Chief; Nwsp Rptr; Yrbk Stf; Hon Roll; NHS; Johnn M Robinson Awd-Most Valbl Staffer 85; Speech Awes 83-85; Elem Creatv Wrtng Cls Teacher 84-86; Journlsm.

HARTT, TRACEY; Fort Kent Community HS; St Francis, ME; (Y); Pres Jr Cls; Var Bsbl; Var Wrstlng; Hon Roll; U ME; Bus Mgmt.

HARVIE, PATRICK; Livermore Falls HS; Livermore Falls, ME; (Y); Rep Am Leg Boys St; Aud/Vis; Church Yth Grp; Science Clb; Band; Jazz Band; Rep Stu Cncl; Stat Bsbl; High Hon Roll; Hon Roll; Student Of Mnth 84; Bio Student Of Yr 84; Comptr Student Of Yr 85; Comptr Design.

HATFIELD, CHRIS; Orono HS; Orono, ME; (S); 16/105; Drama Clb; Math Tm; NFL; Speech Tm; Thesps; Chorus; School Musical; Nwsp Stf; Hon Roll; NHS; All Star Cast ME St 1 Act Play Contest 84; Theatre.

HAVERTY, JANET; Catherine Mc Auley HS; Portland, ME; (Y); VP Pres Church Yth Grp; Drama Clb; French Clb; Key Clb; Stage Crew; Nwsp Stf; Trs Sr Cls; Rep Stu Cncl; Var L Fld Hcky; Var L Sftbl; Math Awd 82; Latin Awd 84.

HAWBAKER, SARAH; Washington Acad; East Machias, ME; (Y); 5/51; Church Yth Grp; Band; Chorus; Pres Jr Cls; Rep Stu Cncl; Vllybl; DAR Awd; NHS; U Of Sthrn ME; Music Ed.

HAWKSLEY, THOMAS W; Bangor HS; Bangor, ME; (Y); Pres Computer Clb; Mathletes; Math Clb; Math Tm; High Hon Roll; Pres Church Yth Grp; FCA; Hon Roll; Cert-Comp Prgmg, Data Entry 84-85; Hghst Comp Prgm Deg 85; Bently Coll; Comp Prgmr.

HAYDEN, MICHELLE RAE; Mt Blue HS; Dryden, ME; (Y); Am Leg Aux Girls St; Band; Chorus; Trs Stu Cncl; JV Capt Bsktbl; JV Fld Hcky; Var L Sftbl; High Hon Roll; NHS; Fine Arts.

HAYES, SAMANTHA; Cape Elizabeth HS; Cape Elizabeth, ME; (Y); Intnl Clb; Spanish Clb; Varsity Clb; Yrbk Stf; Bsktbl; Var L Fld Hcky; JV Sftbl; Var L Swmmng; Hon Roll; CPR Instr 85; Exch Stu Mexico 84; Bowdoin; Bus Exec.

HAZA, STEPHANIE A; George Stevens Acad; Brooklin, ME; (Y); 3/63; Am Leg Aux Girls St; Drama Clb; French Clb; Chorus; Yrbk Stf; Sec Frsh Cls; Sec Soph Cls; Var JV Cheerleading; Hon Roll; NHS; Stevens Spkrs Series Co-Chrmn 86; Brdcstng.

HEATH, RANDY; Fryeburg Acad; Fryeburg, ME; (S); French Clb; Varsity Clb; Var Bsbl; Var Bsktbl; Var Socr; High Hon Roll; Hon Roll; NHS; Frsh Schltc Awd Hgst Rank 83; Frsh In Frsh Cls B W Tinker Chptr; Cls C Bsbl Champ Awd; Embry-Riddle Aeronauticl; Aviat.

HEATH, SUZANNE; Mt Blue HS; Farmington, ME; (Y); Church Yth Grp; Library Aide; Chorus; Color Guard; Yrbk Stf; David Gregory Michael Meml Schlrshp 85; E Nazarene Clg; Psych.

HEBERT, SANDY; Leavitt Area HS; Turner, ME; (Y); 40/165; Church Yth Grp; Debate Tm; French Clb; Varsity Clb; Trk; Algeheny Coll; Nrsng.

HEINE, JENNIFER; Windham HS; Woodinville, WA; (Y); Cmnty Wkr; Acpl Chr; Jazz Band; Mrchg Band; Orch; Pep Band; Swing Chorus; Symp Band; Hon Roll; NHS; Northwest Bible Coll; Chstn Sgr.

HENDERSON, CONNIE; York HS; York, ME; (Y); 13/176; Art Clb; Computer Clb; Girl Scts; Stage Crew; Sec Soph Cls; Sec Jr Cls; Stu Cncl; Mgr(s); Sftbl; Hon Roll; Hghst Grade Comp Cls 84; U FL; Bus Mngmnt.

HENDERSON, ROBERT; Calvary Hill Christian HS; Dryden, ME; (Y); Church Yth Grp; Drama Clb; Chorus; Color Guard; Yrbk Stf; Stu Cncl; Bsktbl; Crs Cntry; Ftbl; Socr; ME Vo-Tech Inst; Auto Mech.

HENDRIX, KEN; Bucksport HS; E Orland, ME; (Y); 48/130; Spanish Clb; Varsity Clb; Band; JV Bsbl; Var Bsktbl; Amer HS Athlt 85.

HENNIN, RAOUL; Morse HS; Woolwich, ME; (Y); French Clb; Math Tm; Science Clb; Stu Cncl; Var Crs Cntry; JV Swmmng; High Hon Roll; JV Trk; 1st ST Sci Fair Physics 85; Acad Hnr Awd Chem,Hist,Frnch V 85.

HENRY, LISA; George Stevens Acad; Penobscot, ME; (Y); Rptr Hst FBLA; Nwsp Rptr; Yrbk Stf; Adv.

HERRMANN, KIM; Cape Elizabeth HS; Cape Elizabeth, ME; (Y); Intnl Clb; Nwsp Rptr; Var Golf; Var L Sftbl; High Hon Roll; Hon Roll; CCC All Star Tm-Sftbl 85.

HERSOM, CATHERINE A; Sanford HS; Sanford, ME; (Y); Am Leg Aux Girls St; Church Yth Grp; Ski Clb; Band; Concert Band; Jazz Band; Mrchg Band; Var Crs Cntry; Var Sftbl; Hon Roll; Bio.

HEWETT, LESLIE; Livermore Falls HS; Fayette, ME; (Y); Varsity Clb; Stu Cncl; Var L Bsbl; Var L Bsktbl; Var Capt Ftbl; Var Wt Lftg; Hon Roll; NHS; Pres Schlr; Pell Grnt 85-86; U ME Orono; Elec Engrng.

HIGER, BRENDA P; Belfast Area HS; Belfast, ME; (Y); 26/141; AFS; Am Leg Aux Girls St; Rep Frsh Cls; Pres Soph Cls; Sec Trs Jr Cls; VP Sr Cls; Var Capt Fld Hcky; Var Capt Gym; Mgr(s); Trk; Mary S Enk Schlrshp 85; Pagon Schlrshp 85; New Hampshire Coll; Mktng.

HILBINGER, CAROL LEE; Deering HS; Portland, ME; (Y); 21/265; Exploring; FTA; Hosp Aide; Key Clb; Math Tm; Concert Band; Mrchg Band; Hon Roll; NHS; Orch; Pres Acadmc Fit Awd 85; U Of Southern ME; Math.

HILDRETH, TIM; South Portland HS; S Portland, ME; (Y); Church Yth Grp; Band; Church Choir; Crs Cntry; Trk; Wrstlng; High Hon Roll; Hon Roll; Sci.

HILL, DAVID; Houlton HS; Houlton, ME; (Y); Math Clb; Band; Mrchg Band; Stage Crew; Bsbl; Bsktbl; Golf; Vllybl; U ME-ORONO.

HIRSCH, JODI A; Deering HS; Portland, ME; (Y); 19/310; Rep Am Leg Aux Girls St; Dance Clb; Drama Clb; French Clb; Chorus; Mrchg Band; School Musical; Lit Mag; French Hon Soc; Hon Roll; 4th Pl ST Natl Frnch Exam 84; Anatomy Ldrshp Bk Awd 84; Frgn Lang.

HISCOCK, MICHAEL L; Leavitt Area HS; North Turner, ME; (Y); 52/125; Boy Scts; Drama Clb; French Clb; Speech Tm; School Play; Variety Show; Nwsp Rptr; Nwsp Stf; Crs Cntry; JV Ftbl; SMVTI; Culinary Arts.

HODGDON, TAMMY; Belfast Area HS; Belfast, ME; (Y); Drama Clb; Capt Cheerleading; Mgr(s); Score Keeper; Timer; Hon Roll; Perf Atten 84; Typng Awd 84; Mrch Dms Awd 84; Acctng.

HODGKIN, VALERIE; Lewiston HS; Lewiston, ME; (Y); Church Yth Grp; Letterman Clb; Bsktbl; Var L Crs Cntry; Var Capt Trk; High Hon Roll; Hon Roll; Ntl Merit Ltr.

HODGKINS, GLENN; Benny Eagle HS; N Windham, ME; (Y); 10/214; Math Tm; Ski Clb; Symp Band; Nwsp Phtg; Stu Cncl; Var L Tennis; Bausch & Lomb Sci Awd; High Hon Roll; Hon Roll; NHS; Math Awd; Pupl Paper Fnd Schlrshp; Standish Alumni Assoc Schrlshp; U ME; Engrng.

HODGKINS, JOHN; Yarmouth HS; Yarmouth, ME; (Y); Church Yth Grp; French Clb; Ski Clb; Band; Chorus; Jazz Band; School Musical; School Play; Yrbk Stf; Crs Cntry; Eagl Sct 84; Biochem.

HODGKINS, LYNNE J; Leavitt Area HS; Greene, ME; (Y); 1/170; Am Leg Aux Girls St; Cmnty Wkr; Math Tm; Speech Tm; School Play; Nwsp Ed-Chief; French Hon Soc; NHS; Trs Church Yth Grp; French Clb; ME Schlrs Day 85; Lng Clb Awd 85; Pre-Law.

HODGSON, KARYN; Fryeburg Acad; Fryeburg, ME; (Y); Mgr Bsbl; Mgr Bsktbl; Hon Roll; Fayeburg Acad Schlrshp 85-86; Acctg.

HOESCHEN, CHRISTINE; Morse HS; Georgetown, ME; (Y); Hosp Aide; Capt Math Tm; Science Clb; Yrbk Stf; High Hon Roll; Ntl Merit Ltr; Intnl Clb; Pep Clb; Im Vllybl; Prfct Atten Awd; US Hstry Awd 85; 1st Pl ME Hstry Day 85; ME Bowdoin Coll Smmr Hmnts Pgm 85; U Of CT; Phrmcy.

HOLIERHOEK, CAROL; Woodland HS; Woodland, ME; (S); French Clb; FBLA; Hosp Aide; Varsity Clb; Yrbk Rptr; Var L Cheerleading; Mgr(s); Hon Roll; VP Soph Cls; VP Jr Cls; Westbrook Coll; Med Secy.

HOPKINS, SETH; Dexter Regional HS; Dexter, ME; (Y); 8/105; Pres Sec 4-H; Pres FBLA; L Bsbl; Mgr Bsktbl; Cit Awd; Dnfth Awd; DAR Awd; 4-H Awd; NHS; Ntl Merit SF; Natl 4-H Congrss Chicago IL 83; 4-H Citznshp WA Foods WA D C 83; Commdty Mktg Symp Chicago IL 84; Syracuse U; Telecomm.

HOPLER, VICKILYNNE; Fryeburg Acad; Fryeburg, ME; (Y); Dance Clb; GAA; Library Aide; Pep Clb; Varsity Clb; Stage Crew; Yrbk Stf; Cheerleading; Mat Maids; Score Keeper; US Air Force; Admin Nurse.

HORNE, FREDERICK; Gardiner Area HS; Gardiner, ME; (Y); VP Aud/Vis; Trs Church Yth Grp; FCA; Nwsp Stf; Rep Frsh Cls; Rep Soph Cls; Rep Sr Cls; JV Ftbl; Hon Roll; Crpntry.

HORTON, ANGELA; Yarmouth JR SR HS; Yarmouth, ME; (Y); Church Yth Grp; French Clb; Latin Clb; Yrbk Ed-Chief; Yrbk Stf; Rep Soph Cls; Rep Jr Cls; Pres Stu Cncl; Cit Awd; French Hon Soc; Smith Clg; Intl Bus Mgmt.

HORTON, LAURIE; Fryeburg Academy; Fryeburg, ME; (Y); Yrbk Stf; Rep Church Yth Grp; Rep Jr Cls; Sec Stu Cncl; Var Trk; Var Hon Roll; Jr NHS; NHS; Lyndon; Ed.

HOTELLING, KIRSTIN R; Deering HS; Freeport, ME; (Y); Art Clb; Cmnty Wkr; Debate Tm; Model UN; Ski Clb; Yrbk Stf; Lit Mag; Fld Hcky; Lcrss; High Hon Roll; Poetry Cnttst Achvts 1st,3rd 84-85; Oberin; Wrtng.

HOTTE, KIRK A; Oxford Hills HS; Oxford, ME; (Y); Debate Tm; Math Clb; NFL; Band; Mrchg Band; Trk; Hon Roll; Debat Troph Lexington MA & Herman H S 84; Debat Troph Deering H S 85; Aerosp Engrng.

HOWARD, LISA; Lawrence HS; Clinton, ME; (Y); 22/201; French Clb; Leo Clb; Band; Chorus; Jazz Band; Mrchg Band; Pep Band; Hon Roll; Prfct Atten Awd; Thomas Coll; Busnss.

HOWARD, PAULA; Windham HS; N Windham, ME; (Y); Sec Soph Cls; Rep Jr Cls; Var Socr; Var Trk; Hon Roll; Sec Jr NHS; US Bus Educ Awd Wnnr 83; Legal Secy.

HOWE, GEORGE; Gorham HS; Gorham, ME; (Y); Hon Roll; US Hist Awd 85; Typng Accrcy Awds 83-85; Andover Coll; Accntnt.

HOWE, STEPHEN; Cony HS; Augusta, ME; (Y); 45/300; Am Leg Boys St; Var Capt Bsbl; Var Capt Bsktbl; Var Capt Crs Cntry; Im Vllybl; High Hon Roll; Hon Roll; NHS; Hon Roll; ME ST Sci Fair 83; Eastern ME Cls A All Trnmnt Bsktbl Tm 85; Amer HS Athlt 85; Husson Coll; Bus Adm.

HOY, NATHAN; Old Orchard Beach HS; Old Orchard Bch, ME; (Y); 17/100; Hon Roll; Comp Achvt Awd 84-85; Comp Troubleshtng.

HUBNER, KATHERINE; Deering HS; Portland, ME; (Y); Key Clb; Varsity Clb; Stu Cncl; Bsktbl; Hon Roll; Jr NHS; Sftbl; Fld Hcky; Antmy Ldrshp Clss 83-84; Hnbl Mntn All Telegram Leag Sftbl Tm 83-84; U Of VT; Lib Arts.

HUFF, LAURIE; Jay HS; Jay, ME; (Y); Math Tm; Varsity Clb; Yrbk Stf; Pres Jr Cls; Var L Bsktbl; Var L Sftbl; Hon Roll; Girls State Alt 85.

HUFF, LISA; Wells HS; Wells, ME; (Y); Cmnty Wkr; FHA; Chorus; Yrbk Stf; Hon Roll; NHS.

HUFF, VERONICA; Bonny Eagle HS; Hollis, ME; (Y); 4/240; Drama Clb; Pres Latin Clb; Math Tm; High Hon Roll; NHS; Pres Schlr; Washington U St Louis; Rssn.

HUGHES, TRACY; Cape Elizabeth HS; Cape Elizabeth, ME; (Y); Exploring; Ski Clb; Spanish Clb; Mgr(s); Var Socr; Stat Swmmng; JV Trk; CPR Instr 84 & 85; Vet.

HUJSAK, ELIZABETH; Bonny Eagle HS; W Buxton, ME; (Y); Am Leg Aux Girls St; JA; Ski Clb; JV Var Bsktbl; Stat Fld Hcky; JV Tennis; Hon Roll; Jr NHS; NHS; Lobbyst Awd 85; ME St Garden Clb Essay Cont 85; Latin II,Span II Awds 85; Stanford U; Comm.

HUNTER, CONNIE; Lawrence HS; Fairfield, ME; (Y); Office Aide; Spanish Clb; Yrbk Stf; VP Frsh Cls; Stu Cncl; JV Bsktbl; Var Crs Cntry; Var Sftbl; Hon Roll; KUUTI; Nutritionist.

HUNTRESS, DIANE; Fryeburg Acad; Brownfield, ME; (Y); GAA; Latin Clb; Varsity Clb; Yrbk Ed-Chief; Yrbk Stf; Sec Soph Cls; Var Fld Hcky; Var Mgr(s); Mgr Wrstlng; Hon Roll; Bus.

HUNTRESS, WENDY LEE; Massabesic HS; Springvale, ME; (Y); 3/145; Pres Church Yth Grp; Chorus; Yrbk Stf; Co-Capt Fld Hcky; Co-Capt Sftbl; High Hon Roll; NHS; Bsktbl; Hon Roll; Kiwanis Awd; SSYA Plyr Sprtsmn Awd 85; Engl Dept Awd 85; Sftbl MVP 83, 85; Thomas Coll; Ofc Admin.

HURLEY, GAIL; Lewiston HS; Lewiston, ME; (Y); 12/450; Letterman Clb; Var Capt Fld Hcky; Trk; Hon Roll; NHS; Natl Sci Merit Awd 83-84; Girls ST Alt 84-85; Outstndg Achvt Frnch III 83-84,Analysis 84-85; Engl 83.

HUTCHINSON, JENNIFER; Houlton HS; Houlton, ME; (Y); Am Leg Aux Girls St; FBLA; FHA; Pres Math Clb; Sec Band; Chorus; Yrbk Stf; Cheerleading; Hon Roll; Church Yth Grp; JR Miss Pgnt Spirit Of JR Miss Awd 84; Dollars For Schlrs 85; Husson Coll; Acctng.

IACONETA, CATHERINE; Portland HS; Portland, ME; (Y); Latin Clb; Rep Frsh Cls; Rep Jr Cls; Trs Sr Cls; Var Bsktbl; Coach Actv; Socr; Sftbl; Hon Roll; NHS; Bsktbl St Champs 83-84 & 84-85; 2nd Tm All St 84-85; Sftbl St Champs 84-85; 1st Tm All Lg All Str 83-84; Phys Ther.

INGERSON, SANDY; Lisbon HS; Lisbon Falls, ME; (Y); Am Leg Aux Girls St; Church Yth Grp; French Clb; Office Aide; Yrbk Stf; Bsktbl; Var Socr; Var JV Sftbl; Hon Roll; Mid ST Auburn; Sec.

IRVING, RICHARD; York HS; Cape Neddick, ME; (Y); Church Yth Grp; Dance Clb; Yrbk Stf; Mgr(s); Prfct Atten Awd; Johnson Wales; Culinary Arts.

IVORY, LISA; Nokomis Regional HS; Detroit, ME; (Y); 6/176; Hst French Clb; Drm Mjr(t); Yrbk Stf; Rep Frsh Cls; Rep Jr Cls; Rep Sr Cls; Twrlr; High Hon Roll; NHS; Pittsfield Scbasticook Hosp Aux Schlrshp 85; Dr John Briggs Mem Schlrshp 85; Eastern ME Vo-Tech Inst; Med.

JACKMAN, AUDREY; Old Orchard Beach HS; Ocean Pk, ME; (Y); 2/74; VP Pres Church Yth Grp; Band; Concert Band; Jazz Band; Mrchg Band; Orch; Symp Band; High Hon Roll; Sal; John Trull Mem Schlrshp 85; Ithaca Coll Ithaca; Musc Ed.

JACKSON, BRIAN; Deering HS; Portland, ME; (Y); Am Leg Boys St; Varsity Clb; Var Coach Actv; Var JV Ftbl; Var Trk; Var Im Vllybl; Var L Wrstlng; Hon Roll; Mst Val JV Wrstlr; Wrstg 4th Regn; Wrstlng ST; Engrng.

JACKSON, LYNN; Bonny Eagle HS; W Buxton, ME; (Y); Library Aide; Mgr(s); Score Keeper; Mgr Socr; Sftbl; Hon Roll; Outstndng Stu Awd 85; Comp.

JACOBS, SHAWN M; Mexico HS; Mexico, ME; (Y); Am Leg Boys St; Aud/Vis; Boy Scts; Chorus; School Musical; VP Jr Cls; VP Sr Cls; Socr; Trk; Church Yth Grp; Natl Schl Choral Awd; Mst For The Schl; Amer Intl Coll; Bio.

JACQUES, ANDREW P; Upper Kennebec Valley Mem HS; Bingham, ME; (Y); Am Leg Boys St; Red Cross Aide; Ski Clb; Yrbk Ed-Chief; Pres Frsh Cls; Pres Soph Cls; Pres Jr Cls; Pres Sr Cls; Var Crs Cntry; Var Trk; Hugh O Brian Yth Fndtn & Ldrshp Smnr 84; ST Cls C Ski Miestr Awd 85; Math Acad Lttr 83-85; U Of ME-ORONO; Elec Engrng.

JACQUES, KATHY; Lewiston Rgional Vocational Ctr; Lewiston, ME; (Y); Hosp Aide; Pres Pep Clb; Stu Cncl; Hon Roll; Bernards Schl Hair Fashn; Barbr.

JACQUES, RICHARD; Livermore Falls HS; Livermore Falls, ME; (Y); 12/96; Am Leg Boys St; L Math Tm; Yrbk Ed-Chief; Yrbk Stf; Bsktbl; Trk; Hon Roll; NHS; Voice Dem Awd; 4th Beam Bus Ed Assn ME 84; Modl ST Legsltr 84; Hstry Awd 84; Pres Acadmc Fit Awd & Acctncy Awd 85; Thomas Coll; CPA.

JALBERT, LORIANN; Sanford HS; Sanford, ME; (Y); Teachers Aide; High Hon Roll; Hon Roll; Cert Waitrss Traing Cours Hm Ec 84; Secy.

JALBERT, MICHELLE; Windham HS; North Windham, ME; (Y); Church Yth Grp; GAA; Yrbk Stf; Cheerleading; Gym; Socr; Prfct Atten Awd; Mrchndsng.

JAMES, JILL; Presque Isle HS; Mapleton, ME; (Y); Debate Tm; Drama Clb; VP NFL; Sec VP Spanish Clb; Speech Tm; Band; School Musical; Nwsp Phtg; Pres Soph Cls; Pres Jr Cls; Poem Publ Magzn Western KY 85; Outstndng Fornscs 85; Govt.

JAMESON, LEA-ANNE; Yarmouth HS; Yarmouth, ME; (Y); 9/86; Am Leg Aux Girls St; Trs French Clb; Political Wkr; Pres Frsh Cls; Pres Soph Cls; Pres Jr Cls; Pres Stu Cncl; Var Swmmng; Var Tennis; Cit Awd; Col Dames Essay Wnnr 85; USM Smmr Inst 85; Intl Rltns.

JAMESON, MICHELLE; Meclomak Valley HS; Friendship, ME; (Y); Pres Art Clb; Latin Clb; Thesps; School Musical; School Play; Variety Show; Hon Roll; Computer Clb; Drama Clb; Stage Crew; Best Actress 84-85; Most Imprvd Thespian 84-85; Hnrbl Ment Bath Certamen Latin Clb 83-84; Psych.

JAMISON, NATHALIE LYNN; Gardiner Area HS; Randolph, ME; (Y); 1/216; Am Leg Aux Girls St; Church Yth Grp; JCL; Pres Latin Clb; Band; Chorus; School Musical; High Hon Roll; NHS.

JANDREAU, KEVIN NILES; Ashland Community HS; Portage, ME; (Y); 2/48; Church Yth Grp; Band; Church Choir; Concert Band; Jazz Band; Mrchg Band; Orch; School Musical; School Play; Variety Show; Pres Acad Ftns Awd 85; Dirigo St ME Hse Rep Awd 85; U Southern ME; Music.

JANDREAU, KIM MARIE; Ashland Community HS; Portage, ME; (Y); 6/44; Band; Sec Church Yth Grp; Pres Jr Cls; Pres Sr Cls; Trs Pres Stu Cncl; Cheerleading; Vllybl; Hon Roll; NHS; Voice Dem Awd; Recpnt Prncpls Assn Secdry Schls 85; Mst Spritd Prsn 85; Hghst In Busnss 85; Northern ME Vo Tech Inst; Bus.

JASPER, ANNA; R W Traip Acad; Kittery, ME; (Y); Church Yth Grp; Drama Clb; Thesps; Chorus; School Musical; School Play; Yrbk Stf; JV Cheerleading; Var Fld Hcky; Var Trk; Home Ec Awd; Actress.

JASPER, BILLY; Livermore Falls HS; Livermore Falls, ME; (Y); Boy Scts; Band; Concert Band; Drm & Bgl; Jazz Band; Mrchg Band; Pep Band; JV Var Bsktbl; Capt Var Crs Cntry; Var L Trk; U Of ME Orono; Elec Engrng.

JEAN, ELLEN; Freeport HS; Freeport, ME; (Y); 12/65; Church Yth Grp; Cmnty Wkr; French Clb; Office Aide; PAVAS; Nwsp Ed-Chief; Lit Mag; VP Stu Cncl; Hon Roll; NHS; Dollars For Schlrs Awd Scholar 85; Stu Cncl Awd Scholar 85; U Of ME Orono; Psych.

JELLISON, DAWN; Kennebunk HS; Kennebunkport, ME; (Y); 4/150; Math Clb; Science Clb; Band; School Play; Nwsp Stf; Lit Mag; Gym; Kiwanis Awd; NHS; Ntl Merit Ltr; 14th Ntl Spnsh Exm 85; Supts Supr 100 Schlrs 84; ME Schlrs Dy Pgm & Half Tuitn Schlrshp UMO 85; Cornell U; Aersp Engrng.

JENKINS, BONNIE; Franklin Schl; Auburn, ME; (Y); Girl Scts; Chorus; Church Choir; Yrbk Phtg; High Hon Roll; Hon Roll.

JEWETT, SUSAN; Jay HS; Jay, ME; (Y); 15/85; Rep Am Leg Aux Girls St; Pres 4-H; Sec FBLA; Office Aide; Band; Yrbk Bus Mgr; VP Sr Cls; Capt Cheerleading; Hon Roll; Thomas Coll; Ofc Admin.

JOHNSON, BELINDA; Caribou HS; New Sweden, ME; (Y); 116/235; Hosp Aide; Key Clb; Letterman Clb; Varsity Clb; Var Socr; Var Capt Sftbl; Mgr Wrstlng; High Hon Roll; Hon Roll; NH Vo-Tech Coll; Occptnl Thrpy.

JOHNSON, HARRISON; Morse HS; Bath, ME; (Y); Boy Scts; Church Yth Grp; Stage Crew; Socr; Trk; Hon Roll; Boys ST 85.

JOHNSON, JENNIFER J; Caribou HS; Stockholm, ME; (Y); 36/240; Church Yth Grp; GAA; Letterman Clb; Library Aide; Office Aide; Ski Clb; Varsity Clb; Band; Chorus; Church Choir; Boston Coll Of Pharmacy; Phrmcy.

JOHNSON, MICHELLE; Kennebunk HS; Kennebunk, ME; (Y); 39/142; Art Clb; Yrbk Stf; Hon Roll; Fash Merch.

JOHNSON, PAUL; Windham HS; S Windham, ME; (Y); Art Clb; Ski Clb; JV Socr; Hon Roll; AF; Aeronutcl Engr.

JOHNSON, REBECCA; Houlton HS; Houlton, ME; (Y); Pres Church Yth Grp; Math Clb; Band; Chorus; Church Choir; School Musical; Vllybl; Hon Roll; U Of ME Orono; Elem Ed.

JOHNSON, ROBYN; Deering HS; Portland, ME; (Y); French Clb; Bsbl; Hon Roll; Marn Bio.

JONES, DEBBIE; Livermore Falls HS; Livermore Falls, ME; (Y); Drama Clb; FNA; Varsity Clb; Band; Concert Band; Mrchg Band; School Play; Stage Crew; Yrbk Stf; JV Bsktbl; Smmr Humanities Pgm 85; Engl Hnrs 85-86; Nrsng.

JONES, MATTHEW; Derring HS; Portland, ME; (Y); 1/255; Debate Tm; JCL; VP Hst Latin Clb; Letterman Clb; Math Tm; NFL; Ski Clb; Var L Crs Cntry; Var L Trk; Bausch & Lomb Sci Awd; Ntl Hnr Soc Schlrshp, Maxima Cum Laude Ntl Lat, 1st Ntl Spnsh Exm 85; Dartmouth Coll; Math.

JONES, MELANIE; Bangor HS; Bangor, ME; (Y); Hosp Aide; Key Clb; Library Aide; Band; Concert Band; Mrchg Band; Pep Band; School Play; Nwsp Stf; Yrbk Ed-Chief; Mary Novak Awd Engl Excllnc 84; Engl Achvt 84-85; U ME Orono; Bus.

JONES, MIKE; Deering HS; Portland, ME; (Y); JA; Key Clb; Latin Clb; Varsity Clb; Trs Soph Cls; Trs Jr Cls; JV Bsktbl; Var L Crs Cntry; Var Trk; Bus Mngmnt.

JONES, PEGGY A; Leavitt Area HS; Turner, ME; (Y); 20/150; Am Leg Aux Girls St; Drama Clb; Office Aide; School Play; Trs Frsh Cls; Trs Soph Cls; Trs Jr Cls; L Cheerleading; Im Coach Actv; L Fld Hcky; All Star Cast 1 Act Ply Fstvl 84; Spch Cntst-Dramtcs-1st Pl 84; Bentley Coll; Hosp Adm.

JONES, ROBERT; York HS; York, ME; (Y); 11/130; German Clb; Yrbk Stf; L Bsktbl; L Ftbl; L Trk; Im Vllybl; Hon Roll; JR Wrtng Awd 85; Worchester Polytech Inst; Engrg.

JORDAN, JAYNE; Lewiston HS; Lewiston, ME; (Y); Office Aide; Yrbk Stf; JV Fld Hcky; Graphic Art.

JORDAN, LISA; Telstar Regional HS; Locke Mills, ME; (Y); 13/61; Drama Clb; Teachers Aide; Flag Corp; Nwsp Stf; Cheerleading; High Hon Roll; Hon Roll; Outstndng Achvt Eng 85; Photo.

JORDAN, RHONDA J; Leavitt Area HS; Turner, ME; (Y); FHA; Pep Clb; Nwsp Stf; Yrbk Stf; Stu Cncl; Trk; High Hon Roll; Hon Roll; Bus.

JORDAN, TRACY; Orono HS; Orono, ME; (S); 15/105; Trs Frsh Cls; Sec Soph Cls; Pres Stu Cncl; Stat Bsbl; JV L Cheerleading; Hon Roll; NHS; Natl Hnr Soc 83-85; U Of ME; Pre-Vet.

JUDGE, MARGARET R; Biddeford HS; Biddeford, ME; (Y); 1/300; Am Leg Aux Girls St; 4-H; Band; Yrbk Bus Mgr; Rep Jr Cls; JV Trk; High Hon Roll; Trs NHS; Hnrs Convctn Awd 2nd Acadmc Achv 84-85; Dartmouth; Pre-Med.

JUERS, JOELLE; Westbrook HS; Weatbrook, ME; (Y); 2/211; Am Leg Aux Girls St; Church Yth Grp; Drama Clb; English Clb; Latin Clb; Math Tm; Rep Stu Cncl; NHS; Sal; Band; ME Assn Scndry Schl Prncpls Awd 85; Rachel Hutchinson Math Schlrshp 85; Outstndng Chem Stu Awd 85; U Of PA; Hstry.

JUTRAS, SANDRA; Lewiston HS; Lewiston, ME; (Y); 44/425; Exploring; Letterman Clb; Ski Clb; Stage Crew; Var Cheerleading; Hon Roll; NHS; Maine Schlrs Day 85; Northeastern U; Comp Sci.

KANGAS, HOLLY; Buckfield HS; W Paris, ME; (Y); Am Leg Aux Girls St; Spanish Clb; Chorus; High Hon Roll; Hon Roll; NHS; Bus.

KARKOS, KERN; Mt Blue HS; Wilton, ME; (Y); 2/220; Exploring; Ski Clb; Var L Crs Cntry; Var L Trk; High Hon Roll; Jr NHS; Ehren Urkunde Hnrs For Hgh Achvt In Grmn 84 & 85; ME Schlrs Day Awd 85; Cert Of Aprctn 85; Lngs.

KEAMY, DIRK; Lisbon HS; Lisbon Falls, ME; (Y); Boy Scts; CAP; French Clb; Ski Clb; Pep Band; Crs Cntry; Socr; Elec Engr.

KEARNEY, JULIE; Deering HS; Portland, ME; (Y); Key Clb; Chorus; School Musical; Nwsp Stf; VP Sec Stu Cncl; Crs Cntry; Trk; French Hon Soc; VP NHS; St Schlr; Boston U Tanglewood Inst Yng Art Vocal Pgm 84; Louis S Black Mem Scholar 85; Accompanist Chorus 81-85; Mt Holyoke Coll.

KEARNS, BRENDA; Hampden Acad; Hampden Highland, ME; (Y); 8/160; Chrmn Sec Church Yth Grp; French Clb; Band; Concert Band; Mrchg Band; High Hon Roll; NHS; Pres Schlr; Hosp Aide; Bsktbl; Eagls Clb Schlrshp 85; ME Schlrs Day 84; Thomas Coll; Comp Inf Sys.

KEATEN, JAMES; Skowhegan Area HS; Skowhegan, ME; (Y); 8/217; Drama Clb; German Clb; Math Tm; Sec Chorus; Nwsp Ed-Chief; NHS; Pres Schlr; Varsity Clb; Nwsp Rptr; Blaine House Schlrshp 85; ARA Schlrshp 85; William Philbrick Schlrshp 85; U ME Farmington; Educ.

KELLER, CHRISTINE; Skowhegan Area HS; Norridgewock, ME; (Y); Art Clb; 4-H; High Hon Roll; Hon Roll; Art Awd 83; Wldlf Cnsrvtnst.

KELLEY, D ANNA; Jonesport-Beals HS; Beals, ME; (Y); Church Yth Grp; Cmnty Wkr; Computer Clb; Drama Clb; 4-H; Girl Scts; Office Aide; Varsity Clb; School Play; Stage Crew; Sewng Clb 84-85; JR Prom Queen 85; Beal Coll; Trvl.

KELLEY, JANE A; Belfast Area HS; Belfast, ME; (Y); Political Wkr; Chorus; School Musical; High Hon Roll; Hon Roll; Jr NHS; Ntl Merit Ltr; Math Tm; VP Spanish Clb; Nwsp Stf; Proj Utopia,Gftd & Tlntd Prog 82-83; Upwd Bnd 84-86; Music Fest 85; Airln Pilt.

KELLEY, JULIA; Livermore Falls HS; Livermore Falls, ME; (Y); Am Leg Aux Girls St; Varsity Clb; Yrbk Stf; Rep Stu Cncl; Bsktbl; JV Var Fld Hcky; Var Sftbl; Trk; Acctng.

KELLY, DEIRDRE; Ft Kent Community HS; St Francis, ME; (Y); 22/145; Art Clb; Yrbk Stf; Vllybl; Hon Roll; Athltc Awd Intrmrl Bsktbl 84; Awd Bio 84; Cert Hnr Hnr Rll 3 Consectv Tmes 83 & 85; Husson Coll; Secy.

KELLY, LEISA; Ft Kent Community HS; St Francis, ME; (Y); 7/150; Yrbk Bus Mgr; Hon Roll; Outstndng Achvt Gnrl Bio 84; ME Bus Educ Assn-Bus Math & Shrthnd I 84-85; Tchng.

KELSO, ROBERT; Skowhegan Area HS; Skowhegan, ME; (Y); Am Leg Boys St; JV Ftbl; JV Wrstlng; Hon Roll; Sheppards Awd 84; Geomtry Hghst Avg 84; Chem Hghst Avg 85; U Of ME-ORENO; Wldlf Cnsrvtn.

KEMP, RITCHIE; Carrabec HS; N Anson, ME; (Y); Chess Clb; German Clb; Var Bsbl; Var Trk; Ntl Merit Schol; Prfct Atten Awd; Comp Pgmmr.

KENDRICK, KRISTIN; Bonny Eagle HS; Hollis, ME; (Y); Church Yth Grp; French Clb; Symp Band; Ed Nwsp Rptr; Nwsp Stf; Trs Soph Cls; Trs Jr Cls; Sec Sr Cls; Var Cheerleading; JV Fld Hcky; U Of ME-ORONO; Intl Affrs.

KENNEDY, CHERYL; Freeport HS; Freeport, ME; (Y); 4/80; Am Leg Aux Girls St; Trs French Clb; Pres Band; Trs Soph Cls; VP Jr Cls; Pres Sr Cls; JV Var Bsktbl; JV Var Fld Hcky; Pres NHS; U S Army Resrv Natl Schlr Athl Awd 85; Schlr Athl Awd 85; Smith Coll Bk Awd Acadmc Achvt & Ldrshp 85; Bio.

KENNEDY, MICHELE; Traip Acad; Kittery, ME; (Y); Am Leg Aux Girls St; Pep Clb; Political Wkr; Chorus; Stage Crew; Yrbk Rptr; Yrbk Stf; Rep Soph Cls; Rep Jr Cls; Sec Stu Cncl; Zoolgy.

KENNEDY, WENDY GRANT; Marshwood HS; South Berwick, ME; (Y); 11/101; French Clb; Math Tm; Trs Frsh Cls; Trs Soph Cls; Trs Jr Cls; Trs Sr Cls; Pres VP Stu Cncl; Var Cheerleading; Var JV Fld Hcky; NHS; Band Cncl Rep; Natl Music Awd; Comm.

KETCH, VICKIE; Caribou HS; Caribou, ME; (Y); 17/230; French Clb; Chorus; High Hon Roll; Hon Roll; U Of ME.

KETOVER, JILL; Deering HS; Portland, ME; (Y); Cmnty Wkr; Pres FTA; Hosp Aide; VP JA; Political Wkr; Teachers Aide; Band; Chorus; School Musical; Yrbk Stf; Poli Sci.

KIDDER, KATHRYN; Cony HS; Augusta, ME; (Y); 2/300; Am Leg Aux Girls St; JCL; Yrbk Sprt Ed; Rep Stu Cncl; Var Capt Bsktbl; Var Capt Fld Hcky; Var Capt Sftbl; Hon Roll; Pres Schlr; Sal; Athl Schlrshp Fld Hcky 85; US Army Resv Ntl Schlr Athl Awd 85; Fld Hcky MVP Awd 84-85; U ME-ORONO; Lib Arts.

KILBORN, KAREN; Lake Region HS; Bridgton, ME; (Y); AFS; Am Leg Boys St; Am Leg Aux Girls St; VP Varsity Clb; Yrbk Ed-Chief; Yrbk Sprt Ed; Yrbk Stf; Rep Jr Cls; Trs Stu Cncl; Var Bsktbl; Psych.

KIMBALL, SCOTT; Deering HS; Portland, ME; (Y); Band; Concert Band; Jazz Band; Mrchg Band; Pep Band; Hon Roll; Comp.

KING, DEBORA A; Mattanawcook Acad; Lincoln Ctr, ME; (Y); 7/110; Church Yth Grp; Band; Chorus; Concert Band; Pep Band; Var Mgr Bsktbl; High Hon Roll; Hon Roll; Grls ST 84; Acadmc Excllnc Awd Top 10 Clss 85; Wilhemina Porter Memrl Schlrshp 85; Casco Bay Coll; Paralegl.

KING, ERIC; Fryeburg Acad; Conway, NH; (Y); Church Yth Grp; Drama Clb; French Clb; JA; School Play; Nwsp Stf; Yrbk Sprt Ed; Yrbk Stf; Var Crs Cntry; Ntl Merit Ltr; FL Inst; Navgtnl Aide.

KING, LANAE; Belfast Area HS; Morrill, ME; (Y); Sec FBLA; Trs Girl Scts; Letterman Clb; Office Aide; Teachers Aide; Band; Hon Roll; Camera Clb; Concert Band; Mrchg Band; 2nd Pl In ST Solo & Ensmbl For Clrnt 82; Slvr & Ldrshp Awd In Grl Scouts 83; Hussen Coll; Lgl Scrtry.

KING, MYA LISA; Hampden Acad; Hampden, ME; (Y); 8/180; Pres Intnl Clb; Key Clb; Band; Yrbk Stf; Capt Crs Cntry; Var Gym; Var Trk; High Hon Roll; Hon Roll; NHS; ME Schlrs Day 85; Smmr Inst Of Unif Of Southern ME 85; Doc.

KINNEY, RANDA CATE; Penquis Valley HS; Atkinson, ME; (Y); Am Leg Aux Girls St; Sec Drama Clb; Band; Church Choir; Jazz Band; Pep Band; School Musical; Nwsp Stf; Yrbk Bus Mgr; Sec Soph Cls; Outstndg Clss Musician Awd 83 & 85; Gftd/Tlntd Music & Theater 83-85; Educ & Music.

KIPPAX, JILL B; Gray-New Gloucester HS; New Gloucester, ME; (Y); 1/115; Ski Clb; Band; Jazz Band; Mrchg Band; Orch; Pep Band; School Musical; Symp Band; Hon Roll; Hon Roll; Portland Yth Symph Orch 82-85; ME All-ST Music Fest 84-85; U Of ME Smmr Inst Gifted & Tlntd 84; Georgetown U; Pre-Med.

KLIVANS, LAURA; Camden-Rockport HS; Camden, ME; (Y); 4/125; French Clb; JCL; Latin Clb; Nwsp Rptr; Lit Mag; Swmmng; High Hon Roll; Hon Roll; Lion Awd; NHS; Delg Dirigo Grls ST 85; Wnnr Cntrl ME Area Agncy On Agng Essy Cntst 85; Schlrs Dy At U Of ME Orono.

KNAPTON, JEFF; Westbrook HS; Westbrook, ME; (Y); Rep Am Leg Boys St; Church Yth Grp; Key Clb; Pres Stu Cncl; Var L Bsktbl; Var L Socr; Hon Roll; NHS; Latin Clb; Rep Frsh Cls; Yale Bk Awd 85; Hugh O Brien Yth Ldrshp Sem 84; Chem Engrng.

KNOWLES, LINDA; Leavitt Area HS; Greene, ME; (Y); 16/110; Var JV Bsktbl; Var Coach Actv; Var L Sftbl; Hon Roll; MVP Vrsty Bsktbl 84-85; Phtogrphy.

KNOWLTON, NANCY J; Hampden Acad; Hampden, ME; (Y); 43/160; French Clb; Girl Scts; Hon Roll; Kiwanis Awd; Fr Clb Awd 85; U Of ME; Bus.

KNOX, CHERYL A; Washington Acad; Pembroke, ME; (Y); 1/49; French Clb; Library Aide; Nwsp Ed-Chief; High Hon Roll; NHS; Ntl Merit SF; Outstndng JR Bk Awd 84; Amy Parker Wiswell Awd 82; U Of ME; Hstry.

KOLLIAS, JANA; Yarmouth HS; Yarmouth, ME; (Y); 5/88; Church Yth Grp; Drama Clb; Latin Clb; Math Tm; Band; Chorus; School Musical; School Play; Yrbk Stf; Lit Mag; Duke U Durham NC.

KOMINSKY, JULIE; Bangor HS; Bangor, ME; (Y); Key Clb; Ski Clb; Ed Nwsp Stf; Yrbk Stf; High Hon Roll; Hon Roll; NHS; Engl Achvt Awd 85.

KOSOFF, TERRI; Westbrook HS; Westbrook, ME; (Y); Dance Clb; Drama Clb; French Clb; School Play; Yrbk Sprt Ed; Hon Roll; Nwsp Sprt Ed; Nwsp Stf; JV Var Bsktbl; JV Trk; Wmns Litry Union 85; Kids/Cops Wrkshp Drg/Alchl Abus 85; Amer U; Pre-Law.

KREIE, JOYCE L; Wells HS; Ogunquit, ME; (Y); 1/115; Trs Church Yth Grp; Math Tm; Nwsp Sprt Ed; Yrbk Sprt Ed; Pres Sr Cls; Var Capt Bsktbl; Var L Fld Hcky; Var Capt Sftbl; Var High Hon Roll; NHS; Outstndng Acad Awd; Coaches Awds Sftbl Fldhcky; Def Awd Bsktbl.

KROOK, BETH; Robert W Traip Acad; Kittery, ME; (Y); 4/8; Camera Clb; French Clb; Yrbk Phtg; JV Fld Hcky; L Trk; High Hon Roll; Hon Roll; NHS; Most Imprvd Awd Girls Trk 85; Art.

KUHN, MARIE; Skowhegan Area HS; Hartland, ME; (Y); 7/170; Art Clb; German Clb; Varsity Clb; Band; Concert Band; Mrchg Band; Pep Band; Variety Show; High Hon Roll; NHS; U Of VT; Anml Sci.

KUIVANEN, ANDERS; Mattanawcook HS; Chester, ME; (Y); Minstr.

KUPERMAN, MARINA; Portland HS; Portland, ME; (Y); 1/250; Am Leg Aux Girls St; Math Tm; Sec Soph Cls; Sec Jr Cls; JV Var Fld Hcky; High Hon Roll; NHS; French Clb; Latin Clb; Chorus; Wellesley Bk Awd 85; Prix D Excllnce Fr 85; ME Schlrs Day UMO 85; Physcn.

LA FRENIERE, RUTH ANNE; Old Orchard Beach HS; Old Orchard Bch, ME; (Y); Computer Clb; Drama Clb; French Clb; Library Aide; Office Aide; Color Guard; Mrchg Band; Yrbk Stf; Score Keeper; Wt Lftg; Air Force.

LA PAN, KAREN ELIZABETH; Mt Blue HS; Wilton, ME; (Y); Trs FBLA; Cheerleading; Hon Roll; Jr NHS; NHS; Bus.

LA POINTE, MANON; Leavitt Area HS; Greene, ME; (Y); Am Leg Aux Girls St; Church Yth Grp; Speech Tm; Y-Teens; School Play; Variety Show; JV Cheerleading; Hon Roll; Busnss Mgmt.

LA POINTE, MICHELE LEE; Piscataquis Community HS; Guilford, ME; (Y); AFS; Am Leg Aux Girls St; FNA; Key Clb; Concert Band; Pep Band; Yrbk Stf; Stu Cncl; Capt Cheerleading; Mgr Fld Hcky; ME Ms TEEN Pgnt 83 & 85; RN.

LA PORTE, RENEE M; Skowhegan Area HS; Skowhegan, ME; (Y); 36/206; Varsity Clb; Band; Concert Band; Mrchg Band; VP Soph Cls; Var Capt Bsktbl; Var Socr; Var Sftbl; Dnfth Awd; Hon Roll; Amer HS Athl 84; Air Force; Air Trffc Cntrlr.

LA ROSE, TAMMIE; Lisbon Falls Christian Acad; Pownal, ME; (S); School Musical; School Play; JV Bsktbl; JV Sftbl; Capt Vllybl; Hon Roll; Missions.

LABBE, MICHAEL; Noble HS; North Berwick, ME; (Y); 1/162; Am Leg Boys St; Church Yth Grp; Key Clb; Capt Math Tm; Var L Bsbl; JV Stat Bsktbl; JV Socr; Dnfth Awd; Elks Awd; High Hon Roll; Engr Week Gftd Tlntd UMO 84; High Score Union Mutual Math Exm 84; Worcester Poly Inst; Elec Engr.

LACEY III, JOHN S; Cape Elizabeth HS; Cape Elizabeth, ME; (Y); Trs Church Yth Grp; Debate Tm; Off Drama Clb; French Clb; Science Clb; School Musical; School Play; Stage Crew; Trs Frsh Cls; Stu Cncl; Ntl Interschlstc Swmmng 83-84; 200 Medly Relay 84-85; Theater Awd 84-85; Pol Sci.

LACHANCE, CHRISTOPHER; Skowhegan Area HS; Norridgewock, ME; (Y); Am Leg Boys St; Varsity Clb; Band; Concert Band; Mrchg Band; Var Bsbl; Var Capt Socr; Hon Roll; Marine Maratime Acad; Engr.

LACHANCE, CLAIRE; Lewiston HS; Lewiston, ME; (Y); 4/400; Rep Am Leg Aux Girls St; Trs Keywanettes; Math Tm; Political Wkr; Yrbk Bus Mgr; High Hon Roll; NHS; Ntl Merit Ltr; Brown U Bk Awd 84; Frnch Dept Awds 85; Eng Dept Awds 82-85; Tufts U; Econ.

LACHANCE, DEBBIE; St Dominic Regional HS; Lewiston, ME; (Y); Church Yth Grp; Drama Clb; JA; Keywanettes; Pep Clb; Church Choir; Sec Jr Cls; Stu Cncl; JV Var Cheerleading; Score Keeper; Bio.

LACHANCE, DOUGLAS; Biddeford HS; Biddeford, ME; (Y); 16/300; Am Leg Boys St; Art Clb; High Hon Roll; Hon Roll; Art.

LACHANCE, GERALD; Lewiston HS; Lewiston, ME; (Y); Church Yth Grp; Var L Ice Hcky; Var Socr; High Hon Roll; Jr NHS; NHS.

LACROIX, ELIZABETH; Yarmouth HS; Yarmouth, ME; (Y); Am Leg Aux Girls St; French Clb; Office Aide; Yrbk Stf; Rep Jr Cls; Rep Stu Cncl; Var Bsktbl; Var Fld Hcky; Var Sftbl; French Hon Soc; Spcl Ed Teacher.

LACROIX, THERESA M; Yarmouth HS; Yarmouth, ME; (Y); Drama Clb; French Clb; Office Aide; Stage Crew; Yrbk Ed-Chief; Yrbk Stf; Mgr Bsktbl; Hon Roll; Westbrook Coll; Med Asst.

LAGASSE, NICHOLE; Westbrook HS; Westbrook, ME; (Y); Am Leg Aux Girls St; Spanish Clb; Stu Cncl; Mgr Wrstlng; Hon Roll.

LAHAIE, DEREK A; St Dominics Regional HS; Lewiston, ME; (Y); 17/80; Boy Scts; Key Clb; Var L Bsbl; Var Capt Bsktbl; Var Capt Socr; Hon Roll; US Army, Ntl Soccer Coaches Assoc MVP 84-85; P & P Fuel, All Male Athl Awd 84-85; ME Maritime Acad; Mrine Engrng.

LAMARCHE, LAURA; Central HS; East Corinth, ME; (Y); 6/82; 4-H; Sec Trs FHA; Office Aide; Chorus; Yrbk Bus Mgr; Trs Sr Cls; Capt L Cheerleading; High Hon Roll; Pres NHS; Trs Frsh Cls; Top 10 SR 85; Acadmc Achvt Awds Engl 84-85; Acadmc Achvt Awds Hstry 84; Beal Coll; Bus Mgmt.

LAMONTAGNE, ANNE; Gorham HS; Gorham, ME; (Y); Pres Sec Church Yth Grp; Debate Tm; Drama Clb; GAA; Leo Clb; Spanish Clb; Chorus; Madrigals; School Musical; School Play; Hugh O Brien Ldrshp Found Sem 82-83; Head Usher Grad 85; Dirgo Electv 85; Chem.

LANDER, STUART; Nokomis Regional HS; Newport, ME; (Y); 19/170; Band; Concert Band; Mrchg Band; Symp Band; Var Crs Cntry; Var Trk; Var L Wrstlng; High Hon Roll; Hon Roll; Mst Outstndng Comp Stu Of The Yr 85; Band Letter 83; Wrstlng Letter-Vrsty 83; U Of ME; AFROTC.

LANDES, WENDY; Caribou HS; Caribou, ME; (Y); 35/285; Am Leg Aux Girls St; Rep Soph Cls; Rep Jr Cls; Rep Stu Cncl; Var Cheerleading; Var Crs Cntry; Hon Roll; NHS.

LANDRY, JEFF; Lewiston HS; Lewiston, ME; (Y); Boy Scts; Church Yth Grp; Exploring; JV Bsktbl; JV Mgr(s); High Hon Roll; Hon Roll; NHS; Cntrl ME Vo Tech Inst; Wldng.

LANDRY, JULIE; Portland HS; Portland, ME; (Y); Latin Clb; JV Var Tennis; Hon Roll; Prfct Atten Awd; Antomy Ldrshp; MVP Tnns; Acctng.

LANE, REBECCA H; Edward Little HS; Auburn, ME; (Y); Spanish Clb; Ed Lit Mag; Hon Roll; NHS; Church Yth Grp; Church Choir; Hnrb Mntn,Outstndng Achvmnt Spnsh 83; Outstndg Achvmnt Awd Spnsh 85.

LANE, TAMMY; Jay HS; Wilton, ME; (Y); VP Sec Church Yth Grp; Exploring; FBLA; Library Aide; Sec Teachers Aide; Yrbk Stf; High Hon Roll; Hon Roll; Band; Color Guard; Legl Sec.

LANEY, KANDI L; Skowhegan Area HS; Skowhegan, ME; (Y); 11/216; Am Leg Aux Girls St; Math Tm; Varsity Clb; Rep Stu Cncl; Var Bsktbl; Var Socr; Sftbl; Var Trk; High Hon Roll; NHS; Alg Awd 83; Chem Awd 84; Past Wrthy Advsr Order Rainbow Girls 81-85; Exch Stu Frnch 84; Solo Airplane 84; GA Inst Tech; Chem Engr.

LANGLAIS, RACHEL I; St Dominics Regional HS; Lewiston, ME; (Y); 7/77; Var L Bsktbl; Var L Sftbl; Dnfth Awd; High Hon Roll; Hon Roll; Trs NHS; Ntl Merit Ltr; Pres Schlr; Beta Sigma Phi Schlrshp 85; P&P Fuel Female Ath Of Yr 85; Bio Excllnc 85; Bates Coll; Bio.

LANPHER, TERESA; Penquis Valley HS; Milo, ME; (Y); Variety Show; Yrbk Stf; JV Capt Bsktbl; Var Sftbl; Hon Roll; Athl Awds, Coaches Awd Var Sftbl 83-84; Bus Ed Assn ME Adv Typ & Shrthnd I 84-85; Exec Secry.

LAPHAM, KEVIN; Freeport HS; Freeport, ME; (Y); Pres Aud/Vis; Cmnty Wkr; Library Aide; Stage Crew; Yrbk Stf; Cit Awd; NHS; Am Leg Boys St; JA; Hon Roll; WCSH Tv Am Future Awd 85; Hugh O Brien Yth Ldrshp Sem 84; 5th Pl New Eng HS Video Comp 85; Tv.

LAPLANTE, CINDY; Lewiston HS; Lewiston, ME; (Y); 94/441; Church Yth Grp; Cmnty Wkr; Girl Scts; Hosp Aide; Church Choir; Drm Mjr(t); Var JV Sftbl; Twrlr; French Hon Soc; Hon Roll; Sarah T Burke Fund 85; Knights Columbus 85; Rev Daniel J Hagerty Scholar 85; St Josephs Coll; Nrsng.

LAPOINTE, LISA; Lewiston HS; Lewiston, ME; (Y); Letterman Clb; Q&S; Rep Frsh Cls; Trs Soph Cls; Trs Jr Cls; Trs Sr Cls; Var Cheerleading; Hon Roll; Child Stdy.

LARGEY, LORINDA; Fryeburg Acad; Denmark, ME; (S); French Clb; Varsity Clb; Chorus; School Play; Nwsp Stf; Yrbk Stf; Fld Hcky; Hon Roll; NHS; Law.

LAROCHELLE, MICHAEL; Lewiston HS; Lewiston, ME; (Y); Am Leg Boys St; Boy Scts; Math Tm; Pres Thesps; Chorus; School Musical; Yrbk Ed-Chief; Off Stu Cncl; JV Capt Bsktbl; High Hon Roll; Eagle Scout 83; All St Chrs 83-86; Rensselaer Awd Math & Sci 85; Holy Cross Bk Awd 85; Engrng.

LARRABEE, MARK; Cony HS; Augusta, ME; (Y); JCL; Latin Clb; Red Cross Aide; Hon Roll; Magna Cum Lauda - JCL Exm 83-84; Hnrb Mntn - Schl Sci Fair 84-85; ADAPT Pgm Awd 83-84; U Of ME At Orono; Chem.

LARRIVEE, TAMMY; Lewiston HS; Lewiston, ME; (Y); Am Leg Aux Girls St; VP Hst Intnl Clb; Pep Clb; Yrbk Stf; Stu Cncl; Stat Bsktbl; JV Fld Hcky; Mgr Ftbl; Var Trk; NHS; Concours Nationale Francais Merit Awd 84; Pol Sci.

LARSON, DONNA MARIE; Wells HS; Wells, ME; (Y); 13/108; Chorus; Stage Crew; Nwsp Rptr; Nwsp Stf; Yrbk Stf; JV Sftbl; Hon Roll; Sec NHS; Ogunquit Wmns Clb & HS Ntl Hnr Soc Schlrshps 85; HS Schlrshp Fund Awd 85; U Of ME Farmington; Bus Mngmt.

LASH, SCOTT; Medomak Valley HS; Waldoboro, ME; (Y); Am Leg Boys St; Church Yth Grp; Cmnty Wkr; Stu Cncl; Var JV Mgr(s); 4-H; Latin Clb; Ski Clb; Comp Prgmmr.

LATTY, NANCY; Rangeley Lakes Regional HS; Rangeley, ME; (Y); Girl Scts; Yrbk Phtg; Yrbk Rptr; Yrbk Stf; Pres Frsh Cls; VP Sr Cls; Sec Pres Stu Cncl; Andover; Bus Admin.

LAUZE, LISA; Edward Little HS; Mechanic Falls, ME; (Y); Drama Clb; Latin Clb; School Musical; School Play; High Hon Roll; NHS; St Schlr; Yrbk Stf; Yale Bk Awd 85; Magna Cum Laude 83-85; Nrs.

LAVALLEY, RAY; Fort Fairfield HS; Ft Fairfield, ME; (Y); Chess Clb; Hon Roll; Accntng.

LAVIGNE, MICHELLE; Brunswick HS; Jacksonville Bch, FL; (Y); 15/221; Church Yth Grp; Office Aide; Chorus; Church Choir; Drm Mjr(t); Variety Show; Var Cheerleading; High Hon Roll; Pres Schlr; North FL U; Bus Admin.

LAYNE, JENNIFER; Fryeburg Acad; N Fryeburg, ME; (S); 5/130; Radio Clb; Yrbk Stf; Lit Mag; Var Capt Bowling; Var Socr; High Hon Roll; NHS; Clarence E Walker Ind Arts Awd 83; Bio.

LE BLANC, ANDRE; Leavitt Area HS; Greene, ME; (Y); Pres Church Yth Grp; JV Var Ftbl; High Hon Roll; Hon Roll.

LE CLAIR JR, ROBERT N; Saint Dominic Regional HS; Lewiston, ME; (Y); 33/100; Pres Drama Clb; Sec Key Clb; Math Clb; Math Tm; School Musical; School Play; Mgr Stage Crew; Variety Show; High Hon Roll; NHS; Key Clbr Of Yr 84-85; Archtctrl Engrng.

LE CLAIR, WENDY J; Portland HS; Portland, ME; (Y); JA; Latin Clb; Teachers Aide; Nwsp Stf; Yrbk Stf; Sftbl; Var Trk; Hon Roll.

LEAR, PAMELA; Deering HS; Portland, ME; (Y); 60/292; Church Yth Grp; Pres Exploring; Pres German Clb; Pres Band; Concert Band; Drm Mjr(t); Jazz Band; Mrchg Band; Hon Roll; Ski Clb; Jordan Marsh Jr Advsry Cncl Schlrshp 84-85; Avtn.

LEAVITT, KAREN; Caribou HS; Caribou, ME; (Y); Church Yth Grp; Library Aide; Church Choir; Hon Roll; St Josephs Coll; Nrsng.

LEBEL, VICKIE; Oak Hill HS; Sabattus, ME; (Y); Am Leg Aux Girls St; Church Yth Grp; Office Aide; VP Frsh Cls; JV Var Bsktbl; JV Var Fld Hcky; JV Var Sftbl; Hon Roll; JR SR Prom Committee Chairman 85; Comp Sci.

LEBLANC, ERIK; Skowhegan Area HS; Canaan, ME; (Y); 41/160; German Clb; Letterman Clb; Ski Clb; Varsity Clb; Var L Ftbl; JV Trk; Wt Lftg; Georetown; Govt.

LEBLOND, LISA D; Lewiston HS; Lewiston, ME; (Y).

LECLAIR, CAROL A; Lewiston HS; Lewiston, ME; (Y); Outstndng Achvt Advncd Math 85; Psych.

LECOMPTE, CARRIE; St Dominic Regional HS; Lisbon, ME; (Y); 3/80; Nwsp Rptr; JV Var Bsktbl; Capt Var Fld Hcky; Var Sftbl; High Hon Roll; VP NHS; Voice Dem Awd; Suppr Perfmnc-NEDT 83-84; Bentley; Math.

LEE, JOYCE; Schenck HS; Medway, ME; (Y); Cmnty Wkr; FNA; Hosp Aide; Office Aide; VICA; Vllybl; Certfd Nrses Aide 85; Mst Imprvd Stu 85; CPR 85; Hesser; Med Asst.

LEE, STEPHEN; Cheverus HS; Portland, ME; (Y); 17/87; Church Yth Grp; Drama Clb; Key Clb; Im Ftbl; Var Swmmng; Im Capt Vllybl; High Hon Roll; Ntl Merit Sci Awd 84; Bronze Acad Awd 83-84; U ME Orono; Cvl Engrng.

LEE, TODD; Gorham HS; Gorham, ME; (Y); Model UN; Ski Clb; Spanish Clb; JV Bsbl; Im Bsktbl; JV Golf; High Hon Roll; Hon Roll; Spanish NHS; Naval ROTC; Nvl Pilot.

LEGENDRE, DIANE; Lewiston HS; Lewistin, ME; (Y); 4/400; Math Tm; Pep Clb; Ski Clb; Lit Mag; High Hon Roll; Exclnc Schlrshp Engl 84; Exclnc Latin 85; Coll Edtrl Stff 85; Pre-Med.

LEGENDRE, THOMAS; Lewiston HS; Lewiston, ME; (Y); Am Leg Boys St; Rep Key Clb; Hon Roll; NHS; WA Wrkshps 85; Mdl ST Leglstre 84; Lbrl Arts.

LEIGHTON, MARY ELLEN; Gorham HS; Gorham, ME; (Y); Church Yth Grp; Latin Clb; Leo Clb; Spanish Clb; Nwsp Ed-Chief; Var Cheerleading; Var Socr; 4-H Awd; Hon Roll; Spanish NHS; JR Clss Marshall 85; Frgn Exchng Stu To Barcelona Spain 85-86; Gordon Coll; Pre-Med.

LEMIEUX, ANN; Deering HS; Portland, ME; (Y); JA; High Hon Roll; Hon Roll; Accntng.

LEMIEUX, RICHARD; Becksport HS; Bucksport, ME; (Y); 6/120; Am Leg Aux Girls St; Boy Scts; Letterman Clb; Nwsp Rptr; JV Bsbl; JV Ftbl; JV Trk; Var L Wrstlng; Hon Roll; Engr.

LENFESTEY, LAURIE; Erskine Acad; Gardiner, ME; (Y); Letterman Clb; Library Aide; Speech Tm; Yrbk Stf; Bsktbl; Var Crs Cntry; Var Mgr(s); Mgr Sftbl; High Hon Roll; Hon Roll; Stu Tutr 84-85; Mdcl Asstnt.

LENFESTEY, SALLY; Jonesport-Beals HS; Beals, ME; (Y); French Clb; Nwsp Rptr; Yrbk Ed-Chief; VP Soph Cls; Pres Jr Cls; JV Cheerleading; Var Sftbl; JV Vllybl; High Hon Roll; Hon Roll; Frnch Awd 83-85; Sci Awe & Englsh Awd 84-85; US Histry Awd 84-85; Jrnslm.

LENTZ, LAURIE; Deering HS; Portland, ME; (Y); Varsity Clb; Band; Concert Band; Mrchg Band; Pep Band; Sftbl; High Hon Roll; Hon Roll; Band Sec; Sectn Ldr Percssn; ST Sftbl Chmp Awd 84-85; U South ME; Bus.

LEONARD, RICK; Nokomis Regional HS; Newport, ME; (Y); 4/180; French Clb; Band; Mrchg Band; Swing Chorus; Pres Jr Cls; Rep Sr Cls; Var L Bsbl; Capt Var Bsktbl; Capt Var Socr; Capt Var Trk; Accntng I Awd; 3rd Pl Bus Ed Assn Of ME Regnl Cont; Syracuse U; Accntng.

LEPAGE, JEFF; Lewiston HS; Lewiston, ME; (Y); Letterman Clb; Varsity Clb; Yrbk Stf; JV Socr; Var Capt Swmmng; Var Trk; Marine Engr.

LEVASSEUR, LISA; Lewiston HS; Lewiston, ME; (Y); Cmnty Wkr; Q&S; Yrbk Ed-Chief; JV Bsktbl; Var Trk; High Hon Roll; Jr NHS; NHS; Wellesley Bk Awd 85; Outstndng Achvt Eng 84-85; Law.

LEVASSEUR, PATTY; Fort Kent Community HS; Ft Kent, ME; (Y); 11/165; Band; Nwsp Rptr; Yrbk Ed-Chief; Pres Sr Cls; Stu Cncl; JV Mgr(s); L Sftbl; Cit Awd; Hon Roll; VP NHS; NHS Rgnl VP 85-86; Colby Coll; Frnch.

LEVECQUE, JOHN; Old Orchard Beach HS; Old Orchard Bch, ME; (Y); 32/74; Teachers Aide; Varsity Clb; Trk; Wt Lftg; Idle Sons Rest Mem Scholar 85; Southern ME Vo-Tech; Mngmnt.

LEVER, ANGIE; Sanford HS; Sanford, ME; (Y); Pres Church Yth Grp; Ski Clb; JV Bsktbl; Mgr(s); Jr NHS; Bus Adm.

LEVESQUE, JULIA; Madison HS; Madison, ME; (S); Spanish Clb; Yrbk Ed-Chief; Yrbk Stf; Trs Jr Cls; Pres Sr Cls; Stu Cncl; Var Fld Hcky; Var Socr; DAR Awd; Hon Roll; Phy Thrpy.

LEVY, MATTHEW A; Bangor HS; Bangor, ME; (Y); 11/321; Chess Clb; Capt Debate Tm; Math Clb; Math Tm; Trs Science Clb; High Hon Roll; NHS; Ntl Merit SF.

LEWIS, AMY; Bangor HS; Bangor, ME; (Y); Rep Jr Cls; JV Var Bsktbl; Var Socr; Var Sftbl; NHS; U Of ME; Pharm.

LIBBY, DEBORAH L; Portland HS; Portland, ME; (Y); Yrbk Stf; Fld Hcky; Tennis; U Of ME Orono; Librl Arts.

LIBBY, GRETCHEN; Bonny Eagle HS; Bar Mills, ME; (Y); French Clb; Varsity Clb; Concert Band; Rep Stu Cncl; JV Var Bsktbl; Var Fld Hcky; Var Capt Sftbl; High Hon Roll; Hon Roll; NHS; Hlth Awd; Frnch I Awd; SMAA 1st Tm All Star Fld Hcky; Dartmouth Coll; Comp.

LIBBY, PAMELA; Westbrook HS; Westbrook, ME; (Y); Cmnty Wkr; Sec Spanish Clb; Church Choir; Yrbk Stf; Capt Var Cheerleading; Hon Roll; Keywanettes; Red Cross Aide; Band; School Musical; Modern Miss Schlrshp Pgnt 84; Miss Natl Teenager Pgnt 85; Clark U; Mus Educ.

LIBBY, RUSSELL; Woodland HS; Woodland, ME; (S); Boy Scts; Chess Clb; Band; Socr; Hon Roll; NHS; Engrng.

LIEBERMAN, JAMES; Bangor HS; Bangor, ME; (Y); 80/316; Am Leg Boys St; Boy Scts; Yrbk Bus Mgr; Yrbk Stf; Im Bsktbl; Im Vllybl; Hon Roll; VP Temple Yth Grp; Phy Ed.

LILLY, BARBARA; Woodland HS; Princeton, ME; (Y); Computer Clb; Drama Clb; Nwsp Stf; Yrbk Stf; Lit Mag; Flight Attndnt.

LINCOURT, STEVE; Sanford HS; Sanford, ME; (Y); Ski Clb; JV Bsbl; Stat Bsktbl; Var Mgr Mgr(s); Pre-Med.

LINDQUIST, KRISTEN E; Camden Rockport HS; Rockport, ME; (Y); 2/130; French Clb; Sec Latin Clb; Nwsp Rptr; Lit Mag; VP Capt Crs Cntry; High Hon Roll; Sec NHS; Ntl Merit SF; Am Leg Aux Girls St; JCL; ME Summer Humanities Bourdoia Coll 84; JR Sci Symposium Univ New Hampshire 84; French Major.

LITTLE, HEATHER A; Skowhegan Area HS; Norridgewock, ME; (Y); 17/204; Hon Roll; Pres Acad Fit Awd 85; Frnch II Awd 85; Faculty-Stu Bdy Scholar Awd 85; U ME Farmington; Elem Ed.

LITTLEFIELD, BARBARA; Sanford HS; Sanford, ME; (Y); JV Var Bsktbl; JV Fld Hcky; JV Capt Sftbl; Hon Roll; 3rd Yrk Cty Typng Cont 85; Rad Tech.

LONG, MELISSA; Brunswick HS; Brunswick, ME; (S); Church Yth Grp; Band; Concert Band; Drm & Bgl; Mrchg Band; Orch; Variety Show; Stat Bsktbl; Stat Sftbl; Hon Roll; All New England Band 85; All ST Band 85; Figure Skatng Bronze Dance 83; Liberal Arts Coll; Forign Svc.

LONGCORE, JEFF; Orono HS; Orono, ME; (Y); 3/104; AFS; Chess Clb; Church Yth Grp; Band; Orch; Nwsp Stf; Stu Cncl; Socr; French Hon Soc; NHS; Hnr Rl 82-85; Ntl Merit Schlrshp 85; U MI Ann Arbor; Aerosp Engrng.

LONGPRE, ANDREA; Fryebury Acad; Stoneham, ME; (Y); French Clb; Varsity Clb; Chorus; Cheerleading; Sftbl; Nrsg.

LOOK, HEIDI; Jonesport-Beals HS; Jonesport, ME; (Y); 3/29; Am Leg Aux Girls St; Pres Church Yth Grp; Drama Clb; Pres 4-H; Yrbk Ed-Chief; Var Capt Bsktbl; Var L Cheerleading; Var Capt Vllybl; DAR Awd; Trs NHS; Delia Houghton Schlrshp 85; DAC All-Star Vllybl Awd 84-85; Wshngton Cnty Union Ctznshp Awd 85; E ME Voc Tech Inst; Rdlgc Tech.

LORD, LISA L; Presque Isle HS; Presque Isle, ME; (Y); 22/260; Intnl Clb; Math Clb; Cheerleading; Trk; Hon Roll; Kiwanis Awd; Kiwanis Clb Schlrshp 85; Bus & Prfsnl Wmns Schlrshp 85; U Of ME; Erly Chldhd Ed.

LOUNSBURY JR, DAN T; Morse HS; Bath, ME; (Y); Am Leg Boys St; Church Yth Grp; Drama Clb; Math Tm; Trs Soph Cls; Stu Cncl; JV Var Bsktbl; Var Socr; Var Trk; Hon Roll; Hnrb Mntn-Schl Sci Fair 84.

LOVEJOY, STACEY; Buckfield HS; Buckfield, ME; (Y); Varsity Clb; Bsktbl; Socr; 4-H Awd; High Hon Roll; Hon Roll; NHS; St Schlr; 4-H; Math Tm; HOBY Sem 84; Mary E Gammon Awd Hghst Avg JR Cls 85; Psych.

LOWTHER, STEPHEN; Cony HS; Augusta, ME; (Y); 4/331; Am Leg Boys St; JCL; Latin Clb; Math Tm; Band; Concert Band; Orch; Yrbk Stf; High Hon Roll; St Schlr; Engrng.

LUCAS, APRIL; Deering HS; Portland, ME; (Y); Church Yth Grp; Exploring; Key Clb; Varsity Clb; Yrbk Stf; Var Fld Hcky; Var Tennis; Hon Roll; French Clb; Variety Show; Anatmy Ldrshp 85; Lib Arts.

LUCE, KATIE; Windham HS; S Windham, ME; (Y); Keywanettes; Varsity Clb; Rep Soph Cls; Rep Jr Cls; Rep Stu Cncl; Var Capt Bsktbl; L Var Socr; Var L Sftbl; Jr NHS; NHS; Sftbl All-Star 83-85,MIP 83-84; Outstndg Achvt Info Proc III 84-85; Bsktbl All-Star 84-85,Bst Plymkr; U Of S ME; Accntnt.

LUMBERT, CAROL; Forest Hills HS; Jackman, ME; (Y); Drama Clb; Math Clb; Math Tm; School Play; Yrbk Ed-Chief; Yrbk Stf; Off Jr Cls; Cheerleading; Coach Actv; Crs Cntry; Sci Awds; Jrnlsm.

LUNDQUIST, STEVE; R D HS; Owls Head, ME; (Y); 1/115; Am Leg Boys St; Capt Debate Tm; JCL; ROTC; Var L Ftbl; Var L Trk; Bausch & Lomb Sci Awd; Hon Roll; NHS; Val; Pres Acad Fit Awd 85; Schlr/Ath 85; Masters, Mates & Pilots Scholar 85; Rensselaer Polytech; Engrng.

LUNT, HOLLY; Boothbay Region HS; West Southport, ME; (S); 3/65; AFS; Am Leg Aux Girls St; French Clb; JCL; Pres Latin Clb; Model UN; Pres Ski Clb; Pres Jr Cls; L Capt Fld Hcky; L Capt Swmmng; Dartmouth Bk Clb Awd 84.

LUTZ, CHRISTINE; George Stevens Acad; Penobscot, ME; (Y); 5/69; Art Clb; Drama Clb; Sec 4-H; French Clb; Varsity Clb; Yrbk Stf; Stu Cncl; VP Co-Capt Socr; Hon Roll; NHS; ME Summer Hum Pgm-Bowdoin Coll 84; Trinity Coll Hartfrd; Phil.

LY, TY; Deering HS; Portland, ME; (Y); Dance Clb; Key Clb; Yrbk Stf; Off Soph Cls; Mgr(s); Hon Roll; Bus Mgt.

LYDON, JESSICA ELIZABETH; Gardiner Area HS; Gardiner, ME; (Y); 6/224; French Clb; Trs Frsh Cls; Trs Soph Cls; Trs Jr Cls; VP Sr Cls; Var Fld Hcky; Capt Swmmng; Trk; High Hon Roll; NHS; Athltc & Acdmc Schlrhsp 85; US Snt Yth Prog; Summr Humnts Prog 84; Bowdoin Coll; Bio.

LYMAN, BARBARA; Livermore Falls HS; Mount Vernon, ME; (Y); Pres Church Yth Grp; Drama Clb; Varsity Clb; Band; Capt Cheerleading; Trk; Hon Roll; Bus.

MAC DONALD, LARISSA; Lawrence HS; Fairfield Ctr, ME; (Y); Church Yth Grp; 4-H; Band; Yrbk Ed-Chief; Yrbk Phtg; JV Var Cheerleading; Im Gym; Var Pom Pon; Var Trk; Im Vllybl; 4-H ST Wnr 2 Tms 85; UNH; Comp Tech.

MAC LEAN, HEATHER; Noble HS; North Berwick, ME; (Y); Am Leg Aux Girls St; Hosp Aide; Nwsp Rptr; L Fld Hcky; Capt L Gym; Capt L Sftbl; Hon Roll; NHS; Band; Chorus; Various Awds For Improvemnt & Achvt In Sports 83-85; Creative Writing Awd; Law.

MAC PHEE, LEONARD; Mt Blue HS; Farmington, ME; (Y); Am Leg Boys St; Pres Church Yth Grp; Letterman Clb; Varsity Clb; School Musical; Var L Bsktbl; Var L Socr; Hon Roll; NHS; Pre-Law.

MAC PHERSON, HEATHER; Oxford Hills HS; Oxford, ME; (Y); French Clb; FHA; Girl Scts; Key Clb; U New England; Phys Thrpy.

MADDISON, CHRISTINE B; Belfast Area HS; Belfast, ME; (Y); 3/141; Math Tm; Yrbk Stf; Sec Trs Sr Cls; Swmmng; High Hon Roll; Trs Jr NHS; NHS; Ntl Merit Ltr; Pres Schlr; St Schlr; U ME; Pre-Med.

MADRID, PAUL S; Bangor HS; Bangor, ME; (Y); Science Clb; JV Crs Cntry; JV Trk; High Hon Roll; Hon Roll; Spnsh Awd 84-85.

MAHLER, TIMOTHY W; Gorham HS; Gorham, ME; (Y); Church Yth Grp; Chorus; Church Choir; Var Bsktbl; JV Var Socr; Sftbl; High Hon Roll; Hon Roll; Outstndng Bible Stu Awd 82-83; Achvt Awds Alg Soc Sci 82-83; Awana Ldr Timing Seaman & Campng Awds 83; TN Temple; Pastrl.

MAINS, CHARLENE; Windham HS; Westbrook, ME; (Y); Keywanettes; Band; Chorus; Jazz Band; JV Var Mgr(s); Hon Roll; Jr NHS; Music Awd 84-85; Bus.

MANDARELLI, RHONDA MARIE; Catherine Mc Cauley HS; S Windham, ME; (Y); 7/65; Am Leg Aux Girls St; Drama Clb; Hosp Aide; Yrbk Stf; Rep Stu Cncl; Hon Roll; Voice Dem Awd; Pres SADD 84-85; Sci Olympd 85; Med.

MANN, THOMAS; Bucksport HS; Bucksport, ME; (Y); Church Yth Grp; Cmnty Wkr; Computer Clb; French Clb; Varsity Clb; Band; Concert Band; Jazz Band; Mrchg Band; Variety Show; Comp Pgrmr.

MARCOTTE, AMY L; Van Buren District Secondary Schl; Van Buren, ME; (Y); 5/80; Am Leg Aux Girls St; Math Clb; Jazz Band; Nwsp Sprt Ed; Yrbk Stf; Pres Sr Cls; Capt Var Bsktbl; Capt Var Socr; Capt Var Sftbl; Hon Roll; Bst Sportsmnshp Awd Sftbl 85; St Josephs Coll; Law.

MARCOUX, LAURA; Lawrence HS; Shawmut, ME; (Y); Am Leg Aux Girls St; Church Yth Grp; Drama Clb; French Clb; Hosp Aide; Chorus; Yrbk Stf; High Hon Roll; Hon Roll; Edna Lawrence Scholar 85; U ME Farmington; Ed.

MARIN, JOSEPH; Fort Kent Coummunity HS; Eagle Lake, ME; (Y); Boy Scts; St Schlr; Hon Roll; Chem Awd 85; Frnch Awd 84; IA ST; Engrng.

MARKS, ALAN; Penquis Valley HS; Milo, ME; (Y); 3/77; Am Leg Boys St; Yrbk Stf; Lit Mag; Var Crs Cntry; High Hon Roll; Hon Roll; ST Sci Fair-1st Pl 85; ME Scholars Day 85; U Of ME Smmr Pgm For Acadmclly Gftd Math/Sci Students 85.

MARKS, JULIE; Lawrence HS; Waterville, ME; (Y); English Clb; Key Clb; Orch; Nwsp Stf; Yrbk Stf; High Hon Roll; Hon Roll; Prfct Atten Awd; Engl.

MARRONE, MICHAEL; Gorham HS; Gorham, ME; (Y); Math Tm; Spanish Clb; Var Bsbl; Var Bsktbl; Var Crs Cntry; Var Golf; Hon Roll; Schl Alg Awd 82-83; Engrng.

MARSANSKIS, MICHAEL; Belfast Area HS; Belfast, ME; (Y); 23/141; Latin Clb; Ski Clb; Band; Mrchg Band; Diving; Ftbl; Swmmng; Trk; Dnfth Awd; Hon Roll; ST Chmp Divng 84 & 85; Rnr-Up Bckstrke 84 & 85; Ath Of Yr 84 & 85; 3rd Plc Vlt ST 83-85; Miami U Oxford.

MARSTON, SHERI; Deering HS; Portland, ME; (Y); 30/350; Band; Concert Band; Drm Mjr(t); Mrchg Band; Orch; Diving; Swmmng; Hon Roll; Swimskin Awd-Southwestern MA Swmmng Chmpnshps & MVP 85; H S Ram Awd-Mst Vlbl Driver 84 & 85.

MARTELL, TAMMY; Bonny Eagle HS; Limerick, ME; (Y); Rep Girl Scts; Rep Library Aide; Rep Ski Clb; Rep Spanish Clb; Rep Teachers Aide; Rep Varsity Clb; Rep Stu Cncl; Stat Bsktbl; Mgr(s); High Hon Roll; Pres SADD 84-85 & 85-86; Corp Law.

MARTIN, GAIL NICOLE; Madawaska HS; Windsor, CT; (Y); 6/97; Am Leg Aux Girls St; Math Tm; Spanish Clb; Yrbk Stf; Pres Frsh Cls; Pres Jr Cls; Var Capt Bsktbl; Var Capt Socr; Var Capt Sftbl; Hon Roll; Key Bnk Of Northern ME Schlrshp 85; Robert Mac Donald Rotary Schlrshp 85; Pres Acadmc Ftnss Awd 85; U Of ME-ORONO; Bus Admin.

MARTIN, SUSAN; Penobscot Valley HS; Lincoln, ME; (Y); 7/76; Drama Clb; French Clb; Pep Clb; Varsity Clb; School Play; Variety Show; Yrbk Bus Mgr; Capt L Cheerleading; Hon Roll; NHS; Miss Grtr Lncln 85-86; Bangor CC; Dntl Hygene.

MARTIN, THOMAS; Fort Kent Com HS; Fort Kent, ME; (Y); 2/160; Math Clb; Science Clb; Varsity Clb; Rep Frsh Cls; Trs Stu Cncl; Bsbl; Cit Awd; Gov Hon Prg Awd; High Hon Roll; Hon Roll; Sci Achvt Awd, Schl Ctznshp, Merit Awd 82-83; Theortcl Sci Achvt Awd, Tutrng Mth 83-84; SWE Awd 84-85; U Of FL Gainesville; Comp Engr.

MARTIN, TINA; Fort Kent Cmnty HS; Eagle Lake, ME; (Y); 12/154; Varsity Clb; Chorus; JV Bsktbl; Var L Sftbl; Var L Tennis; Vllybl; Hon Roll; Prfct Atten Awd; Hghst Achvt In Angegra II, Psychlgy I & II 84-85; Hghst Achvt In Hstry 85; U Of ME Frmngtn; Elem Ed.

MARTINDALE, SCOTT; South Hope Christian Schl; Waldoboro, ME; (S); 1/9; Church Yth Grp; Church Choir; Yrbk Phtg; Yrbk Stf; Var Bsktbl; JV Socr; High Hon Roll; Lion Awd; Acad Excell MSAD 40 Awd 82-83; Hghst Oerall Avg 83-84.

MATHEWS, PAMELA A; Scarborough HS; Scarborough, ME; (Y); 37/132; Church Yth Grp; Science Clb; Nwsp Rptr; Rep Sr Cls; Var L Crs Cntry; Var Mgr(s); JV Var Trk; Hon Roll; NHS; Local Schlrshp Mark Marianne Milliken Schlrshp 85; Gordon Coll; Eng.

MATTINGLY, MATT; Carrabec HS; N Anson, ME; (Y); Am Leg Boys St; Aud/Vis; Boy Scts; Drama Clb; German Clb; Band; Concert Band; School Play; Variety Show; Trs Soph Cls; Hnrry Ctzn Boy ST 85; Theatre.

MATTSON, ERIK T; Bucksport HS; Bucksport, ME; (Y); 12/135; Trs Church Yth Grp; Varsity Clb; Nwsp Stf; VP Stu Cncl; Var Capt Crs Cntry; Var L Trk; Hon Roll; NHS; Voice Dem Awd; Outwrd Bound Course 84; Bus Admin.

MAY, KIMBERLY; Caribou HS; Caribou, ME; (S); 35/235; Am Leg Aux Girls St; Ski Clb; Varsity Clb; Band; Var Capt Crs Cntry; Var Trk; NHS; Girl Scts; Hosp Aide; Key Clb; Mst Valuable Rnnr Crs Cntry 83-84; Ldrshp Delg 83-84; Phys Thrpy.

MAYNARD JR, LLOYD J; Washburn District HS; Washburn, ME; (Y); 3/50; Am Leg Boys St; Church Yth Grp; Var L Crs Cntry; Dnfth Awd; High Hon Roll; NHS; Prfct Atten Awd; JV Mgr(s); Var Score Keeper; JV Timer; Acct I Awd 84; Acct II Awd 85; MSSPA Principls Awd Acad Excllnce & Citznshp 85; N ME Vo Tech Inst; Acctg.

MAZER, FAITH; Deering HS; Portland, ME; (Y); Hosp Aide; Key Clb; Spanish Clb; VP Temple Yth Grp; Hon Roll; Spanish NHS; Natl Spnsh Exam Adv Lvl 9th Pl 85; Phys Ther.

MAZER, LISA; Deering HS; Portland, ME; (Y); French Clb; Hosp Aide; Key Clb; Letterman Clb; Temple Yth Grp; Varsity Clb; Crs Cntry; Trk; Hon Roll; U Of RI; Pharm.

MAZEROLLE, PAULA A; Caribau HS; Caribou, ME; (Y); Ski Clb; Rep Frsh Cls; Rep Soph Cls; Rep Jr Cls; Rep Stu Cncl; JV Cheerleading; Var Crs Cntry; Var Gym; Rep Trk; Hon Roll; Ltr Gyymnstcs 83-84; Track Ltr 83-84; Hnr Roll 83-84; Mech.

MC ALISTER, PAM; Fryeburg Acad; Ctr Lovell, ME; (Y); JV Score Keeper; JV Sftbl; High Hon Roll; Hon Roll; Physcl Thrpy.

MC ALLISTER, PATRICIA; Fryeburg Acad; Center Conway, NH; (Y); 4-H; Franklin Pierce Coll; Lawyr.

MC AULEY, CINNAMON; Cony HS; Augusta, ME; (Y); Church Yth Grp; Dance Clb; Pep Clb; Spanish Clb; Variety Show; Hon Roll; Psych.

MC AUSLIN, JUDY; Gardiner Area HS; Gardiner, ME; (Y); Letterman Clb; Q&S; Yrbk Stf; Var Bsktbl; Var Fld Hcky; Var Sftbl; Hon Roll; Phys Ther.

MC CARTHY, ABBY; Madison HS; New Sharon, ME; (S); 4/99; Yrbk Stf; VP Frsh Cls; VP Soph Cls; VP Jr Cls; Stu Cncl; Bsktbl; Coach Actv; Fld Hcky; Socr; Sftbl; Fld Hcky Awd 83; Bst Defnsve Plyr Soccr 84; New Engld Math Leag Hghst Scrng Fresh 83.

MC CLELLAN, KATHLEEN A; Mt Ararat HS; South Harpswell, ME; (Y); 14/180; Am Leg Aux Girls St; Library Aide; Teachers Aide; Chorus; Variety Show; Yrbk Ed-Chief; VP Stu Cncl; Hon Roll; NHS; SR Svc Awd; SR Eagle Awd; Hm Ec Awd; Johnson & Wales Coll; Clnry Art.

MC CLURE, JOAN; Bangor HS; Bangor, ME; (Y); 1/321; Yrbk Ed-Chief; Trs Sr Cls; Rep Stu Cncl; Capt Cheerleading; Elks Awd; High Hon Roll; NHS; Val; Am Leg Aux Girls St; Church Yth Grp; Clss Of 1925 Hstry Awd 85; Oracle Yrbk Awd 85; U OF ME Orono; Bus Admin.

MC CLURE, LINDEN H; Mt Abram HS; Kingfield, ME; (Y); 1/77; Pres Band; Pres Concert Band; Nwsp Ed-Chief; Yrbk Ed-Chief; Var L Crs Cntry; High Hon Roll; NHS; Ntl Merit SF; Prfct Atten Awd; Hugh O Brian Yth Ldrshp Delg 83; Williams Coll Bk Awd 84; Maine Schlrs Day Delg 84; U Of ME Orono; Chem Engrng.

MC COLLOUGH, KELLY SUSAN; Rumford HS; Rumford, ME; (Y); 2/130; Am Leg Aux Girls St; Drama Clb; Latin Clb; Band; Rep Frsh Cls; Pres Sr Cls; L Trk; High Hon Roll; Hon Roll; NHS; Part In ME Schlrs Day 85; Phy Thrpy.

MC COUBREY, SHERRI; Calais HS; Calais, ME; (Y); 18/61; Yrbk Stf; Sec Sr Cls; Hon Roll; Mabel J De Shon Rainbw Schlrshp 85; U Of ME-ORONO; Elem Educ.

MC DIVITT, SUZETTE; Presque Isle HS; Presque Isle, ME; (Y); VP Varsity Clb; Trs Stu Cncl; Var Capt Cheerleading; Var L Fld Hcky; Hon Roll; SAD 1 Wrtng Cntst Clsrm Wnnr 82; Northern ME Vctnl Tech.

MC DONALD, STEPHANIE; Jay HS; Jay, ME; (Y); Am Leg Aux Girls St; Hosp Aide; Band; Mrchg Band; Yrbk Sprt Ed; Var L Cheerleading; JV Var Fld Hcky; Var L Sftbl; Hon Roll; Pres NHS; Tri-M Music Hnr Soc 85; 2nd Outstndng Rep Grls St 85; Nrsng.

MC DONOUGH, FRANCIS; Orono HS; Orono, ME; (Y); 12/105; Trs Church Yth Grp; Math Tm; Orch; Yrbk Bus Mgr; Trs Sr Cls; Var L Ice Hcky; Var Capt Socr; L Trk; Hon Roll; Pres Schlr; Air Force Acad; Engrng.

MC DOWELL, RUTH; Woodland HS; Princeton, ME; (S); 4/66; Sec FBLA; Hosp Aide; Thesps; Pres Varsity Clb; Yrbk Ed-Chief; Trs Sr Cls; Mgr(s); High Hon Roll; Trs NHS; Drama Clb; Typng Awd 83-84; Hmn Physlgy Awd 83-84; Casco Bay Coll; Med Sec.

MC GILL, LINDY; Lewiston HS; Lewiston, ME; (Y); 100/425; Letterman Clb; Capt Ski Clb; Varsity Clb; Color Guard; Trk; Twrlr; NHS; Ntl Merit Ltr; U AL; Pre-Med.

MC GLAUFLIN, DONNA; Edward Little HS; Mechanic Falls, ME; (Y); Am Leg Aux Girls St; Drama Clb; Pres Latin Clb; Math Tm; School Musical; Yrbk Stf; Var L Trk; Cit Awd; Hon Roll; Prfct Atten Awd.

MC GOWAN, DAVID; Portland HS; Portland, ME; (Y); Debate Tm; VP JA; Latin Clb; Political Wkr; Quiz Bowl; Rep Frsh Cls; Rep Soph Cls; Rep Jr Cls; Rep Sr Cls; Rep Stu Cncl; Natl JR Achvt Cnvntn Dlgt 85; Rgn JR Achvt Cnvntn Dlgt 85.

MC HENRY, FRANKLIN; Wisdom HS; Madawaska, ME; (Y); Leo Clb; Varsity Clb; Var L Bsbl; Ice Hcky; Var L Socr; Hon Roll; U Of ME Orono; Music.

MC INTYRE, EDWARD; Skowmegan Area HS; Norridgewock, ME; (Y); 52/216; Art Clb; Drama Clb; German Clb; PAVAS; Thesps; Chorus; Madrigals; School Play; Stage Crew; Variety Show; St Oratory; U NY; Arts.

MC KINNEY, DEBORAH; Thornton Acad; Saco, ME; (Y); 4/220; AFS; Chrmn Church Yth Grp; Band; Chorus; Nwsp Rptr; Yrbk Stf; NHS; John Deering Schlrshp; ME Smmr Hmnts Inst Gftd & Tlntd; Outstndg Awd Engl, Scl Stds; Polt Sci Schlrshp; U Of ME-ORONO; Engl.

MC MAHON, PENNY; Lewiston HS; Lewiston, ME; (Y); Sec Pep Clb; VP Trs Stu Cncl; Hon Roll; Exec Secy.

MC NEALLY, ALLEGRA; Gorham HS; Gorham, ME; (Y); Art Clb; Camp Fr Inc; Sec 4-H; Chorus; Concert Band; Ed Yrbk Stf; St Schlr; Computer Clb; Dance Clb; Pep Band; Corrspndnt Area Nwsp 83-85; Ntl 4-H Congrss Trp Wnnr ME Plnt/Soil Sci 85; 4-H Ctznshp Trp Wnnr 82-83; Fin Arts.

MC NEIL, PAULINE; Yarmouth JR SR HS; Yarmouth, ME; (Y); Band; Concert Band; Jazz Band; Mrchg Band; Yrbk Ed-Chief; Yrbk Stf; French Hon Soc; High Hon Roll; Yth Wnd Ensmble& Yth Symphny Orchestra 84-85; Bus.

MC NEIL, THOMAS; Caribou HS; Caribou, ME; (S); 5/215; Am Leg Boys St; Church Yth Grp; Band; Chorus; Trs Soph Cls; Pres Jr Cls; Pres Sr Cls; Var Tennis; NHS; U ME Orono; Publ Adm.

MC ORMOND, SHERYL; Monmouth Acad; Georgetown, TX; (Y); 2/37; JCL; Math Tm; Speech Tm; Chorus; Concert Band; Orch; High Hon Roll; NHS; Cmnty Wkr; Latin Clb; Ntl Ltn Exam Lvl II 83; Cert Of Hon Excel In Schlrshp 84; Top Scorer Math Exam Awd 85; Bio.

MC PHERSON, TERESA; Houlton HS; Houlton, ME; (Y); Chess Clb; Church Yth Grp; Drama Clb; FHA; School Play; Hon Roll; Certifed Nrsg Asst; Franklin Pierce Coll; Comm.

MC WHINNIE, JOHN; Lewiston HS; Lewiston, ME; (Y); 10/500; Pres Am Leg Boys St; Church Yth Grp; Pres Key Clb; Pres Q&S; Varsity Clb; JV Bsktbl; JV Socr; Var Capt Tennis; Boys Nation 85; Model Legsltr 83-84; Asst Edtr, Sr Edtr Yrbk 84-86; Boston Coll; Law.

MEALEY, CHERYL ANN; Dexter Regional HS; Dexter, ME; (Y); 5/97; Sec AFS; Am Leg Aux Girls St; Church Yth Grp; Pres French Clb; VP Chorus; Gym; Tennis; Hon Roll; NHS; Scott Hi-Q Quiz Team; Colby Coll; Lang.

MEEKER, LISA; Forest Hills HS; Jackman, ME; (Y); 1/18; Drama Clb; Math Tm; Yrbk Bus Mgr; Hon Roll; NHS; Sal; U Of ME-FARMINGTON; Elem Educ.

MEGATHLIN, MARK; Portland HS; Portland, ME; (Y); 45/256; Church Yth Grp; Spanish Clb; Rep Frsh Cls; Rep Soph Cls; Rep Sr Cls; JV Bsbl; Var L Ice Hcky; Capt L Socr; Im Vllybl; Hon Roll; Maurice Drees Schlrshp; Union Coll; Lib Arts.

MEIR, JOSEFFA; Caribou HS; Caribou, ME; (S); 1/230; Cmnty Wkr; Ski Clb; Varsity Clb; Rep Stu Cncl; Var JV Socr; Trk; High Hon Roll; All Academic American; MIT; Arch Engrng.

MELDRUM, LORI; Lewiston HS; Lewiston, ME; (Y); 24/397; Hosp Aide; Y-Teens; High Hon Roll; Hon Roll; St Marys Schl Nrsng; Nrsng.

MELLEN, DARCY; Portland HS; Portland, ME; (Y); Nwsp Rptr; Lit Mag; Cheerleading; Gym; Vllybl; Hon Roll; U Of Southern ME; Engl.

MENNEL, TIM M; Berwick Acad; Durham, NH; (Y); 3/31; Drama Clb; Political Wkr; Chorus; School Musical; School Play; Yrbk Ed-Chief; Ed Lit Mag; High Hon Roll; Ntl Merit Schol; Sal; Englsh & Math Awds 84 & 85; Englsh Hnr Awd 84 & 85; Kelliher Prz In Englsh 84; Carleton Coll.

MERRIAM, TRACI; Bucksport HS; Bucksport, ME; (Y); Am Leg Aux Girls St; Letterman Clb; Varsity Clb; Band; Jazz Band; Mrchg Band; Nwsp Ed-Chief; Nwsp Rptr; VP Jr Cls; Var Trk; Embry-Riddle U; Air Trfc Cntrlr.

MERRILL, DOUGLASS; Medomak Valley HS; Wasingtn, ME; (Y); Art Clb; Church Yth Grp; Science Clb; Stage Crew; Sci.

MESERVEY, JAMMIE; Bonny Eagle HS; Gorham, ME; (Y); Sec Trs Latin Clb; Hon Roll; Jr NHS; NHS; Aerontcs.

METCALF, CHRISTIAN; Skowhegan Area HS; Norridgewock, ME; (Y); Latin Clb; Varsity Clb; Var Crs Cntry; Var Trk; Pre Med.

METIVIER, KAREN; Westbrook HS; Westbrook, ME; (Y); Camp Fr Inc; French Clb; Keywanettes; Band; Concert Band; Mrchg Band; Yrbk Stf; Var Tennis; Hon Roll; NHS; Mth.

MEYERS, KRIS; Gorham HS; Gorham, ME; (Y); Chorus; Madrigals; School Musical; Sec Frsh Cls; Sec Soph Cls; Sec VP Jr Cls; VP Sr Cls; JV Var Fld Hcky; Spanish NHS; Drama Clb; Bus.

MEYERS, TRACEY; Gorham HS; Gorham, ME; (Y); Debate Tm; Latin Clb; School Play; Sec Jr Cls; Sec Sr Cls; Trs Stu Cncl; Mgr(s); Score Keeper; DAR Awd; High Hon Roll; Histry Awd 85; Syracuse U; Elem Ed.

MICHAUD, CATHIE; Lewiston HS; Lewiston, ME; (Y); Church Yth Grp; Hosp Aide; Fld Hcky; Hon Roll; Jr NHS; Bentley Coll; Acctng.

MICHAUD, CINDY; Wisdom HS; St Agatha, ME; (Y); 8/48; Church Yth Grp; Drama Clb; VP French Clb; Church Choir; School Play; Yrbk Stf; Co-Capt Cheerleading; Mgr(s); Score Keeper; Hon Roll; U Of ME Orono; Psych.

MICHAUD, HEIDI; Windham HS; S Windham, ME; (Y); Chorus; Yrbk Stf; Fld Hcky; Vllybl.

MICHAUD, MARC; St Dominic Regional HS; Lewiston, ME; (Y); Cmnty Wkr; Off Yrbk Stf; Hon Roll; Pres Acad Ftns Awd 85; Concours Natl De Frangois-6th In ST 85; CA ST U Fresno; Enology.

MICHAUD, MICHELLE L; Waterville SR HS; Waterville, ME; (Y); Am Leg Aux Girls St; Var L Bsktbl; JV Var Fld Hcky; Var L Mgr(s); Var L Sftbl; Hon Roll; Aerospace Sci.

MICHAUD JR, ROBERT P; Wisdom HS; St Agatha, ME; (Y); Am Leg Boys St; Church Yth Grp; Band; Mrchg Band; Pep Band; Var Mgr(s); Var Score Keeper; Cit Awd; High Hon Roll; Hon Roll; Engrng.

MICHAUD, TINA; Wells SR HS; Emery Mills, ME; (Y); Church Yth Grp; Dance Clb; Girl Scts; Chorus; Cheerleading; Sftbl; Hon Roll; U ME Orono; Chem Engrng.

MILLER, ADELE A; Skowhegan Area HS; Norridgewock, ME; (Y); 23/226; Church Yth Grp; German Clb; Varsity Clb; Nwsp Stf; Rep Stu Cncl; Stat Bsktbl; JV Capt Fld Hcky; Var L Sftbl; Hon Roll; NHS; Doris Lake Hme Econ Schlrshp 85; Robert P Brown Schlrshp 85; Shorshegan No 1 Extnsn Grp Schlrshp 85; U Of ME-FARMINGTON; Hme Econ.

MILLER, JODY NAN; Houlton HS; Houlton, ME; (Y); Am Leg Aux Girls St; Church Yth Grp; Dance Clb; Speech Tm; Yrbk Ed-Chief; Var Cheerleading; Var Socr; Im Vllybl; Hon Roll; Secdry Ed.

MILLER, TABITHA; Kennebunk HS; Kennebunk Port, ME; (Y); Art Clb; Drama Clb; French Clb; Acpl Chr; Chorus; School Musical; Hon Roll; Rcgntn Choregraphy Schl Mus 85; Boston Ballet Smmr Schl 84; Modern Miss Pgnt 85; Dance.

MILLETT, JILL; Oxford Hills HS; Waterford, ME; (Y); 19/237; 4-H; Letterman Clb; Varsity Clb; JV Var Bsktbl; JV Var Sftbl; High Hon Roll; Hon Roll; NHS; MVP Sftbl 85; Coaches Bsktbl Awd 85; Pres Awd 85; U Of Sthrn ME; Accntng.

MILLIKEN, MATHEW; Deering HS; Portland, ME; (Y); 30/300; Am Leg Boys St; Letterman Clb; Capt Var Ftbl; Var L Wrstlng; High Hon Roll; Ntl Merit SF; Yale Bk Awd 84; Hgst Hnrs German 85; U Maine; Engr.

MILLIKEN, MICHAEL; Deering HS; Portland, ME; (Y); Letterman Clb; JV Ftbl; Var Wrstlng; ST Champ Wrstlng 84-85; UMO.

MILLS, WENDY A; Messalonskee HS; Belgrade, ME; (Y); 3/132; Math Tm; Band; VP Chorus; Concert Band; Mrchg Band; School Musical; Variety Show; Var L Swmmng; Hon Roll; VP NHS; ME H S Tchrs Schlrshp 85; Frnch Awds; Thomas Coll; Accntng.

MILNE, CHRISTINE; Sanford HS; Sanford, ME; (Y); Church Yth Grp; Ski Clb; Comp.

MILSOP, JENNIFER; Windham HS; Westbrook, ME; (Y); Am Leg Aux Girls St; Girl Scts; Pres Key Clb; Orch; Var Capt Fld Hcky; Trk; Hon Roll; Sec NHS; Church Yth Grp; Math Tm; Latin Hnr Soc 84; Hugh O Brien Yth Fndtn Delg 84; ME Delg Ldrshp Today & Tomorrw Conf WA DC 85; Zoology.

MINKOWSKY, JIM; Lewiston HS; Lewiston, ME; (Y); Boy Scts; MMM; Chorus; School Musical; Stage Crew; Hon Roll; Jr NHS; NHS; U Of Southern ME; Music.

MINOTY, PAULA; Cony HS; Augusta, ME; (Y); 7/200; Computer Clb; Pres Library Aide; Yrbk Stf; Rep Jr Cls; High Hon Roll; Hon Roll; St Schlr; Top 10 Pct 83-85; Dartmouth Bk Awd 85; 2nd Pl Schl Sci Fair 85; Comp Sci.

MIRANDA, GINA; Madawaska HS; Madawaska, ME; (Y); 24/103; Am Leg Aux Girls St; Church Yth Grp; Sec Trs Drama Clb; French Clb; Latin Clb; Sec Trs Spanish Clb; Rep Band; Chorus; Church Choir; Drm Mjr(t); All Fest Cast Stu 83-84; Grnd Intl Comm Mrchng Champ 84; Miss Teen All Amer Congnlty 84; Physcl Thrpy.

MITCHELL, CARRIE; Westbrook HS; Westbrook, ME; (Y); Keywanettes; Yrbk Stf; Rep Stu Cncl; Var L Cheerleading; Var L Cheerleading; Var L Trk; Hon Roll; Vet.

RAYMOND, BRENDA L; Bangor HS; Bangor, ME; (Y); 17/303; Hosp Aide; Chorus; High Hon Roll; Pres Schlr; United ME Craftsmn Scholar Awd 85; Excllnce Engl Awd 84-85; EMVTI; Nrsng.

RAYMOND, KATHERINE; Cony HS; Augusta, ME; (Y); Am Leg Aux Girls St; French Clb; Variety Show; Ed Yrbk Phtg; Rep Soph Cls; JV Capt Fld Hcky; High Hon Roll; Ntl Merit SF; St Schlr; 1st Pl Essay ME Commsn Of Women 85; Arch.

RAYNE, CHRIS; Washburn District HS; Crouseville, ME; (Y); 7/48; French Clb; Pep Clb; Varsity Clb; Yrbk Stf; JV Mgr Bsktbl; JV Cheerleading; Var L Socr; High Hon Roll; NHS; NEDT Awd; Ntl Hnr Soc Schlrshp 85; Washburn Teachrs Assoc Schrshp 85; MI Girls V Soccer 83; Emerson Coll; Pub Rel.

READ, JEFFREY; Lewiston HS; Lewiston, ME; (Y); Am Leg Boys St; Sec Key Clb; Varsity Clb; JV Ice Hcky; Var Capt Socr; Var L Tennis; High Hon Roll; SMAA Sccr All STR 1st Tm 84; Havard Bk Prz 85; Sci Awd 83; Pre-Med.

REAMAN, KRISTINE; Deering HS; Cape Elizabeth, ME; (Y); Camera Clb; French Clb; Gym; Hon Roll.

REDDING, KIM; South Hope Christian HS; Union, ME; (S); Church Yth Grp; Var Co-Capt Cheerleading; Var Vllybl; High Hon Roll; Hon Roll.

REDMOND, MARY; Jay HS; Jay, ME; (Y); Drama Clb; FBLA; Pres Y-Teens; School Musical; School Play; Yrbk Ed-Chief; Yrbk Phtg; Sftbl; Hon Roll; Gftd, Tlntd, ME Ntl Ldrs Conf, Exch Stu Intl 85; Lgl Secr.

REDWINE, ELIZABETH A; Lawrence HS; Albion, ME; (Y); 22/250; Am Leg Aux Girls St; Boys Clb Am; French Clb; Key Clb; Math Tm; JV Bsktbl; High Hon Roll; Hon Roll; Pres Schlr; Stu Of Mnth; Pride Clb; U Of ME Orono; Engrng.

REED, MICHELLE; Caribou SR HS; Caribou, ME; (S); Cmnty Wkr; Pres French Clb; GAA; Hosp Aide; Varsity Clb; Bsktbl; Socr; Sftbl; Hon Roll.

REED, TODD M; Edward Little HS; Auburn, ME; (S); 15/350; JCL; Latin Clb; Var Capt Bsktbl; Tennis; Wt Lftg; High Hon Roll; Hon Roll.

REID, BETHANY; Oxford Hills HS; South Paris, ME; (Y); Church Yth Grp; Debate Tm; Drama Clb; Chrmn English Clb; Latin Clb; Color Guard; Concert Band; Jazz Band; Mrchg Band; High Hon Roll; 2nd Pl ST Champ Novice Debate 82-83; Frgn Lang.

RHOADS, ALAN; Kents Hill Schl; Stow, MA; (Y); Concert Band; Var Ice Hcky; JV Lcrss; JV Socr; High Hon Roll; Hon Roll; Mst Imprvd Rcr Vrsty Ski Tm 85; U Of CT Storrs; Engrng.

RICE, NANCY; Stearns HS; Millinocket, ME; (Y); Am Leg Aux Girls St; Chorus; VP Frsh Cls; Cheerleading; Hon Roll; NHS; Tchr.

RICH, LARRY; Orono HS; Bangor, ME; (S); 9/120; Boy Scts; Math Tm; Yrbk Stf; Var L Crs Cntry; High Hon Roll; Eagle Sct Awd 84; Hugh O Brian Yth Ldrshp Conf 84; Eng.

RICHARD, DANIEL; Bridgton Acad; Dover, NH; (Y); 2/186; High Hon Roll; Acadmc Imprvmnt Awd 85; Syracuse U; Aerospace Engr.

RICHARD, PETER; Livermore Falls HS; Livermore Falls, ME; (Y); Am Leg Boys St; Aud/Vis; Computer Clb; Varsity Clb; Pres Jr Cls; Pres Sr Cls; Var Bsktbl; Var Crs Cntry; Hon Roll; NHS; Electrcl Engr.

RICHARD, RANDY; Jay HS; Jay, ME; (Y); 30/82; Im Bsktbl; JV Ftbl; Im Vllybl; Central ME Voc Tech; Electrncs.

RICHARDS, LISA; Belfast Area HS; Morrill, ME; (Y); Var Bsktbl; Var Fld Hcky; Var Sftbl; Hon Roll; Prfct Atten Awd; Pre Law.

RICHARDSON, TAMMY; Morse HS; Bath, ME; (Y); Radio Clb; Science Clb; Stage Crew; Variety Show; Yrbk Stf; Rep Frsh Cls; Rep Soph Cls; Rep Stu Cncl; Var L Tennis; Ntl Merit Ltr; Math Awd-Hghst Achvt JR Cls; Math.

RICKER, LISA; Lewiston HS; Lewiston, ME; (Y); Ski Clb; Yrbk Stf; Crs Cntry; Score Keeper; Trk; Hon Roll; Rotary Awd; Spch Path.

RICKMAN, BRAD; Yarmouth HS; Yarmouth, ME; (Y); Am Leg Boys St; Pres Drama Clb; Math Tm; School Play; Lit Mag; JV Bsktbl; High Hon Roll; Pres NHS; ME Smmr Humnties Bowdoin Coll; Stdnt Advcy Comm.

RIDDLE, CATHERINE JOY; Fryeburg Acad; Brownfield, ME; (Y); Am Leg Aux Girls St; Nwsp Rptr; Yrbk Stf; Capt Bsktbl; Capt Fld Hcky; Capt Sftbl; Cit Awd; High Hon Roll; Kiwanis Awd; NHS; Waltr Rbnsn Clsscl Prz-Ltn 82; Elzbth W Tinkr Hstry Awd 85; Gibson Mem Mdl 85; William Smith Coll.

RIDLEY, RYAN; Jay HS; Jay, ME; (Y); 10/85; Am Leg Boys St; Camera Clb; Science Clb; Stage Crew; Nwsp Phtg; Off Frsh Cls; Socr; Vllybl; Hon Roll; 1st U Parish Schlrshp 86; NH Tech Inst; Assoc Sci.

RIENSTRA, SHERI; Sherilyn Rene Reinstra HS; Fryeburg, ME; (Y); Am Leg Aux Girls St; Church Yth Grp; Cmnty Wkr; French Clb; GAA; Letterman Clb; Varsity Clb; Band; Chorus; Church Choir; Eva Mulford Music Schlrshp 82-83; Bentley; Paralgl.

RILEY, DEBORAH; Windham HS; Raymond, ME; (Y); Am Leg Aux Girls St; JA; VP Keywanettes; Math Tm; Rep Jr Cls; Var Fld Hcky; Jr NHS; NHS; Cmnty Wkr; Latin Hnr Soc 84-86; New England Young Wrtrs Conf 85; Tri St Schlrshp Pagnt Fnl 85; Intl Rel.

RITCHIE, KAREN; Morse HS; Bath, ME; (Y); 5/190; French Clb; Variety Show; Crs Cntry; Hon Roll; NHS; Ntl Merit Ltr; Pres Schlr; St Schlr; Math Tm; Yrbk Stf; Cert Hnr Frnch; Beta Sigma Phi Schlrshp; Colby Coll; E Asian Stds.

RITTER, WILL; Bangor HS; Bangor, ME; (Y); 30/350; Var L Ftbl; Var L Socr; Var L Trk; Wt Lftg; High Hon Roll; Hon Roll; Ntl Merit SF; Soc Stud Dept Awd; All ST Ftbl Tm; MIT; Astrophyscs.

RIVARD, RHONDA-LEE; Central HS; Hudson, ME; (Y); Sec FHA; Chorus; Yrbk Stf; Hon Roll; Eng Acad Achvt Awd 85; Comp.

ROBERTS, CHRISTOPHER C; Wells HS; Wells, ME; (Y); JV Var Bsbl; JV Bsktbl; JV Var Ftbl.

ROBERTS, DAWN; Telstar Regional HS; East Bethel, ME; (Y); 43/78; Girl Scts; Teachers Aide; Temple Yth Grp; Yrbk Stf; Fld Hcky; Sftbl; Hon Roll; Acad Achv Bio 83; Acad Achv Spnsh 84; St Mary Schl Of Nrsng; Nrsng.

ROBERTS, RENEE; Woodland HS; Princeton, ME; (Y); English Clb; FBLA; Office Aide; Yrbk Stf; Lit Mag; SR Typing Awd 83-85; Bus Math Awd 84-85; U Of MA; Bus.

ROBERTS, STACEY; Nokomis Regional HS; Newport, ME; (Y); 37/171; Church Yth Grp; Drama Clb; German Clb; Ski Clb; School Musical; School Play; Crs Cntry; Trk; Hon Roll; ME U Orono; Jrnlsm.

ROBERTSON, ANN; Caribou HS; Caribou, ME; (S); 18/275; Varsity Clb; Band; Mrchg Band; Rep Soph Cls; Cheerleading; Trk; Hon Roll; Jr NHS; NHS; St Schlr; U Of ME-ORONO.

ROBERTSON, JOHNNA; Mt Blue HS; E Wilton, ME; (Y); JV Ski Clb; Nwsp Stf; Yrbk Stf; JV Fld Hcky; Var Gym; Var Trk; Hon Roll.

ROBILLARD, RANDALL; Marshwood HS; Eliot, ME; (Y); 5/120; Boy Scts; Computer Clb; French Clb; Math Tm; Trk; High Hon Roll; Hon Roll; NHS; Lions Clb Schlrshp 85; Pres Acdmc Ftns Awd 85; Highest Math Tm Score Adv Math Ctgry 85; U NH.

ROBINSON, AMY; Lawrence HS; Albion, ME; (Y); Sec Spanish Clb; High Hon Roll; NHS; JV Capt Bsktbl; Var Score Keeper; Var Sftbl.

ROBINSON, KIMBERLY JEAN; Medomak Valley HS; Waldoboro, ME; (Y); 1/150; Church Yth Grp; Pres Intnl Clb; Math Tm; Pres Band; Chorus; JP Sousa Awd; NHS; Pres Schlr; Val; Am Leg Aux Girls St; Frederic Chopin Piano Awd 85; MSSPA Principals Awd 85; Bowdoin Coll; Intl Law.

ROBISHAW, DEREK; Skowhegan Area HS; Norridgewock, ME; (Y); Church Yth Grp; JA; Math Tm; Quiz Bowl; Varsity Clb; Band; Concert Band; Variety Show; Rep Soph Cls; Bowling; Shepard Awd Mst Imprvd Stu 85; U Of ME Orono; Mechncl Engrng.

ROBITAILLE, LOUISE; Lewiston HS; Lewiston, ME; (Y); Office Aide; Stat Bsktbl; Stat Ice Hcky; JV Var Sftbl; USM; Bus Mgmt.

RODERICK, WILLIAM; South Portland HS; S Portland, ME; (Y); 92/325; Key Clb; VP Sr Cls; Var L Debate Tm; JV Var Bsktbl; Var L Ftbl; JV Var Trk; High Hon Roll; Hon Roll; Jr NHS; NHS; John Norton Awd 83.

RODRIGUE, DONNA A; Skowhegan Area HS; Oakland, ME; (Y); 3/215; Varsity Clb; Score Keeper; Var Capt Socr; High Hon Roll; Jr NHS; NHS; Bus Educ Assn Of ME Schlrshp For Plcng 3rd In Shrthnt I; Thomas Coll; Off Adm.

ROGERS, STEPHANIE; Madison HS; Madison, ME; (Y); 13/98; Office Aide; Band; Concert Band; Jazz Band; Mrchg Band; Pep Band; Yrbk Stf; Rep Frsh Cls; Hon Roll; Legal Sec.

ROHDE, D MORGAN; Fryeburg Acad; Ct Lovell, ME; (Y); Latin Clb; Yrbk Phtg; Var L Crs Cntry; Hon Roll; Aerospace Engrng.

ROLFE, STEPHEN; Westbrook HS; Westbrook, ME; (Y); Am Leg Boys St; Boy Scts; Pres Sec Key Clb; Latin Clb; Math Tm; Off Jr Cls; Stu Cncl; Crs Cntry; Swmmng; Trk; All-State Swm Team 84 & 85; Cross Cntry All Star 84; Engrng.

ROLLINS, ANDREW; Cony HS; Augusta, ME; (Y); Spanish Clb; Variety Show; JV Bsktbl; Var Capt Golf; High Hon Roll; Hon Roll; ME JR PGA Trnmnt-Ovrll Wnnr 84 & 85; Ntl JR PGA-QLFD For New Englnd Sctnl 85; Bus.

ROMANET, AMY B; Massabesic HS; Limerick, ME; (Y); 14/142; Am Leg Aux Girls St; Sec Church Yth Grp; Sec 4-H; Nwsp Rptr; High Hon Roll; Hon Roll; Sec NHS; 4-H Awd; Schlrshps, Hnr Sci 85; Creatv Wrtng Gftd Stsu 83; U Southern MI; Frgn Lang.

ROMERO, LINDA; Woodland HS; Woodland, ME; (S); 1/60; Drama Clb; Thesps; Varsity Clb; Nwsp Rptr; Lit Mag; Pres Frsh Cls; Rep Stu Cncl; Capt Cheerleading; High Hon Roll; NHS; Outstndng Stdnt 82-84; Outstndng Schlr Athl 83-84; Bus.

ROSE, RICHARD; Cheverus HS; Portland, ME; (Y); 25/86; Boy Scts; Sec Speech Tm; Teachers Aide; Church Choir; School Musical; Nwsp Rptr; St Anselms; Engl.

ROSSIGNOI, JONI; Westbrook HS; Westbrook, ME; (Y); Camp Fr Inc; Exploring; Yrbk Stf; Capt Swmmng; Hon Roll; Backstroke Swmmng Record; ST Champ.

ROTTHOFF, JOLENE; Old Orchard Beach HS; Old Orchard Bch, ME; (Y); 9/74; Church Yth Grp; French Clb; Chorus; Concert Band; Jazz Band; Mrchg Band; Yrbk Stf; Rep Frsh Cls; Rep Soph Cls; Rep Jr Cls; Cert Mscnshp Berklee Coll Msc Jazz Fstvl 84; Phys Thrpy.

ROUILLARD, LISA C; St Dominic Regional HS; Lewiston, ME; (Y); 8/79; Variety Show; Cheerleading; Sftbl; High Hon Roll; Hon Roll; NHS; Hd Chrldr JV & V Hcky 82-83; Var Chrldr Hcky & Sccr 83-85; Nrsng.

ROWELL, WENDA; Mt Blue HS; Wilton, ME; (Y); Am Leg Aux Girls St; Church Yth Grp; German Clb; Girl Scts; Hosp Aide; Color Guard; JV Bsktbl; JV Cheerleading; Var Trk; Hon Roll; Germ Intl Awd 84; St Josephs; Psych.

ROY, CAROL; Lewiston HS; Lewiston, ME; (Y); 88/411; Acpl Chr; Pres Chorus; Nwsp Stf; Off Soph Cls; Rep Jr Cls; Rep Sr Cls; Hon Roll; NHS; Outstndng Engl Ability Awd 83; AZ ST U; Lib Arts.

ROY, JENNIFER; Lewiston HS; Lewiston, ME; (Y); 8/400; Off Soph Cls; Off Jr Cls; Off Sr Cls; Var Cheerleading; Var Trk; High Hon Roll; Outstndng Scholar Engl & Frnch 85; Rep ME Schlrs Day UMO 85; U New England; Phys Thrpy.

ROY, TRACY H; Windham HS; South Windham, ME; (Y); Rep Am Leg Aux Girls St; Pres Soph Cls; Pres Sr Cls; Var Bsktbl; Var Trk; High Hon Roll; Hon Roll; VP Jr NHS; Pres NHS; Rep Church Yth Grp; Ltn Hnr Soc 82-85; Prsdntl Clsrm 85; PTA Wrtng Cntst Hnrb Mntn 85; Psychlgy.

RUBLEE, VIKKI; Penquis Valley HS; Milo, ME; (Y); Church Yth Grp; Sec Jr Cls; Var Bsktbl; Var L Socr; Var L Sftbl; High Hon Roll; NHS; Sec Frsh Cls; Hon Roll; Al-Estrn ME Cls B 1st Tm Sccr 83; Regnl Typng II Bus Cntst 85; Awd Cls Typr; Bangor CC; Bus Adm.

RUDY, EDWINA KIPPY; South Portland HS; South Portland, ME; (Y); Am Leg Aux Girls St; Cmnty Wkr; Drama Clb; Sec Jr Cls; Rep Sr Cls; Pres Stu Cncl; Hon Roll; Intnl Clb; Keywanettes; Political Wkr; Amer Future Awd 85; ME Smmr Arts Prog 85; Art 3 Awd 85; Hist.

RUFF, DANIEL G; Lewiston HS; Lewiston, ME; (Y); Letterman Clb; Science Clb; Nwsp Rptr; Yrbk Stf; NHS; CT Coll; Physcs.

RUSS, MARJI; Orono HS; Orono, ME; (S); 14/105; Hosp Aide; School Play; Yrbk Stf; Rep Stu Cncl; Var Cheerleading; Socr; Var Capt Swmmng; Trk; Hon Roll; Bio Sci.

RUSSELL, ROBERT; South Portland HS; South Portland, ME; (Y); Rep Soph Cls; Stu Cncl; Capt Var Bsktbl; Var Trk; Im Vllybl; Im Wt Lftg; Coaches Awd Attitude Achvt 84; Mike Andersen Awd Excel Perf Sprtsmnshp 85; Pre-Med.

RUSSELL, TAMISUE; Washburn District HS; Washburn, ME; (Y); 5/50; Am Leg Aux Girls St; Pep Clb; Yrbk Ed-Chief; Ed Yrbk Stf; Pres Frsh Cls; Pres Jr Cls; Pres Sr Cls; Pres Stu Cncl; L Vllybl; Pres Sec NHS; 1st Pl Exh Spkng Cont 84; Washburn Pagnt Schlrshp 85; Mem Schlrshp 85; U Maine; Nrsng.

RYDER, LINDA; Belfast Area HS; Belfast, ME; (Y); Bus Adm.

SABAN, KATHY; Arskine Academy HS; Palermo, ME; (Y); French Clb; Trs Sr Cls; Bsktbl; Mgr(s); Sftbl; High Hon Roll; Hon Roll; NHS.

SADLER, KATHY; Woodland HS; Woodland, ME; (Y); 2/64; Am Leg Aux Girls St; Drama Clb; Math Tm; Varsity Clb; Yrbk Stf; Var L Sftbl; Var L Vllybl; High Hon Roll; Trs NHS; Sal; Outstndng Stu 82-84; St Anselm Coll; Physcl Thrpy.

SAFRAN, MARY JANE; Houlton HS; Houlton, ME; (Y); 5/135; Camera Clb; VP Church Yth Grp; Pres Service Clb; School Play; Stu Cncl; Vllybl; High Hon Roll; Hon Roll; NHS; Delg ME Schlrs Day UMO 85.

SAMPSON, JODY; Leavitt Area HS; North Turner, ME; (Y); DECA; High Hon Roll; 1st Pl Free Entrprse Ec DECA 85; Top Slsmn Magzne Dr 82 & 83; Honry Page ME Hse Of Reps 83; Bus.

SAMPSON, KEVIN; Gorham HS; Gorham, ME; (Y); 7/130; Boy Scts; Pres Church Yth Grp; Library Aide; Spanish Clb; Stu Cncl; Im Ftbl; Im Vllybl; High Hon Roll; Spanish NHS; Im Bsktbl; Acctng I Awd; U Of NH; Acctng.

SAMPSON, PAMELA; Belfast Area HS; Belfast, ME; (Y); Camera Clb; Church Yth Grp; Cmnty Wkr; Dance Clb; Drama Clb; FCA; FBLA; Girl Scts; Library Aide; Office Aide; Ldrshp Awd 85; Word Of Life NY; MP.

SAMSON, ERICA; Jay HS; N Jay, ME; (Y); Am Leg Aux Girls St; Pres Drama Clb; Math Tm; Model UN; Science Clb; School Musical; School Play; Hon Roll; Sec Trs NHS; Var Capt Cheerleading; U ME Farmington; Spec Edc.

SANFORD, SHAWN G; Leavitt Area HS; Greene, ME; (Y); 3/110; Am Leg Boys St; Math Tm; School Play; Var Capt Ftbl; Var Capt Trk; DAR Awd; DAR Awd; High Hon Roll; Hon Roll; Sec Trs NHS; All ST Ftbl Tm-Hnrb Mntn, Qb & 2nd Tm Dfnsv Back 84; Worcester Poly Inst; Cvl Engrng.

SARGENT, LISA; Bonny Eagle HS; W Buxton, ME; (Y); 20/240; Acpl Chr; Concert Band; School Musical; Variety Show; Var Cheerleading; Fld Hcky; High Hon Roll; NHS; St Schlr; Church Yth Grp; Pres Acad Fitnss Awd 85.

SAUCIER, GARY; Ft Fairfield HS; Ft Fairfield, ME; (Y); 5/90; Chess Clb; JA; Nwsp Stf; Yrbk Stf; High Hon Roll; Prfct Atten Awd; Schlrshp Thomas Coll-Typg I, Soc Stud Awds 84; Rgnl Typg II BEAM Cont, Acctg I & Typg II Awds 85; Bus Admin.

SAVAGE, CHERI; Edward Little HS; Auburn, ME; (Y); Church Yth Grp; Cmnty Wkr; FBLA; Latin Clb; Varsity Clb; Chorus; Variety Show; Yrbk Stf; VP Frsh Cls; Rep Soph Cls; Magna Com Laude Awd 82-83; Orono.

SAVAGE, JULIE; Central HS; Stetson, ME; (Y); 14/83; Computer Clb; Drama Clb; Trs French Clb; Girl Scts; Library Aide; School Play; Yrbk Stf; High Hon Roll; Hon Roll; U Of ME Orono.

SAVAGE, WILLIAM; Bonny Eagle HS; W Buxton, ME; (Y); Boy Scts; VP JA; JV Crs Cntry; Hon Roll; NHS; Ntl Merit Ltr; Chess Clb; Latin Clb; Math Tm; Band; Egl Sct 83; VP Prodctn Of Yr 85; Delg ME ST Schlrs Day 85; Law.

SAWYER, DAWN E; Sacopee Valley HS; E Baldwin, ME; (Y); Drama Clb; Sec Stu Cncl; Band; Yrbk Ed-Chief; Hon Roll; VP NHS; NEDT Awd; Voice Dem Awd; HOBY Yth ST Sem 83; Hofstra U; Intl Bus.

SCANLON, TERI; Fryeburg Acad; Fryeburg, ME; (Y); Church Yth Grp; Drama Clb; Varsity Clb; Chorus; School Musical; School Play; Ed Yrbk Stf; Sec Trs Jr Cls; Var Cheerleading; Var Fld Hcky; SADD-EXEC 84-85; Boston Coll; Cnslng.

SCHMIDT, MATTHEW; Orono HS; Orono, ME; (S); 1/105; Pres Church Yth Grp; Computer Clb; Pres Debate Tm; Math Tm; NFL; Lit Mag; Im Bsktbl; High Hon Roll; NHS; Boy Scts; Japan US Senate Schlrshp 84; Elec Engrng.

SCHMITT, CYNTHIA; Livermore Falls HS; Livermore Falls, ME; (Y); Am Leg Aux Girls St; Varsity Clb; Church Choir; Yrbk Stf; Trs Jr Cls; Rep Stu Cncl; Var L Bsktbl; Var L Crs Cntry; NHS; Church Yth Grp; Outstndng Engl, Grmn & Hstry Awds 86; Hofstra U; Pre Law.

SCHOENBROD, TANJA; Kennebunk HS; Kennebunkport, ME; (S); Church Yth Grp; Ski Clb; Spanish Clb; Yrbk Phtg; Yrbk Stf; Var Bsktbl; Var Vllybl; Hon Roll; NHS; Photo.

SCHOFF, MICHAEL; York HS; York, ME; (Y); 25/130; Church Yth Grp; JV Bsbl; JV Var Ftbl; Var Socr; U Of S ME; Acctg.

SCHOLZ, RENATE; Oxford Hills HS; S Paris, ME; (Y); Am Leg Aux Girls St; Church Yth Grp; Debate Tm; Latin Clb; Chorus; Orch; Hon Roll; NHS; Colby Bk Awd 85; Engl.

SCHONBERGER, LISA; Bangor HS; Bangor, ME; (Y); 13/303; Am Leg Aux Girls St; Cmnty Wkr; Key Clb; Orch; Yrbk Ed-Chief; Ed Yrbk Stf; Tennis; Hon Roll; NHS; Pres Acad Fit Awd 85; Michael Pilot Mem Fnd Scholar Awd 85; Barnard Coll; Psych.

SCIGLIANO, LISA; York HS; York, ME; (Y); Art Clb; Church Yth Grp; Drama Clb; French Clb; German Clb; Key Clb; Latin Clb; Math Clb; Math Tm; School Musical; Grmn Clb-Treas 84; Ltr Vrsty Jacket Ernd 85; Fnlst Miss ME Pgnt 85; Law.

SCOTT, CONNIE; Central HS; Old Town, ME; (Y); Church Yth Grp; Drama Clb; Library Aide; 4-H Awd; High Hon Roll; Hon Roll; Math Awd 84; Regnl Cont Typng I Wnnr 84; D Lor Beauty Schl; Csmtlgy.

SCRIBNER, SHARON; Oxford Hills HS; S Paris, ME; (Y); Church Yth Grp; Intnl Clb; Pres Color Guard; Bsktbl; Socr; US Achvt Acad Awd Wnnr Spnsh 85; Phys Thrpy.

SEABREASE, STACEY; Bangor HS; Bangor, ME; (Y); 4-H; Hosp Aide; Band; Orch; Off Jr Cls; L Fld Hcky; Mgr(s); L Swmmng; 4-H Awd; Hon Roll; All Star ST Swm 85; Phrmcy.

SEAMANS, SARAH; Medomak Valley HS; Union, ME; (Y); Pep Clb; Red Cross Aide; Band; Chorus; Drm Mjr(t); Yrbk Stf; VP Pres Stu Cncl; Sftbl; Hon Roll; St Schlr; Mst Outstndng Ctzn-Grls St 85; Rena House Schlrshp 85; Coll Of The Atlantic; Marn Bio.

SEARLES, LORI; Rangeley Lakes Regional HS; Rangeley, ME; (Y); 2/21; Am Leg Aux Girls St; Yrbk Ed-Chief; Capt Bsktbl; JV Coach Actv; DAR Awd; High Hon Roll; NHS; Sal; Office Aide; Nwsp Sprt Ed; MSSPA Princ Awd 85; Husson Clg Awd 85; Math Awd 85; Thomas Clg; Bus Adm.

SEGER, JANET MARIE; Deering HS; Portland, ME; (Y); FTA; German Clb; Hosp Aide; JA; Latin Clb; Mgr(s); Im Trk; Hon Roll; U Of ME Farmington; Ed.

SEIDEN, FERN R; Hebron Acad; Union, ME; (Y); Band; Chorus; School Musical; School Play; Pres Frsh Cls; Rep Stu Cncl; Fld Hcky; Gym; Lcrss; Drama Clb; Natl JR Hnr Soc; Wellesley Awd; Pblc Spkng Awd; Psych.

SENDZIK, MICHELE; Gorham HS; Gorham, ME; (Y); Pres Church Yth Grp; Debate Tm; Pres 4-H; Latin Clb; Spanish Clb; Trk; Cit Awd; 4-H Awd; Hon Roll; NHS; Ntl 4-H Cngrss-Chicago 85.

SEVIGNY, CYNTHIA M; Biddeford HS; Biddeford, ME; (Y); 8/270; Yrbk Bus Mgr; JV Bsktbl; High Hon Roll; Hon Roll; Hghst Acad Achvt 85; ME Schlrs Day U ME Orono 85; Acctng.

SEYMOUR, JAMES; Portland HS; Cliff Island, ME; (Y); Cmnty Wkr; Pres Math Clb; Math Tm; Rep Jr Cls; JV Var Bsbl; Im Vllybl; High Hon Roll; Hon Roll; NHS; Yale Bk Awd; Ntl Sci Olympiad Awd; Anatomy Of Ldrshp; Marine Engrng.

SHACHOY, CATOR; Portland HS; Portland, ME; (Y); AFS; Latin Clb; Chorus; Lit Mag; Im Bskbl; Score Keeper; Var L Swmmng; Var L Trk; Im Vllybl; Hon Roll; U MA Amherst.

SHACKLEY, DEBORAH; Westbrook HS; Westbrook, ME; (Y); Am Leg Aux Girls St; Latin Clb; Yrbk Stf; Off Stu Cncl; JV Bsktbl; Var L Fld Hcky; Var Sftbl; Hon Roll; Westbrook Acad Achvt Hnr 85; Psych.

SHAPIRO, WILLIAM; Bangor HS; Bangor, ME; (Y); Computer Clb; Key Clb; VP Science Clb; Nwsp Rptr; Nwsp Stf; Yrbk Stf; Var Swmmng; Hon Roll; Office Aide; Yrbk Rptr; Ntl Sci Olympiad Awd; New Englnd Math League Awd; Engrng.

SHARPLES, KIM L; Mt Ararat HS; Bowdoinham, ME; (Y); Girl Scts; Nwsp Rptr; Nwsp Stf; Hon Roll; MSAD Dist Spllg Bee Champ 82; Bio Awd 84; Jrnlsm.

SHAW, BRENDA L; Lewiston HS; Lewiston, ME; (Y); 33/411; Off Frsh Cls; Off Soph Cls; Off Jr Cls; Pres Stu Cncl; Var Stat Bsktbl; Score Keeper; High Hon Roll; Hon Roll; NHS; Pres Stu Cncl 85; Stu Cncl Mem Of The Yr 85; Outstndng Achvt In Hist 85; Central ME Med Ctr; Nrsng.

SHAW, DIANE; Lewiston HS; Lewiston, ME; (Y); 65/398; Keywanettes; Y-Teens; Hon Roll; Cntrl ME Med Cntr Schl Nrs.

SHAW, MICHAEL; Oxford Hills HS; South Paris, ME; (Y); 6/237; Church Yth Grp; Debate Tm; Trs FBLA; Political Wkr; Band; Concert Band; Jazz Band; Mrchg Band; Cit Awd; High Hon Roll; Bryant Coll; Acctng.

SHAW, SANDY J; Community HS; Eagle Lake, ME; (Y); 5/165; Am Leg Aux Girls St; Church Yth Grp; Quiz Bowl; Bausch & Lomb Sci Awd; High Hon Roll; Hon Roll; NHS; Pres Schlr; St Schlr; Hgh Achvt Mythlgy & Outstndng Expermntl Physcs 84-85; Socty Wmn Engrs Sci & Math 85; U Of ME; Nrsg.

SHORES, CHARLENE; Lawrence HS; Clinton, ME; (Y); 3/200; FCA; French Clb; VP Sr Cls; JV Bsktbl; JV Sftbl; DAR Awd; High Hon Roll; Hon Roll; NHS; St Schlr; Social Stds Achvt Awd; Husson Coll; Bus Adm.

SHOREY, DARIN; Caribou HS; Washburn, ME; (Y); Church Yth Grp; Var Bsbl; JV Bsktbl; Hon Roll; Theological Coll.

SHOSTAK, ANTHONY; St Dominic Regional HS; Lewiston, ME; (Y); 23/75; Drama Clb; Key Clb; School Musical; School Play; Stage Crew; Variety Show; Rep Frsh Cls; Rep Soph Cls; Kiwanis Awd; Philadelphia Coll Of Art New Talnt Pgm Schlrshp, RI Jewelry Inst Art Achiev Awd 85; Art.

SIDDIQUI, JAVED; Caribou HS; Caribou, ME; (S); 3/240; JV Capt Bsktbl; Im Socr; Var L Vllybl; MA Inst Of Tech; Mathematics.

SIDES, ANNELISE; Bangor HS; Bangor, ME; (Y); Band; Concert Band; Mrchg Band; Pep Band; Yrbk Stf; Hon Roll; Aviatn.

SIMON, JACKIE; Lewiston HS; Lewiston, ME; (Y); CMMC Schl Of Nrsng; Nrsng.

SIMONEAU, DENISE B; Massabesic HS; Biddeford, ME; (Y); 21/145; French Clb; Girl Scts; Math Tm; Yrbk Stf; Var L Bsktbl; Var L Fld Hcky; Var Socr; Var L Trk; Im Vllybl; Hon Roll; Natl Hnr Scty Schlrshp; Leo Clb Schlrshp; Math Hnrs; U Of Southern ME; Comp Sci.

SIMONEAU, LISA; Lewiston HS; Lewiston, ME; (Y); 16/442; Am Leg Aux Girls St; Sec VP Drama Clb; VP Pres Keywanettes; Political Wkr; School Musical; Nwsp Ed-Chief; Hon Roll; NHS; Ntl Merit Ltr; Cmnty Wkr; Advncd Plcmnt Engl Awd 85; Randlph-Macn Wmns Coll Dstngshd Schlr Awd Schlrshp 85; Drma Awds 83 & 85; Randolph-Macon; Poli Sci.

SIMPSON, MARC A; Waterville HS; Waterville, ME; (Y); 3/203; Am Leg Boys St; Latin Clb; Variety Show; JV Bsbl; JV Bsktbl; High Hon Roll; NHS; Ntl Merit SF; Yale Book Awd 84; Biol Awd 84; Scott Hi G Team 84-85; Aero Engr.

SINCLAIR, JAY; Leavitt Area HS; Canton, ME; (Y); Aud/Vis; Sec Church Yth Grp; Cmnty Wkr; Computer Clb; French Clb; Library Aide; Natl Beta Clb; Speech Tm; Concert Band; Jazz Band; ME Smr Hmnts Pgm 85; Acadmc Advct 84-85; Bowdoin Coll; Eng.

SINCLAIR, SANDRA E; Wells HS; Wells, ME; (Y); Spanish Clb; Nwsp Stf; Yrbk Stf; Trs Sr Cls; Hon Roll; Sec NHS; Psych.

SINCLAIR, STEPHEN; Cony HS; Augusta, ME; (Y); CAP; Sec German Clb; ROTC; Color Guard; Drill Tm; JV Crs Cntry; JV Wrstlng; Chess Clb; Exploring; JCL; Caruso-Walker Flght Schlrshp 84; Amelia Earhart & Billy Mitchell Awds 83-84; Pol Sci.

SIROIS, PHILLIP; Ashland Community HS; Ashland, ME; (Y); French Clb; Band; Pep Band; School Musical; Var Bsbl; Var JV Bsktbl; Im Vllybl; High Hon Roll; Hon Roll; U ME Orono; Chem Engrng.

SITES, MELINDA; Lewiston HS; Lewiston, ME; (Y); Church Yth Grp; Debate Tm; Drama Clb; Letterman Clb; Y-Teens; Stage Crew; Var Capt Swmmng; Hon Roll.

SJOBERG, KAREN; Caribou SR HS; Caribou, ME; (S); 17/230; Am Leg Aux Girls St; VP DECA; Drama Clb; Yrbk Phtg; Pres Stu Cncl; JV Var Fld Hcky; Var Sftbl; NHS; Mortician.

SLIVINSKI, SOYON L; Edward Little HS; Auburn, ME; (S); Drama Clb; Latin Clb; Concert Band; Yrbk Rptr; Pres Sr Cls; Pres Stu Cncl; L Cheerleading; JV Diving; High Hon Roll; NHS; Ldrshp Awd 82; Ntl JR Classical Leagues Maxima Cum Laude Ntl Latin Exam 82; Dramatics Awd 82; Legal Studies.

SMITH, ANDREA; Fryeburg Acad; Lovell, ME; (Y); Am Leg Aux Girls St; French Clb; Latin Clb; Varsity Clb; Chorus; Mgr(s); Socr; High Hon Roll; Hon Roll; NHS.

SMITH, ELLEN; Hampden Acad; Winterport, ME; (Y); Drama Clb; French Clb; Girl Scts; Intnl Clb; Band; School Play; JV Fld Hcky; High Hon Roll; Hon Roll; Med.

SMITH, JANUARY; Massabesic HS; Limerick, ME; (Y); Am Leg Aux Girls St; Church Yth Grp; Girl Scts; Trs Soph Cls; Trs Sr Cls; JV Fld Hcky; Var L Tennis; Lion Awd; Trs NHS; Voice Dem Awd; Most Imprvd Player Awd-Tennis 85; Sci Hnrs 83-85; Highest Cls Avg Awd-Sci 82-83; USCG Acad; Govt.

SMITH, JENNIFER JOY; Open Bible Baptist Christian Schl; New Vineyard, ME; (Y); Church Yth Grp; Chorus; Concert Band; School Musical; Yrbk Stf; Soph Cls; High Hon Roll; Jr NHS; Art Clb; Dance Clb; Vocal Solo Competitn All ST Music 82-84; Rnr Up Stu Of Yr 84-85; Cultural Achvt Awd 84-85; Pensacola Chrstn Coll; Elem Ed.

SMITH, KATHRYN MARIE; Caribou HS; Caribou, ME; (Y); 15/210; French Clb; Hosp Aide; Varsity Clb; Band; Yrbk Stf; Trs Stu Cncl; Mgr Bsktbl; Socr; Sftbl; Trk; SADD Offc-Treas 85-86; Behvrl Sci.

SMITH, MARK; Gorham HS; Gorham, ME; (Y); 23/130; Boy Scts; Leo Clb; Spanish Clb; Band; School Musical; School Play; Yrbk Sprt Ed; VP Soph Cls; VP Jr Cls; Pres Sr Cls; Boys ST Alt 85; N Eastrn U; Chem Engrng.

SMITH, RHONDA; Oxford Hills HS; Oxford, ME; (Y); 52/237; FBLA; Hosp Aide; Library Aide; Office Aide; Hon Roll; Most Dedctd Stu Hlth Pgm 84-85; Stephens Mem Hosp Aux Schlrshp 85; U ME; Nrsng.

SMITH, RICK; Edward Little HS; Auburn, ME; (Y); Chess Clb; Key Clb; Latin Clb; Letterman Clb; Varsity Clb; JV Bsbl; Var Bsktbl; Crs Cntry; Trk; Hon Roll; Acctng.

SMITH, TAMI; Oxford Hills HS; Oxford, ME; (Y); 42/215; DECA; 4-H; Office Aide; Mgr(s); High Hon Roll; Hon Roll; Prfct Atten Awd.

SMITH, TERRI; Bangor HS; Bangor, ME; (Y); Church Yth Grp; Pres Service Clb; Chorus; Off Soph Cls; Stu Cncl; Cheerleading; Fld Hcky; Mgr(s); Hon Roll; Trs NHS; U Of Southern ME; Bus Adm.

SMITH, TIFFANY; Piscataquis Comm HS; Abbot Village, ME; (Y); AFS; Drama Clb; French Clb; Teachers Aide; Chorus; School Musical; School Play; JV Cheerleading; Var Trk; Hon Roll; Human Reltns.

SMITH, VALERIE A; Cape Elizabeth HS; Cape Elizabeth, ME; (Y); 12/125; Jazz Band; Yrbk Bus Mgr; Var Diving; Var Tennis; High Hon Roll; Hon Roll; NHS; Pres Schlr; Band; Var Cheerleading; Maroon Medal Scty 85; Scty Of Wmn Engrs 85; Bryant Coll; Htl Mngmnt.

SOKOLYSKI, DIANA; Leavitt Area HS; Leeds, ME; (Y); Girl Scts; Chorus; Nwsp Stf; Yrbk Stf; Fld Hcky; Vllybl; Hon Roll; Nrs.

SOPER, CHERYL; Bucksport HS; Orland, ME; (Y); Mgr Bsktbl; Stat Sftbl; Hon Roll; Eastern ME Vo-Tech Inst; Med.

SOUCY, MATTHEW R; Ft Kent Community HS; Ft Kent, ME; (Y); Sec Drama Clb; Band; Chorus; Rep Sr Cls; Pres Stu Cncl; Capt L Trk; Vllybl; Hon Roll; Trs NHS; Ntl Merit Ltr; U Notre Dame; Philosphy.

SOUZA, JEFFREY; Leavitt Area HS; Greene, ME; (Y); 2/140; Am Leg Boys St; Math Tm; Jazz Band; School Play; Nwsp Phtg; High Hon Roll; NHS; Ntl Merit SF; Voice Dem Awd; Cptns & Coachs Awd Math Team 85; 10th Pl Odyssy Of Mnd Wrld Comptn 85; Physics.

SPIEGEL, BRAD; Deering HS; Portland, ME; (Y); French Clb; Math Clb; Var L Socr; Var L Trk; Hon Roll; Med.

SPOONER, PETER; Messalonskee HS; Waterville, ME; (Y); 5/144; Am Leg Boys St; Math Tm; Quiz Bowl; VP Stu Cncl; L Capt Crs Cntry; Elks Awd; High Hon Roll; Lion Awd; Pres Trs NHS; Church Yth Grp; Colby Coll, Holy Cross Bk Awds; Carnegie-Mellon U; Math.

SPRAGUE, MICHELE; Bangor HS; Bangor, ME; (Y); Band; Chorus; Orch; Nwsp Stf; VP Frsh Cls; Rep Soph Cls; Rep Jr Cls; Rep Stu Cncl; Var L Cheerleading; Var L Diving; Outstndng Stu Leadrshp 83; Accntng.

ST CLAIR, KATHERINE; Lewiston HS; Lewiston, ME; (Y); 109/379; Cmnty Wkr; Letterman Clb; Varsity Clb; Drill Tm; Drm Mjr(t); Var Capt Cheerleading; Var Trk; Mr Bernards Schl Hair Fash; Cos.

ST JEAN, ELISSA D; Mt Ararat HS; Bailey Island, ME; (Y); Library Aide; Chorus; Jazz Band; School Musical; School Play; Variety Show; Hon Roll; Cert Merit Exc Music 83-85; Cert Merit Bio 83-84; Music.

ST ONGE, LOUISE; St Dominic Regional HS; Lewiston, ME; (Y); Drama Clb; French Clb; Hosp Aide; Trs Pres Keywanettes; Math Tm; Var Co-Capt Tennis; Dnfth Awd; Hon Roll; Sec NHS; 3rd & 6th ST Frnch Ntl Exam 83 & 84; Mnr Awd 84; U Of ME-ORONO; Bus

ST PETER, DENIS; Caribou HS; Caribou, ME; (S); Rep Frsh Cls; Var Bsktbl; Var Capt Socr; Var Trk; Hon Roll; Allstar Eastern ME Class A Soccer 84; Engrng.

ST PIERE, DEBBIE; Freeport HS; Freeport, ME; (Y); Church Yth Grp; JA; Chorus; Var Capt Cheerleading; JV Fld Hcky; Im Gym; Im Socr; JV Sftbl; Im Vllybl; Hon Roll; Child Stu.

ST PIERRE, MICHELLE; Westbrook HS; Westbrook, ME; (Y); Keywanettes; Color Guard; Crs Cntry; Score Keeper; Timer; Capt Trk; Hon Roll; Prfct Atten Awd; Westbrook Coll; Dentl Hyg.

STACK, SANDRA; Westbrook HS; Westbrook, ME; (Y); 2/217; Am Leg Aux Girls St; French Clb; Mrchg Band; L Tennis; High Hon Roll; NHS; Harvard Bk Awd 85; Middlebury; Frgn Lang.

STAIRS, DARRIN B; Freeport HS; Freeport, ME; (Y); 2/90; Am Leg Boys St; Cmnty Wkr; Math Tm; Trs Frsh Cls; VP Soph Cls; Trs Sr Cls; JV Var Socr; High Hon Roll; Boy Scts; French Clb; Colby Coll Bk Awd 85; Plummer Acad Achvt Awds 84-85; Comp Sci.

STAPLES, JEANNE; Old Orchard Beach HS; Old Orchard Bch, ME; (Y); Ski Clb; Band; Color Guard; Mrchg Band; JV Capt Cheerleading; Var Fld Hcky; Var L Trk; Twrlr; Var Wt Lftg; Hon Roll; Cmpt Bscs Awd 84-85.

STARR, CAROLE J; South Portland HS; South Portland, ME; (Y); 1/300; Am Leg Aux Girls St; Latin Clb; Co-Capt Math Tm; Chorus; Orch; NCTE Awd; NHS; St Schlr; Val; Cmnty Wkr; Wellesley Bk Awd 84; Cert Socy Womn Engrs 84; Womns Lit Union Wrtng Cntst Hnbl Mntn 84; Wellesley Coll; Pol Sci.

START, SHERRY; Medomak Valley HS; Warren, ME; (Y); Girl Scts; Hon Roll; Prfct Atten Awd; Grl Scts 82-83; Hnr Rll 82-83; Perf Attdnc 82-85; Kennebec Vlly Voc Tech Inst.

STEADMAN, JOEL; Freeport HS; Freeport, ME; (Y); Church Yth Grp; JA; Math Tm; JV Bsbl; JV Bsktbl; JV Socr; Hon Roll; Jr NHS; VP NHS; Schlstc Ath Awd US Army Resv 85; Acctng.

STEEVES, CARLA; Bonny Eagle HS; Saco, ME; (Y); Dance Clb; Latin Clb; Varsity Clb; Bsktbl; Var Sftbl; Hon Roll; Child Psych.

STEINHACKER, DAVID; Skowhegan Area HS; Skowhegan, ME; (Y); 30/170; Am Leg Boys St; Ski Clb; Varsity Clb; Nwsp Phtg; Yrbk Phtg; Bsktbl; Trk; Hon Roll.

STEINMEYER, NICOLE; Cony HS; Augusta, ME; (Y); Exploring; French Clb; FBLA; Cheerleading; Hon Roll; Nora Jackson Schlrshp 85; Judy Patenaude Meml Schlrshp 85; U Of ME Orono; Intl Mgmt.

STEVENS, ALMA-LEA; Lewiston HS; Lewiston, ME; (Y); Chorus; Variety Show; Nwsp Rptr; Nwsp Stf; Yrbk Rptr; Yrbk Stf; VP Frsh Cls; Var L Cheerleading; JV Trk; High Hon Roll; Comp Pgmmng.

STEVENS, CYNTHIA; Lee Acad; Lee, ME; (Y); 3/52; Am Leg Aux Girls St; Letterman Clb; Office Aide; Chorus; School Play; Stage Crew; Yrbk Stf; Var Mgr(s); High Hon Roll; NHS; Schlrshp Awd; W TX ST U; Accntnt.

STEVENS, ELAINE GAIL; Mattanawcook Acad; Lincoln Center, ME; (Y); Am Leg Aux Girls St; Church Yth Grp; Pres Latin Clb; Letterman Clb; Math Tm; Varsity Clb; Nwsp Rptr; Yrbk Stf; L Trk; High Hon Roll; Outstndng Achvt Ltn 84; U Of ME-ORONO; Elec Engr.

STEVENS, MELISSA; Buckfield HS; W Sumner, ME; (Y); 3/40; Am Leg Aux Girls St; 4-H; Pres Frsh Cls; Pres Jr Cls; Co-Capt Cheerleading; Cit Awd; 4-H Awd; NHS; Chorus; Mary Walker Awd; Phys Thrpst.

STEVENS, SHARON; Rumford HS; Rumford, ME; (Y); Am Leg Aux Girls St; Chorus; Yrbk Stf; Bsktbl; Var L Fld Hcky; Var L Tennis; Voice Dem Awd; Scndry Educ.

STEVENSON, DEBORAH; Gorham HS; Gorham, ME; (Y); Church Yth Grp; Computer Clb; 4-H; French Clb; Latin Clb; Leo Clb; Library Aide; Spanish Clb; Ed Nwsp Stf; 4-H Awd; Comp Sci.

STICHT, MICHELLE; Belfast Area HS; Belfast, ME; (Y); Art Clb; School Musical; JV Var Cheerleading; JV Var Mgr(s); Var Score Keeper; Hon Roll; Schl Lttr & Pin Chrldng 85; Com Artst.

STORER, KIM; Livermore Falls HS; Farmington, ME; (Y); 4-H; Chorus; Church Choir; Drill Tm; School Musical; School Play; Modelng.

STOUTAMYER, ADAM; Madison HS; Madison, ME; (S); Letterman Clb; Ftbl; Wt Lftg; Wrstlng; Hon Roll; Peer Cnslr; U Of Southern ME; Ind Arts.

STRAIT, JOHN CHIP; Wells HS; Wells, ME; (Y); Letterman Clb; Ski Clb; Varsity Clb; L Bsktbl; L Trk; 2 Schl Rcrds-Hgh Jmp 84 & 85; Mst Imprvd Plyr-Bsktbl & Trk 85; Cls B ST Chmpnshp Tm-Bsktbl 83; Cmmrcl Pilot.

STRATTON, BRADLEY J; Winthrop HS; Winthrop, ME; (Y); 6/100; AFS; Capt Debate Tm; JCL; Latin Clb; NFL; Band; Jazz Band; Pres Frsh Cls; JV Im Bsktbl; Hon Roll; Spkr Of House ME Model ST Yth Legisltre 83-84; New England Dist Debate Trnmnt Wnr 83-84; Dartmouth; Pre-Law.

STROUT, CYNTHIA; Leavitt Area HS; Greene, ME; (Y); Chrmn FHA; Nwsp Stf; Hon Roll; MAGIC 84-85; Bus Admin.

STRUVEN, CHRISTOPHER; Fryeburg Acad; Fryeburg, ME; (Y); Boy Scts; Computer Clb; Varsity Clb; Yrbk Stf; JV Bsbl; JV Var Socr; Wrstlng; Prfct Atten Awd; Renssealer Polytech; Aeron Engr.

STUBBS, MARK; Bucksport HS; Bucksport, ME; (Y); Varsity Clb; Nwsp Rptr; Bsbl; Bsktbl; Hon Roll; Comp.

STUDLEY, WENDY; Erskine Acad; Albion, ME; (Y); 8/81; Pres FBLA; Letterman Clb; Office Aide; Cheerleading; Mgr(s); Score Keeper; High Hon Roll; Hon Roll; NHS; Prfct Atten Awd; Prfct Atten 4 Yrs 85; Employees Scholar 85; Doris Young Scholar 85; Thomas Coll; Acctg.

STURTEVANT, DIANE; Madison HS; Madison, ME; (Y); French Clb; Key Clb; Spanish Clb; Trs Soph Cls; VP Sr Cls; Var Bsktbl; Var Cheerleading; Capt Trk; Capt Twrlr; Var Vllybl; 110 Pcnt Clb Trk Awd 84; Knights Columbus Freethrow Trnmnt Awd 82; Vllybl MVC Champs Awd 85; Engl.

SULLIVAN, ELIZABETH; Morse HS; Woolwich, ME; (Y); Am Leg Aux Girls St; Church Yth Grp; Variety Show; Var L Bsktbl; Var L Fld Hcky; Var L Sftbl; Hon Roll; Phys Ed.

SUMMERSON, NANCY; Deering HS; Portland, ME; (Y); French Clb; Key Clb; Varsity Clb; Variety Show; Stu Cncl; Var Cheerleading; JV Crs Cntry; JV Fld Hcky; Var Tennis; Hon Roll; Psych.

SUTHERLAND, DIANE; Morse HS; N Bath, ME; (Y); 19/189; Church Yth Grp; Pep Clb; Spanish Clb; School Play; Variety Show; Yrbk Phtg; Yrbk Rptr; Yrbk Stf; JV L Bsktbl; Var L Crs Cntry; Marion E King Schlrshp 85; Morse High Sci Fair 1st 85; Nurses Alumni Assoc Schlrshp 85; U Of NH; Nrsg.

SVENDSEN, LAURA; Bangor HS; Bangor, ME; (Y); 8/316; Church Yth Grp; Service Clb; Chorus; Orch; Ed Nwsp Stf; Yrbk Stf; JV Fld Hcky; High Hon Roll; Hon Roll; NHS; NACEL Cultrl Exchg Schlrshp 85; Archit.

SWARZTRAUBER, HOLLY LYNN; George Stevens Acad; Castine, ME; (Y); Sec Am Leg Aux Girls St; FBLA; Science Clb; Spanish Clb; Chorus; Stage Crew; Nwsp Phtg; Nwsp Rptr; Yrbk Phtg; Yrbk Rptr; Spanish Awd; Typing Tourn Awd; ME Grls ST Sec Of Senate; Princeton; Engl.

SWEATT, JAMES; Portland HS; Portland, ME; (Y); Church Yth Grp; Ftbl; Socr; Im Vllybl; Hon Roll.

SWICKER, BETH; Deering HS; Portland, ME; (Y); 55/275; Church Yth Grp; Drama Clb; Pres Exploring; Pres German Clb; Key Clb; Color Guard; Pom Pon; Hon Roll; Pres Schlr; Colby-Sawyer Coll; Med Tech.

SYLVESTER, STEPHANIE; Portland HS; Portland, ME; (Y); 28/250; Latin Clb; Nwsp Stf; Sr Cls; Stu Cncl; Var Cheerleading; Trk; Hon Roll; Anat Of Ldrshp 84; Cls 1932 Scholar 85; NE U; Jrnlsm.

TAGGETT, LUANN M; Fort Kent Community HS; Fort Kent, ME; (Y); 35/145; Church Yth Grp; Hosp Aide; Im Bsktbl; L Sftbl; Im Vllybl; Hon Roll; U Of New England; Phys Therapy.

TALON, TRACY; Hampden Academy; Hampden, ME; (Y); French Clb; Key Clb; Ski Clb; Var Fld Hcky; JV Gym; Var Vllybl; Hon Roll.

TANGUAY, DENISE MICHELE; Mt Ararat HS; S Harpswell, ME; (Y); 21/185; VP Church Yth Grp; Var Capt Fld Hcky; High Hon Roll; NHS; Ski Clb; Band; Variety Show; Sftbl; Exc Early Child Ed 83-85; Hm Ec Schlrshp 85; Officers Wives Schlrshp 85; Westbrook Coll; Early Childhd.

TANGUAY, TIM; Sanford HS; Sanford, ME; (Y); Band; L Bsbl; L Ftbl; Wt Lftg; High Hon Roll; NHS; Comp Sci.

TARDIE, ROBERT; Fort Kent Community HS; Ft Kent, ME; (Y); Boy Scts; Chess Clb; Church Yth Grp; Var Bsbl; Var JV Bsktbl; Var Mgr(s); Var Score Keeper; Var Trk; Hon Roll; U Of ME; Math.

TARDIE, TOM M; Caribou HS; Caribou, ME; (Y); 57/220; Rep Stu Cncl; JV Socr; Var VP Tennis; Hon Roll; Model ST Legislative Gov Cabnt 85; MVP Ten 85; Bus Admin.

TARDIF, KAREN; Cony HS; Augusta, ME; (Y); Am Leg Aux Girls St; Dance Clb; FBLA; Variety Show; Yrbk Stf; Rep Frsh Cls; Sec Soph Cls; Cheerleading; Hon Roll; Top 10 Pct; Homecoming Chrmn; Davina Slosberg Mudge Schlrshp; Stonehill Coll; Comm.

TARDIFF, JULIE ANN; Winthrop HS; Winthrop, ME; (Y); 15/98; Pres French Clb; German Clb; School Play; Nwsp Ed-Chief; Hon Roll; NHS; Church Yth Grp; English Clb; Pep Clb; Stage Crew; Amer Legion Schlrshp $500 85; French Clb Schlrshp 85; Ramsdell Schlrshp 85; Northeastern U; Jrnlsm.

TARGETT, JILL ALMA; Gray New Gloucester HS; Gray, ME; (Y); 8/160; French Clb; JCL; Latin Clb; Math Tm; Yrbk Phtg; Yrbk Stf; JV Fld Hcky; Im Vllybl; Jr NHS; Val; Med.

TARR, SARAH L; Fort Fairfield HS; Ft Fairfield, ME; (Y); #26 In Class; French Clb; Band; Chorus; Church Choir; Var Bsktbl; Var Socr; Var Sftbl; Hon Roll; Prfct Atten Awd; Mrchg Band; Math Awd 84; U Of ME Preque Isle; Rcrtn.

TATAKIS, ELIZABETH A; UK Valley HS; Bingham, ME; (Y); Church Yth Grp; Cmnty Wkr; Computer Clb; French Clb; Red Cross Aide; Chorus; Stage Crew; Nwsp Phtg; Nwsp Rptr; Nwsp Stf; KUUTI; Nrsg.

TATE, KIMBERLY; Ellsworth Christian HS; Ellsworth, ME; (S); Church Yth Grp; Chorus; Yrbk Stf; Word Of Life Schlrshp 81; Christian Character Awd 80; Pastors Awd 83; Baptist Bible Coll; Elem Ed.

TAYLOR, CHRISTOPHER; Fryeburg Acad; Fryeburg, ME; (S); Boy Scts; Church Yth Grp; French Clb; Varsity Clb; Band; School Musical; Nwsp Rptr; L Var Ftbl; L Var Tennis; NHS; Boston U; Elec Engr.

TAYLOR, DIANE; Skowhegan Area HS; Norridgewock, ME; (Y); Varsity Clb; Yrbk Stf; Var L Bsktbl; Fld Hcky; High Hon Roll; Hon Roll; JV Bsktbl & Fld Hcky Coaches Awd 82-84.

TAYLOR, LAURA; Yarmouth HS; Yarmouth, ME; (Y); Drama Clb; Hosp Aide; Ski Clb; Trs Spanish Clb; Stage Crew; Yrbk Stf; Var Diving; Var Lcrss; Var Socr; High Hon Roll; Stdnt Advocy 83-84; Med.

TAYLOR, LORI; Brewer HS; Brewer, ME; (Y); 13/220; Church Yth Grp; Cmnty Wkr; English Clb; Key Clb; Letterman Clb; Yrbk Sprt Ed; Rep Frsh Cls; Rep Soph Cls; Rep Jr Cls; Rep Sr Cls; U Of ME Orono; Acctng.

TAYLOR, STEPHEN; Mt Blue HS; Wilton, ME; (Y); Am Leg Boys St; Church Yth Grp; Teachers Aide; Chorus; Church Choir; School Play; Var Bsbl; Hon Roll; Jr NHS; NHS; 7 Yr Newspaper Carrier Svc Awd; Optometry.

TAYLOR, STEVEN; Fryeburg Acad; Fryeburg, ME; (S); 3/110; Boy Scts; JV Bsbl; Bowling; JV Socr; High Hon Roll; NHS; B W Tinker Chptr Frshmn Schlstc Awd 82-83.

TEDESCO, BRET; Leavitt Area HS; Turner, ME; (Y); Bsktbl; Ftbl; Trk; Hon Roll; Arch.

TETU, DAWN; Marshwood HS; S Berwick, ME; (Y); 7/98; Cmnty Wkr; JV Bsktbl; JV Var Sftbl; Hon Roll; NHS; Pres Physcl Ftns Awd 83-84; Coaches Awd 85; Nrsng.

THEBARGE, JANELLE; Carrabec HS; Anson, ME; (Y); Am Leg Aux Girls St; Ski Clb; Varsity Clb; Chorus; VP Frsh Cls; Pres Soph Cls; Pres Jr Cls; Var L Cheerleading; Var L Socr; Hon Roll; Al-Star Cheerng 83-85; Clthng Dsgnr.

THERIAULT, AILEEN; Fort Kent Community HS; Fort Kent Mills, ME; (Y); 32/135; Yrbk Sprt Ed; Yrbk Stf; Sec Rep Frsh Cls; Trs Jr Cls; Pres Rep Stu Cncl; Var JV Bsktbl; Var Socr; Var Trk; Cit Awd; Hon Roll; U Of Southern ME; Psych.

THERIAULT, LISA; Fort Kent Community HS; Ft Kent, ME; (Y); 34/145; FNA; Band; Sftbl; Vllybl; Hon Roll; Voice Dem Awd; Nrsng.

THERIAULT, MYSCHA; MSAD No 70 Hodgdon HS; N Amity, ME; (Y); Church Yth Grp; Drama Clb; Varsity Clb; Chorus; School Musical; VP Soph Cls; Stu Cncl; Stat Bsbl; Stat Bsbl; Mgr(s); Hnr V Ltr 82; V Clb Plaques 85; Schlstc Achvt 82; Design.

THERRIAULT, PAULINE; St Dominic Regional HS; Lewiston, ME; (Y); 8/75; Var Capt Bsktbl; Var Capt Fld Hcky; Var Capt Sftbl; DAR Awd; High Hon Roll; Hon Roll; NHS; Prfct Atten Awd; All St Doms Awd 85; Acad All ST Bsktbl Tm 85; Insurance Women Of Androscoggin Vly Scholar 85; Thomas Coll; Acctg.

THIBEAU, LAURA; Lawrence HS; Fairfield, ME; (Y); Art Clb; Spanish Clb; Capt Color Guard; Cheerleading; Capt Pom Pon; Swmmng; Hon Roll; Prfct Atten Awd; Kennebec Valley; Acctg.

THIBODEAU, BETTY; Lee Acad; Springfield, ME; (Y); Am Leg Aux Girls St; Letterman Clb; Varsity Clb; Nwsp Stf; Yrbk Stf; Sec Jr Cls; Bsktbl; Socr; High Hon Roll; Secy Sci.

THIBODEAU, LAURA V; Caribou SR HS; Caribou, ME; (Y); Office Aide; Var Cheerleading; Var Crs Cntry; High Hon Roll; Hon Roll; Vandalism Comm 82-83; BEAM Typg Cont 83-84; U Southern ME; Bus.

THIBODEAU, MARGERY; Morse HS; Bath, ME; (Y); Pep Clb; Stage Crew; Variety Show; Yrbk Stf; Frsh Cls; Pres Stu Cncl; Var Cheerleading; Hon Roll; Pres Physcl Ftns Awd; Art.

THIBODEAU, RENEE; Caribou HS; Caribou, ME; (Y); Drama Clb; Key Clb; Letterman Clb; Varsity Clb; Band; Pep Band; VP Soph Cls; VP Sr Cls; Var Fld Hcky; Var Tennis; Rotary Clb Schlrshp 85; Regis Coll; Econ.

THISSELL, TANYA; Medomak Valley HS; Friendship, ME; (Y); VP Art Clb; Pep Clb; Hon Roll; Grphc Dsgn.

THOMAS, HEIDI; Ellsworth HS; Ellsworth, ME; (Y); French Clb; Var Cheerleading; Hon Roll; Eng.

THOMBS, RHONDA; Ashland Community HS; Ashland, ME; (Y); 1/50; Am Leg Aux Girls St; Sec Church Yth Grp; Pres Band; Rep Stu Cncl; Capt Bsktbl; Capt Socr; Capt Sftbl; Bausch & Lomb Sci Awd; NHS; Val; Ath Of Yr, Stu Of Yr 84-85; Colby Coll Bk Awd 83-84; U Of ME Orono; Elem Ed.

THOMPSON, CARMELA; Mt Blue HS; Farmington, ME; (Y); Art Clb; German Clb; Ski Clb; Varsity Clb; Variety Show; Pres Frsh Cls; Rep Soph Cls; Rep Jr Cls; Rep Stu Cncl; Schlrshp Barbizon Mdlg Schl 85; Ms Photo Ms Teen All Amer 84; 4th Runner Up 84-85; Barbizon; Modeling.

THOMPSON, HEATHER; Hampden Acad; Hampden, ME; (Y); L Socr; Hon Roll; NHS; Cmnty Wkr; GAA; Hosp Aide; Intnl Clb; Pep Clb; Spanish Clb; Variety Show; CPA.

THOMPSON, KIRK B; Freeport HS; Freeport, ME; (Y); 20/63; Boy Scts; Cmnty Wkr; VP JA; Library Aide; Office Aide; Political Wkr; Red Cross Aide; Chorus; Yrbk Ed-Chief; Yrbk Stf; 3rd Pl Typing Contst Regnl BEAM 84; 4th Pl Adv Accntng Contst Regnl BEAM 85; L Carl Bean Schlrshp 85; Husson Coll; Mgmt Accntng.

THORESON, TAMI; Lewiston HS; Lewiston, ME; (Y); 23/411; Sec Trs Exploring; Pres Intnl Clb; Office Aide; Yrbk Stf; Var Fld Hcky; L Capt Gym; Var L Trk; High Hon Roll; Hon Roll; NHS; Eng,French,Captain Awd 83-85; ROTC; Engrng.

THORESON, TAMRA; Lewiston HS; Lewiston, ME; (Y); 24/437; Sec Trs Exploring; Pres Intnl Clb; Office Aide; Yrbk Stf; Off Frsh Cls; Mgr JV Fld Hcky; Capt Gym; Trk; High Hon Roll; NHS.

THURLOW, TODD; Central HS; Kenduskeag, ME; (Y); Aud/Vis; Church Yth Grp; Band; Chorus; Concert Band; Jazz Band; Mrchg Band; Acdmc Achvt Sci & Math 85; Mus.

TIERNEY, SCOTT; Comden-Rockport HS; Camden, ME; (Y); Pres Sr Cls; Capt Ftbl; Capt Wrstlng; High Hon Roll; Ntl Merit Ltr; Debate Tm; Latin Clb; Ski Clb; Varsity Clb; Chorus; US Senate Yth Pgm Del 85; St Champ Wrstlng 167 Lbs 85; Harvard U; Intl Law.

TIMBERLAKE, JAMES; Lewiston HS; Lewiston, ME; (Y); ME Smmr Humnts Prog 85.

TINKHAM, MARK; Deering HS; Portland, ME; (Y); French Clb; Letterman Clb; Rep Frsh Cls; Rep Soph Cls; JV Ftbl; Capt Trk; Anatomy Of Leadrshp 84-85; Pre-Law.

TOBEY, WARREN; Lawrence HS; Albion, ME; (Y); Office Aide; Teachers Aide; Chorus; Hon Roll; Prfct Atten Awd.

TODD, HEIDI; Caribou HS; Caribou, ME; (Y); Church Yth Grp; Drama Clb; Band; Chorus; Church Choir; Mrchg Band; Pep Band; School Play; NH Coll; Bus Admin.

TODD, JENNIFER; Belfast Area HS; Belfast, ME; (Y); Am Leg Aux Girls St; Girl Scts; Band; Chorus; Mrchg Band; School Musical; Variety Show; L Mgr(s); Trk; Hon Roll.

TODD, SHERI L; York HS; Cape Neddick, ME; (Y); 31/120; French Clb; Math Tm; Sec Band; Sec Concert Band; Sec Mrchg Band; School Musical; Sec Frsh Cls; Trs Soph Cls; Crs Cntry; DAR Awd; Outstndg Svc Band 85; Pres Acad Fit Awd Pgm 85; Dollars For Schlrs Scholar 85; Bay Path JC; Trvl Adm.

TOLMAN, SUSAN G; Mattanawcook Acad; Lincoln Ctr, ME; (Y); Letterman Clb; Pep Clb; Varsity Clb; Chorus; Bsktbl; Fld Hcky; Mgr(s); Tennis; Hon Roll; Winter Carnival Qn 84; E ME Vo Tech Inst; Bus Mgmt.

TOPHAM, BONNIE LYNN; Thornton Acad; Saco, ME; (Y); 13/244; Am Leg Aux Girls St; Church Yth Grp; Latin Clb; Rep Sr Cls; Capt L Bsktbl; Sftbl; Elks Awd; NHS; Rotary Awd; Duff B Kreitzberg Schlrshp 85; U Of New England; Phy Thrpy.

TOWLE, MIKE; Yarmouth HS; Yarmouth, ME; (Y); 4/100; Am Leg Boys St; Drama Clb; French Clb; Latin Clb; Math Tm; School Play; Var Bsktbl; Capt Socr; High Hon Roll; Hon Roll; Half Schlrshp U Of ME Orono ME Schlrs Day 85; Engrng.

TOWNSEND, KELLY; Kennebunk HS; Kennebunk, ME; (Y); Church Yth Grp; Dance Clb; Girl Scts; Pep Clb; Spanish Clb; Temple Yth Grp; Varsity Clb; Color Guard; Drm Mjr(t); Var Capt Cheerleading; Miss Teen Kennebunk USA 85; Worthy Advsr Arundel Assb No 35 IORG 83; Natl Art Awd 85; U Of ME; Bus.

TRAHEY, RICHARD; Cony HS; Augusta, ME; (Y); Exploring; FBLA; JCL; Latin Clb; Model UN; Spanish Clb; Pres Variety Show; Ed Nwsp Bus Mgr; Hon Roll; Boy Scts; Jrnlsm.

TRASK, TINA; Messalonskee HS; Oakland, ME; (Y); 59/142; Drama Clb; French Clb; Varsity Clb; Stage Crew; Variety Show; Nwsp Ed-Chief; Var Capt Cheerleading; Var Sftbl; High Hon Roll; Peer Tutr; Bus Tm; Watervl Womns Assoc Schlrshp 85; Thomas Clg; Bus Mgmt.

TREADWELL, MARK; Penquis Valley HS; La Grange, ME; (Y); Var Bsbl; JV Bsktbl; Hon Roll; Truck Driver.

TREBILCOCK, TEDDY; Oxford Hills HS; Oxford, ME; (Y); Am Leg Boys St; Boy Scts; Church Yth Grp; Band; Concert Band; Jazz Band; Mrchg Band; School Musical; Crs Cntry; Ftbl; Al-ST Music 84 & 85; ME Jzz Cmp 81-85; Hnrs ME ST Sol Ensmbl 84; Music.

TREIBER, JOHN; Morse HS; West Bath, ME; (Y); Radio Clb; School Play; Yrbk Phtg; JV Socr; Var Tennis; JV Trk; Comm.

TRUDEL, KELLEY; Gray New Gloucester HS; Gray, ME; (Y); 11/130; Co-Capt Church Yth Grp; French Clb; Chorus; Off Frsh Cls; Bsbl; Sftbl; Hon Roll; Jr NHS; NHS; Prfct Atten Awd; Bowdoin; Psych.

TURCOTTE, KATHRYN M A; Oak Hill HS; Sabattus, ME; (Y); 17/90; Am Leg Aux Girls St; Office Aide; Ski Clb; Speech Tm; Band; Chorus; Variety Show; Nwsp Rptr; Fld Hcky; Mgr(s); Tchr Secndry Educ.

TURCOTTE, WENDY; Madison Area HS; Madison, ME; (S); 1/100; Math Tm; Drm Mjr(t); Yrbk Stf; Sec Frsh Cls; Pres Soph Cls; Twrlr; Cit Awd; High Hon Roll; Hi-Q Tm 83-85; Hugh O Brian Yth Ambssdr 84; Math.

TURMENNE, PENNY L; Edward Little HS; Oxford, ME; (S); Pep Clb; Hon Roll; U Of ME Farmington; Elem Ed.

TURNER, ANTHONY V; Bangor Baptist HS; Bangor, ME; (Y); 4/22; Pres Frsh Cls; Var L Bsbl; Var L Bsktbl; Var L Socr; Hon Roll; Sci Schlrshp Awd 85; Acadmc Athlt Awd 85; U Of ME Orono; Optmtry.

TURNER, MAUREEN; Yarmouth HS; Yarmouth, ME; (Y); Cmnty Wkr; French Clb; Band; Yrbk Ed-Chief; Var Fld Hcky; Capt Var Swmmng; High Hon Roll; Hon Roll.

TUTTLE, DIANE; Lawrence HS; Fairfield, ME; (Y); 16/212; Drama Clb; Keywanettes; Latin Clb; Chorus; School Play; Stage Crew; Swing Chorus; Yrbk Stf; Score Keeper; High Hon Roll; Frfld Snowmobile Clb Schlrshp 85; Keyette Schlrshp 85; Awd & Schlrshp Amer Lgn Post 14 85; Lyndon ST Coll; Thrptc Rec.

TUTTLE, PAMELA LYNN; Portland HS; Portland, ME; (Y); #91 In Class; Latin Clb; Red Cross Aide; Nwsp Rptr; Yrbk Stf; Rep Frsh Cls; Rep Soph Cls; Rep Jr Cls; Rep Stu Cncl; Capt Cheerleading; NHS; Culinary Arts.

TYE, MARCUS J; Sumner Memorial HS; Gouldsboro, ME; (Y); 1/92; Drama Clb; School Musical; School Play; Nwsp Ed-Chief; Rep Sr Cls; High Hon Roll; NHS; Val; Boy Scts; Chess Clb; Schl Mascot; Nthrn New England JR Sci & Humanities Symposium Winner; Princeton U; Global Conquering.

TYLER, JOY; Mt Blue HS; Weld, ME; (Y); Church Yth Grp; Pres 4-H; Library Aide; OEA; Color Guard; Nwsp Stf; 4-H Awd; Hon Roll; Prfct Atten Awd.

TYNE, JENNIFER; Maine Central Inst; Burlington, ME; (Y); 3/97; Pres Camera Clb; Yrbk Ed-Chief; Yrbk Phtg; Rptr Lit Mag; VP Sr Cls; Var Capt Fld Hcky; Var Capt Sftbl; VFW Awd; Am Leg Aux Girls St; Smith Coll; Engl.

ULMER, MALCOLM; Gardiner Area HS; Randolph, ME; (Y); French Clb; Science Clb; Variety Show; JV Bsktbl; Hon Roll; Prfct Atten Awd; Law.

URQUHART, EDWARD; Fryeburg Acad; Fryeburg, ME; (Y); 10/150; Computer Clb; Var Bsbl; Var Socr; Scrkpr Wrstlng; UNH Sci Symposm Awd 85; Engrng.

VALLEE, LANCE; Lewiston HS; Lewiston, ME; (Y); Church Yth Grp; Key Clb; Varsity Clb; Bsbl; Ftbl; Trk; Wt Lftg; High Hon Roll; Hon Roll; NHS; Plymouth St U.

VAMPATELLA, JOAN; Gray-New Gloucester HS; New Gloucester, ME; (Y); Drama Clb; French Clb; Hosp Aide; Band; Pres Soph Cls; Vllybl; Jr NHS; NHS.

VAN BRUNT, CAROLYN SUE; Deering HS; Portland, ME; (Y); 38/251; Aud/Vis; Church Yth Grp; Drama Clb; Office Aide; Spanish Clb; Acpl Chr; Chorus; Church Choir; School Musical; Nwsp Stf; Ntl Spnsh Exam 7th Pl ST 85; Spnsh Clb Schlrshp 85; ME All ST Chrs 85; Gordon Coll; Cmmnctns.

VANE, KATHLYN; Machias Memorial HS; Machias, ME; (Y); 2/53; Drm Mjr(t); Yrbk Stf; Trs Frsh Cls; VP Soph Cls; Pres Jr Cls; VP Sr Cls; Var Bsktbl; Var Sftbl; Var Capt Vllybl; Pres NHS; Hgh Engl Avg 85; Delia Haughton Schlrshp 85; Pres Acad Fitnss Awd 85; U Of ME-ORONO; Medcl Tech.

VANSTEENBURG, DANIEL; Marshwood HS; Papillion, NE; (Y); Boy Scts; Church Yth Grp; Exploring; JA; Band; Chorus; Concert Band; Jazz Band; Mrchg Band; Orch; U Of KY; Comp Sci.

VARNEY, THOMAS H; Lewiston HS; Lewiston, ME; (Y); Church Yth Grp; Computer Clb; Drama Clb; Office Aide; Church Choir; School Musical; School Play; Stage Crew; Variety Show; Rep Jr Cls; CMVTI Auburn; Acting.

VAUGHAN, JESSICA; Gray New Gloucester HS; New Gloucester, ME; (Y); #15 In Class; Am Leg Aux Girls St; Sec Drama Clb; Trs French Clb; Church Choir; Sec School Play; Stu Cncl; JV Fld Hcky; NHS; Trs Frsh Cls; VP Soph Cls; Colby Coll; Psych.

VAZNIS, PAULA; Stearns HS; Millinocket, ME; (Y); Am Leg Aux Girls St; Hosp Aide; Band; Chorus; Concert Band; Mrchg Band; School Musical; Stu Cncl; Cheerleading; Hon Roll; Mst Imprvd Chrldr Awd 84; UM Farmington; Dietcs.

VEILLEUX, MICHELLE; Rumford HS; Rumford, ME; (Y); Church Yth Grp; Cmnty Wkr; Trs FBLA; FHA; Girl Scts; Office Aide; Spanish Clb; Yrbk Stf; Mat Maids; Trk; Ofc Aid & Typwrtng Awds 82-85; Big Bro/Big Sistr 84-85; Husson Coll; Crt Reprtng.

VERMETTE, KIM N; Biddeford HS; Biddeford, ME; (Y); Am Leg Aux Girls St; Cmnty Wkr; Teachers Aide; Off Jr Cls; Off Sr Cls; Stu Cncl; Hon Roll; NHS; Northeastern U; Physcl Thrpy.

VERREAULT, SCOTT; Lisbon HS; Lisbon, ME; (Y); Drama Clb; School Musical; School Play; Stage Crew; Bsktbl; Trk; Wt Lftg; Boy Scts; Varsity Clb; U ME Orono; Elec Engrng.

VIGUE, KIMBERLY ANN; Fort Fairfield HS; Ft Fairfield, ME; (Y); 6/72; Drama Clb; JA; Library Aide; Chorus; Drill Tm; Mrchg Band; School Musical; JV Cheerleading; Geometry Awd 84.

VINING, RHONDA; Lewiston HS; Lewiston, ME; (Y); 27/411; JA; Stat Bsktbl; Score Keeper; Sftbl; High Hon Roll; Hon Roll; NHS; Frnch Awd 82; Lat Awd 85; U ME Orono; Anml Med Tech.

VIOLETTE, CARLENE; Van Buren District Secondary HS; Vanburen, ME; (Y); GAA; Varsity Clb; Rep Frsh Cls; Rep Soph Cls; Rep Stu Cncl; JV Bsktbl; JV Var Cheerleading; Hon Roll; Casco Bay; Bus Adm.

VITALE, VICTORIA; Lawrence HS; Albion, ME; (Y); Am Leg Aux Girls St; Sec Key Clb; Ski Clb; Yrbk Stf; JV Sftbl; Im Vllybl; Hon Roll; Prfct Atten Awd; Hortclture.

VO, AN; Portland HS; Portland, ME; (Y); Boys Clb Am; Exploring; VICA; Swmmng; Vllybl; Hon Roll; Coll; Elec Tech Engrng.

VOISINE, LYNN; Van Buren District Secondary Schl; Vanburen, ME; (Y); Band; Sec Frsh Cls; Rep Stu Cncl; Var Cheerleading; Vllybl; Hon Roll; NHS; Voice Dem Awd; Bus Adm.

VREELAND, LAURA; Yarmouth HS; Yarmouth, ME; (Y); 19/90; Church Yth Grp; Drama Clb; Hosp Aide; Stage Crew; Yrbk Stf; Crs Cntry; Sftbl; High Hon Roll; Hon Roll; Spanish NHS; Accmplshmnt JR Engl Awd 84; Mst Imprvd Cross Cntry Trphy 84; Phys Sci Awd 82; U Of RI; Bio Engnrng.

WAILUS, MICHELLE; Lewiston HS; Lewiston, ME; (Y); Rep Frsh Cls; Rep Soph Cls; Rep Jr Cls; Stat Bsbl; Var Mgr(s); Stat Sftbl; Hon Roll; Pedtrcs.

WAITE, BRIAN D; Calais HS; Calais, ME; (Y); 4/62; Am Leg Boys St; Pres Stu Cncl; Var Capt Bsbl; Var Capt Socr; Bausch & Lomb Sci Awd; High Hon Roll; NHS; Boy Scts; Church Yth Grp; Cmnty Wkr; GA-PAC Schlrshp 85; MVP US Army Natl Sccr Chcs Assn Amer 85; Mst Outstndng Stu Cncl Mbr 85; U Of ME Orono; Engnrg.

WAITE, ELIZABETH M; Mexico HS; Mexico, ME; (Y); 4/69; Am Leg Aux Girls St; Pep Clb; Band; Chorus; Jazz Band; Pep Band; School Musical; Hon Roll; JP Sousa Awd; Kennebec Vly Cncrt Fstvtl JR Chorus 82; Mntn Vly Hnrs Bnd 83/85; Dstrct I & II Solo Ensmbl 83/84.

WAKEFIELD, ROGER P; Cape Elizabeth HS; Cape Elizabeth, ME; (Y); Computer Clb; French Clb; Math Tm; High Hon Roll; JETS Awd; NHS; St Schlr.

WAKEM, CATHY A; Caribou HS; Caribou, ME; (Y); Ski Clb; Varsity Clb; Rep Frsh Cls; Rep Soph Cls; Rep Jr Cls; Rep Stu Cncl; Var Cheerleading; Var Crs Cntry; Trk; Hon Roll; Bus Admin.

WALCH, JENNIFER; Westbrook HS; Westbrook, ME; (Y); 3/200; French Clb; Latin Clb; Math Tm; Quiz Bowl; Yrbk Stf; JV Crs Cntry; Var Fld Hcky; Var Trk; Hon Roll; NHS; ME Schlrs Day 85; Gftd & Tlntd Inst Of Tech USM 85; Williams Bk Awd 85; MIT; Engrng.

WALHER, TODD; Fryeburg Acad; Fryeburg, ME; (Y); Boy Scts; French Clb; Varsity Clb; Var Bsbl; Var Bsktbl; Var Ftbl; Var Socr; Hmcmng Class King; Embry Riddle; Comm Airln Plt.

WALKLING, ELLEN; Brunswick HS; Brunswick, ME; (S); 8/237; Trs Church Yth Grp; Capt Math Tm; Church Choir; Orch; School Musical; Sec Frsh Cls; Ntl Merit Ltr; Brunswick Hnr Soc; All Eastern Orch; All ST Orch; Dartmouth; Med.

WALLACE, ANNETTE; Lisbon Falls Christian Academy; Lisbon Falls, ME; (Y); 2/7; Church Yth Grp; Chorus; School Play; Yrbk Stf; Capt Cheerleading; Vllybl; Elem Ed.

WALLACE, CHRISTOPHER; Cheverus HS; Portland, ME; (Y); 12/77; Debate Tm; JA; School Play; Var Bsbl; Im Ftbl; High Hon Roll; NHS; Ntl Merit SF; Amer Mgt Schlrshp 85; Dale Carnegie Schlrshp 84; Outstndng Yng Busmn Mid Atlntc & New Eng STS 85; U Of ME-ORONO; Schl Bus Adm.

WALLACE, JULIE; Skowhegan Area HS; Norridgewock, ME; (Y); Church Yth Grp; Varsity Clb; Chorus; School Play; Yrbk Sprt Ed; Yrbk Stf; Sec Soph Cls; Var Bsktbl; Capt JV Fld Hcky; JV Sftbl; Orono; Bio.

WALLS, DOROTHY; Gardiner Area HS; W Gardiner, ME; (Y); FBLA; Office Aide; Pep Clb; Color Guard; Mrchg Band; Nwsp Bus Mgr; Nwsp Rptr; Nwsp Stf; Twrlr; Prfct Atten Awd; Schl Nwsp Typst 84-86; Rifle Cmp 85-86; Infrmtn Clb 83-85.

WALLS, KAREN A; Machias Memorial HS; Machias, ME; (Y); Church Yth Grp; Yrbk Stf; Var Capt Bsktbl; Var Sftbl; Var Capt Vllybl; High Hon Roll; Hon Roll; NHS; U S Army Resrv Natl Schlr-Athl Awd 84-85; Govt Awd 83-85; Phy Thrpst.

WALSH, KATHY; Fryeburg Acad; Denmark, ME; (Y); French Clb; Varsity Clb; Yrbk Bus Mgr; Yrbk Stf; Cheerleading; Fld Hcky; Trk.

WALTON, CASEY; Monmouth Acad; Monmouth, ME; (Y); Speech Tm; Band; Jazz Band; Pep Band; Var Bsbl; Var Capt Bsktbl; Var Capt Crs Cntry; Hon Roll; NHS; UMO; Chem Engrng.

WARD, ALLEN; Lisbon HS; Lisbon Falls, ME; (Y); 7/100; Boy Scts; FBLA; Ftbl; Hon Roll; NHS; U ME Orono; Comp Sci.

WARD, RICHARD P; Lewiston HS; Lewiston, ME; (Y); French Clb; Yrbk Stf; Ntl Hnr Roll 85; Frnkln Piece Coll; Frgn Lng.

WARD, RUSSELL; Fryeburg Acad; Wareham, MA; (Y); Church Yth Grp; Radio Clb; Ski Clb; Band; Concert Band; Jazz Band; Mrchg Band; Stage Crew; Variety Show; Yrbk Phtg; Awd For Acad Excell In Frnch I 83-84; Awd For Outstnding Perf In Stage & Mrchng Bnd 82-83; Marine Bio.

WARREN, CAMI; Caluary Hill Christian Schl; Buckfield, ME; (Y); Church Yth Grp; Teachers Aide; School Play; Yrbk Ed-Chief; Yrbk Stf; Rep Frsh Cls; Cheerleading; Hon Roll; Singing Awd 82-83; Adm Awd 84-85; Hyles-Anderson Coll; Mth Tchr.

WARREN, RUSSELL; Vinalhaven HS; Vinalhaven, ME; (Y); Am Leg Boys St; Boy Scts; French Clb; Bsktbl; Socr; Elec.

WARSKY, STEPHANIE; Wiscasset HS; Wiscasset, ME; (Y); French Clb; Speech Tm; VP Frsh Cls; Off Stu Cncl; Stat Bsbl; Stat Bsktbl; Stat Socr; Mgr Trk; Spec Educ.

WATKINS, MELISSA; Lake Region HS; Casco, ME; (Y); 12/150; French Clb; Pep Clb; VP Varsity Clb; Var L Bsktbl; Var Crs Cntry; Var Capt Trk; Hon Roll; Sonja Flanigan Mem Awd 84; MVP X-Cntry & Trk 81, 82, 84; X-Cntry & Trk Athl Schlrshp To UVM 84; U Of VT; Phys Educ.

WATSON, CLYDE; P C H S HS; Cambridge, ME; (Y); 2/83; Church Yth Grp; Computer Clb; Band; Concert Band; Jazz Band; Mrchg Band; Pep Band; Comp Sci.

WATT, KATHY; Orono HS; Orono, ME; (S); 10/112; Math Tm; School Play; Ed Yrbk Phtg; Capt Var Fld Hcky; Var L Swmmng; Var Capt Tennis; French Hon Soc; High Hon Roll; NCTE Awd; Art.

WEATHERBEE, SUZANNE; Mattanawcook Acad; Lincoln, ME; (Y); Computer Clb; Letterman Clb; Pep Clb; Varsity Clb; VICA; Chorus; Variety Show; Im Badmtn; Var L Bsktbl; Im Coach Actv; MVP JV Bsktbl 83-84; MVP Vrsty Bsktbl 84-85; NMUTI Presque Isle; Comp Tech.

WEBB, JAMES; Fryeburg Acad; Fryeburg, ME; (S); 10/128; Boy Scts; Church Yth Grp; Pres French Clb; School Musical; School Play; Nwsp Bus Mgr; Nwsp Phtg; Yrbk Bus Mgr; Yrbk Phtg; Socr; Engrng.

WEBB, LAUNA; Gorham HS; Gorham, ME; (Y); Dance Clb; 4-H; GAA; Girl Scts; Pep Clb; Varsity Clb; Band; Concert Band; Jazz Band; Mrchg Band; Phy Ther.

WEBBER, MICHAEL; Deering HS; Portland, ME; (Y); French Clb; Trs German Clb; JA; Temple Yth Grp; Varsity Clb; Rep Jr Cls; JV Bsbl; Socr; JV Tennis; Rep Frsh Cls; Civil Engrng.

WEBSTER, JEFFRI-LYNN; Lee Acad; Springfield, ME; (Y); AFS; Am Leg Aux Girls St; Math Tm; Ski Clb; Varsity Clb; Chorus; School Musical; School Play; Variety Show; Lit Mag; 2 Yr Full Tuitn Scholar OCU 86-88; OK City U; Comm.

WEBSTER, KELLY; Medomak Valley HS; Waldoboro, ME; (Y); AFS; Church Yth Grp; Cmnty Wkr; Hosp Aide; Red Cross Aide; Chorus; Bsktbl; Socr; Hon Roll; Modelng Boston 85; Med.

WEEKS, TIMOTHY; Cheverus HS; Scarborough, ME; (Y); 23/86; Boy Scts; Drama Clb; Key Clb; Letterman Clb; Ski Clb; School Musical; L Trk; Cit Awd; Hon Roll; Outstndg Achvt Chem 84; Good Ctzns Awd 84; Lyndon ST Coll; Bio.

WEIGELT, EARL; Forest Hills HS; Jackman, ME; (Y); #3 In Class; Church Yth Grp; Chorus; Church Choir; VP Frsh Cls; Var Bsbl; L Var Crs Cntry; Hon Roll; NHS; Mt Vernon Nazarene Coll; Mnstry.

WEINER, DANIEL; Deering HS; Portland, ME; (Y); JA; Office Aide; Ski Clb; Temple Yth Grp; Jazz Band; Variety Show; Yrbk Phtg; Hon Roll; Anesthesiology.

WELCH, CARLA; Deering HS; Portland, ME; (Y); AFS; Girl Scts; Chorus; Church Choir; Im Bsktbl; JV Gym; JV Sftbl; High Hon Roll; Hon Roll; Jr NHS; Cert Of Hnr 84; Peer Helper Training Prog 84; Comp Sci.

WELCH, MICH A; Maine Central Inst; Pittsfield, ME; (Y); JV Bsbl; Var Crs Cntry; Var Trk; JV Wrstlng; Hon Roll; U Of ME; Bus Adm.

WELCH, STACY LEE; Boothbay Region HS; W Boothbay Harbor, ME; (Y); Am Leg Aux Girls St; Band; Yrbk Stf; Hon Roll; NHS; Donor Bk Awd-Bus Educ Courses 85; Beal Coll; Secry.

WELNER, KATHARINE; Morse HS; Bath, ME; (Y); Am Leg Aux Girls St; VP Church Yth Grp; French Clb; Sec Intnl Clb; Yrbk Stf; High Hon Roll; Hon Roll; Prfct Atten Awd; Science Clb; Band; Word Of Life Scholar 83-85; Creat Wrtg Intr Natl Comp 83-85; Qz Tm Natl 83-85; Hougton; Eng.

WESCOTT, JAMES; Skowhegan Area HS; Skowhegan, ME; (Y); 2/175; Am Leg Boys St; Letterman Clb; Math Tm; Scholastic Bowl; Varsity Clb; Nwsp Phtg; Yrbk Phtg; Trs Sr Cls; Bsbl; Var Capt Bsktbl; Sheperd & Sci & Hstry Awds; Dartmouth; Mech Eng.

WEST, MARY; Belfast Area HS; Frankfort, ME; (Y); Church Yth Grp; Nwsp Stf; JC Awd; Prfct Atten Awd; High Avg Alg I Earth Sci 83; Chamberlayne JC; Int Desgn.

WESTLEIGH, LOUISA; Oxford Hills HS; W Paris, ME; (Y); Am Leg Aux Girls St; Church Yth Grp; Drama Clb; Library Aide; Teachers Aide; Acpl Chr; Chorus; Variety Show; Hon Roll; Music Awds 83-85; Vikettes Girls Grp 84-85; Mntn Vly Musicl 84-85; Psych.

WESTON, MARY A; Fryeburg Acad; Fryeburg, ME; (Y); Church Yth Grp; Band; Chorus; Church Choir; School Musical; Stage Crew; Ed Yrbk Stf; ME Smmr Arts Prog 84; Long Isl U Southampton; Dsgn.

WESTORT, JENNIFER; Portland HS; Portland, ME; (Y); JA; Latin Clb; Yrbk Stf; Bsktbl; Var Fld Hcky; JV Sftbl; Hon Roll; St Schlr; Natl Hnr Rl 85; Maine Schlr 85.

WEYBRANT, JILL; Morse HS; Bath, ME; (Y); Am Leg Aux Girls St; Pep Clb; Variety Show; Var Cheerleading; Var Crs Cntry; Var Capt Gym; Var Socr; Var Trk; Hon Roll; Outstndng Achvt French II 83-84; Coaches Awd Track 83-84; Awd Cross Cty 84-85; Phys Thrpy.

WHALEN, CATHY; Sanford HS; Springvale, ME; (Y); 37/243; Trs French Clb; VP Pres Keywanettes; Y-Teens; Nwsp Rptr; Yrbk Stf; Var JV Fld Hcky; Var Capt Tennis; French Hon Soc; Hon Roll; NHS; Sprague Elec Schlrshp 85; Intrct Schlrshp 85; MVP Tnns Tm 84; U Of Southern ME; Htl Admin.

WHEELER, DAVID L; Waterville Schls; Waterville, ME; (Y); 32/202; Am Leg Boys St; Boys Clb Am; Pres Spanish Clb; Var Ftbl; Var Swmmng; Trk; Hon Roll; Ntl Merit SF; Scott Hi-Q Team; Century III Ldrs Awd; Attorney.

WHITAKER, STEPHANIE; Woodland HS; Grand Lake Stream, ME; (S); Trs French Clb; Hosp Aide; Trs Intnl Clb; Lit Mag; Rep Frsh Cls; Rep Soph Cls; Rep Jr Cls; Rep Stu Cncl; Stat Bsktbl; JV Var Mgr(s); St Anselm Coll; Med.

WHITE, ANGI; Traip Acad; Kittery, ME; (Y); Church Yth Grp; Drama Clb; French Clb; Girl Scts; Thesps; Chorus; Church Choir; Nwsp Stf; Cheerleading; Hon Roll; Psych.

WHITE, MICHELLE; Sanford HS; Sanford, ME; (Y); JV Mgr(s); JV Score Keeper; JV Capt Sftbl; Hon Roll; Fashn Merchndsng.

WHITE, PETER; Gorham HS; Scarborough, ME; (Y); Church Yth Grp; Bsbl; Var Bsktbl; ME U; Civil Engr.

WHITE, STACEY; Caribou HS; Caribou, ME; (Y); Drama Clb; Sec Key Clb; Sec Office Aide; Pres Varsity Clb; Church Choir; Yrbk Rptr; Var L Crs Cntry; Var L Trk; Hon Roll; Sec NHS; Westbrook; Med Sec.

WHITMORE, JOANNE L; Edward Little HS; Auburn, ME; (S); Church Yth Grp; Hosp Aide; Latin Clb; Pep Clb; Political Wkr; Teachers Aide; Chorus; Yrbk Stf; JV Trk; Hon Roll; Bus Admin.

WHITNEY, ALICE; Greely HS; N Yarmouth, ME; (Y); 12/147; Church Yth Grp; Drama Clb; VP French Clb; JCL; Trs Latin Clb; Teachers Aide; Chorus; School Play; Stage Crew; Nwsp Sprt Ed; Westbrook Coll Pres Schlr 85-86; Natl Acad Fit Awd 84-85; Natl Latin Exam Maxima Cum Laude 84-85; Westbrook Coll; Dentl Hyg.

WHITNEY, JUNE; Windham HS; N Windham, ME; (Y); 4-H; JA; Yrbk Stf; Trs Soph Cls; Pres Jr Cls; Var Bsktbl; Var Capt Socr; 4-H Awd; High Hon Roll; Hon Roll; MVP Var Bsktbl 85; Triple C All Star Bsktbl 85; Triple C All Star Sftbl 83 & 85; Bus.

WHITNEY, SUSAN; Cony HS; Augusta, ME; (Y); JCL; Variety Show; JV Capt Bsktbl; JV Fld Hcky; JV Var Sftbl; Im Vllybl; Hon Roll; Plymouth ST Coll; Metrlgy.

WHITTEN, SHANNON; Caribou HS; Caribou, ME; (S); Concert Band; Mrchg Band; Pep Band; School Musical; Rep Soph Cls; Sec Jr Cls; Var Cheerleading; Mgr Gym; JV Socr; High Hon Roll; SR All Aroostook Band; USTA Adv Intermed Awd; Sci Fair Prjct Awd; Law.

WIBERG, SONJA; Hampden Acad; Hampden, ME; (Y); Am Leg Aux Girls St; Hosp Aide; Key Clb; Band; Trs Jr Cls; Gym; Socr; Tennis; High Hon Roll; VP NHS; ME Schlrs Day 85; Sprts Rehab Thrpsy.

WIEGLEB, JENNIFER A; Maranacook Community Schl; Manchester, ME; (Y); 8/107; Church Yth Grp; Math Tm; Pres Spanish Clb; Var Capt Socr; Var Capt Tennis; Hon Roll; Political Wkr; Chorus; Yrbk Stf; Kennebec Teen Republcns VP 84-85; Duke U; Econ.

WILCOX, TRINA; Caribou HS; Washburn, ME; (Y); 51/220; Church Yth Grp; VP Key Clb; Yrbk Stf; Rep Jr Cls; Westbrook; Bus Admn.

WILDER, CRYSTAL L; Bonny Eagle HS; Hollis, ME; (Y); Library Aide; Math Tm; Teachers Aide; Symp Band; Mgr(s); High Hon Roll; Hon Roll; NHS; Ntl Merit SF; Earth Sci Awd; Spanish.

WILEY, JENNIFER; Wiscasset HS; Dresden, ME; (Y); Pres 4-H; French Clb; Office Aide; Var L Crs Cntry; L Mgr(s); Var Score Keeper; Var L Trk; Stat Wrstlng; 4-H Awd; High Hon Roll.

WILLETTE, STEVE; Lisbon HS; Lisbon Falls, ME; (Y); 16/115; Am Leg Boys St; Boy Scts; CAP; Drama Clb; French Clb; Drill Tm; Stage Crew; Yrbk Phtg; Horsmnshp.

WILLEY, BEVERLY; Fryeburg Acad; Harrison, ME; (Y); 40/151; Cmnty Wkr; Girl Scts; Sec Leo Clb; Library Aide; Office Aide; Chorus; JV Cheerleading; Mgr Fld Hcky; Hon Roll; Prfct Atten Awd; Wrk Readiness Cert 85; Bus & Prfsnl Womens Clb Prize 84; Dorothy P Ingraham Schlrshp 85; Leo Clb Aprctn; U ME Machias; Secry.

WILLIAMS, BILLY L; Hyde Schl; New York, NY; (Y); Boys Clb Am; Cmnty Wkr; Debate Tm; Drama Clb; Pres Frsh Cls; Var Capt Bsktbl; Trk; High Hon Roll; Pres Schlr; Prep Schl Boys Clb Schlrshp Awd 84; Bsktbl Schlrshp 83; Prncpls Awd 83; Villanova U; Social Wrk.

WILLIAMS, DANIEL; Houlton HS; Houlton, ME; (Y); Sec FFA; Hon Roll; Farming.

WILLIAMS, ELIZABETH; Orono HS; Bangor, ME; (S); Math Tm; Speech Tm; Yrbk Phtg; Yrbk Rptr; Yrbk Stf; Stu Cncl; Cheerleading; L Socr; Tennis; Mgr(s); Grand Svc 84-85; Jrnlsm.

WILLIAMS, KRISTEN; Yarmouth HS; Yarmouth, ME; (Y); Am Leg Aux Girls St; Pres Drama Clb; French Clb; Latin Clb; Math Tm; Science Clb; Thesps; Band; School Musical; School Play; Wellesley Bk Awd 85; Sci Olympcs 6th In Ntn For 1 Evnt 8th In Ntn 85; Anthrplgy.

WILLIAMS, TROY C; Bangor HS; Bangor, ME; (Y); Church Yth Grp; Cert Prtcptn Accntng I Rgnl Cntst 84; Cert Achvt For Outstndng Cntrbtn & Achvt Bus Educ 84; Certfd Pblc Accntnt.

WILLOCKS, CLAUDIA; Bangor HS; Bangor, ME; (Y); Library Aide; Office Aide; Score Keeper; Hon Roll; Prfct Atten Awd; A Hartstone Mrl Schlrshp Awd 85; Husson Coll; Nrsng.

WILLS, SHALE; Belfast Area HS; Union, ME; (Y); 12/143; French Clb; Varsity Clb; Chorus; School Musical; Yrbk Stf; Stu Cncl; Fld Hcky; Gym; Trk; Hon Roll; YFU Schrlshp Japan 84; Searsmont Neighborhd Activts Schlrshp 85; MSAD Tchrs Assoc Schlrshp 85; NY U; Anthrplgy.

WILSON, KRISTINE; Westbrook HS; Westbrook, ME; (Y); Hst FBLA; Yrbk Stf; High Hon Roll; Hon Roll; Ntl Merit Ltr; 2nd Pl BEAM Regnl Bus Cntst Shrthd & 25 Pctl ST Cntst 85; Cert Awd Acadmc Achvt 85; Westbrook Coll ME; Bus Adm.

WILSON, LAURA; Hampden Acad; Hampden, ME; (Y); French Clb; Band; Concert Band; Yrbk Ed-Chief; Yrbk Stf; Vllybl; High Hon Roll; Hon Roll; Sec NHS; Ntl Merit Ltr; ME Schlrs Day Prtcpnt 85; Cvl Engnrng.

WILSON, MARK; Monmouth Acad; North Monmouth, ME; (Y); Math Tm; Speech Tm; Band; Socr; High Hon Roll; Ntl Merit SF; Air Force Acad; Military.

WILSON, MELISSA; Bonny Eagle HS; Steep Falls, ME; (Y); Church Yth Grp; Library Aide; Office Aide; Teachers Aide; Band; Symp Band; Hon Roll; Jr NHS; NHS; Bus.

WINCAPAW, LISA; South Hope Christian Schl; Waldoboro, ME; (Y); 2/7; Church Yth Grp; Latin Clb; Library Aide; Chorus; Yrbk Stf; Var L Vllybl; Hgst Grade Pt Avg Sci,Eng 84-85; Pre-Med.

WINCHENBACH, LYNETTE; Medomak Valley HS; Waldobor, ME; (Y); Cmnty Wkr; Latin Clb; Pep Clb; Band; Chorus; Concert Band; JV Bsktbl; Var Trk; Hon Roll; Med Tech.

WING, IRENE E; Caribou HS; Caribou, ME; (Y); 50/240; Church Yth Grp; Hosp Aide; Key Clb; Yrbk Stf; Hon Roll; Nrsng.

WINN, MIKE; Wells HS; Ogunquit, ME; (Y); Stu Cncl; Var Crs Cntry; Hon Roll; NHS; ROTC; Naval Ofcr.

WINSLOW, SUSAN; Hampden Acad; Hampden, ME; (Y); Drama Clb; French Clb; Girl Scts; Hosp Aide; Intnl Clb; Key Clb; Teachers Aide; Band; Concert Band; Mrchg Band; Math.

WITHAM, ROBYN; Lawrence HS; Shawmut, ME; (Y); 20/221; Church Yth Grp; Cmnty Wkr; Library Aide; Red Cross Aide; Spanish Clb; Band; Chorus; High Hon Roll; Hon Roll; Hnrs Comp I & II & Lit 83-85; U Of ME Orono; Psych.

WITTER, DARCIE; Telstar Regional HS; Bethel, ME; (Y); 15/68; Am Leg Aux Girls St; Red Cross Aide; Ski Clb; Teachers Aide; Varsity Clb; Pres Frsh Cls; JV Var Fld Hcky; Sftbl; Var L Trk; Hon Roll; Eng Hgst Grade Avg 82-85; Bus Mgmt.

WITZKE, DAWN N; Oak Hill HS; Sabattus, ME; (Y); 1/80; Am Leg Aux Girls St; Pres Church Yth Grp; Math Tm; School Play; Yrbk Stf; Var Stat Sftbl; High Hon Roll; Trs NHS; Val; Prjct Discvry 83-85; Ntl Merit Cmmnd Stu 84; AAL All Coll Schlrshp 85; Johns Hopkins U; Math.

WOLFF, KATHLEEN P; Lake Region HS; Bridgton, ME; (Y); 39/147; Church Yth Grp; School Musical; School Play; Swing Chorus; Variety Show; Yrbk Stf; Stu Cncl; Cheerleading; NHS; St Schlr; Kendal C Ham Schlrshp 86; Sebago Schrshp 85; Cong Chrch Schlrshp 86; U ME-FARMINGTON; Spcl Ed.

WOLFORD, LINDA; Mattanawcook Acad; Lincoln Ctr, ME; (Y); Am Leg Aux Girls St; Pres Church Yth Grp; Library Aide; Chorus; High Hon Roll; Hon Roll; Csmtlgy.

WOOD, MELISSA; Winslow HS; N Vassalboro, ME; (Y); Dance Clb; Band; Drm & Bgl; Drm Mjr(t); Mrchg Band; Bsktbl; Crs Cntry; Sftbl; JP Sousa Awd; Prfct Atten Awd; Outstndng Alg,Clarinet,Marcher Geo 83-85; Bus Adm.

WOOD, TRAVIS; Messalonskee HS; Oakland, ME; (Y); 39/165; Chess Clb; Church Yth Grp; Drama Clb; School Musical; Nwsp Stf; Stat Bsktbl; Var Capt Crs Cntry; Im Ftbl; Var L Trk; High Hon Roll; 3rd In Rgnl Bus Mt 85; U Of ME Orono; Acctng.

WOODARD, MICHELLE; Valley HS; Bingham, ME; (Y); Am Leg Aux Girls St; VP Church Yth Grp; Drama Clb; Band; Chorus; Concert Band; Pep Band; Cheerleading; Trk; Hon Roll; Delg ME Schlrs Day 85; Hist.

WOODBURY, JAMES; Portland HS; Portland, ME; (Y); Chess Clb; Exploring; French Clb; JA; Var L Bsktbl; Hon Roll; NHS; Boys Clb Am; Latin Clb; Vllybl; Williams Coll Bk Awd; ME Schlrs Day Prtcpnt; Prtcpnt Antmy Of Ldrshp; Engrng.

WOODWARD, DEAN; Messalonskee HS; Augusta, ME; (Y); 6/145; Am Leg Boys St; Cmnty Wkr; Quiz Bowl; Band; Chorus; Pep Band; Var L Socr; JCL; Latin Clb; Math Tm; Mensa 84-85; All ST Chorus 85; Westinghouse Schlrshp 85; Rose-Hulman Inst Of Tech; Engr.

WOODWARD, HEIDI J; Bonny Eagle HS; W Buxton, ME; (Y); Orch; Symp Band; Nwsp Rptr; Trs Jr Cls; Pres Sr Cls; Capt Var Cheerleading; JV Tennis; Hon Roll; NHS; Outstndng Jrnlst 84; Most Dedicated Chrldr 84; Natl Helper Awd 85; U ME; Educ.

WOODWARD, KAREN S; Sumner Memorial HS; Gouldsboro, ME; (Y); 2/85; Am Leg Aux Girls St; Pres Drama Clb; Band; Chorus; Jazz Band; School Musical; Variety Show; Rep Stu Cncl; JP Sousa Awd; NHS.

WOODWORTH, STEVE; Oxford Hills HS; S Paris, ME; (Y); Rep Jr Cls; Rep Sr Cls; Stu Cncl; JV Bsktbl; Hon Roll.

WORSTER, TRAVIS; Forest Hills HS; Jackman, ME; (Y); 2/22; Am Leg Boys St; Church Yth Grp; Drama Clb; Math Tm; Quiz Bowl; Var Bsbl; Var Socr; Cit Awd; Hon Roll; NHS; Sci Fair Awd 83-84; New England Jr Sci & Humanities Sympsm 84-85; Algebra II Awd 84-85; Engrng.

WORTHLEY, CAROL; Rumford HS; W Peru, ME; (Y); Office Aide; Spanish Clb; Yrbk Stf; Crs Cntry; Sftbl; Hon Roll; Prfct Atten Awd; Shrthnd 1 Awd 85; Bus Educ Assn ME 85; Accntng.

WRIGHT, DEBORAH LOU; Searsport District HS; Winterport, ME; (Y); AFS; Am Leg Aux Girls St; Trs FBLA; Yrbk Stf; Pres Jr Cls; Var L Fld Hcky; Var L Sftbl; Hon Roll; NHS; VP Pep Clb; Outstndng Jr Grl Awd 85.

WRIGHT, GREG; Calvary Hill Christian HS; East Dixfield, ME; (Y); Church Yth Grp; Pep Clb; Yrbk Phtg; Yrbk Stf; Rep Frsh Cls; Rep Soph Cls; VP Jr Cls; Off Stu Cncl; Var Bsktbl; Var Crs Cntry; Mst Imprvd Acdmc 82-83; Mst Improvd Acmdc 84-85; U MA Amherst; Coaching.

WRIGHT, LAUREN E; Maranacook Community HS; Bennington, VT; (Y); 14/150; Pres AFS; Am Leg Aux Girls St; Dance Clb; Trs German Clb; Hosp Aide; School Musical; L Tennis; Hon Roll; Church Yth Grp; Debate Tm; YMCA Camp Cnslr 82-83; Williams Clg Bk Awd Excllnc Eng 84; Cngrs Bundstg Schlrshp 84-85; Wheaton Clg.

WRIGHT, MELISSA; Penquis Valley HS; Milo, ME; (Y); Camera Clb; Computer Clb; Drama Clb; Teachers Aide; Nwsp Stf; Yrbk Stf; High Hon Roll; Hon Roll; 1st Pl Acctg I Regnl Bus Cntst 85; Acctg.

WRIGHT, SHEILA; Lee Acad; Lambert Lk, ME; (Y); 6/42; Am Leg Aux Girls St; Letterman Clb; Library Aide; Nwsp Rptr; Nwsp Stf; Stu Cncl; Sftbl; High Hon Roll; Hon Roll; Comm.

YEATON, BELINDA S; Skowhegan Area HS; Norridgewock, ME; (Y); Ski Clb; Drill Tm; Flag Corp; Mrchg Band; Yrbk Stf; High Hon Roll; Hon Roll; SR Grp; Prom Cmmtte; SR Booth; Vrsty Clb; Accntng I Rgnls.

YEATON, CHRISTINE; Lincoln Acad; Wiscasset, ME; (Y); 40/125; VP AFS; Aud/Vis; Church Yth Grp; Pep Clb; Sec Varsity Clb; Chorus; Trs Frsh Cls; Bsktbl; Capt Fld Hcky; Sftbl; All-ST Fld Hcky 84; MVP Fld Hcky 84; Harold Smithwick Schlrshp 85; Emerson Coll; Brdcstng.

YORK, CHRISTOPHER; Caribou HS; Caribou, ME; (S); High Hon Roll; Ntl Sci, Ldrshp Merit Awd 83-85.

YORK, HEIDI J; Skowhegan Area HS; Skowhegan, ME; (Y); 44/206; Church Yth Grp; Trs French Clb; Pep Clb; Varsity Clb; Band; Chorus; Concert Band; Mrchg Band; Rep Sr Cls; Lion Awd; Dollars For Schlrs Awd 85; Frnch Schlrshp 85; ME All St Band 85; Kennebec Vly Vo Tech; RN.

YOUNG, LYNN; Belfast Area HS; Morrill, ME; (Y); 9/147; Rep Am Leg Aux Girls St; Pres FBLA; Pres Spanish Clb; Chorus; School Musical; School Play; Sec Trs Sr Cls; Hon Roll; Jr NHS; NHS; Blaine House Schlrshp 85; Ms FBLA Of ME 85; Presdntl Acadmc Fitness Awds Pgm 85; U Of ME-ORONO.

ZAHTILA, MARIANN; Winslow HS; Winslow, ME; (Y); 52/205; Trs AFS; Pres Church Yth Grp; Math Tm; Color Guard; Mrchg Band; Yrbk Stf; Rep Sr Cls; Rep Stu Cncl; Hon Roll; Egl Crss Awd Cthlc Yth Org CYO 85; U Of CT; Phrmcy.

ZIMMERMAN, STEVE; Robert W Traip Acad; Kittery, ME; (Y); Boy Scts; Sec Church Yth Grp; JV Ftbl; Acadmc Awd Sci 84; Bus.

ZIPFEL, CATHY; Leavitt Area HS; Turner, ME; (Y); 5/150; Am Leg Aux Girls St; Sec Church Yth Grp; Math Clb; Yrbk Stf; Var L Fld Hcky; Trk; French Hon Soc; High Hon Roll; NHS; St Schlr; Bus Mgmt.

MASSACHUSETTS

AARONSON, STEPHANIE R; Newton South HS; Newton, MA; (Y); Pres Drama Clb; Model UN; Chorus; School Play; Nwsp Stf; Stu Cncl; Ntl Merit Ltr; School Musical; Hon Roll; Newton Educ Wrkshp Dir; Faclty Awd 83-85; Hstry.

ABBOOD, CHERYL; Braintree HS; Braintree, MA; (Y); 41/468; Church Yth Grp; Office Aide; Var Gym; JV Trk; High Hon Roll; Hon Roll; Maximum Hnrs 83-84; Frmnghm ST Coll; Bus.

ABBOTT, SEAN A; Gardner HS; Gardner, MA; (Y); 2/180; Am Leg Boys St; Church Yth Grp; School Musical; Crs Cntry; Hon Roll; NHS; Ntl Merit Ltr; Sal; Trinity Coll; Math.

ABBOTT, SHARON; Notre Dame Acad; Hingham, MA; (Y); Church Yth Grp; French Clb; Science Clb; Ski Clb; Chorus; School Play; Stu Cncl; High Hon Roll; Hon Roll; Soc Sci.

ABGRAB, RUSSELL J; Westport HS; Westport, MA; (Y); 3/158; Drama Clb; French Clb; Intnl Clb; Ski Clb; School Play; Yrbk Stf; Var L Bsbl; Var L Bsktbl; High Hon Roll; NHS; MVP Vrsty Bsebll 84-85; Cpt Frshmn Bsktbl 82-83; Pre Med.

ABNEY, AUDREY; Bridgewater Raynham Regional HS; Raynham, MA; (Y); GAA; Hosp Aide; Varsity Clb; Yrbk Ed-Chief; Yrbk Stf; Off Sr Cls; Coach Actv; JV Var Fld Hcky; JV Var Sftbl; JV Hon Roll; Bridgewater Raynham Hall Of Fame Stflb 85; V Ltr Awd Sftbl 85; Ltr Awd Fld Hcky 85; Bridgewater ST Coll; Soclgy.

ABRAHAM, ROBERT; Westbridge HS; Concord, MA; (S); 2/15; 4-H; Var Bsktbl; Im Ice Hcky; Var Socr; High Hon Roll; Hon Roll; NHS.

ABROMOVITCH, CHRISTINE; Haverhill HS; Haverhill, MA; (Y); Church Yth Grp; Spanish Clb; Var Sftbl; Hon Roll; R Elaine Crouston Mem Schlrshp 85; Northern Essex CC; Accntng.

ABURIDA, WAEL; Northfield Mt Hermon Schl; Lake Forest, IL; (Y); Camera Clb; Intnl Clb; Radio Clb; Nwsp Phtg; Yrbk Phtg; Wt Lftg; High Hon Roll; Hon Roll; Lake Forest Coll; Econ.

ACCIARDO, PAMELA C; Coyle And Cassidy HS; Selkirk, NY; (Y); 13/158; VP French Clb; Ski Clb; Teachers Aide; Yrbk Stf; Var L Cheerleading; Var L Tennis; JV Trk; French Hon Soc; High Hon Roll; Hon Roll; Shaws Schlrshp 85; New Engand Dairy Deli Assoc Schlarhp 85; Lets Shine Awd 85; Babson Coll; Bus.

ACHILLES, REGINALD H; Fitchburg HS; Fitchburg, MA; (Y); 23/227; Am Leg Boys St; French Clb; Varsity Clb; JV Var Bsbl; JV Var Ftbl; High Hon Roll; Drm & Bgl; Hon Roll; HS Alumni Schlrshp 85; Joseph G Flynn Schlrshp 85; Clemson U; Arch.

ADAM, JOHN ANDREW; Barnstable HS; W Barnstable, MA; (Y); 59/425; Church Yth Grp; Drama Clb; Chorus; School Play; Rep Jr Cls; Rep Sr Cls; Crs Cntry; Hon Roll; Ltr Acad; Kirk Mashow Mem Schlrshp; Gold Silver Cert Acad; Northeastern U; Engrng.

ADAMIAK, NEAL F; St Johns HS; Worcester, MA; (Y); 88/280; Am Leg Boys St; Church Yth Grp; Band; High Hon Roll; Hon Roll; Cmnty Wkr; Nwsp Stf; Rep Soph Cls; Im Bsktbl; Arch.

ADAMIK, DAWN L; North Middlesex Regional HS; W Townsend, MA; (Y); 34/212; Political Wkr; Varsity Clb; Variety Show; VP Jr Cls; Pres Sr Cls; Crs Cntry; Powder Puff Ftbl; Trk; Ntl Ldrshp Svc Awd 85; MA Coll Art; Design.

ADAMS, CASSANDRA; Barnstable HS; Centerville, MA; (Y); Church Yth Grp; Drama Clb; Band; Concert Band; Mrchg Band; Mgr Sftbl; Hon Roll.

ADAMS, CHRISTOPHER D; Brockton HS; Brockton, MA; (Y); 3/996; Am Leg Boys St; French Clb; Key Clb; Math Tm; Band; Chorus; Concert Band; Mrchg Band; School Musical; Swing Chorus; Outstndg Prfrmnce Fr 84; Holy Crs Book Awd 85; Jazz.

ADAMS, CYNTHIA; Taunton HS; Taunton, MA; (Y); Am Leg Aux Girls St; Church Yth Grp; Latin Clb; Band; Concert Band; Mrchg Band; High Hon Roll; Hon Roll; NHS; Prfct Atten Awd; JR Cls Mrshl 85; MA Adv Stu Pgm Altrnt 85; Faith Ofcr-Intl Ordr Of Rainbow/Grls 85; Cornell; Ntrtn.

ADAMS, HILARY; Brockton HS; Brockton, MA; (Y); Church Yth Grp; High Hon Roll; Hon Roll; Bus Admin.

ADAMS, MARK; Archbishop Williams HS; Braintree, MA; (Y); 24/209; Church Yth Grp; Ski Clb; Stage Crew; Rep Jr Cls; Im Bsbl; JV Bsktbl; Im Golf; Hon Roll; Jr NHS; NHS; Providence; Bus Admin.

ADAMS, MICHAEL; Holy Name Central Catholic HS; Worcester, MA; (Y); 50/260; Nwsp Ed-Chief; Nwsp Rptr; Nwsp Stf; Ed Lit Mag; Rep Stu Cncl; JV Mgr(s); Hon Roll; Engl Mdl 83; Jrnlsm Cert 84; Creative Wrtng Cert 85.

ADAMS, SCOTT; Holliston HS; Holliston, MA; (Y); Am Leg Boys St; Yrbk Stf; Off Jr Cls; Off Sr Cls; Var L Ftbl; Var L Trk; High Hon Roll; Hon Roll; NHS; Ntl Merit Ltr; Acadmc Lrt; Economics.

ADAMS, TERRENCE; Hull HS; Hull, MA; (Y); Var Bsbl; Coach Actv; Var Ftbl; Ice Hcky; Powder Puff Ftbl; Al-Star Ftbl, Bsbl.

ADAMS, TIM; Hull HS; Hull, MA; (Y); 16/135; Rep Jr Cls; Off Sr Cls; Var Capt Bsbl; Var Capt Ftbl; Powder Puff Ftbl; All Str Tm; Ftbl All Schlstc Bst Back; Awd & Trophy Combination Athl, Schlr & Ctzn; U Lowell.

ADAMS, TINA; South High Community Schl; Worcester, MA; (S); Dance Clb; Stu Cncl; Stdnt Advsry Cncl 85; U Mass Med Hlth Career Prog 84; Proj 50/50 Comp Cmp 83; Holy Cross; Surgn.

ADDERLEY JR, THOMAS JOHN; Ayer HS; Ft Devens, MA; (Y); 32/167; Boy Scts; German Clb; Letterman Clb; Nwsp Phtg; Yrbk Stf; Var L Crs Cntry; Var Socr; Var L Trk; Var L Wrstlng; Hon Roll; ROTC Scholar Air Force 85; Boston U; Aerospc Engrng.

ADDIS, CRAIG E; Northampton HS; Florence, MA; (Y); 31/265; Am Leg Boys St; Boy Scts; Drama Clb; Thesps; School Musical; School Play; Stage Crew; Variety Show; High Hon Roll; NHS; Drama Stage Mgr 85-86; Boy Scts Eagle Sct 85; Thespns Pres 85; Mech Engrng.

ADILETTO, DANIEL; Franklin HS; Franklin, MA; (Y); Boy Scts; French Clb; Ski Clb; Yrbk Stf; Rep Stu Cncl; JV Stat Ftbl; JV Var Golf; Fitchburg ST Coll; Bus.

ADKINS, KIMBERLY; N Andover HS; N Andover, MA; (Y); 110/234; Aud/Vis; Pres Church Yth Grp; Pres Girl Scts; Hosp Aide; Office Aide; Band; Mrchg Band; Pep Band; School Musical; Intl Ordr Of Rnbw Grls-PWA Grnd Crss Of Clr & Grnd Bnr Bearer Of MA 81-85; Gordon Coll; Socl Wk.

ADLER, OONA; Barnstable HS; Centerville, MA; (S); Church Yth Grp; Drama Clb; Acpl Chr; Chorus; Church Choir; Madrigals; School Musical; School Play; Mgr(s); Sftbl; Music.

AGAPITE, JULIE; Boston Latin Schl; Boston, MA; (Y); 91/330; Church Yth Grp; Cmnty Wkr; Drama Clb; Office Aide; Political Wkr; Stage Crew; Hon Roll.

AGBEY, JAMES; Holy Name HS; Worcester, MA; (Y); 113/246; Church Yth Grp; Science Clb; Band; School Play; Stage Crew; Variety Show; Ftbl; Sftbl; U Of Lowell; Math.

AGOSTINI, PAULA; Bishop Feehan HS; Seekonk, MA; (Y); 8/250; Var Trk; Vllybl; French Hon Soc; High Hon Roll; NHS; Chem Cert Of Achvt 85; Math Excllnc Cert 84; Ntl Lang Arts Olympd-With Distctn 83; Accntng.

AGUIAR, RICARDO; New Bedford HS; New Bedford, MA; (Y); 97/640; Computer Clb; JA; Var L Tennis; Hon Roll; SE MA U; Comp Engr.

AHEARN, JOHN; Milford HS; Milford, MA; (Y); 23/300; Band; Concert Band; Jazz Band; Variety Show; Hon Roll; NHS; Concrt Band Awd; Hall Of Fame Band Awd; Pub Comms.

AHEARN, LORI; Natick HS; Natick, MA; (Y); 21/443; Sec Jr Cls; Sec Sr Cls; High Hon Roll; Hon Roll; Trs NHS; Rep Frsh Cls; Rep Soph Cls; Off Stu Cncl; Bus Dept Awd-Exc Typng 85.

AHERN, DEBORAH; Burlington HS; Burlington, MA; (Y); Trs Church Yth Grp; Nwsp Rptr; Yrbk Sprt Ed; Capt Powder Puff Ftbl; Capt Socr; Capt Trk; Hon Roll; NHS; Silver Mdl 300 Low Hrdls New Englnd Trck Mt 85; Ntl Hnr Soc 85; Vrsty Trck Soc 85; Vrsty Trch Hgh Socr; Frgn Corspndnt.

AHERN, JUDY; Dennis Yarmouth HS; W Yarmouth, MA; (Y); 7/316; Am Leg Aux Girls St; VP Civic Clb; Letterman Clb; Ski Clb; Yrbk Ed-Chief; Trs Soph Cls; Trs Jr Cls; Trs Sr Cls; Var L Fld Hcky; JV Sftbl; DAR Excll Amer Hstry Awd 84-85; Cornell U Ithaca.

AICKELIN, CARRIE; Chicopee Comprehensive HS; Chicopee, MA; (Y); 16/308; VP Church Yth Grp; German Clb; JCL; Science Clb; Band; Concert Band; Mrchg Band; Yrbk Sprt Ed; Stu Cncl; Var L Swmmng; Pro Merito VP, Elks Tnagr Mnth 85; Wstrn New Engl Coll; Comp Engr.

AIKENS, GLENN; Gloucester HS; Gloucester, MA; (Y); 2/380; Var L Bsktbl; Im Mgr Ftbl; High Hon Roll; NHS; Ntl Merit Ltr; Sawyer Mdl 83; Phys, Wrld Hist Merit Awds 85; Comp Sci.

AIKINS, G ROBERT; Belmont Hill Schl; Brookline, MA; (Y); Aud/Vis; Nwsp Stf; Ice Hcky; Hon Roll; Ntl Merit Ltr; Pratt Natl Tlnt Srch Fin Arch, Art & Dsgn 85; Prat Inst Schlrshp 85; Film.

AIROLDI, PHILIP; Westfield HS; Westfield, MA; (Y); 50/400; Boy Scts; Drama Clb; School Musical; School Play; Nwsp Rptr; Stu Cncl; Var Swmmng; Var Trk.

AKELL, CYNDIE; Mansfield HS; Mansfield, MA; (Y); 36/170; Drama Clb; School Play; Hon Roll; Augat 85; Nights Phythias 85; Stu Exch Pgm; Bay ST JC; Travel.

AKKER, BARBRA VANDEN; Whitinsville Christian HS; Whitinsville, MA; (Y); 3/17; Art Clb; Church Yth Grp; School Play; Stage Crew; Nwsp Ed-Chief; Yrbk Ed-Chief; Yrbk Phtg; VP Stu Cncl; High Hon Roll; NHS; Calvin Coll.

ALBANESE, JENNIFER; Westport HS; Westport, MA; (Y); Cmnty Wkr; Ski Clb; Yrbk Sprt Ed; Var Capt Bsktbl; Coach Actv; Var Capt Fld Hcky; Mgr(s); Sftbl; Taber Scholar; Globe All Schltc Plyr Yr; All Star Field Hockey, Bsktbl; Stonehill; Lib Arts.

ALBANO, DONNA; Agawam HS; Agawam, MA; (Y); 55/350; Church Yth Grp; JA; JCL; Library Aide; Color Guard; Im JV Sftbl; Var Swmmng; Var Trk; Hon Roll; Med Tech.

ALBEE, CHRIS; Blackstone Valley Reg Voc Tech HS; Bellingham, MA; (Y); Var Capt Crs Cntry; Var L Trk; Hon Roll; Bus.

ALBERGHINI, ERIC; Tahanto Regional HS; Berlin, MA; (Y); 5/50; Math Tm; Stu Cncl; Capt Bsbl; Bsktbl; Trs NHS; Trs JA; Science Clb; Spanish Clb; Capt Socr; Hon Roll.

ALBERTELLI, CHRISTINE; Melrose HS; Boston, MA; (Y); Stu Cncl; Var L Bsktbl; JV Fld Hcky; JV Sftbl; Hon Roll; NHS; Engrng.

ALBERTELLI, SARA; Arlington Catholic HS; Arlington, MA; (Y); 5/149; Drama Clb; JA; Spanish Clb; Church Choir; School Play; Yrbk Phtg; High Hon Roll; Hon Roll; NHS; Ntl Merit SF; Natl Lat Exm Gold Mdlst 82 & 83; Pre-Med.

ALDRED, MICHELLE M; Randolph HS; Randolph, MA; (Y); 13/327; Cmnty Wkr; Pres French Clb; Teachers Aide; Chorus; School Play; Hon Roll; JC Awd; NHS; Church Yth Grp; Dance Clb; MA Forgn Lang Assn Ldrshp 85; Wnnr Dennis F Ryan Essy Cntst Law Day 85; Cert Merit Frnch Cntst 84; Salem ST Coll; Elem Ed.

ALETTO, MARY JO; Presentation Of Mary Acad; Salem, NH; (S); 3/50; Cmnty Wkr; Math Clb; Spanish Clb; Variety Show; Yrbk Stf; Cheerleading; Hon Roll; Sec NHS; Schl Sci Fair Awd 83; Regnl Sci Fair Cert 83; Health Svcs.

ALFE, GERILYN MARIE; Medford HS; Medford, MA; (Y); 2/536; Sec Intnl Clb; Yrbk Stf; Capt Cheerleading; High Hon Roll; NHS; Ntl Merit Ltr; Sal; Dance Clb; Hosp Aide; Letterman Clb; Commnwlth MA Schlr Grnt 85; Suprntndnt Excllnc Awd 85; Danc Tchrs Clb Boston MA Annl Schlrshp 85; Tufts Jackson U; Dntstry.

ALIX, LYNNE; North Attleboro HS; No Attleboro, MA; (S); 1/275; Model UN; Trk; Val; Trs JCL; Trs Latin Clb; Math Tm; Scholastic Bowl; Pres Band; Pres Concert Band; Pres Mrchg Band; Brown Bk Engl Awd; Renssalaer Math/Sci Awd; Ntl JR Clsscl Leag Awd; Govt.

ALLARD, KARILYN; Billerica Memorial HS; Billerica, MA; (Y); #14 In Class; Chorus; Church Choir; School Musical; Variety Show; High Hon Roll; NHS; Pres Schlr; St Schlr; Engl Dept Awd; Friends Music Schlrshp; Stockkbridge Schl Ag; Flrcltr.

ALLEGREZZA, AMY; Milford HS; Milford, MA; (Y); 4/293; Am Leg Aux Girls St; VICA; Band; Yrbk Stf; Rep Soph Cls; Rep Jr Cls; Rep Stu Cncl; JV Capt Fld Hcky; Var L Tennis; High Hon Roll; Chncllrs Awd U MA 4 Yr Schlr 85; Vrs Band Awds 83-85; Law.

ALLEGREZZA, GREGORY; Milford HS; Milford, MA; (Y); 3/300; Am Leg Boys St; Band; Jr Cls; Stu Cncl; JV Var Bsbl; JV Var Bsktbl; Var Socr; High Hon Roll; NHS; Ntl Merit Ltr; Vrsty Bsktbl 84-85; Engrng.

ALLEN, COURTNEY; Greenfield HS; Greenfield, MA; (Y); #1 In Class; Church Yth Grp; School Play; Yrbk Phtg; Trk; High Hon Roll; NHS; Ntl Merit SF; Harvard Bk Awd 85; Frgn Lang Inst Simons Rock Scholar 85; Georgetown; Frgn Lang.

ALLEN, DANIEL; Tantasqua Regional HS; Sturbridge, MA; (Y); 8/200; Am Leg Boys St; Variety Show; Ed Lit Mag; Rep Stu Cncl; Var Crs Cntry; Var Trk; Hon Roll; VP NHS; Ntl Merit Ltr; Pres Schlr; Providence Coll.

ALLEN, DAWN; Reading Memorial HS; Reading, MA; (Y); 4-H; Hosp Aide; Varsity Clb; Band; Var L Trk; 4-H Awd; High Hon Roll; Hon Roll; Church Yth Grp; Concert Band; SADD 84-86; Springfield Coll; Phy Thrpy.

ALLEN, GREG; Seekonk HS; Seekonk, MA; (Y); Boy Scts; Church Yth Grp; Computer Clb; Latin Clb; Letterman Clb; Var L Swmmng; NHS; Exploring; God Cntry Awd; Boy Sct Yr Narragansett Cncl 85; MV Swmr 85; Boston Glb All Schlstc Swm Tm 85; Rensselaer Polytechnic Inst.

ALLEN, IRVING V; Somerville HS; Somerville, MA; (Y); 63/535; Camera Clb; Church Yth Grp; Library Aide; Rep Stu Cncl; High Hon Roll; Hon Roll; Rep Frsh Cls; VA Mc Carthy Mem Awd Accntng 85; Somerville Dist Ct Schlrshp 85; MA U Boston; Accntng.

ALLEN, JACQUELINE; Randolph HS; Randolph, MA; (Y); Debate Tm; Cmnty Wkr; Lib Arts.

ALLEN, KELLY; New Bedford HS; Acushnet, MA; (Y); Ski Clb; Teachers Aide; Band; Vllybl; Bristol CC; RN.

ALLEN, LISA; North Middlesex Regional HS; Pepperell, MA; (Y); Art Clb; 4-H; GAA; Ski Clb; JV Bsktbl; Var Capt Swmmng; Hon Roll; All Star Tm Sftbll 83-84, Co Capt 83-85; U Lowell; Bus.

ALLEN, LISA; Norwood HS; Norwood, MA; (Y); 4/398; Church Yth Grp; Hosp Aide; Key Clb; Red Cross Aide; Concert Band; School Play; Cheerleading; Trk; CC Awd; Cit Awd; UMASS Tlnt Awd 84; Awd Outstndng Achvt Sci 85; Tchrs Assoc Schlrshp 85; Tufts/Jackson U; Med.

ALLEN, MICHELLE; Whitinsville Christian Schl; Millbury, MA; (Y); 7/45; Camera Clb; Church Yth Grp; Drama Clb; Pres 4-H; Hosp Aide; Sec Chorus; School Play; Cheerleading; JV Vllybl; 4-H Awd; Principals Awd 83; MA Cranbry Fest Best Show 83; Creative Wrtng Awd 83; Med.

ALLEN, MONIQUE; Methuen HS; Methuen, MA; (Y); 25/325; Am Leg Aux Girls St; Intnl Clb; Model UN; Teachers Aide; Yrbk Stf; Im JV Bsktbl; Im JV Sftbl; High Hon Roll; Hon Roll; Physcl Thrpy.

ALLEY, ROBIN K; St Louis Acad; Lowell, MA; (Y); 2/35; Drama Clb; French Clb; Stage Crew; Yrbk Phtg; Var Cheerleading; Hon Roll; Alg Awd 85; Comp Sci Awd 85; Hnr Roll Awd 84; U Lowell; Biol.

ALLISON, MARCIA; Haverhill HS; Haverhill, MA; (Y); 72/415; Pres Church Yth Grp; Cmnty Wkr; Sec German Clb; Band; Chorus; Concert Band; Mrchg Band; Variety Show; Yrbk Stf; High Hon Roll; R Elaine Croston Schlrshp 85; Band Parents Awd 85; Pres Schlrshp 85; E Nazarene Coll; Engl.

ALLIX, DEBRA; Christopher Columbus HS; South Boston, MA; (S); Cmnty Wkr; Political Wkr; Variety Show; French Hon Soc; High Hon Roll; Hon Roll; NHS; NEDT Awd; Awd Recongnition Algebra I Competition 82-83; Harvard; Med.

ALLMAN, KRISTIN; Westwood HS; Westwood, MA; (Y); 6/206; AFS; Am Leg Aux Girls St; Key Clb; Orch; Rep Stu Cncl; Var L Fld Hcky; Var L Tennis; Hon Roll; NHS; Ntl Merit Ltr; Tri Vly Leag Tnns Al-Str 84-85; Tri Vly Leag Fld Hocky Al-Star 84; NVP Tnns 85; Mkrtng.

ALMEIDA, CRAIG A; Westport HS; N Dartmouth, MA; (Y); Variety Show; Yrbk Phtg; Yrbk Stf; Hon Roll; NHS; Bridgewater ST Coll; Sec Ed.

ALMEIDA, JACQUELINE; New Bedford HS; New Bedford, MA; (Y); 19/686; Office Aide; Pep Clb; Yrbk Sprt Ed; High Hon Roll; Hon Roll; NHS; Acctg.

ALMEIDA, MARY JO; New Bedford HS; New Bedford, MA; (Y); 35/600; Aud/Vis; Church Yth Grp; Office Aide; Yrbk Stf; High Hon Roll; NHS; Media Comm.

ALOISIO, PAUL; Woburn SR HS; Woburn, MA; (S); Boy Scts; JCL; Ski Clb; Concert Band; Mrchg Band; Symp Band; Rep Stu Cncl; High Hon Roll; Jr NHS; Ntl Latin Hnr Soc 84; Chem.

ALOSI, TIMOTHY B; Sacred Heart HS; Plymouth, MA; (Y); 1/88; Boy Scts; Debate Tm; Pres Key Clb; Stage Crew; Rep Stu Cncl; Var Bsktbl; Var Socr; Var Trk; High Hon Roll; NHS; Chncllrs Tlnt Awd 85-86; Engrng.

ALPER, ERIC J; Sharon HS; Sharon, MA; (Y); 5/200; Am Leg Boys St; Drama Clb; Math Tm; Model UN; Spanish Clb; Nwsp Ed-Chief; Yrbk Bus Mgr; Rep Frsh Cls; Rep Soph Cls; VP Jr Cls; Ntl Hnr Soc Schlrshp 85; Robyn Amy Locke Mem Schlrshp 85; Brown U.

ALPERS, MARIA L; Wilmington HS; Wilmington, MA; (Y); 6/250; French Clb; Trs Frsh Cls; Trs Soph Cls; Trs Jr Cls; Trs Sr Cls; Var Sftbl; Var Vllybl; French Hon Soc; High Hon Roll; NHS; Outstndng Englsh Stu 85; Presdntl Acadmc Ftns Awd 85; Outstndng Achvt Frnch 85; Regis Coll; Comm.

ALTIMARI, OLGA; Christopher Columbus HS; East Boston, MA; (S); 7/120; Hon Roll; NHS; Engrng.

ALTMAN, STEPHANIE A; Marblehead HS; Marblehead, MA; (Y); 1/246; Drama Clb; Chrmn Intnl Clb; Latin Clb; Service Clb; Thesps; Chorus; School Musical; Swing Chorus; Ed Nwsp Stf; Lit Mag; U Of PA Book Awd 85; 1st Pl Awd New Englnd Msc Fstvl 84; Maxima Cum Laude Ntl Lth Tst 85.

ALTMAN, WAYNE J; North Andover HS; North Andover, MA; (Y); 4/268; Am Leg Boys St; Cmnty Wkr; Math Tm; Speech Tm; Temple Yth Grp; Pres Jr Cls; Pres Sr Cls; Stu Cncl; Tennis; High Hon Roll; ST Champ Radio Brdcstng MA Fornscs Lg 85; MA Mth Lg Top 20 85; Hgh Achvt Hnrs Spn Pgm 84-85; Pre-Med.

ALUKONIS, KAREN; Lynn Classical HS; Lynn, MA; (Y); Aud/Vis; Office Aide; Pep Clb; Radio Clb; Stage Crew; Yrbk Stf; Powder Puff Ftbl; Hon Roll; 3 Certs Hgh Hon 84; 2 Certs Hgh Hon 85; Fash Merch.

ALVES, ELIZABETH; New Bedford HS; New Bedford, MA; (Y); 14/600; Library Aide; Orch; Var L Crs Cntry; Var L Trk; High Hon Roll; Hon Roll; NHS; Prfct Atten Awd; Econmst.

ALVES, MARK D; Dartmouth HS; South Dartmouth, MA; (Y); 11/243; AFS; Am Leg Boys St; Church Yth Grp; Cmnty Wkr; Debate Tm; Mrchg Band; JV Crs Cntry; NHS; Math Tm; Band; Hugh O Brien Yth Ldrshp Smnr 84; Grp Ldr Sptlght Prgm For Gftd Stu 85; Pltcl Sci.

ALVES, NATERCIA C; Westport HS; Westport, MA; (Y); 20/140; Debate Tm; Intnl Clb; JA; Office Aide; Nwsp Ed-Chief; Yrbk Stf; Hon Roll; NHS; Jrnlsm Awd 85; Teenagr Of Mnth 85; Betsy Taber Schlrshp 85; Rhode Island Coll; Psych.

ALVES, ROSE MADELEINE; Bishop Connolly HS; Bristol, RI; (Y); 80/177; Sec Church Yth Grp; Girl Scts; VP JA; Spanish Clb; Var Sftbl; Hon Roll; Prfct Atten Awd; Top Achvr JR Achvmnt 84-85; Bst All-Arnd Spnsh Clb 83-84; Barry U; Comp Sci.

ALVES, SUSAN; Madison Park HS; Boston, MA; (Y); Camera Clb; Key Clb; Office Aide; Stu Cncl; Cheerleading; Hon Roll; Prfct Atten Awd; Stu Ldrshp; Northeastern U; Bus Adm.

ALWARDT, ANITA L; Bay Path Reg Vo Tech; North Oxford, MA; (Y); Hosp Aide; Capt Bsktbl; Var Cheerleading; Capt Socr; JV Sftbl; Hon Roll; NHS; MVP & Coaches Awd/Sccr 83-85; Bsktbl Coaches Awd 83-84; Ntl Hnr Soc Awd 84-85; Fshn Dsgn.

AMABILE, CHARLENE; Our Lady Of Nazareth Acad; Malden, MA; (Y); 30/83; Debate Tm; FBLA; GAA; Math Clb; Red Cross Aide; Acpl Chr; Variety Show; Coach Actv; Hon Roll; NCTE Awd; Vrsty Bsktbl Coaches Awd 85; My Solo Xmas Shw 85; Psych.

AMARA, PAUL; Catholic Memorial HS; Hyde Park, MA; (Y); Hosp Aide; Intnl Clb; Teachers Aide; Rep Stu Cncl; JV Bowling; Im Socr; U Of Mass Boston; Educ.

AMARAL, MICHAEL; New Bedford HS; New Bedford, MA; (Y); Sec Chess Clb; Im Bowling; Chem.

AMARELLO, JOHN A; Bishop Connolly HS; Fall River, MA; (Y); Cmnty Wkr; Pres Sr Cls; Stu Cncl; Bsbl; Hon Roll; Sal; SMBA Bowling Awd 85-86; Quimet Schlrshp 85-86; Southeastern MA U; Mech Engrng.

AMATANGELO, SUSAN T; Watertown HS; Watertown, MA; (Y); 10/310; Pres Cmnty Wkr; Scholastic Bowl; Ski Clb; Yrbk Bus Mgr; Sec Frsh Cls; Rep Stu Cncl; Bsktbl; Coach Actv; Powder Puff Ftbl; Trk; Sons Of Italy Italn Awd/Schlrshp; 15th Annl Framingham ST Hstrcl Conf Hnrbl Mntn; Smith Coll; Librl Arts.

AMBACH, KAREN LESLIE; North Brookfield HS; North Brookfield, MA; (Y); 1/44; Church Yth Grp; Band; Chorus; School Musical; Nwsp Stf; Mgr Yrbk Stf; Stu Cncl; Pres NHS; Ntl Merit Ltr; Val; Hnrs Grp Ntl Sci Srch 85; Sci Fair Wnnr 82-84; Stu Gov Day Delg 84; Bio.

AMBROSE, LAURA; Belmont HS; Belmont, MA; (Y); 59/294; Church Yth Grp; Pep Clb; Political Wkr; School Play; Var Bsktbl; JV Var Socr; Var Sftbl; Hon Roll; Grls Div II N Sectnl Champ Bsktbl 84-85; U Of NH; Math.

AMIOTT, WILLIAM; Southbridge HS; Southbridge, MA; (Y); 13/133; Math Tm; Bausch & Lomb Sci Awd; Hon Roll; NHS; Outstndng Physcs Stu Of Yr 85; Sci Awd 85; U Of Lowell; Comp Sci.

AMIRAULT, CHRISTINE; Norton HS; Norton, MA; (Y); Varsity Clb; VP Band; VP Concert Band; VP Mrchg Band; Yrbk Stf; Trs Soph Cls; Trs Jr Cls; Trs Sr Cls; Var Bsktbl; Northeastern U; Nrsg.

AMMERING, CAROL; Medway HS; Medway, MA; (Y); 24/152; Band; Chorus; Concert Band; Jazz Band; Mrchg Band; School Musical; School Play; Swing Chorus; High Hon Roll; NHS; MA Cntrl Dst Band 85; Chrch Pianst 83-85; Vet Med.

AMORE, LISA; Presentation Of Mary Acad; Methuen, MA; (Y); Church Yth Grp; French Clb; Spanish Clb; Chorus; Nwsp Stf; 5th Schl Sci Fair 84.

AMPIAW, EUNICE A; South High Community HS; Worcester, MA; (Y); Trs Art Clb; Chorus; Var Bsktbl; High Hon Roll; NHS; Ntl Merit Schol; Pres Schlr; Church Yth Grp; Debate Tm; Library Aide; Frances Hiatt Schlr 85; Worcester Exc Clb Yth Yr 85; Hlth Occup Stu 84; Yale U; Physcn.

AMSDEN, DAVID KENDRICK; St Johns HS; Holden, MA; (Y); 140/300; Church Yth Grp; Cmnty Wkr; JA; Ski Clb; Variety Show; Yrbk Stf; Rep Jr Cls; Pres Sr Cls; Socr; Tennis; U Of VT; Lib Arts.

AMSTEIN, JILL; Mohawk Trail Regional HS; Shelburne, MA; (Y); 1/123; Am Leg Aux Girls St; Varsity Clb; Yrbk Ed-Chief; Yrbk Stf; VP Sr Cls; Rep Stu Cncl; JV Var Vllybl; High Hon Roll; Pres NHS; Computer Clb; Engrng.

ANACLETO, MARIA; Ware HS; Ware, MA; (Y); 18/120; French Clb; JV Capt Bsktbl; Var Capt Sftbl; Hon Roll; Ware Fndry AC Athl Sftbl Awd 85; Polish Amer Ctzns Clb Schlrshp 85; PFC William Seveney Awd 85; Sprngfld Tech CC; Wrd Prcssng.

ANAND, RAKESH; Saint Johns HS; Shrewsbury, MA; (Y); 5/268; Math Tm; Ski Clb; High Hon Roll; NHS; Ntl Merit Ltr; St Johns Rcqtbl Clb Pres 83-85; Math Lgu Vrsty All Star 84-85; Wstrn MA Math All Star 84-85; Stanford U.

ANDERSON, CARRIE ANN; Methuen HS; Methuen, MA; (Y); 22/350; Am Leg Aux Girls St; Cmnty Wkr; Dance Clb; Intnl Clb; Model UN; Yrbk Stf; Bsktbl; Powder Puff Ftbl; Var Sftbl; Var Swmmng; St Theresas Sprts Comm Awd 83; Cmmrcl Des.

ANDERSON, CHERI; New Bedford HS; New Bedfore, MA; (Y); Library Aide; Red Cross Aide; ROTC; Drill Tm; Yrbk Phtg; Med.

ANDERSON, DAVID; St Johns HS; Shrewsbury, MA; (Y); Boy Scts; Church Yth Grp; CAP; French Clb; Ski Clb; Varsity Clb; Y-Teens; Church Choir; Stage Crew; Altar Boy Awd 85.

ANDERSON, ERIC; Arlington Catholic HS; Medford, MA; (Y); 49/148; French Clb; Bsktbl; Score Keeper; Var Trk; Hon Roll; Prfct Atten Awd.

ANDERSON, GAIL; Woburn HS; Woburn, MA; (S); 80/600; Leo Clb; Ski Clb; Spanish Clb; Yrbk Stf; Pres Stu Cncl; Cheerleading; Sftbl; Trk; High Hon Roll; Hon Roll; Sci Fair 85; Speaking Contest 84; Northeastern U; Nursing.

ANDERSON, JIMMIE L; Newton South HS; Dorchester Boston, MA; (Y); Am Leg Boys St; Cmnty Wkr; Ftbl; Var L Trk; Wrstlng; Hon Roll; Athltc Recgn Awd 85; Robert L Braceland Awd 85; Bus Mgmt.

ANDERSON, JOHN; Maynard HS; Maynard, MA; (Y); 30/100; Radio Clb; Band; Rep Jr Cls; Pres Sr Cls; Var Ftbl; Var Trk; Aud/Vis; Boys Clb Am; Church Yth Grp; Cmnty Wkr; News Dir WAUM Cable 84-86; Bus.

ANDERSON, LISA; St Bernards CC HS; Winchendon, MA; (S); 3/173; Drama Clb; Latin Clb; Church Choir; Orch; JV Trk; High Hon Roll; Hon Roll; NHS.

ANDERSON, PATRICIA; Notre Dame Acad; Scituate, MA; (Y); 22/114; Debate Tm; Band; Chorus; Stage Crew; Sec Sr Cls; Im Bsktbl; Var Trk; Im Vllybl; High Hon Roll; Prfct Atten Awd; U S Naval Sea Cadet-Hnr Cade Awd 84; Brnz Mdl USNSCC Swm Mt 85; 3rd Notre Dame Acad Trck Mt 440m 85; Holy Cross; Bus Mgmt.

ANDERSON, TIMOTHY P; Hopkins Acad; Hadley, MA; (S); Am Leg Boys St; Cmnty Wkr; French Clb; Office Aide; Orch; Nwsp Ed-Chief; Yrbk Stf; Golf; NHS; As Schools Match Wits; Bob Jones U; Prelaw.

ANDON, CHARLES A; Arlington HS; Arlington, MA; (Y); 16/407; Science Clb; Band; Concert Band; Symp Band; Bsbl; Ftbl; Var Capt Trk; NHS; Cmmnwlth Schlr Awd-MA 85; Dgtl Eqpmnt Corp Schlrshp Awd 85; Northeastern U; Mech Engr.

ANDRADE, CHRISTOPHER; B M C Durfee HS; Fall River, MA; (S); 80/680; Sec Computer Clb; Q&S; School Play; Ed Nwsp Ed-Chief; Yrbk Rptr; Lit Mag; Sec Soph Cls; Sec Jr Cls; Var Ice Hcky; Hon Roll; Northeastern U; Elec Engr.

ANDRADE, JOHANNA; Taunton HS; Taunton, MA; (Y); Church Yth Grp; Band; Concert Band; Mrchg Band; Hon Roll; Sci Fair Hnrbl Ment 82; Splng Bee 2nd Pl 79; Nrsng.

ANDREASSEN, CAROLYN; Groton-Dunstable Regional HS; Groton, MA; (Y); Church Yth Grp; Exploring; Hon Roll; Awd Proj BASE 85; Comp Prog.

ANDRY, NATASHA; Boston Technical HS; Boston, MA; (Y); Hon Roll; Northeastern U; Psych.

ANGELO, DEBORAH J; Hamilton-Wenham Regional HS; Hamilton, MA; (Y); 16/196; Chess Clb; Drama Clb; Chorus; Color Guard; School Musical; School Play; Nwsp Stf; Yrbk Stf; Score Keeper; High Hon Roll; U Of Lowell; Music.

ANGUILLA, CAROL; Bishop Connolly HS; Bristol, RI; (S); 11/158; Sec Church Yth Grp; Cmnty Wkr; Drama Clb; French Clb; Church Choir; Stage Crew; Yrbk Ed-Chief; Var L Crs Cntry; High Hon Roll; Trs NHS.

ANIELLO, MARLENE; Notre Dame Acad; Braintree, MA; (Y); Church Yth Grp; Math Tm; Var Bsktbl; Im Socr; Var Trk; Hon Roll; Cochs Awd Bsktbl; Al-Star-Tripl Jmp Cathlc Leag Recrd.

ANISH, DEBORAH LYNN; Pittsfield HS; Pittsfield, MA; (Y); JA; Latin Clb; Yrbk Stf; Var Socr; JV Var Sftbl; High Hon Roll; Hon Roll; VFW Awd; Alt Grls ST 84; Chrprrsn SADD 85; Bentley Coll; Bus.

ANNECHARICO, SONJA M; Monument Mountain Reg HS; Sandisfield, MA; (Y); 17/132; 4-H; Color Guard; Yrbk Stf; Hon Roll; NHS; Stu Cncl 84-85; Stu Advsry Brd Prncpl 83-84.

ANNUNZIATO, MARK; Taunton HS; Taunton, MA; (Y); Church Yth Grp; JCL; Latin Clb; Stage Crew; Yrbk Stf; Rep Frsh Cls; Rep Soph Cls; Rep Jr Cls; Stu Cncl; Var L Ftbl.

ANOLI, JOSEPH; Bishop Fenwick HS; Peabody, MA; (Y); Golf; Ice Hcky; Socr; Hon Roll; UMASS-AMHEARST; Bus.

ANOOSHIAN, MARY; Wakefield HS; Wakefield, MA; (Y); JA; Hon Roll; Jr NHS; NHS.

ANTHONY, DAVID S; Burlington HS; Burlington, MA; (Y); Pres Aud/Vis; Acpl Chr; Chorus; Madrigals; School Musical; Swing Chorus; JV Var Ftbl; Drama Clb; Variety Show; Bsktbl; All Eastern Chorus 85; All ST Chorus 84-85; SR Dist Chorus 82-85; Lowell U; Accntng.

ANTICO, ROBERT; Wilmington HS; Wilmington, MA; (Y); 128/250; Church Yth Grp; Ftbl; Wrstlng; U Lowell; Elec Engrng.

ANTON, MARY; Bishop Feehan HS; Mansfield, MA; (Y); 90/253; Cmnty Wkr; Chorus; Church Choir; Spanish NHS; Typng Cntst Awd 85; Lgl Sec.

ANTON, PETER; Phillips Acad; Lawrence, MA; (Y); Aud/Vis; Math Clb; Teachers Aide; Band; Stage Crew; Im Crs Cntry; Var Trk; Convers Prize Excllnce Geom 1st Pl 83-84; Bailey Prize Excllnce Pre-Calculus 2nd 84-85; Engrng.

ANTONIAN, KIM MARIE; Auburn HS; Auburn, MA; (Y); Yrbk Stf; Rep Frsh Cls; VP Rep Soph Cls; VP Rep Jr Cls; VP Rep Sr Cls; VP Rep Stu Cncl; Score Keeper; CC Awd; High Hon Roll; NHS; Gordon B George Awd Exclnce Sci 85; U MA; Pre-Med.

ANTONIO, JAMES P; Bishop Fenwick HS; Peabody, MA; (Y); Church Yth Grp; Y-Teens; Im Bsktbl; Var Socr; Var Trk; High Hon Roll; Hon Roll; Prfct Atten Awd; Harvard; Law.

ANTONIONI, ELLEN; St Bernards C C HS; Leominster, MA; (S); 19/164; Ed Yrbk Stf; VP Stu Cncl; Hon Roll; NHS; Ntl Merit Ltr; Cmnty Wkr; Math Clb; Chorus; Im JV Bsktbl; JV Sftbl; Bus.

ANTONIOU, JOHN N; Westwood HS; Westwood, MA; (Y); 115/203; Aud/Vis; Key Clb; Lit Mag; Tufts U.

ANTONUCCI, MARIA; St Barnards C C HS; Leominster, MA; (S); 12/172; Trs Drama Clb; Library Aide; Tennis; Hon Roll; Med.

ANTOSCA, ANNMARIE; Mansfield HS; Mansfield, MA; (Y); VP Frsh Cls; Hon Roll; Schlstc Achvt Span & Bnus Depts 84; Schlstc Achvt Bus 85.

ANTROBUS, ELIZABETH; Gloucester HS; Gloucester, MA; (Y); 3/314; Pres Church Yth Grp; French Clb; JA; Math Tm; Nwsp Rptr; Yrbk Stf; Lit Mag; High Hon Roll; Hon Roll; Sec NHS; Cmmwlth MA Schlrshp 85; Sawyer Mdl 84; Wellesley Coll.

APAZIDIS, JOHN; Boston Latin Schl; Boston, MA; (Y); Computer Clb; Key Clb; Science Clb; Lit Mag; Hon Roll; Prfct Atten Awd; Tufts; Dntstry.

APKARIAN, DIANE; Presentation Of Mary Acad; Methuen, MA; (Y); Sec French Clb; Hosp Aide; Rep Frsh Cls; Im Gym; Hon Roll; NEDT Awd; Law.

APONTE, CARMEN; North HS; Worcester, MA; (Y); 4-H; Library Aide; Office Aide; Spanish Clb; Teachers Aide; Bsktbl; Fld Hcky; Vllybl; Hon Roll; ST Mutual Awd 85; Hnry Fitzmaurice Awd 85; Mary O Donnell Schlrshp 85; Quinsigamon CC; Exec Secy.

AQUILINA, ANTONIO J; Westwood HS; Westwood, MA; (Y); 4/241; Church Yth Grp; French Clb; Math Tm; School Play; Yrbk Bus Mgr; Stu Cncl; Tennis; High Hon Roll; NHS; Ntl Merit SF; Frinceton Alumni Assn Of New Engl Awd 84; Engrng.

AQUINO, KRISTIN; Monument Mountain Regional HS; Housatonic, MA; (Y); Church Yth Grp; Hosp Aide; Color Guard; Yrbk Stf; Mgr Ftbl; Mgr(s); Score Keeper; JV Sftbl; High Hon Roll; Hon Roll; Dean JC; Comp Sci.

ARANGIO, ALANA M; Saugus HS; Saugus, MA; (Y); 2/300; Library Aide; Stu Cncl; Var Capt Bsktbl; Fld Hcky; Var Sftbl; Cit Awd; High Hon Roll; Jr NHS; NHS; Voice Dem Awd; Skip Moorehouse Awd 83; Sci Math Cert 85; Achvt Recgntn Awd 83; Pre-Med.

ARANGIO, JENNIFER C; Saugus HS; Saugus, MA; (Y); 15/309; Hosp Aide; Office Aide; Yrbk Stf; Sr Cls; Stu Cncl; High Hon Roll; Hon Roll; Jr NHS; NHS; Hugh O Brian Yth Fndtn Ldrshp Awd 84; Svc Awd 84; Intl Hon Soc Hstry Awd 85; Bio.

ARBIT, LORI; Stoughton HS; Stoughton, MA; (Y); GAA; Girl Scts; Pep Clb; Temple Yth Grp; Chorus; Drm Mjr(t); Mrchg Band; Stage Crew; Yrbk Stf; Stu Cncl; Bus.

ARCHAMBAULT, DAVID; South Hadley HS; S Hadley, MA; (Y); 4-H; Drm & Bgl; Accntng.

ARCHAMBAULT, LISA; South High Community HS; Worcester, MA; (S); 1/250; Var Fld Hcky; Var Trk; Hon Roll; Pres NHS; Val; Brown Bk Awd 84; Supertndnts Cert Awd 85; Stu Achvt Awd 85; Boston Coll; Librl Arts.

ARCHAMBAULT, LYNNE; North Middlesex Regional HS; Pepperell, MA; (Y); Church Yth Grp; Pres Soph Cls; Pres Jr Cls; Stu Cncl; Fld Hcky; Tennis; High Hon Roll; Hon Roll; Jr NHS; Pres NHS; Hugh O Brien Schlrshp; Talentd Gifted Pgm; Stu Cncl Awd; Bus.

ARCHAMBAULT JR, RICHARD A; Georgetown HS; Georgetown, MA; (Y); Pres Sr Cls; Var L Ftbl; High Hon Roll; Hon Roll; Bus Mgmt.

ARCHAMBEAULT, KARIN; Burncoat SR HS; Worcester, MA; (Y); Church Yth Grp; Hosp Aide; Yrbk Stf; Pres Jr Cls; Rep Stu Cncl; Capt Cheerleading; Gym; Hon Roll; Jr NHS; Voluntr Svc Awd 85; Med.

ARCILA, DAFNE; Methuen HS; Methuen, MA; (Y); JV Bsktbl; Var Crs Cntry; Var Trk; High Hon Roll; Hon Roll; U MA.

ARENA, STEPHEN; St Domenic Savio HS; Wilmington, MA; (Y); 9/109; Chess Clb; JA; Ski Clb; Yrbk Rptr; Yrbk Stf; Lit Mag; Var Crs Cntry; Im JV Ice Hcky; Var Trk; High Hon Roll; Med.

ARGYROPLE, STACEY; Milton HS; Milton, MA; (Y); AFS; Church Yth Grp; Drama Clb; Spanish Clb; Band; Chorus; Church Choir; Concert Band; Mrchg Band; Variety Show; Mktg.

ARIETA, MICHAEL; Silver Lake Regional HS; Kingston, MA; (Y); 35/550; Chrmn Am Leg Boys St; Pres Math Clb; Stu Cncl; Capt L Bsktbl; Hon Roll; NHS; MA Boy ST Games Bsktbl 85; Pre-Law.

ARLORO, JULIE; Reading Memorial HS; Reading, MA; (Y); Camera Clb; Band; Mrchg Band; Orch; Ed Yrbk Phtg; High Hon Roll; Hon Roll; Valbl Svc Awd 84; Schlstc Achvt Awd 85; Engrng.

ARMANETTI, LISA; Middleborough HS; Middleboro, MA; (Y); VP Exploring; Quiz Bowl; Variety Show; Yrbk Rptr; Rep Frsh Cls; Rep Soph Cls; Rep Sr Cls; Stat Bsktbl; Var L Fld Hcky; JV Trk; MA Milton Acad Adv Stud Pgm 85; Math.

ARMSTRONG, CAROLYN A; Plymouth-Carver Regional SR HS; S Londonderry, VT; (Y); 58/611; Church Yth Grp; Cmnty Wkr; Debate Tm; Pres Drama Clb; Science Clb; School Musical; School Play; Hon Roll; Hosp Aide; Spanish Clb; Elizabeth B Cushman Schlrshp 85; SEOG Schlrshp 85; Southern VT Coll; Law Enfrcmnt.

ARMSTRONG, PATRICIA; Salem HS; Salem, MA; (Y); 18/332; High Hon Roll; Hon Roll; NHS; Cert Of Mbrshp-Natl Hnr Soc 85; Cert Of Prfcncy For Cntry 21 Accntng 84; Marion Ct JC Of Bus; Lgl Sec.

ARMSTRONG, PEARLANN; Hoosac Valley HS; Adams, MA; (Y); Ski Clb; JV Var Bsktbl; JV Socr; JV Var Sftbl; Var Hon Roll; Crmnlgy.

ARMSTRONG, RICHARD; Quincy HS; Quincy, MA; (Y); 10/360; Am Leg Boys St; JA; Math Tm; Yrbk Stf; Stu Cncl; Var Tennis; High Hon Roll; Ntl Merit SF; Chess Clb; Computer Clb; Air Frc Assn Awd 85; Natl Sojrnrs Awd 84; West Point; Med.

ARNOLD, MICHELLE; Hingham HS; Hingham, MA; (Y); 36/326; Church Yth Grp; Cmnty Wkr; Speech Tm; Yrbk Stf; Hon Roll; Excellence In US Hstry 85; Frgn Svc.

ARNOLD III, WILLIAM P; Longmeadow HS; Springfield, MA; (Y); 123/280; Computer Clb; JA; Variety Show; Ftbl; Wt Lftg; Mnrty Engrng Awd; U Of MA; Comp Engrng.

ARNONE, LISA-MARIE; Our Lady Of Nazareth Acad; Malden, MA; (Y); 20/52; Church Yth Grp; Acpl Chr; Band; Chorus; Church Choir; School Musical; Ed Yrbk Stf; Pres Sr Cls; NEAD Nrthstrn All Dist Chrs 84; Ms MA TEEN Svc Awd 84; Psychlgy.

ARNOTT, MARGARET; Fontbonne Acad; Quincy, MA; (Y); 30/131; Trs Church Yth Grp; Drama Clb; Hosp Aide; Science Clb; Chorus; School Play; Stage Crew; High Hon Roll; Ntl Ltn Exm Cum Laud; Yanke Div Schlrhsp; Suffolk U; Psychlgy.

ARRIGA, MICHAEL J; Burlington HS; Burlington, MA; (Y); 26/315; Am Leg Boys St; Trs Frsh Cls; Ftbl; Ice Hcky; Lcrss; Mgr(s); Wt Lftg; Hon Roll; NHS; U Of Lowell; Mech Engrng.

ARRINGTON, NERESSIA VEMA; Mission Church HS; Jamaica Plain, MA; (S); Art Clb; Church Yth Grp; Cmnty Wkr; Hosp Aide; JA; Office Aide; Chorus; Church Choir; School Play; Rep Jr Cls; Awd For Dancing 82; Northeastern; Health Fld.

ARROYO, LUCY; Salem HS; Salem, MA; (Y); 16/326; Church Yth Grp; Cmnty Wkr; Dance Clb; Church Choir; Yrbk Stf; High Hon Roll; Hon Roll; Jr NHS; NHS; Ntl Merit Ltr; Mss Tn Of MA Schlrshp & Rcgntn Pgnt 85; Bus Admin.

ARRUDA, CHERIE; New Bedford HS; New Bedford, MA; (Y); 47/668; AFS; Church Yth Grp; Drama Clb; Rep Stu Cncl; High Hon Roll; NHS; Tutrng Awd 85.

ARRUDA, CHRISTINE; Bishop Connolly HS; Fall River, MA; (Y); 73/200; Sec Church Yth Grp; Drama Clb; Girl Scts; Hosp Aide; Church Choir; School Play; Stage Crew; Variety Show; High Hon Roll; Hon Roll; Psych.

ARRUDA, ROBIN; Bishop Connolly HS; Westport, MA; (S); 27/158; Church Yth Grp; Cmnty Wkr; Spanish Clb; High Hon Roll; Hon Roll; Jr NHS; NHS; SE MA U; Elem Educ.

ARSENAULT, THEODORE; Beverly HS; Beverly, MA; (Y); Art Clb; Chess Clb; Computer Clb; English Clb; Math Clb; Science Clb; High Hon Roll; Hon Roll; 2nd & 3rd Pl Chem Sci Fair 84-85; Grmn Lvl I Awd 85; Lowell U; Chem Engr.

ARSENAULT, THOMAS; New Bedford HS; New Bedford, MA; (Y); 6/700; Rep Jr Cls; JV Bsktbl; L Var Golf; Hon Roll; NHS; Ntl Merit Ltr; Appld Math.

ARTHUR, GORDON; Braintree HS; Braintree, MA; (Y); 99/430; Church Yth Grp; Cmnty Wkr; Hosp Aide; JA; Teachers Aide; JV Ftbl; Hon Roll; Bntly Coll Bus Wk Stu 85; JR Clclr Waptck Chptr Ordr Dmly 84; Corp Adm.

ARTIOLI, MICHELLE; High School Of Commerce; Springfield, MA; (S); Cmnty Wkr; Red Cross Aide; Chorus; Mrchg Band; Rep Stu Cncl; Var Bsktbl; Var Socr; Var Gov Hon Prg Awd; High Hon Roll; NHS; Natl Quest Prog Devl Ldrshp 84; 3,Th Annl Stdnt Govt Day Rep 85; W New England Coll JR Inst 85; Bus.

ARUIN, RAYA; Peabody Veterans Memorial HS; Peabody, MA; (Y); 18/550; Science Clb; High Hon Roll; Hon Roll; Jr NHS; NHS; Ntl Merit Ltr; Boston U; Engrng.

ASADORIAN, DONNA M; Haverhill HS; Bradford, MA; (Y); 98/415; Church Yth Grp; High Hon Roll; Elaine Croston Awd 85; Donald Freeman Awd 85; Daniel Harrington Awd 85; Merrimack Coll.

ASELTON, CATHY; Burncoat SR HS; Worcester, MA; (Y); 30/280; Drama Clb; Intnl Clb; Teachers Aide; Sftbl; Tennis; NHS; Ntl Hnr Soc 85; Stonehill Coll; Elem Ed.

ASH, GEORGE; St Dominic Savio HS; Revere, MA; (Y); Aud/Vis; Chess Clb; Cmnty Wkr; Computer Clb; Nwsp Rptr; NEDT Awd; H S Scholar 82-86; Film Clb 84-85; Hnr Rl; Northeastern U; Comp Design.

ASHE, THOMAS; Haverhill HS; Haverhill, MA; (Y); 80/400; Church Yth Grp; French Clb; Nwsp Phtg; Ed Yrbk Phtg; Score Keeper; Var Swmmng; High Hon Roll; Hon Roll.

ASHLEY, CHRISTINE; Danvers HS; Danvers, MA; (Y); 110/320; GAA; Bsktbl; Sftbl; Hon Roll; Acctng.

ASHRAFZADEH, ALI; Newton North HS; Newton, MA; (Y); Hosp Aide; Intnl Clb; Bsktbl; Socr; Swmmng; Boston U; Med.

ASSAD, CINDI; Westport HS; Westport, MA; (Y); 6/163; Trs French Clb; Intnl Clb; Ski Clb; Yrbk Stf; Rep Soph Cls; Rep Jr Cls; Var Cheerleading; Var JV Fld Hcky; Hon Roll; NHS; Bus Mgr.

ASTLEY, BONNIE; Chicopee Comprehensive HS; Chicopee, MA; (Y); 42/340; Powder Puff Ftbl; Hon Roll; Jr NHS; Bay Path JR Coll; Exec Sec.

ATHERTON, LUCINDA C; Greenfield HS; Greenfield, MA; (Y); 34/154; Church Yth Grp; Hosp Aide; Pres Pep Clb; Spanish Clb; School Play; Stage Crew; Yrbk Phtg; Yrbk Stf; Off Sr Cls; Rep Stu Cncl; Fred G Wells 85; A K Warner 85; U ME Orono; Elem Ed.

ATHERTON, MELISSA; Milford HS; Milford, MA; (Y); 41/314; JV Sftbl; JV Vllybl; Hon Roll; NHS; Psych.

ATKIN, DAVID S; Westfield HS; Westfield, MA; (Y); 1/354; Am Leg Boys St; Band; Concert Band; Jazz Band; Mrchg Band; Orch; School Musical; School Play; NHS; Val; Louis Armstrng Jazz Awd 85; Westfield Acad Schlrshp 85; Boston Coll; Math.

ATKINS, TRACEY L; Newton South HS; Newton, MA; (Y); Drama Clb; VP Exploring; School Play; Ed Lit Mag; Thtr.

ATWOOD, DEBORAH; Natick HS; Natick, MA; (Y); 1/440; JCL; Speech Tm; Chorus; Flag Corp; School Musical; Twrlr; High Hon Roll; Hon Roll; NHS; Harvard Prize Bk 85; Union Coll; Mth.

AU, ALAN; Deerfield Acad; Amherst, MA; (Y); Computer Clb; Pep Clb; Ski Clb; Band; Pep Band; Nwsp Stf; Im Tennis; Hon Roll; Cornell U.

AUBIN, MICHELLE M; BMC Durfee HS; Fall River, MA; (Y); 65/650; CAP; Girl Scts; Library Aide; Spanish Clb; Band; Chorus; Church Choir; Concert Band; Mrchg Band; Cit Awd; BMC Durfee Almni Schlrshp 85; BMC Durfee Delta 81; U Of MA; Anthrplgy.

AUBIN, TOD; Baypatah Vo Tech Regional; Oxford, MA; (S); 11/236; Ftbl; Wt Lftg; High Hon Roll; NHS; Berkly Sch Music.

AUCIELLO, MARIA; St Clements HS; Somerville, MA; (Y); Girl Scts; Hosp Aide; School Play; Yrbk Stf; Nrsng.

AUDETTE, RENEE; Somerset HS; Somerset, MA; (Y); Band; Concert Band; Mrchg Band; Variety Show; High Hon Roll; Hon Roll; NHS; Prfct Atten Awd; Music Awds 83; Southeastern MA U.

AUFIERO, JEFFREY; Lexington HS; Lexington, MA; (Y); AFS; Church Yth Grp; French Clb; Jazz Band; Nwsp Rptr; Stat Ice Hcky; Hon Roll; Comp Sci.

AUGER, COLLEEN; New Bedford Voc; New Bedford, MA; (Y); 1/402; Hosp Aide; JA; VICA; Yrbk Stf; Trk; Hon Roll; NHS; Med Asst Shop 84-85; ST Comp 3rd 84-85; Bristol CC; Med Tech.

AUGER, JOE; Southbridge HS; Southbridge, MA; (Y); 11/144; Chess Clb; Trs Church Yth Grp; Math Tm; School Play; Var Trk; Im Wt Lftg; Hon Roll; NHS; Ntl Merit SF; Hopwood Smmr Schlrshp 85; Worcester Polytechnic Inst; Eng.

AUGER, JOSEPH; Southbridge HS; Sbridge, MA; (Y); 10/163; Chess Clb; Trs Church Yth Grp; Computer Clb; Math Tm; Var Trk; Im Wt Lftg; Hon Roll; NHS; Ntl Merit SF; Hopwood Smmr Schlrshp Pgm 85; Elec Engr.

AUGERI, MARIA-ROSE; Presentation Of Mary Acad; Methuen, MA; (Y); French Clb; Math Clb; Bausch & Lomb Sci Awd; Hon Roll; Calculus Awd & Prncpls Awd 85; 3rd Prz Sci Fair Wnnr; Regnls Cash Awd-ST Fair 83; Rgnl Sci Fair Awd 84; Merrimack Coll; Bus.

AUGUST, JAMES; King Philip Regional HS; Providence, RI; (Y); Drama Clb; School Play; U Rhode Island; Engr.

AUHAN, HEATHER; Bridgewater Raynham Reg HS; Ft Lee, VA; (Y); 83/364; FTA; Teachers Aide; Drm Mjr(t); Stat Trk; Hon Roll; Schlrshp Dr 84-85; CCD Tchr 85; Spcl Ed.

AUREN, MICHELLE; Auburn SR HS; Auburn, MA; (Y); Church Yth Grp; Band; Concert Band; Mrchg Band; Rep Frsh Cls; High Hon Roll; NHS; Med Asst.

AUSIELLO, ANDREA; Wilmington HS; Wilmington, MA; (Y); 5/270; Church Yth Grp; Dance Clb; VP Frsh Cls; VP Soph Cls; VP Jr Cls; VP Sr Cls; French Hon Soc; NHS; High Hon Roll; Regis Coll; Pltcl Sci.

AUSPITZ, RACHEL B; Commonwealth Schl; Somerville, MA; (Y); Acpl Chr; Chorus; Madrigals; School Play; Lit Mag; Ntl Merit SF; Arts Recognition & Talent Search; Actor.

AUSTIN, DAVID W; Central Catholic HS; Tewksbury, MA; (Y); 12/227; Boy Scts; Sec Drama Clb; Ski Clb; Chorus; School Musical; School Play; Stage Crew; High Hon Roll; NHS; Order Of The Arrow 84; Harvard Bk Awd 83; Columbia U; Engrng.

AUSTIN, SHEILA JO; Malden HS; Malden, MA; (Y); 100/450; Church Yth Grp; Cmnty Wkr; Key Clb; Office Aide; Pep Clb; Red Cross Aide; Variety Show; Rep Soph Cls; Var Cheerleading; Pub Rel.

AUSTIN, STEPHANIE; Weymouth North HS; Weymouth, MA; (Y); 14/393; JV Var Bsktbl; High Hon Roll; Hon Roll; Nrs.

AUSTIN, THOMAS ANDREW; Lincoln-Sudbury Regional HS; Sudbury, MA; (Y); Church Yth Grp; French Clb; Stu Cncl; Crs Cntry; Trk; Gov Hon Prg Awd; High Hon Roll; NHS; St Schlr; Probidence Coll; Finance.

AVELLAR, ANN; Chatham HS; S Chatham, MA; (Y); AFS; Church Yth Grp; Drama Clb; Girl Scts; Ski Clb; Church Choir; School Play; Yrbk Stf; JV Fld Hcky; Balfour Awd Math 85; Merit Achvt Awd 85; Prom Queen, Prom Chrprsn 85; Cls Marshall 85; Bus.

AVILES, REINALDO; Jeremiah E Burke HS; Dorchester, MA; (Y); Spanish Clb; Yrbk Stf; Trs Sr Cls; Stu Cncl; JV Trk; JV Wrstlng; Hon Roll; NHS.

AVILLA, RONNY; Bishop Connolly HS; Westport, MA; (Y); Church Yth Grp; Cmnty Wkr; Stage Crew; Capt Bsbl; Var Bsktbl; JV Crs Cntry; Hon Roll; High Hons 82; Hgst Hon 84; Hlth Care.

AVIS, MICHAEL; Agawam HS; Feeding Hls, MA; (Y); 79/400; Concert Band; Sec Sr Cls; Var Bsktbl; Ftbl; Mgr(s); Trk; Hon Roll; Stonehill Coll; Bus.

AVRUCH, IAN; Waltham HS; Waltham, MA; (Y); 2/600; Am Leg Boys St; JCL; Key Clb; Latin Clb; Sec Science Clb; High Hon Roll; VP NHS; Cert Acad Exclnce MA Assoc Schl Suprntndnts 85; Full-Tuition Scholar Brandeis U 85; Brandeis U; Physics.

AWUMA, JOSHUA; Doherty Memorial HS; Worcester, MA; (Y); Latin Clb; Var Bsktbl; Var Ftbl; Im Socr; Capt Tennis; Hon Roll; Yth Of Yr Grndl YMCA 84.

AXT JR, LOUIS A; Drury SR HS; North Adams, MA; (S); Band; Concert Band; Jazz Band; Mrchg Band; Pep Band; School Musical; Rep Frsh Cls; Trk; Hon Roll; NEDT Awd; Williams Coll; Pre-Law.

AXTMANN, SCOTT; Wilbraham-Monson Acad; Wilbraham, MA; (Y); 13/130; Im Lcrss; Var Socr; Var Tennis; Hon Roll; Bus.

AYENI, AKEEM; Doherty Memorial HS; Worcester, MA; (Y); Pres Frsh Cls; Pres Soph Cls; Var Crs Cntry; Var Socr; Capt Trk; High Hon Roll; Jr NHS; NHS; Boys Clb Am; Alumnus MA Ldrshp Sem 84; Wnnr Career Day Essay Cont 85; Mbr Cty Mgr Yth Cncl 84-85; Bio.

BAACKE, ERIC; Bridgewater Raynham Regional HS; Raynham, MA; (Y); Boys Clb Am; Church Yth Grp; FCA; Varsity Clb; Y-Teens; Bsbl; Bsktbl; Coach Actv; Socr; Hon Roll; Prncpls Awd Ldrshp 82; Bus.

BABINSKI, JOAN; Burncoat SR HS; Worcester, MA; (Y); Church Yth Grp; Intnl Clb; Science Clb; Band; Variety Show; Cheerleading; Pres Jr NHS; NHS; Spanish NHS; Holy Crss Bk Awd 85.

BABNER, DAVID; Barnstable HS; Hyannis, MA; (Y); Letterman Clb; Boy Scts; Varsity Clb; Nwsp Sprt Ed; Rep Frsh Cls; Rep Soph Cls; VP Jr Cls; JV Bsbl; Var Bsktbl; Var Crs Cntry; Syracuse U; Brdcstng.

BACCHUS, TERRANCE; Reading Memorial HS; Dorchester, MA; (Y); Varsity Clb; Bsktbl; Ftbl; Trk; Hon Roll; 3rd Newenglnd Trk Meet 4x100 Rly 85; Accntng.

BACHAND, CHERYL; Leicester HS; Cherry Valley, MA; (S); French Clb; Hosp Aide; Latin Clb; Math Tm; Nwsp Rptr; High Hon Roll; NHS; Prfct Atten Awd; Mgr Sftbl; Cum Laude Natl Lat Exam 83-84; Med.

BACHAND, LINDA; Oxford HS; Oxford, MA; (Y); Pep Clb; Ski Clb; Chorus; Color Guard; School Musical; Stu Cncl; Var Capt Cheerleading; Var Gym; High Hon Roll; Hon Roll; Pre-Law.

BACHE, STEPHEN; Braintree HS; Boston, MA; (Y); 51/400; Ski Clb; Socr; High Hon Roll; Hon Roll; Phy Engr.

BACON, SUSAN A; Holyoke HS; Holyoke, MA; (Y); Dance Clb; GAA; Office Aide; Pep Clb; JV Bsktbl; JV Var Cheerleading; Timer; Hon Roll; Prfct Atten Awd.

BACZEWSKI, CHRISTINA; Gardner HS; Gardner, MA; (Y); 30/182; Chess Clb; Debate Tm; Band; JV Bsktbl; Var Crs Cntry; Var Tennis; Hon Roll; NHS; Acctg.

BADE, SUSAN; Triton Regional HS; Byfield, MA; (Y); Trs AFS; Hosp Aide; Band; Mrchg Band; Variety Show; Yrbk Stf; Rep Stu Cncl; Var Trk; NHS.

BADGER, ANMARIE; Lynn English HS; Lynn, MA; (Y); 10/357; Am Leg Aux Girls St; Drama Clb; Sec JCL; School Play; Variety Show; Yrbk Ed-Chief; VP Soph Cls; VP Jr Cls; Trs Sr Cls; Var Bsktbl; William F O Brien Mem Scholar 85; Lynn Eveng Clb Scholar 85; Lynn Eng Drama Clb Boosters Scholar 85; St Anselm Coll; Pre-Engrng.

BAER, CYNTHIA; Clinton HS; Clinton, MA; (Y); Dance Clb; Drama Clb; Intnl Clb; PAVAS; Band; Chorus; School Play; Yrbk Phtg; Bst Sprtng Actress Awd 85; Drama.

BAER, SUSAN; Bishop Connolly HS; Swansea, MA; (S); 22/158; Church Yth Grp; Cmnty Wkr; Ski Clb; Yrbk Stf; Tennis; Vllybl; NHS; U Of CT; Pharm.

BAGLEY, KELLY; Fontbonne Acad; Quincy, MA; (Y); 59/173; VP Debate Tm; French Clb; Science Clb; Pres Band; Chorus; Lit Mag; Rep Soph Cls; Hon Roll; 3rd Pl Sci Fair; Globe Schlstc Art Fair Seim-Fin; Syracuse U; Comm.

BAGLIONE, MICHELE; Methuen HS; Methuen, MA; (Y); Cheerleading; Coach Actv; High Hon Roll; Northrn Essex CC; Acctng.

BAIER, CATHY L; Dartmouth HS; S Dartmouth, MA; (Y); 60/269; Sec Debate Tm; Band; Concert Band; Drm & Bgl; Mrchg Band; Symp Band; Hon Roll; Almn & Music Assocs Schlrshps 85; MA Brd Regnts 85; U Of MA; Anml Sci.

BAIER, MARGARET; Silver Lake Regional HS; Halifax, MA; (Y); Cmnty Wkr; Varsity Clb; Drama Clb; Girl Scts; Sec Latin Clb; VP Spanish Clb; Off Teachers Aide; Band; Jazz Band; School Play; Stu Mnth 85; Katharine Gibbs; Bus.

BAIL, STEPHEN; Chicopee Comprehensive HS; Chicopee, MA; (Y); German Clb; L Bsbl; L Capt Ftbl; MVP Bsbl 85; Bus Admin.

BAILEY, CELIA; Barnstable HS; Osterville, MA; (Y); Church Yth Grp; Cmnty Wkr; Office Aide; High Hon Roll; Lion Awd; NHS; Ntl Merit Ltr; Outstndng Bus Stu 83-84; Wheaton Bk Awd 85; Barnstable H S Bus Dept Awd 85; John F Kennedy Awd 85; Cape Cod CC; Acctng.

BAILEY, KARA; Nashoba Regional HS; Lancaster, MA; (Y); 15/193; Pep Clb; Rep Jr Cls; Rep Stu Cncl; Bsktbl; Cheerleading; Fld Hcky; Hon Roll; NHS; NHS Scholar 85; Charles P O Connell Mem Scholar 85; Yth Mth Awd 85; U PA; Ped Nrsng.

BAILEY, LEANN; Longmeadow HS; Longmeadow, MA; (Y); 79/297; AFS; Drama Clb; Chorus; School Musical; Stage Crew; Hon Roll; Stu Cncl; Bsktbl; Score Keeper; Church Choir; Dance Awd; U MA; Nrsng.

BAILEY, MICHELLE; Scituate HS; Scituate, MA; (Y); 11/297; Math Clb; Lit Mag; JV Var Cheerleading; Hon Roll; Jr NHS; NHS; NEDT Awd; C A Herter Mem Schlrshp 84; Maxima Cum Laude, Slvr Mdl Ntl Latin Exm 85; Biomed Engrng.

BAILEY, PAUL; Marian HS; Marlborough, MA; (Y); Drama Clb; School Play; Lit Mag; L Var Crs Cntry; L Var Trk; Hon Roll; Oceonogrpy/ Metrolgy Awd 85; St Micheals Coll.

BAILEY, TIM; Gloucester HS; Gloucester, MA; (Y); 30/340; Am Leg Boys St; Cmnty Wkr; Varsity Clb; Yrbk Ed-Chief; Rep Soph Cls; Rep Jr Cls; Crs Cntry; Trk; Hon Roll; NHS; Intl Rel.

BAILEY, TIMOTHY C; Gloucester HS; Gloucester, MA; (Y); 30/340; Am Leg Boys St; Cmnty Wkr; Yrbk Ed-Chief; Off Soph Cls; Off Stu Cncl; Crs Cntry; Trk; Hon Roll; NHS; Ntl Merit Ltr; Intl Rel.

BAILLY, CARIE A; Holyoke HS; Holyoke, MA; (Y); Art Clb; French Clb; GAA; JA; Latin Clb; Science Clb; Acpl Chr; Chorus; High Hon Roll; Hon Roll; Holyoke CC; Rtl Mgmnt.

BAILLY, SHERI L; Holyoke HS; Holyoke, MA; (Y); 23/380; Drama Clb; French Clb; Latin Clb; School Play; Yrbk Ed-Chief; Cheerleading; High Hon Roll; Hon Roll; Jr NHS; NHS; Wmns Clb Schlrshp 85; Pres Acad Ftnss Awd 85; U Of MA; Acctg.

BAIRD, KRISTI; Burlington HS; Burlington, MA; (Y); 15/369; Church Yth Grp; Math Clb; Yrbk Stf; Rep Soph Cls; Rep Sr Cls; Sec Stu Cncl; Elks Awd; Hon Roll; NHS; Stu Cncl Schlrshp 85; Pine Glen PTA Schlrshp 85; Boston U; Sclgy.

BAJGIER, THOMAS; Chicopee Comprehensive HS; Chicopee, MA; (Y); Boy Scts; Church Yth Grp; Cmnty Wkr; Latin Clb; Bsktbl; Ftbl; Mgr(s); Eagle Scout 83; Bus Mgmt.

BAKER, BETH; Barnstable HS; Centerville, MA; (Y); 16/363; Trs Church Yth Grp; 4-H; Q&S; Ed Nwsp Stf; Rep Soph Cls; Var Co-Capt Vllybl; Hon Roll; NHS; Trained & Achvd Companion Dog Obed 81-85; Bst JR Handlr Dog Shws 81-84; Dog Shws Hghst Scoring 83-85; Wheaton Coll; Cmmnctns.

BAKER, CHRISTINE; Stoughton HS; Stoughton, MA; (Y); Church Yth Grp; Math Tm; Drill Tm; Yrbk Stf; Rep Frsh Cls; Rep Soph Cls; Stu Cncl; High Hon Roll; NHS; Asst Rlgn Tchr 83-85; Math.

BAKER, COURTNEY; St Bernards CC HS; Fitchburg, MA; (S); Ski Clb; Rep Soph Cls; Rep Jr Cls; Stu Cncl; JV Bsktbl; Var Fld Hcky; Var Trk; Hon Roll.

BAKER, MICHELLE A; Holyoke HS; Holyoke, MA; (Y); 50/395; JA; Teachers Aide; Color Guard; Socr; High Hon Roll; Hon Roll; NHS; Marine Corp; Spec Intlgnce.

BAKER, WILLIAM; Mohawk Trail Regional HS; Shelburne Fls, MA; (Y); 15/140; Cmnty Wkr; Varsity Clb; Capt Ftbl; Trk; Wt Lftg; Hon Roll; NHS.

BALDASSARRE, NANCY; Swampscott HS; Swampscott, MA; (Y); 11/230; French Clb; Model UN; Political Wkr; Nwsp Rptr; Nwsp Stf; Yrbk Stf; Ed Lit Mag; Off Stu Cncl; Jr NHS; NHS; Hnrb Mntn In Phi Alpha Theta Frmghm ST Coll Hstrcl Conf Tm Paper/Schl Ltry Mag Poetry Cntst 84; Chld Study.

BALDI, DIANE M; Bridgewater-Raynham Regional HS; Raynham, MA; (Y); Art Clb; 4-H; Art.

BALDWIN, AARON E; Marthas Vineyard Regional HS; Vineyard Haven, MA; (Y); 31/103; Art Clb; Boy Scts; Camera Clb; JCL; Latin Clb; Library Aide; Mgr Spanish Clb; Teachers Aide; Yrbk Stf; Bsbl; Delorra Schlrshp; Pell Grant; Baldwin Wallace Grant; Baldwin Wallace Coll; Intl Pol.

BALESTER, WENDY; Randolph HS; Randolph, MA; (Y); Civic Clb; Cmnty Wkr; French Clb; Intnl Clb; Library Aide; Office Aide; Teachers Aide; Drm & Bgl; Nwsp Stf; Hon Roll; Stu Advsry Awd 84-85; Suffolk; Criminal Justc.

BALIKIAN, PHILIP; Belmont HS; Belmont, MA; (Y); Am Leg Boys St; Drama Clb; JA; Spanish Clb; Nwsp Rptr; Var Crs Cntry; JV Trk; Var Wrstlng; High Hon Roll; NHS; PTA Awds In Math & Frgn Lng 85; Med.

BALL, JUDI LYNN; Malden HS; Malden, MA; (Y); 9/511; Political Wkr; Rep Frsh Cls; Rep Soph Cls; Sec Jr Cls; Sec Sr Cls; Var Capt Fld Hcky; Var Sftbl; Elks Awd; NCTE Awd; NHS; Boston Coll; Pre-Law.

BALLARD, MATTHEW; Cathedrae HS; Springfield, MA; (Y); Capt Ftbl; Im Wt Lftg; All Western MA Ftbl Sq 84-85; Bus.

BALLOU, CHERYL; Douglas Memorial HS; Douglas, MA; (Y); Varsity Clb; Band; Concert Band; Mrchg Band; Trs Frsh Cls; Rep Soph Cls; Hon Roll; Jr NHS; NHS.

BAMBAKIDOU, LISA; Cushing Acad; Torrington, CT; (Y); VP Frsh Cls; Pres Soph Cls; Sec Stu Cncl; Var Capt Bsktbl; Var Capt Sftbl; Var Capt Vllybl; Hon Roll; N Cooke Mem Awd 83; Bette Davis Awd 83-85; All League Sftbl & Bsktbl 84-85; Math.

BAMBURY, JIM C; Saugus HS; Saugus, MA; (Y); 67/301; JV Var Bsktbl; JV Var Socr; Hon Roll; Sccr MVP Spnsrd ARMY 85; Unsung Hero Awd Sccr 85; Mambr Saugus Cultrl Exch Tm Plyd Sccr Europe 82; North Shore CC; Engrng Sci.

BANCROFT, JENIFER; Nashoba Regional HS; Stow, MA; (Y); 2/200; Church Yth Grp; Intnl Clb; Chorus; Church Choir; Ed Lit Mag; Rep Soph Cls; Rep Jr Cls; Stu Cncl; L Crs Cntry; Mgr(s); Engl Awd For SR Cls 85; Schlrshp From Commonwealth Of MA 85; Covenant Coll; Philosophy.

BANDLE, KRIS; Malden Catholic HS; Malden, MA; (Y); Church Yth Grp; Hon Roll; NHS; Engrng.

BANKS, CHERYL; Fitchburg HS; Fitchburg, MA; (Y); Church Yth Grp; Hosp Aide; Library Aide; Quiz Bowl; Red Cross Aide; High Hon Roll; Hon Roll; Bio I, Spnsh I & II High Avg 84; Elem Ed.

BANKS, MATT; Wachusett Regional HS; Holden, MA; (Y); 77/400; Boy Scts; VP Model UN; Political Wkr; Ski Clb; Teachers Aide; Band; Concert Band; Symp Band; Econ.

BANNER, SUE; Barnstable HS; Hyannis, MA; (S); 1/400; Temple Yth Grp; Varsity Clb; Concert Band; Mrchg Band; Swmmng; High Hon Roll; Hon Roll; NHS; Ntl Merit SF; Val; Cert Acad Excllnce Awd MA Assoc Schl Supts 85; Bus Admin.

BAPTISTA, MARIA; New Bedford HS; New Bedford, MA; (Y); Intnl Clb; Yrbk Stf; Southeastern MA U; Med Tech.

BAPTISTE, DANIEL; Dartmouth HS; S Dartmouth, MA; (Y); 19/254; AFS; Math Tm; Varsity Clb; Var Trk; Wt Lftg; NHS; Chmcl Engrng.

BARAM, MARCUS S; Belmont HS; Belmont, MA; (Y); Cmnty Wkr; Nwsp Ed-Chief; Nwsp Rptr; Nwsp Stf; Lit Mag; Im Bsktbl; JV Var Crs Cntry; Var Swmmng; JV Trk; Hon Roll; Geothe Inst Awd & Grmn Conslt Awd 84 & 85; Stu Jrnlst Yr Awd 84; N E Young Whiters Conf 85; Jrnlsm.

BARBAGALLO, LESLIE A; Belmont HS; Belmont, MA; (Y); Church Yth Grp; Cmnty Wkr; Letterman Clb; Spanish Clb; Band; Concert Band; Mrchg Band; Crs Cntry; Trk; High Hon Roll; 2 Vrsty Ltrs Crss Cntry; 1 Vrsty Ltr Trk; Law.

BARBARINI, ROBERT; Agawam HS; Feeding Hills, MA; (Y); Church Yth Grp; Band; JV Var Bsbl; JV Var Ice Hcky; Accntng.

BARBEAU, LAURA J; Cathedral HS; Ludlow, MA; (Y); Pep Clb; Band; Flag Corp; Mrchg Band; Pep Band; Sftbl; Hon Roll; All Westtern MA HS Sftbl Team 85; Area HS Coaches All-Lge Sftbl Team 85; Fitchburg ST Coll; Bus.

BARBERA, PATRICK; Belmont HS; Belmont, MA; (Y); 78/304; Church Yth Grp; Cmnty Wkr; Letterman Clb; Varsity Clb; JV Bsktbl; Var L Ftbl; Im Vllybl; Hon Roll; Boston Coll.

BARBERA, TODD; Central Catholic HS; Haverhill, MA; (Y); 60/219; Church Yth Grp; JA; ROTC; JV Crs Cntry; JV Trk; Hon Roll; Bus Mgmnt.

BARBIERI, PAUL; Milford HS; Brookfield, WI; (Y); JV Bsktbl; Coach Actv; Score Keeper; Hon Roll; Unsung Hero-Bsktbl; U Of WI Milwaukee.

BARBOSA, EMA; Mt St Joseph Acad; Dorchester, MA; (Y); Church Yth Grp; Math Clb; Church Choir; Variety Show; Lit Mag; Bio.

BARBOSA, LUIS; Cathedral HS; Boston, MA; (Y); Teachers Aide; Chorus; Mgr(s); Swmmng; Tennis; Hon Roll; NHS; Ntl Merit Ltr; Frnch Awd 82; Suffolk Book Awd 83; Intl Clb Awd 84; Northshore CC; Pilot.

BARCA, AMY; Bishop Feehan HS; Foxboro, MA; (Y); 6/250; Church Yth Grp; Drama Clb; Hosp Aide; Sec Frsh Cls; Sec Soph Cls; Rep Jr Cls; Sec Stu Cncl; Trk; NHS; Spanish NHS; Elem Educ.

BARCA, JOE; Hanover HS; Hanover, MA; (Y); Rep Frsh Cls; Rep Soph Cls; Rep Jr Cls; Rep Sr Cls; Stu Cncl; Capt Tennis; Hon Roll; Boston Herald American Newsppr Artical Prntnd 84; Writer.

BARCK, TIMOTHY; Westbridge Schl; Lowell, MA; (S); 2/16; Chess Clb; Science Clb; Yrbk Stf; Off Jr Cls; Off Sr Cls; Stu Cncl; Stat Bsktbl; High Hon Roll; NHS; Yale U; Arch.

BARDEN, CATHRYN; Chicopee Comprehensive HS; Chicopee, MA; (Y); 26/360; Dance Clb; Sec Girl Scts; Yrbk Stf; Im Powder Puff Ftbl; Var Sftbl; Hon Roll; NHS; Accntng.

BARDSLEY, DAVID; Holyoke HS; Holyoke, MA; (Y); CAP; Chorus; Capt Drill Tm; Stage Crew; Var Swmmng; Hon Roll; Close-Up Wk In Washington-Study Of Govt 85; MIT; Sci.

BARDWELL, CAROLYN; Southwick HS; Southwick, MA; (Y); 20/120; Am Leg Aux Girls St; Office Aide; Red Cross Aide; Concert Band; Jazz Band; Var Capt Bsktbl; Var Trk; Hon Roll; NHS; Louis Armstrong Jazz Awd 85; U MA; Med Tech.

BARI, ROYCE; Amherst Regional HS; Amherst, MA; (Y); Art Clb; Orch; Hon Roll; U Of MA; Bus.

BARILARO, JEAN MARIE; Weymouth North HS; Weymouth, MA; (Y); 11/340; Am Leg Aux Girls St; Pres Key Clb; Math Tm; School Play; Ed Lit Mag; Stu Cncl; Var Swmmng; Cit Awd; Elks Awd; NHS; Boston Coll; Pre-Law.

BARKER, JANE; Andover HS; Andover, MA; (S); VP DECA; Pep Clb; Hon Roll; Distribtvf Clb Of Amer Comptn; 2nd Pl ST Career Dvlpmnt; Northeastern U; Intl Mrktng.

BARKER, SUZI; Taunton HS; Taunton, MA; (Y); Hon Roll; Zoology.

BARLETTA, BONNIE; Matignon HS; Medford, MA; (Y); Rep Soph Cls; Off Stu Cncl; JV Capt Bsktbl; Sftbl; Vllybl; Hon Roll.

BARLETTA, VINCENZO; East Boston HS; Hyde Park, MA; (Y); VP Exploring; Socr; High Hon Roll; Hon Roll; VP NHS; Bio, Civcs, Geom Awds 84; Engl Awds 85; Sci Fair 1st Pl, Mock Trial 84; Bio.

BARLOW, AVLIN; Georgetown HS; Georgetown, MA; (Y); 1/90; Church Yth Grp; Drama Clb; French Clb; Library Aide; Sec Band; Jazz Band; Camera Clb; Yrbk Ed-Chief; High Hon Roll; Pres NHS; Harvard Bk Awdd 85; Rensselaer Polytech Inst Math & Sci Awd 85; Regnl Stu Advsry Cncl 85-86; Bio.

BARNABO, SUSAN; Marian HS; Natick, MA; (Y); 27/177; Church Yth Grp; French Clb; Latin Clb; Red Cross Aide; Yrbk Stf; Rep Soph Cls; Hon Roll; NHS; NEDT Awd; Girl Scts; Cert Of Hnrb Merit Cum Laude Natl Latn Exam 83.

BARNES, MICHELLE L; Everett HS; Everett, MA; (Y); 39/499; Office Aide; School Play; Nwsp Phtg; Yrbk Phtg; Cheerleading; Hon Roll; Bunker Hill CC Acad Exclnc 85; John Hancock Hnrs Awd 85; Bunker Hill CC.

BARNET, LAURA; Hingham HS; Hingham, MA; (Y); 25/325; Church Yth Grp; DECA; Thesps; Church Choir; Pres Orch; School Musical; Yrbk Stf; Hon Roll; NHS; Ntl Merit Ltr; Outstdng Contrib Orch 83 & 85; Mst Imprvd Orch 83; SE MA Schl Bndmstr Assn 83-85; Prfrmng Art.

BARNEY, CHRISTINE; Boston Latin Schl; Jamaica Plain, MA; (Y); VP Camera Clb; Hosp Aide; JA; Church Choir; Photogrphy Cont Ricoh Corp 83-84.

BARNICLE, BRENDAN; Acton Boxboro Reg HS; Acton, MA; (Y); 8/360; Boy Scts; Church Yth Grp; Political Wkr; Trs Sr Cls; Capt Crs Cntry; Trk; NHS; Pres Schlr; Rotary Awd; Spanish NHS; Harvard; Pocitics.

BARR, ANNE; Attleboro HS; Parma Hts, OH; (Y); Church Yth Grp; French Clb; Pep Clb; Band; Concert Band; Mrchg Band; Pep Band; Trs Soph Cls; High Hon Roll; Hon Roll; Supr, 2 Excllnt Ratngs Duets/Qurtet-Sol Ensmbl Cntst 83-84; Elem Ed.

BARR, PATRICIA; Whitman Hanson Regional HS; Hanson, MA; (Y); 4/340; Pres AFS; Trs Camp Fr Inc; Church Yth Grp; Hosp Aide; Yrbk Stf; Rep Frsh Cls; Rep Soph Cls; Rep Jr Cls; Rep Stu Cncl; Hon Roll; Town Hanson Soccer 82-85; Hugh O Brien Yth Ldrshp 84; Proj Contmpry Comptnss 82-83; Nrs.

BARRACLOUGH, JEFFREY; Methuen HS; Methuen, MA; (Y); Church Yth Grp; Yrbk Rptr; Sec Frsh Cls; JV Var Ftbl; Var Golf; Var Ice Hcky; JV Trk; Prntr.

BARREIRA, SHARON; Westport HS; Westport, MA; (Y); JA; Yrbk Stf; Wt Lftg; Hon Roll; NHS; Kinyon Campbell; Bus.

BARRETT, KELLY; Classical HS; Lynn, MA; (Y); 23/173; Church Yth Grp; Office Aide; Pep Clb; Spanish Clb; Stu Cncl; Hon Roll; NHS; Bus Admin.

BARRETTE, MICHAEL; Belmont HS; Belmont, MA; (Y); 23/309; Church Yth Grp; Cmnty Wkr; VP JA; Spanish Clb; Crs Cntry; Capt Trk; High Hon Roll; Hon Roll; Ntl Merit Ltr; Georgetown U; Intl Bus.

BARRICELLI, SUZANNE; Malden HS; Malden, MA; (Y); 17/600; Trs Church Yth Grp; Sec Key Clb; Office Aide; Teachers Aide; Band; Mrchg Band; School Play; Trs Yrbk Stf; NCTE Awd; Ntl Merit Ltr; Mount Holyoke.

BARROS III, BELMIRO J; Old Rochester Regional HS; Marion, MA; (Y); Am Leg Boys St; Off Soph Cls; Off Jr Cls; Ftbl; Trk; Hon Roll; Screeng Comm Schl Prncpl 84; Tres Of SADD 84-85; Spnsh.

BARROS, LUIS; Tounton HS; Taunton, MA; (Y); 58/410; Boys Clb Am; Dance Clb; Variety Show; Rep Frsh Cls; Rep Soph Cls; Rep Jr Cls; Rep Stu Cncl; Var Socr; Hon Roll; Ntl Merit Ltr; WEB Du Bois & Shaws Suprmkts Inc & Portuguese Am Cvc Clb Schlrshps 85; U Of MA Amherst; Mgmt.

BARROS, MARY; Dartmouth HS; S Dartmouth, MA; (Y); 31/251; Aud/Vis; JV Stat Bsktbl; Var Capt Sftbl; Var Capt Vllybl; Hon Roll; NHS; Sthestrn MA Conf Div II Vllybl Al-Star 84; Div I ST Sftbl Chmpns 84; Comnctn Fld.

BARROWS, PETER C; Silver Lake Regional HS; Carver, MA; (Y); 152/457; Chorus; Drftg.

BARRY, DAVID; Hudson HS; Hudson, MA; (Y); Bsbl; Ftbl; Ntl Hist Day Awd 2nd ST 83.

BARRY, JAY; Central Catholic HS; N Andover, MA; (Y); 50/220; Var Bsbl; Var Bsktbl; Var Ftbl; High Hon Roll; Bus Mgmt.

BARRY, JOHN; Everett HS; Everett, MA; (Y); 2/350; Boy Scts; Pres Science Clb; Yrbk Stf; JV Var Bsbl; Var Capt Socr; Sal; NHS; High Hon Roll; Nwsp Rptr; Debate Tm; Rsrch, ST Sci Fair, 3rd Prz Awd 85; Pres Yth Sccr Leag 84-85; Suffolk U Bk Awd 85; MIT; Comp Engr.

BARRY, JOHN JOSEPH; Andover HS; Andover, MA; (Y); Model UN; Varsity Clb; School Musical; School Play; Rep Frsh Cls; Rep Soph Cls; Rep Jr Cls; Rep Sr Cls; Rep Stu Cncl; Capt Ftbl; Most Lkly Succeed Cls 85; Dstngshd Athl Awd 85; Lillian Caplan Schlrshp-Ldrshp, Ctznshp 85; Villanova U; Lbrl Arts.

BARRY, JUDY; Revere HS; Revere, MA; (Y); 57/383; Office Aide; Fld Hcky; Powder Puff Ftbl; Sftbl; Computer Clb; Tracy Ciambelli Mem Schlrshp 85; Irma Wertheim Schlrshp 85; Brdgwtr ST; Bus Mngmnt.

BARRY, KEVIN; Leicester HS; Rochdale, MA; (S); Bsbl; Var Bsktbl; Var Ftbl.

BARRY, KIMBERLY; Presentation Of Mary Acad; Methuen, MA; (Y); Dance Clb; Math Clb; Model UN; Ski Clb; Spanish Clb; School Play; Stage Crew; Nwsp Stf; Yrbk Stf; Im Bsktbl; Worcester ST Coll; Lawyer.

BARRY, LYNNE; Notre Dame Acad; Cohasset, MA; (Y); GAA; Library Aide; Stu Cncl; JV Bsktbl; Var Sftbl; Var Trk; JV Vllybl; High Hon Roll; NHS; Natl Hnr Soc; Law.

BARRY, SHAUN K; Holyoke HS; Holyoke, MA; (Y); CAP; Debate Tm; Drama Clb; NFL; Thesps; School Musical; School Play; Var Tennis; Boy Scts; Church Yth Grp; Engrg.

BARRY, SUSAN; King Philip Regional HS; Norfolk, MA; (S); 24/285; Am Leg Aux Girls St; Pres Church Yth Grp; Var Fld Hcky; Var Capt Gym; Var Capt Trk; Hon Roll; NHS; Bus Finance.

BARRY, THEOLINDA; Marian HS; Hopkinton, MA; (Y); 47/176; Latin Clb; Library Aide; Office Aide; Orch; Variety Show; Yrbk Stf; Hon Roll; NHS; Excllnce In Sr Engl 85; Cum Laude-Natl Latin Exam 84; St Anselm Coll; Bio.

BARSAM, JULIE ROXANNE; Belmont HS; Belmont, MA; (Y); Sec Church Yth Grp; PAVAS; School Musical; School Play; Stage Crew; Nwsp Stf; Val Holy Trinity Sunday Schl 84; Tufts U; Lib Arts.

BARSHAK, JASON; Malden Catholic HS; Malden, MA; (Y); Computer Clb; Math Clb; Math Tm; VP Trs Temple Yth Grp; VP Band; Yrbk Stf; Bsktbl; High Hon Roll; Kiwanis Awd; NEML Mth Awd; B Nai B Rith Yth Grp; Law.

BARTEL, WENDY; Billerica Memorial HS; Pinehurst, MA; (Y); 29/499; Concert Band; Drm Mjr(t); Mrchg Band; Var Capt Bsktbl; Var Trk; JP Sousa Awd; NHS; GAA; Varsity Clb; Band; Best Marcher Awd 83-85; Outstndng Musicianshp 85; Anna Maria Coll; Music.

BARTFAY, ANNE; Northfield Mount Hermon Schl; Fountain Vly, CA; (Y); GAA; Red Cross Aide; Nwsp Stf; Yrbk Stf; Off Soph Cls; Off Jr Cls; Im Capt Socr; Var Swmmng; Var Trk; High Hon Roll; Cornell.

BARTLETT, CHRISTOPHER; Plymouth-Carver HS; Manomet, MA; (Y); 25/536; U Of Rochester; Optcs.

BARTLETT, PENNIE A; Nipmuc Regional HS; Upton, MA; (Y); Church Yth Grp; Computer Clb; FHA; School Play; Stage Crew; Nwsp Ed-Chief; Yrbk Phtg; Yrbk Rptr; Yrbk Sprt Ed; Yrbk Stf; Holy Angels Parish Schlrshp 85; Ella Risteen Schlrshp 85; Mt Ida Coll Grant 85; Mt Ida Coll; Fash Retail.

BARTLEY, MYLES K; Holyoke Catholic HS; Holyoke, MA; (Y); AFS; Chess Clb; Political Wkr; Yrbk Bus Mgr; Var L Bsbl; JV Mgr Bsktbl; Hon Roll; Pres Schlr; Wrld Hist Awd 82; 20th Century Hist Awd 85; U Of MA; Law.

BARTO, BRIAN; Triton Regional HS; Byfield, MA; (Y); 10/180; Rep Stu Cncl; Var L Bsbl; Var L Golf; Hon Roll; NHS; Math Awd 83-84; Schlr Ath6 83-85; MVP Golf Tm 84-85; Engrng.

BARTON, ALLEN R; Lexington HS; Lexington, MA; (Y); Jazz Band; Orch; School Musical; Variety Show; Nwsp Ed-Chief; Yrbk Phtg; Socr; High Hon Roll; Hon Roll; NHS; Physics.

BARTON, DANI; Dana Hall Schl; Wellesley, MA; (Y); Cmnty Wkr; Chorus; School Musical; Yrbk Stf; JV Sftbl; Var Capt Vllybl; Frnch Exch 85.

BARTON, DANIELA; Dana Hall Schl; Wellesly, MA; (Y); Cmnty Wkr; Chorus; School Musical; Yrbk Stf; Sftbl; Capt Vllybl; Frnch Exchng 85.

BARTOW, SHARON; Westwood HS; Westwood, MA; (Y); 40/241; AFS; Key Clb; Stu Cncl; Fld Hcky; Powder Puff Ftbl; Trk; Hon Roll; Finlst Essy Cntst; Bus.

BARUNAS, KRISTINA M; Canton HS; Canton, MA; (Y); Chorus; JV Var Cheerleading; JV Crs Cntry; Hon Roll; NHS; Century Clb 85; Boston Coll; Bus Mgmt.

BASCH, JEFFREY D; Sharon HS; Sharon, MA; (Y); Computer Clb; French Clb; Letterman Clb; Trs Math Tm; Temple Yth Grp; Varsity Clb; Band; Concert Band; Jazz Band; Pep Band; Chem Engr.

BASILE, JOSEPH A; Silver Lake Regional HS; Halifax, MA; (Y); 18/500; Chess Clb; French Clb; Latin Clb; Band; Jazz Band; Bsktbl; Socr; Var Trk; Hon Roll.

BASLER, WILLIAM JOSEPH; Burlington HS; Burlington, MA; (Y); 100/376; Church Yth Grp; Yrbk Rptr; Yrbk Stf; Stu Cncl; Gym; Hon Roll; Natl Hnr Roll 84-85; Excllnce Prof Cookng 83; Northeastern U; Acctg.

BASSETT, KATHERINE T; Norton HS; Norton, MA; (Y); 8/130; Pres Math Tm; VP Band; Jazz Band; VP Mrchg Band; VP Jr Cls; Capt Trk; VP NHS; Voice Dem Awd; Office Aide; Lions Clb All ST Band 85; Band Parent Scholar 85; Colby Coll; Econ.

BAST, JENNIFER; Sacred Heart HS; Braintree, MA; (Y); Civic Clb; Drama Clb; Hosp Aide; Spanish Clb; Variety Show; Nwsp Stf; JV Cheerleading; JV Vllybl; Eng Lit 84; Merit Chem 85; Merit U S Hstry 85; Nrsg Prac.

BASTIAANS, SALLY; Easthampton HS; Easthampton, MA; (Y); Am Leg Aux Girls St; French Clb; Hosp Aide; Chorus; Yrbk Stf; Hon Roll; NHS; Girls All-ST Wmns Aux Legn Alt 85; Chorus Awd 82-85; Pre-Law.

BATEMAN, ROBYN; Williston Northhampton HS; Holyoke, MA; (Y); Church Yth Grp; Dance Clb; Drama Clb; Key Clb; Library Aide; School Play; Nwsp Stf; Swmmng; High Hon Roll; Jr NHS.

BATES, JEFF; Nauset Regional HS; Brewster, MA; (Y); Am Leg Boys St; Math Tm; Ski Clb; Pres Stu Cncl; Var Ice Hcky; JV Socr; Var Tennis; Hon Roll; NHS; Williams Coll Bk Awd 85; Cornell; Engrng.

BATES, NICOLAS K; Andover HS; Andover, MA; (Y); Boy Scts; Church Yth Grp; School Musical; Variety Show; Yrbk Stf; Var Socr; God Cntry Awd; Hon Roll; Eagle Scout; Dickinson Coll; Physics.

BATTISTA, LISA; Holy Name Central Catholic HS; Auburn, MA; (Y); 4/260; Dance Clb; Pep Clb; Teachers Aide; Cheerleading; High Hon Roll; Hon Roll; NHS; Prfct Atten Awd; Church Yth Grp; Varsity Clb; Excell Awd Amer Lit 85; Excel Religion II & III 84-85; Math.

BATTISTA, REBECCA; Shepherd Hill Regional HS; Dudley, MA; (Y); Church Yth Grp; Math Tm; Band; Church Choir; School Musical; Trs Stu Cncl; High Hon Roll; Trs NHS; Bus Adm.

BATTIT, GINA; Belmont HS; Belmont, MA; (Y); 90/309; Sec Church Yth Grp; Pres JA; Key Clb; Pep Clb; Yrbk Stf; Var Crs Cntry; Var L Sftbl; Im Vllybl; High Hon Roll; Hon Roll; St Michael Coll; Acctng.

BAUER, LIANE; Acton-Boxboro Regional HS; Acton, MA; (Y); 44/363; AFS; Church Yth Grp; Red Cross Aide; Swmmng; Hon Roll; NHS; Globe All Schlstc Girls Swim Team 82; Lowell All Star Swmmng 82; Swmmng Schlrshp 85; Villanova U; Math.

BAUM, BRIAN A; Attleboro HS; Attleboro, MA; (Y); 5/450; Am Leg Boys St; Church Yth Grp; Var L Tennis; High Hon Roll; NHS; Cert Excllnce Typ I & Framingham St Hstrcl Conf 84.

BAUMAN, LAURA; Hopkins Acad; Hadley, MA; (S); 7/52; Church Yth Grp; Cmnty Wkr; 4-H; Spanish Clb; Band; Chorus; Church Choir; Concert Band; Mrchg Band; Pep Band; Sci.

BAUMANN, PAIGE F; Newburyport HS; Newburyport, MA; (S); 2/223; Intnl Clb; Model UN; Q&S; School Play; Nwsp Phtg; Nwsp Rptr; Lit Mag; High Hon Roll; Hon Roll; NHS; Lawyer.

BAVARO, MARY ELLEN; Sacred Heart HS; Plymouth, MA; (Y); 1/80; Rep Stu Cncl; Var Capt Bsktbl; JV Capt Sftbl; High Hon Roll; Pres NHS; Val; VFW Awd; Chanclr Tlnt Awd Schlrshp U Of MA; Outstndng Stu; Cornell U; Engrng.

BAVLY, SUZANNE; Maimonides Schl; Newton, MA; (Y); Drama Clb; Temple Yth Grp; Acpl Chr; School Play; Nwsp Stf; Yrbk Ed-Chief; Sec Soph Cls; Brown U Bk Awd 84; Theatre.

BAXENDALE, GREG; Bishop Connolly HS; Swansea, MA; (Y); Var Capt Bsbl; Var Bsktbl; Hon Roll; MVP Bsbl 85; All Star Bsbl 85.

BAXTER, CHRIS; New Bedford HS; New Bedford, MA; (Y); 36/600; Letterman Clb; Varsity Clb; Yrbk Stf; Crs Cntry; Trk; NHS; Church Yth Grp; Drama Clb; Radio Clb; Stu Cncl; Law.

BAXTER, DONNA; Mohawk Trail Regional HS; Ashfield, MA; (Y); Trs AFS; Debate Tm; Political Wkr; Yrbk Sprt Ed; Var Fld Hcky; JV Mgr(s); JV Score Keeper; JV Tennis; Hon Roll; Math.

BAYER, STEPHEN; Taunton HS; Taunton, MA; (Y); Drama Clb; Intnl Clb; Band; Concert Band; Mrchg Band; Nwsp Rptr; Nwsp Stf; Yrbk Stf; Lit Mag; Jrnlsm.

BAYOU, BASSAM; Natick HS; Natick, MA; (Y); 97/443; Boy Scts; Socr; Engrng.

BAZARIAN, ANDREW; Wilbraham And Monson Acad; Wilbraham, MA; (Y); Church Yth Grp; Ed Nwsp Sprt Ed; JV Ftbl; Var Capt Lcrss; Var Capt Wrstlng; Hon Roll; Trs Jr Cls; Law.

BEAGERON, WILLIAM; Central Catholic HS; Lawrence, MA; (Y); 78/219; Boy Scts; Church Yth Grp; Ski Clb; Im Bsktbl; JV Ftbl; JV Trk; Hon Roll; Comp Sci.

BEAL, TODD N; Marblehead HS; Marblehead, MA; (Y); Arch.

BEALL, KATHERINE; Holy Name CC HS; Worcester, MA; (Y); Chorus; School Musical; School Play; Yrbk Stf; Hon Roll; NHS; Hnrb Mntn Histry Papr 84; Theatre Guild Best Actrs Awd 84; SR Rcgntn Plaque 85; ME U; Frstry.

BEAMAN, TANYA D; Hyde Park HS; Mattapan, MA; (Y); Church Yth Grp; Cmnty Wkr; Dance Clb; FBLA; Girl Scts; Library Aide; Office Aide; Pep Clb; Political Wkr; Band; MA ST Schlrshp Awd; ST Fnlst & Pagnt Fnlst-Miss Amer Co-Ed Pgnt 85; Best Singer In Cls Awd; Newbury Coll; Audio-Visual Tech.

BEAN, JULIE; Matignon HS; Somerville, MA; (Y); 34/198; French Clb; Rep Soph Cls; Rep Jr Cls; Stu Cncl; Var Bsktbl; JV Sftbl; Var Vllybl; Hon Roll; Hnrbl Mntn Teenager Of The Yr 82; Hstry Clb 84-85; Nrsng.

BEAN, LUANN; West Bridgewater HS; W Bridgewater, MA; (Y); 14/104; Church Yth Grp; Varsity Clb; JV Cheerleading; Var Trk; Hon Roll; NHS.

BEANDO, CHERIE; Blackstone Valley Reg Vo-Tech; Sutton, MA; (Y); Dance Clb; Library Aide; Red Cross Aide; Lit Mag; High Hon Roll; Hon Roll; Comp Mgt.

BEARD, HOLLY; Taunton HS; Taunton, MA; (Y); Art Clb; GAA; Teachers Aide; Varsity Clb; JV Bsktbl; Var Socr; JV Sftbl; Hon Roll; Mid ST Coll; Sec.

BEATO, RAFAEL; Madison Park HS; Boston, MA; (Y); Hon Roll; NHS; Prfct Atten Awd; Chllng Pgm Recgnzd For Outstndng Acadmc Achvt 85; Electrncs.

BEATRICE, JONATHAN L; Tri-Country Vocational Schl; Franklin, MA; (Y); Chess Clb; Red Cross Aide; Ski Clb; VICA; Yrbk Stf; Rep Frsh Cls; Rep Soph Cls; Rep Jr Cls; Rep Sr Cls; Hon Roll; High Hnrs 85; Shop Awd 85; MIT; Mech Engrng.

BEATTIE, MAUREEN; Dracut HS; Pelham, NH; (Y); Cmnty Wkr; Hosp Aide; Key Clb; Office Aide; Teachers Aide; Yrbk Stf; Hon Roll; Ntl Merit SF; Outstandng Classcl Studs Stdnt; Outstndng Engl Studnt; St John Hosp Schlrshp; Univ Of NH; Agri Sci.

BEATTY, IAN; Amherst Regional HS; Amherst, MA; (Y); Var Lcrss; Hon Roll; Ntl Merit SF; UMASS; Phy Scntst.

BEAUDET, CATHLEEN; Auburn HS; Auburn, MA; (Y); 55/180; Church Yth Grp; Pep Clb; Varsity Clb; Yrbk Phtg; Yrbk Rptr; Yrbk Stf; Cheerleading; Fld Hcky; Sftbl; Hon Roll; Ded Cls; Hnr Rl; Worcester ST; Ed.

BEAUDIN, PAULA; Easthampton HS; Easthampton, MA; (Y); Yrbk Stf; Cheerleading.

BEAUDOIN, MICHELLE; B M C Durfee HS; Fall River, MA; (Y); 27/688; French Clb; Hosp Aide; JA; Library Aide; Yrbk Stf; High Hon Roll; Hon Roll; NHS; Bus Mgr.

BEAULIEU, BRIAN L; Chicopee HS; Chicopee, MA; (Y); 22/260; Yrbk Stf; Pres Jr Cls; Pres Sr Cls; Rep Stu Cncl; Var Capt Socr; Var Capt Trk; NHS; Cmnty Wkr; Yrbk Sprt Ed; Rep Soph Cls; ST H S Champnshp Tm 83; 5th Pl Javelin Western MA Trk Mt 85; Bronze Medal Wnnr Western MA Socr 85; Engrng.

BEAULIEU, SHELLY; Somerset HS; Somerset, MA; (Y); Mrchg Band; School Play; Twrlr; High Hon Roll; Hon Roll; NHS; X-Ray Tech.

BEAUREGARD, RICHARD E; Salem HS; Salem, MA; (Y); 65/328; Var Bsbl; Var Capt Ftbl; Hon Roll; Hero Ftbl Awd 84; Salem ST Coll; Bus Adm.

BEAUREGARD, TREVOR; Garnder HS; Gardner, MA; (Y); 37/190; Chess Clb; Church Yth Grp; JV Var Bsbl; Var L Bsktbl; Capt L Ftbl; Wt Lftg; Bsbl Coaches Awd 84; Htl Rest & Trvl Adm.

BECK, GEORGE C; Xaverian Brothers HS; Wellesley, MA; (S); 4/236; Capt Chess Clb; Church Yth Grp; Math Tm; JV Trk; High Hon Roll; NHS; Ntl Merit SF.

BECK, JULIE; Natick HS; Natick, MA; (Y); 17/443; Trs JA; Ski Clb; Speech Tm; Nwsp Stf; Sec Stu Cncl; JV Fld Hcky; Im Lcrss; JV Tennis; High Hon Roll; Hon Roll; Math.

BECK, ROBERT; Hingham HS; Hingham, MA; (Y); 40/350; AFS; Church Yth Grp; Band; Church Choir; Concert Band; Jazz Band; Mrchg Band; Orch; School Musical; Hon Roll; Natl Assn Of Jazz Educ Outstndng Solist 85; Outstndng Contrbtn To Jazz Bnd 85; Mst Imprvd JR Awd 85; Air Force Acad; Aero Engrng.

BECK, THERESA; Marian HS; Framingham, MA; (Y); Chorus; Spanish NHS; Real Est.

BECKWITH, NADINE; Holy Name CC HS; Auburn, MA; (Y); Drama Clb; Chorus; Church Choir; High Hon Roll; Natl Sci Olympiad Bio 4th Pl 84; Schl Dept Awd French III 85; Cert Achvmnt Art 83-84; Cmpt Sci.

BECKWITH, WAYNE E; Milford HS; Milford, MA; (Y); Var Ftbl; Var Trk; Hon Roll; MIP Ftbl Awd 84-85; Framingham ST; Elec Engr.

BEDARD, SCOTT; Danvers HS; Danvers, MA; (Y); 186/320; Aud/Vis.

BEDIGIAN, PAUL; Northbridge JR SR HS; Whitinsville, MA; (Y); 3/140; Boy Scts; Chess Clb; JV Var Bsbl; High Hon Roll; Hon Roll; Jr NHS; NHS; Chess Trnmnt Champ 80-82 & 85; Eagle Sct 83; U Of Lowell; Civil Engrng.

BEELE, PAMELA; Agawam HS; Agawam, MA; (Y); Church Yth Grp; Ski Clb; Chorus; Rep Stu Cncl; Var Fld Hcky; Var Trk; Var Hon Roll; Var NHS; Bd Of Dir For Natl Hnr Soc 84-85; U Of MA; Bus.

BEGIN, JULIE MARIE; Canton HS; Canton, MA; (Y); 27/280; Church Yth Grp; French Clb; GAA; Girl Scts; Hosp Aide; Varsity Clb; Band; Concert Band; Mrchg Band; School Musical; Jordan Marsh Fshn Brd 84-85; Gold Awd Grl Sctng 84; 1st Clss Awd Grl Sctng 83; U Mass; Pre-Med.

BEHRENS, JEFFREY S; Framingham North HS; Framingham, MA; (Y); 8/330; Cmnty Wkr; Drama Clb; Political Wkr; Nwsp Ed-Chief; Lit Mag; NHS; Ntl Merit SF; Telluride Assn Smmr Prg Schlrshp 84; N E Amer Chem Soc Contst Hnrb Mntn 84; Cert Merit Concours Fr 84; Cornell; Pol Sci.

BEITZEL, ERIK; Milford HS; Pleasent Garden, NC; (Y); Band; Jazz Band; Var Tennis; Marine Bio.

BELAND, BRIAN D; Wachusett Regional HS; Sterling, MA; (Y); Am Leg Boys St; Art Clb; Church Yth Grp; Hon Roll; Wentworth Inst Of Tech; Arch.

BELAND, STEPHEN; Central Catholic HS; Lowell, MA; (Y); 16/219; VP Pres Church Yth Grp; Var Capt Crs Cntry; Var Capt Trk; Hon Roll; Princpl Schlrshps; Legn Hnr; Crim Jstc.

BELANGER, ELIZABETH J; Randolph HS; Randolph, MA; (Y); 37/315; Drama Clb; Mgr Chorus; School Musical; Swing Chorus; Rep Sr Cls; Hon Roll; Kiwanis Awd; NHS; St Schlr; Northeastern U; Bus.

BELAVITCH, DAVID; Central Catholic HS; Salem, NH; (Y); 60/226; Cmnty Wkr; Var Bsktbl; Var Trk; Coachs Awd Bsktbll 84-85; All Star Bsktbll 85; Hnrbl Mntn All Confrnc Trck Team 85; Busn.

BELCASTRO, LORI; Arlington Catholic HS; Woburn, MA; (Y); 6/148; Spanish Clb; Nwsp Stf; Yrbk Stf; Vllybl; NHS; Engrng.

BELEZOS, GEORGE NICHOLAS; Boston Latin Schl; Brighton, MA; (Y); 10/330; Church Yth Grp; Computer Clb; German Clb; Political Wkr; Bsktbl; High Hon Roll; Hon Roll; Boston Splng Champ 80; Hnrs Pgm Boston U 85.

BELEZOS, WILLIAM; Boston Latin Schl; Boston, MA; (Y); 134/330; Church Yth Grp; Drama Clb; German Clb; JA; Stage Crew; Rep Soph Cls; Rep Stu Cncl; Barnes & Noble Good Grds Cert 84; Sls Clb & Co JR Achvt 84; Bus Mgmt.

BELHUMEUR, NICOLE; Northfield Mount Hermon HS; Greenfield, MA; (Y); Church Yth Grp; Varsity Clb; Frsh Cls; Soph Cls; JV Capt Bsktbl; JV Var Fld Hcky; Var JV Sftbl; Hon Roll; Peter Leyden JR Mem Awd Phy-Ed & Athltcs 85; Frgn Lang.

BELISLE, MICHELLE; Milford HS; Milford, MA; (Y); 36/300; Dance Clb; School Musical; Yrbk Stf; Jr Cls; Capt Var Cheerleading; Hon Roll; NHS; USCA Natl Champ 3rd Pl Chrng Ind 84; USCA Natl Champ 1st Pl Tlnt Ind 84; Var Chrldng Bst Sprtswmn 84; Bus Mgmt.

BELIVEAU, ROBERT; Methuen HS; Methuen, MA; (Y); 10/370; Cmnty Wkr; Var Capt Gym; Var JV Trk; High Hon Roll; NHS; Intnl Clb; Library Aide; Model UN; Nwsp Sprt Ed; French Hon Soc; Elec Engr.

BELKEN, KURT; Apponequet Regional HS; Lakeville, MA; (Y); 12/260; Jazz Band; Mrchg Band; Symp Band; Rep Frsh Cls; Rep Soph Cls; Rep Jr Cls; Hon Roll; Trs NHS; Church Yth Grp; Band; Proj Excel-Southeastern MA U 84; Law.

BELL, BETH; St Bernards Cc HS; Westminster, MA; (S); 6/163; Yrbk Stf; Trs Stu Cncl; Cheerleading; Hon Roll; NHS; Ntl Merit Ltr; Engineering.

BELL, KATHLEEN; Framingham South HS; Framingham, MA; (Y); 9/262; Latin Clb; Rep Sec Stu Cncl; Stat Ice Hcky; Var L Socr; Var L Tennis; Var L Trk; NHS; High Hon Roll; Hon Roll; MA ST Chmpn Sccr Team 84.

BELL, MARLENE; Dracut SR HS; Dracut, MA; (Y); Church Yth Grp; Dance Clb; Office Aide; Nwsp Rptr; Sec Soph Cls; Sec Jr Cls; Sec Sr Cls; Var Cheerleading; Var Coach Actv; Variety Show; Pub Cmnctns.

BELLA MURA, JESSIKA; Saugus HS; Saugus, MA; (Y); 17/301; Sec Aud/Vis; Sec Chess Clb; Drama Clb; Trs VP French Clb; JA; Lit Mag; Crs Cntry; Ntl Merit SF; Chorus; School Play; Yrbk Art Edtr.

BELLAROSA, PAUL; Nauset Regional HS; Brewster, MA; (Y); Ski Clb; Off Jr Cls; Off Sr Cls; Var Ice Hcky; Var Socr; Hon Roll; Polit Sci.

BELLE ISLE, PAUL P; Andover HS; Andover, MA; (Y); 11/430; Model UN; Pep Clb; Rep Sr Cls; Coach Actv; Gym; Cit Awd; High Hon Roll; Hon Roll; Ntl Merit SF; Social Stds Dept Awd; Aerontcl Engr.

BELLEROSE, CELESTE; Southbridge HS; Sbridge, MA; (Y); 10/160; Pres Band; Concert Band; Drm Mjr(t); Yrbk Stf; Pres Soph Cls; Stu Cncl; L Trk; Hon Roll; JP Sousa Awd; NHS; Fitchburg ST Coll; Nrsg.

BELLETETE, MICHELLE; St Bernards Central Catholic HS; Winchendon, MA; (S); 19/172; Drama Clb; Yrbk Stf; Hon Roll; Equestrn Sportsmnshp Awd 83; Salve Regina; Psych.

BELLINI, KRISTY; Aguwam HS; Agawam, MA; (Y); 13/340; Dance Clb; Drama Clb; Ski Clb; Color Guard; Variety Show; Trk; High Hon Roll; Hon Roll; NHS; Cert Credit Typng 84; Acctng.

BELLONE, THERESA; Senior HS; E Boston, MA; (Y); Swmmng; Hon Roll; Hgh Acad Achvt Scl Stds 82-83; Psych.

BELMARSH, LISA; Weymouth North HS; Weymouth, MA; (Y); Office Aide; Pep Clb; Ski Clb; Yrbk Ed-Chief; Rep Jr Cls; Rep Sr Cls; Rep Stu Cncl; JV Bsktbl; Var Socr; High Hon Roll; Sci.

BELMONTE, DENISE; Revere HS; Revere, MA; (Y); 34/385; Cmnty Wkr; Red Cross Aide; Ed Yrbk Stf; VP Soph Cls; Rep Jr Cls; Rep Sr Cls; Stu Cncl; Capt Cheerleading; Coach Actv; Elks Awd; Cella Schlrshp Awd 85; Ntn Wide Chrng Awd 84; SADD Cert 85; Suffolk U; Bus Mngmnt.

BELMONTE, JUDITH; Revere HS; Revere, MA; (Y); Church Yth Grp; Library Aide; Office Aide; Science Clb; Church Choir; Yrbk Stf; Rep Jr Cls; Rep Stu Cncl; Cit Awd; Hon Roll; MA Coll Art; Graphic Desgn.

BELMONTE, MICHELLE; Lynn Ciassical HS; Lynn, MA; (Y); Dance Clb; Teachers Aide; Drm & Bgl; JV Bsktbl; Hon Roll; Paralegal.

BELSITO, GINA; Holy Name C C HS; Worcester, MA; (Y); 48/244; Art Clb; Intnl Clb; Science Clb; Capt Bsktbl; Crs Cntry; Capt Trk; Hon Roll; Hnr For Christian Attitude Outstdng Charactr 85; Hnr For Yth Art Mnth In Worcester 85; Worcester ST; Bio.

BELSITO, PETE; St Johns HS; W Boylston, MA; (Y); 151/282; Am Leg Boys St; Church Yth Grp; English Clb; French Clb; Varsity Clb; JV Bsbl; JV Var Ftbl; High Hon Roll; Hon Roll; Finance.

BELTON, THERESA; Holy Name C C HS; Worcester, MA; (Y); 51/241; Debate Tm; Hosp Aide; Science Clb; Spanish Clb; School Musical; School Play; Stage Crew; Nwsp Stf; Hon Roll; MA ST Schlrshp 85; Math Hnrs 81; Fitchburg ST Coll; Nrsng.

BEMBENCK, DEBBIE; Bartlett HS; Webster, MA; (Y); Church Yth Grp; Sec FBLA; Ski Clb; Variety Show; Nwsp Stf; Yrbk Stf; Cheerleading; Tennis; Hon Roll; Psych.

BENDEL, PAULA; Clinton HS; Clinton, MA; (Y); Intnl Clb; JA; School Play; Yrbk Stf; Rep Soph Cls; Vllybl; Hon Roll; Framingham ST Coll; Bus Mngmnt.

BENEDICT, AUGUSTA; Westford Acad; Westford, MA; (Y); 39/222; Cmnty Wkr; Model UN; VP Frsh Cls; VP Soph Cls; VP Jr Cls; VP Sr Cls; Coach Actv; Var Fld Hcky; JV Fld Hcky; Hon Roll; Pltcl Sci.

BENEVIDES JR, ROBERT P; Somerset HS; Somerset, MA; (Y); 4/299; Church Yth Grp; Political Wkr; School Play; Stage Crew; Nwsp Stf; Elks Awd; High Hon Roll; NHS; Pres Schlr; Brown U Bk Awd 84; Elks Teenager Mnth 85; Male Teenager Yr 85; Ctzns Schlrshp Fndtn 85; NY U; Film Dir.

BENHAM, PAUL J; Maynard HS; Maynard, MA; (Y); 5/90; Am Leg Boys St; Boys Clb Am; Radio Clb; VP Jr Cls; VP Sr Cls; Capt Bsktbl; Ftbl; Capt Trk; High Hon Roll; Pres NHS; WPI; Engr.

BENINATI, JANET; Dana Hall Schl; Wilmington, MA; (Y); 1/111; Dance Clb; Drama Clb; Rep Jr Cls; Rep Sr Cls; High Hon Roll; Cum Laude Soc 84-85; Tulane U.

BENNETT, BRENDA A; Dedham HS; Dedham, MA; (S); 4/289; Church Yth Grp; Band; Concert Band; Jazz Band; Mrchg Band; Orch; High Hon Roll; Hon Roll; JP Sousa Awd; Outstndg Soph Math 83-84; Voice Of Democracy Cont Semi-Fnlst 84-85.

BENNETT, CINDY; Gardner HS; Gardner, MA; (S); Art Clb; Camera Clb; 2nd Pl DECA ST Cmptn 84; Bus Mngmnt.

BENNETT, ELIZABETH C; Newburyport HS; Newburyport, MA; (S); Intnl Clb; JCL; Ski Clb; Nwsp Sprt Ed; Hst Frsh Cls; Hst Soph Cls; Hst Jr Cls; L Bsktbl; Coach Actv; Fld Hcky; Jrnlsm Awds 84-85; All Star Tnns Tm 83-84; Dnc Thrpy.

BENNETT, JOHN; Fairhaven HS; Acushnet, MA; (Y); 25/200; Nwsp Stf; JV Bsbl; JV Bsktbl; Var L Tennis; Hon Roll; Jr NHS; Lionard Picansoe Memrl Awd; Jrnlsm.

BENOIT, CHRISTINE; Chicopee Comprehensive HS; Chicopee, MA; (Y); 29/311; Pres Church Yth Grp; Sec Exploring; Office Aide; Yrbk Stf; Powder Puff Ftbl; S Prestley Blake Schlrhsp 85; Anna B Houston Schlrshp 85; Pro Merito Awd 85; Bay Path JR Coll; Law.

BENOIT, GEORGE; St Johns HS; Holden, MA; (Y); Pres Church Yth Grp; Hon Roll; NHS; Var L Socr; Fairfield U; Bus.

BENOIT, JOHN; Chicopee Comprehenisve HS; Chicopee, MA; (Y); 8/373; Boy Scts; Exploring; French Clb; Yrbk Stf; L Ftbl; High Hon Roll; Hon Roll; NHS; Engrng.

BENOIT, NICOLE A; Cathedral HS; Springfield, MA; (Y); Prfct Atten Awd; Airpln Pilot.

BENSON, WILLIAM; Foxboro HS; Foxborough, MA; (Y); Band; Jazz Band; Mrchg Band; ITT Tech; Drftng.

BENSON, WILLIAM E; Needham HS; Needham, MA; (Y); 55/362; Am Leg Boys St; Boy Scts; Yrbk Ed-Chief; VP Jr Cls; VP Sr Cls; God Cntry Awd; Hon Roll; NEDT Awd; Church Yth Grp; JV Ftbl; Boys ST,ST Auditor,Judge 85; Toastmastrs Intl Yth Ldrshp Pgm 84; Colby Coll Bk Awd 85; Pol Sci.

BENTLEY, RHONDA M; Berkshire Schl; New York, NY; (S); 3/110; Band; Vllybl; High Hon Roll; Sec Drama Clb; School Musical; Nwsp Rptr; VP Soph Cls; Mgr Trk; Cum Laude Scty 85; Williams Coll Bk Awd 85; Stephan Spaulding Schlrhsp 85; Pre-Med.

BENTLEY, TONIA; Mission Church HS; Jamaica Plain, MA; (S); Sec Frsh Cls; Trs Soph Cls; Hon Roll; Natl Awd Sci 84; Med.

BERARD, KENNETH; Agawam HS; Feeding Hills, MA; (Y); 51/389; Church Yth Grp; English Clb; Library Aide; Model UN; Quiz Bowl; Teachers Aide; Lit Mag; Var Capt Ftbl; Im Wt Lftg; Hon Roll; All Wstrn MA Running Bck 2nd Tm 84; 1000 Yrd Clb Running Bck 84; Plyr Of Wk Sunday Repub JR Ath 84; Amer U; Crim Just.

BERARDI, KAREN; Woburn SR HS; Woburn, MA; (S); French Clb; Leo Clb; Ski Clb; Color Guard; Flag Corp; Stu Cncl; High Hon Roll; Hon Roll; Jr NHS; Boston Coll; Mgmt.

BERENGUER, JODIE; B M C Durfee HS; Fall River, MA; (Y); French Clb; Variety Show; Yrbk Stf; Hon Roll; Johnson & Wales; Trvl.

BERG, CHRISTOPHER P; Weston HS; Weston, MA; (Y); 25/190; Orch; School Musical; Var L Socr; Var L Trk; Ntl Merit SF; Math Tm; Jazz Band; Nwsp Stf; Hon Roll; Princeton Alumni Assoc Awd Leadership & Academic Promise 84; Astronomer.

BERG, KRISTINA; North Middlesex Regional HS; Pepperell, MA; (Y); Band; Concert Band; Mrchg Band; School Musical; School Play; Trk; Hon Roll; Band Rcgntn Awd 85; U Of MA; Merch.

BERGER, MARK R; Plymouth-Carver HS; Plymouth, MA; (Y); Debate Tm; French Clb; Intnl Clb; Math Clb; Political Wkr; Science Clb; Temple Yth Grp; Nwsp Rptr; Nwsp Stf; JV Capt Socr; Schl Fnlst Sci Fair 82 & 84; Wnnr Schl Wrtg Fest 82; Wrtr.

BERGERON, JUDITH; Southbridge HS; Southridge, MA; (Y); French Clb; High Hon Roll; Hon Roll; Regis Coll; Lib Arts.

BERGERON, RENEE; Holyoke Catholic HS; Chicopee, MA; (Y); Computer Clb; Latin Clb; Spanish Clb; Chorus; School Musical; Lit Mag; Var Crs Cntry; Var Trk; High Hon Roll; NHS; Holy Cross Bk Prze 85.

BERGERON, STEPHEN; Chicopee Comprehensive HS; Chicopee, MA; (Y); Computer Clb; Yrbk Stf; Elks Awd; High Hon Roll; Hon Roll; NHS; Western New England Coll; Compt.

BERGMANN, MALENA N; Chelmsford HS; Tyngsboro, MA; (Y); 54/560; Art Clb; French Clb; Ski Clb; Drill Tm; Yrbk Stf; Powder Puff Ftbl; Trk; High Hon Roll; Hon Roll; Church Yth Grp; Boston Globe Art Show Gold Key Awd 83; Art.

BERKOICS, ROBERT; Boston Latin HS; Boston, MA; (Y); 131/330; Boys Clb Am; Var Ftbl; High Hon Roll; Hon Roll; Fidelity Awd 83; COAC Acad 79; Wentworth; Bldg Constrctn Tech.

BERMANN, JOSEPH; Newton North HS; Newton, MA; (Y); Boy Scts; Math Tm; Socr; Tennis; Trk; High Hon Roll; Hon Roll; Ntl Merit SF; Math Olympd Fnlst 85; Math & Sci.

BERNAL, EDDIE; Bay Path Reg Voc Tech HS; Webster, MA; (Y); Aud/Vis; Computer Clb; Quiz Bowl; Radio Clb; High Hon Roll; Hon Roll; Mst Outstndng SR Stu Sci & Elec 85; Mst Outstndng Elec Tech 85; Elec Fld Engr.

BERNARD, DIANE E; Reading Memorial HS; Reading, MA; (Y); Hosp Aide; JA; Pep Clb; Varsity Clb; Capt Drm Mjr(t); Nwsp Stf; Ed Yrbk Stf; Capt Gym; High Hon Roll; Hon Roll; Schlstc Achvt Awds Hnr Roll Stu 84; English.

BERNARD, KEVIN; Brockton HS; Brockton, MA; (Y); Am Leg Boys St; Art Clb; Church Yth Grp; Cmnty Wkr; Political Wkr; Rep Frsh Cls; Rep Soph Cls; Rep Jr Cls; Rep Sr Cls; JV Bsbl; Clg Of Holy Cross; Hist.

BERNARDES, JOHN; Milford HS; Milford, MA; (Y); 50/300; Science Clb; Church Choir; Var Tennis; Hon Roll; Portuguese Diploma Grad 82-83; Arch.

BERNAT, JENNIFER; Hoosac Valley Regional HS; Cheshire, MA; (Y); Pep Clb; Teachers Aide; Nwsp Stf; Yrbk Stf; Cheerleading; Hon Roll; Mc Cann Vocatnl Schl; Med Asst.

BERNAT, KERRI; Bishop Connolly HS; Fall River, MA; (Y); Drama Clb; Hosp Aide; Ski Clb; School Play; Var Cheerleading; Hon Roll; Bryant Coll; Acctng.

BERNIER, ANNE MARIE; Bartlett HS; Webster, MA; (Y); 35/149; Trs Church Yth Grp; Spanish Clb; Church Choir; JV Var Bsktbl; Var Socr; JV Sftbl; High Hon Roll; Hon Roll; Ltr In Sccr 84-85; Math.

BERNIER, JEANNE; Bishop Connolly HS; Fall River, MA; (Y); Drama Clb; Hosp Aide; Nwsp Rptr; Hon Roll; Southeastern MA U; Nrs.

BERNIER, MARC; Middleboro HS; Middleboro, MA; (Y); Aud/Vis; Boy Scts; Computer Clb; Stage Crew; JV Var Socr; Hon Roll; NHS; Engrng.

BERNIER, PAUL; Algonquin Regional HS; Southboro, MA; (Y); 28/221; Church Yth Grp; Var Bsktbl; High Hon Roll; Hon Roll; Vrsty Ltr Strtg On Bsktbl Tm 85-86; Ec.

BERNSEN, LINDA J; Foxborough HS; Foxborough, MA; (Y); Church Yth Grp; School Play; Nwsp Rptr; Rep Frsh Cls; Rep Sec Soph Cls; Rep Stu Cncl; MA Bus Wk Scholar Bently 84; Hum Rel Yth Awd 85; Mem Scholar 85; Dean JC; Mrktg.

BEROLL, DAVID; Doherty Memorial HS; Worcester, MA; (Y); Latin Clb; Spanish Clb; Teachers Aide; Temple Yth Grp; Pres Orch; Hon Roll; Ntl Sng Wrtng Cmptn Fnlst 84; SITE Pgm 85-86.

BERRIGAN, ROSEANN; Acton Boxborough Regional HS; Acton, MA; (Y); 173/343; AFS; Aud/Vis; Drama Clb; Pep Clb; Radio Clb; School Musical; School Play; Stage Crew; Variety Show; Nwsp Stf; All Star Awd Cls Comp Plys 84; Emerson Coll; Comm.

BERRIOS, JAVIER PALEVI; HS Of Commerce; Springfield, MA; (S); 2/300; Church Yth Grp; Cmnty Wkr; Pep Clb; Spanish Clb; Yrbk Stf; High Hon Roll; Hon Roll; NHS; Sal; U Of MA-AMHERST; Pre-Med.

BERRY, JOHN L; Mahar Regional HS; Petersham, MA; (Y); Am Leg Boys St; Dance Clb; Drama Clb; Chorus; School Play; Variety Show; Stu Cncl; Ftbl; Trk; Wt Lftg.

BERRY, VICKIE; Milford HS; Milford, MA; (Y); Trs Church Yth Grp; Church Choir; Color Guard; Yrbk Phtg; High Hon Roll; Hon Roll; Extraordinary Christian Stu Of Am 85.

BERRYMAN, SCOTT; Leicester HS; Rochdale, MA; (Y); Church Yth Grp; Band; Chorus; Church Choir; School Play; High Hon Roll; Hon Roll; Organ Perfrmnce.

BERTHIAUME, AMY; Clinton HS; Clinton, MA; (Y); 2/150; Church Yth Grp; Cmnty Wkr; Dance Clb; Intnl Clb; Ski Clb; Chorus; Stage Crew; Variety Show; Yrbk Stf; Rep Soph Cls; Hrvrd Bk Awd Of Boston 85; Commnctns.

BERTOCCHI, JEANNIE M; Everett HS; Everett, MA; (Y); 7/260; Letterman Clb; Varsity Clb; Yrbk Stf; Var Bsktbl; Var Fld Hcky; Var Sftbl; CC Awd; Elks Awd; High Hon Roll; NHS; E Clb 85; Anthony J Sarno Awd 85; Itln Amer Assn Everett 85; Malden Hsop Sch Nrsng; Nrse.

BERTOLINO, KIM; Gloucester HS; Gloucester, MA; (Y); 10/350; Drama Clb; German Clb; School Play; Rep Soph Cls; Im Vllybl; Hon Roll; Lib NHS; Sawyr Mdl 84; High Achvt Ger Awd 85; Ger.

BERTONE, DEAN; Medway JR SR HS; Medway, MA; (Y); Varsity Clb; Yrbk Stf; Crs Cntry; Hon Roll; Prfct Atten Awd; Pres Fitns Awd 82-83; Coll Of Holy Cross; Comp Sci.

BERTOZZI, AMELIA P; Falmouth HS; East Falmouth, MA; (Y); JV Sftbl; High Hon Roll; Hon Roll; Advncd Grp For Coll Courses 85; Intl Bus.

BERUBE, DAVID; Joseph Case HS; Swansea, MA; (Y); 24/209; Trs Drama Clb; Pres Chorus; Jazz Band; School Musical; School Play; Nwsp Rptr; Cit Awd; Hon Roll; NHS; Amer Lgn Schl Awd 85; MA HS Drama Gld Actng Awd 81 & 85; Sthestrn MA U; Acctng.

BERUBE, DENISE; Diman Regional Vo Tech HS; Fall River, MA; (Y); Girl Scts; Hon Roll; Culinary Arts.

BERUBE, JAMES; Salem HS; Salem, MA; (Y); 7/382; Am Leg Boys St; Mathletes; Math Tm; Science Clb; Nwsp Stf; High Hon Roll; NHS; Rensselaer Medal; Engr.

BERUBE, MICHELLE M; Norwood SR HS; Norwood, MA; (Y); 22/377; Band; Mrchg Band; Orch; Symp Band; Hon Roll; Jr NHS; Prncpls Awd 83; Contntl Math Leag 83; Lions Clb All-St Band 85; Math.

BESSETTE, CHRISTINE; Belchertown JR SR HS; Belchertown, MA; (Y); Pep Band; Yrbk Stf; VP Sr Cls; JV Cheerleading; JV Pom Pon; Hon Roll; NHS; Hghst Avr Intro Art 82; Outstndng Achvt Art, Hghst Aver Adv Cermanics 85; Springfield Tech CC; Grphs Dsg.

BETHELL, HUGH R; Manchester HS; Manchester, MA; (Y); Debate Tm; English Clb; NFL; Political Wkr; High Hon Roll; Ntl Merit Schol; Prfct Atten Awd; Church Yth Grp; Math Clb; Math Tm; MA ST Debate Champ 84; Ntl Hnr Soc Pres 84-85; Century III Ldrshp Awd Wnnr 84; Stanford U; Pol Sci.

BETT, CHRISTOPHER J; Winchester HS; Winchester, MA; (Y); 2/285; Am Leg Boys St; Church Choir; VP Church Yth Grp; Sftbl Clb; Nwsp Sprt Ed; JV Socr; Var L Trk; High Hon Roll; Ntl Merit Ltr; Eagle Scout 84; Harvard Book Awd 85; Cornell U; Elec Engnrng.

BETTENCOURT, IRENE; New Bedford HS; New Bedford, MA; (Y); Library Aide; Teachers Aide; Yrbk Stf; Hnrbl Mntn Portugs Tst 84; U Of Lowell; Comp Sci.

BETTINGER, SUSAN; King Philip Reginal HS; Plainville, MA; (S); Church Yth Grp; Var L Gym; Var L Socr; Var L Trk; Hon Roll; NHS; Bus.

BEVERIDGE, JAMES; Acton-Boxborough Regional HS; Acton, MA; (Y); 52/362; Boy Scts; Church Yth Grp; Drama Clb; Stage Crew; Hon Roll; Ntl Merit Ltr; Rochester Inst Tech; Comp Engr.

BEVILACQUA, BRENDA A; Medford HS; Medford, MA; (Y); Hon Roll; Ntl Merit SF; Phslgy Hnr 85; Natl Merit Awd; Suffolk U; Gvrnmnt.

BHAN, RENUKA; Brooks Schl; N Andover, MA; (Y); 2/88; Math Tm; Spanish Clb; Off Sr Cls; Var Capt Bsktbl; Var Fld Hcky; Var Lcrss; High Hon Roll; Ntl Merit SF; RPI Medal Math & Sci 84; Harvard Clb Andover Awd 84; Headmasters & Trustees Awd 85; Harvard U; Sci.

BHATT, DEEPAK; Boston Latin Schl; Boston, MA; (Y); #1 In Class; VP Intnl Clb; Math Tm; VP Science Clb; Orch; High Hon Roll; JETS Awd; NHS; Ntl Merit SF; Prfct Atten Awd; Val; Rensselaer Medal Math & Sci 84; Summer Sci Prog At Ojai Ca 84; MIT; Medicine.

BHATTACHARYA, SUBRATA; Randolph HS; Randolph, MA; (Y); 2/378; Camp Fr Inc; Trs Intnl Clb; Math Clb; Math Tm; Science Clb; Spanish Clb; Varsity Clb; School Musical; Nwsp Bus Mgr; Yrbk Rptr; Suffolk U Bk Awd 85; Med.

BIALOCKI, LESIA MELANIE; Milton HS; Milton Village, MA; (Y); 1/200; Pres AFS; Church Yth Grp; Dance Clb; Pres French Clb; Science Clb; Nwsp Rptr; Nwsp Stf; Ed Lit Mag; Rep Frsh Cls; Rep Soph Cls; Outstndng Stu Awd-Hgh Acadmc Schvt 82-83; Wheaton Bk Awd-Outstndng Schltc Achvt & Ldrshp 84; Harvard-Radcliffe.

BIALY, BETH; Bartlett HS; Webster, MA; (Y); 9/149; Cmnty Wkr; French Clb; FBLA; Office Aide; Spanish Clb; Capt Drm Mjr(t); Yrbk Rptr; Tennis; High Hon Roll; NHS; Acctng.

BIANCHI, BRENDA; Taunton HS; Taunton, MA; (Y); 35/400; Hosp Aide; Office Aide; Red Cross Aide; Band; Stu Cncl; Co-Capt Var Bsktbl; Var Sftbl; High Hon Roll; Hon Roll; NHS; March Dimes, M Fishwick Schlrshp 85; MVP Bsktbl Tm 85; Wheaton Coll; Chem.

BIBEAU, KRISTIN A; Longmeadow HS; Longmeadow, MA; (Y); 21/275; JA; VP Keywanettes; Symp Band; Rep Stu Cncl; Fld Hcky; Lcrss; Vllybl; High Hon Roll; Kiwanis Awd; NHS; Longmeadow Maternal Assn Scholar 85; U MA; Mth.

BIBEAULT, MAUREEN; Bishop Feehan HS; Attleboro, MA; (Y); 33/253; Cmnty Wkr; Chorus; Yrbk Stf; Im Coach Actv; Var Crs Cntry; Var Trk; French Hon Soc; High Hon Roll; Hon Roll; NHS; Div II Crs Cntry All Str Tm 84 & 85; Awd Cert Achvt Outstndg Prfmnce Chem 85; Silv Mdl Hghst Eng Avg; Mech Engrng.

BIELLO, MELISSA; Marian HS; Milford, MA; (Y); 77/177; Dance Clb; Hon Roll; NEDT Awd; Advrtsmnt.

BIER, KAREN; Westwood HS; Westwood, MA; (Y); 14/250; AFS; Church Yth Grp; School Play; Ed Lit Mag; Hon Roll; NHS; Ntl Merit Ltr; Key Clb; Library Aide; Teachers Aide; Julia Babineau Awd NHS Chrctr 85; Lutheran Yth Fllwshp New England Rep 83-85; Sunday Schl Tchr 83-85; Concordia Coll; Tchg.

BIKALES, THOMAS J; Belmont HS; Lincoln, MA; (Y); Cmnty Wkr; Political Wkr; Nwsp Ed-Chief; Nwsp Rptr; Lit Mag; JV Socr; Var Trk; High Hon Roll; Ntl Merit SF; Natl Cum Laude Soc 84; LAW.

BILODEAU, MICHELLE A; Salem HS; Salem, MA; (Y); 45/350; Hosp Aide; School Musical; School Play; Stage Crew; Yrbk Stf; Hon Roll.

BINDER, RICHELLE; Haverhill HS; Haverhill, MA; (Y); Color Guard; Cit Awd; High Hon Roll; NHS; Ntl Merit Schol; Key Clb; Spanish Clb.

BING-ZAREMBA, ADRIAN CHARLES; St Marys HS; Southwick, MA; (Y); 5/60; Am Leg Boys St; Ski Clb; Spanish Clb; Nwsp Rptr; JV L Socr; Hon Roll; NHS; Engrng.

BINGHAM, ALEXANDRA; Groton Schl; Alexandria, VA; (Y); Cmnty Wkr; Political Wkr; Teachers Aide; Var Fld Hcky; Var Ice Hcky; JV Lcrss; JV Tennis; Hon Roll; Ntl Merit Ltr; Magna Cum Laude Diploma 85; Hnrb Mntn Teen Mag Cont 83; U VA; Latin Amer Studs.

BINNEY, YLANA; Hingham HS; Plymouth, MA; (Y); 98/335; Church Yth Grp; Cmnty Wkr; Debate Tm; GAA; Hosp Aide; Yrbk Stf; Lcrss; Sftbl; Hnr Rll; Pre-Law.

BIONELLI, JUDY; Malden HS; Malden, MA; (Y); Church Yth Grp; Drama Clb; Key Clb; Acpl Chr; Chorus; Church Choir; Madrigals; Variety Show; Music.

BIRCHLER, CHERYL; Framingham South HS; Framingham, MA; (Y); 90/243; Drama Clb; Spanish Clb; Chorus; Stage Crew; Yrbk Stf; JV Bsktbl; JV Var Crs Cntry; Var Capt Trk; High Hon Roll; Hon Roll; Mst Imprvd in Track 84; St Anselm Coll; Nrs.

BIRD, VINNY; Boston Latin HS; Boston, MA; (Y); 69/300; JA; High Hon Roll; Hon Roll.

BIRNSCHEIN, TIMOTHY A; Watertown SR HS; Watertown, MA; (Y); 5/273; Rep Am Leg Boys St; Pres Drama Clb; Trs JA; Madrigals; School Play; Nwsp Stf; High Hon Roll; NHS; Ntl Merit Ltr; Church Yth Grp; Acad Achvt Awd 84.

BISCOTTI, MICHAEL; Monument-Mountain Regional HS; Gr Barrington, MA; (Y); French Clb; Varsity Clb; School Musical; School Play; Stage Crew; Variety Show; Yrbk Bus Mgr; Yrbk Stf; Stu Cncl; Capt Ftbl; Frnch Achvt Awd 84; Peer Fcltng Awd 85; Bio.

BISHOP, RACHELL; Bedford HS; Bedford, MA; (Y); 43/213; Church Yth Grp; ROTC; High Hon Roll; Hon Roll; SAR Awd; VFW Awd; ROTC Ldrshp Awd 83-84; Georgetown U; Pre-Med.

BISHOP, STEVEN; Wachusett Regional HS; Holden, MA; (Y); Varsity Clb; JV Capt Bsktbl; Var Capt Socr; Dist Sccr MVP 84; Army Sccr MVP 84; Vrsty Team MVP 83-84; Sprts Mgmt.

BISSONNETTE, JACLYN; Hudson HS; Hudson, MA; (Y); Church Yth Grp; Cmnty Wkr; Pep Clb; Ski Clb; Chorus; School Musical; Yrbk Stf; Trs Frsh Cls; Trs Soph Cls; Trs Jr Cls; Photo Wnr Worcester Art Museum 85; 3rd Pl Natl Hstry Day 84; Grphc Dsgn.

BISSONNETTE, JILL; Cathedral HS; Springfield, MA; (Y); Dance Clb; Math Clb; Teachers Aide; Chorus; Hon Roll; Bay Path JC; Bus.

BISTANY, MARIE; Cushing Acad; Ashburnham, MA; (Y); Am Leg Aux Girls St; FBLA; Yrbk Ed-Chief; Off Sr Cls; Stu Cncl; High Hon Roll; Hon Roll; NHS; Val; Psych.

BIXBY, BARBARA; Westport HS; Westport, MA; (Y); 2/150; Church Yth Grp; Pres French Clb; Intnl Clb; VP JA; Yrbk Stf; Sec Pres Stu Cncl; Var Fld Hcky; High Hon Roll; NHS; Ntl Merit Ltr; Georgetown; Intl Bus.

BLACHE, BRIAN; Methuen HS; Methuen, MA; (Y); U MA; Law Enfrcmnt.

BLACK, EILEEN; Doherty Memorial HS; Worcester, MA; (Y); Church Yth Grp; Chorus; Variety Show; Sftbl; High Hon Roll; Hon Roll; SITE 85-86; Nrsng.

BLACK, JAMES L; Algonquin Regional HS; Northboro, MA; (Y); 4/210; Am Leg Boys St; Church Yth Grp; Nwsp Rptr; JV Bsktbl; Stat Ftbl; Mgr(s); Score Keeper; Hon Roll; NHS; Ntl Merit Ltr; Pol Sci.

BLACK, ROBERT A; Methven HS; Methuen, MA; (Y); 6/336; Boys Clb Am; Boy Scts; Spanish Clb; High Hon Roll; Hon Roll; NHS; Spanish NHS; U Of MA; Engl.

BLACK, SHELLY; Framingham South HS; Framingham, MA; (Y); 33/260; GAA; Latin Clb; Rep Frsh Cls; Rep Soph Cls; Rep Jr Cls; Rep Sr Cls; Sec Stu Cncl; Capt L Bsktbl; L Socr; JV Sftbl; Natl Latin Cum Laude.

BLACKBURN, MARIA; Boston Latin HS; Boston, MA; (Y); Drama Clb; VP JA; Band; Yrbk Stf; JV Socr; JV Trk; Hon Roll; Ntl Merit Ltr; Fdlty Awd 82; Law.

BLACKER, DINA; Sharon HS; Sharon, MA; (Y); Spanish Clb; Nwsp Rptr; Nwsp Stf; Yrbk Stf; Fld Hcky; Trk; Hon Roll; Framingham ST Term Paper Comptn 85.

BLACKETT, CARRIE; Reading Memorial HS; Reading, MA; (Y); Camp Fr Inc; Dance Clb; Teachers Aide; Trk; High Hon Roll; Hon Roll; Law.

BLACKINGTON, SUE; Haverhill HS; Haverhill, MA; (Y); Church Yth Grp; French Clb; Hosp Aide; Letterman Clb; Spanish Clb; Varsity Clb; Chorus; School Play; Var L Trk; Cit Awd; Westfield ST Coll; Educ.

BLACKMER, TRACY; Boston Latin HS; Jamaica Pl, MA; (Y); 17/335; VP Key Clb; Concert Band; Yrbk Phtg; Ed Yrbk Stf; Ed Lit Mag; Swmmng; NHS; Pres Schlr; Hosp Aide; Red Cross Aide; Lawrence Mdl For Ptry 85; Capen Schlrshp For Music 85; Yale U; Pre-Med.

BLACKWELL, ROBIN; Moument Mountain Regional HS; Gt Barrington, MA; (Y); Band; JV Bsktbl; Var L Socr; Var L Sftbl; Physcl Eductn.

BLADES, LAURA L; Bellingham Memorial HS; Bellingham, MA; (Y); DECA; Drama Clb; Hosp Aide; Hst OEA; Ski Clb; Yrbk Stf; Stu Cncl; U Of NH; Psychlgy.

BLAIR, DOUG; Bedford HS; Watertown, MA; (Y); Im Cheerleading; Var Capt Crs Cntry; Var L Trk; Hon Roll; Estrn MA Sprng Trck Champ 85; Capt Dual Cnty Lge Cross Cntry Champ 84; Estrn MA Winter Trck Champ 85; Rochestr Inst Tech; Cmptr Engnr.

BLAIR, LAURA L; Doherty Memorial HS; Worcester, MA; (Y); Church Yth Grp; Dance Clb; French Clb; FHA; Girl Scts; Ski Clb; Chorus; Variety Show; Nwsp Rptr; Var Trk; Career Day Essy 85; Clark U; Mktg.

BLAIR, PETER J; Foxboro HS; Foxboro, MA; (Y); 5/243; Am Leg Boys St; VP Trs Church Yth Grp; Model UN; Ski Clb; Rep Stu Cncl; Var Socr; Trk; Hon Roll; NHS; Ntl Merit Ltr; Engr.

BLAKE, CARYN L; Holyoke HS; Holyoke, MA; (Y); Dance Clb; Office Aide; Spanish Clb; Teachers Aide; Nwsp Rptr; Nwsp Stf; Yrbk Stf; Var Cheerleading; JV Tennis; Hon Roll.

BLAKE, SANDRA; Norwell HS; Norwell, MA; (Y); 5/180; Dance Clb; Drama Clb; French Clb; Band; School Musical; Nwsp Stf; Yrbk Stf; JV Socr; High Hon Roll; NHS.

BLAKE, WILLIAM J; Cathedral HS; Springfield, MA; (Y); 93/516; Camera Clb; Letterman Clb; Yrbk Phtg; L Capt Trk; Im Wt Lftg; Ntl Merit Ltr; Franklin Pierce Coll; Adv.

BLANCHARD, CHERYL A; Bourne HS; Monument Beach, MA; (Y); 2/190; Debate Tm; Math Tm; Concert Band; Mrchg Band; Yrbk Ed-Chief; Hon Roll; Jr NHS; NHS; Ntl Merit Ltr; Sal; Wellesley Bk Awd 85; JR Clss Mrshll 85; Pre-Law.

BLANCHARD, KEVIN; Blackstone Valley Tech HS; Uxbridge, MA; (Y); High Hon Roll; Hon Roll; Comp Engrng.

BLANCHARD, MICHAEL; New Bedford HS; New Bedford, MA; (Y); Computer Clb; Exploring; Chess Clb; JA; Hon Roll; Hnry Mntn Art Shw 85; Comp Pgmng.

BLANCHETTE, MARK; Shepherd Hill Regional HS; Dudley, MA; (Y); Cmnty Wkr; Stu Cncl; Var L Crs Cntry; Var L Trk; Hon Roll; Science.

BLANK, ERIC; Deerfield Acad; Golden, CO; (Y); 2/250; Boy Scts; Pres Computer Clb; Pres Debate Tm; Pres Drama Clb; Intnl Clb; Sec Model UN; Science Clb; Speech Tm; Teachers Aide; School Play; Deerfld Acad Mdl UN 85-86; Egl Sct 83; Big Bros-Sis Assn 84-86; Frgn Affrs.

BLASER, CHRISTOPHER J; Lunenburg HS; Lunenburg, MA; (Y); Am Leg Boys St; School Play; Rep Frsh Cls; Rep Soph Cls; Rep Jr Cls; Rep Sr Cls; JV Var Bsktbl; High Hon Roll; Hon Roll; NHS; Acctng.

BLASI, DIANNE; Wakefield HS; Wakefield, MA; (Y); Rep Stu Cncl; Var Fld Hcky; Var Tennis; Hon Roll; Church Yth Grp; Varsity Clb; Variety Show; Im Bsktbl; MVP Awd In Fld Hcky 84; Unsung Hero Awd In Tennis 85.

BLATCHFORD, KEVIN R; Gloucester HS; Magnolia, MA; (Y); 59/320; Cmnty Wkr; Trs Jr Cls; Bsbl; Co-Capt Bsktbl; Tennis; Hon Roll; Athl Schlrshp Awd, Bsktbl All Star, Bst All Around Grd SR 85; Athl Assoc Bsktbl MVP 84-85; Mgmnt.

BLATCHLEY, ELIZABETH; Hudson HS; Hudson, MA; (Y); 4/150; Church Yth Grp; Drama Clb; Pep Clb; Ski Clb; Chorus; School Musical; Yrbk Stf; Var Capt Tennis; High Hon Roll; Jr NHS; Spnsh Awd; Englsh Usag A-P Commn Err Awd; Phy Ed Awd Jr Grls.

BLAUS, MARKUS M; Masconomet Regional HS; Middleton, MA; (Y); 60/200; Am Leg Boys St; School Play; Hon Roll; German Exchng Prog 84; Advertsmnt.

BLEAKNEY, AMY; Nashoka Regional HS; Stow, MA; (S); DECA; Drama Clb; School Musical; Pres Frsh Cls; VP Sr Cls; L Cheerleading; Var Tennis; Hon Roll; Outstndng Frshmn Awd 82; Awd Excel Chrldng 84; Horticultural Soc Comp 2nd Pl 81; Educ.

BLEAU, NORMAND; Holy Name Central Catholic HS; Shrewsbury, MA; (Y); 56/272; Trs Church Yth Grp; Hosp Aide; School Musical; Stage Crew; Var Mgr(s); Readg & Rhetorc 83.

BLEIWAS, MICHAEL; Randolph HS; Randolph, MA; (Y); Computer Clb; Drama Clb; French Clb; JA; Ski Clb; Socr; Hon Roll; NHS; Ntl Merit Ltr; Comp Sci.

BLICK, JACQUELINE; Boston Technical HS; Mattapan, MA; (Y); 61/219; Church Yth Grp; Girl Scts; Chorus; Church Choir; Nwsp Stf; Cit Awd; Hon Roll; Davis Gross Awd 83; U MA Boston; Acctng.

BLISS, JOHN; Blackstone Vly Regnl Vo Tech HS; Uxbridge, MA; (Y); Dance Clb; Rep Stu Cncl; Trk; Hon Roll; Autlo Techncn.

BLONIARZ, TODD MICHAEL; Gateway Regional HS; Blandford, MA; (Y); 2/81; School Play; Rep Stu Cncl; Var JV Bsbl; Cit Awd; Hon Roll; Lion Awd; NHS; Prfct Atten Awd; Pres Schlr; Sal; 1st Prz Gateway Pre Calcls Math Leag Comptn 84; 2nd Prz Ladies Aux VFW Dist 8 Patriotsm Art Cntst 85; Clark U Worcester MA; Math.

BLOUNT, JOHN K; Berkshire Schl; Mill River, MA; (S); 4/100; Sec Soph Cls; Sec Jr Cls; Capt JV Bsbl; Capt JV Ftbl; French Clb; Yrbk Stf; Ice Hcky; High Hon Roll; Awd For Writing 85; Jrnlsm.

BOBALA, ROBERT; Chicopee HS; Chicopee, MA; (Y); 8/250; Church Yth Grp; Yrbk Stf; Sec Jr Cls; Sec Sr Cls; JV Socr; High Hon Roll; NHS.

BOCIAN, KRISTINE; St Peter Marian C C HS; Rutland, MA; (S); 7/171; Boys Clb Am; Teachers Aide; Yrbk Stf; L Bsktbl; L Crs Cntry; Hon Roll; Jr NHS; NHS; Ntl Hnr Scty 84-85; Hahnemann Hosp Schl Nrs; Nrs.

BODENDORF, DAVID; Westfield HS; Westfield, MA; (Y); 33/327; Var Golf; Envrnmntl.

BODIE, MELINDA M; Leominster HS; Leominster, MA; (Y); JV Var Bsktbl; JV Var Sftbl; High Hon Roll; Hon Roll; NHS.

BODIO, LISA A; Milford HS; Milford, MA; (Y); 64/350; Church Yth Grp; Dance Clb; Drama Clb; Exploring; Girl Scts; Key Clb; Pep Clb; School Musical; Yrbk Stf; Hon Roll; Regis Coll Schlrshp 85; Dnc Capers 1st 2nd & Hnrb Mntn 85; Tlnt Amer Semi Fnls 1st 2nd & 3rd Pl 85; Regis Coll; Bio.

BODURTHA, KRISTINE; Agawam HS; Agawam, MA; (Y); Art Clb; Church Yth Grp; Band; Church Choir; Yrbk Stf; Hon Roll; Child Psych.

BODWITCH, SUSAN; Triton Regional HS; Newbury, MA; (Y); AFS; Drama Clb; Hosp Aide; Concert Band; Mrchg Band; Variety Show; Yrbk Phtg; Yrbk Stf; Hon Roll; NHS; All Amer Hall Of Fame Band Hnrs; Ldrs Clb; Thrpy.

BOEHM, KATE; Longmeadow HS; Longmeadow, MA; (Y); 145/287; Camera Clb; Ski Clb; JV Capt Bsktbl; Stat Socr; Var Sftbl; Hon Roll; Phys Thrpy.

BOEHNER, APRIL LYNN; Taunton HS; Taunton, MA; (Y); Cmnty Wkr; Office Aide; Yrbk Stf; Southeastern MA U; Acctng.

BOERMEESTER, DANIEL; Billerica Memorial HS; Billerica, MA; (Y); 58/500; French Clb; JV Capt Bsbl; JV Ftbl; Hon Roll.

BOERSMA, MATT; Phillips Acad; Steamboat Spgs, CO; (Y); Model UN; School Play; Nwsp Ed-Chief; Hon Roll; Ntl Merit SF; French Clb; Key Clb; Band; Concert Band; Mrchg Band; Pol Econ.

BOGER, ROBERT E; Mansfield HS; Mansfield, MA; (Y); 32/174; Trs Church Yth Grp; Drama Clb; Spanish Clb; Chorus; School Musical; School Play; Socr; Hon Roll; Lion Awd; Suffolk U; Govt.

BOGUSLAWSKI, JUDITH; Turners Falls HS; Turners Falls, MA; (Y); 1/96; Computer Clb; Spanish Clb; Varsity Clb; Yrbk Phtg; Yrbk Stf; Soph Cls; L Crs Cntry; L Trk; High Hon Roll; Jr NHS; Exclnc In Math, Englsh & Frgn Lng 85; Pred Acdmc Ftns Awd 85; Stu Of Mnth 85; Bentley Coll; Accntnt.

BOILEAU, MICHELLE; Cathedral HS; Chicopee, MA; (Y); 4/516; Office Aide; Teachers Aide; Frsh Cls; Gym; Capt Trk; NHS; Bio.

BOISSELLE, VINCENT; Holyoke Catholic HS; Chicopee, MA; (Y); 21/140; Chess Clb; Computer Clb; Off Drama Clb; Exploring; Rep Frsh Cls; Hon Roll; Physics.

BOISVERT, KEITH; Leicester HS; Cherry Valley, MA; (S); French Clb; Tennis.

BOISVERT, SCOTT W; Drury SR HS; North Adams, MA; (Y); 2/185; Am Leg Boys St; Computer Clb; Pep Clb; Concert Band; Mrchg Band; L Golf; High Hon Roll; VP NHS; Ntl Merit SF; NEDT Awd; RPI; Sci.

BOLDIGA IV, JOSEPH PAUL; Bishop Stang HS; E Freetown, MA; (Y); 30/215; Yrbk Ed-Chief; Stu Cncl; Bsktbl; High Hon Roll; Hon Roll; Hist Acdmc Awd; Sociology Acdmc Awd; Accntng Acdmc Awd; Newbury JC; Culinary Arts.

BOLTON, CHRISTOPHER A; Mt Greylock Regional HS; Williamstown, MA; (Y); 3/100; Chorus; Madrigals; School Musical; Nwsp Stf; Lit Mag; NHS; Ntl Merit SF; Gym; Socr; Hon Roll; Japan-US Senate Exchng Schlr 84; Rensselaer Polytchnc Inst Mdl 84; Engr.

BOLTON, JULIE; Dana Hall HS; Millis, MA; (Y); Pres Church Yth Grp; Cmnty Wkr; Pres French Clb; Girl Scts; Church Choir; Yrbk Stf; Hon Roll; Jr NHS; ROTC,Navy.

BOLTON, TAMI A; Franklin HS; Franklin, MA; (Y); DECA; OEA.

BONAK, MICHAEL STEVEN; Monoment Mountain Regional HS; Housatonic, MA; (Y); Boy Scts; Drama Clb; ROTC; Band; Concert Band; Jazz Band; Mrchg Band; School Musical; Yrbk Stf; Golf; Law.

BONCZYK, LORI A; Holy Name CC HS; Worcester, MA; (Y); 40/268; Church Yth Grp; Var L Bsktbl; Var L Fld Hcky; Var Capt Sftbl; Hon Roll; Jr NHS; Religion III Awd 84-85; Bus.

BOND IV, GEORGE W; Leominster HS; Leominster, MA; (Y); Am Leg Boys St; School Musical; School Play; Mgr Stage Crew; Yrbk Bus Mgr; Rep Frsh Cls; Rep Soph Cls; Rep Jr Cls; JV Socr; Hon Roll; Pre Med.

BOND, KIM; Framingham South HS; Framingham, MA; (S); 41/270; Cmnty Wkr; Dance Clb; Chorus; School Musical; Variety Show; Var Cheerleading; Var Golf; Hon Roll; NHS.

BONINI, JOHN; Westfield HS; Westfield, MA; (Y); 7/375; Church Yth Grp; Capt Var Bsbl; Var Bsktbl; Var Ftbl; Hon Roll; NHS.

BONK, CHRISTA L; Oakmont Reginal HS; Westminster, MA; (Y); 30/127; Bsktbl; Score Keeper; Sftbl; Hon Roll; Presdntl Schlrshp 85; Amer Lgn Schlrshp 85; Knights Of Columbus Schlrshp 85; New England U; Physcl Thrpy.

BONNER, MARY; Notre Dame Acad; Braintree, MA; (Y); Math Tm; Chorus; Stage Crew; Im Bsktbl; Var Crs Cntry; Trk; MVP JV Crs Cntry Tm 82-83; Cath Lg All Star Hgh Jmp 85; Cert Awd Crfts 85; Bus Mktg.

BONNETTE, DANIEL; South High Community Schl; Worcester, MA; (S); Am Leg Boys St; Yrbk Sprt Ed; VP Jr Cls; Stu Cncl; Var Bsbl; Var Capt Ftbl; Var Trk; Wt Lftg; Hon Roll; Pres NHS; Hugh O Brien Ldrshp Conf 84; Acadmc Olympc Tm 84; Stdnt Govt Day Prog Boston 85; Bus.

BONSIGNORE, FRANK; Arlington Catholic HS; Arlington, MA; (Y); 58/137; Boy Scts; Drama Clb; Math Clb; Office Aide; Spanish Clb; JV Bsktbl; JV Bowling; Merrimack Coll; Acctng.

BONVIN, JEANINE; Franklin HS; Franklin, MA; (Y); Rep Jr Cls; Hon Roll; Cert Appr Math Tutorng 84-85; Ed.

BOOKER, JENNIFER; Dartmouth HS; S Dartmouth, MA; (Y); 8/246; Sec AFS; JA; Office Aide; Teachers Aide; NHS; Pres Schlr; Southeastern MA U; Nrsg.

BOORSTEIN, ALEXA; Newton N HS; Newton, MA; (Y); Sec Exploring; JCL; Math Tm; Band; Mrchg Band; Rep Jr Cls; Var Cheerleading; Stat Gym; Mgr(s); Hon Roll; Ltrs Athl Trnr 84-85; Phy Thrpy.

BOOTH, BETHANY; Bridgewater-Raynham Regional HS; Raynham, MA; (Y); French Clb; Math Tm; Science Clb; Nwsp Stf; Stu Cncl; Bsktbl; High Hon Roll; Pres NHS; Stu Adv Cncl 85-86; Sci Humnties Symp 85; Human Svc.

BOOTH, CAROL; Barnstable HS; Barnstable, MA; (S); Church Yth Grp; Drama Clb; Hosp Aide; Acpl Chr; Chorus; Church Choir; Orch; School Musical; Hon Roll; Slvr Acad Cert 84; All-Cape Music Fstvl Awds 83-85; Psych.

BOOTHROYD, RENEE; Newburyport HS; Newburyport, MA; (S); 1/209; Am Leg Aux Girls St; JCL; Math Tm; Model UN; Q&S; Yrbk Sprt Ed; Lit Mag; Capt Socr; Trk; Super Of Schls Cert Acadmc Excllnc 84; Harvard Bk Prz 84; Amercn Clscl Leag Latin Exam Cert, Gold Key; Biomed Engr.

BORDEAU, BRIAN; Hoosac Valley HS; Adams, MA; (Y); High Hon Roll; Hon Roll.

BORDIERI, PAULA; Reading Memorial HS; Reading, MA; (Y); Hosp Aide; Nwsp Rptr; Rep Soph Cls; Rep Jr Cls; Rep Sr Cls; Sec Stu Cncl; Capt Tennis; French Hon Soc; High Hon Roll; NHS; Mnt Holyoke Awd 85; JR Mrshll 85; Peer Tutorng Awd 85.

BOREN, CARL; Bishop Feehan HS; Mansfield, MA; (Y); 70/260; Aud/Vis; Church Yth Grp; Spanish Clb; Teachers Aide; Band; Concert Band; Mrchg Band; Nwsp Stf; High Hon Roll; Hon Roll; Comp.

BORGES, PAULA; Somerville HS; Somerville, MA; (Y); Church Yth Grp; Spanish Clb; Nwsp Rptr; Yrbk Rptr; Off Soph Cls; Hon Roll; 1st Prz Sprg Wrtg Fest 85; Nrsg.

BOSCHEN, SHARON; Silver Lake Reg HS; Halifax, MA; (Y); 40/465; Church Yth Grp; French Clb; Girl Scts; Library Aide; Chorus; Trk; NHS; Scholar Regis Coll 85-86; Regis Coll; Ed.

BOSWELL, KERRY M; Cardinal Spellman HS; Brockton, MA; (Y); 14/203; Hosp Aide; School Musical; High Hon Roll; NHS; NEDT Awd; Pres Schlr; Rotary Awd; Sci Fair; Mc Donalds Corp Schlrshp 85; Knights Of Columbus Schlrshp 85; Boston U; Bio.

BOSWORTH, LORNA; Brockton Christian Regional HS; Mansfield, MA; (S); Trs Church Yth Grp; Drama Clb; Chorus; Church Choir; School Play; Yrbk Stf; VP Jr Cls; VP Sr Cls; High Hon Roll; Ltry Jrnl Poetry Awd 84; Prncpl & Bio Awd 83-84; Gordon; Marine Bio.

BOTELHO, ALEXANDRE; B M C Durfee High Schl Of Fall River; Fall River, MA; (Y); High Hon Roll; Hon Roll; NHS; St Scholar Stud Adv Alg & Calc I 84 & 85; St Scholar Stud Calc II & Calc II 85 & 86; Chem Engrng.

BOTELHO, JEFFREY; New Bedford HS; New Bedford, MA; (Y); 31/688; Church Yth Grp; Political Wkr; Bsbl; Bsktbl; Crs Cntry; Trk; High Hon Roll; Hon Roll; Jr NHS; NHS; Phys Thrpy.

BOTOLINO, LISA J; Arlington HS; Arlington, MA; (Y); 55/375; Church Yth Grp; Girl Scts; Mathletes; Church Choir; Nwsp Stf; Yrbk Stf; JV Vllybl; Hon Roll; NHS; Wmns Clb Schlrshp 85; MA ST Schlrshp 85; Suffolk U; Acctng.

BOTROS, DAVID; Burlington HS; Burlington, MA; (Y); 12/315; Computer Clb; Exploring; Math Clb; Science Clb; Hon Roll; JETS Awd; NHS; Chmstry Awd 84; Aerospace Engrng.

BOUCHARD, JULIE; St Bernardis C C HS; Leominster, MA; (S); 14/173; Art Clb; Church Yth Grp; Drama Clb; Latin Clb; School Play; Rep Frsh Cls; Rep Soph Cls; Rep Jr Cls; Tennis; Hon Roll; Pre Med.

BOUCHARD, LISA; Durfee HS; Fall River, MA; (Y); Drama Clb; French Clb; JA; Law.

BOUCHARD, SANDRA; B M C Durfee HS; Fall River, MA; (Y); Cmnty Wkr; Computer Clb; Drama Clb; Library Aide; Political Wkr; School Musical; Sftbl; BCC; Comp Engr.

BOUCHER, JOHN; St Domenic Savio HS; Chelsea, MA; (Y); Bsktbl; JV Ftbl; JV Ice Hcky; JV Trk; MA Maritime; Engrng.

BOUCHER, LISA; Southbridge HS; Southridge, MA; (Y); Chorus; School Musical; Hon Roll; Alt Concert Choir; Hnr Roll; Typng Awd; Regis Coll; Law.

BOUCHER, LISA M; Millis Public HS; Millis, MA; (Y); Art Clb; Church Yth Grp; Dance Clb; 4-H; Intnl Clb; School Play; Variety Show; Bridgewater ST Coll; Englsih.

BOUCHER, LYNNE; Methuen HS; Methuen, MA; (Y); 22/346; Church Yth Grp; Intnl Clb; Model UN; Pep Clb; Sec Jr Cls; Sec Sr Cls; Var L Bsktbl; Var L Fld Hcky; Hon Roll; Rep NHS; Elem Educ.

BOUCHER, RENEE; Holyoke Catholic HS; Chicopee, MA; (Y); 15/128; French Clb; Math Clb; Stage Crew; Lit Mag; Hon Roll; Typing I & II Excllnc Awd 84-85; Stngrphy I Excllnc Awd 85; Holyok Cmnty Coll; Exctv Sec.

BOUCHIE JR, GEORGE E; Boston College HS; Medford, MA; (Y); 38/250; Boy Scts; Hosp Aide; Ski Clb; Concert Band; Hon Roll; NHS; Ftbl; Trk; Vllybl; Eagle Scout 82.

BOUCIAS, BRANDON; Mohawk Trail Reg HS; Charlemont, MA; (Y); 12/148; Art Clb; Letterman Clb; Ski Clb; Spanish Clb; Varsity Clb; Nwsp Rptr; Frsh Cls; Var Crs Cntry; Var Socr; Var Trk; VP Frshmn Cls; Vrsty Ski Team; U Of RI; Marine Bio.

BOUDREAU, DONNA; Arlington SR HS; Arlington, MA; (Y); Trs Library Aide; Acpl Chr; Chorus; School Play; SADD; Alcohol Awareness; Middlesex CC; Exec Sec.

BOUDREAU, JANINE; Wakefield HS; Wakefield, MA; (S); 3/372; Church Yth Grp; Pres French Clb; JA; Key Clb; Yrbk Stf; Mgr(s); JV Var Socr; Hon Roll; Hosp Aide; Soph Cls; Chncllrs Tlnt Awd Pgm Schlrshp 85; Dartmouth Coll Bk Clb Awd 85; Coachs Sccr Awd 83-84; U Of NH; Bus Mgmt.

BOUDREAU, KEVIN; Malden Catholic HS; Everett, MA; (Y); Trs Church Yth Grp; Cmnty Wkr; French Clb; Stage Crew; VP Stu Cncl; JV Crs Cntry; Ice Hcky; Var Trk.

BOUDREAU, LAURIANA G; Holy Name CCHS; Whitinsville, MA; (Y); 26/272; Church Yth Grp; Drama Clb; Science Clb; Ski Clb; Teachers Aide; School Play; Hon Roll; NHS; Prfct Atten Awd; Pre-Med.

BOUDREAU, MARILYN ANN; Notre Dame Academy; Worcester, MA; (Y); Cmnty Wkr; Drama Clb; French Clb; Library Aide; Church Choir; Stage Crew; Variety Show; Nwsp Sprt Ed; Elks Awd; MA Commnwlth Schlr 85; Worcester Polytech Inst; Chem.

BOUDREAU, MONIQUE; Arlington Catholic HS; Waltham, MA; (Y); 52/148; Art Clb; Church Choir; School Musical; Variety Show; Yrbk Stf; Cum Laude Natl Latin Exm 83; Cmmnctn Disorders.

BOUDREAU, PAUL SCOTT; New Bedford HS; New Bedford, MA; (Y); 150/600; JCL; Varsity Clb; JV Bsbl; JV Var Ftbl; Gridiron Clb Schlrshp 85; Westfield ST Coll; Crmnl Jstc.

BOUDROT, PAMELA A; Dedham HS; Dedham, MA; (Y); 130/325; Stat Aud/Vis; Pres Drama Clb; Pres Exploring; Chorus; School Musical; School Play; Stage Crew; Variety Show; Nwsp Stf; Yrbk Stf; Odd Flws/Rebeccas Essay Cntst Wnnr 83:Pipe Piux XII Mdl Study Religion 82; Outstndng Soloist Awd 84; Theatre Arts.

BOULANGER, AIMEE; Monson JR/SR HS; Monson, MA; (Y); 8/86; Rep Am Leg Aux Girls St; Drama Clb; French Clb; School Musical; School Play; Yrbk Ed-Chief; JV Var Cheerleading; Hon Roll; NHS; Bst Actrss One-Act Plays 83-85; Bst Spprtng Actrss One-Act Plays 84-85; Engl.

BOULANGER, DANIELLE; N Andover HS; North Andover, MA; (Y); 24/243; AFS; Am Leg Aux Girls St; Drama Clb; Q&S; Pres Chorus; School Musical; School Play; Nwsp Stf; VP Frsh Cls; VP Soph Cls; Natl Arion Music Awd; Natl Schl Choral Awd; Outstndng Achvt Acad Music; Gettysburg Coll; Bus Mgmnt.

BOULANGER, SHARON; New Bedford HS; New Bedford, MA; (Y); French Awd 85; Psych.

BOULGER, SEAN; Xaverian Brothers HS; Norwood, MA; (S); 2/240; Stage Crew; Nwsp Ed-Chief; High Hon Roll; NHS; Ntl Merit Ltr; Drama Clb; Jr NHS; Xaverian Bros Schlrshp 82; Holy Cross Coll Bk Awd 84; NCTE Achvt Awd & Alumni Schlrshp 83-84; Law.

BOUMITRI, RITA; Brockton HS; Brockton, MA; (Y); Church Yth Grp; Cmnty Wkr; Girl Scts; Hosp Aide; Variety Show; Bsbl; Var Sftbl; Hon Roll; Bridgewater ST Coll; Psych.

BOURASSA, PAUL; Methuen HS; Methuen, MA; (Y); 8/390; Am Leg Boys St; French Clb; Intnl Clb; Model UN; Var Wrstlng; French Hon Soc; High Hon Roll; Hon Roll; NHS.

BOURGEOIS, CHERYL; Matignon HS; Waltham, MA; (Y); Church Yth Grp; GAA; Latin Clb; Ski Clb; Spanish Clb; Teachers Aide; JV Tennis; Hon Roll.

BOURGEOIS, GAYNOR; Murdock HS; Winchendon, MA; (Y); 7/120; Model UN; Yrbk Ed-Chief; Stu Cncl; Var Capt Fld Hcky; Var L Sftbl; NHS; Yrbk Stf; Off Frsh Cls; JV Bsktbl; Hon Roll; Wachusett Lg All Star Fld Hcky, JR Usher 84-85; Am Leg Pstr Cont 2nd Pl 84-85; Regnl Stu Advsry Cnslr.

BOURGEOIS, RICHARD M; Joseph Case HS; Swansea, MA; (Y); Am Leg Boys St; Church Yth Grp; French Clb; Var L Bsbl; Var L Bsktbl; Var L Ftbl; High Hon Roll; NHS; Proj Excel 84; Engrng.

BOUTIN, BERNADETTE; Bishop Connolly HS; Fall River, MA; (Y); Pres Church Yth Grp; Drama Clb; Chorus; Church Choir; School Play; Nwsp Stf; High Hon Roll; Hon Roll; Piano Rctl Comptn Trphy 80; SMU Grnt Voice Lssns 80-81; SMU; Music.

BOUTWELL, LISA; Woburn HS; Woburn, MA; (S); 68/511; Church Yth Grp; French Clb; Hosp Aide; Church Choir; Color Guard; Stu Cncl; High Hon Roll; Hon Roll; Jr NHS; French Exchng 85; Tumbling 82-85; Phy Thrpy.

BOUVIER, LYNNE; St Bernards Central Catholic HS; Leominster, MA; (S); 3/162; Camera Clb; Drama Clb; Mgr School Play; Rep Stu Cncl; JV Var Socr; Var Tennis; High Hon Roll; Hon Roll; NHS; Vet.

BOUVIER, THOMAS M; Acton-Boxborough Regional HS; Acton, MA; (Y); 45/343; Var Ice Hcky; Var Lcrss; Var Capt Socr; Hon Roll; NHS; MVP Sccr Tournmnt 84; DCL Hckey & Sccr All Star 84-85; Bst All Arnd Male Athlte 84-85; U Of MA; Mngmnt.

BOVA, MARIA; Wakefield Memorial HS; Wakefield, MA; (S); 31/305; VP OEA; School Musical; School Play; Variety Show; Yrbk Stf; High Hon Roll; Hon Roll; NHS; Schlrshp To Burdett Schl 85; 1st Pl Steno I 83; 1st Pl Steno II 85; Burdett; Exec Sec.

BOVE, KIM; Haverhill HS; Bradford, MA; (Y); 61/413; Church Yth Grp; Latin Clb; Ski Clb; Spanish Clb; Sec Sr Cls; Cheerleading; High Hon Roll; Hon Roll; Nrtheastern U; Psychlgy.

BOVE, LISA; Mt St Joseph Acad; Newton, MA; (Y); 6/162; Church Yth Grp; Drama Clb; Science Clb; Spanish Clb; Stu Cncl; JV Var Bsktbl; JV Vllybl; Hon Roll; Pres NHS; Val; Ntl Ldrshp & Acad All Amer Awds 85; Pre Med.

BOVE JR, MICHAEL; Nauset Regional HS; N Eastham, MA; (Y); Stat Bsktbl; Var L Socr; Hon Roll.

BOWAB, JOSEPH; Central Catholic HS; N Andover, MA; (Y); 72/219; Boys Clb Am; Church Yth Grp; JA; Rep Frsh Cls; Rep Soph Cls; Rep Jr Cls; Rep Stu Cncl; JV Var Bsktbl; Im Vllybl; Hon Roll; Pre-Law.

BOWDEN, JON; Silver Lake Regional HS; Halifax, MA; (Y); 11/500; Var Bsbl; Capt Ftbl; High Hon Roll; Hon Roll; Bus Admin.

BOWDEN, KAREN; Whitman Hanson Regional HS; Whitman, MA; (Y); 13/300; Stu Cncl; Var Capt Cheerleading; Coach Actv; Gym; Cit Awd; High Hon Roll; Hon Roll; Lion Awd; NHS; Pres Schlr; Southeastern MA U; Nrsng.

BOWDOIN, SEAVEY; Melrose HS; Melrose, MA; (Y); 18/450; Aud/Vis; Drama Clb; Stage Crew; Rep Sr Cls; High Hon Roll; Hon Roll; JR SR Forum 85; 735 Yth & Fmly Resrcs; Comm.

BOWEN, DAVID NEVILLE GODDARD; Scituate HS; Scituate, MA; (Y); 122/287; Chess Clb; Exploring; Math Clb; Rep Stu Cncl; Var Ice Hcky; Hon Roll; Ntl Merit Ltr; Assumption Coll; Frgn Affrs.

BOWEN, JOANN; Everett HS; Boston, MA; (Y); Church Yth Grp; Cmnty Wkr; Intnl Clb; Pres Key Clb; Science Clb; Teachers Aide; Nwsp Stf; JV Bsktbl; Var Capt Cheerleading; Var Capt Pom Pon; Cmmnwlth MA Offcl Citation Chrng Champs 85; Holy Cross; Law.

BOWEN JR, JOSEPH; Melrose HS; Melrose, MA; (Y); 77/370; Boy Scts; Church Yth Grp; Hosp Aide; Library Aide; Pres Ski Clb; Hon Roll; Schltc Awd Math, Lang Arts, Indus Arts 83; Elec Engrng.

BOWER, COLIN; Manchester JR SR HS; Manchester, MA; (Y); Rep Am Leg Boys St; Yrbk Sprt Ed; Rep VP Stu Cncl; Im Bsbl; Capt Var Bsktbl; Var Ftbl; Im Socr; Hon Roll; Stu Advsry Cncl 85-86; Stu Advsry Cmmtt 85-86; Peer Educ Ldr 84-86.

BOWER, PETER; Randolph HS; Randolph, MA; (Y); Pres Church Yth Grp.

BOWERS, RUSSELL; Uxbridge HS; Uxbridge, MA; (Y); Boy Scts; Church Yth Grp; Nwsp Stf; JV Var Ftbl; Wt Lftg; Hon Roll; Arch Engr.

BOWERS, SCOTT; Randolph HS; Randolph, MA; (Y); Drm & Bgl; Nwsp Sprt Ed; Nwsp Stf; Yrbk Sprt Ed; Rep Frsh Cls; Rep Soph Cls; Rep Jr Cls; Rep Sr Cls; JV Bsktbl; JV Var Ftbl; Engrng.

BOWES, SHERYLENE; King Philip Regional HS; Plainville, MA; (S); 3/280; Church Yth Grp; Pres DECA; Drama Clb; Yrbk Stf; Cheerleading; Sftbl; Vllybl; Hon Roll; 4th Pl Gen Merch Rtlng; 7th Pl Miss DECA 84; 1st Pl Gen Merch Rtlng; 3rd Pl Entreprenrshp Manl 85; Alfred U; CPA.

BOWLING, LORI ANN; BNC Durfee HS; Fall River, MA; (Y); 150/750; FNA; Hosp Aide; Library Aide; Office Aide; Teachers Aide; School Play; Yrbk Stf; Hon Roll; Spec Needs Aide 83; Sthestrn MA U; Nrsng.

BOYD, STEVE; Haverhill HS; Haverhill, MA; (Y); Boys Clb Am; Wrstlng; Hon Roll; Treas Eclgy Clb 86; Bio Awd 81-82; Aero Engr.

BOYER, LAWRENCE; Smith Acad; Hatfield, MA; (S); Boy Scts; Hosp Aide; Key Clb; Quiz Bowl; Off Jr Cls; JV Bsktbl; Hon Roll; Philosphy Comm 83-84; Schl Solar Systm Monitor 84; U Of MASS Astron Clb 84; Astro-Physcs.

BOYES, SUSAN; Abington HS; Abington, MA; (Y); 33/198; Chorus; Madrigals; Orch; School Musical; French Clb; High Hon Roll; Hon Roll; E Nazarene Clg; Erly Chldhd.

BOYLE, BRIAN D; Holy Name Central Catholic HS; Auburn, MA; (Y); 50/250; Chess Clb; Church Yth Grp; Cmnty Wkr; FBLA; Political Wkr; Var L Golf; JV Socr; Hon Roll; Central MA All Str Golf 84-85; Northeasern U; Crmnl Jstc.

BOYLE, KATHERINE; Bishop Connolly HS; Newport, RI; (Y); Church Yth Grp; Drama Clb; Political Wkr; Ski Clb; Church Choir; School Play; Stage Crew; High Hon Roll; Hon Roll; Frnch Frgn Exchng Stu 85.

BOYNTON, TODD; Amhrest Regional HS; Pelham, MA; (Y); Aud/Vis; Computer Clb; Im Badmtn; Var Ice Hcky; Var Socr; High Hon Roll; Hon Roll; MVP Ice Hcky 81-83; RPI; Engrng.

BOZZI, DAWN M; Saugus HS; Saugus, MA; (Y); 39/307; Church Yth Grp; Office Aide; Pep Clb; Yrbk Stf; Lit Mag; Stu Cncl; High Hon Roll; Hon Roll; Jr NHS; NHS; Exc Bio Awd 83-84; Exc Italian Awd 83-84; Italian Clb 84-85; Boston U; Physcl Thrpy.

BRABANT, SCOTT D; Ashland HS; Ashland, MA; (Y); 1/97; Am Leg Boys St; Intnl Clb; Variety Show; JV Var Bsktbl; Var Socr; Var Tennis; High Hon Roll; Jr NHS; NHS; Schlstc Achvt Awd Hstry, Englsh & Bus 85; Schlstc Achvt Awd Bus, Chem & Bio 84; MVP Tennis Vrsty 84.

BRACCIOTTI, CHRISTINE; Stoneham HS; Stoneham, MA; (Y); 1/207; Latin Clb; Mathletes; Math Tm; Ski Clb; Sec Spanish Clb; Yrbk Stf; High Hon Roll; Jr NHS; Sec NHS; Val; Commonwlth Of MA Schlrshp 85; Engl Mdl 85; Boston Coll; Finance.

BRACKEN, MICHAEL E; Boston College HS; Braintree, MA; (Y); 2/280; Cmnty Wkr; Key Clb; Nwsp Stf; Var Capt Socr; Var L Trk; NHS; Sal; St Schlr; VP Church Yth Grp; Spanish Clb; Principals Svc Awd 85; Commonwealth MA Schlr Awd 85; MAFLA Frgn Lang Assn 85; Cornell U; Engrng.

BRACKEN, SEAN; Malden Catholic HS; Menford, MA; (Y); Latin Clb; Yrbk Stf; NHS; Ntl Merit SF; Bus.

BRACKETT, BRENDA E; Blackstone Millvile Reg HS; Blackstone, MA; (Y); 9/110; Yrbk Stf; Rep Stu Cncl; JV Bsktbl; Var Fld Hcky; JV Sftbl; Var Trk; High Hon Roll; NHS; Bentley Coll.

BRADBARD, BETH; Medford HS; Chelmsford, MA; (Y); 51/437; Hosp Aide; Off Temple Yth Grp; Var L Trk; Vllybl; Hon Roll; Jr NHS; NHS; Roger Williams Coll; Arch.

BRADFORD, LAUREN D; Reading Memorial HS; Reading, MA; (Y); Church Yth Grp; Drama Clb; Hosp Aide; Yrbk Bus Mgr; Lit Mag; High Hon Roll; Latin Clb; Radio Clb; Chorus; Church Choir; Latn Hnr Socty Pres 84; Amer Clg Muscns 83; Cmp Hope Volntr Cnslr 82; Jrnlsm.

BRADLEE, DAVID; St Johns HS; Hudson, MA; (Y); 15/275; Chess Clb; Math Clb; Math Tm; High Hon Roll; NHS; NEDT Awd; Worcester Vo-Tech; Chmcl Engrng.

BRADLEY, KELLEY; Silver Lake Regional HS; Halifax, MA; (Y); 9/500; Camp Fr Inc; Dance Clb; French Clb; GAA; Office Aide; Nwsp Ed-Chief; Nwsp Stf; High Hon Roll; Hon Roll; Variety Show; La Femmina Schl Modlng 85; Med Tech.

BRADLEY, LEE-ANN; Stoughton HS; Stoughton, MA; (Y); Chorus; Drill Tm; Hon Roll; Med.

BRADY, MICHAEL S; Deerfield Acad; Brielle, NJ; (Y); Radio Clb; Service Clb; Spanish Clb; Var JV Lcrss; Var L Socr; Hon Roll.

BRAGA, CHARLES; Bishop Connolly HS; Fall River, MA; (S); 7/158; Church Yth Grp; Computer Clb; JCL; Latin Clb; Nwsp Rptr; Nwsp Stf; High Hon Roll; Jr NHS; NHS; Ntl Clscl Latn League Exm-Magna Cum Laude 82; Med.

BRAGG, HANNAH; Bedford HS; Bedford, MA; (Y); 52/213; Aud/Vis; Girl Scts; Band; Hon Roll; Engrng.

BRAITHWAITE, DAVID; Falmouth HS; Falmouth, MA; (Y); Pres French Clb; Scholastic Bowl; School Play; Nwsp Stf; Rep Jr Cls; High Hon Roll; Hon Roll; NHS; Ntl Merit Ltr; AFS; Stdnt Qrtr Awd Frnch 85; Stdnt Qrtr Awd Latn 85; Brd Membr Cape Cod Untd Natns Assn 82-84; Amherst Coll; Pol Sci.

BRAMANTI, CHRISTOPHER J; Burlington HS; Burlington, MA; (Y); 96/315; JV Var Bsbl; Var Bsktbl; Hon Roll; Acctng.

BRANCATO, SANDRA; East Boston HS; E Boston, MA; (Y); Key Clb; Fld Hcky; Var Fld Hcky; Var Ftbl; Var Sftbl; Hon Roll; Law.

BRANCO, JEFF; Bishop Connolly HS; Swansea, MA; (Y); 35/176; Exploring; Var Crs Cntry; Var L Swmmng; High Hon Roll; Elect Engrng.

BRANDSMA, KIRSTEN; Natick HS; Natick, MA; (Y); 122/420; JCL; Off Jr Cls; Hon Roll; Psych.

BRATHWAITE, SONIA Y; Burlington HS; Burlington, MA; (Y); Church Yth Grp; Chorus; Swing Chorus; Ed Yrbk Stf; Powder Puff Ftbl; Hon Roll; VP Church SR Yth Grp; Burlington Recrtn Dept; Pol Sci.

BRAUDIS, PATRICIA; Fontbonne Acad; Norwood, MA; (Y); 49/134; Drama Clb; Intnl Clb; Science Clb; Stage Crew; Im Bsktbl; JV Capt Fld Hcky; Hon Roll; Ntl Spnsh Exam High Hnrs 85; Law.

BRAWLEY, JOANNE; Westwood HS; Westwood, MA; (Y); 7/211; AFS; Band; Concert Band; Mrchg Band; Pep Band; Stage Crew; Var L Swmmng; NHS; Ntl Merit Ltr; Spanish NHS.

BRAY, STACIE ANN; Saint Clare HS; Roslindale, MA; (Y); JCL; Service Clb; School Play; Variety Show; Nwsp Rptr; Stu Cncl; Hon Roll; NHS; Ntl Merit Ltr; NEDT Awd; Magna Cum Laude-Natl Latin Exam 80-82; Stonehill Coll Acadmc Schlrshp 85; Stonehill Coll; Poltcl Sci.

BRAZIER, JOAN; Falmouth Acad; N Falmouth, MA; (Y); Orch; Socr; Sftbl; Vllybl; High Hon Roll; Hon Roll; NHS; Val; Drama Clb; 4-H; Colby Coll Bk Awd 84.

BRAZIL JR, DAVID M; Bridgewater Raynham Regional HS; Bridgewater, MA; (Y); Am Leg Boys St; Camera Clb; French Clb; Leo Clb; Science Clb; Ski Clb; Spanish Clb; Tennis; Coll Of Holy Cross.

BRAZILE, PATRICIA; St Peter Marian HS; Worcester, MA; (Y); Church Yth Grp; Hosp Aide; Ski Clb; Var Socr; JV Sftbl; U MA; Int Dsgn.

BREAUIT, JAMES; Montachusett Regional Vo Tech Schl; Fitchburg, MA; (Y).

BREAULT, ELLEN M; David Prouty HS; Spencer, MA; (Y); 21/145; Church Yth Grp; Girl Scts; Pep Clb; Trs Band; Concert Band; Jazz Band; Mrchg Band; Mgr(s); Score Keeper; Timer; David Prouty Band Schlrshp 85; Douglas Tatro Meml Schlrshp 85; All Amer Music Awd 84 & 85; Fitchburg ST Coll; Teaching.

BREEN, DANIEL; Boston Latin Schl; Boston, MA; (Y); Rep Frsh Cls; Rep Soph Cls; Rep Jr Cls; Pres Sr Cls; VP Stu Cncl; Var L Trk; NHS; Am Leg Boys St; Church Yth Grp; High Hon Roll; Fidelity Awd 83; Clsscl Awd Latin 83; Clss 1898 Awd 83; Cls Pres 86; Latin.

BREGOLI, PETER J; Braintree HS; Braintree, MA; (Y); 60/481; Art Clb; Lit Mag; High Hon Roll; Yrbk Art & Dsgn Ed 84-85; Bostom Globe Schltc Art Cmptn Awd 85; Ntl Assn For Advncmnt In Art Tlnt Srch; Parsons Schl Of Dsgn; Illstrtn.

BREMER, DAVID; Burlington HS; Burlington, MA; (Y); 8/315; Math Tm; Swmmng; High Hon Roll; Hon Roll; NHS; Coaches Awd Swmmng 84-85; Mth Awd 84-85; Mth Lg Awd 84-85; Chem Engr.

BREMMER, IAN; St Dominic Savio HS; Chelsea, MA; (Y); 8/105; Pres Chess Clb; VP Debate Tm; JA; Math Clb; Ed Yrbk Ed-Chief; Stu Cncl; NHS; Voice Dem Awd; Cmnty Wkr; Computer Clb; Outstndng Prosectr Awds,Regnl Mock Trls; Cent III Ldrs Prog Merit Wnnr,MA Fnlst; Tulane U; Chem Engr.

BRENNAN, BEVERLY; Bishop Fenwick HS; Lynnfld, MA; (Y); 38/222; Sec 4-H; Hosp Aide; Nwsp Rptr; Yrbk Stf; Rep Soph Cls; Rep Jr Cls; Rep Stu Cncl; Capt Cheerleading; High Hon Roll; Ntl Hnr Roll 85; Yrbk/SR Athlte Awd 85; U Of NH; Sci.

BRENNAN, JENNIFER; Hingham HS; Hingham, MA; (Y); 151/350; School Musical; Yrbk Stf; Cheerleading; Hon Roll; Church Yth Grp; Drama Clb; Office Aide; Stage Crew; Trk; Trk Cert 82-83; Vrsty Let Chrldng 84-85; Comm.

BRENNAN, KATHLEEN; New Bedford HS; New Bedford, MA; (Y); 44/599; AFS; Drama Clb; Key Clb; Q&S; Orch; School Play; Nwsp Rptr; Var L Tennis; Var Vllybl; NHS; Portvgvese Amer Civic League Schlrshp 85; U Of NH; Environmental Conserv.

BRENNAN, MICHAEL; Dartmouth HS; S Dartmouth, MA; (Y); Boy Scts; Church Choir; Trk; Wt Lftg; Ovrseer Dartmouth Grange; U Of MA; Engnrng.

BRENNER, CHARLENE; Marblehead HS; Marblehead, MA; (Y); 4/260; Hosp Aide; Trs Spanish Clb; Variety Show; Ed Yrbk Stf; Rep Soph Cls; High Hon Roll; NHS; Bus Mgmt.

BRENNER, STACEY; Randolph HS; Randolph, MA; (Y); Drama Clb; Pres French Clb; Hosp Aide; School Musical; School Play; Rep Soph Cls; Rep Jr Cls; Jr NHS; Ntl Merit Ltr; Fr Clb Awd 84-85; Heart Assn Awd 85; Law.

BRENS, ERNESTO; Lawrence HS; Lawrence, MA; (Y); Boys Clb Am; Chorus; School Play; Trk.

BRESNAHAN, CASSANDRA; Bishop Stang HS; New Bedford, MA; (Y); 51/212; Ski Clb; Teachers Aide; Stage Crew; Yrbk Stf; Rep Soph Cls; Var L Trk; Var L Vllybl; High Hon Roll; Hon Roll; Pres Schlr; U Of MA Amhrst; Lgl Studies.

BRESNAHAN, PATRICK D M; Holyoke HS; Holyoke, MA; (Y); Latin Clb; Varsity Clb; Off Stu Cncl; Var Ice Hcky; Var Socr; Var Tennis; Hon Roll; Political Wkr; Stage Crew; Rook Yr-Hcky; Hnr Rll.

BREZNAY, JENNIFER; Buckingham Browne & Nichols HS; Newton, MA; (S); Dance Clb; Debate Tm; Chorus; School Musical; Nwsp Ed-Chief; Var Lcrss; Var Capt Socr; Ntl Merit Ltr; Orch; JV Bsktbl; Harvard Bk Prz 85; Bio Sci.

BRIAND, NOELLE; Bishop Connolly HS; Westport, MA; (Y); 40/177; Ski Clb; VP Frsh Cls; Pres Soph Cls; Pres Jr Cls; VP Rep Stu Cncl; L Bsktbl; L Trk; High Hon Roll; Church Yth Grp; Girl Scts; Outstndng Soph Awd 83-84; Hugh O Brien Youth Ldrshp Ambssdr 83; Middlebury Coll; Eco.

BRICK, MELINDA; St Peter Marian CC HS; Worcester, MA; (Y); 4/175; Church Yth Grp; Science Clb; Yrbk Stf; Crs Cntry; Hon Roll; NHS; Coaches Awd Grls Crs Cntry 85; Home Ec Awd 82; Hahneman Hosp Schl Nrsng; Nrsng.

BRIDEAU, MICHELLE; Fitchburg HS; Fitchburg, MA; (Y); 2/230; Mgr Band; Concert Band; Mrchg Band; Pep Band; School Play; Yrbk Stf; Stu Cncl; Var Capt Fld Hcky; JV Sftbl; High Hon Roll; French I Awd 83; John P Hagerty Mem Hist Medal 85; Local Hist Conf 1st Prz 85; Engr.

BRIGGS, KARYN; Hoosac Valley HS; Savoy, MA; (Y); French Clb; Pep Clb; Ski Clb; JV Sftbl; High Hon Roll; Hon Roll.

BRIGGS, MONICA A; Wellesky SR HS; Wellesley, MA; (Y); 9/316; Ed Art Clb; Exploring; Sec German Clb; Ski Clb; Teachers Aide; School Play; Nwsp Stf; Lit Mag; Off Soph Cls; Off Sr Cls; Brown U Bk Awd-Achvt In Eng 84; Presdntl Acadmc Ftnss Awd 85; Am Assn Of Tchrs Of Grmn Awd 84; Middlebury Coll; Eng.

BRIGHAM, DAVID G; Sheppard Hill Regional HS; Charlton, MA; (Y); 20/110; Am Leg Boys St; Latin Clb; Pre-Med.

BRIGHAM, SHARON ANN; Weymouth North HS; Weymouth, MA; (Y); 1/340; Am Leg Aux Girls St; Sec Sr Cls; Var Co-Capt Bsktbl; Var Co-Capt Sftbl; Co-Capt Vllybl; High Hon Roll; Sec NHS; Pres Schlr; Rotary Awd; Val; ST Fnlst Colonial Dames Wrtng Cntst; Dartmouth Bk Awd; Chnclrs Awd Schlrshp; MVP Vlybl; Holy Cross.

BRIGHTMAN, HEATH; Newton North HS; Newton, MA; (Y); Aud/Vis; Boy Scts; Ski Clb; Stage Crew; High Hon Roll; Hon Roll; SAR Awd; Eagle Scout Awd 84; Ordeal Mbr 83; Mbr Temple Israel Cong 84; Pilot.

BRIGHTMAN, STEVEN; B M C Durfee HS; Fall River, MA; (Y); 50/687; Var L Crs Cntry; Var L Trk; Hon Roll; NHS; Comp Engr.

BRIN, ALEX; Westfield HS; Westfield, MA; (Y); Boys Clb Am; Cmnty Wkr; Quiz Bowl; JV Bsktbl; JV Ftbl; Var Tennis; Var Trk; High Hon Roll; Hon Roll; NHS; Intl Baccalaureate 85; Western New England Coll; Math.

BRION, WERNER; Bishop Connolly HS; Somerset, MA; (S); Chess Clb; Cmnty Wkr; Drama Clb; Hosp Aide; School Musical; School Play; Stage Crew; Nwsp Rptr; High Hon Roll; Hon Roll; St Annes Hosp Recgnt Servc 83; Engrng.

BRISCOE, ROBERTA; Dracut HS; Dracut, MA; (Y); Computer Clb; 4-H; Key Clb; Library Aide; Office Aide; 4-H Awd; Hon Roll; NHS; 4-H 2-Yr Ldrshp Awd & Merit Awd 83-84; Art Achvt Awd 83; Anml Sci.

BROADBENT, JANIS C; Silver Lake Regional HS; Pembroke, MA; (Y); 11/457; Drama Clb; Pres French Clb; Yrbk Stf; Stu Cncl; Var Cheerleading; Var Tennis; DAR Awd; Sec NHS; Voice Dem Awd; U Of ME-ORONO; Pre-Dnstry.

BROADBENT, LYNNE M; Middleboro Memorial HS; Middleboro, MA; (Y); Hon Roll; Acctg.

BRODIE, HEATHER; St Bernards HS; Ashby, MA; (S); #9 In Class; L Hosp Aide; Model UN; Stat Mgr(s); Sftbl; High Hon Roll; Jr NHS; NHS; Chem,Geo,Alg Awds 83-84; Sci.

BROILES, THOMAS L; Ashland HS; Ashland, MA; (Y); Am Leg Boys St; Drama Clb; FBLA; School Play; Yrbk Stf; Trs Sr Cls; Rep Stu Cncl; Capt Bsktbl; Capt Ftbl; Capt Trk; Philips Acad Summr Sessn Scholar 85; Law.

BROMBERG, ROBIN; Revere HS; Revere, MA; (Y); 4/388; Debate Tm; Math Tm; Scholastic Bowl; Temple Yth Grp; Nwsp Stf; Yrbk Stf; Hon Roll; Am Leg Aux Girls St; Drama Clb; Library Aide; Brown U Bk Awd 85; Pres Stu Fac Sen 85-86; Stu Advis Comm 85-86; Sttu Advis Com ST 85-86; Pre Med.

BROMFIELD, KENNETH S; Sharon HS; Sharon, MA; (Y); Chess Clb; Math Tm; Temple Yth Grp; Band; Chorus; Concert Band; Nwsp Stf; Yrbk Stf; Hon Roll; Ntl Merit Ltr.

BRONNER, MICHELLE; Ayer HS; West Point, NY; (Y); 21/167; Am Leg Aux Girls St; Capt Bsktbl; Fld Hcky; Capt Sftbl; Mu Alp Tht; NHS; Acceptnc 1S Military Acad 85; US Military Acad; Lang.

BRONSON, DIANA; Montachusett Regional Voc-Tech HS; Templeton, MA; (Y); VICA; Yrbk Stf; Cheerleading; NHS; Prom Cmmtte 84-85; Mount Wachusette CC; Bus.

BRONSON, RENEE; Reading Memorial HS; Roxbury, MA; (Y); Church Yth Grp; Dance Clb; Spanish Clb; Band; Chorus; Church Choir; Concert Band; Mrchg Band; Orch; Symp Band; AKA Dnnr Hnr Pres VA ST U & Mel King William Thompson Pagnt 84; Clrnt Duet Berkly Schl Music 82-85; Syracuse U; Bus.

BROOKBUSH, KIMBERLY; King Philip Regional HS; Norfolk, MA; (Y); Powder Puff Ftbl; Score Keeper; Hon Roll; Accntg.

BROOKS, DIONNE S; Cambridge Rindge & Latin Schl; Cambridge, MA; (Y); 19/504; Church Yth Grp; Cmnty Wkr; Drama Clb; FCA; Girl Scts; JA; Key Clb; Office Aide; Quiz Bowl; Church Choir; Harvard Coop Soc Schl 85; Martin Uther King Schl Grad 85; Mass Pep Schlrshp Serv 85; Boston U; Comm.

BROOKS, LISA; Academy Of Notre Dame; Westford, MA; (Y); Church Yth Grp; VP French Clb; Hosp Aide; Key Clb; Sec Soph Cls; Hon Roll; Awd Of Part-Concours De Francais 84; Intl Frgn Lang Awd 84; Lang.

BROOKS, TERI; Quabbin Regional HS; Barre, MA; (Y); 17/156; Red Cross Aide; Pres Ski Clb; Varsity Clb; Yrbk Stf; Cheerleading; Hon Roll; NHS; French Clb; Teachers Aide; Fld Hcky; Bartholomew Schlrshp 85; Barre Cmmnty Imprvmnt Assoc Schlrshp 85; Amer Legion Schlrsh& 85; Anna Maria Coll; Pre-Law.

BROPHY, KAREN; Beverly HS; Beverly, MA; (Y); 19/375; Pres Leo Clb; School Musical; School Play; Stage Crew; Nwsp Rptr; Yrbk Stf; Lit Mag; Off Jr Cls; Off Sr Cls; Var Fld Hcky; Entrtnmnt & Feat Edtr Nswpr 84-86; US Hist Awd 85; Rep Corriculum Cncl 84-85; Eng.

BROSNAN, DANIEL; Matignon HS; Arlington, MA; (S); 11/188; Cmnty Wkr; French Clb; Var Ftbl; French Hon Soc; Hon Roll; NHS; Bus.

BROSNAN, MAUREEN; Burncoat SR HS; Worcester, MA; (Y); Church Yth Grp; Intnl Clb; Science Clb; Yrbk Stf; High Hon Roll; Hon Roll; NHS; Career Day Worcester Essay Wnnr 85.

BROSSEAU, JOSEPH D; West Springfield HS; West Springfield, MA; (Y); 46/231; Ski Clb; Golf; Gym; High Hon Roll; NHS; Mattson-Sullivan Golf Schlrshp 85; Donald Phil Awd Scholar Athlete 85; U Of NH; Mechncl Engrng.

BROUILLETTE, RICHARD; Cathedral HS; Chicopee, MA; (Y); Ski Clb; Teachers Aide; Outstndng Svc Awd; Western New England Coll; Bus.

BROUSSEAU, ERIC; Southbridge HS; Southbridge, MA; (Y); 2/145; Am Leg Boys St; Church Yth Grp; Cmnty Wkr; Math Tm; Political Wkr; Rep Jr Cls; Stat Ftbl; Var Trk; High Hon Roll; NHS; Law.

BROUSSEAU, HEIDI; Dracut HS; Pelham, NH; (Y); French Clb; Yrbk Stf; Capt Bsktbl; JV Sftbl; Var Vllybl; Hon Roll; NHS; Rotary Awd; Engl, Alg & Phy Ed Hnrs 83; Tchrs Assn Schlrshp 85; U Of NM; Nutrtn.

BROUWER, AMY; Northbridge JR SR HS; Whitinsville, MA; (S); 1/153; Church Yth Grp; Office Aide; Pep Clb; Spanish Clb; Var L Bsktbl; Var L Fld Hcky; Powder Puff Ftbl; Var L Sftbl; High Hon Roll; NHS; Outstndng Span Stu 83-84; Umass Chanclrs Talent Awd 85; Yth Understndg Int Stu Exc 84; Chem Engr.

BROWN, ALISON S; Amherst Regional HS; Amherst, MA; (Y); 18/310; Dance Clb; Acpl Chr; Chorus; School Musical; School Play; Stage Crew; Rep Stu Cncl; Hon Roll; NHS; Ntl Merit SF; Pre-Med.

BROWN, ANITA; Randolph HS; Randolph, MA; (Y); Pres Church Yth Grp; Dance Clb; Pres Church Choir; Yrbk Stf; 1st Rnr Up Cotillion 85; 1st Rnr Up Boston Dist Tlnts 85.

BROWN, DANIEL S; Milton Acad; Chicago, IL; (Y); Cmnty Wkr; Debate Tm; Latin Clb; Model UN; Orch; School Play; Var Lcrss; Capt Socr; Ntl Merit SF; Educ Policy Committee 84-85; Hist.

BROWN, DAVID M; Plymouth-Carver HS; Plymouth, MA; (Y); Pres Church Yth Grp; JV Ftbl; Var Golf; Im Lcrss; Capt Var Trk; Comp Sci.

BROWN, DAVID P; W Bridgewater JR SR HS; West Bridgewater, MA; (Y); Am Leg Boys St; Key Clb; JV Ftbl; Comp.

BROWN, DEBORAH; Melrose HS; Melrose, MA; (Y); 22/350; Scholastic Bowl; Ed Yrbk Phtg; Hon Roll; NHS; Schltc Awd Lang Art 83.

BROWN, ELIZABETH; Masconomet Regional HS; Topsfield, MA; (Y); 20/244; Trs French Clb; Model UN; Varsity Clb; Var Capt Socr; High Hon Roll; Hosp Aide; Latin Clb; Yrbk Stf; Rep Sr Cls; Rep Stu Cncl; Cape Ann Lge Allstr Sccr 84; Hist.

BROWN, ERIC; Saugus HS; Saugus, MA; (Y); Aud/Vis; Chess Clb; Computer Clb; Var Crs Cntry; JV Trk; Hon Roll; Jr NHS; NHS; Voice Dem Awd; Physcs.

BROWN, ERICA I; Natick HS; Natick, MA; (Y); 60/450; NFL; Ski Clb; Spanish Clb; Mrchg Band; Pres Symp Band; Nwsp Rptr; Ed Nwsp Stf; Rep Stu Cncl; NCTE Awd; High Hon Roll; Syracuse U; Jrnlsm.

BROWN, JENNIFER ANN; North Broofield HS; N Brookfield, MA; (Y); 2/47; Sec 4-H; Band; Chorus; Trs Frsh Cls; Trs Soph Cls; Trs Jr Cls; Trs Sr Cls; Var L Bsktbl; Var L Fld Hcky; Var Capt Sftbl; Supertndnts Awd 85; Worcester Polytechnic Inst; Eng.

BROWN, JOANN; Marble Head HS; Marblehead, MA; (Y); 40/245; Stage Crew; Yrbk Phtg; Cheerleading; Gym; Powder Puff Ftbl; High Hon Roll; Law.

BROWN, JULIE F; Norton HS; Norton, MA; (Y); 18/120; Key Clb; Pep Clb; Ski Clb; Varsity Clb; School Play; Yrbk Sprt Ed; VP Stu Cncl; L Bsktbl; Trk; Vllybl; Sprtsmans Schlrshp 85; Army Reserve Schlr/Athlete Awd 85; Ithaca Coll; Psych.

BROWN, KATHLEEN; Bartlett HS; Webster, MA; (Y); French Clb; FBLA; Drm Mjr(t); Mgr Trk; High Hon Roll; NHS; Nichols Coll; Bus Mgmt.

BROWN, LISA; Billerica Memorial HS; Billerica, MA; (Y); 23/423; High Hon Roll; Salem ST Clg; Engl.

BROWN, LORI A; Gloucester HS; Gloucester, MA; (Y); Hosp Aide; High Hon Roll; Hon Roll; Outstndng Achvt In Clthng 85; Clothing.

BROWN, MICHAEL; Belmont HS; Belmont, MA; (Y); Am Leg Boys St; Church Yth Grp; Concert Band; Trs Soph Cls; Var Crs Cntry; Var L Trk; Hon Roll; MA ST Champ & Rcrd Holder 600 Yd Run 85; MA ST Champ 400 M Run 85.

BROWN, MICHAEL; Wakefield HS; Wakefield, MA; (Y); Church Yth Grp; Im Mgr Bsbl; Im Mgr Bsktbl; JV Ftbl; Var L Golf; Im Mgr Wt Lftg; Hon Roll; Bus.

BROWN, MICHAEL SPEROS; Manchester JR SR HS; Manchester, MA; (Y); 5/80; Am Leg Boys St; Boy Scts; Debate Tm; Math Tm; Sec Jr Cls; Sec Sr Cls; Var L Bsktbl; Var L Crs Cntry; NHS; NFL; Hrvrd Bk Prz 84; Amer Jwsh War Vet Bro Awd 85; Cornell U; Mech Engrng.

BROWN, PAMELA; Notre Dame Acad; Canton, MA; (Y); 13/114; Cmnty Wkr; Spanish Clb; Chorus; Hon Roll; Educ.

BROWN, ROBYN C; Brockton HS; Brockton, MA; (Y); 160/995; Trs Computer Clb; Drama Clb; Library Aide; Pep Clb; Chorus; School Musical; Nwsp Stf; Yrbk Stf; Ed Lit Mag; Cit Awd; Rainbw Girls Brocktts Anti-Vndlsm Rock Video Fclty 85; Bentley Coll; Acctg.

BROWN, STEPHEN; Milford HS; Milford, MA; (Y); Var Crs Cntry; Var Tennis; Hon Roll; Most Dedicated Tennis 83-85; Bentley Coll; Comp Sci.

BROWN, STEVEN; Maynard HS; Maynard, MA; (Y); 17/100; Mgr Aud/Vis; Radio Clb; Band; Concert Band; Mrchg Band; Stage Crew; JV Bsbl; Var L Ice Hcky; Var L Socr; Hon Roll; Best Dept Of Yr Editg 85; Military.

BROWN, STEVEN C; Waltham HS; Waltham, MA; (Y); Am Leg Boys St; VP Church Yth Grp; Latin Clb; Political Wkr; Swing Chorus; Yrbk Stf; Stu Cncl; Capt Crs Cntry; Var Trk; High Hon Roll; Nobel Prz Athltcs Rnnr Up 83; New Balnc Natl Grss Roots Prog 85; 1st H S Finshr Natl TAE JR Champ 84; Pol Sci.

BROWN, SUSAN; Milford HS; Milford, MA; (Y); 8/292; Cmnty Wkr; Bowling; High Hon Roll; NHS.

BROWN, SUSAN; Ursuline Acad; Dedham, MA; (Y); Church Yth Grp; Drama Clb; Library Aide; Spanish Clb; School Musical; Yrbk Stf; Hon Roll; NHS; Ntl Merit Schol; Commonwlth MA Awd Schrlshp 85; Boston U; Bus.

BROWN, VIVIAN; Mario Umana Harbor Schl; Roxbury, MA; (Y); Im Badmtn; Var Cheerleading; Co-Capt Sftbl; Var Vllybl; Hon Roll; Med Tech.

BROWNE, CAROLYN; Everett HS; Boston, MA; (Y); Church Yth Grp; Key Clb; Trs Jr Cls; Var Cheerleading; JV Trk; Nrsng.

BROWNING, CYNTHIA; Mohawk Trail Reg HS; Colrain, MA; (Y); 23/142; Church Yth Grp; Chorus; Church Choir; School Musical; Yrbk Stf; JV Tennis; Var L Vllybl; High Hon Roll; Hon Roll; Varsity Clb; Elem Ed.

BROWNING, PAUL; Bartlett HS; Webster, MA; (Y); 14/149; Band; Concert Band; Mrchg Band; Ice Hcky; High Hon Roll; Hon Roll; Comp Engrng.

BRUCE, JEFF; Westford Acad; Westford, MA; (Y); French Clb; Ski Clb; Variety Show; Yrbk Phtg; Yrbk Stf; L Golf; Hon Roll; N Eastern U; Comp Sci.

BRULE, MATTHEW L; Blackstone Valley Regional HS; E Douglas, MA; (Y); Band; Concert Band; Mrchg Band; School Musical; Hon Roll; Elctrnics.

BRUNELLE, MARK; Pathfinder Reg Vo Tech; Palmer, MA; (Y); FFA; FFA Grnhnd Deg 82; U MA; Ldnscp Arch.

BRUNELLE, MONIQUE; Barnstable HS; Hyannis, MA; (Y); Drama Clb; Chorus; Concert Band; Sec Mrchg Band; School Musical; School Play; Schl Grnt WA Workshps Congrssnl Sem 85; Hats Off Cmmndtn Schl Comm 85; Polit Sci.

BRUNNER, ELIZABETH A; Dedham HS; Dedham, MA; (Y); 39/298; Church Yth Grp; Drama Clb; VP Sec Band; Concert Band; Jazz Band; Mrchg Band; Rep Jr Cls; Im Bsktbl; Im Sftbl; Hon Roll; Best Sets Tourn Plays 85; Math Awd 83; Schlstc Art Awd 85; Art.

BRUNO, DAVID; Revere HS; Revere, MA; (Y); 5/400; Math Clb; Math Tm; Quiz Bowl; Science Clb; Jr Cls; Var Socr; Var Trk; High Hon Roll; Essay Cntst Wnnr Cert Spcl Cong Recgntn 85; MA Inst Tech; Math.

BRUNO, ROBERTA; Presentation Of Mary Acad; N Salem, NH; (S); 8/51; Church Yth Grp; Cmnty Wkr; Math Clb; Pep Clb; Spanish Clb; School Musical; Cheerleading; Tennis; Hon Roll; NHS; 2nd Prz Sci Fair 83; Schl Rep At MA ST Sci Fair 83; Bentley Coll; Acctng.

BRUSCO, DIANE; Norwood SR HS; Norwood, MA; (Y); 3/341; JA; Key Clb; Drill Tm; Pres Stu Cncl; Var L Tennis; DAR Awd; Elks Awd; JC Awd; NHS; Elks Ntl Schlrshp 85; MA AFL-CIO Schlrshp 85; U Of VA; Lbrl Arts.

BRYANT, AMANDA; Quabbin Regional HS; Barre, MA; (Y); 8/145; Am Leg Aux Girls St; ROTC; Yrbk Bus Mgr; VP Sr Cls; Capt Bsktbl; Capt Sftbl; Pres NHS; Drama Clb; Latin Clb; Math Tm; Schlr/Athl Awd 85; Althc Dir Assoc Awd; MVP Bsktbl Tm, All Star Bsktbl & Sftbl, MVP All-Star Sftbl; NE U; Phy Thrpy.

BRYDA, CAROL A; Medway JR-SR HS; Medway, MA; (Y); 9/142; Church Yth Grp; Drama Clb; Hosp Aide; Nwsp Stf; Yrbk Stf; Stu Cncl; Fld Hcky; Trk; Hon Roll; NHS; Schlstc Awds; Co-Chrmn Prom Commtt; Yth Undrstndg Japan Exch Pgm; Biochem.

BRYSON, ANDREA; Brockton HS; Brockton, MA; (Y); 110/1100; Dance Clb; Teachers Aide; High Hon Roll; Hon Roll; Talent Awd Golden Girl Pagnt 82; Spcl Olympcs 85; UCLA; Dancer.

BUCHALTER, STEPHEN S; Algonquin Regional HS; Northboro, MA; (Y); 124/221; Am Leg Boys St; Red Cross Aide; Rep Frsh Cls; Rep Soph Cls; Rep Jr Cls; Rep Sr Cls; Stu Cncl; Var Capt Ftbl; Var Wrstlng.

BUCHANAN, DANIEL P; North Middlesex Regional HS; Pepperell, MA; (Y); 1/210; Debate Tm; Math Tm; Chorus; Jazz Band; Madrigals; Mrchg Band; Yrbk Stf; Off Sr Cls; NHS; Ntl Merit SF; MA Advanced Studies Pgm 84; MA Yth Ldrshp Sem 83; MA Chancellors Talent Awd; Harvard U; Philosphy.

BUCHANAN, STEPHEN S; Weston HS; Weston, MA; (Y); Yrbk Rptr; JV Socr; Trk; Hon Roll; Ntl Merit SF.

BUCINSKAS, SHELLEY; David Hale Fanning Trade HS; Worcester, MA; (Y); Cmnty Wkr; Hosp Aide; Teachers Aide; Chorus; Yrbk Stf; Wt Lftg; NHS; Quinsigumond CC; Erly Chldhd.

BUCK, JASON P; Athol HS; Athol, MA; (Y); 5/114; Am Leg Boys St; Church Yth Grp; Model UN; Radio Clb; Concert Band; Mrchg Band; School Play; Nwsp Stf; Yrbk Stf; Trs Stu Cncl; Psychtrst.

BUCKEL, DENISE; Holyoke Catholic HS; Chicopee, MA; (Y); 10/140; Math Clb; Hon Roll; NHS; St Josephs Coll; Frch Tchr.

BUCKLAND, CULLEN; Haverhill HS; Haverhill, MA; (Y); Y-Teens; Nwsp Rptr; Stu Cncl; Hon Roll; Emerson Clg; Brdcstg.

BUCKLEY, CHARLES; Archbisop Williams HS; Braintree, MA; (Y); 33/200; Library Aide; Ski Clb; Golf; Trk; Hon Roll; NHS; Eucharistic Minister 85; Cornell; Engrng.

BUCKLEY, JOANNE; Holbrook JR SR HS; Holbrook, MA; (Y); 10/105; French Clb; Library Aide; Chorus; Yrbk Stf; Trs Soph Cls; Trs Jr Cls; Trs Sr Cls; Var Stu Cncl; NHS; Law.

BUCKLEY, KARA; Lexington HS; Lexington, MA; (Y); Church Yth Grp; French Clb; Hosp Aide; Chorus; School Musical; Stu Cncl; Var Bsktbl; Var Cheerleading; Score Keeper; Merrimack Coll; Bus Adm.

BUCKLEY, KEVIN; Woburn HS; Woburn, MA; (S); Boys Clb Am; Church Yth Grp; Drama Clb; French Clb; Leo Clb; Math Tm; Stu Cncl; Var Bsbl; Var Bsktbl; Jr NHS; Cls Treasr 82-83; Hnr Roll; JV Vlybl; Wake Forest Villanova; Med Bio.

BUDD, JEFFREY; Randolph HS; Randolph, MA; (Y); Computer Clb; Intnl Clb; Spanish Clb; Teachers Aide; School Musical; Yrbk Bus Mgr; Hon Roll; NHS; Parapro Hebrew Tchrs Prog 84; Grad Prozdr Div Hebrew Clg 85; Bus.

BUDDE, JAMES; Hingham HS; Hingham, MA; (Y); 46/335; Camera Clb; Church Yth Grp; Computer Clb; Stage Crew; Im Socr; Im Vllybl; High Hon Roll; Hon Roll; Mech Engrng.

BUDDENHAGEN, CURTIS G; Manchester JR SR HS; Manchester, MA; (Y); 2/79; Am Leg Boys St; Boy Scts; Capt Debate Tm; Math Tm; Science Clb; Pres Soph Cls; Pres Stu Cncl; Var Capt Golf; High Hon Roll; NHS; Alice Forbes Perkins Hooper Medcl Schlrshp 85; H S Schlr 85; Salutatorian 85; Dartmouth Coll; Law.

BUDDENHAGEN, KELLY; Bishop Stang HS; Newport, RI; (Y); Aud/Vis; Chess Clb; Church Yth Grp; Cmnty Wkr; Drama Clb; JA; Office Aide; Band; Concert Band; Mrchg Band; Christian Aherter Mem Schlrshp; Jr Olympic Sftbl; Educ.

BUDDING, ANTHONY D; Lexington HS; Lexington, MA; (Y); Ski Clb; Spanish Clb; Lcrss; Socr; Trk; Hon Roll; Psych.

BUELL, JENNIFER; Northfield Mt Hermon HS; Greenfield, MA; (Y); Exploring; Nwsp Stf; Var L Crs Cntry; Var L Fld Hcky; Var L Ice Hcky; Var L Swmmng; Var Capt Trk; Cit Awd; High Hon Roll; Hon Roll; Wellesly Book Awd 84; Peter Leyden Book Awd For Exc In Phy Ed & Athltcs 84; Hdmstr Awd 85; Brown U; Bio Sci.

BUGAN, CHERYL ANN; Bartlett HS; Webster, MA; (Y); 13/174; Church Yth Grp; Trs FBLA; Office Aide; High Hon Roll; NHS; Gld B Awd 85; Roman Wajer Schlrshp 85; Nichols Coll; Bus Admin.

BUGGIERO, DONNA; Fontbonne Acad; Readville, MA; (Y); 5/131; Church Yth Grp; Intnl Clb; Political Wkr; High Hon Roll; Hon Roll; NHS; Prfct Atten Awd; Natl Exm; Hugh O Brian Yth Orgztn; Stu Govt Day.

BUIDRINI, JANINA M; Southwick HS; Southwick, MA; (Y); 4-H; French Clb; Office Aide; Chorus; 4-H Awd; Hon Roll; NHS; VFW Awd; Phy Thrpy.

BULEY, CHRISTINE; Agawam HS; Agawam, MA; (Y); Girl Scts; Chorus; Hon Roll; Acctg.

BULLARD III, WILLIAM A; B M C Durfee HS; Fall River, MA; (Y); 24/700; VP JA; NHS; Boy Scts; Church Yth Grp; Computer Clb; Math Tm; JV Ftbl; Hon Roll; U S Naval Acad; Engrng.

BULLEN, MICHAEL; Franklin HS; Franklin, MA; (Y); Boy Scts; OEA; Ski Clb; Var Socr; Var Trk; Hon Roll; Voice Dem Awd; MA St Soccer Team 83; MA St Soccer Team 84; Athltc Hnr Roll 84; Htl Mngmnt.

BUNDY, CARTER A; Groton Schl; Montrose, NY; (Y); Debate Tm; Ski Clb; Var Socr; JV Tennis; Ntl Merit SF; Cross Country Skiing Captain 84-85; Law.

BUNNELL, LORI; St Mary Regional HS; Lynn, MA; (Y); 12/127; Library Aide; Office Aide; Stage Crew; Variety Show; Yrbk Stf; Rep Stu Cncl; Var Powder Puff Ftbl; High Hon Roll; Hon Roll; Jr NHS; Guidnce Aide; Comp Sci.

BUONCUORE, LISA; Arlington Catholic HS; Burlington, MA; (Y); 3/148; Drama Clb; JA; Spanish Clb; Church Choir; Yrbk Stf; High Hon Roll; NHS; Prfct Atten Awd; MA Adv Studs Pgm 85; Natl Hon Rl 84-85; Tchr.

BUONICONTI, CORINNA; Agawam HS; Agawam, MA; (Y); Cmnty Wkr; Drama Clb; Chorus; School Musical; School Play; Swing Chorus; Variety Show; Sftbl; NY U; Music.

BUONOPANE, JAMES; St Dom Savid HS; Winthrop, MA; (Y); 30/115; Church Yth Grp; Cmnty Wkr; Computer Clb; Key Clb; Math Clb; Math Tm; Nwsp Stf; Yrbk Stf; Crs Cntry; Trk; Boston Coll.

BURBA, RUSSELL; Central Catholic HS; Lawrence, MA; (Y); 80/223; Boys Clb Am; Boy Scts; Church Yth Grp; Computer Clb; Dance Clb; JA; Ski Clb; School Play; Stage Crew; Yrbk Phtg; U Of Lowell; Elect Engr.

BURCKHARDT, JILL; Hopkins Acad; Hadley, MA; (Y); 17/52; Am Leg Aux Girls St; Art Clb; Church Yth Grp; French Clb; Speech Tm; Band; Concert Band; Mrchg Band; Variety Show; Yrbk Bus Mgr; Ln Prize Spkng Cont 1st Pl 83-84; Comm.

BURD, MITCHELL S; Watertown HS; Watertown, MA; (Y); 7/304; Cmnty Wkr; Hosp Aide; Pres Intnl Clb; Temple Yth Grp; Band; Mrchg Band; Nwsp Stf; Var Tennis; High Hon Roll; NHS; Cum Laude Scty 84-85; Chem Awd 84; Awd For Acad Excell 85; Amherst Coll; Math.

BURGE, WILLIAM; Silver Lake Regional HS; Bryantville, MA; (Y); 117/425; Im Bsktbl; Var Socr; Im Vllybl; Church Yth Grp; 4-H; Key Clb; Varsity Clb; Coach Actv; Athl Of Mnth 85; MIP Soccr Tm 84-85; Peter J Mc Cauley Alumni Awd 84-85; Husson Coll; Bus.

BURGER, ANNE; Lunenburg HS; Lunenburg, MA; (Y); 4/139; Var L Bsktbl; Var VP Fld Hcky; Var Capt Trk; High Hon Roll; NHS; Pres Schlr; St Schlr; Elizabeth Haskens Math Awd 83; Lunenburg High Spnsh Awd 85; Luhenburg High Schlr Athlt 85; Colby Coll.

BURGESS, KEN D; Quaboag Regional HS; W Brookfield, MA; (Y); 19/79; Church Yth Grp; JA; Ski Clb; Varsity Clb; Var Golf; Var Socr; Hon Roll.

BURKE, ANN MARIE; Bishop Stano HS; S Dartmouth, MA; (Y); Church Yth Grp; Computer Clb; Key Clb; Pep Clb; Chorus; Church Choir; School Musical; Yrbk Stf; Frsh Cls; Soph Cls; ST Div I Fld Hcky Chmp 84; Wntr Trck & Sprng Trck All Star 82-85; Bentley Coll; Comp Sci.

BURKE, ANNMARIE; Gardner HS; Gardner, MA; (Y); 51/180; Church Yth Grp; Spanish Clb; Teachers Aide; JV Capt Cheerleading; JV Var Sftbl; Mrktng.

BURKE JR, JAMES E; Brockton HS; Brockton, MA; (Y); 30/950; Church Yth Grp; Key Clb; Political Wkr; Rep Soph Cls; Bsbl; Ftbl; High Hon Roll; Hon Roll; Cum Laude In Natl Latin Exam 85; Med.

BURKE, KRIS; Mt St Joseph Acad; Newton, MA; (Y); 16/148; Camera Clb; Dance Clb; Drama Clb; Spanish Clb; Teachers Aide; Chorus; School Play; Lit Mag; NHS; Mary Devercaux Awd Char & Svc 85; Boston Coll; Theatr.

BURKE, MAUREEN; Christopher Columbus HS; S Boston, MA; (S); 1/121; Church Yth Grp; Yrbk Ed-Chief; Var Cheerleading; High Hon Roll; Hon Roll; NHS; NEDT Awd; Spnsh, Chem Awd 84; Princpl List 84; Boston Coll; Pre-Med.

BURKE, TIMOTHY; Sacred Heart HS; Hull, MA; (Y); Church Yth Grp; Math Clb; Bsbl; Bsktbl; Hon Roll; Alg I 82-83; Villinova; Finc.

BURNETT, JOHN; Turners Falls HS; Erving, MA; (Y); 7/95; Church Yth Grp; Computer Clb; Letterman Clb; Yrbk Stf; Capt Swmmng; Var Tennis; Jr NHS; NHS; Pres Schlr; Excellence In Spanish I-III 81-84; James Z Naurison Schlrshp; U Of MA; Comp Sci.

BURNHAM, ANNE; Brimmer And May HS; Chestnut Hill, MA; (S); Church Yth Grp; Model UN; School Musical; Nwsp Ed-Chief; Yrbk Ed-Chief; Pres Frsh Cls; Sec Soph Cls; Var Fld Hcky; Var Lcrss; Hon Roll; Columbia Schlstc Assn Awd 84; Catherine B Mc Coy Awd 82; Soviet Area Studies.

BURNHAM, BETH; Wachusett Regional HS; Holden, MA; (Y); 28/386; Hosp Aide; Yrbk Ed-Chief; High Hon Roll; Hon Roll; NHS; Holden Hosp Auxiliary Schlrshp 85; U Of New England; Physcl Thrpy.

BURNHAM, JILL; Gloucester HS; Gloucester, MA; (Y); 4/375; Drama Clb; Rep Jr Cls; Stu Cncl; Bsktbl; Fld Hcky; Sftbl; Elks Awd; Hon Roll; NHS; Dance Clb; Intl Thespian Soc 83-84; Bio Engr.

BURNS, ANDREA; Plymouth-Carver HS; Manomet, MA; (Y); #103 In Class; Pres AFS; Office Aide; Yrbk Bus Mgr; Rep Stu Cncl; Jr NHS; Publ Rltns.

BURNS, DAVID; Bridgewater Raynham Regional HS; Raynham, MA; (Y); Im Ftbl; Stonehill Coll; Acctng.

BURNS JR, GERALD L; Grafton Memorial HS; N Grafton, MA; (Y); 3/125; Quiz Bowl; Ski Clb; Yrbk Stf; Var Bsbl; JV Var Bsktbl; Var Crs Cntry; Im Vllybl; Hon Roll; NHS.

BURNS, JAMES; Brockton HS; Brockton, MA; (Y); 130/1000; Chess Clb; Church Yth Grp; Drama Clb; Political Wkr; Ski Clb; School Musical; Yrbk Rptr; Off Sr Cls; Wrstlng; U Denver; Bus Adm.

BURNS, JENNIFER; Bishop Connolly HS; Westport, MA; (S); 12/158; Cmnty Wkr; Dance Clb; Drama Clb; French Clb; Ski Clb; School Play; Yrbk Stf; JV Cheerleading; JV Var Golf; Martin L King Jr Essay Cont Wnnr 81-82; Holocaust Essay Cont Wnnr 82-83; Hugh O Brien Yth Ldrshp 83-84; Holy Cross; Frnch.

BURON, MICHELLE M; St Peter Marian Cc HS; Auburn, MA; (Y); VP Church Yth Grp; Cmnty Wkr; Spanish Clb; Variety Show; Rep Frsh Cls; Co-Capt Cheerleading; Co-Capt Pom Pon; Elks Awd; High Hon Roll; Hon Roll; St Josephs Coll; Bio.

BURROWS, CHRISTINA MARIE; Agawam HS; Agawam, MA; (Y); 11/310; AFS; Church Yth Grp; French Clb; Chorus; Swing Chorus; Yrbk Ed-Chief; Trs Soph Cls; NHS; Variety Show; Hon Roll; U-MA Essay Prx 83; Sprngfld Dartmouth Clb Bk Awd 84; Providnence Coll; Engl.

BURT, HEATHER; Fairhaven HS; New Bedford, MA; (Y); Key Clb; Spanish Clb; Band; Concert Band; Orch; Nwsp Stf; Yrbk Stf; Capt Cheerleading; High Hon Roll; Hon Roll; Acad Letter 84; Acad Cert 85; Spnsh Oral Cont 85; Hotel Mgt.

BURTON, VINCENT; Randolph HS; Randolph, MA; (Y); Ftbl; Trk; Wrstlng; Orthdntstry.

BUSA, GINA; Tewksbury Memorial HS; Tewksbury, MA; (Y); 39/335; JA; Mrchg Band; Nwsp Stf; Yrbk Stf; Rep Frsh Cls; Trs Soph Cls; Trs Jr Cls; Rep Stu Cncl; Hon Roll; Ntl Merit Ltr; Ed.

BUSCEMI, CARLA; Ayer HS; Ayer, MA; (Y); 13/160; Am Leg Aux Girls St; Var Capt Bsktbl; Var Capt Fld Hcky; JV Sftbl; Hon Roll; Mu Alp Tht; NHS; Rivier Coll; Parlgl Studys.

BUSCEMI, CHRISTINE; Maynard HS; Maynard, MA; (Y); Letterman Clb; Radio Clb; Rep Sr Cls; JV Fld Hcky; Var Mgr(s); Var Score Keeper; NHS; Fshn Merchndsng.

BUSCEMI, SUSAN; Christopher Columbus Cntrl Cth HS; Boston, MA; (S); Drama Clb; Nwsp Rptr; High Hon Roll; Hon Roll; NEDT Awd; NSMA 85; Sci Fair 2nd Pl 84; Phtgrphy Cntst 1st Pl 84; Emerson Coll; Comms.

BUSH, BRETT M; Gardner HS; Gardner, MA; (Y); 2/200; Am Leg Boys St; Pres Frsh Cls; Rep Soph Cls; Trs Jr Cls; Var L Bsbl; Var L Bsktbl; Var L Crs Cntry; High Hon Roll; NHS; Ntl Merit SF; Harvard Bk Clb Awd; Soph Ath Yr; Hugh O Brien MA Yth Ldrshp Awd; Bus.

BUSH II, SCHUYLER D; Northfield Mount Hermon HS; Gill, MA; (Y); Church Yth Grp; Office Aide; Nwsp Bus Mgr; Yrbk Stf; Lit Mag; JV Swmmng; Var Trk; Wt Lftg; Var Wrstlng; Hon Roll; Isshin Karate Purple Belt Medal 82-84; Media Arts.

BUSKEY, ANN; Gardner HS; Gardner, MA; (Y); 7/160; Am Leg Aux Girls St; Church Yth Grp; Spanish Clb; Band; Mrchg Band; Rep Frsh Cls; Rep Soph Cls; Stu Cncl; Tennis; Hon Roll.

BUSTA, BRENDA; Andover HS; Andover, MA; (Y); 122/425; Girl Scts; Ski Clb; Diving; Sftbl; Swmmng; Hon Roll; Amer Leb Awrnss Assn Schlrshp 85; Villanova U; Comp Sci.

BUSTOS, MARIA; Mario Umana Tech; Brighton, MA; (Y); Camera Clb; Computer Clb; Dance Clb; Math Tm; VICA; Bsktbl; Bowling; Coach Actv; Swmmng; Hon Roll; Most Imprvd Stu Math 85; Cosmotlgst.

BUSWELL, KRISTIN L; Malden HS; Malden, MA; (Y); Key Clb; Hon Roll; Cert Profcncy 85; Schlrshp Awd 85; Bus.

BUTERA, ROBERT; Bishop Feehan HS; Cumberland, RI; (Y); 2/237; Math Clb; Math Tm; Concert Band; Jazz Band; Mrchg Band; School Musical; Dnfth Awd; High Hon Roll; NHS; Spanish NHS.

BUTLER, DAVID; Bishop Stang HS; New Bedford, MA; (Y); 81/211; Dance Clb; Drama Clb; Key Clb; Letterman Clb; Ski Clb; Chorus; Yrbk Stf; Socr; Trk; Hon Roll; Southeastern MA U; Cvl Engrng.

BUTLER, JOHN A; Cogle & Cassidy HS; Taunton, MA; (Y); Orch; Nwsp Rptr; JV Var Bsktbl; JV Var Ftbl; Var Golf; Samuel W Swauze Mem Schlrshp Awd 83.

BUTLER, MARY ELIZABETH; Bishop Stang HS; New Bedford, MA; (Y); 82/211; Cmnty Wkr; Drama Clb; Drm Mjr(t); School Play; Yrbk Ed-Chief; Rep Soph Cls; Rep Sr Cls; Twrlr; Hon Roll; Eng III Awd 83-84; Commnwlth Mass Schlrshp 84-85; Cong Stu Rep 82-85; Rhode Island Coll; Mass Comm.

BUTLER, SAMANTHA; Westfield HS; Westfield, MA; (Y); 20/350; Girl Scts; JA; Band; Concert Band; Pep Band; School Play; Rep Soph Cls; Trk; NHS; Syracuse U; Engrg.

BUTLER, SORAYA D; Boston Latin Schl; Boston, MA; (Y); Sec Drama Clb; Speech Tm; Band; Concert Band; School Play; Stage Crew; Yrbk Ed-Chief; Rep Sr Cls; Francis Grdnr Prz For Exc In Declamation 85; NY U; Acting.

BUTLER, THOMAS; Bridgewater-Raynham HS; Bridgewater, MA; (Y); Boy Scts; Bsbl; Stat Im Bsktbl; Capt Var Golf; Hon Roll; All-Schlstc Golf Team 85; Brdgwtr-Rynhm Sports Hall Fame Golf 85; Cntry Club JR Champ Golf 84; Bus.

BUZZELL, MELISSA; Mohawk Trail Regional HS; Shelburne Falls, MA; (Y); Chorus; Score Keeper; Sftbl; Hon Roll; Law.

BYRNE, PAUL T; Natick HS; Natick, MA; (Y); Church Yth Grp; Cmnty Wkr; Computer Clb; JA; Letterman Clb; Political Wkr; Varsity Clb; Rep Frsh Cls; Rep Soph Cls; Rep Jr Cls; Polit Sci.

BYRNES, CHERYL; Hudson HS; Hudson, MA; (Y); 3/125; Church Yth Grp; Cmnty Wkr; Girl Scts; Pep Clb; Political Wkr; Ski Clb; Var Tennis; High Hon Roll; NHS; Ntl Merit Ltr; Excllnce Fr, Sci, Eng Awds; Hstry.

BYRON, JENNIFER; Hopkins Acad; Hadley, MA; (S); 3/47; 4-H; French Clb; Concert Band; Mrchg Band; Yrbk Stf; VP Capt Bsktbl; JV Sftbl; Trs NHS.

BYRON, RICH; Reading Memorial HS; Reading, MA; (Y); VP Stu Cncl; Var L Trk; French Hon Soc; High Hon Roll; NHS; Dartmouth Bk Clb Awd Ldrshp & Schlrshp 85.

CABANA, GREG; Christopher Columbus HS; South Boston, MA; (S); Church Yth Grp; Stage Crew; Yrbk Phtg; JV Bsktbl; High Hon Roll; Finance.

CABECA, ANTHONY J; New Bedford HS; New Bedford, MA; (Y); 12/650; Am Leg Boys St; Church Yth Grp; Band; Concert Band; Jazz Band; Mrchg Band; Orch; School Musical; Symp Band; High Hon Roll; Psych.

CABRAL, DONNA; Burlington HS; Burlington, MA; (Y); Church Yth Grp; Hon Roll; Ski Clb; JV Socr; Awd Apprctn Drug/Alcohol Task Force 85; Awd Completion & Success Piano Mini-Cncrt 81; Salem ST Coll; Bus Acctg.

CABRAL, DOUGLAS; New Bedford HS; New Bedford, MA; (Y); 96/599; Var L Ftbl; Hon Roll; Gridiron Clb Schlrshp 85; Grad Hnrs 85; Allegheny Coll; Bio.

CABRAL, LAUREN; Lunenburg HS; Lunenburg, MA; (Y); Cmnty Wkr; French Clb; GAA; Varsity Clb; JV Bsktbl; Var Capt Fld Hcky; JV Socr; Var Trk; High Hon Roll; Hon Roll; Pres Phys Fit Awds; Cmmnctns.

CABRAL, MARY JO; B M C Durfee HS; Fall River, MA; (Y); Church Yth Grp; Sec & Treas Cosmtlgy Clb Awd 85; Catherine E Hinds Inst.

CABUCIO, RONALD; Diman Reg Voc Tech HS; Fall River, MA; (Y); High Hon Roll; Hon Roll; SMU.

CADIGAN, DAWN M; Medford HS; Medford, MA; (Y); 29/545; Sec Ski Clb; Varsity Clb; Stu Cncl; Capt Cheerleading; Pom Pon; Trk; Hon Roll; Bio & Engl Hnrs Awds 83; Burdett Schl Boston; Exec Sec.

CADIMA, KEVIN J; B M C Durfee HS; Fall River, MA; (Y); 11/656; Computer Clb; Math Clb; Math Tm; Political Wkr; Teachers Aide; Elks Awd; High Hon Roll; Hon Roll; NHS; Ntl Merit Ltr; Almn Schlrshp 85; Tngr Of Mnth 85; Pres Acadmc Awd 85; Lyndon ST Coll; Metrlgy.

CADLE, JOHN R; Malden HS; Malden, MA; (Y); Boy Scts; Cmnty Wkr; Hon Roll; Navy; Avtn Elctrcns Mate.

CADY, KRISTINA; Ware HS; Ware, MA; (Y); 12/115; Am Leg Aux Girls St; Pep Clb; Chorus; School Play; Ed Yrbk Phtg; Sec Stu Cncl; Wt Lftg; DAR Awd; Hon Roll; VFW Awd; Jane Eddy Lull Music Awd 85; Mt Holyoke Clg; Bio.

CAFARO, MARIA E; Hopedale JR-SR HS; Hopedale, MA; (Y); 3/61; Church Yth Grp; Chorus; School Play; Stage Crew; Yrbk Stf; High Hon Roll; NHS; Ntl Merit SF; Schlstc Decthln 84; Math.

CAFASSO, MICHELLE; Everett HS; Everett, MA; (Y); Cmnty Wkr; Intnl Clb; Key Clb; Office Aide; Chorus; Color Guard; Drill Tm; Hon Roll; Psych.

CAFASSO, MRIE; Gloucester HS; Gloucester, MA; (Y); Church Yth Grp; Yrbk Stf; VP Stu Cncl; Sftbl; Hon Roll; Pres NHS.

CAFFREY, PATRICIA A; Middleborough HS; Middleboro, MA; (Y); Band; Chorus; Rep Frsh Cls; Rep Soph Cls; Rep Jr Cls; Rep Stu Cncl; JV Bsktbl; JV Var Fld Hcky; Slvr M Ctznshp, Band Ldrshp Clb 84.

CAGGIANO, MARK A; Dennis Yarmouth R HS; S Yarmouth, MA; (Y); Am Leg Boys St; Church Yth Grp; Civic Clb; Pres Jr Cls; Var Capt Ice Hcky; Var L Socr; Var L Tennis; Kiwanis Awd; VP Frsh Cls; VP Soph Cls; MVP Hcky; Phy Ed Awd; Good Sprtsmnshp Awd; Hmcmng King; Babson Coll; Bus.

CAGNETTA, PATRICE; Haverhill HS; Bradford, MA; (Y); 26/380; French Clb; Spanish Clb; Color Guard; High Hon Roll; NHS; John Hancock Bus Awd 85; Bus Math Awd 82; NH Coll; Accntng.

CAHILL, MARY; Dedham HS; Dedham, MA; (Y); 85/300; Church Yth Grp; Cmnty Wkr; Ski Clb; Varsity Clb; JV Bsktbl; JV Coach Actv; Powder Puff Ftbl; Var L Socr; Var L Trk; Hon Roll; Prsdntl Phy Ftnss Awd 83-84; Bus.

CAIN, SUSAN; Woburn HS; Woburn, MA; (S); 5/500; Church Yth Grp; Computer Clb; Debate Tm; English Clb; FBLA; Leo Clb; Math Clb; Math Tm; Science Clb; Ski Clb; Histrcl Essay Cont Wnr 84; Girl Of Yr CMO Bsktbl 83; MA ST Sci Fair Wnr MIT 3rd Pl 82; Bus.

CAIRNS, THERESA; Presentation Of Mary Acad; Hampstead, NH; (Y); 15/50; Pres Sec Church Yth Grp; French Clb; Hosp Aide; Cheerleading; Dnfth Awd; Hon Roll; NHS; G H Berube Trst Fnd Schlrshp 85; Trigom Awd 85; Cert Achvt NEDT 83; Providence Coll; Eng.

CAITLIN-AHERN, JEANMARIE; Bishop Feehan HS; Sharon, MA; (Y); Pres 4-H; Chorus; Church Choir; School Musical; School Play; Stage Crew; 4-H Awd; High Hon Roll; Hon Roll; Spanish NHS; Theater.

CALANDRA, FRANK; Matignon HS; Somerville, MA; (Y); 53/175; Boys Clb Am; Boy Scts; Science Clb; Im Bsktbl; Im Vllybl; Wrcstr Polytch Inst; Aero Engrg.

CALARESE, JAMES; Milford HS; Milford, MA; (Y); 7/292; Aud/Vis; Church Yth Grp; Yrbk Stf; Rep Stu Cncl; JV Tennis; High Hon Roll; NHS; WPI; Ind Mgmt Engrng.

CALCAGNI, SCOTT; Milford HS; Milford, MA; (Y); Yrbk Stf; JV Bsbl; Hon Roll; Crew Prsn Mnth Awd Mc Donalds 85; Envrnmntl Sci.

CALDBECK, THOMAS; Classical HS; Springfield, MA; (Y); 11/412; Church Yth Grp; Key Clb; Nwsp Rptr; Yrbk Stf; Hon Roll; Jr NHS; NHS; Ntl Merit Ltr.

CALDICOTT, DEBRA; Fontbonne Acad; Norwood, MA; (Y); 15/131; Sec Church Yth Grp; Dance Clb; Drama Clb; Hosp Aide; Intnl Clb; Drm & Bgl; Yrbk Stf; High Hon Roll; Hon Roll; Lwyr.

CALDON, MAUREEN F; Cathedral HS; Hampden, MA; (Y); Dance Clb; Office Aide; Ski Clb; Outstndng Svc 84-85; Flashtype Muscular Dystrophy 84-85; US Irish Dncng Tm Rep USA 82-84; Smith Coll; Bus Mgt.

CALDWELL, RENEE RACHEL; Medford HS; Medford, MA; (Y); Band; Drm & Bgl; VFW Awd; Outstndg Prgrs Engl; Outstndg Achvt Engl; NE U.

CALISE, LISA; Bishop Connolly HS; Somerset, MA; (S); 5/177; VP JA; Latin Clb; Math Tm; Ski Clb; Vllybl; High Hon Roll; NHS; Magna Cum Laude; Georgetown; Intl Bus.

CALL, KRISTINE M; Bellingham Memorial HS; Bellingham, MA; (Y); 4/201; Drama Clb; Intnl Clb; Ski Clb; Yrbk Stf; High Hon Roll; Jr NHS; NHS; Pauline Ladouceur Mem Schlrshp 86; Framingham St Hstry Cont-Hnrb Mntn 84; Pres Acad Ftnss Awd 85; Worcester ST Coll; Comp Sci.

CALLAGHAN, PATRICIA; Reading Memorial HS; Reading, MA; (Y); 1/355; Nwsp Ed-Chief; NHS; Pres Schlr; Spanish NHS; St Schlr; Val; Church Yth Grp; Debate Tm; Hosp Aide; Math Tm; Princeton Alumni Assn Awd 84; Radcliffe Summr Pgm Sci 84; Pres Stu Advsry Cncl 84-85; Harvard U; Med.

CALLAGHAN, STEPHANIE; Braintree HS; Braintree, MA; (Y); 14/400; Math Tm; Red Cross Aide; High Hon Roll; NHS; Ntl Merit Ltr; Spanish NHS; SADD Stu 85; Essy Accptd Schl Litry Magzne 85.

CALLAHAN, JOANNE; Malden HS; Malden, MA; (Y); 50/500; PAVAS; Church Choir; Madrigals; School Musical; Variety Show; Yrbk Bus Mgr; Yrbk Rptr; Lit Mag; Co-Capt Trk; NEDT Awd; Cornell U; Htl Mngmnt.

CALLAHAN, JOHN; Rev Ere HS; Revere, MA; (Y); Am Leg Boys St; Math Clb; Math Tm; Quiz Bowl; Science Clb; Yrbk Stf; Mgr Bsktbl; Var Trk; High Hon Roll; Dedctd Svc Awd 85; Engrng.

CALLAHAN, KERRY; Leominster HS; Leominster, MA; (Y); Am Leg Boys St; Church Yth Grp; Letterman Clb; Ski Clb; Var L Bsbl; Var L Bsktbl; Var Capt Socr; High Hon Roll; Hon Roll; NHS; All Cape Cod Sr Babe Ruth All Stars 85; All Stars Babe Ruth 83.

CALLAHAN, SUSAN; Easthampton HS; Easthampton, MA; (Y); 25/140; JA; Spanish Clb; Yrbk Stf; Var L Swmmng; Hon Roll; Math.

CALLENDER, MICHAEL; Bedford HS; Bedford, MA; (Y); 72/219; AFS; Boy Scts; Cmnty Wkr; OEA; ROTC; Rep Stu Cncl; Var L Crs Cntry; Var L Trk; Cit Awd; VFW Awd; 100 Hrs Of Vol Wrk For VA 85; Air Force Acad; Austrntcl Engr.

CALUSDIAN, DAVID C; Walpole HS; Walpole, MA; (Y); 45/262; Church Yth Grp; Radio Clb; Band; Jazz Band; NHS; SW MA U; Pol Sci.

CALVERT, CHRISTINE; Melrose HS; Melrose, MA; (Y); 26/365; Ski Clb; Trk; Vllybl; Hon Roll; NHS; Sci Awd 83; Math.

CAMAIONI, CAROL; New Bedford HS; New Bedford, MA; (Y); 2/700; Church Yth Grp; Drama Clb; Chorus; School Musical; VP Pres Stu Cncl; High Hon Roll; NHS; Chancllrs Tlnt Awd Schlrshp-Academc Excllnc 85; Rensselaer Polytech Inst Awd-Math & Sci 85; Engrng.

CAMARA, GRACE; New Bedford HS; New Bedford, MA; (Y); Nrsng.

CAMARA, ROBERT; Somerset HS; Somerset, MA; (Y); Concert Band; Jazz Band; Mrchg Band; Orch; Symp Band; Nwsp Rptr; Nwsp Stf; Yrbk Stf; Per Atten Awds 78-81; Math Awd 79-80; Music Awds 78-81; Pub Rel.

CAMARA, STEPHANIE; BMC Durfee HS; Fall River, MA; (Y); 114/656; Camera Clb; Variety Show; Yrbk Stf; Hon Roll; Johnson & Wales; Fash Merch.

CAMARATA, ANNA; Boston Latin HS; Boston, MA; (Y); 49/325; English Clb; French Clb; JA; Key Clb; Latin Clb; Chorus; Nwsp Stf; Yrbk Stf; Lit Mag; High Hon Roll; Exmplry Conduct & Fidelity 85; Achvt In Reading 83; Tufts U; Intl Relations.

CAMBRA II, ROBERT F; Taunton HS; Taunton, MA; (Y); Latin Clb; Lib Library Aide; Lit Mag; Comm Art.

CAMERON, CHERYL ANN; Trinton Regional HS; Rowley, MA; (Y); 5/182; AFS; Church Yth Grp; Drama Clb; Color Guard; Off Jr Cls; Off Stu Cncl; Elks Awd; High Hon Roll; Hon Roll; NHS; Triton Tchrs Assc Awd Acad Exc 84; AWD Exc In Span 85; Bravo-Encore Awd For Acad Exc 80-85; Bates CollENGL.

CAMERON, CHRISTINE; Notre Dame Acad; S Weymouth, MA; (Y); 23/114; Church Yth Grp; Debate Tm; Hosp Aide; Library Aide; Ski Clb; Chorus; Rep Stu Cncl; Im Vllybl; French Hon Soc; High Hon Roll; Georgetown; Jrnlsm.

CAMERON, GARY ALAN; North Attleboro HS; N Attleboro, MA; (Y); 27/231; Var Letterman Clb; Var Varsity Clb; Var Nwsp Sprt Ed; JV Bsbl; L Ftbl; L Golf; Im Vllybl; Hon Roll; Ntl Merit Schol; MA U; Comp Sci.

CAMERON, KAREN; Salem HS; Salem, MA; (Y); 52/332; German Clb; Girl Scts; Ski Clb; Band; Concert Band; Mrchg Band; Orch; School Musical; Yrbk Stf; High Hon Roll; Girl Sct Gold Awd 84; Music.

CAMILIEN, GLADIS; Fontbonne Acad; Boston, MA; (Y); 16/172; Art Clb; Debate Tm; Drama Clb; Ed English Clb; French Clb; Library Aide; Yrbk Stf; Lit Mag; High Hon Roll; NHS; Boston Glb Art Awds-Blue Rbbn & Gld Key 85; Boston Glb Art Fair 85; 1st Prz-Archdiocesian Art Fair 83; Law.

CAMP, MARK; North Middlesex Regional HS; Pepperell, MA; (Y); 13/216; VP Debate Tm; Drama Clb; Madrigals; Mrchg Band; School Musical; Yrbk Stf; JV Ftbl; Im Socr; Hon Roll; NHS; Citn Stu Govt-ST Hse 85; TAG Intrn 85; Masp Alt 84; U Of MAHSTRY.

CAMPAGNA, DAWN; Methuen HS; Methuen, MA; (Y); 44/340; Drama Clb; Intnl Clb; Chorus; School Musical; Swing Chorus; Variety Show; Sec Stu Cncl; Hon Roll; All ST Chorus 85; HOBY Ldrshp Fndtn 84; Stu Overall Achvt Recgntn Awd 83; Music Ed.

CAMPAGNA, SUZANNE; St Clare HS; Norwood, MA; (Y); Church Yth Grp; Cmnty Wkr; Trs French Clb; Trs Girl Scts; JCL; Church Choir; School Musical; Stage Crew; Nwsp Rptr; Nwsp Stf; Amer Classcl Lg NJCL Cert Cum Laude 82; May Nelson Awd 85; Gold & Silver Awds Grl Scouts 83 & 85; Syracuse U; Cmmnctns.

CAMPANALE, MICHAEL J; Arlington HS; Arlington, MA; (Y); Rep Stu Cncl; JV Var Bsbl; JV Var Bsktbl; Var Ftbl; High Hon Roll; Hon Roll; NHS.

CAMPANELLA, CHRISTINE; Everett HS; Everett, MA; (Y); Church Yth Grp; Key Clb; Office Aide; Northeastern U; Accntng.

CAMPBELL, GARY; Malden Catholic HS; Medford, MA; (Y); 10/185; Sec Computer Clb; Trs French Clb; Intnl Clb; Yrbk Stf; Im Bsktbl; Ftbl; Im Vllybl; High Hon Roll; Jr NHS; NHS; Acctg.

CAMPBELL, KERRY; Taunton HS; Taunton, MA; (Y); Church Yth Grp; JCL; Latin Clb; Yrbk Stf; Lit Mag; Trk; High Hon Roll; NHS.

CAMPBELL, ROBERTA; Holy Name C C HS; Uxbridge, MA; (Y); Drama Clb; Quiz Bowl; Band; Humnties II Awd 84; Lit III Awd 85; Stenogrphy I Awd 85; Bus Adm.

CAMPISI, DEBBIE; Agawam HS; Feeding Hills, MA; (Y); 16/348; Church Yth Grp; Hosp Aide; Band; Concert Band; Mrchg Band; High Hon Roll; Hon Roll; Nrsng.

CAMPO, ELIZABETH; Matignon HS; Somerville, MA; (S); 15/191; Drama Clb; School Musical; Stage Crew; Rep Soph Cls; Rep Stu Cncl; Hon Roll; NHS; Ntl Merit Schol; Spanish Clb; Hstry Awd 83; Babson; Bus.

CAMUS, THEODORE A; Westford Acad; Westford, MA; (Y); 2/205; VP Chess Clb; VP Math Tm; Band; Mrchg Band; Bausch & Lomb Sci Awd; High Hon Roll; NHS; Ntl Merit Ltr; Prfct Atten Awd; Pres Schlr; Alg II, Trig, Chem, Colby Coll Bk Prize; Calc & Physics Awds; Rennsselaer Polytech Inst; Comp.

CANAVAN, MARY; Braintree HS; Braintree, MA; (Y); 172/510; JV Bsktbl; Score Keeper; Var Capt Socr; Var Sftbl; High Hon Roll; Socr All-Star Tm 84; Boston Coll; Polit Sci.

CANAVAN, SHARON; Archbishop Williams HS; Quincy, MA; (Y); #30 In Class; Camera Clb; Church Yth Grp; FNA; Hosp Aide; Yrbk Stf; High Hon Roll; Hon Roll; NEDT Awd; Spnsh Merit Awd 83; Law.

CANDIDO, LISA; Dartmouth HS; N Dartmouth, MA; (Y); 46/261; Church Yth Grp; JA; Key Clb; Yrbk Sprt Ed; Stu Cncl; Cheerleading; Gym; Jr NHS; Gtr New Bedford Jr Miss 85; Dr Deane E Frietas Schlrshp 85; Boton U; Pre-Med.

CANEY, BRIAN F; West Springfield SR HS; W Springfield, MA; (Y); 52/250; Spanish Clb; JV Capt Bsbl; Var L Ftbl; Hon Roll; Spanish NHS; Nrtheastrn U; Elec Engrng.

CANN, LYNNE-ROSE; Methuen HS; Methuen, MA; (Y); 2/350; Computer Clb; Intnl Clb; High Hon Roll; NHS; Spanish NHS; Spnsh Awd.

CANNATELLI, DENISE M; Malden HS; Malden, MA; (Y); 84/500; Art Clb; Cmnty Wkr; Dance Clb; Hosp Aide; Office Aide; Ski Clb; Color Guard; Drm & Bgl; Var Fld Hcky; Var Gym; Albert E Harding & Trstee Schlrshps 85; Boston Coll; RN.

CANNEY, CATHLEEN; Mount Saint Joseph Acad; Brookline, MA; (Y); 10/150; Church Yth Grp; Math Clb; Color Guard; High Hon Roll; Hon Roll; NHS; Chem.

CANNEY, CHRISTOPHER; Haverhill HS; Haverhill, MA; (Y); Cmnty Wkr; Political Wkr; JV Bsktbl; Var Crs Cntry; JV Ftbl; Im Wt Lftg; Hon Roll; Aero Engrng.

CANNEY, JOSEPH; St Johns HS; Shrewsbury, MA; (Y); Letterman Clb; Model UN; Varsity Clb; Nwsp Stf; Im Bsktbl; JV Var Ftbl; Var L Trk; Hon Roll; Bus.

CANNON, JOHN; Hingham HS; Hingham, MA; (Y); 29/300; AFS; Computer Clb; Yrbk Stf; Crs Cntry; JV Tennis; Trk; Vllybl; Pre-Med.

CANTO, MICHAEL A; Greater Boston Acad; Stoneham, MA; (S); 2/12; Band; Chorus; Orch; Rep Soph Cls; Pres Jr Cls; Hon Roll; Socty Distngshd Amer H S Stdnts 85; Buckingham Browne; Pedtrcn.

CANTWELL, JAMES; Burncoat SR HS; Worcester, MA; (Y); Crs Cntry; Hon Roll; Jr NHS; NHS; Comp Sci.

CAPALDO, MATTHEW; Medford HS; Medford, MA; (Y); Cmnty Wkr; Nwsp Stf; Yrbk Stf; Tennis; Hon Roll; NHS; Bio Awd 81-82; Englsh Awds For Acad Excell 81-83; Awd For Cmnty Svc 84; Bus Adm.

CAPARELLIOTIS, DAVID; Marian HS; Framingham, MA; (Y); 26/177; Civic Clb; Ski Clb; School Play; Ed Yrbk Rptr; Pres Frsh Cls; Rep Off Soph Cls; Rep Jr Cls; Stu Cncl; Cit Awd; Hon Roll; Chrmn Stu Cmmnctn Local Nwsppr Grp 85; Bowdoin Coll; Engl.

CAPES, KARYN; North Middlesex Regional HS; Pepperell, MA; (Y); Church Yth Grp; Drama Clb; French Clb; Teachers Aide; Orch; Rep Stu Cncl; JV Crs Cntry; Var Trk; Hon Roll; Sec NHS; Envrmntl Svc.

CAPLETTE, NORA L; Shepherd Hill Regional HS; Southbridge, MA; (Y); Am Leg Aux Girls St; 4-H; Math Tm; Ski Clb; Chorus; School Play; NHS; Pres Athltc Awd 83-85; ST Hnr Scholar 85.

CAPLETTE, PAMELA L; Shepherd Hill Regional HS; Charlton, MA; (Y); 1/158; Dance Clb; Band; School Musical; Elks Awd; High Hon Roll; NHS; Val; Church Yth Grp; Girl Scts; Hosp Aide; Yth Of Yr Awd 85; Chrltn Dmcrtc Cmt Schlrshp 85; Elzb A Carmody Mem Schlrshp 85; Hofston U; Math.

CAPONE, ROBIN; Wakefield HS; Wakefield, MA; (Y); Off Frsh Cls; Sec Soph Cls; Sec Jr Cls; Rep Stu Cncl; Var Capt Tennis; Var Capt Twrlr; Hon Roll; Yrbk Rptr; Yrbk Stf; JV Bsktbl; Stu Advsry Cmt 85; MVP Tennis 84 & 85; Mst Ptntl Awd For Tennis 83.

CAPONE, RONALD V; Masconomet Regional HS; Topsfield, MA; (Y); 12/275; Am Leg Boys St; Cmnty Wkr; Var Socr; Var Trk; CC Awd; Hon Roll; NHS; PTA Schlrshp Awd 85; Thomas W Trst Mem Schlrshp 85; Northeast Reg Chmpnshp Sccr Tm Mbr 84; St Anselm Coll Manchester; Bus.

CAPOSSELA, MINO C; Buckingham Browne & Nichols HS; Boston, MA; (Y); French Clb; Sec Frsh Cls; Rep Soph Cls; Off Jr Cls; Capt Tennis; High Hon Roll; Natl Merit Schlrshp Semi Fnlst; YFU Japn U S Sen Schlrshp; NELTA A #15; Yale; Inv Bnkr.

CAPPELLO, MARIA; Christopher Columbus HS; Boston, MA; (S); Bsktbl; 2nd Hnrs 84; Comp.

CAPPUCCI, JAMES M; Burlington HS; Burlington, MA; (Y); 29/315; Church Yth Grp; Computer Clb; JA; Rep Sr Cls; Var Capt Crs Cntry; Var L Trk; High Hon Roll; Hon Roll; NHS; Comp.

CAPPUCCIO, CAROLYN; Norwood SR HS; Norwood, MA; (Y); Hosp Aide; Key Clb; Mrchg Band; Orch; Symp Band; Rep Stu Cncl; Var L Tennis; Hon Roll; Wheaton Coll.

CAPRIOLI, ANGELA; Holy Name Central Catholic HS; Worcester, MA; (Y); 48/232; Political Wkr; Ski Clb; High Hon Roll; Hon Roll; E Side Imprvmnt Clb Schlrshp 85; SMS Rivs Colon Biscegliese Schlrshp 85; Bio II Cert 85; U MA Amherst; Pre-Vet.

CAPSHAW, JACQUELYN; Greenfield HS; Greenfield, MA; (Y); Church Yth Grp; DECA; GAA; Chorus; Trs Frsh Cls; Trs Stu Cncl; Trs Jr Cls; Var Cheerleading; JV Fld Hcky; JV Tennis; Georgetown; Pltcl Sci.

CARABALLO, EFRAIN; Holyoke HS; Holyoke, MA; (Y); Spanish Clb; High Hon Roll; Hon Roll; U MA-AMHERST; Elect Engrng.

CARBON, ELLINOR; Marthas Vineyard RHS HS; Edgartown, MA; (Y); 8/110; Computer Clb; Spanish Clb; Yrbk Stf; Sec Frsh Cls; Soph Cls; Sec Jr Cls; Sec Sr Cls; Sec Stu Cncl; Bsktbl; Fld Hcky; Wellesley Coll.

CARBONE, MATTHEW; Haverhill HS; Bradford, MA; (Y); Trs Band; Jazz Band; Mrchg Band; Nwsp Phtg; Ed Yrbk Ed-Chief; Yrbk Phtg; JP Sousa Awd; Key Clb; Concert Band; Jewish War Vet USA Brotherhd Awd 85; New England Schltc Hnrs Band 83-85; Natl Assoc Jazz Ed 85; Northern Essex CC; Crimnl Just.

CARCHIO, DONNA; King Philip Regional HS; Wrentham, MA; (S); Church Yth Grp; DECA; Girl Scts; VICA; Mgr(s); Trk; Dist Conf 1st Pl Fd Mktg Evnt, 1st Pl Mktg Supvry 84; 1st Pl Pgm Cvr Dsgn 84; MA DECA Conf 2nd Pl 85; Jhonston & Wales; Fshn Mrch.

CARDARELLI, CHERYL; Malden HS; Malden, MA; (Y); 29/450; Church Yth Grp; Color Guard; Mrchg Band; School Musical; Variety Show; Lit Mag; Ntl Merit Schol; Nrsg.

CARDEIRO, ROBERT; St Johns HS; Westboro, MA; (Y); 103/271; Church Yth Grp; Trs Exploring; Variety Show; Var L Crs Cntry; Var Trk; High Hon Roll; Hon Roll; Bio.

CARDELLO, JOSEPH; Matignon HS; Medford, MA; (Y); 74/181; Nwsp Stf; Rep Frsh Cls; Rep Soph Cls; Rep Jr Cls; Rep Sr Cls; Rep Stu Cncl; JV Bsbl; JV Var Bsktbl; Coach Actv; JV Ftbl; Bus.

CARDILLO, BRENT; Drury HS; N Adams, MA; (Y); 25/163; Spanish Clb; Nwsp Stf; Crs Cntry; Hon Roll; NHS; Ntl Merit Ltr; NEDT Awd; Pres Schlr; Elks Schlshp 85; James Navrison Schlshrp 85; RI Schl Design; Crtnist.

CARDONA, NILDA; Commerce HS; Springfield, MA; (S); Church Yth Grp; Hosp Aide; Spanish Clb; Church Choir; School Play; Bsktbl; Bowling; Tennis; Vllybl; Hon Roll; STCC; Hlth.

CARDOSO, NANCY; B M C Durfee HS; Fall River, MA; (Y); Church Yth Grp; Hon Roll; Accntng.

CARDOZA, KIMBERLY; Maynard HS; Maynard, MA; (Y); 18/100; Trs Church Yth Grp; Radio Clb; VP Frsh Cls; Sec Jr Cls; Var L Fld Hcky; Var L Sftbl; Var L Vllybl; Hon Roll; Premed.

CAREW, JENNIFER; Whitman-Hanson Regional HS; Whitman, MA; (Y); 53/323; AFS; Im Bowling; Var Crs Cntry; Im Tennis; JV Trk; Hon Roll; Grls Crss Cntry MI Rnnr 82; J Conant Mem Schlrshp 85; Town Comm Schlrshp 85; Burdett School; Ex Secy.

CAREY III, WALTER T; Gloucester HS; Gloucester, MA; (Y); 46/314; Math Tm; Off Capt ROTC; Thesps; Drill Tm; School Musical; Stage Crew; Sr Cls; NHS; Pres Rotary Awd; VFW Awd ROTC Comp Outstndng Cmnty Svc 85; Thespain Schlrshp & Intl Thespain Awd 85; ROTC Awds 84; U Lowell; Elec Engrng.

CARINI, FRANK; Medway JR/SR HS; Medway, MA; (Y); 52/146; Var Bsbl; JV Var Socr; Hon Roll; AZ ST; Jrnlsm.

CARISTI, LAURA; Notre Dame Academy; Marshfield, MA; (Y); Cmnty Wkr; Debate Tm; Political Wkr; Chorus; School Musical; Crs Cntry; Trk; High Hon Roll; Hon Roll; Pre Med.

CARLINO, MARY C; Tewksbury HS; Tewksbury, MA; (Y); 30/290; Hon Roll; Spnsh Stu Of The Yr 81-82; U Of Lowell; Med.

CARLISLE, ELIZABETH; Lawrence HS; Lawrence, MA; (S); 15/350; Chorus; School Play; Yrbk Stf; High Hon Roll; Hon Roll; L Pin 84-85; MI ST U; Pre Vet Med.

CARLO, FRANCIS J; Auburn HS; Auburn, MA; (Y); JV Var Bsbl; JV Socr; High Hon Roll; Hon Roll; Ederd Coll; Bus Admn.

CARLO, MICHELLE; St Clare HS; West Roxbury, MA; (Y); Sec Church Yth Grp; French Clb; Stu Cncl; Hon Roll; NHS; Ntl Merit Ltr; Bentley Coll; Accntng.

CARLS, ELIZABETH; Wayland HS; Wayland, MA; (Y); 8/230; Church Yth Grp; Girl Scts; Pres Latin Clb; Var Ski Clb; Chorus; Church Choir; Madrigals; Stu Cncl; JV Var Lcrss; JV Var Socr; Hnrs Bio Awd, Wrld Hstry Awd, Nat Sci Olympiad 81-82; Ntl Sco Stds Olympiad 82-83; Latin IV Awd 83-84; Yale U.

CARLSON, EMELINE M; Cardinal Spellman HS; Brockton, MA; (Y); 4/210; Hosp Aide; Office Aide; Lit Mag; VP Jr Cls; VP Stu Cncl; Capt Cheerleading; Mgr(s); Tennis; High Hon Roll; Kiwanis Awd; MA Yh Ldrshp Hugh O Brian 82; Pres Fitnss Acad Awd 85; George E Keith Plymouh Hm Natl Bank 85; Northeastern U; Nrse Practitnr.

CARLSON, ROSS; Wellesley SR HS; Wellesley, MA; (Y); Pres Church Yth Grp; Band; Concert Band; Jazz Band; Pep Band; Capt Var Swmmng; German Clb; School Musical; School Play; Yrbk Stf; V Ltrs Sailng,Swmmng 84-85; Bay ST Conf Swmmng Awd 3rd Pl 84-85; Cert Achvt Stage Band 83.

CARMEL, LAURA; Southbridge HS; Sbridge, MA; (Y); 17/137; Yrbk Phtg; Yrbk Stf; Rep Frsh Cls; Rep Soph Cls; Rep Jr Cls; Rep Sr Cls; JV Var Fld Hcky; Var Trk; Hon Roll; Pre-Vet.

CARNEGIE, RUTH; Doherty Memorial HS; Worcester, MA; (Y); Trs Church Yth Grp; VP JA; Library Aide; Office Aide; Spanish Clb; Church Choir; Yrbk Stf; High Hon Roll; Jr NHS; Spanish NHS; Ntl Spnsh Exam Awds 85; Biology.

CARNES, GRETCHEN; Shawsheen Valley Vo Tech; Tewksbury, MA; (Y); 13/460; Computer Clb; Hosp Aide; VICA; School Play; Stu Cncl; Sftbl; Swmmng; Hon Roll; Bowling-Patch Trphy, Mdl 82; Law Enfrcmnt.

CARNES, JOHN F; Norwell HS; Norwell, MA; (Y); Varsity Clb; JV Bsbl; Var Ftbl; Im Wt Lftg; Stone Hill; Bus.

CARNEVALE, STEPHANIE A; Beverly HS; Beverly, MA; (Y); 53/378; Off Jr Cls; Pres Stu Cncl; Var Cheerleading; Powder Puff Ftbl; Cmnty Wkr; Ski Clb; Peer Educ & Patria Lavora Schlrshps 85; U Of MA.

CARNEY, COLLEEN; Fontbonne Acad; Quincy, MA; (Y); 15/155; Church Yth Grp; Computer Clb; Intnl Clb; Library Aide; Math Tm; High Hon Roll; Drama Clb; Hosp Aide; Variety Show; Hon Roll; Cert Merit New Eng Math Lg 85; Art Awd 1st Boston Archdioces Art Fair 83; Awd Outstndng Achvt Geom 84; Engrng.

CARNEY, JENNIFER; Easthampton HS; Easthampton, MA; (Y); Hosp Aide; Chorus; Yrbk Stf; Stu Cncl; Var Cheerleading; Capt Twrlr; Hon Roll; Poli Sci.

CARON, CYNTHIA; St Bernards C C HS; Fitchburg, MA; (S); 12/173; Girl Scts; Latin Clb; Office Aide; School Musical; Sec Jr Cls; Var Capt Cheerleading; Var Socr; JV Trk; Hon Roll; Duke U.

CARON, LISA; Agawam HS; Feeding Hls, MA; (Y); 59/300; GAA; Nwsp Sprt Ed; Sec Stu Cncl; Var Bsktbl; Var L Fld Hcky; Var L Sftbl; Var Var Trk; Hon Roll; Church Yth Grp; Drama Clb; All-Star Team Sacred Eart Athltc Assc Softbl 83-84.

CARON, MELISSA; New Bedford HS; New Bedford, MA; (Y); 71/680; Church Yth Grp; Hosp Aide; JA; Var L Trk; High Hon Roll; Hon Roll; Prfct Atten Awd.

CARON, ROSEMARY; Billerica Memorial HS; Billerica, MA; (Y); 2/507; Camera Clb; French Clb; Math Clb; Math Tm; Science Clb; Yrbk Stf; JV Socr; High Hon Roll; L Hon Roll; NHS; Miss Teen Schlrshp Recgntn Pagnt 85; Tufts U; Bio.

CARON, SUZANNE; New Bedford HS; New Bedford, MA; (Y); 14/543; Drama Clb; French Clb; Ski Clb; VP Jr Cls; Pres Stu Cncl; Var Capt Crs Cntry; Var Capt Trk; High Hon Roll; NHS; Citation HS Stu Cngrs 85; Stu Cngrs Scholar 85; New Bedford Ladies Scholar Trust Fnd 85; Wellesley Coll; Bio.

CARPENTER, AMY; Holy Name CC HS; E Douglas, MA; (Y); Church Yth Grp; Yrbk Stf; Lit Mag; High Hon Roll; Hon Roll; NHS; Dept Awd In Engl & Humanities 84; Journ.

CARPENTER, KEVIN; Technical HS; Springfield, MA; (S); 3/210; FBLA; DAR Awd; High Hon Roll; NHS; Renselear Polytchnc Awd For Sci & Math 83; Dartmouth Clb Bk Awd 83; Hmnts Tech.

CARPENTER, LAUREL; Hingham HS; Hingham, MA; (Y); 9/340; Am Leg Boys St; L Debate Tm; Thesps; School Musical; Rep Cmnty Wkr; NHS; Cmnty Wkr; Drama Clb; Band; Church Choir; NCTE Writing Comp Semi Fin; Elected To Stu Advisry Cncl; Manhattenville Book Awd; All Star Acting Awds; Attorney At Law.

CARPENTER, MARYANN; Ayer SR HS; Ayer, MA; (Y); #23 In Class; Drama Clb; Pep Clb; VP Spanish Clb; Hon Roll; Busnss.

CARPENTER, MATTHEW; Saint Bernards C C HS; Leominster, MA; (S); 22/172; Camera Clb; Model UN; Ski Clb; Nwsp Ed-Chief; Nwsp Rptr; Rep Stu Cncl; Var Crs Cntry; Var Trk; Hon Roll; Engrng.

CARPENTER, TRISTRAM C; Norwood SR HS; Norwood, MA; (Y); 25/357; Band; Jazz Band; Mrchg Band; Swing Chorus; Socr; Hon Roll; Ntl Merit Ltr; Harvard; Pre-Law.

CARR, ANDREW E; Burlington HS; Burlington, MA; (Y); 35/400; JA; Math Tm; Ski Clb; Lit Mag; Var Socr; Var Tennis; Var Trk; Hon Roll; NHS; H P Hood Schlrshp 85-89; U Of Notre Dame; Cmnctns.

CARR, CRAIG; Comprehensive HS; Chicopee, MA; (Y); 6/270; Am Leg Boys St; Rep Frsh Cls; Rep Jr Cls; JV Bsbl; JV Ftbl; Hon Roll; NHS; Elec Engrng.

CARR, DEBRA A; Old Colony Reg Tech Voc HS; Carver, MA; (Y); Cmnty Wkr; Computer Clb; Dance Clb; Pres VICA; Yrbk Stf; Rep Frsh Cls; Stu Cncl; DAR Awd; Hon Roll; Ntl Hstry & Govt Awd 84; Acdmc All Amer 84; Ntl Achvt & Srv Awd 85; Brdgwtr ST; Bus Mngmnt.

CARR, KENNETH I; Hingham HS; Hingham, MA; (Y); 1/330; Chess Clb; VP Math Tm; Pres Temple Yth Grp; Chorus; Im Vllybl; High Hon Roll; NHS; Ntl Merit SF; Val; AFS; Harvard Book Awd 84.

CARR, TIMOTHY; Hingham HS; Hingham, MA; (Y); 4/350; Boy Scts; Church Yth Grp; Jazz Band; Symp Band; JV Socr; Hon Roll; NHS; Holy Cross Bk Awd 85.

CARRABIS, SHARON; Westwood HS; Westwood, MA; (Y); 98/215; AFS; Camp Fr Inc; Drama Clb; Thesps; Chorus; Concert Band; Drm Mjr(t); Mrchg Band; School Musical; Swing Chorus; Arion Awd 85; Outstndng Achvt-Music 84; Advertsng.

CARREIRO, GRACE; New Bedford HS; New Bedford, MA; (Y); 4/540; Cmnty Wkr; English Clb; Church Choir; Yrbk Stf; High Hon Roll; NHS; Stonehill Coll Hnrs Schlr 85; Hghst Hnrs Grad 85; Stonehill Coll; Med Tech.

CARREIRO, HELENA; New Bedford HS; New Bedford, MA; (Y); Church Yth Grp; Drama Clb; Church Choir; Stage Crew; Stu Cncl; Crmnl Psych.

CARREIRO, STEVEN H; New Bedford HS; New Bedford, MA; (Y); 133/600; Exploring; Political Wkr; Concert Band; Mrchg Band; Rep Stu Cncl; Badmtn; Trk; Hon Roll; Westfield ST Coll; Music Perf.

CARRIER, MICHELE; Chicopee Comprehensive HS; Chicopee, MA; (Y); 52/340; French Clb; Var L Cheerleading; NHS; Office Aide; Chorus; Variety Show; Var Tennis; Fashion Retlr.

CARRIS, EUGENIA; Boston Latin Schl; Boston, MA; (Y); 43/335; French Clb; Trs Key Clb; Speech Tm; Swing Chorus; Rep Stu Cncl; L Swmmng; VP NHS; Church Yth Grp; Debate Tm; Drama Clb; 2nd Pl Boston Latns Prz Declmtn 85; Prz Clss III & IV 83; Fidlty & Modrn Przs 83-84.

CARROLL, AMY; Middleborough HS; Middleboro, MA; (Y); Church Yth Grp; Drama Clb; Orch; Rep Frsh Cls; Sec Sr Cls; Rep Stu Cncl; Var Bsktbl; Var Swmmng; Cit Awd; Hon Roll; Syracuse U; Cmmctns.

CARROLL, BRIAN; Leominster HS; Leominster, MA; (S); Boy Scts; Ski Clb; School Musical; School Play; Yrbk Stf; Stu Cncl; Ftbl; Swmmng; God Cntry Awd.

CARROLL, LAUREN; Holliston HS; Holliston, MA; (Y); 19/206; Church Yth Grp; Cmnty Wkr; Teachers Aide; Stage Crew; Variety Show; Yrbk Stf; Pres Frsh Cls; Pres Soph Cls; Pres Jr Cls; Pres Sr Cls; Stu Mnth 84; Hugh O Brian Ambssdr 3 Yrs 83-85; MA Bar Assn Awd 85; Boston Coll Schlrshp 85; Boston Coll; Pre Med.

CARROLL, LESA; Old Rochester Regional HS; Mattapoisett, MA; (Y); 28/147; Frsh Cls; Capt Cheerleading; JV Sftbl; Capt Twrlr; Spotlight Prog 84-85; Intl Bus.

CARROLL, SUELLEN; Bishop Feehan HS; Cumberland, RI; (Y); 11/250; JCL; Yrbk Rptr; Rep Jr Cls; Rep Sr Cls; Crs Cntry; L Capt Trk; French Hon Soc; NHS; Poltcl Sci.

CARROLL, TINA; Holy Name Central Catholic HS; Worcester, MA; (Y); 22/243; Dance Clb; Church Choir; High Hon Roll; Hon Roll; Ntl Merit Ltr; MA ST Schlrshp 85-86; Worcester ST Coll; Bus Admin.

CARSON, ANITA; King Philip Regional HS; Norfolk, MA; (S); #2 In Class; Am Leg Aux Girls St; Trs Church Yth Grp; Math Clb; Ski Clb; Varsity Clb; Powder Puff Ftbl; Capt Socr; Sftbl; Hon Roll; NHS; Engrng.

CARTER, DONALD; Dartmouth HS; N Dartmouth, MA; (Y); 5/243; AFS; Boy Scts; Math Tm; Band; Concert Band; Jazz Band; Mrchg Band; Trs NHS; USAF Acad; Engrng.

CARTER, EDDIE; North HS; Worcester, MA; (Y); Boys Clb Am; Boy Scts; Church Yth Grp; Chorus; Church Choir; Var Bsktbl; Var Socr; Hon Roll; NHS; Prfct Atten Awd; Ntl Cnfrnc Chrst & Jews Cert Of Rcgntn 82; Cntrl New Englnd Coll; Accntng.

CARTER, LAURA; Hingham HS; Hingham, MA; (Y); 30/325; Drama Clb; Thesps; Chorus; Mgr Jazz Band; School Musical; Yrbk Stf; Trs Stu Cncl; Cheerleading; Hon Roll; Comm.

CARTER, MICHELLE; Cambridge Rindge & Latin HS; Cambridge, MA; (Y); Cmnty Wkr; School Play; Yrbk Stf; Capt Cheerleading; High Hon Roll; NHS; Georgetown U; Brdcstng.

CARUSO, STEPHEN M; Sacred Heart HS; N Weymouth, MA; (Y); 4/60; Am Leg Boys St; Cmnty Wkr; Math Clb; Concert Band; School Musical; Variety Show; Rep Frsh Cls; Pres Soph Cls; Ftbl; Cit Awd; Notre Dame Coll; Bus.

CARVELLI, ROSEMARY; Newton North HS; W Newton, MA; (Y); Exploring; Sec Frsh Cls; Im Var Cheerleading; Cit Awd; Hon Roll; Bus Mgmt.

CASALIE, CHARLES; Blackstone Valley Vo-Tech; Milford, MA; (Y); Hon Roll; Prfct Atten Awd; Elec Engr.

CASAVANT, LISA; Murdock HS; Winchendon, MA; (Y); 13/113; Model UN; Office Aide; Yrbk Bus Mgr; Yrbk Rptr; Yrbk Stf; Pres Frsh Cls; Var Bsktbl; Var Capt Fld Hcky; Var Sftbl; Hon Roll; Psych.

CASAZZA, CHRISTINE; Wakefield Memorial HS; Wakefield, MA; (Y); Church Yth Grp; Key Clb; Yrbk Stf; Cheerleading; Var L Gym; JV Tennis; Northeastern; Nrsg.

CASAZZA, CORINNE; Everett HS; Everett, MA; (Y); 6/250; Key Clb; Scholastic Bowl; Nwsp Stf; High Hon Roll; Jr NHS; NHS; Pres Schlr; Voice Dem Awd; Hofstra U; Jrnlsm.

CASCIANI, CARLO; Everett HS; Everett, MA; (Y); Merrimack Coll; Comp Sci.

CASE, MICHAEL; Monument Mountain HS; Housatonic, MA; (Y); Varsity Clb; Yrbk Stf; Var Bsbl; Var Ice Hcky; Hon Roll.

CASE, TAMARA; Triton Regional HS; Newbury, MA; (Y); Church Yth Grp; Band; Sec Chorus; Church Choir; Concert Band; Mrchg Band; Crs Cntry; Trk; Hon Roll.

CASELLO, JOSPH; St Johns HS; Shrewsbury, MA; (Y); 30/270; French Clb; JA; Model UN; Stage Crew; NHS; Ntl Merit Ltr; Boston U; Intl Reltns.

CASEY, DIANE; Mount Saint Joseph Acad; Brighton, MA; (Y); 34/155; Math Clb; Science Clb; Variety Show; Yrbk Stf; Hon Roll; Trs NHS; Med Sch.

CASEY, MAUREEN; Reading HS; Reading, MA; (Y); Pep Clb; Varsity Clb; Variety Show; Var Cheerleading; JV Trk; High Hon Roll; Consdrd Natl Hnr Socty 85; Nrsg.

CASEY, MICHAEL; Taunton HS; Taunton, MA; (Y); Am Leg Boys St; Yrbk Stf; Pres Frsh Cls; Pres Soph Cls; Pres Jr Cls; Pres Sr Cls; Trs Stu Cncl; Var L Crs Cntry; Var L Trk; Hon Roll; Taunton Art Assn Annl Art Shw 2nd & 3rd 83-85; Taunton HS Band 82-84.

CASEY, PATRICIA; Natick HS; Natick, MA; (Y); 59/443; Cheerleading; JV Swmmng; JV Trk; JV Vllybl; Hon Roll; Outstndng Typng Awd 83; Bentley Coll; Bus.

CASEY, THERESE; Holy Name CC HS; Boyston, MA; (Y); Ski Clb; Var Fld Hcky; Var Trk; Prfct Atten Awd; Relgn Dept Awd 83; Athl Awds Trck, Fld Hocky 84; Phych.

CASHMON, ROB; Maynard HS; Mayanrd, MA; (Y); 9/99; Computer Clb; Band; Concert Band; Jazz Band; Mrchg Band; School Musical; Hon Roll; NHS; Ntl Merit SF; 1st & 2nd Pl Schl Spllng Bee 84 & 85; Comp Sci.

CASHTON, MICHAEL; Belmont HS; Belmont, MA; (Y); Am Leg Boys St; Spanish Clb; Pres Temple Yth Grp; Nwsp Ed-Chief; Pres Soph Cls; Rep Stu Cncl; Socr; Var Trk; High Hon Roll; Hon Roll; PTA Awd Rcgntn Svc 84; PTA Achvt Awd Soc Stud 85.

CASINEAU, KELLY; Cathedral HS; Springfield, MA; (Y); 112/550; Hosp Aide; Office Aide; Var L Crs Cntry; Var L Swmmng; Var Trk; Nrsng.

CASLER, SEAN; Natick HS; Natick, MA; (Y); 73/450; Boy Scts; Chrmn German Clb; Intnl Clb; JCL; Latin Clb; Band; Concert Band; Drm & Bgl; Jazz Band; Mrchg Band; Bus.

CASS, LISA; Abington HS; Abington, MA; (Y); 11/198; Flag Corp; Yrbk Ed-Chief; VP Sr Cls; Rep Stu Cncl; Cit Awd; High Hon Roll; NHS; Pres Schlr; Acadmc Achv Hnrs Chem 83-84; Boston Coll; Nrsng.

CASSESSO, ROB; Reading Memorial HS; Reading, MA; (Y); Boy Scts; French Clb; JA; Political Wkr; Crs Cntry; Wt Lftg; Var Wrstlng; Rep Soph Cls; U MA; Bus.

CASSIDY, KATHLEEN; Arlington Catholic HS; Burlington, MA; (Y); 14/148; Dance Clb; Hosp Aide; Spanish Clb; Teachers Aide; Nwsp Rptr; Crs Cntry; Sftbl; NHS; Boston 20 Ml Wlk Fr Hngr 85; Soc Wrkr.

CASSIDY, LAURA; Mansfield HS; Mansfield, MA; (Y); 3/207; Key Clb; Ski Clb; Color Guard; Drill Tm; Mrchg Band; Yrbk Stf; High Hon Roll; NHS; Modl Sen; Mt Holyoke; Biochem.

CASSIDY, MARY; Bishop Feehan HS; Attleboro, MA; (Y); 31/216; French Clb; Hosp Aide; Var JV Cheerleading; Trk; JV Vllybl; French Hon Soc; High Hon Roll; Hon Roll; NHS; Exclnce Bio & French 83 & 84.

CASSIE, JONATHAN; Rockland HS; Rockland, MA; (S); Debate Tm; Drama Clb; School Play; Variety Show; Im Bowling; Im Socr; Im Wt Lftg; Hon Roll; NHS; NEDT Awd; Project Contemporary Comp 83.

CASSO, DEBORAH; Falmouth HS; Falmouth, MA; (Y); AFS; French Clb; Var Capt Crs Cntry; Var Tennis; Var Trk; NHS; Church Yth Grp; Stu Cncl; Hon Roll; Jr NHS.

CASTANO, CORINNE; Hudson HS; Hudson, MA; (Y); Math Clb; Pep Clb; Band; Stu Cncl; High Hon Roll; NHS; Ntl Merit Ltr.

CASTANTINO, MELISSA; Groton-Dunstable HS; Groton, MA; (Y); 3/190; Church Yth Grp; Cmnty Wkr; Debate Tm; French Clb; Latin Clb; Political Wkr; Scholastic Bowl; Teachers Aide; Band; High Hon Roll; US Hstry Advncd Plcmnt Awd 84-85; US Hstry Essay Cntst Hnrbl Ment & Fnlst 85; Ethiopis Dnky Proj 85; Cambridge U; Intl Rltns.

CASTRUCCI, KAREN; Milford HS; Milford, MA; (Y); 58/321; Drama Clb; School Musical; School Play; Stage Crew; Vllybl; Hon Roll; NHS; Clss Of 1950 Awd 85; U Of MA Amherst; Bus Mgmt.

CATALANO, JOSEPH; Methuen HS; Methuen, MA; (Y).

CATHCART, DANIEL E; Maynard HS; Maynard, MA; (Y); 20/99; Aud/Vis; Boys Clb Am; Boy Scts; Radio Clb; Teachers Aide; Bsbl; Var L Ftbl; Var L Ice Hcky; Var L Trk; Hon Roll; Comm TV Prog Awd By Adams-Russell Cable TV 85; FL Inst Of Tech; Elec Engrng.

CATINO, ELENA; Revere HS; Revere, MA; (Y); 30/357; French Clb; Pep Clb; Yrbk Stf; Rep Frsh Cls; Rep Soph Cls; Rep Jr Cls; Rep Sr Cls; Rep Stu Cncl; Var Powder Puff Ftbl; NHS; Boston Coll; Nrsng.

CATRON, KATHLEEN; Notre Dame Acad; Dorchester, MA; (Y); 34/114; Church Yth Grp; Debate Tm; Chorus; JV Im Bsktbl; Im Socr; Var Sftbl; Var Co-Capt Vllybl; Geomtry Schltc Awd 83-84; Bentley; Bus.

CAVALLARO, MARLENE; Methuen HS; Andover, MA; (Y); 9/330; Hosp Aide; Intnl Clb; Model UN; Spanish Clb; Band; Color Guard; School Play; Tennis; High Hon Roll; NHS; Hugh O Brian Smnr 83; Exc Clb Yth Of Mnth 85; Stu Overall Achvt Rcgntn 83 & 85; Tufts U; Engrng.

CAVANAUGH, JON R; Rockport HS; Rockport, MA; (Y); 14/72; Am Leg Boys St; Drama Clb; French Clb; Math Tm; Band; Chorus; Bsbl; Bsktbl; Golf; High Hon Roll; Army ROTC & Navy ROTC 4 Yr Schlrshps 85; Providence Coll; Math.

CAVANAUGH, LISA; Billerica Memorial HS; Billerica, MA; (Y); Church Yth Grp; German Clb; Concert Band; Drm Mjr(t); Mrchg Band; Yrbk Stf; Badmtn; Hon Roll; Merrimack; Bus Mgmt.

CAVANAUGH, MICHAEL; Holyoke HS; Holyoke, MA; (Y); Latin Clb; Ski Clb; Nwsp Stf; Yrbk Stf; JV L Bsbl; Capt Var Socr; High Hon Roll; Hon Roll.

CAVANAUGH, NANCY A; Malden HS; Malden, MA; (Y); Church Yth Grp; Yrbk Sprt Ed; Yrbk Stf; Rep Stu Cncl; Var Capt Crs Cntry; Var L Trk.

CAVANAUGH, WILLIAM M; Woburn HS; Woburn, MA; (Y); Computer Clb; Ust Pl Awd Sci Fair 83; 3rd Pl Sci Fair Awd 85; Sci Olympd Awd 83; New Hampshire U; Comp Engr.

CAVIGELLI, SONIA A; Lexington HS; Lexington, MA; (Y); French Clb; Ski Clb; Varsity Clb; Var L Sftbl; Var Vllybl; Hon Roll; Stu Consrvtn Assn 85; Urban-Suburban Pgm 85; Ger & Frnch Awds 84-85.

CAWTHRON, LISA; Senior HS; Billerica, MA; (Y); Boys Clb Am; Exploring; Library Aide; Office Aide; ROTC; Teachers Aide; High Hon Roll; Hon Roll; Rivier Coll; Med Tech.

CEDERHOLM, LAURA; Marlboro HS; Marlboro, MA; (Y); 69/350; Red Cross Aide; Band; Concert Band; Mrchg Band; Orch; Stu Cncl; Mgr(s); Trk; Hon Roll; Faculty Awd Outstndng Achvt In Music 83-84; Bus.

CEDRONE, MICHELE; Braintree HS; Braintree, MA; (Y); 12/397; Nwsp Stf; Rep Frsh Cls; Rep Soph Cls; Rep Jr Cls; Rep Sr Cls; Rep Stu Cncl; Stat Trk; High Hon Roll; Hon Roll; NHS; Bus.

CEDRONE, SILVIA; Newton Catholic HS; Brighton, MA; (S); 2/50; School Play; Yrbk Ed-Chief; VP Stu Cncl; Crs Cntry; High Hon Roll; NHS; Physcl Thrpy.

CELAYA, FRANCISCA; Miss Halls Schl; New Canaan, CT; (Y); 19/63; GAA; Spanish Clb; Varsity Clb; Acpl Chr; Yrbk Stf; JV Bsktbl; Var Lcrss; Var Socr; JV Tennis; Effrt Hnr Roll 84-85.

CELUZZA, STEPHEN; Tantasqua SR HS; Sturbridge, MA; (S); 8/187; Math Tm; MMM; Ski Clb; Concert Band; Jazz Band; Yrbk Phtg; Stu Cncl; High Hon Roll; NHS; Rep Hugh Obrien Youth Ldrshp Semnr 84; Engrng.

CERASUOLO, JOELLE M; Maynard HS; Maynard, MA; (Y); 9/100; Aud/Vis; French Clb; Chorus; Concert Band; Mrchg Band; Sec Frsh Cls; VP Soph Cls; Var Cheerleading; Hon Roll; School Play; Med.

CERRONE, CHRISTINA M; Revere HS; Revere, MA; (Y); Church Yth Grp; Cmnty Wkr; Pep Clb; Spanish Clb; Chorus; School Play; Yrbk Stf; Im Bsktbl; Im Fld Hcky; Im Sftbl; Bentley Coll; Acctng.

CERRONE JR, SALVATORE C; Saint Dominic Savio HS; E Boston, MA; (S); 10/104; Chess Clb; Computer Clb; Debate Tm; VP JA; ROTC; Yrbk Rptr; Var Trk; Outstndng Anatomy & Physiology Stu 83; Outstndng SR Ldrshp Awd 84; MA Delg Region 1 JR Achvt 83; Tufts U; Medicine.

CERULLI, THERESA; Melrose HS; Melrose, MA; (Y); 5/400; Church Yth Grp; Ski Clb; JV Trk; Hon Roll; NHS; Engrng.

CHABOT, KIMBERLY; Somerset HS; Somerset, MA; (Y); 1/320; Drama Clb; School Play; Nwsp Ed-Chief; Yrbk Rptr; Trs Stu Cncl; Var L Trk; Jr NHS; VP NHS; Ntl Merit SF; Val; Harvard Bk Awd 85; Brown Bk Awd 85; Rensselaer Math & Sci Medal 85; Brown U.

CHABOT, THERESA; Bishop Feehan HS; N Attleboro, MA; (Y); Ski Clb; Tennis; Trk; Hon Roll; Spanish NHS; Bus.

CHADOROWSKY, LEISA B; Malden HS; Malden, MA; (Y); 47/500; Library Aide; Sec Temple Yth Grp; Chorus; Church Choir; JV Sftbl; Hon Roll; Prfct Atten Awd; Accntng.

CHAFF, DIANE; Haverhill HS; Haverhill, MA; (Y); Cmnty Wkr; Chorus; Rep Sr Cls; High Hon Roll; Hon Roll; NHS; HEA Annie P Roche Awd 85; Distinctn 82-83; U Lowell; Lib Arts.

CHAGARIS, KEITH E; Norwood HS; Norwood, MA; (Y); Var JV Bsbl; Nubury JC; Physcl Thrpy.

CHAISSON, BRIAN; Weymouth North HS; Weymouth, MA; (Y); 133/393; Key Clb; Ski Clb; Bsbl; Bsktbl; Ftbl; Bus Stu Term 85; Bus Mgmt.

CHALFONTE, JAMES; Drury SR HS; N Adams, MA; (S); Hosp Aide; Ski Clb; Concert Band; Jazz Band; Mrchg Band; Capt Bowling; Hon Roll; NHS; NEDT Awd; Wstrn MA Dist Msc Fest 2nd Tromb 84; Elec Engr.

CHAMBERLIN, STACEY; Revere HS; Revere, MA; (Y); Political Wkr; Yrbk Stf; Stu Cncl; Var L Crs Cntry; Var L Trk; High Hon Roll; Hon Roll; Greater Boston Lgu All Star Cross Cnty 83-84.

CHAMBERS, DAVID; Wareham HS; E Wareham, MA; (Y); Boy Scts; Cheerleading; Computer Clb; Lcrss; Socr; Tennis; Hon Roll; New England Tech; Comp Pgmr.

CHAMNAN, PHAT; South Boston HS; Brighton, MA; (S); Cmnty Wkr; Hosp Aide; Office Aide; Teachers Aide; Nwsp Stf; Stu Cncl; Hon Roll; NHS; Prfct Atten Awd; Havard Book Awd 83-84; Perf Attndce Awd 83-84; Ntl Engl Merit Awd 83-84; Med.

CHAMPAGNE, NICOLE; Bishop Stang HS; Rochester, MA; (Y); 22/215; Chorus; VP Stu Cncl; Var Fld Hcky; Var Capt Sftbl; Hon Roll; VP NHS; Tri Town Dlrs Schlrs Annual Schlrshp 85; Acad Awd Math 85; Stonehill Coll; Bio.

CHAMPLAIN JR, JOSEPH D; Beverly HS; Beverly, MA; (Y); Rep Stu Cncl; JV Trk; Hon Roll; 1st Pl Sci Fair Scholar 85; U S Navy Awd Superior Achvt 85; Civil Engrng.

CHAMPOUX, NOELLE; Revere HS; Revere, MA; (Y); Math Tm; Pep Clb; Yrbk Stf; VP Jr Cls; Stu Cncl; Var L Cheerleading; Coach Actv; JV Fld Hcky; JV Trk; High Hon Roll; Boston Coll; Psych.

CHAN, EVA; Boston Latin Schl; Boston, MA; (Y); 111/299; French Clb; Key Clb; Nwsp Stf; Ed Lit Mag; Rep Stu Cncl.

CHAN, HON KEE; Cushing Acad; Brookline, MA; (Y); #3 In Class; Intnl Clb; Yrbk Phtg; Tennis; Wt Lftg; High Hon Roll; Hon Roll; Bus Mgmt.

CHAN, MARY; Boston Latin Schl; W Roxbury, MA; (Y); 31/328; Pres English Clb; GAA; JA; Key Clb; Model UN; Spanish Clb; Stage Crew; Variety Show; Yrbk Stf; Off Soph Cls; Access Awd 85; Yale; Law.

CHANDLER, CHARLES; Boston Tech HS; Boston, MA; (Y); Boy Scts; Chess Clb; Hon Roll; Prfct Atten Awd; Var Socr; Var Trk; Med Tech.

CHANG, PAUL; Easthampton HS; Easthampton, MA; (Y); Boy Scts; Varsity Clb; Var Socr; High Hon Roll; NHS; Exploring; JV Bsbl; JV Bsktbl; Eagle Scout; Engrng.

CHANG, TERESA K; Algonquin Regional HS; Northborough, MA; (Y); 2/211; Sec Trs Concert Band; Mrchg Band; Yrbk Stf; Sec Frsh Cls; Sec Soph Cls; High Hon Roll; Pres NHS; Prvte Lssns Schlrshp 82-83; Holy Crss Bk Prze Outstndng Acad Accmplshmnts 84-85.

CHANG, TINA; Methuen HS; Methuen, MA; (Y); Church Yth Grp; FCA; Intnl Clb; Spanish Clb; Chorus; Church Choir; Variety Show; Yrbk Stf; Trk; Hon Roll; Mst Achvt Engl 80; Outstndg Chorus 81; Intl Bus.

CHAO, YVONNE Y; Lexington HS; Lexington, MA; (Y); Math Tm; Political Wkr; Red Cross Aide; Orch; School Musical; Stage Crew; Yrbk Stf; Var Crs Cntry; Var Trk; Hon Roll; Hnrbl Mntn X-Cntry 83; Frnch Awd 85.

CHAPIN, MICHELLE; Mt Everett Regional HS; Sheffield, MA; (Y); 11/73; Cmnty Wkr; 4-H; Church Choir; Concert Band; Sec Soph Cls; Sec Sr Cls; Var Cheerleading; Var Socr; Var Sftbl; Hon Roll.

CHAPMAN, MARC; Don Bosco Technical HS; Readville, MA; (S); Cmnty Wkr; Hon Roll; NHS; Comp Fld.

CHAPMAN, MICHELLE; Dracut SR HS; Dracut, MA; (Y); Office Aide; Profcncies Spnsh, Comp Sci & Chem 85; Awd Acad Exclnc Geom 84; Comp Sci.

CHAPMAN, SANDRA L; Belmont HS; Belmont, MA; (Y); Camera Clb; Flag Corp; School Play; Hon Roll; Mt Ida Clg; Parlgl Stud.

CHAPSKI, ROBERT; Boston Latin Schl; Boston, MA; (Y); 7/320; Boy Scts; Church Yth Grp; Cmnty Wkr; Computer Clb; Drama Clb; High Hon Roll; Hon Roll; NHS; Ntl Merit Ltr; Prfct Atten Awd; Acad All Am 85; Harvard U.

CHAPULIS, MARK; St Johns HS; Sutton, MA; (Y); 80/274; Church Yth Grp; Spanish Clb; Band; Jazz Band; Hon Roll; Jr NHS; Ntl Merit Ltr; Bryant Coll; Bus Mgmt.

CHAREST III, GERARD; Bishop Stang HS; Rochester, MA; (Y); 50/230; Ski Clb; Off Frsh Cls; Off Soph Cls; Stu Cncl; Bsktbl; Hon Roll; Bentley Coll Bus Week 85; Bentley; Investmnts Analyst.

CHARETTE, CATHERINE A; Palmer HS; Three Rivers, MA; (Y); 5/97; Pres Math Tm; Pres Soph Cls; Pres Jr Cls; Pres Sr Cls; Var Cheerleading; Dnfth Awd; Hon Roll; NHS; Pres Schlr; Pres Church Yth Grp; Rensselaer Awd Exclnce Math & Sci 84; Highest Score HS Math Exam 85; Bk Awd Exclence Sci 85; Mt Holyoke Coll; Bio-Chem.

CHARLAND, ALICE MARIE; Pittsfield HS; Pittsfield, MA; (Y); Church Yth Grp; Teachers Aide; Orch; Cit Awd; High Hon Roll; NHS; St Schlr; Boy Scts; Exploring; Pep Clb; Wellesley Coll Bk Awd 84; Centry III Ldrshp Awd 85; Pres Acad Ftns Awd 85; Siena; Dnstry.

CHARLES, PATRICK; Andrew Jackson HS; Dorchester, MA; (Y); 71/493; Pres Science Clb; Nwsp Rptr; U Of MA; Bio.

CHARRON, LISA M; Ware HS; Ware, MA; (Y); 14/122; Dance Clb; Spanish Clb; Yrbk Stf; Cheerleading; Gym; High Hon Roll; Hon Roll; Bay Path JC Longmeadow; Acctg.

CHARTRAND, CAROLYN; Cracut HS; Dracut, MA; (Y); French Clb; Office Aide; Teachers Aide; Varsity Clb; Var Cheerleading; JV Fld Hcky; Var Gym; JV Sftbl; JV Vllybl; Med.

CHASE, EDWARD; North Quincy HS; Quincy, MA; (Y); 95/400; Var Swmmng; Var Trk; Capt Var Wrstlng; Hon Roll; Hugh R Simpson Mem Schlrshp 85; Cert Outstndg Achvt Coll Wrtng 85; NE U; Crmnl Just.

CHASE, WILLIAM; Central Catholic HS; Haverhill, MA; (Y); 76/212; Chorus; JV Var Ftbl; Im Wt Lftg; Hon Roll.

CHATALBASH, ROY S; Dover-Sherborn HS; Dover, MA; (Y); Am Leg Boys St; Chess Clb; JA; Chorus; School Musical; School Play; Crs Cntry; Trk; Bus.

CHATFIELD, CHERYL; Milford HS; Milford, MA; (Y); Art Clb; Camera Clb; Ski Clb; Meine U; Recrtnl Mngmnt.

CHAU, HELEN; Boston Latin Schl; Boston, MA; (Y); Art Clb; Camera Clb; Exploring; French Clb; JA; Latin Clb; Band; Lit Mag; VP Frsh Cls; VP Stu Cncl; Oratorical Awd 79; Boston Coll; Comm Arts.

CHECKA, KEVIN; Southbridge HS; Sbridge, MA; (Y); 31/144; Computer Clb; Stu Cncl; Jrnlsm.

CHEN, IVAN; Dartmouth HS; Dartmouth, MA; (Y); Debate Tm; Math Clb; Math Tm; Orch; Rep Frsh Cls; Rep Frsh Cls; Rep Jr Cls; JV Tennis; NHS; Ntl Merit Ltr; 1st Prz Poetry Cont 84; Regnl & ST Sci Fair Part Awd 85; Acad Excell Awd 83 & 85; Pre-Med.

CHENARD, BOB; Medway Jr-Sr HS; Medway, MA; (Y); Church Yth Grp; Pres Jr Cls; Off Stu Cncl; Capt Bsbl; Var Ice Hcky; Capt Var Socr; Hon Roll; MVP Soccer Athl Awd 84-85; SADD Comm Task Force; Engrng.

CHENETTE, DAVID; Sacred Heart HS; Quincy, MA; (Y); Trk; Art.

CHENEY, PAMELA; Dana Hall HS; Acton, MA; (Y); Pres French Clb; Key Clb; Band; Yrbk Stf; JV Trk; Hon Roll; U S Pony Clb 80-86; Pres Ridng Clb Dama Hall 85-86; Frntiers Sci Pgm; Pediatrcs.

CHERETA, ANA; New Bedford HS; New Bedford, MA; (Y); 1/600; Office Aide; Yrbk Ed-Chief; Rep Sr Cls; DAR Awd; High Hon Roll; NHS; Val; English Clb; Hosp Aide; Q&S; MA Commonwlth Schlr 85; Rensselaer Medal 84; Physics Awd 85; Harvard Coll.

CHERIN, ANTHONY; Boston Latin Schl; Boston, MA; (Y); 32/300; Drama Clb; Band; Chorus; Jazz Band; School Play.

CHERRINGTON, COLETTE A; Milford HS; Hopedale, MA; (Y); 19/305; Cmnty Wkr; Key Clb; Pep Clb; Political Wkr; Yrbk Stf; Var Fld Hcky; Var Capt Gym; Var Trk; JV Vllybl; NHS; Claire Stone Winiker Schlrshp Awd 85; MVP/Midland Leag Bm Chmp/Gymnstcs 85; Unsung Heroine/Fld Hockey; Johnson & Wales Coll; Trvl Mgmt.

CHESEBOROUGH, LYNNETTE; West Roxbury HS; Dorchester, MA; (Y); 1/240; Church Yth Grp; Hosp Aide; Office Aide; Teachers Aide; Church Choir; Yrbk Bus Mgr; Yrbk Stf; Trk; DAR Awd; High Hon Roll; Boston U Full Tuitn Schlrshp 85; Economics.

CHESNA, JAMES; Revere HS; Revere, MA; (Y); Letterman Clb; Varsity Clb; School Play; Variety Show; Capt Bsbl; Ftbl; Hon Roll; Parents Ftbl Clb 85; Coaches Awd Baseball 85; N Shore CC Merit Schlrshp Athletic 85; N Shore CC; Pro Baseball.

CHESNICKA, DANIEL J; Westfield HS; Westfield, MA; (Y); 87/334; Sec Am Leg Boys St; Drama Clb; School Play; Nwsp Rptr; Var Capt Diving; Capt L Swmmng; L Var Trk; Aud/Vis; W MA Dvng Chmp, Recrd Hldr 85; Dvng Medls Bay ST 84-85; Bst Actr Awd 84-85.

CHESTER, KELLYANN; Uxbridge HS; Uxbridge, MA; (Y); 9/68; Computer Clb; Concert Band; Jazz Band; Mrchg Band; Yrbk Stf; Hon Roll; NHS; VP Trs Spanish Clb; Chorus; Orch; Central MA Dist Orch 85; MA All St Concert Band 85; Brklne Chamber Music Comp 85; Music Ed.

CHEUNG, YEE; Charlestown HS; Boston, MA; (Y); Art Clb; Church Yth Grp; Dance Clb; GAA; School Musical; Rep Sr Cls; Badmtn; Swmmng; Vllybl; Hon Roll; Newbury JC; Acctng.

CHEVAIRE, NICOLE; Westford Acad; Westford, MA; (Y); 11/205; AFS; Church Yth Grp; French Clb; Model UN; Trs Sr Cls; Var L Fld Hcky; Cit Awd; NHS; Cmnty Wkr; Ski Clb; Joe Shields Mem Schlrshp 85; Spnsh II Best Stu Awd 83; Comm Svc Awd 85; Trustees Of Westford Awd 85; MA U; Intl Bus.

CHI, ROBERT Y; Belmont HS; Belmont, MA; (Y); Spanish Clb; Nwsp Ed-Chief; Lit Mag; JV Trk; High Hon Roll; NHS; PTA Achvt Engl, Sci 84-85; Phi Beta Kappa Awd 85.

CHIANG, CHIN MING; Newton South HS; Newton, MA; (Y); Chess Clb; Church Yth Grp; Math Tm; High Hon Roll; Hon Roll; Elec Engrng.

CHIARENZA, JOSEPH; Medford HS; Medford, MA; (Y); 35/480; Am Leg Boys St; Science Clb; Im Coach Actv; Var L Trk; NHS; Im Bsktbl; Im Ftbl; Comp Sci.

CHIASSON, DANIELLE; Maynard HS; Maynard, MA; (Y); 5/90; Aud/Vis; Radio Clb; Concert Band; Mrchg Band; Var Fld Hcky; Var Score Keeper; High Hon Roll; Hon Roll; NHS; Awd Outstndng Dir Yr-Radio 84; Chrprsn Jr Prom Comm 85; 1 Of 4 Radio Genl Mgrs 84-85.

CHIAVARAS, MARY; Lunenburg HS; Lunenburg, MA; (Y); Debate Tm; Intnl Clb; Library Aide; Math Tm; Cheerleading; Sftbl; High Hon Roll; Hon Roll; NHS; Gld Key Art Awd 83; Hnrb Mntn Ntl Boston Globe Art Comptn 84; Dnstry.

CHIAVETTONE, GERALD HEATH; Joseph Case HS; Seekonk, MA; (Y); 5/205; Am Leg Boys St; Math Tm; Var Crs Cntry; L Var Trk; Hon Roll; NHS; 1st Awd ST Sci Fair 85; Carl S Ell Pres Schlrhsp 85; Northeastern U; Comp Sci.

CHILDS, STEPHANIE; Newburyport HS; Newburyport, MA; (S); 9/194; Am Leg Aux Girls St; JCL; Math Tm; Model UN; Q&S; Nwsp Stf; Var L Fld Hcky; Var L Tennis; Hon Roll; NHS; Ntl Latin Exam-Maxima Cum Laude Slvr Mdl 83-84; Hstry Conf At Salem ST Coll 83-84; Ldrshp Smnr Prgm.

CHILVERS, CHRISTINE M; Grafton HS; N Grafton, MA; (Y); 2/134; Church Yth Grp; Variety Show; Nwsp Sprt Ed; Yrbk Stf; Stat Bsktbl; Stat Trk; Elks Awd; Masonic Awd; NHS; Sal; Outstndng Frgn Lang Stu 85; Wellesley Coll.

CHIN, DAVID; Boston Latin Schl; Boston, MA; (Y); 84/300; Computer Clb; Exploring; Var L Trk; Hon Roll; Dixwell Prz Of Excllnc In Classics 84; Acctg.

CHIN, GLENN; Boston Technical HS; Boston, MA; (Y); Boys Clb Am; Chess Clb; JA; Math Tm; Pep Clb; Sec Sr Cls; Bsbl; Im Bsktbl; Im Ftbl; Var Ice Hcky; Hnr Roll 82-83; Hnrb Mntn & Hnr Roll 84-85; 2nd & 4th Pl In Chinatown Bsktl League 84-85; Phrmcy.

CHIN, VICTOR; Randolph HS; Randolph, MA; (Y); 15/300; VP Computer Clb; Math Tm; Rep Jr Cls; Var Trk; Hon Roll; CBL Bsktbl Lgue 85; Elect Engrng.

CHIROFF, DEBORAH A; Greenfield HS; Greenfield, MA; (Y); 4/159; Drama Clb; School Play; Yrbk Stf; Stu Cncl; High Hon Roll; NHS; Sec Science Clb; Nwsp Phtg; Nwsp Stf; Colby Coll Bk Awd; Engl, Frnch, Bio, Hstry Awds; Frnch Tutorg; Theatr Arts.

CHISHOLM, DONALD P; Reading Memorial HS; Reading, MA; (Y); 1/344; Cmnty Wkr; JA; Political Wkr; Nwsp Rptr; Nwsp Stf; Yrbk Ed-Chief; Bsbl; Ice Hcky; High Hon Roll; NHS; Engrng.

CHMIELEWSKI, STEVEN; Somerset HS; Somerset, MA; (Y); Exploring; Ski Clb; Variety Show; Var L Fld Hcky; Var L Ice Hcky; Im Swmmng; Im Wt Lftg; High Hon Roll; Hon Roll; Jr NHS; Williams Bk Awd 85; Pre-Med.

CHOI, SEUNG HO; Monument Mt Regional HS; Great Barrington, MA; (S); Varsity Clb; Var Socr; Var Wrstlng; Hon Roll; 1st Wstrn MASS Soccer Torun 82; 1st-2nd-5th MASS St Wrstlng Champ Indiv 83 & 84; Worcester Polytech Inst; Engrng.

CHOINIERE, DEBORA; Monson JR SR HS; Monson, MA; (Y); 14/85; Am Leg Aux Girls St; Church Yth Grp; Drama Clb; French Clb; School Play; Pres Jr Cls; Var Capt Cheerleading; Hon Roll; MVP-CHRLDNG 83-84; Comp Sci.

CHOKSHI, SMITA; Monument Mountain RG HS; W Stockbridge, MA; (Y); English Clb; French Clb; Math Tm; Science Clb; School Play; Yrbk Stf; Wt Lftg; High Hon Roll; Med.

CHOQUETTE, JOSEPH R; Silver Lake Regional HS; Halifax, MA; (Y); Art Clb; Boy Scts; Exploring; French Clb; Cit Awd; Karate Chmpnshp Awd 84; Wrld Mltry Mrtl Arts Assoc Blck Rnkng Awd 84; Boston Globe Schlstc Art Awd 85; US Mltry; Cmmrcl Art.

CHOQUETTE, MICHAEL; Central Catholic HS; Tewksbury, MA; (Y); 59/219; JA; Stage Crew; Hon Roll; Bio Chem.

CHOUINARD, KIMBERLY; Bishop Connolly HS; Fall River, MA; (Y); 18/200; Cmnty Wkr; Teachers Aide; Rep Sr Cls; L Var Cheerleading; Stat Score Keeper; High Hon Roll; NHS; MS MA Ntl Tnagr Pgnt Sem Fnlst 85; Pre Med.

CHOW, JIMMY; Boston Latin School; Brighton, MA; (Y); 16/300; Latin Clb; Var Wrstlng; Hon Roll; NHS; Natl Sci Olympd 85; MA St Frstyl Chmpnshp 85; Stanford; Engnrng.

CHOW, JULIO; Boston Technical HS; Boston, MA; (Y).

CHOW, MAT; Berkshire Schl; Hong Kong; (S); Intnl Clb; Science Clb; Off Frsh Cls; Off Soph Cls; Golf; Var Sftbl; High Hon Roll; Cum Laude Soc 84-85; Bus Mngmt.

CHRISTENSEN, CHRISTINE; Bridgewater-Raynham Regional HS; Raynham, MA; (Y); Dance Clb; Capt Color Guard; Capt Flag Corp; Camera Clb; Chorus; Yrbk Stf; Hon Roll; Vrsty Jckt Awd 85; Comp.

CHRISTIANO, SUSAN A; Plymouth Carver HS; Carver, MA; (Y); 3/535; Library Aide; Chorus; Swing Chorus; Variety Show; Ed Lit Mag; High Hon Roll; NHS; St Schlr; MA Suprntndnts Awd For Acad Excel 84-85; Frgn Lang Clb 83-85; Wellesley Coll; Psychtrst.

CHRISTIANSEN, CHARLENA; Bishop Fenwick HS; Salem, MA; (Y); 50/222; Church Yth Grp; Fld Hcky; Hon Roll; U Of Steubensville OH; Psych.

CHRISTO, PAULA SANTO; Westport HS; Westport, MA; (Y); Sec French Clb; Var Capt Vllybl; High Hon Roll; Hon Roll; NHS; Camp Fr Inc; Exploring; Intnl Clb; Ski Clb; Teachers Aide; Salva Regina; Occptnl Thrpst.

CHRISTOPHER, JILL; Nauset Regional HS; Orleans, MA; (Y); Church Yth Grp; JV Bsktbl; JV Socr; JV Sftbl; Hon Roll; Mt Ida Coll; Fshn Dsgn.

CHRISTOPULOS, TINA; Boston Latin Schl; Boston, MA; (Y); 35/300; Dance Clb; Drama Clb; JA; Key Clb; Stage Crew; NHS; Ntl Merit SF.

CHRZANOWSKI, JENNIFER; East Bridgewater HS; E Bridgewtr, MA; (Y); 18/170; Key Clb; Rep Frsh Cls; Rep Soph Cls; Rep Jr Cls; Rep Sr Cls; Rep Stu Cncl; Bsktbl; Fld Hcky; Hon Roll; Kiwanis Awd; Mem Schlrshp 85; Jr Miss Pgnt 85; American U; Law.

CHRZANOWSKI, KERRY J; Cathedral HS; Ludlow, MA; (Y); Gym; NHS; Floral Design.

CHU, RUTH; Boston Latin HS; Boston, MA; (Y); 57/305; Camera Clb; Exploring; French Clb; JV Vllybl; NHS; Bus.

CHU, WINNE; Randolph HS; Randolph, MA; (Y); Sec Intnl Clb; Capt Color Guard; Nwsp Stf; Sec Stu Cncl; High Hon Roll; NHS; Outstndng Randlph Yth Awd 85; Dartmth Bk Awd 85; Natl Hstry Day 85; Rep Grtr Bostn Stu Advs Cncl 84-85.

CHURCH, CHERYL; Monson JR-SR HS; Monson, MA; (Y); 1/86; Am Leg Aux Girls St; Church Yth Grp; Cmnty Wkr; Computer Clb; French Clb; Co-Capt Mathletes; Math Clb; Math Tm; Office Aide; Red Cross Aide; Zero Mfg Math Awd 85; Worcester Polytechnic Inst.

CHURCH, TIMOTHY M; Falmouth HS; Falmouth, MA; (Y); Boy Scts; Math Tm; L Ice Hcky; High Hon Roll; NHS; SAR Awd; First Cngrssnl Chrch Schlrshp 85; Lawrence Assoc Schlrshp 85; Stu Athl Awd 85; NW U; Elec Engr.

CHURCHILL, MARK E; Cardinal Spellman HS; W Bridgewater, MA; (Y); 20/203; Drama Clb; Varsity Clb; Chorus; School Musical; School Play; Hon Roll; NHS; Prfct Atten Awd; Sci Fair 2nd Pl & 3rd Pl 83 & 84; Wrld Hstry Awd 82; Stonehill Coll; Bus.

CHURCHILL, ROBIN; Ayer HS; Shirley, MA; (Y); 16/180; French Clb; Office Aide; Band; Mrchg Band; Pep Band; Rep Jr Cls; Cheerleading; High Hon Roll; NHS; Advtsng.

CIAMARRA, ANNAMARIA; Stoneham HS; Stoneham, MA; (Y); 3/274; Dance Clb; Math Tm; Ski Clb; Spanish Clb; School Musical; School Play; Yrbk Stf; High Hon Roll; Jr NHS; NHS; Mdl Excllnc Math & Sci 84; Sci Mdl 85; Commnwlth Of MA Schlrshp 85; Harvard U.

CIAMPA, PAUL; Matignon HS; Cambridge, MA; (S); 4/174; Boys Clb Am; Church Yth Grp; Spanish Clb; Im Bsktbl; L Crs Cntry; VP NHS; Ntl Merit Ltr; Spanish NHS; Engrng.

CIARCIA, CHRISTOPHER J; Catholic Memorial HS; Dorchester, MA; (Y); 101/277; Boy Scts; Church Yth Grp; Dance Clb; FCA; JA; Science Clb; Ski Clb; Drm & Bgl; Wrstlng; Hon Roll; Coll Schlrshp 85-86; Suffolk U; Bus Mgmnt.

CIARCIA, MICHELE; Christopher Columbus HS; Boston, MA; (Y); 25/132; Hosp Aide; Band; Mrchg Band; Bsbl; Hon Roll; Nrsng.

CIARDI, LAURIE; Boston Latin HS; Boston, MA; (Y); 28/324; Cmnty Wkr; Drama Clb; JA; Political Wkr; School Play; Stage Crew; Nwsp Stf; NHS; Ntl Merit Ltr; Dixwell Prz Exc Clsscs 84; Lib Art.

CIARLONE, DAVID V; Westfield HS; Westfield, MA; (Y); 14/360; Computer Clb; Ski Clb; Trs Spanish Clb; Cit Awd; NHS; Spanish NHS; UNICO Schlrshp 85; Providence Coll; Psychlgy.

CICCIU, LISA J; Milford HS; Milford, MA; (Y); 131/307; Church Yth Grp; Key Clb; Pep Clb; Yrbk Stf; Hon Roll; Nichols Coll; Mgt.

CICCONE JR, RONALD W; Bishop Fee Han HS; Attleboro, MA; (Y); Boy Scts; Debate Tm; Yrbk Stf; Elks Awd; Eagle Scut 84; Smmn Sci Pgm, Bshp Cronin Awd 85; Attn.

CICHOCKI, BARBARA; South Hadley HS; S Hadley, MA; (Y); 5/156; Art Clb; Debate Tm; Drama Clb; Latin Clb; Math Tm; Stage Crew; Camp Fr Inc; Ed Yrbk Stf; Stu Cncl; Trk; Mt Holyoke Coll; Biol.

CIESLAK, CINDY A; Quaboag Regional HS; Warren, MA; (Y); 24/88; Spanish Clb; Varsity Clb; Yrbk Stf; Stu Cncl; Var Bsktbl; Var Crs Cntry; Var Sftbl; Hon Roll; Sec Frsh Cls.

CIMINO, DANIELA; Marian HS; Milford, MA; (Y); Var Capt Bsktbl; Var Timer; High Hon Roll; Hon Roll; NHS; Spanish NHS; Natl Latin Exam Cum Laude, Magna Cum Laude.

CIOSEK, RICHARD F; Bishop Connolly HS; Swansea, MA; (Y); Computer Clb; Band; Church Choir; High Hon Roll; Hon Roll; Fnlst Comp Cntst 84; SMU; Electrncs.

CIPOLLINI, JOHN; B M C Durfee HS; Fall River, MA; (Y); 14/700; Spanish Clb; Bsktbl; Var L Bsbl; High Hon Roll; Hon Roll; NHS; Brown U; Pre Med.

CIVETTA, PETER REGIS; Wellesley HS; Wellesley, MA; (Y); 32/328; Drama Clb; Acpl Chr; Boy Scts; School Musical; School Play; Stage Crew; Variety Show; Hon Roll; NHS; Drama Clb Pres 84-85; Drama Clb VP 83-84; Joseph E Fiste Mem Awd 85; Boston Coll; Theatr.

CIVITARESE, MARC; Beverly HS; Beverly, MA; (Y); Am Leg Boys St; Church Yth Grp; Nwsp Stf; Off Jr Cls; High Hon Roll; NHS; Tufts; Pre-Med.

CLANCY, DEBORAH A; Bollingham Manprial JR SR HS; Bellingham, MA; (Y); Church Yth Grp; DECA; Yrbk Stf; High Hon Roll; Hon Roll; NHS; Travl.

CLAPP, ELIZABETH; Dennis Yarmouth Regional HS; Dennis, MA; (S); 1/316; Church Yth Grp; Pres Girl Scts; Math Tm; Trs Band; School Musical; Bausch & Lomb Sci Awd; NHS; Ntl Merit Ltr; Val; Harvard Bk Awd 84; MA Inst Tech; Chem Engr.

CLAPP, GRETCHEN; King Philip Regional HS; Norfolk, MA; (S); 18/222; Rep Stu Cncl; JV Socr; Hon Roll; NHS; Ntl Merit SF; U Of Lowell; Physcl Therapy.

CLARIMUNDO, ROSA; Bishop Fenwick HS; Peabody, MA; (Y); High Hon Roll; Hon Roll.

CLARK, AMY; Lee HS; Otis, MA; (Y); 13/108; Church Yth Grp; Spanish Clb; Yrbk Stf; Socr; High Hon Roll; Hon Roll; NHS; Accntng.

CLARK, BECKY; Minnechaug Regional HS; Wilbraham, MA; (Y); Church Yth Grp; Church Choir; Mrchg Band; Yrbk Stf; Mgr Trk; Hon Roll; Band; Concert Band; Jazz Band; Pep Band; Hnrb Mntn-Sci Fair 84; Student Hostess 85-86; Clemson U; Accounting.

CLARK, BRIAN E; Medfield HS; Medfield, MA; (Y); Am Leg Boys St; Church Yth Grp; Ski Clb; Var Capt Crs Cntry; Var L Trk; Hon Roll; Jr NHS; Bus Adm.

CLARK, CHRISTINE; Georgetown HS; Georgetown, MA; (Y); Drama Clb; Band; Concert Band; Jazz Band; Mrchg Band; School Play; Var Capt Bsktbl; Var L Socr; Var Capt Socr; Im Tennis; Coaches Awd Bsktbll, Sftbll 84-85; Georgetown Real Est Schlrshp 85; Babson Coll; Mgmt.

CLARK, DARRELL W; Hamilton-Wenham Regional HS; S Hamilton, MA; (Y); 30/200; Am Leg Boys St; Chess Clb; Church Yth Grp; Drama Clb; Band; Chorus; Concert Band; Drm & Bgl; Jazz Band; Mrchg Band; All ST Band 3rd ST; Conn Coll; Pol Sci.

CLARK, DINA; Mario Umana Tech HS; Boston, MA; (Y); Girl Scts; Hosp Aide; Church Choir; Yrbk Stf; Trs Jr Cls; Var Cheerleading; Var Pom Pon; Hon Roll; Prfct Atten Awd; Spch Cont 1st Pl 80; Boston Globe Essay Cont Rnnr-Up 85; Dist Spllng Comptn Chmp 85; Pedtrcn.

CLARK, JAMES E; Oakmont Regional HS; Ashburnham, MA; (Y); 11/135; Am Leg Boys St; Aud/Vis; Band; Concert Band; Mrchg Band; Nwsp Rptr; Yrbk Phtg; Var Bsbl; High Hon Roll; Sprts Jrnlsm.

CLARK, KINO; Blackstone Vly Regnl Vo-Tech HS; Milford, MA; (Y); Computer Clb; Nwsp Stf; Hon Roll; Comp Tech.

CLARK, MELANIE; Bishop Feehan HS; N Attleboro, MA; (Y); Y-Teens; Mrchg Band; Stage Crew; Nwsp Rptr; Nwsp Stf; Soc Wrk.

CLARK, PAUL; Randolph HS; Randolph, MA; (Y); Varsity Clb; Var Capt Socr; Jr NHS; Ntl Merit Ltr; Engrng.

CLARK, PAUL E; West Springfield HS; W Springfield, MA; (Y); 73/253; VP Variety Show; German Bk Awd 85; Roger Williams Coll; Mar Bio.

CLARK, PAULA; Tahanto Regional HS; Berlin, MA; (Y); 2/60; Sec Trs Church Yth Grp; Hosp Aide; Science Clb; Band; JV Bsktbl; High Hon Roll; Lion Awd; VP NHS; Sal; Williams Coll Bk Awd 84; Evangel Coll; Medical.

CLARK, RICHARD; Maynard HS; Maynard, MA; (Y); 8/99; Band; Mrchg Band; JV Bsbl; Var Ftbl; Capt Var Trk; Wt Lftg; High Hon Roll; Hon Roll; NHS; St Schlr; MA Advncd Stud Prog 85; FL Inst Tech; Aviation.

CLARK, STEPHANIE; Norwell HS; Norwell, MA; (Y); 25/174; VP AFS; Drama Clb; Pres 4-H; Intnl Clb; School Play; Nwsp Rptr; Ed Nwsp Stf; Var L Fld Hcky; Cit Awd; Hon Roll; MA 4-H Key & Herdsman Awd 83-84; 4-H Mabel Chandler Awd 84; Best Of Shows Arts & Crafts 79-84; Cornell U; Vet.

CLARK, TARA C; Marblehead HS; Marblehead, MA; (Y); 11/262; Band; Drm Mjr(t); Jazz Band; Mrchg Band; Orch; High Hon Roll; NHS; Ntl Merit SF; Drama Clb; Latin Clb; Fin Mc Donalds All Star Marchng Band 84; Piccolo WBZ TV 35th Anv Mrchng Band 83; Fund Rsng Chrmn Ban; Mus Ind.

CLARK, TODD; Central Catholic HS; Methuen, MA; (Y); Boys Clb Am; Trs Frsh Cls; Trs Soph Cls; VP Sr Cls; JV Var Bsktbl; JV Var Trk; Hon Roll; Arch.

CLARK, WILLIAM; Marian HS; Natick, MA; (Y); 4/177; Latin Clb; Nwsp Sprt Ed; Lit Mag; Rep Frsh Cls; Pres Soph Cls; Pres Jr Cls; Var L Socr; High Hon Roll; Hon Roll; NHS; Hugh O Brian Yth Ldrshp Smnr, Ambssdr 84; Finance.

CLARK, WILLIAM; Mohawk Trl Regional HS; Colrain, MA; (Y); 27/142; Pres AFS; Church Yth Grp; Pres 4-H; French Clb; Political Wkr; Band; Yrbk Stf; Var Tennis; 4-H Awd; Hon Roll; NYSSMA Solo Fest Outstndg 82; Intl Bus.

CLARKE, KELLY; Aquawam HS; Feeding Hills, MA; (Y); 60/350; Library Aide; Office Aide; Yrbk Stf; Var Cheerleading; Hon Roll; NHS; Stu Cadre; Jr Marshall; Engrng.

CLARKE, TRACIE; Saugus HS; Saugus, MA; (Y); 15/309; Ski Clb; Yrbk Stf; Off Soph Cls; Off Jr Cls; Off Sr Cls; Stu Cncl; Trk; Jr NHS; NHS; Camp Fr Inc; Outstndng Achv Math 84.

CLARKSON, DAVID C; Newburyport HS; Newburyport, MA; (Y); Am Leg Boys St; Aud/Vis; Computer Clb; Intnl Clb; Library Aide; Model UN; Science Clb; Sci Tutor 83-86; Franklin Pierce Coll; Psych.

CLAUGHTON, SARAH; Frontier Regional Schl; Sunderland, MA; (Y); Cmnty Wkr; French Clb; Library Aide; Tennis; Hon Roll; Ed.

CLAVEAU, DAVID M; Salem HS; Salem, MA; (Y); Electrncs.

CLAY, NANCY; Georgetown JR SR HS; Georgetown, MA; (Y); 14/89; Drama Clb; Ski Clb; Spanish Clb; Band; Mrchg Band; High Hon Roll; Ryal Lncr Mrchng Bnd 82-83; Supr Prfrmnc US Hstry 84-85; Outstndng Achvt Typng/Keybrdng I 84-85; Mrchndsng.

CLEARY, JOHN; St Johns HS; Grafton, MA; (Y); Church Yth Grp; FCA; School Play; Im Bsktbl; Ftbl; Im Tennis; Hon Roll; Altar Boy; Lttl Leag Umpir; Villanova; Bus Adm.

CLEARY, NANCY; Westford Acad; Westford, MA; (Y); Pres Art Clb; Pep Clb; Spanish Clb; Yrbk Ed-Chief; Var Capt Bsktbl; Var Capt Socr; Var Trk; High Hon Roll; NHS; Bostn Glob Schlstc Art Awd Ntl 83; RI Schl Of Dsgn; Cmmrcl Art.

CLEMENT, ANTHONY; Dorchester HS; Boston, MA; (Y); Am Leg Boys St; Boys Clb Am; Letterman Clb; ROTC; Teachers Aide; Varsity Clb; Band; Drill Tm; Pres Frsh Cls; Bsktbl; Boys ST 85; Sec-Boys ST 85; Apptd To Govrs Cncl; Bus Mgmt.

CLEMENT, JENNIFER; B M C Durfee HS; Fall River, MA; (Y); 34/500; VP French Clb; Yrbk Stf; High Hon Roll; Hon Roll; NHS; Erly Chldhd Educ.

CLEMENT, MARK; Barnstable HS; W Barnstable, MA; (Y); Am Leg Aux Girls St; Off Stu Cncl; Crs Cntry; Trk; Hon Roll; NHS; Holy Cross Coll; Engl.

CLEMONS, TRACEY; The High School Of Commerce; Springfield, MA; (S); #3 In Class; JA; Chorus; Cit Awd; Hon Roll; NHS; Prfct Atten Awd; Acad All Amer Awd 85; U Of MA; Acctnt.

CLERC, MARC; Apponequet HS; Lakeville, MA; (Y); Rep Frsh Cls; Rep Soph Cls; Rep Jr Cls; Pres Sr Cls; Bsktbl; Crs Cntry; Trk; Hon Roll; NHS.

CLERPIAL, KAREN; Bedford HS; Bedford, MA; (Y); 29/213; Am Leg Aux Girls St; Church Yth Grp; Girl Scts; Red Cross Aide; Band; Chorus; Church Choir; Concert Band; Mrchg Band; School Musical; Psych.

CLEVERLY, ANDREA J; Middleboro HS; Middleboro, MA; (Y); Drama Clb; Variety Show; Var Fld Hcky; Mgr Sftbl.

CLIFFORD, AMY L; Gloucester HS; Gloucester, MA; (Y); 42/308; Yrbk Ed-Chief; Trs Frsh Cls; Pres Soph Cls; Off Jr Cls; Stu Cncl; Var Cheerleading; Var Trk; Kiwanis Awd; Syracuse U; Cmnctns.

CLIFFORD, CHERYL; Randolph HS; Randolph, MA; (Y); Yrbk Stf; Illstrtn Dsgn.

CLIFFORD, JOSEPH P; Dedham HS; Dedham, MA; (S); 4/290; Spanish Clb; Nwsp Rptr; Nwsp Sprt Ed; Nwsp Stf; Var L Bsbl; Var L Bsktbl; High Hon Roll; NHS; Ntl Merit Ltr; Pres-Elect Natl Hnr Scty 85-86; MA Boys ST 85; Best JR Sci 85.

CLIFFORD, MARY ELLEN; Sacred Heart HS; Braintree, MA; (Y); Church Yth Grp; Drama Clb; Girl Scts; Spanish Clb; Church Choir; School Play; Stage Crew; Variety Show; Nwsp Stf; VP Frsh Cls; Exclnc In Theolgy 84-85; Archdcsn Yth Cncl 85; Chrstn Ldrshp 84; Theology.

CLOPPER, JEFFREY S; Framingham South HS; Framingham, MA; (Y); 7/285; Trs Drama Clb; Pres Temple Yth Grp; Acpl Chr; Chorus; Madrigals; School Musical; School Play; Stage Crew; Variety Show; High Hon Roll; Drama Clb Schlrshp 85; David Mindess Schlrshp 85; Tufts U; Med.

CLORY, ERIC; Bridgewater-Rayham Reg HS; Raynham, MA; (Y); Ski Clb; Bsktbl; Crs Cntry; Trk; Wt Lftg; Hon Roll; Engrng.

CLOSE, SARAH; Beverly HS; Beverly, MA; (Y); German Clb; Red Cross Aide; Band; Concert Band; Mrchg Band; JV Socr; High Hon Roll; NHS; Wellesley Coll Bk Awd 85; Bassline Awd 85.

CLOUGH, JENNIFER; Holy Name Central Catholic HS; Spencer, MA; (Y); 49/272; Church Yth Grp; Ski Clb; Church Choir; VP Jr Cls; VP Sr Cls; High Hon Roll; Hon Roll; Outstndng Achvt Lit 85; Forsyth; Dentl Hyg.

CLOUGH, JOHN H; Lexington SR HS; Lexington, MA; (Y); Church Yth Grp; Cmnty Wkr; Political Wkr; Rep Jr Cls; Rep Sr Cls; Pres Rep Stu Cncl; Var L Lcrss; Capt Var Socr; Runner-Up Hugh O Brian Ldrshp Fndtn Awd 84; Stu Ldr Pgm 85-86.

CLOUGH, WENDELL M; Chelmsford HS; Chelmsford, MA; (Y); 21/560; Sec Church Yth Grp; School Musical; School Play; Ed Nwsp Stf; Off Stu Cncl; French Hon Soc; NHS; Ntl Merit SF; Art Clb; Aud/Vis; Yth Ftns Achv Awd 82-83; MA Drama Fest All Star Cst Awd 84; CHS Drma Clb Bst Actr Awd; Columbia U; Writing.

CLOUTIER, ROSELLA; Agawam HS; Agawam, MA; (Y); 105/325; AFS; Dance Clb; 4-H; Library Aide; Color Guard; Drill Tm; Hon Roll; Electronic Accntng.

CO-WALLIS, GWEN MARIE; Silver Lake Regional HS; Halifax, MA; (Y); 19/500; Cmnty Wkr; Dance Clb; Yrbk Stf; Pres Soph Cls; JV Var Cheerleading; Var Pom Pon; High Hon Roll; Hon Roll; Hst NHS; Acctnt.

COADY, MARCELLE; Bellingham Memorial HS; Bellingham, MA; (Y); Nwsp Stf; Yrbk Sprt Ed; Var L Fld Hcky; Var L Trk; Woonsockett Call All Str Spg Trck 85; Wntr Trck MVP 84; Wntr Trck TVL All Str Tm 83-85; Johnson & Wales; Clnry Arts.

COAKLEY, ROBERT PAUL; Blackstone Vly Rgnl Vo Tech HS; Northbridge, MA; (Y); Computer Clb; Drm & Bgl; High Hon Roll.

COATES, JENNIFER; Boston Latin Schl; Boston, MA; (Y); 103/324; Lit Mag; Hon Roll; Church Yth Grp; Key Clb; Pep Clb; Brdcstng.

COBB, MELISSA; Bishop Feehan HS; Attleboro, MA; (Y); JCL; Color Guard; Rep Frsh Cls; JV Cheerleading; Var Trk; Hon Roll; Med.

COBE, RUSS; Bedford HS; Bedford, MA; (Y); 14/238; Drama Clb; Temple Yth Grp; Jazz Band; Madrigals; School Musical; Var L Swmmng; Rotary Awd; Aud/Vis; Band; Chorus; Wesleyan U; Liberal Arts.

COBERY, MARC; Bishop Connolly HS; Fall River, MA; (Y); Church Yth Grp; JA; JCL; Latin Clb; JV Crs Cntry; Var Golf; Gov Hon Prg Awd; Natl Lat Exam Magna Cum Laude Lvl I 83; Natl Lat Exam Cum Laude Lvl II 84.

COCCA, ROBERT; Winthrop HS; Winthrop, MA; (Y); 1/250; Am Leg Boys St; Drama Clb; Math Tm; Pres Science Clb; Chorus; School Play; Rep Stu Cncl; L Socr; Trk; NHS; Mst Likly Succd 83-86; Grtr Boston Stu Advsry Cncl 86; Harvarfd Bk Clb Awd Excllnc Schlrshp 85; Med.

CODELIA, ADRIENE; St Peter Marian Cntrl Catholic HS; Worcester, MA; (Y); Ski Clb; School Musical; Nwsp Rptr; Yrbk Rptr; Rep Stu Cncl; Var Crs Cntry; Var Tennis; Earlham Coll.

CODY, GERARD; Christopher Columbus HS; South Boston, MA; (S); 35/115; Nwsp Rptr; Nwsp Sprt Ed; Nwsp Stf; Yrbk Rptr; Yrbk Stf; Var Crs Cntry; Im Capt Trk; Cit Awd; Jr NHS; Employee Of Mnth Dec 84; 2nd Pl Annual Columbus Run 84; Mary Deuereax Chrctr Awd 81; U Of Lowell; Indstrl Engrng.

COE, KATHLEEN; Stoughton HS; Stoughton, MA; (Y); Church Yth Grp; Cmnty Wkr; Office Aide; Pep Clb; Teachers Aide; Drm Mjr(t); Mrchg Band; Stage Crew; Tennis; Twrlr; Merrimack; Tchr.

COE, WAYNE R; Murdock HS; Winchendon, MA; (Y); 1/62; Am Leg Boys St; Model UN; Yrbk Ed-Chief; High Hon Roll; Pres NHS; Prfct Atten Awd; Pres Schlr; Val; Voice Dem Awd; Pres Soph Cls; MA Assn Schl Supt Acad Excllnce Awd 84; U Of MA Amherst; Legl Stud.

COFFEY JR, DENIS M; Bishop Connolly HS; Portsmouth, RI; (Y); 62/157; Boy Scts; Drama Clb; School Play; JV Socr; High Hon Roll; Eagle Scout 85; Ad Altare Del-Pope Pius XII Medals 83-84; The Citadel.

COFFEY, MARK; Don Bosco Vo Tech; West Roxbury, MA; (S); Chorus; Stu Cncl; Crs Cntry; Trk; Hon Roll; Ntl Merit Schol; Var Ltr X-Cntry, Indoor & Outdoor Trck 82-85; Prfct Atten Awd; Law Enforcement.

COFFMAN, MICHAEL; Braintree HS; Braintree, MA; (Y); 26/400; Chess Clb; Math Tm; Spanish Clb; Temple Yth Grp; Var Tennis; Hon Roll; Spanish NHS; Engl Olympia Tst 82; Hnrb Mntn Sci Fair 85; Jewish Theolgcl/Sem; Cantorial.

COGLIANO, MIKE A; Billerica Memorial HS; Billerica, MA; (Y); JV Lcrss.

COGNETTA, MICHAEL; Milford HS; Milford, MA; (Y); 44/311; Church Yth Grp; JV Bsbl; Var L Bsktbl; Coach Actv; Hon Roll; NHS.

COHAN, CAROLYN; Holbrook HS; Holbrook, MA; (Y); 4/102; Sec Latin Clb; Rep Soph Cls; Rep Jr Cls; JV Var Bsktbl; JV Fld Hcky; JV Var Socr; JV Var Sftbl; Hon Roll; NHS; Acad All Amer 84.

COHANE, LISA; Holy Name Central Catholic HS; Worcester, MA; (Y); 14/272; Sec Church Yth Grp; School Musical; School Play; Lit Mag; High Hon Roll; NHS; Bio.

COHEN, BECKY; Chicopee Comprehensive HS; Chicopee, MA; (Y); 28/370; German Clb; Hosp Aide; Ed Yrbk Stf; Rep Soph Cls; Tennis; NHS; Nrsng.

COHEN, CHERI LYN; Natick HS; Natick, MA; (Y); 11/421; Off Jr Cls; Off Sr Cls; Var Capt Swmmng; High Hon Roll; Hon Roll; Trs NHS; John Hnck Ins Co Bus Awd 85; Rtry Clb Schlrshp 85; Bus Law Awd 85; Babson Coll; Bus.

COHEN, JAY; Randolph HS; Randolph, MA; (Y); Drama Clb; Temple Yth Grp; Stage Crew; Var L Crs Cntry; Var Trk; Hon Roll.

COHEN, JEFFREY; Peabody Veterans Memorial HS; Peabody, MA; (Y); Drama Clb; Math Tm; Thesps; Stage Crew; Ftbl; Ice Hcky; Trk; High Hon Roll; NHS; Law.

COHEN, JENNIFER; Brookline HS; Brookline, MA; (Y); Drama Clb; JA; Office Aide; Ski Clb; Spanish Clb; Yrbk Stf; Off Jr Cls; Trk; High Hon Roll; Hon Roll; Robert House Acadmc Achvt Awd 83-85.

COHEN, MELISSA; Framingham South HS; Framingham, MA; (Y); French Clb; Temple Yth Grp; Stu Cncl; Tennis; Hon Roll; Psych.

COHEN, REBECCA; Winthrop HS; Winthrop, MA; (Y); 3/220; Hosp Aide; Math Tm; Science Clb; Nwsp Sprt Ed; Yrbk Ed-Chief; Sec Sr Cls; JV Var Bsktbl; JV Var Tennis; High Hon Roll; NHS; Suffolk U Bk Awd 85; Sci Tm Awd 85; Tnns Awd 84-85; Cornell; Pre-Med.

COHEN, WARREN; Brookline HS; Brookline, MA; (Y); Cmnty Wkr; Political Wkr; Temple Yth Grp; Nwsp Ed-Chief; Off Soph Cls; Off Jr Cls; Off Sr Cls; Band; Hon Roll; Grad Schrlshp 85; Fnlst Sherman H Starr Human Rel Awd 85; Colby Coll Bk Prz 84.

COISH, LORI; New Bedford HS; New Bedford, MA; (Y); 77/640; Office Aide; Yrbk Stf; Hon Roll.

COLBERT, PATRICIA; Norwell HS; Norwell, MA; (Y); Cmnty Wkr; GAA; Hosp Aide; Stage Crew; Variety Show; Nwsp Rptr; Nwsp Stf; Yrbk Stf; Im Bsktbl; Mgr(s); Comm.

COLBY, PAULA M; Billerica Memorial HS; N Billerica, MA; (Y); 100/500; Girl Scts; Hosp Aide; Nwsp Rptr; Stu Cncl; Badmtn; Var Crs Cntry; Capt Powder Puff Ftbl; Var Trk; Var Vllybl; Hon Roll; U Of Lowell; Bus Mgmt.

COLE, CHERYL; Silver Lake Regional HS; Kingston, MA; (Y); 24/458; French Clb; Math Clb; Nwsp Phtg; Yrbk Phtg; Yrbk Stf; Sec Soph Cls; Var Cheerleading; JV Fld Hcky; DAR Awd; NHS; John Hancock Awd 85; Acad All Amer 85; U MA Amherst; Bus Mngmnt.

COLE, CYNTHIA; Norwell HS; Norwell, MA; (Y); VP AFS; Church Yth Grp; Drama Clb; Chorus; Drill Tm; School Musical; School Play; Rep Jr Cls; Var Mgr(s); Var Score Keeper; Bus Admin.

COLE, KIMBERLY; Braintree HS; Braintree, MA; (Y); Art Clb; Church Yth Grp; Cmnty Wkr; Dance Clb; Debate Tm; Drama Clb; Spanish Clb; Chorus; Church Choir; School Musical; Modern Miss ST Fnls Tlnt Wnnr 85; Outstndng Effort Theology 84-85; Spnsh II Awd 84; Emerson Coll; Theatrics.

COLE, LAURA; Silver Lake Reg HS; Halifax, MA; (S); 49/489; Dance Clb; Office Aide; Pres Spanish Clb; Variety Show; Nwsp Ed-Chief; Yrbk Ed-Chief; Hon Roll; Prfct Atten Awd; Ballet Co Stu Of The Year 82; Nursing.

COLE, LISA; Dracut SR HS; Dracut, MA; (Y); Key Clb; Ski Clb; Band; Concert Band; Mrchg Band; Utica Coll Syracuse; Soclgy.

COLE, MICHAEL; Marlboro HS; Marlboro, MA; (Y); Boys Clb Am; Key Clb; Im Bsktbl; Var Crs Cntry; Var Trk; High Hon Roll; Hon Roll; Physics.

COLEMAN, EDWARD; Boston Latin Schl; Boston, MA; (Y); 69/310; Latin Clb; Chorus; Church Choir; Yrbk Bus Mgr; Socr; Swmmng; Hon Roll; NHS; Prfct Atten Awd; Merit Awd 83; Greek Clb 84-85; Profsnl Clb 84-85.

COLEMAN, FRANCIS; Clinton HS; Clinton, MA; (Y); Am Leg Boys St; Church Yth Grp; Intnl Clb; JA; Rep Stu Cncl; Ftbl; Golf; Hon Roll; Elec Engr.

COLLAZO, JOSE; Lawrence HS; Lawrence, MA; (Y); Aud/Vis; Dance Clb; Drama Clb; MMM; Chorus; Swing Chorus; Cheerleading; Gym; Swmmng; Best Athlt Cylpda 80; NY Schl Perf Arts; Sngr.

COLLETTA, VALERIE; Melrose HS; Melrose, MA; (Y); 34/400; German Clb; Stu Cncl; Im Bsktbl; Var Tennis; High Hon Roll; Hon Roll; NHS; Bio.

COLLIER, KAREN; Sacred Heart HS; S Weymouth, MA; (Y); 1/58; Capt Color Guard; Drm & Bgl; Drm Mjr(t); Stage Crew; Nwsp Rptr; Yrbk Stf; Pres Frsh Cls; VP Stu Cncl; JV Var Cheerleading; Var Capt Sftbl; US Army Resrv Natl Schlr/Ath Awd 85; WBZ-TV4 & GM Bst Of Clss Awd 85; MA Cmmnwlth Schlr Awd 85; Coll Of Holy Cross; Chem.

COLLINS, ANDREW M; Millis HS; Millis, MA; (Y); 3/58; Church Yth Grp; Orch; Var Socr; Capt Tennis; Hon Roll; NHS; Ntl Merit Ltr; Med.

COLLINS, CATHERINE; Notre Dame Acad; Billerica, MA; (Y); 8/50; Trs Pep Clb; Political Wkr; Ski Clb; Stage Crew; Im Bsktbl; High Hon Roll; Hon Roll; NHS.

COLLINS, CHRIS; Biship Feehan HS; Mendon, MA; (Y); 44/240; Church Yth Grp; Im Bsktbl; High Hon Roll; Hon Roll; NHS; Spanish NHS; Bio Hnrs Achvt Awd 83 & 84; Span Hnrs Achvt Awd 83; Pol Sci.

COLLINS, CHRISTOPHER H; Millis HS; Millis, MA; (Y); 13/85; Sec Am Leg Boys St; Band; Concert Band; Jazz Band; Mrchg Band; Variety Show; L Socr; L Trk; Hon Roll; Chrmn ST Stu Advsry Cncl MA Brd Ed SSAC 85-86; ST Brd Ed.

COLLINS, DANNY R; Millis HS; Millis, MA; (Y); 34/90; Church Yth Grp; Cmnty Wkr; Science Clb; Spanish Clb; Varsity Clb; Var L Ftbl; Var L Trk; Wt Lftg; Hon Roll; Jr NHS; Wntwrth Inst/Tech; Elec Engrng.

COLLINS, DENNIS; Christopher Columbus HS; Charlestown, MA; (S); 12/125; Boys Clb Am; Church Yth Grp; Cmnty Wkr; JA; JV Ftbl; JV Var Ice Hcky; Im Wt Lftg; High Hon Roll; Hon Roll; NHS; Bus.

COLLINS, GREGORY M; Boston College HS; Quincy, MA; (Y); 19/270; Camera Clb; French Clb; Key Clb; Ski Clb; High Hon Roll; NHS; Undergrad Awds 82-85; Boston Coll; Bus.

COLLINS, JEFF; Westport HS; Westport, MA; (Y); Drama Clb; French Clb; Intnl Clb; Ski Clb; School Play; Nwsp Stf; Yrbk Stf; Bsktbl; Crs Cntry; Golf; SE MA U; Pltcl Sci.

COLLINS, JOHN; Bishop Fenwick HS; Beverly, MA; (Y); Boy Scts; Church Yth Grp; Cmnty Wkr; Ski Clb; Y-Teens; JV Bsktbl; Hon Roll; VP YMCA Ldrs Clb 85; Plt.

COLLINS, KEITH; St Peter-Marian C C HS; Worcester, MA; (Y); Church Yth Grp; JA; Bsbl; Ice Hcky; Wt Lftg; Hon Roll; Assumption Coll; Bus Mgmt.

COLLINS, LINDA; Lunenburg HS; Lunenburg, MA; (Y); Girl Scts; Intnl Clb; Teachers Aide; Variety Show; Var Bsktbl; Var Capt Socr; Var Sftbl; High Hon Roll; Hon Roll; NHS; All Stars Bsktbl Hnrry Mentn 84; All Stars Sftbl 2nd Tm 85; All Stars 1st & 2nd Tm Soccer 84-85; Pre-Med.

COLLINS, MELISSA; Plymouth-Carver HS; Plymouth, MA; (Y); 31/516; AFS; French Clb; Concert Band; Mrchg Band; Variety Show; Yrbk Rptr; Yrbk Stf; Hon Roll; Northeastern U; Advrtsg.

COLLINS, MICHELLE; Smilford HS; Milford, MA; (Y); Church Yth Grp; Yrbk Stf; Coach Actv; Fld Hcky; Gym; Sftbl; Vllybl; Hon Roll; Salva Regina; Psych.

COLLINS, MIKE; Chicopee HS; Chicopee, MA; (Y); Yrbk Stf; VP Sr Cls; Var JV Ftbl; UMASS; Cvl Engrng.

COLLINS, NEAL O; Stoneham HS; Stoneham, MA; (Y); 24/262; Am Leg Boys St; Church Yth Grp; Debate Tm; Exploring; French Clb; Math Tm; Ski Clb; Band; Concert Band; Jazz Band; Var Ltrs Sports 83-85; Navy; Engrng.

COLLINS, PATRICIA; Salem HS; Salem, MA; (Y); 104/456; Church Yth Grp; Spanish Clb; Y-Teens; Drm & Bgl; Yrbk Stf; Var Cheerleading; Var Capt Swmmng; Hon Roll.

COLLINS, RAYMOND; Leominster HS; Leominster, MA; (Y); Quiz Bowl; JV Bsktbl; Var Trk; Boston Coll; Law.

COLLINS, ROSLINDE M; Westford Acad; Westford, MA; (Y); French Clb; Office Aide; Pres Frsh Cls; Capt Cheerleading; L Trk; High Hon Roll; Hon Roll; NHS; 1st Rnr Up Miss MA Amer Co-Ed Pag 85; US Chrldr Achvt Awd 84; Natl Ldrshp & Svc Awd 85; Bio Sci.

COLOMEY, KEVIN G; Catholic Memorial HS; Dedham, MA; (Y); 75/247; Am Leg Boys St; Computer Clb; Drama Clb; JA; Key Clb; Rep Jr Cls; Rep Stu Cncl; Var Swmmng; JV Trk; Hon Roll; Engrng.

COLON, DAVID; Boston Technical HS; Boston, MA; (Y); FBLA; Math Clb; Office Aide; Hon Roll; Boys Clb Am; Chess Clb; Trs Church Yth Grp; Cmnty Wkr; Computer Clb; Pep Clb; Amer Hstry Awd 85; Lowell U; Elec Engr.

COLON, GIEZI; Commerce HS; Springfield, MA; (S); Church Yth Grp; English Clb; Cit Awd; Hon Roll; Jr NHS; NHS; Prfct Atten Awd; Engr.

COLON-FRANCIA, SHIRLITTA; Groton Schl; Washington, DC; (Y); Church Yth Grp; Dance Clb; Pep Clb; Church Choir; Sec Soph Cls; Sec Sr Cls; Sec Stu Cncl; Var Capt Bsktbl; Socr; Pres Alliance Stu Hrmny 85-86; Brown U; Psych.

COLUMBO, JULIA M; Dedham HS; Dedham, MA; (S); 6/280; Church Yth Grp; Concert Band; Mrchg Band; Orch; High Hon Roll; Hon Roll; Chrtr Mbr Interact Club; Psych.

COMBS, JUDITH; North Brookfield HS; N Brookfield, MA; (Y); Chess Clb; Church Yth Grp; Computer Clb; Band; Chorus; Church Choir; Variety Show; Hon Roll; Houghton Coll NY.

COMEAU, JOHN; Lynn Classical HS; Lynn, MA; (Y); 42/200; Chess Clb; French Clb; Science Clb; Rep Sr Cls; Var Stu Cncl; Stu Cncl; Golf; Vllybl; French Hon Soc; Aud/Vis; Intl Frgn Lang Awd 83; U Lowell; Mech Engr.

COMEAU, KEVIN J; Central Catholic HS; N Andover, MA; (Y); 4/227; Science Clb; Ski Clb; Yrbk Ed-Chief; Yrbk Stf; High Hon Roll; NHS; Ntl Merit Ltr; Pres Schlr; St Schlr; Dartmouth Bk Awd 84; Lawrence Eagle Trib Schlrshp 85; N Andover Schlrshp Found Schlrshp 85; Dartmouth Coll; Wrtng.

COMEAU, LISA J; Methuen HS; Methuen, MA; (Y); 98/300; Co-Capt Cheerleading; Com.

COMEAU, MARSHA A; Dracut HS; Dracut, MA; (Y); 1/259; High Hon Roll; VP NHS; Ntl Merit Ltr; Pres Schlr; St Schlr; Mst Outstndng Stu In Comp Sci, Math, Eng & Scl Stds 85; Tchrs Assn Bst All Arnd Stu Awd 85; Worcester Poly Tech Inst; Mech.

COMEAU, NOREEN; Haverhill HS; Haverhill, MA; (Y); 8/379; Latin Clb; Spanish Clb; High Hon Roll; NHS; Achvt Awd Bst All Arnd Lat Stu,Bst All Arnd Frgn Lang Stu 85; Carleton Prz & Speros Katsaros Scholar; Clark U; Comm.

COMMISSO JR, JOSEPH; High School Of Commerce; Springfield, MA; (Y); 52/413; Cmnty Wkr; Office Aide; Rep Sr Cls; Socr; Swmmng; Hon Roll; Jr NHS; Tutor In Math 83-85; Clscl Achvt Schlrshp 85; Alice B Beal PTO Schlrshp 85; Amer Intl Coll; Orthdntst.

COMOSA, JOHN; Malden Catholic HS; Malden, MA; (Y); 93/197; Ftbl; Hon Roll; Lowell Tech Inst; Engrng.

CONARD, BILL T; Canton HS; Canton, MA; (Y); 62/256; Boy Scts; Stu Cncl; Var Capt Bsbl; Var Capt Bsktbl; Hon Roll; Stonehill; Law.

CONATY, CATHLEEN; King Philip Regional HS; Wrentham, MA; (S); Math Tm; Band; Sec Jr Cls; Bsktbl; Powder Puff Ftbl; Hon Roll; NHS; Drama Clb; Concert Band; Jazz Band; Exclince Biol 83; Exclince Chem 84; New England Schltc Hnrs Band 83-84; Biol.

CONBOY, THOMAS L; Central Catholic HS; Salem, NH; (Y); Church Yth Grp; DECA; Scholastic Bowl; Nwsp Stf; Yrbk Stf; Rep Stu Cncl; Var Crs Cntry; JV Var Ice Hcky; High Hon Roll; NHS; Campus Yth Minstr 85-86; Princeton U; Chem Engrng.

CONDIT, DANIEL; Maynard HS; Maynard, MA; (Y); 10/103; Color Guard; Stu Cncl; Var L Ftbl; Var Capt Golf; Var L Ice Hcky; Hon Roll; Athl Awd, MVP Golf 85; USMC Dstngshd Athl Awd 85; Dig Dquip Corp Schlrshp 85; Providence Coll; Engrng.

CONDON, DAVID M; Sudlow HS; Ludlow, MA; (Y); Am Leg Boys St; Math Tm; Nwsp Stf; Yrbk Stf; Rep Jr Cls; Var Golf; Ice Hcky; NHS; Ntl Merit Ltr; Voice Dem Awd; Wnnr Publshrs Amer Bk Rvw 84.

CONDON, MARK; Bishop Connolly HS; Westport, MA; (S); 6/200; Boy Scts; Debate Tm; Math Tm; Ski Clb; JV Crs Cntry; High Hon Roll; NHS; Art Clb; Im Bowling; Vrsty Cyclng; Sci Fair Jdg; Chem Engrng.

CONFORTI, DARIN; BMC Durfee HS; Fall River, MA; (Y); 120/700; Computer Clb; French Clb; JV Bsbl; Ftbl; Hon Roll; Poli Sci.

CONGLETON, GREGG; St Johns Prep; Marlborough, MA; (Y); Boy Scts; Drama Clb; French Clb; Intnl Clb; JA; Model UN; Political Wkr; Ski Clb; Golf; Hon Roll; Intl Mktg.

CONLAN, RICHARD; Reading Memorial HS; Reading, MA; (Y); 17/357; Boy Scts; Concert Band; Jazz Band; Mrchg Band; JV Ice Hcky; JV Trk; God Cntry Awd; High Hon Roll; NHS; All Amer Hall Of Fame Bnd Hnrs 84; U S Wind Bands Accpt 84; Mtrlgy.

CONLEY, SUSAN MARIE; Barnstable HS; West Barnstable, MA; (Y); 40/398; Color Guard; DAR Awd; High Hon Roll; NHS; Hon Roll; Barnstable Ltr Medal 85; Cert Merit Law Day Essay Cont 85; Cape Cod Comm Coll; Exec Adm.

CONLEY, THOMAS; Methuen HS; Methuen, MA; (Y); DECA.

CONLIN, RICHARD F; King Philip Reg HS; Norfolk, MA; (Y); Am Leg Boys St; Math Tm; Stat Ftbl; Var Capt Socr; Hon Roll; NHS; Engrng.

CONLON, MARY; King Philip Regional HS; Norfolk, MA; (Y); Acctg.

CONNALLY, MICHAEL; Chicopee Cmprhnsv; Chicopee, MA; (Y); 39/300; Am Leg Boys St; German Clb; Yrbk Stf; Rep Stu Cncl; Var L Ftbl; Var L Trk; Hon Roll; NHS; Westfield ST Coll; Crmnl Jstc.

CONNELL, DAVID; East Boston HS; E Boston, MA; (Y); CAP; Computer Clb; JA; Hon Roll; Bus Law Schlstc Awd 85; Acctng.

CONNELL, JOHN; Don Boco HS; Brighton, MA; (Y); Church Yth Grp; Rep Jr Cls; JV Bsktbl; Var Capt Ftbl; Hon Roll; Ntl Merit Ltr; Cath Yuth Conv Treas 84; Engrng.

CONNELL, MARY; Academy Of Notre Dame; Westford, MA; (Y); 16/50; French Clb; Hosp Aide; Key Clb; Library Aide; 9th Hstry, 1st Sectn 82-83; 11th Relgn, 1st Sectn 84-85; Indstrl Psychlgy.

CONNELLY, JOHN K; West Bridgewater JR SR HS; W Bridgewater, MA; (Y); Aud/Vis; Varsity Clb; Band; Church Choir; Jazz Band; School Play; Sec Stu Cncl; Var L Bsbl; Var L Bsktbl; Var L Crs Cntry; MA Lions Clb Al-ST Bnd 84; Bus Adm.

CONNELLY, KIMBERLY A; Salem HS; Salem, MA; (Y); 29/375; Church Yth Grp; Ski Clb; Mrchg Band; Orch; Rep Stu Cncl; Var Cheerleading; JV Fld Hcky; High Hon Roll; Sec NHS; Bio.

CONNER, SHERI; Wachusett Regional HS; Princeton, MA; (Y); 4/385; Church Yth Grp; Cmnty Wkr; Girl Scts; Hosp Aide; JA; Ski Clb; Stage Crew; Nwsp Rptr; Nwsp Stf; Cit Awd; Williams Book Awd 84; Rcpnt Prof & Bus Wmns Schlshp 85; Rcpnt AFSM Schlshp 85; PA ST U; Elec Engr.

CONNERY, JULIANNE; Leicester HS; Leicester, MA; (S); Church Yth Grp; Latin Clb; Math Clb; Ski Clb; Chorus; Church Choir; JV Sftbl; Capt Vllybl; High Hon Roll; Hon Roll; Northeastern; Pharmacy.

CONNOLLY, BRENDA M; Malden HS; Malden, MA; (Y); 12/440; Key Clb; Math Clb; Band; Concert Band; Mrchg Band; Variety Show; Stu Cncl; Sftbl; Hon Roll; Kiwanis Awd; COMP Sci.

CONNOLLY, EMILY; Fontbonne Acad; Dorchester, MA; (Y); Church Yth Grp; Drama Clb; Library Aide; U Of ME; Sci.

CONNOLLY, GAIL; Bishop Fenwick HS; S Hamilton, MA; (Y); 27/222; Rep Soph Cls; Var Fld Hcky; Var Sftbl; Var Trk; Hon Roll; Jr NHS; NHS; Prfct Atten Awd; Athltc Intgrty Awd 85; Anat & Phys Awd 85; Scholar U Lowell 85; U Lowell; Phys Ther.

CONNOLLY, KIM M; Bellingham Memorial HS; Bellingham, MA; (Y); 18/201; Capt Drm Mjr(t); Yrbk Stf; Pres Stu Cncl; Cit Awd; DAR Awd; Hon Roll; NHS; Outstndng SR Leadrshp Awd 85; Outstndng SR Srvc Awd 85; Chairman Of Student Advsry Council 85; Providence Coll; Eng.

CONNOLLY, NOREEN; Walpole HS; Walpole, MA; (Y); 92/270; Red Cross Aide; Rep Sr Cls; Pres Stu Cncl; Var L Fld Hcky; Var L Sftbl; Elks Awd; Hon Roll; Rep Frsh Cls; Rep Soph Cls; Rep Jr Cls; Coaches Awd 84-85; Stu Cncl Schlrshp 85; Teen Of Mnth 85; St Anselm Clg; Nrsg.

CONNOLLY, ROBIN A; Bellingham Memorial HS; Bellingham, MA; (Y); Church Choir; Ed Yrbk Stf; Pres Frsh Cls; Pres Soph Cls; Pres Jr Cls; VP Stu Cncl; Tennis; Twrlr; High Hon Roll; NHS; Hugh O Brien Fndtn Ldrshp 84; Mst Outstndng Stu 83-85.

CONNOR, JAN; Phillips Acad; Minneapolis, MN; (Y); Debate Tm; Letterman Clb; Varsity Clb; Nwsp Bus Mgr; Var Crs Cntry; JV Socr; JV Tennis; Kates Amer Hstry Paper Awd 85.

CONNORS, JOSEPH T; Westfield HS; Westfield, MA; (Y); Am Leg Boys St; Debate Tm; Pres Frsh Cls; Pres Soph Cls; Pres Sr Cls; Capt Bsktbl; Crs Cntry; Trk; Jr NHS; NHS; As Schls Match Wits Tm TV Quiz Show; MA Stu Govt Day; 2nd Spkr Awd CT Vly Debate Lg; Pol Sci.

CONNORS, TIMOTHY M; Southwick HS; Granville, MA; (Y); Am Leg Boys St; Ski Clb; JV Bsktbl; Capt Var Socr; Capt Var Trk; Hon Roll; Mst Imprvd JR Vrsty Bsktbl 82; MVP Vrsty Trck 85.

CONORS, MATTHEW J; Medfield HS; Medfield, MA; (Y); Am Leg Boys St; Red Cross Aide; Teachers Aide; Nwsp Rptr; Lit Mag; Var Ftbl; Var L Trk; Hon Roll; Ntl Merit Ltr; Creative Wrtg Awd 85; MA Inst Tech; Engrng.

CONOVER, WILLIAM K; The Rivers Schl; Dover, MA; (Y); 2/64; Drama Clb; Model UN; Acpl Chr; School Musical; School Play; Stage Crew; Var Crs Cntry; Var Lcrss; High Hon Roll; Ntl Merit SF; Cum Laude Soc 84; Hstry.

CONRAD, ROBERT C; Walpole HS; Walpole, MA; (Y); 13/252; Rep Frsh Cls; Rep Soph Cls; Rep Jr Cls; Im JV Bsktbl; JV Trk; Hon Roll; Pres Acad Ftnss Awd 85; Balfour Schlrshp 85; Ntl Hist Cntst Hnrbl Mntn 84; Bryant Coll; Bus.

CONRAD, THOMAS; St Peter-Marian HS; Sterling, MA; (Y); Chess Clb; Exploring; Pep Clb; Spanish Clb; Var Capt Bsbl; Var Capt Socr; Cit Awd; Hon Roll; Boy Scts; Ski Clb; Coaches Awd Socr 85; Outdrs Clb 85; Westfield ST Clg; Comm.

CONROY, KATHLEEN; Arlington HS; Arlington, MA; (S); 7/407; Hosp Aide; Office Aide; Political Wkr; Yrbk Stf; Rep Jr Cls; Var L Fld Hcky; Var L Trk; Hon Roll; Trs NHS; Ntl Merit Ltr; Holy Cross Worcester MA.

CONROY JR, WILLIAM E; Randolph HS; Randolph, MA; (Y); Church Yth Grp; Variety Show; Bridgewater ST; Comp Prgmmr.

CONRY, CHRISTOPHER SCOTT; Don Bosco Technical HS; Chestnut Hill, MA; (S); 20/220; Political Wkr; Nwsp Phtg; Yrbk Sprt Ed; Yrbk Stf; Rep Stu Cncl; Var Bsbl; Var Capt Ice Hcky; Hon Roll; NHS; Rep Don Boso Boston Ldrshp Retroat 84; Bus.

CONSAUL, LISA; Shawsheen Tech HS; Tewksbury, MA; (Y); 29/410; Mgr(s); Im Vllybl.

CONSEDINE, PATRICK; Holyoke Catholic HS; Holyoke, MA; (Y); Cmnty Wkr; Drama Clb; Y-Teens; Stage Crew; Nwsp Stf; Yrbk Stf; L Bsbl; L Bsktbl; Golf; Socr; Flagler Coll; Psych.

CONSOLATI, JEFF; Lee HS; Lee, MA; (Y); 5/100; VP French Clb; Stu Cncl; JV Var Bsbl; High Hon Roll; Hon Roll; NHS; Ntl Merit Ltr; Acad All Amer 85; Frnch Clb Scholar 85; Ithaca Coll; Mktng.

CONSOLATI, MARY; Lee HS; Lee, MA; (Y); #4 In Class; Rep French Clb; Rep Math Tm; Pres Soph Cls; Pres Jr Cls; Pres Sr Cls; Pres Rep Stu Cncl; Mgr Crs Cntry; VP Sftbl; Frnch Achvt Awd; Var Ltr Awds; Lib Arts.

CONSTANT, KONSTANTINOS; Shepherd Hill Regional HS; Dudley, MA; (Y); 30/160; Boys Clb Am; Chess Clb; Debate Tm; Quiz Bowl; Variety Show; Var Bsktbl; JV Var Ftbl; Var Capt Trk; Pinewood Intl Schl In Grce Outstndng Blgy BSCS Stu Awd 82-83; Navy; Bus.

CONTABILE, GIUSEPPE; Chicopee Comprehensive HS; Chicopee, MA; (Y); 12/308; Spanish Clb; Yrbk Rptr; Yrbk Stf; Hon Roll; Jr NHS; NHS; Foreign Lang Awd 84-85; Page/Charles Abbey/Big Y/Fitzpatrick Schlrshp 85; U MA; Interpreter.

CONTE, KAREN; Our Lady Of Nazareth Acad; Methuen, MA; (Y); 13/59; Church Yth Grp; Ski Clb; Spanish Clb; Nwsp Rptr; Nwsp Stf; Yrbk Stf; JV Bsktbl; Hon Roll; Debate Tm; Cheerleading; Currclm Committe 83-84; VP Impct Club 825-82; HOPE Club 82-84; Engnrng.

CONTI, LAINA; Wakefield HS; Wakefield, MA; (Y); Church Yth Grp; OEA; Pep Clb; Yrbk Stf; Var Capt Cheerleading; Fld Hcky; Sftbl; Hon Roll; Boston Coll; Bus.

CONTILLI, PATRICIA A; Peabody Veterans Memorial HS; Peabody, MA; (Y); 32/510; JV Var Sftbl; VP NHS; Hosp Aide; CC Awd; Hon Roll; Pres Schlr; Boston Coll; Pre-Med.

CONWAY, CHRIS; Canton HS; Canton, MA; (Y); 10/265; Math Tm; Socr; Trk; Hon Roll; NHS; Ntl Merit Ltr.

CONWAY, CHRIS C; Wachusett Reg HS; Princeton, MA; (Y); 68/400; Ski Clb; Coach Actv; Hon Roll; Engrng.

CONWAY, KAREN; Agawam HS; Amherst, NY; (Y); 24/340; AFS; Church Yth Grp; Civic Clb; Cmnty Wkr; Hosp Aide; Pep Clb; Ski Clb; Pres Acpl Chr; Pres Chorus; Sec Jazz Band; Creatv Wrtng 83; Rotary Schlrshp 85; Chopin Piano Awd 85; SUNY Geneseo; Spec Educ.

CONWAY, KEVIN P; Billerica Memorial HS; N Billerica, MA; (Y); 20/423; Off Church Yth Grp; Pres Spanish Clb; Nwsp Bus Mgr; Nwsp Stf; Var L Ftbl; Var L Trk; Hon Roll; Stu Of Mnth 85; Billerica Fedrtn Of Tchrs Schlrshp 85; Utica Coll Of Syracuse U; Jrlsm.

CONWAY, PATRICK; Wakefield HS; Wakefield, MA; (Y); Church Yth Grp; JV Socr; JV Trk; Var Wrstlng; Middlesex Leag Wrstlng 84; Middlesex Leag Wrstlng 85; Arch.

COOK JR, HARLAND L; Walpole HS; Walpole, MA; (Y); Am Leg Boys St; Boy Scts; JV Crs Cntry; Var L Trk; Var Capt Wrstlng; NHS; Church Yth Grp; JV Bsbl; Im Gym; Elks Awd; Prse Phys Fit Awd; Outstndg Frsh Svc Awd; Ad Altare Dei Awd; Alter Boy; Phys Ed Ldr; Phrmcy.

COOK, KEVIN; New Bedford HS; New Bedford, MA; (Y); Exploring; Letterman Clb; Yrbk Stf; Rep Stu Cncl; Var L Crs Cntry; Var L Trk; Hon Roll; Stu Of SADD; Stu Grt Outdrs Clb; Rep Stu Cngrss; Brown.

COOK, MARIANNE; Silver Lake Regional HS; Kingston, MA; (Y); 66/576; Girl Scts; Spanish Clb; JV Socr; Hon Roll.

COOK, MELISSA; Hanover HS; Hanover, MA; (Y); Band; Chorus; Concert Band; Drm Mjr(t); Mrchg Band; School Musical; School Play; Hon Roll; Church Yth Grp; Office Aide; 2nd Pl New Englnd HS Video Cmpttn 85; Most Sopportive Durng Marchng Band 85; Theatre Arts.

COOK, STEVE; Georgetown JR SR HS; Goergetown, MA; (Y); High Hon Roll; Hon Roll; Highest Achvt-Intro To Physical Sci 83; Presdntl Physical Fitness Awd 84; U Of MA-AMHERST; Electrcl Engr.

COOKE, FRANCIS; Boston Latin Schl; Boston, MA; (Y); 186/301; JA; Latin Clb; Yrbk Stf; High Hon Roll; Hon Roll; Engrng.

COOKE, PETER; Cohassey HS; Cohasset, MA; (Y); 35/130; Aud/Vis; Cmnty Wkr; Computer Clb; JV Stat Bsktbl; Var L Ftbl; Im Vllybl; Hon Roll; US Naval Acad.

COOLEY, MICHAEL A; Sharon HS; Sharon, MA; (Y); 28/209; Math Tm; Temple Yth Grp; Nwsp Stf; JV Tennis; Hon Roll; Ntl Merit Ltr; Framingham ST Coll Awd For Exclinc On Hist Research Paper 85.

COOMBS, KEVIN C; Malden HS; Malden, MA; (Y); Debate Tm; Scholastic Bowl; Jazz Band; Hon Roll; Bentley Coll.

COON, MICHAEL T; Mt Everett Regional HS; Sheffield, MA; (Y); 2/75; Am Leg Boys St; Church Yth Grp; VP Frsh Cls; Off Stu Cncl; Capt L Bsbl; Capt L Bsktbl; JV Crs Cntry; Capt L Socr; High Hon Roll; Pres NHS; Hugh O Brian Yth Ldrshp Semnr; Engrng.

COONEY, SHAUN; Maynard HS; Maynard, MA; (Y); 22/104; Boy Scts; Radio Clb; Acpl Chr; JV Ftbl; Socr; Hon Roll; Engrng.

COONEY, TRACY; Ayer HS; Ft Devens, MA; (Y); 18/150; Am Leg Aux Girls St; Church Yth Grp; Cmnty Wkr; French Clb; Girl Scts; Ski Clb; Rep Sr Cls; Swmmng; Timer; Pol Sci.

COONS, CHRISTINE M; Monument Mountain Regional HS; Housatonic, MA; (Y); 11/124; Sec Band; Nwsp Sprt Ed; Var Capt Bsktbl; Var Capt Socr; Var Capt Sftbl; Pres NHS.

COOPEE, TODD C; Hampshire Regional HS; Southampton, MA; (Y); 11/110; Am Leg Boys St; Concert Band; Jazz Band; Mrchg Band; Pep Band; Nwsp Rptr; Ice Hcky; Hon Roll; NHS; Dartmouth Bk Clb Awd 85; Co-Chrmn Stu Agnst Drnk Drvng 85; Dartmouth; Engrng.

COOPER, ELIZABETH; Dana Hall Schl; Wellesley, MA; (Y); 4-H; Pres Sec Key Clb; Pres Soph Cls; Hon Roll; Hnbl Mntn Putnam Purchs Prz Awd Drwg 85; Plcd 22nd U19 USFA Natl Fencg Champs 85; Arch.

COOPER, GEORGIA M; Phillips Acad; Ithaca, NY; (Y); Cmnty Wkr; Lit Mag; Hon Roll; Ntl Merit Ltr; Maxima Cum Laude-Ntl Latin Exam 84; Barnard Coll; Psych.

COPPOLA, JOSEPH P; Berkshire Schl; W Springfield, MA; (Y); Science Clb; Varsity Clb; Var Ftbl; JV Capt Ice Hcky; Var Capt Lcrss; Kelts, Colfax & Bkr Schlsrhp 83-84; Chstr W Rice Sci Awd 84-85; Hobart Coll; Biology.

COPPOLINO, NANCY; Westwod HS; Westwood, MA; (Y); 55/214; Spanish Clb; Chorus; Color Guard; Stage Crew; Hon Roll; Spanish NHS; Bus Mgmt.

CORA, AMARILYS; Chelsea HS; Boston, MA; (Y); FHA; Latin Clb; Political Wkr; Science Clb; Spanish Clb; Band; Concert Band; Pres Frsh Cls; Bsbl; Var Bsktbl; Band Pres 85; Brandeis U; Law.

CORACCIO, CAROL; Billerica Memorial HS; Billerica, MA; (Y); 32/400; Church Yth Grp; Drama Clb; Spanish Clb; Chorus; Drm & Bgl; School Musical; School Play; Stage Crew; Variety Show; Yrbk Stf; Ditson Schl Schlrshp 85; Billerica Cmm Theatre Hd Cstrmr 84; Colby-Sawyer Coll; Art.

CORBETT, ANN E; Bridgewater-Raynham Regional HS; Bridgewater, MA; (Y); Drama Clb; French Clb; Model UN; School Play; Stage Crew; Nwsp Rptr; Nwsp Stf; High Hon Roll; Jr NHS; Ntl Merit Ltr; Wrtr.

CORBETT, KAREN M; Medford HS; Medford, MA; (Y); 29/476; Band; Concert Band; Pres Orch; Cheerleading; Hon Roll; NHS; Ntl Symphny Orchstra Awd 85; Cmmnwlth Of MA Schlrshp 85; Boston U; Music.

CORCORAN, HOLLY; Bedford HS; Bedford, MA; (Y); 45/229; Church Yth Grp; Chorus; Rep Soph Cls; Rep Jr Cls; JV Bsktbl; Var Capt Diving; JV Capt Sftbl; Var Capt Swmmng; High Hon Roll; Hon Roll; U MA Amherst; Bus Adm.

CORCORAN, MARY; Arlington Catholic HS; Arlington, MA; (Y); 7/148; Service Clb; VP Rep Jr Cls; Var Trk; Hon Roll; NHS; Natl Latn Exm Silvr Medl, Cum Laude, Magna Cum Laude 83-85; Bus.

CORDEIRO, FRANCISCO P; Old Colony Vocational Tech HS; Acushnet, MA; (Y); 2/121; Sal; Outstndng Schlstc Achvt, Acad Achvt Math, Sci 85; Amer Leg Awd Dstngshd Achvt 80; Nuclr Physc.

CORDEIRO, RICHARD THOMAS; Joseph Case HS; Swansea, MA; (Y); VP Camera Clb; Concert Band; Jazz Band; Mrchg Band; Pep Band; Yrbk Ed-Chief; Hon Roll; Mgr Sec Band; Yrbk Bus Mgr; Yrbk Phtg; Dec Teenagr Mnth 84; Tchrs Assn Schlrshp 85; Band Ltr & Jckt 85; RI Coll; Music Ed.

CORDI, IRENE; Clinton HS; Clinton, MA; (Y); 33/116; French Clb; Intnl Clb; JA; Yrbk Stf; St Schlr; Clinton Arts & Crfts Schlrshp 85; Hesser Coll; Fshn Mrchndsng.

CORDWELL, KAREN; Revere HS; Revere, MA; (Y); Church Yth Grp; Hosp Aide; Math Tm; Yrbk Stf; JV Socr; Hon Roll; Whidden Mem Vlntr Awd 83; Ed.

COREY JR, BRIAN R; B M C Dunfee HS; Fall River, MA; (Y); Boys Clb Am; Boy Scts; French Clb; Political Wkr; Varsity Clb; Concert Band; Mrchg Band; Nwsp Rptr; Lit Mag; Rep Frsh Cls.

CORLISS, CHRISTINE; Taunton HS; Taunton, MA; (Y); Church Yth Grp; 4-H; Girl Scts; Thrpy.

CORMIER, DAVID; Dracut HS; Dracut, MA; (Y); Exploring; JV Var Bsbl; Im Bowling; JV Ftbl; Im Golf; Var Wrstlng; Hon Roll; NHS; Pres Schlr; $750 Schlrshp From Dracut Schlrshp Fndtn 85; U Of Lowell; Mech Engnrng.

CORMIER, JENNIFER; New Bedford HS; Acushnet, MA; (Y); Camera Clb; Exploring; Ed Yrbk Stf; Var Diving; Var Sftbl; Hon Roll; Var Swmmng; Var Trk; PA ST U; Petrolm.

CORMIER, MARK; Gardner HS; Gardner, MA; (Y); 17/170; French Clb; Variety Show; Yrbk Ed-Chief; Yrbk Phtg; Yrbk Rptr; Yrbk Sprt Ed; Yrbk Stf; Rep Frsh Cls; Rep Soph Cls; VP Jr Cls; Stu Govt Schlrshp 85; Chester P Mc Pherson Ctznshp Awd 85; St Anselm Coll.

CORMIER, RENEE; St Bernards C C HS; Leominster, MA; (S); 5/163; Cmnty Wkr; Drama Clb; Service Clb; School Play; Nwsp Stf; Yrbk Stf; Hon Roll; NHS; Ntl Merit SF; Regis Coll; Scl Wrkr.

CORNELIUS, DOUGLAS; Brockton HS; Brockton, MA; (Y); 8/900; Yrbk Ed-Chief; High Hon Roll; Kiwanis Awd; NHS; Ntl Merit Ltr; Pres Schlr; Crosby Bk Awd 84; Summa Cum Laude Gold Mdl On Natl Latin Exam 84; Brandeis U; Vet Med.

CORRADO, JOHN C; Assabet Valley Regional Vo-Tech; Hudson, MA; (Y); 13/315; Ski Clb; Bsbl; Bsktbl; Golf; Hon Roll; NHS; Mech Engrng.

CORREA, EDWARD; Clinton HS; Sterling, MA; (Y); Chess Clb; Hon Roll; Fitchbrg St Coll Math Comp Hnrbl Ment 84.

CORREA, WAYNE J; Quincy Vo Tech Schl; North Quincy, MA; (Y); 8/250; Am Leg Boys St; Capt ROTC; Hon Roll; Amer Lgn Schlstc Excell 85; Elec Engrng.

CORREIA JR, JOSEPH J; Somerville HS; Somerville, MA; (Y); 41/576; Boys Clb Am; High Hon Roll; Hon Roll; Frnch Awd; Tufts U.

CORREIA, LISA; New Bedford HS; New Bedford, MA; (Y); 36/599; Drama Clb; JCL; Latin Clb; Capt Mrchg Band; School Play; Capt Var Twrlr; High Hon Roll; Hon Roll; Jr NHS; NHS; Cum Laude Magna Cum Laude Ntl Ltn Exm 83-84; Ltn Awd; Betsy Taber Schlrshp 85; Band Bstr Schlrshp 85; Stonehill Coll; Chmstry.

CORREIRA, JON PAUL; Coyle-Cassidy HS; Taunton, MA; (Y); 2/180; JCL; Trs Latin Clb; Varsity Clb; Var Ice Hcky; NHS; NEDT Awd; Holy Crs Bk Awd 85; Relgn III Awd 85; Notre Dame; Law.

CORRIGAN, KERRY; Ursuline Acad; Norwood, MA; (Y); Drama Clb; French Clb; Speech Tm; Teachers Aide; School Play; High Hon Roll; NHS; Ntl Merit Ltr; Kathleen Lowney Schlrshps 85; Boston Coll.

CORRIVEAU, JAMES R; Bay Path RVT HS; Charlton City, MA; (Y); Am Leg Boys St; Boy Scts; Library Aide; Socr; Comp Sci.

CORRIVEAU, TRACY; Wachusett Regional HS; Auburn, MA; (Y); 9/381; Church Yth Grp; Dance Clb; Lit Mag; Var L Cheerleading; JV Fld Hcky; High Hon Roll; Hon Roll; Jr NHS; NHS; Spanish NHS; Dance Masters Of Amer Dance Awds 83-85; New England Invitationals Awds 83-85; Journlsm.

CORTINA, CHRISTINE; Winchester HS; Winchester, MA; (Y); Church Yth Grp; French Clb; Hosp Aide; Ski Clb; Nwsp Rptr; Nwsp Stf; Rep Frsh Cls; Rep Soph Cls; Rep Jr Cls; Sec Sr Cls; Art Awds 84 & 85; Cert Merit 84.

COSENTINI, MICHELA; Classical HS; Springfield, MA; (Y); 6/410; Nwsp Ed-Chief; High Hon Roll; VP NHS; Prfct Atten Awd; William C Hill Trst Schlrshp 85; Presdntl Acadmc Ftns Awd 85; Jrnlsm Awd-Exclnc In Edtng 85; Our Lady Of Elms Coll; Intl Bus.

COSNER, SHARON; Ayer HS; Ayer, MA; (Y); Hosp Aide; Library Aide; Var Tennis; Hon Roll; MVP Tnns 85.

COSSABOOM, BRIAN J; Middleboro HS; Middleboro, MA; (Y); 9/207; Am Leg Boys St; Band; Jazz Band; Mrchg Band; Orch; Pep Band; Socr; NHS; Engrng.

COSTA, CHRISTOPHER; New Bedford HS; New Bedford, MA; (Y); Boy Scts; Yrbk Phtg; Yrbk Rptr; Yrbk Stf; Pres Jr Cls; Pres Sr Cls; Rep Stu Cncl; Im Bsktbl; JV Trk; Hon Mntn Martin Luther King Jr Essy Cntst 81.

COSTA, JULIE; North Quincy HS; Quincy, MA; (Y); 17/389; Math Tm; Ski Clb; Spanish Clb; Varsity Clb; Band; Color Guard; Tennis; Vllybl; Elks Awd; High Hon Roll; Boston Coll; Pre-Med.

COSTA, KEITH J; Norwood HS; Norwood, MA; (Y); Am Leg Boys St; Hon Roll; Princ Awd 83; Toastmstrs Yth Ldrshp Pgm 85.

COSTA, MARYBETH; Joseph Case HS; Swansea, MA; (Y); 35/209; Church Yth Grp; Drama Clb; French Clb; VP Ski Clb; Concert Band; Mrchg Band; Yrbk Stf; JV Gym; Hon Roll; NHS; ITT Schlrshp 85; St Josephs Coll ME; Lwyr.

COSTA, NANCY; Brockton HS; Brockton, MA; (Y); 50/1000; Band; Concert Band; Mrchg Band; Nwsp Rptr; Yrbk Stf; Hon Roll; NHS; Cum Laude Natl Ltn Exm 84; Lbrl Arts Coll; Cmmnctns.

COSTA, ROBERT; New Bedford HS; New Bedford, MA; (Y); Boy Scts; Church Yth Grp; Church Choir; Rep Stu Cncl; Swmmng; Timer; Trk; High Hon Roll; Hon Roll; Hnrb Mntn Holocaust Essay Cntst 85; Exc In Portuguese 85; Comp Sci.

COSTANZO, LINDA; Pope John VIII HS; Malden, MA; (S); 18/210; Hosp Aide; JA; Math Clb; Nwsp Stf; Lit Mag; Trk; Hon Roll; Jr NHS; NHS; Stu Cncl Trsr; Ntl Hnr Society; Engrng.

COSTELLO, SUSAN; Girls Catholic HS; Medford, MA; (Y); French Clb; Color Guard; French Hon Soc; High Hon Roll; U Of MA; Law.

COSTIGAN, WILLIAM; St Dominic Savio HS; E Boston, MA; (Y); 37/109; Boys Clb Am; Spanish Clb; Stage Crew; Var L Bsbl; Var L Bsktbl; Var L Ftbl; Hon Roll; Prfct Atten Awd; Var Bsbll & Ftbll Ltrs 83-84; Var Bsbll, Ftbll, & Bsktbll Ltrs 84-85; Comp Sci.

COTE, CELINE; St Louis Acad; Lowell, MA; (Y); Sec Church Yth Grp; Drama Clb; Sec French Clb; School Play; Variety Show; VP Jr Cls; Hon Roll; NE Essex CC; Liberal Arts.

COTE, HEATHER A; Silver Lake Reg HS; Halifax, MA; (Y); 19/457; Drm Mjr(t); Mrchg Band; School Musical; Var L Trk; Hon Roll; JP Sousa Awd; NHS; St Schlr; Church Yth Grp; French Clb; SE Dist Band,Orch 84-85; Soft Touch Dance Band Schlrshp 85; Plympton Fire Dept Aux Schlrshp 85; U MA; Sci.

COTE, LAURIE; Southbridge HS; Southbridge, MA; (Y); 25/142; Dance Clb; Variety Show; Yrbk Stf; Stu Cncl; High Hon Roll; Hon Roll; NHS; Dean JC; Bus Admin.

COTE, LISA; B M C Durfee HS; Fall River, MA; (Y); 350/650; Drama Clb; Teachers Aide; Chorus; School Musical; School Play; Stage Crew; Gym; Hon Roll; Southeastern MASS U; Psychlgy.

COTE, MONIQUE; Bishop Connolly HS; Westport, MA; (S); 9/160; Art Clb; Drama Clb; Chorus; Nwsp Ed-Chief; Nwsp Stf; High Hon Roll; NHS; SE MA U; Dsgn.

COTTEN, JEAN; Natick HS; Natick, MA; (Y); 159/443; Church Yth Grp; Hosp Aide; Hon Roll; Ntl Merit Ltr; Prfct Atten Awd; Bus Awd 85; Natl Hnr Roll; Framingham Union Schl; Nursing.

COTTON, KAREN; Mansfield HS; Mansfield, MA; (Y); Trs Church Yth Grp; Cmnty Wkr; Library Aide; Office Aide; Spanish Clb; Teachers Aide; Church Choir; Hon Roll; Masonic Awd; Outstndng Acad Achvt-Wrk Exprnce Dept 85; Wrk W/Handicppd.

COTTON, STACEY; Norton HS; Norton, MA; (Y); 8/180; Yrbk Sprt Ed; Sec Soph Cls; Sec Jr Cls; Sec Sr Cls; Rep Stu Cncl; Var Capt Bsktbl; Var Capt Sftbl; Var Capt Vllybl; Sec NHS; Voice Dem Awd; Sftbl & Vlybl All Schlstc Tm 84-85; All St Blybl, Bsktbl & Sftbl 84-85; MPV Ylybl & Sftbl 84-85; Bio.

COUGHLIN, KATHLEEN; Arliington Catholic HS; Arlington, MA; (Y); 60/148; JA; Office Aide; Yrbk Sprt Ed; Sec Jr Cls; Capt Cheerleading; Trk; Ntl Merit Ltr; Acadmc All Amer Awd-Eng 85; Cmnctns.

COUGHLIN, STACEY; Franklin HS; Franklin, MA; (Y); 7/235; Math Tm; Trs OEA; Drm & Bgl; High Hon Roll; Hon Roll; Trs NHS; Mrchg Band; Bryant Clg; CPA.

COUILLARD, CRAIG S; Saugus HS; Saugus, MA; (Y); Letterman Clb; Varsity Clb; Band; Off Stu Cncl; Golf; Ice Hcky; Bus.

COULOMBE, DONALD; Chicopee Comprehensive HS; Chicopee, MA; (Y); 34/266; Band; Concert Band; Mrchg Band; Pep Band; High Hon Roll; Hon Roll; Jr NHS; NHS; Comp Sci.

COULON, MICHELLE; Presentation Of Mary Acad; Methuen, MA; (Y); Church Yth Grp; Girl Scts; Pep Clb; Spanish Clb; Stage Crew; Yrbk Stf; High Hon Roll; Hon Roll; NHS; Vet.

COULOURAS, DIANNE; North Quincy HS; N Quincy, MA; (Y); 64/400; Church Yth Grp; Color Guard; High Hon Roll; Hon Roll; Son Of Italy Schlrshp 85; Emerson Coll; Mass Commnctns.

COURNOYER, BRIAN; Southbridge HS; Sbridge, MA; (Y); 48/162; Pres Church Yth Grp; Band; Concert Band; Mrchg Band; JV Bsktbl; Var Capt Socr; Vllybl; Stu Govt Day Delg 85; Poltcl Sci.

COURTEMANCHE, STEPHANIE; Taunton HS; Taunton, MA; (Y); 20/430; Church Yth Grp; Girl Scts; Lit Mag; High Hon Roll; Hon Roll; GSA Gld Awd 85; Elms Coll; Intl Studies.

COURTOIS, MICHELLE; St Clare HS; Jamaica Plain, MA; (Y); 7/154; Church Yth Grp; JCL; Chorus; Nwsp Stf; Pres Frsh Cls; High Hon Roll; NHS; NEDT Awd; Pres Schlr; St Schlr; John Hancock Awd Acad Excllnce 85; Bentley Coll; Mgmt.

COUSIN, SANDRA; Madison Park HS; Boston, MA; (Y); Dance Clb; Drama Clb; School Play; Yrbk Rptr; Yrbk Stf; VP Sr Cls; Cheerleading; Prfct Atten Awd; Typng & Chld Care Awd 84; Comp Sci.

COUTE, STEVEN; Tahanto Regional HS; Berlin, MA; (Y); 1/50; Church Yth Grp; Math Tm; Science Clb; Rep Stu Cncl; JV Var Bsktbl; Var Capt Socr; High Hon Roll; Jr NHS; NHS; U MA Chncllrs Talnt Awd 86; Harvard Bk Awd 85; Hist Term Papr Awd 84; Worcester Polytech Inst; Elc En.

COUTINHO, JESSICA; Marthas Vineyard Regional HS; Oak Bluffs, MA; (Y); 19/105; Exploring; Chorus; Sec Soph Cls; Var Bsktbl; Var L Fld Hcky; Hon Roll; Optmtry.

COUTO, SUZANNE; Sacred Heart HS; Weymouth, MA; (Y); French Clb; Girl Scts; Math Clb; Teachers Aide; Variety Show; Im Crs Cntry; JV Vllybl; Hon Roll; NHS; Excel In Engl & US Hstry 84; Metrs Achvt Chmstry 85; Nrsng.

COUTU, DEBRA; Southbridge HS; Southbridge, MA; (Y); 60/140; Off Band; Chorus; Concert Band; Mrchg Band; Mgr School Play; Variety Show; Hon Roll; JV Sftbl; Gregg Typng Awd 85; Nichols Coll; Bus.

COUTU, LINDA; Holyoke Catholic HS; Chicopee, MA; (Y); Math Clb; Spanish Clb; High Hon Roll; Ntl Merit Ltr; Holyoke Catholic Awd Cert Chem; Math 4 & Amer Lit 84-85; Acctg.

COVIELLO, ROBERT J; Lincoln-Sudbury HS; Sudbury, MA; (Y); Boy Scts; Var Capt Bsbl; JV Bsktbl; Var Ftbl.

COWDEN, WENDIE; Auburn HS; Auburn, MA; (Y); 25/179; Sec Church Yth Grp; Math Tm; Varsity Clb; Variety Show; Var Capt Cheerleading; Var Trk; High Hon Roll; Clifton C Stone Scholar Auburn Grange 85; Auburn Assmbly 85; Natl Hnr Roll 85; U Of CT; Psych.

COWLES, LORI; Agawam HS; Agawam, MA; (Y); Art Clb; Color Guard; Yrbk Stf; Score Keeper; Hon Roll; Jr NHS; NHS; Framingham ST Coll; Bus.

COX, DANIEL; Bridgewater Raynham Regional HS; Bridgewater, MA; (Y); Ftbl; Trk; Wt Lftg; Wrstlng; Engrng.

COX, KERRIE; Holy Name CC HS; Uxbridge, MA; (Y); Dance Clb; Drama Clb; Pep Clb; School Play; JV Cheerleading; Psych.

COX, KIMBERLEIGH; Hingham HS; Hingham, MA; (Y); 12/350; Yrbk Stf; Stu Cncl; Var Cheerleading; Var L Gym; Jr NHS; Cmnty Wkr; School Musical; Variety Show; Yrbk Phtg; Sftbl; Princeton Awd; Spn & Alg Tutor; Ballet & Jazz Prfrmnces; JR Showmnshp Dog Shows.

COX, REBECCA; Pingree Schl; Marblehead, MA; (Y); 2/64; Chorus; Yrbk Ed-Chief; JV Var Bsktbl; JV Var Fld Hcky; JV Var Lcrss; High Hon Roll; Ntl Merit SF; Nwsp Stf; CC Awd; Cit Awd; Cumlaude Soc 84; All Star Grls Bsktbl, R Pesche Awd 85; Princeton U.

COYLE, KATHLEEN; Turners Falls HS; Turners Fls, MA; (Y); 11/96; Model UN; Chorus; VP Madrigals; School Musical; Stage Crew; Yrbk Stf; Swmmng; Jr NHS; NHS; Rtry Club, Civics & Dr Sabato Mem Schlrshps 85; Alice Teed Awd 85; Pres Acad Ftns Awd 85; Schl Svc Awd; U Of MA; Zoology.

COYLE, WILLIAM; Bishop Fenwick HS; Beverly, MA; (Y).

COYNE, MARY; Burncoat SR HS; Worcester, MA; (Y); 24/260; Church Yth Grp; Intnl Clb; Library Aide; Office Aide; Pep Clb; Science Clb; Elks Awd; Hon Roll; VP Jr NHS; NHS; Southeastern MA U; Acctng.

COYNE, MICHAEL; Drury HS; North Adams, MA; (Y); 14/187; Band; Concert Band; Jazz Band; Mrchg Band; Pep Band; School Musical; JV Socr; Var L Tennis; High Hon Roll; JP Sousa Awd; MVP Wstrn MA Jzz Band Finals 85; Williams Coll.

CRADOCK, JOHN; Boston Latin HS; Boston, MA; (Y); 67/300; Drama Clb; Stage Crew; Ed Lit Mag; Ntl Merit SF; High Hnrs-Natl Greek Exam 85; Boston Coll; Comm.

CRAFT, JAMES K; Narragansett Regional HS; Phillipston, MA; (Y); 15/98; Am Leg Boys St; ROTC; Yrbk Phtg; Stu Cncl; Var L Ftbl; Var L Trk; Mu Alp Tht.

CRAFTS, SARAH; Gardner HS; Gardner, MA; (Y); 1/160; Am Leg Aux Girls St; Debate Tm; Chorus; Yrbk Stf; Sec Bsktbl; Var Tennis; High Hon Roll; NHS; Lamp Of Lrnng Awd For Hghst Rnkng 84; Pres Pro Merito Chptr Of Natl Hnr Soc 85-86; TV Rptr.

CRAFTS, SCOTT A; Minnechawg Regional HS; Hampden, MA; (Y); 74/320; Cmnty Wkr; Dance Clb; Intnl Clb; Library Aide; Teachers Aide; School Musical; School Play; Variety Show; Gym; Achvt Awd Hm Ec 83-84; U Of MA; Danc.

CRAIG, LEE A; Easthampton HS; Easthampton, MA; (Y); Var Bsktbl; Var Capt Golf; Var Socr; Accntnt.

CRAIG, LISA ANNE; Natick HS; Natick, MA; (Y); 29/459; Cmnty Wkr; Rep Stu Cncl; Var Cheerleading; Digital Corp Scholar 85; Providence Coll; Mktng.

CRAIG, PATRICIA A; Dedham HS; Dedham, MA; (S); 1/325; Church Yth Grp; Hosp Aide; Nwsp Ed-Chief; Nwsp Stf; Stu Cncl; High Hon Roll; Hon Roll; NHS; Val; VFW Awd; Harvard Prize Book Awd 84; Bst Frshmn In Foreign Language 81; Outstndng Jr In English 84; MA Inst Of Tech.

CRAIN, W CALEB; Shrewsbury HS; Shrewsbury, MA; (Y); 1/269; Capt Math Tm; Variety Show; Nwsp Rptr; Ed Yrbk Rptr; Ed Lit Mag; Stu Cncl; Bausch & Lomb Sci Awd; Pres NHS; Ntl Merit Schol; Val; Harvard U; Writing.

CRANCE, GINA-LYN; Southbridge HS; Southbridge, MA; (Y); 55/133; Drama Clb; Yrbk Stf; VP Frsh Cls; VP Soph Cls; Tennis; Trs VP Stu Cncl; Pres MA Assoc Stu Cncls 84-85; Pres & Treas Central MA Assoc Stu Cncls 82-84; Hofstra U; Cmmnctns.

CRANE, ELIZABETH G; Dana Hall Schl; Belmont, MA; (Y); Church Yth Grp; Lit Mag; Var Capt Tennis; Hon Roll; Graphc Dsgn.

CRANE, WENDY; Fairhaven HS; South Dartmouth, MA; (Y); AFS; French Clb; Band; Chorus; Concert Band; Jazz Band; Mrchg Band; Orch; School Musical; Hon Roll; 3rd Frnch Oral Spnkg 84; Chem.

CRAVEN, MAUREEN; Lowell HS; Lowell, MA; (S); DECA; Hst Jr Cls; DECA ST Ofcr 85; Photo.

CRAVENHO, CHRISTINE A; Sacred Heart HS; Kingston, MA; (Y); Drama Clb; Key Clb; NFL; Chorus; School Musical; Fld Hcky; NHS; Ntl Merit Ltr; Voice Dem Awd; Quartr Fnlst NCFL Ntl Chmpnshps 84; ST Chmpn Ply Rdng MA Frnsc Leag 84; Catholic U Of Amer; Elec Engrng.

CRAW, CARRIE; Taconic HS; Pittsfield, MA; (Y); Cmnty Wkr; Drama Clb; Hosp Aide; Good Ctznshp Awd-Cvtn 83-84; Clarke Schl For Deaf Liasn Mainstrmng 82-83; Don Btlr Memrl Schlrshp 85; Berk CC; Comp Grphcs.

CRAWFORD, DAVID; Cathedral HS; E Longmeadow, MA; (Y); Civic Clb; Model UN; Service Clb; Ski Clb; Var Trk; Bus Mngmnt.

CRAWFORD, HOLLY; Northbridge HS; Northbridge, MA; (Y); 8/139; Sec Pres Latin Clb; Band; Mrchg Band; Sec Sr Cls; Rep Stu Cncl; Var Co-Capt Sftbl; Hon Roll; Jr NHS; NHS; Lit Mag; DAR Good Ctznshp Awd 85; Delg Ntl Conf Chrstns & Jews 83; Fitchburg ST Coll.

CRAWFORD, KIMBERLY; Cohasset HS; Cohasset, MA; (Y); AFS; Hosp Aide; Library Aide; Red Cross Aide; Chorus; Yrbk Ed-Chief; Var Fld Hcky; Var Powder Puff Ftbl; Swmmng; Hon Roll; Bus.

CRAWFORD, ROBERT L; Brookline HS; Brookline, MA; (Y); Acpl Chr; Chorus; Symp Band; Nwsp Sprt Ed; Rep Jr Cls; JV Bsbl; Var Crs Cntry; Stat Ftbl; Var Trk.

CRAWFORD, STANLEY; Masconomet Reg HS; Topsfield, MA; (Y); 58/244; Nwsp Rptr; Rep Soph Cls; VP Jr Cls; VP Sr Cls; Hon Roll; Spanish Clb; Color Guard; School Musical; School Play; Im Ftbl; ABC Stu 82-83; Lead Stu; Corp Law.

CRERAR, MICHELE; Franlin HS; Franklin, MA; (Y); French Clb; Office Aide; OEA; Ski Clb; Yrbk Stf; Hon Roll.

CRESCENZI, CAROLYN; Notre Dame Acad; Hanover, MA; (Y); 29/114; Drama Clb; Spanish Clb; Chorus; School Musical; School Play; Stage Crew; Stat Bsktbl; Score Keeper; Var Sftbl; Vllybl; Coaches Awd Sftbl 85.

CREVECOEUR, JEAN EDWARD; Boston English HS; Dorchester, MA; (Y); Computer Clb; French Clb; JA; Teachers Aide; Varsity Clb; School Play; Nwsp Stf; Rep Soph Cls; Rep Jr Cls; Pres Sr Cls; Newton Silbert Schlrhsp 85; US Histry Awd 85; Boston Commwlth Schlrshp 85; Worcester ST; Crmnl Jstc.

CRIDGE, PATTI; Westford Acad; Westford, MA; (Y); Church Yth Grp; Hosp Aide; Church Choir; Jazz Band; Mrchg Band; Orch; Symp Band; Rep Stu Cncl; Trk; Jr NHS; All Cty Hnrs Orch 84; Outstndng Serv Awd Orch 84; Exc Ratng Cello Solo 84; Comm.

CRIPE, JULIE; Holy Name HS; Northborough, MA; (Y); French Clb; Hosp Aide; School Musical; Nwsp Stf; Crs Cntry; Trk; High Hon Roll; Hon Roll; Educ.

CRISTELLO, MARIANNE; Billerica HS; Billerica, MA; (Y); 20/394; Church Yth Grp; Ski Clb; Hnr Roll; Regis Coll Weston; Med Tech.

CROCHETIERE, RONALD; South Hadley HS; South Hadley, MA; (Y); Boy Scts; Church Yth Grp; Debate Tm; Pres Sr Cls; Hnr-Svrl Radio Apprncs For Chrstn Sta WACE 85; Awd-Acadmc Excllnc-Pth Fndr Voc Regnl 85; U Of MA; Engrng.

CROCKER, BRENDA; Revere HS; Revere, MA; (Y); Trk; Schl Visual Arts; Photogrphy.

CROCKER, JENNY REBECCA; Falmouth HS; East Falmouth, MA; (Y); Spanish Clb; Sec Trs Band; Sec Trs Concert Band; Sec Trs Jazz Band; Sec Trs Mrchg Band; School Musical; Hon Roll; Jr NHS; NHS; Westfield ST Coll; Crmnl Just.

CROFT, DAVID; Framingham South HS; Framingham, MA; (Y); 100/240; Band; Concert Band; Jazz Band; Mrchg Band; Orch; Pep Band; School Musical; Symp Band; Variety Show; Ithaca Clg; Bus Mgmt.

CROGAN, CHRIS; Reading Memorial HS; Reading, MA; (Y); Jazz Band; JV Wrstlng; Comp Sci.

CROKE, LAURIE; Fontbonne Acad; Quincy, MA; (Y); 50/137; Drama Clb; Intnl Clb; Stage Crew; Hon Roll; Art Awd 83-84; Boston Coll; Bus.

CRONE, MELISSA A; Brockton HS; Brockton, MA; (Y); Hosp Aide; SADD 84; Hon Roll 84-85; Lbrl Studys.

CRONIN, COLLEEN; Maiden HS; Malden, MA; (Y); 27/550; Church Yth Grp; Dance Clb; Band; Mrchg Band; Pep Band; Symp Band; Hon Roll; Psych.

CRONIN, JOHN; Archbishop Williams HS; Braintree, MA; (Y); 29/198; Var Ftbl; Var Trk; High Hon Roll; Hon Roll; NHS; Diploma Mert Spn 83-84; Bus.

CRONIN, JOSEPH; Boston College HS; Milton, MA; (Y); 40/280; Church Yth Grp; Cmnty Wkr; VP JA; Nwsp Rptr; Var L Ftbl; Var L Swmmng; Hon Roll; NHS; Carmen Elio Awd Var Swmmng 85; Georgetown U; Pre-Med.

CRONIN, LAURA; Burlington HS; Burlington, MA; (Y); Ski Clb; Chorus; VP Frsh Cls; Cheerleading; Sftbl; Hon Roll; Italian V Awd 85; St Michaels; Bio.

CRONIN, MATT; Boston College HS; Norwell, MA; (Y); 27/300; VP German Clb; Intnl Clb; VP JA; Key Clb; Ski Clb; Nwsp Phtg; Yrbk Phtg; JV Trk; High Hon Roll; NHS; ACL & JCL Magna Cum Laude 84; Bus.

CRONIN, NANCY M; Mount St Joseph Acad; Brighton, MA; (Y); Church Yth Grp; JA; Suffolk U.

CRONIN, SIOBHAN; Burncoat SR HS; Worcester, MA; (Y); French Clb; Science Clb; Ski Clb; Y-Teens; Var Crs Cntry; Hon Roll; Voice Dem Awd; Career Day Awd 85; Hstry Awd 85; Nrsng.

CRONIN, TIM; Boston College HS; Milton, MA; (Y); Trs Church Yth Grp; Cmnty Wkr; Hosp Aide; Pres JA; Political Wkr; Teachers Aide; JV Bsktbl; L Ftbl; L Swmmng; Bus.

CROSBY, MARK; Quincy HS; Quincy, MA; (Y); Am Leg Boys St; Cmnty Wkr; VP Chorus; Madrigals; Swing Chorus; Variety Show; High Hon Roll; Hon Roll; Jr NHS; NHS; Comm.

CROSSEN, BRENDA; Malden HS; Malden, MA; (Y); 24/443; Girl Scts; Key Clb; Variety Show; Rep Soph Cls; Rep Jr Cls; Hon Roll; SADD Pres Pblc Rltns; Physcl Thrpy.

CROVELLO, LISA; Norwell HS; Norwell, MA; (Y); Church Yth Grp; Cmnty Wkr; Girl Scts; Varsity Clb; Chorus; School Musical; School Play; Stage Crew; Variety Show; Stu Cncl; Mgt.

CROWELL, JERELYN J; Woburn HS; Woburn, MA; (Y); Church Yth Grp; French Clb; Girl Scts; Intnl Clb; Key Clb; Ski Clb; Chorus; Drill Tm; School Musical; Sftbl; X-Ray Tech.

CROWELL, TIMOTHY A; Somerset HS; Somerset, MA; (Y); Cmnty Wkr; Political Wkr; Ski Clb; Varsity Clb; Variety Show; Nwsp Rptr; JV Socr; Var L Tennis; Hon Roll; Optmtry.

CROWLEY, CHRISTINE; Silver Lake Regional HS; Kingston, MA; (Y); French Clb; Hosp Aide; Spanish Clb; Yrbk Stf; Rep Soph Cls; Var Mgr(s); JV Var Socr; Comm.

CROWLEY, CHRISTOPHER A; Cohasset HS; Cohasset, MA; (Y); 9/125; Computer Clb; Math Tm; Chorus; Concert Band; Jazz Band; School Musical; NHS; Ntl Merit SF; St Schlr; Aud/Vis; Top Scr MA Div Amer Comp Sci Lg 85; Outstndng Band Mbr Awd 85; MIT; Bio-Elec Engrng.

CROWLEY, FRANCIS H; English HS; Lynn, MA; (Y); 1/360; Am Leg Boys St; Capt Math Tm; Band; Drm Mjr(t); VP Frsh Cls; Soph Cls; Jr Cls; Trs Sr Cls; High Hon Roll; NHS; Duracell Invntn Cntst 83; Dartmouth Bowl Awd 85; Archlgy.

CROWLEY, JAMES; Cathedral HS; Feeding Hls, MA; (Y); 89/519; Boy Scts; Band; Concert Band; Mrchg Band; School Musical; Im Wt Lftg; Var Wrstlng; Hon Roll; Elec.

CROWLEY, KAREN J; Cardinal Spellman HS; Brockton, MA; (Y); 6/210; Church Yth Grp; Latin Clb; Office Aide; Stu Cncl; High Hon Roll; Kiwanis Awd; NHS; Pres Schlr; 2nd Prz Local Sci Fair 84; Cum Laude Awd Ntl Latin Ex 83; Frnch Awd 85; Boston Coll; Mrktng.

CROWLEY, KATHLEEN; Fontbonne Acad; Milton, MA; (Y); Drama Clb; Intnl Clb; Chorus; Vllybl; Hon Roll; Prfct Atten Awd.

CROWLEY, MAUREEN; Franklin HS; Franklin, MA; (Y); Am Leg Aux Girls St; Trs Church Yth Grp; Yrbk Stf; Capt Cheerleading; Socr; Trk; Hon Roll; NHS; Voice Dem Awd; Mddlsx Wllsey Clb Bk Prz.

CROWLEY, STEPHEN; Arlington HS; Arlington, MA; (Y); Cmnty Wkr; Rep Jr Cls; JV Bsbl; JV Var Ice Hcky; Hon Roll; Ntl Merit Ltr; Law.

CROZE, RHONDA; Lee HS; Lee, MA; (Y); Art Clb; French Clb; Yrbk Stf; Mgr(s); Socr; Sftbl; Hon Roll; Bay Path JC; Retl Mgmt.

CRUMB, DAVID; Chicopee Comprehensive HS; Chicopee, MA; (Y); 15/276; Am Leg Boys St; German Clb; Variety Show; Yrbk Stf; Swmmng; Gov Hon Prg Awd; High Hon Roll; Hon Roll; Jr NHS; NHS; UMASS Acad Scholar 85; SHEA Scholar 85; Pro Merito Soc 85; U Of MA.

CRUMBLE, JOANNE; Miss Halls Schl; Boston, MA; (Y); Dance Clb; Hosp Aide; Drill Tm; Nwsp Stf; Sec Stu Cncl; JV Vllybl; Hon Roll; Wellesley Bk Awd 84-85; Schl Secy, Prctr 85-86; Georgetown U; Brdcstng.

CRUZ, MICHAEL J; New Bedford HS; New Bedford, MA; (Y); 250/600; Drama Clb; Rep Soph Cls; Rep Sr Cls; JV Crs Cntry; VP L Trk; Ntl Merit SF; Natl Merit Schlrshp Outstndng Negro Stu, Stu Rep To Boston, Capt Of Track Tm 84; Law.

CUGINI, LISA; Braintree HS; Braintree, MA; (Y); Church Yth Grp; JV Var Cheerleading; JV Sftbl; Hon Roll; Law.

CUKOR, JEFF; Natick HS; Natick, MA; (Y); 11/500; Cmnty Wkr; Hosp Aide; JCL; Pres Temple Yth Grp; VP Soph Cls; Rep Jr Cls; Stu Cncl; JV Capt Socr; High Hon Roll; NHS; Pre-Med.

CULLEN, TIMOTHY M; Hamilton Wenham Regional HS; S Hamilton, MA; (Y); Am Leg Boys St; Church Yth Grp; Ski Clb; Spanish Clb; Chorus; Church Choir; Var Bsbl; JV Bsktbl; Var Socr; Hon Roll; Boys ST Swmmng Awd 85; St Pauls Church Yth Delg 85.

CULLINANE, CAREY; Marian HS; Sudbury, MA; (Y); JV Var Bsktbl; NEDT Awd; MA ST Sci Fair Wnnr 84; Worcester Regnl Sci & Engrng Fair Wnnr 84; Sci.

CUMMINGS, DON; Wakefield Memorial HS; Wakefield, MA; (Y); JA; Ski Clb; Nwsp Rptr; JV Golf; Var Tennis; High Hon Roll; Im Bsbl; Hon Roll; Engr.

CUMMINGS, ELIZABETH D; E Briodgewater HS; E Bridgewater, MA; (Y); 19/150; Drama Clb; Hosp Aide; Key Clb; Library Aide; Band; Chorus; Color Guard; Concert Band; Mrchg Band; School Musical; Law Acad Awd 82; Sarah E Curran Mem Scholar 85; Suffolk U.

CUMMINGS, JAMES; Whitman-Hanson HS; Whitman, MA; (Y); JV Trk; Wt Lftg; JV Wrstlng.

CUNHA, GARY; Malden HS; Malden, MA; (Y); 26/500; Am Leg Boys St; Church Yth Grp; Pres Band; Concert Band; Jazz Band; Trs Madrigals; Mrchg Band; Variety Show; Var Swmmng; Literary Scty 85-86; Comp Sci.

CUNHA, MARY JO; Academy Of Notre Dame; Lowell, MA; (Y); 1/50; Church Yth Grp; Cmnty Wkr; Computer Clb; Hosp Aide; Variety Show; JV Bsktbl; Coach Actv; Var Sftbl; High Hon Roll; NHS; Amer Assn Of Wmns U Hnr 85; Dntstry.

CUNNEY, JOHN; St Johns Prep Schl; Beverly, MA; (Y); Church Yth Grp; Lit Mag; Var L Ftbl; JV Lcrss; Var Trk; Ntl Merit SF; Hnr Rll; Gen Sci.

CUNNIFF, CATHERINE; Tantasqua Regional HS; Sturbridge, MA; (Y); 4/225; Am Leg Aux Girls St; Library Aide; Math Tm; High Hon Roll; Hon Roll; NHS; Ntl Merit SF; Chorus; Stage Crew; MA Adv Stu Pgm 85; Soc Stu Awd; Math Tm Awd; Georgetown Schl Frgn Svc; Pol.

CUNNIFF, JOHN; Holyoke HS; Holyoke, MA; (Y); English Clb; French Clb; Latin Clb; NFL; Speech Tm; Mgr Band; Concert Band; Nwsp Stf; Yrbk Stf; NHS; Holy Cross Bk Prz 85; Math.

CUNNIFF, ROBERT; Silver Lake Regional HS; Kingston, MA; (Y); 72/550; Am Leg Boys St; Church Yth Grp; French Clb; JV Var Bsbl; Im Bsktbl; Hon Roll; U S Military Acad; Engrng.

CUNNINGHAM, CAROLINE; Miss Halls Schl; Lagrangeville, NY; (Y); 27/63; Cmnty Wkr; Drama Clb; French Clb; Spanish Clb; School Play; Stage Crew; Nwsp Phtg; JV Sftbl; Swmmng; Var Vllybl; SR Cls Proctr 85-86; Bus Mngmnt.

CUNNINGHAM, CHARLES; Silver Lake Regional HS; Halifax, MA; (Y); Boy Scts; Church Yth Grp; Band; Concert Band; Jazz Band; Mrchg Band; Orch; Pep Band; School Musical; Symp Band; Berkley Coll Of Music; Music.

CUNNINGHAM, JOHN; Saugus HS; Saugus, MA; (Y); 23/320; French Clb; Ski Clb; Rep Sr Cls; Im Coach Actv; Var L Socr; Var Capt Trk; Var L Wrstlng; Pres NHS; Coach For Saugus Yth Sccr 84-85; U Of MA; Pre Med.

CUNNINGHAM, KEVIN; Boston College HS; Hingham, MA; (Y); 6/280; Church Yth Grp; Key Clb; Nwsp Stf; L Bsktbl; Im Ftbl; High Hon Roll; NHS; Ntl Merit Ltr; Ntl Hnr Rll 85; Ntl Latin Exam-Cum Maxima Laude 84; Georgetown U; Accntng.

CUNNINGHAM, NANCY; Hingham HS; Hingham, MA; (Y); 60/340; Church Yth Grp; Ski Clb; Spanish Clb; Yrbk Stf; Sec Frsh Cls; Rep Soph Cls; Rep Jr Cls; Rep Sr Cls; Im Fld Hcky; Var L Trk; Psych.

CUPP, JASON W; Attleboro HS; Attleboro, MA; (Y); 15/438; Am Leg Boys St; Boy Scts; Yrbk Stf; VP Jr Cls; Pres Sr Cls; Trs Stu Cncl; Capt Crs Cntry; L Trk; High Hon Roll; NHS; U S Military Acad; Biochem Engr.

CURAN, LINDA; Oliver Ames HS; North Easton, MA; (Y); 18/277; Varsity Clb; Yrbk Stf; Sftbl; High Hon Roll; Hon Roll; Jr NHS; NHS; Pres Schlr; St Anselms Coll.

CURCI, KRISTINA M; Auburn HS; Auburn, MA; (Y); 20/179; Church Yth Grp; Ski Clb; Varsity Clb; Yrbk Ed-Chief; Var Capt Cheerleading; Var Fld Hcky; NHS; HS Alumni Schlrshp 85; MA Polic Assoc Schlrshp 85; Fitchburg ST Coll; Cmmnctns.

CURCIO, LYN; Girls Ctholic HS; E Boston, MA; (Y); Hon Roll.

CURCURU, STEPHANIE E; Beverly HS; Beverly, MA; (Y); Am Leg Aux Girls St; Ski Clb; Ed Yrbk Phtg; L Bsktbl; L Socr; L Trk; High Hon Roll; NHS; Ntl Merit Ltr; Aerspc Engr.

CURLEY JR, CHARLES Z; Norwood SR HS; Norwood, MA; (Y); 52/350; Am Leg Boys St; Church Yth Grp; Trs Concert Band; Yrbk Ed-Chief; Trs Jr Cls; Trs Sr Cls; Capt Crs Cntry; Var L Ice Hcky; Capt Var Trk; Band.

CURLEY, JENNIFER; Braintree HS; Braintree, MA; (Y); 30/481; Hosp Aide; Red Cross Aide; Capt Var Pom Pon; Hon Roll; Prfct Atten Awd; Awd Attnded Med Semnrs 85; Boston U; Bio.

CURLEY, PATRICIA A; Sacred Heart HS; Weymouth, MA; (Y); 2/58; Church Yth Grp; Variety Show; High Hon Roll; Hon Roll; NHS; Sal; Essay Law Awd 82-83; MA Police Schlrshp 81-82; Regis Coll; Law.

CURRAN, AMY; Canton HS; Canton, MA; (Y); Drama Clb; German Clb; Band; Concert Band; Mrchg Band; Pep Band; School Musical; School Play; Hon Roll; NHS; Century Clb Awd 84-85; Bnd Achv Awd; Vet Sci.

CURRAN, BARBARA A; Norton HS; Norton, MA; (Y); 2/128; Mrchg Band; Yrbk Ed-Chief; Yrbk Stf; Trs Jr Cls; DAR Awd; High Hon Roll; Trs NHS; Ntl Merit SF; NEDT Awd; Voice Dem Awd; Smith Coll; Law.

CURRAN, ELLEN J; Norton HS; Norton, MA; (Y); 17/154; Computer Clb; Drama Clb; Ed Yrbk Phtg; Yrbk Stf; Hon Roll; Visual Comm.

CURRAN, JAMES L; Malden Catholic HS; Reading, MA; (Y); Church Yth Grp; Im Bsktbl; Im Ice Hcky; Hon Roll; SR Svc Prog 85; Suffolk U; Law.

CURRAN, STEPHEN; Malden Catholic HS; Reading, MA; (Y); 30/179; Im Bsktbl; High Hon Roll; Hon Roll; NHS; Merrimack Coll; Accntng.

CURREY, KAREN E; Greenfield HS; Greenfield, MA; (Y); 8/160; Ski Clb; Trs Sr Cls; Stu Cncl; Var JV Fld Hcky; Var Tennis; High Hon Roll; Hon Roll; NHS; Pres Schlr; Pep Clb; Prsndtl Acadmc Ftns Awd; Acadmc Hnrs Bk Awd; Htl Hnr Soc Schlrshp; Vrsty Ski Tm; Colby Coll; Liberal Arts.

CURRIE, JENNIFER; Fontbonne Acad; Plymouth, MA; (Y); 8/131; Drama Clb; Science Clb; Stage Crew; Lit Mag; Hon Roll; Jr NHS; NHS; Excel Stdy Shkspre 85; Outstndng Achvt Amer Hist 85; Hnrbl Ment Sci Fair 84; Ltr Publhd Newswk Mag 84.

CURRIER, GREG; Nauset Reg HS; N Truro, MA; (Y); Boy Scts; Church Yth Grp; Chorus; Var L Bsktbl; High Hon Roll; Prfct Atten Awd; High Grd Pt Avrge 82-84; Tns Clb 84; Engrg.

CURRIER, HEIDI; Commerce State St HS; Springfield, MA; (S); JA; Trk; Hon Roll; NHS; Church Yth Grp; 4-H; Girl Scts; Gym; Natl Hnr Scty Cert 84; Army; Secy.

CURRY, DIANNE F; Mansfield HS; Mansfield, MA; (Y); 44/182; Yrbk Stf; Lit Mag; Powder Puff Ftbl; JV Sftbl; Hon Roll; Mbr Of Acad Decthln Tm; Spcl Schltc Recgntn From Math & Engl Depts; Wheaton Coll.

CURTI, SABINA B; Berkshire Schl; Hollowville, NY; (S); 6/115; Art Clb; Varsity Clb; Symp Band; Yrbk Stf; Trs Soph Cls; Stat Ice Hcky; Var Socr; Var Sftbl; Var Tennis; Var Capt Vllybl; Mst Imprvd Vllybl Plyr Awd 85; Math.

CURTIN, MAUREEN; Brockton HS; Brockton, MA; (Y); 66/1000; Trk; High Hon Roll; Hon Roll; Bentley; Accntng.

CURTIS, STEVEN; Algonquin Regional HS; Northboro, MA; (Y); Var L Bsktbl; Civil Engr.

CURVING, DOUGLAS; Northbridge JR-SR HS; Whitinsville, MA; (Y); 6/140; Church Yth Grp; Nwsp Stf; Pres Frsh Cls; Var Bsktbl; Var L Crs Cntry; High Hon Roll; Hon Roll; NHS; St Schlr; Gordon Coll; Engrng.

CUSACK, HOLLI; Matignon HS; Melrose, MA; (Y); 9/250; Spanish Clb; High Hon Roll; Hon Roll; NHS; NEDT Awd; Spanish NHS; Ntl Hnr Rll 84; Acad Al-Amer 85; Columbia-Jrnlsm.

CUSACK, MARY ELLEN; Dedham HS; Dedham, MA; (S); 9/290; Aud/Vis; Cmnty Wkr; School Play; Sec Stu Cncl; Var L Trk; Hon Roll; NHS; Magna Cum Laude Cert Ntl Latin Exam 85; SAD Trh Chrpsrn 85; Stdnt Adv Comm; Mrktg.

CUSHING, CAROLYN; Marian HS; Framingham, MA; (Y); Political Wkr; School Musical; Variety Show; Yrbk Ed-Chief; Rep Jr Cls; Rep Sr Cls; NHS; NEDT Awd; Spanish NHS; Cmnty Wkr; AP US Hstry Awd 83-84; Intl Rltns.

CUSHWAY, DENISE; Easthampton HS; Easthampton, MA; (Y); 7/141; Chorus; Yrbk Stf; VP Jr Cls; VP Sr Cls; Stu Cncl; Var Socr; High Hon Roll; NHS; Schlstc Awd Jr Ms Pgnt 84; Ctzns Schlrshp 85; Acadmc Awd Grad 85; Wheaton Coll; Bio.

CUSOLITO, RICHARD; Falmouth HS; W Falmouth, MA; (Y); 25/350; French Clb; Math Clb; Math Tm; JV Socr; Var L Tennis; Hon Roll; NHS; Ntl Merit SF; Math Stu; Math.

CUSSON, THERESA B; Milford HS; Milford, MA; (Y); 22/297; Drama Clb; Hosp Aide; High Hon Roll; NHS; Engl.

CUTRONI, MICHAEL; Saint Marys HS; Worcester, MA; (Y); 4/50; Spanish Clb; School Play; Var Bsbl; Hon Roll; Worcester Polytechnical Inst.

CUTTER, STEPHANIE; Bridgewater-Raynham Regional HS; Raynham, MA; (Y); FTA; Model UN; Science Clb; Ski Clb; Var L Fld Hcky; Var Capt Trk; Hon Roll; NHS; NEDT Awd; Voice Dem Awd; Pre-Law.

CUTTING, STEPHANIE A; Belmont HS; Belmont, MA; (Y); Church Yth Grp; Latin Clb; Sec Frsh Cls; Rep Stu Cncl; Var Bsktbl; Var Socr; Var Sftbl; Varsity Clb; Stu Advsr To Schl Comm 85-86; Middlesex League 2nd Tm All Star 85; Schl Comm Awd-Exclnce In Athltcs 85.

CWALINA, MICHELLE; Westford Acad; Westford, MA; (Y); Office Aide; Pep Clb; Spanish Clb; Teachers Aide; Yrbk Stf; Trk; Hon Roll; Psych.

CYGANIEWICZ, LORI; Gardner HS; Gardner, MA; (Y); Spanish Clb; Var Fld Hcky; Var L Tennis; Elem Educ.

CYR, BRENDA; Gardner HS; Gardner, MA; (S); 84/167; Trs Art Clb; Trs VP DECA; FHA; Office Aide; Teachers Aide; Drm & Bgl; Cheerleading; Bus.

CYR, DAVID; Taunton HS; Taunton, MA; (Y); Var Bsbl.

CYR, JACKIE; North Cambridge Catholic HS; Cambridge, MA; (Y); Score Keeper; Vllybl; Hon Roll; NHS.

CYR, MICHELLE; Bishop Connolly HS; Fall River, MA; (S); 23/177; Model UN; Speech Tm; Var Soph Cls; JETS Awd; Comp Sci.

CYRULIK, TAMMY; King Philip Regional HS; Plainville, MA; (Y); Church Yth Grp; Yrbk Stf; Var Capt Tennis; Hon Roll; Framingham ST Coll; Lib Arts.

CZAJA, PAUL; Monument Mountain Regiolnal HS; Housatonic, MA; (Y); Church Yth Grp; Pres Exploring; Pres Band; Jazz Band; School Musical; Lit Mag; Ftbl; Liberty U; Psych.

CZARNECKI, LYNN M; Westfield HS; Westfield, MA; (Y); Jr NHS; Lwyr.

D AMICO, VINCENT; Methuen HS; Methuen, MA; (Y); 44/450; Capt Bsbl; High Hon Roll; Hon Roll; Prfct Atten Awd; Italian I II Awd Hgst Avg Cls 83-84; U Lowell; Engrng.

D ANDREA, BETSY; Bridgewater-Raynham Regional HS; Raynham, MA; (Y); Ski Clb; L Fld Hcky; L Tennis; Hon Roll; Cmnty Wkr; FTA; Science Clb; JV Bsktbl; Advtsng.

D ANGELO, ANDREW M; Westwood HS; Westwood, MA; (Y); 34/220; Am Leg Boys St; Jazz Band; Yrbk Ed-Chief; Rep Soph Cls; Rep Jr Cls; Rep Sr Cls; Pres Stu Cncl; Var Bsbl; Var Ftbl; Var Trk; Poli Sci.

D ARRIGO, BETH; Notre Dame Acad; Scituate, MA; (Y); Chorus; Var Crs Cntry; Trk.

D ELIA, JENNIFER S; Chelmsford HS; Chelmsford, MA; (Y); 3/560; AFS; French Clb; Girl Scts; Math Tm; Nwsp Rptr; French Hon Soc; High Hon Roll; NHS; Ntl Merit SF; Dartmouth Bk Awd 84.

D ENTREMONT III, EARL; Canton HS; Canton, MA; (Y); 24/250; Church Yth Grp; Rep Jr Cls; Rep Sr Cls; JV Bsbl; Var Bsktbl; Trk; Hon Roll.

D-AGOSTINO, PETER; Medford HS; Medford, MA; (Y); 8/588; English Clb; French Clb; JA; Pep Clb; Political Wkr; Varsity Clb; Pep Band; JV Var Bsbl; JV Var Ftbl; JV Var Ice Hcky; VFW Schlrshp Awd 85; North Eastern; Acctg.

DA SILVA, ALICE; Lowell HS; Lowell, MA; (S); 129/552; DECA; Library Aide; High Hon Roll; Hon Roll; Finance & Crdt-Wrttn DECA Evnt 84; U Of Lowell; Bus.

DA SILVA, HONORIA; Taunton HS; Taunton, MA; (Y); Lit Mag; Hon Roll; Accrdtd Cert In Portuguese Cltr & Lang 82; Ldng Rls In 2 Portuguese Plys-Taunton Sprts Clb 82; Pblc Rel.

DACEY, RICHARD; Bedford HS; Bedford, MA; (Y); Am Leg Boys St; Pres Church Yth Grp; ROTC; Church Choir; Drm Mjr(t); Madrigals; Mrchg Band; School Musical; Hon Roll; PMC Order Of De Molay 85; Gordon Coll; Music.

DACRUZ, SUSANNE; New Bedford HS; New Bedford, MA; (Y); 126/688; Color Guard; Mrchg Band; Hon Roll; Ntl Merit Ltr.

DADAH, MATTHEW; Leominster HS; Leominster, MA; (S); DECA; Drama Clb; Office Aide; School Musical; School Play; Bst Spprtng Actor In Intercls Play Cmptn 84-85; 1st Pl In DECA Cmptn For Dist 84-85; Worcester ST Coll; Bus Mgmt.

DADDARIO, JOSEPH; Franklin HS; Franklin, MA; (Y); JV Bsbl; L Golf; Hon Roll; Prelaw.

DAGENAIS, CHERYL A; Leominster HS; Leominster, MA; (Y); 5/352; Cmnty Wkr; Sec French Clb; Hosp Aide; Political Wkr; School Play; Yrbk Stf; Rep Stu Cncl; Var Capt Tennis; NHS; Pres Schlr; Fortnightly Clb Schlrshp 85; Most Vlbl Plyr Tennis 84-85; Bentley Coll; Acctg.

DAGHLIAN, HOURY; North Andover HS; N Andover, MA; (Y); 19/244; Church Yth Grp; Teachers Aide; Church Choir; Lit Mag; High Hon Roll; A L Sergeant Awd Supr Lat Achvt 84; E Allan Mem Scholar 85; Mak-Tuturijian Supr Achvt Awd Am Lang 85; Merrimack Coll; Polit Sci.

DAGNESE, HEIDI; Leicester HS; Leicester, MA; (Y); 20/113; Church Yth Grp; Drama Clb; Band; Concert Band; School Play; Variety Show; Nwsp Stf; VP Stu Cncl; Fld Hcky; Sftbl; Fitchburg ST; Comm.

DAGOSTINO, CHRIS; Arlington HS; Arlington, MA; (Y); Boys Clb Am; Im Badmtn; JV Bsbl; Im Bsktbl; Var Ftbl; L Trk; Elks Awd; Hon Roll; Engrng.

DAHLQUIST, TAIT; Silver Lake Regional HS; Plympton, MA; (Y); 59/500; Latin Clb; Chorus; Hon Roll; Engr.

DAIGNEAULT, ANGELIQUE; Holy Name CC HS; Worcester, MA; (Y); 111/279; Church Yth Grp; Pep Clb; Cheerleading; Optmtrst.

DALEY, GAYLE B; Mission Church HS; Boston, MA; (Y); 1/51; Cmnty Wkr; Exploring; Red Cross Aide; Trs Jr Cls; Pres Sr Cls; Var Cheerleading; High Hon Roll; NHS; Val; Yrbk Stf; Scholar Mission H S 81-85; Commonwealth Schlr Awd 85; Eng Awd 85; Harvard-Radcliffe Cambridge.

DALEY, JOYCE A; Hyde Park Acad; Hyde Park, MA; (S); Church Yth Grp; Cmnty Wkr; Girl Scts; Teachers Aide; Yrbk Stf.

DALIMONTE, KIM; Bartlett HS; Webster, MA; (Y); 8/174; French Clb; Office Aide; Speech Tm; Drm Mjr(t); Variety Show; Yrbk Stf; Twrlr; High Hon Roll; NHS; Outstndg Stu Awd 83; Philip & Fannie D Pearl Schlrshp 85; Anthony J Sitkowski Schlrshp 85; U Of RI; Psych.

DALPE, MARY T; Hudson Catholic HS; Marlboro, MA; (Y); VP 4-H; VP JA; Science Clb; Ski Clb; Im Powder Puff Ftbl; Elks Awd; Hon Roll; NHS; Chess Clb; Drama Clb; AV Irsh-Amer Assn Schlrshp 85; Awd Dist Natl Sci Olympd Physcs 85; Hudson Emblm Clb Schlrshp 85; Providence Coll; Vet.

DALTERIO, JOHN; St Johns HS; Hyannisport, MA; (Y); Am Leg Boys St; Ski Clb; JV Bsbl; Var L Ftbl; Im Wt Lftg; Hon Roll; Phrmcy.

DALTON, MICHELLE D; North Middlesex Regional HS; Pepperell, MA; (Y); 22/212; Cmnty Wkr; Debate Tm; Political Wkr; Color Guard; School Musical; Nwsp Sprt Ed; Yrbk Ed-Chief; Swmmng; Voice Dem Awd; Church Yth Grp; Debate Awd 84; Knights Of Columbus Schlrshp Awd 85; Mdrn Miss Fnlst 84; Coll Of Wooster; Intl Rltns.

DALTON, THOMAS M; Thayer Acad; Braintree, MA; (Y); 58/103; Church Yth Grp; Cmnty Wkr; School Play; Yrbk Stf; Var L Ftbl; Var L Trk; Suffolk U Boston MA; Govrnmnt.

DALY, CRYSTAL L; Holyoke HS; Holyoke, MA; (Y); Pep Clb; Teachers Aide; JV Cheerleading; Hon Roll; Dancing 10 Yrs 85; Bus.

DALY, JOANNE; Holy Name Central Catholic HS; Worcester, MA; (Y); 19/275; Church Yth Grp; Ski Clb; JV Cheerleading; Var Capt Socr; High Hon Roll; Hon Roll; Natl Sci Olympd Chem Rnnr Up 84-85; Latn III Medl Excllnc 84-85; Centrl MA Grls Sccr All Strs 84-85; Pre-Med.

DALY, MICHAEL KEVIN; Nashoba Regional HS; Stow, MA; (Y); Exploring; Wrstlng; Hon Roll; Ntl Merit Schol; Natl Latin Exam Magna Cum Laude 84-85; Boston U; Mech Engr.

DALY, NANCY; Our Lady Of Nazareth Acad; Wakefield, MA; (Y); Chorus; School Musical; Nwsp Phtg; Yrbk Stf; Hon Roll; NHS; Bus Mgmt.

DAMBROSIO, GENNARO; St Dominic Savio HS; Revere, MA; (Y); 18/109; Computer Clb; JA; Ski Clb; Jr Cls; Rep Stu Cncl; High Hon Roll; Boston Coll; Law.

DAMIANO, ROBERT; Brockton HS; Brockton, MA; (Y); Cmnty Wkr; Hon Roll; Astronomy.

DANDREA, PETER; Holy Name C C HS; Worcester, MA; (Y); Med Field.

DANDY, MICHELE S; West Springfield HS; W Springfield, MA; (Y); 95/275; Hon Roll; Alumni Assn Schlrshp 85; Holyoke CC; Busnss Admin.

DANESE, ANDREA; Haverhill HS; Haverhill, MA; (Y); 43/400; Keywanettes; Spanish Clb; Nwsp Stf; Stu Cncl; Cheerleading; High Hon Roll; Hon Roll; Layout Edtr Yrbk.

DANFORTH, KAREN; West Springfield HS; West Springfield, MA; (Y); 14/279; Am Leg Aux Girls St; School Musical; Nwsp Stf; Yrbk Stf; Off Soph Cls; Off Jr Cls; Off Sr Cls; Sec Stu Cncl; Var Co-Capt Cheerleading; Sec NHS; Elem Educ.

DANGELMAIER, ROBERT; Reading Memorial HS; Reading, MA; (Y); Nwsp Phtg; Nwsp Stf; Lit Mag; Sec Sr Cls; Rep Stu Cncl; Var Crs Cntry; Var Trk; High Hon Roll; Hon Roll; Drama Clb; Peer Tutoring Awd 85.

DANIELL, ADRIENNE; Bedford HS; Bedford, MA; (Y); 120/213; Hosp Aide; Teachers Aide; Mgr Tennis; High Hon Roll.

DANIELS, CYNTHIA; Bishop Stang HS; Acushnet, MA; (Y); Cmnty Wkr; Hosp Aide; Chorus; Yrbk Stf; Quinnipiac Coll.

DANIELS, FRANCES; Dana Hall Schl; Wellesley, MA; (Y); Art Clb; Drama Clb; School Play; Lit Mag; Golf; Hon Roll; Pre Law.

DANIELS, TODD; Smith Acad; Hatfield, MA; (Y); Boy Scts; Church Yth Grp; 4-H; Var Bsbl; 4-H Awd; NHS; Ntl Sci Olym Awd 83; Phy Ed Awd 85; Comp.

DANIELSON, SERENA; Arlington HS; Arlington, MA; (S); 18/412; Church Yth Grp; Cmnty Wkr; Trs Computer Clb; Library Aide; Church Choir; High Hon Roll; NHS; Yrbk Stf; The Bagdasar & Elmas Garabedian Awd 84; Sec Of Media Cntr Clb; Mdrn Jazz Dncng; Comp Sci.

DANNA, JAMES; Westwood HS; Westwood, MA; (Y); 49/214; AFS; Church Yth Grp; Var Swmmng; JV Tennis; Hon Roll; Bus Adm.

DANNER, STEVEN G; Boston Latin Schl; Allston, MA; (Y); 52/299; Drama Clb; Political Wkr; Science Clb; School Play; Chrmn Sr Cls; Hon Roll; Continentl Math Leag Awd 82-83; Natl Sci Chem Olympd Awd 85; Edtr & Pres, Hnbl Mntn BLS Lampoon 84; Engrng.

DAOUST, DONNA; Milford HS; Milford, MA; (Y); 12/292; Church Yth Grp; Hosp Aide; Office Aide; Stage Crew; High Hon Roll; NHS; Occ Ther.

DAPPER, DIANE; Holy Name Central Catholic HS; Worcester, MA; (Y); 88/285; Camp Fr Inc; Church Yth Grp; GAA; Chorus; Socr; Sftbl; 4-H Awd; Hon Roll; Prfct Atten Awd; Typg Awd 85; Assumption; Acctg.

DARON, MICHAEL; Groton-Dustnable Regional HS; Groton, MA; (Y); Yrbk Rptr; Yrbk Stf; Rep Frsh Cls; Rep Soph Cls; Rep Jr Cls; Rep Stu Cncl; L Bsbl; Im Golf; L Ice Hcky; Hon Roll; Bus Adm.

DATEO, ROBERT; St Johns HS; Paxton, MA; (Y); Am Leg Boys St; Church Yth Grp; Ski Clb; Varsity Clb; JV Bsbl; Im Bsktbl; Var Crs Cntry; Var Trk; Bus.

DATTERO, JANET FRANCES; Girls Catholic HS; Malden, MA; (Y); Church Yth Grp; Band; Trs Frsh Cls; Rep Stu Cncl; JV Sftbl; JV Vllybl; Hon Roll; NHS; Boston Coll; Cmnctns.

DAUGHERTY, KELLY; Malden HS; Malden, MA; (Y); 21/500; Band; Concert Band; Mrchg Band; Yrbk Ed-Chief; Yrbk Stf; Sec Frsh Cls; Rep Soph Cls; Psychlgy.

DAUNAIS, MICHELLE; Hoosac Valley HS; Admas, MA; (Y); 2/170; Am Leg Aux Girls St; Debate Tm; Quiz Bowl; Nwsp Ed-Chief; Lit Mag; High Hon Roll; NHS; Chnclrs Tlnt Awd Fnlst 85; Attndng MA Advncd Studies Pgm 85; Ntl Eng Merit Awd 85; Tufts U; Vetrnry Med.

DAUPHIN, LYNDA; New Bedford HS; Acushnet, MA; (Y); 16/688; Drama Clb; Exploring; JCL; Office Aide; Stage Crew; Yrbk Stf; Trk; High Hon Roll; NHS; Delta Kappa Gamma Essy Cont Hon Men 85; Med.

DAUPHINAIS, KEVIN; Braintree HS; Braintree, MA; (Y); 72/416; Var Bsbl; Var Bsktbl; Socr; High Hon Roll; Hon Roll; SADD 84-85; Natl Athletic Placement 85; Arch Engnrng.

DAUPHINAIS, WENDY; Lunenburg HS; Lunenburg, MA; (Y); 4/143; Church Yth Grp; Cmnty Wkr; Debate Tm; Intnl Clb; Service Clb; Ski Clb; School Musical; School Play; Nwsp Rptr; Yrbk Phtg; Rnnr Up Miss United Teenager Pgnt 83; Yth Mnth Natl Exch Clb 84-85; Prin Awd 81; PTO Awd 85; Colby Coll Waterville ME; PR.

DAVEY, COLLEEN; Southbridge HS; Southbridge, MA; (Y); #4 In Class; Art Clb; Math Tm; Var L Fld Hcky; Var L Trk; Hon Roll; NHS.

DAVI, ANGELIQUE; Bishop Connolly HS; Swansea, MA; (S); 7/177; Church Yth Grp; Math Tm; Spanish Clb; Nwsp Stf; NHS; Hghst Hnr Roll 82-85; Vrsty Cycling Womens New Engl Champ 83-84; Cyclng Team Mgr 85; Law.

DAVID, LYNN EMILY; Murdock HS; Winchendon, MA; (Y); 10/120; School Play; Stage Crew; Yrbk Stf; Sec Soph Cls; Var Cheerleading; Var Trk; Hon Roll; NHS; U Of NH; Microbio.

DAVIDSON, BRIDGETTE; Our Lady Of Nazareth Acad; Lynnfield, MA; (Y); Church Yth Grp; Trs 4-H; Pres Science Clb; Stu Cncl; JV Var Bsktbl; Var Sftbl; JV Vllybl; 4-H Awd; Cabot Corp Sci Smnr 85; Bostom Museum Of Sci Smmr Mentrshp 85; H S Chem, Algbr I & Geomtry Awds; Marine Bio.

DAVIDSON, KERRY JAURES; Phillips Acad; Baton Rouge, LA; (Y); Off Sr Cls; JV Capt Bsktbl; Var L Trk; Hon Roll; Radio Clb; Gulf ST Tnns 2nd 85; RJ Reynolds Scholar; Pre-Coll Pgm Duke U; Slvr Mdl Nw Engl Intrschlstc; Trck Awds; Sci.

DAVIDSON, MICHAEL; Chelmsford HS; N Chelmsford, MA; (Y); 162/565; Church Yth Grp; Drama Clb; Spanish Clb; Chorus; School Musical; School Play; Stage Crew; Nwsp Rptr; Nwsp Stf; Stu Cncl; Spnsh Exchange Prog; Holy Cross; Lbrl Arts.

DAVIES, CHRISTOPHER NELSON; Chatham HS; N Chatham, MA; (Y); 9/55; Ed Yrbk Ed-Chief; Pres Sr Cls; Pres Stu Cncl; Var L Bsbl; Var L Bsktbl; Var L Tennis; Cit Awd; Athlt Of The Yr 83-84; Sprtsmnshp Awd 84-85; Stu Of Govt Day Delegate 84-85; U Of MA Amherst; Bus.

DAVIES, TODD M; Billerica Memroial HS; Billerica, MA; (Y); 6/400; L Crs Cntry; L Trk; High Hon Roll; NHS; Ntl Merit SF; Boy Scts; Chess Clb; Church Yth Grp; Math Tm; Science Clb; 2nd Blck Blt 82; Harvard Prz Bk Ad 83; Teen Agr Mnth Awd 84; Physcs.

DAVILA, LILLIAN; Saint Marys HS; Westfield, MA; (Y); Spanish Clb; Teachers Aide; Yrbk Stf; Cheerleading; Trk; Westfield ST Coll; Chld Psych.

DAVIN, KATHLEEN A; Franklin HS; Franklin, MA; (Y); 10/235; Math Tm; OEA; Spanish Clb; Teachers Aide; Yrbk Stf; Hon Roll; 2nd Pl Off Ed Assn ST Comp 85; Bryant Coll Pres Scholar 85; NHS Scholar 85; Bryant Coll; Bus.

DAVIS, BRIDGETTE; Nauset Regional HS; Eastham, MA; (Y); Boys Clb Am; Exploring; Pep Clb; Ski Clb; Nwsp Stf; Yrbk Stf; Rep Stu Cncl; Fld Hcky; Boatswim Pres Sea Explorer Grp 85; Tourism.

DAVIS, CHARLENE; Weymouth North HS; Weymouth, MA; (Y); High Hon Roll; Hon Roll; Hnr Soc 80-82; Drama Awd 80-81; Band Awd 78-82; Pol Sci.

DAVIS, CRYSTAL; Ayer SR HS; Ayer, MA; (Y); 11/160; Am Leg Aux Girls St; Drama Clb; Library Aide; Acpl Chr; Chorus; School Play; Rep Frsh Cls; Off Sr Cls; Rep Stu Cncl; Mgr(s); Amer Hstry Awd 84; Ayer Lions Clb Schlrshp 85; Natl Hnr Soc Schlrshp 85; UMASS; Biochem.

DAVIS, DONNA; Groton-Dunstable Regnl Secondy Schl; Dunstable, MA; (Y); Chorus; Hon Roll; Pres Jr NHS; Pres NHS; Bus Mgmt.

DAVIS, GLEN; Saugus HS; Saugus, MA; (Y); 34/400; Chess Clb; Computer Clb; FCA; Masonic Awd; NHS; Prfct Atten Awd; Comm.

DAVIS, GRIFFIN; Drury SR HS; N Adams, MA; (Y); 59/185; Church Yth Grp; Cmnty Wkr; Pep Clb; Spanish Clb; Varsity Clb; School Play; Var Capt Bsbl; Coach Actv; JV Ftbl; JV Mgr(s); William Robinson Bsbl 85; Peter Foote Bsbl 85; Am Leg 85; St Josephs; Comm.

DAVIS, HEATHER; Peabody Veterans Memorial HS; Peabody, MA; (Y); 9/535; French Clb; Key Clb; Latin Clb; Science Clb; High Hon Roll; Hon Roll; U Of MA; Med.

DAVIS, JAMES; Malden Catholic HS; Everett, MA; (Y); 34/185; Church Yth Grp; Computer Clb; Var L Crs Cntry; Var JV Trk; Vllybl; Strnmy.

DAVIS, JOEL; Wakefield HS; Wakefield, MA; (Y); Boy Scts; JA; VP Prsnnl JA Estrn MA 85; Chrprsn Intl Affrs JA Assn E MA 85-86; Dely NAJAC 83; Aero Sci.

DAVIS, KELLY; Lunenburg HS; Lunenburg, MA; (Y); Sec Pres Intnl Clb; Library Aide; VP Chorus; School Musical; Sec Frsh Cls; Sec Soph Cls; High Hon Roll; Hon Roll; NHS; Chorus Achvt Awd 84-85; MA U Amherst; Phisiolgy.

DAVIS, PALMER; Deerfield Acad; Erie, PA; (Y); Boy Scts; Chess Clb; VP Computer Clb; Debate Tm; French Clb; Model UN; Pres Political Wkr; Radio Clb; Ed Lit Mag; Rep Frsh Cls; Concours Natl De Francais 83; Med.

DAVIS, RENEE; Commerce HS; Springfield, MA; (S); 18/300; Church Yth Grp; Library Aide; Chorus; DAR Awd; Hon Roll; NHS; Advntst Yuth Yr 84; Columbia Union Coll; Bus Mgmnt.

DAVIS, STEVEN R; Sutton HS; Sutton, MA; (Y); 3/70; Am Leg Boys St; Church Yth Grp; Stu Cncl; Var Capt Bsktbl; Var Capt Crs Cntry; Im Golf; Im Vllybl; High Hon Roll; Hon Roll; NHS; Acctng.

DAVIS, SUSAN C; Ipswich HS; Ipswich, MA; (Y); 10/126; Band; Yrbk Bus Mgr; Capt Cheerleading; Var Capt Fld Hcky; Var Capt Sftbl; Hon Roll; NHS; MA Frgn Lang Assoc Excllnc In Frnch & Lang 85; US Arms Rsv Ntl Schlr Athlt Awd 85; Southeastern MA U.

DAVIS, TODD; North Brookfield HS; N Brookfield, MA; (Y); 3/38; Computer Clb; Math Tm; Bsktbl; Socr; Hon Roll; NHS; Comp Sci.

DAVOREN, SHEILA M; Malden HS; Malden, MA; (Y); 27/500; Office Aide; Spanish Clb; School Musical; Variety Show; Rep Hst Sr Cls; Var Crs Cntry; Var Trk; Stat Wrstlng; Hon Roll; VFW Awd; Alumni Scholar 85; Ed Assn Louise De Meu Scholar 85; Pop Warner Assn Scholar 85; U Of MA AmherstBUS.

DAWSON, JAMES; Chicopee Comprehensive HS; Chicopee, MA; (Y); Boy Scts; Hort.

DAWSON, MICHAEL; New Bedford HS; New Bedford, MA; (Y); 141/702; Aud/Vis; Camera Clb; VP JA; Nwsp Phtg; Nwsp Stf; Frsh Cls; Stu Cncl; Hon Roll; Jr NHS; Atmos Sci.

DAWSON, SHEILA; Bishop Connolly HS; Fall River, MA; (Y); Latin Clb; Bsktbl; Trk; High Hon Roll; Law.

DAY, COLIN; Newton North HS; Newtonville, MA; (Y); Boy Scts; Exploring; Band; Chorus; Concert Band; Orch; School Musical; Engrng.

DAY, FRANCIE; Woburn HS; Woburn, MA; (S); Church Yth Grp; GAA; JA; Leo Clb; Letterman Clb; Political Wkr; Ski Clb; Varsity Clb; Band; Color Guard; Fshn Dsgn.

DE ANGELIS, CLARE; Westwood HS; Westwood, MA; (Y); 79/242; 4-H; GAA; Pep Clb; Varsity Clb; Yrbk Stf; Bsktbl; Tennis; Trk; Vllybl; Hon Roll.

DE ANGELIS, KIMBERLY A; Billerica Memorial HS; Billerica, MA; (Y); Dance Clb; Band; Chorus; Flag Corp; Mrchg Band; School Musical; School Play; Stage Crew; Yrbk Stf; Rep Frsh Cls; Clrgrd & Mrchng Band Awd 82-83; Lttr Awd 82-83; MA Coll Of Pharmacy; Phrmcy.

DE CARLO, JOELLE; Matignon HS; Charlestown, MA; (Y); 19/181; Church Yth Grp; Drama Clb; Latin Clb; Science Clb; Spanish Clb; School Musical; School Play; Stage Crew; Nwsp Stf; Rep Frsh Cls; Ldrshp Awd 85; Schltc Excllnce 85; Suffolk U; Law.

DE COSTA, MICHAEL J; Boston College HS; Dorchester, MA; (Y); Am Leg Boys St; Debate Tm; JA; Key Clb; Red Cross Aide; Stu Cncl; Im Bsbl; Im Bsktbl; JV Ftbl; Boston Coll; Polit Sci.

DE COURCY, CHERYL; Wakefield HS; Wakefield, MA; (Y); Yrbk Stf; Fld Hcky; Hon Roll; Church Yth Grp; Cmnty Wkr; GAA; Variety Show; Bsktbl; Trk; Chld Psych.

DE CRISTOFARO, DANIEL; Silver Lake Regional HS; Kingston, MA; (Y); 40/510; Key Clb; Stu Cncl; Var Capt Bsbl; Var JV Bsktbl; Var Capt Ftbl; High Hon Roll; Hon Roll; NHS; Sport Focus Plyr Wk Ftbl 84; Gray Awd Bsktbl.

DE FEO, EVELYN; Christopher Columbus HS; Boston, MA; (Y); Dance Clb; Teachers Aide; Variety Show; Gym; Hon Roll; Nrthestrn OK; Erly Chldhd Ed.

DE FUSCO, ANDREA; Presentation Of Mary Acad; Methuen, MA; (Y); 1/50; Church Yth Grp; Debate Tm; VP Spanish Clb; Chorus; School Musical; Yrbk Stf; Sec Jr Cls; High Hon Roll; Pres NHS; Voice Dem Awd; Dghtrs Of Amer Revltn 83; SADD Rep 84; Sci Olympd & Fair Winr 85; Int Med.

DE GRAAN, CHRISTINE; Notre Dame Acad; Hinghman, MA; (Y); 30/113; Church Yth Grp; Chorus; School Musical; School Play; Stage Crew; Ntl Merit SF; Cmnctns.

DE GREGORIO, ROBERT; Cambridge Rindge And Latin HS; Cambridge, MA; (S); NHS; 1st Hnrs Hnr Roll 83-85; Ed Sci.

DE HAAN, LISA; Sutton Memorial HS; Whitinsville, MA; (Y); 3/68; Church Yth Grp; Drama Clb; School Play; Yrbk Sprt Ed; Var L Bsktbl; L Var Socr; NHS; PAVAS; Varsity Clb; Im Vllybl; Cmmnwlth MA Schlrs 85; Auto Dsmntlrs & Rcyclrs Amer Schlrshp 85; Wrcstr Cnty All Str Comp Swim 81-83; Emerson Coll; Theatre Arts.

DE HART, HENRY; Deerfield Acad; Queens Village, NY; (Y); Trs Computer Clb; Nwsp Stf; Im Bsktbl; Im Socr; JV Trk; Hon Roll; De Witt Wallace Readers Digest Fellow, NY U Medcl CTR Inst Rehab Med 85.

DE JONGH, VAL; North Andover HS; N Andover, MA; (Y); 42/242; Debate Tm; Drama Clb; Pep Clb; JV Socr; JV Trk; High Hon Roll; Hon Roll; Latin Achv For Schlstc Ablty 84; Crew Person Of The Mnth 84; Merrimack Coll; Psych.

DE LARIA, ALLAN; Arlington Catholic HS; Medford, MA; (Y); 30/148; French Clb; JV Bsktbl; Var Crs Cntry; Hon Roll; NHS.

DE LEO, KERRI; Mohawk Trail Regional HS; Buckland, MA; (Y); 18/142; Varsity Clb; Church Choir; School Musical; Swing Chorus; Nwsp Stf; Yrbk Stf; Cheerleading; Crs Cntry; Var L Trk; Excel Physcs Awd 84-85.

DE LISLE, VICTORIA; Governor Dummer Acad; Ipswich, MA; (Y); 2/89; Dance Clb; Drama Clb; French Clb; Speech Tm; Thesps; Nwsp Stf; French Hon Soc; High Hon Roll; NHS; Sal; Tulane U; Engl.

DE LOCHE, JEANNINE; Dana Hall HS; Wellesley, MA; (Y); Sec Exploring; Pres Key Clb; Political Wkr; Q&S; School Play; Nwsp Ed-Chief; High Hon Roll; Church Yth Grp; Dance Clb; Drama Clb; Congdon Prize Scholar Dana Hall Schl 83; Bronze Congrssnl Awd; Brown Bk Prize 85; Jrnlsm.

DE LORIA, DANIEL G; Chicopee Comprehensive HS; Chicopee, MA; (Y); 63/311; Am Leg Boys St; Boy Scts; Debate Tm; German Clb; Concert Band; Jazz Band; Mrchg Band; Stu Cncl; Jr NHS; NHS; Eagle Scout 82; U S Stu Cncl Awd 85; Acad All Amer 85; St Hyacinths Coll.

DE LUCA, ANDREW; Sacred Heart HS; Weymouth, MA; (Y); Am Leg Boys St; English Clb; Art Clb; Spanish Clb; Variety Show; Var Capt Bsbl; Var Bsktbl; Bsbl & Bsktbl Sprtsmshp Awd 84; Math.

DE LUCA, CRISTINA B; Winchester HS; Winchester, MA; (Y); 19/325; JCL; Latin Clb; Spanish Clb; Ed Yrbk Stf; Rep Stu Cncl; JV Socr; High Hon Roll; NHS; Ntl Merit Ltr; HS Hnrs Pgm; New Eng ST Art Contst Grand Wnnr; Bosto Globe Schlstc Art Awds 81; Cert Merit 83.

DE LUCA, JOSEPH; Winchester HS; Winchester, MA; (Y); 5/317; Political Wkr; Spanish Clb; Cit Awd; High Hon Roll; NHS; Pres Acad Ftns Awd 85; Outstndg Acad Achvt Awd 85; Cert Merit Engl, Bus, Sci & Math 84-85; Brandeis U; Pre-Med.

DE LUCA, MICHELLE; St Mary HS; Lawrence, MA; (Y); 32/108; Hosp Aide; JA; Teachers Aide; Rep Jr Cls; Pres Hmrm 84-85; Boston Coll; Econ.

DE LUCIA, JANICE; Presentation Of Mary Acad; Methuen, MA; (S); 4/51; Church Yth Grp; Math Clb; Pep Clb; Pres Sec Spanish Clb; Yrbk Stf; Rep Stu Cncl; Hon Roll; NHS; Comp.

DE MARTIN, LORI ANN; Barnstable HS; Hyannis, MA; (S); 134/398; Drama Clb; Concert Band; Drm Mjr(t); Mrchg Band; School Play; Stu Cncl; Rep Soph Cls; Rep Jr Cls; Rep Sr Cls; Spirit JR Ms Awd, Phys Ftnss Schlrshp 85; Band Cncl; U Of Lowell; Lbrl Arts.

DE MASE II, DELIA; Bishop Feehan HS; Franklin, MA; (Y); Church Yth Grp; Drama Clb; Library Aide; Political Wkr; School Musical; Stage Crew; High Hon Roll; Hon Roll; Hghst Avg In Englsh & Amer Lit 84-83; City Mayors Awd For Cmpstn On Drunk Drvng 85; Culnry Arts.

DE MENDONCA, DANIEL; New Bedford HS; New Bedford, MA; (Y); 8/750; Computer Clb; JA; Office Aide; High Hon Roll; Jr NHS; NHS; Med.

DE MILIA, ROBERT J; Nashoba Regional HS; Stow, MA; (Y); 14/192; Church Yth Grp; Dance Clb; Debate Tm; Spanish Clb; Trs Band; Chorus; Concert Band; Jazz Band; Mrchg Band; Pep Band; All Eastern Recommndtn Band 84-85; All ST Fest 83-85; Central & Wachusett Dist Fest; Worcester Polytech Inst; Engrng.

DE MILLE, CHARLES W; Tewksburg Memorial HS; Tewksbury, MA; (Y); 21/335; Boy Scts; Math Tm; Band; Concert Band; Drm & Bgl; Jazz Band; Mrchg Band; NHS.

DE MORRIS, JEFFREY R; St Marys HS; Westfield, MA; (Y); 7/50; Am Leg Boys St; Cmnty Wkr; Var Bsbl; Var Golf; JV Var Socr; Elks Awd; High Hon Roll; Hon Roll; Jr NHS; Ntl Merit Ltr; ST Schlrshp 85; W New Engl Coll; Accntnt.

DE MUTH, ROBERT J; Xaverian Bros HS; Westwood, MA; (S); 17/236; Chess Clb; Yrbk Stf; High Hon Roll; Hon Roll; Pre-Med.

DE PAOLI, LORI; Leicester HS; N Brookfield, MA; (S); Church Yth Grp; Office Aide; Pep Clb; School Play; Cheerleading; Golf; High Hon Roll; NHS; Prfct Atten Awd; Accntng.

DE PAULIS, CATHY; Greater Lowel Regional Vo Tech; Lowell, MA; (S); Rep Jr Cls; Rep Stu Cncl; JV Trk; Hon Roll; Typing Cert 84-85; Shrthnd Cert 84; Sec.

DE PONTE III, JOSEPH; Ludlow HS; Ludlow, MA; (Y); Church Yth Grp; Math Tm; High Hon Roll; JETS Awd; Ntl Merit SF; NEDT Awd; Voice Dem Awd; WPI Frontiers In Sci & Math Smmr 85; Engrng.

DE ROSA, CHRISTINA E; Lynnfield HS; Lynnfield, MA; (Y); Dance Clb; Political Wkr; Chorus; School Musical; Hon Roll; Royal Acad Of Dance London 84; Dance.

DE RUBEIS, POMPEO; Newton Catholic HS; Newton, MA; (S); Pres Church Yth Grp; Chorus; Yrbk Phtg; Yrbk Sprt Ed; Yrbk Stf; Rep Sec Stu Cncl; High Hon Roll.

DE SIMONE, MICHAEL F; Burlington HS; Burlington, MA; (Y); 32/350; Am Leg Boys St; Church Yth Grp; Math Clb; Yrbk Stf; Rep Frsh Cls; Rep Soph Cls; Trs Stu Cncl; Ice Hcky; Hon Roll; NHS; Best Def Plyr Awd Hockey 85; Engr.

DE SOUZA, REBECCA A; Fairhaven HS; Fairhaven, MA; (Y); 2/200; French Clb; Yrbk Ed-Chief; Yrbk Stf; High Hon Roll; Jr NHS; NHS; Ntl Merit Ltr; NEDT Awd; Civic Clb; Math Tm; Brown U Bk Awd 85; French Oral Spkng Cont 85; Acad Ltr 84-85; Bus Adm.

DE STEFANO, DENISE; Pope John XXIII Central HS; Malden, MA; (S); 8/207; Math Clb; Lit Mag; Sec Stu Cncl; High Hon Roll; NHS; NEDT Awd; Stonehill Coll; Engrng.

DE TORO, CHRISTINE; Coyle And Cassidy HS; Taunton, MA; (Y); #10 In Class; Spanish Clb; Cheerleading; High Hon Roll; Hon Roll; NHS; Spanish NHS; Voice Dem Awd.

DE TROLIO, JOSEPH; Bishop Feehan HS; Mansfield, MA; (Y); Boy Scts; Church Yth Grp; Yrbk Stf; Ad Altere Dei; Alter Boy; Lctr.

DE VELIS, DONNA; Woburn SR HS; Woburn, MA; (S); 100/500; French Clb; Key Clb; Stu Cncl; NHS; Bus Mgmnt.

DE VITO, ALYSSA; Stoneleigh-Burnham Schl; Greenfield, MA; (Y); GAA; Chorus; School Musical; Nwsp Rptr; Lit Mag; Var Socr; Var Sftbl; Hon Roll; NHS; Spanish Clb; Wellesley Club Bk Awd.

DE VOIR, MICHELLE SUZANNE; Andover HS; Andover, MA; (Y); 15/437; Drama Clb; Thesps; Band; Jazz Band; Madrigals; Mrchg Band; School Musical; Swing Chorus; Lit Mag; High Hon Roll; Ntl Schl Choral Awd 85; MA Advncd Stds Pgm 84; Drum Mjr NESBA Hnrs Band 85; Andona Soc Schlrshp 85; Duke U; Lbrl Arts.

DE WOLF, LAUREL A; Billerica Memorial HS; Billerica, MA; (Y); 120/450; Nwsp Ed-Chief; Nwsp Rptr; Nwsp Stf; Chrch Schlrshp 85; Nwspapr Jrnlsm Awd 85; Natl Hnr Rll 85; Salem ST Coll; Jrnlsm.

DE-QUATTRO, NICOLE; Quaboag Regional HS; W Brookfield, MA; (Y); 1/90; Am Leg Aux Girls St; Latin Clb; Science Clb; Yrbk Stf; Pres Soph Cls; High Hon Roll; Pres NHS; Church Yth Grp; Yrbk Stf; Capt L Bsktbl; SADD 84 & 85; Ntl Conf Of Christians & Jews Convntn 84; Bio.

DEAN, MATTHEW; Central Catholic HS; Lowell, MA; (Y); 100/219; Ski Clb; Im Bsktbl; U Of Lowell; Bus.

DEAN, MICHAEL; Milford HS; Milford, MA; (Y); JV Ftbl; Hon Roll; Math.

DEAN, TREVOR; Bishop Feehan HS; Plainville, MA; (Y); Boys Clb Am; Church Yth Grp; Letterman Clb; Spanish Clb; Varsity Clb; Var L Bsktbl; Var L Crs Cntry; Var L Trk; High Hon Roll; Hon Roll; Achiev Awd Lit, Top Five 85; Dent Tech.

DEANGELIS, CHRISTOPHER; Matignon HS; Somerville, MA; (S); 8/179; Drama Clb; Spanish Clb; JV Ice Hcky; Hon Roll; Sec NHS; Spanish NHS; Bio.

DEATON, KATHY R; Hanover HS; Hanover, MA; (Y); Church Yth Grp; Girl Scts; High Hon Roll; Hon Roll; Outstndng Achvt Sci 84; Bus Admin.

DEBAGGIS, JAMES; Franklin HS; Franklin, MA; (Y); 87/237; Variety Show; Var Golf; Hon Roll; ST Golf Tourn H S Golf Tm 84-85; Bus Mgmt.

DEBATIS, MICHELE; Bishop Feehan HS; Bellingham, MA; (Y); French Clb; French Hon Soc; Hon Roll; Prfct Atten Awd.

DEBBIE, JONES; Whitman-Hanson Regional HS; Hanson, MA; (Y); 9/327; AFS; Stu Cncl; Kiwanis Awd; NHS; Natl Hstry Day 1st Pl ST, Fin Natl 84-85; Framingham ST Coll Hstrcl Conf Hnrb Mntn 84, 3rd Pl 85.

DECKER, LISA; Burncoat HS; Worcester, MA; (Y); Church Yth Grp; Dance Clb; Intnl Clb; VP JA; Science Clb; Stu Cncl; Hon Roll; Jr NHS; Trs NHS; Spanish NHS; Williams Coll Bk Awd 85; Vet Med.

DECKER, TIM; Bartlett HS; Webster, MA; (Y); 19/158; Math Tm; Science Clb; Spanish Clb; Yrbk Stf; JV Bsbl; Var Ftbl; Im Vllybl; Im Wt Lftg; Hon Roll; 1st Pl Spllng Bee 85; Awd For Math Achvt 83-84; Air Frce; Civil Engrng.

DECOSTE, ELAINE; Coyle & Cassidy HS; Raynham, MA; (Y); 30/147; Trk; French Hon Soc; Hon Roll.

DEE, COLLEEN; Chelmsford HS; N Chelmsford, MA; (Y); Church Yth Grp; High Hon Roll; Hon Roll; Spanish NHS; Jrnlsm.

DEE, JAMES; Don Bosco HS; Medford, MA; (S); Church Yth Grp; Cmnty Wkr; Lit Mag; Sec Stu Cncl; Socr; JV Trk; Hon Roll; NHS; Cmmnty Svc Awd 84; Elec Engr.

DEEHAN, CHRISTOPHER; Melrose HS; Melrose, MA; (Y); Political Wkr; Off Jr Cls; JV Bsbl; Var Bsktbl; JV Ftbl; Var Golf; Hon Roll; NHS; Boston Coll; Bus.

DEFORGE, CHRISTINE; Holyoke Catholic HS; Holyoke, MA; (Y); Spanish Clb; Stage Crew; Yrbk Ed-Chief; JV Capt Bsktbl; Var Socr; JV Sftbl; Phy Thrpy.

DEGAETANO, GINA; Somerset HS; Somerset, MA; (Y); Drama Clb; MMM; School Musical; School Play; Variety Show; Var Vllybl; Art Clb; Church Yth Grp; Cmnty Wkr; Office Aide; Spokesperson For Roman Catholic Yth Grp; U MA; Acting.

DEGAETANO, KELLI; Bishop Connolly HS; Westport, MA; (Y); 33/170; Church Yth Grp; Cmnty Wkr; Ski Clb; Varsity Clb; Variety Show; Var L Cheerleading; Pom Pon; High Hon Roll; Hon Roll; NHS; Westport JR Miss Contestnt 85; Comp Sci.

DEGNAN, SCOTT P; Monson JR SR HS; Monson, MA; (Y); 3/80; Church Yth Grp; Trs French Clb; Math Tm; Yrbk Bus Mgr; Yrbk Rptr; Sec Trs Jr Cls; VP Sr Cls; Hon Roll; Trs NHS; Teas Frnch Clb 84-86; Mbr Yng Rep 84-86; Bentley Coll; Bus Adm.

DEIGNAN, DEIDRE M; Uxbridge HS; Uxbridge, MA; (Y); 7/70; Girl Scts; Yrbk Ed-Chief; DAR Awd; High Hon Roll; Trs NHS; Ntl Merit Ltr; Pres Schlr; St Schlr; VP Jr Cls; L Var Cheerleading; Rtry Intl Yth Exchng Pgm 85-86; Alt Stu Govt Day Pgm 85; Cls Mrshll 84; Coll Of Holy Cross; Pol Sci.

DEININGER, ROBERT C; Norwell HS; Norwell, MA; (Y); 21/178; AFS; Am Leg Boys St; Boy Scts; Latin Clb; School Play; Yrbk Ed-Chief; Rep Stu Cncl; Var Trk; Hon Roll; NHS; Med.

DEKLE, WILLIAM; Phillips Acad; Register, GA; (Y); Chess Clb; Debate Tm; Drama Clb; Natl Beta Clb; Science Clb; School Play; Nwsp Stf; Hon Roll; NHS; Ntl Merit Ltr; Sci Awd 82-83; E Ratd Fencer USFA 84-85; Natl Latn Exm 85; Yale U; Cogntv Sci.

DEL NEGRO, PHILIP C; Cathedral HS; Springfield, MA; (Y); 25/474; JA; Model UN; Quiz Bowl; High Hon Roll; NHS; Pres Schlr; St Schlr; Dgtl Equip Corp Schlrshp 85; Samuel Bowles Schlrshp 85; Carl R Hellstrom Schlrshp 85; Western New England Coll; Bus.

DEL TUFO, ROSE T; Dedham HS; Dedham, MA; (S); 8/289; Church Yth Grp; Cmnty Wkr; Drama Clb; School Play; Stage Crew; Rep Soph Cls; High Hon Roll; Hon Roll; Hgst Awd Ntl Latn Exm 85; Ms Teen MA 84; Med.

DEL VECCHIO, MICHELE A; Quincy HS; Quincy, MA; (Y); 24/325; Dance Clb; Office Aide; School Musical; Yrbk Stf; Rep Stu Cncl; Var Capt Cheerleading; DAR Awd; Elks Awd; NHS; Ambrose Duggan Mem Schlrshp 85; Stu Cncl Schlrshp 85; Natl Phys Educ Awd 85; Nrtheastrn U; Phys Thrpy.

DELAGE, WILLIAM; Southbridge HS; Sbridge, MA; (Y); 39/160; Tennis; Trk; Hon Roll.

DELANDY, SCOTT; Central Catholic HS; Dracust, MA; (Y); 40/260; Drama Clb; JA; Stage Crew; Principle Scholar Wnr 85; Bus.

DELANEY, DAREN; Matigon HS; Somerville, MA; (S); 2/180; Pres Stu Cncl; JV Bsbl; Var Ftbl; NHS; Spanish NHS; Stdnt Athl Awd Bantam Ftbl Leag 83; Suffolk U Bk Awd Outstndng Schl Svc 84; Natl Hnr Rll & USNLMA; Engrng.

DELANEY, DAVID; Gardner HS; Gardner, MA; (Y); Var Crs Cntry; Var Trk; NHS; Prfct Atten Awd; Bio.

DELANEY, KATY; Marlborough HS; Marlborough, MA; (Y); 30/300; Boys Clb Am; Varsity Clb; Var Capt Bsktbl; Var Socr; Var Sftbl; Central MA Soccer All Star 84; Middlesex Cnty Bsktbl Plyr Of Yr 84-85; Capt New Englnd Wildcats 84-85.

DELANEY, KIMBERLY M; Buckingham Browne & Nichols Schl; Woburn, MA; (Y); Church Yth Grp; JCL; Latin Clb; Yrbk Stf; Stu Cncl; Var Bsktbl; Var Crs Cntry; Hon Roll; Pres Schlr; Var Awd Crs Cntry, Bsktbl, Crew 84-85; Bay ST Metro Tm Bsktbl 85; Yth Games MA 83 & 84; Lib Arts.

DELANEY, MARY; St Bernards CC HS; Fitchburg, MA; (S); 11/172; Camera Clb; Drama Clb; Hosp Aide; Rep Stu Cncl; Hon Roll; NHS; Bio Awd 84; French Awd 84; Holy Cross Coll; Med.

DELANEY, PATRICK; St Johns HS; Grafton, MA; (Y); 160/282; Drama Clb; English Clb; FCA; Ski Clb; Spanish Clb; Varsity Clb; Variety Show; Crs Cntry; Trk; Hon Roll; Holy Cross Coll; Law.

DELAY, TIM; Hingham HS; Hingham, MA; (Y); 53/345; Varsity Clb; Band; Mrchg Band; School Play; Symp Band; Rep Frsh Cls; Var Bsbl; Var Ice Hcky; Var Socr; Hon Roll; Lib Arts.

DELCORE, HENRY D; Catholic Memorial HS; Dedham, MA; (Y); 2/260; Am Leg Boys St; JA; Math Clb; Science Clb; VP Spanish Clb; Rep Frsh Cls; Rep Soph Cls; JV Socr; NHS; Ntl Merit Ltr; Gen Excel Merit; Boblay Orr Sportsmnshp Pgm Wnnr; Us Naval Acad; Engrng.

DELFINO, LISA M; Attleboro HS; Attleboro, MA; (Y); 35/390; Color Guard; High Hon Roll; Jr NHS; NHS; MA Supt Awd 85; N Purchase Clb Scholar 85; Outstndng Bus Stu Awd 85; Fisher JC; Med Asst.

DELISLE, JENNIFER; Danvers HS; Danvers, MA; (Y); 40/315; French Clb; Hosp Aide; Spanish Clb; Color Guard; Yrbk Stf; French Hon Soc; High Hon Roll; Hon Roll; NHS; Spanish NHS; Most Outstndng Colorguard 83-84; U Of New Hampshire; Soc Sci.

DELL ANTONIO, IAN; Northampton HS; Northampton, MA; (Y); 7/210; Debate Tm; Quiz Bowl; Thesps; School Musical; School Play; Stage Crew; Nwsp Rptr; Nwsp Stf; High Hon Roll; NHS; Astrnmy.

DELL ORFANO, DARIA; Christopher Columbus HS; Boston, MA; (S); Hon Roll; Bentley Coll; Bus Mgt.

DELLORFANO, ANTHONY; Xaverian Bros HS; Cohasset, MA; (S); 44/250; Drama Clb; Pep Clb; Political Wkr; Ski Clb; School Play; Variety Show; Yrbk Stf; Rep Frsh Cls; Off Soph Cls; Off Jr Cls; Holy Cross; Pol Sci.

DELLOVO, DEBBIE; Burlington HS; Burlington, MA; (Y); Church Yth Grp; Cmnty Wkr; Girl Scts; JA; Teachers Aide; Swmmng; Tennis; Hon Roll; Mem Elem Awd 81; Sktng Awds 81-85; Lesley Coll; Elem Ed.

DELOREY, CHRISTINE M; Dennis-Yarmouth Regional HS; Yarmouth Port, MA; (Y); 31/330; Varsity Clb; JV L Crs Cntry; Var L Trk; Hon Roll; Chorus; JV Fld Hcky; Im Socr; Grls Ath Achvt Awd 85; Cbls B ST Champ Discus 85; 11th Plyr Awd Crs Cntry 84-85; Providence Coll; Psych.

DELOREY, MICHAEL; Burlington HS; Burlington, MA; (Y); Church Yth Grp; Var Lcrss; Hon Roll; SR SCI Awd 85; Boston Clg; Math.

DELORIE JR, RALPH C; Malden Catholic HS; Melrose, MA; (Y); 3/185; Boy Scts; Computer Clb; Exploring; French Clb; Math Tm; Var Socr; L Swmmng; Var High Hon Roll; NHS; Ntl Merit Ltr; MVP-SWM Tm 84-85; Capt-Swm Tm 85-86; Hgh Hnr Roll 82-85.

DELUCA, WILLIAM; Wakefield Memorial HS; Wakefield, MA; (Y); JV Bsktbl; JV Golf; Hon Roll; Bus Admin.

DEMAR, SHERRI; Montachusett Regional HS; Fitchburg, MA; (Y); Red Cross Aide; Color Guard; Drm & Bgl; Outstndg Stu Awd Exclince Hlth/Nutr 83-84; Med Tech.

DEMEDEIROS, ROSALIND P; New Bedford HS; New Bedford, MA; (Y); Hosp Aide; Office Aide; VP Frsh Cls; Var L Fld Hcky; Var Capt Tennis; Hon Roll; Med.

DEMERS, PAUL; Diman Regional Vo-Tech High Sch; Swansea, MA; (Y); Ski Clb; Bsbl; Bowling; Swmmng; Wt Lftg; New England Trd Schl; Carpentry.

DEMINSKI, CAROLINE; Presentation Of Mary Acad; Methuen, MA; (S); 1/50; Trs Church Yth Grp; Math Clb; Spanish Clb; Yrbk Stf; Pres Stu Cncl; Var Capt Bsktbl; Var Capt Sftbl; Var L Vllybl; High Hon Roll; NHS; Yth Undstng Ex Stu Prog 84; 2nd Pl Chem 84; Pres Stu Cncl 84; Law.

DEMOPOULOS, ELAINE; Boston Latin Schl; Boston, MA; (Y); 28/330; Key Clb; Church Choir; Variety Show; Stu Cncl; Cheerleading; Pom Pon; Score Keeper; Mgr Swmmng; Trk; NHS; Le Cours Francs Frnch Essy Cmptn 83-84; Readng/Lang Arts Cert 85.

DEMOURA, NORMAN; Taunton HS; Taunton, MA; (Y); Jazz Band; Capt Im Vllybl; High Hon Roll; Hon Roll; Mus.

DEMPSEY, DIANNA; Monument Mountain Regional HS; Gt Barrington, MA; (S); 19/134; Spanish Clb; Band; Nwsp Rptr; Sec Stu Cncl; Var Mgr(s); Im Vllybl; Hon Roll; Pep Clb; NE Regnl Stu Advisry Cncl 84-85; Peer Counslng 83-84; Stu Advisry To Principal 84-85; Univ Of Ct; Psychology.

DENAPOLI, JAN; Algonquin R HS; Southboro, MA; (Y); 32/215; Church Yth Grp; Girl Scts; School Musical; Yrbk Stf; Cheerleading; Swmmng.

DENAULT, PAULA; Lawrence HS; Lawrence, MA; (Y); Trk; High Hon Roll; Hon Roll; Bus Effcncy Awd Spllng 85; Gregg Shrthnd Awd 85; M Fazio Inst BC; Csmtlgy.

DENDLER, SCOTT; Reading Memorial HS; Reading, MA; (Y); Computer Clb; Drama Clb; Math Clb; Teachers Aide; School Play; Stage Crew; Nwsp Bus Mgr; JV Bsbl; Var Ice Hcky; Im Sftbl; Engrng.

DENEEN, MICHELE; Arlington Catholic HS; Waltham, MA; (Y); 12/148; Var L Crs Cntry; Var L Trk; Hon Roll; NHS; Magna Cum Laude Natl Latn Exm 85.

DENEHY, KELLY; Salem HS; Salem, MA; (Y); Var Cheerleading; Var Gym; Hon Roll.

DENHAM, MARK; Leicester HS; Leicester, MA; (Y); Ski Clb; Crs Cntry; Capt Trk; Hon Roll; Cntrl New Englnd Coll; Comp Sci.

DENIS, BRUCE; Leominster HS; Leominster, MA; (Y); Am Leg Boys St; Pres Chess Clb; Off Church Yth Grp; Math Clb; Math Tm; Stu Cncl; High Hon Roll; NHS; Exclince Mth Awd 84; Exclince Pre-Calculus Awd 85; Mth.

DENNEHY, DANIEL; Weymouth South HS; S Weymouth, MA; (Y); 57/340; Computer Clb; German Clb; Ski Clb; Yrbk Stf; Var Bsktbl; Var Crs Cntry; Trk; High Hon Roll; Hon Roll; Providence Coll; Acctg.

DENNEN, DONNA; Taunton HS; Taunton, MA; (Y); Church Yth Grp; Cmnty Wkr; DECA; Drama Clb; FBLA; Latin Clb; Varsity Clb; Crs Cntry; Trk; Hon Roll; Parent Educ Prg 82; Cert Of Apprctn Peer Alchl Educ 85; Soc Work.

DENNINGTON, EVERETT; Marblehead HS; Marblehead, MA; (S); Political Wkr; Chrmn Red Cross Aide; Stage Crew; Nwsp Rptr; Nwsp Stf; Rep Soph Cls; Rep Jr Cls; VP Stu Cncl; Gym; Trk; Hon Men Marblehead Arts Fstvl 82.

DENNIS, COLLEEN M; Cathedral HS; Enfield, CT; (Y); Intnl Clb; JA; Office Aide; Yrbk Stf; Rep Frsh Cls; Rep Soph Cls; Rep Jr Cls; Rep Sr Cls; Bus Admin.

DENNISON, DONNA D; Dedham HS; Dedham, MA; (Y); 16/300; VP Stu Cncl; High Hon Roll; Hon Roll; Pres Schlr; French Hon Soc; Outstndg SR In Engl 85; Magna Cum Laual Ntl Classical Latin 85; Outstndg JR In Soc Stu 84; Wheaton Coll; French.

DENT, RAE; Holyoke Catholic HS; Granby, MA; (Y); Chess Clb; French Clb; GAA; School Musical; Yrbk Stf; Bsktbl; Sftbl; Holyoke CC; Culnry Arts.

DEPINA, MARIA; Madison Park HS; Boston, MA; (Y); Office Aide; Rep Stu Cncl; Hon Roll; VP Pres NHS; Prfct Atten Awd; Outstndng Stu Hugh O Brien Yth Ldrshp Org 83-84; Bostn Stu Advsry Cncl 84-85; 2nd Pl Prz Wnnr Sci Fair; Engrng.

DEPPERT, JODI; Milord HS; Milford, MA; (Y); 96/283; Church Yth Grp; Cmnty Wkr; FNA; Hosp Aide; Capt Color Guard; Capt Flag Corp; Trk; Hon Roll; SADD 85; Nrs.

DEPUTAT, DANIELLE; Saugus HS; Saugus, MA; (Y); 72/313; Church Yth Grp; Cmnty Wkr; Drama Clb; VP JA; Library Aide; Ed Lit Mag; Stu Cncl; Gym; Prfct Atten Awd; Camp Fr Inc; JAAEM VP Opertns 85-86; Credit Lst 83-85; NH Coll; Bus.

DESCHENES, JULIE; Weymouth North HS; N Weymouth, MA; (Y); 50/336; Church Yth Grp; Var Bsktbl; Var Socr; Var Trk; Hon Roll; Jr NHS; Phy Ed, Scl Stds & Hlth Awd 85; Air Force Acad; Aeronautics.

DESCHENES III, WILFRID; Central Catholic HS; Lowell, MA; (Y); 37/228; CAP; Science Clb; Ski Clb; Chorus; Im Bsktbl; Capt Bowling; Im Vllybl; Hon Roll; NHS; Pres Schlr; Lgn Hnr 83-84; Ornteerng Awd 84-85; Mission Rep 84-85; U Of Lowell; Bio.

DESELL, KATHY; Presentation Of Mary Acad; Lawrence, MA; (Y); Church Yth Grp; Spanish Clb; Bsktbl; JV Var Sftbl; MVP Awd 85.

DESFORGE, JOHN C; Wilmington HS; Wilmington, MA; (Y); AFS; School Play; Yrbk Sprt Ed; VP Frsh Cls; VP Soph Cls; VP Jr Cls; VP Sr Cls; Stu Cncl; Var L Ftbl; Var Capt Trk; MVP Trck 84-85; Outstndng Achvt Awd Law 84-85; Law.

DESIMONE, PAMELA; Billerica Memorial HS; Billerica, MA; (Y); 45/500; French Clb; Chorus; Madrigals; School Musical; Yrbk Stf; Rep Soph Cls; Rep Jr Cls; Rep Stu Cncl; Pre-Law.

DESJARDINS, BARBARA ELLEN; Triton Regional HS; Rowley, MA; (Y); 12/182; Hosp Aide; Band; Chorus; Concert Band; Mrchg Band; High Hon Roll; Hon Roll; JP Sousa Awd; NHS; Prfct Atten Awd; Nw Englnd Schltsc Band Awd 85; MA Yth Wnd Ensmbl 85; Wilmot Roby Evans Awd 85; Ithaca Coll; Music Prfrmnce.

DESJARDINS-CANADA, PAMELA; North Brookfield HS; N Brookfield, MA; (Y); #9 In Class; Church Yth Grp; Math Tm; Pres Spanish Clb; Chorus; School Musical; Nwsp Ed-Chief; Nwsp Stf; Yrbk Stf; Rep Stu Cncl; Hon Roll; Med.

DESMARAIS, DANIEL; B M C Durfee HS; Fall River, MA; (Y); Camera Clb; Trs Church Yth Grp; French Clb; Library Aide; Teachers Aide; Church Choir; Lit Mag; Hon Roll; Libry Aid Awd 85; Socl Wrk.

DESMARAIS, DEBRA ANN; Blackstne-Millvl Rgnl JR SR HS; Millville, MA; (Y); 6/114; High Hon Roll; Reymond E Trottier Mem Schlrshp 85; Natl Nhr Soc 84-85; Bryant Coll; Acctg.

DESMARAIS, WENDY; Easthampton HS; Easthampton, MA; (Y); 1/132; Am Leg Aux Girls St; Sec Rptr 4-H; Bausch & Lomb Sci Awd; Hon Roll; NHS; NEDT Awd; Val; Dartmouth Clb Bk Awd 84; Supt Awd 85; Pres Acadmc Ftns Awd 85; U Of Connecticut; Jrnlsm.

DESMOND JR, EDWARD A; St Johns Prep Schl; Beverly, MA; (Y); Hon Roll; Med.

DESMOND, KRISTINE; Stoughton HS; Stoughton, MA; (Y); Church Yth Grp; Dance Clb; Hosp Aide; PAVAS; Chorus; Swing Chorus; High Hon Roll; Hon Roll; 1st Swng, Show Choir Awds 82-85; Comm.

DESOURDY, SANDRA; North HS; Worcester, MA; (Y); FBLA; Latin Clb; Pep Clb; Bsktbl; Socr; Tennis; Hon Roll; Prfct Atten Awd; Arch.

DESOUSA, ESTHER; Gardner HS; Gardner, MA; (Y); 14/172; Cmnty Wkr; Spanish Clb; Fld Hcky; Tennis; NHS; Arch.

DESROCHES, STEPHEN G; Southwick HS; Southwick, MA; (Y); 12/129; Am Leg Boys St; Pres Ski Clb; JV Socr; L Trk; Var Capt Wrstlng; High Hon Roll; Hon Roll; NHS; U Of Lowell; Mech Engrng.

DESROSIERS, MONIQUE; Grafton HS; S Grafton, MA; (Y); 85/130; Camp Fr Inc; Church Yth Grp; Hosp Aide; Band; Fld Hcky; Trk; Elks Awd; Rotary Awd; St Schlr; Robert L Mason Scholar 85; Marion Cmp Fire Awd 81; Amer Intl Coll; Med Tech.

DESTREMPES, CHARLES; Northbridge JR SR HS; Whitinsville, MA; (S); 3/160; Am Leg Boys St; Chess Clb; Latin Clb; Quiz Bowl; Scholastic Bowl; Nwsp Stf; Off Frsh Cls; Off Soph Cls; Off Jr Cls; Off Sr Cls; WPI; Elec Engrng.

DESY, MARGARET; Holy Name CCHS; Worcester, MA; (Y); 17/273; Art Clb; JA; Hon Roll; Fshn Dsgn.

DETESO, KIM; Woburn SR HS; Woburn, MA; (S); JA; JCL; Latin Clb; Ski Clb; Stu Cncl; Trk; High Hon Roll; Hon Roll; Jr NHS.

DETORIE, MAURA; Bishop Feehan HS; Lincoln, RI; (Y); 1/260; JCL; Pres Frsh Cls; Pres Soph Cls; Rep Jr Cls; Rep Sr Cls; Stu Cncl; Var Capt Trk; Var Capt Vllybl; Dnfth Awd; French Hon Soc; Princeton U; Engl.

DEVEAU, CHARLES; Don Bosco Tech HS; Roslindale, MA; (S); Boys Clb Am; Cmnty Wkr; JV Var Bsbl; JV Ice Hcky; JV Trk; High Hon Roll; NHS; Elec Engrng.

DEVEAU, SEAN; Deerfield Acad; Branford, CT; (Y); Cmnty Wkr; Spanish Clb; Lit Mag; Capt Var Swmmng; Tennis; Capt Vrsty Swmmg 85; All New Engld Wtr Polo Tm 84-85.

DEVER, JOSEPH B; Thayer Acad; Weymouth, MA; (Y); 1/99; Chess Clb; Nwsp Phtg; Nwsp Rptr; Nwsp Stf; Yrbk Phtg; Off Stu Cncl; Var L Socr; High Hon Roll; NHS; Val; Spcl Hstrn Awd 83; JR Hstry Awd 84; Dartmouth Coll; Rsrch.

DEVINE, ELLEN M; Sacred Heart HS; Halifax, MA; (Y); 27/89; Church Yth Grp; Dance Clb; Girl Scts; Intnl Clb; Ski Clb; Chorus; Variety Show; Yrbk Stf; Var Cheerleading; DAR Awd; Exclnce Dance Danny Hoctors Dance Caravan NYC 83; Providence Coll.

DEVINE, JULIE; Notre Dame Acad; Scituate, MA; (Y); 41/115; Office Aide; Im Bsktbl; Im Vllybl; Hon Roll; Spanish NHS; Mth Awd 85; Svc Awds 84 & 85; Htl Mngmnt.

DEVINE, KATHLEEN; King Philip Regional HS; Plainville, MA; (Y); Hosp Aide; VICA; Var Bsktbl; Var Crs Cntry; Mgr(s); 3rd Pl Local VICA Comp Nrsng 85; RN.

DEVINE, ROBERT; North HS; Worcester, MA; (Y); Boy Scts; Hon Roll; Ntl Merit SF; Acad Olympian; Grad Summesmoth U CT.

DEVLIN, KELLY; Ware HS; Ware, MA; (Y); 12/115; Cmnty Wkr; 4-H; French Clb; Girl Scts; Hosp Aide; Yrbk Stf; High Hon Roll; Hon Roll; Optometry.

DEWEY, MARC; Dennis Yarmouth Regional HS; S Dennis, MA; (Y); Drama Clb; Stage Crew; Variety Show; Im Vllybl; Acctg.

DEWEY, MICHAEL R; Waltham HS; Waltham, MA; (Y); Am Leg Boys St; Science Clb; School Play; Score Keeper; Hon Roll; Cmnty Wkr; NHS; 2nd Essy Cntst 85; Engrng.

DI BONA, SHERRIE; Brockton HS; Brockton, MA; (Y); Church Yth Grp; French Clb; Hosp Aide; High Hon Roll; Hon Roll; NHS; Prfct Atten Awd; Massasoit CC; Nrsng.

DI CAMILLO, ADELE A; Milford HS; Milford, MA; (Y); 32/320; Cmnty Wkr; Drama Clb, PAVAS; School Musical; School Play; Stage Crew; Yrbk Stf; High Hon Roll; Hon Roll; NHS; Northeastern U; Banking.

DI CARLO, JILL; Marian HS; Framingham, MA; (Y); Cmnty Wkr; Chorus; Hon Roll; NEDT Awd; Hmcmng 82-83; Villanova; Bus.

DI CECCA, BENNY; Woburn SR HS; Woburn, MA; (S); Boy Scts; Computer Clb; Band; Concert Band; Mrchg Band; Variety Show; Stu Cncl; Hon Roll; Eagle Scout 84; Lawyer.

DI CRESCE, LAURIE A; Marian HS; Sudbury, MA; (Y); Dance Clb; French Clb; Band; Chorus; Lit Mag; Sec Frsh Cls; JV Cheerleading; JV Golf; Var Stat Swmmng; Jrnlsm.

DI FIORE, ROSE MARIA; Presentation Of Mary Acad; Methuen, MA; (S); Pres Sec Church Yth Grp; Hosp Aide; Math Clb; Political Wkr; Yrbk Stf; Pres Sr Cls; Capt L Bsktbl; NHS; Cmnty Wkr; Pep Clb; Sci Fair 1st Pl 83-84; Stu Gov Day Delg Boston 83-84.

DI GIACOMO, JULIE; Medford HS; Medford, MA; (Y); 7/436; Am Leg Aux Girls St; Church Yth Grp; Math Tm; Varsity Clb; Yrbk Stf; Sr Cls; Var JV Cheerleading; High Hon Roll; Mu Alp Tht; NHS; Hnrs Eng Awd 84 & 85; Mth Awds 84 & 85; Scholar U MA Amherst 85; Med.

DI LULLO, DONNA; Agawam HS; Agawam, MA; (Y); 1/350; Yrbk Stf; Hon Roll; NHS; Spanish NHS; Brown Book Awd 85.

DI MARCO, DIANE; Malden HS; Malden, MA; (Y); 28/550; Key Clb; Variety Show; Trs Soph Cls; Trs Jr Cls; Trs Sr Cls; Var Bsktbl; Var Fld Hcky; Hon Roll; Camp Fr Inc; JV Capt Sftbl; Hugh O Brian Ldrshp Smnr 84; Harvard Book Awd 84; Acting.

DI MARTINO JR, EDWARD P; Norwood HS; Norwood, MA; (Y); 14/350; Am Leg Boys St; CAP; Leo Clb; Crs Cntry; Ftbl; Trk; NHS; Columbia U; Engr.

DI MAURO, ANN MARIE; Dedham HS; Dedham, MA; (S); 9/350; Church Yth Grp; Coach Actv; Var L Sftbl; Hon Roll; Boston Coll; Math.

DI MEO JR, FRANK; St Johns HS; Worcester, MA; (Y); 17/260; Church Yth Grp; Computer Clb; French Clb; Nwsp Rptr; Socr; Vllybl; High Hon Roll; NHS; Ntl Merit Ltr; NEDT Awd; U PA; Engrng.

DI PALMA, HOPE G; Shawsheen Valley Vo Tech; Tewksbury, MA; (Y); 57/396; VICA; Drm Mjr(t); Nwsp Rptr; Sftbl; Twrlr; Hon Roll; R & G Burns Schlrshps 85; Merrimack Coll; Bus Mgmnt.

DI PAOLO, LINDA; Bishop Fenwick HS; Peabody, MA; (Y); Cmnty Wkr; Nwsp Stf; Yrbk Stf; High Hon Roll; Pres NHS; Peabody YMCA Gymnstcs Ldr Awd 83; Schl Latin III Awd 84; Schl Sci Awd 85; Engr.

DI PIERDOMENICO, DANA; Bartlett HS; Webster, MA; (Y); 12/179; Church Yth Grp; Exploring; French Clb; Office Aide; Pep Clb; Science Clb; Variety Show; Nwsp Stf; Yrbk Stf; Swmmng; Manhattanville Clg; Poltc Sci.

DI PIETRANTONIO, GUISEPPE; Rindge & Latin HS; Cambridge, MA; (Y); JA; School Play; Nwsp Phtg; Nwsp Rptr; Yrbk Phtg; Diving; Socr; Swmmng; Coachs Soccr Awd 85; MA Pre Engrng Serv Awd 84; Salem ST Coll.

DI PILATO, VINCENT H; Tahanto Regional HS; Boylston, MA; (Y); Computer Clb; Yrbk Stf; Golf; NHS; U Lowell; Elec Engrng.

DI SABATINO, DENISE; Malden HS; Malden, MA; (Y); 89/500; Art Clb; Hosp Aide; Pep Clb; Flag Corp; Stage Crew; Variety Show; Cheerleading; Pom Pon; Hon Roll; Ntl Merit Ltr; Malden Arts Schlrshp; Ntl Merit Ltr; Mldn Trste Schlrshp; Salem ST Coll; Comrcl Art.

DI SANO, DANIEL; Malden HS; Malden, MA; (Y); 1/650; Key Clb; Quiz Bowl; Rep Soph Cls; Rep Jr Cls; VP Sr Cls; Stu Cncl; Var Tennis; High Hon Roll; Kiwanis Awd; NHS; Brown U Bk Awd 85; Sec Of Litry Scty 85; Rotary Clb Awd 84; Harvard U; Bus Mgmt.

DI TONDO, LYN; Franklin HS; Franklin, MA; (Y); 4/235; Math Tm; OEA; Color Guard; Variety Show; Lit Mag; Elks Awd; VP NHS; Ntl Merit Schol; Church Yth Grp; Math Clb; Wellesley Coll Bk Awd 84; Dwyer Meml Schlrshp 85; MA Advncd Stud Prgm 84; Boston Coll; Librl Arts.

DI ZOGLIO, CAROLINE B; Methuen HS; Methuen, MA; (Y); 15/306; Hosp Aide; Intnl Clb; Var Crs Cntry; Powder Puff Ftbl; JV Trk; High Hon Roll; NHS; Pres Acad Fit Awd 85; Cls 1915 Scholar; Suffolk U; Bio.

DIAB, NADIA; Natick HS; Natick, MA; (Y); 86/432; Exploring; Hosp Aide; Teachers Aide; Yrbk Ed-Chief; Yrbk Stf; JV Fld Hcky; Hon Roll; Tufts U; Dentistry.

DIAMOND, PAMELA; W Springfield HS; W Springfield, MA; (S); Am Leg Aux Girls St; Sec Church Yth Grp; Hosp Aide; JA; Band; JV Sftbl; NHS; Concert Band; Mrchg Band; Hon Roll.

DIATCHENKO, DIMITRI; Newton North HS; Newtonville, MA; (Y); Art Clb; FFA; Natl Beta Clb; Varsity Clb; Variety Show; Ftbl; Gym; Trk; Schlrshp Awd Stetson U 83; Boston Coll; Robtcs.

DIAZ, DAVID; Drury SR HS; North Adams, MA; (Y); Concert Band; Jazz Band; School Musical; High Hon Roll; JP Sousa Awd; NHS; Pres Schlr; Band; Mrchg Band; MA All ST Concert Band,Dist Band 83-85; Am Leg Schl Awd 85; Nuc Engr.

DIAZ, HENRY; Wilbraham Monson Acad; New York, NY; (Y); Intnl Clb; Spanish Clb; Nwsp Rptr; Var L Crs Cntry; JV Lcrss; Var Trk; Var L Wrstlng; Hon Roll; Schlrshp Privt HS Minorts Law 82-86; Wrstlng 1st Pl Medl 83; Wrstlng 4th Pl Medl 84; Accntng.

DIAZ, LAZARO; Boston Latin School; Brighton, MA; (Y); 2/319; Chess Clb; Intnl Clb; Model UN; High Hon Roll; NHS; Commonwlth Scholar 85; Brd Regents Scholar 85; Cls Of 1920 Scholar 85; Harvard U; Chem.

DIBIASE, JULIE A; Belmont HS; Belmont, MA; (Y); 30/310; Cmnty Wkr; Computer Clb; Latin Clb; PAVAS; Nwsp Bus Mgr; Sftbl; Trk; High Hon Roll; Hon Roll; NHS; Ntl Latn Exm Cm Laud Cert 85.

DIBONA, ANNEMARIE; Brockton HS; Brockton, MA; (Y); 32/1200; Band; Concert Band; Mrchg Band; Symp Band; High Hon Roll; Hon Roll; Silv Mdl Latn Exam Natl 83-84; Pre Med.

DICIACCIO, NICOLAS; Arlington Catholic HS; Arlington, MA; (Y); 15/150; JV Crs Cntry; Var Trk; Aerontcl.

DICKINSON, CHARLES; Franklin HS; Franklin, MA; (Y); Cmnty Wkr; Variety Show; JV Bsktbl; Var Golf; JV Socr; Var Trk; Hon Roll; U Of NH; Engrng.

DICKSON, SHANNON; Drury SR HS; Clarksburg, MA; (Y); Pep Clb; Teachers Aide; Yrbk Stf; JV Var Bsktbl; Var L Socr; Mgr Trk; Charls & Olivia Perron Schlrshp 85; Green Mt Coll Athltc Schlrshp 85; Green Mt Coll; Bus Acctng.

DIEP, ANH; Boston Tech HS; Boston, MA; (Y); Computer Clb; Pep Clb; Rep Soph Cls; Sftbl; Score Keeper; Tennis; Vllybl; High Hon Roll; Hon Roll; Prfct Atten Awd; Samuel Gross Davis Awd 83; Cert Of Compltn-Peer Councing Technqs 84; Boston U; Math.

DIFINI, VINCENT; Marian HS; Framingham, MA; (Y); 31/177; Golf; Capt L Socr; Hon Roll; NHS; Engrng.

DIGIORGIO, TRACI; Franklin HS; Franklin, MA; (Y); Ski Clb; Color Guard; Drill Tm; Drm & Bgl; Flag Corp.

DIGIOVANNI, ARTHUR; Central Catholic HS; Lowell, MA; (Y); 32/219; Im Bsktbl; Im Vllybl; High Hon Roll; Hon Roll; Pre Med.

DIGIROLAMO, ELIZABETH; Canton HS; Canton, MA; (Y); 14/255; Church Yth Grp; Cmnty Wkr; German Clb; Sftbl; Hon Roll; NHS; Century Clb 84-85; Engrng.

DIJAK, ALEXANDRA; Stoughton HS; Stoughton, MA; (Y); Art Clb; Chorus; Stage Crew; Yrbk Stf; Socr; Trk; High Hon Roll; NHS; MA Coll Art; Interior Dsgn.

DIMARE, STEPHEN; Hudson HS; Hudson, MA; (Y); Math Clb; Math Tm; Var Crs Cntry; JV Ice Hcky; High Hon Roll; Part On 3rd Pl Math Tm In ST 83; Part On 3rd Pl Math Tm In New Englnd 83; 2nd Pl Hstry Proj In ST 83; Engrng.

DIMO, SCOTT M; Quaboag Regional HS; Warren, MA; (Y); JA; Spanish Clb; Hon Roll; Bio.

DIMUZIO, ANGELA; Rockland HS; Rockland, MA; (Y); 52/270; Church Yth Grp; Nwsp Stf; Yrbk Stf; Hon Roll; Bsktbl; Coach Actv; Var L Trk; Johnson & Wales; Accntng.

DINEN, MAUREEN; Classical HS; Lynn, MA; (Y); Spanish Clb; Rep Jr Cls; Sftbl; Swmmng; Hon Roll; Jr NHS; Prfct Atten Awd; U NH; Engr.

DION, CHERYL M; BMC Durfee HS; Fall River, MA; (Y); 20/679; French Clb; Hosp Aide; Varsity Clb; Chorus; Variety Show; Yrbk Stf; Var Powder Puff Ftbl; Var Capt Twrlr; High Hon Roll; Hon Roll; Schlrshp ILGWU $250 85; Awd Varsity Let For Gunner 84; Co-Capt Of Gunners 84; Assumption Coll; Chem.

DION, DANIEL; Blackstone Valley Reg Vo-Tech; Whitinsville, MA; (Y); Am Leg Boys St; Boy Scts; Bsbl; Ftbl; Swmmng; Hon Roll; Plmbg.

DION, DAVID; Montachusett Regional Vo Tech Schl; Fitchburg, MA; (Y); Ski Clb; Yrbk Stf; Var L Crs Cntry; JV Ftbl; Hon Roll; Trs NHS; Air Force; Pilot.

DION, DENISE; Chelmsford HS; Chelmsford, MA; (Y); 2/560; Church Yth Grp; Hosp Aide; Var L Cheerleading; Cit Awd; French Hon Soc; NHS; Sal; Ski Clb; Nwsp Stf; Off Frsh Cls; Amer Assn U Wmn Schlrshp 84-85; Merrimack Vly Assn Schl Cmmttees Acad Exclnc Awd 85; Oct Stu Of Mth 85; Dartmouth Coll; Engrng.

DION, GREG; Southbridge HS; Southbridge, MA; (Y); 49/144; Var Bsbl; JV Golf; Hon Roll; Acctg.

DION, JOELLE; Agawam HS; Feeding Hls, MA; (Y); AFS; FCA; GAA; Varsity Clb; Chorus; Ed Yrbk Stf; Bsktbl; Tennis; Hon Roll; Tchnd CCD Clss 84-85; Psych.

DION, KATHRYN A; Beverly HS; Beverly, MA; (Y); 147/378; Cmnty Wkr; JV Var Bsktbl; Var Powder Puff Ftbl; JV Var Socr; DAR Awd; Hon Roll; Fnlst Christian Mem Schlrshp 83; Flagler Coll; Educ.

DION, KRISTIN; Hudson HS; Hudson, MA; (Y); FBLA; Pep Clb; Ski Clb; Spanish Clb; Varsity Clb; Chorus; School Musical; Yrbk Stf; Fld Hcky; High Hon Roll; U MA Amherst; Bus.

DION, MICHELLE; St Peter-Marian Cc HS; Sterling Junction, MA; (S); 1/175; Camera Clb; Drama Clb; School Musical; School Play; High Hon Roll; NHS; Northeastern U; Chem Engrng.

DION, THOMAS; Blackstone Valley Reg Voc Tech HS; Uxbridge, MA; (Y); Trs Church Yth Grp; Hon Roll.

DIONNE, JUDITH; Holy Name Central Catholic HS; Worcester, MA; (Y); Aud/Vis; Church Yth Grp; Girl Scts; Church Choir; School Musical; School Play; Nwsp Rptr; Nwsp Stf; Hon Roll; Jr NHS; Girl Scout Silver Awd 83; Marion Awd 82; Comm.

DIONNE, SUSAN ANN; Haverhill HS; Haverhill, MA; (Y); 104/375; School Play; Var Cheerleading; JV Trk; High Hon Roll; Hale Aux Schlrshp Awd; Croston Schlrshp Awd; Hunking Schlrshp Girls; U Of Lowell; Med Tech.

DIRSA, PETER; Haverhill HS; Haverhill, MA; (Y); 41/460; Aud/Vis; Pres Computer Clb; Teachers Aide; High Hon Roll; Comp Sci.

DISIMONE, ANTHONY; Algonquin Regional HS; Northboro, MA; (Y); Computer Clb; Yrbk Stf; High Hon Roll; NHS; Bus.

DITULLIO, ANNE; Marian HS; Framingham, MA; (Y); Color Guard; Drill Tm; Drm & Bgl; Flag Corp; Arch.

DIXON, KRISTI; Northfield Mount Hermon HS; Chatham, MA; (Y); Cmnty Wkr; Varsity Clb; Chorus; Nwsp Rptr; Nwsp Sprt Ed; Var Capt Bsktbl; JV Vllybl; Hon Roll; Lila & Dewitt Wallace Awd Creatv Wrtg 85; Stdnt Ldrshp 85-86; Media Cmmnctns.

DOBSON, ERIC; Auburn HS; Auburn, MA; (Y); Ski Clb; Variety Show; Nwsp Ed-Chief; Nwsp Rptr; Nwsp Stf; Yrbk Phtg; Yrbk Stf; Sec Soph Cls; Sec Jr Cls; Sec Sr Cls; Westfield ST; Law Enfrcmnt.

DODGE, CARRIE; Notre Dame Acad; Lowell, MA; (Y); 4/50; Cmnty Wkr; Drama Clb; Hosp Aide; JA; Key Clb; Spanish Clb; Stage Crew; Sec Soph Cls; VP Jr Cls; VP Stu Cncl; Phys Ther.

DODGE, CHRIS; Burlington HS; Burlington, MA; (Y); Cmnty Wkr; Dance Clb; Yrbk Stf; Lit Mag; Off Sr Cls; Rep Stu Cncl; Bsbl; Ice Hcky; Trk; Hon Roll; Computervision Corp-Engrng Schlrshp 85; U Of MA; Engrng.

DODGE, EVERLYN; Whitman Hanson Regional HS; Whitman, MA; (Y); Church Yth Grp; Drama Clb; Yrbk Stf; Rep Soph Cls; Rep Jr Cls; Rep Sr Cls; VP Stu Cncl; Mgr(s); Score Keeper; Hon Roll; Stu Govt Awd 85; Westfield ST Clg; Educ.

DODGE, JULIE A; Marlboro HS; Marlborough, MA; (Y); 3/280; AFS; French Clb; Rep Stu Cncl; JV Bsktbl; Elks Awd; High Hon Roll; NHS; Richer Home & Schl Assn Awd 85; Alice E & Harry A Barnard Scholar 85; Coll Holy Cross Scholar Awd 85; Coll Holy Cross Worcester MA.

DODSON, DONNA; Algonquin Regional HS; Northboro, MA; (Y); 3/220; Sec Church Yth Grp; Chorus; Church Choir; Var L Crs Cntry; Var L Trk; High Hon Roll; NHS; Outstdng Accmplshmnt In Acad 85; Wellesley; Bio-Chem.

DOHERTY, AMY; Bridgewater-Raynham Regional HS; Bridgewater, MA; (Y); 6/320; Am Leg Aux Girls St; Ski Clb; Nwsp Ed-Chief; Stu Cncl; Var Fld Hcky; Var Capt Trk; Hon Roll; NHS; Ntl Merit Ltr; NEDT Awd; Stheastrn MA Regnl Stu Advsry Cncl 85-86; Engl.

DOHERTY, DANIEL; Leicester HS; Leicester, MA; (Y); Band; High Hon Roll; Hon Roll; Prfct Atten Awd; ROTC; Crmnl Sci.

DOHERTY, JAIME; Braintree HS; Braintree, MA; (Y); Drama Clb; Teachers Aide; Chorus; School Play; Variety Show; Cheerleading; Fld Hcky; Gym; Lcrss; Mgr(s); Real Est.

DOHERTY, JIM P; Burlington HS; Burlington, MA; (Y); 23/315; Aud/Vis; Math Tm; Stage Crew; Yrbk Phtg; NHS; Ntl Merit SF; Frnch Acad Awd 83-84; Elect Engrng.

DOHERTY, JODI; Hingham HS; Hingham, MA; (Y); Drama Clb; Girl Scts; School Musical; Yrbk Stf; JV Var Cheerleading; Hon Roll; Bus.

DOHERTY, JOSEPH P; St Peter Marian HS; Auburn, MA; (Y); VP Jr Cls; Rep Stu Cncl; Var Capt Ice Hcky; Var L Tennis; Hon Roll; Murphy Cup-Awd Outstndg Contrib Ice Hocky 84-85; Air Force Acad; Pilot.

DOHERTY, LAURA; Bridgewater Raynham Regional HS; Bridgewater, MA; (Y); Church Yth Grp; Chorus; Madrigals; Hon Roll; Educ.

DOHERTY, LUANNE; Notre Dame Acad; Hingham, MA; (Y); 10/135; Chorus; School Musical; School Play; Golf; Sftbl; High Hon Roll; NHS; Spanish NHS; Ntl Merit Sci Awd 85; Holy Cross.

DOHERTY, MARGARET; Holbrook JR SR HS; Holbrook, MA; (Y); 15/101; VP Latin Clb; Rep Frsh Cls; Rep Soph Cls; Rep Jr Cls; Rep Sr Cls; Rep Stu Cncl; L Var Crs Cntry; NHS; Chorus; School Musical; Un Sng Hero Crss Cntry 84; MVP Trk Tm 84-85; MVP Trck Mayflwr Leag 85; Nrsg.

DOHERTY, MARY; Matignon HS; Arlington, MA; (Y); 36/181; Hosp Aide; Spanish Clb; Church Choir; Hon Roll; NEDT Awd; Trs Church Yth Grp; Lib Arts.

DOHERTY, WAYNE; Boston Latin Schl; Boston, MA; (Y); VP JA; Latin Clb; Capt ROTC; Rep Jr Cls; Rep Sr Cls; Rep Stu Cncl; JV Var Bsbl; Im Bsktbl; Hon Roll; Exemplry Cndct & Fidlty Boston Latn Schl 83-84; Metro Rifl Tm Rnnr Up 85; Bus.

DOIRON, MARIANNE; Fontbonne Acad; Dor, MA; (Y); 7/132; Church Yth Grp; Cmnty Wkr; Dance Clb; Debate Tm; Drama Clb; Girl Scts; Political Wkr; Teachers Aide; Chorus; School Musical; Hugh Obrien & The Mass Yth Ldrshp Fndtn 84; Silver Medal & Cum Laude Cert Latin I & Ii 83-84; Occup Therp.

DOLAHER, KERRIANNE; Saugus HS; Saugus, MA; (Y); 65/300; Cmnty Wkr; GAA; Office Aide; Pep Clb; Red Cross Aide; Yrbk Stf; Trs Soph Cls; Off Sr Cls; Pres Stu Cncl; Powder Puff Ftbl; Miss MA ST Teen-1st Rnnr Up 85; Court Stenogrphr.

DOLAN, CHRISTINE; Ursuline Acad; Dedham, MA; (Y); Drama Clb; French Clb; Hosp Aide; Nwsp Rptr; Nwsp Stf; Socr; Swmmng; Frnch Clb Pres 84-85; George Washington U; Pre-Med.

DOLAN, ERINN; Chicopee Comprehensived HS; Chicopee, MA; (Y); Var L Sftbl; Hon Roll; NHS; RN.

DOLAN, LORI; Boston Latin Schl; West Roxbury, MA; (Y); 52/300; Church Yth Grp; Cmnty Wkr; Hosp Aide; Latin Clb; Ski Clb; Variety Show; Nwsp Stf; Hon Roll; NHS.

DOLAN, MAUREEN; Franklin HS; Franklin, MA; (Y); 11/235; Trs French Clb; Math Tm; OEA; Ski Clb; Lit Mag; Var L Crs Cntry; JV Tennis; Var L Trk; Hon Roll; NHS; Eugene J & Helen R Mem Scholar 85; Clark U; Lib Arts.

DOLD, SUE G; Southwick HS; Southwich, MA; (Y); Am Leg Aux Girls St; Office Aide; Pep Clb; Ski Clb; Variety Show; Trs Frsh Cls; Trs Soph Cls; Trs Jr Cls; Trs Sr Cls; JV Bsktbl; Bus Admin.

DOLE, GEORGE L; Mohawk Trl Regional HS; Shelburne Falls, MA; (Y); 2/149; Am Leg Boys St; Cmnty Wkr; Varsity Clb; Nwsp Stf; Capt Crs Cntry; Var Trk; High Hon Roll; Hon Roll; VP NHS; Harvard Bk Awd 85; Excell In Englsh 85; Art Awd 85.

DOMAL, LISA; Norwood HS; Norwood, MA; (Y); 6/351; Church Yth Grp; Key Clb; School Play; Variety Show; High Hon Roll; JC Awd; NHS; Holy Cross; Pre-Med.

DOMINIE, ANITA; Ware HS; Ware, MA; (Y); Math Tm; Band; Concert Band; JV Socr; High Hon Roll; Hon Roll; Spnsh Awd 83; Rensselaer Math & Sci Awd 85; Med Tech.

DOMINIK, MELISSA; St Marys HS; Westfield, MA; (Y); VP JA; Nwsp Rptr; Yrbk Stf; JV Var Mgr(s); JV Var Score Keeper; Ctzn Schlrshp Awd 85; E R Behrend Schlrshp 85; Altrnt Pres Senate-Youth & Gvrnmnt 85; Quinnipiac Coll; Accntng.

DONAHUE, NANCY; Matignon HS; Cambridge, MA; (Y); Science Clb; JV Capt Cheerleading; Hon Roll; Boston Coll.

DONAHUE, ROSEMARIE; Boston Latin HS; Boston, MA; (Y); 108/320; French Clb; JA; Latin Clb; Ski Clb; NHS; Camp Fr Inc; Church Yth Grp; Cmnty Wkr; Dance Clb; Hosp Aide; Classcl Awd 82; Fidlty Awd 82; Acctg.

DONATINI, DAWN; Agawam SR HS; Feeding Hls, MA; (Y); 46/350; Ski Clb; Band; Concert Band; Jazz Band; Mrchg Band; Orch; Pep Band; School Musical; Symp Band; Yrbk Stf; Poster Cntst/Ed In Schls Won Svngs Bond 83; MA U; Bus.

DONERTY, KERRY A; Archbishop Williams HS; Quincy, MA; (Y); Dance Clb; Ski Clb; Sec Frsh Cls; Sec Soph Cls; Sec Jr Cls; Var L Cheerleading; Trk; High Hon Roll; VP Sec NHS; Suffolk Book Awd 85.

DONNELLAN, VICKI; Manchester JR SR HS; Manchester, MA; (Y); 4/80; Yrbk Phtg; Yrbk Sprt Ed; Var L Bsktbl; Var L Fld Hcky; Var L Sftbl; Vllybl; CC Awd; High Hon Roll; NHS; Ntl Merit Ltr; Wesleyan U; Bio.

DONNELLY, JENNIFER; Notre Dame Acad; Weymouth, MA; (Y); 15/126; Church Yth Grp; Drama Clb; Spanish Clb; Acpl Chr; Band; Chorus; Church Choir; Concert Band; Madrigals; Orch; Music.

DONNELLY, JENNIFER E; Natick HS; Natick, MA; (Y); 46/456; School Musical; School Play; Stage Crew; Off Frsh Cls; Off Soph Cls; Off Jr Cls; Stu Cncl; Arch.

DONOVAN, AMY; Mohawk Trail Reg HS; Charlemont, MA; (Y); 20/140; Rep Jr Cls; Hon Roll; Bus.

DONOVAN, BRIAN; Westford Acad; Westford, MA; (Y); 15/220; French Clb; Model UN; Var Trk; Ntl Merit SF; Westford Acad French I Awd 83; Georgetown U; Intl Bus.

DONOVAN, EDDIE; Bishop Fenwick HS; Lynnfield, MA; (Y); 25/222; Church Yth Grp; Drama Clb; Teachers Aide; Stage Crew; Rep Sr Cls; JV Bsktbl; Hon Roll; Drama Clb Awd 85; Bentley Coll; Bus.

DONOVAN, ELIZABETH M; Dedham HS; Dedham, MA; (S); 3/325; Church Yth Grp; Band; Mrchg Band; School Musical; Off Stu Cncl; Var Capt Bsktbl; Sftbl; Elks Awd; Hon Roll; VP NHS; Unsung Hero Bsktbl 85; MIP Bsktbl 84; Coll Holy Cross; Pol Sci.

DONOVAN, MARGARET; Somerville HS; Somerville, MA; (Y); 27/539; Church Yth Grp; Capt Color Guard; Var JV Cheerleading; Var Sftbl; Var Vllybl; Hon Roll; NHS; Chrldg Awd 85; Salem ST Clg; Acctg.

DONOVAN, PATRICIA; Arlington Catholic HS; Arlington, MA; (Y); 60/150; Art Clb; Church Yth Grp; Drama Clb; Hosp Aide; Spanish Clb; Church Choir; Stage Crew; Bus.

DONOVAN, ROBERT; Holbrook HS; Holbrook, MA; (Y); 30/110; Chess Clb; Church Yth Grp; Latin Clb; Varsity Clb; School Play; Stage Crew; Yrbk Stf; Trs Jr Cls; Rep Sr Cls; Var L Crs Cntry; Bst Salesman In Schl 85; U Miami; Bus.

DOOLEY, JOHN T; Arlington Catholic HS; Lexington, MA; (Y); 1/160; French Clb; JA; Latin Clb; JV Bsktbl; VP Trk; High Hon Roll; Hon Roll; NHS; RPI Math & Sci Awd 85; Gold Medal Ntl Latin Exam 83-84; Harvard U; Bio.

DOOLEY, KEVIN P; Wakefield HS; Wakefield, MA; (Y); Off Boy Scts; Off JA; Nwsp Ed-Chief; Ed Lit Mag; Im Bsktbl; Im Ftbl; Hon Roll; NRA Marksmn Cert 83; YMCA Red Crs Lifsvg Cert 84; Toastmstr Yth Ldrshp Prog Awd 85; Bus Admin.

DOONER, LISA MARIE; St Marys Regional HS; Lynn, MA; (Y); 20/89; Stu Cncl; Diving; Gym; Powder Puff Ftbl; Swmmng; Italian Cmmnty Ctr Schlrshp 85; HS Pagnt Rep 84; MA ST Schlrshp 85; Bus Wk Schlrshp 84; St Anselm Coll; Pre-Law.

DORAN, MICHELLE; Hingham HS; Hingham, MA; (Y); 27/350; Church Yth Grp; Band; Mrchg Band; Lcrss; Hon Roll; NHS; Spn Heritage Pgm 85; Comm Art.

DOREY, LINDA; Silver Lake Regional HS; Pembroke, MA; (Y); 11/467; Drama Clb; VP French Clb; School Play; Stage Crew; Yrbk Stf; Var Im Socr; U Of MA-AMHERST; Frnch.

DORGAN, KEVIN; Malden Catholic HS; Everett, MA; (Y); Church Yth Grp; Computer Clb; Varsity Clb; Nwsp Rptr; Nwsp Stf; Var JV Ftbl; Vllybl; Hon Roll; Ntl Merit SF; Pre-Med.

DORMER, JAMES; Cohasset HS; Cohasset, MA; (Y); 25/129; AFS; Ski Clb; Varsity Clb; Yrbk Stf; Golf; Socr; Wrstlng; Hon Roll; Computer Clb; Debate Tm; Schltc Achvt Awd 83-84.

DORR, KIM; Franklin HS; Franklin, MA; (Y); Varsity Clb; Yrbk Stf; Fld Hcky; Sftbl; Hon Roll; Nrsg.

DORR, MICHAEL KING; Newton Catholic HS; Newton, MA; (S); 1/80; Chess Clb; Debate Tm; Drama Clb; English Clb; French Clb; Thesps; School Musical; School Play; Stage Crew; Nwsp Stf.

DORRINGTON, MICHAEL; Franklin HS; Franklin, MA; (Y); Rep Stu Cncl; Var Bsbl; Var Bsktbl; Var Ftbl; Var Ice Hcky; Var Trk; Var Vllybl; Cit Awd; Hon Roll; Med Dr.

DORSEY, GEMMA L; Cathedral HS; E Long, MA; (Y); 34/500; Debate Tm; Hosp Aide; Trs Intnl Clb; Model UN; Ski Clb; School Musical; VP Rep Sr Cls; Stu Cncl; Var Tennis; Im Vllybl; Friendliest SR Girl 85; Presdntl Fitness Awd 85; Leadrshp Awd-Georgetown Alumni 84; Holy Cross Coll; Economics.

DOSTOU, CHRISTINE; Bishop Connolly HS; Fall River, MA; (S); 12/177; Math Tm; Spanish Clb; High Hon Roll; Comp Engr.

DOUCETTE, CHRISTINE; North Shore Regional Voc HS; Beverly, MA; (Y); Church Yth Grp; Computer Clb; Ski Clb; Sec Fr Cls; Hon Roll; Comp Sci.

DOUCETTE, JOHN; Whitman-Hanson Regional HS; Whitman, MA; (Y); 7/350; Var L Ftbl; Im Vllybl; Im Wt Lftg; Hon Roll; NHS; Busnss Mgmt.

DOUCETTE, MARK; Silver Lake Reg HS; Plympton, MA; (Y); 64/520; Am Leg Boys St; French Clb; Key Clb; Rep Jr Cls; Rep Sr Cls; JV Bsktbl; Hon Roll; Prom Comm 85; Bentley Coll; Bus Adm.

DOUCOT, CHRISTOPHER J; Malden Catholic HS; Stoneham, MA; (Y); 20/187; Drama Clb; Letterman Clb; Var L Crs Cntry; Var L Trk; High Hon Roll; Hon Roll; NHS; Holy Cross Coll; Bio.

DOUGAN, MARIANNE; Randolph HS; Randolph, MA; (Y); Church Yth Grp; Computer Clb; Drama Clb; Spanish Clb; Nwsp Ed-Chief; Tennis; Nutritn.

DOUGHERTY, JOHN; Lenox Memorial HS; Lenox, MA; (Y); Computer Clb; JCL; Latin Clb; JV Bsktbl; Var Golf; JV Var Wrstlng; High Hon Roll; Hon Roll; Mrktng.

DOUGLAS, JANET; Smith Acad; Hatfield, MA; (Y); VP Pres Drama Clb; School Musical; Variety Show; Yrbk Phtg; Trs Frsh Cls; VP Soph Cls; Capt Cheerleading; Sftbl; High Hon Roll; Hon Roll; Finance.

DOW, CHRISTOPHER; Cushing Acad; Leominster, MA; (Y); Am Leg Boys St; Boy Scts; Model UN; Var L Crs Cntry; JV Lcrss; Var L Trk; JV Wrstlng; Hon Roll; Im Socr; Sci Fair-1st Pl Chem-Physcs 83-84; Cntrl MA Sci Fair-Amer Chemcl Soc Awd 83-84; MA ST Sci Fair MIT.

DOW, ROBERT; Lynn Classical HS; Lynn, MA; (Y); Am Leg Boys St; Chess Clb; JA; Library Aide; VP Science Clb; Hon Roll; Frgn Lang.

DOWD, CHRIS; Bridgewater Raynham Reg HS; Bridgewater, MA; (Y); Am Leg Boys St; JV Wrstlng; High Hon Roll; Hon Roll; Engrng.

DOWNER, MICHAEL E; Trinton Regional HS; Salisbury, MA; (Y); 4/225; Rep Am Leg Boys St; Pres Church Yth Grp; Church Choir; JV Bsbl; JV Ice Hcky; Hon Roll; NHS; Westrn Civ Awd 81-82; Mondial Awd 84-85; West Point; Lwyr.

DOWNES, KATHARINE A; Milton Acad; Brookline, MA; (Y); Cmnty Wkr; Hosp Aide; Key Clb; Speech Tm; Nwsp Ed-Chief; Ntl Merit SF; Church Yth Grp; Intnl Clb; Latin Clb; NFL; State Chmpn Extmporns Spkng 83; Maxima Cum Laude Ntl Ltn Exam 82; Miss MA State Fnlst 84; Lbrl Arts.

DOWNES, MELISSA M; Milford HS; Milford, MA; (Y); 97/282; Pres Chorus; Orch; Stage Crew; Var Trk; Hon Roll; Trk Rookie Yr 83, Unsng Heroine 84; Engrng.

DOWNEY, MARY ELLEN; Girls Catholic HS; Melrose, MA; (Y); Cmnty Wkr; Political Wkr; School Play; Hon Roll.

DOWNEY, PATRICK; St Johns Prep; Peabody, MA; (Y); Drama Clb; School Play; Stage Crew; 2 Set Dgsn Awds & Stat Drama Fstvl Awd 85; Art.

DOWNIE, MARTIN; Classical HS; Springfield, MA; (Y); 2/413; Nwsp Rptr; Lit Mag; Rep Frsh Cls; Capt L Crs Cntry; High Hon Roll; Pres NHS; Sal; Syracuse U; Advrtsng.

DOWNING, KIMBERLY; Agawam HS; Agawam, MA; (Y); 15/340; VP Pres JA; Orch; High Hon Roll; Hon Roll; NHS; Spanish NHS.

DOWNING, TIMOTHY E; Catholic Memorial HS; Dedham, MA; (Y); Am Leg Boys St; Computer Clb; Key Clb; Spanish Clb; Rep Jr Cls; Pres Sr Cls; Pres Stu Cncl; Var L Ftbl; Wt Lftg; Hon Roll; ST Repr Boys ST 85; Pol Sci.

DOYLE, BETH; Archbishop Williams HS; Weymouth, MA; (Y); 18/210; Dance Clb; Drama Clb; Math Tm; School Musical; School Play; Stage Crew; Yrbk Stf; Hon Roll; Jr NHS; Rep For Vocation Day 85; Pre-Law.

DOYLE, CRAIG M; Waltham SR HS; Waltham, MA; (Y); Am Leg Boys St; Boys Clb Am; Church Yth Grp; Library Aide; JV Bsktbl; JV Socr; Var Tennis; Hon Roll; Jr NHS; Ntl Merit Ltr; Cty Wlthm Tnns Fnlst & Chmp 84-85.

DOYLE, KATHERINE; Mohawk Trail Regional HS; Ashfield, MA; (Y); Dance Clb; German Clb; Varsity Clb; Var Capt Crs Cntry; Var Trk; Hon Roll.

DOYLE JR, KENNETH J; Waltham SR HS; Waltham, MA; (Y); 22/630; Am Leg Boys St; Boys Clb Am; Church Yth Grp; Var Bsktbl; Var Socr; Hon Roll; Jr NHS; NHS; Ntl Hnr Roll 85; Ken Harding Awd-Soccer 85; Holy Cross.

DOYLE, MAUREEN; Rockland HS; Rockland, MA; (S); 11/276; Church Yth Grp; Ski Clb; Spanish Clb; Teachers Aide; Im Badmtn; JV Bsktbl; Stat Score Keeper; JV Stat Socr; Im Sftbl; Var Trk; U Of MA Amherst; Ed.

DOYLE, SAMANTHA; Bartlett HS; Webster, MA; (Y); Sec French Clb; Variety Show; Yrbk Stf; Var Crs Cntry; Var Capt Socr; Var Capt Trk; Accntng.

DRAGO, ELIZABETH C; Canton HS; Canton, MA; (Y); Church Yth Grp; French Clb; JV Cheerleading; Hon Roll; Boston Coll; Mgmt.

DRAKE, JOHN; Andover HS; Andover, MA; (Y); 110/464; Pep Clb; Yrbk Stf; Rep Frsh Cls; Rep Soph Cls; Rep Jr Cls; Var Capt Socr; Allied Chem Physics/Chem Awd 85; GCA Sci Awd 85; Worcester Polytech Inst; Engrng.

DRALEAUS, PENELOPE A; Leominster HS; Leominster, MA; (Y); 14/388; Library Aide; Office Aide; Elks Awd; High Hon Roll; Hon Roll; NHS; Pres Schlr; JR Mbr Of The Fortnightly Clb 84-85; Westbrok Coll; Comp Prog.

DRAPER, AMY; Dracut SR HS; Dracut, MA; (Y); Church Yth Grp; Hosp Aide; JV Bsktbl; JV Var Sftbl; Nursng.

DRAYTON, LISA A; Holy Family HS; New Bedford, MA; (Y); 17/59; JA; Yrbk Ed-Chief; Var JV Bsktbl; French Hon Soc; Hon Roll; Jr NHS; NHS; U Of Lowell; Crimnl Justc.

DRESCHER, SANDRA; Ayer SR HS; Ayer, MA; (Y); Pep Clb; Spanish Clb; Nwsp Stf; Yrbk Stf; Powder Puff Ftbl; Pol Ofcr.

DREVITCH, GARY; Malden HS; Malden, MA; (Y); 3/500; Key Clb; Scholastic Bowl; Variety Show; Nwsp Ed-Chief; Ed Lit Mag; Bowling; Hon Roll; NHS; Ntl Merit Ltr.

DREW, KRISTEN; Milford HS; Milford, MA; (Y); 20/286; Vllybl; High Hon Roll; Hon Roll; NHS; Fitchburg ST; Nrsg.

DREW, MICHELE; Lynn Classical HS; Lynn, MA; (Y); Church Yth Grp; Exploring; Hosp Aide; Office Aide; Pep Clb; Hon Roll; VP NHS; USAA Frgn Lang Awd 84; USAA Ldrshp Svc Awd 85.

DRISCOLL, KARIN; Wakefield HS; Wakefield, MA; (Y); DECA; Hosp Aide; Pep Clb; Hon Roll; Ctzns Schlrshp Fndtn 85; Burdett Clg Schlrshp 84; Burdett Coll; Fashn Merch.

DRISCOLL, KRISTINE; Methuen HS; Methuen, MA; (Y); 20/346; Trs Girl Scts; Intnl Clb; Model UN; Pep Clb; VP Stu Cncl; Var L Fld Hcky; Hon Roll; Sec NHS; Stu Advstry Cmte 84-86; Accntng.

DRISCOLL, MAURA; Revere HS; Revere, MA; (Y); 12/389; Cmnty Wkr; Political Wkr; Chorus; Yrbk Sprt Ed; Yrbk Stf; Sec Soph Cls; VP Jr Cls; Off Stu Cncl; Capt Cheerleading; Co-Capt Gym; Suffolk Bk Awd 84; Gym Coaches Awd 83-85; UCLA; Thetr Art.

DRISCOLL, SARAH; Stepherd Hill Regional HS; Dudley, MA; (Y); Church Yth Grp; Variety Show; Off Stu Cncl; Gym; Sftbl; Hon Roll; Math Tm; Chorus; Church Choir; Comp.

DROHAN, SUSAN; Bedford HS; Bedford, MA; (Y); Church Yth Grp; Civic Clb; Drm Mjr(t); Stat Ice Hcky; Var Swmmng; Var Twrlr; Hon Roll; Bus.

DROHAN, WILLIAM; Holyoke HS; Holyoke, MA; (Y); Church Yth Grp; Drama Clb; Latin Clb; Spanish Clb; Teachers Aide; School Play; Stage Crew; Yrbk Stf; JV Socr; Hon Roll; U Of MA.

DROUIN, SCOTT; Methuen HS; Methuen, MA; (Y); Hon Roll; Black Belt Ucchi-Ryu Karate Sys 84; U Lowell; Novelst.

DRUMM, GERALD; Lynn English HS; Lynn, MA; (Y); Boys Clb Am; Letterman Clb; Y-Teens; Socr; Hon Roll; Essex County All Stars Socr 84; Intl Socr Clb 84-85; Naval Rescue Schl; Fire Safety.

DRUMMOND, MAUREEN F; Monsignor Ryan Memorial HS; Dorchester, MA; (Y); 3/88; Cmnty Wkr; Drama Clb; Library Aide; Service Clb; Stage Crew; Yrbk Stf; Bowling; High Hon Roll; VP NHS; Prfct Atten Awd; U Of MA Chancllrs Schlrshp For Excllnc 85; U Of MA-BOSTON; Nrsng.

DRUMMY, PATTY; Fontbonne Acad; Dorchester, MA; (Y); Pres Church Yth Grp; Girl Scts; High Hon Roll; NHS; Drama Clb; Intnl Clb; Stage Crew; Variety Show; Prfct Atten Awd; Natl Latn Exm Magna Cum Laude; Old Dominion U; Ed.

DRURY, STEVEN J; Canton HS; Canton, MA; (Y); Am Leg Boys St; Boy Scts; Church Yth Grp; Political Wkr; Nwsp Stf; Rep Frsh Cls; Rep Soph Cls; Pres Sec Stu Cncl; Golf; Stu Cncl Awd 85.

DU PONT, CELESTE M; Lee HS; Lee, MA; (Y); French Clb; Teachers Aide; Band; Chorus; Church Choir; Concert Band; Drm Mjr(t); Mrchg Band; School Musical; Hon Roll; Scndry Ed.

DU PONT, YVONNE MARY; North Middlesex Regional HS; Pepperell, MA; (Y); 12/200; Church Yth Grp; Chorus; Jazz Band; Variety Show; Nwsp Stf; Hon Roll; Jr NHS; NHS; SADD 84-85; Tlntd & Gftd SR Intrn 84-85; Stardusters Schlrshp 85; MA ST Gnrl Schlrshp 85; U Of Lowell; Music.

DUARTE, PAULA; New Bedford HS; New Bedford, MA; (Y); 46/690; Trk; Hon Roll; NHS; Stu Congrss; Frgn Lang Clb; Bus.

DUBE, KAREN L; St Joseph Regional HS; Lowell, MA; (Y); Church Yth Grp; Hosp Aide; School Musical; Yrbk Ed-Chief; Rep Stu Cncl; Var Cheerleading; High Hon Roll; Sec NHS; Highest Bus Awd 85; Stu Cncl Schrshp 85; Nrthrn Essex Cmnty Coll; Secy.

DUBIN, DAWN; St Clare HS; Chestnut Hill, MA; (Y); 23/158; Chorus; School Musical; Hon Roll; 2nd Hghst Acad Avg Geom 83-84; Pol Offcr.

DUBIN, DEBORAH F; Dennis-Yarmouth Regional HS; E Dennis, MA; (Y); 2/316; Am Leg Aux Girls St; Political Wkr; Ski Clb; Temple Yth Grp; Nwsp Rptr; Yrbk Stf; Lit Mag; Pres Frsh Cls; Pres Stu Cncl; VP NHS; Congrssnl Page 83-84; Hugh O Brian Ldrshp Semnr 83; Big Sistr Prog; Pol Sci.

DUBOIS, KIMBERLEY; Bartlett HS; Webster, MA; (Y); 3/174; Camera Clb; Trs DECA; FBLA; JA; Nwsp Bus Mgr; Yrbk Bus Mgr; Cit Awd; High Hon Roll; Jr NHS; Sec NHS; Cert Of Awd Shrthd 84; Outstndng Schltc Achvt Awd Alumni Assoc 85; Nichls Pres & Achvt Awds 85; Nichols Clg; Acctg.

DUBREVIL, DONNA; Somerset HS; Somerset, MA; (Y); Girl Scts; Hosp Aide; Variety Show; Var Bsktbl; Var Crs Cntry; Score Keeper; Var Trk; High Hon Roll; NHS; U Of MA; Nrs.

DUBRULE, BRUCE G; Athol HS; Athol, MA; (Y); 36/120; Am Leg Boys St; Boy Scts; Church Yth Grp; Model UN; Chorus; Socr; Trk; Robtcs.

DUBY, CAROLYN; Bishop Connolly HS; Adamsville, RI; (S); 3/158; Drama Clb; Math Tm; Chorus; Church Choir; Var L Crs Cntry; Elks Awd; High Hon Roll; NHS; Ntl Merit Ltr; Miss Poise & Persnlty Martins Schl Of Mdlng 84; Wnnr Swansea Mall Phto Contst 84; Luther King Wnnr 82; Brown U; Pre-Med.

DUCHARME, DOUGLAS; Coyle And Cassidy HS; Taunton, MA; (Y); 14/146; Math Clb; Spanish Clb; Sec Frsh Cls; JV Bsbl; Var L Ftbl; Hon Roll; VP NHS; Spanish NHS; All Conf Tm Ftbl 84; John A Needs Awd Ftbl 84.

DUCLOS, ROSANNE; Leicester HS; Leicester, MA; (S); French Clb; Latin Clb; Math Clb; Math Tm; FL Inst Tech; Med.

DUCLOS, THEODORE; Leicester HS; Leicester, MA; (S); French Clb; Latin Clb; U Tampa; Acctng.

DUE, BRICE; Westford Acad; Westford, MA; (Y); Chess Clb; French Clb; Math Tm; Model UN; Jazz Band; Symp Band; Ntl Merit SF; Band; Mrchg Band; Pep Band; Nrthestrn Dist Bnd; Boston Musm Sci Smmr Sci Mentrshp-Comerics Inc 84; Cabot Fndtn Sci Smnrs 83; Physcs.

DUFAULT, DANIEL; Central Catholic HS; Pelham, NH; (Y); 100/260; Art Clb; Church Yth Grp; JA; Band; Concert Band; Jazz Band; School Play; Nwsp Stf; Yrbk Stf; JV Ftbl; Bicyl Motocrss Racg 65 Troph 83-84; U Of NH; Med.

DUFF, RONALD; Bartlett HS; Webster, MA; (Y); 7/170; Pres French Clb; Science Clb; Bausch & Lomb Sci Awd; High Hon Roll; NHS; NEDT Awd; Cranstn Fndtn-G Rockefeller Memrl Schlrshp 85; Normandy Clb Schlrshp 85; G H Bartlett Prz Engl 85; Holy Cross Coll; Pre-Med.

DUFFLEY, SANDRA; Sacred Heart HS; Weymouth, MA; (Y); Variety Show; Yrbk Stf; Hon Roll; Exclnce Typing I 85; Svc Awd 85; Cape Cod CC; Htl/Mtl Mgt.

DUFFY, BRIAN; Bridgewater Raynham HS; Bridgewater, MA; (Y); Boy Scts; Camera Clb; Math Tm; Ski Clb; Band; Concert Band; Jazz Band; Mrchg Band; Hon Roll; Ntl Merit Ltr; Boston U; Engr.

DUFFY, ELENA M; Ursuline Acad; Walpole, MA; (Y); 43/70; Drama Clb; Leo Clb; Spanish Clb; Thesps; Chorus; Church Choir; School Play; Stage Crew; Yrbk Stf; Hon Roll; Spnsh Cert Of Achvt 83; Hon Mntn Postr Cntst 83; Fshn Dsgn.

DUFFY, MARY KATE; Marian HS; Natick, MA; (Y); Cmnty Wkr; Hosp Aide; Office Aide; Ski Clb; Teachers Aide; Yrbk Stf; Var Mgr(s); Hon Roll; Elem Schl Tchr.

DUFFY, THERESA; East Boston HS; E Boston, MA; (Y); Dance Clb; Drama Clb; Cheerleading; Hon Roll; Boston U; Jrnlsm.

DUFFY JR, THOMAS J; Norwood HS; Norwood, MA; (Y); 58/323; Am Leg Boys St; Key Clb; Yrbk Ed-Chief; Off Chrmn Frsh Cls; VP Soph Cls; VP Jr Cls; VP Sr Cls; Rep Stu Cncl; Trk; Hon Roll; Tn TV Dirctr Camramn/Swtchr 85-86alchl Awrns Cmmte 84-86; Schl Cmmte Stu Govt Dy, Sptlght Pgm 85.

DUFFY, WILLIAM J; Oliver Ames HS; South Easton, MA; (Y); 1/278; Am Leg Boys St; Cmnty Wkr; Math Clb; Model UN; Lit Mag; L Socr; Var Trk; Elks Awd; High Hon Roll; Hon Roll; Worcester Polytechnic Inst.

DUFRESNE, CELESTE; New Bedford HS; New Bedford, MA; (Y); 10/688; VP Exploring; Political Wkr; Teachers Aide; Nwsp Rptr; Nwsp Sprt Ed; Nwsp Stf; Lit Mag; Stu Cncl; High Hon Roll; NHS.

DUGAS, AMY E; Shepherd Hill Regional HS; Charlton, MA; (Y); 19/156; Camp Fr Inc; Church Yth Grp; Band; Flag Corp; School Play; Stu Cncl; Cheerleading; Hon Roll; Booster Clb Scholar Awd 85; U MA Amherst; Microbio.

DUGGAN, ANN; North Quincy HS; Quincy, MA; (Y); 7/400; Math Tm; Var Capt Bsktbl; Var Capt Sftbl; Var Capt Vllybl; Elks Awd; French Hon Soc; High Hon Roll; Jr NHS; Spanish NHS; Voice Dem Awd; Sub Lg All Schltc Vllybl Tm 83 & 84; Channel 7 Suprstar Awd 85; Pres Acad Fit Awd 85; Northeastern U; Phys Ther.

DUGGAN, KATHY; St Columbkille HS; Brighton, MA; (Y); 2/60; Yrbk Rptr; Yrbk Stf; Sec Frsh Cls; Trs Soph Cls; Pres Jr Cls; Bausch & Lomb Sci Awd; French Hon Soc; Hon Roll; NHS; Val; Typng, Theolgy, Sci, Engl & Comp Awds 85; Monsgnr Daly & MA Cmmnwlth Schlrshps 85; Boston Coll; Lbrl Arts.

DUKES, JOHN; Braintree HS; Braintree, MA; (Y); JV Bsktbl; Hon Roll; Bus.

DULCHINOS, DEAN; Holyoke HS; Holyoke, MA; (Y); Drama Clb; French Clb; Latin Clb; Nwsp Ed-Chief; Yrbk Ed-Chief; High Hon Roll; Jr NHS; NHS; Ntl Merit SF; School Play; Rensselaer Math & Sci Awd 85; Engnrng.

DULONG, SUSAN; Apponequet Regional HS; East Freetown, MA; (Y); 20/230; Church Yth Grp; Drama Clb; Church Choir; Jazz Band; School Musical; Symp Band; Variety Show; Var Capt Twrlr; Hon Roll; NHS; Apponequet Music Boosters Schlrshp 84-85; Apponequet Drama Clb Awd 85; Rgnl Schl Committee Acad Awd 85; Music.

DULONG, SUZANNE; Billerica Memorial HS; Billerica, MA; (Y); 37/500; French Clb; Ski Clb; Stage Crew; Yrbk Stf; Var Capt Socr; Var L Trk; Hon Roll; Boston U; Eng.

DUMAS, MIRIAM; King Philip Reg HS; Norfolk, MA; (S); Church Yth Grp; French Clb; Math Tm; Capt Crs Cntry; Trk; Hon Roll; NHS; Winter Track Capt Vrsty 84-85; Natl Histy Day Regnls 85; Phy Thrpy.

DUMAS, PAUL; Northbridge JR-SR HS; Whitinsville, MA; (S); 1/160; Am Leg Boys St; Latin Clb; Ski Clb; Yrbk Stf; Stu Cncl; High Hon Roll; NHS; Regnl & ST Stdnt Advsry Cmmttee 85; Bio.

DUNCAN, TAMMY; Somerset HS; Somerset, MA; (Y); Boys Clb Am; Church Yth Grp; Debate Tm; Teachers Aide; Chorus; School Play; Stage Crew; Nwsp Phtg; High Hon Roll; Hon Roll; Nrsng.

DUNCAN, THOMAS W; Lincoln-Sudbury HS; Sudbury, MA; (Y); Var Capt Gym; Var L Lcrss; Var L Socr; Skidmore Coll; Elect Engrng.

DUNHAM JR, WILLIAM H; Apponequet HS; Lakeville, MA; (Y); Church Yth Grp; Cmnty Wkr; Ftbl; Var L Trk; Wt Lftg; Hon Roll; NHS.

DUNIGAN, KATHLEEN; Lowell HS; Lowell, MA; (Y); 5/800; VP Intnl Clb; VP JA; JCL; Science Clb; Rep Spanish Clb; Nwsp Ed-Chief; High Hon Roll; NHS; Church Yth Grp; Latin Clb; Cum Laude Natl Latn Exm 83 & 84; Pre-Law.

DUNLAP, JOHN D; Arlington HS; Arlington, MA; (Y); Am Leg Boys St; Drama Clb; School Musical; Yrbk Stf; Sec Stu Cncl; Stu Advsry Cmmttee 82-86; Stu Rep To Schl Cmmttee 84-85; Pre-Law.

DUNLAP, KIMBERLY B; Norton HS; Norton, MA; (Y); Yrbk Ed-Chief; Sec Stu Cncl; Co-Capt Cheerleading; Hosp Aide; Pep Clb; Band; Color Guard; Rep Frsh Cls; Rep Soph Cls; Co-Capt Pom Pon; Emblem Clb Schlrshp 85; US Chrldng Assn Ntl Chmpn 84y; Northeastern U; Phy Thrpy.

DUNN, CHARLES; Chelmsford HS; Chelmsford, MA; (S); 200/565; Boy Scts; Church Yth Grp; DECA; Ftbl; High Hon Roll; Hon Roll; Johnson & Wales Coll; Hotel Mgt.

DUNN, DARLENE; Shawsheen Valley HS; Bedford, MA; (Y); 4/400; Off VICA; Yrbk Stf; Stu Cncl; High Hon Roll; Hon Roll; VICA Outstndng Ldrshp Awd 84; Stdnt Advsry Cncl Regnl Rep 85-86; Intl Ordr Rainbw Grls 80-85; Bus Adm.

DUNN, DIANE; St Bernards Cc HS; Fitch, MA; (S); 16/176; Ski Clb; Socr; Trk; Hon Roll; Daughters Isabella Schlrshp 82; Soccer League All Stars 83; Tufts U; Veterinarian.

DUNN, KATHRYN LEE; Dennis-Yarmouth Regional HS; West Yarmouth, MA; (S); 16/316; Am Leg Aux Girls St; Model UN; Varsity Clb; Band; Drm Mjr(t); School Musical; Var Capt Cheerleading; Hon Roll; NHS; Holy Cross Book Awd; Dennis Yarmouths JR Miss 85; Boston Coll; Intl Bus.

DUNN, TOM; Marlboro HS; Marlboro, MA; (Y); 16/350; Boys Clb Am; Church Yth Grp; Ski Clb; Var L Trk; High Hon Roll; NHS; Varsity Clb; JV Crs Cntry; Elks Awd; Fclty Awd Outstndng Achvt Art 83-84; Elec Engnr.

DUNNE, CHARLES M; Waltham HS; Waltham, MA; (Y); Am Leg Boys St; JCL; Spanish Clb; Var Lcrss; Var Wrstlng; Hon Roll; Boys Clb Am; JV Ice Hcky; JV Socr; Coaches Awd Wrstlng 85; 7th Plyr Awd Hockey 83-84; U S Naval Acad; Pol Sci.

DUNNE, PATRICK R; Holliston HS; Holliston, MA; (Y); Am Leg Boys St; Variety Show; Im Badmtn; High Hon Roll; Hon Roll; NHS; Acad Ltr; Acad Achvt Gold Ltr Silver Ltr; Elect Engr.

DUONG, VI; Boston Latin Schl; Boston, MA; (Y); French Clb; Intnl Clb; Key Clb; Science Clb; Hon Roll; Cty Of Boston Rdg Arts Cert 85; Concours De Francais Des Cooperants 84; Intl Rel.

DUPONT, ROBERT; Billerica Memorial HS; Billerica, MA; (Y); 23/465; Exploring; French Clb; Yrbk Stf; Var Crs Cntry; Var L Trk; Hon Roll; Ntl Merit Ltr; St Schlr; Im Bowling; U Of Lowell; Elec Engr.

DUPREY, CHERYL; Groton-Dunstable Rgnl Scndry Schl; W Groton, MA; (Y); Girl Scts; Office Aide; Band; Mrchg Band; Yrbk Stf; Wt Lftg; High Hon Roll; Hon Roll; Honry Typg Awd 84-85; Csmtlgy.

DUPREY, PAUL; Weymouth South HS; Weymouth, MA; (Y); 24/340; Am Leg Boys St; Church Yth Grp; Church Choir; Rep Frsh Cls; Rep Soph Cls; Rep Jr Cls; Rep Sr Cls; Var L Bsktbl; Capt Var Socr; Var L Trk; Acad Achvt Schlrshp 85; MVP Soccr 85; MIP 85; Bentley Coll; Bus Adm.

DUPUIS, MICHAEL; Tahanto Regional HS; Boylston, MA; (Y); 3/60; Am Leg Boys St; Pres Church Yth Grp; Math Clb; Math Tm; L Bsktbl; High Hon Roll; St Schlr; MA U Amherst; Engr.

DUQUETTE, JOAN; Monson JR SR HS; Wilbraham, MA; (Y); 13/90; French Clb; Yrbk Stf; Hon Roll; Pres Schlr; Framingham ST Col6; Soclgy.

DUQUETTE, MARIE L; Chicopee HS; Chicopee, MA; (Y); 11/300; Aud/Vis; Library Aide; Color Guard; Nwsp Stf; Yrbk Stf; Var Trk; High Hon Roll; Hon Roll.

DURAND, DANIELLE L; Quaboag Regional HS; Warren, MA; (Y); Church Yth Grp; Hosp Aide; JA; Trs Jr Cls; Trs Sr Cls; Cheerleading; Sec NHS; Pre Law.

DURLACK, CHERYL; Monument Mountain HS; Gr Barrington, MA; (Y); 23/117; Art Clb; Dance Clb; Spanish Clb; Hon Roll; FL Inst Of Tech; Marine Sci.

DUROCHER, STEPHEN A; Holy Name Central Catholic HS; Leicester, MA; (Y); 15/240; Church Yth Grp; Drama Clb; JA; School Musical; School Play; Yrbk Stf; L Var Golf; Hon Roll; NHS; Science Clb; MA Hnr Schlr 85; Worcester Poly Inst; Aero Engnr.

DURONIO, SHARON; Franklin HS; Franklin, MA; (Y); Church Yth Grp; Math Tm; OEA; Trs Frsh Cls; Trs Soph Cls; Trs Jr Cls; Stu Cncl; High Hon Roll; Hon Roll; NHS; Rensselaer Polytchnc Inst Sci & Math Awd85; Math.

DUSO, DOROTHY; Bartlett HS; Webster, MA; (Y); 7/150; Sec Exploring; French Clb; Spanish Clb; Band; Concert Band; Mrchg Band; Yrbk Stf; Tennis; High Hon Roll; NHS; Cert Ed Devl 82-84; Nrsg.

DUSSEAULT, GRACE; Shepherd Hill Regional HS; Dudley, MA; (Y); Trs Church Yth Grp; JV Var Bsktbl; JV Sftbl; High Hon Roll; NHS; Frmngham ST Coll; Dietician.

DUTRA, ROBYN; Natick HS; Natick, MA; (Y); Cmnty Wkr; JA; Stu Cncl; Var L Trk; Hon Roll; Vrsty Lttr-Track 84; Busnss Awd-Typing 84; U MA; Merchndsng.

DUVAL, CHERYL; Holyoke Catholic HS; S Hadley, MA; (Y); 35/140; Church Yth Grp; Exploring; French Clb; Latin Clb; Chorus; Church Choir; Color Guard; Stage Crew; Yrbk Stf; Lit Mag; Spec Educ.

DUVAL, STEPHEN; Leominster HS; Leominster, MA; (Y); Am Leg Boys St; Rep Stu Cncl; Var Bsktbl; High Hon Roll; Pres NHS; Outstndng Bio Achvt 85; Karate Brwn Blt 83; MA Coll Of Phrmcy; Phrmcy.

DWORMAN, SCOTT; Chapel Hill Chauncy Hall HS; Framingham, MA; (Y); Temple Yth Grp; Chorus; Orch; School Musical; Stage Crew; Nwsp Stf; Var Tennis; Var Trk; Hon Roll; Hgh Excllnc Spansh Stu.

DWYER, KIMBERLY; Bellingham Mem HS; Bellingham, MA; (S); 14/201; Trs DECA; Trs Chorus; Yrbk Sprt Ed; L Tennis; Capt L Vllybl; High Hon Roll; Hon Roll; Jr NHS; NHS; Pres Schlr; MASS-DECA Shclrshp 85; Bellingham DECA Schlrshp 85; Stu Cncl Ldrshp Schlrshp 85; Coll Of Holy Cross.

DWYER, MARTHA; Norwell HS; Norwell, MA; (Y); 2/175; French Clb; Concert Band; Jazz Band; Mrchg Band; Orch; School Musical; Nwsp Stf; High Hon Roll; NHS; Ntl Merit SF; Acad All Amer Awd 85; Music Thrpy.

DYE, MICHAEL; Brokcton HS; Brockton, MA; (Y); 66/1150; German Clb; Stage Crew; Nwsp Stf; Trs Jr Cls; JV Socr; Var Wrstlng; Hon Roll; Advncd Plcmnt Am Hstry-Recvd A; Frgn Affrs.

DYER, KAREN; Braintree HS; Braintree, MA; (Y); 143/432; Church Yth Grp; Yrbk Stf; Cheerleading; Pom Pon; High Hon Roll; Hon Roll; Spanish NHS; Pep Clb; Spanish Clb; Nrsg.

DYER, MELISSA; Governor Dummer Acad; Georgetown, MA; (Y); 9/88; VP Church Yth Grp; Dance Clb; Drama Clb; Ski Clb; Church Choir; Ed Nwsp Stf; Ed Yrbk Stf; Capt JV Socr; JV Tennis; Hon Roll; MVP Sccr 84.

DYM, JORDANA; Northampton HS; Northampton, MA; (Y); 1/250; Co-Capt Quiz Bowl; VP Thesps; School Musical; Stage Crew; Nwsp Ed-Chief; Lit Mag; High Hon Roll; NCTE Awd; NHS; Ntl Merit SF; Brown Bk Awd 84.

DZIEL, JOHN; Chicopee HS; Chicopee, MA; (Y); JV Bsktbl.

DZIGAS, JAY J; Marlboro HS; Marlboro, MA; (Y); 50/320; Am Leg Boys St; Key Clb; Ski Clb; Varsity Clb; Band; Variety Show; Trs Jr Cls; Pres Stu Cncl; Capt Trk; Underclsmn Band Awd 83-85; PA ST U; Meteorlgy.

EAGAN, SEAN F; Falmouth HS; Mashpee, MA; (Y); Key Clb; Spanish Clb; Band; Mrchg Band; Bsktbl; High Hon Roll; Hon Roll; NHS.

EARLY, JILL M; St Louis Acad; Lowell, MA; (Y); 3/32; Church Yth Grp; Drama Clb; French Clb; Band; Chorus; Orch; Pres Sr Cls; High Hon Roll; NHS; Stu Govt Day Rep 85; Schl Fund Drv Chairprsn 82; U Of Lowell; Schl Tchr.

EARVOLINO, PATRICK J; Holliston HS; Holliston, MA; (Y); Am Leg Boys St; Mgr(s); High Hon Roll; NHS; Rensselaer Medal Math,Sci 84-85; Ltr Acad 84-85; Med.

EASLER, ERIK; Blackstone Valley Tech; Milford, MA; (Y); Hon Roll; Central New England Coll; Comp.

EAST, KRISTEN; Christopher Columbus HS; Boston, MA; (Y); 27/132; Hosp Aide; VP JA; Y-Teens; Variety Show; Rep Frsh Cls; Rep Jr Cls; Stu Cncl; Socr; Swmmng; Hon Roll; Hghst Spnsh Avg For Yr 83-84; Educ Dev At The Lcl Norm Of 80% Or Abv 83-84; American U; Crmnl Jstc.

EASTMAN, CHRISTINE; Holbrook HS; Holbrook, MA; (Y); 2/102; Latin Clb; Chorus; School Musical; Trk; Hon Roll; Pres NHS; Harvard Book Awd 85; Nrsng.

EASTMAN, KRISTINE; Westford Acad; Cumberland, RI; (Y); Hosp Aide; Ski Clb; Cheerleading; Fld Hcky; Gym; Sftbl; Hon Roll.

EASTMAN, TOBY D; Wellesley HS; Roxbury, MA; (Y); 57/315; Cmnty Wkr; JV Sftbl; Hon Roll; Natl Achvmnt Schlrshp Prgm 84; METCO Awd 84; Comm.

EATON, NANCY L; Bellingham Memorial JR SR HS; Bellingham, MA; (Y); 23/201; Drama Clb; German Clb; Vllybl; High Hon Roll; Hon Roll; Pres Schlr; Boys Clb Am; DECA; Ski Clb; Intl Order Rainbow Grls Schlrshp, Bellingham Stu Actvty Fund Schlrshp 85; MA U Amherst; Astronomy.

EBERSOLE, KIRSTEN M; Bedford HS; Bedford, MA; (Y); 48/218; VP AFS; Girl Scts; Church Choir; Var Mgr Bsbl; Var Mgr Socr; JV Mgr Swmmng; Hon Roll; Scndry Tchng.

ECCLESTON, MISTIE L; Uxbridge HS; Uxbridge, MA; (Y); Art Clb; Stu Cncl; NHS; Chrstn Herter Schlrshp 83; Flagler Coll; Deaf Educ.

ECHEVARRIA, LISA; Norton HS; Norton, MA; (Y); 25/170; Ski Clb; Spanish Clb; Chorus; Flag Corp; Mrchg Band; Yrbk Stf; Sec Rep Stu Cncl; High Hon Roll; Hon Roll; Top Seller Fund Raiser 82-83; Prfct Atten Marchng Band 82-83; Simmons Coll.

EDDY, MARTHA; North Middlesex HS; Pepperell, MA; (Y); 38/185; Church Yth Grp; GAA; Library Aide; Varsity Clb; Variety Show; Yrbk Stf; Var Crs Cntry; Var Trk; Hon Roll; Prfct Atten Awd; Hmrm Rep 84; U MA Amherst.

EDDY, SUSAN; Natick HS; South Natick, MA; (Y); 56/458; Pep Clb; Ski Clb; Spanish Clb; Chorus; School Musical; School Play; Variety Show; Stu Cncl; High Hon Roll; Hon Roll; Bus Awd Typng 83; U Or RI; Cnsmr Affrs.

EDRY, MARK J; Acton Boxborough Regional HS; Acton, MA; (Y); 20/354; AFS; Drama Clb; Radio Clb; Hon Roll; NHS; Ntl Merit SF; Lettered H S Radio Station Music Dir 83; Comp Sci.

EDSON, KIMBERLEY; Chatham JR SR HS; W Chatham, MA; (Y); 9/50; AFS; Church Yth Grp; Drama Clb; Girl Scts; Ski Clb; School Play; Stage Crew; Yrbk Stf; Cheerleading; Fld Hcky; Accntng.

EDSON, MICHAEL R; Athol HS; Athol, MA; (Y); 1/135; Am Leg Boys St; Bausch & Lomb Sci Awd; High Hon Roll; NHS; Ntl Merit Ltr; Pres Schlr; Val; Model UN; Nwsp Stf; Var L Golf; MVP Vrsty Golf 84 & 85; Gld Plaq-4 Yrs Al A's 85; 1st Pl AHS Sci Fair 85; Math & Sci Dept Awd 85; Williams Coll; Psychtrst.

EDWARDS, BRUCE L; Hampshire Regional HS; Haydenville, MA; (Y); 19/111; Am Leg Boys St; Hon Roll; Aerosp Engrng.

EDWARDS, JOHN; Matlgnon HS; Arlington, MA; (S); 12/200; Drama Clb; French Hon Soc; Hon Roll; NHS.

EDWARDS, SANDRA; Shepherd Hill Regioanl HS; Dudley, MA; (Y); 24/158; Pres 4-H; Var Math Tm; School Musical; Pres Stu Cncl; Tennis; Cit Awd; 4-H Awd; High Hon Roll; NHS; Ntl Merit Ltr; Pres Acad Fit Awd 85; Fin Miss MA Coed Pag 85; USMA Invtitnl Acad Wrkshp 84; U MA Amherst; Legal.

EDWARDS, THOMAS M; Scituate HS; Scituate, MA; (Y); 20/294; Am Leg Boys St; Computer Clb; Pres Frsh Cls; Pres Soph Cls; Rep Stu Cncl; Var Bsktbl; Var Ftbl; Var Trk; Hon Roll; NHS; W Pt Smmr Scntfc Smnr 85; Nvl Acad Smmr Scntfc Smnr 85; Engrng.

EGELSTROM, ERIC; Holbrook HS; Holbrook, MA; (Y); 28/102; Bsktbl; Var Socr; Var Trk; Bentley; Acctng.

EGERTON JR, ARTHUR E; Silver Lake Regional HS; Pembroke, MA; (Y); 9/457; Boy Scts; Debate Tm; Camp Fr Inc; Library Aide; Office Aide; Ski Clb; Band; Jazz Band; Yrbk Phtg; Sr Cls; Gen Dynmcs Quincy Mgmt Assn Schlrhsp 85; Sons Itly Schlrshp 85; Allegheny Coll; Pre Med.

EICHORN, BONNIE; Drury SR HS; N Adams, MA; (Y); 51/185; English Clb; Pep Clb; Spanish Clb; Nwsp Rptr; Bsktbl; Mgr Ftbl; Trk; Hon Roll; Hartwick Coll; Jrnslm.

ELA, HOLLY; Ayer HS; Ayer, MA; (Y); 3/160; Sec Computer Clb; Chrmn Model UN; Sec Acpl Chr; Capt Color Guard; School Play; Ntl Merit Schol; Pres Schlr; Drama Clb; Spanish Clb; Chorus; Chncllrs Tlnt Schlrshp 85; MA Hnr Schlrshp 85; Cntrl Dist, All St & Natl Chrl Awd 85; U MA Amherst; Mus Educ.

ELDER, MARK; Hudson HS; Hudson, MA; (Y); Political Wkr; Ski Clb; Off Sr Cls; Stu Cncl; JV Ftbl; Hon Roll; Engrng.

ELDREDGE, MARCIA ANN; Chatham HS; Chatham, MA; (Y); 16/52; Drama Clb; Ski Clb; Nwsp Ed-Chief; Nwsp Phtg; Yrbk Phtg; Yrbk Sprt Ed; Crs Cntry; Tennis; Vllybl; Hon Roll.

ELDRIDGE, MARY E; Westwood HS; Westwood, MA; (Y); 106/221; 4-H; Key Clb; Office Aide; Chorus; Yrbk Stf; Var L Fld Hcky; 4-H Awd; Hon Roll; School Play; Virginia Burke Awd 85; Sr Music Awd 85; Framingham Union Hosp; Nrsng.

ELDRIDGE, PAMELA; Wakefield HS; Wakefield, MA; (Y); 32/305; Church Yth Grp; Yrbk Stf; Crs Cntry; Trk; U VT; Lib Arts.

ELGUEZABAL, LUIS; Marian HS; Framingham, MA; (Y); CAP; Yrbk Sprt Ed; Ftbl; Sec NHS; VP Spanish NHS; SADD 84-85; Engr.

ELIAS, KAREN; Methuen HS; Methuen, MA; (Y); 30/350; Dance Clb; Pres French Clb; Hosp Aide; Intnl Clb; Teachers Aide; Score Keeper; Vllybl; French Hon Soc; High Hon Roll; Hon Roll; Boston Coll; Bus Adm.

ELLIOTT, HEIDI J; Milford HS; Milford, MA; (Y); 16/305; Drama Clb; Hosp Aide; Chorus; Stage Crew; Var Capt Tennis; High Hon Roll; NHS; Syracuse U; Jrnlsm.

ELLIS, JENEPHER; Mauset Regional HS; S Orleans, MA; (Y); Stage Crew; Nwsp Stf; Yrbk Ed-Chief; Coach Actv; Gym; Trk; 2nd Pl MA Mth Olympiad 85; Jrnlsm.

ELLIS, MAUREEN; St Clement HS; Somerville, MA; (Y); Office Aide; Varsity Clb; Y-Teens; Hon Roll; VP NHS; St Clements Mothers Club Decsd Membrs Schlrshp 84; St Clements Priests Schlarhp 85; Med.

ELLIS, MICHAEL G; Nowell HS; Norwell, MA; (Y); 50/184; Am Leg Boys St; Church Yth Grp; FCA; Ed Yrbk Stf; Rep Soph Cls; Rep Jr Cls; Rep Sr Cls; Rep Stu Cncl; JV Bsbl; Var L Bsktbl; Bst Plyr Sthshr Sccr Leag 84; Boston Glob 84; Al-Estrn MA, Al-Star Sccr Tm 84; Al-Schlstc Sccr Tm 84; Pre-Law.

ELSTER, MICHAEL; St Johns HS; Shrewsbury, MA; (Y); 50/272; Am Leg Boys St; Church Yth Grp; VP JA; Model UN; Ski Clb; Nwsp Rptr; Var Capt Socr; High Hon Roll; NHS; Bus.

EMERY, AMY; Pentucket Regional HS; Merrimac, MA; (Y); 27/179; Hon Roll; Lion Awd; Chorus; School Play; Stage Crew; Rep Soph Cls; Rep Jr Cls; Pres Awd Svc Schl & Cls 85; Merrimac PTO Schlrshp 85; Male Hosp Aux Schlrshp 85; U RI; Phrmcy.

EMILIA, DINO D; Bridgewater-Raynham Regional HS; Bridgewater, MA; (Y); Hosp Aide; Ski Clb; Stu Cncl; Ftbl; Engrng.

ENCE, HEIDI; Doherty Memorial HS; Worcester, MA; (Y); Pres Church Yth Grp; Latin Clb; Chorus; Church Choir; Yrbk Stf; L Socr; High Hon Roll; Hon Roll; Jr NHS; Ntl Merit SF; Eng Essay Wnnr 85; Summitteer Awd 85; Yng Womanhd Recgn Awd 85; Brigham Young U.

ENDERLE, PAUL; Agawam HS; Feeding Hls, MA; (Y); 3/350; Boy Scts; Church Yth Grp; JA; Ski Clb; Church Choir; Yrbk Stf; Im Bsbl; Var L Swmmng; French Hon Soc; NHS; Pres Awd BS Energy Ed & Conservtn Pgm 82; Cty Bsbl Champs Trphy 83; Outstndng Alter Boys Awd 82; Air Force Acad; Cmmrcl Pilot.

ENGEL, LAURA M; Bay Path Voc HS; Southbridge, MA; (Y); 3/158; High Hon Roll; Hon Roll; NHS; Stu Mth Fshn Dsgn 85; Outstndng Stu Fshn Dsgn & Engl Awds 85; Missnry.

ENNEGUESS, MARK; Maynard HS; Maynard, MA; (Y); 16/100; Boys Clb Am; Radio Clb; Band; Chorus; Color Guard; Concert Band; Jazz Band; Mrchg Band; Bsbl; Ftbl; Worcester Polytech Inst; Engrng.

ENO, JOANE M; Bellingham Memorial HS; Bellingham, MA; (Y); 46/200; DECA; Ski Clb; Varsity Clb; Yrbk Stf; VP Jr Cls; VP Sr Cls; Rep Stu Cncl; Var L Fld Hcky; Var L Trk; Hon Roll; Frnch Cert 83; Spnsh Cert 84; D P Cert 85; U AZ; Crmnl Jstc.

ENOS, ERIC; Taunton HS; Taunton, MA; (Y); 40/451; Church Yth Grp; Library Aide; Yrbk Stf; Hon Roll; Ntl Merit Ltr; Magna Cum Laude Cert Natl Latin Exam 83; Interpreter.

ENOS, KERRIE; Bishop Connolly HS; Westport, MA; (Y); Drama Clb; Hosp Aide; School Play; Stage Crew; Var Cheerleading; Hon Roll; Pre-Med.

ENRIGHT, MICHELE; Silver Lake Regional HS; Plympton, MA; (Y); 120/511; French Clb; Yrbk Bus Mgr; Hon Roll; French.

ENXUGA, ROSE; N B HS; New Bedford, MA; (Y); 64/688; Nrsng.

ERAMO, ANTHONY; Haverhill HS; Haverhill, MA; (Y); 69/425; Capt VP Bsbl; VP Ice Hcky; Capt VP Socr; High Hon Roll; Hon Roll; Bentley Coll; Accntng.

ERB, DAVID A; Leominster HS; Leominster, MA; (Y); 13/450; Rep Am Leg Boys St; Boy Scts; Office Aide; Service Clb; Teachers Aide; Variety Show; Yrbk Stf; JV Trk; High Hon Roll; NHS; Cls Awd Citznshp,Schlshp 85; Mayo Awd Exc Acctng 85; Grad Hnrs 85; Bentley Coll; Acctng.

ERDLEN, KRISTEN; Dana Hall HS; Wellesley, MA; (Y); Hosp Aide; Key Clb; Teachers Aide; Rep Frsh Cls; Var Bsktbl; Fld Hcky; Lcrss; High Hon Roll; Hon Roll; NHS; Pre-Med.

EREKSON, MELISSA; Danvers HS; Danvers, MA; (Y); 7/350; Science Clb; Spanish Clb; Thesps; Capt Flag Corp; Yrbk Stf; High Hon Roll; NHS; Spanish NHS; Church Yth Grp; Civic Clb; Drtmth Bwl 85; 1st Rnr-Up Ms Tn Schlrshp Pgnt 85; ST Sci Olympd; Spnsh.

ERICKSEN, MICHELLE A; Uxbridge HS; Uxbridge, MA; (Y); Church Yth Grp; Yrbk Stf; JV Var Fld Hcky; Score Keeper; Hon Roll; NHS; Pres Schlr; Krull Schlrshp 85; Presntl Ftnss Awd 85; Calvin Coll; Phys Thrpy.

ERICKSON, GARY; Malden Catholic HS; Malden, MA; (Y); 4/180; Nwsp Sprt Ed; Rep Soph Cls; Rep Jr Cls; Rep Stu Cncl; JV Bsbl; Capt Var Bsktbl; High Hon Roll; Kiwanis Awd; Ntl Merit Ltr; Rotary Awd; Math.

ERICKSON, HARLEY A; Harwich HS; N Harwich, MA; (Y); Drama Clb; Pres 4-H; Spanish Clb; School Musical; High Hon Roll; NHS; Harvard Book Prz 85; Biol.

ERICKSON, JOHN; Milford HS; Milford, MA; (Y); 44/292; JV Bsbl; Var JV Ftbl; Var Trk; High Hon Roll; Hon Roll; NHS; Arch.

ERICKSON, JULIE; Stoughton HS; Stoughton, MA; (Y); 141/365; Lit Mag; Rep Frsh Cls; Rep Soph Cls; Rep Jr Cls; Rep Sr Cls; Capt L Cheerleading; L Trk; Hon Roll; Mst Vlbl Chrldr 85; SR Athlt Awd 85; Notre Dame MD; Pre-Law.

ERICKSON, LORRE; Gardner HS; Gardner, MA; (Y); Art Clb; Chess Clb; L Trk; Hon Roll; Musician.

ERICSON, MARK; Westford Acad; Westford, MA; (Y); 75/220; Boy Scts; German Clb; Concert Band; Jazz Band; Var Capt Bsktbl; Var Capt Ftbl; Var L Trk; Wt Lftg; Hon Roll; Engrng.

ESCOBAR, CARA; Bishop Connolly HS; Portsmouth, RI; (S); 25/158; Drama Clb; VP JA; Math Tm; Chorus; School Play; Yrbk Stf; High Hon Roll; NHS; NEDT Awd; Comp Sci.

ESCOBAR, PAUL G; Somerset HS; Somerset, MA; (Y); 7/299; Boy Scts; Pres Church Yth Grp; Co-Capt Debate Tm; VP French Clb; Co-Capt Math Tm; Concert Band; NHS; NEDT Awd; VP JA; Band; Marjorie Sells Carter Boy Sct Schlrshp 85; Natl Eagle Sct Schlrshp 85; Yale U; Law.

ESPANOLA, DIANA; Phillips Acad; Natick, MA; (Y); Var Bsktbl; JV Fld Hcky; Var Sftbl; Hon Roll.

ESPER, KRISTIN ANN; Leominster HS; Leominster, MA; (Y); 3/401; Office Aide; School Musical; Yrbk Phtg; Yrbk Stf; Rep Frsh Cls; Rep Soph Cls; Cheerleading; High Hon Roll; NHS; Prfct Atten Awd; Admssns Ofc 82-83; Fortnightly Club 84; MA Commnwlth Schlr 85; Holy Cross Coll; Spnsh.

ESPINOLA, CLIFFORD; New Bedford HS; New Bedford, MA; (Y); 24/700; Coach Actv; Ftbl; Golf; Score Keeper; Var Trk; Var Wt Lftg; Cit Awd; High Hon Roll; Hon Roll; Voice Dem Awd; Chem.

ESPOSITO, KRISTIN; Wakefield HS; Wakefield, MA; (Y); Hon Roll; Hnr Roll 85.

ESTABROOK, ALISON; Dracut SR HS; Dracut, MA; (Y); French Clb; Color Guard; Mrchg Band; Trk; High Hon Roll; Hon Roll; NHS; Pres Schlr; Draut Schlrshp Fndtn 85; U Of Lowell; Psychlgy.

ESTABROOK, DAN; Boston Latin Schl; Boston, MA; (Y); 1/300; Math Tm; High Hon Roll; Hon Roll; NHS; Ntl Merit SF; Glover Medl Cicerenian Lat 84; Princeton Alumni Awd 85; Modern & Clsscl Prz 83.

ESTABROOK, TIMOTHY; Chicopee Comprehensive HS; Chicopee, MA; (Y); Art Clb; Band; Concert Band; Jazz Band; Mrchg Band; Pep Band; Yrbk Stf; Cmmrcl Art.

ESTEY, STEPHEN; Brockton HS; Brockton, MA; (Y); 159/1000; Ice Hcky; Wrstlng; High Hon Roll; Hon Roll; Pilgrom Fndtn Schlrshp 85; Bridgewater ST Clg; Law.

ESTIN, PAUL A; Belmont HS; Belmont, MA; (Y); 3/280; Sec Trs Computer Clb; Math Tm; JV Socr; High Hon Roll; NHS; Rensselaer Math & Sci Awd 85; Prnctn Alumni Assn Awd 85; Sci.

ESTRELA, PETER; Bishop Connoly HS; Fall River, MA; (S); 15/160; Boys Clb Am; Boy Scts; Socr; High Hon Roll; NHS; SE MA U; Elec Engr.

ETTER, BRYAN P; Norton HS; Norton, MA; (Y); 3/128; Computer Clb; Math Clb; Math Tm; Tennis; Cit Awd; High Hon Roll; NHS; Pres Acdmc Ftns Awd; Rchstr Inst Of Tech; Comp Sci.

EURBIN, CHARLENE M; Drury SR HS; N Adams, MA; (Y); Chorus; Mc Canns Tech Schl; Cosmtlgy.

EUWART, DONALD; Burncoat SR HS; Worcester, MA; (Y); Pres Frsh Cls; Stu Cncl; Capt Ftbl; Trk; French Hon Soc; Hon Roll; Jr NHS; Pres NHS; Rensselaer Awd 85; Acad Olympic Awd 84; Chem Engrng.

EVANS, DAROLD; Sandwich HS; Forestdale, MA; (S); Church Yth Grp; Cmnty Wkr; DECA; FCA; Red Cross Aide; 2nd Pl DECA Dist Cmptn & 3rd Pl ST Comptn 84-85; Ntl Cntndr DECA 85; 2nd Pl Chmpnshp Moto Crs 83-84; Mrktng.

EVANS, NOREEN; Fontbonne Acad; Quincy, MA; (Y); 10/245; Hosp Aide; Intnl Clb; Office Aide; Band; Chorus; Drm & Bgl; Stage Crew; Score Keeper; Trk; Hon Roll; Alg I Awd; Relgn Awd; Spnsh Awd; Nrsng.

EVANS, SAMUEL J; Sharon HS; Sharon, MA; (Y); Chorus; Pres Concert Band; Jazz Band; School Musical; School Play; Ed Nwsp Stf; VP Jr Cls; Stu Cncl; Pres NHS; Yale; Econ.

EVERETT, BRUCE D; Maynard HS; Maynard, MA; (Y); 29/100; Am Leg Boys St; Aud/Vis; Radio Clb; Band; Concert Band; Jazz Band; Mrchg Band; Socr; Hon Roll; Engrng.

EVITTS, SUSAN; Saugus HS; Saugus, MA; (Y); 9/300; Stu Cncl; Sftbl; Capt Tennis; Hon Roll; Jr NHS; NHS; Sci Cert Merit 85; Frgn Lang Awd Achvt Spn 84; Hnrb Mntn ST Hstrcl Conf Framingham ST Coll 85; Bio.

EVON, PAUL; Chicopee Comprehensive HS; Chicopee, MA; (Y); Ice Hcky; NHS; Co MVP Hcky 84-85; Marine Bio.

EYLES, GREGORY; North Middlesex Regional HS; W Townsend, MA; (Y); Math Tm; Teachers Aide; Color Guard; Badmtn; Bsktbl; Bowling; Coach Actv; Ftbl; Golf; Ice Hcky; MVP Ftbl 79-81; All Star Baseball ST 80-81; Northeastern U; Sci.

EYLES, HEATHER; Tantasqua Regional HS; Sturbridge, MA; (Y); 10/189; Chorus; School Musical; Hon Roll; NHS; Lang.

FABBO, ROSITA; East Boston HS; E Boston, MA; (Y); Dance Clb; Pep Clb; Var Cheerleading; Bst Itln II, III Stu 84 & 85; Prfct Attndnc 82; Fshn Dsgn.

FABBRI, JUDITH F; Saint Rose HS; Chelsea, MA; (Y); 12/45; Office Aide; Band; Concert Band; Mrchg Band; Symp Band; Nwsp Bus Mgr; Nwsp Rptr; High Hon Roll; NHS; Cmnty Wkr; St Rose Meml Schlrshp 85; Cert Hon-Comp 85; Outstndg Band Awd BHS 84; U Of CA Irvine; Engl.

FABERMAN, ROBERT; Leominster HS; Fitchburg, MA; (Y); 1/353; Trs Church Yth Grp; Pres French Clb; Concert Band; School Musical; Elks Awd; High Hon Roll; NHS; Ntl Merit Ltr; Val; Superintendent Schl Hnr Awd; Brandeis U; Med.

FABIANO, MARIO; Boston Latin HS; Boston, MA; (Y); Boys Clb Am; Church Yth Grp; Latin Clb; Var Bsbl; Var Bsktbl; Ntl Merit Ltr; Continental Math Leag Cert Dstnctn 82-83; MA Assn Math Leags Cert Merit 84; MVP Bsbl 85.

FABRI, RICH A; Saugus HS; Saugus, MA; (Y); 47/307; Church Yth Grp; JV Bsbl; JV Var Bsktbl; Jr NHS; NHS; Voice Dem Awd; Saugus JV Bsktbl Coaches Awd 85; CYO Sprtsmnshp Awd 85; Engrng.

FAFARD, AMY LYNN; Bartlett HS; Webster, MA; (Y); 14/175; Aud/Vis; Church Yth Grp; Cmnty Wkr; Drama Clb; Girl Scts; Hosp Aide; Library Aide; Office Aide; Political Wkr; Science Clb; MA St Sci Fair-3rd Pl 85; Am Legn Schlrshps 85; James Lobban Memrl Schlrshp 85; Clark U; Neuropsychlgy.

FAGAN, MICHAEL; Boston College HS; Wellesley, MA; (Y); 52/260; Church Yth Grp; Debate Tm; Political Wkr; VP Spanish Clb; Nwsp Rptr; Yrbk Stf; Hon Roll; NHS; Boston Clg; Pltcl Sci.

FAHEY, ERIN; Hudson HS; Hudson, MA; (Y); 4-H; Pep Clb; Ski Clb; Powder Puff Ftbl; Hon Roll; Lib Arts.

FAHEY, LAWRENCE; Somerville HS; Sommerville, MA; (Y); 63/700; Boys Clb Am; Boy Scts; Computer Clb; French Clb; Rep Frsh Cls; Hon Roll; Bently Coll; Bus Admin.

FAIR, MICHAEL J; Natick HS; Natick, MA; (Y); 70/460; Church Yth Grp; Cmnty Wkr; Letterman Clb; Varsity Clb; Sec Stu Cncl; Var L Bsktbl; Var L Ftbl; Vllybl; Wt Lftg; High Hon Roll; All-Schlstc Ftbl Tm 84; W Agganis All Star Ftbl Tm 85; Estrn MA Div 1 Ftbl Sprbwl Chmpns 82-83; Springfield Coll; Psych.

FAIRFAX, MONT; Medfield HS; Medfield, MA; (Y); Ski Clb; Var Bsbl; Var Ftbl; Im Wt Lftg; Hon Roll; Hon Roll; New England Jr Enduro Grnd Champ; New Englad Trl Rdrs Assoc 84-85; Bus Admin.

FAIRWEATHER, SHEILA A; Woburn HS; Woburn, MA; (Y); Art Clb; French Clb; JA; Leo Clb; Ski Clb; Variety Show; Yrbk Stf; Stu Cncl; Fld Hcky; Score Keeper; Art.

FAITH, WENDY ANN; Brockton HS; Brockton, MA; (Y); Sec Pres Y-Teens; Yrbk Stf; Hon Roll; Ldrshp Awd Ldrs Clb 84 & 85; U Lowell; Phys Ther.

FALCONE, SCOTT; Phillips Acad; Utica, NY; (Y); Model UN; Ski Clb; JV Bsbl; Var Socr; Hon Roll; Ntl Merit Ltr; Trk; SR Cls Discpnry Comm Rep; Friday Forum Cncl 85-86; Peer Suppt Invlvmnt Grp 84-86; Lit.

FALER, SETH; Wakefield Memorial HS; Wakefield, MA; (Y); 4/325; JA; JCL; Latin Clb; Math Tm; Var Socr; Var L Trk; High Hon Roll; Jr NHS; Recrd Hldr Schl Obstacle Course 84; Ofcr Frst Ed Svgs Brch 85-86; Recip Brown U Bk Awd Excllnce Eng 85.

FALLON, JOHN; Natick HS; Natick, MA; (Y); 69/443; Letterman Clb; Var Bsktbl; Capt Socr; Im Wt Lftg; Hon Roll; Prfct Atten Awd.

FALLON, TRACEY; Westford Acad; Westford, MA; (Y); 14/222; Sec German Clb; Model UN; Nwsp Rptr; Var Fld Hcky; Var Gym; Var Tennis; High Hon Roll; NHS; Church Yth Grp; Natl Hon Soc Ldrshp Awd 85; Pres-SADD 85; Pre-Law.

FALVEY, JOAN; Randolph HS; Randolph, MA; (Y); Am Leg Aux Girls St; Cmnty Wkr; Political Wkr; Spanish Clb; Rep Frsh Cls; Pres Soph Cls; Pres Jr Cls; Pres Sr Cls; Pres Stu Cncl; Hon Roll; SADD; Hugh O Brien Outstndng Soph Awd 83-84; Polit Sci.

FANDREYER, CARL; Fitchburg HS; Fitchburg, MA; (Y); Am Leg Boys St; Boy Scts; Church Yth Grp; CAP; Red Cross Aide; Church Choir; Hon Roll; Pre Med.

FANG, KENNETH; Newton South HS; Chestnut Hill, MA; (Y); Debate Tm; Ski Clb; Concert Band; Jazz Band; JV Tennis; Faculty Awd 84-85; Sci.

FARIA, JAMES D; BMC Durfee High Of Fall River; Fall River, MA; (Y); 36/691; Church Yth Grp; Computer Clb; Library Aide; Tennis; High Hon Roll; Hon Roll; NHS; Sthestrn MA U; Bus Mngmnt.

FARIA, LISA; Coyle & Cassidy HS; Taunton, MA; (Y); Church Yth Grp; Dance Clb; Exploring; Hosp Aide; Ski Clb; Spanish Clb; Rep Soph Cls; Rep Jr Cls; Stu Cncl; High Hon Roll; Sci Fair Awd 82; Vol Awd Pin Cert 85; Northeastern U; Nrs.

FARIA, SUSANA; Newbedford HS; Newbedford, MA; (Y); Latin Clb; Office Aide; Yrbk Rptr; Yrbk Stf; Crs Cntry; Trk; High Hon Roll; Hon Roll; NHS; Prfct Atten Awd; Psych.

FARINA, WENDY A; Southwick HS; Southwick, MA; (Y); 5/159; Drama Clb; Pres French Clb; Model UN; Pep Clb; Nwsp Stf; Lit Mag; Var L Bsktbl; Var L Fld Hcky; Capt L Trk; High Hon Roll; Cornell U; Hotel Mgmt.

FARIVAR-SADRI, KAMRAN; Milford HS; Milford, MA; (Y); Boy Scts; Cmnty Wkr; Var Socr; JV Trk; Wt Lftg; Var Wrstlng; High Hon Roll; Jr NHS; NHS; Engr.

FARLEY, BENOIT; St Peter Marian HS; Worcester, MA; (Y); Stage Crew; Variety Show; Ftbl; Ice Hcky; Wt Lftg; New England Coll; Phy Ed.

FARLEY, JAMES; Cathedral HS; Springfield, MA; (Y); NHS; Acadmc Excllnc Engl 85; Acadmc Excllnc Math 84; Comp Engrng.

FARLEY, JOSEPH; Barnstable HS; Osterville, MA; (S); Drama Clb; Concert Band; Drm Mjr(t); Mrchg Band; School Musical; High Hon Roll; Hon Roll; NHS; Computer Clb; Band; Acad Achvt 85; Mus Fstvl 83-84; Hnrbl Mntn Law Day Essay Cntst 85; Comp Sci.

FARNUM, HILARY; Monument Mountain Regional HS; Gr Barrington, MA; (Y); 4/125; Pres Church Yth Grp; Girl Scts; Chorus; Madrigals; School Musical; Variety Show; Stu Cncl; High Hon Roll; Hon Roll; Jr NHS; Jr Erly Schlrshp 85; Acadmc Awd 84; Bio.

FARO, GINA; Winthrop HS; Winthrop, MA; (Y); 12/220; Church Yth Grp; Math Tm; Nwsp Sprt Ed; Nwsp Stf; Yrbk Sprt Ed; Im Bsktbl; Var Fld Hcky; Hon Roll; NHS; Merit Awd 83-84.

FAROOQ, NABIL M; Milford HS; Milford, MA; (Y); 25/300; Hosp Aide; Office Aide; Nwsp Stf; Bsktbl; High Hon Roll; Hon Roll; NHS; Med.

FARR, KELLY ANN; Sacred Heart HS; Hanover, MA; (Y); 23/89; Camp Fr Inc; Cmnty Wkr; Sec Key Clb; Teachers Aide; Nwsp Ed-Chief; Nwsp Rptr; Nwsp Stf; Yrbk Ed-Chief; Yrbk Stf; Hon Roll; Am Schltc Prss Assn, 1st Pl Awd Schl Nwspapr-Hrt Beat-Edtr In Chf 84-85; Comm.

FARRAHER JR, JOHN F; Marshfield HS; Marshfield, MA; (Y); 54/360; Am Leg Boys St; Cmnty Wkr; Key Clb; Band; Ftbl; L Ice Hcky; L Trk; Hon Roll; NHS; SADD Tri-Capt 84-86; Lt Gov New Eng Dstrct Key Clb 84-85; Gov New Eng Dstrct Key Clb.

FARRELL, LOUIS; Methuen HS; Methuen, MA; (Y); 115/350; Drama Clb; Intnl Clb; Spanish Clb; Band; Chorus; Concert Band; Jazz Band; Mrchg Band; Pep Band; School Musical; Solo Awds Mrchng Band 84-85; SR Cls Rep Band Cncl 85; All Dist Band 2nd Trump 1st Chr 85; Drama.

FARRELL, STEPHEN; Holy Name Central Catholic HS; North Grafton, MA; (Y); Church Yth Grp; Variety Show; Var Ftbl; Var Capt Trk; Var Wt Lftg; Hon Roll; Outstndng Achvmnt Chem Awd 84-85; Comp Info Sci.

FASANO, LINDA; Braintree HS; Braintree, MA; (Y); 21/416; Church Yth Grp; Cmnty Wkr; High Hon Roll; Hon Roll; NHS; Spanish NHS; Hnrb Mntn Braintree Sci Fair 82; Volntr Lore & Dedictn Awd 83; Typewrtng Awd 84-85.

FASSELL, SUZANNE MARIE; Hoosac Valley HS; Adams, MA; (Y); 7/168; School Play; Nwsp Ed-Chief; Yrbk Sprt Ed; Crs Cntry; Trk; High Hon Roll; Lion Awd; NCTE Awd; NHS; St Schlr; Frank Kelly Mem Schlrshp 85; William Adams Schrshp 85; Jrnlsm Awd 85; Mt Holyoke Coll; Jrnlsm.

FASTOSO, MARK; Bishop Stang HS; N Dartmouth, MA; (Y); 22/265; Art Clb; Boy Scts; Chess Clb; Church Yth Grp; Stage Crew; Hon Roll; NHS; Top 10 Frshmn 82; MA Coll Of Art; Grphc Dsgn.

FASY, ELIZABETH; Bishop Connolly HS; Portsmouth, RI; (S); 3/177; French Clb; Math Tm; Ski Clb; Var Crs Cntry; JV Socr; Var Trk; High Hon Roll.

FAUCETT, KAREN L; Phillips Academy HS; Danville, VA; (Y); 34/1073; Church Yth Grp; Cmnty Wkr; French Clb; JV Socr; L Var Tennis; Hon Roll; Ntl Merit Ltr; St Schlr; Sec New Stu Wlcmng Clb 83-84; U PA.

FAULKNER IV, CHARLES E; St Johns HS; Worcester, MA; (Y); Var Ftbl; Var Mgr(s); JV Trk; Spanish Clb; Yrbk Phtg; Yrbk Stf; Hon Roll; Babson Coll Holy Cross; Bus Mgt.

FAULKNER, KEVIN JOSEPH; Marshfield HS; Marshfield, MA; (Y); 116/362; Key Clb; Library Aide; Acpl Chr; Chorus; School Musical; L Bsbl; Var Socr; Hon Roll; Prfct Atten Awd; St Schlr; MA ST Schlrshp 85; Marshfield Tchrs Awd 85; Westfield ST Westfield; Bus.

FAUST, MICHAEL JOHN; Hingham HS; Poway, CA; (Y); 13/333; Am Leg Boys St; Nwsp Sprt Ed; Nwsp Stf; Capt Tennis; Im Vllybl; High Hon Roll; Hon Roll; NHS; Chess Clb; Math Tm; RPI Math & Sci Awd 84; Sager Elec Co Schlrshp 85; IL U; Engr.

FAVAZZA, MARY; Gloucester HS; Gloucester, MA; (Y); 6/370; Political Wkr; Thesps; Mgr Stage Crew; Pres Frsh Cls; Rep Soph Cls; Var Bsktbl; Var Sftbl; Hon Roll; VP Pres NHS; Sawyer Medal Achvt 82; Psych.

FAVOLISE, DAVID E; Bishop Connolly HS; Portsmouth, RI; (S); 21/177; Church Yth Grp; 4-H; High Hon Roll; Hon Roll; Comp Engr.

FAY, KEVIN A; Hanover HS; Hanover, MA; (Y); Yrbk Stf; Hon Roll; Ntl Merit Ltr; Syracuse U; Jrnlst.

FAY, PAUL C; Boston College HS; Canton, MA; (Y); 89/293; Rep Am Leg Boys St; Chess Clb; Church Yth Grp; Cmnty Wkr; Debate Tm; Key Clb; Nwsp Rptr; Yrbk Stf; Lit Mag; JV Crs Cntry; Worcester Polytech Inst; Engr.

FEARING, SHARI; Hudson HS; Hudson, MA; (Y); 35/165; Ski Clb; JV Var Fld Hcky; Eng Awd Common Errors 84; Westfield ST Coll; Bus Mgmt.

FEARS, LISA; Rockport HS; San Diego, CA; (Y); Am Leg Aux Girls St; Church Yth Grp; GAA; Score Keeper; Socr.

FEATHERSTON, PAUL; Agawam HS; Feeding Hills, MA; (Y); 95/365; Church Yth Grp; Cmnty Wkr; Var Capt Bsktbl; Im Vllybl; Hon Roll; Pltcl Sci.

FEDDEMA, SUSAN; Northbridge JR SR HS; Whitinsville, MA; (Y); 2/138; French Clb; Yrbk Stf; Stu Cncl; High Hon Roll; Hon Roll; Jr NHS; NHS; Sal; Drm & Bgl; Tlgrm & Gzt Stu Achvr 85; Wrcstr Poly Inst; Engrng.

FEDERICO, ANTHONY; Christopher Columbus HS; Boston, MA; (S).

FEDERICO, LISA; Christopher Columbus HS; Boston, MA; (S); 8/135; Science Clb; Hon Roll; Jr NHS; NHS; NEDT Awd; Fash Shw Mdl; Alg Wnng Tm.

FEDERICO, LISA; Haverhill HS; Haverhill, MA; (Y); Church Yth Grp; German Clb; Political Wkr; Ski Clb; Variety Show; Powder Puff Ftbl; Trk; High Hon Roll; Hon Roll.

FEDOR, CHRISTOPHER; St Johns HS; Sterling, MA; (Y); 153/287; Church Yth Grp; Ski Clb; Var Capt Bsktbl; Var Ftbl.

FEDORA, KELLY; Agawam HS; Feeding Hls, MA; (Y); 61/317; JA; Library Aide; Chorus; Color Guard; Mrchg Band; Yrbk Stf; Hon Roll; Westfield ST; Media.

FEENEY, MICHAEL; Brockton HS; Brockton, MA; (Y); 68/1000; Church Yth Grp; JCL; Red Cross Aide; Hon Roll; Maxima Cum Laude On The Natl Latin Exam 85.

FELDMAN, JAY; Doherty Memorial HS; Worcester, MA; (Y); Chess Clb; French Clb; Temple Yth Grp; Stu Cncl; Var L Crs Cntry; Var L Trk; French Hon Soc; High Hon Roll; Jr NHS; NHS; Horace Mann Schlr 82-85; Drug Abuse Peer Cnslr 85; Med.

FELIX, BARRY; Aqawam HS; Feeding Hills, MA; (Y); 98/320; JA; Library Aide; Teachers Aide; Stage Crew; VP Soph Cls; Im Bsktbl; JV Socr; Var Wrstlng; Hon Roll; Boy Scts; 2nd Pl Wstrn MA Wrstlng Trnmnt, 6th ST 85; St Michaels Coll; Psych.

FELTCH, STACIE; Everett HS; Everett, MA; (Y); Church Yth Grp; Intnl Clb; Trs Key Clb; Varsity Clb; Chorus; Var L Trk; Hon Roll; Jr NHS; Lion Awd; NHS; Trck Relay Tm 3 Rbbns 83-84; Math.

FELTER, SARAH; Cushing Acad; Ashburnham, MA; (Y); Intnl Clb; Chorus; Rep Soph Cls; Rep Stu Cncl; Bsktbl; Fld Hcky; Var Sftbl; Swmmng; Tennis; DAR Awd; Jrnlsm.

FENICK, DEIRDRE A; Braintree HS; Braintree, MA; (Y); 36/416; Church Yth Grp; Off Frsh Cls; Rep Soph Cls; Jr Cls; JV Fld Hcky; JV Sftbl; Hon Roll; Bus.

FENNELL, TIMOTHY; Christopher Columbus HS; Abington, MA; (S); 13/119; Science Clb; Drm & Bgl; Yrbk Ed-Chief; Yrbk Phtg; Hon Roll; NHS; Ntl Merit SF; Sailing Club 82; Yth Soccer Camp Schlrshp 82; Soc Distinguished Am HS Stu 83-85; Engrng.

FENNELLY, WENDY; North Quincy HS; Quincy, MA; (Y); 74/400; Math Tm; Spanish Clb; Rep Jr Cls; Co-Capt Cheerleading; Hon Roll; Stonehill Coll.

FENNESSY, KAREN; New Bedford HS; New Bedford, MA; (Y); 43/600; Church Yth Grp; Drama Clb; English Clb; Teachers Aide; Concert Band; Mrchg Band; School Musical; School Play; Swmmng; Hon Roll; Bio.

FERBER, MICHAEL; Brockton HS; Brockton, MA; (Y); 140/1500; Cmnty Wkr; Computer Clb; German Clb; Key Clb; Temple Yth Grp; Band; High Hon Roll; NHS; German Awd Excell 84; Lowell Tech; Elec Engr.

FERGUSON, DOUGLAS E; Central Catholic HS; Salem, NH; (Y); 1/227; Art Clb; Math Clb; Nwsp Stf; Yrbk Stf; Bowling; High Hon Roll; NHS; Ntl Merit SF; Val; Acad Awds Math,Sci; Johns Hopkins U; Biomed.

FERGUSON, MARTHA L; Dover Sherborn HS; Sherborn, MA; (Y); 22/158; Intnl Clb; Latin Clb; Ski Clb; Varsity Clb; Yrbk Stf; Sec Jr Cls; Var Crs Cntry; Var Trk; Hon Roll; Smll Bus.

FERIOLI, JULIE; Cathedral HS; Feeding Hls, MA; (Y); Cmnty Wkr; Office Aide; Chorus; Nwsp Stf; JV L Cheerleading; NHS; Highest Avg Frnch II & Math II & Frnch III; Engrng.

FERLEZ, JENNIFER A; Leominster HS; Leominster, MA; (S); 50/400; Church Yth Grp; French Clb; Math Tm; Political Wkr; School Musical; School Play; Sec Rep Stu Cncl; JV Var Fld Hcky; Hon Roll; Bst Actrs Awd Intrcls Play 82-84; Acad All-Amer 83-84; Boston Coll; Intl Rltns.

FERNANDES, DOREEN L; Old Colony Regionl Vo Tech HS; Carver, MA; (Y); VICA; Pres Schlr; Presdntl Cert Of Merit; S S Pierce Co-Best Culinary Artist; Commonwealth Of MA Schlrshp Grant; Newbury JC; Culinary Arts.

FERNANDES, JOHN; New Bedford HS; New Bedford, MA; (Y); 245/800; Ski Clb; Teachers Aide; Stage Crew; Yrbk Stf; VP Sr Cls; Var Ice Hcky; Var Socr; Excllnce In Portuguese 85.

FERNANDES, JORGE; Madison Park HS; Boston, MA; (Y); ROTC; Color Guard; Drill Tm; Socr; Hon Roll; Schrlshp Northeastern U 84-85; Med.

FERNANDES, LAURA; Marian HS; Ashland, MA; (Y); Hosp Aide; Chorus; Im Score Keeper; Hon Roll; Compltn 6 Yr Portguese Schl 85; Boston Coll; Nrsg.

FEROAH, MICHELE; Milford HS; Milford, MA; (Y); 17/296; DAR Awd; High Hon Roll; Stat Bsktbl; VP Sftbl; VP Vllybl; Pre Med.

FERRANTE, KAREN; Matignon HS; Medford, MA; (S); 15/179; Church Yth Grp; Library Aide; Political Wkr; Science Clb; Yrbk Ed-Chief; Bsktbl; Crs Cntry; Trk; French Hon Soc; NHS; Hnr Roll; Ntl Merit Ltr.

FERRARA, DIANE; Framingham South HS; Framingham, MA; (Y); 40/270; Color Guard; Yrbk Bus Mgr; Yrbk Stf; Stu Cncl; JV Var Fld Hcky; SADD Mbr 83-85; VP SADD Chptr 85-86.

FERRARA, KEVIN M; Winthrop HS; Winthrop, MA; (Y); 44/220; Am Leg Boys St; Art Clb; Cmnty Wkr; French Clb; Hosp Aide; Ski Clb; Varsity Clb; Yrbk Ed-Chief; Off Soph Cls; Off Jr Cls; Advrtsng.

FERRARA, TONIA; Hudson HS; Hudson, MA; (Y); Pep Clb; Ski Clb; Spanish Clb; Var Fld Hcky; Stat Ice Hcky; Powder Puff Ftbl; Stat Trk; MIAA Tourn Sectnl Team Champ Hocky Mgr 85; St Bonaventure; Mktng.

FERRARI, DONNA; Norwood SR HS; Norwood, MA; (Y); 45/337; Art Clb; Hosp Aide; Band; Concert Band; Mrchg Band; Symp Band; Stu Cncl; Hon Roll; Jr NHS; All Amer Large Div Schlr 84; JR All Amer Hall Fame Bnd Hnr 85; CPA.

FERRARI, KENNETH; Arlington Catholic HS; Wilmington, MA; (Y); 33/167; Church Yth Grp; Variety Show; Capt Var Bsktbl; Var L Ftbl; Hon Roll; St Josephs.

FERRARO, PATTY A; South High Community HS; Worcester, MA; (Y); Church Yth Grp; Cmnty Wkr; FNA; Hosp Aide; Teachers Aide; Rep Stu Cncl; Var Socr; Var Tennis; Jr Prom Committee 85; Fitchburg ST SMU; Nrsng.

FERREIRA, BARRY E; Bishop Connolly HS; Fall River, MA; (Y); 33/158; Cmnty Wkr; Bowling; High Hon Roll; Hon Roll; NHS; Pres Schlr; U Of MA; Comp Prgmr.

FERREIRA, HELEN; Bishop Connolly HS; Fall River, MA; (S); #17 In Class; Church Yth Grp; Ski Clb; High Hon Roll; Funeral Dir.

FERREIRA, IRENE; Keith Catholic HS; Lowell, MA; (Y); #10 In Class; French Clb; Nwsp Stf; Yrbk Bus Mgr; Yrbk Sprt Ed; Var Capt Bsktbl; Var Capt Tennis; Var Capt Vllybl; Hon Roll; NHS; Prfct Atten Awd; MVP Bsktbl 82-83 & 84-85; Vllybl Coaches 82-83; Bsktbl Coaches 83-84; MIP Vllybl 83-84; MVP Vllybl; Bridgewater ST Coll; Phys Ed.

FERREIRA, KARL; Diman Reg Vo Tech HS; Fall River, MA; (Y); Boy Scts; JA; Nwsp Rptr; Nwsp Stf; Emerson; Brdcstg.

FERREIRA, LISA; Taunton HS; Taunton, MA; (Y); Var Cheerleading; Bus.

FERREIROS, MANUEL; St Dominic Savio HS; E Boston, MA; (Y); 10/30; Art Clb; JA; Key Clb; Spanish Clb; Band; Concert Band; School Musical; Nwsp Rptr; Nwsp Stf; Yrbk Rptr; Berkley; Musician.

FERRELLI, MARIA; Matignon HS; Somerville, MA; (S); 1/174; Library Aide; Science Clb; Spanish Clb; Nwsp Rptr; Rep Frsh Cls; Rep Soph Cls; Stu Cncl; Bsktbl; JV Sftbl; Pres NHS; Tufts; Engrng.

FERRENDINO, SHAUN; Agawam HS; Feeding Hills, MA; (Y); Chorus; Hon Roll; Dist Chorus 84; Medical.

FERRIMAN, ROBERT J; Barnstalbe HS; Osterville, MA; (Y); 102/411; Church Yth Grp; Cmnty Wkr; School Musical; Variety Show; Var Bsbl; Var L Ice Hcky; Hon Roll; JR Rtrns VP 85; Leag All-Star Hcky Tm 83; Ice Hcky Capt & MVP 83; Babson Coll; Fin.

FERRINI, SANDRA L; Norton HS; Norton, MA; (Y); 16/124; Key Clb; Pep Clb; Varsity Clb; Pres Soph Cls; Pres Jr Cls; Pres Trs Stu Cncl; Capt Cheerleading; Pres Schlr; Almn Awd 85; JFK Awd Chrldg 85; Pres Awd Acadmc Fit 85; Stonehill Coll; Acctg.

FERRO, ROSANNA; Methuen HS; Methuen, MA; (Y); Chorus; Variety Show; Music Thry 82-85; Show Choir 83-85; Vcl & Instrmntl Ensmbl 84-85; Cmpsr Of Songs; Brkl Coll Of Music; Msc Cmpsr.

FERRY, ANTHONY; BMC Durfee HS; Fall River, MA; (Y); Boys Clb Am; Y-Teens; Hon Roll; Achvt Awd In Cmrcl Art; US Navy; Engrng.

FERRY, VIVIAN; Dighton-Rehoboth Regional HS; Rehoboth, MA; (S); Art Clb; Cmnty Wkr; Hosp Aide; Radio Clb; Ski Clb; Badmtn; Vllybl; Prefect Atten 83-84; Comm.

FERULLO, JOHN; Winthrop HS; Winthrop, MA; (Y); 35/250.

FFRENCH, SHERDON MALHAI; Medford HS; Medford, MA; (Y); 68/445; Key Clb; Red Cross Aide; Science Clb; Spanish Clb; Hon Roll; VFW Awd; Reserve-Netball Team In Jamaica; Amhert U MA; Bio Chem.

FIELD, JOHN; Agawan HS; Agawam, MA; (Y); 99/366; U Of MA; Comp Sci.

FIELD, LAURIE; Beverly HS; Beverly, MA; (Y); 20/400; VP Leo Clb; Chorus; Madrigals; School Musical; School Play; Swing Chorus; Variety Show; Nwsp Stf; NCTE Awd; Ntl Merit Schol; Comm.

FIELD, SHARALEE M; King Phillip Regional HS; Norfolk, MA; (Y); 1/215; Ed French Clb; Key Clb; Math Tm; Nwsp Stf; Ed Lit Mag; Rep Stu Cncl; High Hon Roll; NHS; Ntl Merit SF; Suprtndt Awd Acad Excell 84; Stu Of The Mnth 84; Excell Chem 83; MIT; Nuclr Engr.

FIELD, SHEILA I; Beverly HS; Beverly, MA; (Y); Art Clb; Church Yth Grp; Debate Tm; Library Aide; Office Aide; Spanish Clb; Teachers Aide; VP Soph Cls; Trk; Hon Roll; Merit Awd Aide 85-86; Hnrs Rll 84; Sci Awd 84; U Of NH; Intr Dsgn.

FIELDS, RENEE; Lexington HS; Lexington, MA; (Y); Church Yth Grp; Hosp Aide; Ski Clb; Var Capt Fld Hcky; Gym; Lcrss; Sftbl; Trk; Bus.

FIESTER, GINA; Agawam HS; Feeding Hills, MA; (Y); 27/320; Dance Clb; GAA; Hosp Aide; Varsity Clb; Chorus; JV Bsktbl; Var L Socr; JV Sftbl; Var L Trk; High Hon Roll; Flr Aid Prog Sprngfld Hosp 84; Outstdng Perf Westfld ST Soccor Schl 84; Utility Plyr Sftbl 83; Phy Thrpy.

FIFIELD, DOREEN D; Frontier Regional HS; So Deerfield, MA; (Y); GAA; Spanish Clb; Var Bsktbl; Var Capt Fld Hcky; JV Sftbl; High Hon Roll; Hon Roll; NHS.

FIGAROLA, MONICA; Girls Catholic HS; Medford, MA; (Y); 7/30; Drama Clb; Spanish Clb; School Play; Hon Roll.

FIGUERIDO, ANTHONY; Hopedale HS; Hopedale, MA; (Y); Am Leg Boys St; Band; School Play; Yrbk Stf; Stat Bsktbl; L Golf; High Hon Roll; NHS; Rep Frsh Cls; Rep Soph Cls.

FIGUERIDO, TONY; Hopedale JR-SR HS; Hopedale, MA; (S); Ski Clb; Band; Concert Band; Jazz Band; School Play; Rep Frsh Cls; VP Soph Cls; VP Jr Cls; L Golf; High Hon Roll; Law.

FIJAL, SHERRY L; Classical HS; Springfield, MA; (Y); 16/393; School Musical; Yrbk Sprt Ed; Sec Soph Cls; Sec Jr Cls; Sec Sr Cls; Sec Stu Cncl; Var Mgr(s); Hon Roll; Jr NHS; Hugh O Brien Yth Ldrshp Smnr Ambssdr 83; Pres Acadmc Ftnss Awd 85; Springfield Tchrs Clb Awd 85; Bentley Coll; Bus Mgmt.

FILIAULT, MICHELLE A; Moosac Valley HS; N Adams, MA; (Y); Lit Mag; Hon Roll; Lion Awd; NHS; Berkohire CC; Crmnl Justc.

FILIPPI, MATT; Malden HS; Malden, MA; (Y); 40/560; Church Yth Grp; Band; Church Choir; Color Guard; Concert Band; Drill Tm; Drm & Bgl; Flag Corp; Jazz Band; Mrchg Band; Mst Outstndng Music Frshmn 82-83; Jazz Band Pres 84-85; 1st Pl Trmpt Soloist 83-85; Boston U; Music Educ.

FILKINS, LAURA; Frontier Regional Schl; S Deerfield, MA; (Y); 3/76; Church Yth Grp; Drama Clb; French Clb; GAA; Hosp Aide; Ski Clb; Chorus; Church Choir; School Play; Variety Show; Western Dist Chorus 83; Peer Ed 84-86; Wellesly Bk Awd 85; Stu Gov Day Rep 85; Bus.

FILLETI, CARMEN; Don Bosco Tech; Hyde Park, MA; (S); Church Yth Grp; Yrbk Stf; Rep Soph Cls; Rep Jr Cls; Rep Stu Cncl; Var L Ftbl; High Hon Roll; NHS; Ntl Merit Ltr; Aerosp Engrng.

FILOSA, STEVEN R; Saugus HS; Saugus, MA; (Y); 9/300; Im Bsbl; Var Capt Bsktbl; JV Golf; High Hon Roll; Hon Roll; Jr NHS; NHS; Engrng.

FINE, SHERI; Marblehead HS; Marblehead, MA; (Y); Pres French Clb; Latin Clb; Sec Temple Yth Grp; Ed Yrbk Stf; Stu Cncl; Var Cheerleading; JV Var Fld Hcky; Var Powder Puff Ftbl; Hon Roll; NHS; Frnch Ldrshp Awd 85; MVP JV Fld Hockey 83; Best Def Fld Hcky 84; Tufts U; Orthdntst.

FINEMAN, DEBORAH; Newton North HS; Newton Centre, MA; (Y); Teachers Aide; Pres Temple Yth Grp; JV Fld Hcky; Var Capt Gym; JV Tennis; High Hon Roll; US Hstry Essay Cont Runner Up 85.

FINER, HOWARD; Randolph HS; Randolph, MA; (Y); Am Leg Boys St; Camp Fr Inc; Temple Yth Grp; Stage Crew; Yrbk Bus Mgr; Socr; Hon Roll; JC Awd; NHS; Computer Clb; Lloyd Young Memrl Awd; All Arnd Judean Troph; Schl Store Bus Mgr; Comp Engrng.

FINI, MARIA; St Bernards Central Catholic HS; Lunenburg, MA; (S); 19/173; Art Clb; Trs Ski Clb; Spanish Clb; Rep Jr Cls; Stu Cncl; Var Cheerleading; Var Socr; Var Trk; Hon Roll; Spnsh III Awd 84; Bus Mgmt.

FINK, KATHERINE; Westfield HS; Westfield, MA; (Y); Cmnty Wkr; Library Aide; Red Cross Aide; Ski Clb; Spanish Clb; Teachers Aide; Trk; Hon Roll; Intl Bus.

FINLAYSON, DONNA L; Mansfield HS; Mansfield, MA; (Y); 36/174; French Clb; Hosp Aide; Library Aide; Office Aide; Color Guard; Drill Tm; Flag Corp; Stage Crew; Yrbk Stf; Hon Roll; U Of MA-AMHERST; Anml Sci.

FINN, CHRISTOPHER; Malden HS; Malden, MA; (Y); 17/480; Am Leg Boys St; Key Clb; Variety Show; L Capt Ftbl; L Trk; Wt Lftg; Hon Roll; NHS; Engrng.

FINN, CHRISTY; Acad Of Notre Dame; Dunstable, MA; (Y); 27/50; Church Yth Grp; Dance Clb; Drama Clb; PAVAS; Variety Show; Nwsp Rptr; Nwsp Stf; JV Swmmng; Hon Roll; Comm.

FINN, ERIN; Sacred Heart HS; Plymouth, MA; (Y); 16/90; Key Clb; Ski Clb; Stu Cncl; JV Var Fld Hcky; Capt Lcrss; Socr; Hon Roll; NHS; Band; Yrbk Stf; 1st Prize Sacred Heart Art Shw 85; Boston Globe Art Awd 85; MVP Plymouth Soccr All Stars 84.

FINN, STACY; Randolph HS; Randolph, MA; (Y); FNA; Hosp Aide; Intnl Clb; Temple Yth Grp; Chorus; Yrbk Stf; Hon Roll; JC Awd; NHS; Med.

FINNEGAN, MARTHA; Cathedral HS; Wilbraham, MA; (Y); Hosp Aide; Trk.

FINNERAN, ELLEN; Marshfield HS; Marshfield, MA; (Y); 100/340; Pres AFS; Art Clb; Church Yth Grp; Drama Clb; Sec 4-H; Hosp Aide; Key Clb; Im Bsktbl; 4-H Awd; God Cntry Awd; Psych.

FINNERTY, THOMAS; Malden Catholic HS; Medford, MA; (Y); 22/184; Church Yth Grp; Chrmn Cmnty Wkr; Intnl Clb; JA; Latin Clb; Pep Clb; Nwsp Stf; Im Bsktbl; Im Score Keeper; Im Vllybl; Babe Ruth Leag Bsbl All Str 83; U Of Notre Dame; Elctrcl Engrng.

FIORE, LISA MARIE; Fontbonne Acad; Hyde Park, MA; (Y); 20/128; Church Yth Grp; Drama Clb; Sec Intnl Clb; Teachers Aide; School Musical; School Play; Stage Crew; Variety Show; Hon Roll; NHS; Exclnce Alg I, Span III 82-83 & 84-85; Dramatics Awd 84-85; Accntng.

FIORE, MICHELLE; Christopher Columbus HS; S Boston, MA; (S); Drama Clb; Political Wkr; Variety Show; Vllybl; St Augustine Excllnc Awd 2nd Pl 82; UCLA; Thrtr.

FIORENTINO, DOUGLAS; Fitchburg HS; Fitchburg, MA; (Y); Am Leg Boys St; CAP; Yrbk Phtg; Yrbk Stf; Rep Stu Cncl; JV Crs Cntry; High Hon Roll; Aviatn Mgmt.

FIORENTINO, MICHAEL; Boston Latin Schl; Boston, MA; (Y); 100/300; Physcs Ntl Sci Olympd 85; US Army Rsrv Ntl Essay Cntst Cert 85; Bus Admin.

FIORETTI, CHRISTINE; Marian HS; Natick, MA; (Y); 2/177; Church Choir; School Musical; Yrbk Ed-Chief; Var Capt Socr; Var L Sftbl; High Hon Roll; NHS; Ntl Merit Ltr; Church Yth Grp; Drama Clb; Wellesley Coll Bk Awd; Physc, Math, Bio Awds; Bio.

FIORINO, DEBBIE; Bedford HS; Bedford, MA; (Y); 22/239; Rep Frsh Cls; Trs Soph Cls; Trs Jr Cls; French Hon Soc; High Hon Roll; Hon Roll; NHS; Bus.

FIRDA, THOMAS ALLEN; South Hadley HS; S Hadley, MA; (Y); Latin Clb; Artist Of The Smstr Awd 85; U Of MA; Art.

FISCHLER, MELISSA; Westwood HS; Westwood, MA; (Y); 12/217; Trs AFS; Yrbk Ed-Chief; Var Capt Trk; Var L Vllybl; NHS; Ntl Merit Ltr; Pres Spanish NHS; Camera Clb; Drama Clb; Key Clb; Daily Transcrpt Soph Of Yr, All Star Trk 84-85; Patriot Ledgr All Schltc Awd Trk 85; Bay ST Comp 85; Lib Art.

FISH, CURTIS; Mohawk Trail Regional HS; Colrain, MA; (Y); Aud/Vis; Boy Scts; Ski Clb; Teachers Aide; Varsity Clb; Stage Crew; Ftbl; Trk; Wt Lftg; Peer Educ 84-85; Hnrble Men Ftbll 83-85; Audio Vsl Awd 84-85; Lehigh U; Crmnl Just.

FISHER, ERIC; Leominster HS; Leominster, MA; (Y); 4/380; Ski Clb; Var L Tennis; High Hon Roll; NHS; Boys ST 85; Mst Imprvd Ten 85; Bus.

FISKE, D DANIEL; Mohawk Trail Regional HS; Shelburne, MA; (Y); 4-H; Stage Crew; 4-H Awd; High Hon Roll; Hon Roll; Kiwanis Awd; MA Outstndng Yth Awd 84; Dir MA Jersey Cattle Clb 84 & 85; Spnsh & Math Awds 83-85; Ag.

FISZMAN, LISA; Cushing Acad; Ashburnham, MA; (Y); JV Bsktbl; Var Vllybl; JV Wt Lftg; Fr II Awd 84-85; Bst Overall JR 84-85; Fr I Awd 83-84.

FITCH, BRIAN; Plymouth Carver HS; Plymouth, MA; (Y); Computer Clb; Radio Clb; Ski Clb; Band; Concert Band; Drm & Bgl; Jazz Band; Mrchg Band; Polc Dept Recog Compssn Twrd Fllw Man 85; Hnry Musicn Awd 85; Berklee Schl Of Music; Percssn.

FITCH, MICHELLE; Taconic HS; Pittsfield, MA; (Y); 10/254; Sec Dance Clb; GAA; Girl Scts; Q&S; Nwsp Stf; Sec Yrbk Stf; High Hon Roll; FL Inst Of Tech; Comp Engrng.

FITZGERALD, KATHRYN; Ursuline Acad; Boston, MA; (Y); 29/73; Dance Clb; French Clb; Service Clb; Band; Concert Band; Mrchg Band; Yrbk Phtg; Trs Frsh Cls; Var Tennis; High Hon Roll; Providence Coll; Law.

FITZGERALD, KRISTIN M; Matignon HS; Somerville, MA; (Y); 63/183; Drama Clb; Spanish Clb; School Musical; School Play; JV Var Sftbl; Swmmng; Latin Hnrs 80-81,82-83; Geometry Hnrs 82-83; Salem St Coll.

FITZGERALD, PAT; Cambridge Rindge And Latin Schl; Cambridge, MA; (S); Drama Clb; Pres Key Clb; Pep Clb; Radio Clb; Nwsp Rptr; Nwsp Sprt Ed; Stu Cncl; Var L Ftbl; Var L Trk; Var L Wrstlng; Article Printed Natl Magazine 85; Law.

FITZGIBBONS, STEPHEN; Holyoke HS; Holyoke, MA; (Y); 89/350; Boys Clb Am; Drama Clb; Latin Clb; Yrbk Sprt Ed; Yrbk Stf; JV Var Bsbl; JV Var Bsktbl; Hon Roll; Holyoke Yth Bsebl Leag Schlrshp 85; S Hadley Educ Assoc Schlrshp 85; Ithaca Coll.

FITZLER, KRISTINE; B M C Durfee HS; Fall River, MA; (Y); 34/600; French Clb; Hosp Aide; Chorus; Crs Cntry; Trk; High Hon Roll; Hon Roll; Jr NHS; NHS; Pres Acad Ftnss Awd 85; Southeastern MA U; Nrsng.

FITZPATRICK, ANDREA; Belmont HS; Belmont, MA; (Y); 22/290; Dance Clb; Drama Clb; School Musical; School Play; High Hon Roll; NHS; Mc Gill U Montreal; Rsrch Bio.

FITZPATRICK, COLLEEN; Chelmsford HS; Chelmsford, MA; (Y); Church Yth Grp; JV Bsktbl; Hon Roll.

FITZPATRICK JR, EARL W; Malden Catholic HS; Malden, MA; (Y); Camera Clb; Church Yth Grp; Cmnty Wkr; Latin Clb; Political Wkr; Ski Clb; Nwsp Phtg; Yrbk Phtg; Var Crs Cntry; Var Trk; Boston U; Mech Engr.

FITZPATRICK, MICHAEL F J; Catholic Memorial HS; Dedham, MA; (Y); 16/295; VP Computer Clb; Coach Actv; Var Golf; Var Capt Socr; High Hon Roll; NHS; Ntl Merit Ltr; NEDT Awd; Pres Schlr; Church Yth Grp; Dorothy Devereaux Charctr Schlrshp 85; Worcester Polytech Inst; Engrng.

FITZPATRICK, SUSAN; Canton HS; Canton, MA; (Y); 48/265; Drama Clb; German Clb; Band; Chorus; Concert Band; Mrchg Band; School Musical; School Play; Stage Crew; Variety Show; All Star Cast Awd 85; U Of MA Amherst.

FITZPATRICK, TAMMY; Salem HS; Salem, MA; (Y); 10/363; Yrbk Stf; Off Frsh Cls; Trs Soph Cls; Trs Jr Cls; Trs Sr Cls; Bsktbl; Var Fld Hcky; High Hon Roll; NHS; Chld Ed.

FITZSIMMONS, COLLEEN L; Somerset High HS; Somerset, MA; (Y); 11/299; Church Yth Grp; Trs Debate Tm; Drama Clb; Hosp Aide; JA; Concert Band; Trs Mrchg Band; Symp Band; JV Tennis; High Hon Roll; Musictown Fest Queen X 83-84; Springfield Coll; Phy Thrpy.

FITZSIMMONS, MAURA; Matighon HS; Melrose, MA; (S); 19/187; Sec Y-Teens; Rep Frsh Cls; Rep Soph Cls; Church Yth Grp; Hosp Aide; Ski Clb; French Hon Soc; Hon Roll; NHS; YMCA Ldrs Clb Ldr Of The Yr 83 & 84; Bio.

FITZSIMMONS, PATTI; Taunton HS; Taunton, MA; (Y); Hon Roll; Prfct Atten Awd; Typing Awd 84; Shorthand Achvt Awd 85; Cert Of Proficiency 85; SEC.

FLACHBART, KAREN; Marblehead HS; Marblehead, MA; (Y); Girl Scts; Var L Bsktbl; Var L Socr; Var L Sftbl; Top Scr In Nthestrn Cnfrnc In Soccer 83; N E Cnfrnc All Star Soccer 83 & 84; Intr Dsgn.

FLAGG, MARK D; Athol HS; S Royalston, MA; (Y); Am Leg Boys St; Model UN; DAR Awd; Hon Roll; NHS; Pres Schlr; Schl Accntnt 84-85; MA Bus Wk 84; Excell Hist Awd 85; Bentley Coll; Accntnt.

FLAHERTY, ERIN; Bishop Stang HS; Mattapoisett, MA; (Y); Church Yth Grp; Key Clb; Rep Soph Cls; Rep Jr Cls; Var L Trk; 4th JR Miss Wareham 85; Wntr Trck Awd 84; Div II Chmps Trck 85; Salve Regina Newport; Nrsg.

FLAHERTY, MAUREEN; Notre Dame Acad; N Quincy, MA; (Y); 50/114; Church Yth Grp; Hosp Aide; Political Wkr; Chorus; School Musical; School Play; Stage Crew; Variety Show; JV Var Bsktbl; Mgr(s); Alg I, Geom, & Spnsh II Schltc Excllnc Awds 83-84; St Michaels Coll; Pre-Med.

FLAHERTY, NORA; Marblehead HS; Marblehead, MA; (Y); 12/259; Cmnty Wkr; Sec Drama Clb; Sec Thesps; Stage Crew; Lit Mag; High Hon Roll; Hon Roll; Jr NHS; NHS; Ntl Merit Ltr; Renselaer Medal 85; U MA Chancllrs Tlnt Awd Scholar 85; Gold Key, Blue Rbn Boston Globe Sci Art 84; Pre-Med.

FLAHERTY, PATRICIA; Newton Catholic HS; Newtonville, MA; (Y); Capt Var Cheerleading.

FLAMAND, CHERYL; Ware HS; Ware, MA; (Y); Art Clb; French Clb; Hosp Aide; Model UN; Hon Roll; Comp Sci Awd Excell 85; Psych.

FLANAGAN, BRENDA; Cathedral HS; Springfield, MA; (Y); 29/509; Cmnty Wkr; Office Aide; Political Wkr; Stu Cncl; Tennis; Hon Roll; NHS; Prfct Atten Awd; Rlgn & Outstndng Svc Awds 84-85.

FLANAGAN, DAVID J; Phillips Acad; Andover, MA; (Y); 20/400; Computer Clb; Math Tm; Model UN; Teachers Aide; JV Swmmng; JV Tennis; High Hon Roll; Hon Roll; Ntl Merit SF; Comp Sci.

FLANAGAN, DAVID W; Tewksbury HS; Tewksbury, MA; (Y); 3/284; Mathletes; Political Wkr; Sec Sr Cls; Stu Cncl; L Socr; L Trk; High Hon Roll; Jr NHS; NHS; Wang Lab Schlrshp 85; Navy ROTC Acad Schlrshp 85; Most Likely To Succeed 85; Rensselaer Polytech Inst; Engr.

FLANAGAN, JENNIFER; Bishop Connolly HS; Tiverton, RI; (Y); 35/205; Cmnty Wkr; Ski Clb; Varsity Clb; VICA; School Play; Stage Crew; Yrbk Stf; Bsktbl; Var Trk; High Hon Roll; Southeastern MA U; Fine Arts.

FLANIGAN, ANNMARIE; Bridgewater-Raynham Regional HS; Bridgewater, MA; (Y); Church Yth Grp; Hosp Aide; Ski Clb; Variety Show; Hon Roll; NHS; Stu Govt Day Secry Selectmen 85; Qlfr Grls St Pgm 85; La Femmina Mdlng & Fnshng Schl 82-84.

FLANNAGAN, THOMAS J; Gloucester HS; Gloucester, MA; (Y); 21/320; Am Leg Boys St; Political Wkr; Yrbk Rptr; Yrbk Stf; JV Tennis; Elks Awd; Hon Roll; NHS; Navy Schrlshp Fnlst 85; Stop Shop Co Inc 85; Ithaca Coll; Pilot.

FLANNERY, KEVIN; Auburn HS; Auburn, MA; (Y); 18/182; Band; Concert Band; Jazz Band; Mrchg Band; Nwsp Rptr; JV Bsbl; High Hon Roll; NHS; Worcester Polytech; Elec Engr.

FLAVIN, EDWARD J; Quincy HS; Quincy, MA; (Y); 63/313; Am Leg Boys St; Church Yth Grp; Civic Clb; Cmnty Wkr; FCA; Var Ice Hcky; Hon Roll; Hockey Schlrshp Bruins Camp 83 & 85; Civil Engrng.

FLAXER, ANDREA; Marblehead HS; Marblehead, MA; (Y); Key Clb; Pres Temple Yth Grp; Band; Im Tennis; Tchrs Aide 81; Bus Admin.

FLEMING, DOUGLAS A; Greenfield HS; Greenfield, MA; (Y); 17/159; JV Bsktbl; JV Var Socr; Var L Trk; Excll Boys Phy Ed 85; Excll Drftng Grde II 85; Greenfield CC; Engnrng.

FLEMING, JAMES; Groton Dunstable Regnl Secndry Schl; Groton, MA; (Y); 1/83; Math Tm; Stu Cncl; Var Trk; High Hon Roll; Trs NHS; Amer Clscl Leag & Ntl Jr Clscl Leag Magn Cm Laud 84; E Haskins Math Cntst Awd Outstndng Prfrmnc 85; MIT; Astrphyscs.

FLEMING, KELLY; Burncoat SR HS; Worcester, MA; (Y); 21/260; Church Yth Grp; Cmnty Wkr; JA; Office Aide; Hon Roll; NHS; Southeastern MA U; Poltcl Sci.

FLEMING, KRISTEN; Bishop Connolly HS; Mattapoisett, MA; (S); 2/177; Church Yth Grp; Off Latin Clb; Math Clb; Math Tm; Ski Clb; Rep Soph Cls; JV Trk; Var Vllybl; High Hon Roll; NHS; Sumna Cum Laudi 83; Magnum Cum Laudi 84; Civil Engr.

FLEMING, LINDA; Billerica Memorial HS; Billerica, MA; (Y); 52/477; French Clb; Color Guard; Flag Corp; Mrchg Band; Yrbk Stf; Rep Jr Cls; Hon Roll; Good Sportsmanshp Awd 82; Med.

FLEMING, MARY; Billerich Memorial HS; Billerica, MA; (Y); 60/477; Church Yth Grp; French Clb; Color Guard; Flag Corp; Mrchg Band; Yrbk Stf; Rep Jr Cls; Twrlr; Hon Roll; Ms Imprvd Rifle 84; Bst Flag 83; Med.

FLEMING, MARYA; Bishop Connolly HS; Mattapoisett, MA; (S); 20/158; Church Yth Grp; Cmnty Wkr; Latin Clb; Math Tm; Ski Clb; Trk; Vllybl; Elks Awd; High Hon Roll; NHS; Phys Thrpy.

FLEMING, STEVEN; St Bernards HS; Lunenburg, MA; (S); 5/161; JV Bsbl; Bsktbl; High Hon Roll; NHS.

FLENKE, KAREN; Cathedral HS; Enfield, CT; (Y); Cmnty Wkr; Office Aide; Serv To Schl-Guidnc Aid 84-85; Homerm Rep 83-84; Elem Eductn.

FLODMAN, KRISTIN; South High Community Schl; Worcester, MA; (S); 13/250; Boy Scts; Church Yth Grp; Church Choir; VP Jr Cls; VP Sr Cls; Trs Stu Cncl; DAR Awd; Hon Roll; NHS; Cty Mngr Downtown Yth Cncl; Elks Schlrshp; Hugh O Brian Yth Ldrshp Sem; S Eastern MA U; Bio.

FLOOD, MICHELE; Plymouth-Carver HS; Plymouth, MA; (Y); 5/520; GAA; Latin Clb; Crs Cntry; Trk; High Hon Roll; Hon Roll; Jr NHS; NHS; Pres Schlr; Excel Ltn 85; Bradford Coll; Psych.

FLORES, REBECCA; Academy Of Notre Dame; Concord, NH; (Y); Art Clb; Chorus; Yrbk Stf; Im Bsbl; Hon Roll; NHS; Prfct Atten Awd; Art Awds 82-85.

FLOWERS, APRIL; Holy Name C C HS; Worcester, MA; (Y); Cmnty Wkr; Fld Hcky; Worcester Ballet Assn 81; Engl Excllnc Awd 82; Tufts U; Vet.

FLOYD, NANCY; Chicopee HS; Chicopee, MA; (Y); Church Yth Grp; Teachers Aide; Pres Chorus; Pres Madrigals; Hon Roll; Westfield ST Coll; Elem Eductn.

FLROES, GINA LYNN; Wellesley HS; Wellesley, MA; (Y); Girl Scts; Rep Frsh Cls; Rep Soph Cls; Pres Jr Cls; Coach Actv; Var Capt Trk; Hon Roll; JC Awd; NHS; Rptr Aud/Vis; PA Hse Of Rep Plq Fr Trk ST Chmpn 82-83; Boston Coll; Sprts Med Dr.

FLYNN, JOHN J; Triton Regional HS; Salisbury, MA; (Y); Am Leg Boys St; Nwsp Stf; Yrbk Phtg; Yrbk Stf; Off Soph Cls; Off Jr Cls; Off Sr Cls; Tennis; Fairfield U; Cmmnctns.

FLYNN, MARY; Catherdral HS; Springfield, MA; (Y); 16/529; Cmnty Wkr; JA; JV Sftbl; NHS.

FLYNN, MARY; Hanover HS; Hanover, MA; (Y); Cmnty Wkr; GAA; Political Wkr; Varsity Clb; Yrbk Stf; Bsktbl; Sftbl; Hon Roll.

FLYNN, MELISSA J; Oakmont Regional HS; Westminster, MA; (Y); 27/155; Dance Clb; Chorus; Stu Cncl; Cheerleading; Sftbl; Trk; Hon Roll; Clsscl Bllt Hgh Awds; U Of NH; Bio.

FLYNN, PAUL; Bishop Feehan HS; Walpole, MA; (Y); 100/250; JV Var Ftbl; Var Trk; Var Wt Lftg; Bio,Math Hnrs 82.

FLYNN, PETER Y; Bridgewater-Raynham Regional HS; Bridgewater, MA; (Y); 30/315; Am Leg Boys St; Political Wkr; Ski Clb; Pres Stu Cncl; Var L Trk; Hon Roll; Rotary Awd; Pres Acad Fit Awd 85; Loren Keith Prize 85; Robert G Clark Mem Scholar 85; Syracuse U; Pol Sci.

FLYNN, ROBERT; Marian HS; Framingham, MA; (Y); Rep Frsh Cls; Rep Jr Cls; Im Bsktbl; L Var Golf; L Var Socr.

FOGEL, LAURA; Haverhill HS; Haverhill, MA; (Y); 75/425; NHS; FBLA; High Hon Roll; Credit Women Intl Haverhil Awd 85; Northern Essex Comm Coll; Acctn.

FOGG, KELLEY A; Brockton HS; Brockton, MA; (Y); 15/990; Cmnty Wkr; Office Aide; Ski Clb; High Hon Roll; NHS; Pres Schlr; NCTE Awds 84; Cum Laude Ntl Ltn Exam 84; Bates Coll.

FOLAN, JULIE; Mansfield HS; Mansfield, MA; (Y); 33/205; Pres Sr Cls; Var Capt Bsktbl; JV Sftbl; Hon Roll; Vrsty Bsktbl-6th Player Awd 85; Bsktbl Vrsty Letters 83-86; Honrbl Mentn Sun Chronicle All Star Tm 85; Nursing.

FOLAN, KARL M; Lynn Vocational Technical Inst; Lynn, MA; (Y); Am Leg Boys St; Boy Scts; Church Yth Grp; Cmnty Wkr; Political Wkr; Ski Clb; Hon Roll; Jr NHS; Pres Schlr; Alphonse Drewicz Mem Schlrshp 85; Elec Engr.

FOLB, KAREN J; Ayer HS; Ayer, MA; (Y); 8/160; Am Leg Aux Girls St; Ski Clb; Spanish Clb; Yrbk Stf; Rep Soph Cls; Sec Jr Cls; Sec Sr Cls; High Hon Roll; Mu Alp Tht; NHS; Bus Mgmnt.

FOLEY, BRIAN; Cathedral HS; Springfield, MA; (Y); 192/550; Church Yth Grp; Bsbl; Var Bsktbl; JV Ftbl; JV Wt Lftg; Intl Fnce.

FOLEY, CAROLYN; Braintree HS; Braintree, MA; (Y); 55/418; Rep Soph Cls; Var Cheerleading; Hon Roll; Prfct Atten Awd; Lib Arts.

FOLEY, CHRISTINE MARIE; Wachusett Regional HS; Rutland, MA; (Y); 77/386; Church Yth Grp; Girl Scts; Hon Roll; Spanish NHS; Certfd Adv Lf Svg YWCA 83; Bus Adm.

FOLEY, DANIEL; Franklin HS; Franklin, MA; (Y); 5/235; OEA; Red Cross Aide; Stage Crew; Variety Show; Pres Jr Cls; Pres Sr Cls; Var Capt Bsktbl; Hon Roll; NHS; Digital Eqpt Schlrshp 85; Francis Eddy King Awd 85; Babson Coll; Bus Mgt.

FOLEY, DENISE; Holbrook HS; Holbrook, MA; (Y); 20/102; Am Leg Aux Girls St; Church Yth Grp; Latin Clb; Co-Capt Drm Mjr(t); Pres Jr Cls; Stu Cncl; Bsktbl; Fld Hcky; Socr; Sftbl; ST Stu Advsry Cncl 83-84; Ntl Ldrshp Trnng Cmp, Pres Clb Stu Cncl 84-85; Comm.

FOLEY, LISA; Weymouth North HS; Weymouth, MA; (Y); 72/400; Sftbl; Vllybl; E Weymouth Merchnts Schlrshp 85; Nichols Coll; CPA.

FOLEY, MICHAEL; English HS; Lynn, MA; (Y); 60/395; Camera Clb; Yrbk Stf; Bowling; Golf; Hon Roll; Law Enfrcmnt.

FOLEY, MICHAEL; Mansfield HS; Mansfield, MA; (Y); 4/207; Am Leg Boys St; Nwsp Rptr; Im Bsktbl; High Hon Roll; Hon Roll; NHS; Ntl Merit Ltr; Naval ROTC Schlrshp Ltr 85; Yale U Smmr Prog 85; Cornell U; Physics.

FOLEY, SHEILA; Arlington Catholic HS; Medford, MA; (Y); 23/149; Art Clb; Yrbk Stf; Crs Cntry; Hon Roll; NHS; Magna Cum Laude 84.

FOLLANSBEE, CAROLINE J; Ipswich HS; Ipswich, MA; (Y); Leo Clb; Yrbk Stf; Var Bsktbl; Var Socr; Var Sftbl; Hon Roll; NHS; Rep Frsh Cls; Rep Soph Cls; Rep Jr Cls; Schl Hnr Awd 3 Yrs; Law Day Essy Awd 83; Bsktbl Cape Ann Leag All Str 85.

FOLLANSBEE III, ROBERT S; Nashoba Regional HS; Lancaster, MA; (Y); 18/179; JV Var Bsbl; Var Wrstlng; Hon Roll; Phys Ed Awd 85; Mst Valuable Contribtr Awd Bsbl 85; N Central MA Umpires All Star Tm Bsbl 85; Bucknell U; Bus Mngmnt.

FONNER, SUZANNE; Cathedral HS; Springfield, MA; (Y); Office Aide; Ski Clb; Nwsp Stf; Var Trk; NHS; Tutor Algebra II.

FONTAINE, DANIEL; Classical HS; Lynn, MA; (Y); Church Yth Grp; French Clb; Golf; Hon Roll; Arts.

FONTANA, MICHELLE; East Longmeadow HS; E Long Mdw, MA; (Y); 38/197; French Clb; Intnl Clb; Variety Show; Yrbk Stf; Trs Frsh Cls; Var Capt Cheerleading; Var Tennis; Union Coll; Hstry.

FORAND, DEBORAH; Southbridge HS; Sbridge, MA; (Y); 13/162; Yrbk Stf; Cheerleading; Hon Roll; NHS; Rep Jr Cls; Gym; Hofstra; Chem.

FORBES, MARY; Chicopee HS; Chicopee, MA; (Y); 41/273; Cmnty Wkr; JA; Political Wkr; Church Choir; Nwsp Ed-Chief; Yrbk Stf; Var Score Keeper; Var Timer; Var Trk; Hon Roll; Wstrn New England Coll; Dr.

FORBES, MICHAEL; Whitman Hanson Regional HS; Whitman, MA; (Y); Computer Clb; Library Aide; Var L Crs Cntry; JV Trk; NHS; Prfct Atten Awd; Northeastern U; Elec Engr.

FORBES, PATRICIA; Girls Catholic HS; Malden, MA; (Y); Church Yth Grp; Drama Clb; Girl Scts; Hosp Aide; School Play; High Hon Roll; Hon Roll; MA HS Drama Fstvl All Star Cast 83; Cert Of Ed Dvlpmnt Ntl 83; Bus.

FORBES, RAYMOND; Marblehead HS; Marblehead, MA; (Y); 59/259; French Clb; Ski Clb; Varsity Clb; Pres Pep Band; School Play; Var Capt Ftbl; Var Capt Tennis; Wt Lftg; Hon Roll; Ldrshp Cncl 84-85; MVP Ten 84-85; Boston Coll; Bus Admin.

FORD, KATHRYN; Lexington HS; Lexington, MA; (Y); Church Yth Grp; Chorus; Orch; School Musical; 4-H Awd; Cncrt Chr 84-85; Yth Rep Orch-New England Conservatory 82-84; Gtr Boston Yth Symph Orch 84-85; Educ.

FORERO, JAMES; Holy Name HS; Worcester, MA; (Y); Hon Roll; Comp Pgmmng.

FORGIT, LANCE E; David Prouty HS; Spencer, MA; (Y); Am Leg Boys St; Church Yth Grp; Math Clb; Var Bsktbl; Var Golf; Hon Roll; NHS; Acctng.

FORKEY, JOSEPH N; Lunenburg HS; Lunenburg, MA; (Y); 7/150; Am Leg Boys St; Trs Church Yth Grp; Math Tm; Trs Band; Trs Sr Cls; Trs NHS; Pres Schlr; Chess Clb; Trs 4-H; Intnl Clb; PTO Bst Sci Stu Awd 85; Worcester Telgrm & Gaztt Outstndng Stu 85; Bst Actr-Comptv Cls Plys 85; Cornell U; Physcs.

FORKNALL, JACKIE; Taunton HS; Taunton, MA; (Y); Sci & Math.

FORMAN, BRIAN; Randolph HS; Randolph, MA; (Y); Temple Yth Grp; Rep Stu Cncl; Var Capt Bsktbl; Var Socr; Hon Roll; JC Awd; NHS; Ivy League; Med.

FORMATO, RICHARD M; Saint Johns HS; Shrewsbury, MA; (Y); 27/271; Church Yth Grp; Hosp Aide; Math Tm; Science Clb; Variety Show; Im Bsbl; Im Bsktbl; High Hon Roll; Hon Roll; NHS; Engrng Semnr & Math Clarkson U; Bicyclng Clb; Elec Engr.

FORNARA, CYNTHIA; Georgetown HS; Georgetwon, MA; (Y); 2/88; Drama Clb; Spanish Clb; Yrbk Stf; Trs Sr Cls; High Hon Roll; Hon Roll; NHS; Sal; Dartmouth Clb Awd; Outstndg Achvt Chem, Spnsh IV.

FORREST, JAMES P; Norwood SR HS; Norwood, MA; (Y); Am Leg Boys St; Church Yth Grp; Varsity Clb; Bsbl; JV Bsktbl; Ftbl; Var L Socr; Var Capt Trk; Hon Roll; Indr Trck High Scorer 85; Phy-Ed Awd 85.

FORRESTER, KOLBY; Southbridge HS; Sbridge, MA; (Y); 7/162; Church Yth Grp; Trs Girl Scts; Math Tm; Concert Band; Mrchg Band; Rep Soph Cls; Rep Jr Cls; High Hon Roll; Hon Roll; NHS; Outstndg JR Mrchg & Cncrt Bnd 85; Bus.

FORRESTER, KRISTIN; Algonquin HS; Southboro, MA; (Y); Church Yth Grp; Drama Clb; Chorus; School Musical; School Play; High Hon Roll; Hon Roll; NHS; Theology.

FORSTER, LISA; St Bernards Central Catholic HS; Leominster, MA; (S); 3/164; Sec Ski Clb; Yrbk Stf; Sec Soph Cls; Sec Jr Cls; Sec Sr Cls; Var Tennis; DAR Awd; High Hon Roll; Hon Roll; Sec NHS; Engl, Hist Awds; Hmcmng Court; Boston Coll; Finance.

FORSYTHE, KELLIE; Arlington Catholic HS; Billerica, MA; (Y); 22/150; Art Clb; Church Yth Grp; French Clb; GAA; Girl Scts; JA; Service Clb; School Musical; Yrbk Stf; Var Cheerleading; Special Eductn.

FORTIER, JONATHAN; Holbrook HS; Holbrook, MA; (Y); 19/101; French Clb; JV Bsktbl; Var Crs Cntry; Var Ftbl; Var Ftbl; Var Trk; Var Wrstlng; Hon Roll; NE U; Comp Sci.

FORTIER, LYNN D; Leominster HS; Leominster, MA; (Y); 17/350; Church Yth Grp; Dance Clb; Mgr Yrbk Stf; High Hon Roll; Hon Roll; NHS; Presdntl Acad Fitness Awd 85; Knights Of Columbus Schlrshp 85; Gannon U; Physcns Asst.

FORTIN, DONNA; Bishop Feehan HS; Woonsocket, RI; (Y); Church Yth Grp; JCL; Lit Mag; JV Var Vllybl; French Hon Soc; High Hon Roll; NHS; New England Regnl CYO Bsktbl Champs 84; MVP CYO Vllybl Tm 85; Piano Cert SR II Lvl 85; Bio.

FORTIN, WENDY D; Holyoke HS; Holyoke, MA; (Y); Church Yth Grp; Dance Clb; Political Wkr; Science Clb; Teachers Aide; School Play; Variety Show; High Hon Roll; Hon Roll; Office Aide; U Of MA Wstfld; CPA.

FORZESE, JILL; Methuen HS; Methuen, MA; (Y); 34/345; Intnl Clb; Pep Clb; Im Powder Puff Ftbl; JV Trk; JV Vllybl; High Hon Roll; Hon Roll; Bus Admin.

FORZIATI, CHRISTINE; Easthampton HS; Easthampton, MA; (Y); #12 In Class; Dance Clb; Trs Stu Cncl; Capt Cheerleading; Socr; High Hon Roll; Hon Roll; Trs NHS; Natl Hon Roll Awd 85; Clark U; Psych.

FOSKEY, LISA; Apponequet Regional HS; East Freetown, MA; (Y); 13/200; Cmnty Wkr; Dance Clb; Drama Clb; Variety Show; High Hon Roll; Hon Roll; NHS; Treas FOCUS Clb 85-86; Bus Mngmnt.

FOSSA, JOHN; Beverly HS; Beverly, MA; (Y); Boy Scts; Rep Soph Cls; VP Jr Cls; Pres Sr Cls; Hon Roll; USMA West Point; Engrng.

FOSSELLA, ROBERT M; Stoughton HS; Stoughton, MA; (Y); High Hon Roll; Hon Roll; Pioneering/Bethel Svc; Data Pro.

FOSTER, BENJAMIN; Westwood HS; Westwood, MA; (Y); 29/214; Chess Clb; Church Yth Grp; Stage Crew; Hon Roll; Ntl Merit SF; Outstndg Achvt Intro Comp Sci 82-83; Geol Engrng.

FOSTER JR, JAMES H; Boston Technical HS; Jamaica Plain, MA; (Y); 13/215; Rep Soph Cls; Pres Jr Cls; VP Stu Cncl; High Hon Roll; Hon Roll; NHS; Prfct Atten Awd; Boston Pblc Schls Schlrshp 85; SPC Leadrshp Awd 85; Boston U; Communctns.

FOSTER, JANE; Hingham HS; Hingham, MA; (Y); 70/325; Am Leg Aux Girls St; Church Yth Grp; Sec Spanish Clb; Thesps; School Musical; School Play; Variety Show; Rep Jr Cls; Rep Stu Cncl; Var Capt Cheerleading; Secry MA Assoc Stu Cncls 85-86; Intl Bus.

FOSTER, LAUREN; Brookline HS; Brookline, MA; (Y); Cmnty Wkr; French Clb; Ski Clb; Off Jr Cls; Lcrss; Trk; NHS; Ntl Merit Ltr; Cert Merit AATF 84; Engrng.

FOSTER, STACEY; Bishop Feehan HS; N Attleboro, MA; (Y); Church Yth Grp; Cmnty Wkr; Hosp Aide; French Hon Soc; High Hon Roll; Nrsng.

FOSTER, WAYNE F; Franklin HS; Franklin, MA; (Y); Var Ice Hcky; Miami U; Bus.

FOUCART, PAUL; New Bedford HS; New Bedford, MA; (Y); 27/620; Pres Drama Clb; Band; Chorus; Concert Band; Mrchg Band; School Musical; School Play; Nwsp Rptr; Nwsp Stf; Bst Actr 85; Bst Spprtng Actr 83; Cmmnctns.

FOUGERE, DAVID; Framingham South HS; Framingham, MA; (Y); 19/262; Trs Drama Clb; Latin Clb; Acpl Chr; Chorus; Madrigals; School Musical; School Play; Variety Show; VP Frsh Cls; VP Soph Cls.

FOURNIER, KAREN; Mohawk Trail Regional HS; Charlemont, MA; (Y); Ski Clb; Sec Varsity Clb; Yrbk Sprt Ed; Yrbk Stf; Rep Frsh Cls; Rep Soph Cls; Rep Jr Cls; Rep Sr Cls; JV Var Fld Hcky; Var Mgr(s); Ski Tm; Chem Achvt; Peer Educ; Grp Cnclng.

FOURNIER, LISA; Chicopee HS; Chicopee, MA; (Y); JA; Var L Cheerleading; Westfield ST Coll; Bus Mgr.

FOWLER, HEATHER J; East Bridgewater HS; E Bridgewater, MA; (Y); 8/152; Key Clb; Rep Frsh Cls; Rep Soph Cls; Rep Jr Cls; Rep Sr Cls; Rep Stu Cncl; Var Bsktbl; Var Socr; Var Trk; High Hon Roll; SADD 84-85; Pres Acad Fitnss Awd 85; Continentl Mth Lg Comp Excllnce Awd 83; Vassar Coll; Ed Gifted Chldrn.

FOX, ANNE T; Academy Of Notre Dame HS; Lowell, MA; (Y); Hosp Aide; VP Key Clb; Stage Crew; Yrbk Stf; Co-Capt Cheerleading; NHS; Im Bsktbl; Im Vllybl; Frnch Achv Awd; Cert & Lttr Of Cmmndtn From Jets Inc; St Michaels Coll; Bio.

FOX, DEBRA; Marblehead HS; Marblehead, MA; (Y); 42/267; Drama Clb; Latin Clb; Ski Clb; Pres Band; Concert Band; Mrchg Band; Orch; School Play; Stage Crew; Yrbk Ed-Chief; Soclgy.

FOX, RICHARD; Weymouth South HS; S Weymouth, MA; (Y); Trs Frsh Cls; Trs Soph Cls; VP Jr Cls; VP Sr Cls; JV Crs Cntry; Var Socr; Var Timer; Rotary Awd; Bstn Glb Schltc Art Awd Gld Key; Art Achvt Awd; Art.

FOX, STEVEN; Malden HS; Malden, MA; (Y); 19/468; Pres Exploring; French Clb; Letterman Clb; Pres Temple Yth Grp; Mrchg Band; School Musical; Lit Mag; Rep Jr Cls; Var L Crs Cntry; Var L Trk; Natl Hnr Scty 3rd Qtr Awd 85; Brandeis U; Pre-Med.

FOX, STEVEN; Marblehead HS; Marblehead, MA; (Y); 7/260; Math Tm; Variety Show; Trs Sr Cls; JV Bsktbl; Var Tennis; Var Trk; High Hon Roll; NHS; Ntl Merit Ltr; Bus.

FOY, JOAN M; Weymouth North HS; E Weymouth, MA; (Y); Church Yth Grp; Ski Clb; Var L Bsktbl; Var L Socr; Var L Sftbl; Hon Roll; Old Clny All Star Socr 83-85; Socr Schlrshp Adelphi 85; Adelphi U; Sprts Mgmt.

FOY, KATHY; Archbishop Williams HS; Quincy, MA; (Y); 56/191; Church Yth Grp; Hosp Aide; Yrbk Phtg; Cheerleading; Cit Awd; Hon Roll; Jr NHS; Hgh Hnr Roll 82; Bio.

FRAGALA, THOMAS; North Andover HS; N Andover, MA; (Y); 11/242; Boy Scts; Trs Computer Clb; Hosp Aide; Var L Socr; Var L Trk; Prfct Atten Awd; Rotary Awd; High Hon Roll; Latn Hnr Socty; Eagl Sct Awd; Bst Offnsv Plyr Awd Sccr; Rensselaer Polytechnic Inst.

FRANCESCONI, GINA; Milford HS; Mendon, MA; (Y); 50/314; Dance Clb; Hosp Aide; Ski Clb; Band; Chorus; JV Im Sftbl; JV Vllybl; Bryant Coll; Bus Mktg.

FRANCHI JR, JOHN A; St Johns HS; Worcester, MA; (Y); 70/270; Church Yth Grp; Model UN; School Musical; School Play; Stage Crew; Lit Mag; Rep Stu Cncl; L Crs Cntry; L Trk; Jr NHS; Ltr Cmndtn NA Invtnl Mdl UN 84; Coll Holy Cross; Med.

FRANCIOSE, STEPHANIE; Beverly HS; Beverly, MA; (Y); Church Yth Grp; Rep Frsh Cls; Trs Soph Cls; Trs Jr Cls; Trs Sr Cls; Cheerleading; Fld Hcky; Trk.

FRANCIS, DEBBIE; Concord Carlisle Regional HS; Concord, MA; (Y); 1/273; Band; Concert Band; Mrchg Band; Symp Band; High Hon Roll; NHS; Ntl Merit Ltr.

FRANCIS, JOHN; Central Catholic HS; Bradford, MA; (Y); 18/219; Cmnty Wkr; Exploring; Science Clb; Teachers Aide; School Musical; Im Bsktbl; Im Score Keeper; Im Timer; High Hon Roll; NHS; Biol Sci.

FRANCIS, SCOTT; Holy Name Central Catholic HS; Worcester, MA; (Y); 64/272; Spanish Clb; Chorus; School Musical; JV Bsbl; JV Var Ftbl; Syracuse; Adv.

FRANCISCO, RAYMOND L; Coyle-Cassidy HS; Berkley, MA; (Y); Church Yth Grp; Ski Clb; Bsktbl; Crs Cntry; Tennis; U Lowell; Engrng.

FRANCULLO, LINDA E; Bishop Fenwick HS; Lynn, MA; (Y); 32/222; Church Yth Grp; Hon Roll; James W O Brien Scholar 85; Merrimack Coll.

FRANEK, RONDA; Bartlett HS; Webster, MA; (Y); FNA; Ski Clb; Trk; Hon Roll; Nrsng.

FRANKINA, LEE M; Millis HS; Millis, MA; (Y); 20/80; Chorus; Variety Show; Var L Bsktbl; Var L Ftbl; Var L Trk; Im Vllybl; Hon Roll; Div & League All Star Ftbl 84; Bus.

FRANKLIN, MARITZA R; Mission Church HS; Dorchester, MA; (Y); Hosp Aide; Var Vllybl; Hon Roll; Howard U; Physcl Thrpy.

FRANSON, KIM; Woburn HS; Woburn, MA; (S); French Clb; JA; JCL; Latin Clb; Leo Clb; Chorus; Church Choir; High Hon Roll; Hon Roll; Jr NHS; 3rd Pl Rgnl Sci Fair 82; Med.

FRAPPIER, DONNA M; Cathedral HS; Springfield, MA; (Y); Office Aide; Capt Trk; NHS; Bryant; Bkpng Acctng.

FRASCA, TAMSIN; Beverly HS; Beverly, MA; (Y); JV Cheerleading; JV Fld Hcky; Var Powder Puff Ftbl; Psych.

FRASER, ANDREA J; Boston Latin Schl; Jamaica Plain, MA; (Y); 39/320; Drama Clb; Pres German Clb; Intnl Clb; JA; Political Wkr; School Play; Var L Crs Cntry; JV Socr; NHS; Ntl Merit Ltr; Natl Greek Exam With Merit 84; ST Fnlst Miss Amer Co-Ed Pagnt 85; Harvard.

FRASIER, DAVID; Cambridge Kindge & Latin HS; Cambridge, MA; (S); 25/650; Var Ftbl; Var Wrstlng; Art Clb; Boy Scts; Cmnty Wkr; Dance Clb; Math Clb; Political Wkr; Red Cross Aide; Ski Clb; Co-Cptn Football Vrsty Team; Bus Mgmt.

FRATUS, ANITA; Barnstable HS; Hyannis, MA; (Y); Drama Clb; Hon Roll; Cape Cod CC; Crim Jstc.

FREDERICK, RONALD A; Chicopee HS; Chicopee, MA; (Y); 1/235; Am Leg Boys St; Pres Chess Clb; VP Computer Clb; Capt Debate Tm; Capt Mathletes; Church Choir; Ed Yrbk Stf; Mgr Trk; Bausch & Lomb Sci Awd; CC Awd; RPI Medallion; Roy Lane Awd Math; AHS Math Exam Awd; Rensselaer Polytech Inst:Engrn.

FREDETTE, CHRISTINA; Holyoke Catholic HS; Chicopee, MA; (Y); 52/142; Spanish Clb; Chorus; School Musical; Yrbk Stf; Sftbl; Csmtlgy.

FREDRICKSON, LISA; Newburyport HS; Newburyport, MA; (S); Cmnty Wkr; Drama Clb; JCL; Chorus; School Musical; School Play; NHS; Cum Laude Ntl Lat Exm 82; Prsdntl Phy Fit Awd 83; Marine Bio.

FREE, LAURA; Natick HS; Natick, MA; (Y); Cmnty Wkr; Stu Cncl; Var Cheerleading; JV Trk; Hon Roll; Boston Coll; Cmnctns.

FREEDMAN, JEFFREY; Peabody Veterans Memorial HS; Peabody, MA; (Y); 17/586; Science Clb; Temple Yth Grp; Concert Band; Jazz Band; Mrchg Band; Rep Stu Cncl; NHS; Drummer Local Rock Band 84; Bsktbl Yth Org 83; Most Outstndng Band Mbr Awd 82-83; Sci.

FREEDMAN, LYNN; Haverhill HS; Bradford, MA; (Y); 56/400; French Clb; Latin Clb; Swmmng; Trk; High Hon Roll; NHS; U Of NH; Bus.

FREEDMAN, STEPHANIE; Marblehead HS; Marblehead, MA; (Y); 20/259; Cmnty Wkr; Debate Tm; French Clb; Math Tm; Temple Yth Grp; School Play; Stu Cncl; High Hon Roll; Hon Roll; NHS; MA Mth Lg Awd 84-85; MA Frnch Tchrs Guild Awds 84 & 85; Natl Guild Piano Tchrs Audtns 80-85; Mth.

FREELEY, ELAINE; Woburn SR HS; Woburn, MA; (S); 42/500; Church Yth Grp; Leo Clb; Yrbk Ed-Chief; Stu Cncl; Cheerleading; Gym; High Hon Roll; Jr NHS; NHS; Phy Thrpy.

FREELEY, KATHLEEN A; Milford HS; Milford, MA; (Y); 10/292; Church Yth Grp; Service Clb; JV Tennis; JV Vllybl; High Hon Roll; NHS.

FREEMAN, ALLISON; Stoughton HS; Stoughton, MA; (Y); Hosp Aide; Math Tm; Band; Concert Band; Jazz Band; Mrchg Band; School Musical; Trk; High Hon Roll; 1st Hon Men Sci Fair 83; 5th Grnd Awd Sci Fair 84 & 85; Med.

FREEMAN, DENICE; W Bridgewater JR SR HS; W Bridgewater, MA; (Y); Hosp Aide; Hon Roll; Bentley Coll; Mrktg.

FREEMAN, JILL; Holliston HS; Holliston, MA; (Y); 26/206; Church Yth Grp; Band; Yrbk Stf; Rep Sr Cls; Var Capt Cheerleading; Var Fld Hcky; Var Trk; Hon Roll; NHS; Ntl Merit Ltr; Pres Acdmc Ftns Awd 85; Wheaton Coll; Psych.

FREITAG, LISA; Triton Regional HS; Rowley, MA; (Y); 5/180; Cheerleading; JV Mgr(s); Hon Roll; NHS; Law.

FREITAS, LINDA; Taunton HS; Taunton, MA; (Y); High Hon Roll; Hon Roll; NHS; Prfct Atten Awd; Century 21 Typwrtng & Bkkpng Awd.

FRENCH, W SCOT; Mt Everett Reg HS; Sheffield, MA; (Y); Boy Scts; Church Yth Grp; Ski Clb; Color Guard; Lit Mag; Pres Sr Cls; God Cntry Awd; World Conservation Awd 85; Mile Swim Awd 84; Eagle Scout Plus Bronze & Gold Palms 85.

FRENIEVE, NORM; Holyoke Catholic HS; Chicopee, MA; (Y); Computer Clb; JV Trk; Prfct Atten Awd; Excel Frnch I,Alg II 82-85; Holyoke CC; Metrlgy.

FREYERMUTH, BRIAN F; Tabor Acad; Plymouth, MA; (Y); 1/139; Lit Mag; Im Bsktbl; Im Socr; Im Tennis; High Hon Roll; Ntl Merit SF; Harvard Prize Bk-Harvard Clb Of New Bedford, John C Makepeace Mem Schlrshp, Natl Latin Exam 84; Psych.

FRIEDMAN, FERN N; Milford HS; Milford, MA; (Y); 4/321; VP Exploring; Rep Stu Cncl; JV Capt Bsktbl; JV Fld Hcky; Var Capt Tennis; DAR Awd; High Hon Roll; Hon Roll; Pres NHS; Ntl Merit Ltr; Masschsts Cmnwlth Schlrs Awd 85; Dr John Devalvia Athlt Awd 85; Acdmc Schlrshp Nrthestrn U 85; Nrthestrn U; Cmnctns.

FRIEDMAN, JODI; Marblehead SR HS; Marblehead, MA; (Y); 33/245; Drama Clb; VP French Clb; Intnl Clb; Ski Clb; Mgr Stage Crew; Nwsp Rptr; Nwsp Stf; Yrbk Rptr; Ed Yrbk Stf; Hon Roll; Pre-Med.

FRIEDMAN, LAURIE; Attleboro HS; Attleboro, MA; (Y); Church Yth Grp; JV Fld Hcky; Gym; Var Trk; NHS.

FRIEDMAN, PAUL E; Westwood HS; Westwood, MA; (Y); 1/241; Mathletes; Math Clb; Capt Math Tm; Hon Roll; NHS; Ntl Merit SF; Rotary Awd; MA Assn Schl Suprtndnts Awd 84; Amer Chem Soc A A Ashdown Awd 82; Olympiad Awd 83; MIT; Comp Engr.

FRIEDRICH, MARY; Clinton HS; Clinton, MA; (Y); Intnl Clb; Drm Mjr(t); Yrbk Stf; Rep Stu Cncl; Hon Roll; La Femina Modelng Awd 83; Law.

FRIEL, KERRI A; Andover HS; Andover, MA; (Y); 13/624; Church Yth Grp; Girl Scts; Acpl Chr; Orch; Variety Show; Var Golf; High Hon Roll; Hon Roll; Jr NHS; Girls Golf Ltr 84; Orch Ltr 84; Tchg Deaf.

FRIEND, KAREN; Franklin HS; Franklin, MA; (Y); Church Yth Grp; Cmnty Wkr; Political Wkr; Teachers Aide; Yrbk Stf; Trs Stu Cncl; JV Mgr(s); JV Sftbl; Hon Roll; Voice Dem Awd; Psych.

FRIEZE, KEN; Newton South HS; Waban, MA; (Y); Church Yth Grp; Capt Ski Clb; Nwsp Stf.

FROC, RANDY; Ashland HS; Ashland, MA; (Y); Am Leg Boys St; Church Yth Grp; JA; Tennis; Prfct Atten Awd; Lowell U; Elec Engrng.

FROIO, JOHN; Cohasset HS; Cohasset, MA; (Y); 13/130; Trs AFS; Aud/Vis; Im Bsbl; L Ftbl; L Golf; Im Ice Hcky; L Wrstlng; Hon Roll; JR Clb Champ Golf 85.

FRONGILLO, RICHARD; Franklin HS; Franklin, MA; (Y); 2/233; Boy Scts; Math Tm; Var Capt Socr; Var Trk; Hon Roll; Pres NHS; Sal; MA Al-ST Sccr Tm 84-85; U Of MA-AMHERST; Comp Sci.

FRUHBEIS, TODD; Nashoba Regional HS; Stow, MA; (Y); 21/185; Boy Scts; Church Yth Grp; VP Soph Cls; VP Soph Cls; VP Jr Cls; Pres Sr Cls; Rep Stu Cncl; Bsktbl; Ftbl; Trk; Schlrshp MA Bus Wk 84; Daugh Am Rev Good Cit Awd 85; 6th ST Mile Relay Trk; U MA; Bus.

FRYE, MICHELLE; Haverhill HS; Haverhill, MA; (Y); French Clb; Yrbk Phtg; Cheerleading; Trk; High Hon Roll; Hon Roll; U New England; Phys Thrpy.

FUCHS, JULIUS A; St Joseph Central HS; Pittsfield, MA; (Y); 2/90; Am Leg Boys St; Boy Scts; Quiz Bowl; Nwsp Rptr; VP Stu Cncl; Capt Crs Cntry; Capt Wrstlng; High Hon Roll; NHS; Spanish NHS; Eagle Scout 83; MA Adv Studs Pgm Milton Acad 85; Wrstlng Medals 83-85; U S Naval Acad.

FUHRMANN, ANDREW; Mt Greylock Regional HS; Williamstown, MA; (Y); 6/140; Am Leg Boys St; Crs Cntry; Trk; NHS; RPI; Engrng.

FULGINITI, MARISA; Newton Catholic HS; W Newton, MA; (Y); 5/55; Chorus; Yrbk Stf; Sftbl; Vllybl; High Hon Roll; Hon Roll; Elks Schlrshp Awd 85; Acad All-Amer Schlr 85; Aquinas JC; Accntnt.

FULLER, DAVID; Taunton HS; Taunton, MA; (Y); Camera Clb; VP Intnl Clb; Office Aide; Hstry.

FULLER, ELIZABETH; Reading Memorial HS; Reading, MA; (Y); JA; Stu Cncl; JV Socr; Var Capt Trk; High Hon Roll; NHS; Art.

FULLER, STEPHEN D; Braintree HS; Braintree, MA; (Y); 1/483; Band; Concert Band; Jazz Band; Mrchg Band; Orch; Nwsp Stf; French Hon Soc; High Hon Roll; NHS; Ntl Merit Ltr; Math Olympd Awd 84-85; Hrvrd Bk Awd 84; RPI Mdl 84; Harvard U; Physics.

FULLERTON, CHARLOTTE L; Saint Mary HS; Haverhill, MA; (Y); 4/108; Church Yth Grp; Sec Cmnty Wkr; JA; Service Clb; Nwsp Rptr; Yrbk Stf; NHS; Coachng Trphy Haverhill Yth Hcky 81-85; Stu Of Mth Plq Lawrence Exch Clb 85; Schlrshp Outstndng Stus; U Of Southern CA; Cinema.

FULLERTON, ELIZABETH; Dana Hall Schl; Wellesley, MA; (Y); Church Yth Grp; Cmnty Wkr; Drama Clb; Key Clb; Library Aide; Acpl Chr; Chorus; Jazz Band; Madrigals; School Musical; Law.

FULLERTON, TINA; Stoughton HS; Stoughton, MA; (Y); Swing Chorus; Burdett; Sec.

FUQUA, DAVID R; Mt Greylock Regional HS; Williamstown, MA; (Y); 1/130; Jazz Band; Orch; School Musical; Symp Band; Nwsp Phtg; Yrbk Phtg; Elks Awd; NHS; Ntl Merit SF; Concert Band; MENC All-Estrn Orch 85; Music.

FURBER, JEFF; Haverhill HS; Haverhill, MA; (Y); Aud/Vis; Church Yth Grp; MMM; Band; Concert Band; Jazz Band; Mrchg Band; High Hon Roll; Comp Accntnt.

FURBUSH, ALICIA; Everett HS; Everett, MA; (Y); Church Yth Grp; Hosp Aide; Intnl Clb; Key Clb; Variety Show; Bowling; U Of MA; Nrs.

FUREY, COLLEEN; Natick HS; Natick, MA; (Y); 113/460; Church Yth Grp; Off Frsh Cls; Off Jr Cls; Off Sr Cls; Fld Hcky; Im Lcrss; Im Socr; MVP JV La Crosse 82; Westfield ST Coll; Bus.

FURLONG, JUDITH ANN; Mount Alvernia HS; Natick, MA; (Y); 1/43; Cmnty Wkr; Drama Clb; Latin Clb; Chorus; School Play; Stu Cncl; High Hon Roll; NHS; Ntl Merit Ltr; Val; Serv Merch Schlrshp 85-86; Commwlth Schlr Grant 85-86; Joseph P Considine Mem Schlrshp 85-86; MA Inst Tech; Engrng.

FURLONG, MATT; Bridgewater HS; Bridgewater, MA; (Y); English Clb; French Clb; Ski Clb; Pres Stu Cncl; Bsktbl; Crs Cntry; Diving; Gym; Swmmng; Trk; Bridge Water ST; Health.

FURLONG, MIKE; Watertown HS; Watertown, MA; (Y); 10/285; Pres Intnl Clb; VP JA; Nwsp Rptr; Yrbk Stf; Rep Sr Cls; Var Ftbl; Var Trk; High Hon Roll; VP NHS; Ntl Merit Ltr; JA ROJAC Conf 85; Peer Ldrshp Pgm Offcr 84; Pop Warner Chmpnshp Tms Capt 82 & 83; Sales Engr.

FURLONG JR, ROBERT J; Boston College HS; Hyde Park, MA; (Y); 150/290; Rep Am Leg Boys St; JA; Key Clb; Nwsp Stf; Im Bsktbl; U Of MA At Boston Smr Pgm Fr Crtv Wrtng HS Stu 84; U Of MA-AMHERST; Jrnlsm.

FURTADO, BERNADETTE; Biship Stang HS; New Bedford, MA; (Y); 12/217; Hosp Aide; Ski Clb; Capt Color Guard; Variety Show; Yrbk Stf; High Hon Roll; NHS; Hon Roll; ILGWU Schlrshp 85; Super Hnrs Piano Eval 82-85; Acadmc Awds; Coll Holy Cross; Bio.

FURTADO, CARLA; Plymouth-Carver HS; Carver, MA; (Y); Hon Roll; Jr NHS; Acctng.

FUSARO, MARISA G; North HS; Worcester, MA; (Y); 1/170; Variety Show; Nwsp Rptr; Ed Yrbk Ed-Chief; Stu Cncl; Socr; High Hon Roll; Hon Roll; Jr NHS; NHS; Spanish NHS; Holy Cross Bk Prize 84; Telegram & Gazette Stu Achvt Awd 85; Horace Mann Schlr 82 & 85; Boston Coll; Law.

FUSCO JR, ANTHONY; Central Catholic HS; Methuen, MA; (Y); 90/219; Trs Church Yth Grp; Rep Frsh Cls; Rep Soph Cls; Rep Jr Cls; Rep Sr Cls; Rep Stu Cncl; Var JV Ftbl; Ice Hcky; JV Trk; Im Wt Lftg; Natl Hnr Soc Lgn Hnr Awd; Campus Mnstry; Engnr.

FUSCO, JOAN G; Berkshire Schl; Hillsdale, NY; (S); 4/132; Intnl Clb; Nwsp Ed-Chief; Socr; Val; Church Yth Grp; Dance Clb; 4-H; Variety Show; Gym; Lcrss; Peter Lance Anderson Schlrshp 85; Stanley Prz For Excel In Frnch 85; Tertius Van Dyke Prz In Eng 85; Mcgill U; Languages.

FUSCO, THOMAS; Scituate HS; Scituate, MA; (Y); Drama Clb; Thesps; Chorus; Mrchg Band; School Play; Stage Crew; Swing Chorus; Symp Band; U MA Amherst; Prfrmg Art.

FUSHPANSKI, SUZANNE; Triton Regional HS; Salisbury, MA; (Y); Church Yth Grp; OEA; Hon Roll; Bus Educ Awd 84-85; Evangel Bible Coll; Legal Secy.

GAASCH, HEIDI; Newton North HS; Auburndale, MA; (Y); Church Yth Grp; French Clb; Ski Clb; Chorus; School Musical; Off Jr Cls; Off Stu Cncl; JV Swmmng; Var Trk; Hon Roll; Lbrl Arts.

GABRIEL, JOHN; Monument Mountain Reg HS; Housatonic, MA; (Y); Cmnty Wkr; Office Aide; Red Cross Aide; Stage Crew; Pres Soph Cls; Hon Roll; Great Barrington Fire Dept Vlntr Frfghtr; Housatonic Hose Co; Frfghtng.

GAETA, MARY; Mount Saint Joseph Acad; Medford, MA; (Y); Church Yth Grp; Science Clb; Yrbk Bus Mgr; Lit Mag; Trk; High Hon Roll; NHS; Haberlin Trust Scholar 83 & 84; Natl Sci Merit Awds 83 & 84; Intl Forn Lang Awd 85; Chem Engrng.

GAFFEY, KERRY; Matignon HS; Medford, MA; (S); 14/175; French Clb; JA; Science Clb; Rep Soph Cls; Var Crs Cntry; Co-Capt Trk; French Hon Soc; Hon Roll; NHS.

GAFFNY, KEVIN; Saint Dominic Savio HS; Revere, MA; (S); 19/125; JV Bsktbl; JV Ftbl; Trk; Hon Roll; Italian Lang Awd.

GAGNE, MATTHEW; Manson JR SR HS; Monson, MA; (Y); Aud/Vis; Boys Clb Am; Boy Scts; Exploring; French Clb; JA; PAVAS; School Musical; Awd For Hlpng 2 Slow Kids 80; Comp.

GAGNER, RUSSELL; North Attleboro HS; N Attleboro, MA; (Y); JCL; Latin Clb; Varsity Clb; Var L Ftbl; Powder Puff Ftbl; Hon Roll; N Attleboro Ftbll Schlrshp 85; U Of Lowell; Elec Engnrng.

GAGNON, LYNETTE M; Westfield HS; Westfield, MA; (Y); 9/358; Church Yth Grp; Church Choir; School Play; L Trk; L Vllybl; NHS; Messiah Coll Deans Schlrshp 84; Citzns Schlrshp Fndtn Awd 85; Messiah Coll Grantham PA.

GAGNON, MARY BETH; Bishop Connolly HS; Fall River, MA; (Y); 85/177; Cmnty Wkr; Hosp Aide; Spanish Clb; Vllybl; Hon Roll; Pre-Med.

GAGNON, MICHELLE; BMC Durfee HS; Fall River, MA; (Y); Trs Church Yth Grp; Yrbk Stf; Hon Roll; Toursm.

GAGNON, ROGER H; Norton HS; Norton, MA; (Y); 1/118; Mrchg Band; Yrbk Stf; Pres Frsh Cls; Var Crs Cntry; Bausch & Lomb Sci Awd; High Hon Roll; NHS; Val; Am Leg Boys St; Math Tm; Prsdntl Acad Ftnss Awd, Nvl Rsrv Ofcrs Trngn Crps Schlrshp 85; Hugh O Brien Yuth Ldrshp 83; Worcester Polytech; Nuclr Engr.

GAGNON, SCOTT; Taunton HS; Raynham, MA; (Y); Drama Clb; School Musical; School Play; Stage Crew; Boy Scts; Cmnty Wkr; French Clb; Teachers Aide; Acpl Chr; Chorus; Bridgewater ST Coll; Sec Ed.

GAINES, GRETA; Northfield Mount Hermon HS; S Newbury, NH; (Y); Model UN; Var Capt Ski Clb; School Play; Stage Crew; Lit Mag; Var Fld Hcky; Var Sftbl; Var Tennis; Wt Lftg; High Hon Roll; Dartmouth Clb Bk Awd 84; Georgetown U; Film.

GAINEY, JENNIFER; Malden HS; Malden, MA; (Y); Church Yth Grp; Cmnty Wkr; Girl Scts; Key Clb; Office Aide; Political Wkr; Church Choir; Variety Show; Yrbk Stf; Bowling; Pnmnshp Awd 80; Comptrs.

GAJDA, MELISSA; Taunton HS; Taunton, MA; (Y); 18/410; Drama Clb; Hosp Aide; Red Cross Aide; Ski Clb; Spanish Clb; Band; Concert Band; Mrchg Band; School Play; Polish Am Citzns Clb Schrshp 85; Joseph T Mc Donald Schlrshp 85; U Connecticut; Phrmcy.

GAJDA, MONIQUE MARIE; Hoosac Valley HS; Adams, MA; (Y); 14/185; CAP; Intnl Clb; Radio Clb; School Play; Nwsp Ed-Chief; Yrbk Stf; NHS; Pres Schlr; VFW Awd; MA Cadet Of Yr 83; Cade Ofcr Schl 2nd Pl Spch Awd 83; Outstndg Sqdrn Commndr 83; Daniel Webster Coll; Aviatn.

GAKIS, VASILIOS; Haverhill HS; Haverhill, MA; (Y); Var Socr; U Of Lowell; Engr.

GALANIS, ANGELA; Ispwich HS; Ipswich, MA; (Y); Pres Church Yth Grp; Yrbk Stf; Trs Frsh Cls; Trs Soph Cls; Trs Jr Cls; Trs Sr Cls; Rep Stu Cncl; Var Socr; Var Sftbl; Church Grp Pres 84; MVP Vrsty Sftbl 85; Bus.

GALARIS, SEAN; St Johns Prep; Marblehead, MA; (Y); Church Yth Grp; Cmnty Wkr; JA; Var Capt Bsktbl; Var Ftbl; Var Socr; Im Tennis; Im Wt Lftg; MVP Bsktbl 84-85; Most Outstndng Plyr Greek Am Vet Bsktbl Tourn 85; Bus Adm.

GALEGO, DEBBIE; New Bedford HS; New Bedford, MA; (Y); 85/688; Intnl Clb; Pep Clb; Chorus; Vllybl; Cit Awd; Hon Roll; Delta Kappa Gamma Essy Cntst 85; Southeastern MA U; Bus.

GALIN, DAVID; Lexington HS; Lexington, MA; (Y); Trs Drama Clb; School Musical; School Play; Stage Crew; JV Socr; Natl Hnr Roll 83-84; Elec Engnrng.

GALINDO, ANGELA L; Dana Hall Schl; New York, NY; (Y); Cmnty Wkr; Debate Tm; Political Wkr; Rep Sr Cls; Hon Roll; Ntl Merit Ltr; A Better Chance Schlrshp 82-85; LEAD Pgm 84; Dorm Proctor 84-85; Bus.

GALLA, TRACEY; Our Lady Of Nazareth Acad; Malden, MA; (Y); 41/64; Church Yth Grp; Debate Tm; Ski Clb; Spanish Clb; Acpl Chr; Chorus; School Musical; School Play; Nwsp Stf; Yrbk Stf; Bus Mngmnt.

GALLAGHER, ELIZABETH; Fontbonne Acad; Stoughton, MA; (Y); 3/310; Intnl Clb; Service Clb; Lit Mag; High Hon Roll; NHS; Ntl Merit Ltr; Bio Awd 84; Magna Cum Laude,Maxima Cum Laude,Silver Mdl 83-84; Phy Sci Awd 83; Pre-Med.

GALLAGHER, KIM; Silver Lake Regional HS; Halifax, MA; (Y); 57/454; Sec Church Yth Grp; Library Aide; Sec Spanish Clb; Band; Rep Soph Cls; Im Stat Bsktbl; Mgr(s); Score Keeper; Hon Roll; Halifx Grls Athltc Assn & Rbrt Billr Memrl Schlrshps 85; Southeastern MA U; Bus.

GALLAGHER, MATTHEW E; Catholic Memorial HS; Randolph, MA; (Y); Am Leg Boys St; Chess Clb; Rep Soph Cls; Rep Jr Cls; JV Socr; High Hon Roll; Jr NHS; NHS; Big Bros Prog Chrmn 85-86; Ldrshp Semnrs Estrn Conf Chrstn Bros 84-85.

GALLAGHER, THOMAS; St Peter-Marian CC HS; Worcester, MA; (S); 5/171; Math Tm; Crs Cntry; Off NHS; Boston College.

GALLANT, RENEE; Salem HS; Salem, MA; (Y); Ski Clb; Yrbk Stf; Capt Gym; High Hon Roll; Hon Roll; Anonymous Schlrshp 85; U Of MA; Real Ests Sls.

GALLANT, ROBERT; Don Bosco Tech; Chelsea, MA; (S); Chess Clb; Computer Clb; Political Wkr; Nwsp Rptr; Lit Mag; Wentworth; Electrnc Engr.

GALLIEN, SANDRA; David Prouty HS; E Brookfield, MA; (Y); 38/145; Cmnty Wkr; Latin Clb; Pep Clb; JV L Bsktbl; Var Coach Actv; JV Var Fld Hcky; Jr NHS; NHS; Office Aide; Nwsp Rptr; SAAD Treas; Ntl Hnr Soc Schlrshp; SMU; Pol Sci.

GALLIVAN, TIMOTHY G; Foxboro HS; Foxboro, MA; (Y); 24/243; Rep Am Leg Boys St; Boy Scts; VP Church Yth Grp; Pres French Clb; Varsity Clb; Nwsp Sprt Ed; Yrbk Stf; Rep Frsh Cls; Rep Soph Cls; Rep Jr Cls; Bus Wk Bentley Coll Scholar 85; Notre Dame; Pol Sci.

GALLO, JOSEPH A; Malden Catholic HS; Medford, MA; (Y); #79 In Class; Exploring; 4-H; French Clb; Intnl Clb; Varsity Clb; Nwsp Stf; L Capt Crs Cntry; Capt L Tennis; L Trk; High Hon Roll; U VT; Med.

GALLUZZO, CAROL; Woburn HS; Woburn, MA; (S); Leo Clb; Ski Clb; Variety Show; Rep Stu Cncl; Cheerleading; High Hon Roll; Hon Roll; VP Jr NHS; Ed.

GALUSKI, DAVID; Coyle & Cassidy HS; Raynham, MA; (Y); French Clb; Math Clb; Math Tm; Spanish Clb; Yrbk Stf; Trs Jr Cls; VP Capt Crs Cntry; Var Trk; Pres NHS; NEDT Awd; Dartmouth Coll; Med.

GALVIN, DIANE; Braintree HS; Braintree, MA; (Y); 28/480; Church Yth Grp; High Hon Roll; NHS; Spanish NHS; Law.

GALVIN, PAUL T; BMC Dufee HS; Fall River, MA; (Y); 9/688; Cmnty Wkr; French Clb; JV Bsbl; Var L Bsktbl; Elks Awd; High Hon Roll; NHS; Pres Schlr; Elks Teen Of Mnth 84; Cmmnwlth Schlr Grnt 85; Acadmc All Amer 85; Boston Clg; Engl.

GAMES, DEBBI S; Georgetown HS; Georgetown, MA; (Y); 8/93; Drama Clb; OEA; Yrbk Stf; Sec Jr Cls; Var Socr; Jr NHS; NHS; Church Yth Grp; French Clb; Girl Scts; 2nd Pl Offc Educ Assn Rcrds Mgmt & 4th Pl In Bus Math & Bus Prfrdng 85; Pres Phy Ftnss Awd 84-85; Babson Coll; Bus Mgmt.

GANCARZ, ROBERT M; Cathedral HS; Chicopee, MA; (Y); Wstrn New England; Elec Eng.

GANNON, DAMON; Franklin HS; Franklin, MA; (Y); Ski Clb; Crs Cntry; Trk; Hon Roll; Natl Vrsty Clb Awd 84 & 85.

GANNON, PAUL; Braintree HS; Braintree, MA; (Y); Cmnty Wkr; Trk; Hon Rl; Law Enfrcmnt.

GANONG, TAMMY; Groton Dunstable Reg Secondary Schl; Groton, MA; (Y); Church Yth Grp; Sec Trs 4-H; Rep Stu Cncl; 4-H Awd; Hon Roll; Jr NHS; Ntl Merit Ltr; Drama Clb; Intnl Clb; Rep Hugh O Brien Yth Ldrshp Conf 84; Basic Alchol Safty Ed 85; 1st Pl Ed Display Sci Fair 85; Bio.

GANYARD, JEFFREY P; Northfield Mount Hermon Schl; Boca Raton, FL; (Y); Boy Scts; Chess Clb; Drama Clb; French Clb; Math Clb; Math Tm; School Play; Im Var Ice Hcky; JV Var Lcrss; Im Socr; Tufts; Math.

GANZ, DAN; Natick HS; Natick, MA; (Y); 113/443; Temple Yth Grp; Stu Cncl; JV Bsbl; JV Trk; Hon Roll; 2 Trm Pres Lcl Bnai Brith Orgnztn 83-85; Regnl-VP 85-86; Law.

GAPARRO, PAUL B; Lincoln Sudbury Regional HS; Sudbury, MA; (Y); Bsbl; Ftbl; Trk; Law.

GARANT, LORI A; Seekonk HS; Seekonk, MA; (Y); French Clb; Teachers Aide; Var L Crs Cntry; Trk; Hon Roll; Jr NHS; Bus.

GARBERS, SAMANTHA; Boston Latin Schl; Boston, MA; (Y); 8/332; French Clb; Key Clb; Latin Clb; Yrbk Bus Mgr; Yrbk Stf; Rep Frsh Cls; Rep Soph Cls; Rep Jr Cls; VP Stu Cncl; Var Powder Puff Ftbl; Francis Gardner Prz Exc Studies 83-84; Cls Awd 82-83; Psych.

GARCEAU, DANIEL S; Medfield HS; Medfield, MA; (Y); Am Leg Boys St; Church Yth Grp; Band; JV Bsbl; Var L Ftbl; Var L Trk; Hon Roll; NHS; Ntl Merit Ltr; Engnr.

GARCIA, MARTHA; Lawrence HS; Lawrence, MA; (Y); High Hon Roll; Hon Roll.

GARCIA, PATRICIA; Malden HS; Malden, MA; (Y); 40/500; Hon Roll; Engr.

GARDELLA III, CHARLES; Haverhill HS; Haverhill, MA; (Y); 75/417; Boys Clb Am; Spanish Clb; Off Stu Cncl; High Hon Roll; NHS; James P Ginty Awd 85; Persnl Achv Awd 85; Northestrn U; Elec Engr.

GARELICK, LAURA A; Brookline HS; Chestnut Hill, MA; (Y); Dance Clb; Drama Clb; Ski Clb; School Musical; Diving; Co-Capt Gym; Jr NHS; Ntl Merit SF; Harvard Prize Bk 84; Carlton Warren Mem Sci Awd 84; Psy.

GARIEPY, LISA; Gardner HS; Gardner, MA; (Y); 12/150; Church Yth Grp; French Clb; Intnl Clb; Math Tm; Office Aide; Quiz Bowl; Hon Roll; NHS; Prfct Atten Awd; MA Schlr Grant 85; MA Commonwlth Scholar 85; Pres Acad Fit Awd 85; U MA; Anthroplgy.

GARLAND, AMY K; Brockton HS; Brockton, MA; (Y); 58/900; Church Yth Grp; Office Aide; Band; Concert Band; Mrchg Band; Symp Band; Acctng.

GARNIEWICZ, CHRISTOPHER; St Johns HS; Worcester, MA; (Y); 116/276; Art Clb; Boy Scts; Church Yth Grp; Drama Clb; Model UN; School Musical; Stage Crew; Lit Mag; JV Trk; JETS Awd; Mech Engr.

GARRETT, ANDREW; New Bedford HS; New Bedford, MA; (Y); 51/698; Chess Clb; Computer Clb; Drama Clb; JCL; Concert Band; Mrchg Band; Orch; Stu Cncl; Var Swmmng; Hon Roll; U S Naval Acad; Comp Sci.

GARRETT, KELLY; Burncoat SR HS; Worcester, MA; (Y); Church Yth Grp; French Clb; Intnl Clb; JA; Yrbk Stf; Var Capt Socr; Var Trk; Hon Roll; Career Day Worcester Essay Cntst 85; Engrng.

GARRITY, NANCY; Fontbonne Acad; Dor, MA; (Y); 6/150; Drama Clb; Hosp Aide; Math Tm; Science Clb; Teachers Aide; Crs Cntry; High Hon Roll; Hon Roll; Jr NHS; NHS; Sci Fair-Hnrb Mntn 84; Engrng.

GARRITY, THOMAS; Norwood SR HS; Norwood, MA; (Y); 18/346; Am Leg Boys St; Church Yth Grp; Computer Clb; Key Clb; Math Tm; Ski Clb; Ed Yrbk Bus Mgr; High Hon Roll; Town Gov Officl; Ntl Spnsh Cert; Rensselaer Polytech Inst; Comp.

GARROW, JEFFREY J; Ludlow HS; Ludlow, MA; (Y); Am Leg Boys St; Church Yth Grp; JCL; Var Capt Bsbl; JV Ice Hcky; High Hon Roll; Hon Roll.

GARTH, LYNN VIRGINIA; Lincoln-Sudbury Regional HS; Lincoln, MA; (Y); Church Yth Grp; French Clb; Chorus; Orch; School Musical; School Play; Ed Lit Mag; Cum Laude Soc; Harvard Prz Bk; Brown U Bk Awd.

GARVEY, JOHN; Boston College HS; Winchester, MA; (Y); 163/297; Church Yth Grp; Key Clb; Ski Clb; JV Ftbl; JV Trk; Hon Roll; Most Imprvd Stu; Ltrm Sailng Tm; Selectv Sumr Prog Boston Clg; Bus.

GASCO, BRIAN KEITH; Blackstone Valley Tech; Millbury, MA; (Y); Boy Scts; High Hon Roll; Hon Roll; Plumber.

GASKELL, DONNA; BMC Durfee HS; Fall River, MA; (Y); Hon Roll; SMU; Acctnt.

GATELY, DENNIS P; Governor Dummer Acad; Groveland, MA; (Y); Pres Aud/Vis; Key Clb; Thesps; Stage Crew; Yrbk Sprt Ed; Var Bsbl; Var Socr; Ntl Merit Ltr; Cum Laude Scty 85; GDA Hnr Scty 85; Dodge Bk Prz 85; MA Inst Tech; Chem Engr.

GATSOULIS, IRENE; Mario Umana Tech; Hyde Pk, MA; (Y); Hon Roll; Rensselaer Awd 84-85; Boston U; Bus.

GATZKE, ROBIN; Lexington HS; Lexington, MA; (Y); Natl Schl Orch Dir Awd; Tourg Membr Yng Perfrmrs Of Longy; New England Conservatory Hnrs Quartet.

GAUDET, GLENN; Wakefield HS; Wakefield, MA; (Y); 52/305; Aud/Vis; Pres JA; Key Clb; Ski Clb; School Play; Yrbk Stf; JV Ftbl; Chrmn Offcrs Rgn 1 Jr Achvrs Conf 85; Pres Jr Achvrs Assn Estrn MA 85; Babson Coll; Bus.

GAUDET, HEIDI; High School Of Commerce; Springfield, MA; (S); Hosp Aide; Office Aide; Band; Yrbk Rptr; Yrbk Stf; Trk; Hon Roll; Jr NHS; NHS.

GAUDETTE, BRIAN D; Milford HS; Milford, MA; (Y); 7/320; Yrbk Stf; Rep Frsh Cls; Rep Soph Cls; Rep Jr Cls; Rep Sr Cls; Var L Crs Cntry; Var Capt Golf; High Hon Roll; NHS; Holy Cross Worcester; Pre-Med.

GAUDETTE, MICHAEL; Holyoke HS; Holyoke, MA; (Y); French Clb; Hon Roll; Cum Laude Ntl Ltn Exam 84; Worcester Poly Inst; Engrng.

GAUDINO, FRANCESCA; East Boston HS; E Boston, MA; (Y); Math Clb; Hon Roll; Trvlg.

GAUDRAULT, THOMAS; Masconomet HS; Topsfield, MA; (Y); 20/250; French Clb; Teachers Aide; Var Capt Crs Cntry; Var Capt Trk; Hon Roll; NHS; Indoor Trck-Var, Capt Lttr 85; Sci Fair 2nd Pl 83; Pre-Med.

GAUDREAU, DONALD P; Salem HS; Salem, MA; (Y); Band; Concert Band; Jazz Band; Mrchg Band; Orch; Stu Cncl; Trk; High Hon Roll; Hon Roll; Engrng.

GAUGHEN, ANDREW POWERS; Milton HS; Milton, MA; (Y); AFS; Chess Clb; Stage Crew; Lit Mag; Hon Roll; Cert Hnr Readng Pgm 84; Essy Awd Wnnr Miltn Sr Ctzns Cmptn 84; New Eng Thtr Cmptn Stg Crw Awd Wnnng 85.

GAULIN, PAMELA A; Southbridge HS; Sbridge, MA; (Y); 21/144; Yrbk Ed-Chief; Yrbk Stf; Socr; Hon Roll; Frnch 3 Hnr Rll Awd.

GAUTHIER, MARYBETH; Holy Name CC HS; Millbury, MA; (Y); 16/276; Nwsp Ed-Chief; Yrbk Stf; JV Cheerleading; Hon Roll; NHS; Natl Sci Olympd 84; Dept Awd Amer Lit 85; Dept Awd Jrnlsm 85; Engl.

GAUTHIER, RONALD; Apponequet Regional HS; Lakeville, MA; (Y); Church Yth Grp; Drama Clb; School Musical; School Play; Variety Show; Im Bsktbl; Im Crs Cntry; JV Ftbl; Var Trk; Hon Roll; Southeastern MA U; Bus Mgt.

GAUVIN, KEVIN; Gardner HS; Gardner, MA; (Y); VP VICA; Draftng.

GAVEL, MARC; Central Catholic HS; Lowell, MA; (Y); 37/243; Computer Clb; Math Tm; Stage Crew; Yrbk Stf; Hon Roll; NHS; U Of Lowell; Mech Engr.

GAVONI, BETH; Silver Lake Regional HS; Kingston, MA; (Y); 23/500; Girl Scts; Spanish Clb; Yrbk Stf; Stu Cncl; JV Fld Hcky; High Hon Roll; Hon Roll; Trs NHS.

GAVRON, DAVID; Masconomet Regional HS; W Boxford, MA; (Y); 74/274; Latin Clb; Nwsp Rptr; Pres Soph Cls; Pres Jr Cls; JV Bsbl; JV Capt Bsktbl; JV Socr; Hon Roll; Rep Frsh Cls; Rep Sr Cls; Membr MIAA Div II N Champn Sccr Tm 84; Spkr Salem ST Coll Hstry Conf Wrld War II 85.

GAYNOR, ANN; Randolph HS; Randolph, MA; (Y); Teachers Aide; Yrbk Stf; Rep Stu Cncl; Capt Cheerleading; Var Coach Actv; Var Powder Puff Ftbl; JV Sftbl.

GAYTON, CYNTHIA; Natick HS; Natick, MA; (Y); 52/443; Hon Roll; New England Regnls-Fgr Sktng; Bus Admin.

GAZE, ERIC; Cathedral HS; Hampden, MA; (Y); Mathletes; Math Clb; Office Aide; Var Tennis; Mu Alp Tht; NHS; Holy Cross Bk Awd 85; SR Exec Bd Mbr Natl Hon Soc 85; Asstnt Democrat Chr Modl Senate 85.

GEAGHAN, SCOTT; Andover HS; Andover, MA; (Y); 5/340; Cmnty Wkr; Ski Clb; L Trk; Wt Lftg; High Hon Roll; Hon Roll; MIT; Elctrcl Engrng.

GEARY JR, DANIEL J; Salem HS; Salem, MA; (Y); Political Wkr; Yrbk Stf; Rep Jr Cls; Trk; Bus.

GEARY, ELLEN; Lawrence HS; Lawrence, MA; (S); 5/305; Band; Mrchg Band; High Hon Roll; Acctng.

GEARY, KARYN; Classical HS; Lynn, MA; (Y); 8/173; Church Yth Grp; Debate Tm; Hosp Aide; Spanish Clb; Yrbk Stf; Stu Cncl; Trk; High Hon Roll; Jr NHS; Pres NHS; Schlstc Achvt Awd 83; Miss Lynn Area Pagnt 85.

GEDACHIAN, AUDREY; Doherty Memorial HS; Worcester, MA; (Y); Hosp Aide; VP JA; Math Tm; Ski Clb; Nwsp Rptr; Trs Frsh Cls; Stu Cncl; Var Mgr(s); Hon Roll; Ntl Merit Ltr; 1st Pl Bk Brotherhd Awd 83.

GEIB, MICHELLE; Canton HS; Canton, MA; (Y); Pres Church Yth Grp; German Clb; Band; Concert Band; Mrchg Band; School Musical; Stage Crew; Mktng.

GELB, LAURIE I; Lexington HS; Lexington, MA; (Y); French Clb; Hosp Aide; Ski Clb; Temple Yth Grp; Yrbk Ed-Chief; Yrbk Stf; Stu Cncl; L Crs Cntry; NHS; Med.

GELGUT, JACQUELINE; Westfield HS; Westfield, MA; (Y); VP JA; School Play; Cit Awd; NHS; Natl Hnr Rl 85; St Joseph Coll; Exper Psych.

GELINAS, M; Cathedral HS; Springfield, MA; (Y); 50/500; Im Bsktbl; Hon Roll; Bus.

GELINAS, MARK; St Bernards CC HS; Fitchburg, MA; (S); 23/167; Math Clb; Im Bsktbl; Var L Ftbl; Trk; Wt Lftg; Hon Roll; NHS; Acad All-Amer 85; Law.

GELINAS, PAUL; Dimon Regional Voc-Tech HS; Somerset, MA; (Y); 1/200; Nwsp Stf; Yrbk Stf; JV Golf; MA Boys ST 85; Elect Engr.

GELMAN, RICHARD M; Holbrook HS; Holbrook, MA; (Y); 17/150; Spanish Clb; Chorus; Yrbk Rptr; Yrbk Stf; Var Bsbl; JV Bsktbl; Hon Roll; NHS; Cls 85 Exec Brd; Ntl Spnsh Exm; Sthestrn MA U; Comp Sci.

GEMME, KARA; David Prouty HS; Spencer, MA; (Y); 2/185; Church Yth Grp; Cmnty Wkr; Ski Clb; Sec Frsh Cls; Sec Soph Cls; VP Jr Cls; VP Sr Cls; Rep Stu Cncl; Var Trk; High Hon Roll; Stu Achvr Yr 85; Hnr Grad 85; Sr Hnr Soc 85; U CT; Phys Ther.

GENDREAU, NEIL; Southbridge HS; Southbridge, MA; (Y); 1/144; Cmnty Wkr; Math Clb; Math Tm; ROTC; Capt Ftbl; Trk; Wt Lftg; High Hon Roll; NHS; Val; Dstngshd Athl Awd Marine Corps 85; Natl Ftbl Fndtn Hall Of Fame 85; Best Of Cls 85; 1 Yr Schlrshp ROTC; Aeronaut Engrng.

GENDRON, SUZANNE; Monson JR-SR HS; Monson, MA; (Y); 10/86; Church Yth Grp; French Clb; Yrbk Phtg; Yrbk Stf; High Hon Roll; Hon Roll; Pres NHS; Hon Roll 82-83; Frgn Lang.

GENTILE, SUSAN E; Mount St Joseph Acad; Newton Highlands, MA; (Y); 30/160; Cmnty Wkr; GAA; Science Clb; VP Stu Cncl; Var Capt Bsktbl; Var Capt Socr; Var Capt Socr; Var Capt Vllybl; Hon Roll; Chess Clb; NEAAU Girls Olymp Bsktbl 84-85; Women Sports Found Awd 85; Leag MVP Sftbl 85; Bridgewater St Coll.

GENTILI, GINA; Mansfield HS; Mansfield, MA; (Y); 10/200; Color Guard; Rep Jr Cls; Sec Stu Cncl; JV Sftbl; NHS; Church Yth Grp; Cmnty Wkr; Key Clb; Spanish Clb; Drill Tm; Ctzns Scholar Fndtn Stu Rep 85-86; Advrtsng.

GEOFFROY, JEFFREY W; Marraganset Regional HS; Baldwinville, MA; (Y); 2/98; Am Leg Boys St; Boy Scts; Yrbk Stf; Pres Sr Cls; Var Ftbl; Mgr(s); Capt Tennis; NHS; Pres Schlr; Sal; USMA-WEST Point; Aerontcl Engr.

GEORGE, DOUGLAS; Boston Latin Schl; Boston, MA; (Y); 100/325; Church Yth Grp; Computer Clb; JA; Latin Clb; Trs Science Clb; Ski Clb; Off Stu Cncl; Var Bsbl; Ntl Merit SF; Pres & Fndr :Dtk Socl Orgnztn 84-86; Ran Trip 100 Stu Montreal Canada 85; Engrng.

GEORGE, JENNIFER; Wachusett Regional HS; Holden, MA; (Y); 46/381; Cmnty Wkr; Office Aide; Hon Roll; NHS; Chld Psych.

GEORGE, ROBERT; St Johns HS; Worcester, MA; (Y); 5/272; Am Leg Boys St; Church Yth Grp; Variety Show; Nwsp Rptr; Var Stu Cncl; JV Var Tennis; High Hon Roll; NHS; Schl Rep-MA Ldrshp Smnr 84; VP-NTL Hnr Soc 84-85; Engrng.

GEORGE, TIMOTHY A; Saint Johns HS; Worcester, MA; (Y); 22/272; Am Leg Boys St; Boy Scts; FBLA; Spanish Clb; Nwsp Rptr; Sec Jr Cls; Var Trk; High Hon Roll; NHS; Bowdoin Coll; Econmcs.

GERMAINE, MONIQUE; Westwood HS; Westwood, MA; (Y); 64/284; AFS; Sec Church Yth Grp; Trs Drama Clb; Office Aide; Spanish Clb; Chorus; Color Guard; Drill Tm; Jazz Band; Mrchg Band; Mc Donalds Crew Decthln Fnlst; Boston Coll; Bus Admn.

GEROKOULIS, SCOTT; Medford Voc-Tech HS; Medford, MA; (Y); #17 In Class; Math Clb; Math Tm; Bsbl; Bsktbl; Bowling; Ftbl; Golf; Score Keeper; Wt Lftg; Hon Roll; Most Imprvd Drftng 85; Wentworth Inst; Mech Desgn.

GERONIMO, VAL; Woburn HS; Woburn, MA; (S); 88/500; Drama Clb; French Clb; Leo Clb; Stu Cncl; Cheerleading; Hon Roll; NHS; Northeastern U; Acctng.

GERRISH, KAREN LEE; Franklin HS; Franklin, MA; (Y); 20/235; Church Yth Grp; Latin Clb; Red Cross Aide; Spanish Clb; Stage Crew; Variety Show; Lit Mag; Rep Stu Cncl; Var Capt Cheerleading; Hon Roll; Stonehill Coll Acad Scholar 85; Stonehill Coll; Bus.

GERVASI, DAVID; Weymouth North HS; Weymouth, MA; (Y); JV Var Ice Hcky; Hon Roll; Babe Ruth Bsbl 82-84; Bently Coll; Bus Mgmt.

GETCHELL, STEFANIE ADAMS; Newburyport HS; Newburyport, MA; (Y); Crs Cntry; Trk; Hon Roll; Crs Cntry Rcrd 84; Coaches Awd 85; MVP Crs Cntry 83 & 84; Mary Washington Coll; Envrnmntl.

GETSON, DEBBIE; Framingham South HS; Framingham, MA; (S); 13/270; Latin Clb; Varsity Clb; School Musical; Yrbk Stf; VP Stu Cncl; Var L Cheerleading; NHS; Variety Show; Rep Frsh Cls; Stdnt Govt Day Rep 85; Acadmc All Amer 84; Prom Coord 85.

GEVRY, MARY ELLEN; Shepherd Hill Regional HS; Dudley, MA; (Y); 28/160; Pres Church Yth Grp; French Clb; Girl Scts; Pep Clb; Band; Concert Band; Mrchg Band; Bsktbl; Capt Sftbl; Hon Roll; Alg Awd 82; Sftbl Capt 85; Field Hockey Capt 85; MA Coll Phrmcy; Phrmcy.

GHILARDUCCI, THOMAS; Taunton HS; Berkley, MA; (Y); 97/430; Band; Mrchg Band; Bsbl; Hon Roll; Arch.

GIAKOUMIS, TINA; Bartlett HS; Webster, MA; (Y); 11/148; Spanish Clb; Capt Flag Corp; Variety Show; Nwsp Ed-Chief; Yrbk Rptr; Hon Roll; NHS; Psych.

GIAMMATTEO, KERRI; King Phillip Regional HS; Clearwater, FL; (Y); FBLA; Yrbk Stf; Var Trk; Hon Roll; NHS; Vrsty Trk Ltr 84; Accntng.

GIANATASSIO, JULIE ANNE; Malden HS; Malden, MA; (Y); 8/500; VP Key Clb; Hst Latin Clb; Nwsp Sprt Ed; Rep Frsh Cls; Rep Soph Cls; Rep Jr Cls; Rep Sr Cls; Bsktbl; Lion Awd; NHS; American U; Bio.

GIANCOLA, LUCIA; Cathedral HS; Springfield, MA; (Y); 105/515; Church Yth Grp; Office Aide; Service Clb; Outstndng Svc Awd-Gudnc Aide 84-85; Centry 21 Accntng Cert Of Profcncy 85; Bus Admin.

GIANELLY, ROBERT C; Longmeadow HS; Longmeadow, MA; (Y); 70/278; Am Leg Boys St; Key Clb; Var Bsktbl; Capt Ftbl; Hon Roll; Hnr Mntn All Wstrn MA Ftbl Tm 84-85.

GIANNANOREA, ITALIA; Archbishop Williams HS; Quincy, MA; (Y); Yrbk Stf; Socr; Diplma Of Merit Spnsh II & III 83-85; Inc Law.

GIANNASCA, ROBERT; Matignon HS; Cambridge, MA; (S); 7/190; Drama Clb; French Clb; Hosp Aide; School Musical; French Hon Soc; Hon Roll; NHS; Math.

GIANNINO, JOSEPH; Malden Catholic HS; Revere, MA; (Y); Art Clb; Church Yth Grp; Debate Tm; French Clb; Political Wkr; Chrmn Stu Cncl; Mldn Cthlc Ldrshp Inst Smmr 85; Suffolk U; Bus Law.

GIARAMITA, KARRIE; Bishop Fenwick HS; Saugus, MA; (Y); Var Capt Bsktbl; Var Sftbl; Var Vllybl; High Hon Roll; Hon Roll; New Englnd JR Olympcs Grls Bsktbl Strtng Cntr 84; New Englnd JR Olympcs Ntl Tm Strtng Cnrt 85; Nuclear Med Tech.

GIARDINA, MICHELE; Woburn HS; Woburn, MA; (S); 100/500; Leo Clb; Spanish Clb; Yrbk Stf; Stu Cncl; High Hon Roll; Var Trk; Endicott Coll; Bus Adm.

GIBLIN, ROBERT A; Marian HS; Marlboro, MA; (Y); Ntl Merit Ltr; NEDT Awd; Schlrshp-U Of Miami FL 85; Awrded Frshmn Tutn Grnt-Bently Coll 85; Invtd To U Of MA Hnrs Pgm 85; U Of MA Amherst.

GIDDON, JOANNA; Newton North HS; W Newton, MA; (Y); French Clb; GAA; Letterman Clb; Pep Clb; Teachers Aide; Varsity Clb; School Play; Yrbk Stf; Trk; Vllybl; Coaches Awd, Cpt Vlybl, Bsktbl, Trk 82-83; Cpt Vl Bl, Trk 85-86; Comm.

GILBERT, DIANE; Norwood HS; Norwood, MA; (Y); 60/351; Cmnty Wkr; Yrbk Sprt Ed; Var Bsktbl; Var Fld Hcky; JV Sftbl; Im Vllybl; U MA Amherst; Bus Mgmt.

GILES, LAURA; Hoosac Valley HS; Cheshire, MA; (Y); Ski Clb; Concert Band; Mrchg Band; Yrbk Ed-Chief; Capt Crs Cntry; High Hon Roll; Wellesley Alumnae Bk Awd 85; Ambassdr Hugh O Bryan Yth Ldrshp Fndtn 84; Natl Engl Merit Awd 85.

GILFIX, AMY; Chapel Hill Chauncey Hall; Newton, MA; (Y); 2/45; Intnl Clb; Spanish Clb; Chorus; School Musical; Yrbk Bus Mgr; Yrbk Stf; Stu Cncl; Var Vllybl; High Hon Roll; Ntl Merit Ltr; Drama Awd 85; Stu Math Tutr 85; Pine Mnr Tenis Chmpn 81; Cmmnctns.

GILL, MATTHEW D; Woburn HS; Woburn, MA; (Y); Band; Concert Band; Jazz Band; Mrchg Band; Orch; School Musical; Schlrshp-Smmr Yth Music Schl U Of NH; Outstndg Acad Achvt Awd -Music 85; MA Yth Wind Ensmbl 84-85; Muscn.

GILL, MIKE; Fairhaven HS; Fairhaven, MA; (Y); Bsbl; Ice Hcky; Hon Roll; Standard Times All Star Hcky Tm 85; SE MA All Star Hcky Tm 85.

GILLESPIE, KELLY; South High Community Schl; Worcester, MA; (S); Stu Cncl; High Hon Roll; Hon Roll; NHS; Frnch I Awd 84; Cert For Straight A 83; Coll; Communications.

GILLESPIE, KRISTINE; Randolph HS; Randolph, MA; (Y); FNA; Hosp Aide; Intnl Clb; Spanish Clb; Teachers Aide; Yrbk Stf; Hon Roll; JC Awd; Jr NHS; NHS; Stu Gov Awd 84-85; Hmcmng Parade 84-85; Med.

GILLET, CHRISTINE; Bishop Connolly HS; Westport, MA; (Y); 73/160; Art Clb; Cmnty Wkr; Political Wkr; Yrbk Stf; High Hon Roll; Hon Roll; NHS; Barlizon Schl Of Mdlng Grad 83-84; Outstndng Art Stu; Asstnt Prncpls Awd; Fashion Inst Of Tech; Intr Dsgn.

GILLIATT, PAMELA M; Medway JR SR HS; Medway, MA; (Y); 14/131; Yrbk Stf; Sec Jr Cls; Sec Sr Cls; Var L Cheerleading; Var Powder Puff Ftbl; Hon Roll; Sec NHS; Accntng Awd; Schlstc Awd; Bost U Schlrshp; MA ST Schlrshp; HS Schlrshp; Boston U; Math.

GILLIGAN, LAWRENCE; Malden HS; Malden, MA; (Y); 51/450; Church Yth Grp; Variety Show; VP Soph Cls; VP Jr Cls; VP Sr Cls; Bsbl; Var L Crs Cntry; JV Ftbl; Voice Dem Awd; Political Wkr; Little League Tm Coach 84; Sec Educ.

GILLIGAN, PAUL; Mount Everett Reg; Sheffield, MA; (Y); 1/73; Am Leg Boys St; Boy Scts; Church Yth Grp; Q&S; Trs Sr Cls; JV Bsbl; JV Var Bsktbl; High Hon Roll; Colby Coll Awd Mst Outstdng Stu In Clss 85; Engrng.

GILLIS, MARK J; Reading Memorial HS; Reading, MA; (Y); 59/357; Computer Clb; Debate Tm; High Hon Roll; Hon Roll; Ntl Merit Ltr; Pres Schlr; Womens Assn Schlrshp 85; Boston U; Lit.

GILLMAN, ALEXANDER B; Masconomet Reg SR HS; Boxford, MA; (Y); 59/278; Art Clb; Boy Scts; Thesps; School Musical; School Play; Nwsp Rptr; Nwsp Stf; Yrbk Stf; Badmtn; Var L Trk; Boston Globe Schlstc Arts Awds 84-85; Arts Recognition & Tlnt Srch Hnbl Mntn 84-85; Fine Arts.

GILLMAN, MICHAEL; Easthampton HS; Easthampton, MA; (Y); 2/142; Am Leg Boys St; Math Tm; Var Golf; High Hon Roll; NHS; Rensselaer Mth & Sci Awd; Amer H S Mth Exam Awd; Comp Info Sys.

GILLOOLY, VANESSA; Drury SR HS; North Adams, MA; (S); Church Yth Grp; Dance Clb; Pep Clb; Band; Trs Concert Band; Mrchg Band; Pep Band; School Musical; Rep Frsh Cls; Hon Roll; Rotry Clb Tlnt Show & Prz 83; Music Schlrshp-Drury Band 84.

GILMAN, GALADRIEL; Georgetown HS; Georgetown, MA; (Y); Capt Varsity Clb; Capt Bsktbl; Var Fld Hcky; Var Sftbl; High Hon Roll; NHS; AFS; Church Yth Grp; Cmnty Wkr; Drama Clb; Stu Advsry Comm 84-85; Arch.

GILMAN, STEVEN; Malden HS; Malden, MA; (Y); 30/700; Office Aide; Stage Crew; High Hon Roll; Boston U; Air Trffc Cntrl.

GILMARTIN, BRIAN; St Johns HS; Auburn, MA; (Y); 90/270; Boy Scts; JA; Spanish Clb; Var Capt Crs Cntry; Var L Trk; High Hon Roll; Hon Roll; Ski Clb; WPI Scholar 85-86; Worcester Polytech; Elec Engrng.

GIMILARO, STEPHEN; Arlington HS; Arlington, MA; (S); 13/417; Computer Clb; Debate Tm; NFL; Band; Concert Band; Jazz Band; Mrchg Band; Orch; Symp Band; Im Bsbl; Arlngtn Hstrcl Soc Essay Cntst 84; Pol Sci.

GINNETTY, DAN; Silver Lake Regional HS; Halifax, MA; (Y); 62/500; Math Clb; Spanish Clb; Im Bskbl; Im Wt Lftg.

GINTY, BARBARA; Holyoke Catholic HS; Holyoke, MA; (Y); 8/144; Latin Clb; Spanish Clb; Nwsp Stf; High Hon Roll; Hon Roll; NHS; Ntl Merit Ltr; Prfct Atten Awd; Excllnce Engl I, Religion I Awd 83; Excllnce Hnrs Engl II Awd 84; Cmmnctns.

GIOIOSO, JENNIFER; Danvers HS; Danvers, MA; (Y); 3/310; Hosp Aide; Capt Color Guard; Capt Flag Corp; Yrbk Rptr; Yrbk Stf; French Hon Soc; High Hon Roll; NHS; Outstndng Ldrshp Awd 84; Mktng.

GIONFRIDDO, TOM; Agawam HS; Feeding Hills, MA; (Y); 23/400; Pres Band; Pres Concert Band; Mgr Jazz Band; Pres Mrchg Band; School Musical; Lit Mag; Hon Roll; NHS; Ntl Merit Ltr; Drama Clb; MA Assn Jzz Eductrs Jzz Comp Comptn 84-85; Ntl Assn Jzz Eductrs Outstndng Sol Awd 83; Music Compstn.

GIORDANO, GARY; Malden Catholic HS; Saugus, MA; (Y); 44/187; Chess Clb; Church Yth Grp; CAP; MMM; Pep Clb; Church Choir; Pep Band; L Ftbl; Capt Wt Lftg; NHS.

GIRARD, DIANE; Murdock HS; Winchendon, MA; (Y); 5/107; Model UN; Stage Crew; Yrbk Stf; Rep Stu Cncl; Var Capt Bsktbl; Var L Fld Hcky; Var Capt Sftbl; NHS; Ntl Merit Ltr; Church Yth Grp; Chairprsn Model Congrss 85; Wachusett Lg All Star Sftbl 85; Pre-Med.

GIRARD, MICHELLE; New Bedford HS; New Bedford, MA; (Y); 10/600; Sec Computer Clb; JCL; Rep Jr Cls; Rep Sr Cls; Var Crs Cntry; Var Capt Trk; High Hon Roll; Hon Roll; NHS; NBEA Schlrshp 85; Pres Acadmc Ftns Awd 85; Capts Clb Athlt Of Mnth 85; Georgetown U; Bus.

GIROUARD, DIANE; New Bedford HS; New Bedford, MA; (Y); 142/599; JA; Office Aide; Q&S; Nwsp Rptr; Nwsp Stf; Hon Roll; 1st Prz Jewsh Fdrtn Holocst Essy Cntst 84; AFL-CIO Schlrshp Orgnzd Labr 85; Qull & Scrll Hnr Soc 85; Sthestrn MA U; Jrnlsm.

GIROUARD, JAMES M; Westfield HS; Westfield, MA; (Y); 70/350; VP JA; Nwsp Rptr; Nwsp Stf; Yrbk Stf; Stu Cncl; Var Trk; Var Capt Wrstlng; High Hon Roll; Hon Roll; Ntl Merit Ltr; Ray Mc Donald Schlrshp 85; Ripon Coll; Hstry Ed.

GIROUX, SHIRLEY; Southbridge HS; Southridge, MA; (Y); Hon Roll.

GIRR, CATHERINE; Longmeadow HS; Longmeadow, MA; (Y); 23/281; Capt Quiz Bowl; Nwsp Ed-Chief; Chess Clb; Rep Stu Cncl; Var L Crs Cntry; Var L Lcrss; High Hon Roll; NHS; Prfct Atten Awd; JV L Bsktbl; U Of MA Chnclrs Tlnt Awd Schlrshp 85.

GISMONDI, CAROL; Medway JR SR HS; Medway, MA; (Y); 11/160; Band; Yrbk Stf; Sec Soph Cls; JV Var Bsktbl; Var Tennis; JV Var Vllybl; Hon Roll; NHS; Ntl Merit Ltr; Law.

GITLIN, JOCELYN M; Newton South HS; Newton, MA; (Y); Dance Clb; Ski Clb; Temple Yth Grp; School Musical; School Play; Variety Show; Nwsp Stf; Lit Mag; Rep Sr Cls; Rnr Up Miss MA Amer Co-Ed Pag 85; Lehigh U; Bus.

GITTENS, PATRICIA; E Boston HS; Dorchester, MA; (Y); Church Yth Grp; Trk; Salem ST Coll; Bus Ed.

GIUSTI, SUSAN; St Clare HS; Norwood, MA; (Y); Cmnty Wkr; Varsity Clb; Var Capt Sftbl; Im Vllybl; MVP Sftbl; Mst Outstndng Math Stu; Mst Dstngsd Athlte; MA Acad; Engrng.

GLADSTONE, PAMELA; Methuen HS; Methuen, MA; (Y); 7/336; Intnl Clb; Model UN; Color Guard; Nwsp Bus Mgr; Nwsp Ed-Chief; Nwsp Rptr; Nwsp Stf; Yrbk Ed-Chief; Yrbk Rptr; Yrbk Stf; Awd Excllnc Jrnlsm 85; Hnbl Mntn Annl ST Hstrcl Conf 85; VA Wesleyan; Jrnlsm.

GLADU, KIMBERLY; Holyoke Catholic HS; Chicopee, MA; (Y); Church Yth Grp; French Clb; Yrbk Stf; French Hon Soc; Hon Roll; St Annes Sodality Gld Schlrshp; Gerber Baby Prods Co Schlrshp; Le Cercle Rochambeau Schlrshp; Westfield St; Early Chldhd Educ.

GLASS, BONNIE J; Silver Lane Regional HS; Pembroke, MA; (Y); 205/492; Key Clb; Office Aide; Yrbk Stf; Cheerleading; Crs Cntry; Trk; Hon Roll; Pell Grant 85; MA ST Schlrshp 85; Dean JC; Fashn Merch.

GLASS, KELLEY; Marblehead HS; Marblehead, MA; (Y); 35/259; Church Yth Grp; Debate Tm; Drama Clb; French Clb; Hosp Aide; Capt Color Guard; Trk; Hon Roll; Sunday Schl Tchr 85; Psych.

GLASSER, SUSAN; Phillips Acad; Montclair, NJ; (Y); French Clb; Model UN; Nwsp Ed-Chief; Nwsp Rptr; Var Tennis; Hon Roll; Law.

GLASSMAN, DEBBY; Randolph HS; Randolph, MA; (Y); Spanish Clb; Temple Yth Grp; Drill Tm; Nwsp Stf; Yrbk Ed-Chief; Stu Cncl; Bus Law.

GLAVICKAS, CATHERINE; Easthampton HS; Easthampton, MA; (Y); Hosp Aide; Ski Clb; Rep Jr Cls; VP Sr Cls; Rep Stu Cncl; Var Socr; Bentley Coll; Accountng.

GLEASON, GARY; Boston College HS; Braintree, MA; (Y); Chess Clb; Ski Clb; Im Bsktbl; Im Ftbl; Im Vllybl; Hon Roll; Ntl Merit Ltr.

GLEESON, BRENDAN; Burncoat SR HS; Worcester, MA; (Y); Variety Show; Sec Church Yth Grp; Nwsp Rptr; Var Socr; Var Trk; Hon Roll; Jr NHS; NHS; Prfct Atten Awd; Telegram & Gazette Ace Carrier 85.

GLEESON, LAUREN; Natick HS; Natick, MA; (Y); 31/443; Girl Scts; Hosp Aide; Yrbk Stf; Rep Jr Cls; Rep Stu Cncl; Var Swmmng; JV Trk; High Hon Roll; Hon Roll; Prfct Atten Awd.

GLISPIN, ARTHUR; Grafton Memorial SR HS; North Grafton, MA; (Y); Church Yth Grp; Var JV Bsktbl; Im Vllybl; Hon Roll; NHS; Comp Sci.

GLOSTER, TIMOTHY; Drury SR HS; N Adams, MA; (Y); 47/120; Church Yth Grp; Band; Concert Band; Mrchg Band; Pep Band; School Musical; Var L Tennis; High Hon Roll; Hon Roll; Pep Club Schlrshp 85; Band Schlrshp 85; Westfield ST Coll; His.

GLUECK, JULIET; Christopher Columbus HS; Boston, MA; (S); Art Clb; Drama Clb; French Clb; Hosp Aide; School Play; Lit Mag; JV Bsktbl; JV Fld Hcky; JV Lcrss; Hon Roll; Literary Mag Awd 84; Brown U; Bus.

GLUSHIK, JOHN; Westfield HS; Westfield, MA; (Y); 1/336; Church Yth Grp; Cmnty Wkr; Scholastic Bowl; Band; Rep Stu Cncl; Var Bsktbl; Tennis; NHS; Concert Band; Jazz Band; Dartmouth Clb Bk Awd 85; Wstrn MA Dist Jazz Bank 85; Chncllrs Tlnt Awd 85.

GLYNN, BRIAN J; Whitman-Hanson Regional HS; Whitman, MA; (Y); 95/350; DECA; FBLA; Nwsp Rptr; Stu Cncl; Var Socr; Var Trk; Pres DECA MA 84; Natl Bus Conf 85; DECA Schlrshp 85; Johnson & Wales Coll; Htl Mgt.

GLYNN, KARA; Dana Hall HS; Wellesley, MA; (Y); GAA; Q&S; Varsity Clb; Nwsp Stf; Yrbk Stf; Rep Jr Cls; Rep Sr Cls; Var Socr; Hon Roll; Sibly Law.

GOC, KIMBERLY; Nazareth Acad; Melrose, MA; (Y); 6/60; Pep Clb; Spanish Clb; Var L Bsktbl; Var L Socr; Var Vllybl; High Hon Roll; Hon Roll; NHS; Knights Of Columbus Essay Cntst Wnnr 85; Outstndng Contribtn-Bsktbll Awd 84; Sports Med.

GODARD, TAMMY; Holyoke HS; Holyoke, MA; (Y); 34/380; Church Yth Grp; French Clb; Band; Concert Band; Var Tennis; Hon Roll; Jr NHS; NHS; Pres Schlr; Margaret J Hyland Memrl Schlrshp 85; Cercle Des Dames Francais 85; Springdale PTA Awd 85; U Of MA; Pre-Med.

GODDARD, DEBROAH; Fontbonns Acad; Boston, MA; (Y); 64/160; Art Clb; Dance Clb; Drama Clb; Library Aide; Art Awd; Global Schltcs & Natl Art Awds; Poster Cntst; Simmons Coll; Psych.

GODDEAU, SCOTT; Cathedral HS; Somers, CT; (Y); Library Aide; Office Aide; Bsktbl; NHS; HS Outstndng Svc Awd 85; Boston Coll; Corp Law.

GODEK JR, THOMAS G; Hull HS; Hull, MA; (Y); 10/158; Computer Clb; Math Clb; Pres Band; Jazz Band; Pres Mrchg Band; Var L Bsbl; JV Stat Ftbl; JP Sousa Awd; Trs NHS; Im Vllybl; Reuben A & Lizzie Grossman Awd 85; Pres Acad Ftnss Awd 85; Hull Coachs Trphy 85; Boston U; Math.

GODES, ARLENE; Randolph HS; Randolph, MA; (Y); Trs French Clb; Pres FNA; Hosp Aide; Spanish Clb; Hst Temple Yth Grp; Rep Soph Cls; Hon Roll; VP Jr NHS; NHS; Bowling; Nursng.

GODFREY, MARGARET; Salem HS; Salem, MA; (Y); Rep Stu Cncl; Var Cheerleading; JV Fld Hcky; Hon Roll; Merch Mgmt.

GODFREY, MARK S; Hanover HS; Hanover, MA; (Y); Trs Soph Cls; Trs Jr Cls; Trs Sr Cls; Var Bsbl; Capt Bsktbl; Capt Ftbl; Var Trk; High Hon Roll; Hon Roll; NHS; Engrng.

GOEHRING, MARY LOUISE; Chicopee Comprehensive HS; Chicopee, MA; (Y); 31/321; Church Yth Grp; 4-H; German Clb; Hosp Aide; Church Choir; Drm & Bgl; Yrbk Stf; VP Soph Cls; VP Jr Cls; VP Sr Cls; Northeastern Drum Corp Champ 84; John L Fitzpatrick Schlrshp 85; Abbey Schlrshp 85; Wheelock Coll; Child Ed.

GOGUEN, DEIDRE; Leominster HS; Leominster, MA; (S); 24/344; Political Wkr; School Musical; Rep Stu Cncl; VP Swmmng; VP Trk; NHS; Ntl Merit Ltr; Voice Dem Awd; U Of MA Chancellors Talent Awd 84; Comm.

GOKAS, DIANE; Lynn English HS; Lynn, MA; (Y); 30/352; GAA; Ski Clb; Concert Band; Trs Mrchg Band; High Hon Roll; Hon Roll; Babe Ruth Sftbl All Star Awd 83; Comp Sci.

GOKHALE, AJIT V; Randolph HS; Randolph, MA; (Y); 1/314; Pres Chess Clb; Capt Math Tm; Trs Jr Cls; L JV Bsbl; L Socr; Bausch & Lomb Sci Awd; Ntl Merit Schol; Val; Model UN; Nwsp Sprt Ed; Rensselaer Polytech Inst Mdl Sci & Math 84; MATH Olympiad Finlst 85; Captiol Area Mth Lg MVP 84; MA Inst Of Tech; Elect Engrng.

GOLDBERG, PAULA; Governor Dummer Acad; Andover, MA; (Y); Sec Frsh Cls; Fld Hcky; Lcrss; Vllybl; Hon Roll; Drmtry Prctr 84-85; Lafayette Coll.

GOLDEN, CHRISTOPHER; Marian HS; Framingham, MA; (Y); 21/177; School Musical; Variety Show; Nwsp Rptr; Yrbk Stf; Lit Mag; Hon Roll; NEDT Awd.

GOLDFARB, DEBRA; Westwood SR HS; Westwood, MA; (Y); 36/210; Dance Clb; Key Clb; Teachers Aide; Temple Yth Grp; Capt Var Cheerleading; Var Powder Puff Ftbl; Var Swmmng; Var Trk; Cit Awd; Hon Roll; Abraham Joshua Heschel Hnr Socty Untd Synag Yth 84-85; Pol Sci.

GOLDMAN, JEFF; Brockton HS; Brockton, MA; (Y); 6/950; Am Leg Boys St; Boy Scts; Church Yth Grp; Key Clb; Science Clb; Temple Yth Grp; High Hon Roll; NHS; Rotary Awd; Eagle Sct Schlrshp 85; Phi Delta Kppa Tchng Soc Awd 85; Yeshiva U-NY; Biochem.

GOLDMAN, JEFFREY; Lexington HS; Lexington, MA; (Y); Sec Computer Clb; Scholastic Bowl; VP Temple Yth Grp; Band; Boy Scts; Jazz Band; Mrchg Band; Bsktbl; Hon Roll; Colgate U.

GOLDSTEIN, AMY; Wakefield Memorial HS; Wakefield, MA; (Y); Key Clb; Variety Show; Hon Roll; Jr NHS; NHS; JR Wrtng Awd 85; Endicott Clg; Mktg.

GOLDSTEIN, DAMON; Medford HS; Medford, MA; (Y); 20/416; Pres Drama Clb; Letterman Clb; Var Math Tm; Nwsp Stf; Rep Jr Cls; Var Capt Swmmng; Var L Tennis; Mu Alp Tht; NHS; MVP Boys Var Swim Tm 85.

GOLDSTEIN, ERIC; Westwood HS; Westwood, MA; (Y); 21/225; Chess Clb; Computer Clb; Dance Clb; Temple Yth Grp; School Musical; School Play; Crs Cntry; Score Keeper; Trk; Hon Roll; Natl Rcgntn Piano Plyng 84; Taught Comp Cls Sr Yr; UCLA; Comp.

GOLDSTEIN, JAMES B; Burlington HS; Burlington, MA; (Y); 11/340; Trs Debate Tm; Math Tm; JV Bsktbl; Im Coach Actv; High Hon Roll; Hon Roll; NHS; Drtmth Book Awd 85.

GOLDSTEIN, KEITH; Randolph HS; Randolph, MA; (Y); Intnl Clb; High Hon Roll; Hon Roll; Accntg.

GOLISANO, TINA; Malden HS; Malden, MA; (Y); 10/500; Art Clb; Key Clb; Math Tm; Office Aide; Quiz Bowl; Band; Drm & Bgl; Mrchg Band; Variety Show; NHS; Dartmouth Clb Bk Awd 85; Ntl Hnr Soc Sec 85-86; Wind Endmbl 84; Engrng.

GOLUB, DAVID; Needham HS; Needham, MA; (S); 196/420; Ski Clb; Lit Mag; Lcrss; Ntl Merit Ltr; Poetry.

GOMES, DAVID; New Bedford HS; New Bedford, MA; (Y); 42/688; Church Yth Grp; Office Aide; Yrbk Ed-Chief; Yrbk Stf; Rep Stu Cncl; JV Crs Cntry; Var Trk; Hon Roll; NHS; Natl Latin Exm-Cum Laude 85; 3rd Pl Wnnr-Delta Kappa Gamma Essy 85; S E Rgnl Stu Advsry Cncl Cmtte 85; Boston Coll; Bio.

GOMEZ, ANTONIO C; Salem HS; Salem, MA; (Y); Wentworth Inst Tech; Comp Engr.

GONCALVES, DAVID; Diman Reg Voc Tech HS; Fall River, MA; (Y); Boys Clb Am; Church Yth Grp; FCA; Church Choir; Stage Crew; Rep Stu Cncl; Hon Roll; Zion Bible Inst; Undrsea Wldr.

GONSER, GREGORY; Westwood HS; Westwood, MA; (Y); 95/206; Am Leg Boys St; Church Yth Grp; Drama Clb; Thesps; Acpl Chr; Chorus; Jazz Band; School Play; Stage Crew; Tennis; Natl Arion Awd 85; Dist Singer Hnrs Chorus 83-85; All ST Singer Top 1 Pcnt ST 85; Music.

GONYEA, GREG; Silver Lake Regional HS; Kingston, MA; (Y); Art Clb; French Clb; Ski Clb; Hon Roll; Boston Globe Schltc Art Awd Cert Of Recog 83; Art.

GONYEA, KYLE; St Johns HS; Worcester, MA; (Y); Church Yth Grp; Sec Drama Clb; Spanish Clb; Chorus; School Musical; School Play; Stage Crew; Variety Show; Rep Frsh Cls; Rep Soph Cls; Bst Male Voclst Awd-Schl Varty Shw 83-85; Music.

GONZALES, CLAYTON; Andover HS; Andover, MA; (Y); 100/435; Civic Clb; Drama Clb; Model UN; Orch; School Play; VP Sr Cls; High Hon Roll; Science Clb; Variety Show; Yrbk Stf; Holy Cross Coll; Chem.

GONZALEZ, GLORIA H; Mission Church HS; Randolph, MA; (Y); Varsity Clb; Yrbk Stf; Sec Jr Cls; VP Sr Cls; Var Cheerleading; Hon Roll; NHS; Boston Coll; Comp Sci.

GONZALEZ, LORI; New Bedford HS; New Bedford, MA; (Y); Office Aide; Concert Band; Mrchg Band; Orch; School Musical; Hon Roll; Phy Ther.

GONZALEZ, MICHELE; Bedford HS; Bedford, MA; (Y); 33/213; Band; Concert Band; Jazz Band; Madrigals; Orch; Bsktbl; Trk; Hon Roll; Grls Trple Jump Rcrd 85; Athl Trng Pgm Ltr 84-85; U TX San Antonio; Phy Thrpy.

GOODALE, THOMAS; Newton Catholic HS; Newton, MA; (S); 1/52; Am Leg Boys St; Exploring; Yrbk Ed-Chief; Trs Stu Cncl; High Hon Roll; NHS; Val; Suffolk U Bk Awd 84; Boston Coll; Bio.

GOODE JR, ROBERT; Bishop Feehan HS; Norton, MA; (Y); JCL; JV Ice Hcky; High Hon Roll; Hon Roll; Intl Latin Awd Magnum Cum Laude 85.

GOODFIELD, TANYA; Leicester HS; Leicester, MA; (S); Church Yth Grp; Drama Clb; 4-H; Office Aide; Ski Clb; Varsity Clb; Band; School Play; Variety Show; Pres Jr Cls; Ldrshp Conf 84; Stu Senate In Boston 85; Stu Town Gov 83-85; Holy Cross.

GOODMAN, AMY; Malden HS; Malden, MA; (Y); Pres Dance Clb; Temple Yth Grp; Variety Show; Comp Pgmr.

GOODMAN, KATHERINE; Buckingham Browne & Nichols HS; Brooklin, MA; (S); Jazz Band; School Musical; School Play; Stage Crew; Nwsp Ed-Chief; Nwsp Rptr; Sftbl; Hon Roll; 1st Pl JR Prfl Awd 86.

GOODREAU, TRICIA J; Westfield HS; Westfield, MA; (Y); 15/347; Church Yth Grp; Cmnty Wkr; French Clb; JV Var Sftbl; NHS; Stu Alcohol Advsry Bd; Cmnty Hon Awd-Help On Safe Prom 84; Excllnc Fr Awd 85; Air National Guard; Elec.

GOODRIDGE, SCOTT; North Middlesex Regional HS; Townsend, MA; (Y); Aud/Vis; Church Yth Grp; Letterman Clb; Library Aide; ROTC; Varsity Clb; Variety Show; JV Capt Bsktbl; Var Mgr(s); Var Capt Tennis; Bio.

GOODROW, MISTY; Leicester HS; Leicester, MA; (S); 1/108; Church Yth Grp; Latin Clb; Math Tm; Cheerleading; High Hon Roll; VP NHS; Natl Hnr Soc Schl Rep Natl Schlrshp 85; MA ST Schlr Grnt Schlrshp 85; Mt Holyoke Coll; Bio Sci.

GOODWIN, CAROL; Malden HS; Malden, MA; (Y); 24/465; Camp Fr Inc; Church Yth Grp; Teachers Aide; Color Guard; Mrchg Band; Variety Show; Rep Jr Cls; Hon Roll; Natl Engl Merit Awd; Zonta Intl Ctzn Schlr Awd; Cmmnctns.

GORDON, CARLA; Old Rochester Regional HS; Mattapoisett, MA; (Y); AFS; French Clb; Office Aide; Yrbk Stf; JV Var Sftbl; JV Vllybl; Coaches Awd Softball; MVP Volleyball; French.

GORDON, DONALD; Milford HS; Milford, MA; (Y); Socr; Trk; High Hon Roll; NHS.

GORDON, KELLY; Haverhill HS; Haverhill, MA; (Y); 17/450; Church Yth Grp; Sec German Clb; Hosp Aide; Intnl Clb; Latin Clb; Rep Stu Cncl; High Hon Roll; Hon Roll; NHS; Alg Awd Frshmn Asmbly; PWA Intl Order Rainbow Girls; Nrsng.

GORDON, KIMBERLY; Leicester HS; Roddale, MA; (Y); 24/109; French Clb; Girl Scts; Bst Attitude Awd Modeling 84; Mst Imprvd Model Awd 83; Bay Path JC; Fshn Merch.

GORDON, MICHELLE; Framingham South HS; Framingham, MA; (Y); 90/260; Drama Clb; Sec VP French Clb; Hosp Aide; Sec JA; Capt Color Guard; School Musical; Sec Soph Cls; Sec Jr Cls; Sec Sr Cls; Temple Yth Grp; SAAD Secy & Treas; Advrtsng.

GORDON, PHYLLIS; Marlborough HS; Marlborough, MA; (Y); 5/280; AFS; Sec Am Leg Aux Girls St; Variety Show; Stu Cncl; Capt Crs Cntry; Socr; Trk; High Hon Roll; Kiwanis Awd; NHS; Wesleyan U; Jrnlsm.

GOREN, ROBYN; Natick HS; Canada; (Y); 15/375; Frsh Cls; Stu Cncl; Var L Crs Cntry; Socr; Swmmng; Var L Trk; Hon Roll; Prfct Atten Awd; Canadian Red Cross Bronze Medallion, Bronze Cross Swmmng Awd 83; Royal Conservatory Mus Piano Awd 84; Dntstry.

GORMAN, MICHAEL; Marian HS; Upton, MA; (Y); 55/177; Boy Scts; Church Yth Grp; Band; Concert Band; Var Bsktbl; Music.

GORRIGAN, BETH; Notre Dame Acad; Hanover, MA; (Y); 33/113; Church Yth Grp; Cmnty Wkr; Hosp Aide; Variety Show; Im Bsktbl; Im Coach Actv; Var Vllybl; French Hon Soc; Hon Roll; Ntl Merit Ltr.

GOSLER, KEVIN; St Johns HS; Worcester, MA; (Y); Boy Scts; VP Church Yth Grp; Stage Crew; Nwsp Sprt Ed; Hon Roll; Im Bsbl; Im Bsktbl; JV Crs Cntry; Var Ftbl; Im Sftbl; Syracuse U; Pre-Med.

GOSS, ELIZABETH; Norwood SR HS; Norwood, MA; (Y); 38/400; French Clb; Sec Key Clb; Chorus; Hon Roll; HS Schlrshp 85; Wheaton Coll; Comm.

GOSSELIN, AMY; Lawrence HS; Lawrence, MA; (Y); 5/290; Math Clb; VP Science Clb; Band; Chorus; Rep Soph Cls; Rep Jr Cls; Rep Sr Cls; Vllybl; High Hon Roll; NHS; Mc Donalds Schlrshp 85; Bentley Coll; Accntng.

GOSSELIN, ELIZABETH; Holyoke HS; Holyoke, MA; (Y); 4/394; French Clb; Latin Clb; Var Capt Fld Hcky; Capt Var Sftbl; Jr NHS; NHS; MA Brd Of Ed Commnwlth Schlr 85; Bentley Coll; Acctng.

GOSSELIN, MICHELLE; Bishop Stang HS; Westport, MA; (Y); 24/211; Girl Scts; Hosp Aide; Ski Clb; Yrbk Stf; Var Trk; Hon Roll; Kiwanis Awd; NHS; Ntl Merit Ltr; Ripon Coll Schlrshp 85; Ripon Coll; Bio.

GOSSELIN, RAYMOND; Holyoke HS; Holyoke, MA; (Y); French Clb; Nwsp Phtg; JV Ftbl; JV Trk; Mech Engr.

GOTTLIEB, DAVID; Phillips Acad; Wantagh, NY; (Y); Office Aide; Pep Clb; Teachers Aide; School Play; Im Bsktbl; Im Socr; Im Sftbl; Tennis; High Hon Roll; Hon Roll; Frnch Prz Bst 2nd Yr Stu 83; Taylor Prz, Darling Prz 85; Lang.

GOUCHER, ANGELA; Cathedral HS; Feeding Hills, MA; (Y); JV Capt Sftbl; Outstndng Svc Awd 85; English.

GOUDREAU, ALICIA; Bartlett HS; Webster, MA; (Y); 16/149; French Clb; FBLA; Yrbk Bus Mgr; NHS; Prfct Atten Awd; Accntng.

GOUIN, SUSAN; Shepherd Hill Regional HS; Charlton, MA; (Y); Church Yth Grp; Hon Roll; Yth Ftns Achvt Awd AAHPERD 84; Bus.

GOULD, KENNETH; Central Catholic HS; Lawrence, MA; (Y); 35/220; Var Bowling; JV Ftbl; JV Trk; High Hon Roll; Hon Roll; Arch Engr.

GOULET, DAWNE; Taunton HS; Taunton, MA; (Y); Hosp Aide; Band; Chorus; Concert Band; Jazz Band; Mrchg Band; Var Trk; Hon Roll; Med Tech.

GOULSTON, KENNETH; Newton North HS; Newtonville, MA; (Y); Ski Clb; Temple Yth Grp; Nwsp Stf; Yrbk Stf; L Bsktbl; Ftbl; Var Swmmng; Hon Roll; Pres Jr Natl Assn Deaf 84-85; Wrld Games Deaf 85; Fnlst Bay St Games 84.

GOUTHRO, NANCY; King Philip Regional Voc HS; Wrentham, MA; (Y); Var L Bsktbl; Var L Crs Cntry; Var L Trk; Church Yth Grp; JV Gym; Hon Roll; Pres Phys Fit Awd 82; Acad Excllnce 82; MVP Girls Trk 84; Spn.

GOUVAN, JENNIFER ANN; Minnechaug Regional HS; Hampden, MA; (Y); 18/348; Sec Church Yth Grp; Teachers Aide; Church Choir; Madrigals; School Musical; Stage Crew; Variety Show; Nwsp Ed-Chief; Nwsp Rptr; NHS; Minnechaug Schlrshp 85; Music Awd 85; Clark U; Bio.

GOUVEIA JR, JOSEPH; Malden Catholic HS; Everett, MA; (Y); 56/187; Camera Clb; Church Yth Grp; Cmnty Wkr; Bsktbl; Hon Roll; MA ST Scholar 85; Bentley Coll; Bus Mngmnt.

GOVE, SUSAN; Newburyport HS; Newburyport, MA; (Y); 4/207; Hosp Aide; Model UN; Science Clb; School Musical; Yrbk Stf; Trk; Elks Awd; High Hon Roll; Hon Roll; NHS; Ntl Hon Soc, Carl S Ell Presdntl & Brnze & Slvr Key Schlrshps 85; Northeastern U; Phy Thrpy.

GOVONI, JAMES M; Plymouth Carver HS; Plymouth, MA; (Y); Am Leg Boys St; Church Yth Grp; Latin Clb; Var Capt Socr; Hon Roll; Jr NHS; Old Colony Socr Lg Champs 82 & 83; Boston Coll; Govt Svc.

GOWARD, CHRIS; Natick HS; Natick, MA; (Y); 67/443; Mrchg Band; Symp Band; JV Socr; L Trk; Hon Roll; Hatch Awd 2nd Pl 84; New England Brdcstng Assn Awd 83; New England Interschltc Trk Mt 4th Pl 85; Advrtsng.

GOWING, JENNIFER; Tantasqua Regional HS; Sturbridge, MA; (Y); 38/210; Church Yth Grp; Ski Clb; Varsity Clb; Variety Show; Pres Stu Cncl; Var Capt Cheerleading; Var Tennis; Hon Roll; NHS; Unsung Hero-Vrsty Tennis 85; U Of MA; Cmmnctns.

GOYETCHE, VERNON; Everett HS; Everett, MA; (Y); Church Yth Grp; Variety Show; Bsbl; JV Ice Hcky; Ice Hcky; Im Vllybl; Hon Roll; Charity Wrk Walk-A-Thon Proj 85; Bus Adm.

GRACIA, MATTHEW D; New Bedford HS; New Bedford, MA; (Y); 18/688; Am Leg Boys St; Church Yth Grp; Cmnty Wkr; JV Bsbl; Var Trk; High Hon Roll; Hon Roll; Jr NHS; NHS; Yale U; Engrng.

GRADY, ELIZABETH; Northfield Mt Hermon HS; Harvard, MA; (Y); French Clb; Math Tm; Spanish Clb; School Musical; School Play; Stage Crew; JV Ice Hcky; Mgr(s); High Hon Roll; Hon Roll; Intl Bus.

GRADY, JOHN; Hopedale JR SR HS; Hopedale, MA; (Y); Boy Scts; Church Yth Grp; Political Wkr; Band; Var L Socr; High Hon Roll; Church Choir; Concert Band; Mrchg Band; Pep Band.

GRADY, MATTHEW J; Holyoke HS; Holyoke, MA; (Y); Drama Clb; Latin Clb; Ski Clb; Spanish Clb; Speech Tm; Stage Crew; Nwsp Phtg; Nwsp Stf; Var Golf; Hon Roll; Law.

GRAHAM, KELLY; Auburn HS; Auburn, MA; (Y); Church Yth Grp; Ski Clb; Rep Frsh Cls; Rep Soph Cls; Var Crs Cntry; JV Fld Hcky; High Hon Roll; Trs NHS; Ntl Hon Soc 85-86; Vrsty X-Cntry 84-85; Hgh Hon Roll 82-85; Tchr.

GRAHAM, KIM; Natick HS; Natick, MA; (Y); Church Yth Grp; Cmnty Wkr; Hosp Aide; Political Wkr; Church Choir; Rep Jr Cls; Prfct Atten Awd; Var Cheerleading; Pres-SADD 85; Pres-Chrch Yth Grp 85; Framingham ST; Psych.

GRAHAM, LISA D; East Longmeadow HS; Springfield, MA; (Y); Drama Clb; Hosp Aide; Latin Clb; Library Aide; Office Aide; JV Trk; High Hon Roll; Hon Roll; Mdrn Miss Teen Schlrshp Pgnt 84; U Of MA; RN.

GRAMMENOS, NICHOLAS; Auburn HS; Auburn, MA; (Y); 8/185; Church Yth Grp; Math Tm; High Hon Roll; Lion Awd; NHS; Amer Hellenic Ed Progrssv Assn Scholar 85; Greek Ladies Philoptochos Soc Scholar 85; Worcester Polytech; Mech Engrng.

GRANDE, CYNTHIA; Murthas Vineyard Regional HS; Oak Bluffs, MA; (Y); 13/107; Church Yth Grp; Drama Clb; Chorus; School Musical; Stage Crew; Lit Mag; Rep Jr Cls; Golf; Socr; Hon Roll; Fr Achvt Awd 84; Phys Ed Achvt Awd 85; Navy.

GRANDE, JOANNE; Chelsea HS; Chelsea, MA; (Y); 20/199; Pep Clb; Ski Clb; Yrbk Phtg; Yrbk Rptr; Yrbk Stf; Trk; Hon Roll; NHS; Elks Clb Schlrshp 85; ST Schlrshp 85; Salem ST Coll; Bus Admin.

GRANE, SCOTT; North Quincy HS; Quincy, MA; (Y); 58/350; High Hon Roll; Hon Roll; Prfct Atten Awd; Arch.

GRANGER, RONALD; Andover HS; Andover, MA; (Y); 105/431; Church Yth Grp; Pep Clb; Ski Clb; Rep Frsh Cls; Im Bsbl; Im Bsktbl; JV Ftbl; Im Lcrss; Im Wt Lftg; Hon Roll; Aerntcl Engrng.

GRANT, DEBORAH J; Dracut HS; Dracut, MA; (Y); Hon Roll; NHS; Pres Schlr; Dracut Schlrshp Fndtn Awd 85; U Of Lowell MA; Math.

GRANT, HEATHER LEE; David Prouty Regional HS; E Brookfield, MA; (Y); 29/169; JV Bsktbl; Capt L Fld Hcky; High Hon Roll; Hon Roll; NHS; White Sweater Awd 85; Hnr Stu 85; Sr Hnr Soc 85; Worcester St Coll; Comp Sci.

GRANT, KIMBERLY; Attleboro HS; Attleboro, MA; (Y); Church Yth Grp; Powder Puff Ftbl; High Hon Roll; Hon Roll; NHS; Chamberlayne JR Coll; Rtl Merc.

GRANT, SARAH; Canton HS; Canton, MA; (Y); 71/256; Church Yth Grp; German Clb; VP GAA; VP Varsity Clb; Nwsp Stf; Yrbk Sprt Ed; Rep Soph Cls; Rep Jr Cls; Rep Sr Cls; Fld Hcky; USSCA 84-85.

GRANTHAM, JEFF; Westford Acad; Westford, MA; (Y); 100/250; AFS; German Clb; Office Aide; Varsity Clb; Ftbl; Trk; Wrstlng; Hon Roll; Law.

GRAVES, DAVID; Bellingham Memorial HS; Bellingham, MA; (Y); Boy Scts; Church Yth Grp; Socr; Trk; Engrng.

GRAVES, KRISTEN; Greenfield HS; Greenfield, MA; (Y); Yrbk Sprt Ed; Var L Gym; Var L Trk; Hon Roll; Smith Coll; Frnch.

GRAVES, MELISSA A; Mohawk Trail Regional HS; Shelburne Falls, MA; (Y); 7/139; Rep Stu Cncl; Var Stu Trk; Hon Roll; Awd A Ave Typg I 82-83; Awd Excllnc Frnch I & II 83-85; Prim Ed.

GRAVES, VALERIE A; Milton HS; Milton, MA; (Y); AFS; Library Aide; Chorus; Nwsp Ed-Chief; Var Trk; Hon Roll; NHS; Ntl Merit Ltr; MA Bus Week 84; Suffolk Bk Awd.

GRAY, ALBERT; Ayer JR SR HS; Shirley, MA; (Y); 18/165; Math Clb; JV Bsbl; JV Var Bsktbl; Coach Actv; Var JV Ftbl; NHS; Ntl Merit Schol; Chndlr Mach Co 85; ITPE Schlrshp 85; U Of KY-LOUISVILLE; Elec Engr.

GRAY, BETH; Douglas HS; E Douglas, MA; (Y); Hosp Aide; Varsity Clb; Band; Concert Band; Mrchg Band; Yrbk Ed-Chief; Trs Soph Cls; Trs Jr Cls; Rep Stu Cncl; Psych.

GRAY, CHARLES; Newton North HS; Newton, MA; (Y); German Clb; Latin Clb; Ski Clb; Var Bsktbl; JV Golf; Capt Socr; Var Trk; Hon Roll; Bus.

GRAY, EMILY; Mohawk Trail Regional HS; Shelburne Fls, MA; (Y); 6/125; Debate Tm; Chorus; School Musical; Hon Roll; NHS; Exlnc Comp Math Awd 84-85.

GRAY, GARY; Burlington HS; Burlington, MA; (Y); Computer Clb; Hon Roll; NHS; Comp Sci.

GRAY, JENNIFER; Franklin HS; Franklin, MA; (Y); Trs Church Yth Grp; Church Choir; School Play; Hon Roll; NHS; Tchr.

GRAY, JOSHUA B; Milton Acad; Jericho, VT; (Y); Lit Mag; NCTE Awd.

GRAY, LORI S; Randolph HS; Randolph, MA; (Y); 30/316; Drama Clb; Band; Concert Band; Mrchg Band; Swing Chorus; NHS; Rotary Awd; SEMSBA; All ST Band; Dist Band; Clark U; Bus Mgmt.

GRAY, MICHAEL E; Quincy HS; Quincy, MA; (Y); 9/350; Am Leg Boys St; Nwsp Rptr; Yrbk Bus Mgr; Pres Stu Cncl; Tennis; French Hon Soc; High Hon Roll; Ntl Merit Ltr; VFW Awd; Voice Dem Awd; Quincy Hstrcl Soc Essay Wnr 82; Brown; Pre-Med.

GRAY, NICOLE S; Phillips Acad; Andover, MA; (Y); Spanish Clb; Lit Mag; JA; Latin Clb; Nwsp Rptr; Var Crs Cntry; Im Lcrss; Im Swmmng; Im Trk; Hon Roll; Commentation Ntl Negro Merit Pgm 84; Lang.

GRAY, PETER L; Malden HS; Malden, MA; (Y); 4/550; Key Clb; Quiz Bowl; Temple Yth Grp; Band; Variety Show; Yrbk Stf; Rep Jr Cls; Cit Awd; NHS; Rotary Awd; Pre-Dentl.

GRAY, SHERI; Malden HS; Malden, MA; (Y); #40 In Class; Office Aide; Hon Roll; U Of Lowell; Comp Sci.

GRAZIANI, LAURA; Brockton HS; Brockton, MA; (Y); 53/1200; Exploring; Hosp Aide; Latin Clb; High Hon Roll; Hon Roll; Prfct Atten Awd; Bio.

GREATOREX, PAULA; Christophe Columbus HS; Charlestown, MA; (S); 45/135; Math Clb; Rep Frsh Cls; Rep Soph Cls; Stu Cncl; Nrsg.

GREAVES, SHEILA; Medway HS; Medway, MA; (Y); 15/150; Cmnty Wkr; Chorus; Yrbk Bus Mgr; Yrbk Stf; Stu Cncl; Cheerleading; Var Trk; Var Hon Roll; Sec NHS; MVP Trk 83-85; ST Champ Lng Jmp Trk 85; Schltc Awd Hon Rl 83-85; Bus Mngmnt.

GRECO, CARRIE; Fr Matignon HS; Winchester, MA; (Y); Church Yth Grp; Cmnty Wkr; Spanish Clb; Rep Soph Cls; Rep Jr Cls; Rep Stu Cncl; Var L Crs Cntry; Var L Trk; Vllybl; Hon Roll; Suffolk; Law.

GREELISH, JEFFREY; Holy Home HS; W Brookfield, MA; (Y); 115/242; Cmnty Wkr; Boy Scts; JV Var Bsktbl; Var Trk; Wt Lftg; Bernard J Flanagan Memrl Schlrshp 85; Centrl MS Conf Champ & Recrd Hldr Shotpt 85; Natl Sci Olympd 84; Bridgewater ST Coll; Phy Ed.

GREELISH, MAUREEN; Holy Name C C HS; Fiskdale, MA; (Y); 25/272; Church Yth Grp; French Clb; Chorus; Church Choir; Hon Roll; Christian Theatrcl Grp 84; Yth Minstry.

GREEN, CLIFF; Cathedral HS; Enfield, CT; (Y); 30/515; Boy Scts; Computer Clb; Math Clb; Model UN; JV Tennis; High Hon Roll; Eagle Scout 83; Order Of The Arrow 82; Popg Pnus XII Relgs Awd Scouts 85; Mech Engrng.

GREEN, PAMELA; Archbishop Williams HS; Weymouth, MA; (Y); Church Yth Grp; FHA; Ski Clb; Band; Yrbk Stf; Pres Frsh Cls; Var Sftbl; JV Trk; Flute Awds Solo & Ensmbl Fest 1st & 2nd 82-85; Arch.

GREENBERG, DAVID; Newton North HS; Newton Centre, MA; (Y); School Play; Nwsp Rptr; Trk; High Hon Roll; Ntl Merit SF; Kennedy Bk Prz-Excllnc In U S Hstry 85; Ntl Latin Exam-Outstndng Perfrmnc 85.

GREENBERG, JONATHAN; Newton North HS; Newton, MA; (Y); Latin Clb; Stage Crew; Lit Mag; Var L Socr; Var L Trk; Hon Roll; Ntl Merit SF; Gold Medal Natl Latin Exam 85; U S Acad Decthln 85-86; MA Coaches Invitatnl Trk Mt 85.

GREENBERG, MYLES D; Andover HS; Andover, MA; (Y); 5/425; Chess Clb; Computer Clb; Math Tm; Temple Yth Grp; Yrbk Phtg; Rep Sr Cls; High Hon Roll; Ntl Merit SF; 1st Pl Sci Olympiad-Chem; Excel Amer Hstry; Engrng.

GREENE, CATHERINE M; Weymouth South HS; Weymouth, MA; (Y); 6/341; Am Leg Aux Girls St; VP Key Clb; Library Aide; Math Tm; Red Cross Aide; Yrbk Stf; Rep Frsh Cls; High Hon Roll; NHS; Rocklnd Trst Co Schlrshp Awd 85; Gilbert Schlrshp 85; Boston Coll; Finance.

GREENE, ELLEN; Hopedale JR & SR HS; Hopedale, MA; (S); 3/58; Band; Chorus; School Play; Pres Frsh Cls; Pres Soph Cls; Pres Jr Cls; L Capt Bsktbl; L Fld Hcky; L Sftbl; High Hon Roll.

GREENE, KATHERINE A; Wellesley SR HS; Wellesley, MA; (Y); 63/315; Aud/Vis; Drama Clb; Var Ski Clb; Stage Crew; Cheerleading; Coach Actv; JV Socr; Var Vllybl; Hon Roll; Ntl Merit SF.

GREENE, PAMELA; Bishop Feehan HS; Cumberland, RI; (Y); 102/245; Art Clb; Cmnty Wkr; Hosp Aide; Stu Cncl; Bsktbl; Var Sftbl; Swmmng; High Hon Roll; Hon Roll; Rep Soph Cls; Coaches Awd 83; Kirkbrae Swm Tm 83; Bronz Medl Boy ST Bskbl Tm 84; All Tourn Tm 84; All Star Hon Men 85; Comm.

GREENE, ROBERT A; Westfield HS; Westfield, MA; (Y); 29/330; Am Leg Boys St; Debate Tm; French Clb; Trs Soph Cls; Trs Sr Cls; JV Bsbl; Var Ftbl; Pres NHS; MIT; Engrng.

GREENOUGH, MICHELLE; Boston Latin Schl; Jamaica Plain, MA; (Y); Church Yth Grp; Cmnty Wkr; Girl Scts; Hosp Aide; Suffolk U; Soclgy.

GREENWOOD, ANDREA; Westport HS; Westport, MA; (Y); 8/210; Drama Clb; FBLA; Ski Clb; Nwsp Stf; Yrbk Stf; Crs Cntry; Sftbl; French Hon Soc; Hon Roll; NHS; Aerontcl Engr.

GREGORY, JILL; Dartmouth HS; S Dartmouth, MA; (Y); 30/246; Key Clb; Ski Clb; Var Cheerleading; Var Capt Fld Hcky; Var JV Sftbl; Var Tennis; Hon Roll; Jr NHS; NHS; Med Tech.

GREGORY, LISA; Wareham HS; Wareham, MA; (Y); 32/175; Church Yth Grp; Cmnty Wkr; FHA; Girl Scts; Stu Cncl; Cit Awd; High Hon Roll; Hon Roll.

GREGORY, MICHAEL; Doherty Memorial HS; Worcester, MA; (Y); Boy Scts; Church Yth Grp; French Clb; JA; Yrbk Stf; Hon Roll; Boston Coll; Law.

GREINER, MICHAEL; Cohasset HS; Cohasset, MA; (Y); 7/130; AFS; Aud/Vis; Capt Debate Tm; Nwsp Stf; Var Trk; High Hon Roll; NHS; Golden Tape Awd Comm TV Prod Of Yr 85; Mst Vlbl Debater 85; Ntl Fnlst Wash Wrkshp Essay Cntst 84; Intertl Law.

GRENIER, DEBORAH A; North Shore Regional HS; Salem, MA; (Y); Ski Clb; Trs Jr Cls; Hon Roll; Acad All Amer; Ldrshp Awd.

GREW, LAURIE; Matignon HS; Somerville, MA; (Y); Cmnty Wkr; Spanish Clb; Hon Roll; Ntl Merit Ltr; Spanish NHS; NEDT Awd 83; Proj Close Up Grp 85; Psych.

GRIFFIN, HELEN; Saint Clave HS; Roslindale, MA; (Y); Church Yth Grp; JA; School Musical; Trk; High Hon Roll; Hon Roll; Prfct Atten Awd; Drama.

GRIFFIN, JEANNE M; Archbishop Williams HS; Randolph, MA; (Y); 66/198; Sec VP Church Yth Grp; Cmnty Wkr; Girl Scts; Library Aide; Office Aide; Teachers Aide; Chorus; Church Choir; School Musical; Nwsp Stf; Grandparent Adoption Cert 85; Eucharistic Minister 85-86; CCD Tchr 84-85; Northeastern U; Frnch Intrprtr.

GRIFFIN, KATHLEEN E; Assabeth Valley Regional Vocat HS; Hudson, MA; (Y); Hosp Aide; Stat Bsktbl; Var Socr; Prfct Atten Awd; Genrl Psychlgy.

GRIFFIN, LAUREEN A; Ralph C Mahar Regional HS; Erving, MA; (Y); 6/110; Dance Clb; Band; Chorus; Variety Show; Yrbk Bus Mgr; Yrbk Phtg; Yrbk Stf; Sec Soph Cls; Sec Jr Cls; Sec Sr Cls; MA Assoc Schl Sprtndnt Outstndg SR Awd 84-85; All-Dist Music Fest 85; Intl Frgn Lang Awd 84-85; Boston Coll; Elem Educ.

GRIFFIN, MARK; Somerset HS; Somerset, MA; (Y); JV Var Bsbl; JV Var Ftbl; Wt Lftg; Hon Roll; NHS; Boston U; Engrng.

GRIFFIN, MICHAEL J; Westfield Vocational HS; Westfield, MA; (Y); 8/76; Am Leg Boys St; Service Clb; Yrbk Stf; Stu Cncl; Bsbl; Socr; Cit Awd; Elks Awd; Hon Roll; Kiwanis Awd; Elks Clb Schlrshp 85; Flrnc Tryon Schlrshp 85; Srv V Awd 85; Ctzns Schlrshp Awd 85; Holyoke CC; Bus.

GRIFFIN, VALERIE A; Waltham HS; Waltham, MA; (Y); AFS; Church Yth Grp; Hosp Aide; Church Choir; Yrbk Stf; Cit Awd; Hon Roll; Jr NHS; NHS; Ntl Merit SF; Lang.

GRIFFITH, JEFF; Lexington HS; Lexington, MA; (Y); L Bsbl; L Bsktbl; L Ice Hcky; Lcrss; Hon Roll; Middlesex Lg All Star Hockey Tm 85; Babson Coll; Bus.

GRILLIS, CHRIS; Arlington HS; Arlington, MA; (Y); Yrbk Stf; JV Ftbl; Comp Engrng.

GRINNELL, GARY M; Foxborough HS; Foxboro, MA; (Y); 40/270; Am Leg Boys St; Church Yth Grp; Letterman Clb; Varsity Clb; Var Bsktbl; Var Crs Cntry; Var Trk; Hon Roll; Ntl Merit Ltr; Busnss Mgmt.

GRINSHPAN, MARINA; Doherty Memorial HS; Worcester, MA; (Y); High Hon Roll; Hon Roll; Comp Sci.

GRODEN, WENDI; Medway HS; Walpole, MA; (Y); 40/160; Am Leg Aux Girls St; Church Yth Grp; Drama Clb; Office Aide; Varsity Clb; School Play; Rep Soph Cls; Rep Stu Cncl; JV Bsktbl; Var Fld Hcky; Al-Star Trk 85; Al-Star Fld Hcky 84; Pre-Vet.

GRONDIN, WENDY MARIE; Westport HS; Westport, MA; (Y); Dance Clb; Exploring; Intnl Clb; Library Aide; Office Aide; Political Wkr; Ski Clb; Nwsp Rptr; Nwsp Stf; Hon Roll; U MA; Navy Ofcr.

GROOM, ERICA; Tantasqua Regional HS; Wales, MA; (Y); 28/200; AFS; Latin Clb; Chorus; School Play; Nwsp Rptr; Nwsp Stf; Yrbk Rptr; Lit Mag; Hon Roll; Prfct Atten Awd; Shksprn Lit Tchr.

GROSSMAN, MARC; Malden Catholic HS; Malden, MA; (Y); 14/185; JCL; Latin Clb; Nwsp Rptr; Rep Frsh Cls; Hon Roll; Govt.

GRUBER, JULIE; Dana Hall HS; Wellesley, MA; (Y).

GRUGNALE, STACY; Classical HS; Lynn, MA; (Y); 12/170; Church Yth Grp; Pres Debate Tm; Spanish Clb; Chorus; JV Bsktbl; JV Var Cheerleading; High Hon Roll; Hon Roll.

GUARDABASCIO, PAMELA; Dedham HS; Dedham, MA; (S); 8/350; Church Yth Grp; Band; Concert Band; Jazz Band; Mrchg Band; Orch; School Musical; Gym; NHS; Alt Grtr Boston Yuty Sym Orch 83; Northeastern U; Bio.

GUARDIANI, JOHN; Southbridge HS; S Bridge, MA; (Y); JV Bsbl; JV Bsktbl; Var JV Ftbl; JV Trk; Hon Roll; MIT; Engr.

GUARINO, DANIEL; St Dominic Savio HS; Revere, MA; (Y); 7/109; Church Yth Grp; Key Clb; Math Clb; Yrbk Stf; Lit Mag; Im Bsktbl; JV Ftbl; Hon Roll; Elec Engrng.

GUARINO, HONORIA; Haverhill HS; Bradford, MA; (Y); 1/400; Exploring; Pres French Clb; Latin Clb; Nwsp Stf; Jr NHS; Ntl Merit Ltr; Haverhill Sci Hist 83; Ntl French Ex 85; Wellesly Alumn Bk Awd 85; French.

GUAY, SHARON; Taunton HS; East Taunton, MA; (Y); Latin Clb; Office Aide; Teachers Aide; Yrbk Stf; Bsktbl; Fld Hcky; Med.

GUEN, JOHNNY; Boston Technical HS; Boston, MA; (Y); Bsktbl; Vllybl; Hon Roll; NHS; Rep Asian Cltres Clb 84-85; VP Asian Cltres Clb 85-86.

GUENTHER, LU ELLEN; Bartlett HS; Webster, MA; (Y); 2/174; Church Yth Grp; FBLA; Office Aide; Trs Pep Clb; Ski Clb; Variety Show; High Hon Roll; NHS; Prfct Atten Awd; Coll Of The Holy Cross; Econmcs.

GUERIN, CHRISTINE M; North Middlesex Regional HS; Pepperell, MA; (Y); Dance Clb; Girl Scts; Color Guard; School Musical; Trs Frsh Cls; Trs Soph Cls; Stu Cncl; JV Crs Cntry; JV Trk; Hon Roll; Intr Dsgn.

GUERIN, DONNA; Greater Lowell Voke HS; Lowell, MA; (S); Sec Stu Cncl; Hon Roll; USSCA; Bus Cluster Cert Of Profiency In Typing 83-84.

GUERIN, JOHN; Cushing Acad; Athol, MA; (Y); Church Yth Grp; Chrmn Model UN; Var Ski Clb; VP Soph Cls; Tennis; L Trk; Wt Lftg; Hon Roll; Dorm Proctor SR Yr 85-86; Amer Interntl Schl France 86; Hmncng King 83; Med.

GUERINO, ALISON; Newton North HS; Newton Center, MA; (Y); Art Clb; Letterman Clb; Variety Show; Var Swmmng; JV Trk; High Hon Roll; Hon Roll; Stu Schlr Award 83; Spirit Award 83; Med.

GUERRA, SALVATORE F; Abington HS; Abington, MA; (Y); Am Leg Boys St; Yrbk Stf; Rep Sr Cls; Stu Cncl; Bsktbl; Capt Socr; L Tennis; High Hon Roll; NHS.

GUERRIN, CAROLYN; Hopkins Acad; Hadley, MA; (Y); 16/55; Art Clb; Church Yth Grp; Girl Scts; Spanish Clb; Band; Chorus; Concert Band; Mrchg Band; Bsktbl; Socr; Roger Williams; Comp Sci.

GUERRINI, JAMES; Norton HS; Norton, MA; (Y); Am Leg Boys St; Math Tm; Varsity Clb; JV Var Crs Cntry; High Hon Roll; Hon Roll; NEDT Awd.

GUERRINI, JODI; Saugus HS; Saugus, MA; (Y); 71/320; Church Yth Grp; Cmnty Wkr; Hosp Aide; Library Aide; Office Aide; Yrbk Stf; Ed Lit Mag; Stu Cncl; Newbury JC; Trvl.

GUERTIN, LISA; St Bernards C C HS; Winchendon, MA; (S); 21/172; Church Yth Grp; Drama Clb; Sec 4-H; Library Aide; Pep Clb; Yrbk Stf; JV Trk; Hon Roll; Psychology.

GUGLIELMI, ANN MARIE; Westwood HS; Westwood, MA; (Y); 24/215; L Var Swmmng; NHS; Spanish NHS; Powder Puff Ftbl; Hon Roll; Grls S Sctnl Chmpnshps 84; Freestyle Grls Sctnl Chmpnships 84; Psychology.

GUIBORD, MICHAEL J; St Johns HS; Boylston, MA; (Y); 122/279; Am Leg Boys St; Church Yth Grp; French Clb; Model UN; Rep Jr Cls; JV Bsbl; Im Bsktbl; Im Vllybl; Hon Roll; Head Coach Lg Champ Farm Lg Tm 85; Aero.

GUIDICE, JAMES; Arlington HS; Arlington, MA; (Y); Boy Scts; Band; Chorus; Concert Band; Jazz Band; Mrchg Band; Orch; School Musical; School Play; Symp Band; Suffolk U Bk Awd Outstndng Schl Serv 85; U Of MA.

GUIDOTTI, GUIDO; Newton North HS; Newton, MA; (Y); Boy Scts; Camera Clb; Computer Clb; Exploring; Ski Clb; Yrbk Phtg; Yrbk Rptr; Yrbk Stf; High Hon Roll; Hon Roll; Nmntn Kennedy Bk Prz 85; Engr.

GUIFFRE, CHRISTOPHER DAMIEN; Wellesley Senior HS; Wellesley, MA; (Y); Church Choir; Ftbl; NHS; Ntl Merit Ltr; Bus Mgmt.

GUILLAUME, MATHURIN; Cambridge Latin Schl; Camb, MA; (Y); Church Yth Grp; FCA; French Clb; Chorus; Vllybl; Hon Roll; Wentworth Inst Tech; Elec Engnr.

GUILMETTE, CHRISTINE; BMC Durfee HS; Fall River, MA; (Y); Drama Clb; FBLA; Hosp Aide; JA; Yrbk Stf; Hon Roll; Katherine Gibbs; Bus.

GUILMETTE, TRACEY; Westford Acad; Westford, MA; (Y); French Clb; Teachers Aide; Yrbk Bus Mgr; Yrbk Phtg; Yrbk Stf; Var JV Fld Hcky; Stat Ice Hcky; Trk; High Hon Roll; Hon Roll; Peer Cnslng 86; Deaf Stu Aide 86; Psych.

GULA, BARBARA; Bishop Feehan HS; S Attleboro, MA; (Y); Hosp Aide; Color Guard; Hon Roll; Cmnty Wkr; Nwsp Stf; Stu Cncl; Vrsty Lttr Colorgrd 83-84; 3 Yr Colorgrd Pin 84-85; 100 Hr Pin Voluntr Wrk 82-83; Probtn For Juvnls.

GULA, SUSAN; Fairhaven HS; Fairhaven, MA; (Y); 25/195; Nwsp Stf; Hon Roll; Jr NHS; NHS; Acdmc Ltr; $500 Shaws Sprmrkt Schlrsp; $250 May Delano Schlrshp; Southeastern MA U; Med Tech.

GULLIVER, KAREN A; Leominster HS; Leominster, MA; (Y); 9/388; Church Choir; Var Bsktbl; Var Capt Crs Cntry; Var Trk; Elks Awd; High Hon Roll; NHS; JR Fortnightly Clb 85; Becker JC; Trvl.

GULLUNI, MARIA; Cathedral HS; Springfield, MA; (Y); 19/515; Cmnty Wkr; Intnl Clb; VP JA; Service Clb; Teachers Aide; Ed Yrbk Stf; NHS; GAA; Office Aide; Rep Jr Cls; Edtr-In-Chf Of Yrbk 85-86; Projct Dir Of Natl Hnrs 85-86; Excell In Acad Awd For Rlgn 84; Pol Sci.

GUMLAW, LAURA J; W Springfield HS; W Springfield, MA; (Y); 81/279; Sec Church Yth Grp; Dance Clb; Daisy Chain 84; Westfield ST Coll; Elem Educ.

GUNN, TONJA; Leominster HS; Leominster, MA; (Y); 43/356; Political Wkr; School Musical; Trs Jr Cls; Trs Sr Cls; Rep Stu Cncl; Cit Awd; High Hon Roll; Hon Roll; NHS; Spelman Coll; Ec.

GUNTHER, BENJAMIN; Medford HS; Medford, MA; (Y); 3/450; Cmnty Wkr; Math Tm; Science Clb; Var Tennis; High Hon Roll; Mu Alp Tht; Trs NHS; Rensselaer Awd 85; Geomtry,Intr Math,Adv Math Top Stu Awds 83-85; Bio,Che,Physcs & Engl Awds.

GUPTA, MANISH; Reading Memorial HS; Glastonbury, CT; (Y); 13/359; Camera Clb; Computer Clb; Debate Tm; Socr; High Hon Roll; NHS; Pres Schlr; Reading Schlrshp Awd 85; Analytical Sci Corp Schlrshp 85; Worcester Poly Inst; Aerosp Eng.

GUREVICH, TANYA; Framingham South HS; Sudbury, MA; (Y); French Clb; JA; Temple Yth Grp; Variety Show; Yrbk Stf; JV Tennis; High Hon Roll; Hon Roll; NHS; Ntl Merit Ltr; Harvard U; Pharmacist.

GURRY, ROBERT; Ware HS; Ware, MA; (Y); French Clb; Pres Key Clb; Band; Jazz Band; Mrchg Band; Variety Show; Hon Roll; Stu Gov 85; Engr.

GUSTOWSKI, DIANNE H; St Marys HS; Worcester, MA; (Y); 1/48; Am Leg Aux Girls St; Church Yth Grp; French Clb; Hosp Aide; Pres JA; School Musical; High Hon Roll; Nrsng.

GUTIERREZ, CATHY; Apponequet Regional HS; Lakeville, MA; (Y); 7/220; Drama Clb; French Clb; School Musical; School Play; Nwsp Ed-Chief; Yrbk Stf; Ed Lit Mag; Sec Frsh Cls; High Hon Roll; Jr NHS; Fnlst Pres Schlrs 85; Vassar Coll; Lang.

GUTOWSKI, RICHARD G; West Springfield HS; W Springfield, MA; (Y); 22/240; Church Yth Grp; Computer Clb; JA; Church Choir; French Clb; Hon Soc; Hon Roll; Kiwanis Awd; NHS; Worcester Polytech Inst; Elec.

GUYER, ERIC; Masconomet Regional HS; Middleton, MA; (Y); 18/247; Chess Clb; French Clb; Nwsp Stf; Var L Bsktbl; Var Capt Golf; Hon Roll; Pre-Law.

GUZLEY, YVONNE; Academy Of Notre Dame; Tewksbury, MA; (Y); 11/50; Library Aide; JV Socr; Hon Roll; NHS; Comp Pro.

GUZZETTA, STEPHEN; Gardner HS; Gardner, MA; (Y); 4/182; Am Leg Boys St; Spanish Clb; Band; Concert Band; Mrchg Band; Pep Band; Var Bsktbl; Hon Roll; NHS; Chancellors Tlnt Awd Acad Excllnce 86; Med.

GUZZETTI, JIMMY; Franklin HS; Franklin, MA; (Y); Var Ftbl; Wentworth Inst; Arch Desgn.

GWOZDZ, MARK F; Hoosac Valley HS; Cheshire, MA; (Y); 26/188; Cmnty Wkr; Exploring; Ski Clb; School Play; Socr; Hon Roll; NHS; Black Blt Martl Art Han Pul 83; VP Domstc Exch Clb 84-85; Natl Ski Patrl 84; Westfield ST Coll; Crmnl Justc.

HAALAND, JOHN; Fairhaven HS; Fairhaven, MA; (Y); 3/180; Math Tm; Service Clb; Trs Soph Cls; Trs Jr Cls; Bsbl; Bsktbl; Ftbl; High Hon Roll; NHS; VFW Awd; Williams Coll Bk Awd 85; Engr.

HAAS, JAMES A; Weston HS; Weston, MA; (Y); Chorus; Church Choir; Concert Band; Madrigals; School Musical; Variety Show; Nwsp Rptr; VP Soph Cls; VP Jr Cls; Pres Sr Cls; Harvard Bk Prz 84; Boston Globe All Schltc Swm Team 84; MVP Ftbl 84; Hist.

HABER, VERONICA; North Middlesex Regional HS; Ft Devens, MA; (Y); Hosp Aide; Library Aide; Office Aide; Var Trk; Hon Roll; Med.

HABERSHAW, KAREN; Bishop Feehan HS; Attleboro, MA; (Y); Im Y-Teens; Rep Frsh Cls; Rep Soph Cls; Rep Jr Cls; Sec Sr Cls; Sec Stu Cncl; Capt Var Cheerleading; Capt Trk; JV Vllybl; Fnlst Prelmnry Tlnt Am Mdl 85; Fnlst Tlnt Am Mdl 85; Grad Wrkshps I & II Actng & Mdlng 83-84; Elem Educ.

HABIB, JOHN; Methuen HS; Methuen, MA; (Y); 5/350; Am Leg Boys St; Pres VP Church Yth Grp; Intnl Clb; Model UN; Nwsp Stf; Trs Jr Cls; Trs Sr Cls; Var Trk; High Hon Roll; Pres NHS; Dartmouth Bk Awd 85; Sci.

HABIBULLA, TASNEEM; Groton-Dunstable Rgnl Scndry Schl; Groton, MA; (Y); Church Yth Grp; Dance Clb; Intnl Clb; Church Choir; Variety Show; Yrbk Phtg; Yrbk Stf; JV Sftbl; High Hon Roll; Hon Roll; Psych.

HACKETT, ANGELIQUE; Drury HS; North Adams, MA; (Y); Chorus.

HACKETT, DARLA; Melrose SR HS; Melrose, MA; (S); 46/386; Var L Cheerleading; High Hon Roll; Hon Roll; Jr NHS; NHS; Schlstc Awd Soc Stds 83; Acadmc Achvt Chrldng 85; Bus Mgmt.

HACKETT, JO ANN; Bishop Connolly HS; Fall River, MA; (Y); 42/170; Church Yth Grp; Cmnty Wkr; GAA; Varsity Clb; Var Bsktbl; Var Trk; Im Vllybl; High Hon Roll; Stage Crew; Im Golf; Youth Coord Retreat Pgm 83-85; Secy BCHS Alchol/Drug Awness Team 84-85; Northeastern U; Hlth.

HADDAD, MICHAEL; Triton Regional HS; Byfield, MA; (Y); Math Tm; Variety Show; JV Bsbl; Var JV Bsktbl; JV Socr; High Hon Roll; Hon Roll; NHS; Engl Awd; Spnsh Awd; Williams Coll Bk Awd.

HADDON, RICHARD J; Blackstone Valley Vo Tech HS; E Douglas, MA; (Y); 7/205; Boy Scts; Exploring; Concert Band; Mrchg Band; Yrbk Stf; Var Socr; Hon Roll; Church Yth Grp; Yrbk Phtg; L Mgr(s); Pres Acad Fit Awds Outstndng Acad Achvt 84-85; Supt Commendtn Awd Outstndng Achvt & Perfmnce 84-85; Military.

HADLEY, SUZANNE; Northfield Mount Hermon HS; Herndon, VA; (Y); Cmnty Wkr; Intnl Clb; Political Wkr; Nwsp Rptr; Var Swmmng; Im Tennis; High Hon Roll; Hon Roll; Jr NHS; Awd Excllnce Amer Lit 85; Exch Pgm Stu Trm Abrd Frnce 85; Psych.

HADLEY, WARREN; Central Catholic HS; Lawrence, MA; (Y); 40/220; Ski Clb; Im Bsktbl; Im Vllybl.

HAGERTY, CAROL; Archbishop Williams HS; Holbrook, MA; (Y); 9/198; Girl Scts; Science Clb; Im Bowling; JV Trk; Hon Roll; NHS; NEDT Awd; Pres Schlr; Spanish NHS; Cmmnwlth Schlr 85; Coll Holy Cross; Med.

HAGG, KAREN; Nauset Regional HS; Eastham, MA; (Y); Boy Scts; School Play; Var Capt Gym; Var Tennis; High Hon Roll; Hon Roll; NHS; U Of RI; Phrmcy.

HAGGERTY, MICHELLE; Whitman-Hanson Regional HS; Hanson, MA; (Y); 26/360; Camp Fr Inc; Church Yth Grp; Hosp Aide; Office Aide; Yrbk Stf; Crs Cntry; Mgr(s); Score Keeper; Hon Roll; Jr NHS; Nrs.

HAGGLUND, JOHN; St Johns HS; Sutton, MA; (Y); 42/273; Am Leg Boys St; Church Yth Grp; English Clb; 4-H; French Clb; Office Aide; Rep Frsh Cls; Hon Roll; Jr NHS; NHS; Phrmctcl Rsrch.

HAGGSTROM, CHRISTINE; Fitchburg HS; Fitchburg, MA; (Y); 8/211; Drama Clb; School Play; Stage Crew; Nwsp Ed-Chief; Lit Mag; NHS; Ntl Merit Ltr; Math Tm; High Hon Roll; Hckmck Mdl Sen 84-85; Wmns Clb Wrcstr Cnty Schlrshp 85; Mdl Top 10 Sr 85; Boston U; Comm.

HAGOPIAN, ARDA; Methuen HS; Methuen, MA; (Y); Sec Trs Church Yth Grp; Intnl Clb; Model UN; Band; Mrchg Band; School Musical; Rep Frsh Cls; Rep Soph Cls; Rep Jr Cls; High Hon Roll; Bus Mgmt.

HAGOPIAN, GREGORY S; Belmont HS; Belmont, MA; (Y); 38/300; Church Yth Grp; Computer Clb; Concert Band; Mrchg Band; JV Bsbl; Var Wrstlng; Computer Clb; Ntl Merit Ltr; Im Bsktbl; 2 Schl Cmmttee Awds 84-85; Engrng.

HAGOPIAN, JASON R; Lexington HS; Lexington, MA; (Y); Boy Scts; Church Yth Grp; French Clb; Ski Clb; Nwsp Stf; Lit Mag; Trk; Rensselaer Poly Inst; Arch.

HAGUE, MARC; Northbridge JR SR HS; Whitinsville, MA; (Y); 22/152; Concert Band; Jazz Band; Mrchg Band; Yrbk Stf; Stu Cncl; Im Coach Actv; Var Ftbl; Var Trk; Im Wt Lftg; Hon Roll; Oceanogrphy.

HAIRSTON, ERIC; Boston Latin Schl; Boston, MA; (Y); Hon Roll; Comp Engr.

HAJJAR, KIM; Concord Carlisle HS; Concord, MA; (Y); 60/265; Church Yth Grp; Hosp Aide; Sftbl; High Hon Roll; Hon Roll; Acadmc Excllnc Soc Sci 83; Acadmc Excllnc Spnsh 85; Boston Coll; Bus.

HAJOS, GABOR; St Peter-Marian C C HS; Worcester, MA; (S); 6/177; Church Yth Grp; Computer Clb; Science Clb; Ski Clb; Stage Crew; Var Socr; Im Tennis; High Hon Roll; VP NHS; Worc Polytech Inst; Elec Engr.

HALE, BRADLEY R; Northampton HS; Northampton, MA; (Y); 12/189; Pres Church Yth Grp; Drama Clb; Quiz Bowl; Thesps; School Musical; School Play; High Hon Roll; NHS; Am Leg Boys St; Political Wkr; Robert James La Salle Awd 85; Miss Minnie M Shason Awd 85; Musical Prz 85; Vassar Coll.

HALEY, CATHERINE A; Holyoke HS; Holyoke, MA; (Y); GAA; Latin Clb; Nwsp Rptr; Hon Roll; Irish Way Prgm Ireland Cultural Prgm 85; Psychlgy.

HALEY, CHRIS; New Bedfrod HS; New Bedford, MA; (Y); 80/688; VP Computer Clb; JV Var Ftbl; Stu Cngrss & Interclb Cncl 84-85; Northeastern; Comp Pgmmg.

HALEY, KAREN; Matignon HS; Arlington, MA; (S); 13/183; Church Yth Grp; Spanish Clb; JV Sftbl; JV Vllybl; Hon Roll; NHS; Ntl Merit Ltr.

HALEY, LORRAINE M; Mt St Joseph Acad; Newton Center, MA; (Y); Church Yth Grp; French Clb; Intnl Clb; Science Clb; Spanish Clb; Variety Show; Hon Roll; NHS; Schlrshp From Parish 85; Awd Genrl Excllnc 85; Partl Schlrshp Top 4 Stdnts Clss 82; Boston Coll; Med.

HALEY, MARYKATE; Notre Dame Acad; Weymouth, MA; (Y); Art Clb; GAA; Stage Crew; Variety Show; Var L Crs Cntry; Var Gym; Var L Trk; Hon Roll; Prfct Atten Awd; Schl Art Fair Wnnr & 1st Pl Boston Globe Art Fair 83; All ST Cathlc Schl Cross Cnty Champ 85; Comm Art.

HALEY, NANCY; Bellingham Memorial HS; Bellingham, MA; (Y); 20/201; Mgr DECA; Nwsp Stf; Trs Frsh Cls; Stat Bsbl; Stat Bsktbl; Stat Crs Cntry; Var Score Keeper; High Hon Roll; Hon Roll; NHS; Natl Prtcpnt DECA 84-85; Johnson & Wales Coll; Htl Mgmnt.

HALEY, TRACY; Northbridge JR SR HS; Northbridge, MA; (Y); 10/153; Aud/Vis; Church Yth Grp; Computer Clb; Drama Clb; School Play; Stage Crew; High Hon Roll; NHS; Pres Schlr; Snd Crw Chief MA ST Schlrshp 85-86; U Of Lowell; Elec Engr.

HALL, CHRIS; Arlington Catholic HS; Arlington, MA; (Y); 34/160; Letterman Clb; JV Ftbl; Var Bsbl; JV Capt Bsktbl; Ftbl; High Hon Roll; Hon Roll; NHS; Natl Latin Exam Magna Cum Laude 82-83 & 83-84; Boston Coll.

HALL, JOYCE; Gardner HS; Gardner, MA; (Y); Church Yth Grp; Band; Concert Band; Mrchg Band; JV Sftbl; Hon Roll; NHS; Mont Wachusetts CC; Bus Tech.

HALL, JULIE; Monument Mountain Regional HS; W Stockbridge, MA; (Y); School Play; Yrbk Stf; Lit Mag; Sec Frsh Cls; Pres Jr Cls; Pres Sr Cls; Var Cheerleading; Var Gym; Hon Roll; NHS; Blum Memrl Schlrshp 85; Frgn Lang Awd 85; Peer Fclttng 85; Public Rltns.

HALL, LA RHETTA; HS Of Commerce; Sprinfield, MA; (Y); Cmnty Wkr; Band; Chorus; Off Frsh Cls; Off Soph Cls; Off Jr Cls; Var Cheerleading; Var Trk; Hon Roll; Prfct Atten Awd; Grl Of Yr 83; Debtnte Queen 84; Howard U; Hlth.

HALL JR, WILLIAM RICHARD; Lee HS; Lee, MA; (Y); 27/102; Drama Clb; French Clb; Band; Concert Band; Jazz Band; Mrchg Band; School Musical; School Play; Stage Crew; Ice Hcky; Stu Advsry Cncl 85-86; Exch Stu Prog 82-86; Peer Ldrshp 83-86; Pre Med.

HALLAHAN, MICHAEL; Cathedral HS; Springfield, MA; (Y); Cmnty Wkr; Office Aide; Political Wkr; Var Ftbl; Var Trk; Im Wt Lftg; Bus.

HALLE, DAVID A; New Bedford HS; New Bedford, MA; (Y); 40/571; Computer Clb; Drama Clb; JCL; Red Cross Aide; Stage Crew; High Hon Roll; NHS; Voice Dem Awd; Var L Swmmng; Schl Fin In Voice Of Democrcy Essay 84; Confnc Awd In Sci 85; Southampton Coll; Marine Chem.

HALLER, CHARLOTTE; Tantasqua Regional HS; Holland, MA; (S); 1/196; Latin Clb; Math Tm; Chorus; Ed Yrbk Stf; Stu Cncl; High Hon Roll; Hon Roll; NHS; Librl Arts Coll; Hist.

HALLIGAN, BRIAN; Westwood HS; Westwood, MA; (Y); 45/224; AFS; Boys Clb Am; Church Yth Grp; Yrbk Bus Mgr; Rep Sr Cls; Var L Bsktbl; Var Capt Crs Cntry; Var L Tennis; Rep Stu Cncl; Var Trk; Natl Hnr Rl 85; Med.

HALLISEY, MARTHA; Fontbonne Acad; Avon, MA; (Y); 2/120; Drama Clb; Intnl Clb; Math Clb; Math Tm; Science Clb; School Play; Lit Mag; Var Capt Crs Cntry; Trk; High Hon Roll; Bio, Thlgy, Amer Lit Hnrs, Chem, Thlgy, Britsh Lit, Histry Hnrs Awd; 14th Pl Cathlc Cntrl Cross Cnty.

HALLORAN, SEANA E; Cathedral HS; E Longmeadow, MA; (Y); Cmnty Wkr; Intnl Clb; Math Clb; 1st Le Fest Frnch Poetry Cntst 83; Piano Awds 84; 90th Prcntle St Prize Math Exam 85.

HALPERN, LORI; Holyoke HS; Holyoke, MA; (Y); Drama Clb; French Clb; NFL; Nwsp Rptr; JV Var Trk; High Hon Roll; Jr NHS; NHS; Bio.

HALPIN, JACQUELINE D; Archbishop Williams HS; Weymouth, MA; (Y); 19/198; Church Yth Grp; Cmnty Wkr; FNA; Chorus; Church Choir; School Musical; Variety Show; Pres Stu Cncl; Hon Roll; NHS; Acadmc Excllnc Spnsh Awd 85; Relgn Awd 84 & 85; Grndparnt Adptn Pgm 84 & 85; Emmanuel Coll; Bio.

HALSTEAD, MICHAEL J; Notre Dame Prep; Fitchburg, MA; (Y); Am Leg Boys St; Ski Clb; Yrbk Stf; Stu Cncl; Var Bsbl; Var Bsktbl; Golf; Var Socr; Hon Roll; NHS.

HALTER, JENNIFER L; Scituate HS; Scituate, MA; (Y); 37/277; Pep Clb; Stu Cncl; High Hon Roll; Hon Roll; Jr NHS; SR Booster Schlrshp 85; Babson Coll; Bus Mngmnt.

HAMBERG, JO ANN; Malden HS; Malden, MA; (Y); Sec Temple Yth Grp; Chorus; Variety Show; Mt Ida; Exec Secy.

HAMBY, HENRY; Bedford HS; Bedford, MA; (Y); Church Yth Grp; FBLA; Latin Clb; Crs Cntry; Var Trk; Hon Roll.

HAMEL, KEVIN; Chicopee Comprehensive HS; Chicopee, MA; (Y); #141 In Class; Tennis; Comp Prgrmg.

HAMEL, KIMBERLY; Easthampton HS; Easthampton, MA; (Y); 23/140; Color Guard; Yrbk Stf; Cit Awd; French Hon Soc; High Hon Roll; Johnson & Wales Coll; Fshn Merc.

HAMEL, MICHELLE; Cathedral HS; Springfield, MA; (Y); 87/500; Hosp Aide; Intnl Clb; Library Aide; Office Aide; OEA; Service Clb; School Musical; Stage Crew; Stu Cncl; Var Trk; Track Awd 84; Nursing.

HAMEL, PAUL; St Dominic Savio HS; Revere, MA; (Y); Chess Clb; Computer Clb; JA; Ski Clb; Nwsp Phtg; Yrbk Phtg; Rep Jr Cls; Rep Stu Cncl; Hon Roll; NHS; Al-Amer 85; USSCA 85; Math Awd 85; Pre-Med.

HAMILTON, LINDA; Woburn SR HS; Woburn, MA; (S); Church Yth Grp; Hosp Aide; Rep Stu Cncl; Cheerleading; Hon Roll; Jr NHS; Nrsng.

HAMILTON, NOEL; King Philip Regional HS; Norfolk, MA; (Y); Drama Clb; Var Fld Hcky; Hon Roll; Stu Pilot 85; Sftbl Mngr For Grls 85; Coll; Bus.

HAMILTON, RICHARD; Mohawk Trail Regional HS; Shelburne Falls, MA; (Y); Ski Clb; Varsity Clb; Variety Show; Sr Cls; JV Bsbl; Var Socr; Var Tennis; Hon Roll.

HAMLING, JODY L; Monument Mountain Regional HS; Gt Barrington, MA; (Y); 4/124; Am Leg Aux Girls St; Cmnty Wkr; Office Aide; Stage Crew; Yrbk Stf; High Hon Roll; Hon Roll; Cert Compltn Intrnshp VIP Travl Inc 85; Bay Path Jr Coll Merit Schlrshp 85; Bus Schlrshp 85; Bay Path JC; Trvl Adm.

HAMMER, DARCY; Newburyport HS; Newburyport, MA; (Y); 85/207; Cmnty Wkr; Q&S; Var Fld Hcky; Var Socr; Var Trk; Var Hon Roll; Wilmot Roby Evans Co Scholar 85; MVP Socr 85; Hnrb Mntn Rockport Art Fest 84; Boston U; Art.

HAMMOND, LAURA C; Newburyport HS; Newburyport, MA; (S); 20/209; Math Tm; Political Wkr; Q&S; Spanish Clb; Nwsp Ed-Chief; Lit Mag; Cit Awd; NHS; Ntl Merit Ltr; Newburyport Firemans Ldrshp Awd 84; Jrnslm.

HAMMOND, SANDRA; Wellesley SR HS; Wellesley, MA; (Y); 75/290; School Musical; Stu Cncl; Church Yth Grp; Cmnty Wkr; Drama Clb; French Clb; Chorus; School Play; JV Swmmng; Cit Awd; U Of IN; Music.

HAMPSON, TRACI; Hudson HS; Hudson, MA; (Y); Pep Clb; Civic Clb; Yrbk Stf; Sec Frsh Cls; VP Sr Cls; Var L Cheerleading; L Var Mgr(s); Im Powder Puff Ftbl; Var JV Score Keeper; Stat Socr; Chamberlayne Jr; Int Design.

HAMRE, JOHN T; Cathedral HS; W Springfield, MA; (Y); Church Yth Grp; Rep Frsh Cls; Rep Jr Cls; Var JV Bsktbl; Var JV Socr; 2nd & All Leag Tm Wstrn MA Sccr 85; Mjrty Whip/Model Senate 86.

HANCOCK, DWAYNE; Westport HS; Westport, MA; (Y); 10/180; Debate Tm; Drama Clb; French Clb; Intnl Clb; Ski Clb; School Play; Var L Bsktbl; Var L Crs Cntry; Var L Golf; NHS; Bus Sci.

HANDLER, CINDY M; Sharon HS; Sharon, MA; (Y); 5/209; Drama Clb; Ski Clb; Spanish Clb; Sec Temple Yth Grp; Stage Crew; Rep Jr Cls; Hon Roll; NHS.

HANDLER, MICHAEL; Phillips Acad; W Hartford, CT; (Y); French Clb; Math Tm; Acpl Chr; Chorus; Madrigals; School Musical; School Play; Nwsp Rptr; Lit Mag; High Hon Roll.

HANDREN, MARK; Coyle & Cassidy HS; Taunton, MA; (Y); 3/160; Am Leg Boys St; Boy Scts; JCL; Latin Clb; Varsity Clb; Var Capt Ftbl; L Trk; High Hon Roll; NHS; City Wide Essay Cont Schlrsh& 84-85; Natl Hnr Scty; West Point; Archlgy.

HANDRICH, DEBORAH; Wakefield HS; Wakefield, MA; (Y); 102/305; Church Yth Grp; DECA; 4-H; NHS; Katherine Gibbs Schl; Secy.

HANEGUN, CHARLES; Chelsea HS; Boston, MA; (Y); 16/212; Science Clb; Band; Crs Cntry; High Hon Roll; Hon Roll; NHS; Com Nolan Awd Schlrshp Acadmc Excllnc 85; Northeastern U; Elctrcl Engrng.

HANKINSON, CHRISTINA; Malden HS; Malden, MA; (Y); 12/443; Drama Clb; Girl Scts; Hosp Aide; Office Aide; PAVAS; Yrbk Rptr; Hon Roll; Ntl Merit Ltr; Alt Mass Advncd Stds Pgm 85; Med.

HANLEY, MATTHEW; Sacred Heart HS; Mashpee, MA; (Y); 6/65; Pres FBLA; Rep Frsh Cls; Rep Soph Cls; Rep Jr Cls; Pres Sr Cls; Rep Stu Cncl; Var Bsbl; Var Bsktbl; High Hon Roll; Hon Roll; Suffolk U Boston; Pre-Law.

HANLON, HUBERT; Malden Catholic HS; Medford, MA; (Y); 21/185; French Clb; Chorus; School Play; Rep Stu Cncl; Var Bsktbl; L Ftbl; Im Vllybl; Hon Roll; Jr NHS; NHS.

HANLON, KERRY; Pope John XXIII HS; Chelsea, MA; (Y); Church Yth Grp; Dance Clb; French Clb; Key Clb; Science Clb; School Musical; Bsktbl; Cheerleading; Powder Puff Ftbl; Variety Show; Drama Awd 84; Suffolk U; Pre-Law.

HANLON, SHAWN; Canton HS; Canton, MA; (Y); 32/250; Church Yth Grp; Cmnty Wkr; German Clb; Hon Roll; Jr NHS; Prfct Atten Awd; Century Clb 82-83.

HANNABURY, JOHN; Malden Catholic HS; Malden, MA; (Y); 28/195; Computer Clb; Teachers Aide; Band; Nwsp Rptr; L Trk; Im Vllybl; Hon Roll; Outdoor Trk MVP 85; Sports Med.

HANNAH, JOANETTA; East Boston HS; Roxbury, MA; (Y); JA; OEA; Teachers Aide; Church Choir; Prfct Atten Awd; Wrd Prcssng Schlrshp Awd.

HANNAN, THOMAS J; Xauerian Brothers HS; Medfield, MA; (S); 10/236; Chess Clb; Math Tm; Im Ftbl; Hon Roll; Ntl Merit Ltr; Bio.

HANRAHAN, DAVID; Easthampton HS; Easthampton, MA; (Y); 19/160; Aud/Vis; VP Frsh Cls; VP Soph Cls; JV Bsktbl; Hon Roll; Bentley Coll; Fin.

HANRY, HERMAN; Technical HS; Springfield, MA; (Y); Red Cross Aide; Socr; Engr Sci.

HANSBERRY, KENNETH M; Norwood HS; Norwood, MA; (Y); 2/350; Am Leg Boys St; Key Clb; Trs Soph Cls; Var Golf; JV Socr; Var Tennis; JV Wrstlng; JC Awd; NHS; Ntl Merit Ltr; Law.

HANSON, ERIC; Natick HS; Natick, MA; (Y); 101/493; Pres VP Church Yth Grp; Crs Cntry; Trk; Hon Roll.

HAPENNEY, SANDRA; Burlington HS; Burlington, MA; (Y); 95/315; GAA; JA; JV Socr; Sftbl; Var Trk; Hon Roll; Var Socr Awd 84; Sftbl Lg All Star 85; JV Socr Awd 83; Dietícn.

HAQUE, IMRAN; Cambridge Rindge And Latin HS; Canbrudge, MA; (Y); Math Clb; Math Tm; JV Tennis; High Hon Roll; Hon Roll; NHS; Pres Schlr; Rotary Awd; Cambridge Emblm Awd 85; Algbr I Prz Exm 82; Latn II Prz Exm 84; Pre-Med.

HARAN, REGINA; Burncoat SR HS; Worcester, MA; (Y); Civic Clb; Cmnty Wkr; Hosp Aide; Socr; Hon Roll; Jr NHS; NHS; Horace Mann Honorary 83; Med Illstrtr.

HARASIMOWICZ, MARY ANN; Murdock HS; Winchendon, MA; (Y); 2/107; Am Leg Aux Girls St; Model UN; Yrbk Stf; Trs Jr Cls; Var Bsktbl; Var Fld Hcky; Var Trk; High Hon Roll; NHS; Cntrl MA Pentath 1st Pl Tm 7th Pl Ind 84; Wachusett Lg All Star Fld Hcky 84; Rgnl Hstry 1st Conf 85; Boston Coll.

HARBOLD, KAREN; Algonquin Regional HS; Northboro, MA; (Y); 15/221; Church Yth Grp; PAVAS; Yrbk Ed-Chief; JV Cheerleading; Capt Var Vllybl; Hon Roll; NHS; Music Schlrshp Perfrmg Arts Schl Worcester 83-84; Bus Adm.

HARCOVITZ, KATHERINE; King Philip Regional HS; Norfolk, MA; (S); Girl Scts; Hosp Aide; Band; Concert Band; Jazz Band; Mrchg Band; Jr NHS; UN Song Hero Awd Mrchng Bnd 83; Optometrist.

HARDIMAN, CHRISTOPHER J; Waltham HS; Waltham, MA; (Y); 27/600; Am Leg Boys St; Pres Latin Clb; Var Socr; JV Trk; Hon Roll; Jr NHS; NHS; Waltham Rotary Clb Schlrshp 84-85; Waltham Hgh Clss Of 1985 Schlrshp 84-85; Excell In Englsh Awd 84-85; Holy Crss Coll.

HARDING, JENNIFER A; Georgetown HS; Georgetown, MA; (Y); 5/93; AFS; Church Yth Grp; Drama Clb; Political Wkr; Concert Band; Mrchg Band; Bsktbl; Crs Cntry; Hon Roll; NHS; Presdntl Acadmc Ftnss Awd 85; VFW Auxlry Schlrshp 85; Hank Norman Memrl Schlrshp 85; U Of ME Orono; Engrng.

HARDY III, HUDSON E; Old Rochester Regional HS; Mattapoisett, MA; (Y); 22/150; Am Leg Boys St; Sec Computer Clb; Trs JA; Bsbl; Crs Cntry; Comp Sci.

HARDY, PATRICK; Medford Voc Tech HS; Medford, MA; (Y); 1/140; Boys Clb Am; Church Yth Grp; Cmnty Wkr; Office Aide; Hon Roll; Ntl Merit Schol; Rbt Gorney Awd For Mst Outstndng SR 85; Wntwrth Tech Inst; Mech Dsgn En.

HARE, RODERICK C; Taconic HS; Pittsfield, MA; (Y); 4/280; Key Clb; Acpl Chr; Nwsp Phtg; Nwsp Rptr; Yrbk Phtg; Lit Mag; VP Jr Cls; High Hon Roll; NHS; Voice Dem Awd; Clark U; Ec.

HARGRAVES, LAUREN; Bishop Fenwick HS; Lynn, MA; (Y); English Clb; GAA; Office Aide; Stage Crew; Rep Sr Cls; Rep Stu Cncl; Capt Cheerleading; Powder Puff Ftbl; Hon Roll; Commctns.

HARLOW, MICHAELA; Mohawk Trail Regional HS; Plainfield, MA; (Y); School Musical; Stage Crew; Yrbk Stf; Rep Jr Cls; Trs Stu Cncl; Var Mgr(s); Hon Roll; NHS; Art Clb; Chorus; Outstndng Achvt Bio Sci 84; Excel Spnsh 84; Art Comm 84-85; Comm Art.

HARMON, KRISTEN; King Philip Regional HS; Plainville, MA; (S); 48/215; Civic Clb; Var L Bsktbl; Var L Socr; Hon Roll; NHS; Bryant Coll; Bus Admn.

HARNAIS, SERGIO; Quincy HS; Quincy, MA; (Y); 118/302; Computer Clb; Office Aide; Chorus; Church Choir; Madrigals; School Musical; Variety Show; Nwsp Rptr; Nwsp Stf; Stu Cncl; Law.

HARNEY, CATHERINE; St Peter-Marian CC HS; Worcester, MA; (S); 2/181; Church Yth Grp; Drama Clb; Math Tm; Teachers Aide; VP Jr Cls; Rep Stu Cncl; High Hon Roll; NHS; Prfct Atten Awd; Hnrs U S Hstry & Amer Lit & Chem Awds 84-85; Erly Chldhd Ed.

HARNISCH, SUSAN T; Hamilton-Wenham Regional HS; Wenham, MA; (Y); 8/190; Art Clb; Drama Clb; Band; Capt Fld Hcky; High Hon Roll; Kiwanis Awd; NHS; PAVAS; Ski Clb; Chorus; Boston Globe Gold Key Awd Art 84; Top Rnkng Englsh Stu Awd 85; Bowdoin; Englsh.

HAROOTIAN, PETER; Reading Memorial HS; Reading, MA; (Y); French Clb; Yrbk Phtg; Yrbk Stf; Stu Cncl; Var Crs Cntry; Var Socr; Var Capt Trk; High Hon Roll; Engnr.

HARPER, GARY; Northbridge JR-SR HS; Whitinsville, MA; (S); Boy Scts; Ski Clb; Band; Concert Band; Jazz Band; Mrchg Band; Var Bsbl; High Hon Roll; NHS; Comp Sci.

HARPIN, DAN; Marlboro HS; Marlboro, MA; (Y); 36/800; JV Bsbl; JV Ftbl; High Hon Roll; Fclty Awd Outstndng Achvt Bus 85; Bus Mgmnt.

HARRIES III, RICHARD J; Hingham HS; Hingham, MA; (Y); 18/320; JV Ice Hcky; JV Socr; Hon Roll; NHS; Capt HS Sailing Tm 85; Chrmn Yacht Clb Jr Comm 84 & 85; Sailing Achvt Awds; Yale; Math.

HARRILD, GEOFFREY R; Sharon HS; Sharon, MA; (Y); Debate Tm; JCL; Latin Clb; Yrbk Stf; Socr; Trk; High Hon Roll; Hon Roll; NHS; Ntl Merit SF; Frnch & Latn Stu Mth 82.

HARRIMAN, KATHLEEN; Rockland HS; Rockland, MA; (S); 4/275; Church Yth Grp; Cmnty Wkr; French Clb; Service Clb; Stu Cncl; Im Bsktbl; Var Crs Cntry; Im Sftbl; Im Vllybl; High Hon Roll; Soc Stu Awd 81-82; MA State Schlrs Schlrshp 85.

HARRINGRON, BRIAN; Archbishop Williams HS; Braintree, MA; (Y); Political Wkr; Ski Clb; JV Bsbl; Im Bsktbl; Im Golf; JV Ice Hcky; Jr NHS; Engnrng.

HARRINGTON, BETH; Notre Dame Acad; Hanover, MA; (Y); 40/114; Cmnty Wkr; Drama Clb; Hosp Aide; Chorus; School Musical; School Play; Stage Crew; Im DECA; Im Vllybl; Hon Roll; Excel In Relgn 82-83; 1st Pl Crft Comptn 84-85; Bst Actrss Awd 84-85.

HARRINGTON, BRIAN; Cathedral HS; Springfield, MA; (Y); 53/525; Cmnty Wkr; Political Wkr; Ntl Merit SF; Panelist 83-85; Model Senate 84-85; Lib Art.

HARRINGTON, DENISE; Arlington HS; Arlington, MA; (Y); Office Aide; Yrbk Stf; Comm Art.

HARRINGTON, JOAN; Bishop Stang HS; New Bedford, MA; (Y); 50/222; Ski Clb; Chorus; Yrbk Stf; Capt Jr Cls; Diving; Gym; Swmmng; L Tennis; L Trk; Hon Roll; Acad Awd Religion 85; Acad Awd Engl IV 85; Boston Coll; Ed.

HARRINGTON, KIM; Monson JR SR HS; Monson, MA; (Y); 21/86; Drama Clb; French Clb; School Musical; School Play; L Cheerleading; Hon Roll; Rep Rgnl Stu Advsry Cncl 84-85; JR Prom Committee 84-85; Co Capt JV Chrldng 82-83; Westfield ST Coll; Cldhd Educ.

HARRINGTON, MARK D; Hoosac Valley HS; Adams, MA; (Y); Am Leg Boys St; Nwsp Stf; Yrbk Stf; VP Sr Cls; Rep Stu Cncl; Var Bsktbl; Capt Crs Cntry; Capt Trk; NHS; W-Mass X-Country Champn 84; Brandeis U; Psychlgy.

HARRIS, PETER; Haverhill HS; Haverhill, MA; (Y); 21/440; Letterman Clb; Varsity Clb; Band; Mrchg Band; JV Var Bsbl; JV Bsktbl; Var Golf; Var L Ice Hcky; Var L Trk; High Hon Roll; Harvard; Pyscl Thrpy.

HARRIS, ROBERT E; Malden HS; Malden, MA; (Y); 88/520; Temple Yth Grp; Band; Concert Band; Jazz Band; Mrchg Band; Comm.

HARRISON, JACQUELINE A; Doxbory HS; Duxbury, MA; (Y); Church Yth Grp; Dance Clb; Teachers Aide; Hon Roll; NHS; Duxbury Recreatn Grls Advancd Ten Trnmnt 1st Pl 83; Pres Phys Fitnss Awd 83; Htl Admin.

HARROP, PAMELA M; Bishop Feehan HS; N Attleboro, MA; (Y); 95/270; Drama Clb; JCL; Chorus; Nwsp Rptr; Rptr Lit Mag; High Hon Roll; Prfct Atten Awd; Spanish NHS; Century III Ldrshp Awd 84; 4th Rnr Up Miss Teen Of Amer Schlrshp & Rcgntn Pageant 84; Psychology.

HART, CHERYL L; Lincoln-Sodbury Regional HS; Lincoln, MA; (Y); Model UN; Ski Clb; Spanish Clb; Yrbk Stf; Rep Soph Cls; Rep Jr Cls; Sec Sr Cls; JV Capt Socr; JV Tennis; Hon Roll; Bus.

HART, JOSEPH; West Roxbury HS; Boston, MA; (Y); Am Leg Boys St; Varsity Clb; Band; Jazz Band; Bsktbl; Ftbl; Trk; Hon Roll; NHS; Prfct Atten Awd; U AL; Comp Sci.

HART, TIMOTHY P; Central Catholic HS; Lawrence, MA; (Y); 3/228; Pres Church Yth Grp; Church Choir; School Musical; Var Crs Cntry; Var Trk; High Hon Roll; NHS; Pres Schlr; Rotary Awd; St Schlr; Cmmnty Serv Tngr Of Yr 85; Eagle Tribune Schlrshp 85; Boston Coll.

HARTMANN, DONALD A; Tahanto Regional HS; Boylston, MA; (Y); Concert Band; Yrbk Phtg; Yrbk Stf; JV Bsbl; JV Var Bsktbl; Var Golf; Var Socr; Hon Roll; MVP JV Bsktbl Awd 82-83; U Of Hartford; Studio Art.

HARTNETT, KATHERINE; Leicester HS; Leicester, MA; (S); Cmnty Wkr; Hosp Aide; Nwsp Rptr; Nwsp Stf; Yrbk Phtg; Yrbk Rptr; Yrbk Stf; Var Fld Hcky; Jrnlsm.

HARTNETT, LAUREEN; Cambridge Rindge And Latin HS; Cambridge, MA; (S); Church Yth Grp; Cmnty Wkr; Hosp Aide; Key Clb; Math Tm; Political Wkr; Band; Rep Jr Cls; Hon Roll; Prfct Atten Awd; Princeton; Chem.

HARTZ, KENNETH; North HS; Worcester, MA; (Y); Boys Clb Am; Boy Scts; 4-H; Political Wkr; Ski Clb; Varsity Clb; Church Choir; Yrbk Sprt Ed; Rep Stu Cncl; Capt Trk; Nrthestrn; Bus Mgmt.

HARVANEK, THOMAS; Bartlett HS; Webster, MA; (Y); 27/175; School Play; Stage Crew; Variety Show; Yrbk Stf; Hon Roll; NHS; U Of Lowell; Elec Engrng.

HARWOOD, KIM R; Monument Mountain Reg HS; Gt Barrington, MA; (Y); Band; Concert Band; Mrchg Band; Pep Band; Yrbk Stf; JV Var Trk; Hon Roll; Western New Englnd Coll; Acctng.

HARWOOD, RONALD; Beverly HS; Beverly, MA; (Y); Var Capt Tennis; High Hon Roll; Hon Roll; NHS.

HASAPIDIS, GEORGE P; Governor Dummer Acad; Pinehurst, MA; (Y); 1/88; Aud/Vis; Boy Scts; Key Clb; Quiz Bowl; Varsity Clb; Jazz Band; Yrbk Ed-Chief; Capt L Crs Cntry; JV Golf; JV Trk; Cum Laude Soc; U S Military Acad; Ofcr.

HASELTINE, MICHAEL P; Grafton HS; Grafton, MA; (Y); 7/134; Nwsp Stf; VP Jr Cls; VP Sr Cls; VP Capt Ftbl; VP Capt Ice Hcky; VP Capt Trk; Hon Roll; NHS; Cornell U; Engrng.

HASENFUS, JOSEPH; Dedham HS; Dedham, MA; (Y); 27/325; Aud/Vis; School Play; Variety Show; Rep Sr Cls; Cit Awd; High Hon Roll; Stage Crew; Var L Trk; Rep Frsh Cls; MVP Trck 84; Schlr/Athlte US Army Rsrve 85; Capt Trck 85; U Of MA-BOSTON; Mngmnt.

HASEQAWA, KENNETH; South High Community Schl; Worcester, MA; (S); Cmnty Wkr; Scholastic Bowl; Science Clb; Trs Stu Cncl; High Hon Roll; VP NHS; Comp Sci.

HASKELL, DARYL; Berkshire Schl; Utica, NY; (Y); 3/122; Band; Concert Band; Mrchg Band; Bsbl; Coach Actv; Ice Hcky; Wt Lftg; Wm Brks Noln Memrl Schlrshp 85; Head Prfct 85-86; Cptn Vrsty Bsbl 85-86; Empir ST Gms Ice Hcky; Bus Mngmt.

HASKELL, HEATHER; Hoosac Valey HS; Adams, MA; (Y); 11/169; Cmnty Wkr; Pep Clb; School Play; Yrbk Stf; NHS; Dora & Jacob Wineberg Schlrshp 85; Elsie C & Robert T Arnold Schlrshp 85; St Pauls Schlrshp 85; N Adams ST Coll; Bus Admin.

HASKINS, KENNETH; Bridgewater-Raynham Regional HS; Bridgewater, MA; (Y); FBLA; Mathletes; Math Clb; Pre-Law.

HASLAM, DOUGLAS; Tewksbury Memorial HS; Tewksbury, MA; (Y); 7/330; Boy Scts; Church Yth Grp; Band; Concert Band; Jazz Band; Mrchg Band; God Cntry Awd; Hon Roll; NHS.

HASTINGS, COLLEEN; Brockton HS; Brockton, MA; (Y); 210/1000; Cmnty Wkr; Drama Clb; Band; Mrchg Band; Orch; Stage Crew; Symp Band; Hon Roll; Marine Bio.

HASTINGS, SUSAN; Lunenburg HS; Lunenburg, MA; (Y); Art Clb; Intnl Clb; Stage Crew; Sftbl; High Hon Roll; Hon Roll; Fitchburg ST Coll.

HATCHER, JEFFREY L; Mosconomet Regional HS; Boxford, MA; (Y); 1/220; Am Leg Boys St; Church Yth Grp; Math Tm; Thesps; Acpl Chr; Chorus; Boy Scts; School Musical; School Play; High Hon Roll; Outstdng Englsh Stu; Bio.

HATTON, CHRISTOPHER J; Westfield HS; Westfield, MA; (Y); Church Yth Grp; Nwsp Sprt Ed; Yrbk Sprt Ed; Bsbl; Var Capt Bsktbl; Var Socr; Var Trk; Soccr Vrsty Clb Awd 84; Citzn Schlrshp Awd 85; Providence Coll; Econmcs.

HAUMANN, KAREN L; Billerica Memorial HS; Billerica, MA; (Y); 75/400; Office Aide; Concert Band; Drm & Bgl; Mrchg Band; Stage Crew; Yrbk Stf; Powder Puff Ftbl; Hon Roll; Lawrence Mem Hosp Schl; RN.

HAUSEN, FRANCOISE; Bishop Connolly HS; Middletown, RI; (S); 12/177; Ski Clb; Teachers Aide; Band; Mrchg Band; Yrbk Stf; Trk; Vllybl; High Hon Roll; Jr NHS; German Hnr Scty 83-84; Bus.

HAVENS, LISA; Lawrence HS; Lawrence, MA; (Y); 57/313; JV Cheerleading; High Hon Roll; Hon Roll; Gregg Shrthnd Awd 85; Centruy 21 Typing Awd 85; Backer JC; Sprts Admin.

HAWKINS, BRENDA; Taconic HS; Pittsfield, MA; (Y); 17/300; Pep Clb; Q&S; Radio Clb; Nwsp Rptr; Yrbk Stf; Jr Cls; Co-Capt Cheerleading; Hon Roll; Ltr Merit Excllnc Soclgy 85; Brd Regnts Schlrshp 85; U Of MA; Clncl Psych.

HAWLEY, KENNETH A; Ludlow HS; Ludlow, MA; (Y); 12/272; Am Leg Boys St; CAP; Color Guard; JV Var Bsbl; High Hon Roll; Hon Roll; NHS; Chorus; Concert Band; Mrchg Band; Gov Citation 85; Spkr House Citation ST 83 & 85; Chem Engrng.

HAY, HEATHER; Ware HS; Ware, MA; (Y); Art Clb; French Clb; GAA; Key Clb; Stage Crew; Variety Show; JV Stat Bsktbl; Var Mgr(s); Var Score Keeper; Stat Socr; Var Soccer & Var Bsktbl Ltr Statistician 83 & 84; JV Bsktbl Awd 84; Marine Bio.

HAYES, BRIAN; Melrose HS; Melrose, MA; (Y); 6/370; Boy Scts; Computer Clb; Mrchg Band; Nwsp Rptr; Var L Bsbl; Var L Bsktbl; Hon Roll; NHS; Ntl Merit Ltr.

HAYES, BRYON; Nauset Regional HS; N Eastham, MA; (Y); Drama Clb; School Musical; School Play; Stage Crew; Hon Roll.

HAYES, DEIRDRE L; Sacred Heart HS; Plymouth, MA; (Y); 11/80; Pres Frsh Cls; Var Capt Bsktbl; Var Capt Fld Hcky; Var Capt Sftbl; Hon Roll; NHS; Outstndg Athl 84; Schlr Athl 85; Excell Acad & Athltcs 85; U Of VT; Phy Educ.

HAYES, FRANCES S; Dedham HS; Dedham, MA; (S); 7/350; Drama Clb; Rep Soph Cls; Rep Jr Cls; Rep Sr Cls; Stu Cncl; Hon Roll; VFW Awd; Voice Dem Awd; Suffolk U; Government.

HAYES, KEVIN; Reading Memorial HS; Reading, MA; (Y); JV Wrstlng; Hon Roll; Electrcn.

HAYES, LAUREN; Notre Dame Acad; Hanover, MA; (Y); 30/130; Intnl Clb; Science Clb; Spanish Clb; School Musical; Stage Crew; VP Soph Cls; Var L Crs Cntry; Var L Trk; Hon Roll; Excllnc Alg Awd; Schlrshps-Claire & Marhta Nagie/Nrsng & Hanovr Vstng Nrses; Boston Coll; Nrsng.

HAYES, MICHAEL E; Canton HS; Canton, MA; (Y); 9/265; Mathletes; Math Clb; Math Tm; Nwsp Stf; Yrbk Stf; Rep Sr Cls; Rep Stu Cncl; Var L Crs Cntry; Var L Ice Hcky; JV Socr; Century Clb 84; Eastern Mass Mah All-Star 85; Engrng.

HAYES, STEVE; Central Catholic HS; Lawrence, MA; (Y); Comp Sci.

HAYES, SUSAN; Holbrook HS; Holbrook, MA; (Y); Spanish Clb; Chorus.

HAYES, TANJA; Bishop Connolly HS; Fall River, MA; (S); 21/155; Dance Clb; Off Ski Clb; Yrbk Phtg; High Hon Roll; NHS; Drama Clb; School Play; Nwsp Phtg; Nwsp Stf; Tennis; Scholar Ecology Prgm Teton Sci Schl WY 84; U Of WA Seattle.

HAYMES, MEREDITH L; Sharon HS; Sharon, MA; (Y); Am Leg Aux Girls St; Drama Clb; School Play; Nwsp Stf; Yrbk Stf; Hon Roll; NHS; Library Aide; Math Tm; Spanish Clb; Stu Of Mnth Mth 84; Phi Alpha Theta, Upsilon Alpha Hnrb Mntn 85; Excllnce Acting Drama Fest Guild 85; Med.

HAYNER, STEPHANIE; Newburyport HS; Newburyport, MA; (Y); 40/210; Science Clb; Trk; Hon Roll; U Of AZ; Ranch Mngr.

HAYNES, MARGARET M; Hudson HS; Hudson, MA; (Y); Pep Clb; Ski Clb; Mrchg Band; Orch; Capt Cheerleading; Powder Puff Ftbl; Sftbl; Hon Roll; Bus Adm.

HAYTER, ROYCE; Joseph Case HS; Seekonk, MA; (Y); Boy Scts; Church Yth Grp; Drama Clb; Chorus; Var L Crs Cntry; Var L Trk; Bristol CC; Eng.

HAYWOOD, MARY; Gardner HS; Gardner, MA; (Y); GAA; Band; Concert Band; Mrchg Band; JV Bsktbl; High Hon Roll; Hon Roll; NHS; Engrng.

HAZELL, PATRICIA; Beverly HS; Beverly, MA; (Y); Cmnty Wkr; Hosp Aide; Drm & Bgl; JV Sftbl; JV Trk; Hon Roll; Prfct Atten Awd; Church Yth Grp; Library Aide; Office Aide; Safety Awd 83; Penmnshp Awd 82; Fnncl Mgmt.

HEALEY, DAVID; Randolph HS; Randolph, MA; (Y); Drama Clb; Spanish Clb; Pres Band; Concert Band; Jazz Band; Mrchg Band; Crs Cntry; Swmmng; Trs NHS; School Musical; Outstndng Jzz Solst Dist Jzz Fstvl 85; Sestrn MA Schlstc Bndmbrs Assn Comptn 85; Sci.

HEALEY, DENISE E; Franklin County Christian Acad; Deerfield, MA; (Y); 1/15; Church Yth Grp; Quiz Bowl; Sec Stu Cncl; French Clb; GAA; Band; Concert Band; Mrchg Band; Hghst Schltc Achvt Awd 85; Elem Educ.

HEALY, MARC; St Johns HS; Oxford, MA; (Y); 78/263; JA; Model UN; Var L Trk; High Hon Roll; Hon Roll; NEDT Awd; Church Yth Grp; Headmasters Hnrs 84-85; Merit Schlrshp Ripon Coll 85; Ntl Hnr Roll 85; Ripon Coll; Physics.

HEALY, MICHELLE; Fontbonne Acad; Wollaston, MA; (Y); 10/138; Trs Church Yth Grp; Pres Key Clb; Ed Lit Mag; Var Crs Cntry; Var Capt Trk; NHS; Hosp Aide; Science Clb; Teachers Aide; Chorus; Holy Cross Bk Awd 85; Spnsh Natl Exam Brnz Medal 85; Schl Rcrds Trck & Crss Cntry,Leag Trphys 82-85; Engl.

HEALY, SUZETTE; Tahanto Regional HS; Boylston, MA; (Y); 5/60; Church Yth Grp; French Clb; Hosp Aide; Science Clb; Var Crs Cntry; Var Tennis; Hon Roll; Jr NHS; NHS; Boylston Grad Assn Bk Awd 85; Jeffrey Navin Schlrshp 85; Hahnemann Hosp Schl; Nrsng.

HEALY, THOMAS; Tri-County Reg Tech; Franklin, MA; (Y); 2/237; VICA; High Hon Roll; Hon Roll; Franklin Rotary Club Schlrshp 85; Commnwlth MA Schl 85; Tri-Cnty HS Tchrs Assoc Awd 85; Wentworth Inst Tech; Mech Engr.

HEBARD, ROXANNE; North Attleboro HS; N Attleboro, MA; (Y); Dance Clb; Latin Clb; Powder Puff Ftbl; Sftbl; Vllybl; Hon Roll; YMCA Ldrs Clb; Nrs.

HEBB, REBECCA; Blackstone Valley Reg Voc Tech HS; Upton, MA; (Y); Computer Clb; High Hon Roll; Worcester Poly Tech Isnt Frontiers Sci & Math Prog 85.

HEBERT, CHRISSY; Natick HS; Natick, MA; (Y); Cmnty Wkr; Sftbl.

HEBERT, JEFFREY M; Grafton Memorial SR HS; S Grafton, MA; (Y); Am Leg Boys St; Art Clb; Church Yth Grp; Quiz Bowl; Nwsp Rptr; Rep Stu Cncl; Hon Roll; ELEC Engrng.

HEBERT, LINDA; Smith Acad; Hatfield, MA; (Y); Drama Clb; Key Clb; School Play; Stage Crew; Variety Show; Yrbk Bus Mgr; Yrbk Phtg; Yrbk Stf; JV Bsktbl; Var Fld Hcky; French.

HEBERT, SANDRA; St Bernards HS; Fitchburg, MA; (S); 13/163; Trs French Clb; Church Choir; School Musical; Yrbk Stf; Rep Stu Cncl; Mgr(s); Hon Roll; NHS; Engrng.

HEBERT, TIM; Agawam HS; Feeding Hls, MA; (Y); 39/300; Band; Concert Band; Jazz Band; Mrchg Band; Hon Roll; Mech Drawing Hnry Mntn In ST Comptn 83; Engnrng.

HEDSPETH, RONALD P; Cathedral HS; Springfield, MA; (Y); Boy Scts; Church Yth Grp; Cmnty Wkr; Political Wkr; Ftbl; Hon Roll; Comp Engr.

HEERTER, THOMAS A; Malden HS; Malden, MA; (Y); 26/511; Trk; NHS; Lit Soc; Babe Ruth Asst Coach; U Lowell; Comp Sci.

HEFFERNAN, KATHLEEN; B M C Durfee HS; Fall River, MA; (Y); 32/700; Drama Clb; French Clb; Varsity Clb; Flag Corp; Stage Crew; Yrbk Stf; Twrlr; High Hon Roll; Hon Roll; NHS; Mrktng.

HEFFERNAN, KRISTEN; Methuen HS; Methuen, MA; (Y); 49/450; Intnl Clb; Spanish Clb; Band; Concert Band; Mrchg Band; High Hon Roll; Hon Roll; Bus.

HEFFRON, MICHAEL; St Dominic Savio HS; E Boston, MA; (Y); 36/109; Aud/Vis; Boys Clb Am; Chess Clb; Computer Clb; JA; Trk; Wt Lftg; Hon Roll; Electrcl Engrng.

HEGARTY, KAREN; Norwood HS; Norwood, MA; (Y); 25/351; Cmnty Wkr; Hosp Aide; JA; Band; Jazz Band; Mrchg Band; Orch; Symp Band; Stu Cncl; Elks Awd; Joseph P Zyrek Awd 85; Frncs X Sheehan Schlrshp 85; Paul M Alberta Music Schlrshp 85; U Of NH; Music.

HEGGESTAD, LAUREN; Bedford HS; Bedford, MA; (Y); 8/230; Church Yth Grp; Drama Clb; Church Choir; Var L Diving; Var L Gym; Var L Swmmng; High Hon Roll; NHS; Ntl Merit SF; Harvard Bk Awd.

HEGNER, JEANNE M; Sacred Heart HS; Plymouth, MA; (Y); 4/89; Debate Tm; Intnl Clb; School Musical; Nwsp Rptr; NHS; Ntl Merit Ltr; Dance Clb; Drama Clb; Speech Tm; Intl Yth JA 83-84; Natl Frnsc Leage Key 84-85; 1st Chem Sci 85.

HEIDBRINK, KRISTINE J; Burlington HS; Burlington, MA; (Y); VP Trs Church Yth Grp; Bsktbl; Powder Puff Ftbl; JV Var Socr; Sftbl; Tennis; Var Trk; Hon Roll; Lgu Best Perfrmr 45 Yrd Dash 84-85.

HEIJN, LAURA H; Lincoln-Sudbury Regional HS; Lincoln, MA; (Y); Art Clb; Library Aide; Lit Mag; High Hon Roll; Ntl Merit SF; Art.

HEIMBERG, MARY D; Maynard HS; Maynard, MA; (Y); 1/100; Am Leg Aux Girls St; Radio Clb; Chorus; Concert Band; Mrchg Band; Rep Frsh Cls; Pres Soph Cls; Rep Stu Cncl; Var Cheerleading; Trk; Hugh O Brian Yth Fndtn Ldrshp Smnr 84; Chncllrs Tlnt Awd 85; Bio.

HEINE, JEANNE; Weymouth North HS; Weymouth, MA; (Y); 39/339; Church Yth Grp; Spanish Clb; Yrbk Stf; Stu Cncl; Sftbl; Vllybl; High Hon Roll; Hon Roll; Phys Ther.

HEINEGG, AYO P; Phillips Acad; Saudi Arabia; (Y); Cmnty Wkr; Key Clb; Spanish Clb; Var Crs Cntry; Capt Trk; Jr NHS; M L King JR Awd 84; Ntl Achvt Schlrshp 84; VP Afro-Latino Amer Soc 84-85.

HEINIG, GEORGE; Tahanto HS; Boylston, MA; (Y); 3/47; Pres Church Yth Grp; Math Tm; Band; Jazz Band; Mrchg Band; Yrbk Stf; Rep Stu Cncl; Jr NHS; NHS; Prfct Atten Awd; MA Boys ST; Optmtrst.

HEITMAN, CHRISTOPHER E; Rivers Country Day HS; Newton Centre, MA; (Y); Cmnty Wkr; Key Clb; VP Frsh Cls; Rep Soph Cls; Pres Jr Cls; Pres Stu Cncl; Var Capt Bsbl; Var Ice Hcky; Var Socr; Hon Roll; Headmstrs Awd 85; Rivers Athltc Dept Awd 85; Paul Licht Hockey Awd, Navoni Awd Bsbl 85; ST U NY Plattsburgh; Math.

HELDENBERGH, PAMELA; Holy Name Central Catholic HS; E Douglas, MA; (Y); Varsity Clb; Church Choir; Var Capt Socr; Var Sftbl; High Hon Roll; Hon Roll; Trphy Hgh Screr Worcester Indr Soccer Lge 85; Humanities Awd, Algebra Awd, Rlgn Awd, Hnr Awd 83; Phys Thrpy.

HELMAN, DANIEL S; Granby JR SR HS; South Hadley, MA; (Y); Am Leg Boys St; Pres Church Yth Grp; Band; Chorus; Hon Roll; Var Socr; Var Trk; Var Wrstlng; Excllnce Horticulture 85; Coaches Awd Wrstlng 83 & 84; Horticulture.

HELMS, LISA A; Lincoln-Sudbury Regional HS; Sudbury, MA; (Y); Var Capt Bsktbl; Var Socr; Arch.

HENAULT, CHRISTINE; Medway JR SR HS; Medway, MA; (Y); 1/145; Drama Clb; Jazz Band; School Musical; Yrbk Stf; Stu Cncl; Var Socr; Var Trk; High Hon Roll; VP NHS; Prfct Atten Awd; Wellesley Bk Awd 85; MVP Grls Vrsty Socr Tm 85; MA Advncd Studies Pgm 85.

HENDERSON, MARK; Bridgewater Raynham Regional HS; Bridgewater, MA; (Y); Camera Clb; Science Clb; Spanish Clb; Yrbk Stf; Mgr(s); Score Keeper; Acad All Amer 85; Old Colony Awd 85; Doctr Sprts Med.

HENDERSON, RACHEL MARGARET; Cambridge Rindge And Latin Schl; Cambridge, MA; (Y); 10/500; Cmnty Wkr; Drama Clb; French Clb; School Musical; School Play; Stage Crew; Variety Show; Stu Cncl; NHS; Ntl Merit Ltr; Harvard Coop Scty Schlrshp 85; Wnnr Bnd Crtcl Wrtng Cont 85; Rec For Outstdng Dramatic Achv 84-85; Wesleyan U; Thtr.

HENDRY, JENNIFER; Burncoat SR HS; Worcester, MA; (Y); 3/271; Church Yth Grp; JA; Sftbl; High Hon Roll; Hon Roll; Jr NHS; NHS; Ldrs Club Schlrshp 85; Natl Cncl Yth Ldrshp 84-85; Assumption Coll; Bus.

HENEGHAN, CHRIS; Burlington HS; Burlington, MA; (Y); 50/350; Yrbk Stf; Rep Sr Cls; Hon Roll; Law.

HENNEMANN, JAMES T; Oakmont Regional HS; Westminster, MA; (Y); Nwsp Ed-Chief; Ftbl; Bridgewater ST Coll; Aviation.

HENNEMUTH, GARY; Falmouth HS; N Falmouth, MA; (S); AFS; Drama Clb; Thesps; Acpl Chr; Chorus; School Musical; School Play; Swing Chorus; Hon Roll; Bst Actor 84; Bst Vocalist 83; Bst Actor 85; NY U; Theatre.

HENNESSEY, DONNA; Lawrence HS; Lawrence, MA; (S); 80/300; JA; Band; Chorus; Concert Band; Mrchg Band; Yrbk Stf; Sftbl; Vllybl; Hon Roll; US Achvmnt Acad 83; Newberry JC; Resp Thrphy.

HENNESSEY, JOAN; Arlington Catholic HS; Arlington, MA; (Y); 18/148; Intnl Clb; Spanish Clb; Var L Cheerleading; High Hon Roll; Hon Roll; NHS; Acctng.

HENNESSY, MELISSA; Marian HS; Framingham, MA; (Y); 5/177; Yrbk Stf; Lit Mag; High Hon Roll; Hon Roll; NCTE Awd; NHS; Church Yth Grp; Spanish Clb; School Musical; Cheerleading; Excllnce Geom Awd 84; Jrnlsm.

HENSHAW, JEANETTE; North Middlesex Regional HS; W Townsend, MA; (Y); Church Yth Grp; Computer Clb; Drama Clb; NFL; Red Cross Aide; Teachers Aide; Concert Band; Pep Band; Stage Crew; Jr NHS; Elem Educ.

HENSHAW, ROBIN; Marragansett Regional HS; Templeton, MA; (Y); Am Leg Boys St; Boy Scts; Computer Clb; Letterman Clb; Political Wkr; Rep Stu Cncl; Crs Cntry; Trk; Pres Mu Alp Tht; NHS; Scholar G Washington U Coll Prg Secondary Schl Study 84; Scholar Chancellors Talent Awd 84.

HEPPENSTALL, RICHARD; St Johns HS; Worcester, MA; (Y); 251/290; JA; Ski Clb; Y-Teens; Capt Ftbl; Var Trk; Var Wt Lftg; Syracuse U; Law.

HERBERT JR, ROGER G; Barnstable HS; Centerville, MA; (Y); Computer Clb; Drama Clb; Stage Crew; Hon Roll; Southeastern Acad FL; Travel.

HERMENAU, WAYNE; Brockton HS; Brockton, MA; (Y); 225/1098; Church Yth Grp; Latin Clb; Band; Drm & Bgl; Jazz Band; Mrchg Band; Nwsp Rptr; Ftbl; Vllybl; JP Sousa Awd; Wentworth Inst; Slr Engrng.

HERMISTON, NANCY J; Westwood HS; Westwood, MA; (Y); AFS; Cmnty Wkr; Hosp Aide; Key Clb; School Musical; School Play; Yrbk Stf; Lit Mag; Var L Fld Hcky; Trk; Phy Thrpy.

HERNANDEZ, MAGDALENA; Boston Latin School; Boston, MA; (Y); 76/335; Pres Debate Tm; VP French Clb; VP Sec JA; Chorus; MA Spch ST Fnl Trnmt 1st Pl 83; Francis Gardner Dbtng Awd 83; Francis Gardner Rdng Awd 2nd Pl 85.

HERNANDEZ, RAFAEL; Greenfield HS; Greenfield, MA; (Y); Chess Clb; Church Yth Grp; Spanish Clb; Teachers Aide; Hon Roll; MA U; Pre-Med.

HERNANDO, CAMILLE; Ayer SR HS; Ft Dix, NJ; (Y); Hosp Aide; Pep Clb; Pres Spanish Clb; Chorus; Yrbk Stf; High Hon Roll; NHS; Spanish III Awd Exc 84-85; Nrsng.

HERNON, ANN C; Mission Church HS; Hyde Park, MA; (Y); Girl Scts; Science Clb; School Play; Variety Show; VP Jr Cls; Var Capt Bsktbl; Var Capt Sftbl; Hon Roll; NHS; Prfct Atten Awd; All Star Of Leag Softball 81-85; Outstndng Athlete 85; Schl Athlete Of Yr 85; Framingham ST; Bus Mngmnt.

HERRERA, LISA; Classical HS; Lynn, MA; (Y); Office Aide; Pep Clb; Spanish Clb; Chorus; Variety Show; Yrbk Stf; Stu Cncl; Sftbl; Hon Roll; Stewardess.

HERRERA, SUSANNE G; Mohawk Trail Regional HS; Shelburne Falls, MA; (Y); Aud/Vis; Church Yth Grp; Capt Color Guard; School Musical; School Play; Rep Sr Cls; Stat Bsktbl; High Hon Roll; Hon Roll; NHS; NM ST U; Bus.

HERSEY, STEPHEN; Westford Acad; Westford, MA; (Y); AFS; French Clb; Intnl Clb; Latin Clb; Ski Clb; Spanish Clb; L Golf; L Socr; Hon Roll; Intl Bus.

HERSHENSON, KEITH; Randolph HS; Randolph, MA; (Y); 59/315; Sec Computer Clb; Drama Clb; Chorus; Stage Crew; Yrbk Stf; Hon Roll; NHS; U Of MA; Mngmt.

HERSHFANG, RACHEL E; Commonwealth Schl; Boston, MA; (Y); Political Wkr; Chorus; Lit Mag; High Hon Roll; Ntl Merit SF; Cls 1885 Awd Lat 81-82.

HERVIEUX, LINDA; Keith Catholic HS; Lowell, MA; (Y); 4/55; Nwsp Ed-Chief; Yrbk Ed-Chief; Sec Soph Cls; High Hon Roll; Jr NHS; MA Commnwlth Schlr 85; Acad Schlrshp 85; Boston U Schlrshp 85; Boston U; Jrnlsm.

HESSION, ANN M; Dedham HS; Dedham, MA; (S); 2/300; Church Yth Grp; Concert Band; Sec Mrchg Band; Capt Bsktbl; Swmmng; Trk; High Hon Roll; NHS; Ntl Merit Ltr; Bst Frshmn & Soph In Sci 83 & 84; Renselear Medal 85.

HESSION, EDWARD; Central Catholic HS; Lowell, MA; (Y); Church Yth Grp; Math Clb; Ski Clb; JV Bsktbl; Var Crs Cntry; Var Trk; High Hon Roll; Mth.

HESTER, MICHAEL J; Wellesley HS; Wellesley, MA; (Y); Am Leg Boys St; Chorus; JV Var Bsbl; Var Capt Ftbl; JV Var Ice Hcky; Fac Admin Parents & Stu Org 84-85; Mltry Career.

HEUGHAN, LISA R; Framingham North HS; Boston, MA; (Y); 110/325; Chrmn Cmnty Wkr; Spanish Clb; Yrbk Sprt Ed; Rep Soph Cls; Rep Jr Cls; Rep Stu Cncl; Im Badmtn; Coach Actv; JV Sftbl; Im Vllybl; Mst Lkly Scceed 81-84; METCO Acad Awd 81-83; Boston U; Sys Engr.

HEWETT, KERRIE; Presentation Of Mary Acad; Atkinson, NH; (Y); Dance Clb; Debate Tm; Drama Clb; Model UN; Ski Clb; School Musical; School Play; Yrbk Stf; Cheerleading; Hon Roll; Hnrs In Nature Of Belief Ad 85; U Of NH; Lwyr.

HEWLETT, LINDA; Cathedral HS; Springfield, MA; (Y); GAA; JA; Varsity Clb; Var Bsktbl; Var Sftbl; Im Wt Lftg; U MA; Accntng.

HEWSON, SHERI; Stoughton HS; Stoughton, MA; (Y); Math Tm; Trs Temple Yth Grp; Band; Concert Band; Mrchg Band; School Musical; Capt Vllybl; High Hon Roll; Hon Roll; Law.

HIBBERT, CHRISTINE ANN; New Bedford HS; New Bedford, MA; (Y); Rep Frsh Cls; Rep Soph Cls; Rep Jr Cls; Stu Cncl; Hon Roll; Stheastrn MA U; Accntng.

HICKOK, DEIRDRE; New Bedford HS; New Bedford, MA; (Y); 70/688; Church Yth Grp; Trs Drama Clb; Office Aide; Chorus; School Musical; School Play; Rep Stu Cncl; Swmmng; Ntl Merit SF; Bst Command Spkn Fr 84-85; Theatr.

HICKS, CHRISTINE; Brockton HS; Brockton, MA; (Y); 95/997; Service Clb; Rep Jr Cls; High Hon Roll; Hon Roll; Jr NHS; Hlth Fair Awd 83.

HICKS, CHRISTINE; Holy Name CC HS; Leicester, MA; (Y); 78/245; Church Yth Grp; Pep Clb; School Play; Yrbk Stf; Lit Mag; Var Cheerleading; Hon Roll; Yth Ftns Cncl & Crtv Wrtng Awds 84-85; Hmnts IV 85; Framingham ST Coll; Law.

HICKS, DIANE; Mohawk Trail Reg HS; Charlemont, MA; (Y); 26/120; Church Yth Grp; Debate Tm; Ski Clb; Chorus; Church Choir; Color Guard; Trk; Hon Roll; Float & Fndraisg & SR Receptn Comms; U MA; Bus Mktg.

HICKS, HOLLY; Tri-County Vo Tech HS; E Walpole, MA; (Y); Teachers Aide; Yrbk Stf; Stu Cncl; Score Keeper; Socr; Sftbl; Vllybl; Hon Roll; Good Sprtsmnshp Sccr, Vrsty Pin Sccr 83; Vrsty Sftbll 83-84; Framingham ST; Erly Chldhd Dv.

HICKS, LISA; Bridgewater-Raynham Regional HS; Raynham, MA; (Y); Mgr(s); Wt Lftg; Southeastern MA U; Psych.

HIGBY, SHARON; Cathedral HS; Longmeadow, MA; (Y); Church Yth Grp; 4-H; Spanish Clb; School Musical; School Play; Pres Frsh Cls; Stu Cncl; Vllybl.

HIGGINS, CINDY; Barnstable HS; Hyannis, MA; (S); Drama Clb; Acpl Chr; Chorus; Stage Crew; Swing Chorus; Variety Show; High Hon Roll; Music.

HIGGINS, JACQUELYN A; Norwood HS; Norwood, MA; (Y); 61/332; Cmnty Wkr; Key Clb; Spanish Clb; School Play; Variety Show; Nwsp Stf; Yrbk Stf; Trs Soph Cls; Trs Jr Cls; JV Sftbl; Med.

HIGGINS, SUSAN M; Peabody Veterans Memorial HS; Peabody, MA; (Y); Girl Scts; Band; Church Choir; Concert Band; Mrchg Band; Yrbk Stf; Bsktbl; Sftbl; Tennis; Hon Roll; Burdette; Comp Prog.

HIGH, ELIZABETH; Clinton HS; Clinton, MA; (Y); Dance Clb; Drama Clb; Intnl Clb; Ski Clb; Chorus; School Play; Yrbk Stf; Hon Roll; Prfct Atten Awd; French Clb; Achvt Awd Dncng 85; Theatre Arts.

HILDRETH, VICTORIA; Milford HS; Milford, MA; (Y); 90/300; Dance Clb; Band; Concert Band; Mrchg Band; Stat Socr; Trk; Hon Roll; Ski Clb; Yrbk Stf; Score Keeper; Mst Dedictd Girls Vrsty Trk 85; 1st Pl Jazz Trio, 1st Pl Grp Prodctn 85; 1st Rnr-Up Jazz Trio 85.

HILL, ANTHONY A; West Roxbury HS; Mattapan, MA; (Y); Am Leg Boys St; JA; Stage Crew; Yrbk Phtg; Yrbk Ed-Chief; Var Capt Ftbl; Var Capt Trk; Hon Roll; NHS; Office Aide; Cmnty Lg Asst Ftbl Coach 84; Hugh O Brien ST Sem 84; Comp Engrng.

HILL, BARBARA; B M C Durfee HS; Fall River, MA; (Y); 68/596; Yrbk Stf; Hon Roll; Chef.

HILL, CAROL; Doherty Memorial HS; Worcester, MA; (Y); Rep Church Yth Grp; FHA; Spanish Clb; School Play; Yrbk Stf; Hon Roll; Jr NHS; Fshn Merchndsng.

HILL, CYNTHIA; Agawam HS; Feeding Hills, MA; (Y); 46/310; Office Aide; Chorus; School Musical; Variety Show; JV Capt Cheerleading; Hon Roll; NHS; Ntlhnr Rl 85; U MA; Nrsg.

HILL, GREGORY J; Tewksbury Memorial HS; Tewksbury, MA; (Y); 35/300; JV Bsbl; Capt L Golf; Capt L Ice Hcky; Im Socr; Hon Roll; Coachs Awd Glf Tm 85; Asst Capt HS Hcky ST Fnls 85; U Of NH; Cvl Engrng.

HILL, MALCOLM S; Natick HS; Natick, MA; (Y); 84/442; Am Leg Boys St; Church Yth Grp; JCL; Rep Jr Cls; VP Sr Cls; Capt Crs Cntry; Capt Trk; Hon Roll; Med.

HILL, MICHAEL; Chicopee HS; Chicopee, MA; (Y); Boy Scts; Nwsp Stf; Yrbk Stf; Capt Var Crs Cntry; Var Trk; Engrng.

HILL, TIMOTHY K; Norton HS; Norton, MA; (Y); 9/190; Am Leg Boys St; Varsity Clb; Yrbk Stf; Stu Cncl; JV Bsktbl; JV Var Ftbl; Trk; Hon Roll; NHS; Framingham ST Upsilon Alpha Hist Cntst.

HILLARY, RONALD; Revere HS; Revere, MA; (Y); Am Leg Boys St; Yrbk Stf; Pres Jr Cls; Var Ftbl; Var Trk; Stu SAAD 84-85; Suffolk; Law Enf.

HILLIARD, CATHERINE; Hopedale JR SR HS; Hopedale, MA; (Y); 5/60; Cmnty Wkr; Library Aide; School Play; Stage Crew; Yrbk Stf; High Hon Roll; NHS; Vet.

HIMES, WESLEY; Deerfield Acad; Greensboro, NC; (Y); Boy Scts; Church Yth Grp; Debate Tm; Model UN; Bsktbl; Socr; Hon Roll; Big Bro 85-86; Chrstn Fllwshp, Missions 85; Pol Sci.

HINCHEY, KEVIN; Melrose HS; Melrose, MA; (Y); 11/404; Var L Socr; Hon Roll; NHS; Pres Acad Fit Awd 85; Womns Clb Melrose Inc Scholar 85; Math Awd 85; Worcester Polytech; Elec Engrng.

HINCKLEY, JENNIFER JEAN; Barnstable HS; Centerville, MA; (Y); 32/398; Camera Clb; Cmnty Wkr; Drama Clb; Hosp Aide; Political Wkr; Ski Clb; Nwsp Phtg; Yrbk Phtg; Vllybl; VFW Awd; Centerville-Osterville Vlntrs Scholar 85; VFW Scholar 85; Northeastern U; Resp Thrpy.

HINDS, DAWN; Jeremiah E Burke HS; Dorchester, MA; (Y); 4-H; School Musical; Rep Stu Cncl; JV Vllybl; Prfct Atten Awd; Peer Counslg Tchnques 83; Pr Cnslg Trng Dimock Yth Alc Prog 84; Natl Cmmttee Arts Of Hndcppd 83-85.

HINES, DAVID; Lynn English HS; Lynn, MA; (Y); AFS; Var Ftbl; Var Trk; Bst Off Lnmn JV 83; Coachs Awd Vrsty 84; Annapolis; Nvy.

HINES, DOUGLAS; Boston Latin Schl; Boston, MA; (Y); 146/334; Band; Mrchg Band; Stage Crew; Symp Band; Rep Frsh Cls; Rep Soph Cls; Rep Jr Cls; Rep Stu Cncl; Var Ftbl; Var Trk; Natl Socl Studies Olympd 83-84; Pre-Law.

HINES, EVAN; Boston Technical HS; Boston, MA; (Y); Boys Clb Am; ROTC; Wrstlng; Hon Roll; Hnr Roll Merit 82-85; NYU; Bus.

HINES, KATHLEEN B; Randolph HS; Randolph, MA; (Y); 6/316; Spanish Clb; VP Concert Band; Jazz Band; Mrchg Band; Nwsp Stf; NHS; Ntl Merit Ltr; MA Yth Wind Ensmbl; S Shore Consvrtry Of Music; MA All ST Music Festvl; Music.

HINES, LYNN; Silver Lake Regional HS; Halifax, MA; (Y); 3/450; French Clb; Latin Clb; Mrchg Band; Yrbk Ed-Chief; Stu Cncl; Trk; Hon Roll; NHS; Acadmc All Am 84-85; Rcklnd Trst Schlrshp 85; NLSA 85; U Of MA; Crftd Pblc Accntnt.

HINGSTON, JAMES; Christopher Columbus HS; Boston, MA; (Y); 45/142; Boys Clb Am; Church Yth Grp; Cmnty Wkr; JA; Letterman Clb; Varsity Clb; Var Bsbl; JV Ftbl; Var Ice Hcky; L Tennis; Rookie Yr 82-83; MVP Bsbll 83; Bus Law Awd 84-85; Plattsburgh ST; Bus.

HINTEREGGER, ELLEN; Newton North HS; Newton, MA; (Y); Church Yth Grp; Cmnty Wkr; Dance Clb; Service Clb; Teachers Aide; Band; Concert Band; Mrchg Band; School Musical; Lit Mag; Psych.

HIPPLE, MARIE; Holliston HS; Holliston, MA; (Y); Art Clb; Dance Clb; Exploring; French Clb; Teachers Aide; Y-Teens; Church Choir; Stage Crew; Yrbk Rptr; Yrbk Stf; Ntl Latin Schlr Awd 83; Bst Prfrmnc In Dance Thtr Awd 84; U Of MA Amhrst; Fshn Dsgnr.

HIROSE, KEIKO; Milton Acad; Wellesley, MA; (Y); 3/65; Cmnty Wkr; Math Tm; PAVAS; Chorus; School Play; Nwsp Stf; Rep Frsh Cls; Im Bsktbl; Im Fld Hcky; JV Lcrss; Ben Fosdick Harding Prz Ltn 82.

HIRSHBERG, AMY N; Doherty Memorial HS; Worcester, MA; (Y); Cmnty Wkr; JA; Spanish Clb; Teachers Aide; Temple Yth Grp; Thesps; Nwsp Rptr; Hon Roll; Jr NHS; Spanish NHS; Natl Spnsh Exm Schlstc Achvt Awd 84; JR Achvt Exam Awd 85; Brdcstg.

HIRSHLAG, JENNIFER; Apponequet Regional HS; East Freetown, MA; (Y); 15/250; Band; Drm Mjr(t); Nwsp Stf; Yrbk Stf; Tennis; Capt Twrlr; High Hon Roll; Hon Roll; Jr NHS; NHS; Jrnlsm.

HITCHCOCK, TIMOTHY S; Brookline HS; Brookline, MA; (Y); Church Choir; Madrigals; Symp Band.

HIX, DEAN G; Milford HS; Milford, MA; (Y); 35/314; Boy Scts; VP Church Yth Grp; Drama Clb; Math Clb; Chorus; School Musical; High Hon Roll; Hon Roll; NHS; Stonehill Coll Acad Schlrshp 85-89; Stonehill Coll; Bus Adm.

HIXON, JEANNETTE; East Boston HS; Mattapan, MA; (Y); Church Yth Grp; Library Aide; Teachers Aide; Chorus; Pep Band; Variety Show; Nwsp Rptr; Yrbk Stf; VP Pres Stu Cncl; Capt Cheerleading; Pres Bstn Ctywd Stu Govt 84-85; Sufflk U Awd; Amherst U; Intl Bus.

HO, LUIS; Boston Latin Schl; East Boston, MA; (Y); 28/340; Exploring; French Clb; JA; Science Clb; Orch; High Hon Roll; Hon Roll; Jr NHS; NHS; Prfct Atten Awd; Sci Fair 1st Cty, 3rd ST, Ntl Sci Olym Awd, XXI Math Olym Awd 84-85; MIT; Astrnmy.

HOAG, MICHAEL R; Bishop Feehan HS; Attleboro, MA; (Y); 1/252; Am Leg Boys St; Church Yth Grp; Debate Tm; French Clb; Letterman Clb; Math Clb; Quiz Bowl; Nwsp Rptr; Nwsp Stf; Yrbk Rptr; Holy Cross Book Prz 85; Law.

HOANG, LO; Chelsea HS; Boston, MA; (Y); Chess Clb; Socr; Trk; Hon Roll; Kiwanis Awd; Boston U; Engnrng.

HOCHKEPPEL, GLEN; Cohasset HS; Cohasset, MA; (Y); 3/130; Debate Tm; Drama Clb; Math Tm; Chorus; Jazz Band; School Musical; Nwsp Stf; Lit Mag; High Hon Roll; NHS; Eng.

HOCKER, KRISTEN; Bedford HS; Bedford, MA; (Y); 4/213; AFS; Off Jr Cls; Bsktbl; Var Mgr(s); Var Score Keeper; Var L Socr; High Hon Roll; Hon Roll; NHS; Ntl Merit Ltr; Ldrshp Awd Phys Ed 82-83; Johns Hopkins U; Lib Arts.

HODGE, SHERYL A; Randolph HS; Randolph, MA; (Y); 53/351; Drama Clb; Spanish Clb; Band; Chorus; Concert Band; Jazz Band; Mrchg Band; School Musical; Gym; NHS; SEMSBA Cert 84; Section Ldr Of Trumpets 84-85; Hnr Roll 2nd Term Cert 85; N Adams ST Coll; Childhd Educ.

HODOS, EMILY; Stoneleigh Burnham HS; Greenfield, MA; (Y); DECA; Fld Hcky; Tennis; Hon Roll.

HOFFMAN, SHERYL; Tantasqua Regional HS; Sturbridge, MA; (S); 6/188; Math Tm; Ski Clb; Varsity Clb; Chorus; Pres Stu Cncl; Var L Fld Hcky; Var L Trk; Trk; High Hon Roll; Hon Roll; Lang.

HOFFMEISTER, MITCHELL; Franklin HS; Franklin, MA; (Y); VP DECA; Ski Clb; Variety Show; Var L Socr; Var L Wrstlng; High Hon Roll; NHS; Boy Scts; Hon Roll; Hockomock Lgu Champ Vrsty Soccer Tm 83; 3rd Yr Vrsty Wrstlng Awd 84-85; 2nd Pl Overll Mrktng ST DECA; Marktng.

HOGAN, BRIAN; Don Bosco Technical HS; Whitman, MA; (S); 10/280; Church Yth Grp; High Hon Roll; NHS; Ntl Merit Schol; NEDT Awd; Ntl Ldrshp Awd & Trnng Ctrs; Stonehill Coll; Bus.

HOGAN, CHARLES P; Canton HS; Canton, MA; (Y); 22/250; Am Leg Boys St; Drama Clb; Temple Yth Grp; Acpl Chr; School Musical; School Play; Rep Stu Cncl; Var Capt Tennis; Btty Crckr Awd; DAR Awd; Ponkapoag Civic Assn Scholar 85; Joanna Allison Connors Mem Scholar 85; Betty Crocher Awd 85; Boston Coll.

HOGAN, CHRIS; Woburn HS; Woburn, MA; (S); Church Yth Grp; JCL; Leo Clb; Ski Clb; Variety Show; Stu Cncl.

HOGAN, DANIEL J; Weymouth Vocational Tech HS; Weymouth, MA; (Y); 1/100; Am Leg Boys St; Church Yth Grp; Cmnty Wkr; Math Tm; Church Choir; Nwsp Rptr; VP Sr Cls; High Hon Roll; NHS; Outstdng Soph Area Drftg Stdy 83-84; Outstndg Mth Stu Of Trm 83-84; Fndr Mrnng Bible Stdy Schl 84-85; Chrsn Svc.

HOGAN, LORI; Christopher Columbus HS; Boston, MA; (Y); 20/135; Spanish Clb; Var Vllybl; Nrsng.

HOGAN, MARY; Holy Name C C HS; Grafton, MA; (Y); Ski Clb; Crs Cntry; Trk; Hon Roll.

HOGAN, MELISSA A; Dartmoth HS; S Darmouth, MA; (Y); 6/250; VP JA; Sec Band; Concert Band; Mrchg Band; Trs Frsh Cls; Trs Soph Cls; Trs Jr Cls; Trs Sr Cls; NHS; Acad Excell Awd 82-84; Excell In Amer Govt Hnrs Awd 82-83; Excell In Earth Sci Awd 82-83; Phy Thrpy.

HOGAN, SHAWN P; Brockton HS; Brockton, MA; (Y); 30/820; Am Leg Boys St; Math Tm; High Hon Roll; Gilmore Schl & Knights Of Columbus Schlrshp; 800 Scor SAT Math 83-84; Bucknell U; Bus Mgmt.

HOGARTH, HELEN; Douglas Memorial HS; E Douglas, MA; (Y); 4/35; Chess Clb; Sec Trs 4-H; Sec FHA; Teachers Aide; Bsktbl; Vllybl; Lion Awd; NHS; Voice Of Democrcy 84; 4-H NV ST Chmpn-Pub Spkg 83; Military.

HOHENADEL, KIMBERLY; Cushing Acad; Ashburnham, MA; (Y); 4-H; Library Aide; Teachers Aide; Chorus; School Musical; Yrbk Stf; Pres Stu Cncl; JV Lcrss; Im Tennis; Hon Roll; Chrprsn Scl Committee 85; Prctr In SR Dorm 85-86; Stu Body 85-86; Intl Rltns.

HOIBERG, LESTER; Smith Acad; Hatfield, MA; (S); Key Clb; School Musical; School Play; Variety Show; Bsktbl; High Hon Roll; Hon Roll; Drama.

HOIKALA, ANDREA; Billerica Memorial HS; Billerica, MA; (Y); French Clb; Ski Clb; Chorus; Yrbk Stf; Powder Puff Ftbl; JV Trk; Hon Roll; Ntl Merit Ltr; Sci.

HOLBROOK, KEITH M; Bishop Stang HS; Wareham, MA; (Y); Am Leg Boys St; Ski Clb; Rep Stu Cncl; Capt Var Ftbl; L Trk; Capt Wt Lftg; West Point; Sprts Med.

HOLBROOK, MARINDA; Oxford HS; Oxford, MA; (Y); 3/150; Church Yth Grp; Yrbk Stf; NHS; Am Leg Aux Girls St; Variety Show; Var Fld Hcky; High Hon Roll; Outstndng Bus Stu Yr 85; Brigham Yng U; Bus.

HOLBROOK, STANLEY; West Bridgewater JR SR HS; W Bridgewater, MA; (Y); 27/100; Drama Clb; Varsity Clb; School Play; JV L Ftbl; L Trk; Wentworth; Elec Engrg.

HOLDEN, CHRISTOPHER M; Amherst-Pelham Regional HS; Amherst, MA; (Y); 128/280; Am Leg Boys St; Church Yth Grp; Ski Clb; Jazz Band; Pep Band; Symp Band; Var L Crs Cntry; Var L Trk; Hon Roll; Excllng-Spanch IV Standard 84-85.

HOLDEN, MICHAEL J; Central Catholic HS; Haverhill, MA; (Y); 22/228; High Hon Roll; Hon Roll; Chem Awd 83; Presdntl Acadmc Awds Pgm 85; Merrimack Coll; Cvl Engrng.

HOLLAND, DANIEL; Blackstone Valley Regional Vo Tech; Millbury, MA; (Y); Exploring; Lowell U; Elec Engr.

HOLLAND, JEANNE; Our Lady Of Nazareth Acad; Billerica, MA; (Y); 3/59; Church Yth Grp; Sec Jr Cls; Rep Stu Cncl; Var Bsktbl; Stat Mgr(s); NHS; Prfct Atten Awd; Var Sftbl; High Hon Roll; Dilgnc Chem 85; Excllnc Frnch 84 & 85; Sci.

HOLLAND, MARY; Bishop Connolly HS; Tiverton, RI; (S); 1/177; French Clb; Math Clb; Var Crs Cntry; Var Trk; High Hon Roll; NHS; Med.

HOLLORAN, PATTI A; Winchester HS; Winchester, MA; (Y); 30/284; Church Yth Grp; Cmnty Wkr; French Clb; Hosp Aide; Concert Band; Mrchg Band; Nwsp Rptr; High Hon Roll; Hon Roll; Bus.

HOLLOWAY, MARIE; St Peter-Marian C C HS; Worcester, MA; (Y); Camera Clb; Computer Clb; Ski Clb; Nwsp Phtg; Yrbk Phtg; Trs Soph Cls; Capt Cheerleading; Var Socr; JV Sftbl; Var Tennis; NH Coll; Rest Mgmt.

HOLM, COLLEEN; Malden HS; Malden, MA; (Y); 51/500; Variety Show; Trk; High Hon Roll; Hon Roll; Hnr Rl Strght A; Boston Coll; Lawyer.

HOLMAN, CANDACE A; West Springfield HS; W Springfield, MA; (Y); 15/240; Art Clb; Drama Clb; Spanish Clb; Band; Mrchg Band; School Play; Hon Roll; Ntl Merit SF; Spanish NHS; James Z Naurison Schlrshp 85; Mary Jane Bampos Art Schlrshp 85; W Springfld Coll Clb Schlrshp 85; MA Coll; Art Ed.

HOLMBERG, PAMELA K; Bay Path Regional Vo Tech; Auburn, MA; (Y); 7/159; Hon Roll; Stu Mnth 81-82, 82-83 & 83-84; Shop Competition 3rd 81-82; Make Up Artist.

HOLMES, BROOKS; Scituate HS; Scituate, MA; (S); 72/305; Band; Drm & Bgl; Jazz Band; Symp Band; Bsbl; JV Wrstlng; Hon Roll.

HOLMES, CYNTHIA; Leicester HS; Leicester, MA; (S); Am Leg Aux Girls St; Pres Church Yth Grp; Math Tm; Nwsp Sprt Ed; Nwsp Stf; Capt Crs Cntry; NHS; Cmnty Wkr; Exploring; Latin Clb; Cntry III Ldr For Leicester HS 84; Stu Govrnmnt Day 84; Pol Sci.

HOLMES, KIRSTEN ERICA; Holy Name Central Catholic HS; Auburn, MA; (Y); 2/272; Am Leg Aux Girls St; Dance Clb; Drama Clb; School Musical; School Play; High Hon Roll; Jr NHS; NHS; Ntl Merit Ltr; Yrbk Rptr; Harvard Bk Awd 85.

HOLMES, KRISTEN; Norton HS; Norton, MA; (Y); French Clb; Pep Clb; Ski Clb; Varsity Clb; Chorus; JV Cheerleading; Var Capt Tennis; Hon Roll; NHS; Ntl Merit Ltr; Cmnctns.

HOLMES, MICHAEL; Central Catholic HS; Haverhill, MA; (Y); 21/216; Art Clb; Drama Clb; Ski Clb; Camp Fr Inc; Nwsp Stf; NHS; Jrnlsm.

HOLT, CAROLYN S; Weymouth South HS; S Weymouth, MA; (Y); 17/340; Church Yth Grp; Intnl Clb; Cmnty Wkr; Hosp Aide; Band; Chorus; Church Choir; School Play; Coach Actv; Mgr(s); Surp Rtng Town Mus Fest 82-83; Grnd Cross Color Intl Order Rainbow Girls Svc Awd 84; Chrch Schlrshp 85; Babson Coll; Accntng.

HOLTON, JEFFREY M; West Bridgewater HS; West Bridgewatr, MA; (Y); 25/110; Q&S; Varsity Clb; Stage Crew; Yrbk Sprt Ed; Yrbk Stf; Trs VP Stu Cncl; Var Capt Bsbl; Var Capt Bsktbl; Var Capt Golf; Elks Awd; Ithaca Coll; Bus Acctnt.

HOLWAY III, LOWELL H; Natick HS; S Natick, MA; (Y); 30/500; CAP; Trk; Ntl Merit Ltr; Bentley Coll Spotlight Pgm 85; MA Advncd Stud Pgm 85; Dartmouth Coll; Lwyr.

HOLZER, MICHELE; Cushing Acad; Lunenburg, MA; (Y); 11/96; Dance Clb; Library Aide; Teachers Aide; Varsity Clb; School Musical; Var Cheerleading; Var Fld Hcky; Hon Roll; Lib Arts.

HOLZRICHTER, DAWN; Barnstable HS; Osterville, MA; (Y); 51/385; Art Clb; CAP; Spanish Clb; Rep Frsh Cls; Rep Soph Cls; Rep Jr Cls; Trk; NHS; Wheaton Grant 85; Mass St Schlrshp 85; Kiwanis Schlrshp 85; Wheaton; Russian.

HOMSI, KRISTOPHER L; Natich HS; Natick, MA; (Y); 7/447; Am Leg Aux Girls St; Teachers Aide; Bsbl; Ftbl; Trk; Im Wt Lftg; High Hon Roll; NHS; ST Champ Clss A In Javelin 85; Conf Champ Bay ST League In Javelin 85; Gradtd Magna Cum Laude Boys S; Chem Engrng.

HONEYWELL, KRISTY L; Walpole HS; Walpole, MA; (Y); Sec Church Yth Grp; Ski Clb; Concert Band; Mrchg Band; Rep Jr Cls; Mgr(s); Hon Roll; Jr NHS; NHS.

HOOD, NIALL S V; Hingham HS; Hingham, MA; (Y); 21/340; Chrmn Church Yth Grp; Math Tm; Chorus; Nwsp Stf; Capt Crs Cntry; Capt Trk; Hon Roll; Trs NHS; AFS; Drama Clb; Old Clny Leag Hnrbl Ment Crs Cntry; Wntr Trk Capt; 2nd Pl ST Hersheys Ntl Trk & Fld; Grinnel; Ecolgst.

HOOD JR, ROBERT; Methuen HS; Methuen, MA; (Y); Boy Scts; Computer Clb; Comp Pgmmng.

HOOGHEEM, REBECCA L; Sharon HS; Sharon, MA; (Y); 79/199; VP Church Yth Grp; Cmnty Wkr; Nwsp Stf; Yrbk Stf; Cit Awd; Hon Roll; Bus Awds 82-84; Bus Comm.

HOPCROFT, JENNIFER L; Norwood HS; Norwood, MA; (Y); Hosp Aide; Band; Mrchg Band; Nwsp Stf; Var Capt Socr; Hon Roll; Jr NHS; NHS; Ntl Merit SF; Natl Art Hon Soc 84-86.

HOPE, SUSAN; Walpole HS; Walpole, MA; (S); 26/265; JCL; Latin Clb; Leo Clb; Library Aide; Spanish Clb; Rep Soph Cls; Rep Jr Cls; Rep Sr Cls; Hon Roll; NHS; Silvr Mdl Spn III Hons 83; Gold Medl Summa Cum Laude Natl Lat Exam 83; Hon Men Natl JR Writng Cont; Tufts U; Vet Med.

HOPKINS, ANDREW P; Bishop Connolly HS; Somerset, MA; (Y); 35/167; Cmnty Wkr; High Hon Roll; Ntl Merit Ltr; Distnctn Mdl Awd 85; Ntl Hnr Roll 85; Cmmnty Serv Awd 85; MA Maritime Acad; Marine Engrg.

HOPKINS, MICHAEL S; Westboro HS; Westboro, MA; (Y); 13/158; AFS; Am Leg Boys St; Boy Scts; Band; Capt Crs Cntry; Var Trk; NHS; Ntl Merit Ltr; Cmmndtn Awd Frnch 82; Engrng.

HOPKINSON, MARY B; Milford HS; Milford, MA; (Y); 12/350; Am Leg Aux Girls St; Pres Drama Clb; Pres VP Chorus; Jazz Band; School Musical; School Play; High Hon Roll; NHS; Hugh O Brien Yth Ldrsh Fndtn 83; MA Cmmnwlth Schlrshp 85; U Of MA-AMHERST; Math.

HORACEK, F JOSEPH; Minnechaug Regional HS; Wilbraham, MA; (Y); 33/357; AFS; Am Leg Boys St; Pres Church Yth Grp; Sec Drama Clb; Intnl Clb; JCL; PAVAS; Chorus; Madrigals; School Musical; Dean Mr Pres Wrtng Awd 85; Tufts U; Pre-Med.

HORAN, CATHIE; Reading Memorial HS; Reading, MA; (Y); 30/350; Trs Band; Chorus; Trs Concert Band; Trs Mrchg Band; School Musical; Rep Frsh Cls; Rep Soph Cls; Rep Jr Cls; Hon Roll; Spanish NHS; N E SR Dstrct Chorus 83 & 84; All Amer Music Hall Of Fame 83 & 84; Whlck Coll Bk Awd 85; Music Thrpy.

HORGAN, BETH; Arlington HS; Arlington, MA; (Y); Sec Church Yth Grp; Hosp Aide; Concert Band; Mrchg Band; Symp Band; Yrbk Stf; JV Trk; God Cntry Awd; High Hon Roll; Hon Roll; Nrsng.

HORGAN, KEVIN P; Ayer HS; Ayer, MA; (Y); Am Leg Boys St; Ski Clb; VP Frsh Cls; Pres Soph Cls; Pres Jr Cls; Pres Sr Cls; Off Stu Cncl; Var L Crs Cntry; Var L Trk; Hon Roll; Bus Mgmt.

HORGAN, TIMOTHY J; Woburn SR HS; Woburn, MA; (Y); 7/500; Church Yth Grp; French Clb; Key Clb; Math Tm; Yrbk Stf; High Hon Roll; Jr NHS; NHS; VP NHS; Ntl Merit SF; Drama Clb; Holy Crs Coll Bk Awd; Chem Engrng.

HORLOR, LAURA; Southwick HS; Granville, MA; (Y); Am Leg Aux Girls St; Cmnty Wkr; Math Clb; Office Aide; Stage Crew; Yrbk Stf; Socr; Sftbl; High Hon Roll; NHS; Visl Arts.

HORTON, TRACIE; Hoosac Valley HS; Adams, MA; (Y); 6/165; Am Leg Aux Girls St; Debate Tm; Quiz Bowl; Nwsp Ed-Chief; Nwsp Rptr; Ed Lit Mag; Var L Tennis; High Hon Roll; Hon Men Jr Prze Spkg 85; MA Adv Stud Prog Milton Acad 85; Rschr Bio.

HOSMAN, JOHN; Saint Johns Preparatory HS; Peabody, MA; (Y); Cmnty Wkr; Var Capt Crs Cntry; Var Capt Trk; Hon Roll; Prfct Atten Awd; Im Bsktbl; Im Bowling; Im Ftbl; Im Golf; Im Swmmng; 3rd Eastern MA Champs 2 Mile 85; 6th All-ST Mt 85; Many Trck Accmplshmnts; Phy Thrpy.

HOSMER, CHERI; King Philip Regional HS; Wrentham, MA; (Y); DECA; Hon Roll; Restrnt Comptncy Evnt 85; Miss Deca Comptn 85; Rtl Mgmt.

HOSTETTER, LYNNE; Weymouth North HS; Weymouth, MA; (Y); Cmnty Wkr; French Clb; Pep Clb; Ski Clb; Yrbk Stf; High Hon Roll; Jr NHS; Regnl Essay Fin/Natl Colonial Dames Of Amer 84; Sci Stu Of Term 84; Bus.

HOUGHTON, AMY; Hudson HS; Hudson, MA; (Y); Aud/Vis; Pep Clb; Pep Band; Swmmng; Vllybl; Wt Lftg; High Hon Roll; Hon Roll; Portuguese Awd 82-83; Worcester ST; Nrsng.

HOUGHTON, KARA; Fontbonne Acad; Canton, MA; (Y); 6/135; Drama Clb; Intnl Clb; School Play; Lit Mag; Hon Roll; NHS; Outstndng Wrk Spn III 84-85; Excllnce Theology 84-8; Excllnce Spn II 83-84.

HOULE, DENISE; Chicopee Comprehensive HS; Chicopee, MA; (Y); 21/375; German Clb; Hosp Aide; Chorus; Church Choir; Orch; Stu Cncl; Var Swmmng; Jr NHS; Sec Soph Cls; MA ST Guitar Champ 1st Pl 85; All Dist Chorus 84; Music.

HOULE, MATTHEW; Holyoke Catholic HS; Chicopee, MA; (Y); Chess Clb; Church Yth Grp; French Clb; Science Clb; School Musical; School Play; Acad Achvt Awd Biol 84; U Of MA; Ancient Hstry.

HOULE, ROBERT; St Bernards C C HS; Leominster, MA; (S); 4/164; Am Leg Boys St; Art Clb; Drama Clb; VP Hst French Clb; Model UN; School Musical; School Play; Stage Crew; Variety Show; Yrbk Stf; Polt Sci.

HOULE, SHERYL; Chicopee Comprehensive HS; Chicopee, MA; (Y); Debate Tm; JCL; Quiz Bowl; Color Guard; Drm & Bgl; Yrbk Phtg; Yrbk Stf; Powder Puff Ftbl; NHS; Latin Clb; Army ROTC Schlrshp 85-89; U MA Amherst; Psych.

HOULE, TINA M; Cathedral HS; Chicopee, MA; (Y); Camera Clb; Color Guard; School Musical; Nwsp Phtg; Nwsp Stf; Yrbk Phtg; Yrbk Stf; Twrlr; 4-H; Library Aide; Phtogrphr.

HOWARD, BRENDAN; St Bernards C C HS; Leominster, MA; (S); 1/163; Am Leg Boys St; Pres French Clb; School Musical; School Play; Stage Crew; Yrbk Stf; Im Bsktbl; High Hon Roll; NHS; Prfct Atten Awd; Holy Cross Book Awd 84; 1st Rnkng Frshmn, Soph & Jr 81-84; Sci.

HOWARD, CURTIS; Boston Technical HS; Boston, MA; (Y); FCA; Rep Frsh Cls; Rep Soph Cls; Var L Bsktbl; Var Trk; Hon Roll; Omega Psi Phi Frtrnty Schlrshp 85; MA Pre Engrng Prog Stu Achv Awd 84; Northeastern U; Comp Sci.

HOWARD, INA; Lynn English HS; Lynn, MA; (Y); French Clb; JA; Office Aide; Chorus; Drm & Bgl; Rep Frsh Cls; Rep Jr Cls; Stu Cncl; Var Bsktbl; Var Socr; Upward Bnd 85; Howard U; Law.

HOWARD, WENDY SUE; Seekonk HS; Seekonk, MA; (Y); 10/210; Church Yth Grp; Cmnty Wkr; Varsity Clb; Chorus; VP Frsh Cls; VP Soph Cls; Rep Sr Cls; Sec Stu Cncl; JV Bsktbl; JV Fld Hcky; Benjamin Bates Schlrshp 85; Dorothy Dow Schlrshp 85; Bates Coll; Med.

HOWARTH, JENNIFER; Nipmuc Regional HS; Upton, MA; (Y); Church Yth Grp; Girl Scts; Model UN; Red Cross Aide; Yrbk Stf; Sec Jr Cls; Sec Sr Cls; Rep Stu Cncl; High Hon Roll; NHS; Desgn.

HOWE, REGINA MARIE; Wareham HS; W Wareham, MA; (Y); 6/150; Stage Crew; Yrbk Phtg; Yrbk Rptr; Yrbk Stf; High Hon Roll; NHS; Awd Cert For High Average Hnrs Engl 85; Gilead Schl Brooklyn; Missinry.

HOWE, THOMAS; Dennis Yarmouth Regional HS; Yarmouthport, MA; (S); 52/310; Boys Clb Am; Band; Church Choir; Concert Band; Jazz Band; Mrchg Band; Orch; Pep Band; School Musical; Symp Band; Yth Amer European Concert Tour 85; SE Dist Hnrs Band 85; Musician Yr 82-83; U Of MA-AMHERST; Perf Artist.

HOYE, KATHY; Coyle And Cassidy HS; Taunton, MA; (Y); Var L Bsktbl; Var Vllybl; High Hon Roll; Hon Roll; NHS; Spanish NHS; Arch.

HUANG, CHRISTINE M; Belmont HS; Belmont, MA; (Y); Orch; Var Trk; High Hon Roll; Hon Roll; Physics Awd 85.

HUBACHECK, STEPH; Mount St Joseph Acad; Brighton, MA; (Y); JA; Boston Clg; Psych.

HUBBARD, AMY; Gloucester HS; Gloucester, MA; (Y); 22/350; JV Sftbl; Hon Roll; Trs NHS; Acadmc Recog Nght 85; Awd Acadmc Excllnc 84; Law.

HUBBARD, KAREN LEE; Wakefield HS; Wakefield, MA; (Y); 9/305; Church Yth Grp; Key Clb; School Play; Yrbk Sprt Ed; Trs Stu Cncl; Var Capt Fld Hcky; Var Capt Tennis; DAR Awd; Elks Awd; NHS; Wakefld Schlr-Athl Awd 85; Amer Lgn Awd 85; Holy Cross Coll; Math.

HUBBARD, KIMBERLY; Wakefield HS; Wakefield, MA; (Y); Church Yth Grp; French Clb; Political Wkr; School Play; Lit Mag; JV Fld Hcky; Mgr(s); Var Swmmng; Hon Roll; American U; Amer Studs.

HUBBARD, MICHELLE; Hudson HS; Hudson, MA; (Y); Math Tm; Pep Clb; Ski Clb; Hon Roll; NHS; Worcester Cnty Math Leag Awd 82 & 83; Portuguese Achv Awd 82-83; Accntng.

HUDLIN, MELISSA ANNE; Ayer HS; Ayer, MA; (Y); Am Leg Aux Girls St; Ski Clb; VP Soph Cls; VP Jr Cls; VP Sr Cls; Var Capt Cheerleading; Var Capt Trk; High Hon Roll; Hon Roll; NHS; Holy Cross Coll; Bus.

HUDSON, HOLLY; Mohawk Trail Regional HS; Rowe, MA; (Y); Ski Clb; Color Guard; JV Tennis; JV Vllybl; Color Grd Awd 85; Fitchburg ST Coll; Bus.

HUDSON, PAMELA; Weymouth North HS; Weymouth, MA; (Y); 40/340; Math Tm; Hon Roll; Recog Sci Prfrmnce 83; Natl Sci Olympd 83; Cert Achvt Mth Tm 84; New Englnd Deacnss; Nrsg.

HUDSON-WRIGHT, KIMBERLY; Fontbonne Acad; Dorchester, MA; (Y); Church Yth Grp; Drama Clb; Hosp Aide; Intnl Clb; Library Aide; High Hon Roll; Hon Roll; Library Achvt 85; Prom Queen 85; Georgetown; Dr.

HUFF, SUSAN A; Girls Catholic HS; Everett, MA; (Y); 5/35; Church Yth Grp; Drama Clb; Latin Clb; Spanish Clb; Church Choir; School Musical; School Play; Stage Crew; Variety Show; Rep Soph Cls; Schl Soloist; Treas SADD; Secy Frgn Lang Club; U Of MA-BOSTON; Med.

HUGHES, CHRIS; King Philip HS; Worcester, MA; (Y); Boy Scts; Church Yth Grp; Band; Concert Band; Drm Mjr(t); Jazz Band; Mrchg Band; JV Trk; Im Wt Lftg; Hon Roll; Rookie Yr, Jzz Bnd 84-85; Vrsty Ltr Mrchng Bnd Bishop Feehan HS 83-84.

HUGHES, DONALD C; Newton North HS; Newton Centre, MA; (Y); Newton Art Assn Schlrshp 85; Fine Arts.

HUGHES, KEVIN; Christopher Columbus HS; Dorchester, MA; (S); NHS; Natl Sci Merit Awd 84-85; MA Inst; Computers.

HUGHES, MARY; Doherty Memorial HS; Worcester, MA; (Y); 24/356; Ski Clb; Sec Soph Cls; Sec Jr Cls; Sec Sr Cls; Capt Fld Hcky; Capt Sftbl; Elks Awd; Hon Roll; Jr NHS; NHS; Mt Holyoke Coll; Librl Arts.

HUGHES, SHARON; Medway JR SR HS; Medway, MA; (Y); 6/151; Hosp Aide; High Hon Roll; Hon Roll; NHS; Schlstc Awd 83, 84 & 85; Bio-Chem.

HULL, RICHARD W; Silver Lake HS; Halifax, MA; (Y); 20/472; Pres Church Yth Grp; 4-H; French Clb; Band; Concert Band; Mrchg Band; Stu Cncl; Im Wrstlng; Hon Roll; Voice Dem Awd; Halifax Athltc Assn Scholar 85; Halifax Civic Orgnztn Scholar 85; Syracuse U; Archit.

HULTIN, STEPHEN O; Rockport HS; Rockport, MA; (Y); Am Leg Boys St; Cmnty Wkr; Scholastic Bowl; Science Clb; Stage Crew; Trs Soph Cls; Var Capt Bsktbl; Var Socr; Tennis; NHS; Var Bstkbl MVP 85; Bus.

HULTON, TERRI; East Longmeadow HS; E Longmeadow, MA; (Y); Concert Band; Mrchg Band; Variety Show; Nwsp Sprt Ed; Off Sr Cls; Rep Stu Cncl; Fld Hcky; Swmmng; Trk; NHS; Smith Coll Bk Awd 84; Pres Acadmc Fit Awd 85; Womn Sci Prog 84; Fairfield U; Acctg.

HUMASON, LARRY; Lee HS; Monterey, MA; (Y); Trs French Clb; Math Tm; Band; Concert Band; Jazz Band; Mrchg Band; Orch; Pep Band; School Musical; Hon Roll; Frnch Clb Schlrshp 85; Band Schlrshp 856; Westfield ST Coll; Music.

HUNDLEY, LAURA S; Belmont HS; Belmont, MA; (Y); 6/300; Am Leg Aux Girls St; Latin Clb; Orch; Nwsp Ed-Chief; Nwsp Rptr; Lit Mag; Stu Cncl; Jr NHS; NHS; Ntl Merit Ltr; Violin Solo Carnegie Hall NY Strng Orch 83; Grls Natn Delg Wash DC 84; Wnnr New England Perf Comp 84; Harvard; Lit.

HUNT, BRIAN; Watertown HS; Watertown, MA; (Y); 50/275; Boys Clb Am; Boy Scts; Church Yth Grp; Letterman Clb; Varsity Clb; Var L Bsktbl; Im Coach Actv; JV Ftbl; Im Wt Lftg; Hon Roll; Bus Adm.

HUNT, DEBBIE; Holbrook HS; Holbrook, MA; (Y); 23/110; Church Yth Grp; OEA; Chorus; School Musical; Var Cheerleading; Var Mgr(s); Var Trk; Aquinas; Mgmnt.

HUNT, JOANNE J; Sharon HS; Sharon, MA; (Y); 4/210; Drama Clb; Spanish Clb; Temple Yth Grp; Nwsp Stf; Yrbk Stf; High Hon Roll; Hon Roll.

HUNT, JODIE; Triton Regional HS; Salisbury, MA; (S); Church Yth Grp; OEA; Yrbk Stf; Hon Roll; ST Pres Of Offc Educ Assn 85-86; Lcl Chaptr Pres Of OEA; Stateswoman Awd OEA; LGL Sec.

HUNT, NANCY IRENE; Watertown HS; Watertown, MA; (Y); 17/325; Church Yth Grp; Civic Clb; Color Guard; Yrbk Stf; Sr Cls; Trk; Hon Roll; NHS; Band; Mrchg Band; Sci Dept Top Stu Hnry Awd 85; Stu Athl Awd 85; Westfield ST Coll; Sci Tchr.

HUNT, STEVEN; Ipswich HS; Ipswich, MA; (Y); Am Leg Boys St; Math Tm; Science Clb; Yrbk Stf; Var L Socr; Var L Trk; High Hon Roll; Hon Roll; NHS; Sci Symposium U MS 85; Engrng.

HUNTE, PAMELA L; Academy Of Notre Dame HS; Mason, NH; (Y); 14/79; Computer Clb; Chorus; Stage Crew; Yrbk Stf; NCTE Awd; NHS; Prov Coll Achvt Schlrshp 85-86; Abraham Burtman Trst Schlrshp 85-86; Martha Jones Trst Schlrshp 85-86; Providence Coll; Dentistry.

HUNTER, AMY; Wachusett Regional HS; Jefferson, MA; (Y); 59/387; Yrbk Stf; High Hon Roll; Hon Roll; NHS; Pres Schlr; MA State Schlrshp 85-86; Natl Honor Roll 85; Assumption Coll Partial Schlrshp 85-86; Assumption Coll; Bus Mgmt.

HUNTER, DANIEL; Cushing Acad; Ashburnham, MA; (Y); Boys Clb Am; Church Yth Grp; School Play; Bsbl; Crs Cntry; Ice Hcky; Bus Mgmt.

HUNTER, DEBORAH J; Franklin HS; Franklin, MA; (Y); 31/235; Church Yth Grp; Cmnty Wkr; Pres OEA; Nwsp Stf; Yrbk Bus Mgr; Mgr Bsktbl; Stat Ftbl; Cls 85 Franklin HS Schlrshp; Skidmore Coll; Studio Art.

HUNTER, JOANNE; Notre Dame Acad; Hingham, MA; (Y); 2/115; Red Cross Aide; Chorus; High Hon Roll; Hon Roll; NHS; Prfct Atten Awd; Spanish NHS; Vet.

HUNTLEY, JOANNE; Whitman-Hanson Regional HS; Hanson, MA; (Y); Church Yth Grp; Cmnty Wkr; Hosp Aide; Band; Mrchg Band; Rep Stu Cncl; Crs Cntry; Trk; Hon Roll; NHS; Doctor.

HURD, ROBIN; Georgetown JR SR HS; Georgetown, MA; (Y); Dance Clb; Drama Clb; Trs Girl Scts; Spanish Clb; Chorus; Church Choir; Lib Concert Band; Mrchg Band; Variety Show; Prfct Atten Awd; Eductn.

HURD, STACEY; Holbrook HS; Holbrook, MA; (Y); 5/100; Trs Church Yth Grp; French Clb; Sec Chorus; School Musical; Yrbk Stf; Sec Pres Stu Cncl; Crs Cntry; Var Capt Socr; Trk; NHS; Colby Coll Bk Awd 85; Finances.

HURLEY, BRIAN C; Doherty Memorial HS; Worcester, MA; (Y); Aud/Vis; Boy Scts; Church Yth Grp; Math Clb; Stage Crew; Yrbk Stf; Var L Golf; High Hon Roll; NHS; Spanish NHS; Acad Ltrs 81-82, 84-85; Essay Cont Wnr 85; Vet.

HURLEY, MICHELLE; Archbishop Williams HS; Braintree, MA; (Y); Camera Clb; Chorus; Yrbk Stf; High Hon Roll; Hon Roll; NEDT Awd; Boston Fire Fightrs Local 716 AFL.

HURLEY, THOMAS M; Coyle And Cassidy HS; South Easton, MA; (Y); 7/125; JCL; Latin Clb; Ski Clb; Rep Frsh Cls; Rep Soph Cls; Rep Jr Cls; Tennis; Electrcl Engrng.

HUTCHINS, LAURA; Melrose HS; Boston, MA; (Y); 82/375; Art Clb; Camp Fr Inc; Chess Clb; Dance Clb; Drama Clb; Hosp Aide; Pep Clb; Red Cross Aide; Ski Clb; Spanish Clb; Drug Pgm 84; Dancing 84; UCLA; Jrnlsm.

HUTCHINS, NANCY; Haverhill HS; Haverhill, MA; (Y); 43/415; Dance Clb; Library Aide; Chorus; School Musical; Nwsp Rptr; Nwsp Stf; NHS; Intl Ordr Of Rnbw For Grls Schlrshp 85; Paul Harriman Awd Excel In Engl 85; Mt Holyoke Coll; Bio.

HUTCHINSON, SUZANNE; Beverly HS; Beverly, MA; (Y); 45/378; Cmnty Wkr; Latin Clb; Science Clb; Yrbk Stf; Rep Sr Cls; JV Sftbl; Hon Roll; Lion Awd; Rep Frsh Cls; Rep Soph Cls; Greater Beverly Coll Clb Schlrshp 85; Dr Roberta Forgione Schlrshp 85; Barbara Goldberg Mem Schlrshp; U NH; Hlth.

HUTNAK, REBECCA; Douglas Memorial HS; E Douglas, MA; (Y); 1/36; Church Yth Grp; Band; Yrbk Stf; Cit Awd; Hon Roll; NHS.

HUTNAK, STEPHANIE; Douglas Memorial HS; Douglas, MA; (Y); Church Yth Grp; Quiz Bowl; Varsity Clb; Band; Yrbk Stf; Sftbl; Cit Awd; Hon Roll; NHS; MVP Awd Sftbl 85; Bio.

HUTNER, EDWARD L; Westborough HS; Westboro, MA; (Y); 37/158; Am Leg Boys St; Cmnty Wkr; Political Wkr; Ski Clb; Temple Yth Grp; Stage Crew; Variety Show; Pres Frsh Cls; Pres Jr Cls; Hon Roll; Bsktbl Champs Church Lg 84-85; Pre-Dentstry.

HUUSKONEN, SONENE; Salem HS; Salem, MA; (Y); 7/338; Drama Clb; VP German Clb; Trs Ski Clb; Sec Trs Mrchg Band; School Musical; VP Stu Cncl; High Hon Roll; Kiwanis Awd; VP NHS; Pres Schlr; Goethe Inst Awd Ger 84; NHS Scholar 85; Physics Awd 85; U Of NH; Ger.

HYATT, MATTHEW D; Oliver Ames HS; South Easton, MA; (Y); 11/247; Am Leg Boys St; Church Yth Grp; Lit Mag; VP Jr Cls; Var Socr; Var L Tennis; Jr NHS; Voice Dem Awd; School Musical; Hon Roll; Boston Globe Art Awd Gold Key 85; Natl Lat Exam Cum Laude 85; Hockamock Mod Senate SE MA 84-86; Archit.

HYDE, CHRISTOPHER; Mt Greylock Regional HS; Lanesboro, MA; (S); 26/129; Nwsp Ed-Chief; Lit Mag; Var Crs Cntry; Var Trk; NHS; W MA Crss Cntry Medlst 82-83; Berkshire Cnty 880 Yrd Run Rnnr Up 84; Bowdoin; Engl.

HYNES, KELLY; Georgetown JR SR HS; Georgetown, MA; (Y); AFS; Drama Clb; OEA; Yrbk Stf; Hon Roll; Elem Educ.

HYORA, JENNIFER; Chatham HS; Chathamport, MA; (Y); 4/56; Computer Clb; Math Tm; Teachers Aide; Band; Yrbk Stf; Trs Jr Cls; Var Fld Hcky; Hon Roll; NHS; Grls ST Rep 85; Bus.

HYPPOLITE, KARLA L; Boston Latin Schl; Dorchester, MA; (Y); Aud/Vis; JA; Key Clb; Band; Concert Band; Outstndng Negro Student NASP; Bowdoin Coll:Doctor.

IACONIS, ELIZABETH; Natick HS; Natick, MA; (Y); High Hon Roll; Hon Roll.

IACOPUCCI, WILLIAM J; Medford HS; Medford, MA; (Y); 73/450; Off Jr Cls; Ftbl; Lcrss; Trk; Hon Roll; Banking Pgm 86; Bus Coll; Accntnt.

IACOVELLI, SUSAN; Milford HS; Milford, MA; (Y); 23/305; Am Leg Aux Girls St; Chorus; Jazz Band; School Musical; Sec Soph Cls; Sec Jr Cls; Sec Sr Cls; Ntl Merit Ltr; Commnwlth Schlr Recptnt 85; Stu Advsry Cncl Schl Commtte 85; MA U; Chem Engr.

IANNACCI, MICHAEL; Malden Catholic HS; Malden, MA; (Y); 5/181; Boy Scts; Camera Clb; VP Pres Church Yth Grp; Hosp Aide; Ski Clb; Ftbl; Elks Awd; High Hon Roll; Kiwanis Awd; NHS; Grnd Ldge Of MA Ordr Sons Of Italy In Amer Schlrshp 85; MA Brd Of Rgnts Commonwlth Schlrshp 85; Worcester Polytech Inst; Engrng.

IANNELLI, MICHAEL J; Waltham SR HS; Waltham, MA; (Y); 25/600; Am Leg Boys St; Aud/Vis; JCL; Nwsp Sprt Ed; Yrbk Stf; Pres Stu Cncl; Var L Bsktbl; Var L Ftbl; Hon Roll; Ntl Merit Ltr; Army Ntl Schlr/Athlte Awd 85; Ntl Merit Hnr Roll 85; U Of Notre Dame.

IANNUCCILLI, BETTY ANN; Methuen HS; Methuen, MA; (Y); 60/375; Model UN; Band; Concert Band; Jazz Band; Mrchg Band; VP Jr Cls; VP Sr Cls; Var Trk; DAR Awd; High Hon Roll; 2nd ST Rlys Indr Trck Shotput 83; 2nd ST Rlys Otdr Trck Shotput 85; ST Rly Champs In Discus 84; Northeaster; Chem.

IARROBINO, PAULA; Girls Catholic HS; Medford, MA; (Y); Drama Clb; French Clb; School Play; Trs Soph Cls; JV Cheerleading; Hon Roll; Pysch.

IGNAZIO, NANCY; Matignon HS; Camb, MA; (S); 17/179; Drama Clb; Hosp Aide; Pep Clb; Spanish Clb; Varsity Clb; Sec Sr Cls; Sec Stu Cncl; Var Sftbl; Var Vllybl; High Hon Roll; Engrng.

IHNATKO, ANDREW; Westwood HS; Westwood, MA; (Y); 14/214; Pres Camera Clb; Math Tm; Ed Lit Mag; L Swmmng; Hon Roll; NHS; Ntl Merit SF; Stu Announcer; Cmpt Sci.

IMBRESCIA, PHILIP; Everett HS; Everett, MA; (Y); Church Yth Grp; Letterman Clb; VP Soph Cls; Off Jr Cls; Off Sr Cls; Off Stu Cncl; JV Bsbl; Var Ice Hcky; High Hon Roll; Hon Roll; Engnrng.

IMBRIANO, GREG; Lynn Classical HS; Lynn, MA; (Y); Church Yth Grp; Chorus; School Play; Stage Crew; Rep Soph Cls; Var Golf; JV Socr; Var Tennis; Hon Roll; 1st Pl Sci Fair 81; Engrng.

INDELICATO, DONNA; Christopher Columbus HS; Boston, MA; (Y); 16/132; High Hon Roll; Hon Roll; NHS; Med Tech.

INDRESANO, TRACY; Westford Acad; Westofrd, MA; (Y); AFS; Spanish Clb; Band; Concert Band; Mrchg Band; JV Bsktbl; Var L Trk; High Hon Roll; Hon Roll.

INGEMI, CHRISTINE; Rockland HS; Rockland, MA; (S); 14/277; Pep Clb; Spanish Clb; Var L Socr; Var L Trk; Hon Roll; NHS; Bridgewater ST Coll; Bus Mktg.

INGHAM, ANTHONY NELSON; Agawam HS; Feeding Hills, MA; (Y); Boy Scts; Church Yth Grp; Cmnty Wkr; Teachers Aide; Varsity Clb; Yrbk Rptr; Bsbl; Ftbl; Wrstlng; Hon Roll; Wstrn MA Bsbl Tm 85; Cmnctns.

INTERRANTE, JOYCE MARIE; Girls Catholic HS; N Reading, MA; (Y); 13/35; Yrbk Ed-Chief; Trs Sr Cls; Hon Roll; Voice Dem Awd; Histry Awd 85; SADD Sec 85; Pblshe Edtrl Boston Hrld 83; Anna Maria Coll; Lawyer.

IRELAND, KAREN; Bay Path Regional Vo Tech; North Oxford, MA; (S); 12/244; Church Yth Grp; VP Bsktbl; VP Sftbl; Hon Roll; NHS.

IRISH, TIMOTHY M; Wareham HS; Wareham, MA; (Y); 15/166; Crs Cntry; Trk; Cit Awd; Hon Roll; NHS; Attnd Boys ST Smmr 84; Wentworth Ins Tech; Aero Engr.

IRONS, JOHN C; Marblehead HS; Marblehead, MA; (Y); 4/245; VP Jr Cls; VP Sr Cls; Capt Bsbl; Capt Ftbl; Cit Awd; High Hon Roll; Hon Roll; NHS; Church Yth Grp; Stu Athl 85; Clsmates Today-Neighbors Tomorrow 84; MVP Ftbl 84; Bowdoin Coll; Med.

IRONS, STEPHEN J; Xaverian Bros HS; Norwood, MA; (S); 10/236; Boy Scts; Nwsp Rptr; Nwsp Stf; Bsbl; JV Capt Bsktbl; JV Ftbl; High Hon Roll; Hon Roll; NHS; CYO Basketball Team Captain & MVP 84; SR Christian Svc Project 85; Boston Coll; Bus Mgmt.

ISAKSEN, MARK; Fairhaven HS; Fairhaven, MA; (Y); 19/200; Pres AFS; Nwsp Rptr; Yrbk Ed-Chief; Pres Stu Cncl; Var L Ftbl; Trk; Hon Roll; NEDT Awd; Church Yth Grp; French Clb; AFS Exch Stu Brazil 84; TV News Anchormn 84-85; Georgetown U.

ISHERWOOD, JEFFREY C; Plymouth Carver Regional HS; Plymouth, MA; (Y); 130/500; AFS; Exploring; Mrchg Band; Stage Crew; Yrbk Phtg; Ed Yrbk Stf; Hon Roll; Photo Jrnlsm.

ISLES, DARYL MARY; Our Lady Of Nazareth Acad; Peabody, MA; (Y); 20/64; Pep Clb; Var Capt Bsktbl; Score Keeper; VP Sftbl; Timer; Var Vllybl; Hon Roll; All Star Bsktbl Awd 85; Pro Life Essy Wnnr 85; Sprts Med.

ISSERLIS, DEBRA J; Somerset HS; Somerset, MA; (Y); 9/299; Debate Tm; VP JA; VP Chorus; School Musical; Ed Nwsp Ed-Chief; Stu Cncl; Elks Awd; NHS; Ntl Merit Ltr; Pres Schlr; Miss Teen Of Amer Schlrshp & Rcgntn Pgnt Personal Dept Awd 84; Century III Ldr 85; Proj Excel 83-84; Wesleyan U; Linguistics.

IVERS, JENNIFER; Marian HS; Hopkinton, MA; (Y); 40/177; Dance Clb; Library Aide; VP Frsh Cls; VP Soph Cls; Pres Sr Cls; JV Bsktbl; Var Cheerleading; JV Crs Cntry; Var Tennis; Hon Roll; Track All-Star 85; Stu Advsry Cncl 83-84; Law.

IVORY, CAROLYN; Westford Acad; Westford, MA; (Y); AFS; Model UN; Drm Mjr(t); Mrchg Band; Sec Symp Band; Nwsp Rptr; Trk; High Hon Roll; Hon Roll; Sec NHS; Mst Outstndng Frsh & Jr Musician 83 & 85; Jrnlsm.

IVORY, P GRAHAM; Monument Mountain Reg HS; Gt Barrington, MA; (S); 16/128; Am Leg Boys St; Nwsp Rptr; Lit Mag; Pres Sr Cls; Var Bsbl; Var Socr; Hon Roll; NHS; Boy Scts; JCL; Disc Jock Intrnshp WSBS 84-85; 3rd Pl New Englnd Math Comptn 81; Soclgy.

IZATT, DEBORAH; Chicopee Comp HS; Chicopee, MA; (S); 40/276; Art Clb; Camera Clb; Church Yth Grp; Cmnty Wkr; Exploring; Office Aide; Political Wkr; Q&S; Teachers Aide; Drm & Bgl; Framingham ST; Dietcn.

JACHRIMO, CINDYANN; Melrose HS; Melrose, MA; (Y); 27/365; Cmnty Wkr; Drama Clb; German Clb; School Play; Lit Mag; Ntl Merit Ltr; Outstndng Achvt In Drma & Scl Stds.

JACKMAN, CHRISTOPHER M; Newburyport HS; Newburyport, MA; (Y); 24/196; Am Leg Boys St; JV Bsktbl; JV Ftbl; Hon Roll; NHS; Prfct Atten Awd; Ldrshp Clb 84; Christian A Herter Meml Schlrshp Wnnr 85; Harvard U; Polit Sci.

JACKSON, JENNIFER; St Bernards Central Catholic HS; Peterborough, NH; (S); 10/163; Hosp Aide; JCL; Service Clb; Spanish Clb; Band; Nwsp Ed-Chief; Yrbk Ed-Chief; JV Trk; Hon Roll; NHS; Highest GPA Latin III; Awd In Accelrtd Engl; Mktg.

JACKSON, SHERYL; Lawrence HS; Lawrence, MA; (Y); 13/300; Church Yth Grp; Cmnty Wkr; Hosp Aide; Church Choir; Pres Stu Cncl; Trk; High Hon Roll; NHS; Merrimack Vly Teen Yr 85; Augustian J Lawlor Mem Schlrshp 85; Italian Wmn & Curt Gowdy Schlrshps 85; Gordon Coll; Psych.

JACKSON, TIMANGO; High School Of Commerce; Springfield, MA; (S); Boy Scts; English Clb; JA; Var Capt Ftbl; Cit Awd; Hon Roll; JETS Awd; NHS; Prfct Atten Awd; Comp.

JACOB, MENCILLA C; English HS; Boston, MA; (Y); Dance Clb; English Clb; JA; Prfct Atten Awd; Dnce Awd 85; Pell Grant 85; Gus Saunders Scholar 85; Northeastern U; Bus.

JACOBS, CYNTHIA; Boston Latin HS; Dorchester, MA; (Y); Dance Clb; Exploring; Chorus; Church Choir; Swing Chorus; Lit Mag; Mass Comm.

JACOBS, KAREN; Monson JR SR HS; Monson, MA; (Y); 15/78; Church Yth Grp; Drama Clb; French Clb; Stage Crew; Yrbk Ed-Chief; Sec Frsh Cls; Sec Sr Cls; VP Stu Cncl; Mgr(s); NHS; SADD Pres; Psych.

JACOBSEN, MARK E; Walpole HS; Walpole, MA; (Y); 11/265; Ski Clb; Band; Concert Band; Mrchg Band; JV Bsktbl; Var Capt Socr; Var Capt Tennis; CC Awd; Hon Roll; NHS; Phy Ed Leader 84 & 85; Tufts U; Engrng.

JACOBSON, SARAH G; Lexington HS; Lexington, MA; (Y); French Clb; Ski Clb; School Musical; L Capt Trk; French Hon Soc; Hon Roll; Jr NHS; NHS; Ntl Merit Ltr; Orch; Williams Coll Bk Awd 85; Outstndg Contrib Frgn Lang Dept 85; Fr.

JACQUES, CHERYL C; Leicester HS; Rochdale, MA; (Y); 8/120; Church Yth Grp; Drama Clb; Band; Church Choir; School Play; JV Cheerleading; Hon Roll; NHS; Ntl Merit SF; Chancellors Tlnt Awd From U MA-AMHERST 84; U Of MA-AMHERST; Theater.

JACQUES, ERIC; Gardner HS; Gardner, MA; (Y); 29/190; Am Leg Boys St; Church Yth Grp; Debate Tm; Model UN; NFL; Speech Tm; Yrbk Stf; Stu Cncl; JV Bsbl; JV Bsktbl; Lt Gov YMCA Yth Govt Pgm 85; Gov Am Lg Boys ST Pgm 85; Natl Fin Natl Catholic Forn Trnmnt 84-85; Law.

JAHNCKE, HERB; Bridgewater-Raynham Regional HS; Bridgewater, MA; (Y); Am Leg Boys St; Camera Clb; Math Tm; Political Wkr; Science Clb; Ski Clb; Nwsp Phtg; Tennis; Trk; NHS; Sci Symposium U Mass Amherst 85; 1st Pl Photography Cntst 85.

JAILLET, TINA; Gardner HS; Gardner, MA; (Y); 53/169; Exploring; Girl Scts; Office Aide; Yrbk Stf; Rep Sr Cls; Montachusett CC; Bus Adm.

JAILLET, TRACY; Falmouth HS; Falmouth, MA; (Y); French Clb; Key Clb; School Play; Tennis; NH Coll; Fshn Merch.

JAKUSIK, TODD; Bishop Connolly HS; Westport, MA; (Y); Cmnty Wkr; Var Bsbl; Var Ice Hcky; Providence Coll.

JALBERT, COLLEEN; B M C Durfee HS; Fall River, MA; (Y); #48 In Class; French Clb; MMM; Concert Band; Mrchg Band; Sec Orch; Yrbk Stf; High Hon Roll; Hon Roll; NHS; Ntl Merit Sci Awd; Comp Sci.

JALELIAN, LINCOLN; Arlington HS; Arlington, MA; (S); 13/425; Boy Scts; Latin Clb; Mrchg Band; Symp Band; Ed Yrbk Stf; High Hon Roll; Boys Clb Am; Chess Clb; Political Wkr; Science Clb; Eagle Scout 84.

JAMES, KARTIKA; St Marks Schl; Bronx, NY; (Y); School Play; Lit Mag; JV Bsktbl; JV Lcrss; Mgr(s); JV Socr; Henry Nichols Ervin Schlrshp 84; Bttr Chance Schlr 82, 85; Wellesley Coll; Psychlgy.

JAMES, KIMBERLY L; Natick HS; Natick, MA; (Y); Pep Clb; Nwsp Rptr; Nwsp Stf; Rep Frsh Cls; Rep Soph Cls; Rep Jr Cls; Rep Stu Cncl; Var L Cheerleading; Hon Roll; Engl.

JAMES, LORI K; Phillips Acad; Chatham, NY; (Y); Latin Clb; Radio Clb; School Play; Nwsp Bus Mgr; Nwsp Ed-Chief; Off Sr Cls; Chess Clb; Cmnty Wkr; Debate Tm; Orch; Ntl Achvt Schlr 84-85; Film.

JAMIESON, JODI; Silver Lake Regional HS; Plympton, MA; (Y); 95/422; Church Yth Grp; Drama Clb; 4-H; French Clb; School Play; Nwsp Rptr; Hon Roll; U Of MA Amherst; Englsh.

JANASIEWICZ, LYNN A; Palmer HS; Palmer, MA; (Y); 2/97; Hosp Aide; Pres Ski Clb; Jazz Band; Mrchg Band; Hst Frsh Cls; Hst Soph Cls; Hst Jr Cls; Hst Sr Cls; Var Capt Bsktbl; Var Capt Fld Hcky; MA Commonwlth Schlr 85; Palmer Rotary Clb Scholar 85; U S Army Schlr Ath Awd 85; Boston U; Phys Thrpy.

JANELL, PAUL; Milford HS; Milford, MA; (Y); 15/312; Var L Bsbl; JV Capt Bsktbl; JV Var Socr; High Hon Roll; NHS; Northeastern; Accntng.

JANKIUS, BRIAN C; Quaboag Regional HS; W Brookfield, MA; (Y); Am Leg Boys St; Church Yth Grp; Trs Spanish Clb; Varsity Clb; Var Capt Bsbl; Var Capt Bsktbl; Hon Roll; Comm.

JANKOSKI, KATHIE; Tantasqua Regional HS; Sturbridge, MA; (Y); 2/200; Church Yth Grp; Math Tm; Ski Clb; Chorus; Yrbk Stf; JV Fld Hcky; Var Trk; High Hon Roll; Hon Roll; NHS; Engrng.

JANNINO, GEROGE; Everett HS; Boston, MA; (Y); 35/250; Church Yth Grp; Intnl Clb; Key Clb; Letterman Clb; Science Clb; Varsity Clb; Var Ftbl; JV Ice Hcky; Hon Roll; Elect Engr.

JANOUSEK, J PAUL; Duxbury HS; Duxbury, MA; (Y); Am Leg Boys St; Key Clb; Spanish Clb; Band; Mrchg Band; Pep Band; Nwsp Phtg; Golf; Hon Roll; NHS; WPI; Chem Engr.

JANSEN, JOANIE; Somerville HS; Somerville, MA; (Y); Art Clb; Chorus; Jazz Band; School Musical; Swing Chorus; Hon Roll.

JANSKI, TODD E; Gardner HS; Gardner, MA; (Y); 18/180; Am Leg Boys St; French Clb; Intnl Clb; School Musical; School Play; Hon Roll; Prfct Atten Awd; Bishops Fund Theme Cntst Worcester Diocese 82 & 83; Syracuse U; Cmnctns.

JANVRIN, WAYNE; Methven HS; Methuen, MA; (Y); 7/340; French Clb; Intnl Clb; Model UN; Im Bsbl; Im JV Ftbl; JV Trk; High Hon Roll; NHS; Harvard Almn Bk Awd 85; Frnch Acadmc Excllnc 82-84; Comp Engrng.

JARABEK, ELIZABETH; B M C Durfee HS; Fall River, MA; (Y); 24/680; Drama Clb; French Clb; Yrbk Stf; Trk; Hon Roll; NHS; Psych.

JARDIN, RAQUEL; Bishop Connolly HS; Somerset, MA; (Y); 2/225; Hosp Aide; JA; Nwsp Stf; High Hon Roll; Hon Roll; Jr Achvt Pres 83-84; RI ST Ballet 82-83; Emerson Coll; Busnss Commnctn.

JARGOWSKY, STACY; Dana Hall HS; Ellenville, NY; (Y); Chorus; Madrigals; High Hon Roll; Hon Roll; Awd Lang & Math 82; Hnr Sci, Lang, Music & Hstry 83; U Of Miami; Pre-Law.

JARNAGIN, ROBERTA RUSSELL; Concord Acad; Concord, MA; (Y); Chess Clb; Cmnty Wkr; Computer Clb; English Clb; 4-H; French Clb; Latin Clb; Math Tm; Nwsp Rptr; Yrbk Bus Mgr; Harvard Summer Schl 84.

JAWORSKI, KATRINA; Cathedral HS; E Longmeadow, MA; (Y); 9/425; Dance Clb; German Clb; Yrbk Rptr; High Hon Roll; Olympd Math Semi Fnlst 83; Pres Acaed Ftnss 85; Natl Hnr Rll 85; U MA; Sci.

JEAN-MARY, MARIE ROSE; North Cambridge Catholic HS; Cambridge, MA; (Y); Church Choir; Hon Roll; NHS; Prfct Atten Awd; U MA.

JEDLINSKY, DAVID C; Dover Sherborn Regional HS; Dover, MA; (Y); 14/162; Am Leg Boys St; Chess Clb; Church Yth Grp; Math Tm; Chorus; School Musical; Nwsp Rptr; JV Crs Cntry; Hon Roll; Natl Merit Spec Schlrshp 85; Comp Sci Acad Grad Awd 85; MA Inst Of Tech; Comp Sys Anly.

JEDRASZEK, PAULA; Beverly HS; Beverly, MA; (Y); Trs Frsh Cls; VP Soph Cls; Pres Jr Cls; JV Cheerleading; Sftbl; Hon Roll; Sci Fair Hnrb Mntn 84; Phys Thrpst.

JEFFREY, STEPHEN; Bishop Connolly HS; Fall River, MA; (Y); Boys Clb Am; Church Yth Grp; Latin Clb; Var L Bsbl; Im Bowling; High Hon Roll; Hon Roll; Yth Grp Svc Awd 83; Top Two Awd Bus At Connolly 85; Southeastern MA U; Bus Mgmt.

JENKINS, ELIZABETH; Westford Acad; Westford, MA; (Y); AFS; Church Yth Grp; Exploring; French Clb; Model UN; Band; Concert Band; Drm & Bgl; Mrchg Band; Symp Band; Phi Beta Kappa Hist Paper Hnrbl Ment 85; Bus Adm.

JENKINS, JANET; Taunton HS; Taunton, MA; (Y); 45/491; Library Aide; Spanish Clb; Hon Roll; St Schlr; Framingham ST Coll; Medcl Tech.

JENKINS, MARGARET M; Westford Acad; Westford, MA; (Y); 4/205; Church Yth Grp; French Clb; Sec JCL; Drm & Bgl; Yrbk Bus Mgr; Var Swmmng; Var Capt Trk; High Hon Roll; NHS; Pres Schlr; Pres Clsrm 84; Wellesley Coll; Econ.

JENKS, AMY; Turners Falls HS; Montague, MA; (Y); Rep Soph Cls; Sec Jr Cls; Trs Stu Cncl; Stat Bsbl; JV Cheerleading; Excllnce Accntng, Geo, Shrthnd, Amer Lit & Life; Soc Wrk.

JENSEN, ELIZABETH; Tantasqua Regional SR HS; Brimfield, MA; (S); 7/200; Pres Church Yth Grp; Math Tm; Ski Clb; Yrbk Stf; Var Socr; Var Tennis; Hon Roll; NHS.

JENSSEN, PATRICIA E; Lenox Memorial HS; Eastham, MA; (Y); School Play; Drama Clb; 4-H; Yrbk Bus Mgr; Yrbk Stf; Art.

JERNIC, MARIA; Acton Boxboro R HS; Acton, MA; (Y); 37/343; Ed Lit Mag; NHS; French Clb; Intnl Clb; Variety Show; Nwsp Stf; High Hon Roll; Hon Roll; Pres Schlr; Fred/Robbins Schlrshp 85; Internshp/Acton Brd Of Hlth 84; Wellesley Coll; Hosp Adm.

JERNIGAN, CHRISTOPHER; Buckingham Browne & Nichols HS; Newton, MA; (S); Pres Church Yth Grp; Cmnty Wkr; Model UN; Rep Frsh Cls; Rep Soph Cls; Rep Jr Cls; Pres Sr Cls; Pres Stu Cncl; Var Socr; Ntl Merit Ltr; History 84; Varsity Cross Cntry Skiing 82-85.

JEZAK, KAREN; Dracut HS; Dracut, MA; (Y); Library Aide; Office Aide; Spanish Clb; Cheerleading; Hon Roll; Acad Excel Bio 84; Acad Excel 1st Qtr Hnrs 85.

JEZIERSKI, ANN MARIE; Bartlett HS; Webster, MA; (Y); 12/175; Church Yth Grp; Girl Scts; Science Clb; Spanish Clb; Band; Nwsp Rptr; Nwsp Stf; Yrbk Bus Mgr; Hon Roll; NHS; U MA-AMHERST; Anml Sci.

JOCK, JACQUELINE; Ware HS; Ware, MA; (Y); 1/125; VP French Clb; Stat Socr; French Hon Soc; High Hon Roll; Hon Roll; Psych.

JODOIN, TIM; Mohawk Trail Regional HS; Rowe, MA; (Y); 13/96; Exploring; German Clb; Ski Clb; Varsity Clb; Socr; Trk; Hon Roll; NHS; U S Army Resrv Natl Scholar/Athlete Awd 85; Cert Of Apprectn-MA Heart Assn 85; Syracuse U; Comptr Engrng.

JOERRES, CHRISTINE; Dartmouth HS; N Dartmouth, MA; (Y); 40/256; Office Aide; OEA; Acad Excllnce Soph JR & SR; SE MA U; Acctnt.

JOERRES, MARC; Dartmouth HS; N Dartmouth, MA; (Y); 27/254; U Of HI Monoa; Comp Prog.

JOHN, CINDY; Hopkins Acad; Hadley, MA; (Y); 5/62; Computer Clb; Dance Clb; Math Tm; Varsity Clb; Chorus; Yrbk Stf; Var Capt Bsktbl; JV Socr; Var Trk; Hon Roll; Hugh O Brian Yth Found 83; Obstectrcs.

JOHNSON, AMY; Medford HS; Medford, MA; (Y); 5/450; Letterman Clb; Rptr Nwsp Stf; JV Crs Cntry; JV Tennis; Var Trk; High Hon Roll; NHS; Frank E Call Mem Citznshp Awd 83; Colby Coll Bk Awd 85; Animal Sci.

JOHNSON, BRENDA; South High Community Schl; Worcester, MA; (S); Sec Jr Cls; JV Var Bsktbl; Var Socr; Var Sftbl; High Hon Roll; Hon Roll; NHS; Accntg.

JOHNSON, CHISTINE; Girls Catholic HS; Medford, MA; (Y); Church Yth Grp; French Clb; Rep Jr Cls; VP Stu Cncl; Var Sftbl; Capt Var Vllybl; High Hon Roll; Jr NHS; Lion Awd; NHS; Spanner Clb Scholar Awd 82; MVP Vllybl 85; Mst Imprvd Plyr Vllbyl 84; Bunker Hill CC; Sec Sci.

JOHNSON, CHUCK; Lexington HS; Lexington, MA; (Y); Church Yth Grp; French Clb; Band; Concert Band; Mrchg Band; Im Bsbl; JV Bsktbl; Im Socr; Hon Roll; Nvl Sci.

JOHNSON, COURTNEY; Burncoat SR HS; Worcester, MA; (Y); Church Yth Grp; Hosp Aide; Intnl Clb; Red Cross Aide; Y-Teens; Church Choir; Sec Stu Cncl; JV Var Bsktbl; Var Socr; Hon Roll; Engrng.

JOHNSON, D VONNA SHERESE; Berkshire Schl; Flushing, NY; (Y); 14/130; Pres Drama Clb; Rep Jr Cls; Rep Sr Cls; Var Capt Vllybl; Hon Roll; Spanish Clb; Chorus; School Play; Stage Crew; Variety Show; Ursa Viridis Schlrshp 84; Schoellkopf Schlrshp 84; Natl Scshlrshp Outstndng Negro Stu 84; Welesley Coll; Med.

JOHNSON, DEBORAH; Bridgewater-Raynham Reg HS; Bridgewater, MA; (Y); 10/340; Fld Hcky; Gym; High Hon Roll; Hon Roll; NHS; Schlstc Achvt Ntl Educ Dev Tst 84; Pre Med.

JOHNSON, DOUGLAS; Silver Lake RHS HS; Pembroke, MA; (Y); 116/430; Boy Scts; Church Yth Grp; Im L Socr; Paul J Cuneo Mem Awd-Sccr Plyr 84; Peter Mc Cauley-Almni Schlrshp 85; Husson Coll; Bus Admin.

JOHNSON, ELIZABETH B; Mount Saint Joseph Acad; Watertown, MA; (Y); Sec Civic Clb; Math Clb; Hon Roll; NHS; PSTA Jr Schlrshp 85; Haberlin Inst Schlrshp 83 & 84.

JOHNSON, ERIC R; St Johns HS; Douglas, MA; (Y); 70/272; French Clb; Stage Crew; Ntl Merit SF; Top 10 Prcnt JETS Engrng Tst 84; Physcs.

JOHNSON, HEATHER; Bedford HS; Crownsville, MD; (Y); Church Yth Grp; Varsity Clb; Acpl Chr; Chorus; Madrigals; School Musical; School Play; Variety Show; Mgr(s); Swmmng; Cancer Studies.

JOHNSON, IAN P; Westboro HS; Westboro, MA; (Y); 4/177; Am Leg Boys St; Boy Scts; Pres Church Yth Grp; Rep Stu Cncl; Var Capt Socr; High Hon Roll; NHS; Pres Schlr; Eckerd Coll FL; Pol Sci.

JOHNSON, JEFFREY; Smith Acad; N Hatfield, MA; (Y); Am Leg Boys St; Drama Clb; Trs Jr Cls; Var L Bsktbl; Var L Golf; Var L Socr; Prz Spkg 1st Pl 85; Bus.

JOHNSON, JEFFREY D; Marian HS; Framingham, MA; (Y); Variety Show; JV Crs Cntry; JV Socr; JV Trk; Hon Roll; Prfct Atten Awd; U Of RI; Elec Engrng.

JOHNSON, JENNIFER; Newburyport HS; Newburyport, MA; (Y); 12/208; Intnl Clb; Science Clb; Var Fld Hcky; Var Socr; Var Trk; High Hon Roll; Hon Roll; NHS; SADD; Pres Fitnss Awd; Boston U; Lib Arts.

JOHNSON, JULIE; Algonquin Regional HS; Southborough, MA; (Y); 8/225; Church Yth Grp; High Hon Roll; NHS; Hghst Schlstc Avg Awd 82.

JOHNSON, JULIE; Falmouth HS; Falmouth, MA; (Y); Cmnty Wkr; Hosp Aide; Spanish Clb; School Musical; Tennis; High Hon Roll; Hon Roll; NHS; Dance Clb; School Play; Schlrshp Mt St Charles Acad 82; Mktg.

JOHNSON, KAREN; Malden HS; Malden, MA; (Y); 61/535; Key Clb; Pep Clb; Variety Show; Lit Mag; Im Bsktbl; Im Gym; Var Capt Sftbl; Mrktng.

JOHNSON, KATHERINE; Winchester HS; Winchester, MA; (Y); Trs Church Yth Grp; Hosp Aide; Church Choir; Mrchg Band; Stage Crew; Variety Show; French Hon Soc; High Hon Roll; Hon Roll; Ntl Merit Ltr; Bus.

JOHNSON, KATHRYN; King Philip Regional HS; Norfolk, MA; (S); 23/222; Drama Clb; Hosp Aide; Mrchg Band; Ed Yrbk Stf; Ed Lit Mag; NHS; Natl Svc & Ldrshp Awd 83; Natl Hon Soc 83-84; Southeastern MA U; Visual Desg.

JOHNSON, LISA; David Prouty HS; Spencer, MA; (Y); 43/170; Mgr Bsktbl; Var Fld Hcky; Var Sftbl; Plyr Wk Fld Hcky 84; Southeastern MA U; Med Tech.

JOHNSON, MARK; Leicester HS; Leicester, MA; (S); Boy Scts; Church Yth Grp; Drama Clb; English Clb; Math Tm; Ski Clb; School Play; Nwsp Rptr; Nwsp Stf; Yrbk Rptr; Centry III Ldrshp Prog 1st Rnnr Up 84; Worcester Carrier Awd 83; Capt LHS Var Tenns Tm 83-85; Bentley Coll; Bus.

JOHNSON, MAUREEN; Girls Catholic HS; Melrose, MA; (Y); Church Yth Grp; Dance Clb; PAVAS; Ski Clb; Teachers Aide; Variety Show; Var Capt Cheerleading; Var Coach Actv; Frshmn Of Yr 83; Vrsty Chrldrs Awd 83-86; No Demerits Awd 85; Salem ST Coll; Bus Educ.

JOHNSON, MAUREEN; Weymouth North HS; Weymouth, MA; (Y); 77/430; Church Yth Grp; Hosp Aide; Pep Clb; Spanish Clb; Yrbk Ed-Chief; Sec Soph Cls; Pres Stu Cncl; Var Crs Cntry; Trk; Var Cit Awd; 1st ST Stu Today Nghbrs Tmmrw 85; Hugh O Brian Awd 82-85; Estrn Nazarene Actvty Awd 85; Eastern Nazarene Coll; Accntnt.

JOHNSON, MICHELLE R; Auburn SR HS; Auburn, MA; (Y); Am Leg Aux Girls St; Mgr Acpl Chr; Mgr Chorus; Jazz Band; Rep Jr Cls; Stu Cncl; Var L Socr; High Hon Roll; NHS; Church Yth Grp; Ntl Assn Jazz Ed Mst Vlb Muscn 84; Bio.

JOHNSON, NANCY; Wakefield HS; Wakefield, MA; (S); Church Yth Grp; Rep Sec DECA; Hosp Aide; VP Pep Clb; Orch; Im Gym; Im Mgr(s); High Hon Roll; Hon Roll; 2nd Pl Dist, 4th Pl ST, Top 70 Natl DECA 84; 1st Pl Dist, 1st Pl ST, 2nd & 1st Oral 85; 14th Natl; Middlesex CC; Mktg.

JOHNSON, PETER; Old Rochester Regional HS; Marion, MA; (Y); 13/145; AFS; Ski Clb; Socr; Hon Roll; Jr NHS; Charles R Washburn Outstndng Stu Awd 83; Law.

JOHNSON, REBEKAH; Bridgewater-Raynham Regional HS; Bridgewater, MA; (Y); 13/340; JV Fld Hcky; JV Gym; NHS; Achvt Awd NEDT Test 84; Nrsg.

JOHNSON, RICHARD; Southbridge HS; Southbridge, MA; (Y); 35/179; Boy Scts; Computer Clb; Math Tm; Band; Jazz Band; Mrchg Band; Var Bsktbl; Crs Cntry; Tennis; Var L Trk; U Of Lowell; Mchncl Engrng.

JOHNSON, RUSSELL ERIK; Wachusett Regional HS; Paxton, MA; (Y); 113/400; Off Church Yth Grp; Ski Clb; Var Bsbl; Bsktbl; Var Ftbl; Hon Roll; Bus Admin.

JOHNSON, SHEILA; Mission Church HS; Boston, MA; (Y); 19/50; Church Yth Grp; Dance Clb; Drama Clb; Library Aide; Office Aide; Red Cross Aide; Science Clb; Teachers Aide; Church Choir; School Play; 1st Hnr 85; Accntng Awd 85; 2nd Hnr 85; Paypath JC; Bus Admin.

JOHNSON, SUSAN A; King Philip Regional HS; Plainville, MA; (Y); Church Yth Grp; High Hon Roll; Hon Roll.

JOHNSON, TIMOTHY A; Burlington HS; Burlington, MA; (Y); 50/320; Boys Clb Am; Boy Scts; Pres Church Yth Grp; Var L Swmmng; Timer; Hon Roll; Prfct Atten Awd; Leag All Star Boys Swmmng 83-85; Hon Mntn Boys Swmmng 82-85; Ec.

JOHNSON, VALERIE A; Salem HS; Salem, MA; (Y); 46/348; Yrbk Ed-Chief; Stu Cncl; JV Var Fld Hcky; High Hon Roll; Hon Roll; Schlstc Journ Awd 85; Outstndg Goalie Awd 83; Roger Williams; Marine Bio.

JOHNSTON, LYNN; Arlington HS; Arlington, MA; (S); 4/412; VP French Clb; Jazz Band; Nwsp Bus Mgr; Nwsp Stf; High Hon Roll; NHS; Ntl Merit SF; Church Yth Grp; Yrbk Stf; Williams Coll Bk Awd 84; Schlrshp U NH Yth Mus Schl 82-83; Arlington Histrcl Soc Rsrch Proj Awd 84; Med.

JOLICOEUR, MICHELLE; Plymouth-Carver HS; Center Harbor, NH; (Y); 37/600; Church Yth Grp; Dance Clb; Drama Clb; Band; Concert Band; Mrchg Band; Hon Roll; Bus Mngmnt.

JOLLY, ELIZABETH; Nipmuc Regional HS; Mendon, MA; (Y); Church Yth Grp; Cmnty Wkr; Pres 4-H; Girl Scts; Political Wkr; Quiz Bowl; Var Fld Hcky; Cit Awd; 4-H Awd; FHA; Ctznshp WA Focus Natl 4-H Ctr 83; MA 4-H Key Awd 83; Consecutive Hnr Roll 85; Pre Med.

JONASSAINT, YOLLA; Jeremiah E Burke HS; Boston, MA; (Y); Art Clb; Computer Clb; Engl 82; Home Ec 85; Berkshire Chrstn Coll; Bus.

JONCAS, BRUCE G; Grafton Memorial SR HS; N Grafton, MA; (Y); 5/130; Pres Church Yth Grp; Pres Frsh Cls; Rep Stu Cncl; Var Capt Bsbl; Var Capt Bsktbl; Im Vllybl; Hon Roll; NHS; Pres Schlr; US Army Rsrve Ntl Schlr/Athlte 85; U Of Lowell; Comp Sci.

JONES, ADRIANNE; Scituate Public HS; Scituate, MA; (Y); Church Yth Grp; Drama Clb; Girl Scts; Band; Chorus; Stage Crew; Symp Band; Variety Show; Bsktbl; Hon Roll; Cornell U; Vetrnry Med.

JONES, AMYBETH; Wakefield Memorial HS; Wakefield, MA; (Y); 9/273; Mrchg Band; Symp Band; JV Bsktbl; Var Socr; JV Capt Tennis; Bausch & Lomb Sci Awd; NHS; Ntl Merit Ltr; St Schlr; Pres Schlrshp NE U 85; MA Grand Offcr Intl Order Rnbw Girls 85-86; NE U; Phy Thrpy.

JONES, ANDREW; Bishop Feehan HS; Foxboro, MA; (Y); 20/250; JV Var Bsbl; JV Var Ice Hcky; JV Vllybl; French Hon Soc; High Hon Roll; NHS; Hgh Hnrs 83-85; Frnch Natl Hnr Socty 84; Natl Hnr Socty 84-85.

JONES, ART; King Philip Regional HS; Wrentham, MA; (Y); Am Leg Boys St; Aud/Vis; Varsity Clb; Ftbl; Wt Lftg; Hon Roll; Ntl Hstry Day-St Fnls 85; Harvard; Engr.

JONES JR, CARL; Bishop Fenwick HS; Peabody, MA; (Y); 81/220; Church Yth Grp; Drama Clb; School Play; Stage Crew; Badmtn; Bsbl; Bsktbl; Var Coach Actv; JV Ftbl; Var Socr; Hnr Roll 81-85; Bsktbl 81-82; Ftbl 81; Merrimack Coll; Bus Adm.

JONES, EXTELLA; High School Of Commerce; Springfield, MA; (S); School Play; Variety Show; Yrbk Stf; Rep Jr Cls; High Hon Roll; NHS; Prfct Atten Awd; Frnch Recitn Awd 86; Comp Sci.

JONES, KAREN; Malden HS; Malden, MA; (Y); Ski Clb; North Eastern U; Phy Thrpy.

JONES, KAREN A; Burlington HS; Burlington, MA; (Y); Yrbk Phtg; Yrbk Stf; Powder Puff Ftbl; Hon Roll; Jr NHS; Sec NHS; Yr Bk Photo Editor 85; Secr Of Ntl Hnr Soc 85; Mbr Of JR Prom Comm 84-85; Env Sci.

JONES, LINDA R; Gloucester HS; Gloucester, MA; (Y); 18/314; German Clb; Hosp Aide; Yrbk Stf; Rep Jr Cls; Rep Sr Cls; Trk; Hon Roll; NHS; Sawyer Medal 83; Life Sci Achvt Awd 82; Acad Recgntn 83-85; Bates Coll; Bio.

JONES, MELINDA A; Lincoln-Sudbury Reg HS; Sudbury, MA; (Y); Church Yth Grp; FBLA; Spanish Clb; Yrbk Stf; Rep Stu Cncl; JV Capt Bsktbl; Ntl Merit Ltr; Stu Ambassador Schl Awd 84; Bus Admin.

JONES, MICHELLE; Hanover HS; Rockland, MA; (Y); Sec Yrbk Sprt Ed; VP Capt Cheerleading; Hon Roll; Sec.

JONES, PAUL F; Westfield HS; Westfield, MA; (Y); VP Church Yth Grp; Rep Frsh Cls; Var L Lcrss; Var L Socr; Var Wrstlng; NHS; Stu Ldr Prof Advntre, Spnsh Stu Trp Spain 84-85.

JONES, TRACEY A; Lexington HS; Lexington, MA; (Y); French Clb; Orch; Var Bsktbl; Var Capt Swmmng; Var Capt Trk; Hon Roll; NHS; Mbr Grtr Boston Yth Ymph Orch 84-86.

JONES, WILLIAM; Boston College HS; Braintree, MA; (Y); Boy Scts; Church Yth Grp; Im Crs Cntry; Im Trk; Hon Roll; NHS; Eagle Sct 85; Bus Mgmt.

JORDAN, KELLY; Greenfield HS; Greenfield, MA; (Y); 19/154; DECA; Ski Clb; Yrbk Stf; Sec Frsh Cls; Sec Soph Cls; Sec Sr Cls; Sec Stu Cncl; Var Tennis; Hon Roll; Spec Svc Clss Awd 85; U MA; Lib Arts.

JORDAN, PAMELA R; Boston Lat In HS; Boston, MA; (Y); 91/325; Church Yth Grp; Debate Tm; JA; Key Clb; NFL; Pep Clb; Spanish Clb; Church Choir; Rep Jr Cls; Rep Stu Cncl; Pedtrcs.

JORGE, CHRISTINE; New Bedford HS; New Bedford, MA; (Y); 36/250; Library Aide; Stu Cncl; Hon Roll; NHS; Frnch Excllnc Awd 85; Desgn.

JORGE, LINDA E; Bishop Stang HS; Assonet, MA; (Y); Civic Clb; Cmnty Wkr; Office Aide; Service Clb; Chorus; High Hon Roll; Hon Roll; NHS; Corp Law.

JOSEPH, CHRIS; Brockton HS; Brockton, MA; (Y); 240/1000; Ski Clb; Hon Roll; Stu Govt Day 84-85; Bentley; Bus Mgmt.

JOSLIN, ROBIN; Fitchburg HS; Fitchburg, MA; (Y); Church Yth Grp; Drama Clb; Yrbk Stf; Hon Roll; Crimnl Psychlgst.

JOY, CHRIS; Murdock HS; Winchendon, MA; (Y); Girl Scts; Model UN; School Play; Trs Frsh Cls; Cheerleading; Hon Roll; NHS.

JOYAL, DENISE; St Clare HS; W Roxbury, MA; (Y); VP Church Yth Grp; Dance Clb; Latin Clb; Pep Clb; JV Bsktbl; Variety Show; 1st Prz Latn Oratory 84; 2nd Hghst Ave Math 84; Nrsng.

JOYAL, MICHELLE; Cathedral HS; Somers, CT; (Y); Intnl Clb; Natl Beta Clb; High Hon Roll; NHS; Bus.

JOYCE, CELINA; Boston Latin Schl; Boston, MA; (Y); 52/310; Church Yth Grp; Hosp Aide; Variety Show; Hon Roll; NHS; Latin Clb; Ski Clb; Nwsp Rptr; Yrbk Stf; Employee Svc Awd Bradlees 84; Art.

JOYCE, CHRISTOPHER; Braintree HS; Braintree, MA; (Y); 51/481; Ski Clb; Var JV Bsbl; Var JV Socr; Hon Roll; SADD; Sprts Med.

JOYCE, EILEEN; Coyle & Cassidy Memorial HS; N Easton, MA; (Y); Drama Clb; Hosp Aide; Spanish Clb; Chorus; School Musical; Hon Roll; Sec NHS; Ntl Merit Ltr; NEDT Awd; Spanish NHS; Pre-Med.

JOYCE, KEVAN; Whitman-Hanson HS; Hanson, MA; (Y); Letterman Clb; Varsity Clb; Capt Var Ice Hcky; Hon Roll; MA Tm Al-Star Ic Hcky/ Tnrmnts Al Ovr Wrld, Recnt Trp Germny-Austria; Bus.

JOYCE, SEAN E; Quincy HS; Quincy, MA; (Y); 156/333; Am Leg Boys St; CAP; ROTC; Drill Tm; Hon Roll; JV Bsbl; JV Ftbl; JV Wrstlng; Rtrd Ofcrs Assn Mdl 85; US Army; Law Enfrcmnt.

JOYCE, WILLIAM; Boston College HS; Medford, MA; (Y); 14/270; Math Tm; High Hon Roll; NHS; Ntl Merit Ltr; VFW Awd; Mst Val Mathlete 84; Achvt Math Comp 85; Dartmouth Coll; Math.

JUDGE, BETH; Notre Dame Acad; Scituate, MA; (Y); Hosp Aide; Science Clb; Ski Clb; Chorus; School Musical; School Play; Stage Crew; Mgr(s); Timer; Archdiocesan Cath HS Yth Conv Secy 84-85; Nrs.

JUDSON, JERILYN; Burlington HS; Burlington, MA; (Y); Church Yth Grp; FTA; Girl Scts; Office Aide; Acpl Chr; Chorus; School Musical; Yrbk Stf; Fld Hcky; Powder Puff Ftbl; Grand Offcr To Assmbly Of Intl Order Of Rainbow 85-86; Framington ST Coll; Teach.

JUMP, KERRI-LYNN; Acad Of Notre Dame; Lowell, MA; (Y); Hosp Aide; Key Clb; Chorus; School Play; Hon Roll; Prfct Atten Awd; Algbr I-2nd Pl 83; Comptr Litercy-1st Pl 84; Comptr Pgmmng-1st Pl 85; U Of Lowell; Comptr Sci.

JUNAS, ANDREW; Arlington HS; Arlington, MA; (Y); Radio Clb; JV Bsbl; Im Bsktbl; Var Capt Crs Cntry; Var Trk; Hon Roll; Grtr Boston X-Cntry All-Star 84; Bonnell Bunny Hop 5 Miler 1st Pl 85; Bus Mgmt.

JURCZAK, GERI; Christopher Columbus HS; Chasn, MA; (S); Boys Clb Am; Church Yth Grp; GAA; Latin Clb; Library Aide; Mathletes; Office Aide; Political Wkr; Ski Clb; Spanish Clb; Outstndng Boy/Girls Clbs 82; Bus Mgmt.

JUREK, JAMES; Gill-Montague Regional HS; Turners Falls, MA; (Y); Cmnty Wkr; Letterman Clb; Varsity Clb; Nwsp Stf; VP Frsh Cls; VP Soph Cls; Rep Stu Cncl; JV Church Yth Grp; Var Ftbl; Var Trk; Lg Str Pole Vaulter; Bus.

JUSCZAK, KRISTINE; Dracut HS; Dracut, MA; (Y); JV Bsktbl; Capt Var Vllybl; High Hon Roll; Sec NHS; U Lowell; Bus.

JUSTINSKI, DONNA; North Attleboro HS; N Attleboro, MA; (Y); 39/ 230; Drama Clb; Hosp Aide; Office Aide; Hon Roll; NHS; SECR.

KABADIAN, KIMBERLY; Wachusett Regional HS; Holden, MA; (Y); 42/386; Dance Clb; Chorus; Stage Crew; Clark U; Intl Bus.

KABOTSKY, JOSHUA A; Sharon HS; Sharon, MA; (Y); Computer Clb; Pres JCL; Pres Latin Clb; Math Clb; Math Tm; Band; Concert Band; Pep Band; School Musical; Hon Roll; Mech Drwng, Comp, Ltn, & Sci Stu/ Mnth; Engrng.

KACHEN, SUSAN H; Andover HS; Andover, MA; (Y); 56/412; Hosp Aide; Pep Clb; Acpl Chr; Madrigals; School Musical; Variety Show; Var Cheerleading; High Hon Roll; Hon Roll; Fclty Awd 82-83; Triple A Soc 82-83; Typng Awd 82-83; Comm.

KACHINSKY, KIM; Murdock HS; Winchendon, MA; (Y); 1/107; Am Leg Aux Girls St; Library Aide; Model UN; School Play; Stage Crew; Yrbk Stf; Rep Stu Cncl; Var Cheerleading; High Hon Roll; Sec NHS; Chairprsn Model Cong 84-85; Awd Best Perf Tourn Plays 82-85; Fash Merc.

KACZMAREK, STEPHEN; Berkshire HS; River Hills, WI; (Y); 6/125; Drama Clb; Radio Clb; Jazz Band; School Musical; Stage Crew; Nwsp Ed-Chief; Yrbk Phtg; Socr; Trk; High Hon Roll; Excllnce Stagecraft Awd 84-85; Calvin Fentress Ctznshp Prize 84-85; Cls Agent 85; CO Coll; Pre-Med.

KADILIS, ALEXIA A; Bishop Connolly HS; Middletown, RI; (Y); 14/ 162; Aud/Vis; Drama Clb; Thesps; Chorus; School Musical; School Play; Stage Crew; NHS; Voice Dem Awd; 1st Prz Pntngs 83; Naples Amer HS Tlnt Wnnr 82; Ntl Fndtn Advcmt Arts 84; Barnard Coll; Thrtr.

KAHN, HEATHER J; Malden HS; Malden, MA; (Y); 50/520; Cmnty Wkr; Hosp Aide; Pep Clb; Teachers Aide; Temple Yth Grp; Variety Show; Hst Sr Cls; Var Cheerleading; Sftbl; Hon Roll; Jacob Ruderman Schlrshp 85; Miss Teen MA 84; Union Coll; Pltcl Sci.

KAISER, CHRISTOPHER J; East Longmeadow HS; East Longmeadow, MA; (Y); 17/206; Am Leg Boys St; Church Yth Grp; Boy Scts; Nwsp Ed-Chief; Rep Sr Cls; NHS; Intnl Clb; Scholastic Bowl; Trs Frsh Cls; Trs Soph Cls; Pres Clsrm Dely 85; HOBY Ctznshp Awd 84; Bst Dely Modl Cngrss Amer Intl Coll 84; Intl Rel.

KAISER, ROBERT D; Winthrop HS; Winthrop, MA; (Y); Science Clb; Temple Yth Grp; Band; Concert Band; Jazz Band; Mrchg Band; Hon Roll; NHS; Prfct Atten Awd; Schlrshp Harvard U Physcs Extnsn Lss 85; Acadmc Extr Curremlr Musem Sci Boston; MIT Smmr Stds 83-85; Physcs.

KALANTA, JAY; Central Catholic HS; Methuen, MA; (Y); Church Yth Grp; Cmnty Wkr; Varsity Clb; Im Bsktbl; Var Trk; Im Wt Lftg; Hon Roll; U Of Lowell; Bus Mgt.

KALB, DEBORAH; Marian HS; Sudbury, MA; (Y); Cmnty Wkr; Chorus; Stage Crew; Hon Roll; Jr NHS; NEDT Awd; Bus Admn.

KALDES, CHRISTIAN; Deerfield Acad; Bernarbston, MA; (Y); Camera Clb; Computer Clb; School Play; Nwsp Phtg; Yrbk Phtg; Coach Actv; Ftbl; Lcrss; Hon Roll; Bio Chmstry.

KALIKOW, JOANNA; Natick HS; Natick, MA; (Y); 10/443; French Clb; NFL; Speech Tm; School Musical; School Play; High Hon Roll; Jr NHS; NHS; Ntl Merit SF; Fornsc Teams Sec 85-86; Head Of Ntl Hnr Soc Exec Brd 85-86; 1st & 2nd Pl Ntl Lvl Comptr Fornscs 85.

KALIMERIS, ANGELIKI E; St Clare HS; West Roxbury, MA; (Y); 10/ 153; Cmnty Wkr; Dance Clb; JA; JCL; Teachers Aide; Variety Show; Nwsp Rptr; High Hon Roll; Hon Roll; Ntl Merit Ltr; Cum Laude Awd; Magna Cum Laude Awd Natl Latn Exm; Stonehill Coll; Lwyr.

KALLIO, JAMES R; Medfield HS; Medfield, MA; (Y); Am Leg Boys St; Cmnty Wkr; Nwsp Rptr; Nwsp Stf; Yrbk Rptr; Off Jr Cls; Var Bsbl; Var Bsktbl; Var Socr; Hon Roll; Math.

KALOSHIS, EVA; Silver Lake Regional HS; Halifax, MA; (Y); Camp Fr Inc; Latin Clb; Red Cross Aide; Capt Cheerleading; Var Socr; Var Trk; Matl Merit Foundtn Hnr Roll,Spotlght Prgm SMU,Early Matricultn Frm HS 85; NE U; Psychlgy.

KALP, ANDREW; Randolph HS; Randolph, MA; (Y); Intnl Clb; Crs Cntry; Socr; Wrstlng; Hon Roll; Exec Bd AZA 85; Law.

KAM, PAUL VANG; Burlington HS; Burlington, MA; (Y); 4/323; Am Leg Boys St; Debate Tm; Math Clb; Yrbk Stf; Ed Lit Mag; Stat Bsbl; Stat Bsktbl; High Hon Roll; VP NHS; Acad Exclnce Eng 83, 84 & 85; Med.

KAMERER, JENNIFER; Milford HS; Milford, MA; (Y); 81/305; Office Aide; Yrbk Phtg; Yrbk Stf; JV Var Vllybl; High Hon Roll; Hon Roll; Church Yth Grp; Key Clb; JV Bsktbl; Barbizon Schl Modelng Scholar Cert 85; Hesser Coll; Fashn Merrchndsng.

KAMPF, MATTHEW; Bourne HS; Triangle, VA; (Y); VP Y-Teens; Var Crs Cntry; Var Trk; High Hon Roll; Hon Roll; Prfct Atten Awd; Culinary Schl Of LTD; Prf Chef.

KAMPFER, FAITH; Marlboro HS; Marlboro, MA; (Y); English Clb; Teachers Aide; Acpl Chr; Madrigals; School Musical; Sec Frsh Cls; Rep Soph Cls; High Hon Roll; Hon Roll; Pres Church Yth Grp; Fclty Awd Excel Eng 85; Lead Role Mozrts 82; Marlboro Smmr Band 85; U MA-AMHERST; Eng.

KAMROWSKI, MICHAEL; Wareham HS; Buzzards Bay, MA; (Y); Am Leg Boys St; JV Bsbl; JV Ftbl; Hon Roll; Engrng.

KANDRA, MIKE; Groton Dunstable HS; Groton, MA; (Y); Am Leg Boys St; Varsity Clb; Yrbk Stf; L Var Bsbl; L Var Bsktbl; L Var Socr; Im Vllybl; Im Wt Lftg; Jr NHS; NHS; All Cntrl MA Soccer Plyr 83-84; All Star Soccer 84; Wauchusett Leag Allstr 83-84; Amer Hstry Awd 85; Bus Mgmt.

KANE, COLLEEN; Dennis-Yarmouth HS; West Yarmouth, MA; (Y); 15/ 316; Drm Mjr(t); Twrlr; Hon Roll; NHS; Emmanuel Coll Pes Schlrshp; Emmanuel Coll; Educ.

KANE, KAREN; Agawam HS; Agawam, MA; (Y); 10/340; GAA; Yrbk Stf; Var Capt Socr; Hon Roll; NHS; Spanish NHS; Comp Sci.

KANE, MATTHEW J; Barnstable HS; Hyannis, MA; (Y); Church Yth Grp; Drama Clb; Math Tm; Ski Clb; Band; Concert Band; Drm & Bgl; Jazz Band; Mrchg Band; Orch; Slvr Acadmc Achvt Awd 83; Gld Acadmc Achvt Awd 84; Acadmc Achvt Lttr 85; Engrng.

KANE, NANCY M; St Clare HS; Hyde Park, MA; (Y); 22/153; Church Yth Grp; Church Choir; Nwsp Rptr; Trs Jr Cls; Trk; Hon Roll; Miss Persnlty Miss Amer Coed Pagnt 85; Northeastern; Engrng.

KANE, SEAN; Marian HS; Natick, MA; (Y); 59/177; JV Var Bsbl; JV Var Bsktbl; JV Ftbl; High Hon Roll; Hon Roll; NEDT Awd; Arch.

KANE, TIM K; Woburn HS; Woburn, MA; (Y); Boys Clb Am; JA; Key Clb; Leo Clb; Ski Clb; Im Bsktbl; Var Ice Hcky; Im Wrstlng; Bobby ORR AHA Pgm Plyr Sportsmnshp Awd 83-84; Elec Engrng.

KANNALLY, LEANN; Walpole HS; Walpole, MA; (Y); Church Yth Grp; Drama Clb; Girl Scts; Library Aide; Office Aide; VP Chorus; Church Choir; School Play; Hon Roll; Stu Mth Amer Govt/Str Law 85.

KAO, LIWEN; Newburyport HS; Newburyport, MA; (Y); 2/207; Math Tm; Q&S; Teachers Aide; Lit Mag; High Hon Roll; Trs NHS; Ntl Merit Ltr; Sal; U Of CA Berkeley; Mech Engrng.

KAO, SHIN C; Newburyport HS; Newburyport, MA; (S); 5/194; Model UN; Nwsp Rptr; Nwsp Stf; Lit Mag; Hon Roll; NHS; U S Natl Journlsm Awd.

KAPLANIDIS, MICHAEL; Randolph HS; Randolph, MA; (Y); Am Leg Boys St; Dance Clb; Drama Clb; Intnl Clb; Varsity Clb; Variety Show; Socr; Wt Lftg; Wrstlng; Hon Roll; MA U; Gen Bus.

KAPSAMBELIS, NIKI D; Norwell HS; Norwell, MA; (Y); 23/176; Drama Clb; French Clb; Chorus; School Play; Stage Crew; Variety Show; Nwsp Ed-Chief; Ed Yrbk Stf; High Hon Roll; NHS; Engl.

KAPUR, JAY; Doherty Memorial HS; Worcester, MA; (Y); 27/400; Church Yth Grp; Im Bsktbl; Im Ftbl; Im Vllybl; High Hon Roll; NHS; Hiatt Schlrshp 85; Knghts Vartan Awd 85; Worcester Polytech; Chem Engrng.

KARADIZIAN, RICHARD Z; Watertown HS; Watertown, MA; (Y); 19/ 250; Computer Clb; Intnl Clb; Teachers Aide; Comp Sci.

KARALEKAS, CHRISTOPHER; New Bedford HS; New Bedford, MA; (Y); 21/688; Am Leg Boys St; Art Clb; Trs Church Yth Grp; Yrbk Stf; VP Rep Soph Cls; Rep Jr Cls; Stu Cncl; Crs Cntry; Trk; High Hon Roll; Optometrst.

KARALEKAS, LEEANN; Fontbonne Acad; Milton, MA; (Y); 25/136; Church Yth Grp; Drama Clb; Intnl Clb; Stage Crew; Bsktbl; Fld Hcky; Tennis; Hon Roll; Excllnce Spn Awd 85; Bentley Coll; Bus Admin.

KARAM, THOMAS; B M C Durfee HS; Fall River, MA; (Y); 57/850; Boys Clb Am; Varsity Clb; Nwsp Sprt Ed; Capt Var Bsktbl; Var Ftbl; Hon Roll; NHS; Hnr MA ST Bsktbl Champ 84; JR Bsktbl Leag Acad Ad 81; U Of MA; Bus.

KARCH, ERIC; Randolph HS; Randolph, MA; (Y); Var Bsbl; Var JV Ftbl; Hon Roll; Jr NHS; NHS; Comp Sci.

KARKOS, KAREN; Franklin HS; Franklin, MA; (Y); 19/235; Math Tm; Teachers Aide; Lit Mag; Hon Roll; Stu Sec Drctr Engl Dept 84-85; U MA Boston; Bus.

KARKUTT, KAREN; St Bernards HS; Fitchburg, MA; (S); 8/169; Camera Clb; Cmnty Wkr; Hosp Aide; Latin Clb; Stu Cncl; High Hon Roll; NHS; Ntl Conf Christns Jews 84-85; Tutoring 84-85; Intrmrl Bsktbl 83-84; Boston Coll; Sci.

KARLE, ANDREA; Notre Dame Acad; Hingham, MA; (Y); 70/114; Church Yth Grp; Debate Tm; Drama Clb; Chorus; Yrbk Stf; Var Gym; JV Trk; Hon Roll; Prfct Atten Awd; Essay Cont Awd 82-83; Nrsng.

KARPO, LAUREN A; Marblehead HS; Marblehead, MA; (Y); Art Clb; Cmnty Wkr; Drama Clb; Thesps; School Musical; School Play; Stage Crew; Variety Show; Swmmng; Boston U.

KASABULA, STEPHEN; Saint Johns HS; N Grafton, MA; (Y); 3/287; Church Yth Grp; Lit Mag; Var L Crs Cntry; Var L Trk; Hon Roll; NHS.

KASIERSKI, SCOTT; Northbridge JR-SR HS; Northbridge, MA; (S); 6/ 160; Am Leg Boys St; Latin Clb; Band; VP Sr Cls; Rep Stu Cncl; L Crs Cntry; L Trk; Hon Roll; NHS; Ntl Merit SF; Lbrl Arts.

KASTANGO, KARI; Tantasqua Regional SR HS; Holland, MA; (S); 13/ 193; Church Yth Grp; Pres MMM; Varsity Clb; Jazz Band; Var JV Bsktbl; Var Capt Socr; Var Capt Sftbl; JP Sousa Awd; NHS; U MA; Engrng.

KASUBA, LISA; Fontbonne Acad; Milton, MA; (Y); 72/135; Church Yth Grp; Intnl Clb; JV Fld Hcky; Bus Mgmt.

KATSOS, GEORGE E; Arlington HS; Arlington, MA; (Y); 70/377; Church Choir; Jazz Band; Madrigals; School Musical; Nwsp Rptr; Rep Soph Cls; VP Stu Cncl; Var Tennis; Hon Roll; Army Rsrv Govt Awd 85; Hstry.

KATZ, ANDREW D; Newton South HS; Newton, MA; (Y); Am Leg Boys St; Pres German Clb; Radio Clb; Nwsp Sprt Ed; JV Bsbl; JV Bsktbl; JV Lcrss; Socr; Outstndg Achvt Ger 84-85; Jrnlsm.

KATZ, JESSYCA L; Andover HS; Andover, MA; (Y); 69/405; GAA; Model UN; Pep Clb; Ski Clb; Temple Yth Grp; Fld Hcky; Powder Puff Ftbl; Trk; Hon Roll; Comm.

KATZ, STEPHANIE; Bedford HS; Bedford, MA; (Y); Camp Fr Inc; Hosp Aide; Mgr(s); Powder Puff Ftbl; Hon Roll; Comp Sci.

KATZEN, HOWARD; Randolph HS; Randolph, MA; (Y); Spanish Clb; Temple Yth Grp; Band; Concert Band; Mrchg Band; Hon Roll; NHS; Acad Achvt Awd Band 84; Lttr Awd Band 84; Engr.

KAUFFMAN, STEPHEN M; Tabor Acad; Duxbury, MA; (Y); Madrigals; Orch; School Musical; Symp Band; Radio Clb; Chorus; Concert Band; Jazz Band; Madrigals; Yth Symp Orchstr 82-85; Boston Soc Tromb Comp 84; MA Symph Orchstr Comp 85; MA All State & Dist Comp; Music.

KAUFMAN, ALAN; Newton North HS; W Newton, MA; (Y); Exploring; Ski Clb; Yrbk Stf; Lit Mag; Gov Hon Prg Awd; High Hon Roll; Ntl Merit SF; U MI; Engrng.

KAUFMAN, ALAN H; Waltham HS; Waltham, MA; (Y); Am Leg Boys St; French Clb; JCL; School Play; Nwsp Rptr; Capt Var Tennis; Hon Roll; Cmmnctns.

KAUFMAN, BETH; B M C Durfee HS; Fall River, MA; (Y); 49/687; Cmnty Wkr; Drama Clb; Temple Yth Grp; Nwsp Stf; Yrbk Ed-Chief; Lit Mag; Hon Roll; NHS; Hosp Aide; Sec Math Clb; Soc Action/Fnd Rsng VP Of Nw Englnd Rgn Untd Synagogue Yth 85-86; Abraham Joshua Heschel Hnr Soc.

KAVANAGH, BETSEY L; West Boylston JR SR HS; Sterling Jct, MA; (Y); Art Clb; Cmnty Wkr; Girl Scts; Spanish Clb; Teachers Aide; Sftbl; Cit Awd; God Cntry Awd; Hon Roll; Eclgcl Sci Awd; Art Awd; Erly Chldhd Dvlpmnt.

KAVANAUGH, STEVEN; Georgetown HS; Georgetown, MA; (Y); 10/ 100; Camera Clb; Bsbl; Bsktbl; Socr; High Hon Roll; Hon Roll; NHS; Bus.

KAWA, SHIRLEY; Whitman-Hanson Regional HS; Whitman, MA; (Y); 7/350; Nwsp Ed-Chief; Nwsp Rptr; Nwsp Stf; High Hon Roll; Hon Roll; Kiwanis Awd; NHS; AFS; Church Yth Grp; Drama Clb; Ellen Conway Spellman Ntl Cntst 1st Pl; Amer Legion; Framingham ST Hist Scty Hon Mem Top Ten; Dean JC; Comm.

KAY, CHRISTOPHER J; Walpole HS; Walpole, MA; (Y); Varsity Clb; Nwsp Stf; Var L Bsbl; JV Crs Cntry; High Hon Roll; Hon Roll; NHS; Clsrm Perfrmnce Awd Bio 84; Clsrm Perfrmnce Awd Alg II 85; Cmmnctns.

KEALEY, CHRIS; Bishop Fenwick HS; Newburyport, MA; (Y); 35/220; Var L Ftbl; High Hon Roll; Hon Roll; UNH; Poltcl Sci.

KEAMY, MATTHEW; Methuen HS; Methuen, MA; (Y); 12/400; Am Leg Boys St; Aud/Vis; Boy Scts; VP Church Yth Grp; Cmnty Wkr; Intnl Clb; Math Tm; Spanish Clb; Teachers Aide; Yrbk Ed-Chief; Ortrcl Cont Wnnr 83, 2nd Pl 85; MA Boys ST 85; Williams Coll; Math.

KEANE, JULIE; Malden HS; Malden, MA; (Y); Color Guard; Drill Tm; Drm & Bgl; Nwsp Phtg; Nwsp Rptr; L Nwsp Stf; Human Svcs.

KEANE, KELLY; Holyoke Catholic HS; Holyoke, MA; (Y); 4/133; Latin Clb; Quiz Bowl; Nwsp Ed-Chief; Nwsp Rptr; Ed Yrbk Stf; Var L Socr; Var L Swmmng; Var L Tennis; High Hon Roll; Sec NHS; Jrnlsm.

KEANE, SANDRA; Lexington HS; Lexington, MA; (Y); Church Yth Grp; Dance Clb; French Clb; Chorus; School Musical; Yrbk Stf; Socr; Hon Roll; U RI; Oceangrphy.

KEANEY, ERIN; St Peter-Marian Central Catholic; Worcester, MA; (Y); Camera Clb; Hosp Aide; Ski Clb; School Musical; Yrbk Phtg; Sec Soph Cls; JV Var Cheerleading; Var L Socr; JV Capt Sftbl; Prfct Atten Awd; Chrldng Awd 85; Stheastrn MA U; Acctng.

KEANEY, PATRICK; Cathedral HS; Springfield, MA; (Y); 98/525; Trs Frsh Cls; Stu Cncl; Capt Var Crs Cntry; Ice Hcky; Trk; Aerospc Engr.

KEANY, MICHAEL; Archbishop Williams HS; Braintree, MA; (Y); 31/ 200; Church Yth Grp; Library Aide; Math Tm; Ski Clb; Trk; Hon Roll; Ntl Merit Ltr; Msv Vlble Mathlete 83; Spanish Merit Awd 83; Suffolk U; Accntng.

KEARNAN, TARA; Nipmuc Regional HS; Mendon, MA; (Y); Church Yth Grp; Dance Clb; Yrbk Stf; High Hon Roll; NHS; Cert Awd Acadmc Achvt 83; Outstndng Achvt Awd Soc Sci 85; Publ Spkg Clb 85; Chrprsn Cmmttee 85-86; Psych.

KEARNS, PAUL; Christopher Columbus HS; Boston, MA; (S); Red Cross Aide; JV Ice Hcky; Neponset Youth Hockey & MVP 81-83; ATI In Woburn; Comp Elec.

KEAVANY, KRISTIN ANN; Cathedral HS; Springfield, MA; (Y); Library Aide; Yrbk Rptr; Yrbk Stf; VP Soph Cls; VP Sr Cls; Capt Crs Cntry; Trk; Sprts Med.

KECK, DAVID; Doherty Memorial HS; Worcester, MA; (Y); Chess Clb; JA; Math Clb; Math Tm; Im Ftbl; High Hon Roll; Prfct Atten Awd; U Of Houston; Comp.

KEDDIE, ROBERT; Christopher Columbus HS; Boston, MA; (Y); 26/ 132; Boy Scts; CAP; JA; Science Clb; Ski Clb; Color Guard; Drill Tm; Rep Jr Cls; Stu Cncl; Ftbl; Sci Awd 83-84; Bio Awd 83-84; USAF Acad; Astrophysics.

KEDDY, CAROLYN; Fontbonne Acad; Quincy, MA; (Y); Drama Clb; Intnl Clb; Science Clb; Stage Crew; JV Var Bsktbl; Var Trk; Var Vllybl; High Hon Roll; Hon Roll.

KEEFE, KEVIN; Everett HS; Everett, MA; (Y); VP Intnl Clb; Key Clb; Letterman Clb; Science Clb; Band; Socr; Capt Tennis; Law Enfrcmnt.

KEEFE JR, KEVIN MICHAEL; Boston College HS; Winchester, MA; (Y); 76/280; Cmnty Wkr; Key Clb; Rep Frsh Cls; Rep Soph Cls; Sec Jr Cls; Rep Sr Cls; Stu Cncl; Var Trk; Jr NHS; Sal; Acad Excel Awd Frnch 83; Pres Svc Awd, John Farricy Awd 85; Holy Cross Coll; Psych.

KEEFE, ROBERT M; Charles H Mc Cann Technicall HS; Adams, MA; (Y); Am Leg Boys St; Hon Roll; Co-Wrtr Class Hist; 1st Pl NASC Pgrmg Cont; Crtv Arts.

KEEGAN, MATTHEW; Newton North HS; W Newtonm, MA; (Y); Art Clb; Church Yth Grp; Varsity Clb; Lit Mag; Capt L Ftbl; Var L Lcrss; Hon Roll; Ski Clb; 1st League DVI All Star La Crosse Tm Goalie 85; Rnnr Up MIAA Tourn 85; Chammp MIAA 85.

KEENAN, KATHLEEN A; New Redford HS; New Bedford, MA; (Y); 144/680; Drama Clb; School Play; Stage Crew; Yrbk Stf; Stu Cncl; Hon Roll.

KEENAN, TIMOTHY; Leicester HS; Leicester, MA; (S); Boy Scts; French Clb; Latin Clb; Var L Bsktbl; Var L Ftbl; Hon Roll; Engr.

KEENE, REBECCA; Bishop Fenwick HS; Marblehead, MA; (Y); Var Capt Bsktbl; Var Capt Fld Hcky; Socr; High Hon Roll; NHS; Fresh Capt Bsktbll & MVP Trnmnt 83; All Star Fld Hckry 84; Bay ST Fld Hcky Team 85; Math.

KEHOE, DEAN; Revere HS; Revere, MA; (Y); 1/400; Math Tm; Quiz Bowl; Science Clb; Stage Crew; Ed Yrbk Stf; JV Trk; High Hon Roll; Prfct Atten Awd; Val; Harvard Bk Awd 85; Renssalaer; Elec Engrng.

KEIRAN, KATHLEEN M; Cardinal Spellman HS; N Falmouth, MA; (Y); 40/206; Church Yth Grp; Drama Clb; 4-H; Letterman Clb; Quiz Bowl; Spanish Clb; Chorus; School Musical; School Play; Var Bsktbl; Anne C Hayes Schlrshp Awd 81; Lynch Fontaine Meml Schlrshp 85; Citzns Schlrshp Fndtn 85; Boston Clg; Nrsg.

KEITH, JAMES; Faith Baptist Christian Acad HS; W Springfield, MA; (Y); Church Yth Grp; FCA; Teachers Aide; Yrbk Sprt Ed; Yrbk Stf; Var Capt Bsktbl; Coach Actv; Var Capt Socr; Var Capt Sftbl; Hon Roll; Christian Char 81-85; MIP Bsktbl 83-84; MI & MV Plyr Sccr 82 & 85; Bibl Baptist Coll E; Phy Ed Tch.

KELDSEN, KYLE; Ayer HS; Ft Devens, MA; (Y); 41/353; Am Leg Boys St; Boy Scts; Church Yth Grp; Debate Tm; NFL; JV Ftbl; Hon Roll; KS Cty Tae Kwon Do Open 1st Pl 84; Sparing Presb Chrch Awd 85; Engrng.

KELL, ROBERT; St Johns HS; S Grafton, MA; (Y); 39/289; Hon Roll; NHS; NROTC.

KELLEHER, DOUG; Mohawk Trail Regional HS; Shelburne Fls, MA; (Y); 48/135; Trs Frsh Cls; Trs Soph Cls; Trs Jr Cls; Trs Sr Cls; Socr; Hon Roll; Rogert Williams; Arch.

KELLEHER, HEATHER; Notre Dame Acad; Norwell, MA; (Y); 21/114; Chorus; School Musical; French Hon Soc; High Hon Roll; Hon Roll; Ntl Merit Ltr; Jazz Dance Awd 82-83; Classical Ballet.

KELLEHER, MICHAEL; Whitman-Hanson Regional HS; Whitman, MA; (Y); 19/323; Computer Clb; Varsity Clb; JV Bsktbl; Var L Ftbl; Im Gym; Var L Trk; Im Vllybl; Im Wt Lftg; Hon Roll; NHS; Mech Engrng.

KELLEHER, TIA; Brockton HS; Brockton, MA; (Y); 54/1000; Cmnty Wkr; Political Wkr; Yrbk Stf; High Hon Roll; Hon Roll; NHS; Prfrmnc Awd-Emplye-Shaws Sprmrkts 85.

KELLEY, JANET; Dedham HS; Dedham, MA; (Y); 32/300; Ski Clb; Chorus; JV Bsktbl; Var JV Fld Hcky; Var Trk; JV High Hon Roll; VFW Awd; Voice Dem Awd; Liberat Arts Schl; Psych.

KELLEY, KIM M; Cathedral HS; Springfield, MA; (Y); 155/520; Church Yth Grp; Cmnty Wkr; German Clb; JA; Ski Clb; JV Var Bsktbl; JV Var Mgr(s); Var Trk; Western New England Coll; Mktng.

KELLEY, LEANNE; Boston Latin Schl; Boston, MA; (Y); 106/325; Latin Clb; Political Wkr; Ski Clb; Chorus; Powder Puff Ftbl; Hon Roll; Ltn Advncd Plcmnt Exm 85.

KELLEY, LORI; Shawsheen Tech; E Billerica, MA; (Y); Girl Scts; JA; Chorus; Mrchg Band; School Musical; Trk; Lab Tech.

KELLEY, MICHAEL A; Oakmont Regional HS; Westminster, MA; (Y); 10/132; Am Leg Boys St; Chess Clb; Church Yth Grp; Debate Tm; Latin Clb; Model UN; Quiz Bowl; Scholastic Bowl; Ski Clb; Socr; Digital Equip Corp Schlrshp 85; U MA-AMHERST.

KELLEY, SCOTT; Hoosac Valley HS; Adams, MA; (Y); 15/170; Am Leg Boys St; Ski Clb; Golf; Var L Socr; Hon Roll; Pres Exh Clb 85-86; Vrsty Ltrmn Ski Tm.

KELLEY, THERESE; Coyle And Cassidy HS; Taunton, MA; (Y); Rep Jr Cls; VP Sr Cls; Var Bsktbl; Var Crs Cntry; Var Co-Capt Trk; Hon Roll; NHS; Spanish NHS; Cross Cnty Div All Star 84; Spring Track 84-85; Track Co Cptn 85-86; Intl Mrktng.

KELLEY, TRACEY-LEE; Pope John XXIII Central HS; Revere, MA; (Y); 4/213; High Hon Roll; Hon Roll; Jr NHS; NHS; Ntl Merit Ltr; NEDT Awd; Pres Schlr; U NH; Vet.

KELLIHER, BRENDAN; Norwood SR HS; Norwood, MA; (Y); Hon Roll; JC Awd; Am Leg U S Hstry Mdls 84 & 85; Twn Mgr Stu Govt Day 83; Century III Rep 84; U MA Boston; Hstry.

KELLY, EDWARD; Westford Acad; Westford, MA; (Y); Church Yth Grp; Var Bsbl; Var Bsktbl; Hon Roll; 1st Tm Wachusetts Lg All Star Bsbl 84-85; Greatr Lowell Bsbl Ldrs Battg 85; Lowell Sun 2nd Tm 85; U Lowell; Comp Sci.

KELLY, ERIN; Cathedral HS; Springfield, MA; (Y); Trk; Nrsng.

KELLY, KATHLEEN; Saint Clare HS; Hyde Pk, MA; (Y); French Clb; JCL; VP Soph Cls; Rep Jr Cls; Sec Sr Cls; Sec Rep Stu Cncl; Im Vllybl; Hon Roll; Silver Medal Latin Exam 82-83; Latin Exam Cert 83-84; Hmnts.

KELLY, KEVIN; St Johns Prep; Lynnfield, MA; (Y); Church Yth Grp; Cmnty Wkr; JA; Crs Cntry; Lcrss; Socr; Trk; Hon Roll; NHS; Tufts U; Elec Engrng.

KELLY, KRISTIN; Malden HS; Malden, MA; (Y); 68/500; Sec Church Yth Grp; Cmnty Wkr; Pep Clb; Political Wkr; Teachers Aide; Color Guard; Mrchg Band; Variety Show; Rep Frsh Cls; Rep Soph Cls; Bus Adm.

KELLY, LISA; Bishop Feehan HS; Pawtucket, RI; (Y); 91/270; Drill Tm; Mrchg Band; Nwsp Stf; Tennis; Twrlr; Psych.

KELLY, ROBERT; Boston College HS; Milton, MA; (Y); 65/300; Church Yth Grp; Key Clb; Sec Ski Clb; Nwsp Rptr; Nwsp Stf; Yrbk Stf; Hon Roll; Camera Clb; Cmnty Wkr; Political Wkr; Big Bro Incmng Frsh; Francis Ouimet Schlr; IM Cpt Vlybl, Ftbl, Bsktbl; Boston Coll; Pol Sci.

KELLY, SHARRON; Billerica Memorial HS; Billerica, MA; (Y); 20/500; French Clb; Yrbk Stf; Var Crs Cntry; Var Capt Trk; Hon Roll; Jr NHS; Lowell Sun All Star Indr Trck 84; Lowenn Sun All Star Outdr Trck 83-85; Merrimack Vly Conf All Star; Bus Mgmt.

KELLY, SUSAN MARIE; Barnstable HS; Hyannis, MA; (Y); 5/398; Sec Drama Clb; VP Sec Band; VP Sec Mrchg Band; School Play; Rep Sr Cls; Stu Cncl; Elks Awd; High Hon Roll; Hon Roll; NHS; Teenagr Yr 85; Wheelock Coll Bk Awd 84; Outstndng Yuth Awd 85; Wheelock Coll Boston; Elem Ed.

KELLY, THOMAS; Monument Mountain Regional HS; South Lee, MA; (S); 11/130; Concert Band; Jazz Band; Mrchg Band; School Musical; Nwsp Sprt Ed; Var Bsbl; Var Socr; High Hon Roll; NHS; Music Dept Awd 84; Brandeis U; Engl.

KELLY, THOMAS J; Quincy HS; Quincy, MA; (Y); 50/320; Am Leg Boys St; Church Yth Grp; JA; Variety Show; Yrbk Stf; Var Socr; High Hon Roll; Hon Roll; Bus.

KELLY, TRACY; Bishop Feehan HS; Pawtucket, RI; (Y); 32/237; CAP; Drama Clb; Library Aide; Chorus; School Musical; School Play; Stage Crew; Hon Roll; NHS; Ltr Drama, Chor; U Of RI; Med Tech.

KELNHOFER, ROBERT; Bedford HS; Bedford, MA; (Y); 35/240; Boy Scts; Church Yth Grp; Math Tm; Powder Puff Ftbl; Capt Socr; Capt Trk; Hall Fame Math, Gen Rad Schlrshp, Gary P Hansen Awd Trk 85; Branders U.

KEMP, ARNOLD J; Boston Latin Schl; Boston, MA; (Y); Trs Drama Clb; JA; School Play; Stage Crew; Ed Lit Mag; Rep Stu Cncl; Francis Gardner Debate Awd 84; Schl Of Museum Of Fine Arts-Free Course Tuition 85.

KEMPTON, KIMBERLY; Blackstone Valley Tech; Upton, MA; (Y); 1/300; English Clb; Library Aide; Teachers Aide; Nwsp Bus Mgr; Nwsp Ed-Chief; Nwsp Rptr; Var Sftbl; High Hon Roll; NCTE Awd; Prfct Atten Awd; Columbia U; Jrnlsm.

KENDRA, TANYA A; Chicopee Comprehensive HS; Chicopee, MA; (S); 19/280; Dance Clb; Hosp Aide; Letterman Clb; Office Aide; Ski Clb; Spanish Clb; Variety Show; Yrbk Stf; Rep Jr Cls; Mgr(s); Ntl Ledrshp Org 84-85; Mt Holyoke Coll; Med Tech.

KENEFICK, MOLLY; Holyoke HS; Holyoke, MA; (Y); Pres Am Leg Aux Girls St; English Clb; Hosp Aide; Political Wkr; Quiz Bowl; Spanish Clb; Rep Stu Cncl; JV Capt Fld Hcky; Var L Swmmng; Hon Roll; Norman Knight Awd 85; Psych.

KENNAN, SEAN; Barnstable HS; Hyannis, MA; (S); 3/400; Drama Clb; Math Tm; Concert Band; Mrchg Band; Orch; Hon Roll; VP NHS; Ntl Merit Ltr; Nwspaper Carr Of Mnth 81; Williams Coll Book Awd-Soc Sci 84; Astrnmy.

KENNEDY, CHARLEEN; Classical HS; Lynn, MA; (Y); #18 In Class; Hosp Aide; Spanish Clb; Var Bsktbl; Var Socr; Var Sftbl; Var Tennis; Sftbl MVP 83; Stfbl Varsty 84; Physcl Thrpy.

KENNEDY, CHRIS; Arlington HS; Arlington, MA; (Y); Ski Clb; Capt Crs Cntry; Var L Trk; Hon Roll; MVP Crss Cntry 84; Capt Of Crss Cntry 84-85; Acctg.

KENNEDY, CHRISTINE E; Burlington HS; Burlington, MA; (Y); 157/360; Exploring; Var Fld Hcky; Coaches Awd Field Hockey 84; St Elizabeths Hosp; Nrsng.

KENNEDY, MAUREEN; Fontboone Acad; Quincy, MA; (Y); 11/127; Dance Clb; Debate Tm; Drama Clb; Intnl Clb; Variety Show; Hon Roll; NHS; Hnrb Mntn-Fontbonne Sci Fair 84; Northeastern U; Bio.

KENNEDY, SUSAN; Arlington Catholic HS; Medford, MA; (Y); 25/148; Church Yth Grp; Dance Clb; Intnl Clb; JA; Spanish Clb; JV Bsktbl; Var Tennis; Hon Roll; NHS; 10 1st Pl Awds In Irsh Stp Dncng 82-85; N Subrbn Cathlc Tnns Chmps 85; Bus Admin.

KENNEFICK, KRISTINE; Sacred Heart HS; Halifax, MA; (Y); 11/89; Church Yth Grp; Key Clb; Nwsp Rptr; Nwsp Stf; Trk; High Hon Roll; Hon Roll; NHS; Chem Awd 85; Nwspr Awd 84; Bates Coll; Pre-Med.

KENNEY, MARY KATE; Weymouth North HS; Weymouth, MA; (Y); 3/365; French Clb; Math Clb; Math Tm; Pep Clb; Yrbk Stf; High Hon Roll; Hon Roll; Jr NHS; NHS; Ntl Merit Ltr; Ten Yr Irish Stp Dncng Awd 85; Tm Stu Awds 83-85; Frnch & Engl Prin Awd 85; Dartmouth; Comp Sys Anlysis.

KEOGH, JUDITH A; Mount Saint Joseph Acad; Boston, MA; (Y); 38/164; Church Yth Grp; French Clb; JA; Math Clb; Science Clb; Variety Show; Yrbk Stf; Rep Stu Cncl; Hon Roll; Art Fair 3-3rd Przes, 1 2nd Prz 84.

KERRIGAN, CHRISTINE A; Woburn HS; Woburn, MA; (Y); Hosp Aide; Color Guard; Flag Corp; Yrbk Ed-Chief; Pres Frsh Cls; Hon Roll; Knghts Of Columbus Schlrshp 81-82; Mst Lkly To Sccd In 9th Grd Yrbk 81-82.

KERSHAW, KEVIN; Durfee HS; Fall River, MA; (Y); 169/687; Boy Scts; Computer Clb; 4-H; Lit Mag; 4-H Awd; High Hon Roll; Hon Roll; Comp Engr.

KESSINGER, LAURIE; Hull HS; Hull, MA; (Y); 7/160; Church Yth Grp; Yrbk Stf; Fld Hcky; Powder Puff Ftbl; Trk; High Hon Roll; Hon Roll; Jr NHS; Engl Awd 85; MA ST Schlrshp Awd 85; Boston U; Phy Thrpy.

KEYWORTH, JODI; Mansfield HS; Mansfield, MA; (Y); #9 In Class; Church Yth Grp; Key Clb; VP Band; Concert Band; Mrchg Band; Rep Frsh Cls; Rep Soph Cls; Rep Stu Cncl; JV Bsktbl; JV Capt Sftbl; Natl Frnch Cont Top 10; Key Scty; Pre-Dntl.

KHAMBATY, MURRIAM J; Gloucester HS; Gloucester, MA; (Y); 8/365; Political Wkr; Red Cross Aide; Yrbk Ed-Chief; Rep Soph Cls; Off Jr Cls; Off Stu Cncl; JV Sftbl; Elks Awd; Hon Roll; NHS; Med.

KHAN, ADIL; St Johns HS; Shrewsbury, MA; (Y); 12/272; Debate Tm; Math Tm; Science Clb; Rep Soph Cls; Rep Jr Cls; Hon Roll; NHS; Worcester Acad Compttv Schlrshp 85; US Cst Grd Acad-MITE Slctn 85; Med.

KHOK, MOSORN; South Boston HS; Brookline, MA; (Y); Hon Roll; Prfct Atten Awd; NHS 83-84; Northeastern U; Comp Sci.

KHOXAYO, SOMPONG; Bedford HS; Bedford, MA; (Y); 160/213; Outstndng Stu Awd Cert 83; Northeastern; Comp Math.

KHOZOZIAN, JOHN; Watertown HS; Watertown, MA; (Y); 2/306; Am Leg Aux Girls St; Var L Ice Hcky; Var L Tennis; Bausch & Lomb Sci Awd; High Hon Roll; Hon Roll; Jr NHS; NHS; Sal; Dartmouth Coll; Math.

KIBBE, RANDY; Douglas HS; Douglas, MA; (Y); Boy Scts; Cmnty Wkr; Ski Clb; Varsity Clb; Yrbk Stf; JV Bsktbl; Var Capt Socr; Hon Roll; Nothrestrn U; Bus Admin.

KIDDER, STEPHEN; Tahanto Regional HS; Berlin, MA; (Y); 8/54; Pres Church Yth Grp; Math Clb; Math Tm; Science Clb; Ski Clb; Yrbk Stf; Var Capt Bsbl; JV Bsktbl; Var Golf; Var Socr; Pilot.

KIELTY, TRACEY; Bishop Feehan HS; Attleboro, MA; (Y); Stu Cncl; Trk.

KIJAK, MICHAEL S; Chicopee Comprehensive HS; Chicopee, MA; (S); 2/340; French Clb; Var Bsbl; Var Bsktbl; Mgr(s); Powder Puff Ftbl; Var Socr; French Hon Soc; High Hon Roll; Jr NHS; Sal.

KILDUFF, KATHLEEN; Bishop Feehan HS; E Walpole, MA; (Y); 38/263; Math Clb; Math Tm; Chorus; School Musical; School Play; Stage Crew; Hon Roll; NHS; Ntl Merit SF; 1st Bristol Cnty Ntl Bnk Clb Pres 84; U Of MA-AMHERST; Indstrl Engrg.

KILELEE, MIKE; Medway HS; Medway, MA; (Y); Am Leg Boys St; Intnl Clb; VP Jr Cls; VP Sr Cls; Stu Cncl; JV Var Mgr(s); Hon Roll; Mst Outstdng JR Boy 85; Acctng Awd For Avg Of 90 For 1 Yr 84; Schlstc Awd 84-85; Acctng.

KILEY, ANDREW; Westbridge HS; Woburn, MA; (S); 1/15; Chess Clb; Ski Clb; Nwsp Stf; Stat Bsktbl; Im Golf; Var Score Keeper; Timer; High Hon Roll; NHS; Pres Natl Hnr Soc 86; Math Awd 83-85.

KILEY, MEGAN P; Andover HS; Andover, MA; (Y); 50/400; Dance Clb; Pep Clb; Chorus; Yrbk Stf; Fld Hcky; Trk; High Hon Roll; Hon Roll; Prfct Atten Awd.

KILEY JR, WILLIAM P; Triton Reg HS; Rowley, MA; (Y); AFS; Am Leg Boys St; Boy Scts; Debate Tm; Math Tm; Science Clb; Bsbl; JV Golf; Hon Roll; NHS; Soc Stud Awd; Rgnl Sci Fair 9th Pl; Pre-Med.

KILGORE, LISA B; Braintree HS; Braintree, MA; (Y); Pres Church Yth Grp; Yrbk Stf; Rep Frsh Cls; Rep Soph Cls; Rep Jr Cls; Rep Sr Cls; Var Cheerleading; Pom Pon; Hon Roll; Spanish NHS; Exc Stu Madrid Spain 84; Cls Yrbk Awd 85; Philergians Schlrshp; Eastern Star Schrlshp; Warren Schlrshp; U RI; Bus Adm.

KILLION, PAULA; Blue Hills Regional HS; Holbrook, MA; (Y); VICA; School Musical; Variety Show; Yrbk Phtg; Yrbk Stf; Rep Sr Cls; Var Cheerleading; JV Sftbl; Hon Roll; Pres Schlr; Emmanuel Coll Rita Walsh Fnd Schlrshp; Blue Hills Educ Assn Awd; Cert Of Hnr Awd; Emmanuel Coll; Englsh Comm.

KILLION, RICHARD J; Archbishop Williams HS; Holbrook, MA; (Y); Aud/Vis; Cmnty Wkr; Computer Clb; Key Clb; Political Wkr; Golf; Hon Roll; Stonehill Coll; Comp Sci.

KIM, ANDREW; Malden Catholic HS; Medford, MA; (Y); 9/185; Art Clb; Church Yth Grp; Computer Clb; Drama Clb; VP French Clb; VP Sec Intnl Clb; Math Tm; Quiz Bowl; Acpl Chr; Chorus; New Englnd Math Leag Cert Merit Super Achvt 84, JR High Scr Cert Awd 85; Psych.

KIM, CHARLES; Haverhill HS; Haverhill, MA; (Y); Boy Scts; VP Church Yth Grp; Key Clb; Political Wkr; VP Spanish Clb; Nwsp Rptr; Yrbk Stf; VP Stu Cncl; Prfct Atten Awd; Haverhill Hgh Rep Of Hugh O Brien Yth Ldrshp MS 83-84; Pol Sci.

KIM, HAEMI; Westfield HS; Westfield, MA; (Y); Drama Clb; Latin Clb; School Play; Nwsp Rptr; Nwsp Stf; Lit Mag; Ruth Mc Caffrey Memrl Poetry Awd 85; Lit Fld.

KIM, JULIA; Dana Hall Schl; Canton, OH; (Y); 2/80; Orch; School Play; Hon Roll; NC Outward Bnd, String Chamber Orch 84-85; Best JR Muscn Awd, Lead Prod Columbia U 85; Math.

KIM, PETER; Natick HS; Natick, MA; (Y); 28/443; Art Clb; Computer Clb; French Clb; Var L Swmmng; Arch.

KIMBLE, ERIC WILSON; St Johns Prep; Georgetown, MA; (Y); 11/225; Capt Var Bsbl; Im Bsktbl; Im Ftbl; Im Golf; Var Capt Trk; High Hon Roll; NHS; Ntl Merit Ltr; NEDT Awd; St Schlr; St Johns Prep Stu Athl,Schlr Awd 83-85; Top Eng Stu Yr 82-83; Brown U; Lib Arts.

KIMBLE, KARLA; Woburn HS; Woburn, MA; (S); Church Yth Grp; Drama Clb; Letterman Clb; Office Aide; Pep Clb; School Musical; Yrbk Stf; Stu Cncl; Swmmng; Trk; Fitchburg ST Coll; Spec Ed.

KINCAID, SEAN; St Peter-Marian HS; Worcester, MA; (Y); 57/189; French Clb; Ski Clb; Stage Crew; Var Crs Cntry; Var Golf; Var Ice Hcky; U ME Orono; Bio.

KINDERMAN, SPENCER; Westborough HS; Westboro, MA; (Y); Computer Clb; French Clb; Latin Clb; Media Comm.

KING, ANNE; Weymouth North HS; Weymouth, MA; (Y); 54/393; Girl Scts; Hosp Aide; Var Tennis; Hon Roll; Princpls Commendatn Frnch 85; Bus Mngmnt.

KING, CARL; Marblehead HS; Marblehead, MA; (Y); 97/250; Latin Clb; Ski Clb; L Stat Socr; Hlth Sci.

KING, CHRISTOPHER; Holy Name Central Catholic HS; Spencer, MA; (Y); 101/272; Boy Scts; Ski Clb; Yrbk Stf; VP Soph Cls; Pres Jr Cls; Pres Sr Cls; Var JV Ftbl; Hon Roll; Computer Clb; 4-H; Biol, Rdng, Rhetoric Awds 82-83; Hgh Slsprsn Ad Drve & Mag Drve 82-85; Athltc Trnng.

KING, CHRISTOPHER P; Hamilton Wenham Regional HS; Wenham, MA; (Y); 24/190; Am Leg Boys St; Chess Clb; Science Clb; Physics.

KING, DAVID; Madway JR SR HS; Medway, MA; (Y); Church Yth Grp; Drama Clb; Pres Chorus; School Musical; School Play; Hon Roll; Hugh O Brien Yuth Fdtn Awd 84.

KING, DEANNA; Norton HS; Norton, MA; (Y); Pep Clb; Varsity Clb; Yrbk Ed-Chief; Yrbk Stf; Stu Cncl; Var Cheerleading; High Hon Roll; Hon Roll.

KING, DOUGLAS; Monson JR SR HS; Wilbraham, MA; (Y); 5/83; Boys Clb Am; Boy Scts; Chess Clb; Church Yth Grp; Cmnty Wkr; FTA; German Clb; Mathletes; Math Clb; Quiz Bowl; Westfield ST; Astrnmy.

KING, JOHN; Weymouth North HS; Weymouth, MA; (Y); Drama Clb; Acpl Chr; Chorus; School Musical; School Play; Stage Crew; Lit Mag; Hon Roll; Mdl.

KING, JOHN A; No Middlesex Reg HS; W Townsend, MA; (Y); 58/210; Church Yth Grp; 4-H; Library Aide; Quiz Bowl; Chorus; Church Choir; School Play; 4-H Awd; Hon Roll; Leg Hall Schlrshp 85; Grange Schlrshp 85; Farmingham ST Coll; Dietcs.

KING, LISA; Maynard HS; Maynard, MA; (Y); 4/100; Am Leg Aux Girls St; Radio Clb; Band; Sec Pres Stu Cncl; Var Capt Bsktbl; JV Capt Fld Hcky; Var Capt Trk; Hon Roll; NHS; Ntl Merit Ltr; Engrng.

KING, MELISSA; Mt Everett Regional HS; Mt Washington, MA; (Y); Color Guard; Cheerleading; Mgr(s); Pom Pon; Bay Path JC; Secy Stds.

KING, RENESE E; South Lancaster Acad; South Lancaster, MA; (Y); Computer Clb; Drama Clb; Acpl Chr; Chorus; Orch; School Musical; School Play; Stage Crew; Symp Band; Rep Soph Cls; JR Alumni Awd Scholar 84; Comp Pgrmg.

KING, ROBERTA M; Framingham North HS; Framingham, MA; (Y); 89/330; Acpl Chr; Chorus; Yrbk Stf; Hon Roll; NHS; Var L Bsktbl; JV L Crs Cntry; Var Swmmng; Var Capt Trk; Bay Path JR Bk Awd 84; U Of Miami; Phy Thrpy.

KING, SHERYL; Monson HS; Monson, MA; (Y); Dance Clb; Hosp Aide; Yrbk Stf; Cheerleading; Diving; Swmmng; Wt Lftg; Wrtg.

KING, WILLIAM R; Frontier Regional HS; So Deerfield, MA; (Y); JV Var Bsbl; JV Ftbl; S Deerfield Womns Clb Schlrshp 85; U Of MA; Engr.

KINGMAN, EAMON R; East Bridgewater HS; East Bridgwater, MA; (Y); 7/153; Am Leg Boys St; Pres Key Clb; Var Capt Bsbl; Var Capt Bsktbl; Var Capt Socr; Hon Roll; NHS; MA Stu Govt Day; VP Stu Cncl & SADD; All Lg Bsbl Socr.

KINGSBURY, DALE A; Newburyport HS; Newburyport, MA; (Y); 15/200; Am Leg Boys St; Church Yth Grp; Math Tm; Science Clb; Trs Stu Cncl; Var L Socr; Hon Roll; NHS; Ntl Merit SF; Mth & Sci Tutor 84-85 & 85-86; Head Mth Tutor 85-86; Top Mth Stu 83; Bio.

KINGSBURY, JENNIFER; Watertown HS; Watertown, MA; (Y); 39/350; Color Guard; Hon Roll; Drama Clb; Library Aide; Office Aide; Nwsp Sprt Ed; Yrbk Stf; Hlth Adm.

KINGSBURY, SUSAN; Malden HS; Malden, MA; (Y); Pep Clb; High Hon Roll; Hnr Rl 84-85; Crimson Travel Schl; Travl Agnt.

KINGSLEY, PAMELA; Joseph Case HS; Swansea, MA; (Y); 3/209; French Clb; Yrbk Ed-Chief; Yrbk Stf; High Hon Roll; Hon Roll; NHS; Ntl Merit SF; Southwestern MA U.

KINKEAD, BECKY; Natick HS; Natick, MA; (Y); 14/449; Am Leg Aux Girls St; Church Yth Grp; Yrbk Stf; Off Soph Cls; Off Jr Cls; Off Sr Cls; Stu Cncl; Var Capt Fld Hcky; Var L Trk; Hon Roll; Bus Awd Exclnc Typg 86; Bus Mgmt.

KINSELLA, ERIN; Academy Of Notre Dame; Tewksbury, MA; (Y); 1/50; French Clb; Political Wkr; Sec Jr Cls; Var Capt Bsktbl; Var Capt Tennis; Var Vllybl; High Hon Roll; NHS; Voice Dem Awd; Hlf Tuitn Schlrshp Upon Grad 8th Grd 82; Brown U Bk Awd Outstndng Exprssn Wrtg 85; Ec.

KINSELLA, JEAN; Billeria Memorial HS; Billerica, MA; (Y); 18/394; Sec Chess Clb; Debate Tm; Yrbk Stf; Rep Frsh Cls; Rep Soph Cls; Var L Bsktbl; Var Capt Socr; Var L Trk; High Hon Roll; NHS; Brandeis U; Pre-Med.

KINSLEY, MARY; Sacred Heart HS; Plymouth, MA; (Y); 27/89; Art Clb; Drama Clb; Key Clb; NFL; Speech Tm; Chorus; School Musical; School Play; Hon Roll; Art Achv Schlrshp 84-85; Fornscs Degre Hnr 84-85; Law Schl.

KIPERMAN, PALMER; Marblehead HS; Mablehead, MA; (Y); 68/270; Latin Clb; Ski Clb; Yrbk Stf; JV Bsktbl; Powder Puff Ftbl; Var Socr; Var Trk; Silver Mdl Maxima Cum Laude Natl Latin Exam 85; Frnch.

KIRBY, LISA A; Newburyport HS; Newburyport, MA; (Y); 15/204; Hosp Aide; Hon Roll; NHS; Brnz & Slvr Acad Keys; John Calvin Noyes Schlrshp; Bus Schlrshp; Bentley Coll; Mktg.

KIRBY, TIMOTHY P; Boston College HS; Quincy, MA; (Y); Pres Church Yth Grp; Hosp Aide; Key Clb; Ftbl; High Hon Roll; Ntl Merit Ltr; NEDT Awd; Math Clb; JV Trk; Adv Math Achvt Awd 85; Scripture Achvt Awd 84; Exmplry Behvr Cert 85; Bio.

KIREJCZYK, JANIE; Chicopee Comprehensive HS; Chicopee, MA; (Y); Dance Clb; German Clb; GAA; School Play; Yrbk Rptr; Yrbk Stf; Var Bsktbl; Powder Puff Ftbl; Var Socr; Var Sftbl; Frolics Scholar 85; Transcript Tm 85; MVP Sftbl 85; Baypath JC; Retail.

KIRITSIS, ALISA S; Shepherd Hill Regional HS; Dudley, MA; (Y); 27/156; Dance Clb; Math Tm; Drm Mjr(t); Jazz Band; Mrchg Band; School Musical; Stu Cncl; High Hon Roll; Masonic Awd; NHS.

KIRKENDALL, CHRIS; Cohasset HS; Cohasset, MA; (Y); 35/200; Yrbk Stf; JV Bsktbl; Var Socr; Var Trk; Hon Roll.

KIRKITELOS, PAUL C; Ludlow HS; Ludlow, MA; (Y); 1/300; Am Leg Boys St; Var Crs Cntry; Var Golf; Var Capt Wrstlng; High Hon Roll; NHS; Rep Soph Cls; Bsbl; Ntl Merit SF; MVP Wrstlr 84-85; Ldng Scorer Vrsty Glf 83-85; All Sectnl Wrstlng Tm 84-85; Engrng.

KIRSCHE, STEPHEN M; Southwick HS; Granville, MA; (Y); 2/116; Am Leg Boys St; Trs French Clb; Math Tm; Lit Mag; Rep Stu Cncl; Hon Roll; NHS; Pres Schlr; Sal; Library Aide; NROTC Scholar 85; Rensselaer Polytech; Elec Engrg.

KIRWIN, LAURA; Braintree HS; Braintree, MA; (Y); 60/436; Cmnty Wkr; FCA; Library Aide; Teachers Aide; Yrbk Stf; Lit Mag; Var Bsktbl; High Hon Roll; Hon Roll; Jr NHS; 1st Pl & Hnrb Mntn Indstrl Ed Soc/Crftsmnshp Instrmnt & Frntur Mkng 84-85; Schlstc Press Awd 83-84; Archeology.

KISER, DOUGLAS; Ayer HS; Ft Devens, MA; (Y); Teachers Aide; Varsity Clb; Ftbl; Trk.

KITKA JR, FREDERICK; Bartlett HS; Webster, MA; (Y); Capt Crs Cntry; Capt Trk; Hon Roll; NHS; Unsung Hero Awd Trk Also Ltr 82-83; MVP Trk 85; Cross Cntry Lttr 82-85; Arch.

KIZNER, STEPHANIE; Algonquin Regional HS; Southboro, MA; (Y); 87/259; Yrbk Stf; Rep Frsh Cls; Var Capt Cheerleading; Hon Roll; Boston U.

KLARWASSER, TINA; Bishop Feehan HS; N Attleboro, MA; (Y); Drama Clb; School Musical; School Play; Stage Crew; French Clb; Band; Concert Band; Mrchg Band; Pep Band; French Hon Soc; MA Art; Apprl Dsgn.

KLEINBERGER, SCOTT; BMC Durfee HS; Fall River, MA; (Y); 51/691; Camera Clb; Computer Clb; VP JA; Science Clb; Ski Clb; Swmmng; Tennis.

KLOHN, ANGELINA; Sharon HS; Sharon, MA; (Y); 29/200; Drama Clb; Library Aide; Pres Band; Pres Concert Band; Nwsp Stf; Yrbk Stf; Var Tennis; Hon Roll; FAME Schlrshp 85; French Student Of Mnth 85; Northeastern U; Intl Busnss.

KLOSE, CORNELIA K; Milton Acad; Chicago, IL; (Y); Latin Clb; Math Tm; Model UN; Chorus; Orch; Nwsp Rptr; Lit Mag; Swmmng; High Hon Roll; Ntl Merit SF; Latin Prize 84; 4th Awd Natl Schlstc Creative Writing Contest 81; Scshl Creative Writing Awd 84; Harvard U; Linguistics.

KLOUDA, REBECCA M; South Hadley HS; S Hadley, MA; (Y); 2/180; Latin Clb; Math Tm; Yrbk Rptr; Var Fld Hcky; Var Swmmng; Var Trk; High Hon Roll; NHS; Ntl Merit Ltr.

KMETZ, CHRISTAL; Norton HS; Norton, MA; (Y); 1/180; Church Yth Grp; Varsity Clb; Band; Drm Mjr(t); Pres Frsh Cls; Pres Soph Cls; Pres Jr Cls; Pres Sr Cls; Var L Bsktbl; NHS; Mst Outstndng Drm Mjr 84.

KMON, MATTHEW ALBERT; David Prouty HS; Spencer, MA; (Y); 5/176; Church Yth Grp; Math Tm; Pep Clb; Ski Clb; Spanish Clb; Yrbk Stf; Rep Soph Cls; Rep Jr Cls; Var L Golf; Var Capt Socr; Commonwlth MA Scholar 85; Holy Cross Clb Worcester Scholar 85; Central MA All Star Socr 85; Coll Holy Cross; Pre-Med.

KNAPIK, ROBERT J; Westfield HS; Westfield, MA; (Y); 60/330; Am Leg Boys St; CAP; Trs JA; Var Ski Clb; School Play; Trs Frsh Cls; Var Trk; USAF Acad Smmr Sci Sem 85; Cert PADI Open Water Diver; USAF Acad; Pilot.

KNIGHT, CHRISTINE; Old Rochester Regional HS; Mattapoisett, MA; (Y); 1/175; Church Yth Grp; 4-H; GAA; Math Tm; Var Bsktbl; Var Capt Sftbl; Cit Awd; 4-H Awd; High Hon Roll; Hon Roll; Pres Natl Hnr Soc 85-86; Excllnce Hstry, Eng, Chem, Spn 85; Coll Clb New Bedfrd Excclnce Scholar 85; Phys Ed.

KNIGHT, DANIELLE; St Marys HS; Worcester, MA; (Y); Drama Clb; Church Choir; School Musical; Nwsp Ed-Chief; Yrbk Stf; VP Sr Cls; Cheerleading; Hon Roll; Excllnc Bus Awd 85; Worc Cnty Lgl Sec Bus Schlrshp 85; Joseph & Josephine Koledo Memrl Schlarhp 85; The Salter Schl; Lgl Sec.

KNIGHTLY, JOHNNA; Metheun HS; Methuen, MA; (Y); 1/320; Intnl Clb; Model UN; Pep Clb; Yrbk Ed-Chief; Var Capt Swmmng; Var Trk; High Hon Roll; NHS; Wellesley Bk Awd 85; SOAR Awd 85; Engrng.

KNOTT, JEFFREY; Beverly HS; Beverly, MA; (Y); JV Ice Hcky; Var L Tennis; High Hon Roll; NHS; 1st Pl Chem Sci Fair 84-85; JV MVP 84-85; Biochem.

KNOWLES, ROBERT; Bridgewater-Raynham HS; Raynham, MA; (Y); 20/320; Am Leg Boys St; JV Bsbl; Bsktbl; Var L Golf; Wt Lftg; JV Wrstlng; Hon Roll; NHS; NEDT Awd; Bus Mgmt.

KNOX, HEATHER; Hingham HS; Hingham, MA; (Y); 80/365; Church Yth Grp; Dance Clb; PAVAS; Varsity Clb; Chorus; Yrbk Stf; Rep Stu Cncl; JV Var Cheerleading; Im Fld Hcky; Hon Roll.

KNOX, JOHN ANTHONY; Weymouth Vocational Technical HS; E Weymouth, MA; (Y); Boy Scts; Bsbl; Ice Hcky; Hon Roll; John Major Course Study Carpentry; AF Acad; Pilot.

KNUDSON, INGER; Bridgewater-Raynham Reg HS; Bridgewater, MA; (Y); Drama Clb; French Clb; Chorus; Church Choir; School Play; Stage Crew; Swing Chorus; Fld Hcky; Trk; Wt Lftg; Englsh.

KOCHER, FORREST; Tantasqua HS; Southbridge, MA; (S); 15/195; Letterman Clb; Yrbk Bus Mgr; Yrbk Stf; Lit Mag; Sr Cls; Rep Stu Cncl; Var L Crs Cntry; Var Trk; Hon Roll; NHS; Holy Cross; Law.

KOCHER, MARK; Tantasqua Regional HS; Southbridge, MA; (S); Letterman Clb; Math Tm; Varsity Clb; Crs Cntry; Hon Roll; NHS; Comp Sci.

KOFFMAN, DAVID J; Winchester HS; Winchester, MA; (Y); 3/325; Varsity Clb; Var Bsbl; Var Bsktbl; Var Ftbl; High Hon Roll; Jr NHS; Ntl Merit SF; Nwsp Rptr; Yrbk Rptr; Rep Jr Cls; Dartmouth Minutemn Clb Bk Awd 84; Brown Bk Awd 84; Sci & Mth Dept Scholar Awd 84.

KOH, JANG HOON; Cushing Acad; Ashburnham, MA; (Y); Art Clb; Intnl Clb; Ski Clb; JV Socr; Var Tennis; Hon Roll; Computer Clb; JA; Orch; Nwsp Rptr; UCLA; Busnss.

KOH, KIMBERLY; Buckingham Browne & Nichols; Belmont, MA; (S); JCL; Latin Clb; Letterman Clb; Varsity Clb; Acpl Chr; Orch; Lit Mag; Var Bsktbl; Var Fld Hcky; Var Lcrss; Indep Schl Leag Awd Fld Hcky 82-84; Mythlgy Awd JCL Conv 84; Cum Laude Natl Latn Tst 83; Physlgy.

KOHLI, NEERAJ; Holliston HS; Holliston, MA; (Y); 1/230; AFS; Am Leg Boys St; Chess Clb; VP Debate Tm; Mgr Drama Clb; Orch; Yrbk Ed-Chief; Capt L Tennis; High Hon Roll; NHS; MA Brd Regents ST Schlrshp 85; Pres Schlstc Awdd Acad Excell 85; Syracuse U Engl Awd Top Schlr 85; Boston U; Pre-Med.

KOKERNAK, JOHN; Bartlett HS; Webster, MA; (Y); Rep Boys Clb Am; Rep Boy Scts; Rep CAP; Pres Jr Cls; Rep Stu Cncl; Var Ftbl; Capt Trk; Rep Wt Lftg; 1st Pl Bay ST Trials 85; U Of OK; Mtrlgy.

KOKERNAK, SCOTT J; Bartlett HS; Webster, MA; (Y); 38/165; Boys Clb Am; Var Bsbl; Var Ftbl; Prfct Atten Awd; Prfct Atndnc 81-85; Bsbl & Ftbl Ltrs 83-85; Border Cnfrnc All Star In Ftbl 84-85; Nichols Coll; Mngmnt Info Systm.

KOKOSKI, PAULA; Hopkins Acad; Hadley, MA; (Y); 11/62; Art Clb; French Clb; Sec Frsh Cls; Sec Soph Cls; Sec Jr Cls; Sec Sr Cls; Var Bsktbl; Score Keeper; Stat Sftbl; Hon Roll; Boston Globe Schltc Art Awd 84; Unsung Hero Vrsty Bsktbl 85; Bus Mgmt.

KOKOSZKA, JEAN ANN; Marshfield HS; Marshfield, MA; (Y); 27/396; AFS; Key Clb; Elks Awd; High Hon Roll; Kiwanis Awd; NHS; John P Bunszel Mem Schlrshp 85-86; Am Leg Aux 85-86; U RH; Phrmclgy.

KOLB, SHARON J; Bishop Connolly HS; Fall River, MA; (Y); Art Clb; Cmnty Wkr; Dance Clb; Drama Clb; JA; Stage Crew; High Hon Roll; Hon Roll; Prfct Atten Awd; Citzn Schlrshp Fndtn 85; Harris David Schlrshp 85; Boston U; Chem.

KOLOSEIKE, KATHERINE A; Pittsfield HS; Pittsfield, MA; (Y); 14/340; Am Leg Aux Girls St; Exploring; JCL; Latin Clb; Band; Jazz Band; Mrchg Band; Var Capt Socr; High Hon Roll; Yrbk Stf; Aux Berkshire Dist Med Soc Scholar 85; Sprngfld Coll Humanities Awd 84; U NC; Phys Ther.

KOPANON, SUSAN; Gloucester HS; Gloucester, MA; (Y); 17/314; Capt Gym; Capt Tennis; Im Vllybl; Hon Roll; NHS; Acad Recgntn 85; Stonehill Coll.

KOPEC, SUSAN; Chicopee Comprehensive HS; Chicopee, MA; (Y); Am Leg Aux Girls St; JA; Spanish Clb; Drm & Bgl; Rep Soph Cls; Rep Jr Cls; Nrsg.

KORNET, JOHN; Cohasset JR SR HS; Cohasset, MA; (Y); 2/120; Pres AFS; Computer Clb; Debate Tm; Math Clb; Math Tm; Teachers Aide; Acpl Chr; Band; Chorus; Concert Band; Martial Arts Achvts 85-86; Kogun Awd, Dedictn, Versitlty Band & Jazz 84-85; Swmmng, Sailng, Ten Awds; Bio.

KORTEKAMP, TODD; Monson HS; Monson, MA; (Y); 5/84; Am Leg Boys St; Church Yth Grp; French Clb; Math Clb; Stage Crew; JV Var Bsktbl; Var L Socr; Hon Roll; NHS; Elec Engrng.

KOSAK, CAROLYN; Arlington HS; Arlington, MA; (S); 4/400; Office Aide; Teachers Aide; Mrchg Band; Symp Band; Nwsp Stf; Rep Stu Cncl; High Hon Roll; Sec NHS; Dance Clb; French Clb; MA Assn Of Schl Supt Cert Acad Excllnce 84; 1st Pl Arlngtn Hst Soc Essay 84; French Awd 84; Teacher.

KOSKI, DEBBIE; Silver Lake Regional HS; Kingston, MA; (Y); 47/472; Pres Church Yth Grp; Key Clb; VP Latin Clb; Spanish Clb; Var Bsktbl; Var Socr; Capt Sftbl; Hon Roll; NHS; Ntl Merit Ltr; N Adams ST Coll; Bus Admin.

KOSLOWSKI, CARL C; Quaboag Regional HS; Warren, MA; (Y); 9/90; Math Tm; Science Clb; Varsity Clb; Pres Frsh Cls; Bsbl; Bsktbl; Crs Cntry; High Hon Roll; Hon Roll; Trs NHS; Worcester Poly Tech; Mechncl.

KOSOWICZ, LISA; St Louis Acad; Dracut, MA; (Y); 8/33; Drama Clb; French Clb; School Play; Pres Frsh Cls; Coach Actv; Hon Roll; NHS; Church Choir; Yrbk Stf; Drama Clb Pres 84-85; Prom Chrprsn 84-85; Yrbk Typst 84-85; U Lowell; Fin.

KOSS, DANA; Needham HS; Needham, MA; (Y); 11/380; Spanish Clb; Pres Temple Yth Grp; Yrbk Stf; Var Gym; High Hon Roll; Hon Roll; NHS; Ski Clb; Band; 4th & 7th Pl Ntl Spnsh Exam 84-85; SR Asstnt Frshmn Hmrm 85; U Of PA; Psych.

KOSUDA, RUSSELL R; Smith Vocational HS; Shutesbury, MA; (Y); Am Leg Boys St; Boy Scts; Exploring; Yrbk Stf; Sec Trs Jr Cls; Trs Sr Cls; Stu Cncl; Elks Awd; High Hon Roll; Voice Dem Awd; Comp Progmmng.

KOSUK, NICHOLAS L; Chelsea HS; Chelsea, MA; (Y); 1/199; Model UN; Capt Quiz Bowl; Pres Science Clb; Concert Band; Bausch & Lomb Sci Awd; Trs NHS; Val; Band; Mrchg Band; High Hon Roll; Hrvrd Book Awd 84; SR Dstrct Bnd 84; 3rd Pl MA ST Sci Fair 85; MIT; Gntc Rsrch.

KOUREPENIS, KERRY S; Watertown HS; Watertown, MA; (Y); 1/285; Am Leg Boys St; Intnl Clb; Off Stu Cncl; Var Tennis; High Hon Roll; Hon Roll; NHS; HS Coordntr-Achvt Awd 83-84; Hrvrd Bk Awd 85; Sci Achvt Awd-Bio 84; Harvard U; Bus.

KOVALSKI, KIMBERLY; Easthampton HS; Easthampton, MA; (Y); 32/129; French Clb; JA; Yrbk Stf; Var Swmmng; Trvl.

KOWAL, JENNIFER; Hopkins Acad; Hadley, MA; (Y); 7/60; Cmnty Wkr; 4-H; French Clb; Hosp Aide; Chorus; Nwsp Stf; JV Bsktbl; JV Sftbl; Hon Roll; NHS; Rgstrd Nrs.

KOWALEWSKI, ANTHONY JOHN; Southbridge HS; Southbridge, MA; (Y); 7/135; Math Tm; Sec Chorus; Trs Concert Band; Trs Mrchg Band; School Musical; High Hon Roll; Hon Roll; VP NHS; Ntl Merit Ltr; Ntl Schl Chorl Awd 85; MA Assn Schl Supt Cert Acadmc Exc 84; Commnwlth Schlr Awd 85; Boston U; Cmnctns.

KOWALSKI, DIANE; Chicopee Comprehensive HS; Chicopee, MA; (Y); 79/266; Color Guard; Mrchg Band; JV Var Cheerleading; Bay Path JR Coll; Mngmnt.

KOZIOL, ANNA M; Cathedral HS; Chicopee, MA; (Y); Dance Clb; Var L Swmmng; Var L Trk; Elks Awd; All-Westrn MA Swim Tm 4 Yrs; Northeastern U; Bus Adm.

KOZLOWSKI, DEBRA; Bartlett HS; Webster, MA; (Y); Church Yth Grp; Cmnty Wkr; Trs Spanish Clb; Church Choir; Stu Cncl; Var Cheerleading; Sftbl; High Hon Roll; Hon Roll; Prfct Atten Awd; Mrktng.

KOZLOWSKI, LISA; Bartlett HS; Webster, MA; (Y); 7/140; French Clb; Yrbk Stf; High Hon Roll; NHS.

KRANEFUSS, KRISTIN; Arlington Catholic HS; Stoneham, MA; (Y); Art Clb; Pres Drama Clb; French Clb; Intnl Clb; Office Aide; School Play; Stage Crew; Serv, Hero & Art Postr Cntst Awds 83 & 8; U Of Lowell; Bio.

KRATZ, DAVID F; Central Catholic HS; N Andover, MA; (Y); 98/228; Boys Clb Am; Boy Scts; Church Yth Grp; Civic Clb; Cmnty Wkr; Computer Clb; Debate Tm; English Clb; Exploring; Political Wkr; Lawy Day Hnrs 85; Eagle Scout 80-85; St Chiefsquire K Of C 84-86; Math.

KRAUSE, TONYA; North Brookfield HS; N Brookfield, MA; (Y); Camera Clb; French Clb; Library Aide; VP Spanish Clb; Chorus; School Play; Sec Frsh Cls; Church Yth Grp; Band; Variety Show; Midleburg; Spnsh.

KRAWCZYK, KAREN; Westfield HS; Westfield, MA; (Y); 26/370; Yrbk Stf; JV Bsktbl; Var Capt Fld Hcky; JV Var Sftbl; Timer; High Hon Roll; NHS; Typng II Awd 84-85; Bus.

KRCMARIK, AMY; Coyle & Cassidy HS; N Dighton, MA; (Y); French Clb; Var Trk; French Hon Soc; High Hon Roll; Hon Roll; NHS.

KREIDER, JAMES; Newton North HS; Newton, MA; (Y); Pres Church Yth Grp; Math Tm; Rep Stu Cncl; Var L Crs Cntry; Var L Trk; High Hon Roll; Hon Roll; Prfct Atten Awd; Outstndng Acdmc Achvt 83; Engrng.

KREITZBERG, TINA; Stoughton HS; Stoughton, MA; (Y); Girl Scts; Temple Yth Grp; Acpl Chr; Chorus; Church Choir; Variety Show; Hon Roll; 2nd Awd Schl Sci Fair & 2nd Regnl Fir 81-82; 3 Music Dept Vocl Awds 85; Amelia Greenbaum Schlrshp 85; Northeastern U; Engrng.

KRESS, WALTER P; East Hampton HS; Easthampton, MA; (Y); 5/141; Trs Am Leg Boys St; Church Yth Grp; JA; Chorus; Off Stu Cncl; JV Bsbl; High Hon Roll; Hon Roll; NHS; HOBY Fndnt MA Ldrshp Sem 84; Librty Bel Fstvl Music Chrs 84; Prncpls Revw Comm Behavrl Code 84; Gordon Coll; Eng.

KRIGEST, MITCHELL; Milton HS; Milton, MA; (Y); Temple Yth Grp; L Band; Concert Band; Mrchg Band; L Trk; Bus Admn.

KRIKORIAN, JEAN; Doherty Memorial HS; Worcester, MA; (Y); Art Clb; Dance Clb; Library Aide; Ski Clb; Trk; Jr NHS; Ind Pl Frgn Lang Wk Pstr Cntst 84; Cmmrcl Art.

KRITZAS, ATHENA; Haverhill HS; Bradford, MA; (Y); 35/389; Sec Church Yth Grp; JCL; Latin Clb; Spanish Clb; Yrbk Ed-Chief; Stu Cncl; High Hon Roll; Hon Roll; Dstnctn Awd.

KROLL, DANA; Southbridge HS; Southbridge, MA; (Y); 55/165; Computer Clb; Var Bsbl; JV Bsktbl; Var Bowling; Var Golf; Socr; Bowling Schlrshp; Graphics Engr.

KRONLUND, LISA; Westford Acad; Westford, MA; (Y); AFS; Art Clb; Dance Clb; Drama Clb; French Clb; JCL; Ski Clb; School Play; Stu Cncl; Swmmng; Hugh O Brian Yth Fndtn Schl Rep 84; Pres Clssrm 85; U S Stu Cncl Awd 85.

KRUCKEMEYER, KATHERINE; Boston Latin Schl; Boston, MA; (Y); 1/315; Math Tm; Hon Roll; NHS; Rensselaer Medal 85; Boston Latin Art Medal 85; Blue Rbbn Fnlst Schlstc Art Awds 84-85.

KRUGER, SHARON H; Westwood HS; Westwood, MA; (Y); 5/240; AFS; Capt Math Tm; Lit Mag; Powder Puff Ftbl; High Hon Roll; NHS; Ntl Merit SF; High Score S MA Math Leag 83-84; U Of MA Amherst; Comp Sci.

KUENSTER, TIM; Somerset HS; Somerset, MA; (Y); Drama Clb; 4-H; School Play; Var Capt Socr; JV Wrstlng; High Hon Roll; NHS; Comp Engrng.

KUKLINSKI, EDWARD; Medway JR SR HS; Medway, MA; (Y); 5/150; Golf; Hon Roll; NHS; Engr.

KUKLINSKI, SUSAN; Northfield Mount Herman HS; Wellesley, MA; (Y); Ski Clb; School Musical; Var Crs Cntry; JV Var Socr; Var Trk; Hon Roll; Horse Riding Awds 81-83; Bus.

KUMAR, WANITA; Bridgewater-Raynham Regional HS; Raynham, MA; (Y); 2/335; Computer Clb; French Clb; Math Tm; Sec Science Clb; Nwsp Stf; JV Tennis; High Hon Roll; NHS; Cert Natl Educ Dvlpmnt Tests 84; Brown U; Med.

KUNKEL, DANELE; Shepherd Hill Regional HS; Dudley, MA; (Y); Math Tm; Band; Mrchg Band; Yrbk Ed-Chief; Yrbk Stf; High Hon Roll; Hon Roll; Emerson Coll; Disc Jcky.

KUO, BENJAMIN; Phillips Acad; Starkville, MS; (Y); Boy Scts; Church Yth Grp; Band; Jazz Band; Orch; School Musical; Symp Band; JV Lcrss; JV Socr; Ntl Merit Ltr; MMTA Piano IV Lvl ST Wnnr 80; Baldwin JR Piano ST Wnnr 81; Metrlgcl Soc Awd 81; Chem Engr.

KUPA JR, EDWARD J; Phillips Acad; Andover, MA; (Y); Boy Scts; Church Yth Grp; Chorus; JV Bsktbl; JV Ftbl; High Hon Roll; Hon Roll; Jr NHS; V Crew 85; Blue Key Soc 85; Arch Engrng.

KUPIEC, YAEL; Bedford HS; Bedford, MA; (Y); 19/213; Math Tm; Concert Band; Nwsp Rptr; FCA; Var Trk; High Hon Roll; Jr NHS; NHS; Art Clb; Temple Yth Grp; Art Dept Scholar Awd 83-84.

KURKUL, CHRISTINE; St Clements HS; Somerville, MA; (Y); Cmnty Wkr; Office Aide; Yrbk Stf; Hon Roll; Jr NHS; Commndbl Cond Cert 83-85; Bus Adm.

KURSONIS, KIMBERLY; Chelsea HS; Chelsea, MA; (Y); 15/199; Dance Clb; Science Clb; Teachers Aide; Nwsp Stf; Yrbk Phtg; Yrbk Stf; Var Capt Cheerleading; Var JV Vllybl; 4-H Awd; High Hon Roll; William Kenneley Schlrshp 85; Curry Clg; Nrsg.

KURTO, PETER M; Deerfield Acad & Saratoga Spgs HS; Saratoga Springs, NY; (Y); 15/500; Cmnty Wkr; Rep Stu Cncl; Capt L Ice Hcky; Capt Socr; Var L Trk; High Hon Roll; NHS; NY ST Regents Schlrshp 85; All Amer Sccr Awd 85; Chem Achv Awd 83; Phy Ed Achv Awd 83; Brown U; Bus Mgmt.

KUSEK, MICHAEL; Holyoke HS; Holyoke, MA; (Y); Am Leg Boys St; Church Yth Grp; Debate Tm; Drama Clb; English Clb; JCL; Latin Clb; NFL; Capt Speech Tm; Band; CT Vly Debate Leag; Debate Team Champ 83-84; Close Up Prog 85; As Schls Match Wits Tv Quiz Show 84-86; NY U; Lawyer.

KUSH, SUNDEE; Gardner HS; Gardner, MA; (Y); 71/250; Church Yth Grp; Drama Clb; Red Cross Aide; Ski Clb; Teachers Aide; Y-Teens; Crs Cntry; Pilot.

KUSHMERICK, NICHOLAS; Boston College HS; Natick, MA; (Y); 22/270; Cmnty Wkr; Computer Clb; Math Tm; Science Clb; Yrbk Stf; JV Socr; High Hon Roll; Debate Tm; Hosp Aide; Mathletes; Awd Acad Excll Brit Lit, Clcls, Comp Sci, Advd Math, Comp Prog 83-85; Carnegie-Mellon U; Comp Engnr.

KUTENSKY, CHRIS; Lawrence Central Catholic HS; Atkinson, NH; (Y); 72/239; Ftbl; Wt Lftg; U Of NH; Htl & Rstrnt Mgmt.

KWAN, BRUCE; Boston Latin Schl; Boston, MA; (Y); VP JA; High Hon Roll; Hon Roll; MIT; Elec Engr.

KWAPIEN JR, THOMAS J; Cathedral HS; Springfield, MA; (Y); 90/500; Band; Concert Band; Jazz Band; Mrchg Band; Orch; School Musical; School Play; Var L Crs Cntry; Var L Trk; JP Sousa Awd; 3 Yr ROTC Schlrshp; Clark U; Envirnmntl Engrng.

KWONG, YVONNE; Boston Latin HS; Boston, MA; (Y); 17/321; Cmnty Wkr; Debate Tm; Hosp Aide; Intnl Clb; Science Clb; Orch; Nwsp Stf; Lit Mag; Hon Roll; Pres Schlr; NE Medical 100 Hour Vlntr Awd 82; City Sci Fair 2nd & 3rd Pl 84-85; Harvard U; Econ.

KYAN, MARY; Boston Technical HS; Boston, MA; (Y); Library Aide; Mathletes; Office Aide; Badmtn; Proj Bus Awd 80; Airline Svcs.

L HEUREUX, DAVID; Bishop Connolly HS; Fall River, MA; (Y); 40/117; Cmnty Wkr; Band; Chorus; Church Choir; High Hon Roll; Hon Roll; SE MA U.

LA BARRE, CHRISTOPHER; Holy Name Central Catholic HS; Auburn, MA; (Y); 48/275; Capt Crs Cntry; L Trk; Outstndng Achvt Relgs Studys 84-85; Engrng.

LA BASTIE, CURT; Blackstone Valley Reg Voc Tech HS; Mendon, MA; (Y); Boy Scts; Church Yth Grp; Trk; High Hon Roll.

LA BELLE JR, DAVID A; Turners Falls HS; Millers Falls, MA; (Y); 26/95; Rep Jr Cls; Var Bsbl; Var Bsktbl; Var Golf; Var Socr; Jr NHS; Lion Awd; NHS; Heritg Bnk Schlrshp 85; Reed Libby Memrl Awd 85; Schl Svc Awd 85; U Of MA; Civl Engrng.

LA BRANCHE, JAMES; Central Catholic HS; Lowell, MA; (Y); 60/219; Variety Show; Im Bsbl; Im Bsktbl; Var JV Crs Cntry; Im Lcrss; Im Socr; Im Vllybl; JV Wrstlng; Hon Roll; MA Coll; Phrmcy.

LA BRUNERIE, REBECCA; Dana Hall HS; Columbia, MO; (Y); 17/90; Pres Intnl Clb; JCL; Key Clb; Latin Clb; Pres Science Clb; Bsktbl; Socr; Var Tennis; Hon Roll; Jr NHS; Natl Ltn Exm Cum Laude 83-84; Magna Cum Laude 84-85; AFA Frgn Lang Clb Outstndng Mbr 83-84.

LA CHAPELLE, NICOLE; Holyoke HS; Hartford, CT; (Y); 49/400; Drama Clb; English Clb; NFL; Spanish Clb; Speech Tm; Nwsp Ed-Chief; Hon Roll; NHS; Pres Acadmc Ftns Schlrshp 85; Stu Govt Day Rep 85; Hartford Clg; Intl Fnce.

LA COURT, LORI ANN; Everett HS; Everett, MA; (Y); 37/400; FCA; Varsity Clb; Sftbl; Swmmng; Hon Roll; YMCA Swmng Ntls 82; Bay ST Triathlon 84; 3 Letter Awd 85; U MA Amherst; Sprts Mngmnt.

LA CROIX, LISA; Chicopee Comprehensive HS; Chicopee, MA; (Y); 7/325; Am Leg Aux Girls St; VP French Clb; Yrbk Ed-Chief; Stu Cncl; Powder Puff Ftbl; Trk; Elks Awd; French Hon Soc; High Hon Roll; NHS; Yrbk Effcncy Awd 85; Rensselaer Polytech Inst; Mgmt.

LA FLAMME, MICHELLE; St Peter Marian CC HS; Worcester, MA; (Y); 45/180; Drama Clb; Capt Pep Clb; Spanish Clb; Thesps; Chorus; School Musical; School Play; Nwsp Rptr; Nwsp Stf; Hon Roll; Schlrshps Worcester ST Coll & Froshinn Clb 85; Hnrs Amer Hstry Spnsh 3, Relgn 3, Amer Lit 83-84; Worcester ST Coll; Engl Ed.

LA FLEUR, CHERYL L; Chicopee Comprehensive HS; Chicopee, MA; (S); 72/340; French Clb; Yrbk Stf; Rep Jr Cls; Powder Puff Ftbl; Var L Socr; Var Trk; Phys Thrpst.

LA FRANCE, MARIA; Arlington HS; Kent, WA; (Y); 103/410; Drama Clb; School Play; Stage Crew; Yrbk Phtg; Poems Pub Schl Paper; Dartmouth Coll; Drama.

LA HAIR, LAURIE; South High Ccommunity Schl; Worcester, MA; (S); 35/250; Sec Jr Cls; Sec Sr Cls; Rep Stu Cncl; Var Fld Hcky; Var Trk; Worceste ST Coll; Bus Mgmt.

LA PENSE, MICHELE Y; Nauset Regional HS; Brewster, MA; (Y); 23/160; Drama Clb; Stage Crew; Var Cheerleading; High Hon Roll; Hon Roll; Am Leg Willis S Gould Jr Schlr 85; Delta Kappa Gamma Scholar 85; MA ST Scsholar 85; Northeastern U; Mktg.

LA PLANTE, CHRISTINE M; Westport HS; Westport, MA; (Y); Trs Church Yth Grp; Dance Clb; Political Wkr; Teachers Aide; Chorus; School Play; Var Mgr(s); L Sftbl; Hon Roll; Cmnty Wkr; Stndrd Times Spllng Bee Awd 82; Brown Smmr HS 84; St George Svc Awd 82; SMU; Physch.

LA PLANTE, DARLENE; Methuen HS; Methuen, MA; (Y); 78/310; Pep Clb; School Musical; School Play; Capt Gym; Powder Puff Ftbl; Score Keeper; Swmmng; Timer; Hon Roll; MA ST Schlrshp, Gym Coaches Awd 85; Worchester ST Coll; Erly Ch Ed.

LA ROCHE, STEPHANIE; Barnstable HS; Hyannis, MA; (S); Drama Clb; Teachers Aide; Acpl Chr; Chorus; Color Guard; Madrigals; School Musical; Stu Cncl; High Hon Roll; NHS; All Cape Music Fstvl 85; Sci.

LA ROCHELLE, STEVE; Chicopee Comp HS; Chicopee, MA; (Y); Latin Clb; Var L Ice Hcky; Latin Lang Awd 83-84.

LA ROSA, MARY BETH; Boston Latin Schl; Hyde Park, MA; (Y); 26/332; Church Yth Grp; Computer Clb; Drama Clb; VP JA; Cheerleading; Tennis; NHS; Carnegie-Mellon U Smmr Prog 85; Ntl Greek Exam Won Rbbn 85; Sprts Co-Ordntr Vcntn Bible Schl 85.

LA ROSEE, JEAN-PAUL; Attleboro HS; Chartley, MA; (Y); Am Leg Boys St; Art Clb; Church Yth Grp; Var L Gym; Var L Socr; Var L Trk; French Hon Soc; High Hon Roll; NHS; Prfct Atten Awd; Bio.

LA SCOLA, ERIC; Newton North HS; Newton, MA; (Y); Church Yth Grp; English Clb; Red Cross Aide; Nwsp Stf; Im Socr; Im Vllybl; Im Wrstlng; High Hon Roll; Law.

LA VIOLETTE, LISA; Holyoke HS; Holyoke, MA; (Y); Church Yth Grp; Office Aide; Teachers Aide; High Hon Roll; Hon Roll; Tutored Alg I, Acctng I & II 84-85; Brigham Yng U; Bus.

LA VITA, RACHEL; Christophr Columbus HS; Medford, MA; (Y); 19/132; Hon Roll; NHS; Spanish Awd 84; Accntst.

LAAKSO, ERIK W; Newburyport HS; Newburyport, MA; (Y); 25/200; Am Leg Boys St; Political Wkr; Red Cross Aide; VP Sr Cls; Var Ftbl; Capt Ice Hcky; Hon Roll; Ldrshp Sem 83-84; Stu Advsry Cncl 84-85; Bus.

LABONTE, MICHELLE; Milford HS; Milford, MA; (Y); 27/350; Am Leg Aux Girls St; Dance Clb; Drama Clb; Hosp Aide; School Musical; School Play; Stage Crew; NHS; Med.

LACASSE, ROBERT J; Grafton SR HS; N Grafton, MA; (Y); Prfct Atten Awd; Nichols Coll; Accntng.

LACERTE, MICHELLE; Catherdal HS; Agawam, MA; (Y); 84/474; Dance Clb; Hosp Aide; Library Aide; Varsity Clb; School Musical; School Play; Cheerleading; Hon Roll.

LACH, CHRIS; Southbridge HS; Sbridge, MA; (Y); 49/159; Church Yth Grp; Hon Roll; Mech Engrng.

LACHAPELLE, JULI; Southbridge HS; Southbridge, MA; (Y); Band; Concert Band; Mrchg Band; Nwsp Ed-Chief; Nwsp Stf; Freelnc Wrtr.

LACROIX, RICHARD J; Chicopee Comprehensive HS; Chicopee, MA; (S); 58/299; German Clb; Var Trk; Hon Roll; NHS.

LADEAU, MICHAEL KIRK; Murdock HS; Winchendon, MA; (Y); Boy Scts; Model UN; Stage Crew; L Bsbl; L Capt Bsktbl; Capt L Ftbl; Hon Roll; Modl Congrs-Clrk Senat 85; Ftbl Al-Star Puntr 84; Bsbl MVP 85; Embry Riddle; Aerontcl Sci.

LADETTO, STEPHEN J; Bourne HS; Sagamore, MA; (Y); 9/180; Am Leg Boys St; Boy Scts; Cmnty Wkr; Spanish Clb; Bsbl; Var Tennis; Hon Roll; NHS.

LADURANTAYE, RENEE; Taunton HS; Taunton, MA; (Y); 3/400; Am Leg Aux Girls St; Pres Sec Library Aide; Lit Mag; Hon Roll; Delta Kappa Gamma Schlrshp 85; Taunton HS Home-Ec Schlrshp 85; Bridgewater ST Coll; Spcl Ed.

LAFFERTY, DAWN; Diman Regional Voc Tech HS; Fall River, MA; (Y); Key Clb; VP Soph Cls; Pres Jr Cls; Pres Sr Cls; High Hon Roll; Hon Roll; Womens Support Grp 82-85; Comp Prog.

LAFLAMME, KIM; Catherdal HS; Chicopee, MA; (Y); Swmmng; Accntng.

LAFLAND, TRACEY; Our Lady Of Nazareth Acad; Methuen, MA; (Y); 20/60; Church Yth Grp; Intnl Clb; Pep Clb; Nwsp Stf; Yrbk Stf; Trs Sec Stu Cncl; Mgr(s); Score Keeper; Hon Roll; Prfct Atten Awd; Harvard Boston Coll; Pre-Med.

LAFRANCHI, CHRISO; Saint Dominic Savto HS; E Boston, MA; (Y); 3/110; Computer Clb; Debate Tm; JA; Key Clb; Math Clb; Nwsp Rptr; Yrbk Rptr; Bsktbl; JV Ftbl; High Hon Roll; Schl Scholar 82; Ivy League; Intl Rltns.

LAFRENAIS, KERRY; Southbridge HS; Southbridge, MA; (Y); 7/140; Yrbk Ed-Chief; Rep Frsh Cls; Rep Soph Cls; Rep Jr Cls; Trs Cheerleading; Natl Hnr Soc 85; Stu Govt Day Committee Mbr 84; Med Tech.

LAGACE, MICHAEL; Bridgewater-Raynham Reg HS; Raynham, MA; (Y); Boy Scts; L Socr; JV Wrstlng; High Hon Roll; Hon Roll; Eastern MA ST Champ Soccer Team 82; Lgechampshp Wrstlng Team82-83; Lge Champshp Soccer Team 83-84; Pre-Med.

LAGONAKIS, VALERIE; Bishop Fenwick HS; Salem, MA; (Y); Yrbk Stf; JV Vllybl; Hon Roll; Bus Mgmt.

LAGUE, SUSAN; Milford HS; Milford, MA; (Y); 27/300; High Hon Roll; Hon Roll; NHS; Office Aide; Ski Clb; Band; Orch; Bowling; Bus Mngmnt.

LAHIFF, PAUL; Matigon HS; Somerville, MA; (Y); 54/190; Boys Clb Am; Church Yth Grp; Office Aide; Varsity Clb; JV Var Bsbl; Var JV Bsktbl; Hon Roll; Cthlc Cntrl League All-Star Bsktbl 84-85; Bus.

LAHIKAINEN, KEITH; Gardner HS; Gardner, MA; (Y); DECA; L Bsktbl; JV Ftbl.

LAIDLAW, ANNEMAIRE; Norton HS; Norton, MA; (Y); 21/160; Pep Clb; Ski Clb; Varsity Clb; Yrbk Bus Mgr; Yrbk Stf; Rep Frsh Cls; VP Stu Cncl; Var Capt Cheerleading; Hon Roll; NEDT Awd.

LAIDLAW, CAROL A; Norwell HS; Norwell, MA; (Y); AFS; Church Yth Grp; Latin Clb; Hon Roll; Wrld Wrk Clb 84; SON CITY Chrstn Yth Grp 81-85; Knghts Columbus Schlrshp 85; Stonehill Coll; Bus Adm.

LAING, KATIE; Braintree HS; Boston, MA; (Y); 70/460; Church Yth Grp; Var Pom Pon; Hon Roll; SADD 84-85; Engr.

LAKE, LUELLEN; Madison Park HS; Boston, MA; (Y); Yrbk Stf; Sec Sr Cls; Lwyr.

LALIBERTE, CATHERINE M; Hudson Catholic HS; Hudson, MA; (Y); 9/50; Math Clb; Math Tm; Yrbk Stf; Var Capt Bsktbl; Powder Puff Ftbl; Im Socr; Var L Sftbl; NHS; Prfct Atten Awd; Digital Inc Schlrshp 85; SE MA U; Comp Sci.

LALLIER, SUZANNE; Bishop Feehan HS; N Attleboro, MA; (Y); Exploring; JV Bsktbl; L Var Trk; Vrsty Lttr 85; Pepperdine U; Librl Arts.

LALONDE, ROBERT; Central Catholic HS; Lowell, MA; (Y); U Lowell; Mech Engrng.

LAM, SUE KIN; Doherty Memorial HS; Worcester, MA; (Y); 4/356; High Hon Roll; Hon Roll; Jr NHS; NHS; Career Day Worcester Essy Cntst 84; Cmnwlth Of MA Schlr Awd 85; Worcester Proj Fair 2nd Prz 84; Worcester Polytech Inst; Elec E.

LAMACCHIA, JULIE ANN; Burncoat SR HS; Worcester, MA; (Y); 36/221; Office Aide; Nwsp Ed-Chief; Nwsp Rptr; Nwsp Stf; Hon Roll; Jr NHS; NHS; Rob Roy Beauty Sci Acad Schlrshp 85; Rob Roy Beauty Sci Acad; Csmtlg.

LAMAGDELAINE, LORRI A; Westfield HS; Westfield, MA; (Y); 50/350; Church Yth Grp; Varsity Clb; Chorus; Nwsp Rptr; Off Frsh Cls; Off Soph Cls; Sec Jr Cls; Pres Sr Cls; Stu Cncl; Fld Hcky; MVP Fld Hcky 84-85; Var Ltr Swmmng/Fld Hockey 82-85; Phys Educ.

LAMB, WENDY; Billerica Memorial HS; Billerica, MA; (Y); 31/450; Hosp Aide; Madrigals; School Musical; High Hon Roll; Hon Roll; Bentley; Bus Adm.

LAMBERT, BRIAN M; Central Catholic HS; El Paso, TX; (Y); 7/221; Pres Drama Clb; Science Clb; Ski Clb; School Musical; School Play; Stage Crew; Yrbk Stf; High Hon Roll; NHS; Schl Acad Schlrshp Awds 81-85; Yth Minstry Org 84-85; Baylor U; Chem.

LAMBERT, CHRISTINA; St Bernards CC HS; Leominster, MA; (S); 12/169; Art Clb; Church Yth Grp; Drama Clb; Model UN; Political Wkr; Teachers Aide; School Musical; Nwsp Stf; High Hon Roll; NHS; Pre-Law.

LAMBERT, DEBORAH; Chelmsford HS; Chelmsford, MA; (S); 84/550; DECA; French Clb; Nwsp Stf; French Hon Soc; Hon Roll; DECA-2ND Pl Awd Oval ST Comptn 85; DECA-3RD Pl Awd-Oral Evnt ST Comptn 85; Bus Mngmt.

LAMBERT, DONNA; Bishop Connolly HS; Somerset, MA; (Y); 86/214; Cmnty Wkr; Drama Clb; Hon Roll; Bus.

LAMBERT, KATHLEEN; St Marys HS; Westfield, MA; (Y); 8/60; Debate Tm; English Clb; Socr; Hon Roll; NHS; NEDT Awd; Cmnty Wkr; Intnl Clb; Chorus; Comp Awd 84-85; Engl.

LAMOLY, RON; Georgetown HS; Georgetown, MA; (Y); Political Wkr; Nwsp Rptr; Rep Jr Cls; Hon Roll.

LAMOTHE, CLAUDIE; Cambridge Rindge Latin HS; Cambridge, MA; (Y); French Clb; Quiz Bowl; Science Clb; Swing Chorus; Bsktbl; Gym; Ice Hcky; Swmmng; Vllybl; Wt Lftg.

LAMOTHE, RONALD M; Lunenburg HS; Lunenburg, MA; (Y); Am Leg Boys St; School Play; VP Frsh Cls; VP Soph Cls; VP Jr Cls; VP Sr Cls; Off Stu Cncl; Var Capt Bsbl; Var Capt Bsktbl; Var Capt Ftbl.

LAMOUREUX, TRACEY; Billerica Memorial HS; Billerica, MA; (Y); 96/493; Rep Frsh Cls; Var Gym; Var Socr; High Hon Roll; Hon Roll; Mis Teen Am Schlrshp 85; Med Sec.

LAMPNER, MICHELLE ANN; Randolph HS; Randolph, MA; (Y); 23/351; Am Leg Aux Girls St; Drama Clb; School Play; Mgr Stage Crew; Mgr Variety Show; Hon Roll; JC Awd; Sec NHS; Sec French Clb; Library Aide; Randolph Rotry & Lions Clbs Schlrshps 85; Randolph Shpg Ctr Asscs Schlrshp 85; Boston U; Comp Sci.

LAMSON, BRIAN; South High Comm Schl; Worcester, MA; (Y); Capt Bowling; High Hon Roll; Hon Roll; Bus.

LAMSON, JOHN G; Northampton HS; Northampton, MA; (Y); 8/250; Am Leg Boys St; Cmnty Wkr; Var L Lcrss; Capt Var Swmmng; High Hon Roll; Pres NHS; Teachers Aide; Dartmouth Clb Bk Awd 85; Peer Ed Comm Chrmn 85; All-Wstrn MA Swm Tm 84-85.

LANCASTER, WM; Holy Name HS; Worcester, MA; (Y); Boys Clb Am; Cmnty Wkr; Varsity Clb; Var Bsktbl; Awd Alg II, Ath Recgntn, Vrsty Jckt Awd Bsktbll 85; U Bridgeport; Acctng.

LANCIA, JOHN L; Acton Boy HS; Acton, MA; (Y); 123/365; Boy Scts; Yrbk Stf; Golf; Ice Hcky; Francis J Ouimet 85; U Of CT; Bus.

LANCIANI, JONATHAN; Leominster HS; Leominster, MA; (S); 44/352; Am Leg Boys St; Church Yth Grp; Cmnty Wkr; Political Wkr; Ski Clb; Rep Frsh Cls; Rep Soph Cls; Rep Jr Cls; Rep Sr Cls; Rep Stu Cncl; Pre Med.

LANCIANI, MIKE; Monachusett Regional HS; Sterling, MA; (Y); JV Bsktbl; JV Crs Cntry; JV Var Ftbl; Var Capt Socr; MVP Offns JV Sccr 83-84; U S Army; Airbrn Infntry.

LANCKTON, BENJAMIN E; Newton South HS; Neton, MA; (Y); French Clb; Temple Yth Grp; School Play; French Hon Soc; High Hon Roll; Ntl Merit Ltr; Princeton Awd 85; Zeiderman Awd 83.

LANCTO, MARK E; St Marys HS; Westfield, MA; (Y); 5/50; Am Leg Boys St; Yrbk Stf; Lit Mag; Co-Capt VP Sr Cls; Var Mgr Bsbl; JV Var Bsktbl; Var Mgr Socr; Hon Roll; NHS; U MA; Elec Engr.

LANDERS, BRENDAN M; Chicopee HS; Chicopee, MA; (Y); 38/210; French Clb; Political Wkr; Nwsp Stf; Yrbk Stf; Pres Jr Cls; Stu Cncl; Golf; Socr; Hon Roll; John Bogla O Reilly Clb Schlrshp 85; Siena Coll; Pol Sci.

LANDERS, PAULA A; Mount Saint Joseph Acad; Boston, MA; (Y); Drama Clb; VP JA; School Play; Stage Crew; Yrbk Stf; Cheerleading; Fld Hcky; Mgr(s); Score Keeper; Math Fair Awd 2nd Pl; Ldrshp Awd Jr Achvmnt; Co Star Play; Finalist Miss United Teen Pgt; Bentley; Bus Admin.

LANDGRAF, SUSAN; Chelsea HS; Chelsea, MA; (Y); 7/189; Church Yth Grp; Science Clb; Bsktbl; Sftbl; NHS; Suffolk U; Comp Engr.

LANDO, DIANA; Watertown HS; Watertown, MA; (Y); Nwsp Phtg; Yrbk Rptr; Boston Conservatroy.

LANDRY, JULIE; Taunton HS; Taunton, MA; (Y); 7/389; Drama Clb; Library Aide; Spanish Clb; Lit Mag; High Hon Roll; NHS; Ntl Merit Ltr; Walker Merit Schlrshp 85; Excllnc Awd 85; SW MA U; Engl.

LANDRY, KEITH D; Waltham HS; Waltham, MA; (Y); Am Leg Boys St; VP Church Yth Grp; French Clb; Science Clb; School Play; Nwsp Rptr; JV Trk; Hon Roll; Jr NHS; Emerson Coll; Comm.

LANDRY, MICHELLE; St Bernards Central Catholic HS; Leominster, MA; (S); 16/164; Art Clb; Church Yth Grp; Sec French Clb; Model UN; Stage Crew; Hon Roll; NHS.

LANE, GINGER M; Silver Lake Regional HS; Bryantville, MA; (Y); Capt Bsktbl; Capt Sftbl; High Hon Roll; Hon Roll; NHS; Al-Star Bsktbl & Sftbl 85; Samuel O Gurney Awd 85; MVP Sftbl Tm 85; U Of NH; Phy Ed.

LANE, JOANNE; Braintree HS; Braintree, MA; (Y); 86/416; Art Clb; Cmnty Wkr; Hon Roll; Olympiad Engl Exam Awd 83; Westfield ST Coll; Elem Educ.

LANE, MICHAEL; Wilbraham & Monson Acad; Wilbraham, MA; (Y); 10/112; Boy Scts; Key Clb; Ed Q&S; Nwsp Ed-Chief; Pres Frsh Cls; Pres Jr Cls; Capt Lcrss; Capt Socr; Capt Wrstlng; Hon Roll; Latin IV Awd 85; Davison Schlrshp 85.

LANG, JENNIFER; Randolph HS; Randolph, MA; (Y); Hosp Aide; Ski Clb; Crs Cntry; Trk; Hon Roll; Ntl Hist Fnl 85.

LANGENBACK, KRISTIAN; Hoosac Valley HS; Adams, MA; (Y); Nwsp Rptr; Fld Hcky; God Cntry Awd; Law.

LANGHILL, TODD; St Johns HS; Westboro, MA; (Y); Aud/Vis; Boy Scts; Church Yth Grp; Exploring; Ski Clb; Im Bsbl; Im Bsktbl; Im Socr; Im Sftbl; Im Vllybl; Canimide U; Crmnlgy.

LANGHOFF, KRISTEN A; Old Rochester Reg HS; Mattapoisett, MA; (Y); 35/135; Church Yth Grp; Band; Concert Band; Jazz Band; Mrchg Band; Pep Band; School Musical; Yrbk Stf; Voice Dem Awd; Most Vlbl Perfmr Music 85; Music Schlrshp Form 85; Dollrs For Schlrs Schlrshp 85; Seton Hill Clg; Psych.

LANGIS, DARREN; Lynn Classical HS; Lynn, MA; (Y); 3/190; Am Leg Boys St; Pres Sr Cls; VP Stu Cncl; Bsbl; Ftbl; Trk; Wt Lftg; High Hon Roll; NHS; Political Wkr; Natl H S Ftbl Coaches All Amer 85; Natl H S Acad All Amer 85; Mngmnt.

LANGLAIS, CATHERINE; Bishop Connolly HS; Fall River, MA; (Y); 62/177; Church Yth Grp; Cmnty Wkr; Drama Clb; Chorus; Church Choir; School Play; High Hon Roll; Hon Roll; Merit Awd Muscl Fall Rivr JR Music Clb 85; Hghst Hnr Roll 85; Bus.

LANGLEY, JENNIFER; Arlington Catholic HS; Burlington, MA; (Y); 27/158; Drama Clb; Spanish Clb; Nwsp Stf; Rep Jr Cls; Rep Sr Cls; Rep Stu Cncl; Hon Roll; Pre-Med.

LANGLOIS, JESSICA; New Bedford HS; New Bedford, MA; (Y); JA; Office Aide; Nwsp Bus Mgr; Nwsp Rptr; Nwsp Stf; Stu Cncl; Capt Vllybl; Hon Roll; Jr NHS; Drama Clb; Roger Wlms Coll; Paralgl Trng.

LANGLOIS, KAREN; Shepherdhill Regional HS; Dudley, MA; (Y); Yrbk Stf; High Hon Roll; NHS; Accntnt.

LANGLOIS, TOM C; Saugus HS; Saugus, MA; (Y); 41/350; Pres Frsh Cls; Bsbl; Bsktbl; Cit Awd; Hon Roll; Achvt Rcgntn Awd 83; Stu Ldrhsp Awd 83; Outstndng Contributions Stu Cncl 83; Comp.

LANGNER, MIRIAM; Westford Acad; Westford, MA; (Y); Drama Clb; Exploring; German Clb; Hosp Aide; Pres Mgr Band; Chorus; Symp Band; Nwsp Stf; High Hon Roll; NHS; U Of NH; Med Tech.

LANGONE, LAURIE; Cathedral HS; Springfield, MA; (Y); Cmnty Wkr; Red Cross Aide; Variety Show; Stat Ftbl; JV Gym; Var Score Keeper; JV Trk; Prof Modeling Awds 81; Western New England Coll; Bus.

LANGORD, LAURA L; Algonquin Regional HS; Southborough, MA; (Y); 10/221; Church Yth Grp; Drama Clb; Teachers Aide; Chorus; School Musical; School Play; Hon Roll; NHS.

LANGTON, LORI; Apponequet Regional HS; East Freetown, MA; (Y); Exploring; JA; Science Clb; Diving; Var L Fld Hcky; Bausch & Lomb Sci Awd; Hon Roll; Ntl Merit Schol; St Schlr; Varsity Clb; Focas Club 84-85; Sftbl & Fld Hockey Trphys 84-85; Bio.

LANKARGE, KIM; Hopkins Acad; Hadley, MA; (S); 1/51; Spanish Clb; Band; Chorus; Concert Band; Mrchg Band; Rep Frsh Cls; Pres Jr Cls; Var L Cheerleading; Var L Socr; Var L Sftbl.

LANNI, PASQUALE; Lunenburg HS; Lunenburg, MA; (Y); Intnl Clb; Teachers Aide; Stage Crew; Im Bsktbl; Im Coach Actv; Var Ftbl; Im Wt Lftg; High Hon Roll; Hon Roll; U MA; Ag.

LANSEIGNE, PAMELA MARIE; Haverhill HS; Haverhill, MA; (Y); 98/315; Yrbk Stf; Hon Roll; Acctng.

LANTZ, GRETCHEN; Groton-Dunstable Regional HS; Groton, MA; (Y); Camp Fr Inc; Hosp Aide; Band; Chorus; Church Choir; JV Fld Hcky; JV Trk; Jr NHS; Church Yth Grp; Ski Clb; Exch Stu Yth Undrstndng Finland 83-84; Pro-Arts Smmr MFA Boston Museum Fine Arts 85; Lib Art.

LANUCHA, SUSAN; Easthampton HS; Easthampton, MA; (Y); 15/142; Yrbk Stf; JV Socr; High Hon Roll; NHS; Yrbk Layout Edtr 85-86; Phys Thrpy.

LANZA, MATTHEW D; Winthrop HS; Winthrop, MA; (Y); 40/216; Am Leg Boys St; Nwsp Rptr; Pres Jr Cls; Bsbl; Ftbl; Ice Hcky; Trk; Wt Lftg; Hon Roll; Bus Adm.

LAREAU, CRAIG; Fitchburg HS; Fitchburg, MA; (Y); 3/200; Am Leg Boys St; Mrchg Band; Yrbk Stf; Var Bsbl; Var Ftbl; Var Trk; High Hon Roll.

LAREAU, KEVIN A; Fitchburg HS; Fitchburg, MA; (Y); Am Leg Boys St; Mrchg Band; Rep Soph Cls; Rep Jr Cls; Var Bsbl; Var Ftbl; Var Trk; High Hon Roll; Bio Sci.

LAREAU, RAYMOND; Burnwat SR HS; Worcester, MA; (Y); Boys Clb Am; Boy Scts; Intnl Clb; JA; Science Clb; JV Bsbl; JV Bsktbl; Hon Roll; Accntng.

LARIVIERE, CHRISTINE; Douglas Memorial HS; East Douglas, MA; (Y); 4/45; Varsity Clb; Yrbk Ed-Chief; Stu Cncl; Score Keeper; High Hon Roll; NHS; Schlrs Awd Bd Regents 85; Paul D Manning Svc Awd 85; Douglas High Math Awd 85; U MA-AMHERST; Psych.

LARIVIERE, LYNN; Douglas Memorial HS; E Douglas, MA; (Y); 3/40; Varsity Clb; Yrbk Stf; VP Frsh Cls; VP Soph Cls; VP Jr Cls; VP Sr Cls; Bsbl; Bsktbl; NHS; Nrsg.

LARIVIERE, SUSAN; Bartlett HS; Webster, MA; (Y); 1/174; Sec VP Church Yth Grp; Science Clb; Variety Show; Capt Twrlr; High Hon Roll; NHS; St Schlr; Library Aide; Spanish Clb; Mrchg Band; Lucy T Phillips Math Awd 85; Schltc Achvt Awd Gld B 85; Cyril C Smith Memrl 85; Clark U; Math.

LARKIN, CHRISTOPHER; Hopedale JR SR HS; Hopedale, MA; (S); 6/62; Am Leg Boys St; Church Yth Grp; Band; Yrbk Stf; VP Frsh Cls; VP Jr Cls; VP Sr Cls; VP Bsktbl; VP Socr; NHS; Bus Mgmt.

LARKIN, SHANNON; West Springfield SR HS; W Springfield, MA; (Y); 13/280; Drama Clb; Trs Latin Clb; Acpl Chr; Chorus; Church Choir; School Musical; Cheerleading; High Hon Roll; NHS; Ntl Merit Ltr; Century III Leaders Awd 84; Latin Natl Hnrs Soc 81; Western MA Dist Chorus 84-85; Smith Coll; Psych.

LARKIN, STEPHEN J; Marianhill HS; Southbridge, MA; (Y); 6/20; Am Leg Boys St; French Clb; Ski Clb; School Musical; Nwsp Sprt Ed; VP Frsh Cls; VP Soph Cls; VP Jr Cls; VP Sr Cls; Var Bsbl; Cochs Awd, MVP Vrsty Bsktbl 84-85; Stu Athlt Wk Grtr Media Cabl Ch 13 85; Stonehill Coll; Law.

LARNARD, PAMELA; Presentation Of Mary Acad; Methuen, MA; (Y); Church Yth Grp; Hosp Aide; Rep Soph Cls; Sec Sr Cls; Stu Cncl; Cheerleading; Sci Fair Awd 82-83; U Of Lowell MA; Undclrd Bus.

LARONGA, TONI M; Bellingham Memorial HS; Bellingham, MA; (Y); Church Yth Grp; DECA; Band; Concert Band; Mrchg Band; High Hon Roll; Hon Roll; Bus.

LAROUCO, ANTONIO; Milford HS; Milford, MA; (Y); High Hon Roll; Hon Roll; U MA; Engrng.

LARSON, GEOFFREY OWEN; Mohawk Trail Regional HS; Colrain, MA; (Y); 13/123; Church Yth Grp; JV Crs Cntry; JV Trk; Hon Roll; Jr NHS; Natl Sci Olympiad 1st Schl Chem 84-85; Chem Engrng.

LARSON, JANINE; Dana Hall Schl; Wellesley, MA; (Y); French Clb; Hosp Aide; Library Aide; Lit Mag; Stu Cncl; Var Fld Hcky; JV Lcrss; Var Sftbl; Var Swmmng; Var Vllybl; Achvt Awd Frnch 85; All Star Awd Field Hockey 84; Modern Lang.

LARSON, JENNIFER; Walpole HS; Walpole, MA; (Y); 7/265; Pres Church Yth Grp; French Clb; Band; Chorus; Orch; Trs Sr Cls; Elks Awd; NHS; Ntl Merit Ltr; Pres Schlr; Boston Coll.

LARSON, MARK; Marian HS; Framingham, MA; (Y); 33/177; Church Yth Grp; Capt Bsktbl; JV Crs Cntry; Elks Awd; Hon Roll; Holy Cross.

LASHUA, CHRIS; St Bernards HS; Ashburnham, MA; (S); Boy Scts; Camera Clb; Church Yth Grp; Stage Crew; Variety Show; VP Frsh Cls; Hon Roll; Graph Dsgn.

LASSITER, LAURIE; Salem HS; Salem, MA; (Y); Yrbk Stf; High Hon Roll; Hon Roll; Spanish NHS; Jrnlsm.

LATAWIEC, PAULETTE; Beverly HS; Beverly, MA; (Y); DECA; Girl Scts; Gym; Hon Roll; 1st Pl Apparrel & Acc Rgnl DECA Confrnce 85; Nrsng.

LATESSA, ROBYN; B M C Durfee HS; Fall River, MA; (Y); 2/650; Math Clb; Varsity Clb; Concert Band; Mrchg Band; Yrbk Stf; Lit Mag; Trs Stu Cncl; Cheerleading; High Hon Roll; NHS; Williams Bk Awd 85.

LATHAM, DAVID; Hopkins Acad; Hadley, MA; (S); 1/46; Spanish Clb; Nwsp Rptr; Yrbk Phtg; Var Golf; Var Socr; Capt Var Wrstlng; Hon Roll; NHS; Ntl Merit Ltr; U Of MA Chncllrs Tlnt Awd 84; Rensselaer Polytech Inst Medl 84; Pre-Med.

LATHAM, EDWARD A; Sandwich HS; Sandwich, MA; (Y); 1/152; Am Leg Boys St; Cmnty Wkr; Math Tm; Ski Clb; JV Var Bsbl; L Var Bsktbl; High Hon Roll; Hon Roll; Pres NHS; Ntl Merit SF; Hrvrd Bk Awd 85; Schl Rep For Stu Govt Day 85; Accptd MA Advnc Stdy Pgm 85; US Mltry Acad; Engrng.

LATOUR, DEBRA; Gardner HS; Gardner, MA; (Y); 17/182; GAA; Pep Clb; Spanish Clb; Chorus; Bsktbl; Fld Hcky; Tennis; Bio.

LATTIN, JEFFREY J; Whitman-Hanson Regional HS; Whitman, MA; (Y); 60/330; Am Leg Boys St; Radio Clb; Varsity Clb; Yrbk Stf; Rep Frsh Cls; Pres Soph Cls; Pres Jr Cls; Rep Sr Cls; Rep Stu Cncl; Stat Cocah Actv; USC; Law.

LATULIPPE, MICHELLE; St Marys HS; Westfield, MA; (Y); 2/65; Am Leg Aux Girls St; School Musical; Ed Nwsp Stf; Trs Sr Cls; Var Socr; Var Sftbl; High Hon Roll; NHS; Intrntnl Rltns.

LAUCKS, MELINDA; Dana Hall Schl; Needham, MA; (Y); Key Clb; Q&S; School Play; Nwsp Rptr; Nwsp Stf; Lit Mag; Var Fld Hcky; Im Lcrss; Hon Roll; Putnum Purchase Prz Print Mkng 85.

LAURA, RICHARD; Matignon HS; Somerville, MA; (Y); 47/185; Boy Scts; Drama Clb; School Musical; School Play; Variety Show; Rado.

LAURENZA, LYNDA; Matignon HS; Cambridge, MA; (S); 27/189; JA; Library Aide; Spanish Clb; Hon Roll; NHS; Prfct Atten Awd; Humanitarian Awd 82; Accntnt.

LAURINO, PAUL P; Boston Latin Schl; Roslindale, MA; (Y); 4/324; Math Tm; Lit Mag; Hon Roll; NHS; Ntl Merit SF; Natl Schlstc Wrtng Awd 84; William Kimball Norton Awd 83; Boston Hldy Grtng Crd Cntst 83; Engnrng.

LAVALLEE, DAWN; Southbridge HS; Sbridge, MA; (Y); #18 In Class; Band; Concert Band; Mrchg Band; JV Fld Hcky; Hon Roll.

LAVALLEE, LISE; Ayer HS; Ayer, MA; (Y); Office Aide; Yrbk Stf; Var Trs Stu Cncl; Mgr(s); Hon Roll; Yrbk Art Edtr 85-86; MA Coll Art; Grphc Artst.

LAVELLE, PATRICIA M; Holyoke HS; Holyoke, MA; (Y); Church Yth Grp; Latin Clb; Pep Clb; Spanish Clb; Yrbk Stf; Stu Cncl; Var Capt Bsktbl; Fld Hcky; ST Anselms; Physcl Thrpy.

LAVELLE, TIMOTHY J; Holyoke HS; Holyoke, MA; (Y); Trs German Clb; JCL; Political Wkr; Rep Sr Cls; Rep Stu Cncl; JV Ftbl; High Hon Roll; Hon Roll; Dartmouth Clb Bk Awd 85; Med Clb 84-85; Bio.

LAVERRIERE, WENDY; Methuen HS; Methuen, MA; (Y); 53/383; Intnl Clb; Pep Clb; Varsity Clb; Trk; Vllybl; Hon Roll; Accntng.

LAVIGNE, TODD; Bartlett HS; Webster, MA; (Y); Hon Roll.

LAVOIE, CHERYL; Mcthuen HS; Lowell, MA; (Y); 76/210; Color Guard; High Hon Roll; Burdett Schl Coll Schlrshp 85; Bus Dept Schlrshp 85; Burdett Schl; Acctg.

LAVOIE, JEAN; Bridgewater-Raynham Regional HS; Raynham, MA; (Y); 6/305; French Clb; Science Clb; Spanish Clb; Tennis; High Hon Roll; Hon Roll; NHS; Phys Thrpy.

LAVOIE, NICOLE; Leominster HS; Leominster, MA; (Y); 7/354; Cmnty Wkr; French Clb; JA; School Musical; Cheerleading; High Hon Roll; NHS; Pres Schlr; Rotary Clb Schrlshp 85; Chancellors Talnt Awd 85; John F Joyce Schlrshp 85; U MA; Lawyer.

LAVOIE, PATRICK; Bridgewater-Raynham Regional HS; Raynham, MA; (Y); 4/300; French Clb; Math Clb; Math Tm; Spanish Clb; Tennis; Wt Lftg; High Hon Roll; Hon Roll; NHS; W Point Acad; Acctg.

LAWLER, JULIE; Newton North HS; Newtonville, MA; (Y); Chorus; High Hon Roll; Hon Roll; Outstndng Achvt Awd In Eng 82-83; Stu-Tchr Org To Prvnt Nclr War 84-85; Simons Rock Of Bard Coll; Eng.

LAWLER, KATE; Auburn HS; Auburn, MA; (Y); Sec Church Yth Grp; Latin Clb; Spanish Clb; Yrbk Stf; Rep Soph Cls; Rep Jr Cls; Var L Crs Cntry; JV Fld Hcky; Swmmng; High Hon Roll; MA Frgn Lang Assclth Ltn Awd 84-85; Occptnl Educ Achvt Awd 84.

LAWLER, KATHLEEN; Easthampton HS; Easthampton, MA; (Y); 1/140; Am Leg Aux Girls St; JA; Math Tm; Rep Stu Cncl; Var Capt Socr; Var Sftbl; High Hon Roll; NHS; Val; Ski Clb; Pioneer Vly Dartmouth Club Book Awd 85; Most Dedictd Awd-Vrsty Sftbll 85; Laywer.

LAWLOR, BONNIE; Coyle & Cassidy Memorial HS; Berkley, MA; (Y); 4/140; Drama Clb; JCL; Latin Clb; Spanish Clb; Chorus; School Musical; High Hon Roll; Hon Roll; NHS; Acad Ltr Hgh Hnr & Hnr Rlls; Ltrs Drma/Folkgrp; Pin Folkgrp; MA Coll Of Phar; Phrmcy.

LAWRENCE, JACQUELINE; Mansfield HS; Mansfield, MA; (Y); 39/201; Office Aide; Powder Puff Ftbl; JV Trk; Acctnt.

LAWRENCE, KATHRYN; Bishop Stang HS; Fairhaven, MA; (Y); 9/218; Church Yth Grp; Dance Clb; Ski Clb; Yrbk Phtg; Yrbk Stf; High Hon Roll; NHS; Top Stu In Oceanogrphy Clss; Colgate U; Bio.

LAWRENCE, MARIA A; Notre Dame Academy; Worcester, MA; (Y); Pres Church Yth Grp; Drama Clb; French Clb; Latin Clb; School Musical; Dion Fndtn Schlrshp; Clark U; Bio.

LAWSON, CHAPPELL H; Phillips Acad; Washington, DC; (Y); VP Debate Tm; Key Clb; Pres Model UN; Rep Nwsp Rptr; Nwsp Stf; Hon Roll; Ntl Merit SF; Trnsltn Prz; Princeton; Law.

LAWSON, LISA; Southwick HS; Springfield, MA; (Y); Dance Clb; Church Yth Grp; Spanish Clb; Teachers Aide; Church Choir; Yrbk Stf; Hon Roll; Comp Pgmmng.

LAWTHER, JANINE; Hamilton-Wenham Regional HS; South Hamilton, MA; (Y); Church Yth Grp; Drama Clb; Chorus; Color Guard; School Musical; Stage Crew; Yrbk Stf; Bsktbl; Hon Roll; Hgh Achvt In Phy Ed 83-84; Chmcl Sales.

LAWTON, ALISHA O; Framingham North HS; Hyde Park, MA; (Y); 165/350; Drama Clb; Key Clb; Spanish Clb; Acpl Chr; Church Choir; School Play; Yrbk Rptr; Rep Stu Cncl; Cheerleading; Cit Awd; Psych.

LAYDEN, CAROLINE M; Westwood HS; Westwood, MA; (Y); 27/216; AFS; Key Clb; Yrbk Stf; JV Fld Hcky; Powder Puff Ftbl; Hon Roll; NHS; Spanish NHS; Comp Engrng.

LAZO, MICHAEL L; Boston College HS; W Roxbury, MA; (Y); JA; Rep Frsh Cls; Rep Soph Cls; Rep Stu Cncl; Stat Bsbl; Im JV Ftbl; MVP Hcky W Roxbury 84-85; Citatn US Navl Sea Cadts 84; Psychlgy.

LAZO, SUZAN; Southbridge HS; Southbridge, MA; (Y); School Play; Off Soph Cls; Off Jr Cls; Off Sr Cls; Var Cheerleading; Nrsng.

LE BEL, CHERYL; Southbirdge HS; Southridge, MA; (Y); VP Church Yth Grp; Math Tm; Var Capt Bsktbl; Var Fld Hcky; Var Capt Trk; Hon Roll; Acadmc & Math All Amer 85; Amer Finest Athl 84-85; Framingham ST Coll; Math.

LE BEL, SUZANNE; Pentucket Regional HS; Groveland, MA; (Y); 25/179; Pres Trs OEA; Trs Spanish Clb; Trs Jr Cls; High Hon Roll; Hon Roll; Stu Cncl; Prncpls Awd; Merrimack Coll; Acctg.

LE BLANC, CHARLOTTE; Gardner HS; Gardner, MA; (Y); 27/170; Drama Clb; Pres French Clb; Hosp Aide; Pep Clb; Varsity Clb; Chorus; Drm Mjr(t); School Musical; School Play; Stage Crew; Maude G Cobleigh Awd/Excllnc Dramatics 85; Drama Awd & GEA Awd 85; Knighs Of Columbus Schlrshp; U Of MA; Nrsng.

LE BLANC, KRISTEN; North Attleboro HS; North Attleboro, MA; (Y); JV Var Bsktbl; JV Var Cheerleading; Im Powder Puff Ftbl; Var L Trk; Hon Roll; NHS; Psych.

LE BLANC, LISA; St Bernards C C HS; Fitchburg, MA; (S); 5/173; Cmnty Wkr; Drama Clb; Sec Trs Latin Clb; Library Aide; School Musical; Nwsp Rptr; High Hon Roll; Hon Roll; Jr NHS; NHS; Spec Ed.

LE BLANC, MICHELLE C; New Bedford HS; New Bedford, MA; (Y); 5/541; AFS; Concert Band; Mrchg Band; Orch; School Musical; Chrmn Stu Cncl; French Hon Soc; High Hon Roll; Trs NHS; Pres Schlr; Hghst Avg Engl 85; Southeastern MA U; Bus Admin.

LE BLANC, RICHARD E; Fitchberg HS; Fitchburg, MA; (Y); 6/227; Am Leg Boys St; High Hon Roll; NHS; Physcs Awd 85; Montachusette Regnl Schlrshp Awd 85; Engl Compstn Prz Awd 85; Phys Ther.

LE BRUN, JAMES K; Milford HS; Milford, MA; (Y); 47/470; Am Leg Boys St; Church Yth Grp; Key Clb; Math Clb; Science Clb; Spanish Clb; Rep Stu Cncl; L Bsbl; Capt Bsktbl; Hon Roll; Bus.

LE CLAIR, GEORGE; Boston College HS; Hanover, MA; (Y); 42/250; JCL; Key Clb; Var Trk; Hon Roll; NHS; Natl Latin Exam Hnbl Mntn 84 & 85; In Schl Tutor 85; Dever Schl Tutor 84-85; Bus.

LE CONTI, DAVID; Newton North HS; W Newton, MA; (Y); Church Yth Grp; Cmnty Wkr; Exploring; FCA; Political Wkr; Var Bsbl; Var Ice Hcky.

LE FAVE, SUZANNE; Matignon HS; Medford, MA; (S); 4/185; Hosp Aide; Trs JA; Nwsp Stf; Coach Actv; Var Crs Cntry; Var Trk; NHS; MA Statehouse Tour Guide 83-84; Ntl Sci Merit Awd Bio 84; Harvard; Lawyer.

LE MAY, STEVEN; Methuen HS; Methuen, MA; (Y); Ski Clb; Yrbk Stf; Tennis; Arch.

LE ROY, ELIZABETH; Miss Halls Schl; Laconia, NH; (Y); 22/65; Church Yth Grp; Political Wkr; Ski Clb; Sec Frsh Cls; Off Soph Cls; Pres Jr Cls; Pres Stu Cncl; Var Fld Hcky; Var Capt Lcrss; MVP Ski Tm 82; Pre-Law.

LE TOURNEAU, PAUL; Taunton HS; Berkley, MA; (Y); DECA; Library Aide; Ski Clb; JV Bsbl; JV Ftbl; JV Var Ice Hcky; CC Awd; Im Swmmng; Im Wt Lftg; Im Wrstlng; Amer Cancer Soc Vltr Awd 84; Drug & Alcohol Task Frce Vltr 85; Educ Fair Demnstr For DECA 85; Bus Adm.

LEACH, ARTHUR; Bridgewater-Raynham Regional HS; Bridgewater, MA; (Y); Am Leg Boys St; Boy Scts; Camera Clb; Ski Clb; Spanish Clb; Ftbl; Trk; High Hon Roll; Hon Roll; Natl Riflmns Asn Exprt Smallbore Qualf 85; Engrng.

LEAHEY, CORNELIUS; Bishop Connolly HS; Swansea, MA; (S); 42/158; Ski Clb; Var Capt Crs Cntry; Var Capt Trk; Hon Roll; NHS; Alexander Graham Bell Schlrshp 84-85; Teenager Mnth Fall Rvr Elks Club 84-85; Bio.

LEARY, BETTY ANN; Holy Names Christian HS; Worcester, MA; (Y); 36/295; Ski Clb; Orch; School Musical; JV Trk; DAR Awd; High Hon Roll; Hon Roll; Art Latin Rel Frnch Awd 84-85; Holy Cross Coll; Pre Dentsty.

LEARY, JAMES; St Domenic Savio College Prep; E Boston, MA; (Y); 15/125; Church Yth Grp; Cmnty Wkr; Teachers Aide; Nwsp Rptr; Crs Cntry; Hon Roll; Engrng.

LEAVITT, JOHN R R; Northfield Mt Hermon Schl; Southborough, MA; (Y); Computer Clb; Drama Clb; Math Clb; School Play; Stage Crew; Nwsp Stf; Rptr Lit Mag; JV Crs Cntry; Socr; Ntl Merit SF; Comp Sci.

LEAVITT, STEVEN; Randolph HS; Randolph, MA; (Y); Math Tm; Pres Q&S; Pres Temple Yth Grp; Yrbk Stf; Rep Soph Cls; JV Crs Cntry; Hon Roll; NHS; Engnr.

LEBLANC, BRIAN; Blackstone Valley Reg Voc Tech; Bellingham, MA; (Y); Orch; Hon Roll; Elec.

LEBLANC, DOUG J; Salem HS; Salem, MA; (Y); Band; Concert Band; Jazz Band; Mrchg Band; Orch; Pep Band; School Musical; Symp Band; Nuc Engrng.

LEBOWITZ, JENNIFER; Buckingham Browne & Nichols HS; Chestnut Hill, MA; (S); Dance Clb; Pres Debate Tm; VP French Clb; Madrigals; School Musical; School Play; Rptr Nwsp Stf; Hon Roll.

LEBRASSER, MICHELLE; Lynn Classical HS; Lynn, MA; (Y); Rep Soph Cls; Var Capt Cheerleading; Vllybl; Hon Roll; Bus Admin.

LECLERC, JAY; St Peter Marian HS; Worcester, MA; (Y); 41/177; Boy Scts; Church Yth Grp; Computer Clb; Sec Exploring; JA; Spanish Clb; Stage Crew; Variety Show; Im Bsktbl; Hon Roll; Pope Pius XII Awd 82; IN Inst Tech; Elec Engnrng.

LECLERC, SCOTT; St Peter-Marion CC HS; Worcester, MA; (S); 5/181; Church Yth Grp; Exploring; Concert Band; School Musical; Nwsp Rptr; Hon Roll; NHS; Ntl Merit Ltr; Engrng.

LECOUR, ELIZABETH A; Bishop Connolly HS; Fall River, MA; (Y); 57/175; Drama Clb; Hosp Aide; Chorus; Church Choir; School Play; Stage Crew; Yrbk Stf; High Hon Roll; Natl Piano Auditions 81 & 82; Mass Rgnl Sci Fair 81; Southeastern MA U; Lab Tech.

LECOURS, ANGELA; Monson JR SR HS; Monson, MA; (Y); 9/86; French Clb; School Musical; Ed Yrbk Ed-Chief; Sec Stu Cncl; High Hon Roll; NHS; Pres Schlr; Camera Clb; Cmnty Wkr; Drama Clb; Teachrs Assn Schlrshp & Awd 85; PTO Awd 85; Henry O Holley Schlrshp 85; Hesser Coll; Travl/Tourism.

LECUYER, PHILIP; Bridgewater-Raynham Regional HS; Bridgewater, MA; (Y); Cmnty Wkr; Capt Var Bsbl; Var Bsktbl; Hon Roll; Bus Admin.

LEDGISTER, FLOYD; Randolph HS; Randolph, MA; (Y); Am Leg Boys St; CAP; Varsity Clb; Capt Crs Cntry; Capt Trk; JC Awd; Hon Roll; U S Senator MA Boys ST 85; Boys Natn 85; Old Colony All Str Crss Cntry 85; U S Air Force Acad; Flght Trng.

LEDUC, PAMELA; Southbridge HS; Southbridge, MA; (Y); 28/160; Drm Mjr(t); Co-Capt Twrlr; Accntng.

LEDUC, RACHELLE L; Brockton HS; Brockton, MA; (Y); 41/900; Church Yth Grp; Dance Clb; French Clb; Ski Clb; Nwsp Rptr; Rep Soph Cls; VP Jr Cls; Pres Sr Cls; Score Keeper; High Hon Roll; Hon Mntn Creatve Wrtng Cntst 84; Cmmnctns.

LEE, CALVIN; Boston Technical HS; Boston, MA; (Y); Red Cross Aide; Ice Hcky; High Hon Roll; MIT; Aerosp Engr.

LEE, CHRISTOPHER; Catholic Memorial HS; Notre Dame, IN; (Y); 13/300; Am Leg Boys St; Computer Clb; French Clb; Math Clb; Political Wkr; Ski Clb; Yrbk Sprt Ed; Yrbk Stf; Im Bsktbl; Im Ftbl; French I 81; Yrbk Excllnce 85; Edward Bradley Mem Schlrshp 85; Notre Dame; Mktng.

LEE, DAVID CHUN YOUNG; Cushing Acad; Hong Kong; (Y); Art Clb; Boy Scts; Intnl Clb; Ski Clb; Var Lcrss; Var Socr; French Hon Soc; High Hon Roll; Hon Roll; Pre Med.

LEE, DONNA; Arlington Catholic HS; Arlington, MA; (Y); Ed Yrbk Phtg; Yrbk Stf; Off Frsh Cls; Off Soph Cls; Off Jr Cls; Sec Sr Cls; Var Sftbl; Var Capt Vllybl; Prfct Atten Awd; Church Yth Grp; Outstndg Stu Awd 85; Outstndg Schl Svc 85; Phy Thrpst.

LEE, ELIZABETH K; Winchester HS; Winchester, MA; (Y); Debate Tm; Intnl Clb; Math Clb; Math Tm; VP Sec Science Clb; Spanish Clb; Church Choir; School Musical; Variety Show; Nwsp Rptr; NCTE Achvt Awd Writing 84; 1st Pl Martin Luther King Jr Easay Cont 82; Winchester Smith Coll Bk Awd; Biochem.

LEE, LUCINDA; Boston Latin Schl; Boston, MA; (Y); 44/299; Camera Clb; French Clb; Key Clb; Ski Clb; Trs Jr Cls; Vllybl; Hon Roll; NHS; Busnss.

LEE, MEESOOK; Dedham HS; Needham, MA; (S); 2/350; Am Leg Aux Girls St; Orch; Nwsp Rptr; Lit Mag; Pres Stu Cncl; Trk; Elks Awd; Pres NHS; Sal; Rensselaer Poly Tech Inst Medal For Sci & Math 84; Bst In Math 82-85; MIT; Engrng.

LEE, ROGER; Gloucester HS; Gloucester, MA; (Y); 30/472; Math Tm; Rep Frsh Cls; Rep Soph Cls; Rep Jr Cls; Im Bsktbl; Stat Ftbl; Mgr(s); Hon Roll; Bryont; Bus Adm.

LEE, VIVIE; Shrewsbury HS; Holmdel, NJ; (Y); 2/270; Math Clb; Capt Math Tm; NFL; Nwsp Ed-Chief; Ed Yrbk Stf; Ed Lit Mag; Ntl Merit Schol; Sal; Camera Clb; Nwsp Phtg; Harvard U; Appld Physcs.

LEFEBVRE, STEVE; Dartmouth HS; N Dartmouth, MA; (Y); 26/261; AFS; Key Clb; Ski Clb; Rep Frsh Cls; Rep Soph Cls; Rep Jr Cls; Rep Sr Cls; Var Ftbl; Var Golf; Hon Roll; Ftbl Superbowl Tms 83-85; U MA Amherst; Pre-Med.

LEFKOWITZ, HANNAH; Dana Hall Schl; Wellesley, MA; (Y); Nwsp Rptr; VP Sr Cls; Spanish NHS; Cmnty Wkr; Drama Clb; Key Clb; Quiz Bowl; School Musical; School Play; Stage Crew; Ondy Dean Gilson 52 Prz In Thtr 84-85; Dir 3 Indpndt Prod JR Yr Spec Citation 84-85.

LEGAULT, KEVIN; Bishop Connolly HS; Swansea, MA; (S); 17/200; Chess Clb; Computer Clb; French Clb; Math Clb; Ski Clb; Var Golf; High Hon Roll; Jr NHS; NHS; Worcester Polytechnic Inst; Eng.

LEGER, GINGER S; BMC Durfee HS; Fall River, MA; (Y); 69/633; Cmnty Wkr; Library Aide; Spanish Clb; Variety Show; Hon Roll; NHS; Minister.

LEGER, JOHN; Salem HS; Salem, MA; (Y); 1/15; Am Leg Aux Girls St; Ski Clb; Rep Frsh Cls; Rep Soph Cls; Rep Stu Cncl; Elect Engr.

LEGERE, MICHELLE L; English HS; Lynn, MA; (Y); 16/333; Ski Clb; Nwsp Ed-Chief; Ed Yrbk Ed-Chief; Rep Soph Cls; Stu Cncl; JV Bsktbl; Capt Var Tennis; High Hon Roll; Hon Roll; NHS; Bentley Coll.

LEGGEE, JEFFREY; Nashoba Regional; Bolton, MA; (S); DECA; JV Crs Cntry; Var Trk; JV Wrstlng; 4-H Awd; Hon Roll; DECA 2nd Pl Dist, 3rd Pl ST 85; Martial Arts Excllnc Awd 84; U Of MA; Hotel Rest Mgmt.

LEIGHTON, KIM; North Andover HS; North Andover, MA; (Y); 42/243; Art Clb; Debate Tm; Drama Clb; NFL; Speech Tm; Chorus; Church Choir; School Musical; Lit Mag; Tennis; Schlrshp Andover Artist Guild 85; Blue Rbbn & Gold Key Boston Globe Art Cont 85; Art & Ltry Mag Awds; Sarah Lawrence Coll; Lbrl Arts.

LEINBACH, ROBERT B; Brookline HS; Brookline, MA; (Y); Ski Clb; Chorus; Jazz Band; Mrchg Band; Orch; School Musical; Swing Chorus; Symp Band; Var Capt Lcrss; JV Socr; Music Schl; Jazz.

LEISTRITZ, MICHAEL; Holy Name Central Catholic HS; Worcester, MA; (Y); Boys Clb Am; Church Yth Grp; JA; Var JV Bsbl; Im Bsktbl; Hon Roll; Comm Skills Hnrs Cert 83-84; Chem Hnrs Cert 84-85; Athl Recog Awd 83-85; Dartmouth Coll; Bus Admin.

LELE, SHANTANU A; Natick HS; Natick, MA; (Y); 9/437; JV Bsbl; Im Bsktbl; Var Tennis; High Hon Roll; Hon Roll; NHS; Ntl Merit Ltr; Zayre Corp Schlrshp; Tufts U; Engrng.

LEMAY, LAURA A; Brookline HS; Brookline, MA; (Y); Drama Clb; PAVAS; Acpl Chr; Chorus; School Musical; School Play; Swing Chorus; Variety Show; Hon Roll; NHS.

LEMAY, MICHAEL P; Oakmont Regional HS; Westminster, MA; (Y); #18 In Class; Am Leg Boys St; Var Bsbl; Var Ftbl; JV Trk; Im Wt Lftg; Hon Roll; Bus.

LEMIEUX, CHRISTEN; Bishop Connolly HS; Portsmouth, RI; (Y); Hosp Aide; English.

LEMIEUX, JEANNETTE; Westford Academy HS; Westford, MA; (Y); 6/205; French Clb; Ski Clb; Var L Crs Cntry; Var L Swmmng; Var Capt Trk; High Hon Roll; NHS; MVP Cross Cnty 84; Trustes Awd Schlrshp 85; US Army Rsv Ntl Schlr Athlt Awd 85; MI Tech; Comp Sci.

LEMOFF, BRIAN E; Westborough HS; Westborough, MA; (Y); 1/180; Debate Tm; Exploring; Model UN; VP Temple Yth Grp; Chorus; Madrigals; Lit Mag; Bausch & Lomb Sci Awd; Ntl Merit SF; Chess Clb; Most Schlrly; Calculus Awd 84; Cert Merit, Model Cong 84; CA Inst Tech; Thrtcl Phys.

LENART, PETER C; Cathedral HS; Chicopee, MA; (Y); 41/476; Am Leg Boys St; Boy Scts; Church Yth Grp; Political Wkr; Capt Quiz Bowl; Nwsp Stf; Yrbk Stf; Wrld Cultures Excllnc Acad Awd 82-83; Ldrshp Pstn Model Snt Minrty Whip 85-86; Govt Sci.

LENEHAN, MARGARET; Malden HS; Malden, MA; (Y); 7/700; Church Yth Grp; Dance Clb; Office Aide; Political Wkr; Quiz Bowl; Red Cross Aide; Band; Variety Show; Hon Roll; NHS; Psychlgy.

LENSCH, SARA; Bishop Feehan HS; Dallas, TX; (Y); Drama Clb; Spanish Clb; Drill Tm; School Musical; School Play; Stage Crew; JV Twrlr; Hon Roll; Spanish NHS; Engl Awd Amer Lit 83-84; Shenandoah Coll; Perf Arts.

LENTHALL, BRUCE; Brookline HS; Brookline, MA; (Y); Rep Frsh Cls; Stat Ftbl; Hon Roll; NHS; Ntl Merit Ltr.

LENTINI, ANDREA; Woburn SR HS; Woburn, MA; (S); Varsity Clb; Rep Stu Cncl; JV Bsktbl; VP Capt Fld Hcky; JV Sftbl; Var Trk; High Hon Roll; Jr NHS; Ntl Merit Ltr; Pres Schlr; Fldhcky Schltc Hon Mntn,All Star 84; Med.

LEO, TONI; Bishop Fenwick HS; Danvers, MA; (Y); 14/222; Teachers Aide; Yrbk Ed-Chief; CC Awd; High Hon Roll; Hon Roll; NHS; Nwsp Phtg; Yrbk Phtg; Yrbk Stf; Jr NHS; Outstndng Achvt Psychlgy 85; Am Newspaper Pub Assoc Schlstc Jrnlst Awd 85; Bucknell U; Chem.

LEONARD, ANN-MARIE; Ware HS; Ware, MA; (Y); 16/115; Hosp Aide; Hon Roll; Prfct Atten Awd; VFW Awd; Mary Lane Hosp Axllry Schlrshp 85; Polish Amer Schlrshp 85; Amer Lgn Schlrshp 85; Pro Mexico 83-85; Sprngfld Tech CC; Med Lab Tech.

LEONARD, BRIAN; Nauset Regional HS; E Orleans, MA; (Y); Church Yth Grp; Var L Varsity Clb; Var L Socr; Var L Tennis; Var Hon Roll; Soph Cls; Jr Cls; Sr Cls; Bsbl; JV Bsktbl; Mst Athl 82; Hnrd Tnns Ablty-Radio Sta 85; St Fnls Doubles MA Tennis 85; Bus Cmmnctns.

LEONARD, JEANNE; North Reading HS; North Reading, MA; (Y); Cmnty Wkr; Hosp Aide; Cheerleading; Tennis; Emmanuel Coll; Comm Arts.

LEONARD, KERRY; Woburn HS; Woburn, MA; (S); Church Yth Grp; Ski Clb; Hon Roll.

LEONARD, TINA; Medway JR SR HS; Medway, MA; (Y); 50/150; Church Yth Grp; Flag Corp; Yrbk Stf; High Hon Roll; Hon Roll; Prom Comm 85; Bentley; Acctng.

LEONARDO, LISA A; Somerset HS; Somerset, MA; (Y); 48/300; VP Church Yth Grp; Church Choir; Concert Band; Drm Mjr(t); Orch; School Musical; School Play; Pres Swing Chorus; Symp Band; High Hon Roll; Miss Congeniality Somerset Musictown Fest 83-84; All Eastern Band 85; Bridgewater ST Coll; Chldhd Ed.

LEONE, MICHELLE; Marion HS; Framingham, MA; (Y); 8/177; Dance Clb; Chorus; Var Cheerleading; Hon Roll; NHS; Natl Hnr Soc 85-86; Cheerldng 84-86; Lawyer.

LEONG, MICHELLE; Boston Technical HS; No Quincy, MA; (Y); 1/225; Pep Clb; Bausch & Lomb Sci Awd; High Hon Roll; Hon Roll; NHS; Val; Mc Carthy Awd; Franklin Awd; Boston U; Nrsg.

LEONG, WAIK; Cheisea HS; Boston, MA; (Y); JV Bsktbl; High Hon Roll; Hon Roll; Prfct Atten Awd; Boston U; Comp Sci.

LEPAGE, RICHARD; BMC Durfee HS; Fall River, MA; (Y); Spanish Clb; Varsity Clb; Bsbl; Bsktbl.

LEROY, EMMLYNN L; North Cambridge Catholic HS; Somerville, MA; (Y); Camera Clb; Drama Clb; Intnl Clb; Math Tm; Varsity Clb; Vllybl; French Hon Soc; High Hon Roll; Hon Roll; NHS; Engrng.

LEROY, MICHELLE; Norton HS; Norton, MA; (Y); 32/168; Drama Clb; JA; Office Aide; Varsity Clb; Chorus; School Play; Variety Show; Yrbk Stf; Trk; Bus Wk-Bentley Coll 85; Sls Womn Of Yr JR Achvt 83; Rookie Of Yr JR Achvt 83; Fashn Mdse.

LESCARBEAU, KIM; Drury SR HS; N Adams, MA; (Y); 45/183; Drama Clb; Teachers Aide; Pres Lib Chorus; School Musical; School Play; Stage Crew; Hon Roll; Church Yth Grp; Hosp Aide; Thesps; Vocl Music Schlrshp ST; Pro Merito Hnr Socty & SADD Secy; Soprano I Westrn Dist Music Fest; Westfield ST Coll; Spec Ed.

LESICZKA, JEFF; Haverhill HS; Haverhill, MA; (Y); 42/420; High Hon Roll; NHS; Elaine R Croston Awd 85; U Of Lowell; Mech Engnrng.

LESKO, YVONNE; Our Lady Of Nazareth Acad; Wilmington, MA; (Y); 30/70; Art Clb; Var L Bsktbl; Var Capt Sftbl; Var L Vllybl; Pep Clb; Spanish Clb; Yrbk Phtg; Prfct Atten Awd; Sftbl All Star Tm 83-85; Keene ST; Arch.

LESLIE, CHERYL; Northbridge JR & SR HS; Whitinsville, MA; (S); #6 In Class; Am Leg Aux Girls St; Latin Clb; Sec Latin Clb; Band; Nwsp Ed-Chief; Rep Stu Cncl; Var Cheerleading; Stat Score Keeper; NHS; Ntl Merit SF; Engrng.

LESPERANCE, JENNIFER; Gardner HS; Gardner, MA; (Y); 20/180; Church Yth Grp; Debate Tm; Pres French Clb; Model UN; Chorus; Yrbk Stf; Var Capt Crs Cntry; Trk; Hon Roll; Outstndng Spkr Awd 85; Pre-Med.

LESSARD, PETER; Brockton HS; Brockton, MA; (Y); 33/1000; Drama Clb; JCL; Red Cross Aide; Stage Crew; Nwsp Rptr; High Hon Roll; NHS; Prfct Atten Awd; Chem.

LESTER, JO ELLEN; Dedham HS; Dedham, MA; (Y); 22/285; Chorus; High Hon Roll; Hon Roll; NHS; Pres Schlr; Voice Dem Awd; Outstndng-Wntr Clr Guard 83; Bst Sci 83 & 84; Northeastern U; Phrmcy.

LESTER, JOHN EDWARD; Dartmouth HS; S Dartmouth, MA; (Y); 1/258; Math Tm; Concert Band; Nwsp Rptr; Bausch & Lomb Sci Awd; Elks Awd; NHS; Ntl Merit SF; Pres Schlr; St Schlr; Boy Scts; MA All ST Bnd 83; Harvard U Bk Awd, Brown U Bk Awd 84; MA Inst Of Tech; Biomed Engrng.

LESZCZYNSKI, STEVEN M; Salem HS; Salem, MA; (Y); JV Socr; Hon Roll; Almni Schlrshp 85; U Of Lowell; Cvl Engrng.

LETCHFORD, EMMA E; Franklin HS; Franklin, MA; (S); Band; Chorus; Concert Band; Drm Mjr(t); Jazz Band; Mrchg Band; Pep Band; Variety Show; All ST Chrs 85; Central Dist Chrs 85; Music.

LETIZIO, GINA; Presentation Of Mary Acad; Lawrence, MA; (Y); Church Yth Grp; Computer Clb; French Clb; Ski Clb; Nwsp Stf; Yrbk Phtg; Yrbk Stf; Trs Stu Cncl; MA U Amherst; Hotel Adm.

LETOURNEAU, MICHELLE; Presentation Of Mary Acad; Chester, NH; (S); 8/52; Church Yth Grp; Cmnty Wkr; Computer Clb; Pres French Clb; Math Clb; Chorus; Nwsp Stf; Yrbk Stf; High Hon Roll; Hon Roll; Co Pres Stu Agnst Drvng Drunk 85; Jrnslm.

LEVASSEUR, RONALD; Bishop Connolly HS; Fall River, MA; (Y); 40/170; Drama Clb; French Clb; JA; Thesps; Yrbk Bus Mgr; Pres Frsh Cls; Tennis; High Hon Roll; Hon Roll; Bentley; Acctng.

LEVENTMAN, AARON; Newton North HS; Newton, MA; (Y); Pres Drama Clb; Speech Tm; School Play; Philip J Wolfe Thtr Awd 85; Hon Mntn Nw Englnd HS Video Comptn 85; UC Santa Cruz; Flmmkng.

LEVER, JOANN; Methuen HS; Methuen, MA; (Y); 51/395; 4-H; Var JV Bsktbl; Var JV Powder Puff Ftbl; Var JV Sftbl; Var Swmmng; Var JV Vllybl; 4-H Awd; Hon Roll; Spanish NHS; Merrimac Coll; Math.

LEVERONE, KELLI; Bristol Plymouth Reg Vo Tech; Taunton, MA; (Y); Art Clb; Lit Mag; Pres Jr Cls; Rep Sr Cls; Hon Roll.

LEVESQUE, MICHAEL; Bishop Connolly HS; Bristol, RI; (S); 28/177; Boy Scts; Church Yth Grp; Hon Roll; Intl Bus.

LEVESQUE, SHARON; Joseph Case HS; Swansea, MA; (Y); 31/209; French Clb; Acpl Chr; Band; Chorus; Color Guard; School Play; Hon Roll; Drama Clb; Intnl Clb; Church Choir; Cathlc Orgnz Foresters Schlrshp 85; Storehill Coll; Bus.

LEVINE, ALEX G; Newton South HS; Brookline, MA; (Y); Am Leg Boys St; French Clb; Var Capt Bsktbl; Var Lcrss; JV Var Socr; Hon Roll; All-Schlstc Awds Boston Globe, Boston Herald & Bnai Brith For Lacrosse 85.

LEVINE, DAVID; Randolph HS; Randolph, MA; (Y); French Clb; Math Tm; Ski Clb; Teachers Aide; Temple Yth Grp; Hon Roll; NHS; Engrng.

LEVINE, JEFFREY S; Brockton HS; Brockton, MA; (Y); 55/998; Am Leg Boys St; Temple Yth Grp; Band; Mrchg Band; Orch; Rep Soph Cls; Rep Jr Cls; Rep Sr Cls; Var Ftbl; Var Wt Lftg; Engrg.

LEVINE, JONATHAN M; Taconic HS; Pittsfield, MA; (Y); 2/292; Latin Clb; Quiz Bowl; School Musical; School Play; Nwsp Ed-Chief; Yrbk Stf; Pres Sr Cls; Ntl Merit SF.

LEVINE, JULIE; Framingham South HS; Framingham, MA; (Y); 24/268; Cmnty Wkr; Hosp Aide; Sec Latin Clb; Ski Clb; Spanish Clb; Ed Yrbk Bus Mgr; Off Frsh Cls; Off Soph Cls; Off Jr Cls; Stu Cncl; Lang.

LEVINE, LAUREN; Canton HS; Canton, MA; (Y); 4/275; Am Leg Aux Girls St; 4-H; German Clb; Girl Scts; Science Clb; Band; Concert Band; Mrchg Band; School Musical; School Play; Century Clb Awd 84-85; Pre-Law.

LEVINE, MARK A; Framingham South HS; Framingham, MA; (Y); 1/285; Math Clb; Temple Yth Grp; Nwsp Stf; Var L Crs Cntry; Var Capt Trk; High Hon Roll; NHS; Chess Clb; Computer Clb; French Clb; Harvard Bk Awd 83-84; Trig-Star Awd 84-85; Acad Excel Awd 84-85; Comp Sci.

LEVINE, RACHEL A; Newton North HS; Newton, MA; (Y); Ski Clb; Yrbk Stf; Rep Stu Cncl; Socr; Trk; Hon Roll; Audio-Vis.

LEVINE, STEPHANIE; Randolph HS; Randolph, MA; (Y); Teachers Aide; Temple Yth Grp; Yrbk Stf; Off Frsh Cls; Off Soph Cls; Off Jr Cls; Off Sr Cls; Stu Cncl; Var L Cheerleading; Powder Puff Ftbl; JR Advsrs Awd 85.

LEVINE, TODD; Stoughton HS; Stoughton, MA; (Y); Temple Yth Grp; Stage Crew; Rep Stu Cncl; Var L Bsbl; Var L Bsktbl; Var L Ftbl; High Hon Roll; Exc Brd Class Of 86 83-86; Sprts Med.

LEVITT, MALA; Framingham South HS; Framingham, MA; (Y); 21/265; Drama Clb; Latin Clb; School Musical; JV Gym; JV Lcrss; Capt Pom Pon; High Hon Roll; Hon Roll; NHS; Architecture.

LEVY, ERICA J; Belmont HS; Belmont, MA; (Y); Am Leg Aux Girls St; Hosp Aide; Trs VP Temple Yth Grp; Band; Concert Band; Mrchg Band; JV Bsktbl; Mgr(s); Score Keeper; Hon Roll; Schl Comm Awds Bnd 84 & 85; MA ST Dist Bnd 84; Comp Sci.

LEVY, LANCE; Stoughton HS; Stoughton, MA; (Y); Varsity Clb; Nwsp Stf; Lit Mag; VP Frsh Cls; Rep Soph Cls; Rep Jr Cls; Im Mgr Bsbl; Im Mgr Bsktbl; Var Ice Hcky; Var VP Tennis; Sci Fair Partcpnt 84-84; Hnry Engl Compstn Wrtg Cntst 84; Corp Law.

LEW, JOHN; Weymouth North HS; Weymouth, MA; (Y); Var Trk; Hon Roll; Bentley Coll; Mrktng.

LEWIS, DEBORAH; Haverhill HS; Georgetown, MA; (Y); 41/385; French Clb; MMM; Acpl Chr; Trs Chorus; Church Choir; School Musical; Swing Chorus; Variety Show; High Hon Roll; Hon Roll; Mst Imprvd Frnch Stu 83; Salem ST Coll; Nrsng.

LEWIS, DIANA; North Attleboro HS; No Attleboro, MA; (S); 8/232; GAA; JCL; Latin Clb; Var L Bsktbl; Var L Fld Hcky; Var L Sftbl; NHS; Natl Latin Exam Slvr Mdl 83; Natl Latin Exam Cert Of Merit 84; Med.

LEWIS, FRANCIS J; Phillips Acad; Chicago, IL; (Y); German Clb; Rep Jr Cls; Rep Sr Cls; Rep Stu Cncl; Hon Roll; Ntl Merit SF; Var Lcrss; JV Socr; Pol Sci.

LEWIS, IAN; Newton North HS; W Newton, MA; (Y); Am Leg Boys St; Political Wkr; Yrbk Phtg; Capt Var Gym; Ntl Merit Ltr; Glss Blwg.

LEWIS, JUDITH; Mario Unana HS; Mattapan, MA; (Y); Church Yth Grp; JA; Church Choir; School Play; Yrbk Stf; Sec Jr Cls; Sec Sr Cls; Rep Stu Cncl; Var Bsktbl; Var Trk; MA Pre-Engrng Pgm Ldrshp, Schlstc Awds 83-84; U Lowell; Elec Engrng.

LEWIS, MICHELLE; Woburn SR HS; Woburn, MA; (S); #219 In Class; French Clb; Color Guard; Flag Corp; Rep Stu Cncl; Hon Roll; Sci Fair 3rd Pl 81-82; NE U; Accntnt.

LEWIS, PAMELA; New Bedford HS; New Bedford, MA; (Y); French Clb; Hosp Aide; Red Cross Aide; Chorus; Church Choir; Stu Cncl; Hon Roll; Diocese Fall Rvr; Present Bishops Charty Ball 85; Nrsg.

LEWIS, ROBERT; Whitman-Hanson Regional HS; Hanson, MA; (Y); 16/320; Var Bsbl; Var Bsktbl; Var Ftbl; NHS; Aerontcl Engrng.

LI, LIN TAI; Boston Technical HS; Boston, MA; (Y); Hosp Aide; Rep Jr Cls; Rep Stu Cncl; Hon Roll; NHS; Bentley Coll; Bus Admn.

LIATSOS, EMANUEL S; Lynn English HS; Lynn, MA; (Y); 4/382; Am Leg Boys St; Church Yth Grp; Band; Pep Band; Yrbk Stf; VP Jr Cls; Stu Cncl; Bsktbl; Vllybl; VP NHS; MVP Bsktbl 85; MIT; Chem Engr.

LIAZOS, THEODORE; Saint Johns HS; Wocester, MA; (Y); Church Yth Grp; French Clb; Political Wkr; Nwsp Stf; Trk; High Hon Roll; NHS; Ntl Merit SF; Nwspr Rookie Wrtr Of Yr 83; Harvard Coll; Intl Rel.

LIBBARES, LISA; Greenfield HS; Greenfield, MA; (Y); Computer Clb; Drama Clb; Girl Scts; Band; Concert Band; Mrchg Band; School Play; Hon Roll.

LIBBY, RICHARD; Hingham HS; Hingham, MA; (Y); Cmnty Wkr; Computer Clb; Var Golf; Im Vllybl; High Hon Roll; Hon Roll.

LICOPOLI, MARIA; Holy Name HS; Sutton, MA; (Y); Church Yth Grp; Ski Clb; Bsktbl; JV Var Socr; Trk; Wt Lftg; High Hon Roll; Hon Roll; NHS; Relgn Awd 83; Alg II & Frnch II Awd 84; Alg III, Litrtr III, Rlgn III Awd 85; Engrng.

LICOSKI, SONJA J; Silver Lake Regional HS; Pembroke, MA; (Y); 45/462; Drama Clb; Latin Clb; Office Aide; Var Mgr(s); Var Score Keeper; JV Trk; Hon Roll; Ntl Merit Ltr; Bio.

LIESKE, JONATHAN; Shepherd Hill HS; Dudley, MA; (Y); Hon Roll; Math Awd 82-83; Johnson & Wales; Culinary Arts.

LIEU, TINA; Newton North HS; W Newton, MA; (Y); Orch; High Hon Roll; Hon Roll.

LIFRAK, JOSEPH; Bishop Connolly HS; Fall River, MA; (S); 32/200; Boys Clb Am; Cmnty Wkr; Ski Clb; VP Bsktbl; JV Crs Cntry; Var Capt Golf; Elks Awd; High Hon Roll; NHS; Highest Hnr Roll; Oteting Clb; Homeroom Dir; Harvard; Med.

LIGNOS, KELLY; Bishop Fenwick HS; Peabody, MA; (Y); Yrbk Stf; Math.

LILLIE, JOSEPH E; Murdock HS; Winchendon, MA; (Y); 2/78; Am Leg Boys St; Church Yth Grp; Model UN; Chorus; Church Choir; Concert Band; Jazz Band; Mrchg Band; Orch; School Play; Amer Lgn Awd 85; Pres Hnr Awd Fitchburg ST Coll 85; Fitchburg ST Coll; Engl.

LIM, HERBERT; Boston Latin Schl; Boston, MA; (Y); 22/330; Boys Clb Am; Computer Clb; JA; High Hon Roll; Hon Roll; NHS; Ntl Merit Ltr; Clsscl Prz 81; Fidelity Prz 83; Boston Lat Schl Sci Fair Hon Men 85.

LIMA, BARBARA; New Bedford HS; New Bedford, MA; (Y); Drama Clb; Teachers Aide; School Musical; Var Swmmng.

LIMA, DAVID; New Bedford HS; New Bedford, MA; (Y); Bsbl; Ftbl; Hon Roll.

LIMA, JAMES; Salem HS; Salem, MA; (Y); Band; Chorus; Concert Band; Hon Roll; Music.

LIMA, WENDY JO; New Bedford HS; New Bedford, MA; (Y); Dance Clb; Drama Clb; Girl Scts; ROTC; Color Guard; Drill Tm; Gym; Hon Roll; Cape Verdean Amer Vets Assc Inc & Ladies Aux 85; Eleanor M Williams Schlrshp 85; United Socl Clb 85; Becker JR Coll; Travel.

LIN, I MEI; Westwood HS; Westwood, MA; (Y); 2/241; Capt Math Tm; Jazz Band; School Musical; Ed Lit Mag; JV Tennis; High Hon Roll; VP NHS; Ntl Merit SF; Sal; Spanish NHS; Grtr Bostn Yth Symph Orch 85; MA Assn Schl Suprntndnt Awd 84; Fnlst New England Conservtry Comptn 83; Harvard.

LINCOLN, BETHANY; Medway HS; Medway, MA; (Y); Church Yth Grp; Hosp Aide; Nwsp Stf; VP Trs Stu Cncl; Bsktbl; Capt Sftbl; Vllybl; Phsilosophy Comm 84; SADD Rep 85.

LINCOLN, LINDA J; Medway JR SR HS; Medway, MA; (Y); 7/143; VP Church Yth Grp; Varsity Clb; Yrbk Bus Mgr; Sec Soph Cls; Sec Stu Cncl; Var Bsktbl; Var Sftbl; Var Capt Vllybl; Hon Roll; Jr NHS; Boostr Clb & Dennis Coakley Schlrshps 85; Medway Coach Awd 85; Southeastern MA U; Bio.

LINCOLN, SANDRA; Leicester HS; Leicester, MA; (Y); 38/113; Hon Roll; Bus.

LIND, TIMOTHY; Ayer SR HS; Shirley, MA; (Y); Art Clb; Yrbk Stf; Hon Roll; Achvt In Art 85; Cincinnati Police Acad; Plc Ofc.

LINDSEY, JOAN P; Medway JR SR HS; Medway, MA; (Y); 8/154; Teachers Aide; Lib Band; School Musical; Ed Yrbk Phtg; Hon Roll; NHS; Voice Dem Awd; Hnrb Mntn ST Vdo Comp 85; Prodcr Lcl TV Prog 84-86; Bk Awd Brown U Excllnc Englsh 85; Intl Stu.

LINDSTROM, KRISTINE; Woburn SR HS; Woburn, MA; (S); 160/500; French Clb; Girl Scts; Hosp Aide; Leo Clb; School Musical; Yrbk Stf; Stu Cncl; Var Capt Gym; Hon Roll; Tumblers Capt; Nrsng.

LINDWALL, ASHLEY; East Longmeadow HS; E Longmeadow, MA; (Y); 3/212; Pres NHS; Pres Schlr; AFS; French Clb; Hosp Aide; Intnl Clb; Band; Mrchg Band; Nwsp Stf; Gym; U Lowell; Phys Ther.

LING, MAURICE; Hingham HS; Hingham, MA; (Y); 6/350; Boy Scts; Computer Clb; Math Tm; Band; Concert Band; Jazz Band; Mrchg Band; Orch; School Musical; Symp Band; Outstndng Cntrbtn-Band & Orchestra 83-85; Elect Engrng.

LINGER, DAVE; Holliston HS; Holliston, MA; (Y); 54/206; Church Yth Grp; Ski Clb; Var L Bsktbl; Var L Ftbl; Hon Roll; WV U; Aero Engr.

LINGERMAN, MARK; Newburyport HS; Newburyport, MA; (Y); 53/200; JCL; Band; Jazz Band; School Musical; JV Bsbl; Var Ftbl; Hon Roll; Bus Adm.

LINNELL, AMY; Nauset Regional HS; Brewstr, MA; (Y); Ski Clb; Fld Hcky; Hon Roll; NHS; Frgn Lang.

LINSCOTT, JULIE; Newburyport HS; Newburyport, MA; (Y); GAA; Trs Frsh Cls; Rep Soph Cls; Bsktbl; Capt Var Cheerleading; Hon Roll; Var Lttr In Chrldng 83-84; Capt For Ftbl & Bsktbl Chrldng 85-86; Closeup Prog In WA DC 85; Acctnt.

LINZ, CHRISTINE; Bedford HS; Bedford, MA; (Y); 7/213; Church Yth Grp; Chorus; School Musical; Var Rep Soph Cls; Var Capt Fld Hcky; Powder Puff Ftbl; Hon Roll; NHS.

LIPINSKI, JUSTINE; Matignon HS; Somerville, MA; (Y); 49/182; Cmnty Wkr; Drama Clb; French Clb; Hosp Aide; School Play; Bus.

LIPPENS, STEPHEN A; Georgetown JR SR HS; Georgetown, MA; (Y); 11/93; Nwsp Ed-Chief; Yrbk Ed-Chief; Var L Socr; Hon Roll; NHS; Voice Dem Awd; Pres/Stu Advsry Cncl 84-85; VP SADD 84-85; Schl Wnnr Cent III Ldrshp Schlrshp 84; Boston Coll; Invstmnt Fin.

LIRIANO, DORCAS; Boston Latin HS; Boston, MA; (Y); 91/299; Spanish Clb; Jr Cls; Wnr Natl Fr Cont 83-84; Psych.

LISBOA, MARIA; Commerce HS; Springfield, MA; (S); Cmnty Wkr; Computer Clb; Office Aide; VP Sr Cls; Stu Cncl; JC Awd; NHS; Spnsh Awd 82; STCC; Secr.

LISOWSKI, JAMES; Chicopee HS; Chicopee, MA; (Y); 4/222; JV Bsbl; Var L Golf; High Hon Roll; NHS; Ntl Merit Ltr; Pres Schlr; Acadmc All-Am 84-85; Ntl Sci Achvt Awd 83-84; Hugh O Brien Ldrshp Awd 82-83; Rensselaer Polytechnic Inst.

LISTOVITCH, MARNA; St Peter-Marian HS; Holden, MA; (Y); 21/179; Cmnty Wkr; Band; Concert Band; Jazz Band; Mrchg Band; Nwsp Rptr; Ed Nwsp Stf; Hon Roll; Svc Awd, Schlrshp 85; St Joseph Coll; Nrsg.

LITCHFIELD, KERRY; Bedford HS; Bedford, MA; (Y); Yrbk Stf; Rep Frsh Cls; Rep Soph Cls; Bsktbl; Var JV Swmmng; Hon Roll.

LITCHFIELD, RICHARD J; Brockton HS; Brockton, MA; (Y); 17/943; VP French Clb; Pep Clb; School Musical; Nwsp Stf; Var Swmmng; High Hon Roll; Hon Roll; NHS; Pres Schlr; St Schlr; Cert Achvt Acad Exc 85; Ntl Hnr Rl; Boston Coll; Finance.

LITMAN, DAVID; Natick HS; Natick, MA; (Y); Cmnty Wkr; JA; Political Wkr; Spanish Clb; Temple Yth Grp; Trk; Bus.

LITTLE, CHRISTA; Boston Latin HS; Boston, MA; (Y); 44/342; Trs Camera Clb; Church Yth Grp; Cmnty Wkr; Hosp Aide; JA; Key Clb; Rep Stu Cncl; High Hon Roll; Prfct Atten Awd; Law.

LITTLE, HEATHER; Hoosac Valley HS; Adams, MA; (Y); Exploring; Ski Clb; JV Socr; Trk; Hon Roll.

LITTLEFIELD, MARK A; Newburyport HS; Newburyport, MA; (Y); 11/207; Math Clb; Math Tm; Band; Chorus; Jazz Band; High Hon Roll; Hon Roll; NHS; St Schlr; Outstndng Trombonist Awd 83; Salem ST Coll; Math Tchr.

LITTLEFIELD, SCOTT; St Dominic Savio HS; Saugus, MA; (Y); 40/125; Band; JV Capt Bsbl; L Ftbl; L Trk; Hon Roll.

LIU, AUSTIN; Burlington HS; Carlisle, MA; (Y); 11/315; Church Yth Grp; JA; Math Tm; Hon Roll; NHS.

LIU, JULIE ANNE; Doherty Momeril HS; Worcester, MA; (Y); Chorus; Nwsp Stf; Socr; NHS.

LIVINGSTN, ERIC; Hingham HS; Hingham, MA; (Y); AFS; Cmnty Wkr; Computer Clb; Trs Pres Drama Clb; Ski Clb; Thesps; School Musical; School Play; Hon Roll; VP Schl Gaming Clb 83-84; Syracuse U NY; Engrng.

LIVINGSTON, LOREE; Classical HS; Lynn, MA; (Y); Church Yth Grp; GAA; Phys Ftns Achvt Cert 83; Coach.

LIVINGSTONE, LISA; North Quincy HS; Quincy, MA; (Y); 125/379; Drama Clb; Pep Clb; Quiz Bowl; Ski Clb; Spanish Clb; Stage Crew; Yrbk Stf; Sec Jr Cls; Sec Sr Cls; Stu Cncl; Outstndng Achvt Ldrshp,Pride Commttee 85; U Of MA Amherst; Theatre.

LLEWELYN, DANIEL P; Pioneer Valley Regional HS; Northfield, MA; (Y); 2/55; Am Leg Boys St; Quiz Bowl; Var L Bsbl; Var L Bsktbl; Hon Roll; Trs NHS; Sal; Spanish NHS; Commwlth Schlr 85; Stevens Inst Tech; Engrng.

LOANDO, HEIDI-ANN; Milford HS; Milford, MA; (Y); Am Leg Aux Girls St; Dance Clb; Drama Clb; Hosp Aide; Stage Crew; High Hon Roll; Hon Roll; NHS; Spec Educ.

LOBO, JASON M; Southwick HS; Southwick, MA; (Y); 9/134; Am Leg Boys St; Model UN; Stu Cncl; Var Bsktbl; Hon Roll; NHS; St Schlr; VFW Awd; Church Yth Grp; Band; Street & Smiths All Am Bsktbl 84-85; Am Leg Good Citznshp Awd 85; Billy Wise Awd Sportsmnshp 85; Dartmouth Coll; Comp Sci.

LOCHRIDGE, KELLY; Lexington HS; Lexington, MA; (Y); Church Yth Grp; Cmnty Wkr; Hosp Aide; Ski Clb; Chorus; Church Choir; School Musical; Var L Swmmng; Ithaca Coll NY; Physcl Thrpy.

LOCKE, KIM; Dedham HS; Dedham, MA; (Y); Church Yth Grp; Cmnty Wkr; Library Aide; Church Choir; Hon Roll; Sci Dept Mst Imprvd Awd 83-84; Occptnl Thrpst.

LOCKWOOD, AMY; Natick HS; Natick, MA; (Y); Pres Church Yth Grp; JCL; Key Clb; Band; Off Frsh Cls; Off Stu Cncl; Trk; High Hon Roll; Hon Roll; Ntl Merit SF; MA Assoc Arch Drwng Awd 84; Excllnce Intro Comp Proc Bus Awd 84; Oberlin Coll OH.

LOCKWOOD, TIM; Agawam HS; Feeding Hills, MA; (Y); Boy Scts; JA; Trs Soph Cls; Trs Jr Cls; Var Bsktbl; JV Socr; Hon Roll; St Michaels; Comp Sci.

LODISH, HEIDI; The Brimmer And May Schl; Brookline, MA; (S); Model UN; Office Aide; Chorus; School Musical; School Play; Symp Band; Nwsp Rptr; Yrbk Stf; Fld Hcky; Hon Roll; Catherine Baldwin Mc Coy Schlr 83; Kenyon Coll; Ecnmcs.

LOGAN, BARRY; Newton North HS; Newton, MA; (Y); 12/800; Am Leg Boys St; Church Yth Grp; Ski Clb; Jazz Band; Trs Sr Cls; Capt Crs Cntry; JV Lcrss; Capt Swmmng; Var Trk; Hon Roll; Mdcl.

LOGAN, COLLEEN M; Cathedral HS; Longmeadow, MA; (Y); Cmnty Wkr; Office Aide; Service Clb; Rep Stu Cncl; Hon Roll; Jr NHS; NHS; Pre-Med.

LOHREY, JENNIFER; Acad Of Notre Dame; Tewksbury, MA; (Y); 6/50; Dance Clb; Hosp Aide; Pep Clb; Ski Clb; Hon Roll; Dancing Awd 85; Mission Spirit Awd 85; Dr.

LOHRI, PETER; Georgetown JR SR HS; Georgetown, MA; (Y); 8/100; French Clb; Political Wkr; Var L Ftbl; Im Powder Puff Ftbl; High Hon Roll; Hon Roll; Ntl Merit Ltr; Cvcs Awd; Prfct Atten Awd; Boston U; Engrng.

LOISELLE, LINDA; North Attleboro HS; North Attleboro, MA; (Y); Var Cheerleading; Coach Actv; Var Gym; Powder Puff Ftbl; High Hon Roll; Hon Roll; NHS; VFW Awd; Bronze Medl 3rd Bst Vrsty Chrldr NECA Cheering Camp 83; Writng.

LOISELLE, ROBIN; Chicopee Comprehensive HS; Chicopee, MA; (S); 48/284; Cmnty Wkr; Computer Clb; FNA; German Clb; GAA; Aud/Vis; Powder Puff Ftbl; Socr; Sftbl; NHS; Bay ST Mdcl Ctr; Nrsng.

LOMANO, KRISTINA; Archbishop Williams HS; Marshfield, MA; (Y); #32 In Class; Church Yth Grp; Hosp Aide; Teachers Aide; Chorus; School Play; Hon Roll; NHS; Yrbk Stf; Bsktbl; Spnsh Awds For Mntng A Avr 84 & 85; Pin For Vlntrng At Quincy Cty Hosp 84; Nrs.

LOMBARA, JOHN; St Johns Preparatory Schl; Lynn, MA; (Y); Var Bsbl; Im Bsktbl; Im Ftbl; Var Co-Capt Ice Hcky; Hon Roll; NHS.

LOMBARA, STEPHEN; Wakefield HS; Wakefield, MA; (Y); 8/290; Math Tm; Concert Band; Bsktbl; Crs Cntry; Trk; Hon Roll; NHS; Ntl Merit Ltr; Boy Scts; Key Clb; Stu Ath Awd 85; Catalyst Awd Bst Chem Stu 85; MIT.

LOMBARA, SUZANNE S; Beverly HS; Beverly Farms, MA; (Y); 2/378; Am Leg Aux Girls St; Yrbk Ed-Chief; Trs Sr Cls; VP L Fld Hcky; Powder Puff Ftbl; High Hon Roll; Trs NHS; Ntl Merit SF; Sal; Schl Superintdnts 85; Cert Acad Achvt; Stanford U; Engrng.

LOMBARD, PAMELA J; Northampton HS; Northampton, MA; (Y); 5/250; Ski Clb; Band; School Musical; Variety Show; Var Crs Cntry; Var Swmmng; Var Trk; High Hon Roll; NHS; Ntl Merit SF; Sci.

LOMBARD, THERESA; Norton HS; Norton, MA; (Y); 5/175; Cmnty Wkr; Pep Clb; Ski Clb; VP Pres Concert Band; Mrchg Band; Rep Stu Cncl; Capt Var Bsktbl; High Hon Roll; VP NHS; Ntl Merit Ltr; Psych.

LOMBARDI, JOHN; Doherty Memorial HS; Worcester, MA; (Y); Aud/Vis; Church Yth Grp; Dance Clb; Trs Exploring; Latin Clb; Library Aide; Science Clb; Band; Orch; Hon Roll; Young Columbus Awd 84; Grnd Prze Sci Fair 84; Newsp Carrier Awd 82; Rutgers U; Ceramic Engrng.

LOMBARDI, JOHN; Holy Name HS; Worcester, MA; (Y); Var Bsbl; Bsktbl; Var Ftbl; Hon Roll; Math.

LOMBARDOZZI, LISA A; Malden HS; Malden, MA; (Y); 28/464; Key Clb; Nwsp Sprt Ed; Nwsp Stf; JV Fld Hcky; Hon Roll; Pre-Law.

LOMBERTO, MICHELLE; Mansfield HS; Mansfield, MA; (Y); Church Yth Grp; French Clb; Office Aide; Church Choir; Sec.

LONARDO, EILEEN; Bishop Feehan HS; Attleboro, MA; (Y); 96/260; Exploring; French Clb; Mgr Ftbl; Mgr Sftbl; French Hon Soc; High Hon Roll; Hon Roll.

LONDON, CHARLES; New Bedford HS; New Bedford, MA; (Y); Comp Tech.

LONG, ELAINE; Bishop Feehan HS; S Attleboro, MA; (Y); Prfct Atten Awd; Fshn Dsgn.

LONG, ELEANOR; Archbishop Williams HS; Milton, MA; (Y); School Play; Stage Crew; Nwsp Stf; Hon Roll; NEDT Awd; Church Yth Grp; Nwsp Rptr; Stu Agnst Drnk Drvng Awd 84-85; Hofstra U; Cmnctns.

LONG, JOHN; Bourne HS; Buzzards Bay, MA; (Y); Church Yth Grp; Jr NHS; Ntl Merit SF; Pres Acad Fit Awd 85; Cls Artist 85; SMU; Graphic Arts.

LONG, LUCINDA; Hopedale JR SR HS; Hopedale, MA; (S); 1/58; Chorus; School Play; Stage Crew; Rep Trs Stu Cncl; High Hon Roll.

LONG, MARY ELLEN F; Mansfield HS; Mansfield, MA; (Y); 7/185; French Clb; Acpl Chr; School Musical; School Play; Stage Crew; Var L Trk; High Hon Roll; Hon Roll; NHS; Drama Clb; Pres Acadmc Fit Awd 84-85; Excllnc Frnch Awd 85; Boston Coll; Bus Adm.

LONGLEY, ANDREW; Reading Memorial HS; Reading, MA; (Y); Church Yth Grp; Computer Clb; Math Tm; Church Choir; Lit Mag; JV Trk; High Hon Roll; NHS; Nwsp Rptr; Brown Book Awd 85; Full Schlrshp To Andover Acad Smmr Sessn 85; Aerosp Engr.

LONGO, LEE ANN; Fairhaven HS; Fairhaven, MA; (Y); 29/189; French Clb; Nwsp Rptr; Nwsp Sprt Ed; Nwsp Stf; Yrbk Stf; Trs Stu Cncl; Fld Hcky; Jr NHS; Acdmc Achvmnt Schlrshp 85-89; Johnson & Wales Coll; Hotel.

LONGO, MARK; Leominster HS; Leominster, MA; (Y); 37/193; Am Leg Boys St; French Clb; Math Clb; Office Aide; School Musical; School Play; VP Frsh Cls; Rep Stu Cncl; Hon Roll; Pres Schlr; 1st MA Hist Conf 84; SR Cls Ply, J D Miller Schlrshp, MA HS Drama Fstvl 85; Bentley Coll; Econ.

LONIS, KIMBERLY; Chicopee Comprehensive HS; Chicopee, MA; (Y); 3/314; Band; Variety Show; Yrbk Stf; Var Capt Bsktbl; Powder Puff Ftbl; Var Capt Sftbl; Elks Awd; High Hon Roll; NHS; Elks Teenager Yr 85; Dartmouth Bk Awd 84; Pro Merito 85; U Of VT; Pre-Med.

LONNBERG, KRISTIN; Medford HS; Medford, MA; (Y); 99/413; Letterman Clb; Ski Clb; Var L Socr; L Tennis; Bus Admin.

LOONEY, KACEY; Tantasqua HS; Brimfield, MA; (Y); 40/205; Church Yth Grp; English Clb; Math Tm; Ski Clb; Varsity Clb; Variety Show; Stu Cncl; L Var Socr; Var Trk; Hon Roll; Johnson & Wales Coll; Bus.

LOONEY, KIMBERLY; Lynn English HS; Lynn, MA; (Y); Drama Clb; School Musical; Variety Show; Hon Roll; Dance.

LOPES, DULCE; Brockton HS; Central Falls, RI; (Y); SMU; Nrs.

LOPES, PAUL R; Fairhaven HS; Fairhaven, MA; (Y); 47/225; Aud/Vis; Camera Clb; Intnl Clb; JA; Library Aide; Nwsp Stf; Yrbk Phtg; Var L Trk; Cit Awd; Salve Regina Coll; Comm Dsgn.

LOPES, TERESA; Cambridge Rindge & Latin HS; Cambridge, MA; (Y); 4/580; Debate Tm; JCL; Letterman Clb; Science Clb; Var Socr; Var Wrstlng; High Hon Roll; JA; Latin Clb; Teachers Aide; Harvard U; Comp Sci.

LOPEZ, LISA; Dana Hall Schl; Queens, NY; (Y); Debate Tm; Hosp Aide; Library Aide; Math Clb; Science Clb; Band; School Musical; Lit Mag; Cit Awd; Hon Roll; ABC Schlrshp 83; Arist Hnr Soc 83; Cert Apprctn Peac Corps Prtnrshp Pgm 83; Pre-Med.

LOPEZ, NELSON R; East Boston HS; E Boston, MA; (Y); Art Clb; Boys Clb Am; Chess Clb; CAP; Computer Clb; Math Clb; Office Aide; Science Clb; Spanish Clb; Band; Math Hnr 81; Arts Awd 83; Martial Arts Hnr 81; U MA; Med.

LOPEZ, NOEMI; Technical HS; Springfield, MA; (Y); 3/219; Off Jr Cls; Rep Stu Cncl; Trk; Zoology.

LORD, JENNIFER S; Bellingham Memorial HS; Bellingham, MA; (Y); 33/190; Drama Clb; French Clb; Ski Clb; School Play; Yrbk Rptr; Rep Stu Cncl; Hon Roll; Intrl Order Rainbow For Girls Offcr 82-85; Framingham ST Histrcl Conf 83-84; Fncl Awd Boston U 85; Boston U; Jrnlsm.

LORD, KENNETH RONALD; Westport HS; Westport, MA; (Y); 18/142; Art Clb; Church Yth Grp; Var Capt Bsbl; Var L Bsktbl; Bowling; Var Capt Crs Cntry; Elks Awd; High Hon Roll; NHS; Pres Schlr; B Taber, Col E Brenner, MA ST Schlrshps 85; Southeastern MA U; Comp Engrng.

LORDAN, JODI M; Reading Memorial HS; Reading, MA; (Y); 13/350; French Clb; Pres Pep Clb; Chorus; High Hon Roll; Hon Roll; NHS; Ntl Merit Ltr; Boston U; Nrsng.

LORDAN, TIMOTHY; Arlington Catholic HS; Arlington, MA; (Y); Var Bsbl; Var Crs Cntry; Var Ftbl; JV Var Ice Hcky; Aero Nvgtn.

LORDEN, DIANA; Groton-Dunstable HS; Groton, MA; (Y); Am Leg Aux Girls St; Hosp Aide; Ski Clb; Band; Rep Stu Cncl; JV Sftbl; Hon Roll; Jr NHS; VFW Awd; Voice Dem Awd; Comp Sci.

LORION, KRISTIN; Cathedral HS; Springfield, MA; (Y); Girl Scts; JA; Chorus; Church Choir; School Musical; School Play; Swing Chorus; Variety Show; STCC; Bus.

LOSAW, SANDRA; Lee HS; Lee, MA; (Y); 3/100; Church Yth Grp; Drama Clb; Quiz Bowl; Concert Band; Mrchg Band; School Musical; School Play; DAR Awd; High Hon Roll; NHS; Assumption Coll.

LOTRIONTE, CATHERINE; Bishop Connolly HS; Somerset, MA; (S); 3/177; Church Yth Grp; Computer Clb; Math Tm; Ski Clb; Spanish Clb; Yrbk Rptr; Yrbk Sprt Ed; Bowling; Tennis; Voice Dem Awd; Martin Luther King Jr Essay Awd 84; Piano Awds 83-84; Harvard; Law.

LOUD, KEITH J; Belmont Hill HS; Burlington, MA; (Y); Aud/Vis; Math Tm; Var L Ice Hcky; Var Mgr(s); Score Keeper; Var L Socr; Timer; High Hon Roll; Ntl Merit SF; Cum Laude Soc 84; Harvrd Clb Boston Awd 84; Brown Bk Awd 84; Med.

LOUGEE, MICHELLE; Nashoba Regional HS; Stow, MA; (Y); 35/200; Lit Mag; Var Capt Cheerleading; High Hon Roll; Hon Roll; Perfrmnc Awd From Boston U 85; Intor Art Awd 82-89; Drwg & Paintg I Awd 83; Boto Globe Gld Key 85; Boston U; Art.

LOUGHLIN, THOMAS LESLIE; Brockton HS; Brockton, MA; (Y); Brockton Hstrcl Soc 81-83; U Of Bridgeport CT; Arts & Hmn.

LOUIE, JOSEPHINE; Newton North HS; W Newton, MA; (Y); Speech Tm; Acpl Chr; Chorus; Orch; School Musical; Pres Stu Cncl; Im Golf; JV Socr; High Hon Roll; Colby Coll Bk Prz 85.

LOVATO, CHERYL; Plymouth-Carver HS; Carver, MA; (Y); 27/511; Cmnty Wkr; Science Clb; Band; Concert Band; Mrchg Band; Hon Roll; Ntl Merit Ltr; Pres Acad Fit Awd 85; Boston U; Psych.

LOVE, AMY; Mahowak Trail Regional HS; Shelburne Fls, MA; (Y); 29/142; School Musical; Yrbk Stf; Sec Frsh Cls; Sec Soph Cls; Sec Jr Cls; Sec Sr Cls; Rep Stu Cncl; Score Keeper; Tennis; Hon Roll.

LOVELY, PAM; Haverhill HS; Bradford, MA; (Y); 36/435; Capt Swmmng; High Hon Roll; MVP In Swmng 82, 83 & 85; MVP Tennis.

LOVERRO, JODI; Clinton HS; Clinton, MA; (S); Pres OEA; Yrbk Stf; VP Jr Cls; VP Sr Cls; Capt L Bsktbl; Var L Sftbl; Capt L Vllybl; High Hon Roll; NHS; VP Church Yth Grp; Outstndng Bus Stu Of Yr 85; Athl Of Wk 83 & 84; Bay ST JR Coll Boston; Bus.

LOWDER, AMY JO; Lexington HS; Lexington, MA; (Y); French Clb; Ski Clb; Chorus; Yrbk Stf; Var Tennis; Hon Roll.

LOWENSTEIN, DOUGLAS; Bishop Connolly HS; Newport, RI; (S); 10/200; Latin Clb; Math Tm; JV Bsktbl; L Tennis; High Hon Roll; NHS.

LOWENTHAL, MICAH; Newton South HS; Newton, MA; (Y); Math Tm; Var Trk; Hon Roll; Ntl Merit SF.

LOWERY, RAELEEN; Greater New Bedford Vo Tech; New Bedford, MA; (Y); Hosp Aide; Ski Clb; Yrbk Stf; Var Bsbl; Var L Cheerleading; Var Trk; VICA Gld Mdl-ST Rgnl Partcptd Ntls Phoenix AZ 85; TX Wmns U; Physcl Thrpy.

LOWNEY, JENNIFER; Newton North HS; W Newton, MA; (Y); Cmnty Wkr; Office Aide; Varsity Clb; Stage Crew; Variety Show; Var JV Fld Hcky; Var Capt Gym; Var Trk; Hon Roll; John F Kennedy Hstry Awd 85; H L Wash Chem Cup 85.

LUBIN, SUZANNE; Apponequet Regional HS; East Freetown, MA; (Y); 6/225; Drama Clb; French Clb; Scholastic Bowl; Acpl Chr; Chorus; School Musical; School Play; Variety Show; Sec Frsh Cls; Rep Soph Cls; Drama Clb Awd 85; Acad Excllnce Awd 84; Cmmnctns.

LUCCHETTI, MARY; Fontbonne Acad; Milton, MA; (Y); Camera Clb; Drama Clb; Ski Clb; Chorus; School Play; Hon Roll; Excell In Alg II 84-85; Spnsh Awd Cum Laude 84-85; Chem.

LUCCI, DAVID; Bishop Connolly HS; Portsmouth, RI; (Y); Hon Roll; Comp Engrng.

LUCCIO, DARLENE; Ursuline Acad; Dedham, MA; (Y); Drama Clb; Hosp Aide; Political Wkr; Spanish Clb; School Play; Stage Crew; Nwsp Rptr; Yrbk Stf; Trs Jr Cls; Hon Roll; Congrssnl Aide Congrssmn Moakley Bostn Ofc 85; Ordham U; Pre-Law.

LUCEY, JOANNE; Holy Name CCHS; Worcester, MA; (Y); 42/273; Pres Church Yth Grp; Service Clb; School Musical; Nwsp Rptr; Sec Stu Cncl; Yrbk Rptr; Yrbk Stf; Bsktbl; Var L Fld Hcky; Sftbl; Hmnts II Awd 84; Acad Awds Alg I, Geomtry, Hist I & II, Jrnlsm; Comm Skills Frnch I & II; Pre-Law.

LUCEY, JOHN; Central Catholic HS; Methuen, MA; (Y); Am Leg Boys St; Art Clb; Church Yth Grp; FBLA; FTA; MMM; Red Cross Aide; ROTC; Service Clb; L Ftbl; Legion Hon 85; Music.

LUCHINI, JOSEPH P; Milford HS; Milford, MA; (Y); 72/311; Band; Jazz Band; JV Bsbl; JV Bsktbl; JV Var Socr; Var L Trk; US Army Ntl Soccer Coaches Assn MVP Awd 85; Class Of 85 Mem Schlrshp 85; Kim Miller Awd 85; Syracuse U; Mech Engrng.

LUCHINI, RICHARD; Milford HS; Milford, MA; (Y); 55/292; JV Bsktbl; Var L Socr; Var L Trk; Hon Roll; Vrsty Trck Mst Dedctd 85; Vrsty Trck Rookie Of Yr 83.

LUCIA, MAUREEN; Nortre Dame Acad; Dorchester, MA; (Y); Drama Clb; Girl Scts; Hosp Aide; Key Clb; Ski Clb; Acpl Chr; Chorus; School Musical; School Play; Trk; Nrsng.

LUCIA, RICHARD; Holyoke HS; Holyoke, MA; (Y); Var Crs Cntry; Var Trk; Hon Roll; U MA; Acctng.

LUCIANO, ROBERT; Dedham HS; Dedham, MA; (Y); 34/220; Aud/Vis; Church Yth Grp; Ski Clb; Ftbl; Wrstlng; Hon Roll; Bus.

LUCIER, DAWN; Hopedale Jr-Sr HS; Hopedale, MA; (S); 4/58; Chorus; VP Frsh Cls; Rep Stu Cncl; Var Mgr(s); Var Score Keeper; Var L Sftbl; Var Timer; High Hon Roll; School Play; Stage Crew; Holy Cross Coll; Sprts Med.

LUCIER, TINA; Bay Path RVT HS; Southbridge, MA; (Y); 42/158; DECA; Yrbk Phtg; Yrbk Stf; Stu Cncl; Var Cheerleading; Score Keeper; Hon Roll; Bstr Clb Schlrshp 85; Rotry Clb HS Hnr Day Awd 85; Dudley Hall Inst; Bus Admin.

LUCIUS, ROBERT; Dracut SR HS; Dracut, MA; (Y); Aud/Vis; Pres Computer Clb; Pres Key Clb; Political Wkr; Jazz Band; Mrchg Band; Crs Cntry; Trk; Congrssnl Nom For W Point 85; Mst Outstndng Stu In TV Prodctn 85; Citadel; Intl Rltns.

LUCZYNSKI, REBECCA; Cathedral HS; Springfield, MA; (Y); Nwsp Stf; Var Capt Cheerleading; Intnl Clb; JA.

LUIPPOLD, CAMILLE; Greenfield HS; Greenfield, MA; (Y); Dance Clb; DECA; Pep Clb; Nwsp Stf; Yrbk Stf; Sec Stu Cncl; Var Cheerleading; JV Sftbl; Hon Roll; Law.

LUKEN, BETH; Tewksbury Memorial HS; Tewksbuy, MA; (Y); Library Aide; Office Aide; Chorus; Trk; Vllybl; Hon Roll; Most Vlbl Chrl Offcr 84-85; Dnce.

LUKOWSKI, DOREEN; Masconemet Regional HS; Topsfield, MA; (Y); 4/250; French Clb; Hosp Aide; Sec Frsh Cls; Sec Soph Cls; Stu Cncl; Capt Cheerleading; Var Fld Hcky; Hon Roll; Jr NHS; NHS; Harvard Book Prz 85.

LUND, KRISTIN; Westwood HS; Westwood, MA; (Y); 57/215; AFS; Key Clb; School Play; Yrbk Stf; Capt Fld Hcky; Powder Puff Ftbl; Trk; Hon Roll; Mthmtcs.

LUNDBERG JR, ROBERT S; Shepherd Hill Regional HS; Brookfield, MA; (Y); Am Leg Boys St; School Musical; Rep Soph Cls; Rep Jr Cls; Rep Sr Cls; Rep Stu Cncl; JV Var Socr; Trk; U Lowell; Mech Engrng.

LUNNY, LAUREN; Northampton HS; Northampton, MA; (Y); 69/189; Church Yth Grp; Cmnty Wkr; GAA; Varsity Clb; Yrbk Phtg; Yrbk Stf; Jr Cls; Sr Cls; Stu Cncl; Cheerleading; Samuel Michelson Awd Excllnce Govt 85; Dollars For Schlrs 85; U ME Orono; Polit Sci.

LUOMA, LAUREN J; Hudson Catholic HS; Hudson, MA; (Y); 1/48; Cmnty Wkr; VP Pres JA; Math Tm; Trs Frsh Cls; Pres Jr Cls; JV Sftbl; High Hon Roll; Pres NHS; Pres Schlr; Val; St Michaels Hnr Tuitn Schlrshp 85-89; Frgn Lang Hghst Avg Awd Spnsh 85; St Michaels Coll; Bus Mgt.

LUONG, TRUNG; Doherty Memorial HS; Worcester, MA; (Y); French Clb; FHA; JA; Latin Clb; Library Aide; Rep Jr Cls; High Hon Roll; Hon Roll; Ntl Merit Ltr; Horace Mann Awd 84.

LUPI, ANDREA; Matignon HS; Somerville, MA; (Y); 3/190; Church Yth Grp; Drama Clb; School Musical; JV Trk; French Hon Soc; NHS; NEDT Awd; Bus.

LUPU-SAX, TONI; Newton North HS; Newton, MA; (Y); Pres Drama Clb; NFL; Speech Tm; Mgr Chorus; Mrchg Band; School Musical; School Play; Lit Mag; Thtr.

LURIE, SHARI; Doherty Memorial HS; Worcester, MA; (Y); 43/356; Hosp Aide; Ski Clb; Temple Yth Grp; Stage Crew; Yrbk Stf; Hon Roll; NHS; 100 Hrs Vlntr Wrk Hosp 83; Brandeis U; Bio.

LUSH, DOUGLAS; Agawam HS; Agawam, MA; (Y); 4-H; Chorus; School Musical; School Play; Variety Show; Off Soph Cls; Off Jr Cls; JV Im Socr; High Hon Roll; Hon Roll.

LUSIGNAN, KRISTINA; Lee HS; Lee, MA; (Y); 6/114; Church Yth Grp; Debate Tm; Drama Clb; French Clb; Math Clb; Math Tm; Quiz Bowl; Color Guard; Flag Corp; School Musical; Sec Ed Tchr.

LUSSIER, CHAD; Ware HS; Ware, MA; (Y); 1/140; Am Leg Boys St; Computer Clb; French Clb; Math Clb; Math Tm; Pres Frsh Cls; VP Soph Cls; VP Jr Cls; VP Stu Cncl; Var Capt Bsbl.

LUTER, KELLEY L; Bedford HS; Bedford, MA; (Y); Church Yth Grp; Debate Tm; Pep Clb; ROTC; Variety Show; Cheerleading; Nrthestrn U Bstn MA; Med.

LUZ, TROY; Diman Regional Voke HS; Fall River, MA; (Y); Boys Clb Am; Cmnty Wkr; JV Capt Socr; Boy Of Yr 85; Pres Of JR Bd 85; Best Athlt Of Yr 85; Navy.

LUZAITIS, PAUL; Christopher Columbus HS; South Boston, MA; (S); 3/119; Chess Clb; Debate Tm; JA; Spanish Clb; Yrbk Stf; Rep Soph Cls; Jr Cls; Rep Sr Cls; Stu Cncl; Var L Bsbl; MA Adv Stds Pgm; Boston Coll; Law.

LVOVICH, LEONARD; Newton North HS; W Newton, MA; (Y); Ski Clb; Brandeis U; Law.

LYDON JR, JAMES F; St Dominic Savio HS; Chelsea, MA; (Y); 24/109; Church Yth Grp; Nwsp Rptr; Nwsp Stf; Yrbk Stf; Lit Mag; Trk; Hon Roll; Prfct Atten Awd; Htl Mgmt.

LYFORD, LISA K; Frontier Regional HS; Sunderland, MA; (Y); 2/76; Sec French Clb; Concert Band; Orch; Nwsp Stf; Yrbk Ed-Chief; Lit Mag; Bausch & Lomb Sci Awd; Sal; Fashn Revue Delgt Ntl Cong 84; Commnwlth MA Schlrshp 85; U MA-AMHERST; Biochem.

LYLE, SCOTT; Marian HS; Sudbury, MA; (Y); 60/180; Rep Frsh Cls; JV Bsbl; NHS; 2nd Pl Sci Fair 85; Twn Hcky Leag 81-82; Engrng.

LYMAN, KIMBERLY; Bay Path Reg Voc Tech HS; Oxford, MA; (Y); Nwsp Stf; Yrbk Stf; Sec Jr Cls; Sec Sr Cls; Capt Cheerleading; Capt Pom Pon; JV Sftbl; Hon Roll; Jr NHS; NHS; Comp.

LYNCH, ALLISON; Melrose HS; Melrose, MA; (Y); 11/380; Church Yth Grp; French Clb; Hosp Aide; Acpl Chr; Chorus; Flag Corp; School Musical; Stage Crew; Yrbk Bus Mgr; NHS; SADD; Hunger Project.

LYNCH, JENNIE; Fontbonne Acad; Stoughton, MA; (Y); Church Yth Grp; Pres Drama Clb; Key Clb; Chorus; School Musical; School Play; Variety Show; Crs Cntry; Sftbl; Capt Vllybl; Cum Laude Natl Latin Exam 83; Jordan Marsh JR Cncl 85; Bst Actrss Awd 83.

LYNCH, JEROME F; Cathedral HS; Springfeld, MA; (Y); 19/480; Church Yth Grp; Cmnty Wkr; Office Aide; Nwsp Rptr; Var Capt Golf; Mgr(s); Drama Clb; NHS; Ntl Merit Ltr; High Hon Roll; Gilbert Schlrshp 85-86; Boston Clg; Bus Mgmt.

LYNCH, KAREN; Girls Catholic HS; Medford, MA; (Y); 18/35; Drama Clb; Hosp Aide; School Play; Stage Crew; Yrbk Stf; Cit Awd; Hon Roll; Kiwanis Awd; Ntl Merit Ltr; Stu Quartr; Ntl Merit Hnr Rl; Bay ST JC; Fash Merch.

LYNCH, KELLY; Bridgewater-Raynham Regional HS; Bridgewater, MA; (Y); Ski Clb; Im Bsktbl; JV Socr; Var L Sftbl; Im Vllybl; Hon Roll; Ply Soccr Germny 86; Law Enfrcmnt.

LYNCH, KIMBERLEY; Middleboro HS; Middleboro, MA; (Y); 11/234; Drama Clb; Variety Show; Var Cheerleading; Var Diving; Var Gym; Var Powder Puff Ftbl; Var Swmmng; Var Trk; Hon Roll; NHS; JR Miss Pgnt Schlstc Schlrshp Awd 84; Boston Coll; Intl Bus.

LYNCH, LISA; St Bernards C C HS; Leominster, MA; (S); 14/169; Church Yth Grp; School Play; Hon Roll; NHS; Prfct Atten Awd; Assumption Coll; Polt Sci.

LYNCH, NANCY; Fontbonne Acad; Boston, MA; (Y); Church Yth Grp; Cmnty Wkr; Computer Clb; Debate Tm; Drama Clb; Pres JA; Pep Clb; Political Wkr; Chorus; School Play; Drama Fest 84; Jordan Marsh Fash Bd 85; Boston Clg; Bus/Fnce.

LYONS, DENISE; Our Lady Of Nazareth Acad; Woburn, MA; (Y); 17/53; Drama Clb; Pep Clb; Thesps; Stage Crew; Rep Soph Cls; Swmmng; High Hon Roll; Hon Roll; Awd For Consistent Efford & Christian Svc 85; Awd Outstndng Achvt In Algebra II 85; Grad W/Hnrs 83; Law.

LYONS, ELLEN; Chelmsford HS; Chelmsford, MA; (Y); Camera Clb; Church Yth Grp; Hon Roll.

LYONS, JEAN; Milton HS; Milton, MA; (Y); Drama Clb; School Musical; School Play; Swing Chorus; Variety Show; Yrbk Ed-Chief; Sec Jr Cls; JV Tennis; JV Trk; Hon Roll; Drama Schlrshp 85; UN Pilgrmg Yth Fnlst 84; Cmmnctns.

LYONS, KATHLEEN M; Cardinal Spellman HS; Brockton, MA; (Y); Hosp Aide; Hon Roll; NEDT Awd; Harsco Merit Schlrshp Awd 85; John J Hallisey Mem Schlrshp 85; Pres Acad Ftns Awd 85; Boston U; Pre-Med.

LYONS, PAUL; Winthrop HS; Winthrop, MA; (Y); 7/217; Am Leg Boys St; Boy Scts; Drama Clb; School Play; Trs Frsh Cls; Pres Sr Cls; Var L Bsktbl; Cit Awd; Elks Awd; Hon Roll; Eagle Scout 81; Freedoms Fndtn 85; Amer Legion Schl Awd 83; Engr.

LYONS, ROBERT; Catholic Memorial HS; Brighton, MA; (Y); 19/247; Computer Clb; Math Clb; JV Capt Socr; L Wrstlng; Hon Roll; Jr NHS; NHS; NEDT Awd; Im Ftbl; Math Awd 83-84; Partl Schlrshp Cath Mem 82-86; Providence Coll; Bus.

LYONS, SHARYN L; Sharon HS; Sharon, MA; (Y); 19/210; Nwsp Stf; Hon Roll; Dance Fin Roller Skatng Comptn 84; Hnrb Mntn Framingham ST Coll Annual Hstrcl Conf 85; Babson Coll; Bus.

LYONS, SUSAN; Boston Latin HS; Boston, MA; (Y); 59/334; Church Yth Grp; Rep Stu Cncl; JV Var Bsktbl; Powder Puff Ftbl; JV Var Sftbl; Var Capt Swmmng; NHS; Art Clb; Boys Clb Am; Cmnty Wkr; Clsscl Awd 83; Schlrshp Engl 84; MVP 17 & Undr Swmmr 84; Pre Med.

MAC CORMACK, DENISE; Saint Clare HS; Boston, MA; (Y); 5/150; Church Yth Grp; JCL; Political Wkr; Nwsp Rptr; Nwsp Stf; Rep Jr Cls; Pres Stu Cncl; High Hon Roll; NHS; Boston Coll; Bus.

MAC DONALD, DENNIS; St Dominic Savio HS; Revere, MA; (Y); 15/120; Math Tm; High Hon Roll; Hon Roll; Acad Scholar HS 82-86.

MAC DONALD, LISA; Archbishop Williams HS; Braintree, MA; (Y); 2/200; Key Clb; Math Tm; High Hon Roll; Hon Roll; NHS; 1st Calculs Awd 85, Precalclus Awd 84; Wrld Hist Awd 85; Northeastern U; Engrng.

MAC DONALD, ROBIN; Bridgewater-Raynham Regional HS; Raynham, MA; (Y); Pres Church Yth Grp; Band; Concert Band; Drm Mjr(t); Jazz Band; Mrchg Band; Pep Band; Yrbk Stf; Hon Roll; Prfct Atten Awd; South Shore Consrvtry Mus Schlrshp 84; MA Lions All St Band Schlrshp 85; Oceanography.

MAC DONALD, STEPHEN J; St Patricks HS; Waltham, MA; (Y); 20/50; Am Leg Boys St; Boys Clb Am; VP Frsh Cls; VP Jr Cls; VP Sr Cls; Mgr Bsbl; Var Capt Bsktbl; Var Capt Ftbl; Hon Roll; NEDT Awd; Mass Stu Govt Day 85; Syracuse Coll; Doctor.

MAC DOUGALL, RICHARD; Medway JR SR HS; Medway, MA; (Y); 39/156; Am Leg Boys St; VP Pres Stu Cncl; Capt Ftbl; Capt Golf; Nwsp Sprt Ed; Im Wt Lftg; Prtcptd In Strtng 1st SADD Pgm In Medway 84-85; 1st Teenage Eucharistic Mnstr In Chrch 85; Bus Mngmnt.

MAC ELHINEY, ROBERT; Boston College HS; Weymouth, MA; (Y); 41/293; Cmnty Wkr; Key Clb; Var L Tennis; High Hon Roll; NHS; Cert Awd Acadmc Excllnc Amer Lit; Physcs & Algbr II 85; Tnns Coachs Awd 84; Bus.

MAC INNIS, MARGARET; Holy Name C C HS; Douglas, MA; (Y); 22/296; Church Yth Grp; French Clb; Stage Crew; Yrbk Stf; Lit Mag; Var Fld Hcky; Wt Lftg; High Hon Roll; Hon Roll; NHS; Chld Ed.

MAC INTYRE, SUSAN A; Cardinal Spellman HS; Abington, MA; (Y); 2/202; Dance Clb; Drama Clb; School Play; Tennis; High Hon Roll; NCTE Awd; NHS; Ntl Merit SF; Holy Cross Coll; Pre-Law.

MAC KAY, STEPHEN K; Walpole HS; Walpole, MA; (Y); Church Yth Grp; Leo Clb; Spanish Clb; Teachers Aide; Band; Concert Band; Mrchg Band; Gym; JV Socr; Var L Trk; Perf Awd For Spnsh II, Geo & ESCP 83; Perf Awds Englsh 84; Perf Awd Englsh & Analysis 85.

MAC KEEN, LISA; Maynard HS; Maynard, MA; (Y); 9/100; French Clb; Office Aide; Chorus; School Play; Lit Mag; Capt Cheerleading; Gym; Trk; High Hon Roll; Hon Roll; Princpls Hnr Awd 85; Digtl Equp Corp Schlrshp 85; DAR Hstry Awd 85; Oberlin Coll; Doc Neurlgy.

MAC KENZIE, SUSAN; Tananto Regional HS; Jaffrey, NH; (Y); 12/59; Sec Church Yth Grp; Chorus; School Musical; Yrbk Ed-Chief; Var L Bsktbl; Hon Roll; NHS; Ntl Merit Ltr; Drama Clb; Girl Scts; Outstndng Bus Stu Awd; Tahanto Schlrshp Commte Awd; Keene ST Coll; Bus Adm.

MAC KINNON, CORINNE; Taunton HS; Taunton, MA; (Y); Latin Clb; Teachers Aide; Var Trk; High Hon Roll; Hon Roll; NHS; Magna Cum Laude Natl Latin Exam 85.

MAC KINNON, JOHN; Boston College HS; Hingham, MA; (Y); Church Yth Grp; Im Bsktbl; Capt L Socr; Var L Trk; Hon Roll; Jr NHS; Trck Catholic Conf All-Star & Schl MVP; Sccr Catholic Conf All-Star; Boston Coll; Mgmt.

MAC KIZER, RICHARD; St Johns HS; W Boylston, MA; (Y); 93/288; Church Yth Grp; 4-H; Spanish Clb; Chorus; School Musical; Yrbk Stf; JV Socr; Var Trk; 4-H Awd; Hon Roll; George B Tredwell Cup 4-H Awd Mst Prmsng JR Male 4-Hr 82; Vrsty Jckt Vrsty Trk & Fld St 85; Intl Bus Mgmt.

MAC MILLAN, HELEN; Lunenburg SR HS; Lunenburg, MA; (Y); 2/140; Pres Sec Church Yth Grp; Intnl Clb; Pres Sec Chorus; School Musical; Rep Frsh Cls; Rep Soph Cls; Rep Jr Cls; Rep Sr Cls; Var L Socr; Var L Trk; Chrs, Civics & Adv Bio Awds 83-85; Mc Gill U; Pre Med.

MAC NEIL, MICHELLE; Taunton HS; Taunton, MA; (Y); Cert Credit Cntry Acctng 83-84; Bryant; Acctng.

MAC NEILL, DEBORAH; Algonquin HS; Northboro, MA; (Y); Ski Clb; U MA; Engrng.

MAC NEVIN, COLIN; Newton North HS; Newton Lower Fls, MA; (Y); 120/651; Church Yth Grp; Exploring; School Play; JV Bsbl; Var L Ftbl; JV Lcrss; Im Wt Lftg; 1st Tm Subrbn Leag All Str Offnsv Grd Ftbl 85; Sandy Bartzak Schlrshp 85; U Of MA Amherst; Bus Mgmt.

MAC QUARRIE, MELISSA; Chelmsford HS; Chelmsford, MA; (Y); 204/550; Ski Clb; Orch; Yrbk Rptr; Powder Puff Ftbl; JV Capt Socr; Hon Roll; Arch.

MAC QUILKEN, KATHLEEN; Bedford HS; Bedford, MA; (Y); 78/213; Rep Frsh Cls; Rep Soph Cls; JV Bsktbl; JV Mgr(s); Fin.

MACARIS, STEVEN BARRY; High School Of Commerce; Springfield, MA; (S); 14/300; Church Yth Grp; Political Wkr; Red Cross Aide; Ski Clb; Nwsp Rptr; Yrbk Ed-Chief; Yrbk Rptr; Off Jr Cls; Cit Awd; High Hon Roll; SR Standout; Ldrshop Wkshp Awd; SADD Wrkshp Awd; U Of MA; Comm.

MACDONALD, MELINDA; Wakefield HS; Wakefield, MA; (Y); VP Pres AFS; Pep Clb; Spanish Clb; School Play; Yrbk Stf; Lit Mag; Hon Roll; Jr NHS; Physcl Thrpy.

MACDONALD, MICHELLE; Braintree HS; Braintree, MA; (Y); Cheerleading; Mktg.

MACE, JAMES E; Needham HS; Needham, MA; (Y); 2/406; Pres German Clb; Math Tm; Concert Band; Mrchg Band; Orch; School Musical; JV Crs Cntry; NHS; Ntl Merit SF; Science Clb; Colby Coll Bk Prz 84; Carnegie-Mellon U; Biochem.

MACGLAUFLIN, DONNA; Worcester North HS; Worcester, MA; (Y); Church Yth Grp; Hosp Aide; Office Aide; Spanish Clb; Varsity Clb; Stu Cncl; Var Socr; Zoolgst.

MACHADO, KAREN; Barnstable HS; W Hyannisport, MA; (Y); 60/398; Church Yth Grp; Hosp Aide; Ski Clb; Var L Fld Hcky; Simmons Coll; Phys Thrpy.

MACHADO, NANCY; New Bedford HS; New Bedford, MA; (Y); Art Clb; Cmnty Wkr; Pep Clb; Nwsp Rptr; Yrbk Stf; Stu Cncl; Trk; Church Yth Grp; Office Aide; Nwsp Sprt Ed; Bus Clb Pres 85; South Eastern MA U; Med Tech.

MACHNIK, MICHAEL C; Central Catholic HS; Salem, NH; (Y); 2/227; Stat Bsbl; Stat Ice Hcky; High Hon Roll; NHS; Ntl Merit Ltr; Pres Schlr; Rotary Awd; Sal; VP JA; Math Clb; Lawrence Eagle-Tribune Crrier Schlrshp; 1st Pl Math & Sci; Rensselaer Plytdnc Inst; Engrng.

MACIOLEK, DAVID; Medway JR SR HS; Medway, MA; (Y); 28/160; Church Yth Grp; Var Bsbl; Var Socr; Hon Roll.

MACKEEN, DAVID; Archbishop Williams HS; Canton, MA; (Y); 15/200; Church Yth Grp; Library Aide; JV Ice Hcky; Trk; High Hon Roll; Hon Roll; NHS; Comp Sci.

MACKINNON, LORI; Bishop Feeran HS; Walpole, MA; (Y); Church Yth Grp; Dance Clb; Co-Capt Drill Tm; High Hon Roll; Hon Roll.

MACLELLAN, JEANNE; Notre Dame Acad; Scituate, MA; (Y); Drama Clb; 4-H; School Musical; School Play; Hon Roll; Chem Awd 85; Crnbrry Cookng Cntst 83; Chem.

MACOMBER, DEANNA; Uxbridge HS; Uxbridge, MA; (Y); 8/82; Drama Clb; Band; Mrchg Band; Math.

MACSUGA, MICHAEL J; Holyoke HS; Holyoke, MA; (Y); Art Clb; Camera Clb; JA; Office Aide; Nwsp Phtg; Yrbk Phtg; JV Trk; High Hon Roll; Boy Scts; Hon Roll; Ma Art & Poetry Contest 79; Transcript Teligram Bd Cont 2nd Place 84; MA Coll; Photography.

MACYS, EDWARD J; Malden HS; Malden, MA; (Y); 17/525; Key Clb; Math Tm; Rep Frsh Cls; Rep Soph Cls; Rep Jr Cls; Rep Sr Cls; Hon Roll; Ntl Merit Ltr; Ntl Engl Merit Awd; Wrcestr Poly Inst; Mech Engrng.

MADARAS, KENNETH; Taunton HS; Taunton, MA; (Y); JV Bsktbl; Var Ftbl; Var Capt Swmmng; Jrnlsm.

MADDEN, JENNIFER; Bridgewater-Raynham HS; Bridgewater, MA; (Y); Drama Clb; Model UN; Spanish Clb; School Play; Stage Crew; Nwsp Rptr; Nwsp Stf; Hon Roll; Actng Awd 83; Fin In Intl Mdlng Cont 83; Comm.

MADDOX, H W JEROME; Franklin HS; Franklin, MA; (Y); Am Leg Boys St; Math Tm; Varsity Clb; Variety Show; Pres Jr Cls; L Bsktbl; L Ftbl; L Trk; Hon Roll; Ntl Merit Ltr; Chncllrs Awd Schlrshp UMASS 85; Unsung Hero Ftbl 84; Most Imprvd Bsktbl 84-85; Law.

MADERA, MICHELLE E; Jeremiah E Borke HS; Dorchester, MA; (Y); Dance Clb; Drama Clb; JA; Chorus; School Play; Yrbk Ed-Chief; Yrbk Rptr; Yrbk Stf; Stu Cncl; NHS; Boston U 4-Yr Schlrshp 85; Blck Edctrs Allnc Schlrshp 85; Boston U; Med.

MAFRICI, LISA; Braintree HS; Braintree, MA; (Y); 11/395; French Clb; Library Aide; Nwsp Rptr; VP French Hon Soc; High Hon Roll; Hon Roll; NHS; Cabot Sci Seminar Awd 85; Sci Fair Awd Biol 83.

MAGADINI, SUSIE; Monument Mountain Regional HS; Gr Barrington, MA; (Y); 30/135; Camera Clb; Hosp Aide; Band; Mrchg Band; Yrbk Phtg; Yrbk Stf; Var Cheerleading; Var Crs Cntry; Var Trk; Ski Clb; Nrsg.

MAGALDI, DIANA; Coyle Cassidy Memorial HS; S Easton, MA; (Y); 10/140; Library Aide; Spanish Clb; VP Band; Hon Roll; Jr NHS; NHS; Spanish NHS; Schl Lttr Part Band 84; Top GPA Wrld Hist 83; 3rd Yr Pin Band 85; Bus Admin.

MAGEE, LORI; Burlington HS; Burlington, MA; (Y); 65/315; GAA; Chorus; Var L Socr; Var L Sftbl; Var L Trk; Hon Roll; Hosp Aide; School Musical; Cheerleading; JV Diving; Spec Ed.

MAGNANI, CAROLYN; Boston Latin Schl; W Roxbury, MA; (Y); Drama Clb; Swing Chorus; Nwsp Rptr; Yrbk Ed-Chief; Var L Trk; NHS; Ntl Merit Ltr; Church Yth Grp; Hosp Aide; Key Clb; Miss Teen Am St Fnlst 85; Pres Acdmc Ftns Awd 85; Seaton W Manning Schlrshp 85; Harvard.

MAGNANI, DIANNA; Bostin Latin Schl; Boston, MA; (Y); Art Clb; Chorus; Swing Chorus; Nwsp Rptr; Yrbk Ed-Chief; Var L Crs Cntry; Var L Trk; NHS; Ntl Merit Ltr; Harvard Bk Awd 85; Boston Globe Gold Key Art Awd 84; Samuel Gross Davis Awd 83.

MAGOWAN, JULIE A; Clinton HS; Clinton, MA; (Y); Intnl Clb; Rep Frsh Cls; Rep Soph Cls; Rep Jr Cls; Var L Cheerleading; Hon Roll; Sec NHS; Boston Coll; Cmmnctns.

MAGRANE, DIANE E; St Marys Regional HS; Lynn, MA; (Y); 46/127; Boys Clb Am; Camp Fr Inc; Church Yth Grp; Dance Clb; Drama Clb; Girl Scts; JA; Library Aide; Office Aide; School Musical; Med.

MAGUIRE JR, DENNIS F; Bishop Fenwick HS; Lynn, MA; (Y); Church Yth Grp; Stage Crew; Variety Show; Yrbk Stf; Var L Bsktbl; High Hon Roll; NHS; Ntl Merit Ltr; Algbr II Hnrs Awd 85; Math Olympd MA Awd 85; Brown; Math.

MAGUIRE, FINNY; Medway HS; Medway, MA; (Y); 50/170; Church Yth Grp; Nwsp Sprt Ed; Yrbk Stf; Pres Frsh Cls; Pres Soph Cls; Stu Cncl; JV Bsktbl; Ftbl; JV Mgr(s); Var Capt Socr; League All Star Soccer 84-85; Hnrbl Mntn All-Star Tnns 83-84; Meteorology.

MAHANOR, ELIZABETH; Fontbonne Acad; Milton, MA; (Y); Hosp Aide; Ed Lit Mag; Var Capt Trk; Var Vllybl; Hon Roll; NHS; Varsity Clb; Mgr(s); Score Keeper; NEDT Awd; Cnty Bk Awd 86; Vrsty Ltr Trck, Vlybl & Vrsty Trck Pin 85; Lgu Comptn Track Trphs 83-85; Pre-Med.

MAHER, DAVID; Wellesley HS; Wellesley, MA; (Y); 90/330; Church Yth Grp; Key Clb; Varsity Clb; Var Bsbl; Var Bsktbl; Var Mgr Golf; Outstndng Achvt JETS Natl Engrng Tst 84; All Conf Golf 84-85; Engrng.

MAHER, JANET; Rockland HS; Rockland, MA; (S); 11/277; Ski Clb; Yrbk Stf; Pres Frsh Cls; Rep Soph Cls; Trs Jr Cls; Pres Sr Cls; Stu Cncl; High Hon Roll; Hon Roll; NHS; U MA Amherst; Mgt.

MAHER, LYNNE MARIE; Pentucket Regional HS; Groveland, MA; (Y); 7/174; Church Yth Grp; Drama Clb; Capt Color Guard; School Musical; Nwsp Ed-Chief; Yrbk Ed-Chief; Rep Jr Cls; High Hon Roll; Hon Roll; Boston Coll; Bio.

MAHER, PATRICK; Tri-County Vo Tech; Millis, MA; (Y); Boy Scts; Church Yth Grp; VICA; Chorus; School Musical; Variety Show; Capt Ftbl; Elec Const.

MAHER, REBECCA; Wakefield HS; Wakefield, MA; (Y); 17/305; Church Yth Grp; French Clb; Latin Clb; Orch; School Play; Yrbk Stf; Cheerleading; Gym; Elks Awd; NHS; Purdue U; Engr.

MAHER, REMA; Hoosac Valley HS; Adams, MA; (Y); VP Rep Frsh Cls; VP Rep Soph Cls; VP Rep Jr Cls; VP Rep Sr Cls; VP Rep Stu Cncl; Var Socr; JV Sftbl; Hon Roll; Var Soccer Ltr 83; Chrmn SADD Orgnztn 84; Peer Eductr 85; Intl Bus.

MAHNKEN, TOM; Mohawk Trail Regional HS; Ashfield, MA; (Y); 8/122; Acpl Chr; Jazz Band; School Musical; School Play; VP Soph Cls; Rep Jr Cls; NHS; Drama Clb; Nwsp Stf; Rep Stu Cncl; Williams Coll Bk Awd 85; Dartmouth Clb Bk Awd 85; Asst Dir Middle Schl Jazz Bnd 85; Music Perf.

MAHONEY, CHRISTINE; Somerville HS; Somerville, MA; (Y); 26/535; Spanish Clb; Yrbk Stf; Rep Stu Cncl; High Hon Roll; NHS; Spanish NHS; Pres Acdmc Ftns Awd 85; Suffolk U.

MAHONEY, DANIEL; Buxbury HS; Duxbury, MA; (Y); 1/247; Am Leg Boys St; Capt Golf; Capt Socr; DAR Awd; High Hon Roll; Pres NHS; Ntl Merit Ltr; St Schlr; Val; Dartmouth Bk Awd 84; Commonwlth Schlr 85; Edward Butler Latn Awd; Harvard Clg; Engrng.

MAHONEY, GERALD J; Cardinal Spellman HS; Brockton, MA; (Y); 26/225; Rptr Am Leg Boys St; Boy Scts; Church Yth Grp; Latin Clb; Var Bsktbl; Var Crs Cntry; Var Trk; Hon Roll; NHS; NEDT Awd; Ad Altare Dei Religious Awd 83; Pipe Pius XII Religious Awd 84; Chrch Scholar 85; Intl Rel.

MAHONEY, KERRY; Sacred Heart HS; Weymouth, MA; (Y); 4-H; Spanish Clb; Variety Show; Rep Soph Cls; Hon Roll; Math Schrlshp 81-85; Acctng.

MAHONEY, MARY; Maynard HS; Maynard, MA; (Y); 2/100; French Clb; Band; Chorus; Concert Band; Mrchg Band; School Musical; High Hon Roll; Engrng.

MAHONEY JR, PAUL; Maiden HS; Malden, MA; (Y); 40/550; Am Leg Boys St; Church Yth Grp; Key Clb; Variety Show; Yrbk Stf; Rep Soph Cls; Rep Jr Cls; Trs Sr Cls; Hon Roll; Ntl Merit Ltr.

MAHONEY, PHILIP W; St Bernards C C HS; Fitchburg, MA; (Y); 21/168; Am Leg Boys St; Drama Clb; Ski Clb; Church Choir; School Play; Variety Show; Nwsp Ed-Chief; Nwsp Rptr; Yrbk Stf; Rep Stu Cncl; Archael.

MAHONEY, TIMOTHY; St Bernards CC HS; Fitchburg, MA; (S); 22/170; Am Leg Boys St; Cmnty Wkr; Model UN; Political Wkr; Ski Clb; Chorus; Nwsp Ed-Chief; Rep Jr Cls; Var L Crs Cntry; Var L Trk.

MAHONEY, TINA M; Westspringfield HS; W Springfield, MA; (Y); Teachers Aide; Chorus; Church Choir; Drm & Bgl; Drm Mjr(t); Mrchg Band; Variety Show; Twrlr.

MAILLE, MARY; Dracut SR HS; Dracut, MA; (Y); Church Yth Grp; Office Aide; JV Bsktbl; Capt Var Fld Hcky; Sftbl; Hon Roll; U Of Lowell; Accntnt.

MAILLET, THERESA A; Belmont HS; Belmont, MA; (Y); Band; Concert Band; Mrchg Band; Hon Roll; Schlrshp-Belmont Schl Of Ballet 85; Awd-9 Yrs Of Dancing At Belmont Schl Of Ballet 83; Tchr.

MAJESKI, KRISTINA; Wakefield HS; Wakefield, MA; (Y); Church Yth Grp; French Clb; GAA; Key Clb; Teachers Aide; Varsity Clb; Chorus; Church Choir; Nwsp Rptr; Yrbk Stf; JR Dist Chrs 83; Polit Sci.

MAJEWINSKI, KRISTEN M; Holyoke Catholic HS; S Hadley, MA; (Y); Yrbk Stf; Var Capt Bsktbl; Var Capt Socr; Var Capt Sftbl; Elks Awd; Hon Roll; MVP Awd Sccr 82; All Str Tm Bsktbl JR & SR Yr 83-84; St Anselms Coll; Bio.

MAJKUT, KIMBERLY; Taunton HS; East Taunton, MA; (Y); Latin Clb; Office Aide; Spanish Clb; Yrbk Stf; Lit Mag; Sec Stu Cncl; Fld Hcky; Sftbl; Trk; NHS; Hnrb Mntn All Schltc Fld Hockey 84.

MAJKUT, TRACEY; Bridgewater-Raynham Regional HS; Raynham, MA; (Y); Model UN; Ski Clb; Var L Cheerleading; Fld Hcky; Tennis; Hon Roll; NHS; Bus.

MAKI, AMY; Lunenburg HS; Lunenburg, MA; (Y); Am Leg Aux Girls St; Trs Art Clb; Church Yth Grp; Sec Debate Tm; Trs Intnl Clb; Library Aide; Variety Show; Yrbk Stf; Var L Bsktbl; Coach Actv; MA Grls ST Cty Cncl Hous Rep, Flr Ldr 85; 1st Pl Lip Sync Cmptn 85; Court Prm 85; Hotel/Rest Mgt.

MAKI, SUSAN D; Maynard HS; Maynard, MA; (Y).

MAKUKU, AMENYA K; Phillips Acad; Andover, MA; (Y); Cmnty Wkr; Var Ice Hcky; JV Var Lcrss; Intl Trade.

MALAGRIDA, LISA; King Philip Regional HS; Plainville, MA; (Y); Camera Clb; Church Yth Grp; Dance Clb; Variety Show; Yrbk Phtg; Yrbk Rptr; Off Stu Cncl; Fld Hcky; Socr; Swmmng; Northeastern U; Comp Sci.

MALANDRINOS, PAUL; Chicopee HS; Chicopee, MA; (Y); High Hon Roll; Hon Roll; Comp Sci.

MALDONADO, LUIS A; Holyoke HS; Holyoke, MA; (Y); 40/250; Boys Clb Am; High Hon Roll; Hon Roll; Engrng.

MALDONADO, MICHAEL; Technical HS; Springfield, MA; (Y); 3/150; Off ROTC; Chorus; Color Guard; Drill Tm; Rep Stu Cncl; Var L Tennis; Hon Roll; NHS; AF Assn Awd, Mdl, AFJROTC Cdt Yr 85; Amer Leg Schlstc Excel Awd; US Military Acad Prep Schl.

MALE, LAUREN; Lunenburg HS; Lunenburg, MA; (Y); Sec VP Church Yth Grp; Intnl Clb; Ski Clb; Teachers Aide; Acpl Chr; Chorus; Yrbk Stf; High Hon Roll; NHS; Colby Coll Eng Awd 85; Acad Awd Comp 85; Middlebury Coll; Frgn Lang.

MALENFANT, ROBERT; Central Catholic HS; Methuen, MA; (Y); Boys Clb Am; Sec Rep Frsh Cls; Rep Soph Cls; Rep Jr Cls; VP Sr Cls; VP Stu Cncl; Var Capt Bsktbl; Coach Actv; Var Tennis; High Hon Roll; Math Awd 83; Prncpls Schlrshp 83-84; Most Ptntl Coll Bsktbl Awd 83; All-Star Tnns & Bsktbl MVP 84; Bio Sci.

MALIN, ELIZABETH; Marblehead HS; Marblehead, MA; (Y); 14/289; Drama Clb; French Clb; Hosp Aide; Stage Crew; High Hon Roll; Hon Roll; NHS; Bio.

MALINOSKI, RICHARD; Agawam SR HS; Agawam, MA; (Y); 52/300; Math Clb; Nwsp Bus Mgr; Nwsp Phtg; Nwsp Stf; Stat Bsktbl; JV Capt Socr; Hon Roll; Acctg.

MALKASIAN, MATTHEW H; Northbridge JR SR HS; Whitinsville, MA; (Y); 16/140; French Clb; Ski Clb; Trk; Wt Lftg; Hon Roll; NHS; Bryant Coll; Econmcs.

MALLALIEU, SANDRA; Cathedral HS; Springfield, MA; (Y); Am Leg Aux Girls St; Exploring; Intnl Clb; Math Clb; Chorus; Nwsp Phtg; Nwsp Rptr; Stu Cncl; Cmnty Cncl; Model Snte; Frnch Lang Fndtn Awd; Chem.

MALLEY, CAROLYN; Holy Name CCHS; Worcester, MA; (Y); 68/290; Church Yth Grp; Pep Clb; Bsktbl; Var Sftbl; Hon Roll; Hnrs Awd 83-84; Latin Awd 84; Relgn III Awd 85; Art Advrtsng.

MALLLOUX, DIANE; Fitchburg HS; Fitchburg, MA; (Y); GAA; JA; Varsity Clb; Yrbk Stf; Crs Cntry; Var Trk; High Hon Roll; Ntl Merit Ltr; Pep Clb; Yrbk Phtg; Jr Ftchbrgs Womns Clb 84-85; Jr Amit Awd Phys Ftns 85; Comp Sci.

MALLOY, DANIEL; Hopedale HS; Hopedale, MA; (Y); 11/60; Golf; JV Mgr(s); High Hon Roll; MA Acadmc Decathlon; Worcester Polytech Inst; Engr.

MALNATI, SCOTT; Weymouth North HS; Weymouth, MA; (Y); Art Clb; Bsbl; Bsktbl; Ftbl; High Hon Roll; Hon Roll; Boston Coll; Real Est.

MALONE, EILEEN; St Clare HS; Hyde Pk, MA; (Y); 13/150; Church Yth Grp; JA; Nwsp Rptr; Frgn Svc.

MALONE, MAUREEN; Reading Memorial HS; Reading, MA; (Y); Church Yth Grp; Band; Concert Band; Mrchg Band; Orch; Var Crs Cntry; Var Trk; High Hon Roll; Hon Roll; Biolgcl Fld.

MALONE, SHAWN P; Chicopee Comprehensive HS; Chicopee, MA; (S); 13/340; Var Bsktbl; Var Capt Ftbl; Powder Puff Ftbl; Var L Trk; NHS; MVP Ftbl 82; Defnsv Plyr Ftbl 84; Spnsh Lang Awd 83; Annapolis Naval Acad.

MALONEY, DANIEL; Archbishop Williams HS; Randolph, MA; (Y); 21/220; Church Yth Grp; Nwsp Rptr; Nwsp Stf; JV Var Ftbl; Wt Lftg; High Hon Roll; Hon Roll; NHS; Pres Schlr; Bryant Coll; Mktg.

MALONEY, JIM; Agawam HS; Agawam, MA; (Y); 92/325; Ftbl; Wt Lftg; Wrstlng; Hon Roll; Bridgewater ST Coll; Sprts Med.

MANASSO, LAUREN; Franklin HS; Franklin, MA; (Y); Church Yth Grp; Church Choir; Yrbk Stf; Stu Cncl; Hon Roll; Bus Admin.

MANCUSO, MARC A; Wilbraham & Monson Acad; Palmer, MA; (Y); 2/113; Church Yth Grp; Mathletes; Model UN; Ed Nwsp Stf; Var Bsktbl; Var L Golf; Var L Socr; High Hon Roll; Ntl Merit SF; Hstry.

MANFRA, JEREMIAH J; Ipswich HS; Iswich, MA; (Y); 10/130; Am Leg Boys St; Math Tm; Science Clb; Pres Jr Cls; VP Stu Cncl; Var L Ftbl; Var L Lcrss; NHS; Frsh Cls; Soph Cls; Outstndng Physics Stu Of Yr 85; Eastern MA HS La Crosse Assoc All Star 85; Norwich U; Elec Engrng.

MANGIACOTTI, MICHAEL; Braockton HS; Brockton, MA; (Y); Church Yth Grp; FCA; Pep Clb; Ski Clb; Var JV Trk; High Hon Roll; NHS; John P Bunszel Schlrshp 85; Eva Edgar Wright D W & R A Fields Schlrshp 85; Natl Hnrs Soc 85; Suffolk U; Law.

MANGIULLI, KRISTIN; Millbury Memorial HS; Holden, MA; (Y); 24/116; Dance Clb; School Play; Nwsp Rptr; Yrbk Rptr; Pres Frsh Cls; Pres Soph Cls; Pres Jr Cls; Pres Stu Cncl; Cit Awd; DAR Awd; Springfield Coll; Elem Educ.

MANGUM, PAUL; East Boston HS; Dorchester, MA; (Y); Church Yth Grp; Stu Cncl; JV Bsbl; JV Ftbl; Var Trk; Hon Roll; Mock Trial 1st Tm 85; Law Clb 84-85; Bus Admin.

MANHEIM, FRANCESCA; Falmouth HS; Falmouth, MA; (S); PAVAS; Teachers Aide; Orch; School Musical; Variety Show; Kiwanis Awd; Schlrshp Cape Cod Sympny 81; Kiwns Music Fest 82; 1st Violin Sect All ST Orch 83-85; Boston U; Music.

MANIOUDAKIS, STEPHEN; Chicopee Comprehensive HS; Chicopee, MA; (Y); 46/300; Drama Clb; German Clb; Variety Show; Stu Cncl; NHS; VP & Pres Totl Yth Grp 84-86; Hmrm Rep 82.

MANKODI, SONAL; Peabody Veterans Memorial HS; Peabody, MA; (Y); 1/553; VP French Clb; Mathletes; Math Tm; Office Aide; Science Clb; Capt Tennis; High Hon Roll; NHS; Ntl Merit Ltr; Val; Rensselaer Mdl Outstndng Jr Math & Sci 85; Harvard Clb Bk Awd 85; Chancellors Tlnt Awd 85; Frnch Awd 85; Med.

MANLEY, MICHELLE; St Clare HS; Roslindale, MA; (Y); 15/160; French Clb; Girl Scts; Chorus; Nwsp Rptr; Ntl Merit Ltr; Voice Dem Awd.

MANN, JAMIE C; Brookline HS; Brookline Vlg, MA; (Y); Chess Clb; Science Clb; Latin Clb; Teachers Aide; Hon Roll; Ntl Merit Ltr; Law.

MANN, MARY; Academy Of Notre Dame; Nashua, NH; (Y); 19/50; Church Yth Grp; Hosp Aide; Library Aide; Teachers Aide; Chorus; Church Choir; Hon Roll; Prfct Atten Awd; 1st Pl In Cls-U S Hstry, British/American Lit & Church Hstry; IL ST; Busnss Mgmt.

MANNING, CAREN; Bedford HS; Bedford, MA; (Y); 21/240; Church Yth Grp; Pep Clb; Chorus; School Musical; Stage Crew; Trs Jr Cls; Trs Sr Cls; Bsktbl; Var Cheerleading; JV Var Fld Hcky; Pres Ftnss Awd Acdmcs 85; Clifford Realtors Ctznshp Awds 85; Boston Coll; Spec Ed.

MANNING, DUSTIN M; Nashoba Regional HS; Lancaster, MA; (Y); 43/196; JV Bsbl; Var Capt Bsktbl; Var Capt Crs Cntry; Var Capt Trk; Cntrl MA Dist Trk Chmp 85; U Of NH.

MANNING, LAURA; Bishop Feehan HS; Foxboro, MA; (Y); 90/252; Church Yth Grp; Hosp Aide; Varsity Clb; Color Guard; Trs Frsh Cls; Var L Bsktbl; JV Fld Hcky; Var L Trk; High Hon Roll; Hon Roll; St Anselms; Commnctns.

MANNING, MICHELLE; Fontbonne Acad; N Quincy, MA; (Y); 30/135; Church Yth Grp; Intnl Clb; Teachers Aide; Chorus; Lit Mag; Hon Roll; Ntl Hnr Soc; Spnsh III Merit Awd; Intl Bus.

MANNING, SEAN; Marian HS; Milford, MA; (Y); 52/180; Boy Scts; Church Yth Grp; Cmnty Wkr; Band; School Play; JV Var Bsktbl; Var Ftbl; NEDT Awd; Engrng.

MANNING, SHARON A; Tyngsboro JR-SR HS; Tyngsboro, MA; (Y); Church Yth Grp; Yrbk Stf; Trs Soph Cls; Sec Jr Cls; Sec Sr Cls; Rep Stu Cncl; Var Capt Cheerleading; JV Var Fld Hcky; Typst Yr 84-85; Travel Agent.

MANTEGANI, CATHY; Milford HS; Milford, MA; (Y); 85/320; Girl Scts; Hosp Aide; Teachers Aide; Var Trk; Hon Roll.

MANTHA, GARY P; St Johns HS; Worcester, MA; (Y); Church Yth Grp; JA; Spanish Clb; Variety Show; Nwsp Stf; Trk; High Hon Roll; NHS; Head Master List 84-85; Bates Coll; Bio.

MANTIA, ELAINE; Reading Memorial HS; Reading, MA; (Y); Spanish Clb; Band; Concert Band; Mrchg Band; Bsktbl; Fld Hcky; Var L Socr; High Hon Roll; Hon Roll; Spanish NHS; English.

MANTONE, ERIN; Woburn SR HS; Woburn, MA; (S); 125/500; French Clb; Hosp Aide; Ski Clb; Variety Show; Trs Frsh Cls; Off Stu Cncl; Im JV Sftbl; Hon Roll; Lesley Coll; Human Svcs.

MANUEL, ROB; Drury HS; N Adams, MA; (S); Church Yth Grp; Ski Clb; Y-Teens; Concert Band; Jazz Band; Mrchg Band; School Musical; Nwsp Rptr; Var Capt Crs Cntry; Capt Score Keeper.

MANZELLO, ANNE SUSAN; Holy Name CC HS; Worcester, MA; (Y); 4/233; Chess Clb; Math Clb; Pep Clb; Varsity Clb; Pres Soph Cls; Pres Jr Cls; Pres Sr Cls; JV Bsktbl; Crs Cntry; Var JV Sftbl; Telegrm & Gztte, Dist E & Sons Of Itly Stu Achvrs 85; Holy Cross Coll; Pol Sci.

MANZI, CHRISTOPHER; Bartlett HS; Webster, MA; (Y); 38/178; Church Yth Grp; Cmnty Wkr; Varsity Clb; Stu Cncl; Var Bsktbl; Var Ftbl; Hon Roll; Phrmcy.

MARA, JOSEPH D; Grafton HS; South Grafton, MA; (Y); 4/108; Am Leg Boys St; Band; School Musical; Stage Crew; VP Sr Cls; Var Crs Cntry; Var Tennis; Hon Roll; NHS; Ntl Merit SF; Lions Clb MA All ST Band 83; Engrng.

MARAKAS, GEORGIA; Boston Latin Schl; Boston, MA; (Y); 79/330; Pres Church Yth Grp; JA; Key Clb; Latin Clb; Church Choir; Powder Puff Ftbl; NHS; All NJCL Ntl Greek Exam Awd 85; Mngmnt.

MARBLE, ANDREW; Fitchburg HS; Fitchburg, MA; (Y); Am Leg Boys St; Cmnty Wkr; School Play; Yrbk Stf; Var Capt Crs Cntry; High Hon Roll; Head To Head TV Series 85; Intl Studs.

MARC AURELE, JIM; Holy Name Central Catholic HS; Worcester, MA; (Y); Y-Teens; Var Stat Bsbl; Var Stat Bsktbl; Score Keeper; Hon Roll; Humnts & Relgous Stds Awds 82-85; Pblc Rltns.

MARCELLUS, CARLA; St Gregory HS; Mattapan, MA; (Y); 3/104; Church Yth Grp; Cmnty Wkr; JA; Pep Clb; Nwsp Stf; Yrbk Stf; Rep Soph Cls; Rep Stu Cncl; Hon Roll; NHS; Georgetown U; Foreign Svc Ofcr.

MARCHAND, JULIE; Holy Name CC HS; Worcester, MA; (Y); Church Yth Grp; School Play; Var Trk; Hon Roll; NHS; Relgn 83-84; Northeastern; Phy Thrpy.

MARCHESE, MICHELLE; Medford HS; Medford, MA; (Y); 11/430; Hosp Aide; Science Clb; Band; Color Guard; Trs Orch; Yrbk Stf; Stu Cncl; JV Tennis; Hon Roll; NHS; Acad Excllnc Engl 83-85; Bio.

MARCIANO, SUE; Woburn Senior HS; Woburn, MA; (S); Latin Clb; Varsity Clb; Yrbk Ed-Chief; Pres Frsh Cls; Sec Soph Cls; Stu Cncl; Bsktbl; Fld Hcky; Sftbl; High Hon Roll; Middlesex All Star Awd 84; MVP Def Awd 84; Capt Fld Hcky 85; Boston Coll; Accntng.

MARCOTRIGIANO, VICKI; Dighton-Rehoboth Regional HS; Rehoboth, MA; (Y); 67/277; Church Yth Grp; Drama Clb; 4-H; Office Aide; School Play; Stage Crew; Score Keeper; Hon Roll; Bus.

MARCOTTE, DANIEL; New Bedford HS; New Bedford, MA; (Y); 31/688; Church Yth Grp; French Clb; JCL; Latin Clb; Ed Yrbk Stf; High Hon Roll; Hon Roll; NHS; Voice Dem Awd; Acctg.

MARCOUX, SUZY; Cathedral HS; Springfield, MA; (Y); Awd Grmn II 83-84; Awd Acctg 84-85; Phy Thrpy.

MARCUS, GRETA; Randolph HS; Randolph, MA; (Y); Ski Clb; Band; Yrbk Bus Mgr; Stu Cncl; Var Capt Cheerleading; Var Swmmng; Var Tennis; Hon Roll; JC Awd; NHS; Randolph Outstndng Yth 84-83; SR Black Bett Karate 84; Outstndng Soph Awd 84; Orthdntst.

MARGLIN, DAVID J; Commonwealth HS; Watertown, MA; (Y); Chess Clb; Drama Clb; Chorus; School Play; Nwsp Sprt Ed; Var Capt Bsbl; Ntl Merit SF; Nwsp Stf; Socr; Tennis; Captain Squash Tm; Chrman Theater Bd; Frshmn Math Tchr.

MARIA, MARTIN; Natick HS; Framingham, MA; (Y); Westfield ST Coll; Physcs.

MARIANO, NANETTE; Weymouth North HS; Weymouth, MA; (Y); 22/300; French Clb; Hosp Aide; Math Tm; Sftbl; High Hon Roll; Hon Roll; NHS; Scim Hstry, & Engl Trm Stu 82-84; Northestrn U; Soc Wrkr.

MARIEN JR, LEO; Somerset HS; Somerset, MA; (Y); Ski Clb; Var Bsbl; Crim Just.

MARIN, JOSEPH W; Medfield HS; Medfield, MA; (Y); Am Leg Boys St; Church Yth Grp; Var Ftbl; Im Wt Lftg.

MARINELLI, BRIAN; Malden Catholic HS; Malden, MA; (Y); 18/188; Computer Clb; French Clb; Nwsp Stf; Im Vllybl; High Hon Roll; Hon Roll; NHS; Rotary Awd; Bus.

MARINELLI, LEE; Bridgewater Raynham HS; Bridgewater, MA; (Y); Mgr Gym; Dntl Asst.

MARINO, CHRIS; Malden Catholic HS; Malden, MA; (Y); 26/185; Boy Scts; Computer Clb; JCL; Latin Clb; Band; JV Im Socr; JV Im Trk; Hon Roll; Ntl Merit SF; Pre Med.

MARINO, CHRISTINA; Boston Latin HS; East Boston, MA; (Y); 69/375; Cmnty Wkr; High Hon Roll; Hon Roll; Accntng.

MARINO, DONNA; Arlington HS; Arlington, MA; (Y); Boys Clb Am; Church Yth Grp; Office Aide; Church Choir; Hon Roll; Cosm.

MARINO, PAUL M; Foxboro HS; Foxborough, MA; (Y); 38/250; Pres French Clb; Pres Letterman Clb; Ski Clb; Pres Varsity Clb; Crs Cntry; Trk; Hon Roll; Bentley Coll; Fin.

MARINOS, ILEANA; Haverhill HS; Haverhill, MA; (Y); Letterman Clb; Ski Clb; Spanish Clb; Varsity Clb; Coach Actv; Var Mgr(s); High Hon Roll; Secr Italn Clb 85-86; OH ST; Biol.

MARKELLA, JAY D; Abington HS; Abington, MA; (Y); 64/183; Cmnty Wkr; Political Wkr; JV Bsbl; Var L Ftbl; Hon Roll; Am Red Cross 1st Aid Trning Cert 84; Am Red Cross CPR Cert 84-85; Am Red Cross Adv Lfsvng & Wtr Sfty; Springfield Coll; Hlth.

MARKOWSKI, LISA; Agawam HS; Feeding Hls, MA; (Y); 40/350; Score Keeper; Hon Roll; Fashion.

MARLAND, MARY; Kin Philip Regional HS; Wrentham, MA; (S); 5/203; Math Tm; Sftbl; Trk; Hon Roll; NHS; Girl Scts; Bryant Coll Schlrshp 85; Bryant; Bus Mgmt.

MARLATT, GEOFF; Hingham HS; Hingham, MA; (Y); 50/325; JV Bsktbl; Capt Ftbl; Hon Roll; Bus.

MARLEY, BRENDA M; St Mary HS; Lawrence, MA; (Y); 2/108; Cmnty Wkr; Teachers Aide; Nwsp Rptr; High Hon Roll; Hon Roll; Pres NHS; Sal; Lit Mag; ARA Schlrshp From U Of ME Farmington 85; Chris Antonelli Schlrshp 85; Law Day Awd 85; U Of ME Farmington; Spec Ed Tc.

MARMER, MARK; Andover HS; Andover, MA; (Y); 3/435; Drama Clb; School Musical; Nwsp Stf; Sec Trs Sr Cls; Tennis; Var L Trk; High Hon Roll; NHS; Braown U Bk Awd 85; U MA Chancelors Tlnt Awd 85; Bus.

MAROIS, MICHELLE; St Peter Marian CC HS; Auburn, MA; (S); 12/191; Church Yth Grp; Cmnty Wkr; Hosp Aide; School Play; Yrbk Bus Mgr; Yrbk Stf; Hon Roll; NHS; Prfct Atten Awd; Highest Human Bio & Religion III 84; Hnrs Eng, Hist & Chem 84; Quinsigamond CC; Dntl Hygnst.

MAROTTA, MICHAEL; Falmouth HS; W Falmouth, MA; (S); Band; Drm Mjr(t); Jazz Band; Mrchg Band; School Musical; Im Vllybl; Cape Cod Symphny Schlrshp 84; MA All-State Fstvl & All Estrn Fstvl 84-85; Music Ed.

MARQUARDT, CHARLES J; Winchester HS; Winchester, MA; (Y); Boy Scts; French Clb; JCL; Latin Clb; Ski Clb; Varsity Clb; JV Bsktbl; Var L Golf; High Hon Roll; Hon Roll; Natl Latin Exam Silver Medal; CYO Yth Cncl.

MARQUES, STEVEN O; Diman Reg Voc-Tech HS; Fall River, MA; (Y); Yrbk Stf; JV Bsbl; Im Bowling; Graphc Art.

MARQUIS, CHARLES; English HS; Lynn, MA; (Y); 10/362; AFS; Am Leg Boys St; Drama Clb; JCL; Math Tm; School Play; Yrbk Ed-Chief; Rep Soph Cls; VP Jr Cls; High Hon Roll; Red & Gray Vrsty Awd 85; Natl Hnr Scty Bk Awd 85; Anne T Donald Schlrshp 85; SE MA U; Comp Sci.

MARQUIS, MELISSA W; Andover HS; Andover, MA; (Y); 19/430; VP AFS; Rep Church Yth Grp; Service Clb; Band; Concert Band; Mrchg Band; JV Trk; High Hon Roll; Hon Roll; NHS; Child Psych.

MARQUIS, SHEILA; Presentation Of Mary Acad; Lawrence, MA; (Y); Cmnty Wkr; Stage Crew; Variety Show; Yrbk Stf; Stu Cncl; Hon Roll; NHS; U Of Lowell; Busnss.

MARRONE, PHILIP; Malden Catholic HS; Everett, MA; (Y); 1/185; Church Yth Grp; Trs Computer Clb; Im Bsktbl; Im Vllybl; High Hon Roll; Ntl Merit Ltr; Tuitn Schlrshp 83; Engrng.

MARROU, ANDRE ROSHON; Wareham SR HS; East Wareham, MA; (Y); 7/173; Am Leg Boys St; Boys Clb Am; Varsity Clb; School Play; Nwsp Sprt Ed; Pres Soph Cls; Var L Ftbl; Var L Trk; NHS; Pres Schlr; U Mass; Engnrng.

MARRS, GAIL A; Marblehead HS; Marblehead, MA; (Y); 23/250; Cmnty Wkr; Trs Latin Clb; Jazz Band; Powder Puff Ftbl; Capt Trk; NHS; JR Rotarian 85; Boston Coll; Lib Arts.

MARRYAT, GLENN H; Sandwich HS; Sandwich, MA; (Y); 20/150; Am Leg Boys St; Church Yth Grp; Var Crs Cntry; Var L Tennis; Hon Roll; NHS.

MARSH, DAVID; Medway JR SR HS; Medway, MA; (Y); Church Yth Grp; Var Bsbl; JV Var Ftbl; High Hon Roll; Hon Roll; Achv Cert-Schltc Awd 84-85; Engrng.

MARSHALL, BRUCE D; Quincy HS; Quincy, MA; (Y); 79/378; Am Leg Boys St; Dance Clb; Drama Clb; Chorus; VP School Musical; VP Variety Show; Stu Cncl; Var Bsktbl; Elks Awd; Hon Roll; Cncrt Choir Awd 85; Cmptr Oper.

MARSHALL, JAMES; Burlington HS; Burlington, MA; (Y); Miltry.

MARSOLAIS, DENISE; Triton Regional HS; Salisbury, MA; (Y); 8/185; Hon Roll; NHS; Pres Schlr; Genl Svc Admin Essay Cntst 84; Natural Sci & Eng Awd 83-84; Train Monkeys 82-85; MA PD Assoc Schlrshp; CO ST U; Zoology.

MARTEL, AMY; Boston Lann Schl; Boston, MA; (Y); 86/300; JA; JV Socr; Hon Roll; NHS.

MARTEL, GLEN; Holy Name Central Catholic HS; Paxton, MA; (Y); 57/275; Art Clb; Church Yth Grp; Concert Band; Stage Crew; Nwsp Stf; Ftbl; Excllnce Art 82-83 & 84-85; Berklee Coll Music; Rcrd Engrng.

MARTEL, JOAN; Leicester HS; Leicester, MA; (Y); Art Clb; Church Yth Grp; Cmnty Wkr; Dance Clb; French Clb; Office Aide; Chorus; Church Choir; Var Crs Cntry; Var Trk; Dance Trphy 82; Wilfred Acad; Hrdrsr.

MARTELL, CHRISTINE; Bedford HS; Bedford, MA; (Y); 21/240; AFS; Am Leg Aux Girls St; Church Yth Grp; Girl Scts; Chorus; Var L Gym; JV Var Mgr(s); JV Capt Socr; High Hon Roll; Hon Roll; Mth.

MARTELL, NEIL J; Chicopee Comprehensive HS; Chicopee, MA; (S); 65/340; Church Yth Grp; German Clb; Library Aide; Office Aide; Pep Clb; Teachers Aide; Stage Crew; Variety Show; Rep Frsh Cls; Rep Soph Cls.

MARTIN, DIANE; B M C Durfee HS; Fall River, MA; (Y); #35 In Class; Yrbk Stf; Hon Roll; NHS; SMU; Acctg.

MARTIN, DOREEN; Salem HS; Salem, MA; (Y); Cmnty Wkr; Hosp Aide; Drm & Bgl; School Play; Stu Cncl; JV Fld Hcky; Accntng.

MARTIN, DOUG; New Bedford HS; New Bedford, MA; (Y); 25/534; Var Swmmng; Pres Schlr; High Hon Roll; NHS; Chancellors Tlnt Awd U Of MA 84; NBA Schlrsh 85; Ann Miller Mem Schlrsp 85; Worcester Polytech Inst; Elc En.

MARTIN, HOLLY; Taunton HS; Taunton, MA; (Y); Drama Clb; Trs JCL; Math Tm; Trs Spanish Clb; Band; School Musical; Yrbk Stf; Sec Frsh Cls; Fld Hcky; NHS.

MARTIN, JENNIFER; Governor Dummer Acad; Biddeford Pool, ME; (Y); 29/100; Cmnty Wkr; French Clb; Chorus; Nwsp Stf; Yrbk Stf; JV Lcrss; Var Sftbl; High Hon Roll; Hon Roll; Jr NHS; Sea Pines Acad Wrtng Awd 82-83; Comm.

MARTIN, KEVIN M; Central Catholic HS; Dracut, MA; (Y); 75/250; Boy Scts; Chorus; Bsktbl; Var L Ice Hcky; Var L Trk; Wt Lftg; Hon Roll; New England Coll; Civl Engrng.

MARTIN, LISA; Joseph Cas HS; Swansea, MA; (Y); 15/210; Drama Clb; Exploring; French Clb; Symp Band; Stage Crew; Var L Sftbl; Im Vllybl; Hon Roll; Jr NHS; NHS; Leslie Giroux Mem Schlrshp 85; Southeastern MA U; Nrsg.

MARTIN, MICHAEL; Danuers HS; Danvers, MA; (Y); Aud/Vis; Church Yth Grp; Letterman Clb; Varsity Clb; Var Bsktbl; Im Ice Hcky; Im Socr; Im Sftbl; Wt Lftg; Hon Roll; Pres Phyl Ftnss Awd 85; Sprtsmnshp Awd Bsbll 83; Bus.

MARTIN, MICHAEL; Holyoke HS; Holyoke, MA; (Y); Boys Clb Am; Yrbk Stf; Stu Cncl; Ftbl; Ice Hcky; Socr; Hon Roll; Syracuse U.

MARTIN, ROBERT; Fall River BMC Durfee HS; Fall River, MA; (Y); Bsbl; Hon Roll; Med.

MARTIN, ROBERT P; Norwood SR HS; Norwood, MA; (Y); Band; Chorus; Concert Band; Drm Mjr(t); Madrigals; Mrchg Band; Orch; School Musical; School Play; Swing Chorus; Southest MA Dist Chrs 83-85; MA All ST Chrs 83-85; Prof Musician.

MARTIN, SHERYL; East Bridgewater HS; East Bridgewatr, MA; (Y); 17/154; Key Clb; Yrbk Stf; Stu Cncl; JV Cheerleading; JV Mgr(s); Var Tennis; Hon Roll; NHS; Hmcmng Queen Fnlst; JR Prom Queen; E Bridgewater Natl Hnr Scty Achvt Awd; Bryant Coll; Bus.

MARTINEAU, CHRISTINE; Chicopee Comprehensive HS; Chicopee, MA; (S); Spanish Clb; Nwsp Rptr; Nwsp Stf; Yrbk Stf; JV Var Socr; Hon Roll; Jr NHS; NHS; Pro Merito 84-85; Spn Achvt Awd 83-84.

MARTINEZ, MICHAEL; Brookline HS; San Jose, CA; (Y); Var Capt Ftbl; Cit Awd; Bsktbl Tm Twn Capt 84-85; San Jose ST; Bus.

MARTINEZ, NIEVES; Lawrence HS; Lawrence, MA; (Y); Band; Chorus; JV Bsktbl; Var Trk; JV Vllybl; Hon Roll; Worcester ST Coll; Comp.

MARTINO, MARK J; Westboro HS; Westboro, MA; (Y); 10/177; Exploring; Band; Chorus; Concert Band; Jazz Band; Var Socr; Hon Roll; NHS; Ntl Merit SF; VP Church Yth Grp.

MARTINS, ELIZABETH; Bishop Connolly HS; Fall River, MA; (Y); Cmnty Wkr; Teachers Aide; Portuguese Hnr II & III 83-85; Vet.

MARTINS, JOHN; B M C Durfee HS; Fall River, MA; (Y); 88/700; Red Cross Aide; Var L Wrstlng; Pre Law.

MARTONE II, DINO J; Andover HS; Andover, MA; (Y); Cmnty Wkr; Band; Concert Band; Jazz Band; Mrchg Band; Orch; School Musical; Variety Show; Count Boise Jazz Awd 85; Mst Mscl In HS Yrbk 85; U Of Lowell; Music Ed.

MARTULA, AMY; Hopkins Acad; Hadley, MA; (S); #8 In Class; Ski Clb; Spanish Clb; Chorus; Stu Cncl; Socr; Sftbl; High Hon Roll; Hon Roll.

MARYEA, MINNAH; High School Of Commerce; Springfield, MA; (S); 5/300; JA; Hon Roll; NHS.

MAS, VINCENT J; Belchertown HS; Belchertown, MA; (Y); 6/75; Am Leg Boys St; Church Yth Grp; Cmnty Wkr; MMM; Ski Clb; Spanish Clb; Band; School Play; Pres Frsh Cls; VP Jr Cls; ST Enrgy Cncl Pres & Stu ST Coord 84-85; Boston Coll; Med.

MASNY, LISA; Holy Name HS; Leicester, MA; (Y); Pep Clb; Nwsp Rptr; Nwsp Stf; Trk; Amer Lit Awd 84-85; Athl Recog Awd Trck & Fld 84-85; Psych.

MASON, MICHAEL; St Dominic Savio HS; Revere, MA; (Y); Chess Clb; Cmnty Wkr; Computer Clb; JA; Key Clb; Library Aide; MMM; Ski Clb; Nwsp Phtg; Nwsp Rptr; Arntcl Tech.

MASSA, CHRIS; Bedford HS; Bedford, MA; (Y); 20/213; Var L Socr; Var L Tennis; High Hon Roll; Trs NHS.

MASSARO, DEBBIE; Woburn HS; Woburn, MA; (S); 13/500; VP Latin Clb; Math Tm; Varsity Clb; Rep Frsh Cls; Trs Stu Cncl; Var Bsktbl; JV Fld Hcky; Capt Tennis; High Hon Roll; NHS; MA ST Sci Fair 2nd Pl 82; Ntl Sci Merit Awd 82; Magna Cum Laude Ntl Latin Exam 83; Tufts; Pre-Med.

MASSARO, JENNIFER; Woburn SR HS; Woburn, MA; (S); Art Clb; Letterman Clb; Ski Clb; Spanish Clb; Flag Corp; Stu Cncl; Fld Hcky; Tennis; Hon Roll; Jr NHS; Art School; Dsgnr.

MASSE, THOMAS; Dracut SR HS; Dracut, MA; (Y); Intnl Clb; Concert Band; Jazz Band; Mrchg Band; Im JV Bsktbl; Im Capt Ftbl; JV Var Trk; Hon Roll; Boy Scts; Prfct Atten; Comp Sci.

MASTALERZ, STEVEN J; Ludlow HS; Ludlow, MA; (Y); Am Leg Boys St; Church Yth Grp; JCL; Math Tm; Variety Show; Yrbk Stf; High Hon Roll; Hon Roll; JV Var Bsbl; JV Bsktbl; NEDT Cert 90 Pct Or Bttr; Frsh Bsktbl Capt.

MASTERSON, JAIA; Fontbonne Acad; Braintree, MA; (Y); Art Clb; Drama Clb; Key Clb; Science Clb; School Play; Crs Cntry; Mgr(s); Trk; Natl Latin Exam Cum Laude 82-83; Archdiocese Boston Art Fair 83-84; Boston Globe Schltc Art Awds 84-85; Art.

MASTERSON, JAMES T; Waltham HS; Waltham, MA; (Y); Am Leg Boys St; Church Yth Grp; French Clb; JCL; Latin Clb; JV Bsktbl; Capt Tennis; Hon Roll; Jr NHS; Ntl Merit Ltr.

MASTOVSKY, DANA; Framingham South HS; Framingham, MA; (Y); 14/269; Drama Clb; German Clb; Nwsp Stf; Yrbk Stf; Im Tennis; Hnbl Mntn Sci Comptn 82-83.

MASTROCOLA, PAUL; Malden Catholic HS; Medford, MA; (Y); 6/185; Pres Church Yth Grp; Computer Clb; Drama Clb; School Play; Ed Yrbk Stf; Stu Cncl; Im Bsktbl; Im Vllybl; Pres Jr NHS; NHS; Hdmstrs Lst 82-85; Cls Up Pgm; Bus Adm.

MATARAZZO JR, JAMES M; Winthrop HS; Winthrop, MA; (Y); 11/212; Am Leg Boys St; VP Band; School Play; Yrbk Stf; Trs Sr Cls; NHS; Church Yth Grp; Drama Clb; Library Aide; Office Aide; Law Day Exercises MA Bar Assc 85; Hstry.

MATARAZZO, MICHELLE; Winthrop HS; Winthrop, MA; (Y); 16/221; Hosp Aide; Color Guard; Flag Corp; Im Bsktbl; Hon Roll; NHS; Prfct Atten Awd; Home Ec Awd 83; Nrsng.

MATARAZZO, ROSEANN; Christopher Columbus HS; Boston, MA; (S); #30 In Class; Math Awd 83-84; Suffolk U; Law.

MATARESE, ANTONIO R; Ashland SR HS; Ashland, MA; (Y); 20/100; Am Leg Boys St; Yrbk Stf; Trs Jr Cls; Var Tennis; Stu Achvemnt Awd Busn Admin 81; U Of RI; Intrnatl Mrktng.

MATARESE, JOSEPH; St Dominic Savio HS; Revere, MA; (Y); 20/110; Yrbk Sprt Ed; Yrbk Stf; Var Crs Cntry; Var L Golf; JV Capt Ice Hcky; Hon Roll; Prfct Atten Awd.

MATASSINO, DEBRA K; Landmark Schl; Hilton Head, SC; (Y); Cmnty Wkr; Drama Clb; JA; Political Wkr; Ski Clb; School Play; Stage Crew; Variety Show; Nwsp Phtg; Nwsp Stf; WV Weslyan; Entrtnmnt.

MATEUS, FRANCISCO; B M C Durfee HS; Fall River, MA; (Y); Boys Clb Am; Computer Clb; Band; Coach Actv; Var Socr; High Hon Roll; Hon Roll; Prfct Atten Awd; Herald New Allstar Team; MA Bay ST Gameteam; Eastrn MA United Soccr Club All Stars 84-85.

MATHER, WENDY; Coyle & Cassidy HS; N Easton, MA; (Y); Ski Clb; Yrbk Stf; VP Frsh Cls; Pres Soph Cls; VP Jr Cls; Off Sr Cls; VP Stu Cncl; Socr; Trvl.

MATHIAS, CATHY; Bishop Connolly HS; Fall River, MA; (Y); Cmnty Wkr; Drama Clb; School Play; JV Bsktbl; Var Sftbl; Var Trk; High Hon Roll; Hon Roll; Bridgewater ST Coll; Comm Dsrd.

MATON, GENEVIEVE; Groton Dunstable Regional Sec HS; Groton, MA; (Y); Intnl Clb; Band; Chorus; Church Choir; Yrbk Stf; Hon Roll; NHS; Arch.

MATORIN, ABIGAIL I; Newton South HS; Newton Centre, MA; (Y); Hosp Aide; Var Swmmng; Hon Roll.

MATOSIC, CHRISTOPHER; Central Catholic HS; Lawrence, MA; (Y); 90/225; Ftbl; Trk; Vllybl; Wt Lftg; Hon Roll; Villanova; Hstry.

MATRA, LINCOLN; Boston Latin Schl; Boston, MA; (Y); Computer Clb; Pep Clb; Lit Mag; High Hon Roll; Hon Roll; JETS Awd; Prfct Atten Awd; MA Pre Engrng Prgrm Awd 82-83; Kidney Fndatn MA Bike-A-Thon Awd 85; Elect Engrng.

MATRONI, LISA; Cathedral HS; Springfield, MA; (Y); 88/512; Dance Clb; Library Aide; Ski Clb; Stu Cncl; Mgr(s); Score Keeper; Hon Roll; 1st & 3rd Pl Mdls Ice Sktng Comptns 82-85; Law.

MATTHEWS, CHRISTOPHER; English HS; Boston, MA; (Y); Hon Roll; NHS; Boston Tchrs Union Schlrshp 85; Benjamin Simons Schlrshp 85; Engl Hnrs Awd 85; Nrthstrn U Boston; Comp Pgmmg.

MATTHEWS, JEFFREY A; Catholic Memorial HS; Roslindale, MA; (Y); 3/270; Computer Clb; French Clb; Math Clb; High Hon Roll; Sec NHS; Frnch Awd 83-84; Chemstry Awd 83-84; Worcester Poltch Inst; Elec Eng.

MATTISON, MICHELLE A; Hoosac Valley HS; Cheshire, MA; (Y); 19/169; 4-H; Hosp Aide; Pep Clb; School Play; Nwsp Stf; 4-H Awd; Hon Roll; NHS; Pres Schlr; Soclgy Awd Creatv Wrtng Awd 85; Smith Coll; Englsh.

MATTRESS, MARY; Holy Name CC HS; Worcester, MA; (Y); 205/272; Church Yth Grp; Pep Clb; Trk; Hon Roll; Phys Fit Awds; Revw Grmmr Awd; Humnts Lit I Awd; Bus.

MATULA, CAROLYN ANN; Somerset HS; Somerset, MA; (Y); 11/299; VP French Clb; Mrchg Band; Variety Show; Yrbk Stf; Var L Fld Hcky; High Hon Roll; NHS; NEDT Awd; Prjct Excel 82-83; Boston Coll; Chmstry.

MATYS, MARK; Holy Name Central Catholic HS; Worcester, MA; (Y); Computer Clb; Math Clb; JV Socr; Var Tennis; Hon Roll; Humanties Hist Awd 82-83; Comm Skills 83-84; Am Lit Hnr Awd 84-85.

MAUK, MARIJA; Falmouth HS; Teaticket, MA; (Y); French Clb; Pep Clb; Band; Color Guard; Concert Band; Flag Corp; Mrchg Band; Hon Roll; Jr NHS; Kiwanis Awd; Ntl Hnr Soc, Lawrence Schl, Falmouth Ed Assn Schlrshps 85; Rollins Coll; Math.

MAURELLO, ANTHONY J; St Johns HS; Shrewsbury, MA; (Y); 55/270; Am Leg Boys St; VP JA; Math Tm; Ski Clb; JV Socr; JV Trk; Hon Roll; NHS; 9th Hgh Scorer Var Mth Lg 85; Elec Engrng.

MAURICIO, LINDA; B M C Durfee HS; Fall River, MA; (Y); 99/688; Teachers Aide; Chorus; Variety Show; Yrbk Stf; Mgr Wrstlng; Cit Awd; Hon Roll; Phi Kappa Gamma 85; Boston Coll; Spcl Eductn.

MAXNER, MICHELLE; Beverly HS; Beverly, MA; (Y); Church Yth Grp; Yrbk Phtg; Yrbk Stf; JV Fld Hcky; Hon Roll; Bus.

MAXON, JENNIFER; Bedford HS; Bedford, MA; (Y); 13/213; Church Yth Grp; Yrbk Rptr; Var L Bsktbl; Var L Sftbl; Capt L Swmmng; High Hon Roll; NHS; Ntl Merit Ltr; Yrbk Stf; Rep Jr Cls; Dartmth Bk Awd 85; Leag All-Star Swim Tean 83-85; Outstndg Achvt Engl & Scl Stds 83-84.

MAXWELL, DOUGLAS; East Longmeadow HS; E Longmeadow, MA; (Y); Boy Scts; Computer Clb; Exploring; French Clb; Intnl Clb; Library Aide; L Crs Cntry; L Tennis; Hon Roll; U MA-AMHERST; Comp Sci.

MAY, JEFFREY M; Ludlow HS; Ludlow, MA; (Y); 8/276; Am Leg Boys St; Boy Scts; Band; Drm Mjr(t); Rep Sr Cls; Rep Stu Cncl; High Hon Roll; NHS; St Schlr; Worcester Poly Inst; Elec Engr.

MAYALL, ROBIN; Durfee HS; Fall River, MA; (Y); Church Yth Grp; JA; Math Clb; Math Tm; Spanish Clb; Chorus; Church Choir; VP Frsh Cls; Swmmng; Hon Roll; VP Stu Govt 84-85; Mth.

MAYER, HOLLY; Mount Alvernia HS; W Roxbury, MA; (Y); 4/43; Church Yth Grp; Chorus; School Play; Nwsp Ed-Chief; Yrbk Ed-Chief; VP Pres Stu Cncl; Cheerleading; Hon Roll; NHS; Drama Clb; 8 Yr Pres Cncl Physcl Ftnss Awd 83; Engl.

MAYLOTT, PAUL ANDREW; Grafton Memorial SR HS; N Grafton, MA; (Y); Hosp Aide; Band; Orch; Bsktbl; Hon Roll; NHS; Prfct Atten Awd; Concert Band; Mrchg Band; School Play; Math & Sci Mart Inprv Medl 85; David & Margaret Harvey Schlrshp 85; Clark U; Med.

MAYNARD, JAMES M; Brockton HS; Brockton, MA; (Y); 25/1006; Am Leg Boys St; Church Yth Grp; Cmnty Wkr; Computer Clb; Exploring; Var Trk; High Hon Roll; Hon Roll; NHS; MA Advncd Studies Pgm 85; YMCA Chrch Lg Bsktbl 83-85; Cmnty Bsbl Lg SR Div 83-84; Engrng.

MAYNARD, LEWIS; Salem HS; Salem, MA; (Y); 220/480; Boy Scts; Stage Crew; JV Bsbl; JV Bsktbl; Var L Ftbl; Var Capt Lcrss; Roscoe M Woodward Schlrshp Fund 85; Dean JC; Comm.

MAYNARD, LISA; Southbridge HS; Southbridge, MA; (Y); 48/165; Church Yth Grp; Library Aide; Capt Bsktbl; Fld Hcky; Mgr(s); Tennis; Hon Roll; Accntng.

MAYO, MICHAELA; East Bridgewater HS; E Bridgewater, MA; (Y); Aud/Vis; Church Yth Grp; Dance Clb; Ski Clb; Yrbk Stf; Hon Roll; U Of Las Vegas; Htl Mgmt.

MAYO, THOMAS; Ipswich HS; Ipswich, MA; (Y); 7/124; Art Clb; Aud/Vis; Computer Clb; Leo Clb; Science Clb; Yrbk Stf; Lit Mag; Hon Roll; Ntl Merit Ltr; Northeastern; Electrnc/Comp Eng.

MAZANEC, NANCY; Mohawk Trial Regional HS; Shelburne Fls, MA; (Y); Church Yth Grp; Teachers Aide; Varsity Clb; School Musical; Variety Show; Bsktbl; Crs Cntry; Score Keeper; Trk; Hon Roll; Western New England.

MAZUR, KAREN; Hoosac Valley HS; Savoy, MA; (Y); Hon Roll; Legal Secy.

MAZYCK, DENISE; Lexington HS; Lexington, MA; (Y); Church Yth Grp; Cmnty Wkr; Sec French Clb; Intnl Clb; Office Aide; Yrbk Stf; Stu Cncl; Hon Roll; NHS; Rotary Awd; Josiah W Hayden Rcrtnl Fclity Schlrshp 85; Amanda Payson Schlrshp 85; Allied-Instrmntn Lab Schlrshp 85; Nrthestrn U-Boston; Bus Admin.

MAZZA, ANNE; Cathedral HS; Springfield, MA; (Y); 106/500; GAA; Library Aide; Office Aide; Swmmng; Trk.

MAZZA, TARA; Mohwak Trail Regional HS; Plainfield, MA; (Y); 17/142; Sec Band; Nwsp Stf; Ed Yrbk Stf; Rep Soph Cls; Var Tennis; Trk; JV L Vllybl; Hon Roll; School Musical; School Play; Art Awd 85; Spanish Awd; Athletic Nutrition.

MAZZEL, JOSEPH; Cambridge Rindge & Latin HS; Cambridge, MA; (S); Boy Scts; Church Yth Grp; Dance Clb; Key Clb; Math Clb; Var Capt Ftbl; Wrstlng; Opt Clb Awd; Capt Varsity Ftbl 84.

MAZZEO, ANDREA; Holy Name C C HS; Shrewsbury, MA; (Y); Art Clb; JA; Ski Clb; Varsity Clb; Chorus; School Musical; Var Cheerleading; Var Score Keeper; Hon Roll; Practical Chem Awd 84; Queens Coll.

MAZZOLA, JAMES; Canton HS; Canton, MA; (Y); 66/265; Boy Scts; Church Yth Grp; Cmnty Wkr; German Clb; Var JV Ftbl; Var Trk; Im Vllybl; Im Wt Lftg; Hon Roll.

MC ALVIN, KARIN; Falmouth HS; E Falmouth, MA; (Y); Church Yth Grp; Hon Roll; Bentley; Bus.

MC AULEY JR, DANIEL; Medford HS; Medford, MA; (Y); 30/710; Math Tm; Red Cross Aide; Varsity Clb; Pres Frsh Cls; Var Ftbl; Var Trk; Hon Roll; NHS; Rep Soph Cls; VP Jr Cls; Math & Engl Awds 82-84; Athletic Achvt Awd In Trk 84-85.

MC AULEY, GEOFFREY; Lynn Classical HS; Lynn, MA; (Y); Boy Scts; Camp Fr Inc; Political Wkr; Var Crs Cntry; Var Trk; Hon Roll; Pre-Law.

MC BRIDE, BARBARA E; Burlington HS; Burlington, MA; (Y); Drama Clb; JA; Math Tm; Flag Corp; School Play; Yrbk Stf; High Hon Roll; Hon Roll; NHS; Ntl Merit Schol; Engl Awd 82-83; Elec Engr.

MC BRIDE, COURTNEY; Cathedral HS; Springfield, MA; (Y); 27/515; Model UN; Office Aide; Yrbk Stf; NHS; Pre Med.

MC BRIDE, MARILYN; Archbishop Williams HS; Quincy, MA; (Y); 25/202; Pep Clb; Chorus; Variety Show; JV Var Cheerleading; JV Var Pom Pon; High Hon Roll; Hon Roll; NHS.

MC CABE, BRIAN; Newton North HS; W Newton, MA; (Y); Pres Church Yth Grp; Chorus; Church Choir; Mrchg Band; School Musical; JV Trk; Hon Roll; Harvard Bk Awd 85; Magna Cum Laude Ntl Ltn Exam 84-85; Harvard U; Corp Law.

MC CABE, FRANK; Boston Latin HS; Roslindale, MA; (Y); 63/335; FCA; YMCA; Yth Org Offcr; Boys Clb Am; Chem Clb; Irish Histrcl Soc; Latin Cultural Soc.

MC CAFFREY JR, BERNARD; St Bernards Central Catholic HS; Leominster, MA; (S); 7/163; Nwsp Stf; Var L Bsbl; Var L Ice Hcky; Hon Roll; NHS; Latin Awd 82; Engrng.

MC CAFFREY, MAUREEN; Lynn Classical HS; Lynn, MA; (Y); Cheerleading; Powder Puff Ftbl; Socr; Hon Roll; Jr NHS; Comm.

MC CAIN, GARETH; Tahanto Regional HS; Santa Clara, CA; (Y); 12/60; Math Tm; Science Clb; Trs Sr Cls; Var Bsbl; Var Bsktbl; Var Capt Socr; NHS; JA; Trs Jr Cls; Var Tennis; Amer Lgn Ldrshp Awd 85; Tahanto Schlrshp Cmmtt 85; Cntrl MS Sccr All-Star 84-85; U Of CA Santa Cruz; Marine Bio.

MC CALL, JOYCE RABI; Copley Square HS; Boston, MA; (Y); 18/100; Cmnty Wkr; Library Aide; Office Aide; Teachers Aide; Chorus; School Musical; Hon Roll; Prfct Atten Awd; Volntrng Serv Awd 85; Comp Wrkshp Smmr Prog Awd 83; Comp Sci, Astrnmy & Physcs Hnr Awds 84; U Of MA-AMHERST; Astrnmy.

MC CALL, KATHY M; Maynard HS; Maynard, MA; (Y); Boys Clb Am; JV Var Bsktbl; Hon Roll; Coll; Bus Adm.

MC CALL, MARY; Southwick HS; Granville, MA; (Y); Am Leg Aux Girls St; Exploring; Chorus; High Hon Roll; Soclgy.

MC CANN, KIMBERLY M; Westfield HS; Westfield, MA; (Y); Am Leg Aux Girls St; Pres Spanish Clb; Yrbk Stf; VP Trs Stu Cncl; Var Capt Trk; Jr NHS; Sec NHS; Presdntl Clsrm Yng Amer 85; Mt Holyoke Coll.

MC CANN, MICHAEL; Holy Name C C HS; North Grafton, MA; (Y); Church Yth Grp; Computer Clb; JA; School Musical; Mgr Stage Crew; Bsbl; JV Socr; Var Tennis; Hon Roll; 4th Degree Knights Columbus Schlrshp 82-85; Bio.

MC CANN, SHARON; King Philip Regional HS; Plainville, MA; (Y); Church Yth Grp; Drama Clb; Yrbk Stf; Hofstra U; Bus.

MC CARTHY, ALEXANDER; Mt Everett Regional HS; W Stockbridge, MA; (Y); 4/77; Am Leg Boys St; Ski Clb; Lit Mag; VP Jr Cls; VP Sr Cls; JV Bsbl; Var Socr; Var Wrstlng; High Hon Roll; Hon Roll; Local Ski Area Ski Team 84-85; Area Hockey Team 82-83; Engr.

MC CARTHY, EILEEN; Boston Latin HS; Hyde Pk, MA; (Y); Hosp Aide; Latin Clb; Ski Clb; Var Powder Puff Ftbl; Jordan Marsh Cncl 85-86; Bus.

MC CARTHY, GENEVIEVE; Wellesley HS; Wellesley, MA; (Y); 29/315; Camera Clb; Dance Clb; German Clb; Library Aide; PAVAS; Yrbk Phtg; Badmtn; Gym; Hon Roll; Walnut Hill Schl Ballet Scholar 82; Bio-Chem.

MC CARTHY, JENNIE; Academy Of Notre Dame; Tewksbury, MA; (Y); 12/60; VP Pep Clb; Political Wkr; Stage Crew; Pres Stu Cncl; Hon Roll; VP Soph Cls; Bsktbl; Capt Var Vllybl; Prfct Atten Awd; Brady Schlrshp 82-86; Mc Kinley Schlrshp 82-86; Hugh O Brien Ldrshp Sem Rep 84; Baldwin Wallace; Pre-Med.

MC CARTHY, JOANNA M; Duxbury HS; Duxbury, MA; (Y); 27/243; Orch; School Musical; Yrbk Stf; Var L Crs Cntry; Stat Trk; Hon Roll; NHS; Ntl Merit Ltr; Suffolk U; Humanties.

MC CARTHY, KELLY A; Cathedral HS; Indian Orchard, MA; (Y); 27/465; Model UN; Rep Sr Cls; JV Sftbl; Hon Roll; Pres Schlr; Schlrshp Acad Achvt 85; Indian Orchards Womens Clb Schlrshp 85; Brian Sullivan Schlrshp 85; U Of NH; Vet Med.

MC CARTHY, KIMBERLY; Holyoke Catholic HS; Holyoke, MA; (Y); 4/128; GAA; VP Latin Clb; Spanish Clb; Yrbk Stf; Var Bsktbl; JV Socr; JV Sftbl; High Hon Roll; Trs NHS; Comp Pgmng Awd 85; Law.

MC CARTHY, LINDA; Arlington Catholic HS; Waltham, MA; (Y); 11/148; Church Yth Grp; Drama Clb; JA; Yrbk Rptr; Rep Frsh Cls; Rep Soph Cls; Var L Crs Cntry; JV Trk; High Hon Roll; NHS; Acad All Amer 85; Natl Engl Merit Awd 85; Latin Gold Medl 82; Jrnlsm.

MC CARTHY, MAUREEN E; Boston Latin HS; Boston, MA; (Y); 62/320; Church Yth Grp; Cmnty Wkr; Key Clb; Latin Clb; Stage Crew; Yrbk Stf; Rep Stu Cncl; Var Cheerleading; JV Sftbl; NHS; Pres Amer Fit Awd 85; Open Gate Awd 85; Classcl Awd Latin 82; Boston Coll; Lib Arts.

MC CARTHY, MONICA E; Quaboag Rigional HS; Warren, MA; (Y); 10/87; Library Aide; Math Tm; Science Clb; VP Spanish Clb; Varsity Clb; VP Frsh Cls; Sec Jr Cls; Capt Bsktbl; L Crs Cntry; Var Fld Hcky.

MC CARTHY, PATRICIA; Presentation Of Mary Acad; Lawrence, MA; (S); 1/50; Spanish Clb; Ed Yrbk Ed-Chief; High Hon Roll; NHS.

MC CARTHY, PATRICIA A; Boston Latin Schl; West Roxbury, MA; (Y); 43/319; Church Yth Grp; JA; Latin Clb; Ski Clb; Variety Show; Var Cheerleading; JV Sftbl; Hon Roll; NHS; Prfct Atten Awd; Clscl,Modern Awd 81-82; Boston Latin Schl Schlrshp 85; Colgate U; Sports Med.

MC CARTHY, ROBERT; Everett HS; Everett, MA; (Y); Church Yth Grp; Intnl Clb; Key Clb; Letterman Clb; Political Wkr; Science Clb; Var L Ftbl; Wt Lftg; Hon Roll; Engrng.

MC CARTHY, SEAN; Catholic Memorial HS; W Roxbury, MA; (Y); JA; Pres Key Clb; Variety Show; Rep Frsh Cls; VP Soph Cls; Rep Jr Cls; Rep Sr Cls; Stu Cncl; Score Keeper; Aud/Vis; Outstndg Catholic Yth 84; Pres Catholic Yth Orgn 84-85; MS Southeastern U; Civil Engr.

MC CARTHY, SHEILA; Marblehead HS; Marblehead, MA; (Y); 44/275; Var Cheerleading; JV Var Swmmng; Hlth Prof.

MC CARTHY, STACEY; Chicopee Comprehensive HS; Chicopee, MA; (Y); 87/300; Library Aide; Office Aide; Hon Roll; Bay Path Jr Coll; Sec.

MC CARTHY, THOMAS P; Central Catholic HS; Bradford, MA; (Y); Art Clb; Church Yth Grp; French Clb; Science Clb; Stage Crew; High Hon Roll; Jr NHS; Masonic Awd; NHS; Ntl Merit Ltr; Paul R Koch Essay Wnnr 85; De Molay Fndtn Awd 85; Hntr Awd 85; Amer U Pres Schlr 85; Amer U; Intl Stds.

MC CHESNEY, JACQUES; Deerfield Acad; New Vernon, NJ; (Y); JV Ftbl; Im Ice Hcky; JV Lcrss; Hon Roll; Ntl Merit Ltr; Hd Tour Gd Deerfield Admssns Dept; Hd Tutor Deerfield Tutrng Ctr; Exec Comm Stdnt Blood Drive.

MC CLELLAN, MARK D; Marblehead HS; Marblehead, MA; (Y); 67/258; Rep Stu Cncl; L Bsbl; L Ftbl; Hon Roll; Prfct Atten Awd; Magcn Grdiron Clb Schlrshp 85; Boston Hearld 83; All Schlstc Bsbl Tm 85; Salem New All Schlstc Bsbl 85; U Of MA; Engrng.

MC CLELLAND, SCOTT; Archbishop Williams HS; Quincy, MA; (Y); 50/250; Hon Roll; Prfct Atten Awd; Awd Outstndng Effort Soc Stud 84-85; Doctor.

MC COLLEM, CAROLYN; Bedford HS; Bedford, MA; (Y); 55/213; Church Yth Grp; Girl Scts; Chorus; Swmmng; Hon Roll; Prfct Atten Awd; Comp.

MC CONNELL, HEATHER; Notre Dame Acad; Marshfield, MA; (Y); Art Clb; French Clb; Chorus; Bsktbl; Crs Cntry; Socr; Trk; French Hon Soc; Algebra I Hghst Grd Awd 83; Math.

MC CONNELL, SCOTT; Holyoke Catholic HS; Easthampton, MA; (Y); JV Socr; U Of MA; Engrng.

MC CORMACK, AMY C; Scituate HS; Scituate, MA; (Y); 28/278; Church Yth Grp; Rep Frsh Cls; Rep Soph Cls; Rep Stu Cncl; JV Var Cheerleading; Hon Roll; Jr NHS; NHS; MA Frgn Lng Assn Awd Of Exc 84; Scituate League Of Wmn Vtrs Schlrshp 85; Providence Coll; Pltcl Sci.

MC CORMACK, KATHLEEN; Marblehead HS; Marblehead, MA; (Y); 1/261; Sec Drama Clb; German Clb; Math Tm; Sec Thesps; Yrbk Stf; NHS; Val; Franklin & Marshall Bk Prz 84; MA Sup Assoc Awd 84; U PA; Lib Arts.

MC CORMICK, JOHN; Salem HS; Salem, MA; (Y); 34/350; Church Yth Grp; Nwsp Rptr; VP Capt Bsbl; Var L Bsktbl; High Hon Roll; Hon Roll; Harvard Prz Bk Awd 85; N Eastern Conv All Star Salem Evng News All Star Bsbl 85; MVP Vrsty Bsbl 85; Engr.

MC COY, KEVIN C; Manchester JR SR HS; Manchester, MA; (Y); 34/70; Am Leg Boys St; Boy Scts; Rep Frsh Cls; Var Bsbl; Var Capt Bsktbl; Var Ftbl; Var Golf; High Hon Roll; Grad Cls Mrshll 85; Yrbk Dedctn-To Me 85; U Of FL; Phy Educ.

MC COY, PATRICIA; New Bedford HS; New Bedford, MA; (Y); Church Yth Grp; Drama Clb; Office Aide; Political Wkr; Chorus; Church Choir; Stage Crew; Yrbk Phtg; Rep Stu Cncl; Timer; Syracuse; Photo.

MC CRACKEN, SCOTT D; Monument Mountain HS; Br Barrington, MA; (Y); 21/155; Drama Clb; Ski Clb; School Play; Var Trk; Var Wrstlng; High Hon Roll; Hon Roll; Hawthorne Coll; Pilot.

MC CREA, JOHN; Dighton-Rehoboth Regional HS; Rehoboth, MA; (S); DECA; ROTC; Multiple Awds DECA 83; Bus.

MC CREADY, CINDY; Gateway Regional HS; Huntington, MA; (Y); Band; Yrbk Ed-Chief; Stu Cncl; Stat Bsktbl; Stat Fld Hcky; Mgr(s); Score Keeper; Stat Sftbl; Cit Awd; Hon Roll; WNEC; Bus Admin.

MC CUEN, KELLEY; Dartmouth HS; N Dartmouth, MA; (Y); 11/262; AFS; Hosp Aide; VP Pres JA; Office Aide; OEA; Teachers Aide; Yrbk Stf; NHS; Acad Excllnc Awd 82-85; Engl Excllnc 85; Acushnet Fndtn Schlrshp 85; Bryant Coll; Accntng.

MC CULLOM, PATRICK; Governor Dummer Acad; N Andover, MA; (Y); 40/95; Key Clb; Ski Clb; Bsktbl; Socr; Tennis; Trk; Socl Comm & Big Bros.

MC CURDY, MARCIA; Girls Catholic HS; Malden, MA; (S); 1/35; Church Yth Grp; Spanish Clb; Yrbk Stf; Var Bsktbl; Hon Roll; Kiwanis Awd; Scty Dist Amer HS Stus 82-84; Merrimack Coll; Bus Admin.

MC CUSKER, AMY; Westwood HS; Westwood, MA; (Y); 61/214; Camera Clb; Hosp Aide; Key Clb; Ski Clb; JV Tennis; Var L Vllybl; Fashn Desgn.

MC DERMOTT, JACQUELINE A; Canton HS; Canton, MA; (Y); 39/270; Church Yth Grp; Cmnty Wkr; Pep Clb; Varsity Clb; Yrbk Stf; Rep Sr Cls; Stu Cncl; Capt Cheerleading; Powder Puff Ftbl; Hon Roll; Vol Svc Awd Miss Am Co Ed Pagnt 84; URI; Mrktng.

MC DERMOTT, JAMES; Randolph HS; Randolph, MA; (Y); Church Yth Grp; Q&S; Band; Concert Band; Mrchg Band; Accntng.

MC DERMOTT, KELLY; Academy Of Ntre Dme; Dracut, MA; (Y); 8/50; French Clb; Concert Band; Orch; Sec Soph Cls; Trs Stu Cncl; Capt Var Swmmng; Var Tennis; NHS; Dntst.

MC DERMOTT, TIMOTHY M; Leicester HS; Leicester, MA; (Y); Church Yth Grp; Rep Stu Cncl; Var Ftbl; Stu Govt 84; Ntl Assoc Of Chrstns & Jews 84; Crmnlgy.

MC DEVITT, LISA A; Cathedral HS; Springfield, MA; (Y); Computer Clb; Law.

MC DONALD, DAVID; Salem HS; Salem, MA; (Y); 43/332; Var Bsbl; Var Capt Bsktbl; Socr; High Hon Roll; Hon Roll; Bus.

MC DONALD, EDW; Boston College HS; Rockland, MA; (Y); Key Clb; Ski Clb; Rep Jr Cls; Rep Sr Cls; Stu Cncl; Bsbl; Ftbl; Law.

MC DONALD, JOHN; Boston Latin Schl; Boston, MA; (Y); JA; Latin Clb; Teachers Aide; Nwsp Stf; Yrbk Phtg; Yrbk Stf; Rep Stu Cncl; Var L Ftbl; Var L Trk; Hon Roll; Jrnlsm.

MC DONALD, MEGAN E; Cathedral HS; Springfield, MA; (Y); 1/476; Mathletes; Ski Clb; Ed Nwsp Stf; Var Cheerleading; Var Trk; Mu Alp Tht; Pres NHS; Intnl Clb; Math Clb; Dartmouth Bk Awd 85; Cathedrl Hgh Modl Senat Parlmntrn 85-86; Rep Amer Interntl Coll Modl Congrs 85; Math.

MC DONALD, SHERRIE L; Ludlow HS; Ludlow, MA; (Y); 42/276; JA; Variety Show; Rep Frsh Cls; Rep Soph Cls; Rep Jr Cls; Rep Sr Cls; Stat Sftbl; Hon Roll; Milton Bradley Co Labr Union Scholar 85; Citznshp Cls Of 85 Awd 85; Granby Am Leg Scholar 85; Bryant Coll; Mktg.

MC DONNELL, LISA; Holyoke Catholic HS; Holyoke, MA; (Y); 11/140; Computer Clb; Debate Tm; Sec Trs Latin Clb; Spanish Clb; School Play; Nwsp Rptr; Yrbk Stf; Lit Mag; High Hon Roll; NHS; Elms Coll; Law.

MC DONNELL, THOMAS; Canton HS; Canton, MA; (Y); Boy Scts; Church Yth Grp; Var L Crs Cntry; JV Ftbl; Var L Trk; Hon Roll; Capt Spring Track 85-86; Hlth.

MC DONOUGH, KATHLEEN V; Dedham HS; Dedham, MA; (Y); 44/300; Civic Clb; Dance Clb; Drama Clb; Exploring; Teachers Aide; School Play; Var Swmmng; Cit Awd; Hon Roll; Mst Imprvd Soph Eng Dept 84; Bentley Coll Sptlght Pgm 85; Excllnt Effrt Eng 82; Mktg.

MC DOWELL, CRAIG; Malden Catholic HS; Malden, MA; (Y); 11/185; Latin Clb; Fld Hcky; Golf; NHS; Ntl Merit SF; Rotary Awd.

MC EACHERN, JOHN H; Gloucester HS; Gloucester, MA; (Y); Camera Clb; Church Yth Grp; French Clb; German Clb; Political Wkr; Jazz Band; Mrchg Band; School Musical; Var Crs Cntry; Gordon Coll; Bio.

MC EACHERN, KAREN; Sacred Heart HS; Weymouth, MA; (Y); 1/68; Math Clb; Spanish Clb; Variety Show; Pres Soph Cls; Sec Jr Cls; JV Var Cheerleading; High Hon Roll; NHS; Intl Frgn Lang Awd; Art.

MC ELENEY, PATRICK; Arlington Catholic HS; Arlington, MA; (Y); 22/148; Am Leg Boys St; Var Trk; Hon Roll; NHS; Prfct Atten Awd; Magna Cum Laude 83-84; Cum Laude 85.

MC ELLIGOTT JR, DAVID; Arlington Catholic HS; Arlington, MA; (Y); Boys Clb Am; Var Bsbl; Var L Bsktbl; Var Ftbl; Var Wt Lftg; Merrimack Acadmc & Engrng Schlrshp 85; MA ST Schlrhsp 85; MVP Bsbl 83-84; Merrimack Coll; Civil Engr.

MC ELROY, KERRY A; Dighton-Rehoboth Regional HS; Rehoboth, MA; (Y); 12/250; Art Clb; Science Clb; Chorus; Yrbk Stf; Capt Bsktbl; Capt Fld Hcky; Sftbl; Trk; Hon Roll; NHS; Ntl Found Adv Arts; Boston Globe Schlstc Art Awds; Rhode Island Schl Design; Artis.

MC ENANEY, TIMOTHY; Nauset Regional HS; Brewster, MA; (Y); Church Yth Grp; Ski Clb; Trs Jr Cls; Trs Sr Cls; JV Var Bsbl; JV Var Bsktbl; Var Crs Cntry; JV Var Socr; Var Trk; Hon Roll; Syracuse U; Bus.

MC EWEN, JULIE; Woburn SR HS; Woburn, MA; (S); Church Yth Grp; French Clb; Hosp Aide; Leo Clb; Office Aide; Color Guard; School Musical; Stu Cncl; Swmmng; Hon Roll; Natl Achvt Acad 83; Vol & Cnslr Spec Educ Chldrn 78-85; Fitchburg ST; Spec Educ Tchr.

MC GANTY, CHRIS; Nashoba Regional HS; Bolton, MA; (S); 31/196; Var Capt Bsktbl; Capt Var Socr; Var Trk; Hon Roll; NHS; 2nd Pl DECA 85; 1st Pl DECA Dist Compettn 84; Syracuse U; Mktng.

MC GEE, DAVID; Bishop Fee Han HS; Attleboro, MA; (Y); 91/265; Boy Scts; Nwsp Rptr; Nwsp Stf; Yrbk Stf; Crs Cntry; Trk; High Hon Roll; Hon Roll; Cvl Engrng.

MC GEE, STEVEN; Westwood HS; Westwood, MA; (Y); 90/220; Band; Concert Band; Drm & Bgl; Jazz Band; Mrchg Band; Pep Band; Stage Crew; Hon Roll; Rookie Yr Awd Marching Bnd 82; Bst Marching Mbr Awd 84; Mus Prod.

MC GIBBON, GLENN; Randolph HS; Randolph, MA; (Y); Spanish Clb; Band; Concert Band; Jazz Band; Mrchg Band; School Musical; Hon Roll; NHS; Church Yth Grp; Crs Cntry; Syms Music Schl Schlrshp 85; Semsba, SE Dist Partcpnt 83-85; Comm.

MC GILVRAY, HEATHER; Bedford Public HS; Bedford, MA; (Y); 28/214; Pres Girl Scts; Chorus; Madrigals; School Musical; Yrbk Stf; JV Bsktbl; Var Socr; Hon Roll; Ntl Merit Ltr; Church Yth Grp; Partcptd In A Stu Exchng For 2 Wks To Spain 85; Partcptd In A Bedford Grl Scout Trip To Englnd 2 Wks; Bryn Mawr; Archlgy.

MC GINLEY, BARBARA; Tewksbury Memorial HS; Tewksbury, MA; (Y); Church Yth Grp; Hosp Aide; Color Guard; Stat Bsktbl; Prfct Atten Awd; Ed.

MC GINN, LISA A; B M C Durfee HS; Westport, MA; (Y); 23/688; Sec MMM; Pres Orch; Lit Mag; High Hon Roll; NHS; Pres Acad Fitnss Awd 85; Regents Orch Act Scholar ASU 85-86; Sthestrn MA Dist Orch Concrt 82-85; AZ ST U; Violin Perfmnce.

MC GINN, THOMAS J; Westborough HS; Westboro, MA; (Y); 21/177; Am Leg Boys St; Aud/Vis; Boy Scts; Pres Exploring; School Play; Stage Crew; Stu Cncl; Crs Cntry; Ftbl; Trk; Assumption Coll; Mgmt.

MC GLOIN, JONATHAN; St Johns HS; Uxbridge, MA; (Y); 98/300; Am Leg Boys St; Computer Clb; English Clb; JA; Math Clb; Science Clb; Ski Clb; Spanish Clb; Varsity Clb; Rep Frsh Cls; Law.

MC GLONE, SHAYNE; Silver Lake Regional HS; Kingston, MA; (Y); 85/500; Boy Scts; Exploring; Math Clb; Archit.

MC GLYNN, MAUREEN; Algonquin Regional HS; Northboro, MA; (Y); 19/210; Concert Band; Jazz Band; Mrchg Band; Ed Yrbk Phtg; Trs Frsh Cls; Trs Soph Cls; Trs Jr Cls; Trs Sr Cls; Hon Roll; NHS; Music Lesson Scholar 83; Phi Alpha Theta ST Hstrcl Conf 85; Pre-Law.

MC GONAGLE, MICHAEL D; Sandwich JR SR HS; Sandwich, MA; (Y); 23/152; Am Leg Boys St; Boy Scts; Concert Band; Jazz Band; Var L Lcrss; Hon Roll; NHS; Ordr Of Arrow 83; Spn Merit Awd 84; Cape Cod Cmnty Coll Collabrtve Pgm 85; Engrng.

MC GONAGLE, PAUL C; Burlington HS; Burlington, MA; (Y); Am Leg Boys St; Aud/Vis; Cmnty Wkr; Office Aide; Political Wkr; Radio Clb; School Musical; Nwsp Ed-Chief; Yrbk Stf; Powder Puff Ftbl; Schl Govt Excllnc 83-85; MA Stu Jstc ST House 84-85; Brdcstg Cmmnctns.

MC GONNIGAL, MAUREEN; Weymouth North HS; E Weymouth, MA; (Y); 5/435; Drama Clb; Pres Band; School Musical; Yrbk Stf; Rep Jr Cls; Rep Sr Cls; Vllybl; High Hon Roll; JP Sousa Awd; Trs NHS; Cmmnwlth Schlr 85; Pres Acad Fitnss Awd 85; Chncllrs Tlnt Awd 84; U Of MA-AMHERST; Cmmnctns.

MC GOUGH, KAREN; Arlington Catholic HS; Arlington, MA; (Y); 29/148; Cmnty Wkr; Drama Clb; French Clb; Office Aide; Service Clb; School Musical; School Play; Cheerleading; Hon Roll; NHS; Law.

MC GOURTY, MAURA; Doherty Memorial HS; Worcester, MA; (Y); Pres Debate Tm; VP JA; Nwsp Stf; Var L Socr; Var L Trk; High Hon Roll; Hon Roll; Jr NHS; Band; Chorus; JR Achvt VP Of Yr 84; Dynmy Future Ldrs Prog 85; Publc Reltns.

MC GOVERN, PATRICIA; Natick HS; Natick, MA; (Y); 158/443; Bsktbl; Sftbl; Hon Roll; Prfct Atten Awd; MA Bay CC; Wrd Proc.

MC GOWAN, CHRIS; Wellesley HS; Wellesley, MA; (Y); German Clb; JV Var Socr; Hon Roll; Ntl Merit Ltr; Comp Sci.

MC GOWAN, LAURA; Holbrook JR SR HS; Holbrook, MA; (Y); 22/100; Var Capt Sftbl; Hon Roll; Certfd Scuba Dvr By PADI Dvrs 82; Cst Gurd Axlry Btng Sklls & Seamnshp 85.

MC GOWAN, MARY; Medway HS; Medway, MA; (Y); 42/150; Cmnty Wkr; Yrbk Stf; Rep Stu Cncl; Im Var Bsktbl; Im Coach Actv; Var Capt Socr; High Hon Roll; Hon Roll; Church Yth Grp; Hosp Aide; Schlstc Awd 83 & 85; Spirit & Unsung Hero 84-85; Travel.

MC GRADY JR, JOSEPH P; Westboro HS; Westboro, MA; (Y); 24/158; Am Leg Boys St; Model UN; Concert Band; Variety Show; Stu Cncl; Var Bsbl; JV Bsktbl; Var Ftbl; Hon Roll; NHS; Med.

MC GRAIL, CHRISTINE; Leicester HS; Rochdale, MA; (Y); Church Yth Grp; Latin Clb; Rep Stu Cncl; VP L Fld Hcky; VP L Trk; Hon Roll; Physcl Ftns Awd 85; Psych.

MC GRAIL, SUZANNE; Clinton HS; Clinton, MA; (Y); Church Yth Grp; Intnl Clb; Nwsp Stf; Yrbk Bus Mgr; Var L Cheerleading; L Capt Fld Hcky; L Var Sftbl; NHS; Med.

MC GRATH, MICHAEL; Agawam HS; Feeding Hls, MA; (Y); Library Aide; JV Bsktbl; Var Ftbl; Im Wt Lftg; Hon Roll; Peer Ldrshp Wrkshp Cert 84; Bus.

MC GRATH, MICHELE; Saugus HS; Saugus, MA; (Y); Office Aide; Yrbk Stf; High Hon Roll; Hon Roll; Jr NHS; Bus Mngmnt.

MC GRATH, RICHARD; Milford HS; Milford, MA; (Y); 1/293; Boy Scts; Band; Concert Band; Mrchg Band; Pres Soph Cls; Var Swmmng; Var Tennis; JV Wrstlng; NHS; Hugh O Brian Yth Fndtn Semnr Rep 83-84; Harvard Bk Clb Worcester Awd 85; Engrng.

MC GRATH, ROBERT; St Johns Prep; Lynn, MA; (Y); English Clb; Ski Clb; Spanish Clb; Nwsp Ed-Chief; Nwsp Sprt Ed; Nwsp Stf; JV Bsbl; Bsktbl; Ftbl; JV Ice Hcky; Jrnlsm.

MC GRATH, SCOTT; Bridgewater Raynham Regional HS; Raynham, MA; (Y); Varsity Clb; JV Golf; JV Wrstlng; Stonehill Coll; Crmnl Law.

MC GRATH, SHEILA; Archbishop Williams HS; Quincy, MA; (Y); 27/201; Camera Clb; Church Yth Grp; Drama Clb; Key Clb; Chorus; School Musical; Stage Crew; Yrbk Stf; Rep Frsh Cls; Rep Soph Cls; Spansh Awd 83; Soc Wrk.

MC GRATH, SUSAN; North Andover HS; N Andover, MA; (Y); 9/262; Intnl Clb; Math Tm; Pep Clb; Ski Clb; Chorus; Ed Yrbk Stf; Stu Cncl; Fld Hcky; Mgr Mgr(s); Trk; N Andover Schlrshp Fndtn Awd 85; Lawrence Rotry Schlrshp 85; MA Commnwlth Schlrs Grnt 85; Boston Coll; Math.

MC GREGOR, CAROLINE; Haverhill HS; Haverhill, MA; (Y); 51/380; Pres French Clb; German Clb; Yrbk Stf; JV L Crs Cntry; Var Capt Trk; High Hon Roll; NHS; Latin Clb; Stu Cncl; Powder Puff Ftbl; Prsnl Achvt Awd 85; Mst Valble Perfrmr 85; Frnch Clb Awd 85; St Lawrence U.

MC GUIRE, BOB; Milford HS; Milford, MA; (Y); 34/300; JV Wrstlng; High Hon Roll; Hon Roll; Northeastern; Engrng.

MC GUIRE, NANCY; Melrose HS; Melrose, MA; (Y); 12/375; Girl Scts; Ski Clb; Yrbk Stf; Hon Roll; NHS; Mst Outstndng Mth Stu 82-83; Phys Thrpy.

MC GUIRE, RACHEL; Matgnon HS; Somerville, MA; (S); 8/190; Art Clb; Drama Clb; Chorus; School Musical; School Play; Stage Crew; Nwsp Stf; Lit Mag; Trk; NHS; Hnr Roll 82-84; Ntl Merit Letter 84; Soc Distinguished Amer H S Stu 84; Harvard; Arch.

MC INNIS, DANIEL; Malden HS; Malden, MA; (Y); Art Clb; Boy Scts; Band; Mrchg Band; Bsbl; Ftbl; Swmmng; Trk; Wrstlng; Med Schl; Vet.

MC INNIS, KELLI A; South High Community Schl; Worcester, MA; (Y); Church Yth Grp; Political Wkr; Ski Clb; Teachers Aide; Band; Concert Band; Jazz Band; Mrchg Band; Sec Frsh Cls; Var Tennis; Certified Ski Instrctr 82-83; Ty Cobb Sftbl Lg 82-83; Med Ther.

MC INTOSH, ARTHUR P; Hingham HS; Hingham, MA; (Y); 160/325; AFS; Nwsp Phtg; Rep Stu Cncl; Hon Roll; Photo Cntst; Med.

MC INTYRE, JEAN; Jamaica Plain HS; Boston, MA; (Y); Nwsp Stf.

MC KAY, KATHY; Joseph Case HS; Swansea, MA; (Y); 24/209; French Clb; Church Choir; Var Capt Gym; Trk; Cit Awd; Hon Roll; NHS; Coaches Awd For Gym 84-85; Citizens Schlrshp; U Of Lowell; Phy Ther.

MC KAY, MATTHEW; Bishop Feehan HS; N Attleboro, MA; (Y); Chess Clb; Ski Clb; Off Soph Cls; Bsbl; Bsktbl; Ftbl; Powder Puff Ftbl; U Mass Amhearst; Engr.

MC KAY, ROBIN; Weymouth South HS; Weymouth, MA; (Y); JV Var Cheerleading; Hon Roll; Patriot Ldgr Awds Arts 84; Ntl Sci Olym 83; Fash Ill.

MC KAY, SHEILA; Jeremian E Burke HS; Dorchester, MA; (Y); Stu Cncl; Hon Roll; Cert Achvt 84-85; Jrnlsm.

MC KEE, CYNTHIA; Saugus HS; Saugus, MA; (Y); 60/350; Hon Roll; Fitchburg ST Coll; Nrsng.

MC KENNA, LORI; BMC Durfee HS; Fall River, MA; (Y); 4/688; Office Aide; Varsity Clb; Color Guard; Capt Drm Mjr(t); Nwsp Stf; Yrbk Stf; Lit Mag; CC Awd; High Hon Roll; NHS; Colgate U; Bus Mngmnt.

MC KENNA, MAUREEN; Silver Lake Regional HS; Halifax, MA; (Y); Church Yth Grp; Exploring; Library Aide; Office Aide; Chorus; Church Choir; High Hon Roll; Hon Roll; Dsgn Art.

MC KENNA, PATRICIA; Sacred Heart HS; N Quincy, MA; (Y); 4/68; Church Yth Grp; French Clb; Girl Scts; Math Clb; Church Choir; Variety Show; Var Bsktbl; Capt Var Sftbl; Var Vllybl; Hon Roll.

MC KENZIE, JAMES; Don Bosco Technical HS; Medford, MA; (S); 19/200; Pep Clb; Quiz Bowl; Nwsp Sprt Ed; Yrbk Sprt Ed; Capt Socr; Swmmng; Trk; Hon Roll; Bus Mgmt.

MC KENZIE JR, ROBERT C; Holyoke HS; Holyoke, MA; (Y); Band; Concert Band; Mrchg Band; Yrbk Stf; JV Bsbl; Ftbl; Var Socr; Var Swmmng; High Hon Roll; Hon Roll; Sci.

MC KEOWN, DENISE M; Andover HS; Andover, MA; (Y); 20/406; Model UN; Yrbk Stf; Rep Stu Cncl; JV Fld Hcky; Score Keeper; High Hon Roll; Hon Roll; Pltcl Sci.

MC KILLOP, LOUISE; Norton HS; Norton, MA; (Y); Pep Clb; Varsity Clb; Chorus; Variety Show; Var Capt Cheerleading; Var Capt Pom Pon; Hon Roll; Prfct Atten Awd; Bus.

MC KINNON, PAMELA; Christopher Columbus HS; Charlestown, MA; (S); 9/135; Boys Clb Am; FNA; JA; Cheerleading; Hon Roll; NHS; Ntl Merit Ltr; Spanish NHS; Algbr & Latn Awd; U Of MA Amhurst; Nrsng.

MC LAUGHLIN, CATHERINE; South Boston HS; South Boston, MA; (S); Drama Clb; Girl Scts; Office Aide; Teachers Aide; School Play; Swing Chorus; Nwsp Ed-Chief; Rep Frsh Cls; Rep Soph Cls; Rep Jr Cls; Chrstn Merter Schlrshp 83; Exch Stud Sschlrshp To Japan 84; Stud Of Mnth 84; Lang.

MC LAUGHLIN, CHRISTINE; Triton Regional HS; Salisbury, MA; (Y); AFS; Rep Stu Cncl; Mgr(s); Var JV Trk; Hon Roll; NHS; Med.

MC LAUGHLIN, CLARE; Boston Latin HS; Boston, MA; (Y); 65/322; Church Yth Grp; Bsktbl; Sftbl; French Hon Soc; Hon Roll; Key Clb 82-85; Prfsnl Clb 82-85; Frgn Plcy 83-85; Boston Coll; Pre-Med.

MC LAUGHLIN, JULIE; Lowell HS; Lowell, MA; (S); 130/552; DECA; VP JA; Nwsp Rptr; Rep Soph Cls; High Hon Roll; Hon Roll; Johnson & Wales Natl DECA Scholar 85; JA Sls Awd 82; 2nd Pl Awd ST DECA Creative Mktng 85; Johnson & Wales Coll; Bus Admin.

MC LAUGHLIN, KERRI E; Walpole HS; Walpole, MA; (Y); 29/267; Church Yth Grp; Cmnty Wkr; Hosp Aide; Spanish Clb; Rep Frsh Cls; Rep Soph Cls; Rep Jr Cls; Rep Sr Cls; Hon Roll; Boston Globe Schltc Art Awds Gold Key & Blue Ribbn 81 83 & 85; Boston U; Art.

MC LAUGHLIN, LAUREN A; Hamilton-Wenham Reginal HS; Wenham, MA; (Y); 14/200; Cmnty Wkr; Drama Clb; Chorus; Jazz Band; School Musical; Nwsp Rptr; Nwsp Stf; Lit Mag; Trs Frsh Cls; Trs Soph Cls; Engl.

MC LAUGHLIN, MARY ELLEN; Ursuline Acad; W Roxbury, MA; (Y); 7/73; Cmnty Wkr; Pres Service Clb; Chorus; Drill Tm; Yrbk Stf; Hon Roll; NHS; Church Yth Grp; Drama Clb; Spanish Clb; Latn Awd 85; Peer Mnstry Cert 85; ISIA Figr Sktg 1 Gld, 2 Slvr, 1 Brnz & 2 4th Pl 81-85; Wellesley Coll; Psych.

MC LAUGHLIN, MICHAEL E; Duxbury HS; Duxbury, MA; (Y); 88/274; Am Leg Boys St; Key Clb; Stat Bsktbl; Var JV Ftbl; JV Golf; Bus.

MC LEAN, ADAM J; Chicopee Comprehensive HS; Chicopee, MA; (S); 11/294; German Clb; Var Bsktbl; Var Ftbl; Var Trk; High Hon Roll; Hon Roll; NHS; Air Force Acad; Aerontcl Engrng.

MC LEAN, JOHN B; Acton-Boxborough Reg HS; Acton, MA; (Y); Chess Clb; Computer Clb; Math Tm; School Musical; Var JV Bsktbl; Var Vllybl; Hon Roll; NHS; Rep To Grmn-Amer Reltns Semnr; 1st In European Math Comptn; Elec Engrng.

MC LEAN, SCOTT; Natick HS; Natick, MA; (Y); 109/470; JV Bsbl; Finance.

MC LELLAN, HELENANNE; Marian HS; Hopkinton, MA; (Y); 20/177; Church Yth Grp; Girl Scts; Latin Clb; Office Aide; Yrbk Stf; Var L Bsktbl; Var JV Mgr(s); Var JV Score Keeper; Var JV Timer; Hon Roll; Excllnce Wrtng Adv Engl I 83; Excllnce Final Exam Christian Values 83; Grl Scouts Silver Awd 83; Nrsng.

MC LELLAN, MEGAN; Westwood HS; Westwood, MA; (Y); 70/214; AFS; Church Yth Grp; Intnl Clb; School Musical; Yrbk Stf; Trs Stu Cncl; Var L Fld Hcky; St Schlr; Var Trk; Elks Awd; Cmnctns.

MC MAHON, KOURTNEY; Bridgewater Raynham Regional HS; Bridgewater, MA; (Y); French Clb; Ski Clb; Spanish Clb; Varsity Clb; Var Cheerleading; JV Fld Hcky; JV Sftbl; Nutrition.

MC MANUS, AMY; Coyle And Cassidy HS; Taunton, MA; (Y); Art Clb; French Clb; Hosp Aide; Quiz Bowl; Ski Clb; Church Choir; Yrbk Phtg; Yrbk Stf; Rep Soph Cls; Hon Roll; Fashn Desgn.

MC MANUS, MATTHEW; St Johns HS; Framingham, MA; (Y); 42/278; Church Yth Grp; Dance Clb; English Clb; FCA; Science Clb; Spanish Clb; School Musical; High Hon Roll; Hon Roll; NHS; Bus Adm.

MC MENEMY, NANCY; Doherty Memorial HS; Worcester, MA; (Y); Church Yth Grp; Hosp Aide; Political Wkr; Variety Show; Yrbk Stf; Stu Cncl; Natl Frnch Exam Awd 84; Lib Arts.

MC MULLEN, LYN; Burlington HS; Burlington, MA; (Y); 86/319; Drama Clb; JA; Acpl Chr; Chorus; School Musical; School Play; Stage Crew; Swing Chorus; Variety Show; Hon Roll; Music Hnr Awd 85; Berklee; Music.

MC MULLEN, PETER; Medway JR SR HS; Medway, MA; (Y); 28/150; Boy Scts; Church Yth Grp; Band; Concert Band; Jazz Band; Nwsp Rptr; Yrbk Stf; Ftbl; Golf; Wt Lftg; Bus Mngmnt.

MC MULLIN, JOANNE; Mohawk Trail Regional HS; Hawley, MA; (Y); VP AFS; German Clb; Library Aide; Varsity Clb; Chorus; School Musical; Var Trk; High Hon Roll; Hon Roll; Church Yth Grp; Ger Awd 85.

MC NAIR, KARLA; Boston Latin HS; W Roxbury, MA; (Y); Dance Clb; Key Clb; Ski Clb; Teachers Aide; Variety Show; Lit Mag; Hon Roll.

MC NALL, KEN; Wakefield HS; Wakefield, MA; (Y); Church Yth Grp; JV Bsbl; Var L Ftbl; Var Wrstlng; High Hon Roll; Hon Roll; Ftbll MVP 84; Engnr.

MC NALLY, KATHLEEN; Haverhill HS; E Hempstead, NH; (Y); Key Clb; Nwsp Rptr; NHS; Stu Cncl Awd Outstndng Achvt Frnch 81-82; Schlrshp Awd 85; U NH; Comm.

MC NALLY, PETER R; N Quincy HS; Quincy, MA; (Y); 48/379; Am Leg Boys St; Scholastic Bowl; Var Socr; High Hon Roll; Hon Roll; NHS; Boy Scts; Church Yth Grp; Library Aide; Spanish Clb; Amer Legion Schlrshp 85; Altruso Club Quincy Schlrshp 85; NE U; Comp Sci.

MC NAUGHT, JAMES A; Xaverian Brothers HS; Walpole, MA; (S); 3/236; Boy Scts; Chess Clb; Exploring; Latin Clb; Mgr(s); Socr; Swmmng; High Hon Roll; NHS; Ntl Merit Ltr; 1 Yr Acad Scholar Xaverian Bros H S; Sufflk U Bk Awd 84; Scholar N Amer Acad Of Bagpiping 84; Aero-Sci.

MC NEE, SUSAN; Taunton HS; Taunton, MA; (Y); 107/430; Sec Church Yth Grp; Drama Clb; Trs 4-H; Office Aide; Pep Clb; Var L Cheerleading; Var L Pom Pon; 4-H Awd; Hon Roll; Cert Of Crdt & Prfcncy Cntry 21 Typwrtng 84-85; Bus Mngmnt.

MC NEIL, CRISTON; Malden HS; Malden, MA; (Y); 47/470; Drama Clb; Girl Scts; Acpl Chr; Pres Chorus; Madrigals; Variety Show; Tchng.

MC NEIL, KARYN; Fontbonne Acad; Readville, MA; (Y); 18/127; Debate Tm; Drama Clb; School Play; Stage Crew; Ed Lit Mag; Rep Frsh Cls; Rep Soph Cls; Hon Roll; Hugh O Brien Yth Ldrshp Fnlst; Recgntn Awd-Spn I; Recgntn Awd-Spn III Hnrs; Bio.

MC NEIL, RICHARD; Andover HS; Andover, MA; (Y); 120/435; Church Yth Grp; Ice Hcky; Hon Roll; Ntl Merit Ltr; St Schlr; Sthestrn MA U.

MC NEILLIE, KENT; Medway JR SR HS; Medway, MA; (Y); 23/162; Church Yth Grp; Drama Clb; Band; Chorus; Church Choir; Concert Band; Jazz Band; Mrchg Band; School Musical; School Play; Electrical Engrng.

MC NEILLY, KAREN; Fontbonne Acad; Jamaica Plain, MA; (Y); 37/150; Drama Clb; Library Aide; School Musical; School Play; Lit Mag; Hon Roll; Lbrary Aid Awd; Brnz Mdl Spnsh Achvt; Excllnc Spnsh III; Engl Jrnlsm.

MC NEILLY, LAWRENCE R; Catholic Memorial HS; Jamaica Plain, MA; (Y); 7/269; Am Leg Boys St; Cmnty Wkr; Math Clb; Nwsp Sprt Ed; Bsktbl; L Ftbl; High Hon Roll; Masonic Awd; Sec NHS; Pres Schlr; Hollis Fndtn Schlrshp 85; Catholic Memrl H S Commnty Serv Awd 85; Michael S Bosak Memrl Schlrshp 85; Bryant Coll; Marketng.

MC NTIGNY, DONNY; Bishop Stong HS; Westport, MA; (Y); 61/250; Cmnty Wkr; Ski Clb; Yrbk Stf; Var Bsbl; Var Ftbl; Var Wt Lftg; Masonic Awd; MA Coll Of Pharmacy; Phrmcst.

MC NULTY, LORA; Bishop Feehan HS; Norfolk, MA; (Y); French Clb; Chorus; School Play; Stage Crew; French Hon Soc; High Hon Roll; NHS; Prfct Atten Awd.

MC OUAT, ROB; Nansey Regional HS; East Orelans, MA; (Y); Math Clb; Var Bsbl; L Bsktbl; Hon Roll.

MC PHELIM, LISA; Concord-Carlisle HS; Concord, MA; (S); Civic Clb; CAP; Pres DECA; Var Cheerleading; Var Tennis; Hon Roll; 1st Pl Trphy DECA ST Conf-Apprl & Accssrs 85; Johnson & Whales Coll Schlrshp 85; Providence Coll; Bus Mgmt.

MC QUADE, KATHRYN; Presentation Of Mary Acad; Hampstead, NH; (Y); 14/50; Church Yth Grp; French Clb; Hosp Aide; Math Clb; Yrbk Stf; JV Bsktbl; Var Sftbl; Hon Roll; NHS; Ntl Hnr Soc 84-85; Ntl Hnr Roll 85; Hobart & William Smith; Bio.

MC QUIGGAN, LISA; Maynard HS; Maynard, MA; (Y); Cmnty Wkr; Radio Clb; VP Soph Cls; Sec Sr Cls; JV Bsktbl; JV Sftbl; DAR Awd; Daugh Am Revlutn Schlrshp 85; Framingham Un Hosp; Nrsng.

MC QUISTON, AMY; Tahanto Regional HS; Boylston, MA; (Y); 2/44; Science Clb; Yrbk Stf; Capt Fld Hcky; High Hon Roll; Jr NHS; VP NHS; Williams Coll Bk Awd 85; MVP Fld Hcky 83.

MC STOWE, NORA J; Uxbridge HS; Uxbridge, MA; (Y); 5/70; Office Aide; Sec Spanish Clb; Trs Varsity Clb; VP Soph Cls; Sec Stu Cncl; Var L Fld Hcky; High Hon Roll; NHS; Pres Schlr; Hugh O Brian Yth Ldrshp Smnr 82-83; Brnds U; Pre-Med.

MC SWEENEY, JASON; Nipmuc Reg HS; Mendon, MA; (Y); Church Yth Grp; Cmnty Wkr; Trk; Cmnctns.

MC VEY, MICHAEL; Brockton HS; Brockton, MA; (Y); 47/936; High Hon Roll; Prfct Atten Awd.

MC WHIRK, KIMBERLY; Boston Latin Schl; Boston, MA; (Y); Drama Clb; French Clb; Ski Clb; Elem Ed.

MEAD, ANDREA M; Northfield Mt Herman HS; Ridgefield, CT; (Y); AFS; Art Clb; Drama Clb; Sec Intnl Clb; Ski Clb; Varsity Clb; Chorus; School Musical; Stage Crew; Rep Frsh Cls.

MEAD, ERIC; Westfield HS; Westfield, MA; (Y); #66 In Class; 5 Yr Anniversary Awd Guitar 81; Tri ST Guitar Band Comp 1st&2nd 78,79&82; 2nd&3rd Pl Band Perf 83&84; Musician.

MEAL, KEITH L; Cardinal Spellman HS; W Bridgewater, MA; (Y); 37/217; Boy Scts; Church Yth Grp; Computer Clb; Bsktbl; Var Capt Crs Cntry; Var Capt Trk; Hon Roll; Pres Schlr; Eagle Scout 84; 1st Pl Cardinal Spellman Sci Fair 85; Town Schlrshp 85; Daniel Webster Coll; Comp Sci.

MEDEIROS, CHRISTOPHER; Diman Reg Voc Tech HS; Somerset, MA; (Y); VICA; Concert Band; Wenworth Inst; Crpntry.

MEDEIROS, DEAN; Bishop Connolly HS; Fall River, MA; (S); 23/168; Chess Clb; Drama Clb; German Clb; Hosp Aide; Stage Crew; Variety Show; Var L Bsbl; High Hon Roll; NHS; Moninated Exch Prgm To Finland 84; Providence Coll; Mus.

MEDEIROS, JOYCE L; BMC Durfee HS; Fall River, MA; (Y); 68/650; Cmnty Wkr; Office Aide; Varsity Clb; Color Guard; School Musical; Variety Show; Hon Roll; Vrsty Lttr 84; Ctzn Schlrshp Awd 85; Delta Awd 85; Mrchng Band Certs 85; SE MA U; Psych.

MEDEIROS, KATHLEEN S; Bishop Stang HS; Acushnet, MA; (Y); 7/220; Rep Soph Cls; Sec Jr Cls; Sec Sr Cls; Rep Stu Cncl; Capt Cheerleading; Hon Roll; NHS; St Schlr; Civic Clb; Trk; Century 3 Ldrshp 85; Top 10 In Clss 85 82-85; Acushnet Tchrs Schlrshp 85; Boston Coll; Nrsng.

MEDEIROS, LANCE; New Bedford HS; New Bedford, MA; (Y).

MEDEIROS, LAURIE; Bishop Connolly HS; Westport, MA; (Y); Church Yth Grp; Cmnty Wkr; Var L Cheerleading; High Hon Roll; Hon Roll; Schlrshp & Schlstc Awd From Westport JR Miss Pgnt 85; Math.

MEDEIROS, LINDELLE; Somerset HS; Somerset, MA; (Y); Yrbk Stf; Rep Sr Cls; Stu Cncl; Trk; High Hon Roll; Hon Roll; Fitchburg ST Coll.

MEDEIROS, LISA; Wilmington HS; Wilmington, MA; (Y); 23/249; JA; Spanish Clb; Yrbk Stf; Mgr(s); Var Trk; Hon Roll; Kiwanis Awd; Ntl Merit Schol; Spanish NHS; MA St Schlrshp Rec 85; U New Hampshire; Occup Thrpst.

MEDEIROS, MARYELLEN; Bishop Connolly HS; Fall River, MA; (S); Cmnty Wkr; Hosp Aide; Ski Clb; Rep Soph Cls; High Hon Roll; NHS; Southeastern MA U; Marktng.

MEDEIROS, MICHAEL; B M C Durfee HS; Fall River, MA; (Y); 53/651; Computer Clb; JV Trk; Hon Roll; NHS; Pres Schlr; U Of MA; Bio-Chem.

MEDEIROS, NELSON; New Bedford HS; New Bedford, MA; (Y); 77/598; Church Yth Grp; Drama Clb; JA; Varsity Clb; Stu Cncl; Var Ice Hcky; Var Tennis; Engrng.

MEDEIROS, RICARDO; Diman Reg Vo Tech; Fall River, MA; (Y); Band; Mrchg Band; Orch; Var Bsbl; Var Socr; Trk; Hon Roll; Herald News Small Schl All Schltc 85; Socr Tm; Mech Engrng.

MEDEIROS, SANDRA; New Bedford HS; New Bedford, MA; (Y); 6/580; AFS; Drama Clb; Yrbk Stf; Stu Cncl; Fld Hcky; High Hon Roll; Jr NHS; NHS; Church Yth Grp; Debate Tm; Boston U; Intl Rltns.

MEDEIROS, STEVEN; Arlington Catholic HS; Woburn, MA; (Y); 85/158; Hosp Aide; Spanish Clb; Concert Band; Variety Show; Var Capt Ftbl; Wt Lftg; Chem.

MEDERIS, JOANNE; B M C Durfee HS; Fall River, MA; (Y); Art Clb; French Clb; Band; Color Guard; Concert Band; Var Capt Flag Corp; Mrchg Band; Yrbk Stf; Powder Puff Ftbl; JV Twrlr; Grphc Dsgn.

MEDOFF, LEE J; Needham HS; Needham, MA; (Y); 40/400; Am Leg Boys St; Var L Ftbl; Var L Trk; Wt Lftg; High Hon Roll; Hon Roll; NHS; New Engld Sprts Ldg All Schlstc Tm 85; Needham Sprtsmns Clb Schlrshp 85; Haverford Coll Phila PA; Chem.

MEDVECKY, DEBORAH; Presentation Of Mary Acad; Salem, NH; (Y); Art Clb; Church Yth Grp; Drama Clb; Model UN; Pep Clb; Ski Clb; Varsity Clb; School Play; Tennis; Stu Cncl Schlrshp 85; Humants Awd 85; Plymouth ST Coll; Mrktng.

MEE, EILEEN C; Mount Saint Joseph Acad; Brighton, MA; (Y); Art Clb; French Clb; Girl Scts; Hosp Aide; Variety Show; Hon Roll; NHS; Bus Ntl Hnr Scty 84-85; Bus.

MEEKER, HEATHER; Concord Carlisle HS; Concord, MA; (Y); 10/297; Church Yth Grp; Political Wkr; VP Spanish Clb; High Hon Roll; NHS; Dept Hnrs English Spnsh 83; Dept Hnrs Englsh Spnsh Chem Hstry Gym 84; Dept Hnrs Englsh Spnsh 85.

MEFFAN, ROBERT; Bedford HS; Bedford, MA; (Y); Church Yth Grp; JV Ftbl; Var Lcrss; Hon Roll; Ntl Merit Ltr; U MA Amherst; Cvl Engrng.

MEGA, STEVEN; Hudson HS; Hudson, MA; (Y); Bsktbl; Mgr(s); Hon Roll; Hugh O Brien Ldrshp Awd 84; Mrn Bio.

MEGAN, JOSEPH F; Bishop Feehan HS; Attleboro, MA; (Y); 9/245; Am Leg Boys St; Math Clb; Math Tm; VP Stu Cncl; JV Bsktbl; VP Crs Cntry; VP Trk; High Hon Roll; NHS; Spanish NHS; Hghst Score Mth Tm; Holy Cross; Bus.

MEI, PAM; Marlboro HS; Marlboro, MA; (Y); Ski Clb; High Hon Roll; Hon Roll; Bay ST JR; Flght Atndnt.

MEIGGS, HILLARY; Silver Lake Regional HS; Kingston, MA; (Y); Church Yth Grp; French Clb; Girl Scts; Hosp Aide; Var L Socr; Marion Medl Awd 82-83; Girl Sct Silvr Awd 83-84; Fashn Dsgn.

MEISSNER, EDWARD P; Roxbury Latin Schl; Canton, MA; (Y); Am Leg Boys St; Cmnty Wkr; Chorus; Yrbk Phtg; Socr; Co-Capt Wrstlng; Cit Awd; Hon Roll; NHS; Ntl Merit Ltr; Outstndng Yng Ctzn Canton Citation 85; Boston Coll H S Schltc Scholar 80; U Notre Dame; CPA.

MELANSON, DENISE; Westwood HS; Westwood, MA; (Y); 87/207; Spanish Clb; Swmmng; Trk; Hon Roll; Spanish NHS; Vrsty Swmmng Ltr 83; Bus.

MELANSON, LISA; St Bernards Central Catholic HS; Fitchburg, MA; (S); 17/163; Sec French Clb; Chorus; School Musical; Yrbk Stf; Rep Stu Cncl; Stat Bsktbl; Var Crs Cntry; High Hon Roll; Hon Roll; Prfct Atten Awd; Fr Awd 84; Fitchburg ST Coll; Nrsg.

MELANSON, MARK; Braintree HS; Braintree, MA; (Y); 165/420; Church Yth Grp; Ski Clb; JV Bsbl; Engrng.

MELANSON, NORITA; St Gregory HS; Dorchester, MA; (Y); Drama Clb.

MELANSON, SCOTT; Central Catholic HS; Lawrence, MA; (Y); 33/247; Ski Clb; Capt Bowling; High Hon Roll; U Of Lowell; Elec Engr.

MELEEDY, MICHAEL G; North Quincy HS; Quincy, MA; (Y); 26/372; Am Leg Boys St; Cmnty Wkr; Math Tm; Quiz Bowl; Scholastic Bowl; Var Bsbl; Stat Bsktbl; Coach Actv; High Hon Roll; NHS; U MA Amherst; Bus Admin.

MELIA, MARY; Beverly HS; Beverly, MA; (Y); 191/378; Girl Scts; Acpl Chr; Chorus; Madrigals; School Musical; School Play; Swing Chorus; Hon Roll; Helen Nicols Music Schlrshp 85; Berklee Schl Music; Music Educ.

MELIERE, JANINE; Framingham South HS; Framingham, MA; (S); 22/285; Camp Fr Inc; French Clb; Key Clb; Church Choir; Variety Show; Capt Cheerleading; Socr; Sftbl; Hon Roll; Ntl Vrsty Clb Comptv Tm Awd 84.

MELISI, JEAN M; Whitman-Hanson Regional HS; Whitman, MA; (Y); 9/285; AFS; Am Leg Aux Girls St; Chorus; Yrbk Stf; JV Socr; Hon Roll; Sec NHS; Pres Schlr; Bentley Coll; Bus Mngmnt.

MELLEN, DIONNE; Canton HS; Canton, MA; (Y); 61/265; Pres Sec Church Yth Grp; French Clb; Stage Crew; Nwsp Stf; Yrbk Ed-Chief; Elks Awd; Hon Roll; Canton Comm Clb Schlrsph 85; St Catherines Philotchos Soc Schlrhsp 85; MA U Amherst; Art.

MELLEN, GERARD; N Middlesex Regional HS; Townsend, MA; (Y); Church Yth Grp; Pres Computer Clb; Rep Jr Cls; Golf; Hon Roll; NHS; Comp Sci.

MELLO, BEVERLY A; Fairhaven HS; Fairhaven, MA; (Y); 5/189; VP Spanish Clb; Vllybl; High Hon Roll; Jr NHS; VP NHS; Pres Schlr; Cmmnwlth MA & Thms Liuesey Mem Schlrshps 85; Citatn Schltc Achvt 85; Southeastern MA U; Comp Sci.

MELLO, CHRISTINE; B M C Durfee H S Of Fall River; Fall River, MA; (Y); 120/680; Drama Clb; German Clb; Library Aide; Teachers Aide; School Play; Yrbk Stf; Sthestrn MA U; Psychlgy.

MELLO, DIANE; Bishop Stang HS; S Dartmouth, MA; (S); 3/236; Church Yth Grp; Var Bsktbl; Var Sftbl; High Hon Roll; NHS; Wellesley Coll.

MELLO, GLENDA; Barnstable HS; Centerville, MA; (S); 199/398; AFS; Church Yth Grp; Drama Clb; Chorus; Church Choir; School Musical; Stage Crew; Powder Puff Ftbl; Bay Path JC; Trvl.

MELLO, STACEY ANN; Barnstable HS; Centerville, MA; (Y); 23/398; Sec Church Yth Grp; Ski Clb; Nwsp Stf; JV Trk; DAR Awd; Hon Roll; Lion Awd; NHS; St Schlr; Silver Acad Achvmnt Awd 83; Gold Acad Achvmnt Awd 84; NCTE Wrtng Awd For Excell In Wrtng 84; U Of NH; Bus Adm.

MELO, ANNA; Jeremiah E Burke HS; Dorchester, MA; (Y); 5/18; Dance Clb; Drama Clb; Office Aide; Teachers Aide; School Play; Stage Crew; Yrbk Stf; Pres Stu Cncl; Hon Roll; Handcp Arts Fest Awd 84-85; Schl Spirit Awd 85; Urban Schlr 84-85; Boston U; Crmnl Law.

MEMBRINO, LOUIS; St Bernards Central Catholic HS; Fitchburg, MA; (S); 11/163; Varsity Clb; Nwsp Stf; Pres Soph Cls; Pres Sr Cls; JV Bsbl; Var Bsktbl; Var Ftbl; Var Trk; Hon Roll; NHS; Outstndng Achvt Chem; John H Healy Mem Awd; Mech Engrng.

MEMBRINO, TIMOTHY; Lunenburg HS; Lunenburg, MA; (Y); Pres Frsh Cls; Pres Soph Cls; Pres Jr Cls; Pres Sr Cls; High Hon Roll; NHS; SADD Publ Rel Chrmn 84-85; SADD Pres 85-86; Comp Engrng.

MEMMOLO, CIRIACO A; Malden Catholic HS; Revere, MA; (Y); Drama Clb; Latin Clb; Math Tm; School Musical; NHS; Ntl Merit Ltr; Latin Awd 85; Biographer Awd 85; John Muslo Laborers Locl 22 Mem Scholar 85; Boston U; Med.

MENARD, CHRISTOPHER; Taunton HS; Taunton, MA; (Y); 27/410; Computer Clb; Math Tm; Stu Cncl; L Ftbl; L Trk; Im Wt Lftg; Mass Adu Stds Prog 84; Worcester Polytech Inst; Math.

MENARD, STACEY; Coyle Cassidy HS; Taunton, MA; (Y); 4-H; Spanish Clb; Teachers Aide; Trs Frsh Cls; Rep Soph Cls; Rep Jr Cls; 4-H Awd; Pharm.

MENDEHALL, CHERYL; Tri-County Regional Vocational Tech; Seekonk, MA; (Y); Hon Roll; Comp Info Systms.

MENDEL, ROBERT; Hoosoc Valley HS; Adams, MA; (Y); Cmnty Wkr; Pep Clb; Ski Clb; Band; Concert Band; Jazz Band; Mrchg Band; Pep Band; Hon Roll; Trinity Coll; Bus.

MENDES, STEPHANIE; Somerset HS; Somerset, MA; (Y); 16/326; Dance Clb; Ski Clb; Variety Show; Rep Jr Cls; Rep Stu Cncl; Var L Cheerleading; JV Fld Hcky; Hon Roll; NHS; Bus.

MENDOZA, STEPHANIE; Bourne HS; Monument Beach, MA; (Y); 13/165; Pres Concert Band; Drm Mjr(t); Mrchg Band; School Play; VP Jr Cls; Capt Vllybl; Sec NHS; Pres Schlr; PA ST U; Bus Admin.

MENTZER, LISA; Burncoat SR HS; Worcester, MA; (Y); Church Yth Grp; Intnl Clb; Crs Cntry; Trk; Socl Wrk.

MENTZER JR, ROBERT; Burncoat SR HS; Worcester, MA; (Y); 38/263; Boy Scts; Trs Pres Church Yth Grp; Intnl Clb; Chorus; Church Choir; Hnr Schlrshp 85-86; U Lowell; Metrlgy.

MENZ, KAREN; Weymouth North HS; E Weymouth, MA; (Y); 2/393; Yrbk Ed-Chief; Yrbk Stf; Rep Frsh Cls; Rep Soph Cls; Rep Jr Cls; High Hon Roll; Hon Roll; Jr NHS; NHS; Ski Clb; JR Usherette 85; Med Tech.

MERCER, DANIEL W; Boston College HS; Milton, MA; (Y); Camera Clb; Church Yth Grp; Ski Clb; Cit Awd; Hon Roll; NHS; Im Bsktbl; Im Ftbl; Svc Awd Am Jewish Comm 85; Boston Coll; Med.

MERCER, ROBERT; Malden HS; Malden, MA; (Y); Boy Scts; Brotherhood; Order Arrow Dance Tm Chief 84-85; Creatv Wrtng Proj Poetry Awd 84; Elec.

MERCHANT, JOHN; Bartlett HS; Webster, MA; (Y); 80/171; Boy Scts; Pres Science Clb; Spanish Clb; Variety Show; Hon Roll; Eagle Sct 83; Pres Sci Clb 84-85; Northeastern U; Phrmcy.

MERCHANT, LORRAINE; Fontbonne Acad; Canton, MA; (Y); Art Clb; Pres Church Yth Grp; Cmnty Wkr; Intnl Clb; Political Wkr; Service Clb; Thesps; School Musical; School Play; Stage Crew; Co-Founder Of SADD 85; Yth Rep On Canton Yth Commssn 83-84; Voltr MA Hosp Schl & St John CCD 83-85; Mdrn Lang.

MERCIER, MICHELLE; Marthas Vineyard Regional HS; Edgartown, MA; (Y); 6/102; Church Yth Grp; Socr; Tennis; Hon Roll; NHS; Middlebury Coll; Bio.

MERCURIO, JOSEPH; Arlington Catholic HS; Billerica, MA; (Y); 2/148; Pres Church Yth Grp; Var Trk; High Hon Roll; Hon Roll; Jr NHS; NHS; Prfct Atten Awd; Intnl Clb; JA; Natl Latin Exam Silver Medal 83, Gold Medal 84, Silver Medal 85; Lowell U; Comp Sci.

MERINGER, BRIAN E; Rockport HS; Rockport, MA; (Y); Am Leg Boys St; JA; Spanish Clb; Stage Crew; Pres Frsh Cls; Off Soph Cls; Trs Jr Cls; Trs Sr Cls; Stu Cncl; Var L Bsktbl; JV Bsktbl Mst Imprvd 83; JV Socr Coaches Awd 83; Econ.

MEROLA, CORINNE; East Boston HS; E Boston, MA; (Y); Computer Clb; JA; Key Clb; Rep Jr Cls; Swmmng; Hon Roll; NHS; Bentley; Comp Sci.

MERSELIS III, JOHN G; Mt Greylock Regional HS; Williamstown, MA; (Y); 17/110; Am Leg Boys St; Band; Yrbk Stf; Var Socr; Hon Roll; NHS.

MERSKI, JOHN A; Frontier Regional Schl; South Deerfield, MA; (Y); JV Bsbl; JV Ftbl; High Hon Roll; Hon Roll; NHS; Bus Mngmt.

MERSON, DAVID S; Falmouth HS; Falmouth, MA; (Y); 2/398; AFS; Model UN; Quiz Bowl; Scholastic Bowl; Pres Science Clb; School Play; Variety Show; Elks Awd; High Hon Roll; JETS Awd; Outstng Soc Stud Stu Of Yr 84; Natl Olympiad Comp 84 & 85; 1st Pl Wnr Pafford Essay Cont 84 & 85; Brown U; Biol.

MESICK, ROBERT; Agawam HS; Feeding Hls, MA; (Y); Rep Stu Cncl; JV Ice Hcky; Hon Roll.

MESSALINE, LINDA; Marthas Vineyard Regional HS; Vineyard Haven, MA; (Y); 4/107; AFS; Band; Chorus; Lit Mag; High Hon Roll; Hon Roll; NHS; Schlrshp George Washington U Smmr Sessn 85; Awd Excllnc Chem 85; Chem.

MESSIER, KATHLEEN; Arlington Catholic HS; Bedford, MA; (Y); 66/148; Church Yth Grp; Spanish Clb; Church Choir; Nwsp Stf; Yrbk Stf; Nrthstrn U; Cmmrcl Art.

MESSIER, LISA; Taunton HS; Taunton, MA; (Y); 4-H; Office Aide; Spanish Clb; Yrbk Stf; Hon Roll; Zoology.

MESSIER, MARC; Diman Regional Vocational HS; Fall River, MA; (Y); MA VICAR Pgm 85; SMU; Mech Engr.

MESSINA, LISA; Silver Lake Regional Kingston HS; Kingston, MA; (Y); 111/513; French Clb; Girl Scts; Hosp Aide; Latin Clb; Library Aide; Office Aide; Chorus; Grl Sct Slvr Awd 83; Phy Thrpst.

METZ JR, WALTER C; St Johns HS; Shrewsbury, MA; (Y); 11/270; Cmnty Wkr; Lit Mag; Im Bsktbl; JV Socr; High Hon Roll; NHS; Ntl Merit SF; NEDT Awd; Schlrshp Andover Acad 83; Physics Rsrch Scientist.

METZGER, TRACI; Westfield HS; Westfield, MA; (Y); #52 In Class; Nwsp Rptr; Nwsp Sprt Ed; Nwsp Stf; Var Capt Bsktbl; JV Socr; Var Sftbl; Hon Roll; Jrnlsm.

MEUNIER, DANIELLE; The High School Of Commerce; Springfield, MA; (Y); Yrbk Phtg; Rep Frsh Cls; Rep Soph Cls; Stu Cncl; Trk; Cit Awd; High Hon Roll; Hon Roll; NHS; Stu Rep Schl Comm 84-85; Proj Lead 84-85; Ldrshp Inst Western New England Coll 84-85; Child Psych.

MEYER, DEBRA; High School Of Commerce; Springfield, MA; (Y); Hosp Aide; JA; Teachers Aide; Church Choir; Nwsp Ed-Chief; Yrbk Stf; Soph Cls; Jr Cls; Nrsng.

MEYER, DENISE; Chicopee Comprehensive HS; Chicopee, MA; (Y); 55/350; Dance Clb; German Clb; Library Aide; Var Tennis; Hon Roll; Intrior Dsgn.

MICCICHE, LISA; Maynard HS; Maynard, MA; (Y); 3/109; French Clb; Radio Clb; Band; Jazz Band; Yrbk Phtg; Trk; Hon Roll; NHS; Hrvrd Book Awd 83; Grad Schlrshps 84; Ftchbrg ST Coll; Mass Cmnctns.

MICELOTTA, LISA; Milford HS; Milford, MA; (Y); 38/305; Church Yth Grp; Key Clb; Pep Clb; Hon Roll; NHS; Boston Coll; Bus Mgt.

MICHAEL, LILA A; B M C Durfee HS; Fall River, MA; (Y); 149/590; Church Yth Grp; Pres French Clb; Office Aide; Pep Clb; Yrbk Stf; Hon Roll; Lebanaon Amer Soc; MA ST Scholar; Northeastern U; Radlgy.

MICHAEL, WENDY; Somerset HS; Somerset, MA; (Y); 60/299; JV Bsktbl; JV Capt Fld Hcky; Var Capt Sftbl; High Hon Roll; Hon Roll; Diman Regional Tech Inst; Dntl.

MICHAELES, CHRISTOPHER; St Johns HS; Sturbridge, MA; (Y); 14/268; Math Clb; Math Tm; Ski Clb; Var Trk; High Hon Roll; NHS; Ntl Merit Ltr; Natl Merit Hnr Roll 85; Order Of Ahepa Distrct 8 Schlrshp 85; Order Of Ahepa Local Schlrshp 85; Williams Coll.

MICHALAK, MICHELE; Holy Name C C HS; Millbury, MA; (Y); 35/275; French Clb; Service Clb; School Musical; Lit Mag; High Hon Roll; Hon Roll; Jr NHS.

MICHALEWICH, RICHARD; Bishop Connolly HS; Somerset, MA; (S); 26/250; Computer Clb; Math Tm; Var L Tennis; High Hon Roll; Cmnty Wkr; Worcester Polytch Inst; Mech En.

MICHALIK, MICHELLE; King Philip Regional HS; Plainville, MA; (Y); 40/270; Dance Clb; Yrbk Stf; VP Frsh Cls; JV Socr; JV Sftbl; Hon Roll; Art.

MICHAUD, KAREN JOAN; Holyoke HS; Holyoke, MA; (Y); Computer Clb; FBLA; JA; Bsbl; Bsktbl; Socr; Twrlr; High Hon Roll; Hon Roll; Library Aide; Holyoke CC; Bus.

MICHAUD, KERI M; Westford Acad; Westford, MA; (Y); 26/205; OEA; Ski Clb; Im Ice Hcky; High Hon Roll; Bentley Coll; Acctg.

MICHAUD, LESLIE A; Salem HS; Salem, MA; (Y); 30/332; Yrbk Stf; VP Sr Cls; Stu Cncl; Var Capt Cheerleading; Var JV Socr; Hon Roll; High Hon Roll; Pre-Vet.

MICHAUD, SCOTT; Lawrence HS; Lawrence, MA; (S); 6/300; Acpl Chr; Band; Chorus; Concert Band; Jazz Band; Orch; Swing Chorus; Yrbk Ed-Chief; French Hon Soc; High Hon Roll; Oberlin Conservtry; Prof Violin.

MIDDLEBROOK, LEAH W; Phillips Acad; San Francisco, CA; (Y); Spanish Clb; Lit Mag; Hon Roll; Ntl Merit SF; Bd Govs Phillips Acad.

MIDDLETON, TIM; Billerica Memorial HS; Billerica, MA; (Y); JV Crs Cntry; Var Trk.

MIELE, MONICA; Cathedral HS; Hampden, MA; (Y); 1/520; Intnl Clb; Math Clb; Red Cross Aide; High Hon Roll; Mu Alp Tht; NHS; Wellesley Book Awd 84-85; Acdmc Awds In Englsh, Bio, Spnsh, Rlgn & European Hstry.

MIESZCZANSKI, CHRIS; Bishop Fenwick HS; Salem, MA; (Y); Church Yth Grp; JV Bsktbl; Var Ftbl; High Hon Roll; Hon Roll; Polc Offcr.

MIGA, THEODORE; Holyoke HS; Holyoke, MA; (Y); 28/368; Latin Clb; Gym; Trk; High Hon Roll; Hon Roll; NHS; Outing Clb; Margaret Hyland Schlrshp 85-86; MA Regnts 85-86; U Of MA; Elctrcl Engr.

MIGHORELLI, ANDREA; Holy Name CCHS; Worcester, MA; (Y); #47 In Class; JV Socr; Var L Trk; High Hon Roll; Pre-Law.

MIGUEL, PAULINA; Diman Reg Voc Tech HS; Fall River, MA; (Y); Key Clb; Hon Roll; Library Aide; Endicott Coll; Comp Sci.

MILANI, ANNA; Salem HS; Salem, MA; (Y); #3 In Class; Math Tm; Science Clb; Ski Clb; Orch; School Musical; Yrbk Ed-Chief; Capt Cheerleading; High Hon Roll; Pres NHS; Pres Spanish NHS; Wellesley Bk Awd 84-85.

MILCH, HEIDI; Fontbonne Acad; Milton, MA; (Y); 27/130; Drama Clb; Girl Scts; Intnl Clb; Stage Crew; Variety Show; JV Badmtn; JV Cheerleading; JV Crs Cntry; JV Sftbl; JV Trk; U MA Amherst; Fash Retlng.

MILECKI, IRENE; St Marys HS; Worcester, MA; (Y); 1/60; Church Yth Grp; Drama Clb; Hosp Aide; Chorus; Nwsp Stf; Yrbk Stf; JV Capt Cheerleading; Hon Roll; 1st Pl Sci Fair; Northeastern U; Med Lab.

MILES, CRAIG S; Winthrop HS; Winthrop, MA; (Y); 4/220; Am Leg Boys St; Boy Scts; Science Clb; Yrbk Stf; Rep Frsh Cls; VP Soph Cls; Trs Jr Cls; VP Sr Cls; Var Golf; Var Trk; Ad Altare Dei Boy Scout Medal 80; Pope Pius XII Boy Scout Medal 82; Eagle Scout 82; Cornell U; Diplomacy.

MILES, SHANNON MEGAN; Holyoke HS; Holyoke, MA; (Y); Drama Clb; French Clb; Latin Clb; Speech Tm; Nwsp Rptr; Nwsp Stf; High Hon Roll; NHS; Ntl Merit SF; French Awd, English, Typing Pin; MFL Medal Speech Team; Acad Achv Awd; Ped.

MILLER, ANDREW D; Lexington HS; Lexington, MA; (Y); AFS; French Clb; Political Wkr; Ski Clb; Temple Yth Grp; Nwsp Rptr; Nwsp Sprt Ed; Yrbk Sprt Ed; Lit Mag; Var Tennis; Jrnlsm.

MILLER, BRIAN D; Wareham HS; Wareham, MA; (Y); 50/153; Letterman Clb; Rep Frsh Cls; Rep Soph Cls; Var L Ice Hcky; Southeastern MA U; Mechncl Eng.

MILLER, DEBRA S; Randolph HS; Randolph, MA; (Y); 48/451; Drama Clb; Pep Clb; Temple Yth Grp; Varsity Clb; Boy Scts; Mgr Bsktbl; Im Trk; Hon Roll; Temple Beth Shalom Schlrshp 85; Northeastern U; Bus.

MILLER, GRETCHEN; Dana Hall Schl; St Andrews, TN; (Y); Church Yth Grp; Drama Clb; Key Clb; Political Wkr; Service Clb; School Play; Nwsp Rptr; Rep Frsh Cls; VP Jr Cls; Powder Puff Ftbl; U PA Book Prize 85; All Schl VP 85-86; Camp Alleghany Hnr Grl 84.

MILLER, JULIA; Hudson HS; Hudson, MA; (Y); School Musical; Yrbk Stf; Lit Mag; VP Frsh Cls; VP Soph Cls; VP Jr Cls; Var Bsktbl; Var Fld Hcky; Var Sftbl; Hon Roll; Indnpdnt Cable Inc Schlrshp 85; Southwetern MA U; Lbrl Arts.

MILLER, LISA L; Arlington HS; Arlington, MA; (Y); 35/400; Latin Clb; Yrbk Stf; Rep Frsh Cls; Rep Sr Cls; JV Capt Bsktbl; JV Var Socr; JV Sftbl; Hon Roll; NHS; Tompson Schlrshp 85; U Of VT; Psych.

MILLER, MEGAN; Beverly HS; Beverly, MA; (Y); Trs Leo Clb; Office Aide; Acpl Chr; Chorus; Church Choir; School Musical; School Play; Stage Crew; Lit Mag; Ntl Merit Ltr; Mayrs Appt-Beverly Cncl Arts 85; Wrtng.

MILLER, SETH C; Sharon HS; Sharon, MA; (Y); Boy Scts; Chess Clb; Math Clb; Math Tm; Nwsp Bus Mgr; Nwsp Rptr; Nwsp Sprt Ed; Socr; Trk; High Hon Roll; Rensselaer Awd 85.

MILLER, STACY D; Marblehead HS; Marblehead, MA; (Y); 129/260; Camera Clb; Exploring; Ski Clb; Temple Yth Grp; Trs Frsh Cls; Stu Cncl; Coach Actv; Var Capt Socr; Var Swmmng; Var Trk; Bnai Brith All Schlstc Awd Scr 85; Coachs Awd Scr 85; Unsng Hero Swmg.

MILLETTE, RICHARD; Leominster SR HS; Leominster, MA; (S); Political Wkr; Ski Clb; Varsity Clb; School Musical; Trs Stu Cncl; Ftbl; Golf; Cmnty Wkr; Drama Clb; School Play; Northeastern Babson; Bus Mgmnt.

MILLIKEN, STEVEN C; Agawam HS; Agawam, MA; (Y); 25/375; Am Leg Boys St; Library Aide; Nwsp Stf; JV Bsbl; JV VP Bsktbl; Var Ftbl; Mgr(s); Im Vllybl; French Hon Soc; Hon Roll; Jrnlsm.

MILLMAN, CHERYL; Bedford HS; Bedford, MA; (Y); Aud/Vis; Acpl Chr; Chorus; School Musical; Sec Stu Cncl; Var Capt Cheerleading; Powder Puff Ftbl; JV Tennis; High Hon Roll; Teachers Aide; Frndly Slvr Dllr Awd 84-85; Tv-Actng.

MILLS, CATHERINE; Nashoba Regional HS; Lancaster, MA; (Y); Church Yth Grp; Drama Clb; Sec Band; School Musical; Swing Chorus; Variety Show; Trk; High Hon Roll; NHS; Ntl Merit Ltr; All Estrn Chrs 85; Ruth Amelotte Schlrshp Outstndng Vocl Music 85; All ST Chrs 85; Carleton Coll; Pol Sci.

MILLS, ERIK R; Greenfield HS; Greenfield, MA; (Y); 23/160; Church Yth Grp; Drama Clb; Quiz Bowl; School Play; VP Frsh Cls; Rep Soph Cls; Socr; Hon Roll; NHS; Ntl Merit Ltr; Alfred U; Psych.

MILLS, FRANCIS J; Ayer HS; Springfield, VA; (Y); Am Leg Boys St; Church Yth Grp; Math Clb; Var Golf; Var Tennis; Hon Roll; NHS; 1st Pl Natl Sci Olympd Lf Scncs 84; Engrng.

MILLS, KELLY; Franklin HS; Franklin, MA; (Y); 8/237; VP OEA; Variety Show; Yrbk Bus Mgr; Yrbk Ed-Chief; Stu Cncl; Mgr Bsbl; Mgr Bsktbl; Stat Ftbl; Hon Roll; NHS; Carnegie-Mellon U; Econ.

MILTON, HOLLY; Malden HS; Malden, MA; (Y); 43/600; Church Yth Grp; Key Clb; Band; Concert Band; Mrchg Band; Hon Roll.

MINER, MEREDITH A; Winthrop HS; Winthrop, MA; (Y); Art Clb; Drama Clb; Math Tm; School Musical; School Play; Yrbk Stf; Sec Frsh Cls; Stu Cncl; Cheerleading; Powder Puff Ftbl; Cls Day Comm 85; Richard C Lindsey Mem Awd 85; George James Rutherford Awd 85; Boston Globe Art Awd 84; U MA Amherst.

MING, PAULA A; Holbrook HS; Holbrook, MA; (Y); 7/150; Church Yth Grp; Girl Scts; Hosp Aide; Spanish Clb; Chorus; Yrbk Stf; Fld Hcky; Elks Awd; Hon Roll; NHS; Natl Ldrshp & Svc Awd 83; Natl Sci Merit Awd 84; 1st Cl Awd Grl Scts 81; U Of Lowell; Elec Engrng.

MINGOLELLI, DIANE; Medford HS; Medford, MA; (Y); 74/441; English Awd 84; Burdett Schl; Fashinm Mdse.

MINICHIELLO, SUSAN C; St Bernards HS; Fitchburg, MA; (S); 12/172; Drama Clb; Spanish Clb; School Musical; School Play; Nwsp Rptr; Rep Stu Cncl; Cheerleading; Hon Roll; NHS; Excllnc In Spnsh II 84.

MINKWITZ III, RUSSELL E; Walpole HS; Walpole, MA; (Y); Am Leg Boys St; Ski Clb; Bsktbl; Var L Ftbl; Var Trk; Hon Roll; NHS; Pres Trophy Acdmc & Ath Excllnce; Slvr Mdl Frnch & Hist Dept; Phi Alpha Theat Hist Conf Mnrl Mntn; Cornell U; Chem Engrng.

MINOR, MELISSA; Gardner HS; Gardner, MA; (Y); 34/160; Band; Concert Band; Stage Crew; JV Var Swmmng; JV Var Tennis; Hon Roll; Regis Coll; Med Tech.

MIRANDA, DOMINGOS R; B M C Durfee HS; Fall River, MA; (Y); 52/760; Band; Concert Band; Drill Tm; Mrchg Band; Pep Band; Hon Roll; NHS; Elec Engrng.

MIRANDA, MICHAEL; Westport HS; Westport, MA; (Y); Exploring; JA; Yrbk Stf; Var L Golf; Mgr(s); High Hon Roll; NHS; Elec Engrng.

MIRANDA, MIRIAM; Lynn Classical HS; Lynn, MA; (Y); Cmnty Wkr; Dance Clb; Chorus; Color Guard; Drm & Bgl; School Musical; School Play; Tennis; Var Sftbl; Swmmng; Salem ST Coll; Nrsng.

MIRANDA, PAUL; Somerset HS; Somerset, MA; (Y); Jazz Band; Var Ice Hcky; Var Socr; Im Wt Lftg; Im Wrstlng; High Hon Roll; NHS; Elect Engrng.

MIRASOLO, VINCENT; Saint Dominic Savio HS; Revere, MA; (S); 2/120; Math Clb; Math Tm; Spanish Clb; JV Bsbl; Var Crs Cntry; Var Ice Hcky; Var Trk; Im Wt Lftg; High Hon Roll; NHS; Boston Coll.

MIROLLI, ANNA; Westspringfield SR HS; West Springfield, MA; (Y); 39/279; Office Aide; Var Cheerleading; Hon Roll; Daisy Chain 84; Western New England Coll; Acctg.

MIROVICH, STEPHANIE; St Bernards Central Catholic HS; Fitchburg, MA; (S); 10/172; Church Yth Grp; Hosp Aide; Sec Trs Spanish Clb; Teachers Aide; Mrchg Band; Rep Stu Cncl; L Pom Pon; Im Powder Puff Ftbl; Hon Roll; Spnsh Excel Awd 83; Geom Awd 84; Spanish.

MIRRA, ELAINE; St Clare HS; Roslindale, MA; (Y); 7/130; Church Yth Grp; French Clb; JA; JCL; Political Wkr; Nwsp Rptr; Yrbk Stf; Trs Frsh Cls; NHS; Ntl Merit Ltr; Cert-Sprior Prfrmnc In NED Tsts 82; Maxima Cum Laude Frm JR Clsscl Leag In Ntl Ltn Exam 84; Comm.

MIRSKY, DAVID; Newton North HS; Newton, MA; (Y); Pres Sr Cls; High Hon Roll; Hon Roll; Awd For Part & Notable Achv In Annl Acady Intramural 85; Wrtng.

MITCHEL, STEPHANIE; Reading Memorial HS; Reading, MA; (Y); Church Yth Grp; Drama Clb; Chorus; Church Choir; School Musical; School Play; Nwsp Rptr; Lit Mag; French Hon Soc; High Hon Roll; Frng Lang.

MITCHELL, NAOMI; Bridgewater Raynham Reg HS; Raynham, MA; (Y); Church Yth Grp; Model UN; Spanish Clb; Band; Concert Band; Orch; Bsktbl; Fld Hcky; Trk; Hon Roll; Jacket Awd 84; Bronze Mdl Track 85.

MITCHELL, SHAWN G; Chicopee HS; Chicopee, MA; (Y); 42/212; Nwsp Ed-Chief; Nwsp Sprt Ed; Nwsp Stf; Yrbk Stf; Hon Roll; Var L Bsbl; Var L Ftbl; Navy; Bus Mgmt.

MITRI, RAMZI; Holbrook JR SR HS; Holbrook, MA; (Y); 18/107; Drama Clb; Rep French Clb; Rep Latin Clb; Library Aide; Band; School Musical; School Play; Rep Soph Cls; Rep Jr Cls; Crs Cntry; Mech Engrng.

MITZCAVITCH, JOANNE; Maynard HS; Maynard, MA; (Y); 12/105; Radio Clb; Pres Band; Chorus; VP Frsh Cls; Pres Jr Cls; VP Stu Cncl; Fld Hcky; Sftbl; Hon Roll; NHS; U Of MA-AMHERST.

MOBERG, KRISTEN; East Longmeadow HS; E Longmeadow, MA; (Y); 20/210; French Clb; Intnl Clb; Stage Crew; Variety Show; JV Var Cheerleading; Score Keeper; High Hon Roll; Hon Roll; NHS; Pres Acdmc Ftns Awd 85; U MA Amhurst; Accntng.

MOCCIO, ANTHONY; Agawam HS; Agawam, MA; (Y); #34 In Class; Var Bsbl; Var Ftbl; Im Wt Lftg; Hon Roll; Lion Awd; NHS; Outstndng Vars Soph Ftbl Plyr 83; Grand Mrshl Grad 85; Acctg.

MOCCIO, JOANN; Agawam HS; Feeding Hls, MA; (Y); Office Aide; Band; Mrchg Band; Hon Roll; Hairdrssg.

MOCHEN, PATRICIA; Braintree HS; Braintree, MA; (Y); 25/416; JCL; Spanish Clb; Rep Stu Cncl; Capt Bsktbl; Sftbl; Tennis; Hon Roll; NHS; Spanish NHS; Educ.

MODRY, JOSEPH; Barnstable HS; Marstons Mills, MA; (Y); Ski Clb; JV Golf; Ntl Merit SF; Trout Unltd 83-85; Bio.

MOECKEL, JEFFREY A; St Bernards C C HS; Fitchburg, MA; (Y); 52/178; Am Leg Boys St; Art Clb; Ski Clb; Stage Crew; Variety Show; Nwsp Rptr; Crs Cntry; Tennis; Trk; Hon Roll; Hawthorne Coll; Flght Trng.

MOELLERING, ANNE E; Weston HS; Weston, MA; (Y); Orch; Trs Sr Cls; Bsktbl; Capt Fld Hcky; Lcrss; High Hon Roll; NHS; Ntl Merit SF; Holy Cross Book Prize 84; Sci.

MOES, ERICA; North HS; Worcester, MA; (Y); Varsity Clb; Nwsp Stf; Stu Cncl; Socr; Trk; Hon Roll; NHS; Forsyth Schl; Dentl Hyg.

MOFFAT, JULIE; Arlington HS; Arlington, MA; (Y); 91/385; Art Clb; Dance Clb; Drama Clb; German Clb; Office Aide; PAVAS; Ski Clb; Chorus; Capt Color Guard; Madrigals; Frndly Schlrshp $1000 85; Syracuse U; Physics.

MOGLIA, LOREE; Joseph Case HS; Swansea, MA; (Y); French Clb; Intnl Clb; Chorus; Concert Band; Mrchg Band; Orch; Hon Roll; Ntl Merit Ltr; Manhattanville Coll; Dntst.

MOHAN, BRIAN; Milford HS; Milford, MA; (Y); 2/315; Am Leg Boys St; Trs Frsh Cls; Trs Soph Cls; Trs Jr Cls; Trs Sr Cls; JV Ftbl; Var Timer; Var Capt Wrstlng; Pres NHS; Sal; Harvard Coll; Bus Mngmnt.

MOKRZYCKI, KERRY J; West Springfield HS; W Springfield, MA; (Y); Church Yth Grp; German Clb; Pep Clb; L Ski Clb; Flag Corp; L Var Cheerleading; Im Tennis; Im Trk; Bay Path; Fshn Dsgnr.

MOLA, DEAN; North Reading HS; North Reading, MA; (Y); 49/207; Computer Clb; Var Bsbl; JV Bsktbl; High Hon Roll; Hon Roll; HS Minit & Militia Schlrshp 85; Pres Schlrshp-Coll Boca Rtn 85; Coll Of Boca Raton; Bus Adm.

MOLESKY, KYLE; Quabbin Regional HS; Barre, MA; (Y); 40/138; Varsity Clb; School Play; Yrbk Stf; Var Capt Golf; Var Capt Socr; Var Wrstlng; All Centrl MA H S Sccr Tm 83-84; Wstrn MA Div II Wrstlg 4th Pl Fnshr 138 Lbs 85; U Of MA Amherst; Lndscp Arch.

MOLINARI, ROBERTO; St Johns HS; Worcester, MA; (Y); #10 In Class; JA; Nwsp Rptr; Ed Nwsp Stf; Lit Mag; High Hon Roll; NHS; Engrng.

MOLINARI, SUSAN; Fontbonne Acad; Stoughton, MA; (Y); 30/130; Church Yth Grp; Drama Clb; Hosp Aide; Intnl Clb; Political Wkr; Stage Crew; Im Bsktbl; Var Fld Hcky; Score Keeper; Hon Roll; Magna Cum Laude Outstndng Perf Natl Latin Exam 83; 1st Pl Awd Art Fair 83; Hon Men Globe Schlstc Art; Pysch.

MOLLER, MALINDA; Monson JR-SR HS; Monson, MA; (Y); 18/73; Church Yth Grp; Drama Clb; Mgr School Musical; Mgr Stage Crew; Yrbk Phtg; Pres Soph Cls; Mgr Bsktbl; Mgr(s); Score Keeper; Hon Roll; All ST Cast One Act Pl Comp 85; Doctor.

MONAGHAN, CAROL; Cathedral HS; Springfield, MA; (Y); 30/490; Dance Clb; Math Clb; Yrbk Rptr; Yrbk Stf; NHS; Prfct Atten Awd; Rlgn Awd 84; Phrmcy.

MONAHAN, AMY E; Dedham HS; Dedham, MA; (Y); 5/325; Church Yth Grp; Drama Clb; Band; Color Guard; Sec Concert Band; Drm Mjr(t); Mrchg Band; Orch; School Musical; Variety Show; Pres Acadmc Fit; Suffolk U Bk Awd; Boston Coll; Fin.

MONAST, ROBERT; BMC Durfee HS; Fall River, MA; (Y); 75/650; Science Clb; Band; Concert Band; Jazz Band; Mrchg Band; Orch; Pep Band; School Musical; Hon Roll; Yrbk Stf; Mod Music Masters Tri-M 84; Awd Art Div Solo Fstvl 85; Principal Trumpet Orch 84-85; Lowell U MA; Meteor.

MONCHAMP, LISA; Holyoke Catholic HS; Holyoke, MA; (Y); 28/138; Camera Clb; Church Yth Grp; Cmnty Wkr; Computer Clb; Sec Exploring; Hosp Aide; Pep Clb; Spanish Clb; Speech Tm; School Play; Elms Coll; Librl Arts.

MONDALA, ALEX S; Malden HS; Malden, MA; (Y); 28/550; Tennis; Hon Roll; Bus.

MONEY, PAM; Chelmsford HS; Chelmsford, MA; (Y); 47/575; Ski Clb; Spanish Clb; Bsktbl; Socr; Swmmng; High Hon Roll; NHS; Spanish NHS; Trphy Natl Hstry Day 86; Rec Paper St Hstrcl Conf 86; Law.

MONIAK, JULIE; Billerica Memorial HS; Billerica, MA; (Y); 14/463; Camera Clb; Cmnty Wkr; Dance Clb; French Clb; Yrbk Stf; Powder Puff Ftbl; Hon Roll; NHS; Emerson Coll; Sports Cstr.

MONIZ, ANN; New Bedford HS; New Bedford, MA; (Y); 123/700; Church Yth Grp; JA; Library Aide; Church Choir; Hon Roll; Ntl Merit Ltr; Bryant Coll; Accntnt.

MONIZ, MARC; New Bedford HS; New Bedford, MA; (Y); 21/632; JCL; Band; Concert Band; Mrchg Band; School Musical; Off Stu Cncl; Tennis; NHS; Paleoanthroplgst.

MONKS, JOHN; Wachusett Regional HS; Holden, MA; (Y); 18/400; Pres Church Yth Grp; Ski Clb; School Musical; Rep Stu Cncl; Var L Trk; Hon Roll; NHS; Ntl Merit Ltr; Pres Schlr; Spanish NHS; Tufts U; Biomed Engrng.

MONSEN, LINDA; Acton-Boxboro Regional HS; Acton, MA; (Y); Aud/Vis; Powder Puff Ftbl; Var Swmmng; Hon Roll; NH Coll; Acctng.

MONTANINO, MARIA; S Boston HS; S Boston, MA; (S); Stu Cncl; Cheerleading; Pres NHS; Suffolk U Bk Awd, Proj Excel Spotlt 84; Suffolk U; Acctng.

MONTE, LISA; Monson JR-SR HS; Monson, MA; (Y); Church Yth Grp; Letterman Clb; Spanish Clb; Varsity Clb; JV Bsktbl; Var Socr; Hon Roll; Western MA Rnnr Up Soccer Tm 84; Fitchburg ST Coll; Bio.

MONTEMAGNI, ANGELA; Chicopee Comprehensive HS; Chicopee, MA; (Y); German Clb; Hon Roll; Bus Adm.

MONTGOMERY, JEANNE; Notre Dame Acad; Dorchester, MA; (Y); 8/114; Dance Clb; Office Aide; Chorus; School Musical; Im Socr; French Hon Soc; Hon Roll; NHS; Natl Merit Awd AATSP 84; St Anthonys Fund Awd 84; Comp Sci.

MONTI, PETER; Saint Johns HS; Marlborough, MA; (Y); Boy Scts; JV Trk; Hon Roll; NEDT Awd; Boston U; Psych.

MONTLE, DONNA F; B M C Durfee HS; Fall River, MA; (Y); 22/680; Drama Clb; Spanish Clb; Varsity Clb; School Musical; Var L Gym; High Hon Roll; Hon Roll; NHS; Pres Acad Ftns Awd 85; Stu Athl Trng Act 81-85; SEMC Gymnstcs All-Str Team 82; U Of CT; Phy Thrpy.

MONTMINY, JOHN; Malden Catholic HS; Revere, MA; (Y); 8/185; Aud/Vis; Computer Clb; Debate Tm; Intnl Clb; Ski Clb; Crs Cntry; Trk; Hon Roll; NHS; Ntl Merit Ltr; Hdmstrs List 83; Cert Awd Trk; Engrng.

MOODY, STEPHANIE; Boston Latin HS; Boston, MA; (Y); 32/319; Sec Speech Tm; Band; Trs Sr Cls; NHS; Hon Roll; Prfct Atten Awd; VP Science Clb; Nwsp Stf; Ed Lit Mag; MA Rep; Bk Awd 85; Outstndng Ldrshp Awd 85; Sys Engr.

MOONEY, ANNE; St Gregory HS; Dorchester, MA; (Y); 6/100; Yrbk Ed-Chief; Yrbk Stf; Bsktbl; Hon Roll; NHS; Acadmc Achvt Schlrshp 84 & 85; Boston Coll; Bio.

MOONEY, CHRISTINE; Beverly HS; Beverly, MA; (Y); Pres 4-H; Pres German Clb; Sec Band; Rep Concert Band; Mrchg Band; School Musical; Rep Stu Cncl; 4-H Awd; Math.

MOONEY, JAY F; Quaboag Reg HS; Warren, MA; (Y); Math Tm; Varsity Clb; Sec Stu Cncl; Var Bsbl; JV Bsktbl; Var Golf; Var Socr; Brdr Cnfr All Star Soccer 82-84; All Cntrl Soccer 82-84; SPORTS.

MOONEY, SHARON; Woburn HS; Woburn, MA; (S); 88/569; Boys Clb Am; Leo Clb; Spanish Clb; Varsity Clb; Variety Show; Stu Cncl; Var Cheerleading; Var Sftbl; High Hon Roll; Hon Roll; Schlrshp Providence Coll 85; Providence Coll; Poltcl Sci.

MOORE, CAROLYN; Agawam HS; Feeding Hills, MA; (Y); 64/340; Cmnty Wkr; JA; Math Clb; Chorus; Yrbk Stf; Sthrn Coll; Nrs.

MOORE, GREG D; Berkshire Schl; Bennington, VT; (Y); Pres Computer Clb; Teachers Aide; School Play; Hon Roll; Ntl Merit SF; Chess Clb; Drama Clb; JCL; Library Aide; School Musical; Cum Laud Soc 85; Awd Outstndng Contrbtn Comp Pgm 85; Mst Imprvd 83; Vrsty Ltr Wnnr 83-85; Rensellear Polytech; Comp Sci.

MOORE, JESSICA M; Nipmuc Regional HS; Hopedale, MA; (Y); 2/85; Am Leg Aux Girls St; Drama Clb; Chorus; School Play; Yrbk Ed-Chief; VP Frsh Cls; Stu Cncl; JV Co-Capt Fld Hcky; Mgr(s); VP NHS; MA Adv Stu Pgm 84; Worcester Telegram & Gazette Stu Achvr 85; Skidmore Coll; Theatre.

MOORE, JONATHAN; Newburryport HS; Newburyport, MA; (Y); 48/194; Debate Tm; Drama Clb; Library Aide; Model UN; Q&S; School Play; Nwsp Sprt Ed; Lit Mag; Var L Trk; Hon Roll; Bst Actor Awd 84-85; Wesleyan U; Poltcl Sci.

MOORE, NATHAN F; Ralph C Mahan Reg HS; Orange, MA; (Y); 11/103; Am Leg Boys St; Political Wkr; Band; VP Sr Cls; Cit Awd; DAR Awd; Hon Roll; Pres Schlr; Pres Chrmn Civic Clb; Debate Tm; V-Chrmn Crtcl Issues Cmmtt; Mbr Of Stop Nclr War Cmmtt; U Of MA Amherst; Pol Sci.

MOORE, PHIL; Medway HS; Medway, MA; (Y); 50/150; Church Yth Grp; Yrbk Stf; Hon Roll; Schlstc Awd 84; Bentley Coll Bus Wk 85; Bus.

MOORE, RONA G; Plymouth Carver HS; Orlando, FL; (Y); 63/536; Varsity Clb; Flag Corp; Yrbk Sprt Ed; Yrbk Stf; Capt Cheerleading; Var Sftbl; Ntl Merit Schol; Voice Dem Awd; Chrldr Yr 85; George L & Mary D Gooding Schlrshp 85; Valencia CC; Bus Mgmt.

MOORE, SEAN V; Nashoba Regional HS; Bolton, MA; (Y); Trs Church Yth Grp; JV Bsbl; Im JV Bsktbl; Im Sftbl; Im Tennis; Im Vllybl; Hon Roll; NHS; JV Mgr(s); U MA; Vet Med.

MOORE, STEPHEN; Matignon HS; Medford, MA; (Y); 57/181; Boy Scts; Church Yth Grp; Exploring; JV Bsktbl; JV Ftbl; Vllybl; Hon Roll; Acctg.

MOORE, WILLIAM F; Methven HS; Methuen, MA; (Y); 100/330; Computer Clb; Model UN; Band; Jazz Band; Mrchg Band; Variety Show; Bowling; West Pnt Acad 85; Comp Sci.

MOOREHOUSE, MATTHEW; Lynn Classical HS; Lynn, MA; (Y); Church Yth Grp; Debate Tm; Political Wkr; Var Crs Cntry; JV Ftbl; Var Chess Clb; Hon Roll; Archit Engrng.

MOOY, BRUCE E; Ayer HS; El Paso, TX; (Y); 5/160; Am Leg Boys St; Math Tm; Capt Tennis; High Hon Roll; Pres Mu Alp Tht; Trs NHS; Pres Schlr; Pres Clsrm; MASP Milton Acad; U Of TX; Pre-Law.

MOQUIN, ROBERT; Ludlow HS; Ludlow, MA; (Y); 17/276; High Hon Roll; Hon Roll; Rutgers U; Civl Engrng.

MORAIS, KELLEY; Apponequet Regional HS; Lakeville, MA; (Y); Chorus; Stu Cncl; Im Tennis; JV Trk; Hon Roll; NHS; Thesaurus Schlstc Awd 84-85; Johnson & Wales Coll; Htl Mgt.

MORAN, CRAIG M; Shepherd Hill Regional HS; Dudley, MA; (Y); 7/158; Math Tm; Stu Cncl; Elks Awd; High Hon Roll; Lion Awd; NHS; Ntl Merit Ltr; Pres Schlr; Quo Vadis Schlrshp 85; Grand Furniture Schlrshp 85; Nichols Coll; Bus Admin.

MORAN, PAUL; Longmeadow HS; Long Meadow, MA; (Y); 87/250; Exploring; Trs 4-H; Key Clb; Ski Clb; Stu Cncl; JV Trk; Hon Roll; Ntl Ltn Exam, Magna Cum Laude 83.

MORANDO, LAURIE; Maiden HS; Malden, MA; (Y); 16/500; Office Aide; Variety Show; Bowling; High Hon Roll; NHS; Comp Prog.

MORDO, LISA; Marlboro HS; Marlboro, MA; (Y); 70/300; GAA; Varsity Clb; Capt Socr; High Hon Roll; Hon Roll; Outstndng Achvt Awd Soccer 84; Cntrl MS Lgu 2nd Tm All Star Soccer 84; Girsl ST Soccer Team 85; :Bio Sci.

MOREAU, ELEANOR; Holyoke HS; Holyoke, MA; (Y); 80/360; Latin Clb; Science Clb; Spanish Clb; Chorus; Church Choir; Im Socr; Var Swmmng; Timer; Capt Trk; Im Wt Lftg; Ross, W Weis, & Elms Coll Schlrshps 85; Elms Coll; Nrsng.

MOREHOUSE, ELAINE; Lee HS; South Lee, MA; (Y); 18/113; Church Yth Grp; French Clb; Red Cross Aide; Band; Concert Band; Mrchg Band; School Musical; Yrbk Stf; Cheerleading; Sftbl; U Of Lowell; Law Enf.

MORI, ELLEN; Marian HS; Framingham, MA; (Y); Chorus; School Musical; JV Socr; Hon Roll; NHS; Gen Excllnc Adv Engl I 83; Phy Sci 83; Frnch 83; Cmmnctns.

MORIARTY, KAREN A; Marianhill CC HS; Southbridge, MA; (Y); 3/18; Trs Computer Clb; Nwsp Stf; Pres Jr Cls; Pres Sr Cls; Var Capt Bsktbl; Cit Awd; Hon Roll; NHS; Chess Clb; JA; Christian A Herter Awd 83; Brian A Di Gregorie Awd 85; Babson Coll; Accntnt.

MORIARTY, MATTHEW; Holyoke Catholic HS; Holyoke, MA; (Y); Chess Clb; Church Yth Grp; CAP; Cmnty Wkr; Computer Clb; Drama Clb; Exploring; Political Wkr; Teachers Aide; School Musical; Altar Svr Of Yr Awd 84-85; Isshin-Ryu Of Karate Blk Blt 85; SR Life Svng & CPR 84-85; Comp.

MORIARTY, PATRICIA M; Fontbonne Acad HS; Milton, MA; (Y); 30/136; Church Yth Grp; Drama Clb; Girl Scts; School Play; Yrbk Stf; Im Cheerleading; Im Sftbl; Hon Roll; Outstndng Excllnce In Spnsh II, Spnah III & US Hstry 83-85; Mktng.

MORIARTY, PAULA; New Bedford HS; New Bedford, MA; (Y); Aud/Vis; Camera Clb; Cmnty Wkr; Exploring; Cheerleading; Pom Pon; Hon Roll; U Of MA; Math.

MORIARTY, THOMAS M; Quabbin Reg HS; Gilbertville, MA; (Y); Am Leg Boys St; ROTC; Spanish Clb; Teachers Aide; Yrbk Stf; Var Golf; Jr NHS; NHS; Elec Engrng.

MORIN, DEREK; Braintree HS; Braintree, MA; (Y); Blue Hills Tech Inst; Arch.

MORIN, JILL; Drury SR HS; Adams, MA; (Y); 16/161; Church Yth Grp; Pep Clb; Yrbk Stf; Sec Stu Cncl; Capt Crs Cntry; Capt Trk; High Hon Roll; Hon Roll; NHS; Alice Cummings Scholar 85; Pro Merito Hnr Soc 85; N Adams ST Coll; Educ.

MORIN, MICHELLE; Milford HS; Milford, MA; (Y); 20/300; Sec VP Drama Clb; Key Clb; Chorus; Jazz Band; School Musical; School Play; Stage Crew; Yrbk Stf; Tennis; Hon Roll; Med Tech.

MORIN, PAMELA; St Bernards CC HS; Leominster, MA; (S); 19/164; Nwsp Sprt Ed; VP Soph Cls; VP Jr Cls; VP Sr Cls; JV Var Fld Hcky; JV Capt Sftbl; Hon Roll; Trs NHS; Nwsp Stf; Yrbk Stf; Schl Spirited Class 84-85; Friendly Class 84-85; Acctng.

MORIN, PAUL; Westfield HS; Westfield, MA; (Y); 12/350; French Clb; High Hon Roll; Georgetown; Intl Bus.

MORNEAU, MICHELLE; Easthampton HS; Easthampton, MA; (Y); 7/139; Girl Scts; Intnl Clb; JA; Spanish Clb; Yrbk Bus Mgr; Yrbk Stf; L Capt Swmmng; High Hon Roll; Hon Roll; NHS; ST Candlepin Bowlng 83; Bus Adm.

MORO, RICHARD; Woburn HS; Woburn, MA; (S); School Play; Stu Cncl; L Socr; L Tennis; Wt Lftg; Hon Roll; NHS; Aero Eng.

MOROCHNICK, KIM; Chelsea HS; Chelsea, MA; (Y); 13/200; Pep Clb; Band; Concert Band; Jazz Band; Mrchg Band; VP Sr Cls; Stu Cncl; Var Bsktbl; Trk; NHS; Slctd Ldrshp Smnr 82-83; Hnrd By Jewish Amer War Vets Brotherhood Awd 85; $500 Schlrshp Acdmcs Excllnc; Clark U; Humanities.

MORRELL, CYNTHIA A; Bellingham Memorial JR SR HS; Bellingham, MA; (Y); 20/200; Sec DECA; Varsity Clb; Yrbk Stf; Rep Frsh Cls; Tennis; Trk; High Hon Roll; Hon Roll; NHS; St Schlr; Natl Hnr Soc Scholar 85; Bellingham JR Wmns Clb Scholar 85; MVP Vrsty Ten Tm 85; SMU; Acctg.

MORRIS, KELLY; Arlington Catholic HS; Arlington, MA; (Y); 10/148; Hosp Aide; Office Aide; Ski Clb; Spanish Clb; Rep Jr Cls; Var Gym; Trk; High Hon Roll; Hon Roll; Jr NHS; Prom Commttee; Wnnr 2 Hemlack Hts Canoe Races; Engrng.

MORRIS, LISA; Matignon HS; Medford, MA; (Y); Drama Clb; Girl Scts; School Musical; School Play; Variety Show; Yrbk Stf; Lit Mag; Stu Cncl; Var Cheerleading; Hon Roll; Attndted Stu Govt-Close Up-Pgm 85; Hstry Fair Awd 83; Eng.

MORRIS, MARY ELIZABETH; Weymouth South HS; Weymouth, MA; (Y); 31/340; Am Leg Aux Girls St; Pres Frsh Cls; Pres Soph Cls; Pres Jr Cls; Pres Sr Cls; Var Cheerleading; NHS; St Schlr; Blue & Gld Svc Awd 85; PER Elks Schlrshp 85; Weymouth Catholic Memrl Clb Schlrshp 85; Boston U; Cmmnctns.

MORRIS, MICHAEL; Brockton HS; Brockton, MA; (Y); JV Bsktbl; Hon Roll; Prfct Atten Awd; 1st Pl Ribbn Brockton Cmnty Schls Photo Shw 83; Bst Smle Awd SR Suprlatves 85; Northeastern; Bus.

MORRISON, BRIAN; Matignon HS; Watertown, MA; (Y); 38/179; Church Yth Grp; Cmnty Wkr; Science Clb; Spanish Clb; Varsity Clb; Off Soph Cls; Off Jr Cls; Var Ftbl; Hon Roll; Spanish NHS; Bus Admin.

MORRISON, COLLEEN M; Billerica Memorial HS; Billerica, MA; (Y); Spanish Clb; Yrbk Stf; Rep Stu Cncl; Coach Actv; Hon Roll; Phy Thrpy.

MORRISON, ELIZABETH ANN; Miss Halls Schl; Reading, PA; (Y); Art Clb; Spanish Clb; Pres Frsh Cls; Rep Soph Cls; VP Jr Cls; Stu Cncl; JV Fld Hcky; JV Sftbl; Lawyer.

MORRISON, JAMES; Weymouth North HS; Weymouth, MA; (Y); High Hon Roll; Hon Roll; Commndtn Outstndng Achv Math 84-85; Essy Cntst Awd Demcrcy 83-84; Cert Achv TV Prodctn 84-85; TV Prodctn.

MORRISON, JAMES R; Belmont HS; Belmont, MA; (Y); 23/293; Church Yth Grp; VP Spanish Clb; School Play; Nwsp Rptr; JV Bsktbl; Var Socr; Latin Clb; Varsity Clb; JV Bsbl; Harvard Prz Bk, G Webster Heartz Prz 83-84; Carnegie-Mellon U; Lib Arts.

MORRISSETTE, ANDREA L; Bishop Connolly HS; Fall River, MA; (Y); 15/168; Drama Clb; Hosp Aide; Latin Clb; Ski Clb; Spanish Clb; Yrbk Stf; High Hon Roll; NHS; Providence Coll; Bio.

MORRISSEY, DANIEL E; Brockton HS; Brockton, MA; (Y); 50/988; Am Leg Boys St; JA; Letterman Clb; Varsity Clb; Bsbl; Cit Awd; High Hon Roll; Jr NHS; NHS; Ntl Merit Ltr; Skippy Sgt Mem Awd 82; East Side Imprvmnt Assoc Schlrshp 85; Northeastern U; Engrng.

MORRISSEY, JUDY; Gardner HS; Gardner, MA; (Y); 58/157; VP Exploring; Chorus; School Musical; School Play; Stage Crew; Yrbk Phtg; Yrbk Rptr; Yrbk Stf; Hon Roll; Church Yth Grp; Cosmtlgy.

MORRISSEY, KEITH; Taunton HS; Taunton, MA; (Y); 43/437; Aud/Vis; Church Yth Grp; Latin Clb; Office Aide; Var L Bsbl; Var L Bsktbl; Im Wt Lftg; Hon Roll; Pre-Med.

MORSE, CHRISTINE; Georgetown HS; Georgetown, MA; (Y); Church Yth Grp; Cmnty Wkr; Dance Clb; Drama Clb; Hosp Aide; PAVAS; Spanish Clb; Teachers Aide; School Play; Powder Puff Ftbl; Outstndng Typng Awd 85; U Lowell; Mrktng.

MORSE, SARAH; Hoosac Valley HS; Adams, MA; (Y); Pep Clb; School Play; Stage Crew; Yrbk Stf; Lit Mag; Var JV Mgr(s); Im Powder Puff Ftbl; JV Var Score Keeper; Var JV Sftbl; Sftbl & Bsktbl Vrsty Ltrs 83 & 84; Boston Globe Cert Of Recgntn 84; Marine; Mltry Polce.

MORTELL, SEAN; Holyoke Catholic HS; Chicopee, MA; (Y); 8/132; Chess Clb; CAP; Computer Clb; Latin Clb; Spanish Clb; Nwsp Ed-Chief; High Hon Roll; Hon Roll; Var Trk; Engrng.

MORTON, SARAH; Amherst Regional HS; Amherst, MA; (Y); Chorus; School Play; Capt Cheerleading; Math.

MORYL, TODD; Ware HS; Ware, MA; (Y); French Clb; Off Stu Cncl; JV Var Bsktbl; Hon Roll; Archit.

MOSCATO, TRACY; Silver Lake Regional HS; Kingston, MA; (Y); French Clb; Latin Clb; Ski Clb; Var L Bsktbl; JV Socr; Var L Sftbl; Hon Roll; All Star Sftbl 84-85.

MOSCINSKI, JILL M; Lunenburg HS; Lunenburg, MA; (Y); 5/143; Teachers Aide; Rep Soph Cls; Rep Jr Cls; Rep Sr Cls; High Hon Roll; NHS; Spnsh Awd 85; Contntl Math Leag Awd 85; Pres Acad Ftns Awd 85; Colby Coll.

MOSMAN, DEBORAH; Holy Name Central Catholic HS; Grofton, MA; (Y); Church Yth Grp; Ski Clb; Teachers Aide; Hon Roll; Religious Studies Awd 83, 85; Lit Awd 83-85; Telegrm & Gaz Ace Carrier Awd 82; Poltcl Sci.

MOSSA, MARK; St Johns HS; Wilkinsonville, MA; (Y); 55/270; English Clb; Pres VP JA; Model UN; School Musical; Nwsp Stf; Yrbk Stf; Var Mgr Socr; High Hon Roll; NHS; Ntl Merit Ltr; JA Ofcr Of Yr-Top Slsprsn 83-85; Tmstrs Lcl 170 Schlrshp 85; JA Natl & Rgnl Confs 83-85; Babson Coll; Bus Mgmt.

MOSSOW, SUSAN; Shepherd Hill HS; Charlton, MA; (Y); Hon Roll; Prfsnl Artst.

MOSZCZENSKI III, STAN; Old Rochester HS; Rochester, MA; (Y); 15/149; Drama Clb; Math Tm; School Play; Yrbk Stf; Off Frsh Cls; Bsbl; Ntl Merit Ltr; Weightlftng Awd 85; U Of Notre Dame.

MOTA, ROBERT S; New Bedford HS; New Bedford, MA; (Y); 20/688; Am Leg Boys St; JCL; VP Soph Cls; Stu Cncl; JV Trk; High Hon Roll; Hon Roll; NHS; Voice Dem Awd; Church Yth Grp; Maxima Cum Laude Silvr Medl 83; Phy Thrpy.

MOTTA, AMY; Somerset HS; Somerset, MA; (Y); Lit Mag; High Hon Roll; Ntl Hnr Roll 85; Bristol CC; Sec Sci.

MOTTA, BRIAN; Bristol Plymouth Reg HS; Taunton, MA; (Y); Art Clb; Camera Clb; Church Yth Grp; Hon Roll; Nw Englnd Plmbng & Gas Inspctrs Logo Cntst 85; Art.

MOTYL, STEPHANIE; Bishop Feehan HS; Mansfield, MA; (Y); Chorus; Coach Actv; Swmmng; Trk; Hon Roll; Amer Red Cross Certfd WSI 85; Phy Ed.

MOUNT, BRADLEY; Amherst Regional HS; Amherst, MA; (Y); Boy Scts; Church Yth Grp; Concert Band; Mrchg Band; Symp Band; Off Jr Cls; JV Bsbl; JV Var Ftbl; JV Wrstlng; Letterman Clb; Cnty Fair Jr Hndymkr 84; Cnty Fair Consrvtn Awd Yth 83 & 84; U Of MA-AMHERST; Landscp Arch.

MOUSLEY, JEFFREY R; R C Mahar Regional HS; Orange, MA; (Y); 7/127; Am Leg Boys St; Trs Key Clb; Band; Var L Trk; Model UN; Teachers Aide; Concert Band; Mrchg Band; Variety Show; JV Var Bsktbl.

MOWDUK, STEVE; Hopkins Acad; Hadley, MA; (Y); 15/48; Am Leg Boys St; FBLA; Spanish Clb; Trs Frsh Cls; Trs Jr Cls; Trs Sr Cls; Var Bsbl; Var Score Keeper; Socr; Hon Roll.

MOWER, STEVEN; Central Catholic HS; Dracut, MA; (Y); 83/219; JA; Ski Clb; Trk; High Hon Roll; Hon Roll; U Lowell; Acctng.

MOXHAM, TODD; Marblehead HS; Marblehead, MA; (Y); 19/260; Debate Tm; Drama Clb; French Clb; Ski Clb; Varsity Clb; School Play; Stage Crew; High Hon Roll; Hon Roll; NHS.

MOY, JONATHAN; Malden Catholic HS; Malden, MA; (Y); Im Bsktbl; Im Fld Hcky; Hon Roll.

MOZGALA, MIKE; Ware HS; Ware, MA; (Y); 17/121; Art Clb; Lit Mag; Hon Roll; Chamberlayne JC; Int Desgn.

MOZZONE, CHRISTINE MARIE; Taunton HS; Taunton, MA; (Y); Church Yth Grp; Drama Clb; JCL; Sec Latin Clb; Office Aide; Ski Clb; Yrbk Stf; Var Fld Hcky; Var Trk; Hon Roll; Natl JR Classcl Lg Exam Gold Medl 83, Silver Medl 84; Chem Engrng.

MPOURIS, CHRISANTHI; Natick HS; Natick, MA; (Y); 31/459; Church Yth Grp; German Clb; Intnl Clb; Stu Cncl; Hon Roll; NHS; Bus Awd Typg 81-82; Bus Awd Acctg I & II 82-84; Framingham ST Coll; Pol Sci.

MROZINSKI, EDWARD F; Chicopee Comprehensive HS; Chicopee, MA; (S); 71/396; Boy Scts; Cmnty Wkr; German Clb; Science Clb; Ski Clb; Nwsp Stf; Yrbk Stf; Socr; Trk; Elks Awd; Western New Eng Coll; Mech Engr.

MRUK JR, JOHN F; Chicopee HS; Chicopee, MA; (Y); Debate Tm; Political Wkr; Band; Chorus; Concert Band; Jazz Band; Mrchg Band; Yrbk Stf; NHS; Westfield ST; Crmnl Jstce.

MUCCI, WENDY A; Brockton HS; Brockton, MA; (Y); 47/995; Drama Clb; Sec French Clb; School Musical; School Play; Stage Crew; Nwsp Bus Mgr; Nwsp Ed-Chief; High Hon Roll; NHS; Prfct Atten Awd; Sophie Uburtis Schlrshp 85; Frnch Awd 84-85; Outstdng Morning Anncmnt Awd 85; Bridgewater ST Coll; Spch Comm.

MUCCIARONE, GARY; Franklin HS; Franklin, MA; (Y); 75/275; Varsity Clb; Bsbl; Bsktbl; Tennis; Hon Roll; Northeasern; Engrng.

MUCKIAN, KRISTEN; Classical HS; Lynn, MA; (Y); 20/173; Church Yth Grp; VP Debate Tm; Hosp Aide; Office Aide; Spanish Clb; Yrbk Stf; Capt Var Cheerleading; Hon Roll; Jr NHS; SADD 85; St Mchls Coll; Bus Mngmnt.

MUISE, GARY; Methuen HS; Methuen, MA; (Y); Var Bsbl; Var Socr; Var Trk; High Hon Roll; Capt Bsbl 84; Pres Phys Ftnss Awd 82; Northeastern; Marine.

MUISE, PETER; Haverhill HS; Haverhill, MA; (Y); Art Clb; Concert Band; Mrchg Band; School Play; Nwsp Rptr; High Hon Roll; Hon Roll; NHS; Ntl Merit Ltr; Bates Coll; Bio.

MUISE, RICHARD; Everett HS; Boston, MA; (Y); 1/300; Church Yth Grp; Quiz Bowl; Science Clb; Varsity Clb; JV Im Bsktbl; Im Golf; Var Tennis; NHS; Harvard Bk Awd 86; Brown Bk Awd 86.

MUISE, SHEILA; Newton North HS; Newton, MA; (Y); Var Socr; Hon Roll; Prfct Atten Awd; Church Yth Grp; Variety Show; Im Bsktbl; Im Sftbl; Nrthestrn; Nrsng.

MUKHERJEE, SONJIT; Central Catholic HS; N Andover, MA; (Y); 45/219; Church Yth Grp; Q&S; Nwsp Rptr; Yrbk Stf; Var Trk.

MUKSURIS, STELYIO; Matignon HS; Cambridge, MA; (S); Drama Clb; Lit Mag; Stu Cncl; Mgr Bsktbl; French Hon Soc; High Hon Roll; NHS; Ntl Merit SF; Ntl Sci Merit Awd 84; Schlrshp Distgshd Amer HS Stus 84; Cmmnty Svc 84; Harvard U; Thlgy.

MULCAHY, KATHLEEN E; Doherty Memorial HS; Worcester, MA; (Y); Church Yth Grp; Cmnty Wkr; Dance Clb; Letterman Clb; Spanish Clb; Variety Show; Yrbk Stf; Rep Stu Cncl; Socr; Hon Roll; PSYCH.

MULCAHY, KATHY; Beverly Public HS; Beverly, MA; (Y); Dance Clb; Girl Scts; Hosp Aide; Ski Clb; Spanish Clb; Yrbk Phtg; Fld Hcky; Sftbl; Ntl Merit Schol; U MA; Frgn Transltr.

MULCAHY, LAURA JEAN; Wilbraham Mouson Acad; Glastonbury, CT; (Y); Key Clb; Q&S; Church Choir; Orch; Mgr(s); Var Sftbl; JV Vllybl; Vet.

MULCH, THEODORE; North Quincy HS; Quincy, MA; (Y); 31/380; Pep Clb; Quiz Bowl; Sec Capt Sr Cls; Rep Stu Cncl; Var L Ftbl; Var Tennis; Elks Awd; High Hon Roll; NHS; Val; N Quincy VP Awd 85; Reuben & Lizzie Grossman Awd 85; Pres Acad Fit Awd 85; Penn ST U; Intl Fin.

MULKERN, LORI; Abington HS; Abington, MA; (Y); 1/193; Pres French Clb; Math Tm; Concert Band; Jazz Band; Mrchg Band; Orch; Symp Band; Yrbk Stf; High Hon Roll; VP NHS; Hgst Num Avg Frnch; Hnry Mbr Abngtn Hist Soc; 1st Pl Chem Olym Test; Med.

MULLAN, JENNIFER; Holy Name C C HS; Worcester, MA; (Y); 7/272; Hosp Aide; JA; Nwsp Stf; Yrbk Stf; Lit Mag; High Hon Roll; NHS; Spnsh Dept Awd I, II, III; Hnrbl Mntn-Framingham ST Hstrcl Conf; Certs Engl, Relgn, Chem; Jrnlsm.

MULLANEY, ELIZABETH; Reading Memorial HS; Reading, MA; (Y); Church Yth Grp; Dance Clb; Hosp Aide; Pep Clb; Yrbk Stf; JV Tennis; Hon Roll; RMHS Athltc Cert Awd JV Tnns 83-85; Med.

MULLANEY, KAREN; Melrose HS; Melrose, MA; (Y); Cmnty Wkr; French Clb; Hosp Aide; Ntl Merit SF; Outstndng Achvt Awd Lat 83; Med.

MULLANEY, MARY E; Cardinal Spellman HS; Brockton, MA; (Y); 2/203; High Hon Roll; Kiwanis Awd; NHS; NEDT Awd; Pres Schlr; Computer Clb; Lit Mag; Stonehill Coll Acad Scholar 85; Pilgrim Fndtn Scholar 85; Spn Awd 82, 84-85; Stonehill Coll; Pol Sci.

MULLANEY, STEPHEN; St Bernards Central Catholic HS; Leominster, MA; (S); 1/173; Pres Drama Clb; Pres Latin Clb; School Play; Jr Cls; High Hon Roll; NHS; Voice Dem Awd; Boy Scts; Ski Clb; Hghst Rnkng Fresh 82-83; Rel 2, Hmnts Hist 2, Hmnts Lit 2 Awds 83-84; Hghst Rnkng Soph 83-84; Engr.

MULLANEY, TIMOTHY; St Dominic Savio HS; Chelsea, MA; (Y); 6/109; Chess Clb; Church Yth Grp; Math Tm; Var Bsktbl; High Hon Roll; Prfct Atten Awd; Bus Adm.

MULLARE, JENNIFER; Motre Dame Acad; Norwell, MA; (Y); 41/113; Spanish Clb; Chorus; Stage Crew; Yrbk Stf; Stat Bsktbl; Mgr(s); Score Keeper; Stat Vllybl; Hon Roll; Prfct Atten Awd; Easten Coll; Englsh.

MULLER, KRISTINE; Christopher Columbus HS; Dorchester, MA; (S); 3/119; Cmnty Wkr; NHS; Ntl Merit Schol; Spansh, Bio & Crtv Wrtng Awds; Burdett Bus Schl; Bus Adm.

MULLIGAN, KATHLEEN; New Bedford HS; New Bedford, MA; (Y); 86/600; Office Aide; Var L Crs Cntry; Var L Trk; Hon Roll; Illstratr-Crds, Bks.

MULLIGAN, PAMELA; Burlington HS; Burlington, MA; (Y); 16/369; Am Leg Aux Girls St; Math Clb; Flag Corp; Yrbk Stf; VP Jr Cls; VP Sr Cls; Powder Puff Ftbl; Elks Awd; High Hon Roll; VP NHS; Co-Pres Cathl Yth Orgnztn 84-85; Admnstrtrs Awd 85; Salem ST Coll; Nrs.

MULLIGAN, REBECCA M; Bishop Feehan HS; Pawtucket, RI; (Y); Drm Mjr(t); Twrlr; Hon Roll; Tchr.

MULLINS, MICHAEL; Mission Church HS; Jamaica Plain, MA; (S); Cmnty Wkr; 4-H; Yrbk Phtg; VP Frsh Cls; Sec Soph Cls; Bowling; NHS.

MULLONEY, MAUREEN; Arlington Catholic HS; Arlington, MA; (Y); Spanish Clb; Yrbk Bus Mgr; Hon Roll; Bus Mgt.

MULLY, THADDEUS W; Amherst Regional HS; Leverett, MA; (Y); Band; Orch; School Play; Symp Band; High Hon Roll; Hon Roll; Ntl Merit Ltr; All Eastern Orch 85; Bst Achvt Fr III 84; Vet Med.

MULVANEY, MAURA E; Ware HS; Ware, MA; (Y); 7/122; Art Clb; 4-H; French Clb; Intnl Clb; Trs Stu Cncl; Var Socr; 4-H Awd; Key Clb; Math Clb; Chorus; Hugh O Brian Ldrshp Awd 83; Stdnt Govt Day Delg 84; Natl 4-H Conf Delg 85; Stonehill Coll; Lib Arts.

MUNCY, CHRISTOPHER; Cardinal Spellman HS; Brockton, MA; (Y); 62/250; Am Leg Boys St; Var Capt Bsbl; Var Capt Ftbl.

MUNIES, RONI A; Brockton HS; Brockton, MA; (Y); 123/965; Office Aide; Pep Clb; Political Wkr; Ski Clb; Nwsp Stf; Socr; Sftbl; High Hon Roll; Hon Roll; NHS; Pilgrim Fndtn Schlrshp 85; Brockton City Wrkrs Union Schlrshp 85; Henry J Brides Schlrshp 84; Bridgewater ST Coll; Acctg.

MUNN, RICHARD T; Foxboro HS; Foxborough, MA; (Y); 5/206; Math Tm; Nwsp Rptr; Im Bsktbl; Var Socr; High Hon Roll; Jr NHS; Mgr NHS; Ntl Merit SF; Achvmnt Awds Wrtng Natl Cncl Engl Tchrs; Coll Holy Cross; Acctg.

MUNRO, CHRISTINE; Cohasset HS; Cohasset, MA; (Y); 28/130; Cmnty Wkr; Drama Clb; Chorus; Ed Lit Mag; Hon Roll; Jrnlsm.

MUNRO, JOHN; Gloucester HS; Gloucester, MA; (S); 38/340; ROTC; Band; Concert Band; Jazz Band; Mrchg Band; Pep Band; Yrbk Stf; Hon Roll; NHS; Pre-Med.

MUNROE, DANIEL JOHN; David Prouty HS; East Brookfield, MA; (Y); 48/173; School Musical; Rep Stu Cncl; JV Var Ftbl; JV Var Trk; DAR Awd; Hon Roll; Kiwanis Awd; SR Hnr Socty 85; Schlr Athlt Awd Ftbll Hll Of Fm 85; Hugh Obrian Yth Ldrshp Awd 83; U Of MA; Bus Mgmt.

MUNSON, RICHARD; Bishop Stang HS; S Dartmouth, MA; (S); 4/211; Church Yth Grp; Cmnty Wkr; Pres Soph Cls; VP Stu Cncl; Capt Bsktbl; Capt Socr; Im Wt Lftg; Hon Roll; NHS; Ntl Merit Ltr; SE Mass Conf All-Star Bsktbl 82-84; New Bedford Stndrd Times All-Star Bsktbl 82-84; Med.

MURAD, ELAINE; Saint Clare HS; Roslindale, MA; (Y); 1/150; JA; Library Aide; Quiz Bowl; Nwsp Rptr; Nwsp Stf; High Hon Roll; NHS; Prfct Atten Awd; Maxima Cum Laude Cert & Silver Medal Natl Latin Exam 83, 85; Cum Laude Cert Natl Latin Exam 84.

MURCHIE, MARY BETH; St Bernards C C HS; Fitchburg, MA; (S); 28/162; Ski Clb; Spanish Clb; School Musical; JV Var Cheerleading; Hon Roll; Med Techncn.

MURDOCK, HERNAN; Cathedral HS; Dorchester, MA; (Y); Boy Scts; Teachers Aide; Flag Corp; Mrchg Band; VP Stu Cncl; Mgr(s); Score Keeper; High Hon Roll; NHS; John Gilhooley Schlrshp 85; NE U; Comp Engr.

MURIEL, WANDA; Boston Latin Schl; Roslindale, MA; (Y); Trs Camera Clb; Church Yth Grp; JA; Latin Clb; Pres Spanish Clb; Yrbk Stf; Sr Cls; Hon Roll; Boston Explrtn Soc 84-85; Ntl Scl Stds Olympd, Wth Dstnctn 84; Cert Fshn Shw Betances Fstvl 84; Boston U; Accntng.

MURLEY, CHARLES A; Saugus HS; Saugus, MA; (Y); 8/300; Boy Scts; Chess Clb; Lit Mag; Rensselaer Math, Sci Awd; Hnrbl Ment Math Comp.

MURPHY, BRENDAN; Franklin HS; Franklin, MA; (Y); 13/238; Math Tm; Golf; U Of MA; Elec Engrng.

MURPHY, CAROL; Malden HS; Malden, MA; (Y); 13/600; Band; Concert Band; Mrchg Band; Yrbk Ed-Chief; JV Bsktbl; Hon Roll; NHS; Lit Soc Treas 84-86.

MURPHY, CAROLYN; Holyoke HS; Holyoke, MA; (Y); Cmnty Wkr; GAA; Latin Clb; Spanish Clb; School Play; Nwsp Ed-Chief; JV Var Fld Hcky; JV Var Sftbl; High Hon Roll; Hon Roll; Stu Gov Day 84-85; Liberal Arts.

MURPHY, DANIEL; Matignon HS; Cambridge, MA; (Y); Chess Clb; Ski Clb; Var Bsktbl; Capt Golf; Var Socr; French Hon Soc; High Hon Roll; Hon Roll; Ntl Merit Ltr; Orch; Ec.

MURPHY, DAVID P; Walpole HS; Walpole, MA; (Y); Capt Bsbl; Capt Ftbl; Wt Lftg; Hon Roll; NHS; Boston Glb Ftbl All-Schlstc 84-85; USA Tody Athlt To Wtch-Ftbl 84; Bay ST Leag All Str In Bsbl 85.

MURPHY, GERALDINE; North Quincy HS; Quincy, MA; (Y); 14/400; Cmnty Wkr; Math Tm; Spanish Clb; Color Guard; Var Bsktbl; Vllybl; French Hon Soc; High Hon Roll; Jr NHS; Sec NHS; Boston Coll.

MURPHY, JEFFREY D; Milton HS; Milton, MA; (Y); 12/200; Boy Scts; Chess Clb; Math Tm; Science Clb; Nwsp Stf; Yrbk Stf; NHS; Pres Schlr; Milton P M Clb Schlrshp 85; Milton Town Clb Schlrshp 85; Conrell U; Elec Engrng.

MURPHY, JENNIFER; North Cambridge Catholic HS; Somerville, MA; (Y); Hon Roll; NHS; Gnrl Sci Awd; Physcl Thrpy.

MURPHY, JONATHAN; Saint Johns HS; Worcester, MA; (Y); French Clb; Model UN; Band; Concert Band; Orch; Nwsp Stf; Yrbk Stf; Ntl Merit Ltr.

MURPHY, JULIE; Cardinal Spellman HS; Holbrook, MA; (Y); 5/203; Church Yth Grp; Cmnty Wkr; Library Aide; Office Aide; Political Wkr; Spanish Clb; Chorus; School Play; Bsktbl; Var Sftbl; Hnrs Schlrshp Stonehill Coll 85; Commnwlth MA Schlr 85; Stonehill Coll; Bio.

MURPHY, KATHRYN; BMC Durfee HS; Fall River, MA; (Y); 23/687; Drama Clb; Science Clb; Band; Mrchg Band; Nwsp Ed-Chief; Nwsp Stf; Yrbk Stf; Rep Jr Cls; Cheerleading; Trk.

MURPHY, KIMBERLY; Bedford HS; Bedford, MA; (Y); Church Yth Grp; Girl Scts; Chorus; Yrbk Stf; Lit Mag; JV L Bowling; Hon Roll; Bio.

MURPHY, LISA; Doherty Memorial HS; Worcester, MA; (Y); Dance Clb; French Clb; Hosp Aide; Yrbk Stf; French Hon Soc; Hon Roll; Career Day Essay Awd 85; Nrsng.

MURPHY, MAUREEN; Silverlkae Regional HS; Plympton, MA; (Y); 78/520; 4-H; French Clb; Key Clb; Mrchg Band; Yrbk Sprt Ed; Rep Frsh Cls; Hon Roll; Awd & Recgntn From Gov Dukakis For Wrk Towards Drug Free Yth 85; Awd & Recgntn From Hse Of Reps 85; Engl.

MURPHY, MEREDITH; Taunton HS; Taunton, MA; (Y); Drama Clb; JCL; Latin Clb; OEA; Ski Clb; Varsity Clb; Yrbk Stf; Cheerleading; Tennis; Trk.

MURPHY, MICHAEL J; Milton HS; Milton, MA; (Y); Boy Scts; Cmnty Wkr; Latin Clb; Ski Clb; Im Bsktbl; Var Gym; Var Socr; Im Swmmng; Awd ST Champ Gym Tm 82; Awd Sprtsmn Of Yr Camp 80; Bently; Acctg.

MURPHY, PATRICIA A; Belmont HS; Belmont, MA; (Y); Church Yth Grp; VP Pres JA; Latin Clb; Nwsp Rptr; Socr; Var Trk; Hon Roll; Cmnty Wkr; Debate Tm; Library Aide; Grtr Boston Yth Soccer-Undr 17-84; Brnz Medl Wnng Metro Soccer Tm 84; MA ST Soccer Tm 85; Engl.

MURPHY, SHAWN; Whitman-Hanson Regional HS; Whitman, MA; (Y); 21/323; Am Leg Boys St; Mrchg Band; Rep Church Yth Grp; JV Bsktbl; Vllybl; NHS; Pres Schlr; High Hon Roll; Hon Roll; Abington Hstrcl Soc; Mr Whitman-Hanson 4th Rnr Up; Bst Dressed; U MA Amherst; Pre-Med.

MURPHY, SHEILA; Coyle And Cassidy HS; E Taunton, MA; (Y); Chorus; Church Yth Grp; English Clb; Trs 4-H; Science Clb; Hon Roll; NHS; NEDT Awd; Voice Dem Awd; Lit Awd Poetry; Vet Med.

MURRAY, CAROLYN; Fairhaven HS; Fairhaven, MA; (Y); 1/190; AFS; Key Clb; Yrbk Ed-Chief; French Clb; Girl Scts; Office Aide; Ski Clb; Teachers Aide; Church Choir; Nwsp Rptr; Stu Of Mnth 82; Princpls Awd 83; Demcrcy Regnl Wnr 84; Law.

MURRAY, ELIZABETH; Miss Halls Schl; Belvedere, CA; (S); Computer Clb; English Clb; Latin Clb; Pep Clb; Ski Clb; Spanish Clb; Varsity Clb; Band; Concert Band; Stage Crew; Drum Scholar 84-85; Psych.

MURRAY, JOHN; Williston-Northampton HS; Atlanta, GA; (Y); Boy Scts; French Clb; Key Clb; Chorus; Yrbk Bus Mgr; Yrbk Stf; Var L Ftbl; Var L Lcrss; Im Wt Lftg; Hon Roll; Eagle Scout 82; Bus.

MURRAY, LAURA; Girls Catholic HS; Malden, MA; (Y); Camp Fr Inc; Church Yth Grp; French Clb; Girl Scts; Hosp Aide; JV Sftbl; Hon Roll; Trvl Cnslnt.

MURRAY, LISA; Hingham HS; Hingham, MA; (Y); 40/345; Rep Church Yth Grp; Hosp Aide; Yrbk Stf; Rep Frsh Cls; Rep Soph Cls; Rep Jr Cls; Rep Sr Cls; Sec Stu Cncl; Var L Socr; JV Sftbl; Boston Clg.

MURRAY, PATRICK J; Beverly HS; Beverly Farms, MA; (Y); 124/390; Church Yth Grp; Cmnty Wkr; Red Cross Aide; Varsity Clb; JV Bsktbl; JV L Ftbl; Var L Tennis; Im Tennis; Im Wt Lftg; Swmg Capt 84-85; NE Conf 50 Yd Freestyl Rcrd & MVP 85; ST Fnlst Swmg 50-100 Yd Freestyl 83-85; Northeastern U Boston; Bus Adm.

MURRAY, SEAN; Classical HS; Lynn, MA; (Y); JV Var Bsktbl; Hon Roll; Law.

MURRAY, WILLIAM; Boston Latin HS; Boston, MA; (Y); 10/303; Church Yth Grp; Political Wkr; Y-Teens; JV Bsktbl; Hon Roll; NHS; Ntl Merit SF; Latin Awd 81 & 82; Lbrl Arts.

MUSI, DIANE M; Winthrop HS; Winthrop, MA; (Y); 2/220; Math Tm; Science Clb; JV Bsktbl; Var L Sftbl; Var L Tennis; Elks Awd; High Hon Roll; NHS; Hugh O Brien Yth Ldrshp Smnr 83; Coaches Awd Tennis 84; Sftbl NECD 84.

MUSTO, LEAH; Bishap Feehan HS; Mansfield, MA; (Y); Hosp Aide; Spanish Clb; Nwsp Stf; Trk; High Hon Roll; Hon Roll; Spanish NHS; Cert Of Merit-Math 85; Westfield ST; Bus.

MUSTOE, DAWN; Burlington HS; Burlington, MA; (Y); Church Yth Grp; Dance Clb; Drama Clb; German Clb; Hosp Aide; Science Clb; Chorus; School Musical; School Play; Stage Crew; Salem ST Coll; Socl Wrkr.

MYERS, ANDREW; Barnstable HS; Centerville, MA; (Y); Drama Clb; Temple Yth Grp; School Play; Stu Cncl; Coach Actv; Entrepreneur.

MYERSON, LORY; Natick HS; Natick, MA; (Y); 15/443; Ski Clb; Temple Yth Grp; Rep Frsh Cls; Rep Soph Cls; Rep Jr Cls; Rep Stu Cncl; Var Capt Vllybl; Cit Awd; High Hon Roll; Hon Roll; Typng Excllnc Awd 84-85; Poltcl Sci.

MYLES, STEPHANIE; Technical HS; Springfield, MA; (Y); 3/238; Drama Clb; JA; Rep Frsh Cls; Rep Soph Cls; Rep Jr Cls; Rep Stu Cncl; Bsktbl; Trk; Hon Roll; Cert Achvt Awd 85; RN.

NABBEFELD, CATHY; Chelmsford HS; Chelmsford, MA; (Y); 2/600; Sec French Clb; Ski Clb; Tennis; French Hon Soc; NHS; Church Yth Grp; High Hon Roll; Hlth.

NABI, ROBIN L; Sharon HS; Sharon, MA; (Y); 2/210; VP Drama Clb; Thesps; Jazz Band; Nwsp Rptr; VP Frsh Cls; Stu Cncl; Var L Crs Cntry; Kiwanis Awd; Sal; French Clb; 1st Pl Framingham St Phi Alpha Tehta Hist Conf 85; U PA Bk Awd 85; Stu Mnth Frnch & Soc Stud; Law.

NACEY, SUSAN L; Wellesley SR HS; Wellesley Hills, MA; (Y); 4/324; Sec AFS; French Clb; Spanish Clb; Hon Roll; VP NHS; Ntl Merit SF; Frnch Awd.

NACHAJKO, WENDY; Shepherd Hill Regional HS; Dudley, MA; (Y); 5/158; Band; Mrchg Band; High Hon Roll; NHS; Ntl Merit Ltr; Quo Vadis Schlrshp 85; Pres Acadmc Fit Awd 85; Webstr Womns Clb Schlrshp 85; FL Inst Tech; Moleclr Bio.

NADEAU JR, ELLIOTT L; Shrewsbury SR HS; Shrewsbury, MA; (Y); 41/230; Am Leg Boys St; Boys Clb Am; Stage Crew; Variety Show; Off Sr Cls; Bsktbl; Coach Actv; Ftbl; Score Keeper; Socr; Stu Mnth 85; Phys Ther.

NADEAU, JEAN-PAUL; Somerset HS; Somerset, MA; (Y); Chorus; Church Choir; Swing Chorus; Hon Roll; NHS; Providence Coll Summr Sci Pgm 84; Comp Info Svcs.

NADEAU, MICHELLE; HS Of Commerce; Springfield, MA; (S); 4-H; 4-H Awd; NHS; MA Mutual Intrnshp 85; W New Engl; Bus Mgmt.

NADEAU, STEPHEN; Haverhill HS; Haverhill, MA; (Y); 53/415; Boys Clb Am; Church Yth Grp; Cmnty Wkr; Spanish Clb; Nwsp Stf; Stu Cncl; Var Capt Golf; High Hon Roll; NHS; Outstndng Achvt Awd In Golf 81; Personal Achvt Awd 85; U Of VT; Ec.

NAGGIAR, EDOARDO R; Bishop Connolly HS; Fall River, MA; (S); 9/200; French Clb; Band; JV Socr; JV Tennis; High Hon Roll; Jr NHS; NHS; Naval Acad; Elec Engr.

NAHIGIAN, LAURA; Arlington HS; Arlington, MA; (Y); Church Yth Grp; Hosp Aide; Color Guard; Yrbk Phtg; Rep Frsh Cls; Hon Roll; Ntl Hnr Scty; Ntrtn.

NAMBIAR, SUNITHA N; Lincoln-Sudbury Regional HS; Sudbury, MA; (Y); Art Clb; Sec Intnl Clb; Sec Spanish Clb; Teachers Aide; Variety Show; Lit Mag; High Hon Roll; Lead Role Indian Clsscl Dance Drama 85; Perf Awd NY S Indian Conv 83; Awd Perf New England U Perf 84; Psych.

NAPIERATA, BRETT; Bartlett HS; Webster, MA; (Y); Drama Clb; Library Aide; Political Wkr; Ski Clb; School Play; Var L Ftbl; Var L Tennis; Var L Trk; High Hon Roll; Webstr Sumr Lge Bsktbl All Star Tm 83; Brdr Conf All Star Awd Trk & Fld 85; Poltcl Sci.

NARBIS, CAROL; Falmouth HS; Falmouth, MA; (Y); Aud/Vis; Pres Church Yth Grp; Drama Clb; Hosp Aide; Model UN; Chorus; JV Sftbl; Westfield ST Coll; Comm.

NARCHESE, BETH; St Marys HS; Worcester, MA; (Y); 2/64; Sec Church Yth Grp; Cmnty Wkr; Drama Clb; French Clb; Church Choir; School Play; Variety Show; Hon Roll; NHS; 2nd Pl Sci Fair Awd 83; Comm.

NARDONE, VALERIE; Wakefield HS; Wakefield, MA; (Y); Church Yth Grp; Cmnty Wkr; GAA; JA; Key Clb; Math Tm; Yrbk Stf; Socr; U Of Lowell; Engrng.

NASH, KERRY; North Quincy HS; Quincy, MA; (Y); French Clb; FBLA; Pep Clb; Ski Clb; Spanish Clb; Yrbk Stf; JV Bsktbl; Var Powder Puff Ftbl; Sftbl; Tennis; Bus Adm.

NASH, REBECCA; Burlington HS; Burlington, MA; (Y); 10/315; Im Ski Clb; Concert Band; Mrchg Band; Ed Lit Mag; High Hon Roll; NCTE Awd; NHS; Hon Roll; Englsh Awd 83-84; Srv Awd For Edtng 84-85; Goethe Inst Boston Grmn Awd 83-85; Psychlgy.

NASIFF, KENNETH R; Somerset HS; Somerset, MA; (Y); Varsity Clb; Im Bsktbl; Var Ice Hcky; Im Wt Lftg; High Hon Roll; NHS; Lebanon Amer Scholar 85; CSF Scholar 85; Boston Coll; Bus.

NASON, DANIEL F; St Bernards Central Catholic HS; Westminster, MA; (Y); 63/172; Am Leg Boys St; Camera Clb; Drama Clb; Ski Clb; Chorus; School Play; Nwsp Stf; Yrbk Stf; VP Frsh Cls; Rep Soph Cls; Auto Dsgn.

NASUTI, JOSEPH S; Marlboro HS; Marlboro, MA; (Y); Am Leg Boys St; Boys Clb Am; Church Yth Grp; Ski Clb; Varsity Clb; Variety Show; Crs Cntry; Golf; Tennis; Elks Awd; American Inst Of Plant Engrs Awd; Faculty Awds-Excllnc In Busnss & Excllnc In Socl Studies; U Of Lowell; Engrng.

NATELSON, JAMIE; Milford HS; Milford, MA; (Y); 45/320; NFL; Yrbk Stf; Rep Soph Cls; Rep Sr Cls; Rep Stu Cncl; Var L Fld Hcky; Var Capt Gym; Var Capt Trk; Hon Roll; Amer Lgn Schl Awd 82; Intl Rltns.

NATHAN, ANN L; Commonwealth Schl; Boston, MA; (Y); Cmnty Wkr; Mgr Library Aide; Chorus; Church Choir; School Musical; JV Bsbl; Var JV Bsktbl; Var JV Socr; Swmmng; JV Trk; Lead Pgm U MD College Pk 84; Pres Minority Stu League Commonwealth Schl 84-85; Arts Pgm Music Div 84.

NATOLA, LAURIE; Saugus HS; Saugus, MA; (Y); 3/355; GAA; JV Bsktbl; Capt Socr; Cit Awd; High Hon Roll; Jr NHS; NHS; Physics Awd Acad Achvmnt 85; Bryant; Bus.

NAULT, PATRICIA; Presentation Of Mary Acad; Lawrence, MA; (Y); Art Clb; Church Yth Grp; French Clb; Nwsp Stf; Sec Frsh Cls; MA ST & Bay Path Schlrshp 85-86; Fincl Aid Awd 85-86; Bay Path JC; Bus Mgmt.

NAVAROLI JR, THOMAS J; Leicester HS; Cherry Valley, MA; (Y); Aud/Vis; Pres Church Yth Grp; Math Tm; Office Aide; Yrbk Phtg; Rep Frsh Cls; Stu Cncl; JV Bsbl; Var Capt Tennis; Im Vllybl; Bently Coll Bus Week 85; Bus Admin.

NAVE, MICHAEL; Reading Memorial HS; Reading, MA; (Y); Band; Mrchg Band; Mgr(s); High Hon Roll; Hon Roll; Biochem.

NAVIN, MARK; Lee HS; Lee, MA; (Y); 33/106; Boy Scts; Church Yth Grp; French Clb; Quiz Bowl; Crs Cntry; Trphy For Excllnt Performance On TV Quiz Tm 85; Hist.

NAVIN, PETER; Hingham HS; Hingham, MA; (Y); Political Wkr; Rep Stu Cncl; Im Coach Actv; Var Capt Socr; VP Trk; Church Yth Grp; Cmnty Wkr; Model UN; Nwsp Stf; Yrbk Sprt Ed; Bus Mngmnt.

NAZE, JAMES M; Marlboro HS; Marlboro, MA; (Y); 33/275; Am Leg Boys St; JA; Trs Pep Clb; Political Wkr; Yrbk Stf; Pres Frsh Cls; Pres Soph Cls; Stu Cncl; Var L Ice Hcky; JV Trk; Meteorlgy.

NEARY, LORI; Reading Memorial HS; Reading, MA; (Y); Dance Clb; Pep Clb; Political Wkr; Yrbk Stf; Rep Frsh Cls; JV Var Trk; Hon Roll; Schlstc Achvt 85; Bus.

NECKES, AMY M; Randolh HS; Randolph, MA; (Y); 91/352; Yrbk Sprt Ed; L Bsktbl; Capt Sftbl; Hon Roll; Old Colony Lgu Sftbl All Star 85; Sullivan Awd Schlrhsp Outstndng 85; Female Athlt 85; Johnson & Wales Coll; Accntng.

NEDDER, JOSEPH A; Xaverian Brothers HS; Dedham, MA; (S); 1/215; Ed Nwsp Stf; Yrbk Stf; Swmmng; High Hon Roll; NHS; Ntl Merit Ltr; Acad Schlrshp To Xaverian 81-85; Harvard Bk Awd 84; Med.

NEDEAU, JOSEPH; Bishop Connolly HS; Middletown, RI; (Y); 6/157; Church Yth Grp; Drama Clb; Hosp Aide; Math Tm; School Play; High Hon Roll; NHS; NEDT Awd; Pres Acad Ftns Awd 85; USAF ROTC Schlrshp 85; Math & Sci Div Fresh Merit Awd 85; Norwich U; Math.

NEDZWECKAS, SHELLEY M; Southbridge HS; Southbridge, MA; (Y); 21/140; Sec Church Yth Grp; Spanish Clb; Rep Frsh Cls; Rep Soph Cls; JV Diving; Stat Socr; Hon Roll; Natl Govt Day Awd 84; Brdgwtr ST U; Poltcl Sci.

NEE, ANDREA; Clinton HS; Clinton, MA; (Y); Church Yth Grp; Civic Clb; Dance Clb; Intnl Clb; Off Frsh Cls; Off Soph Cls; Off Jr Cls; CC Awd; Johnson/Wales Coll; Pastry Arts.

NEEDHAM, PAUL; Higham HS; Hingham, MA; (Y); 17/348; Church Yth Grp; Cmnty Wkr; Drama Clb; School Musical; School Play; Rep Stu Cncl; JV Ice Hcky; Var Mgr(s); JV Socr; Hon Roll; Bst Attitde Twrd Pgm Spn Heritge Summr Span 84.

NEEDHAM, RITA; Dedham HS; Dedham, MA; (Y); 28/290; Cmnty Wkr; Nwsp Ed-Chief; Nwsp Stf; Var Socr; Hon Roll; UN Plgrmg Yth Essay & Spch Cont 83-84; Jrnlsm.

NEELY, MAURA; Bisho Feehan HS; N Attleboro, MA; (Y); Hosp Aide; Drill Tm; Mrchg Band; Trk; Var Capt Twrlr; High Hon Roll; Hon Roll; NHS; Spanish NHS; Bus.

NEIBERG, LEONARD; Newton South HS; Newton Centre, MA; (Y); Spanish Clb; Var Crs Cntry; Var Trk; High Hon Roll; Hon Roll; Ntl Merit Ltr; AATSP St Span Exam 5th 84; Comp Sci.

NEIDICH, PAUL I; Leominster HS; Leominster, MA; (Y); Am Leg Boys St; Temple Yth Grp; Stage Crew; Var Capt Swmmng; High Hon Roll; Hon Roll; NHS; Ntl Merit Ltr; Mst Imprvd Swmmr 84; Bio Sci.

NEIL JR, WILLIAM F; Melrose HS; Melrose, MA; (Y); 20/400; Aud/Vis; Church Yth Grp; Drama Clb; Thesps; School Musical; School Play; Stage Crew; High Hon Roll; NHS; Lib Arts.

NEILL, LISA; North Middlesex Regional HS; Pepperell, MA; (Y); 9/219; Drama Clb; Acpl Chr; Madrigals; Ed Yrbk Stf; Powder Puff Ftbl; High Hon Roll; Hon Roll; Jr NHS; NHS; Engl Awd Outstndng Achvs 85; U Of MA; Engl.

NELLIGAN, THOMAS; Medford Vocational Technica HS; Malden, MA; (Y); Varsity Clb; Var Crs Cntry; Var Trk; Hon Roll; Catherine F Caren Memrl Awd 85; Mst Imprvd 85; U Of CO Boulder; Publc Rltns.

NELSON, ABIGAIL; Dana Hall Schl; Weston, MA; (Y); Office Aide; Schl Hnrs List 83 & 84; Econ.

NELSON, CRAIG; Cathedral HS; Chicopee, MA; (Y); 54/500; Boy Scts; Intnl Clb; JA; Nwsp Phtg; Nwsp Rptr; Nwsp Stf; Yrbk Phtg; Off Sr Cls; Eagle Scout 85.

NELSON, DAVID; English HS; Roslindale, MA; (Y); Boy Scts; Model UN; Quiz Bowl; Science Clb; School Play; Stage Crew; Socr; Part In MA Adv Stds Prog 85; Hstry.

NELSON, DEBBIE; Holy Name Central Catholic HS; Worcester, MA; (Y); Church Yth Grp; Office Aide; Chorus; School Musical; High Hon Roll; Hon Roll; Bus Mgmt.

NELSON, ERIC; St Johns Preparatory Schl; Boxford, MA; (Y); 111/269; Spanish Clb; Varsity Clb; Im Bsktbl; Im Ftbl; Im Golf; JV Lcrss; Score Keeper; Im Vllybl; Hon Roll; Vrsty Fencg Tm 83; Altrnt Qualfr JR Olympc Fencg Tm 83; Intl Mktg.

NELSON, IRENE; Barnstable HS; Barnstable, MA; (Y); 11/398; Church Yth Grp; Drama Clb; School Play; Stu Cncl; Fld Hcky; Trk; Hon Roll; NHS; Silvr Cert; Gld Cert; Acadmc Ltr, Medl; Fordham U; Intl Reltns.

NELSON, JAMES; Newburyport HS; Newburyport, MA; (S); 21/207; Am Leg Boys St; JA; JCL; Library Aide; Math Tm; Teachers Aide; Hon Roll; NHS; 3rd St Sci Fair 84; Cum Laude Natl Latin Exam 82; Geol Engrng.

NELSON, KAREN; King Philip Regional HS; Plainville, MA; (Y); 46/167; Church Yth Grp; FBLA; Girl Scts; Intnl Clb; Church Choir; Hon Roll; JC Awd; Hugh O Brien Found 84; Dean Jr Coll; Lib Arts.

NELSON, KARIN; Marlboro HS; Marlboro, MA; (Y); 3/320; Girl Scts; Pep Clb; Ski Clb; Trk; High Hon Roll; NHS; Outstndg Achiev Sci, Engl, Foreign Lang 83-85.

NELSON, MARGARET C; Northfield Mount Hermon HS; Middlebury, VT; (Y); Church Yth Grp; Orch; Var Swmmng; Var Trk; Hon Roll.

NEMET, IRENE; Weymouth North HS; E Weymouth, MA; (Y); 60/333; Cmnty Wkr; Key Clb; Yrbk Stf; High Hon Roll; Hon Roll; Bus Wk At Bentley Coll 84; Miss Quincy Bay Pgnt 83; Mss Teen Pgnt 85; Emerson Coll; Comm.

NENARD, CHRISTINE; Agawam HS; Agawam, MA; (Y); Chorus; Sftware Engr.

NERET, TRACEY A; Milton HS; Milton, MA; (Y); 26/200; Rep AFS; Am Leg Aux Girls St; Chess Clb; Nwsp Stf; Yrbk Stf; Lit Mag; Pres Stu Cncl; Bsktbl; Fld Hcky; Tennis; Norman Knight Schlrshp Awd Grls SR 84; UN Plgrmg Yth Delg 84; U Of NH.

NEUMANN, DAVID; Lexington HS; Lexington, MA; (Y); Art Clb; Cmnty Wkr; Computer Clb; Drama Clb; French Clb; Temple Yth Grp; School Play; Nwsp Stf; Yrbk Bus Mgr; Lit Mag; Gld Key & Hnrb Mntn Ntl Schltc Art Awds 84; Law.

NEUYEN, QUOC; Umana Tech; Brighton, MA; (Y); 1/32; Computer Clb; French Clb; Math Clb; Math Tm; High Hon Roll; Hon Roll; NHS; Prfct Atten Awd; 3rd Pl Cty Wd Sci Fair 85; Dean Lst 84; Elctrnc Engrng.

NEVALA, TOM; Maynard HS; Maynard, MA; (Y); 3/100; Am Leg Boys St; Pres Church Yth Grp; Chorus; Concert Band; Jazz Band; Mrchg Band; Var L Ftbl; Var L Golf; NHS; Aud/Vis; Golf Unsung Hero 83-84.

NEVES, MARIA; Madison Park High HS; Boston, MA; (Y); Stu Cncl; Socr; Swmmng; Hon Roll; Ntl Merit Schol; UCLA; Law.

NEVIUS, KAREN; Chelmsfor HS; Chelmsford, MA; (Y); 100/560; Hon Roll; Bio Sci.

NEWBURN, WILLIAM A; Winchester HS; Winchester, MA; (Y); Church Yth Grp; Varsity Clb; JV Ftbl; Var Ice Hcky; JV Lcrss; JV Socr; Hon Roll; Hcky Ltr Awd; Lib Arts.

NEWCOMER, PATRICIA; Leicester HS; Leicester, MA; (S); 1/110; Church Yth Grp; Latin Clb; Math Tm; Spanish Clb; Band; Pep Band; Var Bsktbl; Var Fld Hcky; Var Tennis; High Hon Roll; Hugh O Brien Yth Ldrshp Smnr 84; Ntl Conf Chrstns & Jews 84; Math.

NEWELL, CHRISTINE A; East Longmeadow HS; E Longmeadow, MA; (Y); 45/197; 4-H; 4-H Awd; Hon Roll; Amer Intl Coll; Med Tech.

NEWELL, TODD; Arlington HS; Arlington, MA; (Y); Am Leg Boys St; Band; Jazz Band; Mrchg Band; Symp Band; Pres Jr Cls; Rep Stu Cncl; Capt Tennis; NHS.

NEWMAN, VANESSA; Haverhill HS; Bradford, MA; (Y); Hosp Aide; Lang Tutor-Italian; Psych.

NEWTON, JAMES; Burlington HS; Burlington, MA; (Y); 55/320; Church Yth Grp; JA; Science Clb; Ed Yrbk Stf; Rep Sr Cls; Rep Stu Cncl.

NEYLON, MARY; Stoneham HS; Stoneham, MA; (Y); VP Dance Clb; Trs Drama Clb; Latin Clb; Chorus; Capt Color Guard; School Play; Variety Show; Var Cheerleading; NHS; Chancellrs Tlnt Awd U MA Amherst 84; U MA Amherst; Theater Arts.

NG, ELAINE; Boston Latin Schl; Boston, MA; (Y); French Clb; JA; Latin Clb; Yrbk Stf; Boston Coll; Comm.

NG, HEUNG KWAN; Boston Latin Schl; Boston, MA; (Y); Camera Clb; Cmnty Wkr; Exploring; French Clb; Hosp Aide; Teachers Aide; Vllybl; Hon Roll; Jr NHS; NHS; Tutrng, BU Lab Pgm 84-85; Exemp Cndct, Fdlty 83-84; Clsscs Awd 82; Engrng.

NG, SUI M; Boston Tech HS; Boston, MA; (Y); Computer Clb; French Clb; Hosp Aide; Rep Cmnty Wkr; Hon Roll; NHS; Psych.

NGUYEN, BICH-NGAN; Boston Latin Schl; Boston, MA; (Y); Cmnty Wkr; Dance Clb; Speech Tm; Temple Yth Grp; Band; Chorus; Concert Band; Yrbk Stf; Hon Roll; NHS; Boston Schl Museum/Fine Arts Schlrshp 85; Boston Globe Schltc Art Cntst Gld Key Awd 85; Babson; Mktg.

NGUYEN, HUNG; Chelsea HS; Chelsea, MA; (Y); Boys Clb Am; Y-Teens; Hon Roll; U Of MA-BOSTON; Elec Engr.

NGUYEN, KIM; Brookline HS; Brookline, MA; (Y); Off Frsh Cls; French Hon Soc; Hon Roll; Frnch Cont Awd I 82, Awd II 83; U Lowell; Comp Sci Engr.

NGUYEN, KIMNGOC; Dracut HS; Dracut, MA; (Y); Church Yth Grp; Key Clb; Ski Clb; Yrbk Stf; JV Socr; NHS.

NGUYEN, LONG; Salem HS; Salem, MA; (Y); 10/332; Am Leg Boys St; Math Clb; Socr; High Hon Roll; NHS; Poli Sci.

NGUYEN, QUANG; Boston Tech HS; Boston, MA; (Y); Pep Clb; Red Cross Aide; Socr; NHS; Hnr Roll 83; Air Force Acad; Aerntcl Engnr.

NGUYEN, VI; Lawrence HS; Lawrence, MA; (Y); Boy Scts; High Hon Roll; Hon Roll; Elec Engr.

NICASTRO, ROBERT V; Bishop Feehan HS; N Attleboro, MA; (Y); 5/268; Boy Scts; Chorus; Jazz Band; School Play; Rptr Nwsp Rptr; L Trk; Dnfth Awd; NCTE Awd; Ntl Merit SF; Church Yth Grp; Crew Sport 85; Brown U; Lang.

NICHINIELLO, DENISE; Georgetown HS; Georgetown, MA; (Y); AFS; Cmnty Wkr; Debate Tm; Drama Clb; Political Wkr; Ski Clb; Nwsp Ed-Chief; Nwsp Rptr; Nwsp Stf; Yrbk Stf; Sccr Cchs Awd 83; Outstndng Cntrb To Blue Prnt 85; Stu Advsry Dscpln Comm 85-86; TV Brdcstng.

NICHOLS, KAREN; Brooklin HS; Brookline, MA; (Y); Computer Clb; French Clb; Intnl Clb; Library Aide; Ski Clb; JV Lcrss; Var Capt Socr; Var Capt Tennis; Hon Roll; NHS; Frnch Awd 83; Undftd Awd Tennis 85; Outstndng Attndnc Awd 85.

NICHOLS, LEONARD; Brockton HS; Brockton, MA; (Y); 210/1100; Boy Scts; CAP; Socr; Hon Roll; Law.

NICHOLS, ROBERT H; Dedham HS; Dedham, MA; (Y); 15/300; Am Leg Boys St; Church Yth Grp; Drama Clb; French Clb; Chorus; School Musical; School Play; Stage Crew; Variety Show; Nwsp Ed-Chief; Jr Engl Essay 1st Pl; Boston U; Psych.

NICHOLS, SANDY; Governor Dummer Acad; Manchester, MA; (Y); 25/90; Camera Clb; French Clb; Hosp Aide; Political Wkr; Nwsp Rptr; Ed Yrbk Stf; Im Crs Cntry; JV Fld Hcky; JV Ice Hcky; JV Lcrss; Efrt Hnr Roll; Vtrnry Med.

NICHOLS, WILLIAM; Marian HS; Hopkinton, MA; (Y); Quiz Bowl; Teachers Aide; Var Capt Crs Cntry; JV Ice Hcky; Var L Trk; High Hon Roll; NHS; Ntl Merit Schol; Achv Awd In NEDT Tst 84; Comp Sci.

NICHOLSON, GARY J; Xaverian Brothers HS; Abington, MA; (S); 17/235; Boy Scts; Church Yth Grp; Trs Exploring; JV Ftbl; High Hon Roll; NHS; Score 5 AP U S Hist Exam 84; Pre-Med.

NICKERSON, NOELLE; Glovcester HS; Gloucester, MA; (Y); 42/321; Yrbk Stf; Capt Cheerleading; Tennis; Hon Roll; NHS; MVP Tennis 84.

NICKERSON, SEAN; Gloucester HS; Gloucester, MA; (Y); 25/319; JV Ice Hcky; JV Socr; Var Tennis; Im Vllybl; Cit Awd; Hon Roll; NHS; Ntl Merit Schol; Co-Capt Tnns Tm 83-85; MVP Tnns Tm Dbls 84-85; Stonehill Coll; Librl Arts.

NICOLOSI, JAMES; Methven HS; Methuen, MA; (Y); 29/350; Var Capt Golf; Var Ice Hcky; High Hon Roll; Math.

NIEBRZYDOWSKI, SUSAN; Peabody Veterans Memorial HS; Peabody, MA; (Y); 3/550; VP Key Clb; Spanish Clb; Chorus; School Play; Sec Stu Cncl; High Hon Roll; NHS; Chncllors Awd; Bus.

NIELSEN, CARL DANIEL; Tantasqua Regional HS; Brookfield, MA; (Y); Ski Clb; Y-Teens; Trs Sr Cls; Stu Cncl; Hon Roll; NHS; Med.

NIELSEN, NATALEE A; Burlington HS; Burlington, MA; (Y); 21/360; Boys Clb Am; Boy Scts; Church Yth Grp; VP Debate Tm; OEA; Yrbk Stf; Var L Swmmng; Hon Roll; NHS; Comp Sci.

NIEMIEC, PAUL F; Chicopee Comprehensive HS; Chicopee, MA; (S); 15/385; Bsbl; Natl Hnr Soc Awd 85-85; Natl Accordian Champ Rch 84; JR Div MA Accordian Champ 84; Syracuse U; Comp Tech.

NIERAD, ANDREA; Revere HS; Revere, MA; (Y); 4-H; FHA; NFL; Pep Clb; Spanish Clb; Thesps; School Musical; School Play; Nwsp Rptr; Hon Roll; Ntl Hstry/Govt Awd 83-85; Ntl Ldrshp Awd 84; Schlstc Ltr 85; Cmnctns.

NIERINTZ, ROBERT; Hudson HS; Hudson, MA; (Y); PAVAS; Acpl Chr; Band; Chorus; Church Choir; Concert Band; Mrchg Band; Orch; School Musical; Hon Roll; Outstndng Achv Band 84; Ntl Hstry Dy Awd 83; Intr Dsgn.

NIESTEPSKI, CHRIS; Barstable HS; Centerville, MA; (S); Concert Band; Mrchg Band; Symp Band; Yrbk Stf; Jr Cls; Tennis; Trk; High Hon Roll; NHS; Church Yth Grp; Silver Certfct 83; Gold Certfct 84; Military.

NIGG, DAVID; Billerica Memorial HS; Billerica, MA; (Y); #14 In Class; JV Ftbl; NHS; Elec Engrng.

NIGHTINGALE, MARK R; Lynnfield HS; Lynnfield, MA; (Y); 51/210; Am Leg Boys St; Church Yth Grp; Political Wkr; Teachers Aide; Varsity Clb; Stage Crew; Nwsp Stf; Rep Sr Cls; JV Capt Bsktbl; Mgr(s); Am Leg Boys ST 85; Bus.

NILES, DANIEL T; Austin Preparatory Schl; Lynn, MA; (Y); 1/130; Chess Clb; French Clb; Math Tm; Science Clb; Church Choir; Wt Lftg; NHS; Ntl Merit SF; Amherst U Jr Sci & Humanities Symposium 84; IN U H S Sci Stu Inst 84; Harvard; Elec Engrng.

NILSEN, SUSAN; Silverlake Regional HS; Kingston, MA; (Y); Drama Clb; French Clb; Office Aide; Radio Clb; Crs Cntry; Hon Roll; Acad All Amer 83-84; Georgetown; Intl Reltns.

NIMMO, SUSAN; Natick HS; Natick, MA; (Y); 115/430; Chorus; School Musical; Sftbl; Swmmng; Hon Roll; Awd Outstndng Perfrmnc Comp Sci 85; Fitchburg ST Coll; Math Ed.

NIRO, JEFFREY M; Milford HS; Milford, MA; (Y); 38/300; Am Leg Boys St; JV Bsbl; L Var Ftbl; Capt Var Trk; L Var Wrstlng; Rookie Of Yr Trk 85; Milford Daily News All-Star Trk 85; 1st 100 Yrd Dsh & 220 Mid Lnd Lg 85; Bus.

NIRO, LATICIA; Milford HS; Milford, MA; (Y); 9/298; Am Leg Aux Girls St; Key Clb; Pep Clb; Yrbk Stf; VP Soph Cls; Rep Stu Cncl; JV Capt Fld Hcky; Tennis; High Hon Roll; NHS; Co-Chair JR Prom Comm 85; Soph Ring Comm 84; Fin.

NISHAN, KELLY; Holy Name C C H S; Worcester, MA; (Y); 21/278; Church Yth Grp; Cmnty Wkr; Exploring; Church Choir; Lit Mag; Hon Roll; Psych.

NITKIN, DEBORAH; Randolph HS; Randolph, MA; (Y); Cmnty Wkr; Dance Clb; Drama Clb; Spanish Clb; Temple Yth Grp; Band; Concert Band; Drill Tm; Mrchg Band; Yrbk Stf; Milton A Braver Mem Schlrshp 83; Polt Sci.

NIVALA, ERIC; Gardner HS; Gardner, MA; (Y); 5/157; Am Leg Boys St; Cmnty Wkr; Political Wkr; Spanish Clb; JV Crs Cntry; Var Tennis; JV Trk; CC Awd; High Hon Roll; NHS; Rotary Club Schlrshp; Knights Columbus Schlrshp; Prospect Schl Schlrshp; SE MA U; Psych.

NOBLE, DAVID; Weymouth North HS; Weymouth, MA; (Y); 11/365; Lcrss; Socr; High Hon Roll; Hon Roll; NHS; Bus Stu 82-83; Spnsh Stu 84; Princeton U; Comp Sci.

NOGUEIRA, PAULA; Classical HS; Springfield, MA; (Y); Church Yth Grp; Hosp Aide; Library Aide; Mathletes; Office Aide; Red Cross Aide; Teachers Aide; Varsity Clb; Church Choir; Var Cheerleading; Pre-Med.

NOLAN, FRANCIS; Boston Latin Schl; Boston, MA; (Y); 33/297; Sec Science Clb; Concert Band; Jazz Band; Pep Band; Nwsp Ed-Chief; Yrbk Stf; NHS; Key Clb; Band; Ntl Merit Ltr; CYO Mrchng Band 81-85; Lttl Leag Bsebl Coach 83-85; Engl.

NOLAN, JENNIFER A; Walpole HS; Walpole, MA; (Y); 102/265; Nwsp Phtg; Nwsp Rptr; Yrbk Phtg; Hon Roll; Stonehill Coll.

NOLAN, KATHLEEN; Whitman-Hanson Regional HS; Hanson, MA; (Y); 1/330; Varsity Clb; Band; Jazz Band; Var Socr; Var Sftbl; High Hon Roll; Hon Roll; NHS; Rensselaer Medal Math,Sci 85; Ntl Latin Ex 85; Engrng.

NOLIN, MARK; New Bedford HS; Acushnet, MA; (Y); 47/588; Church Yth Grp; Drama Clb; French Clb; School Musical; School Play; Stage Crew; Nwsp Stf; Bsktbl; Hon Roll; Jr NHS; Northeastern U; Phys Thrpy.

NOLTEMY, KIM; Archbishop Williams HS; Quincy, MA; (Y); 13/201; Math Tm; School Musical; Yrbk Stf; Var L Crs Cntry; Var L Trk; High Hon Roll; Hon Roll; NHS; Spanish NHS; Saks Fifth Ave Fash Ave 84-86; Psych.

NOONAN, JEANNE-MARIE; Fontbonne Acad; Brockton, MA; (Y); Church Yth Grp; Cmnty Wkr; Drama Clb; Intnl Clb; Math Tm; Political Wkr; Science Clb; Chorus; Nwsp Stf; Lit Mag; Outstndng Yth Chch & Cmmnty Awd 85; 3rd Pl Schl Sci Fair 84.

NOONAN, JOSEPH; Boston College HS; Pembroke, MA; (Y); 80/280; Boys Clb Am; Boy Scts; French Clb; VP JA; Crs Cntry; Swmmng; Trk; Bio.

NOONAN, KEVIN; Everett HS; Boston, MA; (Y); Church Yth Grp; Varsity Clb; Bsbl; Bsktbl; Coach Actv; Score Keeper; E Club 84-86; Phy Ftns.

NORDMAN, MICHAEL; Gardner HS; Gardner, MA; (Y); 63/183; Var JV Bsbl; Var Ice Hcky; Oustndng Frshmn Athl 83; Telgrm & Guzette Hcky All Star 84.

NORMAN, DAVID; St Marys HS; Auburn, MA; (Y); 10/60; Church Yth Grp; Drama Clb; School Play; Stage Crew; Rep VP Stu Cncl; JV Bsktbl; Var Socr; High Hon Roll; Hon Roll.

NORMAN, KRISTEN; Natick HS; Natick, MA; (Y); Bsktbl; Hon Roll; Typng Awd 83-84.

NORRIS, GREGG; Weymouth South HS; S Weymouth, MA; (Y); 27/340; Computer Clb; Sec Jr Cls; Var L Bsbl; Var L Trk; High Hon Roll; Hon Roll; NHS; Pres Schlr; John Kilmurray Schlrshp 85; 2nd 5th Pl Cls B Relays 85; UNH; Comp Engr.

NORRIS, MICHAEL; Malden HS; Malden, MA; (Y); 44/453; Boy Scts; Key Clb; Stage Crew; Var L Swmmng; Ntl Merit Schol; Bentley Coll; Acctg.

NORTH, PATRICIA; Fitchburg HS; Fitchburg, MA; (Y); Band; Chorus; Concert Band; Jazz Band; Mrchg Band; Pep Band; Yrbk Stf; High Hon Roll; Hon Roll; Music Perfrmnce.

NORTON, JO ANN; Fitchburg HS; Fitchburg, MA; (Y); High Hon Roll; Hon Roll; Ftchbrg Wmns Clb 85; Spec Hnr Roll 83-84; Ftchbrg ST Coll; Bus.

NORTON, PATRICIA A; Bartlett HS; Webster, MA; (Y); 4/174; Lcrss; Math Tm; Spanish Clb; Chorus; Drm Mjr(t); Mrchg Band; School Play; High Hon Roll; NHS; NEDT Awd; Brown U Bk Awd 85; Cert Of Profcncy-Typwrtng I 85; Holy Cross.

NOVELLINE, LAURA; Chelmsford HS; Chelmsford, MA; (Y); 146/565; French Clb; Ski Clb; Variety Show; Rptr Yrbk Stf; Rep Sr Cls; VP Stu Cncl; Powder Puff Ftbl; SADD Pres 83-85; Stu Govt Day 83-84; Ntl Hstry Day 82-84; U Of MA Amherst; Cmnctns.

NOVELLO, MARGARET; Academy Of Notre Dame; Pelham, NH; (Y); 12/75; Art Clb; Yrbk Stf; Mgr Sftbl; Hon Roll; NHS; Prfct Atten Awd; 2nd Pl Engl & Hstry Schl Art Fair; 2nd Prz Archdcsn Art Fair; 2 1st Pl Schl Art Fair.

NOWAK, JULIE; Natick HS; Natick, MA; (Y); Latin Clb; Band; Concert Band; Mrchg Band; School Musical; Symp Band; Var L Crs Cntry; JV Gym; JV Socr; Var L Trk; Brown U Bk Awd 85; Sec Bay ST Spdsktng Assc 86; 3rd Bay ST Spdsktng Gms 85; Hgh Dgre Englsh Exprsn; Writing.

NOWLAN, MARK; Holy Name Central Catholic HS; Leicester, MA; (Y); 88/250; Church Yth Grp; Bowling; Ace Carrier Tlgrm & Gazette Nwspr 83; Accntng.

NOYES, CINDY; Agawam HS; Agawam, MA; (Y); Church Yth Grp; Library Aide; Band; Concert Band; Hon Roll; Exec Scrty.

NOYES, DOUGLAS EVAN; Tewksbury Memorial HS; Tewksbury, MA; (Y); 80/323; Spanish Clb; Varsity Clb; JV Socr; Var Trk; Hon Roll; Teachers Aide; Band; Concert Band; Jazz Band; Capt Bowling; Mst Vlbl Plyr Indr Trck 82-83; Merrimac Vly All Str Dscs Trck 83-84; Merrimac Vly Ski Clb Champ 83-84; Maine Maritime; Marine Elect.

NOYES, PHILIP D; Duxbury HS; Duxbury, MA; (Y); Am Leg Boys St; Debate Tm; Nwsp Rptr; Capt Crs Cntry; Var Trk; Hon Roll; Social Sci.

NUNES, ARLENE; New Bedford HS; New Bedford, MA; (Y); Church Yth Grp; JCL; Library Aide; Yrbk Rptr; Yrbk Stf; Stu Cncl; High Hon Roll; Hon Roll; Jr NHS; Cert U Montreal 83-85; Ivy League Coll; Linguist.

NUNNA, PADMINI; Marian HS; Framingham, MA; (Y); Drama Clb; JA; School Musical; School Play; Yrbk Stf; Lit Mag; Var Sftbl; Hon Roll; NCTE Awd; Rep Soph Cls; Hnrbl Mntn Marian H S Fair 84; Finc.

NYE, DENNIS M; Lynn Classical HS; Lynn, MA; (Y); 10/197; Am Leg Boys St; Drama Clb; Sec JA; Science Clb; Yrbk Stf; Stu Cncl; Capt Bowling; High Hon Roll; Hon Roll; NHS; Lynn Tchrs Union Schlrshp 85; JR Achvt Bond 85; JR Achvt Mgmt Awd 83; Elon Coll; Med.

O BRIEN, CAROLYN; Cohasset HS; Cohasset, MA; (Y); 12/130; Church Yth Grp; Drama Clb; Band; School Play; Yrbk Ed-Chief; Rep Frsh Cls; Rep Jr Cls; Rep Stu Cncl; JV Bsktbl; Var Cheerleading; Lmplght Hnrs Acad Awd 82-84; Intl Bus.

O BRIEN, CHRISTINE; Bishop Connolly HS; Portsmouth, RI; (S); 16/177; French Clb; Math Tm; Ski Clb; Crs Cntry; Trk; Med.

O BRIEN, CHRISTINE; Holy Name C C H S; Worcester, MA; (Y); Church Yth Grp; Drama Clb; Girl Scts; Hosp Aide; School Play; Stage Crew; Sftbl; Hon Roll; Hnr Awd Comm Skills; Hmnts II; Rlgs Stds II; Nrs.

O BRIEN, DANIEL G; Hudson Catholic HS; Hudson, MA; (Y); 8/72; Am Leg Boys St; Church Yth Grp; Math Tm; Stage Crew; Nwsp Stf; Yrbk Sprt Ed; Var Bsktbl; Capt Crs Cntry; Capt Trk; Hon Roll; Boston Marathon 85; MVP Crs Cntry 84; Mth.

O BRIEN III, EDWARD ANTHONY; Boston College HS; Belmont, MA; (Y); Church Yth Grp; Cmnty Wkr; Key Clb; Math Clb; Math Tm; Im Bsktbl; Ftbl; Var L Ftbl; Im Tennis; Hon Roll; Acad Schlrshp, C Edward Rowe Fund Schlrshp 81-85; Offcl Amtr Hockey Referee 80-85; Vol Yth Hcky Coach; Boston Coll; Bus Mgmt.

O BRIEN, GLENN P; Chicopee Comp; Chicopee, MA; (S).

O BRIEN, JOHN P; Needham HS; Needham, MA; (Y); #1 In Class; Boy Scts; French Clb; Math Tm; Jazz Band; Mrchg Band; JV Crs Cntry; Var L Swmmng; Var Trk; Ntl Merit SF; Eagle Scout 83; Engrng.

O BRIEN, KEVIN; Blackstone Valley Rgnl Vo-Tech HS; Whitinsville, MA; (Y); Nwsp Stf; Stu Cncl; Hon Roll; Am Leg Boys St; Red Cross Aide; Var Capt Crs Cntry; L Var Trk; Slctd Attnd MA Boys ST 85; X-Cntry All Star 84; Bus.

O BRIEN, KEVIN; Malden HS; Malden, MA; (Y); 19/550; Key Clb; Variety Show; Yrbk Phtg; Lit Mag; Bowling; Hon Roll; NHS; Ntl Merit Ltr.

O BRIEN, LAUREN; Franklin HS; Franklin, MA; (Y); 3/250; Trs Church Yth Grp; Cmnty Wkr; Dance Clb; Math Clb; Political Wkr; Variety Show; Lit Mag; Hon Roll; NHS; St Schlr; Frances Eddy King Schlrshp & Awd 85; MA Schlr Awd & Schlrshp 85; MA Jr Miss-1st Runner Up 85; Clark U; Math.

O BRIEN, MICHELLE A; Boston Latin Schl; West Roxbury, MA; (Y); 40/300; Church Yth Grp; German Clb; Key Clb; Science Clb; Hon Roll; NHS; Natl Sci Olympd Chem 85; Rsrch Apprntc Tufts Nutri Rsrch Lab 85; Chem.

O BRIEN, ROBERT; St Johns HS; Shrewsbury, MA; (Y); 42/270; Var Stu Cncl; Var Capt Bsbl; Var Bsktbl; Var Ftbl; NHS; NEDT Awd; Rep Frsh Cls; High Hon Roll; Outstndng Athl Awd 85; Lgn Bsebl All-Star 85; Cntrl MA Bsebl Hnr Tm 84; U Of PA.

O BRYON, LESLIE; Newburyport HS; Newburyport, MA; (Y); 21/200; Cmnty Wkr; Debate Tm; Drama Clb; Political Wkr; Spanish Clb; School Musical; Stage Crew; Yrbk Stf; Fld Hcky; Hon Roll; Pres Ntl Hnr Soc; Hnrs Am Inst Awd; Law.

O CONNELL, DAVID E; Sacred Heart HS; Plympton, MA; (Y); 22/80; Cmnty Wkr; Key Clb; Political Wkr; Chorus; School Musical; Stage Crew; Nwsp Sprt Ed; Var L Bsbl; Var Capt Bsktbl; Var Capt Crs Cntry; Edward L Hand Awd Tm Loylty/Sprtsmnshp 85; Al-Star Crss Cntry/Bsbl 84-85; Relgn Awd-Svc 85; Stonehill Coll; Hstry Tchr.

O CONNELL, ELLEN M; Seekonk HS; Seekonk, MA; (Y); 1/180; Sec Computer Clb; Yrbk Stf; Var L Swmmng; Sec Trs French Hon Soc; High Hon Roll; NHS; Prfct Atten Awd; Brown Bk Awd 85outstndng Undergraduate Awd 85.

O CONNELL, MATTHEW; St Johns HS; Sudbury, MA; (Y); 15/280; French Clb; Ski Clb; Rep Stu Cncl; High Hon Roll; NHS; Ntl Merit Ltr; NEDT Awd; SR Rtrt Tm Ldr, Bro Alan Awd Excel Frnch, Ntl Hnr Rl 84-85; U PA; Lib Arts.

O CONNELL, MAURA L; Westfield HS; Westfield, MA; (Y); 68/340; Church Yth Grp; Varsity Clb; Var Capt Bsktbl; Var Capt Socr; Var Sftbl; Cit Awd; Hon Roll; Best Athl; ST Micheals Coll.

O CONNELL, PETER; Bishop Connolly HS; Tiverton, RI; (S); 20/177; Latin Clb; JV Socr; High Hon Roll; NHS.

O CONNELL, SHAWN; Chicopee HS; Chicopee, MA; (Y); Church Yth Grp; Political Wkr; Variety Show; Yrbk Stf; Bsktbl; Hon Roll.

O CONNELL, STEPHEN; Boston College HS; Needham, MA; (Y); 4/270; Boy Scts; Church Yth Grp; JA; Math Tm; Yrbk Stf; Im Bsktbl; Im Ftbl; Var Capt Swmmng; Im Tennis; High Hon Roll; Eagle Scout 84; Dartmouth Bk Awd 84; Catholic Conf All Star 84 & 85; Dartmouth Coll; Econ.

O CONNOR, KEVIN M; St Johns HS; Worcester, MA; (Y); Am Leg Boys St; Boy Scts; Church Yth Grp; Trs JA; Spanish Clb; VP Sr Cls; JV Bsktbl; JV Ftbl; Hon Roll; 1st Pl Marine Phys Fit Tsts 85; Dentstry.

O CONNOR, MARY; Woburn SR HS; Woburn, MA; (S); 30/500; Church Yth Grp; Dance Clb; French Clb; Leo Clb; Ski Clb; Yrbk Stf; VP Frsh Cls; Var L Cheerleading; NHS; 2nd All Wrld Irsh Stp Dncng Champ.

O CONNOR, MICHELLE L; Silver Lake Reg HS; Pembroke, MA; (Y); 106/620; Church Yth Grp; Hosp Aide; Latin Clb; Office Aide; Church Choir; Ntl Merit Ltr; Ntl Hnr L 85; Bridgewater ST Coll; Elem Ed.

O CONNOR JR, ROBERT J; Roxbury Latin HS; Wellesley, MA; (Y); Drama Clb; Church Choir; Jazz Band; School Musical; School Play; Yrbk Ed-Chief; Rep Sr Cls; Ntl Merit Ltr; Church Yth Grp; French Clb; Holy Cross Clg Bk Awd 84; Rosbury Latn Schl Music Prz 85; 2 Schlrshps Frm Twn Of Wellesley 85; Wesleyan U.

O CONNOR, SUSAN; Whitman-Hanson Regional HS; Whitman, MA; (Y); 5/300; Color Guard; JV Bsktbl; JV Sftbl; Im Vllybl; High Hon Roll; Hon Roll; NHS.

O DONNELL, BRENDA; Saint Clare HS; Roslindale, MA; (Y); 20/168; Church Yth Grp; JA; Spanish Clb; Band; Bsktbl; Sftbl; Hon Roll; Church Choir; 2nd High Avrg Acctg I 85; Bentley Clg; Bus Admin.

O DONNELL, BRIAN; Hanover HS; Hanover, MA; (Y); Boy Scts; Church Yth Grp; Golf; Socr; Hon Roll; NHS; Med.

O DONNELL, CYNTHIA; Fontbonne Acad; W Roxbury, MA; (Y); Church Yth Grp; Computer Clb; Debate Tm; Drama Clb; Hosp Aide; Library Aide; Science Clb; Chorus; Church Choir; School Musical; Lib Clb Achvt 84 & 85; Cert Recog Boston Glbe Art Comp 83; Pre-Law.

O DONNELL, ERIN P; Mount St Joseph Acad; Boston, MA; (Y); 20/150; Dance Clb; Drama Clb; JA; Spanish Clb; Yrbk Stf; High Hon Roll; NHS; Boston Coll; Educ.

O DONNELL, SEAN; Clinton HS; Clinton, MA; (Y); JA; Math Clb; Yrbk Stf; JV Bsbl; Var L Bsktbl; JV Ftbl; Hon Roll; NHS; Hofstra; Jrnlsm.

O DONNELL, THOMAS P; Chicopee Comprehensive HS; Chicopee, MA; (S); 68/250; Boys Clb Am; Letterman Clb; Socr; NHS.

O KEEFE, DAVID R; Newburyport HS; Newburyport, MA; (Y); 90/194; Am Leg Boys St; Drama Clb; JA; Model UN; Chorus; School Musical; Stage Crew; Trk; Library Aide; Crs Cntry; Coaches Awd Crs Cntry 84; MA Boys ST Spkr House & ST Rep 85; Marshall Staff 85; Pol Sci.

O KEEFE, JAMIE; The Boston Latin Schl; Boston, MA; (Y); 176/322; Strategic Gaming Soc; Drama Clb; Frgn Policy Soc; Lampoon; Educ Studies Prgm-Stu-Adm Liaison; Physcs.

O KEEFE, JOHN; Cathedral HS; Lunlow, MA; (Y); 52/600; Cmnty Wkr; Model UN; Var L Bsktbl; Var L Socr; Hon Roll; All Wstrn MA Soccer Tm & All Lgu Tm 84-85; Bus.

O KEEFE, KAREN; Walpok HS; East Walpole, MA; (Y); 104/265; Var Trk; Var L Vllybl; Hon Roll; MA ST Fed Womns Clb 85; Silvr Art Awd 83; Blue Rbbn Boston Glb Schlstc Art Awds 82; Art Inst Boston; Illus.

O LEARY, KATHLEEN; Arlington Catholic HS; Medford, MA; (Y); Church Yth Grp; Hosp Aide; Var L Cheerleading; Hon Roll; NHS; Bus Adm.

O LEARY, KATHLEEN; Bartlett HS; Webster, MA; (Y); 23/149; Church Yth Grp; FNA; Spanish Clb; Chorus; Capt Drill Tm; Variety Show; Var JV Bsktbl; Var Cheerleading; JV Crs Cntry; Hon Roll.

O LEARY, KELLY ANN; St Bernards C C HS; Fitchburg, MA; (S); 13/163; Cmnty Wkr; School Play; Rep Stu Cncl; Var Bsktbl; Var Capt Fld Hcky; Var Golf; High Hon Roll; Hon Roll; Field Hockey Cntrl Mass Conf All-Star Team; Mass Tri-ST & Inter-City Golf Team; Alg & Trig Cert Awd.

O LEARY, KEVIN; Bishop Feehan HS; Foxboro, MA; (Y); 15/240; Var L Bsbl; Var L Bsktbl; Im Vllybl; High Hon Roll; Hon Roll; NHS; Prfct Atten Awd; Exc In Wrld Hstry 82-83; Exc In Ecnmcs 84-85; Tele Cmnctns.

O LEARY, MAUREEN A; Cardinal Spellman HS; Whitman, MA; (Y); 11/202; 4-H; Pep Clb; Service Clb; School Play; JV Bsktbl; Capt Vllybl; 4-H Awd; High Hon Roll; NHS; Pres Schlr; Sci Fair 2nd Pl 85; Whitman Yth Socr Scholar 85; Whitman Athltc Assn Scholar 85; Wellesley Coll; Biomed Engrng.

O LEARY, SEAN P; Pittsfield HS; Pittsfield, MA; (Y); French Clb; Math Clb; Math Tm; Chorus; Madrigals; Nwsp Rptr; Cit Awd; High Hon Roll; Kiwanis Awd; NHS; MA Cmmnwlth Schlrs Awd 85; James Z Naurison & Pittsfld Schl Cls Of 1915 Schlrshps 85; U Of MA; Pol Sci.

O MALLEY, TANYA; Beverly HS; Beverly, MA; (Y); Y-Teens; Band; Concert Band; Mrchg Band; Orch; Pep Band; School Musical; Variety Show; JV Bsktbl; Ed.

O MEARA, CHRISTINE; Malden HS; Malden, MA; (Y); Key Clb; Sec Band; Concert Band; Mrchg Band; Variety Show; Trk; Kiwanis Awd; NHS; Ntl Merit Ltr; Med.

O NEIL, DAVID; Bedford HS; Bedford, MA; (Y); 56/213; Rep Am Leg Boys St; Church Yth Grp; Exploring; VP Jr Cls; VP Sr Cls; Var Capt Ftbl; Var Lcrss; Powder Puff Ftbl; Var Trk; Hon Roll.

O NEIL, MAUREEN; Newton North HS; Newton, MA; (Y); Aud/Vis; French Clb; Model UN; Pep Clb; Off Frsh Cls; Off Soph Cls; Off Jr Cls; Stu Cncl; Var Cheerleading; Hon Roll; Psychlgy.

O NEIL, MICHAEL; Holbrook HS; Holbrook, MA; (Y); 14/102; L Bsbl; L Socr; NHS; Latin Clb; Band; Concert Band; Mrchg Band; Hon Roll; Outstndng Frshmn Band Stu 83; MVP-SCCR Team 85; SR Leag Bsbl All Star; Busnss.

O NEIL, PAMELA; St Josephs Regional HS; Lowell, MA; (Y); 2/50; Church Yth Grp; Church Choir; Rep Jr Cls; High Hon Roll; Hon Roll; Trs Pres NHS; Stu Cncl Schlrshp 85; Spch Pathlgst.

O NEILL, CATHRYN; Bishop Stang HS; S Dartmouth, MA; (Y); 59/208; Cmnty Wkr; Drama Clb; Girl Scts; VP JA; Hon Roll; Hghst Geom Awd; Fitchburg ST Coll; Spcl Educ.

O ROURKE, ERIN E; Boston Latin Schl; Boston, MA; (Y); 95/330; Key Clb; Latin Clb; Band; Var Diving; Var Gym; Sftbl; Var Swmmng; Hon Roll; Outstndng Prfrmr Swm Tm 85; 12th Pl ST Dvng 85; Lang.

O ROURKE, KATRINA; Borncoat HS; Worcester, MA; (Y); Library Aide; Chorus; Yrbk Stf; Hon Roll; Variety Show; Nursing.

O ROURKE, MARY; Barnstable HS; Hyannis, MA; (Y); 55/400; Drama Clb; PAVAS; Q&S; Nwsp Bus Mgr; Nwsp Ed-Chief; Nwsp Rptr; Hobart; Jrnlst.

O SHAUGHNESSY, JOHN P; Minnechaug R HS; Wilbraham, MA; (Y); 54/310; Am Leg Boys St; Church Yth Grp; Pres Frsh Cls; Pres Soph Cls; Pres Jr Cls; Pres Sr Cls; Stu Cncl; L Ice Hcky; Var L Socr; Var L Tennis; Wstrn MA Hnrbl Mntn Vrsty Hockey 85; Wstrn MA Tnns Champs 85; Lbrl Arts.

O SHAUGHNESSY, MICHAEL F; Lexington HS; Lexington, MA; (Y); Am Leg Boys St; Church Yth Grp; Jazz Band; VP Jr Cls; VP Sr Cls; Rep Stu Cncl; Bsktbl; Var Ftbl; Hon Roll; NHS; Frgn Exch 84-85; Rudolph J Fobert Mem Awd 85; Polit Sci.

O SHEA, PATRICK M; Tantasqua Regional HS; Sturbridge, MA; (Y); 3/200; Pres MMM; Acpl Chr; Band; Pres Chorus; Jazz Band; School Musical; Variety Show; Var Crs Cntry; NHS; Ntl Merit SF; Blue Ridge Music Fstvl Slvr Mdl 83; Oberlin Cnsvrtry Music; Vocal.

O SULLIVAN, COLLEEN; Catherkal HS; Springfield, MA; (Y); Hosp Aide; JA; Flag Corp; Phys Thrpy.

O SULLIVAN, PATTY; Sacred Heart HS; Hanson, MA; (Y); 28/89; Key Clb; Nwsp Rptr; Hon Roll; NEDT Awd; Cert Hnr Outstndg Achvt Alg II 85; Bus Admin.

O TOOLE, AUSTIN A; Uxbridge HS; Uxbridge, MA; (Y); 12/100; Am Leg Boys St; Boy Scts; Computer Clb; Spanish Clb; Varsity Clb; Pres Jr Cls; Var Bsbl; L Var Bsktbl; ST Senator MA Boys ST 85; Chrmn MA Boys ST 85; Comp Law.

OBER, CHERYL E; Franklin HS; Franklin, MA; (Y); Church Yth Grp; Yrbk Stf; Rep Soph Cls; Rep Stu Cncl; Hon Roll; Ntl Merit Ltr; Voice Dem Awd; Psych.

OBERLE, STEVEN H; Agawam HS; Agawam, MA; (Y); 2/285; Am Leg Boys St; Church Yth Grp; Pres Jr Cls; Capt Socr; Capt Tennis; Bausch & Lomb Sci Awd; DAR Awd; Pres NHS; Ntl Merit Ltr; Sal; Abilene Chrst U; Enrgng Physcs.

OBERTON, LEIGH; Braintree HS; Braintree, MA; (Y); 114/314; Drama Clb; Office Aide; Sec VP Chorus; Color Guard; Madrigals; School Musical; School Play; Variety Show; High Hon Roll; Hon Roll; Musical Achvt Ltr 84-85; Cosmtlgy.

OBRIEN, CHRISTINE; Bishop Connolly HS; Portsmouth, RI; (Y); 16/173; French Clb; Math Tm; Crs Cntry; Trk; High Hon Roll; NHS; Med.

OBRIEN, DIANE; Braintree HS; Braintree, MA; (Y); 82/450; Church Yth Grp; Cmnty Wkr; Ski Clb; Varsity Clb; Rep Jr Cls; Stu Cncl; JV Var Bsktbl; JV Var Sftbl; Hon Roll; Sci Fair 85; SADD 84-85; YMCA 85; Med.

OBRIEN, TARA; Fontbonne Academy; Milton, MA; (Y); 27/165; Church Yth Grp; Cmnty Wkr; Dance Clb; Trs Drama Clb; Girl Scts; Hosp Aide; Pres Intnl Clb; Chorus; Church Choir; School Musical; Schlrshp Wnnr Miss Ntl Teen Pagnt 84; Wnnr Best Actrs JR Drama Fest Pl 84; Wnnr Best Sprtng Actrs 84; Comm.

OCONNELL, CHRISTINE; Chatham JR SR HS; Chathamport, MA; (Y); 6/50; AFS; Drama Clb; Trs Chorus; School Musical; School Play; Stage Crew; Variety Show; Hon Roll; Jr NHS; NHS; Balfour Mdl Earth Sci; Balfour Mdl Bio I; Law.

OCONNELL, DANIEL; St Johns HS; Holden, MA; (Y); 90/300; Boys Clb Am; Church Yth Grp; Cmnty Wkr; JV Bsbl; JV Bsktbl; VP Trk; High Hon Roll; Hon Roll; Ntl Merit Ltr; Librl Arts.

OCONNELL, PETER F; Bishop Connolly HS; Tiverton, RI; (Y); Latin Clb; Stage Crew; JV Socr; High Hon Roll; NHS; Ntl Merit Ltr.

OCONNOR, ANDREW; Boston College HS; Weymouth, MA; (Y); 32/278; Boy Scts; Church Yth Grp; Socr; High Hon Roll; Hon Roll; NHS; Boston Coll; Busnss.

OFFLEY, JODI ANN; Bristol Plymouth Regional Tech HS; Taunton, MA; (Y); Church Yth Grp; Church Choir; Rep Jr Cls; Rep Sr Cls; Hon Roll; Merit Clb Awd 85; Zion Bible Inst; Youth Minist.

OFFLEY, KEITH; Taunton HS; Taunton, MA; (Y); Boys Clb Am; Bsktbl; Ftbl; Hon Roll; MVP Bsktbll 84-85; Bus.

OH, SARA S; Weston HS; Weston, MA; (Y); Orch; Nwsp Ed-Chief; Lit Mag; Off Frsh Cls; Off Soph Cls; Rep Jr Cls; Rep Sr Cls; Rep Stu Cncl; Hon Roll; Ntl Merit SF; MA Music Tchrs Assn Comp 1st Prz 82-83; Psych.

OHARA, CHARLES; Newton Catholic HS; Boston, MA; (Y); 15/60; Art Clb; English Clb; Library Aide; Math Clb; Political Wkr; Swing Chorus; Lit Mag; VP Sr Cls; Mgr(s); 1st Prz Sci Fair-Solar Enrgy Paper 85; U Of CO; Arch.

OHEAR, KEVIN J; Sandwich HS; E Sandwich, MA; (Y); 25/150; Am Leg Boys St; Ski Clb; Pres Stu Cncl; Ice Hcky; Capt Socr; Tennis; Hon Roll; NHS; Bus Adm.

OHMAN, PAMELA A; Algbonquin Regional HS; Southboro, MA; (Y); Church Yth Grp; Girl Scts; Church Choir; Orch; God Cntry Awd; High Hon Roll; NHS; Awd For Outstdng Acad During Schl Yr 85; Cabinet Mbr Of Chrch Yth Grp 85.

OJERHOLM, AMY J; Needham HS; Needham, MA; (Y); 30/381; Cmnty Wkr; French Clb; Hosp Aide; Intnl Clb; Service Clb; Yrbk Stf; Var L Swmmng; JV Trk; Hon Roll; NHS; Postcomers Clb Schlrshp 85; MA Bd Rgnts Schlrshp 85; Rutgers U Almni Schlrshp 85; Rutgers Coll Of RU; Pre-Med.

OKEEFE, AUDREY; Wakefield HS; Wakefield, MA; (Y); Key Clb; Varsity Clb; School Play; Yrbk Stf; Rep Stu Cncl; Var L Fld Hcky; L Var Swmmng; JV Tennis.

OKSTEIN, LARRY; Newton South HS; Newton, MA; (Y); Rep Am Leg Boys St; Spanish Clb; Nwsp Stf; Var Capt Tennis; Var Trk; High Hon Roll; 110 Pct Awd 84; Law.

OLBRYCH, KARA; Cathedral HS; Chicopee, MA; (Y); Church Yth Grp; Hosp Aide; JA; Office Aide; Ski Clb; JV Cheerleading; Var Trk; Elks Awd; Elks Schlrshp; Elms Coll Schlrshp; Elms Coll Chicopee; Lib Arts.

OLEARY, BRIAN; Boston Latin HS; Boston, MA; (Y); 106/320; Church Yth Grp; Cmnty Wkr; Mathletes; Band; Hon Roll; Ntl Merit Ltr; Little Leag Team 84-85; Bus.

OLEARY, CHRISTINE; Holbrook JR SR HS; Holbrook, MA; (Y); 6/103; Church Yth Grp; Spanish Clb; Chorus; Yrbk Stf; VP Sr Cls; Var Capt Crs Cntry; Var Trk; Hon Roll; NHS; Ntl Merit Ltr; Bio Sci.

OLES, BRIAN T; Newton South HS; Newton, MA; (Y); Library Aide; Chorus; Hon Roll; Ntl Merit Ltr; Schl Forgn Lang Awds-Frnch & Russn 85; Middlebury Coll; Forgn Lang.

OLIN, LISA M; Greater Lowell Regional Voc; Lowell, MA; (Y); Yrbk Stf; JV Bsktbl; Var Coach Actv; Var Timer; Hon Roll; Outstndng Achvt Bakery Awd 85; Schlrshp MA Rest Assoc 85; Schlrshp Night Schl Culinary Arts 85; Newbury JC; Rest Mgt.

OLIVEIRA, DAVID; New Bedford HS; New Bedford, MA; (Y); 55/688; Church Yth Grp; JCL; Yrbk Stf; Rep Frsh Cls; Sec Soph Cls; VP Jr Cls; Var Trk; High Hon Roll; Hon Roll; Hugh O Brien Awd 83-84; Psych.

OLIVEIRA, MICHAEL; Bishop Feehan HS; Rehoboth, MA; (Y); 47/230; Church Yth Grp; JCL; Latin Clb; Letterman Clb; Im Bsktbl; Var Ice Hcky; Var Tennis; Var Wt Lftg; Hon Roll; JR Classical Lg 84-85; Natl Latin Hon 84-85; Bus Admin.

OLIVEIRA, PAUL; Matignon HS; Somerville, MA; (S); 10/190; High Hon Roll; Hon Roll; NHS; Ntl Merit Ltr; Ntl Sci Merit Awd 84; U Of ME-ORONO; Wldlf Mngmnt.

OLIVER, DEBRA; Maynard HS; Maynard, MA; (Y); 28/105; Am Leg Aux Girls St; Radio Clb; Stage Crew; Yrbk Stf; Pblc Rltns.

OLIVER, REGINA M; Cathedral HS; Springfield, MA; (Y); 65/500; School Musical; School Play; Lit Mag; U MA; Pre Med.

OLIVIERI, MARK; Matignon HS; Somerville, MA; (Y); 28/200; Church Yth Grp; Cmnty Wkr; Varsity Clb; Var Bsktbl; Im Mgr Vllybl; High Hon Roll; Hon Roll.

OLIVIERI, STEPHEN; Don Boso Tech HS; Somerville, MA; (S); Quiz Bowl; Hon Roll; Prfct Atten Awd; Jrnlsm.

OLSON, KEITH E; Auburn HS; Auburn, MA; (Y); 2/179; Var Tennis; High Hon Roll; Trs NHS; Ntl Merit SF; Sal; Trs Church Yth Grp; JV Bsbl; JV Bsktbl; Cert Acad Excell MA Assoc Schl Supt 84; Bus.

OLSON, KENNETH; St Bernards C C HS; Leominster, MA; (S); 22/163; Drama Clb; Model UN; School Play; Swing Chorus; Boys State; Law.

OLSON, KRISTINE; Woodward S For Girls; Holbrook, MA; (Y); 2/13; Dance Clb; Yrbk Bus Mgr; Rep Sr Cls; Bausch & Lomb Sci Awd; High Hon Roll; NHS; Sal; Camp Fr Inc; Computer Clb; Drama Clb; 2nd Pl Sci Fair 85; 3r Dpl Sci Fair 84; 1st Pl Hstry Proj 84; U RI; Vet Med.

OMAN, VICKI A; Hanover HS; Hanover, MA; (Y); 6/180; Church Yth Grp; Cmnty Wkr; Rep Drama Clb; Concert Band; Mrchg Band; School Play; Capt L Crs Cntry; Hon Roll; NHS; Ntl Merit Ltr.

OMEARA, PATRICIA; Randolph HS; Randolph, MA; (Y); Pres Band; Pres Concert Band; Drm & Bgl; Jazz Band; Mrchg Band; Orch; School Musical; Powder Puff Ftbl; Sftbl; VFW Awd; Outstndng Music Awd 84; Army; Music.

ONCAY, WILLIAM; Medway HS; Medway, MA; (Y); 2/150; Aud/Vis; Church Yth Grp; Cmnty Wkr; Golf; High Hon Roll; Hon Roll; NHS; Prfct Atten Awd; Schltc Achvt Awds 82-85; NMSQT Recogntn 85; Comp Engr.

ONEIL, ROBERT; Franklin HS; Franklin, MA; (Y); 24/250; VP Stu Cncl; Var Bsktbl; Var Socr; Hon Roll; Hugh O Briens MA Yth Ldrshp Semnr 84; Mktg.

OPERACH, CHARLOTTE; King Philip Regional HS; Norfolk, MA; (Y); Hosp Aide; Concert Band; Nwsp Bus Mgr; Yrbk Bus Mgr; Rep Sr Cls; Rep Stu Cncl; Fld Hcky; Natl Ldrshp & Serv Awd 83; Microbio.

OPPELT, LAURA E; Marblehead HS; Marblehead, MA; (Y); 55/270; Drama Clb; French Clb; Thesps; Chorus; Church Choir; School Musical; Swing Chorus; Variety Show; Powder Puff Ftbl; Socr; Yng Artst Vcl Pgm Schlrshp 82; HS Musical 81; Marblehead Little Theatre Lead 84; Vocal Perf.

ORDWAY JR, LAWRENCE M; Wilbrahm & Monson Acad; Plaistow, NH; (Y); 6/150; JV Crs Cntry; High Hon Roll; Hon Roll; Latin I Awd 83-84; Berube Awd 83-84; Classics.

ORFAO, JANET L; Woburn SR HS; Woburn, MA; (Y); Sec Leo Clb; Ski Clb; Spanish Clb; Chorus; School Musical; Variety Show; Stu Cncl; Fld Hcky; Sftbl; Hon Roll; New England Coll; Arch Dsgn.

ORKIN, JONATHAN; Randolph HS; Randolph, MA; (Y); Radio Clb; Pres Temple Yth Grp; Nwsp Rptr; Yrbk Ed-Chief; L Crs Cntry; L Trk; Hon Roll; VP NHS; Kesher Chrmn New Englnd Regn USY 84-85.

ORLANDI, LISA A; Westfield HS; Westfield, MA; (Y); 42/300; JA; Fld Hcky; MA Bowling Assoc Champ 84; U MA AMHERST; Bus Admin.

ORMOND, ANNEMARIE; Burlington HS; Burlington, MA; (Y); OEA; Mrchg Band; Music Achvt Awd; Bus.

ORMSBY, KAREN; West Springfield HS; W Springfield, MA; (S); Am Leg Aux Girls St; Library Aide; Ski Clb; Band; Drm Mjr(t); Mrchg Band; Crs Cntry; Tennis; High Hon Roll; NHS; Hugh Obrian Ldrshp Awd 84; Eddie Smith Awd Excellence Ldrshp 84; Outstndg Band Stu Awd 84; Medicine.

OROURKE, KEVIN T; Milford HS; Milford, MA; (Y); 92/375; Boy Scts; Cmnty Wkr; Im Bsktbl; Im Score Keeper; Im Timer; Var L Trk; High Hon Roll; Hon Roll; Med.

ORTIZ, MARIBEL; Boston Tech; Boston, MA; (Y); Church Yth Grp; Cmnty Wkr; Hosp Aide; Library Aide; Teachers Aide; Band; Chorus; Church Choir; Psych.

ORTYL, KEVIN; Holyoke Catholic HS; Easthampton, MA; (Y); Chess Clb; Computer Clb; Var Bsbl; Bsktbl; Var Tennis; Archt.

ORZECHOWSKI, DARREN E; Palmer HS; Palmer, MA; (Y); Band; Concert Band; Jazz Band; Mrchg Band; Orch; Symp Band; Variety Show; Lit Mag; Lion Awd; Prfct Atten Awd; Jrnlsm.

ORZOLEK, MARK C; Chicopee Comp HS; Chicopee, MA; (S); 73/300; FCA; German Clb; Var Golf; Var Trk; Jr NHS; NHS; MA U; Bus.

OSGOOD, JAY; Archbishop Williams HS; Quincy, MA; (Y); Church Yth Grp; Nwsp Sprt Ed; Var Bsktbl; JV Var Ftbl; Var Trk; Hon Roll; Prfct Atten Awd; Leroy Curley Rogers-Good Sprtsmn Awd 81-82; Excllnc Religious Studies Awd 82-83; Excllnc Eng Awd 83-84; Specl Educ.

OSHEA, KAREN; Apponequet Reg HS; Lakeville, MA; (Y); Church Yth Grp; Band; Concert Band; Mrchg Band; School Musical; Rep Frsh Cls; VP Soph Cls; Jr Cls; Rep Sr Cls; Hon Roll; Bio.

OSLEY, KIMBERLY; Smith Acad; Hatfield, MA; (Y); 3/35; Church Yth Grp; Drama Clb; Chorus; Nwsp Stf; Yrbk Stf; Capt Cheerleading; High Hon Roll; Lion Awd; Sophia Smith Schlrshp 85; Ntl Merit Sci Awd 84; Pro-Merito 82-85; Boston U; Math.

OSTERGARD JR, ROBERT; Revere HS; Revere, MA; (Y); Library Aide; Quiz Bowl; Yrbk Stf; Goethe Inst Ger-Am Reltns Awd 85; Awds Achvt Schls Quiz Bwl 85; Stu Senate 85; Pride Comm 85; Intl Reltns.

OSTLER, GARY; Malden HS; Malden, MA; (Y); Quiz Bowl; Variety Show; Ftbl; Wt Lftg; Hon Roll; Law.

OSTROBINSKI, DAVID; Hoosac Valley HS; Adams, MA; (Y); Church Yth Grp; Ski Clb; Bsktbl; Socr; Trk; Hon Roll; 1st Pl Pole Vltng Westrn MA 85; Domestic Exch Clb 85-86; U MA.

OSTROKOLOWICZ, DEBRA J; Bartlett HS; Webster, MA; (Y); 5/175; Camera Clb; Spanish Clb; Nwsp Phtg; Nwsp Rptr; Ed Nwsp Stf; Yrbk Phtg; Ed Yrbk Stf; Crs Cntry; Trk; High Hon Roll; Schl Alumni Assoc Achvt Awd 83; Comm Art.

OTOOLE, CAROLYN ANNE; David Prouty HS; Spencer, MA; (Y); 4/175; Red Cross Aide; Trs Stu Cncl; Trk; High Hon Roll; NHS; Iandoris, Flexcon & Brd Of Rgnts Schlrshps; Clark U.

OTTAVIANELLI, DAVID; Bishop Stang HS; New Bedford, MA; (Y); 65/230; Am Leg Boys St; Trs Jr Cls; Var Capt Bsbl; Var Capt Bsktbl; Var Capt Ftbl; Wt Lftg; Hon Roll; Brenda Stetson Awd Good Overall Person 85; Natl Guard Essay Schl Wnnr 85; Med.

OUELLETTE, JULIE; Marblehead HS; Marblehead, MA; (Y); Drama Clb; French Clb; Ski Clb; Sec Band; Concert Band; Orch; Yrbk Stf; Swmmng; Hon Roll; Church Yth Grp; Blue Medal New England Music Fest 85; Unsung Hero 84.

OUELLETTE, ROBERT; Bishop Connolly HS; Westport, MA; (S); 14/180; Drama Clb; Latin Clb; School Play; Nwsp Stf; Stat Bowling; High Hon Roll; Am MENSA Ltd 84; Silver Medal Ntl Classcs Latin Ex 83; Med.

OULMETTE, DENISE; Mohawk Trail Regional HS; Ashfield, MA; (Y); Band; Yrbk Stf; Var Bsktbl; Var Pres Sftbl; High Hon Roll; Computer Clb.

OVERTON, MICHELLE; Canton HS; Canton, MA; (Y); 49/250; Church Yth Grp; French Clb; Hosp Aide; Varsity Clb; Powder Puff Ftbl; Var L Swmmng; Im Vllybl; Ntl Merit Fndtns Ntl Hnr Roll 85; Ntl Ldrshp & Serv Awd 84; Westfield ST Coll; Elem Educ.

OWEN, EDWARD S; Hudson Catholic HS; Marlboro, MA; (Y); 15/49; JA; School Musical; Stage Crew; Pres Sr Cls; Capt Ftbl; Capt Trk; Hon Roll; Kiwanis Awd; Presdntl Acadmc Fitnss Awd 85; Highest Cls Avg-Socl Studies 85; Schl Most Spirited Awd 85; Boston Coll; Psych.

OWEN, SHARON; Newton North HS; Newton, MA; (Y); Church Yth Grp; Yrbk Stf; Vllybl; Hon Roll; Acctg.

OWENS, SEAN; Somerset HS; Somerset, MA; (Y); 21/315; Boy Scts; Ski Clb; Nwsp Stf; Yrbk Stf; Var L Ftbl; Var L Trk; Im Wt Lftg; NHS; Ntl Merit SF; Ctzns Schlrshp Fndtn 84-85; US Mltry Acad; Engrng.

OWSIANY, LISA; Southwick HS; Southwick, MA; (Y); Hosp Aide; Library Aide; Model UN; JV Fld Hcky; JV Var Trk; Hon Roll; Phys Thrpy.

PACHECO, FRANK; New Bedford HS; New Bedford, MA; (Y); NHS; Cert Of Awd & Excllnc In Portuguese 85; Southeastern MA U; Comp Sci.

PACHECO, PAUL A; Bishop Connolly HS; Bristol, RI; (Y); 9/165; Math Tm; VP Ski Clb; Nwsp Stf; Rep Sr Cls; Capt Var Swmmng; Elks Awd; High Hon Roll; VP NHS; Pres Schlr; Schl Svc Awd 85; MA Govrnrs Outstndng Effort Cittn 85; Top Stu-Bio & Portuguese 85; Boston Coll; Bio.

PACHECO, THOMAS; New Bedford HS; New Bedford, MA; (Y); 41/679; Stu Cncl; JV Var Bsbl; JV Crs Cntry; Var L Trk; High Hon Roll; Hon Roll; Jr NHS; NHS; Engrng.

PACKARD, CARRIE; Wachusett Regional HS; Princeton, MA; (Y); 57/486; Church Yth Grp; Ski Clb; Hon Roll; Arch.

PADULA, DIANE MARIE; Boston Latin Schl; South Boston, MA; (Y); 70/321; Church Yth Grp; Drama Clb; Pres JA; Chorus; NHS; Model UN; Ski Clb; School Play; Yrbk Stf; Powder Puff Ftbl; JR Achvt Mngmnt & Exc Awds In ROJAC 84; Larsen Awd For Schlrshp & Schl Spirit 85; Boston Bus Schl; Exec Scrtry.

PADULA, MICHELE; Marian HS; Hopkinton, MA; (Y); Latin Clb; Nwsp Stf; High Hon Roll; NHS; Library Aide; Office Aide; Yrbk Stf; Lit Mag; Acad Schlrshp 83-85; Ntl Ltn Exam 83; Biochmstry.

PAGE, ADAM; St Johns Preparatory Schl; Topsfield, MA; (Y); JA; Stage Crew; Im Ftbl; JV Lcrss; Im Vllybl; Ducks Unltd.

PAGLIERANI, ANDREA L; Arlington HS; Arlington, MA; (Y); Church Yth Grp; Cmnty Wkr; Hosp Aide; Color Guard; Yrbk Phtg; Yrbk Stf; JV Vllybl; Ed.

PAGNOTTA, PAULA; Brockton Christian Regional HS; Brockton, MA; (S); Drama Clb; Chorus; School Play; High Hon Roll; Hon Roll; NHS; Bible, Algbr, Prncpls Awds 83-84; Boston U; Med.

PAGNOTTARO, ALEXANDER; Haverhill HS; Haverhill, MA; (Y); Cmnty Wkr; Political Wkr; Spanish Clb; High Hon Roll; Hon Roll; Northeastern U; Elctrnc Engrng.

PAINE, JENNIFER; Brockton Christian Regional HS; Mansfield, MA; (S); 1/18; Church Yth Grp; Pres Drama Clb; Chorus; Church Choir; School Play; VP Pres Stu Cncl; Cheerleading; High Hon Roll; Dstngshd Amer High Schl Stu; Messiah Coll; Cmmnctns.

PAINE, MATTHEW; Melrose HS; Melrose, MA; (Y); 13/387; Church Yth Grp; Cmnty Wkr; Chorus; Pres Frsh Cls; Stu Cncl; Var L Socr; Capt L Swmmng; Var Trk; High Hon Roll; Hon Roll; Bus Admin.

PAINE JR, RICHARD S; Narragansett Regional HS; Baldwinville, MA; (Y); 1/98; Am Leg Boys St; Boy Scts; Band; Concert Band; Mrchg Band; Yrbk Stf; High Hon Roll; Hon Roll; NHS; Mt Wachusett CC; Acctng.

PAK, MICHAEL; Groton Schl; Portsmouth, RI; (Y); Drama Clb; Stage Crew; Var L Ftbl; Var L Lcrss; Wt Lftg; Bus Admin.

PALACIOS, JEANINE; Wachusett HS; Holden, MA; (Y); Dance Clb; Ski Clb; Varsity Clb; Chorus; JV Capt Cheerleading; JV Fld Hcky; Vllybl; Hon Roll; Fash Merch.

PALENZUELA, ALEXANDER; Phillips Acad; Miami, FL; (Y); Boy Scts; French Clb; Science Clb; Spanish Clb; Lit Mag; Rep Stu Cncl; Im Tennis; Hon Roll; Ntl Merit SF; Outstndng Schlr 82; Coll; Foreign Srv.

PALERMO, PAUL; Westwood HS; Westwood, MA; (Y); 91/214; Var Bsbl; Capt Var Ftbl; Var Trk; Hon Roll; Promotnl Advrtsr.

PALERMO, RICHARD; Central Catholic HS; Plaiston, NH; (Y); 29/219; JV Bsbl; Boston Coll; Bus.

PALINGO, ANNEMARIE; Braintree HS; Braintree, MA; (Y); 20/416; Spanish Clb; High Hon Roll; Hon Roll; NHS; Spanish NHS; Bus.

PALKEY, MICHELLE; Newton Catholic HS; Newton, MA; (Y); Drama Clb; Model UN; School Musical; Stage Crew; Yrbk Stf; Lit Mag; Sec Sr Cls; Var L Cheerleading; Hon Roll; Acad All Amer 84-85; Fash Dsgn.

PALLADINO, THOMAS; Winthrup HS; Winthrop, MA; (Y); 20/230; Boy Scts; Drama Clb; PAVAS; School Musical; School Play; Stage Crew; Jr NHS; NHS; HS Dramtcs Awd 85; Boston Coll; Dramtcs.

PALMARIN, ELIZABETH; Copley Square HS; Boston, MA; (Y); 2/100; Hosp Aide; JA; Library Aide; School Musical; High Hon Roll; NHS; St Schlr; Stage Crew; Rep Stu Cncl; Hon Roll; Boston HS Schlrshp Awd 85; Cmmnwlth Schlr Awd 85; MA ST Schlrshp; Boston U; Med Crr.

PALMERINO, JOANN; Wakefield HS; Wakefield, MA; (Y); Church Yth Grp; Key Clb; L Pom Pon; JV Socr; Comp.

PANCHY, WENDY; Miss Halls Schl; Stockbridge, MA; (Y); 5/64; School Play; Variety Show; Rep Stu Cncl; Var Socr; Cit Awd; Hon Roll; Cum Laude Scty 85; Hamilton Coll; Engl.

PANICO, DANIEL; Saugus HS; Saugus, MA; (Y); 52/320; Boy Scts; VP Sr Cls; VP Stu Cncl; Capt Socr; Voice Dem Awd; Partcpnt 1st Cultrl Sccr Exch Holland 82; Plnd, Orgnzd & Ran Red Crss Blood Dr Eagl Sct Svc Proj 85; Phy Thrpst.

PANICO, SUZANNE F; Boston Latin Schl; South Boston, MA; (Y); 20/300; Hosp Aide; VP JA; Library Aide; Nwsp Rptr; Ed Yrbk Stf; NHS; Camera Clb; Church Yth Grp; Latin Clb; Science Clb; Awd Cls 85 Prz 83; Irsh Step Dancr 5th Pl Grls Nw Eng Regnl 84; Hnr Stu BU 85; Sci.

PANSEWICZ, ERIC; Christopher Columbus HS; Boston, MA; (Y); 13/132; Crmnl Law.

PANTEKIDIS, JOHN; Boston Latin Schl; Boston, MA; (Y); 13/325; Church Yth Grp; Computer Clb; Science Clb; High Hon Roll; AHEPA Awd 79-83; Chem.

PANTOS, EUGENIA; North HS; Worcester, MA; (Y); 3/170; Pep Clb; Quiz Bowl; Scholastic Bowl; Nwsp Stf; Yrbk Ed-Chief; Yrbk Stf; Stu Cncl; Elks Awd; High Hon Roll; Hon Roll; Advncd Plcmnt Crse Engl,Bio 84-85; Assumption Clg.

PAPACHRISTON, JOHN A; Central Catholic HS; Haverhill, MA; (Y); 13/228; Drama Clb; School Play; Var Capt Ftbl; Sec NHS; Rep Frsh Cls; Pres Soph Cls; Pres Jr Cls; Sr Cls; Stu Cncl; Trk; AFROTC Schlrshp; U Rochester; Mech Engrng.

PAPALIOLIOS, ANDREAS; Wilmington HS; Wilmington, MA; (Y); 8/250; Computer Clb; VP JA; Ski Clb; Stu Cncl; Var Socr; French Hon Soc; High Hon Roll; NHS; Ntl Merit Ltr; Prfct Atten Awd; Recpnt Woburn Dist Ct Schlrshp 85; Outstdng In Math Awd 85; Math Tutrng Awds 81-85; Rensselaer Poltech Inst; Ele En.

PAPANDREA, ANTHONY; West Boylston HS; West Boylston, MA; (Y); 18/80; Church Yth Grp; Computer Clb; Math Clb; Science Clb; Spanish Clb; Varsity Clb; Off Stu Cncl; Capt Ftbl; Trk; Capt Wt Lftg; Engrng.

PAPANDREA JR, JOHN A; St Dominic Savio HS; E Boston, MA; (Y); 25/110; Var Bsbl; Var Crs Cntry; Var Ice Hcky; Hon Roll; Business.

PAPAVIZAS, HELLEN; Boston Latin Schl; Boston, MA; (Y); Key Clb; Science Clb; Tennis; High Hon Roll; Hon Roll; NHS; Med.

PAPPAS, CHRISTOS J; North Quincy HS; Quincy, MA; (Y); 5/400; Am Leg Boys St; Sec Church Yth Grp; Math Tm; Scholastic Bowl; Science Clb; Band; Bsktbl; Elks Awd; High Hon Roll; NHS; Presntl Acad Ftnss Awd 85; Quincy Educ Assn Schlrshp 85; MA St Sci Fair Awds 84-85; Brandeis; Engrng.

PAPPAS, ETHEL; Boston Latin HS; Boston, MA; (Y); 69/332; Church Yth Grp; VP JA; Key Clb; Latin Clb; Office Aide; Pep Clb; NHS; Clss Of 1885 Awd 83; Yrbk Actvts Adtr 85-86.

PAQUETTE, ALICE J; Walpole HS; E Walpole, MA; (Y); 2/265; French Clb; Latin Clb; Math Tm; Band; Orch; Bausch & Lomb Sci Awd; High Hon Roll; NHS; Sal; Outstndng Soph Awd 83; 7A Inst Tech; Chem.

PAQUETTE, JACKIE; Milford HS; Milford, MA; (Y); High Hon Roll; Hon Roll.

PAQUETTE, KATHLEEN M; Quaboag Regional HS; W Brookfield, MA; (Y); 11/79; Church Yth Grp; Var Math Tm; Science Clb; Yrbk Stf; Hst Sr Cls; Var Fld Hcky; Mgr(s); Grls St Alt 85; Engrng.

PAQUETTE, R ERIC; Marblehead HS; Marblehead, MA; (Y); Am Leg Boys St; Math Tm; High Hon Roll; Pres Soph Cls; Pres Jr Cls; Pres Sr Cls; Var L Bsbl; Var L Socr; Var Trk; NHS; Dartmouth Bowl 84-85; Bus Wk Schlrshp Small Bus Fdn Amer 83-84; Bus,Government.

PAQUETTE, THOMAS G; Silver Lake R HS; Kingston, MA; (Y); Model UN; Political Wkr; Band; Concert Band; Mrchg Band; High Hon Roll; Hon Roll; Bus.

PAQUETTE, TRICIA; Silver Lake Regional HS; Kingston, MA; (Y); 72/400; FHA; Model UN; Band; Color Guard; Concert Band; Mrchg Band; School Play; JV Cheerleading; Var Crs Cntry; JV Gym; Sci.

PAQUIN, MARC J; Tewksbury Memorial HS; Tewksbury, MA; (Y); 5/300; Aud/Vis; Mathletes; Math Tm; High Hon Roll; Hon Roll; NHS; Comp Tutor Of Grd Schl Stu 85; High Acadmc Awd Comp Sci 85; High Acadmc Awd Physcs,Math 85; Tufts U; Comp Sci.

PARADIS, DAVID; North Attleboro HS; N Attleboro, MA; (Y); Art Clb; Boy Scts; French Clb; Natl Beta Clb; Spanish Clb; Var Bsbl; Var Crs Cntry; JV Socr; High Hon Roll; NHS; Ntl Art Awd 82; URI; Marn Engnr.

PARADIS, JULIE E; Belmont HS; Belmont, MA; (Y); 8/290; Church Yth Grp; French Clb; VP JA; Concert Band; Mrchg Band; Orch; School Play; High Hon Roll; NHS; Ntl Merit SF; Achvt Physics 84-85; Achvt Music 83-85; Bus.

PARADIS, KENNETH W; Leicester HS; Cherry Valley, MA; (Y); 33/108; Church Yth Grp; Var Bsktbl; Var Crs Cntry; JV Socr; Var Trk; Nichols Coll; Bus Adm.

PARANDELIS, CHERYL; B M C Durfee HS; Fall River, MA; (Y); 87/689; Library Aide; Nwsp Rptr; Nwsp Stf; Yrbk Stf; Rptr Sr Cls; Hon Roll; Sr Clss Reporter 85; Entrtnmnt Editor-Durfee Hilltop 85.

PARENT, ALBERT; New Bedford HS; New Bedford, MA; (Y); Chess Clb; JCL; Bowling; 3rd Prz-Grtr New Bedford Holocaust Meml Essay Cont 85; Concours De Francais Des Cooperants 84; Physcs.

PARENT, MARK; New Bedford HS; New Bedford, MA; (Y); 9/600; Am Leg Boys St; Church Yth Grp; Var Diving; Var Capt Swmmng; Var L Tennis; Var Timer; JV Trk; High Hon Roll; Hon Roll; NHS; FL Inst Of Tech; Aeron Engrng.

PARIS, ROBIN; Oakmont Regional HS; Westminster, MA; (Y); 7/125; Trs 4-H; Math Tm; Varsity Clb; Quiz Bowl; Var L Bsbl; Var L Bsktbl; Var L Fld Hcky; Var L Sftbl; Cit Awd; 4-H Awd; Amer Morgan Horse Inst Schlrshp 84; Resv Grnd Ntl & Wrld Morgan Yth Of Yr 84; Silver Mdl Latin Exam; Med.

PARISI, CARL D; Gloucester HS; Gloucester, MA; (Y); 11/300; Thesps; School Musical; School Play; Stage Crew; Hon Roll; Gloucester Schl Comm Schlr 85; Kiwanis & Municpl Union Schlrshps; U Of Lowell MA; Comp Sci.

PARISI, SCOTT P; Gloucester HS; Gloucester, MA; (S); 74/364; Hst Sec Band; Chorus; Concert Band; Drm & Bgl; Jazz Band; Mrchg Band; Orch; School Musical; Symp Band; Hon Roll; New England Scholastic Bank Assoc 84; Indepndt Study Trombone & Piano Lessons; Music Theory 84-85; U Of Lowell; Music Education.

PARK, GINA; Falmouth HS; E Falmouth, MA; (Y); Church Yth Grp; Dance Clb; Drama Clb; Sec Spanish Clb; Color Guard; School Play; Stage Crew; Yrbk Stf; Badmtn; Socr; Stu Yr Awd Bio 83; Salem ST Coll; Engl.

PARK, ROBERT D; Westboro HS; Westboro, MA; (Y); 15/158; Am Leg Boys St; Computer Clb; Band; Mrchg Band; Stu Cncl; JV Var Bsktbl; JV Var Golf; Hon Roll; Comp Engr.

PARKER, AMY; Longmeadow HS; Long Meadow, MA; (Y); 116/230; Keywanettes; Chorus; Capt Cheerleading; Score Keeper; Stat Trk; Hon Roll; U Of MA; Lbrl Arts.

PARKER, AMY; Matignon HS; Lexington, MA; (Y); 13/173; Hosp Aide; VP Science Clb; Yrbk Stf; Stu Cncl; French Hon Soc; High Hon Roll; Lion Awd; NHS; Pres Schlr; Natl Mrt Fndtn Hnr Role 85; Yth Fndtn Schlrshp 85; St Anselm Coll; Nrsng.

PARKER, ANN M; Sharon SR HS; Sharon, MA; (Y); 53/198; Trs 4-H; Sec Varsity Clb; Variety Show; Nwsp Stf; Fld Hcky; Powder Puff Ftbl; 4-H Awd; Ntl Merit Ltr; Bio Stu Of Mth 81; U Of VT; Bio.

PARKER, CHERYL; Hopkins Acad; Hadley, MA; (S); 4/57; Church Yth Grp; Sec Trs 4-H; Band; Chorus; Concert Band; Jazz Band; Socr; 4-H Awd; Hon Roll; Hugh OBRIAN Yth Ldrshp Awd; Wstrn Mass Dist Chrus; Math.

PARKER, CHRISTINE; Bishop Feehan HS; Attleboro, MA; (Y); Church Yth Grp; Pep Clb; Yrbk Stf; Hon Roll; Psych.

PARKER, DEBRA; Nipmuc Regional HS; Upton, MA; (Y); 14/85; Pres Church Yth Grp; Computer Clb; School Play; Yrbk Stf; Pres Frsh Cls; VP Pres Stu Cncl; NHS; Stu Adv Cncl Schl Rep & SAC Rgnl Del; MA Miss TEEN Cntstnt; Natl Cncl Christian & Jews St Del; Assumption Coll; Law.

PARKER, KRISTINE; Canton HS; Canton, MA; (Y); 22/260; German Clb; Color Guard; Flag Corp; High Hon Roll; Century Clb Canton High; Stonehill Coll.

PARKER, LOIS A; Ralph C Mahar Regional HS; Athol, MA; (Y); Am Leg Aux Girls St; Debate Tm; Model UN; Service Clb; Chorus; Variety Show; Sec Frsh Cls; Sec Soph Cls; VP Jr Cls; Var Sr Cls; Psych.

PARKER, SHANNON L; Middlesex Schl; Bedford, MA; (Y); Stage Crew; Nwsp Phtg; JV Bsbl; Var Bsktbl; JV Crs Cntry; Im Socr; Ntl Merit Ltr; Rensselaer Polytech; Comp Sci.

PARKER, STACEY; Marblehead HS; Marblehead, MA; (S); Drama Clb; Rep Frsh Cls; Rep Soph Cls; Sec Jr Cls; Rep Stu Cncl; Var L Gym; High Hon Roll; Hon Roll; Hugh O Brian Yth Ldrshp Awd.

PARKER, TODD; Silver Lake Regional HS; Kingston, MA; (Y); 7/550; Am Leg Boys St; Computer Clb; Debate Tm; French Clb; Math Clb; Im Wrstlng; NHS; Comp Engr.

PARKS, MATTHEW A; Leominster HS; Fitchburg, MA; (Y); Am Leg Boys St; French Clb; Temple Yth Grp; Band; School Musical; School Play; Stu Cncl; Bsbl; High Hon Roll; NHS; Patnt Law.

PARKS, VICTORIA; Gardner HS; Gardner, MA; (Y); Girl Scts; Math Clb; Color Guard; JV Cheerleading; Hon Roll; Hghst Fnl Grad-A-4 Yrs Alg II; Csmtlgy.

PARMLEE, JAC QUIE; Milton Acad; Columbia, SC; (Y); Aud/Vis; Church Yth Grp; Cmnty Wkr; Dance Clb; French Clb; Latin Clb; Teachers Aide; Church Choir; School Play; Stage Crew.

PARRILLA, JANNETTE; Commerce HS; Springfield, MA; (S); 17/300; Spanish Clb; NHS; Church Yth Grp; Hon Roll; Springfield Tech Comm Coll.

PARRON, JOSE; Central Catholic HS; Andover, MA; (Y); 32/230; Cmnty Wkr; Dance Clb; Drama Clb; Variety Show; High Hon Roll; Hon Roll; Grad Schlrshp 82; Outstndng Stu Awd 82; Comnty Ldr, Camps Mnstry 85; Inter Dsgn.

PARROTT, MARQUERITE; Randolph HS; Randolph, MA; (Y); 60/342; Church Yth Grp; Cmnty Wkr; Intnl Clb; Office Aide; Nwsp Stf; Tennis; Hon Roll; JC Awd; NHS; Concrnd Ctzns Randlph Schlrshp 85; Exmplry Condct Awd 85; Natl Hnr Roll 85; U MA Boston; Cmmnctns.

PARRY, SUZANNE; Marblehead HS; Marblehead, MA; (Y); 28/285; Church Yth Grp; Dance Clb; French Clb; Ski Clb; Yrbk Bus Mgr; Powder Puff Ftbl; Hon Roll; Young Dance Co Of Amer 82-85; In Crew For Spirit Of MA 85; Librl Arts.

PARSA, PARWANE S; Lexington HS; Lexington, MA; (Y); Hosp Aide; Math Tm; Nwsp Stf; Yrbk Ed-Chief; Jr NHS; NHS; Ntl Merit Schol; Sci Schlrshp Comptn; Wnnr Genrad Found Sci Awd; Dartmouth Bk Awd; Mbr MENSA; Harvard U; Med.

PARSONS, CONNIE; Westfield HS; Westfield, MA; (Y); 22/350; Sec Church Yth Grp; JA; Spanish Clb; Band; NHS; MA U; Math.

PARSONS, DIANA; Greenfield HS; Greenfield, MA; (Y); Dance Clb; Flag Corp; School Play; Hon Roll; Rollins Coll; Psychlgy.

PARSONS, LORI; Melrose HS; Melrose, MA; (Y); 34/360; Church Yth Grp; French Clb; Color Guard; Flag Corp; Yrbk Stf; Powder Puff Ftbl; NHS; Ntl Yuth Evnt 84; Wrthy Advsr Rnbw Grls 85; SADD 84-86; Dsgn.

PARSONS, MICHAEL; King Philip Regional HS; Plainville, MA; (Y); Socr; Hon Roll; 4th Pl MA Tech Drwng Tchrs Assn Exm 85; Arch.

PARTENHEIMER, ANN; Leicester HS; Leicester, MA; (S); Church Yth Grp; French Clb; Ski Clb; JV Cheerleading; Hon Roll; Prof Modlng Lafemmina Mdlng Schl; Top 10 Miss JR Dnce New England 83; Semi-Profssnl Dance Co.

PARTHUM, DEBORAH; Lawrence HS; Lawrence, MA; (S); 20/300; Drama Clb; Band; Chorus; Drm Mjr(t); Yrbk Stf; High Hon Roll; NHS; L-Pin 84-85; Merrimack Coll; Accntnt.

PARTICINI, VINCENT; St Johns HS; Palmer, MA; (Y); Ski Clb; Chorus; JV Bsbl; JV Bsktbl; JV Ftbl; NHS; Ntl Merit Schol; Math Tm; Speech Tm; Coll Holy Cross; Hist.

PASCAL, LISA; Methuen HS; Methuen, MA; (Y); 83/364; Church Yth Grp; Girl Scts; Model UN; Pep Clb; Jr Cls; JV Fld Hcky; High Hon Roll; Hon Roll; Comp Sci.

PASCIAK, MARK; Central Catholic HS; Salem, NH; (Y); 64/219; Var Trk.

PASCIUTO, SUSAN; Auburn HS; Auburn, MA; (Y); Church Yth Grp; Varsity Clb; Band; Church Choir; Concert Band; Drm Mjr(t); Jazz Band; Mrchg Band; Orch; Var Fld Hcky; Bio.

PASQUANTONIO, SUSAN M; Foxborough HS; Foxborough, MA; (Y); 22/222; Drama Clb; Chorus; Capt Color Guard; Madrigals; School Musical; School Play; Swing Chorus; Hon Roll; NHS; Louis Armstrong Jazz Awd 85; U MA Amherst; Theatre.

PASQUARIELLO, MIA; Commerce HS; Springfield, MA; (S); Office Aide; Capt Cheerleading; Hon Roll; NHS; Air Trfc Cntrlr.

PASQUINI, CYNTHIA M; Ludlow HS; Ludlow, MA; (Y); 28/276; Church Yth Grp; 4-H; French Clb; Girl Scts; Rep Frsh Cls; Stu Cncl; Hon Roll; Ludlow Fire Dept Socl Clb Schlrshp 85; Holyoke Cmnty Coll; Bus Adm.

PASSETTO, CHRISTINA; Monumnt Mountain Reginal HS; Housatonic, MA; (Y); 13/125; Church Yth Grp; Girl Scts; Hosp Aide; Color Guard; Stage Crew; Yrbk Stf; Lit Mag; JV Sftbl; JV Swmmng; High Hon Roll; JR Early Scholar Wheeler & Taylor 85; Soc Stud Stud Spec Svcs Awds 85; Fitchburg ST; Psych.

PASTERNAK, ROBERT; Hoosac Valley HS; Adams, MA; (Y); Aud/Vis; Boy Scts; School Play; Stage Crew; Yrbk Stf.

PASZUK, NANCY; St Marys HS; Worcester, MA; (Y); Church Yth Grp; Dance Clb; Spanish Clb; School Musical; School Play; Stage Crew; Hon Roll; Erly Chldhd Ed.

PATEL, PIUSH; Franklin HS; Accord, NY; (Y); 18/235; Math Tm; Scholastic Bowl; Science Clb; Spanish Clb; Bausch & Lomb Sci Awd; High Hon Roll; NHS; 1st Pl In MA St Sci Fair 83; RPI Math & Sci Awd 84; Instrl Awd In WPI Rgnl Sci Fair 83; Rutgers; Elec Engrng.

PATEL, PRITI; Woburn HS; Woburn, MA; (S); Chorus; Stu Cncl; High Hon Roll; Comp Sci.

PATEL, SHILPA; Mansfield HS; Mansfield, MA; (Y); Cmnty Wkr; Drama Clb; Hosp Aide; Ski Clb; School Musical; Trk; Hon Roll; Hosp Wrk Awd 83 & 84; Hnrb Mntn CSF Window Paintng 85; Wheaton Coll; Physcn.

PATENAUDE, PAM; Holyoke Catholic HS; Chicopee, MA; (Y); Church Yth Grp; Computer Clb; English Clb; Latin Clb; Spanish Clb; Chorus; School Musical; Lit Mag; Crs Cntry; Hon Roll; Spch Pathlgy.

PATERSON, DAVID; Tewksbury HS; Tewksbury, MA; (Y).

PATNEAUDE, CLAUDINE; Taunton HS; Taunton, MA; (Y); Church Yth Grp; Sec Girl Scts; Band; Concert Band; Jazz Band; VP Frsh Cls; VP Soph Cls; Rep Sr Cls; Stu Cncl; Var Crs Cntry; Marian Medal Awd 83; 1st Cls Grl Sct Awd 84; Gold Awd 85.

PATNEAUDE, KRISTEN; Taunton HS; Taunton, MA; (Y); Latin Clb; Office Aide; Yrbk Stf; Stu Cncl; JV Bsktbl; Var Fld Hcky; JV Sftbl; Var Tennis; NHS; Rep Soph Cls; All Schlstcs Fld Hcky 84.

PATON, MARK; St Johns Preparatory Schl; Marblehead, MA; (Y); 2/270; Cmnty Wkr; VP JA; Capt Ski Clb; Var Socr; Hon Roll; Jr NHS; Sccr Fnlst ST Trnmnt 82-83; Dartmouth; Bus.

PATON, TIMOTHY; Lunenburg HS; Lunenburg, MA; (Y); JV Bsbl; JV Bsktbl; High Hon Roll; NHS; Comp Sci.

PATRACUOLLO, JOSEPH; Franklin HS; Franklin, MA; (Y); Church Yth Grp; JA; Teachers Aide; JV Ice Hcky; Var Trk; Hon Roll; Tutrl Clv 84-85; Merit Achvt Awd 85; Engrng.

PATTARINA, JILL; Methuen HS; Lawrence, MA; (Y); 12/360; Intnl Clb; Model UN; Political Wkr; Yrbk Stf; Stu Cncl; Co-Capt Cheerleading; Powder Puff Ftbl; High Hon Roll; NHS; Spanish NHS; Engr.

PATTAVIDA, JILL; Methuen HS; Methuen, MA; (Y); 12/360; Intnl Clb; Model UN; Political Wkr; Yrbk Stf; Stu Cncl; Co-Capt Cheerleading; Powder Puff Ftbl; Hon Roll; NHS; Spanish NHS; Engrng.

PATTERSON, JEFFREY; Concord-Carlisle HS; Concord, MA; (S); Cmnty Wkr; Pres DECA; Ski Clb; Rep Frsh Cls; 2nd & 5th ST-PETRLEUM Mrktng 84, 85; Ntl Cmptitn DECA 85; U Lowell; Law.

PATTERSON, LEE ANN; Sacred Heart HS; S Weymouth, MA; (Y); 3/65; Math Clb; Spanish Clb; Variety Show; High Hon Roll; Hon Roll; NHS; Prfct Atten Awd; Cert Excel Physcl Sci Eng; Cert Excel Alg,Eng,Spnsh,Chem US Hist.

PATTI, ELEANOR R; St Rose HS; East Boston, MA; (Y); 5/45; Drama Clb; Math Clb; Speech Tm; School Musical; School Play; Nwsp Stf; Yrbk Stf; High Hon Roll; Suffolk U.

PAUL, JOSEPH; Chatham JR-SR HS; Chatham, MA; (Y); 21/54; Political Wkr; Ski Clb; JV Bsbl; Var JV Bsktbl; Im JV Ftbl; JV Socr; Hon Roll; Church Yth Grp; Math Clb; Math Tm; Balfour Awd-Typng 83-84; Ski Tm; Prom King-Jr Prom 85; Math.

PAVELICH, LISA M; Lynnfield HS; Lynnfield, MA; (Y); 1/212; Trs Concert Band; Drm Mjr(t); Mrchg Band; Nwsp Bus Mgr; Yrbk Stf; Ntl Merit Ltr; St Schlr; Val; Church Yth Grp; Cmnty Wkr; Dartmouth Bwl Awd; Chancellors Tlnt Awd; NESBA Hnrs Bnd Drm Mjr; MA Assn Of Schl Supr Acdmc Excln Awd; Harvard U; Med.

PAYNE, KARI; Gloucester HS; Gloucester, MA; (Y); 12/300; Yrbk Stf; Rep Frsh Cls; Rep Soph Cls; Stu Cncl; Bsktbl; Var Capt Cheerleading; Var Capt Crs Cntry; Var Capt Trk; Im Vllybl; Hon Roll; Athlte Of The Yr 85; Ithaca Coll; Accntnt.

PAYSON, WENDY; Easthampton HS; Easthampton, MA; (Y); 28/135; Sec Trs Church Yth Grp; Girl Scts; JA; Library Aide; Church Choir; Hon Roll; Katherine Gibbs; Secr Wrk.

PCOLKA, MELANIE; Norton HS; Norton, MA; (Y); 40/130; Drama Clb; JA; Pep Clb; Chorus; Nwsp Rptr; Yrbk Stf; Trk; Hon Roll; Prfct Atten Awd; Southeastern MA Dist Chrs 83; Fshn Merch.

PEABODY, JULIANNE; W Bridgewater JR SR HS; W Bridgewater, MA; (Y); 13/106; Art Clb; Hon Roll; NHS; Bus.

PEACE, JENNIFER J; Hamilton Wenham Regional HS; Hamilton, MA; (Y); 18/198; Art Clb; Church Yth Grp; Cmnty Wkr; Drama Clb; Varsity Clb; Band; Chorus; Concert Band; Drm Mjr(t); Mrchg Band; Scl Stds Awd; CT Col6; Chld Dvlpmnt.

PEARSON, CHERYL; Westfield HS; Westfield, MA; (Y); 3/330; Am Leg Aux Girls St; Dance Clb; Drama Clb; Spanish Clb; Nwsp Rptr; Jr NHS; NHS; James R Shea Mem Awd Excell In Spnsh 84-85.

PEARSON, KELLIE; Durfee HS; Fall River, MA; (Y); Spanish Clb; Color Guard; Mrchg Band; Twrlr; Hon Roll; SMU; Law Enfrcmnt.

PEARSON, ROBYN; Bellingham Mem HS; Bellingham, MA; (Y); 45/201; Hosp Aide; Yrbk Stf; Rep Stu Cncl; JV Score Keeper; Hon Roll; Violet Mowry Memrl Schlrshp 85; Nrthestrn; Nrsng.

PEASE, JONATHAN W; Milton Acad; San Francisco, CA; (Y); Aud/Vis; Service Clb; Acpl Chr; Church Choir; JV Crs Cntry; Im Socr; Ntl Merit SF; Engr.

PEASLEE, DAVID M; Central Catholic HS; Lowell, MA; (Y); 78/228; Church Yth Grp; Math Clb; Ski Clb; Variety Show; Nwsp Stf; Yrbk Stf; Rep Frsh Cls; Co-Capt Tennis; Hon Roll; Pres Schlr; Oimett Caddie Schlrshp 85-86; Lowell Sun All Star Tnns 85; Coaches Tnns Awd 85; St Anselms Coll; Busnss.

PEATFIELD, GREGORY; Georgetown HS; Georgetown, MA; (Y); 9/89; Computer Clb; Teachers Aide; High Hon Roll; Hon Roll; Prfct Atten Awd; Aud/Vis; Aud/Vis; Boy Scts; Science Clb; Inst Stu Comp Crse 83-85; Outstndng Effort & Achvt 85; Outstndng Alg II; Elect Engrng.

PECK, DAVID C; Norwell HS; Norwell, MA; (Y); Church Yth Grp; Cmnty Wkr; School Play; Stage Crew; Yrbk Stf; Stu Cncl; Var Socr; Var Trk; Im Wt Lftg; Var Wrstlng; Mrktng.

PECK, RONALD J; Central Catholic HS; Andover, MA; (Y); 93/219; Church Yth Grp; Cmnty Wkr; Varsity Clb; Stat Bsktbl; Var Golf; High Hon Roll; Hon Roll; Bus.

PECK, STEPHEN; Norton HS; Norton, MA; (Y); 13/160; Am Leg Boys St; Varsity Clb; Yrbk Sprt Ed; Pres Stu Cncl; JV Bsbl; Var Capt Ftbl; Hon Roll; Capt & MVP All Schlstc Team 85; Babson Coll; Accntnt.

PECK, STEVEN B; Plymouth-Carver HS; Plymouth, MA; (Y); 35/550; Am Leg Boys St; Boy Scts; Church Yth Grp; Var Ftbl; Var Capt Trk; God Cntry Awd; Hon Roll; NHS; USAF; Airation.

PECZKA, STEPHANIE T; Revere HS; Revere, MA; (Y); 40/381; Cmnty Wkr; French Clb; Office Aide; Red Cross Aide; Science Clb; Yrbk Stf; Rep Soph Cls; JV Tennis; French Hon Soc; High Hon Roll; Rudolph Di Prizio Jr Memrl Schlrshp 85-86; Salem ST Coll; Psychlgy.

PEDUZZI, DANIEL C; Wareham HS; Wareham, MA; (Y); Am Leg Boys St; Chess Clb; Band; Chorus; Concert Band; High Hon Roll; Hon Roll; Amer Lgn Outstndng Muscn Awd 85; Lowell U; Elec Engr.

PELCZARSKI, DAVID; Holyoke Catholic HS; Holyoke, MA; (Y); 2/146; Church Yth Grp; Computer Clb; English Clb; Latin Clb; Spanish Clb; Speech Tm; Bsbl; Bsktbl; High Hon Roll; Jr NHS; Recip Hnrs Eng & Spn Awd 83-85; Recip Spn & Relign Awds 83-85; Recip Mth Sci & Phys Sci Awds 83-85; Chem Engr.

PELLAND, RACHEL; Dracut HS; Dracut, MA; (Y); Yrbk Stf; Var Cheerleading; Var Gym; Mgr(s); Var Trk; Hon Roll; NHS; Coll; Lgl Sctry.

PELLETIER, GARY; Taunton HS; Taunton, MA; (Y); Church Yth Grp; JCL; Latin Clb; Ski Clb; Yrbk Stf; Lit Mag; Swmmng; High Hon Roll; NHS; Camera Clb; Taunton Area Chamb Commrce Essay Awd 84; Pol Sci.

PELLETIER, JILL E; Salem HS; Salem, MA; (Y); 11/339; Church Yth Grp; Pres Key Clb; Math Clb; Math Tm; Science Clb; High Hon Roll; NHS; Elctrcl Engrng.

PELLETIER, KAREN; Methuen HS; Methuen, MA; (Y); Camp Fr Inc; Intnl Clb; VP Band; Concert Band; Jazz Band; Mrchg Band; Powder Puff Ftbl; Bus.

PELLETIER, KATHLEEN; Hudson HS; Hudson, MA; (Y); French Clb; GAA; Letterman Clb; Pep Clb; Ski Clb; Band; Concert Band; Jazz Band; Mrchg Band; Pep Band; MVP Sftbl 84; Syracuse U; Arch.

PELLETIER, RENEE; Durfee HS; Fall River, MA; (Y); 30/690; Drama Clb; French Clb; Trs German Clb; Nwsp Rptr; Nwsp Stf; Yrbk Rptr; Yrbk Stf; Hon Roll; NHS; Hrnbl Ment Sci Fair 78; Jrnlsm.

PELLETIER, ROBIN; Bishop Fenwick HS; Beverly, MA; (Y); AFS; Nwsp Stf; Yrbk Stf; Rep Jr Cls; Rep Stu Cncl; JV Crs Cntry; High Hon Roll; NHS; Frnch & Engl Awd 82-85; Brown Bk Awd For Engl 84-85; Intrprtgn.

PELOQUIN, JILL; Easthampton HS; Easthampton, MA; (Y); 24/140; Spanish Clb; Yrbk Stf; Stu Cncl; Var Cheerleading; Hon Roll; Holyoke CC; Radlgy.

PELOQUIN, TINA; Easthampton HS; Easthampton, MA; (Y); 4-H; Yrbk Phtg; Yrbk Stf; Off Stu Cncl; 4-H Awd; High Hon Roll; Prncpls Commtt 85; Obstrcn.

PELOSI, ANDREW; Haverhill HS; Bradford, MA; (Y); Church Yth Grp; JA; Political Wkr; Band; Nwsp Stf; Var L Golf; Var L Socr; High Hon Roll; NHS; Grand Lodge MA Sons Italy 85; St Michaels Coll; Ec.

PELTIER, SANDRA; Agawam HS; Agawam, MA; (Y); 45/330; Dance Clb; GAA; Color Guard; Yrbk Stf; Hon Roll.

PELTO, EDWIN V; Fitchburg HS; Fitchburg, MA; (Y); Am Leg Boys St; Drama Clb; School Play; Stage Crew; Yrbk Stf; Hon Roll; M M Mallahy Jr Engl Awd 84-85; Spnsh I Excel Awd 82-83; Pro Arts 85; Film.

PEMBERTON, SHAWNA; Fairhae HS; Fairhaven, MA; (Y); Drama Clb; Trs Chorus; School Musical; School Play; Stage Crew; Variety Show; Cheerleading; Shcl Mdlng 84; NY Acad Thtrcl Arts 85; Miss MA Teen USA 84, Miss Southern New Engl Teenage 85; SMU; Bus Admn.

PENACHIO, KIM; Governor Dummer Acad; Revere, MA; (Y); French Clb; Ski Clb; Varsity Clb; Nwsp Ed-Chief; Yrbk Stf; Var Socr; JV Trk; JV Vllybl; High Hon Roll; Hon Roll; Ingham Fnd Schlrshp 85; Discpln Comm 85-86; Dorm Prctr 85-6.

PENDENZA, LISA; Everett HS; Everett, MA; (Y); 10/300; Church Yth Grp; Key Clb; Intnl Clb; Key Clb; Office Aide; Yrbk Stf; JV Tennis; High Hon Roll; Sec NHS; Italian-Amer Assn John Marchese Schlrshp Awd 85; Helen F Dyer Schlrshp Awd 85; Intl Clb Schlrshp Awd; Suffolk U; Bus Mgmt.

PENDERGAST, CHRIS; Tahanto Regional HS; Berlin, MA; (Y); 21/59; Boy Scts; Math Tm; Science Clb; Ski Clb; Rep Stu Cncl; Var Golf; Var Socr; U Of Lowell; Cvl Engrng.

PENNA, CLAUDIA; Westfield HS; Westfield, MA; (Y); 27/337; Church Yth Grp; Spanish Clb; Yrbk Sprt Ed; Yrbk Stf; Frsh Cls; Capt Soph Cls; Jr Cls; Sr Cls; Capt Var Socr; Var Sftbl; Acctng.

PENTA, PASQUALE; Medford HS; Medford, MA; (Y); Church Yth Grp; Cmnty Wkr; Office Aide; Ski Clb; Stu Cncl; High Hon Roll; Hon Roll; NHS; Office Aide; Ski Clb; Excllnc-Eng 83-85; Excllnc-Sci Awd 83; Hmrm Rep 85; Boston U; Dentstry.

PENTA, SUSAN; Matignon HS; Somerville, MA; (S); 5/180; Cmnty Wkr; Science Clb; Color Guard; Trk; Vllybl; High Hon Roll; Hon Roll; NHS; Ntl Merit Ltr; Natl Ldrshp Merit Awd 84.

PENTO, LAURA; Holbrook JR SR HS; Holbrook, MA; (Y); 7/102; Chorus; Var Bsktbl; Var Sftbl; Hon Roll; NHS; Bsktbll 84-85; Softbll MVP 83-84.

PEPIN, DAVID; Hocyoke Catholic HS; Chicopee, MA; (Y); 38/135; Computer Clb; Keywanettes; Latin Clb; Spanish Clb; Nwsp Bus Mgr; Yrbk Bus Mgr; Trk; North Adams ST; Lawyer.

PEPIN, SCOTT D; Bartlett HS; Webster, MA; (Y); 2/136; Rep Am Leg Boys St; French Clb; Jazz Band; Socr; NHS.

PEPPE, JOHN; Randolph HS; Randolph, MA; (Y); Am Leg Boys St; Political Wkr; Pol Sci.

PEPPER, STEVEN; Cathedral HS; Springfield, MA; (Y); 150/519; JA; Aeronautics Clb; Clctr Sprts Memrtl.

PERAKSLIS, MARK S; Silver Lake Regional HS; Pembroke, MA; (Y); 35/485; Pres Church Yth Grp; Cmnty Wkr; Concert Band; Jazz Band; Trk; Wt Lftg; DAR Awd; Hon Roll; Kiwanis Awd; NHS; Rockwell Schlrshp 85; UK Temprnce Schlrshp 85; Plymouth Ins Women Schlrshp 85; U Of Lowell; Elec Engrng.

PERCHARD, JACKIE; Weymouth North HS; Weymouth, MA; (Y); 46/400; Church Yth Grp; Dance Clb; Trs Drama Clb; French Clb; Girl Scts; Key Clb; Chorus; Orch; School Musical; School Play; Pilot.

PERDICARO, MICHELLE; Christopher Columbus HS; S Boston, MA; (S); 2/119; Dance Clb; School Play; High Hon Roll; Hon Roll; NHS; 1st Pl Sci Fair.

PERDUE, GAYLE; Clinton HS; Clinton, MA; (Y); 4-H; Spanish Clb; Yrbk Stf; Sftbl; 4-H Awd; Hon Roll.

PERDUE, JAMES H; Hamilton Wenham Regional HS; South Hamilton, MA; (Y); 30/193; Am Leg Boys St; Church Yth Grp; Chorus; VP Frsh Cls; Var Socr; JV Trk; Var Wrstlng; Hon Roll; NHS.

PEREIRA, ANAISA; New Bedford HS; New Bedford, MA; (Y); 59/600; Church Yth Grp; Drama Clb; Intnl Clb; Office Aide; Yrbk Stf; Stu Cncl; Jr NHS; Prfct Atten Awd; Hnr Roll 84-85; Bus Admin.

PEREIRA, DARLENE; Bishop Connolly HS; Fall River, MA; (Y); 42/190; French Clb; Girl Scts; High Hon Roll; Hon Roll; Comp Sci.

PEREIRA, JOSEPH; Diman Reg Voch Tech HS; Fall River, MA; (Y); Boys Clb Am; Socr.

PEREIRA, KATHY; Bishop Connolly HS; Swansea, MA; (S); 5/200; Ski Clb; Cheerleading; High Hon Roll; NHS; Boston U; Speech Path.

PEREIRA, PATRICIA JANE F M; Bishop Connolly HS; Fall River, MA; (Y); 51/174; Church Yth Grp; Cmnty Wkr; Drama Clb; Hosp Aide; Chorus; School Play; Stage Crew; High Hon Roll; Hon Roll; Church Choir; Hghst Hnr Roll 85; Prvdnc Coll; Theology Tchr.

PERILLO, PAUL; Everett HS; Everett, MA; (Y); Church Yth Grp; Var Bsbl; Sec Bsktbl; Var Ftbl; Im Wt Lftg; Hon Roll; Outstdng Defsmn Popwarner Ftbl 82; Jrnlsm.

PERKINS, BETH; Haverhill HS; Haverhill, MA; (Y); Hosp Aide; High Hon Roll; Hon Roll; Modeling.

PERKINS, DANA; Leominster HS; Leominster, MA; (S); 74/352; School Musical; School Play; Stage Crew; Stu Cncl; JV Ftbl; Wrstlng; Hon Roll; Communications.

PERKINS, KRISTINE; Natick HS; Natick, MA; (Y); Church Yth Grp; Chorus; High Hon Roll; Nrsng.

PERLEY, RAYMOND; St Marys HS; Worcester, MA; (Y); 17/30; Church Yth Grp; Church Choir; School Play; Holy Cross Coll; Priest.

PERLMAN, JAY; Malden Catholic HS; Malden, MA; (Y); 19/185; Chess Clb; JCL; Latin Clb; Teachers Aide; Temple Yth Grp; Band; Concert Band; Mrchg Band; Variety Show; Im Bsktbl.

PERLMUTTER, DONNA DIANE; West Springfield HS; W Springfield, MA; (Y); 36/240; Pep Clb; Q&S; Yrbk Sprt Ed; Yrbk Stf; Var Capt Bsktbl; Var Capt Socr; Var Capt Sftbl; Im Vllybl; Hon Roll; NHS; Outstndng Achvt Hstry Mary R Godfrey Scholar 85; All Wstrn MA, All ST, Cls MVP Var Socr 85; U Of MA; Mngmnt.

PERRAS, LORI; Easthampton HS; Easthampton, MA; (Y); 2/144; Am Leg Aux Girls St; Capt Color Guard; Yrbk Stf; Var Cheerleading; Gym; High Hon Roll; Jr NHS; NEDT Awd; North Adams ST Coll; Bio.

PERRAULT, CAROLINE; Taunton HS; East Taunton, MA; (Y); Girl Scts; Hosp Aide; Lit Mag; Nrsng.

PERREAULT, DAVID J; Reading Memorial HS; Reading, MA; (Y); 30/351; Boy Scts; Trs Chess Clb; Sec Exploring; High Hon Roll; Hon Roll; Ntl Merit SF; High Hnr Roll Awd 84; Natl Rifle Assn Expert 84; MA Outdr Prone Champshps 7th Intermed Jr 84; Boston U; Elec Engrng.

PERREAULT, MARTHA; Granby HS; Granby, MA; (S); 1/67; Am Leg Aux Girls St; Yrbk Bus Mgr; Yrbk Ed-Chief; Sec Jr Cls; Rep Stu Cncl; Bausch & Lomb Sci Awd; DAR Awd; NHS; Ntl Merit Ltr; Val; Wellesley Coll Bk Awd 83-84; Grl Sct Slvr Awd 81-82; Chem Engr.

PERRIELLO, KRISTINA; Milford HS; Milford, MA; (Y); 78/370; Hosp Aide; Score Keeper; Hon Roll; Nrsng.

PERRIN, DAVE; Dracut SR HS; Dracut, MA; (Y); Boy Scts; Var L Ftbl; Trk; Var L Wrstlng; NHS; U Of Lowell; Civil Engr.

PERRONE, KIMBERLY E; Pittsfield HS; Pittsfield, MA; (Y); Church Yth Grp; Exploring; Pep Clb; Band; Cit Awd; Hon Roll; Brkshire Med Cre Scholar 85; Reid Middl Sschl Scholar 85; CSF 85; St Anselem; Nrsg.

PERRY, BRIAN K; New Bedford HS; Acushnet, MA; (Y); 83/602; Computer Clb; Office Aide; Science Clb; Hon Roll; Northeastern U; Comp Sci.

PERRY, CHRISTINE M; New Bedford HS; New Bedford, MA; (Y); Cmnty Wkr; Color Guard; Mrchg Band; Hon Roll; MA Coll Pharmacy; Phrmcst.

PERRY, DENISE; West Springfield SR HS; W Springfield, MA; (S); 2/240; Am Leg Aux Girls St; Capt Flag Corp; Jazz Band; School Musical; Frsh Cls; French Hon Soc; NHS; Sal; Pres Spanish NHS; Dartmouth Club Bk Awd 84; Natl Merit Comm Stu 85; Daisy Chain 84; Elms Coll; Accntnt.

PERRY, DENISE; Weymouth North HS; E Weymouth, MA; (Y); 10/333; Math Tm; Spanish Clb; Yrbk Stf; High Hon Roll; Hon Roll; NHS; Louise Frederick Mem Schlrshp 85; Brdgwtr ST Coll; Elem Ed.

PERRY, KAREN; Matignon HS; Somerville, MA; (Y); #17 In Class; Computer Clb; Drama Clb; School Musical; School Play; Yrbk Stf; Lit Mag; Trk; Hon Roll; NHS; Spanish NHS; Natl Hnr Roll 83-84; Ct Rprtr.

PERRY, KRISTINE; Everett HS; Everett, MA; (Y); Church Yth Grp; Office Aide; Bentley; Acctg.

PERRY, KRISTINE; Haverhill HS; Bradford, MA; (Y); 4/415; Church Yth Grp; Latin Clb; Spanish Clb; Yrbk Stf; High Hon Roll; NHS; Student Cncl Awds-Latin & Typng 82; Honrbl Mentn Score-AATSP Test 85; Medcl Technlgy.

PERRY, LISA; Dana Hall Schl; Lake Bronson, MN; (Y); Drama Clb; French Clb; Speech Tm; Chorus; School Musical; School Play; Stage Crew; Swing Chorus; Lit Mag; Ntl Merit Ltr; Congdon Prz Schlrshp 82-85; Smith Coll Bk Prz 83-84; Actng.

PERRY, LISA; Lenox Memorial HS; Lenox, MA; (Y); Pres Church Yth Grp; Church Choir; School Play; Lit Mag; High Hon Roll; NHS; Ntl Merit Ltr; Wellesley Bk Awd 84-85; MA Adv Stds Prog 85; Engl.

PERRY, LISA; Nazareth Acad; Reading, MA; (Y); Church Yth Grp; Drama Clb; Band; Chorus; Church Choir; School Musical; School Play; Stage Crew; High Hon Roll; Med.

PERSSON, RUSSELL; St Johns HS; Sturbridge, MA; (Y); Aud/Vis; Ski Clb; JV Socr; Hon Roll; Bus.

PETCEN, MELISSA; Smith Acad; Hatfield, MA; (Y); 1/35; Nwsp Stf; Yrbk Bus Mgr; Yrbk Stf; Var Capt Bsktbl; Var Capt Sftbl; Bausch & Lomb Sci Awd; High Hon Roll; Val; Sophia Smith Schlrshp 85; Suprntndnt Awd Acadmc Excllnc 84; All Wstrn MA Sftbl 85; Smith Coll; Sci.

PETERS, ERIC; Central Catholic HS; Andover, MA; (Y); 64/219; Boys Clb Am; Boy Scts; Var Bsbl; Im Bsktbl; JV Ftbl; Hon Roll; Bus Mgmt.

PETERSOLI, LISA; Lee HS; Lee, MA; (Y); 15/115; French Clb; Nwsp Rptr; Nwsp Stf; Yrbk Phtg; Yrbk Stf; Mgr Bsktbl; JV Cheerleading; Mgr Socr; High Hon Roll; Hon Roll; Phy Thrpy.

PETERSON, BETH; Cambridge School Of Weston; Waltham, MA; (Y); Church Yth Grp; Girl Scts; Teachers Aide; Chorus; Swmmng; JETS Awd; Ntl Merit Ltr; Boys Clb Am; Church Choir; Var Crs Cntry; Intl Order Of Rainbow Grls Grand Assmbly Schlrshp Awd, SWE Cert Merit Highest Hnr Sci & Math 85; Cornell U; Mech Engr.

PETERSON, CHRISTOPHER; Silver Lake Regional HS; Kingston, MA; (Y); Am Leg Boys St; Boy Scts; Drama Clb; French Clb; Latin Clb; Socr; Hon Roll; Worcester ST Coll; Bio.

PETERSON, JILL; Durfee HS; Fall River, MA; (Y); Pep Clb; Stage Crew; Yrbk Stf; Cit Awd; Hon Roll; Chrst Herter Mem Schlrshp 84; Nrs.

PETERSON, JULIE; New Bedford HS; Acushnet, MA; (Y); Exploring; Library Aide; Lit Mag; Hon Roll; Ntl Merit Ltr; Fnlst Voic Demcrcy Essy Cntst 83-84; Engl APT Tst Engl 84-85; Verbl SAT 780 Scor83-84; Pre-Law.

PETERSON, KEVIN D; Natick HS; Hyde Pk, MA; (Y); Am Leg Boys St; Computer Clb; Band; Church Choir; Drm Mjr(t); Var Coach Actv; Var Ftbl; Var Capt Trk; Wt Lftg; Hon Roll; RIT; Comp Prog.

PETERSON, LEE-ANN; Manchester HS; Manchester, MA; (Y); Yrbk Stf; Capt Cheerleading; Hon Roll; Lion Awd; Manchester Bstrs Clb Schlrshp Awd 85; U Of RI; Math.

PETERSON, NEIL; Scituate HS; Scitaute, MA; (Y); Ski Clb; Rep Jr Cls; Var Ftbl; Var Capt Wrstlng; Hon Roll; Govt.

PETERSON, THOMAS A; Shrewsbury SR HS; Shrewsbury, MA; (Y); 36/223; Am Leg Boys St; Trs Pres Band; School Musical; School Play; Yrbk Sprt Ed; VP Jr Cls; VP Sr Cls; Var L Crs Cntry; Var L Trk; NHS; Indr Trck Recrd 84-85; Finland Forgn Exch Prg 84; Band Awds 83-85; Dartmouth; Comp Sci.

PETERSON, WENDY; Wachusett Regional HS; Holden, MA; (Y); 70/352; Church Yth Grp; Rep Soph Cls; Rep Stu Cncl; Art.

PETRACCA, HEATH A; North Quincy HS; Quincy, MA; (Y); 12/375; Am Leg Boys St; French Clb; Library Aide; Quiz Bowl; ROTC; Science Clb; Spanish Clb; Teachers Aide; Chorus; Rep Frsh Cls; Crss Cntry All Schlstc 84-85; Redmond O Brien Awd In Math 84; NQHS Capt 84-85; Cornell U; Ecnmcs.

PETRAKOS, STEPHANIE; Nroth Quincy HS; Quincy, MA; (Y); 3/372; Camp Fr Inc; French Clb; Library Aide; Math Clb; Quiz Bowl; Bsktbl; Trk; Vllybl; Elks Awd; French Hon Soc; Rbt C Billings Schlrshp 85; Ntl Ed Awd 85; Scty Wmn Engrs Cmndtn & Outstndng Schrlshp In Physics & Mth; U Of NH; Engrng.

PETRALIA, LISA MARIE; Barnstable HS; Hyannis, MA; (S); 40/398; Pres Sec Band; Pres Sec Concert Band; Drm Mjr(t); Mrchg Band; School Musical; Yrbk Ed-Chief; Pres Jr Cls; Pres Sr Cls; DAR Awd; Outstndng Soph; Ldrshp Sem; Most Likely To Succeed; Best Musician; Eng.

PETRICCA, JOHN; Leominster HS; Leominster, MA; (Y); 42/410; Am Leg Boys St; Political Wkr; Var L Ice Hcky; High Hon Roll; Hon Roll; Ntl Merit Ltr; Kngts Of Clmbs Schlrshp 85; Bishop Beaven Asmbly Schlrshp 85; Northeastern U; Comp Sci.

PETRIE, MARIA T; West Bridgewater HS; W Bridgewater, MA; (Y); 1/108; Am Leg Aux Girls St; Chess Clb; Girl Scts; Nwsp Rptr; Nwsp Stf; High Hon Roll; NHS; Ntl Merit Ltr; Voice Dem Awd; Math Tm; U MA Amherst Chnclrs Tlnt Awd Wnnr 84-85; St Johns Coll; Philosophy.

PETRILLI, PATRICIA; Archbishop Williams HS; Quincy, MA; (Y); Key Clb; Sec Ski Clb; Chorus; School Musical; School Play; Rep Frsh Cls; VP Soph Cls; VP Sr Cls.

PETRILLO, KEVIN; Central Catholic HS; Methuen, MA; (Y); 53/219; Art Clb; JA; Ski Clb; Im Vllybl; High Hon Roll; Hon Roll; Bus Mgt.

PETROCCHI, DINA; Acton Boxborough Regional HS; Acton, MA; (Y); Hosp Aide; Band; Powder Puff Ftbl; Providence Coll; Bus.

PEURA, BETH; Turners Falls HS; Montague Ctr, MA; (Y); Girl Scts; Varsity Clb; Capt Trk; NHS; Track Awd 85; USAF.

PFABE, RENATA; Northampton HS; Northampton, MA; (Y); 31/189; Dance Clb; Library Aide; Var Ski Clb; Stage Crew; Nwsp Stf; JV Socr; Var Trk; High Hon Roll; Hon Roll; NHS; Demcrtc Cty Cmmtte Schlrshp; Smith Coll; Pre Med.

PHAN, HUNG; East Boston HS; E Boston, MA; (Y); Key Clb; Teachers Aide; Hon Roll; Jr NHS; NHS; MIT Coll; Elec Engr.

PHANEUF, CARMEN; Bishop Connolly HS; Somerset, MA; (Y); Church Yth Grp; Church Choir; French Clb; Hosp Aide; Pres Ski Clb; JV Tennis; Hon Roll; Southeastern MA U; Nrsng.

PHANEUF, MATTHEW D; Fairhaven HS; Acushnet, MA; (Y); 20/200; Var L Trk; Var Wt Lftg; Jr NHS; Southwestern MA U; Biochem.

PHAT, CHAMNAN; South Boston HS; Brighton, MA; (Y); Cmnty Wkr; Office Aide; Teachers Aide; Nwsp Stf; Stu Cncl; Hon Roll; NHS; St Schlr; Book Awd 85; Sci Awd 85; Stu Of Mnth 85; Boston Coll; Bio.

PHELPS, AIMEE; Falmouth HS; Falmouth, MA; (S); Drama Clb; French Clb; Key Clb; Acpl Chr; Madrigals; School Musical; School Play; Fld Hcky; High Hon Roll; NHS; Schl Play 84; Law.

PHELPS, JEANNE M; Foxboro HS; Foxborough, MA; (Y); 35/206; Art Clb; Church Yth Grp; Yrbk Stf; Trs Stu Cncl; Fld Hcky; Swmmng; Trk; Hon Roll; Ntl Merit Ltr; Jay Crowley Schlrshp 85; Mst Artistc 85; 1st, 2nd & 3rd Pl In Foxboro Art Shw JR Artst 85; Emmanuel Coll; Comm Art.

PHELPS, JEFF; Methuen HS; Methuen, MA; (Y); 120/400; Boy Scts; Church Yth Grp; Intnl Clb; Im JV Bsbl; Im JV Bsktbl; Im Bowling; Im Ftbl; Prfct Atten Awd; U Of MA; Law Enf.

PHILBIN, PATRICK F; The Roxbury Latin Schl; Sherborn, MA; (Y); Debate Tm; Drama Clb; Model UN; Chorus; School Play; Nwsp Stf; Lit Mag; Ntl Merit SF; Latin Prz 83-84; Sci Prz 83-84; Brown U Bk Awd 83-84; Yale.

PHILHOWER, AUDRA; Lincoln-Sudbury Regional HS; Sudbury, MA; (Y); Drama Clb; Hosp Aide; JA; Letterman Clb; Pep Clb; Band; Chorus; Swing Chorus; Cheerleading; Pom Pon; 2nd Rnnr Up JR Miss Pagnt 84; Schl Ltr Wnnr 8 Tms Music 82-85; Schl Ltr Wnnr Swmg & Pom Pon 81-84; U Of MA Amherst; Hotl Adm.

PHILLIPS, BRIAN J; Joseph Case HS; Swansea, MA; (Y); 15/260; Pres JA; Science Clb; Service Clb; Trs Sr Cls; Crs Cntry; Ice Hcky; High Hon Roll; NHS; JA Scholar 85; Chase Truot; Thomas Coll; Bus Admin.

PHILLIPS, CHRISTOPHER; Diman Reginal Vocational HS; Swansea, MA; (Y); VICA; High Hon Roll; Thomas Rodrique Scholar Fnd 85; 2nd Pl ST VICA Comp 85; Outstndg CA Vocatnl Stu Of Yr 85; Culinary Inst Of Amer; Cul Art.

PHILLIPS, DENISE; Saugus HS; Saugus, MA; (Y); Office Aide; Yrbk Stf; Stu Cncl; JV Tennis; Hon Roll; Jr NHS; NHS; Voice Dem Awd; Hotel Admin.

PHILLIPS, JOSEPH; Mansfield HS; Mansfield, MA; (Y); Acpl Chr; Band; Concert Band; Drm Mjr(t); Jazz Band; Mrchg Band; School Musical; JV Ftbl; Trk; Lion Awd; Hnr Rll 84; Key Socty 84; Music Compstn.

PHILLIPS, LISA; Marianhill C C HS; Southbridge, MA; (Y); 2/18; Church Yth Grp; Hosp Aide; Yrbk Ed-Chief; Lit Mag; Var Bsktbl; CC Awd; Hon Roll; NHS; Sal; Computer Clb; Overal Excllnc Awd; Chem Awd; Engl & Relgn Awd; Coll Hly Crss; Orthpdc Srgn.

PHILLIPS, MELANIE; Falmouth HS; E Falmouth, MA; (Y); Pep Clb; Band; Concert Band; Drill Tm; Mrchg Band; School Musical; JV Var Bsktbl; Score Keeper; JV Sftbl; Regis Schlrshp 85; Robert Clulow Mem Awd 85; Cedric Hadley Awd 85; All Star Sftbl 85; Regis Coll; Scndry Educ.

PHILLIPS, MIKE; Medway HS; Medway, MA; (Y); 14/150; Church Yth Grp; Boys Clb Am; L Var Crs Cntry; Im Ftbl; L Var Golf; L Var Ice Hcky; High Hon Roll; Hon Roll; NHS; Engrng.

PHILLIPS, ROBERT; Braintree HS; Braintree, MA; (Y); 2/458; Am Leg Boys St; Chess Clb; Trs Math Tm; Concert Band; Jazz Band; Orch; Lit Mag; Gym; Trk; High Hon Roll; Comp Sci.

PHILLIPS, SHEILA; Greenfield HS; Arden, NC; (Y); 17/154; Church Yth Grp; Cmnty Wkr; High Hon Roll; NHS; Pres Acadmc Ftns Awd 85; High Hnrs Awd 85; U Of NC; Elem Educ.

PHILLIPS, STEPHANIE; Norton HS; Norton, MA; (Y); 20/154; Church Yth Grp; Pep Clb; Teachers Aide; Lib Band; Lib Concert Band; Lib Mrchg Band; Nwsp Stf; Yrbk Stf; Stu Cncl; High Hon Roll; Educ.

PHILLOS, HARRY; Boston Latin Schl; Brighton, MA; (Y); 120/310; Camera Clb; Church Yth Grp; Exploring; Latin Clb; JV Tennis; Hon Roll.

PHIPPS, RICHIE; Wakefield HS; Wakefield, MA; (Y); #76 In Class; Var Bsbl; Var Bsktbl; Var Ftbl; Unsung Hero-Ftbl & Bsktbl 85; Comptr Sci.

PIANTES, SHARON; Arlington Catholic HS; Arlington, MA; (Y); 2/134; Art Clb; French Clb; Church Choir; Nwsp Stf; Yrbk Stf; High Hon Roll; Trs NHS; Sal; Socty Womn Engrs Hgh Hnrs Sci & Math 85; MA Forgn Lang Assn Awd Frnch 85; Tufts U; Ec.

PIANTES, STACEY M; Barnstable HS; Cotvit, MA; (S); Church Yth Grp; Cmnty Wkr; Hosp Aide; Acpl Chr; Chorus; Church Choir; Co Chrprsn SADD; 1st Pl Essy Cntst; Penn ST; Psych.

PIAZZA, JEFF J; Methuen HS; Methuen, MA; (Y); 4/350; Camera Clb; Church Yth Grp; Pres French Clb; Pres Intnl Clb; Red Cross Aide; Science Clb; Speech Tm; Chorus; School Musical; School Play; Wesleyan Olin Schlrshp 85; Wesleyan; Bio Chem.

PIAZZA, JOANNE; Methuen HS; Methuen, MA; (Y); 56/375; Intnl Clb; Spanish Clb; Var L Tennis; Stat Vllybl; Bus.

PICARD, MARY ANN; Bishop Feehan HS; Cumberland, RI; (Y); 59/240; Church Yth Grp; Hosp Aide; Lit Mag; JV Crs Cntry; JV Trk; French Hon Soc; Hon Roll; Achvt Awd Biol II, Amer Hstry 83-84; Achvt Awd Eng Lit 84-85; Achvt Awd Eng Grmmr 82-84.

PICARD, MICHAEL P; Marshfield HS; Marshfield, MA; (Y); 22/400; Am Leg Boys St; Pres Key Clb; Latin Clb; Stu Cncl; Var L Ftbl; Var Capt Trk; Wt Lftg; High Hon Roll; Hon Roll; Jr NHS; Tufts U; Engrng.

PICK, JOHN; New Bedford HS; New Bedford, MA; (Y); AFS; Computer Clb; Trs Key Clb; Rep Jr Cls; Stu Cncl; High Hon Roll; Hon Roll; Mu Alp Tht; NHS; Prfct Scor Math SAT 85; Cls Rnk 1 84; Chem.

PICKARD, CATHERINE LOUISE; Reading Memeorial HS; Reading, MA; (Y); AFS; Powder Puff Ftbl; High Hon Roll; Hon Roll; Pres Schlr; Ara A Karakashien Awd 85; Soc Svcs.

PICKETT, KAREN; Matignon HS; Somerville, MA; (S); 4/192; Cmnty Wkr; Drama Clb; Science Clb; Spanish Clb; School Play; Lit Mag; High Hon Roll; NHS; Ntl Merit Ltr; Schl & Dist Hist Fr Wnr.

PICKETT, YVONNE; Bridgewater-Raynham Regional HS; Raynham, MA; (Y); Girl Scts; Latin Clb; Fld Hcky; High Hon Roll; Hon Roll; Bus.

PICROSKI, FRED; Classical HS; Springfield, MA; (Y); 38/392; Aud/Vis; Chess Clb; Library Aide; Yrbk Rptr; Yrbk Stf; Elks Awd; Masonic Awd; NHS; Comp Pgmmg & Svc 3 Awds; Pres Acad Fit Awd; Northeastern; Comp Sci.

PIEDRA, EDWARD; Holyoke Catholic HS; Holyoke, MA; (Y); 8/140; Chess Clb; Computer Clb; Spanish Clb; Rep Frsh Cls; Pres Soph Cls; Rep Jr Cls; Rep Stu Cncl; Tennis; High Hon Roll; Hon Roll; Western MA Schltc Chess Champ 84; Dartmouth Coll Bk Awd 85; York Steak House Employee Mnth 85; U MA; Engrng.

PIELA, BRENDA; BMC Durfee HS; Fall River, MA; (Y); Math Clb; MMM; Red Cross Aide; Science Clb; Mrchg Band; Orch; Nwsp Stf; Yrbk Stf; Tennis; Church Yth Grp; Orch Librn 84; 1 Yr Mbr Fall Rr Symphny Orch 84; 3 Lttr Sprts 82-85; Envir Control Cmmtt Mbr 82-85; Dntl Hygn.

PIERCE, CHRISTINE; Hungham HS; Hingham, MA; (Y); AFS; Trs Church Yth Grp; Debate Tm; Chorus; Nwsp Stf; High Hon Roll; Hon Roll; Continntl Math Leag-3rd Pl Awd 82-83; Archery Tournmnt-2nd Pl Tm & 2nd Highest Scorer 82-83; Georgetown; Pre-Med.

PIERCE, JOHN C; Cathedral HS; Springfield, MA; (Y); 82/515; Chorus; Church Choir; Madrigals; Mrchg Band; School Musical; Variety Show; Var L Swmmng; Dist Chorus 84-85; All-ST Chorus 85; VP Schl Chorus 85-86.

PIERCE, RONALD; Clinton HS; Clinton, MA; (Y); High Hon Roll; NHS; Law.

PIERI, ANDREA; Agawan HS; Feeding Hls, MA; (Y); Dance Clb; Girl Scts; Hosp Aide; Library Aide; Variety Show; Yrbk Stf; Hon Roll; Mech Engr.

PIESSENS, ANNE; Newton South HS; Newton, MA; (Y); Intnl Clb; Spanish Clb; Nwsp Phtg; Yrbk Phtg; JV Tennis; Cit Awd; Hon Roll; Ntl Merit SF; U PA Clb Boston Bk Awd 85; Fnlst Photogrphcs Form Photo Cntsts 84-85; Faclty Awds Ltrs Cmndtn 84 & 85; Brown U; Bus.

PIETKIEWICZ, KORRINE; Matignon HS; Medford, MA; (Y); Science Clb; Spanish Clb; Teachers Aide; Hon Roll; Jr NHS; Spanish NHS.

PIETRASZEK, JEAN; Bishop Connally HS; Swanse, MA; (S); 28/200; Drama Clb; JA; Latin Clb; Ski Clb; Stage Crew; Yrbk Stf; JV Trk; High Hon Roll; NHS; Outward Bound Pgm; Bus Admin.

PIETRUSIAK JR, WILLIAM J; Xaverian Brothers HS; Medfield, MA; (S); 39/236; Boy Scts; School Musical; Bsktbl; JV Crs Cntry; Ftbl; JV Trk; Hon Roll; Chem Engrng.

PIKE, PETER J; Bridgewater-Raynham Regional HS; Raynham, MA; (Y); 20/305; Am Leg Boys St; French Clb; Yrbk Stf; L Bsktbl; Var L Ftbl; Var L Socr; Var L Trk; Im Wt Lftg; Hon Roll; Old Colony Leag All Schlstc Tm Bsktbl 84-85; Taunton Gaz All Schlstc Tm Bsktbl 84-85; U VT; Psych.

PILAT, MELISSA; Methuen HS; Methuen, MA; (Y); 20/340; Intnl Clb; Model UN; Yrbk Stf; Rep Stu Cncl; Hon Roll; NHS; Human Svc.

PILON, LORALEE; Easthampton HS; Easthampton, MA; (Y); 21/135; Church Yth Grp; Debate Tm; French Clb; JA; Acpl Chr; Chorus; Church Choir; Stage Crew; Var Crs Cntry; Ntl Soc Stds Olympd 85; Schl Match Wits Clb 84-86; Pre-Law.

PIMENTAL, MICHAEL; New Bedford HS; New Bedford, MA; (Y); 30/688; Church Yth Grp; Cmnty Wkr; Intnl Clb; Key Clb; Stage Crew; Yrbk Stf; Rep Jr Cls; Rep Sr Cls; Rep Stu Cncl; Hon Roll; Bus Admin.

PINE, DANIEL R; Matignon HS; Somerville, MA; (Y); 82/178; Hosp Aide; Bowling; Hon Roll; Spanish NHS; Phrmcst.

PINE, JENNIFER; Falmouth HS; Falmouth, MA; (Y); Church Yth Grp; French Clb; Hosp Aide; Key Clb; School Musical; School Play; JV Bsktbl; JV Capt Fld Hcky; Lcrss; Sftbl; Pre-Med.

PINGLEY, MARYBETH; Bishop Connolly HS; Fall River, MA; (Y); 51/200; Church Yth Grp; Trk; High Hon Roll; RI Horsemns Assn Mdl 84; Roseland Acres Drill Tm 84; Bio.

PINKHAM, JIM F; Braintree HS; Braintree, MA; (Y); 69/420; Math Clb; Math Tm; Ski Clb; Bsktbl; Golf; Trk; Hon Roll; Hcky Mgr & Scrkpr 84-85; Arch.

PINNEY, JAY; Southwick HS; Southwick, MA; (Y); Am Leg Boys St; Hon Roll; JETS Awd; NHS; Ntl Merit Schol; Drftsmn.

PINO, LAURA; Norton HS; Norton, MA; (Y); 12/150; Art Clb; Camera Clb; Chess Clb; Cmnty Wkr; Computer Clb; Dance Clb; Debate Tm; Drama Clb; English Clb; Exploring; Govt.

PINSONNEAULT, ERIC P; Nashoba Regional HS; Stow, MA; (Y); 20/190; Church Yth Grp; Cmnty Wkr; Rep Jr Cls; JV Bsbl; JV Bsktbl; Var Capt Tennis; High Hon Roll; Hon Roll; NHS; Math Awd; GA Inst Of Tech; Elec Engrng.

PINSONREAULT, LYNNE; Bishop Feehan HS; N Attleboro, MA; (Y); GAA; L Trk; French Hon Soc; Hon Roll.

PINTO, ANA L; Swampscott HS; Swampscott, MA; (Y); 6/201; Church Yth Grp; Drama Clb; Pres Math Tm; Band; Concert Band; Jazz Band; Nwsp Stf; Rep Jr Cls; Rep Sr Cls; High Hon Roll; Harvard Bk Prz 84; Cont Math Leag Awd 82; Physics.

PINTO, ROSA; Bishop Fenwick HS; Peabody, MA; (Y); Intnl Clb; Church Choir; Hon Roll; Prfct Atten Awd; YMCA Awds Swim 84; Aeronutcs.

PIOTTE, SHARON; Maynard HS; Maynard, MA; (Y); 8/102; Band; Chorus; Fld Hcky; Sftbl; Hon Roll; VP NHS; Church Choir; Concert Band; Mrchg Band; Gym; ROTC Schlr/Athl Awd 85; Digital Schlrshp 85; David Mc Kenna Music Schlrshp 85; New Hampshire Coll; Hotl Mgmt.

PIRES, LUBELIA; Durfee HS; Fall River, MA; (Y); 33/600; Church Yth Grp; Chorus; Yrbk Stf; Hon Roll; Physcl Therpy.

PIRES, NANCY; New Bedford HS; New Bedford, MA; (Y); 26/688; Church Yth Grp; Hosp Aide; JCL; Yrbk Stf; High Hon Roll; NHS; Sthrn MA U; RN.

PIRES, RICHARD; New Bedford HS; New Bedford, MA; (Y); 15/750; Am Leg Boys St; Var Crs Cntry; Var Trk; High Hon Roll; Hon Roll; Jr NHS; NHS; Outstndng Achvt Portuguese 85; Delta Kappa Sama Essay Cnts 3rd Pl Awd 84; Chem.

PISANI, DEBRA ANN; Tri County Reg Vo-Tech HS; Franklin, MA; (Y); JV Var Bsktbl; Var Sftbl; Var L Vllybl; Hon Roll; Cmrcl Art.

PISANO JR, ROBERT; Franklin HS; Franklin, MA; (Y); Varsity Clb; Var Bsbl; Var Golf; Ntl Global Art Awd 84; Boston Globe Schlstc Art Awd 85; Art.

PISARCZYK, DANIEL; Holyoke Catholic HS; Easthampton, MA; (Y); Chess Clb; Computer Clb; Spanish Clb; Sec Stu Cncl; Im Bsktbl; Im Golf; U Of MA; Socl Sci.

PISCITELLO, MICHAEL; Melrose HS; Melrose, MA; (Y); 4/400; Hon Roll; NHS.

PITCHER, SARA HAMPTON; Hingham HS; Hingham, MA; (Y); Mrchg Band; Symp Band; JV Tennis; High Hon Roll; Hon Roll; NCTE Awd; NHS; Yrbk Stf; Brown U Bk Awd 8; Cert Of Hnrbl Mrt Natl Latin Exam 85; Mbr Of S Eastern MA SEMSBA & Dist Cncrt Bnds; Frgn Lang.

PIVA, DARLENE MARIE; B M C Durfee HS; Fall River, MA; (Y); 19/667; Color Guard; Twrlr; High Hon Roll; Hon Roll; NHS; Lwyr.

PIZANA, CLEO R; English HS; Mattapan, MA; (Y); 11/100; Chrmn Church Yth Grp; Drama Clb; FCA; Church Choir; School Play; Yrbk Stf; Sec Soph Cls; Stu Cncl; Hon Roll; Boston Globe Drama Fest-Bst Actr 83, 84 & 85; Emerson Coll Drama Fest-Bst Actr 83; Emerson Schlrshp 85; Emerson; Theatre.

PIZZA, MICHAEL; Clinton HS; Clinton, MA; (Y); 7/130; Trs Am Leg Boys St; Intnl Clb; School Play; Yrbk Stf; Off Jr Cls; Stu Cncl; JV Ftbl; Var Trk; NHS; Alt Cong Exch Pgm 85.

PIZZANO, KYM; Saint Louis Acad; Lowell, MA; (Y); Drama Clb; Pres French Clb; Teachers Aide; Chorus; School Play; Variety Show; VP Frsh Cls; Trs Soph Cls; Hst Jr Cls; Hst Sr Cls; Hon Roll Awd 81-85; Chrstn Awd 85; U Of Lowell; Engl.

PIZZICHEMI, MONIKA; Mt Everrett Regional Schl; Gr Barrington, MA; (Y); 8/75; Girl Scts; Band; Church Choir; Concert Band; Mrchg Band; School Play; Rep Soph Cls; Rep Jr Cls; Rep Sr Cls; Stu Cncl; Acad Achvt In Fine Arts 85; MA Coll Of Art; Commrcl Artst.

PLACE, JACQUELINE; Newton North HS; Newton, MA; (Y); Nwsp Rptr; Nwsp Stf; Off Soph Cls; Off Jr Cls; Off Sr Cls; Stu Cncl; Vllybl; Hon Roll; Schl & Cmmnty Svc Awd 84-85; Outstndng Hse Cncl Membr 84-85; Hse Cncl Pres 84; U MA Amherst; Fshn Mktg.

PLANTE, CAMILLE R; Quaboag Regional HS; Warren, MA; (Y); 18/88; Spanish Clb; Band; Yrbk Stf; Bsktbl; Hon Roll.

PLASSE, LISA; Bartlett HS; Webster, MA; (Y); French Clb; VP Soph Cls; VP Jr Cls; Var Cheerleading; Var Socr; Var Sftbl; Hon Roll; Psych.

PLAYER, TRAVIS M; Lunenburg HS; Lunenburg, MA; (Y); Aud/Vis; Red Cross Aide; Stage Crew; Nwsp Phtg; Yrbk Phtg; Yrbk Stf; Socr; Trk; Wt Lftg; Hon Roll; VP The Travel Clb Awd 84; Fitchburg ST Coll; Business.

PLAZA, BEGONA; Doherty Memorial HS; Worcester, MA; (Y); Art Clb; Church Yth Grp; Office Aide; Cheerleading; Hon Roll; Worcester Art Museum Schlsp 83; Holy Cross; Math.

PLOURDE, CHRIS; New Bedford HS; New Bedford, MA; (Y); Band; Concert Band; Drm & Bgl; Mrchg Band; Orch; School Musical; Symp Band; Var L Tennis; High Hon Roll; Hon Roll; Band Cls A ST Champs & Inaugrl Parade 83; SMU; Chem.

PLUHAR, CHRISTOPHER; Norwood HS; Norwood, MA; (Y); 8/330; Am Leg Boys St; Mrchg Band; Symp Band; NHS; Nwsp Stf; Yrbk Bus Mgr; Trk; Hon Roll; Wnr Hstry & Math Cntst 85; Cert Of Merit In Physcs 85; MIT; Physcs.

PLUNKETT, MARY; Wellesley HS; Wellesley, MA; (Y); AFS; Church Yth Grp; Drama Clb; German Clb; Stage Crew; Stu Cncl; Mrktng.

POCIS, CHERYL; Leicester HS; Cherry Valley, MA; (S); 15/110; Stu Cncl; Hon Roll; NHS; Worcester ST Coll; Child Psych.

PODOSEK, PAULA JEAN; Cathedral HS; Ludlow, MA; (Y); 48/420; Sec Trs Intnl Clb; Hon Roll; Excllnc In French I & II 83-84; Outstndng Svc Intl Clb 85; French.

POIRIER, CAROLYN M; Holy Name C C HS; Rochdale, MA; (Y); 14/239; Pep Clb; School Musical; Lit Mag; Cheerleading; High Hon Roll; Hon Roll; NHS; Hnrb Mntn ST Historical Conf Term Paper Cont 85; U Of Lowell; Phys Therapy.

POIRIER, CARRIE; Holyoke Catholic HS; Granby, MA; (Y); Camera Clb; Hosp Aide; Pep Clb; Spanish Clb; Stage Crew; Yrbk Stf; Holyoke CC; Lab Tech.

POIRIER, DAVID J; Fitchburg HS; Fitchburg, MA; (Y); 24/243; Boy Scts; Bsbl; Coach Actv; Var Trk; Am Leg Boys St; Computer Clb; Political Wkr; Spanish Clb; Im Bsktbl; Cit Awd; Ripon Dstngshd Schlr Awd 85; Maj Gen Wm G Blakefield Army ROTC Hnr Schlrshp 85; Eagle Sct Awd 85; Ripon Coll; Hstry.

POIRIER, GARY; Holyoke Catholic HS; Holyoke, MA; (Y); 4/145; Boy Scts; Chess Clb; Church Yth Grp; Computer Clb; French Clb; JA; Latin Clb; JV Bsbl; High Hon Roll; NHS; Alg,Geo,Physcl Sci Awd 83-84; MIT; Engr.

POIRIER, JONATHAN A; Hampshire Regional HS; Williamsburg, MA; (Y); 16/110; Am Leg Boys St; Ski Clb; Variety Show; Off Stu Cncl; Var L Bsbl; Var L Bsktbl; Var L Socr; Hon Roll; NHS; Engrng.

POIRIER, SEAN; North Attleboro HS; No Attleboro, MA; (S); 3/233; JCL; Model UN; Political Wkr; Nwsp Stf; Bsktbl; Tennis; High Hon Roll; Pres NHS; Stu Govt Rep; Model Senate.

POKORNY, ELIZABETH; Chelmsford HS; Chelmsford, MA; (Y); 62/560; Church Yth Grp; Orch; School Play; Var Capt Socr; French Hon Soc; Hon Roll; NHS; Eugene Doody Schlrshp 85; Acdmc Decathlon 84; Nrthstrn U Bstn; Engrng.

POLASKI, GREG; Malden Catholic HS; Medford, MA; (Y); 43/197; JV Bsbl; Var Ice Hcky; Var Socr; Var Hon Roll; MVP-HOCKEY, Soccer 85; Outstndg Achvt Athl Schlrshp 85; Loomis Chaffee Prep.

POLDERVAART, MICHELLE; Southridge HS; Sbridge, MA; (Y); 25/162; Math Tm; Yrbk Stf; Rep Frsh Cls; Rep Soph Cls; Rep Jr Cls; JV Stat Bsktbl; Var Fld Hcky; Hon Roll; Keybrd I Awd 83; Phy Fit Awd 82-85; Stdnt Govt Awd 83; Pre-Med.

POLES, GABRIELLA; Boston Latin Schl; Boston, MA; (Y); 97/300; Church Yth Grp; JA; Key Clb; Latin Clb; JV Powder Puff Ftbl; Hon Roll; NHS; Ribbon W/Merit For Natl Greek Exam 85; Boston Coll.

POLESNAK, STEPHANIE M; Southbridge HS; Southbridge, MA; (Y); 14/176; GAA; Letterman Clb; VP Soph Cls; VP Jr Cls; Var Capt Bsktbl; Var Crs Cntry; Fld Hcky; Hon Roll; Rotary Awd; Exchng Stu To Thailand For Southbridge Rotary Intl Exchng Prog 85-86.

POLIZIO, GAETANO; Rockland HS; Rockland, MA; (Y); French Clb; Socr; Trk; Hon Roll; Boston U.

POLLARD, WILLIAM J; Wilbraham Monson Acad; Wilbraham, MA; (Y); Ski Clb; Var Ftbl; Var Lcrss.

POLLINO, SUSAN; Randolph HS; Randolph, MA; (Y); Dance Clb; Drama Clb; French Clb; Intnl Clb; Temple Yth Grp; School Play; Stage Crew; Hon Roll; Fshn Mrchndsng.

POLLOCK, JODI; Salem HS; Salem, MA; (Y); #8 In Class; Dance Clb; Spanish Clb; Sftbl; High Hon Roll; Jr NHS; NHS; Spanish NHS; Data Proc.

POLLOCK, WENDY J; Dartmouth HS; S Dartmouth, MA; (Y); 49/245; AFS; Cmnty Wkr; Nwsp Rptr; Nwsp Stf; Frnch II Awd 83-84.

POLUCCI, TAMMI JEAN; Hoosac Valley HS; Adams, MA; (Y); 19/169; Trs Church Yth Grp; Hosp Aide; Yrbk Stf; Var L Bsktbl; Coach Actv; Var L Sftbl; High Hon Roll; Hon Roll; NHS; Exchange Club 84-85; Northeastern U; Busnss Admin.

POMER, KATHRYN J; Belmont HS; Belmont, MA; (Y); Sec Church Yth Grp; Latin Clb; Rep Soph Cls; Rep Jr Cls; JV Bsktbl; JV Capt Socr; Hon Roll; Chem Achvt Awd 85; Holy Cross; Med.

POMICTER, BENJAMIN; Boston Latin Schl; Boston, MA; (Y); 32/300; Drama Clb; Math Tm; School Play; NHS; Ntl Merit Ltr; Cntntl Math Leag Ntl Awd 83; Math Assn Of Amer Achvt Cert 84; Amer Invtnl Math Exmntn Prtcptn Cert 85; MIT; Math.

POND, CYNTHIA J; B M C Durfee HS; Fall River, MA; (Y); Cmnty Wkr; Girl Scts; Hon Roll; Accntnt.

PONTE, MARLENE; Bishop Connolly HS; Fall River, MA; (S); Church Yth Grp; Drama Clb; JA; Ski Clb; School Play; Var Cheerleading; High Hon Roll; NHS; Child Psych.

POOLE, KEITH; Arlington HS; Arlington, MA; (Y); Church Yth Grp; Office Aide; Band; JV Ftbl; Var Golf; Bus Mgt.

POOLE, MIKE; Medway JR SR HS; Medway, MA; (Y); 3/160; Church Yth Grp; Drama Clb; School Play; Yrbk Stf; High Hon Roll; Hon Roll; NHS; Comp Sci.

POOLER, KRISTIN; Nauset Regional HS; N Eastham, MA; (Y); Sec Church Yth Grp; Concert Band; Orch; Sec Soph Cls; JV Bsktbl; Var Mgr(s); Var Score Keeper; Var Socr; JV Sftbl; Hon Roll; Busnss Admin.

POPA, JENICA; Boston Technical HS; Boston, MA; (Y); Art Clb; Church Yth Grp; Exploring; French Clb; FHA; Office Aide; Ski Clb; Teachers Aide; Yrbk Stf; Rep Frsh Cls; Dorothea Devereaux Awd 82; Boston Home Tchrs Assn 82; Cert Of Hnr 85; Harvard U; Lwyr.

POPAT, HARSHA; Norton HS; Norton, MA; (Y); Church Yth Grp; Hosp Aide; Library Aide; Office Aide; Church Choir; Yrbk Stf; Hon Roll; Nrsg.

POPKIN, ALAN; Natick HS; Natick, MA; (Y); 35/450; Jr Cls; Bsktbl; JV Ice Hcky; Capt Socr; High Hon Roll; Hon Roll.

PORCARO, CHRISTOPHER; Medford Vo Tech; Medford, MA; (Y); 18/129; Im Trk; Ntl Merit Ltr; Outstndng SR In Automotive 85; Crftsmn Awd 85; Ntl Merit Hnr Roll; MA Bay CC; Auto Technlgy.

PORCARO, PETER; Everett HS; Everett, MA; (Y); Drama Clb; Key Clb; Letterman Clb; Political Wkr; Science Clb; Varsity Clb; Stage Crew; Capt Var Crs Cntry; Var Socr; Var L Tennis; Tufts; Chem Engrng.

PORTER, CAROLYN NOREEN; Bishop Stang HS; Westport, MA; (Y); 47/214; Pep Clb; Yrbk Ed-Chief; VP Jr Cls; VP Sr Cls; Rep Stu Cncl; Vllybl; High Hon Roll; Hon Roll; Lesley Coll; Elem Ed.

PORTER, CHRIS; Marblehead HS; Marblehead, MA; (Y); 80/240; Ski Clb; Ftbl.

PORTER, KATHLEEN; Everett HS; Charlestown, MA; (Y); Cmnty Wkr; Girl Scts; Chorus; School Musical; Hon Roll; Everett High Music Awd 85; Psychlgy.

PORTER, RICK; New Bedford HS; New Bedford, MA; (Y); 179/700; Drama Clb; French Clb; Q&S; Varsity Clb; Y-Teens; School Musical; School Play; Stage Crew; Nwsp Rptr; Nwsp Sprt Ed; Spec Awd Fr 85; Comm.

PORTER, WENDY; Presentation Of Mary Acad; Lawrence, MA; (Y); Church Yth Grp; Math Clb; Church Choir; Yrbk Stf; Rep Jr Cls; Rep Stu Cncl; Var Sftbl; High Hon Roll; NHS; French Clb; Good Sportsmnshp Awd Sftbl 85; Psychlgy.

PORTO, WENDY; Apponequet Regional HS; East Freetown, MA; (Y); 4/220; Office Aide; Yrbk Ed-Chief; Sec Sr Cls; Cheerleading; High Hon Roll; Hon Roll; Sec NHS; Johnson & Wales; Bus Mgmt.

POSTERA, BRIAN; Mohawk Trail Regional HS; Charlemont, MA; (Y); Church Yth Grp; Var L Socr; Hon Roll; Chld Psych.

POTTER, CHRISTOPHER; Burlington HS; Burlington, MA; (Y); 100/367; Var Golf; Hon Roll; Lowell U; Law Enf.

POTTER, JOHN B; Malden Catholic HS; Lynn, MA; (Y); 14/200; Boy Scts; Church Yth Grp; Hosp Aide; Quiz Bowl; Concert Band; Swmmng; High Hon Roll; Hon Roll; Hghst Hnrs Hstry & Frgn Lang 83; Svc Awd Union Hosp JR Vlntr 84; Intl Bus.

POTTER, MICHAEL; St Johns Prep Schl; Peabody, MA; (Y); Church Yth Grp; Cmnty Wkr; Varsity Clb; Im Bsktbl; L Var Ftbl; Im Vllybl; Hon Roll; Jr NHS; Ntl Merit Ltr; Grouse Patrol Hkng Clb 83-85; Peabdy Yth Ftbl Coach 82-85; Aerontcs.

POTVIN, ANDREW F; Drury SR HS; North Adams, MA; (Y); 1/175; Am Leg Boys St; Crs Cntry; Wrstlng; High Hon Roll; NHS; Ntl Merit SF; NEDT Awd; Val; Grad MA Advncd Studies Pgm Milton Acad 85; Chrch Lectr; Chancllrs Talent Awd Recip; Elec Engrng.

POULE, LISA; Bishop Feehan HS; Attleboro, MA; (Y); Var Bsktbl; Var Crs Cntry; Var Sftbl; Var Vllybl; Var Ltr Sftbl, Bsktbl; Sun Chronicle Bsktbl Hnrb Mntn 85; U ME Orono; Phys Ed.

POULIN, CARA; Southbridge HS; Southridge, MA; (Y); 15/150; Art Clb; Math Tm; Yrbk Stf; Tennis; Trk; High Hon Roll; Hon Roll; NHS; Sec Soph Cls; Sec Jr Cls; John Vangel Memrl Schlrshp 85; U CT; Phrmcy.

POULIOT, CHRISTOPHER J; Nipmuc Regional HS; Mendon, MA; (Y); 5/86; Am Leg Boys St; Boy Scts; Drama Clb; Chorus; School Musical; School Play; Stage Crew; Variety Show; Yrbk Stf; High Hon Roll; Hugh O Brien Yth Ldrshp Sem 83; Achvt Awd Chorus 84; Atnd Ntl Conf Christian & Jews 84; Design.

POULIOT, EVE; Franklin HS; Franklin, MA; (Y); Cmnty Wkr; Dance Clb; Ski Clb; Varsity Clb; Variety Show; Yrbk Stf; Ed Lit Mag; Capt Crs Cntry; Var Trk; NHS; Record Holder For Bld A Better Bridge Physics 85; Bio.

POUSSARD, CATHY A; Salem HS; Salem, MA; (Y); 11/313; Drm & Bgl; Variety Show; Var Cheerleading; Powder Puff Ftbl; Socr; Sftbl; High Hon Roll; NHS; Pres Schlr; St Schlr; Shlrshp 85; Chmbr Comm; U NH; Bio.

POWELL, MICHAEL; Monument Mountain Regional HS; Gt Barrington, MA; (Y); 1/125; Am Leg Boys St; Dance Clb; Variety Show; Yrbk Stf; VP Sr Cls; Stu Cncl; Var L Bsktbl; Var L Socr; Var L Tennis; High Hon Roll; William Sidney Fndtn Schlrshp 85; High Hnrs 82-84.

POWELL, PAMELA; Natick HS; S Natick, MA; (Y); Drama Clb; Service Clb; Chorus; School Musical; Nwsp Rptr; Rep Jr Cls; Cheerleading; Coach Actv; Spirit Awd 85; Comm.

POWELL, WILLIAM C; Belmont HS; Belmont, MA; (Y); Aud/Vis; Church Yth Grp; Pres Computer Clb; JA; Concert Band; Mrchg Band; Orch; Nwsp Stf; Swmmng; Mstr Cnclr Ord De Molay 85.

POWER, STACY; Mission Church HS; Roslindale, MA; (S); Boys Clb Am; Stage Crew; VP Soph Cls; Sec Stu Cncl; Sftbl; High Hon Roll; Hon Roll; NHS; Comm.

POWERS, DAWN; Malden HS; Malden, MA; (Y); 13/440; Camp Fr Inc; Hosp Aide; Nwsp Rptr; Nwsp Stf; Sftbl; Hon Roll; NHS; Ntl Merit Ltr; Nrsng.

POWERS JR, JOHN R; Bourne HS; Buzzards Bay, MA; (Y); Church Yth Grp; Band; Concert Band; Jazz Band; Mrchg Band; Pep Band; De Molay Past Mastr Cnclr Mertors Svc Awd 84; De Molay Fndrs Mbrshp Awd 84; Rep De Molay Awd 84; Law.

POWERS, KELLY; Beverly HS; Beverly, MA; (Y); Band; Concert Band; Mrchg Band; JV Bsktbl; JV Socr; JV Sftbl; JV Trk; Hon Roll; Good Sprtsmnshp Awd; Frnch Levl I Awd; Comptrs.

POWERS, LAURA C; Arlington HS; Arlington, MA; (Y); 23/415; Stage Crew; Nwsp Bus Mgr; Nwsp Stf; NCTE Awd; Ntl Merit Ltr; Brown U Book Awd 84; Writer.

POWERS, MAURA; Southbridge HS; Sbridge, MA; (Y); 29/144; Church Yth Grp; Band; Yrbk Bus Mgr; Sec Soph Cls; Sec Jr Cls; Sec Sr Cls; JV Bsktbl; JV Fld Hcky; Concert Band; Mrchg Band; Head DPW Stu Gvrnmnt Day 84; Frnch Hnr Roll Rcgntn 84.

POWERS, MICHELE; St Peter Marian C C HS; Shrewsbury, MA; (Y); Office Aide; Pep Clb; Spanish Clb; Rep Soph Cls; Var Cheerleading; Comptv Figure Sktr 78-85; Cert Of Awd Hnrs Chem,Hist & Relgn 84; Salve Regina; Bio.

POWERS, THOMAS G; Natick HS; Natick, MA; (Y); 97/472; Band; Church Choir; Concert Band; Jazz Band; Orch; Symp Band; Rep Soph Cls; Rep Jr Cls; Var L Bsbl; Var L Ftbl; Music Schlrshp Awds 82-84; MVP Hcky 84-85; Schlrshp Strng Qrtt-River Music Schl 82-85.

PRAJZNER, CHRIS E; Holyoke HS; Holyoke, MA; (Y); Latin Clb; Spanish Clb; Yrbk Stf; Golf; High Hon Roll; Jr NHS; NHS; Ntl Merit Ltr.

PRATT, GARY; Greenfield HS; Greenfield, MA; (Y); Hon Roll; Rensselaer Polytechnic Awd 85; U Of MA; Biochem.

PRATT, GREGORY; Falmouth HS; E Falmouth, MA; (Y); Key Clb; Var Capt Lcrss; Var L Socr; Im Wrstlng; Hon Roll; Jr NHS; Advrtsng.

PRATT, R WESLEY; Deerfield Acad; Greenwich, CT; (Y); Aud/Vis; Boys Clb Am; Boy Scts; Chess Clb; English Clb; Latin Clb; Pep Clb; Q&S; Band; Drill Tm; Vanderbilt U.

PRATT, SHARON; High School Of Commerce; Springfield, MA; (S); Dance Clb; Hosp Aide; JA; Band; Yrbk Rptr; Yrbk Stf; Hon Roll; NHS.

PRAZAK, WENDY; Bishop Connolly HS; Tiverton, RI; (Y); 70/200; Ski Clb; Spanish Clb; Score Keeper; Var JV Vllybl; Hon Roll; Marine Bio.

PRECOURT, ELISE; North Attleboro HS; N Attleboro, MA; (Y); 54/250; Church Yth Grp; Powder Puff Ftbl; Hon Roll; Kathrine Gibbs; Exec Sec.

PRENDERGAST, MARYBETH; Revere HS; Revere, MA; (Y); Drama Clb; Pep Clb; School Musical; School Play; Yrbk Stf; Rep Soph Cls; Rep Jr Cls; Stu Cncl; Var L Cheerleading; Var L Tennis; SADD 85; Prdcr & Anchr Prsn Of Schl Tlvsd News 85; Cmmnctns.

PRESCOTT, ELIZABETH; Franklin HS; Franklin, MA; (Y); Church Yth Grp; Dance Clb; French Clb; JV Trk; Hon Roll; Voice Dem Awd; Bus.

PRESTON, DAVID J; Belchertown HS; Belchertown, MA; (Y); 9/75; Chrmn Am Leg Boys St; Boy Scts; Church Yth Grp; Cmnty Wkr; Stu Cncl; Var L Bsbl; Var Bsktbl; Var L Socr; Hon Roll; NHS; Amer Lgn Bsbl 85; Military.

PRESTON, DEIRDRE; Arlington HS; Arlington, MA; (Y); 106/411; Yrbk Stf; Stu Cncl; Bsktbl; JV Sftbl; NHS; SADD Adv Comm; Ntl Merit Hnr Rl 84-85; Francis E Thompson Schlrshp 85-86; Boston U; Pol Sci.

PRESTON, JENNIFER; Barnstable HS; Centerville, MA; (Y); 73/398; Pres Church Yth Grp; Hosp Aide; Ski Clb; Nwsp Stf; Yrbk Stf; High Hon Roll; Cmmnty Svc Awd-Cape Cod Hosp 83; Jrnlst Of Mnth Awd 85; Providence Coll; Jrnlsm.

PREVITE, GAIL; Matignon HS; Lexington, MA; (Y); Civic Clb; GAA; Political Wkr; Hon Roll.

PREZEAU, CHERCHE; Dana Hall Schl; Whitefish, MT; (Y); 1/86; Key Clb; Ski Clb; VP Chorus; Swing Chorus; Pres Sr Cls; Var Fld Hcky; Var Lcrss; Var Trk; High Hon Roll; Hon Roll; Pres Ftns Awd 84-85.

PRIDE, CAROL J; Greenfield HS; Greenfield, MA; (Y); 1/160; Sec Science Clb; VP Spanish Clb; Band; JV Bsktbl; High Hon Roll; NHS; Ntl Merit Ltr; Pres Schlr; Val; Oliver S Plantinga Chem Awd 85; Evelyn K Michelman Scholar 85; Fred W Wells Trst Grnt 85; Wesleyan U.

PRIESTLEY, ANDREW; St Peter Marian C C HS; Boylston, MA; (Y); Boy Scts; Church Yth Grp; Drama Clb; School Musical; School Play; Nwsp Rptr; Nwsp Stf; Var L Crs Cntry; Ntl Merit Ltr; Clark U; Engl Lit.

PRIMEAU, BRIAN O; Fitchburg HS; Fitchburg, MA; (Y); 20/220; Am Leg Boys St; Boy Scts; Computer Clb; School Play; Stage Crew; Yrbk Bus Mgr; High Hon Roll; Ntl Merit SF; H S Alumni Schlrshp 85; Rensselaer Polytech; Astrophysc.

PROCTER, SUNDERLAND; Miss Halls HS; New York, NY; (Y); Spanish Clb; Fld Hcky; Gym; Socr; Sftbl; Vllybl; Hon Roll; Eng.

PROCTOR, NANCY A; St Columbkille HS; Brighton, MA; (Y); Quiz Bowl; Spanish Clb; School Play; Yrbk Stf; Sec Sr Cls; Sec Stu Cncl; NHS; Typewrtng Speed Cert Merit 85; Shrthnd Dcttn/Trnscrptn Awd 85; John Hancock Sec Awd 85; Boston Bus Sch; Exec Sec.

PROGIN, CINDY; Leominster HS; Leominster, MA; (Y); 121/400; Band; Concert Band; Drm & Bgl; Drm Mjr(t); Jazz Band; Mrchg Band; Orch; School Musical; Hon Roll; Best Horn Plyr 82-84; Joanette Of Yr 82-84; Band Boosters Awd 85; Mt Wacnusette Comm Coll; Soc Wr.

PROHASKA, KRISTIN; Randolph HS; Randolph, MA; (Y); Am Leg Aux Girls St; Church Yth Grp; Sec Soph Cls; Sec Jr Cls; Sec Sr Cls; Stu Cncl; Var Capt Cheerleading; Powder Puff Ftbl; JV Sftbl; JC Awd; Advsr Intl Ordr Rainbw Grls 82-83; Spec Ed.

PROKOP, JAMES; Don Bosco Tech; S Boston, MA; (S); Var JV Ftbl; Var Trk; Prfct Atten Awd.

PROLMAN, LISA; Methven HS; Methuen, MA; (Y); 3/374; Intnl Clb; Sec Trs Temple Yth Grp; School Musical; School Play; Variety Show; Nwsp Rptr; Yrbk Rptr; Rep Stu Cncl; High Hon Roll; NHS; Eng.

PROPATIER, STEPHEN; St Raphael Acad; Seekonk, MA; (Y); 36/260; Nwsp Rptr; Rep Stu Cncl; U Of Los Angeles; Pre-Med.

PROSKAUER, DANIEL C; Newton South HS; Newton, MA; (Y); Church Yth Grp; Computer Clb; Drama Clb; School Play; Stage Crew; Hon Roll; Ntl Merit Ltr.

PROTANO, MARIO; North Attleboro HS; N Attleboro, MA; (Y); 58/250; Hon Roll; Harry W & Beatrice R Fisher Mem Trust $650; U Of La Verne; Bus.

PROTASOWICKI, STEVEN H; Quincy HS; Quincy, MA; (Y); 2/350; Am Leg Boys St; Nwsp Stf; VP Stu Cncl; Tennis; High Hon Roll; NHS; Sal; Computer Clb; JA; JV Bsktbl; NASA Spcshtl Prjct Cmndtn 82; New Englns Math League Merit Awd 85; Cntntl Math Comp Cntst Awd 85; Engrng Mngr.

PROUT, JOANNE; Archbishop Williams HS; Braintree, MA; (Y); Church Yth Grp; Cmnty Wkr; Hon Roll; Spn III Awd 84-85; Socl Wrkr.

PROVOST, THERESA A; Leicester HS; Rochdale, MA; (Y); 5/106; Church Yth Grp; Latin Clb; Math Tm; Church Choir; School Play; Nwsp Rptr; Fld Hcky; High Hon Roll; Trs NHS; Pres Hon Scholar 85; Horace Mann NHS Scholar 85; Fitchburg ST Coll; Spec Ed.

PRUCNAL, KELLY; Hopkins Acad; Hadley, MA; (S); 2/55; French Clb; Hon Roll; Stu Advisry Comm Sec 84-85; Syracuse; Pre-Law.

PUDE, DIANA; Westford Acad; Westford, MA; (Y); French Clb; Band; Concert Band; Mrchg Band; Symp Band; Rep Stu Cncl; JV Tennis; High Hon Roll; Hon Roll; Mth.

PUGH, MARY; Hopedale JR/SR HS; Hopedale, MA; (S); 2/61; Am Leg Aux Girls St; Church Yth Grp; Band; Chorus; Drm Mjr(t); Yrbk Ed-Chief; High Hon Roll; NHS; Sal; Superintndnts Cert Acad Exclnc 84; Mus.

PUGLIA, WILLIAM; Boston College HS; S Boston, MA; (Y); 9/280; Church Yth Grp; JA; Math Tm; Ski Clb; Nwsp Rptr; Yrbk Stf; Im Bsktbl; Im Ftbl; High Hon Roll; Edwards Schlrshp Rcpnt 85; Boston Neighbrhd Bsktbl Lgu 78-85; Physics Acad 84-85; MA Inst Of Technlgy; Engrng.

PUGLIARES, ROSANNE; Somerville HS; Somerville, MA; (Y); 24/565; French Clb; Hosp Aide; High Hon Roll; Hon Roll; NHS; Clarnc Mc Davitt Schlrshp-Nrsng 85; St Elizbth Schl Nrsng; Reg Nrs.

PULVER, CHRISTINE; Natick HS; Natick, MA; (Y); 92/443; Sec Trs Art Clb; VP JA; Teachers Aide; Rep Frsh Cls; Soph Cls; Rep Jr Cls; Stu Cncl; High Hon Roll; Hon Roll; Prfct Atten Awd; 1st Pl MA Ind Ed Soc Arch Drwng 85; Tech Drwng Cert Of Merit 84; Arch.

PUOPOLO, JOANNE; Malden HS; Malden, MA; (Y); 90/400; JV Sftbl; Bus Mgmnt.

PUOPOLO, RAPHAELA; Christopher Columbus Catholic HS; Boston, MA; (Y); 6/132; Church Choir; Hon Roll; NHS; Soc Sci.

PURI, NITA; Wilbraham Monson Acad; Wilbraham, MA; (Y); Art Clb; Cmnty Wkr; Hosp Aide; Intnl Clb; Key Clb; Band; Concert Band; School Musical; Nwsp Stf; Yrbk Stf; Tufts U; Bio.

PURYEAR, MONIQUE; Medford HS; W Medford, MA; (Y); 134/489; Church Yth Grp; Cmnty Wkr; Dance Clb; Exploring; Girl Scts; Library Aide; Teachers Aide; Color Guard; Hon Roll; Prfct Atten Awd; Sci Fair Cert 82; Lesley Coll; Spcl Ed.

PUSTINGER, MELINDA; Southwick HS; Tolland, MA; (Y); NFL; Acpl Chr; Chorus; Trk; Hon Roll; Voice Dem Awd; Tchng.

PUTNAM, PAUL; Hopkins Acad; Hadley, MA; (S); 6/50; Church Yth Grp; Spanish Clb; Band; Chorus; Church Choir; Jazz Band; Mrchg Band; Pep Band; Yrbk Stf; U Of MA; Bus Admin.

PUZNIAK, LAURA; Presentation Of Mary Acad; Methuen, MA; (S); Drama Clb; French Clb; Yrbk Stf; Pres Frsh Cls; Var Capt Cheerleading; NHS; Church Yth Grp; Dance Clb; Pep Clb; Red Cross Aide; Certi Lifeguard YMCA 81-85; Hugh O Brien Ldrshp Ambass 83; Miss Salem Jr Teen 84; Bio-Schl Sci Fair 83; Languages.

PUZYN, LORI; Matignon HS; Cambridge, MA; (Y); 74/188; Camera Clb; Science Clb; Spanish Clb; JV Crs Cntry; JV Var Sftbl; JV Var Vllybl; Spanish NHS.

PYSCZYNSKI, LINDA; Bedford HS; Bedford, MA; (Y); 89/213; Church Yth Grp; Concert Band; Mrchg Band; Yrbk Stf; Rep Jr Cls; Bowling; Fld Hcky; Mgr(s); Powder Puff Ftbl; Hon Roll; Fash Merch.

QUAGAN, JENNIFER; Reading Memorial HS; Reading, MA; (Y); Drama Clb; Hosp Aide; Math Tm; Band; Yrbk Ed-Chief; Ed Lit Mag; Stu Cncl; VP French Hon Soc; High Hon Roll; NHS; Bst Sprtng Actress 83; All-Dstrct Band 83.

QUAGLIA, CARLENE; Bishop Feehan HS; N Attleboro, MA; (Y); 115/240; Cmnty Wkr; Ski Clb; Yrbk Stf; Rep Frsh Cls; Rep Soph Cls; Var Bsktbl; Var Trk; High Hon Roll; Hon Roll; Nrsng.

QUALTER, DIANNE; Rockland HS; Rockland, MA; (S); 26/288; Church Yth Grp; Cmnty Wkr; Spanish Clb; Varsity Clb; Yrbk Bus Mgr; Var Socr; Var Sftbl; Im Vllybl; Hon Roll; NHS.

QUAN, SEN; Classical HS; Springfield, MA; (Y); 17/392; Library Aide; Badmtn; Cit Awd; Hon Roll; Prfct Atten Awd; Pres Acad Ftns Awd, Acad Achvt Magna Cum Laude 85; Exclnce Frnch 83; Var Schlrshps; Hnbl Mntn Poetry; U MA; Soc.

QUARANTO, CHRISTINE; Natick HS; Natick, MA; (Y); Church Yth Grp; Political Wkr; School Musical; Rep Jr Cls; JV Crs Cntry; Hon Roll; Mansfield Beauty Acad; Beautcn.

QUEALY, ANNEMARIE; Everett HS; Everett, MA; (Y); Church Yth Grp; Hosp Aide; Intnl Clb; Key Clb; Capt Cheerleading; Capt Pom Pon; High Hon Roll; Hon Roll; Nrsg.

QUENTAL JR, LAWRENCE; B M C Durfee HS; Fall River, MA; (Y); NE & SNE Amtr Bxng Champ 85; US Air Force; Comp Tech.

QUILL, SUZANNE; Matignon HS; Winchester, MA; (Y); 30/200; Drama Clb; School Musical; School Play; Off Jr Cls; Sec Sr Cls; Sec Stu Cncl; Var JV Cheerleading; High Hon Roll; Hon Roll; Natl Hnr Roll.

QUINLAN, JOHN V; Plymouth-Carver HS; Plymouth, MA; (Y); 151/500; Am Leg Boys St; Varsity Clb; Capt Ftbl; Trk.

QUINLAN, SHANNON; Notre Dame Acad; Duxbury, MA; (Y); 28/114; Church Yth Grp; French Clb; Band; Concert Band; Variety Show; Im Bsktbl; Im Vllybl; Hon Roll; Corp Lawyer.

QUINN, BRIDGET; Presentation Of Mary Acad; Salisbury, MA; (Y); Art Clb; Debate Tm; Spanish Clb; School Play; Nwsp Ed-Chief; Nwsp Stf; Yrbk Stf; VP Soph Cls; Trs Stu Cncl; JV Vllybl; Pre-Law.

QUINN, JOHN; Bridgewater Raynahm Regional HS; Raynham, MA; (Y); Am Leg Boys St; Math Tm; Hon Roll; NHS; NEDT Awd; Law.

QUIRK, KRISTIN A; Belmont HS; Belmont, MA; (Y); Civic Clb; Cmnty Wkr; Concert Band; Nwsp Rptr; Rep Jr Cls; Rep Sr Cls; JV Var Bsktbl; JV Capt Socr; Var Trk; Jr NHS; Vrsty Bsktbll Div II Northern MA ST Chmps 85; Band-MICA Fest Gold Medlst 85; URI 1st Pl Awd 84-85.

QUIRK, PATRICK J; Boston College HS; Brockton, MA; (Y); 11/300; Am Leg Boys St; Cmnty Wkr; Spanish Clb; Nwsp Stf; Lit Mag; Im Ftbl; NHS; High Hon Roll; BC High Entrnc Exam & James J Dunn Schlrshp 82-86; Coll Holy Crss Bk Awd 85; Stu Rep Cristo Med Tm; Med.

RABATTINI, CHRISTINA; Fontbonne Acad; Stoughton, MA; (Y); 55/135; Church Yth Grp; Drama Clb; Intnl Clb; Pres Chorus; Hon Roll; Jr NHS; Cert Outstng Wrk Spnsh III Hnrs & Bronze Medal 85; Flagler Coll; Spnsh.

RABAZZI, PAUL; Burlington HS; Burlington, MA; (Y); VP Aud/Vis; Debate Tm; Im Bsktbl; Hon Roll; Comp Sci.

RABIN, SCOTT H; Marblehead HS; Marblehead, MA; (Y); 47/256; Nwsp Phtg; Band; Pres Chorus; Jazz Band; School Musical; Swing Chorus; Variety Show; Rep Jr Cls; Fredric Chopin Piano Awd 85; Bus.

RACETTE, JULIE; Drury SR HS; N Adams, MA; (Y); 21/163; Off Band; Chorus; School Musical; Trs Soph Cls; Trs Jr Cls; Trs Sr Cls; High Hon Roll; Drama Clb; Mrchg Band; Western Dist Chorus 84-85; MA All ST Chorus 85; SR Prom Queen 85; Skidmore Coll; Music.

RACETTE, SUSAN; Bishop Stang HS; Fall River, MA; (Y); 24/212; Church Yth Grp; Pep Clb; Band; Yrbk Stf; Var Trk; Var Vllybl; High Hon Roll; NHS; Rck Rnng Clb Schlrshp 85; Physlgy & Relgn Acad Awds 84-85; U Of MA; Anml Sci.

RACHMACIEJ, BRIAN; Holyoke Catholic HS; Southampton, MA; (Y); 25/140; Red Cross Aide; Yrbk Ed-Chief; Yrbk Stf; Rep Stu Cncl; Capt Swmmng; Most Vlble Swimmer 85; Most Dtrmnd Swimmer 84; Psych.

RACZ, JOHN; Clinton HS; Clinton, MA; (Y); Church Yth Grp; Debate Tm; Drama Clb; JA; Math Clb; School Play; Yrbk Ed-Chief; Yrbk Rptr; Yrbk Stf; JV Var Ftbl; Engrng.

RAFFONI, CYNTHIA; St Clare HS; Roslindale, MA; (Y); Church Yth Grp; JA; Nwsp Stf; Yrbk Stf; High Hon Roll; Hon Roll; NHS; NEDT Awd; Prfct Atten Awd; Hghst Acad Avg Biol & Relign II, 2nd Hghst Acad Avg Eng II 84; Hghst Acad Avg Bus Typng I 85; Pre-Med.

RAFTERY, ELLEN; Lynn English HS; Lynn, MA; (Y); Church Yth Grp; Drama Clb; Latin Clb; Office Aide; School Musical; School Play; Yrbk Ed-Chief; Comm.

RAFTERY, MICHAEL; Holyoke Catholic HS; Holyoke, MA; (Y); 40/150; JV Im Bsktbl; Var Capt Socr; Var Trk; Awd MVP Trk Tm 85; Hnr All Western Mass Coaches All Star Tm Trk 85; Ntl Athl 85; Norwich Military Coll; Crmnl Ju.

RAGUE, KURT; Bridgewater-Raynham Regnl HS; Raynham, MA; (Y); Church Yth Grp; Cmnty Wkr; Ski Clb; Off Sr Cls; JV Ftbl; Wt Lftg; JV Wrstlng.

RAGUSA, SCOTT; Malden HS; Malden, MA; (Y); Trs Key Clb; Office Aide; Stage Crew; Variety Show; Rep Frsh Cls; Stu Cncl; Ntl Merit SF; Bentley Coll; Bus.

RAHMAN, FARZANA; Lunenburg HS; Lunenburg, MA; (Y); Hosp Aide; Intnl Clb; Math Tm; Rep Jr Cls; High Hon Roll; Hon Roll; NHS; Ntl Merit Ltr; Math Tutor Lnbrg Elem Schl 84-85; Pre-Med.

RAIMO JR, WILLIAM; Everett HS; Everett, MA; (Y); JV Bsbl; Hon Roll; Engrng.

RAIMONDI, MARIA; Matignon HS; Somerville, MA; (Y); 23/185; Science Clb; Spanish Clb; Church Choir; High Hon Roll; Hon Roll; Spanish NHS; IOF Essay Cont Wnnr 83; Psych.

RAMEY, KENNETH S; Southwick HS; Granville, MA; (Y); 7/113; Am Leg Boys St; Ski Clb; VP Stu Cncl; Var L Bsbl; JV Bsktbl; Var L Socr; VP NHS; Emerald Shield Awd 85; MVP, All Lgu & All Wstrn MA Soccer 84; Exclnc In Art 85; Word Of Life Bible Inst.

RAMIREZ, PATRICIA; Southbridge HS; Southbridge, MA; (Y); 7/140; Hosp Aide; Sec Band; Concert Band; Drm Mjr(t); Mrchg Band; Pep Band; Sftbl; Elks Awd; Trs NHS; Cmnwlth Of MA Schlrshp 85; Ftchbrg ST Coll; Spec Ed.

RAMOS, MONICA; BMC Durfee HS; Fall River, MA; (Y); Church Yth Grp; Variety Show; Yrbk Stf; Gordon Clg; Soclgy.

RAMY, GEORGE; Methuen HS; Methuen, MA; (Y).

RAMY, RAGHIDA; Methuen HS; Methuen, MA; (Y); 65/304; French Clb; Intnl Clb; Library Aide; Spanish Clb; French Hon Soc; Doris Lord Schlrshp, Frnch Awd, Methuen Fdtn Schlrshp 85; Bus Mgmnt.

RANDALL, JOHN C; Norwood HS; Norwood, MA; (Y); Am Leg Boys St; Cmnty Wkr; Var L Ftbl; Var Capt Trk; Hon Roll; Jr NHS; Law Enfrcmnt.

RANDALL, SHARON; Greater Boston Acad; Stoneham, MA; (S); 4/18; Pres Drama Clb; Chorus; Yrbk Ed-Chief; Yrbk Phtg; Pres Jr Cls; Capt Gym; Hon Roll; NHS; Northwestern U; Nrsng.

RANDALL, TANIA E; Holyoke HS; Holyoke, MA; (Y); Church Yth Grp; Cmnty Wkr; French Clb; OEA; Political Wkr; Spanish Clb; Band; Chorus; Orch; School Musical; Am HS Athl 84-85; Lib Arts.

RANDO, MARC; North Andover HS; Mashpee, MA; (Y); 37/242; AFS; Drama Clb; Speech Tm; Chorus; School Musical; Variety Show; JV Var Ftbl; JV Var Trk; Debate Tm; Spanish Clb; Featurve Sub-N Andovers Cls 85; US Cst Grd Axllrys Sailing & Seamnshp Awd 84; Colby Coll; Engl.

RANERI, LEO A; Catholic Memorial HS; Dedham, MA; (Y); 35/277; Key Clb; Rep Frsh Cls; Rep Stu Cncl; Bsbl; Ftbl; Cit Awd; High Hon Roll; Hon Roll; Jr NHS; NHS; Bentley Coll Schlrshp 85; Operation Driver Excell 84; Mrksmnshp Awd 81-82; Bentley Coll; Mrktng.

RANESE, MICHELE; Taunton HS; Berkley/Assonet, MA; (Y); Am Leg Aux Girls St; Church Yth Grp; Office Aide; Ski Clb; Teachers Aide; Drm Mjr(t); Ntl Merit Ltr; Pres Amer Leg JR Aux Unit 121 84-85; Psych.

RANKIN, MICHAEL; Taunton HS; Taunton, MA; (Y); Camera Clb; Nwsp Stf; Yrbk Stf; Ed Lit Mag; High Hon Roll; Hon Roll; Psych.

RANNO, FRAN; Holyoke Catholic HS; East Hampton, MA; (Y); Girl Scts; Latin Clb; Pep Clb; Spanish Clb; Yrbk Phtg; U MA; Bkng.

RANSOM, JOHN A; Marian HS; Framingham, MA; (Y); Chess Clb; Church Yth Grp; French Clb; Varsity Clb; Var JV Bsktbl; Score Keeper; W Catholic Boys Scholar 82.

RAPAGLIA, MICHELLE; Lawrence HS; Lawrence, MA; (S); 40/300; Drama Clb; Band; Chorus; Church Choir; Jazz Band; School Play; Sftbl; Hon Roll.

RAPHEL, BRUCE S; Brockton HS; Brockton, MA; (Y); 53/1000; Am Leg Boys St; Cmnty Wkr; French Clb; Temple Yth Grp; Hon Roll; Prfct Atten Awd; Lbrl Arts.

RAPOZA, DAVID; Mansfield HS; Mansfield, MA; (Y); 35/212; Boy Scts; Dance Clb; Drama Clb; Office Aide; ROTC; Varsity Clb; Chorus; School Musical; School Play; Stage Crew; Boston U; Mgmt.

RAPOZA, MELANIE; Falmouth HS; E Falmouth, MA; (Y); Color Guard; Concert Band; Drill Tm; Mrchg Band; School Musical; School Play; Elks Awd; Hon Roll; Drama Clb; Band; Bus Stu Qtr & Yr 84 & 85; 6 Local Schlrshps 85; Plymouth ST NH; Bus Educ.

RAPOZA, TRACEY; Dartmouth HS; N Dartmouth, MA; (Y); NHS; Acadmc Excllnc Awd 82-85; Portuguese Excllnc Awd & Bk Awd 83-85; Typng Awd 83-84; Southeastern MA U; Psych.

RAPSON, WENDY E; Norfolk County Agricultural HS; Abington, MA; (Y); 2/71; 4-H; FFA; Yrbk Stf; Hon Roll; Pres NHS; Sal; FFA Prfency Awd In Lght Hrs Mngmt; MA Vctnl Assn Awd; Norfolk Cnty Agrcltrl HS Tchrs Fdrtn Awd.

RARICK, TIMOTHY; Wilbraham & Monson Acad; Canaan, NY; (Y); 2/112; Lit Mag; JV Var Ice Hcky; JV Var Tennis; JV Ftbl; Socr; Eveline Barber Dept Prz Acctg 85; Wstrn MI U; Acctg.

RASTAD, MICHAEL; St Johns HS; Grafton, MA; (Y); 50/273; Spanish Clb; Var Tennis; NHS; Ntl Merit Ltr; Boston U; Surgeon.

RATHBONE, MELISSA; Brookline HS; Brookline, MA; (Y); Dance Clb; Drama Clb; French Clb; PAVAS; Variety Show; Yrbk Stf; Hon Roll; Mst Creatv Stu 85; Dnc.

RATTA, SAVERIO; Newton North HS; W Newton, MA; (Y); Radio Clb; Band; Chorus; Concert Band; School Play; Nwsp Stf; Bowling; Hon Roll; Ntl Merit Ltr; Law.

RATTLER, CAROLYN F; Brockton HS; Brockton, MA; (Y); Bsktbl; Sftbl; Wt Lftg; Burdett Schl; Acctg.

RAUCH, JACQUELINE; Natick HS; Natick, MA; (Y); 116/443; Church Yth Grp; GAA; Latin Clb; Band; Chorus; Mrchg Band; Var Capt Fld Hcky; Var Capt Trk; MIP Awd Trk 85; U Mass Boston; Jrnlsm.

RAVIDA, JERALD JOSEPH; Boston Latin HS; E Boston, MA; (Y); Computer Clb; Debate Tm; Political Wkr; Ski Clb; Band; Concert Band; Orch; Symp Band; BHA Full Schlrshp Northeastern U 85; Rafuse Rifle Clb Awd 85; St Olym Rifle Champ 84; Northeastern U Boston; Bus Adm.

RAWDING, BRIDGET; Haverhill HS; Ward Hill, MA; (Y); 3/400; Cmnty Wkr; Latin Clb; Spanish Clb; Nwsp Stf; Yrbk Stf; High Hon Roll; NHS.

RAWSON, LEANNE; Braintree HS; Braintree, MA; (Y); 250/480; Church Yth Grp; Acpl Chr; Chorus; Church Choir; Pres Madrigals; School Musical; School Play; Swing Chorus; Variety Show; Hon Roll; SE Mass Chorale Comp 82-85; SE Mass Bandmasters Assn 83-84; Div II New England Chorale Comp 83; Kings Coll; Elem Educ.

RAY, MICHAEL C; Boston College HS; Braintree, MA; (Y); 1/310; Am Leg Boys St; Chess Clb; Pres Debate Tm; Drama Clb; Pres Intnl Clb; Math Tm; Political Wkr; Nwsp Ed-Chief; Yrbk Ed-Chief; Rep Stu Cncl; Boys Natn US Sen, Princeton & Brown U Awds 86; Natl Lat Exam Silver Medal, Natl Grk Exam Hgh Hnr 86; Harvard U; Lbrl Arts.

RAYDA, STEVE J; Masconomet HS; Boxford, MA; (Y); 32/249; Am Leg Boys St; Boy Scts; Church Yth Grp; JV Socr; JV Trk; JV Var Wrstlng; God Cntry Awd; Hon Roll; Natl JR Olympc Free-Style Wrstlg Rep 85; Ger Exchg Stu 84; Bus.

RAYMOND, HECTOR; Salem HS; Salem, MA; (Y); 11/275; Am Leg Boys St; Nwsp Stf; Yrbk Stf; Var Capt Ftbl; Var Capt Wt Lftg; High Hon Roll; Hon Roll; Jr NHS; NHS; Spanish NHS; MA Maritime Acad; Mech Engr.

RAYMOND, JENNIFER; Bishop Feehan HS; Walpole, MA; (Y); 54/264; Cmnty Wkr; Girl Scts; Library Aide; Color Guard; Flag Corp; Nwsp Stf; French Hon Soc; High Hon Roll; Hon Roll; NHS; Law.

RAYMOND, STEPHEN L; Haverhill HS; Bradford, MA; (Y); 12/400; Church Yth Grp; German Clb; Yrbk Stf; Rep Stu Cncl; Im Bsbl; JV Bsktbl; Im Vllybl; High Hon Roll; Sec NHS; Wnr Germn Poety Rdng Cntst; Stu Of Mnth; Med.

RAYMOND, SUSAN; St Bernards Central Catholic HS; Fitchburg, MA; (S); 5/173; Church Yth Grp; Latin Clb; Yrbk Stf; Pres Frsh Cls; Pres Soph Cls; Pres Jr Cls; Fld Hcky; Sftbl; High Hon Roll; NHS; Harvard U; Med.

RAZZA, CHRISTINA; Ashland HS; Ashland, MA; (Y); Drama Clb; Pep Clb; Poem Pblshd Amer Potry Anthlgy 82; Poem Publshd Glowng Embrs 84; Tutrd Frgn Stus Basc Engl Voc 84; Engl.

RAZZABONI, LORI; North Middlesex Regional HS; E Pepperell, MA; (Y); Trs Jr Cls; JV Var Fld Hcky; Hon Roll; NHS; Rep Frsh Cls; Rep Soph Cls; Powder Puff Ftbl; High Hon Roll.

REA, NELLA; Bridgewater-Raynham Regional HS; Bridgewater, MA; (Y); Latin Clb; Library Aide; Science Clb; Spanish Clb; Teachers Aide; Sec Stu Cncl; Im JV Bsktbl; JV Fld Hcky; JV Tennis; Im Wt Lftg; Pre-Law.

READY, WILLIAM; BMC Durfee HS; Fall River, MA; (Y); Computer Clb; Drama Clb; French Clb; Political Wkr; Science Clb; Ski Clb; Spanish Clb; Varsity Clb; Stage Crew; Variety Show; U Of MA; Elec Engnrng.

REAGAN, DANNY; Natick HS; Natich, MA; (Y); 74/470; Hon Roll; Ntl Merit SF; Engrng.

REAGAN, WILLIAM A; Burlington HS; Burlington, MA; (Y); 2/315; Math Tm; L Var Crs Cntry; L Var Trk; High Hon Roll; NHS; U S Hstry Book Awd 85; Cert Acad Excllnce Italian 83-85; Cert Acad Excllnce Engl 84.

REARDON, B MICHAEL; Falmouth HS; E Falmouth, MA; (Y); Church Yth Grp; Key Clb; Var L Ftbl; Var Capt Lcrss; Var Trk; Wt Lftg; High Hon Roll; Hon Roll; NHS; Natl Sci Olympd Chem Dstnctn 83; Benthos Engrng Schlrshp 85; U Of Vermont; Engrng.

REARDON, NOREEN; Girls Catholic HS; Medford, MA; (Y); Church Yth Grp; Hosp Aide; Trs Soph Cls; VP Jr Cls; Stu Cncl; JV Bsktbl; High Hon Roll; Kiwanis Awd; Sec Pres NHS; Miss TEEN MA Pgnt Cont 85; Math.

REBELLO, ROBERT; Somerset HS; Somerset, MA; (Y); Ski Clb; L Bsbl; L Bsktbl; L Ftbl; Im Wt Lftg; High Hon Roll; Hon Roll; NHS; Chem Engrng.

REBELO, TERESA; Matignon HS; Somerville, MA; (Y); 69/181; Church Yth Grp; Intnl Clb; Chorus; Im Vllybl; 4-H Awd; Hon Roll; Bus.

REBHAN, MARIA; Franklin HS; Franklin, MA; (Y); Librl Arts.

RECK, DEBORAH; Wayland HS; Wayland, MA; (Y); Office Aide; Political Wkr; Ski Clb; Teachers Aide; Sec Temple Yth Grp; Yrbk Ed-Chief; Pres Soph Cls; Pres Sr Cls; Rep Stu Cncl; JV Fld Hcky; Hnrs Bio Achvt Awd 82-83; Hrns Hstry Achvt Awd 83-84; Princpls Lst 82-85.

REDD, LAMONT; Technical HS; Springfield, MA; (Y); Boys Clb Am; Variety Show; Rep Stu Cncl; Var Bsktbl; Var Ftbl; Hon Roll; US Marines; Elec Engr.

REDDING, GEORGE; Joseph Case HS; Swansea, MA; (Y); Aud/Vis; Drama Clb; Band; Drm & Bgl; Jazz Band; Mrchg Band; Rep Stu Cncl; Bsbl; Trk; Actng Merit Of Hnr 84; Indvdl Actng Awd 4-85; MA U; Theatre.

REDDING, JEFFERY B; Nroth Attleboro HS; N Attleboro, MA; (Y); 20/235; Rep Church Yth Grp; Model UN; Capt Tennis; Hon Roll; NHS; Worcester Polytechnic Inst; Eng.

REDFERN, BILLY; Burlington HS; Burlington, MA; (Y); 156/315; Ice Hcky; JV Socr.

REED, CHRISTOPHER; Boston Latin Schl; Boston, MA; (Y); 5/328; Chess Clb; Computer Clb; VP JA; Math Tm; Yrbk Bus Mgr; Var Co-Capt Socr; NHS; Ntl Merit Ltr; U PA Bk Awd Excel Math 83-84; AL Faxon Schlrshp Excel Math, ST All Star Math Tm 3rd 85; MIT; Comp Sci.

REED, MARCIA; Old Rochester Regional HS; Rochester, MA; (Y); 28/146; Art Clb; Drama Clb; Ski Clb; School Musical; Rep Soph Cls; Cheerleading; Crs Cntry; Trk; MMR Tri-Town Dollars For Schlrs 85; Excllnce Art Awd; Southeastern MA U; Visual Arts.

REEDY, CHRISTINE; Marian HS; Framingham, MA; (Y); Rep Jr Cls; Var Cheerleading; Hmcmng Queen; Phys Thrpst.

REEDY, MICHAEL; St Dominic Savio HS; Everett, MA; (Y); Art Clb; Chess Clb; VP Church Yth Grp; Cmnty Wkr; Debate Tm; JA; Ski Clb; Variety Show; Trk.

REGAN, BEVERLY; Woburn SR HS; Woburn, MA; (S); Church Yth Grp; Key Clb; Latin Clb; Spanish Clb; Yrbk Stf; Rep Stu Cncl; Var L Bsktbl; Tennis; Hon Roll; NHS.

REGAN, DENISE M; Cardinal Spellman HS; Hanson, MA; (Y); 32/228; Cmnty Wkr; VP Drama Clb; Office Aide; VP Thesps; VP Chorus; Church Choir; School Musical; School Play; Stage Crew; Variety Show; Eloise Kelly Schlrshp 85; Father Ccallahan Schlrshp 85; Salem ST Coll; Bus Mgmt.

REGAN, KATHERINE; Fontbonne Acad; Readville, MA; (Y); Church Yth Grp; Cmnty Wkr; Library Aide; Teachers Aide; Church Choir; Bowling; Gym; Elem Ed Tchr.

REGAN, SHEILA F; Natick HS; Natick, MA; (Y); 95/426; VP Art Clb; Chorus; School Musical; School Play; Stage Crew; Nwsp Stf; JV Trk; Hon Roll; Hnrb Mntn Boston Ballet Costume Design Cont 5th Prize 84; MA Coll Of Art; Artist.

REGAN, TINA; Fontbonne Acad; Stoughton, MA; (Y); 23/135; Church Yth Grp; Dance Clb; Drama Clb; Hosp Aide; Intnl Clb; Stage Crew; Variety Show; Im Var Bsktbl; Var Fld Hcky; High Hon Roll; Bio Awd 84; Exclnc Chem,Alg II,U S Hist 85; Boston Clg; Nrsg.

REGINA, SUSAN; King Philip Regional HS; Norfolk, MA; (S); Church Yth Grp; DECA; Yrbk Stf; Hon Roll; Pres JR DECA 84-85; 4th Pl DECA Dist Conf 84-85; 3rd Pl DECA ST Conf 84-85; Csmtlgy.

REGIS, CAROLE; Boston Technical HS; Boston, MA; (Y); Debate Tm; JA; Teachers Aide; Frsh Cls; Soph Cls; Jr Cls; Sec Stu Cncl; Sftbl; Ntl Merit Ltr; Prfct Atten Awd; Samuel Morse Awd 82; Cert Merit Stu Govt & Ldrshp 85; Jrnlsm.

REGULUS, MICHELLE L; Phillips Acad; Aurora, IL; (Y); Thesps; Band; Camera Clb; School Musical; School Play; Stage Crew; High Hon Roll; Lbrl Arts.

REICH, MELISSA; Bartlett HS; Webster, MA; (Y); 14/148; Church Yth Grp; FNA; Red Cross Aide; Scholastic Bowl; Spanish Clb; Band; Concert Band; Jazz Band; Mrchg Band; Var L Tennis; Audiology.

REICHERT, HEIDI; North Middlesex Regional HS; E Pepperell, MA; (Y); 2/210; Debate Tm; Hosp Aide; Math Tm; Band; Yrbk Bus Mgr; Trs Soph Cls; Stu Cncl; Co-Capt Powder Puff Ftbl; Trs NHS; Sal; Worcester Poly Tech Inst; Bio.

REID, BARBARA; Bishop Connolly HS; Fall River, MA; (Y); 60/200; Church Yth Grp; Crs Cntry; Trk; High Hon Roll; Hon Roll; Dance Clb; High Hnr Roll 84-85; Trk 82-83; Church Activities 82-85; Phys Thrpy.

REID, BRIAN L; Old Rochester Regional HS; Mattapoisett, MA; (Y); 3/186; Am Leg Boys St; Co-Capt Math Tm; Band; Mrchg Band; Var Co-Capt Socr; Hon Roll; VP NHS; Ntl Merit SF; JV Socr MVP 84; Magna Cum Laude Natl Lat Exam 85.

REID, JUDY; Arlington HS; Arlington, MA; (Y); Cmnty Wkr; Band; Jazz Band; Mrchg Band; Rep Jr Cls; Sec Stu Cncl; Bsktbl; Sftbl; Vllybl.

REID, MARY; Turners Falls HS; Turners Falls, MA; (Y); 24/96; Teachers Aide; Mgr(s); NHS; HS Wmns Clb & Ladies Auxlry Montgu Elks Schlrshps; Keene ST Coll; Erly Chldhd Dev.

REID, MICHELLE; King Philip Regional HS; Norfolk, MA; (S); Sec Soph Cls; VP Jr Cls; Var Tennis; Hon Roll; Jr NHS.

REID, SCOTT K; Lincoln-Sudbury Reg HS; Sudbury, MA; (Y); JV Var Bsbl; JV Var Wrstlng.

REIDY, MARY V; Arlington HS; Arlington, MA; (Y); 105/475; Church Yth Grp; Cmnty Wkr; Exploring; Hosp Aide; Office Aide; Yrbk Stf; Int Dsgnr.

REIDY, PATTI; Dracut SR HS; Dracut, MA; (Y); Diving; NHS; Sailing Inst Lowell Regatta Sailing Mayors Race 2nd 83-85; U Lowell; Chem Prof.

REIL, TERESA; Ware HS; Ware, MA; (Y); Church Yth Grp; Drama Clb; Math Tm; Spanish Clb; Band; Chorus; School Play; Variety Show; Socr; High Hon Roll; Var Socr Ltr 83-84; JR All Amer Band Awd 83-84; U MA Amherst; Biochem.

REILEY, DEBORAH; Bishop Feehan HS; Attleboro, MA; (Y); Sec Church Yth Grp; Drama Clb; Girl Scts; Chorus; Church Choir; Elks Awd; French Hon Soc; God Cntry Awd; Hon Roll; Cmnty Wkr; Intl Order Rainbow Girls 83-85.

REILLY, MARGARET ANN; Academy Of Notre Dame HS; Lowell, MA; (Y); 9/79; Art Clb; Church Yth Grp; Pres French Clb; Key Clb; Library Aide; Stage Crew; Yrbk Stf; Bsktbl; High Hon Roll; Hon Roll; Lngmdw Golf Clb Mem Schlrshp, Svc Merch Schlrshp Fnd 85; Boston Coll; Pol Sci.

REILLY, PAMELA; St Marys HS; Oxford, MA; (Y); 5/50; French Clb; Pres Jr Cls; Trs Stu Cncl; JV Cheerleading; Dstngshd Amer HS Stu 82-85; Engrng.

REILLY, TIMOTHY; Cathedral HS; Springfield, MA; (Y); 5/515; Boy Scts; VP JA; JV Ftbl; L Trk; NHS; Prfct Atten Awd; Mech Engrng.

REIM, MELISSA A; Quaboag Regional HS; W Warren, MA; (Y); Sec VP Church Yth Grp; 4-H; Math Tm; Nwsp Stf; Yrbk Stf; Trs Frsh Cls; Trs Soph Cls; Pres Sr Cls; Sec Stu Cncl; NHS; Chldh Educ.

REINEKE, GRETCHEN; Nauset Regional HS; S Orleans, MA; (Y); 14/150; AFS; French Clb; Intnl Clb; JA; Math Tm; Ski Clb; Teachers Aide; Church Yth Grp; Letterman Clb; Pep Clb; Lndscp Arch.

REINISCH, ULI; Bedford HS; Bedford, MA; (Y); 2/213; VP Pres AFS; Am Leg Aux Girls St; Aud/Vis; Teachers Aide; Lit Mag; Rep Stu Cncl; NHS; Drama Clb; Math Tm; School Play; Foreign Language Awd 82-83; Social Studies Awd 84-85; Best Newcomer Awd-Drama Trnmnt Of Plays 82-83; Bio.

REIS, DANIEL J; Cambridge R & L Schl; Cambridge, MA; (Y); 20/550; Church Yth Grp; Office Aide; Ski Clb; Church Choir; Rep Soph Cls; JV Socr; High Hon Roll; Hon Roll; Jr NHS; Engrng.

REIS, DAWN; Leicester HS; Spencer, MA; (S); Assumption Coll; Corp Lwyr.

REIS, ROSE; BMC Durfee HS; Fall River, MA; (Y); 101/696; Hon Roll; Bristol CC; Accntng.

REMILLARD, KERRI; Methuen HS; Methuen, MA; (Y); 62/395; Yrbk Stf; Powder Puff Ftbl; Sftbl; Merrimack Coll; Soc Wrk.

RENNER, SHEILA; Arlington Catholic HS; Concord, MA; (Y); 32/167; Hon Roll; Magna Cum Laude On Natl Latin Exam 82; Librl Arts.

RENZETTI, JEANETTE D; Foxboro HS; Foxborough, MA; (Y); 30/220; Cmnty Wkr; Band; Concert Band; Jazz Band; Mrchg Band; Tennis; Hon Roll; NHS; Ntl Merit Ltr; Pres Schlr; Hartwick Coll; Bus.

REPPAS, PETER; Cushing Acad; Orange, MA; (Y); Var L Bsbl; Var Capt Bsktbl; Var L Socr; Hon Roll; Jr NHS; NHS; Bettie Davis Awd-Jr Athl Yr 84-85; Rgnl St Sci Fair Awd 84; Bus Admin.

REPPUCCI, LISA M; Cardinal Spellman HS; Stoughton, MA; (Y); 10/202; Cmnty Wkr; Library Aide; Office Aide; Trs NHS; NEDT Awd; High Hon Roll; Hon Roll; 1st Pl Awd Schl Sci Fair; Cardinal Cushng Scholar Regis Coll; Pres Acad Fit Awd; Regis Coll; Bio.

RESENDE, NELSON; Bishop Connolly HS; Bristol, RI; (Y); Computer Clb; Debate Tm; Ski Clb; Bowling; Trk; Hon Roll; Engrng.

RESENDE-SANTOS, JOAO; Boston Latin Schl; Boston, MA; (Y); 53/320; Chess Clb; German Clb; Intnl Clb; Model UN; Yrbk Stf; Lit Mag; Stu Cncl; Socr; High Hon Roll; NHS; Cntry III Natl Ldrs 85; Cert Rcgntn Gvrnr 85; Carleton Coll; Intl Rltns.

RESENDES, ROBERT; Bishop Connolly HS; Tiverton, RI; (S); 15/177; Boy Scts; Computer Clb; Im Bsbl; JV Trk; Hghst Hnr Roll.

RESNICK, JOANNE; Hull HS; Hull, MA; (Y); 10/162; Drama Clb; Chorus; School Musical; Ed Yrbk Stf; Sec Jr Cls; Sr Cls; Var L Cheerleading; Hon Roll; VP NHS; Powder Puff Ftbl; South Shore Regis Club Schlrshp 85; Hull Tchrs Assoc Schlrshp 85; Suffolk U Bk Awd 84; Regis Coll; Educ.

RETT, CHRISTOPHER; Milford HS; Milford, MA; (Y); 77/316; Am Leg Boys St; Church Yth Grp; Band; Concert Band; Mrchg Band; Var JV Bsbl; Var JV Socr; JV Wrstlng; High Hon Roll; Jr NHS; WPI; Mech Engr.

REUL JR, JOHN J; New Bedford HS; New Bedford, MA; (Y); Aud/Vis; Chess Clb; Drama Clb; Teachers Aide; School Musical; School Play; Nwsp Rptr; Stu Cncl; Var Crs Cntry; Var Trk; Excllnce In Ed Awd Tm 84; Accredidtn Tm 84; Rep Sen Kennedy Meetng 84.

REUSCH, MARTHA J; Lawrence HS; Lawrence, MA; (S); 13/390; Cmnty Wkr; Sec Chorus; Off Frsh Cls; Off Soph Cls; Off Jr Cls; VP Stu Cncl; High Hon Roll; JV Bsktbl; Var Sftbl; Merrimack Valley All-Conference Field Hockey Defensive Halfback 83-84; :Lib Arts.

REYNOLDS, JONATHAN; Doherty HS; Worcester, MA; (Y); Art Clb; Chess Clb; Pres JA; Latin Clb; Rep Stu Cncl; Bowling; Law.

REYNOLDS, KRISTIN; Wachusett Regional HS; Sterling, MA; (Y); 12/383; Pres Trs 4-H; School Play; French Hon Soc; 4-H Awd; NHS; Pres Schlr; SADD, Sailing Club, Stu Tutoring Coord Math Dept STUDIA; Wachusett Bld Dr Vol; Bates Coll; Fin.

REYNOLDS, MARYELLEN; Leicester HS; Rochdale, MA; (Y); Stu Cncl; Cheerleading; Fld Hcky; Tennis; Ntl Merit Schol; Accntng.

REYNOLDS, PATRICIA; Taunton HS; Berkley, MA; (Y); 32/400; Cmnty Wkr; Library Aide; Office Aide; Lit Mag; Lbry Svc Awd 85; Real Est Agnt.

REYNOLDS, SCOTT W; Haverhill HS; Haverhill, MA; (Y); 15/400; Cmnty Wkr; Sec Band; Concert Band; Jazz Band; Mrchg Band; School Play; Swing Chorus; Variety Show; Nwsp Rptr; Trk; Fr I Awd 82.

REYNOLDS, TRACY A; Mount St Joseph Acad; Brighton, MA; (Y); 20/168; Church Yth Grp; Cmnty Wkr; French Clb; Hosp Aide; JA; Teachers Aide; JA; Teachers Aide; Variety Show; Im Bsktbl; Boston Coll; Sec Ed.

REZENDES, STEVEN; New Bedford HS; New Bedford, MA; (Y); 33/680; Office Aide; Var Bsbl; High Hon Roll; Hon Roll; Jr NHS; NHS; Engrng.

RHEAUME, MICHELLE M; Westfield HS; Westfield, MA; (Y); 48/364; Hon Roll; Excl Shrthnd I 84; Almnae Assoc 84; Exlcn Typng II 85; Bay Path JC; Cert Prof Sec.

RIBEIRO, DAVID; New Bedford HS; New Bedford, MA; (Y); Church Choir; Aviation.

RIBEIRO, MARIA C; New Bedford HS; New Bedford, MA; (Y); 48/600; AFS; Church Yth Grp; Key Clb; L Fld Hcky; High Hon Roll; Hon Roll; Jr NHS; NHS; S E MA U; Nrs.

RICARDI, LINDA A; Cathedral HS; Ludlow, MA; (Y); Cmnty Wkr; Office Aide; Ski Clb; Concert Band; Yrbk Stf; Prfct Atten Awd; Outstndng Bus Stu Awd, Prsdntnl Acad Ftnss Awd 85; Secr.

RICCI, ROBERT; Doherty HS; Worcester, MA; (Y); Boy Scts; Church Yth Grp; JA; Ski Clb; Varsity Clb; Concert Band; Nwsp Sprt Ed; Var Bsbl; Var Ftbl; L Socr; Holy Cross; Engrng.

RICCIARDI, DEANA; Chelmsford HS; N Chelmsford, MA; (Y); 210/600; Church Yth Grp; DECA; Nwsp Rptr; Lit Mag; JV Gym; JV Trk; Hon Roll; NCTE Awd; Grphc Adv.

RICCIO, JULIE; Burlington HS; Burlington, MA; (Y); 120/369; Yrbk Stf; Rep Frsh Cls; Soph Cls; Stu Cncl; Socr; JV Trk; Cit Awd; Advsrs Awd 83; Brlngtn Pop Warnr & The Shron Impemga Mem Schlrshps 85; Framingham ST; Erly Chlhd Educ.

RICCIO, SHERYL; Bishop Feehan HS; Mansfield, MA; (Y); Sec Church Yth Grp; Pres Frsh Cls; Rep Soph Cls; Rep Jr Cls; Rep Sr Cls; Rep Stu Cncl; Sftbl; Hon Roll; Cmnty Wkr; Drama Clb; Schlrshp Awds In Grammar & Wrtng 83; Srv Awd Outstndng & Cntrbtns To Stu Cncl 83 & 84; U FL Gnsvl; Archtcrl Engrng.

RICCIOLI, KENNETH; St Dominic Savio HS; Revere, MA; (Y); 10/110; Computer Clb; Varsity Clb; Variety Show; Crs Cntry; Ice Hcky; Hon Roll; NHS; Acadmc Al-Amer At Larg Div 85; Bus Law.

RICCIOTTI, MICHAEL; Matignon HS; Arlington, MA; (S); 13/181; Boys Clb Am; Camera Clb; Science Clb; Trk; Hon Roll; NHS; NEDT Awd; 1st Cls Marksman 22 Caliber Rifle 84; Project Zero 84; Woburn Sportsmens Assn 84; US Naval Acad; Engrng.

RICCIUTI, CHRISTOPHER P; North Quincy HS; Quincy, MA; (Y); 8/375; Am Leg Boys St; Nwsp Stf; Off Jr Cls; L Bsbl; L Trk; High Hon Roll; Jr NHS; Cmnty Wkr; Computer Clb; Drama Clb; Lat Natl Hnr Soc 84-85; Brz Mdl Wnr Shotput All Lg Meet 85; Hon Men Schl Sci Fair 83-85; ST Sci Fair; Pre-Med.

RICCIUTI, MARIA; St Bernards CC HS; Fitchburg, MA; (S); 9/169; Office Aide; Pep Clb; Varsity Clb; Nwsp Stf; Sec Stu Cncl; Var Capt Cheerleading; Hon Roll; NHS; Natl Coll Educ Wrkshp 84; Chncllrs Schlrshp 84; Natl Coll Educ Schlrshp 84; Med.

RICHARD, HEIDI; Bishop Fenwick HS; Lynn, MA; (Y); Drama Clb; School Musical; School Play; High Hon Roll; Hon Roll; NHS; Cert Awd Latn III Hnrs 85; Fashn Merch.

RICHARD, MICHELLE; Notre Dame Acad; Groton, MA; (Y); 3/50; Art Clb; VP 4-H; 4-H Awd; High Hon Roll; Hon Roll; NHS.

RICHARD, STEVEN; Leominister HS; Leominster, MA; (Y); Stage Crew; JV Bsbl; JV Bsktbl; Im Mgr Ftbl; Im JV Score Keeper; Im Mgr Vllybl; Hon Roll; Ltr Bsktbl 83; Bus Adm.

RICHARDS, LINDA; Reading Memorial HS; Reading, MA; (Y); Chorus; School Play; Nwsp Rptr; Yrbk Stf; Lit Mag; Rep Stu Cncl; High Hon Roll; NHS; Ntl Merit Ltr; Latin Hnr Soc Treas 84-85; Fin Miss TEEN MA 84; Yth & Family Resources Peer Ldr 84; Cmmnctns.

RICHARDS, STEVEN B; Beverly HS; Beverly, MA; (Y); Boy Scts; Church Yth Grp; Trs Frsh Cls; High Hon Roll; Hon Roll; Educ Enrchmnt Ctr; YMCA & YMCA Swm Tm; Engrng.

RICHARDS, TAMARA L; Franklin HS; Franklin, MA; (Y); Church Yth Grp; DECA; Ski Clb; Speech Tm; Rep Soph Cls; JV Bsktbl; JV Sftbl; Hon Roll; NHS; RI Schl Dsgn; Cmrcl Art.

RICHARDSON, DEBBIE; Methuen HS; Methuen, MA; (Y); 122/365; Church Yth Grp; Intnl Clb; L Bsktbl; Powder Puff Ftbl; L Trk.

RICHARDSON, JODI; Lynn Classical HS; Lynn, MA; (Y); Aud/Vis; Pres Church Yth Grp; Spanish Clb; Variety Show; Stu Cncl; Bsktbl; Sftbl; Tennis; Hon Roll.

RICHARDSON, MARVIN; Technical HS; Springfield, MA; (Y); Aud/Vis; Chess Clb; Computer Clb; JA; Rep Stu Cncl; Var Ftbl; Hon Roll; FL Inst Of Tech; Cmptr Sci.

RICHARDSON JR, NEHEMIAH E; Ayer HS; Shirley, MA; (Y); 2/150; Orch; Nwsp Rptr; Rep Frsh Cls; Rep Soph Cls; Rep Stu Cncl; NHS; Ntl Merit Ltr; High Hon Roll; Mu Alp Tht; 17 Magzn GM Concertio Comp 84; Boston Symph Orch Concerto Comp 83; Harvard Musical Assoc Achvt Awd 85; Harvard; Engr.

RICHMOND, MICHELLR; Archbishop Williams HS; Quincy, MA; (Y); Library Aide; Trs Ski Clb; Stage Crew; Yrbk Stf; Rep Frsh Cls; Rep Soph Cls; Rep Jr Cls; Hon Roll; Jr NHS; NHS; Spnsh Awd 83-84; Hghst Avg Sci Awd 83-84; Spnsh Awd 84-85; Accntnt.

RICHMOND, SHEILA; Matignon HS; W Medford, MA; (S); 3/192; Hosp Aide; Library Aide; Nwsp Rptr; Rep Stu Cncl; Trk; High Hon Roll; NHS; NEDT Awd; Hosp Jr Volunteer 84; ST House Tour Guide Vol 83-84; Tufts; Engrng.

RICK, BRIAN; Northfield Mt Hermon Schl; Reading, PA; (Y); Debate Tm; Var Wrstlng; Ntl Merit SF.

RICKARD, MARK; St Johns HS; Northboro, MA; (Y); 23/273; VP Trs Church Yth Grp; French Clb; Model UN; Im Bsktbl; High Hon Roll; Hon Roll; NHS; Ntl Merit Ltr; Bus.

RICKLEY, CAROL; Methuen HS; Methuen, MA; (Y); 4/365; Church Yth Grp; Intnl Clb; Model UN; Nwsp Stf; Stu Cncl; Powder Puff Ftbl; High Hon Roll; NHS; Hnrbl Men St Histrcl Conf Frmngham ST Coll 85; Elec Engnrng.

RIDDICK, LISA; Lawrence HS; Lawrence, MA; (Y); 40/310; Pres Church Yth Grp; Drama Clb; Model UN; Science Clb; Band; Nwsp Ed-Chief; Yrbk Ed-Chief; Hon Roll; NHS; Prfct Atten Awd; Robert E Sault Mem Scholar 85; Matthew Traynor Scholar 85; Yrbk Awd 85; U MA; Pol Sci.

RIDDICK, TIMOTHY; Madison Park HS; Boston, MA; (Y); Boy Scts; Church Yth Grp; Church Choir; Bsbl; Bsktbl; Ftbl; Gym; Sftbl; Swmmng; Trk; Northeastern U; Bsktbl.

RIDING, BEVERLY JAN; Shrewsbury SR HS; Shrewsbury, MA; (Y); Cmnty Wkr; Debate Tm; Drama Clb; Girl Scts; Letterman Clb; Mathletes; Math Clb; NFL; Speech Tm; Teachers Aide; Fitchburg ST Coll; Spec Ed.

RIEMER, GRETCHEN; Milton HS; Milton, MA; (Y); 33/250; AFS; Art Clb; Drama Clb; School Play; Nwsp Rptr; Nwsp Stf; Lit Mag; Socr; Hon Roll; NHS; Exchng Stu-Finland 85-86; Bus.

RIETH, PATRICIA; Berncoat SR HS; Worcester, MA; (Y); 56/270; JA; Office Aide; Bowling; Crs Cntry; Swmmng; Hon Roll; St Schlr; Boston Globe Schltc Art Awds 82; Schltc Gold Key Awd 82; ST Scholar 85; Worcester ST Coll.

RIGANO, CHARISSA M; Belmont HS; Belmont, MA; (Y); Drama Clb; Hosp Aide; PAVAS; Band; Concert Band; Drm & Bgl; Mrchg Band; Orch; Pep Band; Var Mgr Bsktbl; Belmont Schl Cmmtee Awd Music 84-85; Engrng.

RIGAZIO, DAVID L; Reading Memorial HS; Reading, MA; (Y); 36/360; Camera Clb; Am Leg Aux Girls St; Variety Show; Nwsp Rptr; Nwsp Stf; Yrbk Stf; Stu Cncl; Trk; High Hon Roll; Pres Schlr; Boston Coll; Law.

RIGGS, GLENN R; Tantasqua Regional HS; Brookfield, MA; (Y); 26/189; Band; Concert Band; Jazz Band; Mrchg Band; Pep Band; NHS.

RILEY, BRIDGET; Ayer SR HS; Ayer, MA; (Y); 11/180; Drama Clb; Pep Clb; School Play; Nwsp Rptr; Yrbk Rptr; Yrbk Stf; Pres Frsh Cls; Powder Puff Ftbl; Hon Roll; Boston U; Pre-Law.

RILEY, ELIZABETH; Cohasset HS; Cohasset, MA; (Y); 10/122; Jazz Band; Yrbk Stf; Powder Puff Ftbl; Powder Puff Ftbl; Socr; Trk; High Hon Roll; Hon Roll; Ntl Merit SF.

RILEY, JOANNE; St Clare HS; Dedham, MA; (Y); 15/150; Boys Clb Am; Church Yth Grp; JCL; JV Capt Bsktbl; Sftbl; High Hon Roll; Hon Roll; Prfct Atten Awd; MVP For St Annes CYO Sftbl 83; Chrstian Atlt Awd For St Marys CYO Bsktbl 83; Pre-Med.

RILEY, PATRICIA A; Hanover HS; Hanover, MA; (Y); 31/200; Chorus; Church Choir; School Musical; Yrbk Stf; Cheerleading; Hon Roll; Choral Creed Awd 85; George L Higginson Mem Mus Awd 85; Westfield ST Coll.

RINALDI, JOHN M; Acton-Baxborough Regional HS; Boxborough, MA; (Y); Church Yth Grp; FCA; Spanish Clb; Ice Hcky; Socr; Trk; Wt Lftg; Hon Roll; Denver CO; Mrktng.

RINALDO, MARIA; Holy Wamc Central Catholic HS; Worcester, MA; (Y); 5/270; Ski Clb; School Play; Rep Frsh Cls; Var Bsktbl; High Hon Roll; Hon Roll; Ctzn Law Awd, Outstndng Schlstc Achvt Awd, Amer Lit Awd 85; Corp Law.

RINEHART, LUCY; Newton North HS; West Newton, MA; (Y); Cmnty Wkr; French Clb; Chorus; Yrbk Stf; Ntl Merit SF; Magna Cum Laude Awd; Psych.

RINGUETTE, MICHELLE; Agawam HS; Agawam, MA; (Y); 74/310; Hon Roll; NHS; Arthr Nadeau Schlrshp 85; Western New England Coll; Psych.

RINGUETTE, ROBERT; Bishop Feehan HS; N Attleboro, MA; (Y); Im Bsktbl; JV Crs Cntry; Trk; Hon Roll.

RINKER, CYNTHIA; Tahanto Regional HS; Boylston, MA; (Y); 1/60; Cmnty Wkr; Hosp Aide; Math Tm; Bausch & Lomb Sci Awd; Lion Awd; Pres NHS; Val; Science Clb; Chorus; School Musical; Digtl Equip Corp Schlrshp 85; Worcestr Telegrm Gazette Stdnt Achvt Awd 85; Harvard Bk Awd; Georgetown U; Chem.

RINNIG, ELISA B; Sharon HS; Sharon, MA; (Y); 32/209; Hosp Aide; JCL; Ski Clb; VP Temple Yth Grp; Nwsp Stf; Yrbk Stf; Stu Cncl; Pom Pon; Hon Roll; Drama Clb; Hnbl Mntn ST Wd Phi Alpha Theta U S Hstry Conf Wrttn Essy 85; Bio.

RIORDAN, JOANNE; Billerica Memorial HS; Billerica, MA; (Y); 54/500; French Clb; Varsity Clb; Yrbk Stf; Var L Crs Cntry; Var Powder Puff Ftbl; Trk; Mrktng.

RIOUX, GABRIELLE; Marian HS; Framingham, MA; (Y); Chorus; School Play; Yrbk Stf; Hon Roll; NEDT Awd; Adv Frnch Conv & Holy Crss Clg Bk Awds 85; Bryn Mawr Coll; Frnch.

RIOUX, MICHELE; Mount Saint Joseph Acad; Dorchester, MA; (Y); 11/145; Drama Clb; Girl Scts; Hosp Aide; JA; Pep Clb; Variety Show; Hon Roll; NHS; Math Clb; Holy Cross Bk Awd 85; Natl Bus Hon Soc 85; Gen Excllnce Awd 85; Stonehill Coll; Bus Mngmnt.

RIOUX, RENEE; Westport HS; Westport, MA; (Y); Church Yth Grp; Yrbk Stf; High Hon Roll; Hon Roll; Bristol CC; Drftng.

RIPLEY, REBECCA; Hanover HS; Hanover, MA; (Y); Church Yth Grp; Rep Band; Rep Concert Band; Rep Mrchg Band; School Musical; High Hon Roll; Hon Roll; Typng Awd 83-84; Band Awd 84-85; Nrs.

RISTI, JULIE; St Rose HS; East Boston, MA; (Y); 5/45; Drama Clb; School Play; Variety Show; Yrbk Stf; Trs Soph Cls; VP Jr Cls; Var Capt Cheerleading; High Hon Roll; Hon Roll; NHS; Drama Awd 83; Suffolk U; Accntng.

RISUX, MICHELE; Mount St Joseph Acad; Dorchester, MA; (Y); 11/150; VP Church Yth Grp; Drama Clb; Girl Scts; Hosp Aide; JA; Math Clb; Pep Clb; Chorus; Stage Crew; Variety Show; Ntl Bus Hnr Soc 85; Holy Cross Bk Recpnt Awd Wnnr 84; Gnrl Acadmc Excllnc In H S Medal 85; Stonehill Coll; Bus Mgmt.

RITSHER, W DAVID; Lincoln-Sudbury Reg HS; Lincoln, MA; (Y); Aud/Vis; Computer Clb; Math Tm; Band; Orch; Pep Band; Ntl Merit SF; Count Of ERA 80-84; Space Lab.

RITTENBERG, SHERI R; Burlington HS; Burlington, MA; (Y); 47/310; Cheerleading; Gym; Mgr(s); Powder Puff Ftbl; Score Keeper; Hon Roll; NHS; Coaches Awd For Tumblettes 85; Accntng.

RITUCCI, DONALD M; Brockton HS; Brockton, MA; (Y); 18/1100; Am Leg Boys St; Church Yth Grp; Cmnty Wkr; Key Clb; Nwsp Rptr; Off Frsh Cls; Off Soph Cls; Off Jr Cls; Off Sr Cls; Var Ftbl; David E Crosby Book Awd For Dstngshd Acad & Cmnty Achv 84-85; Cum Laude Natl Latin Exam 84-85; Finc.

RIVERA, JACQUELINE; Boston Technical HS; Boston, MA; (Y); Camera Clb; Ski Clb; High Hon Roll; Hon Roll.

RIVERS, STEPHEN F; Cathedral HS; Springfield, MA; (Y); Church Yth Grp; Ski Clb; Brian Sullivan Scholar Awd 85-86; St Jean Baptiste Ed Fndtn Scholar 85-86; Johnson/Wales Acad Scholar; Johnson & Wales; Cul Art.

RIXHAM, DAVID; St Johns HS; Northborough, MA; (Y); Camera Clb; Church Yth Grp; Debate Tm; French Clb; Model UN; Im Bsktbl; Im Tennis; Ntl Merit SF; Brandeis U.

RIZZO, JOSEPH; Everett HS; Everett, MA; (Y); Chess Clb; Church Yth Grp; Cmnty Wkr; JA; Letterman Clb; Varsity Clb; Var Bsbl; Im Bowling; Im Coach Actv; JV Ftbl; Arch Engr.

RIZZO, RALPH; Christopher Columbus HS; Charlestown, MA; (S); 21/121; School Play; Off Sr Cls; Stu Cncl; Var L Bsbl; Var Capt Ftbl; Var L Ice Hcky; Chrstopher Columbus Awd Athlte Of Yr 83-84; Police Sci.

RIZZOTTO, KERRI; Randolph HS; Randolph, MA; (Y); Church Yth Grp; Cmnty Wkr; GAA; JA; Political Wkr; Spanish Clb; Varsity Clb; Yrbk Sprt Ed; Off Frsh Cls; Off Soph Cls; Capt SADD.

ROACH, THOMAS JAMES; Framingham South HS; Framingham, MA; (Y); French Clb; Red Cross Aide; Nwsp Stf; Yrbk Sprt Ed; Stu Cncl; L Bsktbl; L Capt Crs Cntry; L Capt Trk; High Hon Roll; Hon Roll.

ROBAK, KRISTEN; Billerica Memorial HS; Billerica, MA; (Y); 46/520; French Clb; Drill Tm; Flag Corp; High Hon Roll; Hon Roll; Jr NHS; NHS; Nrthestrn U; Chmcl Engrng.

ROBBINS, DONNA M; Ludlow HS; Ludlow, MA; (Y); 23/276; Church Yth Grp; Variety Show; Yrbk Stf; Rep Frsh Cls; Rep Soph Cls; VP Jr Cls; VP Sr Cls; Off Stu Cncl; JV Var Cheerleading; Hon Roll; Distingshd Amer H S Stu Awd 84 & 85; Bentley Coll; Bus.

ROBBINS, ILYSE; Doherty Memorial HS; Worcester, MA; (Y); 6/356; Red Cross Aide; Yrbk Stf; Sec Frsh Cls; VP Soph Cls; VP Jr Cls; VP NHS; Dance Clb; French Clb; Latin Clb; Library Aide; Hiatt Schlr 85; Jewish War Vet Brthrhd Awd 84; Charlotte Dance Co Schlrshp 85-83; Northwestern U; Theatre Arts.

ROBBINS, SARAH; Dana Hall Schl; Wellesley, MA; (Y); 2/88; Drama Clb; Chorus; School Musical; Lit Mag; Pres Frsh Cls; Var Fld Hcky; Hon Roll; Drama Awd 82-83; Comm.

ROBERT, LISA; Dracut SR HS; Dracut, MA; (Y); Library Aide; Nwsp Rptr; Nwsp Stf; Hon Roll; NHS; Cert Merit Awds Poetry 84-85; 2 Poems Pblshd 85; Golden Poet Award; Engl.

ROBERTS, CAROL; Mahawk Trail Regional HS; Colrain, MA; (Y); 42/142; Varsity Clb; Yrbk Sprt Ed; Yrbk Stf; Rep Frsh Cls; Rep Soph Cls; Rep Jr Cls; Bsktbl; Sftbl; Vllybl; Hon Roll; Peer Eductn Honor 85; Vllybl Awd-Leadrshp & Respnsblty 85; Psych.

ROBERTS, DOUG M; Quaboag Regional HS; Warren, MA; (Y); 3/86; Math Tm; Science Clb; Spanish Clb; Varsity Clb; Bsktbl; Hon Roll; NHS; Vrsty Bsktbl All Star 85; Coll; Anthrplgy.

ROBERTS, ERIC M; Triton Regional HS; Rowley, MA; (Y); 24/182; AFS; Boys Clb Am; Boy Scts; Pres Church Yth Grp; Cmnty Wkr; Drama Clb; Band; VP Chorus; Church Choir; Concert Band; All-Amer Band 85; Band Parents Schlrshp 79-85; Eastern Star Grnd & Lcl Chptrs 85; U Of Lowell; Comp Sci.

ROBERTS, JANET; Marian HS; Framingham, MA; (Y); 50/200; Cmnty Wkr; Drama Clb; Hosp Aide; JCL; Leo Clb; Political Wkr; School Musical; Yrbk Ed-Chief; Lit Mag; Rep Sr Cls; Babson Coll; Mktg.

ROBERTS, JOHN; Malden Catholic HS; E Boston, MA; (Y); Rep Stu Cncl; Var Bsbl; Var Ftbl; Var Ice Hcky; Law.

ROBERTS, JOHN; Wachusett Regional HS; Worcester, MA; (Y); Church Yth Grp; Pres Computer Clb; 4-H; Library Aide; Political Wkr; Radio Clb; Var Socr; 4-H Awd; Ntl Merit SF; MA ST Div 1 Sccr Chmps 84; USAF Acad; Elec Engrng.

ROBERTS, LAURA; Bellingham Memorial HS; Bellingham, MA; (Y); Stu Cncl; JV Var Fld Hcky; Var CAP; High Hon Roll; NHS; NEDT Awd; Outstndng Stu Awd 83-85; Chancellors Talent Awd Prog UMASS 85; BHS Counciling Prog 85-86.

ROBERTS, LISA; Boston Latin Schl; Brighton, MA; (Y); 49/290; Chorus; Yrbk Stf; Hon Roll; Spllng Chmpshp Dist IX Cty Boston 85; 4 Yr Schlrshp Museum Fine Arts 82-86; Dixwell Prz Ex Clsscs 84; Art & Sci.

ROBERTS, MARGO; Bourne HS; Otis AFB, MA; (Y); 4/170; Camera Clb; Variety Show; Elks Awd; High Hon Roll; Hon Roll; NHS; Wellesely Awd 84; Westfield ST Coll; Bus Mktg.

ROBERTS, SALLY; Mohawk Trail Regional HS; Shelburne Falls, MA; (Y); 2/96; Am Leg Aux Girls St; Art Clb; Church Yth Grp; Color Guard; Trs Soph Cls; Trs Jr Cls; Trs Sr Cls; Pres NHS; Pres Schlr; Sal; U Of Hartford; Art Ed.

ROBERTS, TERESA; Archbishop Williams HS; Quincy, MA; (Y); 25/289; Church Yth Grp; Computer Clb; Chorus; Variety Show; JC Awd; Psych.

ROBERTS, W; Cathedral HS; Springfield, MA; (Y); 70/500; JV Socr; JV Var Sftbl; U MA; Pre-Med.

ROBIE, STEPHEN I; Brockton HS; Brockton, MA; (Y); 4/1000; Am Leg Boys St; Key Clb; Temple Yth Grp; Var Bsktbl; Im Coach Actv; High Hon Roll; NHS; Cmnty Wkr; Im Score Keeper; MA Stu Govt Day 85; Williams Clg Book Awd 85; Grad Exercises Ushr 85; Pre Med.

ROBILLARD, JAMES; Leicester HS; Cherry Valley, MA; (Y); #15 In Class; Rep Stu Cncl; Capt Ftbl; Capt Trk; Cit Awd; Hon Roll; NHS; U Of MA; Mech Engr.

ROBILLARD, JOSEPH; St Johns Preparatory Schl; Peabody, MA; (Y); Phys Sci.

ROBILLARD, MICHAEL; Chicopee HS; Chicopee, MA; (Y); 12/250; Boy Scts; Church Yth Grp; JCL; Latin Clb; Science Clb; Ski Clb; Yrbk Stf; Swmmng; Trk; High Hon Roll; Rensselaer Polytech; Elec Engrg.

ROBINSON, HEATHER; Medway JR-SR HS; Medway, MA; (Y); 9/130; Yrbk Stf; JV Bsktbl; Var L Tennis; Var L Vllybl; Hon Roll; Jr NHS; NHS; Temple Yth Grp; Yrbk Rptr.

ROBINSON, JOANNE; Marblehead HS; Marblehead, MA; (Y); Drama Clb; French Clb; Spanish Clb; Thesps; School Musical; School Play; Stage Crew; Nwsp Stf; 2 Outstdng Perf In Thtr Awds 85; Boston Globe Schlstc Art Awd-Cert Of Recgntn 83; 1st Pl MA Drm Fstvl; Thtr.

ROBINSON, JULIE; Medwey JR SR HS; Medway, MA; (Y); Varsity Clb; Var Fld Hcky; Var Sftbl; Hon Roll; V Field Hockey Tri Vly Conf Off MVP, Milford Daily News All Star, All Star Leading Scorer 84.

ROBINSON, KIMBERLY L; Framingham South HS; Framingham, MA; (S); 55/285; Drama Clb; Pep Clb; Spanish Clb; Temple Yth Grp; School Musical; School Play; Variety Show; Lit Mag; Trs Jr Cls; Trs Sr Cls; Bus.

ROBINSON, LAURIE; Hoosac Valley Regional HS; Adams, MA; (Y); Pep Clb; Ski Clb; Band; Concert Band; Mrchg Band; Yrbk Rptr; Ed Yrbk Stf; Crs Cntry; High Hon Roll; Hon Roll; Bnd Ltr 83; Crs Cntry Ltr 85; Phrmcy.

ROBINSON, LISA; Ursuline Acad; West Roxbury, MA; (Y); 2/73; Rptr Church Yth Grp; Hosp Aide; Service Clb; Yrbk Ed-Chief; DAR Awd; Pres NHS; Ntl Merit Ltr; Dance Clb; French Clb; Math Tm; 1st Pl N Atlantic Karate Trnmnt JR Whte Belt 84; Hugh Obrian Mass Yth Ldrshp Smnr 83; Chancellr Tlnt; Med.

ROBINSON, MARY B; Palmer HS; Palmer, MA; (Y); 1/97; Ski Clb; Drama Clb; Band; Var Trk; Bausch & Lomb Sci Awd; Dnfth Awd; High Hon Roll; JP Sousa Awd; St Schlr; Val; Pro Merito Soc 83-85; Mt Holyoke Coll; Chem.

ROBINSON, MICHAEL J; Hingham HS; Hingham, MA; (Y); 2/325; Boy Scts; Math Tm; Band; Concert Band; Jazz Band; Mrchg Band; School Musical; High Hon Roll; NHS; Symp Band; Rensselaer Medal 85; Bio Sci.

ROBINSON, ROBERT E; Assabet Valley Regional Vo Tech; Marlborough, MA; (Y); Aud/Vis; School Play; Prfct Atten Awd; Northeast Inst Tech; Arch Drftg.

ROBINSON, SARAH; Bedford HS; Bedford, MA; (Y); 8/227; Drama Clb; Chorus; Concert Band; Jazz Band; Madrigals; Mrchg Band; Orch; Pep Band; School Musical; School Play; Keith L Phinney Awd For Mst Outstndng Vlclst 85; Skiorsky Piano Awd 84 & 85; Bst Actress Awd 84; Boston U; Intl Rltns.

ROCCAFORTE, DENNIS; Boston College HS; South Boston, MA; (Y); Ski Clb; Spanish Clb; Im Bsktbl; Im Ftbl; JV Swmmng; Bus.

ROCHE, ROBERT; Westwood HS; Westwood, MA; (Y); 50/200; Church Yth Grp; Varsity Clb; Band; Concert Band; Jazz Band; Mrchg Band; Yrbk Stf; Rep Sr Cls; Rep Stu Cncl; JV Capt Ice Hcky; MVP Mrchng Band 85.

ROCHE, THOMAS; Hudson HS; Hudson, MA; (S); 1/154; Math Tm; Yrbk Stf; Mgr(s); NHS; Ntl Merit Ltr; Ntl Latin Exam Maxime Com Laude 83-84; MA Advncd Stu Prog 84; Professor.

ROCHELEAU, DENISE; Gardner HS; Gardner, MA; (Y); 31/200; Church Yth Grp; Girl Scts; JV Var Trk; Accntnt.

ROCKWAL, MICHAEL T; St Marys HS; Westfield, MA; (Y); 11/65; Am Leg Boys St; JV Socr; Hon Roll; NHS; Chem & Englsh Awd.

ROCKWOOD, PAIGE; Bartlett HS; Webster, MA; (Y); 25/149; French Clb; Spanish Clb; Yrbk Stf; High Hon Roll; Hon Roll; Htl & Rstrnt Mngmnt.

ROCKWOOD, SAMANTHA; Malden HS; Malden, MA; (Y); Bunker Hill CC; Bus Adm.

RODA, ANA LUCIA; New Bedford HS; New Bedford, MA; (Y); 101/550; Intnl Clb; Library Aide; Sec Office Aide; Sec Nwsp Stf; JV Fld Hcky; Hon Roll; Prfct Atten Awd; Travel.

RODERICK, STEVEN E; Provincetown HS; Provincetown, MA; (Y); 4/40; Am Leg Boys St; FTA; Library Aide; Nwsp Ed-Chief; Yrbk Bus Mgr; Pres Frsh Cls; Pres Soph Cls; Var Mgr(s); NEDT Awd; Stat Bsktbl; Stu Rep Principal Srch Comm; Stu Govt Day Rep; Htl/Rest Mngmnt.

RODERICKS, RON; Brockton HS; Brockton, MA; (Y); 42/1100; Am Leg Boys St; JCL; Key Clb; Off Frsh Cls; Off Soph Cls; Off Sr Cls; Stu Cncl; Var L Ftbl; Var Wt Lftg; Hon Roll; Cum Laude Natl Latn Exm; MA Boys ST Justc Supr Ct; Dntst.

RODERIGUES, DAWN; Somerset HS; Somerset, MA; (Y); Sec Church Yth Grp; JA; Mrchg Band; Nwsp Stf; Yrbk Stf; Sec Soph Cls; Sec Jr Cls; Trk; Twrlr; High Hon Roll; Illustrtn.

RODNEY, MARC-ROBERT; North Cambridge Catholic HS; Cambridge, MA; (Y); Bsktbl; Hon Roll; NHS; US Army Rsrv Athl Awd 85; NE U; Engr.

RODRIGUES, CAREN; Bishop Fenwick HS; Peabody, MA; (Y); Cmnty Wkr; Stage Crew; Nwsp Rptr; Var Cheerleading; Regis; Sclgy.

RODRIGUES, MARCELINA; Madison Park HS; Boston, MA; (Y); Drama Clb; Church Choir; School Play; Socr; Hon Roll; Prfct Atten Awd; Prfct Attndc 83-84; Outstndng Prfmnc & Acadmc Achvt U MA Coll Prep Pgm Awd 84-85; Emerson; Actrss.

RODRIGUEZ, CARLOS; Newton North HS; Newton, MA; (Y); Intnl Clb; Ski Clb; Bsbl; Socr; Hon Roll; Caracas-Venezuela; Engrng.

RODRIGUEZ DE HOSTOS, JUAN E; Phillips Acad; Guaynabo, PR; (Y); Pres Ski Clb; Pres Spanish Clb; Y-Teens; JV Var Tennis; Var Im Vllybl; High Hon Roll; Hon Roll; Val; Engr.

RODRIQUE, JACQUELINE; Leicester HS; Cherry Valley, MA; (S); Pres Church Yth Grp; French Clb; Latin Clb; Math Tm; Band; NFL; Hon Roll; Math Team Cert 82-85; Top Seller Awds 82-85; Pre-Med.

RODRIQUE, TIMOTHEE; Holy Name CC HS; Leicester, MA; (Y); Church Yth Grp; Chorus; Yrbk Phtg; Var Golf; Hon Roll; Voice Dem Awd; U Of Lowell; Mechncl Engr.

RODSKI, PETER; Gardner HS; Gardner, MA; (Y); 4/180; Am Leg Boys St; Trs Frsh Cls; Trs Jr Cls; Var Bsbl; NHS; Chess Clb; Math Clb; Math Tm; Spanish Clb; Mbr Wachusett Lge 1st Tm All Strs Bsbll 85.

ROESER, STEFAN; Marblehead HS; Marblehead, MA; (Y); 11/249; German Clb; Latin Clb; Var Crs Cntry; L Var Trk; High Hon Roll; NHS; Ntl Latn Exmntn Slvr Medal 85; Ntl JETS Tst 82.

ROFFMAN, DENISE; Randolph HS; Randolph, MA; (Y); Spanish Clb; Temple Yth Grp; Drill Tm; Yrbk Stf; Sec Frsh Cls; Hon Roll; JC Awd; NHS; SADD; Stu Adv For Frshmn; Chrprsn Stu Skills Pgm Frshmn; Engrng.

ROGALIN, CATHERINE I; Braintree HS; Braintree, MA; (Y); 7/480; JCL; Math Tm; Yrbk Stf; Var Pom Pon; French Hon Soc; High Hon Roll; NHS; Ntl Merit SF; Prfct Atten Awd; Eng.

ROGALSKI, APRIL DAWNE; Saugus HS; Saugus, MA; (Y); Intnl Clb; Band; Chorus; Capt Flag Corp; Mrchg Band; Pom Pon; Swmmng; VFW Awd; Voice Dem Awd; Church Yth Grp; Nomnee Miss Greater Lynn Pgnt 85; Boston U; Journ.

ROGERS, BETSY; Stepherd Hill Regional HS; Charlton, MA; (Y); Am Leg Aux Girls St; Math Tm; Chorus; School Musical; Yrbk Bus Mgr; Hon Roll; NHS; Prfct Atten Awd; U Of CT; Engl.

ROGERS, HEIDI; New Bedford HS; New Bedford, MA; (Y); 102/664; Church Yth Grp; Dance Clb; Drama Clb; Library Aide; Office Aide; Stu Cncl; High Hon Roll; Hon Roll; Southeastern MA U; Lab Tech.

ROGERS, J PETER; Bishop Feehan HS; Attleboro, MA; (Y); Chess Clb; Var Ice Hcky; Var Trk; Hon Roll; Accntnt.

ROGERS, JASON; Easthampton HS; Easthampton, MA; (Y); 5/140; Am Leg Boys St; Debate Tm; Band; Chorus; Stu Cncl; High Hon Roll; NHS; Ntl Merit Ltr; NEDT Awd; Easthampton Ed Assn 85; Ctzns Scholar 85; U Of MA; Psych.

ROGERS, JEFFREY; New Bedford HS; New Bedford, MA; (Y); 121/653; Aud/Vis; Office Aide; Stage Crew; Nwsp Stf; Trk; High Hon Roll; Hon Roll; Ntl Merit Ltr; SMU; Mecd Tech.

ROGERS, JEFFREY W; Walpole HS; E Walpole, MA; (Y); Church Yth Grp; Ski Clb; Hon Roll; Var JV Bsbl; Var Golf; Var Capt Wrstlng; Clsrm Prfrmnce Awd Chem 85; Phys Thrpy.

ROGERS, JILL S; Lexington HS; Lexington, MA; (Y); Drama Clb; Latin Clb; School Musical; Stage Crew; Yrbk Stf; Hon Roll; Jr NHS; Ntl Merit Ltr; Lang Awd; Cornell U; Pre-Med.

ROGERS, JULIE; Ursuline Acad; Norwood, MA; (Y); 7/73; Drama Clb; VP French Clb; School Musical; Yrbk Stf; Pres Soph Cls; Pres Stu Cncl; Capt Bsktbl; Sftbl; Hon Roll; NHS; Stu Yr Awd 82; Dist Athl Awd US Marine Corps 85; MVP Vrsty Bsktbl 85; S Suburban Leag All-Star 85; Holy Cross; Hlth Sci.

ROGERS, KAREN M; Hanover HS; Hanover, MA; (Y); Church Yth Grp; GAA; Varsity Clb; Var L Socr; JV Sftbl; Hon Roll; S Shore Lg All Star Tm Socr 84-85; S Shore Sports Ctr 84-85.

ROGERS, KATHLEEN; Fontbonne Acad; Wollaston, MA; (Y); 47/131; Hon Roll; Globe Schltc Art Awd-1st Prz 81; Archdiocese Art Fair-Boston-1st Prz 83; Salem ST Coll; Bio.

ROGERS, PAUL V; Somerset HS; Somerset, MA; (Y); Cmnty Wkr; Acpl Chr; Chorus; School Musical; Stage Crew; Swing Chorus; Var L Bsbl; Var L Bsktbl; Var L Ftbl; Var L Socr; Engrng.

ROGERS, RICHARD; Tewksburg Memorial HS; Tewksbury, MA; (Y); 52/360; Church Yth Grp; Bsbl; JV Ftbl; Wt Lftg; Comp Sci.

ROGERS, SHANNON R; Waring Schl; Marblehead, MA; (Y); Chorus; School Play; Var Bsktbl; Var Lcrss; Var Socr; New Engl Bk Review Contest 1st-Bookstore 84.

ROGERS, TIMOTHY; Burncoat SR HS; Worcester, MA; (Y); Worcester ST Coll; Comp Sci.

ROGERS, TONY; Jeremiah E Burke HS; Dorchester, MA; (Y); Art Clb; Computer Clb; Dance Clb; DECA; FBLA; FTA; Key Clb; Teachers Aide; Yrbk Stf; Pres Sr Cls; Deca Awd 85; Rdng Awd 84; Westworth Inst; Cmptrs.

ROGERSON, HANK; Groton HS; Groton, MA; (Y); Dance Clb; Variety Show; Nwsp Sprt Ed; Yrbk Phtg; Yrbk Stf; Sec Frsh Cls; Var Capt Bsbl; Var Ice Hcky; Var Capt Socr; Dartmouth Coll; Lib Arts.

ROGOWSKI, APRIL MARIE; Greenfield HS; Greenfield, MA; (S); 27/159; Pep Clb; Spanish Clb; Flag Corp; Mrchg Band; Yrbk Ed-Chief; Yrbk Stf; VP Sr Cls; Sec Stu Cncl; Cheerleading; Trk; Heritage Bk Schlrshp 85; Aleca Awd & Schlrshp 85; Fred W Wells Trst Fnd 85; U MA Amherst; Htl/Rest/Trvl Ad.

ROHAN, MAUREEN; St Clare HS; W Roxbury, MA; (Y); 20/156; Church Yth Grp; Cmnty Wkr; Hosp Aide; JA; Trs Stu Cncl; Socr; Swmmng; NHS; Pep Clb; School Play; Latin Cum Laude Awd 83; CCD Tchr 83; CYO 83-84; Boston Coll; Nrs.

ROLLI, AL; Malden Catholic HS; Malden, MA; (Y); 90/185; Church Yth Grp; Im Bsktbl; Im Fld Hcky; JV Var Ftbl; Im Vllybl; Hon Roll; Arch Engrng.

ROMAN, ELISSA; Natick HS; Natick, MA; (Y); 3/443; French Clb; GAA; Latin Clb; Var JV Trk; High Hon Roll; Hon Roll; NHS; Prfct Atten Awd; Natl Hnr Roll; Smith Coll Bk Awd; V P Natl Hnr Soc; Econs.

ROMANI JR, DANIEL A; Framingham South HS; Framingham, MA; (Y); 8/263; Band; Jazz Band; Variety Show; Pres Soph Cls; Pres Jr Cls; Pres Sr Cls; Im Bsktbl; Var Ftbl; Var Golf; Var Trk; Itln Clb 82-86; Stu Govt Rep 84-85.

ROMANO, KERI LEE; Woburn Senior HS; Woburn, MA; (S); French Clb; Leo Clb; Ski Clb; Color Guard; Var Gym; High Hon Roll; Hon Roll; Jr NHS; Pres Schlr; Boston Coll.

ROMEO, JENNIFER; Bishop Connolly HS; Fall River, MA; (S); 30/177; Girl Scts; Church Choir; School Musical; Hon Roll; Bus.

ROMSEY, HEATHER; King Philip Regional HS; Plainville, MA; (S); 27/222; Sec Sr Cls; Im Powder Puff Ftbl; Var L Socr; Var L Sftbl; Cit Awd; DAR Awd; Hon Roll; NHS; Stdnt Mnth 84; Unsung Hero Sccr, Sftbl 84; Stonehill; Pol Sci.

RONAN, EDWARD; North Andover HS; North Andover, MA; (Y); 59/260; Am Leg Boys St; Var Ftbl; Var Capt Ice Hcky; Im Vllybl; Im Wt Lftg; High Hon Roll; Hon Roll; Bus.

RONCARATI, JILL; Archbishop Williams HS; Quincy, MA; (Y); Dance Clb; Drama Clb; Key Clb; School Play; Cheerleading; Hon Roll; Alg I Awd 83; Wrld Hstry Awd 83; Bus.

RONCONE, JAMES A; Minnichaug Regional HS; Wilbraham, MA; (Y); 60/311; Rep Am Leg Boys St; VP JA; JCL; PAVAS; Concert Band; Jazz Band; Var L Swmmng; Hon Roll; Boy Scts; Stage Crew; Eagl Sct 84; Jr Clscl Leag Ntl Cnvntn 84; XV Wrld Jambre 83; Mechncl Engr.

RONDEAU, SALLY ANNE; Hoosac Valley HS; Adams, MA; (Y); Boy Scts; Debate Tm; Quiz Bowl; Nwsp Stf; Yrbk Stf; Lit Mag; JV Crs Cntry; JV Trk; Hon Roll; Silver JV Medal X Cty 82; Law.

RONKIN, STEVEN; Peabody Veterans Memorial HS; Peabody, MA; (Y); 43/575; Im Bsktbl; Var Golf; Im Wt Lftg; High Hon Roll; Hon Roll; Schl Sci Fair Awd 84; Regnl Sci Fair 84; Engrng.

ROONEY, CHRISTINA; Holy Name C C HS; Worcester, MA; (Y); 83/272; Trs Church Yth Grp; Cmnty Wkr; Drama Clb; School Musical; School Play; Nwsp Rptr; Nwsp Stf; Tennis; Chorus; Thtr Gld-Bst Actrss 84; Thtr Gld-Bst Spprtng Actrss 85; Sclh Muscl Minor Prt 85; Spnsh.

ROONEY, CHRISTINE; Cardinal Spellman HS; W Bridgewater, MA; (Y); 17/205; Office Aide; Chorus; Hon Roll; NHS; Ntl Merit SF; NEDT Awd; Pres Schlr; Sci Fair 2nd Prz 84; Coll Holy Cross; Pre-Med.

ROOS, MICHELLE; Dover-Sherborn Regional HS; Dover, MA; (Y); 23/166; AFS; Temple Yth Grp; Nwsp Ed-Chief; Yrbk Ed-Chief; Lit Mag; High Hon Roll; Ntl Merit Ltr; Dover Sherborn Hnr Soc 84-85; Jets Ntl Engrng Aptude Srch 84; Rensselaer; Engr.

ROOT, KENNETH; Diman Regional Voc Tech HS; Somerset, MA; (Y); Var Bsbl; JV Bsktbl; Var Socr; High Hon Roll; Hon Roll; Elec Engrng.

ROQUE, FRANCIS; Bishop Feehan HS; Foxboro, MA; (Y); 35/260; Math Tm; Ski Clb; Yrbk Stf; Var Crs Cntry; Var Trk; Hon Roll; NHS; Poltcl Sci.

ROSANO, ELIZABETH A; Walpole HS; Walpole, MA; (Y); 39/265; Spanish Clb; Hon Roll; NHS; Mtl-Bllws Awd 85; Bird Fndtn Schlrshp 85; JR Cls Gld Scl Stds Mdl 84; Trinity Coll; Engrng.

ROSATI, DONNA; Matignon HS; Watertown, MA; (Y); VP Camera Clb; Hosp Aide; Yrbk Stf; Hon Roll; Drama Clb; JA; Ski Clb; Chorus; Stage Crew; Lit Mag; Northestrn U Boston; Physcl Thp.

ROSATONE, LAURIE; Haverhill HS; Haverhill, MA; (Y); 2/400; Intnl Clb; Political Wkr; Service Clb; Trs Spanish Clb; Nwsp Rptr; Yrbk Ed-Chief; Pres Sec Stu Cncl; High Hon Roll; Hon Roll; NHS; Englsh & Spnsh Awds 82-83; Stu Of Mtn Awd 84-85; Govt.

ROSE, DEIDRA; Sacred Heart HS; Onset, MA; (Y); 7/80; Intnl Clb; Cheerleading; Trk; NHS; Algebra II Awd 84; German II Awd 83; Boston U; Hotel Mngr.

ROSE, PAMELA; Montachusett Regional Vo-Tech; Sterling, MA; (Y); Teachers Aide; Var Capt Bsktbl; Stat Ftbl; Var Capt Sftbl; High Hon Roll; Hon Roll; NHS; U S Marn Corps Distngshd Athl & Outstndng Athl & Vrsty Sftbl Ovrll Defns Awds 85; Worcester ST Coll; Comp Sci.

ROSE, TAMMIE; Bridgewater-Raynham Regional HS; Raynham, MA; (Y); Gym; Wt Lftg; Bay ST JR; Legal Sec.

ROSEAFIELD, LEE; Salem HS; Salem, MA; (Y); 24/334; Science Clb; Nwsp Ed-Chief; Yrbk Stf; High Hon Roll; Spanish NHS; Computer Clb; Hosp Aide; Library Aide; Math Tm; Spanish Clb; Partcpt & Hnbl Mntn MA ST Sci Fair 85; Williams Clg Bk Awd 85; Spnsh.

ROSEBERRY, DEANNA; Montachusett Reg Voc Tech; Sterling, MA; (Y); Church Yth Grp; Trs Exploring; Science Clb; Chorus; High Hon Roll; NHS; Outstndng Stu Awd Grphc Arts 84 & 85; Comm.

ROSEMAN, JESSICA; Newton North HS; Newton, MA; (Y); Dance Clb; School Musical; Lit Mag; Teachers Aide; Chorus; Mrchg Band; School Play; Nwsp Stf; Mgr(s); Stat Vllybl; Schlrshp For Pro-Arts Smmr Prog 84; Schl Exchng With La Coruna Spain 84; Szks 5th Ave Fshn Brd Boston; Trvl.

ROSEN, ERIC B; Lincoln-Sudbury Regional HS; Sudbury, MA; (Y); Chess Clb; Math Tm; Ski Clb; JV Crs Cntry; JV Socr; Ntl Merit SF; Cum Laude Soc 84; Rensselaer Mth & Sci Awd 84; Mth.

ROSEN, LAURA; Needham HS; Needham, MA; (Y); 6/400; Spanish Clb; Chorus; Nwsp Rptr; Hon Roll; NHS; Ntl Merit Ltr; AATG Awd Excell German; Schl Awd Best German Stu; U Of PA.

ROSENBAUM, SHARON B; Lexington HS; Lexington, MA; (Y); Ski Clb; Chorus; Var Frsh Cls; Var Soph Cls; Var Stu Cncl; Var Capt Socr; Var Trk; Bio Sci.

ROSENBERG, LAURA; Canton HS; Canton, MA; (Y); 2/265; German Clb; Hosp Aide; Math Tm; Office Aide; Science Clb; Teachers Aide; Temple Yth Grp; JV Socr; High Hon Roll; Hon Roll; YFU Exch Fnlst; Atlntc Regnl Math Leag Penn ST; Grp Ldr Future Prblm Slvg Grp Gftd Chldrn.

ROSENBERGER, SCOTT A; Framingham South HS; Framingham, MA; (Y); 48/256; Church Yth Grp; German Clb; Band; Concert Band; Jazz Band; Mrchg Band; Orch; Variety Show; L Golf; Var Trk; Engrng.

ROSENFIELD, ROBYN; Framingham South HS; Framingham, MA; (Y); 83/256; DECA; VP JCL; Spanish Clb; Temple Yth Grp; Color Guard; Yrbk Stf; Trs Sr Cls; Stu Cncl; Mgr(s); Hon Roll; Chairprsn Retartd Citzns 85; Schlrshp Jewish Comm Ctr; Bus.

ROSENTHAL, JAMIE; Randolph HS; Randolph, MA; (Y); 22/350; VP French Clb; Teachers Aide; Temple Yth Grp; Trs Band; Trs Concert Band; Trs Mrchg Band; Nwsp Rptr; Nwsp Stf; Cheerleading; Hon Roll; MA Frgn Lang 85; Donovan Schl Awd 85; Greater Boston Sect Natl Cncl Jewsh Womn Awd 85; Clark U; Bilingual Soc Wrkr.

ROSENTHAL, MARJORY; Randolph HS; Randolph, MA; (Y); Am Leg Aux Girls St; Cmnty Wkr; Teachers Aide; School Play; Yrbk Stf; Rep Soph Cls; Rep Jr Cls; Rep Sr Cls; Rep Stu Cncl; Cheerleading; 4th Gymnstcs Meet 84; Adv.

ROSENTHAL, TARA; North HS; Worcester, MA; (Y); Library Aide; Pep Clb; Nwsp Rptr; Rep Stu Cncl; Pres Hon Roll; Chsn Reprsnt ST MA NCCJ Lctd In St Louis MO 83; Harvard; Law.

ROSS, DAVID M; Nantucket HS; Nantucket, MA; (Y); 2/50; Am Leg Boys St; Church Yth Grp; Var Bsbl; DAR Awd; Hon Roll; NHS; Prfct Atten Awd; Hnrs Schlr Stonehill Coll 85; Acdmc Exclnc Bio Drftng His Mcr Cmptrs Trig Phys 84; Stonehill Coll; Engnrng.

ROSS, LESLIE A; Northfield Mount Hermon Schl; Pittsfield, MA; (Y); VP JA; JV Capt Cheerleading; Stat Mgr(s); Hon Roll; Georgetown U; Intl Rltns.

ROSS, SUSAN; Bishop Feeban HS; Warren, RI; (Y); 109/252; Cmnty Wkr; Dance Clb; Drama Clb; Girl Scts; Hosp Aide; School Play; Stage Crew; Rep Soph Cls; Powder Puff Ftbl; Trk; U Of RI; Dental Hygeine.

ROSS, THOMAS; Somerville HS; Somervillle, MA; (Y); 25/595; Latin Clb; Ski Clb; Hon Roll; Outstndng Achvt New Englnd Amth League 84-85; Magna Cume Laude Ntl Latin Exam 84-85; Syracuse U; Aero Engrng.

ROSSELLI, CHARLES W; Stoneham HS; Stoneham, MA; (Y); 13/256; Am Leg Boys St; Debate Tm; French Clb; Ed Yrbk Stf; JV Socr; Trk; Hon Roll; NHS; Voice Dem Awd; Chess Clb; Vrsty Schlr 83-85; Promtn Suprmrkt Chain 84; Bus.

ROSSETSKY, ROBERT G; Norwood SR HS; Norwood, MA; (Y); Spanish Clb; Bowling; Socr; High Hon Roll; Hon Roll; Cert Of Merti In Chmstry 84; Lone Medal 85; Pres Acdmc Ftns Awd 85; Bentley Coll; Accntng.

ROSSI, CHRIS; Everett HS; Everett, MA; (Y); Hon Roll; NHS; Northeastern U; Comp Sci.

ROSSI, CHRISTOPHER; North Quincy HS; North Quincy, MA; (Y); 10/376; Am Leg Boys St; Ski Clb; Off Soph Cls; Pres Jr Cls; Pres Sr Cls; Var Capt Bsbl; Var Capt Bsktbl; High Hon Roll; NHS; Spanish NHS; Stephen A Larsen Awd Sci Fair 83; Embry-Riddle; Airline Mngmnt.

ROSSI, JILL; Belchertown JR SR HS; Belchertown, MA; (Y); 17/75; French Clb; Office Aide; Yrbk Stf; Stu Cncl; High Hon Roll; Hon Roll; NHS; Heritage Bnk Schlrshp 85; Natl Hon Soc Schlrshp 85; U Of MA Amherst; Comp Sci.

ROSSI, MARIA; Weymouth North HS; Weymouth, MA; (Y); 24/393; Key Clb; Ski Clb; Yrbk Stf; High Hon Roll; Hon Roll; Jr NHS; Elem Drug & Peer Preshure Edctnl Prog 84-86; Sci Fld.

ROSSITER, RENEE; Easthampton HS; Easthampton, MA; (Y); Drama Clb; Spanish Clb; School Musical; Ed Yrbk Stf; Rep Stu Cncl; Hon Roll; Theatre.

ROTHKEGEL, CEDRIC EDGARDO C; Amherst Regional HS; Amherst, MA; (Y); FBLA; Intnl Clb; Spanish Clb; Im Bsbl; Im Bsktbl; JV Score Keeper; Omass; Lang.

ROTONDI, ELLEN L; Bishop Fenwick HS; Wakefield, MA; (Y); Cmnty Wkr; Drama Clb; Library Aide; School Musical; School Play; Yrbk Stf; JV Tennis; Hon Roll.

ROTONDO, LISA M; Reading Memorial HS; Reading, MA; (Y); 2/357; Church Yth Grp; Drama Clb; Service Clb; Chorus; Yrbk Stf; Ed Lit Mag; Rep Stu Cncl; NHS; Ntl Merit SF; Cmnty Wkr; Harvard Bk Awd 84.

ROTTENBERG, LINDA; Newton South HS; Newton, MA; (Y); Model UN; Concert Band; Nwsp Ed-Chief; Stu Cncl; Var Lcrss; Var Socr; High Hon Roll; Debate Tm; Chorus; Madrigals; Hugh O Brien Yth Ldrshp Cnfrnc 84; Brown U Alumni Book Awd 85; Fctly Letter Of Rcgntn 83-85; Pltcl Sci.

ROUILLARD, MARC; Easthampton HS; Easthampton, MA; (Y); 5/200; Am Leg Boys St; JV Bsktbl; JV Socr; High Hon Roll; NHS; MA U; Journlsm.

ROULUSONIS, LAURIE; Taunton HS; Taunton, MA; (Y); Church Yth Grp; JCL; Latin Clb; Math Tm; Office Aide; High Hon Roll; NHS; Ntl Latin Exam Awd 84; Foreign Lang.

ROUSSEAU, CHRISTINE; Acad Of Notre Dame; Lowell, MA; (Y); Trs Drama Clb; Hosp Aide; Service Clb; Trs Frsh Cls; Bsktbl; JV Vllybl; Bentley Coll; CPA.

ROUSSEAU, MAUREEN A; Somerset HS; Somerset, MA; (Y); 36/300; Band; Chorus; Church Choir; Concert Band; Mrchg Band; Orch; School Musical; Symp Band; High Hon Roll; Hon Roll; Chem.

ROUSSEAU, NEAL; Bishop Feehan HS; Attleboro, MA; (Y); 123/239; Church Yth Grp; Crs Cntry; Ftbl; Trk; High Hon Roll; Prfct Atten Awd.

ROUSSEAU, NORMAND; Newton North HS; Newton, MA; (Y); Church Yth Grp; Trs Stu Cncl; Var Bsktbl; Im Vllybl; Hon Roll; John B Fuller Secnd Chrch W Newton Scholar 85; Am Leg Scholar 85; Schl & Cmnty Ctznshp & Svc Awd 85; U MA; Bus Mgmt.

ROUTHIER, MICHELLE; Easthampton HS; Easthampton, MA; (Y); 6/140; Aud/Vis; Ed Yrbk Stf; Rep Frsh Cls; Rep Soph Cls; JV Var Bsktbl; JV Var Socr; Jr NHS; NHS; Stanhome Schlrshp 85; Ctznshp Schlrshp Fndtn Awd 85; Bryant Coll; Accntng.

ROWE, CYNTHIA; Salem HS; Salem, MA; (Y); Sec Key Clb; Orch; Nwsp Rptr; Yrbk Stf; High Hon Roll; NHS; Spanish NHS; Computer Clb; Library Aide; Math Tm; Drtmth Bowl Awd 85.

ROWE, MICHAEL; Arlington HS; Arlington, MA; (Y); German Clb; PAVAS; Radio Clb; Nwsp Rptr; Nwsp Stf; Crs Cntry; Ftbl; Trk; Wt Lftg; High Hon Roll; Northeastern U; Police Sci.

ROY, CELESTE; Saint Louis Acad; Lowell, MA; (Y); 2/32; Church Yth Grp; Drama Clb; French Clb; School Play; Coach Actv; High Hon Roll; NHS; Sal; Gen George S Patton JR Scholar 2nd Pl 84-85; Stu Govt 84-85; U Of Lowell; Comp Sci.

ROY, DANIELLE; Agawam HS; Feeding Hills, MA; (Y); 250/300; French Clb; Chorus; Yrbk Stf; Hon Roll; NHS; F M Peirce Meml Schlrshp 85; S Prestley Blake Schlrshp 85; Bay Path JC; Trvl Admin.

ROY, KRISTEN; Wachusett Regional HS; Paxton, MA; (Y); VP FFA; Library Aide; Teachers Aide; Hon Roll; 1st Pl Secy Bk FFA ST Conven 84-85; Horse 84-85; 1st Pl Parlmntry Proc FFA 84-85; Becker JC; Bus Adm.

ROYAL, MICHELLE; Malden HS; Malden, MA; (Y); Frgn Lang.

ROZMAN, MARK; St Johns Prep; Haverhill, MA; (Y); 21/230; Latin Clb; Ski Clb; Pres Temple Yth Grp; Im Bsktbl; JV Crs Cntry; Im Golf; JV Trk; NHS; Ntl Merit Ltr; Tufts U; Engrng.

ROZUMEK HOULE, KAREN ANN; Salem HS; Salem, MA; (Y); Library Aide; Math Tm; Science Clb; Trs Soph Cls; High Hon Roll; Hon Roll; Comp Progrmmr.

ROZZI, RICH; North Andover HS; N Andover, MA; (Y); 36/242; Am Leg Boys St; JV Bsbl; Var L Ftbl; Im Wt Lftg; Hon Roll; James O Brien Schlrshp 85; Northeastern; Engrng.

RUANE, JANICE; Fontbonne Acad; Quincy, MA; (Y); 12/130; Drama Clb; Intnl Clb; Stage Crew; Rep Frsh Cls; Rep Stu Cncl; Trk; Hon Roll; Church Yth Grp; Science Clb; Im Stat Bsktbl; Magn Cm Laud Ntl Ltn Exm 84; Bus.

RUBIN, DOUG W; Natick HS; Natick, MA; (Y); 13/493; Temple Yth Grp; Pres Stu Cncl; Bsktbl; Golf; Socr; Cit Awd; High Hon Roll; Hon Roll; NHS; Ntl Merit Ltr.

RUBIN, ELISA; Randolph HS; Randolph, MA; (Y); 4/349; Pres Drama Clb; Socr; High Hon Roll; JC Awd; NHS; Math Tm; Spanish Clb; School Musical; School Play; Stage Crew; U Of PA; Engrng.

RUBIN, LISA; Bridgewater-Raynhm Regional HS; Raynham, MA; (Y); 8/320; Am Leg Aux Girls St; French Clb; Model UN; Pres Temple Yth Grp; Nwsp Rptr; JV Bsktbl; Hon Roll; NHS; NEDT Awd; Voice Dem Awd; Temple Yth Grp Treas 84; Colgate U; Jrnlsm.

RUBIN, MICHAEL R; Narragansett Regional HS; Phillipston, MA; (Y); 30/103; Am Leg Boys St; Church Yth Grp; Computer Clb; Comp Sci.

RUDALEVIGE, ANDREW C; Watertown HS; Watertown, MA; (Y); 1/306; Chess Clb; VP Church Yth Grp; Concert Band; Jazz Band; Lit Mag; Im Bsktbl; DAR Awd; High Hon Roll; NCTE Awd; Val; Suprntndts Awd Acad Exclnc 84; Top 10 Awd Framingham ST Coll Hist Conf 84; U Of Chicago; Pol Sci.

RUDD, SUSAN; Our Lady Of Nazareth Acad; Arlington, MA; (Y); 16/65; Cmnty Wkr; Pres Drama Clb; Hosp Aide; Science Clb; Ski Clb; Chorus; School Musical; School Play; Nwsp Rptr; Nwsp Stf; Globe Drama Fest Act Awd 83-84.

RUDNICK, BRUCE; Malden Catholic HS; Malden, MA; (Y); 7/200; Camera Clb; JCL; Latin Clb; Temple Yth Grp; Band; Concert Band; Yrbk Stf; Var Tennis; Im Vllybl; High Hon Roll; Brown U Bk Awd 85; Bus.

RUDOLPH, KATHLEEN A; Hanover HS; Hanover, MA; (Y); 36/209; AFS; Church Yth Grp; Drama Clb; Hosp Aide; Math Clb; Band; Concert Band; Mrchg Band; School Musical; School Play; St Elizabeths Schl/Nrsng; Nrsng.

RUFFIN, ADA; Boston Technical HS; Dorchester, MA; (Y); Church Yth Grp; Drama Clb; Library Aide; Office Aide; Teachers Aide; Chorus; Church Choir; Rep Stu Cncl; High Hon Roll; Hon Roll; Psych.

RUGGIERI, MICHAEL; Medway JR SR HS; Medway, MA; (Y); Drama Clb; School Musical; Nwsp Stf; Comp Pgm.

RUGGIERO, LINDA; Revere HS; Revere, MA; (Y); Math Clb; Sec Science Clb; Yrbk Phtg; Yrbk Stf; Stu Cncl; Var L Fld Hcky; Var L Sftbl; NHS; Mt Holyoke Coll; Law.

RUHAN, JONATHAN F; Nipmuc Regional HS; Mendon, MA; (Y); 10/85; Am Leg Boys St; Camera Clb; Church Yth Grp; Cmnty Wkr; 4-H; Library Aide; Model UN; God Cntry Awd; Mendon Lions Clb Schrlshp 85; Mendon Baptist Chrch Schlrshp 85; Janet O Stockwell Mem Schlrshp; RI Coll; Pub Archlgy.

RUHMANN, SUSAN; Methuen HS; Methuen, MA; (Y); 59/404; GAA; Intnl Clb; Capt Band; Capt Concert Band; Capt Mrchg Band; Stu Cncl; JV Sftbl; Hon Roll; Sports Journlsm.

RUIZ, LYNDA; Milton Acad; San Antonio, TX; (Y); Cmnty Wkr; GAA; Model UN; Political Wkr; Spanish Clb; Varsity Clb; Stage Crew; Yrbk Bus Mgr; Var Capt Sftbl; JV Var Vllybl; Sneath Foundtn Schlrshp 83-85; Robert Kennedy Schlrshp 84-85; Radcliffe; Pedtrcn.

RUMACK, BARRIE JANE; North Andover HS; N Andover, MA; (Y); 63/242; AFS; Church Yth Grp; Cmnty Wkr; Hosp Aide; Pep Clb; Variety Show; Yrbk Sprt Ed; Yrbk Stf; Var Mgr Bsbl; Var Mgr Bsktbl; Northeastern; Mrktng.

RUMMO, PAUL; Marian HS; Milford, MA; (Y); 14/178; Church Yth Grp; Cmnty Wkr; Var L Ice Hcky; Var L Socr; Var L Trk; High Hon Roll; Hon Roll; NHS; Pre-Med.

RUOKIS, PHIL; Brockton HS; Brockton, MA; (Y); Church Yth Grp; VP Computer Clb; Key Clb; Band; Concert Band; Mrchg Band; High Hon Roll; Hon Roll; Natl Cncl Eng Tchrs Wrtg Comp 85; New England Consrvtry; Mus Comp.

RUSHTON, CHRISTINE; Christopher Columbus HS; Charlestown, MA; (S); 89/135; Boys Clb Am; GAA; Church Choir; School Musical; Variety Show; Rep Jr Cls; Rep Stu Cncl; Stewardess.

RUSSELL, DAVID; St Johns HS; Shrewsbury, MA; (Y); 33/280; Model UN; Service Clb; School Play; Nwsp Rptr; JV Ftbl; Hon Roll; NHS; Ntl Merit Ltr; Prfct Atten Awd; Library Aide; Phi Alpha Theta Hstrcl Essay Cmptn Hnr Mntn 85; St Annes Retreat Tm CYC Invlvmnt 85; Invst Mgmt.

RUSSELL, DENISE; Notre Dame Acad; Hanover, MA; (Y); 67/113; Art Clb; English Clb; Chorus; Spanish NHS.

RUSSELL, FREDERICK J; Somerville HS; Somerville, MA; (Y); 7/600; Am Leg Boys St; Ski Clb; Yrbk Stf; Stu Cncl; JV Var Bsktbl; Im Var Ftbl; High Hon Roll; Hon Roll; NHS; Ecology Clb-Treas 84-85; Italian Clb 83-84 & 84-85; Comp Sci.

RUSSELL, JEANNETTE; Easthampton HS; Easthampton, MA; (Y); Church Yth Grp; French Clb; Chorus; Church Choir; School Play; Hon Roll; Lght Crw Plyrs Awd 85; North Adams; Mdcl Tech.

RUSSELL, SHARON; Cathedral HS; Springfield, MA; (Y); 131/550; JV Bsktbl; Var L Socr; Var Capt Trk; Ntl Athlc Plcmnt Serv 85; Schl Magzne Drve Capt 85; Caftria Aid 85; Pre Vet.

RUSSELL, VALERIE J; Foxborough HS; Foxborough, MA; (Y); 12/222; Pres Church Yth Grp; Capt Drill Tm; Cheerleading; Fld Hcky; NHS; Ntl Merit Ltr; Pres Schlr; Brigham Young U; Bus Adm.

RUSSES, DENISE; Watertown HS; Watertown, MA; (Y); 125/285; Art Clb; Intnl Clb; Off Frsh Cls; Sec Soph Cls; Off Stu Cncl; Capt Cheerleading; Capt Powder Puff Ftbl; Sftbl; JA; Cantalonga Art Awd 85; NAAA 85; MVP Art Awd 85; MA Coll Of Art; Comm Art.

RUSSO, CRISTINA M; Melrose HS; Melrose, MA; (S); 127/405; 4-H; Pep Clb; Ski Clb; Var Capt Cheerleading; Wt Lftg; 4-H Awd; Hon Roll; JR Prom Qn 84; Capt Hcky Chrldr & Ftbl Co Capt 85; Italn Clb Schlrshp Drv 84-85; Framingham ST Coll; Chldhd Ed.

RUSSO, MARK; Randolph HS; Randolph, MA; (Y); Var Ftbl; Var Trk; Hon Roll; Bus.

RUSSO, MELINDA N; Malden HS; Malden, MA; (Y); Spanish Clb; Teachers Aide; Hon Roll; ST Scholar 85; Trustees Scholar 85; Suffolk U; Finance.

RUSSO, ROSEMARY; Matignon HS; Watertown, MA; (Y); 25/173; Pres Civic Clb; JA; Spanish Clb; Nwsp Rptr; Yrbk Stf; Capt Socr; L Sftbl; Pres Schlr; Spanish NHS; Providence Coll; Englsh.

RUTKOWSKI, EDWARD S; Arlington HS; Arlington, MA; (Y); Drama Clb; Chorus; Madrigals; School Musical; School Play; Stage Crew; Ed Yrbk Stf; Arlington Drama Frnds Awd 84; Arlngtn Cblsystms Schlrshp 85; Acad Dcthln Vrsty Awd 84; Adelphi U; Mscl Theatre.

RYAN, BARBARA; Woburn HS; Woburn, MA; (S); JA; Leo Clb; Stu Cncl; Sftbl; Trk; High Hon Roll; Hon Roll; Ski Clb; Boston Coll.

RYAN, BRITT A; Newton North HS; Newton, MA; (Y); Am Leg Boys St; Boys Clb Am; Bsbl; Capt Bsktbl; Capt Ftbl.

RYAN, DAWN; Bay Path Regional Vocational HS; Charlton, MA; (S); 1/244; Drama Clb; Library Aide; School Play; Stu Cncl; Socr; High Hon Roll; NHS; Stu Of Month Sci, Data Proc, Eng, Lit 82-83; MIT; Comp Sci.

RYAN, HELEN M; Walpole HS; Walpole, MA; (S); 88/265; Rep Am Leg Aux Girls St; Church Yth Grp; JCL; Pres Latin Clb; Leo Clb; JV L Trk; Capt L Vllybl; Prfct Atten Awd; Clssrm Perf Awd Latin III 83-84; Close-Up Wash DC 83-84; Gov.

RYAN, JENNIFER; Natick HS; Natick, MA; (Y); 4/443; High Hon Roll; Sec NHS; Ntl Merit Ltr; Wellesley Bk Awd.

RYAN, JOHN C; Plymouth-Carver HS; Carver, MA; (Y); 100/503; Am Leg Boys St; Bridgewater ST Coll; Phys Ed.

RYAN, KATHLEEN; Hanover HS; Hanover, MA; (Y); Camp Fr Inc; School Musical; Drill Tm; Drm & Bgl; Yrbk Stf; Swmmng; Hon Roll; All Hnrs Math Cls; Ntl Hnr Soc; Keene ST; Law.

RYAN, KRIS; Woburn HS; Woburn, MA; (S); French Clb; Hosp Aide; Leo Clb; Office Aide; Ski Clb; Variety Show; Stu Cncl; Var Cheerleading; Crs Cntry; High Hon Roll; Bus.

RYAN, MARGUERITE; Newton Catholic HS; Watertown, MA; (Y); 10/52; Exploring; Library Aide; Teachers Aide; Chorus; School Play; Yrbk Ed-Chief; Yrbk Phtg; Sec Sr Cls; Hon Roll; Corondalt Awd 85; Fitchburg ST; Spcl Ed.

RYAN, MATTHEW J; Holyoke Catholic HS; S Hadley, MA; (Y); 25/126; Drama Clb; Spanish Clb; Teachers Aide; Yrbk Rptr; Var Capt Bsbl; Swmmng; Hon Roll; Kiwanis Awd; Rep Frsh Cls; Rep Soph Cls; Essays Nuclear Pub 85; Eng Lit Schlr Awd 85; Fairfield U; Psych.

RYAN, MICHAEL; Boston College HS; Boston, MA; (Y); Cmnty Wkr; Key Clb; Political Wkr; Ski Clb; Nwsp Rptr; Im Bsktbl; JV Crs Cntry; Im Ftbl; Im Vllybl; Hon Roll; Law.

RYAN, PAUL; Whitman-Hanson Regional HS; Hanson, MA; (Y); 16/330; Varsity Clb; Var Bsbl; Var Bsktbl; Im Coach Actv; Im Vllybl; Hon Roll; NHS; Comp.

RYAN, SUSAN; Taunton HS; Taunton, MA; (Y); Trs Frsh Cls; Trs Soph Cls; Trs Jr Cls; Trs Sr Cls; Var Stu Cncl; JV Capt Fld Hcky; JV Sftbl; High Hon Roll; Hon Roll; NHS; Simmons Coll; Phys Thrpy.

SABER, STEPHEN; Boston Latin Schl; Boston, MA; (Y); 50/300; Pres VP Church Yth Grp; Computer Clb; German Clb; Intnl Clb; Stu Cncl; Socr; Swmmng; Hon Roll; Ntl Merit Ltr.

SABIN, MICHAEL A; Milton Acad; Wellesley, MA; (Y); Cmnty Wkr; Letterman Clb; Varsity Clb; Nwsp Rptr; Var L Bsktbl; Var L Socr; Ntl Merit SF; Soc Sci.

SABIO, REX; Arlington Catholic HS; Malden, MA; (Y); 4/148; Boys Clb Am; Computer Clb; JA; Ice Hcky; Var Trk; High Hon Roll; NHS; Prfct Atten Awd; Summa Cum Laud-Nat Latin Exm 83; Maxma Cum Laud Slvr Mdl Ntl Ltn Exm 84 & 85; 2nd Pl Offcr Yr JA 84; Engrng.

SABLONE, ALBERT; St Dominic Savio HS; Winthrop, MA; (Y); 17/103; Chess Clb; Church Yth Grp; Key Clb; Service Clb; Stage Crew; Rep Frsh Cls; Rep Soph Cls; Rep Jr Cls; Trs Sr Cls; Trk; Boston Coll; Biol.

SABRA, ADAM A; Lexington HS; Lexington, MA; (Y); French Clb; Hon Roll; Pol Sci.

SABRA, MICHAEL; Bishop Connolly HS; Tiverton, RI; (S); 8/190; VP JA; Off Latin Clb; Math Clb; Ski Clb; Nwsp Rptr; Yrbk Stf; Var Golf; JV Trk; High Hon Roll; Hotel & Restrnt Mgmt.

SACCAMANDO, CHELSEY; Cathedral HS; Spfld, MA; (Y); FBLA; GAA; Girl Scts; Hosp Aide; Intnl Clb; Latin Clb; Office Aide; Teachers Aide; Rep Soph Cls; Rep Stu Cncl; MVP Fld Hcky Sprts Trphy 83; Acad Exclinc Rbbns 82-83; Pre-Law.

SACCONE, CAROLE; Silver Lake Regional HS; Bryantville, MA; (Y); 50/500; Church Yth Grp; Drama Clb; Key Clb; Ski Clb; Yrbk Stf; Trs Sr Cls; Cheerleading; Timer; Hon Roll; Voice Dem Awd; Boston Coll; Econ.

SACHS, KATHERINE A; Monument Mountain Regional HS; Housatonic, MA; (Y); 21/127; Art Clb; Political Wkr; Band; Var Capt Bsktbl; Var Capt Socr; Var Capt Sftbl; Hon Roll; NHS; Concert Band; Mrchg Band; All Western MA Sccr Tm 84; All Berkshire Sccr Tm 83-84; Western MA Sccr Trnmnt MVP 84; St Anselm Coll; Soclgy.

SACOVITCH, LISA; St Marys HS; Worcester, MA; (Y); 3/49; Sec Pres Church Yth Grp; Dance Clb; Drama Clb; French Clb; Capt Hosp Aide; JA; Office Aide; Political Wkr; Teachers Aide; School Musical; Hugh O Brian Yth Ldrshp Smnr 84; Sci Fair Awd-2nd Pl 84; Holy Crss Coll Bk Awd 85; Bus.

SADLIER, STEPHEN; Bishop Feehan HS; Pawtucket, RI; (Y); Ski Clb; School Play; Yrbk Phtg; Yrbk Sprt Ed; Yrbk Stf; Capt Trk; Hon Roll; Sci.

SADOSKI, DARCIA; Salem HS; Salem, MA; (Y); 39/325; Church Yth Grp; German Clb; Y-Teens; Band; Concert Band; Mrchg Band; Ed Yrbk Stf; VP Soph Cls; VP Jr Cls; Var JV Cheerleading; Hnrbl Ment Sci Fair 85; Lib Arts.

SADOSKI, LORI; Frontier Regional HS; Whately, MA; (Y); Drama Clb; French Clb; Sec Trs GAA; School Play; Var Crs Cntry; Var Capt Trk; JV Vllybl; Hon Roll; NHS; Rep Soph Cls; MA U; Bus Mgmt.

SAHADY, KERRY L; BMC Durfee HS; Fall River, MA; (Y); 54/658; French Clb; JA; Teachers Aide; Band; Concert Band; Mrchg Band; Pep Band; Variety Show; Hon Roll; NHS; MA Pol Assn Scholar 85; Lebanon Amer Soc Scholr 85; St Anslem Coll; Chem.

SAIA, FRANK; Bishop Fenwick HS; Boxford, MA; (Y); Art Clb; Hon Roll; Prfct Atten Awd; Metrlgy.

SAIA JR, JOHN J; Billerica Memorial HS; Billerica, MA; (Y); 10/560; Computer Clb; Var L Bsktbl; JV Ftbl; Var L Tennis; High Hon Roll; Hon Roll; NHS; Engrng.

SAINT, ANNE MARIE; Newburyport HS; Newburyport, MA; (Y); 20/209; Art Clb; Model UN; Lit Mag; Sftbl; Swmmng; Tennis; High Hon Roll; Hon Roll; NHS; Rotary Awd; Bronze Silver Gild Hnrs Keys 83-85; Safford Schlrshp 85; Eliot M Gordon Schlrshp 85; Syracuse U; Mktg.

SAKAKEENY, BRANDT; Lexington HS; Lexington, MA; (Y); Political Wkr; Pres Ski Clb; Nwsp Rptr; Hon Roll; VP Sr Cls; Var Bsbl; De Pauw U; Banking.

SAKURA, PETER; Lexington HS; Lexington, MA; (Y); Cmnty Wkr; Computer Clb; Drama Clb; Political Wkr; School Play; Nwsp Ed-Chief; Nwsp Phtg; Rep Soph Cls; Jr Cls; Hon Roll; Outstndng Rcgntn Achvt In Frnch 84-85; MA U.

SALAMONE, BETH A; Andover HS; Andover, MA; (Y); 31/425; Model UN; Pep Clb; Political Wkr; Ski Clb; Nwsp Stf; Yrbk Stf; Var Cheerleading; JV Socr; Hon Roll; NHS; Holy Cross; Cmmnctns.

SALEDAS, GEORGE N; Greenfield HS; Greenfield, MA; (Y); DECA; Bsbl; Ice Hcky; Socr; N Adams ST Coll; Bus.

SALEK, ELISE; Montrose Schl; Belmont, MA; (Y); 1/11; Nwsp Ed-Chief; Yrbk Stf; Pres Sr Cls; Rep Stu Cncl; Var L Bsktbl; High Hon Roll; NHS; Pres Schlr; Val; ST Fnlst Centry III Ldrs 85; Montrose Schl Philsphy Prz 84-85; Boston Coll; Hist.

SALEM, SUSAN JAYE; Notre Dame Acad; Worcester, MA; (Y); 7/70; Sec Church Yth Grp; Cmnty Wkr; Debate Tm; Drama Clb; Latin Clb; Spanish Clb; School Musical; School Play; Ed Yrbk Ed-Chief; Yrbk Stf; Coll Holy Cross; Acctng.

SALETT, DARA; Westwood HS; Westwood, MA; (Y); 47/215; Drama Clb; Sec VP Temple Yth Grp; School Musical; Nwsp Stf; Powder Puff Ftbl; Trk; Hon Roll; Spanish NHS; Northeastern U; Bus Adm.

SALIBA, MAUREEN; Methoen HS; Methuen, MA; (Y); 40/350; Girl Scts; Intnl Clb; Stu Cncl; Im Sftbl; Hon Roll; Bus Mgmt.

SALINES, KRISTEN; Saugus HS; Saugus, MA; (Y); 50/360; Teachers Aide; Varsity Clb; Coach Actv; Var Capt Socr; Hon Roll; Jr NHS; NHS; Sclgy.

SALINETTI, LISA; Lee HS; Lee, MA; (Y); 1/115; French Clb; Math Tm; Nwsp Rptr; Yrbk Ed-Chief; VP Stu Cncl; Var Capt Bsktbl; Var Socr; Var Capt Sftbl; NHS; Yrbk Rptr; Rensselaer Medl Excllnc Math & Sci 85; Wellesley Bk Awd 85; All Berkshire, All Western Sccr, Bsktbl 85; Lib Arts.

SALISBURY, WENDY; King Philip Regional HS; Norfolk, MA; (Y); 27/137; Math Clb; Math Tm; Yrbk Stf; Var L Crs Cntry; Powder Puff Ftbl; Var L Trk; Wt Lftg; Hon Roll; Jr NHS; NHS; Psychology.

SALM, SUSAN; Archbishop Williams HS; Holbrook, MA; (Y); 7/213; Math Tm; Chorus; High Hon Roll; Hon Roll; Jr NHS; NHS; Math Tm Awd 85; Acad Excllnc Awd 85; Spnsh Awds 84-85; Acad Achv Awd 84; Vrsty Lttr.

SALMON, JULIE; Somerset HS; Somerset, MA; (Y); Yrbk Stf; Rep Frsh Cls; Off Jr Cls; Off Sr Cls; VP Stu Cncl; Var Cheerleading; Var Capt Fld Hcky; Trk; High Hon Roll; NHS; Arch.

SALMON, TODD; North Middlesex Regional HS; Ashby, MA; (Y); 20/220; Computer Clb; Math Tm; Capt Ftbl; Var Trk; Comp Sci Awd 85; Fitchburg ST Coll; Bus Adm.

SALOMAO, JOAO; Hudson HS; Hudson, MA; (Y); 8/155; Boys Clb Am; Boy Scts; Church Yth Grp; Chorus; School Musical; School Play; JV Bsbl; JV Bsktbl; Var Socr; High Hon Roll; Excllnce Frgn Lang 83-84.

SALOMAO, MARIA L; Hudson HS; Hudson, MA; (S); 13/160; Band; Pep Band; School Musical; Symp Band; Var Mgr(s); Powder Puff Ftbl; Tennis; Vllybl; NHS; Boys Clb Am; OEA Rcptnst Awd 82; Latin Awd Excell 84; Portugese Awd Excell 82; Holy Cross Coll; Bio.

SALPIETRO, ROGER; Diman Reg Voc Technical HS; Fall River, MA; (Y); Church Yth Grp; JV Bsbl; High Hon Roll; Hon Roll.

SALTALAMACCHIA, THERESE; Our Lady Of Nazareth Acad; Reading, MA; (Y); Camp Fr Inc; Hosp Aide; JA; Office Aide; Chorus; School Musical; School Play; Lit Mag; Rep Soph Cls; Trk; Englsh Essay Awd 85.

SALVATORE, LARA E; Norwood HS; Norwood, MA; (Y); 7/369; Yrbk Stf; Rep Stu Cncl; Var L Cheerleading; Var L Gym; Var L Trk; High Hon Roll; Pres NHS; Town Govt Day 85; Am Leg Awd 83; TONY Awd 83.

SALZMAN, ERIC; Newton North HS; Newton, MA; (Y); Cmnty Wkr; Ski Clb; Temple Yth Grp; Band; Jazz Band; Orch; School Musical; School Play; Variety Show; Nwsp Stf; Suffolk U Stu Awd, E MA Gym Legue Meet Fin 84; Newton N HS Svc Awd 85; U MI Ann Arbor; Econ.

SAM, JONATHAN; Westfield HS; Westfield, MA; (Y); 26/334; Church Yth Grp; NHS; Chem Engrng.

SAMANIEGO, YVONNE C; Phillips Acad; Mesquite, NM; (Y); Yrbk Stf; Pres Soph Cls; Rep Trs Stu Cncl; Stat Bsbl; Stat Bsktbl; Score Keeper; Var Vllybl; High Hon Roll; Hon Roll; Pres Jr NHS; Ntl Spnsh Exam 1st Pl 85; Med.

SAMAR, LISA; Monson JR SR HS; Palmer, MA; (Y); 8/80; Art Clb; Dance Clb; Pep Clb; Spanish Clb; Chorus; Yrbk Stf; Var Cheerleading; High Hon Roll; Hon Roll; Henry O Holly Chptr Natl Hnr Soc 83-85; Scholar Regis Coll 85; Scholar Rotary Clb 85; Regis Coll; Psych.

SAMARELLI, CYNTHIA A; Notre Dame Acad; Weymouth, MA; (Y); Boy Scts; Library Aide; Chorus; School Musical; French Hon Soc; High Hon Roll; VP NHS; Natl Sci Merit Awd Wrrn 85; Hgh Avg Geom Awd 83; Hghst Avg Typg Awd 84; St Anselm Coll; Frnch.

SAMII, ROXANNE; Dana Hall Schl; Dover, MA; (Y); School Play; Im Badmtn; Im Bsktbl; Im Fld Hcky; Im Golf; Im Lcrss; Im Socr; Im Sftbl; Im Tennis; Hon Roll; Jrnlsm.

SAMMA, SAKINA; N Attleboro HS; No Attleboro, MA; (S); 13/246; Rep Art Clb; Trs Boy Scts; JCL; Latin Clb; Yrbk Ed-Chief; Yrbk Stf; Gym; Trk; High Hon Roll; Hon Roll; JR Clscl League-Maxima Cum Laude; Econ.

SAMPSON, ELIZABETH; St Bernards Central Catholic HS; Leominster, MA; (S); 19/162; Drama Clb; Ski Clb; Spanish Clb; School Musical; School Play; Trs Jr Cls; Var Cheerleading; Var Tennis; Hon Roll; Child Psych.

SAMUELSON, MATTHEW C; Mt Greylock Regional HS; Williamstown, MA; (Y); 11/140; Am Leg Boys St; Nwsp Phtg; Nwsp Stf; Yrbk Stf; Lit Mag; VP Trs Frsh Cls; Pres Soph Cls; Var Crs Cntry; NHS; Boys Clb Am; Exch Editr Schl Nwsp 85-86; Pol Sci.

SANDAHL, PAM; Weymouth North HS; Weymouth, MA; (Y); 36/393; Am Leg Aux Girls St; Yrbk Stf; Trs Soph Cls; Var Socr; Var Capt Trk; Cit Awd; Hon Roll; NHS; Yrbk Phtg; God Cntry Awd; Patriot Ledgr All-Schltc 85; MVP Sprng Trck 85.

SANDBERG, JANE; King Philip Regional HS; Plainville, MA; (Y); Yrbk Phtg; Yrbk Stf; Sec Stu Cncl; JV Cheerleading; Var L Gym; Var L Socr; Tennis; Stu Gvrnmnt Day Rep 85; N Adams ST Coll; Mktg.

SANDBERG, KRYSTIN; South High Community Schl; Worcester, MA; (S); Hosp Aide; Hon Roll; NHS; Clark U; Bus.

SANDBERG, SARAH; Groton-Dunstable Reg; Groton, MA; (Y); Yrbk Stf; Var L Cheerleading; JV Fld Hcky; Var Mgr(s); Var Score Keeper; Hon Roll; Jr NHS; Bus Mgmt.

SANDERS, JULIE; Cushing Acad; Atlanta, GA; (Y); 10/121; FBLA; Hosp Aide; Spanish Clb; Teachers Aide; Varsity Clb; Drill Tm; Nwsp Rptr; Capt Cheerleading; Socr; Hon Roll; LEAD UCLA Conf 85; MITNITES MIT Boston 85; MA Inst Tech; Civl Engrng.

SANDERS, KAREN M; Bridgewater-Raynham Regional HS; Raynham, MA; (Y); 76/380; Drama Clb; Stage Crew; JV Socr; Hon Roll; U Of MA-AMHERST; Art.

SANDERSON, ELIZABETH; Malden HS; Malden, MA; (Y); 41/600; Church Yth Grp; Dance Clb; Key Clb; Variety Show; Bowling; Hon Roll.

SANDORFI, CSILLA; North Reading HS; N Reading, MA; (Y); Drama Clb; Chorus; Jazz Band; Mrchg Band; Nwsp Ed-Chief; Yrbk Ed-Chief; Pres Stu Cncl; JV Vllybl; High Hon Roll; NHS; Chnclrs Tlnt Awd 85; U Of MA-AMHERST; Jrnlsm.

SANDQUIST, PAUL ANDREW; Dennis-Yarmouth Regional HS; E Dennis, MA; (Y); 60/350; Am Leg Boys St; Boy Scts; Church Yth Grp; Letterman Clb; Ski Clb; JV Bsbl; Im Bsktbl; Var L Socr; Elks Awd; Hon Roll; Eagle Sct 81; U Of NH; Libl Arts.

SANGUEDOLCE, CYNTHIA M; Methuen HS; Methuen, MA; (Y); 69/300; Girl Scts; Intnl Clb; Office Aide; Pep Clb; Teachers Aide; School Musical; Sec Stu Cncl; JV Bsktbl; JV Fld Hcky; Powder Puff Ftbl; Erly Chldhd Educ.

SANNER, PAUL R; Wellesley SR HS; Wellesley, MA; (Y); German Clb; Chorus; Concert Band; Jazz Band; Madrigals; Mrchg Band; Orch; School Musical; NHS; A Young Burns Chrl Awd 85; S Santostefano Strng Awd 85; Wellesley Frnds Of Music Schlrshp Awd 85; Oberlin Coll; Ec.

SANPAKIT, TONY T; Berkshire Schl; Glenmont, NY; (S); 2/108; Art Clb; Intnl Clb; Science Clb; Var Bsktbl; JV Trk; High Hon Roll; Cum Laude Soc 85; Physcs Tchrs Awd 85; Boston Glb Schlstc Art Awd 85; Tulane U; Biomed Engrng.

SANTAPAOLA, CHRISTINE M; Arllington Catholic HS; Medford, MA; (Y); 16/148; Church Yth Grp; French Clb; JV Bsktbl; Hon Roll.

SANTIAGO, ROBIN; New Bedford HS; New Bedford, MA; (Y); 265/688; Trs JA; JCL; Latin Clb; Political Wkr; Acpl Chr; Chorus; Rep Frsh Cls; Rep Jr Cls; Stu Cncl; CC Awd; Med.

SANTORO, ANGELA; East Boston HS; E Boston, MA; (Y); Teachers Aide; Hon Roll; NHS; Harvard Prz Bk 84-85; Acctng.

SANTOS, ELSA; Brockton HS; Brockton, MA; (Y); Drama Clb; French Clb; Key Clb; School Play; Socr.

SANTOS, JOSEPH; Melrose HS; Melrose, MA; (Y); #14 In Class; Computer Clb; Library Aide; Im JV Socr; NHS; Ntl Merit SF; MIT; Aerontcl Engrng.

SANTOS, JOSEPH M; Central Catholic HS; Lowell, MA; (Y); Hon Roll; E Coast Aero Tech Schl; Aviatn.

SANTOS JR, LEONARD A; New Bedford HS; New Bedford, MA; (Y); 39/700; Aud/Vis; Church Yth Grp; Band; Concert Band; Mrchg Band; High Hon Roll; Hon Roll; Jr NHS; NHS; Sci.

SANTOS, LOUIS; Diman Vacational HS; Fall River, MA; (Y); Boy Scts; Exploring; Top Ten Stu 84-85; SMU Sptlght II Pgm 85; SMU.

SANTOS, MARCOS; Boston Latin Schl; Boston, MA; (Y); 13/300; Chess Clb; JA; Spanish Clb; Rep Soph Cls; Rep Jr Cls; Sr Cls; Rep Stu Cncl; Trk; Bausch & Lomb Sci Awd; High Hon Roll; Suffolk Bk Awd; Jack & Jill Recog Acad Achv; 1885 Cls Awd; Stanford U; Elec Engrng.

SANTOS, PATRICIA; Plymouth-Carver HS; Plymouth, MA; (Y); Hosp Aide; Im Cheerleading; Hon Roll; Awd Sci Fair 83; Fash Merch.

SAPITA, DIANE E; Bishop Feehan HS; N Attleboro, MA; (Y); Yrbk Phtg; Yrbk Stf; Rep Jr Cls; Rep Sr Cls; High Hon Roll; Hon Roll; Chorus; Hugh O Brian Yth Ldrshp Conf St & Intl Del; Rel Educ Tchr; Med Explorers Post BSA; Bio Sci.

SAPKA, STEPHEN P; Central Catholic HS; Methuen, MA; (Y); 100/230; Church Yth Grp; Drama Clb; JA; Nwsp Phtg; Im Bsktbl; Hon Roll; Leg Hnr 84; Worcester ST Coll; Media.

SAQUET, ERIC L; Ipswich HS; Ipswich, MA; (Y); 8/127; Drama Clb; French Clb; Leo Clb; Math Tm; Science Clb; School Play; Nwsp Rptr; Lit Mag; VP Frsh Cls; Stu Cncl; Latin Awd; Pacific U.

SARACENO, SCOTT; Central Catholic HS; N Andover, MA; (Y); 21/219; Art Clb; Dance Clb; Stage Crew; High Hon Roll; Hon Roll; Sci Awd 2nd Pl; Boston U; Comm.

SARDINHA, JEFF; B M C Durfee HS; Fall River, MA; (Y); 135/687; Church Yth Grp; Band; Concert Band; Variety Show; Pep Band; Trk; Educ.

SARGENT JR, JOHN K; Hingham HS; Hingham, MA; (Y); 1/330; Church Yth Grp; Math Tm; Concert Band; Mrchg Band; Symp Band; Var Capt Bsktbl; High Hon Roll; NHS; U Of MA Chancellors Talent Awd Schlrshp 85; Harvard Prize Book Awd 85; Pre Law.

SARKIS, ANTHONY M; Drury SR HS; North Adams, MA; (Y); Am Leg Boys St; Boy Scts; Computer Clb; Trk; Cit Awd; High Hon Roll; Hon Roll; Brkshr Cmnty Coll JR Male 3rd Pl Wnnr-Bike Mrthn 84; Astrnmy.

SARMANIOTE, JANYCE; Ursuline Acad; Boston, MA; (Y); French Clb; Yrbk Stf; NHS; Peer Ministry 84-85; Humanities Grp 81-85; Boston U; Sci.

SARNO, DOREEN; Arlington Catholic HS; Medford, MA; (Y); 35/148; L Art Clb; Church Yth Grp; JA; School Musical; School Play; Yrbk Stf; Pres Jr Cls; Var Tennis; Hon Roll; NHS; Natl Ptry Prss,Essy Prs Awd 83; Hnrbl Mntn Essy Cntst Awd 83; Best Annl Rept; JA Awds 84; Boston Clg.

SARRO, CAREN M; Mansfield HS; Mansfield, MA; (Y); 7/185; Dance Clb; Debate Tm; Key Clb; Math Tm; Ski Clb; School Musical; Stu Cncl; Var Cheerleading; Hon Roll; VP NHS; Dance Tchrs Club Boston 84; Pres Awd 85; Excell Phy Educ Awd 85; Worcester Polytech Inst; Biomed.

SASEN, CINDY D; Bellingham JR SR HS; Bellingham, MA; (Y); 55/205; Church Yth Grp; Dance Clb; Nwsp Stf; Yrbk Stf; Sec Frsh Cls; Sec Soph Cls; Sec Jr Cls; Sec Sr Cls; Rep Stu Cncl; Var JV Score Keeper; SE MA U; Bus.

SAULNIER, MICHAEL S; North Attleboro HS; North Attleboro, MA; (Y); 7/231; Drama Clb; JCL; Math Tm; Scholastic Bowl; Thesps; School Musical; Yrbk Stf; Elks Awd; Ntl Merit SF; St Schlr; Gld Medlst Natl Latn Exms 82-83; MA Inst Tech; Comp Sci.

SAULNIER, ROBERT; Boston Latin Schl; Brighton, MA; (Y); 77/300; Am Leg Boys St; Science Clb; Off Sr Cls; Rep Stu Cncl; Var L Trk; Hon Roll; NHS; Sci Olympiad Awd; MIT; Engrng.

SAULT, MICHELE; Whitman Hanson Regional HS; Hanson, MA; (Y); 5/325; Church Yth Grp; Band; High Hon Roll; Hon Roll; NHS; Pres Schlr; MMEA All-ST Band; MMEA SE Dist Band; MA Yth Wind Ensmbl New Engl Consrvtry; Bates Coll; Phy Sci.

SAUNDERS, CATHERINE W; Berkshire Schl; Sheffield, MA; (Y); 13/127; Drama Clb; English Clb; School Play; Yrbk Stf; Lit Mag; Var Fld Hcky; High Hon Roll; Kiwanis Awd; Macaleser Oll; Envrnmntl Stds.

SAUNDERS, JULIANNE; Bishop Feeban HS; Attleboro, MA; (Y); Art Clb; Church Yth Grp; Pep Clb; Ski Clb; Pres Soph Cls; Off Stu Cncl; JV Cheerleading; Trk; Hon Roll; Art Awd 85; Stu Cncl 83-84; Cmmnctns.

SAURIOL, ROBIN; Holy Name CC HS; Worcester, MA; (Y); 12/278; Church Yth Grp; School Musical; Hon Roll; NHS; Hghst Avr Hum I; Cert Rlgn Hum II Bio; Soc Act Clb; Framingham ST Coll; Psych.

SAUVAN, MIKE C; Newburyport HS; Newburyport, MA; (Y); Am Leg Boys St; JCL; Latin Clb; Var Bsbl; Var Capt Socr; Amer Sccr Ambssdrs Europe Tour 84; Notre Dame; Military Pilot.

SAVAGE, RICHARD; Malden HS; Malden, MA; (Y); 54/550; Stat Bsktbl; JV Ftbl; Var Golf; Score Keeper; Hon Roll; Coin Elec; Electrcn.

SAVIANO, JEFFREY; Danvers HS; Danvers, MA; (Y); 51/350; JA; Yrbk Stf; Var Capt Tennis; Hon Roll; NHS; Boy Scts; Rep Frsh Cls; Iona Coll Tnns & Merit Schlrshp 85; Salem Evenng News Tnns All Star 83; Iona Coll-NY; Bus.

SAVICKI, MICHAEL; Franklin HS; Franklin, MA; (Y); Boy Scts; Math Tm; OEA; Nwsp Phtg; Yrbk Phtg; Lit Mag; VP Stu Cncl; Socr; Hon Roll; NHS; Math.

SAVILONIS, MARGARET; Matignon HS; Somerville, MA; (S); 16/200; Drama Clb; School Musical; School Play; Variety Show; Trk; Hon Roll; NHS; NEDT Awd; Corp Law.

SAVOIE, CRAIG A; Lowell HS; Lowell, MA; (S); DECA; Library Aide; Trk; Mgr Schl Store; Mrktng.

SAVOY, SUZANNE; Maynard HS; Mayanrd, MA; (Y); Office Aide; Band; Chorus; Concert Band; Mrchg Band; Var Crs Cntry; Var Trk; Twrlr.

SAWA, STEVEN; Chicopee Comprehensive HS; Chicopee, MA; (Y); Var L Bsktbl; Var L Socr; Var L Trk.

SAWYER, JOSEPH; Clinton HS; Clinton, MA; (Y); 1/150; FCA; Intnl Clb; Math Tm; Yrbk Stf; Var L Bsbl; Var L Bsktbl; Var Capt Ftbl; High Hon Roll; Pres NHS; Ntl Merit Ltr; Harvard Bk Awd 85; Liberal Arts.

SAYLOR, BEVERLY; Doherty HS; Worcester, MA; (Y); Math Clb; Variety Show; Crs Cntry; Debate Tm; Ski Clb; Nwsp Stf; French Hon Soc; High Hon Roll; NHS; Ntl Merit SF; Williams Bk Awd 85; Geology.

SCACCIA, PAMELA J; Franklin HS; Franklin, MA; (Y); Varsity Clb; Stu Cncl; Cheerleading; Hon Roll.

SCADUTO, MIKE J; Malden Catholic HS; Lynnfield, MA; (Y); Computer Clb; Northeastern U; Comp Sci.

SCAGEL, EDWIN; Deerfield Acad; Northampton, MA; (Y); Spanish Clb; Band; Chorus; Concert Band; Jazz Band; Mrchg Band; Pep Band; Stage Crew; Nwsp Stf; JV Bsbl.

SCALA, JAMES C; Berkshire Schl; Lebanon Springs, NY; (S); 10/110; Radio Clb; Var Crs Cntry; Var Lcrss; JV Socr; High Hon Roll; Rdrs Dgst Schlrshp 84; Harvard Bk Prz 84; MVP Ski Tm 85; Coachs Awd & All-Leag Lacrosse Tm 85; Williams Coll.

SCALETTI, TONY R; Newburyport HS; Newburyport, MA; (Y); Ski Clb; JV Ice Hcky; Trk; Hon Roll; N Shore CC; Arch Desgn.

SCALZO, SILVIO; Malden Catholic HS; Lexington, MA; (Y); Boy Scts; Church Yth Grp; Cmnty Wkr; JA; Im Bsbl; Im Bsktbl; Im Ftbl; Im Gym; Im Mgr(s); Im Powder Puff Ftbl; Middlesex League All-Star Baseball 84; Bentley Coll; Busnss Admin.

SCANGAS, LARRY; Salem HS; Salem, MA; (Y); Im Bsbl; High Hon Roll; Hon Roll; NHS; Merit Schlrshp 85; Mech Eng.

SCANLAN, MARK; North Quincey HS; Quincy, MA; (Y); Am Leg Boys St; Capt Bsktbl; Capt Socr; Capt Tennis; High Hon Roll; Spanish NHS; Chrmn Prid Cmte 85-86; Pre-Law.

SCANLAND, ELIZABETH; Triton Regional HS; Salisbury, MA; (Y); Service Clb; Teachers Aide; Pres Soph Cls; Pres Jr Cls; Pres Sr Cls; Var Fld Hcky; Var Tennis; Var Trk; High Hon Roll; Hon Roll; 2nd Pl Mi Relay Cape Ann Lg Mt Trk 82-83; Engl Awd 82-83; Phys Ed Awd 83-84; Soc Studs Awd 84-85; Intl Bus.

SCANLON, BRIAN J; West Boylston HS; Oakdale, MA; (Y); 11/78; Am Leg Boys St; French Clb; Varsity Clb; Stage Crew; Var L Bsktbl; JV Ftbl; Var L Tennis; Im Vllybl; Hon Roll; NHS; Worcester Polytech; Elec Engrng.

SCANLON, CAROLYN; Wakefield HS; Wakefield, MA; (Y); Church Yth Grp; Key Clb; Variety Show; Yrbk Stf; JV Capt Fld Hcky.

SCARCELLA, LISA; Dedham HS; Dedham, MA; (Y); 13/290; Computer Clb; Teachers Aide; Hon Roll; Bst JR-COMPT Dept 84-85; Attnd Benningtn July Pgm-Comp & Fld Bio 85; Bio.

SCARINGI, STEPHEN; Norton HS; Norton, MA; (Y); 12/156; Aud/Vis; Yrbk Ed-Chief; Var L Ftbl; Trk; Hon Roll; Boys ST 85; Pre-Med.

SCARPINO, CHRIS; Scitvate HS; Scituate, MA; (Y); 33/296; Ski Clb; Trs Rep Stu Cncl; JV Bsktbl; JV Var Fld Hcky; Var Trk; Hon Roll; Scituates Alchl Awrns Day Panl 85; Day Dialog-Plymth Cnty Shrff 85; Plymth Cnty Shrff Advsry Brd 85; Boston Coll Fairield; Bus.

SCENNA, MICHELE; Northbridge JR SR HS; Northbridge, MA; (S); 14/160; French Clb; Girl Scts; VP Pep Clb; Sec Frsh Cls; Pres VP Stu Cncl; L Bsktbl; Capt L Fld Hcky; L Trk; Hon Roll; Jr NHS; Hugh O Brien Ldrshp Awd 84; Med.

SCHAEFER, J DORA; Medford HS; Nashville, TN; (Y); Letterman Clb; Mathletes; Concert Band; Nwsp Ed-Chief; Yrbk Stf; Off Soph Cls; Var Socr; Hon Roll; Mu Alp Tht; NHS; Engrng.

SCHAEFER, MICHELLE; Cardinal Spellman HS; Avon, MA; (Y); Church Yth Grp; Girl Scts; Pep Clb; Ski Clb; School Play; Var JV Cheerleading; Var Trk; Hon Roll.

SCHAEFER, STEPHEN P; Cardinal Spekman HS; Avon,, MA; (Y); 42/212; Church Yth Grp; Computer Clb; Variety Show; Nwsp Rptr; Yrbk Stf; Bsktbl; High Hon Roll; Hon Roll; NEDT Awd; Bentley Coll; Acctg.

SCHAFER, SCOTT; Framingham South HS; Framingham, MA; (Y); 4/263; Sec French Clb; Key Clb; Latin Clb; Stu Cncl; Var Trk; High Hon Roll; NHS; Ntl Merit Ltr; Drama Clb; Prfct Atten Awd; Slvr Mdl ACL-NJCL Ntl Ltn Exm; Freelnc Wrtr Argus Pstr Co; Law.

SCHAFFNER, MOLLYE; Marblehead HS; Marblehead, MA; (Y); #20 In Class; Yrbk Ed-Chief; High Hon Roll; Hon Roll; NHS; JV Crs Cntry; JV Trk; Poltcl Sci.

SCHAUBER, CHERYLENE; Maynard HS; Maynard, MA; (Y); 7/107; JV L Bsktbl; Var L Trk; Var Vllybl; High Hon Roll; Hon Roll; NHS; Med Tech.

SCHEER, DEBBIE; Ludlow HS; Ludlow, MA; (Y); 38/276; Camp Fr Inc; Church Yth Grp; Cmnty Wkr; English Clb; Girl Scts; JA; JCL; Red Cross Aide; School Musical; School Play; Sftbl Coach For 3 Tms 81-85; Sunday Schl Tchr 80-85; Girl Sct Ldr 85; Porter & Chester Inst; Arch Des.

SCHEFFLER, HEIDI; Bridgewater-Rayham Regional HS; Bridgewater, MA; (Y); 1/325; Cmnty Wkr; French Clb; Math Tm; Model UN; Ski Clb; Stage Crew; High Hon Roll; NHS; Church Yth Grp; Science Clb; Alt Japan U S Senate ST Scholar & Semi-Fin Finlnd U S Senate ST Scholar Yth For Undrstndg 84; Lang.

SCHEINMAN, CARRIE; Franklin HS; Franklin, MA; (Y); Pres VP Church Yth Grp; Math Tm; Spanish Clb; Church Choir; Concert Band; Mrchg Band; Yrbk Stf; Capt Cheerleading; Hon Roll; NHS.

SCHERMERHORN, NEAL; Monson JR SR HS; Hampden, MA; (Y); 3/86; Church Yth Grp; Church Choir; Concert Band; Jazz Band; Pep Band; School Play; NHS; Pres Acad Ftns Awd; Louis Armstrong Jazz Awd; All-ST Jazz Ensmbl; Berklee Coll Music; Music.

SCHETZEL, JULIE; Monson JR SR HS; Monson, MA; (Y); Church Yth Grp; Spanish Clb; Band; Church Choir; Concert Band; Mrchg Band; Yrbk Ed-Chief; Yrbk Stf; Hon Roll; Sec NHS; Pre-Elem Educ.

SCHICK, STEPHEN M; Norwood HS; Norwood, MA; (Y); 154/393; Boy Scts; Bsktbl; Ftbl; Trk; Wentworth Inst; Arch.

SCHILLER, LISA CHRISTINE; Miss Halls Schl; Houston, TX; (Y); 1/65; French Clb; Church Choir; Nwsp Stf; Cheerleading; JV Capt Fld Hcky; JV Lcrss; High Hon Roll; U TX; Lbrl Arts.

SCHIPANI, LISA M; Belmont HS; Belmont, MA; (Y); Church Yth Grp; Civic Clb; Cmnty Wkr; Red Cross Aide; School Play; Capt Swmmng; Cit Awd; High Hon Roll; Middlesex Leag All Star 84 & 85; Med.

SCHLEGEL, MICHAEL K; Beverly HS; Beverly, MA; (Y); 51/387; Am Leg Boys St; Off Frsh Cls; Off Soph Cls; Off Jr Cls; Off Sr Cls; Stu Cncl; Bsbl; Bsktbl; Ftbl; Hon Roll; U Of MA Amherst.

SCHLICKE, KEVIN S; Narragansett Regional HS; Phillipston, MA; (Y); 8/98; Am Leg Boys St; Pres Letterman Clb; Yrbk Ed-Chief; Var Capt Bsbl; Var Capt Bsktbl; Var Capt Ftbl; Hon Roll; Mu Alp Tht; NHS; Church Yth Grp.

SCHLICKMANN, DEVIN KURT; Deerfield Acad; Worcester, MA; (Y); English Clb; Varsity Clb; Var L Ftbl; Capt Var Lcrss; L Capt Wrstlng; Hon Roll; Ntl Merit Ltr; SR Editor Yr-Bk 85; Silver-New Engld Prep-Cls A-Wrestlng Champ 85; United Nats Mock Assbly Rep 84-85; Hartford CT, Trinity Coll; Gov.

SCHMIZ, JENNIFER; Somerville HS; Somerville, MA; (Y); 8/634; Math Clb; Math Tm; Off Jr Cls; Stu Cncl; Hon Roll; Jr NHS; NHS; Boston U; Comp Sci.

SCHNEIDERS, SUSAN; Canton HS; Canton, MA; (Y); 20/250; Church Yth Grp; Dance Clb; German Clb; Teachers Aide; Cheerleading; Hon Roll; Psych.

SCHNURR JR, WILLIAM T; Berkshire Schl; Sheffield, MA; (S); 1/130; Quiz Bowl; Radio Clb; School Play; Nwsp Rptr; Nwsp Stf; Lit Mag; Stu Cncl; Golf; Ice Hcky; Socr; Cum Laude Scty 85; Eipper Cup For Math 85; Ntl Assn Physics Tchrs Awd 84; Holy Cross.

SCHOFIELD, KAREN; Lunenburg HS; Lunenburg, MA; (Y); Church Yth Grp; Intnl Clb; Band; Concert Band; Golf; High Hon Roll; Hon Roll; NHS; N Am Famly Campers Assoc Treas VP 83-85.

SCHOLZ, KAREN; Hoosac Valley HS; Adams, MA; (Y); 25/158; JV Bsktbl; JV Var Socr; Var Trk; High Hon Roll; Hon Roll; NHS; All Div Sccr Tm 83; 3rd Yr Ski Instr 82-85; Cert Adv 1st Aid; Bus Admn.

SCHONEMANN, HANS J; Newburyport HS; Newburyport, MA; (Y); 43/195; Am Leg Boys St; Debate Tm; JA; Math Tm; Model UN; Political Wkr; Yrbk Stf; Stu Cncl; Bsktbl; Hon Roll; Engrng.

SCHREIBER, TANYA; Newton South HS; Newton, MA; (Y); German Clb; Chorus; Madrigals; Orch; School Musical; Yrbk Stf; Im Vllybl; Hon Roll; Ntl Merit SF; Schlrshp Merrywood Muisc Camp 82&83; All Newton Schl Music 82; Schlrshp New England Camp 82&83; Music.

SCHROCK, JAMES C; Hamilton-Wenham Regional HS; Hamilton, MA; (Y); 50/200; Am Leg Boys St; Church Yth Grp; Chorus; Var Capt Bsbl; Var L Bsktbl; Var L Ftbl; Wt Lftg; Hon Roll; Cape Ann Lg All Star Bsktbl Tm 85; Small Lib Art Coll; Bus.

SCHULTZ, DEBBIE; Westford Acad; Westford, MA; (Y); AFS; German Clb; Intnl Clb; Pep Clb; Trk; High Hon Roll; Hon Roll; English Awd 82-83; Bio.

SCHULTZ, RICHARD; Barnstable HS; Hyannis, MA; (S); 8/399; VP Church Yth Grp; VP Drama Clb; Concert Band; Mrchg Band; School Play; Stage Crew; JV Socr; Var Trk; High Hon Roll; Pres NHS; Mrchng Band Musicnshp Awd; Mc Donalds All Amer HS Mrch Band; Lions All ST Band; U Miami; Marine Bio.

SCHUMACHER, PAUL M; Groton-Dunstoble Regional Schl; Groton, MA; (Y); Boy Scts; Library Aide; Band; Concert Band; Mrchg Band; Pep Band; Crs Cntry; Hon Roll; Arch.

SCHUMAKER, HEIDI; Malden HS; Malden, MA; (Y); Church Yth Grp; Hosp Aide; Office Aide; Ski Clb; Hon Roll; Lab Tech.

SCHUMAKER, JOHN; Melrose HS; Boston, MA; (Y); 83/370; Boy Scts; Church Yth Grp; US Naval Acad.

SCHWAB, KRISTEN; Marian HS; Framingham, MA; (Y); Latin Clb; Ski Clb; Lit Mag; Trs Soph Cls; Jr Cls; Var Trk; Hon Roll; Hnrbl Mntn Sci Fair 83-84; Quinipiac Coll; Phy Ther.

SCHWARTZ, ANNE; New Bedford HS; New Bedford, MA; (Y); 2/600; JCL; Sec Soph Cls; Rep Stu Cncl; Var L Fld Hcky; Capt Var Gym; Var L Trk; Bausch & Lomb Sci Awd; Elks Awd; NHS; Ntl Merit Ltr; Athl Yr 85; US Army Schlr Athl Awd 85; Murphy Schlrshp Athl Ctznshp Awd 85; Brown U; Pre-Med.

SCHWARTZ, BETH; New Bedford HS; New Bedford, MA; (Y); English Clb; Rep Stu Cncl; Gym; Sftbl; Swmmng; Bstn Glbe Leag All Str Grls Swmmng 83-85; MVP Swm Tms 85; Schl Cmmtte Stu Rep 85-86; Med.

SCHWARTZ, BRYAN; Newton North HS; Newton, MA; (Y); Yrbk Phtg; Rep Soph Cls; Rep Jr Cls; JV Socr; JV Wrstlng; Hon Roll; Bus.

SCHWARTZ, ELLYN; Malden HS; Malden, MA; (Y); #10 In Class; Art Clb; Intnl Clb; Quiz Bowl; Scholastic Bowl; Teachers Aide; Temple Yth Grp; Lit Mag; Socr; MA Coll Arts; Commcl Arts.

SCHWARTZ, LEIGH A; Billerica Memorial HS; Billerica, MA; (Y); 9/420; Hosp Aide; Band; Concert Band; Mrchg Band; Pep Band; Yrbk Stf; Var Trk; High Hon Roll; NHS; Pre-Med.

SCHWARTZ, NEIL D; Newton South HS; Newton, MA; (Y); Am Leg Boys St; Political Wkr; School Play; Nwsp Stf; Ed Yrbk Stf; Socr; Hon Roll; Drama Clb; Spanish Clb; Temple Yth Grp; Frgn Lang Awd & Excllnc In Spnsh 85; Newton S Fclty Awd 83-84; MA Lacrosse Champshp Tm 85; Bus.

SCHWARTZ, PAMELA; North Andover HS; North Andover, MA; (Y); 3/250; Library Aide; Math Tm; Q&S; Temple Yth Grp; Nwsp Rptr; Yrbk Stf; Lit Mag; French Hon Soc; NHS; 1st Hnr Grad Spkr 85; Wellesley Coll; Sci.

SCHWARZ, ANDREW D; Wellesley SR HS; Wellesley Hills, MA; (Y); 1/318; JA; Model UN; Nwsp Ed-Chief; Off Stu Cncl; High Hon Roll; NHS; Ntl Merit SF; Harvard Bk 84; Bradford Awd Jrnlsm 84; Awds Mdrn European & US Hist 84; Poltcl Sci.

SCHWEFLER, JEFFREY K; Masconomet Regional HS; Boxford, MA; (Y); 10/270; Am Leg Boys St; Boy Scts; Math Tm; Model UN; Science Clb; NHS; 1st Pl MA ST Sci Fair 83 & 84; Air Force ROTC Schlrshp 85; MA Inst Of Tech; Comp Sci.

SCHWINGER, LAURIE A; Monson JR SR HS; Monson, MA; (Y); 10/78; Sec Drama Clb; French Clb; Co-Capt Varsity Clb; School Musical; School Play; Yrbk Stf; Var Co-Capt Cheerleading; Socr; ROTC; Boston Coll; Psych.

SCIARAFFA, NANCY; Weymouth North HS; Weymouth, MA; (Y); 14/385; Girl Scts; Yrbk Stf; Trk; High Hon Roll; Hon Roll; Jr NHS; NHS; Richard Canova Scholar Elks 85; U MA Amherst; Lib Art.

SCIBELLI, TERESA; Cathedral HS; Springfield, MA; (Y); 38/500; French Clb; GAA; Intnl Clb; Ski Clb; School Play; Yrbk Bus Mgr; Yrbk Stf; Sec Frsh Cls; Stu Cncl; JV Fld Hcky; Intl Bus.

SCIOLA, KIRK M; Saugus HS; Saugus, MA; (Y); 3/290; Chess Clb; Stu Cncl; High Hon Roll; Hon Roll; Jr NHS; NHS; John J Bucchiere Mem Awd 83; Talent Awd Acad Exc 85; MIT; Comp Engrng.

SCOTT, ANDREW; Reading Memorial HS; Reading, MA; (Y); Yrbk Phtg; Stat Golf; Var Mgr(s); Var Score Keeper; JV Trk; Marine Tech.

SCOTT, DENISE; Bedford HS; Bedford, MA; (Y); 125/213; Pep Clb; Orch; Trk; Schlrshp Awd Hm Ec Dept 84-85; Crimnl Justc.

SCOTT, ELIZABETH; Newton North HS; Newton, MA; (Y); Math Tm; Chorus; School Musical; Hon Roll; Gold Mdl At Olympiad Of Spoken Russian 85; Hstry.

SCOTT, ELIZABETH A; Chicopee HS; Chicopee, MA; (Y); 30/299; Aud/Vis; Church Yth Grp; Cmnty Wkr; U MA; Vtrnrn.

SCOTT, MICHAEL; Scituate HS; Scituate, MA; (Y); 30/304; Church Yth Grp; Ski Clb; JV Bsktbl; Var L Golf; Var L Socr; Cit Awd; High Hon Roll; Hon Roll; Jr NHS; NHS; MA ST Tm Golf Champs 85; S Shore Lg Socr JC Champs 84; JR Clb Champ Golf Hatherly 82 & 84; Furman U; Mth.

SCOTT, ROBERT; Chicopee HS; Chicopee, MA; (Y); Boys Clb Am; Boy Scts; Library Aide; Science Clb; Holyoke CC; Engr.

SCULLY, WILLIAM HAROLD; West Springfield SR HS; W Springfield, MA; (Y); 26/272; Church Yth Grp; Cmnty Wkr; Quiz Bowl; Var Capt Crs Cntry; Var Capt Trk; High Hon Roll; Hon Roll; Digital Scholar 85; NHS 84-85; Latin Hon Soc 84; U NH; Civil Engrng.

SCUTERI, DOROTHY; Malden HS; Malden, MA; (Y); Sec Band; Concert Band; Drm Mjr(t); Jazz Band; Mrchg Band; Variety Show; Bsktbl; Sftbl; Hon Roll; Med.

SCZEPANIK, KIM; Framingham South HS; Framingham, MA; (Y); Spanish Clb; Yrbk Stf; Stat Bsktbl; Stat Socr; JV Var Sftbl; Bus.

SEABROOKS, MICHELLE; Technical HS; Springfield, MA; (Y); JA; ROTC; Drill Tm; Rep Stu Cncl; Var Cheerleading; Var Sftbl; Boston U; Pre-Med.

SEALOCK, PEYTRA; Arlington HS; Arlington, MA; (Y); Church Yth Grp; Drama Clb; Chorus; Madrigals; School Musical; School Play; Rep Soph Cls; Gym; Hon Roll; Intl Order Rainbow For Girls Ofcr.

SEAMAN JR, JOHN T; Dennis-Yarmouth Regional HS; East Dennis, MA; (Y); Drm Mjr(t); Jazz Band; Mrchg Band; Symp Band; Pres Soph Cls; Im JV Bsktbl; NHS; Am Leg Boys St; Pres Church Yth Grp; High Hon Roll; MA Yth Ldrshp Sem Outstndg Soph Ldr 84; Oustndg Ind Music Prfrmnce Awds 84 & 85; Brown U Bk Awd 85; NY League Coll; Engrng.

SEARLEMAN, THERESA; St Marys HS; Westfield, MA; (Y); 11/50; Camera Clb; Church Yth Grp; Cmnty Wkr; Spanish Clb; Bsktbl; Cit Awd; High Hon Roll; Hon Roll; Citzn Schlrshp Fndtn Awd 85; U Of MA; Engrng.

SEARS, NATHAN R; Bedford HS; Bedford, MA; (Y); Aud/Vis; Rep Church Yth Grp; Drama Clb; Actor.

SEARS, STACEY; Georgetown JR SR HS; Georgetown, MA; (Y); French Clb; JV Cheerleading; JV Fld Hcky; High Hon Roll; Hon Roll; NHS; Pres Awd 84 & 85; Exc Prfrmnc In Frnch III 84; Supr Prfrmnc In Chmstry 85; Mech Engrng.

SEAVER, MICHELLE; Whitman Hanson Regional HS; Whitman, MA; (Y); 12/400; Rep Jr Cls; JV Var Cheerleading; Hon Roll; NHS; VFW Awd; Miss Fourth Dwn JR Clss Spirt & Ldrshp; Parker Bates Awd Chrldr Awd Ldrshp; Act.

SEDDON, CARROLL; Hingham HS; Hingham, MA; (Y); 48/438; AFS; Aud/Vis; Church Yth Grp; Girl Scts; School Musical; Hon Roll; Engl.

SEDGWICK, MICHAEL; Metheun HS; Methuen, MA; (Y); Model UN; Trk; Hon Roll; Im Bsktbl; JV Crs Cntry; Var L Ftbl; U ME; Htl Mgmt.

SEETELDT, DEREK; Cushing Acad; Atlanta, GA; (Y); Church Yth Grp; Teachers Aide; Yrbk Stf; Var Crs Cntry; Var Capt Swmmng; Var Trk; Hon Roll; GA Swmmng All Star Incntv Awd; MVP Swmmng Tm; Dormtry Proctr; Bus.

SEGAL, LYNDA; Randolph HS; Randolph, MA; (Y); Sec Temple Yth Grp; Band; Capt Color Guard; Yrbk Stf; Var Cheerleading; Powder Puff Ftbl; Var L Socr; Var Tennis; Hon Roll; NHS; Hotel Mgt.

SEGAL, SHELLI; Newton North HS; W Newton, MA; (Y); Orch; JV Swmmng; Hon Roll.

SEGRE, KATHY; Newton North HS; Newton Centre, MA; (Y); Tennis; Hon Roll; Itln Clb 83-85; Itln Exchng Prg 84; Lang.

SEIDLER, CIPPY; Nantucket HS; Nantucket, MA; (Y); 12/52; Cmnty Wkr; Varsity Clb; Nwsp Rptr; VP Soph Cls; Pres Jr Cls; Stu Cncl; Var Fld Hcky; Rotary Awd; VFW Awd; Voice Dem Awd; Stud Govt Day Rep St Hse; U Chgo; Law.

SELETSKY, ROBERT; Norwoos SR HS; Norwood, MA; (Y); 48/372; Boy Scts; Computer Clb; Orch; JV Crs Cntry; JV Socr; Hon Roll; Eagl Sct 85; U Of Rochester; Comp Sci.

SELOVER, ELIZABETH B; Greenfield HS; Greenfield, MA; (Y); Church Yth Grp; Hosp Aide; Science Clb; Sec Spanish Clb; Concert Band; Capt Flag Corp; Ed Yrbk Stf; JV Fld Hcky; JV Golf; Hon Roll; Med.

SELVA, SERGIO L; Oak Ridge HS; Miami, FL; (Y); Am Leg Boys St; Computer Clb; Natl Beta Clb; Science Clb; JV Bsbl; JV Ftbl; High Hon Roll; Jr NHS; Spanish NHS; Spanish Clb; Amer Legn Aux Awd 85; Med.

SELVAGGIO, FRANCIS A; Haverhill HS; Haverhill, MA; (Y); 9/413; Am Leg Boys St; Aud/Vis; Key Clb; Spanish Clb; Ftbl; NHS; Dist Stu 82-85; Worcester Polytech; Engrng.

SENAY, SCOTT; St Bernards CC HS; Leominster, MA; (S); 8/163; Am Leg Boys St; Boy Scts; Drama Clb; School Play; Yrbk Stf; Hon Roll; NHS; Prfct Atten Awd; Eagle Scout 82; Pope Pius XII 83; Comp Engrng.

SENIER, LAURA; Nazareth Acad; Reading, MA; (Y); 5/61; Drama Clb; Chorus; School Play; Stage Crew; Nwsp Ed-Chief; Hon Roll; NHS; NEDT Awd; Church Choir; Nwsp Rptr; Dartmouth Bk Awd 85; All Star Cast Awds 84-85; Engl.

SEPECH JR, WILLIAM T; Weymouth North HS; Weymouth, MA; (Y); Ski Clb; Capt Var Lcrss; Ski Clb 82-86; Outdoor Clb 82-86; Pre-Med.

SEPUKA, LISA; Holy Name C C HS; Auburn, MA; (Y); Ski Clb; Cheerleading; Fld Hcky; Sftbl; Hon Roll; Pre-Law.

SEQUIN, MICHELLE; New Bedford HS; New Bedford, MA; (Y); 148/700; AFS; JA; Office Aide; Mrchg Band; Cheerleading; Tennis; Hon Roll; SMU-JOHNSON & Whales; Bus.

SERA, LAURIE; Newton North HS; Newton, MA; (Y); Aud/Vis; Cmnty Wkr; Political Wkr; Cheerleading; Score Keeper; Hon Roll; Schlrshp Rll Awds 82-85.

SERA, SUSAN; Ware HS; Ware, MA; (Y); Church Yth Grp; French Clb; Hosp Aide; Library Aide; Model UN; VP Jr Cls; Hon Roll; Prfct Atten Awd; Phrmcy.

SERGEL, THERESA C; Bartlett HS; Webster, MA; (Y); #10 In Class; Cmnty Wkr; Drama Clb; Exploring; French Clb; Hosp Aide; Pres Intnl Clb; Pres Science Clb; Drill Tm; Twrlr; High Hon Roll; 3rd Pl Locl Sci Fair 85; 3rd Pl MA ST Sci Fair 85; Citatn Sec ST Sci Fair 85; Gentc Engr.

SERGIO, AMY; Cardinal Spellman HS; Brockton, MA; (Y); 8/240; Hosp Aide; Pep Clb; Ski Clb; Var Capt Cheerleading; High Hon Roll; Hon Roll; NHS; French II Hnr Awd; Youth Minister; Boston Coll; Public Relations.

SERINGA, KRIS; Bridgewater-Raynham Regnl HS; Bridgewater, MA; (Y); 24/350; Math Tm; Science Clb; Ski Clb; JV Var Socr; Var Trk; Hon Roll; Stu Govt Day JR H S Princpl 85; Brd Dirctrs Intl Soccr Clb 84-85; Trvld Ireland & Germany For Sccr; Boston; Biol.

SERINO, VALERIE; Saugus HS; Saugus, MA; (Y); 7/300; Yrbk Stf; Cheerleading; Gym; Hon Roll; Jr NHS; NHS; Outstndng Sci Stu Awd 85; Saugus Italia Amer Schlrshp 85; John J Bucchiere Hmntrn Schlrshp 85; Boston Coll.

SERRANO, LINDA; Cathedral HS; Spfld, MA; (Y); 76/475; Church Yth Grp; Cmnty Wkr; Dance Clb; Hosp Aide; Library Aide; Office Aide; Rep Frsh Cls; Rep Soph Cls; Rep Jr Cls; Rep Stu Cncl; Awd For Outstdng Svc To Chatedral Hgh 84-85; Bus Mgmt.

SERVINO, RICHARD; Boston Tech; Charlestown, MA; (Y); 25/220; Church Yth Grp; Computer Clb; Library Aide; Pep Clb; Yrbk Stf; Stu Cncl; Hon Roll; Steven Ricci Awd Drftng 85; MA U Boston; Engr.

SERWATKA, CHERYL; Dracut SR HS; Dracut, MA; (Y); Office Aide; Yrbk Stf; Rep Stu Cncl; Hon Roll; NHS; Bridgewater ST; Soc Wrkr.

SEUTTER, DORINNE; English HS; Lynn, MA; (Y); 84/365; AFS; Office Aide; Hon Roll; KC Schlrshp; Salem ST Coll; Nrsg.

SEXTON, LAURA; Ursuline Acad; Dedham, MA; (Y); 11/73; VP Church Yth Grp; Dance Clb; Drama Clb; French Clb; Math Tm; VP Service Clb; School Musical; Yrbk Stf; High Hon Roll; NHS; Prin Awd 85; Wheaton Coll; Comp Engrng.

SEYMOUR, KENNETH; Chicopee Comprhensive HS; Chicopee, MA; (Y); 51/266; Letterman Clb; Varsity Clb; Var L Bsbl; NHS; Bus Admin.

SEYMOUR, MICHELLE; Mohawktrail Regional HS; Colrain, MA; (Y); Band; Jazz Band; Mrchg Band; School Musical; School Play; Stage Crew; Yrbk Stf; Rep Stu Cncl; Var Vllybl; Hon Roll; Pro-Arts Consortium Smmr Pgm 84; MA Coll Art; Art Educ.

SEYMOUR, STEPHANIE; Mohawk Trl Regional HS; Colrain, MA; (Y); 13/142; School Musical; School Play; Nwsp Stf; Yrbk Bus Mgr; Yrbk Stf; Rep Jr Cls; Mgr Socr; Var JV Tennis; Hon Roll; Church Yth Grp; Outstndng Exc Spansh 84-85; Spanish.

SEYMOURIAN, DEANNA; Woodward Schl; Milton, MA; (Y); Church Yth Grp; Hosp Aide; Math Tm; Ski Clb; Yrbk Stf; Trs Jr Cls; Trs Stu Cncl; Im Vllybl; Camera Clb; Drama Clb; Aahperd Sr Achvt Awd 84; Math Awd 85; U Of Lowell; Plstcs Engrng.

SHADLEY, BEVERLY; Randolph HS; Randolph, MA; (Y); Spanish Clb; Stu Cncl; Capt Bsktbl; Var Sftbl; Hon Roll; NHS; Exctv Brd Hnr Soc 84-85; Randolph Stu Art Clndr Cntst Wnnr 84; JR Cls Apprctn Awd 85; Wrtng.

SHAFFER, DARREN; West Springfield HS; W Springfield, MA; (Y); Boy Scts; Chess Clb; Intnl Clb; Ski Clb; Im Coach Actv; L Swmmng; Im Vllybl; High Hon Roll; Hon Roll; Engrng.

SHALKAUSKAS, MELISSA; Bourne HS; Monument Bch, MA; (Y); 4-H; Girl Scts; Band; Concert Band; Mrchg Band; Yrbk Stf; Score Keeper; Hon Roll; Jr NHS; Mark Borrows Mem 85; Thorne Fndtn 85; Harriet M Faunee Trst 85; Westfield ST Coll; Soc Wrk.

SHANAHAN, KIMBERLY; Bishop Stang HS; Wareham, MA; (Y); 37/212; Latin Clb; Ski Clb; Yrbk Stf; Var L Sftbl; Vllybl; Hon Roll; Engl Acad Awd 82; Trig Anlytc Geo Acad Awd 83; Boston Coll; Law.

SHAO, KATHERINE; Winchester HS; Winchester, MA; (Y); 28/325; VP French Clb; Band; Chorus; Church Choir; School Musical; School Play; Stage Crew; French Hon Soc; High Hon Roll; NHS; Mass Music Tchrs Assoc Piano Comp 1st Prz 84; Jrnlsm.

SHAPIRO, DAVID; Malden HS; Malden, MA; (Y); 5/500; Pres Chess Clb; Math Clb; Quiz Bowl; Band; Trs Jazz Band; Variety Show; Bowling; Coach Actv; High Hon Roll; Pres NHS; Suffolk Bk Awd 85; Eng Merit Awd 85; Full Scholar U MA Amherst 85; Stanford; Law.

SHAPIRO, LAURA; Framingham South HS; Framingham, MA; (Y); 49/256; Key Clb; Latin Clb; Spanish Clb; Trs Temple Yth Grp; Stat Bsktbl; Fld Hcky; Hon Roll; Mindy Steinberg Awd 83; Morris Chapman Awd 84; Will Grad From The Prozdor Of Hebrew Coll 86; Lwyr.

SHAPIRO, STEPHANIE; Sharon HS; Sharon, MA; (Y); 50/200; Drama Clb; Hosp Aide; Temple Yth Grp; Trs Band; Nwsp Rptr; Yrbk Stf; Rep Sr Cls; Cit Awd; Hon Roll; Norwood Hosp Aux Schlrshp 85; Paul Stearns Mem Schlrshp 85; Friends Of Art & Music Educ Schlrshp 85; U Of MA Amherst; Med Tech.

SHARMA, RAVI K; Winchester HS; Winchester, MA; (Y); 2/325; JCL; Latin Clb; Radio Clb; Science Clb; French Hon Soc; High Hon Roll; Ntl Merit SF; French Clb; Harvard Book Awd 84; Schlrshp Awd Sci, Engl Ltn, Soc Stud 84; Ntl Ltn Exm Gld, Slvr Mdl 82-83; Astrnmy.

SHAW, BRIAN; North Quincy HS; Wollaston, MA; (Y); 137/380; Boy Scts; Computer Clb; JV Trk; Excel Comp Pgm 83-84; U MA-BOSTON; Comp Engr.

SHAW, CHRISTINE; Smith Acad; N Hatfield, MA; (Y); Camera Clb; Drama Clb; 4-H; School Play; Yrbk Phtg; Yrbk Stf; Sftbl; 4-H Awd; Hon Roll; Art Inst Of Boston; Photogrphy.

SHAW, DOREEN M; Brockton HS; Brockton, MA; (Y); 200/800; Hosp Aide; Var Crs Cntry; Var JV Trk; Hon Roll; NHS; Newburg Coll; Phys Ther.

SHAW, JEAN; Southbridge HS; Sbridge, MA; (Y); 1/160; VP Church Yth Grp; Girl Scts; Math Tm; Band; High Hon Roll; NHS; Voice Dem Awd; Hugh O Brien Yth Fndtn/MA Yth Ldrshp Fndt Ambssdr 84; Chancellors Tlnt Awd 85; U S Achv Acad Mbr 85; Psych.

SHAW, JOHN; Norton HS; Norton, MA; (Y); 1/151; Am Leg Boys St; Math Tm; Band; Concert Band; Drm Mjr(t); Mrchg Band; Yrbk Bus Mgr; L Crs Cntry; L Trk; High Hon Roll; Engrng.

SHAW, SARA; Marlblehead HS; Marblehead, MA; (Y); 29/250; Church Yth Grp; JV Fld Hcky; Hon Roll; NHS; Unsung Hero 83; Salem Evening News Carrier Of The Mnth 84.

SHEA, CATHY; Walpole HS; Walpole, MA; (Y); 36/275; Church Yth Grp; Nwsp Rptr; Ed Lit Mag; Rep Frsh Cls; Rep Soph Cls; Hon Roll; Pres Schlr; Stdnt Mnth March 84; Babson Coll; Mktg.

SHEA, FRANK; Saint Dominic Savio HS; East Boston, MA; (S); 26/110; Trs Jr Cls; JV Capt Bsktbl; Ftbl; Score Keeper; Hon Roll; Aviation.

SHEA, GERALDINE; Girls Catholic HS; Malden, MA; (S); 3/36; Rep Jr Cls; Pres Stu Cncl; Var Capt Bsktbl; Var Capt Sftbl; Var Capt Vllybl; Lion Awd; Voice Dem Awd; Schlrshp Awd Attend Bus Wk At Bentley Coll 84; Athlete Of Yr 84; Villanova U; Bus.

SHEA, JENNIFER; Westwood SR HS; Westwood, MA; (Y); 99/214; AFS; Key Clb; Mgr(s); Socr; Hon Roll; Christian A Herter Memrl Schlrshp 84; Bus.

SHEA, KEVIN; Winthrop HS; Winthrop, MA; (Y); Am Leg Boys St; Boy Scts; Church Yth Grp; Math Tm; School Play; Var Socr; Var Trk; Hon Roll; Eagle Scout 85; Sci Team 85; Cornell; Pre-Med.

SHEA, KIMBERLY; Marblehead HS; Marblehead, MA; (Y); 69/240; Church Yth Grp; Cmnty Wkr; Dance Clb; Off French Clb; Hosp Aide; Intnl Clb; Nwsp Rptr.

SHEA, KRISTEN; Taunton HS; E Taunton, MA; (Y); Aud/Vis; Church Yth Grp; Drama Clb; PAVAS; Spanish Clb; Acpl Chr; Chorus; School Musical; VP Soph Cls; VP Sr Cls; Class Of 1933 Schlrshp 85; Tauton Educ Assoc Schlrshp 85; Amer Assoc U Wmn Bk Awd 85; Wheaton Coll.

SHEA, MATTHEW; Cathedral HS; Springfield, MA; (Y); 12/500; Mathletes; Math Clb; Office Aide; NHS; Prfct Atten Awd; Demcrtc Chrmn Model Senate 85-86; Econ.

SHEAHAN, KELLY; Durfee HS; Fall River, MA; (Y); 13/687; Drama Clb; French Clb; Band; Flag Corp; Mrchg Band; Nwsp Stf; Yrbk Stf; VP Jr Cls; VP Sr Cls; Stu Cncl.

SHEAHAN, KRIS; Brockton HS; Brockton, MA; (Y); 2/950; Math Tm; Concert Band; Mrchg Band; NHS; Ntl Merit Ltr; Sal; MA Assn Of Schl Sprntndnts Awd 84; MIT; Bio Med Engrng.

SHEEHAN, COLLEEN; Brockton HS; Brockton, MA; (Y); 100/1100; Trs Church Yth Grp; Drama Clb; Key Clb; Ski Clb; Trs Church Choir; Stage Crew; Yrbk Stf; Trk; Hon Roll; Psych.

SHEEHAN, JOANNE; Saugus HS; Saugus, MA; (Y); 31/301; Office Aide; Pep Clb; Stu Cncl; Var Fld Hcky; Sftbl; NHS; Mktng.

SHEEHY, SUZANNE; Archbishop Williams HS; Quincy, MA; (Y); Church Yth Grp; Yrbk Stf; NHS; Engrng.

SHELDON, DEBORAH; Leominster HS; Leominster, MA; (Y); Drama Clb; Political Wkr; Mrchg Band; School Musical; School Play; Stu Cncl; Nrsg.

SHELLITO, JULIE; Pioneer Valley Regional Schl; Northfield, MA; (Y); 2/56; 4-H; GAA; Co-Capt Scholastic Bowl; Yrbk Ed-Chief; Pres Jr Cls; Var Capt Bsktbl; JV Var Sftbl; DAR Awd; VP NHS; Sal; Schl Stu Of Yr; Dartmouth Clb Bk Awd Ldrshp; Ithaca Coll.

SHELLITO, MICHAEL; Pioneer Valley Regional Schl; Northfield, MA; (Y); 8/56; Am Leg Boys St; Aud/Vis; Boy Scts; Ski Clb; Band; Concert Band; Mrchg Band; Yrbk Bus Mgr; Yrbk Stf; Socr.

SHEPARD, TIMOTHY F; Buckingham Browne & Nichols HS; Sudbury, MA; (Y); Computer Clb; JV Bsktbl; JV Ftbl; Hon Roll; Ntl Merit SF; Physics.

SHEPARDSON, MARY LOU; Coyle And Cassidy HS; South Easton, MA; (Y); 14/167; 4-H; Spanish Clb; Rep Jr Cls; Trs Sr Cls; Sec Stu Cncl; Var Tennis; Var Vllybl; Cit Awd; 4-H Awd; High Hon Roll; Cmmnwlth MA 85; 4-H Natl Congrss Hm Envrnmt 84; Prncpls Svc Awd 85; Assumption Coll; Forgn Affrs.

SHEPHARD, STEVEN; Methuen HS; Methuen, MA; (Y); 5/340; Am Leg Boys St; Intnl Clb; Model UN; JV Socr; Trk; High Hon Roll; NHS; Bentley Coll; Accntnt.

SHEPPARD, KATHY; Winchester HS; Winchester, MA; (Y); Boys Clb Am; Church Yth Grp; Girl Scts; Latin Clb; Y-Teens; Off Soph Cls; Stu Cncl; Cheerleading; Golf; Rollins Coll Winter Pk; Arch.

SHERAR, SHARON; Haverhill HS; Haverhill, MA; (Y); JV Crs Cntry; JV Fld Hcky; High Hon Roll; Hon Roll; Middlebury Coll VT; Englsh.

SHERF, DAVID E; Marblehead HS; Marblehead, MA; (Y); 42/261; French Clb; School Musical; Rep Stu Cncl; Bsktbl; Hon Roll; J Hancock Hnrs Awds Excel Bus; Vrsty Bsktbl Schlr Ath Awd; JV Bsktbl MVP; U MA Amherst; Pol Sci.

SHERMAN, JEFF; Newton Catholic HS; Newton, MA; (Y); 10/55; Teachers Aide; Varsity Clb; School Musical; Variety Show; Nwsp Rptr; Var Bsbl; Var Capt Bsktbl; Im Coach Actv; Hon Roll; Suburb Cath Leag All Star Bsktbl, Bsbl 85; Outstndng Ath 85; Pol Sci.

SHERMAN, ROBERT S; Bourne HS; Sagamore Beach, MA; (Y); Debate Tm; Math Tm; Elks Awd; Hon Roll; NHS; Ntl Rllr Sktng Comp 84; Northeast Reg Champ Rllr Sktng 84; Mem Schlrshp & Elks Stu Mnth Awd 85; Stonehill Coll; Bus Adm.

SHERTER, SCOTT; Greenfield HS; Greenfield, MA; (Y); Chorus; School Musical; School Play; Variety Show; Hon Roll; Peer Eductn Pgm; SADD; Western MA Dist Chorus Pioneer Vly Symphony Chorus.

SHERWOOD, STACEY L; Billerica Memorial HS; N Billerica, MA; (Y); VP Exploring; Library Aide; Chorus; Rep Stu Cncl; Var Bsktbl; Powder Puff Ftbl; Var Sftbl; Var Vllybl; Hon Roll; U Of ME-ORONO; Pre-Vet.

SHIA, BENEDICT; Boston Latin HS; Brighton, MA; (Y); 22/325; Church Yth Grp; Capt Math Tm; Ski Clb; Capt Swmmng; Hon Roll; NHS; Ntl Merit SF; Mst Imprvd Swm Tm 82; Mst Vlbl Plyr Swm Tm 83-85; Harvard Radcliffe; Engrng.

SHIA, LILIAN; Boston Latin School; Boston, MA; (Y); 18/299; Church Yth Grp; Drama Clb; Sec JA; Key Clb; Stage Crew; Hon Roll; NHS; Ntl Merit Ltr; Approbatn, Modern Awds 82-83.

SHIELDS, CHRISTOPHER; Xaverian Brothers HS; Westwood, MA; (S); 14/236; Am Leg Boys St; Boy Scts; Cmnty Wkr; Rep Stu Cncl; L Ftbl; Var Ice Hcky; Var Trk; High Hon Roll; Prfct Atten Awd; U Lowell; Engr.

SHIELDS JR, MICHAEL T; Dennis-Yarmouth Regional HS; South Yarmouth, MA; (Y); 56/319; Am Leg Boys St; Boy Scts; Computer Clb; Key Clb; Ski Clb; Nwsp Stf; Im Bsktbl; Var Tennis; Hon Roll; VFW Awd; Norwich U; Intl Rltns.

SHIKRALLAH, WILLIAM L; Georgetown JR SR HS; Georgetown, MA; (Y); 4/95; Boy Scts; Drama Clb; School Play; Stage Crew; Var L Socr; Hon Roll; NHS; Presdntl Acadmc Ftns Awd 85; Rensselaer Acadmc Schlrshp 85; Amer Lgn Schlrshp 85; Rensselaer Polytc; Aerntcl Engr.

SHINE, DENNIS F; Holy Name CC HS; Worcester, MA; (Y); Am Leg Boys St; Drama Clb; Spanish Clb; School Musical; Cmmnctn Skills Awd 84; Theatre Guild Awd 85; Bentley; Bus.

SHIVICK, STEVEN J; Oxford HS; Oxford, MA; (Y); 6/160; Am Leg Boys St; Church Yth Grp; Stu Cncl; Var Capt Ftbl; Var L Trk; Vllybl; High Hon Roll; Hon Roll; Jr NHS; NHS; U MA; Bus.

SHOBERT, TODD S; Plymouth-Carver HS; S Carver, MA; (Y); Am Leg Boys St; Boy Scts; Church Yth Grp; Socr; Eastrn Nazarene Coll; Bus Adm.

SHOENER, MARK; Cathedral HS; Chicopee, MA; (Y); 75/513; Acctg.

SHOOLMAN, JENNIFER; Buckingham Browne & Nichols Schl; Boston, MA; (S); Chorus; School Musical; School Play; Nwsp Ed-Chief; Yrbk Stf; Ntl Merit SF; Brnz, Slvr Medls Russian Olympd 84-85.

SHORE, ROBIN B; Randolph HS; Randolph, MA; (Y); 33/315; Nwsp Rptr; Nwsp Stf; Hon Roll; Ntl Merit SF; Jrnlsm.

SHORE, SCOTT; Winthrop HS; Winthrop, MA; (Y); 20/217; Math Tm; Var L Crs Cntry; Var L Trk; Hon Roll; Comp Sci.

SHORES, STEPHANIE PAULETTE; Leominster HS; Leominster, MA; (S); 41/352; Cmnty Wkr; French Clb; Political Wkr; School Musical; School Play; Trs Frsh Cls; Pres Stu Cncl; High Hon Roll; Hon Roll; VP & Pres MA Assoc Stu Cncls Exeec Brd 83-85; Thayer Consrvtry Yth Wnd Ensmbl; Tufts U; Pol Sci.

SHOUM, KATHLEEN; Ware HS; Ware, MA; (Y); 26/120; Dance Clb; French Clb; Hosp Aide; Key Clb; Yrbk Stf; Stu Cncl; Cheerleading; Hon Roll; PACC Scholar Awd 85; Bay ST; Nrsng.

SHRIVER, HOLLY; Chicopee Comprehensive HS; Chicopee, MA; (Y); 3/311; Debate Tm; Drama Clb; French Clb; German Clb; Quiz Bowl; Spanish Clb; Concert Band; Yrbk Stf; High Hon Roll; Ntl Merit SF; Outstndng Frgn Lang Stu 85; Japanese.

SHUBERT, KATIE; Acton Boxboro Regional HS; Acton, MA; (Y); 3/354; Drama Clb; Leo Clb; Math Tm; Ski Clb; Mrchg Band; JV Lcrss; NHS; AFS; Civic Clb; Band; Charles Battit Scholar 85; Outstndng Sci Stu Thru HS 85; Natl Hnr Soc 85; Dartmouth U.

SHUGRUE, MICHAEL; St Johns HS; Shrewsbury, MA; (Y); 152/287; Exploring; French Clb; Model UN; Hon Roll; Hstry Tchng.

SHULTZ, ROBERT; Cohasset HS; Cohasset, MA; (Y); 4/135; Am Leg Boys St; VP Frsh Cls; Var Capt Bsbl; Var Capt Bsktbl; Var Capt Socr; Var L Trk; High Hon Roll; Sec NHS; Holy Cross Dartmouth Clb Bk Awds; Athl Hnrs; All Star Bsbl,Soccer; Bus.

SHURTLUFF, KEVIN; North Quincy HS; Quincy, MA; (Y); 19/378; Cmnty Wkr; Math Tm; Political Wkr; Capt Quiz Bowl; VP Spanish Clb; JV Socr; High Hon Roll; NHS; Pres Schlr; Spanish NHS; Spn Tutor 84-85; Case Western Res U Scholar Competitn Weekend 85; Case Western Res U; Engl.

SIBILIA, ROBERT F; Bishop Feehan HS; Mansfield, MA; (Y); Am Leg Boys St; Church Yth Grp; French Clb; Science Clb; Im Bsktbl; French Hon Soc; High Hon Roll; Hon Roll; NHS; Prfct Atten Awd; Schlrshp Awd Bio,Frnch,Math 83-85; Providence Coll; Antmy.

SIBLEY, CHERYL; Lenox Memorial HS; Lenox, MA; (Y); Rep Stu Cncl; Var Bsktbl; Var Socr; Var Socr; High Hon Roll; Hon Roll; Jrnlsm.

SICLUR, CYNTHIA; Ware HS; Ware, MA; (Y); 5/110; Am Leg Aux Girls St; Church Yth Grp; 4-H; Hosp Aide; Mathletes; Model UN; Yrbk Ed-Chief; Yrbk Phtg; Rep Stu Cncl; Voice Dem Awd; Highest Av US Hist 84-85; Dartmouth Bk Awd 84-85; Engrng.

SIDERI, MARIA; Presentation Of Mary Acad; Methuen, MA; (S); 8/51; Church Yth Grp; Pres Spanish Clb; Yrbk Stf; Trs Frsh Cls; Trs Soph Cls; Trs Jr Cls; DAR Awd; High Hon Roll; Pres NHS; Computer Clb; Bus Mngmnt.

SIDMAN, CINDY; Natick HS; Natick, MA; (Y); 143/443; Girl Scts; Spanish Clb; Teachers Aide; Temple Yth Grp; Lit Mag; Soph Cls; Jr Cls; Var Capt Tennis; Hon Roll; Soc Sci.

SIEGEL, ADAM; Peabody Veterans Memorial HS; Peabody, MA; (Y); 2/550; French Clb; Temple Yth Grp; Pres Sr Cls; Rep Stu Cncl; Var Capt Swmmng; NHS; Ntl Merit SF; Rep Soph Cls; 2nd Prz MA ST Sci Fair 85; Chncllrs Awd 85; Arch.

SIEGEL, STEVE; Hamilton-Wenham Regional HS; Wenham, MA; (Y); 82/200; 4-H; FFA; Ski Clb; Var Socr; 4-H Awd; Hon Roll; Frmng.

SIEMER, SHIRLEY ANNE; Nauset Regional HS; Wellfleet, MA; (Y); German Clb; Math Tm; Ski Clb; Band; Concert Band; Orch; School Play; Bsktbl; Socr; Tennis; Northeastern U; Interprtr.

SIEMIONKO, KATHLEEN; Saint Clare HS; Roslindale, MA; (Y); 9/150; Church Yth Grp; French Clb; JCL; Variety Show; Nwsp Rptr; Rep Soph Cls; Hon Roll; Jr NHS; Higst Avg Frech II,Law 84-85; Mount Ida; Paralegal.

SIFFLARD, JUDILYN; Chatham JR SR HS; W Chatham, MA; (Y); 2/56; AFS; Sec Drama Clb; Sec Chorus; Madrigals; School Musical; Yrbk Stf; Sec Jr Cls; Cit Awd; High Hon Roll; NHS; Wellesley Coll Bk Awd 85; Comm.

SIGLER, ERIC; Marblehead HS; Marblehead, MA; (Y); 50/260; Debate Tm; French Clb; Ski Clb; Stu Cncl; Bsktbl; Lcrss; Socr; Tennis; Trk.

SIGRIST, ALLISON; Manchester JR/SR HS; Manchester, MA; (Y); Concert Band; Jazz Band; Mrchg Band; High Hon Roll; NHS; Mst Imprvd Musician 83; Music.

SILLIKER, KAREN; Malden HS; Malden, MA; (Y); 20/523; Key Clb; Yrbk Stf; Sec Sr Cls; Hon Roll; NHS; Math Tm; Office Aide; Variety Show; Im Bowling; Ntl Eng Merit Awd 85; Med.

SILVA, CHRISTINE; Marian HS; Ashland, MA; (Y); 34/172; Church Yth Grp; Dance Clb; Drama Clb; School Play; Variety Show; Yrbk Stf; Stu Cncl; Cheerleading; Trk; Salve Regina; Librl Arts.

SILVA, DAVID; Reading Memorial HS; Reading, MA; (Y); Camera Clb; Church Yth Grp; Band; Concert Band; Mrchg Band; Mgr(s); Hon Roll; Cncrt & Mrchng Band 83-85; Marine Bio.

SILVA, JAMES; Bishop Geehan HS; Cumberland, RI; (Y); Chess Clb; Var L Trk; Spanish NHS; Awd Of Math Exllnc Trignmtry 85; U Of MA; Bio.

SILVA, SHERIL; Somerset HS; Somerset, MA; (Y); Nwsp Rptr; Nwsp Sprt Ed; Nwsp Stf; Rep Frsh Cls; Rep Soph Cls; Rep Jr Cls; Stu Cncl; NHS; NEDT Awd; Spch Path.

SILVEIRA, CAROL ANN; Coyle & Cassidy Memorial HS; Taunton, MA; (Y); 13/156; Pres Drama Clb; VP French Clb; Math Clb; Chorus; Church Choir; School Musical; Hon Roll; Kiwanis Awd; NHS; Schl Ltrs Drama Clb,Flk Grp 84; Rnr Up Cent III Ldrs Schlrshp Cntst 84-85; Outstndng Serv Awd Flk Grp; U Of Lowell; Phys Thrpy.

SILVEIRA, JAMES; Fairhaven HS; Fairhaven, MA; (Y); 15/160; Computer Clb; French Clb; Math Clb; Math Tm; Var Bsktbl; Var Tennis; Hon Roll; U MA Amherst; Comp Engr.

SILVEIRA, THOMAS; Bishop Stang HS; Mattapolsett, MA; (Y); Am Leg Boys St; Church Yth Grp; JA; Political Wkr; School Musical; School Play; Variety Show; Mgr(s); Trk; Hon Roll; Acadmc Awd Hstry 82-83; MA Bus Wk Recvd Schlrshp 84; Cert Achvt Mngng 84; Forgn Svc.

SILVEIRA, VICTOR; New Bedford HS; New Bedford, MA; (Y); 28/600; Art Clb; Sec Drama Clb; Chorus; School Musical; School Play; High Hon Roll; NHS; Excllnce Frgn Lang 84-85; Comp.

SILVER, DAN; Amherst Regional HS; Amherst, MA; (Y); 5/269; French Clb; Red Cross Aide; Temple Yth Grp; Orch; Stage Crew; Var Capt Swmmng; NHS; Excllnce Spn I 83; Excllnce Frnch IV 84.

SILVER, STACEY; Beverly HS; Chester Field, MO; (Y); VP Sec Church Yth Grp; Dance Clb; Drama Clb; Sec VP Temple Yth Grp; Variety Show; Cheerleading; High Hon Roll; Hon Roll; Leadrshp Awd-Overnight Smmr Camp 84; Israel Smmr Pgm Overnight Camp Rep 84; U Of MO-COLUMBIA.

SILVERMAN, ALISA; Framingham South HS; Framingham, MA; (Y); 16/256; French Clb; Hosp Aide; Office Aide; Lit Mag; High Hon Roll; NHS; Free Lance Wrtr Argus Poster Wrtng Experience; Med.

SILVESTRI, MARC; Brookline HS; Brookline, MA; (Y); Hon Roll; Hnrble Men AATF Tst 83-84; Bus.

SILVIA, PATRICIA M; Bridgewater-Raynham Regional HS; Bridgewater, MA; (Y); 5/309; Church Yth Grp; Cheerleading; CC Awd; High Hon Roll; Hon Roll; NHS; Pres Schlr; Rotary Awd; Dante Alighieri Socty MA Hnrs 85; Stonehill Clg Hnrs Schlr 85; Stonehill Coll; Bio.

SILVIA, VANCE A; Milford HS; Milford, MA; (Y); Boy Scts; Band; Concert Band; Jazz Band; School Musical; School Play; L Golf; L Tennis; Band Parents Music Achvmnt Awd 84-85; All Amer Hall Fame Band Hon 82&83; Meterology.

SIMARD, MARIA; Boston Technical HS; E Boston, MA; (Y); 22/258; Nwsp Stf; Yrbk Stf; Pres Stu Cncl; Capt Cheerleading; Capt Sftbl; Hon Roll; Stu Ledrshp Chrprsn 85; SADD Pres 85; Red Cross Blood Drive Crdntr 85; Emerson; Brdcst Jrnlsm.

SIMARD, MICHELE; Presentation Of Mary Acad; Salem, NH; (S); 4/51; French Clb; Math Clb; Hon Roll; NHS; Stonehill Coll; Bus Admin.

SIMAS, JOSE; New Bedford HS; New Bedford, MA; (Y); 61/800; Church Yth Grp; Stu Cncl; Bsktbl; Trk.

SIMMER, ROBERT; King Philip Regional HS; Plainville, MA; (S); Ski Clb; Var L Ftbl; Var Trk; Wt Lftg; Hon Roll; Jr NHS; NHS; Lib Arts.

SIMMLER, CHRISTOPHER R; Xaverian Brothers HS; Franklin, MA; (S); 9/236; Varsity Clb; Concert Band; Im Bsktbl; Im Ftbl; Im Golf; Var Capt Socr; Im Wt Lftg; High Hon Roll; NHS; Cath Conf All-Star Tm Soccer 84; Worcester Polytech Inst; Engr.

SIMMONS, STACEY C; Brookline HS; Dorchester, MA; (Y); Church Yth Grp; Girl Scts; Intnl Clb; Spanish Clb; Church Choir; Off Stu Cncl; Hon Roll; Hugh O Brian Yth Ldrshp Rep 83; Amer Legion Ortncl Ont 84; Amigos De Las Americas Vol 84; Med.

SIMMONS, STEPHANIE; Cathedral HS; Springfield, MA; (Y); 3/515; Hosp Aide; Math Clb; Office Aide; Stu Cncl; Var L Swmmng; NHS; MA Yth Ldrshp Semnr 84; Engrg.

SIMONDS, MELISSA LEE ALEXIS; Fitchburg HS; Fitchburg, MA; (Y); 37/224; Science Clb; Yrbk Stf; High Hon Roll; Hnrbl Ment My Hero Essay Cntst; Alumni Assoc Schlrshp; Fitchburg Womens Clb; Hortwick Coll-New York; Psych.

SIMONDS, ROBERT; Haverhill HS; Haverhill, MA; (Y); 120/450; Boys Clb Am; Church Yth Grp; Varsity Clb; Capt Crs Cntry; Capt Trk; Hon Roll.

SIMONDS, SAMANTHA; Bishop Feehan HS; Attleboro, MA; (Y); 10/250; Hosp Aide; JCL; Speech Tm; Chorus; Ed Yrbk Stf; NHS; Spanish NHS; Hon Men Natl Spn Exam 84 & 85; Cum Laude Natl Lat Exam 84; Dstngshd Accmplshmnt Spn I, II, III 83-85; Frgn Svc.

SIMONE, TODD; Central Catholic HS; Windham, NH; (Y); 30/240; Church Yth Grp; Ski Clb; JV Ftbl; High Hon Roll; Hon Roll; Prncpls Awd 83-84; SR Cncl; Engrng.

SIMONEAU, LAURIE; Bishop Feehan HS; North Attleboro, MA; (S); Drama Clb; Thesps; Chorus; Church Choir; School Musical; School Play; Stage Crew; High Hon Roll; Schl Letter Chorus, Theater; Music.

SIMPKIN, DONALD; New Bedford HS; New Bedford, MA; (Y); 233/640; Church Yth Grp; Library Aide; SMU Coll; Comp Engrng.

SIMS, HEATHER EUGENIA; Natick HS; West Natick, MA; (Y); 213/421; Church Yth Grp; Cmnty Wkr; Debate Tm; Office Aide; Political Wkr; Red Cross Aide; Ski Clb; Spanish Clb; Speech Tm; Band; Sons Itly & HS Arts Cncl Schlrshps 85; Regis Coll; Lbrl Arts.

SINCLAIR, MICHAEL; Longmeadow HS; Longmeadow, MA; (Y); Key Clb; Stage Crew; Bentley Coll; Bus.

SINKIEWICH, LYNDA; Pittsfield HS; Pittsfield, MA; (Y); Church Yth Grp; Drama Clb; Model UN; Political Wkr; School Musical; School Play; Nwsp Rptr; Hon Roll; U Of SC; Brdcst.

SIROIS, DAVE; Bishop Fenwick HS; Salem, MA; (Y); Church Yth Grp; Science Clb; Yrbk Stf; Rep Frsh Cls; Var L Bsktbl; Var L Crs Cntry; Score Keeper; Var Capt Trk; High Hon Roll; Prfct Atten Awd; Christian Studs I & II Awd; Springfield Coll; Bus.

SIROIS, WILLIAM S; Natick HS; Natick, MA; (Y); Var Bsbl; Coach Actv; Im Ftbl; Var Ice Hcky; Hon Roll; Jr NHS; Prfct Atten Awd; Bus.

SISSON, ASHTON; Doherty Memorial HS; Worcester, MA; (Y); Church Yth Grp; Debate Tm; French Clb; Orch; Var L Fld Hcky; High Hon Roll; Hon Roll; NHS; Ntl Merit Ltr; 5th Ntl Frnch Exam 85, 7th 84; Horace Mann Schlr 83.

SISTO, FRANK; Plymouth Carver HS; Hyannis, MA; (Y); Chess Clb; Jazz Band; Variety Show; Var L Bowling; Var Trk; RH ST Champ Chess 85; 2nd Pl MA Chess 85; SE MA U; Comp Pgmmg.

SIVACEK, TRACY A; Bellingham Memoiral JR SR HS; Bellingham, MA; (Y); Art Clb; GAA; Letterman Clb; Library Aide; Var Trk; Var Hon Roll; MVP Wntr Trck 85; All Star Tm Hrdlr 85; Hnrbl Mntn Hurdls & Long Jmp All Star Tm 85; Vet.

SIVAPIRAGASAM, SANJIVAN; Somerville HS; Somerville, MA; (Y); Math Clb; Math Tm; Science Clb; Stu Cncl; Mgr(s); High Hon Roll; NHS; Prfct Atten Awd; Pres Schlr; Natl Yth Sci Camp Awd Wnnr Sci Fair 85; MIT MA; Engrng.

SIZER, KIM; Ayer JR SR HS; Shirley, MA; (Y); Ski Clb; Yrbk Ed-Chief; Var L Cheerleading; JV Fld Hcky; Var L Trk; Hon Roll; NHS; Teachers Aide; School Play; Yrbk Stf; Mu Alpha Theta 84; Herbert Kipton Christmas Crd Wnnr 83; Jrnlsm Awd 85; Wells Coll; Cmrcl Dsgn.

SKANTZARIS, MARIA; Burlington HS; Burlington, MA; (Y); 3/320; Sec Trs Church Yth Grp; Drama Clb; Math Tm; School Play; Yrbk Ed-Chief; Powder Puff Ftbl; High Hon Roll; NHS; Boston Globe Schlstc Art Awds 84; Bio Hist Cert 83; Physics.

SKARP, SARA; Monson JR SR HS; Monson, MA; (Y); Am Leg Aux Girls St; French Clb; GAA; Letterman Clb; Varsity Clb; Band; Concert Band; Mrchg Band; School Musical; School Play; Ruth Berrian Fox Poetry Awd-Hnrb Mntn 83; Phys Thrpy.

SKELTON, JEFFREY P; Burlington HS; Burlington, MA; (Y); 135/360; Cmnty Wkr; JV Var Bsbl; Ftbl; JV Lcrss; JV Var Wrstlng; MA ST Schlrshp 85; U Of Lowell; Arch Engrng.

SKILTON, DEBORAH; Manchester JR SR HS; Manchester, MA; (Y); 1/65; Math Tm; Science Clb; Band; Chorus; Jazz Band; Trs Jr Cls; Trs Sr Cls; High Hon Roll; Debate Tm; Concert Band; Sci Awd 85; Herbert Hahn Mem Bk Awd 85; Manchester Schlr 85.

SKOLNICK, DANIEL; Beverly HS; Beverly, MA; (Y); Aud/Vis; Exploring; L Math Tm; Temple Yth Grp; Nwsp Stf; VP Stu Cncl; Var Crs Cntry; JV Wrstlng; Hon Roll; Psychlgy.

SKOURAS, THOMAS; Lynn English HS; Lynn, MA; (Y); 21/339; Boys Clb Am; Office Aide; High Hon Roll; Hon Roll; Lowell U; Elctrncs Engr.

SKRZYNIARZ, LISA; Holyoke Catholic HS; S Hadley, MA; (Y); Church Yth Grp; French Clb; Hosp Aide; Pep Clb; Hon Roll; Prfct Atten Awd.

SLATE, KATHLEEN; Chicopee Comprehensive HS; Chicopee, MA; (Y); 64/311; Library Aide; Office Aide; Yrbk Stf; L Crs Cntry; Powder Puff Ftbl; JV Sftbl; Var L Swmmng; Hon Roll; NHS; Coaches Awd 2(Softbl & Swimming 84-85; Swim Team Capt 83-85; Bay Path JC; Exec Sec.

SLATTERY, ANN; Boston Latin Schl; Roslindale, MA; (Y); 149/315; Church Yth Grp; JA; Key Clb; Ski Clb; Bsbl; Cheerleading; Sftbl; Tennis; Hon Roll.

SLATTERY, KATHERINE; Girls Catholic HS; Malden, MA; (Y); Church Yth Grp; School Play; Pres Frsh Cls; Pres Soph Cls; Trs Jr Cls; Trs Stu Cncl; JV Bsktbl; JV Sftbl; JV Vllybl; Hon Roll; Zonta Awd Citznshp & Schlrshp 85; Arch.

SLATTERY, THOMAS J; Catholic Memorial HS; Boston, MA; (Y); Church Yth Grp; Computer Clb; JA; Key Clb; Math Clb; Spanish Clb; Rep Frsh Cls; Trk; NHS; Stage Crew; Boston Coll; Bus.

SLAYTER, STEPHEN R; Hyde Park Acad; Roslindale, MA; (S); #1 In Class; Hon Roll; U MA Boston; Comp Sci.

SLEEPER, RACHEL; Shepherd Hill Regional HS; Charlton City, MA; (Y); 2/149; Math Tm; Chorus; Color Guard; School Musical; Stage Crew; Variety Show; Yrbk Stf; Trk; Twrlr; High Hon Roll; US Air Force Acad; Aerospace.

SLEIN, JULIANA; Coyle & Cassidy HS; S Easton, MA; (Y); Church Yth Grp; Cmnty Wkr; French Clb; Latin Clb; Band; Concert Band; Mrchg Band; Bsktbl; Swmmng; NHS; Hghst Avrg In Frnch I 85; U Of MA-AMHERST; Law.

SLIBY, NICOLE N; Walpole HS; Westwood, MA; (Y); 32/256; Drama Clb; French Clb; JCL; Latin Clb; Ski Clb; Band; Concert Band; Mrchg Band; School Play; Pres Soph Cls; Outstndg Frsh Svc 81-82; Blssd Sacremnt Scholar 84-85; Boston Coll.

SLINEY JR, PHILIP M; Needham HS; Needham, MA; (Y); Am Leg Boys St; Church Yth Grp; French Clb; Bsbl; Bsktbl; Socr; Var Trk; Hon Roll; Yrbk Stf; Comp Sci.

SLOAD, DOUGLAS; Beverly HS; Beverly, MA; (Y); Sec Leo Clb; Political Wkr; Teachers Aide; Rep Stu Cncl; JV Bsbl; High Hon Roll; NHS; Bus Admin.

SLOCUMB, DAMON; Classical HS; Springfield, MA; (Y); Church Yth Grp; Computer Clb; JA; Political Wkr; Band; Im Socr; Hon Roll; Acad Achvt Awd From Lowell U 85; Lowell U; Elec Engr.

SLOMSKI, JEFFREY J; Marian HS; Sudbury, MA; (Y); 5/175; Yrbk Bus Mgr; Trs Soph Cls; Stu Cncl; Var Capt Crs Cntry; Var Capt Trk; High Hon Roll; Hon Roll; NHS; Ntl Merit Ltr; NEDT Awd; Manian Schlr-Athlt 84-85; Manian Math Comptn 1st Pl 84; Crss Cntry MVP-3 Tims 81-84; Dartmouth Coll; Bus.

SLYSZ, LISA; Smith Acad HS; Hatfield, MA; (Y); 5/33; Sec Trs Drama Clb; Ski Clb; School Play; Yrbk Sprt Ed; Yrbk Stf; Var Sftbl; Hon Roll; Ticket Seller 82-85; Natl Sci Merit Awd 85; Acad All Amer Awd 85; Elec Engrng.

SMABY, NIELS; Cambridge Rindge & Latin Schl; Cambridge, MA; (Y); 4/600; Computer Clb; Math Tm; Y-Teens; Nwsp Rptr; Nwsp Stf; JV Bsbl; Var Swmmng; JV Trk; High Hon Roll; Ntl Merit SF; MA Team US Acad Decathalon 84; Harvard Bk Awd 84; Phys Sci.

SMACK, JAMES W; Westborough HS; Westborough, MA; (Y); 47/177; Boy Scts; Chess Clb; Church Yth Grp; Hosp Aide; Library Aide; Church Choir; Var L Golf; Hon Roll; German Clb; Eagle Scout 84; U Of MA-AMHERST; Htl Mgmt.

SMARZ, LAURIE; Smith Acad; Hatfield, MA; (S); Drama Clb; Pres 4-H; School Play; Stage Crew; Yrbk Sprt Ed; JV Bsktbl; Var Mgr(s); Var Sftbl.

SMIGIELSKI, THOMAS; Lynn Classical HS; Lynn, MA; (Y); Church Yth Grp; Exploring; French Clb; JA; Yrbk Stf; High Hon Roll; Hon Roll; Jr NHS; Sal; Breed JR Hgh Schlstc Achv Awd 83; Bus Mgmt.

SMITH, BARRY FRANCIS; Cathedral HS; Westfield, MA; (Y); Chess Clb; VP Math Clb; Stage Crew; High Hon Roll; Mu Alp Tht; NHS; Ntl Merit Ltr; Outstndng Serv Awd 84-85; Pres Acad Fitnss Awd 85; MA Advncd Studys Prog Schlrshp 84; Middlebury Coll; Engl.

SMITH, CARLA; Monument Mountain HS; Gt Barrington, MA; (Y); Dance Clb; Hosp Aide; Stage Crew; Yrbk Phtg; Yrbk Stf; Rep Stu Cncl; Var Bsktbl; Var Socr; Var Sftbl; Var Trk; Midas Touch Athl Of Wk Awd 84; Sccr & Bsktbl Awds-All-Berkshr & All-Wstrn Mass 84-85; Sci.

SMITH, CAROL J; Natick HS; Natick, MA; (Y); 2/450; Computer Clb; Speech Tm; Acpl Chr; Chorus; School Musical; School Play; Ntl Merit SF; Sal; Hon Roll; Wellesley Bk Awd 84; Natick Womens Div Schlrshp Com For Music 1st Pl 83; MIT; Electrical Engr.

SMITH, COLLEEN M; Bishop Connolly HS; Middletown, RI; (Y); Sec Church Yth Grp; Cmnty Wkr; Drama Clb; Office Aide; Quiz Bowl; Ski Clb; Teachers Aide; Trk; High Hon Roll; James Silvia Ldrshp Awd 84; Actng Awd Rgnl CYO Newport Cnty 84; Gov Dukakis Awd For Prmtng Drug & Alc; Salve Regina Coll; Educ.

SMITH, DANNY; Franklin HS; Franklin, MA; (Y); Varsity Clb; Hon Roll; Var L Bsbl; Var Capt Ftbl; Var Capt Ice Hcky; Lg All Star Bsbl 85; Thnksgvg Gm MVP Ftbl 84; Dartmouth Coll.

SMITH, DAVID W B; Dover-Sherborn HS; Dover, MA; (Y); 20/250; Am Leg Boys St; Church Yth Grp; Debate Tm; Concert Band; Variety Show; Stu Cncl; Ftbl; Trk; Wt Lftg; Hon Roll; West Point; Engl.

SMITH, DEAN; Bridgewater-Raynham Reg HS; Raynham, MA; (Y); 4-H; Model UN; Ski Clb; Band; Concert Band; Jazz Band; Mrchg Band; Pep Band; Stage Crew; Symp Band; Lions Allstate Band 85; Bridgewater ST Coll; Bus Admin.

SMITH, DEBRA; Monson JR SR HS; Monson, MA; (Y); 2/76; Church Yth Grp; Dance Clb; Drama Clb; French Clb; Mathletes; Math Tm; School Musical; School Play; Yrbk Stf; Sec Stu Cncl; Cheryal Roberts Awd 82; Intl Busn.

SMITH, DEBRA; St Marys HS; Worcester, MA; (Y); Church Yth Grp; Hosp Aide; Office Aide; Spanish Clb; High Hon Roll; Hon Roll; Quinsigamond CC; Lgl Sec.

SMITH, DONNA; Weymouth North HS; Weymouth, MA; (Y); Church Yth Grp; Hon Roll; Psych.

SMITH, GLENN; Nashoba Regional HS; Lancaster, MA; (S); 24/193; Boy Scts; Pres Church Yth Grp; Debate Tm; DECA; Ski Clb; Lit Mag; Bsktbl; High Hon Roll; U Of NH; Bus Admin.

SMITH, GREGORY D; Navset Regional HS; Orleans, MA; (Y); Am Leg Boys St; Ski Clb; Varsity Clb; Yrbk Stf; Off Jr Cls; Ice Hcky; Socr; Hon Roll.

SMITH, HEATHER; Bishop Feehan HS; Cumberland, RI; (Y); Church Yth Grp; Hosp Aide; Band; Chorus; Mrchg Band; School Musical; School Play; Mgr Sftbl; Twrlr; Spanish NHS; Vrsty Schl Ltgtr 83-84; RI Coll; Nrs.

SMITH, HEIDI; Mohawk Trail Regional HS; Buckland, MA; (Y); 15/142; Church Yth Grp; Band; Chorus; Church Choir; Concert Band; Jazz Band; Mrchg Band; Yrbk Stf; High Hon Roll; Hon Roll; Elem Educ.

SMITH, JANIE; Taunton HS; Taunton, MA; (Y); 70/410; Bridgewater ST Coll; Elem Educ.

SMITH, JENNIFER B; Millis HS; Millis, MA; (Y); 9/88; Church Yth Grp; Intnl Clb; Chorus; Off Soph Cls; Stu Cncl; High Hon Roll; Hon Roll; NHS; Acctg.

SMITH, JOHN; Lenox Memorial HS; Lenox, MA; (Y); Capt Boy Scts; Pres Jr Cls; Pres Sr Cls; Rep Stu Cncl; Var Co-Capt Bsktbl; High Hon Roll; NHS; Church Yth Grp; School Play; Pres Frsh Cls; Renneselaer Polytech Inst Medl-Sci & Math 85; Williams Coll Almni Bk Awd Schlstc Achvt 85.

SMITH, JULIE A; Billerica Memorial HS; Billerica, MA; (Y); 24/506; Ski Clb; Yrbk Phtg; Yrbk Stf; Badmtn; Sftbl; Var Vllybl; High Hon Roll; Hon Roll; NHS; All Str Tm Sftbl 83-85; Guidance Aid/Secry 84-85; Holy Cross; Cmrcl Art.

SMITH, KAREN; Westford Acad; Westford, MA; (Y); French Clb; Concert Band; Jazz Band; Mrchg Band; JV Sftbl; Hon Roll; NHS; MASP 85; Bio.

SMITH, KATHLEEN; Haverhill HS; Haverhill, MA; (Y); 57/405; Key Clb; Spanish Clb; NHS; Daniel Harrington Mem Awd 85; Hale Hosp Aux Schrlshp 85; Southeastern MA U; Nrsng.

SMITH, KIMBERLY; Taunton HS; Taunton, MA; (Y); Am Leg Aux Girls St; Hosp Aide; JCL; Math Tm; Yrbk Ed-Chief; Lit Mag; Capt Cheerleading; High Hon Roll; NHS; Latin Clb; Chancellors Talent Awd U-Mass Amherst 85; Psych.

SMITH, LINDA; Arlington Catholic HS; Woburn, MA; (Y); Church Yth Grp; French Clb; Intnl Clb; JA; Office Aide; Political Wkr; Nwsp Rptr; Yrbk Stf; Hon Roll; Bus Wmn Of Mnth 84; Bus Adm.

SMITH, MARY ELLEN; Methuen HS; Methuen, MA; (Y); 53/330; Cmnty Wkr; Hosp Aide; Intnl Clb; Model UN; Band; Concert Band; Jazz Band; Mrchg Band; Off Soph Cls; High Hon Roll; Bon Secours Hosp Auxlry Schlrshp 85; U MA Amherst; Erly Chldhd Educ.

SMITH, MAURA K; Chicopee Comprehensive HS; Chicopee, MA; (Y); Spanish Clb; Variety Show; Yrbk Stf; Rep Jr Cls; VP Stu Cncl; Im Powder Puff Ftbl; JV Capt Sftbl; High Hon Roll; Hon Roll; Sec NHS; Stu Cncl Actv Prtcptn Lttr Awd 84-85; George Washington U; Med.

SMITH, NICKY; Barnstable HS; W Barnstable, MA; (Y); Church Yth Grp; Drama Clb; Hosp Aide; Band; Chorus; Concert Band; Mrchg Band; School Musical; School Play; Stage Crew.

SMITH, PAM; N Andover HS; N Andover, MA; (Y); 77/243; JA; Pep Clb; Q&S; Yrbk Stf; Rep Stu Cncl; JV Sftbl; Lowell U; Bus Mgmt.

SMITH, ROBERT; Malden HS; Malden, MA; (Y); 77/400; Church Yth Grp; Office Aide; Teachers Aide; Varsity Clb; High Hon Roll; Hon Roll; VFW Awd; Voice Dem Awd; Holy Cross; Med.

SMITH, ROBIN; Bishop Connolly HS; Westport, MA; (Y); Ski Clb; School Play; Lit Mag; Rep Stu Cncl; Fld Hcky; Gym; Trk; Hon Roll; Pres Phys Ftns Awd 83; Gymnstc Tm Stu Of Yr 83; Partcptn Awd Trk,Fld Hcky & Gymnstc 83-85.

SMITH, SARA; Norton HS; Norton, MA; (Y); 3/154; Math Tm; Chorus; Church Choir; Variety Show; High Hon Roll; NHS; Ntl Merit Ltr; NEDT Awd; Southeastern Dist Chrs 83 & 85; MA All ST Chrs 85.

SMITH, SIDNEY R; Phillips Acad; Ridgewood, NJ; (Y); Pep Clb; Capt Bsktbl; Var L Trk; Ntl Merit Ltr; Pres Afro Latino Amer Soc 84-85; Oxfam Amer; Political Sci.

SMITH, STACEY; Chelsea HS; Chelsea, MA; (Y); 40/208; Camera Clb; Dance Clb; Sec Office Aide; Rep Frsh Cls; Rep Soph Cls; JV Cheerleading; JV Sftbl; Var Trk; Hon Roll; Saunders Asbestos Svc Awd Excllnce Sci 85; Bridgewater ST Coll; Lib Arts.

SMITH, SUSAN LEE; Braintree HS; Braintree, MA; (Y); 149/482; Drama Clb; Ski Clb; Cheerleading; Hon Roll.

SMITH, TIMOTHY; Bishop Feehan HS; Cumberland, RI; (Y); 26/239; Ski Clb; Spanish Clb; L Var Bsbl; L Var Bsktbl; Hon Roll; NHS; Spanish NHS.

SMITH, TIMOTHY R; Xaverian Brothers HS; Medfield, MA; (S); 35/236; Im Ftbl; Hon Roll; NHS; Ntl Merit Ltr; AP Hghst Hist Score 83; Amherst Coll; Hist.

SMITH, TINA; Aqawam HS; Agawam, MA; (Y); Band; Concert Band; Mrchg Band; Trk; Hon Roll; Exec Sec.

SMITH, WILHELMINA W; Amherst Regional HS; Amherst, MA; (Y); Acpl Chr; Orch; Sr Cls; Hon Roll; NHS; Office Aide; School Musical; Natl HS Slavic Hnr Scty 84-85; Var Music Awds 82-85; Russian I Awd 83; STOP Mbr; Music.

SMOOLCA, CAROL A; Shepherd Hill Regional HS; Dudley, MA; (Y); 4/150; Church Yth Grp; Math Tm; School Musical; Stu Cncl; Capt Var Bsktbl; Var Capt Trk; High Hon Roll; Pres NHS; Fairfield U; Bus.

SNEIRSON, STACEY; Framingham South HS; Framingham, MA; (Y); 12/350; French Clb; Hosp Aide; Nwsp Stf; NHS; Pre-Med.

SNELGROVE, JENNIFER; Brockton HS; Brockton, MA; (Y); Camp Fr Inc; Church Yth Grp; Cmnty Wkr; Dance Clb; Band; Concert Band; Hon Roll; Bentley; Acctng.

SNELL, CYNTHIA; Gardner HS; Gardner, MA; (Y); 45/184; Church Yth Grp; Cmnty Wkr; VP French Clb; GAA; Model UN; School Musical; Yrbk Ed-Chief; Crs Cntry; Co-Capt Trk; Hon Roll; Syracuse Coll NY; Comm.

SNELL, ERIK M; Foxboro HS; Foxboro, MA; (Y); 27/250; Am Leg Boys St; Church Yth Grp; JA; Ski Clb; Ed Nwsp Phtg; Rep Frsh Cls; Rep Soph Cls; JV Capt Socr; JV Var Trk; Drtfsmn Of Term; Arch.

SNELLING, TRACEY; Leicester HS; Leicester, MA; (S); Camera Clb; Church Yth Grp; Political Wkr; Variety Show; Yrbk Phtg; Yrbk Stf; Trs Soph Cls; Trs Rep Jr Cls; Trs Sr Cls; Sec Stu Cncl; Psych.

SNIEZEK, JASON H; Chas H Mc Cann Voc Tech HS; Adams, MA; (Y); Am Leg Boys St; Church Yth Grp; Rep Frsh Cls; Rep Soph Cls; JV Var Bsktbl; High Hon Roll; Hon Roll; Jr NHS; NHS.

SNOONIAN, GARY D; Central Catholic HS; Tewksbury, MA; (Y); 5/238; Math Clb; Science Clb; Stage Crew; Nwsp Rptr; Nwsp Stf; JV Trk; High Hon Roll; Hon Roll; NHS; Ntl Merit Ltr; SR Day Jrnlsm & Stage Crew Awds; Tufts U; Cehm.

SNOW, NANCY; Shepherd Hill Regional HS; Charlton, MA; (Y); 10/159; Color Guard; Mrchg Band; NHS; Spanish Clb; Band; Flag Corp; Stage Crew; Yrbk Stf; High Hon Roll; Hon Roll; Tandoli Schlrshp 85; ST Of MA Schlrshp 85; Untd Food & Comm Wrks Un Schlrshp 85; Nichols Coll; Bus Mgmt.

SNYER, KRISTYN; Academy Of Norte Dame; Tyngsboro, MA; (Y); Church Yth Grp; Girl Scts; Key Clb; Chorus; School Musical; Nwsp Rptr; Rep Stu Cncl; Hon Roll; NHS; Challnge Pgm Rivier Coll 84-85; Pol Sci.

SO, DAVID; Boston Technical HS; Everett, MA; (Y); Bsktbl; Wt Lftg; Hon Roll; Engrng.

SOARES, JOHN R; Diman Reg Voc Tech HS; Somerset, MA; (Y); Cmnty Wkr; VICA; Carpentry.

SOARES, VICKI; BMC Durfee HS; Fall River, MA; (Y); 41/670; French Clb; Hosp Aide; Varsity Clb; Concert Band; Mrchg Band; Yrbk Stf; Var Cheerleading; Capt Twrlr; Hon Roll; NHS; Acctng.

SOBOCZINSKI, JULIE; Salem HS; Salem, MA; (Y); 26/332; Stu Cncl; Var Cheerleading; JV Fld Hcky; High Hon Roll; Hon Roll.

SOCCORSO, ANDREA; Melrose HS; Melrose, MA; (S); 4/404; French Clb; Ski Clb; Yrbk Stf; VP Frsh Cls; VP Soph Cls; Pres Jr Cls; L Cheerleading; L Gym; Pres NHS; Dartmouth Minutemn Bk Clb Awd 84; Boston Coll; Pre-Law.

SODEN, KELLY; Agawam HS; Feeding Hls, MA; (Y); Church Yth Grp; Cmnty Wkr; GAA; JA; Color Guard; Tennis; Hon Roll; Pre-Law.

SODERSTROM, CAROLYN; Bedford HS; Bedford, MA; (Y); 70/250; Exec Sec.

SOJKA, TANIA; Taunton HS; Taunton, MA; (Y); Church Yth Grp; French Clb; JCL; Ski Clb; JV Cheerleading; Trk; High Hon Roll; Hon Roll; NHS; Med.

SOKOLOSKY, NANCY; Turners Falls HS; Turners Falls, MA; (Y); 11/96; Pres Frsh Cls; Sec Jr Cls; Sec Sr Cls; Sec Stu Cncl; Stat Socr; Mgr Swmmng; NHS; Rotary Awd; GAA; Letterman Clb; Stu Of Mnth 83-84; Williams Clg Bk Awd 84; St Michaels Clg; Elem Educ.

SOLANO, MICHAEL; St Dominic Savio HS; Saugus, MA; (Y); 16/103; JA; Nwsp Sprt Ed; Hon Roll; NHS; Rep Frsh Cls; Capt Bsbl; Im Bsktbl; Var Ftbl; Im Golf; Im Ice Hcky; U Of NH; Mech Engrng.

SOLIS, MICHELLE; Greater Boston Acad; Stoneham, MA; (S); Drama Clb; School Play; Yrbk Stf; Sec Frsh Cls; Sec Jr Cls; VP Pres Stu Cncl; Vllybl; High Hon Roll; Hon Roll; NHS; Natl Hnr Rll 85; Intl Forgn Lang Awds 85; Comp Anlyst.

SOLOD, RANDI LEE; Randolph HS; Randolph, MA; (Y); 40/357; Dance Clb; Drama Clb; Spanish Clb; School Musical; School Play; Stage Crew; Variety Show; Ed Yrbk Stf; Stu Cncl; Var Capt Cheerleading; 1st Rnnr Up-Jr Miss Dance Of New England 83; Boston U; Gnrl Hlth Sci.

SOLOMON, JEFFREY H; Quincy HS; Quincy, MA; (Y); 56/318; Am Leg Boys St; Boy Scts; Wrstlng; High Hon Roll; St Schlr; JWV Scholar 85; USC L A Scholar 85; Pres Acad Fit Awd 85; USC.

SOLOMON, STEVEN D; Wachusett Regional HS; Sterling, MA; (Y); 118/348; JV Ice Hcky.

SOLOMONIDES, JOHN; Bedford HS; Bedford, MA; (Y); 6/228; Exploring; Var JV Bsbl; High Hon Roll; NHS; Ntl Merit SF; Lahey Clnc Explr Post 83-84; Babe Ruth-Valuable Fldr Trophy 83 & 84; Indstrl Arts Hnr Awd 84-85; Harvard; Med.

SOMERS, MICHAEL; East Boston HS; E Boston, MA; (Y); Boys Clb Am; Computer Clb; Hon Roll; Prfct Atten Awd.

SOMES, DANNY; Tahanto Regional HS; S Berlin, MA; (Y); 11/46; Am Leg Boys St; Boy Scts; Stu Cncl; Var Golf; Var Socr; NHS.

SONNENBERG, NATHAN; Doherty HS; Virginia Beach, VA; (Y); 30/356; Chess Clb; French Clb; JA; Math Clb; Ski Clb; Temple Yth Grp; Var L Socr; High Hon Roll; Hon Roll; NHS; Acadmc Olympcs 82-83; Carer Dy Essy Wnnr 83-84; U Of VA; Comp Sci.

SONTAG, ANDREW; Monty Tech HS; Fitchburg, MA; (Y); 1/170; Computer Clb; VICA; Var Bsktbl; High Hon Roll; Hon Roll; NHS; Val; Schlrshp New England 85; Superintndt Awd Outstndng Stu 85; Best Stu Math Bus 85; Central N E Coll; Comp.

SOPER, DAWN; Whitman-Hanson HS; Hanson, MA; (Y); DECA; Chorus; Yrbk Stf; Soph Cls; Jr Cls; Sr Cls; Stu Cncl; Gym; Home Rm Rep; Elliot Rozen Mem Awd; Pres Distribtv Ed Clbs Amer; Wilma Boyd Travel/Toursm; Travl.

SOPHAVETH, KHEN; Newton North HS; Newton, MA; (Y); French Clb; Intnl Clb; Diving; Gym; Swmmng; Vllybl; 1st Escher Drwg Cont 82; Pres Phys Ftns Awd 82; Gymnstc Awd 84; Math.

SOPHY, KEO; South Boston HS; Brighton, MA; (S); Nwsp Rptr; Nwsp Stf; Lit Mag; Off Sr Cls; High Hon Roll; Bentley Coll; Acctng.

SOREL, JOHN; Norton HS; Norton, MA; (Y); 7/150; Am Leg Boys St; Boy Scts; Computer Clb; Math Clb; Math Tm; Varsity Clb; Crs Cntry; Trk; High Hon Roll; Hon Roll; Eagl Sct 83; Engrng.

SOREL, LAURIE; Agawam HS; Agawam, MA; (Y); 25/375; AFS; Math Clb; High Hon Roll; Hon Roll; NHS; Acctng.

SOSA, KAREN; Martha Vineyard Regional HS; Oak Bluffs, MA; (Y); 3/107; AFS; Yrbk Stf; Lit Mag; High Hon Roll; Hon Roll; NHS; Consistnt Effort Engl 84; Excllnce Pre-Calculus 85; Wellesley Bk Awd 85; Art Hstry.

SOUCIE JR, NORMAN A; Leicester HS; Leicester, MA; (Y); Am Leg Boys St; Church Yth Grp; Math Tm; VP Sr Cls; Bsktbl; Ftbl; Trk; Dnfth Awd; VP NHS; Schl Rep Govt Dy ST Hous-Boston 85; Engrng.

SOUCY, LISA; Bishop Fenwick HS; Salem, MA; (Y); Cmnty Wkr; Office Aide; Yrbk Stf; High Hon Roll; Hon Roll; Jr NHS; NHS; Ntl Merit Ltr; Excllnc Awd In Geo, French & Alg 84-85.

SOUCY, PAUL R; Lawrence HS; Londonderry, NH; (Y); Boys Clb Am; Computer Clb; FCA; JV Bsktbl; Score Keeper; JV Trk; High Hon Roll; Hon Roll; Cert Of Profncy 84-85; 1st Aide CPR Cert 82-83; NH U; Math.

SOUDEN, STEPHANIE L; Falmouth HS; E Falmouth, MA; (Y); AFS; High Hon Roll; Hon Roll; Jr NHS; NHS; Co-Op Bank Awd 85; Keene ST Coll; Spnsh.

SOURDIFFE, RAY; South Hadley HS; S Hadley, MA; (Y); Visual Cmmnctns.

SOUSA, KIMBERLY; Acad Of Notre Dame; Westford, MA; (Y); 17/52; Girl Scts; Hosp Aide; Key Clb; Library Aide; Chorus; Yrbk Stf; Ntl Merit Ltr; Art Clb; Band; Grl Sct Gold Awd 84; Grl Sct Interntl Japan Smmr Prog 85; Spch Pathlgy.

SOUSA, LAWRENCE W; Brockton HS; Brockton, MA; (Y); 152/996; Am Leg Boys St; Aud/Vis; Cmnty Wkr; Drama Clb; Key Clb; Political Wkr; Nwsp Ed-Chief; High Hon Roll; Pep Clb; Radio Clb; Gus Giordano Awd Excllnce Musical Comedy 82; MA H S Drama Fest Awds 84 & 85; Outstndng Thtrcl Awd 85; Set Design.

SOUSA, LORI; North Cambridge Catholic HS; Cambridge, MA; (Y); High Hon Roll; Hon Roll; NHS; Span III Awd 85; Relgn III Awd 85; Span II Awd 84.

SOUSA, MARIA; New Bedford HS; New Bedford, MA; (Y); 4/688; Varsity Clb; Yrbk Stf; Sec Stu Cncl; Var Capt Gym; High Hon Roll; Pres NHS; Prfct Atten Awd; Top Stu French IV 84-85; Med Tech.

SOUSA, RICHARD; New Bedford HS; New Bedford, MA; (Y); Yrbk Bus Mgr; Var Tennis; High Hon Roll; Hon Roll; NHS; Vrsty Lttr Tennis 85; Econ.

SOUSA, SHELLI; Bishop Connolly HS; Fall River, MA; (Y); 34/179; Ski Clb; Spanish Clb; JV Bsktbl; Var Vllybl; High Hon Roll; Hon Roll; Comm Disorders.

SOUZA, BARBARA; Bellingham JR SR Memorial HS; Bellingham, MA; (Y); Stu Cncl; Pres NHS; Yearbk Stff 84-85 & 85-86; Mgmt.

SOUZA, DIANE; Westport HS; Westport, MA; (Y); French Clb; School Play; JV Sftbl; Bridgewater; TV Prodctn.

SOUZA, PAMELA E; New Bedford HS; New Bedford, MA; (Y); 3/543; Library Aide; Office Aide; Service Clb; Gov Hon Prg Awd; High Hon Roll; NHS; Pres Schlr; St Schlr; Intnl Clb; JCL; Williams Coll Bk Awd 84; Pres Acad Fit Awd, MA ST Hnr Scholar 85; S Shennan Awd 85; Natl JR Clscl Lg; U Of MA Amherst; Comm Dsordr.

SPADEA, JAMIE; Brockton HS; Brockton, MA; (Y); 86/976; Church Yth Grp; Drama Clb; Office Aide; Teachers Aide; Band; Mrchg Band; Symp Band; Yrbk Stf; High Hon Roll; Hon Roll; Vet Med.

SPARKES, JANET; Ayer SR HS; Ayer, MA; (Y); 18/160; Intnl Clb; Math Clb; Powder Puff Ftbl; Sftbl; High Hon Roll; Hon Roll; NHS; Church Yth Grp; Library Aide; Band; Excllnc In Bkkpng I Awd; Excllnc In Bkkpng II Awd 85; Fletcher Fund Schlrshp 85; Burdett Schl; Accntng.

SPARKS, SHARON; Hopedale JR SR HS; Hopedale, MA; (S); 6/63; Church Yth Grp; Band; Chorus; Church Choir; School Play; Yrbk Stf; VP Bsktbl; VP Crs Cntry; High Hon Roll; VP Pres NHS; Rep Shl Acad Decathlon Comp 84; Music Schlrshp SYMS Summer Music Camp 83; Bu Mgmnt.

SPAULDING, GARY B; Tahanto Regional HS; Berlin, MA; (Y); 8/59; Am Leg Boys St; Boy Scts; Math Tm; Band; Pres Stu Cncl; Var Bsbl; Var Socr; High Hon Roll; Hon Roll; Jr NHS; Scholar Awd Berlin Lions Clb 85; Schltc Excllnce Awd Soph Rsrch 83; Regnl Scholar Awd 85; Daniel Webster Coll; Aviat Mgmt.

SPEARIN, SUSIE; Taunton HS; Berkley, MA; (Y); 31/420; Exploring; Hosp Aide; Office Aide; Spanish Clb; Hon Roll; U MA Amherst; Nutrtn.

SPECHT, NANCY; N Reading HS; North Reading, MA; (Y); 6/208; Church Yth Grp; Nwsp Stf; Var Capt Bsktbl; Var Capt Fld Hcky; Powder Puff Ftbl; Var Capt Sftbl; Cit Awd; High Hon Roll; Jr NHS; Sec NHS; Knghts Of Columbus Schlrshp 85; Schlr-Athlt Schlrshp 85; Soc Of Wmn Engr Awd 85; U Of Lowell; Physcl Therpy.

SPEIGHT, MONIQUE; B M C Durfee HS; Fall River, MA; (Y); Church Yth Grp; Drama Clb; French Clb; Sec Trs Chorus; Church Choir; Yrbk Stf; Cert Secy & Treas Chrs 84-85; Durfee Vocalaires 8-85; Fshn Merch.

SPELIOTES, ELIZABETH K; Newton North HS; W Newton, MA; (Y); Pres VP Exploring; Pres Intnl Clb; Ed Yrbk Stf; JV Capt Bsktbl; Var L Socr; Cmnty Wkr; Math Tm; Yrbk Ed-Chief; JV Sftbl; High Hon Roll; Williams Book Awd 85; Math Team High Scorer 84 & 85; Bio.

SPELLMAN, MARYELLEN; St Clare HS; W Roxbury, MA; (Y); Church Yth Grp; Cmnty Wkr; Dance Clb; Drama Clb; Hosp Aide; Political Wkr; Teachers Aide; School Musical; Variety Show; Rep Stu Cncl; Theatre Arts.

SPEREDELOZZI, JOHN; Braintree HS; Braintree, MA; (Y); 32/420; Ski Clb; Teachers Aide; High Hon Roll; Hon Roll; Hnrb Mntn Schl Sci Fair; 2nd Pl Schl Sci Fair; Aerontcl Engrng.

SPERRY, JAMES M; Gloucester HS; Gloucester, MA; (Y); Church Yth Grp; JV Bsbl; Im Bsktbl; Coach Actv; Var Crs Cntry; Cit Awd; Elks Awd; Hon Roll; Stonehill Coll.

SPICER, THOMAS D; Westford Acad; Westford, MA; (Y); 60/230; Pres Frsh Cls; Pres Soph Cls; Pres Jr Cls; Pres Sr Cls; Var Capt Crs Cntry; Hon Roll; AFS; Church Yth Grp; Cmnty Wkr; Ski Clb; Excel Phy Ed 85; Assn Chmpn Athltcs Cngrss JR Olympcs 84; Bus.

SPICKLER, CAROL; Stoughton HS; Stoughton, MA; (Y); Dance Clb; Rep Jr Cls; Var Cheerleading; Var Gym; Var Tennis; Bus.

SPILLANE, MAUREEN; Boston Latin Schl; Boston, MA; (Y); 2/325; Cmnty Wkr; Nwsp Ed-Chief; NHS; Commdtn Merit Natl Greek Exam 85; Dartmouth Book Awd 85; Lawrence Prz Frnch Transltn 85.

SPINDLER, BRIAN; Somerville HS; Somerville, MA; (Y); Boys Clb Am; Computer Clb; Math Clb; High Hon Roll; Hon Roll; 3rd & 1st Pl HS Comp Fair 84, 85; 3rd Pl Wntwrth Tm Comp Comptn 85; Comp Engrng.

SPINELLI, RICHARD; St Dominic Savio HS; Chelsea, MA; (S); 7/117; Chess Clb; CAP; Cmnty Wkr; Library Aide; Pres Stu Cncl; L Ftbl; Capt L Trk; High Hon Roll; NHS; West Point; Army Ofcr.

SPLAGOUNIAS, GREGORY; Lexington HS; Lexington, MA; (Y); Sec Church Yth Grp; Capt FCA; Math Tm; Chorus; Church Choir; Var Ftbl; Var L Wrstlng; Hon Roll; Continentl Mth Lg Cont 1st Pl 83; Middlesex Lg Champs 84; Law.

SPLAINE, KAREN; Silver Lake Regional HS; Kingston, MA; (Y); 49/500; Cmnty Wkr; French Clb; Girl Scts; Hosp Aide; Latin Clb; Trs Math Clb; Hon Roll; Bus.

SPOSITO, CARL; Malden Catholic HS; Revere, MA; (Y); Var Golf; JV Ice Hcky; Nrthestrn U; Engrng.

SPRINDZUNAS, DEBBIE; Algonquin Regional HS; Northboro, MA; (Y); 13/215; Library Aide; Vllybl; Cit Awd; Hon Roll; NHS; Med.

SPRINGER, WILLIAM C; Norwell HS; Norwell, MA; (Y); 85/175; Drama Clb; School Play; Stu Cncl; JV Bsbl; JV Var Bsktbl; JV Ftbl; Var Socr; Var Tennis; Hon Roll; Marquette U; Engl.

ST AMOUR, PAUL; Bedford HS; Bedford, MA; (Y); 35/212; Am Leg Boys St; Boy Scts; Church Yth Grp; Exploring; Ski Clb; Var L Lcrss; Var L Socr; JV Trk; Hon Roll.

ST CYR, ANDREA; Notre Dame Acad; Brockton, MA; (Y); Church Yth Grp; Girl Scts; Hosp Aide; Pres Spanish Clb; Church Choir; Orch; Var Crs Cntry; High Hon Roll; Math Clb; Office Aide; Schl Peer Counselor 84-85; Freedoms Fndtn Yth Leadrshp Seminar 84; Nursing.

ST GERMAIN, JENNIFER; Mohawk Trail Regional HS; Charlemont, MA; (Y); Pres Exploring; Chorus; School Musical; Variety Show; Stu Cncl; Swmmng; Kiwanis Awd; Lion Awd; Hugh O Brian Ldrshp Sem Delg 84; Nrsng.

ST GERMAIN, TRACY; Holy Name C C HS; Sutton, MA; (Y); 23/273; Camp Fr Inc; Church Yth Grp; Dance Clb; Ski Clb; Hon Roll; Natl Sci Olympd-Bio 84; Comp Pgmr Awd 5; Latin Awd 83; Engrng.

ST LOUIS, DEBORAH; St Bernards C C HS; Fitchburg, MA; (S); 2/163; School Play; Nwsp Rptr; Yrbk Stf; Var L Fld Hcky; Mgr(s); Var L Trk; High Hon Roll; Pres NHS; Hon Roll; Ntl Merit Ltr; Harvard Bk Club Awd; Hnrbl Ment Cntrl MA Conf Field Hockey All-Stars; Engl.

ST LOUIS, DONNA; St Bernards HS; Fitchburg, MA; (S); 8/161; Latin Clb; Library Aide; Varsity Clb; School Musical; Nwsp Rptr; Mgr Fld Hcky; Gym; Trk; High Hon Roll; NHS.

ST MARTIN, BRENDA; Easthampton HS; Easthampton, MA; (Y); Church Yth Grp; JA; Spanish Clb; Church Choir; Stage Crew; JV Var Sftbl; Hon Roll; South Eastern Acad; Trvl Adm.

ST MARTIN, DONNA; Doherty Memorial HS; Worcester, MA; (Y); 61/356; Church Yth Grp; Trs Frsh Cls; Trs Soph Cls; Trs Jr Cls; Trs Sr Cls; Stu Cncl; Fld Hcky; Cit Awd; DAR Awd; High Hon Roll; Smfnlst Ntl Cncl Yth Ldrs Sch 85; Only Stu Rep The Schl Comm 85; Assumption Coll; Bio.

ST ONGE, CHRISTIAN; Haverhill HS; Haverhill, MA; (Y); 84/378; German Clb; JA; NHS; Haverhill HS Ski Tm & Vrsty Ltrs; Private Pilot Lic 85; Merimac Coll; Bus.

ST ONGE, JENNIFER ANN; Wilmington HS; Wilmington, MA; (Y); 1/249; Trs Church Yth Grp; Trs Exploring; French Clb; Trs Girl Scts; JV Crs Cntry; French Hon Soc; God Cntry Awd; Hon Roll; NHS; Val; Rensselaer Medl 84; Dartmouth Bk Clb Awd 84; Natl Merit Specl Schlrshp & Cmmnd Stdnt 84-85; Purdue U; Engrng.

ST PETERS, JEFF; Smith Acad; Hatfield, MA; (Y); Boy Scts; Church Yth Grp; Drama Clb; Key Clb; Stage Crew; Pres Frsh Cls; Rep Church Yth Grp; Rep Jr Cls; Pres Stu Cncl; Var Capt Bsbl; Bartmouth Bk Clb Awd 85; All Wstrn MA Bsebl & Sccr 84-85; Bus.

ST PIERRE, JAMES; Dartmouth HS; N Dartmouth, MA; (Y); 41/300; Varsity Clb; JV Bsbl; Var L Ftbl.

ST PIERRE, JAMES F; Attleboro HS; South Attleboro, MA; (Y); Am Leg Boys St; Cmnty Wkr; Rep Jr Cls; Pres Stu Cncl; Powder Puff Ftbl; JV Var Socr; JV Var Trk; High Hon Roll; Hon Roll; NHS; 2nd Pl ST Wide Wrtng Cont 85; Bio Sci.

ST PIERRE, PATRICIA ANN; Salem HS; Salem, MA; (Y); Art Clb; Church Yth Grp; Teachers Aide; Chorus; High Hon Roll; Hon Roll; NHS; Sunday Schl Tchr Chrch 83-85; Berkeley Art Achl; Singer.

STACHOWSKI, KIM; Woburn SR HS; Woburn, MA; (S); Church Yth Grp; Leo Clb; Ski Clb; Spanish Clb; Stu Cncl; High Hon Roll; Hon Roll; Bus.

STAFFIER, LISA; Medway JR SR HS; Medway, MA; (Y); 1/132; Yrbk Bus Mgr; Elks Awd; High Hon Roll; NHS; Ntl Merit Ltr; Pres Schlr; Val; VFW Awd; Voice Dem Awd; Govrnmnt Intershp Prog; Pierce Hart Mem Schlrshp; Chaplain David San Ford Mem Awd & Schlrshp; Bryant Coll; Mgmt.

STALEY II, JAMES R; Newton No HS; Auburndale, MA; (Y); 134/630; Church Yth Grp; CAP; Ski Clb; Concert Band; Jazz Band; Mrchg Band; Var L Ftbl; Var L Lcrss; Hon Roll; Music Dept Schlrshp 85; Beals Hse Svc Awd 85; Wind Ensmbl-Most Impvd Muscn 85; U Of CO Boulder; Engrng.

STALLINGS, REBECCA; North HS; Worcester, MA; (Y); Church Yth Grp; VP Frsh Cls; Var Bsktbl; Rep NHS; Spanish Clb; Varsity Clb; Chorus; Var Sftbl; Var Vllybl; High Hon Roll; Career Day Essay Awd 85; Comp Sci.

STAMOULIS, EVAN; Natick HS; Natick, MA; (Y); 32/435; Trs Church Yth Grp; Cmnty Wkr; Computer Clb; Political Wkr; Band; Concert Band; School Musical; Hon Roll; Mbr Natl Cncl Christians & Jews 84 & 85; St Anselm Coll Manchester; Comp.

STANITSAS, GERASIMOS; Cambridge Rindge & Latin Schl; Cambridge, MA; (Y); Church Yth Grp; Rep Soph Cls; High Hon Roll; Hon Roll; Prfct Atten Awd; Morse Schl PTO Scholar 85; MA ST Scholar 85; Michael A Sullivan Mem Scholar 85; Civil Engrng.

STANSEL, TIMOTHY; Fitchburg HS; Fitchburg, MA; (Y); Am Leg Boys St; Boy Scts; Pres Church Yth Grp; Yrbk Phtg; Hofstra U; Pre-Med.

STANTON, CHRIS; Fontbonne Acad; Milton, MA; (Y); 15/140; Church Yth Grp; Dance Clb; Intnl Clb; Office Aide; Pres Science Clb; Service Clb; Varsity Clb; Nwsp Bus Mgr; Var Capt Bsktbl; Coach Actv; Boston Globe Schltc Art Awd 84-85; Excllnc Nutritn 84; Excllnc Bio Honrs II 85.

STANTON, LYNN; Westford Acad; Westford, MA; (Y); Trs Art Clb; Spanish Clb; High Hon Roll; Artst Art Clb Calndr; Indstl Desgnr.

STANWOOD, MICHELLE; Beverly HS; Beverly, MA; (Y); Nwsp Rptr; Yrbk Stf; Var Capt Bsktbl; Var Fld Hcky; Im Powder Puff Ftbl; Var Trk; Cert Awd Salem ST Coll Hstry Conf 85; Bowdoin Coll; Polit Sci.

STAPEL, SHARON; North Middlesex Regional HS; Townsend, MA; (Y); Cmnty Wkr; Nwsp Rptr; Yrbk Stf; Stat Trk; Hon Roll; NHS; Northeastern; Psych.

STARK, NICOLE VANESSA; Brimmer And May HS; Chestnut Hill, MA; (S); 3/16; Nwsp Ed-Chief; Nwsp Rptr; Nwsp Stf; Pres Frsh Cls; Pres Soph Cls; VP Jr Cls; Pres Stu Cncl; Holy Crss Bk Prz 84; Brown U Bk Prz 84; Nichols Schlrshp 84.

STARK, ROBERT; Wachusett Regional HS; Sterling Jct, MA; (Y); 110/386; Hon Roll; Fitchburg ST Coll; Bus Admn.

STARKIE, JANET; Braintree HS; Braintree, MA; (Y); Church Yth Grp; 4-H; Girl Scts; JV Sftbl; Hon Roll.

STARR, DEBORAH; Doherty Memorial HS; Worcester, MA; (Y); Debate Tm; French Clb; VP JA; VP Temple Yth Grp; Orch; Ed Nwsp Stf; French Hon Soc; High Hon Roll; Jr NHS; NHS; New Engl Rgn Unitd Synagog Yth Exec VP 85-86; Abraham Joshua Heschel Hnr Soc 84; Dns Lst Grad 85; Intl Rltns.

START, NATALIE; Barnstable HS; Cotait, MA; (S); Church Yth Grp; Drama Clb; Hosp Aide; NFL; Speech Tm; Chorus; School Play; Natl Fornsc Leag Awd 85; Candy Strp Cape Cod Hosp 50 Hr Pin 83.

STATHATOS, JAMES; Holyoke HS; Holyoke, MA; (Y); 2/373; Hosp Aide; Band; Nwsp Ed-Chief; Yrbk Stf; High Hon Roll; Pres Jr NHS; Pres NHS; Natl Sci Merit Awd 84-85; Chnclrs Merit Tlnt Awdd 85; Williams Coll Bk Awdd 85; Acad All-Amer 84-85; Med.

STATHIS, ANDREW; Brockton HS; Brockton, MA; (Y); Ski Clb; High Hon Roll; Hon Roll; NHS.

STEAD, ANDREW; St Johns HS; S Bridge, MA; (Y); Aud/Vis; Chess Clb; High Hon Roll; Hon Roll.

STEADMAN, SUSAN; Agawam HS; Feeding Hls, MA; (Y); Church Yth Grp; Hon Roll; Psychlgy.

STEARNS, LORI; Hudson Catholic HS; Marlboro, MA; (Y); 2/82; Church Yth Grp; English Clb; JA; Key Clb; School Musical; Yrbk Stf; Lit Mag; Capt Cheerleading; High Hon Roll; NHS; Boston Coll; Linguistics.

STEC, KATHLEEN; Chicopee Comprehensive HS; Chicopee, MA; (Y); 43/266; Aud/Vis; Church Yth Grp; Cmnty Wkr; Yrbk Stf; Pres Jr Cls; Pres Stu Cncl; Capt Var Bsktbl; Powder Puff Ftbl; Jr NHS; Prom Campgn 85; Telecmmnctns.

STECHENFINGER, WILLIAM A; Hamilton-Wenham Regional HS; S Hamilton, MA; (Y); Cmnty Wkr; VP DECA; VP FBLA; Political Wkr; Bsktbl; Coach Actv; Sftbl; Hon Roll; Distrbtv Eductn Clss Schlrshp 85; Teachers Assn Schlrshp 85; Big Buddy Pgm 83-85; Nichols Coll; CPA.

STEEN, JENNIFER I; Bancorft Schl; Southbridge, MA; (Y); 1/28; Art Clb; Pres Church Yth Grp; Ed Lit Mag; Ntl Merit Ltr; French Clb; Chorus; Church Choir; High Hon Roll; Hon Roll; Spcl Mntn-Wrld Poetry Contst 84; Hnrb Mntn Quinnebay Vly Cncl Arts 84; Creatv Wrtng Awd 84; Journalism.

STEEN, JOHN; Quincy HS; Quincy, MA; (Y); Drama Clb; JA; Band; Concert Band; School Play; Socr; Trk; French Clb; Drill Tm; Stage Crew; Actors Wrkshp; Acting.

STEER, DYLAN; Newton South HS; Newton Centre, MA; (Y); Stage Crew; Nwsp Stf; Yrbk Stf; Im Socr; Hon Roll; Law.

STEFFON, MICHAEL N; Auburn HS; Auburn, MA; (Y); 31/181; Ski Clb; Pres Soph Cls; Pres Jr Cls; Pres Sr Cls; Pres Stu Cncl; Var Socr; Cit Awd; DAR Awd; High Hon Roll; NHS; SADD; Goodrow & AAND Schlrshps 85; Bryant Coll; Mktg.

STEIN, BRENDA; St Clare HS; Roslindale, MA; (Y); 30/159; Dance Clb; Girl Scts; JCL; Library Aide; Nwsp Rptr; Most Impvd Stu Lat II 84; Chld Psych.

STEINBERG, NOAH; Buckingham Browne & Nichols HS; Cambridge, MA; (S); Debate Tm; French Clb; German Clb; Chorus; School Musical; Nwsp Ed-Chief; L Ftbl; Var Ice Hcky; High Hon Roll; Ntl Merit Ltr; Crew Lettrmn 85; Politcs.

STEINBERG, ROBIN; Natick HS; Natick, MA; (Y); 17/442; Am Leg Aux Girls St; JCL; Teachers Aide; Rep Jr Cls; Rep Stu Cncl; Var Socr; Hon Roll; SADD VP 85-86; Oceanography.

STEINKRAUSS, MICHAEL; Boston College HS; Cambridge, MA; (Y); 60/272; Cmnty Wkr; Im Bsktbl; Im Ftbl; High Hon Roll; Ntl Merit Ltr; MA/Com Schlrshp 85; MA Bd Rgnts Schlrshp 85; No 1 Physcs & Adv Math Cls 84; GA Tech; Elec Engrng.

STEPHANIAN, JULIE D; Middleboro HS; Middleboro, MA; (Y); 16/234; Exploring; Rep Sr Cls; Var L Bsktbl; Var Capt Fld Hcky; Var L Tennis; Elks Awd; Hon Roll; NHS; Leonard O Tillson Schlrshp 85; SE MA U; Acctng.

STEPHENS, CARRIE LYNNE; Wareham HS; Buzzards Bay, MA; (Y); Drama Clb; Band; Chorus; Concert Band; Mrchg Band; Twrlr; Psych.

STEPHENS, TRACY; Danvers HS; Danvers, MA; (Y); 52/307; Yrbk Stf; Hon Roll; NHS; Rep Jr Cls; Graphc Arts.

STERCZALA, BETH; Bartlett HS; Webster, MA; (Y); 1/157; Exploring; Science Clb; Spanish Clb; Sec Mrchg Band; Yrbk Stf; Crs Cntry; Capt L Tennis; High Hon Roll; NHS; Bartlett Alumni Assn Achvt Awd 84-85; CT Vly Bio Supply Co Awd 85; 2nd Pl Awd MA ST Sci Fair 85; Orthopedic Physcn.

STERN, ANDREW; Weymouth North HS; Weymouth, MA; (Y); 42/356; Boy Scts; Computer Clb; Exploring; Math Tm; Varsity Clb; JV Var Ftbl; JV Lcrss; JV Wt Lftg; Hon Roll; Outstndng Math,Electrncs,Physcly Stu 82-85; Syracuse; Comp Engr.

STERN, LESLEY; Hopkins Acad; Hadley, MA; (S); French Clb; Band; Concert Band; Mrchg Band; Var Bsktbl; Var Socr; Var Sftbl; High Hon Roll; Hon Roll; U Of MA; Business.

STEVENS, SHANON; Marlboro HS; Marlboro, MA; (Y); Drama Clb; Radio Clb; Science Clb; High Hon Roll; Hon Roll; Im Bsktbl; Acad Achvt Awd US Govt 84; Advr.

STEWART, CHRISTOPHER; Medway SR SR HS; Medway, MA; (Y); 4/172; Boy Scts; Nwsp Stf; Ed Yrbk Stf; Bsktbl; Golf; High Hon Roll; Hon Roll; Jr NHS; NHS; Church Yth Grp; Govt Intrnsp Grp; Prom Comm; Ring Comm; Engrng.

STEWART, DONNA L; Salem HS; Salem, MA; (Y); Spanish Clb; Yrbk Stf; JV Var Bsktbl; JV Socr; JV Sftbl; High Hon Roll; Hon Roll; NHS; Spanish NHS; Profncy Typng Awd 85; Salm ST Coll Hstry Conf Awd 85.

STEWART, JILL; Lunenburg HS; Lunenburg, MA; (Y); Church Yth Grp; Dance Clb; Girl Scts; Hosp Aide; Intnl Clb; Library Aide; PAVAS; Chorus; Church Choir; Madrigals; Athl Awd 84-85; Perf Atten Awd 82; Out Lady Elms Coll; Spch Pthlgy.

STEWART, LESLEY; Gardener HS; Gardner, MA; (Y); 22/169; Church Yth Grp; DECA; Chorus; School Musical; Variety Show; Trs Frsh Cls; VP Soph Cls; Pres Jr Cls; Stu Cncl; Capt Cheerleading; Homecmg Qn 82; Pro Merito 85; Little Oscar Awd Mst Carefree 85; Johnson & Wales; Comp Sys Mgmt.

STEWART, MICHAEL; Central Catholic HS; Hampstead, NH; (Y); 52/220; VP Trs Church Yth Grp; Computer Clb; French Clb; JA; Math Tm; Capt Ski Clb; Concert Band; Jazz Band; Mrchg Band; Symp Band; Purdue; Engrng.

STEWART, PAMELA J; Newburyport HS; Newburyport, MA; (Y); 30/207; Hosp Aide; Capt Flag Corp; Hst Jr Cls; Hst Sr Cls; Stu Cncl; Hon Roll; NHS; Library Aide; Hugh O Brien Yth Ldrshp Sem 83; Salem ST Clg; Elem Educ.

STIBLEY, GLENRAY; Holyoke HS; Holyoke, MA; (Y); Boys Clb Am; Red Cross Aide; Stu Cncl; JV Var Ftbl; L Trk; Wt Lftg; Hon Roll.

STIFTER, ANN; Natick HS; Natick, MA; (Y); Sec JA; JCL; Ski Clb; Nwsp Ed-Chief; Nwsp Rptr; Off Frsh Cls; Off Soph Cls; Stu Cncl; JV Fld Hcky; Hon Roll; U CT; Cmmnctns.

STILL II, DAVID B; Barnstable HS; W Hyannisport, MA; (Y); Q&S; Nwsp Sprt Ed; Sutfoly U Awds For Newswrtng & Edtrls 85; Intl 1st Pl For Schl Paper 84; N Adams ST Coll; Engl.

STILLER, MICHAEL; Melrose HS; Melrose, MA; (Y); 32/370; Yrbk Stf; Im Bsktbl; Var Golf; Hon Roll; NHS; Drug & Alchl Prvntn Pgm 83-84; Outstndg Achvt Phy Educ Awdd 83; Elec Engr.

STIMER, SHARI DAWN; Gardner HS; Gardner, MA; (Y); 3/157; Am Leg Aux Girls St; Trs Spanish Clb; Concert Band; Yrbk Ed-Chief; Sec Sr Cls; Capt Var Cheerleading; L Trk; DAR Awd; Trs NHS; Letterman Clb; Gardner Exchange Club Yth Of Yr 85; Bates Coll; Bio.

STOCKTON, PHILIP L; Newton North HS; Auburndale, MA; (Y); Cmnty Wkr; Dance Clb; Acpl Chr; Madrigals; Orch; School Musical; Bsktbl; Coach Actv; Socr; Ntl Merit SF.

STOICO, TINA; Milford HS; Milford, MA; (Y); 51/315; Hosp Aide; Pep Clb; Yrbk Stf; Sec Frsh Cls; Sec Soph Cls; Sec Jr Cls; Sec Sr Cls; VP Rep Stu Cncl; Tennis; Hon Roll; Nrs.

STOKES, TAMMY; Dracut SR HS; Dracut, MA; (Y); Key Clb; Teachers Aide; Hon Roll; Salem ST; Crmnlgy.

STOLLE, KIRSTEN; Douglas Memorial HS; Douglas, MA; (Y); 1/47; Trs Girl Scts; Flag Corp; Trs Jr Cls; Trs Sr Cls; Capt Cheerleading; God Cntry Awd; High Hon Roll; Trs VP NHS; Val; Voice Dem Awd; Yrbk Artist 85; Mc Donalds Stu Tchr 85; Hugh O Brian Yth Ldrshp Sem 83; Framingham St Coll; Art.

STONE, HEATHER A; Falmouth HS; Mashpee, MA; (Y); Church Yth Grp; Sec Key Clb; Spanish Clb; Drm Mjr(t); School Musical; Rep Stu Cncl; Sftbl; High Hon Roll; Hon Roll; NHS; NW; Psych.

STONE, SUE; Hingham HS; Hingham, MA; (Y); Aud/Vis; Church Yth Grp; Civic Clb; Dance Clb; Office Aide; JV Tennis; Spanish Clb; Orch; Yrbk Stf; Im Badmtn; Math.

STONE, SUSAN J; Minnechaug Regional HS; Hampden, MA; (Y); 10/340; Girl Scts; Intnl Clb; Key Clb; Library Aide; Teachers Aide; Yrbk Stf; Hon Roll; NHS; Chld Stdy Acadmc Awd 84; U Of CT; Phrmcy.

STONE, TAMMY; Agawam HS; Agawam, MA; (Y); 6/350; French Clb; Chorus; Yrbk Stf; French Hon Soc; Chnclrs Tlnt Awd 85.

STOOPS, MELANIE; Ayer HS; Woodbridge, VA; (Y); 4/165; Math Clb; Yrbk Stf; Rep Jr Cls; Rep Stu Cncl; Cheerleading; Powder Puff Ftbl; High Hon Roll; Hon Roll; NHS.

STOROZUK, SCOTT R; Holyoke Catholic HS; Chicopee, MA; (Y); Computer Clb; Latin Clb; JV Var Bsbl; Im Bsktbl; Trk; U Of MA; Phy Thrpst.

STRAKA, ERIKA J; Belmont HS; Belmont, MA; (Y); Concert Band; Mrchg Band; Var L Diving; Im Socr; NHS; Ntl Merit Ltr; French Clb; Band; Orch; Var L Mgr(s); U Of MA Chnclirs Tlnt Schlrshp Awd 85; Belmont Schl Cmmtt Awds 84-85.

STRAKA, SONYA E; Belmont HS; Belmont, MA; (Y); Church Yth Grp; Cmnty Wkr; French Clb; Concert Band; Mrchg Band; Nwsp Stf; Socr; High Hon Roll; Hon Roll; Ntl Merit Ltr.

STRANGIO, MARK J; Watertown SR HS; Watertown, MA; (Y); 7/260; Var Golf; High Hon Roll; Hon Roll; Ntl Merit Ltr; Top 5 In Clss Awd 82-83; Outstndng Sci Stu Awd 82-83; Invtd Take Math Tst U Of Lowell 84-85; Acctng.

STRASNICK, LISA; Milford HS; Milford, MA; (Y); Cmnty Wkr; GAA; Hosp Aide; Bsktbl; Cheerleading; Score Keeper; Sftbl; Trk; Twrlr; Vllybl; Obstetrc Nrs; Nrsng.

STRATTON, CLIFF; St Johns HS; Spencer, MA; (Y); 40/264; Stage Crew; Trk; High Hon Roll; Hon Roll; NHS; Ntl Merit Ltr; Northeastern U; Comp Sci.

STRAUSS, MICHAEL; English HS; Lynn, MA; (Y); Comp.

STRAWN, EMILY; Dpherty Memorial HS; Worcester, MA; (Y); Church Yth Grp; Hosp Aide; VP Spanish Clb; Nwsp Stf; Bsktbl; Var Socr; Var Trk; Hon Roll; Ski Clb; School Play; Awd High Score Ntl Spnsh Ex 84; Schl Coor Newpeer Ed Pgm Drugs 85-86; Med.

STRINGER, KRISTY; Barnstable HS; Osterville, MA; (S); 106/400; Church Yth Grp; Cmnty Wkr; Office Aide; Acpl Chr; Chorus; Church Choir; Madrigals; Cit Awd; High Hon Roll; Hon Roll; Gregg Shrthnd Spdbldng Awd 83-84; Cape Cod CC; Sec.

STROK, CRAIG A; Franklin HS; Franklin, MA; (Y); 24/235; Ski Clb; Variety Show; Yrbk Rptr; Lit Mag; Trk; Hon Roll; NHS; Jean Thackaberry Awd-Excllnc In X-Cntry 83; Colgate U; Bio.

STROUD, CHERYL; New Bedford HS; New Bedford, MA; (Y); Dance Clb; Gym; GAA; Hosp Aide; School Musical; Stage Crew; Off Jr Cls; Bsktbl; Trk; Hon Roll; Ms Les Bourgeois Pgnt Bsktbl 85; Gymnstcs Trk, Dancng 80-81; Untd Hous Pryr Tp Cls Wrkr; DR.

STROUT, AARON; Melrose HS; Melrose, MA; (Y); 25/471; French Clb; Library Aide; Q&S; Thesps; School Musical; Yrbk Sprt Ed; Rep Frsh Cls; Rep Soph Cls; Rep Jr Cls; Rep Sr Cls; Georgetown; Frgn Rel.

STROUT, CYNTHIA; South High Community HS; Worcester, MA; (S); Church Yth Grp; Dance Clb; JV Tennis; Hon Roll; NHS; Worcester H S Acadmc Olympcs 84.

STRUSKI, BARRY P; Plymouth Carver HS; Carver, MA; (Y); 107/500; Am Leg Boys St; Trs 4-H; Capt Crs Cntry; Capt Trk; Comm.

STUART, KAPLAN; Wellesley SR HS; Wellesley, MA; (Y); 3/325; Boys Clb Am; Key Clb; Latin Clb; Math Clb; Teachers Aide; Nwsp Stf; Bsbl; Golf; High Hon Roll; Jr NHS; Surgcl Rsrch Harvrd Med Schl; Vlntr Med Settgs; MA Adv Stds Prog At Milton Acad; Dartmouth Coll; Pre-Med.

STUART, KRISTIN PAGE; Triton Regional Schl; Newbury, MA; (Y); 12/190; AFS; Drama Clb; Service Clb; Teachers Aide; School Musical; School Play; Variety Show; Yrbk Ed-Chief; Yrbk Sprt Ed; Stu Cncl; Scl Stds Awd 82 & 84; Engl & Outstndng SR Awds 85; U Of PA.

STYCZYNSKI JR, ROGER S; Hoosac Valley HS; Adams, MA; (Y); Aud/Vis; Boys Clb Am; Boy Scts; Church Yth Grp; Cmnty Wkr; Computer Clb; Exploring; Latin Clb; Math Clb; Pep Clb; Awd Bsbll 84 & 85; Eng Awd 82; Bio.

SU, JOCELYN; Lincoln/Sudbury Regional HS; Lincoln, MA; (Y); Church Yth Grp; Spanish Clb; Church Choir; Math Tm; Cit Awd; Hon Roll.

SUCHODOLSKI, GRETCHEN K; Andover HS; Andover, MA; (Y); 140/420; Church Yth Grp; Hon Roll; Trs Frsh Cls; Rep Jr Cls; JV Bsktbl; JV Socr; Ch Altar Guild 83-85; Bus Mgmt.

SULEWSKI, KAREN M; Southwick HS; Southwick, MA; (Y); 1/123; Library Aide; Math Tm; Office Aide; Hon Roll; NHS; Ntl Merit SF; Val; Voice Dem Awd; French Clb; Spanish Clb; Model Congress; Mgr Schl Store; Math.

SULIN, MELISSA; Fitchburg HS; Fitchburg, MA; (Y); 32/227; French Clb; Band; Concert Band; Capt Drm Mjr(t); Mrchg Band; Trk; High Hon Roll; Hon Roll; Fitchbrg High Alumni Assc Schlrshp 85; U Of NH; Pre Vet Med.

SULIVAN, LYNN; Newton North HS; Newtonville, MA; (Y); Stu Cncl; Lcrss; Bus.

SULLIVAN, AMY MARIE; Pittsfield HS; Pittsfield, MA; (Y); Cmnty Wkr; Trs Exploring; Hst FBLA; Pep Clb; Red Cross Aide; Capt Varsity Clb; Mrchg Band; Yrbk Stf; Var L Trk; Vllybl; Intrnl Scholar 85-86; Boston Coll; Psych.

SULLIVAN, ASHLEY M; Chatham HS; Chatham, MA; (Y); AFS; Camera Clb; Drama Clb; GAA; Pep Clb; Ski Clb; Spanish Clb; Varsity Clb; Concert Band; Jazz Band.

SULLIVAN, BETH; Arlington Catholic HS; Waltham, MA; (Y); 74/148; Church Yth Grp; JA; Spanish Clb; Yrbk Stf; JV Crs Cntry; Trk; Hon Roll; Outstndng Wrk In Comm 85; Magna Cum Laude-Natl Latin Exam 83; U Of NH; Comm.

SULLIVAN, CASSANDRA; Hingham HS; Hingham, MA; (Y); Acpl Chr; Chorus; Church Choir; Madrigals; Orch; School Musical; School Play; Variety Show; Hon Roll; Dist Chrs Cncrt Prfm/Rec 85; Grtr Boston Piano Bar Sngoff 1st Pl 84; All ST Chrs 85; Boston U; Prfsnl Sngr.

SULLIVAN, CHRISTINA; Westwood HS; Westwood, MA; (Y); 95/214; AFS; Key Clb; Powder Puff Ftbl; JV Tennis; Var Trk; L Vllybl; Hon Roll; Mst Tm Spirt Troph Grls Vllybl 82-83; Fairfield U; Pedtrc Nrs.

SULLIVAN, CHRISTOPHER; Waltham HS; Waltham, MA; (Y); French Clb; Band; Stu Cncl; Var Ftbl; Capt Wrstlng; Hon Roll; NHS; Sci, Englsh & Athltcs PTO Excllnc Awds 83; Rensselaer Poly-Tech; Engr.

SULLIVAN, DANIEL; Weymouth North HS; Weymouth, MA; (Y); 22/300; Am Leg Boys St; Boy Scts; Church Yth Grp; Math Tm; Spanish Clb; Stu Cncl; Bsktbl; Ftbl; Var Ice Hcky; Swmmng.

SULLIVAN, DAVID; Malden Catholic HS; Medford, MA; (Y); 1/179; Computer Clb; Math Tm; Quiz Bowl; Yrbk Ed-Chief; Stu Cncl; Trk; NHS; Ntl Merit Schol; Val; Nwsp Rptr; Edtr Chf Microcmptr Nws 85; Harvard U; Physcs.

SULLIVAN, DONNA; North Andover HS; N Andover, MA; (Y); 22/243; Drama Clb; Pep Clb; Acpl Chr; Sec Trs Chorus; Church Choir; School Musical; School Play; Variety Show; Yrbk Stf; Off Sr Cls; Mary Wacklin & Cyr Assoc Schlrshp 85; Merit Schlrshp 85; Bradford Coll; Comm.

SULLIVAN, DOUGLAS; Marian HS; Framingham, MA; (Y); 15/177; Var Ftbl; Sci.

SULLIVAN, JAMES; Matignon HS; Somerville, MA; (S); 7/174; Cmnty Wkr; Pres Library Aide; Spanish Clb; Lit Mag; Elks Awd; Hon Roll; NHS; Spanish NHS; Ntl Scndry Ed Cncl, Acad All-Amer 83-84; Sci Fair 83-84; St Johns Seminary Coll; Priest.

SULLIVAN, JENIFER; Lynn English HS; Lynn, MA; (Y); AFS; Church Yth Grp; Drama Clb; Hosp Aide; Ski Clb; Stage Crew; Variety Show; NEDT Awd.

SULLIVAN, JOANNE; Holy Name C C HS; N Grafton, MA; (Y); 27/272; Pep Clb; Ski Clb; Frsh Cls; Sec Soph Cls; Sec VP Jr Cls; Stu Cncl; High Hon Roll; Hon Roll; NHS; Comm Skills Dept Awd 84; Religion & Am Lit Dept Awds 85; Bryant Coll; Accntng.

SULLIVAN, JOHN; Andover HS; Andover, MA; (Y); Model UN; Pep Clb; Var JV Ftbl; Var JV Trk; Crmnl Jstc.

SULLIVAN, KATHLEEN; Somerset HS; Somerset, MA; (Y); 15/300; Church Yth Grp; Cmnty Wkr; Nwsp Stf; Var Fld Hcky; Var Trk; Elks Awd; High Hon Roll; Kiwanis Awd; Pres NHS; Val; Teenager Yr 85; Providence Coll; Soc Wrk.

SULLIVAN, KELLY; Lenox Memorial HS; Lenox, MA; (Y); Church Yth Grp; Cmnty Wkr; School Play; Hon Roll; Kiwanis Awd; Boston Coll.

SULLIVAN, KEVIN; Bishop Feehan HS; Foxboro, MA; (Y); Chess Clb; Im Bsktbl; Golf; Ice Hcky; Im Vllybl; Hon Roll; Pre-Law.

SULLIVAN, KEVIN M; Walpole HS; Walpole, MA; (Y); 9/262; JCL; Political Wkr; Spanish Clb; Teachers Aide; Varsity Clb; Var Ftbl; Var Trk; Var Wrstlng; High Hon Roll; Hon Roll; Brown U; Med.

SULLIVAN, LAURA; Danvers HS; Danvers, MA; (Y); 2/305; Church Yth Grp; Teachers Aide; Chorus; Yrbk Stf; Var Capt Bsktbl; Var Capt Fld Hcky; Var Sftbl; Var L Trk; French Hon Soc; High Hon Roll; Music Hnr Soc 83-84; Unsung Hnr Def Fld Hocky 84-85; Mst Imprvd Trk 82-83.

SULLIVAN, MARY ELLEN; Westfield HS; Westfield, MA; (Y); Church Yth Grp; Ski Clb; Var Socr; Var Sftbl; Hon Roll; MVP Skiing 84 & 85; Coachs Awd Sftbl 85.

SULLIVAN, MAURA; Presentation Of Mary Academy HS; Lawrence, MA; (S); 11/50; Church Yth Grp; VP Drama Clb; Ski Clb; Spanish Clb; School Musical; School Play; Nwsp Stf; Yrbk Stf; Hon Roll; Trs NHS; Phys Therapy.

SULLIVAN, MAURA A; Newburyport HS; Newburyport, MA; (S); 22/300; JCL; Math Tm; Model UN; Office Aide; Q&S; Ed Nwsp Rptr; Lit Mag; Hon Roll; NHS.

SULLIVAN, MAUREEN; Bishop Connolly HS; Westport, MA; (S); 20/159; French Clb; Yrbk Stf; Capt Bsktbl; Capt Sftbl; L Vllybl; High Hon Roll; NHS; Bsktbl All-Star 81; Schlrshp Franklin Pierce Coll 85; U Of MA; Psych.

SULLIVAN, MICHAEL P; Palmer HS; Three Rivers, MA; (Y); 3/100; Am Leg Boys St; Chess Clb; Drama Clb; Math Tm; School Play; High Hon Roll; Hon Roll; Pro Merito Soc 85-86; Civil Engrng.

SULLIVAN, NADINE; Marian HS; Framingham, MA; (Y); 19/177; Hon Roll; NHS; Hnbl Mntn Sci Fair 83; Vet.

SULLIVAN, NORA; Monument Mountain Regional HS; Gr Barrington, MA; (Y); 10/133; French Clb; Band; Nwsp Stf; Yrbk Stf; Lit Mag; DAR Awd; High Hon Roll; Hon Roll; NHS; Ntl Merit Ltr; JR Early Schlr Berkshire Crafts Fair Schlr 84-85; Skidmore Coll; Bio.

SULLIVAN, PAULA; Weston HS; Weston, MA; (Y); 52/180; Church Yth Grp; Exploring; Girl Scts; Spanish Clb; Lit Mag; Rep Soph Cls; JV Bsktbl; JV Var Fld Hcky; JV Golf; JV Trk; Providence Coll.

SULLIVAN, ROBERT; Falmouth HS; N Falmouth, MA; (Y); Band; Concert Band; Mrchg Band; Trk; School Play; Stage Crew; U MA Tufts; Music.

SULLIVAN, SCOTT EDWARD; Quincy Vo Tech; Weymouth, MA; (Y); 4/195; Am Leg Boys St; Science Clb; Ski Clb; VICA; Var Ice Hcky; High Hon Roll; Pres Schlr; US Army Resv Schlr/Athl Medl 85; Wnnr Dennis F Ryan Essay-Alcohol & The Law 85; Electrcn.

SULLIVAN, SUSAN MARIE; East Bridgewater HS; East Bridgewatr, MA; (Y); 1/152; Church Yth Grp; Key Clb; Pres Science Clb; Rep Sr Cls; Rep Stu Cncl; Var Capt Cheerleading; Trk; NHS; Pres Schlr; Val; Supt Schls Acad Excllnce Awd 85; MA Math Lg Olympiad 83; Williams Coll; Comp Sci.

SULLIVAN, TIMOTHY; Billerica Memorial HS; Billerica, MA; (Y); 11/500; French Clb; Band; Chorus; Mrchg Band; School Musical; Yrbk Stf; Hon Roll; NHS; Ntl Merit Ltr; MA Advncd Stds Prgm 85.

SULLIVAN, VALERIE; Arlington Catholic HS; Medford, MA; (Y); 20/150; Service Clb; School Musical; Yrbk Stf; Rep Soph Cls; Rep Jr Cls; VP Stu Cncl; Capt Crs Cntry; Var L Trk; Hon Roll; NHS; Natl Latin Exam Awd 83-85; Boston Coll.

SULSKI, JOHN L; Doherty Memorial HS; Worcester, MA; (Y); 12/360; Boy Scts; Church Yth Grp; Latin Clb; Variety Show; Nwsp Rptr; Crs Cntry; NHS; Recpnt Holy Crss Prog Gftd HS Stu Schlrshp 84-85; Dartmouth; Elec Engrng.

SUMMERS, JENNIFER; Chatham JR SR HS; N Chatham, MA; (Y); Drama Clb; Math Tm; Chorus; Madrigals; School Musical; Var Cheerleading; HLSS Schlrshp Braemar Smmr Schl Highland Dancg 83.

SURETTE, KAREN; Malden HS; Malden, MA; (Y); 6/543; Am Leg Aux Girls St; Math Tm; Office Aide; Variety Show; Swmmng; Hon Roll; Kiwanis Awd; Trs NHS; Comp Sci.

SURETTE, SHAUN; St Bernards HS; Fitchburg, MA; (S); 21/163; Drama Clb; Science Clb; School Play; Stage Crew; Ed Yrbk Stf; Rep Stu Cncl; Hon Roll; NHS; Intl Reltns.

SUTCLIFFE, ERIK; King Philip Regional HS; Sheldonville, MA; (S); Am Leg Boys St; Model UN; JV Socr; JV Tennis; Hon Roll; NHS; MA Inst Of Tech; Aero Engr.

SUTHERLAND, SHARON D; Ayer SR HS; Ft Devens, MA; (Y); 10/165; Church Yth Grp; Natl Beta Clb; Color Guard; Yrbk Phtg; Powder Puff Ftbl; Hon Roll; Mu Alp Tht; NHS; Awd Excllnc & Chrctr 85; Pres Acdmc Ftnss Awd 85.

SUTTON, SHERRI; North Middlesex Regional HS; Townsend, MA; (Y); Co-Capt Color Guard; School Musical; Stage Crew; High Hon Roll; Hon Roll; Trs VP Jr NHS; NHS; Study & Prof Awd Microcomp 84; Spnsh.

SWAN, SUSAN P; Holyoke HS; Holyoke, MA; (Y); Pres Latin Clb; Spanish Clb; Band; Concert Band; Mgr Jazz Band; Mrchg Band; Pep Band; Stage Crew; Variety Show; Socr.

SWANSON, KRIS; Tahanto Reg HS; Boylston, MA; (Y); 8/50; Church Yth Grp; Hosp Aide; Yrbk Rptr; VP Frsh Cls; VP Soph Cls; VP Jr Cls; Capt L Bsktbl; Capt L Fld Hcky; Var Sftbl; Var Tennis; U Of NH.

SWARDSTROM, MARK W; Bourne HS; Bourne, MA; (Y); 11/170; Capt Math Tm; ROTC; Band; Nwsp Stf; Yrbk Stf; Var L Ftbl; Var L Trk; High Hon Roll; NHS; Pres Schlr; Cornell U; Engrng.

SWARTZ, DENISE; Gardner HS; Gardner, MA; (Y); French Clb; GAA; Office Aide; Band; Chorus; Mrchg Band; School Musical; Cheerleading; Crs Cntry; Co-Capt Trk; Fitchburg ST Coll; Ele Ed/Math.

SWARTZEL, LISA M; Newburyport HS; Newburyport, MA; (S); 11/194; Math Tm; Model UN; Q&S; Teachers Aide; Chorus; School Musical; Nwsp Rptr; Nwsp Stf; Lit Mag; Socr.

SWEDBERG, RICHARD; Burncoat SR HS; Worcester, MA; (Y); Church Yth Grp; Var Bsktbl; Capt Socr; Var Trk; Phys Ed.

SWEENEY, BRANDON S; Catholic Memorial HS; Medfield, MA; (Y); 12/277; Am Leg Boys St; Debate Tm; Yrbk Sprt Ed; Var Crs Cntry; Var Ice Hcky; Var Tennis; High Hon Roll; VP NHS; Pres Schlr; Bowdoin Coll; Lawyer.

SWEENEY, CHERYL; Matignon HS; Somerville, MA; (Y); 58/196; Camera Clb; Drama Clb; Church Choir; Mrchg Band; Orch; School Musical; School Play; Variety Show; Hon Roll; NEDT Awd; Pre-Med.

SWEENEY, DANIEL A; Ludlow HS; Ludlow, MA; (Y); 30/267; Am Leg Boys St; Yrbk Stf; Var Bsbl; Var Capt Bsktbl; Trs 4-H; Rep Frsh Cls; Rep Soph Cls; Off Jr Cls; Top 30 Govt Test Boys ST 85; Outstndng Underclsmn Bsktbl Tm 85; Bsbl Plyr Of Wk 85; Libl Arts.

SWEENEY, EILEEN; Bishop Fenwick HS; Peabody, MA; (Y); Art Clb; Church Yth Grp; Computer Clb; Science Clb; School Play; Rep Frsh Cls; Rep Soph Cls; Rep Jr Cls; Capt Bsktbl; Var Capt Fld Hcky; Vrsty Fld Hcky Coaches Awd; Comm.

SWEENEY, JOHN; Central Catholic HS; Andover, MA; (Y); 125/219; Church Yth Grp; Library Aide; Math Tm; Ski Clb; Rep Stu Cncl; Stat Bsbl; JV Ftbl; Mgr Ice Hcky; Var Mgr(s); Intrmrl Bsktbl & Vllybl; Mtrlgy.

SWEENEY, JOHN; Peabody Veterans Memorial HS; Peabody, MA; (Y); 40/510; Chess Clb; Latin Clb; L Bsktbl; L Lcrss; Capt Socr; Im Vllybl; Hon Roll; NHS; Pres Schlr; U Vermont; Elect Engr.

SWEENEY, JOSEPH; North Quincy HS; N Quincy, MA; (Y); 110/358; JV Var Crs Cntry; Trk; Hon Roll; NE U; Comp Sci.

SWEENEY, JULIE E; Dedham HS; Dedham, MA; (S); 12/325; Church Yth Grp; Band; Jazz Band; Mrchg Band; Orch; School Musical; NHS; Cmnty Wkr; Concert Band; Hon Roll; Arion Awd 84; Purdue; Comms.

SWEENEY, KATHLEEN; Chicopee Comprehensive HS; Chicopee, MA; (Y); 33/300; NHS; Acctg.

SWEENEY, MARGARET; Whitman Hanson Regional HS; Whitman, MA; (Y); Cmnty Wkr; Yrbk Stf; Rep Stu Cncl; JV Sftbl; Hist Club 83-84; Bus.

SWEENEY, MARY BETH; Franklin HS; Franklin, MA; (Y); Varsity Clb; Yrbk Phtg; Yrbk Stf; VP Capt Cheerleading; Hon Roll; NHS; Math Tutr 84-85; Boston Globe Schlstc Art Awd Cert Recog 85; Frnch Exch Stdnt 84; Mktg.

SWEENEY, WILLIAM; Bishop Connolly HS; Bristol, RI; (Y); Latin Clb; Nwsp Stf; Off Sr Cls; Bsktbl; Socr; Swmmng; Trk; Hon Roll; Law.

SWEET, STUART; Haverhill HS; Haverhill, MA; (Y); 22/375; Aud/Vis; Acpl Chr; Band; Chorus; Stage Crew; Nwsp Ed-Chief; NHS; Boy Scts; Concert Band; Cramm Musical Schlrshp, Elmer Johnson Awd, Modern Music Masters 85; Boston U; TV Prod.

SWEETSER, NATHAN V; Mansfield HS; Mansfield, MA; (Y); Am Leg Boys St; Boy Scts; Math Tm; L Capt Crs Cntry; Capt L Trk; Hon Roll; NHS; Regnl Ed Cncl Rep; Regnl Stu Advsry Cncl Rep; U S Military Acad; Army Officer.

SWEEZEY, KEN; Archbishop Williams HS; Abington, MA; (Y); 56/198; Var L Bsbl; Var Capt Ice Hcky; Jr NHS.

SWENSON, DANIEL F; Waltham HS; Waltham, MA; (Y); Am Leg Boys St; French Clb; Varsity Clb; Band; Chorus; Symp Band; Pres Frsh Cls; Var JV Bsktbl; JV Trk; Hon Roll; Noble Prize & Athltc Awd; Bentley Clg; Bus.

SWIERZEWSKI, ANN M; Holyoke HS; Holyoke, MA; (Y); Church Yth Grp; Latin Clb; Office Aide; Science Clb; Spanish Clb; Rep Frsh Cls; Tennis; High Hon Roll; NHS.

SWIRE, DIANE; New Bedford HS; New Bedford, MA; (Y); GAA; Library Aide; Varsity Clb; Var L Sftbl; Var Capt Vllybl; Northeastern U; Phy Thrpy.

SWISTAK, DAWN MARIE; Hoosac Valley HS; Adams, MA; (Y); 48/169; Girl Scts; Pep Clb; Yrbk Stf; JV Var Sftbl; Hon Roll; NHS; Acad Achvt Typng 85; Acad Achvt Bus Offc Prctcs 85; Berkshire CC; Exec Secy.

SWYMER, CHRISTINE; Marian HS; Milford, MA; (Y); Band; Concert Band; Orch; School Musical; Yrbk Stf; Rep Sr Cls; Var Bsktbl; Var Sftbl; High Hon Roll; NHS; Gen Exclince Advncd Biol 84; Gen Exclince Advncd Eng II; Med.

SYLVESTER, ERIC K; Middleboro HS; Middleboro, MA; (Y); Computer Clb; Library Aide; Hon Roll; NHS; Elctrcl Engr.

SYLVESTER, JULIE; Marblehead HS; Marblehead, MA; (Y); 44/250; Rep Frsh Cls; Rep Soph Cls; Rep Jr Cls; Var Capt Cheerleading; Var Capt Fld Hcky; Var Swmmng; Var Capt Trk; Hon Roll; Powder Puff Ftbl; JV, MVP Field Hockey 82-83; Mst Outstndng Var Trk 82-83; Mst Imprvd Var Swmmng 83-84; Unsung Hero Trk.

SYLVESTER, KRISTIN; Nipmuc Regional HS; Upton, MA; (Y); Pres Church Yth Grp; Drama Clb; 4-H; French Clb; Hosp Aide; Chorus; Church Choir; Nwsp Rptr; Nwsp Stf; Yrbk Stf; U Of MA; Anml Sci.

SYLVIA, EDWARD; Middleboro HS; Middleboro, MA; (Y); Drama Clb; Acpl Chr; School Musical; School Play; Symp Band; Trk; High Hon Roll; NHS; Band; Chorus; Yth Amer European Cncrt Tour Chorus 84; SE Dist Chorus 84-85; SEMSBA Chorus 84-85; ALL ST Chorus 85; Theatre Arts.

SYLVIA, LORI; New Bedford HS; New Bedford, MA; (Y); 22/688; Hosp Aide; Library Aide; Var Gym; High Hon Roll; Jr NHS; NHS; Amer Clscl League Cert Of Hnrb Mntn/Mgna Cum Laude In Latin 85; Hnrb Mntn For Essay 85; Nrs.

SYLVIAN, PATRICK; Camb-Rindge And Latin HS; Cambridge, MA; (Y); Camera Clb; Cmnty Wkr; Debate Tm; French Clb; Political Wkr; Varsity Clb; Nwsp Rptr; Nwsp Stf; Var Socr; Capt Trk; Outstndng Prfmnc-Trk 84-85; Sbrbn Lge All Star Indr Trk 84-85; Outstndng Ldrshp-Hatian Pac Assoc 85; U Of MA; Pol Sci.

SYMONDS, JENNIFER; Bishop Fenwick HS; Essex, MA; (Y); GAA; Drill Tm; Computer Clb; Hon Roll; NHS; Pasd US Figr Sktng Assn Tsts 83-85; Gld Medl Juvnl Complsry Movs 85; Librl Arts.

SYNGAY, SUSAN; Franklin HS; Franklin, MA; (Y); Church Yth Grp; Math Tm; Yrbk Stf; Mgr(s); Sftbl; Hon Roll.

SYRIGOS, JOANNE; Girls Catholic HS; Malden, MA; (S); 2/35; Church Yth Grp; Spanish Clb; Yrbk Stf; Hon Roll; NHS; Stu Of The Quarter 83; Acctng.

SZARGOWICZ, DIANE; Bishop Connolly HS; Fall River, MA; (S); 8/158; Latin Clb; Yrbk Stf; High Hon Roll; Hon Roll; Jr NHS; NHS; SE MA U; Elec Engr.

SZAX, MARIA; Dracut SR HS; Dracut, MA; (Y); Art Clb; Key Clb; Hon Roll; NHS; Adv Crftsmnshp Art Awd 82-83; Bio Eng Awd 83-84; Comm Artist.

SZCZUKA, SUSAN M; Newburyport HS; Newburyport, MA; (S); 13/209; Model UN; Teachers Aide; Yrbk Stf; Stu Cncl; High Hon Roll; Hon Roll; NHS; MA Coll Of Pharmacy; Phrmcst.

SZELA, WENDY; Southwick HS; Granville, MA; (Y); Pres Sec 4-H; Library Aide; Ski Clb; Drill Tm; School Play; Nwsp Stf; Rep Capt Stu Cncl; 4-H Awd; Hon Roll; Hi Pnt Awd-4-H 84; Outstndng 4-H Rcrds 84.

SZEMEREDY, MELISSA O; Hyde Park Acad; Hyde Park, MA; (S); 1/24; Art Clb; Computer Clb; Debate Tm; Drama Clb; English Clb; Math Tm; School Play; Stage Crew; Variety Show; Yrbk Bus Mgr; Sci Awd 83; Math, Engl Awd 84; Cosmtlgy.

SZLYK, LAURA; Shepherd Hill Regional HS; Dudley, MA; (Y); Math Tm; Chorus; School Musical; Yrbk Stf; Sec Sr Cls; Rep Stu Cncl; JV Bsktbl; Var Tennis; NHS; Ntl Merit Ltr; Brdr Cnfrnc All-Star Tennis Plyr 85; Lbrl Arts.

SZPILA, KERRY; Hoosac Valley HS; Cheshire, MA; (Y); Church Yth Grp; Dance Clb; Exploring; Ski Clb; Yrbk Stf; Crs Cntry; High Hon Roll; Hon Roll; Ntl Merit Schol; Psychlgy.

SZUCHAN, KRISTIN; Doherty Memorial HS; Worcester, MA; (Y); Art Clb; Church Yth Grp; French Clb; Letterman Clb; Ski Clb; Trk; RI Schl Dsgn; Adv.

TACCINI, AMY; Weymouth North HS; Weymouth, MA; (Y); Cmmndtn In Algbra II; Dntl Hygnst.

TAIT, ANTHONY; Deerfield Acad; Arlington, VA; (Y); Computer Clb; French Clb; Mgr VP Ice Hcky; Socr; VP Mgr Ftbl.

TALBOT, LORI; Braintree HS; Braintree, MA; (Y); Church Yth Grp; Cmnty Wkr; Drama Clb; Chorus; Church Choir; Color Guard; Madrigals; School Musical; School Play; Yrbk Stf; BHS Chorale Pres & 1st Pl Wnr NY Fest 82-84; SE Dist SEMSBA 83-84; Soc Psych.

TALBOT, LYNNE; Billerica Memorial HS; Billerica, MA; (Y); 6/500; Boys Clb Am; French Clb; Yrbk Stf; Rep Frsh Cls; Rep Soph Cls; Trs Jr Cls; Var Capt Crs Cntry; Powder Puff Ftbl; Var Capt Trk; Sec Jr NHS; Spg Trck MVC All Strs 85; Bio.

TALBOT, RENEE; Agawam HS; Agawam, MA; (Y); 104/350; Cmnty Wkr; Drill Tm; Yrbk Stf; Minnie Barden Mem Scholar 85; Fed Pell Grant 85; Northland Coll Grant 85; Northland Coll; Bio.

TALBOTT, DEREK; Dennis-Yarmouth Regional HS; Dennis, MA; (Y); Am Leg Boys St; Cmnty Wkr; JV Golf; Im Lcrss; L Socr; L Tennis; Im Vllybl; Hon Roll; Pres NHS.

TALCOFF, MATHEW; Newton South HS; Newton Centre, MA; (Y); 2/323; Varsity Clb; Hon Roll; Ntl Merit Ltr; Var L Ice Hcky; Frgn Lang Cert Hnr 84-85; Chaffin Ed Fund Scholar 85; Murray Peter Karger Mem Awd 81; Bentley Coll; Acctng.

TAM, HO CHUEN; Cushing Acad; Kowloon; (Y); 3/96; VP Intnl Clb; Math Tm; Science Clb; Variety Show; JV Var Socr; Var Trk; Wt Lftg; High Hon Roll; Hon Roll; 1st Pl Fitchburg ST Coll JR Math Cntst85; Smmr Schl Ping-Pong Chmpn 84; Renselaer Sci & Math Awd 85; Engrng.

TAM, WAI; Boston Latin Schl; Boston, MA; (Y); Computer Clb; JA; Science Clb; Hon Roll; NHS; Mech Engrng.

TAMAGINI, LISA A; Lexington Christian Acad; Wakefield, MA; (Y); 3/50; Church Yth Grp; High Hon Roll; NHS; Cmnty Wkr; Drama Clb; English Clb; French Clb; Teachers Aide; Thesps; Acpl Chr; MTNA Voice Wnnr 84; MTNA Eastern Div Cntstnt 85; Gtr Bostonian Chorus 81-82; Ne Dist Chor 81-85; Opera.

TAMBURRINO, GINA; Barnstable HS; Hyannis, MA; (Y); Ski Clb; Wheelock Coll Alumni Book Awd 85; Cert Merit Span 84-85.

TAMIS, SHELLEY; Methuen HS; Methuen, MA; (Y); 7/350; Intnl Clb; Bsktbl; Sftbl; Vllybl; High Hon Roll; NHS; Ntl Hnr Soc-Histrn 85; Sci.

TAN, ROWENA; Brockton HS; Brockton, MA; (Y); French Clb; Yrbk Stf; Intrprtr.

TANAGNI, PAUL; Milford HS; Milford, MA; (Y); Church Yth Grp; Computer Clb; Exploring; FBLA; Ski Clb; Spanish Clb; Swing Chorus; Yrbk Sprt Ed; Var Bsbl; Var Socr; Bus Mngmnt.

TANNER, ALAN; St Johns Prep; Peabody, MA; (Y); Temple Yth Grp; Im Bsktbl; Hon Roll; Temple Ner Tamid Brotherhd Schlrshp 85; Harold B Stone Mem Schlrshp 85; U MA; Mgmt.

TARANTO, TODD A; Saint Johns HS; Bolton, MA; (Y); 24/269; Am Leg Boys St; Model UN; Spanish Clb; Teachers Aide; Stu Cncl; Var Bsbl; Im Bsktbl; High Hon Roll; NHS; Ntl Hnr Soc Math Tutor 84-85; Engr.

TARARA, DANIEL; Central Catholic HS; Bradford, MA; (Y); 80/220; Boy Scts; Church Yth Grp; Var Bsbl; Var Bsktbl; Bowling; Var Ftbl; Legn Hnr 84; Nwscarrier Mnth Dec 83; Comp Sci.

TARDANICO, CHRISTINE M; Stoughton HS; Stoughton, MA; (Y); Office Aide; Chorus; Drill Tm; Swing Chorus; Rep Stu Cncl; Twrlr; Stonehill Coll; Bus Mrktng.

TARDIFF, STACEY M; Middleboro HS; Middleboro, MA; (Y); VP Drama Clb; Mgr Stage Crew; Nwsp Rptr; Nwsp Stf; Rep Frsh Cls; Rep Soph Cls; Rep Jr Cls; Rep Stu Cncl; Var JV Fld Hcky; Hon Roll; Russian.

TARDO, GINA; Coyle And Cassidy HS; Taunton, MA; (Y); 55/140; JV Bsktbl; JV Var Cheerleading; JV Trk; Hon Roll; Alg I Awd 82; Med.

TARPEY, JOHN; Gardner HS; Gardner, MA; (Y); DECA; Stat Mgr Ftbl; DECA ST Comptn 1st Pl Awd Wrtn Mnl Comptn 85; John S Gearan Mem Schlrshp 85; Albert H Stone Fund 85; Cntrl Connecticut ST; Bus.

TARTAGLIA, LYNNE; Brockton HS; Brockton, MA; (Y); 153/960; Camera Clb; Drama Clb; Var Capt Bsktbl; Var Socr; Var Capt Sftbl; Hon Roll; Exec Cmmtt Mbr 84-86; Acctng.

TARTARINI, KIM; Natick HS; Natick, MA; (Y); 27/443; Teachers Aide; Var L Bsktbl; Capt Bowling; Var L Trk; Var L Vllybl; High Hon Roll; Hon Roll; Prfct Atten Awd; Schlrshp At Framingham ST Coll Genetics Crs 85; Bus Ed Awd Law 84-85; Vllybl Unsung Hero Awd 84-85; Bio.

TASCA, ANGELA; Methuen HS; Methuen, MA; (Y); 45/465; Powder Puff Ftbl; JV Var Vllybl; High Hon Roll; Hon Roll; Bio.

TASSINARI, ANDY D; North Shore Regional Voc HS; Salem, MA; (Y); Hon Roll; Atten Awd 84-85.

TATEM, ELIZABETH; Bishop Connolly HS; Portsmouth, RI; (S); 29/179; Latin Clb; Math Clb; Math Tm; Ski Clb; Band; Color Guard; Concert Band; Mrchg Band; Pep Band; Stage Crew; Holy Cross; Math.

TATRO, GORDON F; Westfield HS; Westfield, MA; (Y); School Musical; High Hon Roll; Nuc Physics.

TATTAN, KATHLEEN; Quabbin Regional JR SR HS; Hubbardston, MA; (Y); 17/143; French Clb; Band; Concert Band; Symp Band; Yrbk Stf; Trs Jr Cls; Stu Cncl; Cit Awd; French Hon Soc; Hon Roll; Frnch Clb Awd 84; Boston Coll; Ped Nrsng.

TATTRIE, KEVIN; Franklin HS; Franklin, MA; (Y); Am Leg Boys St; Capt Bsktbl; L Var Ftbl; L Var Ice Hcky; Hon Roll; Ntl Merit Ltr; Math Tutor 85; Natl Varsity Clb 85; William O Lord Mem Trophy/Mst Imprvd Ftbl 85; Rookie Of Yr 83-84; Comp Sci.

TATUM, CHRISTOPHER S; Scituate HS; Scituate, MA; (Y); 4/296; Am Leg Boys St; Ftbl; Ice Hcky; Trk; Cit Awd; Hon Roll; NHS; Ntl Merit Ltr; Boston Globe Ice Hcky All Schltc 84-85; Patriot Ledger Ice Hcky All Schltc 84-85; Engrng.

TAUSEK, JENNIFER; Bishop Feehan HS; Attleboro, MA; (Y); 30/255; Exploring; Concert Band; Yrbk Stf; Rep Frsh Cls; Rep Soph Cls; Rep Jr Cls; Rep Sr Cls; Rep Stu Cncl; Trk; High Hon Roll; Awd Exclinc Math 84-85.

TAVANO, LYNN; Milford HS; Milford, MA; (Y); Dance Clb; Hosp Aide; Yrbk Stf; High Hon Roll; Hon Roll; NHS; Nrsng.

TAVARES, MICHELLE; Marian HS; Framingham, MA; (Y); French Clb; Ski Clb; Chorus; Rep Soph Cls; Rep Jr Cls; Hon Roll; NHS; Portuguese Schl 84; Portuguese Lang Tchr 85; Holy Cross; Hstry.

TAVARES, PATRICIA; Westport HS; Westport, MA; (Y); Dance Clb; Exploring; French Clb; Ski Clb; Band; Yrbk Phtg; Yrbk Stf; Capt Cheerleading; Camp Fr Inc; Church Yth Grp; Stu Govt Dy Dely ST Hous Boston 85; Emerson Coll; Cmnctns Media.

TAVARES, PAULINE; New Bedford HS; New Bedford, MA; (Y); 34/688; Drama Clb; Hosp Aide; JCL; Library Aide; School Musical; Yrbk Stf; High Hon Roll; Jr NHS; NHS; Stu Congrss 84-85; MD.

TAWCZYNSKI, CHRISTINE; Monument Mountain Regional HS; Gr Barrington, MA; (Y); 26/119; Band; Concert Band; Mrchg Band; School Musical; Nwsp Bus Mgr; Yrbk Stf; Lit Mag; Var Mgr(s); JV Socr; Hon Roll; Bus Adm.

TAYAG, RAQUEL; Arlington Catholic HS; Billerica, MA; (Y); 27/148; French Clb; Girl Scts; Rptr Nwsp Stf; Yrbk Phtg; Yrbk Stf; Bsktbl; Bowling; Hon Roll; NHS; Dnstry.

TAYLOR, CATHY; Rockland HS; Rockland, MA; (S); 1/287; Church Yth Grp; Variety Show; Socr; Sftbl; High Hon Roll; NHS; NEDT Awd; Rensselaer Mdl 84; Math Awd 82-84; Cert Of Acdmc Exclinc 84; Vetrnrn.

TAYLOR, KIMBERLY; Drury SR HS; Stamford, VT; (Y); 4-H; Girl Scts; Nwsp Rptr; Nwsp Stf; Var L Ice Hcky; Jrnlsm.

TAYLOR, LEEANNE T; Frontier Regional Schl; S Deerfield, MA; (Y); Drama Clb; VP Spanish Clb; School Play; Nwsp Rptr; Yrbk Stf; VP Frsh Cls; Rep Soph Cls; Tennis; L Trk; Hon Roll; Intl Rel.

TAYLOR, LESLIE; Brockton HS; Brockton, MA; (Y); 60/1000; Drama Clb; JCL; Key Clb; Var Trk; US Nvl Rsrvs; Bentley Coll; Bus.

TAYLOR, RICK; Burlington HS; Burlington, MA; (Y); 37/375; Var Ice Hcky; Var Socr; Hon Roll; Boston Globe Art 82-83; Gld Key Awd 82-83; Acdmc Sculptr Awd & Cert 84-85; Drftg.

TAYLOR, ROBERT; Algonquin Reginal HS; Northborough, MA; (Y); Church Yth Grp; Cmnty Wkr; Drama Clb; PAVAS; Chorus; School Musical; School Play; Stage Crew; Variety Show; MS HG Drama Fstvl 84; Recgntn Awd Drama; Cert Awd HS Chorus; Dean JC; Lbrl Arts.

TAYLOR, RONALD; N Reading HS; N Reading, MA; (Y); Church Yth Grp; Drama Clb; Thesps; Band; Chorus; Church Choir; Jazz Band; Mrchg Band; School Musical; Nwsp Rptr; Gordon Coll.

TEAGUE, ANDREA; Beverly HS; Beverly, MA; (Y); 12/399; Mgr Chorus; School Musical; School Play; Stage Crew; Swing Chorus; Nwsp Stf; Trs Stu Cncl; Hon Roll; NHS; Aud/Vis; Mst Imprvd Sngr Awd 84; Hrdst Worker 85; Amer Chem Soc Awd 85; Emmerson; Comm.

TEAGUE, SANDRA G; Classical HS; Springfield, MA; (Y); 3/400; Cmnty Wkr; Debate Tm; Mathletes; Nwsp Rptr; High Hon Roll; Hon Roll; NHS; Ntl Merit Ltr; Quiz Bowl; Nwsp Bus Mgr; Latin I & II Achvmnt 83 & 84; Holy Cross Clg Bk Awd 84; Achvmnt Greek I; Vanerbilt U; Res Bio.

TEBEAU, MARIA; Medway HS; Medway, MA; (Y); Girl Scts; Varsity Clb; Yrbk Sprt Ed; Var Bsktbl; Var Sftbl; Var Vllybl; Hon Roll; Vet Asst.

TECCE, MARIA A; Wellesley SR HS; Wellesley, MA; (Y); Church Yth Grp; Drama Clb; Spanish Clb; Chorus; Church Choir; Orch; School Musical; Variety Show; Var Trk; Boston Coll; Marine Bio.

TEEBAGY, DONNA; Arlington HS; Arlington, MA; (S); 3/400; Sec Church Yth Grp; Cmnty Wkr; Variety Show; Nwsp Stf; Var Tennis; High Hon Roll; Hon Roll; NHS; Smith Coll Clb Of Arlington Bk Awd 84; Arl Cable TV Discussion Women In Todays Society 84; Communications.

TEFTS, VALERIE; Holyoke Catholic HS; Easthampton, MA; (Y); Church Yth Grp; Computer Clb; 4-H; Math Clb; Spanish Clb; Teachers Aide; Swmmng; Exc Chem Awd 85; Math.

TELFORD, LYNNE; Bedford HS; Bedford, MA; (Y); 2/229; Am Leg Aux Girls St; VP Church Yth Grp; Band; Chorus; Jazz Band; School Musical; Nwsp Stf; Yrbk Stf; Sec Soph Cls; Var Swmmng; MA Grls ST 84; Colby Coll Bk Awd 84; Middlebury Coll; Pre-Med.

TEMBENIS, HARRY T; Doherty Memorial HS; Worcester, MA; (Y); Church Yth Grp; JA; ROTC; Spanish Clb; Teachers Aide; Variety Show; Wt Lftg; Hon Roll; Prfct Atten Awd; Career Day Essy Cntst 85; WPI; Cvl Engrng.

TEMKIN, MARK; Newton South HS; Newton, MA; (Y); Chess Clb; Var Debate Tm; JA; NFL; Office Aide; Red Cross Aide; VP Science Clb; Crs Cntry; Tennis; Hon Roll; Faculty Awd 82; Johns Hopkins U; Poltcl Sci.

TEMPLE, BECKY D; Presentation Of Mary Acad; Bradford, MA; (Y); Church Yth Grp; Church Choir; Pres Frsh Cls; VP Jr Cls; Rep Stu Cncl; High Hon Roll; Hon Roll; NHS; NEDT Awd; Math Clb; 2nd Pl Schl Sci Fair 85; Natl Frtrnty Stdnt Musicns 84; Psych.

TEN BROECK, CHRISTINA; Mt Everett Regional HS; Great Barrington, MA; (Y); JV Cheerleading.

TENG, EMMA J; Amherst Regional HS; Amherst, MA; (Y); 9/310; Debate Tm; Drama Clb; French Clb; School Play; Stage Crew; Symp Band; Stu Cncl; Fld Hcky; Hon Roll; Ntl Merit SF; Boston Globe Schlstc Art Comp Gold Key & Schlstc Art Comp Blue Rib 84; Best In The West Art Awd 83; Fine Arts.

TENNEY, BOBBY; Milford HS; Milford, MA; (Y); 30/310; Band; Concert Band; Mrchg Band; JV Bsbl; Var Bsktbl; Var Socr; Hon Roll; Jr NHS; NHS; Law.

TERENZI, DOLORES; Pope John XXIII Central HS; East Boston, MA; (Y); 28/207; Key Clb; NHS; Variety Show; High Hon Roll; Hon Roll; Lilafrance Viles Schlrshp 84; Asst Dance Tchr 81-85; Salem St Coll; Bus Adm.

TESSIER, LISA A; Ayer JR SR HS; Ft Benning, GA; (Y); Church Yth Grp; Girl Scts; Pep Clb; Ski Clb; Spanish Clb; Yrbk Stf; JV Fld Hcky; Powder Puff Ftbl; Hon Roll; JV Fld Hocky Ltr 84-85; U Of Lowell; Comp Sci.

TESTA, SAL; No Andover HS; North Andover, MA; (Y); AFS; Am Leg Boys St; Drama Clb; JA; Pep Clb; Ski Clb; School Musical; School Play; Sec Jr Cls; Sec Sr Cls; Sr Clss Marshal; Cmnty Invlvmt; Rgnl Stu Advsry Brd; U Of MA; Hotel Adm.

TESTAGROSSA, JOSEPH; Montachusett Regional Vo-Tech; Ashburnham, MA; (Y); JV Bsbl; JV Bsktbl; Var Capt Socr; Hon Roll; NHS; Outstndng Achvt Elec 84-85; Elec.

TESTASECCA, BRENDA; Drury SR HS; North Adams, MA; (S); Church Yth Grp; Drama Clb; Spanish Clb; Sec Concert Band; School Musical; Hon Roll; School Play; Swing Chorus; Variety Show; Rep Frsh Cls; W MA Dist Chorus 83-85; S New England Dist Teen Tlnt 1st Pl 83; Evangel Coll MO; Mus.

TESTAVERDE, JILL MARIE PARSONS; Glaucester HS; Gloucester, MA; (Y); Office Aide; Yrbk Stf; Rep Soph Cls; Rep Jr Cls; Sec Stu Cncl; JV Cheerleading; Var Swmmng; JV Trk; Vllybl; Hon Roll; Hnrs Bus Clb 84-85; 8th In Nation 200 Medley Relay Swmmng 82; Outstndng Achvt In Stenography 84-85; Burdett Schl Of Bus; Bus Admin.

TETI, PATRICIA A; Dedham HS; Dedham, MA; (S); 1/280; Drama Clb; Band; Concert Band; Jazz Band; Mrchg Band; Orch; School Musical; School Play; Stage Crew; Rep Frsh Cls; Bst Stdnt Frgn Lang 83, 85, Soc Studies 84; Lions All ST Band 84.

TETREAU, TERESE; Douglas Memorial HS; E Douglas, MA; (Y); Church Yth Grp; FHA; Hosp Aide; Varsity Clb; Band; Chorus; Yrbk Phtg; Pres Soph Cls; Pres Jr Cls; Pres Sr Cls; JR Cls Pres 84-85; Hon Roll 84-85; Nrsng.

TETREAULT, CAROLYN E; Millis HS; Millis, MA; (Y); 13/85; Trs AFS; Trs Band; Jazz Band; Trs Mrchg Band; Yrbk Bus Mgr; Yrbk Phtg; Sec Soph Cls; Sec Crs Cntry; Var L Tennis; Var L Vllybl; GAF Corp Schlrshp 85; Ctzns Fndtn Schlrshp 85; Outstndng Musicn Awd 84-85; Norwich U; Nrsng.

TETREAULT, PAULINE; Holyoke HS; Holyoke, MA; (Y); Church Yth Grp; Speech Tm; Vllybl; High Hon Roll; Hon Roll; Phys Therapy.

TETREAULT, TOM; Southbridge HS; Southbridge, MA; (Y); 36/162; Cmnty Wkr; Nwsp Sprt Ed; Nwsp Stf; Bsktbl; Socr; Hon Roll; Jrnlsm.

TEVEROVSKY, VADIM; Concord-Carlisle HS; Concord, MA; (Y); 7/290; Chess Clb; Co-Capt Math Tm; Ski Clb; Im Socr; NHS; Ntl Merit SF; MA Math Olymp 84; Dept Awd In Math Sci Frnch 82-84; Amer Invit Math Exam 84.

THATCHER, MARK S; Athol HS; Athol, MA; (Y); 5/120; Am Leg Boys St; Model UN; Teachers Aide; Stage Crew; JV Bsktbl; Var L Trk; Var L Vllybl; Hon Roll; NHS; Engrng.

THAYER, CHRIS; Hingham HS; Hingham, MA; (Y); #19 In Class; Church Yth Grp; Ski Clb.

THEODORE, BENZNEY; Boston Latin Schl; Dorchester, MA; (Y); 47/319; Church Yth Grp; Computer Clb; Sec French Clb; Intnl Clb; Orch; Hon Roll; NHS; Early Acceptnc-MIT 85; Presdntl Acadmc Fitness Awd 85; MIT.

THEODORE, DICKENS; Boston Latin Schl; Boston, MA; (Y); 25/320; Church Yth Grp; Computer Clb; Orch; Var Socr; High Hon Roll; NHS; Dixwell Prz Exc Clssics 83; Lawrence Prz 83; Harvard; Med.

THERIAULT, JANET; Salem HS; Salem, MA; (Y); German Clb; Hosp Aide; Band; Concert Band; Mrchg Band; Orch; Socr; Hon Roll; JV Cochs Awd Soccr 84; Acctng.

THEROUX, CHERYL; Chicopee Comprehensive HS; Chicopee, MA; (Y); 1/330; Teachers Aide; Stu Cncl; Var Crs Cntry; Var L Trk; High Hon Roll; NHS; Church Yth Grp; Dance Clb; Hnr In Sci & Mth Cert Merit 85; French Awd 84-85.

THEROUX, DENISE M; Belingham Memorial JR/SR HS; Bellingham, MA; (Y); 96/200; Drama Clb; Hosp Aide; PAVAS; Teachers Aide; Church Choir; School Musical; Im Bsktbl; Im Fld Hcky; Im Ftbl; Im Socr; 1st Woonsocket Fine Arts Scty Fstvl 83-84; Art Grant & Featured Artist Bellinghm Arts Cncl 84; Chamberlayne JC; Fash Design.

THERRIAULT, WILLIAM; Bishop Connolly HS; Tiverton, RI; (S); Computer Clb; Math Tm; Band; Nwsp Phtg; Nwsp Rptr; Yrbk Phtg; Capt Bowling; High Hon Roll; NHS; CA Poly Tech; Chem Engr.

THETREAULT, LYNN; E Longmeadow HS; E Longmeadow, MA; (Y); 11/211; French Clb; Key Clb; Concert Band; Mrchg Band; Variety Show; Nwsp Rptr; Yrbk Stf; Bsktbl; High Hon Roll; NHS; Lions Clb All ST Band 85; Wellesley Bk Awd 84; Westin Mass Dist Band 84-85; Fairfield U; Lib Arts.

THIBAULT, LAURIE; Blackstone Millville Reg SR HS; Blackstone, MA; (Y); Church Yth Grp; Hosp Aide; Band; Chorus; Concert Band; Mrchg Band; Var Bsktbl; Var Trk; Candy Strppr Schlrshp; St Vincents Schl Nrsng; Nrsng.

THIBAULT, SUSAN; B M C Durfee HS; Fall River, MA; (Y); 97/600; Office Aide; Drill Tm; Mrchg Band; Yrbk Stf; Score Keeper; Church Yth Grp; Science Clb; Band; Fld Hcky; Mgr(s); Bryant Coll; Bus Adm.

THIBODEAU, CHERYL ANN; Weymouth South HS; South Weymouth, MA; (Y); 42/340; Church Yth Grp; Hosp Aide; Key Clb; Yrbk Stf; Tennis; Natl Anti-Vivisection Awd 85; Westfield ST Coll; Bus.

THIRUMALAISAMY, PILLAN K; Newton South HS; Newton, MA; (Y); Am Leg Boys St; Var Capt Bsbl; Var Capt Bsktbl; Var Capt Socr; Hon Roll; Fclty Awd Rcgntn 83 85; Colby Coll Bk Prz 85; Tp Scr Vrsty Sccr 83-84.

THOMAS, ANDREW; Bishop Stang HS; New Bedford, MA; (Y); 37/218; Pres Church Yth Grp; Drama Clb; Chorus; Church Choir; School Musical; School Play; Ed Yrbk Stf; U Of New England; Pre-Med.

THOMAS, CHRISTINE; Presentation Of Mary Acad; Salem, NH; (Y); Church Yth Grp; Drama Clb; French Clb; Office Aide; Church Choir; School Musical; School Play; Yrbk Stf; Quota Clb Gr Lawrnce Schlrshp; Amer Lebhnese Assn Schlrshp; Merrimack Coll; Bnkng.

THOMAS, GENA M; Northampton HS; Northampton, MA; (Y); Aud/Vis; Church Yth Grp; Cmnty Wkr; Drama Clb; Girl Scts; Thesps; Chorus; Church Choir; School Musical; School Play; Anna Maria; Chld Psych.

THOMAS, GREGORY SCOTT; Technical HS; Indian Orchard, MA; (Y); Aud/Vis; Pres JA; ROTC; Color Guard; Drill Tm; Drm & Bgl; Yrbk Stf; Stu Cncl; JV Bsbl; Hon Roll; Comp Sci.

THOMAS, JANINE; Norfolk County Agricultural HS; South Weymouth, MA; (S); FFA; Yrbk Stf; Var Bsktbl; Var Vllybl; Hon Roll; Pres Frsh Cls; Sec Soph Cls; Pres Jr Cls; Pres Sr Cls; Rep Stu Cncl; FFA Star Chp Grnhnd 81, Bayst Dgr, Pub Spkng Awds 83; Mst Valu Bsktbl; Iowa U; Agri.

THOMAS, KRISTIN; Matignon HS; Medford, MA; (Y); VP Church Yth Grp; Dance Clb; Hosp Aide; Cheerleading; 1st Somerville Rec Sfbl 84; Cert Of Prog Partcptn 85; St Anslems Clg; Psych.

THOMAS, LINDA SUE; Silver Lake Regional HS; W Wareham, MA; (Y); 7/422; Drama Clb; Key Clb; Political Wkr; Chorus; VP Frsh Cls; Stu Cncl; High Hon Roll; NHS; Ntl Merit Ltr; Page US House Reps 84; Emhart Schlrshp 85; Halifax PTA Schlrshp 85; American U; Librl Arts.

THOMAS, LISA; Mount Saint Joseph Acad; Brighton, MA; (Y); 31/127; Church Yth Grp; Cmnty Wkr; Dance Clb; Drama Clb; Hosp Aide; Latin Clb; Red Cross Aide; Ski Clb; Variety Show; Swmmng; Southeastern MA U; Bus Mgt.

THOMAS, MARK; Silver Lake Reigonal HS; Kingston, MA; (Y); Cmnty Wkr; Computer Clb; Library Aide; Political Wkr; Ski Clb; Spanish Clb; Teachers Aide; Stat Bsktbl; JV Socr; L Wrstlng; Comp Sci.

THOMAS, MICHAEL; Taunton HS; Taunton, MA; (Y); 14/410; Computer Clb; JCL; Latin Clb; Math Tm; Ski Clb; Lit Mag; Taunton Ed Assn Schlrshp 85; Ntl JR Clscl League Key Awd 85; Mildred Atwell Awd For Exc In Latin; J MA Amherst; Orthpdc Srgrn.

THOMAS, REBEKAH; Winthrop HS; Winthrop, MA; (Y); 8/217; Math Clb; Science Clb; Teachers Aide; Temple Yth Grp; Church Choir; School Musical; Yrbk Stf; Mgr JV Bsktbl; Hon Roll; NHS; Jdg Chrls A Rome Awd-Excllnc Rlgious Stds 84; Awd Merit Outstndng Achvt 84; Bus.

THOMAS, RICHARD E; Springfield Technical HS; Springfield, MA; (Y); Am Leg Boys St; Pres Church Yth Grp; CAP; JA; ROTC; Color Guard; Capt Drill Tm; Wrstlng; Hon Roll; Ntl Merit SF; Cert Drftng Recomm 84-85; Hse Repr Ofcl Citation, Outstndng Cadet Yr Cvln Patrol 83; U MA; Frstry.

THOMAS, SUSAN; Boston Latin HS; Boston, MA; (Y); 42/320; Sec Church Yth Grp; Latin Clb; Ski Clb; Variety Show; High Hon Roll; Sec NHS; Ntl Creek Ex Awd 85; Readng Lang Arts Cert 85; Ed.

THOMEN, REBECCA; Monument Mountain HS; Gt Barr, MA; (S); Hon Roll; Army.

THOMPSON, CHRIS; Westwood HS; Westwood, MA; (Y); Aud/Vis; Cmnty Wkr; Ski Clb; Varsity Clb; Variety Show; JV Ice Hcky; Var L Socr; Hon Roll; Silver Mdl Ski Comp; Semi-Fnlst ST Sccr Trnmnt 84; Bus.

THOMPSON, CHRISTOPHER P; Marblehead HS; Marblehead, MA; (Y); 96/259; Band; Concert Band; Mrchg Band; Variety Show; Ed Yrbk Stf; Sec Soph Cls; Trs Sr Cls; Capt Var Trk; Ski Clb; JV Socr.

THOMPSON, JOSEPH; Bay Pathh Regional Voc Tech HS; Oxford, MA; (S); 6/244; Library Aide; Mgr Bsktbl; Score Keeper; Var Socr; Hon Roll; NHS; Prfct Atten Awd; Voc Crfts Cmmtt 84; USSF Sccr Ref 83; Sccr-Thon MD 83-84; Mech Engr.

THOMPSON, MICHAEL J; Mansfield HS; Mansfield, MA; (Y); 22/176; Hon Roll; Ctzns Schlrshp Fdntn 84-85; Pres Acad Fitnss Awd 84-85; Fred L Doolittle Schlrshp Awd 84-85; Bryant Coll; Comp Inf Sys.

THOMPSON, SARA; Groton-Dunstable Regional Sec Schl; Dunstable, MA; (Y); Ski Clb; JV Cheerleading; Hon Roll; Shrthnd Excel 85; Lowell.

THOMPSON, SHAUNA; Groton-Dunstable Regnl Secndry HS; Groton, MA; (Y); Ski Clb; Crs Cntry; Hon Roll; U Of ME; Bus.

THOMPSON, SHAUNA; Hamilton Wenham Reg HS; S Hamilton, MA; (Y); Fld Hcky; Hon Roll; MA U; Art Educ.

THOMPSON, SUSAN; Georgetown HS; Georgetown, MA; (Y); Church Yth Grp; Drama Clb; Spanish Clb; Band; Pres Concert Band; Jazz Band; Mrchg Band; Hon Roll; Outstndg Achvt Typng I 84; Pre-Elem Educ.

THOMPSON, WILLIAM; Fitchburg HS; Fitchburg, MA; (Y); Am Leg Boys St; Bsbl; Ftbl; Trk; High Hon Roll; Centrl MA Conf-All Conf Dfnsv Tckle; Engrng.

THOMSON, JEFFREY M; Lynn English HS; Lynn, MA; (Y); 13/400; Am Leg Boys St; Drama Clb; Teachers Aide; Concert Band; Mrchg Band; School Musical; School Play; High Hon Roll; NHS; Prfct Atten Awd; James W O Brien Schlrshp 85; S Essex Med Aux Sci Bk Awd 85; Boston Coll; Mgmt.

THOMSON, RONALD; Reading Memorial HS; Reading, MA; (Y); Cmnty Wkr; Library Aide; Hon Roll; Ntl Merit Ltr; Film.

THONG, JULIE; Rockland HS; Rockland, MA; (S); 12/275; AFS; High Hon Roll; Hon Roll; NHS; Eng Achvt Awd 83-84; Sci Outstndg Coop & Accomplshmnt Awd 82-83; Northeastern U; Bus.

THONG, YOEUN; South Boston HS; Brighton, MA; (S); Dance Clb; Swmmng; Tennis; Vllybl; NHS; Prfct Atten 83-84; Dstrbtv Ed Clb Amer 83-84; Bus.

THORNDIKE JR, C JOHN; Boston College HS; Abington, MA; (Y); 60/292; JV Ftbl; Var Trk; Hon Roll; Ntl Merit Ltr.

THORP, MICHELE; Hingham HS; Hingham, MA; (Y); 42/329; Church Yth Grp; FCA; Yrbk Stf; Var L Lcrss; Var L Socr; Hon Roll; NCTE Wrtg Cntst 84-85; Outstndng Wrtr 83-84; Old Colony Leag Sccr All Str 84-85.

THORPE JR, WILLIAM H; Algonquin Regional HS; Southborough, MA; (Y); 45/250; Boy Scts; Church Yth Grp; Computer Clb; Hon Roll; Ntl Merit Ltr; Eagle Scout Boy Scouts 84; Comp Sci.

THRASHER, MARY; North Middlesex Regional HS; W Townsend, MA; (Y); VP Church Yth Grp; Ski Clb; Nwsp Stf; Yrbk Stf; Crs Cntry; Hon Roll; Prfct Atten Awd; :Chiropractic.

TIBBETTS, GARY; Monument Mountain Reg HS; W Stockbridge, MA; (Y); 18/113; Socr; Hon Roll; Indstrl Arts Achv Awd 84; Bus.

TIBBETTS, JOHN; Wakefield HS; Wakefield, MA; (Y); Church Yth Grp; Var Bsbl; Coach Actv; Var L Ftbl; U Of HI Hilo; Bus Mgt.

TIBERI, JOCELYN; Everett HS; Everett, MA; (Y); 1/260; Cmnty Wkr; Dance Clb; Pres Intnl Clb; Key Clb; Library Aide; Office Aide; Political Wkr; Quiz Bowl; Scholastic Bowl; High Hon Roll; Brown Book Awd 84; Best Of Class 85; Wellesley Coll; Political Sci.

TIERNEY, CHRISTINE; Marion HS; Framingham, MA; (Y); 22/177; Hosp Aide; Political Wkr; Chorus; Church Choir; School Musical; Crs Cntry; Trk; Hon Roll; NHS; Sec Legn Of Mary Clb; 1st & 3rd Pl Schl Cndy Dr 82-83; Lang Clb.

TIERNEY, MATTHEW; Matignon HS; Cambridge, MA; (Y); 29/185; Off Frsh Cls; Var Capt Crs Cntry; Var Capt Trk; French Hon Soc; Hon Roll; Natl Hnr Rll 85.

TIGHE, SUSAN; Grafton Memorial SR HS; N Grafton, MA; (Y); 12/130; VP Church Yth Grp; Band; Concert Band; Yrbk Stf; Var L Fld Hcky; Var L Score Keeper; Var L Sftbl; Hon Roll; Sec NHS; Pres Schlr; Cmmnwlth MA Schlr 85; U S Army Rsrv Ntl Schlr/Athlt Awd 85; Grtr Media Cable Athlt Wk 85; Bentley Coll; Bus Mgmt.

TILGHMAN, JENNIFER F; Andover HS; Andover, MA; (Y); 2/425; Var Swmmng; Model UN; Pep Clb; Acpl Chr; Chorus; School Play; French Hon Soc; High Hon Roll; NHS; Ntl Merit SF; Dartmouth Book Awd 84; Coll; Geology.

TILLOTSON, LISA E; Grafton HS; Grafton, MA; (Y); Cmnty Wkr; Teachers Aide; Nwsp Phtg; Yrbk Stf; Var JV Bsktbl; Var Crs Cntry; Var JV Fld Hcky; Var Trk; Hon Roll; Art Clb; Acdmc Ltr 83-84; Tp 20 In Mss Amer Coed Pgnt 85; Accntng.

TILLOTSON, MARY; Chicopee Comprehensive HS; Chicopee, MA; (Y); 6/300; Am Leg Aux Girls St; Spanish Clb; Yrbk Rptr; Yrbk Stf; Sec Soph Cls; Sec Jr Cls; Sec Sr Cls; Stu Cncl; Powder Puff Ftbl; Var Capt Socr; Coaches Awd-Trk; Villanova U; Sci.

TILMAN, TERESSA; Bedford HS; Boston, MA; (Y); 53/213; Church Yth Grp; Library Aide; Office Aide; Ski Clb; Church Choir; Yrbk Stf; Mgr(s); Var L Trk; Hon Roll; Home Ec Hnr Awd; Law.

TILSON, WHITNEY R; Northfield Mount Hermon Schl; Northfield, MA; (Y); Cmnty Wkr; Radio Clb; Acpl Chr; Chorus; Rep Jr Cls; Rep Sr Cls; JV Bsktbl; Score Keeper; JV Socr; Var Tennis; Presdntl Clssrm Young Amercns 84.

TIMMER, ASHLEY; Newton South HS; Waban, MA; (Y); Model UN; Ed Nwsp Stf; Ed Yrbk Stf; French Clb; Hosp Aide; High Hon Roll; Hon Roll; Ntl Merit SF; Am Assoc Tchrs Frnch; Design.

TINGLEY, VINCENT J; Natick HS; Natick, MA; (Y); Church Yth Grp; Teachers Aide; Band; Mrchg Band; Sec Stu Cncl; Elec.

TINO, VINCENT; St Dominic Savio HS; E Boston, MA; (S); 2/106; Key Clb; Stat Bsktbl; JV Crs Cntry; JV Trk; High Hon Roll; Hon Roll; Sec NHS; NEDT Awd; Prfct Atten Awd; Metrlgy.

TOAL, MICHAEL; Apponequet Regional HS; Assonet, MA; (Y); Swmmng; Sthestrn MA U; Engrng Tech.

TOBIASON, JENNIFER L; Winchester HS; Winchester, MA; (Y); 6/284; Church Yth Grp; French Clb; Latin Clb; Flag Corp; French Hon Soc; High Hon Roll; Hon Roll; Williams Coll Bk Awd 85; Natl Latin Exam Gold Mdl 85; Lttr 2 Yrs In Flag Corps 85.

TOBIN, ALANA A; Billerica Memorial HS; Billerica, MA; (Y); 49/411; Badmtn; Powder Puff Ftbl; JV Sftbl; High Hon Roll; Hon Roll; U Of Lowell; Acctg.

TOBIN, KELLY; St Clement HS; Somerville, MA; (Y); Hon Roll; NHS; Hgst Avg Bus,Math,Typng,Relgn 85; Comm Arts.

TOBIN, MARK J; Weymouth North HS; Weymouth, MA; (Y); 6/356; Math Tm; High Hon Roll; NHS; Elec Engr.

TOCCI, LYNDA E; Leominster HS; Leominster, MA; (S); 33/240; Political Wkr; Ski Clb; VP Stu Cncl; Var Crs Cntry; Var Capt Fld Hcky; JV Var Trk; Hon Roll; Lawyer.

TOCCI, WENDY; Archbishop Williams HS; Braintree, MA; (Y); Camera Clb; FNA; Girl Scts; Yrbk Stf; Hon Roll; Math Awd 84.

TODD, DEBORAH A; Everett HS; Everett, MA; (Y); Key Clb; NHS; PTA Schlrshp Awd 85; Lois & Lillian Daniele Schlrshp Awd 85; Comp.

TODRES, JONATHAN; Dennis Yarmouth Regional HS; South Yarmouth, MA; (Y); Am Leg Boys St; Nwsp Stf; Im Bsktbl; JV Crs Cntry; JV Trk; High Hon Roll; Hon Roll; NHS; Grad MA Adv Studies Pgm 85; Williams Coll Bk Awd 85; Psych.

TOLIOS, CONSTANTIA; Haverhill HS; Bradford, MA; (Y); 5/400; Church Yth Grp; Latin Clb; Spanish Clb; Nwsp Stf; Yrbk Stf; Trs Soph Cls; Rep Jr Cls; High Hon Roll; Pres NHS; Spnsh Poetry Rdng Wnnr, Stu Cncl Awd 84; Stu Cncl Awd Sci 83; Pol Sci.

TOLLEFSON, REBECCA R; Thayer Acad; Hull, MA; (Y); Chorus; School Play; Ed Lit Mag; Cheerleading; Crs Cntry; High Hon Roll; Ntl Merit SF; Curtn Call Thtr Awd 84; Bio.

TOLOCZKO, JOSEPH; St Peter Marian C C HS; Worcester, MA; (S); 8/177; Church Yth Grp; Nwsp Rptr; Nwsp Stf; JV Var Bsktbl; Ftbl; Vllybl; NHS; St Josephs Coll Schlrshp 85; Syracuse U Schlrshp 85; Vrsty Bsktbl Sprtsmnshp Awd 84-85; St Josephs Coll; Comm.

TOLPA, CHRIS ANN; Chicopee Comprehensive HS; Chicopee, MA; (Y); School Play; Stage Crew; Yrbk Stf; High Hon Roll; Hon Roll; NHS; U MA; Int Desgn.

TOMLINSON, LISA; Bartlett HS; Webster, MA; (Y); Church Yth Grp; French Clb; Pep Clb; Red Cross Aide; Var L Socr; Trk; French Hon Soc; High Hon Roll; Hon Roll; Real Est.

TOMLINSON, MARK; West Springfield HS; W Springfield, MA; (S); Computer Clb; Concert Band; Jazz Band; Mrchg Band; School Musical; High Hon Roll; NHS; Amer Mus Fndtn Band Hnrs 83; Outstng Musnshp 84-85.

TOMSU, DANIELLE; Holy Name Central Catholic HS; Sulton, MA; (Y); 25/269; Church Yth Grp; English Clb; 4-H; Quiz Bowl; God Cntry Awd; High Hon Roll; Hon Roll; Acctng Hon Cert 85; Natl Sci Olympd Bio 3rd Pl 83-84; Equestrian Awds 81-85; Acctng.

TONER, ROBERT; Matignon HS; Cambridge, MA; (S); 10/179; Concert Band; Nwsp Bus Mgr; Rep Stu Cncl; French Hon Soc; Hon Roll; NHS; Broadcstng.

TONG, GREGG; Newton South HS; Newton Centre, MA; (Y); Stage Crew; Rep Jr Cls; JV Socr; Hon Roll; Ltr Of Rcgntn From Schl Faculty 84/85; Pilot.

TONINI, CARMEN D; Monument Mountain Regional HS; W Stockbridge, MA; (Y); 48/128; Hosp Aide; Intnl Clb; Yrbk Stf; JV Socr; Var Trk; Lion Awd; Boy Scts; Exploring; Pep Clb; Yrbk Stf; Schlstc Art Awd 85; Hillcrest Hosp Schlrshp 85; West Stockbridge Wmns Auxiliary Fire Dept 85; Albany Med Ctr Schl/Nrsng; RN.

TOOLE, TIM; North Attleboro HS; N Attleboro, MA; (Y); Church Yth Grp; Civic Clb; Y-Teens; JV Bsbl; JV Bsktbl; Var Crs Cntry; Var Golf; Var Trk; High Hon Roll; Bus.

TOOMEY, CHRISTOPHER; Arlington Catholic HS; Medford, MA; (Y); 24/150; Church Yth Grp; French Clb; JA; Latin Clb; Political Wkr; Thesps; Rep Frsh Cls; Rep Soph Cls; Rep Jr Cls; Rep Sr Cls; Dartmouth Clb Bk Awd 85; Natl Latin Exam Magna Cum Laude 84; Pol Sci.

TOROSYAN, ROBEN; Peabody HS; W Peabody, MA; (Y); 15/560; Drama Clb; French Clb; Science Clb; Concert Band; Jazz Band; Stage Crew; Stu Cncl; Var Swmmng; High Hon Roll; NHS; Cornell U; Arch.

TORRES, MELISSA; Apponequet Reg HS; Assonet, MA; (Y); Church Yth Grp; Rep Frsh Cls; Rep Soph Cls; Rep Jr Cls; High Hon Roll; Pres NHS; Hon Roll; Schl Comm Awd 83; Proj Excel SMU 83; Intl Rel.

TORREY, THERESA; Silver Lake Regional HS; Kingston, MA; (Y); French Clb; Office Aide; Spanish Clb; Yrbk Stf; Bus Mgt.

TOTH, MICHELLE; Weymouth S HS; S Weymouth, MA; (Y); Church Yth Grp; Pres Frsh Cls; Pres Jr Cls; Var JV Cheerleading; Coach Actv; High Hon Roll; Hon Roll; Simmons Coll; Bus Admin.

TOUGAS, COLETTE J; Duxbury HS; Greenharbor, MA; (Y); 5/247; Teachers Aide; High Hon Roll; Hon Roll; Acad Achvt Awd 85; Equestrian Comptns Awds 80-83; Grad Barbizon Modlng Schl, Prfct Atten 84; Wheaton Coll; Psych.

TOUSIGNANT, MIKE; Tri-County Reg Vo-Tech; Attleboro, MA; (Y); Church Yth Grp; Rep Frsh Cls; Rep Soph Cls; Rep Jr Cls; Rep Sr Cls; Var Bsbl; VICA Comptn 84; New England Tech; Tool & Die.

TOUSSAINT, JASON R; Beverly HS; Beverly, MA; (Y); Computer Clb; Math Tm; Political Wkr; Science Clb; Ski Clb; Nwsp Rptr; JV Var Ftbl; Var Golf; Var Lcrss; Im Wt Lftg; Pre-Med.

TOWERS, DANIEL; Westford Acad; Westford, MA; (Y); Boy Scts; Trs Exploring; Band; Socr; Trk; High Hon Roll; Hon Roll; NHS; Engnrng.

TOWNE, MICHELLE; Ayer HS; Shirley, MA; (Y); 34/160; Library Aide; Ski Clb; Yrbk Stf; Var Capt Cheerleading; Powder Puff Ftbl; Var Sftbl; Var Trk; Cit Awd; High Hon Roll; Hon Roll; Hmcmng Queen 84-85; Shirley Fire Dept Awd 85; Word Proc.

TOWNE, SHERRIE L; Classical HS; Springfield, MA; (Y); 13/396; Chorus; Sec Madrigals; Yrbk Stf; Tennis; High Hon Roll; Hon Roll; NHS; Pres Schlr; MMEA Wstrn Dstrct Chorus 84-85; MENC/MMEA All-State Shorus 85; U Of NH; Spnsh Tchr.

TRAFICANTE, DANIEL; Central Catholic HS; Methuen, MA; (Y); 60/260; Church Yth Grp; JA; Var Bsktbl; JV Ftbl; Im Vllybl; Hon Roll; Bus Mgmt.

TRAFICANTE, JOSEPH; Methuen HS; Methuen, MA; (Y); Am Leg Boys St; Cmnty Wkr; Computer Clb; Intnl Clb; Y-Teens; High Hon Roll; NHS; 2 Dplms Of Merit For Hghst GPA 82-81 & 84-85; Engrng.

TRAGHELLA, DEBBY; Tri-County HS; North Attleboro, MA; (Y); VICA; Rep Frsh Cls; Rep Jr Cls; Hon Roll; 1st Pl VICA Dist 84-85; Lab Tech.

TRAGHELLA, GREG; Tri-County Reg Voc; N Attleboro, MA; (Y); 1/230; Ski Clb; High Hon Roll; Hon Roll; Val; MA Cmmnwlth Schlr Grnt 85-86; Bstn Glb Schlstc Art Awd Hnrbl Mntns 84; John Lane Schlrshp Awd 85; Sthestrn MA U; Cmmrcl Art.

TRAINOR, DAVID P; St Johns HS; Fitchburg, MA; (Y); 13/266; Am Leg Boys St; Model UN; Spanish Clb; Im Bsktbl; JV Trk; Im Wt Lftg; High Hon Roll; NHS; Med.

TRAN, HIEP; Newton North HS; Newton, MA; (Y); Computer Clb; Intnl Clb; Math Tm; Nwsp Phtg; Bsktbl; Socr; Vllybl; Hon Roll; Prfct Atten Awd; Excel Alg I 83; Wentworth; Electcl Engrg.

TRAN, HUONG NGOC; Burncoat SR HS; Worcester, MA; (Y); #32 In Class; NHS; Becker JC; Word Proc Admin.

TRAN, KHIEM T; Clinton HS; Clinton, MA; (Y); Am Leg Boys St; Aud/Vis; Boy Scts; Camera Clb; Cmnty Wkr; French Clb; Intnl Clb; JA; Library Aide; Math Tm; Awd Compltn Hlth Career Prog U MA Med Ctr Boys ST 85; Natl Hnr CPR Cert 85; Socty Pin 85; Med.

TRANT, SHEILA; Westfield HS; Westfield, MA; (Y); 111/363; Church Yth Grp; Hosp Aide; Variety Show; Yrbk Stf; Var Bsktbl; JV Var Mat Maids; Var Trk; Bridgewater ST Coll.

TRASK, MICHAEL A; Xaverian Brothers HS; Randolph, MA; (S); 6/236; Sec Drama Clb; French Clb; School Musical; School Play; Nwsp Ed-Chief; Yrbk Stf; Ed Lit Mag; High Hon Roll; NCTE Awd; NHS; Xaverian Alumn Schlrshp; Wesleyan U CT; Engl.

TRAUBER, ROBERT S; Dover-Sherborn Regional HS; Brookline, MA; (Y); AFS; Am Leg Boys St; Exploring; Political Wkr; Stage Crew; Variety Show; Nwsp Rptr; Nwsp Stf; JV Bsktbl; Var Crs Cntry; Law Explrers VP & Co-Treas 84-85; SADD 84-85; Bus.

TRAVASSOS, ELIZABETH; Bishop Connolly HS; Somerset, MA; (Y); Latin Clb; Ski Clb; Cheerleading; Pom Pon; Trk; Spch Ther.

TRAVERS, AMY M; Hopedale JR SR HS; Hopedale, MA; (S); 1/58; Band; Chorus; Trs Stu Cncl; Var L Tennis; High Hon Roll; Acadmc Decthln Team 84.

TRAVIS, MARK W; Norwell HS; Norwell, MA; (Y); Am Leg Boys St; Aud/Vis; Church Yth Grp; Cmnty Wkr; Office Aide; Teachers Aide; School Play; Rep Soph Cls; Rep Sr Cls; Stu Cncl.

TRAVIS, ROBERT; Hingham HS; Hingham, MA; (Y); 79/342; JV Bsbl; Socr; Hon Roll; WPI; Elec Engrng.

TRAVNICEK, JULIE; Southbridge HS; Sbridge, MA; (Y); 6/155; Sec Church Yth Grp; Math Tm; Hon Roll; Lion Awd; NHS; Rep Frsh Cls; Rep Soph Cls; Rep Jr Cls; Var Trk; Bio.

TRAYNOR, LISA; Holyoke HS; Holyoke, MA; (Y); 17/380; Church Yth Grp; French Clb; Latin Clb; High Hon Roll; Hon Roll; Jr NHS; NHS; St Schlr; Bentley Coll.

TRCZCINSKI, PAUL; Christopher Columbus HS; Dorchester, MA; (S); Chess Clb; Cvl Engr.

TREADUP, ANNE MARIE; Bishop Stang HS; New Bedford, MA; (S); 1/220; GAA; Yrbk Stf; Rep Jr Cls; Var Bsktbl; Var Sftbl; Var Vllybl; High Hon Roll; NHS; Ntl Merit Ltr; Hugh O Brian Yth Fndtn Ldrshp Semnr 84; Med.

TREANOR, SHEILA; Girls Catholic HS; Malden, MA; (S); 4/35; Art Clb; Drama Clb; Political Wkr; Yrbk Stf; Sec Chrmn Stu Cncl; Stnt Gov Day Rep 84.

TREEN, ERIN; Bishop Feehan HS; Attleboro, MA; (Y); 45/254; Church Yth Grp; Hosp Aide; French Hon Soc; NHS; Ski Clb; Elks Awd; High Hon Roll; Arch.

TREMBA, STEPHANIE; Holy Name HS; Shrewsbury, MA; (Y); 37/272; Pep Clb; School Musical; Yrbk Stf; Hon Roll; Lit, Histrn & Comm Awds; Mrktng.

TREMBLAY, DAVID A; Old Rochester Regional HS; Marion, MA; (Y); 4/150; Am Leg Boys St; Math Tm; Ski Clb; Nwsp Stf; L Socr; Hon Roll; NHS; Harvard Book Awd 85; Engrng.

TREMBLAY, JILL M; Cathedral HS; Springfield, MA; (Y); 75/519; Intnl Clb; VP Jr Cls; Pres Stu Cncl; Hon Roll; Jr NHS; Springfield Colleen & Ct 85; Frnch Poetry Cntst-1st Prz 85; Commnty Cncl Chrprsn 85; Fnnc.

TREMBLAY, JOYCE; Melrose HS; Melrose, MA; (Y); 45/367; GAA; Y-Teens; L Swmmng; Hon Roll; NHS; Exploring; Pep Clb; Orch; Timer; Trk; Melrose-Wkfld Hosp Swmmng Awd 84; NE YMCA Ldr Schl Hnr Bowl Awd 84; YMCA Swmmng Natl Comp 83-84; Hlth Sci.

TREMBLAY, MICHELLE; Montachusett RVTS; Fitchburg, MA; (Y); Pres Church Yth Grp; Sec VICA; Sec Frsh Cls; Sec Soph Cls; Capt Cheerleading; L Crs Cntry; High Hon Roll; Hon Roll; NHS; Prfct Atten Awd; Most Outstndng Med Asst Stu 85; Med.

TREMBLAY, SCOTT; Newbedford HS; New Bedford, MA; (Y); 190/600; Drama Clb; Teachers Aide; Stage Crew; Var Bsbl; Bsktbl; Var Capt Ftbl; Wt Lftg; Hon Roll; Teenrs Lge All Star Bsbl 84; Tri-Capt Ftbl Tm 85; Plyd For Nwbdfrd Amer Lgn Tm; Crim Just.

TREMBLAY, TRACI; Hamilton-Wenham Regional HS; S Hamilton, MA; (Y); 9/190; Church Yth Grp; Yrbk Stf; Var L Fld Hcky; Mgr(s); Im Sftbl; High Hon Roll; Hon Roll; NHS; Frgn Lang & Pres Acadmc Ftns Awds; Boston Coll; Mngmnt.

TRIANT, DEBORAH; Everett HS; Everett, MA; (Y); Church Yth Grp; Sec Key Clb; Letterman Clb; Science Clb; Var Trk; High Hon Roll; NHS.

TRICKETT, LAURIE; Malden HS; Malden, MA; (Y); 18/440; Stage Crew; Variety Show; Yrbk Stf; Rep Frsh Cls; Rep Soph Cls; Trs Jr Cls; Hon Roll; Phi Delta Phi-Sorority; Ofc Worker; Dance Committee; Engrng.

TRICKETT, SEAN; Malden HS; Malden, MA; (Y); #112 In Class; Band; Mrchg Band; Schltc Art Recgntn Cert 85; GIA; Jewlry Dsgn.

TRIGGS, JENNIFER; Cathedral HS; Wilbraham, MA; (Y); Hosp Aide; Library Aide; Red Cross Aide; Sec Frsh Cls; Nrsng.

TRIMBLE, RANSOM D; Cambridge Pilot Schl; Cambridge, MA; (Y); 24/510; NHS; Pilot Schl Scholar 85; Dollars For Schlrs Scholar 85; Cambridge Rindge & Latin Bicycling Clb 84; Northeastern U; Mech Engrng.

TRINGALE, DAVID; Malden Catholic HS; Everett, MA; (Y); Church Yth Grp; Frsh Cls; Stu Cncl; Var Socr; Var Capt Trk; Hon Roll; Lion Awd; Outstndng Dtrmntn In Indr Track 85; Lions Clb Stu Athlt Awd 85; Stonehill Coll; Hstry.

TRIONFI, ANGELA; Revere HS; Revere, MA; (Y); Office Aide; Yrbk Stf; Rep Soph Cls; Sec Jr Cls; Rep Stu Cncl; JV Fld Hcky; JV Score Keeper; Hon Roll; Johnson & Wales Coll; Arts.

TRIPOLI, MARIA; Bishop Fenwick HS; Peabody, MA; (Y); 22/250; Hosp Aide; JV Sftbl; High Hon Roll; NHS; Prfct Atten Awd.

TRIPP, CARY; Old Rochester Regional HS; Mattapoisett, MA; (Y); 2/103; Sec AFS; Am Leg Aux Girls St; Soph Cls; Jr Cls; Sr Cls; Rep Stu Cncl; JV Sftbl; High Hon Roll; Sec NHS; Clss Pres 86; Law.

TRIPP, CHRISTOPHER; New Bedford HS; Acushnet, MA; (Y); JA; JCL; ROTC; Yrbk Stf; High Hon Roll; NHS; Ntl Merit Ltr; Yth Ldrshp Conf 85; Natl Latn Exm Slvr Medl 84; Astrphyscs.

TROIANI, ALLISON; Westwood HS; Westwood, MA; (Y); Hosp Aide; Var L Swmmng; Camp Fr Inc; Church Yth Grp; Drama Clb; Pep Clb; Chorus; Stage Crew; JV Diving; Im Gym; Stone Hill; Acctng.

TROIANO, TIMOTHY; Newton North HS; Newton, MA; (Y); Am Leg Boys St; Boy Scts; Church Yth Grp; Teachers Aide; Orch; School Musical; Stu Cncl; Var Crs Cntry; JV Capt Lcrss; Var Capt Swmmng; Outstndng Athl 83; Swmmng High Pt Awd 84-85; Suburbn Leag All Star-Swmmng 85; Phys Thrpy.

TRONGONE, TRACEY; Clinton HS; Clinton, MA; (Y); 10/126; Drama Clb; Pres Intnl Clb; Ed Yrbk Stf; Capt Vllybl; Hon Roll; NHS; Voice Dem Awd; Lion Awd; VFW Awd; Lions Club & VFW Ortrcl Comps 84-85; Exch Club Yth Mnth 85; MA Hse Reps Offcl Citn Ortrcl Achvt 85; U Of MA-AMHERST; Frnch.

TROTTO, TIM; St Johns HS; Shrewsbury, MA; (Y); 148/272; Ski Clb; Ftbl; Trk; Wt Lftg; Hon Roll; Rochester Inst Of Tech; Mch Eng.

TRUDEAU, GUY; Saint Johns HS; W Boylston, MA; (Y); 204/269; Boy Scts; French Clb; Pep Clb; Church Choir; Rep Jr Cls; JV Socr; Var Hon Roll; U Of MA Lowell/Chem Engr.

TRUDEAU, MATTHEW J; Quaboag Regional HS; W Brookfield, MA; (Y); 19/95; Church Yth Grp; Drama Clb; Latin Clb; Spanish Clb; Chorus; Church Choir; Yrbk Bus Mgr; Yrbk Phtg; Hon Roll; NHS.

TRUDEAU, WILLIAM O; Fast Longmeadow HS; East Longmeadow, MA; (Y); 70/212; Am Leg Boys St; Pres Soph Cls; Pres Jr Cls; Pres Sr Cls; Stu Cncl; Capt L Swmmng; Hon Roll; Boy Scts; Band; Yrbk Stf; Stu Advsry Cncl Schl Cmmte; Dely Stu Advsry Cncl ST Brd Ed; Civitan Clb; Engrng.

TRUEIRA, CYNTHIA; Danvers HS; Danvers, MA; (Y); 34/300; 4-H; Band; Concert Band; Mrchg Band; Bsktbl; Hon Roll; NHS.

TRUESDALE, JENNIFER; Arlington HS; Arlington, MA; (Y); Drama Clb; Radio Clb; Chorus; Madrigals; School Musical; School Play; Stage Crew; Swing Chorus; Fld Hcky; Hon Roll; Arlington Frnds Of Drama Awd 85-86; Music.

TRUONG, DU MY; Charleston HS; Brighton, MA; (Y); Hon Roll.

TRUONG, TOAN; Boston Latin HS; Boston, MA; (Y); 149/326; Boy Scts; Pres JA; Concert Band; Drm Mjr(t); Rep Stu Cncl; JV Bsbl; Var Crs Cntry; Var JV Socr; Vllybl; Hon Roll; Musicl Band Tours 83-85; Boston U; Med Doctr.

TRZCINSKI, PAUL; Christopher Columbus HS; Dorchester, MA; (Y); Political Wkr; Hon Roll; Civil Engrng.

TSIRIGOTIS, PETROS; Bishop Guertin HS; Lowell, MA; (Y); Church Yth Grp; Nwsp Bus Mgr; Hon Roll; Harvard; Econ.

TSITOS, ANDREAS; Malden Catholic HS; Malden, MA; (Y); 62/184; Bus.

TUBEROSA, MICHAEL; Silver Lake Regional HS; Kingston, MA; (Y); Cmnty Wkr; Latin Clb; Nwsp Rptr; Im Stat Bsktbl; Hon Roll; Brdcstng.

TUERCK, JOHN; Braintree HS; Braintree, MA; (Y); 8/481; French Clb; Orch; Var L Tennis; High Hon Roll; NHS; Ntl Merit Ltr; Opt Clb Awd; US Al-Estrn Orchstr 85; 5th Chr Al-ST Orchstr 85; Tanglewood Inst Music Acptnc 84; Tufts U.

TUFFIN, AMALIE; Acton Boxborough Regional HS; Acton, MA; (Y); 18/354; Drama Clb; Stage Crew; Nwsp Stf; Off Jr Cls; Hon Roll; NHS; NHS; Ntl Merit SF; Intnl Clb; PAVAS; Spanish III Hnrs Achvt Cert; TV Panelist Young Editors Show; Soviet Studies.

TUFTS, MARA; Marblehead HS; Marblehead, MA; (Y); 77/388; Dance Clb; Teachers Aide; Yrbk Stf; Rep Sr Cls; Rep Stu Cncl; Powder Puff Ftbl; Trk; Hon Roll.

TULLY, CYNDI; Woburn HS; Woburn, MA; (S); 10/530; Boys Clb Am; Church Yth Grp; Cmnty Wkr; GAA; Intnl Clb; Leo Clb; Math Clb; Math Tm; Science Clb; Ski Clb; Woburn Womans Clb Hnrd Guest 85; Hist Essay Awd Wnnr 84; Bowdoin Coll; Intl Bus.

TULLY, DONNA; Groton Dunstable Rgnl Secondry Schl; Dunstable, MA; (Y); 4-H; Hosp Aide.

TUNEWICZ, LORI-ANN; Bridgewater-Raynham Reg HS; Bridgewater, MA; (Y); 52/350; 4-H; Girl Scts; Ski Clb; Yrbk Stf; Var Fld Hcky; Trk; Vrsty Ler & Jckt Awd Fld Hcky 85; Bridgewater ST; Soc Wrk.

TURCOTTE, ELAINE; Bishop Connolly HS; Fall River, MA; (S); 4/158; Art Clb; Coach Actv; Mgr Drama Clb; French Clb; Pres JA; Math Tm; Church Choir; School Play; Variety Show; Yrbk Bus Mgr; Century III Ldrs Schlrshp 85; Carl S Ell Pres Schlrshp 85; Elks Teenager Mnth Oct 84; NE U; Elec Engr.

TURCOTTE, JAYNE; Attleboro HS; Attleboro, MA; (Y); Mrchg Band; Powder Puff Ftbl; L Swmmng; Tennis; High Hon Roll; Trs NHS; Ntl Merit SF; NEDT Awd; Engr.

TUREK, TODD; Ware HS; Ware, MA; (Y); Spanish Clb; Bsbl; NHS; Spanish NHS; Law Enfrcmnt.

TURMENNE, LISA; Classical HS; Lynn, MA; (Y); Aud/Vis; Chorus; Drm & Bgl; Yrbk Stf; Bowling; Hon Roll; NHS; Exploring; Library Aide; Pep Clb; Phsy Thrpy.

TURNER, CLEM; Deerfield Acad; Queens Village, NY; (Y); Church Yth Grp; Computer Clb; Debate Tm; Model UN; Radio Clb; JV Ftbl; JV Trk; Hon Roll; Civic Clb; Im Bsktbl; Law.

TURNER, ELIZABETH ANN; Nashoba Regional HS; Lancaster, MA; (Y); Var Capt Cheerleading; Var Tennis; Mst Valuable Contributor Chrldng 84; U Of RI; Mrktng.

TURNER, JEFFREY B; Oxford HS; Oxford, MA; (Y); 2/152; Am Leg Boys St; VP Math Tm; VP Band; Jazz Band; Variety Show; Var Trk; High Hon Roll; NHS; MA Lions Al-ST Bnd 85; Ntl Sci Olympiad Physcs Tm 2nd Pl Schl 85; Cls Rng Cmte 84; Sci.

TURNER, JOSEPH F; Weymouth Vocational Techncial HS; Weymouth, MA; (Y); Am Leg Boys St; Art Clb; Debate Tm; FBLA; Intnl Clb; JA; OEA; Political Wkr; Varsity Clb; VICA; Hnr Rl; Wentworth; Arch.

TURNER, MICHAEL; St Dominic Savio HS; S Boston, MA; (Y); Boys Clb Am; Chess Clb; Church Yth Grp; Cmnty Wkr; Lit Mag; Rep Frsh Cls; Bsbl; Bsktbl; Ice Hcky; High Hon Roll; Lit.

TURNER, TIMOTHY J; Norwood HS; Norwood, MA; (Y); 35/367; Church Yth Grp; Math Clb; Political Wkr; Varsity Clb; Rep Jr Cls; Trs Sr Cls; Capt Ftbl; Wrstlng; High Hon Roll; Comp Sci.

TUTTLE, ANNE; Norwell HS; Norwell, MA; (Y); 1/174; AFS; Drama Clb; Pres Latin Clb; Band; Yrbk Ed-Chief; Rep Stu Cncl; L Var Trk; High Hon Roll; NHS; Ntl Merit Ltr; Dartmouth Club Bk Awd 84-85; Rep MASC 84-85.

TWIGG, MICHELE; Wellesley HS; Wellesley, MA; (Y); 8/284; AFS; Cmnty Wkr; French Clb; Intnl Clb; Key Clb; Band; Concert Band; Yrbk Phtg; Yrbk Stf; Pres Stu Cncl; Med.

TWORIG, MICHELLE; Drury HS; N Adams, MA; (Y); Am Leg Aux Girls St; French Clb; Sec Frsh Cls; VP Soph Cls; Trs Sr Cls; JV Sftbl; Capt Swmmng; Var Tennis; High Hon Roll; NHS; Pre Med.

TYER III, VINCENT D; Bedford HS; Bedford, MA; (Y); 31/213; Bsbl; Ftbl; Wt Lftg; Hon Roll; Engrng.

UCHNEAT, MICHAEL S; Frontier Regional HS; Sunderland, MA; (Y); Var JV Bsbl; Var JV Bsktbl; High Hon Roll; Hon Roll; NHS; Peer Educ 84-85; Engrng.

UHLENDORF, KARL; Marthas Vineyard Regional HS; Vineyard Haven, MA; (Y); 21/117; Varsity Clb; Chorus; Madrigals; School Musical; School Play; Nwsp Stf; Yrbk Stf; Socr; L Tennis; Hon Roll; All ST Music Fest 85; Law.

ULLRICH, PETER; Deerfield Acad; Oceanside, NY; (Y); Aud/Vis; German Clb; Ski Clb; Spanish Clb; Band; School Play; JV Lcrss; Hon Roll.

ULRICH, JENNIFER; Lenox Memorial HS; Lenox, MA; (Y); Church Yth Grp; Chorus; Church Choir; Yrbk Stf; Rep Frsh Cls; High Hon Roll; Hon Roll; Jr NHS; Kiwanis Awd; Skin Ther.

UNDERWOOD, JAMES; South Hadley HS; S Hadley, MA; (Y); 84/188; Aud/Vis; JV Var Mgr(s); Arch Drftng.

UNDERWOOD, LYNN ANN; Chicopee HS; Chicopee, MA; (Y); 28/250; Art Clb; Church Yth Grp; Hosp Aide; Red Cross Aide; Yrbk Stf; Crs Cntry; Swmmng; Trk; NHS; Chicopee Bus & Prfsnl Womens Schlrshp 85; RI Schl Dsgn; Graph Dsgn.

UNNI, PAUL; North Reading HS; N Reding, MA; (Y); Chorus; Color Guard; Concert Band; Drm & Bgl; Jazz Band; Mrchg Band; School Musical; School Play; Nwsp Stf; Yrbk Stf; Psych.

UNWIN, DONNA; Silver Lake Regional HS; Halifax, MA; (Y); 15/424; French Clb; Latin Clb; Math Clb; Fld Hcky; JV Trk; Hon Roll; NHS; Ntl Merit Ltr; Rotary Awd; Providence Coll; Pre Engrng.

UPHAM, RANDALL; Reading Memorial HS; Reading, MA; (Y); Chess Clb; Computer Clb; German Clb; Math Tm; Band; Chorus; Church Choir; Rep Frsh Cls; Capt L Crs Cntry; L Trk; Comp Sci.

URAUHART, MATTHEW; Bedford HS; Bedford, MA; (Y); 90/214; Aud/Vis; Church Yth Grp; CAP; ROTC; Cert Partcptn Amer Wldrnss Ldrshp Schl 84; Fin.

URBAN, DAWN ANNE; Westport HS; Westport, MA; (Y); Girl Scts; School Play; Bsbl; Var Bsktbl; Var Sftbl; Tennis; JV Vllybl; Wt Lftg; Hon Roll; Plyd Piano 4 Yrs; Southeastern MA U; Med Tech.

URBANO, MARIA; Medway JR SR HS; Medway, MA; (Y); 27/160; Dance Clb; Teachers Aide; Lib Yrbk Stf; JV Socr; Hon Roll; Prfct Atten Awd; Pres Italian Club 82-83; Ring Dance Staff 83-84; Pedtrcn.

URBINA, DAVID; Umana Vo Tech; Jamaica Plain, MA; (Y); Intnl Clb; ROTC; Off Stu Cncl; Bsbl; Daniel Webster; Comm Pilot.

URMSTON, JOHN; Tahanto Reg HS; Boylston, MA; (Y); 3/49; JA; High Hon Roll; Hon Roll; NHS; U Of San Francisco; Trvl.

USALIS, INGA; Thayer Acad; Hanover, MA; (Y); 7/106; Church Yth Grp; GAA; Girl Scts; Ed Yrbk Phtg; Yrbk Stf; JV Var Fld Hcky; JV Var Lcrss; JV Var Mgr(s); High Hon Roll; Hon Roll; Spnsh II Excllnc Awd; Com Sci.

USALIS, KARLA; Thayer Acad; Hanover, MA; (Y); 1/106; Church Yth Grp; GAA; Girl Scts; Yrbk Stf; Lit Mag; L Bsktbl; L Fld Hcky; L Lcrss; High Hon Roll; JETS Awd; Rensslaer Polytech Inst Mdl Tp Math/Sci Hnrs; W Holbrook Schlrshp Excllnc 84-85; Cum Laud Soc 85; Sci.

USHAKOFF, NICOLE; Beverly HS; Beverly, MA; (Y); 8/385; Am Leg Aux Girls St; Pres Band; Jazz Band; NHS; German Clb; Concert Band; Mrchg Band; Stage Crew; Nwsp Bus Mgr; High Hon Roll; Dartmouth Bowl Awd 85; Band Bass-Line Awd 83-85; Natl Hnrs Blazr 84-85; Sls.

USTAS, BETH; Saugus HS; Saugus, MA; (Y); 15/300; Church Yth Grp; High Hon Roll; Hon Roll; Jr NHS; NHS; Ntl Merit Ltr; Pres Schlr; Presdntl Schlrshp 85; Partcptn Math Olympd Exm 85; Supr Acadmc Achv 82; Eckerd Coll FL; Pre-Med.

UTLEY, WENDY; Bedford HS; Bedford, MA; (Y); 9/241; Drama Clb; Band; Chorus; Jazz Band; Mrchg Band; School Musical; School Play; NHS; Stouffers Bedford Glen Hotel Schlrshp 85; Boston U.

UTTLEY, KRISTINE; North Andover HS; N Andover, MA; (Y); 42/241; Rep Frsh Cls; Rep Soph Cls; Rep Stu Cncl; Var Capt Bsktbl; Coach Actv; Golf; Swmmng; Var Capt Trk; Hon Roll; Full Athltc Schlrshp To Benley Coll 85; MVP-CAPE Ann Leag Bsktbl 85; Mbr New Englnd JR Olympcs 84-85; Bentley Coll.

UZDAVINIS, KAREN; Frontier Regional Schl; S Deerfield, MA; (Y); 12/76; Exploring; Pres French Clb; Nwsp Phtg; Yrbk Phtg; Lit Mag; Sec Jr Cls; Sec Sr Cls; Sec Stu Cncl; Stat Bsktbl; High Hon Roll; Stu Govt Day 85; Long Island U; Phtgrphy.

VAANANEN, ROXANNE; Fitchburg HS; Fitchburg, MA; (Y); 2/160; Sec Soph Cls; Sec Jr Cls; Var Crs Cntry; Var JV Trk; High Hon Roll; Hrvrd Bk Awd 85; Frnch & Geom Awds; Fitchburg Wmns Clb; Accntng.

VACCARO, PETER; Falmouth HS; W Falmouth, MA; (Y); Pres Latin Clb; Math Tm; Spanish Clb; Mrchg Band; VP Frsh Cls; VP Soph Cls; JV Var Ice Hcky; JV Var Socr; Hon Roll; VP Chess Clb; Lt Pafford Awd Wrtng 84.

VADALA, MARIE; Gloucester HS; Gloucester, MA; (S); Math Tm; Band; Concert Band; Off Mrchg Band; Nwsp Rptr; Nwsp Stf; Yrbk Stf; Rep Soph Cls; Hon Roll; Math Clb; Little League Volunteer 82-85; New England Scholastic Band Assoc 84-85; Business.

VAFIDES, JULIE; Hingham HS; Hingham, MA; (Y); 86/325; Church Yth Grp; Var JV Cheerleading; Im Fld Hcky; Hon Roll; Bus Mngmnt.

VAGOS, VIRGINIA; New Bedford HS; New Bedford, MA; (Y); Sec Intnl Clb; Pep Clb; Hon Roll; Southeastern MA U; Lang.

VAILLANCOURT, MARC; Diman Reg Voch Tech HS; Fall River, MA; (Y); Var Tennis; Air Force; Tele Comm Exprt.

VALANTE, MARY A; Notre Dame Acad; Hanover, MA; (Y); Church Yth Grp; Pres Girl Scts; Pres Spanish Clb; Band; Im Vllybl; High Hon Roll; NHS; Ntl Merit Ltr; Prfct Atten Awd; Spanish NHS; Marion Mdl GSA 83; 1st Cls GSA Awd 83; Freedom & Ldrshp Yth Cngrs Vly Forge 84-85.

VALCOURT, DAWN; Westport HS; Westport, MA; (Y); French Clb; VP JA; Var Sftbl; High Hon Roll; NHS; Pres Schlr; B W Taber Schlrshp, Engl Acad Awd 85; Bridgeater ST Coll; Psych.

VALENCOURT, MICHELLE; North Brookfield HS; N Brookfield, MA; (Y); Church Yth Grp; Computer Clb; Office Aide; Red Cross Aide; Spanish Clb; Yrbk Stf; Sec Jr Cls; Sec Sr Cls; Rep Stu Cncl; Var Cheerleading; Miss Chrldr Awd 85; Hnrbl Mntn Sci Fair 83-85; Child Psych.

VALENTGAS, HARRY; North HS; Worcester, MA; (Y); Varsity Clb; Var L Ftbl; Var L Tennis; Var L Trk; Hon Roll; Bentley Coll; Bus Mngmnt.

VALENTINE, TINA; Springfield Technical HS; Springfield, MA; (Y); VP JA; Stage Crew; Nwsp Ed-Chief; Mgr(s); Mgr Swmmng; Jr Ldrshp Inst 85; Exclnc Typg 85; Lithogrphr.

VALERIO, ELISHA A; Clinton HS; Clinton, MA; (Y); 24/130; Art Clb; Spanish Clb; High Hon Roll; Hon Roll.

VALLAS, KIM C; Falmouth HS; Falmouth, MA; (S); AFS; Drama Clb; Key Clb; Chorus; Madrigals; School Musical; School Play; Hon Roll; NHS; Perfrmg Arts Bst Actrss Awd 82; SE MA Dist SR H S Music Fest 84-85; MA AL ST Music Fest 85; Engrng.

VALLEE, JOSEPH; Joseph Case HS; Swansea, MA; (Y); 42/209; Band; Concert Band; Jazz Band; Mrchg Band; Pep Band; NEIT Tech Bk Awd, RCA Carer Schlrshp 85; New England Inst Tech; Comp Sci.

VALOIS, KATHERINE; Gardner HS; Gardner, MA; (Y); 8/178; Am Leg Aux Girls St; Church Yth Grp; French Clb; Chorus; Var L Trk; NHS; Ltr Commendatn PSAT Score 85.

VANASSE, ANDREW; Reading Memorial HS; Reading, MA; (Y); Church Yth Grp; JA; Trs Frsh Cls; Rep Soph Cls; Rep Jr Cls; Rep Stu Cncl; Bsktbl; Var JV Socr; Trk; French Hon Soc; New Englnd Math League Cert Of Merit 85; Engrng.

VANASSE, CATHERINE; Notre Dame Acad; Weymouth, MA; (Y); French Clb; Latin Clb; Office Aide; Ski Clb; Im Bsktbl; Var Gym; Score Keeper; Drama Clb; Hon Roll; Prfct Atten Awd; Cert Of Merit In Frnch Exam 85; Bus.

VANASSE, PHILIP; Boston College HS; Weymouth, MA; (Y); 6/273; Hosp Aide; Math Tm; Science Clb; Jazz Band; Im Bsktbl; Im Wt Lftg; High Hon Roll; NHS; Ntl Merit Ltr; Wilson Schlr U Of Rochester 85; NROTC Schlrshp 85; U Of Rochester; Astronmy.

VANCELETTE, THOMAS; Saint Marys HS; Worcester, MA; (Y); Church Yth Grp; Drama Clb; Latin Clb; Spanish Clb; School Musical; School Play; Stage Crew; Variety Show; Trs Soph Cls; Hon Roll; Assumpton Coll.

VANERIAN, SALLY S; Watertown HS; Watertown, MA; (Y); 3/310; Cmnty Wkr; Dance Clb; Hosp Aide; Quiz Bowl; Temple Yth Grp; Chorus; Nwsp Rptr; DAR Awd; High Hon Roll; NHS; Commonwlth MA Schlr Grant 85; Supt Awd 84; Trophy Acad Excllnce 85; MA Inst Tech; Bio.

VANHOOK, LEONORA; Leicester HS; Leicester, MA; (Y); Intnl Clb; 1st Pl Equire Expo & Art Shw 84-85; Art.

VANIA, METTA; Miss Halls Schl; Canaan, NY; (Y); Variety Show; Yrbk Stf; Stu Cncl; Capt Bsktbl; JV Socr; Timer; Hon Roll; Exprmntl Psych.

VANSEGHI, ROBERT L; South Boston HS; South Boston, MA; (Y); Am Leg Boys St; Boys Clb Am; Boy Scts; Teachers Aide; Var Capt Bsbl; Var Capt Ftbl; Var Swmmng; Var Wt Lftg; Miami U; Sci.

VANT, LAUREL; Reading Memorial HS; Reading, MA; (Y); VP AFS; Church Yth Grp; Girl Scts; Chorus; Church Choir; JV Bsktbl; Var Socr; JV Trk; Hon Roll; Masonic Awd; Math.

VARIO, TAMARA; St Marys HS; Auburn, MA; (Y); 10/68; Church Yth Grp; School Play; Hon Roll; Framingham Coll; Commnctns.

VARNEY, MARIE; Lawrence HS; Lawrence, MA; (S); Intnl Clb; Band; Chorus; Mrchg Band; Rep Frsh Cls; Rep Jr Cls; High Hon Roll; Hon Roll; Mus Bus.

VARNEY, SUSAN E; Oliver Ames HS; N Easton, MA; (Y); 30/280; Model UN; Spanish Clb; Yrbk Stf; Rep Sr Cls; Var Bsktbl; Var Capt Fld Hcky; Powder Puff Ftbl; Var Capt Sftbl; Hon Roll; Jr NHS; Leag All Star Fld Hcky, Sftbl 84-85; Rotary, Outlook Clb Schlrshp 85; U RI; Lat Amer Stds.

VASALLO, SUSANA; Christopher Columbus HS; Boston, MA; (Y); 24/132; 4-H; Var Bsktbl.

VASILE, ANGELINA; Beverly HS; Beverly, MA; (Y); Girl Scts; Rep Frsh Cls; Trs Soph Cls; Trs Sr Cls; Var L Cheerleading; Hon Roll; Fashn Retail Merchndsng.

VASILE, RICHARD; Milford HS; Milford, MA; (Y); Boy Scts; Pres Sr Cls; Var L Socr; Var L Trk; Var L Wrstlng; Church Yth Grp.

VASQUEZ, GEORGE; Lawrence HS; Lawrence, MA; (Y).

VASQUEZ, LUCIA; Christopher Columbus HS; Boston, MA; (Y); 27/132; Knghts Of Columbus Schlrshp 83; MA ST Art Fair Awd 84; Bus.

VASSALLO, ROSEMARY ANNE; Doherty Memorial HS; Worcester, MA; (Y); 57/356; Church Yth Grp; Latin Clb; Spanish Clb; Varsity Clb; Stage Crew; Variety Show; Yrbk Stf; Var Cheerleading; High Hon Roll; Jr NHS; Worcester Polytechnic Inst; Bio.

VAUGHAN, ALICE; Methuen HS; Methuen, MA; (Y); Church Yth Grp; Dance Clb; Intnl Clb; Model UN; Y-Teens; Soph Cls; Jr Cls; Powder Puff Ftbl; High Hon Roll; Hon Roll.

VAUGHEY, TOM; Marlobough HS; Marlboro, MA; (Y); Church Yth Grp; Cmnty Wkr; JV Bsbl; Im Bsktbl; JV Ice Hcky; Hon Roll; VA Poly Tech; Statistcs.

VAUGHN, JANAN; Reading Memorial HS; Reading, MA; (Y); Church Yth Grp; Drama Clb; Nwsp Rptr; Nwsp Stf; Lit Mag; Rep Jr Cls; Stat Bsktbl; High Hon Roll; Hon Roll; Church Yth Grp; Natl Hstry Day-1st Pl Rgnl & Dist, 2nd Pl ST Cmptn 84; Smnr Prsntn At Northeastern U 84; Brdcstg.

VAUTOUR, MICHELLE; Lynn Classical HS; Lynn, MA; (Y); 15/200; Computer Clb; VP JA; Office Aide; Rep Pep Clb; Chorus; Stage Crew; Yrbk Stf; Elks Awd; High Hon Roll; Hon Roll; JR Achvt Exctv Of Yr 85; Accntng.

VEARA, E JAMES; Dennis-Yarmouth Regional HS; East Dennis, MA; (Y); Am Leg Boys St; Church Yth Grp; Letterman Clb; Varsity Clb; Yrbk Stf; Capt Crs Cntry; Capt Trk; High Hon Roll; Hon Roll; NHS; Boston Coll; Pol Sci.

VECCHIONE, CHRIS; St Dominic Savio HS; E Boston, MA; (S); 4/109; Computer Clb; Sec JA; Math Clb; Bsktbl; Bowling; JV Crs Cntry; Ftbl; JV Trk; High Hon Roll; Hon Roll; Italn II Awd 83-84; Boston Coll; Comp Sci.

VEIGA, MARIA A; Madison Park HS; Dorchester, MA; (Y); Hon Roll; NHS; Prfct Atten Awd; Shclrshp Trip France ACIS 85; Comp Sci.

VELOSO, YANNICK; East Boston HS; Boston, MA; (Y); Dance Clb; Key Clb; Prfct Atten Awd; Burdett; Exec Secy.

VELYVIS, KRISTEN; Drury SR HS; N Adams, MA; (Y); 2/180; Church Yth Grp; Cmnty Wkr; Pres 4-H; Pres French Clb; Band; Stage Crew; Var L Socr; Var Capt Trk; NHS; Sal; Wellesley Bk Awd 85; U PA; Biomech.

VENEZIA, LORI; Matignon HS; Medford, MA; (S); 14/179; Cmnty Wkr; Drama Clb; Library Aide; High Hon Roll; NHS; Spanish NHS; Lawyer.

VENICE, KELLY ANN; Bishop Connolly HS; Swansea, MA; (Y); Church Yth Grp; Cmnty Wkr; Drama Clb; Spanish Clb; School Play; Stage Crew; Var Trk; Kathy Lynn De Mello Meml Schlrshp 85; Northeastern; Radlgc Tech.

VENTOLA, STEVEN; Chris Columbus HS; Boston, MA; (Y); #10 In Class; Ski Clb; Nwsp Rptr; Nwsp Stf; Jr NHS; NHS; NEDT Awd; Acad All-Amer 84-85; U Of Lowell; Med Tech.

VENTRESCA, MARIA; Classical HS; Lynn, MA; (Y); Aud/Vis; Library Aide; OEA; High Hon Roll; Hon Roll; Jr NHS; NHS; Prfct Atten Awd; Katherine Gibbs; Leg Secy.

VENTURA, EDYTHAN; Cushing Acad; Wakefield, MA; (Y); Hosp Aide; Sec Soph Cls; Var Socr; Capt Var Trk; High Hon Roll; Hon Roll; Sci Clb Bio Prize; Comp Sci Awd; Psych.

VERDERBER, CATHY; Walpole HS; Walpole, MA; (Y); 40/265; Ski Clb; Rep Stu Cncl; Var Cheerleading; JV Var Fld Hcky; Var Capt Tennis; NHS; Regis Coll; Mgmt.

VERDERICO, PATRICK; Dom Savio HS; Saugus, MA; (Y); 30/105; Ftbl; Trk; Wt Lftg; Bus Mgmt.

VERGOTH, LARA; Dartmouth HS; S Dartmouth, MA; (Y); 17/250; AFS; Math Tm; Ed Yrbk Stf; L Capt Crs Cntry; L Capt Trk; NHS; Acad Let 84-85; Bus.

VERICK, PAMELA; Leicester HS; Cherry Valley, MA; (S); Church Yth Grp; Computer Clb; Latin Clb; Math Tm; Office Aide; Political Wkr; Nwsp Rptr; Nwsp Stf; Var L Cheerleading; High Hon Roll; Rep Ntl Conf Chrstns & Jews 84; Cum Laude Recgntn Ntl Merit Lat Exam 84; Wellesley Coll; Engl.

VERRAS, KATRINA; Woburn SR HS; Woburn, MA; (S); 26/500; Church Yth Grp; Cmnty Wkr; Leo Clb; Ski Clb; Spanish Clb; Variety Show; Yrbk Stf; Stu Cncl; High Hon Roll; Sec NHS; Engrng.

VERRE, TOM F; Middleboro HS; Middleboro, MA; (Y); Aud/Vis; Drama Clb; Chorus; School Musical; School Play; Stage Crew; Variety Show; Yrbk Stf; Art.

VERROCHI, LYNNE; Cambridge Rindge & Latin HS; Cambridge, MA; (Y); Ski Clb; Yrbk Stf; Off Soph Cls; Off Jr Cls; Off Sr Cls; Stu Cncl; Jr NHS; NHS; Ashawmut Bank Schlrshp 85-89; U Of MA At Amherst.

VERVILLE, ANN; New Bedford HS; New Bedford, MA; (Y); 87/700; Drama Clb; Stage Crew; Sec Sr Cls; Stu Cncl; Var Capt Swmmng; Var L Trk; Hon Roll; Jr NHS; Nwsp Stf; Steering Committee; Stu Advisory Committee.

VIA, FELICIA; Jeremiah E Burke HS; Dorchester, MA; (Y); Dance Clb; Drama Clb; JA; Chorus; Yrbk Stf; Sftbl; Trk; High Hon Roll; Hon Roll; Jr NHS; Merit Awd 85; Stu Ldrshp 85; Med.

VICTOR, MARC; Randolph HS; Randolph, MA; (Y); Latin Clb; Temple Yth Grp; Band; Jazz Band; Mrchg Band; Nwsp Bus Mgr; Nwsp Ed-Chief; Nwsp Rptr; Nwsp Stf; Hon Roll; Metropathways 84-85; Pol Sci.

VIDOLI, DIANNE; Burlington HS; Burlington, MA; (Y); 100/389; Church Yth Grp; Drama Clb; Girl Scts; JA; Chorus; Sec Jr Cls; Var Cheerleading; Var Powder Puff Ftbl; High Hon Roll; Hon Roll; Alchohol/ Drug Surveillance Pgm; Salem ST Coll; Trvl Indstry.

VIEIRA JR, FRANK J; Salem HS; Salem, MA; (Y); Nwsp Ed-Chief; Stu Cncl; Bsbl; Swmmng; Wt Lftg; Wrstlng; High Hon Roll; Chess Clb; Yrbk Stf; Bsktbl; HS Var Ltr Wrstlng 85; Trophy Coaches Awd Wrstlr 84; HS Rec Wrstlng Quickest Pin 85; U Honolulu; Mgt.

VIEIRA, KAREN; Joseph Case HS; Swansea, MA; (Y); 11/210; Am Leg Aux Girls St; Ski Clb; L Capt Crs Cntry; L Capt Trk; Elks Awd; High Hon Roll; Hon Roll; Sec NHS; Crss Cntry Coachs Awd 83-84; Trk Tm Outstndng Rnnr 85; Elks Stu Mnth 84; Clark U Worcester; Bio.

VIEITES III, ROLANDO R; Matignon HS; Cambridge, MA; (S); 9/198; JA; Spanish Clb; Rep Frsh Cls; Rep Stu Cncl; Im Bsktbl; Im Vllybl; Hon Roll; NHS; Ntl Merit Ltr; Boston Coll; Bus.

VIERA, JOANN; Dartmouth HS; N Dartmouth, MA; (Y); 58/264; JV Var Bsktbl; JV Var Fld Hcky; JV Var Sftbl; Bstn Globe All Schltc Fld Hockey 84; St Julies Ladies Guild Scholar 85; Dartmth Alumni Assn Scholar 85; Southeastern MA U; Comp Sci.

VIETAS, STEFANIE; Bishop Stang HS; N Dartmouth, MA; (Y); 3/218; Dance Clb; Ski Clb; Mrchg Band; Yrbk Stf; Var Bsktbl; JV Var Sftbl; High Hon Roll; NHS; Frndly Sons St Patrick Schlrshp 85; Coll Club New Bedford 85; Top 10 Awd 85; Boston Coll.

VIGLIETTI, TINA; Everett HS; Everett, MA; (Y); Intnl Clb; Key Clb; Letterman Clb; Var Bsktbl; JV Score Keeper; Hon Roll.

VIGNEAU, STEPHANIE; Whitman Hanson HS; Hanson, MA; (Y); 20/365; Cmnty Wkr; Ski Clb; Varsity Clb; Band; Concert Band; Mrchg Band; Var L Socr; JV L Sftbl; Hon Roll; NHS; Law.

VILLIOTTE, RICHARD; St Dominic Savio HS; Revere, MA; (Y); 12/110; Cmnty Wkr; Math Tm; Ski Clb; Im Bsktbl; Var Golf; Im Ice Hcky; Im Tennis; JV Trk; Law.

VINCENT, JANA; Bishop Connolly HS; Fall River, MA; (Y); 50/180; High Hon Roll; Psych.

VINCENT, JON T; Marblehead HS; Marblehead, MA; (Y); Art Clb; Rep Frsh Cls; Hon Roll; Blckblt Karate 83; Bst Shw Stdnt Art Arts Fest 84; Fine Arts.

VINCENT, LUKE; Bishop Connolly HS; Fall River, MA; (S); 27/177; Computer Clb; Drama Clb; Office Aide; Teachers Aide; School Play; Nwsp Rptr; High Hon Roll.

VINER, KIERSTEN; Lee HS; Lee, MA; (Y); 2/115; French Clb; Math Tm; Band; Sec Soph Cls; Sec Jr Cls; Stu Cncl; Var Bsktbl; Var Socr; Var Sftbl; High Hon Roll; Dartmouth Bk Awd 85; Engrng.

VINOCOUR, DANIEL S; Chicopee HS; Chicopee, MA; (Y); 14/250; Debate Tm; JA; Model UN; Band; Concert Band; Mrchg Band; Yrbk Stf; Co-Capt Ftbl; Tennis; NHS; Elec Engrng.

VINSON, YVETTE; Cushing Acad; Depew, NY; (Y); Intnl Clb; Teachers Aide; Church Choir; Madrigals; School Musical; School Play; Trk; Vllybl; High Hon Roll; Jr NHS; Hrvrd Prz Bk For Schlrshp, Ldrshp & Chrctr 85; Med.

VIRGIN, KATHLEEN; Saugus HS; Saugus, MA; (Y); 12/300; JV Fld Hcky; Var JV Sftbl; Jr NHS; Yrbk Stf; High Hon Roll; Hon Roll; Salem ST Coll; Bus.

VISCONTI JR, JOHN A; Medford HS; Medford, MA; (Y); Am Leg Boys St; Cmnty Wkr; Math Tm; Varsity Clb; Stu Cncl; Var L Tennis; High Hon Roll; Mu Alp Tht; Pres NHS; NEDT Awd; Hnr Biol & Hnr Geom Awd 82-83; Hnr Engl & Intro To Comptrs Awd 83-84; Hnr Eng & Apphyscs Awds 84-85; Med.

VITAL, LISA; Bishop Feehan HS; Norton, MA; (Y); 7/240; Hosp Aide; Math Tm; Drm Mjr(t); Jazz Band; Mrchg Band; Orch; Var L Tennis; High Hon Roll; NHS; Spanish NHS; Engrng.

VITALE, CHRISTOPHER; B M C Durfee HS; Fall River, MA; (Y); Band; Concert Band; Drm Mjr(t); Jazz Band; Orch; Pep Band; Math.

VITALE, JENNIFER; Everett HS; Everett, MA; (Y); Church Yth Grp; Jr Cls; Var Cheerleading.

VIVEIROS, JOHN; Old Rochester Regional HS; Rochester, MA; (Y); 10/150; Trs AFS; Am Leg Boys St; Math Tm; Ski Clb; Teachers Aide; JV Bsbl; JV Var Socr; Trk; Math Clb; Jr NHS; Top Eng Stu; Chem Olympd; MVP V Soccer; Dentstry.

VIVIER, JAMES; Mohawk Trail Reg HS; Rowe, MA; (Y); 28/142; Pres Church Yth Grp; Library Aide; School Musical; Stu Cncl; Var Bsbl; JV Bsktbl; Var Socr; Var Hon Roll; Peer Educ Prog 84-86; Schll Cmmtt Stu Rep 84-86; Engrng.

VO, TUAN; Doherty Memorial HS; Worcester, MA; (Y); Computer Clb; Math Tm; High Hon Roll; Hon Roll; Jr NHS; NHS; WPI; Elctrcl Engrng.

VOGEL, FRED; Northfield Mt Hermon Schl; Lake George, NY; (Y); Rep Frsh Cls; Rep Soph Cls; Rep Jr Cls; Bsbl; Ftbl; Ice Hcky; Wt Lftg; Trs Jr NHS; Dance Clb; Letterman Clb; Union Coll; Law.

VOLPE, DIANNE; St Peter-Marian C C HS; Worcester, MA; (Y); 7/179; Computer Clb; Library Aide; Math Tm; Office Aide; Yrbk Bus Mgr; Yrbk Stf; High Hon Roll; Math Clb; Pep Clb; JV Bsktbl; Hghst Acad Avg Scl Stds 85; Elgs Essay Cont Wnnr 85; East Side Imprv Club Schlrshp 85; U Of MA-AMHERST; Brdcst Jrnlsm.

VON LOSSNITZER, PETER D; Holyoke HS; Holyoke, MA; (Y); 50/450; Aud/Vis; Boy Scts; Church Yth Grp; German Clb; Spanish Clb; Band; Envrmntl Sci.

VOORHIS, SARAH M; Middlesex Schl; Concord, MA; (Y); Cmnty Wkr; Dance Clb; Teachers Aide; Chorus; School Musical; Nwsp Stf; Im Tennis; High Hon Roll; Ntl Merit SF; Office Aide; Psych.

VOYER, KEVIN; Agawam HS; Feeding Hls, MA; (Y); Library Aide; Variety Show; Ftbl; Var Socr; Im Wt Lftg; Var Wrstlng; Hon Roll; Advrtsng.

VRABLIK, KEVIN ALLEN; Acton-Boxborough Regional HS; Acton, MA; (Y); 110/360; Hosp Aide; Office Aide; Radio Clb; Teachers Aide; Nwsp Phtg; Nwsp Stf; Yrbk Phtg; Yrbk Stf; Hon Roll; Yng Wrtrs Cntst Hnbl Mntn; Boston U; Physcs.

VYRAVANADAN, KAUSHALYA; Somerville HS; Somerville, MA; (Y); 7/569; Intnl Clb; Math Clb; Math Tm; Nwsp Phtg; Nwsp Stf; Yrbk Phtg; Yrbk Stf; Vllybl; High Hon Roll; Hon Roll; Hnbl Mntn Schl Sci Fair 85; Contntl Math Leag Excllnc 85; CA ST U Sacramento; Elctrnc.

WACLAWIK, JAMES M; Millis HS; Millis, MA; (Y); 1/96; Am Leg Boys St; Intnl Clb; Band; Stu Cncl; Capt Crs Cntry; Var L Tennis; High Hon Roll; NHS; Ntl Merit Ltr; Voice Dem Awd; Harvard Book Awd 85; Engrng.

WADSWORTH, TRACY; Bishop Fenwick HS; Gloucester, MA; (Y); Camera Clb; Exploring; Mathletes; Color Guard; Drm & Bgl; Stu Cncl; High Hon Roll; Hon Roll; GPA Awd In Geo 83-84; SATS Eng & Math 84-85; Pblshd Artcl Wrt For Drm Corps News 82-83; Boston Coll.

WAGNER, HEATHER; Plymouth-Carver HS; Plymouth, MA; (Y); AFS; Art Clb; DECA; GAA; Variety Show; JV Bsktbl; Var L Cheerleading; JV Sftbl; JV Trk; Hon Roll; St Anselms Coll; Psych.

WAHNON, SANDRA H; Seekonk HS; Seekonk, MA; (Y); 2/211; Science Clb; Pres Spanish Clb; Chorus; Trk; High Hon Roll; NHS; Sal; Pres Spanish NHS; Young Peoples Schl Schlrshp Prfmng Arts 79; Acad Excllnc HS Awd 85; Brown U; Pre-Med.

WAITKEVICH, KEVIN J; Foxboro HS; Foxboro, MA; (Y); 32/222; JA; Varsity Clb; JV Var Ftbl; Wt Lftg; Hon Roll; Stu Of The Qtr In Mtl Wrkng & Acctng II 85; Pamela Kelley Mem Schlrshp 85; Bridgewater ST Coll; Acctng.

WALD, DEBBIE; Natick HS; Natick, MA; (Y); 37/449; JA; Library Aide; Speech Tm; Stu Cncl; Var L Swmmng; Hon Roll; Bus Admin.

WALDMAN, ROBIN L; Framingham South HS; Framingham, MA; (Y); 26/256; Pres French Clb; Hosp Aide; Latin Clb; VP Temple Yth Grp; Variety Show; Ed Yrbk Stf; JV Lcrss; VP Swmmng; Hon Roll; NHS; Mayna Cum Laude Ntl Latin Exam; Intl Bus.

WALDMANN, HELENA; Dana Hall HS; Westwood, MA; (Y); Church Yth Grp; Hosp Aide; Orch; Trk; Hon Roll; Bio.

WALDRON, MICHAEL; Maynard HS; Maynard, MA; (Y); 24/99; Am Leg Boys St; Radio Clb; Ski Clb; Radio Clb.

WALENTY, MARGARET; Uxbridge HS; Uxbridge, MA; (Y); 2/85; Church Yth Grp; Band; Concert Band; Jazz Band; Mrchg Band; Yrbk Phtg; Yrbk Stf; Rep Stu Cncl; Crs Cntry; Powder Puff Ftbl; Mbr LSAC Chrmn 2nd Yr 84-86; Cntrl Dist Bnd 82-85; Phtgrphy Edtr JR & SR Yrs For Yrbk 84-86; Northeastern U; Ind Engr.

WALGREEN, ALBERT; Bishop Feehan HS; Mansfield, MA; (Y); Boy Scts; Chess Clb; Math Tm; Var Trk; High Hon Roll; Hon Roll; NHS; Spanish NHS; Colby Coll Book Prize 85; Eagle St 83; USMA Invtnl Acadmc Wrkshp 85.

WALKER, DARLENE L; Rockland HS; Rockland, MA; (Y); AFS; Dance Clb; Drama Clb; Girl Scts; VP Chorus; Drill Tm; School Musical; School Play; Gym; Hon Roll; SEMSBA 84; Dstrct Chorus 85; Grl Scout Slvr Awd 81; Howard U; Cmnctns.

WALKER, DAVID; Somerset HS; Somerset, MA; (Y); Cmnty Wkr; Computer Clb; Band; Concert Band; Mrchg Band; School Play; Symp Band; Yrbk Stf; Hon Roll; NHS; Natl Hnr Soc 84; NEDT Certs 83 & 84; U Of MA Amherst; Elec Engrng.

WALKER, JANET; Malden HS; Malden, MA; (Y); Church Yth Grp; VP Chorus; Madrigals; Variety Show; Hon Roll; Chamberlayne JC; Bus Admin.

WALKER, JENNIFER E; Newburyport HS; Newburyport, MA; (S); 21/200; German Clb; JCL; Math Tm; Pres Model UN; Ed Nwsp Stf; Lit Mag; Trs Frsh Cls; Rep Stu Cncl; Hon Roll; Yale; Econ.

WALKER, MELISSA; Reading Memorial HS; Reading, MA; (Y); Pres French Clb; Band; Jazz Band; Mrchg Band; Nwsp Rptr; Yrbk Sprt Ed; Lit Mag; Rep Stu Cncl; High Hon Roll; Northeast Dist Bnd Mbr 84; Psych.

WALKER, PATRICK; Billerica HS; Billerica, MA; (Y); 15/512; Church Yth Grp; French Clb; Var Capt Socr; Var Capt Tennis; Merrimck Vlly Conf Most Vlbl 83-84; Tenns Plyr 84-85; Phys Sci.

WALKER, ROBERT; Cathedral HS; Springfield, MA; (Y); Ice Hcky; Socr; Wrstlng; Bus.

WALKER, ROBIN; Natick HS; Natick, MA; (Y); 32/443; French Clb; JA; Var Fld Hcky; JV Var Lcrss; High Hon Roll; Hon Roll; Ntl Merit SF; Bus Awd Typg 82; Engrng.

WALKER, STEPHANIE; Marblehead HS; Marblehead, MA; (Y); 2/240; French Clb; Hosp Aide; Latin Clb; Yrbk Stf; JV Swmmng; High Hon Roll; NHS; Princeton Awd 85; Summa Cum Laude Cert Natl Latn Exm 85.

WALKER, SUE; Hingham HS; Hingham, MA; (Y); 106/326; Church Yth Grp; School Musical; Trk; Hon Roll; Bus Mgmt.

WALL, EILEEN; Marblehead HS; Marblehead, MA; (Y); 6/250; Church Yth Grp; Ed Yrbk Rptr; Var Socr; Var Capt Trk; NHS; Excllnc Engl 85; Engl.

WALL, PHILIP; Mansfield HS; Mansfield, MA; (Y); 44/283; Boys Clb Am; Boy Scts; Letterman Clb; Varsity Clb; Y-Teens; JV Var Bsktbl; JV Var Ftbl; Im Wt Lftg; Hon Roll; Northeastern U; Electrcl Engr.

WALL, ROBERT A; Methuen HS; Methuen, MA; (Y); Cmnty Wkr; Intnl Clb; Model UN; Band; Concert Band; Mrchg Band; School Musical; School Play; Hon Roll; Drama Clb; Ind Mngmnt Engrng.

WALLACE, ANDREA; Haverhill HS; Bradford, MA; (Y); 100/400; Church Yth Grp; French Clb; JA; Office Aide; Red Cross Aide; Spanish Clb; Yrbk Sprt Ed; Swmmng; Timer; Mu Alp Tht; Vrsty Letter-Girls Swimming 83; Jr Achvt 85; Nrthrn Essex Cmnty Coll; Lb Art.

WALLACE, BRENDEN; Taunton HS; Taunton, MA; (Y); Ftbl; Northeastern U; Engrng.

WALLACE, DELROY; Framingham North HS; Framingham, MA; (Y); 76/312; 4-H; Socr; 4-H Awd; Hon Roll; Natl Hon Soc 85; Cert Hon Bio 83; Warren Wilson; Elec Engrng.

WALLACE, ELIZABETH; Tri-County Reg Tech Voc Schl; Franklin, MA; (Y); Boy Scts; Exploring; Var Capt Vllybl; Hon Roll; Belmont Abbey Coll; Hstry.

WALLACE, JAMES; B M C Durfee HS; Fall River, MA; (Y); 10/600; Camera Clb; French Clb; JA; Math Clb; Math Tm; Science Clb; Yrbk Stf; Rep Sr Cls; Var Tennis; High Hon Roll; Cmmnctns.

WALLACE, KARYN; St Mary HS; Newton, NH; (Y); 5/89; Spanish Clb; Yrbk Stf; Var Cheerleading; Im Gym; Var L Trk; High Hon Roll; Prfct Atten Awd; Varsity Clb; Var Powder Puff Ftbl; Im Vllybl; Acad Excell Anatomy 85; Acad Achvt Physics 85; Acad Excell Amer & Brtsh Lit 85; UCLA; Ob-Gyn.

WALLACE, MIKE; Christopher Columbus HS; South Boston, MA; (S); CAP; JA; Political Wkr; Ski Clb; Spanish Clb; Varsity Clb; Variety Show; Nwsp Rptr; Nwsp Stf; Yrbk Stf; Awd Of Excllnc 83-84; Bridgewater ST; Accntng.

WALLEN, ROBERT; Nipmuc Regional HS; West Upton, MA; (Y); 1/86; Boy Scts; Science Clb; Teachers Aide; Varsity Clb; Nwsp Rptr; Nwsp Stf; Off Soph Cls; Stu Cncl; Capt Vllybl; Elks Awd; Chrstn A Herter Schlrshp 85; Rgnl Stu Advsry Cncl Rep; ASTROPHYSCS.

WALLENMAIER, LISA; Bridgewater Raynham Reg HS; Raynham, MA; (Y); Model UN; Band; Chorus; Concert Band; Drm Mjr(t); Mrchg Band; Co-Capt Capt Twrlr; SEMSBA 83-84; Lions Clb Banqt 83; Lions All ST Band; Home Ec.

WALSH, BRIAN K; Boston Latin Acad; Brighton, MA; (Y); Am Leg Boys St; Political Wkr; Band; Concert Band; Jazz Band; Pres Jr Cls; VP Sr Cls; Rep Stu Cncl; L Ftbl; L Capt Trk; Jewish War Vets Brotherhd Awd 85; Am Leg MA Boys ST Joseph Nasiatka Mem Awd 85; Boston-Kyoto Scholar; Harvard U; Pre-Law.

WALSH, CHRIS; Medway JR SR HS; Medway, MA; (Y); 20/152; Church Yth Grp; VP Drama Clb; Chorus; School Musical; School Play; Stu Cncl; Hon Roll; Pres NHS; IPEC Ldr 84-85; Govt Intrns-Anchr Man TV 84-86; Emerson; Cmnctns.

WALSH, DAVID M; Matignon HS; Somerville, MA; (Y); 59/173; Nwsp Sprt Ed; Lit Mag; Im Bsktbl; Im Vllybl; Hon Roll; Westfield ST Coll; Englsh.

WALSH, DEBBIE; Newton Catholic HS; W Roxbury, MA; (Y); Drama Clb; Acpl Chr; School Musical; Variety Show; Lit Mag; VP Sr Cls; Cheerleading; Trk; High Hon Roll; Church Yth Grp; Hmcmng Ct 84; New England Conservatory; Music.

WALSH, DEBORAH; Bishop Connolly HS; Tiverton, RI; (S); 24/177; Church Yth Grp; Ski Clb; Var Crs Cntry; Tennis; Var L Trk; NHS; Mrktg.

WALSH, EDWARD; BMC Durfee HS; Fall River, MA; (Y); 7/650; Church Yth Grp; Letterman Clb; Math Clb; Math Tm; Swmmng; Trk; High Hon Roll; Hon Roll; NHS; Var Swmmng Ltr 82-85; Pre-Med.

WALSH, EDWARD; Marian HS; Framingham, MA; (Y); Boy Scts; Band; Sec Frsh Cls; JV Im Bsktbl; JV Crs Cntry; JV Var Ftbl; JV Socr; JV Trk; Hon Roll; Richard T Swann Sportsmnshp Awd 81-82; Engrng.

WALSH, GARY D; Pioneer Valley Regional HS; Bernardston, MA; (Y); 7/60; Rep Am Leg Boys St; Ski Clb; Var Bsbl; JV Bsktbl; Var Socr; Hon Roll; Bus.

WALSH, GERARD J; Malden HS; Malden, MA; (Y); Chorus; Trk; Hon Roll; NHS; Kiwanis Awd; MA Hghr Ed Schlrshp 85; Salem ST; Drftsmn.

WALSH, JOSEPH C; Lexington HS; Lexington, MA; (Y); Ski Clb; L Bsbl; L Ftbl; L Trk; Stu Ldrs; Lexington Yth Cmmsn; Providence Coll; Bus.

WALSH, JUDITH; Arlington Catholic HS; Medford, MA; (Y); 27/148; Art Clb; French Clb; Service Clb; Var Cheerleading; Var Trk; Hon Roll; Psych.

WALSH, JULIE; Braintree HS; Braintree, MA; (Y); 12/400; Church Yth Grp; Rep Jr Cls; Var Capt Bsktbl; JV Capt Fld Hcky; Var L Sftbl; High Hon Roll; NHS; Prfct Atten Awd; Sec Spanish NHS.

WALSH, KERRY; Medway JR SR HS; Medway, MA; (Y); 29/150; Mgr(s); Var Socr; High Hon Roll; Hon Roll; Physcl Thrpy.

WALSH III, MICHAEL J; Randolph HS; Randolph, MA; (Y); Am Leg Boys St; VP Church Yth Grp; Spanish Clb; Sec Band; Sec Concert Band; Jazz Band; Sec Mrchg Band; School Musical; Yrbk Stf; Capt Crs Cntry; Educ.

WALSH, PATRICIA; Arlington Catholic HS; Medford, MA; (Y); 19/147; Church Yth Grp; Hosp Aide; Intnl Clb; JA; Spanish Clb; Nwsp Stf; Hon Roll; NHS; Tchr.

WALSH, SUSANNE; Wellesley HS; Wellesley, MA; (Y); 46/295; AFS; Church Yth Grp; French Clb; Key Clb; Stage Crew; Nwsp Rptr; Yrbk Stf; Cit Awd; Hon Roll; NHS; Pre-Law.

WALSH, WILLIAM; Condor-Carlisle HS; Concord, MA; (Y); Engr.

WALTMAN, FAY E; Malden HS; Malden, MA; (Y); 23/511; English Clb; Trs Key Clb; Math Tm; Stage Crew; Variety Show; Var L Crs Cntry; JV Sftbl; Var L Trk; Hon Roll; Most Dedctd Cross-Cntry 84; U Of NH; Vet.

WALTON, JENNIFER; Northfield Mt Hermn; Mystic, CT; (Y); Girl Scts; Chorus; Jr Cls; JV Bsktbl; JV Fld Hcky; JV Ice Hcky; Mgr(s); Score Keeper; Sftbl; JV Trk; 1st Cls Girl Sct 83.

WALTON, JOHN W; Taconic HS; Pittsfield, MA; (Y); Am Leg Boys St; Boys Clb Am; Church Yth Grp; Cmnty Wkr; Bsbl; Bsktbl; Hon Roll; Math.

WALTON, SCOTT; Dedham HS; Dedham, MA; (Y); Stage Crew; Rep Stu Cncl; NCTE Awd; Comm Artist.

WANAT, KARI; Easthampton HS; Easthampton, MA; (Y); 22/140; Church Yth Grp; Yrbk Stf; High Hon Roll; Hon Roll; Acctng.

WANDELOSKI, MARY E; Greenfield HS; Greenfield, MA; (Y); DECA; Spanish Clb; JV Stat Bsktbl; Mgr(s); Timer; Var L Trk; Hon Roll; Girl Scts; Flag Corp; Ice Hcky; Peer Edctr-Rptg Sec; SADD; Wheelock Coll; Nrsry Schl.

WANDS, JEFFREY A; Agawam HS; Feeding Hills, MA; (Y); 4/285; Am Leg Boys St; VP Soph Cls; Var L Trk; High Hon Roll; NHS; Spanish NHS; Mst Lkly Succeed 82, 85; Wmns Aux, Agawam Dem Twn Comm Schlrshps 85; Bryant Coll; Bus Mgmnt.

WANIEWSKI, LISA; Agawam HS; Feeding Hills, MA; (Y); 30/365; French Clb; Ski Clb; Ed Yrbk Stf; JV Var Sftbl; NHS; Bus Mgmt.

WARD, BRIAN; Christopher Columbus HS; South Boston, MA; (S); 40/121; Var L Bsbl; Var L Ice Hcky; NHS; Awd Of Excllnc 83; Bus.

WARD, EDMUND F; Sacred Heart HS; Kingston, MA; (Y); 20/89; Art Clb; Debate Tm; German Clb; Hon Roll; NHS; Geom Awd 83; Hstry Awd Scholar 85; Debate Awd 85; Bridgewater ST; Govt.

WARD, JOSEPH; Bishop Fenwick HS; Ipswich, MA; (Y); Cmnty Wkr; JV Var Ftbl; Hon Roll; Engrng.

WARD, JOSEPH A; St Columbkille HS; Brighton, MA; (Y); Church Yth Grp; French Clb; Quiz Bowl; Variety Show; Lit Mag; Rep Jr Cls; VP Sr Cls; VP Stu Cncl; Hon Roll; Burdett Schl; Acctng.

WARD, MICHAEL; Salem HS; Salem, MA; (Y); 15/300; Nwsp Rptr; Nwsp Stf; Stu Cncl; Var L Bsbl; Var L Bsktbl; Var L Ftbl; High Hon Roll; Jr NHS; NHS; Spanish NHS.

WARE, PAUL J; Sandwich JR SR HS; Forestdale, MA; (Y); 20/160; Am Leg Boys St; Boy Scts; Debate Tm; Im JV Bsbl; JV Bsktbl; Var Golf; JV Socr; L Trk; Hon Roll; Marine ROTC; MOWW Spch Cntst; Southern CA U; Pilot.

WAREING, RICHARD F; Bishop Stang HS; New Bedford, MA; (Y); 6/240; Mgr(s); Cmnty Wkr; School Musical; Stage Crew; Rep Soph Cls; Stat Ftbl; High Hon Roll; NHS; Ntl Merit SF; Holy Cross Book Awd 85; Top 10 Stu 83-85; ST Senator/MA Stu Govt Day 85; Coll Holy Cross; Hstry.

WARK, DAVID; Groton-Dunstable Regl Secndry Schl; Groton, MA; (Y); 10/70; Varsity Clb; Bsktbl; Hon Roll; Jr NHS; Burdette Business Schl; Bus.

WARREN, BARBARA; North Reading HS; North Reading, MA; (Y); 82/202; 4-H; Girl Scts; Chorus; Rep Frsh Cls; Rep Soph Cls; Rep Jr Cls; Rep Sr Cls; Rep Stu Cncl; Powder Puff Ftbl; Socr; George Shurmack Schlrshp 85; CSF Schlrshp 85; Var Schlstc Awds 82-85; Salem ST; Bus Adm.

WARREN, CATHLEEN; Bishop Feehan HS; Mansfield, MA; (Y); 69/260; Band; Church Choir; Concert Band; Mrchg Band; School Musical; High Hon Roll; Hon Roll; Spanish NHS; Ed.

WASEL, CHRISTOPHER J; Joseph Case HS; Swansea, MA; (Y); Am Leg Boys St; Computer Clb; Var Bsbl; Var Bsktbl; JV Crs Cntry; Hon Roll; Jr NHS; Lion Awd; NHS; Comp Engnrng.

WASHER, GLENN A; Mohawk Trl Reg HS; Shelburne Falls, MA; (Y); Boy Scts; Jazz Band; School Musical; Capt Bsbl; Capt Bsktbl; Capt Ftbl; Varsity Clb; Band; Concert Band; School Play; Eagle Scout Awd 85; All Leag, All Wstrn MA Ftbl Team 84; Best Athl Awd 85; Worcester Poly Tech; Mech Engr.

WASHER, SHARAN; King Philip Regional HS; Wrentham, MA; (Y); Church Yth Grp; Dance Clb; Spanish Clb; Band; Color Guard; Drill Tm; Yrbk Ed-Chief; Trk; Wt Lftg; Hon Roll.

WASHINGTON, CHARLES B; Madison Park HS; Dorchester, MA; (Y); Am Leg Boys St; JA; Off Jr Cls; Bsktbl; Coach Actv; NCTE Awd; Bus Mgmt.

WASILEWSKI, DAVID; Hoosac Valley HS; Adams, MA; (Y); Var L Bsktbl; Var L Golf; High Hon Roll; Hon Roll; Bus.

WASS, ELIZABETH; Leominster HS; Leominster, MA; (S); #2 In Class; Band; Concert Band; Mrchg Band; School Musical; School Play; Rep Stu Cncl; NHS; Sal; Sr Class Play 85; Ntl Hnr Soc 85; Salutatoarian 85; Fitchburg ST Coll; Educ.

WASSMANN, JULIE M; Grafton SR HS; North Grafton, MA; (Y); Girl Scts; Band; Variety Show; Nwsp Rptr; Hon Roll; Newbury JR Coll; Anml Tech.

WASTLER, KIMBERLY; Miss Halls Schl; Marblehead, MA; (Y); French Clb; Stage Crew; Yrbk Phtg; Yrbk Stf; Lit Mag; Vllybl; High Hon Roll; Hon Roll; Cum Laude Soc 84-85; Geogrphy Prz 84-85; Acadmc Awds-Frnch & Sci 84-85; Lehigh U; Chem Engrng.

WATERMAN, BRAD; Dighton-Rehoboth Regional HS; Rehoboth, MA; (Y); 54/238; Church Yth Grp; Hon Roll; Econ.

WATERMAN, DAVID M; Boston College HS; Hanover, MA; (Y); Am Leg Boys St; Boys Clb Am; Boy Scts; Church Yth Grp; Key Clb; Varsity Clb; Nwsp Rptr; JV Bsktbl; Score Keeper; JV Var Socr; 3 Yr Strtr Socr Tm 84-86; Boys ST Schl Comm Chrmn 85; Boston Coll; Eng.

WATERMAN, JOHN; Somerset HS; Somerset, MA; (Y); 23/300; Nwsp Rptr; Nwsp Stf; Stu Cncl; Im Ftbl; Capt Trk; Cit Awd; High Hon Roll; Hon Roll; NEDT Awd; Pres Acdmc Ftns Awd; U Of MA; Cmnctns.

WATERMAN, MICHAEL; Coyle & Cassidy Memorial HS; Taunton, MA; (Y); French Clb; Ski Clb; Yrbk Stf; Bsktbl; Crs Cntry; Golf; Trk; Hon Roll; The Consumer Educ Excllnce Awd 85; Bryant Coll Smithfield; Bus Adm.

WATERS, DOLORES; East Boston HS; E Boston, MA; (Y); Pep Clb; Teachers Aide; Varsity Clb; Var Capt Sftbl; Mock Trial Wnrs Law Day 85; U S Hstry Awd 83-84; JR Comm Awd 84-85; Northeastern U; Crim Just.

WATERS, KATHLEEN; Whitman Hanson Regional HS; Whitman, MA; (Y); 2/350; Am Leg Aux Girls St; Church Yth Grp; Color Guard; Im Tennis; High Hon Roll; Hon Roll; Kiwanis Awd; NHS; Ntl Merit SF; Spellman Essay Cont 2nd Pl 85; St Hist Day 2nd Pl 84freg St Hist Day 1st Pl 84; Pathlgy.

WATERS, MARIE; King Philip Regional HS; Norfolk, MA; (Y); 20/167; Library Aide; Lit Mag; NHS; Essay Cntst Wnnr Trp Frnc Swtz & Itly; Med.

WATJUS, DEBBIE; Maynard HS; Maynard, MA; (Y); 13/99; Letterman Clb; Spanish Clb; Chorus; Yrbk Stf; Sec Soph Cls; Rep Sr Cls; Sec Rep Stu Cncl; Capt Cheerleading; Trk; Hon Roll; Bio.

WATKINS, DORIS M; Foxboro HS; Foxborough, MA; (Y); 15/202; Church Yth Grp; Pres JA; Varsity Clb; Yrbk Stf; Rep Frsh Cls; Rep Soph Cls; Rep Jr Cls; Rep Sr Cls; Stu Cncl; Var L Socr; SADD Pres 84-85; JV Soccer MVP 82-83; Ntl Merit Ldrshp Awd 84-85; George Washington U; Pre-Law.

WATROBA, LISA; Easthampton HS; Easthampton, MA; (Y); 20/133; Nwsp Stf; Yrbk Sprt Ed; Pres Sr Cls; Stu Cncl; DAR Awd; Hon Roll; NHS; Pres Soph Cls; Bsktbl; Gym; Grtr Easthampton Jr Miss 85; MA Kraft Awd 85; John Donaven Awd 85; Bio-Chem.

WATSON, HEIDI; Hingham HS; Hingham, MA; (Y); 10/350; Band; Mrchg Band; Stat Lcrss; Var Mgr(s); Var Timer; High Hon Roll; Hon Roll; NCTE Awd; Var Score Keeper; Mt Holyoke Bk Awd 85; Soc Of Wmn Engrs Cert Of Merit 85; Nrsg.

WATSON, JEFF; Medway HS; Medway, MA; (Y); 80/150; Church Yth Grp; Yrbk Stf; Rep Stu Cncl; Capt Var Ftbl; Im Wt Lftg; Im Wrstlng; Hon Roll; Im Bsktbl; ST Stu Advsry Chrmn 85-86; Bst Attitude Awd & Hnrbl Mntn All Star Vrsty Ftbl 84-85; Law Enfrcmnt.

WATSON, KIMBERLY; Leominster HS; Leominster, MA; (Y); 6/352; Church Yth Grp; School Musical; School Play; Sec Frsh Cls; Sec Soph Cls; Sec Jr Cls; Sec Sr Cls; Stu Cncl; Tennis; Jr NHS; Mt Holyoke Coll; Bio.

WATT, LINDA; Fontbonne Acad; Hyde Pk, MA; (Y); 15/127; Pres Church Yth Grp; Debate Tm; Drama Clb; Intnl Clb; Math Tm; Chorus; School Musical; School Play; Trk; Hon Roll; Child Psychlgy.

WAUGH, SCOTT; Hingham HS; Hingham, MA; (Y); 100/360; Pres Cmnty Wkr; Drama Clb; Pres Band; Jazz Band; Yrbk Ed-Chief; Rep Stu Cncl; Var L Bsbl; Var L Ftbl; Var L Trk; Hon Roll; Mst For Schl Awd; Dir Awd.

WAYMAN, PAULA J; Bartlett HS; Webster, MA; (Y); 6/155; Drm Mjr(t); Nwsp Stf; Ed Yrbk Rptr; Trs Soph Cls; Trs Jr Cls; Trs Sr Cls; Stu Cncl; High Hon Roll; Hon Roll; NHS; Soclgy.

WAYNEN, STEPHEN; Hingham HS; Hingham, MA; (Y); Church Yth Grp; Cmnty Wkr; School Musical; School Play; Nwsp Stf; Hon Roll; Gld Key Art Awd 85; Schlstc Art Awd Cert Of Merit 85; JR Cls Art Awd 85; Skidmore Coll; Cmmrcl Arts.

WEAGLE, SUZANNE; Methuen HS; Methuen, MA; (Y); 37/350; Dance Clb; Intnl Clb; Model UN; Political Wkr; Rep Stu Cncl; Hon Roll; Clncl Psychlgy.

WEAVER, MARK A; Bishop Connolly HS; Swansea, MA; (Y); Var L Crs Cntry; Var L Swmmng; Var L Trk.

WEBB, SCOTT; Hingham HS; Hingham, MA; (Y); 11/325; Band; Var Capt Crs Cntry; JV Var Trk; High Hon Roll; Hon Roll; NHS; Cum Laude Ntl Ltn Exam 85; MA Boys ST Rep 85; NCTE Wrtng Cntst 85; Bus Mngmnt.

WEBB, TRACEY; Taunton HS; Taunton, MA; (Y); Var Sftbl; Hon Roll.

WEBBER, KIMBERLY; Greenfield HS; Greenfield, MA; (Y); 14/140; Science Clb; Band; Yrbk Stf; Rep Sr Cls; Stu Cncl; Var L Trk; Cit Awd; Hon Roll; NHS; Pres Schlr; Outstdng Ldrshp & Ctznshp 85; Oustdng Abilities In Chem/Physcs 85; Outstdng Abilities In Drftng 84-85; Worcester Polytechnic Inst; Ele.

WEBER, ROBERT L; Bethesda Chevy Cahse HS; Washington, DC; (Y); Jazz Band; Hon Roll; Boy Scts; Computer Clb; French Clb; Mrchg Band; Eagle Scout With Brnz, Gld & Slvr Palms 84; Brnz Merit Schlr 85; Georgetown U; Dentstry.

WEBSTER, HEIDI; Lunenurg HS; Lunenburg, MA; (Y); Math Tm; Teachers Aide; Chorus; School Play; Trs Soph Cls; Trs Jr Cls; Trs Sr Cls; JV Var Cheerleading; JV Var Sftbl; Trs NHS; Eng.

WEED, KARLA; Wilmington HS; Wilmington, MA; (Y); 44/269; Spanish Clb; Yrbk Stf; JV Crs Cntry; JV Trk; JV Vllybl; Hon Roll; Chem Awd 82-83; Middlesex Comm; Dental Hy.

WEEGO, PATRICIA; Clinton HS; Clinton, MA; (Y); Church Yth Grp; Intnl Clb; Sec JA; Rep Frsh Cls; Off Jr Cls; JV Var Vllybl; Hon Roll; Hst NHS; Engrng.

WEEKS, LESLEY; Masconomet Regional HS; Topsfield, MA; (Y); 14/244; Model UN; Var Fld Hcky; Var Capt Gym; Var Sftbl; Hon Roll; Pres NHS; Ntl Merit SF; Wellesley Bk Awd 85; Fld Hcky Coaches Awd 84; Gymnstc Coaches Awd 85; Bus.

WEINBERG, LISA; Somerset HS; Somerset, MA; (Y); Drama Clb; School Play; Stage Crew; Variety Show; Capt Var Bsktbl; Var L Trk; Var L Vllybl; High Hon Roll; Hon Roll; NHS; Commnctns.

WEINER, LISA; Milford HS; Milford, MA; (Y); 29/310; Drama Clb; Band; Concert Band; Mrchg Band; School Musical; Yrbk Stf; Hon Roll; NHS; Syracuse U; Psych.

WEINFELD, DANIEL R; Newton North HS; Newton Centre, MA; (Y); Scholastic Bowl; Temple Yth Grp; Jazz Band; School Musical; Yrbk Stf; Var JV Trk; Hon Roll; Ntl Merit SF; MA Chmpnshp Tm Acad Decath Gld Mdl Soc Sci Silvr Mdl Eng Mth & Sci 84-85; Hstry.

WEINSTEIN, STEPHANIE; Andover HS; Andover, MA; (Y); 4/400; Pep Clb; Red Cross Aide; Trs Pres Temple Yth Grp; JV Fld Hcky; JV Socr; Cit Awd; High Hon Roll; Hon Roll; L NHS; Ntl Merit SF; Harvard Bk Awd 84; GTE Corp Schlrshp 85; Phy Sci Inc Schlrshp 85; Tufts U.

WEIR, KRISTAL; Silver Lake Regional HS; Halifax, MA; (Y); 4-H; French Clb; Hon Roll; Newbury Coll; Fashn Merch.

WEISBERG, MICHELLE; Revere HS; Revere, MA; (Y); 20/386; Cmnty Wkr; Political Wkr; Quiz Bowl; Red Cross Aide; Yrbk Stf; Rep Sr Cls; High Hon Roll; NHS; Rep Soph Cls; Rep Jr Cls; W Arthur Mognihan Schlrshp; Brandeis U Grant; Schl Frgn Lang Awd French; Brandeis U; English.

WEISENSEE, BRENDA S; Memorial HS; Tewksbury, MA; (Y); 70/335; Ski Clb; Cheerleading; Hon Roll; U Of Lowell; Bus Mngmnt.

WEISENSEE, SCOTT; Memorial HS; Tewksbury, MA; (Y); 29/335; Church Yth Grp; Var Ftbl; Var Trk; Var Wrstlng; Hon Roll; NHS; Bus Mngmnt.

WEISS, CATHERINE; Bishop Feehan HS; Foxboro, MA; (Y); 90/250; Church Yth Grp; Dance Clb; Hosp Aide; Trs Soph Cls; Rep Jr Cls; Pres Sec Sr Cls; Pres Sec Stu Cncl; Var JV Tennis; Dnfth Awd; Elks Awd; Psych.

WEISS, CHRISTINE; Cathedral HS; Springfield, MA; (Y); Stage Crew; Nwsp Rptr; Nwsp Stf; Outstndng Displynrt Awd 85; Outstndng Svc 85; Jrnslsm.

WEISS, ILANA J; Natick HS; Natick, MA; (Y); 250/500; Art Clb; Political Wkr; Band; Mrchg Band; Yrbk Stf; Off Frsh Cls; Off Soph Cls; Stu Cncl; Tennis; Hon Roll; MA U Amhurst; Intr Desgn.

WEISS, THOMAS P; Xaverian Brothers HS; Norwood, MA; (S); 8/236; Chess Clb; Church Yth Grp; School Musical; Pres Frsh Cls; Rep Stu Cncl; JV Var Ice Hcky; JV Socr; High Hon Roll; NHS; Stage Crew; Xaverian Ldrshp Inst 84; Engrng.

WEISSMAN, BRIAN; B M C Durfee HS; Fall River, MA; (Y); 4/663; JA; MMM; Science Clb; Concert Band; Mrchg Band; Pep Band; High Hon Roll; NHS.

WELBY, JOHN; Westwood HS; Westwood, MA; (Y); Camera Clb; Hosp Aide; Key Clb; Color Guard; Drm & Bgl; Nwsp Phtg; Yrbk Phtg; JV Tennis; JV Trk; Trvl Admin.

WELCH, KATHLEEN; Chicopee Comprehensive HS; Chicopee, MA; (Y); 46/340; German Clb; Hosp Aide; Jr Cls; Trk; Hon Roll; NHS; Bay Path JC; Mgmt.

WELCH, LAURENCE J; Methuen HS; Methuen, MA; (Y); Intnl Clb; Hon Roll; MBA.

WELCH, RICHARD; Hingham HS; Hingham, MA; (Y); 29/340; Church Yth Grp; Variety Show; Stu Cncl; Var L Bsbl; Var Capt Bsktbl; Im Vllybl; Hon Roll; Chrprsn Stu Cncl 84-85, Exec Chrprsn 85-86; Vrsty Bsktbl, Ltrs 84-85; Capt 85-86; Chrch Fnds Cntr; Bus Adm.

WELCH, VERONICA; Bedford HS; Bedford, MA; (Y); 5/238; Drama Clb; Chorus; Church Choir; School Musical; Var Diving; Var Gym; Var Swmmng; High Hon Roll; NHS; Ntl Merit Ltr; Chancllrs Tlnt Awd Pgm 85.

WELDON, LOUISE; Arlington Catholic HS; Burlington, MA; (Y); 39/159; JA; Church Choir; Phy Sci.

WELHAM, ANDREW R; Northfield Mt Hermon Schl; Annandale, VA; (Y); Var L Diving; Var Ftbl; JV Lcrss.

WELLER, CYNTHIA ALYCE; West Roxbury HS; West Roxbury, MA; (Y); AFS; Dance Clb; Drama Clb; Hosp Aide; Red Cross Aide; ROTC; Concert Band; Variety Show; Stu Cncl; DAR Awd; Atten, Ctzn Svc, Fld Svc, Heart Fnd 80; Aid Svc, Red Crss 81; Cmnty Svc, Swmmg Awd 83; Lawyr.

WELLES, STEPHEN M; Dennis Yarmouth Regional HS; West Dennis, MA; (Y); 4/335; Am Leg Boys St; Church Yth Grp; Civic Clb; Band; Concert Band; Jazz Band; Mrchg Band; Orch; High Hon Roll; Hon Roll; Excllnc-Engl 83; Bstn Coll Bk Awd 85; Outstndng Musicnshp-S E MA Jazz Ensmbl Comptn 84.

WELLS, JENNIFER; Lexington HS; Lexington, MA; (Y); French Clb; Ski Clb; Spanish Clb; Off Frsh Cls; Var L Lcrss; Var L Socr; NHS; Rtry Clb MVP-SCCR 85; Spnsh Awd-Recog Of Fine Wk 85; Middlesex Lge All Star-Sccr 85; Wellesley Coll; Frnch.

WELLS, LISA; Chicopee Comprehensive HS; Easthampton, MA; (Y); Church Yth Grp; Dance Clb; Drama Clb; JA; Spanish Clb; School Play; Holyoke CC; Bus.

WELLS, SUZANNE; Natick HS; Natick, MA; (Y); 79/443; Am Leg Aux Girls St; Cmnty Wkr; Bsktbl; Var Capt Sftbl; Var Capt Swmmng; Hon Roll; SADD 83-85; JR Exec Brd 84-85; All Star Swm Tm 83 & 84; Phy Thrpy.

WELLS, TIMOTHY R; Wahconah Regional HS; Windsor, MA; (Y); 25/203; Stu Cncl; JV Var Bsbl; JV Bsktbl; Var Capt Ftbl; Hon Roll; NHS; Holy Cross; Bus.

WELLSPEAK, JOSEPH; West Field HS; Westfield, MA; (Y); 72/385; U Of MA Amherst; Elec Engrng.

WENSTROM, TRICIA; Norwood HS; Norwood, MA; (Y); 21/375; Church Yth Grp; Key Clb; School Play; Rep Stu Cncl; Capt Cheerleading; Hon Roll; JC Awd; Norwood Tchrs Assoc Schlrshp 85; Norwood HS Schlrshp 85; U NH; Hotel Admin.

WENTZEL, MARILYN; Hopkins Acad; Hadley, MA; (S); 5/45; French Clb; Band; Chorus; Concert Band; Mrchg Band; Yrbk Ed-Chief; Score Keeper; Sftbl; NHS.

WENTZELL, STEVE; Tahanto Regional HS; Boylston, MA; (Y); 13/46; Am Leg Boys St; Church Yth Grp; JA; Var Bsktbl; Var Golf; Hon Roll.

WESER, JOSEPH; Tewksbury HS; Tewksbury, MA; (Y); 40/336; Church Yth Grp; Math Tm; Varsity Clb; Band; Church Choir; Mrchg Band; Socr; Trk; Hon Roll; Teen Tlnt Dstrct Fnls 83; Jmy Swgrt Bible Coll.

WEST JR, CHARLES M; Brockton HS; Brockton, MA; (Y); Computer Clb; Drama Clb; Office Aide; Acpl Chr; Chorus; School Musical; School Play; Stage Crew; VP Concert Choir 84-85; Natl Choral Awd 84-85; Rep De Molay Awd 82-83; MA Maritime Acad; Marine Trans.

WEST, CHRIS P; Woburn HS; Woburn, MA; (Y); Boys Clb Am; Leo Clb; Ski Clb; Var Ftbl; Wt Lftg; Var Wrstlng; High Hon Roll.

WEST, JAMES; Burncoat SR HS; Worcester, MA; (Y); Church Yth Grp; Ski Clb; Stu Cncl; Bsktbl; Ftbl; Sftbl; Trk; Vllybl; Wt Lftg; Ace Carrier 83.

WEST, RICHARD; Coyle And Cassidy HS; Lakeville, MA; (Y); Church Yth Grp; Band; JV Var Bsbl; Hon Roll; Archit Engrng.

WEST, ROBIN L; Fitchburg HS; Fitchburg, MA; (Y); Cmnty Wkr; Church Choir; Im Bsktbl; Hon Roll; Local Advsry Cncl Fed & Priv Grants 84-85; Fitchburg ST Coll; Bus Admin.

WHALEN, ELEANOR; Arlington Catholic HS; Medford, MA; (Y); Hosp Aide; Office Aide; Spanish Clb; Var L Bsktbl; Var Sftbl; JV Vllybl; MVP In Bsktbl For Intl Ordr Of Rnbw 85; Erly Chldhd Ed.

WHALEN, JENNIFER; Silver Lake Regional HS; N Pembroke, MA; (Y); 14/457; Church Yth Grp; Trs French Clb; Girl Scts; Latin Clb; Yrbk Stf; JV Cheerleading; Hon Roll; Kiwanis Awd; Trs NHS; VFW Awd; Hnrd Muscl Excel Organ, Nuclr Disarmnt Essay Awd 84; Fr R Callahan Schlrshp 85; U NH; Bio.

WHALEN, MARY; Brockton HS; Brockton, MA; (Y); 63/1000; JCL; High Hon Roll; NHS; Magna Cum Laude Natl Latin Exam 85; Law.

WHEATON, SANDRA; Wakefield HS; Wakefield, MA; (Y); AFS; Rep Church Yth Grp; GAA; Trs Key Clb; School Play; Yrbk Stf; Stat Bsktbl; JV Stat Fld Hcky; Jr NHS; Elem Ed.

WHEELER, DAVID B; Greater Boston Acad; Stoneham, MA; (Y); 5/18; Drama Clb; Rep Frsh Cls; Pres Soph Cls; VP Jr Cls; Trs Pres Stu Cncl; Im Bsktbl; Im Vllybl; Hon Roll; Ntl Merit Schol; Ldrshp Awd; Rotary Outstndng Stu Schlrshp; Gymnastic Awd; Atlantic Union Coll; Engr.

WHEELER, ROGER J; Medfield HS; Medfield, MA; (Y); Am Leg Boys St; Church Yth Grp; Political Wkr; Trs Sr Cls; Var Bsbl; Var Ftbl; High Hon Roll; Hon Roll; NHS; Rep Ntl Conv Page 84; Mem Lib Wrkshop Yng Politcns 84; West Point.

WHELAN, WILLIAM; Bishop Stang HS; New Bedford, MA; (Y); 52/250; Aud/Vis; Boy Scts; Chess Clb; Computer Clb; Drama Clb; Office Aide; School Play; Stage Crew; Lit Mag; JV Var Trk; Fairfield U; Bus Adm.

WHIFFEN, JENNIFER; Holbrook HS; Holbrook, MA; (Y); Library Aide; Band; Concert Band; Jazz Band; Mrchg Band; Pep Band; Symp Band; Variety Show; JV Bsktbl; JV Fld Hcky; MVP In Track 84; All League Chmp In Shtpt 85; UCLA; Sprts Med.

WHITAKER, DONNA; Sacred Heart HS; Duxbury, MA; (Y); 33/89; Intnl Clb; Key Clb; JV Var Bsktbl; Capt Bowling; Var Capt Fld Hcky; Var Sftbl; Hon Roll; NHS; MA ST Bwlng Champ 83; Spnsh Awd 84.

WHITE, CHERYL; Weymouth North HS; Weymouth, MA; (Y); 7/393; French Clb; FHA; Math Tm; Rep Jr Cls; Capt Crs Cntry; Trk; Electrncs & Frnch; Elctrnc Engr.

WHITE, ELIZABETH; Bishop Connolly HS; Fall River, MA; (S); 23/177; Hosp Aide; Math Tm; Ski Clb; School Play; Var Cheerleading; Trk; High Hon Roll; Pre-Med.

WHITE, ELLEN P; Frontier Reg HS; Whately, MA; (Y); Mgr Yrbk Stf; Stu Cncl; Trk; Vllybl; High Hon Roll; Hon Roll; French Clb; German Clb; GAA; Rep Jr Cls; Coachs Trphy Vlybl 84; Engr.

WHITE, FRANCES M; Malden HS; Malden, MA; (Y); 107/520; Boy Scts; Church Yth Grp; Hosp Aide; Variety Show; Var L Fld Hcky; Var L Trk; Almni Schlrshp 84-85; Fld Hcky & Trck Ltrs; George A Hanna Jr Memrl Schlrshp 84-85; U Of MA; Bio.

WHITE, ISOBEL T; Lexington HS; Lexington, MA; (Y); French Clb; Political Wkr; School Musical; Swing Chorus; Yrbk Stf; Sec Soph Cls; Sec Jr Cls; Sec Sr Cls; Jr NHS; NHS; Humanities.

WHITE, JOHN; Classical HS; Springfield, MA; (Y); 13/392; Am Leg Boys St; Debate Tm; Nwsp Sprt Ed; Yrbk Stf; Im Bsbl; Var Ftbl; JV Tennis; Im Wt Lftg; Jr NHS; NHS; Pres Physcl Ftnss Awd 81; Jesse Law Schlrshp Awd 85; Western New Eng Coll; Htl Mgmt.

WHITE, KELLY; Woburn SR HS; Woburn, MA; (Y); French Clb; Ski Clb; Off Frsh Cls; Off Soph Cls; Off Jr Cls; Off Sr Cls; Stu Cncl; Trk; Nrsng.

WHITE, LAURIE; Haverhill HS; Haverhill, MA; (Y); 20/386; French Clb; High Hon Roll; NHS; Hoverhill Kiwanis Clb Acad Achvt Hnrs 85; N Essex CC; Bus.

WHITE, RICHARD; Holy Name Catholic Chrch HS; Worcester, MA; (Y); Var Bsbl; JV Bsktbl; Var L Ftbl; Hon Roll; Jr NHS; Accntng.

WHITE, ROBIN; Braintree HS; Braintree, MA; (Y); 46/397; Hon Roll; Comps.

WHITEHEAD, LARA; St Bernards Central Catholic HS; Rindge, NH; (S); 18/170; Girl Scts; Model UN; Nwsp Ed-Chief; Yrbk Phtg; Yrbk Stf; Stat Bsktbl; Var Fld Hcky; JV Trk; NHS; Ntl Merit Ltr; Anne Boy Schlrshp GSUSA 83.

WHITESIDE, KEVIN; Wellesley HS; Wellesley, MA; (Y); Church Yth Grp; Hosp Aide; Key Clb; Latin Clb; Nwsp Bus Mgr; JV Bsbl; Var Crs Cntry; Var Trk; Hon Roll; NHS; U Notre Dame; Bus Adm.

WHITING, IAN; Beverly HS; Beverly, MA; (Y); Band; Concert Band; Jazz Band; Mrchg Band; School Musical; Hon Roll; Hnr Musician Awd New Englnd Mus Camp 85; U MA; Mus Perf.

WHITLEY, KAREN; Framingham South HS; Framingham, MA; (Y); Drama Clb; Band; Mrchg Band; Orch; School Musical; Var Bsktbl; Var Lcrss; Var Socr; High Hon Roll; NHS; MVP & All Star Sccr & La Crosse 85; US Marines Dstngshd Athlte Awd 85; Biomdcl Engrng.

WHITMARSH, CHERYL; Silver Lake Reg HS; Kingston, MA; (Y); 33/457; Library Aide; Office Aide; JV Trk; High Hon Roll; Hon Roll; Rotary Awd; Kingston Repblcn Twn Cmmtt Schlrshp 85; Edna Maglathlin Schlrshps 85; St Josephs; Acctng.

WHITMORE, LAURA; Triton Regional HS; Byfield, MA; (Y); AFS; Church Yth Grp; Girl Scts; Hosp Aide; Ski Clb; Color Guard; Drill Tm; Mrchg Band; Hon Roll; Bus.

WHITNEY, DEVON DARCEY; Everett HS; Everett, MA; (Y); Church Yth Grp; FTA; Intnl Clb; Key Clb; Yrbk Stf; NHS; Hugh O Brian Ldrshp Awd 84; Bus Mngmnt.

WHITNEY, GLEN T; Medfield HS; Medfield, MA; (Y); Chess Clb; Math Tm; Pres Science Clb; School Musical; High Hon Roll; NHS; Ntl Merit SF; St Schlr; US Math Olympd 84; 2nd Pl Intl Comp Pgmng Cntst U Of WI 82; Awd To Dr Ross Pure Math Pgm OSU 83; Math.

WHITNEY, JENNIFER; Arlington HS; Arlington, MA; (Y); Church Yth Grp; Chorus; Church Choir; Madrigals; School Musical; School Play; Rep Jr Cls; Hon Roll; Intl Order Of Rainbow For Girls Worthy Advisor 84-85; Yth Of America Choir 84; Communications.

WHITNEY, JULIA; North Reading HS; North Reading, MA; (Y); 19/207; Band; Yrbk Stf; Var Bsktbl; Var Capt Tennis; Var Capt Vllybl; Hon Roll; Vllybl MVP 83-85; Athltc Boostr Schlrshp 85; Ctzns Schlrshp Fndtn Awd 85; U Of ME Orono; Nutrtn.

WHITNEY, KEVIN B; Oakmont Regional HS; Ashburnham, MA; (Y); 45/135; Am Leg Boys St; Pres Aud/Vis; Concert Band; Jazz Band; Mrchg Band; Yrbk Stf; High Hon Roll; Hon Roll; Art Clb; Boy Scts; MA Lions Clb All ST Band 84; MVP Mrchg Band 85; Fitchburg ST; Med Tech.

WHITTAKER, SUZANNE L; Stoneham HS; Stoneham, MA; (Y); 9/259; Trs Dance Clb; Math Tm; School Play; Variety Show; Yrbk Stf; High Hon Roll; Hon Roll; Trs NHS; Bus Wk 84; Annie Bailey Trowbridge Awd 85; SADD 83-85; U Of MA; Math.

WHITTEN, RUSSELL; Marblehead HS; Mablehead, MA; (Y); 40/240; Nwsp Rptr; Var Gym; Var Swmmng; JV Trk; High Hon Roll; Hon Roll; Boston Globe Swmmng All Star Lst 2nd Pl 84 & 85; Swmmr Of Yr 84 & 85; S CA Coll.

WHRITENOUR, AMY J; Frontier Regional HS; So Deerfield, MA; (Y); 1/76; Drama Clb; Chorus; Nwsp Stf; Ed Yrbk Stf; Ed Lit Mag; Tennis; NHS; Ntl Merit SF; Pres Spanish Clb; Hst Frsh Cls; Hopwood Scholar Lynchbrg Coll 85; Chncllrs Talnt Awd U MA; Dartmouth Bk Awd; Sci.

WICKS, PATRICIA S; Haverhill HS; Haverhill, MA; (Y); 81/385; Nwsp Stf; Yrbk Stf; High Hon Roll; Slvr Mdl In Intl Piano Rcrdng Cmptn 85; Fine Arts.

WIDBERG, SUSAN; Brockton Christian Regional HS; Canton, MA; (S); Drama Clb; Hosp Aide; Church Choir; School Play; Co-Capt Cheerleading; Vllybl; Natl Leadership Org 83-84.

WIDMYER, GREGORY W; North Andover HS; North Andover, MA; (Y); 3/275; Am Leg Boys St; Rep Jr Cls; Rep Sr Cls; VP Stu Cncl; Var L Ftbl; Var Capt Tennis; French Hon Soc; High Hon Roll; Ntl Merit Ltr; FCA; Natl Cncl Of Tchrs Engl Wrtng Cntst 85; Bread Loaf/New England Yng Wrtrs Conf 85; Intl Bus.

WIEDL, CRAIG J; Middleborough HS; Middleboro, MA; (Y); Am Leg Boys St; Band; Orch; JV Var Crs Cntry; JV Var Trk; JV Var Wrstlng; NHS.

WIERBOWICZ, PAULA; Everett HS; Everett, MA; (Y); #10 In Class; Cmnty Wkr; High Hon Roll; Hon Roll; NHS.

WIERLING, ROBERT; Weymouth North HS; Weymouth, MA; (Y); Boy Scts; Math Tm; JV Ftbl; JV Trk; High Hon Roll; Hon Roll; Prfct Atten Awd; Stu Of Term Indstrl Arts Dept 85; CA U Berkley; Comp Engr.

WIESNER, CHRISTOPHER F; Brockton HS; Brockton, MA; (Y); Church Yth Grp; JCL; Var Tennis; High Hon Roll; Hon Roll; NHS; Magna Cum Laude Natl Latn Exm 85; 1st Prz-Amer Heart Assn Heart Fair 83; Bentley Coll; Acctg.

WIGGIN, CINDY; South Hadley HS; S Hadley, MA; (Y); 81/180; Art Clb; Church Yth Grp; Latin Clb; Band; Mrchg Band; 1st Teen Bible Time 85; Hnrbl Mntn Etna Ins Drunk Drvng Cntst 85; 1st Art Baptist Yth Fndtn 84-85; Artist.

WIGHTMAN, JANICE; Greenfield HS; Greenfield, MA; (S); 53/165; Church Yth Grp; Dance Clb; DECA; Pres 4-H; Band; Yrbk Stf; Pres Sr Cls; Stu Cncl; Var Trk; Var DAR Awd; Gribbns Band Instru Schlrshp 85; Porter Awd 85; Dstrbtv Ed Clbs Amer Bk Awd 85; Estrn KY U; Ed Of Def.

WIKAR, CHRISTINE; Classical HS; Springfield, MA; (Y); Church Yth Grp; Yrbk Bus Mgr; Yrbk Stf; Sftbl; Tennis; Cit Awd; Hon Roll; Engrng.

WILANDER, MICHELE; Gateway Regional HS; Blanford, MA; (Y); Cmnty Wkr; Office Aide; Sec Sr Cls; Sec Stu Cncl; Var L Bsktbl; Var L Fld Hcky; Var L Sftbl; High Hon Roll; Hon Roll; Stage Crew; Schlr Ath 85; SAC 83-85; Wstrn New Eng Coll; Acctg.

WILCOX, JAMES; Durfee HS; Fall River, MA; (Y); 16/687; Aud/Vis; Varsity Clb; Var L Crs Cntry; Var L Trk; High Hon Roll; Hon Roll; NHS; Engrng.

WILCOX, MICHAEL; New Bedford HS; New Bedford, MA; (Y); 21/543; Am Leg Boys St; Computer Clb; Drama Clb; Lit Mag; Stu Cncl; High Hon Roll; NHS; Ntl Merit Ltr; Pres Schlr; Sci Confidence Awd 85; Rensselaer Polytech; Elec Engrn.

WILCOX, RUSSELL J; Masconomet HS; Boxford, MA; (Y); 1/278; Capt Math Tm; Model UN; Radio Clb; Speech Tm; VP Wrstlng; Val; Mathletes; NFL; Scholastic Bowl; Science Clb; MA St Sci Fair 3rd At ISEF 84; MA Future Problem Solvers Champs 84; Harvard Book 84; MIT.

WILDE, GERALDINE; New Bedford HS; New Bedford, MA; (Y); Church Yth Grp; Hosp Aide; Trk; High Hon Roll; NHS; Portuguese Excllnc Awd 85; Cert Of Apprctn 84; Athltc Awd-Sprng Trck 85.

WILDE, MARCIE A; Barnstable HS; Hyannis, MA; (Y); 56/398; Ski Clb; Var Trk; Hon Roll; Providence Coll; Engl.

WILEY, PATRICK; Chicopee Comprehensive HS; Chicopee, MA; (Y); Spanish Clb; Variety Show; Bsktbl; Ftbl; Trk; Spanish NHS.

WILHELMSEN, KIM; Doherty Memorial HS; Worcester, MA; (Y); 10/356; VP JA; Math Tm; Ski Clb; VP Band; Orch; Yrbk Ed-Chief; High Hon Roll; Jr NHS; NHS; Ntl Merit Ltr; NW U; Bus.

WILK, JOHN; Hoosac Valley HS; Cheshire, MA; (Y); Church Yth Grp; Exploring; School Play; Yrbk Rptr; Yrbk Stf; Hon Roll; Phy Thrpst.

WILKENS, MELISSA; Bishop Stang HS; Westport, MA; (Y); 80/240; Hosp Aide; Ski Clb; Flag Corp; Pharm.

WILKINS, NANCY; Hudson HS; Hudson, MA; (Y); Aud/Vis; Service Clb; Teachers Aide; Concert Band; School Musical; Nwsp Rptr; L Trk; Hon Roll; Band; Mrchg Band; Natl Hstry Day Awd 83-85; Girls Trck Coachs Awd 83; Comm.

WILKINS, SCOTT; Groton-Dynstable Regional HS; Dunstable, MA; (Y); Boy Scts; Church Yth Grp; Cmnty Wkr; Ski Clb; Ice Hcky; Lowell U; Comp Engr.

WILKINS, SCOTT B; Andover HS; Andover, MA; (Y); 98/405; Church Yth Grp; Model UN; Ski Clb; Rep Frsh Cls; Rep Soph Cls; Rep Jr Cls; Off Sr Cls; Var Bsbl; JV Bsktbl; Var Capt Socr; Selctd Ply Bay ST Games Sccr 84; Bus.

WILKINSON, REBECCA E; Walpole HS; Walpole, MA; (Y); Church Yth Grp; Drama Clb; Exploring; GAA; Varsity Clb; Band; Chorus; Flag Corp; School Play; JV Crs Cntry; Burdett; Fashn Merch.

WILKS, SABRINA; Notre Dame Acad; Hanover, MA; (Y); 4/120; Cmnty Wkr; French Clb; Science Clb; School Musical; French Hon Soc; High Hon Roll; Trs NHS; Prfct Atten Awd; Schl Rep Archdiocese Of Boston 84-85; Bus Mgmt.

WILLIAMS, CATHERINE M; Frontier Regional HS; Conway, MA; (Y); 4/75; Drama Clb; Latin Clb; Office Aide; Tennis; High Hon Roll; Hon Roll; Pres NHS; Ntl Merit Ltr; 4 Yrs Exclnce Hist,Engl,Lat 85; U Of Chicago.

WILLIAMS, DANIEL; Ayer HS; Shirley, MA; (Y); 35/160; Chess Clb; Computer Clb; Debate Tm; FBLA; Spanish Clb; Acpl Chr; Var Bsktbl; Coach Actv; Socr; Vllybl; John E Morrisey Schlrshp 85; MA U; Finance.

WILLIAMS, DARNYL; Fiarhaven HS; Acushnet, MA; (Y); Church Yth Grp; Concert Band; Mrchg Band; Vllybl; Hon Roll; Jr NHS; French Instructors Awd 83.

WILLIAMS, GREGORY R; Athol HS; Athol, MA; (Y); 3/120; Am Leg Boys St; Cmnty Wkr; Political Wkr; Band; Mrchg Band; Nwsp Bus Mgr; Nwsp Stf; Pres Stu Cncl; Bsktbl; Trk; Hnrb Mntn Sci Fair 83-84; Stu Govt Day Delg 84-85; Model Congrss Delg 84-85; Bus.

WILLIAMS, JULIE ELIZABETH; Minnechaug Regional HS; Hampden, MA; (Y); JA; Nwsp Stf; Bay Path Schlrshp 85; Rotry Clb Schlrshp 85; MA ST Schlrshp 85; Bay Path JC; Fshn Merchndsng.

WILLIAMS, KAREN; Christopher Columbus HS; Charlestown, MA; (S); Library Aide; Yrbk Stf; Hon Roll; NHS; Chem, All Amer Acad Awds; U MA Amherst; Chldhd Ed.

WILLIAMS, KAREN; Concord-Carlisle HS; Concord, MA; (S); DECA; MA Deca St Comp 1st Pl 84-85; Deca Career Conf San Francisco 3rd Pl 84-85; U Of MA-AMHERST; Rstrnt Mngmnt.

WILLIAMS, KELLY; Lexington HS; Lexington, MA; (Y); Church Yth Grp; Cmnty Wkr; French Clb; Natl Hnr Soc 83-85; Schlrshp Acadmc Achvt 85; Mt Saint Marys; Bus Mgmt.

WILLIAMS, MARY RUTH; Smith Acad; North Hatfield, MA; (Y); 2/35; Church Yth Grp; Drama Clb; Chorus; School Musical; Stu Cncl; Capt Cheerleading; Capt Fld Hcky; Elks Awd; High Hon Roll; Sal; MA Commonwlth Scholar 85; Boston Coll; Nrsng.

WILLIAMS, MAY L; Norton HS; Norton, MA; (Y); Debate Tm; Girl Scts; JA; Political Wkr; Chorus; Nwsp Rptr; Yrbk Stf; Var Sec Vllybl; NEDT Awd; Voice Dem Awd; Ntl JR Achvt Conf 83 & 85; MIT Educ Stds Pgm Stu, Tchr, Adminstr & JR SR Prom Commtte 82-85; U Of MA Amherst; Ntl Pk Mngmnt.

WILLIAMS, MELODY; New Bedford HS; New Bedford, MA; (Y); Boys Clb Am; Cmnty Wkr; Dance Clb; School Musical; JV Bsktbl; Trk; Hon Roll; Hnbl Mntn Lit Essy 85; NAACP 84-85; Howard U; Fine Arts.

WILLIAMS, MICHELLE; Notre Dame Acad; Marshfield, MA; (Y); 22/120; Camera Clb; Church Yth Grp; Debate Tm; Drama Clb; English Clb; Intnl Clb; Band; Chorus; Hon Roll; NHS; Catholic U; Intl Rel.

WILLIAMS, TANYA J; Boston Latin Acad; Dorchester, MA; (Y); Church Yth Grp; Debate Tm; Latin Clb; Band; School Musical; Symp Band; Rep Soph Cls; JV Sftbl; U Of MA-BOSTON; Psych.

WILLIAMSON, DEBRA; Hoosac Valley HS; Adams, MA; (Y); JA; Ski Clb; Rep Frsh Cls; Rep Soph Cls; Rep Jr Cls; Rep Sr Cls; Trs Stu Cncl; JV Crs Cntry; Stat Ftbl; Var Socr; Peer Edctr 84-85; Exch Club Mbr 85; Bus.

WILLIAMSON, JAMES; Catholic Memorial HS; Roslindale, MA; (Y); 5/277; FBLA; Hosp Aide; Key Clb; ROTC; Pep Band; Nwsp Bus Mgr; Bsktbl; Capt Ftbl; Im Sftbl; NHS; Frvw Co Inc Employee Of Mnth 85; Bstn Plc Dept JR Ptrlmns Awd 85; Hnrb Mntn MIT Sci Fair 85; Harvard U.

WILLIAMSON, JEANNETTE; Lynn Classical HS; Lynn, MA; (Y); Church Yth Grp; JA; Library Aide; Office Aide; Pep Clb; Spanish Clb; Chorus; Church Choir; Drm & Bgl; Variety Show; Intl Forgn Lang Awd-Spansh 84; Williams Coll; Pediatrcn.

WILLIAMSON, SANDRA L; Cardinal Spellman HS; Hanover, MA; (Y); 19/203; Sec Drama Clb; Sec Chorus; School Musical; Variety Show; Ed Lit Mag; NHS; Pres Schlr; Sci Fair-1st Pl 85; MIT St Sci Fair-2nd Pl 85; Cardinal Spellman Schlrshp 85; Stonehill Coll; Comm.

WILLIE, JAMES T; Concord-Carlisle HS; Concord, MA; (Y); 77/276; Boy Scts; Church Yth Grp; Varsity Clb; Off Concert Band; Jazz Band; Off Mrchg Band; School Musical; Im Bsktbl; JV Lcrss; Var Socr; Dept Awd Mus 84.

WILLIS, DAVID; Brockton HS; Brockton, MA; (Y); 98/1100; Boys Clb Am; Church Yth Grp; Bsbl; Tennis; Wt Lftg; High Hon Roll; Hon Roll; Comp Sci.

WILLMAN, WENDY A; Algonquin HS; Southboro, MA; (Y); 12/221; Var L Bsktbl; Var L Vllybl; High Hon Roll; NHS; Athl Awd Bsktbl 85.

WILSON, AMANDA LYNN; Ayer SR HS; Ayer, MA; (Y); Sec Church Yth Grp; Cmnty Wkr; 4-H; Hosp Aide; Ski Clb; Yrbk Stf; Powder Puff Ftbl; 4-H Awd; Hon Roll; Mcdonalds Crw Prsn Of Mth 85; Accntng.

WILSON, BETH E; Grafton SR HS; N Grafton, MA; (Y); 14/130; Band; Chorus; Yrbk Stf; Pres Stu Cncl; Var L Fld Hcky; Capt Trk; Hon Roll; VP NHS; St Schlr; Athltc Awd 85; Music, Soc Studys & Phy Ed Awds 85; Grew/Grange/Sideline/Theresa Taft & Giles Schlrshps; Boston Coll; Erly Chldhd.

WILSON, CRAIG; Mansfield HS; Mansfield, MA; (Y); 3/177; Am Leg Boys St; Varsity Clb; Band; Capt Ftbl; Capt Trk; DAR Awd; Lion Awd; Pres NHS; Prncpls Am Flag Awd 85; Prncpls Awrd Outstndg Stdnt Athlte 85; US Nvl Acad; Nvl Offcer.

WILSON, DIANE; Barnstable HS; Centerville, MA; (Y); VP Pres AFS; Drama Clb; Key Clb; Stat Bsktbl; Powder Puff Ftbl; Trk; Bio.

WILSON, ELIZABETH; Commerce HS; Springfield, MA; (Y); Sec Church Yth Grp; Cmnty Wkr; Dance Clb; Teachers Aide; Drill Tm; Nwsp Phtg; Nwsp Rptr; Rep Stu Cncl; Gym; Hon Roll; Miss Teenage Bethel 85; Accntng.

WILSON, MARY; Chelsea HS; Chelsea, MA; (Y); 11/220; Cmnty Wkr; Rep Soph Cls; High Hon Roll; Hon Roll; VP NHS; Church Yth Grp; Political Wkr; Science Clb; Var Bsktbl; Var Crs Cntry; Hrbrt Kuprsmth Schlrshp Gvn To Outstndng Schlr-Athl 85; Cert Awd Ntl Hnr Soc-VP 85; Clark U.

WILSON, MARY ELLEN; Holy Name Central Catholic HS; Northbridge, MA; (Y); Drama Clb; French Clb; Pep Clb; Science Clb; School Musical; School Play; JV Trk; High Hon Roll; NHS; Most Outstndg Stu Frnch I; Most Outstndg Stu German I; Intrprtr.

WILSON, MICHELE; Ayer SR HS; Shirley, MA; (Y); 18/160; Am Leg Aux Girls St; Band; Orch; High Hon Roll; Hon Roll; NHS; Fitchburg ST Clg; Bus Admin.

WILSON, PAMELA; Somerset HS; Somerset, MA; (Y); 20/350; Debate Tm; Hosp Aide; JA; Math Tm; Ski Clb; Color Guard; Mrchg Band; Orch; High Hon Roll; NHS; U MA-AMHERST; Biochem.

WILSON, PENNY W; Lexington HS; Lexington, MA; (Y); Am Leg Aux Girls St; Concert Band; Mrchg Band; Nwsp Rptr; Ed Yrbk Sprt Ed; Var Crs Cntry; Var Capt Trk; Jr NHS; NHS; Crss Cntry Al-Star 84; Wintr Trk Al-Star 2 Mi 85.

WILSON, RONALD; Holyoke Catholic HS; Chicopee, MA; (Y); 45/149; Boys Clb Am; Computer Clb; JA; Spanish Clb; Band; School Musical; School Play; Sec Jr Cls; Sec Sr Cls; Rep Stu Cncl; Syracuse; Lbrl Arts.

WILSON, SANDY; Lexington HS; Lexington, MA; (Y); Yrbk Stf; Mgr Ftbl; Engl.

WINDOLOSKI, MARK D; Agawam HS; Feeding Hills, MA; (Y); 2/350; Am Leg Boys St; High Hon Roll; Spanish NHS; Physcs.

WING, GARY W; Burlington HS; Burlington, MA; (Y); 25/315; Boy Scts; Math Tm; Var Capt Swmmng; Hon Roll; NHS; Lowell Son All Star Swmmng 84 & 85; Mech Engrng.

WING, WILLIAM; Marian HS; Framingham, MA; (Y); Boy Scts; Camera Clb; Exploring; Ski Clb; Nwsp Phtg; Yrbk Phtg; Crs Cntry; Wt Lftg.

WINGOOD, PAMELA; Bedford HS; Bedford, MA; (Y); 3/229; Math Tm; Band; Concert Band; Nwsp Stf; Crs Cntry; Trk; Cit Awd; DAR Awd; High Hon Roll; NHS; Commonwealth Schlr Schlrshp 85; MA Soc Of Prfssnl Engr Awd 85; Tufts U; Engrng.

WINKELMES JR, DON; Westwood HS; Westwood, MA; (Y); 52/214; AFS; Church Yth Grp; School Musical; Stage Crew; Variety Show; Lit Mag; JV Socr; JV Tennis; Hon Roll; Coll.

WINKLER, ALFRED C; Groton Schl; Jamaica, NY; (Y); VP Frsh Cls; Pres Soph Cls; Sec Jr Cls; VP Sr Cls; Stu Cncl; Var JV Bsbl; JV Bsktbl; Im Capt Socr; Cmndtn Natl Achvt Schlrshp Pgm-Minority Stu For SAT Scores 84; Med.

WINKLER, MARK; Longmeadow HS; Longmeadow, MA; (Y); Boy Scts; Church Yth Grp; Exploring; German Clb; Office Aide; Political Wkr; Teachers Aide; Im Var Mgr(s); Im JV Tennis; Hon Roll; Bently Coll; Bus Mgmt.

WINKLER, RICHARD A; Sharon HS; Sharon, MA; (Y); 10/225; Am Leg Boys St; Spanish Clb; Temple Yth Grp; Nwsp Rptr; Nwsp Stf; Rep Sr Cls; Trs Stu Cncl; Var Socr; Hon Roll; NHS; Hnrbl Ment Rsrch Paper Phi Alpha Theta Hist Conf 85; Liberal Arts.

WINNING, KELLY; Whitman-Hanson Regional HS; Hanson, MA; (Y); Yrbk Stf; Rep Stu Cncl; Bsktbl; JV Crs Cntry; JV Trk; Hon Roll; NHS; Hstry Clb; Prm Cmmtte; Intntl Bus.

WINTER, KAREN; St Marys HS; Worcester, MA; (Y); Drama Clb; School Musical; Nwsp Rptr; Nwsp Stf; Yrbk Rptr; Yrbk Stf; VP Soph Cls; Sec Sr Cls; Capt Var Cheerleading; Frances Hiatt Schlrshp 85-86; Boston Coll Acadmc Schlrshp 85-86; MA ST Schlrshp 85-86; Boston Coll; Pre-Dental.

WINTER, MARK A; Fitchburg HS; Fitchburg, MA; (Y); 48/225; Am Leg Boys St; Chess Clb; Computer Clb; Latin Clb; Math Clb; Math Tm; Pep Clb; Political Wkr; Concert Band; Mrchg Band; U Of Lowell; Mech Engr.

WIRTH, AMY; Nipmuc Regional HS; Upton, MA; (Y); 5/85; Model UN; Ski Clb; Yrbk Stf; Rep Frsh Cls; VP Soph Cls; VP Jr Cls; VP Sr Cls; Trs Stu Cncl; JV Bsktbl; JV Crs Cntry; Stu Gov Day Alt 85; Vrsty Fld Hockey-Most Impvd 84-85; Prom Cmmttee 85; Biology.

WISNASKAS, WILLIAM; Whitman Hanson Regional HS; Whitman, MA; (Y); Boy Scts; Cmnty Wkr; Political Wkr; JV Crs Cntry; Var L Trk; High Hon Roll; Hon Roll; NHS; Northeastern U; Comp Prog.

WISSELL, MATTHEW; St Peter-Marian HS; Rochdale, MA; (Y); Church Yth Grp; JA; Political Wkr; Stat Ice Hcky; Stat Socr; Hon Roll; Exec Bd Mbr SADD 84-85; Framingham ST Coll; Atty.

WITHBROE, NANCY; Arlington HS; Arlington, MA; (Y); Church Yth Grp; Sec French Clb; Office Aide; Chorus; Church Choir; Madrigals; School Musical; High Hon Roll; NHS; Church Music Comm 84-86; Am Assoc Teachers French Awd 83-84.

WITHINGTON, WENDY; St Bernards C C HS; Fitchburg, MA; (S); 17/173; Drama Clb; French Clb; Yrbk Stf; Var Fld Hcky; JV Sftbl; Hon Roll; Med.

WITKOP, THERESA; Minnechaug R HS; Wilbraham, MA; (Y); Church Yth Grp; Intnl Clb; Chorus; School Musical; School Play; Nwsp Stf; NCTE Awd.

WITKOSKI, DAVID; Dennis-Yarmouth Regional HS; Dennis, MA; (Y); Art Clb; Church Yth Grp; FCA; Ski Clb; JV Bsktbl; JV Golf; Var L Tennis; Boston Globe Art Hon Men 85; D-Y Tchrs Assn Awd Art & Arch 84; Boys State 85; Coaches Awd Bsktbll 85; Comm Art.

WITOVER, JULIE; Andover HS; Andover, MA; (S); 110/435; DECA; VP Sec Temple Yth Grp; Yrbk Ed-Chief; Swmmng; DECA Ntls 3rd Pl 85; U Of MA-AMHERST; Fshn Merchndg.

WITZMANN, STEPHEN W; Dennis Yarmouth Regional HS; South Yarmouth, MA; (Y); L Crs Cntry; Underground ZZ Top Fan Clb; US Military Acad.

WIZWER, HEIDI; Greenfield HS; Greenfield, MA; (Y); Exploring; Spanish Clb; Temple Yth Grp; Var L Tennis; Var L Vllybl; Hon Roll; Bay ST Games Vlybl 85; Bus.

WOIDYLA, STEVE; Haverhill HS; Haverhill, MA; (Y); VP Trs Church Yth Grp; JV Ice Hcky; Auto Tech.

WOJCIK, LISA M; Ludlow HS; Ludlow, MA; (Y); 6/275; JA; High Hon Roll; Hon Roll; Ntl Merit Fdtn, Outstndng Bus Stu 85, 84; Holyoke CC; Exec Secy.

WOLF, ED; Stoughton HS; Stoughton, MA; (Y); Boy Scts; Intnl Clb; Temple Yth Grp; Nwsp Rptr; Nwsp Stf; Trk; High Hon Roll; Hon Roll; Bus.

WOLFE, ANNA; Hingham HS; Hingham, MA; (Y); Band; Mrchg Band; Yrbk Ed-Chief; Sec Frsh Cls; Var Bsktbl; Var Fld Hcky; Var Lcrss; Hnr Rl.

WOLFE, DEREK; Monument Mountain Regional HS; Lee, MA; (Y); Church Yth Grp; Computer Clb; Yrbk Stf; JV Var Bsbl; JV Bsktbl; Var Golf; High Hon Roll; Hon Roll; NHS; Rensselaer Medal Math,Sci 85; Bus Comm Schlrshp 85; RPI; Nuc Physics.

WOLK, AMY; Natick HS; Natick, MA; (Y); 58/468; Sec Pres Temple Yth Grp; School Musical; Rep Frsh Cls; Rep Soph Cls; Rep Jr Cls; Rep Stu Cncl; Score Keeper; JV Vllybl; Hon Roll; Pol Sci.

WOLLENHAUPT, THOMAS; St Dominic Savio HS; Winthrop, MA; (Y); 8/103; Ski Clb; Variety Show; Var L Crs Cntry; Im Ftbl; Var L Trk; High Hon Roll; NHS; Chess Clb; JA; Letterman Clb; 2nd Pl Dist Medley CCL Rly Crnvl Trck 85; NTA Chmp Winthrop Yacht Clb 83; Awd Lawdy Oratry Cntst 83; St Anselm Coll; Bus.

WOLOSZ, BARBARA; St Marys HS; Worcester, MA; (Y); 8/56; Church Yth Grp; Spanish Clb; Var Bsktbl; Var Sftbl; Hon Roll; Jr NHS; Ace Carrier Awd 85; ST Champ K Of C Free Throsw 84; ST Champ ST Police Ftbl Throw 84.

WOLRICH, ELYSE; Randolph HS; Randolph, MA; (Y); Hosp Aide; Pres Intnl Clb; Spanish Clb; Sec Temple Yth Grp; Color Guard; High Hon Roll; JC Awd; NHS; Stage Crew; Yrbk Stf; Intrstdy 1st Prz Smmr Trp Europe 85; Smith Coll Bk Awd 85; Natl Hstry Day Locl Comptn Wnnr 85; Pre-Med.

WONG, BRENDA; Boston Latin Schl; Brighton, MA; (Y); 48/318; Concert Band; NHS; Pres Schlr; Grls HS Schlrshp 85; ACCESS Schlrshp 85; SR Music Awd 85; Boston U; Comm.

WONG, DIANA S; Randolph HS; Randolph, MA; (Y); Intnl Clb; Co-Capt Color Guard; Trs Stu Cncl; L Crs Cntry; Trk; High Hon Roll; Hon Roll; NHS; Bus.

WONG, FRED J; Xaverian Brothers HS; Brockton, MA; (S); Math Tm; Yrbk Stf; High Hon Roll; Hon Roll; NHS; Ntl Merit Ltr; Green Belt-Karate 83; Math.

WONG, FUNGWAH; Cambridge Rindge & Latin Schl; Cambridge, MA; (Y); Accounting.

WONG, HUBERT S; Drury SR HS; N Adams, MA; (Y); 44/178; Camera Clb; Church Yth Grp; Var L Golf; Hon Roll; Accntng.

WONG, LOUISA; Boston Latin Schl; Allston, MA; (Y); 56/319; Church Yth Grp; Chorus; Swing Chorus; Yrbk Stf; NHS; VP Boston Exploration Soc; Treas Aslan Cultures Clb; Activities Coordntr Aeroncl Engrng Soc; Tufts U; Librl Arts.

WONG, MONICA SIU; Randolph HS; Randolph, MA; (Y); French Clb; Intnl Clb; Math Tm; Nwsp Stf; Trk; Hon Roll; NHS; Econ.

WONG, PETER; Boston Latin HS; Boston, MA; (Y); 90/319; Camera Clb; JA; Pres Science Clb; Yrbk Phtg; Sr Cls; Vllybl; NHS; Prfct Atten Awd; Fidelty Prz 82; Branders U; Bio.

WONG, PETER; Boston Latin Schl; Boston, MA; (Y); JA; Science Clb; Hon Roll; NHS; Natl Sci Olympiad Physics W/Distnctn 85.

WOO, REBECCA A; Lowell HS; Lowell, MA; (Y); 9/552; Church Yth Grp; Cmnty Wkr; Trs VP Intnl Clb; Latin Clb; Yrbk Stf; Rep Soph Cls; Rep Jr Cls; Rep Sr Cls; Rep Stu Cncl; High Hon Roll; Natl Hnr Socty Schlrshp 85; Friends Of Lowell H S Schlrshp 85; Trinity Coll; Frnch.

WOOD, CHRISSY; Monument Mountain HS; Lenox, MA; (Y); 4/150; Band; Concert Band; Mrchg Band; Orch; School Musical; School Play; Rep Stu Cncl; L Gym; JV Sftbl; Var Trk; Pittsfield Music Schl Cncrt Band 82-83; Westrn Mass Dist Cncrt Band & 77l Musicl Orch 83-84; Lib Arts.

WOOD, CHRISTOPHER; Brooks Schl; Westport, CT; (Y); Letterman Clb; Acpl Chr; Band; Chorus; Jazz Band; School Musical; School Play; Pres Frsh Cls; Ftbl; Wt Lftg; Rep/Pres Mnrty Stu Affrs 83-85; Jazz Octet 83-85; Georgetown; Law.

WOOD, DARLEEN; Holy Name HS; Auburn, MA; (Y); Church Yth Grp; Computer Clb; 4-H; Pep Clb; Church Choir; School Musical; Fld Hcky; Sftbl; Swmmng; Trk; Certs In Humnts, Biol & Cmmnctns 84; Tuffs U; Vet.

WOOD, HEIDI E; Reading Memorial HS; Peoria, IL; (Y); Church Yth Grp; Trs French Clb; Band; Concert Band; Jazz Band; Mrchg Band; Hon Roll; SR Dist Band 84; Merrimack Coll; Early Chldhd Ed.

WOOD, JULIE; W Springfield SR HS; W Springfield, MA; (S); 8/240; Am Leg Aux Girls St; Band; Flag Corp; Jazz Band; Sftbl; Hon Roll; NHS; Ntl Merit Ltr; Spanish NHS; Mc Donald All Amer Band 84; Amer Muscl Fdtn Awd 84; Stdnt Dir HS Band 84-85; Tufts U; Econ.

WOOD, LORALEE; Saugus HS; Saugus, MA; (Y); 34/322; Teachers Aide; Bsktbl; Powder Puff Ftbl; JV Sftbl; Swmmng; Trk; Hon Roll; Jr NHS; NHS; Computer Clb; Pres Phy Ftns 85; Comp Svc Awd 85; NE U; Comp Sys Mgmt.

WOOD, MARGARET; Manchester JR SR HS; Manchester, MA; (Y); Church Yth Grp; Teachers Aide; Var JV Bsktbl; JV Fld Hcky; Var Capt Sftbl; Im Vllybl; High Hon Roll; Hon Roll; Erly Chldhd Ed.

WOOD, MICHAEL; Arlington Catholic HS; Wilmington, MA; (Y); 30/158; VP JA; Spanish Clb; Ftbl; Hon Roll; Wlmngn SR Bsbl League Chmps 84; JR Achvt Prfct Atndnc 84-85; Engrng.

WOODFORD, JONATHAN; Hudson HS; Hudson, MA; (Y); 11/150; Boys Clb Am; Church Yth Grp; Cmnty Wkr; Math Tm; JV Var Bsktbl; JV Ftbl; Score Keeper; Timer; Hon Roll; Ntl Merit Ltr; Wocomal Math Leag Hgh Scr 83; Contntl Math Leag Hgh Scr 83; Aeron Engrng.

WOODIN, SARA; Monument Mountain HS; Stockbridge, MA; (Y); Hosp Aide; High Hon Roll; Hon Roll; Nrsng.

WOODMAN, SANDY; Revere HS; Revere, MA; (Y); Rep Jr Cls; JV Bsktbl; Var Fld Hcky; Var Trk; Babson Coll; Chld Psych.

WOODRUFF, JASE; Mt Everett HS; N Egremont, MA; (Y); Am Leg Boys St; Drama Clb; Ski Clb; Lit Mag; JV Bsbl; Var Socr; Var Wrstlng; Hon Roll; Skidmore U; Bus Ownrshp.

WOODS, ANNE; Fontbonne Acad; Milton, MA; (Y); 62/130; Art Clb; Church Yth Grp; Drama Clb; Library Aide; Science Clb; Stage Crew; Var L Fld Hcky; Var L Sftbl; Art Awd 81; U Of MA-BOSTON; Ec.

WOODS, JOANNE; Holyoke Catholic HS; S Hadley, MA; (Y); 22/138; Church Yth Grp; Computer Clb; French Clb; Latin Clb; Color Guard; Stage Crew; Hon Roll; Prfct Atten Awd; Frnch III Cert Awd 84; Alg II Cert Awd 85; Frnch II Cert Awd 83.

WOODS, JOSEPH; Chicopee Comprehensive HS; Chicopee, MA; (Y); 1/311; Math Tm; Science Clb; Spanish Clb; Rep Jr Cls; Rep Sr Cls; Rep Stu Cncl; CC Awd; High Hon Roll; NHS; Val; MA Schl Sprntdnts Cert Acad Exclnc 85; Elks Most Vlbl Stu Schlrshp Awd 85; U Of Notre Dame; Aerosp Engrng.

WOODS, KATHLEEN; Bishop Fenwick HS; Wenham, MA; (Y); 24/216; Church Yth Grp; Cmnty Wkr; Drama Clb; Speech Tm; School Musical; School Play; Nwsp Ed-Chief; Yrbk Phtg; Hist Excel Achvt; MIAA Swmmng ST Chmpshp Rnnr Up; Boston U; Comm.

WOODS, MICHELLE; Holyoke Catholic HS; S Hadley, MA; (Y); 15/138; Church Yth Grp; Computer Clb; French Clb; Latin Clb; Yrbk Stf; High Hon Roll; French II,IV,Chem Awd 83-85.

WORCESTER, SHARON L; Andover HS; Andover, MA; (Y); 43/424; AFS; Church Yth Grp; Debate Tm; DECA; Yrbk Stf; Var Trk; Cit Awd; High Hon Roll; Hon Roll; NHS; Perfmg Arts-Piano; Twn Soccer; Chrch Bsktbl; Bus Admin.

WORDEN, JAMES; Arlington HS; Arlington, MA; (S); 16/417; Boys Clb Am; Camera Clb; Computer Clb; Math Clb; Math Tm; Political Wkr; Pres Science Clb; Band; Concert Band; Jazz Band; 1st MA ST Sci Fair 84; W O Taylor Schrlshp 84; Rotary Awd 83-84; MIT; Mec Engr.

WORKMAN, KERRI LYNNE; Somerset HS; Somerset, MA; (Y); 5/300; Math Tm; Concert Band; Mrchg Band; Orch; Symp Band; High Hon Roll; NHS; Musctwn Fest Prncss; PM Clb Schlrshp; Friends Of Mus Schlrshp; Wellesley Coll; Math.

WORRELL, A BABETTE; Tantasgua Rgnl SR HS; Brimfield, MA; (Y); 36/193; Pres Church Yth Grp; Drama Clb; Varsity Clb; Chorus; Drill Tm; School Play; Bsktbl; Fld Hcky; Sftbl; Comm.

WORSH, LISA; Wellesley SR HS; Wellesley, MA; (Y); 29/289; Church Yth Grp; Key Clb; Chorus; Badmtn; Gym; Socr; Hon Roll; Jr NHS; NHS; Acadia U.

WRENN, KATHRYN; Doherty Memorial HS; Worcester, MA; (Y); 42/356; Church Yth Grp; Spanish Clb; Chorus; Church Choir; Yrbk Stf; High Hon Roll; Hon Roll; Jr NHS; Hst NHS; Spanish NHS; Boston Glbe Schltc Art Comp 84; Art Illustr.

WRIGHT, ANITA T; Leominster HS; Leominster, MA; (Y); Debate Tm; Pres DECA; Stage Crew; Yrbk Stf; Rep Soph Cls; Rep Jr Cls; Rep Stu Cncl; Trk; Peer Ldr Pgm 84-85; Gov Dukakis Drug & Alcohl Comm 84; Lwyr.

WRIGHT, HELEN; Lexington HS; Lexington, MA; (Y); Math Clb; Chorus; School Musical; School Play; Athl Awds 82-83; Hstry.

WRIGHT, JANET E; Whitman-Hanson Regional HS; Whitman, MA; (Y); 18/325; Red Cross Aide; Varsity Clb; Variety Show; Yrbk Ed-Chief; Rep Frsh Cls; Rep Soph Cls; Rep Jr Cls; Rep Sr Cls; Sec Stu Cncl; Stat Bsktbl; Dr Dnld Mc Enroe Memrl Schlrshp 85; Boston U; Phys Thrpy.

WRIGHT, PAMELA; Haverhill HS; Haverhill, MA; (Y); 119/390; Civic Clb; Spanish Clb; Band; Chorus; Church Choir; Concert Band; Mrchg Band; Masonic Awd; Mst Imprvd JR HHS Band 84; Gordon Coll; Bus Admin.

WRIGHT, PAMELA L; Chelmsford HS; N Chelmsford, MA; (Y); 20/565; French Clb; Varsity Clb; Band; Concert Band; Mrchg Band; School Musical; French Hon Soc; High Hon Roll; NHS; Ntl Merit SF; Engr.

WRIGHT, ROBERT E; Melrose HS; Melrose, MA; (Y); Am Leg Boys St; Boy Scts; Var Ftbl; Trk; Wt Lftg; U MA Amherst; Bus.

WRIGHT-HUDSON, KIMBERLY; Fontbonne Acad; Dorchstr, MA; (Y); Church Yth Grp; Drama Clb; Hosp Aide; Intnl Clb; Library Aide; High Hon Roll; JC Awd; Libry Achv 85; JR Prom Queen 85; Georgetown U.

WRIGHTINGTON, TAMMY; BMC Durfee HS; Fall River, MA; (Y); Drama Clb; Intnl Clb; Spanish Clb; Nrsg.

WRONA, MARGUERITE; Ludlow SR HS; Ludlow, MA; (Y); Am Leg Aux Girls St; Chorus; High Hon Roll; JETS Awd; Sec NHS; NEDT Awd; Voice Dem Awd; Hosp Aide; Math Tm; Band; Rensselaer Medal Of Hnr 85; Wellesley Coll Bk Awd 85; Smith Coll Bk Awd 85; Dartmouth; Engrng.

WRUBEL, TINA; North HS; Worcester, MA; (Y); Church Yth Grp; Office Aide; Varsity Clb; Socr; Hon Roll; Career Day Worcester Essay Cont Wnnr 85; Holy Cross; Bus Mngmnt.

WU, CURTIS Q; Agawam HS; Agawam, MA; (Y); AFS; Am Leg Boys St; Capt Quiz Bowl; Band; Lit Mag; Var Tennis; French Hon Soc; NHS; Ntl Merit SF; Cmnty Wkr; Rensselaer Awd; Dartmouth Bk Awd; Engrng.

WU, MICHAEL; Boston Vo-Tech; Boston, MA; (Y); Chess Clb; Cmnty Wkr; JV Socr; Hon Roll.

WYNNE, MEGAN; Framingham South HS; Framingham, MA; (Y); 10/263; Latin Clb; Color Guard; School Musical; Yrbk Ed-Chief; Var Bsktbl; High Hon Roll; Hon Roll; Pres NHS; Ntl Merit Ltr; Brown U Book Awd Excllnc In Englsh 85.

WYSOCKI, CHRISTOPHER; Weymouth North HS; N Weymouth, MA; (Y); Key Clb; Spanish Clb; Nwsp Phtg; Nwsp Sprt Ed; Yrbk Stf; JV Lcrss; Var Tennis; Hon Roll; Wessagusset Prnt Cncl Schlrshp 85; MA ST Schlrshp 85; Suffolk U; Engl.

WYSOCKI, MARK; Cathedral HS; Springfield, MA; (Y); 64/465; Math Clb; Model UN; Science Clb; Ski Clb; Teachers Aide; Jr NHS; Ntl Merit Ltr; New N Middle Schl Schrlshp 85; Semi Fin St Prz Math Ex 84; Embry Riddle Aeronautcl U; Engr.

YABLONSKI, CHRISTINE; Gardner HS; Gardner, MA; (Y); 14/169; Pep Clb; Spanish Clb; Chorus; School Musical; Variety Show; Clark U; Psych.

YACUZZO, MARY A; Easthampton HS; Easthampton, MA; (Y); Church Yth Grp; Teachers Aide; Chorus; Off Stu Cncl; Var Cheerleading; Score Keeper; Hon Roll; Holoyke CC; Elem Ed.

YAN, ALBERT; Boston Latin Schl; Boston, MA; (Y); 22/300; JA; Science Clb; High Hon Roll; NHS; Ntl Merit Ltr; Prfct Atten Awd; Lawrnc Prz For Gen Excell In Condct & Stds 83-84; Engrng.

YARUSH, TIMOTHY; Franklin HS; Franklin, MA; (Y); Church Yth Grp; Exploring; School Play; JV Ftbl; Var Wrstlng; Hon Roll; 4th Pl Belmont Wrestling Invitational 85; Lawyer.

YEE, JEANNE N; Northfield Mount Hermon HS; Malden, MA; (Y); Cmnty Wkr; Debate Tm; Ed Yrbk Stf; Rep Stu Cncl; High Hon Roll; Ntl Merit Ltr; Harvard Bk Prize 85; Robert Cade Wilson Schlrhsp 85; Baxter Prize 85.

YEE, KENT; Umana Tech; Boston, MA; (Y); ROTC; Hon Roll.

YEE, MARY; Salem HS; Salem, MA; (Y); German Clb; Math Tm; Science Clb; Orch; High Hon Roll; NHS; School Musical; Rep Frsh Cls; Fld Hcky; Engrng.

YEGERLEHNER, DEBORAH; Doherty Memorial HS; Worcester, MA; (Y); Church Yth Grp; Drama Clb; Girl Scts; Hosp Aide; Library Aide; Chorus; Church Choir; Orch; School Play; Hon Roll.

YENS, CHRISTOPHER R; The Cambridge Schl; Boston, MA; (Y); Am Leg Boys St; Capt Chess Clb; Debate Tm; Chrmn Math Clb; Bsktbl; Lcrss; Socr.

YERARDI, KRIS; Woburn SR HS; Woburn, MA; (S); Drama Clb; JA; Leo Clb; Ski Clb; Spanish Clb; Off Jr Cls; Stu Cncl; JV Bsktbl; Var Fld Hcky; Sftbl; U Of ; Nh.

YERKES, JEFF; Newton South HS; Newton, MA; (Y); Civic Clb; French Clb; Political Wkr; Radio Clb; JV Tennis; Hon Roll.

YEZERSKI, JONATHAN A; Andover HS; Andover, MA; (Y); 37/403; Rep Frsh Cls; Rep Stu Cncl; Capt Var Crs Cntry; Capt Var Trk; Hon Roll; NHS; Educ.

YIP, MARGARET; Boston Technical HS; Boston, MA; (Y); 2/230; High Hon Roll; Hon Roll; NHS; St Schlr; Boston U; Pre-Med.

YIU, TRACY; Boston Technical HS; Boston, MA; (Y); 28/250; Intnl Clb; Library Aide; Off Sr Cls; Hon Roll; U MA-AMHERST; Bus.

YON, KERRI; Franklin HS; Franklin, MA; (Y); Church Yth Grp; Yrbk Ed-Chief; Lit Mag; Trk; Hon Roll; Advrtsng.

YORNS, MARK; Ware HS; Ware, MA; (Y); Am Leg Boys St; Math Clb; Math Tm; Stu Cncl; Capt Var Bsbl; Ftbl; High Hon Roll; Hon Roll; Excell In Comp Sci 85; Pro Merito 85; Comp Prog.

YOUNG, ADAM; Gardner HS; Gardner, MA; (Y); 7/170; Am Leg Boys St; Stage Crew; Var L Bsktbl; JV Crs Cntry; JV Ice Hcky; Var L Tennis; Var L Trk; Hon Roll; Ntl Merit Ltr; Coll Holy Cross.

YOUNG, ELIZABETH; Scituate HS; Scituate, MA; (Y); 18/280; Pres Church Yth Grp; Ski Clb; Yrbk Stf; JV Bsktbl; JV Socr; Hon Roll; NHS; Zoolgy.

YOUNG, JAY C; Pioneer Valley Regional HS; Bernardston, MA; (Y); Am Leg Boys St; Chess Clb; Church Yth Grp; Drama Clb; Varsity Clb; School Play; Var Bsbl; Var Bsktbl; Var Capt Socr; JV Trk; Ldrshp Gro 84-86; Mgmt.

YOUNG, KATHERINE; Arlington Catholic HS; Billerica, MA; (Y); 41/148; Church Yth Grp; French Clb; Hosp Aide; Intnl Clb; Teachers Aide; Nwsp Ed-Chief; Hon Roll; Nrthestrn U; Physcl Thrpst.

YOUNG, SEAN D; Xaverian Br HS; Foxboro, MA; (S); 20/235; Art Clb; French Clb; Letterman Clb; Varsity Clb; Yrbk Rptr; Var Capt Swmmng; Wt Lftg; Hon Roll; Ntl Merit Ltr; Leag All-Star Swmmng 82-84; Ntl Art Hnr Soc 83.

YOUNG, TRACY; Dracut SR HS; Dracut, MA; (Y); Key Clb; Yrbk Stf; Hon Roll; U Lowell; Nrsng.

YOVAN, JOHN; Shepherd Hill Regional HS; Charlton, MA; (Y); Am Leg Boys St; Ski Clb; Spanish Clb; JV Bsbl; Var Ftbl; Var Golf; Var Ice Hcky; Im Wt Lftg; Outstndng Achvt Bio 84; Fin.

YPHANTES, STEPHANIE; Westwood HS; Westwood, MA; (Y); 63/220; AFS; Key Clb; Stat L Bsktbl; JV Fld Hcky; L Mgr(s); Hon Roll; Psych.

YU, ANGELA Y H; North Quincy HS; Quincy, MA; (Y); 42/389; Computer Clb; Science Clb; Spanish Clb; School Musical; Vllybl; High Hon Roll; Hon Roll; NHS; Pres Schlr; Spanish NHS; Pres Acadmc Fit Awd 85; Outstndng Achvt Spnsh 84; Boston Coll; Law.

YU, LUCATHY; Belmont HS; Belmont, MA; (Y); 15/300; Church Yth Grp; Intnl Clb; PAVAS; Color Guard; Mrchg Band; Stage Crew; Hon Roll; NHS; Carl A Westphal Memrl Schlrshp 85; U C Berkeley; Bus.

YUE, PETER; Boston Technical HS; Brighton, MA; (Y); Church Yth Grp; Church Choir; Rep Jr Cls; Hon Roll.

YURKINS, MARK; Bridgewater-Rayham Regional HS; Bridgewater, MA; (Y); JV Bsbl; JV Bsktbl; Im Ftbl; JV Scrkpr Socr; Cit Awd; Hon Roll; JETS Awd; Wentworth; Engrng.

YVON, SHARI; Chicopee Comprehensive HS; Chicopee, MA; (Y); 5/308; JCL; Latin Clb; Band; Concert Band; Mrchg Band; Bausch & Lomb Sci Awd; NHS; St Schlr; Smith Coll Bk Awd 84; Ltr & Pin Schls Match Wits Tm 84-85; Natl Latin Exam Awd 82; U Of MA; Chem.

ZABLE, MARJORIE E; New Bedford HS; New Bedford, MA; (Y); 11/600; Cmnty Wkr; Math Tm; Lit Mag; Rep Jr Cls; Var Tennis; Var Vllybl; NHS; Voice Dem Awd; Debate Tm; Intnl Clb; Cent III Ldrshp Cntst 84; Guidepstyth Wrtng Cntst 85; Boston Clg; Intl Fnce.

ZACCARDI, DEBORAH A; Norton HS; Norton, MA; (Y); 7/118; Church Yth Grp; Sec Pep Clb; Rep Varsity Clb; Sec Band; Sec Concert Band; Sec Mrchg Band; School Play; Yrbk Stf; Rep Stu Cncl; JV Bsktbl; Chnclrs Talnt Awd UMASS 85-86; J F Kennedy Mem Awd Trk 85; Tchrs Assn Scholar 85; U Of MA; Nrsg.

ZACCHEO, JOSEPH; Boston College HS; Quincy, MA; (Y); 28/300; JA; Bsktbl; JV Trk; Vllybl; High Hon Roll; Hon Roll; NHS; MIT; Chem Engrg.

ZACHARAKIS, GEORGE; Arlington HS; Arlington, MA; (Y); Sec Church Yth Grp; Nwsp Stf; Pre Law.

ZACHARIAS, RUSSELL; Methuen HS; Methuen, MA; (Y); 78/360; Var L Ftbl; Var L Ice Hcky; Var L Trk; Hon Roll; Comp Sci.

ZAFFINO, BRIAN; Dennis Yarmouth Regional HS; Dennis, MA; (Y); Am Leg Boys St; Church Yth Grp; Ski Clb; JV Trk; Vllybl; High Hon Roll; Hon Roll; Jr NHS; Trs NHS; Delg UN Pilgrmg Yth 85; ECHO 84-85; Knight Altar 82-85; Bus Admin.

ZAGRODNIK, NICOLE L; Frontier Regional HS; S Deerfield, MA; (Y); Girl Scts; Ski Clb; Spanish Clb; Nwsp Stf; Yrbk Stf; Trs Frsh Cls; Stat Bsbl; Var Cheerleading; Hon Roll; 10 Yr Mbr Grl Sctng 85; Eng.

ZAHKA, CYNTHIA L; Belmont HS; Belmont, MA; (Y); Church Yth Grp; Cmnty Wkr; Orch; Variety Show; Socr; Trk.

ZAJK, MELISSA J; Wilbraham & Monson Acad; Ware, MA; (Y); #4 In Class; Model UN; Chorus; Lit Mag; Sec Soph Cls; L Var Tennis; Var Capt Vllybl; Rtry Exchng Schlrshp Sweden 83-84; Hmntrn Awd 83; Cum Laude Soc 85; Georgetown U; Rssn.

ZALK, JULIE; Malden HS; Malden, MA; (Y); 11/500; Girl Scts; Hosp Aide; Key Clb; Office Aide; Pres Temple Yth Grp; Band; Variety Show; Cit Awd; High Hon Roll; Kiwanis Awd; NEMA Engl Awd 85.

ZAMAGNI, ANDY; Malden HS; Malden, MA; (Y); Key Clb; Bowling; Golf; Capt Swmmng; Hon Roll; Bunker Hill; Bus Mgmt.

ZANGARI II, RONALD L; Haverhill HS; Haverhill, MA; (Y); Political Wkr; High Hon Roll; Hon Roll; Elctrncs.

ZAPPITELLI, MICHELE; Everett HS; Everett, MA; (Y); Intnl Clb; Key Clb; Bus Schl; Beautcn.

ZARDESKAS, DONNA; Milford HS; Milford, MA; (Y); #86 In Class; Cmnty Wkr; Hosp Aide; Band; Hon Roll; U MA; Mngmnt.

ZAREMBA, SUSAN; Methuen HS; Methuen, MA; (Y); 12/355; Intnl Clb; Model UN; Var Swmmng; High Hon Roll; NHS; Bus Adm.

ZARINETCHI, FARISA; Brookline HS; Brookline, MA; (Y); Drama Clb; Pres Key Clb; Stage Crew; Variety Show; Yrbk Stf; Ed Lit Mag; JV Sftbl; JV Vllybl; High Hon Roll; Bus.

ZARLE, STIG; Lexington HS; Lexington, MA; (Y); FBLA; Ski Clb; Var L Bsbl; Im Bsktbl; Hon Roll; Bates Clg; Ecnmcs.

ZARTARIAN, VALERIE; Canton HS; Canton, MA; (Y); 1/272; Drama Clb; Math Tm; School Musical; School Play; Yrbk Bus Mgr; Stat Score Keeper; High Hon Roll; NHS; Ntl Merit Ltr; Val; Cntry Clb Ensmb Awd For Drama 83; All-Star Cst Awd Bst Play 84; Prnctn U; Elec Engrng.

ZASKEY, CHRISTINE; Cathedral HS; Chicopee, MA; (Y); 15/500; Am Leg Aux Girls St; Hosp Aide; School Musical; Yrbk Stf; Stu Cncl; Trk; NHS; Polit Sci.

ZASTAWNY, TODD M; Grafton HS; Grafton, MA; (Y); 35/115; Am Leg Boys St; Church Yth Grp; Band; Mrchg Band; School Musical; School Play; Variety Show; Var L Ftbl; Var L Trk; Hon Roll; Comp Drftg.

ZASTREA, LEE; Newton North HS; Auburndale, MA; (Y); Fashion.

ZATERKA, AMY; Tahanto Regional HS; Boylston, MA; (Y); 5/50; 4-H; Girl Scts; Band; Chorus; School Musical; Pres Jr Cls; Rep Stu Cncl; JV Cheerleading; Var Crs Cntry; Sftbl; Math Alg Awd 84; Nrs.

ZAWISLAK, LINDA; Bartlett HS; Webster, MA; (Y); Variety Show; Yrbk Stf; Rep Frsh Cls; Rep Soph Cls; Sec Jr Cls; Sec Sr Cls; Rep Stu Cncl; JV Var Cheerleading; Var Socr; JV Var Sftbl; Bus Admin.

ZDROJEWSKI, MIKE; Woburn SR HS; Woburn, MA; (S); 21/511; Church Yth Grp; Drama Clb; Pres Q&S; Rep Stu Cncl; Im Bsktbl; Var Tennis; Pres NHS; Spanish NHS; Engr.

ZDZIARSKI, JULIE ANN; Monument Mountain HS; Great Barrington, MA; (S); 7/140; Band; School Musical; Nwsp Rptr; VP Stu Cncl; Capt Gym; Trk; High Hon Roll; NHS; Voice Dem Awd; Church Yth Grp; Wstrn MA Primary Prevention Prog 85; Law.

ZEMBA, CHRISTINE; Easthampton HS; Easthampton, MA; (Y); Drama Clb; 4-H; French Clb; Mgr JA; Political Wkr; Teachers Aide; Sec Chorus; School Play; Rep Stu Cncl; Hon Roll; Elem Educ.

ZEMUI, DAWIT; Cambridge Rindge And Latin HS; Cambridge, MA; (Y); 13/543; Art Clb; English Clb; Key Clb; Math Clb; Math Tm; Science Clb; Ski Clb; Varsity Clb; Frsh Cls; Soph Cls; 1st Hon Roll 84-85; Awds Vrsty Tennis 83-84; Northeastern U; Cvl Engrng.

ZERESKI, JENNIFER; Bellingham Memorial HS; Bellingham, MA; (Y); 17/201; VP DECA; Varsity Clb; Color Guard; Nwsp Ed-Chief; Ed Yrbk Stf; Stu Cncl; Var Cheerleading; Var Trk; NHS; Pres Schlr; Providence Coll Acad Schlrshp; 1st Pl MA DECA Rgnl & ST Conf; Providence Coll; Engl.

ZGRODNIK, KIMBERLY; Hopkins Academy HS; Hadley, MA; (S); 1/45; French Clb; Political Wkr; Chorus; Nwsp Ed-Chief; Pres Stu Cncl; Var Sftbl; Elks Awd; NHS; Sci.

ZIAJA, MARK; Hoosac Valley HS; Adams, MA; (Y); Stu Cncl; Var L Socr; Var L Tennis; Voice Dem Awd; Stu Gov Day Rep 85; Boys ST 85; Wgner Coll; Ed.

ZICARO, ANGELA M; St Peter-Morian C C HS; Worcester, MA; (Y); Church Yth Grp; Dance Clb; Drama Clb; School Musical; Nwsp Rptr; Nwsp Stf; Hon Roll; Assumption Coll; Bus.

ZICHELLE, KATHRYN; St Bernards Central Catholic HS; Leominster, MA; (S); 6/162; Church Yth Grp; Latin Clb; Ski Clb; Church Choir; Fld Hcky; Trk; Wt Lftg; High Hon Roll; Hon Roll; NHS.

ZIDES, MARK; Bridgewater-Raynham Regional HS; Raynham, MA; (Y); Am Leg Boys St; Boys Clb Am; FCA; Temple Yth Grp; Nwsp Rptr; Var Bsbl; Var Bsktbl; Coach Actv; Var Socr; Hon Roll; MVP Awd Soccer Clb 85; Sports Bdcstng.

ZIELINSKI, DAN; Cathedral HS; Springfield, MA; (Y); 37/520; Mathletes; Math Clb; Acpl Chr; School Musical; NHS; Prfct Atten Awd; Math Tm; Chorus; Madrigals; School Play; Math.

ZIEMBA, JOHN S; Ludlow HS; Ludlow, MA; (Y); 7/250; Am Leg Boys St; JCL; Yrbk Ed-Chief; Rep Jr Cls; Rep Sr Cls; JV Bsbl; Var Crs Cntry; High Hon Roll; NEDT Awd; Voice Dem Awd; Authr.

ZIKAS, TOMAS; Canton HS; Canton, MA; (Y); 3/265; Boy Scts; Debate Tm; VP Jr Cls; Pres Sr Cls; Var Crs Cntry; JV Socr; JV Tennis; Var Trk; Hon Roll; NHS; Elec Engrng.

ZILLMER, LESLEE; Chicopee Comprehensive HS; Chicopee, MA; (Y); Camera Clb; 4-H; German Clb; Yrbk Phtg; Yrbk Stf; L Crs Cntry; Powder Puff Ftbl; L Swmmng; NHS; Ntl Merit Ltr; Ntl Merit Ltr 83; U Southern CA.

ZIMMERMAN, KRISTIN; King Philip Regional HS; Norfolk, MA; (S); 3/220; Model UN; Ed Nwsp Ed-Chief; Ed Lit Mag; Sec Jr Cls; Rep Stu Cncl; Capt L Fld Hcky; NHS; Ntl Merit SF; SADD Co-Fndr 84; All-Star Fld Hckey Team 84; Intl Law.

ZINGARELLI, KAREN; Haverhill HS; Haverhill, MA; (Y); 50/430; Cmnty Wkr; Key Clb; Acpl Chr; Chorus; Color Guard; Mrchg Band; Swing Chorus; Hon Roll; Jr Dist Chrs 83; Sr Dist Chrs/All ST Recmndtn 85; U Of NH; Phys Thrpy.

ZIRLEN, DAVID B; Natick HS; Natick, MA; (Y); 35/490; Capt Bsktbl; Capt Socr; Hon Roll; 2nd Tm Boston Globe All Star Soccer 84; Law.

ZISCH, HEIDI MARIE; Academy Of Notre Dame HS; Chelmsford, MA; (Y); 3/78; Girl Scts; Hosp Aide; Capt L Socr; High Hon Roll; Pres NHS; Prfct Atten Awd; St Schlr; Cmnty Wkr; Intnl Clb; Library Aide; MA Yth Ldrshp Rep 83; MA Stu Govt Day Rep 84; USPA IRA Scholar 85; Brandeis U; Pre-Med.

ZOINO, PAULA; Brockton HS; Brockton, MA; (Y); 6/1000; JCL; Library Aide; Math Tm; Yrbk Phtg; Rep Frsh Cls; Rep Soph Cls; Rep Sr Cls; High Hon Roll; NHS.

ZOKOWSKI, MARGARET; Smith Acad; Hatfield, MA; (S); Church Yth Grp; Nwsp Stf; Sec Soph Cls; VP Jr Cls; Var Bsktbl; Var Sftbl; Hon Roll; Natl Phys Ed Awd 83-84; Lat III Only Stu 84-85; NSTA NASA Spce Shuttl Stu Invlvmt Pg 83-84; Hstry.

ZOLDAK, KAREN; Gardner HS; Gardner, MA; (Y); French Clb; Pep Clb; Chorus; School Musical; JV Var Cheerleading; Gardner Embl Clb Schlrshp 85; Mt Wachusett Comm Coll; Bus Adm.

ZOLNAY, KAREN; Bedford HS; Bedford, MA; (Y); 12/229; Church Yth Grp; GAA; Hosp Aide; Varsity Clb; Band; Chorus; Concert Band; Mrchg Band; Orch; Symp Band; Boston Globe Swm All-Stars 80-83; Lowell Sun Swm All-Stars 80-83; Bowdoin Coll; Biochem.

ZUBER, KATHLEEN M; Pittsfield HS; Pittsfield, MA; (Y); Boy Scts; Pep Clb; Yrbk Stf; Var L Sftbl; Var L Swmmng; Im Vllybl; High Hon Roll; Hon Roll; David Landa Mem Awd 85; Vrsty Ltr Sftbl 85; Quinnipiac Coll; Radiogrphy.

ZUFFANTE, LORI; Winthrop HS; Winthrop, MA; (Y); 21/217; Band; Capt Color Guard; Capt Drill Tm; Co-Capt Flag Corp; School Musical; High Hon Roll; Hon Roll; NHS; Elem Ed.

ZULFIQUAR, AMIR; St Johns HS; N Grafton, MA; (Y); 23/270; Sec Computer Clb; Pres Exploring; French Clb; Math Tm; Science Clb; JV Crs Cntry; High Hon Roll; Ntl Merit Ltr; Boston U; Biomed Engrng.

ZURZOLO, GABRIELA; Ursuline Acad; Stoughton, MA; (Y); Drama Clb; French Clb; Hosp Aide; Spanish Clb; Chorus; School Musical; School Play; Yrbk Ed-Chief; VP Frsh Cls; Pres Sr Cls; VMP Tnns Tm, Capt 84-85; Ldrshp Awd 85; Sr Advsr Saks 5th Ave Teen Fshn Bd 84-85; Wellesley Coll; Intl Rel.

ZWICKER, JAMES L; St Peter-Marian HS; Worcester, MA; (Y); Boy Scts; Church Yth Grp; Cmnty Wkr; Drama Clb; Ski Clb; Y-Teens; School Play; Variety Show; Rep Frsh Cls; Rep Soph Cls; Asmptn Coll Wrchsr MN; Bus.

ZYMROZ, WENDI; Agawan HS; Feeding Hls, MA; (Y); Dance Clb; Ski Clb; Variety Show; Nwsp Rptr; Nwsp Stf; Yrbk Bus Mgr; Gym; Trk; High Hon Roll; Psych.

ZYWNA, KEVIN; Turners Falls HS; Turners Fls, MA; (Y); 12/96; Exploring; Ski Clb; Varsity Clb; Var L Bsbl; Var L Crs Cntry; Var L Ftbl; Hon Roll; NHS; Dartmouth Clb Bk Awd; Cannon Novak Awd; U Of Notre Dame; Bus Admin.

NEW HAMPSHIRE

ABBADESSA, STEPHEN; St Thomas Aquisas HS; Dover, NH; (Y); Cmnty Wkr; French Clb; Variety Show; High Hon Roll; NHS; U Of NH-DURHAM; Elec Engr.

ABELE, APRIL; Alvirne HS; Hudson, NH; (Y); Ski Clb; Var L Sftbl; Hon Roll; Prom Cmmttee Recog 85; U Of NH.

ABORJAILY, LAUREN; Mascoma Valley Regional HS; Enfield, NH; (Y); Rep Am Leg Aux Girls St; Yrbk Stf; VP Frsh Cls; Rep Stu Cncl; Var Bsktbl; Mgr JV Fld Hcky; Var Sftbl; Awd Wnnr Peace Essy Cntst 84; Stdnt Cncl Undrclssmn Awd 84-85; Publ Rel.

ACHTMANN, ERIC; Hanover HS; Sunapee, NH; (Y); 5/65; German Clb; Math Tm; Ski Clb; Lit Mag; JV Crs Cntry; JV Lcrss; JV Tennis; JV Trk; High Hon Roll; Ntl Merit Ltr; Astrontcl Engrng.

ACKERSON, MATTHEW; Frnaklin HS; Franklin, NH; (Y); 1/91; Computer Clb; French Clb; Math Tm; Golf; Trk; High Hon Roll; NHS; Prfct Atten Awd; Voice Dem Awd; High Math Ave,Math Tm Scr 82-85; Hugh O Brian Ldrshp Conf 83-84; Math.

ADKINS, WENDY; Franklin HS; Franklin, NH; (Y); 18/92; Spanish Clb; Yrbk Stf; Rep Stu Cncl; Var Capt Cheerleading; JV Sftbl; Hon Roll; Hlth Occptns.

AGUIAR, TRACEY; Presentation Of Mary HS; Hudson, NH; (Y); Art Clb; Library Aide; Science Clb; Service Clb; Hon Roll; Awd Of Appreciation Outstndng & Dedicated Svd In Lib 83-84; Aymouth ST Coll; Bio.

ALBAHARY, RONALD; Nashua HS; Nashua, NH; (Y); 1/927; Debate Tm; Drama Clb; Model UN; JV Bsbl; Im Bsktbl; High Hon Roll; NHS; Rotary Awd; Full Scholar Econ Sem Fndtn Econ Ed 85; Hnrary Spkr Clb Richelieus Mnthl Meetg 84; U PA Wharton; Econ.

ALBRITTON, NEAL E; Nashua SR HS; Nashua, NH; (Y); 95/804; Am Leg Boys St; Library Aide; School Play; Ed Yrbk Ed-Chief; Rep Soph Cls; Im Wt Lftg; Hon Roll; NHS; Rotary Awd; Nashua Rotary Clb Schlrshp 85; 1st Pl Wnnr-H S Logo Contst 84; NH Techncl Inst; Electrnc Engr.

ALCORN, CHARLENE; Stevens HS; Claremont, NH; (Y); Am Leg Aux Girls St; Key Clb; Pres Stu Cncl; JV Sftbl; High Hon Roll; Hon Roll; Stu Agnst Drnk Drvng Pres 82-84; Plymouth ST Coll; Elem Ed.

ALCOTT, KRIS; Hopkinton HS; Concord, NH; (Y); DECA; Drama Clb; School Play; Im JV Cheerleading; Cert Achiev & Partcptn DECA 85; Johnston & Wales; Fashn Merch.

ALDRICH, KEN; Spaulding HS; Rochester, NH; (S); 49/418; Church Yth Grp; Band; JV Golf; L Socr; Var Trk; Hon Roll; Jr NHS; Engr.

ALETTO, PAMELA JAYNE; Salem HS; Salem, NH; (Y); Hosp Aide; Math Tm; Model UN; Teachers Aide; Concert Band; Capt Drm & Bgl; Mrchg Band; Mgr School Play; Hon Roll; MA Coll Pharm; Pharm.

ALEXANDER, SCOTT; Portsmouth HS; Portsmouth, NH; (Y); 16/390; CAP; Latin Clb; Var L Bsbl; High Hon Roll; Hon Roll; NHS; Chrmn JR Wrld Cncls Modl Congrss 85; Aviatn.

ALLAIN, DAWN C; Pinkerton Acad; Auburn, NH; (Y); 44/440; Trs Exploring; Hosp Aide; Church Choir; Ed Yrbk Stf; Rep Frsh Cls; Rep Soph Cls; Rep Jr Cls; Rep Sr Cls; Im Powder Puff Ftbl; Hon Roll; Carol Riley Mem Schlrshp 85; Derry Kiwanis Clb Schlrshp 85; Pres Acad Ftnss Awd; U Of NH; Genetcs.

ALLAN, CHRISTIAN D; Exeter Area HS; Exeter, NH; (Y); Am Leg Boys St; VICA; Capt Crs Cntry; Socr; Trk; High Hon Roll; Hon Roll; Arch.

ALLBEE, TRACY; Woodsville HS; N Haverhill, NH; (Y); Math Tm; Office Aide; High Hon Roll; Hon Roll; Jr NHS; NHS; Bus Stu Mnth 84; Bus Stu Yr 85; Bus.

ALLEN, BONNIE; Newport HS; Newport, NH; (Y); Dance Clb; Math Clb; Math Tm; Pep Clb; Spanish Clb; Band; Concert Band; Jazz Band; Mrchg Band; Pep Band; Travel/Tourism.

ALLEN, VICKI; Concord HS; Concord, NH; (Y); 78/329; Chorus; High Hon Roll; BAP I 84; BAP II 85; Basic Geom 85; Soc Stud 85; IAC 85; Chem 85; Law.

ALLMAN, GAIL; Derryfield Schl; Manchester, NH; (Y); Drama Clb; Science Clb; Varsity Clb; Stage Crew; Yrbk Ed-Chief; Yrbk Stf; Trs Frsh Cls; Co-Capt Fld Hcky; Lcrss; Hon Roll.

AMMON, KIMBERLY; Salem HS; Salem, NH; (S); 3/405; Spanish Clb; Teachers Aide; Band; Concert Band; Mrchg Band; High Hon Roll; NHS; Spnsh Achvt Awd 84; Med.

AMNOTT, LYNNE; Woodsville HS; Haverhill, NH; (Y); Church Yth Grp; Drama Clb; Office Aide; Sec Spanish Clb; Band; JV Bsktbl; Var Mgr(s); Hon Roll; Trs Jr NHS; NHS; Newport VT N Country Woodwind Ensmble 85; NH Vo Tech Schl; Nrsng.

ANDERSON III, CARL F; Exeter Area HS; Exeter, NH; (Y); Am Leg Boys St; Chess Clb; Church Yth Grp; Cmnty Wkr; Im JV Bsktbl; Im JV Socr; Wt Lftg; High Hon Roll; Hon Roll; Rotary Awd; St Anselms Clg Schlrshp,Donald Gaulin Awd 84-85; Cent III Ldr Yth & Govt YMCA 84-85; US Acadm Decth; St Anselms Clg; Polit Sci.

ANDERSON, MICHAEL; Wilton-Lyndeboro Cooperative HS; Lyndeboro, NH; (Y); 1/43; Computer Clb; Math Tm; Var Bsktbl; Bausch & Lomb Sci Awd; NHS; Val; Chess Clb; School Play; High Hon Roll; Amer Lgn Schlrshp Mdl Wnnr 85; WBZ-TV & GM Corp Best Of Class Awd 85; WLC Hghst Score Math Cntst; Lowell U; Elect Engr.

ANDREWS, CURTIS; Gorham HS; Gorham, NH; (Y); Aud/Vis; Drama Clb; JV Bsktbl; JV Score Keeper; High Hon Roll; Hon Roll; Elect Engrng.

ANDREWS, PETER J; Keene HS; Keene, NH; (Y); 1/354; Acpl Chr; Jazz Band; Yrbk Phtg; Rep Jr Cls; VP Sr Cls; Rep Stu Cncl; NCTE Awd; NHS; Ntl Merit SF; Camera Clb; St Pauls Schl Advncd Studies Prg 84; Engrng.

ANNIS, KAREN; Merrimack HS; Merrimack, NH; (S); Sec DECA; Pres Girl Scts; Band; Mrchg Band; Hon Roll; Food Svc Dist Ed 1st Pl 84; Girl Scts Silver Ldrshp Awd 84; DECA Hmn Rel Svc Silver Mdl 84; Bus Admn.

ARANOSIAN, LISA R; Tilton Schl; Concord, NH; (S); 5/80; Math Tm; Spanish Clb; Stage Crew; Nwsp Stf; Yrbk Stf; Rep Sr Cls; Bsktbl; Lcrss; Socr; High Hon Roll; Foreign Lngs.

ARMSTRONG, THERESA; Kingswood Regional HS; Center Ossipee, NH; (Y); Trs Pres FBLA; ST Histrn FBLA 85-86; Trvl & Toursm.

ARNOLD, LYNNE; Trinity HS; Merrimack, NH; (Y); 33/170; Church Yth Grp; Teachers Aide; Var Bsktbl; Var Sftbl; Var Vllybl; Hon Roll; NHS; Ntl Educ Dvlpmnt Tsts 84.

ARNOTT IV, WILLIAM; Keene HS; Keene, NH; (Y); 122/358; Am Leg Boys St; Drama Clb; German Clb; Yrbk Stf; Wrstlng.

ARONSON, JOHN; Laconia HS; Laconia, NH; (Y); Hon Roll; Ntl Merit SF.

ATKINSON, DEVIN S; Groveton HS; Groveton, NH; (Y); Cmnty Wkr; Drama Clb; Ski Clb; School Play; Variety Show; Yrbk Ed-Chief; Yrbk Phtg; Yrbk Rptr; Yrbk Stf; Mgr(s); Drftg.

AUBIN, DONNA; Berlin SR HS; Berlin, NH; (Y); 64/206; Church Yth Grp; Hon Roll; NHS; Ntl Merit Ltr; Associated Schls Inc; Airline.

AUCLAIR, TIMOTNY; Spaulding HS; Rochester, NH; (S); 25/392; Hon Roll; UNH; Acctng.

AUGUSTINOWICZ, WALTER; Stevens HS; Venice, FL; (Y); 8/188; Am Leg Boys St; Church Yth Grp; Letterman Clb; Math Tm; JV Bsbl; Score Keeper; High Hon Roll; Hon Roll; Robotics.

AUSTEN, SCOTT; Milford Area SR HS; Amherst, NH; (Y); Am Leg Boys St; Cmnty Wkr; Var Crs Cntry; Var JV Socr; Var L Trk; High Hon Roll; Hon Roll; NHS; Im Vllybl; 1st Pl MASH Art Shw-Drwng 83; 2nd Pl MASH Art Shw-Grphcs 84; Cmmrcl Art.

AUTNAM, MARTHA; Fall Mountain Regional HS; Charlestown, NH; (Y); French Clb; Hosp Aide; Cheerleading; Sftbl; Swmmng; Ntl Ldrshp & Serv Awd 85; Vlntr Srvcs 85; Nrsng.

AVARD, JOHN; West HS; Manchester, NH; (Y); 55/352; Church Yth Grp; Variety Show; 1st Degree Blck Belt; 2nd Pl Adult Male Blck Belts Sparring; 2nd Pl Adult Male Black Blt Kata; U Of HI; Chiroprctc.

AYER, DEBRA; White Mountains Regional HS; Hudson, NH; (Y); 16/88; Art Clb; FBLA; Spanish Clb; Yrbk Rptr; Hon Roll; Nevers Schlrshp 85; Art Hnr Soc 83-84; Becker JC; Trvl.

AYER, PHILIP; Stevens HS; Cornish, NH; (Y); Aud/Vis; Math Tm; School Play; Yrbk Stf; JV Stat Bsbl; Var Ftbl; Hon Roll; Raymond Johnson Memrl Ftbl Awd 84; Cornish Fair Assn Schlrshp 85; Plymouth ST Coll; Acctnt.

AYOTTE, SCOTT; Berlin HS; Berlin, NH; (Y); 28/202; Boy Scts; NHS; USAF.

AZZAPARDI, NADINE; Spaubling HS; Rochester, NH; (Y); 17/350; Am Leg Aux Girls St; Computer Clb; French Clb; High Hon Roll; Hon Roll; NHS; Natl Hnr Soc 85; Acctg.

BABAIAN, LISA; Salem HS; Salem, NH; (Y); VP Church Yth Grp; Pres Latin Clb; Model UN; Spanish Clb; Yrbk Stf; Rep Sr Cls; Rep Stu Cncl; High Hon Roll; Latin Awd 85; Frgn Lang Awd 85; Fairfield U; Law.

BACK, TAMMY J; Salem HS; Salem, NH; (Y); 74/345; Cmnty Wkr; FHA; Hosp Aide; Model UN; Teachers Aide; Hon Roll; Northern Essex CC; Sci.

BACON, REBECCA; Fall Mountain Regional HS; Alstead, NH; (Y); 51/151; Spanish Clb; Var JV Bsktbl; Hon Roll; Gym Awd.

BAILAT, CLAUDE P; Pembroke Acad; Chichester, NH; (Y); 19/156; Boy Scts; Exploring; Latin Clb; Math Tm; Varsity Clb; Trk; NHS; Prfct Atten Awd; Am Legn Schlrshp Awd 81; U Of NH; Mech Engrng.

BAILEY, BRENDA J; Pembroke Acad; Chichester, NH; (Y); 8/173; Pres Art Clb; Church Yth Grp; Pres Latin Clb; Science Clb; Spanish Clb; Yrbk Stf; High Hon Roll; Hon Roll; NHS; Pres Schlr; All Around Schltc Awd; Schltc Awd Latin; Scholar Awd Engl; All Around Hnrs Awd; MA Coll Phrmcy; Phrmclgy.

BAILEY, KATHRYN; A Crosby Kennett HS; Jackson, NH; (Y); Church Yth Grp; French Clb; Girl Scts; Key Clb; Ski Clb; Teachers Aide; Varsity Clb; Rep Jr Cls; Trk; French Hon Soc; Frnch Clb,Girl Scts 83-85; Pblctn Amer Poetry Anthlgy 85; Lib Arts.

BAILLARGEON, DAVID; Franklin HS; Franklin, NH; (Y); JV Var Ftbl; Hon Roll; US Army; Mechnc.

BAKANEC, BRADLEY S; Londonderry HS; Londonderry, NH; (Y); Ski Clb; Var L Lcrss; Var Capt Socr; Hon Roll; BUS.

BAKER, KIMBERLY; Mascoma Valley Regional HS; Canaan, NH; (Y); 1/150; French Clb; Quiz Bowl; Pep Band; School Musical; School Play; Yrbk Ed-Chief; VP Jr Cls; NHS; Drama Clb 83-85; St Pauls Schl Adv Stds Prog 85; Englsh, Soc Stds, Offc Aid & Stu Cncl Awds 85.

BAKER, TAMMY L; Kimball Union Acad; Cornish, NH; (Y); Camera Clb; Cmnty Wkr; French Clb; Ski Clb; Chorus; Var Socr; Var Tennis; High Hon Roll; Hon Roll; High Hnr Awd In Mth & Sci For Soc Of Womens Engrs 85; Bates; Bus.

BALDI, MATTHEW; Bishop Guertin HS; Nashua, NH; (Y); 7/150; Am Leg Boys St; Key Clb; Spanish Clb; Yrbk Stf; Im Bsktbl; JV Crs Cntry; JV Trk; NHS; Spanish NHS.

BARE, DANNA; Winnisquam Regional HS; Tilton, NH; (Y); 10/91; Am Leg Aux Girls St; Camera Clb; Ed Nwsp Stf; Sec Jr Cls; Rep Stu Cncl; Var L Cheerleading; JV Sftbl; Hon Roll; Gftd & Tlntd Prog NH 82-86; Simmons Coll Boston; Mktg.

BARKER, SCOTT; Spaulding HS; Rochester, NH; (Y); 78/357; Church Yth Grp; Rep Jr Cls; Im Bsbl; JV Var Bsktbl; Var Capt Ftbl; JV Gym; Hon Roll; JC Awd; Athltc Trnr.

BARLOW, GREGORY; Bishop Brady HS; Suncook, NH; (S); 3/58; Yrbk Stf; Pres Frsh Cls; Pres Soph Cls; JV VP Crs Cntry; Hon Roll; NHS; Boy Scts; Political Wkr; Ski Clb; Hugh Obrien Youth Ldrshp Seminar Ambassdr 84; Class Engl Awd 83-84; Class Frnch Awd 83; Pre Med.

BARNOCKY JR, JOHN A; Saint Thomas Aquinas HS; Pease Afb, NH; (Y); Boy Scts; Church Yth Grp; French Clb; Key Clb; Mathletes; Math Tm; ROTC; VP Rep Jr Cls; Rep Sr Cls; Trs Stu Cncl; Engr.

BARON, JONATHAN E; Manchester High School Central; Manchester, NH; (Y); 75/409; Am Leg Boys St; Temple Yth Grp; Rep Stu Cncl; High Hon Roll; Hon Roll.

BARON, PAUL; Bishop Brady HS; Laconia, NH; (S); 2/58; Ski Clb; VP Frsh Cls; Sec Jr Cls; Var Bsbl; Var Ftbl; Hon Roll; Bus.

BARRY, AMY; Woodsville HS; N Haverhill, NH; (Y); Ski Clb; Pres Frsh Cls; Sec Stu Cncl; Var Fld Hcky; Var Sftbl; Hon Roll; JR Englsh Awd 85; Anatomy & Psychlgy Awds 85; U Of Denver; Englsh.

BARTER, MARIANNE; Concord HS; Bow, NH; (Y); Cmnty Wkr; Drama Clb; Hosp Aide; Varsity Clb; Stage Crew; Lit Mag; Hon Roll; Outstndg Achvt Engl 85; Engl.

BARTLETT, CHRISTINE; Pinkerton Acad; Windham, NH; (Y); 23/540; Drama Clb; VP French Clb; Chorus; Stage Crew; Variety Show; Yrbk Stf; Crs Cntry; Trk; Hon Roll; NHS; U Of NH; Cmnctns.

BARTON, DEBBIE; Pembroke Acad; Epsom, NH; (Y); FHA.

BARTZ, MARGO; Franklin JR SR HS; Franklin, NH; (Y); Yrbk Phtg; Yrbk Stf; Bsktbl; Sftbl; Hon Roll; Bus.

BASCIO, JAMES M; Salem HS; Salem, NH; (S); Model UN; Capt Var Bsktbl; Var Ftbl; Var Trk.

BASCOM, KIMBERLEY; Salem HS; Salem, NH; (Y); Art Clb; Aud/Vis; Camera Clb; FHA; GAA; Girl Scts; Model UN; PAVAS; VICA; Band.

BAUM, SHONA; Portsmouth HS; Portsmouth, NH; (Y); Drama Clb; Exploring; French Clb; Chorus; School Musical; School Play; Stage Crew; Hon Roll; Ntl Merit SF; Brandeis; Wrtng.

BAXTER, CARA; Memorial HS; Manchester, NH; (Y); 69/366; Sec Church Yth Grp; Cmnty Wkr; Hosp Aide; Teachers Aide; Nwsp Rptr; Nwsp Stf; Var Powder Puff Ftbl; JV Socr; Hon Roll; Stu Aide Svc Awd 83-85; Jrnlsm.

BAYBUTT, SHARON; A Crosby Kenneth HS; Tamworth, NH; (Y); 51/200; Art Clb; Cmnty Wkr; Drama Clb; Key Clb; Ski Clb; Yrbk Stf; Var L Cheerleading; Hon Roll; Moore Coll Of Art; Comm Art.

BAYEK, WENDY; Timberlane Regional HS; Plaistow, NH; (Y); French Clb; Hon Roll; UNH; Bus.

BEACH, KEVIN; Salem HS; Salem, NH; (S); Church Yth Grp; Latin Clb; Model UN; Bsktbl; Hon Roll; Dartmouth Coll; Med.

BEADLE, KATHERINE; Winnisquam Regional HS; Franklin, NH; (Y); 15/80; Pres Camera Clb; French Clb; Nwsp Phtg; Ed Yrbk Phtg; Var Trk; Var Vllybl; Hon Roll; Prfct Atten Awd; Church Yth Grp; 4-H; Presdntl Physcl Ftns Awd 82-85; Robert H Gertrude E Sedgley Chartbl Fndtn Awd 85; Endicott Coll; Photojrnlsm.

BEALS, JOHN; Alvirne HS; Hudson, NH; (Y); 23/360; Var Bsbl; Var Socr; Hon Roll.

BEAUBIEN, SUZANNE; Milford Area SR HS; Milford, NH; (Y); 67/286; Sec FBLA; Mgr(s); High Hon Roll; Hon Roll; NHS; Bentley Coll; Bus Comm.

BEAUCHESNE JR, ROBERT G; Newmarket HS; Newmarket, NH; (Y); Am Leg Boys St; Church Yth Grp; Trs FHA; Teachers Aide; Band; Concert Band; Mrchg Band; Pep Band; Yrbk Stf; JV Bsbl; Hugh O Brian Ldrshp Sem 84; Johnson & Wales Coll; Cul Arts.

BEAUCHESNE, ROBIN; Alvirne HS; Hudson, NH; (Y); 24/357; Church Yth Grp; Yrbk Stf; Rep Stu Cncl; Hon Roll; Med Lab Tech.

BEAUDET, MARC; Salem HS; Salem, NH; (S); 44/363; Boys Clb Am; Church Yth Grp; French Clb; Model UN; Ski Clb; Teachers Aide; School Play; Variety Show; Off Sr Cls; JV Bsbl; Voice Of Demcrcy Wnnr 84; Bus Admin.

BEAUDET, TAMI; Memorial HS; Manchester, NH; (Y); 42/400; French Clb; Math Clb; Nwsp Stf; JV Socr; JV Trk; High Hon Roll; Hon Roll; Miss Hsplty Ntl Tngr Pgt 86-87; Johnson Wales; Fash Merch.

BEAUDIN, DEBRA A; Salem HS; Salem, NH; (Y); Model UN; Ski Clb; Var Cheerleading; Hon Roll; Dip Tchrs Training Clb Boston 85; BU; Psych.

BEAUDOIN, MARIE; Laconia HS; Laconia, NH; (Y); Trs French Clb; Service Clb; Hon Roll; NHS.

BECHARD, KATHI; Londonderry HS; Londonderry, NH; (Y); Math Tm; Rep Frsh Cls; Rep Soph Cls; JV Cheerleading; Var Socr; French Hon Soc; High Hon Roll; NHS; Var Trk; Lang Trnsltr.

BECHTEL, LESLEE; Bishop Brady HS; Bow, NH; (Y); 13/79; Am Leg Aux Girls St; Pres Stu Cncl; Var Capt Bsktbl; Var Capt Fld Hcky; Var Capt Sftbl; Trs NHS; Am Leg Aux Awd 85; Mst Vlbl Plyr Fld Hcky 84; Bst Def Plyr Bsktbl 84-85; US Military Acad; Pol Sci.

BECKER, JOHN; Portsmouth HS; Portsmouth, NH; (Y); Stu Cncl; Var Ftbl; Trk; Bus Mgmt.

BECKETT, BRIAN L; Hopkinton HS; Contoocook, NH; (Y); Am Leg Boys St; Yrbk Stf; Crs Cntry; Socr; Trk; High Hon Roll; Hon Roll; Schlrshp 85; OK ST U; Hotel Mgmt.

BEDARD, JOEL T; Bishop Guertin HS; Nashua, NH; (Y); Im JV Socr; Im Sftbl; Im Vllybl; Hon Roll; Yth Consrvtn Corps 85; Med Tech.

BEDARD, LAURIE; Presentation Of Mary Acad; Pelham, NH; (Y); 12/35; Church Yth Grp; French Clb; Science Clb; Ski Clb; Vllybl; Hon Roll; U Lowell; Bus.

BEDARD, LORRICE; Mt St Mary Seminary HS; Nashua, NH; (Y); Pres Debate Tm; Pres French Clb; Ed Yrbk Phtg; Sec Sr Cls; High Hon Roll; Rep NHS; Ntl Merit Ltr; Am Leg Aux Girls St; Drama Clb; Model UN; Natl Fornsc Leag Degr Distnctn 85; NH Delg Grls Natn 85; Dartmouth Clb Bk Awd 85; Socl Sci.

BELAND, JUNE; Manchester West HS; Manchester, NH; (Y); 24/364; Ski Clb; High Hon Roll; Hon Roll; Acctg.

BELANGER, DIANE; Hillsboro-Deering HS; Deering, NH; (Y); Computer Clb; Library Aide; Off Jr Cls; JV Bsktbl; JV Sftbl; Sci Fair Awd 2nd Pl 83-85; Art Awd 85.

BELANGER, LAURA L; Manchester West HS; Bedford, NH; (Y); Ski Clb; Hon Roll; U Of NH; Bus.

BELANGER, SCOTT; Salem HS; Salem, NH; (Y); Model UN; JV Ftbl; Var JV Trk; Hon Roll; Comp Sci.

BELCASTRO, TINA; Pittsfield HS; Pittsfield, NH; (Y); Church Yth Grp; JA; Teachers Aide; Varsity Clb; Yrbk Stf; JV Var Bsktbl; Hon Roll; NHS; Comp Sci.

BELL, JAMES; Coe-Brown Northwood Acad; Strafford, NH; (Y); Drama Clb; FFA; School Musical; School Play; Nwsp Rptr; Nwsp Stf; JV Bsbl; VP Socr; Hon Roll; NHS; Real Estate.

BELL, MARK; Hopkinton HS; Contoocook, NH; (Y); 5/71; Band; Pres Frsh Cls; Co-Capt Crs Cntry; Trk; High Hon Roll; Hon Roll; NHS; Ntl Merit Ltr; Boy Scts; Church Yth Grp; Frnch II Profcncy Awd; Outstndng Band Awd; Adv Studies Prog St Paul Schl; Lang.

BELLEROSE, SUZANNE; Presentation Of Mary Acad; Lowell, MA; (Y); Church Yth Grp; Drama Clb; Science Clb; Service Clb; Chrmn Sr Cls; Cheerleading; Vllybl; High Hon Roll; Hon Roll; NHS; U Lowell; Comp Sci.

BELLOWS, MELANIE; Fall Mountain Regional HS; Alstead, NH; (Y); 8/140; Am Leg Aux Girls St; Spanish Clb; Band; Drm Mjr(t); Mrchg Band; Pep Band; Yrbk Ed-Chief; Yrbk Phtg; Pres Frsh Cls; Pres Soph Cls; Hnrs Awd; Spnsh Awd; Scl Stds Awdd; U Of NH; Hlth.

BENNETT, KIM; Moultonborough Acad; Center Hrbr, NH; (Y); 5/40; Ski Clb; Spanish Clb; Variety Show; Var Cheerleading; Hon Roll; Art Hnr Soc 84-85.

BERG, MARY C; Tilton Schl; Duxbury, MA; (S); Art Clb; Camera Clb; GAA; Hosp Aide; Key Clb; Teachers Aide; Mgr Lit Mag; Pres Frsh Cls; Var Capt Fld Hcky; Hon Roll; Stu Supv Awd 83-84; Stu Ctr Worker 84-85; Ledrshp Supv Of Stu Morning Kitchen Crew 84-85; Archetecture.

BERGERON, CARRIE; Laconia HS; Laconia, NH; (Y); Church Yth Grp; FHA; Hosp Aide; VICA; Var Cheerleading; Hon Roll; NH FHA HERO Profcncy Evnt Awd 85; Cert Modrn Miss Pagnt Prog 85; Chld Devl.

BERGERON, TAMMY; Memorial HS; Manchester, NH; (Y); 28/366; French Clb; Crs Cntry; Trk; Twrlr; High Hon Roll; Hon Roll; Med Tech.

BERMAN, KIM; Nashua HS; Nashua, NH; (Y); Camera Clb; Cmnty Wkr; Political Wkr; Soph Cls; Trs Jr Cls; Rgnl VP Yng Judea 85-86; Yth Gvrnmnt Rep 83-85; St Pauls Smmr Pgm 85; Intl Rltns.

BERNARDUCCI, MARC; Bishop Buertin HS; Hudson, NH; (Y); 17/158; FCA; ROTC; Nwsp Stf; Var L Cheerleading; Var L Socr; Im Vllybl; Im Wt Lftg; Var Wrstlng; NHS; Natl Hnr Scty Svc Awd 85; U Of RI; Pharm.

BERUBE, JEANNE; Spaulding HS; Rochester, NH; (S); 57/418; JV Var Bsktbl; Var Mgr(s); Var Score Keeper; Var Socr; Stat Sftbl; Hon Roll; Excllnc In Home Ec 82; Rookie Of The Yr Awd Bsktbl 82; UNH.

BIBBINS, JUDITH; Pembroue Acad; Concord, NH; (Y); Church Yth Grp; Spanish Clb; Cheerleading; Crs Cntry; Mgr(s); Hon Roll.

BICKFORD, CHRIS C; Concord HS; Concord, NH; (Y); 23/340; Debate Tm; Math Tm; NFL; Var Wrstlng; Hon Roll; Ntl Merit SF; New Eng Math Awd 80; Engrng.

BICKFORD, PENNY; Spaulding HS; Barrington, NH; (Y); 49/360; Band; Co-Capt Color Guard; Concert Band; Mrchg Band; Hon Roll; Elem Educ.

BICKFORD, WENDY; Spaulding HS; Barrington, NH; (S); Band; Concert Band; Jazz Band; Mrchg Band; Hon Roll; UNH; Lib Arts.

BILODEAU, PAULA; Manchester H S West; Manchester, NH; (Y); 32/352; Ski Clb; Chorus; Trs Soph Cls; Trs Jr Cls; Trs Sr Cls; High Hon Roll; Hon Roll; Jr NHS; Bus Admin.

BIRCH, PETER; Bishop Guertin HS; Westford, MA; (Y); 13/177; FCA; Spanish Clb; Var Bsbl; Var Capt Ice Hcky; JV Socr; NHS; VP Spanish NHS; Math Sci Awd 85; MVP Ice Hcky Tm 85; Ntl Hnr Soc Serv Awd 85; Pre-Med.

BIRON, KELLEY; Cogswell Memorial HS; Henniker, NH; (Y); 2/24; Drama Clb; VP French Clb; Hosp Aide; Math Clb; Math Tm; School Musical; VP Stu Cncl; Var Cheerleading; Sftbl; Vllybl; Mst Outstndng Englsh, Wrld Hstry, Adv French 82-83; High Acadmc Achvt Psychlgy, Soclgy 84-85; NH U; Speech Thrpy.

BISHOP, RON; Goffstown HS; New Boston, NH; (Y); Chess Clb; Math Tm; Hon Roll; 1st Pl Ntl Sci Olympd 84; Airline Pilot.

BISSON, CAROL; Berlin HS; Berlin, NH; (Y); Girl Scts; Church Choir; Hon Roll.

BLAIR, MICHELLE; Mascoma V R HS; West Canaan, NH; (Y); Hst 4-H; Chorus; School Musical; Var JV Cheerleading; Var JV Fld Hcky; JV Mgr(s); Mgr Sftbl; Twrlr; Mst Imprvd Vrsty Chrldr 83-84; Mascoma Yth Prjct 82; Prm Committee 85; Recrtnl Ldrshp.

BLAIS, SHANE; Berlin HS; Berlin, NH; (Y); Band; Concert Band; Jazz Band; Mrchg Band; School Musical; Im Bsktbl; Var Crs Cntry; Var Trk; Im Vllybl; U Of NH; Chem Engrng.

BLAKE, DAVID; Hillsboro-Deering HS; Hillsboro, NH; (Y); Church Yth Grp; Math Tm; Teachers Aide; Varsity Clb; Trs Soph Cls; Rep Stu Cncl; Capt Bsbl; Var Bsktbl; Var Socr; Cmmnctns.

BLAKE, EDWARD; Concord HS; Bow, NH; (Y); 16/335; Letterman Clb; Math Clb; Math Tm; Quiz Bowl; Varsity Clb; JV Bsktbl; Var L Socr; Var L Trk; Im Vllybl; High Hon Roll; Excel Awds Engl 85, Econ 84, Soc Stds 85; Bus.

BLANCHARD, ANITA; Hillsboro-Deering HS; Hillsboro, NH; (Y); 4/57; Library Aide; Math Tm; Teachers Aide; Ed Yrbk Stf; Hon Roll; Lion Awd; NHS; GTE Sci & HS Sci Awds 85; Albany Coll Of Pharmacy; Phrmst.

BLANCHETTE, KIM RENEE; Keene HS; Keene, NH; (Y); Am Leg Aux Girls St; Pep Clb; Var Capt Gym; Powder Puff Ftbl; JV Trk; Ushers Clb Schlrshp 85; Most Vlbl Gmnst 83-85; 6th Pl ST All Around Cmptn 85; Springfield Coll; Phy Educ.

BLANCHETTE, SHAY M; Plymouth Area HS; Plymouth, NH; (Y); 3/145; Pres Church Yth Grp; Pres French Clb; Math Clb; School Musical; Yrbk Ed-Chief; Var Bsktbl; Var Sftbl; High Hon Roll; NHS; Voice Dem Awd; JR Yr 85; Outstndg Alg II Stu 84; Outstndg Alg I Stu 82; Arch.

BLANTON, CHARLIE M; Spaulding HS; Rochester, NH; (Y); #9 In Class; Band; Chorus; Drm & Bgl; Jazz Band; Mrchg Band; School Play; Variety Show; Rep Frsh Cls; High Hon Roll; NHS; All St Band 83-84; Dartmouth; Musician.

BLANTON, JOSEPH; Spaulding HS; Rochester, NH; (S); 49/415; Boys Clb Am; JV Bsbl; Var L Ftbl; Var L Trk; Wt Lftg; Hon Roll; Won JR Clb Golf Chmpnshp 81; Rnnr-Up Golf Chmpnshp 82; 3rd Pl SENH Trck Meet 84.

BLECKMANN, KAREN; Pittsfield HS; Pittsfield, NH; (Y); 1/90; VP Pres Church Yth Grp; School Play; Pres Frsh Cls; Rep Stu Cncl; Var Stat Bsktbl; Capt Var Fld Hcky; High Hon Roll; NCTE Awd; Pres NHS; Ntl Merit Schol; 1st Pl Sci Fair 85; Hghst Achv Frnch III Alg II Chem Intermed Wrtng & Amer Studs 85; Lang.

BLISH, BRITTA; Fall Mountain Regional HS; Charlestown, NH; (Y); 7/160; French Clb; Tennis; Hon Roll; Gen Bus 83; Frnch I & Typng I 84; Plymouth ST; Offc Admin.

BLOOM, KAREN A; Newmarket HS; Newmarket, NH; (Y); 1/47; Am Leg Aux Girls St; Math Tm; Band; Yrbk Bus Mgr; Sec Sr Cls; Var Stu Cncl; Var Capt Cheerleading; Fld Hcky; Hon Roll; Jr NHS; Pre-Med.

BLOUIN, MONIQUE; Manchester Memrl HS; Manchester, NH; (Y); Camera Clb; Cmnty Wkr; French Clb; FBLA; PAVAS; Chorus; Church Choir; School Musical; Nwsp Stf; Swmmng; Manchester Mem Crusader Awd 85; SADD VP 83-84; SADD Pres 84-85; SADD Stu Advsr 85-86; NH Coll; Bus Mgmt.

BLUNT, DEBBY; Salem HS; Salem, NH; (S); Debate Tm; Key Clb; Model UN; Teachers Aide; School Play; Rep Stu Cncl; JV Fld Hcky; Hon Roll; J A D D 84-85; Sr Actvts 84-85; Bates Coll; Pol Sci.

BOEMIG, TRACI; Hinsdale HS; Hinsdale, NH; (Y); 8/60; Drama Clb; VP French Clb; Band; Concert Band; Mrchg Band; School Play; Variety Show; Yrbk Ed-Chief; Trs Frsh Cls; Var Cheerleading; Smith Coll Book Awd 85; Frnch Hnr Awd 84; High Hnrs Awds 84-85; Frnch Intrprtn.

BOISVERT, DENISE M; Pembroke Acad; Suncook, NH; (Y); Latin Clb; Fld Hcky; Hon Roll; NH Tech Inst; Dntl Hygnst.

BOISVERT, PAUL; Alvirne HS; Hudson, NH; (Y); 94/332; Band; Concert Band; Jazz Band; Orch; Hon Roll; NH ST Accrdn Chmpn 84; 1st Pl Opn Pop Solo Estrn Cup Cmptn 83; 1st Pl US Opn Pop Combo 85; Music.

BOLAND, STEPHEN J; Bishop Guertin HS; Nashua, NH; (Y); 8/150; Am Leg Boys St; VP Church Yth Grp; Trs Key Clb; Nwsp Rptr; Ed Yrbk Stf; Sec Stu Cncl; Var L Crs Cntry; JV Trk; High Hon Roll; Trs NHS; Mst Outstndng Soph Crs Cntry 83; 3rd Pl Dance Marathon 85; Outstndng Perfrmnce Stu Cncl 85; Cmmnctns.

BOLKO, THOMAS; Portsmouth HS; Portsmouth, NH; (S); 19/394; Var Capt Socr; Var L Trk; High Hon Roll; NHS; Schlr Athl Awd Soccer 83 & 84; Schlr Athl Awd Track 84-85.

BOND, DANIELLE; Spaulding HS; Rochester, NH; (Y).

BOSA, JOSEPH; Kingswood Regional HS; Wolfeboro, NH; (Y); 50/200; Church Yth Grp; Model UN; Band; Concert Band; Jazz Band; Symp Band; Golf; Tennis; High Hon Roll; Hon Roll; Music.

BOUCHER, MICHAEL C; Trinity HS; Manchester, NH; (Y); 1/163; Boy Scts; Pres Stu Cncl; Capt Crs Cntry; Trk; High Hon Roll; NHS; Ntl Merit Ltr; NEDT Awd; Prfct Atten Awd; Val; US Air Force Acad Smr Scntfc Smnr 85; Rnslr Plytch Inst Rnslr Medal 85; St Pauls Advnc Stu Prgm 85; Englsh.

BOUTIN, MICHELLE ANNETTE; Somersworth HS; Somersworth, NH; (Y); 9/165; French Clb; VP Pres FBLA; Hosp Aide; Red Cross Aide; VP Pres Stu Cncl; Hon Roll; NHS; Hugh O Brien Yth Ldrshp Sem 84; Srch Adv Stu Pgm UNH 85; Alt Girls Nation 85; U NH; Nrsng.

BOWEN, CHRISTOPHER J; Salem HS; Salem, NH; (S); German Clb; Model UN; Var Crs Cntry; Ftbl; Var Trk; High Hon Roll; Hon Roll; Goethe Inst Boston Grmn Awd 83-84; Harvard U; Law.

BOWIE, SANDI; Timberlane Regional HS; Plaistow, NH; (Y); Pres Trs 4-H; Quiz Bowl; Chorus; Color Guard; Crs Cntry; Trk; Cit Awd; 4-H Awd; Hon Roll; Cnty Medal Of Hnr-Rockingham 4-H 85; Western New England Coll; Comp.

BOWLER, GREGG; Concord HS; Concord, NH; (Y); 35/323; L Bsbl; Var Bsktbl; Hon Roll; NHS; Bus.

BOWSE, KERRY; Dorer HS; Raymond, NH; (Y); 34/346; Drama Clb; French Clb; Key Clb; Yrbk Phtg; Yrbk Stf; Elwin Cilley Scholar 85; Key Clb Svc Awd 85; U NH; Med Tech.

BOYLE, PAULA J; Lin-Wood Schl; N Woodstock, NH; (S); Cmnty Wkr; FBLA; Pres FFA; Teachers Aide; Chorus; Nwsp Rptr; Nwsp Stf; Yrbk Stf; Cheerleading; Vllybl; Plymouth ST Coll; Elem Educ.

BRADLEY, INGRID; Kimball Union Acad; Plainfield, NH; (Y); Yrbk Stf; Lit Mag; Var Fld Hcky; Var Capt Ice Hcky; Var Lcrss; Var Swmmng; Var Tennis; Hon Roll; U NH; Lib Arts.

BRASSARD, DAWN; Central HS; Manchester, NH; (S); 128/435; DECA; Rep Soph Cls; Rep Jr Cls; Rep Stu Cncl; Hon Roll; Fash Mktg.

BRAWN, JAMES; Portsmouth HS; Newington, NH; (S); Latin Clb; Model UN; Political Wkr; Socr; Swmmng; High Hon Roll; Hon Roll; NHS; Jr World Cncl 84-85; Colubia.

BRAZELIS, GITA BRIGITA; Salem HS; Salem, NH; (S); German Clb; Key Clb; Ski Clb; Color Guard; School Play; Stage Crew; Cheerleading; Mgr(s); High Hon Roll; NHS; German Awd Das Goothe Inst Of Boston 83; Mdrn Miss Pageant Cert Of Achvmnt 84; Model.

BRAZINSKY, CATHERINE M; Nashua SR HS; Nashua, NH; (Y); 59/816; AFS; French Clb; Hosp Aide; Ski Clb; VP Stu Cncl; Swmmng; High Hon Roll; Hon Roll; Jr NHS; NHS; Presdntl Acadmc Fitness Awd 85; Marquette U; Physcl Thrpy.

BRENT, COLIN; Trinity HS; Manchester, NH; (Y); Chess Clb; Church Yth Grp; Computer Clb; Exploring; Model UN; Stage Crew; Nwsp Ed-Chief; Hon Roll; Trs NHS; Ntl Merit SF; German & Greek Awd; Genetics.

BRETON, SANDRA L; Spaulding HS; Rochester, NH; (Y); VP Church Yth Grp; FBLA; Key Clb; Sec Frsh Cls; JV Bsktbl; JV Mgr(s); JV Score Keeper; Var L Socr; JV Stat Sftbl; Hon Roll; Pre Law.

BRETTON, DEBRA; Timberlane HS; Plaistow, NH; (Y); Art Clb; German Clb; Pep Clb; Var Cheerleading; Ftbl; Gym; Pom Pon; Tennis; Wt Lftg; Hon Roll; New England Schl Art; Cmrcl Art.

BRIGGS, JENNIFER; Belmont HS; Belmont, NH; (S); 3/80; French Clb; Varsity Clb; Band; Sec Soph Cls; Sec Jr Cls; Cheerleading; Co-Capt Crs Cntry; Co-Capt Trk; High Hon Roll; NHS; MVP X-Cntry 82, 83 & 84; MVP Chrldng 84; MIP Track 84; Holy Cross; Math.

BROADY, JOEL; West HS; Bedford, NH; (Y); 90/352; Ski Clb; Var L Bsbl; Hon Roll.

BROCKNEY, RICHARD; Spauldine HS; Rochester, NH; (Y); ROTC; Socr; Trk; Hon Roll.

BROOKS, DARLENE; Conant HS; Jaffrey, NH; (Y); Church Yth Grp; JCL; Pres Latin Clb; Church Choir; Jazz Band; Mrchg Band; School Musical; High Hon Roll; Hon Roll; Girl Scts; Natl Latin Exam Magna Cum Laude 83; Bryn Mawr; Arch.

BROOKS, DAVID; Milford Area SR HS; Amherst, NH; (Y); Nwsp Sprt Ed; Yrbk Sprt Ed; High Hon Roll; Hon Roll; Ntl Merit SF; St Pauls Advcd Studies Pgm-Advcd Frnch 85; Pol Sci.

BROOKS, DAVID; Portsmouth HS; Greenland, NH; (S); 1/413; CAP; VP German Clb; Exploring; Math Tm; Trk; High Hon Roll; NHS; Most Improved Cadet NH Wing CAP 84; German Book Awd 84; Air Force Acad; Aerospace Engr.

BROOKS, ETHEL; Spaulding HS; Rochester, NH; (S); 2/390; Church Yth Grp; Math Clb; Math Tm; Yrbk Stf; Rep Frsh Cls; VP Soph Cls; High Hon Roll; NHS; Ordr Of Rainbow Grls 79-84; N H Meth Chrch Yth Cncl Sec 84; Politics.

BROOKS, KEVIN; Kennett HS; Freedom, NH; (Y); 10/200; Varsity Clb; JV Bsbl; Var Bsktbl; High Hon Roll; NHS; Pres Schlr; Thomas Coll; Accntng.

BROUILLETTE, DIANE; Spaulding HS; Rochester, NH; (S); 23/418; Math Clb; High Hon Roll; Banking.

BROWALL, SCOTT; Salem HS; Salem, NH; (S); 78/363; German Clb; Sec Model UN; Hon Roll; Cert Exclnce In Germ Goethe Inst Boston 83-85; Natl Hist & Govt Awd 84; Invlvmnt Am Kennel Clb 82-85; Arch.

BROWN, CRYSTAL A; Phillips Exeter Acad; Cleveland, OH; (Y); Rep Stu Cncl; Var JV Bsktbl; Im Lcrss; Im Socr; Hon Roll; Pres Jr NHS; Ntl Merit Ltr; Ntl Achvt Semi Fnlst; Outstndng Stu 82; Acad ACT Tm 82; U PA; Fin.

BROWN, DAVID P; Concord HS; Concord, NH; (Y); 7/361; Church Yth Grp; Math Tm; Varsity Clb; Pres Stu Cncl; VP L Socr; VP L Trk; Cit Awd; High Hon Roll; Pres VP NHS; Ntl Merit SF; Biomed Engrng.

BROWN JR, DOUGLAS; Hopkinton HS; Contoocook, NH; (Y); 6/76; Church Yth Grp; Debate Tm; Band; Nwsp Ed-Chief; Yrbk Phtg; High Hon Roll; NHS; St Pauls Schl Adv Stu Pgm 85; Med.

BROWN, HEATHER; Belmont HS; Canterbury, NH; (S); Church Yth Grp; French Clb; Girl Scts; Band; Chorus; Concert Band; Mrchg Band; Pep Band; Hon Roll; NHS; Anml Sci.

BROWN, KAREN; Profile JR SR HS; Bethlehem, NH; (Y); Political Wkr; School Musical; School Play; Yrbk Ed-Chief; VP Frsh Cls; Sec Soph Cls; Sec Jr Cls; Sec Sr Cls; JV Var Bsktbl; JV Var Fld Hcky; Sprts Brdcstng.

BROWN, KEITH; Coe Brown HS; Strafford, NH; (Y); JV Bsbl; JV Capt Bsktbl; Var Capt Socr; Hon Roll; NHS; Engrng.

BROWN, KELLY; Somersworth HS; Rollinsford, NH; (Y); 10/170; French Clb; GAA; Ski Clb; Yrbk Stf; Stu Cncl; Var Capt Bsktbl; Var Sftbl; Var Capt Swmmng; High Hon Roll; Kiwanis Awd; Tufts U; Pre-Med.

BROWN, MIKE; Portsmouth SR HS; Portsmouth, NH; (Y); Bsbl; Bsktbl; Bowling; Socr; Wrstlng.

BROWN, SANDY; Farmington HS; Farmington, NH; (Y); Am Leg Aux Girls St; Pres 4-H; Yrbk Bus Mgr; Mgr(s); JV Vllybl; Hon Roll; Hghst Spnsh Grde Avg 85; Farmington Wmns Clb & NH Coll Schlrshps 85; NH Coll; Clnry Arts.

BROWN, SARAH; Derryfield HS; Manchester, NH; (Y); 5/49; Cmnty Wkr; Drama Clb; Intnl Clb; Science Clb; Nwsp Stf; Yrbk Ed-Chief; Pres Frsh Cls; Rep Soph Cls; Rep Jr Cls; Var Fld Hcky; Wellsley Bk Awd 84-85.

BROWN, WENDY; Belmont HS; Laconia, NH; (S); 4-H; French Clb; Band; Chorus; Pep Band; JV Sftbl; Hon Roll; NHS; Keywanettes; Concert Band.

BRUNETTE, CARRIE; Memorial HS; Manchester, NH; (Y); 63/366; Dance Clb; French Clb; Variety Show; JV Socr; Hon Roll; Dance Scholar 83; Cmmnctns.

BRUSSEAU, WILLIAM; Littleton HS; Littleton, NH; (Y); 5/98; Pres Soph Cls; Pres Jr Cls; Bsbl; Bsktbl; Im Coach Actv; Ftbl; Im Wt Lftg; Hon Roll; NHS; Boy Scts; Psychlgy.

BRYANT, DEBORAH; Spaulding HS; Rochester, NH; (S); Church Yth Grp; Cmnty Wkr; Key Clb; Math Clb; Band; Color Guard; Concert Band; Mrchg Band; High Hon Roll; Hon Roll; U Of NH; Nutritional Sci.

BRYANT, DIANE E; Salem HS; Salem, NH; (S); 32/363; Model UN; Teachers Aide; School Play; High Hon Roll; Hon Roll.

BUCO, ANDREA; Salem HS; Salem, NH; (S); Drama Clb; Key Clb; Model UN; School Play; Stu Cncl; JV Fld Hcky; Mgr(s); Vllybl; Hon Roll; St Anselms; Law.

BULKLEY, LYNN ANNE; Mount St Mary Seminary HS; Londonderry, NH; (Y); 13/87; Am Leg Aux Girls St; Yrbk Rptr; Lit Mag; Pres Frsh Cls; Pres Frsh Cls; Pres Sec Stu Cncl; DAR Awd; JCL; Latin Clb; Model UN; Exch Clb Yth Yr Awd Nashua NH Area 85; MV Stdnt Cncl 83-85; 1st Altrnt NH US Yth Senat Schlrshp 85; Stonehill Coll; Cmmnctns.

BULLIS, PENNY; Nute HS; Milton, NH; (S); 4/42; FBLA; Library Aide; Math Tm; Trs Soph Cls; Hon Roll; NHS; Bus Ed.

BUONOPANE, SHARON; Spaulding HS; Center Strafford, NH; (S); 6/387; Rep Jr Cls; High Hon Roll; NHS.

BURBANK, BARBARA; Spaulding HS; Rochester, NH; (Y); 107/356; Office Aide; Red Cross Aide; Cheerleading; Hon Roll; HOSA 84-85; Prm Ste 85; Nrsng.

BURBANK, KERRI; Plymouth Area HS; Thornton, NH; (Y); Church Yth Grp; 4-H; JV Mgr Crs Cntry; JV Sftbl; Mgr Trk; Elem Ed.

BURGESS, ROBERT; Bishop Guertin HS; Nashua, NH; (Y); 6/155; Am Leg Boys St; Camera Clb; French Clb; Math Clb; Nwsp Phtg; Nwsp Stf; Yrbk Stf; High Hon Roll; Jr NHS; NHS.

BURKE, JUSTINE; Salem HS; Salem, NH; (Y); Pres Sec Church Yth Grp; French Clb; Model UN; High Hon Roll; Hon Roll; Cert De Merite 83-84; Gregg Shorthand Awd 85; Bus Admin.

BURKE, MATTHEW; Hillsboro-Deering HS; Deering, NH; (Y); Teachers Aide; Varsity Clb; Yrbk Stf; Rep Sr Cls; Rep Stu Cncl; Var Capt Bsbl; JV Var Bsktbl; JV Var Socr; Hon Roll; Bus.

BURLEIGH, BRET; Trinity HS; Hooksett, NH; (Y); 13/169; Art Clb; Computer Clb; Model UN; Pres Sr Cls; Var Trk; DAR Awd; High Hon Roll; NHS; NEDT Awd; Holy Crs Book Awd 85; Biol.

BURNELL, SCOTT; Timberlane Regional HS; Atkinson, NH; (Y); 21/216; Aud/Vis; Chess Clb; Model UN; School Play; Stat Bsktbl; Im Socr; Hon Roll; Ntl Merit Ltr; Outstndng Soc Studies Stu 85; U S Army; Educ.

BURNEY, SHERYL K; Somersworth HS; Somersworth, NH; (Y); 25/168; FBLA; Latin Clb; Pres Band; Drm Mjr(t); Mrchg Band; School Musical; Trk; Twrlr; JP Sousa Awd; NHS; U KY; Med Tech.

BURNHAM, VICTORIA J; Plymouth Area HS; Plymouth, NH; (Y); 12/143; French Clb; Math Tm; Teachers Aide; Nwsp Stf; Stu Cncl; Hon Roll; Tufts U; Vet.

BURNS, KELLIE; Salem HS; Salem, NH; (Y); 20/347; Key Clb; Trs Latin Clb; Model UN; Teachers Aide; Chorus; School Play; High Hon Roll; Hon Roll; NHS; Ntl Merit Ltr; Rivier Coll Grnt Schlrshp 85-86; Julia Keene Chrtble Trust Fund Schlrshp 85-86; Rivier Coll; Elem Educ.

BURR, BRIGET; Stevens HS; Claremont, NH; (Y); Yrbk Stf; Sec Soph Cls; Sec Jr Cls; Sec Sr Cls; JV Var Fld Hcky; JV Var Trk; Hon Roll; Prfct Atten Awd; V S Clb; Prom Commttee; Movie Set Dir.

BUSHNELL, ANDREW; Inter-Lakes HS; Meredith, NH; (Y); 3/50; Var Bsbl; JV Var Bsktbl; Hon Roll; NHS.

BUSSIERE, KRISTINA; Goffstown HS; Goffstown, NH; (Y); 24/190; Office Aide; Ski Clb; Yrbk Stf; Stu Cncl; Var Co-Capt Cheerleading; High Hon Roll; Hon Roll; GASP Schlrshp 85; Hon Mntn Frnch Awd 83; Plymouth ST Coll; Bus Admin.

BUTTRICK, MELANIE; Concord HS; Bow, NH; (Y); Church Yth Grp; Cmnty Wkr; Dance Clb; FCA; Science Clb; Chorus; Church Choir; Variety Show; Cheerleading; Sftbl; Bio Awd Outstndng Achvt 83-84; Bible Schlrshp Awd 83-85; Bio.

BUXTON, RONALD E; Exeter Area HS; Exeter, NH; (Y); Am Leg Boys St; Trs 4-H; Math Tm; Band; Concert Band; Mrchg Band; Wrstlng; 4-H Awd; Hon Roll; Ntl Merit Ltr; MVP-WRESTLNG 85; Engrng.

BUZZELL, MARK; Saint Thomas Aquinas HS; Dover, NH; (Y); 16/87; Art Clb; Camp Fr Inc; CAP; Debate Tm; Exploring; Letterman Clb; Natl Beta Clb; Ski Clb; Color Guard; Flag Corp; U Of HI.

BUZZELL JR, WARREN A; Spaulding HS; Rochester, NH; (Y); 52/400; Am Leg Boys St; Boy Scts; 4-H; Letterman Clb; Rep Frsh Cls; L Ftbl; Hon Roll; Arch.

CABRAL, SCOTT; Gorham HS; Berlin, NH; (Y); Drama Clb; School Play; Yrbk Bus Mgr; High Hon Roll; Hon Roll; Trs NHS; Mst Outstndng-Pre Algbr 83; Mst Imprvd Perfrmnc-Comptrs 84; Mst Imprvd-U S Hstry 85; Northeastern U; Comp Info Systm.

CACCIOLA, VINCENT; Concord HS; Concord, NH; (Y); Hon Roll; Prfct Atten Awd.

CADIEUX, LAURIE A; Exeter Area HS; Exeter, NH; (Y); 11/289; Capt Color Guard; Concert Band; Nwsp Rptr; High Hon Roll; Kiwanis Awd; NHS; Pres Schlr; U Of NH; Bus Adm.

CADREACT, RICHARD; Masconia Valley Regional HS; Enfield, NH; (Y); JV Bsbl; JV Bsktbl; JV Socr; Comp.

CALLAGHAN, CHRISTOPHER; Spaulding HS; Rochester, NH; (S); 32/460; Church Yth Grp; Key Clb; Rep Frsh Cls; Im Bsktbl; Im Ftbl; Var L Socr; Hon Roll; NHS; Natl Eng Merit Awd 84.

CALLAGHAN, SHEILA BETH; Spaulding HS; Rochester, NH; (Y); 60/347; Am Leg Aux Girls St; GAA; Girl Scts; Key Clb; Yrbk Sprt Ed; Rep Frsh Cls; Rep Soph Cls; Sec Jr Cls; Sec Sr Cls; Var Capt Bsktbl; Fosters Dream Tm Bsktbll 84-85; Elem Educ.

CALLAHAN, DENNIS; St Thomas Aquinas HS; Dover, NH; (Y); 25/90; Capt Bsktbl; Ftbl; Exeter Chrstms Bsktbl Tourney All-Tourney Tm 84-85; St Thomas Aquinas Bsktbl MVP 84-85; U Of NH.

CALLAHAN, KAREN; The Derryfield Schl; Nashua, NH; (Y); VP Church Yth Grp; Cmnty Wkr; Drama Clb; Intnl Clb; Thesps; Acpl Chr; Chorus; Church Choir; Madrigals; School Musical.

CAMP, KIRSTEN; Hopkinton HS; Contoocook, NH; (Y); Church Yth Grp; Cmnty Wkr; Dance Clb; Drama Clb; Hosp Aide; Chorus; School Musical; School Play; Stage Crew; Yrbk Phtg; Child Psych.

CAMPBELL, DEVRA J; Holderness School; N Conway, NH; (Y); 5/78; Church Yth Grp; French Clb; Key Clb; Service Clb; Ski Clb; School Play; Rep Frsh Cls; Rep Soph Cls; Rep Sr Cls; Stu Cncl; Elctd Job Ldr 85-86; Pre-Med.

CAMPBELL, KEVIN; Portsmouth HS; Rye, NH; (Y); 24/340; VP Latin Clb; Model UN; Hon Roll; Northeastern U; Chem Engrng.

CARBERRY, KASSY LEIGH; Winnisguam Regional HS; Tilton, NH; (Y); 23/70; FBLA; Girl Scts; Band; Color Guard; Concert Band; Drm & Bgl; Jazz Band; Mrchg Band; Yrbk Phtg; Yrbk Stf; Athltc Schlrshp 85; Franklin Tilton Northfield Schlrshp 85; Irving C & Katherine M Johnson Awd 85; Mount Ida Coll; Human Svc.

CAREY, JACQUELINE; Manchester West HS; Manchester, NH; (Y); 94/377; Debate Tm; Ski Clb; Lib Band; Lib Concert Band; Lib Mrchg Band; Lib Pep Band; High Hon Roll; Hon Roll; A Ratng Solo & Ensmble Music Fest 85; Animal Sci.

CARIELLO, WENDY; Moulton Borough Acad; Center Hrbr, NH; (Y); Drama Clb; Chorus; School Musical; School Play; Nwsp Rptr; Yrbk Stf; Sec Jr Cls; Lib Sr Cls; Var L Sftbl; Hon Roll; Sec Educ.

CARIGNAN, ANNE MARIE; Spaulding HS; Rochester, NH; (S); 43/418; JV Bsktbl; Var JV Sftbl; Capt L Vllybl; Hon Roll; Vllybl Capt 84; Vllybl Hgh Scor 82-83; Vllybl Drm Tm Hnrb Mntn 82-84; FL S Coll; Bus Adm.

CARLETON, CHERYL; Milford Area SR HS; Mt Vernon, NH; (Y); 35/270; Church Yth Grp; Girl Scts; Hosp Aide; Nwsp Stf; Hon Roll; Candy Striping Schlrshp 85; Hgh Pwr Rifle Comptn Awds 84 & 85; Dollars For Schlrs Schlrshp 85; Rivier Coll-Nashua NH; Nrsng.

CARLOW, TAMI A; Trinity HS; Manchester, NH; (Y); 18/198; Math Tm; Political Wkr; Red Cross Aide; Yrbk Stf; Trk; Hon Roll; NHS; Qlfd-Jr Natls Swmng-Bkstrk 85; Spnsh Awd 83; 1000 Dlrs Wms Clb Schlrshp 85; Cornell U; Entomolgy.

CARMODY, BERNADETTE THERESE; Merrimack Valley HS; Penacook, NH; (Y); 4/120; Am Leg Aux Girls St; Trs Church Yth Grp; Rep Stu Cncl; Var L Fld Hcky; Hon Roll; Sec NHS; Voice Dem Awd; Stu Cncl Yr 85; Pres Awd Acad Ftns 85; Hlth Occup Stu Am Treas 84; Coll St Scholastica; Phys Thrpy.

CARPENTIERE, DAVID; Milford Area SR HS; Milford, NH; (Y); Computer Clb; Hosp Aide; Vllybl; Bldng Trades Awd 85; Elect Engr.

CARR, TROY D; Newmarket Central Schl; Newmarket, NH; (Y); 3/46; Am Leg Boys St; Pres Frsh Cls; Trs Jr Cls; VP Sr Cls; Pres Stu Cncl; Var Bsktbl; Var Socr; Hghst Achvt Hstry & Chem 85; All Arnd Jr Boy 85; Bus Admn.

CARSON, HEATHER; Bishop Brady HS; N Chichester, NH; (S); 1/76; French Clb; Band; Yrbk Ed-Chief; NHS; Ntl Merit Schol; Val; Wellesley Bk Awd 84; Hstry Clb 84-85; St Pauls Adv Stu Pgm 84; Law.

CARTER, KEVIN; Christian Fellowship Schl; Laconia, NH; (Y); Var Crs Cntry; Var Socr; Var Trk; Hon Roll; Prfct Atten Awd; Schlstc Awd For Englsh & Wrtng 84; Chriastian Fllwshp Schl Hnr Pinn 84; CFS Pin Bst Exemplfs Stnds Sc; Messiah Coll; Bus Mgmt.

CARTER, REBECCA; Salem HS; Salem, NH; (Y); Cmnty Wkr; FHA; School Play; Nwsp Rptr; Nwsp Stf; Lit Mag; Hon Roll; Hon Roll; Cert Child Care Aide 84-85; Minister.

CARTER, TIM; Dover HS; Dover, NH; (Y); High Hon Roll; Hon Roll; Comp Prgrmr.

CARTIER, DANIEL; Saint Thomas Aquinas HS; Dover, NH; (Y); Am Leg Boys St; Var JV Ftbl; Hon Roll; UNH; Elec Engr.

CASSELBERRY, DIANE; Spaulding HS; Rochester, NH; (S); 27/400; Drama Clb; Math Clb; PAVAS; Band; Color Guard; Mrchg Band; Stage Crew; Variety Show; High Hon Roll; Hon Roll; UNH; Teachng.

CASSIDY, WILLIAM T; Milford Area SR HS; Amherst, NH; (Y); Computer Clb; Var L Socr; Var L Trk; Var Wrstlng; Hon Roll; Physics.

CATALFIMO, NADINE; Salem HS; Salem, NH; (Y); 83/374; French Clb; Mgr(s); Hon Roll; Jr Castle Coll; Bus.

CEA, STEPHEN; Salem HS; Salem, NH; (Y); 23/353; Model UN; Ftbl; Var Trk; High Hon Roll; Hon Roll; NEDT Awd; Elec Engrng.

CHAMPAGNE, SUSAN; Trinity HS; Manchester, NH; (Y); 1/180; Hosp Aide; Capt Math Tm; Yrbk Stf; Var Socr; High Hon Roll; Pres NHS; Val; Outstndng Sci & Math Stdnt 85; Dghtrs Amer Revltn Good Ctzn ST Wnnr 85; Dartmouth Coll; Med.

CHANG, CHIU LIEN; Phillips Exeter Academy; Blacksburg, VA; (Y); Art Clb; Cmnty Wkr; Dance Clb; Debate Tm; Drama Clb; French Clb; German Clb; Library Aide; Math Clb; Science Clb; 1st Pl PEA French Poetry 84; 2nd Pl Reptr 84; Intl Winner Piano Comp 82; Res.

CHAPDELAINE, GARY J; Tilton Schl; Manchester, NH; (Y); French Clb; Varsity Clb; School Play; Nwsp Stf; Rep Frsh Cls; Rep Soph Cls; Stu Cncl; Capt Bsktbl; Var Ftbl; Socr.

CHAPIN, GREG; Winnisquam Regional HS; Northfield, NH; (Y); JV Socr; Auto Mech.

CHAPMAN, DENISE; Fall Mtn Regional HS; Charlestown, NH; (Y); Drama Clb; Pres 4-H; VP Spanish Clb; Chorus; School Musical; Yrbk Stf; Socr; Sftbl; 4-H Awd; High Hon Roll; Westbrook Coll; Bus.

CHAPMAN, MARTHA; Weare HS; Weare, NH; (S); 5/50; Pres 4-H; French Clb; Trs Jr Cls; Var Bsktbl; Vllybl; 4-H Awd; Hon Roll; NHS; Quiz Bowl; Varsity Clb; Acadmc All Amer Schlr Prog 84; All ST Vllybl Tm 84.

CHARLEBOIS, NICOLE; Newport JR SR HS; Newport, NH; (Y); Church Yth Grp; Math Tm; Var L Cheerleading; Var L Fld Hcky; Var L Sftbl; DAR Awd; Hon Roll; NHS; Rotary Awd; Law.

CHARRON, DAVID; Manchester H S West; Manchester, NH; (Y); 48/366; Cmnty Wkr; Ski Clb; Yrbk Phtg; Yrbk Stf; Wrstlng; High Hon Roll; Yth Of Yr-Manchstr YMCA 82; Pres-Manchstr YMCA Ldr Corps 84-85; UNH; Elec Engrng.

CHARRON, KRISTEN; Memorial HS; Manchester, NH; (Y); 6/366; Chorus; Lit Mag; Var Capt Crs Cntry; Var Capt Trk; High Hon Roll; UNH Manchester; Sgn Lang Intrp.

CHASE, CHRISTINE; Mascoma Valley Regional HS; Enfield, NH; (Y); French Clb; Math Tm; Concert Band; JV Var Cheerleading; High Hon Roll; Hon Roll; NHS; Computer Science.

CHASE, HEATHER M; Phillips Exeter Acad; Muncie, IN; (Y); French Clb; Orch; School Play; Nwsp Bus Mgr; High Hon Roll; Ntl Merit SF; Blackmar Hist Prize 84; Cum Laude Soc 85; Pre-Med.

CHASE, NONA; Berlin SR HS; Berlin, NH; (Y); 137/202; Cmnty Wkr; Pep Clb; Band; Stage Crew; Yrbk Stf; Off Jr Cls; Bsktbl; Score Keeper; Hmcmng Queens Crt 83-84; UNH; Bus Mgmt.

CHASE, SHARON; Kennett HS; Redstone, NH; (Y); 11/200; Key Clb; Var L Fld Hcky; Var L Sftbl; French Hon Soc; Hon Roll; Bus.

CHASSE, CHRISTINE; Spaulding HS; Rochester, NH; (S); 39/418; FBLA; Key Clb; Church Choir; Rep Sr Cls; Hon Roll; NHS; U Of NH.

CHELLIS, RACHEL; Kingswood Regional HS; Center Ossipee, NH; (Y); Church Yth Grp; FBLA; Trs Spanish Clb; Yrbk Stf; Fld Hcky; Hon Roll.

CHENEY, SHAWN; Concord HS; Concord, NH; (Y); Latin Clb; Im Bsktbl; JV Ice Hcky; JV Socr; High Hon Roll; Hon Roll; JV Ice Hockey Partcptn Awd 83-85; NH U; Aerntcl Engr.

CHIASSON, ALLAN; Nute HS; Milton Mills, NH; (S); 5/42; VP Art Clb; Church Yth Grp; Drama Clb; Pres FBLA; Math Tm; Varsity Clb; Pres Soph Cls; Stu Cncl; Capt Var Bsbl; Capt Var Bsktbl; Hugh O Brian Fndtn 82-83; Arch.

CHILD, MARY E; Manchester Central HS; Manchester, NH; (Y); 1/470; Pres Drama Clb; Hosp Aide; Church Choir; Rep Sr Cls; Swmmng; DAR Awd; VP NHS; Val; Church Yth Grp; Math Clb; Harvard Bk; Rensselaer Polytech Inst Mdl; NH JR Miss 85, ST Schlrshp Wnnr.

CHIN, LISA; Salem HS; Salem, NH; (Y); 40/345; Math Tm; Model UN; Yrbk Ed-Chief; JV Fld Hcky; Mgr(s); JV Var Trk; High Hon Roll; Hon Roll; French Clb; Band; Dollars For Schlrs Schlrshp 85; Dgtl Eqpt Corp Schlrshp 85; PA ST U; Engrng.

CHIN, WINNIE Y; Coffstown HS; Manchester, NH; (Y); 5/210; Drama Clb; FNA; Red Cross Aide; Teachers Aide; Var Crs Cntry; Hon Roll; NHS; Stage Crew; Nwsp Stf; Frnch II Awd 83; Natl Hnr Rl 85; Boston U; Med.

CHINCHAR, CHRIS ANN; Portsmouth HS; Rye, NH; (S); 14/430; CAP; Model UN; Ski Clb; Rep Jr Cls; Bsktbl; JV Sftbl; High Hon Roll; Hon Roll; NHS; Sci.

CHRISTOFORE, CASSANDRA; Kingswood Regional HS; New Durham, NH; (Y); Church Yth Grp; Concert Band; School Musical; School Play; Symp Band; High Hon Roll; Hon Roll; Bio 83-84; Spanish Civics 82-83; Stevens Schl Bible; Mssnry.

CIESLA, KIMBERLY; Londonderry HS; Londonderry, NH; (Y); Ski Clb; Spanish Clb; Teachers Aide; VP Soph Cls; JV Gym; Hon Roll; Spanish NHS; 13th Pl Amer Assn Of Tchrs Natl Span & Portgs Exm 84; UNH; Bus.

CLAIRMONT, PETER; Belmont HS; Belmont, NH; (S); 7/78; Math Tm; Varsity Clb; Bsbl; Socr; Trk; Hon Roll; NHS; 1st Pl Sci Fair 85; Comp.

CLARK, CELIA; Fall Mountian Regional HS; Charlestown, NH; (Y); Church Yth Grp; 4-H; French Clb; JA; Yrbk Stf; Socr; Trk; 4-H Awd; Hon Roll; NHS; NH Girls Socr Selct Tm 85; Schl Red Trk Shotput 84; Biol.

CLARK, JESSE; Fall Mountain Regional HS; Charlestown, NH; (Y); 5/150; Am Leg Boys St; CAP; Sec Trs 4-H; Library Aide; Science Clb; Yrbk Sprt Ed; Trk; High Hon Roll; Hon Roll; Pres NHS; Cvl Air Ptrl Flght Schlrshp 83; Air Frc ROTC Schlrshp 85-89; Am Lgn Schlrshp 85; Embry-Riddle Aero U; Aero Engrn.

CLARK, KELLY P; Hopkinton HS; Concord, NH; (Y); 5/69; German Clb; Math Tm; Model UN; Ed Yrbk Phtg; Var Capt Fld Hcky; Var Capt Sftbl; High Hon Roll; NHS; Pres Schlr; Yth For Undrstndg Semi-Fnlst US Sen Japan Scholar 84; SR Female Athlte Awd 85; U S Army Resrve Schlr; Cornell U; Intl Relatns.

CLARK, MISSY; Alvirne HS; Hudson, NH; (Y); 139/332; Hosp Aide; Nwsp Stf; Lit Mag; Sftbl; Trk; Hon Roll; U Of San Francisco; Cmmnctns.

CLARK, TERRI L; Littleton HS; Littleton, NH; (Y); 5/69; Am Leg Aux Girls St; Lit Mag; Pres Frsh Cls; Pres Stu Cncl; Sftbl; Cit Awd; DAR Awd; Elks Awd; High Hon Roll; NHS; Wheaton Coll; Economics.

CLARKE, BENJAMIN; Spaulding HS; Strafford, NH; (S); 45/418; Debate Tm; Drama Clb; Latin Clb; Ftbl; Var Trk; Ntl Engl Merit Awd 84; Law.

CLEARY, LAURA; Moultonborough Acad; Center Hrbr, NH; (Y); 12/30; Art Clb; French Clb; FHA; Sec Sr Cls; Stat Bsktbl; Mgr(s); JV Stat Sftbl; Hon Roll; Endicott Johnson Coll; Intr Des.

CLEMENT, LISA; Newport JR SR HS; Newport, NH; (Y); Exploring; German Clb; Chorus; School Musical; School Play; Swing Chorus; Yrbk Bus Mgr; Yrbk Stf; DAR Awd; High Hon Roll; Psych.

CLERMONT, NICOLE; Lin-Wood HS; N Woodstock, NH; (Y); 4/20; Am Leg Aux Girls St; Church Yth Grp; Stage Crew; Nwsp Stf; Rep Frsh Cls; Pres Soph Cls; VP Stu Cncl; Var Bsktbl; Var Cheerleading; JV Vllybl; Law.

CLOSSON, TOM; Bishop Guertin HS; Nashua, NH; (Y); Church Yth Grp; FCA; Spanish Clb; Var Bsbl; L Socr; Spanish NHS; Outstndng Achvt Medal 82.

COCCHIARO, LISA; Salem HS; Salem, NH; (S); 21/405; French Clb; Model UN; Color Guard; High Hon Roll; Cert Of Merit Frnch 83-84; UN Steerng Cmmte 84; JR Prom Cmmtee 84; Csmtlgst.

COCCHIARO, LYNNE EILEEN; Salem HS; Salem, NH; (S); 3/405; French Clb; High Hon Roll; NHS; Miss NH TEEN 3rd Rnnr-Up 84; Bus.

COHEN, TODD; Lebanon HS; Lebanon, NH; (Y); Exploring; Yrbk Stf; Rep Soph Cls; Rep Jr Cls; Rep Sr Cls; Ftbl; Hon Roll; Genl Ordr Dedctn & Diligne 85; Cobleskill SU; Ag.

COLE, MONTGOMERY; Salem HS; Salem, NH; (Y); 75/350; Drama Clb; Model UN; Lit Mag; Hon Roll; Ntl Merit SF; Cert Frnch Achvt 82-83; U Of Lowell; Elctrcl Engr.

COLE, NORMA; Spaulding HS; Barrington, NH; (S); 40/418; Church Yth Grp; Drama Clb; 4-H; Library Aide; Stage Crew; High Hon Roll; Hon Roll; Ntl Merit Ltr; Outstndng Achvt Alg I, Civics, Frnch I 81-82; Early Chldhd Educ.

COLEMAN, THOMAS; Spaulding HS; Rochester, NH; (S); 30/418; Drama Clb; JA; Key Clb; Capt ROTC; School Play; Yrbk Bus Mgr; Tennis; Hon Roll; Natl Engl Merit Awd 84-85; Cornell; Hotel Admin.

COLLIGAN, THOMAS; Trinity HS; Bedford, NH; (Y); 15/200; Am Leg Boys St; Cmnty Wkr; L Bsktbl; L Ice Hcky; L Socr; High Hon Roll; Hon Roll; NHS; NEDT Awd; Top Algbra Stu 83; UNH; Commnctn.

COLLINS, GREG; Spaulding HS; Rochester, NH; (Y); Key Clb; Hon Roll.

COLLINS, MICHAEL; Colebrook Acad; Colebrook, NH; (Y); Drama Clb; Band; Chorus; Jazz Band; Mrchg Band; Yrbk Phtg; NH All ST Chrs 83-85; All Eastrn Chrs 85; Comp Techncn.

COMEAU, STEPHEN; Bishop Guertin HS; New Boston, NH; (Y); Computer Clb; Debate Tm; French Clb; Math Clb; Math Tm; Speech Tm; Yrbk Rptr; Yrbk Stf; Im Bsktbl; Hon Roll; ST Novice Debate 1st Pl Spkr Awd ST Fin 84; ST Novice & Var Debate 1st Pl Spkr Awd 2nd Prelmnry 85; Pre Med.

CONKLIN, HEATHER; Oyster River HS; Madbury, NH; (Y); 11/165; Drama Clb; VP 4-H; VP French Clb; Math Tm; School Play; Stage Crew; Nwsp Rptr; JV Capt Bsktbl; Dnfth Awd; French Hon Soc; ST 4-H Wnnr Food & Ntrtn 84; Make It Yrslf Wool Swng Cont 83; Natl Frnch Exam 83; Econ.

CONLY, LINDA; Fall Mountain Regional HS; Charlestown, NH; (Y); 29/100; Varsity Clb; Band; Chorus; Church Choir; Concert Band; Mrchg Band; Pep Band; Crs Cntry; Socr; Swmmng; Concord Tech Schl; Dent Hyg.

CONNER, W SEAN; Trinity HS; Bedford, NH; (Y); Am Leg Boys St; Ski Clb; JV Bsktbl; Var Capt Ftbl; Wt Lftg; Hon Roll; Var Ski Tm Ltrmn 84-85; Coaches Awd Bsktbl 83-84; NEDT Mth Awd 83-84; Engrng.

CONNOLLY, RICHARD; Dover HS; Dover, NH; (Y); FFA; Yrbk Stf; JV Ice Hcky; JV Var Socr; High Hon Roll; Hon Roll; Engr.

CONNORS, BRYCE; Manchester Memorial HS; Manchester, NH; (Y); 44/366; Am Leg Boys St; Trs Church Yth Grp; Cmnty Wkr; Red Cross Aide; Ski Clb; VICA; Nwsp Rptr; Off Stu Cncl; High Hon Roll; Hon Roll; VICA Skills Olympcs ST Spch Cont 2nd Pl 85; VICA Skills Olympcs Opening/Closng Cermny 2nd Pl 85; Merrimack; Mktng.

CONNORS, S; Manchester West HS; Manchester, NH; (Y); Bsktbl; Ftbl; Wt Lftg; Hon Roll.

CONVERY, CHRISTINE; Timberlane Reg HS; Plaistow, NH; (Y); 22/274; German Clb; Model UN; Teachers Aide; Band; Jazz Band; Mrchg Band; Pep Band; Rep Sr Cls; Hon Roll; NHS; 1st Pl Wnnr Natl Hstry Day Cmptn, Wash DC 83; 1st Pl Wnnr Natl Hstry Day NH 84; Dartmouth; Lawyr.

COOK, CHRISTINE G; Concord Christian Schl; Franklin, NH; (Y); Hosp Aide; Band; Chorus; Concert Band; Pep Band; School Musical; Yrbk Stf; JV Bsktbl; JV Sftbl; Hon Roll; Concord Hosp Nrsng Schl; Nrsng.

COOKE, DEBORAH; Fall Mountain Regional HS; Charlestown, NH; (Y); Math Tm; Spanish Clb; Band; Flag Corp; Mrchg Band; Hon Roll; Bus Finance.

COOMBS, JULIE; Laconia HS; Laconia, NH; (Y); Church Yth Grp; Drama Clb; Band; Chorus; Concert Band; Mrchg Band; Orch; Pep Band; School Play; Hon Roll; Northeastern Christian JC.

CORDWELL, DANIEL J; Berlin HS; Milan, NH; (Y); 96/202; Ftbl; Mgr(s); Diesel Mech.

CORMIER, MELISSA; Pinkerton Acad; Derry, NH; (Y); Band; Mrchg Band; Hon Roll; Franklin Pierce Coll.

CORRETTE, AMY; Lebanon HS; Londonderry, NH; (Y); Drama Clb; Varsity Clb; Band; Mrchg Band; School Play; Rep Frsh Cls; Rep Soph Cls; Rep Jr Cls; Rep Sr Cls; Var Cheerleading; Joel Hesser Mem Schlrshp 85; Lebanon Ctzns Schlrshp Fndtn 85; Lebanon Lions Clb 85; Hesser Coll; Trvl.

CORYEA, PAUL; Salem HS; Salem, NH; (Y); 40/360; French Clb; Key Clb; Math Tm; Model UN; Ski Clb; Capt Var Bsktbl; Capt Var Crs Cntry; French Hon Soc; Hon Roll; Dollars Schlrs Schlrshp 85; Derry Salem Elks Schlrshp 85; Worcester Poly Tech Inst; Engr.

COSTELLO, ANGELA; Central HS; Manchester, NH; (S); Sec DECA; Hon Roll; DECA ST Secy & Natl Delg 85; NH Grnd Champ Baton Twrlr & Strttr 82-84; JR Miss NH 83; Fshn Dsgnr.

COSTELLO, LOREEN; Salem HS; Salem, NH; (S); Latin Clb; Model UN; Political Wkr; Band; Stage Crew; Var Cheerleading; High Hon Roll; Teachers Aide; Concert Band; Mrchg Band; Jr Prom Committee 84-85; Greek Clb 84-85; Latin Outstndg Stu Awd 83-84; Lang.

COTE, DENNIS; Portsmouth SR HS; Portsmouth, NH; (Y); Model UN; JV Var Ftbl.

COTTER, JOHN; Bishop Guertin HS; Nashua, NH; (Y); 30/138; Church Yth Grp; French Clb; Stage Crew; Nwsp Stf; Yrbk Stf; Trk; High Hon Roll; Hon Roll; NHS; Pres Schlr; Gordon Coll; Bus.

COTTING, SHARON; Pembroke Acad; Allenstown, NH; (Y); FHA; High Hon Roll; Hon Roll; Ntl Merit Schol; Cert Concord Regnl Voctnl Ctr Data Proc 85; Bus.

COUSER, ALISON; Concord HS; Concord, NH; (Y); 26/331; Dance Clb; Orch; Yrbk Phtg; Pres Soph Cls; Trs Jr Cls; Rep Stu Cncl; High Hon Roll; NHS; Modern Lang.

COUTURE, LISA; Spaulding HS; Rochester, NH; (S); 1/390; Math Tm; High Hon Roll; Mu Alp Tht; NHS; Search UNH Prog Advanced Students.

COWAN, SHERYL S; Plymouth Area HS; Plymouth, NH; (Y); 2/138; VP French Clb; VP Temple Yth Grp; Yrbk Stf; Soph Cls; Sec Stu Cncl; JV Sftbl; JV Tennis; High Hon Roll; Hon Roll; NHS; French II Schlrshp Awd 84; Chem Hnr Awd 8k.

COX, MARTHA; Kingswood Regional HS; Ossipee, NH; (Y); 3/123; Church Yth Grp; Dance Clb; Pres Band; School Musical; Trs Soph Cls; Trs Sr Cls; Fld Hcky; High Hon Roll; NHS; Pres Schlr; Chem Awd; US Hstry Awd; Latn Awd; Boston Coll; Law Schl.

COYNE, ROBERT; Bishop Guertin HS; Hollis, NH; (Y); 27/157; Am Leg Boys St; French Clb; Nwsp Ed-Chief; Hon Roll; Boy Scts; Church Yth Grp; FCA; Key Clb; Ski Clb; Band; Amer Legion Boys Nation 85; Law.

CRANAGE, ROBIN; Kennett HS; Freedom, NH; (Y); 7/206; Cmnty Wkr; Key Clb; Yrbk Stf; Rep Frsh Cls; Rep Jr Cls; Rep Stu Cncl; Crs Cntry; Fld Hcky; Trk; Hon Roll; Bus.

CRANE, CYNTHIA E; Hanover HS; Grantham, NH; (Y); Debate Tm; Drama Clb; School Play; Nwsp Phtg; JV Lcrss; L Mgr(s); Trk; High Hon Roll; Ntl Merit Schol; Amer Assoc Tchrs Frnch Cntst 82-83; Germn Hnr Socty 84; Calcls Leag 85; U Of NH; Ec.

CRISP, STEPHEN; Bishop Guertin HS; Hollis, NH; (Y); FCA; Ski Clb; Bsbl.

CRONIN, JON ANDREW; Portsmouth HS; Rye, NH; (Y); 18/344; Church Yth Grp; Drama Clb; Acpl Chr; Chorus; Church Choir; Jazz Band; School Musical; School Play; Swing Chorus; Trk; All New England Chorus Solo Ensmble 84 & 85; Manhattanville Coll; Pre-Med.

CRONIN, SUSAN; Salem HS; Salem, NH; (Y); Exploring; Latin Clb; Math Tm; Model UN; Yrbk Ed-Chief; Bsktbl; JV Trk; High Hon Roll; NHS; Latn Awd 85; Med.

CROSS, DIANNE; Salem HS; Salem, NH; (Y); Church Yth Grp; Model UN; Band; Mrchg Band; School Musical; Variety Show; Hon Roll; NEDT Awd; Tlnt Amer Natl Finals 1st Pl Dncng Awd 82; Tlnt Amer Regnl Finals 1st Rnnr-Up Singing Awd 83; Acctg.

CROTEAU, CRAIG; Berlin HS; Berlin, NH; (Y); Boy Scts; Church Yth Grp; VICA; UNH; Mech Engrng.

CROTEAU, JULIE A; Salem HS; Salem, NH; (S); 97/363; Church Yth Grp; Model UN; Teachers Aide; Band; Concert Band; Mrchg Band; Gym; Hon Roll; New Hampshire Tech I; Den Hyg.

CROTEAU, LYNN; Berlin HS; Berlin, NH; (Y); 45/225; Cmnty Wkr; Pep Clb; Pep Band; Nwsp Rptr; Nwsp Stf; Var Cheerleading; Var Mgr(s); Hon Roll; Law.

CROWLEY, LISA; Newport HS; Newport, NH; (Y); Am Leg Aux Girls St; Computer Clb; French Clb; Ski Clb; School Musical; Yrbk Stf; Var L Bsktbl; Var L Fld Hcky; Var L Sftbl; Hon Roll; Hotl Mgmt.

CROWLEY, SHERRY; Pembroke Acad; Concord, NH; (Y); Spanish Clb; Yrbk Stf; JV Bsktbl; Hon Roll; NW Coll; Culnry Arts.

CULLEN, DEBORAH; Merrimack Valley HS; Penacook, NH; (Y); 42/120; FBLA; Spanish Clb; Chorus; School Musical; School Play; Stage Crew; Variety Show; JV Bsktbl; JV Socr; Im Tennis; Chrs Partcptn Awd Musicl Dept Awd 85; Music Partcptn Medl 85; Johnson ST Coll; Theatr Art.

CULLEN, MELISSA; Winnissquam Regional HS; Northfield, NH; (Y); 6/78; Var Cheerleading; Var Off Sftbl; NHS; Pres Schlr; Natl H S Awd Excllnc 85; Pres Acdmc Fit Awd 85; Utica Coll; Bus.

CUNNIFF, THOMAS A; Oyster River HS; Durham, NH; (Y); 4/120; Chess Clb; Drama Clb; Math Tm; Political Wkr; Capt Quiz Bowl; Concert Band; Orch; Mgr Stage Crew; Bsbl; Swmmng.

CUNNINGHAM, DAN; Bishop Guertin HS; Merrimack, NH; (Y); 40/150; Camera Clb; Church Yth Grp; JV Crs Cntry; Im Mgr Socr; Timer; JV Trk; Im Mgr Wt Lftg; Hon Roll; Sprtsmn Awd IM Soccer 83; Engrng.

CUNNINGHAM, LYNN; Salem HS; Salem, NH; (Y); Boys Clb Am; Model UN; Ed Yrbk Phtg; Var Bsktbl; Var Crs Cntry; JV Sftbl; JV Trk; High Hon Roll; Hon Roll; Spanish NHS; Chllng Prm For Gftd/Tlntd Stu 84-85; Coaches Awd-Bsktbl 82-83 & 84-85; Spn Hnr Awd 83-84; Pre-Schl Eductn.

CURLEY, DEIRDRE MARY; Stratford Public Schl; Stratford, NH; (Y); German Clb; Chorus; School Musical; Yrbk Rptr; Yrbk Stf; Sec Frsh Cls; Sec Soph Cls; Sec Jr Cls; Sec Sr Cls; Var Capt Cheerleading; Stratford High SR Clss Schlrshp 85; Colebrook Frst Ntl Bnk Schlrshp 85; N Cntry Music Fstvl Awd 82-85; Nw Hmpshre Tech Inst; Hmn Serv.

CURRIER, ANN-MARIE; Penbroke Acad; Manchester, NH; (Y); Intnl Clb; Latin Clb; Science Clb; VP Frsh Cls; VP Soph Cls; VP Jr Cls; Rep Stu Cncl; Stat Fld Hcky; Hon Roll; Ntl Merit Ltr; Chem Engr.

CURRIER, EDITH; Hillsboro-Deering HS; Hillsboro, NH; (Y); 7/60; Am Leg Aux Girls St; French Clb; Teachers Aide; Varsity Clb; Band; Mrchg Band; Pep Band; Yrbk Stf; Sr Cls; Var Capt Bsktbl; Coachs Awd For Athltc & Acad Achvt 84-85; Henry J Auclair Awd 85; Keene ST Coll; Phy Educ.

CURRIER, LYNN; Hopkinton HS; Contoocook, NH; (Y); 7/77; Am Leg Aux Girls St; Drama Clb; German Clb; Math Tm; Model UN; Chorus; School Play; Yrbk Phtg; Pres Stu Cncl; Hon Roll; Hugh O Brian Yth Found Awd 84; Grmn I & II Awd 84 & 85; UVM; Psych.

CZARNEC, STACIA ARIANNA; Pinkerton Acad; Chester, NH; (Y); Am Leg Aux Girls St; Cmnty Wkr; Hosp Aide; JCL; Latin Clb; Rep Soph Cls; Rep Jr Cls; Tennis; Hon Roll; NHS; Dvlpmntl Psych.

D AMANTE, RICHARD; Concord HS; Concord, NH; (Y); 19/335; German Clb; Tennis; High Hon Roll; NCTE Awd; NHS; Ntl Merit Ltr.

D ANGELO, DIANE; Alvirne HS; Nashua, NH; (Y); 13/350; Am Leg Aux Girls St; Rep Stu Cncl; Var Bsktbl; Bowling; Trk; Wt Lftg; High Hon Roll; Hon Roll; Trs NHS; Rivier Challange Pgm.

D AUTEUIL, MONICA; Salem HS; Salem, NH; (Y); 28/363; French Clb; FHA; Model UN; Band; Concert Band; Mrchg Band; School Play; Var Mgr(s); High Hon Roll; Hon Roll; Hofstra U Fresh Acadmc Recog Schlrshp 85; Hofstra U; Bio.

DABROWSKI, JOE; Dover HS; Dover, NH; (Y); Church Yth Grp; JV Bsbl; JV Bsktbl; Hon Roll; MVP JV Bsktbl 84-85; Good Sportsmnshp Bsbl 84; Drafting.

DAHL, NICHOLAS H; Bishop Guertin HS; Nashua, NH; (Y); 31/135; Am Leg Boys St; VP Jr Cls; VP Stu Cncl; Capt Bsktbl; Capt Vllybl; Dnfth Awd; Hon Roll; NHS; Pres Schlr; Sec Spanish NHS; SR Cls Schlrshp 85; Schl Lylty Awd 85; U Of NH; Bus.

DAIGNEAULT, KRISTEN; Londonderry HS; Londonderry, NH; (Y); Art Clb; Office Aide; Trs Stu Cncl; Var Capt Bsktbl; Socr; JV Sftbl; Hon Roll; Recvd Unsng Hero Awd Bsktbl 85; Bio.

DALLAIRE, MICHELE; Concord HS; Concord, NH; (Y); 40/329; Church Yth Grp; Varsity Clb; Band; Color Guard; Mrchg Band; L Var Cheerleading; Var Socr; Var Tennis; Hon Roll; NHS; Latin I Achvmnt Awd 82.

DANIELS, JEAN; Winnesquam Regional HS; Tilton, NH; (Y); Trs Jr Cls; Trs Sr Cls; Stu Cncl; Var Cheerleading; Var Fld Hcky; Var Trk; Hon Roll.

DANIELS, MICHELLE; Winnisuam Regional HS; Tilton, NH; (Y); Church Yth Grp; French Clb; Math Tm; Ski Clb; Yrbk Stf; Trs Frsh Cls; Pres Soph Cls; Rep Stu Cncl; Var Mgr(s); Trk; Orthpdc Surgn.

DANISEVICH, TERRI; Timberlane Regional HS; Danville, NH; (Y); German Clb; Model UN; Quiz Bowl; Ski Clb; JV Trk; 4-H Awd; Hon Roll; Pres VP 4-H; Bio.

DARLINGTON, ELLEN S; Oyster River HS; Durham, NH; (Y); 20/121; Drama Clb; Spanish Clb; School Musical; School Play; Stage Crew; High Hon Roll; Ntl Merit SF; Oyster River Schlstc Hnr Soc 84-85; Letter In Drama 84; 1st Prize 2nd Yr Spnsh In St Spnsh Exam 84.

DAVIS, LEE-ANNE; Timberlane Regional HS; Plaistow, NH; (Y); Church Yth Grp; Office Aide; Teachers Aide; Hon Roll; Hghst Avg Achvt Awd-Am Hstry; Achvt Awds-Ger II & Bio; Wldlf Technlgs.

DAVIS, LESLIE A; Moultonborough Acad; Center Harbor, NH; (Y); 15/39; Pres FBLA; Hst FFA; Cit Awd; Prfct Atten Awd; Nwsp Bus Mgr; Nwsp Stf; Yrbk Bus Mgr; Yrbk Ed-Chief; Yrbk Stf; Sec Jr Cls; Burdett Schl; Co Op Sec.

DAVIS, LESLIE ANN; Wilton-Lyndeborough Coop HS; Wilton, NH; (Y); 2/45; Sec Church Yth Grp; School Musical; Variety Show; Hon Roll; NHS; Sal; Natl Sci Merit Awd 82; Natl Ldrshp Awd 83; Am Lg Awd 85; Northeastern KY; Med Tech.

DAVIS, TODD; Milford Area SR HS; Amherst, NH; (Y); 24/281; Am Leg Boys St; VP Debate Tm; Q&S; Quiz Bowl; Scholastic Bowl; Nwsp Ed-Chief; Im Vllybl; High Hon Roll; Hon Roll; Ntl Merit Ltr; Soc Stds Awd Best In Fld 85; Yth & Govt NH YMCA Suprm Ct Jstc 84-85; Prnclpl For Day Cntst Wnnr 85; NH U; Pltcl Sci.

DE FLIPPIO, STEPHANIE; Milford Area SR HS; Amherst, NH; (S); 33/286; Church Yth Grp; Spanish Clb; Teachers Aide; VP Sr Cls; Var JV Socr; Trk; Hon Roll; UNH; Liberal Arts.

DE GRANDPRE, BETSY; Conant HS; Jaffrey, NH; (Y); Teachers Aide; Concert Band; Jazz Band; Mrchg Band; Orch; Pep Band; Stage Crew; High Hon Roll; Hon Roll; NEDT Awd.

DE LUCA, JAMES; Manchester Central HS; Manchester, NH; (Y); 33/403; Am Leg Boys St; Boys Clb Am; Cmnty Wkr; Computer Clb; Exploring; Political Wkr; Nwsp Bus Mgr; Rep Frsh Cls; Rep Soph Cls; Rep Jr Cls; Hugh O Brian Natl Delg 83; U S Japn Sent Prog ST Fnlst 84; Exch Clb Awd Recpnt Mayrs Awd 85; U Of NH; Intl Bus.

DEABLER, GREG; Profile HS; Bethlehem, NH; (Y); 2/40; Chess Clb; Cmnty Wkr; Computer Clb; Math Clb; Math Tm; Office Aide; Ski Clb; Teachers Aide; Band; Rep Frsh Cls; Essy Wnnr Bethlehem NH 85; Wrld Affrs Semnr U Of WI 85; Exchng Stu Frnc Rotry Clb 83; Math.

DEARBORN, LEIGH ANN; Franklin JR SR HS; Hill, NH; (Y); Hon Roll; Acctg III Speed Typg Cont NH Coll 85; Actg.

DECARVALHO, ANTHONY; Kennett HS; Eaton Cnt, NH; (Y); 25/200; Tennis; Spanish NHS; Band; Crs Cntry; Socr; Hon Roll; Spnsh Awd 85; FL Inst Of Tech; Photgrc Tech.

DECOST, RICHARD; Spaulding HS; Rochester, NH; (S); 57/450; Drama Clb; ROTC; Speech Tm; School Play; Hon Roll; ROTC Asst Flght Cmmndr 84; U Of NH; Engl.

DEERING, TERRI ANN; Nashua SR HS; Nashua, NH; (Y); Sec DECA; Hosp Aide; Chorus; Flag Corp; VFW Awd; DECA Schlrshp 85; Spnsh Hnr Rll Awd 83; DECA Awds 85; Johnson & Wales Coll; Bus Mgt.

DEERY, PHYLLIS ANNE; Aluirne HS; Hudson, NH; (Y); Quiz Bowl; Varsity Clb; School Play; Var Bsktbl; Var Capt Crs Cntry; Var Capt Trk; Hon Roll; NHS; Stu Yr 85; Fmle Athl Yr 85; Sprtsmnshp Awd 85; Tufts U; Educ.

DEL GIUDICE, KERRY L; Central HS; Manchester, NH; (Y); 60/439; Church Yth Grp; Cmnty Wkr; Exploring; Hosp Aide; Mgr Var Ice Hcky; Mgr(s); Pom Pon; Im Powder Puff Ftbl; Var Score Keeper; Var Socr; U Of CT; Phrmcy.

DELAGE, GREGORY S; Nashua HS; Nashua, NH; (Y); 200/985; Am Leg Boys St; Church Yth Grp; Pep Clb; Spanish Clb; Varsity Clb; Pres Frsh Cls; Stu Cncl; Bsbl; Bsktbl; Ftbl; U VT; Pol Sci.

DELISLE, DALE; Portsmouth SR HS; Portsmouth, NH; (Y); JV Bsbl; Var Trk; Var Tnk; High Hon Roll; Aero Sp Engr.

DELLA GATTA, JAMES; Bishop Guertin HS; Nashua, NH; (Y); 24/159; FCA; Key Clb; Math Clb; Yrbk Stf; Var L Ice Hcky; JV Socr; Hon Roll; NHS; Bsktbl; Wt Lftg; SADD 84-85; Math Tutor 84-85; Math.

DELUCA, TED; Bishop Guertin HS; Lowell, MA; (Y); Boys Clb Am; Church Yth Grp; Im Bsktbl; Ftbl; Wt Lftg; Hon Roll; Syracuse; Jrnlsm.

DEMERITT, EDWARD; Coe-Brown Northwood Acad; Barrington, NH; (Y); Boy Scts; Church Yth Grp; Drama Clb; Office Aide; Chorus; Church Choir; Pep Band; School Play; Variety Show; Nwsp Rptr; St Pauls Schl Advncd Studs Pgm 85; Excllnc Frnch I & III Awds 83-85; Excllnc Alg I & II/Geom 83-85; Bryant Coll; Bus Adm.

DEMERS, MIKE J; Pelham HS; Pelham, NH; (Y); 11/116; Hon Roll; NHS; NHS Awd 85; Frnch Awd 85; St Anselms Coll; Crimnl Justc.

DES LAURIERS, STEPHEN; Bishop Guertia HS; Dracut, MA; (Y); 33/150; Boy Scts; Computer Clb; Hon Roll; U Of CA Los Angeles; Pre-Med.

DESBIENS, MICHAEL M; Pelham HS; Pelham, NH; (Y); 14/126; Am Leg Boys St; Model UN; Spanish Clb; JV Var Bsbl; JV Socr; High Hon Roll; Hon Roll; Stanford U; Nuc Power.

DESCHENES, CHRISTINE; Trinity HS; Manchester, NH; (Y); Trs Frsh Cls; VP Soph Cls; Rep Stu Cncl; Capt Crs Cntry; Score Keeper; Var Trk; Hon Roll; Jr NHS; NHS; NEDT Awd.

DESPRES III, ALFRED S; Bishop Guertin HS; Hudson, NH; (Y); 2/147; Boy Scts; Cmnty Wkr; French Clb; Ski Clb; Off Sr Cls; Capt Var Crs Cntry; Socr; Wt Lftg; God Cntry Awd; High Hon Roll; Colby Coll Bk Awd 84; Elks, Rotary & Digital Scholars; Eng Dept Awd; Rensselaer Polytechnic; Bio-Med.

DESROCHERS, COLETTE R; Presentation Of Mary Acad; Lowell, MA; (Y); Church Yth Grp; Drama Clb; Hosp Aide; Science Clb; Ski Clb; Pres Soph Cls; NEDT Awd; Bio.

DESROCHERS, LISA; Trinity HS; Manchester, NH; (Y); 7/160; Church Yth Grp; Math Tm; Co-Capt Color Guard; Yrbk Stf; High Hon Roll; Hon Roll; NHS; Ntl Merit SF; Comp Sci.

DESROCHERS, MICHAEL R; Goffstown HS; Manchester, NH; (Y); 36/182; Boy Scts; Church Yth Grp; Cmnty Wkr; Debate Tm; Political Wkr; Cit Awd; God Cntry Awd; Hon Roll; NHS; Ntl Merit Ltr; Eagle Sct 83; Cert Hnr Soc Stds, M Stark Schlrshp Awd 85; Norwich U; Cvl Engr.

DESRUISSEAUX, MICHAEL; Manchester H S West; Manchester, NH; (Y); 38/352; Trs Exploring; 2nd N H Indstrl Arts Comp Drftng 85; Arch.

DEVINE JR, EDWARD F; Salem HS; Salem, NH; (S); 22/363; Boys Clb Am; German Clb; Model UN; Var L Bsktbl; Var L Ftbl; Var L Trk; Hon Roll; Athl Schlr Awd 84; Salems Outstndng Athl Trck 83; Athl Wk 83; Pre Med.

DEVOE, STEVE; Pembroke Acad; Concord, NH; (Y); Aud/Vis; French Clb; Key Clb; Band; Bsbl; Socr; Hon Roll; Engrng.

DEXTER, DAVID; Spaulding HS; Gonic, NH; (Y); 57/357; Hon Roll; Comp Drftng.

DEXTER, REBECCA; Stevens HS; Claremont, NH; (Y); Stu Cncl; High Hon Roll; Hon Roll; Prfct Atten Awd; Typg, Alg Cont 85; Exec Bus Sec.

DI PRIZIO, PETER; Spaulding HS; Rochester, NH; (S); 23/390; VP Jr Cls; JV Bsbl; JV Bsktbl; Var L Ftbl; Im Tennis; Im Wt Lftg; High Hon Roll; Hon Roll.

DICK JR, STRATFORD L M; Phillips Exeter Acad; Lake Forest, IL; (Y); Cmnty Wkr; French Clb; Ski Clb; Acpl Chr; Band; Pres Chorus; JV Crs Cntry; Im Socr; Var Trk; Ntl Merit SF; 6th Pl ST, 1st Pl Cnty IL ST Math Contest 82; Davies Music Prize 82; Econ.

DICKERMAN, KIMBERLEY; Profile JR SR HS; Littleton, NH; (Y); Pres Church Yth Grp; School Musical; High Hon Roll; Hon Roll; Voice.

DICKEY, DAVID; Central Catholic HS; Salem, NH; (Y); 90/220; Ski Clb; Var Ftbl; Im Trk; Im Wrstlng; Hon Roll; Bus.

DICKEY, MARYANN; Salem HS; Salem, NH; (Y); 34/335; Debate Tm; Latin Clb; Model UN; Band; Jazz Band; Stage Crew; Nwsp Ed-Chief; Hon Roll; Cert Awd Jrnlsm 84-85; Cert Awd HS Stu Rptr Pgm 84-85; Del Model UN 84-85; U NH; Eng Educ.

DIDERIKSEN, DEIDRE; Portsmouth SR HS; Portsmouth, NH; (Y); Am Leg Aux Girls St; Drama Clb; JA; Chorus; Concert Band; Jazz Band; Mrchg Band; School Musical; High Hon Roll; NHS; Amer Legion Aux Schlrshp 85; Castleton ST Coll; Mass Comm.

DIKEMAN, GLENN W; Phillips Exeter Acad; Joplin, MO; (Y); Chess Clb; Trs Key Clb; Math Tm; Lit Mag; JV L Ftbl; Trk; Var Capt Wrstlng; High Hon Roll; Hon Roll; Ntl Merit Schol; Naval Reserve Ofcs Trnng Corps Schlrshp 85; Natl Hnr Roll 85; Cls A New England Wrstlng Brnz Mdl 85; Tulane U New Orleans; Med.

DILLON, CHARLES; Concord HS; Bow, NH; (Y); 14/330; Cmnty Wkr; Math Tm; Rep Stu Cncl; Im Sftbl; L Trk; Im Vllybl; High Hon Roll; NHS; Ntl Merit SF; Olympics Of Mind Div III ST Champs 84; Proj Excel Keene ST Coll 85; Mech Engr.

DILORENZO, MARNELL; Stevens HS; Claremont, NH; (Y); Am Leg Aux Girls St; Pres Key Clb; Yrbk Stf; Rep Jr Cls; Trs Sr Cls; Stu Cncl; Var Mgr(s); JV Socr; Explorer Cadet 85; Acctng.

DINCO, AMY; Colebrook Acad; Colebrook, NH; (Y); Art Clb; Church Yth Grp; Cmnty Wkr; Drama Clb; French Clb; FBLA; Girl Scts; JA; Science Clb; Varsity Clb; Rep Hugh O Brien Ldrshp Fndn 83-84; ST Offcr FBLA 83-85; Social Wrk.

DINEEN, JANE; Salem HS; Salem, NH; (Y); 151/347; Key Clb; Model UN; Teachers Aide; Yrbk Ed-Chief; Yrbk Stf; Sec Frsh Cls; Sec Jr Cls; Sec Sr Cls; Var Capt Crs Cntry; Var Gym; X-Cntry Coaches Awd; MVP X-Cntry; Kiwanis Ath Of Wk Awd; Keene ST Coll; Bus Mgmt.

DINORSCE, WENDY; Memorial HS; Manchester, NH; (Y); 21/366; Hosp Aide; Pres Band; Pep Band; Bowling; Boston U; Astrnmy.

DION, CHERYL; Alvirne HS; Hudson, NH; (Y); 1/350; Math Tm; Teachers Aide; Lit Mag; Trs Jr Cls; Rep Stu Cncl; High Hon Roll; NHS; Wellesley Bk Awd 85; St Pauls Adv Studies Pgm 85; Math Cntst Awd 84; Elect Engr.

DIONNE, DANIELLE; Presentation Of Mary Acad; Hudson, NH; (Y); 4/32; Cmnty Wkr; French Clb; Hosp Aide; Library Aide; Science Clb; Service Clb; High Hon Roll; NHS; Ntl Merit Ltr; Prfct Atten Awd; Highest Recgntn Awd-Bio 83; Highest Recgntn Awd-Physiolgy 85; Highest Recgntn Awds-Eng & Eng Lit 83-85; St Anselm Coll; Bio.

DISCIULLO, KAREN; Milford Area SR HS; Amherst, NH; (Y); 46/255; Hosp Aide; Yrbk Stf; Rep Frsh Cls; Rep Stu Cncl; Var Capt Cheerleading; Powder Puff Ftbl.

DIVNEY, ROBERT; Colebrook Acad; Colebrook, NH; (Y); 7/47; Varsity Clb; Band; Chorus; Concert Band; Mrchg Band; Yrbk Stf; Var L Bsbl; Co-Capt Socr; Im Vllybl; NHS; All ST Chrs 85; N Cntry 82-85; Marquette U; Cvl Engr.

DOBSON, TERESA; Spaulding HS; Barrington, NH; (S); 3/300; Church Yth Grp; Math Clb; Math Tm; Yrbk Stf; High Hon Roll; Psych.

DOD, BETSY ANN; Mount St Mary Seminary; Merrimack, NH; (Y); Am Leg Aux Girls St; Ski Clb; Yrbk Stf; Stat Var Bsbl; Stat Var Bsktbl; Stat Var Crs Cntry; Var Mgr(s); Var Score Keeper; Var Timer; Girls St 85; Maryland Inst Art; Int Desgn.

DODD, BARBRA; Inter-Lakes HS; Ctr Sandwich, NH; (Y); Am Leg Aux Girls St; Church Yth Grp; Band; Chorus; School Musical; Yrbk Ed-Chief; Yrbk Stf; JV Var Bsktbl; Var Trk; Hon Roll; Law.

DODGE, RUTH; Fall Mountain Regional HS; Charlestown, NH; (Y); 32/150; AFS; Church Yth Grp; Drama Clb; Girl Scts; Trs Latin Clb; Ski Clb; VP Spanish Clb; Chorus; Capt Color Guard; School Musical; U Of NH.

DOLAN, SEAN; Dover HS; Barnstead, NH; (Y); JV Bsktbl; JV Ftbl; JV Var Socr; Hon Roll; U Of NH; Marine Bio.

DOLAN, TIMOTHY S; Central Catholic HS; Pelham, NH; (Y); Church Yth Grp; Chorus; Yrbk Stf; Var Ice Hcky; Var Trk; Hon Roll; Engr Schlrshp UNH, Engr Schlrshp Merrimack Coll, Keene ST & Plymouth ST Schlrshps 85-86; New Hampshire U; Civil Engr.

DOLCINO, CARINA; Concord HS; Concord, NH; (Y); Pres Varsity Clb; Band; Variety Show; Rep Soph Cls; VP Jr Cls; Pres Sr Cls; L Bsktbl; L Fld Hcky; L Trk; Hon Roll.

DOLLARD, JONATHAN; Manchester Memorial HS; Auburn, NH; (Y); 24/366; Pres Leo Clb; Capt Bowling; High Hon Roll; Hon Roll; Prfct Atten Awd; Arch.

DONAVAN, HANNAH; Holderness HS; Bennington, VT; (Y); Drama Clb; Spanish Clb; School Musical; School Play; Crs Cntry; Lcrss; Socr; Tennis; Hon Roll.

DONNELLY, MICHAEL P; Mascoma Valley Regional HS; Grafton, NH; (Y); 10/105; Boy Scts; French Clb; Concert Band; Pep Band; Yrbk Stf; Pres Jr Cls; Pres Sr Cls; JP Sousa Awd; Pres Schlr; Pres Leo Clb; Boston U; Intl Diplomatics.

DONNELLY, THERESA; Woodsville HS; Pike, NH; (Y); 4/51; Drama Clb; Hosp Aide; School Musical; Yrbk Ed-Chief; Cheerleading; High Hon Roll; NHS; Church Yth Grp; FBLA; FHA; Latin Schlrshp 85; Walter & Carole Young Schlrshp 85; St Anselms; Med.

DONOVAN, BRIAN J; Berlin HS; Berlin, NH; (Y); 9/209; Am Leg Boys St; Pres Jr Cls; Pres Sr Cls; Bsktbl; Var Capt Ice Hcky; Hon Roll; NHS; Pres Acad Fit Awd 85; Terrance Sullivan Awd 85; Bobby Ore Sprtsmnshp Awd 84; Clarkson U; Acctg.

DONOVAN, HEATHER LYNN; Londonderry HS; Londonderry, NH; (Y); Varsity Clb; Lit Mag; Pres Frsh Cls; Rep Soph Cls; Rep Jr Cls; Pres Sr Cls; Rep Stu Cncl; JV Var Cheerleading; Stat Lcrss; Stat Socr; NH Acad Danc Jzz Awd 1st Pl 84; UNH; Humn Resrc Mgmt.

DONOVAN, JIM; Timberland Regional HS; Plaistow, NH; (Y); Cmnty Wkr; French Clb; Model UN; Ski Clb; Off Frsh Cls; Trs Stu Cncl; Var Capt Socr; Tennis; Law.

DOOLEY, ROBIN; Milford Area SR HS; Milford, NH; (Y); Yrbk Stf; Bsktbl; Capt Powder Puff Ftbl; Var Sftbl.

DORR, JEFFERSON A; Central HS; Manchester, NH; (Y); 32/437; Art Clb; Drama Clb; Band; Concert Band; Jazz Band; Mrchg Band; School Play; Stage Crew; Var Golf; High Hon Roll; Manchester Leag Woman Voters Awd 85; U NH; Hist.

DORVAL, DIANA; Pinkerton Acad; E Hampstead, NH; (Y); 17/485; Church Yth Grp; Var Fld Hcky; Sftbl; Hon Roll; Kiwanis Awd; NHS; Keene St Coll; Psych.

DOUBEK, CHRISTOPHER; Winnacunnet HS; Hampton, NH; (Y); Cmnty Wkr; Drama Clb; School Play; Stage Crew; Stu Cncl; Bsktbl; Var Crs Cntry; Var Trk; Hon Roll; NHS; Outstdng Achv In Art 85; Salve Regina; Thtr.

DOUCET, MATTHEW; Nashua Senior HS; Nashua, NH; (Y); 54/807; Am Leg Boys St; Boys Clb Am; Church Yth Grp; School Play; Pres Frsh Cls; Rep Soph Cls; Rep Jr Cls; Rep Sr Cls; Rep Stu Cncl; Var L Bsbl; Athltc Of Yr 83; All ST Qurtbck 85; All Area Qurtbck 85; Rennselaer Poly Inst; Mngmt.

DOUCETTE, HEATHER A; Pinkerton Acad; Windham, NH; (Y); GAA; Var Capt Bsktbl; Var Capt Socr; Var Sftbl; Prfct Atten Awd; All ST & All Rgn Sccr 83-85; Sccr Hnrbl Ment 83-85; All Star Hnrbl Ment Bsktbl 83-85.

DOWARD, JOAN; Manchester HS West; Allenstown, NH; (Y); 12/364; Math Tm; ROTC; Lit Mag; Var Trk; High Hon Roll; NHS; NJROTC Mrtrs Achvt Awd 85; Am Leg ROTC Schlstc Achvt Awd 83; ROTC Dstngshd Cadet Awd 82, 84 & 85; Boston U; Law.

DOWNS, TRACEY; Fall Mountain Regional HS; Charlestown, NH; (Y); 6/150; Camera Clb; 4-H; Spanish Clb; Yrbk Stf; JV Capt Bsktbl; Score Keeper; Socr; Sftbl; Tennis; Hon Roll; St Pauls Schl Adv Stud Pgm 85; Pre-Law.

DOYLE, CHRISTINE M; Londonderry HS; Londonderry, NH; (Y); Church Yth Grp; Ski Clb; Chorus; Color Guard; Var L Bsktbl; Var L Socr; Var L Trk; High Hon Roll; Hon Roll; Phy Ed-Outstndng Indiv Achvt & Svc Awd 83-84; Adver.

DRESCHER, TERRI; Hopkinton HS; Contoocook, NH; (Y); Church Yth Grp; German Clb; Intnl Clb; Math Clb; Var Ski Clb; Varsity Clb; Yrbk Stf; Var Cheerleading; Hon Roll; Htl Mtl Admin.

DRESSER, SCOTT G; Milford Area SR HS; Amherst, NH; (Y); 48/286; Nwsp Rptr; Nwsp Sprt Ed; Var L Bsbl; Var L Ftbl; Im Wt Lftg; High Hon Roll; Hon Roll; Pwdr Pff Ftbl Coach 84-85; U Of NH.

DREW, PHILIP; Kennett HS; Redstone, NH; (Y); 53/200; 4-H; Var L Bsbl; Var L Socr; Roger Williams Inst; Arch.

DRISCOLL, MAURA; Portsmouth HS; Portsmouth, NH; (Y); 23/373; Am Leg Aux Girls St; Church Yth Grp; Latin Clb; Rep Frsh Cls; Rep Soph Cls; Rep Jr Cls; Rep Stu Cncl; JV Bsktbl; JV Fld Hcky; Trk.

DROGO, MARIE; Salem HS; Salem, NH; (S); 3/370; Sec French Clb; Key Clb; Model UN; Ski Clb; Teachers Aide; School Musical; High Hon Roll; NHS; Acctg.

DROUIN, JOANNE; West HS; Manchester, NH; (Y); 87/350; Church Yth Grp; Cmnty Wkr; Office Aide; Political Wkr; Varsity Clb; Y-Teens; JV Capt Bsktbl; Var Crs Cntry; Trk; High Hon Roll; Plymouth ST Coll; Lib Arts.

DU BOIS, CYNTHIA; Belmont HS; Canterbury, NH; (Y); #5 In Class; French Clb; Girl Scts; Ski Clb; Varsity Clb; Band; Pep Band; Yrbk Stf; Rep Frsh Cls; Sec Soph Cls; VP Jr Cls; NH Cmnty Serv Awd 81-82; Most Vlbl Skier 84-85; U Of New England; Pre Med.

DUBE, CHRISTOPHER; Berlin HS; Berlin, NH; (Y); 24/235; Var Trk; Hon Roll; Aviation Mgmt.

DUBE, MICHAEL D; Kearsarge Regional HS; Contoocook, NH; (Y); Am Leg Boys St; Chess Clb; Model UN; Hon Roll; NHS; Ntl Merit SF; Wrtng.

DUBE, STEPHEN; Spaulding HS; Rochester, NH; (Y); 78/349; Church Yth Grp; Hon Roll; U NH; Frgn Lang.

DUCHESNAYE, KATHLEEN; Hopkinton HS; Contoocook, NH; (Y); Church Yth Grp; FBLA; Spanish Clb; Chorus; Church Choir; U Fo NH; Medcl Sci.

DUFF, PAULA; Concord HS; Concord, NH; (Y); 46/329; Drama Clb; French Clb; Chorus; School Musical; Stage Crew; Yrbk Bus Mgr; High Hon Roll; Hon Roll; NHS; Outstndng Achvt Bio & Music 83-84; Hlth Educ.

DUFFIELD, TRACY; Salem HS; Salem, NH; (Y); Model UN; Ski Clb; VP Band; Concert Band; Drm & Bgl; Jazz Band; Pep Band; Nwsp Rptr; Yrbk Stf; Hon Roll; Franklin Pierce Coll; Acctng.

DUFFY, PATRICK; Pinkerton Acad; Windham, NH; (S); 29/413; Ski Clb; Concert Band; Jazz Band; Mrchg Band; Pep Band; School Musical; Socr; Trk; Hon Roll; NHS; Physics.

DUFORD, SHERYL; Winnisquam Regional HS; Sanbornton, NH; (Y); 6/87; Sec French Clb; Math Clb; Pres Jr Cls; Pres Sr Cls; Rep Stu Cncl; Hon Roll; Comp.

DUFOUR, NICOLE; Milford Area SR HS; Amherst, NH; (Y); 35/324; Yrbk Phtg; Trk; Hon Roll; Scholar Frgn Lang Inst Simons Rock Bard Coll 85; Spn.

DUHAIME, GARY; Memorial HS; Manchester, NH; (Y); 48/366; JV Var Socr; Norman Caron Sprtsmnshp Awd 83; Comp Engrng.

DUHAMEL, MICHELE; Memorial HS; Manchester, NH; (Y); 63/366; French Clb; Rptr FBLA; Hosp Aide; Variety Show; Powder Puff Ftbl; Hon Roll; Acctng.

DUMOULIN, DEBBRA; Manchester H S West; Manchester, NH; (Y); 53/364; Hon Roll; Bentley Clg; Comp Info Sysm.

DUNBAR, AMY; Hollis Area HS; Hollis, NH; (Y); 10/130; Church Yth Grp; Cmnty Wkr; Political Wkr; Concert Band; Jazz Band; High Hon Roll; NHS; Spanish NHS; Spanish Clb; Band; Govs Excllnc Awd 85; Engl Excllnc Awd 85; 1st Deg Black Belt Shaolin Kenpo Arts Assn 84; Rivier Coll; Socl Work.

DUNBAR, WENDY; Milford Area SR HS; Amherst, NH; (Y); FBLA; Rep Jr Cls; Powder Puff Ftbl; Im Vllybl; Amer Guild Englsh Handbell Rngrs 83-85; Intl Ordr Of Rainbow Dir Of Chrch Bell Choir 83; Bus.

DUNCAN, SARAH; Hanover HS; Hanover, NH; (Y); 4/136; German Clb; Latin Clb; Band; School Play; Yrbk Stf; High Hon Roll; Hon Roll; Excllnce Prize German 84; Excllnce Prize Latin 84; Law.

DUNHAM, MELISSA; Nashua SR HS; Nashua, NH; (Y); 63/820; Drama Clb; Hosp Aide; Latin Clb; Library Aide; High Hon Roll; Hon Roll; Jr NHS; NHS; Pres Acad Ftns Awd; Biochem.

DUNN, DENISE J; Milford Area SR HS; Amherst, NH; (Y); 27/265; Trs Church Yth Grp; Math Tm; Acpl Chr; Chorus; Church Choir; Variety Show; Im Vllybl; High Hon Roll; Hon Roll; NHS; Hgh Scorer ST Math Cntst 85; Intl Ordr Of Rnbw For Grls 80-85; NH Coll; Acctng.

DUNNE, JOHN; Pittsfield HS; Pittsfield, NH; (Y); 2/77; Capt Quiz Bowl; Yrbk Sprt Ed; Var L Bsbl; JV L Bsktbl; Capt L Socr; DAR Awd; NHS; Pilot.

DUNNING, TASHA; Hopkinton HS; Concord, NH; (Y); Cmnty Wkr; Varsity Clb; Band; Var Bsktbl; Var Fld Hcky; Var Golf; Var Sftbl; Hon Roll.

DUPUIS, ANN MARIE; Trinity HS; Manchester, NH; (Y); Church Yth Grp; School Musical; Nwsp Rptr; Ice Hcky; Mgr(s); Score Keeper; JV Sftbl; Var L Vllybl; Hon Roll; NHS; SADD; Stonehill Coll; Med Tech.

DUPUIS, JOEL; Woodsville HS; Woodsville, NH; (Y); Sec Trs FBLA; Pres Soph Cls; VP Jr Cls; Rep Stu Cncl; Mgr(s); Score Keeper; Var JV Timer; Mngmnt.

DUPUIS, KURT; Spaulding HS; Rochester, NH; (S); Church Yth Grp; Band; Chorus; Concert Band; Jazz Band; Mrchg Band; Orch; Pep Band; School Play; Swing Chorus; Tanglewood Inst Schlrshp 84; All Estrn Band 85; Grtr Boston Yth Symph Orch 84; Boston U; Music.

DUPUIS, MARK; Spaulding HS; Rochester, NH; (Y); VICA; Yrbk Rptr; Yrbk Stf; Var L Bsktbl; High Hon Roll; Hon Roll; U Of NH; Electro Mech Engnrng.

DUPUIS, PAMELA; Spaulding HS; Rochester, NH; (S); 17/351; Band; Chorus; Concert Band; Jazz Band; Mrchg Band; Pep Band; Rep Jr Cls; Hon Roll; Drm & Bgl; Orch; Hugh O Brien Yth Fndtn Ambassador 83-84; NH All-St Bnd 83-84.

DURHAM, PETER; Phillips Exeter Acad; Andover, MA; (Y); Pres Computer Clb; Math Clb; Math Tm; Im Bsktbl; JV Crs Cntry; High Hon Roll; Ntl Merit SF; Rensselaer Medl Math, Sci 84; Math.

DURKEE, ROBERT M; Portsmouth HS; Porstmouth, NH; (Y); 62/394; Model UN; Pres Sr Cls; Rep Stu Cncl; Var L Bsbl; Var L Ice Hcky; High Hon Roll; Hon Roll; JR Prom King 84-55; U Of NH; Industrial Engr.

DUSTIN, SCOTT ALLEN; Hillsboro-Deering HS; Hillsboro, NH; (Y); 12/59; Varsity Clb; Band; Yrbk Stf; Sr Cls; Var Capt Bsktbl; Hon Roll; Cmnty Wkr; Mrchg Band; Var L Bsbl; MVP Bsbl Vrsty 85; Ctzn Schlrshp Awd 85; U S Army Resrv Schlr & Athl Awd 85; Plymouth ST Coll; Bus Mgmt.

DUTILE, DALE; Manchester Memorial HS; Manchester, NH; (Y); 2/402; Yrbk Stf; Stu Cncl; Capt Socr; High Hon Roll; NHS; Pres Schlr; Sal; St Pauls Schl Adv Stds 85; Harvard Bk Awdd 84; Clinton H Scovell Awd 85; Boston Coll; Bus.

DUVAL, MICHAEL; Bishop Guertin HS; Nashua, NH; (Y); 98/157; FCA; Pep Clb; Pres Ski Clb; Stu Cncl; Im Bsktbl; Im Ice Hcky; Mgr(s); Im Socr; Im Sftbl; Var L Tennis; Boston Col6; Law.

DUVAL, NATALIE; Central HS; Manchester, NH; (Y); 2/436; Exploring; Concert Band; Mrchg Band; Ed Lit Mag; Capt Socr; JV Trk; High Hon Roll; NHS; Ntl Merit Ltr; Sal; Ski Tm Capt 85; Cabardina Troph 85; Dartmouth.

DUVALL, MARK; Salem HS; Salem, NH; (S); 25/405; Latin Clb; Model UN; Ski Clb; Stu Cncl; Var JV Ftbl; Trk; High Hon Roll; Hon Roll.

DWYER, DAVID; Manchester Memorial HS; Manchester, NH; (Y); 91/366; VICA; School Play; Nwsp Phtg; Nwsp Rptr; Var L Trk; Hon Roll; Manchester Policemns Wives Schlrshp 86; Voctnl Indstrl Clbs Amer Secy 85; Boston Coll; Psychtry Wrk.

DZICZEK, JENNIFER; Londonderry HS; Manchester, NH; (Y); Sec Art Clb; Drama Clb; VP French Clb; Office Aide; Chorus; Color Guard; Nwsp Rptr; Yrbk Ed-Chief; Yrbk Phtg; High Hon Roll; Yrbk Awd 84 & 85; U NH; Secy.

EDWARDS, WILLIAM R; Winnacunnet HS; Hampton, NH; (Y); Am Leg Boys St; JA; High Hon Roll; Hon Roll; NHS; Prfct Atten Awd; Sci Symposium Attendnc Awd; UNH; Mechncl Engrng.

EGLINTON, KENNETH; Milford Area HS; Amherst, NH; (Y); Am Leg Boys St; Church Yth Grp; Pres Band; Concert Band; Jazz Band; Mrchg Band.

EILERS, ERIKA; Concord HS; Concord, NH; (Y); 35/330; Drama Clb; Orch; School Musical; Stage Crew; L Var Crs Cntry; Var Trk; High Hon Roll; Hon Roll; Rotary Club Yth Exch Pgm 85-86; Lang.

EISFELLER, JUSTIN; Portsmouth HS; Greenland, NH; (S); 13/362; Model UN; Spanish Clb; JV Bsktbl; High Hon Roll; Hon Roll; Jr NHS.

ELLIS, JON; Spaulding HS; E Rochester, NH; (Y); JV Bsbl; Var Capt Ice Hcky; JV Socr; Hon Roll; Vrsty Hockey MVP 83-85, 7th Plyr Awd 82-83; Vrsty Soccer MIP 83.

ELLS, BRUCE; Mascoma Valley Regional HS; Grafton, NH; (Y); 3/117; Art Clb; VP 4-H; Chorus; Nwsp Phtg; Yrbk Phtg; Cit Awd; High Hon Roll; NHS; Church Yth Grp; Ski Clb; ST 4-H Teen Cncl 85; Undrclssmn Sci Awd 85; Schlrshp Consrvtn Cmp 84; Aerontcl Engrng.

EMOND, DAWN MARIE; Alvirne HS; Hudson, NH; (Y); Lit Mag; Soph Cls; High Hon Roll; NHS; Med.

ERBSTEIN, NANCY; Oyster River HS; Durham, NH; (Y); 8/130; Drama Clb; VP French Clb; Chorus; Orch; Yrbk Stf; Rep Stu Cncl; French Hon Soc; Hon Roll; NHS; Ntl Merit SF; Cogntve Sci.

ERICKSON, KRISTIN; Presentation Of Mary Acad; Nashua, NH; (Y); 6/33; Pres French Clb; Science Clb; Nwsp Stf; High Hon Roll; Hon Roll; NHS; Rnkd 1st Engl & Relgn 82-85; Intrior Dsgn.

ERRERA JR, LEONARD J; Mascenic Regional HS; New Ipswich, NH; (Y); Nwsp Rptr; Pres Frsh Cls; Rep Stu Cncl; Var L Bsbl; JV Bsktbl; Var L Socr; Hon Roll; UNH; Jrnlsm.

ESENWINE, MATTHEW; Weare HS; Weare, NH; (Y); 1/41; Drama Clb; French Clb; Nwsp Ed-Chief; Nwsp Stf; Mgr L Bsktbl; Score Keeper; High Hon Roll; NHS; Val; Drama Clbs Prmsng Actr Awd 85; NH Eductnl Thtre Gulds Cast 85; Pres Schlrshp 85; Castleton ST Clg; Brdcst Comm.

ESPINOLA, LAURIE ANN; Salem HS; Hampstead, NH; (S); 60/343; Key Clb; Ski Clb; Bsktbl; Capt Var Fld Hcky; JV Sftbl; Psych.

ESTES, KIM; Dover HS; Dover, NH; (Y); 4-H; 4-H Awd; High Hon Roll; Hon Roll; UNH; Mar Biol.

EVANS, KRISTEN; Stevens HS; Claremont, NH; (Y); Sec Key Clb; Yrbk Bus Mgr; Yrbk Stf; Pres Stu Cncl; Var Tennis; Cit Awd; 4-H Awd; High Hon Roll; NHS; Church Yth Grp; Harvard Bk Awd 85; 4 H Ctznshp WA Trp 84; Pre-Med.

EVENSON, KRISAN; Spaulding HS; Rochester, NH; (S); 10/418; Am Leg Aux Girls St; Drama Clb; High Hon Roll; Hon Roll; NHS; Smnr Adv HS Stu; Frnch.

EZEKIEL, MICHAEL; Bishop Guertin HS; Hudson, NH; (Y); 55/125; Boy Scts; Church Yth Grp; Hosp Aide; Key Clb; Ski Clb; JV Crs Cntry; Im Socr; Hon Roll; 1 Yr Hnr Rold Awd 84; Hour Pin Hosp Vol 84; Med.

FAFORD, MICHELLE; Londonderry HS; Londonderry, NH; (Y); VP Church Yth Grp; VP Spanish Clb; Stat Bsktbl; Var Crs Cntry; Var Socr; Var Trk; Hon Roll; Spanish NHS.

FANNING, JUDITH; Spaulding HS; Rochester, NH; (S); 31/415; VP Church Yth Grp; Cmnty Wkr; Trs Drama Clb; Key Clb; School Play; Yrbk Stf; NHS; Search Tm 84-85; Bio.

FARAH, DANIEL JAY; Christian Fellowship HS; Ctr Harbor, NH; (Y); Church Yth Grp; Scholastic Bowl; School Play; Bsktbl; Score Keeper; Socr; NEDT Awd; Bibl Awd 82-85; Oral Roberts U; Theolgy.

FARAR, DEBORAH; Alvirne HS; Hudson, NH; (Y); Pres Church Yth Grp; FBLA; Chorus; Church Choir; School Musical; School Play; Var Cheerleading; Hon Roll; Brigham Yng U; Illstrtn.

FARMER, TERESA; Winnisquam Regional HS; Tilton, NH; (Y); 12/77; Pres FBLA; Spanish Clb; Hon Roll; Shaws Schlrshp 85; Womens Club Schlrshp 85; Hesser Coll; Travel.

FARMER, TOM; Goffstown Area Public HS; Goffstown, NH; (Y); 2/201; Boy Scts; Church Yth Grp; Math Tm; Var Tennis; High Hon Roll; Lion Awd; NHS; Rotary Awd; Sal; Superior Grd-Chem St Pauls Advncd Stud Pgm 84; Schlrshps Recogntn-Chem, Coll Bio I, II 83-85; Tufts U; Engrng.

FARR, ROCHELLE; Woodsville HS; Monroe, NH; (Y); 11/75; Church Yth Grp; Pres 4-H; FHA; Yrbk Stf; Var Bsktbl; Coach Actv; Fld Hcky; Dnfth Awd; Hon Roll; NHS; Typing & Bst Contrbtn Bsktbl Awds 83-84; Alg I & Bst Contrbtn Bsktbl Awds 83; Comp.

FARRELL, DENISE; Concord HS; Concord, NH; (Y); Girl Scts; Hosp Aide; Sec Spanish Clb; Band; Chorus; Color Guard; Jazz Band; Mrchg Band; Concord Antrim Schlrshp 85; Outstndg Attitude Mrchg Bnd 85; U NH; Vet.

FARWELL, DAVID M; Trinity HS; Hooksett, NH; (Y); 19/190; Am Leg Boys St; Var Bsbl; Var Ice Hcky; Hon Roll; NHS; Bus.

FAULHABER, SHERRY; Spaulding HS; Rochester, NH; (Y); FNA; Hosp Aide; Office Aide; Red Cross Aide; JV Bsktbl; JV Trk; Hon Roll; U Of NH; Nrs.

FAULKNER, BLAINE; Spaulding HS; Rochester, NH; (Y); 36/256; Hon Roll; NH Tech Inst.

FAUTEUX, LUCY; Presentation Of Mary HS; Nashua, NH; (Y); 1/33; VP French Clb; Ski Clb; Yrbk Stf; Sec Soph Cls; Pres Jr Cls; VP Sr Cls; Bausch & Lomb Sci Awd; High Hon Roll; NHS; Val; Bates Coll; Bio.

FECTEAU, KELLIE; Farmington HS; Farmington, NH; (Y); 7/67; Am Leg Aux Girls St; Church Yth Grp; French Clb; Yrbk Stf; VP Jr Cls; Hon Roll; NHS; Abraham Burtman Schlrshp 85; U Of NH; Pre Vet.

FECTEAU, RICHARD; Franklin JR-SR HS; Franklin, NH; (Y); 6/100; Boy Scts; Church Yth Grp; Trk; Hon Roll; NHS; Prfct Atten Awd; Elec Engr.

FELIX, LOUIS; Mascoma Valley Regional HS; Enfield, NH; (Y); 25/130; Church Yth Grp; Math Tm; Pep Clb; Band; Chorus; Concert Band; Mrchg Band; Pep Band; School Musical; High Hon Roll; Outstndng Chorus Mbr 83-85; Engrng.

FERRARI, PAUL; Milford Area SR HS; Amherst, NH; (Y); Am Leg Boys St; Boy Scts; English Clb; Kaley Plbc Spkng Cntst 84; Law.

FEVERSTEIN, ABRA; Franklin HS; Franklin, NH; (Y); 1/100; Band; Trs Frsh Cls; Trs Soph Cls; Trs Jr Cls; Trs Sr Cls; Rep Stu Cncl; Var Ftbl; Bausch & Lomb Sci Awd; DAR Awd; Val; Natl Hnr Soc Schlrshp Wnnr 85; Arion Awd Mus 85; Lakes Region Discus Champ 85; Dartmouth Coll; Chem.

FIKE, KRISTEN L; Somersworth HS; Somersworth, NH; (Y); 4/150; Dance Clb; Math Tm; Quiz Bowl; Chorus; Swing Chorus; Nwsp Ed-Chief; Nwsp Stf; High Hon Roll; NHS; St Pauls Advncd Studies Prog Chem 85; Jrnlsm.

FILIMONOV, MARK G; Hanover HS; Etna, NH; (Y); 14/143; Stage Crew; Nwsp Bus Mgr; Yrbk Stf; Rep Jr Cls; Rep Sr Cls; Swmmng; JV Trk; High Hon Roll; Ntl Merit SF; Cunningham Trust & Dresden Schlrshps 85; Dartmouth Coll; Physcs.

FILIPPINI, ANGELA; Nashua SR HS; Nashua, NH; (Y); Am Leg Aux Girls St; Color Guard; Orch; Variety Show; Hon Roll; Rifle Team 83-84; Nrthestrn U; Elec Engr.

FILIPPONE, MARIA; Salem HS; Salem, NH; (Y); FTA; Girl Scts; Key Clb; Latin Clb; Model UN; Hon Roll; River Coll Nashua NH; RN.

FILLIO, CHRISTOPHER P; Exeter Area HS; East Kingston, NH; (Y); Am Leg Boys St; Nwsp Stf; Sec Jr Cls; Rep Stu Cncl; Var Bsbl; Socr; Trk; High Hon Roll; NHS; Boy Scts; Quebec-Hydro Frnch Awd 84; Ivy Leag Schl; Comp Sci.

FILLION, JOE; Franklin HS; Franklin, NH; (Y); Band; Concert Band; Jazz Band; Mrchg Band; Pep Band; Var L Bsbl; Hon Roll; Prfct Atten Awd; De Vry Inst Elctrncs; Comp Repr.

FILTEAU, LIESL; Newfound Memorial HS; E Hebron, NH; (Y); Chorus; Var Capt Trk; High Hon Roll; Hon Roll; NHS; Mst Imprvd On Trk Tm 85; 10th NH Trk Meet Discus 85; SR Ways & Means Committee 85; Plymouth ST Coll; Bio.

FINAN, KATHLEEN M; Portsmouth SR HS; Portsmouth, NH; (Y); Drama Clb; Office Aide; School Musical; School Play; Stage Crew; Yrbk Stf; JV Sftbl; Hon Roll; Comp Sci.

FISCHER, DAN; Bishop Guertin HS; Nashua, NH; (Y); 3/150; French Clb; Math Clb; Sec Sr Cls; Rep Stu Cncl; Var L Socr; High Hon Roll; Jr NHS; NHS.

FITCHETT, SHARON; White Mountians Regional HS; Whitefield, NH; (Y); 4/88; Church Yth Grp; Drama Clb; Teachers Aide; Mgr(s); NHS; Art Clb; French Clb; Radio Clb; Stage Crew; Hon Roll; Hugh O Brian Ldrshp Awd 84; Century II Ldrshp Awd 85; St Pauls Adv Stds Prog 85; Gordon Coll; Spec Ed.

FITZGERALD, KELLY; Dover HS; Dover, NH; (Y); GAA; Girl Scts; Mgr Bsktbl; Mgr Fld Hcky; Powder Puff Ftbl; Hon Roll; Hotel Mgmt.

FLAHERTY, KATHLEEN; Gilford Middle HS; Gilford, NH; (S); 7/104; Drama Clb; Thesps; Sec VP Chorus; School Play; Ed Nwsp Rptr; Sec Jr Cls; JV Bsktbl; Var L Fld Hcky; Sec German Clb; VP Swing Chorus; NH All-ST Chorus 83-84; All-Estrn Chorus 84-85; Newspaper Feature Editor 84-85; Theatre.

FLANDERS, CHARLES; Inter Lakes HS; Meredith, NH; (Y); Boy Scts; Church Yth Grp; Computer Clb; Pep Clb; Im Badmtn; Im Bsbl; Im Bsktbl; Var Socr; Var Trk; Hon Roll; Sci Fair Awd 85; Econ.

FLANDERS, DAVID; Keene HS; Keene, NH; (Y); Am Leg Boys St; Latin Clb; Acpl Chr; Chorus; Variety Show; Pres Sr Cls; Pres Stu Cncl; JV Wrstlng; NHS; Rotary Awd; GMI; Elctrnc Engr.

FLANDERS, DOUGLAS P; Keene HS; Keene, NH; (Y); 23/390; Am Leg Boys St; VP VICA; Rep Frsh Cls; Rep Soph Cls; Rep Jr Cls; Rep Sr Cls; Trs VP Stu Cncl; JV L Wrstlng; Hon Roll; JR Lion 85; Elec Engrng.

FLEMING, SHANNON; Inter-Lakes HS; Center Harbor, NH; (Y); 9/54; Church Yth Grp; Library Aide; Varsity Clb; Band; Pep Band; JV Bsktbl; L Sftbl; JV Vllybl; High Hon Roll; Hon Roll; U Of Tampa; Biol.

FLETCHER, BARRY; Fall Mountain Regional HS; Walpole, NH; (Y); FFA; Var Ftbl; Ntl FFA Cnvntn Rep 84; Dairy Frmr.

FLETCHER, SUSAN; Pinkerton Acad; Derry, NH; (Y); Church Yth Grp; Chorus; Church Choir; Var Vllybl; Hon Roll; NHS; Typng Awd 85; Chrs Accmpnst Awd, Bible Awd 84; Liberty U; Music.

FLINN III, LEWIS B; Phillips Exeter Acad; Richmond, VA; (Y); Boy Scts; VP French Clb; Drama Clb; Pres Acpl Chr; Off Chorus; Madrigals; Orch; Ed Yrbk Stf; High Hon Roll; Wnnr Cncrto Cmptn Org Cncrto 83; Soloist Ten Cncrts; Cmpstn.

FLOYD, JULIE E; Plymouth Area HS; Plymouth, NH; (Y); French Clb; Ski Clb; Bsktbl; Crs Cntry; Fld Hcky; Sftbl; Hon Roll; Score Keeper; Timer.

FLYNN, ROBERT; Spaulding HS; Barrington, NH; (S); 6/384; Church Yth Grp; Drama Clb; Key Clb; ROTC; School Play; High Hon Roll; Search Gftd, Tlntd UNH Smnr Sessions 84-85; Decoration Comm Cty Xmas Parade 84.

FLYNN, ROCK; Spaulding HS; Barrrington, NH; (Y); 5/400; Am Leg Boys St; Church Yth Grp; Cmnty Wkr; Drama Clb; Key Clb; Capt ROTC; School Play; High Hon Roll; NHS; St Pauls Schl Advanced Stud Pgm 85.

FOLLANSBEE, REGINA; Concord HS; Concord, NH; (Y); Orch; Yrbk Stf; Tennis; Hon Roll; Outstndg Achvt Acct I 85; Hon Men Acctg Cont 85; Ten Ltr 85; Acctg.

FONG, ROLAND; Nashua HS; Nashua, NH; (Y); Church Yth Grp; JA; Pep Clb; Varsity Clb; Var Trk; High Hon Roll; Hon Roll; Jr NHS; NH NHS; Bsbl Ltr Grad 85; NH U; Comp Engr.

FONTAINE II, ARTHUR; Franklin JR SR HS; W Franklin, NH; (Y); 20/90; Rptr DECA; Mgr Drama Clb; Teachers Aide; Trs Band; Trs Chorus; School Play; Yrbk Phtg; JV Var Mgr(s); JV Score Keeper; Hon Roll; Cazenovia; Fash Desgn.

FONTAINE, MARK; Laconia HS; Laconia, NH; (Y); Boy Scts; Church Yth Grp; Letterman Clb; Ski Clb; Crs Cntry; Trk; Hon Roll; Natl Eagle Of Cross Awd 85; Med.

FONTAINE, TIM; Pembroke Acad; Suncook, NH; (Y); VICA; Rep Soph Cls; Socr; Elecl.

FORD, BENTLEY; Profile HS; Franconia, NH; (Y); 3/40; Chess Clb; VP Computer Clb; Math Tm; Ski Clb; Var Tennis; High Hon Roll; Comp Sci.

FORET, GRETCHEN; Merrimack HS; Merrimack, NH; (S); 24/240; Pres DECA; Office Aide; VP Jr Cls; Im Gym; Var Mgr(s); Im Vllybl; Hon Roll; 3rd Pl Apparel & Access Suprvisry Level DECA ST Comp 84; Mgr Week Schl Store 84; Johnson & Wales; Mktg.

FORTE, RACHELLE; Salem HS; Salem, NH; (S); French Clb; GAA; Latin Clb; JV Cheerleading; Var JV Mgr(s); JV Sftbl; High Hon Roll; Cert Of Merit Frnch 83-84; C Of C Miss Congeniality 84-85; Boston Coll.

FOSTER, KRISTI; Farmington HS; Farmington, NH; (Y); Yrbk Stf; Bsktbl; Sftbl; Bsktbl Awd 84; Sftbl MVP 84-85; Hair Drssr.

FOURNIER, NICOLE; Spaulding HS; Barrington, NH; (S); Chorus; School Musical; Swing Chorus; Socr; Hon Roll; Ctznshp Awd 80; Mus.

FRAMBACH, BARBARA; Portsmouth SR HS; Pease AFB, NH; (Y); German Clb; Pep Clb; Mrchg Band; Symp Band; Trk; High Hon Roll; Hon Roll; U Of NH; Trvl.

FRANK, ELIZABETH S; Phillips Exeter Acad; Winchester, MA; (Y); Drama Clb; Thesps; School Musical; School Play; Rep Stu Cncl; Fld Hcky; Lcrss; Sftbl; High Hon Roll; Ntl Merit SF.

FRANTZ, TIMOTHY; Hillsboro-Deering HS; Hillsboro, NH; (Y); 13/65; Church Yth Grp; Drama Clb; Math Tm; Quiz Bowl; Chorus; Church Choir; School Play; Trs Stu Cncl; JV Socr; Hon Roll; Chem.

FRASER, ERIC; Salem HS; Salem, NH; (Y); Model UN; Var L Ftbl; JV Trk; Var L Wrstlng; Hon Roll; Lowell U; Electrnc Engr.

FRASER, JUDITH; Salem HS; Salem, NH; (Y); FHA; Key Clb; School Play; Hon Roll; NHS; Merrimack Coll; Acctng.

FRECHETTE, NAOMI; Hopkinton HS; Hopkinton, NH; (Y); Pres Jr Cls; Var Trk; Church Yth Grp; Wt Lftg; Bay ST JC; Csmtlgy.

FREITAS, STEVEN; Salem HS; Salem, NH; (Y); 3/344; Key Clb; Chrmn Model UN; Off Ski Clb; Spanish Clb; Bausch & Lomb Sci Awd; High Hon Roll; Sec NHS; Spanish NHS; Cls Essyst 3rd 85; Acadmc Excllnc Physcs Awd 85; Acadmc Excllnc Math Awd 85; Worcestr Plytech Inst; Elec Eng.

FRENCH, MIKE J; Milford Area SR HS; Amherst, NH; (Y); 64/220; Computer Clb; Math Tm; Hon Roll; U NH; Comp Sci.

FREYENHOGEN, LORI; Thayer HS; Winchester, NH; (Y); Girl Scts; Hosp Aide; Teachers Aide; Off Frsh Cls; Off Soph Cls; Off Jr Cls; Stu Cncl; Bsktbl; Fld Hcky; Score Keeper; Acctg.

FRIEDMAN, VANESSA V; Phillips Exeter Acad; New York City, NY; (Y); Office Aide; Nwsp Bus Mgr; Ed Lit Mag; Ntl Merit SF.

FRIES, LISA V; Pittsfield HS; Pittsfield, NH; (Y); 2/63; Pres Church Yth Grp; VP Pres 4-H; Varsity Clb; Band; Sec Pres Stu Cncl; JV Bsktbl; Var Fld Hcky; Hon Roll; Pres NHS; Sal; Algbr II Achvt 83-84; 2nd Pl Sci Fair 82-83; Geomtry Achvt 82-83; Plymouth ST Coll; Elem Eductn.

FRIZZELL, LYLE; Groveton HS; Groveton, NH; (Y); 17/48; 4-H; Dnfth Awd; Embry-Riddle Aeron U; Comp Sci.

FROST, KELLEY; Spaulding HS; Rochester, NH; (S); 8/392; Key Clb; Rep Jr Cls; High Hon Roll; Hon Roll; NHS; Soap Box Derby Sptsmnsp Awd 80; Quinipiac; Phys Thrpy.

FROST, MICHEAL; Manchester Memorial HS; Manchester, NH; (Y); 5/366; Boy Scts; JV Ice Hcky; High Hon Roll; NHS; Colby Coll Bk Awd 85; MA Inst Tech; Chem.

FULGONI, ELAINE M; Nashua HS; Nashua, NH; (Y); 62/807; Church Yth Grp; Hosp Aide; Library Aide; Yrbk Stf; Hon Roll; Jr NHS; NHS; Swmmng Awd 81; Art Awds 81-82; Pres Acad Ftnss Awd 85; Rivier Coll; Art.

FULLER, CHRISTOPHER P; Phillips Exeter Acad; Arlington Hts, IL; (Y); Pres Debate Tm; Pres Model UN; Ed Yrbk Phtg; JV Socr; Hon Roll; Ntl Merit SF; Prfct Atten Awd; Intl Bus Law.

GAGNE, JENNIFER; Saint Thomas Aquinas HS; Farmington, NH; (Y); Debate Tm; French Clb; Hosp Aide; NFL; Yrbk Stf; Art Hnrs 84.

GAGNE, SCOTT; Mascoma Valley Regional HS; Enfield, NH; (Y); Art Clb; Ski Clb; Band; Concert Band; Mrchg Band; Lit Mag; High Hon Roll; Hon Roll; 1st Pl Awds Art Show 83-84; Portland Schl Art Painting Competitn Fin 84; RI Schl Desgn; Graphic Desgn.

GAGNON, MICHELE; Manchester HS West; Bedford, NH; (Y); 39/364; Art Clb; Hon Roll; Nw Englnd IKS Blck Blt Chmpn 85; Publc Reltns Prsn Ntl Art Hnr Soc 84-85; Nw Eng Kart Blk Blt Chmp 84; St Anselm Coll; Educ.

GAGNON, SHELLY; Londonderry HS; Londonderry, NH; (Y); GAA; Teachers Aide; Varsity Clb; VP JV Bsktbl; VP Capt Socr; VP JV Sftbl; Hon Roll; Sccr Coaches Awd Div II All-ST Nashua Telegrph 84; All-Area Goalie, MHCA Hnrbl Mntn Awd; Phy Thrpy.

GAIMARI, STEPHEN; Bishop Guertin HS; Nashua, NH; (Y); 15/150; FCA; French Clb; Var Bsktbl; Var Socr; Var Trk; High Hon Roll; NHS; All Area Sccr 84; Bio.

GALVIN, MATTHEW DUANE; The Derryfield Schl; Auburn, NH; (Y); VP Soph Cls; Pres Sr Cls; JV Sr Cls; JV Bsbl; Var L Ice Hcky; Capt L Lcrss; JV Socr; 4-H Awd; Drama Clb; 4-H; NH U; Bio Chem.

GANNON, DAVID; Concord HS; Concord, NH; (Y); 52/329; Pres Spanish Clb; Im Golf; Var Tennis; Im Vllybl; Hon Roll; Accntng.

GARABEDIAN, MICHELE; Timberlane Regional HS; Plaistow, NH; (Y); 37/215; French Clb; Model UN; Office Aide; Ski Clb; Yrbk Stf; Trs Stu Cncl; High Hon Roll; Hon Roll; Armenian Yth Fdrtn 83; Armenian Yth Fed Smmr Olympics Bronze 84; Natl Merit Fndtn Hnr Rl 84-85; Hofstra U; Pub Rel.

GARDEN, CHRISTINA L; Milford Area SR HS; Amherst, NH; (Y); 18/290; Computer Clb; Exploring; Math Tm; Q&S; Nwsp Rptr; Hon Roll; JETS Awd; NHS; Vrsty Alpine Ski Tm-St Chmpns 85.

GARDNER, MARK; Coe-Brown Northwood Acad; Northwood, NH; (Y); 5/60; Yrbk Ed-Chief; Yrbk Sprt Ed; VP Frsh Cls; VP Soph Cls; VP Jr Cls; VP Sr Cls; Var Bsbl; Mgr(s); Stat Socr; NHS; MVP Bsbl 85; VP NHS 86; Law.

GARTNER, MARY; The Derryfield School; Hollis, NH; (Y); French Clb; Math Clb; Yrbk Stf; Ed Lit Mag; Crs Cntry; Tennis; French Hon Soc; Hon Roll; NHS; Spanish NHS; Frnch III Awd 84; 6th Pl Buttrfly, ST Swm Chmpnshps 83.

GARVEY, JAMES; Alvirne HS; Hudson, NH; (Y); Math Tm; Science Clb; Concert Band; Jazz Band; Var Capt Tennis; High Hon Roll; Hon Roll; VP NHS; Yth Govt Prss Ed 83-85; Quen City Musc Festvl 83-84; U Of NH.

GAUCHER, DANIEL; Trinity HS; Manchester, NH; (Y); Am Leg Boys St; Church Yth Grp; Exploring; Nwsp Phtg; Nwsp Rptr; Var JV Ftbl; Hon Roll; NEDT Awd; Phtgrphr.

GAUDET, BILL; Nute HS; Milton, NH; (Y); VP Church Yth Grp; Pres Band; Pres Chorus; Jazz Band; Stage Crew; Variety Show; JV Bsbl; Hon Roll; JC Awd; Kiwanis Awd; Natl Hnr Rl 85; Evangel Clg; Music.

GAUDREAU, BRENDA; Concord HS; Concord, NH; (Y); 113/323; Church Yth Grp; Varsity Clb; School Play; Variety Show; Rep Stu Cncl; Var Bsktbl; Var Crs Cntry; Var L Sftbl; High Hon Roll; Hon Roll; All Amer Phy Ftnss 83-84; Outstndng Prfmnc In Chem 85; Athlt Of Wk 85; Elem Ed.

GAUTHIER, LYNN; Spaulding HS; Rochester, NH; (Y); 92/416; Pres 4-H; VP FBLA; Key Clb; Band; Capt Color Guard; Concert Band; Mrchg Band; Yrbk Bus Mgr; VP Sr Cls; Cit Awd; Ntl Cngrss Trp To Chcgo 83; Johnson & Wales; Htl Mgt.

GAY, LISSETT; Farmington HS; Farmington, NH; (Y); Yrbk Stf; Sec Soph Cls; Sec Jr Cls; Sec Sr Cls; JV Bsktbl; JV Sftbl; JV Var Vllybl; Hon Roll; NHS; New Hampshire Tech Inst; Bus.

GELINAS, PAULA JEAN; Memorial HS; Manchester, NH; (Y); 17/366; Church Yth Grp; Math Clb; Yrbk Stf; Pres Jr Cls; Pres Sr Cls; Rep Stu Cncl; JV Var Socr; JV Var Sftbl; Var Trk; Hon Roll; Boston Coll; Law.

GELINAS, ROSEMARY; Farmington HS; Farmington, NH; (Y); Teachers Aide; Varsity Clb; Yrbk Phtg; Yrbk Stf; High Hon Roll; Hon Roll; Pres NHS; Var JV Bsktbl; Var JV Sftbl; Keene ST Coll; Comp.

GEMBINSKI, THERESA; Dover HS; Dover, NH; (Y); 7/287; Key Clb; Math Tm; Var L Fld Hcky; High Hon Roll; Cmnty Wkr; French Clb; Variety Show; Stat Bsktbl; Coach Actv; Mu Alp Tht; Hgh Scorer ST Math Meet 85; Intl Rel.

GENDRON, WENDY; Pembroke Acad; Suncook, NH; (Y); Dance Clb; Drama Clb; Spanish Clb; Chorus; Church Choir; School Play; Nwsp Rptr; Lit Mag; Frsh Cls; Trs Church Yth Grp; Hugh O Brien Yth Schlrhsp Awd 84; Jrnlsm.

GENEST, JOHN; Pittsfield HS; Pittsfield, NH; (Y); Am Leg Boys St; Drama Clb; Q&S; Varsity Clb; School Play; Yrbk Bus Mgr; Yrbk Sprt Ed; Rep Frsh Cls; VP Jr Cls; Pres Stu Cncl; Mark Munroe Sccr Hustle Awd 84-85; Engrng.

GENEST, STEVE; Salem HS; Salem, NH; (Y); Boys Clb Am; JV Crs Cntry; Hon Roll; NEDT Awd; UNH; Forestry.

GERARD, ANDREW; Lebanon HS; Lebanon, NH; (Y); 1/150; AFS; Latin Clb; Math Tm; Ski Clb; Varsity Clb; Band; Pep Band; Yrbk Rptr; Capt Var Crs Cntry; Capt Var Trk; 3rd Pl CVC 800 M 85; St Pauls Schl Adv Studs Pgm Bio 85; Outstndng Perfrmnce Sci 84-85; Amherst Coll; Marine Bio.

GERATH, JENNIFER; Gorham JR SR HS; Gorham, NH; (Y); Girl Scts; Yrbk Ed-Chief; Yrbk Stf; High Hon Roll; Hon Roll; Drama Clb; Pep Clb; Stage Crew; Nwsp Stf; NHS; Eng.

GIAQUINTO, MICHAEL A; Bishop Geurtin HS; Nashua, NH; (Y); 14/135; Am Leg Boys St; Debate Tm; French Clb; NFL; Speech Tm; Im Bsktbl; JV Socr; Im Sftbl; High Hon Roll; NHS; Green & Gold Debating Awd 85; ST Champ Vrsty Debate Rnnr-Up 85; Boston Coll; Fin.

GIBBS, MARGARET; Milford Area SR HS; Amherst, NH; (Y); Acpl Chr; Chorus; Rep Soph Cls; Rep Jr Cls; Stu Cncl; Powder Puff Ftbl; Hon Roll; Chrmn Work Study Comm, Prom Comm 85; U NH; Comm.

GIFFIN, KAREN; Spaulding HS; Sanbornville, NH; (S); #21 In Class; Pres Church Yth Grp; VP Drama Clb; Key Clb; School Musical; School Play; High Hon Roll; Hon Roll; NHS; Ntl Engl Merit Awd 84 & 85; Bio.

GILBERT, CHRISTINE; Spaulding HS; Rochester, NH; (S); Church Yth Grp; Rep Jr Cls; Cheerleading; Hon Roll.

GILBERT, COLLEEN MARIE; Timberlane Reg HS; Plaistow, NH; (Y); 13/219; Am Leg Aux Girls St; French Clb; Pres Stu Cncl; Var Capt Crs Cntry; JV Socr; Var Capt Trk; High Hon Roll; Hon Roll; NHS; Clark U; Psych.

GILCHRIST, MICHELE S; St Pauls Schl; Columbus, OH; (Y); Church Yth Grp; Intnl Clb; Political Wkr; Stage Crew; Variety Show; Nwsp Stf; Yrbk Stf; Var Mgr(s); JV Socr; Var Swmmng; ABC Schlrshp Awd 81; Grls Trck Awd Mst Outstndng Stu 84; Frgn Exch Stu 84-85; Stanford; Bus Admin.

GILETT, BETH; Hillsboro-Deering HS; Hillsboro, NH; (S); Drama Clb; Library Aide; Math Tm; Model UN; Quiz Bowl; Rep Frsh Cls; JV Var Cheerleading; Hon Roll; Typing Achvt Awd 84; Hugh O Brian Yth Fndtn Ldrshp Hillsboro Deering 83-84; Tufts U; Intl Rel.

GILLETT, BETH; Hillsboro-Deering HS; Hillsboro, NH; (S); 2/70; Am Leg Aux Girls St; Math Tm; Rep Frsh Cls; JV Cheerleading; Hon Roll; NHS; Hugh O Brian Yth Ldrshp Sem 84; Typing Awd 84; U NH; Intl Affairs.

GILMAN, SHERRI; White Mountains Regional HS; Lancaster, NH; (Y); 11/110; Church Yth Grp; Office Aide; Spanish Clb; Yrbk Stf; Rep Frsh Cls; Rep Soph Cls; Rep Jr Cls; Sec Sr Cls; Rep Stu Cncl; Cheerleading; Chld Thrpy.

GILMAN, SUSAN A; Kennett HS; Conway, NH; (Y); 48/205; VP Key Clb; Sec Frsh Cls; Rep Jr Cls; Stu Cncl; JV VP Bsktbl; JV Fld Hcky; JV Sftbl; Hon Roll; Hon Stu Cncl 83-84; U RI.

GILMORE, JENNIFER; The Derryfield Schl; Amherst, NH; (Y); Drama Clb; Intnl Clb; Chorus; School Musical; School Play; Stage Crew; Nwsp Ed-Chief; Nwsp Stf; Off Jr Cls; Crs Cntry; Frnch.

GIRARD, DIANE JEAN; Memorial HS; Manchester, NH; (Y); 13/402; Nwsp Stf; Yrbk Stf; VP Jr Cls; VP Sr Cls; Rep Stu Cncl; JV Bsktbl; Var Crs Cntry; Var Trk; High Hon Roll; NHS; Eckerd Coll; Biochmstry.

GIRARD, MICHELLE; Am Goffstown HS; Manchester, NH; (S); DECA; JV Cheerleading; ST DECA Conf Hghst Ovrall Scr 85; NH ST Rep Natl DECA Conf; Fnlst Voctl Skill Ctr Hghst Ovrall; Champlain Coll; Retlg Mrchg.

GIRARD, VICKY; Berlin HS; Berlin, NH; (Y); 135/210; Library Aide; Stu Cncl; Cit Awd; Hon Roll; JV Cheerleading; Var Trk; NH Voc Coll; Scrtrl Sci.

GIROUARD, KELLY; Concord HS; Concord, NH; (Y); 80/329; Rep Frsh Cls; Rep Jr Cls; Trk; Hon Roll.

GIROUX, SUSAN MARIE; Nashua SR HS; Nashua, NH; (Y); 34/881; Am Leg Aux Girls St; Nwsp Sprt Ed; Pres Frsh Cls; Rep Stu Cncl; JV Bsktbl; Var L Sftbl; Hon Roll; Jr NHS; NHS; Keene ST Coll Hon Scholar; Kenne ST Coll; Jrnlsm.

GLADU, NICOLE; Tilton Acad; Lakeville, CT; (S); High Hon Roll; Hon Roll; French Clb; Math Tm; Varsity Clb; School Musical; Stage Crew; Off Soph Cls; Capt Crs Cntry; L Var Lcrss; Mst Vlble U-X-Cntry Skng 83; Burnham Geo Awd 84; Athltc Cmmtte 83-85; Bates; Engl.

GLASS, DAVID; Hanover HS; Hanover, NH; (Y); JCL; Latin Clb; Jazz Band; School Play; Trs Frsh Cls; Capt Ice Hcky; Lcrss; Socr; Hon Roll; Ntl Merit Ltr; Lbrl Arts.

GLIDDEN, BOBBIE-JO; Farmington HS; Farmington, NH; (S); Band; JV Sftbl; Photgrphy.

GLIDDEN, JANET; Spaulding HS; E Wakefield, NH; (Y); School Play; Culinary Arts.

GOBIN, MARK STEPHEN; Goffstown Area HS; Goffstown, NH; (Y); Band; Concert Band; Jazz Band; Mrchg Band; Pep Band; Var Crs Cntry; Var Trk; High Hon Roll; NHS; Chem Engrng.

GODDARD, THOMAS; Portsmouth HS; Portsmouth, NH; (Y); 100/373; Pres Latin Clb; Ftbl; High Hon Roll; Hon Roll; Bhcnng Comp YMCA 85; Outstndg Perf Math 82; UNH Durham; Comp Sci.

GODZYK, MELANIE; Colebrook Acad; Colebrook, NH; (Y); 4/70; Church Yth Grp; French Clb; Band; Chorus; Mrchg Band; Hon Roll; NHS; Mth.

GOLDTHWAITE, JAE-ANN D; Alvirne HS; Hudson, NH; (Y); 7/350; Cmnty Wkr; Exploring; Sec French Clb; Library Aide; Science Clb; Teachers Aide; Hon Roll; NHS; U Of NH; Nrsng.

GOODY, MATTHEW; Saint Thomas Aquinas HS; Newmarket, NH; (Y); Cmnty Wkr; Drama Clb; Ski Clb; Varsity Clb; Y-Teens; Rep Stu Cncl; Var L Ftbl; Swmmng; Comm.

GORDON, CLINT; Calvary Christian HS; E Kingston, NH; (Y); Math Tm; Chorus; School Play; Hon Roll; Am Leg Oratorcl Cont 84; Bus Adm.

GORSKI, JOHN M; Exeter Area HS; Exeter, NH; (Y); 2/284; Boy Scts; Nwsp Stf; Hon Roll; Natl Hnr Rll 84-85; Lodg Secy Ordr Arrw 84-85; Grnd Concours Natl Frnch Exm 82-83; Tacon Awd 82-83; U Of NH; Comp Sci.

GOSSELIN, CELESTE; Pembroke Acad; Allenstown, NH; (Y); Church Yth Grp; French Clb; Red Cross Aide; Yrbk Stf; Stu Cncl; Hon Roll; Ped Nrs.

GOSSELIN, GREG; Lebanon HS; Lebanon, NH; (Y); Church Yth Grp; Spanish Clb; Sec Frsh Cls; JV Bsbl; Var L Ice Hcky; Var L Socr; High Hon Roll; Hon Roll; MVP Ice Hockey 84-85; Mth.

GOSSELIN, JEANINE; Salem HS; Salem, NH; (Y); GAA; Key Clb; Model UN; Office Aide; Teachers Aide; Bsktbl; Fld Hcky; Trk; Hon Roll; Bsktbll MVP; Rebound Rec For A Yr; 3 Yrs Vrsty Bsktbll; Capt Bsktbll; Track-Hurdling Rec 100 Meters; U Of New Hampshire; Health.

GOUDREAU, CELESTE; Presentation Of Mary Acad; Nashua, NH; (Y); Church Yth Grp; Drama Clb; French Clb; Hosp Aide; Science Clb; Ski Clb; Vllybl; Hon Roll; Acct I Type II Shthnd 84; Off Prct Wrd Proc 85; Daniel Webster Coll; Bus Mgmnt.

GOUDREAULT, CYNTHIA E; Timberlane Regional HS; Plaistow, NH; (Y); French Clb; Concert Band; Drm Mjr(t); Mrchg Band; High Hon Roll; NHS; Band; Stage Crew; Off Frsh Cls; Hon Roll; Schlrshp Geo N Parks Drum Major Acad 83 & 84; Outstndng Pronunciation Frnch; Coll Schlrshp; U NH; Bus Mgt.

GOULD, AARON; Alvirne HS; Hancock, NH; (Y); 32/250; Am Leg Boys St; Key Clb; Ski Clb; Band; Jazz Band; Var L Trk; Hon Roll; Ntl Merit Ltr; NY U; Bus.

GOULD, GREGORY; Trinity HS; Manchester, NH; (Y); 2/170; Computer Clb; Math Tm; Model UN; Yrbk Phtg; Yrbk Stf; Trk; Ntl Merit Schol; Mech Engrng.

GOULET, S; West HS; Manchester, NH; (Y); 53/352; Nwsp Phtg; Nwsp Stf; Yrbk Phtg; Yrbk Stf; UNH; Bus.

GOURDEAU, RAYMOND L; Timberlane Regionel HS; Atkinson, NH; (Y); French Clb; Ski Clb; Var JV Ftbl; Im Bsbl; Im Sftbl; Im Wt Lftg; Var Capt Wrstlng; High Hon Roll; Hon Roll; Achv Awds Hghst Avg-Chem Bio, Engl; U Of NH; Elec Engr.

GOYETTE, DONNA; Timberland Reg HS; Plaistow, NH; (Y); Model UN; Speech Tm; Yrbk Sprt Ed; Sec Soph Cls; Off Jr Cls; Off Sr Cls; Var JV Fld Hcky; Var L Sftbl; High Hon Roll; Hon Roll; Gregg Typng Awd 84; Achvmnt Awd 84; Bst Dfnsv Plyr 83; Springfld Coll; Phy Educ.

GRACE, THERESA; Trinity HS; Manchester, NH; (Y); Am Leg Aux Girls St; Church Yth Grp; Band; Pep Band; Sec Stu Cncl; Var Capt Crs Cntry; Var Capt Trk; Hon Roll; MVP X-Cntry 84; MVP Spring Trck 85; Parents Clb Schlrshp 85; Bio.

GRAF, SIOBHAN; The Living Word HS; Claremont, NH; (Y); Church Yth Grp; Cmnty Wkr; Dance Clb; Debate Tm; Drama Clb; Library Aide; Teachers Aide; Acpl Chr; Chorus; School Musical.

GRALENSKI, DAN; Gorham JR-SR HS; Shelburne, NH; (Y); Drama Clb; Pep Clb; Quiz Bowl; Spanish Clb; Thesps; Varsity Clb; School Play; Nwsp Rptr; Nwsp Sprt Ed; Nwsp Stf; Gorham HS Granite St Challenge Tm 85; U NH; Engrng.

GRANT, CHARLENE; Concord HS; Concord, NH; (Y); 4/350; Math Tm; Capt Band; Color Guard; Capt Concert Band; Jazz Band; Capt Mrchg Band; NHS; Drama Clb; Pep Band; L Cheerleading; Top 10 Awd 82-85; Adv Stds Pgm 85; Math.

GRAY, ANNE; Spaulding HS; Rochester, NH; (S); 8/415; Am Leg Aux Girls St; Key Clb; Math Tm; Yrbk Stf; Var Bsktbl; Var Sftbl; High Hon Roll; Hon Roll; Mu Alp Tht; NHS; Search UNH Sem For Advncd High Schl Stud 84-85; Elec Engrng.

GRAY, DONALD M; Phillips Exter Acad; Bronxville, NY; (Y); Radio Clb; Science Clb; Stage Crew; Wrstlng; High Hon Roll; Ntl Merit SF; Varsity Crew 84-85; Pres Sci Soc 84-85; Elec Engrng.

GREENBERG, GLENN; Manchester Central HS; Manchester, NH; (Y); 45/440; VP Temple Yth Grp; Nwsp Rptr; Yrbk Sprt Ed; Trs Soph Cls; Trs Jr Cls; Trs Sr Cls; Var Tennis; NHS; Rep Frsh Cls; JV Socr; Scovel Schlrshp For Acad 85; Novak Schlrshp 83; Superior Schlr St Pauls Schl Advncd Stds Prog 84; Syracuse U; Public Rel.

GREENE, SHERRA D; Keene HS; Keene, NH; (Y); 11/322; Drama Clb; Model UN; Pep Clb; Spanish Clb; Band; Cheerleading; Fld Hcky; Sftbl; Hon Roll; NHS; Pres Acadmc Fit Awd 85; Wheaton IL; Pol Sci.

GRIECO, LYNDA S; Salem HS; Salem, NH; (Y); Key Clb; Model UN; Political Wkr; Spanish Clb; Teachers Aide; Yrbk Bus Mgr; Yrbk Rptr; Yrbk Stf; Merrimack Coll; Poli Sci.

GRIFFIN, GLENNA; Presentation Of Mary Acad; Nahsua, NH; (Y); Drama Clb; 4-H; French Clb; Hosp Aide; Library Aide; Science Clb; Service Clb; Church Choir; Stage Crew; Nwsp Ed-Chief; Engl I Cert Hnrb Mntn 83; Chllng Pgm Cert Cmpltn Rivier Coll 85; Amer Inst Frgn Stud Partcptn Cert 85; Psychtry.

GRIFFIN, JEAN; Pembroke Acad; Epsom, NH; (Y); FFA; Teachers Aide; Yrbk Stf; High Hon Roll; Hon Roll; FHA Disply-Slvr Medl Ntl 85; Empire Acad; Cosmtlgy.

GRIFFIN, MICHAEL; Concord HS; Concord, NH; (Y); 16/323; Latin Clb; Im Ice Hcky; High Hon Roll; Hon Roll; NHS; Im Bsktbl; Im Sftbl; Im Vllybl; Latin Natl Hon Soc 83; Geom Awd 84; Spnsh I, Bio 84; Boston Coll; Art.

GRIFFIN, PETER RAYMOND; Raymond HS; Raymond, NH; (Y); Am Leg Boys St; Q&S; Nwsp Sprt Ed; Var L Bsktbl; Var L Socr; Hon Roll; All State Soccer 85; NE Soccer Clb MVP 85; Clss Mrshl Snr Clss 85; Journalism.

GRIMES, WILLIAM J; Milford Area Senior HS; Amherst, NH; (Y); 2/286; Math Tm; Ski Clb; Var Socr; Im Vllybl; Hon Roll; NHS; Ntl Merit SF; Sal; Top Engl Student 83-84; Engrng.

GRIVOIS, SCOTT; Pembroke Acad; Chichester, NH; (Y); Var L Bsbl; JV Var Bsktbl; JV Crs Cntry; Hon Roll.

GROUT, DAVID A; Phillips Exeter Acad; Valatre, NY; (Y); Cmnty Wkr; Ski Clb; Spanish Clb; Band; VP Jazz Band; Mrchg Band; School Play; Variety Show; Var L Diving; Ntl Merit SF; Crew Vrsty; Howard.

GRUMBLING, KIMBERLEY; Dublin Schl; Newmarket, NH; (Y); Church Yth Grp; 4-H; GAA; Chorus; School Play; JV Var Bsktbl; JV Var Socr; JV Var Vllybl; Hon Roll; Most Imp Vllybl Plyr 83; Law.

GUANGA, MARIE; Sanborn Reginal Kingston; Fremont, NH; (Y); 45/143; 4-H; FFA; Girl Scts; Chorus; Stage Crew; Cit Awd; 4-H Awd; Hon Roll; 4-H Homemakers Awd 84; Conservation Camp Cert 84; An Sci.

GUARALDI, NAOMI STARR; Lebanon HS; Lebanon, NH; (Y); AFS; DECA; French Clb; Drm Mjr(t); Mrchg Band; Rep Frsh Cls; Rep Soph Cls; Pres Jr Cls; Mgr(s); Hon Roll; Bus Mgmt.

GUERIN, PAULA; Berlin HS; Berlin, NH; (Y); Rep Frsh Cls; Rep Soph Cls; Rep Jr Cls; JV L Bsktbl; JV L Sftbl; Hon Roll; Berlin Vo Coll; Adv.

GUERIN, RICHARD E; Laconia HS; Laconia, NH; (Y); 1/142; Trs Chess Clb; Drama Clb; Math Tm; Rep Stu Cncl; Scrkpr L Bsktbl; High Hon Roll; Pres NHS; Val; Voice Dem Awd; Harvard Bk 84; St Pauls ASP 84; Presdntl Clsrm 84; Hugh Obrien Yth Ldrshp Smnrs 83; SR Math Awd; Clarkson U; Chem Engr.

GUERTIN, TRACEY; Belmont HS; Canterbury, NH; (S); Hosp Aide; Varsity Clb; Band; Yrbk Stf; Var L Crs Cntry; Var L Trk; Hon Roll; NHS; Girl Scts; Concert Band; YMCA Yth Gov 85; Phys Thrpy.

GUILBEAULT, STACIE; Memorial HS; Manchester, NH; (Y); 8/394; French Clb; Variety Show; Nwsp Stf; VP Stu Cncl; Var L Cheerleading.

GUILMETT, BRENDA; Laconia HS; Laconia, NH; (Y); French Clb; GAA; JV Capt Bsktbl; Var Sftbl; Hon Roll; NHS; Trvl.

GULLA, BRUNO; Hillsboro-Derring HS; Hillsboro, NH; (Y); Boy Scts; Model UN; Jazz Band; Camera Clb; Symp Band; Pres Soph Cls; Pres Jr Cls; Pres Sr Cls; Rep Stu Cncl; Aud/Vis; Boy Scts Cmnty Serv Awd 83; Pltcl Sci.

GUTWILLIG, BARRY; Nashua HS; Nashua, NH; (Y); 85/850; German Clb; Temple Yth Grp; Stage Crew; Hon Roll; Jr NHS; NHS; UNH; Bus Adm.

HACKETT, CATHERINE; Portsmouth SR HS; Rye Beach, NH; (S); 3/361; Math Tm; Mgr Crs Cntry; Swmmng; Var Trk; High Hon Roll; Sec NHS; New England Bk Assn Awd 84; JR Wrld Cncl 84.

HALBEDEL, RHONDA; Mascenic Regional HS; Greenville, NH; (Y); 9/65; French Clb; Yrbk Stf; Trs Soph Cls; Trs Jr Cls; Trs Sr Cls; Rep Stu Cncl; Var Fld Hcky; High Hon Roll; Hon Roll; NHS; Mst Outstndng Spnsh 83-84; JR Yr Awd 83-84; MI Sci 84-85; NH Technical Inst; Dentl Hyg.

HALFMANN, ANDREA; Gilford Middle HS; Gilford, NH; (S); Computer Clb; Math Tm; Q&S; Nwsp Bus Mgr; Var Capt Sftbl; Hon Roll; NHS; French Clb; Library Aide; Ski Clb; Ski Team Capt; Interact.

HALL, BRAD L; Memorial HS; Manchester, NH; (S); 58/402; Boy Scts; Church Yth Grp; VP DECA; FHA; Nwsp Stf; High Hon Roll; Hon Roll; Boys Clb Am; Trk; DECA Schlrshp 85; Voc Excllnc Schlrshp 85; FHA Schlrshp 85; Htl/Rstrnt Mgmt.

HALL, HEATHER; Fall Mountain Regional HS; Walpole, NH; (Y); 39/137; Trs Am Leg Aux Girls St; Chorus; Madrigals; Var Capt Cheerleading; JV Socr; Hon Roll; Sandra Wilson Schlrshp; Dllrs/Schlrs Schlrshp; Fnlst Miss NH Chrldr; Oceanside Coll/Beauty; Csmtlgy.

HALLWORTH, ROBERT; Dover HS; Dover, NH; (Y); 40/345; Am Leg Boys St; Spanish Clb; Ice Hcky; High Hon Roll; Hon Roll; Lit.

HAMBLET, ROBERT S; Salem HS; Windham, NH; (S); 1/380; VP Key Clb; Chrmn Model UN; Yrbk Bus Mgr; Pres Jr Cls; Swmmng; DAR Awd; High Hon Roll; Pres NHS; Spanish NHS; Val; Dartmouth Bk Awd Outstndng Schlr Athl 84; Intl Rel.

HAMEL, DONNA J; Salem HS; Salem, NH; (S); 14/380; Church Yth Grp; Capt Var Gym; High Hon Roll; NHS; Spanish NHS; Coaches Awd 83; Bus.

HAMEL, SHARON D; Salem HS; Salem, NH; (S); 9/405; Model UN; High Hon Roll; Challnge Pgm Rivier Coll 84-85; Fr Acad Awd 84.

HAMILTON, JILL M; Portsmouth SR HS; Greenland, NH; (Y); 30/380; Rep Am Leg Aux Girls St; Pres French Clb; Model UN; Var Bsktbl; Var Fld Hcky; Var Sftbl; High Hon Roll; Hon Roll; NHS; Coaches Awd Bsktbl 84; Six V Ltrs 82-85; U NH; Media.

HAMMOND, KRISTINE MARIE; Concord HS; Bow, NH; (Y); 1/361; Pres Sec Church Yth Grp; Hosp Aide; Math Tm; Chorus; Concert Band; Mrchg Band; Bausch & Lomb Sci Awd; High Hon Roll; Ntl Merit SF; Drama Clb; Rensselaer Med Math & Sci Awd 84; Math.

HANEY, REBECCA; Fall Mountain Regional HS; Newport, NH; (Y); 2/141; French Clb; Concert Band; Mrchg Band; Pep Band; School Musical; High Hon Roll; Hon Roll; NHS.

HANKEY, GRAHAM W; Milford Area SR HS; Amherst, NH; (Y); Am Leg Boys St; Boy Scts; Chess Clb; Cmnty Wkr; Debate Tm; Vllybl; Hon Roll; NHS; Biol Stdy Pgm UNH 85; Yth & Govt Pgm 84-85; Astrnmy.

HANKS, NANCY; Nashua HS; Nashua, NH; (Y); Church Yth Grp; Dance Clb; Prfct Atten Awd; FL Inst Tech; Psych.

HANKUS, CHERYL; Timberlane Regional HS; Hampstead, NH; (Y); Church Yth Grp; 4-H; FBLA; Teachers Aide; Band; Concert Band; Hon Roll; Most Imprvd Plyr Band 81; Merit Awd Math 81; Bus Ed Prof Growth Awd 85; Plymouth ST Coll; Legal Sec.

HANSON, MARY BETH; Spaulding HS; Rochester, NH; (Y); Yrbk Stf; Rep Frsh Cls; Rep Soph Cls; Trs Jr Cls; Rep Sr Cls; JV Sftbl; High Hon Roll; Hon Roll.

HANSON, ROGER; Hopkinton HS; Contoocook, NH; (Y); French Clb; Teachers Aide; Stage Crew; Yrbk Stf; Im Bsbl; Im Bsktbl; Art Awd 82-83; Hawthorne Coll; Aviatn Mgmt.

HANSON, WENDY JO; Woodsville HS; Haverhill, NH; (Y); FBLA; Hon Roll; Jr NHS; NHS; Cert Awd Frnch II 83; Awd Accntng I 85; Awd Chem 85; Plymouth ST Coll; Accntng.

HARDING, DEBORAH M; Moultonbaraugh Acad; Center Harbor, NH; (Y); 3/40; JCL; Math Tm; Office Aide; Spanish Clb; Band; Chorus; Mrchg Band; Pep Band; School Musical; Nwsp Rptr; Outstndng Awds Ldrshp, Math, Sprtsmnshp; Amer U; Intl Studies.

HARLAN, MICHELLE M; Portsmouth SR HS; Greenland, NH; (Y); 7/342; Church Yth Grp; Drama Clb; Latin Clb; Model UN; Rep Stu Cncl; High Hon Roll; Trs NHS; Ntl Merit Ltr; Pres Schlr; German Clb; German Natl Hnr Soc; Natl Piano Awd; USAF Art Awds; Harvard U; Comp Eng.

HARMACINSKI, JIM; Salem HS; Salem, NH; (S); Boys Clb Am; Model UN; Ski Clb; Bsktbl; Crs Cntry; Socr; Trk; Wt Lftg; High Hon Roll; Hon Roll.

HARMON, TAMMY; Concord HS; Manchester, NH; (Y); 11/360; Drama Clb; Model UN; Chorus; Yrbk Stf; High Hon Roll; NHS; Chairprsn Peer Cnslng Teens-Need-Teens 84-85; SADD; Psych, Engl 11-A, Alg II Achvt Awds 85; Psych.

HARRINGTON, ELLEN; Fall Mountain Reginal HS; Charlestown, NH; (Y); 50/150; French Clb; Chorus; School Musical; School Play; Pre-Law.

HARRIS, ELIZABETH A; Manchester West HS; Bedford, NH; (Y); 9/364; Hosp Aide; Nwsp Stf; Rep Jr Cls; Rep Sr Cls; Var Tennis; Var Vllybl; High Hon Roll; Lion Awd; Trs NHS; Bedford Womans Clb Schlrshp 85; Princpls Meritrus Serv Awd 85; Bedfrd Fire Dept Schlrshp; Clark U; Pre-Med.

HARTFORD, SCOTT; Concord HS; Concord, NH; (Y); Nwsp Rptr; Ftbl; Im Wrstlng; Hon Roll; Chem Achvt Awd 85; Bowdion; Socl Wrk.

HARTLEN, LAURIE; Colebrook Acad; Colebrook, NH; (Y); 8/51; NHS; Med.

HARTMAN, KIMBERLY S; West HS; Bedford, NH; (Y); Am Leg Aux Girls St; Ski Clb; Nwsp Bus Mgr; Pres Soph Cls; Pres Jr Cls; Pres Sr Cls; Hon Roll.

HARTWELL, DANA; Manchester West HS; Bedford, NH; (Y); 94/352; Church Yth Grp; JV Ftbl; Var Capt Swmmng; JV Wrstlng; High Hon Roll; Hon Roll; U NH; Bus.

HARVEY, BARBARA; Salem HS; Salem, NH; (Y); Model UN; Var L Cheerleading; Mgr(s); DAR Awd; High Hon Roll; Hon Roll; Spanish NHS; Danc Tchrs Clb Boston 85; UNH; Bio.

HARVEY, LORI; Farmington HS; Middleton, NH; (Y); Yrbk Stf; JV Bsktbl; Hon Roll; Spanish NHS.

HARVEY, SHAWN MARIE; Salem HS; Salem, NH; (S); 11/363; Model UN; JV Sftbl; Ftbl; Hon Roll; NHS; Spanish NHS; Civil Engr.

HASTINGS, DOREEN; St Thomas Aquinas HS; Farmington, NH; (Y); #9 In Class; Church Yth Grp; Spanish Clb; Yrbk Stf; Stat Sftbl; JV Vllybl; NHS; Pres Schlr; Pres Spanish NHS; VA Paul Dee Schlrshp 85; U Of NH; Elctrcl Engr.

HATEM, JOANNE MARIE; Salem HS; Salem, NH; (S); 55/350; VP Sec Church Yth Grp; Debate Tm; VP Sec FHA; Model UN; Spanish Clb; Capt Color Guard; Hon Roll; Prfct Atten Awd; Stage Crew; Sftbl; Voice Dem Schlrshp 2nd Pl 84; Paralegal Lawyer.

HATFIELD, STEVEN; Hillsboro-Deering HS; Hillsboro, NH; (S); Church Yth Grp; Math Tm; Band; Mrchg Band; Pep Band; Symp Band; Bsbl; Bsktbl; Socr; Hon Roll; Arch.

HATTORI, DAVID A; Salem HS; Salem, NH; (S); Model UN; Spanish Clb; Off Stu Cncl; High Hon Roll; Hon Roll; Spanish NHS.

HAVRDA, CHRISTINE; Stratford Public HS; N Stratford, NH; (Y); 4/17; 4-H; Teachers Aide; Yrbk Stf; VP Stu Cncl; Sftbl; Bausch & Lomb Sci Awd; High Hon Roll; Hon Roll; NHS; Prfct Atten Awd; U Of NH; Anml Sci.

HAWES, JAMES W; Central HS; Manchester, NH; (Y); 125/450; Am Leg Boys St; L Var Ftbl; JV Socr; Var Trk; High Hon Roll; Hon Roll.

HAWKO, CHRISTINE; Laconia HS; Laconia, NH; (Y); 14/148; Am Leg Aux Girls St; Rep Stu Cncl; Hon Roll; NHS; Church Yth Grp; Cmnty Wkr; French Clb; Elinor Prkr Lit Awd; St Anselm Coll; Bio.

HAYES, JACQUELINE J; Phillips Exeter Acad; Washington, DC; (Y); Pres Drama Clb; PAVAS; Quiz Bowl; Acpl Chr; School Musical; School Play; Im Tennis; Im Vllybl; Hon Roll; Ntl Merit Ltr; Eng Prz 83-84; Merrill Speaking Prz 84; Theatre Arts.

HAYES, JEFFREY R; Kennett HS; Bartlett, NH; (Y); 15/275; Pres Soph Cls; Bsktbl; Ftbl; Hon Roll; Spec Studies Pgm 84; Lib Art.

HAYNES, JEFFREY LYNN; Stevens HS; Claremont, NH; (Y); Am Leg Boys St; Computer Clb; Ski Clb; JV Bsbl; JV Golf; Cit Awd; Hon Roll; Prfct Atten Awd; NH Boys ST 85; ABC JR Bowlng Natls 85; Claremont Cntry Clb JR Clb Champ 84; Acctng.

HAYWARD, JEANETTE; Dover HS; Dover, NH; (Y); Robert C Varney Awd Fig Sktg Great Bay Fig Sktg Clb 80-81; Mac Intosh Coll; Trvl.

HEALEY, KELLY; Manchester Central HS; Deerfield, NH; (Y); Am Leg Aux Girls St; Var Bsktbl; Var Capt Socr; Var Capt Trk; Hon Roll; Springfield Clg; Phy Ed.

HEATH, HEATHER A; Concord HS; Concord, NH; (Y); 69/371; Varsity Clb; Yrbk Stf; Lit Mag; Rep Stu Cncl; Crs Cntry; L Trk; Hon Roll; Pres Acad Ftnss Awd 85; Sprague Elec Schlrshp 85; Ntl Cncl Tchrs Engl Awd 84; U Of NH; Comm.

HEBERT, GREGORY; Milford Area SR HS; Amherst, NH; (Y); Hon Roll; Bio.

HEBERT, JIMMY; Salem HS; Salem, NH; (Y); Boys Clb Am; Model UN; JV Bsktbl; Var Crs Cntry; Var Mgr(s); JV Trk; Plymouth ST Coll; Bus Admn.

HEDSTROM, CHRIS; Winnisquam Regionaql HS; Northfield, NH; (Y); Church Yth Grp; Library Aide; Math Tm; Chorus; High Hon Roll; Hon Roll; Hnrbl Mntn In A Concord Art Exhbt 84-85; Modrn Lang.

HEFFERNAN, ELAINE; Nashua HS; Nashua, NH; (Y); 20/840; Red Cross Aide; Trs Church Choir; Mrchg Band; School Musical; Swing Chorus; Var Bsktbl; High Hon Roll; Church Yth Grp; Drama Clb; Ski Clb; Hnr & Bst Thespian Awds; Prsdentl Acad Ftness Awd; Outstndng Musician; Boston U; Brdcstng.

HEIM, DAVID; Saint Thomas Aquinas HS; Exeter, NH; (Y); French Clb; Ski Clb; Var Ftbl; Var Golf; U Of MA; Engrng.

HENAULT, MARK; West HS; Bedford, NH; (Y); 2/366; Exploring; Math Tm; Yrbk Stf; Lit Mag; Cit Awd; High Hon Roll; Jr NHS; NHS; NEDT Awd; Comp Sci.

HENDERSON, GINA; Spaulding HS; Rochester, NH; (S); 55/351; Trk; Hon Roll; Rep Frsh Cls; Airline Stwrds.

HENDERSON, ROBERT; Spaulding HS; Rochester, NH; (Y); ROTC; JV Bsktbl; Hon Roll; Bus.

HENNESSEY, ELLEN; White Mountains Regional HS; Whitefield, NH; (Y); 3/100; Band; Mrchg Band; Pep Band; Yrbk Stf; Sec Soph Cls; Sec Jr Cls; JV L Bsktbl; Var Fld Hcky; Var L Sftbl; NHS; UNH; Med.

HENRY, JAY S; Kennett HS; North Conway, NH; (Y); 14/200; Concert Band; Mrchg Band; Pep Band; Rep Stu Cncl; JV Socr; Hon Roll; Century III Ldrs Schl Wnnr; U Of NH; Econ.

HENRY, PATRICK L J; Berlin HS; Berlin, NH; (Y); 35/202; JV Var Bsktbl; Im Coach Actv; JV Im Score Keeper; Im Vllybl; Im Wt Lftg; Machnst.

HERMAN, MELISSA R; Contoocook Valley Regional HS; Windsor, NH; (Y); 15/160; Drama Clb; Temple Yth Grp; Chorus; School Musical; School Play; Yrbk Ed-Chief; JV Swmmng; High Hon Roll; JCL; Variety Show; MENC All Estrn Chorus 85; St Pauls Adv Smmr Pgm 84; NH All-ST Poetry Rctl 1st Pl 83; Wesleyan U; Psych.

HERRICK, MONIKA E; Timberlane Regional HS; Danville, NH; (Y); 4/206; Rptr FBLA; German Clb; Model UN; Church Choir; Rep Stu Cncl; High Hon Roll; NHS; Ski Clb; Teachers Aide; Rep VICA; Dartmouth Bk Awd 84; Hgh Achvt Bio, Germn II & III, Amer Demcrcy 84; SR Engl Awd 85; Wheaton Coll; Pol Sci.

HICKEY, CHRISTOPHER; Spaulding HS; Rochester, NH; (S); Math Clb; Math Tm; Var Tennis; High Hon Roll; Hon Roll.

HICKS, SHAWNA; Hopkinton HS; Contoocook, NH; (Y); DECA; 4-H; German Clb; Intnl Clb; Office Aide; Mgr(s); 4-H Awd; Hon Roll; Masonic Awd; Cmnty Wkr; Co-Chrmn-Prm Comm; Fash Merch.

HIGGINS, STEPHEN; Coe-Brown Northwood Acad; Barrington, NH; (Y); 15/51; Church Yth Grp; Var Bsktbl; Prfct Atten Awd.

HILDERBRAND, STACEY; Milford Area SR HS; Milford, NH; (Y); Chorus; Mgr(s); Var JV Socr; UNH; Cmmnctns.

HILL, MICHAEL; Kennett HS; Conway, NH; (Y); Church Yth Grp; Ftbl; Hon Roll; OH Valley Coll; Bus Mgmt.

HINRICHSEN, KIM; Portsmouth SR HS; Rye, NH; (Y); Church Yth Grp; JA; Model UN; JV Fld Hcky; High Hon Roll; NHS; Rye Bus Assn Schlrshp 85; Portsmouth Nvl Shpyrd Schlrshp 85; Wokott Soc Schlrshp 85; U NH; Botany.

HIPWELL, STUART; Stevens HS; Claremont, NH; (Y); Yrbk Stf; Rep Stu Cncl; Hon Roll; Law.

HIRAI, AKIRA; Mascoma Valley Regional HS; Enfield, NH; (Y); 1/108; Am Leg Boys St; Capt Math Tm; Quiz Bowl; Yrbk Ed-Chief; Lit Mag; NHS; Pres Schlr; Val; Drama Clb; JV Bsbl; Smmr Sci Prog 85; Harvard U; Elec Engrng.

HO, FRANCES; Portsmouth HS; Portsmouth, NH; (S); 6/350; Pres Exploring; Hosp Aide; Sec JA; Y-Teens; Color Guard; Stage Crew; High Hon Roll; VP NHS; Pre-Med.

HOAG, DANIEL; Bishop Guertin HS; Chelmsford, MA; (Y); 34/172; Computer Clb; FCA; Spanish Clb; Im Bsktbl; JV Crs Cntry; Var Swmmng; Var L Tennis; Hon Roll; Spanish NHS; Westfrd Tnns Tm; Chelmsfrd Swm Tm & Tnns Tm; Pre-Law.

HOCH, REBECCA; St Pauls Schl; Poolesville, MD; (Y); Dance Clb; Variety Show; Dickey Prize Dance 82-84; Schlrshp Ballet 84-85; Ballet Dancer.

HOCKMAN, ERIC; West HS; Bedford, NH; (Y); Cmnty Wkr; Computer Clb; Exploring; Band; Concert Band; Jazz Band; Pep Band; Var Swmmng; Var Trk; Hon Roll; Jrnlsm.

HOEFLICH, JOSEPH; Portsmouth HS; Greenland, NH; (S); 43/405; Seacoast Spllng Bee 2nd Pl 82; Ldrshp Awd 84; Comp Pgmmr.

HOFFMAN, JON; Pembroke Acad; Concord, NH; (Y); Boy Scts; FBLA; Hon Roll; Prfct Atten Awd; Comp Engr.

HOK, KATHARYN; Concord HS; Concord, NH; (Y); 20/330; Hosp Aide; Varsity Clb; Mrchg Band; Symp Band; Lit Mag; Rep Stu Cncl; Var Crs Cntry; Var Fld Hcky; NHS; Variety Show.

HOLBROOK, MARCIA J; Memorial HS; Manchester, NH; (Y); 1/396; Math Tm; Capt Quiz Bowl; Nwsp Ed-Chief; Rep Stu Cncl; DAR Awd; High Hon Roll; Pres NHS; Ntl Merit SF; Val; Yrbk Stf; Rensselaer Medal; Cent III Ldr; Darmouth Bk; Eng.

HOLDEN, HELEN; Milford Area HS; Amherst, NH; (Y); 3/290; Yrbk Ed-Chief; Var L Tennis; Pres NHS; Ntl Merit Ltr; Coll Holy Cross; Econ.

HOLMES, PATTI; Salem HS; Salem, NH; (Y); French Clb; Key Clb; Model UN; Pep Clb; Teachers Aide; Yrbk Stf; JV Cheerleading; JV Fld Hcky; Stat Score Keeper; JV Sftbl; Ecnmcs.

HONG, EUGENE S; Phillips Exeter Acad; Weston, MA; (Y); Ski Clb; Mgr Nwsp Bus Mgr; Ed Lit Mag; Stu Cncl; Var Lcrss; JV Socr; High Hon Roll; Ntl Merit SF; Asian Society VP 84-85; Bio-Med.

HOPKINS, PENNY; Fall Mountain Regional HS; Claremont, NH; (Y); 4/110; 4-H; French Clb; Girl Scts; High Hon Roll; Hon Roll; Fshn Mrch.

HOPKINS, ROSS; Laconia HS; Laconia, NH; (Y); Trs Art Clb; Trs Soph Cls; Trs Jr Cls; Trs Sr Cls; Im Swmmng; Im Tennis; Hon Roll; Trs NHS; Accntng.

HORYMSKI, DAVID; Concord HS; Concord, NH; (Y); 35/361; Math Tm; Im Ftbl; NHS; Ntl Merit SF; St Pauls Advncd Studies Pgm 84.

HOVATTER, GINA; Manchester High School West; Manchester, NH; (Y); 45/352; VP Band; VP Mrchg Band; Jr Cls; Chld Psych.

HOWARD, BRIAN; Dovr HS; Dover, NH; (Y); French Clb; High Hon Roll; Hon Roll; U Of NH.

HOWARD, CLINT; Spaulding HS; Rochester, NH; (S); 15/390; 4-H Awd; High Hon Roll; NHS; Bryant; Accntng.

HOWARD, TIMOTHY; Plymouth Area HS; Plymouth, NH; (Y); Am Leg Boys St; Drama Clb; Band; Mrchg Band; Pep Band; School Play; Im Bsktbl; JV Capt Ftbl; Hon Roll; ST Drama Fstvl 85; Park & Rec Sprtsmnshp Awd Bsktbl 85; Dist All ST Bnd 85; U IL Emerson; Drama.

HOYT, STEVE; Kennett HS; E Madison, NH; (Y); 34/200; Boy Scts; Cmnty Wkr; 4-H; Ski Clb; JV Bsktbl; Var Trk; Hon Roll; UNH; Engrng.

HUBBARD, ROBIN; Saint Thomas Aquinas HS; Barrington, NH; (Y); Church Yth Grp; Girl Scts; Latin Clb; Office Aide; Nwsp Stf; Spec Ed.

HUBER, DONNA; Memorial HS; Manchester, NH; (Y); 68/386; Nwsp Stf; Mgr(s); Var Powder Puff Ftbl; Var High Hon Roll; Var Hon Roll.

HUDSON, CHRISTINE; Woodsville HS; Woodsville, NH; (Y); Office Aide; Ski Clb; Band; Mrchg Band; Capt Crs Cntry; Hon Roll; Ctzns For Schlrs Awd 85; X-Cntry Rnng Mdlln 83; Odd Fllws & Rebeccas Lodge Schlrshp 85; Wilma Boyd Career Schl; Trvl.

HUDSON, JANE; Alvirne HS; Hudson, NH; (Y); 8/272; Pres Computer Clb; Girl Scts; Science Clb; School Play; Mgr Stage Crew; JV Mgr Bsktbl; Var JV Trk; Hon Roll; Princpls Hnr Rll 4.0 GPA 82; Alvivne SR Clss Schlrshp 85; Plymouth ST Coll; Comp Sci.

HUEBNER, PATRICIA; Conant HS; Jaffrey, NH; (Y); 4/47; Church Yth Grp; Latin Clb; Office Aide; Teachers Aide; Powder Puff Ftbl; High Hon Roll; Hon Roll; Cheshive Cnty Med Soc Bk Awd Sci 85; Jaffrey Hstrcl Soc Schlrshp 85; Bridgewater ST Coll; Anthrplgy.

HUFF, MARY; Portsmouth HS; Pease AFB, NH; (Y); 45/395; Yrbk Stf; High Hon Roll; Hon Roll; JR Wrld Cncl 84-86; Model Cngrss 85; Chld Psych.

HUFF, MELISSA LEIGH; Somersworth HS; Somersworth, NH; (Y); 8/165; Am Leg Aux Girls St; Mathletes; Math Tm; Spanish Clb; Color Guard; Trs Sr Cls; Rep Stu Cncl; Hon Roll; NHS; Natl Engl Merit Awd 82; Math.

HUGHES, CRAIG; Portsmouth HS; Rye, NH; (Y); 32/400; Model UN; Ftbl; Trk; High Hon Roll; Hon Roll; Ntl Merit Ltr.

HUTCHINS, WILLIAM; Raymond JR SR HS; Manchester, NH; (Y); 4-H; Ski Clb; Sec VICA; Coach Actv; Var Capt Crs Cntry; Var Capt Trk; 4-H Awd; Hon Roll; Lion Awd; Coaching Awd-Crs Cntry 82; Ldrshp Awd 4-H 84; Mach Trades.

HUYCK, KEVIN; Bishop Guertin HS; Hudson, NH; (Y); 11/168; Computer Clb; FCA; Ski Clb; JV Stat Bsktbl; Var Score Keeper; Im JV Socr; Swmmng; Im Vllybl; Hon Roll; NHS; ST Chmpns Indr Sccr 84-85; USAFA; Engrng.

INGERSON, LOGAN; Timberlane Regional HS; Plaistow, NH; (Y); Boy Scts; JV Bsktbl; Hon Roll; Mst Outstndng Indstrl Arts Awd 85; Crpntry.

IRELAND, KELLY L; Alvirne HS; Hudson, NH; (Y); 1/300; Key Clb; Science Clb; Ski Clb; Rep Stu Cncl; Bausch & Lomb Sci Awd; Cit Awd; High Hon Roll; Pres NHS; Ntl Merit Ltr; Val; Princpls Acad Excllnce Awd 85; Stu Yr 83; Dartmouth Coll; Comp Sci.

JACKSON, CORI; Belmont HS; Laconia, NH; (S); 5/80; Sec French Clb; Math Tm; Varsity Clb; VP Frsh Cls; Pres Soph Cls; Pres Jr Cls; Var L Trk; High Hon Roll; Hon Roll; NHS; Hugh O Brien Ldrshp Fndtn 84; Yth & Govt 85.

JACKSON, KELLY; Fall Mountain Regional HS; Charlestown, NH; (Y); 41/156; Am Leg Aux Girls St; Spanish Clb; Yrbk Ed-Chief; Yrbk Stf; Hon Roll; Law.

JACOBSON, JUDY; Fall Mountain HS; Alstead, NH; (Y); #54 In Class; Am Leg Aux Girls St; Camera Clb; Drama Clb; Band; Concert Band; Mrchg Band; Pep Band; Crs Cntry; Socr; Trk; Math,Gym Awd 81-85; Cosmtlgy.

JANKOWSKY, DEBBIE; Fall Mountain Regional HS; Walpole, NH; (Y); 13/160; Am Leg Aux Girls St; Band; Concert Band; Mrchg Band; VP Stu Cncl; Capt Twrlr; High Hon Roll; Hon Roll; Sec NHS; Histry Awd 85; Physcl Ftns Awd 83; Bus.

JANO, LONNIE; Portsmouth HS; Portsmouth, NH; (Y); Church Yth Grp; Computer Clb; Math Tm; Model UN; Church Choir; Var JV Ftbl; High Hon Roll; Hon Roll; Ftbl Cert & Patch; Comp Sci.

JANOS, CHRISTOPHER M; Salem HS; Salem, NH; (Y); Pres 4-H; French Clb; Hosp Aide; Model UN; Ski Clb; JV Bsktbl; High Hon Roll; Hon Roll; NH Vo Tech Coll; Ind Elec.

JARVIS, KRISTIN; Central HS; Manchester, NH; (S); Trs DECA; Nwsp Phtg; High Hon Roll; Hon Roll; Merchndsng.

JAURON, KATHY; Manchester Central HS; Manchester, NH; (Y); 42/437; Church Yth Grp; Church Choir; Ed Yrbk Stf; Lit Mag; Rep Jr Cls; Rep Sr Cls; Stu Cncl; Socr; High Hon Roll; Hon Roll; U Of NH; Math.

JEFFERY, ELIZABETH; Hanover HS; Etna, NH; (Y); Cmnty Wkr; Varsity Clb; Acpl Chr; Bsktbl; Fld Hcky; High Hon Roll; Acad Excell Latin 85; Sprtsmnshp Athl Awd 85.

JENKINS, JILL; Claremont Christian Acad; Bradford, NH; (Y); 1/4; Dance Clb; Scholastic Bowl; Church Choir; School Play; Yrbk Stf; Trs Stu Cncl; Cit Awd; Hon Roll; Pres Schlr; Val; Supv Awd 81; Schlrshp Awd 83; Liberty U Lynchburg.

JENNINGS, TIMOTHY; Bishop Guertin HS; Merrimack, NH; (Y); 62/180; Camera Clb; Church Yth Grp; Church Choir; Nwsp Phtg; Stu Cncl; Crs Cntry; Trk; Wt Lftg; Hon Roll; Outstndg Part Awd/Proj Outreach 82-83; MA Coll Pharm; Pharm.

JENNISON, SHERI; Rochester Spaulding HS; Barrington, NH; (S); Girl Scts; Hon Roll; Candidate For St Pauls Schl,Advanced Studies Program 85; UVM; Medicine.

JENSEN, IRENE; Nashua SR HS; Nashua, NH; (Y); Church Yth Grp; Drama Clb; Science Clb; Pres Soph Cls; Rep Stu Cncl; High Hon Roll; Hon Roll; Exchng Stu 83-84; Chllng Pgm-Rivier Coll 84-85; Biochem.

JEWELL, MICHELLE; Fall Mountain Regional HS; S Charlestown, NH; (Y); 19/154; Am Leg Aux Girls St; Science Clb; Spanish Clb; Yrbk Stf; Bsktbl; Crs Cntry; Mgr Sftbl; Hon Roll; Pres Schlr; Keene ST Coll Hnrs Schlrshp 85; Keene ST Coll; Envrnmnt Study.

JEWETT, KELLIE A; Raymond JR SR HS; Raymond, NH; (Y); 7/73; Hosp Aide; Yrbk Bus Mgr; Trs Soph Cls; Trs Jr Cls; Trs Stu Cncl; Var Capt Bsktbl; Var Capt Sftbl; Var Capt Vllybl; Hon Roll; NHS; All Arnd Girl Awd 85; Schl Sci Awd 85; Schl Math Awd 85; Embry Riddle Aerontcl U.

JOHNS, JONATHAN; Hillsboro-Deering HS; Hillsboro, NH; (Y); Model UN; Yrbk Stf; Var Bsbl; Var Capt Bsktbl; Var Capt Bowling; Var Capt Socr; Prfct Atten Awd; Coaches Awd 84-85; Thompson Schl Appl Sci; Cvl Eng.

JOHNSON, F SCOTT; Salem HS; Windham, NH; (Y); 50/363; Church Yth Grp; Pres German Clb; School Play; Yrbk Ed-Chief; Capt Crs Cntry; Socr; Trk; Coaches Awds Crss Cntry 84-85; Goethe Grmn Spkng Awd 85; Teen Of The Mnth Salem Elks 85; Clark U; Intl Rel.

JOHNSON, KARIN; Spaulding HS; Rochester, NH; (S); 2/379; Sec Key Clb; Math Tm; Band; Concert Band; Jazz Band; Mrchg Band; Yrbk Ed-Chief; VP L Socr; VP L Trk; High Hon Roll; Dartmouth Bk Awd 84; Bio Sci.

JOHNSON, KERI ANN; Newport HS; Goshen, NH; (Y); Am Leg Aux Girls St; French Clb; Hosp Aide; Chorus; Swing Chorus; Fld Hcky; Sftbl; NHS; Voice Dem Awd; Wrkg Peopl.

JOHNSON, KRISTIN A; Pinkerton Acad; Derry, NH; (Y); 85/400; Am Leg Aux Girls St; Cmnty Wkr; Ski Clb; Drill Tm; Rep Soph Cls; Rep Jr Cls; JV Socr; JV Trk; Hon Roll; U Of CT; Chld Psych.

JOHNSON, PATRICIA M; Fall Mountain HS; Charlestown, NH; (Y); Am Leg Aux Girls St; French Clb; Yrbk Stf; Stu Cncl; Var L Cheerleading; Var Trk; Hon Roll; Prfct Atten Awd.

JOHNSON, PETER G; Milford Area SR HS; Milford, NH; (Y); 29/286; Computer Clb; Math Clb; Math Tm; Lit Mag; High Hon Roll; Hon Roll; NHS; Ntl Merit Schol; NEDT Awd; Ski Clb; Alpine Ski Tm Var Ltrs 82-84; West Point Invtnl Acad Wrkshp 84; Comp Sci.

JOHNSON, SUSAN; Concord HS; Bow, NH; (Y); Pres Church Yth Grp; Drama Clb; 4-H; Acpl Chr; Chorus; School Musical; School Play; Stage Crew; Variety Show; Hon Roll; Outstndng Achvt Acctg I 2nd 85; Hnbl Mntn ST Wd Acctg Cntst 85; Phy Effcncy Awd 85; Acctg.

JOHNSON, TAMARA LEIGH; Franklin HS; Franklin, NH; (Y); 4/91; Church Yth Grp; French Clb; Yrbk Stf; JV Var Cheerleading; JV Sftbl; High Hon Roll; NHS; Youth Gov-Welf Dir 84; Youth Gov-Libr 85; Acctng.

JOHNSON, WALTER; Bishop Guertin HS; Nashua, NH; (Y); Boys Clb Am; Ski Clb; Spanish Clb; JV Swmmng; Var Wt Lftg; Var Wrstlng; Hon Roll; Air Force ROTC; Engr.

JONES, JEFF; Spaulding HS; Rochester, NH; (S); Chorus; Gym; Robtcs.

JORDAN, MIKE; Pembroke Acad; Concord, NH; (Y); Church Yth Grp; Stat Crs Cntry; Stat Trk; Hon Roll; NHS; Arch.

JORDAN JR, ROBERT E; Newmarket Central HS; Newmarket, NH; (Y); 2/50; Am Leg Boys St; Math Clb; Math Tm; VP Soph Cls; Bsbl; Bsktbl; Timer; High Hon Roll; Hon Roll; NHS; Bus.

JURANTY, LAURIE; Pembroke Acad; Suncook, NH; (Y); Latin Clb; Science Clb; Spanish Clb; JV Bsktbl; JV Var Fld Hcky; Stat Sftbl; High Hon Roll; Prfct Atten Awd; Comp Sci.

KAEPPELER, DAVID JAMES; Nashua SR HS; Nashua, NH; (Y); 14/807; Am Leg Boys St; Boy Scts; Computer Clb; Sec Band; Chorus; Drm & Bgl; School Musical; French Hon Soc; High Hon Roll; NHS; Schlrshps-Digtl Eqptmnt Corp & Band 85; Pres Acad Ftnss Awd 85; U Of NH; Comp Sci.

KAISER, DEE; Woodsville HS; Woodsville, NH; (Y); 15/67; Ski Clb; Teachers Aide; Chorus; Concert Band; School Play; Yrbk Phtg; Lit Mag; Stu Cncl; Hon Roll; NHS; Nrthestrn Music Fstvl 85; N Cntry Band & Chrs 84-85; Castleton ST U; Comm.

KALKBRENNER, SHAWNTELLE; Pembroke Acad; Concord, NH; (Y); German Clb; Spanish Clb; Teachers Aide; Mansfield U; Elem Educ.

KALVAITIS, LINAS; Hopkinton HS; Contoocook, NH; (Y); Chess Clb; Math Tm; Variety Show; JV Bsktbl; Var Crs Cntry; Hon Roll; Prfct Atten Awd; ST Champ Math Tm 85; U Of Southern CA; Math.

KARCZ, KEVIN; Salem HS; Salem, NH; (S); 29/405; German Clb; Math Clb; Math Tm; Model UN; Ski Clb; Spanish Clb; Trs Soph Cls; Trs Jr Cls; Socr; Trk; Engrng.

KARCZ, LAURIE; Salem HS; Salem, NH; (S); 34/381; Math Clb; Math Tm; Model UN; Ski Clb; JV Trk; High Hon Roll; Hon Roll; NEDT Awd; Spanish NHS; Engrng.

KARNACEWICZ, MARTIN; Portsmouth SR HS; Greenland, NH; (S); Ski Clb; Band; Concert Band; Jazz Band; Mrchg Band; Pep Band; High Hon Roll; NHS; JV Bsbl; JV Bsktbl; A F Acad; Navgtr.

KASS, MICHAEL J; Milford Area SR HS; Milford, NH; (Y); Am Leg Boys St; Computer Clb; Debate Tm; Stu Cncl; JV Bsktbl; Var Ftbl; Var L Golf; Var L Trk; Bys ST Amer Lgn; Schl Brd Stu Rep 85-86; Yth, Govt Stu.

KAZAKIS, CYNTHIA R; Memorial HS; Manchester, NH; (Y); 30/393; Rep Church Yth Grp; Lit Mag; Sec Jr Cls; Rep Stu Cncl; Ftbl; High Hon Roll; Hon Roll; ST Anselm Coll; Chem.

KEALEY, JOLEEN M; Salem HS; Salem, NH; (Y); Debate Tm; Spanish Clb; Speech Tm; Band; Hon Roll; NEDT Awd; Spanish NHS; Lincoln-Douglass Debate Awd 85; Novice ST Debate Fin 83; U Of NH; Botany.

KEEFE, KIMBERLY; Spaulding HS; Rochester, NH; (S); 40/400; Am Leg Aux Girls St; Church Yth Grp; Key Clb; Yrbk Stf; Sec Frsh Cls; Sec Soph Cls; Sec Jr Cls; Sec Sr Cls; Hon Roll; NHS; Pvt Clb Gymnstcs Cls I Comp Gymnst; 2nd Pl NH Gymnstcs ST Meet 83.

KEEGAL, JOYCE; Belmont HS; Laconia, NH; (S); 15/80; Pres Trs 4-H; Quiz Bowl; Chorus; 4-H Awd; Hon Roll; NHS; NH ST Horse Shw 84; Animal Sci.

KEENAN, LORI; Epping HS; Epping, NH; (S); Drama Clb; Hosp Aide; Office Aide; School Play; Yrbk Ed-Chief; Yrbk Phtg; Yrbk Stf; Pres Stu Cncl; Bsktbl; Vllybl; Health Aide Awd 82; U Of NH; Bus Mgmt.

KELLEHER, THOMAS; Saint Thomas Aquinas HS; Dover, NH; (Y); 4/85; French Clb; Letterman Clb; Mathletes; Math Tm; Varsity Clb; Var Bsktbl; Var Crs Cntry; Hon Roll; JV Bsbl; JV Bsktbl; Exclnc Frnch; Math.

KELLEY, JOHN; Milford Area SR HS; Amherst, NH; (Y); Quiz Bowl; Nwsp Sprt Ed; Rep Stu Cncl; Golf; Powder Puff Ftbl; Hon Roll; Outstndng Chmstry Stu 85; Bsktbl Anncr 85; NH Boys ST 85; Syracuse; Cmmnctns.

KELSEY, KRISTINE; Spaulding HS; Rochester, NH; (S); 37/418; Cmnty Wkr; French Clb; Girl Scts; Key Clb; Yrbk Stf; Var Capt Trk; Stat Vllybl; High Hon Roll; Hon Roll; NHS; JR Miss State Fnls 84; Mst Imprvd Rnnr-Trck 83; Wentworth Inst; Elec Engrng.

KENYON, DAVID R; Merrimack HS; Bedford, NH; (Y); 20/285; JV Bsktbl; Hon Roll; Pres Schlr; UNH; Elec Engrng.

KERN, LISA; Nute HS; Milton, NH; (Y); Drama Clb; FBLA; JCL; Math Tm; Band; School Musical; School Play; Yrbk Stf; Sec Sr Cls; Capt Var Cheerleading; Csmtlgy.

KHAN, FELICIA; Portsmouth HS; Portsmouth, NH; (S); 1/300; Am Leg Aux Girls St; Drama Clb; Ski Clb; Band; School Play; High Hon Roll; Havard Bk Awd 84; Haven Mdl 84; Engrng.

KIDDER, LAURIE J; Tilton School; Franklin, NH; (S); Pres Key Clb; Yrbk Ed-Chief; Yrbk Stf; Pres Stu Cncl; Var Bsktbl; Var Golf; Capt Socr; Hon Roll; Charctr Awd, Ellsie Beaumont Awd 84; Sports Psych.

KINCEL, DEBORAH; Spaulding HS; Union, NH; (S); High Hon Roll; Hon Roll; Hnrb Mntn Acctg Contest 82-83; Acctg.

KING, KAREN J; Somersworth HS; Somersworth, NH; (Y); 37/165; GAA; Latin Clb; Rep Stu Cncl; Var Bsktbl; Var L Fld Hcky; Var L Sftbl; Office Aide; Spanish Clb; Im Vllybl; ST Chmps, 2nd Dream Tm Sftbl 85; Ntl Sftbl Trnmnt 84-85; Phy Ed.

KING, LARA D; Somersworth HS; Rollinsford, NH; (Y); 23/170; CAP; Latin Clb; Var L Bsktbl; Var L Crs Cntry; Var L Sftbl; Var Trk; Hon Roll; U Of NH; Engrng.

KING, NEAL; Spaulding HS; Rochester, NH; (S); 27/387; Pres 4-H; Key Clb; Math Clb; Math Tm; Yrbk Stf; Hon Roll; Math.

KINSLEY, DONALD; Concord HS; Bow, NH; (Y); 65/360; Bsktbl; Im Bowling; Var Golf; Hon Roll; NHS; Natl Hnr Roll 84-85; Bow Mens Club Schlrshp 85; Outstndg Achvt Engl 85; U Of NH; Rcrtn Admin.

KINSMAN, LINH; Concord HS; Concord, NH; (Y); 59/323; Dance Clb; Varsity Clb; Yrbk Stf; Rep Soph Cls; Sec Jr Cls; Sec Sr Cls; Rep Stu Cncl; JV Bsktbl; Stat Fld Hcky; L Mgr(s); Achvt Awd-Exclnc In Human Psych 85; Achvt Awd-Exclnc In Engl 85; Psych.

KIRETA, ANDREW; Merrimack HS; Merrimack, NH; (Y); 10/280; Church Yth Grp; Ski Clb; Bsktbl; Hon Roll; NHS; Pres Schlr; Griffin Fund Schlrshp 85-86; Ntl Hnr Soc Schlrshp 85-86; Purdue U; Mech Engr.

KITA, DAVID; Bishop Guertin HS; Mont Vernon, NH; (Y); 3/150; French Clb; Ed Nwsp Bus Mgr; Crs Cntry; Golf; Tennis; High Hon Roll; NHS; Ntl Merit SF; Slvr Metlst Natl Latin Exm 82-84; Schltc Achvt Bio 83-84; Astro Phys.

KITCHEN, AMY JENNIFER; Milford Area SR HS; Amherst, NH; (Y); Am Leg Aux Girls St; Yrbk Bus Mgr; Pres Frsh Cls; Rep Stu Cncl; Var Capt Cheerleading; JV Var Mgr(s); Hon Roll; Wrk 16-20 Hrs Wk 84-85.

KIVLER, KELLY; Kimball Union Acad; White River Jctn, VT; (Y); Stu Cncl; Var L Bsbl; Var L Bsktbl; Var L Crs Cntry; JV Ftbl; JV Lcrss; High Hon Roll; Hon Roll; U C Berkeley; Pol Sci.

KLAMKA, PETER; Bishop Guertin HS; Nashua, NH; (Y); Debate Tm; NFL; Speech Tm; Ed Nwsp Rptr; Trs Frsh Cls; Trs Soph Cls; VP Jr Cls; Trs Stu Cncl; Hon Roll; Jr NHS; NH ST Vrsty Debat Chmpn 85; Ntl HS Inst Nrthwstrn U 85; Dartmouth Smmr Inst 85.

KLENA, KALI; Portsmouth HS; Portsmouth, NH; (S); 35/394; Sec AFS; 4-H; VP Model UN; Band; Concert Band; Mrchg Band; Pep Band; High Hon Roll; NHS; Intl Law.

KLOTZ, EMILY; Porstmouth HS; New Castle, NH; (S); 3/394; Church Yth Grp; Sec French Clb; Math Tm; Quiz Bowl; Fld Hcky; Var L Swmmng; High Hon Roll; NHS; Frnch Schlrshp Awd 84; Biology.

KNIGHT, JOANNE CHRISTINA; Moultonborough Acad; Center Harbor, NH; (Y); 1/42; French Clb; Math Tm; Yrbk Stf; Trs Sr Cls; Rep Stu Cncl; Var L Bsktbl; Var Capt Vllybl; High Hon Roll; Pres NHS; Val; Hghst Avg Math 85; Outstndng Achvt Amer Lit 84; Hghst Avg Ltn II 85; U Of NH.

KNIGHT, SHERYL; Londonderry HS; Londonderry, NH; (Y); Office Aide; Teachers Aide; Chorus; Bus.

KNOWLES, STEPHANIE; Inter Lakes HS; Meredith, NH; (Y); Church Yth Grp; Band; Chorus; School Musical; Yrbk Stf; Rep Frsh Cls; Rep Soph Cls; Sec Sr Cls; Var Capt Cheerleading; Hon Roll; Langgs.

KOBILARCSIK, M GREGORY; Trinity HS; Windham, NH; (Y); 9/165; Ski Clb; Spanish Clb; Capt Ftbl; Wt Lftg; Hon Roll; Sec NHS; NEDT Awd; Amer H S Athl 85; Outstndng Spnsh Stdnt Awd 83 & 85; Outstndng Hnrs Geom Awd 84; Pre-Med.

KOERBER, HEATHER; The Derryfield Schl; Concord, NH; (Y); 1/51; Thesps; Chorus; School Musical; Nwsp Rptr; Stu Cncl; Var JV Bsktbl; Var JV Fld Hcky; Capt Var Sftbl; High Hon Roll; NHS; Frnch Prz 83-85; Yale Bk Awd 85; Rensselaer Medl 85.

KOLOK, KURTISS; Christian Fellowship HS; Laconia, NH; (Y); Church Yth Grp; Political Wkr; School Musical; Var Bsktbl; Var Socr; 4th Pl Awd For Schl Sci Fair 83; Christian Educ Clss Awd 83-84; Bus Adm.

KOLTOOKIAN, CHRISTINE S; Tilton Schl; Canterbury, NH; (Y); GAA; Key Clb; Math Tm; Varsity Clb; Chorus; Yrbk Ed-Chief; Var Capt Lcrss; Var Socr; Hon Roll; Cls Awd 84-85; Most Imprvd Plyr 82-83; William Smith Coll; Chem.

KORNRUMPF, CHANCE; Spaulding HS; Rochester, NH; (S); 17/415; Am Leg Boys St; Boy Scts; Math Clb; ROTC; Band; Drill Tm; Jazz Band; Mrchg Band; Symp Band; High Hon Roll; AF ROTC Schlrshp; Eagle Scout; Sojourners Awd; Astronautical Engrng.

KOURY, LINDA; London Derry HS; Londonderry, NH; (Y); High Hon Roll; Hon Roll; Band; Music.

KOZIELL, PAUL; Newport HS; Newport, NH; (Y); Math Tm; Band; Chorus; Concert Band; Mrchg Band; Orch; Pep Band; School Musical; School Play; Stage Crew; St Pauls Schl Advncd Stds Pgm 85; Gvrnmnt.

KRAMER, KIM; Alvirne HS; Hudson, NH; (Y); 27/311; Church Yth Grp; Var Nwsp Ed-Chief; Im JV Bsktbl; Im Var Socr; Hon Roll; U Of NH; Pre-Law.

KREBS, MICHAEL; Fall Mt Regional HS; Walpole, NH; (Y); 35/145; Am Leg Boys St; Band; Chorus; Madrigals; Mrchg Band; School Musical; School Play; Tennis; Annapolis; Hstry.

KRETSCHMAR, TERRI LYNNE; Somersworth HS; Somersworth, NH; (Y); 34/167; Am Leg Aux Girls St; French Clb; VP Pres FBLA; Office Aide; Red Cross Aide; Yrbk Bus Mgr; Yrbk Stf; Pres Stu Cncl; DAR Awd; Hugh O Brian Yth Fndtn Ldrshp Sem Rep 83; Schl Accredtn Comm Schl Atmosph 83; Prog SEARCH 84; Becker JC; Trvl/Trsm.

KRONENFELD, NATHAN; Londonderry HS; Londonderry, NH; (Y); Drama Clb; Exploring; Quiz Bowl; Temple Yth Grp; Jazz Band; Stat Mgr(s); High Hon Roll; Sec NHS; Band; Pep Band; Yrbk Ed 83-85; Physcs Awds 85; Physcs.

KUDLA, CRISTINA; Pelham HS; Pelham, NH; (Y); Drama Clb; Band; Chorus; Church Choir; Drm Mjr(t); School Musical; School Play; Lit Mag; Thtr Arts.

KULLGREN, PETER; Contoocook Valley Regional HS; Peterborough, NH; (Y); Am Leg Boys St; Boy Scts; Church Yth Grp; Band; Jazz Band; Stage Crew; Lit Mag; Stu Cncl; Hon Roll; Graphic Arts.

KUTZELMAN, JULIE; Timberlane Regional HS; Atkinson, NH; (Y); 48/206; 4-H; French Clb; FBLA; Ski Clb; JV Bsktbl; JV Trk; U Of MA; Comp Sci.

LA PLANTE, TROY; Franklin JR SR HS; Franklin, NH; (Y); 5/90; Am Leg Boys St; Boy Scts; VP Sec Computer Clb; Debate Tm; Pres Sec Exploring; French Clb; Teachers Aide; Nwsp Rptr; Nwsp Stf; JV L Ftbl; NH ST Cert Firefghtr Levl I 84; Ldrshp Awd 84; Kelloggs Citznshp Prog Hnr Rl 85; Schlstc Awd 80-85; NH Voc Tech Coll; Firefghtr.

LA PLUME, AMY LYNN; Salem HS; Salem, NH; (S); 24/363; Church Yth Grp; Key Clb; Model UN; Ski Clb; Spanish Clb; Teachers Aide; School Play; Capt Fld Hcky; Capt Trk; High Hon Roll; Mktng.

LA ROCHE, ERIC; Merrimack Valley HS; Penacook, NH; (Y); Am Leg Boys St; Boy Scts; Var L Bsbl; Var L Bsktbl; JV Capt Ftbl; CT Vly Lg 1st Tm Utlty Plyr Bsbl 84; Cls I Battg Avg 84; Med Tech.

LA ROSE, LISA; Laconia HS; Weirs Beach, NH; (Y); 31/144; Var L Tennis; Voice Dem Awd; ASTRA Clb 84-85; Gldn Tnns Rkt Awd 85; U Of NH; Lib Arts.

LABER, ANNIE; Newport JR SR HS; Newport, NH; (Y); Pres Church Yth Grp; Pres Spanish Clb; Chorus; Color Guard; School Musical; Nwsp Stf; Crs Cntry; NHS; Social Psych.

LABRECQUE, MARK; Berlin HS; Berlin, NH; (Y); 29/220; Church Yth Grp; JV Bsbl; Coach Actv; JV Ice Hcky; Hon Roll; Bus.

LABRECQUE, SONIA; Goffstown Area HS; Goffstown, NH; (Y); Church Yth Grp; Dance Clb; Drama Clb; Pres FNA; Pep Clb; Red Cross Aide; Ski Clb; Teachers Aide; French Hon Soc; High Hon Roll; French IV Awd 85; Adv Bio Awd 85; Dance Fest Schlrshp 83.

LACASSE, NICHOLAS; Lebanon SR HS; W Lebanon, NH; (Y); Pres AFS; Debate Tm; Latin Clb; Letterman Clb; Ed Q&S; Band; Pres Chorus; Swing Chorus; Nwsp Ed-Chief; Yrbk Stf; Psych.

LACHANCE, JOHN; Spaulding HS; Gonic, NH; (S); 59/470; Boys Clb Am; Church Yth Grp; ROTC; JV Var Bsbl; Var Capt Ice Hcky; Var Socr; JV Var Wt Lftg; Hon Roll; DAR ROTC 84.

LADOUCEUR, KRISTEN; Memorial HS; Auburn, NH; (Y); 38/402; Art Clb; Ed Yrbk Stf; Ed Lit Mag; Powder Puff Ftbl; Trk; Hon Roll; Lucy Lamontagne Art Awd 85; U Of NH; Art.

LAFERTE, DENISE; Spaulding HS; Barrington, NH; (S); 4/388; Yrbk Stf; High Hon Roll; NHS; U Of NH Smnrs Adv Stu 84.

LAMARCHE, NANCY; Laconia HS; Laconia, NH; (Y); 11/148; Hosp Aide; Math Tm; Service Clb; Band; Drm Mjr(t); Mrchg Band; Nwsp Ed-Chief; Capt Twrlr; Elks Awd; High Hon Roll; Natural Sci Awd 85; Knights Columbus Scholar 85; Outstndng Mjrt Awd 85; Bentley Coll; Acctng.

LAMARRE, JACQUES; Milford Area SR HS; Amherst, NH; (Y); Am Leg Boys St; Boy Scts; Sec FBLA; Acpl Chr; Lib Band; Yrbk Bus Mgr; Sec Soph Cls; Sec Jr Cls; Stu Cncl; Hon Roll; Dgtl Schlrshp Attnd Phllps Andvr Acad Smmr Sessn 84; Hugh O Brian Yth Ldrshp Smnr Rep 83-84.

LAMB, BETH ANNE; Milford Area SR HS; Milford, NH; (Y); Computer Clb; Exploring; Chorus; Flag Corp; Trs Frsh Cls; Trs Soph Cls; Trs Jr Cls; Rep Stu Cncl; Mgr(s); Mat Maids; Comp Sci.

LAMB, KIM; Salem HS; Salem, NH; (Y); 80/353; Girl Scts; Latin Clb; Model UN; Ski Clb; Band; Mrchg Band; School Musical; School Play; JV Bsktbl; Var Trk; Jrnlsm.

LAMBERT, DEBRA; Manchester Central HS; Manchester, NH; (S); 188/424; VP DECA; Hon Roll; 1st Pl Trophy In Gen Merchnds Manuel 85; 2nd Pl Mdl In Math 85; Bus Mgmt.

LAMONT, ELIZABETH; Merrimack HS; Merrimack, NH; (Y); 12/250; Church Yth Grp; Yrbk Stf; High Hon Roll; Hon Roll; NHS; Pres Schlr; Balfour Awd Engl Lit & Acctng 85; Keene ST Coll; Engl.

LAMONTAGNE, ANNE-LOUISE; St Thomas Aquinas HS; Rochester, NH; (Y); Church Yth Grp; Debate Tm; Drama Clb; VP Pres French Clb; Key Clb; Yrbk Stf; Stu Cncl; High Hon Roll; Hon Roll; Jr NHS; Bio.

LAMOUREUX, KRISTI LEE; Berlin SR HS; St Paul, MN; (Y); 6/220; Am Leg Aux Girls St; Church Yth Grp; Cmnty Wkr; JA; Pep Clb; Band; Concert Band; Yrbk Stf; Sec Trs Jr Cls; Sec Trs Sr Cls; Century III Ldrshp Scholar 85; James River Corp Hgh Achvt Scholar 85; Gustavus Adolphus Coll; Phys Th.

LAMSON, JAMES; Weare HS; Weare, NH; (S); 3/50; Rep Stu Cncl; Crs Cntry; Socr; Var Trk; Hon Roll; NHS.

LAMY, ANGELA M; Manchester H S West; Manchester, NH; (Y); 110/435; Art Clb; Church Yth Grp; Acpl Chr; Band; Chorus; Concert Band; Mrchg Band; Pep Band; School Musical; School Play; Rotary Clb Fine Arts Awd Schlrshp 85; Prfct Attnd Four Yrs HS 85; Brooks Coll; Fashn Desgn.

LANCEY, WENDY; Spaulding HS; Rochester, NH; (S); 8/415; Key Clb; Trs Frsh Cls; Rep Soph Cls; Rep Jr Cls; Capt Bsktbl; Capt Socr; Sftbl; NHS; St Pauls Adv Studies Prog 84; Clncl Psych.

LANDRIGAN, TERENCE; Bishop Guertin HS; Nashua, NH; (Y); 18/160; Sec Am Leg Boys St; 4-H; Key Clb; Nwsp Sprt Ed; Yrbk Sprt Ed; Stu Cncl; JV Bsbl; Var L Golf; Sec NHS; NEDT Awd; Outstndng Svc Awd NHS 84-85; Outstndng Perfrmnce Awd Stu Cncl 84-85; Intl Stud.

LANDRY, ANNE; Bishop Brady HS; Concord, NH; (S); 2/74; Intnl Clb; Yrbk Ed-Chief; High Hon Roll; Hon Roll; NHS; Sal; Engl Awd; Theolgy Awd; St Pauls Schl Adv Stds Pgm; Pre-Med.

LANDRY, CHERI; Presentation Of Mary HS; Pelham, NH; (Y); Science Clb; Ski Clb; Rep Frsh Cls; JV Vllybl; High Hon Roll; Hon Roll; Cert Of Hnr IPS 83; Accntnt.

LANDRY, CINDY; Salem HS; Salem, NH; (Y); 50/347; Model UN; Band; Concert Band; Mrchg Band; High Hon Roll; Hon Roll; Dlrs For Schlrs Schlrshp 85; Acadmc Achvt Awd-Bus Ed 85; Castle JC; Exec Sec.

LANDRY, DAVID; Bishop Guertin HS; Nashua, NH; (Y); Ski Clb; Im Bsktbl; Im Socr; Var L Trk; Im Wt Lftg; Kiwanis Awd.

LANDRY, DAVID; Hopkinton HS; Contoocook, NH; (Y); 19/75; Chess Clb; Computer Clb; Math Tm; Nwsp Rptr; Yrbk Stf; VP Soph Cls; Hon Roll; U Of NM; Poltcs.

LANGELIER, KYM E; Mount Saint Mary Seminary; Nashua, NH; (Y); 41/92; Art Clb; Girl Scts; Spanish Clb; Church Choir; School Play; Bowling; Gym; Hon Roll; Prfct Atten Awd; Bst Shw & 1st Pl Art Awds 84; Memrl Awd Trans Watrclr Nashua Artst Assn Art Shw 83; Grphc Arts.

LANGLEY, PENNY; Oyster River HS; Madbury, NH; (Y); Drama Clb; 4-H; French Clb; Dnfth Awd; 4-H Awd; Hon Roll; Ntl 4 H Cngrss 83, Conf 85.

LANGS, DEBBIE; Dover HS; Dover, NH; (Y); Drama Clb; Latin Clb; Stage Crew; Var Crs Cntry; Mgr(s); Var Trk; Hon Roll; Natl Fed Drug-Free Yth 84; Arch.

LANK, STEPHEN; Pittsfield Middle HS; Barnstead, NH; (Y); Church Yth Grp; Varsity Clb; Yrbk Stf; JV Bsktbl; JV Socr; Bus Mgmt.

LAPIERRE, CHANTAL; Colebrook Acad; N Stratford, NH; (Y); 2/48; French Clb; Varsity Clb; Chorus; Hon Roll; NHS; Prfct Atten Awd; Sal; Yrbk Stf; Sftbl; C A Alumni Scholar 85; Hghst Yr Pt Avg Frnch I, II, III 81-84; Hghst Yr Pt Avg Alg II 83-84; U NH; Comp Sci.

LAPOINTE, JANE; Stevens HS; Claremont, NH; (Y); Cmnty Wkr; Math Tm; Yrbk Bus Mgr; Yrbk Stf; JV Socr; Hon Roll; Margaret Lawlor Mckee Mem Schlrshp 85; Tappan Fund Schlrshp Awd 85; Sweet Briar Coll.

LARAMIE, MATTHEW; Fall Mountain Regional HS; Charlestown, NH; (Y); 37/157; Drama Clb; FTA; Political Wkr; Spanish Clb; Acpl Chr; Band; Chorus; Drm Mjr(t); Madrigals; Pep Band; JR Cls Awd 85; U Of NH; Scndry Ed.

LAROSE, LOUISE; Presentation Of Mary Acad; Dracut, MA; (Y); Pres 4-H; VP French Clb; Hosp Aide; Science Clb; Nwsp Rptr; Rep Frsh Cls; Pres Soph Cls; High Hon Roll; Hon Roll; Ladies Of St Johns Hosp Schlrshp 85; U Of Lowell; Physcl Thrpy.

LASSEY, KAREN; Concord HS; Bow, NH; (Y); 7/325; Debate Tm; German Clb; Math Tm; Ski Clb; Speech Tm; Lit Mag; JV Fld Hcky; Trk; High Hon Roll; NHS; Physcs.

LASTOVICA, HELEN M; Milford Area SR HS; Milford, NH; (Y); Var Bsktbl; Capt Powder Puff Ftbl; Capt Var Trk; Hon Roll; Providence Coll.

LATAILLE, MICHAEL R; Alvirine HS; Hudson, NH; (Y); 19/332; Church Yth Grp; French Clb; Band; Concert Band; Mrchg Band; Pep Band; Yrbk Bus Mgr; High Hon Roll; Hon Roll; Concours Natl De Francais Cert Dhonneur 83-84; Math.

LAVALLEE, DENISE; Goffstown HS; Manchester, NH; (Y); 3/200; Math Tm; Band; Pep Band; High Hon Roll; Advanced Chem Awd 85; Advanced Bio Awd 85; Spnsh 2 Awd 85; U Of RHODE Island; Phrmcy.

LAVALLEE, ROBERT; Bishop Guertin HS; Pelham, NH; (Y); 6/150; FCA; French Clb; Im Bsktbl; JV Trk; Im Vllybl; High Hon Roll; Hon Roll; NHS.

LAVENTURE, KEVIN; Winnisquam Regional HS; Tilton, NH; (Y); Spanish Clb; Bsktbl; Trk; Hon Roll; Prfct Atten Awd; Mst Imprvd Bsktbl Plyr JV 83; MVP Bsktbl JV 84; Comp Sci.

LAVERTU, CHRIS; Trinity HS; Bedford, NH; (Y); Am Leg Boys St; Stage Crew; JV Capt Bsktbl; JV Capt Socr; Hon Roll; Syracuse; Advertsng.

LAVOIE, JENNY; Spaulding HS; Barrington, NH; (Y); 22/348; Math Clb; JV Bsktbl; JV Trk; Hon Roll; Mu Alp Tht; Ntl Merit Ltr; Math.

LAVOIE, PAUL J; Fall Mountain Regional HS; Walpole, NH; (Y); 6/155; French Clb; JCL; Latin Clb; Pres Math Tm; Rep Stu Cncl; High Hon Roll; Hon Roll; NHS; Stu Rep FMR Schl Bd 84-85; Renselar Polytech Inst; Engrng.

LAVOIE JR, RAYMOND V; Bishop Guertin HS; Nashua, NH; (Y); 9/130; Debate Tm; Drama Clb; French Clb; Nwsp Stf; Ed Yrbk Stf; Var Trk; High Hon Roll; NHS; Ntl Merit Schol; Am Leg Boys St; Natl Assoc Ltr Carriers Wm H Doherty Scholar 85; Disabled Amvets Scholar 85; Amherst Coll; Eng.

LAWN, MELODY; Conant HS; Jaffrey, NH; (Y); Trs Frsh Cls; Trs Soph Cls; Bsktbl; Fld Hcky; Sftbl; High Hon Roll; NEDT Awd; Granite Grls ST Cert Grad 85; Hugh O Brian Yth Fndtn 84; Natl Latn Exm Cert Hnbl Merit 84; Acctg.

LAY, MARNIE; Colebrook Acad; Canaan, VT; (Y); Yrbk Stf; Typng Awd 85; Retalng.

LAZOTT, JOHN; Manchester High Schl West; Bedford, NH; (Y); 111/377; Boy Scts; Church Yth Grp; Exploring; Red Cross Aide; Ski Clb; Varsity Clb; Stage Crew; Variety Show; Mgr(s); Score Keeper; UNH; Pilot.

LAZZARO, ANTHONY L; Spaulding HS; Rochester, NH; (Y); Im Badmtn; Im Bsbl; Im Bsktbl; Im Ftbl; Im Socr; Im Sftbl; Im Tennis; Im Vllybl; Im Wrstlng; Hon Roll; Elec Engrng.

LE BOEUF, ANN; Milford Area SR HS; Mt Vernon, NH; (Y); 5/286; Capt Ski Clb; Ed Yrbk Stf; Var Fld Hcky; Trs NHS; Hon Roll; Schlr/Athl Awd 85; Colgate U; Math.

LE DUC, KAREN E; Pinkerton Acad; East Hampstead, NH; (Y); Civic Clb; Band; JV Bsktbl; Var Fld Hcky; Var Sftbl; Hon Roll; NHS; Asst Bsktbll Coach At Hampstead Mdl Schl; Lawrence Eagle Tribune All-Str Fld Hcky Hnrbl Mntn; Art.

LEAOR, KIMBERLY; Milford Area SR HS; Milford, NH; (Y); Yrbk Stf; Bsktbl; Mgr(s); Powder Puff Ftbl; JV Socr; Hon Roll; Retl Mktg.

LEARY, CHRISTOPHER P; Kearsarge Regioanl HS; Warner, NH; (Y); AFS; Am Leg Boys St; Boy Scts; Chess Clb; 4-H; Model UN; Pres Jr Cls; Var Crs Cntry; Var Trk; Hon Roll.

LEBEAU, ANDREW; Portsmouth HS; Portsmouth, NH; (Y); Drama Clb; School Musical; School Play; Stage Crew; High Hon Roll; Hon Roll; U Of NH; Elec Engrng.

LEDUC, NICOLE; Presentation Of Mary Acad; Pelham, NH; (Y); Art Clb; Science Clb; Service Clb; Chorus; School Musical; Im VP Sftbl; Im Vllybl.

LEE, BERNARD; Pinkerton Acad; Manchester, NH; (S); Church Yth Grp; Drama Clb; Pep Clb; Band; Concert Band; Jazz Band; Mrchg Band; Pep Band; School Musical; School Play; Two Yr Band Awd 83; Four Yr Band Awd 85; NH Voc Tech; Auto Tech.

LEE, KAREN L; Kearsarge Regional HS; New London, NH; (Y); 47/110; AFS; Debate Tm; Drama Clb; Latin Clb; Math Tm; Sec Model UN; Stage Crew; Yrbk Stf; JV Var Fld Hcky; Hon Roll; Theatre.

LEGASSE, SCOTT; Memorial HS; Manchester, NH; (Y); 41/402; L Bsbl; Capt Ice Hcky; L Socr; Hon Roll; Crusader Awd 85; Ntl Hnr Roll 84-85; Amer HS Athlt 84-85; Berwick Acad.

LEHMAN, KIM; Hopkinton HS; Contoocook, NH; (Y); Yrbk Phtg; JV Var Bsktbl; JV Var Sftbl; Office Aide; Political Wkr; Chorus; Yrbk Stf; Hon Roll; MIP In Bsktbl 83-84.

LEIGHTON, MEGAN; St Thomas Aquinas HS; Durham, NH; (Y); Boy Scts; Nwsp Stf; Yrbk Stf; Sec Jr Cls; VP Sr Cls; Var Bsktbl; Var Cheerleading; JV Var Fld Hcky; Var Sftbl; Var Trk; Mst Outstndng Frshmn Wntr Trck; NH ST Chrldg Comptn Fnlst 85; JR Prom Cmmttee & Ct For Qn; Stonehill Coll; Cmmnctns.

LELAND, WENDY; Pinkerton Acad; E Hampstead, NH; (Y); 15/535; Pres 4-H; Band; Mrchg Band; School Musical; 4-H Awd; High Hon Roll; Hon Roll; NHS; Jrnlst.

LEMEK, JENNIFER; Pinkerton Acad; Windham, NH; (S); 1/450; Pres VP Girl Scts; Co-Capt Math Tm; Band; School Musical; Yrbk Stf; NHS; Ntl Merit Ltr; Val; Church Yth Grp; Drama Clb; First Class GSA 81; Gold & Slvr Ldrshp Awds 82-83; St Pauls Schl Advance Stu Pgm 84; Carleton Coll; Mus.

LEMIEUX, MAURENE; Alvirne HS; Hudson, NH; (Y); 20/272; Church Yth Grp; Ski Clb; School Musical; Var Socr; Var Trk; Var Wt Lftg; Hon Roll; Kiwanis Awd; Lion Awd; Mst Profcnt In Engl Awd 85; Boston U; Commnctns.

LEMIRE, MARK; Bishop Guertin HS; Wilton, NH; (Y); Church Yth Grp; FCA; JV Var Ftbl; JV Trk; Wt Lftg; Wrstlng; Bus Mgmt.

LENESS, AMANDA V; Phillips Exeter Acad; New York, NY; (Y); Art Clb; JCL; Math Clb; Office Aide; Chorus; Nwsp Rptr; Stu Cncl; High Hon Roll; Ntl Merit Schol; Natl Latin Exam, Summa Cum Laude 83; Bio Olympiad Gold 83; NY Math League Highest 83; Medicine.

LENESS, THOMAS G; Phillipes Exeter Acad; New York, NY; (Y); Band; Jazz Band; Nwsp Rptr; Ed Nwsp Stf; Ed Lit Mag; Rep Stu Cncl; Plywrtng Awd.

LENNERTON, BRETT ALAN; Salem HS; Salem, NH; (S); 37/405; Computer Clb; Math Tm; Model UN; Band; Concert Band; Mrchg Band; JV Var Bsbl; JV Ftbl; Ice Hcky; JV Var Trk; Princeton Coll; Comp Sci.

LEONE, WENDY; Timberlane Regional HS; Atkinson, NH; (Y); Cmnty Wkr; VP 4-H; French Clb; Hosp Aide; Model UN; Office Aide; Concert Band; Mrchg Band; Stat Bsktbl; Hon Roll; Psych.

LESSARD, SUSY; Presentation Of Mary Acad; Dracut, MA; (Y); 4-H; French Clb; Library Aide; Science Clb; Ski Clb; Nwsp Stf; Trs Frsh Cls; Sec Soph Cls; Rep Jr Cls; Trs Stu Cncl; AATF 3rd St 83; Gregg Typng Awd 83; AATF 5th St 84-85; U Lowell.

LEVASSEUR, ROBERT M; St Thomas Aquinas HS; Hampton Falls, NH; (Y); 11/180; Aud/Vis; Latin Clb; Band; Variety Show; JV Bsktbl; Var Capt Socr; Var Capt Tennis; Hon Roll; Pres Schlr; St Pauls Adv Studies Pgm 84; Essay Wnnr 85; Schlr Athl Schlrshp 85; Carleton Coll; Econ.

LEVESQUE, KATHLEEN M; Pinkerton Academy; Derry, NH; (Y); 5/450; Co-Capt Math Clb; Ski Clb; Yrbk Stf; High Hon Roll; Pres NHS; Rensselaer Polytechnic Inst Med; Wellesly Bk Awd; Pres Acad Ftns Awd; Cornell U; Engrng.

LEVESQUE, MIKE; Manchester Memorial HS; Manchester, NH; (Y); 10/369; Math Tm; Teachers Aide; Nwsp Stf; High Hon Roll; St Pauls Adv Stu Pgm 85; Engr.

LEVINE, SHARYN; Goffstown Area HS; Goffstown, NH; (Y); 5/225; Exploring; Girl Scts; Math Tm; Temple Yth Grp; Band; Chorus; Concert Band; Mrchg Band; Pep Band; Swing Chorus; St Pauls Schl Advncd Studies Prgm 85; Sci.

LEWIS, RICHRD G; Oyster River HS; Durham, NH; (Y); 52/132; Aud/Vis; PAVAS; School Play; Schl Museum Fine Arts Sculptr.

LEWIS, TIFFANY J; Memorial HS; Manchester, NH; (Y); 35/402; Drama Clb; Nwsp Stf; Yrbk Stf; Hon Roll; Prfct Atten Awd; French Clb; Quiz Bowl; Lit Mag; Stu Cncl; Cheerleading; Faclty Schlrshp 85; U Of NH; Cmmnctns.

LEWIS, TRACEY; Portsmouth HS; Dyess Afb, TX; (Y); 40/400; Am Leg Aux Girls St; German Clb; Office Aide; Band; High Hon Roll; Hon Roll; AR U; Law & Poltcl Sci.

LIBBY, WAYNE; Spaulding HS; Rochester, NH; (Y); Var Ftbl; Hon Roll; Comp Sci.

LILLY, REBECCA; Coe-Brown Northwood Acad; Northwood, NH; (Y); 1/60; Church Yth Grp; Nwsp Ed-Chief; Yrbk Stf; Sec Frsh Cls; Sec Soph Cls; Pres Jr Cls; Rep Sr Cls; Hon Roll; NHS; Awd Excllnce Eng; Hist.

LIM, HYE-JIN; Phillips Exeter Acad; Schenectady, NY; (Y); Dance Clb; Hosp Aide; Ski Clb; Acpl Chr; Chorus; Rep Stu Cncl; Ntl Merit SF; Church Yth Grp; French Clb; Service Clb; Negley Hstry Prz 84.

LIND, ROBERTA; Hillsboro-Deering HS; Hillsboro, NH; (S); 1/61; French Clb; Math Tm; Band; Yrbk Ed-Chief; Var Mgr(s); High Hon Roll; NHS; Val; Church Yth Grp; Teachers Aide; Rensellaer Medl Excllnce Sci & Math 84; Sci Awd; U Of NH; Pre-Vet.

LIND, ROBIN; Hillsboro Deering HS; Hillsboro, NH; (S); 1/63; Church Yth Grp; French Clb; Math Tm; Teachers Aide; Concert Band; Mrchg Band; Pep Band; Yrbk Bus Mgr; Yrbk Ed-Chief; Yrbk Stf; Rensselaer Awd Excllnc Sci & Math 84; Sci Dept Awd 84; UNH; Pre Vet.

LINDSAY, CHRISTINE MARY; Oyster River HS; Durham, NH; (Y); Am Leg Aux Girls St; Cmnty Wkr; Office Aide; School Play; Var Capt Cheerleading; Swmmng; High Hon Roll; Hon Roll; MIP Chrldng 82-83; MVP Chrldng 84-85; Sound Rcrdng.

LINEHAN, DANYA; Concord HS; Concord, NH; (Y); 12/300; VP Dance Clb; Drama Clb; School Musical; School Play; Stage Crew; Wt Lftg; High Hon Roll; NHS; Pres Schlr; Am Leg Awd 85; Wellesley Bk Awd 84; U NH; Pre-Vet.

LINZETTO, LINDA; Salem HS; Salem, NH; (Y); Church Yth Grp; FBLA; Model UN; Teachers Aide; Hon Roll; Fazios; Beauty Tech.

LISTZWAN, STEPHEN; Profile HS; Franconia, NH; (Y); 4/52; Pres Computer Clb; Library Aide; Math Tm; Rep Jr Cls; Rep Stu Cncl; Var Crs Cntry; L Var Socr; Var Tennis; High Hon Roll; Prfct Atten Awd; Lucy Phozi Awd 80; Engrng.

LITCHFIELD, CYNTHIA; Milford Area SR HS; Amherst, NH; (Y); DECA; FBLA; FHA; Band; Color Guard; Flag Corp; Mrchg Band; Capt Cheerleading; Sftbl; DECA Schlrshp 85; Wilma Boyd Schl; Trvl.

LITTLE, CAYLENE; Pembroke Acad; Pembroke, NH; (Y); Church Yth Grp; FBLA; Math Tm; Band; Nwsp Stf; Bsktbl; Cheerleading; Sftbl; Vllybl; Hon Roll; FL ST U; Bus Admin.

LIVERNOIS, ANDREW; Winnisquam Regional HS; Laconia, NH; (Y); 3/90; Drama Clb; Band; Chorus; Jazz Band; Var Socr; Bausch & Lomb Sci Awd; JP Sousa Awd; NHS; Prfct Atten Awd; Union Coll.

LIZOTTE, DAVID; Stevens HS; Claremont, NH; (Y); 2/212; Math Tm; Model UN; Varsity Clb; Yrbk Bus Mgr; Yrbk Stf; Pres Sr Cls; Tennis; Elks Awd; Trs NHS; Sal; St Pauls Attendee 84; Fitch Scholar 85; Alden Lit Prize; U Of VA; Pre-Med.

LOGUE JR, DENNIS; Hanover HS; Hanover, NH; (Y); Capt Debate Tm; Quiz Bowl; Scholastic Bowl; Yrbk Bus Mgr; Rep Stu Cncl; Bsktbl; JV Crs Cntry; Ftbl; Var L Trk; Hon Roll; Poli Sci.

LOMBARDI, VINCE; Milford Area SR HS; Amherst, NH; (Y); Debate Tm; Pres FBLA; Acpl Chr; Band; Chorus; Mrchg Band; Yrbk Stf; Rep Stu Cncl; Var Trk; Var Vllybl; Pres FBLA 84-85; 3rd Pl Mr FBLA ST NH 85; Stdnt Mnth Milford Area SR Hgh 85; Acctg.

LONG, BONNIE-LEE; Portsmouth HS; Portsmouth, NH; (S); Church Yth Grp; Chorus; Jazz Band; Mrchg Band; School Musical; Sec Frsh Cls; Var JV Cheerleading; Gym; Trk; NHS; Jr Ntl Hnr Sco; High Hnr Rl; Hnr Rl; Int Dec.

LOOMIS, MIKE; Concord HS; Concord, NH; (Y); 35/350; German Clb; L Trk; High Hon Roll; NHS; Comp Sci.

LOPEZ, FELICIA; Portsmouth HS; Portsmouth, NH; (Y); 119/379; Drama Clb; Model UN; Acpl Chr; Band; Chorus; Color Guard; Flag Corp; Madrigals; Mrchg Band; School Musical; NH All ST Chrs 85; NH All ST Drama Cst 85; All New Engl Drama Cst 85; Stephens Coll; Music Theatr.

LORD, SUSAN; Memorial HS; Auburn, NH; (Y); Art Clb; Nwsp Stf; NHS; Bus Admin.

LORD, VALERIE ANN; Fall Mountain Regional HS; S Acworth, NH; (Y); 28/162; Spanish Clb; Sec Band; Mrchg Band; Pep Band; Socr; Sftbl; Cheshire Hosp Axlry Schlrshp 85; NH U; Nrsng.

LORING, MARK; Colebrook Acad; Colebrook, NH; (Y); 5/50; Church Yth Grp; Drama Clb; Chorus; School Musical; Bsktbl; Vllybl; JC Awd; NHS; Music & Amer Legn Awds 85; UNH.

LOVELL, MICHELE; Keene HS; Keene, NH; (Y); Church Yth Grp; Dance Clb; JA; Band; Rep Frsh Cls; Sftbl; Swmmng; Hon Roll; JR Dist Band New Engl Schlrshp 83; U NH; Acctng.

LUJAN, MALU I; Mascenic Reginal; Greenville, NH; (Y); 10/65; Drama Clb; Boys Clb Am; School Play; Stage Crew; Nwsp Rptr; Nwsp Sprt Ed; Rep Sr Cls; Hon Roll; NHS; Wellesley Bk Awd; Acad Engl Awd; Engl Dept Bk Awd & Cert; Spnsh Acad Cert; Boston U; Hlth Sci.

LUOPA, JOHN; Monadnock Regional HS; Troy, NH; (Y); 29/160; Chorus; Var Bsbl; Var Bsktbl; Var Ftbl; Hon Roll; MVP Ftbl Bsktbl All ST 83-84; ST Titles Bsbl 84-85; Bus.

LYNCH, HELEN; Colebrook Acad; Colebrook, NH; (Y); 1/60; CAP; Hosp Aide; Science Clb; Chorus; School Musical; Swing Chorus; High Hon Roll; Hon Roll; NHS; Pres Church Yth Grp; Outstndng Achvt Alg & Frnch 83-85; Bst Actress Jr Cls 85; Bio.

LYNCH, MAUREEN M; Somersworth HS; Somersworth, NH; (Y); 27/175; VP Soph Cls; VP Jr Cls; VP Sr Cls; Stu Cncl; High Hon Roll; Cmnty Wkr; French Clb; Hosp Aide; Acpl Chr; Chorus; Somersworth Cathlc Fndtn & Amer Legn & Mary E Riley Schlrshps Awds 85; U Of NH; Hlth Stds.

MAC KENZIE, PAMELA D; Salem HS; Salem, NH; (Y); 6/346; French Clb; Concert Band; Drm & Bgl; Jazz Band; Mrchg Band; Orch; Pep Band; Nwsp Stf; High Hon Roll; Kiwanis Awd; NH All ST Orchstra & Band 83-85; Univ Lowell Prep Div Hnrs Ensmble 83-85; Frnch Lang & Band Awd 85; Georgetown U; Frnch.

MAC LEOD, DANA K; Community Baptist Schl; Gorham, NH; (Y); Church Yth Grp; Cmnty Wkr; Political Wkr; Church Choir; School Play; Yrbk Rptr; Yrbk Stf; Pres Sr Cls; Socr; Sftbl; Liberyt U Chncllrs Schlrshp 85; Outstndng Phltlc Clmnst Awds 84; Young Amer Freedm ST Chrmnshp 85; Liberty U; Poltcl Sci.

MAC SWEENEY, DARLENE M; Alvirne HS; Hudson, NH; (Y); 18/332; Am Leg Aux Girls St; Intnl Clb; Quiz Bowl; Teachers Aide; Sec Jr Cls; Stu Cncl; Var Capt Cheerleading; Hon Roll; Sec NHS; Supr Psychd Chrldr Awd 83-84; Tchr.

MAC SWEENEY, JOHN; Alvirne HS; Hudson, NH; (Y); 10/275; Am Leg Boys St; VP Math Tm; School Play; Trs Sr Cls; Var Bsktbl; NHS; Stu Of Yr 85; Mst Imprvd Plyr Awd Vrsty Bsktbl 85; Cntry III Ldrshp Awd Wnnr 85; Bently Coll; Acctng.

MACDONALD, SHELLEY; Inter-Lakes HS; Meredith, NH; (Y); Art Clb; Dance Clb; French Clb; High Hon Roll; NHS; Helen Pynn Memrl Hstry Awd 84; Advncd Studys Prog 85; Elem Schl Tchr.

MACKEY, BRIAN D; Dover HS; Dover, NH; (Y); Am Leg Boys St; Boy Scts; Trs Exploring; High Hon Roll; Hon Roll; Eagle Scout 83; Yth Ldrshp Amer Awd 83; U NH; Elec Engrng.

MACOMBER, ROBERTA; Alvirne HS; Hudson, NH; (Y); 12/331; Cheerleading; Trk; Hon Roll; NHS; UNH; Vet Med.

MACRI, LISA; Alvirne HS; Hudson, NH; (Y); Cmnty Wkr; Drama Clb; French Clb; Variety Show; Yrbk Ed-Chief; Im Bsktbl; Im Socr; Law.

MAGNELL, LAUREEN M; Mascoma Valley Regional HS; Enfield, NH; (Y); 15/103; French Clb; Math Tm; Yrbk Stf; Sec Jr Cls; Sec Sr Cls; JV Bsktbl; JV Sftbl; Twrlr; NHS; Ntl Merit Ltr; Wmn Engrs Awd 85; NHS Scholar 85; Pres Acad Fit Awd 85; Syracuse U; Telecmmnctns.

MAHANNA, PAM; Pittsfield HS; Pittsfield, NH; (Y); Trs Church Yth Grp; Band; Church Choir; Rep Trs Stu Cncl; Var Stat Bsktbl; Stat Fld Hcky; Mgr(s); Hon Roll; NHS; 4-H.

MAHEU, MARY; Mascoma Valley Regional HS; Enfield Ctr, NH; (Y); Var Cheerleading; Var Pom Pon; High Hon Roll; Hon Roll; Med Secy.

MAHONEY, TIM; Goffstown Area JR/SR HS; Goffstown, NH; (Y); 20/250; Ski Clb; Rep Sr Cls; Stu Cncl; Var L Socr; High Hon Roll; Hon Roll; NHS; Ntl Merit Ltr; Boy Scts; Church Yth Grp; Hnrb Mntn Excllnce Geom; St Pauls Schl Adv Studs Pgm; Genetics.

MALCOLM, TODD; Winnisquam Regional HS; Franklin, NH; (Y); Math Clb; Math Tm; Ski Clb; Var JV Socr; Hon Roll; New England Math Leag Awd Of Excllnc-1st Pl 84-85; Chem.

MALIK, DEBBIE; Manchester Memorial HS; Manchester, NH; (Y); 11/366; Sec Church Yth Grp; Drama Clb; French Clb; Teachers Aide; Yrbk Stf; High Hon Roll; NHS; St Pauls Sschl Adv Stud Pgm 85; Hnbl Mntn Schltc Wrtng Awd 83; Rep Richelieu Clb Frnch Cntst 85; Frgn Lang Tchr.

MALM, KAREN; Mascoma Valley Regional HS; Enfield, NH; (Y); Church Yth Grp; Spanish Clb; Teachers Aide; Band; Concert Band; Var Capt Cheerleading; High Hon Roll; Hon Roll; NHS; Coachs Awd Vrsty Chrldng 83-84; MVP Vrsty Chrldng 84-85; Fshn Dsgn.

MALONEY, KEVIN; Bishop Guertin HS; Merrimack, NH; (Y); 38/150; Church Yth Grp; French Clb; Im Bsktbl; Wt Lftg; Hon Roll; U Of NH; Bio.

MANN, JULIE; Pinkerton Acad; Windham, NH; (S); Church Yth Grp; Ski Clb; Band; Concert Band; Mrchg Band; Pep Band; School Musical; Hon Roll; Med.

MANWARING, SANDY; Monadnock Regional HS; Keene, NH; (Y); 28/150; Cmnty Wkr; Hosp Aide; Band; Chorus; Yrbk Stf; Var Cheerleading; JV Tennis; Hon Roll; Cls Marshall; Queens Ct; Keene ST Coll; Elem Ed.

MARCHANT, JAMES; Nute HS; Farmington, NH; (S); 1/42; French Clb; FBLA; Math Tm; School Play; Yrbk Stf; High Hon Roll; NHS; Pres Schlr; Val; Balfour Accntng I Awd 83-84; Intl Stds.

MARCHI, LISA; Alvirne HS; Hudson, NH; (Y); 3/350; Church Yth Grp; Yrbk Stf; Stu Cncl; High Hon Roll; Hon Roll; NHS; Natl Sci Merit Awd 85; Natl All-Schlstc Merit Awd 85; Zoology.

MARQUIS, KEVIN; Memorial HS; Manchester, NH; (Y); 33/393; Art Clb; Church Yth Grp; Exploring; Golf; High Hon Roll; Hon Roll; U VT; Med Tech.

MARQUIS, MARIA L; Nashua SR HS; Nashua, NH; (Y); 88/807; AFS; Pres Computer Clb; Ski Clb; Stage Crew; Variety Show; Nwsp Stf; JV Score Keeper; Hon Roll; Jr NHS; NHS; U Of NH; Bus Adm.

MARSH, SHAWN; Spaulding HS; Rochester, NH; (Y); Boy Scts; Var L Ftbl; Hon Roll; Engrng.

MARSTON, BRENDA; Concord HS; Concord, NH; (Y); 50/369; Trs Church Yth Grp; Drama Clb; School Play; Lit Mag; Hon Roll; NCTE Awd; Genl Svc Admin Awd Essay 85; Exclnce Eng 85; Effort Am Culture 84; Cmnctns.

MARTEL, PATRICIA; Mascoma Valley Regional HS; Enfield, NH; (Y); French Clb; Library Aide; Office Aide; Variety Show; Im Badmtn; Var Cheerleading; Var Crs Cntry; Var Trk; Hon Roll; People To People HS Stu Ambssdr Prgm 83; Elem Educ.

MARTEL, SCOTT; Pembroke Acad; Allentown, NH; (Y).

MARTELL, WILLIAM F; Concord HS; Concord, NH; (Y); Latin Clb; Chorus; Yrbk Stf; Var L Crs Cntry; Var L Trk; Hon Roll.

MARTIN, DAVID; Profile HS; Franconia, NH; (Y); Cmnty Wkr; Pep Clb; Capt Coach Actv; High Hon Roll; Hon Roll; Sec Frsh Cls; VP Jr Cls; JV Var Bsbl; JV Var Bsktbl; JV Socr; U Of Southern FL; Cmmnctns.

MARTIN, LYNN; Saint Thomas Awuinas HS; Eliot, ME; (Y); French Clb; Pep Clb; Nwsp Rptr; Nwsp Stf; Cheerleading; Psych.

MARTINEZ, JOSE A; Salem HS; Salem, NH; (S); 12/400; Drama Clb; Model UN; Nwsp Rptr; Trs Frsh Cls; Rep Stu Cncl; Gym; High Hon Roll; NHS; Ntl Merit Ltr; Spanish NHS; American U; Comm.

MARZLOFF, KRISTIN; The Derryfield Schl; Auburn, NH; (Y); Church Yth Grp; Drama Clb; 4-H; Chorus; School Musical; Yrbk Stf; Var Bsktbl; 4-H Awd; Hon Roll; Ntl Merit Ltr; Med.

MASON, DEBORAH; Littleton HS; Littleton, NH; (Y); Sec FBLA; Teachers Aide; Bsktbl; Fld Hcky; Sftbl; Hon Roll; Frnch I Awd 83-84; Bus Awd 84-85; Plymouth ST Clg; Bus Admin.

MASON, KRISTIN; Kennett HS; N Conway, NH; (Y); 29/200; Hosp Aide; Letterman Clb; Fld Hcky; Hon Roll; Nrsng.

MASON, MATTHEW C; Winnisquam Reginal HS; Tilton, NH; (Y); 1/95; Am Leg Boys St; Ski Clb; Variety Show; VP Lib Jr Cls; VP Sr Cls; Stu Cncl; Im Vllybl; High Hon Roll; Hon Roll; Pres NHS; US Histry & Govt Awd 84; YMCA Yth & Govt Prog 83; Vet.

MASON, MICHELLE; Orford HS; Orford, NH; (Y); Drama Clb; French Clb; School Musical; School Play; Nwsp Rptr; Yrbk Stf; Pres Jr Cls; Pres VP Jr Cls; Stu Cncl; Var Cheerleading; Miss NH Natl Teenager Pgnt 84 & 85; Royal Acad Of Modeling Partl Schlrshp 84; Nursng.

MASSARI, PAUL; Portsmouth HS; Portsmouth, NH; (S); 11/400; Math Tm; Political Wkr; Quiz Bowl; Scholastic Bowl; Pres Jr Cls; High Hon Roll; Hon Roll; NHS; Ntl Merit Ltr; JR Wrld Cncl 85; Purpl Belt Shoalin-Kempo Karate 84; Close Up Prog WA DC; Brown U; Law.

MASTERS, BROOKE A; Phillips Exeter Acad; New York, NY; (Y); Service Clb; Chorus; Stage Crew; Ed Nwsp Stf; Var Mgr(s); JV Swmmng; Var L Trk; High Hon Roll; Ntl Merit SF; Amer Hstry Prz 83-84; Eng Hstry Prz 82-83; Law.

MASTERS, LORI; Concord HS; Bow, NH; (Y); Drama Clb; Hosp Aide; Math Tm; Chorus; School Play; Stage Crew; Yrbk Stf; Rep Stu Cncl; High Hon Roll; Hon Roll; Exclnce Art,Engl Awd 84-85; RI Schl Of Desgn Pre Clg Prog 85; Art.

MATSON, CHARLOTTE; St Thomas Aquinas HS; Eliot, ME; (Y); Latin Clb; Chorus; Stage Crew; Variety Show; Nwsp Stf; Marine Bio.

MATTSON, KRISTI; Pinkerton Acad; Derry, NH; (Y); 27/441; Dance Clb; Band; Concert Band; Mrchg Band; Var Trk; Hon Roll; Ltr Of Comm Natl Merit Scholar Prgrm 83; 85 Editn Natl Hnr Roll 85; Grand Vly ST Coll ; Phys Ther.

MAYER, LLOYD H; Phillips Exeter Acad; Philadelphia, PA; (Y); Sec Computer Clb; Drama Clb; Pres Science Clb; Var Crs Cntry; JV Trk; High Hon Roll; Ntl Merit SF; Assn Amer Prof Frnch Cert Of Merit 82; PA Hghr Ed Asst Cert Of Merit 84; Phillips Exeter Acad 84; Gen Engrng.

MAYHEW, KAREN; Milford Area SR HS; Amherst, NH; (Y); Church Yth Grp; Cmnty Wkr; Dance Clb; Hon Roll; Bus Mngmnt.

MAYNARD, ELIZABETH; Pinkerton Acad; Hempstead, NY; (Y); 41/400; Civic Clb; Dance Clb; FBLA; Math Clb; Yrbk Stf; Stu Cncl; Var Swmmng; Vllybl; Hon Roll; Natl Hnr Socty Schlrshp 85; Math Tutr 82-85; Hofstra U; Lib Arts.

MAYO, LISA; Kingswood Regional HS; New Durham, NH; (Y); French Clb; Yrbk Stf; High Hon Roll; Hon Roll; Law.

MAZIARZ, JEFFREY J; Salem HS; Salem, NH; (S); Latin Clb; Teachers Aide; High Hon Roll; Hon Roll.

MAZUR, PATRICIA J; Winnisquam HS; Tilton, NH; (Y); Am Leg Aux Girls St; Ski Clb; Rep Soph Cls; Stu Cncl; JV Cheerleading; Var Fld Hcky; Var Sftbl; Bus Mgmt.

MC ALARY, PATRICK; Goffstown HS; Goffstown, NH; (Y); 3/220; Computer Clb; Exploring; Math Tm; Varsity Clb; Off Frsh Cls; Bsktbl; Socr; High Hon Roll; NHS; Bio Awd 83; Chem, Geom & Algeb II Awds 84; Princeton U; Bio Med.

MC BIRDE, AMANDA; Farmington HS; Farmington, NH; (S); Church Yth Grp; Drama Clb; Band; Rep Frsh Cls; Rep Soph Cls; Rep Jr Cls; Score Keeper; Sftbl; Hon Roll; Soc Wrkr.

MC CABE, BRIAN S; Laconia HS; Laconia, NH; (Y); Am Leg Boys St; Trs Key Clb; Quiz Bowl; Yrbk Sprt Ed; Var Ftbl; VP Capt Tennis; Wt Lftg; Hon Roll; Am Leg Oratrcl Cont ST Fnlst 84; Pres Clsrm WA D C 85; Bus.

MC CABE JR, EDMUND JAMES; Dover HS; Dover, NH; (Y); Pres Am Leg Boys St; Church Yth Grp; Political Wkr; Church Choir; School Play; Elks Awd; Hon Roll; Prfct Atten Awd; Civics Cls Tm Capt 82-83; Law Cls Tm Capt 84-85; Western World Hstry Tm Capt 83-84; St Anselm; Tchr.

MC CALL, DARRYLL A; Conant HS; Jaffrey, NH; (Y); Am Leg Boys St; Band; Mrchg Band; Pep Band; Var Socr; JV Trk; Hon Roll; Williams.

MC CALLISTER, SUSAN; Nute HS; Milton, NH; (S); 2/42; Sec FBLA; Yrbk Bus Mgr; Yrbk Ed-Chief; Trs Frsh Cls; Rep Soph Cls; Pres Trs Stu Cncl; High Hon Roll; NHS; Sal; Sec Art Clb; Blfr Sci Hist & Yrbk Awds 82-84; Accntng.

MC CANN, KEVIN; Trinity HS; Manchester, NH; (Y); 19/161; Computer Clb; Math Clb; Math Tm; Model UN; Trk; Hon Roll; Pres NHS; Ntl Merit Ltr; NEDT Awd; Aero Engrng.

MC CLAIN, CHRISTOPHER J; Londonderry HS; Londonderry, NH; (Y); VP French Clb; Drama Clb; School Play; Yrbk Stf; Ntl Merit SF; NEDT Awd; Hon Roll; U Of Rochester; Physics.

MC COOLE, KAREN; Dover HS; Dover, NH; (Y); 27/275; JV Capt Bsktbl; Var L Sftbl; High Hon Roll; Phrmcy.

MC CORMICK, SHAWN; Salem HS; Salem, NH; (S); 15/363; Aud/Vis; Drama Clb; Letterman Clb; Model UN; School Play; Nwsp Rptr; Var Ftbl; JV Trk; High Hon Roll; Hon Roll; Voice Of Dem 82; U Of SC; Telecmnctns.

MC CRACKEN, KRISTEN; Kennett HS; Freedom, NH; (Y); 24/204; Drama Clb; Key Clb; Math Tm; Spanish Clb; Chorus; Madrigals; Rep Stu Cncl; Stat Sftbl; Var Tennis; Hon Roll; Spnsh I Awd 84; Spnsh II Awd 85; Engrng.

MC DEVITT, MELISSA; Spaulding HS; Rochester, NH; (S); 48/388; Church Yth Grp; Band; Church Choir; Jazz Band; Mrchg Band; Pep Band; Rep Jr Cls; Sftbl; Trk; Hon Roll; Health.

MC DONALD, HOLLY; Kennett HS; N Conway, NH; (Y); Exploring; Library Aide; Math Tm; Hon Roll.

MC DONALD, PAM; Winnisquam Regional HS; Tilton, NH; (Y); Chorus.

MC DONALD, SUSAN; Timberlane Regional HS; Plaistow, NH; (Y); VP Church Yth Grp; Model UN; Ski Clb; Band; Mrchg Band; Yrbk Stf; JV Fld Hcky; Tennis; U NH; Law.

MC GHEE, NANCY J; Merrimack HS; Merrimack, NH; (Y); 20/250; Church Yth Grp; VP Chorus; Concert Band; Jazz Band; Mrchg Band; School Musical; Swing Chorus; Variety Show; Var Fld Hcky; Hnbl Mntn Music Natl Fndtn Advncmnt Arts 85; U Miami; Jazz Vocal.

MC GINNIS, JOY; Pinkerton Acad; Hampstead, NH; (Y); 12/441; Dance Clb; Drama Clb; JA; JCL; Latin Clb; Ski Clb; Rep Sr Cls; 4-H Awd; Hon Roll; NHS; Math Achvt Awd 83; NH ST Champ Gymstcs 83; Ballet Hnrs 84; Oral Roberts U; Chld Psychlgy.

MC GIVERN, SHAWN; Bishop Guertin HS; Hudson, NH; (Y); 14/152; Cmnty Wkr; Bsbl; Bsktbl; JV Crs Cntry; High Hon Roll; Hon Roll; NHS; CYO ST Bsktbll Trmnt All Trny Tm, Rnnrup 85.

MC GRATH, ROBERT K; Nashua SR HS; Nashua, NH; (Y); Am Leg Boys St; FCA; Pep Clb; Pres Frsh Cls; Pres Sr Cls; Off Stu Cncl; JV Bsbl; JV Var Ftbl; Trk; Law.

MC GREGOR, JOHN; Hopkinton HS; Contoocook, NH; (Y); Hon Roll; Aviatn.

MC GRODY, FRANCIS; Hanover HS; Hanover, NH; (Y); AFS; German Clb; Spanish Clb; Var L Ftbl; Archtctr.

MC GUIRE, LIS; Hillsboro-Deering Coop; Hillsboro, NH; (Y); 7/59; Math Tm; Teachers Aide; Yrbk Ed-Chief; Pres Jr Cls; Pres Sr Cls; Hon Roll; NHS; Plymouth ST Coll; Comp Sci.

MC HALE, JUDY; Portsmouth HS; Portsmouth, NH; (Y); Ski Clb; Stage Crew; JV Fld Hcky; Mgr(s); High Hon Roll; Hon Roll; Bus Admin.

MC KENNA, KIMBERLY A; Pinkerton Acad; Derry, NH; (Y); Girl Scts; Math Clb; School Musical; Rep Jr Cls; Rep Sr Cls; Hon Roll; Abraham Burtman Trst Schlrshp 85; Ntl Hnr Roll 85; Daemen Coll; Phy Thrpst.

MC LAUGHLIN, BETH; Hanover HS; Lebanon, NH; (Y); Drama Clb; Stage Crew; Nwsp Ed-Chief; Yrbk Stf; Im Fld Hcky; Hon Roll; Cert Merit Amer Assn Profsrs Frnch 85; Cmmnctns.

MC NALLY, SHANNON; Spaulding HS; Rochester, NH; (Y); Boys Clb Am; Dance Clb; Library Aide; Office Aide; Chorus; Cheerleading; Hon Roll; Prfct Atten Awd; Comp Sci.

MC NULTY, MARGARET; Portsmouth HS; Portsmouth, NH; (Y); Pres Church Yth Grp; Nrsg.

MC PHILLIPS, MARY R; Pinkerton Acad; Windham, NH; (Y); 3/435; Latin Clb; Ski Clb; Pres Sr Cls; Pres Stu Cncl; DAR Awd; Elks Awd; NHS; Church Yth Grp; Cmnty Wkr; Debate Tm; SADD Pres; Century III Ldrshp Comp ST Alt; Stu Yr; Wells Coll; Corp Law.

MC SHANE, ELIZABETH CAROL; Salem HS; Salem, NH; (S); 1/391; Church Yth Grp; French Clb; Girl Scts; Hosp Aide; Latin Clb; Model UN; Church Choir; High Hon Roll; NHS; Hghst Acad Avg In Cls 83 & 84; Frnch Acad Awd 84; Boston Coll; Pre-Med.

MC VICAR, KAREN; Nute HS; Milton, NH; (S); 7/44; FBLA; Girl Scts; Latin Clb; Band; Chorus; Jazz Band; Mrchg Band; Yrbk Stf; Sec Soph Cls; Sec Jr Cls; Culinary Arts.

MEACHAM, MICHAEL; Pembroke Acad; Suncook, NH; (Y); Boy Scts; Church Yth Grp; FFA; Var Bsktbl; JV Socr; Hon Roll.

MEAD, MATTHEW; Concord HS; Concord, NH; (Y); Church Yth Grp; Cmnty Wkr; Variety Show; Nwsp Rptr; Nwsp Stf; Engl.

MEARS, JENNIFER; Belmont HS; Canterbury, NH; (S); 2/80; VP French Clb; Math Tm; Varsity Clb; Band; Pep Band; VP Jr Cls; Sec Stu Cncl; JV Var Bsktbl; Var Crs Cntry; Trk.

MEDRICK, STEPHEN; Derryfield Schl; Merrimack, NH; (Y); Aud/Vis; Computer Clb; Exploring; German Clb; Intnl Clb; Science Clb; Ski Clb; Hon Roll; L Ice Hcky; Var Lcrss; Merit Scholar Comp 85; Engrng.

MELANSON, LISA; Timberlane Regional HS; Sandown, NH; (Y); Model UN; Teachers Aide; Yrbk Sprt Ed; Trs Frsh Cls; VP Soph Cls; VP Jr Cls; Rep Sr Cls; Var Bsktbl; Var Capt Sftbl; Hon Roll; Widener U; Polt Sci.

MELLETT, JENNIFER L; Lin-Wood Public Schl; N Woodstock, NH; (S); 6/21; Church Yth Grp; VP FBLA; Band; Chorus; Church Choir; Pep Band; Stage Crew; Rep Soph Cls; Sec Trs Stu Cncl; Hon Roll; Hugh O Brien Yth Fndtn Ldrshp Sem/Outstndng Soph 83-84; Yth Gvrnmnt 83-85; Prz Spkng 1st Pl Awd 82-83.

MERCER, GREG; Oyster River HS; Madbury, NH; (Y); 6/130; Church Yth Grp; Math Tm; Red Cross Aide; Ski Clb; Var L Crs Cntry; JV Var Trk; High Hon Roll; Ntl Merit SF; Boy Scts; Latin Clb; Air Force ROTC Schlrshp 85; Natl Merit Fnlst 85; Cornell U; Elec Engrng.

MEROTH, WENDY; Epping HS; Epping, NH; (Y); 5/60; Church Yth Grp; French Clb; Chorus; Church Choir; School Musical; Sec Soph Cls; Sec Sr Cls; Bsktbl; Cit Awd; DAR Awd; 2nd US Hist Term Paper Cntst ST Of NH 84; U Of NH; Music.

MERRIHEW, MICHAEL; Spaulding HS; Rochester, NH; (S); Var Tennis; High Hon Roll; Hon Roll; NHS; NH Tech Inst; Arch.

MERRILL, GREGORY; Littleton HS; Littleton, NH; (Y); 3/98; Rep Frsh Cls; Trs Soph Cls; Pres Jr Cls; Pres Sr Cls; Rep Stu Cncl; Crs Cntry; High Hon Roll; NHS; Voice Dem Awd; St Pauls Schl Advncd Stud Pgm 85; Supr Rnkng Advncd Bio St Pauls Schl 85; Dartmouth; Med.

METES, DANA; Manchester Central HS; Manchester, NH; (Y); 49/409; Ed Yrbk Stf; Rep Frsh Cls; Rep Stu Cncl; Var Crs Cntry; Citatn Svc Manchester Untd Way; Law.

METIVIER, LISE; Manchester Memorial HS; Manchester, NH; (Y); French Clb; Ski Clb; Teachers Aide; Chorus; Variety Show; Rep Stu Cncl; Var Cheerleading; CAP; Hon Roll; Barbizon Schl Of Modelng Schlrshp 84; NH Technel Inst; Dental Hygn.

MICALI, PAUL; Bishop Guertin HS; Merrimack, NH; (Y); 68/151; Church Yth Grp; FCA; Var L Bsbl; Var L Bsktbl; Var L Ftbl; Coachs Awd 82; Natl Athl Plcmnt 85; Accntng.

MICHAELS, JULIE; Co-Brown Acad; Strafford, NH; (Y); FFA; Girl Scts; Hosp Aide; Band; Concert Band; Mrchg Band; Orch; Hon Roll; Nursing.

MICHAUD, CELESTE; Presentation Of Mary Acad; Nashua, NH; (Y); Cmnty Wkr; Drama Clb; French Clb; Ski Clb; Variety Show; Trs Sr Cls; Hon Roll; Jr NHS; NHS; Science Clb; Natl Frnch Cont Wnnr; Assumption Coll; Intl Bus.

MICHIE, ALAN; Milford Area HS; Amherst, NH; (Y); Art Clb; Chorus; School Play; Nwsp Stf; Yrbk Stf; Hon Roll; Bus Mgmnt.

MILES, RUSSELL; Spaulding HS; E Rochester, NH; (Y); Yrbk Stf; VP Frsh Cls; VP Soph Cls; VP Jr Cls; Var L Socr; Hon Roll; NHS; Ntl Merit Ltr; Proj Srch 84-85; George A Hattie A Pray Schlrshp 85; Pres Acad Ftns Awd 85; UNH; Mech Engr.

MILEWSKI, DAWN MICHELE; Nashua SR HS; Nashua, NH; (Y); 25/807; Am Leg Aux Girls St; Key Clb; Chorus; School Musical; School Play; Yrbk Stf; Cit Awd; Hon Roll; NHS; Spanish NHS.

MILLER, ELLEN; White Mtns Regional HS; Whitefield, NH; (Y); 1/114; Drama Clb; Spanish Clb; Y-Teens; Trs Jr Cls; Trs Sr Cls; Var Mgr(s); JV Var Score Keeper; Hon Roll; NHS; Prncpls Awd 85; Ntl JR Sci & Hmnts 85; Physcl Thrpy.

MILLER, KAREN; Mascoma Valley Regional HS; Canaan, NH; (Y); Pres Church Yth Grp; 4-H; French Clb; Math Tm; Teachers Aide; Band; Church Choir; Concert Band; Mrchg Band; Trs Frsh Cls; Bus.

MILLER, KEVIN DAVID; Salem HS; Salem, NH; (Y); Ski Clb; High Hon Roll; Hon Roll; Ntl Merit Ltr; U Of Lowell MA; Elec Engrng.

MILLIKEN, ERIC; Pembroke Academy; Suncook, NH; (Y); Chess Clb; 4-H; FBLA; Spanish Clb; Hon Roll; Comp Pgmmng.

MILLS, CHRISTOPHER D; Contoocook Valley Regional HS; Weare, NH; (Y); 39/147; 4-H; Concert Band; Mrchg Band; Orch; Nwsp Stf; Lit Mag; JV Socr; High Hon Roll; Hon Roll; 4th Horn NH All ST Orch 85; Portland Schl Art; Visl Arts.

MILLS, DEIRDRE; St Thomas Aquinas HS; Kittery, ME; (Y); 17/86; Orch; Yrbk Ed-Chief; Church Yth Grp; Debate Tm; Latin Clb; Yrbk Stf; Prfct Atten Awd; NH All-ST Orch 84-85; Natl Yth Event Delg 84; UCC Gen Synod Yth Delg 85; Bates Coll.

MILLS, POLLY; Belmont HS; Canterbury, NH; (S); 5/80; Trs French Clb; Ski Clb; Varsity Clb; Band; Pep Band; Trk; Var Vllybl; Hon Roll; NHS; Vrsty Track MVP 83.

MINTON, NORA; Kennett HS; Jackson, NH; (Y); 31/160; AFS; Drama Clb; Girl Scts; School Play; Rep Frsh Cls; Var L Tennis; Hon Roll; Mst Vlbl Plyr Tennis 85; Frgn Lng.

MITCHELL, BRYAN; Londonderry HS; Londonderry, NH; (Y); Var Crs Cntry; JV Ftbl; JV Lcrss; Var Trk; Hon Roll; Engr.

MITCHELL, CHERYL A; Timerlane Regional HS; Atkinson, NH; (Y); 26/211; Church Yth Grp; German Clb; Yrbk Stf; JV Bsktbl; Capt Fld Hcky; Var Trk; Hon Roll; NHS; Outstndng Athlt Awd 82; Timberlane Alumni Schlrsp 85; Keene ST Coll; Drftng.

MLOCEK, JONATHAN; Salem HS; Salem, NH; (S); 11/405; Church Yth Grp; Cmnty Wkr; Model UN; Trk; High Hon Roll; Med.

MOLLICA, MARISA; Concord HS; Concord, NH; (Y); 47/329; Hosp Aide; Concert Band; Ed Yrbk Stf; JV Trk; High Hon Roll; Hon Roll; NHS.

MONIGLE, DEBBIE; Milford Area SR HS; Amherst, NH; (Y); Church Yth Grp; Acpl Chr; Chorus; School Musical; U NH.

MONSON, ELIZABETH; The Derryfield Schl; Bedford, NH; (Y); Cmnty Wkr; Dance Clb; Drama Clb; Ski Clb; Chorus; School Musical; School Play; Stage Crew; Lit Mag; VP Soph Cls; Med.

MOODY, CARIANNE; Pembroke Acad; Chichester, NH; (Y); Drama Clb; Pres 4-H; Chorus; Variety Show; Yrbk Stf; Pres Soph Cls; Co-Capt Cheerleading; Sftbl; 4-H Awd; Hon Roll; Bus.

MOODY, KIM; Weare HS; Weare, NH; (S); Nwsp Stf; VP Frsh Cls; Trs Soph Cls; High Hon Roll; Hon Roll; NHS; Acad All-Amer 84.

MOONEY, RISHLENE N; Tilton HS; Tilton, NH; (S); 1/79; Church Yth Grp; Drama Clb; Math Tm; Ski Clb; Church Choir; School Musical; Stage Crew; Yrbk Stf; Var Capt Lcrss; Var Socr; Faculty Wives Prz 83-84; Burnham Chem Awd 83-84; Cornell U; Biochem Engr.

MOORE, MEGAN B; Phillips Exeter Acad; Berkeley, CA; (Y); Pres Computer Clb; JV Socr; High Hon Roll; Ntl Merit SF; Mathletes; Im Bsktbl; Im Lcrss; Hon Roll; Calculus Prz 83-84; Chem.

MOREAU, JOSEPH; Dover HS; Dover, NH; (Y); 2/350; Am Leg Boys St; French Clb; Var Trk; High Hon Roll; NCTE Awd; NHS; Sal; Beta Sigma Phi Schlrshp 85; U S Hstry & Gv Awd 84; U Of NH; Jrnlsm.

MORGAN, MAUREEN MOLLY; Spaulding SR HS; Rochester, NH; (Y); Church Yth Grp; Political Wkr; Hon Roll; Lilac Mall Art Showngs 83-85; Plymouth ST Tchrs Coll Art Showngs 84; NHAAE Art Wknd Dartmouth 85; Colby/Sawyer Coll; Engl.

MORIN, ANGELA; Concord HS; Concord, NH; (Y); 13/326; Church Yth Grp; Math Tm; Orch; Yrbk Bus Mgr; Var Tennis; High Hon Roll; NHS; Teachers Aide; Outstndng Achvt Acclrtd Gemtry 83; Outstndng Perfmn Adv Algbr II 84; Outstndng Perfmn Englsh 84-85; Bus Adm.

MORIN, MARC; Gilford HS; Gilford, NH; (S); 1/107; Computer Clb; German Clb; Math Tm; Q&S; Nwsp Ed-Chief; Trs Sr Cls; Var L Bsbl; Camera Clb; Church Yth Grp; Nwsp Rptr; Dartmouth Club Book Awd; DAR Good Citizen; Engrng.

MORIN, SCOTT; Memorial HS; Manchester, NH; (Y); 27/366; Var Crs Cntry; Engr.

MORNEAU, ROLAND JOE; Farmington HS; Farmington, NH; (Y); 6/69; Am Leg Boys St; Church Yth Grp; Socr; Hon Roll; NHS; Sal; Mrshl For Grad 84; Dlrs For Schlrs Awd 85; FHS Wntr Crnvl 82-85; NH Vo Tech Inst; Ind Electrncs.

MORRISON, JENNIFER; Hanover HS; Hanover, NH; (Y); Chorus; Yrbk Bus Mgr; JV Var Bsktbl; Var Capt Socr; Var Capt Sftbl; High Hon Roll; Cmnty Wkr; French Clb; Acpl Chr; All Star Soccer Team 82-84; NH All ST Soccer Team 82-84; All Star Bsktbl Team 84-85; Foreign Lang.

MORRISON, SHERRI; Timberlane Regional HS; Plaistow, NH; (Y); French Clb; Teachers Aide; Ed Yrbk Stf; Var Capt Cheerleading; Mgr(s); Hon Roll; NHS; Chrldr Of Yr 84; Hnr Guard 84; Boston U.

MORSE, BERNARD L; Plymouth Area HS; Campton, NH; (Y); Boy Scts; Military.

MORSE, DONALD E; Memorial HS; Manchester, NH; (Y); 19/366; Golf; High Hon Roll; Hon Roll; Comp.

MORSE, KAREN; Pembroke Acad; Concord, NH; (Y); Church Yth Grp; Exploring; VP Spanish Clb; Band; Concert Band; Stu Cncl; Cheerleading; Hon Roll; All-Amer Acdmc Hnrs 85; Psychlgy.

MORTON, CHRISTINE; Timberlane Regional HS; Atkinson, NH; (Y); Church Yth Grp; German Clb; Teachers Aide; Band; Church Choir; Concert Band; Jazz Band; Mrchg Band; Pep Band; JV Bsktbl; Hosp Lab Tech.

MOULTON, ROBERT; Nashua HS; Nashua, NH; (Y); 225/925; Am Leg Boys St; JV Bsbl; JV Ftbl; Var Ice Hcky; U NH; Bus.

MOUSHEGIAN, MICHAEL; Bishop Guertin HS; Nashua, NH; (Y); 70/200; Nwsp Rptr; Yrbk Ed-Chief; Bsktbl; Var Crs Cntry; Var Trk; High Hon Roll; Computer Clb; Var Swmmng; Founder & Pres Table Ten Clb 83-84; SADD 84-85; Aerontcs.

MOYER, JENNIFER; Pinkerton Acad; Hampstead, NH; (Y); Aud/Vis; Pres 4-H; Pres FFA; Quiz Bowl; Band; School Musical; 4-H Awd; 4-H Chicago Trp 84; FFA Kansas Cty Trp 83; ST Lvstck Tm Harrisburg Trp 84; Frstry Tm WV Trp 83; Bio.

MUDGE, KRISTINE P; Manchester Memorial HS; Manchester, NH; (Y); Sec Church Yth Grp; French Clb; Teachers Aide; Powder Puff Ftbl; Elem Ed.

MUELLER, SCOTT A; Salem HS; Salem, NH; (S); 52/405; Church Yth Grp; German Clb; Math Tm; Model UN; Band; Concert Band; Jazz Band; Mrchg Band; Pep Band; Hon Roll; Seige Prls Awd 83; Chlnge Pgm 84-85; Accntnt.

MULLALY, BRENDAN; Portsmouth HS; Portsmouth, NH; (S); 2/425; Math Tm; Band; Concert Band; Drm Mjr(t); Jazz Band; Mrchg Band; JV Var Bsbl; JV Bsktbl; High Hon Roll; NHS; Dartmouth; Engrng.

MULLEN, DONALD; Concord HS; Concord, NH; (Y); Am Leg Boys St; Boy Scts; Church Yth Grp; FCA; Varsity Clb; Church Choir; Variety Show; Yrbk Stf; Rep Stu Cncl; Var L Ftbl; Awd Prfcncy Law 85; U Systm Of UNH; ROTC.

MUNROE, YVETTE; Hillsboro-Deering HS; Hillsboro, NH; (S); Teachers Aide; Rep Stu Cncl; JV Cheerleading; Hon Roll; Prfct Atten Awd; U NH; Hlth.

MURPHY, ERIN; St Thomas Aquinas HS; Rye Bch, NH; (Y); 12/87; Debate Tm; Sec French Clb; Sec Key Clb; Latin Clb; Co-Capt Yrbk Ed-Chief; DAR Awd; High Hon Roll; Hon Roll; NHS; Awd For Excllnc In Engl, Frnch II, Frnch III, Frnch IV & Latin II 83-85; Miss NH Teengr 85; Hosp Admin.

MURPHY, KATHLEEN; Kennett HS; N Conway, NH; (Y); 10/204; AFS; Am Leg Aux Girls St; French Clb; Girl Scts; Ski Clb; Crs Cntry; Fld Hcky; Trk; DAR Awd; French Hon Soc; Yth & Govt 84 & 85; Ski Miester 85; Boudoin; Math Educ.

MURPHY, KATHLEEN; West HS; Bedford, NH; (Y); 98/361; Ski Clb; Capt Cheerleading; Mgr(s); Hon Roll; U Of NH; Bus.

MURPHY, KELLY; Winnisguam Regional HS; Laconia, NH; (Y); Math Tm; Ski Clb; Drm & Bgl; Capt Var Bsktbl; Capt Var Sftbl; Capt Var Vllybl; Hon Roll; Robt H & Gertrude E Sedgley Chartble Fndtn Awd 85; Athl Cncl Awd 85; Endicott Coll; Trvl & Trsm.

MURPHY, MICHELE; Memorial HS; Manchester, NH; (Y); 111/366; Lit Mag; Cheerleading; Powder Puff Ftbl; U Of NH; Bus Mgmt.

MURRAY, GERRIANN; Salem HS; Salem, NH; (S); 48/363; Church Yth Grp; Debate Tm; Hosp Aide; Key Clb; Ski Clb; Spanish Clb; Band; Concert Band; Drm Mjr(t); Mrchg Band; All-St Band 81-82; Mvp Jv Bsktbll 82-83; Sadd Chairprsn 84-85; Phys Thrpy.

MURRAY, MICHAEL; Bishop Guertin HS; Salem, NH; (Y); Boys Clb Am; Capt FCA; Key Clb; Var Bsktbl; Var Socr; Var Trk; Hon Roll; Gld Medl Phy Ed 82; Pres Phy Fit Awd 82; Bus.

MUSCARELLA, LORI; Salem HS; Salem, NH; (Y); JV Trk; Hon Roll; Ntl Spnsh Exam Awd 85; Yth Assoc For Retrd Ctzn Grp 82-83; Rivier Coll; Ed.

MUSIAL, MELISSA; Manchester Memorial HS; Manchester, NH; (Y); 43/366; Spanish Clb; Variety Show; Lit Mag; Capt JV Sftbl; High Hon Roll; Hon Roll; St Josphs Coll; Nrsng.

MYERS, ROBIN; Portsmouth SR HS; Portsmouth, NH; (Y); Church Yth Grp; Chorus; Church Choir; Color Guard; Stage Crew; High Hon Roll; Hon Roll; Alice M Lee Schlrshp 85; Keene ST Coll; Spcl Ed.

NADEAU, COURTNEY LYNNE; Portsmouth HS; Portsmouth, NH; (Y); NH Rsrv Chmp In Sdl Seat Equitation 83-84; Grnf Ntl Equestrian Eventing 83-85; U Of VT; Equine Rsrch.

NADEAU, MATTHEW; Berlin HS; Milan, NH; (Y); Boy Scts; Church Yth Grp; Eagle Sct 84; Ad-Altere Dei Hghst Relgs Awd 82; Engr.

NADEAU, WILFRED; Spaulding HS; Rochester, NH; (S); Computer Clb; High Hon Roll; Hon Roll; NHS; NH Coll; Accntng.

NARASIMHAN, MICHAEL; Salem HS; Salem, NH; (S); 30/405; Boys Clb Am; Model UN; Ski Clb; Var Mgr Bsktbl; Var Crs Cntry; High Hon Roll; Hon Roll; Yth Of The Yr 84; Ivory Leag Schl; Math.

NASS, CHRIS A; Berwick Acad; Milton Hills, NH; (Y); 6/33; Boy Scts; Var Crs Cntry; JV Socr; Hon Roll; Ntl Merit Ltr; Mech Engrng.

NAULT, DARLENE; Salem HS; Salem, NH; (S); Teachers Aide; High Hon Roll; Comp.

NEALEY, PAMELA JEAN; Salem HS; Salem, NH; (Y); French Clb; Key Clb; Ski Clb; Band; Concert Band; Mrchg Band; Pep Band; High Hon Roll; Hon Roll; Nrs.

NELSON, DAVID; Pinkerton Acad; E Hampstead, NH; (Y); Boy Scts; Sec Pres 4-H; FBLA; Rep Jr Cls; Cit Awd; Dnfth Awd; Bus Math 3rd Pl Trphy 83; Acctng.

NELSON, DONNA; Milford Area HS; Milford, NH; (Y); Church Yth Grp; Band; Concert Band; Mrchg Band; Im Ftbl; Im Vllybl; U Of NH; Phy Ed.

NEMETH, JAMES M; Lin-Wood HS; Lincoln, NH; (S); 1/17; Math Tm; Jazz Band; Yrbk Ed-Chief; Pres Soph Cls; Pres Jr Cls; Var Capt Bsbl; Var L Bsktbl; Var Capt Socr; High Hon Roll; NHS; Dartmouth Coll; Advtsng.

NEWCOMB, ROSS J; Conval Regional HS; Hancock, NH; (Y); 37/163; Art Clb; VP Church Yth Grp; Hon Roll; Ntl Merit SF; U Of ME At Oreno.

NEWELL III, RONALD; Pembroke Acad; Suncook, NH; (Y); 17/175; Exploring; Red Cross Aide; Var L Socr; Hon Roll; Top Stu-Frnch I & Chem 82-83; Hnr Roll All Yr 82-84; Plymouth ST Coll; Sci.

NEWMAN, SPENCER; Perryfield HS; Bedford, NH; (Y); Am Leg Boys St; Science Clb; Ski Clb; Stage Crew; Ed Nwsp Stf; Yrbk Phtg; Rep Stu Cncl; Socr; High Hon Roll; NHS; Samuel Green Am Hist Awd 85.

NEWMAN, TAMI; Alvirne HS; Hudson, NH; (Y); 9/331; Ski Clb; Var Cheerleading; High Hon Roll; Hon Roll; NHS; Varsity Clb; U NH; Bus.

NIEWALD, THOMAS L; Laconia HS; Laconia, NH; (S); 5/150; Drama Clb; Math Tm; Quiz Bowl; Ski Clb; Band; Jazz Band; Im Wrstlng; Hon Roll; NHS; Ntl Merit SF; Army ROTC 4-Yr Schlrshp 85-89; Engrng.

NOBLE, JEFF; Franklin HS; Franklin, NH; (Y); 14/100; French Clb; JV Trk; High Hon Roll; Hon Roll; NHS; Prfct Atten Awd; Elec Engr.

NOEL, JOY C; Salem HS; Salem, NH; (Y); Model UN; Ski Clb; Band; Mrchg Band; JV Trk; Hon Roll; UNH; Sci.

NOLAN, DANIEL A; Salem HS; Salem, NH; (S); 15/405; Math Tm; Model UN; Ski Clb; Elks Awd; High Hon Roll; Hon Roll; Comp Sci.

NOOHAN, SANDY; Fall Mt Reg HS; Alstead, NH; (Y); 5/155; Camera Clb; Drama Clb; French Clb; Color Guard; Yrbk Stf; Bsktbl; Crs Cntry; Trk; Hon Roll; SYRACUSE U; Mktng Mngmnt.

NORRIS, GEOFFREY S; Nashua HS; Nashua, NH; (Y); 30/900; Am Leg Boys St; Church Yth Grp; Science Clb; Debate Tm; JV Capt Bsktbl; High Hon Roll; Hon Roll; Jr NHS; NHS; Spanish NHS; MVP Bsktbl Tm 83; Bus.

NORRIS, LYN ELIZABETH; Salem HS; Salem, NH; (Y); Sec Key Clb; Chrmn Model UN; Off Ski Clb; School Play; Ed Yrbk Phtg; Yrbk Stf; Var Fld Hcky; Var Capt Trk; Hon Roll; School Play; Mrs Arnold Dexter Otis Womens Club & NH Fed 85; Coaches Aw Girls Sprng Trck 83, Fld Hcky 84; U Of NH; Occptnl Thrpy.

NORTON, JAMES P; Salem HS; Salem, NH; (S); 11/405; Model UN; Trk; French Hon Soc; High Hon Roll; Challng Prog 84-85.

NORTON, KELLY JON; Winnisquam Regional HS; Laconia, NH; (Y); 4/77; Math Clb; Math Tm; Band; Jazz Band; Mrchg Band; Pep Band; Var Capt Socr; Var NHS; Prfct Atten Awd; Rensselaer Poly Inst; Mngmt.

NORWOOD, HEATHER; Spaulding HS; Rochester, NH; (S); 42/425; Concert Band; Drm & Bgl; Mrchg Band; Symp Band; Hon Roll; Church Yth Grp; 4-H; Girl Scts; Band; Pep Band; Mac Intosh Coll; Bus Sec.

NOSEWORTHY, RUSSELL; Portsmouth SR HS; Newington, NH; (S); 8/362; JA; Latin Clb; Math Tm; High Hon Roll; NHS; Ntl Merit SF; Elec Engrng.

NUTILE, CHRISTOPHER A; Bishop Guertin HS; Nashua, NH; (Y); Am Leg Boys St; Church Yth Grp; FCA; JV Ftbl; JV Trk; Wt Lftg; Dnfth Awd; Pres SADD 84-85; Scholar Amer Yth Fndtn Ldrshp Conf 84-85; Mayors Task Force 84-85; Pol Sci.

NYHAN, KEITH; Concord HS; Concord, NH; (Y); 23/329; Ftbl; Trk; High Hon Roll; NHS; Latin Hnr Scty 83-84.

O CONNOR, PATRICIA ANNE; Salem HS; Salem, NH; (S); 63/363; Girl Scts; Trs Spanish Clb; Lib Band; Concert Band; Mrchg Band; Pep Band; Nwsp Stf; Yrbk Stf; Twrlr; Hon Roll; Ntl Spnsh Exam Cert 83-84; Miss Majorette 1st Rnnr-Up 84; Nrthrn Esseex CC; Chldhd Dev.

O DEA, CHRISTINE; Portsmouth HS; Portsmouth, NH; (S); Political Wkr; School Musical; School Play; Stage Crew; High Hon Roll; NHS; Church Yth Grp; Drama Clb; Hon Roll; Ntl Hnr Soc JR Chrprsn Fall Conv 84; Prd Asst Schl Plys 83-84; Gentc Engrng.

O HARA, DWIGHT; Hanover HS; Hanover, NH; (Y); Cmnty Wkr; Latin Clb; Quiz Bowl; JV Ftbl; Var JV Ice Hcky; JV Trk; High Hon Roll; Hon Roll; Ntl Merit Ltr; Jrnlsm.

O HEARN, SCOTT; Fall Mountain Regional HS; Alstead, NH; (Y); 1/160; Trs Drama Clb; Pres Latin Clb; Chorus; Concert Band; Jazz Band; Madrigals; School Musical; Yrbk Stf; Var Crs Cntry; NHS; Dartmouth Book Awd 83-84; Psych.

O NEIL III, MICHAEL F; Winnacunnet HS; N Hampton, NH; (Y); 50/284; Sec Chorus; Swing Chorus; Nwsp Stf; High Hon Roll; Hon Roll; Natl Schl Chrl Awd 85; Seacoast Educ Assn 85; NH All St Chrs & Jazz All St Chorus 84-85; AZ ST U; Bus Admin.

O REILLEY, HEATHER; Londonderry HS; Londonderry, NH; (Y); Dance Clb; Drama Clb; Hosp Aide; Math Tm; Color Guard; Rep Frsh Cls; Trs Jr Cls; Rep Sr Cls; JV Bsktbl; Hon Roll; 2nd & 3rd Pls In Dnc Amer Comp 84; New Englnd Math Leag Awd 85.

O ROURKE II, GERARD P; Alton Central HS; Laconia, NH; (Y); Am Leg Boys St; Drama Clb; Pres Intnl Clb; School Play; Stage Crew; Pres Frsh Cls; Pres Jr Cls; Hon Roll; NHS; Law.

O ROURKE, KEVIN J; West HS; Manchester, NH; (Y); 87/364; Boy Scts; ROTC; Pres VICA; Stage Crew; Hon Roll; Douglas Mac Arthur Awd 85; Hnr Cadet ROTC 85; NH Tech Inst; Arch.

O ROURKE, PATRICK; Bishop Guertin HS; Amherst, NH; (Y); 35/150; Computer Clb; Key Clb; Ski Clb; Im Bsktbl; Im JV Socr; JV Trk; Hon Roll; SADD 85; Arch.

O SHEA, KEVIN M; St Thomas Aquinas HS; Madbury, NH; (Y); 75/97; Am Leg Boys St; Debate Tm; VP Drama Clb; NFL; Pres Frsh Cls; Pres Sr Cls; Rep Stu Cncl; VP Socr; Gov Hon Prg Awd; Eagle Sct, BSA 83; NH ST Chmp Am Leg Oratrcl Cont 85; Providence Coll; Polit Sci.

O SULLIVAN, MARYELIZABETH; Portsmouth SR HS; Portsmouth, NH; (Y); Model UN; Flag Corp; Yrbk Stf; Navy; Bus.

OLECHNOWICZ, BECKY J; Portsmouth HS; Portsmouth, NH; (Y); High Hon Roll; U Of NH; Frnc Intrprtr.

OLIVIER, BRYAN M; Dover HS; Dover, NH; (Y); Am Leg Boys St; French Clb; Var L Ice Hcky; High Hon Roll; U Of NH.

OMBERG, PETER D; Aloirne HS; Hudson, NH; (Y); Am Leg Boys St; Letterman Clb; Political Wkr; Science Clb; Ski Clb; Im Socr; Var L Trk; Engrng.

ORDWAY, CATHY L; Pembroke Acad; Epsom, NH; (Y); 5/159; Cmnty Wkr; Pres 4-H; Hosp Aide; Latin Clb; Trs Soph Cls; Stu Cncl; Capt Cheerleading; Sec Trs NHS; Miss TEEN Pgnt 84 & 85; Am Leg Awd; Concord Hosp Schl Nrsng; Nrsng.

ORDWAY, HEIDI; Kingswood Regional HS; Center Ossipee, NH; (Y); Art Clb; Church Yth Grp; DECA; FHA; Church Choir; Hon Roll; Kent Christian.

OTIS, LAUREN; Milford Area SR HS; Mt Vernon, NH; (Y); Church Yth Grp; Nwsp Stf; Yrbk Phtg; Hon Roll; Photo.

OUELLETTE, DEBBIE; Winnacunnet HS; Seabrook, NH; (Y); Nwsp Sprt Ed; JV Bsktbl; Coach Actv; Capt L Fld Hcky; Var L Trk; High Hon Roll; NHS; MVP Awd Fld Hockey 83; Acad Exc Alg I Hnrs 83; Acad Exc Awds French II,III 84-85; Jrnlsm.

OUELLETTE, JENNIFER; Spaulding HS; Rochester, NH; (S); 18/392; Church Yth Grp; Trk; Hon Roll; UNH; Biology.

OUELLETTE, MAUREEN; Conant HS; Jaffrey, NH; (Y); Stage Crew; Rep Stu Cncl; Var Capt Cheerleading; Pom Pon; CC Awd; Hon Roll; Kiwanis Awd; VFW Awd; Voice Dem Awd; All-Amer Chrldr Fnlst 84; Most Outstndg Chrldr Awd 85; Secy.

OUELLETTE, THOMAS J; Memorial HS; Manchester, NH; (Y); 14/396; Am Leg Boys St; Ftbl; High Hon Roll; NHS; Elec Engr.

OXFORD, ALLISON LEA; Milford Area SR HS; Milford, NH; (Y); Am Leg Aux Girls St; Chorus; Yrbk Stf; Rep Frsh Cls; Var Fld Hcky; Im Vllybl; Hon Roll; U Of NH; Psych.

PABLO, DOMINIQUE; Trinity HS; Manchester, NH; (Y); Art Clb; Exploring; Ski Clb; Yrbk Stf; Score Keeper; Socr; Sftbl; Hon Roll; Soccer Rookie Of Yr; Art Therapy.

PADDOCK JR, ROBERT E; Littleton HS; Littleton, NH; (Y); 5/78; Church Yth Grp; Pres Drama Clb; Political Wkr; School Play; Var L Crs Cntry; NHS; Ntl Merit SF; Library Aide; Thesps; Band; Presidential Classroom 85; St Pauls Schl-Advanced Studies Prog 84; USAF Acad Summer Sci Seminar 84; Lawyer.

PAGE, JONATHAN; Concord HS; Concord, NH; (Y); 66/330; Chrmn Varsity Clb; Lit Mag; Im JV Bsktbl; JV Var Socr; Im Sftbl; High Hon Roll; Hon Roll; Pres Schlr; Harvard Grad Schl Design/Career Discovry Pgm 85; Syracuse U; Arch.

PAIGE, DANIEL; Spaulding HS; Rochester, NH; (S); 40/430; Camera Clb; Band; Concert Band; Mrchg Band; Hon Roll; UNH; Mech Engr.

PAINI, CINDY J; Memorial HS; Manchester, NH; (Y); 67/366; Hst FBLA; Var Capt Cheerleading; Mgr(s); Powder Puff Ftbl; High Hon Roll; Hon Roll; Colby Sawyer Clg; Admin.

PALARDIS, TINA; Salem HS; Salem, NH; (Y); 71/347; Cmnty Wkr; Model UN; Spanish Clb; Teachers Aide; Band; Concert Band; Drm & Bgl; Mrchg Band; Hon Roll; Salem NH Lioness Clb Scholar 85; Regis Coll; Mth.

PALMER, LISA; Nashua SR HS; Ayer, MA; (Y); Library Aide.

PANAGOS, CHRISTINE; Memorial HS; Manchester, NH; (Y); 39/394; Band; Rep Frsh Cls; Rep Soph Cls; Rep Sr Cls; Rep Stu Cncl; Powder Puff Ftbl; Sftbl; All City Concert Band 83; Physcl Thrpy.

PANGRAZE, MELISSA; Memorial HS; Auburn, NH; (Y); 42/394; Red Cross Aide; Capt Ski Clb; Co-Capt Tennis; Hon Roll; Vet Med.

PANKH, RAJIV; Goffstown HS; Goffstown, NH; (Y); 2/240; Ski Clb; VP Sr Cls; Trs Stu Cncl; Var Trk; High Hon Roll; NHS; Natl Sci Olympd Bio Top 10; Mth Awd; Elec Awd; New England JR Sci & Humanities Sympsm; Engrng.

PAPP, KATIE; Memorial HS; Manchester, NH; (Y); 4/366; Band; Stu Cncl; Cheerleading; Powder Puff Ftbl; High Hon Roll; Trs NHS; Yale Book Awd 85; Phrmcy.

PAQUETTE, RENE; Winnisquam Regional HS; Tilton, NH; (Y); Drama Clb; Ski Clb; Thesps; School Play; Pres Frsh Cls; Pres Sec Stu Cncl; JV Cheerleading; Var Fld Hcky; Eng.

PARADISE, DEBRA; Milford Area SR HS; Amherst, NH; (Y); Girl Scts; Chorus; Powder Puff Ftbl; Hon Roll; Child Psych.

PARADISE, STEVEN; Milford Area SR HS; Amherst, NH; (Y); Band; Concert Band; Mrchg Band; Hon Roll; Mech Engrng.

PARENT, CELESTE; Berlin SR HS; Berlin, NH; (Y); 7/201; Am Leg Aux Girls St; Church Yth Grp; French Clb; Hon Roll; Jr NHS; NHS; Robt Waugh Mem Awd In Frnch 84; Frnch.

PARENT, DAVE; Londonderry HS; Londonderry, NH; (Y); Ski Clb; Im Bsktbl; JV L Crs Cntry; Var Tennis; JV Trk; French Hon Soc; High Hon Roll; Hon Roll; Fr Hnr Soc 84-85; Schltc Achvt Schl Hnr Awd 84-85.

PARENTEAU, REBECCA; Concord HS; Concord, NH; (Y); Drama Clb; Varsity Clb; School Play; Stage Crew; Yrbk Stf; Sec Sr Cls; Stu Cncl; Crs Cntry; Trk.

PARKER, C; West HS; Manchester, NH; (Y); 100/342; Boy Scts; FHA; Nwsp Phtg; Yrbk Phtg; Hon Roll; Pope Pius Awd 85; Boy Scout Eagle Awd 85; Scout Yr 84; Culnary Inst Am; Mgmt.

PARKER, VICKIE; Kennett HS; Rutland, VT; (Y); Math Tm; Spanish Clb; Hon Roll; Math.

PARNELL, JUDITH; Manchester Memorial HS; Manchester, NH; (Y); 37/366; French Clb; Variety Show; Im Powder Puff Ftbl; L Tennis; Engine Studies.

PARSONS, MARY; Fall Mt Reg HS; Charlestown, NH; (Y); 4-H; Girl Scts; Band; Chorus; Concert Band; Jazz Band; Orch; Yrbk Ed-Chief; Hon Roll; NHS; Prlgl Music.

PASQUALONI, SARA ELIZABETH; Milford Area SR HS; Amherst, NH; (Y); Am Leg Aux Girls St; Church Yth Grp; Math Tm; Science Clb; Yrbk Sprt Ed; High Hon Roll; NHS; Ntl Merit SF; Crs Cntry Ski Tm Vrsty Ltr 82-86; JR Mth Excllnce Awd 85; Pre-Med.

PATTEN, ASHLEE; Saint Pauls Schl; Flintstone, GA; (Y); Latin Clb; Science Clb; Rep Soph Cls; Var Bsktbl; Var Capt Socr; Var Tennis.

PAUL, CHARLENE; Hopkinton HS; Concord, NH; (Y); Church Yth Grp; Cmnty Wkr; Hosp Aide; Band; Concert Band; School Play; Bus Admin.

PAWSON, JOHN; Southeastern N H Christian Acad; Portsmouth, NH; (S); 1/14; Church Yth Grp; Band; Yrbk Stf; Bsktbl; Socr; High Hon Roll; Areonomics.

PEACOCK, CHRIS; Kennett HS; Silver Lk, NH; (Y); French Clb; VP Frsh Cls; Stu Cncl; JV Var Ftbl; JV Var Ice Hcky; Hon Roll; Bentley Schl Of Acctng; Bus Mgt.

PEARSON, MICHAEL; Colebrook Acad; Dixville Notch, NH; (Y); 3/51; Band; Chorus; Mrchg Band; Swing Chorus; Yrbk Phtg; Hon Roll; NHS; Yth & Govt Pgm-Suprm Crt Justc 85; Georgetown U; Attrny.

PEARSON, STUART; Concord HS; Bow, NH; (Y); 8/350; JV Math Tm; Bsktbl; JV Socr; Trk; High Hon Roll; NHS; Outstndng Achvt Awds Engl, Physics, Comp Progmng & Chmstry 84-85; Engrng.

PELCZAR, JANE; Dover HS; Dover, NH; (Y); 18/350; Am Leg Aux Girls St; French Clb; Trs FBLA; Hosp Aide; Key Clb; Rep Stu Cncl; High Hon Roll; NHS; Aud/Vis; Plymouth ST Schlr 85; Kiwanis Clb Schlrshp 85; Plymouth ST Clg; Math Educ.

PELLERIN, PAULA; Mount Saint Mary Seminary HS; Pelham, NH; (Y); 9/89; Drama Clb; Science Clb; School Play; Rep Stu Cncl; Var L Cheerleading; JV Fld Hcky; NHS; Pres Schlr; Pelham Dollrs For Schlrs 85; U Of NH; Chem.

PELLETIER, SCOTT; Dover HS; Dover, NH; (Y); 4-H; Var Crs Cntry; Hnr Roll, Hgh Hnrs 84-85; Plymouth ST Coll; Scl Sci.

PENNELL, PAUL; Merrimack HS; Merrimack, NH; (Y); 33/300; Boy Scts; Church Yth Grp; Cmnty Wkr; Computer Clb; Math Tm; Ski Clb; School Play; Bsktbl; Hon Roll; Prfct Atten Awd; Ski Team 82-84; Flag Bearer 81-82; Northeastern; Software Engr.

PENNYPACKER, BRUCE; Brewster Acad; Stamford, CT; (Y); 10/62; Aud/Vis; Drama Clb; Ski Clb; School Play; Stage Crew; Nwsp Phtg; Yrbk Phtg; Bsbl; Hon Roll; Prfct Atten Awd; Comp Sci.

PEPIN, MICHELLE; Spaulding HS; Rochester, NH; (Y); FHA; FNA; Sec Key Clb; Red Cross Aide; Trk; Hon Roll; U Bridgeport CT; Med Tech.

PERKINS II, JOHN J; Lin-Wood HS; Lincoln, NH; (S); 1/30; Model UN; Teachers Aide; Bsbl; Bsktbl; Socr; Hon Roll; JETS Awd.

PERKINS, PATRICK; Nute HS; Union, NH; (Y); Latin Clb; Band; Jazz Band; Mrchg Band; Orch; Stu Cncl; JV Bsktbl; Socr; Hon Roll; Auto Schl Stratham; Auto Mech.

PERO, DENA; Pembroke Acad; Epsom, NH; (Y); FHA; Hon Roll; Bus.

PERO, STACEY; Nute HS; Farmington, NH; (S); 7/49; French Clb; Concert Band; Variety Show; Yrbk Stf; Pres Frsh Cls; Rep Soph Cls; Trs Stu Cncl; JV Var Bsktbl; JV Var Sftbl; JV Var Vllybl; X-Ray Tech.

PERREAULT, DENISE MARIE; Berlin HS; Berlin, NH; (Y); 2/202; Am Leg Aux Girls St; Concert Band; Jazz Band; Mrchg Band; Pep Band; Ed Yrbk Stf; JV Cheerleading; High Hon Roll; NHS; Ntl Merit Ltr; Wellesley Bk Prz 85; Phys.

PERRON, SUSAN R; Pelham HS; Pelham, NH; (Y); 2/116; Church Yth Grp; Drama Clb; VP Sr Cls; Var L Fld Hcky; Var L Sftbl; Bausch & Lomb Sci Awd; High Hon Roll; NHS; Sal; Science Clb; Granite ST Hnr Schlrshp 85; Pres Acdmc Ftnss Awd 85; Purity Supreme & Svc Merch Schlrshps 85; U Of NH; Chem Engr.

PERRY, EDMUND; Phillips Exeter Acad; Harlem, NY; (Y); Spanish Clb; JV Bsktbl; JV Var Ftbl; High Hon Roll; Hon Roll; Ntl Merit SF; Stanford U; Bus Admn.

PERRY, MATTHEW; Belmont HS; Belmont, NH; (Y); 23/87; Am Leg Boys St; 4-H; Pres Stu Cncl; Bsbl; Stat Bsktbl; JV Crs Cntry; JV Socr; Mgr Sftbl; 4-H Awd; Hon Roll; Ed.

PERVERE, MICHAEL S; Milford Area SR HS; Milford, NH; (Y); 31/286; Aud/Vis; Boy Scts; Trs Church Yth Grp; Computer Clb; Trs Acpl Chr; Trs Chorus; Hon Roll; Math Tm; Mgr(s); Dollars For Schlrs Scholar 85; Knights Columbus Scholar 85; U NH; Mth Ed.

PESULA, JEFFREY; Bishop Guertin HS; Litchfield, NH; (Y); 10/151; Computer Clb; Debate Tm; French Clb; Math Clb; Yrbk Ed-Chief; Yrbk Stf; Var Trk; High Hon Roll; NHS; NEDT; U Of CA-BERKELY; Physcs.

PETERSON, BRADLEY; Bishop Guertin HS; Hollis, NH; (Y); 17/151; Church Yth Grp; FCA; Pres Jr Cls; Var L Bsbl; Var Ftbl; Dnfth Awd; Gov Hon Prg Awd; High Hon Roll; NHS; Sec Frsh Cls; Hugh O Brian Yth Fndtn Intl Ldrshp Semnr 84; U S Natl Ldrshp Mrt Awd 85; U S Stu Cncl Awd 85; Ministry.

PETERSON, PAULA; Timberlane Regional HS; Atkinson, NH; (Y); Church Yth Grp; German Clb; Girl Scts; Math Tm; Model UN; Teachers Aide; Church Choir; Yrbk Stf; High Hon Roll; NHS; Awd Exc German,Chem,Physcs 83-84; Nrsng.

PETTIS, SARAH; Portsmouth SR HS; Portsmouth, NH; (Y); 65/350; Civic Clb; Exploring; FHA; Latin Clb; Model UN; Office Aide; Swmmng; Trk; Hon Roll; Masonic Awd; Swm Tm Capt 83-85; George B Ward Schlrshp 85; Concord Tech Coll; Dntl Asst.

PETTY, LINDA; Manchester West HS; Bedford, NH; (Y); 74/352; FHA; High Hon Roll; Hon Roll; NH Coll; Accntng.

PHELPS, DARLENE; Pembroke Acad; Chichester, NH; (Y); Aud/Vis; DECA; Drama Clb; Sec Trs 4-H; French Clb; FBLA; Pres FHA; Teachers Aide; Sec Frsh Cls; 4-H Awd; Travl.

PHILBRICK, CHRISTINE; Manchester Central HS; Candia, NH; (Y); 30/500; L Ski Clb; L Crs Cntry; L Trk; Am Leg Aux Girls St; Band; Lit Mag; Hon Roll; NHS; Sportsmnshp Of Yr Awd 85; MVP Ski Tm 85; NH U; Nrs.

PHILBRICK, JENNIFER; Milford Area SR HS; Milford, NH; (Y); 98/280; DECA; Pres 4-H; Btty Crckr Awd; 4-H Awd; High Hon Roll; Hon Roll; Distrbtv Ed Outstndng Stdnt Yr 85; Elctd Stdnt Mnth May 85.

PHILIPPON, CONNIE; Goffstown HS; Manchester, NH; (Y); Trs FNA; Library Aide; Ski Clb; JV Cheerleading; High Hon Roll; Hon Roll; Mgr NHS; Northern New England JR Sci & Hummanities Symposium 85; Hist Ledrs In Training 85; Pre Med.

PHILLIPS, JEFFREY; Pembroke Acad; Suncook, NH; (Y); 10/180; French Clb; Pres Key Clb; Varsity Clb; Rep Frsh Cls; VP Rep Stu Cncl; Var L Trk; Hon Roll; NHS; Church Yth Grp; Cmnty Wkr; Hugh Obrien Yth Ldrshp Awd & Smnrs 84; Boston Coll Smmr Exp 85; Psych.

PHILLIPS, KIMBERLY; St Thomas Aquinas HS; Rye, NH; (Y); Church Yth Grp; French Clb; Latin Clb; JV Cheerleading; JV Lcrss; JV Socr; High Hon Roll; Var Bsktbl; Cogswell Bk Hghst Rnkd Berwick Acad 82; Rep Stu Govt Dy 85; Excllnc Latn II 85; Frgn Lang.

PICHETTE, JAMES; S E New Hampshire Christian Acad; Berwick, ME; (Y); Teachers Aide; Yrbk Stf; Var L Bsbl; Var L Socr; Hon Roll.

PICONE, CHRISTOPHER; Bishop Guertin HS; Groton, MA; (Y); 2/180; Pep Clb; School Musical; Nwsp Ed-Chief; Stu Cncl; Mgr(s); High Hon Roll; NHS; Ntl Merit SF; Exploring; Dartmouth Bk Awd 85; Rsrch Bio.

PICOTTE, MICHELLE A; Salem HS; Salem, NH; (S); 49/363; Church Yth Grp; French Clb; Key Clb; Model UN; Ski Clb; School Play; Sec Stu Cncl; Mgr(s); Hon Roll; Mrktng Mngmnt.

PILLSBURY, CANDY; Lebanon HS; Grantham, NH; (Y); JV Bsktbl; Hon Roll; Amer Cancer Socty Volntr 83; Elctrncs.

PLACEY, KATHERINE; White Mountains Reginal HS; Guildhall, VT; (Y); 2/88; Trs FBLA; Nwsp Rptr; Yrbk Stf; High Hon Roll; Hon Roll; Trs NHS; Sal; Pres Acad Ftnss, U VT Schlr 85; 2nd FBLA Acctng I 84; U VT; Bus Mgmnt.

PLAISTED, MARK; Moultonborough Acad; Moultonboro, NH; (Y); 3/30; Chess Clb; Math Clb; Math Tm; Ski Clb; Spanish Clb; Socr; High Hon Roll; Hon Roll; Prfct Atten Awd; Hghst Achvt Sci 83-84; Accntnt.

PLANTE, CHRIS; Pittsfield HS; Pittsfield, NH; (Y); Yrbk Stf; Pres Jr Cls; Var Capt Bsktbl; Var JV Socr; Hon Roll; Sec NHS; Quiz Bowl; Varsity Clb.

POELMAN, CONRAD; Laconia HS; Laconia, NH; (Y); 1/159; Math Tm; Band; Hon Roll; NHS; Val; AHSME NH Tp Scrr 85; Hgh Scrr New England Asscn Of Mth Leags 84-85; NH ST Mth Mt Tp Scrr 84; Air Force Acad.

POIRIER, JENNIFER; Portsmouth SR HS; Portsmouth, NH; (Y); Capt Bsktbl; Sftbl; Vllybl; Hon Roll; Schlr Athlt Awd 83-85; JR Wrld Cncl 85.

POIRIER, JUDITH M; Manchester West HS; Manchester, NH; (Y); 25/364; French Clb; VP FHA; Yrbk Stf; High Hon Roll; Jr NHS; NHS; Bus Prof Womens Schlrshp 85; W HS Alumni Friends Schlrshp 85; St Anselm; Crimnl Just.

POISSON, GINA RE; Franklin HS; Franklin, NH; (Y); 14/92; French Clb; Rptr Stu Cncl; Var Cheerleading; Hon Roll; NHS; Elks Clb Yth Govt Cnclprsn 85; Fshn Merch.

POLLARD, DEBORAH A; Hollis Area HS; Hollis, NH; (Y); 4/122; Church Yth Grp; Rep French Clb; Math Tm; Rep Spanish Clb; Yrbk Ed-Chief; French Hon Soc; NHS; Girl Scts; High Hon Roll; Hon Roll; St Pauls Schl Adv Stu Pgm 84; GSA Gold Awd 85; Nashua Telepraph Jrnlsm Awd 85; Tufts U; Bio.

POLLARD, DONNIE; Lebanon HS; Enfield, NH; (Y); Church Yth Grp; Letterman Clb; Spanish Clb; Varsity Clb; Var L Golf; L Var Ice Hcky; JV Socr; Hon Roll; MA U Amherst; Agronomy.

POMEROY, MICHAEL; Hanover HS; Lyme Center, NH; (Y); 68/144; Church Yth Grp; Quiz Bowl; Yrbk Phtg; JV Var Bsbl; JV Ftbl; Hon Roll; Dresdn Schlrshp; U Of New Hampshire.

PORTER, GERRI; Belmont HS; Belmont, NH; (Y); Church Yth Grp; Varsity Clb; Yrbk Stf; JV Capt Cheerleading; Crs Cntry; Trk; Hon Roll; NHS; NH Tech Inst Of Concord; Radio.

POTTER, MARK; Salem HS; Salem, NH; (S); Boys Clb Am; Model UN; Ski Clb; Socr; Trk; Wt Lftg; Wrstlng; Hon Roll.

POWELL, LAURI; Milford Area SR HS; Amherst, NH; (Y); Church Yth Grp; Cmnty Wkr; 4-H; French Clb; Girl Scts; Letterman Clb; Var Capt Socr; Var L Trk; Var L Vllybl; Hon Roll; Mntl Attd Awd Vrsty Vlybl 84.

POWERS, MICHAEL; Milford Area SR HS; Amherst, NH; (Y); Computer Clb; Exploring; Math Tm; Var Golf; Hon Roll; Worcester Poly Tech; Aero Sp En.

PRAGER, KEVIN L; Phillips Exeter Acad; New York, NY; (Y); Church Yth Grp; Office Aide; Ski Clb; Acpl Chr; Chorus; School Musical; School Play; Rep Soph Cls; Rep Stu Cncl; Var L Lcrss; Yale U; Jrnlsm.

PRAMAS, TIMOTHY; Bishop Guertin HS; Dracut, MA; (Y); 33/150; Church Yth Grp; Debate Tm; NFL; Speech Tm; Nwsp Stf; Yrbk Stf; High Hon Roll; NHS; NEDT Awd; Bsbl; Merit Schlrshp Northwestern Forn Smmr Inst & Natl Forn Inst Smmr Wrksh 85; Cert Outstndng Chrch Svc; Law.

PRATT, CINDY; Salem HS; Salem, NH; (Y); 68/347; Model UN; Chorus; Church Choir; School Musical; JV Cheerleading; Var Gym; Var Mgr(s); Var Trk; Plymouth ST Coll; Phy Ed.

PRESLEY, KRISTIN; Londonderry HS; Manchester, NH; (Y); Ski Clb; Cheerleading; Powder Puff Ftbl; High Hon Roll; Hon Roll; Spanish NHS; Excllnt Acad Grds Achvt Awd 83; Spnsh Achvt Awd 83-85; UVM; Bio.

PRESTON, MICHAEL S; Alvirne HS; Hudson, NH; (Y); 3/297; Church Yth Grp; Computer Clb; FBLA; Pres Intnl Clb; Math Tm; Science Clb; Lit Mag; High Hon Roll; Hon Roll; NHS; Benjamin Bates Schlrshp 85; St Joseph Hosp Auxiliary Schlrshp 85; Calculus Leag 3rd Hghst Scr In H S; Bates Coll; Chem.

PRIDHAM, SHELLEY; Portsmouth SR HS; Portsmouth, NH; (Y); 32/344; Am Leg Boys St; Spanish Clb; Band; Yrbk Stf; Swmmng; Hon Roll; NHS; U Of NH; Psych.

PRIGGE, CHRIS; Monadnock Regional HS; Fitzwilliam, NH; (Y); 3/144; Model UN; Yrbk Stf; VP Jr Cls; Pres Sr Cls; Trk; DAR Awd; NHS; JV Socr; Cit Awd; Ntl Merit SF; Harvard Bk Awd 83-84; John J Kennedy Amer Hist Awd 83-84; Chem Awd 83-84; Adv Stds Prog St Pauls Schl; West Pt; Engrng.

PROCEK, MICHAEL; Nashua SR HS; Nashua, NH; (Y); Am Leg Boys St; Chess Clb; Ski Clb; Im Bsktbl; Coach Actv; Hon Roll; Ntl Jr Beta Clb 82-83; Elec Engr.

PROULX, TIM; Goffstown Area HS; Manchester, NH; (Y); 5/222; Church Yth Grp; Exploring; Math Tm; Ski Clb; Variety Show; Nwsp Rptr; Trs Jr Cls; Off Sr Cls; JV Var Bsbl; High Hon Roll; Chem Awd 85; JR Prom King 85; Engrng.

PRZYGRODZKI, ROBERT; Trinity HS; Manchester, NH; (Y); 4/163; Hosp Aide; Math Tm; Model UN; Yrbk Ed-Chief; High Hon Roll; NHS; NEDT Awd; Yrbk Stf; Tchrs Assn Schlrshp 84; Cath U; Bio.

QUARATIELLO, FRANCIS; Bishop Guertin HS; Nashua, NH; (Y); 3/150; Am Leg Boys St; Debate Tm; Trs French Clb; VP Key Clb; NFL; Nwsp Stf; Yrbk Stf; High Hon Roll; Jr NHS; NHS; Colby Coll Bk Prz 85; V Deb Rnnr Up 84; Novice Deb Champ 83.

QUEENAN, JAMES; Bishop Guertin HS; Hudson, NH; (Y); 54/129; Boy Scts; Church Yth Grp; FCA; Ski Clb; Nwsp Stf; JV Crs Cntry; Im Socr; Im Wt Lftg; Lib Arts.

QUINT, KERRY; Kennett HS; Conway, NH; (Y); Drama Clb; Thesps; School Musical; School Play; Hon Roll.

RAFFERTY, LAURIANN; Winnacunnet HS; Hampton Beach, NH; (Y); 3/285; Church Yth Grp; Capt Mathletes; Math Tm; Teachers Aide; Stage Crew; High Hon Roll; Hon Roll; VP NHS; Ntl Merit SF; Pres Schlr; NH U; Math.

RALPH JR, KENNETH A; Salem HS; Salem, NH; (S); 36/405; Model UN; Spanish Clb; Hon Roll; YMCA All-Amer 84; MVP Swmmng 84.

RAMELOW, NANCY L; Merrimack HS; Simi Valley, CA; (Y); 4/241; Ed Church Yth Grp; Quiz Bowl; Stage Crew; JV Bsktbl; Var Capt Fld Hcky; Mgr(s); Hon Roll; NHS; Pres Schlr; Balfour Awds Spn, Hstry, All Arnd Eng, Natl Hnr Soc; UCLA; Psych.

RAMSDEN, CATHERINE; Pinkerton Acad; Windham, NH; (S); Girl Scts; Hosp Aide; Ski Clb; Band; Church Choir; Concert Band; Pep Band; School Musical; Socr; Sftbl; 1st Cls Highest Awd Girl Sctg 83; Pratt Inst; Comm Art.

RAND, ROBERT D; Spaulding HS; Rochester, NH; (Y); ROTC; Var L Bsbl; Im Bsktbl; Im Golf; Var L Ice Hcky; Im Socr; Im Swmmng; Im Wt Lftg; High Hon Roll; Hon Roll; Bsbl V Most Imprvd Plyr Awd 85; Bsbl Rookie Yr 84; Arch.

RAND, TROY L; Spaulding HS; Rochester, NH; (Y); Var L Bsktbl; Mu Alp Tht.

RANDMERE, ALAR; Inter Lakes JR SR HS; New Hampton, NH; (Y); 3/60; French Clb; Var Bsktbl; Var Crs Cntry; JV Trk; High Hon Roll; Ntl Merit Ltr; Nuclr Engrng.

RAUTIO, KIT; Conant HS; Jaffrey, NH; (Y); Church Yth Grp; ROTC; Color Guard; Ice Hcky; Socr; Hon Roll; Arch.

RAWNSLEY, ROSS; Merrimack HS; Merrimack, NH; (Y); Boy Scts; Church Yth Grp; JV Var Socr; Im Vllybl; Hon Roll; Eagle Sct Awd 85; U Lowell; Acctng.

RAY, KRISTIN; Milford Area SR HS; Amherst, NH; (Y); Yrbk Stf; Rep Frsh Cls; Rep Jr Cls; Sec Sr Cls; Rep Stu Cncl; JV Bsktbl; JV Socr; Hon Roll; NHS; Prom Comm.

RAYMOND, DOMINIQUE A; Nashua HS; Nashua, NH; (Y); 48/907; Mrchg Band; School Play; Yrbk Stf; Hon Roll; Jr NHS; NHS; Pres Schlr; Nashua Rotary Clb Scholar 85; U NH; Bus Admin.

RAYMOND, NANCY; Manchester Central HS; Manchester, NH; (Y); 30/453; Pres Church Yth Grp; Pres FBLA; VP Boy Scts; Yrbk Stf; Lit Mag; Rep Frsh Cls; Rep Soph Cls; Rep Jr Cls; Rep Sr Cls; Rep Stu Cncl; Pres Acad Fitnss Awd 85; Clark U; Psych.

RAYMOND, PAULA M; Nashua HS; Nashua, NH; (Y); 150/800; Aud/Vis; Drama Clb; Hosp Aide; VP JA; Library Aide; School Musical; School Play; Stage Crew; Cheerleading; Hon Roll; Rose ST Coll Cert Awd Gen Bus 84; TV.

RAYMOND, TERRI; Pembroke Acad; Epsom, NH; (Y); DECA; French Clb; Hon Roll; Accnt.

REA, DAVID P; Phillips Exeter Acad; Auburn, ME; (Y); Computer Clb; German Clb; School Play; JV Lcrss; Ntl Merit SF; 1st Place Xerox Essay Cntst 82; Jr Cmmdr Ycht Clb 84; Intl Rel.

READ, LAURIANNE; Kennett HS; Conway, NH; (Y); 7/160; Church Yth Grp; French Clb; FBLA; Teachers Aide; Church Choir; French Hon Soc; High Hon Roll; Hon Roll; Spn.

REARDON, JOHNATHAN; Bishop Guertin HS; Nashua, NH; (Y); 20/180; FCA; Var L Bsbl; Var L Ice Hcky; Wt Lftg; High Hon Roll; Hon Roll; Jr NHS; NHS; Ntl Merit Ltr; NEDT Awd; Undr Rtd Plyr Awd Bsbl 85; Bus.

REES, CARLA; Manchester West HS; Manchester, NH; (Y); 5/352; Am Leg Aux Girls St; Hosp Aide; Nwsp Stf; Yrbk Stf; Rep Frsh Cls; JV Socr; Var L Swmmng; Var L Tennis; High Hon Roll; NHS; Ambsdr To Hugh O Brian Yth Fndtn 84; Bus Admin.

REESE, ROBERT A; Salem HS; Salem, NH; (Y); U Of NH; Opthamology.

REID, SUSAN; Londonderry HS; Londonderry, NH; (Y); Science Clb; Acpl Chr; Chorus; School Musical; Variety Show; Nwsp Stf; Powder Puff Ftbl; High Hon Roll; Hon Roll; NHS; NH All ST Music Fest 85; Queen City Music Fest 85; Summa Cum Laude 85; Rutgers; Genetic Engrng.

REILLY, PETER; Bishop Avertin HS; Lowell, MA; (Y); 65/160; Church Yth Grp; FCA; Varsity Clb; Boys Clb Am; Boy Scts; Im Bsbl; Im Bsktbl; Var Ftbl; Im Wt Lftg; Boston U; Aeros Engrng.

RENNIE, JON S; Trinity HS; Manchester, NH; (Y); Art Clb; Math Tm; Yrbk Stf; NHS; Worchester Polytech; Mech Engrg.

RENSELAER, SUSANNE; Phillips Exeter Acad; Hampton, NH; (Y); 4-H; Library Aide; Im Bsbl; Im JV Socr; Mgr Swmmng; High Hon Roll; Ntl Merit SF; Georgetown U; Engl.

RENY, GARY J; Hillsboro-Deering HS; Hillsboro, NH; (Y); Am Leg Boys St; Band; Flag Corp; Pep Band; Trs Frsh Cls; Trs Jr Cls; Sec Trs Sr Cls; Var Bsbl; Var Crs Cntry; Var Socr; Arch.

REORDON, THOMAS E; Timberlane HS; Plaistow, NH; (Y); 3/215; German Clb; Var Bsktbl; High Hon Roll; NHS; Am Leg Boys St; Chess Clb; Model UN; Political Wkr; Pres Frsh Cls; Rep Soph Cls; Var Bsktbl Coaches Awd 84 & 85; Corp Law.

RHODES, STEVEN D; Concord HS; Concord, NH; (Y); Boy Scts; Jazz Band; Mrchg Band; Symp Band; Var L Socr; Var L Trk; Hon Roll; NHS; Pres Acad Ftnss Awd 85; ST Champ 4x400m Relay Tm 85; USAF Acad; Aerosp Engrng.

RICCIO, ANTHONY; Milford Area SR HS; Amherst, NH; (Y); Am Leg Boys St; Political Wkr; Var Bsbl; Var Bsktbl; Powder Puff Ftbl; Hon Roll; Im Wrstlng; Bsktbl-Lcl Radio Sta All Star Tm, All Trnmnt & Plyr Of Wk 82-85; U Of NH; Pol Sci.

RICE, KRISTEN; Portsmouth HS; Portsmouth, NH; (Y); 32/436; Church Yth Grp; Exploring; Latin Clb; Band; Concert Band; Jazz Band; Mrchg Band; Pep Band; School Musical; JV Var Sftbl; Pre Med.

RICHARDS, DAVID; Fall Mountain Regional HS; Alstead, NH; (Y); 1/150; Am Leg Boys St; Math Tm; Var Capt Bsktbl; JV Var Ftbl; Var Socr; Tennis; Elks Awd; High Hon Roll; NHS; Pres Schlr; Schlr-Athl Awd 85; Cheshire Cnty Med Sci Awd 85; Amer H S Schlr Athl 85; U Of NH; Bus Adm.

RICHARDS, JOHN D; Alvirre HS; Hudson, NH; (Y); Am Leg Boys St; Cmnty Wkr; Hosp Aide; Ski Clb; Hon Roll; Aernutcl Engr.

RICHER, NATHAN; Newport JR SR HS; Newport, NH; (Y); Ski Clb; Band; Chorus; Jazz Band; Mrchg Band; School Musical; School Play; Pres Soph Cls; Var Bsbl; Capt Ftbl; Geraldine Rudenfeldt Music Scholar 84; Bst Actor Awd 83; Dramatics Awd 82; Cmmnctns.

RICKER, CHERI; Nute HS; Union, NH; (Y); Library Aide; Band; Chorus; Variety Show; Cheerleading; Hon Roll; Ntl Merit Schol; Vet Med.

RIEL, ELIZABETH; Moultonborough Acad; Moultonboro, NH; (Y); 2/30; Drama Clb; Latin Clb; Math Tm; Spanish Clb; School Play; Nwsp Rptr; Pres Jr Cls; Rep Stu Cncl; Var Vllybl; NHS; Hgh Hnr Rll 83-84; Stu Cncl Ldrshp Awd 84-85; Dept Engl Awd 84-85; Intl Rel.

RIEL, LURENE M; Pittsfield HS; Pittsfield, NH; (Y); 4/60; Am Leg Aux Girls St; Pres VP 4-H; Science Clb; Varsity Clb; Pres Jr Cls; Bausch & Lomb Sci Awd; 4-H Awd; Church Yth Grp; French Clb; Band; Moody Kent Awd 85; Forrest B Arque & 4-H Schlrshps 85; MA Coll Of Pharmacy; Pharm.

RIES, ALAYNA; Merrimack HS; Merrimack, NH; (S); Computer Clb; Pres DECA; Mgr(s); Vllybl; Hon Roll; Genl Merch Suprvsry Lvl 3rd Pl DECA 84; Genl Merch Suprvsry Lvl Sllng 2nd Pl DECA 84.

RILEY, WANDA; Nute HS; Milton, NH; (Y); JCL; VP Latin Clb; Library Aide; Chorus; Sec Frsh Cls; Hon Roll; FL Inst Tech; Bus Adm.

ROBBINS, CARL W; Nashua SR HS; Nashua, NH; (Y); 96/900; Pres Camera Clb; Computer Clb; Drama Clb; Nwsp Phtg; Nwsp Stf; Yrbk Phtg; Yrbk Stf; Hon Roll; Jr NHS; NHS; Outstndng Electrns Stu Of Yr 85; Presdntl Voctnl Indstrl Arts Stu Of Amer 85; NH Vctnl Tech Coll; Elec Engr.

ROBBINS, CHARLES; Portsmouth HS; Portsmouth, NH; (S); 10/362; Drama Clb; Latin Clb; Quiz Bowl; Capt Golf; NHS; Ntl Merit Ltr; Attended St Pauls Schl Advanced Studies Pgm SPS ASP 84; Yale U; Polit Sci.

ROBERGE, PENNY; Berlin HS; Berlin, NH; (Y); 48/210; Hon Roll; YMCA Yth & Govt 83-85; SADD 84-85; Plymouth ST; Acctng.

ROBERT, CHANTAL; Presentation Of Mary Acad; Nashua, NH; (Y); 2/35; Pres French Clb; School Play; Nwsp Rptr; Yrbk Ed-Chief; High Hon Roll; Jr NHS; Pres Trk; Sal; Val; Hosp Aide; Keene ST Coll; Journlsm.

ROBIDOUX, SCOT J; Pelham HS; Pelham, NH; (Y); Pres Frsh Cls; Pres Soph Cls; Pres Jr Cls; Pres Sr Cls; Pres Stu Cncl; JV Bsbl; JV Var Bsktbl; JV Var Socr; Jr NHS; NHS; U Of NH; Hotel Admin.

ROBINSON, DERYCK; Spaulding HS; Rochester, NH; (Y); Fld Hcky; Ftbl; Trk; Ntl Merit Ltr; Hon Roll; Plymouth ST Coll; Sound Rcrdng.

ROBINSON, LYNN; Salem HS; Salem, NH; (Y); Church Yth Grp; French Clb; Model UN; Hon Roll.

ROBINSON, MICHAEL; Bishop Brady HS; Pittsfield, NH; (Y); Am Leg Boys St; Capt Crs Cntry; Capt Trk; Var Tennis; MVP & Coachs Awd Crss Cntry; Rnnr Yr Awd.

ROBLEE, CHRISTOPHER; Portsmouth HS; Rye, NH; (S); Cmnty Wkr; Exploring; Pres German Clb; JV Socr; JV Trk; High Hon Roll; NHS; Demuan SR Cnclr; ST Pauls Appl.

ROCHEFORT, SONIA; Concord HS; Bow, NH; (Y); Hst Varsity Clb; Var JV Fld Hcky; High Hon Roll; Hon Roll; NHS; Yrbk Stf; Lit Mag; JV Stat Bsktbl; JV L Sftbl; Exc Eng 84-85; Robert D Wheeler Athl Awd 83; Christina Maria Paveglio Mem Hcky Awd 83; Bus Adm.

ROCHELEAU, LYNNE; Saint Thomas Aquinas HS; Rochester, NH; (Y); Debate Tm; Drama Clb; French Clb; Chorus; Stage Crew; JV Bsktbl; JV Var Vllybl; Eng.

ROCKEY, JILL C; Dover HS; Dover, NH; (Y); 27/300; Drama Clb; NHS; Hosp Aide; Math Clb; Pep Clb; Drill Tm; Hon Roll; Walton Acad Scholar 85-86; Albright Coll; Biochem.

RODDY, ANTHONY A; Bishop Guertin HS; Lowell, MA; (Y); 10/137; Nwsp Rptr; Sec Sr Cls; Stu Cncl; Im Bsktbl; Var Crs Cntry; JV Trk; High Hon Roll; Hon Roll; NHS; Spanish NHS; Boston U; Comm.

RODGERS, LINDA A; Presentation Of Mary Acad; Hudson, NH; (Y); Drama Clb; Library Aide; Science Clb; Ski Clb; Band; Orch; Variety Show; Nwsp Ed-Chief; Nwsp Stf; Pres Frsh Cls; Grls ST 85; Bus.

ROGERS, KATHERINE; Spaulding HS; Rochester, NH; (Y); Key Clb; Rep Jr Cls; Rep Sr Cls; Var Socr; Var Trk; Hon Roll; MVP Girls Sprng Trck 84; ST Champ Gymnstcs 83; John Scala Awd 83; NE U; Bus Admin.

ROGERS, TRACY; Concord HS; Bow, NH; (Y); 3/330; Dance Clb; Math Tm; Varsity Clb; Yrbk Stf; Cheerleading; High Hon Roll; NHS; Ntl Merit SF; Lit Mag; Mgr Bsbl; Natl Lat Hnr Soc 84; Proj Excel Keene ST Coll 85; Recip Lat I, II, Fr I, II, Adv Trig, Eng Achvts; Boston Coll; Lib Art.

ROLLINS, JONATHAN J; Ashland HS; Ashland, NH; (Y); Am Leg Boys St; Church Yth Grp; Cmnty Wkr; Band; School Play; Yrbk Phtg; Yrbk Stf; Stu Cncl; Hon Roll; Stu Cncl Awd 85; Boys ST Amer Lgn Diploma 85; Arch.

RONDEAU, MICHELLE M; Timberlane Regional HS; Plaistow, NH; (Y); Trs Church Yth Grp; French Clb; Teachers Aide; JV Trk; Trinity Clge Vermont.

ROSE, KARYN; Salem HS; Salem, NH; (Y); 60/466; JA; Model UN; Ski Clb; Acpl Chr; VP Chorus; School Musical; School Play; Capt Cheerleading; High Hon Roll; Hon Roll; BUS Mgmnt.

ROSE, TODD J; Berlin HS; Dummer, NH; (Y); 9/202; Am Leg Boys St; Boy Scts; Yrbk Stf; Trk; Hon Roll; Jr NHS; NHS; Elec Engrng.

ROSS, DAVID; Concord HS; Concord, NH; (Y); Boy Scts; Band; Concert Band; Mrchg Band; Symp Band; High Hon Roll; Hon Roll; Bus Adm.

ROSS, NICOLE; Partsmouth HS; Dover, NH; (Y); 21/367; VP Spanish Clb; JV Capt Bsktbl; JV Crs Cntry; Capt L Trk; High Hon Roll; Hon Roll; NHS; Trk Field Schlrshp 85; All Am Trk Tm 83-84; Model Cong Minty Ldr 85; Central MI U; Sports Med.

ROSS, NICOLE; Portsmouth HS; Pease AFB, NH; (S); 17/390; Latin Clb; Spanish Clb; JV Capt Bsktbl; JV Bsktbl; JV Crs Cntry; VP Capt Trk; High Hon Roll; Hon Roll; NHS; Phys Ther.

ROULSTON, JUSTIN; Salem HS; Salem, NH; (Y); Model UN; Ski Clb; Spanish Clb; JV Socr; JV Wrstlng; Hon Roll.

ROUTHIER, MICHAEL R; Nashua SR HS; Nashua, NH; (Y); Am Leg Boys St; Hon Roll.

ROUX, STEPHEN R; Saint Thomas Aquinas HS; Eliot, ME; (Y); Key Clb; Var L Bsbl; Var Capt Ftbl; Var L Ice Hcky; St Schlr; Key Clb Sgrnt At Arms; All ST Hnrb Mntn Ftbl; All ST Ftbl, All Seacoast & Hcky; Bio.

ROWE, DIANE; Thayer HS; Winchester, NH; (Y); Church Yth Grp; Latin Clb; Service Clb; Spanish Clb; Teachers Aide; Var Fld Hcky; High Hon Roll; NHS; Voice Dem Awd; Trs Frsh Cls; Dartmouth Bk Prz Engl 83-84.

ROWE, JENNIFER; Portsmouth SR HS; Rye, NH; (Y); 125/375; Drama Clb; Exploring; Model UN; School Musical; School Play; Thesps; Color Guard; Variety Show; Nwsp Rptr; Coach Actv; Ldng Role St Drama Festvl Awd Wnnr 85; Minor Role St Drama Fest Awd 84; Audio Engrng.

ROY, VONDA; Fall Mt Regional HS; Walpole, NH; (Y); Trs FBLA; Color Guard; Girl Scts; Office Aide; Swmmng; Tennis; Cit Awd; Hon Roll.

RUEL, THERESA; Gorham HS; Gorham, NH; (Y); 1/40; Pep Clb; Band; Pep Band; Yrbk Bus Mgr; Yrbk Rptr; Yrbk Stf; Cheerleading; High Hon Roll; Jr NHS; VP NHS; Wellesley Coll Bk Prz 84; Berlin City Bnk Schlrshp 85; Gorham Alumni Assn Schlrshp 85; Franklin Pierce Coll; Pre-Law.

RUGGERIO, JOANNE; Salem HS; Salem, NH; (Y); Church Yth Grp; Model UN; Chorus; Color Guard; Stage Crew; Var Mgr(s); Hon Roll; Cmmrcl Arts.

RUGGERIO, KAREN; Salem HS; Salem, NH; (Y); Church Yth Grp; FBLA; Hosp Aide; Stage Crew; Hon Roll; Cert Nurses Aide 85; Rivier Coll; RN.

RUOFF, DAVID W; Mascour Regional HS; Brookline, NH; (Y); 4/67; Am Leg Boys St; Boy Scts; Camera Clb; Pres Drama Clb; French Clb; School Play; Stage Crew; Nwsp Rptr; Yrbk Phtg; Athl Of Yr 85; Voctnl Schl-Athl Awd 85; U Of NH; Bio.

RUSHTON, NANCY; Salem HS; Salem, NH; (Y); Model UN; Band; Concert Band; Mrchg Band; Yrbk Stf; Hesser JC; Acctg.

RUSSELL, JEFFRY; Dover HS; Dover, NH; (Y); 67/263; JV Bsktbl; Var L Ftbl; Hon Roll; Imprv Var Ftbl Awd 84; UNH; Culnry Arts.

RUSSELL, STEPHANIE; Spaulding HS; Rochester, NH; (Y); Art Clb; Key Clb; Yrbk Stf; Rep Stu Cncl; Trk; Hon Roll; IN U; Comm Art.

RUSSILILLO, ROSE; Laconia HS; Laconia, NH; (Y); French Clb; High Hon Roll; Hon Roll; U NH; Bus Adm.

RYAN, DAVE; Bishop Guertin HS; Nashua, NH; (Y); 97/151; Am Leg Boys St; FCA; JV Bsbl; JV Crs Cntry; Var L Ice Hcky; Im Wt Lftg; Ntl Merit Schol; Hofstra U; Adv.

RYAN, DAWN; Milford Area SR HS; Milford, NH; (Y); Am Leg Aux Girls St; Church Yth Grp; Computer Clb; FBLA; Hon Roll; Comp.

SAGE, JEFFERY; Winnisquam Regional HS; Tilton, NH; (Y); Boy Scts; High Hon Roll; Hon Roll; Comp Sci.

SALYARDS, BRIAN A; Exeter Area HS; Exeter, NH; (Y); Am Leg Boys St; Church Yth Grp; JV Var Ftbl; JV Wrstlng; Hon Roll; Hstry.

SAMSEL, J PATRICK; Bishop Guertin HS; Nashua, NH; (Y); 30/150; FCA; Ski Clb; Im Bsktbl; JV Ftbl; Wt Lftg; Hon Roll; NHS; Ldr Confrmtn Cls St Patricks Chrch 84; Bus.

SAMSON, ELAINE; Pinkerton Acad; Auburn, NH; (Y); 23/485; Pres Dance Clb; 4-H; Math Tm; Red Cross Aide; Teachers Aide; Stage Crew; Im Bowling; Var Tennis; 4-H Awd; NHS; Hm Rm Repr 83-85; Hunts Swm Tm 81-82; Pub Rel Dance Clb 84; U NH; Elec Engrng.

SAMSON, RICHARD C; Colebrook Acad; W Stewartstown, NH; (Y); 4/47; Church Yth Grp; Varsity Clb; Chorus; VP Soph Cls; Var Bsbl; Var Bsktbl; Bowling; Capt Socr; Hon Roll; Pres NHS; ROTC Scholar; U S Naval Acad Appntmnt; RPI Scholar; U S Naval Acad; Aerospc Engrng.

SANBORN, CARRIE L; Plymouth Area HS; Wentworth, NH; (Y); 8/150; Sec French Clb; Hosp Aide; Math Tm; Yrbk Bus Mgr; Off Jr Cls; Rep Stu Cncl; JV Bsktbl; JV Var Tennis; High Hon Roll; Hon Roll; Chem Awd 85; Hmcmg Qn 85; Engrng.

SANBORN, VON; Manchester Memorial HS; Manchester, NH; (Y); 26/366; JV Ftbl; JV Trk; Var High Hon Roll; Var Hon Roll; Var Ntl Merit Ltr; St Anselms; Bus.

SANPHY, REBECCA A; Kennett HS; Glen, NH; (Y); 18/201; Am Leg Aux Girls St; Chorus; Flag Corp; High Hon Roll; Hon Roll; Bio Awdy 82-83; Ntl Sci Olympiad Chmstry 83-84; Berlin Voc Coll; Accntng.

SANTANIELLO, CHRIS; Gilford HS; Gilford, NH; (S); 18/105; Am Leg Aux Girls St; Hosp Aide; Q&S; Spanish Clb; Nwsp Rptr; Nwsp Stf; VP Frsh Cls; JV Bsktbl; Var L Crs Cntry; Var L Fld Hcky; Trib Rookie Yr 83-84; Trib News Ed 84-85; Jrnlsm.

SAUCIER, LINDA; Pembroke Acad; Suncook, NH; (Y); JV Cheerleading; Hon Roll; Cert Acdmc Hnr 84; Awd JV Chrldng 83-84; Halth Occ I Excllnce 85; HOSA Conv 85; Nrsng.

SAVERY, ROBERT T; Pembroke Acad; Concord, NH; (Y); 15/160; Boy Scts; Pep Band; Yrbk Ed-Chief; Bsktbl; Socr; NHS; Socl Stds Awd 85; Bridgewater ST Coll; Bus Mgmt.

SAVOIE, KATHLEEN; Fall Mountain Regional HS; Charlestown, NH; (Y); 10/154; Art Clb; French Clb; Girl Scts; Yrbk Bus Mgr; Yrbk Ed-Chief; Yrbk Phtg; Sec Sr Cls; Bsktbl; Crs Cntry; Socr; Gemtry Awd & Bio Awd; Dietician.

SAWICKI, CHRISTINE; Tilton Schl; Lochmere, NH; (S); 2/80; Varsity Clb; Stage Crew; Yrbk Stf; Var L Lcrss; JV Var Socr; High Hon Roll; Ntl Merit Ltr; NEDT Awd; Library Aide; Math Tm; Rensselaer Math, Sci Medl 84; Bio, Chem Prz 83-84; Chem Engr.

SAWYER, STEPHEN R; Phillips Exeter Acad; Hampton, NH; (Y); 1/300; Church Yth Grp; Mathletes; Math Tm; Rep Soph Cls; Var L Bsbl; JV Bsktbl; JV Socr; High Hon Roll; Hon Roll; Ottaway Schlrshp Awd 83; Exc Soc Studies Anthroplgy 83; Exc Sci Bio 83; Sci.

SCACCIA, LISA; Salem HS; Salem, NH; (Y); Cmnty Wkr; Cheerleading; High Hon Roll; Hon Roll; Trvl Agent.

SCHEIBER, KIMBERLY H; Mount St Mary Seminary HS; Nashua, NH; (Y); 36/90; Drama Clb; Acpl Chr; Chorus; School Musical; School Play; Swing Chorus; Var Capt Cheerleading; Hon Roll; NH All ST Chrs 84-85; All Estrn Chrs 85; Musc Ed.

SCHER, JASON P; Phillips Exeter Acad; Exeter, NH; (Y); Lit Mag; Ntl Merit SF; Writing.

SCHER, JASON P; Phillips Exeter Acad; Great Neck, NY; (Y); Lit Mag; Ntl Merit SF; Exeter Awd-Crtv Wrtng & Expostry Wrtng 85; Wesleyan U; Wrtng.

SCHIFFGENS, LISA; Timberlane Regional HS; Atkinson, NH; (Y); 45/207; FHA; Hosp Aide; Ski Clb; Spanish Clb; Yrbk Phtg; JV Fld Hcky; JV Mgr(s); Hon Roll; Am Leg Schlrshp 85-86; 1st Pl Awd Reg FHA Conf 85; Bringham Young U; Elem Ed.

SCHLAEFER, TRACEY JANE; Lin-Wood Public HS; Lincoln, NH; (Y); Cmnty Wkr; Speech Tm; Teachers Aide; Chorus; School Musical; Stage Crew; Yrbk Stf; Vllybl; Hon Roll; NHS; Plymouth ST; Elem Ed.

SCHOEN, ALLISON; Kennett HS; Bartlett, NH; (Y); 15/201; Drama Clb; Teachers Aide; Thesps; School Play; Stage Crew; Swing Chorus; VP Soph Cls; Coach Actv; High Hon Roll; Hon Roll; NY U; Rec Thrpy.

SCHOLZ, KERRY; Salem HS; Salem, NH; (Y); Church Yth Grp; German Clb; Key Clb; Model UN; Varsity Clb; VP Band; Mrchg Band; Fld Hcky; Mgr(s); Hon Roll; Field Hockey Capt Vrsty 85-86; VP Salem Hgh Schl Bnd 85-86; Cert Achvmnts German 84; Physcl Thrpy.

SCHRAMM, THOMAS; Nashua SR HS; Nashua, NH; (Y); Am Leg Boys St; Ski Clb; Im Bsktbl; JV Socr; High Hon Roll; Jr NHS; NHS; Aeronautcl Engr.

SCORDO, MARIA A; Concord HS; Concord, NH; (Y); 74/350; Var Trk; High Hon Roll; Hon Roll; Arch.

SCOURAS, GREG; Portsmouth SR HS; Portsmouth, NH; (Y); 12/412; Math Tm; High Hon Roll; NHS; Exec Bd Jr Wrld Cncl 84-85; Elect Engrng.

SCRIPTURE, KAREN; Belmont HS; Canterbury, NH; (S); 1/76; Church Yth Grp; Math Tm; Teachers Aide; Concert Band; Jazz Band; Mrchg Band; Pep Band; High Hon Roll; NHS; Cmnty Wkr; Lakes Rgn Math Leag-Hgh Scorer 83-84.

SEARLE, NATALIE; The Derryfield Schl; Amherst, NH; (Y); Cmnty Wkr; Exploring; Intnl Clb; Office Aide; Ski Clb; Teachers Aide; Nwsp Stf; Yrbk Stf; Hon Roll.

SECKER, DIANE B; Mascenic Regional HS; New Ipswich, NH; (Y); 1/65; Church Yth Grp; Drama Clb; French Clb; Yrbk Rptr; Var L Crs Cntry; Var Fld Hcky; NHS; Ntl Merit SF; Val; Math, Engl, Art Awds 83; Frnch, S S, Sci Awds 84.

SEDDON, DAWN; Fall Mountain Regional HS; Alstead, NH; (Y); 13/154; Am Leg Aux Girls St; French Clb; Color Guard; Yrbk Stf; Trs Jr Cls; Var Capt Crs Cntry; Var L Trk; Hon Roll; NHS; Johnson & Wales; Htl Mgmt.

SEGAL, REBECCA E; Concord HS; Bow, NH; (Y); 87/330; Yrbk Phtg; Yrbk Stf; Var Cheerleading; High Hon Roll; Hon Roll; Acad Achvt Awd IA Chem 84-85; Close-Up WA DC 84.

SELLINGER, WILLIAM; Woodsville HS; N Haverhill, NH; (Y); Debate Tm; Drama Clb; French Clb; FBLA; Latin Clb; Library Aide; School Play; Stage Crew; Yrbk Sprt Ed; Yrbk Stf; Southeastern USA; Pol Sci.

SELLINGHAM, BEVERLY J; Plymouth Area HS; Campton, NH; (Y); 24/138; Church Yth Grp; French Clb; Yrbk Stf; Stu Cncl; Var Capt Cheerleading; JV Sftbl; Var Tennis; Hon Roll; Pre Law.

SENECABAUGH, TERRI A; Plymouth Area HS; Plymouth, NH; (Y); 9/160; Am Leg Aux Girls St; VP French Clb; Variety Show; Rep Frsh Cls; Rep Soph Cls; JV Bsktbl; Var Crs Cntry; JV Capt Sftbl; JV Tennis; High Hon Roll; U Of NH.

SERAFIN, THOMAS; Pembroke Acad; Suncook, NH; (Y); 18/190; Boy Scts; Church Yth Grp; French Clb; Key Clb; Band; Pep Band; Hon Roll; Pre-Med.

SEVIGNY, LISA; Trinity HS; Manchester, NH; (Y); 17/150; Yrbk Stf; Bsktbl; Sftbl; High Hon Roll; Hon Roll; NHS; Socl Studies Awd 83-84; Law.

SHAFFER, CINDY; Pembroke Acad; Concord, NH; (Y); Church Yth Grp; Latin Clb; Rep Sr Cls; Hon Roll; NHS; Phy Thrpy.

SHAKLIK, MICHAEL; Bishop Guertin HS; Hudson, NH; (Y); FCA; Key Clb; JV Var Ftbl; Wt Lftg; OH ST U; Aviatn.

SHAUGHNESSY, JEANNE; Ashland HS; Plymouth, NH; (Y); 7/26; Math Tm; Varsity Clb; Band; Trs Sr Cls; VP Stu Cncl; Var Capt Cheerleading; Var Sftbl; Church Yth Grp; Spanish Clb; Teachers Aide; Old Grls Conf 84-85; Faclty Awd 85; Good Sprtsmnshp Awd 85; Plymouth ST Clg; Elem Educ.

SHEARER, KARRIE; Londonderry HS; Londonderry, NH; (Y); Ski Clb; Varsity Clb; Rep Jr Cls; High Hon Roll; Hon Roll; JV Cheerleading; Var Socr; Var Trk; Pilot.

SHELLING, HOPE; Hanover HS; Lyme, NH; (Y); Cmnty Wkr; Dance Clb; Hosp Aide; Pres Temple Yth Grp; Yrbk Phtg; JV Capt Fld Hcky; Var Lcrss.

SHERIDAN, CHRIS; Gilford Middle HS; Gilford, NH; (S); 3/105; Q&S; Nwsp Sprt Ed; Yrbk Sprt Ed; Pres Jr Cls; Var L Bsbl; Var L Bsktbl; Hon Roll; NHS; Math Tm; Spanish Clb; Century III Ldrs Schlrshp 84-85; Math Leag Outsndng Scorer Awd Soph 83.

SHERWOOD, MARK; Kennett HS; Madison, NH; (Y); 21/201; 4-H; Latin Clb; Ski Clb; JV Bsbl; Var Bsktbl; JV Ftbl; U Of NH; Bus.

SHOREY, LISA; Lebanon HS; W Lebanon, NH; (Y); Church Yth Grp; Band; Concert Band; Mrchg Band; Pep Band; Yrbk Stf; Hon Roll.

SHYNE, KENDRA DENISE; Salem HS; Salem, NH; (S); 27/405; Church Yth Grp; German Clb; Key Clb; Model UN; Ski Clb; Color Guard; School Play; High Hon Roll; Hon Roll; Grmn Hnr Awd 84; Goethe Inst 84; U Of TX-AUSTIN; Occptnl Thrpst.

SIBULKIN, LISA; Colebrook Acad; Colebrook, NH; (Y); Drama Clb; School Play; Yrbk Stf; Sftbl; Hesser Coll; Trvl.

SIEVERT, STEVE; Stevens HS; Claremont, NH; (Y); Am Leg Boys St; Aud/Vis; Letterman Clb; Radio Clb; Varsity Clb; School Play; Variety Show; Nwsp Sprt Ed; Nwsp Stf; Yrbk Stf; U SC; Jrnlsm.

SIGNORELLO, ROBERT; Bishop Guertin HS; Nashua, NH; (Y); 30/176; Boys Clb Am; Pres French Clb; Stu Cncl; Var JV Bsbl; JV Im Bsktbl; JV Ftbl; High Hon Roll; Hon Roll; Jr NHS; NHS; CYO Yth Of Yr 82; Holy Cross; Engrng.

SILK, AMANDA MANDI; Keene HS; Keene, NH; (Y); 106/363; Pres Church Yth Grp; Cmnty Wkr; Office Aide; Pep Clb; Spanish Clb; Yrbk Stf; VP Frsh Cls; VP Soph Cls; Pres Jr Cls; Pres Sr Cls; Hugh O Brian Yth Ldrshp NH Ambssdr; Excllnc Educ-NH Schl Brd; Slippery Rock; Scl Wrk.

SILLITTA, ANGELA; Spaulding HS; Rochester, NH; (Y); Office Aide; Rep Frsh Cls; Rep Soph Cls; Off Stu Cncl; Capt L Coach Actv; JV Crs Cntry; JV Gym; JV Socr; JV Sftbl; JV Trk; Mst Imprvd Stu 83; Johnson & Wales; Hotl Mgmt.

SILVERMAN, CATHY; Salem HS; Salem, NH; (S); 6/405; Capt Debate Tm; Key Clb; VP Latin Clb; Ski Clb; Spanish Clb; Teachers Aide; Chorus; Trs Frsh Cls; Mgr Gym; JV Trk; Schlstc Awd Miss Teen New England Pgnt 84; Best Spkr Natl Debate U Mass/Amherst 84; High Acad Avg 83; Intl Law.

SILVERMAN, LISA J; Salem HS; Salem, NH; (Y); French Clb; FBLA; FHA; Model UN; Chorus; School Musical; School Play; Nwsp Stf; Pres Frsh Cls; Pres Soph Cls; Castleton ST Coll Pres Schlrshp 85; Castleton ST Coll; Elem Educ.

SILVERMAN, STACEY; Milford Area SR HS; Amherst, NH; (Y); Q&S; Nwsp Ed-Chief; Nwsp Rptr; Yrbk Stf; Hon Roll; Quill & Scroll Awd 84; ANPA Scholastic Journlst Awd 85; Boston U; Communictn.

SIMARD, CHRIS; Memorial HS; Manchester, NH; (Y); 1/366; Cmnty Wkr; German Clb; Yrbk Stf; Var L Ice Hcky; Var L Trk; High Hon Roll; Pres NHS; Crusader Awd 83-84; NH Intrschlstc Athl Assoc All-Tourn Hcky Team 84-85; Coaches Awd Hcky 84-85.

SIMMS, TAMMY; Stevens HS; Claremont, NH; (Y); Library Aide; Hon Roll; Accntng.

SISTI, ROBYN; St Thomas Aquinas HS; Smithfield, RI; (Y); 22/87; Yrbk Stf; JV Bsktbl; Socr; Var Sftbl; Hon Roll; Army Resv Ntl Schlr Awd 85; Ltr Sftbl 84-85; Clark U; Pre-Law.

SKIDMORE JR, KENNETH J; Pinkerton Acad; Derry, NH; (Y); 160/450; Am Leg Boys St; Boys Clb Am; Rep Frsh Cls; Rep Soph Cls; Rep Jr Cls; Rep Sr Cls; Trs Stu Cncl; JV Bsktbl; Socr; Hon Roll; Mr Pinkerton Cntstnt 2nd Pl 85; Stu Cncl Schlrshp 85; Am Leg Schlrshp 85; U New Hampshire; Ed.

SKORKO, NANCY; Alvirne HS; Hudson, NH; (Y); 22/332; Hosp Aide; Teachers Aide; JV Bsktbl; JV Var Sftbl; Hon Roll; NHS; Boston Coll; Bio.

SLEATH, AMANDA; Trinity HS; Bedford, NH; (Y); Am Leg Aux Girls St; Church Yth Grp; Math Tm; Model UN; NFL; Yrbk Phtg; Var Socr; Hon Roll; NHS; NEDT Awd; Bst Hnrs Geom Stu 82-83; Bst Hnrs Alg II/Trig Stu 83-84; Bst Chem Stu 84-85; Oral Roberts U; Elem Ed.

SMALL, KATHY; Stevens HS; Claremont, NH; (Y); Church Yth Grp; Hosp Aide; Science Clb; Church Choir; Mrchg Band; Cheerleading; High Hon Roll; Hon Roll; RN.

SMILEY, DAVID; Spaulding HS; Rochester, NH; (S); 6/390; High Hon Roll; NHS; Liberal Arts Coll; Law.

SMILIKIS, ROBERT; Bishop Guertin HS; Nashua, NH; (Y); 15/170; Am Leg Boys St; Boys Clb Am; JV Bsktbl; Im Vllybl; High Hon Roll; Hon Roll; Hnr Rll 3 Strght Yrs 83-85; Grndmstr Fo Confrtrnty Of St James 86; U Of Notre Dame; Elec Engrng.

SMITH, ALEXIS E; Conant HS; Rindge, NH; (Y); 5/92; Am Leg Aux Girls St; Computer Clb; Girl Scts; Pres Jr Cls; Pres Sr Cls; JV Bsktbl; High Hon Roll; Ntl Merit Ltr; NEDT Awd; Wellesley Bk Awd 85; Georgetown; Intl Rel.

SMITH, ALICIA A; Lebanon SR HS; Lebanon, NH; (Y); 57/175; AFS; Church Yth Grp; Cmnty Wkr; French Clb; Varsity Clb; Drill Tm; Cheerleading; Golf; Elks Awd; Hon Roll; Barbers Scholar 85; Elks Scholar 85; Bay Path JC; Travel.

SMITH, AMY; Kennett HS; Freedom, NH; (Y); 91/201; 4-H; Hosp Aide; Hon Roll; Psych.

SMITH, DANIEL; Bishop Guertin HS; Lowell, MA; (Y); 14/170; Var Crs Cntry; JV Trk; High Hon Roll; NHS; Engrng.

SMITH, DAVE; Portsmouth HS; Portsmouth, NH; (Y); 98/362; Ski Clb; JV Bsbl; High Hon Roll; Hon Roll; Gray & Para-Prfssnls Schlrshps 85; U Of NH; Bus Adm.

SMITH, DEBBY S; Pembroke Acad; Epsom, NH; (Y); 15/200; French Clb; Rep Soph Cls; Trs Jr Cls; Var L Bsktbl; Var L Fld Hcky; Var L Sftbl; Hon Roll; NHS; Rep Frsh Cls; Female Athlt Of The Yr 84-85; Photo.

SMITH, JASON; A Crosby Kennett HS; Ctr Conway, NH; (Y); 51/201; French Clb; Var L Bsbl; JV Bsktbl; Var L Ftbl; Hon Roll; Archit.

SMITH, JEAN; Lebanon HS; Lebanon, NH; (Y); Church Yth Grp; French Clb; Hosp Aide; Concert Band; Mrchg Band; Stu Cncl; Trk; High Hon Roll; Hon Roll; U Of NH; Occptnl Thrpy.

SMITH, JONATHAN; Spaulding HS; Rochester, NH; (S); 18/361; Boy Scts; Key Clb; Math Tm; High Hon Roll; Mu Alp Tht; NHS; Arch.

SMITH, KATHERINE E; Lebanon HS; Lebanon, NH; (Y); 47/175; AFS; Sec Church Yth Grp; Cmnty Wkr; French Clb; Girl Scts; Pep Clb; Varsity Clb; Band; Color Guard; Mrchg Band; Elizabeth Parkhill Dllrs Schlrs 85; Bay Path JC; Fshn Merchndsng.

SMITH, KATHLEEN; Stevens HS; Windsor, VT; (Y); Am Leg Aux Girls St; Church Yth Grp; Yrbk Stf; Stu Cncl; JV Socr; High Hon Roll; Hon Roll; Var Ski Tm Capt; Mktng.

SMITH, KELLY; Portsmouth HS; Rye, NH; (S); 8/374; Church Yth Grp; Model UN; JV Var Cheerleading; High Hon Roll; Hon Roll; NHS; Scholar Athletic Award 83-84; Physical Therapist.

SMITH, KIM; Timberlane Regional HS; Atkinson, NH; (Y); Lib Concert Band; Mrchg Band; Yrbk Stf; Cheerleading; Hon Roll; Bus Adm.

SMITH, LESLEY; Portsmouth SR HS; Portsmouth, NH; (S); 15/362; Sec Church Yth Grp; Hosp Aide; VP Latin Clb; Model UN; Ski Clb; Var L Fld Hcky; Swmmng; NHS; Schlr Athl Awd 83-84; Hghst Hgh Hnrs 81-85; Pre Med.

SMITH, SHERI; Concord HS; Concord, NH; (Y); VP Church Yth Grp; Drama Clb; School Play; Stage Crew; Variety Show; Var Crs Cntry; Im Sftbl; Im Trk; High Hon Roll; Hon Roll; Engl & Art Achvt Awds 85.

SOCZEWINSKI, RICHARD; Franklin HS; Franklin, NH; (Y); 10/108; Am Leg Boys St; Church Yth Grp; Computer Clb; Library Aide; Math Tm; Rep Stu Cncl; Bsktbl; Trk; Elks Awd; Hon Roll.

SOLOSKO, THOMAS A; Nashua SR HS; Nashua, NH; (Y); 16/808; Am Leg Boys St; Boy Scts; Pres Church Yth Grp; Band; Chorus; Orch; Trk; NHS; Pres Schlr; Voice Dem Awd; Brigham Young U; Elec Engr.

SOSA, CHRISTOPHER; Bishop Guertin HS; Nashua, NH; (Y); VP Church Yth Grp; Drama Clb; Spanish Clb; Thesps; School Play; Stage Crew; Nwsp Stf; Im Mgr Bsktbl; Wt Lftg; JV Wrstlng; Grphc Arts.

SOUCY, DENISE; Memorial HS; Manchester, NH; (Y); 27/402; Camera Clb; Nwsp Phtg; Yrbk Phtg; JV Trk; Hon Roll; Prfct Atten Awd; NH ST Polc Benevolen Assn 85; Notre Dame Coll; Comm Art.

SOUCY, DONNA; Trinity HS; Manchester, NH; (Y); 19/194; Model UN; Political Wkr; Hon Roll; NHS; St Anselms; Bus.

SOYCHAK, ELIZABETH; Winnisquam Regional HS; Laconia, NH; (Y); 8/80; Drama Clb; Model UN; Ski Clb; Thesps; Chorus; School Musical; School Play; Swing Chorus; Yrbk Phtg; Yrbk Stf; Ntl Awd Excllnc 85; Mst Vlbl Soprno 85; Al-Star Cst Awd Drma Fstvl 85; Boston U; Cmnctns.

SPALDING, KENNETH; Milford Area SR HS; Amherst, NH; (Y); Boy Scts; Church Yth Grp; Debate Tm; Ski Clb; Band; Concert Band; Jazz Band; Mrchg Band; JV Socr; Elks Awd; US Naval Acad.

SPATES, SHARON LEE; Salem HS; Salem, NH; (S); 71/373; Boys Clb Am; Sec Church Yth Grp; Cmnty Wkr; Model UN; Teachers Aide; High Hon Roll; Hon Roll; Chldhd Educ.

SPAULDING, RICHARD; Kearsarge Regional HS; New London, NH; (Y); Boy Scts; Church Yth Grp; Drama Clb; Hosp Aide; Model UN; Varsity Clb; Chorus; School Musical; School Play; Pres Jr Cls; HOSA 85-86; Norwich U; Marines.

SPEAR, RICHARD; Spaulding HS; Rochester, NH; (Y); 49/352; Key Clb; Yrbk Ed-Chief; Pres Jr Cls; Rep Sr Cls; Hon Roll; Bus Adm.

SPEIDEL, JOE; Trinity HS; Manchester, NH; (Y); 19/190; Cmnty Wkr; School Play; Nwsp Rptr; Nwsp Stf; JV Bsktbl; Var Capt Socr; Var Tennis; High Hon Roll; Hon Roll; Ntl Merit SF; Boston Coll; Psych.

SPENCER, JEANNE; Mount St Mary Seminary; Nashua, NH; (Y); 1/90; Ski Clb; Yrbk Stf; Pres NHS; Ntl Merit SF; Voice Dem Awd; Drama Clb; Hosp Aide; Model UN; School Play; Im Gym.

SPENCER, JOHN; Salem HS; Salem, NH; (Y); 63/350; Math Tm; U Of NH; Elctrcl Engrng.

SPENCER, JULIE A; Plymouth Area HS; Plymouth, NH; (Y); 6/144; AFS; Church Yth Grp; Ski Clb; Varsity Clb; Rep Stu Cncl; Var Fld Hcky; Var Capt Tennis; High Hon Roll; NHS; Variety Show.

SPENCER, STEVEN M; Nashua SR HS; Nashua, NH; (Y); 12/807; Am Leg Boys St; Boys Clb Am; Var L Bsbl; Var L Bsktbl; High Hon Roll; VP Jr NHS; VP NHS; Hon Roll; MIP Bsktbl & Bsebl 84-85; Rensselaer Polytech; Chem.

SPERO-MICHAELS, LYNDA JOAN; Londonderry HS; Londonderry, NH; (Y); Spanish Clb; JV Sftbl; High Hon Roll; Hon Roll; Spanish NHS; Vet Sci.

ST GELAIS, JOANNE; Manchester HS West; Bedford, NH; (Y); 58/375; Trs Drama Clb; School Play; Stage Crew; Variety Show; Trk; Plymouth ST Coll; Acctg.

ST HILAIRE, RICARDO A; Concord HS; Concord, NH; (Y); 2/330; Am Leg Boys St; Cmnty Wkr; Exploring; Model UN; Political Wkr; Pres Speech Tm; Pres Jr Cls; Pres NHS; Sal; Harvard Bk Awd 85; Rotary Intl Wrld Affrs Smnr 85; Intl Bus.

ST JOHN, RONNA; St Thomas Aquinas HS; Dover, NH; (Y); Sec Church Yth Grp; Cmnty Wkr; Sec French Clb; Sec JA; Key Clb; Office Aide; Yrbk Ed-Chief; Sec Jr Cls; Trs Sr Cls; Crs Cntry; Hugh O Brien Yth Fndtn; Red Crss Vlntr Awd; Rep Regnl JA Conf; Exc Secy.

ST LAURENT, ELLIE; Note HS; Sambornville, NH; (Y); 4-H; FBLA; Girl Scts; Chorus; Army.

ST LAWRENCE, JOAN; Spaulding HS; Rochester, NH; (S); 51/485; Rep Frsh Cls; Rep Jr Cls; Stu Cncl; Var Capt Cheerleading; Hon Roll.

ST LOUIS, JAMES P; Londonderry HS; Londonderry, NH; (Y); Am Leg Boys St; Boy Scts; Concert Band; Jazz Band; Orch; Stage Crew; Yrbk Ed-Chief; Exploring; Math Tm; Band; Egl Sct 83; Project Venture Bcycld Acrss Cntry & Montreal Cnsqtvly 84-85; Audio Prdctn.

ST LOUIS, PAULA; Loconia HS; Laconia, NH; (Y); 18/157; Drama Clb; French Clb; Service Clb; Fld Hcky; Hon Roll; WA U Smmr Schlr 85; Pre Law.

STALLINGS, CARLTON; Alvirne HS; Hudson, NH; (Y); 54/375; Am Leg Boys St; 4-H; School Play; Trk; Cit Awd; Hon Roll; ST Recrd 100-M Dash-10.8-84-85; All Area Star Tm Outstndg Athls 84-85; VP ; Nh Trckstrs Trck Clb 85; Sprts Psych.

STAMMERS, ROBERT; Stevens HS; Cornish, NH; (Y); Boy Scts; Computer Clb; JV Bsbl; Im Bsktbl; Hon Roll; Egl Sct Awd 85; Air Force; Law.

STANHOPE, MARY; Goffstown Area HS; Goffstown, NH; (Y); 6/180; Drama Clb; School Play; Yrbk Ed-Chief; Pres Jr Cls; High Hon Roll; NHS; ST Arts Schlrshp 1st Pl; Math & Art Pins; Syracuse U; Comp Grphcs.

STEINER, PATRICIA ANNE; Goffstown Area HS; Manchester, NH; (Y); 7/212; Aud/Vis; Church Yth Grp; Drama Clb; Exploring; Ski Clb; Concert Band; Jazz Band; Mrchg Band; Pep Band; School Play; All ST Music Awd; Fr Awd; Cmmnctns.

STEINER, STEPHEN; Goffstown Area HS; Manchester, NH; (Y); 1/200; Boy Scts; Capt Chess Clb; Capt Math Clb; Ski Clb; Stage Crew; Yrbk Stf; Var L Crs Cntry; Var L Trk; Ntl Merit Schol; Val; Sanders Assoc Schlrshp 85; Air Force ROTC Schlrshp 85; Hugh O Brian Schl Nominee 83; USAF Acad; Engrng.

STETSON, KIMBERLY; Milford Area SR HS; Milford, NH; (Y); 13/289; Nwsp Phtg; Nwsp Rptr; JV Bsktbl; Var L Socr; Var L Sftbl; Hon Roll; NHS; Pres Schlr; Harley Sanford Aux No 4368 Schlrshp $300 85; U Of NH; Pol Sci.

STETSON, SHERI; Laconia HS; Laconia, NH; (Y); French Clb; Rep Frsh Cls; Rep Soph Cls; Rep Jr Cls; Rep Stu Cncl; JV Fld Hcky; Var Capt Tennis; Hon Roll; MV Jr Stu Cncl Mbr 85; Law.

STEVENS, BETSY; Farmington HS; Middleton, NH; (Y); 3/70; Pres Trs 4-H; French Clb; Teachers Aide; 4-H Awd; High Hon Roll; Hon Roll; NHS; Hugh O Brian Yth Ldrshp Fndtn 84.

STEVENS, MICHELLE; Dover HS; Dover, NH; (Y); 39/281; Spanish Clb; Band; Color Guard; Concert Band; Jazz Band; Mrchg Band; Variety Show; Rep Stu Cncl; High Hon Roll; Hon Roll; Trvl & Trsm.

STEVENS, ROBYN; Salem HS; Salem, NH; (Y); FHA; Key Clb; Model UN; School Play; Trs Sr Cls; Mgr(s); Score Keeper; Timer; Hon Roll; Emerson Coll; Theatr.

STEVENS, SHEILA; Exeter Area HS; Stratham, NH; (Y); 35/300; 4-H; School Play; Yrbk Stf; Var Tennis; 4-H Awd; Hon Roll; Home Ec Awd 84; 4-H Spirit Awd 83; U NH.

STEVENSON, REBECCA; The Derryfield Schl; Amherst, NH; (Y); Intnl Clb; PAVAS; Yrbk Bus Mgr; Var Fld Hcky; Var Tennis; Hon Roll; Art Hstry.

STEVENSON, ROBERT J; Pinkerton Acad; East Derry, NH; (Y); 15/592; Am Leg Boys St; Boys Clb Am; Math Tm; Ski Clb; Crs Cntry; Lcrss; Trk; Hon Roll; Jr NHS; NHS; Proj Challnge 84-85; Manchester Fed Arts Art Awd; Engrng.

STEWART, JEFFREY; Profile JR SR HS; Franconia, NH; (Y); Church Yth Grp; Math Tm; Yrbk Stf; Off Soph Cls; Cheerleading; High Hon Roll; Hon Roll; U S Army; Med.

STEWART, SHERRI; Thayer HS; Winchester, NH; (Y); Church Yth Grp; Teachers Aide; Hon Roll; NHS; Prfct Atten Awd; Var Cheerleading; Cls Treas 82-85; Nrs.

STILLINGS, TINA; Littleton HS; Littleton, NH; (Y); 2/100; Church Yth Grp; Band; Concert Band; Jazz Band; Mrchg Band; Sec Jr Cls; Sec Sr Cls; Var L Bsktbl; Coach Actv; Var L Fld Hcky; St Pauls Adv Studies Pgm 85; Alg II, Hstry, Frnch I Excllnc Awds 84; Engl, Bio, Govt, Band Excllnc 83.

STOCKING, THOMAS; Concord HS; Concord, NH; (Y); 58/360; Church Yth Grp; Var Socr; Var L Trk; NHS; U Santa Clara.

STONE, MICHELE; Dover HS; Dover, NH; (Y); Cheerleading; Trk; Hon Roll.

STONGE, MATTHEW; Milford Area SR HS; Milford, NH; (Y); JV Bsktbl; Hon Roll; Accntng Awd 85; Arch.

STOTZ, LAURA C; Milfrod Area SR HS; Milford, NH; (Y); 18/280; Computer Clb; Math Tm; Acpl Chr; Pres Sec Band; Drm Mjr(t); Jazz Band; JP Sousa Awd; Intnl Clb; Leo Clb; Chorus; Stu Mnth 85; Sole Rcpnt Eng Dept Sr Outstndng Achvt Eng Awd 85; Coll William & Mary; Intl Bus.

STPIERRE, ERIC; Concord HS; Concord, NH; (Y); 83/400; Church Yth Grp; Science Clb; High Hon Roll; Hon Roll; Prfct Atten Awd; Cornell U; Astrnmy.

STRABLIZKY, JAMES; Franklin JR-SR HS; Franklin, NH; (Y); Hon Roll; Ski Clb; Spanish Clb; Teachers Aide; Spn Awd 83; Bus.

STRATZ, ANDREW; Dover HS; Barrington, NH; (Y); 102/350; Var L Ftbl; NH Coll.

STREET, TAVIA; Holderness Schl; Meredith, NH; (Y); 28/78; Church Yth Grp; Var Crs Cntry; Var Socr; Library Aide; Nwsp Stf; Yrbk Stf; Var Bsktbl; Var Cheerleading; Var Sftbl; High Hon Roll; 1st Pl Awd Track Meet 83; Exc US Hstry Awd 83; 1st Pl & Grnd Prz Sci Fair 82; St Anselms; Music.

STROUT, LINETTE MARCIA; Timberlane Regional HS; Plaistow, NH; (Y); Drama Clb; Chorus; School Play; Off Frsh Cls; VP Soph Cls; Off Jr Cls; Off Sr Cls; Dnfth Awd; Hon Roll; NHS; Stu Of Mnth 85; NH Frgn Lang Poetry Rectn-2nd Pl 85; Muscl Theatre.

STUART, JANICE; S Estrn New Hampshire Chrstian Acad; Lebanon, ME; (S); 24/296; Church Yth Grp; School Play; Nwsp Stf; Yrbk Ed-Chief; Pres Sr Cls; Var Bsktbl; Var Vllybl; High Hon Roll; Val; Chrh Pianist N Lebanon 84-85; Sndy Schl Tchr 83-85; Mc Intosh Coll; Accntng.

STUART, JILL; Southeastern NH Christian Acad; Lebanon, ME; (S); Church Yth Grp; Nwsp Rptr; Yrbk Stf; Bsktbl; Cheerleading; Sftbl; Vllybl; High Hon Roll; Bio Awd 84; Hstry Awd 84.

SUGHRUE, BILL; Trinity HS; Manchester, NH; (Y); Am Leg Boys St; Ice Hcky; Socr; Hon Roll; Wagner Hosser Scholar 85; Parents W/Out Partners Intl Scholar 85; NH All ST Socr Tm 85; Lions Cup 85; Boston Coll; Bus.

SULLIVAN, ANN MARIE; Portsmouth HS; Pease AFB, NH; (S); Boy Scts; Drama Clb; Model UN; School Musical; Stage Crew; High Hon Roll; NHS; Dartmouth; Math.

SULLIVAN, DEBRA; Trinity HS; Manchester, NH; (Y); Am Leg Aux Girls St; Sec Pres Church Yth Grp; Model UN; Yrbk Ed-Chief; Yrbk Stf; JV Var Bsktbl; Hon Roll; NHS; Soc Studs Awd 85; Religion Awd 85; Pol Sci.

SULLIVAN, JAMES; Bishop Guertin HS; Lowell, MA; (Y); 22/180; Church Yth Grp; Spanish Clb; Band; Church Choir; JV Bsbl; Im Bsktbl; Im Wt Lftg; Hon Roll; Spanish NHS; Boys Clb Am; Lowell Maj Leag Bsbl; Hyder Meml Schlrshp; Bishop Guertin Schlrshp; Plastc Engrng.

SULLIVAN, JAMES D; Nashua HS; Nashua, NH; (Y); Computer Clb; Math Tm; Ski Clb; Nwsp Rptr; Var Co-Capt Golf; Var Tennis; NHS; Ntl Merit SF; Boys Clb Am; Office Aide; St Pauls Advcd Stds Prog Physics 84; Sftwr Engr.

SULLIVAN, JEAN E; Pembroke Acad; Pembroke, NH; (Y); Var Cheerleading; Hon Roll; Nrs.

SULLIVAN, MICHAEL E; Kimball Union Acad; Alton, NH; (Y); 2/75; Math Tm; School Play; Nwsp Ed-Chief; Off Sr Cls; Var L Bsbl; Var L Socr; Var L Wrstlng; High Hon Roll; Church Yth Grp; Pres Sec Computer Clb; Cum Laude Assn 84-85; Tellurice Assn Summr Pgm Scholar 84; Jrnlsm.

SUNUNU, MICHAEL; Salem HS; Salem, NH; (S); 5/405; Debate Tm; Pres Math Tm; Model UN; Ski Clb; Pres Jr Cls; Stu Cncl; JV Var Socr; Trk; High Hon Roll; NHS.

SWIFT, ELIZABETH; Inter-Lakes HS; Center Harbor, NH; (Y); Church Yth Grp; French Clb; Chorus; Ed Yrbk Phtg; Yrbk Stf; Var Vllybl; High Hon Roll; Hon Roll; Trs Frsh Cls; Trs Soph Cls.

TABER, TIMOTHY; Inter-Lakes HS; Meredith, NH; (Y); 10/57; 4-H; Var Bsbl; JV Capt Bsktbl; JV Socr; Hon Roll; Sci Fair 3rd Pl Physcl Sci 83; Sci Fair 2nd Pl Advncd Bio 85; Plymouth ST Coll; Phy Ed.

TAILLON, SHARI ANN; Timberlane Regional HS; Plaistow, NH; (Y); 42/220; French Clb; Teachers Aide; Yrbk Stf; Sftbl; U NH; Pre-Med.

TALBOT, MICHELLE; Presentation Of Mary HS; Pelham, NH; (Y); Art Clb; Church Yth Grp; Drama Clb; Ski Clb; Variety Show; Nwsp Bus Mgr; Nwsp Phtg; Nwsp Stf; Yrbk Phtg; Yrbk Stf; Endicott Coll; Cmrcl Art.

TANGUAY, GINA; Spaulding HS; E Rochester, NH; (Y); Rep Frsh Cls; Pres Soph Cls; Rep Jr Cls; Rep Sr Cls; Stat Bsbl; L Crs Cntry; L Socr; L Trk; Var Hon Roll; Phy Thrpy.

TARBELL, LISA V; Nashua HS; Nashua, NH; (Y); 118/831; Church Yth Grp; Drama Clb; Nwsp Stf; Yrbk Stf; Hon Roll; Jr NHS; NHS; U Of NH; Bus Admin.

TARDIF, ANDREA; Laconia HS; Laconia, NH; (Y); French Clb; Hosp Aide; Sec Stu Cncl; Crs Cntry; Tennis; Hon Roll; JC Awd; NHS; Mdcl.

TARDIF, GERARD P; Bishop Guertin HS; Nashua, NH; (Y); FCA; Var L Bsbl; Var L Ice Hcky; Bus.

TAYLOR, DONALD; Berlin HS; Berlin, NH; (Y); 14/200; Lit Mag; Var Trk; Hon Roll; NHS; U Of New Hampshire; Teach.

TAYLOR, ERIK; Moultonborough Acad; Moultonboro, NH; (Y); 11/35; School Play; Nwsp Rptr; Nwsp Stf; Yrbk Stf; VP Jr Cls; Rep Stu Cncl; L Bsbl; L Ftbl; Wt Lftg; Hon Roll; U Of NH; Jrnlsm.

TAYLOR, KRISTINE; Spaulding HS; Rochester, NH; (S); 1/416; VP Key Clb; Sec Math Clb; Math Tm; Yrbk Ed-Chief; DAR Awd; High Hon Roll; NHS; Ntl Merit Ltr; Century III Ldrshp Schlrshp; CCD Teacher-St Marys Parish; Dartmouth; Pre-Med.

TAYLOR, TRACY; Portsmouth HS; Pease Afb, NH; (Y); 4/400; Concert Band; Symp Band; Mgr(s); Var L Trk; High Hon Roll; Jr NHS; NHS; Band; Mrchg Band; Stat Bsktbl; St Pauls Advncd Study Pgm 85; 1st Chr Flute 83-84; Strep Pgm 84-85; Vet.

TAYLOR, TROY; Spaulding HS; Rochester, NH; (S); Hon Roll.

TERRAVECCHIA, SUSAN JENNIFER; Pinkerton Acad; Chester, NH; (Y); 40/450; Am Leg Aux Girls St; Church Yth Grp; Spanish Clb; JV L Bsktbl; L Var Sftbl; Hon Roll; Trs NHS; SADD 84-85; Life Savng, First Aid & CPR Certfd; Colby; Tchng.

TEWKSBURY, CRYSTAL; Pittsfield HS; Pittsfield, NH; (S); 13/60; DECA; Varsity Clb; Yrbk Ed-Chief; Var Capt Bsktbl; Coach Actv; Var Sftbl; High Hon Roll; Bay Path JC; Trvl Adm.

THAYER, JAMES; Woodsville HS; Woodsville, NH; (Y); Cmnty Wkr; Drama Clb; FBLA; Math Tm; Radio Clb; School Play; Stage Crew; Nwsp Ed-Chief; Nwsp Rptr; Nwsp Stf; Comp Sci Outstndg Achvt 84-85; 3rd Pl New England Yng Poet Cont Boston Globe 83; U Of NH; Pre-Law.

THERIAULT, KIM; Spaulding HS; Rochester, NH; (S); 27/420; Yrbk Phtg; Pres Frsh Cls; Pres Soph Cls; Pres Jr Cls; Pres Sr Cls; Var Cheerleading; Hon Roll; Camera Clb; FBLA; Math Clb; Hugh O Brian Yuth Fdtn Ldrshp Smnr 83; Adv Studies Pgm 84; NH Jr Ms Schlrshp Pgm Wnner 85; Frgn Rel.

THERRIEN, DONNA; Dover HS; Dover, NH; (Y); Church Yth Grp; Cmnty Wkr; Hosp Aide; Key Clb; Service Clb; Yrbk Ed-Chief; Yrbk Stf; Sec Soph Cls; Hon Roll; U NH; Bus Admin.

THERRIEN, KAREN; Winnisquam Regional HS; Tilton, NH; (Y); 2/78; Math Tm; Ski Clb; Pres Band; Yrbk Ed-Chief; Var Capt Fld Hcky; Var Capt Sftbl; Sec NHS; Sal; Acad Achvt Awd 84; US Army Rsrv Natl Schlr/Athl Awd 85; Pres Acad/Ftns Awd 85; Utica Coll; Bus Admin.

THIBAULT, CARRIE J; Franklin JR SR HS; Franklin, NH; (Y); 2/97; Am Leg Aux Girls St; French Clb; Sec Jr Cls; Off Stu Cncl; JV Var Bsktbl; JV Var Fld Hcky; JV Var Sftbl; NHS; Prfct Atten Awd; Sal; NH Frdtn Wmns Club Schlrshp 85; Mst Otstndng Yng Wmns Awd 85; Bentley Coll; Sccntng.

THIBAULT, JODIE; Mascenic Regional HS; Greenville, NH; (Y); Church Yth Grp; Trs Frsh Cls; Score Keeper; Hon Roll; NHS; Am Leg Schlrshp 85; Am Leg Aux Schlrshp 85; Long Island U; Acctng.

THIBAULT, SCOTT; Memorial HS; Manchester, NH; (Y); 18/366; Boy Scts; Nwsp Rptr; Nwsp Stf; Rep Stu Cncl; Var L Ftbl; JV Ice Hcky; Im Wt Lftg; High Hon Roll; Sci.

THIBODEAU, DEBORAH L; Milford Area SR HS; Milford, NH; (Y); Am Leg Aux Girls St; 4-H; Yrbk Stf; Stu Cncl; Im Powder Puff Ftbl; Im Vllybl; High Hon Roll; Hon Roll; VP NHS; Wellesley Bk Awd 85; Vrsty Cross Cntry Ski Tm 84-85; Comp Sci.

THISTLE, PETER; Pinkerton Acad; E Hampstead, NH; (S); 62/400; Church Yth Grp; Ski Clb; Band; Concert Band; Jazz Band; Mrchg Band; School Musical; Variety Show; 4-H Awd; Hon Roll; 4-H Awd Rgnl UNH 84; Asmbly God Teen Talent 3rd Lvl Comp DC 84 & 85; Bus Mktg.

THOMAS, DEBORAH ANN; Salem HS; Salem, NH; (S); 30/380; Pres French Clb; Key Clb; Latin Clb; Model UN; Teachers Aide; Ed Nwsp Rptr; JV Sftbl; U Of NH; Orthodontist.

THOMAS, JOELLE; Spaulding HS; Sanbornville, NH; (Y); 37/350; JV L Bsktbl; Var Mgr Sftbl; Hon Roll; Stratham Vo Tech; Comp.

THOMPSON, KEVIN; Stevens HS; Claremont, NH; (Y); Dance Clb; Nwsp Rptr; Yrbk Stf; JV Var Bsbl; JV Bsktbl; High Hon Roll; Hon Roll; JC Awd; JP Sousa Awd; Cmmnctns.

THORNTON, TIM; Salem HS; Windham, NH; (Y); 50/400; Capt Debate Tm; Exploring; Var Trk; Hon Roll; Spanish NHS; Law.

THURSTON, ANTHONY; Concord HS; Concord, NH; (Y); Var L Trk; Hon Roll; Grphcs Art Awd 83; Soc Stud 84; Holy Cross; Nvl Ofcr.

THURSTON, KEREN; St Thomas Aquinas HS; Dover, NH; (Y); Am Leg Aux Girls St; Church Yth Grp; GAA; Yrbk Stf; Bsktbl; Sftbl; High Hon Roll; Hon Roll; NHS; MVP Sftbl; MIP Bsktbl; Bst All Arnd Ath Sftbl; Med.

TIERNEY, BRAIN; Manchester Memorial HS; Manchester, NH; (Y); 15/366; Am Leg Boys St; Intnl Clb; Teachers Aide; Coach Actv; Golf; Tennis; High Hon Roll; Hon Roll; NHS; Frgn Lang Nwsp Chf Edtr 86; Frgn Lang Nwsp Stff 83-85; Dntstry.

TIERNEY, BRIAN; Manchester Memorial HS; Litchfield, NH; (Y); 15/366; Am Leg Boys St; Intnl Clb; Teachers Aide; Nwsp Ed-Chief; Var Golf; JV Socr; Var Tennis; High Hon Roll; NHS; Outstndng Physcl Ed 82; Dentstry.

TILTON, STEPHANIE; Conant HS; Jaffrey, NH; (Y); Pres Frsh Cls; Pres Soph Cls; Var Bsktbl; Var Capt Fld Hcky; Var Sftbl; Swmmng; Var Tennis; Dartmouth Bk Awd; All St Bsktbl; MVP Bsktbl; Pre-Law.

TITUS, MICHELLE; Salem HS; Salem, NH; (Y); Debate Tm; Sec Latin Clb; Math Clb; Yrbk Stf; Var Stu Cncl; Var Fld Hcky; JV Trk; High Hon Roll; NHS; Key Clb; VP NHASC 85-86; Yrbk Tri-Edtr 85-86; Jrnlsm.

TODD, DOIRON; Newport JR SR HS; Newport, NH; (Y); Computer Clb; Science Clb; VP Spanish Clb; Stage Crew; Trs Frsh Cls; Stu Cncl; Var Bsbl; Var Bsktbl; Var Ftbl; Var Tennis; NH Al-ST Ftbl Tm 84-85; Cmnctns.

TOLMAN, MARGUERITE; Keene HS; Keene, NH; (Y); Am Leg Aux Girls St; Pep Clb; Ski Clb; Band; Concert Band; Stage Crew; Off Soph Cls; Rep Jr Cls; JV Fld Hcky; JV Gym; Graphic Design.

TOMASELLI, DANIEL J; Salem HS; Salem, NH; (Y); Hon Roll; Med Tech.

TOMPKINS, JENNIFER L; Salem HS; Salem, NH; (Y); 5/363; Key Clb; Math Tm; Model UN; Ski Clb; Teachers Aide; School Play; Stage Crew; Yrbk Ed-Chief; Stu Cncl; High Hon Roll; Elks Teenager Mnth 85; Stu Cncl Reg VP 84-85; U PA; Intl Bus.

TONNESEN, GREGORY; Milford Area SR HS; Amherst, NH; (Y); Var L Golf; JV Socr; Hon Roll; Solor Engry Awd 82; Stanford.

TOTH, SUSAN; Salem HS; Salem, NH; (S); 17/405; Ski Clb; Off Jr Cls; JV Bsktbl; Trk; Elks Awd; High Hon Roll; MVP Bsktbl 83; Coaches Awd Bsktbl 84.

TRAHAN, PATRICIA; Littleton HS; Littleton, NH; (Y); 10/97; Church Yth Grp; Yrbk Stf; Var L Fld Hcky; Hon Roll; Archtctre.

TRASATTI, SUSAN; Milford Area SR HS; Amherst, NH; (Y); 22/200; Hosp Aide; Ski Clb; Yrbk Bus Mgr; Sec Stu Cncl; Powder Puff Ftbl; Var L Socr; High Hon Roll; Hon Roll; NHS; Dollars Schlrs Schlrshp 85; Pres Acad Ftns Awd 85; Holy Cross Coll; Math.

TREEN, KARL; Derryfields Schl; Merrimack, NH; (Y); Sec Camera Clb; French Clb; Key Clb; Ski Clb; Nwsp Rptr; Wt Lftg; Hon Roll; Jrnlsm.

TRELA, CYNTHIA; Dover HS; Dover, NH; (Y); Church Yth Grp; French Clb; Girl Scts; Key Clb; Library Aide; Chorus; High Hon Roll; NHS.

TREMBLAY, BRIAN; Manchester High School West; Bedford, NH; (Y); 111/365; Cmnty Wkr; Exploring; Nwsp Bus Mgr; Nwsp Ed-Chief; Nwsp Phtg; Lit Mag; Var Capt Crs Cntry; Var Trk; High Hon Roll; Hon Roll; Manchester Mayors Citznshp Awd 85; Srvc Awd/Princpls Awd 85; Faculty Schlrshp 85; Castleton ST Coll; Communctns.

TREMBLAY, JACQUELINE; Portsmouth SR HS; New Castle, NH; (S); 5/424; Mathletes; Math Clb; Math Tm; Sec Ski Clb; High Hon Roll; NHS; JR Wrld Cncl 84-85; Dartmouth; Med.

TREMBLAY, JASON; Laconia HS; Lakeport, NH; (Y); Boy Scts; Church Yth Grp; Ski Clb; Var Capt Crs Cntry; Var Trk; Im Wt Lftg; Hon Roll; MVP Cross Cty 84; Outstndng Rnnr Trk 82-85; Physcl Thrpy.

TRISCIANI, BRENDA LEE; Manchester Memorial HS; Manchester, NH; (Y); 14/366; Am Leg Aux Girls St; Girl Scts; Yrbk Stf; Ed Lit Mag; Rep Stu Cncl; Var L Cheerleading; Powder Puff Ftbl; High Hon Roll; NHS; Mem Crusader Awd For Pblctns 85; 1st Clss Awd Grl Sct 83; ROTC; Engrng.

TRUAX, MELINDA; Portsmouth SR HS; Greenland, NH; (Y); Latin Clb; Bowling; Fld Hcky; Sftbl; High Hon Roll; Hon Roll; Nrthwstrn; Crmnl Law.

TUCKER JR, LEON; Concord HS; Concord, NH; (Y); 5/330; Intnl Clb; Math Tm; Model UN; Im Bsktbl; High Hon Roll; NHS; Top 10 In Clss 83-85; Rnnr-Up Lcl Rotary Intl Spch Cont 85; Econ.

TUCKER, MICHAEL; Mascoma Valley Regional HS; Lebanon, NH; (Y); Art Clb; Math Tm; Ski Clb; Concert Band; Mrchg Band; Socr; High Hon Roll; Hon Roll; NHS; MIP Var Sccr 84; Engrng.

TUMMINELLO, MATTHEW; Bishop Guertin HS; Chelmsford, MA; (Y); Ski Clb; Trk; Comm.

TUPICK, BONNIE; Berlin SR HS; Berlin, NH; (Y); 69/210; VP Sr Cls; Var Badmtn; Trk; VFW Awd; Voice Dem Awd; Miss Ntl Teenager Berlin 85; NH Vo-Tech Coll; Bus Adm.

TURGEON, KRISTINE; Concord HS; Concord, NH; (Y); 29/323; Dance Clb; Mrchg Band; Yrbk Stf; Sec Soph Cls; Rep Jr Cls; Twrlr; High Hon Roll; Hon Roll; NHS; Achvt Cert In Intrmdt Typng 84; Cert Of Exc In Englsh 85; Intl Bus.

TURMELLE, ELIZABETH; Londonderry HS; Londonderry, NH; (Y); 4-H; Ski Clb; Rep Soph Cls; Hon Roll; Bus.

TURNER, JOHN; Milford Area SR HS; Amherst, NH; (Y); 15/289; Debate Tm; Math Tm; Political Wkr; Trs Rep Frsh Cls; Trs Rep Soph Cls; Trs Jr Cls; Trs Sr Cls; Stu Cncl; Var L Crs Cntry; Cit Awd; Ldrshp & Physcs 85; Holy Crss Bk Awd 84; Duracell SF 85; Hnr Cncl 85; U Of ME Orono; Elctrcl Engr.

TUROTTE, CHRISTINE; Presentation Of Mary Academy; Lowell, MA; (Y); Church Yth Grp; Drama Clb; Science Clb; Ski Clb; Yrbk Stf; Pres Jr Cls; Pres Stu Cncl; NHS; NEDT Awd; Rivier Clg Chllng Prog 84-85.

TUSON, GWEN LOUISE; Manchester HS; Manchester, NH; (Y); Am Leg Aux Girls St; Math Tm; School Play; Nwsp Stf; Lit Mag; Rep Stu Cncl; Var Crs Cntry; High Hon Roll; NHS; Sec Church Yth Grp.

TUTTLE, KRISTEN; Mascoma Valley Regional HS; Naalehu, HI; (Y); Drama Clb; Library Aide; Ski Clb; Tennis; High Hon Roll; Hon Roll; Aerontcs.

TUTTLE, MATTHEW J; Nashua SR HS; Nashua, NH; (Y); 3/807; Am Leg Boys St; Debate Tm; Pres Latin Clb; Pres Band; School Musical; Var Capt Golf; High Hon Roll; JP Sousa Awd; NHS; NFL; Rensselaer Mdl; Boston Coll.

TUTTLE, MELISSA; Spaulding HS; E Rochester, NH; (Y); Key Clb; Var Trk; Hon Roll; New Hamp Coll; Bus.

TUTTLE, TIMOTHY D; Nashua SR HS; Nashua, NH; (Y); Am Leg Boys St; Concert Band; Jazz Band; Mrchg Band; Variety Show; Rep Stu Cncl; Var Capt Golf; VP NHS; High Hon Roll; Debate Tm; 3rd Pl ST Orgnl Oratry Spch Comptn 84; Art Awd 83.

TUXILL, JOHN; Hopkinton HS; Concord, NH; (Y); 1/75; Math Tm; Model UN; Yrbk Stf; Trs Stu Cncl; Var Capt Crs Cntry; Var Trk; High Hon Roll; NHS; Ntl Merit Ltr; French Clb; Colby Coll Bk Awd 85; Adv Studies Pgm 85; Bio Sci.

TWOMBLEY, SCOTT; Spaulding HS; Sanbornville, NH; (Y); Camera Clb; Drama Clb; School Musical; School Play; Stage Crew; Variety Show; Hon Roll; Drama.

TYLER, JAY; Mascoma Valley Regional HS; Enfield, NH; (Y); Nwsp Rptr; VP Rep Frsh Cls; Rep Soph Cls; Rep Jr Cls; Rep Sr Cls; JV Var Bsbl; Var Capt Bsktbl; Var Socr; Hon Roll; Physical Therapy.

ULRICH, KAREN; Londonderry HS; Londonderry, NH; (Y); Ski Clb; Yrbk Phtg; Yrbk Stf; Rep Pres Stu Cncl; Bsktbl; Socr; Hon Roll.

URDA, PAMELA; Kingswood Regional HS; Wolfeboro, NH; (Y); 33/143; Church Yth Grp; Temple Yth Grp; Band; Chorus; Concert Band; Mrchg Band; School Musical; Symp Band; Var JV Fld Hcky; JV Sftbl; Bates Coll; Surgy.

VACHON, CINDY; Spaulding HS; Rochester, NH; (S); High Hon Roll; NHS; Acctng.

VAILLANCOURT, LESLIE; Fall Mountain Regional HS; Walpole, NH; (Y); Art Clb; Hon Roll; Mt Ida Coll; Trvl.

VALDEZ, TRICIA; Hillsboro-Deering HS; Deering, NH; (S); Church Yth Grp; Drama Clb; Library Aide; Math Tm; Model UN; Quiz Bowl; Teachers Aide; Chorus; Hon Roll; Prfct Atten Awd; Pre-Med.

VAN DYKE, MARK; Machest West HS; Bedford, NH; (Y); 18/384; Math Tm; Band; Concert Band; Mrchg Band; Pep Band; Ed Yrbk Stf; Var L Trk; High Hon Roll; Hon Roll; Bus.

VAN HORN, PAMELA SUE; Colebrook Acad; Colebrook, NH; (Y); 1/47; Drama Clb; French Clb; Y-Teens; Band; Chorus; Yrbk Stf; Bausch & Lomb Sci Awd; Hon Roll; NHS; Val; Navy ROTC 4 Yr Scholar 85-89; Boston U; Aero Engrng.

VAN VLIET, MARK J; Plymouth Area HS; Plymouth, NH; (Y); Boy Scts; Model UN; Ski Clb; Lit Mag; Pres Jr Cls; Var Capt Crs Cntry; Var Trk; Skiing Alpine Jumpng 82-85; Appalacian Mtn Clb Footer Awd 84; Long Trl End To End 84; Arch.

VAN VLIET, MILLER J; Concord HS; Bow, NH; (Y); 42/323; German Clb; Ski Clb; Yrbk Phtg; JV Var Ftbl; High Hon Roll; Hon Roll; NHS; Engl Awd 85; Photogrphy Awd 85; Pre-Med.

VANDIS, CHARLES; Concord HS; Concord, NH; (Y); 35/330; German Clb; Ed Yrbk Phtg; Bsbl; Ftbl; Tennis; High Hon Roll; Hon Roll; NHS; Eng,German 82-85.

VANETTI, CHRISTINE; Milford Area SR HS; Milford, NH; (Y); Yrbk Ed-Chief; Pres Soph Cls; Pres Jr Cls; Pres Sr Cls; Rep Stu Cncl; High Hon Roll; Hon Roll; Teachers Aide; Powder Puff Ftbl; Holy Cross Bk Awd 85; Bus Mgt.

VANHOOSER, JOHN O; The Derryfield Schl; Amherst, NH; (Y); 1/29; Am Leg Boys St; Yrbk Ed-Chief; Pres Soph Cls; Pres Sr Cls; Var Lcrss; Var Socr; High Hon Roll; NHS; Rotary Awd; Val; Hugh O Brien Yth Fndtn Ldrshp Sem 83; Rensselaer Mdl 84; Dartmouth Bk Awd 84; Dartmouth Coll.

VARNEY, ALEXANDRA; Manchester Memorial HS; Manchester, NH; (Y); 39/369; Variety Show; Yrbk Stf; Stu Cncl; Cheerleading; Powder Puff Ftbl; Socr; Hon Roll.

VERHEUL, JOHN; Tilton HS; Ithaca, NY; (Y); 2/79; Drama Clb; Ski Clb; School Play; Rep Jr Cls; Crs Cntry; Lcrss; NHS; NEDT Awd; Spanish NHS; Brown U Bode Awd 84; Cornell U; Comp Engrng.

VERHEUL, JOHN B; Tilton Schl; Tilton, NH; (S); Cmnty Wkr; Drama Clb; Math Tm; Ski Clb; School Play; Jr Cls; Crs Cntry; Lcrss; Hon Roll; NEDT Awd; Brown U Book Awd 84; Cornell U; Comp Engr.

VERMETTE, CAREY; Spaulding HS; Rochester, NH; (S); 23/380; Band; Chorus; Church Choir; Color Guard; Concert Band; Mrchg Band; Pep Band; High Hon Roll; Hon Roll.

VERNADAKIS, BENN; Bishop Giertin HS; Tyngsboro, MA; (Y); 70/160; Boy Scts; Church Yth Grp; Key Clb; Ski Clb; Im Bsktbl; Im Ice Hcky; JV Socr; Var Swmmng; French Hon Soc; Hon Roll; Order Arrow 84; Alcholyte 81-85.

VIEL, JENNIFER L; Somersworth HS; Rollinsford, NH; (Y); 43/165; Drama Clb; French Clb; Latin Clb; Office Aide; Ski Clb; Yrbk Stf; Bsktbl; Tennis; Hon Roll; U Of NH; Nrsg.

VIOLETTE, ANDREW; Concord HS; Bow, NH; (S); 8/331; Boy Scts; Sec Stu Cncl; Var Socr; Var Trk; Elks Awd; High Hon Roll; Pres NHS; Air Force ROTC Schlrshp 85; Duke U; Mech Engr.

VIOLETTE, LISA; Belmont HS; Laconia, NH; (Y); Library Aide; Varsity Clb; Yrbk Stf; Rep Stu Cncl; Var Capt Bsktbl; JV Var Sftbl; Var Co-Capt Vllybl; Hon Roll; MVP Awds-Bsktbl & Sftbl 84-85; Mst Outstndng Vllybl 84-85; Dntl Hygnst.

VOGEL, JOSEPH JAY; Londonderry HS; Londonderry, NH; (Y); Ski Clb; Yrbk Stf; High Hon Roll; Hon Roll; NHS; Hnr Awd Recgntn Outstndng Schlstc Achvt 82-83; Bus Mgmt.

WADE JR, MICHAEL D; Bishop Guertin HS; Salem, NH; (Y); 12/180; Am Leg Boys St; FCA; Key Clb; Nwsp Rptr; Yrbk Stf; Trk; High Hon Roll; NHS; Ntl Merit SF; Spanish NHS; Daniel Webster Coll Comp Sci Credits 85; Archit.

WAGNER, CHARLES; Bishop Guertin HS; Pelham, NH; (Y); 1/160; Rep Jr Cls; Stu Cncl; Var Crs Cntry; Var L Trk; High Hon Roll; Pres NHS; Ntl Merit Ltr; VP Spanish NHS; Holy Cross Bk Awd 85.

WAGNER, CHARLES L; Hopkinton HS; Contoocook, NH; (Y); Capt Math Tm; Trs Frsh Cls; Trs Jr Cls; Trs Sr Cls; High Hon Roll; Trs NHS; Ntl Merit SF; St Pauls Advncd Studies Pgm; US Air Force Acad Summer Scientific Sem.

WAGNER, LISA; Hillsboro-Deering HS; Hillsboro, NH; (Y); 9/59; Am Leg Aux Girls St; Model UN; Yrbk Bus Mgr; Pres Frsh Cls; Pres Soph Cls; Pres Jr Cls; Rep Sr Cls; VP Stu Cncl; Bsbl; Pres NHS; Campbell Schlrshp 85; Natl Hnr Soc Schlrshp 85; Amer Lgn Ctzn Schlrshp 85; U NH; Hstry Tchr.

WAGNER, MATT; Portsmouth HS; Rye, NH; (S); 11/362; Am Leg Boys St; Latin Clb; Model UN; Ski Clb; Var Capt Bsktbl; Var L Golf; High Hon Roll; Hon Roll; NHS; Ntl Merit Ltr; Pres JR World Council Frgn Affairs 84; Schlr Athlete Awds 83-84; Dartmouth; English.

WALKER, PETER; Bishop Brady HS; Tilton, NH; (S); Church Yth Grp; Intnl Clb; VP Soph Cls; Var Bsbl; Var Ftbl; Hon Roll; NEDT Awd; Geometry, Algebra Awds 83-84; History Awd 82-83.

WALKER JR, THOMAS E; Community Baptist HS; Meadows, NH; (Y); Am Leg Boys St; Church Yth Grp; Political Wkr; Yrbk Ed-Chief; VP Frsh Cls; VP Soph Cls; Pres Jr Cls; Im Sftbl; Hon Roll; Voice Dem Awd; Poltcl Sci.

WALKER, WENDY S; White Mtn Schl; Littleton, NH; (Y); Chess Clb; Drama Clb; Quiz Bowl; Chorus; School Musical; School Play; Var Socr; Hon Roll; Eng.

WALLACE, SUSAN; Franklin HS; Franklin, NH; (Y); 3/96; Math Tm; Trs Frsh Cls; Trs Soph Cls; Trs Jr Cls; Pres Trs Stu Cncl; L Var Bsktbl; L Var Fld Hcky; L Var Sftbl; High Hon Roll; NHS; Law.

WALLENT, KAREN; Nashua HS; Nashua, NH; (Y); 2/807; Key Clb; Ski Clb; Band; Camp Fr Inc; Yrbk Stf; High Hon Roll; NHS; Sal; Spanish NHS; AFS; Presdntl Acad Fitness Awd 85; Fairfield U.

WALTERS, JEAN ELIZABETH; Alvirne HS; Hudson, NH; (Y); Am Leg Aux Girls St; Pres Key Clb; Chorus; School Play; Lit Mag; Trs Jr Cls; Stu Cncl; Var Fld Hcky; Var Trk; Hon Roll; Ntl Hnr Roll 85; Keene ST Coll Hnrs Schlrshp 85-89; YMCA Yth/Gvrnmnt Pgm; Keene ST Coll; Elem Educ.

WALTHER, TODD B; Pinkerton Acad; Windham, NH; (Y); Am Leg Boys St; Latin Clb; Ski Clb; JV Lcrss; Var Capt Socr; JV Wrstlng; High Hon Roll; NHS.

WALTZ, MARK; Kennett HS; N Conway, NH; (Y); 3/201; Boy Scts; Drama Clb; Pres Band; Church Choir; Jazz Band; Mrchg Band; Pep Band; Swing Chorus; NHS; Marine Band Awd 85; Ernie Mills Music Spirit Awd 84; Bowdoin Coll; Polit Sci.

WARD, LORI; Nute HS; Milton, NH; (S); 1/45; French Clb; Math Tm; Office Aide; Variety Show; Yrbk Rptr; Pres Soph Cls; Sec Soph Cls; Rep Jr Cls; Sec Stu Cncl; Var Cheerleading; Bus Mgmt.

WASHBURN, LESLIE; Salem HS; Salem, NH; (Y); German Clb; Model UN; Church Choir; School Play; Stage Crew; Nwsp Rptr; Elks Awd; Hon Roll; Dollrs For Schlrs Schlrshp 85; U Of NH; Psych.

WASHBURNE, DENISE; Spaulding HS; Rochester, NH; (Y); Girl Scts; Office Aide; High Hon Roll; Hon Roll; Mc Intosh; Acctng.

WASMER, CHRIS; Timberlane Regional HS; Plaistow, NH; (Y); Camera Clb; Sec Exploring; German Clb; Office Aide; Spanish Clb; Yrbk Stf; Cheerleading; Mgr(s); Tennis; Hon Roll; UNH; Zoology.

WATERMAN, ANDREA BETH; West HS; Bedford, NH; (Y); 84/352; Art Clb; Ski Clb; Color Guard; Drm Mjr(t); Yrbk Stf; Swmmng; Visual Arts.

WATTS, CHERYL A; Salem HS; Salem, NH; (S); 25/363; Trs French Clb; Model UN; Ski Clb; Band; Concert Band; Mrchg Band; School Play; JV Trk; High Hon Roll; Hon Roll; Bentley Coll; Comp.

WEBSTER, GREG; Manchester West HS; Manchester, NH; (Y); Bsktbl; Hon Roll; Bus.

WEEKS, PAMELA; Portsmouth HS; Portsmouth, NH; (S); 14/362; Cmnty Wkr; Drm Mjr(t); Mrchg Band; Sec Stu Cncl; Cheerleading; High Hon Roll; NHS; Latin Clb; Political Wkr; Band; Hmcmng Qn 84-85; JR Wrld Cncl 83-85; Class Musician 84-85; Psych.

WEINHOLD, MARIBETH; Winnacunnet HS; Hampton, NH; (Y); Hosp Aide; Teachers Aide; Chorus; Church Choir; Color Guard; Flag Corp; School Musical; Stage Crew; Hon Roll; Pedtrcn.

WELCH, DANIEL; Plymouth Area HS; Plymouth, NH; (Y); Master Counclr Plymouth Chptr-Order Of Demolay 83 & 84; Bryant Coll; Busnss.

WELCOME, STEVE; Pembroke Acad; Epsom, NH; (Y); 4/200; French Clb; VP Key Clb; Science Clb; Pres Jr Cls; Pres Sr Cls; Var Capt Socr; Var Capt Trk; High Hon Roll; Hon Roll; NHS; Rensselaer Scholar Mdl Mst Outstndg Mth & Sci Stu 85; Rensselaer Polytech Inst Summr Pgm 85; MVP Trk; USAF Acad; Aero Engrng.

WELLS, FERMOR; Concord Christian HS; Concord, NH; (Y); Church Yth Grp; Cmnty Wkr; FCA; Chorus; School Play; Cheerleading; Crs Cntry; Score Keeper; Trk; Hon Roll; Word Of Life Bible Inst Schlrshp 84-85; Phys Ftns Awd 83-85; Mst Imprvd Stu In JR Cls 85; Wrd/Life Bible Inst; Chld Wrkr.

WENDELOWSKI, LAUREN; Littleton HS; Littleton, NH; (Y); 8/98; Drama Clb; Concert Band; Yrbk Stf; Pres Soph Cls; Rep Stu Cncl; JV Var Bsktbl; Band; Mrchg Band; Pep Band; VP Frsh Cls; Chem Bst Achv Awd 85; Concrt Bnd Cert Of Achv 83-85; Marine Bio.

WERDERMAN, JOHN PETER; Hollis Area HS; Hollis, NH; (Y); 10/104; Am Leg Boys St; Rep Church Yth Grp; Rep Spanish Clb; Rep Sr Cls; JV Bsktbl; High Hon Roll; Hon Roll; NHS; Spanish NHS; Teachers Aide; Top Spn III Stu 85; Engrng.

WESTCOTT, ROBIN; Nashua SR HS; Nashua, NH; (Y); 75/806; Office Aide; Teachers Aide; High Hon Roll; Hon Roll; Jr NHS; NHS; Pres Schlr; Rivier Coll Schlrshp; Rivier Coll; Accntng.

WHEELER, CHAROLETTE; Pittsfield HS; Pittsfield, NH; (Y); Church Yth Grp; Cmnty Wkr; 4-H; French Clb; Science Clb; Yrbk Rptr; Yrbk Sprt Ed; Yrbk Stf; 4-H Awd; Hon Roll; 4-H Schlrshp Awd To WA DC 83; 4-H Natl Rcrd Wnnr Chgo Trp 83; NH Tech Inst; Dntl Hygn.

WHEELER, MICHAEL; Kennett HS; Conway, NH; (Y); 13/255; Key Clb; Var Capt Bsbl; JV Var Bsktbl; Hon Roll; NHS; Bus.

WHIPPLE, SUE; Monadneck HS; Fitzwilliam, NH; (Y); French Clb; JV Fld Hcky; Hon Roll; Acctnt.

WHITE, ANN COUTURE; Concord HS; Concord, NH; (Y); 83/323; Church Yth Grp; Computer Clb; VP Band; VP Concert Band; Drm Mjr(t); Jazz Band; VP Mrchg Band; Orch; Pep Band; VP Symp Band; Bst Rsrch Papr In Bio 85; Arthur R Virgin Music Comptn 2nd Pl 85; Achvt Solo Perfrmnc 83.

WHITE, CAROLYN; Trinity HS; Manchester, NH; (Y); 4/180; Drama Clb; School Play; Capt Crs Cntry; High Hon Roll; NHS; Outstndng Eng Stu 85; St Fnl Schlrshp 84; St Pauls Adv Studies Pgm 84; Holy Cross; Eng.

WHITE, JAMES; Pinkerton Acad; Derry, NH; (S); Aud/Vis; Boys Clb Am; DECA; Spanish Clb; JV Bsbl; Mrktng Mgmt.

WHITE, JANA; Pinkerton Acad; Windham, NH; (Y); 63/471; Yrbk Stf; Off Sr Cls; Var Capt Fld Hcky; Trk; Hon Roll; Prfct Atten Awd; Derry Firefghtrs Assoc Schlrshp 85; New Hampshire U; Med Technlgst.

WHITE, MATTHEW; Coe-Brown Northwood Acad; Barrington, NH; (Y); Drama Clb; Office Aide; School Musical; Var Bsbl; JV Stat Bsktbl; JV Score Keeper; JV Socr; NHS; Math.

WHITE, SCOTT N; Bishop Guertin HS; Nashua, NH; (Y); 32/135; Am Leg Boys St; Church Yth Grp; FCA; Pres Soph Cls; Rep Stu Cncl; Var Bsktbl; Capt Socr; Trk; Hon Roll; NHS; Lwyr.

WHITEHOUSE, CORRIE; Milford Area SR HS; Amherst, NH; (Y); 45/290; Pres Church Yth Grp; Intnl Clb; Acpl Chr; Chorus; Drill Tm; Jazz Band; School Play; Variety Show; Nwsp Stf; Hon Roll; Souhegan Vly Cmmnty Chrs Accmpnst 84; Granite ST Wd Piano Aud 4th Pl 85; Bus Adm.

WHITING, JARED; Kingswood Regional HS; Melvin, NH; (Y); Hon Roll; U S Coast Guard Reserves.

WHITNEY, LE TISHIA; Portsmouth SR HS; Portsmouth, NH; (Y); 27/400; Spanish Clb; Acpl Chr; Chorus; Drill Tm; Madrigals; School Musical; Stage Crew; Hon Roll; Spn Recitatn Cont 1st Pl 83-84; U NH; Cmmnctns.

WHITTUM, CHRISTOPHER; Farmington HS; Rochester, NH; (Y); Computer Clb; Drama Clb; Pres 4-H; French Clb; JA; Thesps; Chorus; 4-H Awd; Hon Roll; Psychlgy.

WIGGIN, STACEY; Spaulding HS; East Rochester, NH; (S); 37/418; Trs FBLA; Hosp Aide; Yrbk Ed-Chief; Hon Roll; Hnrbl Ment ST Acctng Cntst 83-84; FBLA ST Ldrshp Conf Typing I 83, Typing II 84; Acctng.

WILDER, SAMANTHA; Hopkinton HS; Concord, NH; (Y); VP Church Yth Grp; Drama Clb; German Clb; Girl Scts; Hosp Aide; Varsity Clb; Chorus; School Musical; Yrbk Stf; Mgr Stu Cncl; BAC; Arch.

WILEY, BARBARA; Concord HS; Concord, NH; (Y); 21/350; Trs Varsity Clb; Variety Show; Trs Sr Cls; Var L Bsktbl; Var L Fld Hcky; JV Sftbl; Var L Trk; High Hon Roll; Hon Roll; Sec NHS; 2nd Tm All ST Bsktbl 84-85; NH ST Hpthalon 85.

WILKENS, STEVE; Hillsboro-Deering HS; Hillsboro, NH; (S); Math Tm; NHS; Metrlgy.

WILKINS, JUDITH A; Pelham HS; Pelham, NH; (Y); 29/125; Office Aide; Teachers Aide; JV Bsktbl; JV Fld Hcky; Score Keeper; Stat Sftbl; Hon Roll; Ruth Rchrdsn Schlrshp Awd 85; U ME Farmington; Hlth Educ.

WILLIAMS, MICHAEL; Concord HS; Concord, NH; (Y); Boy Scts; Church Yth Grp; Band; Hon Roll; Drftng I & II Achvt Awd; Engl Outstndng Prfrmnc; Envrnmntl Dsgn.

WILLIAMSON, CRAIG; Bishop Guertin HS; Amherst, NH; (Y); French Clb; Bsbl; Golf; Im Ice Hcky; Hon Roll; Athl Wk 84-85.

WILSON, CASSIE; Stevens HS; Claremont, NH; (Y); GAA; Math Tm; Office Aide; Pep Clb; Teachers Aide; Concert Band; Mrchg Band; Pep Band; Var Cheerleading; JV Sftbl; Nrsng.

WILSON, CHRISTOPHER; Hanover HS; Strafford, VT; (Y); Band; Drm & Bgl; Jazz Band; Mrchg Band; Orch; School Musical; Swing Chorus; Symp Band; Bsktbl; Trk; All Regn Jazz & Band All Area 83-84; All ST Band & Jazz 84-85; 1st Div Tympani Solo 83-85; Syracuse Coll; Music.

WILSON, JOHN; Coe Brown Northwood Acad; Northwood, NH; (Y); Cmnty Wkr; French Clb; FFA; Quiz Bowl; JV Bsktbl; Hon Roll; Bsktbl 85; Relgs Aid For The Tchrs 84; Recmmdtn For Natl Hnr Soc & SEARCH 84-85; NH Tech Concord; Engrng.

WILSON, PAULINE; Central HS; Goffstown, NH; (Y); 116/409; JA; Band; Var Bsktbl; Im Sftbl; High Hon Roll; Hon Roll; Stu All Trnamnt Bsktbl Tm-Church Leag 85; Stu Sftbl Tm-Chrch Leag 83 & 84; Pol Sci.

WILT, MICHELLE; Lebanon HS; Lebanon, NH; (Y); AFS; French Clb; Varsity Clb; Concert Band; Mrchg Band; Rep Stu Cncl; JV Bsktbl; Var L Crs Cntry; Var Socr; Var L Sftbl; Hlth Med.

WINCKLER, BETSEY; Spaulding HS; Rochester, NH; (S); 22/372; Band; Chorus; Concert Band; Jazz Band; Mrchg Band; School Musical; Rep Sr Cls; Var Trk; High Hon Roll; NHS; All-ST Band 84-85; All-ST Jazz Band 84-85; All New Engl Band 85; Comm.

WINIECKI, JESSICA A; Milford Area SR HS; Amherst, NH; (Y); 46/286; French Clb; VP FBLA; Acpl Chr; Band; Drm Mjr(t); Jazz Band; Orch; Symp Band; Variety Show; Hon Roll; Music Performance.

WISHNEFSKY, LISA; Lebanon HS; Lebanon, NH; (Y); AFS; Drama Clb; Sec French Clb; School Play; Stage Crew; Var L Cheerleading; Ntl Merit SF; Rotary Clb Lebanon Scholar 85; Anna & Benjamin Goodman Scholar 85; Cls 85 Scholar 85; Bryant Coll; Hotl Mgmt.

WISWELL, BRENDA; Pembroke Acad; Concord, NH; (Y); French Clb; Pres Trs Girl Scts; Teachers Aide; Varsity Clb; Band; Concert Band; Nwsp Ed-Chief; JV Bsktbl; JV Var Sftbl; Im Vllybl; Phy Ed.

WITHAM, HEIDI; Portsmouth Senior HS; Portsmouth, NH; (S); 16/362; Church Yth Grp; Exploring; Hosp Aide; Latin Clb; Flag Corp; High Hon Roll; Hon Roll; NHS; U Of NH; Bus Mgmt.

WOFFORD, WILLIAM N; Phillips Exeter Acad; Port Washington, NY; (Y); Radio Clb; Band; JV Lcrss; Tennis; Var Wrstlng; High Hon Roll; Ntl Merit SF; Rssn Spkn Olympd 83-84; Rssn Wrtn Olympd 83; Latin Prz 82; Harvard; Poly Sci.

WOLFE, JENNIFER; Milford Area SR HS; Amherst, NH; (Y); Church Choir; Yrbk Stf; VP Frsh Cls; Rep Soph Cls; VP Jr Cls; VP Sr Cls; Stu Cncl; Var Capt Cheerleading; JV Var Mgr(s); NHS; Intl Bus.

WOOD, JODI; Goffstown Aren HS; Manchester, NH; (Y); 13/180; Trs Pres Church Yth Grp; Math Tm; Ski Clb; Var Mgr Bsbl; Capt Bowling; Mgr(s); Var Mgr Sftbl; High Hon Roll; Hon Roll; VP NHS; Goffstown Ed Assn Scholar 85; Mildred Stark Scholar 85; U RI; Phrmcy.

WOODWARD, CATHY; Milford Area SR HS; Milford, NH; (Y); JV Bsktbl; JV Var Fld Hcky; Var Sftbl; Nrsg.

WOODWARD, MARK A; Kearsarge Regional HS; New London, NH; (Y); AFS; Church Yth Grp; Drama Clb; French Clb; Model UN; Band; Trs Chorus; Yrbk Stf; JV Socr; Hon Roll; All ST Chorus 84; All Eastern Chorus 85; St Pauls Schl Adv Studs Pgm 85; Intl Bus.

WOODWORTH, GRETCHEN H; Londonderry HS; Natick, MA; (Y); Art Clb; Drama Clb; Chorus; School Musical; High Hon Roll; Hon Roll; Graphic Arts.

WOOLBERT, TERRY; Fall Mountain Regional HS; Walpole, NH; (Y); Nwsp Phtg; Hon Roll; Perfect Attndnc Awd 83-84; Spch Baccalaureate 84-85; US Air Force; Accntnt.

WORRELL, KURT; St Thomas Aquinas HS; Rye, NH; (Y); Trs Key Clb; Pres Soph Cls; Pres Jr Cls; Pres Sr Cls; Rep Stu Cncl; NHS; Comm.

WOTTON, WENDI; Spaulding HS; Rochester, NH; (S); 13/416; Mathletes; Trs Math Tm; Office Aide; Var Bsktbl; Var Capt Socr; Var Sftbl; Var Trk; High Hon Roll; NHS; Ntl Merit Schol; Hnrbl Mntn All ST Sccr 85; Dream Tm 1st Tm Sccr 85; Dartmouth; Pre-Med.

WRIGHT JR, ALLAN E; Winnacunnet HS; North Hampton, NH; (Y); Am Leg Boys St; Chess Clb; Exploring; Nwsp Phtg; Nwsp Stf; Var Trk; High Hon Roll; Hon Roll; Stu Tchr Asst Comp Sci 85; Physcs Lab Asst 85; U Of NH; Comp Sci.

WRIGHT, PAMELA; Mascoma Valley Regional HS; Canaan, NH; (Y); Am Leg Aux Girls St; French Clb; GAA; Math Tm; Office Aide; Varsity Clb; Band; Yrbk Stf; Var Fld Hcky; Hon Roll; U VT; Pol Sci.

WU, GRANT P; Phillips Exeter Acad; Shrewsbury, MA; (Y); Hosp Aide; Mathletes; Pres Math Clb; PAVAS; Political Wkr; High Hon Roll; Hon Roll; Ntl Merit SF; Cmnty Wkr; Math Tm; VP Envrnmntl Studies Clb 84; Sherman Hoar Prz Achvt Amer Hstry 84; Cum Laude Soc Phillips Exetr Acad; Biol.

WYATT III, CLARENCE; Nute HS; Milton, NH; (S); 3/47; French Clb; Math Tm; Jazz Band; Yrbk Stf; Rep Jr Cls; Stu Cncl; Bsktbl; Socr; Hon Roll; NHS; Chem Eng.

YACOPUCCI, WILLIAM; Franklin HS; Franklin, NH; (Y); Pres Exploring; Hon Roll; NHS; Ltr Cmndtn Police Chf, Law Enforcement Explr 83; Prin Awd Soc Stu 83; U NH; Law Enfrcmnt.

YANDOW, LORI; Londonderry HS; Londonderry, NH; (Y); Band; Concert Band; VP Stu Cncl; Socr; Hon Roll; Bus.

YEMMA, TRACY; Londonderry HS; Londonderry, NH; (Y); Ski Clb; Spanish Clb; Band; Concert Band; Mrchg Band; Sftbl; High Hon Roll; Hon Roll; Spanish NHS.

YOUNG, APRIL; Coe-Brown Acad; Northwood, NH; (Y); Trs Frsh Cls; French Hon Soc; Hon Roll; French.

YOUNG, EUGENE S; Merrimack Valley HS; Andover, NH; (Y); 3/122; Am Leg Boys St; Boy Scts; Var Capt Bsbl; Var Capt Bsktbl; Var Capt Socr; Hon Roll; Kiwanis Awd; NHS; Norwich U VT; Accntnt.

ZANNINI, JILL M; Salem HS; Salem, NH; (S); 2nd Deg Blck Belt 84; Frnch Cert Of Merit Awd 84; Boston U; Sci.

ZIESKE, WILLIAM; Goffstown HS; New Boston, NH; (Y); #7 In Class; Chess Clb; Computer Clb; Exploring; FNA; Math Clb; Math Tm; Political Wkr; Nwsp Ed-Chief; Nwsp Rptr; Nwsp Sprt Ed; Lafayette Coll; Pol Sci.

ZIMMER, DAWN; Laconia HS; Laconia, NH; (Y); Church Yth Grp; Pep Clb; Ski Clb; VP Frsh Cls; VP Soph Cls; Pres Jr Cls; Stu Cncl; Var Fld Hcky; Var Keywanettes; High Hon Roll; Hugh O Brien Ldrshp Awd 84; Dartmouth Bk Awd 85; Boston Coll.

ZIMMER, TIM; Laconia HS; Laconia, NH; (Y); 2/160; Key Clb; Math Tm; Trs Frsh Cls; JV Tennis; Var Trk; Im Wt Lftg; JV Wrstlng; NHS; Engrng.

NEW YORK

AARON, TIMOTHY S; Brockport HS; Hamlin, NY; (Y); 4/300; Mathletes; Nwsp Stf; Yrbk Phtg; Ed Yrbk Stf; High Hon Roll; NHS; Ntl Merit Ltr; Regnts Schlrshp Wnr 84-85; Trigonmtry Awd 83; 1st Clss Rank Soph Yr 83; Duke U; Medicine.

AARONS, CELESTE A; La Guardia H S Of Music & The Arts; Bronx, NY; (Y); 13/588; Chorus; Nwsp Rptr; Yrbk Stf; Vllybl; Hon Roll; NHS; Music Hnr Leag 84-85; Bio.

ABADINSKY, JUDY; Sheepshead Bay HS; Brooklyn, NY; (Y); Cmnty Wkr; Dance Clb; Drama Clb; Teachers Aide; Temple Yth Grp; Thesps; Y-Teens; Band; Concert Band; School Musical; Alumni Assn Awd Character & Svc 85; Law Assn Awd 85; Brooklyn Coll; Elem Ed.

ABADIR, ESTHER H; Union Springs Acad; Lancaster, NY; (Y); Church Yth Grp; Ski Clb; Varsity Clb; Band; Chorus; Concert Band; Bsktbl; Gym; Cmnty Wkr; FCA; Pathfinder Clb Awds 77-82; Suny Coll-Buffalo; Psych.

ABARE, DEBBIE; Sodus Central HS; Athens, AL; (Y); 12/104; AFS; Science Clb; Rep Stu Cncl; High Hon Roll; Hon Roll; Pres Acad Fit Awd 85; AL U Huntzville; Engr.

ABATE, CATHERINE; St Gabriel HS; Mt Vernon, NY; (Y); 5/61; Cmnty Wkr; Library Aide; Spanish Clb; Hon Roll; NHS; Iona; Elem Ed.

ABATE, DENISE; Moore Catholic HS; Staten Island, NY; (Y); Girl Scts; Ski Clb; Bowling; JV Var Sftbl; Hon Roll; Educ.

ABATE, LIDIA; Saint Gabriel HS; Mt Vernon, NY; (Y); Hosp Aide; JA; Library Aide; Office Aide; Spanish Clb; Teachers Aide; Stage Crew; Nwsp Stf; Yrbk Phtg; Yrbk Stf; Lang.

ABATO, VINCENT J; Patchogue-Medford HS; Medford, NY; (Y); 15/750; Rep Frsh Cls; Rep Sr Cls; JV Socr; Hon Roll; Jr NHS; NHS; Regents Schlrshp Wnnr; U Rochester; Surgeon.

ABATTO, TERESA; Bishop Maginn HS; Albany, NY; (S); 18/118; Cmnty Wkr; Hosp Aide; Latin Clb; Nwsp Rptr; High Hon Roll; Hon Roll; NHS; Albany Med Ctr; Nrsng.

ABBATE, JENNIFER; Jamestown HS; Jamestown, NY; (Y); Church Yth Grp; Color Guard; Ed Nwsp Stf; Ed Yrbk Ed-Chief; Yrbk Phtg; Yrbk Stf; Jamestwn Pst Jrnl Stu Rep 83-84; Advrtsng.

ABBATE, KATHLEEN; Curtis HS; Staten Island, NY; (Y); 42/356; Cmnty Wkr; GAA; Girl Scts; ROTC; Color Guard; Drill Tm; School Play; JV Cheerleading; Off Accos Medal ROTC 85; Yankees Super Yth 85; Med Tech.

ABBATE, SAL; Spackenkill HS; Poughkeepsie, NY; (Y); 24/174; Church Yth Grp; FCA; Spanish Clb; Nwsp Sprt Ed; Rep Frsh Cls; Rep Soph Cls; JV Capt Bsbl; Var Bowling; JV Capt Ftbl; Hon Roll; MVP JV Baseball 84; Clemson U; Elec Engrng.

ABBATE, THOMAS; Eastridge HS; Rochester, NY; (Y); 40/236; Boys Clb Am; Boy Scts; Church Yth Grp; Computer Clb; Drama Clb; Exploring; JA; Math Clb; Varsity Clb; Band; Cornell U; Elec Engrng.

ABBATIELLO, MICHAEL; A G Berner HS; Massapequa Park, NY; (Y); 132/412; Ice Hcky; Socr; Nassau Cnty Pub H S Athltc Assn All Div Socr Glkpr 884-85.

ABBEY, CINDI; Whitney Point CS HS; Whitney Pt, NY; (Y); Church Yth Grp; Pres Sec 4-H; Pres Sec JCL; Pres Latin Clb; Pres Band; Chorus; Pres Concert Band; Drm Mjr(t); Jazz Band; Mrchg Band; Schlrshp SUNY Cortland Music Cmp 85; Al-Str Awd Jzz Fstvl Imprvsd Slo Sax 85.

ABBEY, DONALEA; Cicero North Syracuse HS; Mattydale, NY; (S); 25/711; Capt Bsktbl; Hon Roll; Natl Honor Soc 82-85; Phys Ther.

ABBOTT, CRAIG; G Ray Bodley HS; Fulton, NY; (Y); Pres French Clb; Science Clb; Var L Ice Hcky; Var L Lcrss; Var L Socr; High Hon Roll; NHS; Prfct Atten Awd; Amer H S Athl 85; 2nd Tm Cnty Socr 84; Coaches Choice Wk Hcky & Sccr 84-85; Math.

ABBOTT, JOHN; Randolph Central Schl; Randolph, NY; (Y); Am Leg Boys St; Drama Clb; Quiz Bowl; Varsity Clb; VP Acpl Chr; Chorus; School Musical; School Play; Stage Crew; Trs Frsh Cls; Syracuse.

ABBOTT, KIMBERLY; Skaneateles Central HS; Skaneateles, NY; (S); JV Socr; Var Sftbl; High Hon Roll; Hon Roll; NHS.

ABBOTT, KRISTEN; Onindaga Central HS; Syracuse, NY; (Y); Spanish Clb; Band; Chorus; JV Socr; Var Vllybl; High Hon Roll; Hon Roll; Schlrshp-Canisius Coll 85; Cochs Apprctn Awd Sftbl 85; Al-Star Sftbl Tm 85; Law.

ABBOTT, MIKE; Gray Bodley HS; Fulton, NY; (Y); 5/300; Science Clb; Capt Gym; Ice Hcky; Lcrss; Socr; High Hon Roll; NHS; CSEA NY ST 85; Presdnts & Deans List 84-85; Suny Stone Brook; Elec Engr.

ABBRUSCATO, VIRGINIA; Marlboro HS; Milton, NY; (Y); 64/164; Hon Roll; Home Ec Clthng,Clng Awd 84-85; Oneonta; Hme Ec.

ABBRUZZESE, STEFAN E; The Doane Stuart Schl; Clifton Park, NY; (Y); Ski Clb; Yrbk Stf; Var Capt Bsbl; Var Capt Bsktbl; Var Capt Socr; High Hon Roll; Hon Roll; NHS; St Schlr; MVP Scr 81 & 84; Outstndng Achvmnt Awd Scr 82; Scr All Star 81-84; Holy Cross Coll.

ABBUHL, DALE; Rome Free Acad; Ava, NY; (Y); 118/534; Intnl Clb; Spanish Clb; Capt JV Bsbl; JV Ftbl; Hon Roll; Jr NHS; NHS; Prfct Atten Awd; Pres Schlr; F Parsons Awd JV Bsbl 83; Cpt Frshm Bsbll 82; Castleton ST Coll; Crmnl Just.

ABDALLAH, MAHER; Roosevelt HS; Yonkers, NY; (Y); Rep Soph Cls; Rep Jr Cls; Var Socr; High Hon Roll; NHS; Suprntndnts Awd 83-85; Pres Acad Ftnss Awd 84-85; Natl Hnr Rll 84-85; Manhattan Coll; Med.

ABDELLA, CHRISTOPHER; Notre Dame HS; Oakfield, NY; (S); 10/66; 4-H; Wrstlng; High Hon Roll; NHS; Ftbl; Score Keeper; Hon Roll; Police.

ABDULLAH, NADIA R; East Meadow HS; East Meadow, NY; (Y); 8/414; Drama Clb; Key Clb; Chorus; School Musical; School Play; Yrbk Stf; Crs Cntry; Tennis; Trk; Cit Awd; Regents Schlrshp Wnnr 85; Schlsct Achvt Acad Awd 82; SUNY-BINGHAMPTON; Drmtlgst.

ABDUSSHAKUR, ANEESAH; Holy Trinity HS; Wyandanch, NY; (Y); 5/367; Library Aide; Mathletes; Math Tm; Yrbk Stf; Hon Roll; NHS; Ntl Merit Ltr; NEDT Awd; Intl Studes.

ABEL, JEANNE E; Madison Central HS; Knoxboro, NY; (Y); Band; Concert Band; Jazz Band; Mrchg Band; School Musical; Swing Chorus; Yrbk Stf; High Hon Roll; NHS; Ntl Merit Ltr; Regnts Schlrshp 85; Geneseo; Acctng.

ABEL JR, L DAVID; Oneida ST HS; Oneida, NY; (Y); 37/225; Aud/Vis; Latin Clb; Varsity Clb; Stage Crew; Yrbk Stf; Capt L Bsktbl; L Ftbl; Trk; Hon Roll; Rotary Awd; Regents Schlrshp 85; Albany ST U; Econ Corp Mgmt.

ABEL, LEIGH R; Gloversville HS; Gloversville, NY; (Y); Camera Clb; Computer Clb; Drama Clb; Ski Clb; Band; Chorus; Mrchg Band; Ed Yrbk Phtg; Hon Roll; High Hon Roll; Regnts Schlrshp Awd 85; Buffalo SUNY; Aerosp Engrng.

ABELES, GWEN D; Jericho HS; Jericho, NY; (Y); 11/230; Cmnty Wkr; Dance Clb; Varsity Clb; Variety Show; VP Soph Cls; Pres Jr Cls; Pres Sr Cls; Var L Cheerleading; High Hon Roll; NHS; Bio.

ABELEV, ARKADY; Solomon Schechter SR Of Brooklyn; Brooklyn, NY; (Y); 2/42; Math Tm; Nwsp Stf; Rep Sr Cls; NHS; Sal; Bsktbl; Ice Hcky; Socr; Rgents Schlrshp 85; Congrssnl Recgntn Awd 85; All-City Awd Math 84; Polytechnic Inst Of NY; Comp E.

ABELL, JOYCE; Jordan-Elbridge HS; Memphis, NY; (Y); Hosp Aide; Spanish Clb; Color Guard; Mrchg Band; High Hon Roll; Jr NHS; U S Army; Trnsltn.

ABER, GERALD B; Elmira Southside HS; Elmira, NY; (Y); Am Leg Boys St; Latin Clb; Varsity Clb; Band; Concert Band; Mrchg Band; Symp Band; Yrbk Sprt Ed; Yrbk Stf; JV Var Bsktbl; Citadel.

ABER, JEFFREY C; Port Jervis HS; Middletown, NY; (Y); 49/190; Aud/Vis; Drama Clb; FBLA; Key Clb; Band; Mrchg Band; School Musical; School Play; Stage Crew; Yrbk Stf; NY ST Rgnts Coll Schrlshp 85; Orange Cnty Comm Coll; Bus.

ABLORH-ODJIDJA, ALBERT; St Agnes Boys HS; Rego Park, NY; (Y); 20/104; VP Socr; NHS.

ABNEY, DANA; Joseph C Wilson Magnet HS; Rochester, NY; (Y); Teachers Aide; Church Choir; Yrbk Stf; High Hon Roll; Hon Roll; Prfct Atten Awd; Rep Jr Cls; Sec Stu Cncl; Im Bsktbl; Var Cheerleading; Outstndng Achv Engl 85; Outstndng Imprvmnt Socl Stud 85; FL ST U; Comp Prcssng.

ABOUD, KATHY; Fontbonne Hall Acad; Brooklyn, NY; (Y); Variety Show; Var Pom Pon; Var Tennis; Hon Roll; Cert Of Compltn-NY St Ldrshp Course 85; JR Ring Night Commtt 85; Math.

ABRAHAM, AJAMU; Cardinal Hayes HS; Manhattan, NY; (Y); 7/264; Chess Clb; Dance Clb; Science Clb; JV Crs Cntry; Im Ftbl; JV Socr; JV Trk; High Hon Roll; Hon Roll; Air Force Acad; Pilot.

ABRAHAM, BIJU; Susan Wagner HS; Staten Is, NY; (Y); Art Clb; Aud/Vis; JA; Math Clb; Cit Awd; Hon Roll; Elec Engr.

ABRAHAM, JOANNE R; Lewiston-Porter Central HS; Youngstown, NY; (Y); 1/280; Dance Clb; Hosp Aide; Intnl Clb; Pres Temple Yth Grp; Orch; Rep Sr Cls; Rep Stu Cncl; Var Gym; Sec NHS; Val; Cornell Natl Schlrshp 85; Commnty Ambssdr 84-85; Cornell; Bio.

ABRAHAM, SHEENA; Brighton HS; Rochester, NY; (Y); 25/315; Church Yth Grp; Cmnty Wkr; Chorus; School Musical; Rep Frsh Cls; Rep Soph Cls; Rep Jr Cls; Rep Stu Cncl; Prfct Atten Awd; Dance Schlrshp Awd 84; Med.

ABRAHAM, SUZANNE M; Liverpool HS; Liverpool, NY; (Y); 104/792; High Hon Roll; Hon Roll; Jr NHS; Ntl Merit Ltr; St Schlr; NYS Regnts Schlrshp 85; Acad Achvt Engl 82 & 84; NY ST U Oswego; Art/Mus.

ABRAHAMS, ELIZABETH A; Smithtown HS West; Smithtown, NY; (Y); Church Yth Grp; Girl Scts; Thesps; Chorus; School Musical; School Play; Stage Crew; Swing Chorus; Stu Cncl; JV Fld Hcky; Pres Acad Ftnss Awd 85; NYS Regnts Schlrshp 85; All State Choir 84; Bucknell U; Bio Engr.

ABRALDES, ALEXANDER L; St Anthonys HS; Selden, NY; (Y); Coach Actv; Var Socr; Var Trk; High Hon Roll; Hon Roll; NHS; Spanish NHS; Church Yth Grp; Office Aide; Spanish Clb; Princpls List 83-85; Engrng.

ABRAMAITYS, CHERYL M; Niagara Wheatfield SR HS; Niagara Falls, NY; (Y); 4/313; Church Yth Grp; Latin Clb; Varsity Clb; Rep Stu Cncl; Mgr(s); Var Swmmng; High Hon Roll; Hon Roll; NHS; Coll Clb Niagara Fls, NYS Rgnts Schlrshp 85; Daemen Coll; Bus Admn.

ABRAMOSKI, LISA; Southampton HS; Southampton, NY; (Y); Spanish Clb; Band; Chorus; Mrchg Band; Fld Hcky; High Hon Roll; NHS; Stage Crew; Hon Roll; Jr NHS; Summr Sessn Eastman Schl Music 85; Hampton Music Fest 82-85.

ABRAMOWITZ, DAVID N; Stuyvesant HS; Jamaica, NY; (Y); VP Computer Clb; Co-Capt Math Tm; Science Clb; Im Vllybl; High Hon Roll; NHS; Ntl Merit Ltr; St Schlr; Westinghouse Semifnlst 85; Mock Trial Tm Cty Qrtrfnlst 84; Edtr Schl Sci Mag 82-85.

ABRAMS, BARRY; Copiaque HS; Amityville, NY; (Y); Band; Concert Band; Mrchg Band; Ftbl; Lcrss; Capt Var Wrstlng; Cert Of Merit Distngshd Achvt Sports 83; 1st Pl Physcl Ftns Test 84-85; Empire ST Tm Wrestlng 85; Old Dominion; Radio & TV.

ABRAMS, LAWRENCE; Manhattan Ctr For Science Math; Bronx, NY; (Y); Debate Tm; JA; Chorus; Nwsp Ed-Chief; Yrbk Ed-Chief; High Hon Roll; Prfct Atten Awd; Manhattan Borough Pres Cert Exclnce 84; Saul Sigelschiffer Awd 83; Otto P Burgdorf Awd Bio-Sci 84; Jrnlsm.

ABRAMS, SHERI; Great Neck North HS; Great Neck, NY; (Y); Political Wkr; Nwsp Stf; Yrbk Stf; Rep Stu Cncl; Var Sftbl; Pres Schlr; Schl Serv Awd 85; NY Regnts Schlrshp 85; Peer Cnslr 85; Boston U; Bus.

ABRAMSON, APRIL; Commack High School South; Dix Hills, NY; (S); MMM; Teachers Aide; Temple Yth Grp; Chorus; School Musical; Variety Show; High Hon Roll; Hon Roll; ST U NY Smmr Schl Choral Stds 84; NYSSMA Awds 83-84.

ABRAMSON, JODI L; Massapequa HS; Massapequa, NY; (Y); 1/448; Hosp Aide; Nwsp Sprt Ed; Rep Sr Cls; Var Socr; Elks Awd; NHS; Ntl Merit SF; Val; Cmnty Wkr; Computer Clb; Westnghse Sci Tlnt Srch Hnrs Grp 85; Bk Awd Princeton Alumni Assn 84; Newsday Ldng Schltc Achvr Awd 85; Northwestern U; Med.

ABREU, CARMEN; Aquinas HS; New York, NY; (Y); 7/162; Cmnty Wkr; Nwsp Stf; Yrbk Stf; Hon Roll; Spanish NHS; Pace U; Computer Sci.

ABREU, ESMILDA M; The Bronx HS Of Science; New York, NY; (Y); Cmnty Wkr; VP JA; Spanish Clb; Office Aide; Teachers Aide; Chorus; Im Bsktbl; Spac Shuttl Steu Invlvmnt Projct Cert-Ntl Tchrs Assn & NASA 83; Bio.

ABRUZZO, STEPHEN; St John The Baptist HS; Central Islip, NY; (Y); MMM; Band; Concert Band; Drm Mjr(t); Jazz Band; Mrchg Band; Hon Roll.

ACAMPORA, KENNETH; Sachem HS; Lk Ronkonkoma, NY; (Y); Science Clb; Ski Clb; Varsity Clb; Chorus; Im Badmtn; Im Bsktbl; Var Socr; JV Wrstlng; NY Coll; Comp Prog.

ACAMPORA, MARC R; Chaminade HS; East Rockaway, NY; (Y); 17/337; Pres French Clb; Band; Concert Band; Mrchg Band; Hon Roll; NHS; Ntl Merit Ltr; Pres Schlr; Excllnc Chractr Awd; Lafayette Coll; Engr.

ACANFORA, JO ANN; Lafayette HS; Brooklyn, NY; (Y); 6/400; Ed Yrbk Stf; Cit Awd; Hon Roll; NHS; Ntl Merit Schol; Kiwanis Awd; Loyalty & Svc Awd 85; Schlrshp Awd HS 85; Gov Comm Schlstc Achvt 85; Brooklyn Coll; Elem Educ.

ACARD, BARBARA; Westhampton Beach HS; Westhampton Bch, NY; (Y); Cmnty Wkr; French Clb; FBLA; Library Aide; Office Aide; Teachers Aide; Temple Yth Grp; Drill Tm; Lit Mag; Hon Roll; Lesley Coll; Spec Educ.

ACCARDO, ANNA MARIE; Stella Maris HS; Howard Beach, NY; (Y); 20/248; Church Yth Grp; Dance Clb; Drama Clb; Girl Scts; School Play; Hon Roll; St Johns U; Pedtrtn.

ACCARDO, MARIO; Oceanside HS; Oceanside, NY; (Y); Boy Scts; CAP; Band; Concert Band; Jazz Band; Mrchg Band; Hon Roll; Civil Air Patrol Mitchell Awd 85; Cadet Yr Nassau Compst Sqdrn 84; AEROSP Engr.

ACCOLLA, MICHAEL; Commack High Schl North; East Northport, NY; (Y); Church Yth Grp; Nwsp Rptr; JV Var Bsbl; Engrng.

ACEVEDO, BRUNILDA; St Pius V HS; Bronx, NY; (Y); 20/75; Yrbk Bus Mgr; Sec Jr Cls; Pres Sr Cls; Stu Cncl; Bsktbl; Dnfth Awd; Hon Roll; Mary Mount Coll; English.

ACEVEDO, EFRAIN; Richmond Hill HS; Queens, NY; (Y); Boys Clb Am.

ACEVEDO, MARGARITA; Cathedral HS; Ny, NY; (Y); Hosp Aide; Red Cross Aide; Gym; Citznshp Awd 82; Fash Show Awd 84; Thpry.

ACEVEDO, MARGARITA; St John Th Baptist HS; Central Islip, NY; (Y); Hon Roll; NHS; Spanish NHS; Intl Law.

ACEVEDO, MIGUEL; Cardinal Hayes HS; Bronx, NY; (Y); 10/264; Trs Church Yth Grp; Library Aide; Chorus; School Musical; Stage Crew; Yrbk Stf; VP Frsh Cls; VP Soph Cls; VP Jr Cls; VP Sr Cls; Diamond H Clb Awd 84-85; Cert Of Hspnc Ldrshp Prjct 85; Gnrl Excel Mdl 4th Rnk 84; Comp Sci.

ACEVEDO, NANCY; Hillcrest HS; Forest Hills, NY; (Y); 50/793; Intnl Clb; Library Aide; Natl Hnr Rll 83-85; NY U; Finc.

ACHANZAR, WILLIAM; Mechanicville HS; Mays Landing, NJ; (Y); 2/104; Math Tm; Spanish Clb; Band; Im Ftbl; JV Trk; High Hon Roll; Jr NHS; NHS; Sal; Spnsh Awd; Rchrd Stockton Coll Fndtn Schlrshp; Stockton ST Coll; Micro Bio.

ACHENBACH, LINDA M; Starpoint Central Schl; North Tonawanda, NY; (Y); 12/207; Church Yth Grp; Drama Clb; School Musical; School Play; Stu Cncl; Var Powder Puff Ftbl; JV Sftbl; Hon Roll; Trs Jr NHS; NHS; NY St Regents Schlrshp 85; Fredonia St U.

ACHURY, ANGELA; St Johns Preparatory HS; Jackson Heights, NY; (S); Dance Clb; Variety Show; Yrbk Phtg; Rep Soph Cls; JV Tennis; Wt Lftg; High Hon Roll; NHS; Phys Sci Cert Distnctn 82; GA Inst Technology; Engrng.

ACKER, TINA; East Meadow HS; East Meadow, NY; (S); 95/414; Church Yth Grp; FBLA; Girl Scts; Concert Band; Mrchg Band; Suny Of Farmingdale; Comp.

ACKERBAUER, MICHAEL; Lakeland HS; Mohegan Lake, NY; (Y); Church Yth Grp; Computer Clb; Office Aide; Nwsp Ed-Chief; Nwsp Rptr; Nwsp Stf; Rep Sr Cls; Stu Cncl; Cmmnctns.

ACKERMAN, BRIAN M; Curtis HS; Staten Island, NY; (Y); 43/330; Am Leg Boys St; Boy Scts; Cmnty Wkr; ROTC; Drill Tm; God Cntry Awd; Eagle Scout; Horatio Alger Assoc Distngshd Amer Escort 85; Staten Island Fleet Res Assoc Wnnr 85; Military.

ACKERMAN, LISA; Cicero-North Syracuse HS; Clay, NY; (S); 67/622; German Clb; JA; Office Aide; Band; Concert Band; Mrchg Band; Powder Puff Ftbl; Hon Roll; Arch Engr.

ACKERMAN, MICHAEL; Tottenville HS; Staten Island, NY; (Y); Nwsp Rptr; Nwsp Stf; Var Capt Trk; Jrnlsm.

ACKERMAN, NAOMI; West Hempstead HS; Island Park, NY; (Y); Debate Tm; Key Clb; Model UN; DAR Awd; Hon Roll; Jr NHS; NHS; Speech Tm; Temple Yth Grp; Stonybrook.

ACKERMAN, TERRY L; Rome Free Acad; Taberg, NY; (Y); 72/512; Sec Church Yth Grp; Drama Clb; Intnl Clb; School Play; SUNY Agr & Tech Coll; Bus Adm.

ACKERMAN, WENDI A; Paul V Moore HS; Constantia, NY; (Y); 37/297; Chorus; Hon Roll; NHS; Le Moyne Coll Smmr Schlr 84; NYS Regents Schlrshp 85; SADD Treas; Le Moyne Coll; Engl.

ACKERT, GERALD; Roosevelt HS; Yonkers, NY; (S); Hst FBLA; Capt Band; Capt Mrchg Band; Ed Yrbk Stf; Rep Frsh Cls; VP Soph Cls; Rep Jr Cls; Pres Sr Cls; Trk; Cit Awd; SUNY Stonybrook; Cmmnctns.

ACLUCHE, PIERRE MAX; Springfield Gardens HS; Rosedale, NY; (Y); Church Yth Grp; Computer Clb; English Clb; French Clb; Intnl Clb; Math Clb; NFL; School Musical; Nwsp Rptr; Tennis; Pacific Union Coll; Comp Sci.

ACOSTA, ABDIEL; Walton HS; Bronx, NY; (Y); Boy Scts; Var Bsbl; Var Vllybl; Hon Roll; Prfct Atten Awd; Var Sftbl; Cert Of Merit Mth Having 95 Avg 85; Hnr Roll 5th In Cls 83; Phys Ed.

ACOSTA, ANGELO; All Hallows HS; New York, NY; (Y); 3/26; Dance Clb; Score Keeper; High Hon Roll; Hon Roll; COMP Sci.

ACOSTA, CATHERINE; Bronx High School Of Science; Bronx, NY; (Y); Teachers Aide; Excel In Engl 85; SUNY Stony Brook; Pre Soc Wel.

ACOSTA, JENNY; St Johns Preparatory HS; Woodside, NY; (Y); Chorus; Stage Crew; Hon Roll; NHS; Microbio.

ACOSTA, OLGA; Ellenville HS; Ellenville, NY; (Y); Yrbk Ed-Chief; Yrbk Stf; Trs Jr Cls; VP Sr Cls; Tennis; High Hon Roll; Hon Roll; NHS; Variety Show; Trk; NEMA Eng Merit Awd; Sci.

ACOSTA, SHARLENE; Hudson HS; Livingston, NY; (Y); Church Yth Grp; Chorus; Church Choir; Drill Tm; JV Sftbl; Hon Roll; NHS; Soc Sci.

ACOSTA, YOLANDA; Grace Dodge HS; Bronx, NY; (Y); 83/439; Chorus; Hon Roll; Baroch; Exec Sec.

ACQUILANO, KATHY; Fairport HS; Fairport, NY; (Y); Church Yth Grp; Spanish Clb; Chorus; Drill Tm; School Play; Stu Cncl; Hon Roll; Prfct Atten Awd.

ADAM, LAUREN; Mount Mercy Acad; Lackawanna, NY; (S); 58/199; Computer Clb; French Clb; Hosp Aide; JA; Red Cross Aide; Nwsp Stf; Lit Mag; Prfct Atten Awd; Frgn Languare Fair 3rd Pl 82; ST U Of NY; Comp Sci.

ADAM, TIMOTHY; Jamestown HS; Jamestown, NY; (Y); 35/389; Church Yth Grp; JA; Ski Clb; Spanish Clb; Jr Cls; Stu Cncl; Var Socr; Hon Roll; Prfct Attndnce 83-84; Pre Med.

ADAMAKIS, KRISTINA; Riverside HS; Buffalo, NY; (Y); French Clb; Hosp Aide; Pep Clb; Yrbk Stf; Lit Mag; Rep Frsh Cls; VP Soph Cls; Rep Stu Cncl; DAR Awd; Hon Roll; U NY Buffalo; Acctg.

ADAMCYK, VALERIE; Manhasset HS; Manhasset, NY; (Y); Hosp Aide; VP Service Clb; Thesps; School Musical; School Play; Nwsp Rptr; Ed Lit Mag; Stu Cncl; High Hon Roll; NHS.

ADAMCZAK, JOSEPH T; Guilderland HS; Schenectady, NY; (Y); 82/369; Bsbl; Var JV Bowling; Im Ftbl; Ice Hcky; Im Sftbl; Vllybl; Im Wt Lftg; Hon Roll; Hudson Vly; Engr.

ADAMEC, JILL; Broadalbin Central HS; Broadalbin, NY; (Y); Drama Clb; Letterman Clb; Library Aide; Pep Clb; Varsity Clb; Band; Chorus; Concert Band; Mrchg Band; Var Cheerleading; CPA.

ADAMEC, STEPHEN F; Lancaster HS; Lancaster, NY; (Y); 83/452; Key Clb; Spanish Clb; Varsity Clb; Stat Stu Cncl; Im Stat Bowling; Var Bowling; Stat Ftbl; Stat Ice Hcky; Im Var Socr; Hon Roll; Buffalo ST U; Comm.

ADAMEK, KATHLEEN; North Tonawanda S HS; N Tonawanda, NY; (Y); Church Yth Grp; DECA; FBLA; Nwsp Stf; Rep Stu Cncl; NCCC; Dentl Asst.

ADAMOWICZ, GERALD K; Chatham HS; East Chatham, NY; (Y); 40/143; Boy Scts; Computer Clb; Exploring; Ski Clb; JV Bsbl; Var Bowling; 4-H Awd; High Hon Roll; Hon Roll; Pres Schlr; NY ST Regents Schlrshp; Lyndon ST Coll; Ski Mngmnt.

ADAMS, ALICE; Grand Island HS; Grand Island, NY; (Y); 36/325; Hosp Aide; Ski Clb; Band; Yrbk Stf; JV Diving; Var Gym; JV Trk; Hon Roll; NHS; Vrsty Letter For Acad Exellnce 84-85; Millard Filmore Hosp Vlntr Svc Pin 84; Fshn Inst Of Tech; Fshn Dsgnr.

ADAMS, ANNE; Kenmore East Senior HS; Kenmore, NY; (Y); 47/330; Office Aide; Var L Tennis; Cit Awd; High Hon Roll; Hon Roll; Jr NHS; NHS; Prfct Atten Awd; Pres Schlr; Cert Achvt Math, Prsdntl Acad Ftnss Awd 85; Buffalo ST Coll; Pol Sci.

ADAMS, DIANNE; St John The Baptist D H S; Lindenhurst, NY; (Y); Sec Church Yth Grp; 4-H; Hon Roll; CA U Los Angeles.

ADAMS, GREGORY; Fayetteville-Manlius HS; Fayetteville, NY; (Y); Church Yth Grp; Var Capt Wrstlng; Hon Roll; Cmnty Wkr; Red Cross Aide; Im Bsktbl; JV Lcrss; Var Mgr(s); Im Wt Lftg; Chrch Yth Grp Ldr 84-85; Wrstg Mst Takedwns & Pins 83-84; Fstst Pin Tm 83-84; Sprts Med.

ADAMS, JACQUELIN M; John Jay HS; Pound Ridge, NY; (Y); Drama Clb; Teachers Aide; Chorus; School Play; Variety Show; Lit Mag; Cit Awd; High Hon Roll; Church Yth Grp; Cmnty Wkr; 1st Prz Schls Lit Mag 85; James Jackowski Jrnl Awd 85; Plattsburgh; Eng.

ADAMS, JEFFREY P; Union Springs Central HS; Auburn, NY; (Y); 3/104; Am Leg Boys St; Chess Clb; English Clb; School Musical; School Play; Yrbk Ed-Chief; JV Var Bsktbl; Var Capt Tennis; High Hon Roll; NHS; Elmira Coll Key Schlrshp; Cls Of 85 Schlrshp; Intrschltc Athl Conf MVP Bsktbl; U Of Buffalo; Fine Arts.

ADAMS, JULIE; Greene Central HS; Greene, NY; (Y); 6/115; French Clb; GAA; JV Var Bsktbl; JV Var Fld Hcky; Var L Trk; High Hon Roll; Red Cross Aide; Spanish Clb; Band; Acad Awd 85; Mst Dedicated Trk 85; Ath Awd 85; Siena Coll; Comp Sci.

ADAMS, KATIE; Ithaca HS; Brooktondale, NY; (Y); 4-H; Math Clb; Chorus; Orch; NHS; Ntl Merit Schol; Zonta Clb Math & Sci Awd 85; Albert W Crawford Awd 85; Cntntl Math Leag Cert-Clcls 85; Oberlin Coll.

ADAMS, MARK; Manhatton Center For Science & Math; New York, NY; (Y); Art Clb; Boy Scts; Computer Clb; School Musical; School Play; Stage Crew; Variety Show; Bowling; Cit Awd; Hon Roll; Comp Engr.

ADAMS, MARK P; Palmyra-Macedon Central HS; Palmyra, NY; (S); 12/205; Hon Roll; NHS; Prfct Atten Awd; Woodshp & Mtlshp Awds 83; Comp Engrng.

ADAMS, MICHAEL; R C S SR HS; Coeymans Hollow, NY; (Y); Camera Clb; JA; Hon Roll; Boca Raton; Comp Sci.

ADAMS, MICHELLE L; The Mary Louis Acad; Queens Village, NY; (Y); Cmnty Wkr; Library Aide; Office Aide; Chorus; Im Trk; Commnded Natl Acht Schlrshp Prog Outstndng Negr Stu 84; Cornell U; Vet Med.

ADAMS, PATRICIA; Victor SR HS; Victor, NY; (Y); Ski Clb; Varsity Clb; Band; Stu Cncl; Socr; Trk; Hon Roll.

ADAMS, PAULA M; Copiague HS; Copiague, NY; (Y); 46/350; CAP; Cmnty Wkr; Computer Clb; Dance Clb; VP Sr Cls; Rep Stu Cncl; Var Capt Cheerleading; Var Capt Gym; FBLA; GAA; Miss NY St Natl Chrldr 83-84; All-Leag Gymnast 81-83; Hnbl Mntn Arts Rec & Talent Srch 85; U Of Buffalo; Dance.

ADAMS, RACHEL D; Pinsford Sutherland HS; Pittsford, NY; (Y); Art Clb; Church Yth Grp; Cmnty Wkr; Stage Crew; Sec Frsh Cls; Bsktbl; Fld Hcky; Hon Roll; NHS; Yrbk Stf; NYS Piano Comp 83; Sibleys Schlstc Awds Art 85; Arts Ntl Talent Hnr Mntn 85; Parsons Schl Of Design; Illustr.

ADAMS, REBECCA; Berlin Central HS; Petersburg, NY; (S); 7/89; GAA; Pep Clb; Red Cross Aide; Chorus; School Musical; Cheerleading; Cit Awd; High Hon Roll; Co Chairman Of Prom Committee; Math.

ADAMS, ROBYN; Monticello HS; Brooklyn, NY; (Y); Intnl Clb; Math Tm; Varsity Clb; Nwsp Rptr; Nwsp Stf; Yrbk Stf; Crs Cntry; Trk; Hon Roll; Regnts NYS Schlrshp 85; Russell-Sage Schlrshp 85; Albany ST U.

ADAMS, SAMUEL J; Keshequa Central HS; Hunt, NY; (Y); 10/99; Key Clb; Math Tm; Concert Band; Nwsp Rptr; Var Crs Cntry; Var Trk; Hon Roll; Ntl Merit Ltr; NY ST Regents Schlrshp; SUNY At Geneseo; Comp Sci.

ADAMS, TAMMY J; Clifton Fine Central HS; Oswegatchie, NY; (Y); 15/50; 4-H; Chorus; Stage Crew; Stat Bsktbl; Hon Roll; Mr & Mrs E La Londe Awd; Fredonia; Elem Ed.

ADAMSON, NANCY E; Spring Valley SR HS; Spring Valley, NY; (Y); 46/436; Cmnty Wkr; Key Clb; Jazz Band; Stage Crew; Co-Capt Swmmng; Hon Roll; NHS; Hosp Aide; Spanish Clb; School Play; NY ST Regnts Schlrshp 85; Columbia Schlstc Press Awd 84; Yr Bk Edtr Acadmc & Actvts 84-85; U Of MI.

ADAMSON, SHAWN; Geneseo Central HS; Geneseo, NY; (Y); 9/87; Boy Scts; Computer Clb; Pres 4-H; Spanish Clb; Im Wt Lftg; High Hon Roll; Jr NHS; Spanish NHS; MIT; Comp Prog.

ADDARICH, JOSETTE; St Johns Prep; New York, NY; (S); 64/416; Drama Clb; Chorus; Rep Soph Cls; Rep Jr Cls; High Hon Roll; Hon Roll; NHS; Johnson Wales Acad Schlrshp 85; Johnson Wales Coll; Culnry Art.

ADDEO, GINA; St Gabriel HS; Bronx, NY; (Y); 10/61; Hon Roll; Bus.

ADELMANN, CHARLENE; West Seneca West SR HS; W Seneca, NY; (Y); 89/543; Cmnty Wkr; Key Clb; Red Cross Aide; Teachers Aide; Chorus; Rep Stu Cncl; Cit Awd; Hon Roll; Art Clb; GAA; Natl Cncl Chrstns & Jews Brthrhd/Strhd Yth Awd 84; Girl Scout Gold Awd 85; Med.

ADEY, ROBERT; Maryvale HS; Cheektowaga, NY; (Y); German Clb; JA; Mrchg Band; Symp Band; Crs Cntry; Tennis; Trk; Hon Roll; NHS; SUNY-BUFFALO; Elec Engrng.

ADGERSON, DETRA R; HS Of Fashion Inds; New York, NY; (Y); 78/312; Chess Clb; Teachers Aide; Church Choir; Atten & Punctlty Awd; Morgan ST; Bus Admin.

ADLAM, KAREN; Hillcrest HS; Laurelton, NY; (Y); Sec Church Yth Grp; Hosp Aide; JA; Office Aide; Church Choir; Concert Band; Orch; School Musical; Hon Roll; Teachers Aide; Hillcrest Sci Congress-2nd Pl Medal 83; Nursng.

ADLE, KELLY; Oneida HS; Oneida, NY; (Y); Civic Clb; Drama Clb; 4-H; French Clb; Intnl Clb; Yrbk Phtg; Im Vllybl; Engl.

ADLER, ANDREW F; Horace Mann Barnard Schl; Holliswood, NY; (Y); Debate Tm; Nwsp Rptr; JV Socr; Var Capt Tennis; Wrstlng; Eastern Tnns Assoc 84; Queen NY Dist Rankng 84; U MI; Math.

ADLER, BRIAN S; Clarkstown South HS; Nanuet, NY; (Y); 71/540; Cmnty Wkr; Scholastic Bowl; Nwsp Rptr; Ntl Merit SF; Ntl Merit SF; NHS; Schlrshp Smmr Coll Prog Sec Schl Stu Geo Washington U 84; Ny St Regents Scholarship Winner; Law.

ADLER, DAVID; New Rochelle HS; New Rochelle, NY; (Y); Drama Clb; Teachers Aide; School Musical; Yrbk Stf; High Hon Roll; NHS; Spanish NHS; Natl Ldrshp Orgnztn 84; Battle Of Bands Winner 85; Music.

ADLER, ELIZABETH; The Masters Schl; Dobbs Ferry, NY; (Y); French Clb; Hosp Aide; Key Clb; Yrbk Stf; Ed Lit Mag; Sec Trs Soph Cls; Sec Trs Jr Cls; VP Sr Cls; JV Fld Hcky; Hon Roll.

ADLER, LAURENT; Ramaz Schl; New York, NY; (Y); Chess Clb; Computer Clb; Math Tm; Science Clb; Nwsp Stf; Regents Scholarship; Johns Hopkins U; Med.

ADLER, LEONARD; Bronx High School Of Science; New York, NY; (Y); Chess Clb; Math Tm; Im Tennis; Gov Hon Prg Awd; NHS; Prfct Atten Awd; Pres Schlr; Aud/Vis; Mathletes; Math Clb; Ntl Soc Of Prof Engrs Schlrshp 85; Started Collectors Clb & Was VP & Treas 83-85; Math Mdl; Stanford U; Comp Engrng.

ADLER, LORI J; Irvington HS; Irvington, NY; (Y); 40/122; Mgr Drama Clb; Chorus; School Musical; School Play; Stage Crew; JV Bsktbl; Im Sftbl; Var Tennis; Hon Roll; George Washington U; Chld Psych.

ADLER, MICHAEL; New Rochelle HS; New Rochelle, NY; (Y); Model UN; Political Wkr; Ski Clb; Yrbk Phtg; Rep Jr Cls; Var Lcrss; Var Wrstlng; Bus Adm.

ADLER, PETER; Franklin K Lane HS; Glendale, NY; (Y); #98 In Class; Teachers Aide; High Hon Roll; NHS; St Johns Schlrshp Wnnr Comptv Tst 84; St Johns U; CPA.

ADLERBERT, MARK G; Shenendehowa HS; Ballston Lake, NY; (Y); Boy Scts; FBLA; Ski Clb; Varsity Clb; Church Choir; JV Ftbl; JV Lcrss; SADD 84-85; DECA 84-85; Regnl Plcmt DECNY Comptn 84-85; Bus Mgmt.

ADOLPHE, MIMOSE; La Fayette HS; Brooklyn, NY; (Y); 35/407; Dance Clb; Debate Tm; English Clb; French Clb; FBLA; Intnl Clb; Library Aide; Office Aide; Pep Clb; Service Clb; Brooklyn Coll; Bus Mngmnt.

ADOMEIT, ADRIANNE; Liverpool HS; Liverpool, NY; (Y); 4/789; Exploring; Ski Clb; Varsity Clb; Orch; Off Stu Cncl; Var Socr; High Hon Roll; NHS; Ntl Merit SF; French Clb; Harvard Book Awd 84.

ADRION, CHERENE; East Islip SR HS; East Islip, NY; (Y); Aud/Vis; Dance Clb; Pep Clb; Cheerleading; Fld Hcky; Accntg.

AEBI, NINA; La Guardia HS Of The Music & Arts; New York, NY; (Y); 66/589; Office Aide; Nwsp Rptr; Yrbk Stf; Lit Mag; NHS; Prfct Atten Awd; NYS Rgnts Schlrshp 85; Art Hnr Leag 83-85; Cornell.

AEGERTER, RENEE; Sewanhaka HS; Stewart Manor, NY; (Y); Cmnty Wkr; French Clb; Chorus; Variety Show; Yrbk Stf; Jr Cls; Hon Roll; Law.

AEPELBACHER, LOU ANN; Maryvale SR HS; Cheektowaga, NY; (Y); Church Yth Grp; German Clb; Acpl Chr; Band; Church Choir; Drm Mjr(t); Orch; High Hon Roll; NHS; Ntl Merit Ltr; NY All-ST Wind Ensmbl 84; Its Acad Tm 83-85; Math.

AFFINITO, JAMES J; Marlboro Central HS; Marlboro, NY; (Y); Regents Math,Soc Studies,Eng 85; Wake Forest; Radlgy.

AFIFI, GHADA Y; Shaker HS; Latham, NY; (Y); Art Clb; Cmnty Wkr; Sec German Clb; Math Tm; Speech Tm; Nwsp Rptr; Off Frsh Cls; Var Swmmng; Hon Roll; Regents Schlrshp & Hnry Awd 84-85; Rensselaer Mdl Math & Sci 84-85; GE Hall-Hist Essay Cntst Wnnr 84; Rensselaer Polytech; Bio-Med.

AFIFI, HAZEM Y; Shaker HS; Latham, NY; (Y); German Clb; Hosp Aide; Varsity Clb; Nwsp Rptr; Frsh Cls; Var Swmmng; JV Trk; Hon Roll; Regents Schlrshp & Hnry Awd 84-85; Pres Schlrshp 83-84; Pres List 84; Siena Coll; Pre-Med.

AFRICA, DAVID; Liverpool HS; Syracuse, NY; (Y); VP Frsh Cls; Pres Soph Cls; Pres Jr Cls; Rep Stu Cncl; Hon Roll; Prfct Atten Awd; Im Bsktbl; Lemoyne; Finc.

AGABAYEV, MAGGIE; Solomon Schechter HS; Brooklyn, NY; (Y); Drama Clb; English Clb; Band; School Musical; Vllybl; NYU; Intl Bus Mgmt.

AGAJANIAN, ANITA S; Roy C Ketcham SR HS; Poughkeepsie, NY; (Y); Sec Church Yth Grp; Drama Clb; Math Clb; Band; Chorus; Church Choir; Concert Band; Jazz Band; Sec Mrchg Band; Orch.

AGAN, STEPHEN L; Hoosic Valley Central HS; Johnsonville, NY; (Y); 3/88; Church Yth Grp; Drama Clb; Band; Chorus; Mrchg Band; School Musical; School Play; Swing Chorus; Var Crs Cntry; Var Trk; Northeastern U; Comp Engrng.

AGAN, WILLIAM; Elmira Free Acad; Elmira, NY; (Y); Boy Scts; French Clb; VP Ski Clb; Rep Stu Cncl; High Hon Roll; Hon Roll; Engnr.

AGARABI, DARIO A; La Salle Military Acad; Sea Cliff, NY; (Y); 15/100; Computer Clb; ROTC; Ski Clb; School Play; Var Capt Ftbl; Im Sftbl; Im Swmmng; Var L Trk; Im Wt Lftg; High Hon Roll; Clrksn U; Engrng.

AGARD, MARCELLE; Copiaque HS; N Amityville, NY; (Y); FBLA; High Hon Roll; Hon Roll; Med.

AGATE, DEBORAH L; West Seneca West SR HS; W Seneca, NY; (Y); 28/550; Dance Clb; Hosp Aide; Hon Roll; Jr NHS; Cmnty Wkr; NY ST Regents Schlrshp 85; Cert Of Rcgntn In Chemistry 84; U Of NY Buffalo; Phy Therapy.

AGBUYA, GEORGE; Bishop Ford CC HS; Brooklyn, NY; (Y); 70/400; Church Yth Grp; Cmnty Wkr; Pep Clb; Science Clb; Ski Clb; Teachers Aide; Yrbk Stf; Hon Roll; NY U; Law.

AGELICOLA, ROBERT M; La Salle Acad; Brooklyn, NY; (S); Church Yth Grp; Band; Church Choir; Music.

AGGARWAL, PUNAM; Hornell HS; Hornell, NY; (Y); Church Yth Grp; Exploring; Math Clb; Band; Mrchg Band; Symp Band; Capt Twrlr; High Hon Roll; NHS; Harvard Bk Awd 85.

AGGRIPPINO, JEANNE; Hudson HS; Hudson, NY; (Y); Church Yth Grp; Dance Clb; Spanish Clb; Color Guard; Yrbk Stf; Pom Pon; Sftbl; Trk; Hon Roll; Herkimer CC; Occptnl Thrpy Ast.

AGNANT, MANAKEL; Bishop Loughlin M H S; Brooklyn, NY; (Y); Cmnty Wkr; FBLA; FTA; Im Bsktbl; Im Ftbl; Im Gym; Im Trk; Im Wt Lftg; Hon Roll; NEDT Awd; Purple L Hnr 83 & 84.

AGNE, DEBBIE A; Brewster HS; Patterson, NY; (Y); Church Yth Grp; Girl Scts; Spanish Clb; Stage Crew; Yrbk Rptr; Yrbk Stf; Jr Cls; Mgr(s); Score Keeper; Var Trk; Ntl Englsh Merit Assoc 82-85; Ntl Sci & Ldrshp Assoc 82-85; Art Cllctn Awd 83-84; Math.

AGNELLO, JOANNA; Gates-Chili SR HS; Rochester, NY; (S); Drama Clb; Service Clb; School Musical; Cit Awd; High Hon Roll; Hon Roll; Prfct Atten Awd; Aud/Vis; Library Aide; Chorus; Schl Soc Studies Awd 83-84; Schl Eng Awd 83-84; Schl Health Awd 83-84; Teaching.

AGNES, ADU; Sheapshead Bay HS; Brooklyn, NY; (Y); Library Aide; Pre-Med.

AGODON, ANALILIA; Midwood HS; Brooklyn, NY; (Y); Drama Clb; Stu Cncl; Cheerleading; Med.

AGOSTA, ANNMARIE; Fontbonne Hall Acad; Brooklyn, NY; (Y); Drama Clb; Teachers Aide; Chorus; School Play; Variety Show; Nwsp Rptr; Stu Cncl; Hon Roll; Excllnc Awds Engl Relgn Chorus, Itln 83-85; Ladies Auxlry Ftbonn Schlrshp 82-83; SOCL Wrk.

AGOSTO, BEATRIZ; Adlai E Stevenson HS; Bronx, NY; (Y); Chorus; Rep Jr Cls; JV Bsktbl; JV Bowling; JV Gym; JV Vllybl; JV Wt Lftg; Hon Roll; Prfct Atten Awd; Pace U; Bus Mgmt.

AGOSTO, JOHN; Harry S Truman HS; New York, NY; (Y); 29/544; JV Var Ftbl; JV Var Trk; NHS; Natl Sci Olympd Cert 82-83; Amer Chem Soc NY Sect Cert 83; Regnts Schlrshp 85; Manhattan Coll; Envrnmtlsm.

AGRESTA, EUGENE; Amsterdam HS; Amsterdam, NY; (Y); 4/332; Am Leg Boys St; Nwsp Rptr; Yrbk Rptr; Pres Sr Cls; Var Bsbl; Var Ftbl; Elks Awd; High Hon Roll; VP NHS; Ntl Merit SF; Ans Please TV Quz 84; U Rochester; Psych.

AGRO, JOSEPH L; Sleepy Hollow HS; Tarrytown, NY; (Y); 30/169; Boy Scts; Concert Band; Mrchg Band; Orch; Nwsp Phtg; Yrbk Phtg; Trs Stu Cncl; Tennis; High Hon Roll; Hon Roll; PTSA 85; Amer HS Math Exam Awd 84; Semper Fidelis Awd 85; Pace U; Bus.

AGRO, PETER; Mc Kee Technical HS; Staten Island, NY; (Y); 18/238; Debate Tm; Library Aide; Vllybl; Cit Awd; Hon Roll; Prfct Atten Awd; Physical Fitness Awd 82-85; Elec Engnrng.

AGRO, PETER V; St Francis Prep; Whitestone, NY; (Y); Camera Clb; Computer Clb; JA; Service Clb; Teachers Aide; Vllybl; Hon Roll; Ski Clb; Im Capt Socr; Regents Schlrshp; Judo Var Awd 83-84; Baruch Coll Full Schlrshp; Baruch Coll CUNY; Bus.

AGUILAR, SANDRA ELIZABETH; Dominican Commercial HS; Jamaica Ests, NY; (Y); 53/273; Art Clb; Dance Clb; Rep Sr Cls; High Hon Roll; Hon Roll; Ntl Merit Ltr; Prfct Atten Awd; Girl Scts; Office Aide; Spanish Clb; Princpls Honor Roll 81-85; SIENA Clb Acadmc Achvts Clb 81-85; St Johns U; Busnss Admin.

AGUIRRE, DENNIS; Archbishop Molloy HS; Brooklyn, NY; (Y); Art Clb; French Clb; Science Clb; Spanish Clb; Bowling; The Amer Inst Of Sci & Technlgy Of NYC Awd 83; 1st Hnrs; Med.

AGUIRRE, JOSEPH M; Archbishop Molloy HS; New Hyde Pk, NY; (Y); 135/400; Intnl Clb; Pep Clb; Im Bsktbl; Im Ftbl; Im Sftbl; Psych.

AHART, LORI L; Watkins Glen Central HS; Watkins Glen, NY; (Y); Drama Clb; 4-H; Girl Scts; Ski Clb; Varsity Clb; Chorus; School Play; Cheerleading; Sftbl; Swmmng; NY Nrsng Schlrshp 85; Morrisville ST U; Nrs.

AHEARNE, PATRICK; Valley Stream Central HS; Valley Stream, NY; (Y); 74/360; JV Bsbl; Var Bsktbl; Var Crs Cntry; NHS; PTA Achvt Awd 85; St Johns U; Med.

AHERN, ALICE; Bayshore HS; Bay Shore, NY; (Y); Art Clb; Drama Clb; Hosp Aide; Library Aide; Office Aide; School Musical; Stage Crew; Sftbl; Hon Roll; Awd Hlpng Libr, Awd Drma Clb 83; Awd Oustndng Achvt Enl 85; Nrsg.

AHLERS, CHRIS; Bishop Timon HS; Buffalo, NY; (Y); 1/160; Chess Clb; Quiz Bowl; Nwsp Stf; Lit Mag; Vllybl; Bausch & Lomb Sci Awd; High Hon Roll; NHS; Baush & Laumb Sci Awd 85; Jr Eng Awd 85; Soph Math Awd 84; Econ.

AHLERS, CHRISTOPH M; The Albany Acad; Albany, NY; (Y); Drama Clb; Band; Chorus; Jazz Band; Orch; School Musical; School Play; High Hon Roll; Ntl Merit Schol.

AHLMAN, MARK; Curtis HS; Staten Island, NY; (Y); Church Yth Grp; Church Choir; Concert Band; Mrchg Band; School Musical; Hon Roll; Stu Mnth 85; Borough Pres Awdd Spec Rcgntn 85; SUNY-BINGHAMTON; Zoology.

AHRENS, MICHAEL; Hudson Falls HS; Hudson Falls, NY; (Y); 2/206; Band; Bsktbl; Ftbl; Trk; High Hon Roll; NHS; Spanish NHS; Engnrng.

AHRERS, MICHAEL; Hudson Falls HS; Hudson Falls, NY; (Y); 2/225; Band; Var Bsktbl; Var Ftbl; JV Trk; High Hon Roll; NHS; Spanish NHS; Engrng.

AIELLO, DEBRA; Saint Gabriels HS; New Rochelle, NY; (Y); 20/61; Bsbl; Cheerleading; Sftbl; Vllybl; Hon Roll; Italian Clb.

AIELLO, JOHN F; Julia Richman HS; New York, NY; (Y); 115/479; Var Ftbl; NY ST Regents Coll Schlrshp 85; Hnrbl Ment All-City Ftbl Plyr 84; MVP Ftbl 84; Comp Sci.

AILLET, CHRIS; Minisink Valley HS; Westtown, NY; (Y); 21/290; Art Clb; Church Yth Grp; Cmnty Wkr; Var Capt Crs Cntry; Var Capt Trk; High Hon Roll; JETS Awd; Letterman Clb; Ski Clb; Varsity Clb; Marathon Awds 83-85; OR ST; Civil Engr.

AILLONI-CHARAS, ORRIN; Blind Brook HS; Rye Brook, NY; (Y); Boy Scts; VP English Clb; Var Ski Clb; School Play; Ed Lit Mag; Rep Frsh Cls; Rep Soph Cls; Rep Sr Cls; Var Crs Cntry; Ntl Merit Ltr; Yth Ldrshp Amer Awd BSA 83; Eagle Scout 9 Palms 84; Regent Schlrshp Awd 85; UCLA.

AINSPAN, HERSCHEL A; Albany HS; Albany, NY; (Y); 1/600; Latin Clb; Science Clb; VP Temple Yth Grp; Yrbk Stf; Bausch & Lomb Sci Awd; High Hon Roll; NHS; Ntl Merit SF; Val; RPI Awd For Excel In Math & Sci; Cert Of Merit & Achvt In Math; Cert Awd By Assoc Of Tchrs Of Frnch; Columbia U; Elec Engrng.

AIOSA, GREGORY F; Holy Family HS; Huntington, NY; (Y); 9/282; Church Yth Grp; Nwsp Rptr; Nwsp Stf; Rep Frsh Cls; Var Golf; NHS; Pres Schlr; Fordham U Schlrshp 85; Catholic U Schlrshp 85; Cncl Of Adm & Supv 85; Fordham U; Law.

AIRD, LISA; Cardinal Spellman HS; Bronx, NY; (Y); Girl Scts; Variety Show; Off Sr Cls; Stu Cncl; Trk; Mgr Vllybl; Hon Roll; Brdcst Jrnlst.

AISTARS, SANDRA; Fayetteville Manlius HS; Manlius, NY; (Y); Church Yth Grp; Model UN; Chorus; School Musical; School Play; Variety Show; Hon Roll; DSAT Coll Srch Optn High Scorers 84-85; Amer Latuian Assoc Awds 82-85; Lib Arts.

AITORO, LORRAINE; New Rochelle HS; New Rochelle, NY; (Y); Aud/Vis; Hon Roll; NHS; Engl Achvmnt Awd 82; Regent Diploma 85; Fordham Coll.

AKAGI, LANCE; Union Endicott HS; Endicott, NY; (Y); Computer Clb; Key Clb; High Hon Roll.

AKEL, NICOLE; Binghamton HS; Binghamton, NY; (Y); Church Yth Grp; Pres Key Clb; Ski Clb; Church Choir; Var Tennis; High Hon Roll; Hon Roll; NHS; Bus.

AKERS, DARIA; Trott Vocational HS; Niagara Falls, NY; (Y); Library Aide; Nwsp Stf; Pres Frsh Cls; Hon Roll; Jr NHS; NHS; Outstndng Svc 83; Nrs.

AKERS, ELIZABETH; Weedsport Central HS; Weedsport, NY; (Y); 8/90; Church Yth Grp; French Clb; Intnl Clb; Chorus; Church Choir; Ed Yrbk Stf; High Hon Roll; Hon Roll; NHS; Prfct Atten Awd; Musicianshp Awd 85; Rlgn & Music.

AKESON, NANCYANN; Garden City HS; Garden City, NY; (Y); Trs Pep Clb; Sec Frsh Cls; Sec Jr Cls; Trs Sr Cls; Pom Pon; Jr NHS; NHS; Badmtn; JV Lcrss; JV Tennis; Intl Stu Ex Amb Spain 83; Georgetown U; Int Bus.

ALADIN, MARIE-ALAN; The Bronx High Schl Of Science; Cambria Hts, NY; (Y); Computer Clb; Debate Tm; Library Aide; NFL; Office Aide; Speech Tm; Nwsp Rptr; Rptr Nwsp Stf; Var L Socr; Pres Jr NHS; ST Champ Oral Intrprtn Awd 84; Yng Gftd & Blck Awd 83; Miss Ed Awd 83; Frgn Plcy Essy Awd 84; Bus.

ALAIMO, CATHERINE; St Marys Acad; Glens Falls, NY; (S); 9/43; Drama Clb; Teachers Aide; Band; Chorus; School Musical; Yrbk Bus Mgr; Yrbk Stf; Im Powder Puff Ftbl; Hon Roll; St Joseph Provider; Educ.

ALAIMO, MARIA; New Utrecht HS; Brooklyn, NY; (Y); 32/430; Key Clb; Teachers Aide; School Musical; School Play; Math.

ALAIMO, MARK A; Cardinal Mooney HS; Hilton, NY; (Y); Am Leg Boys St; Var Crs Cntry; Var Capt Trk; Wrstlng; US Army.

ALAMILLA, ANSELMO; Midwood HS; Brooklyn, NY; (Y); Chorus; JV Var Ftbl; Med.

ALAPECK, SCOTT; Union Endicott HS; Endicott, NY; (Y); Latin Clb; Var L Bsbl; Var L Socr; Im Wt Lftg; SPEC Sthrn Piedmont Educ Consrtm 85; Schlrshp SPEC 85; Math.

ALARCON, JORGE; East New York Vo-Tech HS; Brooklyn, NY; (Y); Acad Of Aeronautics; Avtn Tech.

ALATAS, FAWZIA; New Rochelle HS; New Rochelle, NY; (Y); French Clb; French Hon Soc; Hon Roll; NHS; Ind Engrng.

ALBAN, JORGE; Rocky Point HS; Rocky Point, NY; (Y); French Clb; Spanish Clb; School Musical; Nwsp Phtg; Yrbk Phtg; JV Trk; Art Dept Gold Awd 84; Mth Silvr Awd Geom 84; Cooper Union; Art.

ALBAN, PHILIP; So Kortright Central HS; Bloomville, NY; (Y); Am Leg Boys St; Band; Yrbk Stf; Pres Jr Cls; Var Bsbl; JV Var Bsktbl; Var Socr; NHS; Teachers Aide; Varsity Clb; Catskill Area Schl Study Cncl VP; Hghst Regents Bio Exam; USMA.

ALBANESE, CHRISTINA; Gloversville HS; Gloversville, NY; (Y); Church Yth Grp; Teachers Aide; Yrbk Stf; Var Cheerleading; Var L Crs Cntry; Stat Score Keeper; Var L Trk; High Hon Roll; Hon Roll; Art.

ALBANESE, GINA; Saint Edmunds HS; Brooklyn, NY; (Y); 49/187; Church Yth Grp; Cmnty Wkr; Church Choir; Nwsp Stf; Bowling; Hon Roll; Tablet HS Press Awd 85; Kingsborough Coll; Jrnlsm.

ALBANESE, LISA MARIE; Academy Of St Joseph; Smithtown, NY; (Y); GAA; Hosp Aide; Library Aide; Model UN; Political Wkr; Radio Clb; Science Clb; Spanish Clb; Nwsp Ed-Chief; Nwsp Rptr; Cert Hnr NY ST Bar Assoc 85; Cert Supr Acad Achvt Spnsh 83 & 85; Svc Awd Spnsh Nwsltr Edtr Chief 85; Hofstra U; Pre-Law.

ALBANESE, ROSEANN; Sewanhaka HS; Elmont, NY; (Y); 19/362; FBLA; Scholastic Bowl; Variety Show; Trs Jr Cls; JV Bsktbl; Capt Cheerleading; JV Var Sftbl; Cit Awd; High Hon Roll; NHS; Stu Mnth Health 84; Scl Stds Hnr Scty May 84; Stu Mnth Comp Math 84; Comp Pgrmr.

ALBANESE, SAL; Lafayette HS; New York, NY; (Y); JV Bsbl.

ALBANIS, EFSEVIA; St Francis Prep Schl; Jamaica, NY; (S); 29/693; Girl Scts; Library Aide; Math Clb; Trk; Wrstlng; High Hon Roll; NHS; Prncpls List Certs 83-85; Pre-Med.

ALBANO, CAROLINE; Lindenhurst SR HS; Lindenhurst, NY; (Y); Sec Spanish Clb; Band; Concert Band; Mrchg Band; School Play; Nwsp Rptr; Nwsp Stf; Hon Roll; NHS; Hon Men DWI Essay Cont 83; Mdl Wnr NYSMA 82; Engrng.

ALBANO, MATTHEW; Walter Panas HS; Peekskill, NY; (Y); 17/230; Band; Concert Band; Mrchg Band; Orch; Capt Var Crs Cntry; Var Trk; High Hon Roll; Hon Roll; Jr NHS; NHS; Regnts Schlrshp NYS 84; SUNY Albany; Comp Sci.

ALBARRAN, MAGDALENA; Eastern District HS; Brooklyn, NY; (Y); Church Yth Grp; Teachers Aide; Band; Church Choir; Photo.

ALBEE, RICHARD BURR; Cohocton Central HS; Cohocton, NY; (Y); 3/28; Am Leg Boys St; French Clb; Band; Concert Band; Mrchg Band; Pres Sec Stu Cncl; JV Var Bsktbl; JV Var Socr; Tennis; Trs NHS; Hghst Mrk Geometry Rgnts Tst 84; Comp.

AMBROSIO, DAVID C; Northport HS; Northport, NY; (Y); Computer Clb; Radio Clb; Acpl Chr; Chorus; Concert Band; Jazz Band; School Play; Variety Show; Hon Roll.

AMBROSIO, JENNIFER ROSE; Chatham Central HS; E Chatham, NY; (Y); Trs Girl Scts; Chorus; School Musical; High Hon Roll; Hon Roll; Merit Schlrshp-Pittsfield Comm Music Schl 84-85; NYSSMA-DUET Lvl 5 Excllnt Rtng 85; Choir Let 83-85; Music Perfrmnc.

AMELIO, FRANK; South Shore HS; Brooklyn, NY; (Y); Computer Clb; Math Tm; Band; High Hon Roll; NHS; Hstry, Math Hnrs 82-84; Chem Hnrs 83-84.

AMELL, FRANCINE; Linton HS; Schenectady, NY; (Y); 41/273; AFS; Drama Clb; Sec Intnl Clb; Pres Sec JA; Service Clb; School Play; Hon Roll; D Carnegie Yuth Schlrshp Awd 85; Bst Indvdl Achvr 84; Reg 1 JR Achvt 85; Acctng.

AMENDOLARE, MARYBETH; Frankfort-Schuyler HS; Frankfort, NY; (S); GAA; Spanish Clb; JV Bsktbl; Hon Roll; NHS; Law.

AMENDOLIA, ANGELA; Kings Park SR HS; Kings Park, NY; (Y); VICA; Hon Roll; Doc Of Comp Bty Cltr Oper & Gear-Trainee & Hands Patches 85; Beautcn.

AMENDOLIA, LISA; Bishop Kearney HS; Brooklyn, NY; (S); 4/360; Math Tm; Band; NHS; Prsdntl Schlrshp 85; Gen Excllnce St Johns U 85; Fresh Recogntn Hofstra U 85; Hofstra U; Math.

AMENO, CHARLES; Lancaster Central HS; Lancaster, NY; (S); VP Pres AFS; DECA; Key Clb; Yrbk Stf; Rep Stu Cncl; Hon Roll; NHS; Aws Acadmc Exc 84; Hugh O Brian Yth Found 84; V Rifle Team 84.

AMES, EILEEN; Heuvelton Central Schl; Heuvelton, NY; (S); 1/45; Pres GAA; Pres Latin Clb; Trs Band; Capt Flag Corp; VP Frsh Cls; Pres Soph Cls; Pres Jr Cls; Stat Bsktbl; JV Cheerleading; Var Capt Socr; Soccer MVP Awd 83-84; St Lawrence U.

AMES, NADINE; Dundee Central HS; Dundee, NY; (Y); VP AFS; Am Leg Aux Girls St; Chorus; Concert Band; Jazz Band; Mrchg Band; School Musical; NHS; Pres Schlr; Local Choral Awd 85; Area All ST Choir 85; Area All ST Orch 85; Ithaca Coll.

AMES, NANCI; Massena Central HS; Massena, NY; (Y); Cmnty Wkr; French Clb; Rep Frsh Cls; Rep Soph Cls; Rep Jr Cls; Rep Stu Cncl; Powder Puff Ftbl; Var JV Vllybl; Hon Roll; Prfct Atten Awd; GMI; Aero Engr.

AMIAMA, AUDREY; St Michaels Acad; New York, NY; (Y); Hosp Aide; Pres Pep Clb; Red Cross Aide; Teachers Aide; Yrbk Stf; Bsktbl; Gym; Sftbl; Vllybl; Prfct Atten Awd; Medaille Schlrshp 4 Yrs St Josephs Coll 85; 1st Prize In Sci Fair 82; Spnsh Achvmnt Awd 83; St Josephs Coll; Bio.

AMICO, SUZANNE; E J Wilson HS; Rochester, NY; (Y); Trs Exploring; 4-H; Mathletes; Symp Band; Var L Cheerleading; Var L Pom Pon; High Hon Roll; NHS; NYSSMA Outstndng Solo Music Awd 83-84; Geo,Spnsh II Awd 82-83; U Dayton; Crimnl Justc.

AMICONE, EILEEN; Mt Mercy Acad; Buffalo, NY; (S); Church Yth Grp; Nwsp Stf; Lit Mag; Pres Sr Cls; Rep Stu Cncl; Jr NHS; NHS; 2nd Pl Frgn Lang Fair 83; Comm Art.

AMIDON, STEVEN; Canisteo Central Schl; Hornell, NY; (Y); Hon Roll.

AMITRANO, RALPH; Bishop Ford Central Catholic HS; Brooklyn, NY; (Y); Var Bsbl; Var Bsktbl; Intramurals Sec 84-85.

AMMANN, LISA; West Genesee HS; Syracuse, NY; (Y); Key Clb; Color Guard; DAR Awd; High Hon Roll; Hon Roll; Jr NHS; NHS; FL ST; Bus Mgt.

AMMERMAN, JOHN; Tonawanda HS; Tonawanda, NY; (Y); Band; Color Guard; Concert Band; Drm & Bgl; Drm Mjr(t); Jazz Band; Mrchg Band; Orch; Pep Band; NHS; Secndry Ed.

AMMIRATO, ANTHONY; Mineola HS; Mineola, NY; (Y); Cmnty Wkr; Yrbk Stf; Bsbl; Ice Hcky; High Hon Roll; Hon Roll; Sci.

AMMONDS, JERENE; Midwood HS; Brooklyn, NY; (Y); Exploring; GAA; Intnl Clb; Office Aide; Teachers Aide; Varsity Clb; Band; Variety Show; Badmtn; Coach Actv; Colgate Wmns Games Fnlst 6th Pl Trphy 83; Trck Awd 84; Irwin Tobin Phy Ed Awd 82-83; Jrnlsm.

AMODIO, MICHELLE; Pulaski JR & SR HS; Pulaski, NY; (S); 6/95; Church Yth Grp; Cmnty Wkr; French Clb; Math Clb; Band; Im Powder Puff Ftbl; Var Tennis; Cit Awd; Hon Roll; Trs NHS; Spcl Educ.

AMOIA, NANCY; Bishop Kearney HS; Brooklyn, NY; (S); 5/343; Pres FNA; Yrbk Stf; Stu Cncl; High Hon Roll; NHS; Trustee Schlrshp NY U 85; Hnry Pres Schlrshp 85; 3rd Pl Lang Cntst 84; NY U; Mdcl Doc.

AMORETTI, MARTHA; La Salle SR HS; Niagara Falls, NY; (Y); Bsktbl; Coach Actv; Sftbl; Vllybl; Hon Roll.

AMOROSANA, JEFFREY M; Harrison HS; Harrison, NY; (Y); 1/220; Am Leg Boys St; Math Tm; Nwsp Sprt Ed; Yrbk Stf; Lit Mag; Var Capt Bsbl; Var Diving; Var Capt Ftbl; French Hon Soc; High Hon Roll; Harvard Bk Awd Engl 85; RPI Awd Math & Sci 85; French Embsy Of NY Cert Exclnc 85; Librl Arts.

AMOROSANO, DENNIS; Warwick Valley HS; Warwick, NY; (Y); 13/200; Rep Frsh Cls; Var Bsbl; Var Socr; Var Trk; High Hon Roll; Hon Roll; 3rd Tm Tri-Cnty Bsebl 85; Law.

AMOROSI, GREGORY; Fairport HS; Fairport, NY; (Y); Church Yth Grp; Ski Clb; Rep Soph Cls; Im Coach Actv; JV Socr; Im Tennis; Im Trk; Im Vllybl; Regnts Schlrshp 84; St Bonaventure; Pre-Law.

AMOROSO, GREGORY; Rome Free Acad; Rome, NY; (Y); 4/512; Drama Clb; Band; Mrchg Band; Orch; School Play; Nwsp Rptr; Nwsp Stf; Hon Roll; Jr NHS; NHS; All ST Band 84; Utica Coll; Commnctns.

AMOS, GUY; John Jay HS; Hopewell Junction, NY; (Y); Church Yth Grp; Ski Clb; Concert Band; Symp Band; Hon Roll; Prfct Atten Awd; Mech Engrng.

AMPUERO, GEORGE; Msgr Mc Clancy Mem HS; Flushing, NY; (S); 28/229; Cmnty Wkr; Spanish Clb; Teachers Aide; Y-Teens; Var Capt Socr; JV Var Trk; High Hon Roll; Hon Roll; NHS; Principals List; Deans List; IA Coll; Comp Sci.

AMRHEIN, ELEANOR; St Johns Prep; Middle Vlg, NY; (Y); Church Yth Grp; Band; Concert Band; Jazz Band; Hon Roll; St Johns U; Accntng.

AMROSE, DAVID; Sachem HS; Holtsville, NY; (Y); 38/1400; Ski Clb; Spanish Clb; Varsity Clb; JV Var Socr; High Hon Roll; NHS; Ldrs Clb 83; Sci.

AMSEL, JODY; Ossining HS; Ossining, NY; (Y); Mrchg Band; School Musical; School Play; Symp Band; Nwsp Stf; Sec Stu Cncl; Var Fld Hcky; High Hon Roll; Band; Concert Band; Natl Hnr Soc Schlrshp Awd 83-85; Frnch Achvt Awd 83-84; Smith Clg Bk Awd 85; Hist.

AMSTER, DAVID; East Meadow HS; East Meadow, NY; (S); FBLA; Key Clb; Jazz Band; Mrchg Band; Orch; Symp Band; Nwsp Rptr; L Bsbl; High Hon Roll; NHS.

AMSTER, ROBERT; Locust Valley HS; Bayville, NY; (Y); Am Leg Boys St; Drama Clb; Band; Chorus; Concert Band; Drm Mjr(t); School Musical; School Play; Sr Cls; JV Wrstlng; Advrtsng.

AMYOT, MAUREEN; Keveny Memorial Acad; Clifton Park, NY; (S); Girl Scts; Library Aide; Concert Band; Jazz Band; Mrchg Band; Yrbk Phtg; Capt Vllybl; High Hon Roll; Grl Sct Slvr Awd 84; Grl Sct Widr Opprtnts 82-84; Forgn Lang.

AMYOT, TODD; Athena HS; Rochester, NY; (Y); Church Yth Grp; French Clb; Ski Clb; JV Golf; Im Socr; Hon Roll; CPA.

ANA, CABRERA; Richmond Hill HS; Richmond, NY; (Y); Library Aide; Math Clb; Science Clb; Spanish Clb; Teachers Aide; Sftbl; Vllybl; Hon Roll; Prfct Atten Awd.

ANABLE, ANGELA; Coxsackie-Athens HS; Coxsackie, NY; (Y); 10/92; Church Yth Grp; VP Spanish Clb; Band; Chorus; Pep Band; Nwsp Rptr; Yrbk Stf; High Hon Roll; NHS; All St Womens Chr NYSSMA 84; NYS Rgnts Schlrshp 85; Tchrs Assoc Schlrshp 85; SUC Potsdam; Mus Educ.

ANAND, MALA; Longwood HS; Yaphank, NY; (S); Debate Tm; Drama Clb; VP Intnl Clb; Math Clb; NFL; Speech Tm; Ed Lit Mag; Var JV Badmtn; Var JV Bsktbl; Rotary Awd; Forensic Cntst 1st 85; Rotary Exch Stu Schlrshp India 84-85; Interacy Clb Awd 83; U MA; Comp Sci.

ANAND, PAVAN K; Shenendehowa HS; Ballston Lake, NY; (Y); Boy Scts; Pres Computer Clb; Hosp Aide; Intnl Clb; Key Clb; Library Aide; Science Clb; Yrbk Ed-Chief; Crs Cntry; Var Trk; Tri-City India Assn Awd For Dancing 83; Union Comp Crs 83; Med.

ANAND, SAVINDER; Richmond Hill HS; Richmond Hill, NY; (Y); Chess Clb; Math Clb; Office Aide; Teachers Aide; Var Crs Cntry; Hon Roll; NHS; Math Hnr Soc 83-85; Englsh Hnr Soc 84-85; Nalt Arista Hnr Soc 84-85; Bio.

ANANDA, ANUPAMA; Far-Rockaway HS; Far Rockaway, NY; (Y); VP Exploring; Key Clb; Teachers Aide; Nwsp Phtg; Sec Trs Stu Cncl; Hon Roll; NHS; Prfct Atten Awd; Pride Of Yankees 84-85; Biol.

ANANTHAKRISHNAN, DHEERA; John Jay HS; Hopewell Junction, NY; (Y); Cmnty Wkr; Computer Clb; Hosp Aide; Math Tm; Var Tennis; High Hon Roll; Hon Roll; Jr NHS; NHS; Ntl Merit Ltr; Girls 16 Distr Tennis Rankng 5,Finlst ETA Tenis Tourn 84; Schlstc Tenns Dutchess Cty Toun Chmp 83; :Premed.

ANASTASIO, ALEXI; Corning East HS; Corning, NY; (Y); #17 In Class; Computer Clb; Varsity Clb; Stage Crew; L Crs Cntry; L Capt Trk; High Hon Roll; Sec NHS; Rotary Awd; Prsdntl Acad Ftnss Awd, NY Rgnts Schlrshp 84-85; VA Tech; Comp Sci.

ANBAR, ARIEL D; Amherst Central SR HS; Amherst, NY; (Y); 5/310; Pres Aud/Vis; French Clb; Math Tm; Sec Model UN; VP Quiz Bowl; VP Temple Yth Grp; Nwsp Ed-Chief; Im Vllybl; High Hon Roll; NHS; Svc Awd Temple Beth El Jr Cngrtn 82-84; Chem.

ANCEWICZ, LORELEI A; St Dominic HS; Westbury, NY; (Y); Girl Scts; Quiz Bowl; Chorus; Stu Cncl; Var Bowling; Im Vllybl; NY ST Regnts Schlrshp Nrsng; U Of Miami FL; Bio.

ANCONA, LARA JEAN; Earl L Vandermeulen HS; Mt Sinai, NY; (Y); 19/260; Hosp Aide; High Hon Roll; Hon Roll; Math.

ANCTIL, ELIZABETH; Northeastern Clinton Central HS; Rouses Pt, NY; (Y); Drama Clb; Model UN; Ski Clb; Spanish Clb; Varsity Clb; School Musical; School Play; Yrbk Stf; Capt Cheerleading; Capt Pom Pon; Bus.

ANDERLIK, JOELLE; Cicero-North Syracuse HS; Clay, NY; (Y); Debate Tm; Drama Clb; Science Clb; School Play; Rep Stu Cncl; Var Trk; High Hon Roll; Hon Roll; NHS; Frnch Promounciation Cntst 83 & 85; Bus Wrld 84; Intl Bus Law.

ANDERSEN, CHRISTIAN T; Archbishop Stepiival HS; Yonkers, NY; (Y); 52/206; Capt Vrsty Rifl Tm Hnry 84-85; Manhattan; Engrng.

ANDERSEN, JOHN; John Jay HS; Hopewell Juncti, NY; (Y); Ski Clb; Orch; Ntl Merit Ltr.

ANDERSEN, KAREN; G Ray Bodley HS; Fulton, NY; (Y); 89/250; French Clb; Latin Clb; Pres Ski Clb; Variety Show; Yrbk Stf; Stu Cncl; Socr; Swmmng; Trk; Hon Roll; Rgnts Schlrshp 85; Svc Awd 85; Achvmnt Awd Soccer 84; Morrisville Coll.

ANDERSEN, LORI; Centereach HS; Centereach, NY; (Y); 4/475; Debate Tm; FTA; NFL; Co-Capt Speech Tm; Band; Mrchg Band; Var Tennis; High Hon Roll; NHS; Ntl Merit Ltr; Acad Exc Awd From C W Post 85; Regents Schlrshp 85; C W Post Cntr; Physics.

ANDERSEN, VICKY; Newfield HS; Centerreach, NY; (Y); Church Yth Grp; German Clb; JA; Chorus; Hon Roll; German Hnr Awd; Sci.

ANDERSON, ALEX; Bishop Loughlin Memorial HS; Brooklyn, NY; (Y); Computer Clb; Im Ftbl; Hon Roll; Prfct Attdnce Awd 84-85; La Guardia CC; Comp Progmmng.

ANDERSON, ALLIE; Falconer Central Schl; Conewango Vly, NY; (Y); 3/134; Church Yth Grp; Trs Computer Clb; French Clb; JA; Quiz Bowl; Spanish Clb; Trs Orch; Yrbk Sprt Ed; Hon Roll; NHS; Emphasis Excllnce Scholar JCC 85; Summr Study Scholar Violin 83 & 84; Frgn Lang.

ANDERSON, AMY; Westmoreland Central HS; Rome, NY; (Y); 10/76; Church Yth Grp; Drama Clb; Band; Chorus; Yrbk Stf; Pres Soph Cls; Pres Jr Cls; VP Stu Cncl; High Hon Roll; NHS; US Stu Cncl Awd, Acad All Amer 85; Acctng.

ANDERSON, ANNETTE I; Raldoph Central HS; Randolph, NY; (Y); 4/68; 4-H; Ski Clb; Spanish Clb; Teachers Aide; Yrbk Stf; 4-H Awd; Hon Roll; NHS; Drama Clb; FFA; Cornell U; Anml Sci.

ANDERSON, BETH; Mayville Central HS; Mayville, NY; (Y); 7/52; Trs Church Yth Grp; Trs Spanish Clb; Nwsp Phtg; Yrbk Stf; Trs Sr Cls; Rep Stu Cncl; Stat JV Bsktbl; High Hon Roll; NHS; Rgnts Schlrshp 85; Jmstwn CC; Bus Adm.

ANDERSON, CHRISTOPHER P; Gouverneur Central HS; Gouverneur, NY; (Y); VP Band; Chorus; Concert Band; School Musical; School Play; Yrbk Stf; Trs Jr Cls; Ntl Merit Ltr; NYS Regents Schlrshp 85; NYSSMA All ST Conf Choir 84; Potsdam Coll; Music.

ANDERSON, DAREN; Westhampton Beach HS; Westhampton Bch, NY; (Y); 2/240; Am Leg Boys St; Band; Chorus; VP Soph Cls; VP Jr Cls; Rep Stu Cncl; High Hon Roll; NHS; Quiz Bowl; Ski Clb; Pres Clsrm Stu-Wash DC 85; Cmptn Schl Tm Natl Acad Chmpnshp Dallas 85; Sailng Trphy Wnnr.

ANDERSON, DARNELL; Bishop Loughlin M HS; Brooklyn, NY; (S); Band; Chorus; Jazz Band; School Musical; School Play; VP Jr Cls; Stu Cncl; Hon Roll; Duke U; Htl Mgmt.

ANDERSON, DEBIE L; Ripley Central HS; Ripley, NY; (Y); 8/25; Chorus; School Musical; Cheerleading; Crs Cntry; Gym; Vllybl; NHS; Ntl Merit Ltr; VFW Awd; Voice Dem Awd; ST U Of NY; Bus Adm.

ANDERSON, DIANA; St Edmund HS; Brooklyn, NY; (S); 3/187; Spanish Clb; Yrbk Stf; Im Gym; Gov Hon Prg Awd; Hon Roll; Pres NHS; NEDT Awd; Pres Schlr; Pres Schlrshp St Francis U 85; St Francis U; Law.

ANDERSON, DIANE L; Holland Patent Central HS; Barneveld, NY; (Y); Chorus; Drm & Bgl; VP Frsh Cls; Rep Soph Cls; Rep Jr Cls; Rep Sr Cls; Var L Fld Hcky; Var L Trk; Var L Vllybl; High Hon Roll.

ANDERSON, DONNYLE; Letchworth Crntral HS; Castile, NY; (Y); 4/93; Church Yth Grp; Drama Clb; FBLA; Varsity Clb; Yrbk Stf; Cheerleading; Pom Pon; Hon Roll; Silver Days Neighbordays Qn 84-85; Exec Sec.

ANDERSON, GLEN; Walter Panas HS; Peekskill, NY; (Y); Boy Scts; Varsity Clb; Band; Concert Band; Mrchg Band; JV Ftbl; Var Capt Swmmng; High Hon Roll; Jr NHS; NHS; FL Inst Of Tech; Chem Engrng.

ANDERSON, JADE; Dominican Commercial HS; Jamaica, NY; (Y); Church Yth Grp; Civic Clb; Hosp Aide; Hon Roll; Prfct Atten Awd; Off Broadway Shw 81; Peer Ldr In Relig 85; Sienna Clb; Hofstra; Med.

ANDERSON, JANET E; Tottenville HS; Staten Island, NY; (Y); 43/897; Church Yth Grp; Cmnty Wkr; Girl Scts; Key Clb; Teachers Aide; Chorus; Nwsp Stf; Trs Frsh Cls; Hon Roll; NHS; NY ST Spllng Bee Cont 81; 1st Rnnr Up Schlwd Spllng Bee 83; NY U; Comp Pgmmng.

ANDERSON, JEANNE; Our Lady Of Mercy Acad; Hicksville, NY; (Y); 1/117; Church Yth Grp; Lit Mag; Coach Actv; Sftbl; Vllybl; High Hon Roll; Trs NHS; NEDT Awd; Full Schlrshp Molloy Coll & C W Post Coll 85; Adelphi U & St Johns U Schlrhsp 85; Gen Excllnc Awd 85; St Johns U; Math.

ANDERSON, JEFFREY T; Manhatte Center For Science & Math; New York City, NY; (Y); Debate Tm; Church Choir; Concert Band; Nwsp Rptr; High Hon Roll; Prfct Atten Awd; Band; Diving; Trk; Acad All Amer Schlr 84-85; Acad Music Schlr Harlem Scholofart 83-85; Engr.

ANDERSON, KAREN; Bishop Kearney HS; Brooklyn, NY; (Y); Church Yth Grp; Yrbk Stf; Hon Roll; NHS; Scientific Research.

ANDERSON, KAREN L; Uniondale HS; Uniondale, NY; (Y); 127/482; Political Wkr; High Hon Roll; Hon Roll; Hshld Intl Schlrs Awd 85; NY ST Regnts Schlrshp 85; SUNY Coll; Drama.

ANDERSON, KEVIN; Harry S Truman HS; Bronx, NY; (Y); Hlth Med.

ANDERSON, KIM; Waterford-Halfmoon HS; Waterford, NY; (Y); Church Yth Grp; 4-H; Math Clb; Yrbk Stf; Stu Cncl; Fld Hcky; Hon Roll; NHS; NEDT Awd; Chorus; Sprtsmnshp Awd Bwlng 84-85; SADD Pres 84-85; Zoolgy.

ANDERSON, LORI; Binghamton HS; Binghamton, NY; (Y); High Hon Roll; Hon Roll; Prfct Atten Awd; Gregg Typing & Shrthnd Awd 85; Spnsh Awdh 85; Broome CC; Exec Scrtry.

ANDERSON, LORI; Dundee Central Schl; Dundee, NY; (Y); Church Yth Grp; Drama Clb; 4-H; JA; Office Aide; Chorus; Church Choir; St Schlr; Hosp Aide; Spanish Clb; Hlth Careers Clb Awd 83-84; Sci Schlrhsp Nrs 84-85; Armot-Ogden; RN.

ANDERSON, MARK; Chautauqua Central HS; Ashville, NY; (Y); 5/36; Pres Church Yth Grp; Band; Church Choir; Concert Band; Bsktbl; Bowling; Sftbl; Trk; Hon Roll; NHS; MVP Church Bsktbl 85; Tchrs Assn Scholar; Jamestown CC; Missions.

ANDERSON, MICHAEL; Mynderse Acad; Seneca Falls, NY; (Y); Varsity Clb; JV Var Bsbl; JV Var Bsktbl; JV Var Ftbl; Im Mgr Wt Lftg; All-League Running Back Ftbll 84-85; All League Outfield Baseball 85; Art.

ANDERSON, MICHAEL; St Johns Prep; Long Island Cty, NY; (Y); Nwsp Rptr; Nwsp Stf; Yrbk Stf; JV Bowling; Im Mgr Ftbl; High Hon Roll; Hon Roll; NHS; Bio Med.

ANDERSON, MIKE; Middletown HS; Middletown, NY; (Y); Computer Clb; Library Aide; Nwsp Sprt Ed; Yrbk Phtg; Diving; Fld Hcky; Lcrss; Trk; Wt Lftg; Hon Roll; Engrng.

ANDERSON, MOLLY LYNN; Dunkirk HS; Dunkirk, NY; (Y); 31/211; Pres Church Yth Grp; VP Computer Clb; Pres 4-H; Band; Chorus; Rep Stu Cncl; Var L Tennis; NHS; NYS Regnts Schlrshp 85; Kathryn C Reber Music Schlrshp 85; Alfred ST Coll; Comp Aid Dsgn.

ANDERSON, PETER; Lindenhurst HS; Lindenhurst, NY; (Y); ROTC; Ski Clb; Var Bsktbl; JV Var Ftbl; Lcrss; Bio.

ANDERSON, RANDY; Salmon River Central HS; Constable, NY; (S); 8/100; Hon Roll; NHS; Comp Sci.

ANDERSON, ROBERT; Delaware Acad; Delhi, NY; (Y); Spanish Clb; Yrbk Stf; Var L Bsbl; Var L Crs Cntry; Hon Roll; JV Bsktbl; Var Trk; JR Legn Bsbl Allstar; Crmnl Law.

ANDERSON, ROXANNE; Park West HS; East Elmhurst, NY; (Y); 1/25; Aud/Vis; Hosp Aide; Office Aide; Teachers Aide; Rep Sr Cls; Jobs Yuth, Schl Vltnr 84; UCLA; Med.

ANDERSON, RUTH A; Sachem HS North; Farmingville, NY; (Y); 114/1383; Church Yth Grp; Cmnty Wkr; VP Drama Clb; Radio Clb; Stage Crew; Nwsp Phtg; Jr NHS; Soc Stud Cmptn Awd 84; Brdcstg.

ANDERSON, SHERRI; Alden HS; Lancaster, NY; (Y); VP Art Clb; Trs Church Yth Grp; Science Clb; VP Band; Jazz Band; Mrchg Band; JV Trk; Hon Roll; NHS; Acad Ltr Wnnr 83-85; U Of Buffalo; Med.

ANDERSON, STEVEN B; Berne-Knox-Westerlo Central HS; East Berne, NY; (Y); Cmnty Wkr; Ski Clb; Teachers Aide; Stage Crew; Nwsp Stf; Yrbk Stf; JV Bsktbl; Hon Roll; Engrng.

ANDERSON, SUSAN; Falconer Central HS; Falconer, NY; (Y); 16/105; French Clb; Hosp Aide; Quiz Bowl; Hon Roll; NHS; Jamestown CC; Med.

ANDERSON, THERESA; Farmingdale HS; Massapequa Pk, NY; (Y); 1/600; Cmnty Wkr; Key Clb; Yrbk Ed-Chief; Yrbk Sprt Ed; High Hon Roll; NHS; Ntl Merit SF; Sal; Val; Schlrshp-Adelphi U Smr Acad For Intl Stds 85; 1st Pl-Yrbk Cpy Of Columbia U 84-85 Twice; Intl Bus.

ANDERSON, VALERIE G; Maple Grove HS; Bemus Point, NY; (Y); 5/81; Church Yth Grp; Ski Clb; Spanish Clb; Yrbk Ed-Chief; VP L Bsktbl; Cit Awd; DAR Awd; High Hon Roll; Jr NHS; NHS; Regents Schlrshp 85; Miami U Oxford OH; Engrng.

ANDERSON, WENDY; Byron-Bergen C S HS; Batavia, NY; (Y); 14/88; Pres Art Clb; Mrchg Band; Yrbk Phtg; Yrbk Stf; Rep Stu Cncl; Score Keeper; JV Var Vllybl; High Hon Roll; Merit Tuitn Awd 85; Ralph & Mina Gillette Awd 85; Genesee CC; Bus Adm.

ANDES, JENNIFER; Mountainside Acad; Schroon Lake, NY; (Y); French Clb; School Musical; School Play; Yrbk Rptr; Yrbk Stf; Var JV Cheerleading; Var Sftbl; Var Vllybl; Hon Roll; Church Yth Grp; Most Imprvd Stu Awd 83; Scripture Memory Awd 83-85; ST Coll; Bus Adm.

ANDINO, LUIS; Alfred E Smith HS; Bronx, NY; (Y); Wt Lftg; Hon Roll; Acdmc Awds 82-86; NY Inst Tech; Arch.

ANDINO, NATALIE; Francis HS; Staten Island, NY; (S); #2 In Class; Girl Scts; Office Aide; Hon Roll.

ANDJEVSKY, CYNTHIA; Connetauot HS; Ronkonkoma, NY; (Y); 139/694; Var Capt Swmmng; MVP Swmmng 81-84; Coaches Awd Swmmng 84-85; Comp Engrng.

ANDOLINA, CHRISTOPHER M; Amsterdam HS; Amsterdam, NY; (Y); Capt JV Ftbl; Wt Lftg; Hon Roll; Engr.

ANDOLSEK, PHYLLIS; Gowanda Central HS; Gowanda, NY; (Y); 6/139; Church Yth Grp; Drama Clb; Thesps; School Musical; School Play; Off Soph Cls; Stu Cncl; High Hon Roll; NHS; Prfct Atten Awd; Hilbert Coll; Sectrl.

ANDOR, SHARON; Lindenhurst HS; Lindenhurst, NY; (Y); Cmnty Wkr; German Clb; GAA; Spanish Clb; Teachers Aide; Var Badmtn; Var Fld Hcky; Hon Roll; NHS; VFW Awd; Phys Thrpy.

ANDRADE, JOSE A; La Salle Academy HS; Brooklyn, NY; (S); FBLA; Science Clb; Church Choir; Drill Tm; Drm & Bgl; Drm Mjr(t); Flag Corp; Hon Roll; Accounting.

ANDRADE, KRISTIN; Lake Placid Central Schl; Lake Placid, NY; (Y); 3/53; Key Clb; Varsity Clb; VP Sr Cls; Stu Cncl; Var JV Socr; Var Sftbl; Sec NHS; VP Frsh Cls; Xmas Wreath Meml Fund Awd 85; L P Ed Fndtn Schlrshp 85; Tri-Lks Bus & Profssnl Wmns Clb 85; Skidmore Coll.

ANDRE, ELLA; Mabel Dean Bacon V HS; New York, NY; (S); 18/299; JA; Office Aide; Church Choir; Rep Frsh Cls; Rep Soph Cls; Rep Jr Cls; Pres Sr Cls; Rep Stu Cncl; Hon Roll; Prfct Atten Awd; Yth Of NY Awd; Baruch Coll; Acctng.

ANDRE, MIRLENE; Mabel Dean Bacon Vocational HS; Miami, FL; (S); 16/299; Hosp Aide; VP Sec JA; Library Aide; Chorus; Church Choir; Yrbk Phtg; Yrbk Stf; Hon Roll; Prfct Atten Awd; Math Awd 83; Psychlgy.

ANDREANI, MARIANNE; St Vincent Ferrer HS; Jackson Hts, NY; (Y); 28/126; Hon Roll; Jrnlsm.

ANDREOLA, CHRIS; Fallburg Central HS; Hurleyville, NY; (Y); 9/59; Art Clb; Concert Band; School Musical; School Play; Var Socr; Capt Vllybl; Hon Roll; NHS; Grphc Arts.

ANDREOLAS, WILLIAM; Bethpage HS; Bethpage, NY; (Y); 155/290; Hon Roll; Bus Mngmnt; Deree-Pierce Athns Grc; Bus Adm.

ANDRESEN, LISA; Salmon River HS; Brasher Falls, NY; (S); 12/112; Cmnty Wkr; Drama Clb; Pres 4-H; FNA; Library Aide; Pep Clb; Chorus; School Play; 4-H Awd; Hon Roll; Bio.

ANDRESEN, STACEY; Moore Catholic HS; Staten Island, NY; (Y); Math Tm; Ski Clb; Bowling; High Hon Roll; Hon Roll; NHS; Coll Of STATEN Island; Nrsng.

ANDREW, MICHAEL; Charles O Dickerson HS; Trumansburg, NY; (Y); Cmnty Wkr; Stat Bsktbl; Mgr Ftbl; JV Var Mgr(s); Var Score Keeper; Var Socr; Stat Sftbl; Timer; High Hon Roll; Hon Roll; Bus.

ANDREW, TOUMA; Niagara Catholic HS; Niagara Falls, NY; (Y); 35/100; Church Yth Grp; Church Choir; Bsbl; Bowling; Golf; Cit Awd; Bus.

ANDREW, VIRGINIA; Niagara Falls HS; Niagara Falls, NY; (Y); AFS; Pres Church Yth Grp; Hosp Aide; Sec Science Clb; Chorus; Church Choir; School Play; Yrbk Stf; VP Badmtn; Cnslr Mntly & Physclly Hndcppd Smmr Camps 83-85; Natl Hnr Rll 85; Gordon Coll Wenham; Spec Educ.

ANDREWS, ALAN; Gouv Central HS; Gouverneur, NY; (Y); Var Bsbl; JV Var Wrstlng; Hon Roll; Jr NHS; NHS.

ANDREWS, AMY B; Holland Patent Central HS; North Western, NY; (Y); 3/154; Pres Church Yth Grp; Band; Chorus; Church Choir; Jazz Band; Orch; Symp Band; Rep Stu Cncl; High Hon Roll; NHS; Elect Engrng.

ANDREWS, BURCE; Nottingham HS; Syracuse, NY; (Y); Rep Jr Cls; Rep Sr Cls; JV Var Ftbl; JV Var Lcrss; Hon Roll; NHS; Pol Sci.

ANDREWS, GEORGE; John Dewey HS; Brooklyn, NY; (Y); Dance Clb; Teachers Aide; School Play; Off Jr Cls; Bsbl; Trk; Vllybl; Hon Roll; JHS Hndbll Chmp 80-81; Kingsborough; Sci.

ANDREWS, JOHN J; Rome Catholic HS; Rome, NY; (Y); Civic Clb; Drama Clb; Spanish Clb; Capt Varsity Clb; School Musical; Nwsp Stf; Yrbk Stf; Rep Sr Cls; CC Awd; JV Bsbl; Myrs Cncl On Alchl & Drug Abuse.

ANDREWS, KAREN; Hornell HS; Harnell, NY; (S); 2/200; Church Yth Grp; Latin Clb; Varsity Clb; Chorus; Stu Cncl; Var Capt Bsktbl; High Hon Roll; NHS; Lycoming Coll Of PA; Med Tech.

ANDREWS, KATHLEEN; Indian River Central HS; Evans Mills, NY; (S); 1/103; Am Leg Aux Girls St; 4-H; Drm Mjr(t); School Musical; School Play; Yrbk Stf; Pres Sr Cls; Var JV Cheerleading; Var JV Trk; Var JV Twrlr; Elmira Key Awd 84; Clarkson Sci Stdnt Recog Awd 84; Regnts Schlrshp 85; Potsdam ST U Coll; Math.

ANDREWS, LISA; Niagara Catholic HS; Niagara Falls, NY; (Y); Key Clb; Science Clb; Sec Spanish Clb; VP Frsh Cls; Pres Soph Cls; Pres Jr Cls; Rep Stu Cncl; Var Co-Capt Cheerleading; Var Sftbl; High Hon Roll; Hugh O Brien Yth Found Awd 83-84; Med.

ANDREWS, STEPHEN C; St Anthonys HS; Northport, NY; (Y); Boy Scts; Church Yth Grp; Hosp Aide; Jazz Band; Stage Crew; Yrbk Ed-Chief; JV Trk; NHS; Eagle Scout 85; Polit Sci.

ANDREWS, SUSAN; Grand Island HS; Grand Island, NY; (Y); 20/325; Art Clb; L GAA; Spanish Clb; Teachers Aide; Varsity Clb; Variety Show; Coach Actv; Var Diving; Var Swmmng; Hon Roll; Acdmc Ltr; Diving & Swmng Letter & Bar; Bio.

ANDREWS, WESMOND C; Kaiserslautern American HS; New York, NY; (Y); 23/191; ROTC; Teachers Aide; Varsity Clb; Y-Teens; Rep Stu Cncl; Bsbl; Var L Bsktbl; JV Var Ftbl; Powder Puff Ftbl; DAR Awd; Syracuse U; Elec Engr.

ANDRIANO, CLARE; St Francis Prep; College Point, NY; (S); 81/693; Dance Clb; Math Tm; Varsity Clb; Band; Var Socr; Swmmng; NHS; Opt Clb Awd.

ANDRIANOS, JOHN T; Vestal SR HS; Vestal, NY; (Y); 126/450; Hosp Aide; Ski Clb; Mrchg Band; Pep Band; JV Swmmng; Var L Trk; Hon Roll; NYS Regents Schlrshp 85; ST U NY Binghamton; Med.

ANDROSS, DOUGLAS; Fairport HS; Fairport, NY; (Y); Boy Scts; Ski Clb; Spanish Clb; Order Arrow BSA 85; US Merchant Marine Acad.

ANDRUS, GREGORY; Paul V Moore HS; Hastings, NY; (Y); 57/297; Var JV Crs Cntry; Var Trk; High Hon Roll; Hon Roll.

ANDRUS, WENDY; Granville Central HS; Granville, NY; (Y); 1/133; AFS; Am Leg Aux Girls St; Pres VP Church Yth Grp; Math Tm; Band; Chorus; Jazz Band; School Musical; Variety Show; Yrbk Ed-Chief; Mst Outstndng Stu 83; Mst Outstndng Soc Studs Stu 84-85; Mst Outstndng Frnch II Stu 84; Music Perfrmnce.

ANDRYSHAK, COLEEN LYNN; S S Seward Inst; Goshen, NY; (Y); 12/57; Church Yth Grp; GAA; Girl Scts; Ski Clb; Spanish Clb; Chorus; Yrbk Stf; VP Jr Cls; Rep Sr Cls; Capt Bsktbl.

ANDRYSICK, JIM E; Corning Painted Post West HS; Painted Post, NY; (Y); Drama Clb; Ski Clb; Varsity Clb; Acpl Chr; Chorus; Madrigals; School Musical; School Play; Stage Crew; Variety Show; Rgnts Schlrshp 85; SUNY Alfred; Bus Admin.

ANDRYSKI, MARY; West Genesee HS; Syracuse, NY; (Y); Key Clb; Color Guard; Im Bsktbl; Stat Lcrss; Score Keeper; Central City Busnss Inst; Mgmt.

ANDRZEJEWSKI, KIM M; Mayrvale HS; Depew, NY; (Y); 56/333; Sec GAA; Library Aide; Var L Bowling; Stat Score Keeper; Var L Tennis; NHS; Church Yth Grp; Cmnty Wkr; French Clb; Varsity Clb; Grad Hnrs Regnts Diplm 85; ST U Of NY Buffalo; Comp Sci.

ANDUIZA, LIANA M; Saint Marys Girls HS; Manhasset, NY; (Y); Camera Clb; Drama Clb; Hosp Aide; Office Aide; Ski Clb; School Musical; Mgr Stage Crew; Ice Hcky; Hon Roll; Ntl Merit Ltr; Superior Lvl-Spanish 84; Fairfield U; Intl Studies.

ANELLO, ANGELO; La Salle SR HS; Niagara Falls, NY; (Y); Boy Scts; Band; VP Concert Band; Pres Jazz Band; Mrchg Band; Orch; School Musical; Hon Roll; Jr NHS; NHS; Mst Outstndng Talnt Music 84; Hnr Roll Awd 40 Wk 85; Lou Armstrong Music Awd 85; Rit West Point; Acctg.

ANELLO, DENISE; Connetquot HS; Sayville, NY; (Y); 116/865; French Clb; Sr Cls; Cheerleading; JV Vllybl; Hon Roll; Boston U; Advrtsng.

ANELLO, JANE; Manhasset HS; Manhasset, NY; (Y); Debate Tm; Sec French Clb; Hosp Aide; Color Guard; Yrbk Stf; Var Swmmng; Var Trk; NHS; Jr NHS; Schlrshp U Of PA 85; Sci.

ANGARANO, DAVID; Solvay HS; Syracuse, NY; (Y); Excllnc Awd-Amer Studies 84-85; Busnss.

ANGE, CAROLYN; Webster HS; Rochester, NY; (Y); 54/540; Ski Clb; Rep Sr Cls; Capt Socr; Capt Sftbl; Hon Roll; NHS; Lemoyne Coll; Bus.

ANGELES, MARIA; Southwestern Central HS; Lakewood, NY; (Y); VP Church Yth Grp; Pep Clb; Spanish Clb; Yrbk Stf; Pres Frsh Cls; Pres Jr Cls; JV Var Cheerleading; Var Tennis; NHS; Opt Clb Awd; Amer Cancer Scty Top Fund Raiser 81-84; Pre-Med.

ANGELL, DIANNA J; Rome Free Acad; Rome, NY; (Y); 17/530; Drama Clb; 4-H; Girl Scts; Chorus; School Play; Cit Awd; High Hon Roll; Jr NHS; NHS; Pres Schlr; Bus & Profsnl Wmn Clb Schlrshp 85; Cmmnty Thtrs Pres Awd 84; Rgnts Schlrshp 85; SUNY; Spch Cmmnctns.

ANGELONE, MARGARET ANNE; Bishop Kearney HS; Brooklyn, NY; (Y); Hon Roll; NHS; Pres Acad Fit Awd 85; St Francis Coll; Bus Adm.

ANGERER, JEFFREY E; Lansing HS; Lansing, NY; (Y); Rep Sr Cls; Var Capt Bsbl; Var Capt Bsktbl; High Hon Roll; NHS; Ntl Merit Ltr; Boy Scts; English Clb; Variety Show; Rep Frsh Cls; US Army Rsrv Ntl Schl, Ath Awd, Prsdntl Acad Ftnss Awd 85; Pace U; Jrnlsm.

ANGERHOFER, TIMOTHY E; Pittsford-Mendon HS; Pittsford, NY; (Y); Exploring; Radio Clb; Im Bsktbl; JV Ftbl; Hon Roll; NHS; Pres Schlr; Purdue, NYS Regnts Schlrshps 85; Purdue U; Ind Mgt.

ANGERTHAL, MICHAEL A; Valley Stream Central HS; Valley Stream, NY; (Y); 128/365; Var Bsbl; JV Bsktbl; Pace U; Acctng.

ANGILERI, ANGELA; Islip HS; Islip, NY; (Y); Cmnty Wkr; Office Aide; High Hon Roll; Hon Roll; Hist.

ANGILILLI, JEAN M; York Central HS; Mt Morris, NY; (Y); 9/68; AFS; Key Clb; Nwsp Rptr; Yrbk Ed-Chief; VP Sr Cls; Stat Bsktbl; Var Sftbl; NHS; NY ST Regents Schlrshp 85; Gannon U; Law.

ANGIONE, CHRIS; Commack South HS; Commack, NY; (Y); Cmnty Wkr; Letterman Clb; Q&S; Variety Show; Gym; Lcrss; High Hon Roll; Hon Roll; Golden Quill Awrd 85.

ANGIULI, CONSTANCE; Roosvelt HS; Yonkers, NY; (S); Camera Clb; Church Yth Grp; Drama Clb; Girl Scts; Hosp Aide; Ski Clb; Band; Yrbk Stf; Lit Mag; Rep Frsh Cls; Le High U; Ind Mgmt.

ANGLADE, STEVEN; Chaminade HS; Westbury, NY; (Y); 103/416; Cmnty Wkr; Computer Clb; Debate Tm; Intnl Clb; Mathletes; NFL; Science Clb; Speech Tm; Nwsp Rptr; Trk; 1st Sci Fair 83; Jdg Chaminade Invtnl 84; Fnlst LIFA ST Frnsc Leag Trnmnt 85; Bio.

ANGLIN, MICHAEL; Middletown HS; Middletown, NY; (Y); 3/275; Key Clb; Math Tm; Hon Roll; NHS; Ntl Merit Ltr.

ANGLISANO, TONI ANN; Lindenhurst HS; Lindenhurst, NY; (Y); Leo Clb; Ski Clb; High Hon Roll; Hon Roll; NHS; Voice Dem Awd; FBLA; Girl Scts; Nwsdy Hnr Carrier 82; Cert Outstndng Mbr & Slsprsn FLBA 82 & 83; Cert Awds Bst Skier & Italian 83-84; Clarkson; Accntng.

ANGONA, ERIKE; Taconic Hills HS; Hillsdale, NY; (Y); Boy Scts; Cmnty Wkr; 4-H; FFA; German Clb; Library Aide; Political Wkr; Band; Chorus; Church Choir; Coast Guard; Rsturant Bus.

ANGOTTI, ROSEMARY; Cicero-North Syracuse HS; Liverpool, NY; (S); 78/711; Stage Crew; NHS; Bryant & Stratton; Bus.

ANGOTTI, SUSAN; Nazareth Acad; Rochester, NY; (S); Girl Scts; Intnl Clb; Latin Clb; Ski Clb; Chorus; Pres Frsh Cls; Rep Stu Cncl; Hon Roll; Drftng.

ANGRUM, ANITA; Saint Pius V HS; Bronx, NY; (Y); English Clb; French Clb; Hosp Aide; Latin Clb; Nwsp Ed-Chief; Yrbk Stf; Pres Jr Cls; Rep Sr Cls; Hon Roll; NHS; Columbia Coll Double Day Discvry Schlrshp 85; Engl Awd 85; Urban Advntrs Schlrshp & Dnce & Relg Awd 84; Bio.

ANGUS, GABRIELLE M; Hammondsport Central HS; Hammondsport, NY; (Y); 11/71; Rep GAA; Band; Chorus; Concert Band; Mrchg Band; Symp Band; Capt Socr; High Hon Roll; Hon Roll; Val; All ST Band 85; NY ST Regnts Schlrshp 85; SUNY Fredonia; Math.

ANHWERE, ALEXANDRA; New Rochelle HS; New Rochelle, NY; (Y); 112/700; French Clb; Library Aide; Temple Yth Grp; French Hon Soc; NHS; Alfred U; Engr.

ANKER, JOEL B; Vestal SR HS; Binghamton, NY; (Y); 6/450; Am Leg Boys St; FBLA; Mathletes; Varsity Clb; Pres Sr Cls; Capt Bsbl; Capt Socr; NHS; Thomas J Watson Mem Schlrshp 85; All Div Goal Tender Soccer 84; Natl Yth Ldrshp Awd 84; Cornell U; Elec Engr.

ANKROM, MICHAEL; John A Coleman HS; Rifton, NY; (Y); Boy Scts; Pres Computer Clb; Drama Clb; French Clb; Ski Clb; Stage Crew; Rep Soph Cls; Im JV Bsktbl; Hon Roll; Comp Sci.

ANNABEL, NOEL; East Aurora HS; Orchard Park, NY; (S); 16/182; Pres JA; Ski Clb; Varsity Clb; Band; Yrbk Stf; Var L Tennis; Hon Roll; NHS; NY Regents Schlrshp 85; Babson Coll; Accntng.

ANNABI, AMGED; Sacred Heart HS; Yonkers, NY; (Y); Camera Clb; Church Yth Grp; Office Aide; School Play; Stage Crew; Nwsp Phtg; Yrbk Phtg; Trk; Wt Lftg; Prfct Atten Awd; Fordham U; Pre-Law.

ANNABLE, MAUREEN; Barker Central HS; Middleport, NY; (Y); 13/91; AFS; Church Yth Grp; French Clb; FBLA; Teachers Aide; JV Bsktbl; Score Keeper; JV Sftbl; Hon Roll; Hnr Rll Awd-Brnz Pin 84; Hnr Rll Awd-Slvr Pin 85; Early Advncmnt Pgm-Genesee CC 85-86; Genesee CC; Nrsng.

ANNARUMMA, TOM; Port Richmond HS; Staten Isld, NY; (Y); 25/500; Church Yth Grp; Ski Clb; Ed Lit Mag; Wt Lftg; Hon Roll; NHS; Jets Comptn Tstng Prog 85; Princeton; Lwyr.

ANNIBALE, LILLINA; St Johns Prep; Astoria, NY; (Y); 78/550; High Hon Roll; Hon Roll; NHS; Bus Mgmt.

ANNIS, SUSAN; Union-Endicott HS; Endicott, NY; (Y); Church Yth Grp; Key Clb; Concert Band; Capt Flag Corp; Mrchg Band; Rep Soph Cls; Rep Jr Cls; Stu Cncl; High Hon Roll; NHS; Ntl Cncl Yth Ldrshp 85; Ntl Band Awds 83; Marine Studies Enrchmnt Pgm 85; Engrng.

ANNUNZIATA, LISA; Acad Of The Rsrrctn; Easchester, NY; (Y); GAA; Chorus; Stage Crew; Variety Show; Nwsp Stf; Yrbk Stf; Rep Stu Cncl; Capt Bsktbl; L Var Tennis; Hon Roll; MVP Vrsty Tnns Tm 84-85.

ANSARI, MEHRANGIZ; John A Coleman HS; Kingston, NY; (S); 7/66; Pres French Clb; PAVAS; Ski Clb; Teachers Aide; Yrbk Stf; High Hon Roll; NHS; Political Sci.

ANSBACHER, DEBORAH; Wantagh HS; Wantagh, NY; (Y); Capt Math Tm; Band; Concert Band; Mrchg Band; Orch; School Musical; Sftbl; Var Capt Tennis; High Hon Roll; NHS; Cnty Yuth Career Law Dy 85.

ANSLOW, ANNE; Bishop Ludden HS; Baldwinsville, NY; (Y); MMM; Band; Chorus; Jazz Band; Swing Chorus; Hon Roll; Band Awd Am Musical Found 85; All Am Hall Fame Band Hnrs 85; Bishop Ludden Band Awd 85; Music.

ANSTETT, BERNADETTE; St Marys HS; Lancaster, NY; (S); 19/194; Church Yth Grp; Debate Tm; Quiz Bowl; Spanish Clb; Nwsp Ed-Chief; Yrbk Ed-Chief; Yrbk Stf; Im Vllybl; Hon Roll; VP NHS; Canisuis Coll; Pre-Law.

ANTALEK, SUSAN; Beacon HS; Beacon, NY; (S); 18/160; Pres Key Clb; Flag Corp; Trs Jr Cls; Pres Stu Cncl; Socr; Tennis; Elec Grls State 84; Math Awd 83; Acctng.

ANTHONY, ADELLE R; Midwood HS; Brooklyn, NY; (Y); 64/605; Science Clb; Chorus; School Musical; Rep Stu Cncl; Hon Roll; Prfct Atten Awd; Med.

ANTHONY, ANNE MARIE; Aquinas Inst; Rochester, NY; (Y); Dance Clb; Ski Clb; Teachers Aide; Color Guard; Cheerleading; Sftbl; 4-H Awd; Elmyra Coll Key Awd Schlrshp; Acad Schlrshp Aquinas; Math.

ANTHONY II, DENNIS P; Gates-Chili HS; Rochester, NY; (Y); 117/463; Boy Scts; Church Yth Grp; Cmnty Wkr; Computer Clb; Spanish Clb; Var JV Wrstlng; High Hon Roll; Hon Roll; Prfct Atten Awd; Eagle Scout Awd 83; Regents Schlrshp 85; Geneseo ST U; Comp Sci.

ANTHONY, FISCELLA; Port Chester HS; Port Chester, NY; (Y); Thesps; School Musical; School Play; JV Ftbl; L Var Trk; JV Var Wt Lftg; Crimnl Justc.

ANTHONY, JULIE; Haverling Central School; Bath, NY; (S); 21/147; Drama Clb; Exploring; JCL; Band; Chorus; Nwsp Stf; Var Capt Bsktbl; JV Socr; JV Sftbl; NHS; Jamestown CC; Med.

ANTHONY, LYNN; Mount Vernon HS; Mount Vernon, NY; (Y); Church Yth Grp; 4-H; Church Choir; Orch; Hon Roll; NHS; Pre-Med.

ANTHONY, MARTHA S; Midwood HS; Brooklyn, NY; (Y); 103/650; Drama Clb; Hosp Aide; Chorus; Yrbk Phtg; Co-Capt Cheerleading; Archon 84.

ANTICO, LISA; Preston HS; Bronx, NY; (S); Nwsp Rptr; Hon Roll; NHS; 4 Yr Fl Tuition Schlrshp Prstn HS 83; Bus Mngmnt.

ANTONACCI, KATHRYN; Bishop Grimes HS; Syracuse, NY; (Y); Ski Clb; Score Keeper; Sftbl; Timer; Vllybl; Hon Roll; CCBI; Ct Rprtng.

ANTONAZZO, ANNMARIE; Maria Regina HS; Hawthorne, NY; (Y); Church Yth Grp; Computer Clb; Chorus; Hmrm Asst Awd 85; NYU; Bus.

ANTONELLI, DAVID; Germantown Central HS; Hudson, NY; (Y); 10/50; CAP; Varsity Clb; Bsktbl; Socr; Vllybl; Cit Awd; Pilot.

ANTONELLIS, CHRISTIAN; St Francis Prep; Jackson Hgts, NY; (Y); Boy Scts; Church Yth Grp; Teachers Aide; JV Bsbl; Ftbl; High Hon Roll; Hon Roll; Bus Adm.

ANTONOVICH, DAVID; Union Springs Acad; Woodside, NY; (S); 5/48; Ski Clb; Rep Frsh Cls; Pres Soph Cls; Pres Jr Cls; Rep Stu Cncl; Gym; Vllybl; High Hon Roll; Hon Roll; Bus.

ANTONSEN, STEVE; Victor Central HS; Macedon, NY; (Y); 40/250; Church Yth Grp; Drama Clb; Chorus; Church Choir; Orch; School Musical; School Play; Trs Jr Cls; Diving; Hon Roll; SUNY Oswego; Elem Educ.

ANTONUCCI, ANGELA; Aquinas HS; Bronx, NY; (Y); 6/178; Art Clb; Exploring; Key Clb; Science Clb; Teachers Aide; Stage Crew; High Hon Roll; Hon Roll; Prfct Atten Awd; 2 Serv Bar Awds; Hon Mntn Sci Fair; Fordham U; Comp Progmmng.

ANTOSH, MARK; La Salle SR HS; Niagara Falls, NY; (Y); Var L Ice Hcky; Comp Pgmng.

ANZALONE, FRANCESCA; Bishop Kearney HS; Brooklyn, NY; (Y); Library Aide; Rep Jr Cls; Hon Roll; 2nd Hnrs 82-83.

ANZALONE, JULIE A; Lake Shore Central HS; Derby, NY; (Y); Church Yth Grp; Quiz Bowl; Chorus; Church Choir; Madrigals; School Musical; Yrbk Stf; Bausch & Lomb Sci Awd; Jr NHS; NHS; Hlth Svc.

ANZALONE JR, ROBERT G; Seton Catholic Central HS; Binghamton, NY; (Y); Art Clb; Aud/Vis; Boy Scts; Exploring; Crs Cntry; Trk; Embry-Riddle; Airpln Plt.

ANZEL, BRIAN; Niagara Wheatfield HS; Niagara Falls, NY; (Y); Latin Clb; Math Clb; PAVAS; Varsity Clb; Concert Band; Mrchg Band; Stu Cncl; Var L Bsbl; Var L Bsktbl; Var L Golf; MVP Awd Golf 80-85; All Cnty & All ST Band 83; Med.

ANZELON, THERESA; Longwood HS; Sound Beach, NY; (Y); Church Yth Grp; Band; Concert Band; Mrchg Band; Orch; JV Vllybl; High Hon Roll; Hon Roll; Air Force; Music.

APARICIO, FRANCES; Saint Vincent Ferrer HS; New York, NY; (Y); 35/117; Church Yth Grp; FBLA; Library Aide; Political Wkr; Rep Frsh Cls; Rep Soph Cls; VP Jr Cls; Pres Sr Cls; Stu Cncl; Hon Roll; 2nd Hnrs Iona Spnsh Cntst 84; Pace U; Accntng.

APARICIO, MONICA; St John The Baptist D H S; Brentwood, NY; (Y); 5/601; Church Yth Grp; Variety Show; Socr; French Hon Soc; High Hon Roll; Hon Roll; Jr NHS; NHS; Pres Schlr; Alfred U Pres Schlrshp 85-86; Adelphi U Schlrshp 85-86; Alfred U; Comp Sci.

APARICIO, RUBEN; View Rochelle HS; New Rochelle, NY; (Y); Chess Clb; Computer Clb; Acpl Chr; Chorus; Madrigals; Stage Crew; Swing Chorus; Var L Ftbl; Var L Lcrss; NHS; Stu Athl Ftbl 84; NY ST Schlr Athl Assoc Hnry Ment; U Of MA-AMHERST; Elec Engr.

APFEL, ERIN; Ossining HS; Briarcliff, NY; (Y); Rep Am Leg Aux Girls St; Model UN; Acpl Chr; Chorus; Swing Chorus; Sec Stu Cncl; High Hon Roll; Radio Clb; School Musical; School Play; Engl Dept-Soc Studies Dept Awds Ret NYSSSO 82-83; Engl Dept-Foreign Lang Dept Awds 83-84; Liberal Arts.

APMANN, TODD; Westhampton Beach HS; E Moriches, NY; (Y); 6/232; Church Yth Grp; Yrbk Phtg; Stu Cncl; L Tennis; Hon Roll; Jr NHS; NHS; Ntl Merit Ltr; Hghst Av Span III 84-85; Treas Hnr Soc 85-86; Acolyte Chrch 80-86.

APOLLO, JAMES; Farmingdlae HS; Farmingdale, NY; (Y); Library Aide; High Hon Roll; Hon Roll; Stonybrook U; Elctrcl Engrng.

APOLLO, LUCIA; Scotia-Glenville HS; Scotia, NY; (Y); Church Yth Grp; Cmnty Wkr; Drama Clb; French Clb; Hosp Aide; Ski Clb; Chorus; Church Choir; School Play; Yrbk Stf; Frnch.

APONTE, JUAN; Regis HS; Astoria, NY; (Y); German Clb; Service Clb; Varsity Clb; Yrbk Stf; Rep Frsh Cls; Rep Sr Cls; Rep Stu Cncl; JV Crs Cntry; Var Capt Trk; NHS; Natl Hnr Roll 85; MVP-TRK 82-83; Williams Coll; Pre Med.

APONTE, KENNETH; Aquinas Inst; Rochester, NY; (Y); JV Bsbl; Hon Roll; NY ST Regents Schlrshp 84-85; Aquinas Msn Bouzs Slvr Medlst; Rochester Tech Inst; Comp Sci.

APONTE, NANCY; Stella Maris HS; Reog Park, NY; (Y); Med.

APONTE, WAYNE L; La Guardia H S Of Music And Arts; New York, NY; (Y); Teachers Aide; Chorus; School Musical; Nwsp Rptr; Nwsp Stf; Pres Stu Cncl; Adam Clayton Powell JR Ldrshp Awd 82; Jrnlsm.

APPEL, DAVID M; Half Hollow Hills High School East; Dix Hills, NY; (Y); 121/580; Computer Clb; German Clb; Band; Concert Band; Jazz Band; Mrchg Band; Orch; School Musical; Symp Band; Wt Lftg; NYSSMA Cmptn 82; Al-Cnty Jzz Band Cmptn 84 & 85; Germn Hnr Soc 83-85; SUNY Binghamton; Math.

APPEL, JAMES; Woodmere Acad; Atlantic Beach, NY; (Y); Key Clb; Latin Clb; Yrbk Ed-Chief; Bsktbl; Tennis; St Schlr; CT Coll; Math.

APPEL, SHERI; Colonie Central HS; Albany, NY; (Y); 11/511; Intnl Clb; Temple Yth Grp; High Hon Roll; NHS; Ntl Merit Ltr; Law.

APPEL, SHERRI; Commack North HS; Commack, NY; (Y); Cmnty Wkr; Spanish Clb; Temple Yth Grp; Var Badmtn; High Hon Roll; NHS; Med.

APPELBLATT, JAY; Sheepshead Bay HS; Brooklyn, NY; (Y); Library Aide; Chorus; School Musical; Hon Roll; Dly Nws Physcl Ftns Awd 83; Brooklyn Coll.

APPELL, BRECK; Faith Bible Acad; Ames, NY; (Y); 1/4; Drama Clb; Stage Crew; Yrbk Phtg; JV Var Bsktbl; Var Socr; Var Trk; High Hon Roll; Hon Roll; Prfct Atten Awd; Pensacola Christian Coll; Prela.

APPENHEIMER, CYNTHIA R; Sacred Heart Acad; Buffalo, NY; (Y); 15/113; Cmnty Wkr; JA; Stage Crew; Yrbk Phtg; Yrbk Stf; Hon Roll; NHS; Prfct Atten Awd; Pres Schlr; St Schlr; Rgnts Schlrshp 85; SUNYAB; Mechncl Engrng.

APPENHEIMER, MICHELLE; Buffalo Acad Of The Sacred Heart; Buffalo, NY; (Y); French Clb; Library Aide; Red Cross Aide; Chorus; Lit Mag; High Hon Roll; Hon Roll; NHS; Prfct Atten Awd.

APPIAH, AMA; Niagara Catholic HS; Niagara Falls, NY; (Y); Drama Clb; French Clb; Hosp Aide; Sec JA; Pres Key Clb; Nwsp Rptr; Ed Nwsp Stf; Yrbk Stf; Stage Crew; Nwsp Phtg; Apprctn From Mrch Of Dimes Awd 84; U Of FL; Jrnlsm.

APPLEBY, BARBARA; Frontier SR HS; Lakeview, NY; (S); 14/500; Latin Clb; Office Aide; Yrbk Stf; Stu Cncl; JV Var Socr; Sftbl; Hon Roll; NHS; Med.

APPLEGATE, ROBIN LYN; Port Jervis HS; Middletown, NY; (Y); 96/196; Dance Clb; Varsity Clb; School Musical; Yrbk Stf; Mat Maids; Score Keeper; Trk; Hon Roll; Rotary Awd; Dover Bus Coll; Word Proc.

APPLETON, TIM; Palmyra-Macedon Central HS; Macedon, NY; (Y); Boy Scts; Rep Church Yth Grp; Pres Exploring; Acpl Chr; Var L Ftbl; CC Awd; CC Of Finger Lakes; Natrl Rsrc.

APTHORPE, AMY; Mayville Central Schl; Mayville, NY; (Y); VP Church Yth Grp; French Clb; Girl Scts; Band; Chorus; Mrchg Band; School Musical; Nwsp Stf; Yrbk Ed-Chief; Yrbk Stf; Pre-Law.

APTMAN, SUZANNE; Horace Greeley HS; Chappaqua, NY; (Y); Temple Yth Grp; School Musical; Nwsp Bus Mgr; Nwsp Stf; Var Capt Tennis; NYS Rgnts Schlrshp; Div I All Star Squad & All-Cnty Tnns 83-84; Tufts U; Spnsh.

APUN, SHEENA C; Hillcrest HS; Elmhurst, NY; (Y); 4/793; Computer Clb; Hosp Aide; Math Tm; Office Aide; Teachers Aide; Orch; School Play; Hon Roll; Jr NHS; Sec NHS; Regents Schlrshp 85-86; Trustees Schlrshp 85-8; NY U; Med.

APYSHKOV, PAUL; Aviation HS; Richmond Hill, NY; (Y); 12/417; Boys Clb Am; Boy Scts; Exploring; Rep Jr Cls; Aero Engrng.

AQUILA, VINCENT DELL; St John The Baptist HS; Deer Park, NY; (Y); Cmnty Wkr; JV Tennis; JV Trk; JV Wrstlng; C W Post; Engr.

AQUILANO, JOHN; Geneva HS; Geneva, NY; (Y); 70/180; JV Var Score Keeper; Rochester Inst Of Tech; Math.

AQUILINA, ANNA MARIE; Bishop Kearney HS; Brooklyn, NY; (Y); Hon Roll; Comp Sci.

AQUILINO, CHRISTOPHER T; Pelham Memorial HS; Pelham, NY; (Y); 4/177; Am Leg Boys St; Band; Jazz Band; Lit Mag; Var Capt Socr; Var L Tennis; NHS; Ntl Merit Ltr; Pres Schlr; Computer Clb; Ntl Ltn Exam Cert Of Maxima Cum Laude 83 & 85; Leokemia Scty Swm For Life Awd; Mdlbry Coll.

AQUINO, DANIEL; Nazareth Regional HS; Brooklyn, NY; (Y); 8/261; Aud/Vis; Concert Band; Jazz Band; High Hon Roll; Hon Roll; NHS; Bio, Physcs, Italian & Relgn 85; Citaion Of Hnr Form Dist Atty Haltyman 85; Princpls Awd 85; Hofstra U; Bio.

AQUINO, THERESA P; Shaker HS; Latham, NY; (Y); Dance Clb; Hosp Aide; JA; Service Clb; JV Fld Hcky; JV Var Score Keeper; Var Tennis; JV Capt Vllybl; Hon Roll; NHS; Regnts Schlrshp 85; Union Coll; Bio.

ARAGHI, MEHRZAD N; Webster HS; Webster, NY; (Y); 5/562; Trs German Clb; Pres Model UN; Ed Lit Mag; Crs Cntry; JETS Awd; NHS; Ntl Merit SF; Chorus; Nwsp Rptr; Hon Roll; Amer Assn Tchrs German Stdy Trp 84; Wellesley Book Awd 84; Sect Champ Mock Trial Tm 84; Engl.

ARAJE, MICHAEL; St Francis Prep Schl; Jamaica Estates, NY; (S); 130/700; Chess Clb; Math Tm; Model UN; Capt Golf; Hon Roll; NHS; Ntl Merit Ltr; Stck Mkt Clb Pres; Poltcl Sci Clb Pres; Princeton; Law.

ARAUZ, BRENDA LEE; Walton HS; Bronx, NY; (Y); Dance Clb; Chorus; Variety Show; Vllybl; Prfct Atten Awd; Cert Merit 85; Cert Merit Schlstc Achvt 85; Acctnt.

ARBIZU, WILLIAM; Martin Van Buren HS; Bellerose, NY; (Y); 71/621; Art Clb; School Musical; School Play; Stage Crew; Nwsp Rptr; Nwsp Stf; Ed Lit Mag; Hon Roll; Regents Scholar 85; Daily News Super Yth 84; Ind Design.

ARBORE, MARIO; Bethpage HS; Plainview, NY; (Y); 3/200; Intnl Clb; Nwsp Rptr; Hon Roll; NHS.

ARCARA, CHRISTOPHER; Tonawanda SR HS; Tonawanda, NY; (Y); JV Socr; High Hon Roll; 4.0 Grdpt Avg In Art Cert; 1st Pl In Drwng Catgr Awd; Buffalo ST; Englsh.

ARCARA, JO ANNE; Cardinal O Hara HS; Tonawanda, NY; (Y); Art Clb; School Play; Hon Roll; Ntl Hnr Rl 83-85; Buffalo ST Coll; Bio.

ARCE, CHRISTINE; Sachem North HS; Holbrook, NY; (Y); Dance Clb; Human Rltn Comm Clb 82-83; Merit Cert Poetry 85; Bus.

ARCENTALES, ERIKA; St Johns Prep; Long Isld Cty, NY; (Y); Chorus; Variety Show; Psych.

ARCHER, CINDY; Mohawk Central HS; Mohawk, NY; (S); Spanish Clb; High Hon Roll; Jr NHS; NHS.

ARCHER, JASME I; Richmond Hill HS; Richmond Hill, NY; (Y); 23/298; Drama Clb; English Clb; 4-H; French Clb; Math Clb; Science Clb; Service Clb; School Musical; School Play; French Hon Soc; Hunter Schlrshp 85-89; Regents Schlrshp Awd 85-89; Hunter; Psychology.

ARCHER, MARGARET MARY; Beacon HS; Beacon, NY; (Y); 38/160; Girl Scts; Library Aide; Varsity Clb; VP Soph Cls; Co-Capt Sftbl; Co-Capt Vllybl; God Cntry Awd; Grl Scts Gld Awd 85; Sftbl Al-Conf 85; Schlr Athlt Awd 85; Kings Coll; Acctng.

ARCHIBEE, ANN; Camden HS; Camden, NY; (Y); Chorus; High Hon Roll; Hon Roll; Bus Mgmnt.

ARCIERI, ELIZABETH; Bishop Kearney HS; Brooklyn, NY; (Y); Dance Clb; Girl Scts; JA; Library Aide; Pep Clb; Nwsp Stf; Yrbk Stf; Rep Frsh Cls; High Hon Roll; Hon Roll; 1st & 2nd Hnrs.

ARCIERO, DENISE; Tottenville HS; Staten Island, NY; (Y); Art Clb; Camera Clb; Girl Scts; Pep Clb; Church Choir; Tobe Coburn; Advrtsng Desgnr.

ARCIOLD, CHRISTINE; Grover Cleveland HS; Ridgewood, NY; (Y); 24/658; Church Yth Grp; Key Clb; Science Clb; Var Bsktbl; Var Sftbl; Var Tennis; Hon Roll; Cmnty Wkr; English Clb; Girl Scts; Biolgcl Sccssn Awd 85; Acad Olympcs Awd 85; Schlrshp To New Rochelle Coll; SUNY At Stony Brook; Pre-Dntl.

ARCORACI, DAVID A; Dunkirk SR HS; Dunkirk, NY; (Y); 14/212; Computer Clb; Science Clb; Stage Crew; Hon Roll; NHS; NYS Regnts, Al Tech Steel Corp Schlrshps 85; SUNY Fredonia; Comp Engr.

ARCORACI, GARRETT P; Dunkirk HS; Dunkirk, NY; (Y); Am Leg Boys St; Boy Scts; Camera Clb; Computer Clb; French Clb; School Musical; School Play; Yrbk Stf; VP Stu Cncl; NHS; Pol Sci.

ARCUNI, PHYLLIS; Mount Vernon HS; Mount Vernon, NY; (Y); Aud/Vis; Key Clb; Cheerleading; Var JV Sftbl; Data Prcssng.

ARCURI, JENNIFER; Bishop Kearney HS; Brooklyn, NY; (Y); 15/364; Key Clb; Library Aide; Math Tm; Yrbk Stf; Bowling; High Hon Roll; NHS; 3rd Pl Brnz Medl Bowlng Trnmnt 84; Comp Sci.

ARCURI, JUDITH; Thomas R Proctor HS; Utica, NY; (Y); School Play; Yrbk Stf; Sec Soph Cls; Sec Jr Cls; Sec Sr Cls; Var Cheerleading; Hon Roll; Kiwanis Awd; NHS; Opt Clb Awd; Stu Cncl Awd 85; Cornell U.

ARCURI, MIA; Moore Catholic HS; Staten Island, NY; (Y); Church Choir; Yrbk Phtg; Yrbk Stf; VP Bsktbl; Hon Roll; Phy Thrpy.

ARCURI, WILLIAM F; Irondequoit HS; Rochester, NY; (Y); Boy Scts; Service Clb; School Musical; School Play; Hon Roll; NHS; Drama Clb; Science Clb; NYS Regnts Schlrshp 85; BSA Ldrshp Corps Coordntr 84-85; Hnrb Mntn Lcl Photo Shw 85; U Of Rochester; Comp Sci.

ARDISTER, LAWRENCENE; Kensington HS; Buffalo, NY; (Y); Prof Typing Skills 85; Highest Grade Biography 84; Kensington Bus Inst; Wrd Proc.

ARDITO, JOSEPH; Archbishop Molloy HS; W Hempstead, NY; (Y); 78/428; Art Clb; Computer Clb; Math Tm; Science Clb; Yrbk Stf; Bsktbl; JV Crs Cntry; Ftbl; Score Keeper; Sftbl; Hofstra; Bus.

ARDITO, MICHAEL; North Babylon SR HS; North Babylon, NY; (Y); Computer Clb; VICA; Hon Roll; Prfct Atten Awd; Camera Clb; 1st Pl VICA Cont 85; Comp Oper.

ARDRON, JANET; Oxford Acad; Oxford, NY; (Y); Camp Fr Inc; Church Yth Grp; French Clb; Pep Clb; Band; Chorus; Color Guard; Concert Band; Jazz Band; Mrchg Band; Sec.

ARENA, JANE; Preston HS; Bronx, NY; (S); 12/76; Nwsp Rptr; Trs Sr Cls; Bowling; Swmmng; Hon Roll; NHS; Pace U; Nrsg.

ARENA, JO ANN; St John Villa Acad; Staten Island, NY; (Y); 5/140; Art Clb; Camera Clb; Math Tm; Model UN; School Play; Stage Crew; Nwsp Rptr; Nwsp Stf; Yrbk Phtg; Yrbk Rptr; 2nd Gen Hnr Awd Excllnc 82; Hnrb Mntn Achv Art Engl Spnsh, Music 83; Exclnc Europn Studs & Relgn 84; Med.

ARENA, KIM; Gates-Chili HS; Rochester, NY; (Y); 57/464; French Clb; Math Clb; Office Aide; Stu Cncl; Var Capt Cheerleading; High Hon Roll; Soc Studies Awd European Cultrs 83; SUNY-GENESEO; Bio.

ARENA, MARK A; G Ray Bodley HS; Fulton, NY; (Y); 24/256; Latin Clb; Bsbl; Bsktbl; Ftbl; Hon Roll; NHS; Prfct Atten Awd; Syracuse U; Arts.

ARENT, LAURIE; John Jay SR HS; Wappingers Fall, NY; (Y); Church Yth Grp; Drama Clb; Girl Scts; Band; Concert Band; Jazz Band; Mrchg Band; Mgr(s); JV Sftbl; JV Swmmng; Slvr Ldrshp Awd 83; Pre Elem Educ.

AREZZA, ANGELA; St Raymond Acad; Bronx, NY; (Y); 2/86; Hon Roll; Prfct Atten Awd; Spnsh Awd Hgst GPA 84; Sec.

ARFI, MARY; Christ Th King R HS; Forest Hls, NY; (Y); 6/487; Computer Clb; Office Aide; Nwsp Stf; Rep Frsh Cls; Trk; Im Vllybl; Gov Hon Prg Awd; NHS; Sal; Engrng Cert Merit 85; Comptrollers Awd 85; Gov Citation 85; St Johns U; Quantitative Anal.

ARGAMASO, SHARLEEN; Mount Vernon HS; Mount Vernon, NY; (Y); Pres Church Yth Grp; Hosp Aide; Key Clb; Jazz Band; Orch; Trs Jr Cls; Capt Pom Pon; High Hon Roll; Pres NHS; Computer Clb; Rensselaer Awd Excllnc Sci & Math 85; 2nd Hrs Iona Coll Lang Cntst Frnch 84; All Cnty Orch 82-83; Pre-Med.

ARGENTIERI, RICHARD; St Josephs Collegiate Inst; Buffalo, NY; (Y); 25/198; Pres Church Yth Grp; VP JA; Political Wkr; Im Bsktbl; Im Bowling; High Hon Roll; NHS; Prfct Atten Awd; Bus Admin.

ARGENTINE, STEPHANIE L; Oneida SR HS; Oneida, NY; (Y); 6/225; Debate Tm; Chorus; School Musical; School Play; Yrbk Phtg; Trk; High Hon Roll; NHS; Ntl Merit Ltr; Am Leg Aux Girls St; NYS Mus Assn Cmptn; SADD; Corp Law.

ARGYROPOULOS, PAUL; Sachem HS; Holtsville, NY; (Y); 107/1400; Hon Roll; Jr NHS; Regnts Schlrshp 85; Pres Acadmc Fit Awd 85; SUNY Stony Brook; Psych.

ARIANO, ANTHONY K; Canarsie HS; Brooklyn, NY; (Y); 63/567; Baruch Schlrshp 85; ST Rgnts Schlrshp 85; Baruch Coll; Acctng.

ARIAS, FRANCISCO; The Bronx HS Of Science; New York, NY; (Y); Math Tm; Band; Engrng.

ARIAS, LESLIE D; St Johns Prep; Queens, NY; (Y); 30/500; NHS; St Johns U; Accntng.

ARIAS, MARIA; Forest Hills HS; Brooklyn, NY; (Y); 170/800; Cmnty Wkr; JA; Science Clb; Spanish Clb; Orch; School Play; Yrbk Rptr; Yrbk Stf; Rep Frsh Cls; Rep Soph Cls; Spn Awd 83-84; Typng/Word Proc Awd 83-84; NY U; Med.

ARICO, FRANCINE; St Raymond Acad; Bronx, NY; (Y); 5/68; Cmnty Wkr; Capt Cheerleading; Hon Roll; Chsn Compte Typng Cntst Wood Bus Schl 85; St Johns U; Educ.

ARISTA, ISABEL; Mother Cabrini HS; New York, NY; (Y); 3/94; Library Aide; Capt Service Clb; Color Guard; Nwsp Phtg; Yrbk Stf; Var Vllybl; Hon Roll; NHS; NEDT Awd; U Of VA LEAD Pgm Scholar 85; Rennselaer Polytech Inst Summr Pgm Scholar 85.

ARKI, CINDY; Riverside HS; Buffalo, NY; (Y); Church Yth Grp; French Clb; Teachers Aide; Yrbk Stf; Lit Mag; Rep Stu Cncl; Hon Roll; NHS; Bryant & Stratton; Bus.

ARMANO, DIANE; Bethpage HS; Bethpage, NY; (Y); School Musical; Yrbk Stf; Cheerleading; Italian Soc 83-86.

ARMANT, KEVIN; Vestal SR HS; Vestal, NY; (Y); Am Leg Boys St; Concert Band; Jazz Band; Orch; Trs Jr Cls; VP Stu Cncl; Var JV Wrstlng; Hon Roll; NHS; Natl Cncl Yth Ldrshp 85; Pol Sci.

ARMELI, TRACY; Hornell HS; Hornell, NY; (Y); Latin Clb; Chorus; JV Var Cheerleading; JV Var Pom Pon; Hon Roll; Alfred U; Psychlgy.

ARMSTRONG, DEBORAH; Washington Irving HS; Brooklyn, NY; (Y); Hosp Aide; Band; Jr Cls; Supr Achvt Hlth Tchng 84; NY Heart Assoc & NYC Bd Of Ed 84; Physcl Ftns Achvt Awd 84; Howard U Tuskegee Inst; Nrs.

ARMSTRONG, DIANE; Vestal SR HS; Vestal, NY; (Y); Sec Church Yth Grp; Band; Color Guard; Concert Band; Drill Tm; VP Mrchg Band; Pep Band; Symp Band; Twrlr; Hon Roll; Broome CC; Exec Sec.

ARMSTRONG, LORRAINE; Lansingburgh HS; Troy, NY; (Y); Drama Clb; JA; Key Clb; Chorus; School Musical; School Play; Hon Roll; Hudson Valley CC; Bus.

ARMSTRONG, PATRICIA; Ticonderoga HS; Ticonderoga, NY; (Y); 7/110; Cmnty Wkr; Pres FCA; Pres Latin Clb; Pres Y-Teens; Pres Frsh Cls; Var JV Bsktbl; Var Socr; Var Sftbl; NHS; Church Yth Grp; Amer Legn Oratrcl Cntst 85; Springfield Coll; Hmnts.

ARMSTRONG, TREVOR; Nazareth Regional HS; Brooklyn, NY; (Y); Church Yth Grp; Hosp Aide; Concert Band; Drill Tm; Drm & Bgl; Flag Corp; Jazz Band; School Play; Im Ftbl; Camera Clb; Engl 85; Photo 85; Bio.

ARNALDOS, MARIA; Notre Dame Acad; Staten Island, NY; (Y); French Clb; Hosp Aide; Science Clb; JV Socr; Trk; NHS; Natl Frnch Cont Lvl I 83; Intl Bus.

ARNDT, GRETCHEN; Webutuck Central HS; Millerton, NY; (Y); 4-H; Band; Chorus; Church Choir; Pres Frsh Cls; Var Bsktbl; Highest Grad Bus Math 85; Tutor Lrngn Disabled Chldrn.

ARNDT, KAREN; Pelham Memorial HS; Pelham, NY; (Y); Am Leg Aux Girls St; Cmnty Wkr; Drama Clb; School Play; Cit Awd; High Hon Roll; NCTE Awd; NHS; Spanish NHS; School Musical; Columbia U Almn Awd Excllnc Hstry 85; Edward Hardy Awd Sci & Ctznshp 85; Govt.

ARNDT, SANDRA J; Geneseo Central HS; Geneseo, NY; (Y); 24/96; Church Yth Grp; Pres 4-H; Quiz Bowl; Spanish Clb; Yrbk Rptr; Yrbk Stf; Stu Cncl; Stat Bsktbl; Score Keeper; 4-H Awd; Calvin Coll.

ARNDT, SARAH L; The Elisabeth Irwin HS; New York, NY; (Y); Cmnty Wkr; Political Wkr; Yrbk Phtg; Yrbk Stf; Lit Mag; Rep Sr Cls; Var Gym; Sftbl; Ntl Merit Ltr; Excllnc Physcs, Hstry, Latn, Hghst Clss Ave Awd 81-82; Excllnc Bio 82-83; Excllnc Sci, Engl 83-84; Brown U; Comp Lit.

ARNELL JR, MALCOLM M; Baro Hall Acad; Brooklyn, NY; (Y); 4/35; Boy Scts; Church Yth Grp; Cmnty Wkr; Political Wkr; ROTC; Color Guard; Drill Tm; Yrbk Stf; Socr; Swmmng; NY ST Regents Schlrshp 85; Hampton U; Medicine.

ARNETT, SUZANNE; Hicksville SR HS; Hicksvl, NY; (Y); Dance Clb; Drama Clb; Trs Exploring; Nwsp Rptr; Nwsp Stf; Yrbk Stf; Rep Stu Cncl; JV Bsktbl; JV Trk; Church Yth Grp; Purdue U; Dietcs.

ARNEY, DOREEN M; Nanuet SR HS; Nanuet, NY; (Y); 11/174; Chrmn Debate Tm; Political Wkr; Scholastic Bowl; School Musical; School Play; Ed Nwsp Rptr; Ed Yrbk Rptr; Hon Roll; Mu Alp Tht; NHS; Am Leg Ortrcl 1st Schl, 2nd Cnty Hstrcl Soc Awd 85; NY Piano Tchrs Cngrss Hnr Rctl 82; Cornell U; Ind Rel.

ARNOLD, ANNE; Le Roy HS; Le Roy, NY; (Y); AFS; Spanish Clb; Varsity Clb; Yrbk Stf; JV Var Cheerleading; Var Tennis; Var Trk; High Hon Roll; Jr NHS; NHS; Silver Mdl In Natl Latin Exam 84.

ARNOLD, PATRICIA H; South Side HS; Rockville Ctr, NY; (Y); Key Clb; Science Clb; Concert Band; Mrchg Band; Yrbk Stf; Cit Awd; High Hon Roll; Jr NHS; Sec NHS; Exploring; Psych.

ARNOLD, SONJA; Le Roy HS; Leroy, NY; (Y); 2/120; VP AFS; VP Spanish Clb; Var Capt Cheerleading; Var Tennis; High Hon Roll; Jr NHS; NHS; Sal; Allen Seymour Olmsted Englsh Prz 85; Dr Emil Kimaid Mem 85; Michael Pridgeon Mem 85; Kent ST U; Pre-Med.

ARNOLD, TRICIA; South Side HS; Rockville Ctr, NY; (Y); Exploring; Key Clb; Science Clb; Teachers Aide; Band; Yrbk Stf; Cit Awd; High Hon Roll; Jr NHS; Sec NHS; Psych.

ARNOLD JR, WILLIE; Our Savior Lutheran HS; New York, NY; (Y); Library Aide; Office Aide; Church Choir; JV Var Bsktbl; Im Vllybl.

ARNONE, JOHN; Holy Cross HS; Jackson Hts, NY; (Y); 72/312; Bsktbl; Hon Roll; Polytech Inst; Elec Engr.

ARNONE, PAUL F; Mt Saint Michael Acad; Yonkers, NY; (S); 25/308; Chess Clb; Rep Stu Cncl; Im Bsktbl; Im Sftbl; JV Trk; NHS; Spanish NHS.

ARNS, RON P; Paul V Moore HS; Brewerton, NY; (Y); 14/276; Computer Clb; Math Tm; Jazz Band; Mrchg Band; Pep Band; Stu Cncl; Tennis; High Hon Roll; Hon Roll; NHS; Whipple Schlrshp 85; Pres Acad Achvt Awd 85; NY ST Regents Schlrshp Awd 85; SUNY-MORRISVILLE; Engr Sci.

ARO, CHRISTINA A; Wantagh HS; Wantagh, NY; (Y); 43/291; French Clb; Ski Clb; Nwsp Ed-Chief; Nwsp Phtg; Lit Mag; Var Stu Cncl; ROTC; NHS; Regnts Schlrshp Awd 85; Colgate U.

ARONICA, MICHAEL J; Amherst Central HS; Amherst, NY; (Y); 57/325; Aud/Vis; VP Church Yth Grp; JCL; Pres Latin Clb; Math Tm; Quiz Bowl; Concert Band; Nwsp Stf; Var Vllybl; NHS; Regents Schlrshp; U Rochester; Bio.

ARONOV, IRINA; Forest Hills HS; Forest Hills, NY; (Y); 11/881; Boy Scts; Dance Clb; Exploring; Office Aide; Science Clb; Teachers Aide; Y-Teens; Nwsp Rptr; High Hon Roll; Hon Roll; Cncl Jewish Women Lit Cont 85; Borough Sci Fair 1st Pl 84; Arista Jr Forest Hills HS 85; Psych.

ARRANCE, JILL; Randolph Central HS; Randolph, NY; (Y); 21/83; Sec Drama Clb; French Clb; Pep Clb; Ski Clb; Acpl Chr; School Musical; Yrbk Stf; Crs Cntry; Score Keeper; Trk; Trck Rcrrds 85; Jrnlsm.

ARREAGA, GIOVANNY; Msgr Mc Clancy HS; Jackson Hts, NY; (S); 12/225; Library Aide; Math Tm; Spanish Clb; Socr; High Hon Roll; Hon Roll; Sec NHS; Spanish NHS; Schls Princpls List 81-83; Pace U; Bus.

ARRIEUX, ROGER G; Holy Trinity HS; Freeport, NY; (Y); Rep Frsh Cls; Rep Soph Cls; Rep Sr Cls; Rep Stu Cncl; Var Crs Cntry; JV Ftbl; JV Var Trk; Varsity Letters 82-84; Track & Field Awds 83-84; Hofstra U; Bus Major.

ARRIGENNA, JULIE; York Central HS; Piffard, NY; (Y); Band; Mrchg Band; Capt Cheerleading; Socr; Sftbl; Vllybl; High Hon Roll; Pres NHS; Fin Girls St 85; Res Pgm St Lawrence U 85; SUNY; Med.

ARRIGO, JOSEPH; Msgr Mc Clancy Memorial HS; Jackson Hgts, NY; (Y); Church Yth Grp; High Hon Roll; Hon Roll; Bus.

ARRILLAGA, JORGE; New Rochelle HS; New Rochelle, NY; (Y); 52/690; Computer Clb; Drama Clb; French Clb; Pres Intnl Clb; Spanish Clb; Chorus; Lit Mag; French Hon Soc; NHS; Ntl Merit Schol; Tufts U; Medicine.

ARRINGTON, BETTY; A Philip Randolph HS; New York, NY; (Y); 53/166; Science Clb; Chorus; Yrbk Stf; Cheerleading; Phys Fit Achvt Awd 83; Pre-Med.

ARRINGTON, KIMBERLY; HS Of Fashion Industri; Queens, NY; (Y); 56/365; Yrbk Stf; Hon Roll; U Of MA; Mgmt Info Sci.

ARROYO, DAISY; Eastern District HS; Brooklyn, NY; (Y); Dance Clb; Debate Tm; Drama Clb; FBLA; Teachers Aide; School Play; Badmtn; Tennis; Hon Roll; Mdl For Bus 85; Cert Of Awd-Schltc Achvt In Spnsh 85; Cert Of Awd-Schltc Achvt In Eng 5; Brnard M Baruch Coll; Bus Admin.

ARROYO, TISHA; Central HS; Valley Stream, NY; (Y); 39/365; VP FBLA; NHS; Rgnts Schlrshp 85; Natl Bus Hnr Soc 83-85; Bus & Profssnl Womens Clb Of Nassau Cnty Schlrshp 85; Albany ST U; CPA.

ARSENAULT, MARC WM; Niskayuna SR HS; Scotia, NY; (Y); Art Clb; Nwsp Rptr; Nwsp Stf; Yrbk Stf; Lit Mag; Rexford Wmns Clb Art Cont-2nd Water Colors 85; NHSART Dept Cert Of Mrt; Schl Of Visual Arts; Comm Art.

ARTHUR, DOUGLAS J; Clayton A Bouton HS; Voorheesville, NY; (Y); 27/122; Math Tm; Nwsp Rptr; Yrbk Stf; Lit Mag; Var L Crs Cntry; JV Socr; Var L Trk; Var L Vllybl; High Hon Roll; NHS; NYS Regnts Schlrshp 85; Artstc Achvt Awd 82 & 84; SUNY Buffalo; Comp Sci.

ARTHUR, GEORGE; Hutch Tech HS; Buffalo, NY; (Y); 86/262; JA; Political Wkr; Variety Show; Off Sr Cls; Stu Cncl; Ftbl; Trk; Wt Lftg; Hon Roll; ECC; Elec Engrng.

ARTHUR, MARGARET; Clayton A Bouton JR SR HS; Voorheesville, NY; (Y); Drama Clb; Exploring; Girl Scts; Chorus; Concert Band; Jazz Band; Var L Crs Cntry; Var L Vllybl; High Hon Roll; NHS; Hopwood Summr Scholar Pgm Lynchburg Coll 85; Hudson Vly Girl Sct Cncl Wrld Conf 85; Silvr Awd Girl Sct.

ARTHURS, MADELEINE HOPE; The Calhoun Schl; New York, NY; (Y); Art Clb; FTA; Chorus; School Play; Lit Mag; Gym; DAR Awd; NY ST Smmr Schl Arts 84; Brklyn Museum Hnrs Ptng Crse 84-85; Drawng Comp 84.

ARTIN, JOE; Rocky Point JR SR HS; Rocky Pt, NY; (Y); Hon Roll; Acctg.

ARTIN, KATHRYN; Villa Maria Acad; Cheektowaga, NY; (Y); Computer Clb; Girl Scts; Red Cross Aide; Church Choir; School Play; Yrbk Stf; Rep Stu Cncl; Stat Sftbl; Swmmng; Hon Roll; U NY Buffalo; Mth.

ARTL, MICHELLE; Fairport HS; Fairport, NY; (Y); Capt Red Cross Aide; Drill Tm; Yrbk Stf; Pres Frsh Cls; Pres Stu Cncl; JV Var Cheerleading; Ldrshp Awd 84-85; Excllnc Art Awd 84; Congrssnl Secy Stdnt Cncl Monroe Cnty 85-86; Advrtsg.

ARTMAN, JENNIFER J; Batavia HS; Batavia, NY; (Y); 40/240; Drama Clb; 4-H; Chorus; Church Choir; Stage Crew; Lit Mag; 4-H Awd; Hon Roll; NHS; Natl Regents Schlrshp 85; Am Leg Schlrshp 85; Geneseo ST Coll; Sec Educ.

ARZONETTI, TINA M; Pine Bush HS; Middletown, NY; (Y); Church Yth Grp; Science Clb; Ski Clb; Nwsp Rptr; High Hon Roll; Jr NHS; NHS; St Schlr; Deans List Orange Cty Comm Coll 85; NY U; Phys Sci.

ASCHETTINO, DIANA; Manhasset SR/JR HS; Manhasset, NY; (Y); Dance Clb; Service Clb; Teachers Aide; Band; Chorus; Concert Band; Drm Mjr(t); School Musical; Var Cheerleading; Sec NHS; Med.

ASCHOFF, KELLY; Port Jervis HS; Port Jervis, NY; (Y); Rep Stu Cncl; Cheerleading; Hon Roll; Office Aide; Ski Clb; Varsity Clb; Nwsp Phtg; Yrbk Phtg; Yrbk Sprt Ed; Score Keeper; U CO; Photo.

ASH, NICOLE; Boys & Girls HS; Brooklyn, NY; (Y); Computer Clb; Science Clb; Church Choir; Rep Stu Cncl; Hon Roll; Prfct Atten Awd; Regents Schlrshp 85; Bus Hnr Socty 84; Frnch Awd 84.

ASHBAUGH, ERIC; Falconer Central HS; Falconer, NY; (Y); 1/105; Concert Band; Sec Trs Mrchg Band; Bsbl; Bsktbl; Ftbl; Hon Roll; NHS; Sal; Band; Chorus; Regnts Schlrshp 85; Falconer Ed Assn Grnt 85; Jamestown Community; Comp Sci.

ASHBURN JR, JOHN B; Roy C Ketcham HS; Wappingers Fall, NY; (Y); 70/500; Capt Boy Scts; Capt Exploring; Rptr Jr Cls; Var Ftbl; Var Wrstlng; High Hon Roll; Hon Roll; Awd Achvt Bus Dynmanics 83; Hofstra; Pre-Law.

ASHBURN, RALPH; New Utrecht HS; Brooklyn, NY; (Y); 33/605; Band; Mrchg Band; Pep Band; Nwsp Stf; Cit Awd; High Hon Roll; Hon Roll; Prfct Atten Awd; Val.

ASHBY, DANITZA; Eli Whitney Voch HS; Brooklyn, NY; (Y); Cheerleading; Gym; Socr; Sftbl; Vllybl; Wt Lftg; Hon Roll; Pride Op Yankees Outstndng Achvt 85; Comp Sci.

ASHBY, TAMMY; West Genesee SR HS; Syracuse, NY; (Y); French Clb; Sec Jr Cls; Sec Sr Cls; Im Badmtn; Im Bsktbl; Im Diving; Im Fld Hcky; Im Gym; Im Lcrss; Im Socr; Comp.

ASHCROFT, JOHN M; Whitesboro Central HS; Marcy, NY; (Y); 4/327; Math Tm; Varsity Clb; Var L Socr; Capt L Tennis; High Hon Roll; NHS; Ntl Merit SF; Opt Clb Awd; Rotary Awd; NY ST Regents Schlrshp 85; Clarkson U; Engrng.

ASHE, DAVID B; Bethlehem Central HS; Delmar, NY; (Y); 28/338; Church Yth Grp; Chorus; Church Choir; Swing Chorus; Var Crs Cntry; Var Trk; High Hon Roll; NHS; Natl Achvt Schlrshp Pgm Negro Stus 84; Renssealer Polytech Inst Preface Pgm 84; Rensselaer Polytech; Comp Engr.

ASHE, KELLY; The Franciscan Acad; Syracuse, NY; (Y); FBLA; Yrbk Stf; High Hon Roll; Ntl Merit Ltr; Rep Stu Cncl; Niagara U; Pre-Law.

ASHE, MEGAN M; Southampton HS; Southampton, NY; (Y); GAA; Girl Scts; Spanish Clb; Band; Chorus; Jazz Band; Mrchg Band; Stage Crew; Var JV Cheerleading; Var JV Fld Hcky; Cookng.

ASHER, MATTHEW M; Christopher Columbus HS; New York, NY; (Y); 114/676; School Musical; Yrbk Stf; Hon Roll; Val; Regents Schlrshp 85.

ASHLEY, ALICIA VERONA; Murry Bergtraum HS; Brooklyn, NY; (Y); 157/576; Dance Clb; PAVAS; Chorus; School Musical; Variety Show; Gym; Cit Awd; Hon Roll; Prfct Atten Awd; Cert Of Art Awd 85; Future Tchrs Awd 82; Marymount Manhattan Coll; Dnce.

ASHLEY KELLY, GREGORY; Shaker HS; Latham, NY; (Y); Church Yth Grp; Key Clb; Band; Mrchg Band; Nwsp Stf; Pres Sr Cls; Stu Cncl; Capt JV Lcrss; NHS; St Schlr; Pres Schlrshp 85; Boston Coll & U Schlrshps 85; Siena Coll; Pre Med.

ASHLINE, LYNN; Franklin Acad; Malone, NY; (Y); French Clb; Hosp Aide; Pep Clb; Yrbk Stf; Hon Roll; Acad All-Amer 85; Phy Thrpy.

ASHMAN, MICHELLE A; The Mary Louis Acad; Cambria Heights, NY; (Y); Camera Clb; French Clb; Orch; Yrbk Phtg; Im Bowling; JV Trk; Ntl Merit Ltr; Osteopathic Physician.

ASHODIAN, LISA; Williamson SR HS; Pultneyville, NY; (Y); Chorus; Drill Tm; Sec Frsh Cls; Sec Sr Cls; Stat Mgr Bsktbl; JV Cheerleading; JV Var Socr; JV Trk; Fredonia; Accntnt.

ASKHAM, ERIC; Warwick HS; Warwick, NY; (Y); #26 In Class; Science Clb; Hon Roll.

ASKIN, MIKE; Victor Scentral HS; Fishers, NY; (Y); Computer Clb; Model UN; Science Clb; Drm & Bgl; Wrstlng; High Hon Roll; Hon Roll; Sprts Med.

ASKLAR, SUSAN; Niagara Falls HS; Niagara Falls, NY; (Y); Library Aide; Office Aide; Yrbk Bus Mgr; Yrbk Ed-Chief; Yrbk Stf; Rep Soph Cls; Rep Jr Cls; Rep Sr Cls; Rep Stu Cncl; Stat Bsbl; Amer Lgn Awd 83; Syracuse U; Bus Mgmt.

ASPROMONTI, VINCENT; Smithtown H S West HS; Smithtown, NY; (Y); Boy Scts; Cmnty Wkr; JV Bsktbl; Var Ice Hcky; Socr; Hon Roll; Cert Achvt Spn III 92 Avg 85; Acctng.

ASSAF, YAFA L; Yeshiva University HS For Girls; New York, NY; (Y); 5/67; Cmnty Wkr; Hosp Aide; Temple Yth Grp; Schl Wnnr Foreign Pol Assn 85; Hunter Coll; Bio.

ASSALIAN, DENISE; Minisink Valley HS; Middletown, NY; (Y); 34/236; 4-H; VICA; Y-Teens; Crs Cntry; High Hon Roll; NHS; BOCES Gold Plq Wnr 85; NYS 1st Pl Wnr VICA Skill Olympcs Prac Nrsg 85; Hlth Scholar Awds 85; Orange Cnty CC; Nrsg.

ASSIMAKOPOULOS, NICOLLE; John F Kennedy HS; New York, NY; (Y); 25/982; Pres Church Yth Grp; Cmnty Wkr; Dance Clb; Math Tm; Science Clb; Orch; Im Bsktbl; Hon Roll; Chrmn NHS; Sal; Natl Sci Talnt Srch Comp 85; Bronx Borough Sci Fair 2nd Place Wnnr 85; Ldrshp Medal 82; Columbia; Sci Resrch.

ASTORINO, BENJAMIN; Warwick Valley HS; Warwick, NY; (Y); FFA; VICA; High Hon Roll; Hon Roll; FFA Engl Awd, Grnhnd Awd 84.

ASVAZADOURIAN, CORRINE; Our Lady Of Victory Acad; Pleasantville, NY; (S); 21/137; Hosp Aide; Color Guard; School Play; Yrbk Stf; Sec Frsh Cls; Sec Soph Cls; High Hon Roll; Hon Roll; NHS; Awd Prfcncy Typing 83; Pre Med.

ASWAD, EILEEN G; Vestal SR HS; Vestal, NY; (Y); 64/450; French Clb; FBLA; Capt Color Guard; Concert Band; Mrchg Band; Hon Roll; NHS; NYS Regnts Schlrshp 85-89; Ntl Ldrshp, Svc Awd 84; SUNY Binghamton; Acctng.

ASWAD, STACEY; Binghamton HS; Binghamton, NY; (Y); 28/460; Cmnty Wkr; Dance Clb; French Clb; Key Clb; Stu Cncl; Stat Lcrss; Var Score Keeper; High Hon Roll; Hon Roll; NHS; SUNY Binghamton; Pre-Med.

ATAMIAN, CHRISTOPHER P; Collegiate Schl; New York, NY; (Y); Debate Tm; French Clb; Math Tm; Spanish Clb; Speech Tm; Lit Mag; Pres Frsh Cls; Pres Stu Cncl; Var Socr; 1st Pl Atlntc Pcfc Math Comp 84; 3rd Pl NY Math League Comp 83; Hnrbl Mntn Burgdorff Sci Comp 82.

ATCHIE, MEGAN; Haverling Central HS; Bath, NY; (Y); 68/147; GAA; JCL; Latin Clb; Crs Cntry; Trk; Hon Roll; AFS; French Clb; Spanish Clb; Band; All-Nrthrn Hnrbl Mntn 81-83; Natl Latin Test Silver Medal 85; Potsdam ST; Secndry Educ.

ATHANASSIADES, JOHN; Bronx High School Of Sci; Bayside, NY; (Y); VP Church Yth Grp; Math Clb; Math Tm; Teachers Aide; Bowling; Hon Roll; Ntl Merit Ltr; Stu Ath Trainer Pgm 84.

ATHANS, ROBERT; Cicero-North Syracuse HS; N Syracuse, NY; (S); 15/622; Exploring; German Clb; Mathletes; Math Tm; Ski Clb; Trk; Hon Roll; Sci.

ATHILL, ANDREA M; Bishop Kearney HS; Brooklyn, NY; (Y); 28/366; Science Clb; Teachers Aide; Chorus; NHS; Cmnty Wkr; Y-Teens; Hon Roll; Hnrs Spnsh Lang Cont; Columbia Coll; Life Sci.

ATKINS, KRISTIN; Lindenhurst SR HS; Lindenhurst, NY; (Y); JV Gym; Exec Sec.

ATKINS, PAUL; Sheepshead Bay HS; Brooklyn, NY; (Y); Am Leg Boys St; Intnl Clb; Ed Nwsp Rptr; VP Sr Cls; Boy Scts; Office Aide; Ntl Merit Ltr.

ATKINSON, ERIN; Far Rockaway HS; Far Rockaway, NY; (Y); Key Clb; Hon Roll; Arista 85; Hlth Assistng Pgm Cert 85; Nrsng.

ATKINSON, KEN N; St Anthonys HS; Northport, NY; (Y); Var Capt Bsktbl; Var Capt Socr; Empire ST Games Bsktbl 84; All Lng Islnd Nwsdy & Daily Nws Str Bsktbl 85; Bus.

ATKINSON, LEASHA; Northern Adirondack Central HS; Standish, NY; (Y); Yrbk Stf; Hon Roll; OLVSS; Bus.

ATKINSON, MARY; James A Green HS; Stratford, NY; (Y); Church Yth Grp; GAA; Girl Scts; Teachers Aide; Varsity Clb; Chorus; Off Frsh Cls; Stu Cncl; JV Bsktbl; Mgr(s); Herkimer Cnty CC; Prison Grd.

ATKINSON, MARY; Whitesboro SR HS; Whitesboor, NY; (Y); Sec GAA; Yrbk Phtg; Var Fld Hcky; Var Trk; Var Capt Vllybl.

ATKINSON, RICHARD; Fowler HS; Syracuse, NY; (S); Exploring; Acpl Chr; Chorus; Lit Mag; Rep Stu Cncl; Ftbl; Wt Lftg; Wrstlng; High Hon Roll; NHS; Earth Sci & Bio Awds 83-84; Outstndng Svc As Gen Assembly Rep 84; Marine Bio.

ATKINSON, ROSA; Springfield Gardens HS; Laurelton, NY; (S); 2/508; Church Yth Grp; Science Clb; Band; School Play; Off Soph Cls; Off Sr Cls; High Hon Roll; Hon Roll; NHS; Sal; Attndnc & Bio Awd 83; Chem Awd 84; Pre Med.

ATKINSON, SCOTT; Pulaski JR SR HS; Pulaski, NY; (Y); Letterman Clb; Varsity Clb; Band; Concert Band; Mrchg Band; Cit Awd; Prfct Atten Awd; Var Bsbl; Var Bsktbl; JV Ftbl; Phys Ed.

ATLOW, NEAL JAY; Tappan Zee HS; Tappan, NY; (Y); 101/294; Cmnty Wkr; Math Tm; Sec Temple Yth Grp; Thesps; Sec Chorus; School Musical; School Play; Stage Crew; Cit Awd; Natl Cncl Jwsh Wmn Comm Svc Awd 85; Schl Svcx Awd 85; SUNY Geneseo; Spch Comm.

ATTANASIO, ADRIANNE; Academy Of Mt St Ursula; New York, NY; (Y); Drama Clb; School Musical; School Play; Stage Crew; Variety Show; Yrbk Stf; Rep Frsh Cls; Rep Jr Cls; Trs Stu Cncl; NHS; 2nd Excel; Soc Studies,Spnsh Awd.

ATTICO, DEREK; William Howard Taft HS; Bronx, NY; (Y); Aud/Vis; Camera Clb; Hosp Aide; Church Choir; Hon Roll; Library Aide; Office Aide; Teachers Aide; Wt Lftg; Exclnce Playwrtng NY Bd Ed & Fndtn Dramatists Guild 84; NYU; Dramatist.

ATTIE, ELI G; Hunter College HS; New York, NY; (Y); VP PAVAS; Nwsp Ed-Chief; Yrbk Stf; Ntl Merit Ltr; Co-Authored 1 Act Play 83; NY ST Regents Schlrshp 85; Jrnlst.

ATWATER, AMY; Barker Central HS; Barker, NY; (Y); AFS; Church Yth Grp; VP Sec French Clb; Chorus; Church Choir; Var Trk; 4-H Awd; Accntng.

ATWOOD, SUSAN; Victor Cental HS; Victor, NY; (Y); Church Yth Grp; 4-H; Orch; Stage Crew; Stu Cncl; 4-H Awd; High Hon Roll; Hon Roll; Zoology.

AUBLE, TINA; Thomas A Edison JR SR HS; Elmira Heights, NY; (Y); 2/83; Pres French Clb; Varsity Clb; Band; Chorus; School Musical; Yrbk Stf; Capt Cheerleading; DAR Awd; High Hon Roll; Sal; Elmira Rollege Key Awd 84; Rtry Clb Awd 85; Pres Acdmc Ftns Awd 85; St Bonaventure U; Intl Bus.

AUBREY, RENEE; La Salle SR HS; Niagara Falls, NY; (Y); Drama Clb; Hosp Aide; Color Guard; Stat Bsktbl; Im Sftbl; Var Trk; Hon Roll; Jr NHS; NHS; Syracuse U; Pre-Med.

AUCHMAN, STEVEN E; Waterloo HS; Waterloo, NY; (Y); Am Leg Boys St; JA; Pep Clb; Varsity Clb; Ftbl; Lcrss; Wrstlng; Hon Roll; US Air Frce; Elec.

AUCKLAND, WENDY ANNETTE; Arkport Central Schl; Arkport, NY; (Y); 1/60; Am Leg Aux Girls St; Church Yth Grp; Band; Chorus; School Play; Pres Frsh Cls; VP Stu Cncl; Var JV Socr; Var Sftbl; High Hon Roll; Arkport Acadmc Scty 85; Geneses ST U NY; Bio.

AUDOUIN, ELIZABETH; Nazareth Regional HS; Brooklyn, NY; (Y); Office Aide; Speech Tm; Acpl Chr; Chorus; VP Frsh Cls; Rep Soph Cls; Rep Jr Cls; Principals List Awd 82-83; Frnch Awd 84; Hlth Sci.

AUER, JACQUELINE LEE; Newfield HS; Coram, NY; (Y); Boy Scts; Drama Clb; Concert Band; Mrchg Band; School Musical; School Play; Hon Roll; Jr NHS; NHS; Vet.

AUERBACH, MARC A; La Guardia H S Of Music/Arts Perf Art; Brooklyn, NY; (Y); 22/600; Cmnty Wkr; Political Wkr; School Play; Nwsp Rptr; VP Pres Stu Cncl; Ntl Merit SF; Jrnlsm.

AUERHAHN, JENNIFER; Roosevelt HS; Yonkers, NY; (S); Cmnty Wkr; Drama Clb; Exploring; Hosp Aide; Key Clb; VP Ski Clb; Band; Concert Band; Mrchg Band; School Musical; NY ST Rgnts Schlrshp 84; Boston U; Psych.

AUGERI, RICHARD; H Frank Carey HS; W Hempstead, NY; (Y); 21/230; Chrmn Church Yth Grp; Ed Nwsp Sprt Ed; Var Bsbl; Hon Roll; NHS; Optmtry.

AUGLIERA, ANNEMARIE; Moore Catholic HS; Staten Island, NY; (Y); Hosp Aide; Spanish Clb; Nwsp Stf; Yrbk Stf; High Hon Roll; St Johns U.

AUGUGLIARO, DIANNE; Sachem HS; Holbrook, NY; (Y); 18/1406; Pres Exploring; Office Aide; Science Clb; Nwsp Rptr; NHS; Rgnts Schlrshp, Prsdntl Acad Ftnss Awd 85; Wilkes Coll; Engrng.

AUGUSTINE, BRIAN; Rhinebeck HS; Rhinebeck, NY; (Y); Quiz Bowl; Concert Band; Jazz Band; Yrbk Bus Mgr; Yrbk Stf; Var L Golf; Var L Socr; High Hon Roll; Hon Roll; NHS; Elmira Key Awd 85; Hghst Soc Stud Regnts Cls Avg 85; Biomed Engrng.

AUGUSTINI, JOHN F; Allegany Central HS; Allegany, NY; (Y); 14/90; Art Clb; Varsity Clb; Var Crs Cntry; Stat Timer; Var Trk; Hon Roll; Prfct Atten Awd; Miriam Barcroft Blaisdell & Allegany PTA Memrl Schlrshp 85; Accptd Natl Hnr Rll Publctn 85; U Of Pittsburgh Bradford; Wrtg.

AUGUSTINOS, ELENA; Liverpool HS; Liverpool, NY; (S); 87/792; Chorus; School Musical; Variety Show; Rep Frsh Cls; Rep Soph Cls; Rep Jr Cls; Rep Sr Cls; Rep Stu Cncl; High Hon Roll; Jr NHS; Syracuse U.

AULET, TRACIE; Nyack HS; Nyack, NY; (Y); 22/277; Spanish Clb; Chorus; Church Choir; Var Trk; High Hon Roll; Hon Roll; NHS; Spanish NHS; Awd In Recngtn Of Outstdng Accmplshmnt In Msc 85; Abeny Hnr Svc Cert 83; Cert Of Mrt-Excell Wrtng 83; Bus Adm.

AULETTA, LISA; Lindenhurst HS; Lindenhurst, NY; (Y); Aud/Vis; Key Clb; Spanish Clb; Chorus; Yrbk Stf; Sftbl; Hon Roll; Jr NHS; Law.

AULETTA, ROSEANN; Herbert H Lehman HS; Bronx, NY; (Y); 7/444; Science Clb; Nwsp Rptr; High Hon Roll; NHS; USNMA US Natl Math Awds; Bus.

AULICINO, NICOLE; Huntington Christian HS; Farmingville, NY; (Y); 3/20; Church Yth Grp; Drama Clb; Political Wkr; School Play; VP Sr Cls; Mgr Bsktbl; JV Fld Hcky; Var Socr; NHS; Ntl Merit SF; Pres Schlrshp Gordon Clg 85; Gordon Clg; Polit Sci.

AULT, CHRISTOPHER; Onondaga Central HS; Nedrow, NY; (Y); 21/80; Yrbk Stf; Hon Roll; Newbold Coll; Eng.

AURIEMMA, MARIA ANTONIETTA; Mineola HS; Mineola, NY; (Y); 13/257; Art Clb; Nwsp Bus Mgr; NHS; Intnl Clb; Key Clb; Service Clb; JV Bowling; High Hon Roll; Hon Roll; Arch.

AURINGER, MARLENE; Bainbridge Guilford HS; Bainbridge, NY; (Y); 10/76; Hosp Aide; Spanish Clb; Concert Band; Mrchg Band; Orch; JV Vllybl; Pre-Med.

AUSTIN, BUCKY; Cohocton Central HS; Cohocton, NY; (Y); 3/26; Camera Clb; Computer Clb; Band; School Play; Yrbk Stf; VP Sr Cls; Var L Bsbl; Var L Bsktbl; Var L Socr; High Hon Roll; U Of Buffalo; Phy Thrpy.

AUSTIN, CAROLYN; Sacred Heart Acad; Beuerose, NY; (S); 10/190; FTA; Math Tm; Pep Clb; School Play; Hon Roll.

AUSTIN, DAVID; South Side HS; Elmira, NY; (Y); Boy Scts; Library Aide; U S Air Force; Aviation.

AUSTIN, DEBRA J; Fairport HS; Fairport, NY; (Y); 77/600; Camp Fr Inc; Church Yth Grp; French Clb; Service Clb; Band; Mrchg Band; Symp Band; Yrbk Stf; Lit Mag; Hon Roll; SUNY; Psych.

AUSTIN, DERON N; Wellsville HS; Wellsville, NY; (Y); 17/135; Var Capt Bsbl; Var Capt Bsktbl; High Hon Roll; Hon Roll; Bucknell U; Cvl Engrng.

AUSTIN, DIANA D; White Plains HS; White Plains, NY; (Y); Sec Church Yth Grp; Drama Clb; JA; Office Aide; Acpl Chr; Church Choir; Mrchg Band; School Musical; Variety Show; Band; Natl Achvt Schlrshp Pgm Outstndg Negro Stus 85; Wrtng Fair 84; Oakwood Coll; Theolgy.

AUSTIN, DOUG; Cazenovia Central Schl; Cazenovia, NY; (Y); Church Yth Grp; FFA; Ftbl; High Hon Roll; Hon Roll; Cert Wrstlg 81; FFA Camp 84; Sci.

AUSTIN, ELIZABETH; Bloomfield Central Schl; Holcomb, NY; (Y); 1/109; Latin Clb; Varsity Clb; Chorus; Trs Jr Cls; Rep Stu Cncl; Cheerleading; Socr; High Hon Roll; NHS; Prfct Atten Awd; Outstndng Rslts In St Math Comp 82; Vrsty Chrldng 83; U Of PA; Attrny.

AUSTIN, HEATHER; Lake George JR SR HS; Pilot Knob, NY; (Y); Church Yth Grp; Chorus; JV Var Cheerleading; JV Var Pom Pon; Hon Roll; Lk George Yth Theater-Best Supprtng Actrss 82-83; Ballet & Jazz Dncng 74-85; Trvl.

AUSTIN, KENNETH W; The Bronx High School Science; Jamaica, NY; (Y); Camera Clb; Cmnty Wkr; Drama Clb; JA; Sec Key Clb; Political Wkr; Science Clb; Chorus; Yrbk Stf; NHS; Pol Sci.

AUSTIN, KEVIN; Wellsville HS; Wellsville, NY; (Y); 10/120; Am Leg Boys St; Stage Crew; Nwsp Rptr; Nwsp Sprt Ed; JV Var Bsbl; JV Var Bsktbl; High Hon Roll; NHS; Lehigh U; Biol.

AUSTIN, PAUL ANDREW MICHAEL; Liverpool HS; North Syracuse, NY; (Y); 263/792; AFS; Art Clb; Thesps; Lit Mag; Crs Cntry; Hon Roll; NY ST Regnts Schlrshp PSAT NAISQT 85; Upstate Medical Ctr; Med Tech.

AUSTIN, VELMA; New Rochelle HS; New Rochelle, NY; (Y); NHS; Lehman Coll; Bus Adm.

AUSUBEL, LARA J; South Side HS; Rockville Centre, NY; (Y); 1/286; Computer Clb; Exploring; Mathletes; Math Tm; Science Clb; Service Clb; Orch; School Musical; Nwsp Bus Mgr; Nwsp Rptr; Highest Hnrs-NY St Sci Cngrs, LI Sci Cngrs 84; NY St Sci Supv Chem Awd 84; Princeton Bk Awd 84; Sci Rsrch.

AUTENRIETH, ANN; Stissing Mt JR SR HS; Pine Plains, NY; (Y); Church Yth Grp; Dance Clb; Pep Clb; Yrbk Stf; Cheerleading; Score Keeper; Trk; COSMTLGY.

AUTIO, KRIS; Candor Central HS; Candor, NY; (Y); 4/88; School Play; Trs Sr Cls; Crs Cntry; Trk; High Hon Roll; NHS; Ntl Merit Ltr; Church Yth Grp; Varsity Clb; Band; ROTC, Harold E Jansen Mem, Owego Bus & Prof Womens Clb Schlrshps 85; SUNY Fredonia; Acctng.

AUTORINO, SILVIA; Bishop Kearney HS; Brooklyn, NY; (Y).

AVALLONE, ROSANNE; Valley Stream Central HS; Valley Stream, NY; (Y); Church Yth Grp; Jr NHS; Accntng.

AVANT, KRISTEN; Churchville-Chili SR HS; Churchville, NY; (Y); 7/350; Hosp Aide; Pres JCL; Pres Latin Clb; Ski Clb; Chorus; Capt Sftbl; Capt Swmmng; High Hon Roll; NHS; ATAD Exchng Stu W Germny 85; ADEPT 84-85; MI ST U; Botny.

AVDOIAN, SUSAN; Niagara Falls HS; Niagara Falls, NY; (Y); 44/256; French Clb; Key Clb; Red Cross Aide; Ski Clb; Church Choir; School Musical; School Play; Hon Roll; Jr NHS; NHS; Boston U; Specl Ed.

AVELLEZ, OLGA; De Witt Clinton HS; Bronx, NY; (Y); Hosp Aide; Chorus; Capt Cheerleading; Cit Awd; Hon Roll; Surgcl Nrs.

AVERY, BRIAN; Skaneateles HS; Auburn, NY; (Y); Band; Concert Band; Drm & Bgl; Jazz Band; Camera Clb; Orch.

AVERY JR, GARY M; South Side HS; Millport, NY; (Y); JA; Drm & Bgl; Corning CC; Data Proc.

AVERY, JENNIFER E; Westhill HS; Syracuse, NY; (Y); 3/167; Sec AFS; Key Clb; Math Tm; Band; Nwsp Stf; Yrbk Stf; Var Capt Crs Cntry; Capt Var Trk; Hon Roll; NHS; Rgnts Schlrshp 85; Ithaca Coll Schlrshp 85; NYSMA Mdls 81-84; Ithaca Coll; Phy Thrpy.

AVERY, JULIA L; F H Laguardia H S Of The Music & Arts; Bronx, NY; (Y); Church Yth Grp; Cmnty Wkr; Band; Yrbk Stf; Cheerleading; Prfct Atten Awd; NYS Regents Schlrshp 85; Long Island U; Finance.

AVERY, KERRY; Union Endicott HS; Endicott, NY; (S); Am Leg Boys St; Boys Clb Am; Varsity Clb; Var L Bsbl; Var L Bsktbl; Var L Bowling; Var L Ftbl; Elks Awd; Amer Legn Bsbl Rookie Yr 84; WNBG TV HS Bwlng Champ 3rd Pl 85.

AVERY, LAURA MICKEY; Fonda-Fultonville Central HS; Ft Hunter, NY; (Y); #8 In Class; Key Clb; Var Bsktbl; Capt Socr; Capt Sftbl; Var Vllybl; High Hon Roll; NHS; VFW Awd; Swmmng; Wrkd As A Stu Aide In Schls Comp Lab 82-85; Schlrshp To Utica Coll Of Syracuse Sccr 85-86; Utica Coll; Comp Sci.

AVERY, PATRICK W; East Syuracuse-Minoa HS; East Syracuse, NY; (Y); Am Leg Boys St; JV Var Bsbl; JV Var Bsktbl; JV Var Ftbl; High Hon Roll; Hon Roll; NHS.

AVERY, PHILIP; Cicero-North Syracuse HS; Clay, NY; (S); 8/771; Mathletes; Math Clb; Math Tm; Var Trk; Bausch & Lomb Sci Awd; High Hon Roll; Hon Roll; NHS; Opt Clb Awd; Physic Awd Dnnr 84; U Dayton; Math.

AVIDAR, AVA; Midwood HS; Brooklyn, NY; (Y); Drama Clb; Math Tm; Service Clb; Temple Yth Grp; Chorus; School Musical; School Play; Rep Stu Cncl; Model Congrss Exec Staff; Electn Commsnr; Med Sci Inst.

AVILA, LISA; Lindenhurst HS; Lindenhurst, NY; (Y); Am Leg Aux Girls St; Camera Clb; German Clb; Drill Tm; Yrbk Phtg; JV Fld Hcky; Law.

AVILA, MARIA; Holy Trinity HS; Hicksville, NY; (S); Camera Clb; Library Aide; Stage Crew; Nwsp Stf; Yrbk Stf.

AVILES, LISETTE; Mabel Dean Bacon V HS; New York, NY; (S); Teachers Aide; Hon Roll; Regents Geo 84; Schlrshp Awd 84; Comp Pgrm.

AVLICINO, NICOLE; Huntington Christian HS; Farmingville, NY; (S); 2/20; Drama Clb; Political Wkr; Ski Clb; Varsity Clb; Chorus; School Play; VP Sr Cls; Var L Socr; Ntl Merit SF; Sal; Pol Sci.

AVOLIO, DAVE; South New Berlin Central HS; South New Berlin, NY; (Y); Yrbk Stf; JV L Bsktbl; Var L Ftbl; High Hon Roll; Hon Roll; Rochester Inst Of Tech; Elec.

AWAD, ANDREW D; West Genesee HS; Syracuse, NY; (Y); Exploring; JA; JV Bsbl; Im Bsktbl; Im Golf; Im Tennis; Hartwick SUNY Oswego; Sales.

AWOBULUYI, MARCIA KEHINDE; Hillcrest HS; Cambria Hts, NY; (Y); 20/793; Church Yth Grp; Math Tm; Church Choir; Nwsp Bus Mgr; Nwsp Stf; Soph Cls; Jr Cls; Cit Awd; Hon Roll; Ntl Arista Hnr Soc 82 & 85; Ntl Rgnts Schlrshp 85; Boruch Coll; Accntng.

AXELROD, JAMIE; Susan E Wagner HS; Staten Island, NY; (Y); School Musical; School Play; Stage Crew; Frsh Cls; Pres Soph Cls; Jr Cls; Sr Cls; Stu Cncl; Golf; Socr; Supr Yth 85.

AXENFELD, DOUG; Jamesville-Dewitt HS; Dewitt, NY; (Y); Cmnty Wkr; Letterman Clb; Political Wkr; Var Ftbl; Var Lcrss; Hon Roll.

AYAD, ALEXANDER; Camisius HS; Buffalo, NY; (Y); Aud/Vis; Church Yth Grp; Drama Clb; Radio Clb; School Play; Stage Crew; Nwsp Stf; Off Soph Cls; Im Bsktbl; Im Ftbl; Comm.

AYALA, HUGO MARIO; La Salle Military Acad; Oakdale LI, NY; (Y); 5/93; Computer Clb; Intnl Clb; Math Clb; Capt ROTC; Chorus; School Play; Stage Crew; Yrbk Stf; Sec Sr Cls; NHS; Gld Hnrs Every Sem; MA Inst Tech; Elec Engnrng.

AYALA, LAURIE; John F Kennedy HS; New York, NY; (Y); Band; Concert Band; Orch; Hon Roll; Manhattan Coll; Bus Mgmt.

AYDELOTTE, TODD; Pittsford Mendon HS; Pittsford, NY; (Y); 2/300; Boy Scts; Church Yth Grp; Ski Clb; Jazz Band; Nwsp Ed-Chief; Yrbk Stf; Socr; Trk; Hon Roll; Eagle Sct 83; Law.

AYDIN, ALISA A; St Hildas & St Huens Schl; New York, NY; (Y); Drama Clb; Nwsp Ed-Chief; Yrbk Stf; Frnch & Art Awds 83; The Apprntcc Wrtr 85; Yale U; Fine Arts.

AYDIN, TAYKUT; Warwick Valley HS; Ridgewood, NJ; (Y); 35/207; FFA; Coach Actv; Capt Socr; Hon Roll; Yth Ldrshp Awd 84; NYS Regents Schlrshp 85; Rutgers U; Engrng.

AYERS, JODI; Corning West HS; Painted Post, NY; (Y); Pres Sec Ski Clb; Thesps; Varsity Clb; Mrchg Band; Trs Stu Cncl; Var Capt Trk; JV Capt Vllybl; High Hon Roll; Hon Roll; NHS; Trvl.

AYLANGAN, ARZU; Greece Arcadia HS; Rochester, NY; (Y); 4/292; Hosp Aide; Mathletes; Math Clb; Math Tm; High Hon Roll; Hon Roll; Jr NHS; NHS; NYS Rgnts Schlrshp 85; Acad Schrlsphp Pin 84; Frnch Awd 84; U Rochester.

AYLWARD, ANDY; Union Endicott HS; Endwell, NY; (Y); Letterman Clb; Jazz Band; Stu Cncl; JV Swmmng; Var Trk; Hon Roll; RIT; Elec Engrng.

AYOS, AMELIA A; Susan E Wagner HS; Staten Island, NY; (Y); 8/497; Library Aide; Office Aide; Teachers Aide; School Musical; Stage Crew; High Hon Roll; Regnts Schlrshp Awd 85; Acad Olympics-Engl Tm 85; NYU Ttee Schlrshp 85; NY U; Comp Sci.

AYOTTE, THOMAS; Smithtown H S West; Hauppauge, NY; (Y); Am Leg Boys St; Exploring; Political Wkr; Y-Teens; Rep Soph Cls; Rep Jr Cls; Stu Cncl; JV Capt Bsbl; Im Vllybl; Hon Roll; Naval Acad; Aero Engrng.

AYRE, OWEN; Unatego JR SR HS; Unadilla, NY; (Y); 9/89; Am Leg Boys St; Trs Frsh Cls; Trs Soph Cls; Pres Jr Cls; Pres Stu Cncl; Capt Var Crs Cntry; NHS; Dance Clb; Keystone Awd Frnch III 83; De Mulder Mang Awd Frnch IV 84; David W Patchin Mem Scholar 85; Bus Finance.

AYRES, CYNTHIA; Newfield HS; Coram, NY; (Y); Band; Mrchg Band; Var Capt Jr Cls; JV Fld Hcky; Var Capt Trk; Hon Roll; Newfield H S All Time Top 10 In Crss-Cntry 84-85; Suffolk Cnty All Cnty Crss Cntry Tm 84; Phy Ed.

AYRULOVSKI, LEMAN; Curtis HS; Staten Island, NY; (Y); Library Aide; Teachers Aide; Orch; Badmtn; Gym; Vllybl; Cit Awd; Hon Roll; Ntl Merit Ltr; Physcl Ftnss Awd 80-81; Awd Outstndng Perfrmc Strng Quartet 85; Banuch; Cert Pub Accntnt.

AZAR, MICHAEL; Fort Hamilton HS; Brooklyn, NY; (Y); Aud/Vis; Teachers Aide; Chorus; Church Choir; School Musical; Sec Jr Cls; VP Sr Cls; Audio-Visual Awd; Berkeley Coll; Rcrd Prod.

AZINARO, SUSAN; Preston HS; Bronx, NY; (S); 5/100; Cmnty Wkr; Drama Clb; Stage Crew; Yrbk Stf; Co-Capt Twrlr; High Hon Roll; NHS; Archbshp John J O Connor Spcl 84; Rec Awd; Fordham U; Acctng.

AZNAR, SILVINA; St Vincent Ferrer HS; Long Isl City, NY; (Y); Dance Clb; French Clb; JA; Teachers Aide; Nwsp Sprt Ed; Yrbk Phtg; Yrbk Stf; French Hon Soc; High Hon Roll; Georgetown; Diplomacy.

AZZARELLA, DARCY LEE; Alexander Central HS; Alexander, NY; (Y); Sec AFS; Church Yth Grp; FNA; Hosp Aide; Sec Trs Varsity Clb; VP Stu Cncl; Var Capt Crs Cntry; Var Capt Trk; Trs 4-H; Color Guard; Sectnl Cros Cty Champ 82-84; MVP Cross Cty 84-85; Nrsng.

AZZARELLA, PHILIP; Silver Creek Central Schl; Silver Creek, NY; (Y); Math Tm; Spanish Clb; Nwsp Sprt Ed; Bowling; NHS; Fredonia ST; Math.

AZZI, CHERYL; West Seneca East SR HS; Buffalo, NY; (Y); Church Yth Grp; Hon Roll; Bus.

BAASE, JEFFREY; Brockport HS; Hamlin, NY; (Y); 52/320; Church Yth Grp; French Clb; Bsbl; Bsktbl; High Hon Roll; Hon Roll; NHS; Allegheny Coll; Frgn Lang.

BABCOCK, BARBRA; Granviille JR & SR HS; Granville, NY; (S); 6/121; Math Tm; Band; Jazz Band; Swing Chorus; Variety Show; Yrbk Ed-Chief; Rep Frsh Cls; JV Fld Hcky; High Hon Roll; NHS; Berklee Coll Of Mus; Mus.

BABCOCK, CARLA; Niagra Falls HS; Niagara Falls, NY; (Y); Camera Clb; Church Yth Grp; Cmnty Wkr; GAA; Pep Clb; Ski Clb; Spanish Clb; Chorus; Church Choir; Variety Show; Psych.

BABCOCK, CHRISTINA; Sandy Creek Central HS; Lacona, NY; (Y); Art Clb; FFA; Office Aide; VICA; Stat Bsbl; Stat Bsktbl; Var Score Keeper; Otto Mills Fish, Game Clb Schlrshp 85; Morrisville Ag Tech; Flrcultre.

BABCOCK, KIMBERLY; Hornell SR HS; Hornell, NY; (S); 12/204; JCL; Latin Clb; Band; Color Guard; Mrchg Band; Yrbk Stf; Rep Frsh Cls; Rep Soph Cls; Rep Jr Cls; Rep Sr Cls; Hnr Achvt Awds Math, Latin I & II 81-83; Outsdndng Female Athlete Hronell Inv Track Meet 84; Bucknell U; Bus Adm.

BABCOCK, KIMBERLY; Linton HS; Schenectady, NY; (Y); Church Yth Grp; Key Clb; Acpl Chr; Chorus; Church Choir; Jr Cls; Stu Cncl; JV Var Tennis; NHS; Ntl Merit SF.

BABCOCK, LERA; St Marys Acad; Hoosick Falls, NY; (Y); 5/20; Church Yth Grp; Letterman Clb; Pep Clb; Nwsp Stf; Trs Soph Cls; Trs Stu Cncl; Bsktbl; Powder Puff Ftbl; Score Keeper; Sftbl; Amer HS Math Medal & Awd 85; New England Coll; Comp Sci.

BABCOCK, MICHAEL; Herkimer HS; Herkimer, NY; (Y); 5/120; VP Aud/Vis; Drama Clb; Chorus; School Musical; Swing Chorus; JV Bsbl; JV Bsktbl; High Hon Roll; Hon Roll; NHS; Vrsty Ltr A Avr 84; Svc Bar 85; Med.

BABCOCK, ROYALE; Oneida HS; Canastota, NY; (Y); Spanish Clb; Concert Band; Jazz Band; Mrchg Band; Yrbk Stf; High Hon Roll; NHS; Ntl Merit SF; Im Vllybl; Law.

BABIARZ, CYNTHIA L; Churchville-Chili SR HS; Rochester, NY; (Y); Nwsp Stf; Lit Mag; Rep Frsh Cls; Rep Soph Cls; Rep Jr Cls; Rep Stu Cncl; Var Tennis; High Hon Roll; NHS; NY ST Regnts Schlrshp 85; Geneseo U.

BABILOT, MICHAEL; Weedsport JR SR HS; Weedsport, NY; (Y); 9/90; Am Leg Boys St; Boy Scts; Pres Chess Clb; Intnl Clb; Math Tm; Yrbk Sprt Ed; Var L Ftbl; Var L Swmmng; Var L Trk; Pres NHS; Annapolis Naval Acad; Mech Engr.

BABINGTON, TOBIE; Shenendehowa HS; Clifton Pk, NY; (Y); Ski Clb; Yrbk Stf; Off Frsh Cls; Off Soph Cls; Off Jr Cls; Var Capt Cheerleading; JV Powder Puff Ftbl; Im Trk; High Hon Roll; Hon Roll; Best Drsd Grl 83; Cpt Chrldrs 85-86; FL ST U; Fashn Merch.

BABINO, GIOVANNI S; La Salle Acad; Brooklyn, NY; (S); Science Clb; Bowling; Soc Distgnshd Amer HS Stus 84; Cardinal Hayes Hnr Soc 82-84; Math.

BABORE, CONCETTA; Dominican Acad; Astoria, NY; (Y); Computer Clb; Hosp Aide; Nwsp Bus Mgr; Nwsp Rptr; Yrbk Stf; Hon Roll; Regents Schlrshp 85; NY U; Business Mgmt.

BABOWICZ, COLLEEN; John F Kennedy HS; Utica, NY; (Y); Aud/Vis; Key Clb; Nwsp Rptr; Hon Roll; Jr NHS; Mohawk Vly CC; Bus.

BACAL, DARRON A; Port Richmond HS; Staten Island, NY; (Y); 1/750; Pres Computer Clb; Debate Tm; Hosp Aide; Math Tm; School Musical; Nwsp Ed-Chief; Var Tennis; High Hon Roll; NHS; Ntl Merit SF; Hghst SAT Grd 85; Electd Boy Ldr Arista Schl 85; Harvard U; Med.

BACCHUS, PAUL; South Shore HS; Brooklyn, NY; (Y); Church Yth Grp; School Play; Socr; Bus Admin.

BACH, JONATHAN; Northeastern Clinton Central HS; Alburg, VT; (Y); Model UN; Hon Roll; Jrnlsm.

BACH, LARRY; Voorheesville JR SR HS; Voorheesville, NY; (Y); VP Temple Yth Grp; Band; Chorus; Jazz Band; Yrbk Ed-Chief; Crs Cntry; Hon Roll; Ntl Merit Ltr; Music.

BACHER, FRANCESCA; St Joh The Baptist HS; Smithtown, NY; (Y); Dance Clb; Chorus; Yrbk Stf; Rep Jr Cls; Rep Stu Cncl; French Hon Soc; Hon Roll; Med.

BACHINI, CHRISTINA; Cornwal Central HS; Highland Mills, NY; (Y); 14/199; Church Yth Grp; Hosp Aide; Variety Show; Var JV Bsbl; JV Bsktbl; High Hon Roll; Hon Roll; Trs NHS; SUNY Binghamton; Pre-Med.

BACHMAN, AMY; South Side HS; Rockville Ctr, NY; (Y); 80/276; Drama Clb; Key Clb; Latin Clb; Thesps; Chorus; Concert Band; Jazz Band; Madrigals; Mrchg Band; School Musical; NYSSMA-PIANO/A 81; NYSSMA-VOICE/A 84-85; NYSSMA-PIANO/E 83; Intl Thespian Soc 84; Music.

BACHOFFER, LORI; Avon JR SR HS; Avon, NY; (Y); Church Yth Grp; Spanish Clb; JV Bsktbl; Var Diving; JV Var Socr; JV Var Sftbl; JV Vllybl; High Hon Roll; Hon Roll; Jr NHS; Rookie Of Yr Swmmg 84; Swmmr Of Yr 85; Aviatn.

BACHOP, MARY; Sacred Heart HS; Yonkers, NY; (Y); Nwsp Stf; Yrbk Stf; High Hon Roll; 1st Prz Womens Intl Leag Peace & Freedom Essay Cont 84; SUNY; Art.

BACK, RONALD; Valhalla HS; White Plains, NY; (Y); 27/120; Am Leg Boys St; Band; Sec Sr Cls; Im Bsktbl; Var L Ice Hcky; JV Socr; Var L Tennis; Helping Hands Clb 84-86; SADD 84-86; VIF Exch Pgm 84-86; Ithaca Coll; Bus.

BACKENSTROSS, KURT; East Syracuse Minoa C HS; Kirkville, NY; (Y); JV Lcrss; Cert Awd Drftg 85; Delhi; Drftg.

BACKO, SUE; Susquehanna Valley HS; Binghamton, NY; (Y); Chorus; Bsktbl; Sftbl; Tennis; Vllybl; Hon Roll; Jr NHS; NY ST Presdntl Plyscl Ftnss Awd 85; Music Achv Cert 83; In Apprctn Cert-Yth Cncl Smkng Pgm 85; Broome CC; Bus.

BACKUS, GREGG; Bishop Timon HS; W Seneca, NY; (Y); Ski Clb; Spanish Clb; Chorus; Im Bsktbl; Im Ice Hcky; Im Vllybl; Hon Roll; Bus Mgmt.

BACON, ASA MICHAEL; Roosevelt HS; Roosevelt, NY; (Y); Art Clb; Wrstlng; NHS; Ntl Hnr Soc 84; NYS Rgnts Schlrshp 85; Hampton U; Comp Sci.

BACON, ROBERT; Central Islip HS; Central Islip, NY; (Y); Boy Scts; Church Yth Grp; Var Bowling; NHS; Ntl Merit Ltr; NEDT Awd.

BACON, SARA E; Bronx HS Of Science; New York, NY; (Y); Ed Yrbk Stf; Lit Mag; Vllybl; NHS; Crtv Wrtng Awd 85; UFT Schlrshp 85; St Gandens Medl Drftsmnshp 85; Wesleyan U.

BACON, SUZANNE; Attmar-Parish-Williamstown HS; Altmar, NY; (Y); 2/94; Band; Color Guard; Mrchg Band; Pep Band; School Play; Var Stat Bsktbl; Var L Socr; Trk; Stat Wrstlng; Cit Awd; SUNY-BINGHAMTON; Acctng.

BACON, SUZANNE; Lowville Acad Central; Lowville, NY; (Y); FBLA; Bus.

BACZKIEWICZ, ALAN; St Marys HS; Alden, NY; (S); 7/235; Science Clb; Lit Mag; Score Keeper; Im Vllybl; Hon Roll; NHS; RIT; Physics.

BADALAMENT, RACQUEL; Commack H S North; Commack, NY; (Y); MMM; Chorus; Madrigals; School Musical; Swing Chorus; Variety Show; Rep Frsh Cls; Cheerleading; Hon Roll; Chr Cncl Outstndng Serv Awd 83; Music.

BADALAMENTI, CLAUDIA N; Martin Van Buren HS; Queens Village, NY; (Y); 22/671; Teachers Aide; School Musical; Yrbk Stf; Vllybl; French Hon Soc; Hon Roll; Jr NHS; NHS; NY ST Regents Schlrshp 85; Engl Honor Society 85; Sci Honor Society 85; U Of MI; Accounting.

BADALATO, NICHOLAS F; Kingston HS; Kingston, NY; (Y); Am Leg Boys St; Rep Stu Cncl; Var L Ftbl; Var L Trk; Var L Wrstlng; High Hon Roll; Jr NHS; NHS.

BADAMO, MICHAEL; Seaford HS; Seaford, NY; (Y); Camera Clb; Church Yth Grp; Computer Clb; Drama Clb; Exploring; Math Clb; Math Tm; NFL; School Play; JV Ftbl; Med.

BADER, MARIE; Academy Of Mount Saint Ursual; Bronx, NY; (Y); High Hon Roll; NEDT Awd; Music Hnrs Awd 83-84; First Hnrs Awd 82-83; Comp Sci.

BADGER, AMY; Massena Central HS; Massena, NY; (Y); French Clb; Band; Concert Band; Mrchg Band; School Musical; JV Var Cheerleading; Var Trk; Hon Roll; Bus Adm.

BADGER, JENNIFER; Jordan-Elbridge JR SR HS; Jordan, NY; (Y); 5/130; Political Wkr; Sec Jr Cls; Rep Stu Cncl; JV Var Cheerleading; High Hon Roll; Jr NHS; NHS; Church Yth Grp; Dance Clb; Drama Clb; Math Symposium 1st Pl 83; Hi-Quiz Cont TV Shw 84; Mst Outstdng Chrldr 84; Alfred U; Pol Sci.

BADGER, KIMBERLY; Mexico Academy And HS; Mexico, NY; (Y); Camera Clb; Church Yth Grp; Dance Clb; Drama Clb; 4-H; German Clb; Science Clb; Church Choir; Concert Band; Mrchg Band; Grmn Hnr Soc Alpha Beta Phy; 4-H Amb, Hghst Gr Recgntn Grmn; SUNY Upstate Med Ctr; Radiolgy.

BADIA, DARLENE DELLA; Academy Of Mt St Ursula HS; Bronx, NY; (Y); Art Clb; Dance Clb; Teachers Aide; Stage Crew; Nwsp Stf; Yrbk Stf; Soph Cls; Jr Cls; Sr Cls; Hon Roll; 2nd Hnrs Frsh, Soph & JR.

BADOLATO, MARY ANN; Rome Free Acad; Rome, NY; (Y); Concert Band; Mrchg Band; Pep Band; Symp Band; Yrbk Stf; Sec Frsh Cls; JV Vllybl; Jr NHS; Opt Clb Awd; Med Tech.

BADSTEIN, JOSEPH; Pine Bush Central HS; Pine Bush, NY; (Y); 23/300; JV Bsbl; Var Capt Swmmng; NHS; Prfct Atten Awd; Comm Longfellow Awd Adv Aquatcs, Drvr Trnng Awd 84-85; William Paterson Coll; Phy Thpy.

BAENSCH, MICHAEL H; Hastings HS; Hastings-On-Hudsn, NY; (Y); Computer Clb; Key Clb; Lit Mag; Hon Roll; U ST NY Rgnts Schlrshp Awd 85; Comp Sci.

BAER, CHRIS; Westhampton Beach HS; E Moriches, NY; (Y); 68/233; VICA; Cullinary Inst Amer; Cull Arts.

BAETZHOLD, JAMES; Kenmore West SR HS; Kenmore, NY; (Y); Civic Clb; Cmnty Wkr; Service Clb; Rep Soph Cls; Rep Jr Cls; JV Bsbl; Im Bsktbl; Im Socr; Im Vllybl; Columbian Squrs Squr Yr 83.

BAEZ, BRENDA; Cathedral HS; Ny, NY; (Y); Chess Clb; Church Yth Grp; Dance Clb; French Clb; JA; Acpl Chr; Tennis; French Hon Soc; FIT; Intl Mktng.

BAEZ, MILTON; Midwood HS; Brooklyn, NY; (Y); Rep Latin Clb; JV Bsbl; JV Ftbl; Im Sftbl; JV Wrstlng; Hon Roll; A Better Chance-Full Schlrshp 82-84; Busnss Admin.

BAEZ, ROSAURA; St Francis Preparatory Schl; Bayside, NY; (Y); 16/690; Dance Clb; Drama Clb; Science Clb; Spanish Clb; School Musical; Hon Roll; NHS; Natl Hispanic Schlr Awd SF 84-85; Dakin Mem Stu Awd 85; Med.

BAEZ, SUZETTE; Adlai E Stevenson HS; Bronx, NY; (Y); 20/445; Church Yth Grp; Nwsp Ed-Chief; Nwsp Rptr; Yrbk Stf; Tennis; Fordham U; Jrnlsm.

BAGAN, STEVEN; Auburn HS; Auburn, NY; (Y); 21/431; German Clb; ROTC; Drill Tm; High Hon Roll; Hon Roll; NHS; Ntl Merit Ltr; Prfct Atten Awd; ROTC Schlrshp 85; Regents Schlrshp 85; Syracuse U; Mech Engr.

BAGDON, TRACY; Amsterdam HS; Amsterdam, NY; (Y); VP DECA; Varsity Clb; Yrbk Stf; Off Soph Cls; Trs Stu Cncl; Co-Capt Cheerleading; Pom Pon; Hon Roll; Physcl Thrpy.

BAGGIA, CATHERINE; Hunter College HS; Forest Hills, NY; (Y); Math Tm; Science Clb; School Musical; Nwsp Ed-Chief; Yrbk Stf; Var Sftbl; Var Tennis; French Hon Soc; Mu Alp Tht; Ntl Merit Ltr; Dartmouth Coll; Med.

BAGLA, SANGEETA; Kings Park HS; Kings Park, NY; (Y); 2/444; Pres VP Art Clb; JV Hosp Aide; Math Tm; VP Trs Science Clb; Ed Yrbk Stf; Crs Cntry; Trk; High Hon Roll; NHS; Ntl Merit SF; Mth Achvt Trphy 84-85; Frgn Lang Awd Frnch, Spn, Latin 84-85; Chem Achvt 84-85; U Of PA; Biochem.

BAGLI, PETER D; Walt Whitman HS; Huntington, NY; (Y); 152/625; Band; Concert Band; Mrchg Band; Pep Band; JV Golf; JV Socr; Hon Roll; St Schlr; ST U NY Albany.

BAGLIO, BETH ANN; Springville Griffith Inst; Springville, NY; (Y); 31/201; Church Yth Grp; Spanish Clb; Band; Orch; Pres Frsh Cls; Pres Trs Stu Cncl; Var Cheerleading; NHS; Amer Lgn Hnr Schlrshp Awd 85; Prsdntl Acadmc Ftns Awd 85; ST U Buffalo; Accntng.

BAGUIO, MIRIAM; The Stony Brook Schl; Setauket, NY; (Y); 7/84; Library Aide; Ski Clb; Spanish Clb; Chorus; Orch; School Musical; School Play; Yrbk Phtg; Off Stu Cncl; Bsktbl; NYSSMA Piano Comp Natl Piano Guild 80-85; King Awd Emerging Artst Photo 85; Nrsg.

BAHAMONDE, PEDRO; Cardinal Hayes HS; Bronx, NY; (Y); 4/264; Exploring; Library Aide; Service Clb; Prfct Atten Awd; 1st Hnrs Awd 83-85; 2nd Hnrs Awd 85; Lang Medal 83-85; Med.

BAHAR, YALE; Port Richmond HS; Staten Isld, NY; (Y); School Musical; School Play; Stage Crew; Pharm.

BAHL, RENEE; Fayetteville-Manlius HS; Fayetteville, NY; (Y); Letterman Clb; Model UN; Nwsp Rptr; Rep Stu Cncl; Var L Swmmng; Var Trk; Hon Roll; Schltc Art Awds Blue Rbn & Hnrb Mntn 83; Luella A Hurdman Mem Awd Swmmng 83; Mth.

BAHRENBURG, KRISTI K; Arlington HS; Poughkeepsie, NY; (Y); 24/580; German Clb; Ski Clb; Mrchg Band; Orch; Hon Roll; Cert Of Merit Achvt German 83-84; NY ST Conf All ST Band Clrnt 84; NY ST Rgnts Schlrhsp 85; Cornellu; Econ.

BAIDY, KATHLEEN M; Scotia-Glenville HS; Scotia, NY; (Y); 18/244; German Clb; Varsity Clb; Concert Band; Mrchg Band; Yrbk Sprt Ed; Yrbk Stf; Var Im Bsktbl; L Socr; NHS; Pres Acad Fit Awd; Le Moyne Coll; Bio.

BAILER, LYNN; Solvay HS; Syracuse, NY; (Y); Sec JA; Ski Clb; Band; Chorus; Concert Band; School Musical; School Play; Swing Chorus; Yrbk Phtg; Yrbk Stf; Ind Arts Cert Merit 85; NYSSMA Excllnt Grdng Flute Solo 83-84; RIT; Film.

BAILEY, CANUTE; Alfred E Smith HS; Bronx, NY; (Y); Library Aide; Teachers Aide; Band; Concert Band; School Musical; Stage Crew; Nwsp Rptr; Nwsp Stf; Yrbk Stf; Hon Roll; Regnts Schlrshp 85; SUNY-BUFFALO U; Engr.

BAILEY, CHRISTOPHER; Whitesboro SR HS; Whitesboro, NY; (Y); 3/350; Drama Clb; Varsity Clb; Chorus; Mgr Stage Crew; Rep Jr Cls; Pres Sr Cls; Rep Stu Cncl; Var Capt Wrstlng; High Hon Roll; NHS; Centrl Oneida Lg All Str Wrstlng 84; Bst Defnsv Wrstlr 84; Pre-Med.

BAILEY, DAVID A; Mohonasen SR HS; Schenectady, NY; (Y); 10/216; Drama Clb; German Clb; Concert Band; Jazz Band; Mrchg Band; Orch; Pep Band; School Play; Symp Band; NHS; Regents Schlrshp 85; Trustees Schlrshp Clarkson U 85; Clarkson U; Elec Engrng.

BAILEY, ELISABETH A; Keene Central HS; Keene, NY; (S); 1/13; Yrbk Ed-Chief; Pres Frsh Cls; Pres Jr Cls; Pres Sr Cls; JV Cheerleading; High Hon Roll; NHS; Val; VFW Awd; Physics 84; Trigonometry 84; French 84; Cornell U.

BAILEY, FRANK; Clyde Savannah Central HS; Clyde, NY; (Y); Band; Concert Band; Bsktbl; Golf; Hon Roll; Regnts Schlrshp 85; Pres Acadmc Fit Awd 85; Math Awd 85; Upstate Med Ctr; Radlgcl Tech.

BAILEY III, JACK S; Jamesville-De Witt HS; Dewitt, NY; (Y); Church Yth Grp; Orch; Pep Band; High Hon Roll; Model UN; Spanish Clb; Rep Jr Cls; NHS; Schl Spn Awds 83-85; Orch Awd 84 & 85; Fr Awd 84; Africn Asn St 83; Dyplmcy.

BAILEY, JAMES T; Columbia HS; East Greenbush, NY; (Y); Am Leg Boys St; Math Tm; Concert Band; Rep Stu Cncl; Var Capt Ftbl; Var JV Golf; Var Capt Wrstlng; High Hon Roll; NHS; Engrng.

BAILEY, JANE; W C Mepham HS; Bellmore, NY; (Y); Art Clb; Sec Church Yth Grp; Drama Clb; Acpl Chr; Church Choir; Madrigals; School Play; Stage Crew; Yrbk Stf; Off Jr Cls; Natl Sci & Engl Olympd 83; Advrtsg Art.

BAILEY, JOSEPH; Newark SR HS; Newark, NY; (Y); 100/250; Service Clb; Varsity Clb; JV L Bsktbl; Var Capt Ftbl; Var Capt Lcrss; 2nd Tm Finger Lakes All Str Ftbl Tm 84; MVP JV Lacrosse Tm 84; Bst Defnsvmn Vrsty Lacrosse Tm 85; Crmnl Jstc.

BAILEY, KATHRYN; Freeport HS; Freeport, NY; (Y); Pres Church Yth Grp; French Clb; Church Choir; School Musical; Variety Show; Yrbk Stf; Rep Soph Cls; Rep Jr Cls; JV Gym; JV Vllybl.

BAILEY, KAY; Horseheads HS; Erin, NY; (Y); 131/407; Sec Church Yth Grp; Sec Pres 4-H; JCL; Hst Latin Clb; Library Aide; Quiz Bowl; Church Choir; Hon Roll; Hrse Show Awds 81-85; Hippology & Hrse Jdgng Tm Awds 84-85; USAF; Spch Ther.

BAILEY, KELVIN; Newtown HS; Queens Village, NY; (Y); Math Tm; Jr Cls; Capt Socr; Trk.

BAILEY, KEVIN; Huntington Christian HS; Seaford, NY; (Y); 9/22; Church Yth Grp; Varsity Clb; Chorus; Variety Show; Var Bsbl; Var Bsktbl; Var Crs Cntry; Var Socr; Hon Roll; NHS; ORU; Voice Perf.

BAILEY, KIMBERLY A; Lansingburgh HS; Troy, NY; (Y); Cmnty Wkr; JA; Hon Roll; Home Ec Awd 82; Hudson Vly CC; Bus.

BAILEY, MARY; Norwood-Norfolk Central HS; Norfolk, NY; (Y); GAA; JCL; Latin Clb; Band; Concert Band; Mrchg Band; Rep Frsh Cls; Rep Soph Cls; Rep Jr Cls; Rep Stu Cncl.

BAILEY, MARY A; Averill Park HS; W Sand Lk, NY; (Y); Hosp Aide; Ski Clb; Varsity Clb; Nwsp Stf; Var Tennis; JV Var Vllybl; High Hon Roll; NHS; Bus.

BAILEY II, MICHAEL J; Whitesboro SR HS; Whitesboro, NY; (Y); 41/327; Am Leg Boys St; Acpl Chr; Band; Concert Band; Mrchg Band; School Musical; Swing Chorus; Pres Stu Cncl; High Hon Roll; Opt Clb Awd; Genetaska Clb Ctznshp Awd 85; Potsdam Coll; Music Ed.

BAILEY, MICHELLE; Nazareth Acad; Rochester, NY; (Y); French Clb; Varsity Clb; Trk; Hon Roll; Hghst Grd-Amer Hstry; Asian Afrcn Stud Imprvmnt Effrt Awds; Comp Sci.

BAILEY, SHARON M; Clara Barton HS; Brooklyn, NY; (Y); Pres Church Yth Grp; Cmnty Wkr; Hosp Aide; Teachers Aide; VP Chorus; Nwsp Stf; Yrbk Stf; Rep Frsh Cls; Rep Jr Cls; Capt Vllybl; LI U; Med.

BAILEY, SHERRY; Springfield Gardens HS; Laurelton, NY; (Y); 6/443; Math Clb; Math Tm; Off Frsh Cls; Off Jr Cls; Stu Cncl; Tennis; Trk; High Hon Roll; Hon Roll; Jr NHS; NHS; Aerontc Engrng.

BAILEY, TAMMY; Bradford Central HS; Bradford, NY; (S); Church Yth Grp; Band; Chorus; Church Choir; Mrchg Band; Ed Nwsp Stf; Trs Frsh Cls; Trs Soph Cls; Trs Jr Cls; High Hon Roll; Corning CC; Acctng.

BAILEY, TAMMY; Whitney Point HS; Lisle, NY; (S); 11/122; JCL; Sec Latin Clb; High Hon Roll; Hon Roll; Natl Yth Slte 84; Excel Lat I, II & III 84; Acctng.

BAIN, THOMAS C; Ticonderoga HS; Putnam Station, NY; (Y); Church Yth Grp; Chorus; Yrbk Phtg; High Hon Roll; NHS; Regnts Schlrshp NY 85; Flight Safety Intl; Cmmrcl Plot.

BAINS, DAVID F; Gananda Central School District; Macedon, NY; (Y); #1 In Class; Computer Clb; Model UN; Trs Frsh Cls; Trs Soph Cls; Trs Jr Cls; Trs Sr Cls; Rep Stu Cncl; Var Bsktbl; Bausch & Lomb Sci Awd; High Hon Roll; Air Force ROTC Schlrshp 85; NY ST Regents Schlrshp 85; Harvard Bk Awd 84; Aerontcl Engr.

BAIO, HOLLYANNE; Oxford Academy HS; Oxford, NY; (Y); 16/81; FFA; Ski Clb; High Hon Roll; Hon Roll; Pres Schlr; 2nd Bar Acadmc 85; Anna L Mabey Schlrshp 85; Delhi Ag & Tech; Vet.

BAIOCCO, LARA; West Seneca East SR HS; W Seneca, NY; (Y); Church Yth Grp; DECA; GAA; Var JV Sftbl; Var Capt Vllybl; High Hon Roll; JC Awd; Pres Jr NHS; NHS; Stu Cncl; Spnsh Merit Awd 83-84.

BAIR, JAMES; J C Birdlebough HS; Baldwinsville, NY; (Y); 13/180; Trs Church Yth Grp; Latin Clb; Ski Clb; Concert Band; Jazz Band; Mrchg Band; Ftbl; Golf; NHS; Louis Armstrong Jazz Awd; Rochester Inst Of Tech; Mech En.

BAIRD, ANDRE G; Mount Saint Michael Acad; Bronx, NY; (Y); Chess Clb; Computer Clb; Debate Tm; Science Clb; Im Bsktbl; JV Socr; Tennis; Hon Roll; Spanish NHS; NYS Rgnts Schlrshp 85; Fordham U-Bronx NY; Bio.

BAIRD, ANTHONY; Hillcrest HS; New York, NY; (Y); PAVAS; Band; Concert Band; Drm & Bgl; Jazz Band; Mrchg Band; Orch; Crs Cntry; Mth.

BAIRD, DEREK; Greece Athena HS; Rochester, NY; (Y); Drama Clb; Math Tm; Science Clb; Thesps; Chorus; Church Choir; Jazz Band; Madrigals; Symp Band; Rep Frsh Cls; ST U NY Albany; Sec Mth Tchr.

BAIRD, DONALD; Oneonta SR HS; Oneonta, NY; (Y); Church Yth Grp; Key Clb; Spanish Clb; Var Gym; Var Wrstlng; STAC Awd Wrstlng.

BAIRES, ANA; Dominican Commercial HS; Jamaica, NY; (Y); Am Leg Aux Girls St; Nwsp Rptr; NHS; Schlrshp To Dominican Commercial 82-86; Pol Sci.

BAJOR, ROBERT; Christ The King Regional HS; Woodhaven, NY; (Y).

BAK, GREG; Niagara Catholic HS; Niagara Falls, NY; (Y); Church Yth Grp; Cmnty Wkr; French Clb; Office Aide; Fld Hcky; Ftbl; Vllybl; Yth Ldr YMCA 84-86; Knghts Altar Medal Ftbl & Hockey 83-84; Niagara U; Miltry Sci.

BAKER III, ALFRED J; Northport HS; Northport, NY; (Y); English Clb; Ski Clb; Nwsp Rptr; Nwsp Sprt Ed; Yrbk Rptr; Yrbk Sprt Ed; Var Ftbl; Var Wt Lftg; Hon Roll; NHS; SUNY Albany; Engl.

BAKER, AMY; East Aurora HS; West Falls, NY; (Y); 33/182; Church Yth Grp; Pres 4-H; Co-Capt Pep Clb; Varsity Clb; Frsh Cls; Jr Cls; Co-Capt Cheerleading; 4-H Awd; Hon Roll; Outstndng Bus Stu 85; Canisius Clg; Bus Mgmt.

BAKER, BRANDI; Jeffersonville-Youngsville HS; Livingston Manor, NY; (S); 1/60; Chorus; Church Choir; Pres Stu Cncl; Var Socr; High Hon Roll; NHS; Val; VFW Awd; Im Badmtn; Im Bsktbl; Athl Merit Awd 83; Clarkson; Engr.

BAKER, CHRISTINE; Letchworth Central HS; Castile, NY; (Y); Cmnty Wkr; 4-H; Spanish Clb; Band; Color Guard; Concert Band; Mrchg Band; Stage Crew; Yrbk Stf; Off Frsh Cls; Pres Acad Fit Awd 85; Semper Fidelis Awd 85; Alfred Tech; Med Tech.

BAKER, CHRISTINE R; Shenendahowa HS; Round Lake, NY; (Y); Pres Church Yth Grp; Stat Bsktbl; JV Stat Sftbl; High Hon Roll; Hon Roll; Geneseo; Bus Adm.

BAKER, DEAN; Northeastern Clinton Central HS; Champlain, NY; (Y); 12/150; 4-H; Model UN; Var Ice Hcky; Var Socr; Im Vllybl; High Hon Roll; Hon Roll; Arab Bloc Chrmn In UN Cls 83-84; Clarkson U; Elec Engr.

BAKER, ELIZABETH; Watertown HS; Watertown, NY; (Y); 13/321; Chorus; Tennis; Trk; DAR Awd; High Hon Roll; Hon Roll; Jr NHS; NHS; W Walker Mem Schlrshp 85; Ithaca Coll; Comm Hlty.

BAKER, ELLEN; Corning-Painted Post West HS; Coopers Plains, NY; (Y); Pres Church Yth Grp; Band; Church Choir; Concert Band; Jazz Band; Mrchg Band; School Musical; School Play; Capt Bowling; Hon Roll; Corning CC; Mth.

BAKER, GREGORY; Cicero North Syracuse HS; Cicero, NY; (S); 62/622; German Clb; Ski Clb; Off Soph Cls; Off Jr Cls; Bsbl; Diving; Lcrss; Socr; Swmmng; Hon Roll; U MD; Law.

BAKER, JACQUELINE M; Moriah Central Schl; Port Henry, NY; (Y); 3/87; Am Leg Aux Girls St; Drama Clb; Variety Show; Yrbk Stf; Rep Stu Cncl; High Hon Roll; NHS; 1st Rnnr Up JR Ms 84; Hnrbl Dark Shadws Soc 80-85; SUNY Albany.

BAKER, JAMES; Griffith Inst; Collins Center, NY; (Y); Band; Concert Band; Drill Tm; Jazz Band; Mrchg Band; Pep Band; Symp Band; Bsbl; Navy; Nuclr Engr.

BAKER, JIM; Mexico HS; Oswego, NY; (Y); Church Yth Grp; Cmnty Wkr; Band; Concert Band; Jazz Band; Mrchg Band; School Musical; Nwsp Ed-Chief; Nwsp Rptr; Nwsp Stf; Mst Imprvd Drmmr 83-85; Oswego; Engl.

BAKER, JODIE; Mechanicville HS; Mechanicville, NY; (S); 27/104; Pres French Clb; Nwsp Stf; Yrbk Stf; Trs Soph Cls; Trs Jr Cls; Pres Sr Cls; Stu Cncl; Cheerleading; Liberal Arts.

BAKER, JOHN G; Le Roy Central Schl; Le Roy, NY; (Y); 16/114; School Musical; Trs Stu Cncl; Var Socr; Naval ROTC Schlrshp 85; NY St Rgnts Schlrshp 85; Amer Legion Hstry Awd 85; Union Coll; Mgrl Econ.

BAKER, JOYCE; Akron Central Schl; Lockport, NY; (Y); 12/157; Aud/Vis; Chess Clb; Library Aide; Chorus; Orch; School Play; Swing Chorus; Nwsp Stf; Yrbk Phtg; Hon Roll; Niagara Cnty Alt Dairy Princess 84-85; NY ST Regents Schlrshp 85; Bus.

BAKER, K LATONIA; Pittsford Mendon HS; Pittsford, NY; (Y); Civic Clb; JA; Model UN; Var Capt Bsktbl; JV L Socr; Var L Trk; High Hon Roll; Hon Roll; JR Achiev Officer Trng Awd 83-84; Lib Arts.

BAKER, LARA; Schuylerville Central HS; Stillwater, NY; (Y); Church Yth Grp; Drama Clb; 4-H; French Clb; Pep Clb; Chorus; Nwsp Stf; Sec Frsh Cls; VP Soph Cls; Pres Jr Cls; A C C Hartwick; Travel.

BAKER, LEANNE; Williamson Central HS; Williamson, NY; (Y); AFS; Camera Clb; Church Yth Grp; French Clb; Band; Chorus; Concert Band; Mrchg Band; School Musical; School Play; Medcl Fld.

BAKER, MARY; Keveny Memorial Acad; Waterford, NY; (Y); 10/40; JA; Office Aide; Red Cross Aide; Service Clb; Color Guard; Mrchg Band; Variety Show; Dnfth Awd; High Hon Roll; Hon Roll; Ntl Bus Hnr Soc; Schl Sprt Awd; Schl Ldrshp Awd; Peer Cnslng; St Rose; Psych.

BAKER, MARY; The Franciscan Acad; Syracuse, NY; (Y); 3/26; Church Yth Grp; GAA; Hosp Aide; Chorus; School Musical; Sec Soph Cls; Var Sftbl; Var Tennis; High Hon Roll; NHS; Franciscan Scholar 85; Spec Ed.

BAKER, MICHAEL; Forest Hills HS; Forest Hills, NY; (Y); 116/881; Political Wkr; Science Clb; Orch; Hon Roll; US Air Force Acad; Pilot.

BAKER, MICHAEL T; Elmira Free Acad; Elmira, NY; (Y); 20/250; Am Leg Boys St; Church Yth Grp; Cmnty Wkr; Latin Clb; Science Clb; Varsity Clb; School Musical; Variety Show; Rep Frsh Cls; VP Soph Cls; Red Cross Yth Yr 85; Martin M Harngar Awd 85; Hamilton Coll; Pre Med.

BAKER, ROBERT; Coxsackie Athens Central HS; Coxsackie, NY; (Y); 10/104; Church Yth Grp; CAP; Math Tm; Spanish Clb; JV Socr; Var Trk; High Hon Roll; NHS; Frgn Exch Stu Mexico 83-84; Law.

BAKER, ROBERT; Northeastern Clinton Central HS; Alburg Springs, VT; (Y); 4-H; Pres Key Clb; Model UN; Band; Concert Band; Jazz Band; Mrchg Band; Var Socr; High Hon Roll; NHS; Harvard Mod U N 85; Pilot.

BAKER, ROCHELLE; Jamestown HS; Jamestown, NY; (Y); 38/376; Drama Clb; French Clb; Intnl Clb; Trs Acpl Chr; Drill Tm; Pres Yrbk Stf; Hon Roll; Jr NHS; NHS; Rep Frsh Cls; Hazzard/Kent Fund Scholar 85; U Dayton; Lang.

BAKER, RUSS; Tonawanda JR SR HS; Tonawanda, NY; (Y); Spanish Clb; JV Bsktbl; JV Ftbl; Cit Awd; Hon Roll; NHS; Bio Sci.

BAKER, SHARON; Connetquot HS; Bohemia, NY; (Y); 104/808; Spanish Clb; Temple Yth Grp; Mrchg Band; Symp Band; JV Socr; JV Trk; Hon Roll; Math Cont 1st Pl 83; NYSSMA Medals Clarinet & Piano 83-84; SUNY At Stony Brook; Math.

BAKER, STEPHEN B; Salamanca HS; Salamanca, NY; (S); 4/129; French Clb; Varsity Clb; Var L Bsbl; JV Var Bsktbl; Var L Ftbl; Wt Lftg; French Hon Soc; High Hon Roll; NHS; Engr.

BAKER, STEWART; Franklin Academy SR HS; Malone, NY; (Y); DECA; 4-H; Varsity Clb; Acpl Chr; Chorus; Stage Crew; Swing Chorus; Timer; Trk; Vrsty Lttr Trck 85; Bus.

BAKER, SYDNEY; Midwood HS; Brooklyn, NY; (Y); School Musical; Cheerleading; Wt Lftg; Hon Roll; Med Sci Inst 82-86; Med.

BAKER, THOMAS; Attica HS; Attica, NY; (S); 6/150; Boy Scts; Math Tm; Band; Yrbk Stf; VP Sr Cls; Var L Bsktbl; Var L Crs Cntry; Var L Trk; NHS; Church Yth Grp; Natl Cncl Yth Ldrshp 84; USAF Acad; Pilot.

BAKER, TODD; Attica HS; Attica, NY; (S); 1/150; Math Tm; Hon Roll; U Of Buffalo; Math.

BAKER, TOM; Thomas A Edison HS; Elmira Hts, NY; (Y); Am Leg Boys St; French Clb; Varsity Clb; Jr Cls; Sr Cls; Stu Cncl; High Hon Roll; Acad All Amer 85; Bio.

BAKKE, KRISTIN; Mynderse Acad; Seneca Falls, NY; (S); VP Church Yth Grp; Drama Clb; Hosp Aide; Color Guard; Mrchg Band; School Play; Sec Frsh Cls; Rep Stu Cncl; High Hon Roll; Hghst Avg Scl Stds 83; Natl Hnr Roll Yrbk 84; Crmnl Just.

BAKKER, KAREN A; Newburgh Free Academy; Newburgh, NY; (Y); Math Tm; Socr; High Hon Roll; NHS; Spanish NHS.

BAKOWSKI, DARLENE; Mattituck HS; Cutchogue, NY; (Y); 21/118; Dance Clb; German Clb; Variety Show; Yrbk Bus Mgr; Yrbk Stf; Var Co-Capt Bsktbl; JV Var Fld Hcky; JV Var Sftbl; Hon Roll; NHS; 1st Rnr-Up Girls ST Comp 85; Ger Exch Stu 84; Red Crs Blood Drve 84-85; Bus Mgmt.

BAKSH, JAMAL; Jamaica HS; Queens, NY; (Y); Drama Clb; Library Aide; Office Aide; Teachers Aide; Band; Concert Band; School Play; Yrbk Phtg; Vllybl; Wt Lftg; Arista Hnr Soc Awd 82-83; Baruch; Comp Sci.

BALA, GREGORY J; St Francis HS; Lackawanna, NY; (Y); 4/150; Coach Actv; JV Var Ice Hcky; Hon Roll; NHS; U Of Buffalo; Mech Engr.

BALA, ROBERT J; The Loyola Schl; Jackson Heights, NY; (Y); Computer Clb; Drama Clb; Ski Clb; Spanish Clb; School Play; Stage Crew; Variety Show; Nwsp Rptr; Nwsp Stf; Yrbk Stf; NY St Regents Schlrshp 85; Fordham U.

BALACIC, YURI; Msgr Mc Clancy HS; Elmhurst, NY; (Y); Church Yth Grp; Sec Frsh Cls; Im Bsktbl; Im Fld Hcky; Im Ftbl; High Hon Roll; Hon Roll; St Johns; Law.

BALAKRISHNAN, MALINI; Bright HS; Rochester, NY; (Y); 8/320; Exploring; Intnl Clb; Math Tm; Model UN; Sec Spanish Clb; Chorus; Madrigals; Rep Jr Cls; JV Trk; Ntl Merit SF; Ntl Spnsh Cntst Wnnr 81-82; Assn Indians Amer Yth Awd 84; Stu Of Week 84 84; Med.

BALCARCE, IVAN A; The Bronx High School Of Science; New York, NY; (Y); Library Aide; Yrbk Stf; Lit Mag; Natl Hispnic Schlr Awds Pgm Semi-Fin 84-85.

BALCERZAK, BARBARA R; West Valley Central Schl; Machias, NY; (Y); 7/44; Drama Clb; 4-H; Band; Chorus; Concert Band; Jazz Band; Mrchg Band; School Musical; School Play; Variety Show; D Youville Coll; Nrsng.

BALCH, ALLEN; Waterloo SR HS; Waterloo, NY; (Y); Am Leg Boys St; Drama Clb; Model UN; Chorus; School Musical; School Play; Stage Crew; Nwsp Stf; Trk; Hon Roll; Navy; Law Enfrcmnt.

BALCHANDANI, CHETNA G; Forest Hills HS; Rego Park, NY; (Y); 9/881; Dance Clb; English Clb; Nwsp Ed-Chief; Nwsp Rptr; Lit Mag; Jr NHS; NHS; Debate Tm; Intnl Clb; Math Clb; Queens Coll Schlrshp Awd 84; Scntst & Mthmtcn Of Yr 83; Daily News Awd For Ecx & Ex Crclr Actvts 85; Accntng.

BALCHIKONIS, KAREN; Susquehanna Valley HS; Conklin, NY; (Y); Spanish Clb; Drm Mjr(t); Mrchg Band; Orch; Nwsp Stf; Var Capt Bsktbl; Var Fld Hcky; JV Sftbl; Var Trk; Capt Twrlr; Pre-Dntstry.

BALCOM, KIRK; Pulaski JR SR HS; Pulaski, NY; (Y); Church Yth Grp; Cmnty Wkr; Drama Clb; French Clb; Math Clb; Pep Clb; Red Cross Aide; Ski Clb; Varsity Clb; Chorus; Vet Tchnlgy.

BALCOM, RICHARD; West Islip HS; W Islip, NY; (Y); 42/600; High Hon Roll; Hon Roll; SUNY Stony Brook; Elec Engrng.

BALCOMB, SOPHIA; Rhinebeck Centracl HS; Rhinebeck, NY; (Y); AFS; Drama Clb; Varsity Clb; Chorus; School Musical; Ed Yrbk Stf; JV Var Fld Hcky; High Hon Roll; NHS; Bio.

BALDAUF, GERARD; St Agnes Cathedral HS; Merrick, NY; (Y); NHS; NEDT Awd; Cum Laude Mdl 85; Hofstra U Distngshd Schlrs Schlrshp 85; Adelphi U Schlrshp 85; NY ST Regenst Schlrs; Hofstra U Hempstead NY; Acctng.

BALDI, STACY; Walton Central HS; Walton, NY; (Y); AFS; Model UN; Varsity Clb; Color Guard; Sec Frsh Cls; VP Soph Cls; VP Sr Cls; Rep Stu Cncl; Var Tennis; Leaders Clb; Comp Sci.

BALDINO, TRACY A; The Mary Louis Acad; Richmond Hill, NY; (Y); 19/283; Art Clb; Church Yth Grp; Cmnty Wkr; Pep Clb; Chorus; Im Socr; High Hon Roll; Hon Roll; NHS; Pres Schlr; Ntl Hnr Soc Sec 84-85; Catholic U Of America; Bus Adm.

BALDUCCI, ANTHONY T; St Anthonys HS; St James, NY; (Y); 27/201; Camera Clb; Stage Crew; Nwsp Sprt Ed; Yrbk Phtg; Var L Trk; NHS; St Schlr; Hon Roll; Boy Scts; Duns Scotus Awd 83-85; Catholic U Of America; Engr.

BALDUCCI, JEANNINE MARIE; Irvington HS; Irvington, NY; (Y); Library Aide; Chorus; Var Capt Cheerleading; Var Capt Gym; Var Sftbl; JV Var Trk; Hon Roll; Westchester Bus Instute Bus Ed Awd 85; Merit Achvmnt Awd 85; Cobleskill; Bus.

BALDWIN, BETH; Unatego JR SR HS; Unadilla, NY; (Y); 5/88; FHA; Band; Concert Band; Mrchg Band; Pep Band; Yrbk Stf; High Hon Roll; NHS; Poem Accptd Catskill Revw Lit Magzn 85; Coll Of St Rose; Acctg.

BALDWIN, DIXIE LEE; Northville Central Schl; Mayfield, NY; (Y); 1/65; Pres Exploring; Hosp Aide; Ed Yrbk Stf; High Hon Roll; NHS; Hosp Ade 82 & 83; Mth & Sci Regnts Awds 85; Treas Circulus Anagnostarum 84-85; Fulton Montgomery CC; Nrsg.

BALDWIN, GREGORY; Fayetteville-Manius HS; Fayetteville, NY; (Y); Church Yth Grp; Model UN; Variety Show; JV Capt Bsbl; Crs Cntry; JV Var Ftbl; Var Trk; High Hon Roll; NCTE Awd; NHS; Gold Key Art Awd 85; Librl Arts.

BALDWIN, JENNIFER; Alexander Central HS; Darien, NY; (S); Drama Clb; Band; Color Guard; Concert Band; Mrchg Band; Sec Frsh Cls; Sec Soph Cls; Rep Stu Cncl; Hon Roll; Jr NHS.

BALDWIN, KERRY; St Patricks CCHS; Cairo, NY; (Y); Yrbk Phtg; Rep Stu Cncl; Bsktbl; Capt Socr; Sftbl; Drama Clb; Girl Scts; Civic Clb; French Hon Soc; Hon Roll; SUNY Oneonha; Ed.

BALDWIN, KEVIN; Union-Undicott HS; Endicott, NY; (Y); Computer Clb; Mathletes; Ed Lit Mag; High Hon Roll; Hon Roll; Chem Engrng.

BALDWIN, LYNN; Cicero-North Syracuse HS; N Syracuse, NY; (S); 19/711; Girl Scts; Band; Color Guard; Concert Band; Mrchg Band; Trs Stu Cncl; Stat Trk; Hon Roll; NHS; CO ST U; Vet Med.

BALDWIN, MARSHA; Mattituck HS; Mattituck, NY; (Y); 2/120; Spanish Clb; Band; JV Sftbl; High Hon Roll; Hon Roll; Sal; Hghst Avg Spnsh Awd 84; Tchng.

BALDWIN, SUMMERFIELD M; Packer Collegiate Inst; Brooklyn, NY; (Y); 2/37; School Play; Nwsp Rptr; Bsktbl; Hon Roll; Prfct Atten Awd; Gold Mdl NY ST JR Olyp 83; Sprtsprsnshp Awd 83; Parker Schlr Awd 82, 84; Johns Hopkins U; Hist.

BALDYGO, WILLIAM; Rome Free Acad; Rome, NY; (Y); Boy Scts; Ski Clb; Elec Engrng.

BALENTS, LEON M; Honeoye Falls-Lima HS; Honeoye Falls, NY; (Y); Trs Math Clb; Math Tm; Science Clb; Band; High Hon Roll; NHS; Ntl Merit Schol; German Clb; JA; Drill Tm; Second Place CWS Sci Congress 85; Monroe Cnty Math League 85; 2nd Place Overall NYS Acad Decathln 85; Caltech; Physics.

BALFOORT, BARBARA M; Oriskany Central HS; Oriskany, NY; (Y); 12/89; Am Leg Aux Girls St; Cmnty Wkr; GAA; Color Guard; Nwsp Rptr; Var Crs Cntry; Var Trk; Cit Awd; Jr NHS; NHS; Schlrshps-Shomkr Memrl & Ida J Butchr 85-86; Intrvly Leag All Star Trk & Crss Cntry 84-85; Farmingdale ST U; Vet Tech.

BALFOUR, SCOT; Heuvelton Central School Dist; Heuvelton, NY; (S); 2/55; Aud/Vis; Cmnty Wkr; Computer Clb; Library Aide; Concert Band; Jazz Band; Variety Show; Yrbk Stf; Trs Sr Cls; High Hon Roll; Mus Course Crane Potsdam 82; French III, Eng & Algebra Regents Marks 83; Clarkson U Potsdam; Comp Sci.

BALINT, REBECCA; Walter Panas HS; Peekskill, NY; (Y); Pres Drama Clb; Chorus; School Musical; VP Soph Cls; VP Jr Cls; Stu Cncl; Var Vllybl; High Hon Roll; NHS.

BALISTRERI, JIM G; Tamarac HS; Troy, NY; (Y); Drama Clb; Science Clb; Service Clb; Band; Chorus; Mrchg Band; School Musical; Swing Chorus; JV Bsbl; Var Wrstlng; Outstndg Phys Ed Achvt 81-82; Cert Acad Excllnce; Hudson Vly; Phys Ed.

BALK, ALLISON M; F D Roosevelt HS; Brooklyn, NY; (Y); #27 In Class; Sec Church Yth Grp; Office Aide; VICA; Band; Chorus; Church Choir; Jazz Band; Var Gym; NHS; Ntl Merit Ltr; NY U Trustee Schlr 85; NY U.

BALKO, THOMAS M; Hamburg SR HS; Hamburg, NY; (Y); VP Church Yth Grp; German Clb; Concert Band; Orch; Symp Band; L Socr; VP Swmmng; Acadmc All Am 84-85; All Star Socr 84-85; Embry Riddle Aero U; Aerontcl.

BALL, BERNADETTE; St John Baptist District HS; W Islip, NY; (Y); Hosp Aide; Chorus; Variety Show; Nwsp Rptr; Nwsp Stf; Rep Frsh Cls; High Hon Roll; Hon Roll; Molloy Coll; Nrsng.

BALL, MARY; Weedsport Central HS; Weedsport, NY; (Y); 16/90; French Clb; Band; Yrbk Ed-Chief; Yrbk Phtg; Sec Soph Cls; JV Fld Hcky; Var L Trk; High Hon Roll; Hon Roll; NHS; Art Dsgn.

BALL, MICHAEL; Half Hollow Hills High Schl East; Melville, NY; (Y); Leo Clb; Capt Crs Cntry; Trk; High Hon Roll; Pre-Law.

BALL, TERRI; Wilson Central HS; Ransomville, NY; (Y); Red Cross Aide; Ed Yrbk Stf; Sec Frsh Cls; Stat Bsktbl; Var L Fld Hcky; Powder Puff Ftbl; Var L Trk; Var L Vllybl; High Hon Roll; VP NHS; Coachs Trphy Fld Hcky 83; Art.

BALL, TIMOTHY G; West Seneca East Senior HS; Cheektowaga, NY; (Y); 74/385; Church Yth Grp; DECA; Ski Clb; Yrbk Phtg; Hon Roll; German Language Awd 82-83; First Place ST Competition Petroleum Marketing 85; Canisius; Business Admin.

BALL, TOM; Pittsford Sutherland HS; Rochester, NY; (Y); Ski Clb; School Play; Stage Crew; Nwsp Phtg; Yrbk Phtg; Crs Cntry; Trk; Air Force; Math.

BALLA, ANGELIKA; Art And Design HS; New York, NY; (Y); 5/350; NHS; Natl Art Hnr Socty 84-85; NY ST Regnts Schlrshp 85; Brooklyn Coll Frshmn Schlrshp 85; Brooklyn Coll; Pre-Med.

BALLARD, ANITA T; Midwood HS; Brooklyn, NY; (Y); Church Yth Grp; Cmnty Wkr; Dance Clb; Debate Tm; Office Aide; School Play; Lit Mag; NY ST Regnts Schlrshp; Syracuse U; CPA.

BALLARD, DOREEN; Milford Central HS; Milford, NY; (S); 3/30; French Clb; Hosp Aide; Band; Chorus; School Musical; JV Var Cheerleading; Socr; High Hon Roll; Sec NHS; MCS Schlstc Achvt Sci 9 R 83; Pre-Med.

BALLARD, SUSAN M; Holland Patent Central Schl; Barneveld, NY; (Y); 49/195; Cmnty Wkr; Pep Clb; Chorus; School Musical; School Play; Yrbk Rptr; Rep Jr Cls; Rep Sr Cls; Stu Cncl; JV Var Cheerleading; Ntl Cheerldng Athltc Assn-Most Imprvd Dance 83; SUNY-FREDONIA; Spcl Eductn.

BALLARD, TAD; Gilboa-Conesville Central Schl; Gilboa, NY; (S); Boy Scts; Church Yth Grp; 4-H; Band; Mrchg Band; Var Bsbl; JV Bsktbl; High Hon Roll; NHS.

BALLES, LAURA LYNNE; Pittsford Mendon HS; Pittsford, NY; (Y); 1/282; VP Trs Exploring; Model UN; Chorus; Madrigals; School Musical; Yrbk Bus Mgr; NHS; Drama Clb; Latin Clb; Library Aide; Eng,Frnch,Yale Bk Awd 84-85; Lang.

BALLESTER, VIRGINIA; Grand Island SR HS; Gr Island, NY; (Y); Concert Band; Pep Band; School Musical; Hon Roll; Cert Of Achvt 84-85; Med Tech.

BALLESTEROS, GEORGE; Archbishop Molloy HS; Long Is Cty, NY; (Y); 68/409; French Clb; Im Bsktbl; Im Ftbl; Im Score Keeper; Im Sftbl; Hon Roll; Hunter Coll; Med.

BALLINGER, TEENA; Corning Painted Post West HS; Corning, NY; (Y); Church Yth Grp; Computer Clb; Dance Clb; JA; Band; Chorus; Color Guard; School Musical; School Play; Hon Roll; Elmira Coll; Med Secy.

BALLOG, MICHAEL C; Mc Graw Central HS; E Freetown, NY; (Y); 5/65; Boy Scts; Drama Clb; Library Aide; Political Wkr; School Play; Hon Roll; Prfct Atten Awd; NY ST Regnts Schlrshp 85; Hghst Ave Rifl Tm 82-83; ST U Ctr Binghamton; Bio Chem.

BALLOU, ELLEN M; Colton-Pierrepont Central HS; Potsdam, NY; (Y); 1/32; Trs French Clb; Capt Quiz Bowl; Speech Tm; School Play; Variety Show; Yrbk Ed-Chief; Stat JV Bsktbl; Sftbl; NHS; Drama Clb; Stu Of Year 81-82; Natl Sci Olympiad Metal Winnder 81-84; Regents Schlrshp Winner 85; Marist; Communication Arts.

BALLOU, JAMES; Cicero North Syracuse HS; Bridgeport, NY; (S); 103/711; Nwsp Rptr; Ntl Merit SF; Biol.

BALLOU, KELLY; Pioneer Central HS; Arcade, NY; (Y); Cmnty Wkr; Dance Clb; French Clb; FBLA; GAA; Pep Clb; Varsity Clb; School Musical; School Play; Rep Soph Cls; Outstndng Chrlder Awd 85; Parsons; Fshn Coorntn.

BALON, KIM; Forestville Central HS; Forestville, NY; (Y); Quiz Bowl; Radio Clb; Scholastic Bowl; Yrbk Stf; Stat Bsktbl; Stat Ftbl; Mgr(s); High Hon Roll; NHS; Ntl Merit Schol; Outstdng Typst Awd 83; Alfred Ag & Tech; Ct Rprtng.

BALSAM, MICHAEL; Riverdale Country Schl; New York, NY; (Y); Cmnty Wkr; Exploring; Letterman Clb; Q&S; Varsity Clb; Band; Jazz Band; Off Frsh Cls; Var JV Bsbl; Var Ftbl; 4th Pl NY ST Wrstlng 85; 3 Ltr Vrsty Awd Ftbl Wrstlng La Crosse 85; 3 Ltr Vrsty Awd Ftbl Bsbl Wrstlg.

BALSAMO, JOSEPH C; James Madison HS; Brooklyn, NY; (Y); 9/850; Art Clb; Cmnty Wkr; Hosp Aide; Intnl Clb; Mathletes; Math Tm; Chorus; Yrbk Stf; Stu Cncl; Cit Awd; Coney Is Hosp Svc Awd 84; Parish Awd 84; Rgnts Schlrshp 85; SUNY Albany; Pre Med.

BALSAMO, RENEE; Copiague SR HS; Amity Harbor, NY; (Y); 32/350; Art Clb; French Clb; Yrbk Ed-Chief; Sftbl; Hon Roll; Lion Awd; Schl Visual Arts; Media Arts.

BALSHUWEIT, DODI; Odessa Montour HS; Montour Falls, NY; (Y); Drama Clb; FHA; VICA; JV Var Cheerleading; Var Sftbl; High Hon Roll; Hon Roll; Csmtlgy.

BALSTAD, KRISTIN; Pelham HS; Pelham, NY; (Y); AFS; Church Yth Grp; French Clb; Nwsp Stf; Yrbk Stf; Lit Mag; JV Var Fld Hcky; JV L Lcrss; Twrlr; Natl Latin Exam Cum Laude 83; Early Childhd Develpmnt.

BALTAY, MATTHEW C; Horace Greeley HS; Chappaqua, NY; (Y); Ski Clb; JV Var Lcrss; JV Socr; Union Coll; Hstry.

BALTER, KAREN L A; Cathedral HS; Ny, NY; (Y); 5/298; Chess Clb; French Clb; Library Aide; Political Wkr; Speech Tm; Nwsp Rptr; Nwsp Stf; Sftbl; High Hon Roll; Hon Roll; Pol Sci.

BALTIERRA, DAVID; Soesterberg American HS; A P O, NY; (Y); 1/21; Pres Church Yth Grp; School Play; Pres Sr Cls; VP Rep Stu Cncl; Var Capt Socr; NHS; Val; Drama Clb; Nwsp Rptr; Yrbk Phtg; Ntl Hispanc Awds Schlrshp 85; European JR Sci & Humanities Symposm Fnlst 85; Notre Dame Schlr 85.

BALTRUS, TRACI; Our Lady Of Mercy Acad; Sea Cliff, NY; (Y); 16/115; Drama Clb; Stage Crew; Nwsp Rptr; Nwsp Stf; Yrbk Stf; NHS; Ntl Merit Ltr; NEDT Awd; Rensselaer Polytechnic Inst.

BALTZ, STACEY; Long Island Lutheran HS; Massapequa, NY; (S); Dance Clb; Drama Clb; Ski Clb; Chorus; School Musical; School Play; Var Cheerleading; Hon Roll; NHS; RIT; Design.

BALTZER, DAVID A; Watkins Glen Central HS; Watkins Glen, NY; (Y); 31/150; English Clb; French Clb; Q&S; Nwsp Rptr; Nwsp Stf; Hon Roll; NYU ST Regents Schlrshp 85; Corning CC; Jrnlsm.

BALZAN, JAMES; Saugerties HS; Saugerties, NY; (S); 1/250; German Clb; Math Clb; Math Tm; Varsity Clb; Band; Var Capt Bsbl; Var Capt Wrstlng; DAR Awd; High Hon Roll; NHS; Pilot.

BALZANO, SILVIO; Cardinal Spellman HS; Bronx, NY; (Y); Trs Computer Clb; Latin Clb; Pres Bowling; Score Keeper; Hon Roll; NY U Trustee Schlrshp 85; Manhattan Coll Acad Schlrshp 85; Fordham Deans & NY ST Regents Schlrshp; Fordham.

BALZARINI, ANDREA; St Francis Prep; Richmond Hill, NY; (S); 86/760; Ntl Merit Ltr; Opt Clb Awd; Psychlgy.

BAMBERGER, TODD; Yeshiva Univ High Schl For Boys; Bronx, NY; (Y); Boy Scts; Chess Clb; Mgr Bsktbl; Yeshiva U.

BAMBINO, ANNEMARIE; Huntington Christian HS; Massapequa Pk, NY; (S); Church Yth Grp; Chorus; School Play; Pres Jr Cls; Var L Bsktbl; Var L Socr; Sftbl; Hon Roll; Varsity Clb; Mst Imprvd Bsktbl 83; Hnr Guard 84; Messiah; Comm.

BAMBURY, TERESA E; C W Baker HS; Baldwinsville, NY; (Y); 86/441; Key Clb; Ski Clb; Spanish Clb; Yrbk Stf; Off Jr Cls; Off Sr Cls; Trk; Hon Roll; Am Leg, Baldlwnvl Tchrs Assn Schlrshps, Prsdntl Ftnss Awd 85; Biemhardt Coll.

BAMFORD, SUZANNE; Cardinal O Hara HS; Lockport, NY; (Y); Cmnty Wkr; French Clb; JA; Political Wkr; Chorus; School Play; Yrbk Phtg; Yrbk Stf; Rep Frsh Cls; Rep Soph Cls; Corprt Lawyer.

BAN, WANNIE; Bronx H S Of Science; New York, NY; (Y); Pres Church Yth Grp; Cmnty Wkr; Hosp Aide; Pres JA; Yrbk Stf; Rep Jr Cls; Im Vllybl; High Hon Roll; NHS; St Schlr; Svc Awd Medallion 85; Awd Exclnce Phys Ed 85; Pres Acad Ftns Awd 85; U Chicago; Chem.

BANACH, DENISE; Liverpool HS; Liverpool, NY; (S); 57/791; Hon Roll; Jr NHS; NHS; Prfct Atten Awd; Bus Awd; Fd & Nutrtn Awd 82; Rochester Inst; Dietetics.

BANASZEK, ANNAMARIA; Bishop Kearney HS; Brooklyn, NY; (Y); Aud/Vis; Math Tm; NFL; Spanish Clb; Speech Tm; Rep Frsh Cls; High Hon Roll; Hon Roll; Mth Tm Awd 85; Mth.

BANCKS, JENNIFER L; Herbet H Lehman HS; Bronx, NY; (Y); 18/500; Hon Roll; Natl Arista Hnr Soc 84; Rgnts Schlrshp 85; Berkeley Schlrshp 85; Berkeley Bus Instit; Sec.

BANE, BRENDAN M; Mt St Michael HS; Bronx, NY; (S); 64/308; JA; ROTC; Spanish Clb; Im Bsktbl; Im Ftbl; JV Var Ice Hcky; JV Wt Lftg; Hon Roll; Spanish NHS; Fordham U; Law.

BANG, ALLISON; East Meadow HS; East Meadow, NY; (Y); FBLA; Key Clb; Band; Concert Band; Mrchg Band; Var Score Keeper; Stat Socr; JV Sftbl; St Johns U; Bus Mgt.

BANGER, CRAIG; Commack H S North; E Northport, NY; (Y); Boy Scts; Off Jr Cls; Off Sr Cls; Off Stu Cncl; JV Ftbl; Trk; Hon Roll; Arch.

BANISTER, JENNIFER; Sayville HS; Sayville, NY; (Y); Key Clb; JV Vllybl; High Hon Roll; Hon Roll; SUNY; Jrnlsm.

BANK, MARIE E; North Tonawanda HS; N Tonawanda, NY; (Y); 35/470; Hosp Aide; Office Aide; Cit Awd; Hon Roll; Jr NHS; NHS; Pres Schlr; Acadmc Schlrshp-Niagara U 85; Presdntl Awd-Niagara U 85; Budwey Memrl Schlrshp-Zonta Clb 85; Niagara U; Bus Admin.

BANKER, NANCY; Houghton Acad; Plattsburgh, NY; (Y); Church Yth Grp; GAA; Varsity Clb; Chorus; Sec Soph Cls; VP Jr Cls; Stat Var Bsktbl; Var Vllybl; Hon Roll; NHS; Puerto Rico Exhcng Stu 85; Vrsty Sccr 83-85; Houghton Coll; Phy Educ.

BANKOSKE, ROBERT P; St Josephs Collegiate Inst; Williamsville, NY; (Y); 19/202; Ski Clb; Rep Jr Cls; Rep Sr Cls; Stu Cncl; Var Bsbl; Var Golf; Ice Hcky; Hon Roll; VP NHS; 2nd Tm All Catholic Bsbl 85; Merit Brother Pompian Awd Frnch 85; U Notre Dame; Chem Engrng.

BANKS, CHRISTOPHER A; Waterloo SR HS; Waterloo, NY; (Y); Am Leg Boys St; French Clb; JA; Pep Clb; Teachers Aide; Varsity Clb; Rep Frsh Cls; Rep Soph Cls; Rep Jr Cls; Rep Sr Cls; USAF; Aerontcl Engrng Prof.

BANKS, SHERRIL A; Northport HS; E Northport, NY; (Y); 22/585; Pep Clb; Spanish Clb; Yrbk Stf; High Hon Roll; Prfct Atten Awd; Psych.

BANKS, STACY; Eliwhitney Vo Tech; Brooklyn, NY; (Y); Debate Tm; Girl Scts; Office Aide; Church Choir; Bus.

BANKS, YUBERKIS; Yonkers HS; Yonkers, NY; (Y); Art Clb; Church Yth Grp; Dance Clb; French Clb; Latin Clb; PAVAS; Chorus; School Musical; School Play; Stage Crew; Actg.

BANMASSA, RENEE; South Shore HS; Brooklyn, NY; (Y); Orch; Pres Schlr; Rgnts Nrsng Schlrshp 85; Music Svc Awd 85; Hunter Coll; Nrsng.

BANNAN, LISA; Kenmore East Senior HS; Tonawanda, NY; (Y); Sec German Clb; GAA; Girl Scts; Pep Clb; Var Bowling; Var JV Mgr(s); Vllybl; High Hon Roll; Prfct Atten Awd; Score Keeper; Bwlng Sect 3rd Pl 85; Tchng.

BANNISTER, CLEVELAND; Bishop Louglin HS; Brooklyn, NY; (S); Speech Tm; Hon Roll; Hunter U; Elect Engr.

BANNISTER, LANCE; Letchworth Central HS; Gainesville, NY; (Y); 12/83; Varsity Clb; VP Soph Cls; VP Sr Cls; Trs Stu Cncl; Var JV Bsbl; Var JV Socr; Var Wrstlng; Hon Roll; Pres Schlr; Computer Clb; Wrstlng Scholar GCC 85-86; Wrstlg MVP Cnty Tourn Sam Cappadonia Awd 85; Alfred Tech; Chem Tech.

BANYI, SHARON; Sacred Heart Acad; Buffalo, NY; (Y); Latin Clb; Library Aide; Model UN; Quiz Bowl; Cheerleading; Hon Roll; NHS; Amer HC Stu Distngshd; Ecology Clb; NY U Buff; Law.

BAPTISTE, YVONNE; La Salle SR HS; Niagara Falls, NY; (Y); 34/278; Var Capt Cheerleading; Hon Roll; NHS; Pres Acadmc Ftns Awd 85; Syracuse U; Bio.

BARAHAL, HELEN L; Smithtown H S West; Smithtown, NY; (Y); Art Clb; Drama Clb; Thesps; Chorus; School Musical; School Play; Stage Crew; Variety Show; Lit Mag; Var Trk; Regents Schlrshp 85; NY U; Psych.

BARAN, RON; Weedsport Central HS; Auburn, NY; (Y); 20/90; Boy Scts; Intnl Clb; Yrbk Stf; Var Ftbl; Var Trk; Wt Lftg; Hon Roll; Jr NHS; Law Enfrcmnt.

BARANDES, MITCHELL D; James Madison HS; Brooklyn, NY; (Y); 207/809; VP Chess Clb; Math Clb; Math Tm; Temple Yth Grp; NYS Regnts Schlrshp 85; SUNY New Paltz.

BARANKEWICZ, STEPHEN; Bronx High School Of Science; Flushing, NY; (Y); Church Yth Grp; Band; Am Inst Of Aeronautics & Astronautics Chap; Bio.

BARANSKI, GINA; Newburgh Free Academy; Newburgh, NY; (Y); 16/600; Church Yth Grp; Drama Clb; Hosp Aide; Yrbk Stf; High Hon Roll; Htl/Restrnt Mngmnt.

BARBA, JAMES; Nazareth Regional HS; Brooklyn, NY; (Y); Boy Scts; JA; Ski Clb; Varsity Clb; Jazz Band; Stage Crew; Nwsp Rptr; Trk; Hon Roll; Fordham U; Bus.

BARBAGALLO, LORI; Saint Francis Prep; Bayside, NY; (Y); Cmnty Wkr; Hosp Aide; Nwsp Ed-Chief; Nwsp Rptr; Nwsp Sprt Ed; Ed Nwsp Stf; Jr Svc Awd 84; SUNY-GENESEO; Spcl Educ.

BARBAGLIA, SUZANNE; Jordan-Elbridge JR SR HS; Jordan, NY; (Y); Exploring; Hosp Aide; Concert Band; Mrchg Band; School Play; Sec Stu Cncl; Var JV Bsktbl; Var Trk; High Hon Roll; NHS; Carnegie Tutorl Grant 84-85; Most Spirtd Awd 83-84; Stu Cncl Achvt Awd 82-83; Phys Thrpy.

BARBARELLO, MATTHEW P; A G Berner HS; Massapequa Park, NY; (Y); 4/426; Im Bsbl; Im Bsktbl; Im Ftbl; JV Ice Hcky; High Hon Roll; NHS; NYS Rgnts Schlrshp 85; US Coast Guard Acad Proj Aim Prog 84; Hofstra U; Pre-Law.

BARBARINE, NICK J; Sachem North HS; Holbrook, NY; (Y); 170/1500; Varsity Clb; Var JV Bsbl; Hon Roll; NHS; BMX Bicycle Rcng; Little Leag Umpire.

BARBATO, JOHN; Camden Central HS; Taberg, NY; (Y); Im Lcrss; JV Tennis; Biolgy.

BARBATSULY, DENISE; West Hempstead HS; W Hempstead, NY; (Y); Drama Clb; Ski Clb; Band; Drill Tm; Mrchg Band; School Musical; School Play; Var Pom Pon; NHS; Ntl Merit SF; Fnlst-St John Chrysostm Ortrcl Cntst 85; Cornell U; Htl & Rstrnt Mngmt.

BARBEN, LORA LEE; Gerneral Brown HS; Watertown, NY; (Y); 4-H; Pres FHA; Library Aide; Chorus; School Play; Nwsp Rptr; NY ST Pres FHA 84-85; Pbl Rltns.

BARBER, CATHLEEN; Southampton HS; Water Mill, NY; (Y); Debate Tm; Drama Clb; Chorus; Nwsp Phtg; Nwsp Rptr; Yrbk Phtg; Yrbk Stf; High Hon Roll; Hon Roll; Cmnty Wkr; Hghst Engl Avg; Jrnlsm.

BARBER, KEITH; Middletown HS; Middletown, NY; (Y); JV Bsbl; Hon Roll; Pace U; Accntng.

BARBER, KELLY; Irondequoit HS; Rochester, NY; (Y); Church Yth Grp; Ski Clb; Varsity Clb; Band; Concert Band; Mrchg Band; Pep Band; JV Var Socr; Var Trk; Acctng.

BARBER, MALINDA D; Ellicottville Central Schl; Salamanca, NY; (Y); Church Yth Grp; Cmnty Wkr; Chorus; Hon Roll; Vet.

BARBER, SAM; Bishop Grimes HS; Syracuse, NY; (Y); Boys Clb Am; Church Yth Grp; Cmnty Wkr; Dance Clb; Drama Clb; Exploring; FBLA; JA; Political Wkr; Ski Clb.

BARBER, THOMAS; H C Williams HS; Canton, NY; (Y); 15/137; VP Thesps; Band; Concert Band; Jazz Band; Lit Mag; Hon Roll; Ntl Merit SF; Area All ST Bnd 84-85; All-Cnty Jazz Bnd 84-85; Jazz Prfrmr.

BARBER, THOMAS A; Belfast Central Schl; Belfast, NY; (Y); 1/25; Am Leg Boys St; Bausch & Lomb Sci Awd; Cit Awd; High Hon Roll; NHS; Val; Educ Fndtn Schlrshp Alfred ST Coll 85; Rgnts Scshlrshp NYS.

BARBERA, LISA; Central Islip HS; Central Islip, NY; (Y); 8/300; Drama Clb; Office Aide; Chorus; School Musical; School Play; Yrbk Stf; Lit Mag; Rep Soph Cls; Hon Roll; NHS; USDAN Music Schlrshp, Music Tempo Hnry 85.

BARBERA, LISA M; Palmyra-Macedon Central HS; Macedon, NY; (S); 16/205; Math Tm; Chorus; School Musical; School Play; Yrbk Bus Mgr; Yrbk Phtg; Hst Frsh Cls; Hst Soph Cls; Hst NHS; Prfct Atten Awd; All-State Mxd Chrs 84; Math.

BARBERA, STEPHEN; Iona Preparatory HS; New Rochelle, NY; (Y); 30/200; Nwsp Stf; Rep Stu Cncl; Var Bsbl; JV Bsktbl; Var Golf; Var Swmmng; Var Trk; Hon Roll; NHS; Prfct Atten Awd; Bus.

BARBIC, CRAIG; Schoharie Central HS; Schoharie, NY; (Y); 18/80; Varsity Clb; Trs Frsh Cls; Trs Soph Cls; Trs Jr Cls; JV Var Bsktbl; JV Var Socr; Var Capt Tennis; MIP Vrsty Tnns 84; MVP Vrsty Tnns 85; Schoharie Cnty Sngls Champ 85; St Lawrence; Psych.

BARBIERE, CARMELINA VICTORIA; John Dewey HS; Brooklyn, NY; (Y); Church Yth Grp; School Play; Stage Crew; Yrbk Stf; Trk; Hm Ecnmcs Spec Recgntn Awd 84; Busn.

BARBIERO, STEPHANIE C; Notre Dame Acad; Staten Island, NY; (Y); 5/91; Math Clb; Science Clb; Teachers Aide; Yrbk Stf; Jr NHS; NHS; Stevens Inst; Engrng.

BARBOSA, GLORIRMA; James Monroe HS; Bronx, NY; (Y); Dance Clb; Drama Clb; Band; Im Cheerleading; Im Vllybl; Cit Awd; Sci Metals 83; Music Awd 83; Law.

BARBOWSKI, ADAM; Copiague HS; Lindenhurst, NY; (Y); Aud/Vis; Exploring; PAVAS; Variety Show; Hon Roll; Humanties Awd 85; USC; Film.

BARBOWSKI, JAMES; Copiague HS; Lindenhurst, NY; (Y); Aud/Vis; Variety Show; UCLA; Film.

BARBRO, STEVE; Mohonasen HS; Schenectady, NY; (Y); 12/177; French Clb; Key Clb; Band; Concert Band; Jazz Band; Mrchg Band; Pep Band; NHS; Chess Clb; Church Yth Grp; Union Coll; Engr.

BARCLAY, DEBORAH; Kenmore East HS; Tonawanda, NY; (Y); Cmnty Wkr; Drama Clb; Pep Clb; PAVAS; Teachers Aide; Chorus; School Musical; Yrbk Stf; Var Cheerleading; Var Trk; Pep Clb Pres,VP,Treas 83-86; Hugh O Brien Outstndng Stu Ldr 84; Ltr Cnclman Peer Tm 85; Endicott; Comm.

BARCOMB, CINDY; Northern Adirondack Central HS; Altona, NY; (Y); VP 4-H; Band; Concert Band; Mrchg Band; 4-H Awd; Cosmtlgy.

BARCZAK, ANDREA; Amsterdam HS; Amsterdam, NY; (S); 9/362; Concert Band; Trs Stu Cncl; NHS; Mrchg Band; Yrbk Stf; Var Capt Bsktbl; Var Tennis; Var Trk; High Hon Roll; NYSSMA 83; Genetic Engrng.

BARCZEWSKI, RICHARD; George W Fowler HS; Syracuse, NY; (Y); Hon Roll; Presdntl Acadmc Ftnss Awd 85; US Navy.

BARD, CHRISTOPHER; Seaford HS; Seaford, NY; (Y); VP Drama Clb; Capt Math Tm; Concert Band; Drm Mjr(t); Jazz Band; Mrchg Band; Lit Mag; NHS; Scholastic Bowl; Concert Band; SNYSSMA Outstndg Awd Piano 85; Tae Kwon Do Brown Belt; Natl Physics Olympd Awd Dist; MENSA; Physics.

BARD, KERRIAN; Seaford HS; Seaford, NY; (Y); Drama Clb; Math Clb; Chorus; Nwsp Bus Mgr; Lit Mag; JV Socr; High Hon Roll; NHS; Long Isl Yth Orch Prncpl Violinist 84-85; All-ST NY Orch 84; Natl Physics Olympiad Awd Dist 85; Mensa.

BARDEN, CAROLE; Catham Central HS; Chatham, NY; (Y); Chorus; JV Bsktbl; JV Cheerleading; Score Keeper; Var Socr; Var Trk; Columbia Greene; Chem Tech.

BARDEN, JAMES; John S Burke Catholic HS; Middletown, NY; (Y); 18/195; Boy Scts; VP Church Yth Grp; Trk; Hon Roll; NHS; Hnr Roll 83-85; Ntl Hnr Soc 85; Trk 82-85; Engrng.

BARDINELLI, MARA; Fox Lane HS; Bedford, NY; (Y); 28/275; Ski Clb; Spanish Clb; Band; Concert Band; Mrchg Band; Var JV Fld Hcky; JV Capt Lcrss; NHS.

BAREA, JEFFREY SCOTT; Walton HS; Bronx, NY; (Y); Computer Clb; Debate Tm; JA; School Play; Trs Stu Cncl; Coach Actv; Capt Vllybl; Cit Awd; Boy Scts; Drama Clb; James K Warner Hgst Profcny Oratory Awd 85; Un Fed Tchrs Awd Acad Excel 85; Hm Ec Cert 85; City Coll; Engrng.

BARES, KIMBERLY; Susquehanna Valley HS; Conklin, NY; (Y); Drama Clb; Jazz Band; School Musical; Nwsp Sprt Ed; Sec Jr Cls; Rep Stu Cncl; Var Bsktbl; NHS; Band; All-St Bnd Trmbne 85; Psych.

BARFF, MYRNA; Hempstead HS; Hempstead, NY; (S); Church Yth Grp; Library Aide; Nwsp Stf; Vllybl; High Hon Roll; Hon Roll; NHS; Data Processing.

BARGER, CAROL A; Arkport Central Schl; Hornell, NY; (Y); 1/46; Am Leg Aux Girls St; Science Clb; Band; Chorus; Nwsp Rptr; Yrbk Stf; NHS; Ntl Merit Ltr; Val; Yth Of Yr 85; Pres Schlrshp U Pittsburgh 85; Spnsh Awd 84; U Of Pittsburgh Bradford; Wrtr.

BARHITE, LISA; Groton Central HS; Groton, NY; (Y); Am Leg Aux Girls St; VP Stu Cncl; Capt Var Bsktbl; Capt Var Socr; Var L Sftbl; High Hon Roll; Hon Roll; Sec Church Yth Grp; Ski Clb; Spanish Clb; Al-Star Sccr & Sftbl 83-84; Al-Star Sccr & Sftbll 84-85; Prm Crt 85; Math.

BARI, SAMINA; Notre Dame Academy HS; Staten Island, NY; (Y); Cmnty Wkr; Chorus; Yrbk Stf; JV Cheerleading; Untd Hosp Fnd Awd; Richmond Mem Hosp Vlntr Cert Awd & Apprctn 84-85; Natl Frnch Cntst Cert Mrt 83-85.

BARIE, KAREN; Alexander Central HS; E Bethany, NY; (S); Pres Sec Church Yth Grp; Trs Band; Sec Chorus; Mrchg Band; Swing Chorus; Rep Stu Cncl; Socr; Hon Roll; Jr NHS; NHS; All Cnty Band & Chorus 83-85; Western N Y Drft Hrs Qn 85; Solo Fstvls 83-85; Vet.

BARILE, LISA M; Our Lady Of Lourdes; Wappingers Fls, NY; (Y); 11/144; Church Yth Grp; Ed Yrbk Stf; Rep Stu Cncl; Var Capt Bsktbl; Var Capt Crs Cntry; Mgr(s); Var L Trk; Jr NHS; NHS; Our Lady Lourdes 2nd Comp Sci Awd 85; Loyola Coll MD; Comp Sci.

BARILE, ROSARIA; The Mary Louis Acad; Richmond Hill, NY; (Y); Cmnty Wkr; Chorus; Church Choir; School Musical; Nwsp Stf; Hon Roll; NEDT Awd; Nrsng.

BARILEC, MARY; Holland Central HS; Holland, NY; (Y); 14/125; Pres Soph Cls; Var Cheerleading; JV Var Socr; Hon Roll; Lgl Asstnt.

BARILLA, MARIA-LOUISE; Mineola HS; Mineola, NY; (Y); Trs French Clb; Hosp Aide; Key Clb; Mathletes; Teachers Aide; Church Choir; High Hon Roll; NHS; Ntl Merit Ltr; Church Yth Grp; Harvard Prz Bk 85; Cath Daughtrs Of Amer Scholar 82; Pre-Med.

BARILLO, MARY JO; Allegany Central HS; Allegany, NY; (Y); 12/90; Letterman Clb; Varsity Clb; Nwsp Stf; Yrbk Bus Mgr; Yrbk Stf; Rep Soph Cls; Rep Jr Cls; Rep Sr Cls; Rep Stu Cncl; Var Swmmng; Recvr Regnts & Zonta Clb Schlrshps 85; Duquesne U; Gentc Cnslg.

BARISH, SEAN; North Babylon SR HS; North Babylon, NY; (Y); Art Clb; French Hon Soc; High Hon Roll; NY Inst Tech; Film.

BARITEAU, PHILIP H; Hammond Central HS; Hammond, NY; (Y); Aud/Vis; Church Yth Grp; 4-H; French Clb; Office Aide; Band; Chorus; Church Choir; Concert Band; Jazz Band; Arion Awd; All ST Concert Band; Amer Lgn Awd; Ithaca Coll; Music Educ.

BARITEAU, STEVE; Shenendehowa Central Schl; Clifton Pk, NY; (Y); Hon Roll; Auto Tech.

BARKAI, AYELET R; Clarkstown High School North; New City, NY; (Y); Math Clb; Pres Soph Cls; Trs Jr Cls; JV Bsktbl; JV Fld Hcky; JV Socr; JV Sftbl; Hon Roll; Mu Alp Tht; NHS; Engrng.

BARKAN, PAUL A; Southshore HS; New York, NY; (Y); 6/450; Capt Debate Tm; Stage Crew; NHS; Math Tm; Science Clb; Nwsp Rptr; Hon Roll; Prfct Atten Awd; Pre-Law.

BARKER, CAROLYN; Beacon HS; Fishkill, NY; (S); 23/200; French Clb; Office Aide; Yrbk Stf; JV Bsktbl; High Hon Roll; Hon Roll; Jr NHS; French Awd.

BARKER, DALE; Edwards Central HS; Gouverneur, NY; (Y); 13/26; Aud/Vis; Computer Clb; Math Tm; Varsity Clb; Band; Mrchg Band; School Play; Ed Yrbk Stf; Bsbl; Socr; Mst Imprvd Through Sr Yr 85; 4 Yr Band Awd 84; 5 Yr Band Pin 85.

BARKER, ERIC; Kenmore East HS; Tonawanda, NY; (Y); Service Clb; Varsity Clb; Variety Show; Ice Hcky; Hon Roll; NHS; U Of Rochester; Elec Engr.

BARKER, MICHAEL; Kenmore West HS; Buffalo, NY; (Y); Boys Clb Am; Band; Concert Band; Jazz Band; Mrchg Band; Var L Ftbl; Freshmn Mrchng Band Awd 83-84; Citadel Of NC; Comp Sci.

BARKER, SHERI M; Half Hollow Hills High School East; Dix Hills, NY; (Y); 10/566; Mathletes; Orch; Office Aide; Symp Band; High Hon Roll; NHS; Ntl Merit Ltr; Spanish NHS; Grumman Schlr 85; Westnghse Hnrs Grp 85; Natl Conf Synag Yth Yr 85; Columbia U; Engrng.

BARKER, SUSAN; West Irondequoit HS; Rochester, NY; (Y); 68/321; Latin Clb; Varsity Clb; Chorus; Yrbk Stf; Rep Frsh Cls; Rep Stu Cncl; Var L Tennis; JV Vllybl; Hon Roll; NHS; U Of Rochester; Educ.

BARKER, WENDY M; Scotia-Glenville HS; Scotia, NY; (Y); Key Clb; Varsity Clb; Var L Socr; Var L Trk; Var L Vllybl; Hon Roll; Acctng.

BARKEVICH, DIANE; Bishop Scully HS; Amsterdam, NY; (S); 10/75; Drama Clb; Red Cross Aide; Varsity Clb; School Play; Bowling; VP Cheerleading; High Hon Roll; NHS; Bus.

BARKHUFF, STEPHEN E; F D Roosevelt HS; Staatsburg, NY; (Y); 16/325; Boy Scts; Math Tm; Ski Clb; Band; Jazz Band; Mrchg Band; Var Golf; Var Tennis; Pres NHS; NY ST Rgnts Schlrshp 85; Eng.

BARKIDJIJA, CHRISTOPHER; Archbishop Molloy HS; Richmond Hill, NY; (Y); 1/361; Yrbk Rptr; JV Bsktbl; Var L Socr; Var L Trk; Pres NHS; Ntl Merit Ltr; Val; Yng Achvr Of Yr 85; Newsday Ldng Schlstc Achvr 85; Tablet All Schlstc Tm 85; Wesleyan U; Poltc Sci.

BARKLEY, JAMES; Archbishop Stepinac HS; Pleasantville, NY; (Y); 13/201; Computer Clb; Yrbk Sprt Ed; Var Capt Tennis; High Hon Roll; Jr NHS; NHS; Awds In Tennis 85.

BARKMAN, PETER; Ossining HS; Ossining, NY; (Y); Chess Clb; Jazz Band; Mrchg Band; Variety Show; Lit Mag; High Hon Roll; Hon Roll; NY ST HS Chess Chmpn 85; 2nd Pl CT ST Open Chess Trnmnt 85.

BARKSDALE, LAURA; Maria Regina HS; New Rochelle, NY; (Y); Hosp Aide; JV Bsktbl; Awd Apprctn Homerm Asst 84-85; St Johns U; Phrmcy.

BARKUN, DEBBI S; Jamesville-Dewitt HS; Dewitt, NY; (Y); 82/225; Exploring; Temple Yth Grp; Sec Chorus; Concert Band; Madrigals; School Musical; School Play; Hon Roll; Hnrb Mntn Visual Arts 85; MONY Schlstc Art Awds 84-85; Visual Arts.

BARLEBEN, JON; Irondequit HS; Rochester, NY; (Y); 100/398; Aud/Vis; Church Yth Grp; Exploring; Var L Bsbl; Im Bsktbl; JV Socr; Ntl Merit Ltr; Hnr Rl; Eng.

BARLOW, DARREN; John Jay HS; Hopewell Junction, NY; (Y); English Clb; French Clb; Varsity Clb; Band; Concert Band; Bsktbl; Socr; Hon Roll; Hofstra.

BARNARD, SHAWN; Canisteo Central HS; Canisteo, NY; (Y); 12/82; Exploring; Model UN; Band; Chorus; Cit Awd; Hon Roll; NHS; Regnts Schlrshp 85; Delhi; Anml Husbndry.

BARNAS, LAURA; Buffalo Traditional HS; Buffalo, NY; (S); 18/118; Art Clb; Church Yth Grp; Drama Clb; Hosp Aide; Church Choir; Stu Cncl; Swmmng; Hon Roll; Sisters Of Charity Hosp; Nrsng.

BARNER, VICTORIA; Twin Turn Baptist HS; Corning, NY; (Y); Camera Clb; Chess Clb; Church Yth Grp; Computer Clb; Drama Clb; Hosp Aide; Chorus; Church Choir; School Play; Hon Roll; Assoc Music Awd 81; Liberty Baptist U.

BARNES, CHRISTINE; Fashion Industries HS; Brooklyn, NY; (Y); Church Yth Grp; Dance Clb; Teachers Aide; Band; Church Choir; School Play; Yrbk Stf; Im Bowling; Music, Soc Stud, Art, & Attd Awds 80-82; Merit Cert 82; Spellmon U; Chld Soclgy.

BARNES, COLLIN; Half Hollow High East; Dix Hills, NY; (Y); Computer Clb; Chorus; Nwsp Stf; Trk; Med.

BARNES, DAWN; Narrowsburg Central HS; Narrowsburg, NY; (Y); 1/24; Pres Church Yth Grp; Band; Chorus; School Musical; Trs Frsh Cls; Trs Soph Cls; Trs Jr Cls; Trs Sr Cls; Var Capt Bsktbl; Var L Sftbl; Greenville Coll; Math.

BARNES, DERRYALE D; Norman Thomas HS; New York, NY; (S); 2/671; JA; Band; Church Choir; School Musical; High Hon Roll; NHS; Prfct Atten Awd; NY U Trustee Schlrshp 85; Untd Fedrtn Of Tchrs Schlrshp 85; Cert Of Profcncy Stenogrphy 85; NY U Schl Of Arts; TV.

BARNES JR, GARRY E; Marlboro HS; Marlboro, NY; (Y); Trk; Wrstlng; Hon Roll; Schl Vis Arts; Animatn.

BARNES, HOLLY; Ticonderoga HS; Ticonderoga, NY; (Y); Church Yth Grp; Drama Clb; Hosp Aide; Chorus; Color Guard; School Play; Rep Soph Cls; Hosp Aide Over 200 Hrs 82-83; Socl Wrkr.

BARNES, JOSEPH H; Roy C Ketcham HS; Poughkeepsie, NY; (Y); Math Clb; Ski Clb; Concert Band; Jazz Band; Yrbk Stf; Rep Jr Cls; Var Capt Bsktbl; High Hon Roll; Hon Roll; Jr NHS; Duke U; Comp Sytms Anlyst.

BARNES, JULIE; Chester HS; Chester, NY; (Y); GAA; Varsity Clb; Var Capt Bsktbl; Var L Socr; Var L Sftbl; High Hon Roll; Hon Roll; NHS; Voice Dem Awd; 1st Team All-Star Sccr 84; Athltc Trng.

BARNES, KENNETH; Oppenheim Ephrathan Central HS; Dolgeville, NY; (S); 3/25; Am Leg Boys St; Band; Color Guard; Jazz Band; Mrchg Band; Nwsp Ed-Chief; Nwsp Sprt Ed; Yrbk Bus Mgr; Roberts Wesleyan; Music.

BARNES, KIMLEE; Ballston Spa HS; Ballston Spa, NY; (Y); 4-H; Varsity Clb; Orch; Off Frsh Cls; Bsktbl; Fld Hcky; Trk; High Hon Roll; Hon Roll; Presdntl Ftnss Awd 85; Spnsh Excllnc Frgn Lang Awd 84; Rochester Inst Tech; Hotl Tech.

BARNES, MELANIE; St Gabriel HS; New Rochelle, NY; (Y); Church Yth Grp; Civic Clb; Dance Clb; Hosp Aide; Office Aide; Spanish Clb; Chorus; Church Choir; School Musical; School Play; Albany ST NY; Law.

BARNES, MELISSA; Bishop Loughlin HS; Brooklyn, NY; (S); 4/254; Church Yth Grp; Girl Scts; Science Clb; Band; Vllybl; High Hon Roll; NHS; Prfct Atten Awd; PYSCH.

BARNES, MICHELLE A; Bay Shore HS; Bay Shore, NY; (Y); 28/358; Church Yth Grp; Cmnty Wkr; Mathletes; Math Tm; Frsh Cls; Soph Cls; Jr Cls; Rep Stu Cncl; Capt Cheerleading; NHS; NY ST Regents Schlrshp 85; Boston U; Bio-Chem.

BARNES, PRISCILLA; Minisink Valley HS; Howells, NY; (Y); Sec Key Clb; Drill Tm; Flag Corp; Mrchg Band; JV Var Vllybl; Hon Roll; OCIAA Athl Awd Vlybl 85; V M Ltr 85; 5 Band Front Pins Hnr 82-84; OCCC; Art.

BARNES, RUSSELL; Lackawanna HS; Lackawanna, NY; (Y); 28/275; Var L Bsktbl; High Hon Roll; Hon Roll; Al-Conf Bsktbl 85; All-Western NY 2nd Tm Bsktbl 85; MVP Of Yr JV Tm 82; Engrng.

BARNES, STEVEN B; Schalmont HS; Schenectady, NY; (Y); Camera Clb; VP Drama Clb; Quiz Bowl; Ski Clb; Acpl Chr; Band; Chorus; Church Choir; Concert Band; Mrchg Band; Outstndng Achvt Frnch Awd 85; Pre Med.

BARNES, SUSAN; Notre Dame HS; Clay, NY; (Y); ROTC; Color Guard; Drill Tm; Nwsp Stf; Yrbk Stf; Var Socr; Var Sftbl; High Hon Roll; Debate Tm; Drama Clb; Top Gun Awd 84-85; Capt Cup; Onondaga CC; Acctg.

BARNES, TRACY; Coxsackie Athens Central HS; Athens, NY; (Y); Am Leg Aux Girls St; Red Cross Aide; Spanish Clb; Band; Pep Band; Rep Stu Cncl; Var L Socr; Var L Sftbl; High Hon Roll; NHS; Mrt Awd From Hnr Soc 83; All-Cnty Concert Bnd 83-85; NYSMA Solo Comp 82-85; Pol Sci.

BARNES, VEDA D; Poughkeepsie HS; Poughkeepsie, NY; (Y); Math Tm; Jazz Band; Yrbk Stf; Var L Socr; Var L Vllybl; Church Yth Grp; Cmnty Wkr; Drama Clb; Radio Clb; Band; Natl Achvt Outstndng Negro Stu; Awd Outstndng Perf Coast Grd 85; Acad Eng Minorty Stu 84; Eng.

BARNETT, PIETER; Onteora HS; Woodstock, NY; (S); 16/235; Art Clb; Cmnty Wkr; Teachers Aide; Acpl Chr; Chorus; School Musical; School Play; Crs Cntry; Trk; High Hon Roll; Seascope Marn Bio Rsrch In RI 84; Unltd Paramtrs Indep Rsrch Thesis Music Socty 83; Med.

BARNETT JR, WILLIAM; Northville Central HS; Mayfield, NY; (Y); 3/34; Am Leg Boys St; Library Aide; Varsity Clb; Yrbk Stf; Rep Stu Cncl; Var Bsktbl; Ftbl; L Trk; Hon Roll; NHS; Med.

BARNEY, HILDA; Franklin Acad; N Bangor, NY; (Y); Hon Roll.

BARNEY, MAUREEN; Our Lady Of Mercy HS; Penfield, NY; (Y); Model UN; Ed Yrbk Stf; Rep Stu Cncl; Im Bsktbl; Im Sftbl; High Hon Roll; Hon Roll; Merit Rll 82-85; Our Lady Of Mercy Engl Awd 84-85; NY ST Sci Sprvsrs Assn Chem Awd 84-85.

BARNHART, KIMBERLY; Tioga Central HS; Barton, NY; (S); Ski Clb; JV Capt Cheerleading; JV Mgr(s); JV Sftbl; Hon Roll; NHS; Phys Thrpst.

BARNHART, KIMBERLY; Valley Central HS; Walden, NY; (Y); 59/350; Church Yth Grp; Sec Trs 4-H; Office Aide; Service Clb; Church Choir; Rep Jr Cls; Im Gym; 4-H Awd; God Cntry Awd; Hon Roll; Natural Rsrcs Sci Awd 83; Pres Phys Fitness Awd 81&82; Marist U; Bus Admin.

BARNI, NEIL A; Mahopac HS; Mahopac, NY; (Y); 25/400; Am Leg Boys St; Math Tm; Jazz Band; Mrchg Band; Swing Chorus; Nwsp Stf; Off Jr Cls; Stu Cncl; JV Ftbl; Var Golf; U Of Pittsburgh; Bus.

BARNIAK, BECKY; Lowville Academy Central; Turin, NY; (Y); 5/120; Spanish Clb; Chorus; Church Choir; School Musical; Rep Frsh Cls; JV Var Cheerleading; Swmmng; High Hon Roll; Hon Roll; NHS; Regents Schlrshp 84; Capt Elizabeth Bush Schlrshp 85; Presdntl Acadmc Ftnss Awd 85; Albany Coll Phar; Pharmcy.

BARNICKEL, NORA; St Peters High School For Girls; Staten Isl, NY; (Y); Math Clb; JV Var Cheerleading; Hon Roll; Prfct Atten Awd.

BARNNART, KIMBERLY; Tioga Central HS; Barton, NY; (Y); 16/90; Ski Clb; Var Capt Cheerleading; JV Mgr(s); Var JV Sftbl; Hon Roll; NHS; Chrldng Awd 84-85; Mst Outstndng Chrldr Awd 84-85; Phy Thrpy.

BARNOSKI, ALEXA A; Amsterdam HS; Amsterdam, NY; (Y); 7/330; Varsity Clb; Concert Band; Drm Mjr(t); Jazz Band; Mrchg Band; Swmmng; Trk; NHS; Ntl Merit SF; Band; PHI THETA KAPPA Natl Hnr Soc 85; U RI; Zoology.

BARNUM, ANDRA; Medina SR HS; Medina, NY; (Y); AFS; VICA; Acpl Chr; School Musical; Pres Frsh Cls; Rep Stu Cncl; Var Capt Cheerleading; Var Capt Mat Maids; JV Var Pom Pon; Prfct Atten Awd; Csmtlgst.

BARNUM, DOUG; Fairport HS; Fairport, NY; (Y); Computer Clb; Capt Math Tm; Concert Band; Mrchg Band; Orch; High Hon Roll; NHS; Amer HS Math Exm Hnr Rll 85; Physics.

BARNWELL, MICHELE R; Notre Dame Schl; New York, NY; (Y); Hosp Aide; Teachers Aide; Yrbk Phtg; Var Cheerleading; 1st & 2nd Academic Hnrs; Schlrshp NY Schl Of Ballet 82; Classical Ballet.

BAROCAS, JUSTIN; Xavier HS; Hoboken, NJ; (Y); Computer Clb; Letterman Clb; Thesps; Bsbl; Coach Actv; Mgr(s); Score Keeper; UCLA; Comp Sci.

BAROLO, MATTHEW; Niskayuna HS; Niskayuna, NY; (Y); AFS; Boy Scts; Cmnty Wkr; Drama Clb; Pep Clb; Red Cross Aide; Pres Service Clb; Ski Clb; Chorus; School Play; Delg Italy Pres Yth Exc 85; Red Cross Yth Rep Ntl Conv 85; Cornell U; Hotel Mgmt.

BARON, AMY; York Central HS; York, NY; (Y); AFS; Key Clb; Office Aide; Var Cheerleading; Var Mgr(s); Var Score Keeper; Stat Sftbl; JV Vllybl; Hon Roll; Pediatric Nrs.

BARON II, JAIME; Smithtown H S East; St James, NY; (Y); Nwsp Rptr; Crs Cntry; Hon Roll; SUNY Stony Brook; Engrng.

BARON, JOELLE; Lockport SR HS; Lockport, NY; (Y); Drama Clb; Intnl Clb; Ski Clb; Rep Frsh Cls; Swmmng; St John Fisher; Brdcstng.

BARON, LISA; Riverside HS; Buffalo, NY; (S); #15 In Class; Key Clb; Rep Stu Cncl; High Hon Roll; Hon Roll; Pre-Law.

BARON, MARY; Mohawk Central Schl; Mohawk, NY; (Y); 1/100; French Clb; Spanish Clb; Varsity Clb; Mrchg Band; Yrbk Stf; Var JV Bsktbl; Var JV Fld Hcky; High Hon Roll; NHS; Model UN; Rensselaer Plytechnc Inst Math & Sci Awd; Acadmc M Awd Mohawk; MIP Vrsty Bsktbl.

BARON III, PAUL; York Central HS; York, NY; (Y); 7/65; Math Tm; Ski Clb; Var L Bsbl; Var Capt Ftbl; Var L Trk; Var Capt Wrstlng; NHS; Pres Schlr; NY Rgts Schlrshp 85; Agri Schlrshp Awd 85; Ftbl Schlrshp Awd 85; SUNY Geneseo; Forestry.

BARONE, AMY; Batavia Ssr HS; Batavia, NY; (Y); Ski Clb; Color Guard; Concert Band; Mrchg Band; Yrbk Bus Mgr; Yrbk Stf; VP Soph Cls; Stat Bsbl; Stat Bsktbl; Var Capt Cheerleading; Spanish Hnrs 83; Hnr Cert 83; Comm.

BARONE, CARLA; Cardinal Mooney HS; Rochester, NY; (Y); VP Exploring; Sec Girl Scts; Hon Roll; Nrsng.

BARONE, FRANCES; Bishop Kenney HS; Brooklyn, NY; (S); Art Clb; Chorus; Yrbk Rptr; Yrbk Stf; NHS; NY U; Pre-Med.

BARONE, LINDA; Carmel HS; Carmel, NY; (Y); High Hon Roll; Hon Roll; Chem.

BARONE, LISA; St Vincent Ferrer HS; New York, NY; (S); 10/103; Art Clb; Church Yth Grp; Girl Scts; Library Aide; Q&S; Science Clb; Chorus; Nwsp Ed-Chief; Nwsp Rptr; Nwsp Stf; Regnts Schlrshp 85; Iona Coll; Psychlgst.

BARONE, LISA; West Genesee SR HS; Camillus, NY; (Y); Concert Band; Mrchg Band; Yrbk Stf; High Hon Roll; Hon Roll; Secndry Ed.

BARONE, MARIA; Bishop Kearney HS; Brooklyn, NY; (Y); 1st Hnrs 83; 2nd Hnrs 84; Phrmcst.

BARONE, MICHAEL; Auburn HS; Auburn, NY; (Y); Boy Scts; School Play; Im Ftbl; JV Trk; Civitan Awd 82; Chem Engrng.

BAROULETTE, LORNA; Dominican Commercial HS; Queens Vlge, NY; (Y); Church Yth Grp; Hosp Aide; Chorus; Church Choir; Hon Roll; Jr NHS; Princpls Lst 83-85; Nrsng.

BAROUS, MARIA; St Johns Prep HS; Astoria, NY; (Y); Church Yth Grp; Cmnty Wkr; Rep Frsh Cls; Rep Stu Cncl; High Hon Roll; NHS; Prfct Atten Awd; St Johns Prep 1st Hnrs Acad Awd 85; St Johns U Acad Grnt 85; St Johns U; Jrnlsm.

BARPEY, MITCHELL; Mamarcheck HS; Larchmont, NY; (Y); 29/380; French Clb; Ski Clb; Spanish Clb; Var L Swmmng; NHS; Spanish NHS; Tufts U; Engrng.

BARR, BEVERLY; Mt Mercy HS; W Seneca, NY; (S); 19/199; JA; JCL; Latin Clb; Math Clb; Model UN; Chorus; Nwsp Stf; Hon Roll; NHS.

BARR, KIMBERLY; Miagara Falls HS; Niagara Falls, NY; (Y); Key Clb; Office Aide; Red Cross Aide; Teachers Aide; Rep Frsh Cls; Rep Soph Cls; Rep Jr Cls; Var Sftbl; JV Swmmng; French Hon Soc; Frnch Cert Merit 1st, 3rd & 8th Pl Wstrn NY 82-84; U Of AZ Tucson; Wldlf Prsrvtn.

BARR, LEWIS; Corning Painted Post West HS; Coopers Plains, NY; (Y); Boy Scts; Key Clb; Letterman Clb; Varsity Clb; JV Var Bsbl; JV Var Crs Cntry; Hon Roll; Hnr Camper Outstndng Boy Scout Camp 82; Awd Eagle Scout Bdg 85; Crnml Justc.

BARR, LISA; Camden HS; Camden, NY; (Y); Pep Clb; Varsity Clb; Rep Jr Cls; Trs Rep Stu Cncl; Stat Bsktbl; JV Cheerleading; Score Keeper; JV Var Sftbl; High Hon Roll; Prfct Atten Awd; MVCC; Mth.

BARRA, RITA T; The Mary Louis Acad; Bayside, NY; (Y); 16/283; French Clb; Hosp Aide; Library Aide; Stage Crew; Lit Mag; French Hon Soc; High Hon Roll; NHS; Pres Schlr; Manhattanville Coll; Bus.

BARRACATO, NICHOLAS; New Dorp HS; Staten Island, NY; (Y); Wnet 7th Annual Stu Art Fstvl 85; Mortician.

BARRACO, LIDIA; Stella Maris HS; Howard Beach, NY; (Y); 4/206; Church Yth Grp; Cmnty Wkr; Math Clb; Math Tm; Political Wkr; Teachers Aide; Yrbk Stf; Var Bowling; Cit Awd; High Hon Roll; Cath HS Math League Awd 84-85; Ntl Hnr Society 84-85; St Johns U; Comp Pgm.

BARRESI III, ANTHONY V; Hendrick Hudson HS; Croton, NY; (Y); Cmnty Wkr; Computer Clb; Spanish Clb; VP Stu Cncl; High Hon Roll; Hon Roll; Bus Admin.

BARRETO, CARMEN I; Cardinal Spellman HS; Bronx, NY; (Y); 25/536; Dance Clb; French Clb; Hon Roll; Trustee Schlrshp From Pace U 85; Regents Schlrshp 85; Pace U; Pub Accntnt.

BARRETO, ISRAEL; Aviation HS; Bronx, NY; (Y); 92/508; Trs Church Yth Grp; Church Choir; Nwsp Rptr; Ed Nwsp Stf; Rep Sr Cls; NYS Regents Schlrshp 85; Bernard M Baroch; Lib Arts.

BARRETT, CHERRIE; Mynderse Academy; Seneca Falls, NY; (Y); GAA; Girl Scts; Red Cross Aide; Coach Actv; JV Capt Socr; Sftbl; Bsktbl; Cheerleading; Trk; Vllybl; Mst Imprvd Soccr Awd; All Trnmnt Tm Bsktbl Awd; Bus.

BARRETT, COURTNEY; Lansingburgh HS; Troy, NY; (Y); Church Yth Grp; French Clb; Varsity Clb; Band; Chorus; Nwsp Stf; L Var Cheerleading; Var L Sftbl; High Hon Roll; Jr NHS; Elem Educ.

BARRETT, DANELLE; Frontier Central HS; Hamburg, NY; (Y); 98/500; VP Sec Drama Clb; Varsity Clb; School Musical; School Play; Stage Crew; Capt Var Tennis; NHS; Prfct Atten Awd; Thesps; Chorus; Sons & Dughtrs Of Teachrs Schlrshp 85; Coaches Awd & Sprtsmnshp Awd 84; Outstndng Contrbtn Actress Awd; Boston U; Theatre.

BARRETT, ELIZABETH; Bishop Kearney HS; Brooklyn, NY; (Y); Church Yth Grp; Girl Scts; JA; Political Wkr; Spanish Clb; Sec Chorus; Hon Roll; Church Choir; Girl Sct Merit Awd 10 Yrs Svc 85; JA Blue Chip Co 83; Acctg.

BARRETT, ROBERT C; Livonia HS; Livonia, NY; (Y); 2/130; Nwsp Ed-Chief; Var Socr; Var Trk; Jr NHS; NHS; Rgnts Schlrshp Awd 85; SUNY Oswego; Frgn Lang.

BARRETT, SUE; Skaneateles HS; Skaneateles, NY; (S); Tennis; High Hon Roll; Hon Roll; Jr NHS; Capt JV Bsktbl; Powder Puff Ftbl; Trk.

BARRIGAR, BETH; Odessa-Montour Central HS; Odessa, NY; (Y); Church Yth Grp; Teachers Aide; VP Chorus; Church Choir; School Musical; Swing Chorus; Variety Show; Lit Mag; High Hon Roll; Most Outstndng Choral Stu 84-85; Chorus Pianst 82-85; Elmira Hair Ciare Ctr; Cosmtlgy.

BARRON, SHEILA M; Shaker HS; Loudonville, NY; (Y); Chess Clb; Pres German Clb; Library Aide; Ski Clb; Chorus; Hon Roll; Ntl Merit SF; Sierra Clb Vlntr, Alid Rain Campgn 84; Foreign Svc.

BARROSO, TANIA; St Gabriel HS; Mt Vernon, NY; (Y); 16/61; Camera Clb; Drama Clb; Sftbl; Hon Roll; Wnnr Engl Comptn Cntst 83; 3 Time Certfd Wnnr Hstry Olympd 82-85; Iona Coll; Intrntl Bus.

BARROW, ARLETTE; Brooklyn Technical HS; Brooklyn, NY; (Y); Exploring; Office Aide; Color Guard; Yrbk Stf; Rep Sr Cls; Hon Roll; Rensselaer Polytech Inst 85; Organic Chem Awd 85; Yrbk Staff Awd 85; Rensselaer Polytech Inst; Biomd.

BARROW, JOSETTE; Preston HS; Bronx, NY; (Y); Hosp Aide; Im Bsktbl; Im Socr; Im Sftbl; Im Vllybl; Hon Roll; Prfct Atten Awd; Natl Hnr Socty Aux Membr 85; Acctg.

BARROWS, MICHELLE; Cathedral HS; Ny, NY; (Y); 97/298; JA; Library Aide; Ski Clb; Yrbk Stf; Cheerleading.

BARROWS, SEAN; Oxford Academy And Central HS; Oxford, NY; (Y); Church Yth Grp; VP Pres 4-H; VP FFA; Church Choir; 4-H Awd; Kiwanis Awd; FFA Empire Degree 85; SUNY Morrisville; Excavator.

BARRY, CAROLYN; Victor SR HS; Victor, NY; (Y); RBI; Bus.

BARRY, CHRISTINE J; Holy Trinity HS; Levittown, NY; (S); Teachers Aide; Stage Crew; Bowling; High Hon Roll; Hon Roll; NHS; Mth Awd 84; Iona.

BARRY, COLEEN; Southampton HS; Blue Point, NY; (Y); Cmnty Wkr; Dance Clb; Chorus; School Musical; School Play; Stage Crew; Variety Show; Bus Adm.

BARRY, CYNTHIA; Victor Central HS; Victor, NY; (S); 30/207; Ski Clb; Varsity Clb; Acpl Chr; Band; Chorus; Madrigals; School Musical; School Play; Var Tennis; NHS; NYS Regents Schlrshp 85; NYSSMA All-ST Mixed Choir 84; Clarkson; Engr.

BARRY, JOHN; Marlboro HS; Marlboro, NY; (Y); 10/120; High Hon Roll; NHS; Mechncl Engr.

BARRY, MARJORIE; Lake Placid Central HS; Lake Placid, NY; (Y); AFS; Trs Drama Clb; Chorus; Yrbk Ed-Chief; Rep Stu Cncl; Cheerleading; Socr; Trk; Vllybl; Hon Roll; North Country CC; Bus Mgmt.

BARRY, NORA; Mary Louis Acad; Floral Park, NY; (Y); 8/283; Pep Clb; Nwsp Stf; Pres VP Stu Cncl; Bowling; Score Keeper; Gov Hon Prg Awd; High Hon Roll; Hon Roll; NHS; Ntl Merit Ltr; Governors Citation 85; Newsday High Scholastic Achievement 85; Boston College.

BARRY, REBECCA; Lansing HS; Groton, NY; (Y); 5/90; Pres French Clb; School Musical; Nwsp Rptr; Powder Puff Ftbl; Score Keeper; Swmmng; Timer; High Hon Roll; VP NHS; Natl Fr Cont 2nd & 3rd Pl Regnl 85; Natl Fr Cont 1st Pl Schl 83-85; MIP Swmmr 84; Acad Eng Awd 84; Theatr.

BARSKY, VICTORIA; F D Roosevelt HS; Brooklyn, NY; (Y); 40/720; Pres Chess Clb; Cmnty Wkr; Intnl Clb; Science Clb; Chorus; School Musical; School Play; Ed Lit Mag; Gov Hon Prg Awd; Hon Roll; Cncllrs Rl Hnr, Cert Apprectn 84; Cert Distnctn 84-85; Med.

BARSOUM, SUZETTE; Columbia HS; Rensselaer, NY; (Y); Yrbk Stf; Score Keeper; Socr; Vllybl; High Hon Roll.

BARSTOW, BRIAN R; Massena Central HS; Massena, NY; (Y); Boy Scts; JV Var Socr; High Hon Roll; NHS; Ntl Merit Ltr; Lake St Lawrence Yacht Club Sailng Chmpnshps 83-84; Indstrl Engnrng.

BARTELL, JENIFER; Lindenhurst HS; Lindenhurst, NY; (Y); Thesps; Orch; Acting.

BARTELS, JOSEPH R; Cardinal Spellman HS; New York, NY; (Y); Boy Scts; Manhattan Coll; Engrng.

BARTH, GEOFFREY; Plattsburgh HS; Plattsburgh, NY; (Y); Model UN; Ski Clb; Swmmng; Trk; Comp.

BARTH, PAMELA A; New Hartford HS; New Hartford, NY; (Y); 61/264; Camera Clb; Hosp Aide; Tennis; Regents Schlrshp 85; Mohawk Vly CCFACCNTNT.

BARTHE, SUSAN; Bishop Maginn HS; Albany, NY; (Y); Art Clb; Drama Clb; Pep Clb; School Musical; School Play; Stage Crew; Variety Show; Nwsp Stf; Yrbk Stf; Hon Roll; Hudson Vly; Fine Arts.

BARTHEL, KATHLEEN; Bishop Ludden HS; Syracuse, NY; (Y); 6/180; VP Speech Tm; Nwsp Rptr; Yrbk Rptr; Rep Frsh Cls; Rep Soph Cls; Rep Jr Cls; Rep Sr Cls; L Bsktbl; L Trk; NHS; Hghst Avg Sci 85; Hghst Avg Acclrd Physics 85; Marquette U Hnry Schlrshp 85; Marquette U; Comm.

BARTHOLOMEW, DIANA J; Berlin American HS; Apo New York, NY; (S); Church Yth Grp; German Clb; Rep Stu Cncl; Var Bsktbl; Var Crs Cntry; JV Trk; Hon Roll; NHS; Bio Sci.

BARTHOLOMEW, SELMA K; Clara Barton HS; New York, NY; (Y); Yrbk Stf; Hon Roll; Prprtry In EAK 82-84; Poly Tech Inst; Neuro Srgn.

BARTKOWSKI, DAVID; Bishop Maginn HS; Albany, NY; (Y); Latin Clb; Math Clb; Ski Clb; Trs Soph Cls; Stat Bsktbl; Crs Cntry; High Hon Roll; NHS; Acctg.

BARTLE, ROBERTA; New Berlin Central HS; Norwich, NY; (Y); Trs FFA; Bsktbl; Score Keeper; Socr; Sftbl; Army.

BARTLETT, BETH; Camden Central HS; Camden, NY; (Y); Ski Clb; Varsity Clb; JV Var Tennis; High Hon Roll; Hon Roll; Bus.

BARTLETT, CHRISTINE; HS Of Fashion Inds; Brooklyn, NY; (Y); Dance Clb; French Clb; Library Aide; Yrbk Stf; Stu Cncl; Hon Roll; Lawyer.

BARTLETT, DEBORAH; Liverpool HS; Liverpool, NY; (S); 72/791; Church Yth Grp; Symp Band; NHS; Area All ST Wind Ensmble 84; All Cnty Music Assoc 83-84; Clarkson; Math.

BARTLETT, DENISE; Sheepshead Bay HS; Brooklyn, NY; (Y); Church Yth Grp; Band; Concert Band; Variety Show; Hon Roll; Obstet.

BARTLEY, MAUREEN; Aquinas HS; Bronx, NY; (Y); 47/178; Aud/Vis; Exploring; Office Aide; Chorus; Church Choir; Nwsp Rptr; Im Swmmng; Annual Eddy Awd 85; Columbia; Real Est.

BARTO, RONALD D; Harpursville HS; Port Crane, NY; (Y); 1/100; Am Leg Boys St; Art Clb; Church Yth Grp; Computer Clb; Exploring; Nwsp Rptr; Nwsp Stf; High Hon Roll; NHS; Voice Dem Awd; Hghst Rnkd JR Awd 85; JETS Prog Ithaca Coll 85; Comp Sci Apprntshp Bridge Prog 83; Suny Binghamton; Lndscp Arch.

BARTOLA, DIANE L; Susquehanna Valley HS; Binghamton, NY; (Y); 11/177; Church Yth Grp; Cmnty Wkr; Drama Clb; French Clb; School Musical; School Play; Sec Jr Cls; High Hon Roll; NHS; Hosp Aide; Broome CC; Elem Ed.

BARTOLOMUCCI, DONNA J; Mahopac HS; Mahopac, NY; (Y); 60/400; Drama Clb; Thesps; School Play; Stage Crew; Trs Soph Cls; NHS; Ntl Merit Schol; Wnnr Regents Schlrshp 85; Stu Of Mnth Math 85; Fordham; Elem Ed.

BARTOLOTTA, KEVIN G; St Patricks C C HS; Hudson, NY; (Y); 3/39; Am Leg Boys St; Drama Clb; Ski Clb; Yrbk Stf; JV Bsktbl; Im Socr; NHS; SUNY Maritime Coll; Marine Trn.

BARTOLOTTI, CHRISTINE; Whitesboro Sr HS; Utica, NY; (Y); 4-H; GAA; Letterman Clb; Ski Clb; Lit Mag; Rep Stu Cncl; Bus Admin.

BARTOLOTTI, FRANCINE; Dover JR SR HS; Millbrook, NY; (Y); 6/95; Dance Clb; Spanish Clb; Band; Jazz Band; VP Frsh Cls; Rep Jr Cls; Pres Sr Cls; Capt Cheerleading; L Fld Hcky; Stat Ftbl; Hofsta U; Pol Sci.

BARTOLOZZI, KAREN L; Clarkstown HS; New City, NY; (Y); 4/541; Math Tm; Scholastic Bowl; Mrchg Band; Nwsp Stf; Yrbk Stf; Sec Stu Cncl; Vllybl; NHS; Ntl Merit Ltr; Church Yth Grp; 1st Hnrs Iona Lang Cntst Spnsh III & IV 84-85; Georgetown U; Mktg.

BARTON, COLLEEN; Buffalo Academy Of The Sacred Heart; Amherst, NY; (Y); Model UN; Political Wkr; Ski Clb; Spanish Clb; Teachers Aide; Orch; Stage Crew; Nwsp Rptr; Rep Jr Cls; Var Socr; Bus.

BARTON, DANIEL; F D Roosevelt HS; Hyde Park, NY; (Y); 57/325; Boy Scts; French Clb; Nwsp Stf; Pres Stu Cncl; Hon Roll; NHS; Ntl Merit SF; Suny At Albany.

BARTON, JAMES C; Wallkill SR HS; Wallkill, NY; (Y); 30/200; Var Bsktbl; Var Trk; High Hon Roll; Hon Roll; St Schlr; Jr Great Bks Pgm 82; Vister County Comm Coll; Bus Ad.

BARTON, JANIE; Schoharie Central HS; Schoharie, NY; (Y); 42/80; Key Clb; Drill Tm; Sec Soph Cls; Capt VP Cheerleading; Swmmng; Cit Awd; Chorus; Cobleskill Coll; Sec.

BARTON, MATTHEW; Smithtown H S West; Smithtown, NY; (Y); Trs Church Yth Grp; Leo Clb; Math Tm; Spanish Clb; Chorus; Church Choir; Orch; Var Bsbl; Bowling; Hon Roll; Math.

BARTON, MELISSA; Garden City HS; Garden City, NY; (Y); Church Yth Grp; Key Clb; Lbrl Arts.

BARTON, ROBERT; St Marys Acad; Johnsonville, NY; (Y); Hon Roll; NHS; Ag.

BARTON, WENDY; Greece Olympia HS; Rochester, NY; (Y); 31/319; VP Drama Clb; Chorus; Madrigals; School Musical; Symp Band; High Hon Roll; NHS; Ntl Merit Ltr; Pres Schlr; Thesps; Natl Schl Chrl Awd 85; Chrs, Bnd Ltrs 81-85; 50 Pt Drama Clb 81-85; SUNY Coll Geneseo; Soclgy.

BARTOSZEK, CHRISTINE; Acad Of The Resrrctn; Pelham, NY; (Y); Church Yth Grp; Dance Clb; Ski Clb; Trs Soph Cls; Var Cheerleading; Var L Sftbl; Var L Vllybl; Hon Roll; Pulaski Assn NY Cty Police Dept Schlrhsp Awd 83; Crmnl Jstc.

BARTOW, DANIELLE D; Parishville Hopkinton Central HS; Potsdam, NY; (Y); 4/42; Math Tm; Concert Band; Stu Cncl; Cheerleading; Socr; Sftbl; Elks Awd; High Hon Roll; NHS; GAA; Alumni Schlrshp-Crtlnd Coll 85; Tchrs Assoc Schlrshp-Prshvl-Hpkntn Cen Schl 85; SUNY At Cortland; Phy Ed.

BARTUS, GREG; Chenango Forks HS; Chenango Forks, NY; (Y); Ski Clb; Bsbl; Bsktbl; Ftbl; Trk; Hon Roll; NHS; Prfct Atten Awd; All Susquenango Leag Off Guard 84; Stu Yr 84-85; Cornell U.

BARTUS, KELLY A; Lake Shore Central HS; Angola, NY; (Y); 19/259; Trs Drama Clb; Political Wkr; Chorus; Church Choir; Madrigals; Orch; Pres School Musical; School Play; Pres Stu Cncl; High Hon Roll; Presidential Scholr Nominee 85; U S Natl Speech & Drama Awd 85; Beauty Pageant Winner 85; Utica College; Public Relations.

BARTZSCH, JAMES D; Mc Kee Tech HS; Staten Island, NY; (Y); 12/ 271; Church Yth Grp; Debate Tm; Teachers Aide; Church Choir; Nwsp Ed-Chief; Rep Jr Cls; Golf; NHS; Pride Of Yankees Awd NY Cty 83-84; Concordia Lutheran Coll; Semnry.

BARUKHIN, YANA; John Dewey HS; Brooklyn, NY; (Y); Girl Scts; Band; Hon Roll; Cert Merit Awd 85; Comp.

BARVIAN, MARK; Attica SR HS; Strykersville, NY; (Y); Concert Band; Jazz Band; Mrchg Band; Stu Cncl; Var L Bsbl; Var Capt Wrstlng; Bio.

BARWALD, LAURA; Hilton HS; Rochester, NY; (Y); Church Yth Grp; Cmnty Wkr; 4-H; Teachers Aide; Concert Band; Symp Band; 4-H Awd; High Hon Roll; Hon Roll; Brockport; Bus Mgmt.

BASBASINO, LISA; Port Jervis HS; Port Jervis, NY; (Y); Varsity Clb; JV Var Bsktbl; JV Var Sftbl; Var Tennis; All Tri-County 1st Tm Sftbl 85; Mst Dedicated & Imprvd Plyr Sftbl 85; Bus.

BASEDOW, JOHN; Baldwin SR HS; Baldwin, NY; (Y); 2/502; Drama Clb; Mathletes; Science Clb; School Play; Nwsp Rptr; Tennis; High Hon Roll; NHS; Ntl Merit Ltr; Sal; Bio Medl; Spnsh Awds; Spnsh Hnr Socty; Natl Hnr Socty; Math Silvr Medl; Regnts Schlrshp; Hgh Hnr Rll; William Coll; Nwscstg.

BASEL, EILEEN C; Holy Trinity HS; Westbury, NY; (S); 27/356; Math Clb; Variety Show; Capt Bsktbl; Capt Sftbl; High Hon Roll; Hon Roll; NHS; Coaches Awd Vrsty Sftbl 84; Soc Distngshd Amer High Schl Stu 84; Marist Coll; Fash Merch.

BASELICE, STEVEN; St Raymonds HS; Bronx, NY; (Y); 42/191; English Clb; Exploring; ROTC; Ski Clb; Nwsp Bus Mgr; Nwsp Phtg; Yrbk Phtg; Yrbk Stf; Bowling; Trk; New Paltz Coll; Mgmt.

BASELLO, JULIE A; The Mary Louis Acad; Flushing, NY; (Y); 42/283; Drama Clb; Intnl Clb; Socr; Hon Roll; Adelphi U Trustee Schlrshp; CW Post Schlrshp; Regents Schlrshp; Adelphi U; Writer.

BASFORD, KIMBERLY; Heuvelton Central HS; Heuvelton, NY; (Y); 4-H; Sec French Clb; Color Guard; Concert Band; Capt Drill Tm; Jazz Band; Mrchg Band; School Musical; Cheerleading; Socr; Thomas Nelson CC; Cosmtlgst.

BASHAW, MICHELLE ANNA-LISA; Elizabethtown-Lewis Central Schl; Lewis, NY; (Y); Am Leg Aux Girls St; 4-H; Library Aide; Nwsp Stf; 4-H Awd; Hon Roll; NHS; Frgn Svc.

BASHKOFF, LARA; Hauppauge HS; Smithtown, NY; (Y); Cmnty Wkr; Band; Orch; School Musical; Symp Band; Yrbk Rptr; Yrbk Stf; High Hon Roll; NHS; FBLA; All ST NYSSMA Awd 84-85; Music Awds 82-84; Music Camp Merit Schlrshp 83; Athltc Awds 83-85; Bio Med Engrng.

BASHOFF, SUZANNE; Spackenkill HS; Poughkeepsie, NY; (Y); Leo Clb; Temple Yth Grp; Thesps; Church Choir; School Musical; Nwsp Stf; Yrbk Stf; Lit Mag; High Hon Roll; NHS; Natl Frnch Cont 4th Pl 2nd Level 83, 3rd Pl 3rd Level 84, 3rd Pl 4th Level 85; Psych.

BASI, MICHAEL; John F Kennedy HS; Utica, NY; (Y); 40/110; Church Yth Grp; Computer Clb; Mathletes; Math Clb; Pep Clb; Ski Clb; Varsity Clb; Variety Show; Rep Sr Cls; Stu Cncl; Potsdam Coll; Comp Sci.

BASIC, ANTONELLA; St Johns Prep; Queens, NY; (Y); Dance Clb; Chorus; Vllybl; DAR Awd; Prfct Atten Awd.

BASIL, CATHERINE M; Wilson Central HS; Wilson, NY; (Y); 47/134; Church Yth Grp; Library Aide; Ski Clb; School Play; Yrbk Stf; VP Jr Cls; VP Sr Cls; Fld Hcky; High Hon Roll; Homemcng Prncs 84; Prom Qn 85; SUNY Corland; Elem Educ.

BASIL, LISA; Horseheads HS; Horseheads, NY; (S); 30/407; Varsity Clb; Color Guard; Concert Band; Orch; Yrbk Phtg; Rep Soph Cls; Rep Jr Cls; Rep Sr Cls; Var Sftbl; L Tennis; U Of Jacksonville; Art.

BASILA, CATHERINE; Catholic Central HS; Cohoes, NY; (S); 7/203; French Clb; Math Clb; Nwsp Rptr; Rep Soph Cls; Rep Jr Cls; Rep Sr Cls; Rep Stu Cncl; JV Crs Cntry; High Hon Roll; Sec NHS; Natl Ldrshp Merit Awd; Fr Awd; Bus.

BASILE, RITA M; Vestal SR HS; Apalachin, NY; (Y); 66/450; Varsity Clb; School Play; Symp Band; Rep Soph Cls; Var Bsktbl; Var L Civic Clb; Var L Socr; Var L Sftbl; High Hon Roll; NHS; Vrsty Clb 4 Yr Awd For Soccer 84; Gold Tassel 85; Villanova U; Bus Adm.

BASKIN, STACY; Tottenville HS; Staten Island, NY; (Y); 12/897; Math Tm; School Play; Nwsp Stf; Var Cheerleading; Hon Roll; NHS; Prd Of Yankees Awd-Daily Nws Super Youth 83; Regents Schlrshp 85; Cornell U; Statistics.

BASSANI, MARK; Mount St Michael Acad; Bronx, NY; (Y); 48/308; Church Yth Grp; Socr; Spanish NHS.

BASSARATH JR, C SHELDON; L I Lutheran HS; Westbury, NY; (S); Pres Church Yth Grp; NFL; Speech Tm; Jazz Band; School Musical; Nwsp Rptr; Lit Mag; JV Tennis; French Hon Soc; NHS; Columbia; Actng.

BASSETT, E SCOTT; Churchville-Chili SR HS; Rochester, NY; (Y); Boy Scts; Church Choir; Var Socr; Swmmng; Trk; Roberts Wesleyan Coll; Comp Sci.

BASSLER, HOLLY; Berne-Knox-Westerlo HS; East Berne, NY; (Y); Chorus; Color Guard; Mrchg Band; School Musical; Socr; Trk; Vllybl; Hon Roll; NHS; Prfct Atten Awd.

BAST, WILLIAM; St Francis Prep; Forest Hills, NY; (Y); Boy Scts; JV Bsbl; Peer Counselor 85-86; City Coll; Pre-Med.

BAST, WM; St Francis Prep; Forest Hills, NY; (Y); Boy Scts; Red Cross Aide; Bsbl; STAR Boy Scout 84; Peer Cnslr 84-85; Queens Coll; Pre Med.

BASTIAN, DOUGLAS E; Wellsville HS; Wellsville, NY; (Y); 10/130; Am Leg Boys St; CAP; Hon Roll; Cvl Air Patrl Mitchel Awd 83; U Of Buffalo; Mech Engrng.

BASTIAN, JEAN J; Brewster HS; Brewster, NY; (Y); 4/170; Yrbk Stf; Var Capt Trk; High Hon Roll; Hon Roll; NHS; Ntl Merit Ltr; Regents Schlrshp 85; 2nd Pl League Womn Votrs Eassy Cont 84; Vassar Coll.

BASTIANI, JOHN; Colonie Central HS; Albany, NY; (Y); Ski Clb; Hon Roll; Berkley; Music.

BASTY, CHERYL ANN; Hamburg SR HS; Hamburg, NY; (Y); 8/387; 4-H; Girl Scts; Teachers Aide; Chorus; Church Choir; Madrigals; School Musical; School Play; High Hon Roll; Hon Roll; Recip Spn Hnr Roll Awd 3 Yr 82-83; SUNY Buffalo; Mth.

BASUINO, LEONARD C; Xaverian HS; Brooklyn, NY; (Y); 4/347; Sec Chess Clb; JA; Math Tm; Pres Spanish Clb; Hst Stu Cncl; Bsktbl; High Hon Roll; Sec NHS; United HS Chess Leag 1st 85; Aurelio Baldor Awd Exclnce Math 85; Polytechnic Inst NY; Elect.

BATCHELOR, MARK D; Pembroke Central HS; Corfu, NY; (Y); 27/110; Varsity Clb; Variety Show; Pres Sr Cls; Capt Var Bsktbl; Capt Var Ftbl; Hon Roll; NYS Rgnts Schlrshp 85; MVP Bsktbl 84-85; FL ST U; Mkt.

BATCHO, LISA; Tonawanda JR SR HS; Tonawanda, NY; (Y); 13/235; French Clb; School Musical; Var L Cheerleading; JV Swmmng; Hon Roll; NHS; Ntl Merit Ltr; Outstndg Vrsty Chrldr 83-84; Outstndg Stu 85; Pres Athltc Awd 85; U Buffalo; Frgn Lang.

BATEMAN, MICHAEL; Clarkstown South HS; W Nyack, NY; (Y); Aud/ Vis; CAP; Band; Concert Band; Jazz Band; Mrchg Band; Pep Band; Ftbl; Wt Lftg; Inspctr Clousaeu Awd 84; OSWEGO; Tv Prod.

BATES, CORRIE; Glens Falls HS; Glen Falls, NY; (Y); 1/230; AFS; Drama Clb; Key Clb; Pep Clb; Stage Crew; Var JV Cheerleading; Var Mgr(s); High Hon Roll; NHS; Rep Frsh Cls; Hi-Y Club 85-86; Snd Rcrdng Tech.

BATES, DAWN; Churchville-Chili HS; Rochester, NY; (Y); Chorus; Nwsp Rptr; Rep Stu Cncl; Asst Sec-Choral Council 84-85; Sectn Leader-Chorus Choral Council 85-86; Physical Thrpy.

BATES JR, DENNIS G; Royalton-Hartland Central Schl; Middleport, NY; (Y); Am Leg Boys St; Cmnty Wkr; French Clb; Hosp Aide; Varsity Clb; Var L Crs Cntry; Var L Trk; Church Yth Grp; Drama Clb; 4-H; Most Imprvd Cross Cty Trk Plyr 83-84; Asst Mgr Bk Store 83-84; Mgr Schl Bk Store 84-85; Niagara U; Pre-Med.

BATES, JHVONNE; Tamarac HS; Troy, NY; (Y); Church Yth Grp; Science Clb; Chorus; Church Choir; School Musical; Stage Crew; Yrbk Ed-Chief; Yrbk Stf; Rep Jr Cls; Music.

BATES, JOHN; Cicero-North Syracuse HS; N Syracuse, NY; (S); 14/711; Cmnty Wkr; Exploring; Spanish Clb; Hon Roll; NHS; Ntl Merit Ltr.

BATES, JOHN; Thousand Islands HS; Clayton, NY; (Y); 8/78; Varsity Clb; Band; Chorus; Jazz Band; School Play; JV Bsbl; Var Golf; JV Var Ice Hcky; JV Var Socr; High Hon Roll; NYS Rgnts Schlrshp 84; Marlin Firearms Essay Cntst NY St Wnnr 84; Louis Armstrong Jazz Awd 85; NC ST U; Civil Engrng.

BATESON, THOMAS; Whitesboro SR HS; Whitesboro, NY; (Y); Church Yth Grp; Cmnty Wkr; Speech Tm; Variety Show; JV Bsbl; JV Bsktbl; Hon Roll; Opt Clb Awd; Jrnlsm.

BATHGATE, JON; Skaneateles HS; Skaneateles, NY; (Y); Exploring; Band; JV Bsktbl; JV Var Crs Cntry; Var L Trk; High Hon Roll; NHS; Bio.

BATISTA, BERNARDO; Lindenhurst HS; Lindenhurst, NY; (Y); French Clb; Science Clb; Art Clb; Computer Clb; Yrbk Stf; Var Crs Cntry; Var Trk; Prfct Atten Awd; Biochem.

BATISTA, VICTORIA; Seward Park HS; New York, NY; (Y); 60/760; Teachers Aide; Hon Roll; Prfct Atten Awd; Sal; Bernard Baruch Coll; Accntng.

BATSCHE, LAUREN; St John The Baptist HS; Central Islip, NY; (Y); Office Aide; Cheerleading; Hon Roll; Nursing.

BATSFORD, PENNY P; Homer Central HS; Truxton, NY; (Y); Im Vllybl; Doris Walter Schlrshp; Ag Awd Hmkng; Cortland ST Coll; Scl Stds.

BATSON, HENRIETTA P; Dominican Commercial HS; St Albans, NY; (Y); Red Cross Aide; Chorus; Church Choir; Hon Roll; Wagner Coll; Chld Psych.

BATT, LINDA J; West Seneca E SR HS; West Seneca, NY; (Y); 4/365; Pres Trs Exploring; Library Aide; Science Clb; Ed Yrbk Stf; High Hon Roll; JC Awd; Jr NHS; NHS; Ntl Merit Ltr; St Schlr; WA U Schlrshp 85-89; Chancellors Hnry Schlrshp WA U 85-89; Union Coll Schlrshp 85-89; Med.

BATT, LISA; West Seneca East SR HS; Cheektowaga, NY; (S); 17/365; DECA; Key Clb; Ski Clb; Spanish Clb; Rep Soph Cls; Rep Jr Cls; Rep Sr Cls; Rep Stu Cncl; High Hon Roll; NHS; U Of Buffalo; Bus.

BATTAGLIA JR, RONALD J; Amherst Central SR HS; Amherst, NY; (Y); Trs Model UN; Var Gym; Var Swmmng; Hon Roll; Pres NHS; U Of Rochester; Polt Sci.

BATTAGLIA, STEVE; Moore Catholic HS; Staten Island, NY; (Y); Boy Scts; Computer Clb; Var Math Tm; Spanish Clb; Stage Crew; Bowling; NHS; Comp Sci.

BATTAGLIA, SUZANNE; Bishop Ludden HS; Solvay, NY; (S); Spanish Clb; Var JV Socr; Var Capt Trk; DAR Awd; High Hon Roll; NHS; Wellesley Coll Bk Awd 84; Le Moyne Coll Smmr Schlrshp 84; Mdrn Lang.

BATTAGLINO, MIKE P; Schalmont HS; Schenectady, NY; (Y); VP Church Yth Grp; French Clb; Political Wkr; Trs Frsh Cls; Jr Cls; Rep Stu Cncl; Var L Bsbl; Var L Wrstlng; High Hon Roll; Hon Roll; Med.

BATTERMAN, ROD; Connetquot HS; Ronkonkoma, NY; (S); 4/671; Math Tm; Ed Nwsp Stf; Rep Stu Cncl; Pres NHS; Ntl Merit Ltr.

BATTEY, ERIK; Cardinal Spellman HS; Bronx, NY; (Y); Var Capt Ftbl; Regnts Schlrshp 85; 11A Div All Leag Ftbl 1st Tm 84; Hofstra U; Ntrl Sci.

BATTIGE JR, C KENNETH; Christian Brothers Acad; Latham, NY; (Y); 2/145; Am Leg Boys St; Church Yth Grp; Speech Tm; Yrbk Stf; High Hon Roll; NEDT Awd; Sal; Aud/Vis; Camera Clb; Schl Scholar 84-86; Bro Alaysius Myers FSC Guidnce Awd 85; Holy Crs Chltc Achvt Awd 85; Rensselaer Polytech; Engrng.

BATZ, KENNETH A; Churchville Chili SR HS; Churchville, NY; (Y); Ski Clb; Band; Concert Band; Drill Tm; Mrchg Band; Pep Band; Symp Band; JV Bsktbl; JV Crs Cntry; Var Golf; NYS Rgnts Schlrshp; Rochester Inst Of Tech; Comp.

BATZ, RICHARD; Byron Bergen HS; Bergen, NY; (Y); Band; Mrchg Band; Stage Crew; Var Bsbl; Var Golf; Embry-Riddle U; Aerntcl Engr.

BAUDANZA, LORI; Bishop Kearney HS; Brooklyn, NY; (Y); Girl Scts; Rep Frsh Cls; Rep Soph Cls; Co-Capt Cheerleading; NHS; Driver Ed Awd 85; Fash Inst Tech; Fash Buyng.

BAUDIN, KATIA; St Marys Girls HS; Port Washington, NY; (Y); 11/ 152; Art Clb; Pres French Clb; Ski Clb; Chorus; School Play; High Hon Roll; Hon Roll; NHS; St Marys Gold Medal Excel Frnch 85; Iona Coll Lang Comptn Fnlst 83; Iona Coll Lang Comptn 1st Hnrs 84; Hofstra U; Intl Bus.

BAUDISCH, DEBRA; Cardinal Mooney HS; Rochester, NY; (Y); Bsktbl; Hon Roll; Eng Mrt Awd 82; Dncng Awds-Toe, Bllt, Jzz, Tap, & Baton 71-80; MCC; Dietition.

BAUER, BETH ANN; Washingtonville SR HS; Monroe, NY; (Y); 3/292; Girl Scts; Temple Yth Grp; Chorus; Pep Band; Symp Band; Nwsp Stf; Yrbk Stf; Band; Concert Band; Hon Roll; NY ST Schl Vsl Arts Prgrm 82-83; Sec/Treas SADD 84-85; Syracuse U; Fash Dsgn.

BAUER, JENNIFER; Andes Central Schl; Andes, NY; (Y); Cmnty Wkr; Girl Scts; Red Cross Aide; Varsity Clb; Band; Chorus; Mrchg Band; Var Stu Cncl; Cheerleading; Hon Roll; Mst Imprvd, Mst Effrt Engl 85; Mst Effrt Phys Ed 85; Mst Effrt Bio & Chem 84-85.

BAUER, KRISTA M; Amherst Central HS; Eggertsville, NY; (Y); 47/310; Church Yth Grp; French Clb; Pres Trs Ski Clb; Orch; Symp Band; Yrbk Ed-Chief; NHS; Debate Tm; GAA; Band; U Of MI Bndsmn Yr 85; Pres Phys Fit Awd 85; JOY Mfg Co Scholar Awd 85; Case Wstrn Resrve; Biomd Engrng.

BAUER, ROBERT; Frontier Central HS; Hamburg, NY; (S); 28/550; Chess Clb; Science Clb; Varsity Clb; Rep Soph Cls; Rep Jr Cls; Var Swmmng; High Hon Roll; Hon Roll; Bronze & Silver Medal In Lecture For Sci Fair 83; 1st & 2nd Pl Indstrl Arts Fair 83-84; U Of Buffalo; Mech Engrng.

BAUER, SUSAN; Mt St Mary Acad; Tonawanda, NY; (Y); Cmnty Wkr; Ski Clb; Chorus; Hon Roll; Outstndng Cmnty Svc Awd 84; Outstndng Svc YES Pgm 84; YES Ldrshp Training Pgm 83 & 84; ST U NY; Accntng.

BAUM, DEBRA; George W Hewlett HS; Hewlett, NY; (Y); Pres Temple Yth Grp; Nwsp Rptr; Nwsp Stf; Yrbk Stf; JV Capt Vllybl; Hon Roll; Bus.

BAUM, JONATHAN; Monticello HS; Monticello, NY; (Y); 4/170; Nwsp Ed-Chief; Trs Wrstlng; Bausch & Lomb Sci Awd; High Hon Roll; NHS; Ntl Merit Ltr; Pres Schlr; Chess Clb; Teachers Aide; Varsity Clb; SAT Grnt For Excllnc-Geneva Coll 85; NY St Regnts Schlrshp 85; Bucknell U; Med.

BAUM, KYM; Plattsburgh SR HS; Plattsburgh, NY; (Y); 1/159; Cmnty Wkr; Varsity Clb; Trs Jr Cls; Trs Sr Cls; Rep Stu Cncl; Var Capt Socr; Var Capt Vllybl; High Hon Roll; NHS; GAA; Acad Achv Awds In Sci, Sol Stds & Math 83-84; Acad Achv Awd In Sci 85; Cornell; Psych.

BAUMACH, BARBARA; Sachem H S North Campus; Lk Ronkonkoma, NY; (Y); 62/1389; GAA; Hosp Aide; Pres Science Clb; Spanish Clb; Orch; Yrbk Stf; JV Bsktbl; Var L Bowling; JV Fld Hcky; JV Sftbl; MVP Vrsty Bwlng 84; 1st Pl Fstvl Of Music/Chmbr Orch WA D C 85; Cornell; Vet Med.

BAUMAN, ERIC S; Mahopac HS; Mahopac, NY; (Y); 19/378; Chess Clb; Computer Clb; Drama Clb; Library Aide; School Play; Variety Show; Lit Mag; Capt Var Bowling; High Hon Roll; Sec NHS; All Leag Hnrs Bwlng 82-84; SUNY Stonybrook; Comp Sci.

BAUMAN, PATRICIA; Cassadaga Valley HS; Stockton, NY; (Y); 1/118; Quiz Bowl; Thesps; Acpl Chr; Jazz Band; School Musical; Swing Chorus; Lit Mag; Elks Awd; NHS; Rotary Awd; Leg Intrn 85; Tolerton Essy Merit Awd 85; Middlebury Coll VT; Lang.

BAUMAN, TIMOTHY R; Bishop Kearney HS; Rochester, NY; (Y); Math Clb; Model UN; Ski Clb; Im Bowling; Var L Socr; Var L Tennis; High Hon Roll; NHS; Ntl Merit Ltr; Cert Merit NY St Math Legue 84; Coachs Awd Tnns 85; Econ.

BAUMANN, CAMILLE; Wallkill SR HS; Wallkill, NY; (Y); 4/200; Am Leg Aux Girls St; Drama Clb; Chorus; Lit Mag; Capt Socr; Var Trk; Pres NHS; Ntl Merit Ltr; School Play; Nwsp Rptr; Clss Frnch Awd 82-85; Drama Awd 85; Harvard U MA.

BAUMANN JR, EDMUND; Southold HS; Peconic, NY; (Y); 6/53; Am Leg Boys St; Boy Scts; Church Yth Grp; Red Cross Aide; Band; Chorus; Yrbk Stf; Stu Cncl; High Hon Roll; Lion Awd; Eagle Scout 85; NY Inst Tech; Physics.

BAUMANN, MICHAEL R; Smithtown High Schl East; Nesconset, NY; (Y); Exploring; Trs German Clb; L Math Tm; Jazz Band; Symp Band; Nwsp Stf; Pres Soph Cls; NHS; Ntl Merit Ltr; Pres Rotary Awd; Germn Hnr Soc; Portmouth Coll; Bio.

BAUMBERGER, ALEX; South Side HS; Rockville Ctr, NY; (Y); Boy Scts; Band; Concert Band; Jazz Band; Pep Band; JV Wrstlng; Hon Roll.

BAUMGARTNER, BARBARA; North Babylon SR HS; North Babylon, NY; (Y); Yrbk Phtg; Lit Mag; VP Sr Cls; Mgr(s); Sftbl; Vllybl; High Hon Roll; Hon Roll; Jr NHS; NHS; Soclgy.

BAUMGARTNER, MARK; Fort Plain Central Schl; Fort Plain, NY; (S); 4/68; Computer Clb; VP Drama Clb; VP French Clb; Band; Chorus; Jazz Band; Bsktbl; Golf; High Hon Roll; VP NHS.

BAUMGARTNER, THOMAS; Kenmore East HS; Tonawanda, NY; (Y); Varsity Clb; Var L Ftbl; JV Trk; Bus Admin.

BAUSBACK, DEBRA; C A Bouton JR-SR HS; Slingerlands, NY; (Y); 1/ 125; Trs French Clb; Concert Band; Yrbk Ed-Chief; Trs Soph Cls; Var Capt Bsktbl; Var Capt Fld Hcky; Kiwanis Awd; Val; Rennselaer Polytechnic Inst Math & Sci Awd 84; Schlr Athlt Awd 85; Yrbk Awd 84 & 85; Hartwick Coll; Pre-Dentstry.

BAUTER, STACY; General Brown HS; Dexter, NY; (Y); JCL; Key Clb; Rep Frsh Cls; VP Soph Cls; VP Stu Cncl; Var Capt Bsktbl; Var Capt Lcrss; Hon Roll; NHS; Prfct Atten Awd; Jefferson CC; Bus Admin.

BAUTZ, CRAIG; Lakeland HS; Mahopac, NY; (Y); Pres Boy Scts; Letterman Clb; Var Bsbl; Var Crs Cntry; JV Ftbl; Var Golf; Score Keeper; Var Trk; Egl Sct 83; Hfstra Coll; Acctng.

BAVARO, JOSEPH; Clarkstown South HS; New City, NY; (Y); Boy Scts; Im JV Bsbl; Im Bsktbl; Im JV Ftbl; Jr NHS.

BAVETTA, CHRISTINE; Nazareth Regional HS; Brooklyn, NY; (Y); 16/261; French Clb; Math Tm; School Musical; Nwsp Rptr; Rep Sr Cls; Var Capt Bsktbl; Var Sftbl; Var Vllybl; Rep NHS; Rep Ntl Merit Ltr; Hlth Medl 85; Chem Medl 84; Bio Medl 83; Manhattonville Coll; Bus.

BAXTER, CHERYL L; Williamsville North HS; East Amherst, NY; (Y); Church Yth Grp; DECA; Drama Clb; Trs French Clb; JA; Latin Clb; Pres Spanish Clb; High Hon Roll; NHS; Ntl Merit Ltr; Michigan Annual Giving Awd 85; New York Board Of Regents Schlrshp 85; U Of MI; Business.

BAXTER, HERMIA Y; Norman Thomas HS; New York, NY; (S); Aud/Vis; DECA; Office Aide; Teachers Aide; Stage Crew; Color Guard; JV Socr; DECA Achvt Awd 84; Prncpls Cmmndtn Awd Schl Svc 85; DECA Regnl Troph Genl Merch Event 84; Syracuse U; Advrtsg.

BAXTER, JOHN; Walt Whitman HS; Huntington, NY; (Y); 76/550; Spanish Clb; Hon Roll; Spanish NHS.

BAXTER, LAURIE; South Lewis Central HS; Turin, NY; (Y); Var Cheerleading; Var Sftbl; Hon Roll; Acctg.

BAXTER, LILLIAN; Monsignor Scanlan HS; Bronx, NY; (Y); 95/250; JA; Bsktbl; Sftbl; Prfct Atten Awd; Interschltc Achvt 84-85; Psychiatrist.

BAXTER, MEREDITH; Potsdam Central HS; Potsdam, NY; (S); 13/157; AFS; Drama Clb; French Clb; Varsity Clb; Band; Concert Band; Jazz Band; Mrchg Band; Orch; Pep Band; SUNY Fredonia; Cmmnctns.

BAXTER, RICHARD C; South Lewis Central HS; Glenfield, NY; (Y); #4 In Class; Am Leg Boys St; Varsity Clb; Trs Sr Cls; Ftbl; Swmmng; Trk; Wt Lftg; High Hon Roll; NHS; Math.

BAXTER, SHEILA; Hermon-Dekalb Central HS; Hermon, NY; (S); Church Yth Grp; Drama Clb; French Clb; Band; Chorus; Concert Band; Mrchg Band; School Play; Stage Crew; High Hon Roll; Bus.

BAXTER, TERRI; South Glens Falls SR HS; S Glens Falls, NY; (Y); 18/242; Key Clb; Latin Clb; Varsity Clb; Yrbk Stf; Sec Soph Cls; Stu Cncl; Var Capt Cheerleading; Powder Puff Ftbl; Hon Roll; Top 10 Pct Cls 83-84; Grand Champ Chrldng Camp 85; Pre-Med.

BAYER, BARBARA; Lincoln HS; Yonkers, NY; (S); #1 In Class; Drama Clb; School Play; Stage Crew; Nwsp Rptr; Nwsp Stf; High Hon Roll; Aristeon Hnr Soc 84-85; PSYCH.

BAYER, JENNIFER G; Ramaz Schl; New York, NY; (Y); Art Clb; Political Wkr; Temple Yth Grp; Chorus; Nwsp Stf; Yrbk Ed-Chief; Ed Yrbk Stf; Lit Mag; Sftbl; Ntl Merit Ltr.

BAYER, LORNA E; George W Hewlett HS; Hewlett, NY; (Y); Hosp Aide; Mathletes; Math Clb; Math Tm; Science Clb; Chorus; Lit Mag; Gym; Hon Roll; NHS; Slvr Pin For Math Tm Cmptn 84-85; 6th Pl In Cnt Natl Frnch Cont 85; Med.

BAYER, RAYMOND; Moore Catholic HS; Staten Island, NY; (Y); Math Clb; Math Tm; Ski Clb; Pres Soph Cls; Rep Stu Cncl; JV Capt Bsbl; Tennis; Hon Roll; Mrt Awd 84-85; Engrng.

BAYLISS, JACKIE; Oneida SR HS; Oneida, NY; (S); 10/250; Trs 4-H; FBLA; Concert Band; Mrchg Band; God Cntry Awd; High Hon Roll; NHS; NY ST Regents Schlrshp 85; Alfred ST Coll; Exec Secy.

BAYLOR, LISA; Binghamton HS; Binghamton, NY; (Y); Ski Clb; Sec Soph Cls; Rep Stu Cncl; JV Var Cheerleading; Var Crs Cntry; Var Diving; Var Swmmng; Var Trk; High Hon Roll; NHS; Outstndng Stu Cert Spn III 84; Var Crs Cntry Sectnl & STAC Tm Champs 84; Pre-Med.

BAYONA, YARA; Walton HS; Bronx, NY; (Y); Church Yth Grp; Dance Clb; Rep Frsh Cls; Capt Tennis; Capt Vllybl; Lehman Coll; Phy Thrpst.

BAYRASLI, SERVER; Aviation HS; Brooklyn, NY; (Y); 33/509; VP JA; Office Aide; Capt Var Crs Cntry; Capt Var Trk; NHS; Prfct Atten Awd; Outstndng Awds Technical Achvt 84-85; Polytechnic Inst NY; Engrng.

BAYSE, JUDIE; Grand Island HS; Grand Island, NY; (Y); 2/334; French Clb; Color Guard; Trs Drm & Bgl; Flag Corp; Variety Show; High Hon Roll; Hon Roll; NHS; Acadmc Achvt Awds 83-85; NY Penn Clr Grd Circuit Champ 84; Natl Clr Grd Champ 10th Pl 84; Geneseo; Mgmt.

BAZIGOS, SPIRO; St Francis Prep; New York, NY; (Y); JA; Cit Awd; Hon Roll; Ntl Merit Ltr; Aviatn.

BAZIGOS, SPYRIDON; St Francis Prep; Flushing, NY; (S); 152/693; Hon Roll; Ntl Merit Ltr; Acad All Amer Awd; 7 Karate Trophies; Sci.

BAZIN, PAUL; Adlai E Stevenson HS; New York, NY; (Y); 16/445; Debate Tm; JA; Jazz Band; Mrchg Band; Orch; Wrstlng; Hon Roll; NHS; Arista 84-85; Pace U; Bus Mgt.

BEACH, CHRISTINE; Fairport HS; Fairport, NY; (Y); Church Yth Grp; Cmnty Wkr; Dance Clb; Ski Clb; Yrbk Stf; Cheerleading; Coach Actv; Lcrss; Score Keeper; Trk; Hmcmng Prncss 83; Modl Fairport Harold Nwsp 85; NV ST Fnlst Mrs Amer Co-Ed Pgnt 84; Toursm.

BEACH, LORRAINE V; Patchogue-Medford HS; Patchogue, NY; (Y); Trs Church Yth Grp; Sec German Clb; Rep Sr Cls; Hon Roll; NHS; NYS Regents Schlrshp 85; SUNY Coll Geneseo; Deaf Educ.

BEACH, MELISSA; Little Falls HS; St Johnsville, NY; (Y); Church Yth Grp; 4-H; French Clb; Girl Scts; Spanish Clb; Band; Chorus; Church Choir; Mrchg Band; 4-H Awd; Coll; Comptrs.

BEACH, SANDI; Liberty Central HS; Livingston Manor, NY; (Y); Church Yth Grp; Girl Scts; Chorus; Capt Bowling; Var JV Socr; Hon Roll; Prfct Atten Awd; 1st Rnnr Up Miss Lylty Day Pagnt 85; Krissler Bus Inst; Bus.

BEAMISH, WILLIAM J; Bay Shore HS; Bayshore, NY; (Y); 28/400; Boy Scts; Intnl Clb; Concert Band; Mrchg Band; Nwsp Ed-Chief; Rep Stu Cncl; NHS; Eagle Sct Awd, Prsdntl Awd Envrnmntl Prot, Snrklng BSA 85; Embry Riddle Aero U; Pilot.

BEAN, GARY; Rome Free Acad; Rome, NY; (Y); Science Clb; High Hon Roll; Jr NHS; NHS; Pre-Med.

BEAN, MICHELLE; Maryvale HS; Cheektowaga, NY; (Y); Dance Clb; Spanish Clb; Yrbk Stf; Pom Pon; High Hon Roll; Hon Roll; Prfct Atten Awd; Early Ed.

BEARD, JENNIFER MAY; Henninger HS; Syracuse, NY; (Y); 1/400; Rep Soph Cls; Rep Sr Cls; Socr; Trk; Vllybl; Hon Roll; Prfct Atten Awd; Robert Oliver Awd 85; Regents Diploma 85; Syracuse U; Mgmt.

BEASLEY, JOHNITA; Hutchinson Central Technical HS; Buffalo, NY; (Y); 10/262; Church Yth Grp; Dance Clb; Girl Scts; Hosp Aide; JA; Church Choir; Color Guard; Drill Tm; Variety Show; Nwsp Stf; Buffalo Alumnae Panhellenic Awd 85; Alfred JA Scholar 85; Minrty Stu Scholar UNY Binghamton 85; SUNY Binghamton; Comp Pgmmr.

BEATON, PATRICK; La Salle SR HS; Niagara Falls, NY; (S); 2/278; AFS; Mathletes; Varsity Clb; School Play; L Var Crs Cntry; L Var Trk; High Hon Roll; NHS; Sal; U Of Rochester; Engrng.

BEATTIE, RACHEL H; Hunter College HS; Flushing, NY; (Y); Math Tm; Chorus; Madrigals; Swing Chorus; Lit Mag; L Crs Cntry; L Trk; Mu Alp Tht; Ntl Merit SF; Schlrshp Intl Stud Abroad 83.

BEATTY, HEATHER; Fox Lane HS; Pound Ridge, NY; (Y); Church Yth Grp; Mathletes; Math Tm; Ski Clb; Fld Hcky; Lcrss; High Hon Roll; Rep Stu Cncl; Bedford/Pound Ridge Drug Cncl Rep 84-86; Natl Yth Conf Chrstns & Jews 84; Annl Math Exam 83; Math.

BEATTY, HOLLY; Fox Lane HS; Pound Ridge, NY; (Y); Church Yth Grp; Ski Clb; Rep Stu Cncl; JV Fld Hcky; Var Lcrss; High Hon Roll; Rep For The Bedford Pound Ridge Drug Cncl 84-86.

BEATY, TERRI; Corning-Painted Post West HS; Painted Post, NY; (Y); Cmnty Wkr; Exploring; Girl Scts; Hosp Aide; Yrbk Stf; Bowling; Sftbl; 2nd Rnr Up Colonial Days Qn 85; NY Natl Teen-Age Pagnt Volnteer Svc Awd 83; Phys Ther.

BEAUCHAMP, LAURIE; Ogdensburg Free Acad; Ogdensburg, NY; (Y); 20/196; Church Yth Grp; Cmnty Wkr; Math Clb; Yrbk Stf; Rep Stu Cncl; Var Capt Bsktbl; Golf; Var Capt Socr; Var Capt Sftbl; Tennis; Acad Banqt 81-85; Outstndng Grl Athlte & Acad Hnrs 85; Frank La Vigne & Ralph Wiber Memrl Schlrshps 85; Clarkson U; Math.

BEAUDIN, CHRISSY; Glens Falls HS; Glens Falls, NY; (Y); 2/230; Dance Clb; Math Tm; Sec Stu Cncl; JV Var Bsktbl; Var L Cheerleading; Var L Pom Pon; Powder Puff Ftbl; JV Var Sftbl; JV Var Vllybl; High Hon Roll; Mth.

BEAUMONT, JESSE; Albion HS; Albion, NY; (Y); Boy Scts; 4-H; Band; Chorus; Church Choir; Concert Band; Jazz Band; Mrchg Band; School Musical; Swing Chorus; Bio.

BEAUREGARD, MARIA; Grand Island HS; Grand Island, NY; (Y); 3/250; French Clb; Ski Clb; Variety Show; Trs Soph Cls; Cheerleading; Gym; Trk; Hon Roll; NHS; Wellesley Awd 85; PTSA Awd 83-85; Pre-Dntstry.

BEAUREGARD, NICOLE; Charles O Dickerson HS; Trumansburg, NY; (Y); 11/85; French Clb; Varsity Clb; Chorus; Yrbk Stf; Sec Frsh Cls; Rep Stu Cncl; Socr; Tennis; Vllybl; High Hon Roll; High Hnr Awd 85; Eng Awds 83; Lib Art.

BEAUTER, TAMMY; Clyde Savannah HS; Savahhan, NY; (Y); 19/71; Band; Chorus; Concert Band; Mrchg Band; Pep Band; Var L Cheerleading; Hon Roll; Prfct Atten Awd; Dentl Hygn Schlrshp 85; Onondaga CC; Dntl Hygn.

BEAUVAIS, CASSANDRE; Uniondale HS; Baldwin, NY; (Y); Church Yth Grp; Acpl Chr; Chorus; Variety Show; VP Frsh Cls; Sec Sr Cls; Capt Cheerleading; JV Var Fld Hcky; Capt Pom Pon; JV Var Vllybl; NAACP Ind Crmny 85; NY Tech Sch; Comp Tech.

BEAUZILE, NADINE; St Johns Prep; S Ozone Pk, NY; (Y); French Clb; Band; JV Cheerleading; JV Var Trk; Coaches Awd Trk & Field 82-83; NY U; Psych.

BEAZER, DAWN; Acad Of Mst St Ursula; New York, NY; (Y); Howard U; Bus Mgmt.

BECALLO, FRANCES; The Franciscan Acad; West Monroe, NY; (S); 11/25; Pres FBLA; Yrbk Sprt Ed; Sec Stu Cncl; Cit Awd; Hon Roll; NHS; Athltc Awd 81-82; Shorthand I Schlrshp Awd 83-84; Maria Regina Coll; Bus Admin.

BECEIRO, LESLIE; Dominican Commercial HS; Bayside, NY; (Y); 116/384; Intnl Clb; Spanish Clb; School Play; Stage Crew; Yrbk Stf; Vllybl; High Hon Roll; Hon Roll; Prfct Atten Awd; Spanish NHS; Bus Admin.

BECHARD, JENNIFER; Liverpool HS; Liverpool, NY; (S); 160/792; Church Yth Grp; Orch; Symp Band; Stat Lcrss; Hon Roll; NYSMA 82-83; Law.

BECHARD, LISA; Liverpool HS; Liverpool, NY; (S); 100/800; VP JA; Ski Clb; Teachers Aide; Co-Capt Mrchg Band; School Musical; Stu Cncl; High Hon Roll; Jr NHS; NHS; Prfct Atten Awd; NBTA Troph & Awds 82-84; RIT; Hlth.

BECHARD, STEPHEN; Waterford-Halfmoon HS; Waterford, NY; (Y); Cmnty Wkr; Yrbk Stf; CAP; Troph Ml Hi-Lo Comptn Green Isl Rod & Gun Clb 84; Hudson Valley Coll; Hrdwr Bus.

BECHTEL, RANDY; Hamburg SR HS; Hamburg, NY; (Y); 106/406; JA; JV Var Ice Hcky; JV Socr; Wrkr Of Mnth & Hr Twn Yth Emplymnt Srv 84; U NY Bflo; Archtctr.

BECK, CHERYL; Watertown HS; Watertown, NY; (Y); 21/321; GAA; JA; Bsktbl; Trk; Vllybl; High Hon Roll; Jr NHS; NHS; Prfct Atten Awd; Comp.

BECK, DAVID A; Ardsley HS; Ardsley, NY; (Y); Am Leg Boys St; Temple Yth Grp; Nwsp Bus Mgr; Chess Clb; Debate Tm; Math Tm; Nwsp Rptr; Frsbee Clb Capt 84-86; Cmnty Hebrew HS 81-85; Comp Rm Asstnt; Comp Engrng.

BECK, JENS; Gates/Chili HS; Rochester, NY; (Y); 46/463; Aud/Vis; VP Church Yth Grp; Cmnty Wkr; Quiz Bowl; Varsity Clb; Band; Chorus; Church Choir; Concert Band; Jazz Band; Schlrshps Perf Piano 84, Music Dpt Houghton Coll, Tchrs Assn 85; Houghton Coll; Music.

BECK, JONATHAN S; City Honors HS; Buffalo, NY; (Y); 2/97; Math Tm; Pres Science Clb; Orch; School Musical; Symp Band; Ntl Merit SF; Sal; VP Band; Chorus; VP Concert Band; Wnnr Sclp & Blde Soc & Pllsbry Schlrshp; U PA; Bio.

BECK, KELLY; North Babyon SR HS; North Babylon, NY; (Y); Church Yth Grp; Cmnty Wkr; Drama Clb; Girl Scts; School Play; Lit Mag; Cheerleading; Pom Pon; High Hon Roll; NHS; 1st Pl Oratrcl Awd 83; Bus.

BECK, LAURIE; Albion HS; Albion, NY; (S); 20/168; 4-H; Ski Clb; Spanish Clb; Jazz Band; Mrchg Band; Sec Soph Cls; Rep Stu Cncl; Gym; Socr; NHS; Zoology.

BECK, LINDA; Grand Island HS; Gr Island, NY; (Y); Art Clb; Church Yth Grp; Dance Clb; Teachers Aide; Trs Frsh Cls; Trs Soph Cls; Stu Cncl; JV Mgr(s); Socr; Cit Awd; Mgr Of Grnd Island Mc Donalds 85; Bus Mgmt.

BECK, MICHELE; Alexander Central Schl; Darien, NY; (S); 8/88; Church Yth Grp; FTA; Ski Clb; Spanish Clb; Stu Cncl; Var Cheerleading; JV Tennis; Jr NHS; NHS; SUNY-OSWEGO; Comm.

BECK, NANCY K; Brockport HS; Brockport, NY; (Y); 8/300; Trs Jr Cls; Trs Sr Cls; Var Capt Bsktbl; Coach Actv; Var Capt Socr; Var Trk; High Hon Roll; Jr NHS; NHS; Ntl Merit Schol; Schlrshp Banquet Awd; Ldrshp Awd; Capt Empire St Games Westrn Div Bsktbl 83-84; Cornell U; Bus.

BECK, PAMELA J; Long Island Lutheran HS; E Meadow, NY; (S); Drama Clb; Ski Clb; Band; Yrbk Stf; Rep Frsh Cls; Rep Soph Cls; Var Bsktbl; Var Vllybl; NHS; Ctznshp Awd 82 & 84.

BECK, PAUL RAYMOND; New Hartford HS; New Hartford, NY; (S); 10/263; German Clb; VP Chorus; L Bsbl; Bsktbl; L Ftbl; Powder Puff Ftbl; High Hon Roll; Jr NHS; NHS; NY ST Regents Scholar 85; U S Air Force Acad; Engrng.

BECK, SANDRA; Clarence Central HS; Clarence, NY; (Y); 10/280; JCL; Latin Clb; Ski Clb; Concert Band; School Musical; School Play; Nwsp Ed-Chief; Var Socr; Cit Awd; High Hon Roll; Ruel Mavis Awd For Good Schl Ctznshp 85; USAA For Englsh 84; Schlrshp To Northwestern U 85; Northwestern U; Pub Rel.

BECKER, BETSY MARIE; Homer HS; Homer, NY; (Y); 7/199; Am Leg Aux Girls St; Yrbk Stf; Sec Jr Cls; Pres Stu Cncl; Var Fld Hcky; Elks Awd; High Hon Roll; Kiwanis Awd; NHS; Church Yth Grp; William H Morgan Memrl Awd-Poltcl Sci 85; ST U-Albany.

BECKER, BRENDA; Fonda-Fultonville HS; Fultonville, NY; (Y); Church Yth Grp; Band; Chorus; Concert Band; Mrchg Band; Var Socr; Capt Var Vllybl; Stat Wrstlng; Hudson Vly CC; Lab Tech.

BECKER, BRIAN; Riverhead HS; Wading River, NY; (Y); 24/184; Red Cross Aide; Varsity Clb; Band; Concert Band; Jazz Band; Orch; Crs Cntry; Ftbl; Trk; Wt Lftg; Stony Brook U; Pre-Med.

BECKER, CASSANDRA; Garden City HS; Garden City, NY; (Y); Office Aide; Pep Clb; Spanish Clb; Chorus; School Musical; Variety Show; Trk; Im Mgr Vllybl; Stat Wrstlng; Hon Roll; Nassau CC; Nrsg.

BECKER, CATHY; Bainbridge-Guilford HS; Bainbridge, NY; (Y); 11/70; Church Yth Grp; French Clb; Girl Scts; Intnl Clb; Band; Chorus; Concert Band; Jazz Band; Mrchg Band; Orch; Amer Lgn Ortrcl Cntst 2nd 85; Psych.

BECKER, CHRISTA; Depew HS; Depew, NY; (Y); 7/254; Cmnty Wkr; GAA; VP Chorus; Variety Show; Rep Soph Cls; Tennis; Jr NHS; NHS; MVP Frsh Awd Music 82; Gen Bus Awd 85; ST U Coll Buffalo; Psych.

BECKER, DONALD C; Depew HS; Depew, NY; (Y); 19/254; Boy Scts; Cmnty Wkr; Red Cross Aide; Yrbk Stf; Lit Mag; JV Trk; Var Vllybl; Hon Roll; Jr NHS; Ntl Merit Ltr; NY ST Regents Schlrshp 85; Karr Parker Schlrshp 85; NY ST Assembly Cert Of Merit 85; NY ST U Buffalo; Elec Engrng.

BECKER, DOUGLAS; Maple Hill HS; Castleton, NY; (S); Aud/Vis; French Clb; Math Tm; Symp Band; Hon Roll; NHS; 1st Pl Lang Art Olympics Creat Comptng 84; SMPY; Comp Sci.

BECKER, ELAINE; Alden HS; Alden, NY; (Y); 2/198; Sec Church Yth Grp; French Clb; Girl Scts; Band; Chorus; Concert Band; Drm Mjr(t); Mrchg Band; School Musical; School Play; Wnnr Yth Writers Search 84; Nazareth Coll Rochester; Music.

BECKER, JOHN; Auburn HS; Auburn, NY; (S); 9/520; Latin Clb; Varsity Clb; Acpl Chr; Chorus; School Musical; Stage Crew; Swing Chorus; Variety Show; Var L Ftbl; High Hon Roll; U Of Rochester; Chem Engrng.

BECKER II, JOHN C; Mynderse Acad; Seneca Falls, NY; (S); 1/140; Boy Scts; Church Yth Grp; Trs Ski Clb; Concert Band; Jazz Band; Mrchg Band; School Musical; L Crs Cntry; L Golf; High Hon Roll.

BECKER, JUDITH; St Edmund HS; Brooklyn, NY; (S); 16/187; Church Yth Grp; Spanish Clb; Teachers Aide; Color Guard; Drm & Bgl; Drm Mjr(t); Variety Show; Yrbk Stf; Im Gym; Hon Roll; English Merit Awd 83; John Jay College; Criminal Just.

BECKER, KARIN; Colonie Central HS; Albany, NY; (Y); Intnl Clb; Band; Mrchg Band; Yrbk Stf; Rep Stu Cncl; JV Var Score Keeper; JV Vllybl; Hon Roll; U Of Denver; Accntng.

BECKER, RICHARD; Alden Central HS; Alden, NY; (Y); 25/212; Aud/Vis; Church Yth Grp; French Clb; Band; Concert Band; Jazz Band; Mrchg Band; Swmmng; Trk; Hon Roll; Acad Awd 82-84; Vrsty Ltr Swmmng 82-83.

BECKER, SANDRA; Frontier Central HS; Lakeview, NY; (Y); 88/500; Girl Scts; Pep Clb; Ski Clb; Stage Crew; Nwsp Rptr; Nwsp Stf; Rep Frsh Cls; Rep Soph Cls; Rep Jr Cls; Im Socr; St Bonaventure U; Bus Adm.

BECKER, SANFORD; Ballston Spa HS; Ballston Spa, NY; (Y); 7/240; Pres 4-H; Math Tm; JV Bsbl; Capt Var Bowling; JV Trk; 4-H Awd; High Hon Roll; NHS; Air Force ROTC Scholar 85; Physics Awd 85; Pres Fit Awd 85; Clarkson; Elec Engrng.

BECKERINK, JANNA; Clymer Central HS; Clymer, NY; (Y); Church Yth Grp; Pres 4-H; Band; Chorus; Yrbk Ed-Chief; Var L Bsktbl; 4-H Awd; Hon Roll; NHS; Prfct Atten Awd; Elem Educ.

BECKETT, MICHAEL W; Scarsdale HS; Scarsdale, NY; (Y); Computer Clb; Political Wkr; Stu Cncl; Ntl Merit SF; Intl Rel.

BECKETT, WILLIAM; Niagara Falls HS; Niagara Falls, NY; (Y); 25/272; Aud/Vis; Camera Clb; Church Yth Grp; Cmnty Wkr; Computer Clb; JA; Key Clb; Math Clb; Ski Clb; Nwsp Ed-Chief; JR Achvt Awd 85; Alfred ST; Elec Engrng.

BECKFORD, KAREN VERONICA; Bishop Loughlin HS; Brooklyn, NY; (S); 2/282; Dance Clb; Debate Tm; JA; Science Clb; Teachers Aide; Capt Varsity Clb; Capt Crs Cntry; Im Gym; Capt Trk; Im Vllybl; Tchr.

BECKHANS, RONI; Mercy HS; Watermill, NY; (Y); Sec Cmnty Wkr; Ski Clb; Spanish Clb; Varsity Clb; Cheerleading; Gym; Hon Roll; Prfct Atten Awd; Girl Scts; Chorus; Mission Clb Sec; Gym Awds; Ldrs Clb Sec; Acctng.

BECKINGHAUSEN, MARIA S; Sacred Heart Acad; Williamsville, NY; (Y); Cmnty Wkr; Sec Trs German Clb; JA; Red Cross Aide; Chorus; School Musical; Hon Roll; NHS; Church Choir; JR Achvt Awd 83; Outstndng Amherst YES Awd 84; Swm-A-Thon Apprctn Awd 82.

BECKMAN, HEIDI A; Bay Shore HS; Bay Shore, NY; (Y); 7/400; Cmnty Wkr; JV Crs Cntry; High Hon Roll; NHS; Pres Envrnmntl Yth Awd 83-85; Regnts Schlrshp 85; Canisius Coll; Bio.

BECKNER, STEPHANIE; Jordan-Elbridge HS; Elbridge, NY; (Y); Pres GAA; Chorus; Yrbk Ed-Chief; Pres Frsh Cls; Var Cheerleading; JV Fld Hcky; Var Tennis; Var Trk; High Hon Roll; Rep Jr NHS; Mst Outstndng Girls Vrsty Tnns Awd 84; Prom Ct; Law.

BECKSTEAD, KEVIN; Indian River HS; Calcium, NY; (Y); 12/126; Camera Clb; Church Yth Grp; Cmnty Wkr; French Clb; Band; School Play; Rep Jr Cls; JV Wrstlng; Hon Roll; NEDT Awd; Med.

BECKWITH, NOELLE; Hannibal Central HS; Hannibal, NY; (Y); Church Yth Grp; Sec 4-H; French Clb; Varsity Clb; Band; Chorus; Church Choir; Mrchg Band; School Musical; School Play.

BEDARD, AMY; Plattsburgh SR HS; Plattsburgh, NY; (Y); Cmnty Wkr; German Clb; Hosp Aide; Trs Service Clb; Varsity Clb; Chorus; Nwsp Rptr; Nwsp Stf; Cheerleading; Swmmng; Plattsburgh ST U; Culinary.

BEDDOME, DAVID W; Williamsville H S North; N Tonawanda, NY; (Y); 43/315; Ntl Merit SF; MIT; Aerontcl Engrng.

BEDELL, DAWN; Academy Of St Joseph; Kings Pk, NY; (Y); Church Yth Grp; Cmnty Wkr; Debate Tm; Hosp Aide; Library Aide; Spanish Clb; JV Cheerleading; Coach Actv; Hon Roll; Cert Hnr Ind Effrt NYS Mock Trial Tourn; Intl Law.

BEDELL, ELLEN; St John The Baptist D HS; Massapequa, NY; (Y); 8/550; Nwsp Rptr; Rep Frsh Cls; High Hon Roll; Hon Roll; NHS; Spanish NHS; Nrsng.

BEDELL, GEORGE; Seaford HS; Seaford, NY; (Y); Church Yth Grp; Computer Clb; Library Aide; Band; Concert Band; Mrchg Band; Trk; Hon Roll; NYSSMA 85; Comp Sci.

BEDELL, MICHAEL J; Wantagh SR HS; Wantagh, NY; (Y); 25/200; Pres Church Yth Grp; Debate Tm; JA; Ski Clb; Yrbk Rptr; Stu Cncl; JV Var Bsbl; JV Var Ftbl; Var Wt Lftg; Hon Roll; U Of S FL; Pub Rltns.

BEDELL, ROBERT; Whitesboro SR HS; Utica, NY; (Y); 86/320; Boy Scts; Trs Church Yth Grp; Y-Teens; Yrbk Bus Mgr; Rep Stu Cncl; Hon Roll; Opt Clb Awd; SADD Treas 84-85; Ordr Of Arrw-Vgl Hnr 84; Strtd Sml Lndscpng, Pantng & Drvwy Wrk Bus 83-85; MVCC; Bus.

BEDFORD, CHERYL; St John The Baptist D HS; Amityville, NY; (Y); Girl Scts; Rep JA; Stu Cncl; Cheerleading; Powder Puff Ftbl; Comp Sci.

BEDFORD, TRINA; Cicero-N Syracuse HS; Clay, NY; (S); 3/661; Mathletes; Chorus; School Musical; Rep Soph Cls; Rep Stu Cncl; Hon Roll; Prelaw.

BEDIA, DARALYN; Long Beach HS; Long Beach, NY; (S); 18/316; Capt Bsktbl; Var Sftbl; NHS; Adelphi U Trustee Scholar.

BEDNAR, ANTHONY; Union-Endicott HS; Endicott, NY; (Y); 127/462; Hon Roll; Opt Clb Awd; ST U Cortland; Comp Sci.

BEDNARZ, BLAKE; Frontier HS; Blasell, NY; (S); Varsity Clb; School Musical; School Play; Coach Actv; Ftbl; Trk; Wt Lftg; Wrstlng; Hon Roll; NHS; All Star Ftbl Player 83-84; State Finalist In Shot Put 83-84; All State Ftbl Player 84.

BEDNARZ, MARIANNE M; Glen Cove HS; Glen Cove, NY; (Y); 13/265; French Clb; Science Clb; Varsity Clb; Nwsp Sprt Ed; Bsktbl; Capt Socr; JV Var Sftbl; VP NHS; Pep Clb; Regents Schlrshp 85; Suny Binghamton; Med.

BEDORTHA, KATHERINE; Bishop Grimes HS; Fayetteville, NY; (Y); Church Yth Grp; French Clb; Varsity Clb; JV Bsktbl; Im Bowling; Im Ftbl; Var Socr; French Hon Soc; Hon Roll; Socl Wkr.

BEDORTHA, MARY EILEEN; Bishop Grimes HS; Fayetteville, NY; (Y); 28/207; Church Yth Grp; GAA; Variety Show; Rep Frsh Cls; Rep Soph Cls; Sec Sr Cls; JV Bsktbl; Var Capt Socr; Hon Roll; NHS; All-Cnty Soccr; NY Rgnts Schlrshp; Marquette U; Journalism.

BEEBE, KEN; Niagara Wheatfield HS; Lewiston, NY; (Y); 39/313; Church Yth Grp; French Clb; Var Capt Ice Hcky; Var Lcrss; Hon Roll; Lion Awd; NHS; MVP For Var Hcky 83-84; MVP For Var Lacrosse 84; RIT; Elec Engrng.

BEEBE, MICHELLE; Shenendehowa HS; Clifton Park, NY; (Y); 100/700; Church Yth Grp; GAA; Leo Clb; Varsity Clb; Concert Band; Orch; Yrbk Sprt Ed; Var Socr; High Hon Roll; NHS; Conf All ST Bnd NY 84; Empire ST Yth Orch 84-86; Subrbn Cncl 83-84; Law.

BEECHER, JAMES; Elmira Free Acad; Elmira, NY; (Y); Boy Scts; Church Yth Grp; Computer Clb; Latin Clb; Ski Clb; Varsity Clb; Chorus; Swing Chorus; Var L Ftbl; Stage Crew; Entrprnr.

BEECHLER JR, CARLTON R; Midlakes HS; Phelps, NY; (Y); Camera Clb; Church Yth Grp; Computer Clb; Band; Concert Band; Jazz Band; Mrchg Band; Orch; Pep Band; Stage Crew; Paul Smith Coll Syracuse; Eclgy.

BEELES, SCOTT D; Salamanca Central HS; Great Valley, NY; (Y); Am Leg Boys St; Ski Clb; Spanish Clb; Var Trk; Hon Roll; NHS; Spanish NHS; 3rd Pl Cty Art Shw 84; Med.

BEER, DEBORAH M; Eastchester HS; Eastchester, NY; (Y); 6/163; Sec French Clb; Key Clb; Band; Concert Band; Mrchg Band; High Hon Roll; Hon Roll; Ntl Merit Ltr; Alternative School Member 82-85; Wellsley In Westchester Awd 84; Beautification Comm Member 82-84; Cornell U.

BEERS, JAMES; Alexander Central HS; Darien Center, NY; (S); 3/102; Pres Frsh Cls; Pres Soph Cls; Pres Jr Cls; Var Bsbl; Var Stat Bsktbl; Var Ftbl; NHS; Math Tm; Pres Varsity Clb; Pres Band; Acadmc Tm 83-84; Donald Judd Memrl Awd Sprtsmnshp Awd 84; Outstndng Schlr Athl 83-84; Math.

BEERS, LORIE; Walton Central HS; Walton, NY; (Y); Church Yth Grp; FHA; Library Aide; Church Choir; DAR Awd; Hon Roll; NHS; Prfct Atten Awd; Bus Math Awd 83-84; Phy Thrpst.

BEERS, TIFFNEY; Union Endicott HS; Endicott, NY; (Y); 87/430; Ski Clb; Spanish Clb; Band; Color Guard; Drill Tm; Flag Corp; Jazz Band; Mrchg Band; Symp Band; Yrbk Stf; Prsdntl Acad Ftnss Awd; Broome CC; Arch.

BEETOW, CHRISTINE; Springville Griffith Inst; Springville, NY; (Y); Art Clb; Debate Tm; Political Wkr; Yrbk Phtg; Yrbk Stf; Artstc Achvt Awd 83-84.

BEGANY, ALISON; Sacred Heart HS; Yonkers, NY; (Y); 19/239; Intnl Clb; Library Aide; Hon Roll; NHS; St Rose; Bio.

BEGGS, NYALL B; Midwood College; Brooklyn, NY; (Y); 94/630; Boy Scts; Acpl Chr; Chorus; Church Choir; Madrigals; Variety Show; Yrbk Phtg; Ftbl; NHS; Med.

BEGHINI, KENNETH; Cardinal Mooney HS; Rochester, NY; (Y); 55/317; Boy Scts; Band; School Musical; High Hon Roll; Hon Roll; Eagle Scout Awd 84; Engrng.

BEGLEY, JANET; Commack High School North; E Northport, NY; (Y); Hosp Aide; Band; Concert Band; Jazz Band; Mrchg Band; Pep Band; Symp Band; Var Badmtn; Wt Lftg; Hon Roll; All Star Plyr CYO Sftbl Leage 83.

BEGLEY, MICHAEL; Valley Stram Central HS; Valley Stream, NY; (Y); Computer Clb; Stage Crew; Variety Show; Yrbk Stf; Crs Cntry; Trk; Engrng.

BEHARI JR, JOSEPH; Savona Central Schl; Savona, NY; (Y); 1/37; Am Leg Boys St; Church Yth Grp; Stage Crew; JV Crs Cntry; JV Socr; Var Trk; Acad All Stars; Miltry.

BEHNKE, MICHELE E; Brockport HS; Hamlin, NY; (Y); Yrbk Stf; Genesee CC; Fash Merch.

BEHR, DARRIN J; Performin Arts At La Guardia HS; New York, NY; (Y); Temple Yth Grp; Thesps; Chorus; School Musical; School Play; Stage Crew; Rep Sr Cls; JV Lcrss; JV Socr; Arts 85; Lighting Mngr 84; Theatre.

BEHREND, MARLENE A; Kendall JR SR HS; Kent, NY; (Y); 2/95; AFS; Spanish Clb; Band; Church Choir; Concert Band; Mrchg Band; Pep Band; Yrbk Stf; Jr NHS; Sec NHS; Regents Schlrshp 85; Cortland ST Outstndg Fresh Schlrshp 85; All-ST Band 84; Cortland ST; Math.

BEHRENS, KELLY ANN; Lindenhurst HS; Lindenhurst, NY; (Y); Dance Clb; Drama Clb; German Clb; Girl Scts; Thesps; Chorus; School Musical; School Play; Stage Crew; Yrbk Stf; Boces III Cmp Gftd & Tlntd Chldrn 85; NYU; Bus.

BEHRENS, STACY; Lafayette HS; Buffalo, NY; (Y); Band; Pep Band; Var Bsbl; All Hgh Bsbl 2nd Team 85.

BEHRMANN, KARIN; Smithtown High School East; Smithtown, NY; (Y); Concert Band; Stu Cncl; Cheerleading; Crs Cntry; Gym; Trk; French Hon Soc; High Hon Roll; Jr NHS; NHS; 1st Pl Frnch Ptry Cntst Hofstra U 83; Harvard Bk Prz Engl Achvt 85; All Leag Awd Trck 85; Sprts Med.

BEIN, DEBORAH; Roosevelt HS; Yonkers, NY; (S); Trs Band; Concert Band; Mrchg Band; VP Frsh Cls; Rep Soph Cls; Rep Jr Cls; Crs Cntry; Trk; High Hon Roll; NHS; Natl Bnd Assn 82-85; Collegiate Bnd 82-85; RPI Medal 85; Elect Engrng.

BEIO, NANCY; Richmond Hill HS; Woodhaven, NY; (Y); 14/300; English Clb; Library Aide; Office Aide; Service Clb; Teachers Aide; Hon Roll; NHS; Arista 85-86; Engl & Bus Hnr Society 84-85; Acctng.

BEIRNE, ANDREW; Ossining HS; Scarborough, NY; (Y); Model UN; Rep Stu Cncl; Var L Ice Hcky; Var L Lcrss; High Hon Roll; NHS; Political Wkr; Radio Clb; Nwsp Rptr; Ed Nwsp Stf; Statn Mgr, DJ, Nwcstr, Co Sprts Ed Radio Sta 82-85; Atty Mck Trl Tm 83-85; Mgr Ed Schl Nwspr 84-86.

BEIRNE, ANDREW E; Newtown HS; Elmhurst, NY; (Y); Aud/Vis; Boy Scts; Cmnty Wkr; Computer Clb; Exploring; Office Aide; PAVAS; Teachers Aide; School Play; Off Stu Cncl; Svc Cmmndtn Video Sqd 84; TV Prod.

BEITER, JULIE; Cleveland Hill HS; Cheektowaga, NY; (Y); Aud/Vis; GAA; Girl Scts; Stage Crew; Symp Band; Var L Sftbl; Grl Sctg Slvr Awd 81-85; 10 Yrs Perf Attndnc Mullen Sistrs Schl Of Dance 82; Erie CC; Bus Adm.

BEKKERING II, DON; Scotia Glenville HS; Scotia, NY; (Y); 51/250; Key Clb; Ski Clb; Concert Band; Rep Sr Cls; JV Golf; JV Trk; Bst Drssd Male 85; Excllnce Music 85; CO ST U; Accntng.

BELAIR, CASSANDRA; Allegany Central Schl; Allegany, NY; (Y); French Clb; Band; Concert Band; Mrchg Band; Nwsp Rptr; Nwsp Stf; Yrbk Stf; Tennis; High Hon Roll; NHS; Band Schlrshp Music Cmp 84; Medcl Tech.

BELANGER, DANIEL; Auburn HS; Auburn, NY; (Y); Boy Scts; Pres German Clb; Intnl Clb; Ski Clb; Varsity Clb; Chorus; L Golf; Var Capt Socr; L Tennis; Hon Roll; SADD Pres 82-85; Hstry Clb 83; Niagara U; Bus.

BELANGER, PAUL; Lindehurst HS; Lindenhurst, NY; (Y); Trs Art Clb; Varsity Clb; School Play; Yrbk Ed-Chief; VP Sr Cls; Capt Crs Cntry; Var Trk; Hon Roll; NHS; Voice Dem Awd; Natl Sci Olympd-1st Pl Trajctry Cntst 85; Engrng.

BELAS, EDWARD; Webutuck Central HS; Wassaic, NY; (Y); Am Leg Boys St; JV Var Bsktbl; Hon Roll; NHS; Math.

BELASKY, ALISA; East Meadow HS; East Meadow, NY; (S); FBLA; Key Clb; Temple Yth Grp; Band; Concert Band; Mrchg Band; Cheerleading; JV Var Lcrss; Tennis; Hon Roll.

BELE, CARA; Niagara Falls HS; Niagara Falls, NY; (Y); Boys Clb Am; Chess Clb; Church Yth Grp; Civic Clb; Cmnty Wkr; Computer Clb; Exploring; French Clb; Pep Clb; Band; Marines; FBI.

BELE, MARY; Cardinal Spellman HS; Bronx, NY; (Y); Cmnty Wkr; German Clb; Stage Crew; Hon Roll; Chrstn Action Corps Silver Medal 2nd Pl 85; Accntng.

BELEC, ANDREA LYNNE; North Babylon SR HS; N Babylon, NY; (Y); 41/556; Drama Clb; Acpl Chr; Chorus; Madrigals; School Musical; School Play; Swing Chorus; Nwsp Rptr; Nwsp Stf; Yrbk Stf; Potsdam Coll Acad Scholar 85; SUNY Potsdam; Mth.

BELEN, KENDRICK E; La Salle Acad; New York, NY; (S); #2 In Class; Doc Of Med.

BELEVICH, MARIANNE; Westlake HS; Hawthorne, NY; (Y); 15/153; Sec Church Yth Grp; Church Yth Grp; Cmnty Wkr; French Clb; Spanish Clb; Chorus; Church Choir; Yrbk Stf; Stu Cncl; Cheerleading; Mt Pleasant Tchrs Assoc Awd 85; Am Assoc U Womn Awd 85; Pres Acadmc Ftns Awd 85; W Grogan Schlrshp 85; Siena Clg; Bus.

BELFIELD, MATTHEW; Royalton Hartland Central HS; Gasport, NY; (Y); 4/141; Am Leg Boys St; Boy Scts; Church Yth Grp; Cmnty Wkr; Pres Varsity Clb; Chorus; School Musical; Var L Bsktbl; Var L Ftbl; Var L Trk; Mst Outstndng Arch Drwg Stu 85; MVP Trk & Fld 85; All Leag High Jump 85.

BELFIGLIO, BRIAN; Middletown SR HS; Middletown, NY; (Y); School Musical; Swing Chorus; Rep Jr Cls; JV Var Bsbl; Bsktbl; JV Var Socr; Hon Roll; Cmnty Wkr; Drama Clb; Political Wkr; Concert Choir 82-85; Eastern Jazz Pop Festvl 85; Dem Boys 82-84; NYSSMA Choir Evalutn 85; Bus.

BELIK, BARBARA I; Canandaigua Acad; Canandaigua, NY; (Y); French Clb; Trs Frsh Cls; Trs Soph Cls; JV Tennis; High Hon Roll; NHS; NYS Regents Schlrshp 85; Med.

BELIZARE, MARGARET; Bishop Ford Central Catholic HS; Brooklyn, NY; (Y); Church Yth Grp; Dance Clb; French Clb; Hosp Aide; Science Clb; Chorus; Rep Frsh Cls; Rep Stu Cncl; Tennis; Hon Roll; Cornell; Pre-Med.

BELKNAP, DAVID S; Thomas A Edison HS; Elmira Heights, NY; (Y); 21/85; Am Leg Boys St; Varsity Clb; VICA; Var L Bsbl; Var L Bsktbl; Var L Ftbl; Wt Lftg; Fire Dept JR Firemn Yr 84; Rtry Clb JR Rotrn 83-84; Navy; Machnst.

BELKOWITZ, HAROLD; Fayetteville-Manlius HS; Manlius, NY; (Y); 28/332; Exploring; Math Tm; Trs Temple Yth Grp; Nwsp Stf; Hon Roll; NHS; Ntl Merit Ltr; Spanish Clb; Im Bsktbl; JV Golf; NY ST Rgnts Schlrshp 85; Prsdntl Awd Acdmc Ftnss 85; Brandieis U.

BELL, ANN MARIE; Westbury SR HS; Westbury, NY; (Y); 16/200; Computer Clb; Varsity Clb; Nwsp Rptr; VP Frsh Cls; Rep Stu Cncl; L Badmtn; Cit Awd; Hon Roll; Kiwanis Awd; NHS; Schlrshp Awd; Hobart & William Smith Coll; Ps.

BELL, ANTHONY JOSEPH; East Rockaway HS; E Rockaway, NY; (Y); 2/122; Cmnty Wkr; School Play; Yrbk Stf; Pres Jr Cls; Pres Sr Cls; Rep Stu Cncl; NHS; Sal; Church Yth Grp; Exploring; Clark U Schlrshp 85; Citation For Cmnty Srv & Acad Excllnc 85; Clark U; Bio.

BELL, CASEY L; Laguardia H S Of Music & The Arts; Bronx, NY; (Y); 26/538; Chorus; Hon Roll; NHS; Art Hnr League 84; Regents Schlrshp 85; Daily News Princpl 83; Med.

BELL, CYNTHIA; Sachem High School North; Lk Ronkonkoma, NY; (Y); German Clb; Science Clb; Varsity Clb; Chorus; Madrigals; Gym; MVP V Gymnstcs 83.

BELL, DARYL C; Moravia Central HS; Skaneateles, NY; (Y); 1/109; Chorus; Jazz Band; Mrchg Band; School Play; VP Jr Cls; Rep Stu Cncl; Var Tennis; Val; Quiz Bowl; Concert Band; NY ST Rgnts Schlrshp 85; Amer Lgn Awd-MIV Band Mbr 81-82; A T Atwood Prz For Deprtmnt 83-84; Cayuga Cnty Comm Coll; Engr.

BELL, DEBI; Centereach HS; Centereach, NY; (S); VP DECA; FBLA; Hosp Aide; Temple Yth Grp; Chorus; Variety Show; Hon Roll; Prfct Atten Awd; 3rd Pl In DECA ST Conf At Concord 84-85; Suffolk CC; Bus Adm.

BELL, ERIC; Cold Spring Harbor HS; Cold Sprg Harbor, NY; (Y); Boy Scts; French Clb; Intnl Clb; Band; Chorus; Pep Band; Wrstlng; Cit Awd; Hon Roll; Cmnty Svc Awd 84 & 85; Bus.

BELL, IRENE M; John Jay HS; Wappingers Fls, NY; (Y); Sec Church Yth Grp; Sec Trs 4-H; Ski Clb; Band; Stat Crs Cntry; Stat Socr; God Cntry Awd; Hon Roll; Crftsmn Yr Awd 82; Nrsng.

BELL, JEANINE; Brighton HS; Rochester, NY; (Y); 17/315; French Clb; Girl Scts; Sec VP Thesps; Chorus; Madrigals; School Musical; School Play; Stage Crew; Ntl Merit Ltr.

BELL, JEFF; Liverpool Central HS; Liverpool, NY; (S); 87/880; School Musical; Hon Roll; Jr NHS; Embry-Riddle; Aero Engr.

BELL, JENNIFER A; Norman Thomas HS; Bronx, NY; (S); 52/671; Cmnty Wkr; VP JA; Chorus; Rep Frsh Cls; Rep Soph Cls; Cit Awd; Hon Roll; NHS; Prfct Atten Awd; Cert Profcncy Stengrphy 85; Cert Profcncy Wrd Procssg 85; ST U NY Albany; Bus Adm.

BELL, JOSEPH W; Greece Arcadia HS; Rochester, NY; (Y); 12/292; Boy Scts; Church Yth Grp; Math Clb; Math Tm; Yrbk Stf; VP Sr Cls; Capt L Crs Cntry; High Hon Roll; JETS Awd; VP NHS; Rochester Gannett Schlrshp 85; NYS Sci Supervsrs Bio Awd 82; Regents Schlrshp 85; SUNY-BINGHAMTON; Pre-Med.

BELL, KELLEY; Greenwich HS; Greenwich, NY; (Y); Art Clb; FHA; Girl Scts; VICA; Var Bsktbl; Var Mgr(s); Var Score Keeper; Var Sftbl; Prfct Atten Awd; Hnr Roll For Southern Adironack Educnl Ctr 84; Prof Hair Dresser.

BELL, KELLY; Franklin Acad; Malone, NY; (Y); Church Yth Grp; Pep Clb; Church Choir; Stu Cncl; Bus.

BELL, MARIA; Harpursville JR-SR HS; Harpursville, NY; (S); 8/102; Church Yth Grp; French Clb; Girl Scts; Hosp Aide; Chorus; Stu Cncl; Vllybl; High Hon Roll; NHS; Prfct Atten Awd; Hnr Banqt Engl 9; Voice Of Democracy 9th Pl ST 84; Syracuse; Phy Thrphy.

BELL, MARY BETH; Canandaigua SR Acad; Canandaigua, NY; (Y); 21/277; Am Leg Aux Girls St; German Clb; Chorus; VP Frsh Cls; VP Soph Cls; Pres Stu Cncl; Var Capt Tennis; Var VP Vllybl; High Hon Roll; NHS; Regents Schlrshp Winner; Hamilton; Pre Law.

BELL, MICHAEL J; Perry Central HS; Perry, NY; (S); 14/79; Am Leg Boys St; 4-H; FFA.

BELL, MONIQUE; St Catharine Acad; Bronx, NY; (Y); 74/264; Church Yth Grp; Dance Clb; Girl Scts; Church Choir; Fld Hcky; Trk; Hon Roll; 2nd Pl Dbtante 85; Ntrl Artstc Ablty Awd-Tlnt Shw 85; Intr Dsgnr.

BELL, TIMISHA; Hempstead HS; Hempstead, NY; (S); 78/365; Cmnty Wkr; Debate Tm; Spanish Clb; Chorus; Church Choir; Rep Stu Cncl; Bowling; 3rd Pl Elem Schl Math B 80; Biomed.

BELLADONNA, JOSEPH; La Salle Acad; New York, NY; (Y); 12/250; Boy Scts; Hosp Aide; Math Clb; Math Tm; Trs Sr Cls; Bowling; Crs Cntry; Trk; NHS; CPA.

BELLAMY, ANGELA; Henninger HS; Syracuse, NY; (Y); DECA; Church Choir; Variety Show; Bus.

BELLAMY, SPENCER; Holy Trinity HS; Uniondale, NY; (Y); Boy Scts; Office Aide; Variety Show; Rep Stu Cncl; JV Var Bsbl; JV Bsktbl; JV Var Ftbl; JV Var Trk; JV Var Wt Lftg; Hon Roll; Bus Mgmt.

BELLANCA, RICHARD; Bishop Kearney HS; Rochester, NY; (Y); Var Ice Hcky; Var Tennis; JV Wrstlng; U Of Dayton; Accntng.

BELLANGER, KIM; South Colonie HS; Albany, NY; (Y); 79/423; Spanish Clb; Nwsp Stf; Trs Frsh Cls; Pres Soph Cls; Rep Stu Cncl; Var Capt Bsktbl; Var Fld Hcky; Var Socr; Var Trk; NHS; Pace U; Blgy.

BELLANTONI, JOHN; Miller Place HS; Miller Pl, NY; (Y); 3/206; Church Yth Grp; Debate Tm; FBLA; Mathletes; Math Tm; Capt Var Crs Cntry; JV Socr; Var Tennis; Capt Var Trk; Cit Awd; John Douglas Mem Schlrshp For Outstdng Stu/Athlt 85; All-ST & All-NE Rgn In Crss Cntry 84; Duke U; Law.

BELLARDINI, THOMAS M; Pulaski JR SR HS; Pulaski, NY; (S); Math Clb; Ski Clb; Varsity Clb; Band; Mrchg Band; VP Jr Cls; Capt L Ftbl; Im Wt Lftg; Hon Roll; Aerntcl Engr.

BELLAVIA, REGINA; Rocky Point JR SR HS; Rocky Point, NY; (S); 10/189; Varsity Clb; Band; Concert Band; Mrchg Band; Capt Bsktbl; Capt Fld Hcky; Capt Sftbl; Hon Roll; NHS; Orch; LILCO Stdnt Ath Awd 84; PA ST U.

BELLE, GERMAINE A; Midwood HS; Brooklyn, NY; (Y); 143/605; Sec Service Clb; School Musical; Yrbk Stf; Ed Lit Mag; Rep Stu Cncl; Prfct Atten Awd; Super Yth Awd 84; Cert De Merit 82.

BELLE, MARIA; Mahopac HS; Mahopac, NY; (Y); 57/423; Church Yth Grp; Chorus; Nwsp Stf; Pres Soph Cls; Pres Jr Cls; Rep Pres Stu Cncl; JV Var Cheerleading; Mgr(s); Score Keeper; JV Var Sftbl; Comm Arts.

BELLEFOND, LISA; Notre Dame HS; New York City, NY; (Y); Political Wkr; Cmnty Wkr; Drama Clb; Hosp Aide; School Play; Yrbk Stf; Tennis; NYS Regents Schlrshp 85; SF Natl Hisp Schlr Awds 85; Schlrshp CT Coll 85; CT Coll; Eng.

BELLEVILLE, CAROL; Victor SR HS; Victor, NY; (Y); Church Yth Grp; Ski Clb; Varsity Clb; Acpl Chr; Chorus; Orch; School Musical; School Play; Sec Soph Cls; Rep Stu Cncl; Htl Rstrnt Mgmt.

BELLINGER, JODI; Thomas A Edison HS; Hoseheads, NY; (Y); 3/90; Am Leg Aux Girls St; Acpl Chr; Concert Band; Drm Mjr(t); Jazz Band; Orch; Pres Frsh Cls; Trs Soph Cls; Trs Jr Cls; Psych.

BELLINGER, MICHAEL A; West Genesee SR HS; Syracuse, NY; (Y); 1/460; Concert Band; Jazz Band; Mrchg Band; Orch; Symp Band; Rep Jr Cls; Elks Awd; High Hon Roll; NHS; Ntl Merit Ltr; Intl Frgn Lang Awd 82; NY ST Regents Scholar 85; Sci Fellowshp 85; Lehigh U; Engrng.

BELLISARIO, ANDREA; Columbia HS; East Greenbush, NY; (Y); 25/353; Hosp Aide; Var Tennis; Var Trk; Hon Roll; NHS; SADD Pres & Fndr; Boston U; Physcl Thrpy.

BELLIZZI, MARIA; Cardinal Spellman HS; Bronx, NY; (Y); Rep Jr Cls; Hon Roll; Ed.

BELLIZZI, PATRICIA; John Jay SR HS; Hopewell Juncti, NY; (Y); Church Yth Grp; Chorus; Yrbk Stf; JV Bsktbl; JV Fld Hcky; Var Sftbl; JV Var Vllybl; Var High Hon Roll; Hon Roll; Fine Arts.

BELLO, JOHN; South Shore HS; Brooklyn, NY; (Y); Cmnty Wkr; Medal Schlrshp 85; Brooklyn Coll; Comp Sci.

BELLOMO, STEPHEN; St Francis Prep; Whitestone, NY; (S); 11/693; Math Tm; Science Clb; Band; Im Ftbl; Im Sftbl; Im Capt Vllybl; NHS; Prncpls List.

BELLON, NICHOLAS A; H Frank Carey HS; Garden City, NY; (Y); 15/281; Boy Scts; Cmnty Wkr; Pres Drama Clb; School Musical; School Play; Ed Nwsp Stf; L Trk; NHS; Ntl Merit Ltr; Natl Merit Cmmndtn 85; Century III Ldrs Amer Awd 84; Tlntd & Gftd Prog; NY U; Cmmnctns.

BELLOS, MARIA; Mahopac HS; Mahopac Falls, NY; (Y); 58/423; Hon Roll; NHS; Pol Sci.

BELLOW, JOHN; Pulaski HS; Richland, NY; (S); 9/101; Am Leg Boys St; Drama Clb; Letterman Clb; Varsity Clb; Capt Var Ftbl; Capt Var Trk; Hon Roll; Ntl Merit Ltr; Bowdoin Coll; Physcs.

BELLUCCI, ANGELA M; West Babylon HS; West Babylon, NY; (Y); 4/416; DECA; Band; Concert Band; Nwsp Ed-Chief; VP Pres Lit Mag; Hon Roll; NHS; Rgnts Schlrshp 84-85; DECA Radio Adv 1st In Cnty Lvl, 3rd In ST Lvl 84-85; Hofstra U; Comm.

BELLUM, KAROLINE; Cooperstown Central Schl; Cooperstown, NY; (Y); GAA; Chorus; Trk; Vllybl; Sci.

BELMONT, DEBBIE; Frankfort-Schuyler Central HS; Frankfort, NY; (S); FBLA; Library Aide; Spanish Clb; Hon Roll; NHS; Herkimer County Comm; Bus.

BELMONT, GREGORY C; Lynbrook HS; Hewlett, NY; (Y); Debate Tm; VP Mathletes; NFL; Quiz Bowl; Speech Tm; Temple Yth Grp; School Play; Nwsp Bus Mgr; Yrbk Ed-Chief; VP Stu Cncl; Harvard U; Engrng.

BELROSE, GINA; East Islip HS; Great River, NY; (Y); DECA; Hon Roll; Johnson & Wales; Adm Asst.

BELT, KATHERINE; Northport HS; Northport, NY; (Y); 70/585; Art Clb; Dance Clb; Exploring; Political Wkr; Chorus; Variety Show; Stat Wrstlng; Hon Roll; Typing/Bus Awd 83; Svr Anouncer 83; Art Achvt 83-84; Med.

BELTON, KRISTINE; Commack High School South; Commack, NY; (Y); Computer Clb; Math Tm; Office Aide; Teachers Aide; Var Badmtn; JV Tennis; High Hon Roll; NHS; Ntl Merit Ltr; Natl Sci Olympiad Chem 85; Comp Sci.

BELTRAN, JESUS; All Hallows HS; New York, NY; (Y); Teachers Aide; Bsbl; Bsktbl; Bowling; Ftbl; Score Keeper; Timer; Wt Lftg; High Hon Roll; Hon Roll; 2nd Hnr 82; 1st Hnr 83; Bio.

BELTRANO, TONI MARIE; Trott Vocational HS; Niagara Falls, NY; (Y); Girl Scts; Chorus; Nwsp Rptr; RN.

BELVISO, MARGARET; Pelham Memorial HS; Pelham, NY; (Y); VP Drama Clb; Band; Chorus; Concert Band; Mrchg Band; School Musical; School Play; Lit Mag; Hon Roll; NHS; Peer Cnslr 85-86; Model Cngrs 85-86.

BENA, VICTOR; Lindenhurst SR HS; Lindenhurst, NY; (Y); Church Yth Grp; Computer Clb; Science Clb; Yrbk Stf; Bsbl; Wrstlng; High Hon Roll; Comp Engr.

BENALT, LAURA; Southside HS; Rockville Ctr, NY; (Y); 32/291; Art Clb; Drama Clb; Science Clb; Temple Yth Grp; Thesps; Chorus; School Musical; Yrbk Stf; High Hon Roll; NHS; 3rd Pl Grphcs Molloy Coll 85; Music Spnsrs Awd-Chrs 85.

BENASUTTI, KRISTINE; Bethpage HS; Bethpage, NY; (Y); 45/281; Var Capt Bsktbl; Var Capt Sftbl; Var Capt Vllybl; High Hon Roll; Prfct Atten Awd; Outstndng Athl Yr 83-84; Outstndng Athl 4 Yrs 81-85; All Cnty Sftbl Plyr, Daily News All Star 85; St Johns U; Acctng.

BENAVIDES, GRACE; Hutchinson Central Technical HS; Buffalo, NY; (Y); VP Math Clb; VP Math Tm; Pres Band; Church Choir; Pres Concert Band; Pres Jazz Band; Mrchg Band; Swmmng; Hon Roll; Arch Dsgn.

BENBOW, CURIN; The Knox Schl; East Setauket, NY; (S); Orch; Yrbk Sprt Ed; Var Bsktbl; Var Cheerleading; Var Socr; Var Sftbl; JV Vllybl; 4-H Awd; Hon Roll; Prfct Atten Awd; Sci Hnr Roll 82-83; Vrsty Ltr Chrldng 82-83; Medal For Fine Work In Orchstr 80-83; Pepperdine U; Comm.

BENCE, CHRIS; Emma Willard Schl; N Adams, MA; (Y); Dance Clb; French Clb; Office Aide; PAVAS; Ski Clb; School Musical; School Play; Yrbk Stf; VP Sr Cls; Crs Cntry; Mdrn/Jzz Dncr.

BENCHER, JOHN M; Arlington HS; Poughkeepsie, NY; (Y); 15/548; Ski Clb; JV L Socr; High Hon Roll; IBM Watson Memrl Schlrshp Semi Fnlst 85; U Of MI Alumni Schlrshp Semi Fnlst 85; U Of MI; Arch.

BENCIVENGA, LAURA; John H Glenn HS; E Northport, NY; (Y); Chorus; School Play; Stage Crew; Variety Show; Stu Cncl; Mgr Cheerleading; Framingdale; Secy Sci.

BENDELL, BRUCE; New Rochelle HS; New Rochelle, NY; (Y); Debate Tm; VP Ski Clb; VP Golf.

BENDER, CATHY; Coxsackie-Athens HS; West Coxsackie, NY; (Y); 26/92; Church Yth Grp; VP 4-H; Spanish Clb; 4-H Awd; Hon Roll; Columbia Grene; Phrmcy.

BENDER, CHARLES; Schoharie Central Schl; Schoharie, NY; (S); 9/89; Var Bowling; Var Socr; Hon Roll; Math.

BENDER, CHRISTINE; Villa Maria Acad; Cheektowaga, NY; (Y); 15/115; Church Yth Grp; JCL; Latin Clb; Math Clb; Chorus; Rep VP Stu Cncl; Hon Roll; NHS; NEDT Awd; Law.

BENDER, ERIKA; Walton Central HS; Walton, NY; (Y); 8/140; AFS; Girl Scts; Varsity Clb; Concert Band; L Orch; Trs Sr Cls; Var L Cheerleading; Var L Trk; High Hon Roll; Sec NHS; Soph,Jr Schlrshp; NYSMUH; Dntstry.

BENDER, MARCIA; Doane Stuart Schl; Hudson, NY; (S); Ski Clb; Yrbk Ed-Chief; Var L Socr; Var L Sftbl; Var L Vllybl; The Sue De Lew Schlrsph Awd 84; Chem.

BENDER, SARAH; East Syracuse Minda HS; Fayetteville, NY; (Y); 28/338; Sec Pres Church Yth Grp; Variety Show; Yrbk Stf; Gym; Var JV Socr; High Hon Roll; NHS; Hartwick Pres Schlr Schlrshp 85; Amer Legn Post Schlrshp 85; Harwick Coll; Intl Bus Mgmt.

BENDER, STEFFANY; Fayetteville Manlius HS; Fayetteville, NY; (Y); JV Var Socr; Capt Sftbl; NHS; Church Yth Grp; Church Choir; High Hon Roll; Hon Roll; NHS; Sftbl 2nd Tm All Cnty 84-85; Sftbl Hnrb Mntn All Cnty 83; Socr Hnrb Mntn All Cnty 85; Law.

BENEDETTO, RENEE; St Agnes HS; Rockville Centre, NY; (Y); Drama Clb; French Clb; Hosp Aide; School Play; Yrbk Bus Mgr; Var Capt Cheerleading; Var Crs Cntry; Var Trk; NHS; Teachers Aide; Latin Hnr Soc 84-85; Ldrs Clb 83-85; Ldng Nassau Schlstc Achvr 85; Catholic U Of Amer; Chld Psyclg.

BENEDICT, JANICE; Skaneateles HS; Skaneateles, NY; (Y); 4-H; Girl Scts; Chorus; 4-H Awd; Hon Roll; GSA Slvr Awd 84; GSA Gold Awd 85; Food Svc.

BENEDICT, JILL; Fairport HS; Fairport, NY; (Y); Exploring; Girl Scts; Ski Clb; Yrbk Sprt Ed; Cheerleading; Im Coach Actv; JV Diving; Stat Ftbl; Var Mgr(s); Sftbl; Natl Schltc Art Awd 82; MI ST U; Biol.

BENEDICT, JOANNE; Immaculta Acad; Derby, NY; (Y); Trs Church Yth Grp; Debate Tm; Hosp Aide; JA; Math Clb; Ski Clb; Spanish Clb; Variety Show; Nwsp Stf; Lit Mag; Spec Ed.

BENEDICT, STACY; Susquehanna Valley HS; Binghamton, NY; (Y); Art Clb; Band; Mrchg Band; Bsbl; Socr; Hon Roll; Broome CC; Engrng.

BENEK, SUSAN; Maine Endwell SR HS; Johnson, NY; (Y); 35/250; Art Clb; Key Clb; Stage Crew; Yrbk Stf; High Hon Roll; Hon Roll; NHS; Harriet W Coughlin Mem Schlrshp 85; Broome Cnty Med Scty Aux Schlrshp 85; ME Masonic Schlrshp 85; Broome CC; Med Tech.

BENES, TED R; Hamburg Central HS; Hamburg, NY; (Y); Chess Clb; CAP; Computer Clb; Var Ftbl; Im Socr; Var Wt Lftg; Var Wrstlng; SUNY Coll Buffalo; Bus.

BENEVENTO, RICHARD; De Sales HS; Lockport, NY; (Y); Cmnty Wkr; Var Capt Bsbl; Var Ftbl; Ntl Merit Ltr; All Catholics Hnr-Bsbl 85; Chris Chase-Mark Ritzenthaler Memrl Awd-Sprtsmnshp 85; Bus.

BENEWAY, MELISSA ANN; Franklin D Roosevelt HS; Poughkeepsie, NY; (Y); 13/325; Cmnty Wkr; Hosp Aide; Office Aide; Teachers Aide; Rep Frsh Cls; Rep Jr Cls; Elks Awd; Hon Roll; NHS; Craft Construction Co Awd/Schlrshp 85; Dutchess Fd Svc Schlrshp 85; Hyde Pk Assn Schlrshp 85; Rochester Inst Tech; Bus Admin.

BENFORD, PATTY; School Of The Holy Child; Larchmont, NY; (Y); Art Clb; Dance Clb; Key Clb; Yrbk Stf; Rep Frsh Cls; JV Fld Hcky; Var Sftbl; Var Swmmng; Hon Roll; Ntl Merit Ltr.

BENIAMINO, MELANIE; Midlakes HS; Phelps, NY; (Y); 54/154; Church Yth Grp; GAA; Letterman Clb; Varsity Clb; Nwsp Rptr; Yrbk Stf; Capt Cheerleading; Coach Actv; Socr; Hon Roll; ST U Oswego; Actg.

BENIMOWITZ, APRIL L; G W Hewlett HS; Woodmere, NY; (Y); 67/278; FBLA; Nwsp Phtg; Nwsp Stf; Yrbk Phtg; Stu Cncl; NYS Regnts Schlrshp; Washington U St Louis; Law.

BENINATO, RENEE; New Dorp HS; Staten Island, NY; (Y); Intnl Clb; JA; Key Clb; Library Aide; Math Tm; Spanish Clb; Bowling; Pom Pon; Jr NHS; NHS; Engrng.

BENINGO, ANGELA; Trott Vocational HS; Niagara Falls, NY; (Y); Hosp Aide; Nwsp Stf; Hon Roll; NHS; Nrsng.

BENINGO, KARYN; Niagara Wheatfield HS; Niagara Falls, NY; (Y); 1/315; PAVAS; Concert Band; Mrchg Band; High Hon Roll; NHS; Regents Schlrshp 85; Acad Schlrshp 85; Pres Schlrshp 85; Niagara U; Biol.

BENITEZ, JOHN A; La Salle Acad; Brooklyn, NY; (S); Art Clb; Nwsp Sprt Ed; Nwsp Stf; Bowling; Crs Cntry; Im Fld Hcky; Im Ftbl; Trk; Hon Roll; NHS; Track Ltr Frshmn 83; Schl Swtr 83; 2nd Hnrs Awd 83; Acctng.

BENJAMIN, AMY L; Homer HS; Homer, NY; (Y); 32/200; Spanish Clb; Cheerleading; Hon Roll; Morrisville Ag & Tech; Accntng.

BENJAMIN, KELI S; Franklin Acad; Malone, NY; (Y); 60/275; Ski Clb; Spanish Clb; Varsity Clb; Off Frsh Cls; Off Soph Cls; Off Jr Cls; Stu Cncl; Vllybl; NY ST Rgnts Schlrshp 85; Cortland ST.

BENJAMIN, LISA; North Babylon SR HS; Wheatley Heights, NY; (Y); 40/556; Church Yth Grp; Dance Clb; Key Clb; Pep Clb; Capt Varsity Clb; Nwsp Rptr; Yrbk Sprt Ed; Capt Trk; High Hon Roll; NHS; Bst Athl 85; MVP Trck 84-85; Georgetown U; Poli Sci.

BENJAMIN, LISA S; Hunter College HS; Cambria Hts, NY; (Y); Cmnty Wkr; Math Clb; Political Wkr; Princeton U; Psych.

BENJAMIN, MARY L; Mt Markham HS; Cassville, NY; (Y); 1/118; Church Yth Grp; Model UN; Band; Chorus; Church Choir; Yrbk Bus Mgr; DAR Awd; Trs NHS; Val; E E Hallbeck Mem Pstl Schlrshp 85; Optimist Yth Mnth 84; Frnch Awd 84; Word Of Life Bible Inst; Engr.

BENJAMIN, STEVE; Hendrick Hudson HS; Peekskill, NY; (Y); Chess Clb; Debate Tm; Nwsp Stf; Yrbk Stf; Pres Soph Cls; Pres Jr Cls; Pres Sr Cls; Var L Bsktbl; Var Capt Socr; Var L Trk; All Lg Tm Socr 84; Sport For Understndng Socr Tm Brazil 85; Engl.

BENJAMIN, VICKI; Limestone Union Free HS; Limestone, NY; (Y); 7/20; GAA; Latin Clb; Pep Clb; Chorus; Yrbk Stf; JV Cheerleading; Var Sftbl; Var Vllybl; Hon Roll; VP Frsh Cls; Rgnts Diplma Bus; Miss Teen NY Cntstnt; Solost Sprng Concrt; Jamestown Bus Coll; Mrktng.

BENKOVIC, LINDA; Binghamton HS; Binghamton, NY; (Y); Am Leg Aux Girls St; Teachers Aide; Orch; Var L Bsktbl; Var Capt Crs Cntry; Var L Sftbl; JV Swmmng; Var L Btty Crckr Awd; High Hon Roll; Rotary Awd; Sect 4 Class A Cross Cntry Champ 84; Seleall-Confrnce Tm-Bsktbl 85; Rotary Ldrshp Confrnce 85.

BENN, ALFRED; Our Saviour Lutheran HS; Bronx, NY; (Y); Boy Scts; Computer Clb; Var Bsktbl; Var Ftbl; Var Socr; Rep Wt Lftg; Ntl Merit Ltr; Prfct Atten Awd; NY U; Medcl Dr.

BENNEAR, ELISABETH RUTH; Jamesville Dewitt HS; Dewitt, NY; (Y); Art Clb; Ski Clb; Chorus; Stage Crew; Yrbk Stf; Vllybl; Grphc Dsgnr.

BENNETT, BARBARA; Elmira Southside HS; Elmira, NY; (Y); Latin Clb; Pep Clb; Hon Roll; Accntng.

BENNETT, CRYSTAL; Walton HS; Bronx, NY; (Y); 20/500; Church Yth Grp; Cmnty Wkr; Library Aide; Office Aide; Chorus; Yrbk Rptr; Yrbk Stf; Cit Awd; Hon Roll; Secy Yth Clb NY Natl Assn Negro Bus & Prof Wmns Clbs 84-85; Baruch Coll New York; Bus Admn.

BENNETT, DERICK; Bishop Loughlin Memorial HS; Brooklyn, NY; (S); Band; Concert Band; Drm Mjr(t); Jazz Band; Orch; School Musical; School Play; Stage Crew; Im Bsbl; Im Bsktbl; NY Technical Coll; Arch Tech.

BENNETT, ELIZABETH M; West Genesee SR HS; Camillus, NY; (Y); French Clb; Girl Scts; Chorus; Nwsp Rptr; Yrbk Ed-Chief; French Hon Soc; High Hon Roll; NHS; Hosp Aide; JA; SADD VP 84-85; SADD Pres 85-86; Mc Gill U Montreal; Chld Psych.

BENNETT, IRIS E; La Guardia High School Of The Arts; New York, NY; (Y); 1/588; Cmnty Wkr; Office Aide; Service Clb; Yrbk Stf; Lit Mag; Gov Hon Prg Awd; High Hon Roll; Ntl Merit SF; Val; 1st Prize City Coll Poetry Cont 84; Hnrb Mntn NYC HS Poetry Cont 83; Soph Most Potential Art 83; Brown; Writer.

BENNETT, JEFFREY; West Canada Valley Central HS; Poland, NY; (S); 1/81; Aud/Vis; Computer Clb; Model UN; Band; Concert Band; Mrchg Band; Orch; Yrbk Sprt Ed; Yrbk Stf; Var L Golf; Natl Latin Exam 80; Mind Olympcs 83; Ntl Frnch Test Cert Merit; Rensselaer; Elec Engr.

BENNETT, KERRY L; Lockport SR HS; Lockport, NY; (Y); 27/414; Hosp Aide; Latin Clb; Nwsp Rptr; Nwsp Stf; Yrbk Phtg; Yrbk Stf; Rep Jr Cls; Mgr Tennis; Hon Roll; Jr NHS; Niagara Cnty Legislative Intern 85; Pre Law.

BENNETT, KRISTIE; Cato-Meridian HS; Cato, NY; (Y); Church Yth Grp; French Clb; JV Fld Hcky; Var Trk; Im Vllybl; Hon Roll; Jr NHS; Mst Imprvd Frnch Awd 83; SUNY-OSWEGO; Zoolgy.

BENNETT, LISA; Longwood HS; Coram, NY; (S); 9/500; Cmnty Wkr; Speech Tm; Nwsp Ed-Chief; Yrbk Stf; High Hon Roll; NHS; Key Clb; Lit Mag; Acad All Am 84; Engl.

BENNETT, MARITA; Andrew Jackson HS; Queens, NY; (Y); Church Yth Grp; Office Aide; Teachers Aide; Band; Yrbk Stf; Cheerleading; Socr; Vllybl; Cit Awd; High Hon Roll; Triple C Awd 83; Dvlpmntl Ecnmc Ed Pgm Awd 83; Schlrshp Awd 83; C W Post; Premed.

BENNETT, MATTHEW; Millbrook HS; Millbrook, NY; (Y); Church Yth Grp; Ski Clb; Church Choir; Var L Crs Cntry; Var L Trk; Hon Roll.

BENNETT, MICHAEL; Sheepshead Bay HS; Brooklyn, NY; (Y); Boys Clb Am; Chess Clb; Computer Clb; Intnl Clb; Pres JA; Varsity Clb; Variety Show; Var Ftbl; Var Socr; Var Leo Clb; Outstndng Achvt Awd-Ftbl Vrsty 83-84; Spcl Tms Awd In Ftbl Vrsty 83-84; U Of Syracuse; Bus Mgt.

BENNETT, NEIL; Archbishop Molloy HS; E Elmhurst, NY; (Y); Yrbk Phtg; Rep Soph Cls; Trk; Bus Mngmnt.

BENNETT, NORA J; Cazenovia HS; Cazenovia, NY; (Y); 50/150; Am Leg Aux Girls St; Var Bsktbl; Capt Var Fld Hcky; Var Sftbl; Hon Roll; NHS; Nrsng Regnts Schlrshp 85; Bst Defns Grls Vrsty Bsktbl 83; Niagara U; Nrsng.

BENNETT, PATRICIA; Walton HS; Bronx, NY; (Y); English Clb; Girl Scts; Library Aide; Teachers Aide; Gym; Swmmng; Tennis; Vllybl; Hon Roll; Dncng 83 & 84; Soclgy.

BENNETT, PATRICIA A; Charles O Dickerson HS; Trumansburg, NY; (Y); 12/90; Science Clb; High Hon Roll; NHS; Ntl Merit Ltr; French Clb; Thesps; Band; Concert Band; Mrchg Band; Yrbk Stf; Ithara Coll; Biology.

BENNETT, RICHARD L; Franklin Delano Roosevelt HS; Brooklyn, NY; (Y); Cmnty Wkr; Nwsp Ed-Chief; Nwsp Rptr; Wt Lftg; Ntl Merit Schol; St Johns U; Jrnlsm.

BENNETT, ROBERT; De Witt Clinton HS; Bronx, NY; (Y); 24/250; Debate Tm; FCA; Office Aide; Science Clb; Concert Band; Crs Cntry; Socr; Capt Trk; Cit Awd; High Hon Roll; Buffalo U; Bio Sci.

BENNETT, ROBT; Moore Catholic HS; Staten Isl, NY; (Y); 55/176; Church Yth Grp; Drama Clb; Spanish Clb; Stage Crew; Bowling; High Hon Roll; Coll Of Staten Islnd; Comps.

BENNETT, TIFFANY; Sacred Heart Acad; Garden City, NY; (S); 25/186; Math Tm; Yrbk Stf; Im Tennis; Hon Roll; NHS.

BENNETT, VICTORIA A; Saratoga Springs SR HS; Saratoga Springs, NY; (Y); Am Leg Aux Girls St; Ski Clb; Chorus; Nwsp Stf; Rep Stu Cncl; Var Capt Cheerleading; Stat Ice Hcky; Score Keeper; High Hon Roll; Skidmore Recogntn Dinnr Schltc Achvt 84-85; Comp Sci.

BENNIS, SUZANNE; Washingtonville HS; Monroe, NY; (Y); 2/308; Spanish Clb; Band; Symp Band; Crs Cntry; Fld Hcky; Trk; High Hon Roll; Hon Roll; NHS; Siena; Accntng.

BENNS JR, GEORGE; Burgard Vocational HS; Buffalo, NY; (Y); Boy Scts; Pres Church Yth Grp; Cmnty Wkr; Rep Frsh Cls; Rep Soph Cls; Rep Jr Cls; Cit Awd; High Hon Roll; Hon Roll; Nwsp Phtg; Aviatn.

BENOWITZ, ERIKA; Warwick Valley HS; Warwick, NY; (Y); 6/217; French Clb; Chorus; Yrbk Phtg; JV Cheerleading; Var Tennis; Var Trk; NHS; Rotry Ldrshp Camp 83; Pres SADD 84; Asthma Athlt Of Yr Hnrb Mntn 85; Brandeis U; Poltcs.

BENSON, DOROTHY; Linton HS; Schenectady, NY; (Y); AFS; Church Yth Grp; Drama Clb; Intnl Clb; JA; JCL; Thesps; Chorus; School Musical; School Play; Regnts Schlrshp 85; Pres Awd Acadmc Ftns 85; Fordham U; Comm.

BENSON, ERIC GERARD; Mahopac HS; Mahopac, NY; (Y); 65/423; Boy Scts; Church Yth Grp; Cmnty Wkr; Concert Band; Tennis; Wrstlng; High Hon Roll; Hon Roll; NHS; Marine Engrng.

BENSON, JEFFRY; Hoosic Valley HS; Melrose, NY; (Y); Drama Clb; Latin Clb; Band; Chorus; Church Choir; School Musical; Swing Chorus; Variety Show; Math Assn Amer Math Awd 85; Marine Bio.

BENSON, KEVIN W; West Islip HS; W Islip, NY; (Y); Boy Scts; Hosp Aide; Band; NHS; Over 90 Pct Av; Soc Stud Awd 85; Natl Sci Olym Awd Physics 85; Med.

BENSON, KIM; Rocky Point JR SR HS; Rocky Point, NY; (S); 7/238; Trs Church Yth Grp; Math Tm; Spanish Clb; Concert Band; Madrigals; Mrchg Band; Hon Roll; Sufflok Cty Math Test 84; Suffolk Cty Mus Fest 84; Engrng.

BENSON, KRISTYN; Bainbridge-Guilford C S HS; Bainbridge, NY; (Y); French Clb; Band; Chorus; Color Guard; Concert Band; Mrchg Band; Orch; JV Capt Bsktbl; Cit Awd; Hon Roll; Sci.

BENSON III, ROBERT L; Canastota HS; Canastota, NY; (Y); Teachers Aide; Band; Church Choir; Concert Band; Mrchg Band; Stage Crew; Comp Repair.

BENSON, STACEY; Hudson Falls SR HS; Hudson Falls, NY; (Y); 17/201; Trs Church Yth Grp; French Clb; Key Clb; Band; Yrbk Stf; Rep Frsh Cls; Rep Soph Cls; Cheerleading; Sftbl; NHS; Law.

BENSON JR, VAN NESS; Dover JR-SR HS; Wingdale, NY; (S); Boy Scts; Chess Clb; Church Yth Grp; Cmnty Wkr; Computer Clb; FNA; Office Aide; OEA; Teachers Aide; Ftbl; Regents Schlrshp 85; U Of MD; Chem Engr.

BENTLEY, CHRISTOPHER S; Cold Spring Harbor HS; Cold Spring Har, NY; (Y); 25/144; Church Yth Grp; Mathletes; Trs Varsity Clb; Orch; School Play; Var Bsktbl; Var Lcrss; Var Socr; High Hon Roll; NHS.

BENTLEY, JACQUELYN; Copiague HS; Copiague, NY; (Y); Cmnty Wkr; Hosp Aide; Library Aide; Mrchg Band; Stu Cncl; Gym; Trk; High Hon Roll; Hon Roll; NHS; Sci Fair Awd 84; 100 Hr Awd 85; Spcl Ed Tchr Of CCD 85; Nrsng.

BENTLEY, KELLY; Scio Central HS; Scio, NY; (S); 3/44; Rep Spanish Clb; Color Guard; Yrbk Ed-Chief; Pres Soph Cls; Pres Jr Cls; Stu Cncl; Capt Socr; High Hon Roll; NHS; USAA Ldrshp Awd 84; Bio Sci.

BENTLEY, MICHAEL; Berlin Central HS; Berlin, NY; (Y); 15/85; Boy Scts; French Clb; Yrbk Phtg; Bsktbl; Socr; Hon Roll; NHS; Ntl Rifle Assn 82-85; 1st Rnnr Up Times Recrd Nwspr Carrier Of Yr 84; Envrnmntl Sci.

BENTLEY, MICHELLE; Albertus Magnus HS; Blauvelt, NY; (Y); 53/190; Sec Church Yth Grp; Latin Clb; Service Clb; Varsity Clb; Var Socr; JV Sftbl; High Hon Roll; Hon Roll; Natl Latin Exam Magna Cum Laude 82; Dntl.

BENTLEY, SHEILA; Hartford Central HS; Granville, NY; (Y); Pep Clb; Science Clb; Teachers Aide; Chorus; Yrbk Rptr; Yrbk Stf; Bsktbl; Vllybl; Hon Roll; St Lawrence U; Pre-Law.

BENTLEY, WILLIAM; Belmont Central HS; Belmont, NY; (Y); Spanish Clb; Yrbk Stf; Var Bsbl; Var Bsktbl; Var Socr; Christine Lewis Mem Awd Geom Rgnts 84; Willets & Paul Awd Math II Rgnts 85; Math.

BENTON, CAROLYN; Cato Meridian HS; Cato, NY; (Y); French Clb; Girl Scts; Office Aide; Yrbk Stf; Vllybl; Hon Roll; Jr NHS; Bryant & Straton; Legal Sec.

BENTON, JETONE; Kensington HS; Buffalo, NY; (Y); Boy Scts; Church Yth Grp; Chorus; Off Soph Cls; Ftbl; Swmmng; Trk; Hon Roll; FIT; Fshn Dsgn.

BENTREWICZ, JOHN; Hicksville HS; Hicksville, NY; (Y); Stage Crew; Rep Stu Cncl; Var L Bsktbl; Hon Roll; Jr NHS; NHS; Rep Frsh Cls; Rep Soph Cls; Rep Jr Cls; Amer Legn Schl Awd 83; Archt.

BENVENUTO, MARIA; Bishop Keatney HS; Brooklyn, NY; (Y); Hon Roll; 1st Hnrs 82-85; Psych.

BENWARE, TODD R; Gouverneur Central HS; Gouverneur, NY; (Y); Church Yth Grp; Varsity Clb; JV Var Bsktbl; Capt Var Golf; Var Socr; Hon Roll; Most Valubl Plyr-Golf Tm 84-85; All Northern, All ST Golf 85; Math.

BENZ, TAMI; Fairport HS; Fairport, NY; (Y); Exploring; VP German Clb; Yrbk Stf; Rep Stu Cncl; Var L Crs Cntry; JV L Socr; Var L Trk; High Hon Roll; Hon Roll; NHS; Sci.

BENZEL, WILLIAM; Newark SR HS; Newark, NY; (Y); Chess Clb; Service Clb; Band; Jazz Band; Mrchg Band; Pep Band; Im Badmtn; JV Bsktbl; JV Socr; Var Swmmng; Pres RTFC; Syracuse U.

BENZER, JILL; Performing Arts At Laguardi; New York, NY; (Y); 2/155; School Play; Jr NHS; NHS; Prfct Atten Awd; Sal; Untd Fdrtn Tchrs Awd; Rgnts Schlrshp; Govnrs Schlstc Achvt Citatn 85; Friends World Coll; Thtre.

BENZIN, MARGARET; Eden Central SR HS; Eden, NY; (Y); 28/194; Pres Church Yth Grp; GAA; Chorus; Church Choir; Concert Band; School Musical; Nwsp Rptr; JV Var Tennis; NHS; VFW Awd; Mst Imprv Plyr-Grls Tnns Tm 84-85; Dequesne U; Phrmcy.

BENZINGER, JULIE; Newburgh Free Acad; Newburgh, NY; (Y); Var JV Cheerleading; US Chrldr Achvt Awd 85; 3rd Pl Newburgh Chrldg Cmptn 85.

BENZO, SUSAN M; Bishop Grimes HS; Syracuse, NY; (Y); 20/207; Debate Tm; FBLA; NFL; High Hon Roll; Hon Roll; NHS; Acad All-Am 85; Natl Eng Merit Awd 85; US Bus Educ Awd 85; Canisius Coll Buffalo; Accntng.

BENZONI, FRANCISC J; Bloomfield JR SR HS; Victor, NY; (Y); 1/92; VP Stu Cncl; Var L Bsktbl; Var Capt Socr; Var L Trk; Var L Vllybl; High Hon Roll; NHS; Val; Computer Clb; Latin Clb; Cornell; Engrng.

BENZONI, LINDA; Herricks HS; Albertson, NY; (Y); Am Leg Aux Girls St; Hosp Aide; Science Clb; Stage Crew; Nwsp Ed-Chief; Nwsp Rptr; Hon Roll; Jr NHS; NHS; Rep Frsh Cls; Astrnmy Clb 85.

BERAN, LINDA; Port Jervis HS; Pt Jervis, NY; (Y); Spanish Clb; Teachers Aide; VICA; Chorus; Yrbk Stf; Volntr Student Teacher Aid 81-82; Data Processor.

BERARDELLI, CHRISTINA; St Catherine Acad; Bronx, NY; (Y); 24/205; Nwsp Rptr; Yrbk Stf; Hon Roll; Jr NHS; NHS; Ntl Merit Schol; Prfct Atten Awd; Acadmc Al-Amer Awd 85; NY U; Med.

BERARDI, JOHN; Wellsville HS; Wellsville, NY; (Y); 3/135; Pres Stu Cncl; High Hon Roll; Hon Roll; NHS; VP Pres Jr Cls; Southrn Tier Schlrshp 85; NYS Regents Schlrshp 85; Stu Leader Com Mem:Pres Acad Fit Awd:Stu Coun Ss; Alfred U.

BERCOVICI, MARIUS; Brooklyn Tech HS; New York, NY; (Y); Boy Scts; Debate Tm; Office Aide; Ner Tamid Awd 84; Wrd Cnsrvtn Awd 85; Baruch; Bus.

BERECH, ROBERT A; Seaford HS; Seaford, NY; (Y); 39/252; Concert Band; Yrbk Stf; Hon Roll; NYS Regents Schlrshp 85; SUNY-ALBANY; Math.

BEREND, JODI; Half Hollow Hills East HS; Dix Hills, NY; (Y); Cmnty Wkr; Office Aide; Service Clb; Temple Yth Grp; Varsity Clb; Swmmng; JV Vllybl; High Hon Roll; Hon Roll; Jr NHS; Psych.

BERENSHTEYN, RUSANA; Solomon Schechter HS; Brooklyn, NY; (Y); 5/40; Art Clb; Debate Tm; English Clb; Math Clb; Math Tm; Nwsp Rptr; Nwsp Stf; Hon Roll; NY U; Pre Law.

BERG, STACEY; Clarkston SR H S South; Spring Valley, NY; (Y); 3/541; Pres Cmnty Wkr; Math Clb; Ski Clb; Temple Yth Grp; Yrbk Stf; Var Capt Vllybl; Lion Awd; NHS; Ntl Merit Ltr; Pres Schlr; Vlybl Coachs Awd 85; Comm Svc Vol Awd 85; Rocklnd Surgcl Co Hgst Ap Bio Avg Medal 85; Harvard Coll.

BERGAGLIO, CHARLENE; Kings Park SR HS; Kings Pk, NY; (Y); 132/393; Pres Trs Church Yth Grp; Office Aide; Rptr Spanish Clb; Rptr Yrbk Stf; Sec Sr Cls; Hon Roll; Rif Awd 85; Merchndzng.

BERGAMO, GREGORY J; Pine Bush HS; Thompson Ridge, NY; (Y); 4/285; Church Yth Grp; Cmnty Wkr; Math Tm; Rep Soph Cls; Rep Jr Cls; Rep Stu Cncl; Bsktbl; Ftbl; Trk; High Hon Roll; NY ST Regnts Schlrshp 85; Pres Acadmc Ftnss Awd 85; NY ST Bstkbl Coaches Assn-All Acadmc Tm 85; U Of NC-CHAPEL Hill; Med.

BERGAMO, KAREN; Mynderse Acad; Seneca Falls, NY; (Y); 32/130; Sec Drama Clb; Sec Model UN; Band; Chorus; Color Guard; Concert Band; Mrchg Band; School Musical; Swing Chorus; Yrbk Stf; Mansfield U; Cretv Wrtg.

BERGAN, BETH; Henninger HS; Syracuse, NY; (Y); 25/500; Church Yth Grp; French Clb; GAA; Concert Band; Mrchg Band; Capt Var Tennis; Var Trk; JV Var Vllybl; High Hon Roll; NHS.

BERGAN, KAREN; St John The Baptist D H S HS; Massapequa Pk, NY; (Y); Church Yth Grp; Chorus; School Musical.

BERGEN, DAWN; Bishop Kearney HS; Brooklyn, NY; (Y); Spanish Clb; Teachers Aide; Bowling; Sftbl; Hon Roll; NHS.

BERGER, BRENDA; South Shore HS; Brooklyn, NY; (Y); 4/668; Math Tm; Service Clb; Orch; School Musical; Rptr Yrbk Stf; High Hon Roll; NHS; Office Aide; Gvnrs Cmt Schlrst Achvt Ctn Awd 84; Brandeis U; Bio Sci.

BERGER, DENISE; North Babylon SR HS; N Babylon, NY; (Y); 51/556; Intnl Clb; Spanish Clb; Nwsp Rptr; Yrbk Stf; VP Stu Cncl; Mgr(s); Tennis; High Hon Roll; NHS; Pres Schlr; Hofstra U; Psych.

BERGER, JAMES; Oneonta HS; Oneonta, NY; (Y); 5/185; Am Leg Boys St; Key Clb; Quiz Bowl; Varsity Clb; Chorus; Madrigals; Nwsp Stf; Pres Sr Cls; Rep VP Stu Cncl; Var L Ftbl; God & Chrch Awd 80; Outsndng Svc Awd 85; Siena Coll Schlrshp Fnlst 85; Valley Forge Military JC.

BERGER, THOMAS J; MSGR Mc Clancy HS; Jackson Hgts, NY; (Y); 10/100; Camera Clb; Nwsp Phtg; Yrbk Phtg; Yrbk Stf; Pres Frsh Cls; Pres Church Yth Grp; 1st & 2nd Hnrs 84-85; 2nd Hnrs Cathedrl Prep H S Elmhurst NY 82-83; John Jay Coll; Crmnl Law.

BERGERON, JANET; Immaculate Heart Central HS; Watertown, NY; (Y); Drama Clb; French Clb; Band; Variety Show; Yrbk Stf; Golf; Hon Roll; Ntl Merit SF; Pres Schlr; Rgnts Schlrshp 84-85; Potsdam Coll; Comp Sci.

BERGEVIN, ROBERT; Plattsburgh HS; Plattsburgh, NY; (Y); 2/160; Am Leg Boys St; Quiz Bowl; Jazz Band; Off Stu Cncl; Var Golf; Var Socr; Capt Swmmng; High Hon Roll; NHS; Sal; AFROTC 4 Yr Schlrshp 85; MA Inst Tech; Elctrcl Engrng.

BERGGREN, PETER; Ballston Spa HS; Ballston Spa, NY; (S); 49/217; 4-H; Acpl Chr; Concert Band; Cit Awd; Dnfth Awd; High Hon Roll; FFA; Chorus; Jazz Band; Orch; 4H Awds; Cnsrvtn.

BERGIN, WILLIAM; St Marys HS; Port Washington, NY; (S); 1/167; Church Yth Grp; Band; Sec Stu Cncl; JV L Bsktbl; Var L Lcrss; JV L Swmmng; Cit Awd; High Hon Roll; NHS; Ntl Merit SF; Engr.

BERGMAN, LINDA; Canastota HS; Canastota, NY; (Y); Church Yth Grp; Dance Clb; Capt Band; Church Choir; Concert Band; Mrchg Band; Pep Band; School Musical; Bowling; Cheerleading; Most Imprvd Band Stu 83-84; Potsdam; Physcl Thrpy.

BERGMAN, MEREDITH; Mamaroneck HS; Mamaroneck, NY; (Y); Dance Clb; Service Clb; Thesps; School Play; Yrbk Phtg; Rep Stu Cncl; Var Capt Socr; Var Capt Tennis; Hon Roll; NHS; NSDAA Awd 84; Northwestern U; Comm.

BERGMANN, ANDREW; Huntington HS; Huntington, NY; (Y); Capt Aud/Vis; Boy Scts; Drama Clb; Band; Chorus; Stage Crew; Hon Roll; Computer Clb; Acpl Chr; Concert Band; Aud Vsl Awd 82; Comptr Lit Awd 82; NY ST Rgnts Schlrshp 85; Hofstra U; Bus Mgmt.

BERGOINE, JENNIFER; Monroe Woodbury Central HS; Highland Mills, NY; (Y); Cmnty Wkr; Math Tm; Orch; Swmmng; NHS; Bio Awd 85; Phy Ftns Awd 84; Vet Med.

BERGSON, DANIELLE E; John F Kennedy HS; Bronx, NY; (Y); 52/982; Cmnty Wkr; Yrbk Rptr; Var Tennis; Jr NHS; NHS; St Schlr; NYS Rgnts Schlrshp 85; Clark U.

BERGSTROM, CHRIS; Rome Free Acad; Rome, NY; (Y); Church Yth Grp; Band; Concert Band; Jazz Band; Mrchg Band; Orch; Hon Roll; Jr NHS; One Hundred Clb Alg 9 83; Bio.

BERINGHAUSE, KIM; Smithtown High School East; Nesconset, NY; (Y); Off Frsh Cls; Off Soph Cls; Off Jr Cls; Off Stu Cncl; Hon Roll; NHS.

BERKMAN, DEBORAH A; Lyme Central HS; Chaumont, NY; (Y); 6/28; Band; Concert Band; Jazz Band; Mrchg Band; Pep Band; Yrbk Stf; Sec Frsh Cls; Var Score Keeper; Var Socr; Hon Roll.

BERKOFF, MELISSA K; Smithtown East HS; Nesconset, NY; (Y); Dance Clb; VP DECA; Spanish Clb; Temple Yth Grp; Yrbk Stf; Stu Cncl; Cheerleading; Hon Roll; NHS; DECA Reg Finalist 84; NY Regents Schlrshp 85; SUNY-BINGHAMTON; Mgmt.

BERKOWITZ, ELLEN; Washingtonville HS; Monroe, NY; (Y); Cmnty Wkr; Drama Clb; French Clb; Math Tm; Temple Yth Grp; Pep Band; School Musical; Yrbk Ed-Chief; Ed Yrbk Stf; NHS; Orange Cnty CC; Elem Ed.

BERKOWITZ, JEFFREY L; Lawrence HS; Woodmere, NY; (Y); 20/390; Var Bsbl; Co-Capt Ftbl; NHS; Ntl Merit Schol; Wharton Schl-U PA; Bus.

BERKOWITZ, JENNIFER; Walter Panas HS; Peekskill, NY; (Y); Ski Clb; Nwsp Stf; Rep Frsh Cls; Rep Soph Cls; Rep Jr Cls; JV Var Cheerleading; JV Vllybl; Hon Roll; Jr NHS; Bus.

BERKSHIRE, LAURIE; Fredonia HS; Fredonia, NY; (Y); Science Clb; Rep Service Clb; Spanish Clb; Orch; Nwsp Stf; Yrbk Stf; Lit Mag; Var Cheerleading; Hon Roll; Phy Educ.

BERLIN, KIM; Valley Stream Central HS; Malverne, NY; (Y); AFS; Art Clb; Hosp Aide; Ski Clb; Orch; Yrbk Phtg; Var Crs Cntry; Var Trk; French Hon Soc; NHS; Med.

BERLIN, MERIDITH P; Sheepshead Bay HS; Brooklyn, NY; (Y); 73/465; School Musical; Hon Roll; Buffalo U; Pol Sci.

BERLINER, JAIMI; Bronx High School Of Sci; New York, NY; (Y); VP JA; Office Aide; Temple Yth Grp; Frsh Cls; Soph Cls; Rep Jr Cls; Rep Sr Cls; Outstndng Srv In Bio 83-85; Bckgmn Clb Trnmnt Wnr 85; ST U Of NY Albany.

BERLYNE, SUZANNAH; Lawrence HS; Lawrence, NY; (Y); 26/379; Spanish Clb; Band; High Hon Roll; Hon Roll; NHS; Regents Schlrshp 85; Hebrew Awd 83; Binghamton U; Pre-Med.

BERMAN, ALEXANDER S; Yeshiva Univ HS; Forest Hills, NY; (Y); 17/105; Pres Temple Yth Grp; Rep Frsh Cls; Rep Jr Cls; Rep Sr Cls; Stu Cncl; Im Fld Hcky; NHS; Ntl Merit Ltr; NEDT Awd; Arista; Nys Regents Schlrshp.

BERMAN, SHARON; Commack High School North; East Northport, NY; (Y); French Clb; Teachers Aide; Off Frsh Cls; Off Soph Cls; Off Jr Cls; Stat Badmtn; Mgr(s); French Hon Soc; High Hon Roll; NHS.

BERMEJO, PATRICIA J; Washington Irving HS; New York, NY; (Y); FBLA; Service Clb; Trs Sr Cls; Trs Stu Cncl; Hon Roll; Gen Oak Scholar 85; Comp Awd Word Proc Excllnce 85; Atten Awds 83-84; Albany U; Psych.

BERMEJO, WANDA; Cardinal Spellman HS; Bronx, NY; (Y); Church Yth Grp; French Clb; Latin Clb; Ski Clb; Church Choir; High Hon Roll; Rgnts Schlrshp 85; Cornell; Ind Engrng.

BERMEL, BETH; West Seneca East SR HS; Buffalo, NY; (Y); German Clb; L Chorus; Church Choir; School Musical; L Swing Chorus; JV Bowling; Hon Roll; Prfct Atten Awd; Church Yth Grp; Girl Scts; German Schvt Awd 83-84; NYSMA Music Awd 84; ST U Coll New York; Tchr.

BERMINGHAM, DAVID A; Canisius HS; Williamsville, NY; (Y); 30/148; Cmnty Wkr; Ski Clb; Acpl Chr; Hon Roll; Ntl Merit Ltr; Drama Clb; Madrigals; School Play; Im Ftbl; JV Mgr(s); NY ST Rgnts Schlrshp 85; Capt/Pres HS Bicycl Clb-Racng Tm 83-85; Navy ROTC Sclrshp Altnt; IL Inst Tech; Mechncl Engrng.

BERMUNDEZ, ARACELYS; Eastern District HS; Brooklyn, NY; (Y); 42/337; Chorus; Nwsp Rptr; Nwsp Stf; Gym; Trk; Hon Roll; Hnr Cert-Math & Rdng Sklls 82; Steno, Typng 83; Spnsh Accntng, Spnsh 2 & Actng 84; Baruch Coll; Comp Stds.

BERNARD, ANDREW; Sheepshead Bay HS; Brooklyn, NY; (Y); Computer Clb; Math Tm; Trk; Hall Fame-Outdr Trk 85; Poly Inst Of Tech; Elec Engrng.

BERNARD, DINA; Acad Mt Saint Ursula; Bronx, NY; (Y); 49/161; Spanish Clb; Stu Cncl; Cheerleading; NYS Rgnts Nrsng Schlrshp 86; Lehman Coll; Nrsng.

BERNARD, JUDITH A; Starpoint Central HS; Lockport, NY; (Y); 13/196; Drama Clb; Spanish Clb; Stage Crew; Rep Stu Cncl; Powder Puff Ftbl; Jr NHS; NHS; E B Morgan, NYS Regnts Schlrshps 85; Wells Coll; Med.

BERNARD, LERIS G; Pittsford-Mendon HS; Pittsford, NY; (Y); 3/270; Church Yth Grp; Drama Clb; Exploring; Math Clb; Pep Clb; Concert Band; Orch; School Musical; Ed Lit Mag; Rep Soph Cls; Urban Leag Rochester Blck Schlrs Awd 85; Teen Tlnt Lkshore Dist Keybrd Wnnr 83 & 84; Psych.

BERNARD, TIFFANNY; Port Chester SR HS; Portchester, NY; (Y); French Clb; Band; Var Sftbl; Hon Roll; Color Guard; Mrchg Band; School Play; Stage Crew; Yrbk Stf; Gym; Greenwich Country Day Schl Scholar 80; Georgetown; Acctng.

BERNARD, YOLAND; Spring Valley SR HS; Spring Valley, NY; (Y); Socr; Bus Adm.

BERNARDOT, EMILE; Franklin Academy HS; Malone, NY; (Y); Boy Scts; French Clb; Ski Clb; Varsity Clb; Band; Concert Band; Stage Crew; Var L Golf; Var L Swmmng; Pre Med.

BERNAS, MICHELLE; Mount St Mary Acad; N Tonawanda, NY; (Y); 19/120; Cmnty Wkr; Lit Mag; Hon Roll; NEDT Awd; U Buffalo; Econ.

BERNAT, ELIZABETH R; Niagara Wheatfield SR HS; Niagara Falls, NY; (Y); 10/313; Church Yth Grp; Pres Latin Clb; Trs PAVAS; Nwsp Ed-Chief; Var L Bsktbl; Var L Socr; Var L Sftbl; Var Capt Vllybl; High Hon Roll; NHS; NYS Regents Schlrshp 84-85; Heidelberg Coll Merit & Acad Schlrshps 84-85; Niagara Whtfld Hnr Awds 85; Heidelberg Coll Tiffin; Comm.

BERNATH, BRETT; Walt Whitman HS; Huntington, NY; (Y); 101/600; Rep Stu Cncl; Crs Cntry; Trk; Hon Roll; Jr NHS; NHS; NY Rgnt Schlrshp 85; Frnch Exch Pgm 85; Boston U Boston; Engl.

BERNHARDT, ROBERT; Aviation HS; Brooklyn, NY; (Y); Church Yth Grp; JA; Hon Roll.

BERNIER, ARTHUR M; Baldwin SR HS; Baldwin, NY; (Y); 108/502; Aud/Vis; Debate Tm; Model UN; Nwsp Ed-Chief; Nwsp Stf; VP Stu Cncl; Bsbl; Tennis; NHS; Presdntl Acadmc Ftns Awd 84-85; Europn Hstry Outstndng Achv 82-83; ST U Of NY Binghamton; Atty.

BERNINGER, DAVID; Longwood HS; Ridge, NY; (S); 18/551; Am Leg Boys St; Key Clb; Pres Stu Cncl; Var L Socr; Var L Trk; NHS; Voice Dem Awd; School Musical; Nwsp Stf; Gym; Suffolk Cnty Pole Vltng Champ 84; NYS Regnl Brdg Bldng Cntst 1st, Natl B B Cntst 12th Pl 84; Orthdntst.

BERNREUTHER, PAUL; Fairport HS; Fairport, NY; (Y); Math Tm; Varsity Clb; Var L Ftbl; JV L Lcrss; Var Capt Wt Lftg; Spanish NHS; Police Ofcr.

BERNS, JON; Mamaroneck HS; Mamaroneck, NY; (Y); French Clb; JA; Mathletes; Math Clb; Math Tm; Service Clb; Spanish Clb; Yrbk Phtg; Yrbk Stf; JV Socr; Outstndng Soc Stud Achvt 85; Harvard; Bio.

BERNSTEIN, ABBY; Commack High Schl North; Commack, NY; (Y); French Clb; Capt Drill Tm; Mrchg Band; School Musical; French Hon Soc; High Hon Roll; NHS; Off Frsh Cls; Off Soph Cls; Off Jr Cls; Most Outstandng Soph Kickline 84; Treas Ldrs Corps 84-85; Acctng.

BERNSTEIN, CHERYL; Jamesville De Witt HS; Fayetteville, NY; (Y); Debate Tm; Girl Scts; Key Clb; Teachers Aide; Chorus; Orch; School Musical; School Play; Swing Chorus; Yrbk Stf; NY ST Regents Schlrshp 85; Med.

BERNSTEIN, JEFF; John H Glenn HS; Greenlawn, NY; (Y); Debate Tm; Yrbk Sprt Ed; Yrbk Stf; JV Lcrss; JV Trk; High Hon Roll; Hon Roll; NY Metny Soc Actns 85-86; Pre-Law.

BERNSTEIN, JORDANA SIMONE; John H Glenn HS; Huntington, NY; (Y); 1/260; Pres French Clb; Pres Mathletes; VP Hst MMM; Pres Science Clb; Teachers Aide; Orch; Ed Lit Mag; Bausch & Lomb Sci Awd; Ntl Merit SF; Val; Am Assn Of Frnch Trchrs; Poetry Cntst-1st Pl 82; Cntry III Ldrs Prog 84; Cnty Rnk 83; Team Cap Tv Show; Biophysics.

BERNSTEIN, JOY; Lynbrook HS; Hewlett, NY; (Y); Hosp Aide; Mathletes; Spanish Clb; Teachers Aide; Temple Yth Grp; School Play; Nwsp Stf; Cheerleading; NHS; Ntl Merit Ltr; Edit E Rockaway Nrsng Home Paper 84-85; Sci Olympiad Awd 83; Sci Rsrch Pgm 84-85.

BERNSTEIN, LARA; Oceanside HS; Oceanside, NY; (Y); 55/500; Drama Clb; Model UN; Spanish Clb; Temple Yth Grp; Acpl Chr; Chorus; School Musical; Variety Show; Rep Frsh Cls; Trs Soph Cls; All-Cnty Tnns Tm 85; All Cnty & ST Chrs 86; SUNY-ALBANY; Pre-Law.

BERNSTEIN, LEWIS A; Voorheesville JR SR HS; Voorheesville, NY; (Y); 12/120; Trs Drama Clb; Band; Chorus; Jazz Band; School Play; Stage Crew; Var Ftbl; Var Trk; NHS; Ntl Merit Ltr; SUNY Buffalo; Chemical Engnrg.

BERNSTEIN, LISA; George W Hewlett HS; Woodmere, NY; (Y); 42/285; Nwsp Stf; Yrbk Sprt Ed; Yrbk Stf; Var Capt Cheerleading; JV Var Swmmng; U Of VT; Bus.

BERNSTEIN, NINA; St Hildas And St Hughs HS; New York, NY; (Y); 12/23; Varsity Clb; Yrbk Stf; Sftbl; Vllybl; Hon Roll; Pedtrcn.

BERNSTEIN, WENDY; Commack High Schl North; East Northport, NY; (Y); Cmnty Wkr; Exploring; Hosp Aide; Teachers Aide; Rep Frsh Cls; Rep Soph Cls; Rep Jr Cls; Stu Cncl; Hon Roll; Med.

BERRAFATI, JOSEPH F; Irvington HS; Ardsley On Hudson, NY; (Y); Cmnty Wkr; Band; Yrbk Stf; Lit Mag; Rep Stu Cncl; Var L Bsbl; Var L Ftbl; Church Yth Grp; Key Clb; Science Clb; Westinghouse Sci Tlnt Srch Comp Semi-Fnlst 85; NY ST Sci Cong Hnrs Awd 84; Wstchstr Sci Cong Awd 84.

BERRHALTER, JOHN; North Babylon SR HS; North Babylon, NY; (Y); Chorus; JV Ftbl; JV Trk; JV Wrstlng; Pilot.

BERRIER, PENNY A; Columbia HS; E Greenbush, NY; (Y); 9/360; VP Varsity Clb; Sec Frsh Cls; Sec Soph Cls; VP Sr Cls; Trs Stu Cncl; Var Capt Fld Hcky; Swmmng; Var Capt Vllybl; High Hon Roll; NHS; Empire ST Games 80-84; Swarthmore; Engr.

BERRIGAN V, THOMAS; Schuylerville Central HS; Schuylerville, NY; (Y); Am Leg Boys St; French Clb; Math Clb; Math Tm; Chorus; School Play; Yrbk Stf; VP Frsh Cls; VP Soph Cls; Rep Jr Cls; Psych.

BERRIN, EILEEN M; Holy Trinity D HS; Freeport, NY; (S); 22/362; Camera Clb; French Clb; Capt Math Clb; Ski Clb; Nwsp Phtg; Yrbk Phtg; Rep Stu Cncl; High Hon Roll; NHS; Spec Educ.

BERRIOS, LUIS; Monroe HS; Rochester, NY; (Y); Church Yth Grp; Chorus; High Hon Roll; Hon Roll; Cert Bio 84.

BERRY, CHRISTOPHER; Camden HS; Camden, NY; (Y); Church Yth Grp; High Hon Roll; NHS; Navy; Nuclr Propulsn Pgm.

BERRY, CLAIR; Baldwin SR HS; Baldwin, NY; (S); 203/536; Church Yth Grp; Chorus; Church Choir; Rep Stu Cncl; 100 Pct NY ST Schl Music Assoc Vocl Solo 84; All Nassau, NY ST, Eastern Choirs 85; St Leo Coll; Psych.

BERRY, COURTNEY A; The Mary Louis Acad; Flushing, NY; (Y); 54/283; Pres VP Chorus; Cit Awd; Ntl Merit Ltr; NEDT Awd; Prfct Atten Awd; Concouse Ntl De Francais Cert De Merite 83; Law.

BERRY JR, JOHN F; Mephan HS; North Bellmore, NY; (Y); 52/385; Boy Scts; Var Socr; Var Swmmng; Im Vllybl; Hon Roll; NHS; Hofstra U; Acctng.

BERRY, MATTHEW C; Fairport HS; Fairport, NY; (Y); Chorus; Syracuse U; Business.

BERRY, MICHELLE C; Narrowsburg Central HS; Narrowsburg, NY; (Y); 1/25; Sec Church Yth Grp; Drama Clb; Radio Clb; Ed Nwsp Ed-Chief; Tennis; High Hon Roll; Kiwanis Awd; NHS; Pres Schlr; Val; Vassar Coll Smmr Schlrshp 85; Pres Acadmc Fit Awd & Parent-Fclty 1 Yr Schlrshp 85; ST U NY; Engl Jrnlsm.

BERRY, MONA; Clara Barton HS; New York, NY; (Y); 4-H; Hosp Aide; Teachers Aide; Chorus; Hon Roll; Spelman Coll; Pre Med.

BERSHADKER, ANDREW; Blind Brook HS; Rye Brook, NY; (Y); Hosp Aide; Model UN; Acpl Chr; Chorus; School Musical; School Play; Crs Cntry; Ntl Merit Ltr.

BERSTEIN, BRADFORD; Wheatley HS; Old Westbery, NY; (Y); Civic Clb; Debate Tm; Model UN; Political Wkr; Temple Yth Grp; School Musical; School Play; Variety Show; Nwsp Stf; Yrbk Stf; Mock Trial Wnnr 85; AP Hstry 84-85; Lwyr.

BERTE, PAUL; Westlake HS; Pleasantville, NY; (Y); 22/155; FBLA; Ski Clb; Band; Jazz Band; Mrchg Band; Pep Band; School Musical; School Play; Yrbk Stf; Pres Sr Cls; Pres Schlrshp-Manhattan Coll 85; Stu Cncl Ldrshp Awd 85; Bucknell U; Engrng.

BERTHOLD, ANITA M; Maryvale HS; Cheektowaga, NY; (Y); German Clb; Band; Mrchg Band; Orch; Symp Band; Variety Show; Yrbk Stf; Var Cheerleading; Hon Roll; NHS; Cmmnctns.

BERTLESMAN, DOUGLAS G; New Hartford HS; Utica, NY; (Y); Debate Tm; Drama Clb; School Musical; Var L Golf; Hon Roll; JETS Awd; Jr NHS.

BERTOLINO, ANDREA; Canastota HS; Canastota, NY; (S); 1/140; Band; Chorus; School Musical; School Play; JV Cheerleading; High Hon Roll; VP NHS; USAA Natl Sci Awd 85; 1st Piano Comp 83; Le Moyne; Med.

BERTON III, GERALD A; Hackley Schl; Mamaroneck, NY; (Y); 18/87; Computer Clb; Model UN; Nwsp Phtg; Nwsp Rptr; Yrbk Phtg; Yrbk Rptr; JV Bsbl; High Hon Roll; Hon Roll; Regnts Schlrshp 85; TUFTS U; Intl Rel.

BERUBE, JANINE; Bishop Kearney HS; Rochester, NY; (Y); Var Bsktbl; Var Sftbl; Var Tennis; Var Vllybl; Hon Roll; MVP Tennis 83-84; Sectn 5 Cls A Dbls Fnlst 84-85; Bus Mgmt.

BESANSON, ELLEN A; Paul V Moore HS; Central Square, NY; (Y); 76/297; AFS; Drama Clb; Hosp Aide; Hon Roll; Regents Schlrshp 85; Intern Civic Ctr 83-85; Prof Pantomime 83-85; Syracuse U; Tech Thtre.

BESCH, ROSE ANN; Cleveland Hill HS; Cheektowaga, NY; (Y); Merit Rll 85; Synchrnzd Swmmng Achvt Awd 83; Profcncy Awd-Accntng 85; ST U Of NY; Accntng.

BESDANSKY, BARBARA A; W T Clarke HS; Westbury, NY; (Y); 27/193; Key Clb; Yrbk Phtg; Yrbk Stf; Lit Mag; Badmtn; Crs Cntry; Tennis; Trk; NHS; NY St Regents Schlrshp 85; Hofstra U.

BESSE, KARL; Queensbury HS; Glens Falls, NY; (Y); 13/226; Ski Clb; Yrbk Phtg; Stu Cncl; JV Bsbl; JV Ftbl; High Hon Roll; NHS; NY ST Regents Schlrshp; Clarkson Trustees Awd; Clarkson U; Chem Engrng.

BESSEE, CARMONA D; St Josephs HS; Brooklyn, NY; (Y); Dance Clb; Drama Clb; Leo Clb; Varsity Clb; Drill Tm; School Play; Yrbk Stf; Cheerleading; St Johns U.

BESSER, GLENN R; Batavia HS; Batavia, NY; (Y); 85/240; Nwsp Rptr; Nwsp Stf; Im JV Bsktbl; Im JV Ftbl; Hon Roll; Regnt Schlrshp NY ST 85; Genesee CC; Bus Adm.

BESSER, TIMOTHY C; Valley Central HS; Walden, NY; (Y); 27/255; Pres Church Yth Grp; Natl Beta Clb; Band; Concert Band; Mrchg Band; Yrbk Phtg; Yrbk Sprt Ed; Rep Sr Cls; Hon Roll; NHS; NYS Regnts Schlrshp 85; Marist Coll; Jrnlsm.

BESSETTE JR, WARREN D; Hugh C Williams HS; Canton, NY; (Y); Orch; Bowling; Ftbl; High Hon Roll; Hon Roll; NHS; Regents Coll Schlrshp; Clarkson U; Civil Engr.

BESSEY, JAMES; Saranac Central Schl; Saranac, NY; (S); 33/126; Boy Scts; Computer Clb; Dance Clb; Letterman Clb; Office Aide; Varsity Clb; Variety Show; Var Bsbl; Var Capt Ftbl; Im Wt Lftg; JV Offnsv Plyr Of Yr 81; JV Mst Outstndg Plyr 82-83; Vrsty Offnsv Plyr 84; Gym Tchr.

BESSEY, JENNIFER A; Schroon Lake Central Schl; N Hudson, NY; (S); Sec Varsity Clb; School Play; Variety Show; Pres Soph Cls; VP Stu Cncl; Capt Cheerleading; Var Score Keeper; Var Sftbl; High Hon Roll; NHS.

BEST, BRIAN; North Babylon SR HS; North Babylon, NY; (Y); Art Clb; Boy Scts; Camera Clb; Church Yth Grp; Computer Clb; Drama Clb; FBLA; Intnl Clb; VICA; Chorus; UICLA Awd; Int Dsign.

BEST, RHONDA C; Bronx High School Of Science; Queens, NY; (Y); Cmnty Wkr; Teachers Aide; Latin Clb; Office Aide; Yrbk Phtg; Biol Congress Awd 84; Hnrs Eng Prgrm 82-85; Hnrs Fr Prgrm 85; Comp Sci.

BESTRY, JULIE ANNE; Williamsville South HS; Williamsville, NY; (Y); 15/247; Sec Chess Clb; Political Wkr; Capt Quiz Bowl; Sec Science Clb; Thesps; Acpl Chr; High Hon Roll; NHS; Cert Excllnce Alliance Francaise 85; NYS Regnts Scholar 84; Its Acad Awds Capt 83-85; Cornell U; Comm.

BESWICK, HEATHER; Mont Pleasant HS; Schenectady, NY; (Y); 61/209; French Clb; Sec Key Clb; Pep Clb; Varsity Clb; Symp Band; Rep Stu Cncl; Var JV Bsktbl; French Hon Soc; Hon Roll; Prfct Atten Awd 82-85; Northeastern; Elec Engrng.

BETANCES, YOLANDA; Bishop Kearney HS; Brooklyn, NY; (Y); Art Clb; Camera Clb; Church Yth Grp; Office Aide; Spanish Clb; Trk; Hon Roll; NHS; Jrnlsm.

BETANCOURT, ALEX; MSGR Mc Clancy HS; Jackson Hgts, NY; (Y); Church Yth Grp; JV Var Socr; JV Var Trk; Hon Roll; NHS; Princpls Lst 85; Ivey League Coll; Lbrl Arts.

BETANCOURT, DANEEN; Longwood HS; Shirley, NY; (Y); 60/420; Key Clb; Office Aide; Pep Clb; Chorus; Stage Crew; Nwsp Stf; Yrbk Stf; JV Var Cheerleading; Score Keeper; Tennis; JV Awd 83-84; Musculr Dystrphy Assoc Awd 84; Phy Thrpy.

BETANCOURT, ROSITA; The Mary Louis Acad; Woodside, NY; (Y); Teachers Aide; NEDT Awd; Ed.

BETANCOURT, STEVEN; La Salle Acad; New York, NY; (S); Boys Clb Am; Math Clb; Rep Jr Cls; Rep Stu Cncl; Ftbl; Hon Roll; Columbia; Pediatrician.

BETHGE, ROB; North Shore HS; Glen Head, NY; (Y); 20/220; Debate Tm; Thesps; Chorus; School Play; Stage Crew; Hon Roll; NHS; Faclty Hnr Awd 84; Spn Schlr 85; Carnegie-Mellon U; Bus Admin.

BETHUNE, SHAWN; George W Wingate HS; Brooklyn, NY; (Y); Library Aide; Teachers Aide; Hon Roll; Prfct Atten Awd; Rensseloer Polytech Inst Maths & Sci Awd 85; Achvt Awd Math & Sci Acad 84; Ivy League; Doctor.

BETTIN, WILLIAM; John Jay SR HS; Hopewell Junction, NY; (Y); Pres Church Yth Grp; Math Tm; Church Choir; VP Ftbl; Im Ice Hcky; High Hon Roll; NHS; 1st Pl SR Div 5th Annual Microcomp Cont 85; Congrss-Bundestag Yth Exch Scholar SF 85; Engrng.

BETTINO, RITA; Westlake HS; Valhalla, NY; (Y); #10 In Class; Church Yth Grp; Drama Clb; Model UN; Thesps; School Play; Capt Bsktbl; NHS; Ntl Merit Ltr; FBLA; Ski Clb; Spnsh Lang Awd 84; All Leag Hnrbl Ment Vlybl & Bsktbl 84; Stu Mnth Rotary Club 85; Boston Coll.

BETTS, JOSEPH; Cicero North Syracuse HS; Clay, NY; (S); 52/620; Mathletes; Math Tm; Hon Roll; NY ST League Math Awd 83-84; Mech Drwng.

BETTS, LAURINA A; Miller Place HS; Miller Place, NY; (Y); Church Yth Grp; Drama Clb; FBLA; Ski Clb; Church Choir; School Musical; School Play; Nwsp Rptr; Yrbk Stf; Var Badmtn; Kybrdng & Bus Comm Awds 83; Accntng II Awd 85; Winthrop Coll; Bus Admin.

BETTS, STEPHANIE L; East JR & SR HS; Rochester, NY; (Y); 15/267; Math Tm; Ski Clb; Band; Yrbk Stf; Var Crs Cntry; Var Socr; Hon Roll; NHS; Lttr Cmmndtn PSAT NMSQT 83; NY ST Regnts Schlrshp 83; Bryn Mawr.

BETZ, LISA; Central HS; Valley Stream, NY; (Y); Art Clb; Band; Chorus; Orch; Nwsp Ed-Chief; Nwsp Rptr; Nwsp Stf; Yrbk Stf; Var Cheerleading; Var Tennis.

BEURKET, MEGAN; Seton Catholic Central HS; Binghamton, NY; (Y); GAA; Key Clb; Ski Clb; Varsity Clb; Band; School Musical; JV Bsktbl; Sftbl; Var Tennis; Hon Roll; STAC Allstar 84-85; Div III Allstar 83-84; Fin.

BEUTEL, ANN; Mount Saint Mary Acad; Tonawanda, NY; (Y); Computer Clb; Hosp Aide; NFL; Service Clb; Speech Tm; Lit Mag; High Hon Roll; Hon Roll; NHS; NEDT Awd; Yth Engagd Svc Outstndng Cert 84; Nichols Schl Wrm Up Spch Tourn 1st Pl Extempor Spkg 84; Socl Wrk.

BEUTEL, LINDA; Niagara Wheatfield SR HS; Sanborn, NY; (Y); Church Yth Grp; German Clb; Chorus; Cheerleading; Hon Roll; Chrch Bsktbl Team 82-85; Secy.

BEVERLY, BRUCE; Eden Central HS; Eden, NY; (Y); AFS; Computer Clb; Drama Clb; Thesps; Varsity Clb; Acpl Chr; Band; Chorus; Concert Band; Jazz Band; All Eastern Chorus Hartford CT 85; Syracuse U; Aerospace Engnrng.

BEVILACQUA, CARL; Ticonderoga HS; Ticonderoga, NY; (Y); Am Leg Boys St; Bowling; Ftbl; Trk; Hon Roll; BUS.

BEVILACQUA, PATRICK; St Josephs Collegiate Inst; Buffalo, NY; (Y); Art Clb; Thesps; School Musical; Stage Crew; Yrbk Rptr; Trk; Hon Roll; Prfct Atten Awd; Bst Shw Art Awd; Mxd Media Hon Mntn; U Of Buffalo; Law.

BEVILACQUA, PAUL; East Islip HS; East Islip, NY; (Y); JV Var Bsbl; Im Wt Lftg; High Hon Roll; Hon Roll; NHS; Outstndng Physcl Ed Awd; Frgn Lang Hnr Soc; Leaders Clb; Accntng.

BEVILACQUA, RALPH; Port Richmond HS; New York, NY; (Y); 10/581; Key Clb; Science Clb; Nwsp Rptr; Yrbk Stf; Sec Stu Cncl; Var Crs Cntry; Var Trk; High Hon Roll; NHS; Spanish NHS; Permant Hon Rl 85; Comptrollrs Awd 85; Pres Acad Fitnss Awd 85; Case Wstrn Resrv U; Biomed Engr.

BEVILACQUA, STEVEN; North Collins Central HS; N Collins, NY; (Y); 3/79; Drama Clb; Concert Band; Mrchg Band; JV Var Bsktbl; Var Capt Socr; Im Sftbl; Var Tennis; High Hon Roll; NHS; Ntl Merit Ltr; Clarkson U; Comp Engrng.

BEYER, DOLPH; Mexico HS; Mexico, NY; (Y); Aud/Vis; Camera Clb; Church Yth Grp; Dance Clb; Science Clb; Spanish Clb; Varsity Clb; Band; Concert Band; Mrchg Band; Le Moyne CYO Scholar 85; Ind Arts Awd 85; Le Moyne Coll.

BEYER, SCOTT; York Central HS; Leicester, NY; (Y); Art Clb; Aud/Vis; Church Yth Grp; Cmnty Wkr; Computer Clb; Drama Clb; FCA; JA; Key Clb; Library Aide; Bus Mgt.

BEYRODT, CATHRYN M; East Meadow HS; East Meadow, NY; (Y); Color Guard; JV Score Keeper; Jrnlsm.

BEZMAN, STEVEN A; Elmont Memorial HS; Elmont, NY; (Y); 21/247; Pres Computer Clb; FBLA; Pres Math Tm; Pres Concert Band; Pres Mrchg Band; Orch; Variety Show; Capt Bowling; NHS; MAA Math Awd 83-85; Rensselaer Plly Inst; Com Sci.

BHALLA, RAJESH F; Arlington HS; Poughkeepsie, NY; (Y); 30/590; ROTC; Hon Roll; NHS; Ntl Merit Ltr; Regnts Schlrshp 85; U Of TX Austin; Aero Engr.

BHALLA, ROHIT; New Rochelle HS; New Rochelle, NY; (Y); 29/597; Chess Clb; Computer Clb; Service Clb; Temple Yth Grp; Nwsp Sprt Ed; Rep Stu Cncl; Var Tennis; NHS; NYS Regents Schlrshp 85; Pres Schlrshp SUNY Plattsburgh 85; Pre-Med.

BHATIA, VIVEK; John Jay HS; Wappingers Fall, NY; (Y); Math Clb; Math Tm; High Hon Roll; Jr NHS; Ntl Merit Ltr; Intl Sci Olympd Sci Tm 85; Comp Sci.

BHATT, JAY; Pittsford Mendon HS; Pittsford, NY; (Y); Chess Clb; Cmnty Wkr; Math Clb; Math Tm; Nwsp Stf; JV Var Bsbl; JV Im Bsktbl; Ftbl; High Hon Roll; NHS; Outstndng Mth Stu 85; Magna Cum Laude Latin Cont Awd 83; Frnch Cont Awd 83 & 85; Sci.

BHAUMIK, KAUSHIK; H Frank Carey HS; Franklin Sq, NY; (Y); 10/230; Boy Scts; Mathletes; Orch; Red Cross Aide; Sec Jr NHS; NHS; Spanish NHS; Lng Islnd Sci Cong Hghst Hnrs 84-85; NY ST Sci Cong High Hnrs Wnnr 84-85; Aerospc.

BIAMONTE, MARY KAY; Niagara Falls HS; Niagara Falls, NY; (Y); 48/257; Hosp Aide; Key Clb; Library Aide; Yrbk Stf; Stu Cncl; Bsktbl; Sftbl; NHS; Niagara Cnty CC; Exec Secy Sci.

BIANCHI, DONALD; Union Springs Acad; North Syracuse, NY; (S); 14/52; Church Yth Grp; Drama Clb; Acpl Chr; Chorus; Church Choir; Variety Show; Tennis; Wt Lftg; High Hon Roll; Hon Roll; Comp Tech.

BIANCHI, VICTOR; Holy Cross HS; Whitestone, NY; (Y); 33/389; Wt Lftg; High Hon Roll; Ntl Merit Ltr; Schlr Yr Awd 83; Fine Arts Clb 84; Law.

BIANCO, JUDI A; T R Proctor HS; Utica, NY; (Y); Drama Clb; Pep Clb; School Musical; Yrbk Stf; Mohawk Vly CC; Sec.

BIANCO, LYNN; Broadalbin HS; Broadalbin, NY; (Y); 7/86; 4-H; Pep Clb; Spanish Clb; Yrbk Stf; Rep Jr Cls; VP Stu Cncl; High Hon Roll; Hon Roll; Jr NHS; NHS; Natl Sci Merit Awd 82; Cornell; Psych.

BIANCO, STACIE; Corning East HS; Corning, NY; (Y); Varsity Clb; Yrbk Stf; Rep Frsh Cls; Rep Soph Cls; Rep Jr Cls; Rep Sr Cls; Capt Cheerleading; Lcrss; High Hon Roll; NHS; Barbizon Schl Modlg 85; Recvd Awd Top Models; Recvd Plaque Small Frey Ftbl Chrldrs 84; Interior Dsgn.

BIANCULLI, ROSEMARY; Academy Of St Joseph; N Babylon, NY; (Y); Drama Clb; Library Aide; Service Clb; School Musical; School Play; Variety Show; Syracuse; Comm.

BIAS, CRAIG; Albion HS; Albion, NY; (S); 2/180; Aud/Vis; Band; Var Crs Cntry; Swmmng; Trk; Bausch & Lomb Sci Awd; NHS; Sal; Rep Jr Cls; Rep U S Coast Guard Acad Project AIM 84; MI ST U; Engrng.

BIASI, JOSEPH F; Bishop Grimes HS; Syracuse, NY; (Y); 1/207; FBLA; NFL; Band; Trs Frsh Cls; Trs Soph Cls; Trs Jr Cls; Trs Sr Cls; JV Ftbl; High Hon Roll; NHS; RPI Math & Sci Awds; Double-Octo Fnlst Natl Cath For Trnmnt; Regents Schlrshp; Le Moyre Coll; Econ.

BIBAWY, NERMIN; Haverling Central HS; Bath, NY; (S); 1/150; Sec French Clb; JCL; Pres Latin Clb; Math Clb; Jazz Band; Yrbk Stf; VP Stu Cncl; JV Var Cheerleading; High Hon Roll; NHS; Physician.

BIBKO, EDWARD A; John C Birdlebough HS; Phoenix, NY; (Y); 12/200; AFS; Church Yth Grp; Latin Clb; Political Wkr; Ski Clb; Yrbk Stf; NHS; NY ST Regnts Schlrshp 85; U Of VT; Elctrcl Engrng.

BICKERT, SCOTT A; Starpoint Central HS; N Tonawanda, NY; (Y); Boy Scts; Varsity Clb; JV Var Bsbl; JV Var Ftbl; Hon Roll; Jr NHS; NHS; Rep Frsh Cls; Rep Soph Cls; Rep Jr Cls; NY ST Regents Scholarshp 85; Suny At Oswego; Computer Sci.

BICKFORD, CARL; Dryden Central HS; Dryden, NY; (Y); Ski Clb; Spanish Clb; Band; Swmmng; High Hon Roll; NHS; Hnr Awd Draftng,Bio,Chem 83-85; Mech Engrng.

BICOVNY, WENDY; Bronx High School Of Science; New York, NY; (Y); Science Clb; Temple Yth Grp; Lit Mag; Rep Soph Cls; High Hon Roll; Hon Roll; Jr NHS; NHS; Pres Schlr; Pres Acadmc Ftnss Awd 85; Otto P Burgdof Sci Conf Semi-Fnlst 85; Mdl For Svc To Holocgust Stds 85; Brandeis U; Doc Of Med.

BIDDLE, MARY KAY; West Seneca West SR HS; Buffalo, NY; (Y); Cmnty Wkr; Hon Roll; Prfct Atten Awd; Sci Awd-Regents Earth Sci 83-84; Sci Awd-Regents Chem 84-85; Princpls Awd 84-85; Canisius Coll; Bus.

BIDLACK JR, HAROLD A; Twin Tiers Baptist HS; Milan, PA; (Y); Church Yth Grp; Computer Clb; Debate Tm; FFA; Bsbl; Socr; Sftbl; Wt Lftg; Wrstlng; Hon Roll; Lincoln Tech Inst; Elctrnc-Rbtc.

BIE, KATHRYN; Academy Of St Joseph HS; Commack, NY; (Y); Church Yth Grp; Dance Clb; FHA; Hosp Aide; Service Clb; Spanish Clb; Yrbk Stf.

BIEAR, MATTHEW; Fox Lane HS; South Salem, NY; (Y); 23/260; Boy Scts; Lcrss; High Hon Roll; NHS; Cert Merit Sen Mary B Goodhue 85.

BIEDRON, MICHELE; Villa Maria Acad; Buffalo, NY; (Y); Art Clb; Church Yth Grp; Pep Clb; Cheerleading; Hon Roll; Prfct Atten Awd; Deans Schlrshp Canisius Coll 85; Prnts Wthout Prtnrs Inc Awd Excllnc 85; Canisius; Bio.

BIEG, ALICIA; Keveny Memorial Acad; Troy, NY; (Y); 12/35; Red Cross Aide; Band; Concert Band; Jazz Band; Mrchg Band; Capt Cheerleading; Hon Roll; Natl Hon Rl 84-85; Marine Corps Semper Fidelis Music Awd 85; Mst Talented & Musical 85; U Hartford; Lib Arts.

BIEHLER, TIMOTHY; Olean HS; Olean, NY; (Y); 1/215; Drama Clb; Political Wkr; Radio Clb; Capt Scholastic Bowl; Thesps; Chorus; NHS; Val; Jazz Band; School Play; Excllnce Latin; Natl Sci Olympd Awd Bio; Bio.

BIELAWSKI, ANDREW; Archbishop Molloy HS; Maspeth, NY; (Y); Mathletes; Math Tm; Im Bsktbl; Im Ftbl; Im Sftbl; Acctng.

BIELAWSKI, JOHN; Averill Park HS; Troy, NY; (Y); 24/207; Im Bsktbl; High Hon Roll; Hon Roll; Pres Schlr; Regnts Schlrshp 85; Hudson Valley CC; Engrng Sci.

BIELE, LISA; New Rochelle HS; New Rochelle, NY; (Y); FBLA; Chorus; Hon Roll; NHS.

BIELEC, BEVERLY A; Frontier Central HS; Lakeview, NY; (Y); 22/500; Church Yth Grp; Pres 4-H; Latin Clb; Office Aide; Chorus; Yrbk Stf; 4-H Awd; High Hon Roll; Hon Roll; NHS; Regnst Schlrshp Nrsng 84-85; Trocaire, Niagara Frontier Pol Athl Assn Schlrshps 84-85; Trocaire Coll; Nrs.

BIELEC, JOE; La Salle SR HS; Niagara Falls, NY; (Y); Var L Ftbl; Var L Wrstlng; Memphis ST; CPA Accntng.

BIELLAK, STEPHEN; Fairport HS; Fairport, NY; (Y); Math Tm; Concert Band; Orch; High Hon Roll; NHS; Ntl Merit Schol; St Schlr; Cnty Prof Engrs Scty Schlrshp 85; Math Schlrshp 85; Chem Awd 85; Cornell U.

BIENIEK, REBECCA L; Northville Central HS; Northville, NY; (Y); Sec Trs GAA; Sec Library Aide; Yrbk Stf; Sec Jr Cls; Trs Sr Cls; Rep Stu Cncl; Var Bsktbl; Var Socr; Var Capt Sftbl; High Hon Roll; Natl Schlr Athl Awd 82-84; Le Moyne Coll; Comp Sci.

BIER, ELIZABETH M; Bishop Ludden HS; Syracuse, NY; (S); Hosp Aide; JA; High Hon Roll; NHS; Med Hnr Bio 84; Cert Achvt Spnsh 84; JR Achvt JR Exec Awd 84; Nrs.

BIERBAUM, ELIZABETH; Germantown Central Schl; Germantown, NY; (Y); 13/45; Pres Church Yth Grp; Hosp Aide; Acpl Chr; Church Choir; School Musical; Rep Stu Cncl; Var Fld Hcky; JV Mgr(s); Capt JV Sftbl; Hon Roll; Phrmcy.

BIERBRAUER, JENNIFER; Grand Island HS; Grand Island, NY; (Y); 45/335; Church Yth Grp; Debate Tm; English Clb; GAA; Model UN; Ski Clb; Variety Show; Pres Frsh Cls; Pres Soph Cls; Pres Jr Cls; Varsity Letter In Girls Soccer 84; US Naval Acad; Pol Sci.

BIEREDER, CLAUDIA; Christ The King Regional HS; Ridgwood, NY; (Y); 11/349; NHS; 1st & 2nd Hnrs 81-85; St Johns U; Comptr Sci.

BIERLY, CAROLYN M; Niagara Wheatfield HS; Niagara Falls, NY; (Y); 17/313; Latin Clb; Pep Clb; PAVAS; Rep Stu Cncl; Cheerleading; Var Tennis; Hon Roll; Jr NHS; Sec NHS; NY ST Regents Schlrshp 85; Rochester Inst Tech.

BIERNAT, KRISTINE; Buffalo Traditional HS; Buffalo, NY; (S); 2/140; Church Yth Grp; Nwsp Stf; Yrbk Stf; Bausch & Lomb Sci Awd; Hon Roll; NHS; Prfct Atten Awd; Sal; Canisius Coll; Comp Sci.

BIERNBAUM, MARK; Pittsford Mendon HS; Pittsford, NY; (Y); Debate Tm; Drama Clb; Pres Model UN; Chorus; School Musical; School Play; Yrbk Stf; Rep Stu Cncl; NHS; Ntl Merit Ltr; Bst Del Rchstr Annul UN 85; All Cnty Choir, All Area All ST Choir 83-85; Mst Outstndng Chrus.

BIFFER, MICHAEL H; Beach Channel HS; New York, NY; (Y); Art Clb; Cmnty Wkr; Math Clb; Office Aide; Varsity Clb; Concert Band; Jazz Band; Stage Crew; JV Bsbl; JV Ftbl; Boston U; Bus.

BIFONE, SUZANNE; Glen Cove HS; Glen Cove, NY; (Y); 16/256; Cmnty Wkr; Hosp Aide; Key Clb; Pep Clb; Teachers Aide; Nwsp Rptr; Yrbk Stf; Sec Stu Cncl; JV Bowling; Var Stat Lcrss; SUNY-ALBANY; Comp Sci.

BIGEL, MINDY F; Alfred G Berner HS; Massapequa, NY; (Y); 6/426; Computer Clb; Drama Clb; Pres Temple Yth Grp; Acpl Chr; Chorus; High Hon Roll; NHS; SUNY; Acctg.

BIGELOW, CANDIE; Whitney Point Central HS; Lisle, NY; (Y); 4-H; Chorus; Bsktbl; Fld Hcky; Sftbl; Vllybl; 4-H Awd; High Hon Roll; Hon Roll; School Musical; Ithaca Coll; Psych.

BIGELOW, LINDA J; Sachem H S North; Lk Ronkonkoma, NY; (Y); 143/1360; Church Yth Grp; Chorus; Church Choir; Madrigals; School Musical; Lit Mag; Jr NHS; Sec Educ.

BIGGIE, MONICA; Cardinal O Hara HS; Kenmore, NY; (S); 10/150; Hosp Aide; Yrbk Stf; Sec Soph Cls; Stu Cncl; Cheerleading; High Hon Roll; NHS; Geneseo:Educ.

BIGGS, WILLIAM; St Nicholas Of Tolentine HS; New York, NY; (S); School Play; Stage Crew; Yrbk Stf; Var Swmmng; High Hon Roll; Prfct Atten Awd; Merit Awd For Bio & Physcl Educ 83; NY Cty Dept Of Prks & Recrtn.

BIGHAM, CHRISTOPHER H; Attica HS; Attica, NY; (Y); AFS; Drama Clb; Ski Clb; Spanish Clb; School Musical; School Play; Stage Crew; Keene ST Coll; Spn.

BIGHAM, PAMELA; Ten Broeck Academy; Franklinville, NY; (Y); 2/60; Church Yth Grp; VP 4-H; VP Spanish Clb; VP Varsity Clb; Yrbk Stf; Capt Bsktbl; Capt Crs Cntry; Capt Trk; High Hon Roll; NHS; Elmira Coll Key Awd 85; Deaf Ed.

BIGLER, PAMELA; East HS; Big Flats, NY; (Y); Ski Clb; Thesps; Church Choir; Madrigals; Orch; School Musical; Stu Cncl; High Hon Roll; Trs NHS; Trs Drama Clb; Rensselaer Math-Sci Awd 84-85.

BIKOWSKY, DANIEL M; Rocky Point JR SR HS; Rocky Point, NY; (Y); 25/198; Varsity Clb; Var Capt Bsbl; Var Bsktbl; Var Bowling; JV Crs Cntry; JV Wrstlng; Hon Roll; Ntl Merit Schol; Cmnty Wkr; Exploring; NY Regents Schlrshp 85; NJ Coll Rider; Child Psychlgst.

BILANCIA, LINCOLN L; Laguardia High School Of Music & The Ar; Brooklyn, NY; (Y); Political Wkr; Teachers Aide; Yrbk Stf; Lit Mag; Socr; Tennis; Hon Roll; NHS; Portland Schl Art Exhibit 84; Fine Arts Awd Pratt Inst 83; Semi-Annual Exhibit 81-85; Boston Coll; Fine Arts.

BILCO, JEFF; Fayetteville-Manlius HS; Fayetteville, NY; (Y); Church Yth Grp; Cmnty Wkr; Varsity Clb; Var Bsbl; JV Bsktbl; Var Ftbl; Hon Roll; Arspc Engrng.

BILELLO, CHRISTOPHER M; Berner HS; Massapequa Park, NY; (Y); 33/430; Drama Clb; Quiz Bowl; Acpl Chr; Chorus; Stage Crew; Tennis; NHS; All Conf Tnns 84 & 85; Capt Vrsty Tnns 84 & 85; US Coast Guar Acad; Bus.

BILLA, MARK; Johnstown HS; Johnstown, NY; (Y); Computer Clb; FCA; Letterman Clb; Varsity Clb; Chorus; Variety Show; Nwsp Rptr; Im Var Bowling; Im Ftbl; Fulton Montgomery CC; Comp Sci.

BILLINGHAM, FRANK; Massena Central HS; Massena, NY; (Y); 4-H; Hon Roll; Prfct Atten Awd; Fall Sessn Beggng Actg & Sprng Sessn Humn Behvr Tlntd JR St Lawrence U 84-85.

BILLOTTI, DENA; Hilton Central HS; Hilton, NY; (Y); Ski Clb; Nwsp Stf; Yrbk Bus Mgr; Sec Sr Cls; JV Var Fld Hcky; JV Trk; High Hon Roll; Hon Roll; NHS; Jrnlsm.

BILLUPS, RHONDA; Christopher Columbus HS; Bronx, NY; (Y); Church Yth Grp; Office Aide; Color Guard; Yrbk Phtg; Yrbk Stf; Frsh Cls; Vllybl; Merit & Hon Awd 84; Atndnc Awd 83-85; Soc Stds Awd 84; Law.

BILOWUS, TIMOTHY A; Lackawanna SR HS; Lackawanna, NY; (Y); Boy Scts; French Clb; Red Cross Aide; Hon Roll; Canisius Coll; Bio.

BILSON, PAUL; Bishop Grimes HS; Syracuse, NY; (Y); Debate Tm; Drama Clb; VP JA; Model UN; NFL; School Musical; Rep Stu Cncl; Tennis; Hon Roll; NHS; Acad Amer 85; Natl Engl Merit Awd 85; Law.

BINDER, CATHLEEN L; Vestal HS; Apalachin, NY; (Y); 33/450; Drama Clb; Bsktbl; High Hon Roll; NHS; AP Anatomy & Physlgy Coll Credits 82-83; SUNY Albany; Biochem.

BINDER, STUART; Spring Valley HS; Spring Vly, NY; (Y); Rep Temple Yth Grp; Scl Stds Awd 85; Jrnlsm.

BINDER, TERRY; Brewster HS; Brewster, NY; (S); Sec Church Yth Grp; Office Aide; Varsity Clb; Sec Soph Cls; Sec Jr Cls; JV Bsktbl; Var JV Cheerleading; Stat Socr; Hon Roll; MVP Chrldng 84.

BINGAMAN, ERIC A; Corning East HS; Corning, NY; (Y); Exploring; Y-Teens; Bsbl; Ftbl; Trk; Wt Lftg; High Hon Roll; Civl Engrng.

BINGHAM, NIKKI; Salmon River Central HS; Ft Covington, NY; (S); 13/95; FFA; GAA; Var Bsktbl; Var Socr; Var Sftbl; Hon Roll; Prfct Atten Awd; Spec Ed Tchr.

BINI, JACQUELINE; Commack H S South; Dix Hills, NY; (Y); Office Aide; Mrchg Band; Yrbk Stf; Rep Stu Cncl; Cheerleading; Pom Pon; Tennis; High Hon Roll; Hon Roll; NHS; Bus Mgmt.

BINNS, LAUREEN; Saranac Central HS; Morrisonville, NY; (S); 1/130; Church Yth Grp; FBLA; Red Cross Aide; Comm.

BINYARD, TAMMY; Prospect Heights HS; Brooklyn, NY; (Y); Var Bsktbl; Cheerleading; JV Var Vllybl; Engl.

BIOLSI, PETER; Deer Park HS; Deer Park, NY; (Y); 11/450; Varsity Clb; Band; Concert Band; Yrbk Ed-Chief; Var Tennis; High Hon Roll; Jr NHS; VP NHS; Mrchg Band; Orch; Bio Awd; Coaches Awd Tenns; SUNY Stonybrook; Bio.

BIONDI, LISA R A; Kenmore West SR HS; Kenmore, NY; (Y); Church Yth Grp; French Clb; Ski Clb; Church Choir; Stage Crew; Ed Yrbk Stf; Rep Frsh Cls; Rep Soph Cls; Badmtn; Tennis; Optmtrst.

BIONDO, FRANK; Richmond Hill HS; Newyork, NY; (Y); Debate Tm; Pres Church Yth Grp; Pres Jr Cls; Var Bsbl; Var Bowling; Hon Roll; NHS; Daily News Supr Yth Awd 84 & 85; Eng Hnr Soc 85; Mth Hnr Soc 85.

BIONDOLILLO, KIMBERLY; Indian River Central HS; Watertown, NY; (Y); Key Clb; Latin Clb; Var JV Cheerleading; Gym; Var Capt Socr; Var Trk; Hon Roll; Prfct Atten Awd; Church Yth Grp; Band; All-Amer Chrlder 83-84; Ntl Chrlderes Assc 83-84; Law.

BIRCH, BETH; Oakfield-Alabama Central HS; Oakfield, NY; (Y); Church Yth Grp; Exploring; Girl Scts; Office Aide; Pep Clb; School Musical; Cheerleading; Pom Pon; Swmmng; Cazenovia Coll; Erly Chldhd Ed.

BIRD, CARLTON; Port Jervis HS; Sparrowbush, NY; (Y); Boy Scts; Church Yth Grp; Computer Clb; Debate Tm; Math Tm; Band; Concert Band; Jazz Band; Mrchg Band; Pep Band.

BIRD, JEFFREY A; Jamesville-Dewitt HS; Fayetteville, NY; (Y); 20/225; Cmnty Wkr; Exploring; German Clb; Hosp Aide; Intnl Clb; Letterman Clb; Band; Concert Band; Jazz Band; School Musical; Phtgrphy Awds 83, 84 & 85; Bates Coll; Envrnmntl Sci.

BIRD, JOHN; Olean HS; Olean, NY; (Y); Hon Roll; Sci Olympd Bio 84; St Bonaventure; Crmnl Jstc.

BIRD, MICHELE; Moore Catholic HS; Staten Isl, NY; (Y); 44/180; Hosp Aide; JV Var Cheerleading; JV Golf; Var Pom Pon; High Hon Roll; Hon Roll; NHS; Ntl Merit Ltr; JR Svc Awd 83; Coll Staten Islnd; Nrsng.

BIRDSALL, NANCY; Walton Central HS; Walton, NY; (Y); AFS; Girl Scts; Library Aide; VICA; Color Guard; Mrchg Band; Cit Awd; High Hon Roll; Hon Roll; Prfct Atten Awd; Grl Scts 1st Cls Awd 82; Sec.

BIRDSEY, DARYL JEAN; Fabius-Pompey HS; La Fayette, NY; (Y); 2/65; Am Leg Aux Girls St; 4-H; Band; Rep Stu Cncl; High Hon Roll; NHS; Cortland Schlrs Day 85; Stu Cncl Achvt Awd 85; Syracuse U; Envrnmntl Sci.

BIRGER, TAMAR; Mamaroneck HS; Larchmont, NY; (Y); AFS; Aud/Vis; Drama Clb; Key Clb; School Play; Yrbk Stf; Lit Mag; Lcrss; Socr; Natl HS Inst At Northwestern U 85; Tele Comm.

BIRNBAUM, DENNIS; Saugerties HS; Saugerties, NY; (Y); 62/240; Chess Clb; Library Aide; Political Wkr; Science Clb; Spanish Clb; Teachers Aide; Band; Chorus; Church Choir; Concert Band; St Rose Coll; Pre-Med.

BIRNBAUM, NINA R; Pittsford Sutherland HS; Pittsford, NY; (Y); Dance Clb; Model UN; VP Temple Yth Grp; High Hon Roll; VP NHS.

BIRNIE, LAURA; Amherst Central HS; Amherst, NY; (Y); Dance Clb; French Clb; Hosp Aide; Model UN; Ski Clb; Church Choir; Pres Jr Cls; Socr; Sftbl; High Hon Roll; Ntl Mrt Cntntl Math 82; Ntl Frnch 2nd 83, 8th 84 Cntst.

BIRNSTEIN, LARA; Riverhead HS; Riverhead, NY; (Y); Trs Church Yth Grp; JCL; Latin Clb; Orch; School Musical; Valparaiso U; Educ.

BISAILLON, TERESA; Franciscan Acad; N Syracuse, NY; (S); FBLA; NFL; Speech Tm; Yrbk Stf; High Hon Roll; NHS; Ntl Merit Ltr; Stage Crew; 2nd NY ST Frshmn Of The Yr 83; 4th Pl Public Spkng NY ST. Future Bus Ldrs Of Amer 84; Amer Leg Awd; Sci.

BISAILLON, TODD; Mechanicville HS; Mechanicville, NY; (S); 11/110; Computer Clb; Varsity Clb; Rep Soph Cls; Sec Jr Cls; JV Var Ftbl; Var Wrstlng; High Hon Roll; Hon Roll; Earth Sci Awd 82-83; Social Awd 81-82; Math.

BISANTZ, ANN M; Kenmore West HS; Kenmore, NY; (Y); 2/445; Church Yth Grp; Math Tm; Band; Mrchg Band; Yrbk Bus Mgr; Yrbk Ed-Chief; NHS; Ntl Merit SF; Sal; French Clb; Presdntl Schlrhsp ST U NY 85; SUNY Buffalo; Indstrl Engr.

BISCARR, HARRY; Lindenhurst HS; Lindenhurst, NY; (Y); Art Clb; Spanish Clb; Stage Crew; Variety Show; Nwsp Stf; Yrbk Stf; Sec Sr Cls; JV Var Trk; Hon Roll; Ntl Merit SF; Donald Seaman Trck Awd 84; Hamilton Coll; Engrng.

BISCHEL, JULIE; Fayetteville-Manlius HS; Manlius, NY; (Y); Cmnty Wkr; Hosp Aide; JA; JCL; Teachers Aide; Var Swmmng; Var Trk; Hon Roll; NHS; Hon Men Schltc Art Awd 84; Supr Rnk Natl Fed Music Tchrs Locl Piano Comp 84; Med.

BISCUP, THOMAS; Salamania Central HS; Salamanca, NY; (S); 15/150; French Clb; Ski Clb; Var Capt Ftbl; Var Capt Trk; French Hon Soc; High Hon Roll; Hon Roll; NHS; St Bonaventure U; Acctng.

BISGAIER, LARRY M; South Side HS; Rockville Ctr, NY; (Y); 25/280; Boy Scts; Band; Concert Band; Jazz Band; Mrchg Band; School Musical; High Hon Roll.

BISH, CONNIE JO; Frontier Central Senior HS; Hamburg, NY; (Y); 18/500; Church Yth Grp; JA; Spanish Clb; High Hon Roll; Hon Roll; NHS; Daemen Deans Schlrshp 85-86; Pres Acadmc Awd 82-85; Julia Platt Memrl Awd 85; Daemen; Physcl Therpy.

BISH, PAMELA; Mayville Central Schl; Mayville, NY; (S); 2/34; French Clb; Girl Scts; Office Aide; School Musical; Stage Crew; Score Keeper; Dnfth Awd; High Hon Roll; Jr NHS; NHS; Top 5 Pct Natnlly PSAT 84; Secdry Ed.

BISH, REBECCA; Kenmore West SR HS; Tonawanda, NY; (Y); 23/460; Math Tm; Rep Frsh Cls; Rep Soph Cls; Rep Jr Cls; Rep Stu Cncl; JV Swmmng; Var Tennis; Var Vllybl; High Hon Roll; Hon Roll; Rgnts Schlrshp 85; Presntl Hnrs Prgrm At St U Of NY At Buffalo 85; Hnr Clb 85; ST U Of NY; Arch.

BISHARA, ELIZABETH; Niagara Falls HS; Niagara Falls, NY; (Y); 2/200; Pres Church Yth Grp; VP Drama Clb; VP Band; Church Choir; School Musical; Pres Frsh Cls; VP Jr Cls; VP Rep Stu Cncl; JV Sftbl; NHS; V Chairprsn Yorkers Hist Assoc 85-86; Niagara Falls Bd Realtrs Citznshp Awd 85; Med.

BISHKO, DAVID; New Paltz HS; New Paltz, NY; (Y); 4/160; Nwsp Rptr; Var Tennis; Capt Var Wrstlng; High Hon Roll; NHS; Stanford U.

BISHOP, ANN; Roy C Ketcham HS; Poughkeepsie, NY; (Y); Concert Band; Mrchg Band; Stage Crew; Yrbk Sprt Ed; High Hon Roll; Hon Roll; Prjct Advntr Clb 82-83; Achvt Cert Fash Advsr 85; Syracuse U; Cmnctns.

BISHOP, DAVID; Tupper Lake HS; Tupper Lake, NY; (Y); VP Sr Cls; Var Ftbl; Var Socr; Var Trk; Var Wt Lftg; Canton ATC; Crmnl Justice.

BISHOP, KERRI; Bishop Kearney HS; Rochester, NY; (Y); Rep Frsh Cls; JV Var Bsktbl; JV Var Sftbl; JV Var Vllybl; Hon Roll; NHS.

BISHOP, LOU J; Union Endicott HS; Endwell, NY; (Y); 100/425; Church Yth Grp; Cmnty Wkr; Computer Clb; Band; Stu Cncl; Var JV Bsktbl; Coach Actv; Sftbl; MVP-BSKTBL 85; Jennie F Snapp Schlrshp 85; Sportsmnshp Awd 84 & 85; Albright Coll Trustee Awd 85; Albright Coll; Comptr Sci.

BISHOP, MICHAEL J; Auburn HS; Auburn, NY; (Y); 37/440; Church Yth Grp; VP JA; Math Clb; Ski Clb; School Play; JV L Tennis; High Hon Roll; Pres Schlr; Hon Roll; NY St Rgnts Schlrshp 85-89; Brd Of Educ Alumni Schlrshp 85; Cayuga Cmnty Coll; Pre-Law.

BISHOP, SUSAN K; Saratoga Springs HS; Porter Corners, NY; (Y); 21/465; Spanish Clb; Var L Sftbl; High Hon Roll; NHS; Regnts Schlrshp 85; Rensselaer Polytech; Aero Engr.

BISHOP, THOMAS; East Islip HS; East Islip, NY; (Y); Rep Frsh Cls; Rep Soph Cls; JV Bsbl; JV Ftbl; High Hon Roll; Hon Roll; Top 10 Brookhaven Natl Labs Model Bridge Cont 85; Sci Fair Rbbn 83-84; Engrng.

BISIGNANO, NANCY; Our Lady Of Perpetual Help HS; Brooklyn, NY; (Y); 63/162; Library Aide; Teachers Aide; School Play; Sec Sr Cls; Hon Roll; Spn Achvt Awd 85; Sec.

BISKI, BRIAN R; Schalmont HS; Schenectady, NY; (Y); Concert Band; Jazz Band; Mrchg Band; Rep Frsh Cls; Rep Soph Cls; Rep Jr Cls; Stu Cncl; JV Bsktbl; Coach Actv; Var Trk.

BISLAND, LINDA; Eldred Central HS; Glen Spey, NY; (S); 11/41; Cmnty Wkr; Spanish Clb; Pres Varsity Clb; Band; Chorus; Pres Jr Cls; Rep Stu Cncl; Var Capt Bsktbl; Var Capt Socr; Var Sftbl; Athl Yr 84; Times Herald Recd Reg Sccr Tm 83-84; Phy Thrpy.

BISSELL, ALISANDRA; Tamarac HS; Troy, NY; (Y); #14 In Class; Intnl Clb; Variety Show; Yrbk Sprt Ed; Rep Frsh Cls; Rep Soph Cls; Rep Jr Cls; Rep Sr Cls; Var Capt Cheerleading; Cit Awd; NHS; Brittonkill Tchrs Assoc Awd 85; NY St Rgnts Schlrshp 85; Sony Albany; Lbrl Arts.

BISSELL, HENRY; Sodus Central HS; Sodus Pt, NY; (Y); 15/120; Stu Cncl; Bsktbl; Golf; High Hon Roll; MI Glfr 84; 1st Pl Glf Tourn 84-85; 1st Pl Forgn Lang Fair WAFFLE 84; Engrng.

BISSINGER, BARBARA; John H Glenn HS; Huntington, NY; (Y); Church Yth Grp; MMM; Band; Jazz Band; Mrchg Band; School Musical; JV Stat Bsbl; Hon Roll; NHS; Spanish NHS; NYSSMA 85; Secy Band Cnsl 85.

BISTOR, TAD J; Valley Central HS; Newburgh, NY; (Y); 6/251; Am Leg Boys St; Boy Scts; Math Tm; Concert Band; French Hon Soc; High Hon Roll; NHS; Chess Clb; Computer Clb; Mrchg Band; Vigil Hnr 84; NYS Rgnts, Orange Cnty CC Alumni Assn Schlrshps 85; Orange County CC; Chem.

BISTRAIS, BRIAN W; E L Vandermeulen HS; Pt Jefferson Sta, NY; (Y); Orch; Suffolk CC; Audio Rcrdg.

BIVENS, ITINA R; Herbert H Lehman HS; Bronx, NY; (Y); 123/473; Church Yth Grp; Church Choir; Hon Roll; Miss NY Conf AME Zion Church 84; Perf Attndnc Awd 83-85; Sci.

BIVETTO, FRED; St Johns Prep; Howard Bch, NY; (Y); 35/355; Church Yth Grp; Yrbk Stf; Rep Stu Cncl; Im Bsbl; Coach Actv; Var Crs Cntry; Im Ftbl; Mgr(s); Var Socr; Im Sftbl.

BIXBY, BRYCE T; Charles H Roth HS; W Henrietta, NY; (Y); 6/210; Radio Clb; Stage Crew; Nwsp Stf; High Hon Roll; Hon Roll; Jr NHS; NHS; Prfct Atten Awd; NYS Regents Schlrshp 85; Syracuse U.

BIXLER, BRIAN D; Norwich SR HS; Norwich, NY; (Y); Boy Scts; Band; Jazz Band; Mrchg Band; L Swmmng; High Hon Roll; NHS; Pres Schlr; Olym Mind Cpt; Ntl Merit Corp Schlr; U Buffalo; Bio.

BIZEKIS, HELENE; Hebert H Lehman HS; Bronx, NY; (Y); 29/495; Hon Roll; Hnrs Soc; Arista; Fordham Coll; Bus Mgt.

BJORK, JOSEPH; Ogdensburg Free Acad; Ogdensburg, NY; (Y); 14/210; Boys Clb Am; Cmnty Wkr; Math Clb; ROTC; Varsity Clb; School Play; Nwsp Ed-Chief; Nwsp Sprt Ed; Bsbl; Crs Cntry; Zonta Clb Schlrshp 85; Conway Schlrshp 85; ROTC Cadet Schlrshp 85; St Lawrence U; Econ.

BLACK, ANDREW J; Pelham Memorial HS; Pelham, NY; (Y); Church Yth Grp; Orch; Nwsp Sprt Ed; Nwsp Stf; Socr; Var Trk; NY ST Regents Schlrshp 85; NY ST U Buffalo; Elec Engrng.

BLACK, CAROL; John Jay HS; Hopewell Jct, NY; (Y); AFS; Drama Clb; 4-H; Hosp Aide; Band; School Play; Stage Crew; JV Capt Fld Hcky; JV Vllybl; 4-H Awd; Bus.

BLACK, CAROLYN M; Jamestown HS; Jamestown, NY; (Y); 90/374; French Clb; Intnl Clb; Ski Clb; Band; Concert Band; Mrchg Band; Orch; School Musical; Symp Band; Yrbk Stf; Miami U; Bus Mgmt.

BLACK, DAVID THUNEY; Albany Acad; Albany, NY; (Y); 2/43; Am Leg Boys St; Church Yth Grp; Cmnty Wkr; Library Aide; Nwsp Rptr; Ed Lit Mag; Sec Trs Soph Cls; Mgr Bsktbl; Var Crs Cntry; JV Var Socr; Captn Cadet Co; Cum Laude Recgn Top 10 Pct Cls; Holy Cross Bk Awd; US Military Acad; Engr.

BLACK JR, JOHN; Auburn HS; Auburn, NY; (Y); JV Bsbl; Hon Roll; Arch.

BLACK, KAREN; Smithtown East HS; Nesconset, NY; (Y); School Musical; Variety Show; Stu Cncl; Jr NHS; NHS; Spanish NHS; Certfd Lifegd 84-85; J C Lynn Prof Dance Co 85; NYSSMA 85; Jrnlsm.

BLACK, KAREN; William Nottingham HS; Syracuse, NY; (Y); 41/220; Church Choir; Hon Roll; NHS; Outstndng SR Achvt Awd For Schl & Cmnty Imvlvmnt 85; Delta Sigma Theta Awd & Schlrshp Acdmc Achvt 85; Rochester Inst Tech; Engrng.

BLACK, MARK; Letchworth Central HS; Bliss, NY; (Y); Trs VP 4-H; FFA; 4-H Awd; Hon Roll; 3rd Pl Prepared Pblc Spkng 84-85; Star Ag Mech 85; OH Diesel Tech; Diesel Tech.

BLACK, MAUREEN; Mckinley Vocational HS; Buffalo, NY; (Y); Var Crs Cntry; Var Sftbl; Var Swmmng; Var Trk; Hon Roll; NHS.

BLACK, PAULA C; De Witt Clinton HS; New York, NY; (Y); Library Aide; Science Clb; Teachers Aide; Chorus; School Play; VP Frsh Cls; Sec Jr Cls; Rep Stu Cncl; Var Bsktbl; Hon Roll; Engl Spllg, Readg Awds 84-85; Outstndng Effrt 84; Bsktbl Awds MVP 84; UCLA; Secrty Slsprsn.

BLACK, SUZANNE M; Thomas J Corcoran HS; Syracuse, NY; (Y); 2/250; Spanish Clb; Concert Band; Pep Band; Rep Sr Cls; Var Capt Gym; Var Stat Sftbl; Bausch & Lomb Sci Awd; NHS; Pres Schlr; Sal; MVP For Var Gymnstcs 81-85; Outstndng Ldrshp Cncl Of Svc Clbs 85; JR All-Amer Hall Of Fm Bnd Hnrs 84; Renneselaer Plytchnc Inst; Engr.

BLACKBURN, DAVID F; Rome Free Acad; Rome, NY; (Y); Boys Clb Am; Church Yth Grp; Intnl Clb; Red Cross Aide; Rep Sr Cls; Rep Stu Cncl; Var Capt Diving; Var JV Lcrss; Var Capt Swmmng; High Hon Roll; US Air Force Acad; Aero Engnrg.

BLACKBURN, ELIZABETH; Oakfield-Alabama Central HS; Basom, NY; (Y); 5/95; Art Clb; Sec 4-H; Sec French Clb; Ski Clb; JV Socr; High Hon Roll; NHS; Genesee CC; Bus Admin.

BLACKBURN, MARA; Frewsburg Central HS; Frewsburg, NY; (Y); Pres Church Yth Grp; Quiz Bowl; Chorus; Concert Band; Jazz Band; School Musical; Nwsp Rptr; Sec Jr Cls; NHS; Pep Clb; Cedarville Coll; Med.

BLACKBURN, MICHAEL A; Smithtown HS West; Smithtown, NY; (Y); Key Clb; Var L Crs Cntry; Var Lcrss; Var L Trk; Hon Roll; NYS Regents Schlrshp 85; Gold Key Club Awd 85; ST U NY Albany; Bus Fin.

BLACKLER, CATHERINE; Skaneateles Central HS; Skaneateles, NY; (S); 1/165; Church Yth Grp; Rep Stu Cncl; Var Sftbl; Var Capt Tennis; Bausch & Lomb Sci Awd; NHS; Val; High Hon Roll; Jr NHS; Renseler Mdl 84; Wellesley Bk Awd 84; Engrng.

BLACKMAN, CRYSTAL; Farmingdale SR HS; Amityville, NY; (Y); Computer Clb; Office Aide; JV Bsktbl; JV Trk; JV Vllybl; Hon Roll; Amer Blck Assn Clb 83; Howitt U; Fshn Modl.

BLACKMAN, KIRK R; Francis Lewis HS; Laurelton, NY; (Y); 59/527; Church Yth Grp; Computer Clb; JA; Band; Var Bsktbl; Wt Lftg; Hon Roll; Prfct Atten Awd; NYS Regnts Schlrshp 85; Georgetown U; Acctng.

BLACKMAN, MISHAEL; Central Islip SNR HS; Central Islip, NY; (Y); Church Yth Grp; FTA; Teachers Aide; Mrchg Band; Stat Pom Pon; Hon Roll; NHS; Cornell U; Bus.

BLACKMAN, SUSAN DANA; Byram Hills HS; Armonk, NY; (Y); 1/180; Am Leg Aux Girls St; Intnl Clb; Ski Clb; Thesps; School Musical; Nwsp Ed-Chief; Rep Frsh Cls; Rep Soph Cls; Jr Cls; Sr Cls; Co Chrmn Humanities Fstvl 84-85; Fr Prze; Brown U.

BLACKMAN, WADE; Waverly JR SR HS; Waverly, NY; (Y); Computer Clb; Chorus; Madrigals; Nwsp Phtg; Hon Roll; NHS; Pres Acad Awd 85; Valley Chorus Awd 85; Air Force; Food Svc.

BLACKMAR, MICHAEL P; Stissing Mountain JR SR HS; Pine Plains, NY; (Y); Am Leg Boys St; Church Yth Grp; Yrbk Stf; JV Var Bsktbl; Var Capt Ftbl; Hon Roll; NHS; Elect Engr.

BLACKTON, STEVE; No Babylon SR HS; North Babylon, NY; (Y); Boy Scts; Chess Clb; Ftbl; Wrstlng.

BLACKWELL, RENEE; New Rochelle HS; New Rochelle, NY; (Y); Drama Clb; MMM; Chorus; School Play; Variety Show; Nwsp Stf; Lit Mag; Var Bsktbl; JCL; Vllybl; Cvl Svc Awd 83; U Of Miami; Bus Mgmt.

BLACKWOOD, JOY; Flushing HS; E Elmhurst, NY; (Y); Cheerleading; Perfect Atten 85; Comp.

BLADES, ALLEN; Ellenville HS; Ellenville, NY; (Y); Computer Clb; Spanish Clb; JV Bsbl; JV Wrstlng; Hon Roll; Ntl Engl Merit Awd.

BLADES, JENNIFER; Bethpage HS; Bethpage, NY; (Y); 8/270; Off Drama Clb; Off Band; Chorus; Concert Band; Off Mrchg Band; School Musical; Variety Show; Var L Fld Hcky; NHS; Ntl Merit Ltr; Singng SR 85; Clmbtts Awd 85; Bethpage Bicent Comm Awd 85; Clg Of Holy Cross; Indl Psychl.

BLAETZ, ELKE MONIKA; Canajoharie HS; Canajoharie, NY; (Y); 8/90; Intnl Clb; High Hon Roll; Hon Roll; Trs Jr NHS; NHS; Hugh Obrien Yth Fndtn Ambssdr 84; Empre Glrs ST 85; George M Vosburgh Mem Hndbl Choir; Pharmcy.

BLAHA, DAVID; Notre Dame Bishop Gibbons HS; Schenectady, NY; (S); 13/108; Var Bsbl; Var Capt Bsktbl; Var Golf; High Hon Roll; Masonic Awd; NHS; Notre Dame-Bishop Gibbons Phys Ed Awd; Sprts All-Star Tm; Sec Schl Math.

BLAHOWICZ, JAMES; West Seneca West SR HS; West Seneca, NY; (Y); Spanish Clb; Rep Jr Cls; Stu Cncl; Ftbl; Hon Roll; Music.

BLAHUT, JEFF; Union-Endicott HS; Endicott, NY; (Y); Boy Scts; Church Yth Grp; Ski Clb; Bsbl; Bsktbl; JV L Crs Cntry; Hon Roll; Lbrl Arts.

BLAIN, DANIEL; Uniondale HS; Hempstead, NY; (Y); Art Clb; Band; Mrchg Band; Bsktbl; Ftbl; High Hon Roll; Hon Roll; NHS; Art Awd 82-83; Art Awd Photogrph 82-83; Comm Art.

BLAIR, BARBARA; Webster HS; Webster, NY; (Y); 30/500; Church Yth Grp; Cmnty Wkr; Rep Jr Cls; Var Cheerleading; Jr NHS; NHS; Ntl Merit Ltr; German Clb; Teachers Aide; Rep Frsh Cls; Rochester Schl Deaf Svc Awd 85; Delta Epsilon Phi 85; Cert Cmmndtn Afro-Asian Stds 83; Ed.

BLAIR, CHARMINE M; Northeastern Acad; Bronx, NY; (Y); Chorus; Church Choir; Drill Tm; Trs Frsh Cls; Pres Soph Cls; Pres Jr Cls; Capt Bsktbl; Im Vllybl; Hon Roll; Outstndng Chem Awd 85; Outstndng Bio Awd 84; Frnch Pin 85; Oakwood Coll; Bio.

BLAIR, CHRISTINE; Lincoln HS; Yonkers, NY; (Y); 29/306; Girl Scts; Yrbk Stf; Stu Cncl; Capt JV Cheerleading; JV Var Sftbl; High Hon Roll; Hon Roll; NHS; Aristeon Soc; Fordham U.

BLAIR, DONNA; Dundee Central HS; Dundee, NY; (Y); 19/65; Church Yth Grp; JV Var Bsktbl; JV Var Sftbl; French Hon Soc; Hon Roll; Cortland ST U; Math.

BLAIR, KELLY; Schoharie Central HS; Central Bridge, NY; (S); 3/85; Ski Clb; Sftbl; High Hon Roll; Spansh Awd 84.

BLAIR, KIMBERLY; Cortland JR SR HS; Cortland, NY; (Y); MMM; Band; Orch; School Musical; Nwsp Rptr; Lit Mag; High Hon Roll; NHS; Church Yth Grp; Girl Scts; Elmira Coll Key Awd 85; 1st Pl Cmmty Fllwshp Talent Show 85; Wrld Poetry Golden Poet Awd 85; Bio.

BLAIR, MARGARET A; Rome Catholic HS; Rome, NY; (Y); 6/81; JA; Church Choir; School Musical; Yrbk Stf; Trs Sr Cls; Var Bsktbl; JV Socr; High Hon Roll; NHS; NYS Regents Schlrshp 85; FL Inst Of Tech; Engrng.

BLAIR, PAULA; Cohoes HS; Cohoes, NY; (Y); Chorus; Color Guard; Phy Ther.

BLAIR, SUSAN; Queensburg HS; Glens Falls, NY; (Y); 5/226; Pres French Clb; Library Aide; Office Aide; Yrbk Stf; High Hon Roll; NHS; Ntl Merit SF; Pres Schlr; NY Telephone Co Schlrshp 85; Outstndng Achvt Soc Studies Awd 85; Pres Acad Ftns Awd 85; Hartwick Coll; Bio.

BLAIR, VALERIE A; Sachem North HS; Lk Ronkonkoma, NY; (Y); Drama Clb; Girl Scts; Orch; School Play; Bsktbl; Mgr(s); Score Keeper; Sftbl; Miss Teen NY Fnlst 85; Perf Atten; Hotel Mgmt.

BLAIS, KRISTIN A; Southold HS; Peconic, NY; (Y); 2/56; Am Leg Aux Girls St; VP French Clb; Hosp Aide; Quiz Bowl; Radio Clb; Trs Ski Clb; Yrbk Stf; Cheerleading; Sftbl; Bausch & Lomb Sci Awd; NY ST Regents Schlrshp 85; Wellesley Coll; Intnl Relations.

BLAISDELL, EMILY; Cicero-North Syracuse HS; N Syracuse, NY; (S); 30/711; Church Yth Grp; Math Tm; Band; Symp Band; Var L Fld Hcky; Im Powder Puff Ftbl; Hon Roll; NHS; Mst Impr Plyr 84; Vrsty Bar Fld Hcky 84; Houghton Coll; Elem Ed.

BLAISDELL, TIMOTHY; Lyons HS; Lyons, NY; (Y); 11/97; Am Leg Boys St; Varsity Clb; Sec Jr Cls; Bsbl; Bsktbl; Hon Roll; NHS; Church Yth Grp; French Clb; Male Athl Of Yr 85; Prom King 84; MVP Bsktbl 85; Rochstr Inst Of Tech; Mech Engr.

BLAKE, DAVID; R C Ketcham HS; Wappingers Falls, NY; (S); 22/550; Quiz Bowl; JV Var Bsktbl; Var Trk; High Hon Roll; Jr NHS; NHS; Ntl Merit Ltr; Elec Engrng.

BLAKE, DOUGLAS; The Stony Brook Schl; Coram, NY; (Y); 6/81; Church Yth Grp; Office Aide; Acpl Chr; Church Choir; Var L Swmmng; High Hon Roll; Cum Laude Recgntn 83-85; Catherine M Diefendorf Mem Schlrshp 85; Physcs.

BLAKE, MONICA; Professional Childrens Schl; Edison, NJ; (Y); Drama Clb; Model UN; PAVAS; Thesps; Chorus; Nwsp Stf; Rep Stu Cncl; Tennis; Debate Tm; Hosp Aide; Scrn Actrs Guild; NY U; Music.

BLAKE, ROBIN; Chenango Valley HS; Pt Crane, NY; (Y); Church Yth Grp; Drama Clb; French Clb; Varsity Clb; Band; Chorus; Church Choir; Concert Band; Jazz Band; Madrigals; NY ST Schl Music Assn-Excllnt Rtngs 83-85; French.

BLAKE, TAMMY; Vernon Verona Sherrill Central HS; Sherrill, NY; (Y); Trs Church Yth Grp; Sec Soph Cls; Rep Stu Cncl; Cheerleading; JV Sftbl; Var Vllybl; High Hon Roll; NHS; NEDT Awd; Buddy Spcl Olymp Winter Games 85.

BLAKE, VIRGINIA; Chatham Central HS; Chatham, NY; (Y); 13/134; Hosp Aide; Latin Clb; Ski Clb; Chorus; Orch; School Musical; Var Tennis; High Hon Roll; NHS; Ntl Merit SF; Natl Schl Orch Awd 85; Boston U; Phys Ther.

BLAKELOCK, LISA; Niagara Wheatfield HS; Sanborn, NY; (Y); Sec Church Yth Grp; Chorus; Var JV Socr; Var Trk; Hon Roll; Sec.

BLAKES, MICHAEL; Immaculata HS; New York, NY; (Y); Church Yth Grp; English Clb; Service Clb; Teachers Aide; Color Guard; Nwsp Stf; Lit Mag.

BLAKOWSKI, KATHERINE; Holy Angels Acad; Buffalo, NY; (Y); French Clb; Hon Roll; Prfct Atten Awd; HANDS 84; Frnch Achv Awd 84; Canisius Coll; Phy Thrpst.

BLAM, HOLLY; East Islip SR HS; Great River, NY; (Y); Church Yth Grp; Hosp Aide; Score Keeper; High Hon Roll; Hon Roll; Bus Adm.

BLAMOWSKI, LISA A; Immaculata Acad; Orchard Park, NY; (Y); 22/77; French Clb; Trs Sr Cls; Trs Stu Cncl; JV Var Bsktbl; Mgr(s); Stat Trk; Hon Roll; NEDT Awd; Prfct Atten Awd; Regents Schlrshp 85; Suny-Geneseo; Comm.

BLANC, PATRICK; Andrew Jackson HS; Queens Vlg, NY; (Y); Computer Clb; Service Clb; Teachers Aide; Varsity Clb; JV Capt Ftbl; Score Keeper; Wt Lftg; Cit Awd; Prfct Atten Awd; Typng Awds 83-84; Syracuse; Dr.

BLANCHARD, CARRIE; Roy C Ketcham SR HS; Poughkeepsie, NY; (Y); 43/507; VP AFS; French Clb; Girl Scts; Band; Yrbk Stf; Var Stat Ftbl; Var Stat Sftbl; High Hon Roll; NHS; Pres Schlr; NYS Regents Scholar; Dutchess CC; Lib Art.

BLANCHARD, DONALD M; Germantown Central Schl; Elizaville, NY; (Y); 6/60; Varsity Clb; Band; Pres Stu Cncl; Var L Bsbl; Var L Socr; High Hon Roll; Hon Roll; Sec NHS; Regnts Schlrshp 85; AZ ST U; Mech Engr.

BLANCHARD, HYACINTH B; Erasmus Hall HS; Brooklyn, NY; (Y); 22/433; Cmnty Wkr; Debate Tm; VP FBLA; Math Clb; Office Aide; Science Clb; Teachers Aide; Nwsp Stf; Yrbk Ed-Chief; Lit Mag; Regnts Schlrshp 85; Arista 83-85; CMSP Engrng Awd 84-85; Cornell U; Law.

BLANCHARD, LAURIE; Webster HS; Webster, NY; (Y); 12/550; Church Yth Grp; Rep Stu Cncl; Var L Bsktbl; Var L Socr; Var L Vllybl; NHS; Ntl Merit Ltr; Spanish NHS; Letterman Clb; Spanish Clb; Full Scholar Fld Hockey Boston U 85-90; Chl Rcds 800m 1600m 3200m Relay 84; All Cnty Fld Hcky & Trk 84; Boston U; Biomed Engrng.

BLANCHARD, PAUL; Iona HS; Yonkers, NY; (Y); Church Yth Grp; Yrbk Sprt Ed; Off Jr Cls; Pres Sr Cls; Pres Stu Cncl; Capt Bsktbl; Coach Actv; Crs Cntry; Capt VP Lcrss; Capt Trk; Bus.

BLANCHARD, THOMAS S; Canton Central HS; Canton, NY; (Y); 9/132; VP French Clb; Ski Clb; Varsity Clb; VP Y-Teens; School Play; Var Capt Bsbl; Var JV Bsktbl; Var JV Socr; High Hon Roll; NHS; Social Olympiad Awd; Lafayette; Chem Engr.

BLANCHFORD, PHOEBE; John Glenn HS; Greenlawn, NY; (Y); 34/260; French Clb; Intnl Clb; Science Clb; Nwsp Stf; Lit Mag; Var Sftbl; High Hon Roll; Hon Roll; NHS; Ntl Merit SF; Natl Mrt Semi Fnlst 84.

BLANCO, ROBERT; Archbishop Molloy HS; Flushing, NY; (Y); 125/409; Boy Scts; Exploring; French Clb; Science Clb; Spanish Clb; Capt Swmmng; Hon Roll; Im Crs Cntry; Im Trk; Boy Scts Vice Chptr Chief 85-86; Eagle Sct Rnk 85; Asst Coach Flshng Flyrs B Swm Tm 85-86; Biomed Engrng.

BLAND, LYNN; Mt St Ursula HS; Bronx, NY; (Y); Teachers Aide; Nwsp Stf; Stu Cncl; Bus.

BLAND III, ROBERT L; Roosevelt HS; Yonkers, NY; (Y); Chess Clb; Key Clb; Color Guard; Nwsp Rptr; Lit Mag; Sec Soph Cls; Rep Jr Cls; High Hon Roll; Math.

BLANDING, KAREN; Chenango Forks HS; Binghamton, NY; (Y); 4/180; Church Yth Grp; Ski Clb; Spanish Clb; VP Jr Cls; Swmmng; Hon Roll; NHS; Stu Of Yr Awd Spn I; Stu Of Yr Awd Spn II, Soc Stu 84; Psych.

BLANDINO, VINCENT; Archbishop Molloy HS; Ozone Pk, NY; (Y); Church Yth Grp; Cmnty Wkr; Band; Church Choir; Drill Tm; Jazz Band; Mrchg Band; Hon Roll.

BLANEY, KAREN E; St Marys Girls HS; Manhasset, NY; (Y); Drama Clb; Girl Scts; Chorus; School Musical; Stage Crew; Yrbk Phtg; Yrbk Stf; Hon Roll; Rotary Awd; Fordham U; Bus.

BLANK, MATTHEW A; Spring Valley HS; Spring Valley, NY; (Y); 36/440; Cmnty Wkr; Key Clb; Yrbk Phtg; Im Bsbl; Var Capt Swmmng; Im Vllybl; Hon Roll; NHS; Ntl Merit Ltr; Tulane; Medicine.

BLANKENHORN, DAWN; Long Island Lutheran HS; Lindenhurst, NY; (S); Church Yth Grp; Cmnty Wkr; French Clb; German Clb; Spanish Clb; Var L Trk; Var L Vllybl; High Hon Roll; Jr NHS; NHS; Med.

BLASHEARS, SCOTT; Hudson HS; Hudson, NY; (Y); Boys Clb Am; Boy Scts; Rep Frsh Cls; Rep Soph Cls; Stu Cncl; JV Bsbl; JV Bsktbl; Var L Ftbl; JV Var Socr; Hon Roll; Rsprty Thrpy.

BLASI, VALERIE; Southside HS; Rockville Ctr, NY; (Y); 100/300; Church Yth Grp; 4-H; Church Choir; Orch; L Trk; Hon Roll; Amer Classcl Lgs 8th Annual Latin Exam Magna Cum Laude Cert 85; Vet.

BLASK, DAVID V; Herkimer HS; Herkimer, NY; (Y); 14/115; Drama Clb; School Musical; School Play; Badmtn; Bsktbl; Rgnts Schlrshp Awd 84-85; Herkimer Cnty CC; Acctng.

BLASLOV, GEORGE; Msgr Mc Clancy HS; Astoria, NY; (S); 32/225; Chess Clb; Cmnty Wkr; Math Clb; Math Tm; Hon Roll; Communication Arts Awd; Engrng.

BLASSBERG, ADRIENNE; Spring Valley SR HS; Spring Vly, NY; (Y); French Clb; Temple Yth Grp; Chorus; Cheerleading; Hon Roll; Sprng Hill Amblnce Corps Yth Sqd VP 85, Pres 85-86; Nrsg.

BLASUCCI, BARBARA; Preston HS; Bronx, NY; (S); Drama Clb; School Musical; Stage Crew; Variety Show; Nwsp Rptr; Nwsp Stf; NHS; Fordham U; Cmmnctns.

BLASZAK, TOM M; L C Obourn HS; E Rochester, NY; (Y); 30/120; Boy Scts; Model UN; Ski Clb; Spanish Clb; Merit Roll 82-85; St Bonaventure; Bus.

BLATTEIS, MICHELLE; Mineola HS; Roslyn Heights, NY; (Y); Key Clb; Service Clb; Spanish Clb; Temple Yth Grp; Off Frsh Cls; Off Soph Cls; Off Jr Cls; Off Stu Cncl; Var L Socr; High Hon Roll; Tchr Arts & Crfts Elem Aftr Schl Prog 83-85; Mentor Prog Comp 84-85; Math.

BLATZ, ARLENE A; Our Lady Of Lourdes HS; Wappingers Fls, NY; (Y); Church Yth Grp; Girl Scts; Nwsp Rptr; Yrbk Stf; Score Keeper; High Hon Roll; Jr NHS; NHS; Ntl Merit Ltr; Pres Schlr; 1st Class Grl Scout Awd 82; Dutchess C; Med Tech.

BLAUFOX, SHARI; Smithtown West HS; Hauppauge, NY; (Y); Drama Clb; German Clb; Thesps; Chorus; School Musical; School Play; Swing Chorus; Stu Cncl; Tennis; High Hon Roll; Essay Awd 81; Vassar Coll.

BLAUFUSS, MARY; St Marys HS; West Seneca, NY; (S); 25/200; Science Clb; Yrbk Stf; Lit Mag; Var Crs Cntry; Var Trk; Hon Roll; Natl Hnr Socty 85; Canisius Coll; Engl.

BLAYZOR, ROBIN A; Johnstown HS; Johnstown, NY; (Y); Band; Flag Corp; Mrchg Band; Nwsp Stf; Sec Frsh Cls; JV Cheerleading; High Hon Roll; Jr NHS; NHS; GAA; Regents Scholarship Winner 85; Fulton Montgomery; Accounting.

BLAZEJEWSKI, CHRISTINE M; F D Roosevelt HS; Salt Point, NY; (Y); 50/350; Art Clb; Church Yth Grp; 4-H; French Clb; Girl Scts; School Musical; Hon Roll; NHS; Ntl Merit SF; Dutchess CC; Psych.

BLEDSOE, ANGELA; Belmont Central HS; Belmont, NY; (Y); 6/17; GAA; Spanish Clb; Band; Chorus; School Play; Nwsp Stf; Yrbk Stf; Var Capt Bsktbl; Var Capt Socr; Var Capt Sftbl; Otstndng SR Grl Athlt 85; Rotary Club Svc Above Self; MVP Vllybll & Sccr Achvmnt 85; Alfred Ag Tech; Cmptr Sci.

BLEILER, KATHY; Mynaerse Acad; Seneca Falls, NY; (Y); 25/127; Band; Chorus; Concert Band; Drm Mjr(t); Jazz Band; School Musical; Swing Chorus; Rep Stu Cncl; Hon Roll; Music.

BLEILER, STEVEN; Mynderse Acad; Seneca Falls, NY; (Y); 23/132; Am Leg Boys St; School Musical; Swing Chorus; Capt Crs Cntry; Capt Trk; Cit Awd; Hon Roll; NHS; Drama Clb; Anne Dido Mscl Thtr Awd 85; Natl Chrl Awd 85; Fredonia; Comm.

BLEIWEISS, MICHAEL; Commack H S South; Dix Hills, NY; (Y); Computer Clb; Mathletes; Math Clb; Math Tm; Spanish Clb; Teachers Aide; High Hon Roll; NHS; Dscrptv Wrtng Englsh Awd 85; Ntl Sci Olypiad For Chmstry 85; Amer HS Math Exam 84.

BLENCOWE, KATHLEEN; Corning-Painted Post West HS; Coopers Plains, NY; (Y); Sec VP Thesps; Madrigals; Sec Frsh Cls; Sec Soph Cls; Sec Jr Cls; Sec Sr Cls; Pres Stu Cncl; Cheerleading; French Hon Soc; NHS; Geneseo ST Coll; Elem Educ.

BLENCOWE, KATHY; Corning-Painted Post West HS; Coopers Plains, NY; (Y); Thesps; Madrigals; Sec Frsh Cls; Sec Soph Cls; Sec Jr Cls; Sec Sr Cls; Pres Stu Cncl; Cheerleading; High Hon Roll; Hon Roll; Donovan Acad Brd Dir 85-86; Ithaca ST U; Educ.

BLENK, MICHAEL B; Lewiston-Porter SR HS; Youngstown, NY; (Y); 1/273; Boy Scts; Church Yth Grp; Ski Clb; Rep Soph Cls; Rep Jr Cls; Rep Sr Cls; Rep Stu Cncl; Var L Trk; NHS; Ntl Merit Ltr; Eagle Sct 83; VI Tech; Engrng.

BLESKOSKI, NANCY K; Roth HS; W Henrietta, NY; (Y); 62/240; Hon Roll; NHS; Regnts Schlrshp 85; Monroe CC; Law.

BLESSING, THOMAS S; Lockport SR HS; Lockport, NY; (Y); Computer Clb; Drama Clb; Intnl Clb; Latin Clb; ROTC; School Play; Nwsp Sprt Ed; Trk; Hon Roll; Jr NHS; Drama Awd 82-83; Sci Fair Awds 82; Parnts Wthout Prtnrs IYEA 82; U Of CA-BERKELEY; Social Sci.

BLEWETT, BRANDEE; Berlin American HS; Apo New York, NY; (Y); 6/63; ROTC; Band; JV Bsktbl; Mgr Ftbl; Mgr Socr; Trk; NHS; Pres Schlr; All Germany Hnrs Band; TX A & M; Mech Engr.

BLEWETT, CAROLYN; Groton Central HS; Groton, NY; (Y); Girl Scts; Chorus; Yrbk Bus Mgr; Yrbk Stf; Var Bsktbl; Var Stat Trk; JV Var Vllybl; MIP Track; Data Proc.

BLEYLE, KYLE; Williamsville South HS; Williamsville, NY; (Y); JA; Jazz Band; School Musical; JV Vllybl; Ntl Merit Ltr.

BLINN, LAURIE; Lake Placid HS; Lake Placid, NY; (Y); Church Yth Grp; Stage Crew; Yrbk Stf; Sec Jr Cls; VP Sftbl; Hon Roll; Prfct Atten Awd; Cmndbl Atten Awd 85; Cmndbl Atten Awd 83; Suny Agr Tec Canton; Vet Sci.

BLINSTON, KAREN; Tonaswanda JR SR HS; Tonawanda, NY; (Y); Church Yth Grp; Hosp Aide; School Musical; Yrbk Stf; Rep Stu Cncl; Cheerleading; Var Sftbl; Var Swmmng; Hon Roll; NHS; Comp Sci.

BLISS, DIANNE M; Kendall JR SR HS; Hamlin, NY; (Y); 9/92; Ski Clb; Jazz Band; Score Keeper; Band; Concert Band; Mrchg Band; JV Bsktbl; High Hon Roll; Jr NHS; Trs NHS; Regents Schlrshp 85; Acad Decathalon; NYSBA Mock Trial Cmptn; GMI Engrng Inst; Ind Engrng.

BLISS, JEFFREY D; Troupsburg Central Schl; Troupsburg, NY; (Y); 6/13; Aud/Vis; Band; Chorus; Mrchg Band; Trs Stu Cncl; Var L Bsktbl; Var L Socr; Timer; Hon Roll; Prfct Atten Awd; Herkimer CC; Mortuary Sci.

BLITZ, ERICA; Carmel HS; Carmel, NY; (Y); 30/400; Computer Clb; Pres Trs 4-H; Math Tm; School Musical; Stage Crew; Nwsp Phtg; Nwsp Rptr; Nwsp Stf; Yrbk Ed-Chief; Yrbk Phtg; Engrng.

BLIVEN, BRENDA; Belmont Central HS; Belmont, NY; (Y); 1/17; Pres Church Yth Grp; Pres Spanish Clb; Chorus; Pres Concert Band; Nwsp Ed-Chief; Sec Sr Cls; Sec Stu Cncl; Capt Cheerleading; Bausch & Lomb Sci Awd; Val; Daughters Of Amer Revolutn Good Ctzn Awd 85; Amer Chemcl Soc Chem Awd 85; NY ST Regents Schlrshp 85; Houghton Coll; Engl.

BLIZIOTIS, WILLIAM; The High School Of Art & Design; Flushing, NY; (Y); 6/380; Hon Roll; NCTE Awd; NHS; 3rd Pl Pstr Cntst 84; Art Inst Of Chgo; Grphc Dsgn.

BLOCH, ERIKA; New Paltz Central HS; New Paltz, NY; (Y); Pres Church Yth Grp; Sec Drama Clb; Band; Chorus; Concert Band; Drm Mjr(t); Mrchg Band; School Play; Swing Chorus; Symp Band; NE Music Camp Schlrshp 83; All-Eastrn US Music Schl Schlrshp 85; Chrch Ctznshp Awd 84-85; Hope Coll; Music Ed.

BLOCK, GAIL S; Lawrnece HS; Woodmere, NY; (Y); French Clb; Science Clb; Temple Yth Grp; Nwsp Rptr; Nwsp Stf; High Hon Roll; Hon Roll; NHS; Emory U.

BLOCK, JOHN; Farmingdale HS; Massapequa Pk, NY; (Y); Computer Clb; Bsktbl; Crs Cntry; Swmmng; Trk; Hon Roll; Vrsty Ltr Trk 85.

BLOCK, LAUREN H; Northport HS; E Northport, NY; (Y); Hosp Aide; PAVAS; School Musical; School Play; Nwsp Rptr; Nwsp Stf; Yrbk Rptr; Yrbk Stf; Hon Roll; NHS; SUNY-BINGHAMTON; Cmmnctn Arts.

BLOCK, ROBERT J; Horrace Mann Schl; Larchmont, NY; (Y); Chess Clb; Math Tm; Temple Yth Grp; Chorus; Orch; School Musical; Lit Mag; Crs Cntry; Cum Laude Socty 85; U Of Chicago; Sci.

BLODGETT, TOM; Hilton Central HS; Hilton, NY; (Y); Var Swmmng; High Hon Roll; All County Swmmng 84-85; Empire ST Games Fin Swmmng 83-85; Mst Valuable Swmmng 84-85; Physlgy.

BLOISE, MICHAEL G; St Anthonys HS; Kings Park, NY; (Y); 1/400; Nwsp Sprt Ed; Yrbk Rptr; Lit Mag; Im Bowling; JV Crs Cntry; French Hon Soc; High Hon Roll; NHS; Ntl Merit SF; Val; Schlr Yr Awds 82-84; Engr.

BLOM, KIRSTEN; Port Richmond HS; Staten Isld, NY; (Y); 60/650; Cmnty Wkr; Girl Scts; Hosp Aide; Service Clb; School Musical; Nwsp Rptr; French Hon Soc; Civic Clb; Office Aide; Political Wkr; Prncpls Pride Yankee Awd NYC 85; Amer-Israel Yth Ambssdr 83; NYC Brd Of Ed Chncllr Rll Of Hnr 83; Middlebury Coll; Forgn Svc.

BLOMGREN, CHRISTOPHER S; East JR SR HS; Rochester, NY; (Y); 17/267; Am Leg Boys St; Model UN; Band; School Musical; Capt Crs Cntry; Trk; Hon Roll; NHS; Ntl Merit Ltr; VFW Awd; Oswego.

BLOOD, COLLEEN; Jamestown HS; Jamestown, NY; (Y); Church Yth Grp; Acpl Chr; School Musical; Nwsp Rptr; Yrbk Stf; Rep Frsh Cls; Capt Cheerleading; Jr NHS; NHS; Opt Clb Awd; St Bonaventure U; Psych.

BLOOD, JOHN J; Alfred G Berner HS; Massapequa, NY; (Y); #3 In Class; Drama Clb; Scholastic Bowl; School Play; Sec Soph Cls; Sec Jr Cls; Sec Sr Cls; Socr; High Hon Roll; NHS; Ntl Merit Ltr; Amherst; Hstry.

BLOODGOOD, JOSEPHINE P; New Paltz Central HS; New Paltz, NY; (Y); 6/160; Art Clb; Drama Clb; French Clb; Chorus; School Play; Yrbk Ed-Chief; Stu Cncl; High Hon Roll; NHS; NYS Summer Schl Visual Arts 84-85; Recog & Talnts Srch Mst Artistic Cls 85; Fine Art.

BLOOM, JANET F; Central HS; Valley Stream, NY; (Y); 20/390; Leo Clb; Spanish Clb; Var Capt Bsktbl; Var Sftbl; Var Capt Vllybl; Hon Roll; Jr NHS; Mu Alp Tht; NHS; Spanish NHS; PTA Schlrshp 85; Rgnts Schlrshp 85; SUNY Binghamton; Acctng.

BLOOM, KRISTIN; F D Roosevelt HS; Hyde Park, NY; (Y); Hosp Aide; Ski Clb; Band; Mrchg Band; Trk; SUNY Albany; Med.

BLOOM, SUSAN D; Spring Valley SR HS; Spring Valley, NY; (Y); 7/435; Thesps; School Musical; Yrbk Stf; Lit Mag; DAR Awd; French Hon Soc; High Hon Roll; NHS; Ntl Merit Ltr; CIBA-GEIHY Sci Awd 85; Regents Schlrshp Wnnr 85; Cornell U; Bus Mgmt.

BLOOMBERG, NEIL A; Islip HS; Islip, NY; (Y); 99/360; Temple Yth Grp; Y-Teens; Stage Crew; Yrbk Phtg; Yrbk Rptr; Yrbk Stf; Stu Cncl; Var Tennis; Rotary Awd; Boy Scts; Stu Union 85; Kent ST U; Acctng.

BLOSHINSKY, GREGORY; Middletown HS; Suffern, NY; (Y); 19/396; Nwsp Sprt Ed; Yrbk Stf; Var L Socr; Var Capt Tennis; NHS; St Schlr; All Cty Soccer Team 84; Orange Cty Doubles Champ 84; Binghamton; Mgmt Sci.

BLOWE, JOSEPHINE; East Hampton HS; E Hampton, NY; (Y); Trs Church Yth Grp; Spanish Clb; Chorus; Church Choir; School Musical; Hon Roll; Schlrshp Awd For Spnsh I 83; Cert Of Merit For Bio 84; Accntnt.

BLUEMELL, ELIZABETH; Kings Park HS; Kings Park, NY; (Y); Debate Tm; DECA; Drama Clb; NFL; Science Clb; Speech Tm; Chorus; School Play; Lit Mag; High Hon Roll; Hugh O Brien Yth Semnr 84; Rnnr Up Grls Empir ST Contst 85; Bus.

BLUM, SANDRA; Shulamith HS; Brooklyn, NY; (Y); Cmnty Wkr; School Musical; School Play; Nwsp Rptr; Yrbk Bus Mgr; Trs Frsh Cls; Trs Soph Cls; Trs Jr Cls; Hon Roll; NHS; Regents Schlrshp 85; Brooklyn Coll; Comp.

BLUM, TRACY ANN; Charles H Roth HS; Rochester, NY; (Y); 31/210; Spanish Clb; Nwsp Stf; Yrbk Stf; VP Frsh Cls; Pres Soph Cls; Pres Jr Cls; JV Capt Cheerleading; Hon Roll; Jr NHS; NHS; Friars Scholar 85; Regnts Scholar 85; Henrietta Yth Bd Hall Of Fame 84; St Bonaventure U; Acctg.

BLUMAN, ERIC M; Jamesville-Dewitt HS; Jamesville, NY; (Y); Boy Scts; Exploring; German Clb; Temple Yth Grp; Band; Bsbl; Var Crs Cntry; Var Wrstlng; High Hon Roll; Hon Roll; Pre Med.

BLUMAN, ERIC S; Jamesville-Dewitt HS; Dewitt, NY; (Y); 102/225; Boy Scts; Key Clb; Band; School Musical; Var Bsktbl; Var Bowling; JV Var Socr; Var Swmmng; Var Tennis; Rgnts Schlrshp 85; Eagle Scout Awd 85; SUNY Albany; Bus.

BLUMBERG, JASON; Hutch-Tech Lafayette HS; Buffalo, NY; (Y); Rep Frsh Cls; Var Socr; Hon Roll; NHS; Pres Schlr; Rgnts Schlrshp 85; Acadmc Math 85; Pres Acadmc Ftns Awds Pgm 85; Siena Coll; Bus Mngmt.

BLUMBERG, LOREEN; Little Falls JR SR HS; Little Falls, NY; (Y); Drama Clb; FBLA; GAA; Band; Concert Band; Mrchg Band; Yrbk Stf; JV Bsktbl; JV Var Bowling; Var Fld Hcky; Medcl Lab Technlgy.

BLUMENAUER, MICHAEL; Bishop Maginn HS; Albany, NY; (Y); 39/114; Drama Clb; PAVAS; Spanish Clb; Thesps; School Musical; Rep Soph Cls; Stu Cncl; Hon Roll; Intrnshp Empire ST Inst Prfmng Arts 84-85; Best Perfmnc Intrcl Play Comptn 82-84; Suny Coll Brockport; Theatre.

BLUMENKRANZ, ADAM; East Meadow HS; East Meadow, NY; (S); Pres FBLA; Concert Band; Mrchg Band; Nwsp Bus Mgr; VP Soph Cls; VP Jr Cls; Off Stu Cncl; Lcrss; Socr; Hst NHS; 4th Pl NY ST FBLA Spkng Event 85; Accptd Cornell U Smmr Coll Law Prog 85; Cornell U; Law.

BLUMENTHAL, ANDREW; Ohc Torah Inst; Riverdale, NY; (Y); Ntl Merit Ltr; Let Of Commendation From Natl Merit Schlrshp Prog 83; Baruch Schlr 84; Baruch Coll; Bus Admin.

BLUMETTI, LISA D; Srartoaga Springs SR HS; Wilton, NY; (Y); 65/465; Drama Clb; Exploring; French Clb; Spanish Clb; Var JV Socr; JV Trk; High Hon Roll; Hon Roll; NHS; St Schlr; U Buffalo SUNY; Intl Bus.

BLUMREICH, JANNA; Barker Central HS; Barker, NY; (Y); AFS; Drama Clb; French Clb; FBLA; Spanish Clb; Thesps; Band; Chorus; Pep Band; School Play; Niagara County CC; Acctng.

BLUTHARDT, GAYE; Pioneer Central HS; Arcade, NY; (Y); 7/225; 4-H; Spanish Clb; Chorus; School Musical; School Play; Swing Chorus; Lit Mag; Hon Roll; NHS; Ntl Merit Ltr; Regents Schlrshp 85; Cornell U; Bio.

BLY, JENNIFER; Southside SR HS; Pine City, NY; (Y); Drama Clb; Hosp Aide; Varsity Clb; Chorus; Concert Band; Madrigals; Mrchg Band; School Musical; Var L Socr; Hon Roll; NYS Bus, Prof Wmns Conv 82; Hrs Vltnr Svc Awd 84; Muscl Perf.

BLY, MICHAEL P; Brentwood Sunderling HS; Brentwood, NY; (Y); Boys Clb Am; Ski Clb; Stu Cncl; Im Bsbl; JV Ftbl; Im Sftbl; Im Wt Lftg; Voice Dem Awd; U Of HI At Manoa; Bus Mgmt.

BLYTHE, JEFF; John A Coleman HS; Kingston, NY; (S); 3/68; Boy Scts; Key Clb; Varsity Clb; School Musical; Pres Frsh Cls; Rep Stu Cncl; Var L Crs Cntry; Var L Trk; NHS; Ntl Merit Ltr; Natl Achvt Outstndg Negro Stu Semi-Fin 84; Harvard; Pre-Med.

BOADWAY, TINA; Union Springs Acad; Chateaugay, NY; (Y); 3/50; French Clb; Varsity Clb; Variety Show; Var Gym; High Hon Roll; Andrews U; Math.

BOARDMAN, KIMBERLY A; Sherman Central Schl; Sherman, NY; (Y); 1/38; Drama Clb; 4-H; Chorus; Yrbk Ed-Chief; VP Sr Cls; Vllybl; Bausch & Lomb Sci Awd; Hon Roll; NHS; Chautauqua Cnty Alt Dairy Prncss 84-85; Acadmc All Amer Awd Engl 84; Alfed U; Bio.

BOARDWAY, KRISTINE; Gloversville HS; Gloversville, NY; (Y); Intnl Clb; Pep Clb; Teachers Aide; Yrbk Stf; Rep Stu Cncl; Cheerleading; Powder Puff Ftbl; High Hon Roll; Hon Roll; NY ST Rgnts Schlrshp 85; Ithaca Coll; Accntng.

BOATE, CHRISTINE; Connetquot HS; Bohemia, NY; (Y); Church Yth Grp; Hosp Aide; Teachers Aide; Chorus; Mrchg Band; Symp Band; Rep Frsh Cls; High Hon Roll; Jr NHS; NHS; Phy Thrpy.

BOBBY, MICHELE; West Genesee SR HS; Camillus, NY; (Y); Church Yth Grp; French Clb; Key Clb; Ski Clb; Off Soph Cls; Off Jr Cls; Off Sr Cls; Off Stu Cncl; Var Cheerleading; Hon Roll; Nic Kid Awd 80-81 & 82-83.

BOBE, ROSALIA; Cathedral HS; Bkly, NY; (Y); 16/298; Science Clb; Hon Roll; Engl Hnrbl Ment 83; Engl Hnr Medal 85; Cornell U; Optmtry.

BOBOWSKI, CYNTHIA; Scotia Glenville HS; Holiday, FL; (Y); 4-H; French Clb; German Clb; JA; Key Clb; Pep Clb; Red Cross Aide; Ski Clb; Chorus; Church Choir; Int Desgn.

BOBROWSKI, LAURA; Union Endicott HS; Endicott, NY; (S); Sec Church Yth Grp; Spanish Clb; Band; Concert Band; Mrchg Band; School Musical; High Hon Roll; NY ST Schl Music Assn Awd 83; All-County Band 83; Area All ST Band 84; Engrng.

BOBURKA, JOHN; Seton Catholic Central HS; Endicott, NY; (S); Chess Clb; Varsity Clb; JV Bsktbl; JV Var Ftbl; Im Vllybl; High Hon Roll; NHS; Bio.

BOCCHIMUZZO, FRANCO; Saugerties HS; Glasco, NY; (Y); Band; Symp Band; JV Var Ftbl; NHS; Ntl Sci Stds Olpmpd 85; Bus.

BOCCHIMUZZO, SAL; Saugerties JR-SR HS; Glasco, NY; (Y); Band; Concert Band; Symp Band; JV Var Ftbl; Hon Roll; NHS; Comp Sci.

BOCCHINO, MARY E; Arlington HS; Poughkeepsie, NY; (Y); Church Yth Grp; Office Aide; Political Wkr; Hon Roll; Deans List 84-85; Erly Adm Dusthcess Coll 84-85; Bus Adm.

BOCCHINO, ROSSELLA; Bishop Ford CC HS; Brooklyn, NY; (Y); Computer Clb; Dance Clb; Intnl Clb; JA; Science Clb; Sr Cls; Hon Roll; Frgn Lang Clb 1st Hnrs Plaq 82; Hnrs 83; Hmrm Rep Hnrs 84; Bus Law.

BOCCONE, STEVE; East Meadow HS; E Meadow, NY; (Y); Boy Scts; Computer Clb; FBLA; Key Clb; Radio Clb; Science Clb; Varsity Clb; Var JV Ftbl; Var JV Lcrss; Var JV Wrstlng; Best Written Story Awd 84; FBL Am 86; All Star Tm Goals 86; Bus Mgmt.

BOCHSLER, HEIDI; Medina SR HS; Medina, NY; (Y); 15/156; AFS; Chess Clb; Model UN; Orch; Im Badmtn; Im Bowling; Im Vllybl; Cit Awd; Hon Roll; NHS; Accntnt.

BOCI, TODD; Royalton-Hartland HS; Gasport, NY; (Y); 29/208; French Clb; Varsity Clb; Stu Cncl; Im Bsbl; Var Crs Cntry; Im Socr; Tennis; Hon Roll.

BOCK, GEORGE; Union Endicott HS; Endicott, NY; (Y); VP Church Yth Grp; German Clb; Ski Clb; Varsity Clb; Church Choir; Var Capt Bowling; Var JV Ftbl; Hon Roll; Gov NYS Dist Fed Russian Orthodox Clbs 83; Law.

BOCKLAGE, MICHAEL H; Naples Central Schl; Naples, NY; (Y); 13/83; Bsbl; Socr; Vllybl; Bio.

BOCOCK, JENNIFER; Haverling Central Schl; Bath, NY; (S); 5/147; Church Yth Grp; French Clb; Math Clb; School Play; Yrbk Stf; Capt Cheerleading; Swmmng; High Hon Roll; NHS; Ntl Merit Ltr; Alfred ST Coll; Med.

BODDIE, MICHELE L; Cardinal Spellman HS; Brooklyn, NY; (Y); Dance Clb; Girl Scts; Stu Cncl; Var Crs Cntry; Var Capt Trk; 2nd Achvt Hnrs 81-85; Major Track Awds 82-85; Acad Perf Awd 85; LIU; Comp Sci.

BODENSTEINER, DONNA; Nazareth Acad; Webster, NY; (Y); Spanish Clb; Acpl Chr; Band; Chorus; Concert Band; Stage Crew; Trs Stu Cncl; Hon Roll; Excllnt NYSSMA Solo Level 4 Clarinet 84.

BODER, ROBERT; Newfield HS; Selden, NY; (S); 18/568; Cmnty Wkr; Math Tm; Scholastic Bowl; Spanish Clb; Varsity Clb; Tennis; High Hon Roll; Hon Roll; NHS; Regents Schlrshp 85; St U-Binghamton.

BODEWES, SANDY L; Kenmore East HS; Tonawanda, NY; (Y); Ski Clb; Sftbl; Hon Roll; Sci.

BODIE, KAREN; Tonawanda JR SR HS; Tonawanda, NY; (Y); Ski Clb; Yrbk Stf; Rep Stu Cncl; Var L Bsktbl; Var L Socr; Var L Sftbl; Var L Trk; Var L Vllybl; Hon Roll; Sec NHS; Rotry Clb Tonawandas Art Shw 1st Paintg 83; Trck Schl Rcrds 3 Relys 83; Art.

BODINE, BRENT; Penn Yan Acad; Penn Yan, NY; (Y); 37/167; Am Leg Boys St; Varsity Clb; Sec Stu Cncl; JV Bsbl; Var Capt Ftbl; Var Lcrss; Cit Awd; SUNY Alfred Ag & Tech; CAD.

BODKIN, MATTHEW; Mercy HS; Centereach, NY; (Y); Chess Clb; Ski Clb; Hon Roll; Artst.

BODNAR, JACQUELINE; St Catharines HS; Bronx, NY; (Y); Yrbk Stf; Lit Mag; Cheerleading; NHS; Ntl Merit Ltr; NY ST Regents Schlrshp 85; Iona Coll; Bus.

BODNAR, LIZ; Washingtonville HS; Washingtonville, NY; (Y); Chess Clb; Library Aide; Chorus; Nwsp Rptr; Im Bsktbl; JV Var Sftbl; Hon Roll; Mst Imprvd Plyr-Vrsty Sftbll 84-85; Bus Mgmt.

BODNER, LIOR; Huntington HS; Huntington, NY; (Y); Computer Clb; Mathletes; Lit Mag; Reagents Schlrhsp 84-85; JV Fencing; Syracuse U; Bio Engr.

BOEHLECKE, ROBERT; Lansing HS; Ithaca, NY; (Y); Var L Bsktbl; Var L Socr; Var L Trk; Hon Roll; Marine Bio.

BOEHMCKE, SUZANNE; Cold Spring Harbor HS; Huntington, NY; (Y); 46/129; Hosp Aide; Intnl Clb; Chorus; School Musical; Yrbk Stf; Var Lcrss; Nrsng.

BOEHME, CELESTE; Academy Of St Joseph HS; Ft Salonga, NY; (Y); Aud/Vis; Drama Clb; Math Tm; Pep Clb; Spanish Clb; School Play; Ntl Merit Ltr; NEDT Awd; Latn, Spnsh Excel.

BOEMIO, NEIL; Mount Saint Michael Acad; Bronx, NY; (Y); 14/286; Off Chess Clb; Computer Clb; High Hon Roll; Hon Roll; Spanish NHS; Rgnts Schlrshp 85; New York U; Comp Sci.

BOEMIO, TINA; Smithtown H S East; Nesconset, NY; (Y); Dance Clb; Yrbk Stf; Off Frsh Cls; Stu Cncl; Hon Roll; Pres Acad Fit Awd 85; SUNY Geneseo; Engl.

BOENING, LYDIA C; Lancaster Central HS; Lancaster, NY; (Y); Church Yth Grp; Key Clb; Pep Clb; Chorus; School Musical; Rep Stu Cncl; Var Trk; Hon Roll; Vet Med.

BOERGERS, JULIE A; Mount St Mary Acad; Buffalo, NY; (Y); 2/96; Church Yth Grp; Computer Clb; Intnl Clb; Chorus; School Musical; Stage Crew; Nwsp Rptr; Yrbk Ed-Chief; NHS; Schlrshp For Study In Madrid Spain Intl Studies Assn 84; Natl Science Merit Awd 84; U Of Rochester; Computer Sci.

BOGAN, KELLY; New Utrecht HS; Brooklyn, NY; (Y); 28/557; Cmnty Wkr; Pres Key Clb; Office Aide; Teachers Aide; Yrbk Ed-Chief; Bowling; Hon Roll; Kiwanis Awd; Chncllrs Hnr Rll, NUHS Alumi Assn Gld Mdl Govt, Cngrssman Awd Comm Svc 85; Long Island U; Phy Thrpst.

BOGARDUS, BRIDGET; Haverling Central HS; Bath, NY; (S); 26/147; Church Yth Grp; Jazz Band; Mrchg Band; Nwsp Stf; Yrbk Sprt Ed; Rep Stu Cncl; Capt Var Bsktbl; Capt Var Socr; Var Sftbl; NHS; Bryant & Stratton; Bus Admn.

BOGARDUS, DALE; Coxsackie Athens HS; Climax, NY; (Y); 6/105; Boy Scts; 4-H; Pep Clb; Red Cross Aide; Soroptimist; Spanish Clb; Teachers Aide; Yrbk Ed-Chief; Yrbk Stf; Rep Frsh Cls; Merchant Marine Acad; Law.

BOGARDUS, MICHAEL; Harverling Central Schl; Bath, NY; (Y); Am Leg Boys St; Boy Scts; French Clb; Math Clb; Band; Jazz Band; Yrbk Stf; Ftbl; God Cntry Awd; Hon Roll; Syracuse U; Envrnmntl Sci.

BOGARDUS, SETHANN; Ravena-Coeymans-Selkirk HS; Alcove, NY; (Y); Hon Roll; Stat Trk; Acctg.

BOGART, CORINNE F; Holy Trinity HS; Bellmore, NY; (S); 5/356; Cmnty Wkr; French Clb; Math Clb; Math Tm; Teachers Aide; Stage Crew; Nwsp Stf; Stu Cncl; High Hon Roll; NHS; Schlrshp To Univ Of Caen France 84; Psychology.

BOGART, ROBERT; Bishop Timon HS; Buffalo, NY; (Y); 35/160; Am Leg Boys St; Drama Clb; Thesps; Chorus; School Musical; School Play; Nwsp Rptr; Yrbk Rptr; Lit Mag; VP Church Yth Grp; Niagara Canisius; Psych.

BOGART, STEVEN M; Commack High School South; Commack, NY; (Y); Computer Clb; Math Tm; Spanish Clb; Teachers Aide; High Hon Roll; NHS.

BOGATS, ANDREW; James Madison HS; Brooklyn, NY; (Y); Bsktbl; Baruch Coll; Bus Ed.

BOGENSCHUTZ, TODD R; General Brown HS; Watertown, NY; (Y); Boy Scts; French Clb; JV Var Bsbl; JV Mgr(s); NHS; Rgnts Schlrshp 85; Jefferson CC; Comp Sci.

BOGGESS, ANN; Ithaca HS; Ithaca, NY; (Y); Drama Clb; Pres Pep Clb; Ski Clb; Chorus; Madrigals; School Musical; Jr NHS; NHS; Ntl Merit Ltr; Hope Coll Dstngshd Schlr Awd 85; Hope Coll; Bio Psych.

BOGLIA, JOSEPH; Longwood HS; Coram, NY; (S); 3/550; High Hon Roll; Jr NHS; NHS; Prfct Atten Awd; Awd Perf Scor Chem Regnts 84; SUNY Stony Brook; Sprts Med.

BOGUE, MAUREEN; Penn Yan Acad; Naples, NY; (Y); 3/167; Pres 4-H; Pres Band; Church Choir; Jazz Band; Swing Chorus; Elks Awd; 4-H Awd; JP Sousa Awd; Sec NHS; Ntl Merit Ltr; Demper Fidelis Awd 85; Amer Legion Aux Intl Reltns Prize 85; Arion Awd 85; Wells Coll; Hstry.

BOGURSKY, MELISSA L; Lawrence HS; Cedarhurst, NY; (Y); 18/379; Girl Scts; Trs MMM; Temple Yth Grp; Chorus; School Musical; School Play; Lit Mag; High Hon Roll; NHS; Ntl Merit SF; 5 Towns Mus & Art Fndtn Theatre Awd 84; Tufts U; Engl Ed.

BOGUS, MICHELLE; Bishop Loughlin HS; Brooklyn, NY; (Y); Dance Clb; Chorus; School Play; Vllybl; NHS; 1st Hnrs Awd Cert 83; Bio.

BOHALL, JOHN; Weedsport Central Schl; Weedsport, NY; (Y); French Clb; Intnl Clb; Math Clb; Band; Mrchg Band; Yrbk Stf; Swmmng; Comp Sci.

BOHAN, MARY B; The Norte Dame Schl; Richmond Hill, NY; (Y); 23/55; Church Yth Grp; Yrbk Stf; Var L Bsktbl; Var L Sftbl; Capt L Vllybl; NHS; U MD.

BOHAN, MICHAEL; Olean HS; Olean, NY; (Y); 3/210; Church Yth Grp; Quiz Bowl; Science Clb; Ski Clb; Var L Swmmng; Var L Tennis; NHS; Ntl Merit Ltr; French Clb; Ntl Sci Awd-Bio 84; Ntl Sci Awd-Chem 85; Latin Awd 84; Pre-Med.

BOHANNON, RANDY A; Glens Falls SR HS; Glens Falls, NY; (Y); 71/235; VICA; Pres Sr Cls; Hon Roll; Linguistics.

BOHAYETS, STEPHANIE; Auburn HS; Auburn, NY; (Y); Mathletes; Varsity Clb; Yrbk Stf; Var JV Fld Hcky; Var Score Keeper; High Hon Roll; Hon Roll; NHS; Med.

BOHEMIER, CHRIS; West Genesee HS; Warners, NY; (Y); Chess Clb; Church Yth Grp; Cmnty Wkr; Computer Clb; Library Aide; Office Aide; Drm & Bgl.

BOHNET, REBEKAH; LasalleSR HS; Niagara Falls, NY; (S); 20/278; Dance Clb; Girl Scts; Hosp Aide; Band; Cheerleading; High Hon Roll; NHS; Schlrshp Schl Buffalo Ballet 83-84; Schlrshp NYS Schl Arts & Dance 84; Zoolgy.

BOHOSIAN, CHARLES SCOTT; West Genesee HS; Syracuse, NY; (Y); Boy Scts; Church Yth Grp; Hosp Aide; JV Ftbl; JV Trk; High Hon Roll; Hon Roll.

BOHRER, CHARLES; Fairport HS; Fairport, NY; (Y); Library Aide; Varsity Clb; Nwsp Rptr; Nwsp Sprt Ed; Nwsp Stf; Im Bsktbl; L Crs Cntry; Im Socr; L Trk; Im Vllybl; Law Enfrcmnt.

BOICE, DON; Bishop Kearney HS; Rochester, NY; (Y); 10/300; Church Yth Grp; Model UN; Var Socr; Var Trk; NHS; MIP Track 84; Coaches Trck Awd 85; Psychlgy.

BOICE, HEATH P; Cambridge Central HS; Cambridge, NY; (Y); Am Leg Boys St; Drama Clb; French Clb; Band; School Musical; Ed Lit Mag; Sec Stu Cncl; Cit Awd; Hon Roll; NHS; TV Cmmnctns.

BOIES, AMY S; Niagara Wheatfield HS; Niagara Falls, NY; (Y); 20/315; Hosp Aide; Sec PAVAS; Pres Symp Band; Rep Stu Cncl; Var L Bsktbl; Crs Cntry; Var L Trk; Dnfth Awd; High Hon Roll; NHS; Clark Foster Schlrshp 85; Sharon Kroening Awd; Acad All Am; Ithaca Coll; Physcl Thrpy.

BOINK JR, JAMES N; Liverpool HS; Liverpool, NY; (S); 87/772; Camera Clb; Exploring; German Clb; Im Bsbl; High Hon Roll; Hon Roll; Jr NHS; NHS; Pre-Med.

BOJAK, JANICE; Villa Maria Acad; Buffalo, NY; (Y); Computer Clb; Hgst Avg Graphic Art,Drwng,Patng 84-85; Perf Atten 85; Canisius Coll; Jrnlsm.

BOJARSKI, THOMAS; Roy C Ketcham HS; Poughkeepsie, NY; (Y); Computer Clb; Pres Radio Clb; Band; Concert Band; Jazz Band; High Hon Roll; Hon Roll; NC ST U Raleigh; Elec Engr.

BOJMAN, JACOB L; Yesliva Torah Timemah HS; Brooklyn, NY; (Y); Yrbk Stf; Hon Roll; Ntl Merit Ltr; Comp Pgrmr.

BOKAT, TANYA E; Hugh C Williams HS; Canton, NY; (Y); 21/138; Var Capt Socr; High Hon Roll; NHS; VFW Awd; Voice Dem Awd; JV Bsktbl; Var Cheerleading; JV Sftbl; Var Trk; CC Awd; Dickinson Coll.

BOKMAN, OLGA; Bronx HS Of Science; Rego Park, NY; (Y); Library Aide; Math Clb; Office Aide; Nwsp Stf; Hon Roll; Borough Sci Fair 2nd Pl 84; Harvard; Law.

BOKSER, ALEX; Richmond Hill HS; Kew Gardens, NY; (Y); Hon Roll; Prfct Atten Awd; Pre-Dntl.

BOLAND, DAVID; Notre Dame HS; Albion, NY; (S); 10/90; French Clb; Ski Clb; Band; Yrbk Phtg; Yrbk Stf; JV Var Ftbl; Var Golf; JV Var Wrstlng; Hon Roll; NHS; Aer Engrng.

BOLANOS, CAROLINA; Springfield Gardens HS; Hollis, NY; (Y); 141/426; Salute To Yth Schlstc Achvt Awd 85; Educ.

BOLANOS, JEFFREY; St Agnes HS; Richmond Hill, NY; (Y); 19/130; Boys Clb Am; Dance Clb; Church Choir; Lit Mag; Rep Frsh Cls; Rep Soph Cls; Rep Jr Cls; Pres Sr Cls; Pres Stu Cncl; Trk; Law.

BOLARIS, MARIA; Holy Trinity HS; Farmingdale, NY; (Y); 26/356; Chess Clb; Church Yth Grp; Drama Clb; French Clb; Math Clb; Teachers Aide; Stage Crew; Nwsp Ed-Chief; Nwsp Rptr; Nwsp Stf; Cathlc Dghts Amer Poetry 1st Pl Awd; Vrsty Ltr; Math Achvt Awd; Fordham U; Pre-Law.

BOLD, KRISTEN; Victor Central HS; Victor, NY; (Y); 12/192; Teachers Aide; Varsity Clb; Orch; School Musical; Nwsp Stf; Yrbk Stf; Stu Cncl; Trk; High Hon Roll; NHS; Regnts Schlrshp 85; Presdntl Acadmc Ftns Awd 85; Rochester U; Health Sci.

BOLDEN, VERNIE; James E Sperry HS; Rochester, NY; (Y); Rep Jr Cls; JV Bsbl; Var Crs Cntry; Var Trk; Hon Roll; NHS; Hnrbl Mntn Schltc Art Awd Show 83.

BOLDT, WENDY; Batavia SR HS; Batavia, NY; (Y); 12/234; Yrbk Stf; Capt Bowling; JV Tennis; High Hon Roll; NHS; Zonta Clb Schlrshp 85; NY ST Rgnts Schlrshp 85; Pres Acdmc Ftns Awd 85; Le Moyne Coll NY; Accntng.

BOLEBRUCH, MARK R; Mayfield HS; Gloversville, NY; (Y); 15/80; Varsity Clb; Chorus; Var L Bsbl; Var L Bsktbl; Var L Crs Cntry; High Hon Roll; Hon Roll; Rgnts Schlrshp 85; MIP Bsktbl 82; Coaches Awd-Bsbl 82; Cobleskill Ag & Tech; Lib Art.

BOLES, TAMMIE; Corinth Central HS; Corinth, NY; (S); 10/80; French Clb; Key Clb; Pep Clb; Stat Trk; High Hon Roll; Hon Roll; Jr NHS; NHS.

BOLGER, MICHELLE; James I O Neill HS; Apo New York, NY; (Y); 1/118; Church Yth Grp; School Musical; Pres Jr Cls; Sec Sr Cls; Rep Stu Cncl; Capt Cheerleading; Bausch & Lomb Sci Awd; NHS; Val; Homecmg Qn 84; Marshal 83-84; Westpoint Ofcrs Wives Clb Scholar Recip 85; U Of MY Munich; Intl Rel.

BOLGER, PETER; St Anthonys HS; Commack, NY; (Y); 20/235; Chorus; Madrigals; School Musical; Nwsp Rptr; Rep Frsh Cls; Rep Soph Cls; Crs Cntry; Trk; High Hon Roll; NHS; Fordham U Acadmc Schlrshp 85; All Cnty Chrs 83-84; Fairfield U.

BOLGER, THERESA M; Franklin K Lane HS; Ridgewood, NY; (Y); 15/708; Church Yth Grp; Cmnty Wkr; Girl Scts; Office Aide; Hon Roll; NHS; Prfct Atten Awd; St Johns U.

BOLLENTIN, JOHN; Bishop Scully HS; Amsterdam, NY; (Y); French Clb; JA; Band; Concert Band; Jazz Band; Mrchg Band; JV Var Bsktbl; JV Ftbl; Var Mgr(s); Hon Roll; Hghst Avg Art 83-84; Arch.

BOLLER, SCOTT; Hilton Central HS; Hilton, NY; (Y); Ski Clb; Band; Mrchg Band; School Play; Variety Show; JV Trk; Hon Roll; NHS; Essy Cntst,Slf Img Good Mntl Hlth 85; De Paul U; Cretve Wrtng.

BOLLERMAN, FAITH M; Bayport-Blue Point HS; Blue Point, NY; (Y); 25/243; Art Clb; Drama Clb; Orch; School Play; Fld Hcky; NHS; Rgnts Schlrshp 85; NY U; CPA.

BOLMER, STEPHANIE; Town Of Webb HS; Old Forge, NY; (S); Spanish Clb; Varsity Clb; Band; Chorus; Concert Band; Mrchg Band; VP Soph Cls; Var Capt Bsktbl; Var Capt Socr; Var Sftbl; Plattsburgh; Env Sci.

BOLNENONUS, PHILLIP; Forest Hills HS; Elmhurst, NY; (Y); Columbia U; Arch.

BOLOWSKY, DANIEL P; Lake Shore HS; Derby, NY; (Y); 16/259; Sec Sr Cls; Var Ftbl; Wt Lftg; High Hon Roll; NHS; Regents Schlrshp 85; OH ST; Engr.

BOLTON, BRENDA; Albion HS; Albion, NY; (S); 5/178; Off Church Yth Grp; Drama Clb; Political Wkr; Off Acpl Chr; Sec Band; Chorus; Church Choir; Concert Band; Jazz Band; Mrchg Band; Houghton Coll NY; Secdry Ed.

BOLTON, KEVIN J; Red Jacket Central HS; Shortsville, NY; (Y); Boy Scts; Chess Clb; French Clb; Band; Chorus; Drm & Bgl; Jazz Band; Pep Band; High Hon Roll; NHS; NY ST Regents Schlrshp 85; Alfred U; Bus Adm.

BOLTON, STEVEN C; Red Creek Central HS; Sterling, NY; (Y); 5/75; French Clb; Ski Clb; Bsktbl; Var Capt Socr; High Hon Roll; NHS; St Schlr; Regents Schlrshp; Ski Clb Pres; Rochester Inst Of Technlgy; Bus.

BOLTON, TABETHA L; Columbia HS; Rensselaer, NY; (Y); 55/400; Pres Art Clb; Drama Clb; VP Model UN; Lit Mag; JV Fld Hcky; JV Socr; Hon Roll; NHS; NY St Regents Schlrshp 85; NY St Schl Of Ind; Industrial.

BOLTON, THOMAS B; Glen Cove HS; Glen Cove, NY; (Y); 11/271; Pres Computer Clb; Debate Tm; Latin Clb; Nwsp Stf; Tennis; High Hon Roll; NHS; Ntl Merit SF; Amer Chem Soc Awd 84; Elec Engr.

BOLTON, TRACEY; Bishop Mc Mahon HS; Buffalo, NY; (Y); Var Bsktbl; Dr.

BOLTUCH, MARIANNA; Midwood HS; Brooklyn, NY; (Y); 15/605; Church Yth Grp; Varsity Clb; Var Capt Bsktbl; Var Cheerleading; Var Sftbl; Var Vllybl; High Hon Roll; Math Tm; Yrbk Stf; Rep Frsh Cls; H S Schlrshp 85; Louisa Wingate Underhill Awd 85; Summa Cum Laude 85; SUNY-BINGHAMTON; Sprts Med.

BOMBARD, DAVID; Franklin Acad; Constable, NY; (Y); Epsilon Membr; Altr Boy; TCI; Auto Bdy.

BOMMER, MICHAEL; Maryvale HS; Cheektowaga, NY; (Y); German Clb; Swmmng; Accntng.

BONACCIO, CECILIA; Nazareth Acad; Rochester, NY; (S); Latin Clb; Library Aide; Math Clb; Math Tm; Ed Yrbk Rptr; Ed Lit Mag; Tennis; High Hon Roll; NHS; Ntl Ltn Ex Awd Mdl Hnr 82; High Avg Cert Ltn & Itln 82-84; 4 Yrs Mth In 2 Yrs 84; Jrnlsm.

BONAKEY, CAMILLE M; Pioneer Central HS; Machias, NY; (Y); 46/208; JV Trk; Regents Diploma 85; 1st Pl Schl Painting Cont 84-85; U Buffalo; Arch.

BONANNO, LYNN M; Newburgh Free Acad; New Windsor, NY; (Y); Dance Clb; Yrbk Stf; Cheerleading; Mgr(s); Pom Pon; French Hon Soc; High Hon Roll; Hon Roll; Jr NHS; Prfct Atten Awd; Fashn Desgn.

BONANNO, TINAMARIE; Bethlehem Central HS; Slingerlands, NY; (Y); Hosp Aide; Rep Key Clb; Sec Natl Beta Clb; Yrbk Stf; Rep Frsh Cls; Rep Soph Cls; Rep Jr Cls; Rep Sr Cls; Stu Cncl; JV Var Cheerleading; Natl Chrldng Awd 83-84; Phy Thrpy.

BONAPACE, EUGENE S; Mahopac HS; Mahopac, NY; (Y); 6/375; Cmnty Wkr; Math Clb; Trs Science Clb; Band; Chorus; Jazz Band; School Musical; Nwsp Rptr; Bausch & Lomb Sci Awd; High Hon Roll; Cornell U; Pre Med.

BONARO, DOUGLAS WILLIAM; Mahopac HS; Mahopac, NY; (Y); 226/357; JV Wrstlng; Pace; Acctng.

BONARRIGO, NICK; Frankfort-Schuyler Central HS; Frankfort, NY; (S); 1/115; French Clb; FBLA; Pres Key Clb; Varsity Clb; VP Soph Cls; Rep Stu Cncl; JV Capt Bsktbl; Tennis; High Hon Roll; NHS; Math Clb 2nd Fresh 83; Cntrl Vly Tnns Champ 84; Hgh Rnk Dist II Tnns 84; Acctng.

BONASERA, MARK A; Saint Anthonys HS; Huntington, NY; (Y); 3/250; Art Clb; Boy Scts; Church Yth Grp; Exploring; Orch; Symp Band; Nwsp Rptr; Yrbk Rptr; Yrbk Stf; Ed Lit Mag; Princeton Bk Awd Fnlst 85; Msgr Peter Nolan Schlrshp 84; Med.

BONCALDO, GERMANTE M; Nichols HS; Orchard Park, NY; (Y); Debate Tm; Speech Tm; Orch; Var L Ftbl; SCCA Rallies 85; GMI Engr Inst; Mech Engr.

BONCARO, DAVID; Colonie Central HS; Albany, NY; (Y); 20/544; Pres Aud/Vis; Camera Clb; Y-Teens; Stage Crew; Variety Show; High Hon Roll; Hon Roll; NHS; Prfct Atten Awd.

BONCZEK, CHRISTINE; Vestal HS; Vestal, NY; (Y); 33/450; Sec Varsity Clb; Capt Var Socr; Var Sftbl; Var Trk; High Hon Roll; NHS; Ntl Merit Ltr; Rep Soph Cls; Rep Jr Cls; US Army Schlr Athlt Awd 85; MVP US Army Soccer Plyr 85; NY ST Rgnts Schlrshp 85; SUNY Buffalo; Phys Thrpy.

BOND, COLIN; E J Wilson HS; Rochester, NY; (Y); Boy Scts; Ski Clb; Varsity Clb; JV Crs Cntry; JV Golf; Var Swmmng; Hon Roll; Mrn Bio.

BOND, MEGAN; Catholic Central HS; Watervliet, NY; (S); 8/203; Cmnty Wkr; German Clb; Hosp Aide; Spanish Clb; Yrbk Stf; High Hon Roll; Hon Roll; NHS; Spanish, German Awd 82-84; Pre-Law.

BOND, PENNY L; Mexico Acad & Central; Mexico, NY; (Y); 3/200; Ski Clb; Varsity Clb; Trs Acpl Chr; Trs Band; Drm & Bgl; Sec Jr Cls; Sec Sr Cls; Capt Var Socr; Vllybl; Sec NHS; NYS Regnts Schlrshp 85; Coach Awd 83; ST U Coll Oswego NY; Math.

BONDELLIO, CAROLYN; Potsdam HS; Potsdam, NY; (Y); 16/135; French Clb; Nwsp Stf; Yrbk Bus Mgr; Pres Frsh Cls; Var Powder Puff Ftbl; Var Socr; Var Trk; Hon Roll; NHS; Pre-Law.

BONDER, RICHARD; Briarcliff HS; Briarcliff, NY; (Y); Nwsp Stf; Yrbk Stf; Lit Mag; Im Badmtn; Im Bsktbl; JV Crs Cntry; Var Socr; Var Tennis; Var Trk; Hon Roll; Archtctr.

BONESKY, SUSAN; Niagara Wheatfield SR HS; North Tonawanda, NY; (Y); Church Yth Grp; Teachers Aide; Chorus; Var Gym; JV Capt Socr; Hon Roll; Niagara County CC; Bus.

BONFIGLIO, DONNA; Valley Central HS; Newburgh, NY; (Y); 52/300; French Clb; French Hon Soc; Hon Roll; Mrktng.

BONGIORNO, JOSEPH; St John The Baptist D HS; East Islip, NY; (Y); 60/660; Cmnty Wkr; JV Var Ice Hcky; High Hon Roll; Hon Roll; Ntl Bus Hnr Soc 83-85; NYS Regnts Schlrshp 84-85; Acad Achvt Awd 84-85; Hofstra U; Bus Adm.

BONGIOVANNI, MIA; Manlius Pebble Hill HS; Syracuse, NY; (S); Model UN; Stage Crew; Yrbk Stf; Lit Mag; Var Socr; Var Tennis; JV Vllybl; High Hon Roll; Hon Roll; Bst Preprtn Delg-Rep Lebanon Awd 84.

BONGIOVI, CAROLEE H; Seaford HS; Seaford, NY; (Y); 2/250; Church Yth Grp; Band; Concert Band; Mrchg Band; Nwsp Rptr; Nwsp Sprt Ed; Nwsp Stf; Yrbk Stf; Var L Cheerleading; Coach Actv; Soc Stds Awd 84; NYS Regnts Schlrshp; Band; Ntl Hnr Soc; Chrldr; SS Hghst Avg; Duke U; Econmcs.

BONIFACE, BETH; Rensselaer JR SR HS; Rensselaer, NY; (Y); Capt Pep Clb; Nwsp Rptr; Yrbk Ed-Chief; Trs Frsh Cls; Trs Soph Cls; Stu Cncl; Capt Cheerleading; JV Sftbl; High Hon Roll; Hon Roll; Coll Of Saint Rose; Teach.

BONILLA, CECILIA; Yonkers HS; Yonkers, NY; (Y); 123/478; FBLA; Key Clb; Library Aide; ROTC; Spanish Clb; Nwsp Stf; Yrbk Stf; Hon Roll; Cmnty Wkr; Drama Clb; Kiwanis Schlrshp Athln Soc 85; Cert Excllnc In Acad 83 & 85; Cert Awd 83-85; Westchester CC; Med Tech.

BONINA, ANDREA E; St Saviour HS; Brooklyn, NY; (Y); Hosp Aide; Political Wkr; Ed Lit Mag; Rep Soph Cls; JV Bsktbl; Var Fld Hcky; St Schlr; Villanoa U; Law.

BONNER, BARBARA; Tioga Central HS; Candor, NY; (S); 8/96; Nwsp Rptr; Nwsp Stf; High Hon Roll; NHS; Prfct Atten Awd; Herkimer Coll; Admin Secr.

BONNER, CATHERINE; Beach Channel HS; Rockaway Beach, NY; (Y); Library Aide; Yrbk Sprt Ed; Var Socr; Hon Roll.

BONNER, MADELYN; Manhasset HS; Manhasset, NY; (Y); Service Clb; JV Lcrss; JV Var Socr; JV Swmmng; High Hon Roll; Jr NHS; NHS; GAA; Flag Corp; Ntl Sci Comp Bio 84; Med.

BONO, RENAE; St Francis Prep; Whitestone, NY; (Y); Art Clb; Dance Clb; Hon Roll; Cooper Union; Arch.

BONOFFSKI, BEVERLY J; G Ray Bodley HS; Fulton, NY; (Y); 79/257; Science Clb; SUNY At Oswego; Zoolgy.

BONOMI, GINA; Fontbonne Hall Acad; Brooklyn, NY; (Y); Art Clb; Cmnty Wkr; Teachers Aide; Nwsp Rptr; Vllybl.

BONURA, PAULA; St John The Baptist HS; Nesconset, NY; (Y); 200/501; Cmnty Wkr; Dance Clb; FTA; Speech Tm; Orch; Nwsp Rptr; Yrbk Stf; Farmingdale U; Hygnst.

BONVENTRE, DINA; Lindenhurst HS; Lindenhurst, NY; (Y); Spanish Clb; Band; Concert Band; Mrchg Band; Orch; Symp Band; Nwsp Stf; Yrbk Phtg; High Hon Roll; Hon Roll; NYSMA Music Awd Duet, Solo, Trio 83; Comp.

BONVIN, JANET; Fayetteville-Manlius HS; Fayetteville, NY; (Y); Pep Clb; Stage Crew; Variety Show; Yrbk Phtg; Yrbk Stf; Vet Med.

BONVISSUTO, BRIAN; Lafayette HS; Buffalo, NY; (Y); Am Leg Boys St; Church Yth Grp; Band; Pep Band; Var Bsbl; Var Crs Cntry; Var Tennis; Prfct Atten Awd; AZ ST.

BOOAN, THERESA; Cooperstown Central Schl; Cooperstown, NY; (Y); Am Leg Aux Girls St; GAA; Pres Sr Cls; Fld Hcky; Sftbl; Cit Awd; Hon Roll; Church Yth Grp; Band; Chorus; Van Horne Schlrshp 85; Alumni Assoc Awd 85; Cooperstown Comm Awd 85; Springfield Clg.

BOOKMAN, TOM R; Mac Arthur HS; Levittown, NY; (Y); Church Yth Grp; VICA; Var JV Bsbl; Var JV Ftbl; Miami U; Engr.

BOONE, JANICE L; Emmanuel Baptist Acad; Prattsburg, NY; (Y); Yrbk Stf; Var Co-Capt Cheerleading; Var Capt Socr; Var Vllybl; Hon Roll; Recogntn Awd Music 84-85.

BOOTH, JIM; Massapequa HS; Massapequa, NY; (Y); 15/448; Pres Key Clb; Band; Concert Band; Drm Mjr(t); Jazz Band; Mrchg Band; Nwsp Sprt Ed; Var Capt Crs Cntry; Var Capt Trk; JP Sousa Awd; AFROTC 4 Yr Schlrshp 85; NY Rgnts Schlrshp 85; Duke U; Aerosp Engrng.

BOOTH, KAREN; Hilton Central HS; Hilton, NY; (Y); 9/310; VP JA; Math Clb; Ski Clb; Concert Band; Mrchg Band; Symp Band; Var Crs Cntry; Var Trk; High Hon Roll; NHS; Bio.

BOOTHE, LISA; Andrew Jackson HS; St Albans, NY; (Y); 3/450; Church Yth Grp; Girl Scts; Church Choir; Sec Sr Cls; Var Cheerleading; High Hon Roll; Prfct Atten Awd; Pres Chch Yth Cncl 84-85; Med.

BOOTHE, NICOLA; Spring Valley SR HS; Spring Vly, NY; (Y); Dance Clb; Varsity Clb; Rep Frsh Cls; Cheerleading; Hon Roll; Pre-Law.

BORCHERS, ELISHA; Union Endicott HS; Endicott, NY; (Y); Hosp Aide; Key Clb; Latin Clb; Drill Tm; Orch; Yrbk Stf; Hon Roll; NHS.

BORCHERT, ANNE; Marlboro Central HS; Marlboro, NY; (Y); 15/164; Girl Scts; VICA; Band; Chorus; Concert Band; Stage Crew; High Hon Roll; NHS; Gold Awd 83-84; Hm Ec Cooking Awd 83-84; Prof Chef.

BORD, BRUCE T; Tottenville HS; Staten Island, NY; (Y); 11/897; Key Clb; Ski Clb; School Play; Rep Frsh Cls; Var Tennis; NHS; Sci Grant NYC Sci Fair 83; Sci Grant SI Sci Fair 85; Regents Schlrshp 85; Lafayette Coll; Bio Engrng.

BORDEN, DAWN; Cohoes HS; Cohoes, NY; (Y); Church Yth Grp; DECA; Library Aide; Chorus; Rep Frsh Cls; Rep Church Yth Grp; Im Gym; Im Sftbl; Im Swmmng; Hon Roll; SR Schlrshp Awd 85; Hudson Valley Coll; Mrktng.

BORDEN, KIMBERLY; Onteora Central HS; Pine Hill, NY; (S); 34/245; Church Yth Grp; Capt Quiz Bowl; Band; Concert Band; Mrchg Band; Sftbl; NHS; Bus Ed Awd 84; Briarwood Coll; Sec Stud.

BORDEN, VIRGINIA; Kenmore East SR HS; Tonawanda, NY; (Y); Cmnty Wkr; Band; Color Guard; Concert Band; Mrchg Band; School Musical; School Play; High Hon Roll; NHS; Drama Clb; Sci.

BORDERON, ARNEL; Bishop Loughlin M HS; Brooklyn, NY; (S); Band; Church Choir; Jazz Band; School Musical; Im Bsktbl; Im Ftbl; Hon Roll; Holstra U; Elec Engr.

BORDERON, MICHAEL; Bishop Loughlin HS; Brooklyn, NY; (Y); Computer Clb; Science Clb; Var Im Bsktbl; JV Ftbl; JV Mgr(s); JV Score Keeper; JV Timer; Hon Roll; Jr NHS; Bus.

BORDI, JULIE; Commack H S South; Commack, NY; (Y); Hosp Aide; Math Tm; Teachers Aide; Yrbk Stf; Badmtn; Tennis; High Hon Roll; NHS; Church Yth Grp; French Clb; Natl Sci Olympiad Bio 84; Natl Sci Olympiad Chem 85; Pre-Med.

BOREALI, LAWRENCE F; Cobleskill Central HS; Howes Cave, NY; (Y); Am Leg Boys St; Boy Scts; VP Varsity Clb; Band; Stu Cncl; Var Bsbl; JV Var Bsktbl; Var Capt Ftbl; High Hon Roll; VP NHS; Elec Engr.

BORELL, CAROLINE; M Frank Carey HS; Franklin Sq, NY; (Y); 1/400; Camera Clb; French Clb; Band; Yrbk Ed-Chief; Rep Frsh Cls; Rep Soph Cls; Sec Jr Cls; Tennis; French Hon Soc; High Hon Roll; Engrng Medl Excllnc Stdy Math & Sci 85; Pre-Law.

BORELLA, ANNAMARIE; Sachem HS; Lk Ronkonkoma, NY; (Y); 246/1400; Boy Scts; Drama Clb; Exploring; Ski Clb; Spanish Clb; Chorus; Madrigals; School Musical; School Play; Stat Swmmng; Vet.

BORG, JENNY; Brighton HS; Rochester, NY; (Y); 88/318; Spanish Clb; Nwsp Bus Mgr; Nwsp Stf; Rep Jr Cls; VP Sr Cls; JV Bsktbl; JV Socr; JV Trk; Relgs Philsphy Awd 85; Cmmnctns.

BORGELLA, JACQUES; New Utrecht HS; Brooklyn, NY; (Y); 116/557; Cit Awd; Coll Rep; CCNY; Comp Sci.

BORGES, GORDON D; De Sales Catholic HS; Lockport, NY; (Y); French Clb; Var Bsbl; Var Bsktbl; Coach Actv; Var Socr; Hon Roll; NEDT Awd; Regents Schlrshp 84-85; U Rochester; Med.

BORGIA, PATRICIA; Icabod Crane HS; Valatie, NY; (Y); 22/185; Church Yth Grp; Debate Tm; GAA; Nwsp Rptr; Yrbk Rptr; Var Fld Hcky; Var Sftbl; Hon Roll; NHS; Voice Dem Awd; Regents Schlrshp 85; SUNY-POTSDAM; Ind Rltns.

BORGOS, PATRICIA M; Queensbury HS; Glens Falls, NY; (Y); 21/227; Church Yth Grp; French Clb; Spanish Clb; Teachers Aide; Yrbk Bus Mgr; Yrbk Stf; Ed Lit Mag; Stu Cncl; Mgr(s); High Hon Roll; Natl Frnch Cont Awd 84; NYS Regents Schlrshp 85; Lang Stu Qrtr 84; U Of VT; Elem Educ.

BORKO, STEVEN E; Monticello HS; Wurtsboro, NY; (Y); 12/163; Am Leg Boys St; Boy Scts; Quiz Bowl; Ski Clb; Nwsp Bus Mgr; Yrbk Bus Mgr; Stu Cncl; High Hon Roll; Trs NHS; NYS Rgnts Schlrshp 85; SUNY Albany; Lib Arts.

BORLAND, PETER; Altmar-Parish-Williamstown HS; Parish, NY; (Y); Exploring; Mathletes; Varsity Clb; Ftbl; Hon Roll; Aviatn.

BORLAND, RENEE; J C Birdlebough HS; Pennellville, NY; (Y); 9/112; AFS; Band; Concert Band; Mrchg Band; Yrbk Stf; High Hon Roll; Hon Roll; Regnl Schlstc Art Awd 85; Outstndng Achv Drawng-Pntng 85; Art.

BORNHEIMER, JOHN; Lyons HS; Lyons, NY; (Y); 6/92; Am Leg Boys St; Band; Chorus; Pres Sr Cls; Var Tennis; High Hon Roll; NHS; Ntl Merit SF; French Clb; Model UN; NY ST Regents Schlrshp 85; Music Schlrshp From Roberts Wesleyan Coll 85; Roberts Wesleyan; Music Educ.

BORNHOLDT, ELIZABETH A; Schreiber HS; Port Washington, NY; (Y); 1/413; Exploring; Hosp Aide; Pres Service Clb; Yrbk Sprt Ed; Var Badmtn; Var Capt Cheerleading; Cit Awd; NHS; Pres French Clb; Latin Clb; Hosptl Vlntr 400 Hr Awd 85; Vrsty Bdmntn Cochs Awd 85; Rep/Lng Islnd HS Yr Comptn 85; Biopsychlgy.

BORNO, RACHELLE; Lakeland HS; Shrub Oak, NY; (Y); Dance Clb; Ski Clb; Chorus; Jr NHS; Trvl.

BORNSCHEIN, ARTHUR; Connetquot SR HS; Sayville, NY; (S); 3/671; Math Tm; Jazz Band; Pres Jr Cls; Rep Sr Cls; Im Bsbl; Im Bsktbl; Capt Var Ftbl; Var L Wrstlng; High Hon Roll; Jr NHS; US Naval Acad; Aerosp Engr.

BORNSTEIN, DANIEL; Tuxedo HS; Tuxedo Park, NY; (Y); 4/75; School Play; Yrbk Stf; Rep Stu Cncl; Var Bsbl; Var Crs Cntry; High Hon Roll; NHS; NYS Rgnts Coll Scholar 85; Pres Acad Fit Awd 85; Colgate U.

BORNSTEIN, JOANNE; Jamesville-De Witt HS; Dewitt, NY; (Y); 17/280; Latin Clb; Math Tm; Pres Pep Clb; Temple Yth Grp; Orch; Nwsp Stf; High Hon Roll; NHS; Orch Awd 85; Latin Awd 84; Sci.

BORONCZYK, JOSEPH; Fowler HS; Syracuse, NY; (S); Boys Clb Am; Bsktbl; Crs Cntry; High Hon Roll; NHS.

BOROSKI, CHRISTOPHER D; Pittsford-Mendon HS; Pittsford, NY; (Y); Cmnty Wkr; Var Golf; Var Socr; NHS; Ntl Merit Ltr; Chess Clb; Church Yth Grp; Model UN; Im Bsktbl; Hon Roll; Monroe Cnty SR All Str Sccr Tm 84; All Cnty Sccr Tm 84; Air Forc ROTC Schlrshp 85-89; U Of Notre Dame; Aerosp Engrng.

BOROSON, CRAIG; Gloversville HS; Gloversville, NY; (Y); Chess Clb; Computer Clb; Intnl Clb; JA; Temple Yth Grp; Var Capt Tennis; High Hon Roll; Hon Roll; Arch.

BOROVICKA, KRISTINA R; Bayside HS; Bayside, NY; (Y); 7/677; Acpl Chr; Concert Band; Madrigals; School Musical; Nwsp Stf; Lit Mag; Gov Hon Prg Awd; High Hon Roll; Jr NHS; NHS; Cornell U; Cmmnctns.

BOROWITZ, CHRISTINE; Hastings-On-Hudson HS; Hastngs-On-Hudson, NY; (S); 3/115; Key Clb; Model UN; Band; Sec Sr Cls; Capt Pom Pon; L Socr; L Tennis; High Hon Roll; NHS; Ntl Merit Ltr; Ind Engrng.

BOROWSKI, KENNETH J; West Seneca E SR HS; Cheektowaga, NY; (Y); 1/365; Church Yth Grp; Teachers Aide; JV Var Swmmng; JV Var Trk; Bausch & Lomb Sci Awd; JC Awd; Jr NHS; NHS; Prfct Atten Awd; Val; Grmn Natl Hnr Scty 83; MIP & Mvp Swmmng Awds 83 & 85; Hghst Schlstc Avg Tgrck & Crss Cntry 81-85; U Of Rochester; Chem Engr.

BORRAS, AIDA; Aquinas HS; Bronx, NY; (Y); 4/160; Church Yth Grp; VP Yrbk Stf; VP Rep Sr Cls; Capt Sftbl; Vllybl; NHS; Pres Schlr; Cmnty Wkr; Computer Clb; Chorus; Presdntl Schlrshp 85; USEPA 81; Sister Mary Cncpta Awd Natl Hnr Soc 85; Manhattan Coll; Mech Engr.

BORRAS, MARTHA; Aquinas HS; Bronx, NY; (Y); 76/178; Art Clb; Church Yth Grp; Chorus; Church Choir; Pres Frsh Cls; Var Sftbl; Vllybl; Fashn Inst Tech; Fshn Dsgn.

BORRAZZO, EDWARD C; Clarkstown HS South; Nanuet, NY; (Y); 10/550; Church Yth Grp; Math Tm; Science Clb; Pres Band; Jazz Band; Ed Yrbk Stf; JV Bsbl; L Trk; Mu Alp Tht; Pres NHS; NY ST Regents Schlrshp; PTA Council Schlrshp; Cornell U; Engrng.

BORRELLI, JENNIFER; Lynbrook SR HS; Lynbrook, NY; (Y); Leo Clb; Spanish Clb; Yrbk Stf; Cheerleading; Mgr(s); Pom Pon; Trk.

BORRERO, ALEJANDRO; Adlai E Stevenson HS; Bronx, NY; (Y); 2/250; Church Yth Grp; VP JA; Office Aide; Teachers Aide; Rep Soph Cls; Hon Roll; NHS; Prfct Atten Awd; Elmira Coll Key Awd 85; Hghst Acad Ave Engl, Math, Soc Stds 85; Pre-Law.

BORRERO, ARLENE; Cardinal Spellman HS; Bronx, NY; (Y); Church Yth Grp; Computer Clb; Girl Scts; Teachers Aide; High Hon Roll; Hon Roll; Pace; Comp Pgmr.

BORRERO, DENIRA; Moore Catholic HS; Staten Island, NY; (Y); Sec Art Clb; Yrbk Stf; Rep Sr Cls; Stu Cncl; Bowling; NHS; Acad All Amer 85; Acctng.

BORS, DEBORAH; Ithaca HS; Ithaca, NY; (Y); Math Clb; Chorus; Stage Crew; Variety Show; Nwsp Rptr; JV Tennis; Jr NHS; NHS; Ntl Merit Ltr; VFW Awd; Gannett Corp NYS Regnl Carrier Of Yr Awd 83; Spnsh Merit Diploma 84; Soc Wmn Engrs Cert Merit 85; Coll Wm & Mary; Bio.

BORST, NANCY MARIE; Phoenix Central HS; Phoenix, NY; (Y); 61/210; French Clb; FBLA; Speech Tm; Drm Mjr(t); Mrchg Band; Nwsp Stf; Yrbk Stf; Var Trk; High Hon Roll; Hon Roll; Cal ST U.

BORTKIEWICZ, ANNA; Saunders Trades & Technical HS; Yonkers, NY; (Y); 9/198; Pres Church Yth Grp; Intnl Clb; Off Varsity Clb; Ed Yrbk Phtg; Var Trk; Var Vllybl; High Hon Roll; Trs NHS; Cmnty Wkr; Dance Clb; Vrsty 3 Yr Sprt Trphy Trck & Fld 85; Hgh Nrs Algbr Regnts 81; Century III Ldrs Cert Of Merit 84; Manhattan Coll; Chem.

BORYSENKO, NATALIA; Cathedral HS; Brooklyn, NY; (Y); Girl Scts; Am Leg Aux Girls St; Chorus; Hon Roll; JR Yr Art Awd Creatv Art Ukrnian 84; Grl Scts Phtgrphy Awd Outstndng Achvt 84; ST U NY; Psych.

BORZA, JOHN; Solvay HS; Syracuse, NY; (Y); Chorus; School Musical; School Play; Swing Chorus; Variety Show; JV Capt Ftbl; Bus.

BORZELLO, JEANNINE; East Islip HS; East Islip, NY; (Y); Chorus; Capt Drill Tm; Mrchg Band; Orch; School Musical; Yrbk Ed-Chief; Lit Mag; Capt Pom Pon; Jr NHS; NHS.

BOSACK, MARY ANN K; Mahopac HS; Carmel, NY; (Y); 8/358; Am Leg Aux Girls St; Pres Leo Clb; Nwsp Rptr; Ed Nwsp Stf; Ed Lit Mag; Rep Frsh Cls; Rep Soph Cls; Rep Jr Cls; DAR Awd; High Hon Roll; 1st Pl Leg Wmn Votrs Campgn Essay Cont 84; Hugh O Brian Yth Fndnt Ldrshp Sem 83; Stu Of Mnth 84; Yale U; Engl.

BOSCH, MARGARET A; Fairport HS; Fairport, NY; (Y); French Clb; JA; Orch; Hon Roll; Rgnts Schlrshp 85-86; SUNY Geneseo; Bio.

BOSER, CHERI; Allegany Central HS; Allegany, NY; (Y); 4-H; Sec FFA; Girl Scts; Library Aide; Chorus; High Hon Roll; Hon Roll; Star Greenhnd Awd FFA 84-85; Indvdl Accomp Awd 85; Chaptr Farmer Degree 85; RN.

BOSHART, MARK; Charles Dickerson HS; Trumansburg, NY; (Y); 6/98; Am Leg Boys St; Church Yth Grp; Varsity Clb; Yrbk Stf; Trs Soph Cls; Pres Jr Cls; Bsbl; Ftbl; High Hon Roll; NHS; Trphy Top Ten SR Cls 85; Coachs Awd Ftbl 85; GMI; Engrng.

BOSLEY, TAMMY M; Northern Adirondack Central HS; Mooers Forks, NY; (Y); Church Yth Grp; Drama Clb; Hosp Aide; VP L Band; Chorus; Church Choir; VP Concert Band; Mrchg Band; Nwsp Rptr; Variety Show; Regents Schlrshp In Nrsng 85; Mus Solo Awd 83; Albany Med Ctr; Nrsng.

BOSS, DUANE; John Jay SR HS; Hopewell Junction, NY; (Y); Aud/Vis; Chess Clb; High Hon Roll; Hon Roll; Jr NHS; Comp.

BOSS, MARIA; Richmond Hill HS; Richmond Hill, NY; (Y); 1/298; Radio Clb; School Play; Nwsp Rptr; Var L Bsktbl; JV L Crs Cntry; Var L Socr; High Hon Roll; NHS; Pres Schlr; Val; Phi Beta Kappa Schlrshp 85; Abc Cls Awd 85fminerva Awd 85; Hofstra U; Comm.

BOSSARD, HEATHER; Canisteo Central Schl; Hornell, NY; (Y); Pres 4-H; Sec FFA; Yrbk Bus Mgr; Sec Stu Cncl; JV Golf; Cit Awd; High Hon Roll; Sec Canisteo Enrgy Awrns Grp 85; Intern Steuben Cnty Govt Prog 85; Alfred U; Engr.

BOSSELER, GEORGIA; Corning East HS; Corning, NY; (Y); Model UN; Ski Clb; Spanish Clb; Varsity Clb; Chorus; Madrigals; Off Frsh Cls; Trs Soph Cls; Off Jr Cls; Var Capt Diving; 4th Pl Divng Empire ST Games 85; Southrn Tier All Star Swim Tm 85.

BOSSERT, CHARLES; Greece-Athena HS; Rochester, NY; (Y); 43/258; Boy Scts; Church Yth Grp; Band; Concert Band; Jazz Band; Orch; School Musical; Stage Crew; Symp Band; Var Swmmng; Amer Legion Scout Yr 85; Eagle Scout 84.

BOSSERT, JAY; New Dorp HS; Staten Island, NY; (Y); Computer Clb; Exploring; French Clb; Intnl Clb; Office Aide; Science Clb; Service Clb; Teachers Aide; Stu Cncl; Trk; ALISI Concours Natl Fr Cont Excllnce Awd 1st Schl; TX Christian U.

BOSSERT, STEVEN; Greece-Athena HS; Rochester, NY; (Y); 37/260; Boy Scts; Concert Band; Orch; Symp Band; NHS; Church Yth Grp; Exploring; Band; Jazz Band; School Musical; Amer Legn Sct Yr 85; Eagl Sct 84.

BOSSINAS, JIM; Ossining HS; Ossining, NY; (Y); Church Yth Grp; Band; Orch; Symp Band; Bowling; Capt Socr; Tennis; High Hon Roll; Hon Roll; Prfct Atten Awd; Sccr Sprtsmnshp Awd 83; Frnch Awd 85; Strght A Fr 6 Yrs Grk Schl; Archtctr.

BOSSLER, ANNA L; Bainbridge-Guilford HS; Bainbridge, NY; (Y); 14/70; French Clb; Band; Concert Band; Orch; VP Bsktbl; Cheerleading; High Hon Roll; Regents Schlrshp Wnnr 85; Junita Coll; Chem.

BOTHE, CATHERINE; Horseheads HS; Big Flats, NY; (S); 5/407; Concert Band; Jazz Band; Mrchg Band; Orch; Golf; Gym; High Hon Roll; NHS; Secy Ntl Hnr Soc 84-85; Capt Vrsty Golf Tm 84-85; Ohio ST U; Math.

BOTNEY, JULIA; Commack High School South; Dix Hills, NY; (Y); Chess Clb; Intnl Clb; Math Tm; Chorus; Concert Band; Mrchg Band; School Musical; Nwsp Stf; Var Badmtn; JV Socr.

BOTT, HAROLD J; Mount Saint Michael Acad; Bronx, NY; (Y); Band; Jazz Band; Var Trk; Hon Roll; Jr NHS; NHS.

BOTTKE, IRENE; Westhampton Beach HS; Westhampton, NY; (Y); 3/232; Computer Clb; French Clb; Hst Latin Clb; Library Aide; High Hon Roll; NHS; Southampton Coll; Math.

BOTTONE, MARIA ELENA; Hornell SR HS; Hornell, NY; (Y); 19/198; AFS; Aud/Vis; Camp Fr Inc; Church Yth Grp; Cmnty Wkr; Dance Clb; FCA; Pres Trs 4-H; FHA; GAA; Al-Amer 84 & 85; Alfred U; Sprts Med.

BOUBOULIS, EVE; Oneonta SR HS; Maryland, NY; (Y); Key Clb; Ski Clb; Spanish Clb; Varsity Clb; Band; Chorus; Var JV Bsktbl; Var Capt Socr; Var Sftbl; Hon Roll; Excllnc-Bus Math 84; STAC All Star Sftbl 84; Sccr Lge Champ 84; Law Psych.

BOUCARD, DJENANE; Albertus Magnus HS; Nyack, NY; (Y); French Clb; Church Choir; French Hon Soc; Hon Roll; Biochem.

BOUCHER, JEFF; Hartford Central HS; Hartford, NY; (Y); Church Yth Grp; Debate Tm; FFA; Pep Clb; Yrbk Phtg; Yrbk Stf; VP Frsh Cls; Rep Stu Cncl; JV Bsktbl; JV Socr; Blt & Drv Mini-Mod Pllng Trctr In Tri-ST Evnts 83-85; Const Bus.

BOUCHER, LISA; Berne-Knox-Westerlo Central HS; Berne, NY; (Y); 1/85; Nwsp Rptr; Trs Jr Cls; Stu Cncl; Var Crs Cntry; Var Capt Trk; JV Capt Vllybl; High Hon Roll; Sec NHS; Band; Natl Sci Merit Awd 83; Biochem.

BOUCHER, MICHELLE; Horseheads HS; Horseheads, NY; (S); 41/421; French Clb; JV Vllybl; Hon Roll; NHS; Yth Cnty 84; Ushrs Clb 83-85; SUNY Oswego; Bus.

BOUCHER, MICHELLE L; Cardinal Spellman HS; New York, NY; (Y); Church Yth Grp; Debate Tm; Girl Scts; Latin Clb; NFL; Science Clb; Mrchg Band; Hon Roll; Band; Stage Crew; M L K Jr Memrl Schlrshp 85-88; NYS Rgnts Schlrshp; Utica Coll; Intl Study.

BOUCHEREAU, TANYA; Bishop Loughlin Memorial HS; Brooklyn, NY; (Y); Church Yth Grp; Cmnty Wkr; Service Clb; Stage Crew; Trs Stu Cncl; JV Var Cheerleading; High Hon Roll; Hon Roll; Ascent Pgm John Jay Coll Crmnl Jstce 85-86; Cmmnty Svc Hosp Training Pgm 85-86; Eng.

BOUCHEY, MICAHEL; Lansingburgh HS; Troy, NY; (S); #12 In Class; German Clb; Varsity Clb; Band; Jazz Band; Yrbk Phtg; Pres Sr Cls; Var Capt Crs Cntry; Var Trk; High Hon Roll; NHS; Hudson Valley CC; Engrng Sci.

BOUCK, ANDREA; Fort Plain HS; Fort Plain, NY; (S); Drama Clb; Varsity Clb; Chorus; Pres Soph Cls; Pres Jr Cls; Cheerleading; Score Keeper; Hon Roll; NHS; Bus.

BOUDREAU, ANGELA; Victor Central Schl; Victor, NY; (Y); Ski Clb; Chorus; Color Guard; High Hon Roll; Hon Roll; Soclgy.

BOUDREAU, DALE; Auburn HS; Auburn, NY; (Y); 15/460; Aud/Vis; Drama Clb; Band; Concert Band; Jazz Band; Mrchg Band; Stage Crew; High Hon Roll; Vrsty Letter Music 84; Sr Pin-Music 85; Cert Of Part-Music 81-85; US Air Natl Guard; Satl Comm.

BOUDREAU, GORDON; Bishop Grimes HS; North Syracuse, NY; (Y); Drama Clb; French Clb; School Play; Socr; Hon Roll; Rgnts Schlrshp 85; Lemoyne Coll; Envir Sci.

BOUDREAU, JOSEPH; Massena Central HS; Massena, NY; (Y); Boy Scts; French Clb; Ed Lit Mag; Trk; High Hon Roll; Hon Roll; NHS; Acad Awds At Acad Banquet In Massena 83 & 84.

BOUDREAU, SUE; Fairport HS; Fairport, NY; (Y); Drama Clb; 4-H; Spanish Clb; School Play; Hon Roll; Spanish NHS; Geneseo; Comp Sci.

BOUGHTON, JANETTE L; Paul V Moore HS; W Monroe, NY; (Y); 59/297; VP AFS; Drama Clb; Science Clb; Chorus; School Musical; School Play; Nwsp Bus Mgr; Mgr(s); Score Keeper; Sftbl; VP Of SADD; Sunday Schl Teacher; Exchange Stu With AFS To Greece; Suny Morrisville; Bus Admin.

BOUGIAMAS, JOHN; Bronx High School Of Science; Woodside, NY; (Y); Math Tm; Teachers Aide; Church Choir; Nwsp Ed-Chief; Nwsp Rptr; Nwsp Sprt Ed; Nwsp Stf; Rep Frsh Cls; Jr NHS; NY U; Pre-Law.

BOULE, EUGENE; Fort Ann Central Schl; Ft Ann, NY; (Y); 1/60; Am Leg Boys St; French Clb; Math Clb; Ski Clb; Ed Yrbk Stf; Pres Frsh Cls; Pres Soph Cls; Pres Jr Cls; JV Bsktbl; Var Golf.

BOUNATSOS, MARIA; St Johns Preparatory HS; Woodside, NY; (Y); Intnl Clb; Science Clb; Yrbk Stf; Socr; Hon Roll; NHS; Med.

BOUNAUGURIO, JOHN; E J Wislon-Spencerport HS; Rochester, NY; (Y); Aud/Vis; Letterman Clb; VICA; Band; Var Capt Bsbl; Hon Roll; Prfct Atten Awd; Voice Dem Awd; Mgr(s); Score Keeper; 3rd Pl NY ST Job Intrvw Cntst VICA 85; Spk To Lions, Rtry & Kwans Clb On Sccss ST Comptn VICA 85; Northeastern U; Mass Comm.

BOURCY, ANNE; Bishop Grimes HS; Syracuse, NY; (Y); Church Yth Grp; Ski Clb; Chorus; School Musical; JV Socr; Hon Roll; NHS; Marine Bio.

BOURDEAU, PENNY; Plattsburgh HS; Plattsburgh, NY; (Y); Church Yth Grp; Ski Clb; Varsity Clb; Yrbk Stf; VP Sr Cls; Stu Cncl; Bowling; Var Gym; Var Capt Socr; Var Capt Sftbl; Stu Cncl, Evelyn Merritt & Booster Club Schlrshps 85; Class Of 1955 Rcgntn Awd 85; Endicott Coll; Fshn Merch.

BOURDEAU, VIRGINIA L; Averill Park HS; Averill Pk, NY; (Y); 7/216; Chorus; Church Choir; Yrbk Ed-Chief; Tennis; High Hon Roll; Hon Roll; NHS; Snd Lk Hstrcl Scty Schlrshp 85; Fclty Awd 85; Arlene M Hayner Mem Schlrshp Awd 85; Albny Coll; Phrmcy.

BOURGAULT, BRIAN; Tamarac HS; Troy, NY; (Y); Intnl Clb; Science Clb; Yrbk Stf; Stat Bsbl; Mgr(s); Score Keeper; Hon Roll; NHS; Rensselaer Mdl RPI 85; Elmira Key Awd 4-Yr Schlrshp 85; Pre-Med.

BOURGEOIS, TRAMPESS; Camden Central HS; Cleveland, NY; (Y); Cmnty Wkr; Chorus; School Musical; School Play; JV Bsbl; High Hon Roll; Hon Roll; NHS; Law.

BOURGOIS, DANIELLE; Camden Central HS; Camden, NY; (Y); Drama Clb; Chorus; School Musical; School Play; Stage Crew; Nwsp Stf; Hon Roll; Acting.

BOURQUIN, RAMONA; Saranac Lake HS; Bloomingdale, NY; (Y); 28/134; Church Yth Grp; Band; Mrchg Band; Cazenovia Coll; Intr Dsgn.

BOUSQUET, JAMES; Saranac Central Schl; Cadyville, NY; (S); JV Bsbl; JV Var Bsktbl; JV Var Ftbl; High Hon Roll; Hon Roll; MVP JV Bsktbl, Bsbl 84; All Star Team Christmas Tournament 83; Pilot.

BOUSQUET, RONALD D; Northeastern Clinton HS; Champlain, NY; (Y); 3/146; Model UN; PAVAS; Church Choir; School Musical; High Hon Roll; NHS; Ntl Merit Ltr; Pres Schlr; Cmnty Wkr; Natl Sci Merit Awd 84; Natl Ldrshp And Service Awd 85; Acceptance Into All Eastern Chorus 85; Potsdam U; Computer Sci.

BOUTIN, ARTURO; Cardinal Hayes HS; New York, NY; (Y); Boy Scts; Dance Clb; Stage Crew; Nwsp Phtg; Yrbk Phtg; Rep Stu Cncl; JV Crs Cntry; JV Ftbl; Im Ice Hcky; JV Trk; Baruck Coll; Intl Bus.

BOUTIS, HARRY; Herricks HS; New Hyde Pk, NY; (Y); JV Var Bsbl; Bio Engrng.

BOUTON, MONICA L; Guilderland Central HS; Guilderland, NY; (Y); 110/369; FBLA; Var JV Score Keeper; Var JV Socr; Var JV Vllybl; Hon Roll; Ntl Merit SF.

BOUTON, RACHEL K; Roy C Ketcham HS; Wappinger Fls, NY; (Y); Camera Clb; Church Yth Grp; Drama Clb; Color Guard; School Musical; Stage Crew; Ed Yrbk Phtg; Yrbk Stf; Rep Frsh Cls; Hon Roll; Ntl Merit Found Hnr Rl 85.

BOUTON, TAMMY; Harpursville HS; Nineveh, NY; (S); 14/76; Sec Am Leg Aux Girls St; Color Guard; Drill Tm; High Hon Roll; Hon Roll; NHS; Prfct Atten Awd; Voice Dem Awd; SUNY; Vet Tech.

BOUWENS, ALAN; Le Roy HS; Leroy, NY; (Y); Art Clb; School Play; Trk; Hon Roll; Schlstic Art Exhibitr 85; Stu Pilot 85; Graphic Arts.

BOUZA, SUSANA; Academy Of St Joseph HS; Bayshore, NY; (Y); Cmnty Wkr; Hosp Aide; Library Aide; Stage Crew.

BOVAIR, SUSAN; Lake George HS; Lake George, NY; (Y); Girl Scts; Chorus; Color Guard; Yrbk Stf; Trk; Med Secy.

BOWDEN, DEBBIE; Longwood HS; Coram, NY; (Y); 38/488; Math Tm; NFL; Stage Crew; JV Var Cheerleading; Var Vllybl; High Hon Roll; Hon Roll; Jr NHS.

BOWDEN, TRACY; Martin Luther King JR HS; Bklyn, NY; (Y); Debate Tm; Library Aide; Teachers Aide; Wt Lftg; High Hon Roll; Hon Roll; Prfct Atten Awd; Mth Awd 85; Engl Awd 85; Med.

BOWEN, CARON L; New Rochelle HS; Mt Vernon, NY; (Y); 126/600; Church Yth Grp; French Clb; Church Choir; French Hon Soc; NHS; SUNY Stonybrook; Bio-Chem.

BOWEN, CHARLENE; Alexander Hamilton HS; Elmsford, NY; (S); 7/54; Art Clb; Pres Key Clb; Office Aide; Trs Spanish Clb; Color Guard; Nwsp Ed-Chief; Yrbk Stf; Lit Mag; JV Var Vllybl; Jr NHS.

BOWEN, DIANNE; Portville Central HS; Portville, NY; (Y); Am Leg Aux Girls St; Pep Clb; Teachers Aide; Band; Pres Stu Cncl; Capt Var Cheerleading; Diving; Swmmng; High Hon Roll; Hon Roll; Math.

BOWEN, ELIZABETH ANN; Lake Placid HS; Wilmington, NY; (Y); 7/45; Band; Concert Band; Jazz Band; Mrchg Band; JV Vllybl; Hon Roll; St Schlr; SUNY Potsdam; Bio.

BOWEN, JAYNE; John A Coleman HS; Kingston, NY; (S); #1 In Class; Pres Church Yth Grp; Trs French Clb; Key Clb; Yrbk Stf; Trs Jr Cls; Cheerleading; High Hon Roll; Hon Roll; Jr NHS; Dartmouth:Med.

BOWEN, KIMBERLY A; Fort Ann Central Schl; W Fort Ann, NY; (Y); 14/43; French Clb; Math Clb; Yrbk Stf; JV Sftbl; JV Var Vllybl; High Hon Roll; Hon Roll; Church Yth Grp; Office Aide; Rgnts Schlrshp 85; Adirondack Comm Coll; Comp Sci.

BOWEN, MELISSA L; Lockport SR HS; Lockport, NY; (Y); AFS; Camera Clb; Intnl Clb; JA; Library Aide; Spanish Clb; Y-Teens; Hon Roll; Pres Schlr; Canton Ag & Tech Coll; Vet.

BOWENS, PHILLIP; Utica Free Acad; Utica, NY; (Y); Church Yth Grp; Civic Clb; Cmnty Wkr; Key Clb; Pep Clb; Service Clb; Varsity Clb; Band; Church Choir; Concert Band; Semper Fidelis Awd 85; Acdmc Achvt Awd 84-85; Julius Albert Duhart Awd 85; U Buffalo; Arch.

BOWER, BONNI; Sodus Central HS; Sodus, NY; (Y); 18/110; Concert Band; Mrchg Band; Trs Frsh Cls; Trs Soph Cls; Trs Jr Cls; Trs Sr Cls; Cheerleading; Trk; High Hon Roll; Hon Roll; Buffalo ST; Intr Dsgn.

BOWERS, DANIEL; St Marys HS; Williamsville, NY; (S); Var Bsbl; Var L Crs Cntry; Var Ice Hcky; Var L Socr; Hon Roll; NHS; Lawyr.

BOWERS, DAVID S; Arlington HS; Poughkeepsie, NY; (Y); 23/596; Variety Show; Lit Mag; Hon Roll; Ntl Merit Ltr; U Of Rochester Alumni Schlrshp 85; Arlington Crew Team Vrsty Crsmn 81-84; U Of Rochester; Math.

BOWERS, DAWN MARIE; Cardinal Spellman HS; New York, NY; (Y); 144/561; Cmnty Wkr; Rep Soph Cls; Rep Jr Cls; Rep Sr Cls; Vllybl; Hon Roll; Regnts Schlrshp 85; Fordham U; Bus Adm.

BOWERS, LHAG; Haverling Central HS; Bath, NY; (S); French Clb; Latin Clb; Math Clb; Yrbk Stf; High Hon Roll; NHS.

BOWLER, ROBERTA; Faith Bible Acad; Fort Plain, NY; (Y); Church Yth Grp; Drama Clb; Chorus; Church Choir; School Musical; School Play; Var Vllybl; Hon Roll; Spanish Clb; Yrbk Rptr; Schl Spirit Awd 83-85; Bst Girl Ath 84; 5th Pl Sewng Frmls Natn 85; Bible.

BOWLES, ROBYN SUE; Perry Central HS; Perry, NY; (Y); 1/93; Sec Jazz Band; Bsktbl; Socr; Bausch & Lomb Sci Awd; High Hon Roll; NHS; Val; Church Yth Grp; Math Tm; Varsity Clb; Hugh O Brian Ldrshp Semnr; Arion Music Awd; Yth For Understdng; U Of Rochester; Bio.

BOWLES, RODNEY; North Babylon SR HS; North Babylon, NY; (S); 179/592; DECA; Office Aide; Orch; School Musical; Nwsp Rptr; Nwsp Stf; Lit Mag; Bowling; Hon Roll; Prfct Atten Awd; Wren Beverage Schlrshp 84; Decny ST Career Conf Awd 84; Suffolk Cnty DECA Reg Fnlst 84; Cornell U; Hotel Tech.

BOWMAN JR, BURFORD N; Wilson Central Schl; Wilson, NY; (Y); Am Leg Boys St; Boy Scts; Exploring; Im Bsbl; Im Bsktbl; Var Ftbl; Hon Roll; Prfct Atten Awd; NY ST Regnts Dip 86; Mech Engnrng.

BOWMAN, HEATHER M; Roy C Ketcham HS; Poughkeepsie, NY; (Y); Cmnty Wkr; Band; Concert Band; Jazz Band; Mrchg Band; Stage Crew; Symp Band; Hon Roll; Media Comm.

BOWMAN, JULIA A; Oswego HS; Oswego, NY; (Y); Drama Clb; Ski Clb; Chorus; Mrchg Band; School Musical; Symp Band; Var Crs Cntry; JV Powder Puff Ftbl; Var Trk; Hon Roll; U Of AL; Relgn.

BOWMAN, LAURIE A; Union Springs Central Schl; Cayuga, NY; (Y); 13/100; Trs Church Yth Grp; Trs Girl Scts; Ski Clb; Chorus; Church Choir; School Musical; JV Bsktbl; Var JV Score Keeper; Hon Roll; NHS; Paul Smiths Coll; Hotel Mgmt.

BOWMAN, LYNNE; Linton HS; Schenectady, NY; (Y); Sec VICA; Vllybl; Hon Roll; Lintonians & Peer Ldrs Clbs; Russell Sage U; Nrsng.

BOWMAN, MARC; Poughkeepsie HS; Poughkeepsie, NY; (Y); Church Yth Grp; Nwsp Stf; Yrbk Stf; Bowling; Trk; Prfct Atten Awd; Hghst Avg Bus Law I, II 85; Dutchess CC; Bus Adm.

BOWMAN, SHERRILYN; Batavia HS; Batavia, NY; (Y); 8/239; Drama Clb; Math Tm; Chorus; School Musical; Yrbk Ed-Chief; High Hon Roll; NHS; Regnts, Ithaca Coll Schlrshp 85; Yth Awd 85; Ithaca Coll; Accntg.

BOWMAN, THERESA; John C Birdlebough HS; Pennellville, NY; (Y); Art Clb; Camera Clb; Trs Church Yth Grp; Dance Clb; Girl Scts; Library Aide; Red Cross Aide; Ski Clb; Band; Chorus; Comm Art Cert Awd 84; Rochester Inst Tech; Grphc Arts.

BOWMAN, TIM; Albion HS; Albion, NY; (Y); Church Yth Grp; FFA; Star Chptr Greenhand 82; Mech Awd 85; OH Diesel; Mech.

BOYCE, CATHERINE; Hicksville SR HS; Hicksville, NY; (Y); Chorus; Comp Pgmng.

BOYCE, JEFF J; Northern Adirondack Central HS; Altona, NY; (Y); Boy Scts; School Play; Variety Show; Nwsp Stf; Rep Stu Cncl; JV Var Bsktbl; Hon Roll; NY ST Regents Schlrshp 85; Foundation Schlrshp 85; All Star SR Bsktbl 85; SUNY Plattsburgh; Computer Prg.

BOYCE, JOHN W; Greenwich Central HS; Schaghtcoke, NY; (Y); 13/91; FFA; JV Var Golf; JV Var Trk; Hon Roll; Elctrncs.

BOYCE, ROBERT; Ed Clark HS; Las Vegas, NV; (Y); U NV Las Vegas; Comm Art.

BOYCHECK, ANN MARIE; Henninger HS; Syracuse, NY; (Y); Am Leg Aux Girls St; Concert Band; Pep Band; Rep Frsh Cls; Rep Soph Cls; Rep Jr Cls; High Hon Roll; NHS; Pres Amer Legion JR Aux 83-85; Scndry Educ.

BOYD, BETH; Richburg Central Schl; Friendship, NY; (S); Lib Concert Band; Mrchg Band; Nwsp Rptr; Ed Nwsp Stf; Yrbk Stf; Sec Frsh Cls; Sec Soph Cls; Sec Jr Cls; High Hon Roll; Jr NHS.

BOYD, DALE; Frewsburg Central Schl; Frewsburg, NY; (Y); 8/92; Am Leg Boys St; Church Yth Grp; Chorus; Church Choir; School Musical; Yrbk Sprt Ed; Yrbk Stf; Capt Bowling; Hon Roll; NHS; Hazzard Scholar 85-86; Cummins Engine Scholar 85-86; Mt Vernon Nazarene Coll; Relgn.

BOYD, ERNIE; Richburg Central HS; Friendship, NY; (S); 2/16; Band; Concert Band; Jazz Band; Mrchg Band; Yrbk Stf; High Hon Roll; JP Sousa Awd; Jr NHS; NHS; Sal; Med Labrtry Tech.

BOYD, KELLY; Adlai E Stevenson HS; Bronx, NY; (Y); Computer Clb; Ftbl; Wt Lftg; Regents Schlrshp 84-85; Northeastern; Engrng.

BOYD, LEDELL; North Babylon SR HS; North Babylon, NY; (Y); Office Aide; ROTC; Varsity Clb; Nwsp Sprt Ed; Btty Crckr Awd; Hon Roll; JV Bsbl; JV Bsktbl; Bsktbl 83-84; Bakg 85-86; Bus.

BOYD, TIM; Beacon HS; Beacon, NY; (Y); Cmnty Wkr; Key Clb; JV Bsbl; JV Wrstlng; High Hon Roll; Hon Roll; Pres Jr NHS; Pres NHS; Trgnmtry Awd 84-85; Geo Awd 83-84; Am Hist Awd; West Point; Pol Sci.

BOYD, TIMOTHY J; Union Spring Acad; Cayuga, NY; (S); 1/48; Church Yth Grp; Computer Clb; Ski Clb; Varsity Clb; Band; Orch; Pres Frsh Cls; Capt Bsktbl; High Hon Roll; Val; Engrng; Engrng.

BOYD, WILLIAM; Scotia-Glenville HS; Scotia, NY; (Y); 12/250; Church Yth Grp; Computer Clb; Drama Clb; Science Clb; Band; Chorus; Church Choir; Concert Band; Jazz Band; Mrchg Band.

BOYEN, ANDREA N; West Islip HS; W Islip, NY; (Y); Church Yth Grp; Hosp Aide; Band; Im Badmtn; Var CAP; Var L Vllybl; High Hon Roll; NHS; Eng Exc Awd 83.

BOYER, KIMBERLY; Buffalo Acad Of Sacred Hearts; Buffalo, NY; (Y); 25/136; Church Yth Grp; French Clb; Girl Scts; Band; Chorus; Hon Roll; Prfct Atten Awd; Canisius Coll; Engr.

BOYER, MICHELE; Tioga Central HS; Nichols, NY; (S); Computer Clb; GAA; Ski Clb; Varsity Clb; Band; Fld Hcky; JV Capt Vllybl; High Hon Roll; NHS; Concert Band; Bus Mgt.

BOYER, SHAWN; Addison Central HS; Addison, NY; (Y); Boy Scts; Ski Clb; Acpl Chr; Band; Chorus; Mrchg Band; School Musical; Stage Crew; Yrbk Stf; Var Socr; Eagle Scout Awd 85; Electrnc.

BOYKO, SUSAN MARIE; Oneida HS; Verona Bch, NY; (Y); 63/225; Chorus; High Hon Roll; Hon Roll; Office Aide; Capt Cheerleading; Vrsty O Bnd & Pres Ftns Awd 85; Cncert Choir 83-84; Brynt & Strtn Bus Inst; Trv Agn.

BOYLAN, ANN; Our Lady Of Mercy HS; Rochester, NY; (Y); VP GAA; Spanish Clb; Rep Jr Cls; Stu Cncl; Var L Bsktbl; Var L Socr; JV Trk; Hon Roll; Library Aide; Model UN; Accntng.

BOYLAN, JEAN; Newfield HS; Selden, NY; (Y); Church Yth Grp; Drama Clb; Chorus; Church Choir; School Musical; School Play; Yrbk Stf; Rep Jr Cls; Hon Roll; Girl Scts; NY All ST Chrs 85; All Cnty Chrs 85; IN U; Dr.

BOYLAN, LAURENCE; Le Roy Central HS; Leroy, NY; (Y); Rep AFS; Rep Church Yth Grp; VP Spanish Clb; Band; Chorus; Church Choir; Concert Band; Mrchg Band; Orch; School Musical; Natl Latin Exam Magna Cum Laude.

BOYLE, JANICE; The Mary Louis Acad; Jamaica, NY; (Y); Drama Clb; Intnl Clb; John Jay Coll; Law Enfrcmnt.

BOYLE, KELLY; Bishop Ford C C HS; Brooklyn, NY; (Y); Church Yth Grp; Cmnty Wkr; Girl Scts; Hosp Aide; Science Clb; Bowling; Tennis; Hon Roll; Acadmc Excllnc 82; Physcn Asst.

BOYLE, MARGARET A; The Buffalo Smnry; Williamsville, NY; (Y); 3/35; Drama Clb; French Clb; Yrbk Ed-Chief; Pres Frsh Cls; Var Stu Cncl; Lcrss; Vllybl; High Hon Roll; NHS; Ntl Merit Ltr; L Gertrude Angell Schlrshp 81-85; Trstee Awd 82; Engl.

BOYLE, MATTHEW T; Vestal SR HS; Binghamton, NY; (Y); Boy Scts; Chess Clb; Band; Jazz Band; Hon Roll; Eagle Scout & Asst Scout Master 83-85; Regents Schlrshp; SUNY-MARITIME; Comp Sci.

BOYLE, ROBERT E; A G Berner HS; Massapegna Park, NY; (Y); 71/426; Computer Clb; Spanish Clb; Band; Variety Show; Im Bsbl; Hon Roll; NYS Rgnts Schlrshp 85; Phy Sci.

BOYLE, SANDY; Cardinal Spellman HS; Bronx, NY; (Y); Dance Clb; Pep Clb; Pres Stu Cncl; Var Swmmng; Hon Roll; Ntl Ldrshp Merit Awd 85.

BOYLE, SUZANNE; Preston HS; Bronx, NY; (S); Var Bsktbl; Var Sftbl; Var Vllybl; Hon Roll; NHS.

BOYNTON, KARI; Mynderse Acad; Seneca Falls, NY; (Y); 4-H; Office Aide; Var L Bsktbl; Var L Socr; JV Sftbl; 4-H Awd; Hon Roll; US Soccer Ambssdr To Europe, Holland, Belgium & E/W Germany 85; Cazenovia Coll; Hrse Mgt.

BOZAN, ERIK; Cardinal Hayes HS; New York, NY; (Y); 68/267; Chess Clb; Bus.

BRABANDER, JULIE A; Nanuet SR HS; Nanuet, NY; (Y); 3/190; Church Yth Grp; Mathletes; Band; Concert Band; Mrchg Band; Yrbk Stf; High Hon Roll; Jr NHS; Mu Alp Tht; NHS; NY ST Regents Schlrshp 85; NY ST Sci Suprvsrs Assoc Awd 85; Iona Coll; Math.

BRABANT, PETER; Thousand Islands HS; Clayton, NY; (Y); School Musical; School Play; Variety Show; Ftbl; Golf; Ice Hcky; Hon Roll; Lbrl Arts.

BRACCIA, ANTHONY; Lasalle Acad; Brooklyn, NY; (S); Nwsp Stf; Bsktbl; Hon Roll; NHS; Dstngshd Amer HS Stu 84.

BRACE, MELISSA; Odessa Montour Central HS; Millport, NY; (Y); Drama Clb; Ski Clb; Sec Trs Varsity Clb; Sec Concert Band; Sec Mrchg Band; Pep Band; JV Var Bsktbl; Var L Trk; High Hon Roll; Hon Roll; Busn Admin.

BRACERO, LISA; Washingtonville HS; Monroe, NY; (Y); Band; School Play; Var Capt Cheerleading; Hon Roll; Vrsty Chrldng Capt 84-85; Schl Ply 84; Hnr Rll 82-85; Orange Cnty CC; Exec Scrtry.

BRACH, BONNIE LEE; Kenmore West SR HS; Tonawanda, NY; (Y); School Musical; Variety Show; Rep Stu Cncl; High Hon Roll; Hon Roll; Co-Chrprsn Schl Carnvl 85; Asst Dir Cmnty Musicl 85; Cornell U; Vet.

BRACHMAN, JAY; Martin Van Buren HS; Hollis Hls, NY; (Y); 18/579; JA; Library Aide; Mathletes; Math Clb; Math Tm; Chorus; School Play; Yrbk Stf; VP Frsh Cls; Stu Cncl; Acctng.

BRACHT, PATRICIA; Smithtown West HS; Smithtown, NY; (Y); 1/327; Cmnty Wkr; Dance Clb; Teachers Aide; Yrbk Stf; Rep Jr Cls; Stu Cncl; Badmtn; Tennis; French Hon Soc; NHS; Spec Educ.

BRACIKOWSKI, JENNIFER; Griffith Inst; Springville, NY; (Y); Camera Clb; Sec 4-H; Teachers Aide; Color Guard; Var Mgr(s); Vllybl; 4-H Awd; High Hon Roll; Hon Roll; NHS; Pre-Law.

BRACKEN, ANNE; Saint Joseph Acad; E Setarkat, NY; (Y); Church Yth Grp; Spanish Clb; Yrbk Stf; VP Sr Cls; Eng Achvmnt Awd 83-84; Span Awd Applctn & Endeavor 83-84; Bus.

BRACKMAN, JAMES; Ellenville HS; Napanoch, NY; (Y); Spanish Clb; Band; Jazz Band; Stu Cncl; Ftbl; Trk; Vllybl; Hon Roll; NHS; Bio.

BRACY, THEDA; Murry Bergtraum HS; Woodside, NY; (Y); Church Yth Grp; Girl Scts; JA; Office Aide; Chorus; Church Choir; Cheerleading; Hunter Coll; Acctng.

BRADBURY, HEATHER; James I O Neill HS; Highland Fls, NY; (Y); Debate Tm; Letterman Clb; Pep Clb; Varsity Clb; Yrbk Stf; Sec Stu Cncl; Capt Vllybl; Sftbl; U Of MD; Intl Bnkg.

BRADE, GAIL A; Cleveland Hill HS; Cheektowaga, NY; (Y); 1/105; GAA; Band; VP Frsh Cls; Var Bsktbl; JV Cheerleading; Powder Puff Ftbl; Hon Roll; Pres NHS; Val; Ntl Merit Schlrshp Letter Of Commendation 83; Regents Schlrshp 85; Canisius Coll; Sci.

BRADFORD, TERRY; Anthony A Henninger HS; Syracuse, NY; (Y); Aud/Vis; GAA; Crs Cntry; Trk; Cit Awd; Hon Roll; NHS; Jr NHS; Amer Mgmt Assocs Cert Achvt 85; Dir Live TV Shw Rough Times Live 82-85; Annapolis Naval Acad; Aerontcs.

BRADIGAN, KYLE; Forestville Central HS; Forestville, NY; (Y); Boy Scts; Science Clb; Ski Clb; VICA; Bsbl; Bowling; Ftbl; High Hon Roll; Hon Roll; Outstndng Stu Awd 84-85; Plymuth Trouble Shooter 84-85; Auto Mech.

BRADLEY, ANTWAIN; Mc Kinley Vo Tech; Buffalo, NY; (Y); 17/209; JA; Church Choir; Yrbk Stf; Rep Stu Cncl; Var Capt Ftbl; Hon Roll; Pres Schlr; Awd Excel Art 83; 1st Pl Local Drwng Wnnr 85; RIT; Comm Art.

BRADLEY, AVERY; Bennett HS; Buffalo, NY; (Y); Swmmng; Hon Roll; Med.

BRADLEY, CATHERINE; St Peters High School For Girls; Staten Isl, NY; (Y); FNA; Hosp Aide; Spanish Clb; Chorus; School Musical; School Play; Rep Stu Cncl; VP NHS; Prfct Atten Awd; Rep Jr Cls.

BRADLEY, DAWN; Washingtonville HS; Newburgh, NY; (Y); Church Yth Grp; Cmnty Wkr; Im Tennis; Im Trk; High Hon Roll; Jr NHS; Frgn Lang Fest 1st Pl Local 3rd Pl Rgnl 84; Tbar K Horse Show 2 1st 1 2nd & 1 3rd 84; Spec Educ.

BRADLEY, JOHN; Fairport HS; Fairport, NY; (Y); 9/625; Computer Clb; VP JA; Math Tm; Science Clb; Ski Clb; Rep Stu Cncl; Im Bsktbl; High Hon Roll; Hon Roll; Ntl Merit Ltr; JETS Awd; Comp Engr.

BRADLEY, MAUREEN J; Saratoga Springs HS; Saratoga Sprgs, NY; (Y); 51/465; Church Yth Grp; Drama Clb; GAA; Chorus; Chrmn Sr Cls; Rep Stu Cncl; L Fld Hcky; High Hon Roll; NHS; Key Clb, Knights Of Columbus & CSEA Schlrshps; St Rose Coll; Bus.

BRADLEY, TED; Brewster HS; Brewster, NY; (Y); 4-H; JV Socr; Var Trk.

BRADLEY, VINCENT; John A Coleman HS; Kingston, NY; (S); Key Clb; Latin Clb; Ski Clb; School Play; Frsh Cls; Soph Cls; JV Bsbl; Var Bsktbl; Var Socr; Hon Roll.

BRADSHAW, MARY M; East HS; Rochester, NY; (Y); 42/269; Exploring; French Clb; Ski Clb; Chorus; Rep Soph Cls; Rep Jr Cls; VP Sr Cls; Rep Stu Cncl; Swmmng; Hon Roll; Actng Rlls 85; Choir & Mus 78-84; Stu Cncl 83-85; Hnr Roll; Schlrshp Syracuse U; Syracuse U; Perfrmng Arts.

BRADT, BARBARA; Johnstown HS; Johnstown, NY; (Y); Girl Scts; Intnl Clb; Library Aide; Varsity Clb; Rep Stu Cncl; Var Bsktbl; Var Crs Cntry; Var Trk; Hon Roll; Prfct Atten Awd; Mst Promising Ath Acad Ability 82-83; Mst Dedicatd Plyr Bsktbl 83-84; Mst Valuable Trk 84-85; Cortland ST; Phys Ed.

BRADT, CHRIS; Union Springs Acad; Fairport, NY; (Y); Camera Clb; Church Yth Grp; Drama Clb; Ski Clb; School Play; Stage Crew; Capt Var Gym; Cit Awd; Hon Roll; Outstndng Rm Grds & Deans Lst; Ping Pong Trnmnt Trphy 83; Schl Ltr Gymnstcs 84-85; Andrews U; Med.

BRADT, JAMES; Notre Dame HS; Elmira, NY; (Y); JV Bsktbl.

BRADT, SUSAN; Bethlehem Central HS; Glenmont, NY; (Y); Teachers Aide; High Hon Roll; Art Exhbtr & Art Achv Awds 84-85; Betbleheru Bus Wmns Clb Awd 84-85; Gladys E Newell Hnr Soc Schlrshp; JR Coll Of Albany; Fine Arts.

BRADY, ITA; Our Lady Of Victory Acad; Yonkers, NY; (S); 13/159; VP Jr Cls; Sftbl; NHS; Spanish NHS.

BRADY, JENNIFER; Long Beach HS; Long Beach, NY; (S); 8/316; Aud/Vis; Church Yth Grp; Cmnty Wkr; Key Clb; Band; Mrchg Band; Nwsp Ed-Chief; Yrbk Stf; High Hon Roll; NHS; Principals Adv Comm Rep 84-85; Hofstra U; Bus.

BRADY, LEO; H C Wi HS; Canton, NY; (Y); JV Ftbl; JV Ice Hcky; Hon Roll.

BRADY, MICHAEL; Earl L Vandermeulen HS; Mt Sinai, NY; (Y); JV Ftbl; JV Var Trk; High Hon Roll; Hon Roll; Engrng.

BRADY, MICHAEL; St Francis Prep Schl; Queens Village, NY; (S); 34/700; Debate Tm; Model UN; Science Clb; JV Crs Cntry; High Hon Roll; Hon Roll; Prfct Atten Awd; Intl Ec.

BRADY, SANDRA; Madison Central Schl; Oriskany Falls, NY; (S); Varsity Clb; Color Guard; School Musical; Swing Chorus; Variety Show; Yrbk Stf; Stu Cncl; JV Var Cheerleading; Trk; 4-H Awd; Mst Valubl Chrldr 84; Mst Imprv Colorgrd 83; Gregg Typg Awd 84; Mohawk Vlly CC; Secy Stds.

BRADY, TYE; Mexico Academy And Central Schls; Mexico, NY; (Y); 7/250; Science Clb; Pres Ski Clb; VP Stu Cncl; Capt Bsbl; Capt Socr; High Hon Roll; NHS; Ntl Merit SF; VP Spanish NHS; Schlr Athl Awd 80-84; Boston U; Arch.

BRAFF, LANNY; Deer Park HS; Deer Park, NY; (Y); 29/450; Computer Clb; Math Clb; Math Tm; Temple Yth Grp; Band; Concert Band; Jazz Band; Mrchg Band; Orch; Pep Band; Rgnts & A David Yadlouker Scholar 85; Pres Acad Ftns Pgm 85; Stevens Inst Tech; Comp Sci.

BRAGIN, WILLIAM M; Lawrence HS; Cedarhurst, NY; (Y); 10/379; Chrmn Debate Tm; Temple Yth Grp; Mgr Band; Chorus; School Musical; School Play; Pres Soph Cls; Pres Jr Cls; VP Sr Cls; NHS; All Cnty Band 82-85; Ofrd Pres Schlrshp SUNY Buffalo Hnrs Prog 85; Ofrd Schlrshp Penn ST Prog 84; Haverford Coll; Humnts.

BRAHAM, THIERRY J; Holy Trinity HS; Westbury, NY; (S); Chess Clb; Computer Clb; Ski Clb; Mgr(s); High Hon Roll; Hon Roll; NEDT Awd; Highest Avg In Math Ii Awd 83-84; Georgetown; Law.

BRAHM, SHERRY L; Naples Central HS; Naples, NY; (Y); 18/83; Band; Nwsp Stf; Yrbk Stf; Var JV Bsktbl; Stat JV Socr; JV Socr; JV Capt Vllybl; High Hon Roll; Hon Roll; Co-Chrmn-Operation Santa 84-85; Schltc Art Awds 83-85; Intr Dsgn.

BRAIDER, JOHN W; St Anthonys HS; St James, NY; (Y); Church Yth Grp; French Clb; Pep Clb; Varsity Clb; Chorus; Nwsp Rptr; Pres Frsh Cls; Rep Jr Cls; JV Bsktbl; JV Var Ftbl.

BRAINERD, LORI; Fairport HS; Fairport, NY; (Y); Drama Clb; VP 4-H; Ski Clb; Chorus; School Musical; Stage Crew; Nwsp Rptr; 4-H Awd.

BRAITHWAITE, BILLIE; John Dewey HS; Brooklyn, NY; (Y); Nwsp Rptr; Rep Jr Cls; Sal; Brdcst Jrnlsm.

BRAIUNSCHEIDEL, JULIE; Starpoint HS; Lockport, NY; (S); #1 In Class; French Clb; Band; Mrchg Band; High Hon Roll; Jr NHS; Prfct Atten Awd; Schlstc Achvt Awd 83-84; Starpoint Schlr Prg Cert 84-85; Medical.

BRAKE, BRET; Victor Central Schl; Victor, NY; (Y); High Hon Roll; Hon Roll; USAF; Comp Pgmmng.

BRALEY, JEFF; Albion HS; Albion, NY; (Y); Boy Scts; Ski Clb; Hon Roll; US Army; Carpntry.

BRAMER, ROBERT; Alden Central HS; Alden, NY; (Y); Aud/Vis; Boy Scts; Exploring; Spanish Clb; Stage Crew; Golf; Socr; NHS; Natl Hnr Socty 85; MVP Alden Rifle Team 85; Crim Law.

BRAMLEY, MELISSA A; Rome Free Acad; Rome, NY; (Y); Church Yth Grp; Drama Clb; Intnl Clb; Concert Band; Mrchg Band; School Musical; Hon Roll; Jr NHS; Prfct Atten Awd; School Play; Ldrshp Training Pgm 82; Lib Arts.

BRANCATELLI, FRANCES; Saint Edmund HS; Brooklyn, NY; (S); 16/187; Church Yth Grp; Ed Yrbk Ed-Chief; Lit Mag; Im Bsktbl; Bowling; High Hon Roll; Christian Svcs Awd 82-84; Hstry Awd 83; Engl Awd 84; Jrnlsm.

BRANCATO, FRANCIS; Bishop Ford C C HS; Brooklyn, NY; (Y); Boy Scts; Church Yth Grp; Cmnty Wkr; Nwsp Stf; Im Fld Hcky; Im Ftbl.

BRANCATO, PETER J; Kenmore West HS; Kenmore, NY; (Y); Boy Scts; Computer Clb; High Hon Roll; Hon Roll; Ntl Merit Ltr; Philosphy.

BRANCH, GABRIELLE; The Ursuline Schl; Bronx, NY; (Y); Cmnty Wkr; PAVAS; Stage Crew; Lit Mag; Var Trk; Ntl Merit Ltr; Drama Clb; French Clb; School Play; Variety Show; Brent Mc Call-Joffrey Ltd Ldrshp Awd 85; Typg Awd Excllnc 85; Cert Ldrshp Blck Essnc Clb 85; U Of MA Amherst; Flm Prodctn.

BRANCH, MICHELLE; Norman Thomas HS; Bronx, NY; (S); 32/677; JA; Hon Roll; NHS; Future Sectys Assn 83-84; Cert Of Proficncy Stenogrphy 85.

BRAND, FAY-ELISA; Shulamith HS; Brooklyn, NY; (Y); School Play; Variety Show; Ed Yrbk Stf; Rep Soph Cls; VP Jr Cls; VP Stu Cncl; Cit Awd; Gov Hon Prg Awd; Hon Roll; Ntl Merit Schol; Brooklyn Coll; Dentstry.

BRAND, HILARY; Bishop Grimes HS; Manlius, NY; (Y); 4-H; Latin Clb; Ski Clb; Socr; Sftbl; Vllybl; Hon Roll; Acadmc All Amer 85; Amer Athltc 85.

BRAND, KIM; Grand Island SR HS; Gr Island, NY; (Y); GAA; Hosp Aide; Varsity Clb; Variety Show; Var Socr; Hon Roll; 1st & 3rd Pl NY Dance Olympcs 85; NY ST U-Buffalo; Law.

BRAND, LISSA; Marlboro HS; Marlboro, NY; (Y); Office Aide; Varsity Clb; Trs Frsh Cls; Trs Soph Cls; Sec Jr Cls; Sec Sr Cls; Stat Bsktbl; JV Cheerleading; Var JV Sftbl; Var JV Vllybl; Fash Merch.

BRAND, PETER B; Smithtown H S East; Smithtown, NY; (Y); Cmnty Wkr; NY ST Regents Awd; GA Inst Of Tech; Elect Engrng.

BRANDES, KAREN; Campbell Central Schl; Campbell, NY; (S); 1/46; Pres French Clb; Pres Band; Chorus; School Musical; Bsktbl; Socr; Sftbl; Vllybl; NHS; Regents Schlrsph NY ST 85; NY ST Lions Club Band 85; Math.

BRANDEWIEDE, JEANNE M; Garden City HS; Garden City, NY; (Y); Church Yth Grp; French Clb; GAA; Key Clb; Spanish Clb; Rep Jr Cls; Rep Sr Cls; Stu Cncl; JV L Badmtn; Cheerleading; Stu Citznshp Brd; NYS Regnts Schlrshp 85.

BRANDI, THEODORE F; Ardsley HS; Ardsley, NY; (Y); 3/139; Aud/Vis; Pres Church Yth Grp; Chorus; Orch; Stage Crew; Nwsp Stf; Off Soph Cls; Var L Crs Cntry; Trk; French Hon Soc; Franklin & Marshall Coll.

BRANDL JR, JEROME J; Akron Central HS; Akron, NY; (Y); Church Yth Grp; Acpl Chr; Band; Chorus; Church Choir; Color Guard; Jazz Band; Mrchg Band; Orch; Pep Band; Mrchng Band Schlrshp 85; Area All-Cnty 84; SR Cncrt Band Lttr 85; Genessee CC; Music.

BRANDOW, DOUG; Southwestern Central HS; Ce Loron, NY; (Y); German Clb; Bsktbl; Trk; Vllybl; Wt Lftg; Law Enfrcmnt.

BRANDT, CHRISTINE; Saint Joseph By-The-Sea HS; Staten Island, NY; (Y); Girl Scts; Hosp Aide; Stage Crew; Lit Mag; JV Crs Cntry; JV Trk; NHS; NEDT Awd; Pre-Med.

BRANDT, ELEANOR; Hugh C Williams HS; Canton, NY; (Y); 4/132; Pres Church Yth Grp; Drama Clb; Pres Exploring; Trs French Clb; Sec Thesps; Chorus; Church Choir; School Musical; School Play; Stage Crew; Ntl Spch Semi-Fnlst 82; Dartmouth Outstndng Stu Alumni Awd 84; Elks Clb Awd 85; Yale U; Vet.

BRANDT, LISA; Maria Regina HS; White Plains, NY; (Y); Hosp Aide; Nwsp Rptr; Nwsp Stf; Yrbk Stf; High Hon Roll; NHS; Bus.

BRANDT, THOMAS A; Johnstown HS; Fort Plain, NY; (Y); 3/177; Am Leg Boys St; Mrchg Band; Nwsp Ed-Chief; Yrbk Ed-Chief; Sec Stu Cncl; JV Crs Cntry; JV Trk; Pres NHS; 4-H; Band; Amer Legn Ortrcl Cntst 2nd Pl 84-85; SUNY Geneseo; Pol Sci.

BRANEY, R CHRISTOPHER; Fayeteville-Manlius HS; Manlius, NY; (Y); Church Yth Grp; JCL; Latin Clb; JV Var Lcrss; JV Var Socr; Var Swmmng; Natl Latin Exam Cum Laude 83; Swmmng Timothy Crowley Mem 83; Engnrng.

BRANFORD, ANGELICA; Midwood HS; Brooklyn, NY; (Y); Chorus; School Musical; Stage Crew; Variety Show; Yrbk Phtg; Rep Stu Cncl; Twrlr; Prfct Atten Awd; Daily News Princpls Pride Of The Yankees Awd 86; Acting.

BRANKER, HAYDEN; Uniondale HS; Uniondale, NY; (Y); 49/488; Dance Clb; Key Clb; School Play; Variety Show; Capt Trk; Wt Lftg; Hon Roll; Prfct Atten Awd; Hnrry Flg Hldr-NY St Trk Chmpnshp 85; Martin Luther King Schlrshp 85; Trk Schlrshp; C W Post; Advrtsmnt.

BRANN, CHRISTINE C; Wells Central HS; Speculator, NY; (S); 2/30; Church Yth Grp; Teachers Aide; Yrbk Stf; Rep Stu Cncl; High Hon Roll; Hon Roll; NHS; Sal; Chorus; Stage Crew; Art Awd 81; Sci Fair Awd & Gen Bus 82; Potsdam ST U; Ele Education.

BRANSON, ELIZABETH A; Rome Free Acad; Tinker AFB, OK; (Y); Intnl Clb; Pep Clb; Ski Clb; Concert Band; Mrchg Band; Var Cheerleading; JV Sftbl; High Hon Roll; Jr NHS; U Of SC; Study Poli Sci.

BRANT, AMY; Stissing Mountain HS; Ancramdale, NY; (Y); VP FFA; Yrbk Stf; Pres Frsh Cls; Pres Soph Cls; Excllnc Occptnl Ed 85; Cobleskill Coll; Hortcltr.

BRASHAW, CORLIN; Ogdensburg Free Acad; Ogdensburg, NY; (Y); 24/188; Key Clb; Math Clb; Concert Band; Mrchg Band; Pep Band; School Musical; Yrbk Stf; Score Keeper; Hon Roll; Suny Coll; Comm.

BRASINGTON, KIM; St Regis Falls Central Schl; St Regis Falls, NY; (S); Spanish Clb; Teachers Aide; Band; Chorus; Concert Band; Cheerleading; Mgr(s); Var Socr; Var Vllybl; Hon Roll; Paul Smiths; Trvl.

BRASLOW, MICHELE; White Plains HS; White Plains, NY; (Y); JA; JCL; Latin Clb; Pep Clb; Political Wkr; Teachers Aide; Ed Yrbk Phtg; Trs Pres Stu Cncl; Math.

BRASS, CHRISTINE; St Francis Prep; Whitestone, NY; (Y); 60/700; Church Yth Grp; Band; Chorus; Hon Roll; NHS; Opt Clb Awd; Knights Columbus Schlrshp 82-86; Bio.

BRASS, STACEY; Lawrence HS; N Woodmere, NY; (Y); Pres Drama Clb; French Clb; Service Clb; Rep Chorus; School Musical; Variety Show; French Hon Soc; High Hon Roll; NHS; AFS; Five Twns Mus & Art Fndtn Awd Mus 85; Prfrmng Arts.

BRASS, TRACEY A; Lewiston-Porter HS; Youngstown, NY; (Y); 1/250; Church Yth Grp; Cmnty Wkr; Drama Clb; VP French Clb; JA; Quiz Bowl; High Hon Roll; NHS; Wellesley Bk 85; Mst Outstndng AP Hstry 85; Biochem.

BRATHWAITE, ADRIAN; Eli Whitney Vocational HS; Brooklyn, NY; (Y); Boys Clb Am; Boy Scts; Chorus; Prfct Atten Awd; Syracuse U; Comp Engr.

BRATHWAITE, JACQUELINE; Cathedral HS; New York, NY; (Y); 110/298; Art Clb; Dance Clb; Church Choir; Church Yth Grp; Girl Scts; JA; Variety Show; Hon Roll; Acad Hnr Awd 83; Cert Comptr Ltrcy I 84; Acctg.

BRAULT, TERESA; Hornell SR HS; Ft Lauderdale, FL; (Y); Art Clb; Camp Fr Inc; Latin Clb; Library Aide; Chorus; School Musical; School Play; JV Socr; Var Tennis; Schlstc Awd Mrt Spnsh 85; U Of SF; Pre-Med.

BRAUN, RUSSELL R; John F Kennedy HS; Mahopac, NY; (Y); Nwsp Stf; Yrbk Stf; NHS; Ntl Merit SF; Schl Of Vsl Arts Schlrshp 85; Regnts Schlrshp 85; Schl Of Visual Arts NYC; Illus.

BRAUN, STEVEN M; Richmond Hill HS; Woodhaven, NY; (Y); Math Clb; Quiz Bowl; Rep Stu Cncl; French Hon Soc; High Hon Roll; NHS; Polytech Inst; Aerontc Engrng.

BRAUND, PAMELA; Fayetteville-Manlius SR HS; Fayetteville, NY; (Y); Church Yth Grp; JCL; Model UN; Yrbk Ed-Chief; Rep Frsh Cls; Rep Soph Cls; Rep Stu Cncl; JV Socr; NCTE Awd; Ntl Cncl Englsh Tchrs Awd 85; Englsh.

BRAUNSCHEIDEL, LORI; Williamsville East HS; East Amherst, NY; (Y); 139/300; Latin Clb; Rep Frsh Cls; Rep Soph Cls; Var Fld Hcky; Outstndng Amherst 83-84; Buffalo U; Med.

BRAUNSTEIN, JARED; Oceanside HS; Oceanside, NY; (Y); Temple Yth Grp; Concert Band; JV Bsktbl; JV Socr; JV Tennis; Hon Roll; Prfct Atten Awd.

BRAVE III, ANDREW; Woodlands HS; White Plains, NY; (Y); 45/180; Key Clb; Spanish Clb; Nwsp Ed-Chief; Var JV Ftbl; NHS; Prfct Atten Awd; Natl Achvt Semi Fnlst.

BRAVO, LIGIA; Far Rockaway HS; Far Rockaway, NY; (Y); Teachers Aide; Tennis; Hon Roll; Prfct Atten Awd; Ten Awd 84; Daily News Pride Of Yankees Awd 84; Cert Scholar Algbr 83, Geom 85; Lg Arista 85; Bus Admin.

BRAWDY, AMY; Rome Free Acad; Rome, NY; (Y); Exploring; Band; Mrchg Band; Pep Band; JV Var Bsktbl; JV Sftbl; JV Vllybl; Hon Roll; Jr NHS; NHS; Boston U; Pre Med.

BRAWN, TANYA; Wilson Central HS; Wilson, NY; (Y); 36/146; Dance Clb; Library Aide; School Musical; Nwsp Ed-Chief; VP Pres Stu Cncl; Cheerleading; Socr; Hon Roll; Caznova Coll Intrior/Archtrl Dsgn Schlrshp 85; Nigra Cnty Peach Queen Pgnt 84; Cazenovia Coll; Intror/Arch Dsg.

BRAY, DANIEL; Hermon De Kalb Central Schl; Hermon, NY; (S); 1/45; Boy Scts; Chess Clb; Drama Clb; French Clb; Trs Frsh Cls; Trs Soph Cls; Trs Jr Cls; Var Socr; Wrstlng; Trs NHS; Hugh O Brien Yth Fndtn Ambssdr 84; Acadmc Hnr Rll 84; Army Rsrvs Stu Schlr Athlt Awd 82-84; GMI; Engrng.

BRAY, GREG L; Attica Central HS; Attica, NY; (Y); 10/143; Am Leg Boys St; 4-H; Pres FFA; Band; Capt Var Crs Cntry; Var Trk; NHS; US Navy; Elec.

BRAZILL, CHRISTINE; Vestal SR HS; Vestal, NY; (Y); Pres Drama Clb; Nwsp Stf; Yrbk Stf; JV Vllybl; Comm.

BRECHER, LILA M; Mineola HS; Mineola, NY; (Y); 3/357; VP French Clb; Color Guard; Orch; School Musical; School Play; Lit Mag; Var Badmtn; High Hon Roll; Cmnty Wkr; Drama Clb; French Awd; Bucknell U; Pre Med.

BRECKER, MARGARET; Our Lady Of Mercy; Rochester, NY; (Y); 67/250; Hosp Aide; JA; JV Trk; Hon Roll; Nrsng Rgnts Schlrshp Alt 85; Monroe CC; Nrsng.

BREDA, GLENN M; Nanuet SR HS; Nanuet, NY; (Y); Church Yth Grp; Cmnty Wkr; Math Clb; Nwsp Phtg; Nwsp Rptr; Nwsp Stf; JV Crs Cntry; High Hon Roll; Hon Roll; NHS; Math Leag Cnty Fnlst 85; Cornell U; Htl Mgmt.

BREED II, CHARLES L; Chittenango HS; Chittenango, NY; (Y); 11/177; Am Leg Boys St; Church Yth Grp; Rep Sr Cls; Var L Bsbl; Var L Crs Cntry; Var L Trk; Hon Roll; Jr NHS; NHS; Law Enf.

BREEN, JOHN PATRICK; West Hempstead HS; Island Park, NY; (Y); Boy Scts; Drama Clb; JA; Band; Concert Band; Drill Tm; Drm & Bgl; Drm Mjr(t); Mrchg Band; Orch; MIP Golf 82-83.

BREEN, JULIE M; Ogdensburg Free Acad; Ogdensburg, NY; (Y); 16/189; Church Yth Grp; Chorus; Church Choir; School Musical; Swing Chorus; Rep Stu Cncl; CC Awd; Hon Roll; NHS; Syracuse U.

BREEN, RIOBART E; Lansingburgh HS; Troy, NY; (Y); 2/157; German Clb; Concert Band; Jazz Band; Nwsp Ed-Chief; High Hon Roll; NHS; Ntl Merit Ltr; Pres Schlr; Sal; Geneseo Alumni Fellows Scholar; SUNY; Physics.

BREEZE, CHRISTINA; Kings Park SR HS; Kings Pk, NY; (Y); Busnss Admin.

BREGE, KIMBERLY; Midlakes HS; Phelps, NY; (Y); 22/160; Church Yth Grp; Cmnty Wkr; VP English Clb; French Clb; Chorus; Nwsp Stf; Yrbk Ed-Chief; High Hon Roll; Hon Roll; Griswold Tlphn Schlrshp 85; Ontario Cnty Teen Ldr ADAA 85; Teri Rckfllr Awd Lit Promise 85; Ithoca Coll; Brdcst Comm.

BREHENY, BRIAN; St Marys Boys HS; New Hyde Park, NY; (Y); Pres Church Yth Grp; Hosp Aide; Office Aide; Service Clb; Yrbk Stf; Pres Sr Cls; Pres Schlr; Queens Chldrns Psych Volunteer 85; K Of C Squire; Bus.

BREHM, CHERYL M; Wayland Central Schl; Springwater, NY; (Y); 12/91; Am Leg Aux Girls St; Pres Church Yth Grp; Drama Clb; Chorus; Church Choir; Yrbk Phtg; Trs Jr Cls; Sec Stu Cncl; JV Var Cheerleading; Var Tennis; Regents Schlrshp 84-85; Estrn Nazarene Coll; Comp.

BREHM, DOUGLAS; E L Vandermeulen HS; Mt Sinai, NY; (Y); 9/286; Capt Chess Clb; Church Yth Grp; Mathletes; Var L Bowling; High Hon Roll; NHS; Swmmng; Tennis; Math Awd; Law.

BREHM, KELLY K; Watertown HS; Watertown, NY; (Y); Exploring; Hosp Aide; Intnl Clb; Red Cross Aide; Ski Clb; Yrbk Stf; VP Sr Cls; Stu Cncl; Var L Fld Hcky; Boston Coll.

BREITENSTEIN, JEFFREY T; Duanesburg Central HS; Delanson, NY; (Y); 6/65; Am Leg Boys St; Drama Clb; Chorus; Church Choir; School Musical; Stage Crew; Yrbk Ed-Chief; VP Sr Cls; High Hon Roll; NHS; Rgnts Schlrhsp 85; Steinmetz Awd 85; Dar Good Citzn Awd 85; Penn ST U.

BREMER, CELINE M; Christ Community Church HS; Brockport, NY; (Y); Debate Tm; Chorus; School Musical; School Play; Pres Stu Cncl; Var Crs Cntry; Im Socr; Im Sftbl; Var Trk; High Hon Roll; Schlrhsp Banqut 81-82; Distngsh Christian HS Stu; Suny Brockport; Ed.

BREMER, TIMMY G; Palmyra-Macedon Central HS; Macedon, NY; (S); 4/200; Pres Math Clb; Varsity Clb; Capt Crs Cntry; Trk; Hon Roll; NHS; Ntl Merit SF; Math.

BRENDEL, DAVID H; W C Mepham HS; North Bellmore, NY; (Y); 1/385; Nwsp Ed-Chief; Ed Nwsp Stf; Var L Bsktbl; Hon Roll; NHS; Ntl Merit SF; Prfct Atten Awd; Val; Rensselaer Sci & Mth Medl 84; Penn ST Schlr Awd 84.

BRENDEL, STEPHANIE; Lindenhurst SR HS; Lindenhurst, NY; (Y); Hon Roll; Farmingdale; Bus.

BRENNAN, ALICIA; Manhasset HS; Manhasset, NY; (Y); GAA; Service Clb; Var Bsktbl; High Hon Roll; NHS; Flag Corp; Var Socr; Var Sftbl; Med.

BRENNAN, BRENDA; Cohoes HS; Cohoes, NY; (Y); 10/190; Exploring; Pres GAA; Trs Jr Cls; Trs Sr Cls; Rep Stu Cncl; Var Capt Bsktbl; Stat Socr; Var Capt Sftbl; Hon Roll; NHS; ST U Of NY Geneseo; Comp Sci.

BRENNAN, BRIAN; Island Trees HS; Levittown, NY; (Y); CAP; Office Aide; ROTC; Ski Clb; Teachers Aide; Chorus; Color Guard; Drill Tm; Nwsp Stf; Var Ftbl; Retrd Ofcrs Assn 83; Resrv Ofcrs Assn 84; USAF; Nrs.

BRENNAN, BRIGID T; Cairo-Durham HS; E Durham, NY; (Y); Q&S; Concert Band; Mrchg Band; Orch; Nwsp Rptr; Yrbk Stf; Jr NHS; Trs NHS; Acad All Am Bnd 85; NY Mary Of Dungloe 85; U Rochester; Psych.

BRENNAN, JOHN J; Poly Prep C O S; Breezy Pt, NY; (Y); Chess Clb; Varsity Clb; School Play; Stage Crew; JV Bsbl; JV Var Bsktbl; JV Var Ftbl; Var Golf; JV Var Trk; St Louis U; Med.

BRENNAN, LYNN A; St Joseph Hill Acad; Staten Island, NY; (Y); 11/103; Church Yth Grp; Hosp Aide; JA; Political Wkr; Science Clb; Spanish Clb; Rep Stu Cncl; High Hon Roll; NHS; Spanish NHS; NEDT Lttr Of Commndtn 82; U Of VA; Bio.

BRENNAN, MARTIN F; Bishop Ford HS; Brooklyn, NY; (Y); 1/375; JA; Political Wkr; Nwsp Ed-Chief; Pres Sr Cls; Im Bsktbl; Im Coach Actv; Var Socr; DAR Awd; Gov Hon Prg Awd; NHS; Regnts Schlrshp NY ST 85; Harvard U; Pol.

BRENNAN, PEGGY; Cardinal Spellman HS; Yonkers, NY; (Y); 45/600; Dance Clb; Trk; High Hon Roll; NHS; Accntng.

BRENNAN, SCOTT; Amsterdam HS; Amsterdam, NY; (Y); Church Yth Grp; Rep Soph Cls; Bsktbl; Cobleskill Ag & Tech; Bus Mgmt.

BRENNAN, STACEY; Argyle Central Schl; Argyle, NY; (Y); French Clb; Band; Chorus; Concert Band; Mrchg Band; Rep Stu Cncl; JV Sftbl; Hon Roll; Prfct Atten Awd.

BRENNAN, THOMAS; Silver Creek Central HS; Silver Creek, NY; (Y); Church Yth Grp; Key Clb; Math Tm; Spanish Clb; Varsity Clb; Pres Jr Cls; Rep Stu Cncl; High Hon Roll; NHS; Voice Dem Awd; U Of TX Austin; Arch.

BRENNER, JOEL S; Williamsville North HS; Williamsville, NY; (Y); 9/311; Hosp Aide; Pres JA; Ski Clb; Pres Temple Yth Grp; Concert Band; Crs Cntry; High Hon Roll; NHS; Off Frsh Cls; Off Soph Cls; Hobart Presdntl Schlrshp 85-89; Regents Schlrshp 85-89; Hobart Coll; Pre-Med.

BRENNER, ROBERT A; Stissing Mountain HS; Elizaville, NY; (Y); AFS; Aud/Vis; Boy Scts; Church Yth Grp; Church Choir; Yrbk Stf; VP Jr Cls; Var Tennis; Hon Roll; Rotary Awd; Rotary Yth Ldrshp Conf 84; Yth Day Camp Rising Sun 85; Crmnl Justice.

BRENS, AMERICA; John Jay HS; Brooklyn, NY; (Y); Variety Show; Amer Hist I, Ecnmcs, Schlstc Achvt & Spnsh Cert Awd 84-85; Bnk Bus.

BRENT, STEPHEN; Fairport HS; Fairport, NY; (Y); Boy Scts; Band; Concert Band; Jazz Band; Mrchg Band; Orch; JV Trk; JV Wrstlng; Hon Roll; NHS; Eagle Scout Boy Scout 83; NHS 84.

BRENTNALL, KAREN; Newark SR HS; Lyons, NY; (Y); Pres Church Yth Grp; Chorus; Mrchg Band; Yrbk Stf; French Hon Soc; High Hon Roll; Hon Roll; Prfct Atten Awd; Law.

BRERETON, ANDREW; All Hallows Inst; Bronx, NY; (Y); Computer Clb; Stu Cncl; Var Bsktbl; Hon Roll; NHS; US Ntl Ldrshp Merit Awds 85; Am HS Athl 85.

BRESCIA, JACQUELINE A; Utica Free Acad; Utica, NY; (Y); 24/300; Church Yth Grp; Cmnty Wkr; Drama Clb; French Clb; Service Clb; Chorus; Hon Roll; NHS; Prfct Atten Awd; NY ST Regents Schlrshp 85; U Of Rochester; Bio.

BRESCIA, RAYMOND H; St Anthonys HS; Huntington, NY; (Y); Jazz Band; School Musical; Im Sftbl; JV Var Wrstlng; Cath Daugh Amer Schlrshp 81-85; Duns Scotus Acad Awd 82-85; St Johns U Comp Schlrshp 85; Fordham U; Law.

BRESKY, STACEY D; Fallsburg Central HS; South Fallsburg, NY; (Y); 6/56; Cmnty Wkr; Ski Clb; Mrchg Band; Symp Band; Yrbk Stf; Stu Cncl; Score Keeper; High Hon Roll; NHS; Pres Schlr; Rgnts Schlrshp 85; The American U; Psych.

BRESLIN, CINDY A; Mercy HS; Albany, NY; (Y); 36/67; Church Yth Grp; Drama Clb; School Play; Stage Crew; Variety Show; Rep Frsh Cls; High Hon Roll; Hon Roll; ST U Of NY Albany; Psych.

BRESLIN, MARY CLAIRE; Vestal SR HS; Vestal, NY; (Y); 110/450; Debate Tm; Political Wkr; School Play; Yrbk Bus Mgr; Sec Jr Cls; Sec Stu Cncl; Var L Tennis; Hon Roll; Susie Gunglach Schlrshp; Sr Prom Queen 85; Lemoyne Coll; Pol Sci.

BRESLIN, MICHAEL; Cathedral Preparatory Seminary; Bronx, NY; (Y); JV Var Bsktbl; Schlrshp 82-85; Yth Ftns Achvt Awd 82-83 & 85; Hnrs Awd 84-85.

BRESLOW, ADAM; Clarkstown High School North; New City, NY; (Y); Spanish Clb; Bowling; JV Tennis; Hon Roll; Bus.

BRESLOW, SHERRY; Clarkstown High School North; New City, NY; (Y); 56/530; Temple Yth Grp; Frsh Cls; Pres Soph Cls; Rep Jr Cls; Rep Sr Cls; Rep Stu Cncl; JV Var Cheerleading; Hon Roll; Pres Jr NHS; Sec NHS; Outstndng Chrldr & West Chester Cnty Chrldg Assn Schlrshp 85; PTA & Felix V Festa Schlrshp Awds 85; Tufts U.

BRESLOW, STEVEN; Spackenhill HS; Poughkeepsie, NY; (Y); 9/135; Drama Clb; School Musical; School Play; Nwsp Rptr; Nwsp Stf; Yrbk Phtg; Rep Soph Cls; Rep Jr Cls; Rep Sr Cls; Rep Stu Cncl; MIP Vrsty Sccr; Cntry III Ldrshp Awd-Rnnr Up; Ntl Merit Achvt Awd-Ldrshp; Cornell U; Photojrnlsm.

BRESSLER, DAVID J; Hillcrest HS; Flushing, NY; (Y); Hon Roll; 2nd & 5th Pl AAU NY ST & Ntl Karate Chmpsnshp 83; Blck Blt Shotokan Karate 85; Queens Coll Columbia; Elec Engr.

BRETT, AMY K; Amherst Central SR HS; Amherst, NY; (Y); 41/310; Cmnty Wkr; GAA; Intnl Clb; Model UN; Ski Clb; Spanish Clb; Orch; School Musical; Gym; High Hon Roll; Tufts U Medford; Liberal Arts.

BRETT, JASON; Lawrence HS; Woodmere, NY; (Y); Spanish Clb; Var Bsktbl; Im Sftbl; High Hon Roll; NHS; Rensselaer Poly Tech Inst Awd; Ntl Sci Olympd Physcs.

BREUER, CHRIS; Lindenhurst HS; Lindenhurst, NY; (Y); Spanish Clb; Varsity Clb; Band; Off Frsh Cls; Im Bsktbl; Lcrss; Capt Var Socr; Im Vllybl; Im Wt Lftg; Hon Roll; Comp Sci.

BREUER, KRISTIN; North Warren Central HS; Chestertown, NY; (Y); 12/42; Math Clb; Chorus; Color Guard; School Musical; Yrbk Stf; Trs Stu Cncl; Var Capt Vllybl; Adirondack CC; Accntng.

BREUNIG, DAVID; Blessed Sacrament HS; New Rochelle, NY; (Y); 10/85; NFL; Nwsp Ed-Chief; Hon Roll; David Sutton Schlrshp Awd 82; Acad Awd 83; Comp.

BREW, WILLIAM; Byron Bergen Central HS; Bergen, NY; (Y); 1/90; Math Tm; JV Var Bsbl; Bausch & Lomb Sci Awd; High Hon Roll; Jr NHS; Prfct Atten Awd; Val; Ntl Regents Schlrshp 85; Pres Acad Fit Awd 85; AM Hist Awd 85; Byron-Bergen Faculty Assoc Schlrshp 85; Rochestr Inst-Tech; Elect Engr.

BREWER, CINDY; Maple Hill HS; Castleton, NY; (Y); Church Yth Grp; Library Aide; Office Aide; Nwsp Stf; Yrbk Stf; Stu Cncl; Trk; Hon Roll; Stdnt Cncl Secy Awd; Hmnty & Envrnmnt Awds; Hnr Rll.

BREWER, DINA; Eli Whitney Voc HS; Brooklyn, NY; (Y); Library Aide; Teachers Aide; School Play; Gym; Tennis; Vllybl; Wt Lftg; High Hon Roll; NHS; Prfct Atten Awd; Cert Of Achvt-Physcl Eductn 83; Exec Sectry.

BREWER, JENNIFER; Elmira Southside HS; Elmira, NY; (Y); 25/330; Pres Latin Clb; Chorus; School Musical; Symp Band; Yrbk Stf; VP Stu Cncl; Var Capt Bsktbl; Var Capt Vllybl; NHS; Pres Schlr; Soroptmst Clb Intl 85; Am Leg Aux 85; All Stc Vlybl Tm 84; Hofstra U; Law.

BREWER, PAUL; Hornell HS; Hornell, NY; (Y); Boy Scts; Cmnty Wkr; Letterman Clb; Varsity Clb; Var L Bsbl; Var L Bsktbl; Accntng.

BREWER, REBECCA; Good Counsel Acad; Mamaroneck, NY; (Y); 14/56; Hosp Aide; Science Clb; Service Clb; Teachers Aide; Nwsp Stf; Bowling; High Hon Roll; Hon Roll; Chem Lab Asst; Bio Lab Asst; Vol St Agnes Hosp Bld Bk; SUNY-PURCHASE; Bio Sci.

BREWER, ROY L; Elmont Memorail HS; Elmont, NY; (Y); 3/24; Math Tm; Model UN; Band; Orch; Variety Show; NHS; Ntl Merit SF; Computer Clb; FBLA; Mathletes; George Washngton U Medl Mth & Sci 84; Grumman Scholar 84; Silvr Medl Long Island Mth Fair 83; Engrng.

BREWSTER, MICHELLE; Thomas A Edison HS; Elmira, NY; (Y); French Clb; Varsity Clb; Band; Chorus; Concert Band; Jazz Band; Mrchg Band; Trs Frsh Cls; VP Soph Cls; Trs Jr Cls; Louis Armstrong Jazz Awd 85; Penn ST U Music Camp 84; Most Outstndg Musician Awd 83-84; Nrs.

BREZOVSKY, ELLEN; Academy Of The Resrctn; Pt Chester, NY; (Y); 1/63; Drama Clb; Hosp Aide; Service Clb; Chorus; School Musical; Nwsp Stf; Pres Jr Cls; High Hon Roll; NHS; Val; Fairfld Schlr 85; Drama Clb Awd 85; Cath Daugh Am Essay Cont 82-83; Holy Cross.

BRICCO, MICHAEL T; Lyons Central HS; Lyons, NY; (Y); 30/92; Am Leg Boys St; Aud/Vis; Boy Scts; Exploring; Band; School Musical; Yrbk Phtg; Yrbk Stf; JV Ftbl; Var Mgr(s); Eagl Sct; Partcpnt NYS Enrgy Consrvtn Comptn; Plmbg.

BRICE, MELISSA; Woodlands HS; White Plains, NY; (Y); Drama Clb; Mathletes; School Musical; Soph Cls; Jr Cls; Stu Cncl; Cheerleading; Fld Hcky; Hon Roll; NHS; Psych.

BRICK, JEFFREY; Cardinal O Hara HS; Kenmore, NY; (Y); JV Bsbl; JV Socr; Food Svc.

BRICKEL, THOMAS; Baldwin SR HS; Baldwin, NY; (S); 30/502; Debate Tm; Political Wkr; Red Cross Aide; Trs Thesps; Acpl Chr; Pres Chorus; JV Trk; NHS; Ntl Merit Ltr; Spanish NHS; Choir Stu Of Mnth 84; Intl Rel.

BRIDGE, BONITA; Oakfield-Alabama Central HS; Oakfield, NY; (Y); 1/100; Church Yth Grp; Dance Clb; French Clb; Math Tm; Rep Stu Cncl; JV Cheerleading; High Hon Roll; NHS; Acad All Am 84; Rochester Inst Tech; Comp Sci.

BRIDGES, ERIC; Mc Kinley HS; Buffalo, NY; (Y); 18/206; Yrbk Phtg; Yrbk Stf; Score Keeper; Hon Roll; Prfct Atten Awd; Sherman Fyler Awd 85; Hnrs Awd 85; Buffalo Art Yth Awd 85; ST U Coll Buffalo; Fine Arts.

BRIDGEWATER, ETHELEEN; Peekskill HS; Peekskill, NY; (S); 7/157; Church Yth Grp; Chorus; School Play; Var Capt Cheerleading; High Hon Roll; Hon Roll; NHS; Silvr Schlstc Achvt Awd 83; Brnz Schlstc Achvt Awd 84; Gld Schlstc Achvt Awd 85; Law.

BRIDGMAN, FARRON; Attica HS; Varysburg, NY; (Y); 45/175; Band; Concert Band; Mrchg Band; Rep Frsh Cls; Rep Soph Cls; Rep Sr Cls; Rep Stu Cncl; JV Var Bsktbl; Var Capt Crs Cntry; Swmmng; Nlt J Owens Champ 82; Empire ST Games 84-85; Penthln Champ 81-85; Eastern KY U; Phy Thrpy.

BRIDGWOOD, JENNIFER; G Ray Bodley HS; Fulton, NY; (Y); French Clb; Math Clb; Science Clb; Drm Mjr(t); Bowling; Mgr(s); Twrlr; Hon Roll; NHS; Acad Excllnce 85; U Of MI; Psych.

BRIDSON, SUSAN E; North Rose-Wolcott HS; Wolcott, NY; (Y); Art Clb; VP Church Yth Grp; FBLA; Ski Clb; Pres Spanish Clb; Stage Crew; Yrbk Stf; Socr; High Hon Roll; Hon Roll; Pre Med.

BRIGANTI, TINA; Niagara Catholic HS; Niagara Falls, NY; (Y); 10/75; Dance Clb; Sec Key Clb; Yrbk Stf; High Hon Roll; Hon Roll; Jr NHS; Kiwanis Awd; Lion Awd; Church Yth Grp; French Clb; Key Clb Schlrshp 85; Father Krupa Mem Awd 84-85; Nrsng Hm Vol 85; Boston U; Physcl Thrpy.

BRIGGINS, VIVIAN; Acad Of Mt St Ursula; Bronx, NY; (Y); Dance Clb; Girl Scts; JA; Off Soph Cls; Stu Cncl; Trk; Ntl Lang Arts Olympd 83; Bus Adm.

BRIGGS, ALLEN; Chautauqua Central HS; Mayville, NY; (Y); Chorus; Var Capt Bsbl; JV Var Bsktbl; Socr.

BRIGGS, CINDY; Charlotte Valley Central HS; Oneonta, NY; (S); 3/30; Computer Clb; Girl Scts; Spanish Clb; Bsktbl; Sftbl; Hon Roll; NHS; Trs Frsh Cls; Trs Soph Cls; Trs Jr Cls; Bus.

BRIGGS, JAMES L; Rome Free Acad; Rome, NY; (Y); Boy Scts; Cmnty Wkr; Intnl Clb; Ski Clb; Pep Band; Yrbk Bus Mgr; Var Golf; Hon Roll; Jr NHS; Sci Awd; Bus Ind Mgmnt.

BRIGGS, JIM; Churchville-Chili HS; Spencerport, NY; (Y); Spanish Clb; Coach Actv; Mgr(s); Score Keeper; Var L Socr; Var L Trk; Var L Wrstlng; Hon Roll; U Buffalo; Athltc Trnnr.

BRIGGS, MARGIE; Glens Falls HS; Glens Falls, NY; (Y); AFS; Church Yth Grp; Math Clb; Pep Clb; Teachers Aide; Band; Mrchg Band; Powder Puff Ftbl; High Hon Roll; Hon Roll; Math.

BRIGGS, MICHAEL; Victor Central HS; Victor, NY; (S); Church Yth Grp; Acpl Chr; Band; Chorus; Church Choir; Color Guard; Concert Band; Orch; School Musical; Talents For Christ Schlrshp 85; Baptist Bible Coll; Mus Ed.

BRIGGS, MICHAEL WILLIAM; Hilton Central HS; Hilton, NY; (Y); 4/310; Trs Church Yth Grp; Trs Math Clb; Ski Clb; Mrchg Band; Trs Yrbk Phtg; JV Var Tennis; JETS Awd; NHS; Ntl Merit Ltr; Band; All Cnty Orch 1st Chr 84; Cornell U; Gentc Engrng.

BRIGGS, SCOTT D; Gouverneur JR SR HS; Gouverneur, NY; (Y); Varsity Clb; Var Capt Ftbl; Jr NHS; Ntl Merit SF; Trs Frsh Cls; Im Wt Lftg; Hon Roll; Acadm Ltr; Shkspr Clb Eng Awd; Clarkson U; Accntng.

BRIGGS, TINA; Springfield Gardens HS; Lauvelton, NY; (S); 14/508; Red Cross Aide; Hon Roll; NHS; Arista 84; Salute To Yth 84; Psych.

BRIGHT, JULIE; Bishop Ludden HS; Syracuse, NY; (S); Co-Capt Math Tm; Capt L Tennis; High Hon Roll; NHS; Church Yth Grp; Chorus; Engl, Spnsh Awd 84; Algbr Awd 82; Math.

BRIGHT, SEDONIA; Grace H Dodge V HS; New York, NY; (Y); 27/439; Chorus; Rep Frsh Cls; Rep Soph Cls; Rep Jr Cls; Stu Cncl; Bsktbl; Sftbl; Hon Roll; NHS; Prfct Atten Awd; Mt Siani Schl Of Nrsng; Nrsng.

BRIGMAN, BRIAN; Seneca Vocational HS; Buffalo, NY; (Y); 29/200; NHS; Alfred ST Coll; Mech Engr.

BRIGNALL, ALAN J; Waterloo SR HS; Fayette, NY; (Y); 3/175; Varsity Clb; JV Crs Cntry; Im Sftbl; Var Capt Tennis; DAR Awd; High Hon Roll; Pres NHS; Prfct Atten Awd; Voice Dem Awd; Hgh Ave Chem Cash Awd 84; Syracuse U; Brdcst Jrnlsm.

BRIGNOL, SHEILA M; St Johns Prep; Brooklyn, NY; (Y); Church Yth Grp; Exploring; Hosp Aide; Office Aide; Teachers Aide; Chorus; Church Choir; School Musical; Pres Frsh Cls; VP Soph Cls; St Josephs; Pediatrcn.

BRILBECK, SALLYANNE; George W Fowler HS; Syracuse, NY; (Y); 2/211; Exploring; Pep Clb; VP Science Clb; Yrbk Stf; Rep Stu Cncl; Swmmng; High Hon Roll; Pres NHS; Sal; Suny Coll; Earth Sci.

BRILEY, ANTONN M; Mount Vernon HS; Mt Vernon, NY; (Y); Aud/Vis; Dance Clb; FBLA; Variety Show; Ftbl; Trk; Hon Roll; Mt Vernon High Talent Show 83-84; Hnrd Black Yth Achvt Awd 85; Accntng II Awd 84-85; NY Tech; Certified Pblc Accnt.

BRILL, MARIE C; Valley Stream Central HS; Valley Stream, NY; (Y); 17/350; Drama Clb; Thesps; Chorus; Madrigals; School Musical; School Play; Capt JV Cheerleading; Mu Alp Tht; NHS; Pres Schlr; John M Smith Music Awd 85; PTA Schlrshp 85; Allegheny Coll Schlrshp 85; Allegheny Coll.

BRILLI, THERESA; Our Lady Of Mercy HS; Rochester, NY; (Y); Ski Clb; Varsity Clb; Chorus; Var L Gym; JV Trk; Hon Roll; Monroe CC; Pol Sci.

BRINDISI, RICHARD; Pittsford Sutherland HS; Pittsford, NY; (Y); Letterman Clb; Varsity Clb; Bsbl; Ftbl; Hon Roll; NHS; PTSA Achvt Awd-Bus 85; Bus.

BRINK, BRIAN J; Allegany Central HS; Allegany, NY; (Y); 18/100; Computer Clb; Spanish Clb; Concert Band; Mrchg Band; Pep Band; Yrbk Stf; Bsbl; Bowling; Golf; Vllybl; Var Lttrs 82-85; Mus Schlrshp 82; NYS Regnts Schlrshp 85; St Bonaventure U; Bus.

BRINK, CAREY; Saranac Lake HS; Saranac Lake, NY; (Y); 11/124; Sec Jr Cls; Var L Bsktbl; JV Var Powder Puff Ftbl; Var L Socr; JV Var Trk; JV L Vllybl; NHS; Church Yth Grp; Chorus; Church Choir; HS Svc Awd 84; Yth Ctr Staff 82-85; St Bernards Yth Ministry Tm & Retreat Tm 85; Psych.

BRINK, TIMOTHY; East Meadow HS; East Meadow, NY; (S); FBLA; Capt Var Ftbl; Capt Var Lcrss; Capt Var Wrstlng; High Hon Roll; NHS; Male Athlete Yr Awd; MVP La Crosse & Wrstlng; Math.

BRINTON, SCOTT; Longwood HS; Medford, NY; (S); 44/485; Boy Scts; Speech Tm; Orch; Nwsp Rptr; Yrbk Bus Mgr; Lit Mag; Crs Cntry; High Hon Roll; Voice Dem Awd; Nwsp Stf; Egl Scout 85; Mddl Islnd Bd Of Educ Commended Stu 84; Nyssma Violin Solo Excllnt 83; Syracuse U; Nwspapr Jrnlsm.

BRIOT, LEWIS; Beaver River Central Schl; Croghan, NY; (Y); 13/90; Church Yth Grp; Varsity Clb; JV Crs Cntry; Var Mgr(s); Var Score Keeper; Var Timer; High Hon Roll; NHS; Mst Outstdng Stu Awd Howard G Sachett Educ Ctr 83-84; Elec Engrng.

BRISMAN, ANDREW; George W Hewlett HS; Valley Stream, NY; (Y); 18/300; Bsktbl; Hon Roll; NCTE Awd; NHS; Ntl Merit Ltr.

BRISTOL, ELIZABETH; Avon Central HS; Avon, NY; (Y); 5/105; AFS; Yrbk Ed-Chief; VP Frsh Cls; Trs Soph Cls; Trs Jr Cls; Trs Sr Cls; Socr; Trk; High Hon Roll; NHS; Natl Educ Devlpmnt Test Awd 83.

BRISTOL, TODD; Fayetteville Manlius HS; Manlius, NY; (Y); Church Yth Grp; Political Wkr; Ski Clb; Im Badmtn; Var Crs Cntry; JV Lcrss; Hon Roll; Partcptn Merit Awd-Yth Poltcl Clb 84; Bus Entrprs Smnr Schlrshp 85; Psych.

BRITTEN, RICHARD; The Albany Acad; Averill Park, NY; (Y); Camera Clb; Church Yth Grp; Varsity Clb; School Musical; Nwsp Sprt Ed; Yrbk Phtg; Capt Var Ftbl; Capt Var Trk; Var Wrstlng; Ntl Merit Ltr; Wesleyan U; Biol.

BRITTIS, NICOLE; The Masters Schl; Yonkers, NY; (Y); Key Clb; Yrbk Stf; JV Fld Hcky; Hon Roll; French Clb; Hosp Aide; Office Aide; Spanish Clb; Teachers Aide; Lit Mag; Stu Ldr Proctor 84-85.

BROADBENT, SCOTT A; Frontier Central HS; Hamburg, NY; (Y); 84/500; NHS; Rgnts, Presdntl Schlrshp 85; Niagara U; Bio.

BROADWATER, ELIZABETH; Columbia HS; Rensselear, NY; (Y); 4-H; Band; Mrchg Band; Crs Cntry; Capt Trk; High Hon Roll; Hon Roll; NHS; Poltcl Sci.

BROADY, VINCENT; Stony Brook Schl; Dallas, TX; (Y); 12/84; Church Yth Grp; Drama Clb; Math Tm; Political Wkr; Church Choir; School Play; Rep Frsh Cls; Rep Soph Cls; Rep Jr Cls; Bsbl; Bst European Hstry Stu 85; Prfct Hd Of Schl; Stanford; Eng.

BROCATO, CARMINE; John Dewey HS; Brooklyn, NY; (Y); Intnl Clb; Quiz Bowl; Science Clb; Teachers Aide; Stage Crew; Bsktbl; Coach Actv; Ftbl; Sftbl; Vllybl; Leader Tchrs Asst Gym 83-85; 2nd Pl PAL Art 84-85; Exch Pgm 84-85; Fordham; Fin.

BROCCOLI, RENEE; Whitesboro HS; Marcy, NY; (Y); GAA; Powder Puff Ftbl; Var Sftbl; Var Tennis; JV Vllybl; Hon Roll; Biomed Engr.

BROCCOLO, RICHARD; Bishop Kearney HS; Rochester, NY; (Y); Church Yth Grp; Ice Hcky; High Hon Roll; Roch Inst Tech; Engrng.

BROCKHUM, CONNIE L; Gloversville HS; Gloversville, NY; (Y); DECA; Hosp Aide; Spanish Clb; JV Sftbl; JV Trk; Hon Roll; RN.

BROCKMANN, WALTER; Southampton HS; Southampton, NY; (Y); 62/108; Chess Clb; Church Yth Grp; French Clb; Var Trk; Ltrmn Awd; Track Awd; Suffolk Cnty Comm; Accntng.

BROCKOR, DOUGLAS J; Romo Frog Acad; Ava, NY; (Y); 19/528; Intnl Clb; Var L Bsktbl; Var L Trk; Hon Roll; Jr NHS; NHS; Pres Schlr; Colgate Smnr 84-85; U Of Rochester; Law.

BRODERICK, COLLEEN; Nazareth Acad; Rochester, NY; (Y); 10/114; Exploring; JA; Scholastic Bowl; JV Sftbl; NHS; Pres Schlr; Exch Stu Peru SA 84; Syracuse U Sclrshp 85; Syracuse U; Intl Stds.

BRODERICK, ELLEN; Saint Francis Prep; Glendale, NY; (Y); Kiwanis Awd; Var Bsktbl; Var Sftbl; Var Vllybl; Phy Thrpst.

BRODEUR, THOMAS; Pulaski Academy & Central Schls; Richland, NY; (Y); Boys Clb Am; Boy Scts; Stage Crew; Var Capt Bsbl; Var Capt Ftbl; Wt Lftg; MVP Bsebl 85; All Tournmnt Amer Legn Bsebl 85; Joyce Curry Memrl Bsebl Awd 85; Herkimer; Crmnl Justice.

BRODHEAD, NANCY; Warwick Valley HS; Warwick, NY; (Y); 8/205; Hosp Aide; Chorus; Nwsp Rptr; Yrbk Phtg; Yrbk Stf; High Hon Roll; Hon Roll; Ntl Merit SF; Berkeley Alumni Scholar 85; Emily Vail Edctnl Trust Loan 85; Orange & Rockland Employee Scholar 85; Berkeley Of Westchester; Secr.

BRODIN, LAURA; Mamaroneck HS; Larchmont, NY; (Y); Dance Clb; Drama Clb; French Clb; Thesps; School Play; Lit Mag; Hon Roll; PACE Awds 83-84; Sci Awd-Chem 84; Russian Clb 85; Russian Stds.

BRODLIEB, WENDY B; Lawrence HS; Lawrence, NY; (Y); 12/379; Drama Clb; Key Clb; Scholastic Bowl; Sec Spanish Clb; Rep Sr Cls; Cit Awd; Jr NHS; NHS; Schlstc Hnr Awd 82; Spnsh Awd 82; SUNY Binghamton; Bus.

BRODMAN, KEITH; Saint George Acad; Brooklyn, NY; (Y); Computer Clb; Nwsp Stf; Sec Soph Cls; Sec Jr Cls; Hon Roll; NHS; MIT; Comp Sci.

BRODOCK, JUDY; Rome Free Acad; Rome, NY; (Y); Aud/Vis; Pres Church Yth Grp; Girl Scts; Chorus; Pres Frsh Cls; JV Var Fld Hcky; Hon Roll; Jr NHS; Intnl Clb; Im Bsktbl; Girl Scout Silvr Awd 82; Girl Scout Silvr Ldrshp 82; Biomed.

BRODSKY, STEPHEN; Commack HS; Commack, NY; (Y); 5/440; Debate Tm; Temple Yth Grp; Ed Lit Mag; Frsh Cls; Soph Cls; Sr Cls; VP Stu Cncl; Var Socr; NCTE Awd; NHS; Natl French Cntst Laureat 81.

BRODY, DENNIS; Lindenhurst HS; Lindenhurst, NY; (Y); Varsity Clb; JV Bsktbl; Var Ftbl; Var L Lcrss; Graphics.

BROEKER, MICHAEL; Grand Island HS; Gr Island, NY; (Y); Art Clb; School Musical; School Play; Art Svc Awd 83-84; Chrprcty.

BROGAN, SUZANNE; Cardinal Spellman HS; Bronx, NY; (Y); Dance Clb; Girl Scts; Rep Frsh Cls; Rep Stu Cncl; Var Crs Cntry; Mgr(s); Var Score Keeper; Var Sftbl; Var Swmmng; Var Trk; 2nd Honors 83; Marist; Accntng.

BROKALIS, STEPHANIE; Berlin Central Schl; Stephentown, NY; (Y); 4-H; Ski Clb; Varsity Clb; Chorus; School Musical; Yrbk Stf; Crs Cntry; Im Var Sftbl; Var Im Vllybl.

BROMBERG, IZZY S; Voshiua Universtiy HS; Brooklyn, NY; (Y); 39/115; Speech Tm; Temple Yth Grp; Nwsp Rptr; Yrbk Stf; Pres Frsh Cls; Var Diving; Var Swmmng; Im Wrstlng; Hon Roll; Judaic Hnr Rll 82-83.

BROMIRSKI, JUDY; St Marys Acad; Hoosick Falls, NY; (Y); 3/18; French Clb; Service Clb; Nwsp Stf; Sec Frsh Cls; VP Jr Cls; Var Capt Bsktbl; Powder Puff Ftbl; Score Keeper; Var Sftbl; Var Vllybl; Phy Thrpy.

BROMIRSKI, TIMOTHY; Hoosick Falls Central HS; Hoosick Falls, NY; (Y); 10/110; French Clb; Stu Cncl; JV Ftbl; Hon Roll; NHS; West Point; Engrng.

BROMLEY, MARK; Gates-Chili HS; Rochester, NY; (S); Ski Clb; Spanish Clb; School Play; Yrbk Phtg; Rep Frsh Cls; Rep Soph Cls; Rep Jr Cls; JV Diving; High Hon Roll; NHS; Polt Sci.

BROMSON, JONATHAN A; Irvington HS; Tarrytown, NY; (Y); 1/122; Yrbk Stf; Trs Sr Cls; VP Capt Socr; High Hon Roll; Ntl Merit SF; Val; Columbia U Sci Hnrs Prg 82-85.

BRONSKI, LINDA; Onteora Central HS; Woodstock, NY; (S); 24/245; High Hon Roll; NHS; Acpl Chr; Band; Chorus; Color Guard; Drill Tm; Mrchg Band; Orch; Hon Roll; U S Pony Clb MVP 84; Chmbr Orch 1st Chr Cello 84; Clr Grd Solo; Math.

BRONZINO, LISA; Sachem North HS; Lk Ronkonkoma, NY; (Y); 420/1500; Girl Scts; Ski Clb; Spanish Clb; Chorus; Orch; Stat Im Bsktbl; Im Sftbl; NYSSMA 83-84; Achvt Awd In Bsktbl 82-83; Sftbl Awd 82-83; Sclgst.

BROOK, MARJORIE E; East Meadow HS; East Meadow, NY; (Y); 56/414; Debate Tm; Drama Clb; Thesps; Band; Concert Band; Flag Corp; Mrchg Band; School Musical; Stage Crew; Symp Band; Natl Hon Soc 83-85; Soc Dstngshd Stdt 83-85; Oswego U; Comm.

BROOKS, BETH; The Stony Brook Schl; Sewickley, PA; (Y); Var L Fld Hcky; Var L Swmmng; Hon Roll; Elem Educ.

BROOKS, BRENDA J; John Marshall HS; Rochester, NY; (Y); 11/172; French Clb; Office Aide; Sec Pep Clb; Spanish Clb; Yrbk Stf; JV Var Vllybl; DAR Awd; High Hon Roll; Hon Roll; FBLA; Ann Turula Awd 85; SUNY Geneseo; Spcl Educ.

BROOKS, CARRIE; Tioga Central Schl; Barton, NY; (S); 1/96; Nwsp Rptr; Nwsp Stf; High Hon Roll; NHS; Prfct Atten Awd; Vet.

BROOKS, CHRISTIN M; Saratoga Springs HS; Saratoga Spgs, NY; (Y); 44/465; Var L Bowling; High Hon Roll; Hon Roll; AATF Natl Frnch Exam Mdl 83 & 84; Regents Schlrshp 85; Alfred U; Ceramic Engrng.

BROOKS, CYNTHIA; Bishop Ford C C HS; Brooklyn, NY; (Y); Ski Clb; Psych.

BROOKS, ELLEN; Mayfiled Central HS; Gloversville, NY; (Y); 14/77; VP Church Yth Grp; Girl Scts; Concert Band; Jazz Band; Mrchg Band; Symp Band; Math Tm; Varsity Clb; Nwsp Rptr; Miss Bannertown Cont 82; NYSMA Comptn Awds 82-83; Fulton Co Music Awds 84-85; Gold Awd Grl Scouts; Cobleskill Coll; Lib Arts.

BROOKS, ESTELLE; Wells Central Schl; Speculator, NY; (S); 3/35; Drama Clb; Band; Chorus; Mrchg Band; Variety Show; Im Cheerleading; Im Socr; Var Capt Vllybl; Utica Schl Of Commerce; Bus.

BROOKS, GLENROY A; Canarsie HS; Brooklyn, NY; (Y); Boy Scts; MMM; Varsity Clb; Chorus; School Play; Soph Cls; Crs Cntry; Tennis; NEDT Awd; John Jay Coll; Plce Sci.

BROOKS, GREG; Nyack HS; Nyack, NY; (Y); Boy Scts; Cul Art.

BROOKS, JOHN L; Mattituck HS; Mattituck, NY; (Y); 8/120; Am Leg Boys St; Drama Clb; Chorus; School Musical; School Play; Variety Show; Rep Stu Cncl; Var L Bsbl; Var L Socr; NHS; U S Naval Acad Summr Sem 85; Mst Outstndg Ath Soph Cls 84; All ST Chrs 83-85; Georgetown U; Pre-Med.

BROOKS, JOSEPH; Auburn HS; Auburn, NY; (Y); 12/400; Off ROTC; JV Golf; Aero Engr.

BROOKS, LEONIE; St Agnes Cathedral HS; Westbury, NY; (Y); 15/385; Red Cross Aide; Band; Variety Show; Nwsp Phtg; Yrbk Rptr; Pres Stu Cncl; Var L Trk; High Hon Roll; NHS; Prsdng Suprvsr Town Of Hempstead 85; Cum Lade 85; Ntl Merit Fndtn 84; SUNY Stony Brook; Psych.

BROOKS, LISA; Norwood Norfolk Central HS; Norwood, NY; (Y); 18/114; French Clb; JCL; Trs Latin Clb; Band; Concert Band; Mrchg Band; Yrbk Phtg; Cheerleading; Hon Roll; Canton Ag Tech Coll; Acctng.

BROOKS, MARGARET; Gates Chili SR HS; Rochester, NY; (S); 7/463; Church Yth Grp; JA; Service Clb; Ski Clb; Church Choir; High Hon Roll; NHS; Ntl Merit Ltr; Therapist.

BROOKS, MARY B; Alexander Central HS; Alexander, NY; (S); French Clb; Pres Sec Band; Pres Sec Concert Band; Jazz Band; Pres Sec Mrchg Band; Orch; Symp Band; JV Socr; JV Sftbl; Hon Roll.

BROOKS, PAUL T; Bishop Ludden HS; Syracuse, NY; (S); #10 In Class; NFL; Political Wkr; Speech Tm; Pres Jr Cls; Var JV Ftbl; Var JV Lcrss; Var Wt Lftg; Var Wrstlng; High Hon Roll; NHS; Law.

BROOKS, RANDAL; Midlakes HS; Clifton Springs, NY; (Y); Aud/Vis; French Clb; Varsity Clb; Bsbl; YMCA Stu Rep 84-86; Military; Police Ofcr.

BROOKS, STEPHANIE; South Park HS; Buffalo, NY; (Y); German Clb; Rep Jr Cls; Hon Roll; Art Awd; Journlst.

BROOKS, STEPHEN P; Clarkstown HS; New City, NY; (Y); 7/486; Boy Scts; German Clb; Scholastic Bowl; Ed Nwsp Rptr; Trk; Mu Alp Tht; NHS; Ftbl; High Hon Roll; Natl Hnr Roll 85; Pres Acad Ftns Awds Pgm 85; Excell Hmnts 85; Haverford Coll; Hist.

BROPHY, BLAKEMAN B; Westhampton Beach HS; Remsenburg, NY; (Y); 2/200; Am Leg Boys St; Band; Mrchg Band; Yrbk Bus Mgr; VP Sec Stu Cncl; JV Tennis; NHS; Ntl Merit Ltr; Sal; Trs Church Yth Grp; Pres Clsrm Yng Am 85; Brown U Bk Awd 84; Hamilton Coll; Pre-Med.

BROPHY, CHRISTINE; St Francis Preparatory Schl; Flushing, NY; (S); 138/693; Varsity Clb; Score Keeper; Opt Clb Awd; U S Achvt Acad 85; Emerald Soc Awd 82; Holy Name Soc Awd 82; Bus.

BROPHY, THOMAS; St Francis Prep; Flushing, NY; (S); 152/700; Computer Clb; Ski Clb; Varsity Clb; Stage Crew; Tennis; Var Wt Lftg; Holy Name, Emerald Soc Schlrshp 80; Trustee Schlrshp 85; Adelphi; Law.

BROSCH, ERIC; Amsterdam HS; Amsterdam, NY; (S); 30/250; Jazz Band; Rep Frsh Cls; Rep Soph Cls; Sec Jr Cls; Stu Cncl; JV Capt Ftbl; Var Trk; JV Wrstlng; Hon Roll; Mst Imprvd Wrestler 82; Cap Dist All-Star Jazz Ensemble 84; Optometrist.

BROSE, DENNIS; Roy C Ketcham HS; Hughsonville, NY; (Y); Var Capt Socr; Hon Roll; NHS; All Star Soccer Tm 84-85; Ulster County CC; Engrng.

BROSSEAU, DAWN MARIE; L C Obown HS; Rochester, NY; (Y); Sec Exploring; Girl Scts; Sec Pep Clb; Nwsp Rptr; Ed Nwsp Stf; Yrbk Stf; Stu Cncl; Girl Sct Silv Awd,Ldrshp Awd 83; First Pl Compet Med Tm USA 84; Paul Smiths Clg; Chf Trng.

BROSSEAU, KRISTI-LYNN; Schalmont Central HS; Schenectady, NY; (Y); 8/179; Var Pres 4-H; Band; Chorus; Rep Soph Cls; Rep Jr Cls; Rep Sr Cls; Trs NHS; Pres Schlr; Drama Clb; Concert Band; Schalmont Tchrs Assn/Geraldine Corrigan Mem Schlrshp 85; Outstdng Soc Stds Stu 85; Coll Of St Rose.

BROSTEK, ANNEMARIE; St Francis Prep; Flushing, NY; (Y); Church Yth Grp; Var Capt Cheerleading; Comm.

BROTHERS, LISA; Thomas A Edison HS; Elmira Hts, NY; (Y); 15/89; Sec JCL; Sec Latin Clb; Office Aide; Teachers Aide; Chorus; Yrbk Ed-Chief; Rep Stu Cncl; Hon Roll; NHS; Cncl 82; AFSCME Schlrshp 85; Paul J Headd Aptitude Achv Schlrshp 85; Cntrl Cit Bus Inst; Lgl Sec.

BROTMANN, MATTHEW; Woodlands HS; Hartsdale, NY; (Y); Key Clb; Concert Band; Mrchg Band; Nwsp Phtg; Yrbk Phtg; Off Stu Cncl.

BROTSIS, PANAGIOTA; Gloversville HS; Gloversville, NY; (Y); 13/220; Drama Clb; French Clb; Concert Band; Mgr Jazz Band; Mrchg Band; Symp Band; Yrbk Ed-Chief; Stu Cncl; NHS; Regnts Schlrshp 85; Siena Coll; Pol Sci.

BROUGH, KELLY M; Gates-Chili SR HS; Rochester, NY; (Y); 90/465; Drama Clb; Pres VP JA; School Play; Yrbk Stf; Lit Mag; Rep Frsh Cls; Rep Soph Cls; Rep Jr Cls; Rep Sr Cls; Var Timer; Regents Schlrshp 84-85; Genesee CC; Trl Mgmt.

BROUGHTON, FRANCINE; Warwick Valley HS; Warwick, NY; (Y); 75/200; Girl Scts; Var Sftbl; Hon Roll; Prfct Atten Awd; Top 10 Rgnts In Bio Awd 84; Comp Oprtr.

BROUSHET, ANGELIQUE E; Jamaica HS; Flushing, NY; (Y); GAA; Library Aide; Office Aide; Chorus; Variety Show; Capt Vllybl; Cit Awd; Hon Roll; Prfct Atten Awd; NAACP Acad Achvt Awd 84; Pediatrcn.

BROWN, ADAM C; De Sales Catholic HS; Lockport, NY; (Y); 10/50; Am Leg Boys St; Nwsp Stf; Lit Mag; Coach Actv; Capt Golf; Capt Tennis; Hon Roll; Ntl Merit Ltr; Acad All-Amer 85; US Natl Ldrshp Awd 85; Oblates Provncl Awd 85; Niagara U; Hist.

BROWN, ALISON; Postdam Central HS; Potsdom, NY; (Y); 17/150; AFS; French Clb; Latin Clb; Varsity Clb; Nwsp Rptr; Yrbk Bus Mgr; Var L Crs Cntry; Var L Trk; High Hon Roll; Hon Roll; Bard; Comm.

BROWN, AMY; Wyoming Central Schl; Wyoming, NY; (S); 1/25; AFS; Debate Tm; Drama Clb; Band; Church Choir; Concert Band; Mrchg Band; School Play; Pres Jr Cls; Sftbl; Acad Awds 82-85; Lib Arts.

BROWN, ANDREA; Tamarac HS; Melrose, NY; (Y); 25/100; Church Yth Grp; Dance Clb; Hosp Aide; Band; Chorus; Concert Band; Jazz Band; Mrchg Band; JV Var Cheerleading; Hon Roll; Coll Of Boca Raton; Fash Merch.

BROWN, ANGELA; Prospect Heights HS; Brooklyn, NY; (Y); Chorus; Yrbk Stf; Rep Frsh Cls; Trk; High Hon Roll; Hon Roll; Outstndng Wrtg Achvt 85; Excllnc Engl 85; Outstndng Perfrmnc Art 82; Hunters Coll; Soclgy.

BROWN, ANITA; Bishop Maginn HS; Loudonville, NY; (S); Drama Clb; Hosp Aide; Spanish Clb; School Play; Nwsp Sprt Ed; Pres Jr Cls; JV Capt Bsktbl; Sftbl; High Hon Roll; NHS.

BROWN, AUDREY; Our Savior Lutheran HS; Bronx, NY; (S); 4/22; Office Aide; Yrbk Stf; Sr Cls; Stu Cncl; Bsktbl; Trk; Prfct Atten Awd; Our Savior Luth Achvt Awd 84; NY ST U Buffalo; Bus Admin.

BROWN, BENNIE; Port Richmond HS; Staten Isld, NY; (Y); Boy Scts; Church Yth Grp; Church Choir; Yrbk Stf; Trk; Albany; Sociolgy.

BROWN, BILL; Pulaski HS; Pulaski, NY; (Y); Church Yth Grp; 4-H; Math Clb; Varsity Clb; Chorus; Swing Chorus; Crs Cntry; Trk; Wrstlng; High Hon Roll.

BROWN, BILLY; Walton HS; Bronx, NY; (Y); Drama Clb; English Clb; Math Clb; MMM; Science Clb; Spanish Clb; Band; Drm & Bgl; Mrchg Band; School Play; Music.

BROWN, CANDICE LYNN; Frontier SR HS; Lakeview, NY; (S); Church Yth Grp; 4-H; Political Wkr; School Musical; Nwsp Rptr; Sec Stu Cncl; Var Socr; NHS; NEDT Awd; Drama Clb; Cert Hnr NY ST Bar Assoc 85; Psych.

BROWN, CHRIS; Kenmore East HS; Tonawanda, NY; (Y); Hosp Aide; Sftbl; Hon Roll; U Of Buffalo; Med.

BROWN, CHRISTINE; Gilboa Conesville Central HS; Gilboa, NY; (S); 1/26; GAA; Hosp Aide; Band; Chorus; Yrbk Ed-Chief; Bsktbl; Var Socr; High Hon Roll; NHS; Math Regents Awd; Fire Queen Rnr Up.

BROWN, COLLEEN; Bishop Kearney HS; Brooklyn, NY; (Y); Church Yth Grp; Hosp Aide; Library Aide; Political Wkr; Spanish Clb; Hon Roll; Bio.

BROWN, DANIEL; Herkimer SR HS; Herkimer, NY; (Y); Boy Scts; JA; VP Model UN; Var L Trk; Var L Vllybl; Hon Roll; Syracuse U; Bus.

BROWN, DANIEL J; Chenango Valley HS; Binghamton, NY; (Y); Spanish Clb; Chorus; Rep Frsh Cls; High Hon Roll; NY ST Regents Schlrshp 85; Elec Engr.

BROWN, DARIN C; East Syracuse-Minoa Central HS; E Syracuse, NY; (Y); 5/338; Pres Church Yth Grp; Pres Latin Clb; Co-Capt Quiz Bowl; Variety Show; Yrbk Stf; Sec Frsh Cls; Capt Crs Cntry; Capt Trk; High Hon Roll; Ntl Merit SF; Mst Val Rnnr Cross Country, Indoor Track, Track 83-84; Empire St Games 800 M Run 5th Pl 84; Cornell U; Nat Sci.

BROWN, DAVID C; Wallkill SR HS; Wallkill, NY; (Y); Am Leg Boys St; Pres Sr Cls; JV Bsbl; Var Capt Ftbl; Var Capt Socr; Var Capt Trk; High Hon Roll; Pres Jr NHS; NHS; Opt Clb Awd; Air Force Acad; Bus.

BROWN, DAWN R; Elba Central HS; Elba, NY; (Y); 2/40; Church Yth Grp; Band; Chorus; Church Choir; L Crs Cntry; NHS; Sal; French Clb; Math Tm; Genesee CC Merit Tuition Schlrshp 85; NY ST Regents Schlrshp 85; Genesee CC; Music.

BROWN, DIANE; Union-Endicott HS; Endicott, NY; (Y); 59/430; Church Yth Grp; Hosp Aide; Key Clb; Band; Concert Band; Mrchg Band; Orch; Yrbk Stf; Var Trk; Hon Roll; Pres Acad Ftns Awd 85; Suny Binghamton; Soclgy.

BROWN, DIONNE; Christopher Columbus HS; Bronx, NY; (Y); 114/792; Civic Clb; Cmnty Wkr; Political Wkr; Teachers Aide; Chorus; Nwsp Rptr; Nwsp Stf; Cheerleading; Hon Roll; Prfct Atten Awd; Cert Of Merit 82; Math Schlrshp Cert 82; Dist Storytlng Awd 80; Jrnlsm.

BROWN, DIONNE; Mt Vernon HS; Mount Vernon, NY; (Y); Drama Clb; FBLA; School Play; Badmtn; Swmmng; Hon Roll.

BROWN, DONNA LYN; Depew HS; Depew, NY; (S); Sec Ed DECA; Radio Clb; Varsity Clb; Variety Show; Stat Bsktbl; Cheerleading; Crs Cntry; Socr; Trk; Jr NHS.

BROWN, DOROTHY DIANE; Amityville Memorial HS; Amityville, NY; (Y); 2/193; Math Tm; Band; Nwsp Stf; Yrbk Ed-Chief; Pres Sr Cls; Sftbl; NHS; Pres Schlr; Sal; Mary Mc Leod Bethune Blck Achvrs Awd 84; Blck Wmns Alliance Schlrshp 85; Rensselaer Poly Inst; Elec Engr.

BROWN, ELYDA; Clifton-Fine Central HS; Harrisville, NY; (S); 6/50; Camera Clb; Yrbk Stf; Score Keeper; High Hon Roll; Hon Roll; Tlntd JR Pgm St Lawrence U 83.

BROWN, ERIC; Pelham Memorial HS; Pelham, NY; (Y); Pres Trs AFS; Drama Clb; French Clb; Model UN; Political Wkr; School Musical; Stage Crew; Lit Mag; Stu Cncl; Cit Awd; Art.

BROWN, GABRIELLE M; Laguardia H S Of The Arts; New York City, NY; (Y); 259/588; Trs Sec Drama Clb; Thesps; Chorus; Madrigals; School Musical; School Play; Rptr Nwsp Rptr; NHS; Rotary Awd; St Schlr; ARTS Hnrbl Ment Awd 85; Schl Visul Arts; Fine Arts.

BROWN, GEORGE; Washingtonville HS; Monroe, NY; (Y); Crs Cntry; Trk; Hon Roll; Suny Fredonia; Accntng.

BROWN, GEORGIA PATRICIA; Mount Vernon HS; Mt Vernon, NY; (Y); 87/590; Computer Clb; FBLA; Spanish Clb; High Hon Roll; Hon Roll; 4-H; Intnl Clb; Office Aide; Science Clb; Chorus; Spn & Amer Hstry Hgh Hon Rls 83-84; Mythology, Shakespeare, Art Hgh Hon Rls 84-85; Hofstra U; Bio.

BROWN, GRACE; St Catharine Acad; Bronx, NY; (Y); 14/205; Teachers Aide; NHS; Ntl Merit Ltr; Prfct Atten Awd; Rep Frsh Cls; Rep Soph Cls; Pres Jr Cls; Rep Pres Stu Cncl; Acad All Amer 84-85; Natl Hstry & Govt Awd 84-85; NY U; Bus.

BROWN, HOWARD; Deer Park HS; Deer Park, NY; (Y); 99/422; Y-Teens; JV Lcrss; Var Tennis; High Hon Roll; Hon Roll.

BROWN, JAN; Newark Valley HS; Newark Vly, NY; (Y); 15/121; Boy Scts; 4-H; Varsity Clb; JV Var Bsktbl; JV Var Ftbl; Var Trk; Wt Lftg; High Hon Roll; Hon Roll; Defnsv Plyr Yr Bsktbl 85; Carpntry.

BROWN, JANET; Columbia HS; Troy, NY; (Y); Sec Spanish Clb; Band; Concert Band; Sec Drm & Bgl; Mrchg Band; JV Trk; High Hon Roll; NHS; Archtctr.

BROWN, JEFFREY A; Mac Arthur HS; Wantagh, NY; (Y); 16/319; Var Capt Tennis; NHS; NYS Regnts Schlrshp 85; All-Conf Tnns 84; SUNY Albany; Bio.

BROWN, JENNIFER; Long Island Lutheran HS; Wantagh, NY; (S); 1/101; Debate Tm; French Clb; Scholastic Bowl; Nwsp Rptr; Lit Mag; Bowling; High Hon Roll; NHS; German Clb; Mathletes; Highest Class Rank 83-84; Med.

BROWN, JOAN T; Bronx Of Science HS; Brooklyn, NY; (Y); Library Aide; Office Aide; Teachers Aide; Var Cheerleading.

BROWN, KATHY; Amsterdam HS; Hagaman, NY; (Y); Cmnty Wkr; Drm Mjr(t); Yrbk Stf; Stu Cncl; Hon Roll; Prfct Atten Awd; 1st Pl Great Amer Smoke-Out Cntst 84-85; Bio.

BROWN, KATHY; St Marys HS; Lancaster, NY; (S); Varsity Clb; Rep Frsh Cls; Rep Soph Cls; VP Jr Cls; Stat Badmtn; JV Var Cheerleading; Var Sftbl; Var Trk; High Hon Roll; Hon Roll; Law.

BROWN, KENNETH E; Msgr Farrell HS; Staten Island, NY; (Y); Am Leg Boys St; Boy Scts; Camera Clb; Hosp Aide; Im Bowling; Crs Cntry; Trk; Hon Roll; Law.

BROWN, KIM; St Marys HS; Depew, NY; (S); Camera Clb; Ski Clb; NHS; Commnctns.

BROWN, KRISTEN; Mynderse Acad; Seneca Falls, NY; (S); 10/140; 4-H; GAA; Intnl Clb; Var JV Socr; JV Sftbl; Var Trk; High Hon Roll; Hon Roll.

BROWN, KURT E; Faith Heritage Schl; West Chester, PA; (Y); 3/22; Church Yth Grp; Yrbk Stf; Pres Jr Cls; Pres Sr Cls; L Capt Bsktbl; L Capt Socr; L Capt Trk; High Hon Roll; Hon Roll; NHS; Houghton Coll; Bio.

BROWN, LARA L; Mynderse Acad; Seneca Falls, NY; (Y); 11/132; Model UN; Ski Clb; Yrbk Stf; Trs Soph Cls; Trs Jr Cls; Trs Sr Cls; VP Stu Cncl; Socr; Hon Roll; NHS; Regents Scholarship 85; Suny Binghamton; Math.

BROWN, LISA; Lackawanna SR HS; Lackawanna, NY; (Y); Church Yth Grp; Cmnty Wkr; Spanish Clb; Church Choir; Trs Stu Cncl; High Hon Roll; Hon Roll; VP NHS; Psych.

BROWN, LUANNE; C W Baker HS; Baldwinsville, NY; (Y); 28/500; Art Clb; Drama Clb; VP Intnl Clb; JA; Pres Spanish Clb; Chorus; School Musical; School Play; Nwsp Rptr; Nwsp Stf; Frgn Lang Awd & Scholar 85; Oswego; Interprtr.

BROWN, LYNETTE; Cicero-North Syracuse HS; Clay, NY; (S); 85/622; German Clb; Hon Roll; Bryant S Stratton; Bus.

BROWN, MALINDA; Gloversville HS; Gloversville, NY; (Y); Sec Trs Church Yth Grp; Sec Trs 4-H; Teachers Aide; Nwsp Rptr; JV Fld Hcky; Mgr(s); Var Sftbl; Cit Awd; 4-H Awd; High Hon Roll; Math.

BROWN, MARC A; High School Of Art & Design; Bronx, NY; (Y); Art Clb; Yrbk Bus Mgr; Hon Roll; Regents Schlrshp 85; Certfct For WNET/Thirteens Stu Art Festvl 82; Parsons Schl Of Design; Illus.

BROWN, MARCO; Mynderse Acad; Seneca Falls, NY; (Y); 12/150; Yrbk Stf; Rep Stu Cncl; Var L Lcrss; High Hon Roll; NHS; Ntl Merit Ltr; Seneca Cty Med Soc 85; Bio.

BROWN, MARK E; Hornll SR HS; Hornell, NY; (Y); 42/198; Art Clb; Camera Clb; Church Yth Grp; Exploring; Chorus; Ftbl; Socr; Trk; Hon Roll; Art Clb 84; Ceramics 85; St James; Radiogrphy.

BROWN, MARTHA; John Dewey HS; Brooklyn, NY; (Y); AFS; Church Yth Grp; Cmnty Wkr; FCA; GAA; Office Aide; Teachers Aide; Orch; Rep Soph Cls; Capt Trk; Barauch Coll; Bus Admin.

BROWN, MARY; York Central HS; York, NY; (Y); Spanish Clb; Chorus; School Musical; Stat Sftbl; Gov Hon Prg Awd; NHS; Soc Stud 84; Lang 84; Nursing.

BROWN, MICHELE; Attica SR HS; Cowlesville, NY; (S); 15/150; VP Church Yth Grp; Yrbk Stf; Cheerleading; Fld Hcky; Hon Roll; Math.

BROWN, MICHELLE; Commack South HS; Dix Hills, NY; (Y); Art Clb; Dance Clb; Temple Yth Grp; School Musical; School Play; Yrbk Stf; JV Cheerleading; High Hon Roll; NHS; Ntl Merit Ltr; Natl Art Hnr Soc 84-86; Goldn Quil Awd 85.

BROWN, MICHELLE; Scotia Genville HS; Scotia, NY; (Y); Sec JA; Varsity Clb; Chorus; Yrbk Stf; JV Var Bsktbl; JV Capt Fld Hcky; JV Var Sftbl; JV Var Vllybl; High Hon Roll; Hon Roll; Bio.

BROWN, MONICA; Villa Maria Acad; Buffalo, NY; (Y); Church Yth Grp; Computer Clb; French Clb; Hosp Aide; Math Clb; Church Choir; Vllybl; Hon Roll; High Avrg Gen Chem 85; Comp Sci.

BROWN, MONICA TIAHISE; Adlie Stevenson HS; Bronx, NY; (Y); Hon Roll; Law.

BROWN, NATASHA; Clara Barton HS; Brooklyn, NY; (Y); Pres Church Yth Grp; Girl Scts; Hosp Aide; Teachers Aide; Pres Chorus; Pres Church Choir; School Musical; Nwsp Stf; Rep Jr Cls; Cit Awd; Academic Olympics 84-85; Community Work; Medicine.

BROWN, PAMELA; George W Wingate HS; Bklyn, NY; (Y); Dance Clb; Library Aide; Teachers Aide; Color Guard; Concert Band; Yrbk Stf; Var Capt Bowling; Var Cheerleading; Var Capt Sftbl; Var Capt Tennis; Law.

BROWN, PAMELA SUE; Cicero-N Syracuse HS; N Syracuse, NY; (S); 50/622; Church Yth Grp; Capt Color Guard; Mrchg Band; Stu Cncl; High Hon Roll; Child Psych.

BROWN, PATRICIA; Bishop Scully HS; Amsterdam, NY; (S); 3/69; Drama Clb; French Clb; Latin Clb; Math Clb; Stage Crew; Yrbk Phtg; High Hon Roll; NHS; Ntl Merit SF; Art Ntl Hnr Soc; Big Brthrs/Big Sistrs; Williams Coll.

BROWN, PAUL F; B N Cardozo HS; Little Neck, NY; (Y); 106/476; Capt Aud/Vis; Pres Church Yth Grp; Computer Clb; Math Tm; Office Aide; Teachers Aide; Orch; Yrbk Stf; Boy Scts; Math Clb; Ind Arts Awd 82; Schl Serv Awd 82; Polytechnic Inst; Civil Engr.

BROWN, PAULA; Morrisville-Easton Central Schl; Morrisville, NY; (Y); 10/67; Sec Drama Clb; Mathletes; Band; Mrchg Band; School Play; Nwsp Stf; Pres Soph Cls; Pres Jr Cls; Rep Stu Cncl; Score Keeper; Crmnl Jstce.

BROWN, REBECCA; Groton Central HS; Groton, NY; (Y); Church Yth Grp; 4-H; Stage Crew; Rep Stu Cncl; JV Cheerleading; Stat Trk; Stat Wrstlng; Cit Awd; 4-H Awd; NY Distngshd JR Holstein Breed 85; Tompkins Cnty Dairy Princess 85; Grnd Champ Shwmn NY ST Fair 84; Cornell U; Ag.

BROWN, RUTH; Cathedral HS; Ny, NY; (Y); 60/298; Hosp Aide; JA; Office Aide; Chorus; Church Choir; School Play; Hon Roll; Choral Awd 82-85; JR Achvt Awd 82; Prfct Atten Awd 82-83; NY U; Gynclgy.

BROWN, SHERYLL; Springfield Gardens HS; Rosedale, NY; (S); Teachers Aide; Band; Cit Awd; Hon Roll; Jr NHS; Prfct Atten Awd; IS/JHS Sprg Ptry Cont 82; Asst Prncpl Lst 83; Schlstc Achvmnt 84; Psych.

BROWN, SOPHIE; William Howard Taft HS; Bronx, NY; (Y); Computer Clb; Dance Clb; Science Clb; Stu Cncl; Crs Cntry; Timer; Prfct Atten Awd; Supr Yth Of Bronc 85; Pre Med.

BROWN, STEPHANIA; The Masters Schl; Ardsley, NY; (Y); Church Yth Grp; Library Aide; Office Aide; Teachers Aide; Band; Concert Band; Pep Band; Equestrn Awd AHSA, PHA Medls Clss 85; Qlfd For USET Fnls-Gladstone NJ 85; Auburn U; Vet Med.

BROWN, STEPHANIE; Canisteo Central HS; S Hornell, NY; (Y); Ski Clb; Band; Mrchg Band; Yrbk Stf; Var Capt Cheerleading; Hon Roll; Psych.

BROWN, STEPHEN; Plattsburgh SR HS; Plattsburgh, NY; (Y); Var L Ftbl; Var L Swmmng; High Hon Roll; Ntl Merit SF; Var L Trk; U S Military Acad; Bio Sci.

BROWN, STEPHEN J; Holy Trinity HS; Seaford, NY; (S); 16/320; Bsktbl; NHS; Math Awd 83; Math.

BROWN, STEVE; Jamestown HS; Jamestown, NY; (Y); 5/381; Church Yth Grp; French Clb; Quiz Bowl; Concert Band; Jazz Band; Mrchg Band; High Hon Roll; NHS; Natl Ldrshp Orgnztn 84-85; Richard Black Math Awd 85; Theodore Peterson Chem Awd 85; Carnegie-Mellon U; Chem Engrng.

BROWN, SUSAN; Jamaica HS; Flushing, NY; (Y); Art Clb; Church Yth Grp; Drama Clb; Girl Scts; Hosp Aide; JA; Library Aide; Office Aide; PAVAS; Teachers Aide; Awd Poetry Cntst Wnnr 83; Schlstc Awd Art 84; Awd Sci Proj 85; Pre Med.

BROWN, SUSANNAH L; Briarcliff HS; Briarcliff Manor, NY; (Y); AFS; French Clb; Hosp Aide; Yrbk Phtg; Ed Lit Mag; Tennis; Vllybl; High Hon Roll; Hon Roll; Ntl Merit SF; Econ.

BROWN, TAMMY; Newfield HS; Newfield, NY; (Y); 1/50; Varsity Clb; Nwsp Rptr; Yrbk Stf; Bsktbl; Fld Hcky; Ftbl; Sftbl; Wrstlng; High Hon Roll; NHS; JR Cls Sci Awd 85.

BROWN, TERESA A; Academy Of St Joseph; Stony Brook, NY; (Y); Church Yth Grp; Hosp Aide; Math Clb; Science Clb; Service Clb; Acpl Chr; Chorus; Yrbk Stf; Hon Roll; Catholic Dghtrs Amer Schlrshp 82; ASJ Schlrshp 85; Natl Piano Gld 81-85; Acadmc Achvt Math 84-85; Spec Ed.

BROWN, TIMOTHY; Longwood HS; Middle Island, NY; (Y); Church Yth Grp; Cmnty Wkr; Computer Clb; Drama Clb; Math Clb; Jr Cls; Ftbl; Capt Wt Lftg; Wrstlng; High Hon Roll; Outstndng Acadmc Achvt Awd 83; Apprntcshp Brookhaven Natl Lab 84; Med.

BROWN, VALERIE; Camden HS; Blossvale, NY; (Y); 4-H; Chorus; Orch; School Musical; Bowling; Trk.

BROWN, WILLARD R; Marcus Whitman Central Schl; Stanley, NY; (Y); 8/123; Am Leg Boys St; JCL; Ski Clb; Band; Jazz Band; School Play; Yrbk Stf; Var Ftbl; Var Trk; Ntl Merit Ltr; Finger Lakes Regnl Sci Fair Rep 84; 1st Pl Lat Drmtc Rdg Wayne-Finger Lakes Lang Expstn 84-85; Chem.

BROWN, WILLIAM D; Massena Central HS; Massena, NY; (Y); Church Yth Grp; Hon Roll; Math.

BROWN, YOLANDA; New Utrecht HS; Brooklyn, NY; (Y); Dance Clb; Baruch Coll; Acctng.

BROWNE, AMY; Beacon HS; Fishkill, NY; (Y); Key Clb; Varsity Clb; Var Cheerleading; JV Var Sftbl; Hon Roll.

BROWNE, BILL; Roscoe Central HS; Roscoe, NY; (Y); Varsity Clb; VICA; Bsbl; Ftbl; Trk; Kiwanis Awd; Orange Cty Comm Coll; Crimnl Ju.

BROWNE, DERRICK; Cardinal Hayes Power Memorial HS; New York, NY; (Y); Church Yth Grp; Bsktbl; Ftbl; Gym; Score Keeper; Hon Roll; Bus Law.

BROWNE, KEVIN; La Salle Acad; New York, NY; (S); 128/254; Am Leg Boys St; Church Yth Grp; Intnl Clb; School Play; Jr Cls; Stu Cncl; Crs Cntry; Trk; St Johns U; Jrnlst.

BROWNE, MICHELE ANNE; Friends Smnry; New York, NY; (Y); Cmnty Wkr; School Musical; School Play; Nwsp Phtg; Nwsp Rptr; Yrbk Phtg; Rptr Lit Mag; Mgr(s); Vllybl; Ntl Merit Schol; NYS Rgnt Schlrshp 85; Browns U; Jrnlst.

BROWNE, THOMAS D; Msgr Mc Clancy HS; Elmhurst, NY; (Y); Church Yth Grp; Varsity Clb; Crs Cntry; Trk; Hon Roll; NHS; Prfct Atten Awd; Spanish NHS.

BROWNELL, MELESSA; Notre Dame HS; Batavia, NY; (S); 9/81; Pep Clb; Teachers Aide; Yrbk Stf; Trk; High Hon Roll; NHS; Advncd Keybrdng Hghst Avg Medal 84; Sec Sci.

BROWNELL, TODD A; Johnstown HS; Johnstown, NY; (Y); Varsity Clb; Nwsp Stf; Rep Stu Cncl; JV Bsbl; Capt Var Bsktbl; Im Ftbl; Var Tennis; High Hon Roll; Hon Roll; Rgnts Schlrshp 84-85; ST U Of New York; Physcs.

BROWNHILL, ROBERT; Onteora HS; Woodstock, NY; (S); 2/245; Quiz Bowl; Var L Tennis; NHS; Ntl Merit SF; Sal; Mid-Hudson Ath Leag Tnns Trnmnt Rnnr Up 84; Mgmnt Engrng.

BROWNING, EDWIN A; Scio Central School; Scio, NY; (S); Boy Scts; Spanish Clb; Rep Stu Cncl; Bsbl; Capt Tennis; High Hon Roll; NHS; Hugh O Brien Youth Ldrshp Awd 83; Ad Altare Dei Awd 82; Pre Med.

BROWNING, GENE; Tamarac HS; Johnsonville, NY; (Y); Intnl Clb; Math Tm; Political Wkr; Science Clb; Ski Clb; School Play; Yrbk Stf; Off Frsh Cls; Off Soph Cls; Pres Stu Cncl; Cornell U; Arch.

BROWNING, TINA; Maryvale SR HS; Depew, NY; (S); DECA; Hosp Aide; Spanish Clb; Chorus; Pres Frsh Cls; Pres Soph Cls; Rep Jr Cls; Rep Stu Cncl; Var Capt Pom Pon; Hon Roll.

BROWNSEY, MARTIN; Bishop Timon HS; Buffalo, NY; (S); Computer Clb; Nwsp Ed-Chief; Rep Frsh Cls; Rep Soph Cls; High Hon Roll; Frsh Spn Awd 83; Soph Chem Awd 84; NY ST Senate Achvt Awd 84.

BROZOST, TANYA; Vestal Central HS; Vestal, NY; (Y); Orch; JV Bsktbl; Var Crs Cntry; Im Socr; Var Trk; High Hon Roll; Regnts Schlrshp 85; Karate 82; NY ST U Geneseo; Elem Ed.

BRUBAKER, DINA; Watkins Glen HS; Watkins Glen, NY; (S); 6/126; Pep Clb; Stat Bsbl; JV Var Cheerleading; Score Keeper; French Hon Soc; High Hon Roll; Hon Roll; NHS; Bicknell U; Math.

BRUCCULERI, JOSEPHINE; St Johns Prep; Jackson Hts, NY; (Y); Busnss.

BRUCE, CARYN; Fayettevile Manlius HS; Fayetteville, NY; (Y); Church Yth Grp; Cmnty Wkr; Girl Scts; JCL; Pep Clb; Orch; Variety Show; Stat Bsbl; Var JV Socr; Hon Roll; Cum Laude Ntl Latin Exam 83; Hom Ec Awd 84; Physcl Ed Awd 84; Psychlgy.

BRUCE, KEVIN; Fort Ann Central HS; Fort Ann, NY; (Y); 3/60; French Clb; Math Clb; Math Tm; Vllybl; High Hon Roll; Hon Roll; NHS; Prfct Atten Awd; Rgnts Schlrshp 85; Hudson Vlly; Chem Engrng.

BRUCE, LISA; Saranac HS; Saranac, NY; (S); 35/128; Library Aide; Teachers Aide; Var Socr; Var Trk; High Hon Roll; Hon Roll; OLVA; Accntng.

BRUCE, PATRICIA L; Gloversville HS; Gloversville, NY; (Y); 41/265; Teachers Aide; Capt Color Guard; Mgr Jazz Band; Mrchg Band; School Musical; Swing Chorus; Yrbk Stf; Cheerleading; Hon Roll; St Schlr; Syracuse U Ny; Acctng.

BRUCE, SHAWN; Ft Ann Central HS; Ft Ann, NY; (Y); Boy Scts; French Clb; VP Jr Cls; Var JV Bsbl; Im Bsktbl; Var Socr; Phy Ed.

BRUCE, SHEILA; Saranac HS; Saranac, NY; (S); 36/128; Library Aide; Office Aide; Teachers Aide; Socr; Trk; High Hon Roll; Hon Roll; VT Coll; Csmtlgy.

BRUCE, VALERIE; Our Lady Of Victory HS; Thornwood, NY; (S); 2/139; Spanish Clb; Drill Tm; Nwsp Rptr; Yrbk Ed-Chief; Lit Mag; High Hon Roll; NHS; NEDT Awd; Spanish NHS; 1/2 Schlrshp OLV 82; 2nd Mrt Awd-Rank In Cls 84; Chem Awd 83; Communications.

BRUCHHAUSER, ANNE; H Frank Carey HS; Franklin Sq, NY; (Y); 35/222; VP Art Clb; Cmnty Wkr; Debate Tm; Drama Clb; Camera Clb; School Play; Yrbk Stf; Rep Jr Cls; Rep Sr Cls; Adelphi; Comm Art.

BRUCK, MICHAEL L; G W Hewlett HS; N Woodmere, NY; (Y); 59/277; Cmnty Wkr; Math Tm; Science Clb; Pres Soph Cls; Pres Jr Cls; VP Stu Cncl; Hon Roll; Mathletes; Math Clb; Temple Yth Grp; Stu Against Drunk Drvng Awd 84; Temple Bsktbl League 81-85; Regents Schlrshp Awd 85; SUNY Binghamton; Doctor.

BRUCKNER, MICHELLE; Islip HS; Islip, NY; (Y); Dance Clb; Drama Clb; Chorus; School Musical; Rep Frsh Cls; NHS; 3rd Yr Boces Cultrl Arts Ctr 83-86; Mus.

BRUEN, LEANNA; Cortland JR-SR HS; Cortland, NY; (Y); Pres Church Yth Grp; Ski Clb; Thesps; Concert Band; Jazz Band; School Musical; Lit Mag; Rep Stu Cncl; Swmmng; NHS; Tri-M Modrn Music Mstrs 84; Biochem.

BRUGGMAN, JENNIFER; Attica Central Schl; Attica, NY; (Y); Art Clb; Band; Chorus; Mrchg Band; School Musical; Stage Crew; Rep Stu Cncl; Stat Bsbl; Cheerleading; Hon Roll; Engr.

BRUGGMAN, THOMAS; Alexander Central Schl; Alexander, NY; (Y); Art Clb; Aud/Vis; Camera Clb; Cmnty Wkr; Drama Clb; English Clb; Science Clb; Band; Yrbk Phtg; Stu Cncl; Fire Prevntn Essy 1st Pl 84; Forest Range NY; Frst Rngr.

BRUHN, JUDETH E; Kingston HS; Kingston, NY; (Y); 40/600; Am Leg Aux Girls St; Church Yth Grp; 4-H; French Clb; Key Clb; Pep Clb; Ski Clb; Band; Concert Band; Mrchg Band; NYS Rgnts Schlrshp 85; NYSSMA Solo Comp 81-85; Clb Congrss 84; Union Coll; Pre Med.

BRUINSMA, SUSAN; Mercy HS; Rochester, NY; (Y); 99/200; Ski Clb; Hon Roll; Cert Merit Sibley Lindsey & Curr Schlstc Art Awd Exhibit 85; Rochester Bus Inst; Exec Secry.

BRUMBAUGH, IDA; Ft Plain Central HS; Ft Plain, NY; (Y); Church Yth Grp; Girl Scts; Teachers Aide; High Hon Roll; Hon Roll; NHS; Outstdng Hstry Stu 85; Outstdng Englsh Stu 85; Math Awd 83; Bus.

BRUMBAUGH, MARK; G Ray Bodley HS; Fulton, NY; (Y); 51/246; Drama Clb; Thesps; Jazz Band; Mrchg Band; Orch; School Musical; School Play; Stage Crew; Hon Roll; Band; William Quick Mem Awd 85; ST U Of NY; Tech Theatre.

BRUMME, PETER; Mahopac HS; Mahopac, NY; (Y); 49/425; Computer Clb; Science Clb; Nwsp Phtg; High Hon Roll; Hon Roll; NHS; Stu Of Mnth Sci 84; Sci.

BRUNER, GEOFFREY; Plattsburgh HS; Plattsburgh, NY; (Y); French Clb; Ski Clb; High Hon Roll; Arch.

BRUNER, GWENETH; North Rose-Wolcott HS; Wolcott, NY; (Y); Church Yth Grp; Ski Clb; Band; Chorus; Yrbk Ed-Chief; Socr; Swmmng; High Hon Roll; NHS; NY ST Regents Schlrshp 85; Muskingum Coll Presdntl Schlrshp 85; Muskingum Coll; Math.

BRUNETT, SANDRA; Bishop Kearney HS; Webster, NY; (Y); JA; Mrchg Band; Co-Capt Twrlr; High Hon Roll; Hon Roll; Cmnty Wkr; Ski Clb; Ind Engrng.

BRUNETTI, JACQUELINE; St Francis Prep; Uniondale, NY; (S); 130/694; Band; School Musical; Crs Cntry; Trk; Wt Lftg; NHS; Optimate Scty.

BRUNHOFER, KRISTEN; Bethlehem Central HS; Glenmont, NY; (Y); French Clb; Girl Scts; Model UN; Chorus; Swing Chorus; Rep Soph Cls; Rep Jr Cls; Vllybl; French Hon Soc; Hon Roll; Acad Achvt Awd Frnch; Serv Awd; Achvt Awd Music; Med.

BRUNKEN, MIKE; Smithtown High School East; St James, NY; (Y); Computer Clb; Var Socr; Elec Engrng.

BRUNNER, CAROLYN; Bishop Ludden HS; Camillus, NY; (S); Exploring; High Hon Roll; NHS; JV Bsktbl; JV Sftbl; H S Acadmc Schlrshp 82-86; Acadmc Achvt Awds Spnsh I & II, Engl, Earth Sci 82-84; Pre-Med.

BRUNNER, DON; Mercy HS; Middle Island, NY; (Y); Bsbl; Hon Roll; NEDT Awd.

BRUNNER, KIMBERLY; Rye HS; Rye, NY; (Y); 60/210; Cmnty Wkr; Political Wkr; Ski Clb; Orch; VP Frsh Cls; Pres Jr Cls; Rep Stu Cncl; JV Fld Hcky; Stat Ice Hcky; Var L Lcrss; Clemson U; Pre-Law.

BRUNNER, SCOTT; Bethpage HS; Bethpage, NY; (Y); Band; Concert Band; Mrchg Band; Bowling; Golf; Cit Awd; High Hon Roll; Hon Roll.

BRUNO, NANCY; Warwick Valley HS; Sugar Lf, NY; (Y); Art Clb; Computer Clb; Dance Clb; Drama Clb; FBLA; Ski Clb; Teachers Aide; School Play; Stage Crew; Cheerleading; Pace; Bus.

BRUNO III, THOMAS A; Curtis HS; Staten Island, NY; (Y); 59/328; Am Leg Boys St; ROTC; Science Clb; Ski Clb; Var L Golf; JV Ice Hcky; NY ST Regents Schlrshp Wnnr 84-85; Naval Acad Fndtn Aschlrshp Wnnr 85; Outstndg Cadet ; Njrotc 84-85; Ocngrphy.

BRUNS, LAURA DAWN; Holland Patent HS; Barneveld, NY; (Y); 15/155; Orch; School Play; Trs Frsh Cls; Trs Soph Cls; Trs Jr Cls; Rep Stu Cncl; JV Var Cheerleading; High Hon Roll; NHS; Church Yth Grp; Natl Chrldng Champ 84; Brigham Young U.

BRUNSON, CELESTE; Norman Thomas HS; Bronx, NY; (S); 89/671; Aud/Vis; Boys Clb Am; Dance Clb; DECA; Girl Scts; Nwsp Rptr; Rep Soph Cls; Hon Roll; NHS; Prfct Atten Awd.

BRUNSWICK, JIM; Caledonia-Mumford Central Schl; Caledonia, NY; (Y); 8/85; Am Leg Boys St; Church Yth Grp; VP Soph Cls; JV Var Bsktbl; Var Crs Cntry; JV Ftbl; Var Trk; High Hon Roll; NHS; Prfct Atten Awd.

BRUSH, DUANE; Walton Central HS; Walton, NY; (Y); 15/100; Computer Clb; Var Tennis; High Hon Roll; Hon Roll; Engr.

BRUST, ANN M; Chatham HS; Ghent, NY; (Y); Chorus; Church Choir; Yrbk Stf; JV Vllybl; Hon Roll; Rep Stu Cncl; Metrolgy.

BRUZIO, ROBERT; Christopher Columbus HS; New York, NY; (Y); Drama Clb; Chorus; School Musical; Cit Awd; Hnr Cert Excel Schlrshp Art 83; Cert Merit Italian 84.

BRUZZESE, JEAN-MARIE; John Dewey HS; Brooklyn, NY; (Y); JA; Spanish Clb; Nwsp Ed-Chief; Lit Mag; Var L Bowling; Im Sftbl; Hon Roll; Acad Of Fnc; Barauch Coll; Stkbrkr.

BRUZZESE, LARA; Saint John Villa Acad; Staten Is, NY; (Y); 18/125; Art Clb; Church Yth Grp; Cmnty Wkr; Yrbk Stf; Var Cheerleading; Sftbl; Tennis; High Hon Roll; Hon Roll; Sci Affr Awd 83; Eng Hnr Rl 84; Am Stu Hnr Rl 84; St Johns U.

BRUZZESE, STEPHAN J; S Wagner HS; Staten Island, NY; (Y); Am Leg Boys St; Art Clb; JA; Band; Stage Crew; Yrbk Phtg; Yrbk Stf; Lit Mag; Hon Roll.

BRYAN, CHEVARLO; Frt Hamilton HS; Brooklyn, NY; (Y); Science Clb; Nwsp Rptr; Nwsp Stf; Swmmng; Tennis; Trk; French Hon Soc; Hon Roll; Sci Fair Awd 84-85; Math, Engl, Art, Chem & Bio Awds 83-84; UCLA; Med.

BRYAN, DONNA M; Uniondale HS; Uniondale, NY; (Y); 4/480; Cmnty Wkr; Teachers Aide; Ed Nwsp Rptr; Var Cheerleading; Var Vllybl; High Hon Roll; VP NHS; Ntl Merit SF; FBLA; Amer Legn Cert Schl Awd 80; U PA; Bus Adm.

BRYAN, JAN; Victor Central HS; Victor, NY; (Y); 80/210; Ski Clb; School Musical; School Play; Stu Cncl; Cheerleading; Sftbl; High Hon Roll; Hon Roll; Fredonia ST U; Bus Adm.

BRYANT, ALICE; Bishop Ford HS; Brooklyn, NY; (Y); Var Sftbl; Hon Roll.

BRYANT, BERNADETTE; Amsterdam HS; Pattersonville, NY; (Y); 3/332; Trs 4-H; 4-H Awd; Hon Roll; NHS; Rensselear Polytechnic Inst Medal Math & Sci 84; Comp Sci.

BRYANT, CALVIN; Roosevelt JR SR HS; Roosevelt, NY; (Y); Chess Clb; FTA; Mathletes; Spanish Clb; Band; Concert Band; Mrchg Band; Nwsp Stf; Yrbk Stf; Bsbl; Med.

BRYANT, DIANA; Greene Central HS; Greene, NY; (Y); 23/110; Pres VP Church Yth Grp; Drama Clb; French Clb; Chorus; Trs Frsh Cls; Stu Cncl; Var Co-Capt Bsktbl; Sftbl; Tennis; Hon Roll; Broome CC; Cytotech.

BRYANT, JILL MEREDITH; Shenendehowa HS; Clifton Park, NY; (Y); Trs Art Clb; Church Yth Grp; Trk; High Hon Roll; Art.

BRYANT, LEANNE; Heidelberg American HS; Apo New York, NY; (Y); Church Yth Grp; Drama Clb; Model UN; Office Aide; Teachers Aide; Chorus; Church Choir; School Play; Nwsp Rptr; Yrbk Ed-Chief; Med Club Vp; Brdcstng Jrnlsm.

BRYANT, MARY; St Johns Prep; Astoria, NY; (Y); Chorus; Nwsp Stf; High Hon Roll; NHS; Pre-Law.

BRYANT, NOEL L; Stissing Mt JR SR HS; Ancramdale, NY; (Y); 13/78; Church Yth Grp; High Hon Roll; Hon Roll; Prfct Atten Awd; Outstndng Bus & BOCES Stu 85; Krissler Bus Inst; Accntng.

BRYANT, OTIS; Stony Brook College Prep; Central Islip, NY; (Y); 48/84; Civic Clb; Drama Clb; Chorus; School Play; Yrbk Stf; Rep Jr Cls; Im Bsbl; Var Crs Cntry; Im Swmmng; Var Trk; Dr Martin Luther King Scholar Awd 85; Chem.

BRYANT, PEGGY; Moriah Central HS; Pt Henry, NY; (Y); AFS; French Clb; GAA; Ski Clb; JV Bsktbl; JV Var Diving; Im Gym; Im Powder Puff Ftbl; Var Score Keeper; JV Var Sftbl; Bus.

BRYANT, SANDY; Northstar Christian Acad; Hilton, NY; (S); #3 In Class; Debate Tm; Speech Tm; Teachers Aide; Stat Bsktbl; Var Score Keeper; Var Socr; Soc Dist Am HS Stu 84-85; Amer-Christian Hnr Soc 83-84 & 84-85; Roberts Wesleyan Coll; Elem Ed.

BRYANT, VALENTINA; West Babylon HS; W Babylon, NY; (Y); 29/488; Varsity Clb; Yrbk Stf; Var Capt Bsktbl; Var Fld Hcky; JV Sftbl; Var Vllybl; Hon Roll; NHS; Sci.

BRYCELAND, SANDRA; Oneonta HS; Oneonta, NY; (Y); 125/190; Chrmn Ski Clb; Varsity Clb; L Color Guard; Off Sr Cls; Rep Stu Cncl; Var JV Cheerleading; JV Var Trk; Legal Secy.

BRYNE, TIMOTHY; Iona Preparatory HS; Yonkers, NY; (Y); Boy Scts; Chess Clb; Intnl Clb; Letterman Clb; Trs Library Aide; L Crs Cntry; Var L Trk; Eagle Scout 85; Extre Curricular Actvts Awd 85; Eng Hnrs 82-84; Intl Econ.

BRYNIARSKI, MICHELE A; Kenmore East SR HS; Tonawanda, NY; (Y); Dance Clb; Mrchg Band; High Hon Roll; Hon Roll; Canisius Coll; Psych.

BRYNSKI, ADRIENNE; Lewiston Porter HS; Youngstown, NY; (Y); 113/276; VP Church Yth Grp; Trs Drama Clb; Hosp Aide; Band; Color Guard; Mrchg Band; Orch; Mgr(s); Trk; Prfct Atten Awd 82-83; Niagara County CC; Nrs.

BRZEZINSKI, KATHRYN; North Collins Central Schl; N Collins, NY; (Y); 41/79; Church Yth Grp; Trs FTA; Library Aide; Science Clb; Chorus; Church Choir; Nwsp Stf; Yrbk Stf; Var Tennis; Hon Roll; Albert J Hammond Mem Scholar 85; Daemen Coll; Comp Sci.

BRZYTWA, STEVE; Wellsville HS; Wellsville, NY; (Y); Ski Clb; Bsbl; High Hon Roll; Engnrng.

BUBAR, PATRICIA; Maryvale SR HS; Cheektowaga, NY; (Y); 10/333; Pres Church Yth Grp; Drama Clb; Pres French Clb; Band; Chorus; Mrchg Band; Rep Stu Cncl; Hon Roll; NHS; Ntl Merit Ltr; Canisius Coll; Polt Sci.

BUBEL, STEPHANIE; Whitesboro SR HS; Utica, NY; (Y); 26/313; Exploring; Band; Stu Cncl; Powder Puff Ftbl; Hon Roll; NY ST U Geneseo.

BUBLE, ROGER J; Averill Park HS; Poestenkill, NY; (Y); High Hon Roll; Hon Roll; Hudson Vly CC; Autmtve Tech.

BUBOLO, DEAN; Pine Bush HS; Walden, NY; (Y); 13/281; Civic Clb; Computer Clb; Teachers Aide; Varsity Clb; Yrbk Phtg; Rep Frsh Cls; Rep Soph Cls; Rep Jr Cls; Trs Sr Cls; Rep Stu Cncl; Orange Cnty Wrstlg Champ 85; Notre Dame U; Bus Mgmt Adm.

BUCCI, MICHAEL; Union Endicott HS; Endicott, NY; (Y); Church Yth Grp; Varsity Clb; Im Bsktbl; JV L Ftbl; JV L Trk; Hon Roll; NHS; All Conf Trk-Mile Relay 85; Engrng.

BUCCI, MICHAEL J; Elmira Free Acad; Elmira, NY; (Y); 7/250; Ntl Merit Schol; High Hon Roll; Capt Socr; Rep Frsh Cls; Rep Soph Cls; Rep Jr Cls; Rep Sr Cls; Rep Stu Cncl; Am Leg Boys St; Church Yth Grp; Bucknell U; Econ.

BUCCI, PATRICIA; Henninger HS; Syracuse, NY; (Y); 24/300; Debate Tm; Hosp Aide; Spanish Clb; Yrbk Stf; VP Frsh Cls; Rep Soph Cls; Rep Jr Cls; Rep Stu Cncl; Stat Score Keeper; High Hon Roll; Inter Dsgn.

BUCHAL, BETSY; Copenhagen Central HS; Copenhagen, NY; (Y); 5/43; Am Leg Aux Girls St; Drama Clb; Library Aide; School Play; Yrbk Stf; Hon Roll; NHS; Am Hist Tchr.

BUCHANAN, JOE M; Catholic Central HS; Troy, NY; (Y); Cmnty Wkr; Math Clb; Band; Variety Show; High Hon Roll; Hon Roll; Sec Soph Cls; JV Bowling; JV Var Ftbl; JV Tennis; Rgnts Dplma 85; Excllnc Accntng I 84; Hudson Vlly CC; Accntng.

BUCHANAN, MICHAEL D; Portville Central HS; Shinglehouse, PA; (Y); 10/122; Concert Band; Mrchg Band; Nwsp Ed-Chief; Nwsp Phtg; Yrbk Phtg; Yrbk Sprt Ed; Capt Swmmng; Var Trk; High Hon Roll; NHS; Frsh Hnrs Schlrshp Edinboro U 85-86; USAF Sci Fair Awd 84; NY Press Assoc Photo Awd 84; Edinboro U PA; Bio.

BUCHANAN, SCOTT; Homec HS; Cortland, NY; (Y); 32/200; Dance Clb; 4-H; Band; Concert Band; Jazz Band; Mrchg Band; Orch; Symp Band; Crs Cntry; 4-H Awd; Morrisville; Comp Progrmr.

BUCHER, FRED; Pelham Memorial HS; Pelham, NY; (Y); AFS; Am Leg Boys St; Church Yth Grp; Drama Clb; Radio Clb; Ski Clb; Band; Mrchg Band; School Play; Nwsp Rptr; Bus Adm.

BUCHERATI, THERESA; Seaford HS; Seaford, NY; (Y); 22/248; Band; Concert Band; Mrchg Band; Stat Lcrss; Mgr(s); Score Keeper; Timer; Stat Wrstlng; High Hon Roll; NHS; Spanish I,II & III Awds 82-8; Fchemistry Awd 84; Trigonometry Awd 84; Adelphi U; Bus Adm.

BUCHLER, ROBERT; Union-Endicott HS; Owego, NY; (S); Band; Concert Band; Jazz Band; Mrchg Band; Pep Band; Symp Band; Hon Roll; SUNY; Elec Engrng.

BUCHWALDER, LISA; Rocky Point HS; Rocky Point, NY; (S); 5/189; French Clb; NFL; Chorus; Sec Frsh Cls; Sec Soph Cls; Var Crs Cntry; Var Trk; JV Vllybl; High Hon Roll; NHS; Psych.

BUCK, BRIAN C; Irondequoit HS; Rochester, NY; (Y); 57/350; Church Yth Grp; Band; Church Choir; Jazz Band; JV Bsbl; NHS; Ntl Merit Ltr; Mrchg Band; Orch; NY ST Rgnts Schlrshp; SUNY-POTSDAM; Physics.

BUCK, DEBRA; Le Roy HS; Leroy, NY; (Y); Spanish Clb; Hon Roll; Law.

BUCK, DIANE; Sachem North HS; Holbrook, NY; (Y); 41/1389; German Clb; Hosp Aide; Math Tm; Chorus; Yrbk Sprt Ed; Yrbk Stf; Jr NHS; 2nd Schl Sci Fair 84; Recog Long Island Sci Congress 84; Honorable Mentn German 83; Nursng.

BUCK, JARE A; Hilton Central HS; Hilton, NY; (Y); German Clb; Symp Band; Pres Frsh Cls; Off Sr Cls; Bsktbl; Socr; Sftbl; Cit Awd; NHS; Band; Hmecmng Queen & Overall Queen 84; Prom Ct 84; Sr Ball Ct 85; Aswego.

BUCK, JOHN R; Mc Quaid Jesuit HS; Rochester, NY; (Y); 1/183; Chorus; School Musical; School Play; Ed Nwsp Stf; Rep Jr Cls; Rep Sr Cls; Mgr Ftbl; Var JV Trk; High Hon Roll; Ntl Merit SF; Phi Beta Kappa; Elec Engrng.

BUCK, KAREN A; Bethpage HS; Bethpage, NY; (Y); 5/277; Mathletes; MMM; Concert Band; Jazz Band; Orch; School Musical; Var Tennis; NHS; Ntl Merit Ltr; Spanish Clb; Regents Schlrshp; Fredonia ST Fshmn Merit Awd 85-86; Boston U; Mus.

BUCK, KAREN E; Faith Heritage HS; Fulton, NY; (Y); 1/24; Church Yth Grp; Drama Clb; Teachers Aide; Chorus; Orch; School Play; Nwsp Ed-Chief; Nwsp Rptr; Capt Bsktbl; Capt Socr; Bus/Profsnl Womens Schlrshp 85; S W Paine Acad Schlrshp 85; Yth Symphny; Houghton Coll; Engl Ed.

BUCK, MARILYN; Tamarac HS; Troy, NY; (Y); Intnl Clb; Band; Chorus; Church Choir; Cobleskill; Hrtcltr.

BUCKHEIT, JULIE; John Burke Catholic HS; Greenwood Lake, NY; (Y); 1/140; Church Yth Grp; Yrbk Stf; Var Capt Bsktbl; Var L Socr; Var Capt Vllybl; High Hon Roll; VP NHS; Val; Oyaron Schlrshp 85; Englsh Awd 85; Burke Gold Seal 85; Hartwick Coll; Bus.

BUCKINGHAM, LANCE; Camden HS; Tabeig, NY; (Y); Pep Clb; Varsity Clb; Band; Jazz Band; Stu Cncl; Bsktbl; Crs Cntry; Trk; Hon Roll; Rotary Awd; Mech Engr.

BUCKINGHAM, MICHELLE L; Beaver River Central Schl; Croghan, NY; (Y); 17/90; Church Yth Grp; Church Yth Grp; French Clb; Nwsp Stf; Yrbk Stf; Cheerleading; Socr; Hon Roll; NHS; Paul Smiths Coll; Trvl.

BUCKLAND, SANDRA M; Mt St Mary Acad; N Tonawanda, NY; (Y); 32/113; Cmnty Wkr; Hosp Aide; Model UN; Red Cross Aide; Chorus; JV Var Bsktbl; Hon Roll; Computer Clb; French Clb; Library Aide; Alumnae Schlrshp Mt St Mary Acad 82; NEDT Scr Top 10 Pct Natly 83; MIP-BSKTBL 84-85; Phy Thrpy.

BUCKLEY, BRENDA; Commack High School North; Commack, NY; (Y); Hosp Aide; Math Tm; MMM; Spanish Clb; Acpl Chr; School Musical; Swing Chorus; Off Jr Cls; Var Trk; High Hon Roll; 2nd Pl Singing Comptn 85; Bus.

BUCKLEY, CORA A; Smithtown West HS; Smithtown, NY; (Y); Camp Fr Inc; Ski Clb; Thesps; Varsity Clb; Yrbk Rptr; Yrbk Stf; Capt Gym; Hon Roll; MVP Gymnastic Tm 82-85.

BUCKLEY, KIMBERLY; Freeport HS; Freeport, NY; (Y); Key Clb; Ski Clb; Lit Mag; Pres Soph Cls; Pres Jr Cls; Pres Sr Cls; JV Sftbl; Tennis; High Hon Roll; Hon Roll; Pol Sci.

BUCKLEY, SHANNON; Fayetteville-Manlius HS; Manlius, NY; (Y); Cmnty Wkr; JCL; Ski Clb; Rep Jr Cls; Rep Stu Cncl; Var Capt Diving; Var L Swmmng; Var Trk; Hon Roll; NHS; NYS Divng Champ 82-84; Swim Tm 82-84; NYS Swmmng Intrsctnls 82-84; Cornell U.

BUCKMASTER, DAVID; St Francis Prep; Jamaica, NY; (S); 64/693; Math Clb; Church Choir; Im Ftbl; Im Tennis; Hon Roll; NHS; Aerosp Engr.

BUCKNER, STEPHANNIE; Barker Central HS; Appleton, NY; (Y); AFS; Drama Clb; French Clb; Spanish Clb; Band; Concert Band; Orch; Stage Crew; Frgn Tchr.

BUCKOWSKI, PAUL; Saranac Lake HS; Saranac Lake, NY; (Y); Church Yth Grp; Stage Crew; Yrbk Phtg; Rep Stu Cncl; Bsktbl; Capt Lcrss; Capt Socr; Elks Awd; Red Ltr Awd Soccer 83-84; Dawn Sovak Art Schlrshp 84-85; Richard M & Lillian B Johnson Schlrshp; RIT; Photo.

BUCKSHAW, LISA; Sachem North HS; Holbrook, NY; (Y); 21/1383; Cmnty Wkr; VP Exploring; Pres VP Science Clb; Trs Spanish Clb; Chorus; Nwsp Rptr; Badmtn; Jr NHS; Hst NHS; Math Tm; 1st Pl Medal Sci Proj 83; Local Museum Interact Clb 84; Env Engrng.

BUCOLO, CATHLEEN; De Sales Catholic HS; Gasport, NY; (Y); 12/47; Varsity Clb; Y-Teens; Nwsp Stf; Var Socr; Var Capt Sftbl; Hon Roll; NHS; Acad All-Amer 85; Geneseo ST Coll; Math.

BUCZACKI, JAMES; Catholic Central HS; Latham, NY; (S); 5/203; Drama Clb; Math Clb; Red Cross Aide; Service Clb; School Musical; Yrbk Stf; High Hon Roll; VP NHS; Ntl Merit Ltr; Arch.

BUCZEK, TODD C; Chittenango HS; Chittenango, NY; (Y); Am Leg Boys St; Concert Band; Jazz Band; Bsbl; Bsktbl; Hon Roll; Jr NHS; Boy Scts; Spanish Clb; Band; Eagle Sct 86; Govt Intern 84-85; All Cnty Band 79-85; Lwyr.

BUCZYNSKI, BRENDA; Salamanca Central HS; Salamanca, NY; (Y); 35/125; Trs Church Yth Grp; DECA; Model UN; Red Cross Aide; Varsity Clb; Ed Nwsp Stf; Rep Sr Cls; JV Var Cheerleading; High Hon Roll; VP Sec Spanish NHS; Ladies Aux Cash Awd 85; Teachrs Assn Cash Awd 85; Spansh Hnr Soc Serv Awd 85; SUNY-BROCKPORT; Journlsm.

BUDD, BONNIE S; Vestal SR HS; Binghamton, NY; (Y); 115/450; Drama Clb; Hosp Aide; School Play; Im Bowling; NYS Rgnts Schlrshp 85; Robert-Packer Schl Nrsg; Nrsg.

BUDD, JEANETTE; Ellenville Central Schl; Spring Glen, NY; (Y); AFS; Drama Clb; School Musical; School Play; Yrbk Phtg; Stu Cncl; Var Tennis; Chorus; Mst Prmsng Awd Tnns 82-83; Mst Vlbl Plyr Awd Tnns 83-84; Broward County CC; Bus.

BUDD, JODI; Middletown HS; Middletown, NY; (Y); 62/380; Key Clb; Chorus; Hon Roll; Regents Schlrshp 84-85; Orange Cnty CC; Optmtry.

BUDD, MICHAEL; Hugh C Williams HS; Canton, NY; (Y); 20/100; Radio Clb; Varsity Clb; Lit Mag; JV Bsktbl; Coach Actv; JV Var Socr; JV Var Trk; Hon Roll; St Lawrence U; Engl.

BUDDINGTON, WINTON; Potsdam HS; Potsdam, NY; (S); 16/160; Pres AFS; Boy Scts; French Clb; Math Clb; Varsity Clb; Band; Yrbk Phtg; Ftbl; Trk; Vllybl; All Nrthrn Ftbl Off Tckl 84; Sprtsmnshp Var Bsktbl Chrldng 84; Suny Coll; Hist.

BUDELMANN, JON EDWARD; Manlins Pebble Hills HS; Manlins, NY; (Y); Yrbk Sprt Ed; Var Capt Trk; Dnfth Awd; High Hon Roll; NHS; Ntl Merit Ltr; Boy Scts; Office Aide; Congssmns Medal 85; Fay Mc Carthy Schlrshp 81-85; Class Of 38 Ctznshp Awd 84; Johns Hopkins U; Econ.

BUDENHAGEN, TRACEY; Charles C D Aminco HS; Albion, NY; (Y); Spanish Clb; Teachers Aide; Color Guard; Ntl Merit Schol; Gftd & Tlntd Studs 84-85; Police Sci.

BUDINE, KIM; Charlotte Valley Central HS; Davenport, NY; (S); GAA; Yrbk Rptr; Trs Jr Cls; Trs Sr Cls; Pres Stu Cncl; JV Var Bsktbl; VP Socr; VP Sftbl; Trs NHS; Plattsburgh Coll; Crmnl Jstc.

BUDINE, MICHELE; Chenango Forks HS; Binghamton, NY; (Y); Church Yth Grp; Teachers Aide; Stage Crew; Cheerleading; High Hon Roll; Hon Roll; NHS; Stdnt Yr Eng 83; Achvmnt Awds Math 83-85; Achvmnt Awd Chem 85; SUNY Binghamton Coll; Pre Med.

BUDRIES, LAUREN L; Mahopac HS; Carmel, NY; (Y); 29/390; Hosp Aide; Varsity Clb; Yrbk Stf; VP Socr; Vllybl; NHS; Hgh Hnrs Roll 79-80; James Madison U; Ntrtn.

BUDZINSKI, RANDY; Salamanca HS; Killbuck, NY; (S); 6/127; Am Leg Boys St; French Clb; Ski Clb; Varsity Clb; Var JV Bsbl; Var JV Bsktbl; French Hon Soc; High Hon Roll; NHS; Elec Engr.

BUDZISZEWSKI, LYNN; Alexander Central HS; Corfu, NY; (S); #3 In Class; FNA; Yrbk Stf; Rep Stu Cncl; Var Bsktbl; Hon Roll; Jr NHS; Lion Awd; NHS; Canisius Coll; Bus Mgmt.

BUECHLER, JEFFREY; Mohonasen SR HS; Schenectady, NY; (Y); Boy Scts; Chess Clb; Church Yth Grp; Debate Tm; Drama Clb; Nwsp Stf; Capt L Tennis; L Vllybl; The Kings Coll; Psych.

BUECHLER, SIMONE; Geneva HS; Geneva, NY; (S); 6/174; Model UN; Ski Clb; VP Spanish Clb; Band; Concert Band; Yrbk Rptr; Jr Cls; Var L Swmmng; NHS; Ntl Yth Salute 84; Dstngshd Amer HS Stu 84; Intl Rel.

BUECHLER, STEPHANIE; Geneva HS; Geneva, NY; (S); Model UN; Ski Clb; Spanish Clb; Band; Yrbk Stf; Swmmng; Cit Awd; High Hon Roll; Hon Roll; NHS; Intl Rltns.

BUEFORD, SEAN; Rice HS; New York, NY; (Y); Dance Clb; Yrbk Ed-Chief; Rep Jr Cls; Var Capt Bsbl; Im Bsktbl; U S Stdnt Cncl Awds 85; Pedtrcn.

BUEHL, SUSAN A; Westhill SR HS; Syracuse, NY; (Y); 9/167; 4-H; Lit Mag; 4-H Awd; Hon Roll; NHS; Ntl Merit Ltr; NYS Regents Schlrshp 85; Cornell U; Ag Engr.

BUENO, MAIDA; Cathedral HS; Ny, NY; (Y); 1/299; Intnl Clb; Library Aide; Chorus; Nwsp Stf; Hon Roll; Iona Coll Lang Cont 1st Pl 85; Scl Stds Awd 85; Relgn Awd 85; Spnsh Awd 84-85; Arch.

BUETTGENS, JEFFERY; Bishop Ludden HS; Marietta, NY; (S); NHS; Model UN; Im Bsbl; Var Ice Hcky; Var Lcrss; High Hon Roll; ST U Schlr Days Particpnt; Civil Engrng.

BUETTI, MARYANN; Moore Catholic HS; Staten Island, NY; (Y); 5/180; Math Clb; Speech Tm; Chorus; School Musical; School Play; Nwsp Stf; Lit Mag; NHS; Cath Dtrs Of Amer Sngwrtng Awd 84; Med.

BUFALINI, JOE; Guilderland Central HS; Schenectady, NY; (Y); Im Ski Clb; JV Ftbl; Var Lcrss; Var Wrstlng; Empire ST Games 85; 2nd Tm Star Subrbn Cncl 85; Weightlftng 83-85.

BUFFA, MELISSA; Frankfort Schuyler Central Schl; Frankfort, NY; (Y); FBLA; High Hon Roll; Regents Schlrshp 85; Mohawk Valley CC; Acctng.

BUFFA, ROSEMARY C; Earl L Vandermuelen HS; Mt Sinai, NY; (Y); 9/280; Trs French Clb; Sec Leo Clb; Mathletes; Concert Band; Mrchg Band; Nwsp Rptr; Yrbk Rptr; High Hon Roll; NHS; Holy Cross Coll; Psych.

BUFFAMONTI, ANNE MARIE; Williamsville East HS; Buffalo, NY; (Y); 200/300; FBLA; Latin Clb; Rep Stu Cncl; Var Bowling; Powder Puff Ftbl; JV Sftbl; Hon Roll; 3rd Pl Prlmntry Proc Tm FBLA 85; 1st Pl Bus Law FBLA 85; 1st Pl Bus Math I Dist Awd 84; Gdnce Cnslr.

BUGAJ, GREG M; Hamburg SR HS; Hamburg, NY; (Y); 5/387; Rep Frsh Cls; Rep Soph Cls; Rep Jr Cls; Rep Sr Cls; Rep Trs Stu Cncl; JV Bsbl; JV Var Ftbl; Im Socr; Hon Roll; NHS; Pre Med.

BUGEJA, ELLEN; Hauppauge HS; Hauppauge, NY; (Y); Church Yth Grp; Hosp Aide; Var Tennis; Var Capt Trk; Plattsburgh ST; Speech Pathlgy.

BUGGY, KEVIN; Archbishop Molloy HS; Middle Vlg, NY; (Y); 110/420; Boy Scts; Science Clb; Im Ftbl; Im Sftbl; Hofstra U; Busn.

BUGMAN, DAWN; Immaculata Acad; Hamburg, NY; (Y); Spanish Clb; Variety Show; Nwsp Rptr; VP Soph Cls; Hon Roll; Ldrshp Awd For VP Of Soph Clss 83; Erie CC; Exec Sec.

BUHL, ANN L; Saugerties SR HS; Saugerties, NY; (Y); 1/242; Am Leg Aux Girls St; Teachers Aide; Yrbk Ed-Chief; Yrbk Stf; High Hon Roll; NHS; Ntl Merit SF; Val; AP American Hstry; AP Englsh/Biolgy; Wesleyan U; Pre-Med.

BUHRER, DONELLE; Vernon-Verona-Sherrill HS; Vernon, NY; (Y); Church Yth Grp; FCA; Pep Clb; Varsity Clb; Yrbk Stf; Var L Crs Cntry; Var L Trk; High Hon Roll; All Conf CC 83; Grls ST Chmpshps CC 82-83; Fash Merch.

BUI, TON; Canisius HS; Buffalo, NY; (Y); Aud/Vis; Science Clb; High Hon Roll; Hon Roll; NHS; Regents Schrlshp 85; Minrty Schlstc Achvt Awds; ST U NY; Physics.

BUIER, ROSE M; Buffalo Seminary HS; Derby, NY; (Y); 7/36; Church Yth Grp; Girl Scts; Science Clb; Pres Orch; Yrbk Stf; Scrkpr Bsktbl; Mgr Fld Hcky; Mgr(s); Score Keeper; Mgr Sftbl; Wheaton Coll IL; Psych.

BUIST, HONG LOAN; La Guardia H S Of The Arts; Bronx, NY; (Y); 91/588; Cit Awd; Hon Roll; NHS; Ntl Merit SF; Library Aide; Chorus; Yrbk Stf; Stu Cncl; Vllybl; Regents Schlrshp Awd 85; Pace U; Bus Mgmt.

BUJNO, AMY; Walton Central Schl; Walton, NY; (Y); 6/104; Pres Church Yth Grp; Cmnty Wkr; Drama Clb; Key Clb; School Musical; Var Cheerleading; JV Fld Hcky; High Hon Roll; Hon Roll; Jr Schlrshp 84-85; Sci.

BUJOLD, MICHAEL; Martin Van Buren HS; Bayside, NY; (Y); 14/500; Office Aide; Varsity Clb; Band; Hon Roll; Prfct Atten Awd; Sci Hnr Scty 84-86; Hofstra; Accntng.

BUKOVSKY, ANNE MARIE; Sacred Heart HS; Yonkers, NY; (Y); JV Var Vllybl; Hon Roll; SEC Sci.

BUKOWIECKI, JOAN E; Bronx High School Of Science; Bronx, NY; (Y); Hon Roll; Jr NHS; Cngrssnl Medal Of Hnr 83; Fordham U; Comm.

BULAN, GLENN; Ellenville HS; Napanoch, NY; (Y); 1/90; Computer Clb; Band; Yrbk Phtg; Trs Sr Cls; Trs Stu Cncl; Tennis; High Hon Roll; Val; Renssealer Medl Math & Sci; Area All ST Band/Orch; Most Vlbl & Most Constnt Tennis.

BULGER, JUDY; Moore Catholic HS; Staten Island, NY; (Y); VP Intnl Clb; Yrbk Stf; Stat Var Bsktbl; JV Cheerleading; Var CAP; High Hon Roll; Hon Roll.

BULGER, MARCY E; Notre Dame Bishop Gibbons HS; Schenectady, NY; (Y); 18/104; Capt Hosp Aide; Nwsp Rptr; Nwsp Stf; Lit Mag; JV Vllybl; High Hon Roll; NHS; Regents Schlrshp 85; Comp Engrng.

BULKO, DAVID; Roy C Ketcham SR HS; Sparta, NJ; (Y); Band; Jazz Band; Symp Band; Ftbl; High Hon Roll; Jr NHS; NHS; Dixie Classics Jazz Comp Outstnndg Sax Section 85.

BULL, LISA; Amsterdam HS; Amsterdam, NY; (Y); 25/320; Band; Concert Band; Mrchg Band; Pep Band; Trk; Hon Roll; NHS; Fulton Montgomery CC; Nrs.

BULL, MARCIA; Far Rockaway HS; Hempstead, NY; (Y); 1/295; Cmnty Wkr; Math Tm; Scholastic Bowl; Teachers Aide; Yrbk Stf; High Hon Roll; NCTE Awd; NHS; Ntl Merit Schol; Val; Harvard U; Med.

BULL, MICHELLE; Bishop Grimes HS; Manlius, NY; (Y); Ski Clb; Ed Yrbk Stf; Im Var Swmmng; High Hon Roll; Hon Roll; NHS; Italn Hnr Socty; AP Socl Stds & Italn; Pre Dentl.

BULL, PATRICIA; Goshen Central HS; Goshen, NY; (Y); Church Yth Grp; Cmnty Wkr; Sec 4-H; Sec Frsh Cls; VP Soph Cls; VP Jr Cls; Pres Stu Cncl; Var L Socr; Var L Trk; Rep Senate Stdnt Assmbly 85; Chrmn Hungr Relf Cmmttee 85; Pol Sci.

BULL, SHARON; Akron HS; Akron, NY; (Y); Church Yth Grp; Cmnty Wkr; Drama Clb; French Clb; FHA; Teachers Aide; Chorus; Color Guard; School Musical; School Play; Indl Schlrshp 85; NY St Rgnts Nrsng Schlrshp 85; Salvation Army Schlrshp 85; Genosee Cmnty Coll; Nrsng.

BULLIS, JANINE; Port Jervis HS; Huguenot, NY; (Y); Key Clb; Spanish Clb; Varsity Clb; Score Keeper; Socr; Sftbl; Timer; NHS; Rotary Awd; Bus.

BULLOCK, AMY; West Genesee SR HS; Syracuse, NY; (Y); Sec Church Yth Grp; Key Clb; Library Aide; Color Guard; Mrchg Band; Orch; Off Jr Cls; Off Sr Cls; High Hon Roll; NHS; Prfct Atten 84; Med.

BULLOCK, GLORIA; Cicero North Syracuse HS; N Syracuse, NY; (S); 21/622; Sec Trs Church Yth Grp; Band; Concert Band; Mrchg Band; School Musical; Symp Band; High Hon Roll; Hon Roll; Voice Dem Awd; All Cnty Concert Band 84; Cert Mrt High Avg Frnch 83; Cornell U; Bio.

BULLOCK, KIMBERLY; Dominican Commercial HS; Jamaica, NY; (Y); Political Wkr; Nwsp Ed-Chief; Pres Stu Cncl; Church Yth Grp; Nwsp Rptr; Rep Frsh Cls; Rep Soph Cls; Hon Roll; Goldn Poets Awd 85; Wrld Of Poetry 85; Natl Ldrshp Trng Ctr Delgt 85; Natl Assoc Sec Schl Prncpls; Commctns.

BULSON, DAVID; Berlin Central HS; Grafton, NY; (S); 6/111; Church Yth Grp; 4-H; Ski Clb; Trs Frsh Cls; High Hon Roll; Stu Transitional Educ Pgm STEP 84.

BULTERMAN, DARA ANNE; Thousand Islands HS; Clayton, NY; (Y); AFS; Art Clb; Church Yth Grp; GAA; Varsity Clb; School Play; Yrbk Ed-Chief; Stu Cncl; Socr; Hon Roll; Cert Varden Smmr Wrkshp For Yrbk Eds 85; Hgh Sls Rep 83-85; V Ltr Vlybl, Sftbl, Glf & Sccr 83-86; JCC; Trvl & Toursm.

BUMBULSKY, DENISE; Cohoes HS; Cohoes, NY; (Y); Exploring; Im Cheerleading; Hon Roll; Prfct Atten Awd; Acctng.

BUNCH, TREMAINE; Cathedral HS; Bronx, NY; (Y); Hosp Aide; Office Aide; Nwsp Rptr; Nwsp Stf; Hon Roll; Cert Of Awds For Arbutus 82-83; Stoney Brook U; Doctor.

BUNDRICK, JEANNE P; John Jay SR HS; South Salem, NY; (Y); Chorus; School Play; Stage Crew; Variety Show; High Hon Roll; Hon Roll; Ntl Merit Schol; Temple U; Radio.

BUNDY, KELLY; Liverpool HS; Liverpool, NY; (S); 165/792; AFS; Art Clb; Political Wkr; Red Cross Aide; Spanish Clb; School Musical; Rep Stu Cncl; L Var Tennis; Hon Roll; GAA; Outstndng Achvt Awd-Am Hist 84; American U; Intl Rel.

BUNDY, TARA; Seton Catholic Central HS; Vestal, NY; (Y); Church Yth Grp; Science Clb; Ski Clb; Off Stu Cncl; JV Socr; Physcl Thrpy.

BUNKE, DORIS; Elmira Christian Acd; Elmira, NY; (Y); 1/5; Church Yth Grp; Chorus; Yrbk Stf; Sec Frsh Cls; Pres Jr Cls; Pres Sr Cls; Var L Socr; DAR Awd; Hon Roll; Prfct Atten Awd; Corning CC; Drftg.

BUNT, WRAY C; Johnson City HS; Johnson City, NY; (Y); Church Yth Grp; Hon Roll; NY St Regents Schlrshp 85; Schlstc Exc Awd 82-85; Baptist Bible; Arch.

BUNTING, VALISSA L; Woodlands HS; White Plains, NY; (Y); 39/180; FBLA; Spanish Clb; Var L Crs Cntry; Var Mgr(s); Var Capt Socr; Var L Trk; JV Vllybl; Hon Roll; NHS; Ntl Merit SF; Pfct Att 80-81; Girl Scts 79-80; Mth Tm 80-81; Pre-Med.

BUONAFEDE, JENNIFER; Bishop Ford Central Catholic HS; Brooklyn, NY; (Y); 128/470; Church Yth Grp; Computer Clb; GAA; Office Aide; Stu Cncl; Var Sftbl; Hon Roll; St Francis Coll; Finc.

BUONAGURIO, JOSEPH; Connetquot Central School; Ronkonkoma, NY; (Y); 91/750; Boy Scts; Church Yth Grp; Teachers Aide; Chorus; Nwsp Sprt Ed; Off Frsh Cls; Off Soph Cls; Off Jr Cls; Stu Cncl; Bsktbl; Psych.

BUONAIUTO, CINDY A; West Islip HS; W Islip, NY; (Y); Cmnty Wkr; Drama Clb; Spanish Clb; Nwsp Rptr; Yrbk Stf; Lit Mag; High Hon Roll; VP Jr NHS; NHS; Ntl Merit Ltr; Biolgcl Sci.

BUONINFANTE, TERESA; Cardinal Spellman HS; Yonkers, NY; (Y); Hon Roll.

BUONO, DENISE; Bishop Maginn HS; Rensselaer, NY; (Y); Data Procsng.

BUONO, PATRICK; Saugerties HS; Saugerties, NY; (S); Sec Boy Scts; German Clb; Math Tm; Quiz Bowl; Rep Soph Cls; Trs Jr Cls; Trs Stu Cncl; High Hon Roll; Pres Schlr; German Clb; CYO County & Parish Pres 81-85; Med Doctr.

BUONO, VALERIE; Attica Central HS; Attica, NY; (S); Concert Band; Mrchg Band; Rep Stu Cncl; Var Swmmng; Hon Roll; Natl Merit Sci Awd 84; Phys Ther.

BUONTEMPO, PATRICIA; Herbert H Lehman HS; Bronx, NY; (Y); 54/473; Orch; Yrbk Stf; Lit Mag; High Hon Roll; Cmmnctns.

BUPP, MICHAEL; Union Endicott HS; Endwell, NY; (Y); Var L Tennis; Aerontcl Engrng.

BURACK, LAUREN; Riverdale Country Schl; Harrison, NY; (Y); Cmnty Wkr; Key Clb; Math Tm; Nwsp Stf; Var JV Fld Hcky; Var Lcrss; Var Tennis; Var Trk; Hon Roll; Lttr Of Cmmndtn 84-85; Math.

BURAK, MELISSA; Sacred Heart Acad; Lynbrook, NY; (S); 6/186; Church Yth Grp; Speech Tm; Church Choir; Yrbk Bus Mgr; Hon Roll; Iona College; Comp Sci.

BURCH, BARBARA; Haverling Central HS; Bath, NY; (S); 29/147; AFS; FTA; Girl Scts; Math Clb; Teachers Aide; Color Guard; Flag Corp; Yrbk Stf; Stu Cncl; High Hon Roll; Acctng.

BURCH, DAVID M; Martin Van Buren HS; Queens Village, NY; (Y); 32/579; Computer Clb; Math Clb; Math Tm; Science Clb; School Musical; Nwsp Stf; Tennis; Hon Roll; NYS Bar Assoc Mock Trl Comptn-Chmpnshp Stu 85; Martin Van Buren St Chmpns; MD.

BURCH, TIMOTHY J; Hudson Falls Central HS; Hudson Falls, NY; (Y); French Clb; Rep Stu Cncl; French Hon Soc; Hon Roll; NHS; NYS Regnts, St Lawrence U Schlrshps 85; Ciba-Geigy Sci Awd 85; St Lawrence U; Premed.

BURCHILL, JOE; West Genesee SR HS; Syracuse, NY; (Y); Aud/Vis; Boy Scts; Church Yth Grp; German Clb; JV Var Ftbl; JV Lcrss; Capt JV Wrstlng; Tchng.

BURCZYNSKI, MARIA; Lancaster HS; Lancaster, NY; (Y); DECA; Pep Clb; Mrchg Band; Fld Hcky; Trk; Deca VP 84-85; 1st Pl Restrnt Mktng Rgnl/ST Wnnr 84-85; Deca Stu Yr 84-85; Buffalo ST Coll; Bus Adm.

BURD, KIMBERLY; Henninger HS; Syracuse, NY; (Y); Cosmtlgst.

BURDASH, ANN; Susquehanna Valley HS; Binghamton, NY; (Y); 10/200; Dance Clb; Library Aide; Mathletes; Spanish Clb; Orch; Fld Hcky; High Hon Roll; Jr NHS; NHS; Spanish NHS; Fash Mgmt.

BURDASH, PETER; Highland HS; Highland, NY; (Y); 8/120; Band; Pres Frsh Cls; Pres Soph Cls; Rep Stu Cncl; JV Bsbl; JV Socr; Var Capt Vllybl; Trs NHS; Spanish NHS; Bio Lab Awd 84; Physics.

BURDICK, BRENDA; John F Kennedy HS; Utica, NY; (Y); 13/145; Exploring; Mathletes; Chorus; Bsktbl; Rotary Awd; Rotary Intl 85-86; Clarkson; Electcl Engr.

BURDICK, MICHELLE; Cicero-North Syracuse HS; Liverpool, NY; (S); 70/711; Art Clb; Chess Clb; Church Yth Grp; Cmnty Wkr; German Clb; Library Aide; Math Clb; Office Aide; Red Cross Aide; Science Clb; Completion Of Army Basic Training Awd 84; Law.

BURDICK, PETER; Hudson HS; Hudson, NY; (Y); 16/160; Ski Clb; Varsity Clb; Rep Stu Cncl; Var L Bsbl; Var L Ftbl; High Hon Roll; Hon Roll; Annapolis; Engr.

BURDO, BRIDGETTE; Cicero North Syracuse HS; Clay, NY; (S); 58/622; Office Aide; Teachers Aide; Nursing.

BUREK, JILL; Forestville Central HS; Forestville, NY; (Y); 8/61; Church Yth Grp; Radio Clb; Ski Clb; Spanish Clb; Varsity Clb; Pres Jr Cls; Rep Stu Cncl; Var Cheerleading; Hon Roll; NHS; NY ST Rgnts Scholar 85; Hugh O Brien Ldrshp Awd 83; JCC Emphsis Excllnce Awd 84; UNY Geneso; Intl Bus.

BUREK, MICHAEL; Cicero-North Syracuse HS; Clay, NY; (S); 26/711; Ski Clb; JV Bsbl; Var Bsktbl; High Hon Roll; NHS; Natl Hist Govt Awd; Dir Distinguished Young Ldrshp; Pre-Med.

BUREK, PAUL; Attica HS; Cowlesville, NY; (Y); 13/155; Computer Clb; Math Tm; Varsity Clb; Var L Bsbl; Var L Socr; Hon Roll; Math.

BURFORD, DARNELL; Mount Vernon HS; Mt Vernon, NY; (Y); Boy Scts; Church Yth Grp; Aviatn.

BURFORD, JASON L; Attica SR HS; Cowlesville, NY; (Y); Concert Band; Mrchg Band; NHS; Ntl Merit SF.

BURG, PATRICIA; Grand Island HS; Grand Island, NY; (Y); Pres Trs Art Clb; Mathletes; Quiz Bowl; Stage Crew; Yrbk Stf; Hon Roll; NHS; Awds Erie Cnty Fair Expo; Acadmc Achvt & Outstndg Art Awds; Partcpt WNY High Art Exhbt; Art.

BURG, REBECCA; Grand Island HS; Grand Is, NY; (Y); 7/270; Art Clb; Math Tm; Concert Band; High Hon Roll; JP Sousa Awd; NHS; Ntl Merit Ltr; Mathletes; Quiz Bowl; Band; 85 Sr Math Awd; Pres Acadmc Ftns Awd; Pres Hnrs Schlrshp; Karr Parker Engrrng Schlrshp; State U Of NY; Engr.

BURG, STEVEN; Onteora Central HS; Woodstock, NY; (S); Boy Scts; Drama Clb; Capt Quiz Bowl; Jazz Band; Nwsp Stf; VP Frsh Cls; VP Soph Cls; Stu Cncl; Dnfth Awd; NHS.

BURGER, ALFRED; Bishop Ford HS; Brooklyn, NY; (Y); Art Clb; Math Clb; ROTC; School Play; Bowling; Fld Hcky; Sftbl; Wt Lftg; High Hon Roll; Hon Roll; Math League Awd 84-85; 1st Pl Art Cls 85; Fshn Inst & Tech; Cmrcl Art.

BURGER, MELISSA; Mc Kinley HS; Buffalo, NY; (Y); Church Yth Grp; Trs FFA; Pres Sr Cls; Stu Cncl; High Hon Roll; NHS; Prfct Atten Awd; 2nd In ST Flouriclt Cntst, 6th In Indiv 84; 1st In ST Flouriclt Cntst 85; Alfred ST Coll; Fluoriclt Mer.

BURGER, RACHEL A; Hamburg HS; Hamburg, NY; (Y); 25/390; Church Yth Grp; Band; Chorus; Drm Mjr(t); Jazz Band; Orch; School Musical; Stat JV Socr; NHS; Church Choir; Music.

BURGER, RICHARD; St Marys Boys Manhasse; Glen Head, NY; (S); 13/132; Boy Scts; Nwsp Rptr; NHS; Order Arrow Boy Scouts 83; Nassau CC; Librl Arts.

BURGER, SHERI; Connetquot HS; Oakdale, NY; (S); 6/723; Pres Art Clb; Cmnty Wkr; VP Spanish Clb; VP Temple Yth Grp; High Hon Roll; Jr NHS; NHS; Ntl Merit Ltr; Simons Fellwshp U Of NY Stony Brook 84; Psych.

BURGER, WENDY; Roy C Ketcham SR HS; Poughkeepsie, NY; (Y); Church Yth Grp; Computer Clb; Girl Scts; Math Clb; Church Choir; High Hon Roll; Hon Roll; Jr NHS; NHS; Natl Sci Merit Awd 84; Optometry.

BURGESS, BRIAN; Union Springs Acad; Elmira, NY; (Y); Varsity Clb; Chorus; Church Choir; Pres Stu Cncl; Var Bsktbl; Im Sftbl; Hon Roll; Atlantic Union Coll Scholar 84-85; U S Bus Awd Wnnr 84-85; Atlantic Union Coll; Bus.

BURGESS, DANIEL A; Lockport SR HS; Lockport, NY; (Y); Jazz Band; Mrchg Band; School Musical; School Play; Rep School Play; Rep Stu Cncl; JP Sousa Awd; Music.

BURGESS, MAUREEN; Roy C Ketcham HS; Wappingers Fls, NY; (Y); Color Guard; Yrbk Stf; Lit Mag; Stu Cncl; High Hon Roll; NHS; Cert Of Awd Excllnc Amer Stdies II 85; Pre-Law.

BURGGRAF, JAMES P; Bay Shore HS; Bay Shore, NY; (Y); 7/376; Math Clb; Math Tm; JV Bsbl; NHS; Alfred U; Ceramic Engrng.

BURGHART, KELLEY; Unatago JR-SR HS; Otego, NY; (Y); AFS; Library Aide; Rochester Inst Tech; Secry.

BURGLER, CRAIG A; Cardinal OHARA HS; N Tonawanda, NY; (S); Spanish Clb; JV Bsbl; Bowling; Var Wrstlng; High Hon Roll; Engrng.

BURGOS, BIENVENIDO; Thomas A Edison Vo Tech; Brooklyn, NY; (Y); 4/419; Pres Sr Cls; Rep Stu Cncl; Var Capt Gym; NHS; Regents Scholar 85; Natl Hispanic Scholar Semi-Fin 85; City Coll; Chem Engrng.

BURGOS, BLANCA; Aviation HS; Bronx, NY; (Y); 21/417; Debate Tm; Drama Clb; VP JA; Library Aide; Math Tm; Political Wkr; Ski Clb; Color Guard; Drill Tm; Cooper Union; Engr.

BURGOS, LAURA; Spring Valley HS; Spring Valley, NY; (Y); Drama Clb; Library Aide; Chorus; Catherin Gibbs; Exec Sec.

BURGOS, MERCEDES I; Islip HS; Islip, NY; (Y); Hon Roll; Comp Sci.

BURGY, JOHN T; Camden Central HS; Camden, NY; (Y); Pep Clb; Varsity Clb; JV Var Bowling; Rotry Clb Awd High Grades 85; Bus Mgmt.

BURICH, JAMEE; Cornwall HS; Cornwall, NY; (Y); Ski Clb; Y-Teens; Yrbk Stf; Sec Frsh Cls; JV Bsktbl; Stat Ftbl; Var Powder Puff Ftbl; JV Var Sftbl; Hon Roll.

BURICH, LUCY; St Francis Prep; Elmhurst, NY; (S); 23/693; Church Yth Grp; Dance Clb; Pres Frsh Cls; Rep Soph Cls; VP Jr Cls; High Hon Roll; NHS; Acctng.

BURK, ELIZABETH; Williamsville East HS; Buffalo, NY; (Y); 147/299; Var L Bowling; Var L Sftbl; JV Vllybl; Hon Roll; Prfct Atten Awd; Secndry Educ.

BURKARD, MELISSA; Brighton HS; Rochester, NY; (Y); JA; Varsity Clb; Band; Jazz Band; JV Stat Bsktbl; JV Var Sftbl; JV Var Tennis; JV Vllybl; Hon Roll; Compeer Vol 1 Yr Awd 85; Fnlst Tnns Tourn, Club Midtown 85; Lib Arts.

BURKART, KIMBERLY; Bethlehem Central HS; Delmar, NY; (Y); Church Yth Grp; GAA; Ski Clb; Concert Band; Jazz Band; JV Var Sftbl; JV Tennis; High Hon Roll; NHS; NYJMA 85; Psych.

BURKART, MARY L; Herbert H Lehman HS; Bronx, NY; (Y); 3/444; Jazz Band; Orch; Lit Mag; Var L Tennis; Hon Roll; NHS; St Johns U; Journalism.

BURKE, ANN; Hornell HS; Hornell, NY; (Y); Latin Clb; Math Clb; Ski Clb; Pres Frsh Cls; Pres Jr Cls; Rep Stu Cncl; Var L Bsktbl; Stat Ftbl; Gov Hon Prg Awd; High Hon Roll; Pre Law.

BURKE, BRIAN; Byron-Bergen Central Schl; Bergen, NY; (Y); Library Aide; Model UN; Band; Concert Band; Mrchg Band; Stage Crew; Pres Jr Cls; Var Bsktbl; Var Socr; Hon Roll; Comp Sci.

BURKE, BRIGID; Stella Maris HS; Breezy Point, NY; (Y); Debate Tm; French Clb; Math Tm; NFL; Nwsp Rptr; Pres Stu Cncl; Cheerleading.

BURKE, CATHLEEN P; H Frank Carey HS; Garden City So, NY; (Y); 30/222; Cmnty Wkr; Pres Frsh Cls; Off Soph Cls; Off Jr Cls; Sec Stu Cncl; Var L Tennis; High Hon Roll; Jr NHS; Im Sftbl; Im Vllybl; HS Dmstc Stu Exchng Pgm 84-85; Stu Rep Elgblty Cmmtte 84-85; Pres Stu Cncl Upcmng Yr 85-86; Bus.

BURKE, CHARLES T; Canastota HS; Canastota, NY; (Y); 1/132; JV Socr; Var Tennis; JV Wrstlng; High Hon Roll; Lion Awd; NHS; Val; Schlrshp Physcs Chem, Math 81-85; Tp 4 Cls, Hghst Avg Soc Studs 81-85; Whippl Schlrshp SUNY 84-85; SUNY Morrisvl; Plastcs Engrng.

BURKE, CHARLES T; Notre Dame HS; Elmira, NY; (Y); 27/88; Ski Clb; Rep Jr Cls; Pres Stu Cncl; Stat Bsktbl; JV Var Ftbl; Hon Roll; People To People Ambssdr 85; Chem.

BURKE, CHRISTINA M; Ballston Spa HS; Ballston Spa, NY; (Y); 1/250; Trs Varsity Clb; School Musical; Stage Crew; Var Crs Cntry; Capt Swmmng; Capt Var Trk; High Hon Roll; NHS; Val; Outstndng Acad & Athl 84; Regents Schlrshp Wnnr 85; Bio & Chem Awd 83 & 84; Colgate U; Psych.

BURKE, CHRISTINE M; Acad Holy Names; Delmar, NY; (Y); Church Yth Grp; Dance Clb; Drama Clb; School Play; Rep Frsh Cls; VP Jr Cls; Var Bsktbl; JV Socr; High Hon Roll; Pres Schlr; Physcl Sci, Thelgy, Bio & Englsh Awd 81-83; Englsh, Latin, Chem Awd 83-84; Gen Excllnc Awd; Scranton U PA; Physcl Thrpy.

BURKE, EILEEN A; Sacred Heart Acad; Massapequa, NY; (Y); 25/189; VP FNA; Hosp Aide; Stage Crew; Yrbk Bus Mgr; Ed Yrbk Ed-Chief; JV Var Bsktbl; Coach Actv; Var Capt Sftbl; NHS; Villanova U; Nursing.

BURKE, GARY; Webutuck Central Schl; Millerton, NY; (Y); Boy Scts; Nwsp Stf; Var Capt Bsbl; JV Var Bsktbl; JV Var Socr; JV Vllybl; Comp Sci.

BURKE, JENA T; Peekskill HS; Peekskill, NY; (Y); 9/168; Aud/Vis; French Clb; Yrbk Stf; Cheerleading; Score Keeper; Tennis; High Hon Roll; NHS; Rotary Awd; Fordham U; Comm.

BURKE, JENNIFER; Saratoga Springs HS; Greenfield Ctr, NY; (Y); 42/473; Church Yth Grp; Drama Clb; Trs GAA; Hosp Aide; Red Cross Aide; Ski Clb; Chorus; Orch; Yrbk Stf; Coach Actv; Rcgntn Dinner Top 10 Pct Cls 84-85; Natl Frnch Cntst Awd 82-85; Var Mus Ltr & Pin 84-85; Nrsng.

BURKE, JOSEPH; Lindenhurst HS; Lindenhurst, NY; (Y); Ski Clb; Varsity Clb; Band; Var Ftbl; JV Lcrss; Var Trk; Var Wt Lftg; Engrng.

BURKE, KATHLEEN; Kenmore East HS; Tonawanda, NY; (Y); 67/330; Hst Church Yth Grp; Drama Clb; Pres 4-H; Teachers Aide; School Musical; Nwsp Rptr; JV Sftbl; JV Tennis; Var L Trk; NHS; Coach Spec Olympcs 85; Millard Fillmore Hosp Volntr 84; Irene Pearson Mem Awd 85; Buffalo ST Coll; Cmmnctn.

BURKE, KEVIN; Bethpage HS; Bethpage, NY; (Y); Boy Scts; Var Capt Crs Cntry; Var Capt Trk; High Hon Roll; Hon Roll; Outstndng Athltc Awd Crs Cntry,Trk 84-85; Natl Hist Olympd Awd Of Merit 84-85; Tchr Of Hist/Engl.

BURKE, KIMBERLY L; Hempstead HS; Hempstead, NY; (Y); 11/333; VP Frsh Cls; VP Jr Cls; VP Sr Cls; Hon Roll; NHS; L I Sci Congr Awd; Comp Sci.

BURKE, KRISTEN; Rocky Point HS; Rocky Point, NY; (S); 4/195; Girl Scts; Hosp Aide; Yrbk Stf; Hon Roll; NHS; Trustee Achvt Awd 85; Adelphi U; Hlth Fld.

BURKE, LORI; Deer Park HS; N Babylon, NY; (Y); 201/422; FBLA; Tinermedte Typng Awd 84-85; Bus.

BURKE, MARTIN; Voorheesville Central HS; Voorheesville, NY; (Y); Church Yth Grp; Intnl Clb; Band; Concert Band; Symp Band; JV Bsbl; JV Bsktbl; Var L Golf; Var L Trk; High Hon Roll; Hnr Roll 82-86; Vrsty Ltr Swmmng 84; Typng Awd 84; Elec Engr.

BURKE, MARY; Albertus Magnus HS; Spring Vly, NY; (Y); 84/185; Spanish Clb; Hon Roll; Mt St Vincent Coll; Comm.

BURKE, MAURITA B; Notre Dame HS; Elmira, NY; (Y); Cmnty Wkr; Key Clb; Latin Clb; Var JV Bsktbl; L Sftbl; Var L Vllybl; Hon Roll; Regents Nrsng NY ST Schlrshp 85; Suny Alfred; Nrsng.

BURKE, MICAHEL; Sachem HS; Lk Grove, NY; (Y); 132/1309; Science Clb; Ski Clb; Bio.

BURKE, ROBERT; Mohonasen SR HS; Schenectady, NY; (Y); Boy Scts; Exploring; Key Clb; Im JV Bsbl; Im JV Socr; Var Vllybl; High Hon Roll; Hon Roll; Vrsty Sprts Ltr & Pins 84-85; Buffalo U SUNY; Archit.

BURKE, SHAUN; Hillcrest HS; Hollis, NY; (Y); Anml Behvr.

BURKE, SUZANNE E; Schroon Lake Central HS; Schroon Lake, NY; (S); 3/24; French Clb; Model UN; Orch; School Musical; School Play; Pres Frsh Cls; Stu Cncl; Var Cheerleading; High Hon Roll; VP NHS; Hnr Swtr 84; Rgnts Schlrshp Wnnr 85; Daemen Coll; Phy Thrpy.

BURKE, THOMAS; Mt St Michael HS; Yonkers, NY; (S); 29/308; Hon Roll; Rec 2nd Hnrs 83-85; Fordham U; Lib Arts.

BURKE, TIMOTHY; Glens Falls SR HS; Glens Falls, NY; (Y); 45/227; Am Leg Boys St; Key Clb; Var Diving; High Hon Roll; Hon Roll; NYS Swm Coach Assoc Smmr Of Yr 85; Bus Mngmnt.

BURKE, WILLIAM J; Babylon SR HS; Babylon, NY; (Y); Am Leg Boys St; Nwsp Rptr; Rep Jr Cls; VP Sr Cls; Rep Stu Cncl; Var Bsbl; Var Capt Bsktbl; Var Capt Socr; High Hon Roll; NHS; All Lg Socr 85; Princpls Hgh Hnrs List 83-85; Bus.

BURKER, LESLIE; Lowville Academy & Central Schl; Lowville, NY; (Y); French Clb; GAA; Mrchg Band; Orch; School Play; Nwsp Rptr; Nwsp Stf; Var L Socr; Hon Roll; Sec 4-H; Jrnlsm.

BURKHARDT, DIANE; Sachem HS; Farmingville, NY; (Y); 151/1428; German Clb; Pres GAA; Nwsp Rptr; Rep Jr Cls; Jr NHS; JV Capt Fld Hcky; Var Sftbl; Var Trk; Grls Athltc Assn Schlrshp 82-85; Gld Key Wnnr; Syracuse U; Engl.

BURKHARDT, WILLIAM A; Friends Acad; Old Brookville, NY; (Y); Cmnty Wkr; Computer Clb; Ski Clb; Variety Show; Yrbk Stf; Var L Ftbl; Var L Lcrss; Ntl Merit Ltr; NYS Rgnts Schlrshp 85; Colgate U; Comp Sci.

BURKHART, KAREN M; Charles D Baker HS; Baldwinsville, NY; (Y); 69/451; Art Clb; Key Clb; VP Jr Cls; VP Sr Cls; Sec Stu Cncl; JV Var Bsktbl; JV Sftbl; Cit Awd; Jr NHS; NHS; DAR Good Ctznshp Awd 84-85; SUNY Cblskl; Bus Adm.

BURKHART, PAUL; Churchville Chili SR HS; North Chili, NY; (Y); 85/335; Boy Scts; Church Yth Grp; Ski Clb; Varsity Clb; JV Bsbl; Im Bowling; JV Crs Cntry; Var Trk; Im Vllybl; Im Wt Lftg; Navy; Nuclr Powr.

BURKLAND, LESLIE J; Harverling Central HS; Bath, NY; (Y); 35/154; French Clb; Sec Latin Clb; Math Clb; Color Guard; Mrchg Band; School Musical; School Play; Nwsp Rptr; Nwsp Stf; Yrbk Stf; NYS Nrsg Schlrshp.

BURKOWSKE, JESSICA; Stissing Mountain JR-SR HS; Pine Plains, NY; (Y); 4-H; Yrbk Stf; Sec Frsh Cls; Sec Soph Cls; Sec Jr Cls; Sec Sr Cls; Cheerleading; Hon Roll; Comp Sci.

BURKWIT, MARY IRENE; Nazareth Academy HS; Webster, NY; (Y); Boy Scts; Math Tm; Ski Clb; Chorus; School Musical; School Play; High Hon Roll; Hon Roll; Yeomn Ofcr Postn Boy Scts 84-86; Bst Attrny Awd NY ST Yth Govt 83; Nacels Cultr Exch Prog Frnc 83-86.

BURL, TRACY; Salmon River Central HS; Fort Covington, NY; (S); 2/95; Ice Hcky; Hon Roll; NHS; Prfct Atten Awd.

BURLEW, KIP; Mynderse Acad; Seneca Falls, NY; (Y); 35/142; Var L Bsbl; JV Ftbl; High Hon Roll; Hon Roll; Prfct Atten Awd; Math.

BURLINGTON, LEIGH ANN; St Patricks Central Catholic Schl; Athens, NY; (Y); 15/40; Cmnty Wkr; Yrbk Stf; JV Var Cheerleading; High Hon Roll; Hon Roll; Jr NHS; NHS; Natl Hnr Roll Awd 84; NY ST Regents Schlrshp 85; Columbia-Mem Hosp Schl; Nrs.

BURMASTER, JOY; Wilson Central HS; Ransonville, NY; (Y); 14/134; Sec Band; Sec Concert Band; Jazz Band; Pep Band; Yrbk Stf; High Hon Roll; NHS; Pres Schlr; Girl Scts; Library Aide; ST U Of NY; Phys Thrpy.

BURNAH, PRISCILLA; Saranac Central HS; Cadyville, NY; (Y); 40/125; Dance Clb; 4-H; Math Tm; Varsity Clb; Chorus; Var Cheerleading; Var Gym; Var Trk; JV Var Vllybl; High Hon Roll; Regents Schlrshp 85; U VT; Psych.

BURNELL, BRENDA J; Northeastern Clinton Central Schl; Champlain, NY; (Y); 9/146; Am Leg Aux Girls St; Church Yth Grp; Model UN; Pep Clb; Var Capt Bowling; Var Sftbl; Var Capt Swmmng; High Hon Roll; NHS; JV Bsktbl; NYS Regnts Schlrshp 85; Rochester Inst Tech; Comp Sci.

BURNETT, BRIAN; William Howard Taft HS; Bronx, NY; (Y); Off Jr Cls; Vllybl; Hon Roll; Baruch Coll; Bus Adm.

BURNETT, CHERYL; Fairport HS; Fairport, NY; (Y); 42/600; Intnl Clb; Chorus; School Musical; Rep Stu Cncl; High Hon Roll; NHS; Pres Schlr; Drama Clb; JA; Acpl Chr; NYS Rgnts Schlrshp, Prsdntl Awd Acad Ftnss, Grad Hnrs 85; SUNY Geneseo; Mrktg.

BURNETT, COREY; Cicero North Syracuse HS; North Syracuse, NY; (S); 172/711; Exploring; Nwsp Ed-Chief; Nwsp Phtg; Nwsp Stf; Yrbk Ed-Chief; Yrbk Phtg; Lcrss; 2nd Pl Awd Photo In Syracuse Nwspr 84; Photo Jrnlsm.

BURNETT, DAVID T; John Jay HS; Hopewell Jct, NY; (Y); Boy Scts; Chess Clb; Church Yth Grp; Cmnty Wkr; Computer Clb; Science Clb; Ski Clb; Capt Socr; Wrstlng; Hon Roll; Rep NYS Soccr Tournmnt Scotlnd 84; Air Force Acad; Aerntcl Engrng.

BURNETT, KELLY J; Long Lake Central HS; Long Lake, NY; (Y); 2/12; Yrbk Stf; Trs Frsh Cls; Trs Soph Cls; Pres Jr Cls; Rep Stu Cncl; Bausch & Lomb Sci Awd; High Hon Roll; NHS; Regnts Schlrshp 85; Adirondack CC; Gen Sci.

BURNETT, RICHLIN; Clara Barton HS; Brooklyn, NY; (Y); Camera Clb; Dance Clb; Drama Clb; Color Guard; Nwsp Stf; Yrbk Stf; Stu Cncl; Hon Roll; NHS; Ntl Merit Ltr; Daily Nws Prncpls Pride Of Yankees Awd 84; Comp Engrng.

BURNETTE, THOMAS; Washingtonville HS; Washingtonville, NY; (Y); Ski Clb; Band; Jazz Band; Pep Band; Symp Band; Im Bsktbl; JV Socr; High Hon Roll; NHS; All Cty Band Awd 82-84; Med.

BURNHAM, MARY ROSE; Saratoga Catholic Central HS; Ballston Spa, NY; (S); JA; Ski Clb; Yrbk Stf; JV Var Cheerleading; Var Crs Cntry; Score Keeper; Stat Vllybl; High Hon Roll; NHS; Ntl Merit Schol; Bio.

BURNICHE, AMY; Waterford-Halfmoon HS; Waterford, NY; (Y); Math Clb; Ski Clb; Color Guard; Yrbk Stf; Trs Soph Cls; JV Var Cheerleading; Var Crs Cntry; JV Fld Hcky; JV Sftbl; Hon Roll; Physcl Thrpy.

BURNS, ALICE E; Mt Markham Central HS; W Winfield, NY; (Y); 26/126; French Clb; Intnl Clb; Model UN; Yrbk Stf; JV Var Bsktbl; DAR Awd; High Hon Roll; Opt Clb Awd; Aud/Vis; Clark Fndtn Schlrshp 85-86; SUNY Cortland; Pol Sci.

BURNS, ALISA; Niagara Falls HS; Niagara Falls, NY; (Y); Trs Church Yth Grp; Office Aide; Sec Varsity Clb; Church Choir; Prfct Atten Awd; Commendble Achvt 83-85; Comp Sci.

BURNS, BRADLEY; Gouverneur HS; Gouverneur, NY; (Y); 4/140; VP Computer Clb; Pres 4-H; Pres Soph Cls; Capt Crs Cntry; L Socr; High Hon Roll; Trs Jr NHS; Pres NHS; Quiz Bowl; Acpl Chr; Gov Trophy Rsrch Cntst 1st; Whos Who Yorkers; NYS Yorker Hist Bowl Champ; Syracuse U; Appld Sci.

BURNS, CHANDRICKA; Cathedral HS; Ny, NY; (Y); 102/298; Cmnty Wkr; Dance Clb; Drama Clb; Girl Scts; Mrchg Band; Nwsp Stf; Hon Roll; Prfct Attdnce 82-85; Howard U; Psych.

BURNS, CHRISTINA; St Edmund HS; Brooklyn, NY; (Y); 33/187; Cmnty Wkr; Hon Roll; Natl Bus Hnr Soc 84-85.

BURNS, HOLLY; Connetquot HS; Bohemia, NY; (Y); 1/694; Sec Church Yth Grp; Ed French Clb; Ed Girl Scts; Hosp Aide; Ed Library Aide; Ed Math Tm; Red Cross Aide; Band; Ed Chorus; Ed Concert Band; NYSSMA Music Awd 84; Dentst.

BURNS, JODI LYNN; Indian River Central HS; Phildelphia, NY; (Y); AFS; Chorus; Capt Color Guard; Capt Flag Corp; Mrchg Band; School Musical; Yrbk Ed-Chief; Yrbk Sprt Ed; Yrbk Stf; Prfct Atten Awd; JCC; Music.

BURNS, KAREN; Knox Memorial Central HS; Russell, NY; (S); Color Guard; Mrchg Band; Yrbk Stf; Rep Jr Cls; JV Var Bsktbl; Var Socr; Var Sftbl; JV Var Vllybl; High Hon Roll; NHS; League MVP Vllybl & 1st Tm Northern 84; 2nd Tm Northern Soccer & Bsktbl 84; Hon Mntn Vllybl 83; Teach.

BURNS, KELLEY C; Westhill HS; Syracuse, NY; (Y); 1/168; Trs Art Clb; Drama Clb; School Musical; Swing Chorus; Yrbk Stf; Var Capt Cheerleading; Pres NHS; Val; Church Yth Grp; Girl Scts; Hugh O Brian Yth Ldrshp 83; Onondaga Comm Awd 84; Ftbl Chrldng Awd 81; Boston Coll; Bus.

BURNS, KENNETH; Hannibal Central HS; Hannibal, NY; (S); Am Leg Boys St; French Clb; Key Clb; Yrbk Bus Mgr; High Hon Roll; NHS; Buzzy Grant Memrl Awd 81; Engl.

BURNS, LISA; Sachem HS; Holtsville, NY; (S); 81/1600; Pres Hst DECA; Trs French Clb; FBLA; Intnl Clb; Ski Clb; Chorus; Rep Stu Cncl; Hon Roll; NHS; OH U Manasseh Cutler Schlrshp 85; 3rd Pl NYS Bus Comptnt Mrktng; 1st Pl Suffolk Cnty Bus Comp; OH U; Hlth Care Adminstn.

BURNS, LISA; Stella Maris HS; Howard Beach, NY; (Y); 30/250; Library Aide; Math Clb; Science Clb; Yrbk Stf; Hon Roll; Advncd Plcmnt In Englsh & Amer Stds 85; Pre-Med.

BURNS, MARGARET; North Babylon HS; Babylon, NY; (Y); 12/550; Intnl Clb; Var Fld Hcky; JV Sftbl; NHS; Microbio Rsrch.

BURNS, MAURA L; Arlington HS; Hopewell Junction, NY; (Y); 68/597; Cmnty Wkr; Pres Spanish Clb; Color Guard; Orch; Hon Roll; Church Yth Grp; Drama Clb; Stage Crew; NY Regents Schlrshp 85; 4 Yr Excell Avg Awd In Spnsh 84; 5 Yr Excell Avg Awd In Spnsh 85; Marywood Coll; Intl Bus.

BURNS, PATRICIA; S S Seward Inst; Florida, NY; (Y); FHA; GAA; Yrbk Phtg; Stu Cncl; Bsktbl; Cheerleading; Socr; Vllybl; Hon Roll; Burkely; Bus Adm.

BURNS, PATRICK; Forestville Central HS; Perrysburg, NY; (Y); Var Bsbl; Im Bsktbl; Sci.

BURNS, RICHARD; Northstar Christian Acad; Rochester, NY; (S); 3/30; Church Yth Grp; JA; Rep Stu Cncl; High Hon Roll; Hon Roll; Natl Chrstn Hnr Scty 83-85; Acad All Amer 84-85; Accntnt.

BURNS, RICHARD; St Marys Acad; S Glens Falls, NY; (S); 1/43; Am Leg Boys St; Drama Clb; Varsity Clb; Stage Crew; Yrbk Stf; Trs Pres Stu Cncl; Var Bsktbl; Var Ftbl; St Schlr; Val; RPI Mdl 84; All Leag Hnrbl Ment All Reg Ftbl 83-84; U Notre Dame; Engrng.

BURNS, SANDRA; Connetquot HS; Oakdale, NY; (S); 18/700; Sec Cmnty Wkr; GAA; Symp Band; Capt Swmmng; High Hon Roll; Jr NHS; VP NHS; Synchrnd Swmmng, Empire State Games; DE U; Phys Thrpy.

BURNS, SHANNON; Kenmore East SR HS; Tonawanda, NY; (Y); Dance Clb; Pom Pon; High Hon Roll; Hon Roll; NHS; Prfct Atten Awd; Achvt Awd Poetry Anthlgy 83.

BURNS, STEPHEN J; The Wheatley Schl; Old Westbury, NY; (Y); Model UN; Ski Clb; Varsity Clb; Orch; VP Frsh Cls; Socr; Trk; NY St JR II Ski Team 84; Cornell U; Chemistry.

BURNS, TAMMY; Maryvale SR HS; Cheektowaga, NY; (Y); Chorus; School Musical; Ed Yrbk Sprt Ed; Yrbk Stf; Stu Cncl; Cheerleading; Gym; High Hon Roll; Hon Roll; Jr NHS; Bryant & Stratton; Bus.

BURNS, TARA; Seaford HS; Seaford, NY; (Y); Cmnty Wkr; Dance Clb; Hosp Aide; Var Vllybl; High Hon Roll; Hon Roll; Sec.

BURNS, VALARIE; Maple Hill HS; Castleton, NY; (S); Trs Jr Cls; Trs Stu Cncl; JV Var Fld Hcky; JV Var Vllybl; Hon Roll; Rotary Awd; Girl Scts; Math Clb; VP Spanish Clb; Yrbk Stf; Miami U; Tax Atty.

BURNS, VINCENT; Holy Cross HS; Bayside, NY; (Y); 74/348; Art Clb; Im Socr; Var Tennis; High Hon Roll; Bus Admin.

BURNS, WALTER E; Camden HS; Camden, NY; (Y); 26/211; Ski Clb; High Hon Roll; Amer Lgn Boys ST Altrnt 85; Alter Boy 76-85; Wildlife Biolgst.

BURNS III, WILLIAM J; Monsignor Farrell HS; Staten Island, NY; (Y); 35/294; Am Leg Boys St; Boy Scts; Church Yth Grp; Exploring; French Clb; Hosp Aide; Yrbk Phtg; Yrbk Rptr; Pres Frsh Cls; Crs Cntry; Boy Sct Egl Sct Awd 82; Engr.

BURNSIDE, CHRISTINE; Mineola HS; Mineola, NY; (Y); Aud/Vis; VP Camera Clb; Church Yth Grp; Computer Clb; Teachers Aide; Church Choir; Hon Roll; Jr NHS; Prfct Atten Awd; Volntr Serv Tutr Asstnce Prog Awd 85; Hofstra U; Math.

BURNSIDE, JOEL; Attica HS; Attica, NY; (S); 13/150; Am Leg Boys St; Church Yth Grp; Ski Clb; Acpl Chr; Concert Band; Mrchg Band; Socr; NHS; Merit Tuition Awd 85; Vet.

BURR, CHERYL; Our Lady Of Victory Acad; Scarsdale, NY; (S); 33/161; English Clb; French Clb; Yrbk Stf; Lit Mag; Sec Frsh Cls; Trs Soph Cls; Sec Jr Cls; Sec Sr Cls; Bsktbl; Sftbl; Villanova U; Bio.

BURR, KRISTIE; Oneonta SR HS; Oneonta, NY; (Y); French Clb; Varsity Clb; Yrbk Phtg; Var Sftbl; Hon Roll; Math.

BURR, MELISSA; West Genesee HS; Camillus, NY; (Y); Chorus; Concert Band; Mrchg Band; Orch; Rep Soph Cls; Rep Jr Cls; Rep Sr Cls; Var Swmmng; Var JV Vllybl; Hon Roll; A Ratg NYSSMA Solo Fstvl Flute 84; Cornell U; Archit.

BURR, TAMMY; Paul V Moore HS; W Monroe, NY; (Y); 9/297; Church Yth Grp; French Clb; Stage Crew; Nwsp Rptr; Yrbk Stf; Stu Cncl; High Hon Roll; NHS; Regents Schlrshp Wnnr; Acad Schlrshp Houghton; Houghton Coll; CPA.

BURRELL, JUDY M; West Seneca Christian HS; Clarence, NY; (Y); Church Yth Grp; Teachers Aide; Band; Chorus; Church Choir; Concert Band; School Play; Var Socr; Var Vllybl; Prfct Atten Awd; Merit Awd For Grades; Pensacola Chrstan Coll; Elem Ed.

BURRI, LISA; Midlakes HS; Phelps, NY; (Y); VP Sec Cmnty Wkr; French Clb; GAA; Intnl Clb; Yrbk Ed-Chief; Yrbk Sprt Ed; Trs Frsh Cls; Bsktbl; Cheerleading; Socr; Heart Awd Socr 83; CC Of Finger Lks; Retail Mgmt.

BURROUGHS, DERRICK; Cardinal Mooney HS; Rochester, NY; (Y); School Musical; Variety Show; Yrbk Phtg; Yrbk Stf; Stu Cncl; Trk; Hon Roll; Morris Brown; Bus Admin.

BURROWS, DARCI; Andover Central Schl; Andover, NY; (Y); 10/29; Office Aide; Band; Chorus; School Play; Yrbk Ed-Chief; Sec Stu Cncl; Capt Var Sftbl; Capt Var Vllybl; High Hon Roll; All County Music Awd 85; 2nd Alt Robert Mc Clure Awd 85; SUNY Alfred; Exec Sec Sci.

BURROWS, LOREN; Mexico Acad & Central Schl; Mexico, NY; (Y); Bsbl; Bowling; Golf; Socr; Mech Engrng.

BURROWS, SANDRA; Valley Central HS; Montgomery, NY; (Y); 32/350; Church Yth Grp; Trs Soph Cls; Pres Jr Cls; Stat Timer; Stat Trk; Hon Roll; NHS; Comp Sci.

BURROWS, STEPHEN; Monsignor Farrell HS; Staten Island, NY; (Y); 93/300; Camera Clb; Computer Clb; Band; Concert Band; Mrchg Band; Yrbk Stf; Brooklyn Coll; Aerontcl Engrng.

BURSTEIN, ARI; Hebrew Acad; Plainview, NY; (S); 5/80; Debate Tm; Drama Clb; NFL; Pres Temple Yth Grp; Nwsp Sprt Ed; Rep Soph Cls; JV Socr; NHS; Chess Clb; Computer Clb; 1st Pl Long Isl Sci Cngrss 83; Pres Cultrl Apprctn Orgnztn 85; Law.

BURTCH, SCOTT; Alexandria Central Schl; Alexandria By, NY; (Y); Boy Scts; Church Yth Grp; Drama Clb; School Play; Stage Crew; Symp Band; Yrbk Stf; JV Var Fld Hcky; Hon Roll; Masques Drama Clb Mst Imprvd Actor Trphy 85; High Pt Avrg Art Cls & Mech Drwng 3 83-85; Mohawk Vly CC; Graphic Dsgn.

BURTON, CHERYL; Fort Plain HS; Fort Plain, NY; (S); 17/82; Drama Clb; Chorus; School Musical; Variety Show; DAR Awd; Hon Roll; Alfred Tech; Bus Mgmt.

BURTON, DONNA; Fort Plain Central; Ft Plain, NY; (S); Drama Clb; Chorus; Concert Band; Jazz Band; Yrbk Phtg; Var Sftbl; High Hon Roll; NHS; Voice Dem Awd; Vet Med.

BURTON, KRISTEN M; Fairport HS; Fairport, NY; (Y); 40/600; Drama Clb; Intnl Clb; Chorus; School Musical; School Play; Stage Crew; Swing Chorus; Yrbk Stf; Hon Roll; St Schlr; Miami U; Zoology.

BURTON, SHERRY A; Westmoreland Central Schl; Rome, NY; (Y); 22/80; Church Yth Grp; GAA; VP Model UN; Ski Clb; Chorus; Nwsp Stf; Yrbk Stf; Sec Jr Cls; Stu Cncl; High Hon Roll; Lambda Kappa Mus Cert Achvt Awd Art 83; Music Awd-Chrs 85; ST Fnlst Miss NY ST Ntl Tnagr Pagnt 85; Hampton U; Fshn Mrchndsng.

BURTON, TERRY; Schoharie HS; Gallupville, NY; (Y); Church Yth Grp; Computer Clb; Stage Crew; Sec Sr Cls; Mgr(s); Tennis; Trk; Hon Roll; U Of VT; Elem Educ.

BURTON, YVONNE; Amityville Memorial HS; Amityville, NY; (Y); 7/196; AFS; Math Tm; Yrbk Stf; Pres Soph Cls; Bsktbl; Vllybl; Cit Awd; High Hon Roll; Kiwanis Awd; NHS; U Of FL; Interior Design.

BURTS, MARILYN; Clara Barton HS; Brooklyn, NY; (Y); Dance Clb; Science Clb; Spanish Clb; Chorus; Hon Roll; Prfct Atten Awd; Spanish NHS; Socl Stds Schlrshp 85; Arista 83; Awd For Excell In Music 83; Pre-Med.

BURZYNSKI, MARIA; Lancaster HS; Lancaster, NY; (S); Church Yth Grp; Cmnty Wkr; DECA; Pep Clb; Mrchg Band; Fld Hcky; Trk; Vp Lncstr Deca Chptr 84-85; Bus Adm.

BUSCEMI, MICHELLE; Smithtown East HS; Saint James, NY; (Y); Church Yth Grp; Yrbk Stf; Rep Jr Cls; Rep Sr Cls; Crs Cntry; JV Var Tennis; Var Trk; Hon Roll; NHS; Hosp Aide; Italian Hnr Soc 84; Spch Ther.

BUSCEMI, RICHARD; St Josephs Collegiate Inst; Kenmore, NY; (Y); Varsity Clb; Yrbk Sprt Ed; Var Socr; Hon Roll; Philip Scafide Mem Scholar 83-84; Socr All Catholic, All Star Tm 84-85; Keaney Scholar 84-85; Dentistry.

BUSCH, DOLORES; Taconic Hills HS; Hillsdale, NY; (Y); 19/130; Nwsp Rptr; Yrbk Rptr; Yrbk Stf; Hon Roll; NEDT Awd; Co-Vice Pres Lang Clb 83-84; Regents Schlrshp 85; Residence Schlrshp Dyouville Coll 85; Dyouville Coll; Educ.

BUSCH, GREGORY H; Saint Anthonys HS; Ronkonkoma, NY; (Y); Church Yth Grp; Band; Chorus; Nwsp Rptr; NHS; Spanish NHS; Duns Scotus Cert 84; Prncipls List 85; Med.

BUSH, DIANE; Amsterdam HS; Amsterdam, NY; (Y); Drm Mjr(t); Sec Frsh Cls; High Hon Roll; Hon Roll; Fulton Montgomery CC.

BUSH, JACK; Canisteo Central Schl; Canisteo, NY; (Y); Boy Scts; CAP; Computer Clb; Hosp Aide; Ski Clb; Band; Chorus; Mrchg Band; School Musical; Trs Jr Cls; Electrician.

BUSH, JODI; Newark Valley HS; Berkshire, NY; (Y); 17/130; Church Yth Grp; Varsity Clb; Band; Chorus; Church Choir; Rep Stu Cncl; Var L Fld Hcky; Var L Sftbl; High Hon Roll; Hon Roll; Phy Thrpy.

BUSH, JONATHAN; Lafayette HS; Lafayette, NY; (Y); Boy Scts; FFA; High Hon Roll; Hon Roll; SUNY Morrisville; Mechnc.

BUSH, JULIE; Perry Central HS; Warsaw, NY; (Y); Chess Clb; VP 4-H; Math Clb; Math Tm; Yrbk Stf; Trs Soph Cls; Bsktbl; High Hon Roll; Case Inst Of Tech; Comp Engrng.

BUSH, KRISTINA; Bishop Scully HS; Amsterdam, NY; (Y); 15/56; Math Clb; Spanish Clb; Sec VP Stu Cncl; Tennis; High Hon Roll; NHS; Siena Coll; Math Tchr.

BUSH, MICHAEL; Chenango Forks Central HS; Binghamton, NY; (Y); JV Swmmng; Var Tennis; Schlstc Art Awd Gold Key 82; Mock Trial Tourn Hnr 85; Arch.

BUSH, PHYLLIS; Homer Central HS; Homer, NY; (Y); Varsity Clb; Sec Soph Cls; Sec Sr Cls; Rep Stu Cncl; JV Var Cheerleading; JV Var Fld Hcky; JV Var Sftbl; High Hon Roll; Hon Roll; 2nd Tm Al-Star Fld Hocky 84; Cortlnd Cnty Dairy Prncss 84-85; Alfred ST Coll; Accntng.

BUSH, RICHARD; East Aurora HS; West Falls, NY; (S); 17/182; Church Yth Grp; Yrbk Ed-Chief; JV Bsbl; Hon Roll; NHS; Ntl Merit Ltr; Gannon U; Jrnlsm.

BUSH, TARA; Plattsburgh HS; Plattsburgh, NY; (Y); 4/158; French Clb; Bsktbl; Socr; Trk; Vllybl; French Hon Soc; High Hon Roll; NHS; Pres Schlrshp Utica Coll Syracuse U 85; MV Athl 85; Regnts Schlrshps 85; Utica Coll Syracuse U; Acctg.

BUSHA, DANNY B; Au Sable Valley Central HS; Keeserville, NY; (Y); 2/128; FBLA; Model UN; Hon Roll; NHS; Pres Schlr; Sal; Voice Dem Awd; NYS Rgnts Schlrshp; NROTC Fnlst; Clarkson U; Comp Sci.

BUSHEY, MICHELE; Saranac Central HS; Redford, NY; (S); 4/127; French Clb; Sec Trs Band; Concert Band; Jazz Band; Mrchg Band; Trs Soph Cls; Trs Jr Cls; Trs Sr Cls; High Hon Roll; Jr NHS; Plattsburgh ST U.

BUSHMAN, LINDA; Linton HS; Schenectady, NY; (Y); 40/250; AFS; Drama Clb; School Play; Stage Crew; Nwsp Rptr; Nwsp Stf; Yrbk Phtg; Rep Soph Cls; Var JV Cheerleading; Comm.

BUSHNELL, TIM; Olean HS; Olean, NY; (Y); Varsity Clb; VP Frsh Cls; VP Soph Cls; Bsbl; Var Wrstlng; Hon Roll; NHS; Hnr Roll; Natl Hnr Soc; Vrsty Clb; Accntng.

BUSHNELL JR, TIMOTHY; Victor Central HS; Victor, NY; (Y); Boy Scts; Trs French Clb; Trs Library Aide; Pres Model UN; Science Clb; Yrbk Phtg; JV Trk; JV Vllybl; High Hon Roll; NHS; Amer Chem Soc Fnlst 85; Eagle Sct 83; Pre-Med.

BUSHWAY, S; Canisius HS; E Aurora, NY; (Y); 2/152; Am Leg Boys St; Pres Model UN; Quiz Bowl; Acpl Chr; Nwsp Stf; Yrbk Bus Mgr; Var L Wrstlng; Mu Alp Tht; NHS; Sal; Notre Dame U; Math.

BUSKIRK III, MARTIN C; Arlington HS; Pleasant Valley, NY; (Y); Am Leg Boys St; Church Yth Grp; Hon Roll; Bridge Prog Early Admttnce Marist Coll 85-86; RPI; EE.

BUSMIRE, TINA; Kendall JR SR HS; Kendall, NY; (Y); 27/85; Church Yth Grp; Band; Concert Band; Drm Mjr(t); Mrchg Band; School Musical; Variety Show; JV L Bsktbl; Var L Socr; Hon Roll; Bus.

BUSSENO, WILLIAM; Amsterdam HS; Amsterdam, NY; (Y); 15/294; Orch; Hon Roll; Prfct Atten Awd; U Of Buffalo; Chem Engr.

BUSSI, CHRISTINE; Frontier Central HS; Hamburg, NY; (Y); Drama Clb; German Clb; JA; Ski Clb; Concert Band; Mrchg Band; Stu Cncl; Socr; Hon Roll; Prfct Atten Awd; Bus Mgmt.

BUSSI, DOREEN C; Kenmore East HS; Tonawanda, NY; (Y); Church Yth Grp; Math Clb; PAVAS; Mrchg Band; Nwsp Rptr; NHS; Prfct Atten Awd; Drama Clb; Girl Scts; Chorus; Ed Argy Awd-Cmnty Svc 84; All ST Orchstra 83; Grl Sct Ten Yr Pin 84; Law.

BUSUTTIL, LAURA; St Francis Prep; Flushing, NY; (S); Dance Clb; Cheerleading; Ftbl; Gym; Vllybl; Hon Roll; NHS; Ntl Merit Ltr; Scholar Berkeley Schl 85-86; Optimate List 81-85; Italian Natl Hnr Soc 84-85; Berkeley Schl; Exec Sec.

BUTCHER, LISA RENEE; Washingtonville HS; New Windsor, NY; (Y); Delhi; Vet Tech.

BUTCHKO, GREG; Vestal SR HS; Vestal, NY; (Y); German Clb; Band; Concert Band; Jazz Band; Mrchg Band; Psych.

BUTCRELLO, STEPHANIE; Valley Stream Central HS; Valley Stream, NY; (Y); Hosp Aide; Orch; Socr; Jr NHS; NHS; Pre-Med.

BUTENKO, OLESSIA; Jamesville-De Witt HS; Jamesville, NY; (Y); German Clb; Girl Scts; Pres Latin Clb; Pep Clb; Ski Clb; Vllybl; High Hon Roll; NHS; Hon Roll; Econ Entrprs Wrkshp Schlrshp 85; Grad Hnrs Ukrainian Schl 84; Sci.

BUTKOVICH, LEA; Ossining HS; Ossining, NY; (Y); Band; Concert Band; Mrchg Band; Pep Band; Stage Crew; Symp Band; Socr; High Hon Roll; Hon Roll; Wrtng Cntst 1st Pl Essy 82-83; Envrnmntl Sci.

BUTLER, ALAN; Rice HS; Jamaica, NY; (Y); Church Yth Grp; Church Choir; Yrbk Stf; Rep Frsh Cls; Rep Soph Cls; Rep Jr Cls; Rep Sr Cls; Im Bsktbl; Im Ftbl; Hon Roll; 500 Dllr Scholar 84-86; Med.

BUTLER, ANTWANN; Manlius Pebble Hill; Syracuse, NY; (S); Office Aide; Red Cross Aide; Band; Chorus; School Musical; VP L Socr; VP L Trk; High Hon Roll; Hon Roll; J E Crosby Schlrshp 81; All ST Chorus 84; U Of Rochester; Hematologist.

BUTLER, BARBARA; Hicksville SR HS; Hicksvl, NY; (Y); Chorus; Rep Stu Cncl; Stat Lcrss; Stat Wrstlng; Hon Roll; Jrnlsm.

BUTLER, CURTIS; Vestal SR HS; Vestal, NY; (Y); Boys Clb Am; Debate Tm; Band; JV Ftbl; Capt Im Vllybl; High Hon Roll; NHS; Bus.

BUTLER, CYRANO; All Hallows HS; Bronx, NY; (Y); #332 In Class; Teachers Aide; Chorus; Bsbl; Bsktbl; Bowling.

BUTLER, DAVID T; Plattsburgh HS; Plattsburgh, NY; (Y); Aud/Vis; Camera Clb; Church Yth Grp; Model UN; Radio Clb; Church Choir; Nwsp Rptr; SUNY Plattsburgh; Bus Admin.

BUTLER, GRANT; Waldorf Schl; Jaffrey Ctr, NH; (Y); Am Leg Boys St; Acpl Chr; Chorus; Madrigals; Orch; School Musical; Yrbk Stf; VP Sr Cls; Bsktbl; Lcrss; NH U; Envrmntl Cosvrtn.

BUTLER, JEFFERY; Olean HS; Olean, NY; (Y); Hon Roll; Natl Sci Olympiad 83-84; Med Tech.

BUTLER, LYNNETTE; Springfield Gardens HS; Rosedale, NY; (Y); 29/528; Debate Tm; English Clb; FBLA; PAVAS; Service Clb; Spanish Clb; Diving; Vllybl; High Hon Roll; Hon Roll; Dist Spelling Bee Champ 79-80 & 80-81; Fashion Show Awd 84; Bus Adm.

BUTLER, MICHAEL; Harpursville Central Schl; Harpursville, NY; (S); Camera Clb; Spanish Clb; Varsity Clb; Sec Frsh Cls; Pres Soph Cls; Pres Jr Cls; Stu Cncl; JV Var Ftbl; JV Wrstlng; Phtgrphy.

BUTLER, MICHAEL; La Salle Inst; Schenectady, NY; (Y); 1/76; High Hon Roll; Hon Roll; NHS; Ntl Merit Ltr; Biol Awd 82; Eng Awd 81; Fr Awd 83; VA Polytech Inst; Elec Engrng.

BUTMAN, BETH; Altmar-Parish-Williamstown Ch HS; Williamstown, NY; (Y); Art Clb; Varsity Clb; Band; Color Guard; Concert Band; Mrchg Band; Pep Band; Pres Stu Cncl; Pres Bowling; Capt Cheerleading; Won 3 Mony/Schltc Art Awds 85; Hmcmng Prncss 84; Cmmrcl Arts.

BUTTERFIELD, DAVE; South Glenns Falls Central HS; S Glens Falls, NY; (Y); Boy Scts; Trs Varsity Clb; Chorus; School Play; Rep Jr Cls; Rep Stu Cncl; Var Socr; Var Trk; Var Capt Wrstlng; Jr NHS; 1st Tm Al-Foothills Sccr Tm 84; Econmcs.

BUTTERFIELD, LEANNE D; Pulaski JR SR HS; Pulaski, NY; (S); 6/95; Church Yth Grp; Drama Clb; GAA; Ski Clb; Band; Chorus; School Musical; Yrbk Ed-Chief; Var Trk; NHS; Harding U; Psychology.

BUTTERMORE, ALANNA; Webster HS; Webster, NY; (Y); 23/519; Spanish Clb; Church Choir; Yrbk Stf; Swmmng; High Hon Roll; Jr NHS; Spanish NHS; Office Aide; Science Clb; Outstndng Stu Eng,Psnsh Soc Studies 83-85.

BUTTERWORTH, LYNN; Maryvale SR HS; Cheektowaga, NY; (Y); Church Yth Grp; DECA; French Clb; GAA; Spanish Clb; Varsity Clb; Chorus; Var Socr; JV Swmmng; Hon Roll; NC U; Law Enfrcmnt.

BUTTIGIEG, KEVIN M; Floral Park Memorial HS; Floral Park, NY; (Y); 22/186; Band; Nwsp Sprt Ed; JV Soph Cls; Var Ftbl; Var Trk; High Hon Roll; Hon Roll; Sec NHS; Union Coll; Engr.

BUTTITTA, HOLLY; Rocky Point JR SR HS; Rocky Pt, NY; (Y); Ski Clb; Thesps; Chorus; Madrigals; Mrchg Band; School Musical; Socr; Mgr Tennis; Hon Roll; Drama Clb; Music.

BUTTNER, MARGARETH; Carmel HS; Holmes, NY; (Y); Office Aide; School Musical; School Play; High Hon Roll; Hon Roll; NHS; Italian Amer Clb; NY U; Bus Admin.

BUTTON, DENELLE M; Avoca Central HS; Cohocton, NY; (Y); 4/50; 4-H; JCL; Band; School Play; Yrbk Stf; Var Bsktbl; Var Socr; Hon Roll; Prfct Atten Awd; Rep Jr Cls; Vet Sci.

BUTTON, GWENNA; Jasper Central HS; Jasper, NY; (Y); 1/29; Drama Clb; French Clb; Chorus; Yrbk Ed-Chief; Pres Sr Cls; Var Trk; Var Vllybl; High Hon Roll; Val; Elmira Coll Key Awd Scholar 84; Harry J Sargent Scholar 85; Elmira Coll; Bus Admin.

BUTTREY, MIKE; Smithtown H S East; Saint James, NY; (Y); Art Clb; Pres Church Yth Grp; VP 4-H; Coach Actv; Ftbl; Socr; Sftbl; Swmmng; Trk; Wt Lftg; OH ST; Mktg.

BUTTS, CANDY L; Livonia HS; Geneseo, NY; (Y); 2/135; VP Church Yth Grp; Computer Clb; Trs Drama Clb; Math Tm; Science Clb; Spanish Clb; Chorus; Color Guard; Rep Stu Cncl; NHS; Comp Prmg.

BUTZER, DIANE; North Collins HS; Lawtons, NY; (Y); 6/79; 4-H; Band; Concert Band; Mrchg Band; Trs Jr Cls; Trs Sr Cls; Sftbl; 4-H Awd; Hon Roll; NHS; Hghst Avg SR Cls 84-85; Am Leg Scholar 85; Cls Treas 3 Yrs; Herkimer CC; Trvl.

BUTZER, RITA; North Collins Central HS; Lawtons, NY; (Y); 2/70; Pres Sec 4-H; Band; Mrchg Band; School Musical; Trs Sr Cls; Pres Stu Cncl; Stat Bsktbl; JV Vllybl; Trs Jr NHS; NHS; Math.

BUXTON, LISA; Newburgh Free Acad; Newburgh, NY; (Y); Bsktbl; High Hon Roll; Hon Roll; Dutchess Coll; Comp Prog.

BUYDOS, CAROLYN; Shenendehowa SR HS; Clifton Pk, NY; (Y); Aud/Vis; Camera Clb; PAVAS; Ski Clb; Yrbk Stf; JV Fld Hcky; JV Powder Puff Ftbl; Hon Roll; Rhd Isl Schl Phtgrphy; Phtgrphy.

BUYEA, CATHLEEN; Immaculata Acad; W Seneca, NY; (Y); Church Yth Grp; Chorus; Church Choir; Hon Roll; Nrsng.

BUZZELLI, ROBERT; La Salle SR HS; Niagara Falls, NY; (S); 6/278; High Hon Roll; Hon Roll; Lion Awd; Pres NHS; Var JV Ftbl; Mech Engrng.

BYASS, ROMAYNE; Academy Of Mt St Ursula; Bronx, NY; (Y); Church Yth Grp; Computer Clb; Dance Clb; GAA; Church Choir; Howard U; Physclgy.

BYBARCZYK, SUSAN; Lasalle SR HS; Niagara Falls, NY; (S); 27/278; Church Yth Grp; Hosp Aide; Lit Mag; VP Stu Cncl; Mgr(s); Vllybl; Engrng.

BYER, PETER; Onteora HS; Phoenicia, NY; (S); 23/245; Math Tm; Mrchg Band; Ed Nwsp Stf; Ed Yrbk Stf; Hon Roll; NHS; Mst Artstc SR 85; MVP Awd Ski Tm 84; Graph Dsgn.

BYERS, JUDITH L; Fayetteville-Manlius HS; Manlius, NY; (Y); Aud/Vis; Church Yth Grp; Thesps; Chorus; School Musical; School Play; Stage Crew; Hon Roll; Ntl Merit Ltr; St Schlr; Portflio Ntl Comptn 85; Gld Key Schlstc Art Comptn 82; Syracuse U; Art Educ.

BYFIELD, MARJORIE; Walton HS; Bronx, NY; (Y); JA; Chorus; Variety Show; Socr; Prfct Atten Awd; Slctd New York Ctys Outstndg HS Stdnt 84; Fordam U; Psych.

BYINGTON, KRISTEN; Walton Central School; Walton, NY; (Y); 2/102; Sec AFS; Girl Scts; Trs Model UN; Color Guard; Nwsp Rptr; JV Var Cheerleading; Var Crs Cntry; Var Trk; High Hon Roll; NHS; Socl Studies Hghst Avg Awd 83-84; GS Silver Awd 83; Spch Path.

BYNOE, JULIETTE; Mount Saint Ursula HS; Bronx, NY; (Y); Drama Clb; Library Aide; Office Aide; School Musical; Hon Roll; Ntl Lang Arts Olym Awd 83; Cert Hnr Soc Studies 83; Med.

BYNUM, CARMENA; Holy Trinity HS; Freeport, NY; (Y); Camera Clb; Girl Scts; Spanish Clb; Prfct Atten Awd; NY Tech; Comp Engrng.

BYOUS, STACY; Carthage Centra HS; W Carthage, NY; (Y); Chess Clb; Varsity Clb; Yrbk Bus Mgr; Yrbk Stf; Stu Cncl; Var Swmmng; High Hon Roll; AFS; French Clb; Variety Show.

BYRN, THOMAS J; Baldwin SR HS; Baldwin, NY; (Y); 32/503; Church Yth Grp; Drama Clb; Thesps; Chorus; School Musical; School Play; Stage Crew; Lit Mag; NHS; NY St Summer Schl Theatre 84; Am Leg Awd 81; Drama Awd 81; Vassar Coll; Drama.

BYRNE, EDWARD; Archbishop Stepinac HS; White Plains, NY; (Y); 22/207; Church Yth Grp; Rep Frsh Cls; Rep Soph Cls; Rep Jr Cls; Capt Bsktbl; Coach Actv; Cit Awd; High Hon Roll; NHS; Camera Clb; Yth Of Mnth 85; Boston Coll; Acctg.

BYRNE, ELIZABETH; Lindenhurst SR HS; Lindenhurst, NY; (Y); Girl Scts; Hosp Aide; Spanish Clb; Chorus; Yrbk Stf; High Hon Roll; Jr NHS; NHS; Regents Prof Nrsng Schlrshp 85; Pres Acad Ftns Awd 85; Frshmn Recgntn Acad Schlrshp 85; Hofstra U.

BYRNE, KEVIN O; St Anthonys HS; Pt Jeff Stat, NY; (Y); Art Clb; Chorus; Yrbk Phtg; Crs Cntry; Trk; Duns Scotus 83-84; U Dayton; Acctg.

BYRNE, LINDA M; The Masters Schl; Riverdale, NY; (Y); Am Leg Aux Girls St; GAA; Yrbk Ed-Chief; Pres Frsh Cls; Pres Stu Cncl; Fld Hcky; Tennis; Ntl Merit Ltr; Yale U.

BYRNE, LISA; Lansingburgh HS; Troy, NY; (Y); Chorus; School Play; VP Frsh Cls; Rep Sr Cls; Var Capt Cheerleading; Var Fld Hcky; JV Var Score Keeper; High Hon Roll; Hon Roll; Sprtsmnshp & Athl Awd 84; Cobelskill; Clnry Arts.

BYRNE, MEGAN; Fort Plain Central HS; Ft Plain, NY; (Y); Girl Scts; Varsity Clb; Rep Frsh Cls; Capt Cheerleading; Twrlr; Morrisville; Bus Adm.

BYRNE, RENEE; Solvay HS; Syracuse, NY; (Y); French Clb; Ski Clb; Off Frsh Cls; Off Soph Cls; Off Jr Cls; Var Bsktbl; Var Socr; Var Sftbl; High Hon Roll; Hon Roll; 1st Strng, 1st Team All Cnty Soccer 84; 2nd Team All Cnty Soccer 83; Empire ST Games Soccer 85; Syracuse U; Vtrnrn.

BYRNE, SARAH ELIZABETH; Hastings HS; Hastings-On-Hudsn, NY; (S); 14/117; AFS; Chorus; Pres Madrigals; Orch; Ed Yrbk Stf; Crs Cntry; Trk; High Hon Roll; NHS; Ntl Merit Ltr; Psychology.

BYRNE, SEAN; Norwood Norfolk Central HS; Norwood, NY; (Y); Boy Scts; Soph Cls; Rep Stu Cncl; JV Bsbl; JV Socr; High Hon Roll; Hon Roll; Engrng.

BYRNES, ANDREA; North Babylon SR HS; North Babylon, NY; (Y); Band; Concert Band; Var Bsktbl; JV Var Fld Hcky; Sftbl; JV Var Vllybl; High Hon Roll; Hon Roll; Jr NHS; NHS; Vllybl Mst Imprvd Vrsty Plyr 85; Bus.

BYRNES, CHRISTIAN; Bethpage HS; Bethpage, NY; (Y); Spanish Clb; Var L Bsbl; Im Bsktbl; JV L Ftbl; Im Sftbl; Im Trk; Var L Wrstlng; All Lg Gldn Glv Awd 85; Plyr Of Wk 85; NY Rep In Palomino Wrld Srs In Cincinnati OH 85; Crmnl Jstc.

BYRNES, JOANNE; Academy Of The Resurrec; New Rochelle, NY; (Y); GAA; Var L Bsktbl; Var L Trk; High Hon Roll; NHS; Prfct Atten Awd; Pre-Med.

BYRNES, KAREN; Bishop Ludden HS; Camillus, NY; (S); School Play; JV Sftbl; Hon Roll; Spnsh Awd 83; Math.

BYRNES, MICHAEL; Bishop Grimes HS; N Syracuse, NY; (Y); Church Yth Grp; FBLA; Stage Crew; Rep Soph Cls; Rep Jr Cls; Rep Stu Cncl; JV Var Bsktbl; Var Ftbl; Var Golf; SADD 84-85.

BYRNES, PATRICK; Longwood HS; Shirley, NY; (Y); 39/500; Intnl Clb; Key Clb; Q&S; Chorus; Madrigals; School Musical; Nwsp Stf; Lit Mag; High Hon Roll; Jr NHS; Engl.

BZINAK, STEPHEN; Niagara Wheatfield SR HS; Niagara Falls, NY; (Y); Am Leg Boys St; Pres German Clb; VP Math Clb; Model UN; Jazz Band; Pres Stu Cncl; JV Var Tennis; High Hon Roll; NHS; Ntl Merit SF; Clarkson U; Elec Engr.

CA VALLETTI, SUSAN; Hornell HS; Hornell, NY; (Y); Math Clb; Color Guard; Mrchg Band; School Musical; Symp Band; High Hon Roll; Rensselaer Medl Achvt Math & Sci 85.

CAAMANO, LUIS M; Seward Park HS; New York, NY; (Y); Computer Clb; Library Aide; Teachers Aide; Band; Chorus; Orch; Prfct Atten Awd; Comp Pgmmng.

CABALLERO, MICHELE; Bishop Kearney HS; Brooklyn, NY; (Y); Math Tm; Spanish Clb; High Hon Roll; Sec NHS; Math Team Outstndg Achvt 84; 1st Hnrs Iona Coll Lang Cont Spnsh Lvl III 85; Math.

CABALUNA, ELEANOR P; Franklin Acad; Malone, NY; (Y); Church Yth Grp; NFL; Spanish Clb; Church Choir; Swing Chorus; Symp Band; Vllybl; VP Phi Sigma 85; Trea Franklin Acad Tfvl Clb 83-85; Outstndng Voice,Piano,Bass Clrnt; Music.

CABAN, LILLIAN; Clara Barton HS; Brooklyn, NY; (Y); Church Yth Grp; Chorus; Church Choir; Stage Crew; Pres Frsh Cls; Hon Roll; Prfct Atten Awd; Cardlgst.

CABERA, WALDO; HS Of Art & Design; Bronx, NY; (S); 14/439; Computer Clb; Math Clb; Ski Clb; Variety Show; Rep Frsh Cls; Rep Soph Cls; VP Jr Cls; Pres Sr Cls; Pres Stu Cncl; Cit Awd; Ntl AA Hrn Soc 85; Untd Negro Coll Fund Schlrshp 85; Syracuse U Schlrshp 85; Syracuse U; Art.

CABLE, BRENDA L; Whitney Point HS; Whitney Point, NY; (Y); 5/122; Chorus; Mgr(s); High Hon Roll; Hon Roll; Pres NHS; Regnts Schlrshp 85; Broome CC; Comp Sci.

CABRAL, LINDA; Ossining HS; Ossining, NY; (Y); 16/267; Sftbl; High Hon Roll; Hon Roll; All-Div Sftbll 84-85; Bus Stu Of The Mnth 85.

CABRAL, LISA; Earl L Vandermuelen HS; Mt Sinai, NY; (Y); 48/280; FBLA; Pep Clb; Band; Yrbk Ed-Chief; Rep Stu Cncl; Var JV Cheerleading; Coach Actv; JV Capt Sftbl; JV Trk; High Hon Roll; Suffolk Cnty CC; Busnss Admin.

CABRERA, CATHERINE; John Dewey HS; Brooklyn, NY; (Y); GAA; JA; Library Aide; Math Tm; Spanish Clb; Teachers Aide; Band; Gym; Sftbl; Vllybl; Roberto Clemente Awd 83; Pace U; Bus.

CABRERA, JOSUE; Monroe HS; Rochester, NY; (Y); Church Yth Grp; Band; Chorus; Church Choir; JV Bsbl; JV Vllybl; Mth Medl 9th Schl 80.

CABRERA, MATTHEW; Warwick Valley HS; Warwick, NY; (Y); 19/215; FFA; Math Tm; Science Clb; Yrbk Sprt Ed; Var Capt Bsbl; Var Capt Ftbl; Var JV Trk; Hon Roll; NHS; Bridgewater; Bus.

CABRERA, RUTHY; High School Of Fashion Industrs; Bronx, NY; (Y); #89 In Class; Eng Hnr Rll 82-84; Math Hnr Rll 82; Columbia; Psych.

CABRERA, ZORAIDA; John Dewey HS; Brooklyn, NY; (Y); Aud/Vis; Dance Clb; Drama Clb; GAA; Library Aide; School Play; Stage Crew; Sftbl; Vllybl; Cit Awd; Perfm Art Awd 82; Pace U; Exec Comp.

CACCAMISE, DINA; Notre Dame HS; Le Roy, NY; (S); 5/65; Sec Library Aide; Sec Frsh Cls; Sec Soph Cls; Rep Jr Cls; Rep Stu Cncl; Var Socr; JV Sftbl; Hon Roll; NHS; JA; Student Of The Month For November 84; Public Rel.

CACCIOLA, BARBARA; Our Lady Of Victory Acad; Elmsford, NY; (S); 4/150; Science Clb; Spanish Clb; High Hon Roll; Trs NHS; Spanish NHS; Partial Scshlrshp-Our Lady Victory Acad; Bio Awd; Span Awd; Math Awd; Physician.

CACIOPPO, ANTHONY; Richmond Hill HS; Woodhaven, NY; (Y); Radio Clb; Var Bsbl; JV Trk; Hon Roll; Italian Hon Soc 84; Engl Hon Soc 85; Bus Hon Soc 85; Pace U Pleasantville; Mktg Sls.

CACIOPPO, LAURA M; Tottenville HS; Staten Island, NY; (Y); Church Yth Grp; Hosp Aide; Teachers Aide; School Play; Nwsp Stf; Yrbk Rptr; Yrbk Stf; Lit Mag; Rep Soph Cls; Vllybl; Regents Coll Schlrshp 85; Full Tuition Schlrshp To Pace U 85; SUNY At Albany; Educ.

CACIOPPO, ROSE; Uniondale HS; Uniondale, NY; (Y); 29/485; Church Yth Grp; Key Clb; Drm & Bgl; Flag Corp; Yrbk Stf; Cheerleading; JV Sftbl; Cit Awd; Jr NHS; NHS; Spirit Awd Rhythmtls 83; Actvty Awd 84-85; Nassau Comm Coll; Lib Arts.

CADAVID, ADRIANA; Sacred Heart Acad; Uniondale, NY; (S); 19/196; Hosp Aide; Math Clb; Math Tm; Scholastic Bowl; School Musical; School Play; Bowling; Bausch & Lomb Sci Awd; High Hon Roll; NHS; Iona Lang Comp 2nd Hnrs Span 84; Natl French Contest 84; Hofstra U; Engrng.

CADET, BELLA; Christ The King Regional HS; Hollis, NY; (Y); Art Clb; Debate Tm; Speech Tm; Chorus; Hon Roll; Pre-Med.

CADIEUX, ROCHELLE; Oakfield-Alabama CS HS; Basom, NY; (Y); VP 4-H; Sec FFA; Office Aide; JV Var Socr; Hon Roll; Cntnentl Schl Bty; Csmtlgy.

CADMUS, JUDY; Moriah Central Schl; Moriah Center, NY; (Y); Trs AFS; Aud/Vis; Ski Clb; Band; Concert Band; Mrchg Band; Rep Jr Cls; Var Socr; High Hon Roll; Hon Roll; Comp Analyst.

CADRE, GIANNI; Cardinal Spellman HS; Bronx, NY; (Y); Church Yth Grp; Cmnty Wkr; Dance Clb; Hosp Aide; Spanish Clb; Nwsp Stf; Yrbk Stf; Stu Cncl; Hon Roll; NHS; Regnts Schlrshp 85; Schlrshp U Of Dallas 85; Vassar Coll; Med.

CADY, BARBARA; Madrid-Waddington Central HS; Madrid, NY; (Y); Drama Clb; GAA; Girl Scts; Band; Chorus; School Musical; School Play; Stage Crew; Var Score Keeper; JV Var Socr; Potsdam ST; Psych.

CADY, KAREN; Holland Patent Central Schl; Holland Patent, NY; (Y); 69/194; Color Guard; Drm & Bgl; Var JV Cheerleading; Hon Roll; Pep Clb; Chorus; Score Keeper; Cosmetology.

CADY, KIMBERLY; Thomas A Edison HS; Elmira Heights, NY; (Y); 5/87; Stage Crew; Nwsp Stf; Yrbk Stf; High Hon Roll; Pres Schlr; Harrison Earl & Frances Smith Schlrshp 85; Writing Awd 85; Amer Leg Aux Awd 85; Corning CC; Lbrl Arts.

CAESAR, MIMIEUX; St Barnabas HS; Bronx, NY; (S); 21/188; Library Aide; NFL; Chorus; School Musical; Nwsp Rptr; Stu Cncl; Swmmng; Hon Roll; NHS; Spanish NHS; Ntl Sci Olympiad, Bio Awd 84; Prfct Attndnc Awd 83-84; Bio.

CAEZZA, JENNIFER; Commack High School North; E Northport, NY; (Y); Church Yth Grp; Chorus; Nwsp Rptr; Nwsp Stf; Ed Lit Mag; Var Trk; High Hon Roll; NHS; Poli Sci.

CAFERRO, CHERYL A; Lackawanna HS; Lackawanna, NY; (Y); Spanish Clb; Var Sftbl; Hon Roll; GAA; Ski Clb; Rep Soph Cls; Powder Puff Ftbl; Chapman; Psychlgy.

CAFFIN, MICHAEL S; New Rochelle HS; Scarsdale, NY; (Y); 55/597; Boys Clb Am; Boy Scts; Pres Church Yth Grp; Computer Clb; Service Clb; Nwsp Sprt Ed; Lit Mag; JV Var Bowling; Hon Roll; NHS; Jrnlsm.

CAFFO, PAUL; Batavia SR HS; Batavia, NY; (Y); Ftbl; Ag.

CAFIERO, VICTORIA; Bishop Kearney HS; Brooklyn, NY; (S); FNA; Science Clb; Ski Clb; Yrbk Stf; Hon Roll; NHS; Pres Schlr; St Schlr; Semi-Fin ILA Teddy Gleason Scholar Prgm 85; Biol.

CAGGIA, MICHAEL; W C Mepham HS; N Bellmore, NY; (Y); Badmtn; Var Bsbl, Var Golf, JV Lcrss, Im Sftbl; Var Wt Lftg; Hon Roll; Ntl Merit Ltr; Prfct Atten Awd; Fll Accntng Schlrshp Five Twns Coll 85-89; Bus Adm.

CAGGIANELLI, GREGG; Onteora HS; Shokan, NY; (S); 8/212; Am Leg Boys St; Church Yth Grp; Exploring; Math Tm; Quiz Bowl; Chorus; School Musical; Rep Frsh Cls; Rep Soph Cls; Rep Jr Cls; U S Coast Guard Proj AIM 85; Pres Clssrm Yng Amer 85; Engrng.

CAGGIANO, PAMELA G; Holy Trinity HS; East Meadow, NY; (S); 36/349; Cmnty Wkr; Math Clb; Varsity Clb; Band; Church Choir; Jazz Band; School Musical; Cheerleading; Gym; Hon Roll; Psy.

CAHBACK, LEAH J; La Guardia H S Of Music & The Arts; New York, NY; (Y); 54/570; Art Clb; Nwsp Stf; Hon Roll; Office Aide; Nwsp Rptr; Schlstcs Art Awd 83; Art Hnr Leag 84-86; Vet.

CAHILL, BERNADETTE; Northport HS; E Northport, NY; (Y); Hosp Aide; Acpl Chr; Jazz Band; Mrchg Band; School Musical; Symp Band; Stu Cncl; JV Socr; JV Vllybl; NHS; Mary Washington Coll; Pre-Vet.

CAHILL, HEATHER ANN; Maria Regina HS; Bronx, NY; (Y); 3/147; Cmnty Wkr; Hst Dance Clb; Key Clb; Chorus; Nwsp Stf; Yrbk Stf; High Hon Roll; NHS; HS Schlrshp 82; Leatrice Kopera Schlrshp 82; Fashn Inst Tech; Txtl Dsgn.

CAHILL, KENNETH A; Island Trees SR HS; Levittown, NY; (Y); 4/212; Mathletes; School Play; Nwsp Stf; Trs Sr Cls; Stu Cncl; High Hon Roll; Jr NHS; NHS; Debate Tm; NY St Regents Schlrshp 85; Ntl Acad Achvt Sci; Cornell U; Vet.

CAHILL, LAUREN; Bishop Ludden HS; Camillus, NY; (Y); Tennis; High Hon Roll; Hon Roll; Frnch Cert Awd Of Merit 82-83; Soc Studys Awd 85; SUNY-BINGHAMTON; Reg Nrse.

CAHILL, MOLLY; Catholic Central HS; Troy, NY; (S); 6/203; Dance Clb; Drama Clb; French Clb; Math Tm; School Musical; Trs Frsh Cls; Var Bsktbl; JV Var Vllybl; High Hon Roll; NHS; Eastern Regnl Irish Dncng Chmpshp 2nd Pl 82; N A.

CAHILL, SARA; Pelham Memorial HS; Pelham, NY; (Y); Church Yth Grp; Nwsp Rptr; Yrbk Stf; Lit Mag; VP Crs Cntry; JV Lcrss; Hon Roll; NHS.

CAHILL, TERRANCE P; Albany HS; Albany, NY; (Y); Boy Scts; Church Yth Grp; French Clb; Latin Clb; Pep Clb; Var L Swmmng; Var Trk; Regents Schlrshp Awd 85; Pres M & M Better Am 81-85; Suny-Albany.

CAIN, BOB; Schobarie HS; Schoharie, NY; (Y); JV Var Bsbl; JV Bsktbl; Herkimer County CC; Cmmnctns.

CAIN, JOHN; Mercy HS; Jamesport, NY; (Y); JCL; Latin Clb; Band; Pres Frsh Cls; Rep Soph Cls; Rep Jr Cls; Var Capt Bsktbl; JV Ftbl; Var Trk; Hon Roll; 110 Prcnt JV Bsktbl & V Trk 84; Med.

CAINE, SHERRY A; West Seneca Christian Schl; Depew, NY; (Y); Church Yth Grp; Chorus; Church Choir; Stage Crew; Var L Cheerleading; Outstndng Sr Christian Ldrshp Schlrshp 85; James Shriver Schlrshp To Lbrty U 85; Liberty U; Jrnlsm.

CAISSE, SHIRLEY; Scotia Glenville SR HS; Scotia, NY; (Y); JA; Spanish Clb; Chorus; JV Trk; JV Vllybl; Comm Tsk Frc Day Drg, Alchl Abse 85; Schenectady County CC; Hum Svc.

CAJIGAS, JACQUELYN; St John Th Baptist HS; Bayshore, NY; (Y); Cmnty Wkr; Math Tm; Political Wkr; Band; Concert Band; Mrchg Band; Pep Band; Hon Roll; Adelphi U; Acctg.

CALABRESE, ANTHONY M; Island Trees HS; Bethpage, NY; (Y); 1/213; Debate Tm; Model UN; Sec Sr Cls; Trs Stu Cncl; Var Bsktbl; Bausch & Lomb Sci Awd; Hon Roll; Ntl Merit Ltr; Rotary Awd; Val; Rgnts Schlrshp 85; Johns Hopkins; Med.

CALABRESE, CHRISTINE; Tottenville HS; Staten Island, NY; (Y); Chorus; Cit Awd; Hon Roll; NHS; Prfct Atten Awd; Hnr Typwrtng Awd 85; Accntnt.

CALABRESE, REGINA ANN; St Edmund HS; Brooklyn, NY; (S); 26/190; Latin Clb; Rep Soph Cls; Cheerleading; Coach Actv; JV Sftbl; NHS; Cert Merit Awd-High Cls Aver Math 84; Acctng.

CALABRIA, CAROL; Bishop Grimes HS; Syracuse, NY; (Y); 4/207; FBLA; Political Wkr; Trk; DAR Awd; High Hon Roll; NHS; Ntl Engl Merit Awd 85; Rgnts Schlrshp Wnner 85; Itln Ntl Hnr Soc 84; Engrng.

CALABRO, DIANE; Westhampton Beach HS; E Quogue, NY; (Y); Girl Scts; Hosp Aide; Office Aide; UCLA; Law.

CALABRO, PATRICIA I; Sachem HS; Holbrook, NY; (Y); 40/1500; Cmnty Wkr; Color Guard; Orch; School Play; Nwsp Rptr; Sec Sr Cls; Var Tennis; High Hon Roll; Jr NHS; NHS; Bus.

CALAMARI, ROBERT; Fordham Preparatory Schl; Bronx, NY; (Y); Var Bsbl; Hon Roll; Bsbl Lg All-Str 82; Italian Clb 85; Cmnctns.

CALANDRA, WENDY A; Rome Free Acad; Rome, NY; (Y); 254/577; JV Var Sftbl; High Hon Roll; Hon Roll; Rome Profssnl Nursng Schlrshp, Rome Mo Ose Nursng Schlrshp & Cynthia C Chetnik Nursng Schlrshp 85; Monawk Valley CC; Nursng.

CALANDRINO, DONNA; Marlboro HS; Milton, NY; (Y); Church Yth Grp; Girl Scts; Yrbk Stf; Trk; Hon Roll; Ntl Sci Olymp Awd 85; Bio.

CALAPAI, DOMINIQUE; Valley Stream Central HS; Malvern, NY; (Y); 44/375; Art Clb; French Clb; Hosp Aide; Nwsp Stf; Var Badmtn; French Hon Soc; NHS; Regents Scholar 84-85; Adelphi U Trustee Scholar 85; 2nd Pl Grp Imprvistn Old Westbury Coll 85; Adelphi U; Art.

CALARCO, JOE; Irondequoit HS; Rochester, NY; (Y); Thesps; Chorus; School Musical; School Play; Yrbk Stf; Ntl Merit Ltr; Drama Clb; Temple Yth Grp; Acpl Chr; Madrigals; Monroe Cty Area All ST Music Fstvl 84; NYSSMA Fstvl 86; Thtre.

CALARCO, TAMMI; Odessa Montour Central HS; Odessa, NY; (Y); Drama Clb; Teachers Aide; VICA; Var JV Bsktbl; Var Crs Cntry; Var Trk; High Hon Roll; Hon Roll; JV Sprts Ltr Awd Cert Bsktbl 83-84; Vrsty Sprts Ltr Awd Cert Trck 84-85; Bus.

CALCAGNI, EILEEN; Albertus Magnus HS; Garnerville, NY; (Y); 17/190; Pres Church Yth Grp; Girl Scts; Math Clb; Varsity Clb; Capt Socr; High Hon Roll; Hon Roll; Mu Alp Tht; NHS; JV Var Bsktbl; Knghts Of Col Yth Parish Rep 82; Apostolic Yth Awd 84; Card Spellman CYO Awd, Qn Of Parish 83-84; Med.

CALCAGNO, CAROLYN A; Eastridge HS; Rochester, NY; (Y); 63/228; DECA; FBLA; Ski Clb; Yrbk Stf.

CALDAIO, DONNA; Susan E Wagner HS; Staten Island, NY; (Y); Hon Roll; NHS; Acctg.

CALDERON, AARON; Archbishop Molloy HS; Forest Hills, NY; (Y); 56/409; Chess Clb; Computer Clb; Red Cross Aide; Im Bsbl; Crs Cntry; Im Ftbl; Im Sftbl; L Trk; High Hon Roll; NHS; Med.

CALDERON, F; Richmond Hill HS; Richmond Hill, NY; (Y); 15/350; Cmnty Wkr; Dance Clb; Drama Clb; JA; Key Clb; Math Clb; Sec Office Aide; Spanish Clb; Sec Teachers Aide; School Play; Pride Of Yankees 85; Profncy Engl & Humnties 85; Schltc Achvt 84; Best Spkr Spch Clss 85; Math Hon Roll; Soc Sci.

CALDERON, LISA; The Mary Louis Acad; Bellerose, NY; (Y); Camera Clb; Library Aide; Spanish Clb; Variety Show; Bowling; Swmmng; Hon Roll; Queens Coll; Tchng.

CALDERON, WENDY; John Dewey HS; Brooklyn, NY; (Y); 4-H; Girl Scts; JA; Latin Clb; Math Tm; Political Wkr; Science Clb; Spanish Clb; Teachers Aide; Chorus; Govt Committee Scholastic 84-85; Ntl Hispanic Schlrshp Achievement; Brown U; Mathematics.

CALDERONE, SHIRLEY; Bishop Cunningham HS; Oswego, NY; (Y); Pep Clb; Spanish Clb; Chorus; Variety Show; Yrbk Rptr; Yrbk Stf; Rep Frsh Cls; Rep Soph Cls; Pres Stu Cncl; Cheerleading; Le Moyne Coll; Pedtrcn.

CALDOVINO, DENISE; St Edmund HS; Brooklyn, NY; (Y); 50/190; Art Clb; Nwsp Rptr; Gym; High Hon Roll; Hnr Rl 85.

CALDWELL, CHRISTOPHER; St Josephs Collegiate Inst; Bowmansville, NY; (Y); 71/193; Boy Scts; Exploring; Sec Jr Cls; Trs Stu Cncl; Ftbl; Trk; Hon Roll; Northeastern U; Bus Admn.

CALDWELL, MICHELLE; Watervliet HS; Watervliet, NY; (Y); 3/121; Rptr French Clb; Pres Key Clb; School Play; Nwsp Stf; Yrbk Stf; Rep Stu Cncl; High Hon Roll; NHS; Pres Schlr; Voice Dem Awd; Fordham U; Russian Trnsltr.

CALDWELL, STEVEN M; Seaford HS; Seaford, NY; (Y); 24/246; Nwsp Stf; JV Bsktbl; JV Ftbl; Var Capt Lcrss; NHS; SUNY Binghamton; Bus Mngmnt.

CALEGA, ANTHONY; Marlboro HS; Marlboro, NY; (Y); Library Aide; Office Aide; Yrbk Rptr; Var Crs Cntry; Var Tennis; Var Trk; Syracuse U; Brdcstng.

CALERO, MAIDA; Epstern District HS; Bklyn, NY; (Y); Math Clb; English Clb; JA; Spanish Clb; Band; Hon Roll; U PR.

CALHOUN, COLLEEN; Hartford Central HS; Hartford, NY; (Y); French Clb; Pep Clb; Ski Clb; Varsity Clb; Band; Chorus; Drm & Bgl; Mrchg Band; Orch; Yrbk Stf; CCBT; Med Sec.

CALHOUN, KIMBERLY; Johnstown HS; Johnstown, NY; (Y); Drama Clb; Band; Chorus; School Musical; School Play; Swing Chorus; Variety Show; Cheerleading; 4-H; Concert Band; Vrsty J Ftbl & Bsktbl Chrng 84-85; Music.

CALHOUN, WILLIAM; General Brown HS; Dexter, NY; (Y); 5/94; JCL; Band; Chorus; Concert Band; Mrchg Band; School Musical; Hon Roll; NHS; Magna Cum Laude 83-84; 3rd NY Lang Fair Latin Rdng Lwr Level 84; Cornell; Math.

CALI III, JOSEPH L; Sayville HS; Sayville, NY; (Y); 70/350; Church Yth Grp; Key Clb; Political Wkr; Concert Band; Mrchg Band; Var Bowling; Var Socr; High Hon Roll; Hon Roll; 1st Pl Innovative Arch Desgn 85; Elec Engrng.

CALI, PHILIP; Canisteo Central Schl; Canisteo, NY; (Y); Orch; Trs Frsh Cls; Pres Soph Cls; Rep Stu Cncl; Var L Bsktbl; Var L Golf; Cit Awd; High Hon Roll; Pres VP NHS; Ntl Merit Ltr; RPI Smmr Pgm Schlrshp 85; SF Congress Bundestag Exc Pgm 85; Aero Sp Engr.

CALI, ROBERT R; West Islip HS; West Islip, NY; (Y); 46/525; Cmnty Wkr; Mathletes; Band; Chorus; Concert Band; Jazz Band; Madrigals; Mrchg Band; Orch; Pep Band; Bst Mscn Awd 82; SUNY Binghamton; Pre Med.

CALIENDO, ANDREW J; Pelham Memorial HS; Pelham, NY; (Y); Hon Roll; Prfct Atten Awd; Aeron Engrng.

CALIENDO, FRANK J; Holy Trinity HS; East Meadow, NY; (S); 21/400; Drama Clb; Math Clb; Math Tm; Ski Clb; Stage Crew; Stu Cncl; High Hon Roll; Mu Alp Tht; NHS; Hofstra U; Bio.

CALIENDO, JERI-LYNN; North Babylon HS; North Babylon, NY; (Y); Rep Cmnty Wkr; Intnl Clb; Mathletes; Yrbk Ed-Chief; Pom Pon; Trk; French Hon Soc; NHS; Prfct Atten Awd; AAPHERD Tsk Force Phy Fitnss Awd 84 & 85; Acctng.

CALIFANO, ANDREA; Port Richmond HS; Staten Isld, NY; (Y); 6/500; Hosp Aide; Library Aide; Math Tm; School Musical; Nwsp Rptr; Yrbk Stf; Sec Stu Cncl; High Hon Roll; Jr NHS; NHS; Atty.

CALIFANO, CHRISTINA; Mont Pleasant HS; Schenectady, NY; (Y); Church Yth Grp; JA; Office Aide; Pep Clb; Ski Clb; Band; Mrchg Band; Rep Stu Cncl; Var L Cheerleading; Hon Roll; Miss NY Coed Pagnt-Miss Photogne 85; Advrtsng.

CALIGIURI, W PAUL; Queensbury HS; Glens Falls, NY; (Y); Boy Scts; Band; Plattsburg SUNY; Psych.

CALIMERI, ANNA MARIA; Jamestown HS; Jamestown, NY; (Y); 51/384; Chorus; Nwsp Stf; Stu Cncl; Hon Roll; Jr NHS; NHS; Class 1917 Prz Fund Awd 85; Jamestown CC; Elec Tech.

CALIMERI, CATHERINE; Auburn HS; Auburn, NY; (Y); Girl Scts; Ski Clb; Socr; Bus.

CALKINS, ANN; G Ray Bodley HS; Fulton, NY; (Y); Church Yth Grp; Latin Clb; Concert Band; School Musical; VP Jr Cls; Var Capt Crs Cntry; Elks Awd; High Hon Roll; NHS; Red Cross Aide; Prom Quenn 85; Police Benvlnt Assoc Sav Bond 83-84; MVP Girls Corss Cty Cptn 83; Aeronutcl Engr.

CALKINS, ANNE; Bishop Grimes HS; Syracuse, NY; (Y); #2 In Class; Math Clb; Pres Chorus; Church Choir; School Musical; Yrbk Ed-Chief; High Hon Roll; NHS; Sal; Gen Elec Found STAR Awd 85; Harvard U Smr Schl 84; Merit Schlrshp; Le Moyne Coll; Bio.

CALKINS, CARYN; Cardinal Mooney HS; Rochester, NY; (Y); 229/315; JV Socr; Hon Roll; Monroe CC; Psych; Monroe CC; Psych.

CALKINS, NANCY; Cato-Meridian HS; Memphis, NY; (Y); 4-H; JA; Office Aide; Im Badmtn; Im Vllybl; 4-H Awd; Hon Roll; Kiwanis Awd; Prfct Atten Awd; Mst Imprvd Bus Ed 85; Drvr Ed Achv Awd 85; 1st Pl Bsktbl Foul Shtng Awd 83; Bryant T Stratton; Bus.

CALKINS, TINA; Prattsburg Baptist Christian Schl; Pulteney, NY; (Y); Church Yth Grp; Church Choir; School Musical; Stu Cncl; High Hon Roll; Val; Cedarville Coll; Elem Educ.

CALL, ANDREW; Carmel HS; Carmel, NY; (Y); Y-Teens; Nwsp Phtg; Nwsp Rptr; Nwsp Stf; Socr; High Hon Roll; NHS; Voice Dem Awd; Frnsc Med.

CALL, LISA; Horseheads SR HS; Horseheads, NY; (Y); Drama Clb; Chorus; Color Guard; School Play; Stage Crew; Variety Show; Rep Stu Cncl; Hon Roll; Habilitative Sci.

CALL, STACY; West Hampton Beach HS; E Moriches, NY; (Y); 60/232; Church Yth Grp; French Clb; Girl Scts; Ski Clb; Rep Stu Cncl; Var Fld Hcky; Var Sftbl; JV Var Vllybl; Chorus; Hon Roll; Rookie Yr Fild Hockey 82; Artist Mnth 83; Bus.

CALL, STEVEN; Greece Athena HS; Rochester, NY; (Y); 37/280; Boy Scts; Pres Church Yth Grp; Drama Clb; Church Choir; School Musical; School Play; Hon Roll; NHS; St Schlr; Chess Clb; Member Of District & Confernce Council Of Yth Ministries 84-85; Geneseo ST U; Ordaine Ministry.

CALLA, ANGELA; Oakfield Alabama Central HS; Oakfield, NY; (Y); Cmnty Wkr; Drama Clb; French Clb; Office Aide; Ski Clb; Stu Cncl; Socr; Trk; High Hon Roll; Hon Roll; Rgnts Schlrshp Frnch Awd; Potsdam Coll; Comp.

CALLA, GUY; East Islip HS; East Islip, NY; (Y); Pres Sr Cls; Var Bsbl; JV Bsktbl; Im Ftbl; Ice Hcky; Im Socr; Wt Lftg; Hon Roll; Bus.

CALLA, LINDA; Oakfield Alabama Central HS; Oakfield, NY; (Y); Boys Clb Am; Cmnty Wkr; Exploring; GAA; Ski Clb; Band; Concert Band; Jazz Band; Mrchg Band; Orch.

CALLAGHAN, SUSAN; Saratoga Central Catholic HS; Saratoga Spg, NY; (S); 4/40; Drama Clb; Varsity Clb; Stage Crew; VP Jr Cls; JV Var Cheerleading; Vllybl; High Hon Roll; NHS; Inter Design.

CALLAHAN, DANIEL T; Elmira Southside HS; Elmira, NY; (Y); 19/333; Am Leg Boys St; Spanish Clb; Pres Varsity Clb; Rep Frsh Cls; Capt Bsktbl; Capt Ftbl; Hon Roll; NHS; Pres Schlr; Earnie Davis Memrl Awd 84; Regents Schlrshp 85; Alfred U; Med.

CALLAHAN, GERARD; John Jay SR HS; Wappingers Fall, NY; (Y); Var Wrstlng; Hon Roll; Prfct Atten Awd; Acad Of Aeronautics; Pilot.

CALLAHAN, GREG H; Corning East HS; Beaver Dams, NY; (Y); VP Church Yth Grp; 4-H; Letterman Clb; Yrbk Stf; Rep Soph Cls; Rep Jr Cls; Rep Sr Cls; JV Bsktbl; JV Ftbl; JV Lcrss; Engrng.

CALLAHAN, JAMES A; St Anthonys HS; Huntington, NY; (Y); Spanish Clb; JV Var Bsktbl; Var Capt Golf; NHS; Spanish NHS; Capt Glf Tm 83-84; MVP Glf 85; Bus.

CALLAHAN, JAMES J; W C Mepham HS; N Bellmore, NY; (Y); Cmnty Wkr; French Clb; Capt Band; Var Capt Crs Cntry; JV Capt Socr; Var Capt Trk; Hon Roll; All Div Crss-Cntry 84; Natl Sci Olympiad-Bio 84; IN U; Bus.

CALLAHAN, KATHLEEN MARIE; Fayetteville-Manlius HS; Fayetteville, NY; (Y); Am Leg Aux Girls St; Sec JCL; Rep Sr Cls; Var Capt Cheerleading; Hon Roll; NHS; Ntl Merit Ltr; NY ST Rgnts Schlrshp 85; Cornell U; Lab Rel.

CALLAHAN, SHAWN R; Watkins Glen Central HS; Watkins Glen, NY; (Y); Am Leg Boys St; Bsktbl; Trk; Hon Roll; MVP In Track & Fld 84 & 85; St Bonaventure U; Mrktng.

CALLAHAN, TRACEY; St Peters High School For Girls; Staten Island, NY; (Y); Church Yth Grp; Cmnty Wkr; Ski Clb; Yrbk Stf; High Hon Roll; NHS; Med.

CALLANAN, CONSTANCE; Watkins Glen HS; Watkins Glen, NY; (Y); 15/150; VP Letterman Clb; Math Clb; Quiz Bowl; Scholastic Bowl; Drm & Bgl; Var Capt Bsktbl; Var Capt Trk; Var Capt Vllybl; Pres French Hon Soc; Church Yth Grp; NY ST Schlrshp; SUNY-CORTLAND; Athl Trng.

CALLEJA, MARK; Archbishop Molloy HS; Briarwood, NY; (Y); 94/409; French Clb; Spanish Clb; Yrbk Phtg; Trk; Hon Roll; Hndbll Tm Var 84-85; Ebony Yth Cltre Clb Mbr 84-85; Stony Brook; Engnr.

CALLEN, KEITH; Fredonia HS; Fredonia, NY; (Y); Art Clb; Computer Clb; Radio Clb; Science Clb; Spanish Clb; Swmmng; SUNY; Bus Admin.

CALLERY JR, PATRICK; Biship Kearney HS; Rochester, NY; (Y); Var Lcrss; Im Sftbl; High Hon Roll; Hon Roll.

CALLESTO, REBECCA; Attica Senior HS; Attica, NY; (S); 3/150; AFS; Church Yth Grp; Teachers Aide; Concert Band; Jazz Band; Mrchg Band; Nwsp Rptr; Acad All Amer 84; Intl Frgn Lang Awd 85.

CALLI, WILLIAM S; New Hartford SR HS; Utica, NY; (Y); 66/256; Latin Clb; Var Bsbl; Var Mgr(s); Score Keeper; Hon Roll; NY ST Rgnts Schlrshp 85; Cert Of Merit 85; Rensselaer Poly Inst; Attrny.

CALLIGHERIS, MICHAEL; Ward Melville HS; Stony Brook, NY; (Y); 195/725; Church Yth Grp; Var Bsbl; Var Bsktbl; Var Ftbl; Var Wt Lftg; High Hon Roll; Hon Roll; Var Vllybl; Engrng.

CALLOVI, FRANK; La Salle Acad; Brooklyn, NY; (Y); 33/257; Rep Frsh Cls; VP Soph Cls; Sec Jr Cls; Im Bsktbl; Im Fld Hcky; Im Ftbl; Im Vllybl; Hon Roll; Computer Clb; Hon Roll 81-84; Baruch Coll; Acctng.

CALOBRISI, DONNA; John H Glenn HS; E Northport, NY; (Y); 58/260; Dance Clb; Girl Scts; Variety Show; Stu Cncl; Bowling; Cheerleading; Pom Pon; Swmmng; Vllybl; High Hon Roll; Chrldg Awd; SUNY Stonybrook; Math.

CALOGERO, MARY; Mercury HS; Albany, NY; (Y); 1/65; Math Clb; Nwsp Stf; High Hon Roll; NHS; Val; Martin Luther King Schlrshp 85; Siena Coll; Bio.

CALTABELLOTTA, FRAN; Lincoln HS; Yonkers, NY; (Y); 76/303; Cmnty Wkr; Yrbk Stf; Schlrshp Westchester Bus Inst 85-87; Bus Cert 85; Regnst Diplma 85; Westchester Bus Inst; Secy.

CALTEAUX, KELLY A; Hutch Tech; Buffalo, NY; (Y); Library Aide; Rep Sr Cls; Nrsng.

CALVAO, MARIA; Mount Vernon HS; Mount Vernon, NY; (Y); Computer Clb; French Clb; Spanish Clb; Church Choir; High Hon Roll; Hon Roll; Hnrs Math 83; Data Proc.

CALVERT, KEVIN; Southampton HS; Southampton, NY; (Y); Trs Spanish Clb; VP Frsh Cls; Rep Stu Cncl; JV Bsbl; Var Capt Socr; High Hon Roll; Hon Roll; Ntl Hnr Soc 84-85; Boston Coll; Sci.

CALVO, CARMELA; Lafayette HS; New York, NY; (Y); Math Tm; MMM; Concert Band; Jazz Band; Yrbk Stf; High Hon Roll; NHS; NY U; Med.

CALVO, NELLA; Lafayette HS; New York, NY; (Y); Math Tm; Model UN; Concert Band; Jazz Band; Yrbk Stf; High Hon Roll; NHS; NY U; Bus.

CAMACHO, DOMENIQUE; Sachem High School North Campus; Holbrook, NY; (Y); 44/1389; Intnl Clb; Spanish Clb; Chorus; Concert Band; Mrchg Band; Orch; School Musical; Symp Band; Jr NHS; NHS; GSA Slvr Awd 82-83; 2nd Sci Fair 84; Pre-Med.

CAMACHO, EMELINA; St Johns Prep; Woodside, NY; (S); 7/570; Dance Clb; Drama Clb; Leo Clb; Chorus; School Musical; School Play; Rep Frsh Cls; Pres Soph Cls; Pres Jr Cls; Pres Stu Cncl; Amer Chem Scty Awd 84; 1st Hnrs; Columbia U; Psych.

CAMACHO, GRISELL; Grover Cleveland HS; Brooklyn, NY; (Y); 24/659; Cmnty Wkr; Rptr FBLA; Hosp Aide; Office Aide; Red Cross Aide; Spanish Clb; Teachers Aide; Hon Roll; NHS; St Schlr; Pre-Med.

CAMACHO, HELAN; Nazareth Acad; Rochester, NY; (S); Office Aide; Spanish Clb; Spanish NHS; Distngshed Achvt European Cul Stus 84; Francie Nolan Awd 84; Hghst Mark African-Asian Cultrs 83.

CAMACHO, NOEL; Cardinal Hayes HS; Bronx, NY; (Y); 2/264; Dance Clb; Library Aide; Service Clb; Nwsp Ed-Chief; Yrbk Phtg; Hon Roll; NHS; Prfct Atten Awd; Val; Voice Dem Awd; Awd From Diamond H Clb 82-85; Comp.

CAMACHO, PATRICIA M; St Catharine Acad; Bronx, NY; (Y); Church Yth Grp; Stu Cncl; NHS; Prfct Atten Awd; Wood Bus Schl; Legal Secr.

CAMACHO JR, RAMON; St Johns Preparatory HS; Brooklyn, NY; (Y); 20/540; Science Clb; High Hon Roll; Hon Roll; NHS; Schl Sci Fair Wnnr 1st Pl 84; Cornell U; Vet Med.

CAMANN, MOLLY; No Tonawanda SR HS; N Tonawanda, NY; (Y); Drama Clb; Spanish Clb; School Play; Nwsp Ed-Chief; VP Stu Cncl; JV Var Cheerleading; Cit Awd; Hon Roll; Jr NHS; NHS; Spnsh.

CAMARA, JANETTE; Adlai E Stevenson HS; Bronx, NY; (Y); Chorus; Stage Crew; Cheerleading; Tennis; Hon Roll; Burmingham Coll; Lwyr.

CAMBI, MICHAEL G; Yorktown HS; Yorktown Heights, NY; (Y); 2/364; Key Clb; Teachers Aide; Orch; Var Capt Bsbl; Bausch & Lomb Sci Awd; Pres NHS; Ntl Merit Ltr; Val; Church Yth Grp; French Clb; TJ Watson Mem Schlrshp 85; PTSA Awd; Notr Dame Schlr; Pres Astronomy Clb; U Of Notre Dame; Engrng.

CAMBIO, ELENA M; Notre Dame HS; Elmira, NY; (Y); French Clb; Hosp Aide; Service Clb; Church Choir; Orch; School Musical; Nwsp Ed-Chief; Nwsp Rptr; Lit Mag; Hon Roll; Fr Reagan Schlrshp 82-84; Jrnlsm.

CAMERON, CATHY; Massena Central HS; Massena, NY; (Y); Pres Church Yth Grp; Leo Clb; Color Guard; Hon Roll; Prfct Atten Awd; Canton ATC; Elem Educ.

CAMERON, CHRISTINA JEAN; Longwood HS; Coram, NY; (Y); 32/495; Chrmn Am Leg Aux Girls St; Pres VP Exploring; Q&S; Chorus; Lit Mag; Var L Socr; Var L Trk; High Hon Roll; Jr NHS; Ntl Merit SF; Mrn Corps NROTC Schlrshp Fnlst 85-86; U Of CA Berkley; Intl Rltns.

CAMERON, DEBBIE; South Shore HS; Brooklyn, NY; (Y); Cmnty Wkr; Drama Clb; Teachers Aide; School Play; Long Island U; Bus.

CAMERON, GREGORY; Queensbury HS; Glens Falls, NY; (Y); Varsity Clb; JV Bsbl; JV Civic Clb; JV Var Ftbl; JV Var Wrstlng; Hon Roll; Econ.

CAMERON, MATTHEW; James Madison HS; Brooklyn, NY; (Y); Chess Clb; School Musical; Trk; Wrstlng; Chopin Fndtn U S NY Chptr Awd 83; Brooklyn Arts & Cultr Assn Awd 82; Syracuse JR Olymp 84; Music.

CAMERON, RICHARD R; Shenendehowa HS; Ballston Lake, NY; (Y); VP Chess Clb; Computer Clb; Church Choir; Ed Yrbk Phtg; Rep Jr Cls; Rep Stu Cncl; High Hon Roll; NHS; Ntl Merit Ltr; Outstndng Physics Stu Awd 84-85; Peer Cnclng 83-85; Physcl Sci.

CAMERON, SCOTT; Farmingdale HS; Farmingdale, NY; (Y); Cmnty Wkr; German Clb; Varsity Clb; Var L Crs Cntry; Var L Trk; Hon Roll; Rotary Awd.

CAMIC, JAMES; Henninger HS; Syracuse, NY; (Y); French Clb; High Hon Roll; NY ST Regents Schlrshp $250 85; Palmer Coll; Chiropractics.

CAMILE, LAWRENCE; Adlai E Stevenson HS; Bronx, NY; (Y); Church Yth Grp; Church Choir; Socr; Hnr Outstndng Svc Stevenson Vol 84; Nrs.

CAMINITI, KRISTEN; Union Endicott HS; Endwell, NY; (Y); Var Trk; Hon Roll; Photo.

CAMINITI, LISA A; Bishop Kearney HS; Brooklyn, NY; (Y); Ski Clb; Bowling; Var Tennis; Cathlc HS Schlrshp 85; NY ST Regents Schlrshp 85; St Johns U; Bus Mgmt.

CAMINITI, PAUL J; Pelham Memorial HS; Pelham Manor, NY; (Y); 1/177; Pres Spanish Clb; Lit Mag; Trk; High Hon Roll; Hon Roll; NHS; Spanish NHS; Val; SR Dble Sculls Champ Schlstc Rowing Assn 84; SR Dble Sculls Champ Stotesbory Cup Regatta 84; Princeton U; Comp Prog.

CAMINITI, SUSAN M; Bishop Kearney HS; Brooklyn, NY; (Y); Ski Clb; Bowling; Var Tennis; Regents Schlrshp 85; St Johns U; Phy Asst.

CAMINITO, MARIE; Deer Park HS; Deer Park, NY; (Y); Chorus; Mrchg Band; Variety Show; Socr; High Hon Roll; Hon Roll; Comp Pgmr.

CAMLOH, KAREN; Tully Central Schl; Lafayette, NY; (Y); Drama Clb; Varsity Clb; School Musical; Yrbk Stf; Sec Stu Cncl; Var Cheerleading; JV Socr; Var Trk; JV Var Vllybl; Hon Roll; Ad.

CAMMACK III, WILLIAM C; Bronx High School Of Science; New York, NY; (Y); Boys Clb Am; Chess Clb; Church Yth Grp; Computer Clb; Office Aide; Teachers Aide; Ntl Merit SF; Comp Pgmr.

CAMMARATA, CHARLES V; Tottenville HS; Staten Island, NY; (Y); Camera Clb; Hon Roll; NHS; NYS Regents Schlrshp; Rutgers Engineering; Electronic.

CAMMARATA, SALVATRICE; Nardin Acad; Buffalo, NY; (Y); Debate Tm; Office Aide; Political Wkr; Speech Tm; Yrbk Stf; Lit Mag; Hon Roll; Girl Scts; Hosp Aide; Science Clb; American Legn Oratrcl Awd-3rd Pl 83-84; Canisius/Nichols Oratrcl Contst-6th Pl 83-84; Keuka Coll; Law.

CAMMARERI, MARIEANN; Our Lady Of Perpetual Help HS; Brooklyn, NY; (Y); Art Clb; Hon Roll.

CAMMAROTA, JEANINE; Rocky Point HS; Rocky Pt, NY; (Y); 35/200; Band; Mrchg Band; JV Var Cheerleading; JV Sftbl; Hon Roll; Fash Design.

CAMMILLERI, JAMES; Northstar Christian Acad; Brockport, NY; (S); JA; Ski Clb; VP Jr Cls; Socr; Sftbl; Wt Lftg; Wrstlng; High Hon Roll; Hon Roll; NHS; Wrstlng Awd 84; Aviatn.

CAMP, ANDY; Queensburg HS; Glens Falls, NY; (Y); Art Clb; Yrbk Stf; Lit Mag; JV Bsbl; Var Bowling; JV Ftbl; High Hon Roll; Hon Roll; Rookie Yr Vrsty Bsebl 85; MVP Vrsty Bowling 85; Art.

CAMP, ELIZABETH; North Rose-Wolcott HS; Wolcott, NY; (Y); Church Yth Grp; Cmnty Wkr; Ski Clb; Varsity Clb; Variety Show; Yrbk Bus Mgr; Stu Cncl; Var Socr; Cit Awd; Hon Roll.

CAMP, MICHAEL D; Lockport SR HS; Lockport, NY; (Y); AFS; Church Yth Grp; Teachers Aide; Church Choir; JV Ice Hcky; Jr NHS; Niagare U; Optmtrst.

CAMP, PAUL E; Highland HS; Highland, NY; (Y); 2/120; Pres French Clb; Quiz Bowl; School Play; Yrbk Stf; Rep Stu Cncl; Var L Tennis; French Hon Soc; VP NHS; Drama Clb; JA; Acad Achvt Awd Chem & Eng 85; Acad Achvt French 84; Intl Bus Law.

CAMPAGNA, MICHELE; Sheepshead Bay HS; Brooklyn, NY; (Y); Cmnty Wkr; French Clb; Science Clb; Service Clb; Spanish Clb; School Play; High Hon Roll; Hon Roll; Stu Cncl; Daily News Pride Of Yankees Awd 85; Hnr Schl Chrprsn 85; Mock City Cncl Rep 85.

CAMPANELLA, CHERYL; Mount Mercy Acad; Derby, NY; (Y); VP Church Yth Grp; JA; Spanish Clb; Im Powder Puff Ftbl; JV Vllybl; Hon Roll; Pol Sci.

CAMPANELLA, PETER; Smithtown High Schl East; Nesconset, NY; (Y); Exploring; VP Frsh Cls; Rep Soph Cls; VP Stu Cncl; JV Bsbl; JV Ftbl; Wrstlng; Cit Awd; High Hon Roll; Jr NHS; Pre-Med.

CAMPANELLI, LEEANN; West Seneca East SR HS; Buffalo, NY; (Y); Ski Clb; Chorus; JV Cheerleading; High Hon Roll; NHS; Peer Cnslng Substance Abuse 84-85; St Bonaventure U; Pre-Med.

CAMPANILE, MICHAEL; Chaminade HS; Inwood L I, NY; (Y); 114/416; Boy Scts; Church Yth Grp; Cmnty Wkr; FBLA; Mathletes; Science Clb; Band; Concert Band; Mrchg Band; Orch; Spllg Bee 84; Hofstra U; Acctg.

CAMPBELL, ALISON; Manhasset HS; Manhasset, NY; (Y); Service Clb; Pres Frsh Cls; Pres Soph Cls; VP Jr Cls; Pres Sr Cls; Var Socr; High Hon Roll; Jr NHS; NHS; Sprts Nght Comptn 83-85; Natl Sci Olympd Physcs Distnctn 85; Bus.

CAMPBELL, ALISON J; Wheatland-Chili HS; Scottsville, NY; (Y); 2/68; VP Model UN; Band; VP Chorus; Yrbk Stf; Var Diving; Var Socr; Hon Roll; NHS; Sal; VFW Awd; Pres Of Stu Cncl 84-85; Cornell U; Cons Econ.

CAMPBELL, CARA E; Shenendehowa HS; Ballston Lake, NY; (Y); 41/750; Intnl Clb; Flag Corp; Varsity Clb; Concert Band; Stu Cncl; Mgr(s); JV Powder Puff Ftbl; Trk; High Hon Roll; NHS; Scientific.

CAMPBELL, CATHLEEN; Southwestern Central HS; Jamestown, NY; (Y); French Clb; Ski Clb; Band; Trs Chorus; Mrchg Band; School Musical; Yrbk Stf; Hon Roll; Fredonia; Commnctns.

CAMPBELL, CHARLES EDWARD; Bishop Maginn HS; Albany, NY; (Y); 42/114; JA; Yrbk Stf; Rep Frsh Cls; Var Capt Bowling; Crs Cntry; Hon Roll; Prfct Atten Awd; Albany Jr Bowling Assc High Sngle Awd 82-83; Outstndng Bowler HS Awd 85; Hudson Vlly Cmnty Coll; Comp.

CAMPBELL, CHRISTINE M; Nyack HS; Valley Cottage, NY; (Y); 22/270; Drama Clb; Sec Intnl Clb; Sec Spanish Clb; Band; Concert Band; Drill Tm; Stage Crew; Yrbk Stf; High Hon Roll; NHS; Knights Of Puthias Schlstc Achvt Awd 85; Spansh Clb & Hnr Soc Svc Awds 83-85; SUNY Binghamton; Librl Arts.

CAMPBELL, DAVE; Churchville-Chili SR HS; Churchville, NY; (Y); Library Aide; Pep Clb; High Hon Roll; Hon Roll; Natrl Sci.

CAMPBELL, DAVE; Sougerties HS; Saugerties, NY; (Y); Varsity Clb; Symp Band; JV Var Bsktbl; JV Capt Socr; Var Trk; Hon Roll; NHS; Ntl Merit SF.

CAMPBELL, DAWN; Dominican Commercial HS; S Ozone Park, NY; (Y); Rep Church Yth Grp; Hosp Aide; Spanish Clb; Church Choir; Swmmng; Var Wt Lftg; High Hon Roll; Comp.

CAMPBELL, DUFF; Vernon Verona Sherrill Central HS; Vernon Ctr, NY; (Y); Boy Scts; 4-H; Rep Frsh Cls; Rep Stu Cncl; Stat Score Keeper; Hon Roll; Morrisville Coll; Acctg.

CAMPBELL, HEATHER ROSEMARY; Baldwin SR HS; Baldwin, NY; (Y); 3/503; Trs Debate Tm; Drama Clb; Hosp Aide; Model UN; Pres Science Clb; Pres Orch; School Musical; School Play; Lit Mag; Stu Cncl; March Dimes Hlth Prof Schlrshp 85; Discvr Mag Sci Schlrshp Rnnr Up 85; Akron Awd Music 85; Cornell U; Bio.

CAMPBELL, JAMES P; Paul V Moore HS; Bernhards Bay, NY; (Y); 84/297; JV Bsbl; Hon Roll; Regents Schlrshp 85; Oswego Coll; Comp Sci.

CAMPBELL, JENNIFER; Williamsville East HS; Williamsville, NY; (Y); 6/299; French Clb; Trs Latin Clb; Ski Clb; Rep Stu Cncl; Var L Fld Hcky; Trk; High Hon Roll; Outstndg Mbr Yth Engd Svc 84; Gold Medal ACLNJCL Antl Latin Exam 84; Math.

CAMPBELL, KAREN; St Nicholas Of Tolentine HS; Bronx, NY; (S); Pres Stu Cncl; Swmmng; Vllybl; 1st & 2nd Hnrs 81-85; Barlich Coll; Mngmnt.

CAMPBELL, KAREN; Stella Maris HS; Far Rockaway, NY; (Y); Church Yth Grp; French Clb; Hosp Aide; Bowling; Hon Roll; St Johns U; Bio.

CAMPBELL, KATHLEEN; Catholic Central HS; Troy, NY; (S); 11/207; Hosp Aide; Math Tm; Office Aide; Yrbk Stf; Rep Sr Cls; Rep Stu Cncl; Capt Cheerleading; Pom Pon; High Hon Roll; NHS; Nrsng.

CAMPBELL, KAY; Cuba Central Schl; Friendship, NY; (Y); 3/65; Spanish Clb; Varsity Clb; Yrbk Stf; Trs Frsh Cls; VP Sr Cls; Tennis; Vllybl; High Hon Roll; NHS; St Engy Res Comp 85; Acctant.

CAMPBELL, KRISTINA; Peekskill HS; Peekskill, NY; (Y); 28/165; VP Jr Cls; High Hon Roll; Hon Roll; Peekskill Retird Tchrs Assn 85; Edward Shulman Awd 85; Silvr Schlr Pin 85; SUNY New Paltz; Elem Ed.

CAMPBELL, LAURA; St Saviour HS; Brooklyn, NY; (Y); 30/79; Drama Clb; Stage Crew; Variety Show; Nwsp Phtg; Nwsp Stf; Cheerleading; NYS Rgnts Nrsng Schlrshp 85; Cert Of Part 85; St Johns U; Librl Arts.

CAMPBELL, LORRAINE; Sanford H Calhoun HS; Merrick, NY; (Y); Church Yth Grp; Chorus; Rep Soph Cls; Rep Jr Cls; Hon Roll; NHS; Hm Econ Medal 82-83; Englsh Achvmnt Awd 8-83; Spnsh Achvmnt Awd 82-83; Northeastern U; Bus Adm.

CAMPBELL, MATTHEW C; Mynderse Acad; Seneca Falls, NY; (Y); 12/130; Boy Scts; Model UN; School Musical; Rep Frsh Cls; Crs Cntry; Tennis; High Hon Roll; Hon Roll; NHS; St Schlr; Secrty Cncl Awd 84; Mbl Corp Sci Olympc 84; U Of Rochester; Pol Sci.

CAMPBELL, MICHELLE; Christopher Columbus HS; Mt Vernon, NY; (Y); Camp Fr Inc; Church Yth Grp; Cmnty Wkr; Dance Clb; Drama Clb; 4-H; FHA; Hosp Aide; Key Clb; Math Clb; Outstndng Attdnce 84; Bus.

CAMPBELL, PAMELA JEAN; Tioga Central HS; Sayre, PA; (Y); Hosp Aide; Teachers Aide; Band; Chorus; Drm & Bgl; Variety Show; Vllybl; Hon Roll; RIT; Acctng.

CAMPBELL, RANDY; Midwood HS; Brooklyn, NY; (Y); Drama Clb; Chorus; Color Guard; Lit Mag; Cheerleading; JV Crs Cntry; Var Trk; Hon Roll; Borough Pres Goldn Rec Of Achvt 83; Air Force Acad; Pilot.

CAMPBELL, RICHELLE; North Rose-Wolcott HS; North Rose, NY; (Y); 14/125; FBLA; FFA; Spanish Clb; Teachers Aide; Yrbk Ed-Chief; VP Sec Stu Cncl; Var Cheerleading; High Hon Roll; Hon Roll; NHS; Mst Imprvd Chrldr 83; Mst Val Chrldr 85; UNY Geneseo; Acctg.

CAMPBELL, ROBERT; Lansingburgh HS; Troy, NY; (S); 1/190; Trs German Clb; Jazz Band; Mrchg Band; Trs Sr Cls; High Hon Roll; Jr NHS; Pres NHS; Pres Schlr; St Schlr; Val; Rensselaer Medl Excel Math, Sci 84.

CAMPBELL, SANDRA; Sherburne-Earlville HS; Sherburne, NY; (S); 5/142; Pres Band; Concert Band; Drm Mjr(t); Mrchg Band; Trs Frsh Cls; Sec Soph Cls; Sec Jr Cls; High Hon Roll; NHS; Ntl Sci Merit Awd 85; Hartwick Coll; Comp Sci.

CAMPBELL, SANDRA; South Park HS; Buffalo, NY; (Y); 10/350; Nwsp Stf; Bus.

CAMPBELL, SHAUN; Wellsville HS; Wellsville, NY; (Y); Debate Tm; Intnl Clb; Key Clb; Ski Clb; School Musical; Stage Crew; Nwsp Bus Mgr; Rep Stu Cncl.

CAMPBELL, SHERYL; Norwood Norfolk Central HS; Raymondville, NY; (Y); Cmnty Wkr; Drama Clb; French Clb; Girl Scts; Lit Mag; Rep Stu Cncl; Trk; Cit Awd; High Hon Roll; Hon Roll; Bus Adm.

CAMPBELL, THERESA A; E Syracuse Minoa Central HS; E Syracuse, NY; (Y); 20/338; Science Clb; Var Capt Tennis; NHS; Ntl Merit Ltr; St Schlr; Voice Dem Awd; NFL; Ski Clb; Speech Tm; Variety Show; SUNY-ALBANY; Comm.

CAMPBELL, TROY; John Jay HS; Wappinger Falls, NY; (S); 258/570; DECA; Rgnl, Silver Merit & Natl Merit Awds For DECA 84-85; Johnson ST; Bus Ad.

CAMPFIELD, MARYBETH; Commack HS North; E Northport, NY; (Y); Civic Clb; Spanish Clb; Chorus; School Musical; School Play; Yrbk Stf; Jr Cls; Trk; High Hon Roll; NHS.

CAMPIERI, LISA; Mc Kinley HS; Buffalo, NY; (Y); 39/198; Cmnty Wkr; Dance Clb; JA; Office Aide; Pep Clb; Ski Clb; Varsity Clb; Rep Soph Cls; Rep Jr Cls; Rep Sr Cls; I Dare You Awd 85; Amer Legn Cert Schl Awd 85; Canisius Coll; Pol Sci.

CAMPIONE, MARK; Tottenville HS; Staten Island, NY; (Y); 249/897; Spanish Clb; Teachers Aide; Stage Crew; Wt Lftg; Wrstlng; JETS Awd; Ind Arts, Tech Awd 85; Drftsmnshp Awd 85; Arch.

CAMPISANO, DONALD J; Eden Central HS; Eden, NY; (Y); Am Leg Boys St; Debate Tm; Model UN; School Musical; Rep Stu Cncl; Bsbl; Bsktbl; Vllybl; Hon Roll; NHS; Bus Mgt.

CAMPISE, KAREN; Kings Park HS; Kings Pk, NY; (Y); 8/398; Band; Mrchg Band; Symp Band; Jr NHS; NHS; Cmnty Wkr; Hosp Aide; Spanish Clb; Teachers Aide; Yrbk Stf; Ntl Math Exam-Hnrbl Mntn 83-84; Untd Cerebral Palsy Vlntr Awd For Svc 82-84.

CAMPISI, MARK; St Marys Boys HS; Sands Point, NY; (S); VP Stu Cncl; Mgr Bsktbl; Var Lcrss; JV Swmmng; Ski Clb; Hon Roll.

CAMPO, CINDY A; School Of The Holy Child; Syosset, NY; (Y); Church Yth Grp; Dance Clb; Drama Clb; Chorus; Church Choir; School Musical; School Play; Variety Show; Stu Cncl; Socr; Desire Parenti Awd 84; Achvt Awds In Mus, Dance & Drama 83-84; Mus.

CAMPO, JOHANNA; Amsterdam HS; Amsterdam, NY; (Y); 26/300; Yrbk Stf; Hon Roll; NHS; Prfct Atten Awd; Engl Club Awd 85; Math.

CAMPOLI, JAMES; Valley Central HS; Montgomery, NY; (Y); 5/300; Ed Lit Mag; Var L Crs Cntry; Var L Trk; High Hon Roll; NHS; Ntl Merit Ltr; Spanish NHS; JR Olymps 1500 Mtr Wlk 84; 7th TAC Natl Schltc Clssc 1600 Mtr Wlk 85; Empre ST Gmes 5000 Mtr Wlk 85; Sys Anlyst.

CAMPOLO III, PHILIP A; Bishop Grimes HS; E Syracuse, NY; (Y); 8/250; Exploring; FBLA; Trs VP Stu Cncl; JV Var Bsktbl; Var Golf; JV Socr; JV Trk; Hon Roll; NHS; Hon Amer HS Athl 85; Acad All Amer Schlr 85; Pres Natl Hon Soc 85-86; Acctg.

CAMPOREALE, GRACE; St John Villa Acad; Staten Island, NY; (Y); 20/144; Math Tm; Chorus; School Musical; School Play; Yrbk Stf; Sftbl; Hon Roll; Acdmc Schlrshp Frm Seton Hall 85-89; Seton Hall U; Pltcl Sci.

CAMPOS, ALFRED; Bishop Ford Central Catholic HS; Brooklyn, NY; (Y); #44 In Class; Boy Scts; Drama Clb; Exploring; Ski Clb; School Play; VP Stu Cncl; JV Bsbl; Im Ftbl; Swmmng; Hon Roll; Law.

CAMPOS, ILEANA; Norman Thomas HS; New York, NY; (S); 28/671; Computer Clb; Spanish Clb; Band; Nwsp Stf; Cit Awd; Hon Roll; Prfct Atten Awd; Engrng.

CAMPS, ELIZABETH; St Vincent Ferrer HS; Woodside, NY; (Y); 5/114; Math Tm; Color Guard; Drm & Bgl; High Hon Roll; Hon Roll; Ntl Merit Ltr; NEDT Awd; Mrchg Band; Medal Exc Geo 84; Cert Merit Eng,Spnsh 85; Columbia; Astrophysics.

CANADY, SUSAN ROBERTA KAY; Clarkstown South SR HS; W Nyack, NY; (Y); Girl Scts; Office Aide; Band; Color Guard; Concert Band; Mrchg Band; Symp Band; Stu Cncl; Im Powder Puff Ftbl; IN U; Pre-Law.

CANAGUIER, MICHELE; Sauquoit Valley Central HS; Clayville, NY; (Y); 12/100; GAA; Chorus; Rep Sr Cls; Capt Bowling; JV Var Fld Hcky; Var Mgr(s); High Hon Roll; NHS; NEDT Awd; Rotary Awd; Accntnt.

CANAL, REGINALD; Brooklyn Technical HS; Queens, NY; (Y); French Clb; JA; Office Aide; Teachers Aide; Rep Frsh Cls; Hon Roll; NHS; Comprehensive Math & Sci Pgm Awd 85; Tech Drwng & Arch Dept Awd-Cert Of Excllnc 84; Med.

CANALES ACEVEDO, HAYDEE E; St Pius V HS; Bronx, NY; (Y); 20/70; Church Yth Grp; Intnl Clb; JA; Service Clb; Spanish Clb; Nwsp Stf; Yrbk Stf; Hon Roll; Ntl Merit Ltr; Prfct Atten Awd; Eng Hon Men 83; Europn Cultr Excptnl Effrt 84; Alg II & Trig Excptnl Effrt 85; Marymount Manhattan Coll; Psych.

CANALES ACEVEDO, VILMA MARIA; St Pius V HS; Bronx, NY; (Y); 1/71; Church Yth Grp; Cmnty Wkr; Intnl Clb; Scholastic Bowl; Service Clb; Spanish Clb; Stage Crew; Yrbk Rptr; Yrbk Sprt Ed; Yrbk Stf; Gen Excell & Sci Medals 85; Natl Hnr Scty Outstndg Cert Awd 85; NY City Comptrlr Awd Math & Sci 85; Gaudalajara U Of Mexico; Med.

CANAN, MAUREEN; Fairport HS; Fairport, NY; (Y); Art Clb; Varsity Clb; Var Cheerleading; Hon Roll; Ntl Hnr 82-85; WV U; Bus.

CANAROZZI, CHRISTINA; Brewster HS; Brewster, NY; (S); 36/176; Varsity Clb; Chorus; Sec Jr Cls; Sec Sr Cls; Capt Crs Cntry; Trk; Jr NHS; Sec NHS; MVP, MIP X-Cntry 83-84; Spnsh Achvt 83; Plattsburg; Spec Ed.

CANCEL, MELISSA; St Johns Prepartory HS; Long Isld Cty, NY; (Y); Girl Scts; Chorus; Church Choir; Off Jr Cls; Mgr(s); Sftbl; Ed.

CANDELARIA, MARCELINO; Theodore Roosevelt HS; Bronx, NY; (Y); 5/595; Computer Clb; Trk; Hon Roll; Crs Cntry; Intntl Plytx Schlrshp 85; Assn Tchrs Socl Studs UFT Cert 85; Parnts Assn Awds Outstndng Achv 85; Embry-Riddle U; Aerontcl Sci.

CANDELL, SCOT; Half Hollow Hills HS; Dix Hills, NY; (Y); 47/500; Capt Debate Tm; Model UN; Jazz Band; VP Jr Cls; Pres Stu Cncl; Capt Tennis; High Hon Roll; VP NHS; Leo Clb; NFL; NYS Debate Champshp 5th Pl 84; NYS Mod Cngrss 4th Pl 85; Law.

CANDEMERES, PATRICIA; St Francis Prep; Flushing, NY; (S); 105/704; Cmnty Wkr; GAA; Varsity Clb; Lit Mag; Var Bsktbl; Coach Actv; Trk; Hon Roll; NHS; Opt Clb Awd; Comm Art.

CANDINO, BETH A; Mt St Mary Acad; Kenmore, NY; (Y); 13/96; Intnl Clb; Teachers Aide; Stage Crew; Var Tennis; Hon Roll; Part Scolar Intl Stdy Madrd Spain 84; Canisius Coll; Biochem.

CANDY, MATTHEW E; North Tonawanda SR HS; N Tonawanda, NY; (Y), Am Leg Boys St; Boy Scts; Rep Jr Cls; Stu Cncl; Var L Crs Cntry; Var L Socr; Var L Swmmng; Var L Trk; NHS; Boys Clb Am; Eagl Sct 82; Ad & Alfare & Dei 81; Engrng.

CANE, TRACY; Saranac Central Schl; Dannemora, NY; (S); 1/106; Trs Church Yth Grp; Sec Drama Clb; Pres Sec 4-H; Sec French Clb; Band; School Musical; Yrbk Rptr; Yrbk Stf; High Hon Roll; NHS; Med.

CANEDO, NANCY; St Anthony HS; Smithtown, NY; (S); 30/264; Rep Frsh Cls; Sec Soph Cls; Rep Jr Cls; Rep Stu Cncl; Var Capt Cheerleading; Stat Sftbl; Spanish NHS; Algebra Exclnce Awd; Loyola U; Psych.

CANESTRARO, KENNETH; East Syracuse-Minoa Central HS; Clay, NY; (Y); Pres Computer Clb; DECA; Spanish Clb; Stu Cncl; Im JV Socr; Bus Admin.

CANFIELD JR, DAVID A; Averill Park HS; W Sand Lk, NY; (Y); 49/225; Varsity Clb; JV Var Ftbl; Im Wt Lftg; JV Wrstlng; Hon Roll; 3rd Pl Capital Dist Ind Arts Comp 83; NY St Rgnts Schlrshp 85; Excllnc Mechanical Drwng Awd 85; ST U Of NY; Civil Engrng.

CANFIELD, JENNIFER; Williamsville South HS; Williamsville, NY; (Y); Art Clb; Camera Clb; Dance Clb; Drama Clb; French Clb; Thesps; Acpl Chr; School Musical; School Play; Yrbk Phtg; ST U Of NY Buffalo.

CANLAS, JULIUS; St Francis Prep; Bellerose, NY; (S); Science Clb; Wrstlng; Hon Roll; Engrng.

CANNATO, VINCENT J; Byram Hills HS; Armonk, NY; (Y); Am Leg Boys St; Church Yth Grp; Radio Clb; Var L Bsbl; Var L Socr; High Hon Roll; Ntl Merit Ltr; Poli Sci.

CANNAVO, THOMAS J; St Josephs Collegiate Inst; Kenmore, NY; (Y); 8/200; JA; Office Aide; Chorus; Var L Crs Cntry; Var L Trk; Var Capt Wrstlng; High Hon Roll; NHS; Ntl Merit Ltr; Im Bowling; Mst Outstndng Wrstlr 84-85; Bus.

CANNELLA, JOANNE; Liverpool HS; Liverpool, NY; (S); 36/850; Ski Clb; Chorus; Concert Band; Stu Cncl; Var Tennis; Hon Roll; Jr NHS; NHS; Opt Clb Awd; Siena Coll; Intrl Stds.

CANNER, PATTI; Oneonta HS; Oneonta, NY; (Y); Key Clb; Trs Ski Clb; Varsity Clb; Var Capt Bsktbl; Var Socr; Var Sftbl; High Hon Roll; Hon Roll; VP NHS; All Star Soccr Awds 83 & 84; Bus.

CANNESTRA, SAL; Moore Catholic HS; Staten Island, NY; (S); Aud/Vis; Drama Clb; School Musical; School Play; Nwsp Rptr; VP Jr Cls; Bowling; NHS; Jrnlst.

CANNIFF, DEBRA; Union-Endicott HS; Endwell, NY; (S); Band; Mrchg Band; Engl.

CANNISI, GINA; Saint Francis Prep; Rego Pk, NY; (Y); Am Leg Aux Girls St; Band; Concert Band; JV Crs Cntry; JV Trk.

CANNISTA, NICHOLAS; Spackenkill HS; Poughkeepsie, NY; (Y); Church Yth Grp; Drama Clb; 4-H; Thesps; Band; Chorus; Concert Band; Jazz Band; Mrchg Band; Orch; Elec Engrng.

CANNON, AUSTIN E; Holy Trinity HS; N Bellmore, NY; (Y); 180/396; Am Leg Boys St; Boy Scts; Church Yth Grp; Drama Clb; Exploring; School Musical; School Play; Stage Crew; Variety Show; Rep Jr Cls; Nassau CC; Engrng.

CANNON, JOAN-MARIE; Fontbonne Hall Acad; Brooklyn, NY; (Y); 18/130; Church Yth Grp; Drama Clb; Teachers Aide; Hon Roll; NEDT Awd; Amer Classical Leag Natl JR Classical Leag 85; Magna Cum Laude Natl Latin Exam; Profssnl Wrtng.

CANNON, KELLYANNE; East Islip HS; Islip Terr, NY; (Y); 92/478; Church Yth Grp; Dance Clb; School Musical; Yrbk Ed-Chief; Yrbk Stf; Rep Sr Cls; Pom Pon; Hon Roll; Drama Clb; Sec FTA; Roothbert Schlrshp Fund 85; St Josephs Coll Awd 85; St Josephs Coll; Spcl Ed.

CANNON, LAURA; Clarkstown High School North; New City, NY; (Y); Spanish Clb; Var Bsktbl; High Hon Roll; Hon Roll; Jr NHS; Villanova; Corp Law.

CANNON, MARILYN; Brewster HS; Brewster, NY; (S); 28/217; Church Yth Grp; Ski Clb; Yrbk Stf; Stat Bsbl; Capt Cheerleading; Hon Roll; Sec NHS; Engrng.

CANNUCCIARI, JANICE A; Thomas R Proctor HS; Utica, NY; (Y); 1/203; Drama Clb; Math Tm; Political Wkr; Chorus; Stage Crew; Bausch & Lomb Sci Awd; Trs NHS; Opt Clb Awd; Pres Schlr; Val; Elmira Coll Outstndng Jr 83-84; Schlrshp Piaono 83-85; Hugh O Brian Ldrshp Smnr Mst Outstndt Soph 83; Utica Coll; Pre Med.

CANONICO, MELISSA; Sheepshead Bay HS; Brooklyn, NY; (Y); Cmnty Wkr; Office Aide; Teachers Aide; Chorus; Yrbk Stf; Cert Schrlshp Eng,Am Civics,Typng 85; Child Psych.

CANTANNO, ROSEMARIE; St Johns Prep; Long Island City, NY; (S); Drama Clb; Math Tm; Science Clb; Chorus; School Play; Variety Show; High Hon Roll; Pre-Med.

CANTONE, MICHAEL S; Roy C Ketcham SR HS; Poughkeepsie, NY; (Y); 88/507; Am Leg Boys St; Var L Bsbl; Var L Bsktbl; JV Ftbl; Im Golf; High Hon Roll; NHS; Pres Schlr; Rotary Awd; Var Bsbl ST Fin Tm 85; Brnz Mdl Empire ST Games 84; All Sectn Var Bsktbl 84-85; Ithaca Coll; Comm.

CANTOR, STEVEN; Lenox Schl; New York City, NY; (Y); Var Bsktbl; Var Capt Tennis; Var Sftbl.

CANTOR, STUART; Clarkstown South HS; W Nyack, NY; (Y); Im Bsktbl; Var Golf; Econ.

CANTY, KEVIN; William Nottingham HS; Syracuse, NY; (Y); Boy Scts; Var L Bsktbl; JV L Ftbl; Var L Trk; Excel Comp Sci Awd 85; Yth Ldrshp Dev Prog 84-85; Comp Engrng.

CANUP, ROBIN; Roy C Ketcham HS; Poughkeepsie, NY; (Y); Drama Clb; School Play; Nwsp Stf; Yrbk Stf; High Hon Roll; Jr NHS; NHS; Cornell; Bio-Chem Sci.

CANZANO, TERESA; Henninger HS; Syracuse, NY; (Y); Library Aide; Hon Roll; Cert Achvt Vol Svcs 84; Cleveland ST U; Tchng.

CAPACCI, CHRISTINE; Our Lady Of Mercy; Rochester, NY; (Y); 46/240; Cmnty Wkr; Dance Clb; French Clb; Hosp Aide; JA; Ski Clb; Varsity Clb; Var L Socr; High Hon Roll; Hon Roll; Amer U; Intl Bus.

CAPANNOLA, MARC; Niagara Catholic HS; Niagara Falls, NY; (Y); 15/90; Var L Bsbl; Var L Bsktbl; Var L Ftbl; High Hon Roll; Hon Roll; Jr NHS; NHS; U Of WV; Bus Mgmt.

CAPANO, ALLISON; Seaford HS; Seaford, NY; (Y); Am Leg Aux Girls St; Pres Jr Cls; VP Rep Stu Cncl; Var Badmtn; JV Cheerleading; Vllybl; High Hon Roll; Pres NHS; Eng Scholar Awd; Amer Stud Scholar Awd; Admin Awd Outstndg Svc & Schl Spirit.

CAPECE, LORENDA F; Dominican Commercial HS; Bayside, NY; (Y); Intnl Clb; Chorus; Church Choir; Iona Coll Lang Cont 85; Cnslr Oper FUN 83-84; Peer Grp Cnslr 85-86; Law.

CAPECI, JOANN; Moore Catholic HS; Staten Island, NY; (Y); Hosp Aide; Math Clb; Spanish Clb; Hon Roll; NHS; Pres Schlr; Coll Of Staten Island; Comp Sci.

CAPEL, ANNETTE; Bishop Scully HS; Amsterdam, NY; (Y); 18/69; French Clb; Yrbk Stf; Sec Soph Cls; French Hon Soc; Hon Roll; NHS; Profssnl Bus Womens Assn Schlrshp 85; Oswego ST; Bus.

CAPELLUPO, ANTHONY J; Mount St Michaels Acad; Bronx, NY; (S); 2/309; Church Yth Grp; Var Capt Bsbl; High Hon Roll; Hon Roll; NHS; Spanish NHS; NY U; Engrng.

CAPELLUPO, LISA A; Fairport HS; Fairport, NY; (Y); JA; Nwsp Ed-Chief; Nwsp Rptr; Yrbk Ed-Chief; Sec Soph Cls; Sec Sr Cls; Rep Stu Cncl; Hon Roll; Spanish NHS; Mss Lilac Tn Smi-Fnlst Rochester NY 85; SADA 84-85; Mc Curdy Tn Brd 84-85; Mrktng.

CAPERS, VICTOR; North Babylon SR HS; New York, NY; (Y); Chess Clb; Cmnty Wkr; Office Aide; Oswego ST U; Bio Hlth Sci.

CAPETANAKIS, MARIA; Fontbonne Hall Acad; Brooklyn, NY; (Y); French Clb; NCTE Awd; Drctns Adlt Lvng Acad Hnr Cert 85; Hlth Educ Acad Hnr Cert 84; Phy Thrpst.

CAPICOTTO, TONI; Newburgh Free Acad; Newburgh, NY; (Y); Art Clb; Computer Clb; FBLA; JA; Spanish Clb; Yrbk Stf; Hon Roll; Prfct Atten Awd; Laboratory Inst Fshn; Fshn Dsgn.

CAPIZZUTO, BARBARA; Herbert H Lehman HS; Bronx, NY; (Y); 13/444; Concert Band; Orch; School Musical; Hon Roll; Jr NHS; NHS; Acadmc All Amer 85; Hunter Coll; Elem Ed.

CAPLE, PAUL; Dover JR SR HS; Wingdale, NY; (Y); 11/113; Am Leg Boys St; Boy Scts; Drama Clb; School Musical; Nwsp Rptr; Sec Stu Cncl; Crs Cntry; High Hon Roll; Sec VP NHS; Voice Dem Awd; Area All St Chorus 83-84 & 84-85; Alfred U; Bus Law.

CAPOBIANCO, JENNIFER; Farmingdale HS; Farmingdale, NY; (Y); Computer Clb; Dance Clb; FBLA; Cheerleading; Im Gym; Oswego Coll; Data Proc.

CAPOCCI, GINA; Academy Of The Resrrctn; Pt Chester, NY; (Y); 5/63; Math Tm; Ed Yrbk Ed-Chief; Hon Roll; NHS; Acadmc Achvt Grnt 85; Iona Clg Schlrshp 85; Pace U Schlrshp 85; Manhattanville Clg; Bus Mgmt.

CAPODANNO, ANDREA T; Acad Of The Resrrctn; Larchmont, NY; (Y); 10/62; Art Clb; Aud/Vis; Camera Clb; NFL; Speech Tm; Chorus; Sec Sr Cls; NHS; Fordham U Deans Shlrshp 85; NYS Regnts Schlrshp 85; Fordham U.

CAPODANNO, NICOLE; Tottenville HS; Staten Island, NY; (Y); Teachers Aide; Variety Show; Fashion Inst Tech; Bus.

CAPOGNA, LISA; Smithtown High School West; Smithtown, NY; (Y); Church Yth Grp; Cmnty Wkr; Hon Roll; NHS; ITLN Clb, Hnr Soc Pres; Intl Bus.

CAPONE, DANIEL E; Shaker HS; Latham, NY; (Y); 9/409; Computer Clb; Drama Clb; Political Wkr; Spanish Clb; Church Choir; Stage Crew; Lit Mag; Ntl Merit Ltr; Grinnell Coll; Religion.

CAPONE, MICHAEL; Fowler HS; Syracuse, NY; (Y); Lit Mag; VP Sr Cls; Capt Ftbl; Trk; Wt Lftg; Capt Wrstlng; Hon Roll; NHS; Rotary Awd; Itln Amer Athlt Awd Outstndng Stu Athlt 85; Outstndng Mal Athlt Yr 85; Hobart Coll.

CAPONEGRO, CHERYL A; Smithtown HS West; Smithtown, NY; (Y); Scholastic Bowl; Orch; School Musical; Symp Band; French Hon Soc; High Hon Roll; Sec NHS; Ntl Merit Ltr; Princeton Bk Awd Semi Fnlst 82; NY All ST Band & Orch To Japan; Duke U.

CAPORIN, GEORGE; Altmar - Parish - Williamstown HS; Parish, NY; (Y); 3/115; French Clb; JV Var Bsktbl; JV Var Ftbl; Golf; Var Trk; Wt Lftg; High Hon Roll; VP NHS; Prfct Atten Awd; Meteorology.

CAPORUSCIO, ANDREA; Henninger HS; Syracuse, NY; (Y); GAA; Rep Frsh Cls; Rep Soph Cls; Rep Jr Cls; Off Sr Cls; Var Sftbl; Var Capt Swmmng; Var Vllybl; High Hon Roll; Patrick Spadafora Awd/Outstndng JR Fml Stu Athlt Awd 85; Pre-Med.

CAPOUS, TEDDY; Holy Cross HS; Bayside, NY; (Y); 83/320; Chess Clb; Church Yth Grp; Computer Clb; Drama Clb; JA; Library Aide; NFL; Science Clb; Ski Clb; Ice Hcky; Maritime Coll; Marine Engr.

CAPOZZI, SHAWN; Notre Dame HS; Pine City, NY; (Y); Church Yth Grp; Key Clb; Letterman Clb; Pep Clb; Ski Clb; Spanish Clb; Varsity Clb; Stage Crew; Nwsp Stf; VP Frsh Cls; Psych.

CAPPARA, DARLENE; Frontier Central SR HS; Hamburg, NY; (S); Cmnty Wkr; French Clb; Girl Scts; Office Aide; Hon Roll; NHS; Trocaire; Medical Technology.

CAPPELLETTI, KATHLEEN; Jamesville-Dewitt HS; Syracuse, NY; (Y); Church Yth Grp; Hosp Aide; Red Cross Aide; Im Cheerleading; Stat Lcrss; Var Swmmng; JV Trk; Hon Roll; Leag Champ Swim Team 82-84; 13th Pl Sctnl Meet 100 Yrd Brststrk 83; Wnng Swim Team Sctnls 83; Bus.

CAPPELLO, DEBBIE; Solvay HS; Syracuse, NY; (Y); VP JA; Sec VICA; Concert Band; Mrchg Band; Pep Band; Bowling; Sftbl; High Hon Roll; NHS; JR Achvrs Exec Of The Yr 84; NC All-St Concert Bnd 83; NC Cumberland All-Cnty Bnd 83; SUNY Envrnmntl Sci; Chem.

CAPPELLUZZO, PAUL; Minisink Valley HS; Slate Hill, NY; (Y); Church Yth Grp; Ski Clb; Yrbk Phtg; Socr; High Hon Roll; 6th Gup Natl Tang Soo Do Fed 85.

CAPRIO, DARLENE; St Francis Prep; Jamaica, NY; (S); 46/704; Math Clb; Office Aide; Color Guard; Nwsp Rptr; Im Sftbl; Hon Roll; NHS; Acad All Amer Schlr 85; Acad All Amer Schlar Large Div 85.

CAPRIOLI, PAUL; Arlington HS; Lagrangeville, NY; (Y); 10/596; Math Clb; Math Tm; Ntl Merit SF; Natl H S Slavic Hnr Soc 84; AATSEEL Awd Russian 84; Albany Coll; Pharmacy.

CAPUANO JR, PATRICK C; Bishop Ford Central Catholic HS; Brooklyn, NY; (Y); Cmnty Wkr; Dance Clb; Service Clb; Ftbl; Manhattan Schl Vis Arts; Film.

CAPUTI, MAURO; Mineola HS; Mineola, NY; (Y); Trs Computer Clb; Key Clb; Spanish Clb; Band; Concert Band; Mrchg Band; High Hon Roll; Jr NHS; Mgmnt.

CAPUTO, GINA; Pulaski Acad; Pulaski, NY; (S); Church Yth Grp; Drama Clb; French Clb; Math Clb; Color Guard; Concert Band; Mrchg Band; Var Cheerleading; Im Powder Puff Ftbl; Var L Vllybl; Snow Awd 84; Orthdntst.

CAPUTO, JACQUELINE; Pulaski Acad; Pulaski, NY; (S); Drama Clb; GAA; Math Clb; Color Guard; Var Cheerleading; Stat Ftbl; Var Tennis; Var Vllybl; Hon Roll; Schl Psych.

CAPUTO, JAMES R; Arlington HS; Poughkeepsie, NY; (Y); 88/590; Drama Clb; Model UN; Chorus; School Musical; School Play; JV Bsktbl; Golf; High Hon Roll; Engrng.

CAPUTO, JOHANNA; West Seneca East SR HS; West Seneca, NY; (S); VP DECA; Pep Clb; School Play; Rep Frsh Cls; Stu Cncl; Hon Roll; Jr NHS; W Seneca Yth Ct 84; 1st Pl Reg Comptn Jb Intrvw Techs 85; Tp 30 ST Offcrs Exm 85; Attrny.

CAPWELL, CAROLINE J; Vestal .sr HS; Vestal, NY; (Y); 25/450; Cmnty Wkr; French Clb; Hosp Aide; Varsity Clb; Yrbk Stf; Rep Stu Cncl; Var L Fld Hcky; Var L Trk; High Hon Roll; NHS; NY ST Regnts Schlrshp; Cornell U; Bus.

CARABALLO, JULIO; Cardinal Hayes HS; Bronx, NY; (Y); 139/264; St Johns U; Elec Engr.

CARACAPPA, DEIRDRE; Clarkstown H S South; W Nyack, NY; (Y); Office Aide; Ed Lit Mag; Felix V Festa Schlrshp 85; Ntl Hnr Rl 85; Temple U; Jrnlsm.

CARACCI, DIANA L; Gates-Chili HS; Rochester, NY; (Y); 19/464; Exploring; VP JA; Chorus; Yrbk Stf; Rep Jr Cls; High Hon Roll; Hon Roll; NHS; Regents Schlrshp 85; Monroe Comm Coll; Psych.

CARACCILO, CHRISTOPHER; Mynderse Acad; Seneca Falls, NY; (S); 9/140; Boy Scts; Drama Clb; Science Clb; Band; Chorus; VP Frsh Cls; VP Soph Cls; Rep Stu Cncl; Trk; High Hon Roll; Ntl Hnr 83-84; Eagle Scout 82; Lndscp Arch.

CARACCILO, LISA ANN; Myndeuse Acad; Seneca Falls, NY; (Y); GAA; Capt Bsktbl; Capt Socr; Sftbl; Hon Roll; Soccer Tm Empire ST Games 84-85.

CARACCIO, LISA; West Genesee HS; Syracuse, NY; (Y); GAA; Orch; JV Bsktbl; JV Socr; JV Sftbl; High Hon Roll; NHS; Silver Medl Empire St Games 84; Silver Medl 23 Mile Rd Race 84; Most Ded Awd Sprts 85; Bnkng.

CARAGINE, JOSEPH M; Walter Panas HS; Peekskill, NY; (Y); Band; Concert Band; Mrchg Band; Yrbk Stf; JV Bsbl; JV Var Ftbl; JV Lcrss; JV Socr; High Hon Roll; Hon Roll; Sci.

CARAMADRE, GINA; Sauquoit Valley Central HS; Sauquoit, NY; (Y); Art Clb; Camp Fr Inc; Church Yth Grp; Civic Clb; Cmnty Wkr; Exploring; FCA; 4-H; French Clb; GAA; Above Avg Home Ec, Engl, Art, Music, Sci 82; Above Avg Home Ec, Art, Music, Engl, Scl Stds 83; Art.

CARAMANNA, PATRICIA; Cicero N Syracuse HS; North Syracuse, NY; (S); 46/711; DECA; Exploring; French Clb; Math Tm; Band; Color Guard; Mrchg Band; Powder Puff Ftbl; Var Socr; Twrlr; Lemoyne College; Accountant.

CARAMES, KRISTINA; Richmond Hill HS; Richmond Hill, NY; (Y); Pres Key Clb; Spanish Clb; Yrbk Stf; Hon Roll; Fshn Merch.

CARAMORE, ROBERT; St Francis Prep; Queens Village, NY; (S); Band; Concert Band; School Musical; Im Ftbl; Im Sftbl; Im Vllybl; Hon Roll.

CARANELLA, CINDY; Connetquot HS; Ronkonkoma, NY; (S); 12/671; Rep Chorus; Trs Soph Cls; Trs Civic Clb; VP Sr Cls; VP Stu Cncl; JV Vllybl; Pres Jr NHS; NHS; Ntl Merit Ltr; Outstdng Span Stu Awd 82; Pol Sci.

CARANGELO, CHRISTIAN F; Gloversville HS; Gloversville, NY; (Y); Am Leg Boys St; Sec French Clb; Concert Band; Yrbk Stf; Rep Trs Stu Cncl; Capt Crs Cntry; Trk; Sec NHS; Mgt.

CARAPELLA, ELISSA E; Corning East HS; Corning, NY; (Y); Ski Clb; Concert Band; Yrbk Sprt Ed; Rep Soph Cls; Rep Jr Cls; Var Capt Cheerleading; Coach Actv; Trk; High Hon Roll; NHS; Chem.

CARAPELLA, JENNIFER; Eastchester SR HS; Eastchester, NY; (Y); Pres Leo Clb; Sec Jr Cls; Var Capt Bsktbl; JV Var Cheerleading; JV Var Sftbl; Jr NHS; NHS; MVP Bsktbl 84-85; All Lg Bsktbl 83-85; Ath Trainer.

CARBER, JUDITH T; St Catharine Acad; Bronx, NY; (Y); 12/190; VP Soph Cls; Rep Stu Cncl; High Hon Roll; NHS; Regents Schlrshp 85; Srgcl Nrs.

CARBINO, BURTON JOHN; L I Luthern JR/SR HS; Massapequa, NY; (S); 11/59; Computer Clb; Band; Nwsp Ed-Chief; Pres Soph Cls; Pres Jr Cls; Var Ftbl; High Hon Roll; NHS; NY ST Regents Scholar 85; Long Island JR Socr Lg Sportsmnshp Awd 81-83; Law.

CARBINSKI, JOHN; Jamesville Dewitt HS; Dewitt, NY; (Y); 110/250; Church Yth Grp; Exploring; FBLA; Yrbk Sprt Ed; Yrbk Stf; VP Frsh Cls; Var L Bsbl; Var Capt Bsktbl; Hon Roll; All Cty Bsbl,Bsktbl; Bus Mktg.

CARBONARO, MICHAEL J; Kings Park SR HS; Northport, NY; (Y); 94/446; Church Yth Grp; DECA; Band; Ed Yrbk Phtg; Rep Frsh Cls; Var L Lcrss; JV Score Keeper; High Hon Roll; Hon Roll; NHS; NY ST Regnts Schlrshp 85; Siena Coll; Comp Sci.

CARBONE, CHRISTINE; John Jay HS; Hopewell Jct, NY; (Y); Sec Boy Scts; Drama Clb; Girl Scts; Teachers Aide; Y-Teens; Chorus; School Musical; School Play; High Hon Roll; Hon Roll; All Cnty Chorus 83; Psych.

CARBONE, FRANK P; Regis HS; Brooklyn, NY; (Y); Church Yth Grp; Variety Show; Yrbk Sprt Ed; Rep Frsh Cls; Stu Cncl; Capt Bowling; Coach Actv; Hon Roll; Trsts Schlrshp NYU 85; Regnts, Fordham U Schlrshps 85; NYU; Bus Mgt.

CARBONE, JANELLE M; Adlai E Stevenson HS; Bronx, NY; (Y); 49/445; Debate Tm; Rep Sr Cls; Prfct Atten Awd; Var Sftbl; Rgnts Schlrshp 85; Pre Law.

CARBONE, NINA; Mount Vernon HS; Mount Vernon, NY; (Y); 4/750; Key Clb; Latin Clb; Office Aide; Sec Science Clb; Spanish Clb; School Musical; Nwsp Ed-Chief; Nwsp Rptr; Yrbk Rptr; Lit Mag; Stu Of Mnth-Lang & A P Amrcn Hstry; Stu ST Senate Forum Rep; Law.

CARBONE, SUSAN; Whitesboro SR HS; Utica, NY; (Y); Church Yth Grp; Cmnty Wkr; GAA; Hosp Aide; VP Stu Cncl; JV Sftbl; High Hon Roll; NHS; Chorus; Powder Puff Ftbl; Rep NY ST Summr Ldr Traing Inst 84.

CARBONE, SUSAN J; Maryvale SR HS; Cheektowaga, NY; (Y); 33/333; DECA; Drama Clb; French Clb; Acpl Chr; Yrbk Stf; Rep Stu Cncl; JV Capt Cheerleading; High Hon Roll; NHS; Prfct Atten Awd; Canisius Coll; Mrktng.

CARBONE, TOM; Warwick Valley HS; Warwick, NY; (Y); 72/200; Rep Sr Cls; Rep Stu Cncl; Bausch & Lomb Sci Awd; Hon Roll; Pres Cmnty Wkr; Stage Crew; Variety Show; Cert Of Mrt 84; Aero-SP Tech.

CARBONE, TRINA; Rochester Christian HS; Penfield, NY; (S); 1/7; Chorus; Concert Band; Camp Fr Inc; VP Sr Cls; Bsktbl; Socr; High Hon Roll; Prfct Atten Awd; Val; Excell Geomtry 83-84; Excell Wrld Hist 83-84; St John Fisher; Bus.

CARBONI, CHRIS; Hutch-Tech HS; Buffalo, NY; (Y); 50/262; Chess Clb; Computer Clb; Capt Debate Tm; VP Band; VP Concert Band; Jazz Band; Mrchg Band; Rep Stu Cncl; Mgr Socr; Rgnts Schlrshp 85; SUNY Buffalo; Engr.

CARBONNETTI, ANTHONY; La Salle Acad; New York, NY; (Y); Nwsp Rptr; VP Soph Cls; Pres Jr Cls; Sec Stu Cncl; Im Mgr Bsktbl; Pre-Law.

CARCACI, LISA; Churchville-Chili SR HS; Rochester, NY; (Y); Sec GAA; Band; Mrchg Band; Mgr(s); JV Var Socr; Hon Roll; NHS; Rochester Inst Tech.

CARCAMO, MARIA; George Washington HS; New York, NY; (Y); School Play; Bsktbl; Gym; Socr; Swmmng; Prfct Atten Awd; Cosmetology.

CARCATERRA, JOANN; Lawrence HS; Lawrence, NY; (Y); Cmnty Wkr; Pep Clb; Sec Frsh Cls; Sec Soph Cls; VP Jr Cls; Var Capt Bsktbl; Var Sftbl; Var Capt Tennis; Var Trk; Var Capt Vllybl; MVP Vlybl & Tennis 83; Ntl Archon Soc 85.

CARD, LESLIE A; Vestal Central HS; Apalachin, NY; (Y); 83/450; Church Yth Grp; Varsity Clb; Rep Frsh Cls; Rep Soph Cls; Rep Jr Cls; Rep Sr Cls; Rep Stu Cncl; Var L Cheerleading; Stat Socr; Hon Roll; Gold Tassle Cap Hnr Roll 85; SUNY Albany; Lingstcs.

CARDEN, DIANE MICHELLE; Saranac Lake HS; Saranac Lake, NY; (Y); Library Aide; Band; Chorus; Stage Crew; High Hon Roll; NHS; Ntl Merit Ltr; Prfct Atten Awd; Pres Acad Ftns Awd 85; Womens Coll Schlrshp Clb 85; Clarkson U; Tech Comm.

CARDIERI, CATHY; St Edmunds HS; Brooklyn, NY; (Y); 13/187; High Hon Roll; Hon Roll; NHS; Excl Math III 85; Italian Awd 84; Awds Eng,Soc Studies,Rel,Math,Italian 83; Psych.

CARDILLO, ANTHONY M; Xaverian HS; Brooklyn, NY; (Y); 150/400; Am Leg Boys St; Boy Scts; Camera Clb; Cmnty Wkr; Yrbk Phtg; Law.

CARDILLO, MARISA A; T R Proctor HS; Utica, NY; (Y); Art Clb; Pep Clb; Yrbk Rptr; Yrbk Stf; Rep Stu Cncl; Hon Roll; Jr NHS; Italian Excllnce Awd 83-84; Therapist.

CARDINALI, ANGELA; Jericho SR HS; Syosset, NY; (Y); 34/230; Key Clb; Varsity Clb; Var Mgr(s); JV Socr; Var Sftbl; Var Trk; High Hon Roll; NHS; Nuclear Disamnt Clb 82-83; Hofstra U; Bus.

CARDONA, ANGELA; Christ The King Regional HS; Brooklyn, NY; (Y); 32/398; Girl Scts; Service Clb; Spanish Clb; Teachers Aide; High Hon Roll; Hon Roll; Jr NHS; NHS; Spanish NHS; U Of S FL; Crmnl Jstc.

CARDONE, JENNIFER; Longwood HS; Middle Island, NY; (Y); 66/487; Stu Cncl; Var L Bsktbl; Var L Socr; Var Capt Sftbl; Hon Roll; All Suffolk County Sftbl Plyr Shortstop 83-84 & 84-85; Phys Ed.

CARDOZO, HEDY R; Scarsdale HS; Scarsdale, NY; (Y); Debate Tm; French Clb; Library Aide; Teachers Aide; Temple Yth Grp; School Play; Yrbk Stf; Hon Roll; NHS; Ntl Merit Ltr; Ntl Merit Lttr Cmmndtn 85; NYS Regnts Schlrshp 85; Ntl Hnr Soc 85; Brandeis U; Pol Sci.

CARDWELL, JOI B; Hillcrest HS; S Ozone Park, NY; (Y); Church Yth Grp; Drama Clb; Office Aide; Political Wkr; Thesps; School Musical; Yrbk Stf; Lit Mag; Off Jr Cls; Rep Sr Cls; NY U; Acctng.

CARETTA, ALAN; Bishop Kearney HS; Rochester, NY; (Y); Rep Frsh Cls; Rep Jr Cls; Var Ftbl; Im Sftbl; JV Wrstlng; HS Entrnc Exm Schlrshp 83-86; Law.

CAREY, ALBERT; Island Trees HS; Seaford, NY; (Y); 17/220; Bsktbl; Lcrss; Cit Awd; High Hon Roll; Jr NHS; Prfct Atten Awd; Pres Schlr; St Schlr; PTA Cncl M F Stokes Schl Schlrshp 85; Nassau Cnty Police Wives Inc 85-88; Assembly ST NY Cert 85; SUNY Albany; Acctg.

CAREY, BRIAN; Hilton Central HS; Hilton, NY; (Y); Concert Band; Jazz Band; Mrchg Band; Symp Band; Ftbl; Trk; Hon Roll; Band; Pep Band; Variety Show; Engrng.

CAREY, BRIAN N; St Anthonys HS; Kings Park, NY; (Y); Church Yth Grp; Hosp Aide; Nwsp Sprt Ed; Im Bsktbl; Im Bowling; Im Ftbl; Im Ice Hcky; Jr NHS; NHS; NY ST Rgnts Schlrshp 84-85; U Of Rochester; Econ.

CAREY, DAVID; John Jay HS; Hopewell Jct, NY; (Y); Camera Clb; Chorus; Yrbk Phtg; Im Socr; Dutchess Cmnty Coll; Bus Admin.

CAREY, EILEEN N; Northport SR HS; Northport, NY; (Y); Art Clb; Office Aide; Spanish Clb; Teachers Aide; Chorus; Yrbk Stf; Crs Cntry; Trk; Svc Awds For Guidnc Dept 81-83; Vlntr Awd Hlpng Hndicap 81; St Johns U; Educ.

CAREY, JAMES; Tonawanda HS; Tonawanda, NY; (Y); Cmnty Wkr; Varsity Clb; Stu Cncl; Var Bsbl; JV Bsktbl; Var Capt Ftbl; Im Socr; Hon Roll; NHS; Canisius Coll; Bio.

CAREY, PATRICIA; The Mary Louis Acad; Flushing, NY; (Y); Art Clb; Yrbk Stf; Hon Roll; NEDT Awd; Excel Soc Studies 83-84; Ad.

CAREY, PATTI A; Alden Central HS; Marilla, NY; (Y); 20/198; 4-H; Quiz Bowl; Science Clb; Sec Spanish Clb; School Play; Stu Cncl; 4-H Awd; Hon Roll; 4-H Horse Bwl Tm 78-85; High Awds Horse Shws 85; 4-H Hipplgy Rgnl Tm 80-85; Cornell U; Vet.

CAREY, REBECCA L; Nardin Acad; Buffalo, NY; (Y); School Musical; School Play; Stage Crew; Variety Show; Nwsp Rptr; Nwsp Stf; Yrbk Stf; Hon Roll; NHS; Ntl Merit Ltr.

CAREY, THOMAS; Oneonta HS; Oneonta, NY; (Y); Boys Clb Am; JA; Mathletes; Y-Teens; Hon Roll.

CARFAGNO, LISA; Henninger HS; Syracuse, NY; (Y); Church Yth Grp; Swmmng; Hon Roll; Criminal Justice.

CARFAGNO, MARYKAY; West Genesee HS; Camillus, NY; (Y); Chrmn Key Clb; Chorus; Capt Color Guard; Capt Mrchg Band; Hon Roll; NHS; Rgnts Schlrshp Rcpnt 85; Syracuse Univ Schlrshp 85; Syracuse U; Engr.

CARFORA, DAVID; Myrderse Acad; Seneca Falls, NY; (S); JV Ftbl; High Hon Roll; Hon Roll; Fredonia; Recordng Tech.

CARGES, ROGER; Irondequoit HS; Rochester, NY; (Y); Boy Scts; Varsity Clb; Im Bsktbl; Var L Ftbl; Wt Lftg; Prfct Atten Awd; Trk; All Cnty & All Grtr Rochstr Ftbl 85; Egl Sct 85; Bus Mgn Mt.

CARGIN, DALE G; Whitney Point Central Schl; Whitney Pt, NY; (Y); #11 In Class; Am Leg Boys St; Church Yth Grp; Band; Chorus; Concert Band; Jazz Band; Var JV Bsktbl; Var JV Ftbl; High Hon Roll; NHS; Cmmnctns.

CARIDI, MARY ANN; St Johns Prep; Astoria, NY; (Y); Var Sftbl; High Hon Roll; NHS; Engr.

CARILLI, LEANDER; Carmel HS; Carmel, NY; (Y); 25/300; Chess Clb; Computer Clb; Math Tm; Orch; Nwsp Sprt Ed; Var Trk; High Hon Roll; Hon Roll; Pres Tibet Lk Lepidoptera Soc 83; Bio.

CARILLION, DIANE C; Baldwin SR HS; Baldwin, NY; (Y); 51/503; Cmnty Wkr; Mgr Drama Clb; Hosp Aide; Stage Crew; Lit Mag; High Hon Roll; Hon Roll; NHS; Ntl Merit Ltr; Rgnts Schlrshp 85; Psych Soc Wrkr.

CARINGI, TERI; Parishville-Hopkinton CS; Parishville, NY; (Y); Art Clb; FBLA; Ski Clb; Chorus; Color Guard; School Musical; JV Var Socr; Prfct Atten Awd; Outstndng BOCES 85; Cazenovia Coll; Intr Desgn.

CARINO, DIANE L; Lakeland HS; Mohegan Lake, NY; (Y); Dance Clb; German Clb; Office Aide; Orch; Var Crs Cntry; Var Trk; JV Vllybl; Psych.

CARIOTI, JOE; John C Birdlebough HS; Phoenix, NY; (Y); Pres AFS; Trs Drama Clb; Pres Band; Concert Band; Jazz Band; Mrchg Band; School Musical; School Play; Trs Jr Cls; Hon Roll; JR All Amer Hall Fame Bnd 85.

CARKNARD, EVA M; Hoosic Valley Central HS; Valley Falls, NY; (Y); 9/90; Ski Clb; Band; Chorus; School Musical; School Play; Nwsp Bus Mgr; Nwsp Rptr; NHS; Regents Schlrshp 85; Russell Sage; English.

CARL, BILL; Liverpool HS; Liverpool, NY; (Y); Art Clb; Church Yth Grp; Hosp Aide; Stage Crew; Hon Roll; NHS; Merit Awd Urbn Dsgn 85; Cert Persnl Achv MONY Regnl Schlstc Art Cmptn 85; Arch.

CARL, SUSAN; Liverpool HS; Liverpool, NY; (S); 53/792; Art Clb; Church Yth Grp; School Musical; Stage Crew; Yrbk Stf; Hon Roll; Jr NHS; NHS; Hnrbl Mntn MONY Schlstc Art Awds 84; :Advtsg Dsgn.

CARLE, STACY; Hudson HS; Stottville, NY; (Y); Church Yth Grp; 4-H; GAA; Spanish Clb; Band; Church Choir; Mrchg Band; School Musical; Var Bowling; Var JV Socr; Albany Bus Coll; Exec Sec.

CARLETT, PAM; Palmyra Maredon HS; Palmyra, NY; (Y); 31/189; AFS; Pres Sec Church Yth Grp; Math Clb; Concert Band; Flag Corp; Mrchg Band; School Musical; School Play; Yrbk Ed-Chief; Yrbk Stf; St John Fisher Coll; Phrmcy.

CARLEY, CHRISTINE; Vernon Verona Sherrill HS; Verona, NY; (Y); GAA; Concert Band; Rep Frsh Cls; Trs Soph Cls; Rep Jr Cls; VP Stu Cncl; Var Bsktbl; Var Capt Ftbl; Var Trk; Hon Roll; 1st Chr Piccolo All Cnty Cncrt Band 83; Intl Bus.

CARLINEO, ANNE; Corning Painted Post West HS; Painted Post, NY; (Y); Ski Clb; Thesps; Varsity Clb; Chorus; Madrigals; School Musical; Pres Soph Cls; Pres Sr Cls; Mgr Ftbl; NHS; Music.

CARLINO, BARBARA; Susan Wagner HS; Staten Isld, NY; (Y); JV Crs Cntry; Hon Roll; St Johns U; Dentstry.

CARLO, GEORGE; La Salle Academy HS; New York, NY; (S); 15/237; Crs Cntry; Socr; Trk; High Hon Roll; Hon Roll; NHS; Biology.

CARLO, MONTY; Plattsburgh HS; Plattsburgh, NY; (Y); Computer Clb; Model UN; Teachers Aide; Im Vllybl; Hon Roll; Rochester Inst Of Tech; Comp.

CARLO, VENITA M; Fairport HS; Fairport, NY; (Y); Chorus; Rep Stu Cncl; Crs Cntry; Var Capt Trk; Hon Roll; Prfct Atten Awd; Ldrshp Awd Indoor Trk 84; NY Regnts Schlrshp 85; Mount Union Coll; Sprts Med.

CARLOS, ELEANOR; Cathedral HS; Queens, NY; (Y); 70/298; Intnl Clb; Hon Roll; Ntl Merit Ltr; St Johns; Accntng.

CARLOS, GONZALEZ JUAN; Eastern District HS; Brooklyn, NY; (Y); 1/415; Math Tm; Band; Rep Stu Cncl; Gym; Gov Hon Prg Awd; Hon Roll; Spanish NHS; Val; Dist Atty Citation Of Hnr 85; NY Pblc Lib Minerva Awd For Val 85; Untd Fdrtn Of Tchrs Awd Crt Of Hnr; Hampshire Coll; Elec Engr.

CARLOS, ROBERT M; Lakeland HS; Yorktown Heights, NY; (Y); Boy Scts; Cmnty Wkr; Computer Clb; Var L Swmmng; NY ST Rgnts Schlrshp 85; Rochester Inst Of Tech Schlrshp 85; Rochester Inst Of Tech; Mech En.

CARLOW, PEGGY; Catholic Central HS; Green Isl, NY; (Y); German Clb; Math Clb; Drm & Bgl; Var Cheerleading; Var Trk; High Hon Roll; NHS; Res Sci.

CARLSON, CATHERINE; Foxlane HS; Bedford, NY; (Y); 58/300; Art Clb; Church Yth Grp; Pres Intnl Clb; Yrbk Phtg; JV Var Fld Hcky; JV Var Socr; High Hon Roll; Hon Roll; Bus.

CARLSON, CYNTHIA; Patchague-Medford HS; Medford, NY; (Y); 60/750; Concert Band; Hon Roll; NHS; Band; Chorus; Mrchg Band; Regnts Schlrshp 85; NYSMA Grd 6 Exclint Cntst 83-85; BIOCES Cert Achvmt Gft & Tlntd 84; St Lawrence U; Optmtry.

CARLSON, CYNTHIA; St John Villa Acad; Staten Island, NY; (Y); Cmnty Wkr; Hosp Aide; Stage Crew; Bowling; Hon Roll; Ntl Merit Ltr; Natl Hnr Rll 85; Generoso Pope Awd 85; Achv Awd In Bus Law 85; St Johns U.

CARLSON, DEBRA; South Park HS; Buffalo, NY; (Y); 10/402; FHA; Im Tennis; Im Vllybl; High Hon Roll; Hon Roll; U Of NY Buffalo; Comp Prgmng.

CARLSON, DOUG; Odessa-Montour Central HS; Montour Falls, NY; (Y).

CARLSON, EILEEN; Whitesboro SR HS; Whitesboro, NY; (Y); 16/313; Trs Church Yth Grp; Exploring; Intnl Clb; Trs Ski Clb; Ed Yrbk Stf; High Hon Roll; Jr NHS; NHS; Wellesley Clg Clb Awd 84; Pres Acad Ftns Awd 85; St Anselm Clg; Math.

CARLSON, ERIK; Kings Park SR HS; Kings Pk, NY; (Y); Art Clb; Church Yth Grp; Spanish Clb; Yrbk Phtg; Yrbk Stf; JV Var Ice Hcky; Var Lcrss; Sftbl; NHS.

CARLSON, GREG; Highland Central HS; Highland, NY; (Y); Stage Crew; Ftbl; Wt Lftg; Indstrl Arts Awd 83-84; Craftsmn Yr 84; Delhi; Carpentry.

CARLSON, JOSEPH; Falconer Central Schl; Ellington, NY; (Y); 1/130; Cmnty Wkr; Stage Crew; Dnfth Awd; High Hon Roll; 1st Pl Bl & Wht Art Shw 84; Watchtowr Bible; Minister.

CARLSON, KAREN; Fox Lane HS; Pound Ridge, NY; (Y); 119/300; Church Yth Grp; Ski Clb; Var Bsktbl; Var Capt Fld Hcky; Var Socr; Camille Pulise Memorial Awd Outstndng Defensive Player 84; Elementary Ed.

CARLSON, KRISTIN; Emma Willard Schl; Potsdam, NY; (Y); Intnl Clb; Rep Stu Cncl; JV Cheerleading; Var Trk; High Hon Roll; Stage Crew; Peer Cnslr; Nwsp Arts Ed; Interact Pres; Stu Adm Comm; Outng Clb.

CARLSON, KRISTIN; Westport Central HS; Westport, NY; (Y); 4/21; Drama Clb; 4-H; Chorus; Bsktbl; Cheerleading; Sftbl; Hon Roll; SUNY Albany; Med Tech.

CARLSON, ROHN; Batovia HS; Batavia, NY; (Y); Am Leg Boys St; Radio Clb; Acpl Chr; Chorus; School Musical; Variety Show; Var Capt Crs Cntry; Var Trk; Hon Roll; Aeronutcl Engr.

CARLSON, TODD A; Rushford Central Schl; Houghton, NY; (Y); Am Leg Boys St; Pres FFA; Teachers Aide; Rep Stu Cncl; High Hon Roll; Hon Roll; NHS; Bus Adm.

CARLUCCI, ELEANOR; Riverhead HS; Calverton, NY; (Y); French Clb; FBLA; Library Aide; Suffolk CC; Bus Mgmt.

CARLUCCI, KAREN; St Saviour HS; Brooklyn, NY; (Y); 8/70; VP Soph Cls; Pres Sr Cls; Bausch & Lomb Sci Awd; French Hon Soc; NHS; Regents Schlrshp NYS 85-86; Pace U NYC; Accntng.

CARMAN, DIANE; St Francis Prep; Woodhaven, NY; (S); 7/692; Drama Clb; Service Clb; Chorus; School Musical; Var Tennis; Var Trk; Gov Hon Prg Awd; High Hon Roll; NHS; Pres Schlr; Psychologist.

CARMAN, LISA; Plainedge HS; Massapequa, NY; (Y); Band; Chorus; Yrbk Stf; Stu Cncl; Mat Maids; Capt Socr; JV Var Sftbl; Hon Roll; Legl Secy.

CARMEN, DEBORAH; Nazareth Acad; Spencerport, NY; (Y); 1/160; Exploring; French Clb; Math Clb; Math Tm; Concert Band; Jazz Band; Yrbk Stf; Lit Mag; NHS; Church Yth Grp; Nuclr Tech.

CARMICHAEL, JEFFREY; Cicero-North Syracuse HS; N Syracuse, NY; (S); 63/711; VP Church Yth Grp; VP Trs German Clb; JA; Ski Clb; Hon Roll; NHS; Bus.

CARMICHAEL, KEVIN; Le Roy HS; Leroy, NY; (Y); Spanish Clb; Y-Teens; Chorus; Rep Jr Cls; Var L Bsbl; Var L Ftbl; Capt Ice Hcky; High Hon Roll; Hon Roll; Varsity Clb; Ftbl All County Tight End 85; Bsbl All County Pitcher 85; Inclusn Amer H S Ath 85; Phrmcy.

CARMODY, EDWARD; S S Seward Inst; Florida, NY; (S); 1/55; Art Clb; Computer Clb; Yrbk Phtg; Bsbl; High Hon Roll; Hon Roll; NHS; Ntl Merit SF; Val; 1st Pl Orange Cnty Olympics Of The Mind 83; English Awd 3 Consec Yrs.

CARMODY, JILL; Delaware Acad; Treadwell, NY; (Y); Trs Soph Cls; Trs Jr Cls; JV Bsktbl; Hon Roll; Delhi Coll Louis & Mildred Resnick Awd 85; O Connor Hosp Guild Schlrshp 85; Delhi Ag & Tech Coll; RN.

CARMODY, KAREN A; Arlington HS; Poughkeepsie, NY; (Y); 101/596; Cmnty Wkr; Ski Clb; Mrchg Band; Orch; Symp Band; Russn Clb; Purdue U; Bus.

CARMONA, LISA MARIA; Saint Joseph HS; Brooklyn, NY; (Y); Church Yth Grp; Hosp Aide; Intnl Clb; Service Clb; Chorus; Church Choir; School Musical; Variety Show; Yrbk Stf; Bowling; U Of Bridgeport; Pre Med.

CARNEY, ALLEN; Saugerties HS; Saugerties, NY; (Y); Ski Clb; Var Ftbl; High Hon Roll; Hon Roll; NHS; Comp Sci.

CARNEY, CHRIS; Bishop Ford Central Catholic HS; Brooklyn, NY; (Y); Potsdam ST U-NY.

CARNEY, JAMES; Bishop Timon HS; W Seneca, NY; (Y); 14/190; Computer Clb; Latin Clb; Political Wkr; Ski Clb; Nwsp Rptr; Yrbk Stf; Lit Mag; JV Trk; Hon Roll; Religion Awd 83; Cornell U; Vet.

CARNEY, JAMES; Kenmore East HS; Tonawanda, NY; (Y); Yrbk Bus Mgr; Yrbk Phtg; Yrbk Stf; Rep Stu Cncl; Stu Senate Pres 85; Accntng.

CARNEY, KELLY; Hamburg SR HS; Hamburg, NY; (Y); Girl Scts; JA; Nwsp Stf; High Hon Roll; Hon Roll; Sec.

CARNEY, LYNETTE; Corinth Central HS; Corinth, NY; (S); Spanish Clb; Varsity Clb; Band; Chorus; Pres Jr Cls; Fld Hcky; Sftbl; Vllybl; High Hon Roll; NHS; MVP Fld Hcky Plyr Awd 84; Mst Coachable Awd Vllybl 84; Psych.

CARNIELLO, GLENN; N Babylon HS; North Babylon, NY; (Y); Church Yth Grp; Intnl Clb; Spanish Clb; JV Socr; Var Tennis; High Hon Roll; Jr NHS; NHS; Rgnts Schlrshp Wnnr 86; Accntng.

CAROLAN, CHRISTOPHER S; Fordham Prep Schl; Bronx, NY; (Y); Letterman Clb; Y-Teens; Bsbl; Swmmng; Hon Roll; Ntl Merit SF; Pres Schlr.

CAROLEO, CHRISTINE; St Catharine Acad; Bronx, NY; (Y); Cmnty Wkr; Hosp Aide; Office Aide; Teachers Aide; Yrbk Phtg; Gov Hon Prg Awd; Hon Roll; NHS; Ntl Merit Ltr; Prfct Atten Awd; Chem, Math, Engl Hnrs 83; Schlrshps To Iona Coll, Manhatten Coll & York U 85; Iona Coll; Comp Sci.

CAROLLO, GINA; Cardinal Spellman HS; Bronx, NY; (Y); Im Vllybl; Columbia U; Dntl Hygnst.

CAROLLO, JAMES P; Uniondale HS; Uniondale, NY; (Y); 1/480; Am Leg Boys St; Math Tm; Office Aide; Yrbk Sprt Ed; Cit Awd; High Hon Roll; Sec NHS; Ntl Merit Ltr; Val; Amer Lgn Schlstc Achvmnt Awd 81; Rensselaer Polytechnic Inst; Bi.

CARON, DANIEL; Ctr Moriches HS; Ctr Moriches, NY; (Y); 49/97; Art Clb; Camera Clb; Church Yth Grp; French Clb; Hon Roll; High Hnrs Elect 84-85; Poly Inst; Elect Engrng.

CARON, JENNIFER; Avoca Central HS; Avoca, NY; (Y); 2/45; Trs FBLA; Yrbk Bus Mgr; Pres Soph Cls; Pres Jr Cls; JV Var Cheerleading; High Hon Roll; NHS; Acctg.

CAROSA, MARY LEE; Gates-Chili HS; Henrietta, NY; (Y); 81/463; 4-H; Service Clb; Nwsp Rptr; Lit Mag; Rep Frsh Cls; Rep Soph Cls; Rep Jr Cls; Rep Sr Cls; Rep Stu Cncl; 4-H Awd; Publ Spkng Cnty Motal 4-H 84; Teen Ambssdr 4-H 83; Jrnlsm.

CAROTENUTO, DANIEL; John Dewey HS; Brooklyn, NY; (Y); Pres Chess Clb; Library Aide; Lit Mag; Wt Lftg; 1st Pl John Dewey H S Chess Tourn 85; Polytechnic Inst NY; Engrng.

CAROW, ANDY; Lake Placid Central Schl; Lake Placid, NY; (Y); 1/53; Key Clb; Var Bsbl; Var Crs Cntry; Var Socr; Var Trk; Wt Lftg; Bausch & Lomb Sci Awd; Cit Awd; High Hon Roll; Kiwanis Awd; Amer Lgn Englsh Awd 85; Key Bank Awd Excllnc In Math 85; Cornell U; Elec Engr.

CAROZZA, ARIANE; Charles E Gorton HS; Pleasantville, NY; (Y); 9/209; Computer Clb; FBLA; Cheerleading; Sftbl; High Hon Roll; Hon Roll; Supt Awd 83-85; Natl Hnr Rl 84; Halran Clb 83; NY U; Comp.

CARPENTER, BARBARA; Minisink Valley HS; Slate Hill, NY; (Y); Church Yth Grp; 4-H; Girl Scts; Hosp Aide; Key Clb; Teachers Aide; Varsity Clb; Chorus; 4-H Awd; High Hon Roll; Mercy Hosp Schlrshp 85; Tchrs Assoc Schlrshp 85; Morrisville Coll; Nrsng.

CARPENTER JR, CHARLES W; Eden SR HS; Eden, NY; (Y); 25/200; Chorus; School Musical; Nwsp Rptr; Rep Sr Cls; Pres Stu Cncl; Var Capt Vllybl; NHS; Rotary Awd; All Wstrn NY Vlybl 83-85; U Of Richmond; Bus.

CARPENTER, CHRISTINE; Fonda Fultonville HS; Fonda, NY; (Y); Church Yth Grp; Hosp Aide; Teachers Aide; Chorus; Stat Score Keeper; Sftbl; Bus Adm.

CARPENTER, CHRISTINE C; Rome Free Acad; Rome, NY; (Y); 203/536; Intnl Clb; Chorus; Mohawk Vly CC; Comp Pgmr.

CARPENTER, JEFFREY M; Rome Free Acad; Rome, NY; (Y); 32/536; Hon Roll; NHS; Prfct Atten Awd; Regents Coll Schlrshp 85; CC; Bus Mgmt.

CARPENTER, KELLY; Allegany Central HS; Allegany, NY; (Y); Var Gym; High Hon Roll; NHS; Schlrshp Soc 84 & 85; Giant Step St Bonaventure U 85; Solo Fest 82.

CARPENTER, KIMBERLY; Avoca Central HS; Wallace, NY; (Y); Pres FBLA; JCL; Latin Clb; Color Guard; Yrbk Stf; Var Bsktbl; JV Var Socr; Bus.

CARPENTER, KRISTIN J; Greece Athena HS; Rochester, NY; (Y); 11/306; Trs DECA; FBLA; Ski Clb; Yrbk Ed-Chief; Rep Sr Cls; Rep Stu Cncl; Stat L Vllybl; High Hon Roll; NHS; Math Tm; Regents Schlrshp 85; Syracuse U.

CARPENTER, LYNNE; North Warren Central HS; Chestertown, NY; (S); 2/50; Chorus; VP Frsh Cls; Pres Soph Cls; Pres Jr Cls; Var Bsktbl; Var Cheerleading; Var Fld Hcky; Var Tennis; Var High Hon Roll; Outstndng Sprtsmshp 84; Rotary Stu Of Mnth Awd 84.

CARPENTER, ROBERT D; West Islip HS; W Islip, NY; (Y); Drama Clb; Exploring; Political Wkr; Ski Clb; Band; Concert Band; Mrchg Band; Pep Band; Stage Crew; Symp Band; H S Fest The Arts SUNY Old Westburg Imprv & Comptn 85; Hofstra U Clsscl Band Fest 85; Music.

CARPENTER, VANESSA; St Hildas HS; New York, NY; (Y); Chorus; Orch; Yrbk Phtg; Yrbk Stf; Var Bsktbl; Var Vllybl; Prfct Atten Awd; American U; Psych.

CARPENTER, WENDY; Fort Plain HS; Fort Plain, NY; (S); 10/81; Pres Church Yth Grp; Drama Clb; Math Clb; Chorus; Rep Stu Cncl; L Cheerleading; NHS.

CARPINI, LINA DELLI; Preston HS; Bronx, NY; (S); Drama Clb; School Play; Stage Crew; Nwsp Stf; Sec Frsh Cls; Sec Soph Cls; Sec Jr Cls; Sec NHS; Cert Apprectn & Grat Vlntr Svc 84.

CARPINO, DOUGLAS; Coledonia-Mumford Central Schl; Le Roy, NY; (Y); Art Clb; 4-H; Science Clb; JV Ftbl; Var Mgr(s); JV Socr; Var Trk; Var Wrstlng; 4-H Awd; Long Jmp-Schl Rcrd 85; Grnd Champ Shwmn At Caledonia Fair 85; Morrisville Coll; Tchr.

CARR III, EDWARD A T; Northport HS; Nothpot, NY; (Y); 81/588; Church Yth Grp; DECA; Political Wkr; Science Clb; Service Clb; School Musical; Stu Cncl; NHS; Chess Clb; Soph Cls; Bus Awd 1st Pl 85; Bio Resrch Pgm 83-85.

CARR, HEATHER L; Alfred-Almond Central HS; Arlington, VA; (Y); JCL; Yrbk Stf; Cheerleading; Score Keeper; Socr; Sftbl; High Hon Roll; Hon Roll; NYS Regents Schlrshp 85; VA Tech; Genl Arts.

CARR, HOLLISE; Cicero-North Syracuse HS; Clay, NY; (S); 72/711; Boy Scts; Exploring; Hosp Aide; Var JV Crs Cntry; Var Tennis; Var Trk; NHS; Recognition Awd 82.

CARR, KATHLEEN; Liverpool HS; Liverpool, NY; (Y); Cmnty Wkr; VP JA; Office Aide; Color Guard; Mrchg Band; Rep Stu Cncl; Var L Twrlr; Hon Roll; Jr NHS; NHS; Tchng.

CARR, KELLIE; Gilbertsville Central HS; Gilbertsville, NY; (Y); 7/24; Pres Sec Varsity Clb; Trs Pres Chorus; Capt Color Guard; Pres Concert Band; Pres Jazz Band; Pres Swing Chorus; Var Socr; Var Capt Sftbl; High Hon Roll; Church Yth Grp; Scholar NY ST Music Camp Hartwick Coll 85; Excllnce Spn Awd; Music.

CARR, LAURA M; Walt Whitman HS; Hunt Sta, NY; (Y); 17/625; Computer Clb; Orch; School Musical; Symp Band; Fld Hcky; French Hon Soc; High Hon Roll; NHS; Ntl Merit Ltr; Natl Frnch Cntst 4th 85; NYSSMA Awd Solo 83 & 84; Outstndng Non-Strng Plyr Orch Awd 85; Binghamton; Psych.

CARR JR, LESTER W; Clyde-Savannah HS; Clyde, NY; (Y); Am Leg Boys St; Science Clb; Pres Frsh Cls; Pres Soph Cls; Rep Stu Cncl; Im Bsktbl; JV Ftbl; Var Tennis; Vet.

CARR, MARY PAULA; Our Lady Of Mercy HS; Fairport, NY; (Y); 86/200; JA; Library Aide; Spanish Clb; Stage Crew; Nwsp Stf; Merit Rll 82-84; Hnr Rll 82-85; St Bonaventure U; Accntng.

CARR, MELISSA; Cato Meridian HS; Cato, NY; (Y); Church Yth Grp; JV Cheerleading; High Hon Roll; Hon Roll; Outstndng Achvt Awd 84-85; Child Care.

CARR, ROBERT D; Schuylerville Central HS; Schuylerville, NY; (Y); Church Yth Grp; French Clb; Math Tm; Ski Clb; Band; Chorus; Church Choir; School Musical; School Play; Var Crs Cntry; Pres Of Ntl Hnr Scty 85-86.

CARR, SUSAN; Samuel J Tildan HS; Brooklyn, NY; (Y); Cmnty Wkr; Office Aide; Teachers Aide; Cit Awd; Hon Roll; Long Island U; Nrsng.

CARR, TRACEY; Union Springs Academy; Attica, NY; (S); 1/50; Art Clb; Ski Clb; Spanish Clb; Yrbk Stf; Gym; High Hon Roll; NHS; Val; USBEA 84-85; Atlantic Union Coll; Nrsg.

CARRADINI, BRENDA; Batavia HS; Batavia, NY; (Y); Band; Chorus; Concert Band; Mrchg Band; Yrbk Stf; Sec Jr Cls; High Hon Roll; Hon Roll; Church Yth Grp; Girl Scts; Hgh Avg Spnsh Awd 83; Peer Mentor Svc 83; Vrsty Ltr-Band 85; Syracuse U; Bus.

CARRAHER, CAROLYN; Mahopac HS; Carmel, NY; (Y); 42/423; Political Wkr; Yrbk Stf; VP Soph Cls; VP Jr Cls; Mgr Trs Stu Cncl; Stat Bsbl; Pres VP Cheerleading; High Hon Roll; Hon Roll; NHS; Ed.

CARRANO, KIMMARIE; Bishop Ford HS; Brooklyn, NY; (Y); Regents Schlrshp 85; Med.

CARRARA, DENISE M; South Shore HS; Brooklyn, NY; (Y); 42/668; Library Aide; Teachers Aide; Band; Chorus; Variety Show; Lit Mag; Hon Roll; NHS; St Johns Coll; Psych.

CARRASQUILLO, EZRA U; The Packer Collegiate Inst; Brooklyn, NY; (Y); Cmnty Wkr; Debate Tm; French Clb; Political Wkr; Varsity Clb; Chorus; School Play; Variety Show; Nwsp Bus Mgr; Nwsp Rptr; Exprmnt & Entl Living Schlrshp 84; NY ST Regents Schlrshp 85; Dartmouth.

CARRASQUILLO, YOLANDA; Aquinas HS; Bronx, NY; (Y); Computer Clb; Drama Clb; English Clb; Key Clb; Math Clb; Office Aide; Spanish Clb; Band; School Musical; School Play; Pace U; Comp Pgmnr.

CARRATALA, BARBARA; Cardinal Spellman HS; New York, NY; (Y); Camera Clb; Computer Clb; Spanish Clb; Chorus; Drill Tm; Flag Corp; Yrbk Phtg; Stu Cncl; High Hon Roll; Hon Roll; Advncd Plcmnt Crdt 85; Corp Law.

CARRENO, CARMEN MARIA; Schalmont HS; Schenectady, NY; (Y); 15/188; Church Yth Grp; Cmnty Wkr; Ski Clb; Concert Band; Mrchg Band; Yrbk Stf; JV Var Bsktbl; Tennis; High Hon Roll; NHS; Elmira Coll Key Awd 84; Cornell U.

CARRERAS, ELISSA; Cardinal Spellman HS; Bronx, NY; (Y); Camera Clb; Spanish Clb; Capt Flag Corp; Stage Crew; Yrbk Stf; Vllybl; Hon Roll; Cornell U; Med.

CARRICK, LISA; South Park HS; Buffalo, NY; (Y); Band; Concert Band; Jazz Band; Mrchg Band; Stu Cncl; Var L Tennis; Hon Roll; NHS; Prfct Atten Awd; Library Aide; Ntl Hnr Soc Svc Corp 82-84; Tutor Libfary 83-85; Physcl Thrpy.

CARRIER, DEBORAH; Holland Patent Central HS; Rome, NY; (Y); 4-H; Csmtlgy.

CARRIER, ELIZABETH A; Niagara Wheatfield SR HS; Niagara Falls, NY; (Y); 76/313; Girl Scts; Nwsp Stf; JV Socr; Var Trk; NYS Regnts Schlrshp 85; Canisius Coll; Mktg.

CARRIER, SHARON; Jordon-Elbridge Cen HS; Weedsport, NY; (Y); Sec Church Yth Grp; Yrbk Stf; Rep Stu Cncl; Cheerleading; Var Powder Puff Ftbl; High Hon Roll; Hon Roll; Jr NHS.

CARRIERO, GINA MARIE; Lancaster SR HS; Depew, NY; (Y); 139/437; Pres Church Yth Grp; JA; Trs Soph Cls; Var Bsktbl; Var Bowling; Var Capt Vllybl; Prfct Atten Awd; Sftbl; St Barnabas Athltc Assoc Sftbl All Star 85; Canisius Clg; Acctg.

CARRIG, TOBY; Little Falls JR SR HS; Little Falls, NY; (Y); 5/85; Am Leg Boys St; Pres FBLA; Varsity Clb; Nwsp Ed-Chief; Pres Stu Cncl; Var Crs Cntry; Capt Tennis; Var Vllybl; High Hon Roll; NHS; NYS Mr Future Bus Ldr 85; Natl Mr Future Ldr 9th Pl 85; Vanderbilt U Scholar; Vanderbilt U; Comm.

CARRIOLA, JOHN A; Amsterdam HS; Amsterdam, NY; (Y); 49/340; Rep Sr Cls; Rep Stu Cncl; JV Bsktbl; JV Var Ftbl; Mgr(s); Score Keeper; Hon Roll; Rgnts Schlrshp 85; St Agnllo Clb Awd 85; Albany Coll Of Phrmcy; Phrmcy.

CARRO, ROBERT; Seton Catholic Central HS; Johnson City, NY; (Y); Art Clb; Var Trk.

CARROCCIO, BENJAMIN; Copiague HS; Copiague, NY; (Y); 4/350; DECA; FBLA; Latin Clb; Yrbk Stf; Pres Sr Cls; Var Bowling; Hon Roll; NHS; Cornell U; Htl Adm.

CARROLL, ANNEMARIE; Cicero-N Syracuse HS; Clay, NY; (S); 11/622; Church Yth Grp; Cmnty Wkr; Drama Clb; Exploring; Mathletes; Math Tm; School Play; Stage Crew; High Hon Roll.

CARROLL, CHARLES; Oakfield-Alabama Central HS; Oakfield, NY; (Y); Art Clb; JV Bsbl; JV Bsktbl; JV Ftbl; Hon Roll; Bst Artst Aws 84-85; Elec Tech.

CARROLL, DAWN; Newfield HS; Selden, NY; (Y); Aud/Vis; Drama Clb; Pep Clb; Varsity Clb; Chorus; School Musical; Stage Crew; Lit Mag; JV Socr; Merit Awd For Drawing In Lit Magazine; Awd For Painting In Dist Wide Show.

CARROLL, ELEANOR; St Anthonys HS; Long Beach, NY; (Y); 29/330; Church Yth Grp; GAA; Office Aide; Church Choir; School Play; Nwsp Rptr; Yrbk Rptr; Yrbk Stf; Rep Frsh Cls; VP Soph Cls; Duns Scotus Achvt Awd 85; Ladies Aux Vet Frgn War Outstndng 84; William & Mary; Bus.

CARROLL, JAMES; Saugerties HS; Saugerties, NY; (Y); 21/236; Boy Scts; Cmnty Wkr; French Clb; Quiz Bowl; Varsity Clb; Yrbk Stf; Socr; Trk; Vllybl; DAR Awd; Regents Schlrshp; Mbr Of The Natl Hnr Soc 85; Engrng.

CARROLL, JANET; St Francis Prep; Great Neck, NY; (S); 5/690; Am Leg Aux Girls St; Drama Clb; Hosp Aide; Pres Speech Tm; Nwsp Rptr; JV Bsktbl; Gov Hon Prg Awd; High Hon Roll; NHS; Ntl Merit Ltr; Georgetown; Frgn Svc.

CARROLL, JENNIFER; Cicero-North Syracuse HS; Mattydale, NY; (S); 30/622; Church Yth Grp; Co-Capt Dance Clb; Latin Clb; Teachers Aide; Co-Capt Drill Tm; Co-Capt Mrchg Band; Trs Stu Cncl; Stat Ftbl; JV Capt Powder Puff Ftbl; High Hon Roll; FL Inst Of Technology; Aerosp.

CARROLL, JOHN; St Francis Prep; Jamaica, NY; (Y); 289/685; Boys Clb Am; Church Yth Grp; Computer Clb; Im Bsktbl; JV Ftbl; Im Socr; Im Sftbl; Im Vllybl; NYS Regents Schlrshp 85; Disciplinary Excell Doans Awd 84; Baruch Coll; Fin & Invstmnt.

CARROLL, MARIA; Fontbonne Hall Academy; Brooklyn, NY; (Y); 5/135; Church Yth Grp; French Clb; Chorus; Flag Corp; School Play; Nwsp Stf; Yrbk Stf; Swmmng; NHS; Freshmn Schlrshp Fontbonne Hall 82.

CARROLL, SCOTT A; Liverpool HS; Liverpool, NY; (Y); 116/782; Drama Clb; Chorus; School Musical; School Play; High Hon Roll; Hon Roll; Jr NHS; NHS; NYS Regents Schlrshp 84-85; SUNY Potsdam; Comp Sci.

CARROLL, WILLIAM; William Nottingham HS; Syracuse, NY; (Y); 84/220; French Clb; Ski Clb; Spanish Clb; Band; Chorus; Yrbk Stf; Trs Sr Cls; Hotel Mngmnt.

CARRON, EILEEN; Clarkstown North HS; Congers, NY; (Y); Hosp Aide; Fld Hcky; Spec Educ.

CARRUBA, DONNA M; The Mary Louis Acad; S Ozone Park, NY; (Y); High Hon Roll; NHS; NYS Rgnts Schlrshp 85; Comptv Schlrshp St Johns U 85; St Johns U; Quantv Anlys.

CARSKY, MARGARET K; Bronxville HS; Bronxville, NY; (Y); 20/80; AFS; 4-H; Math Tm; Lit Mag; Crs Cntry; JV Capt Vllybl; High Hon Roll; Hon Roll; Ntl Merit Cmmdntn; U Of MI; Engl Lit.

CARSON, JOHN; Saint Marys HS; Williamsville, NY; (S); Science Clb; Var L Bsbl; Im Bsktbl; Hon Roll; NHS; Schlrshp Chrstn Bro Acad 81; 13 Acad Cmmndtns 82-85; Canisius Coll; Pol Sci.

CARSON, MARY; New Rochelle HS; New Rochelle, NY; (Y); IA Coll; Jrnlsm.

CARSON, SCOTT; Nottingham HS; Syracuse, NY; (Y); Latin Clb; Spanish Clb; JV Var Lcrss; Im Var Socr; Var Swmmng; NY ST U-Buffalo; Lndscpe Arch.

CARTAGENA, EVYETTE; John Dewey HS; Brooklyn, NY; (Y); Church Yth Grp; Library Aide; Math Tm; Chorus; Rep Jr Cls; Hon Roll; Jr NHS; Cncl Unity Clb 85; Bernard Buruch; Acctng.

CARTER, CANDY; Coxsackie-Athens Central HS; Coxsackie, NY; (Y); Art Clb; Chess Clb; Dance Clb; 4-H; Girl Scts; Chorus; Yrbk Stf; Stu Cncl; 4-H Awd; Hon Roll.

CARTER, DAVID; Union Springs Acad; Mercer, ME; (Y); 5/50; VP Camera Clb; Radio Clb; Spanish Clb; Varsity Clb; Drill Tm; Yrbk Phtg; Var Bsktbl; Im Ftbl; High Hon Roll; Voice Dem Awd; Act Tests 84-85; Atlantic Union Coll; Biolgy.

CARTER, DEBBIE; Hendrick Hudson HS; Montrose, NY; (Y); Church Choir; VP Frsh Cls; JV Var Fld Hcky; JV Socr; Cit Awd; Hon Roll; Varsity Clb; Stu Cncl; JV Trk; Cobleskill; Hotel Tech.

CARTER, ELIZABETH A; Uniondale HS; Uniondale, NY; (Y); 36/480; Am Leg Aux Girls St; Trs Girl Scts; Math Tm; NFL; Speech Tm; Acpl Chr; Band; Chorus; Concert Band; Drm & Bgl; Acadmc Al-Amer Pres, Presdntl Acadmc Ftns Awd 85; Medl Excllnc Music, Outstndng Achv Coll Acctng 85; Hofstra U; Acctng.

CARTER, JASON E J; Long Island Lutheran HS; Roosevelt, NY; (S); 3/56; Church Yth Grp; Spanish Clb; Bowling; High Hon Roll; NHS; NCTE Awd; Ntl Merit Ltr; St Schlr; NYS Rgnts Schlrshp 85; Columbia U; Pre-Med.

CARTER, JENNIFER; Alexandria Central HS; Redwood, NY; (Y); Var Bowling; Var Sftbl.

CARTER, KATIE; Lockport SR HS; Lockport, NY; (Y); 26/441; Yrbk Stf; Rep Frsh Cls; Rep Soph Cls; Rep Jr Cls; Rep Sr Cls; Rep Stu Cncl; Var Mgr(s); Var Capt Swmmng; Hon Roll; NHS; YMCA Wm J Smith Swmg Awd 85; Niagara County CC.

CARTER, KEVIN M; Park West HS; New York, NY; (Y); 186/531; Computer Clb; ROTC; Drill Tm; Sec Jr Cls; JV Bsbl; JV Bsktbl; JV Ftbl; Cit Awd; High Hon Roll; Hon Roll; City Cncl Citation 82; Air Force Acad; Pilot.

CARTER, KIMBERLY A; Holy Trinity HS; Levittown, NY; (S); 36/318; Cmnty Wkr; Nwsp Rptr; Var Capt Gym; Stat Score Keeper; Var Trk; Hon Roll; Prfct Atten Awd; Stat Timer; 2nd Varsity All Around Indivdl Champ Gymnastics 83; Most Imprvd Varsity Gymnast 82-83; Hnr Roll 82-84; Spc Educ.

CARTER, MARK R; Saranac Central HS; Cadyville, NY; (Y); 39/126; Am Leg Boys St; Drama Clb; Trs Library Aide; School Musical; School Play; Stage Crew; Rep Stu Cncl; Var Trk; Capt Wrstlng; U S Army.

CARTER, MAUREEN; Northern Adirondack HS; Lyon Mountain, NY; (Y); Varsity Clb; Capt L Socr; Var L Sftbl; High Hon Roll; Hon Roll; Bst Def Sccr 83-84; Bst Offns 84-85; MI Sftbl 84-85; Thomas Coll ME; Bus.

CARTER, RUSSELL; Copiaque HS; Copiaque, NY; (Y); CAP; Computer Clb; Intnl Clb; Science Clb; Im Bsktbl; Im Ftbl; Hon Roll; Sci.

CARTER, TIMOTHY P; Kenmore West HS; Kenmore, NY; (Y); Temple Yth Grp; Varsity Clb; Var Ftbl; Var Trk; Buffalo ST; Elem Ed.

CARTIER, CATHY; Salmon River Central Schl; Ft Covington, NY; (Y); 24/87; Pres Church Yth Grp; Pres Drama Clb; Rep Sr Cls; Rep Stu Cncl; Stat Bsbl; JV Bsktbl; Var Capt Swmmng; High Hon Roll; NHS; Admin Ldrshp Awd 85; SUNY-MORRISVILLE; Jrnlsm.

CARTINI, JAY; Bishop Grimes HS; Jamesville, NY; (Y); Boy Scts; Exploring; Trs FBLA; VP JA; Ftbl; DAR Awd; High Hon Roll; Rotary Awd; Acctng.

CARTLEDGE, TRACY N; Shenendehowa Central Schl; Clifton Park, NY; (Y); Drama Clb; Key Clb; School Play; Stage Crew; Yrbk Stf; Var L Cheerleading; High Hon Roll; Hon Roll; NHS; Prfct Atten Awd; Bus Mgmt.

CARTY, JACQUELINE; Newfield HS; Selden, NY; (Y); Cmnty Wkr; French Clb; Girl Scts; Office Aide; Political Wkr; Varsity Clb; Band; Var Fld Hcky; High Hon Roll; Hon Roll; Stony Brook U; Pre Med.

CARUANA, JOHN; Lindenhurst HS; Lindenhurst, NY; (Y); 5/600; Church Yth Grp; Science Clb; Hon Roll; NHS; Italian Natl Hnr Socty 84; Gold Mdl NY ST Sci Olympics At Wst Pt 85; 1st Pl SADD Essa Cont 84.

CARUSANE, DEAN; Altmar-Parish-Williamstown HS; Williamston, NY; (Y); French Clb; Varsity Clb; Rep Stu Cncl; JV Bsbl; Var Bsktbl; Trk; High Hon Roll; Hnr Soc.

CARUSO, JARED; Smithtown High School East; St James, NY; (Y); Camera Clb; Pres Church Yth Grp; JV Bsbl; JV Ftbl; Hon Roll; FL Inst Of Tech; Marine Bio.

CARUSO, MARIE; St John Villa Acad; Brooklyn, NY; (Y); 27/125; Nwsp Rptr; Nwsp Stf; Ed Yrbk Stf; VP Jr Cls; Pres Stu Cncl; JV Sftbl; Hon Roll; Church Yth Grp; Yrbk Rptr; JV Var Tennis; Borough Pres Awd Outstndng Achvt 85; Excllnce Bus Law & Engl 85; Schl Spirit 85; St Johns U; Legal Asst.

CARUSO, MARK; Frankfort Schuyler Central HS; Frankfort, NY; (S); Rptr FBLA; Key Clb; Math Tm; Spanish Clb; Yrbk Stf; High Hon Roll; Hon Roll; NHS; 1st Pl Math Leag 82; 2nd Pl Math Leag 83; Regents Schlrshp 85; SUNY Geneseo; Bio Std.

CARUSO, MICHAEL; Fordham Prep; Yonkers, NY; (Y); Camera Clb; Dance Clb; English Clb; Hosp Aide; Latin Clb; Math Clb; Science Clb; Ski Clb; Nwsp Phtg; Var Ftbl; Columbia; Pre-Med.

CARUSO, MICHAEL J; Our Lady Of Lourdes HS; Poughquag, NY; (Y); 52/144; Boy Scts; Cmnty Wkr; Drama Clb; Band; School Play; Variety Show; NHS; Bio 2nd Hghst Awd 82-83; Rochester Inst Of Tech Schlrshp 84-85; Arlington Brd Of Educ Schlrshp 84-85; Rochester Inst Of Tech; Engrng.

CARUSO, MIKE; Mc Kee V & T HS; Staten Is, NY; (Y); 64/258; Church Yth Grp; Debate Tm; Ski Clb; VICA; Nwsp Rptr; Rep Frsh Cls; Rep Soph Cls; Rep Jr Cls; Stu Cncl; Ftbl; Mst Vlbl Plyr Ftbl; Capt Ftbl Tm; Plumbng Shp Formn.

CARUSO, SUSAN; Frankfort-Schuyler HS; Frankfort, NY; (S); Exploring; French Clb; Math Clb; Nwsp Rptr; High Hon Roll; NHS; Dnstry.

CARUSO, TERI ANN; John H Glenn HS; E Northport, NY; (Y); Chorus; Drill Tm; Stage Crew; Ed Yrbk Stf; Rep Frsh Cls; JV Var Fld Hcky; Cit Awd; AFS; School Musical; Pom Pon; Mert, Acdmc Decath Suffork Co 85; LI Lang Comp, 1st Cultrl Exhbt 83; Outstndng Schlstc Accmplshmnts; Arch.

CARVALLO, SUSAN; Long Island City HS; Astoria, NY; (Y); 100/500; JA; Teachers Aide; Stage Crew; Yrbk Ed-Chief; Yrbk Rptr; Yrbk Sprt Ed; Yrbk Stf; Pres Frsh Cls; Cit Awd; Hon Roll; Outstndng Schl Svc; ST U Coll Buffalo; Law.

CARVER, DANIELLE F; Scarsdale HS; Scarsdale, NY; (Y); Concert Band; Symp Band; Var Capt Bsktbl; Coach Actv; Var Capt Socr; NYS Regnt Schlrshp 85; Amherst Coll.

CARVILL, BILLEE; Massena Central HS; Massena, NY; (Y); Church Yth Grp; French Clb; Radio Clb; Thesps; School Musical; School Play; Rep Jr Cls; High Hon Roll; Hon Roll; Fashion Merch.

CARVILLE, LISA; Broadalbin Central HS; Houston, TX; (Y); 3/100; Church Yth Grp; Cmnty Wkr; Drama Clb; English Clb; French Clb; GAA; Library Aide; Pep Clb; PAVAS; School Musical; MVP Socr 84-85; Jrnlsm.

CARWAY, MARGOT; John Dewey HS; Brooklyn, NY; (Y); Dance Clb; English Clb; Orch; Rep Jr Cls; Hon Roll; Adolescent Voctnl Explortn Pgm-Most Outstndng Stu 82-83; Columbia U; Pre-Law.

CARY, RICHARD; Potsdam Central HS; Potsdam, NY; (Y); Var Trk; Var Wrstlng; Natl Sci Olympd Cert Of Distnctn 85; Tlntd Jrs Pgm 85; Bio.

CARY, SEAN; Albertus Magnus HS; Pearl River, NY; (Y); Cmnty Wkr; Varsity Clb; Nwsp Sprt Ed; Yrbk Stf; Bsktbl; Coach Actv; Crs Cntry; Lcrss; Vllybl; Wt Lftg; Cmmnctns.

CASA, DOUGLAS; Newfield HS; Selden, NY; (Y); Letterman Clb; Varsity Clb; Capt Var Crs Cntry; JV Socr; Capt Var Trk; High Hon Roll; Jr NHS; Med.

CASADO, CHRISTINE; Norman Thomas Commercial HS; New York, NY; (Y); 174/644; Church Yth Grp; Cmnty Wkr; Office Aide; Teachers Aide; Church Choir; Nwsp Rptr; ASL Cert, Rgnts Diplma 85; Borough Manhattan CC; Bus Admn.

CASADONTE, KELLY; Mohawk Central Schl; Mohawk, NY; (Y); 16/97; Trs French Clb; Teachers Aide; Concert Band; Mrchg Band; VP Frsh Cls; JV Var Cheerleading; JV Fld Hcky; High Hon Roll; Hon Roll; NHS; Ed.

CASALE, CHRISTINE; Newwburgh Free Acad; New Windsor, NY; (Y); 24/720; Hosp Aide; Key Clb; Acpl Chr; Chorus; Stat Bsbl; Capt Pom Pon; High Hon Roll; NHS; NY ST Rgnts Schlrshp 85; Slena Coll; Bio.

CASAMENTO, THEODORE; Niagara Wheatfield SR HS; Niagara Falls, NY; (Y); Latin Clb; Varsity Clb; Jazz Band; Rep Stu Cncl; Var Ftbl; Var Ice Hcky; JV Lcrss; High Hon Roll; NHS; Dentistry.

CASANOVA, MELVA; South Shore HS; Brooklyn, NY; (Y); Chorus; Cheerleading; U Of CA; Bus Mgt.

CASCIANO, KAREN; Bishop Grimes HS; E Syracuse, NY; (Y); Variety Show; JV Socr; NEMA 85; Italian Hnr Soc 84-85; Spch Thrpy.

CASCIATO, LISA; Mahopac HS; Mahopac, NY; (Y); 40/400; Cmnty Wkr; Yrbk Stf; Socr; Twrlr; Hon Roll; NHS; SUNY Oneonta; Elem Educ.

CASCIO, MICHAEL; Bethpage HS; Bethpage, NY; (Y); 18/290; Var Bsktbl; High Hon Roll; Bus.

CASCONE, JO ANNE; Our Lady Of Victory Acad; Tuckahoe, NY; (S); 15/159; FBLA; Spanish Clb; High Hon Roll; Spanish NHS; Bus.

CASCONE, KAREN; Mahopac HS; Mahopac, NY; (Y); 7/380; Math Tm; Yrbk Stf; Var Fld Hcky; Var Socr; Cit Awd; High Hon Roll; NHS; Ntl Merit Ltr; Pres Schlr; NY St Regnts Schlrshp 85-86; Rensselaer Polytech Inst Schlrshp 85-86; Syracuse U Schlrshp 85-86; Rensselaer Polytech Inst; Comp.

CASE, JACK; Little Falls JR SR HS; St Johnsville, NY; (Y); Ski Clb; Spanish Clb; Nwsp Rptr; Yrbk Stf; Tennis; Hon Roll; Psych.

CASE JR, JAMES L; Nyack HS; Nyack, NY; (Y); 22/257; Am Leg Boys St; Band; Church Choir; Jazz Band; Rep Soph Cls; Rep Jr Cls; Rep Sr Cls; Var Ftbl; High Hon Roll; Hon Roll; Vrsty Ftlb Tm Cptn 85-86; Stu Exchng Japan 85; Accntng.

CASE, MELINDA; Smithtown HS West; Smithtown, NY; (Y); Mrchg Band; Symp Band; Var L Crs Cntry; JV Var Socr; Capt Var Trk; High Hon Roll; Hon Roll; Spanish NHS; Spanish Clb; Varsity Clb; Hon Men Natl H S Trk All Amer 84; NY ST Hgh Jmp Chmp 84 & 85; NY ST Proclmtn ST & Cnty Legis 84; Sprts Med.

CASE, MONICA; Bradford Central HS; Bradford, NY; (S); FBLA; Band; Chorus; Mrchg Band; Capt Vllybl; Hon Roll; NHS; Honry Mntn In Bus Dynamics For FBLA At ST Conf 84; Corning Comm; Accntng.

CASE, STEPHEN; Hendrick Hudson HS; Peekskill, NY; (Y); 4/200; Art Clb; French Clb; NFL; Speech Tm; Ed Yrbk Stf; Var Capt Socr; High Hon Roll; NHS; Pres Schlr; NY ST Regents Scholar 85; Harvard Spch Trnmnt Outstndng Spkr 85; Princeton U; Arch.

CASE, TIMOTHY J; Chenango Valley JR-SR HS; Binghamton, NY; (Y); 4/185; Boy Scts; Band; Chorus; Jazz Band; Orch; School Musical; DAR Awd; Church Yth Grp; Church Choir; NYS Regnts Schlrshp 85; NYSSMA All ST Cncrt Band Tuba 84; Broome CC; Elctrcl Engrng.

CASELLA, DENISE; East Meadow HS; East Meadow, NY; (S); Key Clb; Band; Mrchg Band; Symp Band; JV Var Lcrss; Hon Roll; NHS; Acadmc All Amer Awd 85; Vet Sci Tech.

CASELLA, JACQUELYN A; Union Endicott HS; Endwell, NY; (Y); 11/435; Key Clb; Ski Clb; Concert Band; Flag Corp; Yrbk Stf; VP Jr Cls; VP Sr Cls; Rep Stu Cncl; High Hon Roll; NHS; NY ST Regnts Schlrshp 85; Natl Yth Ldrshp Cncl 84; Bucknell U; Engrng.

CASEY, BRIAN; Bishop Kearney HS; Rochester, NY; (Y); Varsity Clb; Capt L Ftbl; Capt L Lcrss; Trk; Wt Lftg; Wrstlng; Coaches Awd La Crosse 85; Archael.

CASEY, DIANNE; Nazareth Acad; Rochester, NY; (Y); Church Yth Grp; Hosp Aide; Ski Clb; Varsity Clb; School Musical; Swing Chorus; Off Soph Cls; Sec Stu Cncl; Var Socr; NHS; Natn Latn Exam 83-84; Cnslr.

CASEY, JENNIFER; Warwick Valley HS; Warwick, NY; (Y); Drama Clb; French Clb; Hosp Aide; Math Tm; School Play; JV Cheerleading; Var Diving; Var Swmmng; Trk; Hon Roll; Lawyer.

CASEY, JENNIFER; West Islip HS; West Islip, NY; (Y); 53/525; Drama Clb; School Musical; School Play; Yrbk Stf; VP Soph Cls; VP Jr Cls; VP Sr Cls; Rep Stu Cncl; Hon Roll; PTA Ldrshp Awd 84; Rgnts Schlrshp 85; U Of Richmond; Pol Sci.

CASEY, MARY; Batavia SR HS; Batavia, NY; (Y); Service Clb; Varsity Clb; Chorus; School Musical; Sec Soph Cls; Var L Diving; Var Capt Socr; Var L Swmmng; Hon Roll; MVP Sccr 84; Monroe Cty W All Leag Sccr 84; All Cty Chors 83-84; PA ST U; Athl Trnr.

CASEY, MAUREEN E; Sayville HS; West Sayville, NY; (Y); 79/365; Key Clb; Political Wkr; Ski Clb; Orch; Yrbk Stf; Stat Sftbl; Trk; Hon Roll; St Schlr; NY St Music Awd 81-83; Pres Schlrshp Marit Coll 85; Pol Sci.

CASEY, TARA; Acad Of St Joseph; N Babylon, NY; (Y); Dance Clb; Hosp Aide; Math Clb; Math Tm; Science Clb; Orch; Stage Crew; Yrbk Stf; Var Cheerleading; JV Swmmng; Math Achvt Awd; Bio Achvt Awd; Engrng.

CASEY, VICKI; Rensselaer JR SR HS; Rensselaer, NY; (S); 8/83; Q&S; Nwsp Rptr; Yrbk Ed-Chief; Pres Stu Cncl; Cheerleading; Hudson Vlly CC; Dentl Hyg.

CASH, DAVID; St Joseph Collegiate Inst; Kenmore, NY; (Y); 99/200; Boy Scts; Church Yth Grp; Band; Jazz Band; School Play; Bsbl; Ftbl; JV Var Ice Hcky; High Hon Roll; U Of Buffalo; Elec Engrng.

CASH, MICHELLE; Pavilion Central HS; Pavilion, NY; (Y); Pres Trs FHA; Color Guard; Nwsp Stf; Hon Roll; Home Ec Awd 85.

CASHATT, MICHAEL; La Salle SR HS; Niagara Falls, NY; (Y); 90/279; JV Var Bsbl; JV Var Ftbl; Wstrn NY All Star Bsbl Tm 85; Niag Frontr Leag All Star Bsbl Tm 85; Cabl 3 TV Sprts Rap-Up Allstr Tm; Niagara U; Comp Sci.

CASIANO, JOHN; All Hallows Inst; Bronx, NY; (Y); Bsbl; Crs Cntry; Sftbl; Trk; Wt Lftg; St Johns U; Trk Ltrmn 84.

CASILLO, MICHELLE; Depew HS; Depew, NY; (S); Cmnty Wkr; Pres DECA; Sec French Clb; GAA; Trs Radio Clb; Red Cross Aide; Yrbk Stf; Stu Cncl; Stat Crs Cntry; Stat Diving; Distributive Ed Outstndng Svc Awd 85; Phillips Petroleum Free Enterprise Proj Wnnr 85; Bryant & Stratton; Travel.

CASIMIR, VOLEL JUNE; Bishop Loughlin M HS; Brooklyn, NY; (S); 1/180; Drama Clb; Speech Tm; Teachers Aide; Band; School Musical; Nwsp Stf; Im Ftbl; Hon Roll; NHS; Ntl Hnr Roll 84-85; Ntl Ldrshp Org 84-85; Hofstro U; Pre Med.

CASLAKE, JOANNE; Solvay HS; Syracuse, NY; (Y); 29/181; Trs Key Clb; Yrbk Ed-Chief; Yrbk Phtg; VP Jr Cls; Trs Sr Cls; JV Socr; Art Clb; Math Clb; Drm & Bgl; Photgrphy Awd, Key Clb Svc Awd, Balfour Mdl Comp Sci 85; Rochester Isnt Tech; Phtgrphr.

CASLER, CHRISTINE; Canastota JR SR HS; Canastota, NY; (Y); Office Aide; Chorus; High Hon Roll; Hon Roll; Enriched Sci Prgm 82-85; Advncd Math & Lang Prgms 82-84; Engl.

CASLER, LORI; Fort Plain HS; Ft Plain, NY; (Y); Cmnty Wkr; French Clb; Band; Chorus; School Musical; Rep Stu Cncl; Var Crs Cntry; 4-H Awd; Hon Roll; Hugh O Brian Yth Fndtn Abmssdr 84.

CASO, LOURDES; Bishop Kearney HS; Brooklyn, NY; (Y); Drama Clb; FHA; Trs Key Clb; Spanish Clb; Teachers Aide; Stage Crew; Hon Roll; NHS; Ntl Sci Merit Awds 83; Ntl Ldrshp, Svc Awds 84; 2nd Iona Lang Cnsts 85; Cert Merit Ntl Frnch 84; Columbia; Chem Engrng.

CASOLARE, STEPHANIE; Canastota HS; Canastota, NY; (Y); Pres Church Yth Grp; Teachers Aide; Band; Concert Band; Drm Mjr(t); Mrchg Band; Pep Band; School Musical; Yrbk Stf; Var Capt Cheerleading; Outstndg Ldrshp Bnd 84-85; Flagler U; Deaf Ed.

CASPER, JAMIE; Newfield HS; Selden, NY; (Y); 90/562; Drama Clb; Sec Q&S; Chorus; Madrigals; School Musical; School Play; Swing Chorus; Sec Frsh Cls; Stu Cncl; Voice Dem Awd; Choral Awd 82-85; Drama Awd 85; Quill & Scroll Awd 85; Montclaire Coll; Music.

CASS, ROBERT; Horseheads HS; Horseheads, NY; (Y); 137/407; Church Yth Grp; Hosp Aide; Band; Chorus; Church Choir; Concert Band; Mrchg Band; Hon Roll; Aurelia Whitenack Mem Awd 85; Rodney Faught Mem Awd 85; Pprby Mnth August 81; Corning CC; Nrs.

CASSADAY, JAMES M; Minisink Valley HS; Port Jervis, NY; (Y); 10/232; Scholastic Bowl; Jazz Band; Mrchg Band; Rep Stu Cncl; Var L Bsktbl; Var L Socr; NHS; 3rd Wrld Olym Mind Fnls Akron Oh 84; 3rd St Olym Mnd Fnls Buffalo Ny 85; Natl Acad Chmpnshps Dallas 84; Albright Coll; Med Teach.

CASSANO, KHARA; Longwood HS; Yaphank, NY; (Y); Art Clb; Girl Scts; PAVAS; Q&S; Red Cross Aide; Stage Crew; Yrbk Stf; Lit Mag; Gftd & Tlntd 85.

CASSATA, BARBARA; Bishop Kearney HS; Brooklyn, NY; (Y); Dance Clb; Baruch Coll; Mgmt.

CASSATA, JUDY A; St Francis Preparatory HS; Rosedale, NY; (Y); 106/690; Art Clb; Dance Clb; Service Clb; Variety Show; Yrbk Stf; Im Vllybl; NHS; Opt Clb Awd; St Johns U; Law.

CASSCLES, MICHAEL; Highland HS; Highland, NY; (Y); 25/132; Aud/Vis; Boy Scts; Computer Clb; Concert Band; Jazz Band; Crs Cntry; Tennis; AFS; Band; Mrchg Band; Phys Fit Hon 82-85; U S Natnly Ranked Speed Skater 84; Northern MI U; Cmmnctns.

CASSELLA, ABBY; Kings Park SR HS; Kings Park, NY; (Y); Debate Tm; Drama Clb; Hosp Aide; Spanish Clb; Teachers Aide; Var Cheerleading; Hon Roll; NHS; Natl Lang Arts Olympiad Medal; Mrktng Trophy 1st Pl; Bus Admin.

CASSELMAN, MAUREEN; Nazareth Acad; Rochester, NY; (Y); Debate Tm; Math Clb; NFL; Rep Frsh Cls; VP Soph Cls; High Hon Roll; Hon Roll; St John Fisher; Pre-Med.

CASSERA, LISA; Linton HS; Schenectady, NY; (Y); 6/273; Boys Clb Am; Intnl Clb; JA; Yrbk Stf; Stu Cncl; Hon Roll; NHS; Math.

CASSETTA, CATHERINE; Lyons JR SR HS; Lyons, NY; (Y); 15/96; Ski Clb; Concert Band; Drm Mjr(t); School Musical; Yrbk Stf; Tennis; JP Sousa Awd; NHS; Teachers Aide; Trs Soph Cls; Stndrd Bearer 84-85; Stu Cncl Awd 85; Ithaca Clg; Acctng.

CASSIDY, MICHAEL E; St Francis Prep Schl; Woodside, NY; (S); 102/690; Office Aide; Hon Roll; Jr NHS; NHS; Opt Clb Awd; Spanish NHS; Acad All-Amer Schlr Prog 85; Spnsh Cert Acadmc Hnrs 83; Fordham U; Jurisprdnc.

CASSIDY, PRISCILLA A; Our Lady Of Mercy HS; Rochester, NY; (Y); 19/200; French Clb; School Play; Ed Yrbk Phtg; NHS; Ntl Merit Ltr; Clarkson U Trstee Schlrshp 85; NYS Rgnts Schlrshp 85; Pres Acad Fitnss Awd 85; Clarkson U; Elec Engrng.

CASSINY, CHRISTINE; Franciscan HS; Ft Montgomery, NY; (Y); Cmnty Wkr; Stage Crew; Capt Var Bsktbl; Crs Cntry; Score Keeper; Sftbl; Vllybl; Hon Roll; NHS; Spanish NHS; All Leag Bsktbl, Hnrbl Ment All Cnty 85; Med.

CASTAGLIOLA, NANCY A; Cityh As Schl; Richmond Hill, NY; (Y); Cmnty Wkr; Drama Clb; PAVAS; Church Choir; School Musical; School Play; Stage Crew; Variety Show; Music.

CASTAGNINO, DINA; St John The Baptist HS; Brightwaters, NY; (Y); 5/550; Hosp Aide; Math Tm; Science Clb; Orch; Nwsp Stf; Lit Mag; Mgr(s); High Hon Roll; NHS; Soc Studys Awd; Med.

CASTALDI, RALPH; Beacon HS; Hopewell Jct, NY; (Y); 24/205; Spanish Clb; Varsity Clb; Sec Frsh Cls; Coach Actv; Capt L Ftbl; JV Trk; Capt Wt Lftg; High Hon Roll; Hon Roll; Jr NHS; Ithaca; Phy Thrpy.

CASTALDO, CHRISTOPHER; Newfield HS; Selden, NY; (S); 2/542; Computer Clb; Pres Math Tm; Stu Cncl; High Hon Roll; Jr NHS; NHS; Prfct Atten Awd; Sal; Awd Excel Germn Steuben Soc Am 84; NY ST Rgnts Schlrshp 85; Lamp Knowledge 83; Comp Sci.

CASTALDO, MARIA; Preston HS; Bronx, NY; (S); Drama Clb; School Musical; School Play; Trs Soph Cls; Sec Jr Cls; Capt Cheerleading; NHS; Schlrshp To Preston 82; SUNY Coll At NY; Drama.

CASTANEDA, ISAAC; H S Of Art & Design; Flushing, NY; (Y); 1/439; Debate Tm; FTA; Intnl Clb; Latin Clb; Math Tm; Nwsp Rptr; Socr; Hon Roll; NHS; Prfct Atten Awd; Cornell U; Engr.

CASTANEDA, MARIA L; St Nicholas Of Tolentine HS; New York, NY; (S); 4/138; Yrbk Stf; Math, Hist, Spnsh I & II Awds 82-84; Manhattan Coll; Bus Adm.

CASTANZA, PAUL A; Frontier SR HS; Blasdell, NY; (Y); Ftbl; NE; Bus.

CASTELLA, KRYSTINA; Notre Dame Acad; Staten Island, NY; (Y); Art Clb; Church Yth Grp; Computer Clb; Yrbk Stf; Lit Mag; Bsktbl; Swmmng; Art Awd 85; Natl Art Awd 84; RISD Scholar 84; RI Schl Design; Graphic Desgn.

CASTELLAN, RITZA; Clara Barton HS; Brooklyn, NY; (Y); Dance Clb; French Clb; Chorus; Cit Awd; High Hon Roll; Hon Roll; Prfct Atten Awd; UFT; Pre-Med.

CASTELLANO, BRENDA; New Hyde Park Memorial HS; New Hyde Park, NY; (S); 77/269; Hst DECA; Chorus; School Play; Nwsp Rptr; Lit Mag; Jr NHS; NHS; Nassau Cnty DECA 1st Pl 85; Hofstra U; Advertising.

CASTELLANO, DENISE; Lindenhurst HS; Lindenhurst, NY; (Y); Drama Clb; Hosp Aide; Thesps; Band; Jazz Band; Mrchg Band; Orch; NHS; Arion Awd, Rgnts Schlrshp Nrsg 85; Molloy; Nrsg.

CASTELLANO, FRANK; Babylon SR HS; N Babylon, NY; (Y); 9/150; School Play; Variety Show; Yrbk Stf; Lit Mag; Bsbl; Crs Cntry; Gym; Lcrss; Hon Roll; Jr NHS; Pres Phy Ftnss Awd 85; Oneonta; Envir Sci.

CASTELLANO, FRANK X; Bellport SR HS; Ballport, NY; (Y); 8/320; Swing Chorus; Church Yth Grp; Science Clb; JV Capt Bsbl; High Hon Roll; Jr NHS; NHS; Prfct Atten Awd; Rotary Awd; Presdntl Clsrm Yng Amer 85; US Navl Acad; Med.

CASTELLANO, JILL; Connetquot HS; Bohemia, NY; (Y); 261/806; Church Yth Grp; Teachers Aide; Chorus; Stage Crew; JV Gym; Var Tennis; Hon Roll; Coaches Awd Tennis 82-83; Mid-Sflk Nrsng Schl; Hlth.

CASTELLANO, MARIA; St Barnabas HS; Bronx, NY; (Y); Office Aide; Teachers Aide; Hon Roll; NHS; Prfct Atten Awd; Iona Coll; Bus.

CASTELLI, MICHAEL; St Francis Preparatory Schl; Ozone Park, NY; (S); 60/690; Am Leg Boys St; Varsity Clb; Bsbl; Bsktbl; Score Keeper; High Hon Roll; Hon Roll; NHS; Regent Scholar 85; Little Lg Bsbl Coach; Cornell U; Nutrition.

CASTELLINI, JOANNE; Henninger HS; Syracuse, NY; (Y); 6/400; Exploring; Intnl Clb; Yrbk Stf; Rep Jr Cls; Sec Sr Cls; JV Var Socr; High Hon Roll; Trs NHS; Hlth II Bst Over-All Perf 84-85; The Wellesley Coll Bk Awd 84-85; Comp Prog.

CASTELLINO, SAMUEL; Elmira Free Acad; Elmira, NY; (Y); Am Leg Boys St; JCL; Latin Clb; Letterman Clb; Ski Clb; Off Frsh Cls; Off Soph Cls; Pres Jr Cls; VP Stu Cncl; Var L Tennis; Pol Sci.

CASTER, SUSAN; Union Springs Acad; Caneadea, NY; (S); Church Yth Grp; Varsity Clb; Acpl Chr; Pres Concert Band; Pres Stu Cncl; Cheerleading; High Hon Roll; US Bus Educ Awd 84-85; Bryant & Stratton Bus Schl Schlrshp 1st Alt 84-85; Houghton Wesleyan Ny; Phys Ther.

CASTIGLIA, PATRICIA R; Hamburg SR HS; Hamburg, NY; (Y); 2/350; French Clb; Quiz Bowl; High Hon Roll; NHS; Mth.

CASTIGLIONE, DAVID; Jamestown HS; Jamestown, NY; (Y); French Clb; Capt Quiz Bowl; Concert Band; Jazz Band; Mrchg Band; High Hon Roll; Jr NHS; NHS; Natl Hnr Rll 85; Chem Engrng.

CASTIGLIONE, RALPH; Sachem HS; Holbrook, NY; (Y); 251/1383; Chess Clb; Cmnty Wkr; Office Aide; JV Bsbl; Im Bsktbl; JV Ftbl; Im Wt Lftg; Hockey Dfsmn Yr 84; Hockey MIP 84; Hockey MVP 85; Med.

CASTIGLIONE, STEVE L; Corning East HS; Corning, NY; (Y); Aud/Vis; Drama Clb; Exploring; School Musical; School Play; Stage Crew; Variety Show; Yrbk Bus Mgr; Yrbk Stf; Stu Cncl; Blue Belt; Corning CC; Bio.

CASTILLO, ALBIN; Brooklyn Tech; Flushing, NY; (Y); Boys Clb Am; Boy Scts; Library Aide; Spanish Clb; Teachers Aide; Gym; Hon Roll; Gym Scholar YMCA 83; Slippery Rock ST Coll; Bus.

CASTILLO, LISETTE; Eli Whitney V HS; Brooklyn, NY; (Y); Latin Clb; Red Cross Aide; VICA; Yrbk Stf; Gov Hon Prg Awd; High Hon Roll; Jr NHS; NHS; Steno Cert Achvt 84 & 85; Keybrdng/Word Proc Cert Achvt 85; Marymount Coll; Cmmnctns Offcr.

CASTILLO, TERESA; Cathedral HS; Bx, NY; (Y); 82/298; Intnl Clb; Off Jr Cls; Vllybl; Lehman Coll; CPA.

CASTILLO, VIVIAN; Herbert H Lehman HS; New York, NY; (Y); 63/444; Cmnty Wkr; Dance Clb; Drama Clb; English Clb; French Clb; PAVAS; Service Clb; Teachers Aide; Cit Awd; Excllnc Psycho Literature & F L Spanish 84-85; SUNY In Albany; Psych.

CASTINE, SALLY; Northeastern Clinton HS; Champlain, NY; (Y); CAP; Computer Clb; English Clb; FBLA; FNA; FTA; Hosp Aide; Math Clb; Science Clb; Yrbk Bus Mgr; Clinton CC; Sci.

CASTINE, TODD; Northeastern Clinton Central HS; Chazy, NY; (Y); 45/153; Drama Clb; Speech Tm; Band; Chorus; Concert Band; Mrchg Band; Orch; School Musical; Ice Hcky; Socr; Crane Schl Music; Music Ed.

CASTLE, AMANDA; Sacred Heart Acad; Hempstead, NY; (S); 10/175; Math Tm; Pep Clb; Acpl Chr; Chorus; Church Choir; Madrigals; School Musical; School Play; Hon Roll; NHS; American Biographical Inst Inc 84-85; Oberlin; Music.

CASTLE, JENNIFER R; Briarcliff HS; Briarcliff Mnr, NY; (Y); Drama Clb; Political Wkr; Chorus; School Play; Nwsp Rptr; Lit Mag; High Hon Roll; NHS; Brwn U Bk Awd 84; Wrtng Comp 2nd Pl 83; Engl.

CASTLE, LORI; Lakeland HS; Mohegan Lake, NY; (Y); Yrbk Stf; Pre-Law.

CASTOE, BRENDA; Arlington High North; Wapp Falls, NY; (Y); Computer Clb; Office Aide; Golf; Vllybl; Cert Merit 85; Miss United Teen 84.

CASTRO, AIDA; Clara Barton HS; New York, NY; (Y); Church Yth Grp; Cmnty Wkr; Chorus; Color Guard; Variety Show; Nwsp Stf; Tennis; Hon Roll; Cert Rcgntn Of Achvt Wmns Hist Mnth Outstndg Pstr 84; Pride Of Ynks Awd 84-85; NYC Super Yth 84; Psych.

CASTRO, CELIA; H S Of Music And Art; Brooklyn, NY; (Y); 88/590; Chorus; Madrigals; Hon Roll; NHS; Music Hnr Leag 82-85; Regents Schlrshp 85; Opera Sngr.

CASTRO, JORGE; Adlai E Stevenson HS; Bronx, NY; (Y); Computer Clb; Office Aide; ROTC; Spanish Clb; Color Guard; Drill Tm; Mrchg Band; Prfct Atten Awd; Bus Exec.

CASTRO, MARIA AURORA R; Academy Of St Joseph HS; Kings Park, NY; (Y); 2/121; Library Aide; Science Clb; Chorus; NHS; Var Tennis; NY ST Regents Schlrshp 84-85; Hofstra U; Bus.

CASTRO, RAPHAEL ANGEL; Cardinal Hayes HS; New York, NY; (Y); 36/264; Church Yth Grp; Dance Clb; Exploring; Hosp Aide; JA; Office Aide; Band; Concert Band; Mrchg Band; School Musical; JR Achvt 84; Hnr Rl 83-85; Perf Atten Awd 84; Med.

CASTRO, SONIA; Our Lady Of Perpetual Help; Brooklyn, NY; (Y); 11/165; Intnl Clb; Chorus; School Musical; Pres Soph Cls; Pres Jr Cls; Rep Stu Cncl; Cheerleading; Swmmng; High Hon Roll; NY Regnts Schlrshp 85; Acad All Amer Schlr 85; Cornell U; Bio.

CASTROGIOVANNI, CHRIS; North Babylon SR HS; N Babylon, NY; (Y); 32/527; Art Clb; French Clb; Band; Var Capt Trk; French Hon Soc; High Hon Roll; Jr NHS; NHS; Pres Acad Ftnss Awd 85; Sprvsr Merit Cert 84; Rchstr Inst/Tech; Nwsp Prdctn.

CASULLO JR, ANTHONY J; St Joes Collegiate HS; Kenmore, NY; (Y); JV Bsbl; Var Ice Hcky; Geneseo SUNY; Bus.

CASULLO, MARIA; St Barnabas HS; Yonkers, NY; (Y); 32/136; Computer Clb; Hon Roll; Ntl Sci Olympiad/Chmstry 84; Iona Coll; Accntnt.

CASVIKES, MARIA; Bronx H S Of Science; Bronx, NY; (Y); Church Yth Grp; JA; Teachers Aide; Vllybl; Med.

CASWELL, TRUDY; Madrid-Waddington JR SR HS; Waddington, NY; (Y); 12/50; Sec AFS; VP Pres Drama Clb; Trs GAA; Pres Speech Tm; School Musical; School Play; Yrbk Stf; Crs Cntry; Trk; NHS; Whiz Quiz Tm Mbr 84 & 85; Jzz Pop Fstvl Jersey St 1st Pop Choral Grp 83 & 84; Plattsburgh ST U; Comm.

CATALA, CAROLINE; Academy Of Mount St Ursula HS; Bronx, NY; (Y); Girl Scts; Chorus; Church Choir; Color Guard; Drill Tm; Drm & Bgl; Flag Corp; Cit Awd; Rookie Of Yr Drm & Bgl Corp 83; Flag Line Instrctr Of Yr 84-85; Bio.

CATALANO, GINA; Edison Tech; Rochester, NY; (Y); Exploring; Library Aide; Office Aide; Red Cross Aide; Var Sftbl; Hon Roll; Prfct Atten Awd; Library Aide; Math Clb; Model UN; Nrs.

CATALANO, JENNIFER; Silver Creek Central HS; Silver Creek, NY; (Y); AFS; Ski Clb; Spanish Clb; Band; Yrbk Stf; Im Bowling; Elem Eductn.

CATALDO, WILLIAM; Washingtonville HS; Chester, NY; (Y); Ski Clb; Trk; High Hon Roll; NHS; Hnrs Sqntl Math 82-85; Lndscp Arch.

CATALFAMO, LAURA; Solvay HS; Syracuse, NY; (Y); Frsh Cls; Soph Cls; Jr Cls; DAR Awd; High Hon Roll; Hon Roll; Alg Awd Hghst Avg; Math.

CATANESE, ELIZABETH; Union-Endicott HS; Endicott, NY; (Y); Drama Clb; French Clb; Mathletes; Speech Tm; Concert Band; School Musical; Rep Frsh Cls; High Hon Roll; Jr NHS; NHS; Rotary Yth Ldrshp Awd 85; Area All St Orch 83-84; Math.

CATANESE, JAMES; Churchville-Chili Central HS; Churchville, NY; (Y); 5/302; Model UN; Trk; Wrstlng; High Hon Roll; NHS; Schltc Athlte Awd Wrstlng 84; Highst Hnr Roll 84 & 85; Sci.

CATANIA III, PETER M; Alexander Central Schl; Darien Ctr, NY; (Y); Varsity Clb; Pres Frsh Cls; Rep Soph Cls; Rep Jr Cls; Off Sr Cls; Rep Stu Cncl; JV Bsbl; Stat Bsktbl; Var Capt Golf; Hon Roll; Sectnl Golf 84-85; Co Chairmn Ntl Hnr Soc 85; Fin Mgmt.

CATANIA, STEVE; Kenmore West SR HS; Kenmore, NY; (Y); Varsity Clb; Pres Frsh Cls; VP Soph Cls; VP Jr Cls; Rep Stu Cncl; Var Capt Bsbl; Var Capt Bowling; Var Ftbl; Hon Roll; Prfct Atten Awd; MVP-BSBL & Ftbl 82; MVP-BSBL & Ftbl 83; 2nd Tm All Star-Bsbl 84; U Of Pittsburg; Engrng.

CATANZARO, JACK; Lancaster Central HS; Lancaster, NY; (S); Boys Clb Am; Church Yth Grp; Chrmn Dance Clb; DECA; Rep Stu Cncl; Im Bsbl; JV Bsktbl; Var Ftbl; Im Trk; Bus Admn.

CATANZARO, JOSEPH; Valley Stroam Central HS; Valley Stream, NY; (Y); Boys Clb Am; Boy Scts; Dance Clb; FCA; FBLA; FHA; Off Sr Cls; Wt Lftg; Bst Friend Awd 85; Boston U; Bus.

CATANZARO, MICHELLE; Kenmore East HS; Kenmore, NY; (Y); Mrchg Band; Var Pom Pon; Im Vllybl; NHS; Regents Math Awd 83-85; Nrs.

CATEFORIS, THEODORE; Potsdam HS; Potsdam, NY; (Y); Pres Church Yth Grp; Computer Clb; Band; Jazz Band; Mrchg Band; Orch; Pep Band; Nwsp Stf; Hon Roll; NHS; Tlntd Jrs 84.

CATELLI, ROSE V; Faith Heritage HS; Syracuse, NY; (Y); Chorus; Nwsp Sprt Ed; Var L Cheerleading; Var L Trk; Hon Roll; Jr NHS; NHS; Head Masters List 85; Schl Singing Grp 84-85; Wells Coll; Liberal Arts.

CATENA, JOHN; Amsterdam HS; Amsterdam, NY; (Y); Varsity Clb; Yrbk Stf; Rep Frsh Cls; Rep Soph Cls; Trs Sr Cls; Stu Cncl; Ftbl; Trk; Hon Roll; Sci.

CATERINA, ANNIE; St John Villa Acad; Staten Is, NY; (Y); 7/120; VP Church Yth Grp; Math Tm; Rep Model UN; Teachers Aide; Stage Crew; Nwsp Rptr; Yrbk Stf; Pres Soph Cls; Pres Jr Cls; Pres Stu Cncl; 2nd Gen Excell 83-84; Engl Awd 83-85; Trig Awd 84-85; Holy Cross Coll; Jrnlsm.

CATES, SUSAN M; Holy Trinity HS; E Meadow, NY; (Y); 68/370; Math Clb; Math Tm; Ski Clb; Stu Cncl; Var Badmtn; JV Var Cheerleading; Var Capt Socr; Var Trk; Var Hon Roll; Pres Schlr; Hmcmng Queen 84; Mst Sportsmnlike Plyr Var Badmintn 85, Var Socr 84; U Scranton; Cmmnctns.

CATIZONE, LAURIE A; St Francis Prep; Brooklyn, NY; (Y); 98/690; Dance Clb; Hon Roll; NHS; Opt Clb Awd; FIT; Merch.

CATLIN, LORI; Lowville Acad Central; Castorland, NY; (Y); Girl Scts; Rep Frsh Cls; Rep Soph Cls; Jr Cls; Rep Stu Cncl; JV Capt Bsktbl; JV Var Socr; JV Var Sftbl; JCC; Accntng.

CATNEY, JENNIFER A; Jamesville De Witt HS; Gainesville, NY; (Y); 3/225; Church Yth Grp; Model UN; Chorus; School Musical; Swing Chorus; Im JV Cheerleading; High Hon Roll; Pres NHS; Ntl Merit Ltr; Schlstc Art Awds Blue Rbbn 82-84; Schlstc Art Awds Hnbl Mntn 82 & 84; Coll William & Mary; Bio.

CATONE, DENA; Sachem North HS; Holbrook, NY; (Y); 237/1400; Church Yth Grp; FHA; JA; Science Clb; Ski Clb; Spanish Clb; Yrbk Stf; Im Socr; Var JV Tennis; Var Im Vllybl; Hnrb Mntn-Poetry Cntst 84; NYSSMA Comptn Awd-Piano 84 & 85; Sccr Awd 83; Boston U; Pre-Med.

CATONE, JOSEPH D; Aquinas Inst; Rochester, NY; (Y); Ski Clb; Teachers Aide; Varsity Clb; Stu Cncl; L Capt Bsbl; Bsktbl; L Capt Ftbl; Im Wt Lftg; High Hon Roll; Hon Roll; Acad Schlrshp 80-85; All-Leag Ftbl, Bsbl 84-85; Cornell U; Bus.

CATRAIN, CLAUDINE J; New Dorp HS; Staten Island, NY; (Y); French Clb; Intnl Clb; Hon Roll; Intl Rel.

CATRUNA, LORI; Lyndonville Central HS; Medina, NY; (Y); 8/65; Church Yth Grp; Computer Clb; 4-H; Math Clb; Trs Frsh Cls; JV Bsktbl; Hon Roll; Rgnts Schlrshp 85; U Of Buffalo; Comp Sci.

CATTANEO, MARYANNE; Newfield HS; Coram, NY; (Y); Art Clb; Drama Clb; Chorus; School Play; Trs Sr Cls; Socr; Trk; High Hon Roll; Hon Roll; Jr NHS; VP Natl Art Hnr Socty 84-85; Arch.

CATUCCI, CAROL-ANN; Commack High School North; E Northport, NY; (Y); 38/440; Cmnty Wkr; French Clb; MMM; Orch; Yrbk Stf; Lit Mag; Off Frsh Cls; High Hon Roll; NHS; Joseph Porcino Music Awd 85; Wmns Clb Of Huntington Schlrshp 85; Marist Coll Pres Schlrshp 85; Marist Coll; Psych.

CATUOSCO, ANN MARIE; West Islip HS; W Islip, NY; (Y); 43/525; Drama Clb; Exploring; Hosp Aide; Service Clb; Spanish Clb; Yrbk Stf; Var Capt Cheerleading; Im Capt Trk; Sec Jr NHS; NHS; W Islip PTA Scholar 85; W Islip Little Conf Ftbl Lg Scholar 85; Yvonne Bellow Daher Mem Scholar 85; C W Post Coll; Frgn Lang Tchr.

CAVACCHIOLI, JOANNE; Preston HS; Bronx, NY; (Y); 15/78; VP Soph Cls; Twrlr; Hon Roll; NHS; Rgnts Schlrshp 85; Ntl Hnr Roll 85; Manhattan Coll; Engr.

CAVALIER, LINDA; Campbell Central HS; Campbell, NY; (S); 11/47; Church Yth Grp; French Clb; Varsity Clb; School Musical; Yrbk Stf; Var Capt Bsktbl; Var Capt Socr; Var Capt Trk; High Hon Roll; NHS; SUNY-GENESEO; Spec Educ.

CAVALIERE, ANDREW; Yorktown HS; Yorktown Hts, NY; (Y); 21/360; Key Clb; Rep Stu Cncl; Var L Ftbl; JV Lcrss; Var L Trk; Cit Awd; High Hon Roll; Hon Roll; NHS; Golden Dozen Ftbl Awd Hnrb Mntn 85; All Leag SR Ftbl 84; Bucknell U.

CAVALIERI, LISA; Williamsville East HS; Williamsville, NY; (Y); Cmnty Wkr; Political Wkr; Teachers Aide; Rep Jr Cls; High Hon Roll; Prfct Atten Awd, Outstndng Yth Svc 85; Conisius Coll; Accntng.

CAVALLARO, ANN; South Kortright Central HS; Hobart, NY; (Y); 4-H; Pep Clb; Quiz Bowl; Varsity Clb; School Play; Var Capt Bsktbl; High Hon Roll; Lion Awd; Teachers Aide; Yrbk Stf; Thompson Mem Schlrshp Of $500 Per Yr 85; All Star Bsktbl Team 85; Newbury JC; Animal Tech.

CAVALLARO, DONNA; Solvay HS; Solvay, NY; (Y); VP Frsh Cls; Off Soph Cls; Off Jr Cls; Var Bsktbl; Var Capt Socr; Var Capt Trk; High Hon Roll; Hon Roll; Mu Alp Tht; Mst Coachable 84; MVP Trck 85; Acctng.

CAVALLARO, JO ANN; Bishop Kearney HS; Brooklyn, NY; (S); 6/367; Boy Scts; Exploring; Hosp Aide; Stage Crew; Hon Roll; NHS; Rgnts Schlrshp Awd 85; Dante Awd For Excel In Itln 84; Pace U; Finance.

CAVALLARO, KATHY A; Coming-Painted Post East HS; Corning, NY; (Y); Am Leg Aux Girls St; JA; Letterman Clb; Office Aide; Red Cross Aide; Ski Clb; Spanish Clb; Varsity Clb; School Play; Yrbk Stf; Organizd Girls Lacrosse Leag 84-85; Most Imprvd Swmmr Awd 82; Elbow Greece Studnt Govt Projct 84; Comptrs.

CAVALLARO, LAURA; East Meadow HS; East Meadow, NY; (S); 72/414; Key Clb; Orch; JV Cheerleading; Var Crs Cntry; Var Lcrss; Hon Roll; Schlrshp Acadmc Achvt C W Post 85; Fordham U; Psych.

CAVALLO, LISA M; Plainedge HS; Bethpage, NY; (Y); 10/311; Aud/Vis; GAA; Science Clb; Spanish Clb; Orch; School Play; JV Sftbl; High Hon Roll; Sec NHS; Spanish NHS; NY Regents Schlrshp 85; Pres Acad Fitness Awd 85; Adelphi U; Nrsng.

CAVALLO, THERESA; Mahopac HS; Mahopac, NY; (Y); 51/423; Leo Clb; Nwsp Rptr; Cheerleading; Fld Hcky; High Hon Roll; Hon Roll; NHS; Biology.

CAVALLUZZI, ANGELA; Hicksville HS; Hicksvl, NY; (Y); Chorus; French Hon Soc; Hon Roll; NHS; Adelphi U.

CAVANAGH, MONICA; Midwood HS; Brooklyn, NY; (Y); French Clb; Science Clb; Cit Awd; Hon Roll; French, Sci, Phys Fit Awds 83; Eugene Lang Coll; Lang.

CAVELLO, CHRISTOPHER; Monticello HS; Rock Hill, NY; (Y); Band; Concert Band; Jazz Band; Orch; Stage Crew; Var Bsbl; Hon Roll; Jr NHS; Sci.

CAVIC, PARIS; Richfield Springs Central HS; Richfield Spgs, NY; (Y); 4/70; Am Leg Boys St; Band; Rep Bsktbl; VP Jr Cls; Pres Stu Cncl; JV Bsbl; JV Var Bsktbl; Var L Crs Cntry; Var L Tennis; Var L Trk; SUNY-CORTLAND; Comp Sci.

CAVUOTO, MARIA; Franklin K Lane HS; Ozone Park, NY; (Y); 2/708; Camera Clb; Teachers Aide; Stage Crew; Nwsp Bus Mgr; Nwsp Phtg; Yrbk Ed-Chief; Hon Roll; NHS; Sal; Gov Comm Schlstc Achvt Schlrshp 85; Mem Schlrhsp 85; Regents Schlrshp 85; Syracuse U; Bio.

CAWEIN, GRETCHEN; Pine Bush HS; Bloomingburg, NY; (Y); Mrchg Band; Symp Band; Nwsp Rptr; Yrbk Phtg; Hon Roll; Jr NHS; NY Rgnts Schlrshp 85; Frgn Lang.

CAWLEY, PATRICIA; Alfred G Berner HS; Massapequa, NY; (Y); Cmnty Wkr; Dance Clb; Pep Clb; Acpl Chr; Chorus; Nwsp Rptr; Yrbk Stf; Lit Mag; Awd Hnrbl Mntn For Wrld Of Poetrys Poetry Cont 85; Mbr Of Hofstras Gray Wig Repertory Thtr 85; Perf Arts.

CAYER, JOHN; Frewsburg HS; Jamestown, NY; (Y); 1/90; Am Leg Boys St; Church Yth Grp; FCA; JV Bsbl; Var Bsktbl; JV Ftbl; Var Golf; Hon Roll; Opt Clb Awd; Gentc Engr.

CAZAURANG, CATHY; Earl L Vandermeulen HS; Mt Sinai, NY; (Y); 97/286; French Clb; Fld Hcky; Score Keeper; Timer.

CAZZOLA, PATRICIA; Liverpool HS; Liverpool, NY; (S); 145/781; Hosp Aide; Ski Clb; JV Bsktbl; Var Capt Fld Hcky; Im Powder Puff Ftbl; JV Sftbl; JV Trk; NHS; U Of Buffalo; Phys Thrpy.

CEA, PATRICIA ANN; Richmond Hill HS; Richmond Hill, NY; (Y); Church Yth Grp; Cmnty Wkr; Key Clb; Spanish Clb; School Musical; Nwsp Ed-Chief; VP Jr Cls; VP Sr Cls; NHS; Dance Clb; Supr Yth Pride NY Yankees 84 & 85; Natl Span Tst Queens Coll Awd 85; Cert Dnce & Rec Tap Macys 84; Temple U; Dnce.

CEBALLO, SELENE; Richmond Hill HS; Bklyn, NY; (Y); Rep Frsh Cls; Hon Roll; Prfct Atten Awd; Engl Hnr Soc 84-85; Spn Hnr Soc 84; Hunter Coll; Phys Thrpst.

CEBULA, MICHAEL D; Amsterdam HS; Hagaman, NY; (Y); High Hon Roll; St Schlr; Hon Roll; NY St Regents Schlrshp 85; Empire St Games Archry 82-84; SUNY Albany; Math.

CECALA, PHILIP; Bishop Ford HS; Brooklyn, NY; (Y).

CECCHERELLI, HOLLY; Union Endicott HS; Endwell, NY; (S); 2/430; Debate Tm; Pres Key Clb; Concert Band; Mrchg Band; Orch; Nwsp Rptr; Yrbk Phtg; Var L Trk; High Hon Roll; Hon Roll; Rotary Yth Ldrshp Awd 84; Acad All-Amer 84; Binghamton Yth Symph 84-85; SUNY; Music Ed.

CECERE, REGINA; Cardinal Spellman HS; Bronx, NY; (Y); Sec Church Yth Grp; Cmnty Wkr; Computer Clb; Math Clb; Pep Clb; Lit Mag; Fordham U; Acctng.

CECI, JULIANNE; Bishop Kearney HS; Brooklyn, NY; (Y); Church Yth Grp; Office Aide; Ski Clb; Teachers Aide; Chorus; Church Choir; NHS; Ntl Enrgy Fndtn Essy Awd 83.

CECIL, JANE; Dryden Central HS; Dryden, NY; (Y); 7/150; Church Yth Grp; Cmnty Wkr; Drama Clb; Pres VP 4-H; Ski Clb; Spanish Clb; Varsity Clb; Trs Band; Concert Band; Mrchg Band; Donald Crispell DVM Memrl Schlrshp 85; Outstndng Demnstrtr-Tompkins Co 84; Roy Langdon Memrl Awd 85; Cornell U-Arts & Sci; Bio.

CEDENO, ANGELO; James A Beneway HS; Macedon, NY; (Y); 12/214; Boy Scts; Mathletes; Math Clb; Math Tm; High Hon Roll; Hon Roll; NHS; Prfct Atten Awd; St Schlr; Im Bsktbl; 1st In Wayne Chem Exam 84; Rochester Inst Of Tech; Biotech.

CEDENO, VIVIAN; Herbert H Lehman HS; New York, NY; (Y); 27/444; Sec Sr Cls; Drama Clb; Math Tm; School Play; Nwsp Rptr; Nwsp Stf; Cheerleading; Hon Roll; NHS; CPBA Schlrshp NYU 85; NYU; Bus.

CEDER, AMY; Kenmore West SR HS; Kenmore, NY; (Y); JV Trk; Hon Roll; Mth.

CEDRI, CATHY; Bishop Mc Mahon HS; Buffalo, NY; (Y); Hosp Aide; Bus.

CEECE, RICHARD; Unatego HS; Unadilla, NY; (Y); Stat Boy Scts; Ski Clb; Var Golf; Var Trk; Hon Roll; Ntl Merit Ltr; Prfct Atten Awd; Art.

CEFARATTI, DAVID A; West Seneca West SR HS; West Seneca, NY; (Y); 42/543; JV Bsbl; JV Ftbl; NHS; Regnts Schlrshp 85; SUNY U Buffalo; Elec Engr.

CELANI, DAVID; Maryvale SR HS; Depew, NY; (Y); DECA; Chorus; Variety Show; Hon Roll; Bus Adm.

CELENTANO, KAREN; H Frank Carey HS; Garden City S, NY; (Y); 44/222; Thesps; Band; School Musical; School Play; JV Cheerleading; Hon Roll; Hstry.

CELENTANO, KAREN; Our Lady Of Perpetual Help; Brooklyn, NY; (Y); 4-H; Pres Sr Cls; Stu Cncl; Coach Actv; High Hon Roll; NHS; Catechist Dvlpmnt Course Tchng Chldrn 82; Crmnl Law.

CELENTANO, NANCY; Minisink Valley HS; Otisville, NY; (Y); 6/232; Library Aide; Spanish Clb; High Hon Roll; NHS; Pres Acadmc Fit Awd 85; Humanitarian Awd 85; Kings Coll; Psych.

CELESTINE, JAMES; Andrew Jackson HS; Jamaica, NY; (Y); Computer Clb; Debate Tm; Office Aide; Yrbk Stf; Cornell U; Comp Progmr.

CELOTTO, DANIEL T; Lackawanna SR HS; Lackawanna, NY; (Y); 43/270; Am Leg Boys St; Pres Church Yth Grp; Drama Clb; VP French Clb; School Play; Var Golf; Var Tennis; Canisius Coll; Bus Adm.

CENNI, ROBERT J; Pioneer Central HS; Arcade, NY; (Y); 42/161; Ftbl; NY ST Regnts Schlrshp 85.

CENTENO, EVELYN; Bishop Loughlin Memorial HS; Brooklyn, NY; (S); 11/185; PAVAS; Spanish Clb; Chorus; Concert Band; Capt Vllybl; NHS; Cornell Schlrshp 85-89; Cornell U; Law.

CENTENO, LURDY; Central Islip HS; Central Islip, NY; (Y); Orch; Hon Roll.

CENTENO, MARIA T; A E Stevenson HS; Bronx, NY; (Y); Cmnty Wkr; Office Aide; Spanish Clb; Teachers Aide; Chorus; Mrchg Band; Variety Show; Nwsp Ed-Chief; Vllybl; Bronx Starlte Twrls Awd, Bronx CC Smmr Yuth Sprts Cmp Swmmng Awd 81; City Coll NY; Phy Asst.

CENTENO, PRISCILLA; Acad Of Mt St Vesula; New York, NY; (Y); 35/150; Variety Show; Yrbk Stf; Pace U; Optomtry.

CENTUORI, CHRISTINA; Franciscan HS; Peekskill, NY; (Y); 9/52; Spanish Clb; Chorus; Stage Crew; Nwsp Rptr; Nwsp Stf; Yrbk Stf; Hon Roll; NHS; Spanish NHS; Spnsh Hnr Soc Pres 84-85; Ntl Hnr Soc 84-85; Manhattanville Coll; Librl Arts.

CEPALE, JONATHAN; Commack South HS; Commack, NY; (Y); 43/383; Aud/Vis; Boy Scts; Computer Clb; Math Tm; High Hon Roll; Ntl Merit SF; NYS Regents Schlrshp 85; NYC FD Columbian Soc SAT Schlrshp 84; Schlrshp Awd Rensselaer Polytech 85; Rensselaer Polytech Inst; Comp.

CEPARANO, CHRISTOPHER; Newburgh Free Acad; Newburgh, NY; (Y); Varsity Clb; Ice Hcky; Mgr(s); Socr; High Hon Roll; Hon Roll; Prfct Atten Awd; Sci.

CEPARSKI, JEFFREY J; Marcellus HS; Marcellus, NY; (Y); Hon Roll; Regents Schlrshp 85; Cayuga CC; Comp Sci.

CEPEDA, DIANA; Queen Of The Rosary Acad; Copiague, NY; (Y); Cmnty Wkr; Hosp Aide; Library Aide; Sec Math Clb; Hon Roll; Mu Alp Tht; Dstngshd Yng Ldrshp Awd 85; Phy Aid.

CERAVOLO, JOSEPH A; Henninger HS; Syracuse, NY; (Y); 60/442; Am Leg Boys St; Debate Tm; Intnl Clb; Leo Clb; Rep Stu Cncl; JV Lcrss; Im Tennis; Im Wt Lftg; High Hon Roll; Hon Roll; Cornell; Bio.

CERBONE, EDWARD J; St Anthonys HS; Ronkonkoma, NY; (Y); 22/250; Boy Scts; Chess Clb; High Hon Roll; Hon Roll; NHS; Ntl Merit SF; GA Inst Tech; Elctrcl Engrng.

CERIELLO, ANTHONY; St Marys Boys HS; Glen Cove, NY; (Y); 8/160; Church Yth Grp; Bowling; High Hon Roll; Sheet Metl Wrkrs Union Schlrshp 85.

CERIELLO, CHRIS; St John The Baptist HS; S Farmingdale, NY; (Y); Art Clb; Yrbk Stf; Golf; High Hon Roll; Hon Roll; Arch.

CERILLI, ANNA; St Catharine Acad; Bronx, NY; (Y); 21/205; Hon Roll; NHS; Hghst Avg Italian III 85; 1st Hnrs Iona Italina Cntst 83; 2nd Pl Prty Cntst 85; Princeton U; Bio.

CERINO, ANGELA M; F D Roosevelt HS; Hyde Pk, NY; (Y); JV Cheerleading; Hon Roll; Dutchess Coll.

CERMAK, DENISE; St John The Baptist HS; Smithtown, NY; (Y); 65/550; Cmnty Wkr; Office Aide; Chorus; High Hon Roll; Hon Roll; Cmmnctns.

CEROSKY, ROBERT; Whitesboro SR HS; Whitesboro, NY; (Y); Church Yth Grp; Science Clb; Hon Roll.

CERPA, DESIREE; Herbert H Lehman HS; Bronx, NY; (Y); 5/473; Cmnty Wkr; Office Aide; Chorus; Variety Show; Yrbk Stf; Im Cheerleading; Elem Ed.

CERRATO, MARIA; Herbert H Lehman HS; Bronx, NY; (Y); 3/544; Math Tm; Band; Concert Band; Orch; Yrbk Stf; Lit Mag; Hon Roll; NHS; Val; Hon Arista Soc 83-85; Natl Math Soc 84-85; Bronze Mtl Math 85; Katharine Gibbs Schl; Wrd Proc.

CERRUTO, MICHELE L; Sayville HS; Sayville, NY; (Y); 18/355; 4-H; Y-Teens; Band; Mrchg Band; JV Var Tennis; Cit Awd; Hon Roll; NHS; Pres Schlr; Rotary Awd; Union Coll; Pre Med.

CERTAIN, CHAD; Uniondale HS; Hempstead, NY; (Y); Am Leg Boys St; FBLA; Yrbk Stf; VP Stu Cncl; JV L Crs Cntry; Var L Trk; High Hon Roll; Hon Roll; Jr NHS; USNA; Comp Sci.

CERULLI, CHRISTOPHER; Catholic Central HS; Clifton Park, NY; (S); 4/203; Trs Church Yth Grp; Yrbk Phtg; Rep Frsh Cls; Pres Soph Cls; Pres Jr Cls; Pres Sr Cls; Sec Trs Stu Cncl; JV Var Ftbl; JC Awd; NHS; Bio.

CERUTTI, JEFFREY; Fordham Prep; Bedford, NY; (Y); Political Wkr; Ski Clb; Nwsp Rptr; Pres Frsh Cls; Rep Soph Cls; Rep Stu Cncl; Bsktbl; Im Ftbl; Var Socr; Im Vllybl; Cert Honrs Math Hist Art.

CERVONI, CHRISTINE M; The Ursuline Schl; New Rochelle, NY; (Y); 13/131; Cmnty Wkr; Computer Clb; Debate Tm; Girl Scts; Hosp Aide; NFL; Political Wkr; Speech Tm; Variety Show; Yrbk Phtg; Trinity Coll Hartford; Law.

CESARIO, MICHAEL; Hewlett HS; Hewlett, NY; (Y); Var L Bsktbl; Capt L Ftbl.

CESTONE, ANGIE; School Holy Child HS; White Plains, NY; (Y); Pres GAA; Yrbk Stf; Rep Frsh Cls; Rep Soph Cls; Rep Jr Cls; Rep Sr Cls; Rep Stu Cncl; Var Capt Bsktbl; Coach Actv; NHS; Art I II III 82-85; Applctn Bio 83-84.

CHACE, SHARON; Williamsville South HS; Williamsville, NY; (Y); 106/247; Church Yth Grp; Drama Clb; Girl Scts; Hosp Aide; Red Cross Aide; Acpl Chr; Church Choir; School Play; Stage Crew; Yrbk Phtg; ST Coll At Oswego; Bus Admin.

CHACONA, MICHELLE; Fairport HS; Fairport, NY; (Y); Ski Clb; Mrchg Band; Symp Band; Rep Stu Cncl; Stat Swmmng; Hon Roll; Bio Med.

CHADDERDON, LAUREEN H; Cairo-Durham JR & SR HS; Acra, NY; (Y); 5/89; Church Yth Grp; Dance Clb; Girl Scts; Red Cross Aide; School Play; High Hon Roll; Jr NHS; Trs NHS; Girl Scout Silver Awd 85; Vol Awds 80-85; Cnclr Trning Camp 84-85; Elem Ed.

CHADWICK, MARY BETH; Lakeland HS; New York, NY; (Y); Ski Clb; Spanish Clb; Flag Corp; Yrbk Ed-Chief; Yrbk Stf; High Hon Roll; NHS; Syracuse U; Law.

CHAFFEE, AMY; Hannibal HS; Sterling, NY; (S); Cmnty Wkr; Varsity Clb; Sec Frsh Cls; Trs Soph Cls; Trs Jr Cls; Rep Stu Cncl; Var L Bsktbl; Var L Socr; Var L Sftbl; Hon Roll; Accntnt.

CHAGAS, MARIA; New Rochelle HS; New Rochelle, NY; (Y); NHS; Spanish NHS; Pres Acdmc Ftns Awd 85; PTSA Awd For Ofc Prctc 85; Iona Coll; Intl Stds.

CHAIFETZ, FRANCINE; Commack North HS; Commack, NY; (Y); Hosp Aide; Spanish Clb; Teachers Aide; Trs Temple Yth Grp; Varsity Clb; Chorus; Yrbk Stf; Rep Frsh Cls; Rep Soph Cls; Rep Jr Cls; Law.

CHAIKEN, MARCY H; John Adams HS; Howard Beach, NY; (Y); 1/591; Drama Clb; Nwsp Rptr; Yrbk Stf; Var Sftbl; NHS; Val; AZ ST U Schlrshp 85-89; Queens Coll Ped Awd Foc Achvt 83 & 84; NY ST Regents Schlrshp 85; AZ ST U; Acting.

CHAINTREUIL, COLETTE; Fairport HS; Fairport, NY; (Y); Church Yth Grp; Drama Clb; Ski Clb; Mrchg Band; School Play; Symp Band; Stat Bsktbl; Stat Vllybl; Hon Roll; NHS; Pre-Med.

CHAIRES, PENNY; Stockbridge Valley Central HS; Munnsville, NY; (S); 5/47; Church Yth Grp; Drama Clb; Hosp Aide; Office Aide; Teachers Aide; Chorus; Rep Stu Cncl; High Hon Roll; Hon Roll; Jr NHS; Bryant & Stratton; Med Asst.

CHAKALES, ALLYCE; Bishop Maginn HS; Albany, NY; (Y); Ski Clb; Spanish Clb; School Play; Cheerleading; Pom Pon; Trk; High Hon Roll; Hon Roll; Ntl Merit Ltr; Pre-Law.

CHALSON, MELISSA; W C Mepham HS; N Bellmore, NY; (Y); Cmnty Wkr; Debate Tm; Temple Yth Grp; Band; Yrbk Stf; Off Stu Cncl; Var Socr; High Hon Roll; Jr NHS; NHS; Law.

CHAMBERLAIN, DAVE; Gloversville HS; Gloversville, NY; (Y); JV Var Bsktbl; Ftbl; Var Golf; JV Socr; High Hon Roll; Hon Roll.

CHAMBERLAIN, LAURA; Elmira Southside HS; Elmira, NY; (Y); Latin Clb; Pep Clb; Ski Clb; Varsity Clb; Chorus; Mrchg Band; Yrbk Stf; Bowling; Pom Pon; Trk; Miss Cngnlty Fire Dept 85; Corning CC; Arch Dsgnng.

CHAMBERLAIN, LAURIE; Salamanca Central HS; Salamanca, NY; (Y); 29/140; Art Clb; Ski Clb; Spanish Clb; Score Keeper; High Hon Roll; Hon Roll; NHS; Spanish NHS; Rev R Walsh Mem Schlrshp 85; St Bonaventure U; Pre Law.

CHAMBERLAIN, NATHAN; Cardinal Mooney HS; Hilton, NY; (Y); 117/323; Band; Crs Cntry; Trk; Hon Roll; Roch Inst Tech; Comp Engr.

CHAMBERS, ANN MARIE; John F Kennedy HS; New York, NY; (Y); 165/982; Church Yth Grp; Spanish Clb; Teachers Aide; Co-Capt Flag Corp; Mrchg Band; Prfct Atten Awd; Reseach Apprntc Prog Smmr Schlr U Of VT 84; Pre-Med.

CHAMBERS, JOHN; Victor Central SR HS; Victor, NY; (Y); 34/225; VP Model UN; Scholastic Bowl; Stage Crew; Yrbk Phtg; Im Badmtn; JV Ftbl; Im Sftbl; Var Trk; Var Capt Vllybl; Hon Roll; Mngmt.

CHAMBERS, KEITH; Hutchinson C Technical HS; Buffalo, NY; (Y); Rep Stu Cncl; Var Swmmng; Hon Roll; RPI Awd Math/Sci 85.

CHAMBERS, NATALIE; Sheepshead Bay HS; Brooklyn, NY; (Y); Hosp Aide; JA; Library Aide; Office Aide; Bowling; Sftbl; Vllybl; Hnr Cert Law Stud 84-85; Long Island U; Reg Nrsn.

CHAMBERS-WEBB, CHERYL; Edison Tech & Occupatnl Educ Ctr; Rochester, NY; (Y); Church Yth Grp; Exploring; JA; Office Aide; Church Choir; Rep Sr Cls; JV Mgr(s); Hon Roll; Prfct Atten Awd; Sci Awd; Syracuse U; Bus.

CHAMBLISS, CIAN; Ithaca HS; Brooktondale, NY; (Y); Aud/Vis; Science Clb; Nwsp Stf; JV Crs Cntry; Var Trk; Ntl Merit Ltr; Art Awd 82; NYC Schl Of Visual Arts; Art.

CHAMORRO, HENRY F; St Francis Prep Schl; South Ozone Park, NY; (Y); 279/690; Science Clb; Band; Rgnts Schlrshp 85; Comp Sci.

CHAMPLIN, MICHAEL; Lynbrook HS; E Rockaway, NY; (Y); Cmnty Wkr; Drama Clb; School Musical; School Play; Stage Crew; Pres Frsh Cls; JV Var Bsktbl; Var Tennis; Hon Roll; NHS.

CHAMSON, AMY R; The New Lincoln Schl; New York, NY; (Y); Math Clb; Political Wkr; Jazz Band; Bsktbl; High Hon Roll; NYS Regnts Schlrshp 85; Duke U; Math.

CHAN, AUDREY; Dobbs Ferry HS; Dobbs Ferry, NY; (Y); 2/103; Drama Clb; Pres Key Clb; Stage Crew; Yrbk Bus Mgr; Pres French Hon Soc; High Hon Roll; Sec NHS; Ntl Merit Ltr; Sal; VP Church Yth Grp; Natl Hnr Roll 85; Pres Acadmc Fit Awd 85; Regnts Schlrshp Diploma With Hnrs 85; Williams Coll; Engl.

CHAN, FANNY; Cardinal Spellman HS; Bronx, NY; (Y); 75/550; Art Clb; Dance Clb; Pep Clb; Ski Clb; Speech Tm; Pep Band; Stage Crew; Twrlr; Vllybl; Hon Roll; Hnr Roll 84-85; Pblc Rltns.

CHAN, IRENE; Bishop Kearney HS; Brooklyn, NY; (Y); Math Tm; Ski Clb; Nwsp Rptr; Tennis; High Hon Roll; NY U; Law.

CHAN, JEANNIE; Sodus Central HS; Sodus Point, NY; (Y); 1/107; Am Leg Aux Girls St; Model UN; Science Clb; Concert Band; Nwsp Ed-Chief; Stu Cncl; Tennis; DAR Awd; NHS; Val; NY ST Oratorial Cont 85; Piano Comp 83; Wellesley Book Awd 84; Yale U; Pre Law.

CHAN, KIN SING; Brooklyn Technical HS; New York, NY; (Y); Chess Clb; Math Clb; Math Tm; Hon Roll.

CHAN, LILLIAN; Bishop Kearney HS; Brooklyn, NY; (Y); Math Tm; Ski Clb; Tennis; St Schlr; Media Arts.

CHAN, LO YAT; August Martin HS; New York, NY; (Y); 22/305; Chess Clb; CAP; Cmnty Wkr; Computer Clb; Math Tm; Band; Concert Band; Cit Awd; High Hon Roll; Hon Roll; NY St Regents Schlrshp 85; Boston U; Biomed.

CHAN, MEI Y; Bronx H S Of Science; Elmhurst, NY; (Y); Cmnty Wkr; Hosp Aide; Teachers Aide; Yrbk Stf; Stu Cncl; Ntl Merit Ltr; Engrng.

CHAN, MELVYN G; Midwood HS; Brooklyn, NY; (Y); 5/605; Mathletes; Science Clb; Gov Hon Prg Awd; Hon Roll.

CHAN, PAUL; Stuyvesant HS; Elmhurst, NY; (Y); Church Yth Grp; Cmnty Wkr; German Clb; Hosp Aide; Library Aide; Science Clb; Church Choir; Ntl Merit Ltr; Seer 1st Pl Sci 84; Westinghouse Fnlst 85; MIT; Rsrch Orgnc.

CHAN, SEE WAI; Midwood HS; Brooklyn, NY; (Y); 41/633; Hosp Aide; Math Tm; Lit Mag; Hon Roll; Prfct Atten Awd; Arista Hnrs Soc 84; Chancelrs NY Hnr Roll 85; Hnrs Of Sci Tlnt Srch 85; Chem.

CHAN, SIU-WAN; Norman Thomas HS; New York, NY; (S); 33/671; FBLA; JA; Chorus; Hon Roll; Prfct Atten Awd; 2nd Pl Essay Cntst 84; JR Svc Awd 83.

CHAN, STEVEN; Brooklyn Technical HS; New York, NY; (Y); Chem & Physcs Excllnc Cert 84-85; Engrng Modelng Achvt Cert 84; Long Island U; Comm Arts.

CHAN, SUK MAN; Seward Park HS; New York, NY; (Y); 31/760; Drama Clb; VP Intnl Clb; Service Clb; Teachers Aide; School Play; Variety Show; Stu Cncl; NHS; Starr Schlrshp 85; Sarah Ollesheimer Awd 85; Cornell U; Comp Prog.

CHAN, VIVIAN; Norman Thomas HS; Woodside, NY; (S); 77/671; Cmnty Wkr; Math Tm; Chorus; Schlrshp Cond Cert 82; Cert Achvt Bus 83-85; Hunter Coll; Jrnlsm.

CHAN, WING-KEE THOMAS; Mamaroneck HS; Larchmont, NY; (Y); Library Aide; Spanish Clb; Yrbk Stf; High Hon Roll; NHS; Spanish NHS; Regents Schlrshp 85; Cornell U; Elec Engrng.

CHAN, YEELIN; Baldwin SR HS; Baldwin, NY; (Y); 3/503; Pres Mathletes; Pres Science Clb; Sec Stu Cncl; Bausch & Lomb Sci Awd; French Hon Soc; High Hon Roll; Pres NHS; NHS; U Rochester; Bio.

CHAN, YIMMAE; Norman Thomas HS; New York, NY; (Y); 3/671; FBLA; Office Aide; Var Hon Roll; Var NHS; Var Prfct Atten Awd; Teachers Aide; NYS Rgnts, U Fed Tchrs Schlrshp 85; NY U; Acctng.

CHAN, YIN-MAE; Horman Thomas HS; New York, NY; (S); 3/671; FBLA; Variety Show; Hon Roll; NHS; Prfct Atten Awd; JA; Math Tm; Office Aide; NY ST Regents Schlrshp 85-89; United Fedrtn Of Tchrs Schlrshp 85-89; NY U; Acctng.

CHANCER, ROBERT; Lakeland SR HS; Mohegan Lake, NY; (Y); Chess Clb; Computer Clb; PAVAS; Orch; School Musical; Im Bsbl; Im Bsktbl; Var Capt Ftbl; NHS; Schlrshp Aaron Copland Music & Arts Prog 85; Music Ed.

CHANDLER, JOHN; Hudson HS; Claverack, NY; (Y); Computer Clb; Varsity Clb; Band; Yrbk Stf; Var L Bsbl; Var Capt Golf; Var L Tennis; High Hon Roll; Hon Roll; NHS; GA Tech; Engrng.

CHANDLER, KARLA A; Newark SR HS; Newark, NY; (Y); French Clb; Service Clb; Varsity Clb; Nwsp Rptr; Pres Soph Cls; Rep Sr Cls; Var Capt Cheerleading; Var Capt Swmmng; Sec Trs French Hon Soc; Lion Awd; NYS Regnts Scholar 85; Wegemans Scholar 85; Newark Plyrs Scholar 85; Syracuse U; Advrtsg.

CHANDLER, MARK; Chenango Valley HS; Binghamton, NY; (Y); Cmnty Wkr; Exploring; Stage Crew; Var Diving; JV Var Ftbl; Var Swmmng; Var Trk; Var Vllybl; Jr NHS; NHS; Arch.

CHANDLER, RICHARD; Cairo-Durham HS; Acra, NY; (Y); 24/89; Socr; Trk; Vllybl; Mst Prmsng Phtogrphr 85.

CHANG, ANDREW K; Homer Central HS; Homer, NY; (Y); 1/200; Am Leg Boys St; Church Yth Grp; Quiz Bowl; Varsity Clb; Rptr Nwsp Ed-Chief; JV Var Bsktbl; Var Golf; Var Ice Hcky; NHS; Ntl Merit Ltr; Stanford; Pre-Med.

CHANG, CHRIS; Aviation HS; Jackson Hts, NY; (Y); 70/417; Math Tm; Varsity Clb; Crs Cntry; Tennis; Trk; Cit Awd; Prfct Atten Awd; Pegasus Soc 85; 84 Supr Yth 84; Engrng.

CHANG, JIM; Valley Stream Central HS; Valley Stream, NY; (Y); Church Yth Grp; Computer Clb; Church Choir; Var L Bowling; Var L Ftbl; Var L Trk; Im Mgr Bsktbl; Im Mgr Lcrss; Im Mgr Sftbl; Im Mgr Tennis; NYU; Bus.

CHANG, LISA; James I O Neill HS; West Point, NY; (Y); 17/122; Church Yth Grp; Cmnty Wkr; French Clb; Red Cross Aide; School Musical; Nwsp Rptr; Yrbk Stf; Var L Trk; NHS; Ntl Merit Ltr; NY St Schlrshp 85; U CA-SANTA Cruz; Intl Rel.

CHANG, NAN N; B N Cardozo HS; Bayside, NY; (Y); 6/476; Capt Math Clb; Capt Math Tm; Scholastic Bowl; Westinghouse Semi Fnlst 85; Yale U; Physics.

CHANG, NOEL L; Hunter College HS; New York, NY; (Y); Library Aide; Art Clb; Science Clb; Church Choir; Yrbk Stf; Bowling; L Tennis; Mu Alp Tht; Ntl Science Olympiad 84; Rice At Houston TX; Engrng.

CHANG, WILLIAM; Liverpool HS; Liverpool, NY; (S); 5/792; Math Tm; Yrbk Bus Mgr; Pres Stu Cncl; Var L Tennis; High Hon Roll; Jr NHS; NHS; Chess Clb; Concours Ntl De Francais Hnr Ment 82; Ntl Latin Hnrbl Merit 84; Onondaga Math Leag 84; Bio.

CHANG, WYNMAN; St Johns Prep; New York, NY; (S); Intnl Clb; Bowling; Tennis; Vllybl; Hon Roll; NHS; Polytechnic Inst; Elec Engrng.

CHANG, YAHLIN; High Schl Of Art & Design; Howard Beach, NY; (Y); 4/439; Art Clb; Computer Clb; FTA; Intnl Clb; Library Aide; Math Tm; Office Aide; Teachers Aide; Sr Cls; High Hon Roll; Ntl Art Hnr Soc 82-84; Merit Cert Peer Tutrng Pgm 83; Comp Sci.

CHANI, HARSHILA; Forest Hills HS; Forest Hills, NY; (Y); Exploring; Hosp Aide; Office Aide; Science Clb; Nwsp Rptr; Ed Nwsp Stf; High Hon Roll; Hon Roll; NHS; Prfct Atten Awd; Sophie Davis; Pre-Med.

CHANIN, ALLISON S; Walt Whitman HS; Huntington, NY; (Y); 11/625; Cmnty Wkr; German Clb; GAA; Girl Scts; Pres Key Clb; Mathletes; Band; Chorus; Concert Band; Mrchg Band; 5th Pl NY ST Sci & Enrgy Cnsrvtn 82; Schlr Athlt 84-85; Colgate U; Sci.

CHANIN, DEBBIE; Jericho HS; Westbury, NY; (Y); Key Clb; Office Aide; Varsity Clb; Nwsp Stf; Rep Jr Cls; Rep Sr Cls; Socr; Hon Roll; Camera Clb; PAVAS; Awd Achvt Perf Arts 83; SUNY Albany; Sci.

CHANIN, KATHRYN S; Walt Whitman HS; Huntington, NY; (Y); 1/625; Sec French Clb; Key Clb; Chorus; Orch; Rep Frsh Cls; Tennis; Var Capt Trk; French Hon Soc; NHS; Val; All ST Choir & All Eastern Choir 84-85; NY ST Energy Resrch & Dev Expostn 81-82; Dartmouth Coll; Englsh.

CHAO, CECILIA E; Stuyvesant HS; Holliswood, NY; (Y); Hosp Aide; Nwsp Ed-Chief; VP NHS; Val; Science Clb; Teachers Aide; Hon Roll; Intl Chinese Arts Comptn 3rd Pl 83; Natl Inst Of Hlth H S Stu Smmr Rsrch Intrnshp Awd 84; Chem.

CHAO, GRACE L; Rye Country Day HS; Harrison, NY; (Y); AFS; Church Yth Grp; Cmnty Wkr; Hosp Aide; Nwsp Stf; Lcrss; Socr; Hon Roll; Pre Med.

CHAO, MELODY; St Pius V HS; Bronx, NY; (Y); Office Aide; Pres Frsh Cls; Sec Jr Cls; Sftbl; NHS; Hsptl Aid Vlntr Awd 85; Prfct Attndnc Awd 84-85; Comp Sci.

CHAO, ROBERTA; Spackenkill HS; Poughkeepsie, NY; (Y); Cmnty Wkr; Hosp Aide; Trs Leo Clb; Band; Yrbk Stf; Lit Mag; High Hon Roll; NHS; Camera Clb; Teachers Aide; Vassar Hosp 1 Yr Svc Awd 84; Frnch Essy Shrtstry Cntst 3rd Pl 85.

CHAO, WARREN; Stuyvesant HS; Flushing, NY; (Y); Debate Tm; NFL; Political Wkr; School Musical; School Play; Nwsp Stf; Off Jr Cls; Off Stu Cncl; Cit Awd; High Hon Roll; Hgst Serv Awd 85; Century III Ldrs Cont 84; Super Yth Awd 84; Harvard U; Pol Sci.

CHAPARRO, NELIDA; Mabel Dean Bacon HS; New York, NY; (S); 9/299; Teachers Aide; Chorus; Vllybl; Hon Roll; Bus Ed Dept Cert Of Merit 83-84; Bus Ed Assn Of Metro NY Cert Of Achvt 83-84; Antillian Coll; Comp.

CHAPIN, JILL; Perry Central HS; Perry, NY; (Y); 1/95; FTA; Math Tm; Chorus; Concert Band; Jazz Band; Mrchg Band; Pres Jr Cls; JV Var Socr; 4-H Awd; NHS; Instrmntl Music Eductn.

CHAPIN, REBECCA; New Berlin Centrla HS; New Berlin, NY; (Y); 4/45; FFA; French Clb; Yrbk Stf; Lit Mag; High Hon Roll; Hon Roll; Jr NHS; Lion Awd; Sec NHS.

CHAPIN, STEVEN H; North Babylon SR HS; North Babylon, NY; (Y); 46/556; Chess Clb; Church Yth Grp; Mathletes; Church Choir; Crs Cntry; High Hon Roll; Jr NHS; NHS; Prfct Atten Awd; NY ST Regnts Schlrshp 85; NY ST Assn Of Trnsprtn Engrs Schlrshp 85; U Of Penn ST; Archtctrl Engrng.

CHAPMAN, BENJAMIN; Hudson Falls Central HS; Hudson Falls, NY; (Y); Am Leg Boys St; Exploring; Key Clb; Var Im Ftbl; JV Var Trk; Im Wt Lftg; High Hon Roll; Hon Roll; NHS; Ntl Merit SF; Med.

CHAPMAN, BEVERLY; T R Proctor HS; Utica, NY; (Y); Chorus; Hon Roll; SAR Awd; Bryant & Stratton Bus Inst; Sec.

CHAPMAN, BRENDA; Canastota HS; Canastota, NY; (Y); GAA; VP Intnl Clb; Var Capt Bsktbl; Var Fld Hcky; Var Capt Sftbl; High Hon Roll; NHS; 2nd Tm Dfns All Star Fld Hockey; Hon Mntn Sftball; Hon Lions Clb.

CHAPMAN, GAIL; Lindenhurst HS; Lindenhurst, NY; (Y); Camera Clb; Church Yth Grp; Flag Corp; Mrchg Band; School Musical; Nwsp Stf; Sec Frsh Cls; JV Badmtn; High Hon Roll; Jr NHS.

CHAPMAN, JANET; Northeastern Clinton Central Schl; Champlain, NY; (Y); 39/153; Drama Clb; Ski Clb; Band; Chorus; Concert Band; Camera Clb; School Musical; Variety Show; Crs Cntry; Score Keeper; Central City Bus Inst; Exec Sec.

CHAPMAN, JENNIFER J; Hudson Falls Central Schl; Hudson Falls, NY; (Y); #30 In Class; Art Clb; Camera Clb; Drama Clb; French Clb; Hosp Aide; Thesps; School Musical; School Play; Yrbk Sprt Ed; French Hon Soc; Frnch Hnr Soc 84; Regents Schlrshp 85; Geneseo; Theatre.

CHAPMAN, KRISTINE; Cardinal Mooney HS; Rochester, NY; (Y); 6/317; Exploring; Yrbk Stf; French Hon Soc; High Hon Roll; Hon Roll.

CHAPMAN, MARGARET; Harborfields HS; Centerport, NY; (Y); Dance Clb; Hosp Aide; School Musical; Nurse.

CHAPMAN, ROBERT; Susquehanna Valley HS; Conklin, NY; (Y); Chess Clb; Pep Clb; Spanish Clb; Var Bsbl; Var Ice Hcky; Var Socr; All Star Sprts Awds Socr 83-85; All Star Awds Hockey 82-85; All Star Tm Bsbl 84-85.

CHAPPELL, DARLENE; Riverside HS; Buffalo, NY; (Y); Math Tm; Spanish Clb; Rep Soph Cls; Bsktbl; Sftbl; Trk; Hon Roll; Prfct Atten Awd; Outstndng Stu Spnsh I Awd 82-83; Merit Rl 82-85; Weldng Metal 85-86; Frgn Lang.

CHAPPLE, JAMES F; Palmyra-Macedon Central; Macedon, NY; (S); 9/205; Math Tm; Concert Band; Jazz Band; Mrchg Band; VP Frsh Cls; Trs Stu Cncl; Var L Crs Cntry; JV Var Tennis; Hon Roll; NHS; PSAT 84; Cert Hnr Schlrshp 82-84; Pre Law.

CHAPUK, AMY; Moriah Central Schl; Moriah, NY; (Y); 1/83; AFS; Yrbk Stf; Pres Frsh Cls; Pres Soph Cls; Pres Jr Cls; Pres Sr Cls; Co-Capt Cheerleading; High Hon Roll; Sec NHS; Regents Schlrshp 85; Suny; Elec Engrng.

CHARLAP, RICHARD R; St Francis HS; Hamburg, NY; (Y); 58/143; JV Bsbl; JV Var Ice Hcky; Hon Roll; NY ST Regents Coll Schlrshp 85; Hobart & William Smith; Bio.

CHARLES, CHRISTOPHER; Southwestern Central HS; Jamestown, NY; (Y); FCA; Letterman Clb; Ski Clb; Spanish Clb; Chorus; Var L Bsbl; Var L Ftbl; Secnd Tm All Confrnc Ftbl 85; Jamestown CC; Law Enfrcmnt.

CHARLES, KEVIN; Elmira Free Acad; Elmira, NY; (Y); Aud/Vis; Boy Scts; Church Yth Grp; Spanish Clb; Chorus; Yrbk Stf; Rep Stu Cncl; Var Swmmng; High Hon Roll; Hon Roll; Clarkson & Corning CC; Engrng.

CHARLES, MARILYN; John Dewey HS; Brooklyn, NY; (Y); Church Yth Grp; Dance Clb; Drama Clb; FBLA; Library Aide; Teachers Aide; Chorus; Trk; Prfct Atten Awd; U Of Bridgeport CT; Bus.

CHARLES, SHERRINE; Bishop Kearney HS; Brooklyn, NY; (Y); Library Aide; Church Choir; Var Swmmng; Hon Roll; NHS; Cath Charities 83; St Josephs Coll; Corp Lawyr.

CHARLES, YVES; F D Roosevelt HS; Brooklyn, NY; (Y); Distnctn Paintng Cert 85; Amer Assn Frnch Tchrs 84; Bilingual Ed Ctr 84; Mth.

CHARNEY, DANIEL; East Meadow HS; East Meadow, NY; (S); 62/414; Computer Clb; Drama Clb; Key Clb; Band; Concert Band; Mrchg Band; School Musical; School Play; Stage Crew; NHS; Suny Binghamton; Comp Sci.

CHAROW, RACHAEL; Mamaroneck HS; Rye, NY; (Y); Ski Clb; Temple Yth Grp; Band; Concert Band; Jazz Band; Mrchg Band; Orch; Trk; Safe Rides; Bus.

CHARRON, ANDREA; Bloomfield Central Schl; West Bloomfield, NY; (Y); AFS; Sec Trs Band; Jazz Band; School Musical; Variety Show; Yrbk Sprt Ed; Pres Frsh Cls; Pres Soph Cls; Pres Stu Cncl; NHS; More Able Lrnr Pgm 82-86; Monroe CC; Bus Mngmt.

CHARRON, AURORA; Saint George Acad; New York, NY; (Y); Aud/Vis; Exploring; German Clb; Radio Clb; Stage Crew; Nwsp Rptr; JV Bsktbl; JV Socr; JV Sftbl; Vllybl; Explrs Awd 84.

CHARTON, KIMBERLY; Mont Pleasant HS; Schenectady, NY; (Y); 10/265; Church Yth Grp; Sec Ski Clb; Mrchg Band; Pres Jr Cls; JV Var Socr; Var Sftbl; High Hon Roll; NHS; Spanish NHS; Cmnty Wkr; St George Lodge Awd 85; Sci.

CHARTRAND, MIKE J; Massena Central HS; Massena, NY; (Y); 27/255; Boy Scts; Church Yth Grp; Key Clb; Hon Roll; Ntl Merit Ltr; Cornell; Aero Engrng.

CHARTRAND, THERESA L; Beaver River Central Schl; Croghan, NY; (Y); 4/90; Pres VP FHA; Pres Spanish Clb; Yrbk Stf; Rep Stu Cncl; Var Socr; Trk; High Hon Roll; NHS; Hon Roll; Gftd, Tlntd Pgm 84-85; SAAD Coord 84-85; SUNY Canton; Paper Sci Engrng.

CHARTRAW, STEPHEN; Oakfield Alabama Central HS; Oakfield, NY; (Y); 6/93; Math Tm; Var Crs Cntry; JV Ftbl; Var Tennis; Hon Roll; Comp Sci.

CHASE, BETH; Vernon Verona Sherrill HS; Verona, NY; (Y); Girl Scts; Band; Concert Band; Drm & Bgl; Var Bowling; Var Socr; Cit Awd; High Hon Roll; Hon Roll; MIP Socr 84; Fshn Mrch.

CHASE, CATHERINE; Spackenkill HS; Poughkeepsie, NY; (Y); 22/167; Sftbl; Vllybl; All-Cnty All-Conf Athlt-Sftbl 84 & 85; Ntl Sci Merit Awd 83.

CHASE, EDITH; Clara Barton HS; Brooklyn, NY; (Y); Art Clb; Church Yth Grp; Computer Clb; Library Aide; Office Aide; Teachers Aide; Chorus; Church Choir; Hon Roll; Howard U; Gynclgy.

CHASE, JOHN; Herkimer SR HS; Herkimer, NY; (Y); 57/126; JA; Ski Clb; Spanish Clb; JV Bsktbl; Hon Roll; Navy; Nuclear Power.

CHASE, KATHY; Camden Central HS; Blossvale, NY; (Y); FBLA; Ski Clb; Chorus; Lgl Sec.

CHASE, KIMBERLY; Pioneer Central HS; Machias, NY; (Y); Pres FHA; Spanish Clb; Chorus; School Play; Swing Chorus; Var Swmmng; Hon Roll; Miss Congnlty In Arcade Winterfest 85; 2nd Rnnr Up In Arcade Winterfest 85; ST Fin In Mss NY Coed Pg; Jamestown Cmnty; Med Lab Tech.

CHASE, MOLLY; Fayetteville-Manlius HS; Fayetteville, NY; (Y); AFS; Church Yth Grp; Cmnty Wkr; JCL; Teachers Aide; Trs Frsh Cls; Trs Soph Cls; Trs Jr Cls; Trs Sr Cls; Coach Actv.

CHASE, NELSON; Hudson Falls SR HS; Hudson Falls, NY; (Y); 3/215; Chorus; Bowling; DAR Awd; French Hon Soc; High Hon Roll; NHS; Potsdam, NY; Math Educ.

CHASE, NICOLE; Fort Ann Central HS; Fort Ann, NY; (Y); 6/42; French Clb; Math Clb; Math Tm; Yrbk Stf; JV Bsktbl; High Hon Roll; NHS; Tchrs Assn Awd 85; Pres Fitnss Awd 85; Tngr Of Mnth 82; Adirondack CC; Arch.

CHASE, SUSAN C; Gloversville HS; Gloversville, NY; (Y); Church Yth Grp; Cmnty Wkr; French Clb; Intnl Clb; Spanish Clb; Endicott JC; Bus Adm.

CHASE JR, WAYNE; Cicero-North Syracuse HS; Clay, NY; (S); 37/622; Camera Clb; Ski Clb; Nwsp Phtg; JV Trk; High Hon Roll; Hon Roll; NHS; MONY Schlstc Awd Phtogrphy 83; Princeton; Engrng Sci.

CHASEN, MICHAEL; Hewlett HS; Hewlett Harbor, NY; (Y); Drama Clb; Temple Yth Grp; Thesps; School Musical; School Play; Stage Crew; Variety Show; Yrbk Stf; Rep Stu Cncl; JV Var Trk; Drama Awd 85; CPA.

CHASNEY, WAYNE; Franklin Acad; Malone, NY; (Y); Pres AFS; Pres Trs Church Yth Grp; VP Intnl Clb; Model UN; Stage Crew; Crs Cntry; Trk; Hon Roll; NHS; Ntl Merit Ltr; Physcl Thrpy.

CHATOS, TIMOTHY J; Elmira Southside HS; Elmira, NY; (Y); Pep Clb; Spanish Clb; Varsity Clb; Chorus; School Musical; Stage Crew; VP Frsh Cls; Pres Soph Cls; Rep Jr Cls; Rep Sr Cls; Le Monne; Cmmnctns.

CHATTERJI, MINKI; Vestal HS; Binghamton, NY; (Y); FBLA; Ski Clb; Varsity Clb; Var L Tennis; NHS; Colgate U; Math.

CHATTERTON, ANDREW; Saranac Lake HS; Saranac Lk, NY; (Y); Band; Chorus; Church Choir; Concert Band; Jazz Band; Mrchg Band; Pep Band; Var Crs Cntry; Var Trk; Church Yth Grp; Arch.

CHATTERTON, MICHELE; Cardinal Mooney HS; Rochester, NY; (Y); 185/290; Church Yth Grp; Cmnty Wkr; Teachers Aide; Rep Stu Cncl; Hon Roll; Miss Monroe Cty Teenager 83; Barbizon Schl Modeling 84; Nazareth; Acctng.

CHAU, KARA; Bronx High School Of Science; New York, NY; (Y); Cmnty Wkr; Hosp Aide; Intnl Clb; Band; Pace Grant 85; Pace U; Lib Arts.

CHAU, MABEL; Stuyvesant HS; New York, NY; (Y); NHS; Ntl Merit Ltr; Manhattan Math/Sci Smnrs 84; Med.

CHAUHAN, ARCHANA; Monsignor Scanlan HS; Bronx, NY; (Y); High Hon Roll; Hon Roll; NHS; Prfct Atten Awd; Berkley Bus Schl; Secy.

CHAUNCEY, MICHELLE; Riverhead HS; Wading River, NY; (Y); Church Yth Grp; Office Aide; Chorus; Yrbk Stf; Trs Sr Cls; Aspirng Toward Excel Awd 85; Suffolk CC; Eng.

CHAVARRO, HAROLD; Franklin Delano Roosevelt HS; Brooklyn, NY; (Y); Band; Hon Roll; Awd Of Excllnc-Ind Arts 83; Excllnt Attndnc 83; Pace U; Comp Elec.

CHAVEZ, ANDREW; The Bronx HS Of Sci; Bronx, NY; (Y); Office Aide; Ski Clb; Rep Frsh Cls; Rep Soph Cls; Crs Cntry; Mgr(s); Capt Swmmng; Trk; Prfct Attndnc 84-85; Dentistry.

CHAVEZ, FELIPA T; St Catherine Acad; Bronx, NY; (Y); 11/205; Dance Clb; Drama Clb; Teachers Aide; Chorus; Church Choir; School Musical; School Play; Sec Jr Cls; Sec Stu Cncl; Hon Roll; Jrnlsm.

CHAVEZ, SUSANA; Brooklyn Tech HS; Brooklyn, NY; (Y); Church Yth Grp; Math Tm; Rep Stu Cncl; Vllybl; Hon Roll; Jr NHS; NHS; Val; Eng Mdl 83; Cert Excll Soc Stud 84 & 85; Cert Excll Chem 84; NYU; Bus Admn.

CHAWGO, TAMMIE L; Mexico Academy & Central HS; Fulton, NY; (Y); 5/189; Sec Dance Clb; Pres 4-H; Girl Scts; Nwsp Bus Mgr; Nwsp Rptr; Hon Roll; Spanish Clb; Stu Cncl; Perfect Regents Exam Algebra 82; Regents Schlrshp 85 Series 85; St Josephs; Registered Nurse.

CHAYBAN, JENNY; Riverside HS; Buffalo, NY; (S); 30/212; Dance Clb; French Clb; Intnl Clb; JA; Mathletes; French Hon Soc; Hon Roll; U Of Buffalo; Doctor.

CHEATHAM, DEBRA M; Holy Trinity D HS; Bethpage, NY; (S); 26/318; High Hon Roll; Ntl Merit Ltr; Soc Distngshd Amer HS Stus 84; Cmmnctns.

CHECHILE, LISA; Resurrection Acad; Rye, NY; (Y); Drama Clb; Hosp Aide; Red Cross Aide; Chorus; School Musical; Var Swmmng; Hon Roll; Physcian.

CHECO, JOANNE; Cathedral HS; Newyork, NY; (Y); 170/298; Band; Mrchg Band; St Johns U; Med Tech.

CHEEMA, ARIANA; New Rochelle HS; New Rochelle, NY; (Y); 63/590; Hosp Aide; Hon Roll; NHS; Bryn Mawr Coll.

CHEN, BONNIE; Emma Willard Schl; Limerick, PA; (Y); Yrbk Stf; Im Fld Hcky; Im Lcrss; Im Vllybl; Ntl Merit Ltr; Bus.

CHEN, CATHERINE A; Geneseo Central HS; Geneseo, NY; (Y); 2/65; Ski Clb; Pres Jr Cls; Rep Stu Cncl; Var Capt Socr; Var Trk; Var Vllybl; High Hon Roll; NHS; Spanish NHS; Choir, Hockstein Mus Schl 82-85; Bst Ldr 85; Colgate U; Comp Sci.

CHEN, CHAI T; North Shore HS; Glen Head, NY; (Y); 19/210; Pres Camera Clb; Cmnty Wkr; Exploring; Key Clb; Ski Clb; Jazz Band; Ed Nwsp Phtg; Rep Stu Cncl; JV Var Crs Cntry; JV Lcrss; Sci Congrss Red Rbbn 84; Cooper Union/Adv Sci & Art; Eng.

CHEN, DANIEL; Forest Hills HS; Rego Park, NY; (Y); 28/762; Boy Scts; Exploring; Math Clb; Math Tm; Science Clb; Service Clb; Gym; High Hon Roll; Jr NHS; NHS; Hnrs Group-Westinghouse Sci Tlnt Srch Semifnlst 85; Mayor Hnr Citation 85; Fnlst Sci Fair 85; Med.

CHEN, HELEN; Brooklyn Technical HS; Brooklyn, NY; (Y); 1/1139; VP JA; Math Tm; Office Aide; VP Service Clb; Gov Hon Prg Awd; NHS; Ntl Merit Ltr; Val; Minrty Schltc Awd 84; GM/ABC Bst Of Cls Awd 85; Harvard; Oper Rsrch.

CHEN, HSIEN-CHUN; Seward Park HS; New York, NY; (Y); Cmnty Wkr; Exploring; FBLA; Hosp Aide; Library Aide; Teachers Aide; Hon Roll; Arista 85; Schl Svc Awd 84-85; Excllnt Atten Awd 83-85; NY U; Pre-Med.

CHEN, HUMPHREY; Bronx HS Of Science; New York, NY; (Y); Camera Clb; Church Yth Grp; Computer Clb; Debate Tm; Math Tm; NFL; Teachers Aide; Stu Cncl; High Hon Roll; Ntl Merit Ltr; MAA Hnr Roll 83; Qrtr Fnlst NY Leag 85; 1st Pl Tm Cthlc Frnsc Leag 85; Princeton; Bus.

CHEN, JENNY; Flushing HS; Flushing, NY; (Y); Sec Church Yth Grp; Library Aide; Math Tm; Office Aide; Church Choir; Orch; High Hon Roll; Hon Roll; Prfct Atten Awd; Spec Achvt Awd Of Music 83.

CHEN, JERRY C; Shaker HS; Loudonville, NY; (Y); Church Yth Grp; Rptr Debate Tm; Pres German Clb; Pres Science Clb; Nwsp Rptr; Ed Yrbk Stf; High Hon Roll; Ntl Merit SF; Secy Sci Fi Clb; Stanford U; Elec Engrng.

CHEN, LIQUAN; Seward Park HS; New York, NY; (Y); 3/27; Teachers Aide; School Musical; Prfct Atten Awd; Chinese Cult Club 84; Elect Engrng.

CHEN, LORRAINE; Eastridge HS; Rochester, NY; (Y); 11/210; German Clb; Math Clb; Spanish Clb; Rep Sr Cls; Cit Awd; High Hon Roll; Hon Roll; NHS; U Of Buffalo; Busnss Admin.

CHEN, MARJORIE; Liverpool HS; Liverpool, NY; (S); 149/792; Church Yth Grp; Hosp Aide; Ski Clb; Concert Band; Mrchg Band; Pep Band; Rep Stu Cncl; Jr NHS; NHS; Comm.

CHEN, PAULINA; John Jay SR HS; Wappingers Falls, NY; (Y); AFS; Hosp Aide; Math Tm; Model UN; Lit Mag; Stu Cncl; Var Tennis; NHS; Ski Clb; Nwsp Rptr; Columbia U Sci Hnrs Prog 84-86; Engr.

CHEN, RICHARD; West Islip SR HS; West Islip, NY; (Y); 4/525; Mathletes; Jazz Band; Mrchg Band; Symp Band; Var Tennis; Im Capt Vllybl; High Hon Roll; NHS; Rotary Awd; W Islip Tchrs Assn Mem Schrlshp, Ath Acad Achvt Awd 85; Stanford U; Pre Med.

CHEN, SHAING-CHUNG; The Knox Schl; Centerport, NY; (S); French Clb; Math Clb; Varsity Clb; Chorus; Yrbk Ed-Chief; Stu Cncl; Var Bsktbl; Var Bowling; Var Crs Cntry; Var Lcrss; Engr.

CHEN, SHARON; Warsaw Central HS; Warsaw, NY; (S); 1/93; VP French Clb; Math Tm; Orch; Bausch & Lomb Sci Awd; Jr NHS; NHS; Ntl Merit Ltr; Val; U S Youth Senate Prg Semi-Finalist 84; Minority Scholastic Achvt Awds 84; Century III Ldr Winner 84; Violin.

CHEN, SHEN PENG; St John The Baptist D HS; Lindenhurst, NY; (Y); Chess Clb; Science Clb; High Hon Roll; Hon Roll; Engrng.

CHEN, TY T; Scarsdale HS; Scarsdale, NY; (Y); Boy Scts; Chess Clb; Computer Clb; Hosp Aide; Math Tm; Science Clb; Teachers Aide; Orch; School Play; Ntl Merit SF; Eagle Scout Awd 84; Area-All State Orchestra 81-84; Pre-Med.

CHEN, TYAN; Forest Hills HS; Jamaica Est, NY; (Y); 62/881; English Clb; OEA; Teachers Aide; Nwsp Rptr; Nwsp Stf; Hon Roll; JR Arista Lg 85; NYU.

CHEN, WENDY Y; Garden City HS; Garden City, NY; (Y); Drama Clb; French Clb; VP Chorus; School Musical; School Play; Bausch & Lomb Sci Awd; High Hon Roll; NHS; Ntl Merit SF; Med.

CHENAILLE, JEANETTE; Massena Central HS; Massena, NY; (Y); Church Yth Grp; JV Var Bsktbl; Var JV Sftbl; Hon Roll; Awd Trophy Defense Bsktbl 84-85; 2nd Tm All Northern 85; Math.

CHENALLOY, CATHY M; The Bronx High School Of Science; Bronx, NY; (Y); Hosp Aide; Key Clb; Teachers Aide; BA; Mdrn Lang.

CHENG, DELTON; Midwood HS; Brooklyn, NY; (Y); Cmnty Wkr; PAVAS; Orch; Prfct Atten Awd; Chancy Music Awd, Orch Awd, Hnr Svc Roll 83; Cooper Union; Engrng.

CHENG, JOAN; East Meadow HS; East Meadow, NY; (S); 105/414; FBLA; Service Clb; Nassau CC; Accntnt.

CHENG, YI TING; Christopher Columbus HS; Bronx, NY; (S); 3/35; FTA; Hosp Aide; Math Clb; Science Clb; Service Clb; Teachers Aide; Band; Hon Roll; Prfct Atten Awd; U Of CA Los Angeles; Elec Engr.

CHENOUDA, DINA; Lawrence HS; N Woodmere, NY; (Y); Church Yth Grp; FHA; Library Aide; Science Clb; Spanish Clb; Teachers Aide; Church Choir; Yrbk Stf; Lit Mag; High Hon Roll; Cecil C Mac Donald Awd Ltn Orgns 85; 4th Yr Spnsh Awd 85; Intgrtd Math III Awd 83; Cornell U; Med.

CHEREW, GINA; Avon JR SR HS; Avon, NY; (Y); 8/105; AFS; Church Yth Grp; Library Aide; Spanish Clb; Yrbk Stf; Var Stat Mgr(s); Var Tennis; High Hon Roll; Jr NHS; NEDT Awd; Lab Tech.

CHERKAUER, BRIAN; Kenmore West SR HS; Kenmore, NY; (Y); Computer Clb; JA; Mathletes; Math Clb; Math Tm; Orch; High Hon Roll; Ntl Merit SF; Olympics Of The Mind Wrld Fin 83 & 85; NY ST Sec Bnd 83-85; ST U Of NY Buffalo; Comp Engr.

CHERKAUER, KEVIN; Kenmore West SR HS; Kenmore, NY; (Y); 4/496; VP Math Tm; Band; Orch; High Hon Roll; Hon Roll; NHS; Ntl Merit Ltr; Pres Schlr; Olympcs Of Mind 3rd Pl Wrld Fnls 85; Pres Awd Acad Fit 85; U Of Buffalo; Comp Sci.

CHERNER, ADRIENNE; Coxsackie-Athens Central HS; Coxsackie, NY; (Y); Spanish Clb; Yrbk Phtg; Yrbk Stf; Sec Frsh Cls; Rep Stu Cncl; Capt Var Vllybl; Hon Roll; PA ST U; Biochem.

CHERNIGOFF, STEVE; Bronx H S Of Science; Bronx, NY; (S); Cmnty Wkr; Temple Yth Grp; Band; Concert Band; Nwsp Ed-Chief; Nwsp Rptr; Nwsp Sprt Ed; Yrbk Rptr; Var Capt Bsktbl; Acad All-Amer 84; Engl.

CHERNOFF, HARRY A; Stuyvesant HS; Brooklyn, NY; (Y); Debate Tm; Capt Model UN; Political Wkr; Pres Ski Clb; VP Jr Cls; Trs Stu Cncl; Ntl Merit Schol; Frsh Cls; Soph Cls; French Hon Soc; Westnghse STS Hnrs Grp 85; NY ST Deleg U S Senat Yth Prog 84; NY Cty Supr Yth 83; Poltcs.

CHERON, TERESA M; Saunders Trades & Tech HS; Yonkers, NY; (Y); 10/198; VICA; Lit Mag; Mgr(s); Vllybl; High Hon Roll; NHS; Ntl Merit Ltr; Acad Excl Awd 84-85; Ciba Geigy Sci Awd 85; Manhattan Coll; Chem.

CHERRY, ALETHA; Roosevelt JR SR HS; Freeport, NY; (Y); 42/220; Drama Clb; Exploring; Pres FHA; Hosp Aide; Band; School Musical; Swing Chorus; Pres Soph Cls; Lion Awd; Marvin Erving Soph Mem Awd 85; Roosevelt Ptsa Comm Schlrshp 85; Lioness Clb Schlrshp 85; U NC-GREENSBORO; Art.

CHERRY, MALCOLM; Freeport HS; Freeport, NY; (Y); 276/450; Art Clb; FBLA; Teachers Aide; Variety Show; JV Ftbl; JV Lcrss; Sftbl; Trk; JV Var Wt Lftg; JV Var Wrstlng; Comp Engr.

CHERRY, RICHARD; Forestville Central HS; Gowanda, NY; (Y); 5/45; Aud/Vis; Computer Clb; Exploring; 4-H; Stage Crew; Yrbk Stf; JV Crs Cntry; JV Trk; Var Wrstlng; Natl Sci Olympiad 3rd Schl Chem 85; Rochester U; Med.

CHERVENAK, MARY; Corning-Painted Post East HS; Corning, NY; (Y); Girl Scts; Quiz Bowl; Chorus; Yrbk Stf; JV Vllybl; High Hon Roll; NHS; Grl Sct Silver Awd 84; Grl Sct Marian Medl 82; SOAR Gifted & Talented Pgm 82-86; Biochem.

CHESK, KEITH; Union Endicott HS; Endicott, NY; (Y); 87/450; Church Yth Grp; Cmnty Wkr; Var L Bsbl; Hon Roll; CYO Bsktbl M V P Awd 85; Comp Sci.

CHESLOCK, PAULINE; Hicksville SR HS; Hicksville, NY; (Y); French Clb; Ski Clb; Nwsp Rptr; Stu Cncl; Capt Var Bsktbl; Capt Var Vllybl; Hon Roll; GAA; Varsity Clb; Im Socr; All Conf Vlybl Plyr 84; Best Athlt Schlr 83; Exc Piano 83; Bus Adm.

CHESNAIS, VERONIQUE S; United Nations Intl Schl; Elmhurst, NY; (Y); Ski Clb; Chorus; School Musical; Chess Clb; Crs Cntry; UNIS/UN Stu Orgnsng Comm Chrprsn; Lafayette Coll; Intl Affrs.

CHESTER, KRISTINE; Susquehanna Valley HS; Kirkwood, NY; (Y); Camera Clb; Band; Concert Band; Yrbk Stf; Gym; Vllybl; Exec Sec.

CHESTNUT, DARREN; Kensington HS; Buffalo, NY; (Y); Aud/Vis; Science Clb; Teachers Aide; Var Crs Cntry; Var Tennis; Prfct Atten Awd; Var Swmmng; John & Wales; Data Proc.

CHEUNG, JOHNNY M T; Brooklyn Technical HS; New York, NY; (Y); Boys Clb Am; Camera Clb; Computer Clb; Math Clb; Math Tm; Office Aide; Science Clb; Service Clb; Orch.

CHEUNG, MING; Copiague HS; Copiague, NY; (Y); Math Clb; Math Tm; Teachers Aide; Yrbk Ed-Chief; Rep Jr Cls; Sec Stu Cncl; High Hon Roll; NHS; Med.

CHEUNG, PUI; John F Kennedy HS; New York, NY; (Y); Math Tm; Teachers Aide; Band; Sec Sr Cls; High Hon Roll; Hon Roll; NHS; Prfct Atten Awd; Cert Merit Outstndg Prfrmnce Regnts Exam 84 & 85; Cert Merit Excllnce Soc Stud 84 & 85.

CHEUNG, WAI YIM; Susan E Wagner HS; Staten Island, NY; (Y); 5/500; French Clb; Sec JA; Key Clb; Math Tm; Teachers Aide; Stage Crew; Soph Cls; Jr Cls; High Hon Roll; Ntl Merit Schol; Frnch Cont 82-83; Regents 85; U Of Rocester; Biochem.

CHEUNG, WING SZE; Smithtown East HS; Saint James, NY; (Y); Symp Band; Trs Jr Cls; Var L Tennis; Var L Vllybl; NHS; Spanish NHS; Teachers Aide; Off Frsh Cls; Off Soph Cls; Trs Sr Cls; Vllybl All-Conf/All-Leag Awd 85.

CHEVIER, LINDA; Gouverneur Central HS; Gouverneur, NY; (Y); Pres Computer Clb; 4-H; Math Tm; JV Var Bsktbl; Mgr(s); Bausch & Lomb Sci Awd; High Hon Roll; Hon Roll; Jr NHS; NHS; Comp Sci Awd 84-85; Hannah Mosher Awd 85; Latin Awd 85; Potsdam ST; Comp Sci.

CHEW, STEPHEN W; John Dewey HS; Brooklyn, NY; (Y); Computer Clb; Teachers Aide; Band; Hon Roll; Prfct Atten Awd; Achvt Awdd Math 83; Achvt Awd Ind Arts 83; Pratt Inst; Elec Engr.

CHI, ROSEMARY C; Scarsdale HS; Scarsdale, NY; (Y); Trs French Clb; Capt Math Tm; Off Stu Cncl; Bus Mgmt.

CHI, SUSAN; Bishop Kearney HS; Brooklyn, NY; (S); 19/355; Ski Clb; Nwsp Rptr; Nwsp Stf; Rep Yrbk Stf; Tennis; Hon Roll; NHS; Acad All-Amer 84; Bus Admin.

CHI, SUSAN; Lynbrook SR HS; Hewlett Harbor, NY; (Y); Key Clb; Sec Mathletes; Orch; Yrbk Stf; Pres Jr Cls; Hon Roll; Pres NHS; Ntl Merit Ltr; Arion Awd Musical Achvt 84-85; Med.

CHIA, LI-WAN; Stuyvesant HS; E Elmhurst, NY; (Y); Hosp Aide; Science Clb; Chorus; Nwsp Ed-Chief; Nwsp Stf; Yrbk Stf; High Hon Roll; Hon Roll; Library Aide; Office Aide; Mayors Vol Svc Awd 84; Cert Excell Bio Lab Tech 84; Citation Merit Mayor 85; Pre-Med.

CHIAMPOU, KATIE; St John The Baptist HS; Bay Shore, NY; (Y); 7/750; Church Yth Grp; French Clb; Hosp Aide; Math Clb; Church Choir; Nwsp Stf; Tennis; High Hon Roll; Hon Roll; NHS; Law.

CHIANCA, PETER; Carmel HS; Carmel, NY; (Y); 9/399; Pres Leo Clb; Y-Teens; School Musical; Nwsp Ed-Chief; Yrbk Rptr; Lit Mag; High Hon Roll; Hon Roll; Pres NHS; Ntl Merit Ltr; Cmnctns.

CHIAPPERI, JOSEPH M; Cardinal Mooney HS; Rochester, NY; (Y); Ed Chess Clb; Var L Socr; L Var Trk; High Hon Roll; Hon Roll; NHS; Ntl Merit SF; Spanish NHS; Mgr Concert Band; School Play; Theolgy Awd 82; NYSPHSAA Sec V Cls AAA Socr Champs NY ST Cls A Champ 83; U Of Rochester; Engrng.

CHIARAMONTE, DEIRDRE; Emma Willard Schl; Staatsburg, NY; (Y); Pres 4-H; Capt Drill Tm; JV Bsktbl; Var Socr; 4-H Awd; Hon Roll; NHS; Drama Clb; Girl Scts; Natl Chmp Grnd Natl & Wrld Chmpnshps Morgan Hrse Show Dressage Huntr Ovr Fnces & Seat Eqtatn 83 & 84; Biol.

CHIARAMONTE, ROBERT; South Side HS; Rockville Ctr, NY; (Y); 20/270; Band; Concert Band; Jazz Band; Mrchg Band; Orch; Pep Band; School Musical; Trk; Wrstlng.

CHIARELLA, CAROLYN; Northport HS; E Npt, NY; (Y); Cmnty Wkr; French Clb; Office Aide; Teachers Aide; Yrbk Stf; Rep Frsh Cls; Rep Stu Cncl; Hon Roll; Accntng.

CHIASSON, CHRISTOPHER A; Bishop Grimes HS; Fayetteville, NY; (Y); 17/207; Quiz Bowl; Pres Jr Cls; Rep Sr Cls; Var L Ftbl; Hon Roll; Ntl Merit Ltr; NY ST Regents Schlrshp 85; College.

CHIASSON, CLAIRE; Bishop Grimes HS; Fayetteville, NY; (Y); Church Yth Grp; Im Bsktbl; JV Capt Socr; Var Trk; Stat Vllybl; High Hon Roll; NHS; Natl Soc Stud Olmpd 85.

CHIDLOW, CARL; Pelham Memorial HS; Pelham, NY; (Y); Radio Clb; Stage Crew; Nwsp Phtg; Yrbk Sprt Ed; Rep Soph Cls; Rep Jr Cls; JV Stu Cncl; JV Bsktbl; Var Ftbl; Bst Spkr Cmmtte-Modl Cngrss 85; Strtd Rado Clb 84-85; JR Cls Prom Chrmn 85; Pol Sci.

CHIEN, DAVID; Commack High Schl North; Commack, NY; (Y); Aud/Vis; Exploring; Math Tm; Acpl Chr; School Musical; Swing Chorus; Nwsp Rptr; JV L Crs Cntry; Var L Trk; High Hon Roll; Vrsty Athl Awd Trck 83-85; 3rd Pl Mile Walk Rly Middle Cntry Relays Trck 85; 1st Pl Crss Cntry 84; Med.

CHILDERS, PAMELA J; Paul V Moore HS; Brewerton, NY; (Y); 3/297; 4-H; Girl Scts; Science Clb; High Hon Roll; NHS; Lcl Hnr Soc 84-85; NY ST Rgnts Schlrshp 85; Accptnc To Cornell U 84; Cornell U; Vet.

CHILDERS, TIMMY; Hudson HS; Hudson, NY; (Y); Ftbl; Hon Roll; NHS; USAF; Law Enfrcmnt.

CHILDS, BRYAN; Franklin Acad; Bangor, NY; (S); 3/255; AFS; Drama Clb; Pres Speech Tm; Jazz Band; High Hon Roll; VP NHS; Ntl Merit Ltr; ST Reps Natl 4-H Yth Conf 85; Amer Legion Ortrcl Lcl, Cnty, Dist & Zone 85; Potsdam SUNY; Math Tchr.

CHILDS, CRYSTAL; Mt Vernon HS; Mount Vernon, NY; (Y); Computer Clb; Drama Clb; Key Clb; Latin Clb; Mrchg Band; High Hon Roll; Hon Roll; Pres Phys Ftns Awd 85; GA Inst Tech; Comp Sci.

CHILDS, LORI; Heuvelton Central Schl; Heuvelton, NY; (Y); Pres French Clb; GAA; Hosp Aide; Var Sftbl; Sqntl Math I 83; Bus Dynmcs 83; Bus Kybrdng/Cmnctn 85; Bus Adm.

CHILDS, REBECCA; Indian River Central Schl; Philadelphia, NY; (Y); AFS; Ski Clb; Chorus; School Musical; Yrbk Phtg; Stu Cncl; Cheerleading; Score Keeper; Sftbl; Church Yth Grp; Advrtsng.

CHILDS, ROBIN L; New Paltz Central HS; New Paltz, NY; (Y); Girl Scts; Chorus; Capt Color Guard; Rep Soph Cls; Rep Jr Cls; Bowling; SUNY-CORTLAND; Elem Ed.

CHILDS, WILLIAM H; East Islip HS; East Islip, NY; (Y); 50/475; Concert Band; Im Sftbl; Im Vllybl; High Hon Roll; Hon Roll; St Schlr; FL Inst Of Tech; Space Sci.

CHILJEAN, TRACY; Wantagh HS; Wantagh, NY; (Y); VP Stu Cncl; Var L Tennis; Hon Roll; NHS; Church Yth Grp; Math Tm; Band; Concert Band; Mrchg Band.

CHILLE, RALPH; Niagara Falls HS; Niagara Falls, NY; (Y); Computer Clb; Pres Key Clb; Var L Bsbl; Var L Bowling; Var L Golf; High Hon Roll; Jr NHS; NHS; Amer Legn Awd 83; Niagara U; Comp Sci.

CHIM, AMY-YUKLING; Richmond Hill HS; Richmond Hill, NY; (Y); Office Aide; Spanish Clb; Teachers Aide; Hon Roll.

CHIMELIS, JOEL; Eastern District HS; Brooklyn, NY; (Y); 43/400; Computer Clb; Sr Cls; Var Capt Bsbl; Harvard JC; Comp Sci.

CHIMENTO, CARA; Albertus Magnus HS; Pomona, NY; (Y); Drama Clb; Hosp Aide; School Musical; Yrbk Phtg; Yrbk Stf; Hon Roll; Chiropractor.

CHIMILESKI, ROBERT; Notre Dame HS; Elmira, NY; (Y); Varsity Clb; Bsktbl; Ftbl; Trk; Hon Roll; Hon Mentn Ftbl 84; All Twin Keys Trck 85; Engrg.

CHIN, AUDREY; Mac Arthur HS; Wantagh, NY; (Y); 2/319; AFS; Science Clb; Yrbk Stf; VP Stu Cncl; Var Tennis; High Hon Roll; Hon Roll; Pres Jr NHS; Pres NHS; Sal; NY ST Rgnts Schlrshp 85; Cornell U; Pre-Med.

CHIN, BRYAN; Archbishop Molloy HS; Sunnyside, NY; (Y); 5/409; Computer Clb; Bsktbl; Ftbl; Sftbl; High Hon Roll; NHS; Pre-Law.

CHIN, CEDRIC; Bishop Loughlin Memorial HS; Brooklyn, NY; (Y); Chess Clb; Nwsp Rptr; Hon Roll; Cmnctns.

CHIN, CHARMAINE; Far Rockaway HS; Far Rockaway, NY; (Y); Sec Church Yth Grp; Key Clb; Library Aide; Office Aide; Ski Clb; Teachers Aide; Nwsp Rptr; Hon Roll; NHS; Prfct Atten Awd; Bus Mngmnt.

CHIN, CHRISTOPHER; Kings Park HS; Kings Park, NY; (Y); 5/393; Computer Clb; Debate Tm; DECA; Science Clb; Varsity Clb; Var L Lcrss; Var L Wrstlng; High Hon Roll; NHS; 1st Kaleidescope Shrt Stry Cntst 85; Awd Bst Physics Lab Tech & Accuracy 85; 1st Wrestlng Tourn 84-85; Elec Engnrng.

CHIN, HENRY; Murry Bergtraum HS; Brooklyn, NY; (Y); 80/576; JA; Teachers Aide; Hon Roll; NY U; Bus.

CHIN, HERBERT; Bronx High School Of Science; New York, NY; (Y); Chess Clb; Band; Pres Frsh Cls; Otstndg Schlrshp Awd 85; Rgnts Schlrshp 85; Cooper Union; Elec Engrng.

CHIN, KAREN K; Northport HS; E Northport, NY; (Y); 66/585; Sec Pres DECA; VP French Clb; Hosp Aide; Mathletes; Mrchg Band; Rep Stu Cncl; Hon Roll; NHS; Debate Tm; Political Wkr; Hosp Ade 150 Hrs 85; Svc Awd Pin 83; DECA Rgnl Fnlst Real Est 85; Bus.

CHIN, SHIRLEY; Hillcrest HS; Jamaica, NY; (Y); 17/783; Church Yth Grp; Hosp Aide; JA; Office Aide; Teachers Aide; Church Choir; Hon Roll; Food & Drug, Kodak Awds For Sci Proj 82; Gold Medl Sci Proj 83; NY U; Biochem.

CHIN, SU SHAN; Norman Thomas HS; New York, NY; (Y); 55/671; Cmnty Wkr; FBLA; Library Aide; Office Aide; Red Cross Aide; Teachers Aide; Chorus; Hon Roll; NHS; Prfct Atten Awd; Pres Acad Ftnss Awds 85; Red Crss Vlntr Svc Awd 84-85; NY U; Comp Sci.

CHIN, WILLIAM; Archbishop Molloy HS; Rego Pk, NY; (Y); 150/420; Art Clb; Church Yth Grp; Drama Clb; Math Clb; VICA; Stage Crew; Hon Roll; ASOSP Cert Achvt Aicrft Elec Instlltn At Brd Eductns 84; Engrng.

CHIN, WILLING; New Dorp HS; Staten Island, NY; (Y); French Clb; Intnl Clb; Band; Church Choir; School Play; French Hon Soc; Hon Roll; Prfct Atten Awd; NYU; Med.

CHING, BLANCA; Midwood HS; Brooklyn, NY; (Y); #99 In Class; Art Clb; Church Yth Grp; French Clb; Intnl Clb; Math Tm; Band; Concert Band; Orch; Lit Mag; Hon Roll.

CHIOCCHIO, LUCIA; Our Lady Of Victory Acad; Scarsdale, NY; (S); 3/40; Church Yth Grp; Girl Scts; Spanish Clb; NHS; Spanish NHS; Genl Excllnc 82-83; Caritas Awd.

CHIODI, SANDY; H H Lehman HS; Bronx, NY; (Y); 16/473; JA; Hon Roll; Arista Hnr Scty Mbr & Awd Recpnt 85; Acctncy.

CHIRIATTI, ROBIN; Poughkeepsie HS; Poughkeepsie, NY; (Y); Drama Clb; Girl Scts; Yrbk Stf; Stu Cncl; Stat Bsbl; Mgr(s); Score Keeper; Northeastern U; Bus.

CHIRICO, LISA; Notre Dame HS; Utica, NY; (Y); 41/168; Hosp Aide; School Musical; Nwsp Ed-Chief; Yrbk Stf; Sec Soph Cls; Stu Cncl; JV Tennis; High Hon Roll; Hon Roll; Pres Schlr; Syracuse U; Pub Rel.

CHISLOM, DANIEL R; Roosevelt JR SR HS; Roosevelt, NY; (Y); Drama Clb; FBLA; Yrbk Stf; Cmmnctns.

CHITTENDEN, ALAN; Maple Hill HS; Schodack Landing, NY; (S); 2/85; Church Yth Grp; Pres 4-H; Spanish Clb; JV Capt Bsktbl; 4-H Awd; High Hon Roll; NHS; Ntl Merit Ltr; Sci Awd; Geom Awd; NYS Math Leag Awd; Cornell; Dairy Sci.

CHITUK, DIANE; Mattitreb HS; Cutchogue, NY; (Y); Church Yth Grp; Cmnty Wkr; 4-H; FNA; German Clb; Intnl Clb; Office Aide; Church Choir; Stage Crew; Nwsp Stf; Ltr & Plaq Vrsty Vllybl 85; Med.

CHIU, JO SWAN; Julia Richman HS; Flushing, NY; (Y); 3/479; JA; Math Tm; Hon Roll; Chorus; Manhattn Borough Pres Cert Merit 85; Math Awd & Cert Merit Sci 85; Fclty Schlrshp Awd 85; NY U.

CHIU, LISA; Murry Bergstraum HS; New York, NY; (Y); Chess Clb; JA; Library Aide; Teachers Aide; Chorus; Bsktbl; Sftbl; Maritime Coll; Elec Engrng.

CHIU, PIK CHUN; Seeward Park HS; Brooklyn, NY; (Y); English Clb; Office Aide; Chorus; School Musical; NHS; Prfct Atten Awd; Essay Cont 1st Pl 82, 4th Pl 84; Rgnts Schlrshp 85; Pol Sci.

CHIU, REX S; Smithtown High School East; Nesconset, NY; (Y); 1/550; Hosp Aide; Math Tm; Spanish Clb; Orch; Stu Cncl; Var Tennis; High Hon Roll; NHS; Prfct Atten Awd; Spanish NHS; ST Math Test 83-84; NTUMCAA Tennis Trnmnt; Brown U; Med.

CHIU, TIMOTHY Z; Sachme High School N Campus; Holbrook, NY; (Y); 5/1428; Sec Exploring; Pres Math Tm; Rep Service Clb; Orch; Nwsp Ed-Chief; Ed Lit Mag; NHS; Ntl Merit Ltr; Pres Schlr; NYS Sci Olympiad 2nd Pl Comp Pgmng 85; U Of PA; Mgmt.

CHMIELEWICZ, KIM; Fayetteville-Manlius HS; Manlius, NY; (Y); Model UN; Orch; School Musical; Nwsp Stf; Lit Mag; Hon Roll; NHS; JCL; Math Clb; Natl Latn Exm Magna Cum Laude 83; Natl Latn Exm Cum Laude 84; Engl Lit Awd 84; Crtv Wrtg.

CHMIELEWSKI, KIMBERLY; Altmar Parish Williamstown HS; Parish, NY; (Y); Church Yth Grp; Varsity Clb; Color Guard; Concert Band; Bowling; Cheerleading; Vllybl; High Hon Roll; Hon Roll; NHS; Elmira Key Awd 85; Suny Of Oswego; Accntng.

CHO, BAEK Y; Brooklyn Tech HS; Queens, NY; (Y); 15/1036; Church Yth Grp; Computer Clb; Hosp Aide; Science Clb; Hon Roll; Hnr Grp 1985 Westnghs Sci Tlnt Srch 85; Chancellors Rll Hnr 85; Rsrch Sci.

CHO, JANET; Pittsford Mendon HS; Pittsford, NY; (Y); Art Clb; Boy Scts; Church Yth Grp; Civic Clb; Cmnty Wkr; Computer Clb; Debate Tm; Drama Clb; English Clb; French Clb; Natl Frnch Cntst 7th Pl 83; Mst Valbl Artst 83; Natl Chem Socty Exm Awd 84; Harvard U; Pre-Med.

CHO, KRIS; Bronx High Schl Of Sci; Bronx, NY; (Y); Office Aide; Ski Clb; Teachers Aide; Yrbk Stf; Lit Mag; Stu Cncl; Trk; Engl.

CHOCKO, SHARON; St John The Baptist HS; W Islip, NY; (Y); Hosp Aide; Hon Roll; Accntng I & Typng I-Centry 21 85; Accntng.

CHODAK, JAMES; Bishop Kearney HS; Rochester, NY; (Y); Boy Scts; Hosp Aide; Model UN; Im Bowling; Sencond Hnrs Awd 83-85; Intl Studies.

CHODOCK, ROBERT I; Blind Brook HS; Rye Brook, NY; (Y); Pres AFS; Model UN; Pres Spanish Clb; School Musical; Nwsp Stf; Capt Var Golf; JV Socr; Regnts Coll Schlrshp 85; Cornell.

CHOI, KAM CHOI; Norman Thomas HS; New York, NY; (S); 50/671; Math Clb; Hon Roll; Story Brook U; Teacher.

CHOI, MARK; Bronx H S Of Sceince; Bronx, NY; (Y); Chess Clb; Church Yth Grp; Library Aide; Mathletes; Office Aide; Teachers Aide; Band; Concert Band; Prfct Atten Awd; Doctor.

CHOI, MARY; Grand Island SR HS; Grand Island, NY; (Y); 11/325; Church Yth Grp; Mathletes; Ski Clb; Orch; School Musical; Variety Show; Sec Stu Cncl; Var Crs Cntry; Hon Roll; VP NHS; Vrsty Ltr Awd Hgh Acad Excel 85.

CHOI, PAMELA; Smithtown High School West; Smithtown, NY; (Y); Ski Clb; Drill Tm; Orch; Stage Crew; Yrbk Stf; Rep Frsh Cls; Rep Soph Cls; Rep Jr Cls; Trs French Hon Soc; NHS; Hgh Hnr Rll 84-85; Hnr Rll 82-84; NSSMA 2 Mdls 83; Bus.

CHOKSHI, PARAG; New Rochelle HS; New Rochelle, NY; (Y); Cmnty Wkr; Computer Clb; Hosp Aide; Library Aide; Math Tm; Spanish Clb; Band; High Hon Roll; NHS; Spanish NHS; Am Leg Schl Awd 83; Mth Awd 83; Nwspapr Carr Of Mnth 85; Med.

CHOLLET, MICHELLE; Horseheads HS; Elmira, NY; (S); 52/407; Pres DECA; French Clb; Ski Clb; Orch; Pres Frsh Cls; Rep Soph Cls; Hst Jr Cls; Rep Sr Cls; Rep Stu Cncl; NHS; Deca Reg 1st 85; Endicott Coll; Fash Rtlng.

CHORAZAK, JENNIFER; Frontier Central HS; Blasdell, NY; (S); Trs Drama Clb; French Clb; Girl Scts; Pep Clb; Chorus; School Musical; Stage Crew; Rep Stu Cncl; Hon Roll; NHS; Theatre.

CHOTKOWSKI, STEVEN C; Scotia Glenville HS; Scotia, NY; (Y); Aud/Vis; Stage Crew; Var JV Ftbl; Var Trk; Var Wt Lftg; Var Wrstlng; God Cntry Awd; Cultural Exc Stu 84; Scotia Glenvl Athl Awd 85; S G SR Assist Awd 85; Mgr Awd 84; Herkimer County CC; Radio.

CHOU, ALBERT E; Williamsville South HS; Buffalo, NY; (Y); 3/245; Math Clb; Math Tm; Trs Orch; School Musical; Var Trk; Bausch & Lomb Sci Awd; High Hon Roll; Hon Roll; NHS; Ntl Merit Ltr; Yale Bk Awd 84; Co Conctmstr Schl Orchstra 84-85; Cornell U; Engrng.

CHOVAN, JOE R; Cicero North Syracuse HS; N Syracuse, NY; (S); 13/711; Im Bowling; Im Tennis; NHS; Ntl Merit Ltr; Cornell U; Engr.

CHOVNICK, GARY; James Madison HS; Brooklyn, NY; (Y); 231/812; Cmnty Wkr; Office Aide; Band; Concert Band; Orch; Im Tennis; Cit Awd; Ntl Merit Schol; Bus Mgmt.

CHOW, ALICE; Lansingburgh HS; Troy, NY; (Y); Dance Clb; Political Wkr; Teachers Aide; Yrbk Bus Mgr; Yrbk Phtg; Yrbk Rptr; Yrbk Stf; Pres Frsh Cls; JV Capt Bsktbl; Jr NHS; Beth Lansing Rebekah, Svc Schl & Comm 83; Bus Mgt.

CHOW, RAE; Mohonasen SR HS; Schenectady, NY; (Y); 14/216; VP Band; Concert Band; Drm Mjr(t); Jazz Band; Mrchg Band; Orch; Pep Band; Trs Sr Cls; High Hon Roll; NHS; Mus Schlrshp 83; NY ST Regnts Schlrshp 85; Rennselaer Polytech; Bio Engr.

CHOY, WANDA W Y; Stuyvesant HS; Forest Hills, NY; (Y); Cmnty Wkr; Science Clb; Service Clb; Ed Lit Mag; NHS; Ntl Merit Ltr; Hon Roll; Church Yth Grp; Office Aide; JR Acad Of Sci Certificate 85; Harvard U; Med.

CHRISLEY, CHRISTINA; Byron-Bergen Central Schl; S Byron, NY; (Y); Church Yth Grp; Teachers Aide; Hon Roll; Buffalo ST U; Elem Ed.

CHRISLEY JR, WILEY L; Holland Patent Central Schl; Rome, NY; (Y); Boy Scts; Church Yth Grp; NYS Regents Schlrshp Awd 85; Conaty Coll Morris; Math.

CHRISMAN, CAROLE; Cicero N Syracuse HS; Mattydale, NY; (S); 55/711; Cmnty Wkr; German Clb; VP JA; Onocloger CC; Sci.

CHRISS, BINNIE-AYN; Cohoes HS; Ballston Spa, NY; (Y); Art Clb; Drama Clb; Exploring; FTA; Keywanettes; School Play; Stage Crew; Rep Soph Cls; Rep Jr Cls; Rep Stu Cncl; Coll Of St Rose; Art Eductn.

CHRISS, NEIL A; Whtie Plains HS; White Plains, NY; (Y); 2/538; VP Mathletes; Nwsp Stf; Var Wrstlng; High Hon Roll; Jr NHS; NHS; Ntl Merit SF; Sal; Outstndng JR Var Wrestling 84; All Cnty Hnbl Mntn Var Wrestling 84; Willions Coll Alumni Book Awd 84; Harvard; Psychiatry.

CHRISTENSEN, CARENE; Wells Central HS; Northville, NY; (S); 2/34; Church Yth Grp; French Clb; Library Aide; Band; Chorus; Church Choir; Trs Jr Cls; Var Bsktbl; Var Sftbl; Var Vllybl; Elem Tchr.

CHRISTENSEN, INGRID; Oneonta SR HS; Oneonta, NY; (Y); Varsity Clb; Sec Sr Cls; Rep Stu Cncl; Gym; Church Yth Grp; Spanish Clb; Yrbk Stf; Cheerleading; Diving; Trk; Mst Physclly Fit Grl 83.

CHRISTENSEN, KARA; Houghton Acad; Houghton, NY; (Y); 2/18; Church Yth Grp; Chorus; Yrbk Stf; JV L Cheerleading; Var L Tennis; Var L Vllybl; High Hon Roll; NHS; Mst Imprvd & MVP Awds-Vllybl 84-85; Spn Merit Awd-Hghst Avg 83-84; Houghton Coll; Clncl Chem.

CHRISTENSEN, KIRK W; Shenendehowa Central Schl; Ballston Lake, NY; (Y); Exploring; Key Clb; High Hon Roll; NHS; Cert Schlstc Achvt 82-85; Acad Achct Awd Skidmore Coll 84-85; Cert Merit Sntr Joseph Bruno 84-85; Union Coll; Comp Sci.

CHRISTENSEN, LAURA; William Nottingham HS; Syracuse, NY; (Y); 23/240; Latin Clb; Ski Clb; Chorus; Nwsp Stf; Lit Mag; Stu Cncl; Var Tennis; High Hon Roll; Hon Roll; NHS; R J O Toole Awd 84; Sprtsmnshp Awd 85; N L E-Magna Cum Laude 84-85; William Smith Coll.

CHRISTIAN, CATHY; Academy Fo St Joseph; Northport, NY; (Y); Pep Clb; Stage Crew; Yrbk Stf; Hon Roll; Prfct Atten Awd; Elem Educ.

CHRISTIAN, KIMBERLY ANN; Hartford Central HS; Ft Ann, NY; (Y); 14/43; Church Yth Grp; 4-H; French Clb; GAA; Pep Clb; Varsity Clb; Band; Chorus; Church Choir; Concert Band; Daemen Coll Amherst; Travel.

CHRISTIAN, SAN JAY; F D Roosevelt HS; Brooklyn, NY; (Y); 1/45; Church Yth Grp; Drama Clb; Hosp Aide; Math Clb; Science Clb; Socr; Swmmng; Vllybl; Middle HS Schlrshp 80-81; Bst Stu Awd 83; Elec Engrng.

CHRISTIAN, SIMONE; Roosevelt JR SR HS; Roosevelt, NY; (Y); 21/200; Church Yth Grp; Dance Clb; Drama Clb; Sec VP Girl Scts; Pres Church Choir; School Play; Sec Stu Cncl; Im FHA; Hon Roll; Hampton U; Arch.

CHRISTIANA JR, JOSEPH W; John F Kennedy HS; Waccabuc, NY; (Y); Debate Tm; Political Wkr; Teachers Aide; Rep Soph Cls; Var Golf; Hon Roll; Natl Physics Olympiad Awd 85; Chiropractor.

CHRISTIANO, MICHAEL; Liverpool HS; Liverpool, NY; (S); VP JA; Rep Stu Cncl; JV Im Bsktbl; Wt Lftg; Hon Roll; Jr NHS; NHS; YMCA Vlntr, Cnslr Awds 83-84; Bus Adm.

CHRISTIE, OTIS; August Martin HS; Jamaica, NY; (Y); Church Yth Grp; Church Choir; Concert Band; Orch; Hon Roll; Health Ed 83; Elec Engr.

CHRISTIE, THOMAS C; Syosset HS; Syosset, NY; (Y); 154/508; AFS; Boy Scts; Church Yth Grp; Chorus; Church Choir; Stage Crew; Nwsp Phtg; Yrbk Phtg; Var L Wrstlng; NYSSMA All-Cty, State Choir 83-85; NYS Regnts Schlrshp 84-85; Lehigh U.

CHRISTMAN, KATHLEEN; Our Lady Of Perpetual Help HS; Brooklyn, NY; (Y); 1/160; Church Yth Grp; Library Aide; Sec Jr Cls; Coach Actv; Socr; High Hon Roll; Hon Roll; Jr NHS; NHS; Psych.

CHRISTMAN, SHAWN; Susquehanna Valley HS; Conklin, NY; (Y); Boy Scts; Chess Clb; Computer Clb; French Clb; Concert Band; JV Bsktbl; Var Crs Cntry; Var Trk; Aerospc Engr.

CHRISTMANN, TAMMY B; Wallkill HS; Clintondale, NY; (Y); 20/209; Church Yth Grp; Drama Clb; Office Aide; Service Clb; Chorus; Church Choir; Hon Roll; NHS; Regents Schlrshp Awd 85; Marist Coll; Pltcl Sci.

CHRISTODOULOU, CHRISTINE; St Johns Prep; Astoria, NY; (Y); Church Yth Grp; Band; High Hon Roll; Hon Roll; St Johns U; Bus.

CHRISTON, LORRIE; Narrowsburg Central Schl; Narrowsburg, NY; (Y); 2/27; Pres Church Yth Grp; Sec FHA; Pep Clb; Band; Chorus; School Musical; Yrbk Phtg; Trs Stu Cncl; NHS; Stat Bsbl; Hugh O Brien Ldrshp Smnr Ambsdr 84; NYS Senate Forum 85; Engl.

CHRISTOPHER, MICHELE; Albion Central HS; Albion, NY; (Y); Color Guard; Ntl Merit Schol; Commndtn Awds Alg, Typg I & II 83-85; Bus.

CHRISTOPOULOS, JILL; The Mary Louis Acad; Flushing, NY; (Y); Art Clb; Aud/Vis; NEDT Awd; Fashn Desgn.

CHRZANOWSKI, KIM; Villa Maria Acad; Cheektowaga, NY; (Y); Computer Clb; Math Clb; Natl Beta Clb; Chorus; Cit Awd; Hon Roll; NHS; Prfct Atten Awd; Latin Awd 83; Hgh Lvl Acad Brnz Medal 85; Outstndng Plsh Wrk Polish Awd 85; Canisius Coll; Intl Rltns.

CHRZANOWSKI, MICHAEL J; St Joseph Collegiate Inst; E Amherst, NY; (Y); 5/201; French Clb; Math Tm; JV Im Bsbl; JV Im Ftbl; JV Var Trk; High Hon Roll; Hon Roll; NHS; Ntl Merit Ltr; NY ST Rgnts Schlrshp 84-85; Navy ROTC Schlrshp 85; Pres Acdmc Ftns Awd 85; U Of Buffalo; Chem Engrng.

CHU, AHN; Rome Free Acad; Rome, NY; (Y); Var Tennis; NHS; RPI Sci & Math Medal Hnr 85.

CHU, ANNE; St Michael HS; New York, NY; (Y); Yrbk Stf; Hon Roll; NHS; Prfct Atten Awd; Presndtl Phy Ftns Awd 84; St Michael HS Seal Awd 85; NY U.

CHU, CAVY; Bishop Kearney HS; Brooklyn, NY; (S); Var Math Tm; Chorus; Yrbk Stf; JV Badmtn; JV Gym; NHS; Gold Mdls Schl Badminton Teams 81-82; 1st Hnrs Report Card 83-84; 2nd Hnrs Report Card 84; SUNY-STONY Brook; Sci.

CHU, DOUGLAS C; Hackley Schl; Montrose, NY; (Y); 2/87; Computer Clb; Var Capt Crs Cntry; Swmmng; Var Capt Trk; High Hon Roll; Ntl Merit SF; Brown U Eng Awd 83-84; Yrbk Photogrphy Edtr 84-85; Most Imprvd Runr Vrsty Cross Cntry 84; Engrng.

CHU, JULIE; Newtown HS; Jackson Heights, NY; (Y); Hon Roll; Ntl Merit Schol; Prfct Atten Awd; Outstndng Achvt Awd Bus Ed 85; Hunter Coll; Acctng.

CHU, THOMAS K; Hunter College HS; New York, NY; (Y); Pres Church Yth Grp; Trs Model UN; Teachers Aide; Church Choir; Lit Mag; Ntl Merit Ltr; St Schlr; Cong Bundstg Schlrshp 84; Columbia Coll NY; Pol Sci.

CHUA, DAVID V; Batavia HS; Batavia, NY; (Y); 40/241; Church Yth Grp; Ski Clb; VP Jr Cls; Stu Cncl; JV Tennis; High Hon Roll; NHS; Ntl Eng Merit Awd; Regents Schlrshp; Potsdam ST.

CHUBA, TERRY; Saranac Lake HS; Saranac Lk, NY; (Y); Chess Clb; English Clb; MMM; Bsbl; Tennis; Jrnlsm.

CHUBIRKA, CHRISTINE; Dominican Commercial HS; College Point, NY; (Y); 29/329; Nwsp Rptr; Capt Gym; NHS; Prin Lst 82-85; Sienna Clb 82-85; Jr Ring Day Dance 84-85; PSAT Prep Crse 84; RN.

CHUDOBA, DONNA; Mount Mercy HS; Buffalo, NY; (S); 37/168; Church Yth Grp; FHA; Girl Scts; JA; Science Clb; Nwsp Stf; Lit Mag; Jesse Ketchum Schlrshp Mdl Wnnr 82; Sherman F Teyler Awd 82; Hnr Roll 82; Trocaire Coll; Sci.

CHUEN, YAU; Midwood HS; Brooklyn, NY; (Y); Cmnty Wkr; Office Aide; Prfct Atten Awd; Engrng.

CHUHTA, STEVEN; Tamarac HS; Troy, NY; (Y); Church Yth Grp; Intnl Clb; Math Tm; Political Wkr; Varsity Clb; Chorus; JV Bsbl; Var L Ftbl; Hon Roll; NHS; Cornell; Vet.

CHUN, CARLOS J; Woodmere Acad; Bayside, NY; (Y); Church Choir; JV Var Bsbl; JV Var Socr; Wt Lftg; Regnts Schlrshp 85; NY U; Pub Adm.

CHUN, JOAN; Elmira Free Acad; Elmira, NY; (Y); Am Leg Aux Girls St; Cmnty Wkr; Pres JA; Orch; Nwsp Ed-Chief; Yrbk Ed-Chief; Rep Stu Cncl; Var L Tennis; High Hon Roll; NHS; Essay Cntst Wnr Nrtest Dstrct In Music 85; Rgnl & Ntl Cnfrnc For JA 84; Coll; Pre-Med.

CHUN, SUN; Roosevelt HS; Yonkers, NY; (S); Trs Band; Nwsp Stf; Lit Mag; Off Frsh Cls; Off Soph Cls; Rep Jr Cls; Rep Sr Cls; High Hon Roll; Sec NHS; Fstvl Of Arts & Sci 83; Law.

CHUNG, JAEHOON; St Johns Preparatory Schl; Astoria, NY; (Y); 28/415; VP Science Clb; Var Tennis; Jr NHS; NHS; Rgnts Schlrshp 85; Mdcl Doc.

CHUNG, KAM HUNG; Seward Park HS; New York, NY; (Y); Comp.

CHUNG, SUSAN; Long Island City HS; Long Island City, NY; (S); 10/579; Church Yth Grp; Church Choir; Nwsp Rptr; Hon Roll; Mu Alp Tht; Optmtry.

CHUNG, SUSAN J; Newburgh Free Acad; Newburgh, NY; (Y); Drama Clb; Math Tm; Chorus; Trs Orch; Stage Crew; Var Golf; High Hon Roll; Jr NHS; Spanish NHS; B Dowd Mem Trnmnt Champs 82; Med.

CHUNG, WAI; Sheepshead Bay HS; Brooklyn, NY; (Y); Computer Clb; Library Aide; Math Tm; Science Clb; Yrbk Stf; Cit Awd; Hon Roll; Elect Engr.

CHUNG CHIU WU, ALAN; Brooklyn Technical HS; Elmhurst Corona, NY; (Y); Hosp Aide; Red Cross Aide; Science Clb; Teachers Aide; High Hon Roll; Hon Roll; NHS; Otto P Burgdorf Awd 85; Hnr Cert 82-84; Regents Schrlshp 85; Cornell U; Pre-Med.

CHUNKA, DENISE; Fayetteville Manlius HS; Manlius, NY; (Y); Church Yth Grp; Trs German Clb; Chorus; Church Choir; School Musical; Stage Crew; Vllybl; Hon Roll; PHY Educ Awd 83; Bus.

CHURCH, CLINT S; C W Baker HS; Baldwinsville, NY; (Y); 7/441; Ski Clb; Pres Stu Cncl; Lcrss; Hon Roll; Pres Jr NHS; VP NHS; Cmmnty Schlrshp; Engrng Fllwshp 85; U Of VA; Engrng.

CHURCH, MARY; Mynderse Acad; Seneca Falls, NY; (S); 28/120; Ski Clb; Yrbk Stf; Rep Sr Cls; Rep Stu Cncl; Var Socr; JV Sftbl; Var Trk; High Hon Roll; Hon Roll; JR & SR Ball Crt Attndnt 84 & 85; RIT; Bus.

CHURCH, SALLY; Fox Lane HS; Bedford, NY; (Y); 16/260; Intnl Clb; VP JA; Band; JV Fld Hcky; JV Lcrss; French Hon Soc; High Hon Roll; NHS; Ntl Merit Ltr; Hnrs Bio 84; Outbound Amb Status 84; Pre-Med.

CHURCHILL, KRISTEN; Herkimer SR HS; Herkimer, NY; (Y); 12/135; Drama Clb; Concert Band; Jazz Band; Mrchg Band; JV Var Bsktbl; Var Capt Crs Cntry; Var Trk; High Hon Roll; Hon Roll; NHS; Lib Arts.

CHWE, CHRISTINE; New Rochelle HS; New Rochelle, NY; (Y); Debate Tm; French Clb; Ski Clb; Chorus; Rep Jr Cls; Var Socr; French Hon Soc; High Hon Roll; NHS; Val; Frnch II Awd 83.

CIACCIO, CONNIE; John Dewey HS; Brooklyn, NY; (Y); Italian Clb; St Johns U.

CIACH, LUISA; Mount St Joseph Acad; Buffalo, NY; (Y); 5/48; Church Yth Grp; Sec Office Aide; Hon Roll; Relgn Awd 84-85; Ceramic, Art & Artsts Awd 84; Eric CC; Paralgl Asst.

CIAMPA, DENISE; Our Lady Of Victory Acad; Younkers, NY; (Y); 24/143; Drama Clb; Exploring; Science Clb; Church Choir; Yrbk Stf; Trk; Vllybl; Hon Roll; NHS; Best Fld Plyr Trck & Fld 83-84; Manhattan Coll; Engrng.

CIANCIO, DAVID E; Notre Dame HS; Whitesboro, NY; (Y); 12/178; Letterman Clb; Math Tm; Ski Clb; Varsity Clb; Y-Teens; Yrbk Bus Mgr; Var Ftbl; Im Ftbl; High Hon Roll; NHS; Clarkson U; Elec Engr.

CIANCIOTTA, LAURIE; Bishop Kearney HS; Brooklyn, NY; (Y); 94/365; Church Yth Grp; Cmnty Wkr; Dance Clb; Teachers Aide; High Hon Roll; Jr NHS; NHS; CCD Tchr St Athanisus Bklyn 83; Brooklyn Coll; Mth Ed.

CIANFROCCO, DIANNA; Rome Free Acad; Rome, NY; (Y); 152/526; JA; Orch; Nwsp Sprt Ed; Sec Frsh Cls; Rep Soph Cls; Rep Jr Cls; Rep Sr Cls; Rep Stu Cncl; Var Im Cheerleading; NHS; Prfct Atten 81-84; Hnr Rll 81-85; Fredonia; Lbrl Arts.

CIANO, CHERYL; Mahopac HS; Mahopac, NY; (Y); 11/378; Church Yth Grp; Math Tm; Band; Chorus; Church Choir; Concert Band; Mrchg Band; Orch; High Hon Roll; NHS; Regents Schlrshp Wnnr 85; Area All-ST Orch 82-84; Crane Schl Music; Music.

CIANO, LINDA; Benjamin N Cardozo HS; Little Neck, NY; (Y); Key Clb; Math Clb; Orch; School Play; Im Vllybl; Cit Awd; Hon Roll; Jr NHS; NHS; Computer Clb; Awd Wnnr Artcrvd Clss Rng Essy Cntst 85.

CIANO, MIKE D; Sachem HS North; Holtsville, NY; (Y); Dance Clb; Drama Clb; 4-H; Band; Chorus; Jazz Band; Orch; School Musical; School Play; Stage Crew; Intgrtd Thtr Arts Gftd & Tlntd 85; Music.

CIAPPINA, ANGELA; John Dewey HS; Brooklyn, NY; (Y); JA; Teachers Aide; Yrbk Stf; Off Jr Cls; Off Sr Cls; St John U; Med.

CIARDULLO, AMY C; St Barnabas HS; Yonkers, NY; (Y); 2/143; Library Aide; Office Aide; High Hon Roll; Hon Roll; Jr NHS; NHS; Itallian Hon Soc 83-84; Schlrshp Iona & Manhatten Colls 85; 3rd Plz Essay Cont 82; Iona Coll; Bus.

CIARDULLO, JOHN; Valley Central HS; Walden, NY; (Y); 6/300; Church Yth Grp; Math Tm; Band; Trs Stu Cncl; High Hon Roll; NHS; Spanish NHS; Rensslr Mdl Math & Sci 84-85; Hghts Math Avg; Comp Sci.

CIARFELLA, LISA M; Lockport SR HS; Lockport, NY; (Y); Camera Clb; Cmnty Wkr; French Clb; Intnl Clb; JA; Nwsp Rptr; JV Vllybl.

CIARLONE, KEVIN M; La Salle Inst; Troy, NY; (Y); Off ROTC; Ski Clb; Rep Soph Cls; NY ST Regents Scholarship 85; Hudson Valley; Psychologist.

CIAVARRI, NANCY; Nazareth Acad; Rochester, NY; (Y); 7/165; Cmnty Wkr; Math Clb; Ski Clb; Varsity Clb; Rep Jr Cls; Var Bsktbl; Var Sftbl; High Hon Roll; NHS; Eng Awd 85; Ntl Merit PSAT Recgntn 85.

CIBELLI, MARIO; Minisink Valley HS; Middletown, NY; (Y); Math Tm; Ski Clb; Rep Stu Cncl; JV Bsktbl; JV Var Socr; Var High Hon Roll; Var Hon Roll; NHS; Bus.

CIBULSKY, JEANNE M; Johnson City SR HS; Johnson City, NY; (Y); 12/212; Sec Pres Key Clb; Latin Clb; Ski Clb; Rep Hst Stu Cncl; Var L Cheerleading; Var L Fld Hcky; Var L Tennis; Var L Trk; Hon Roll; Pres NHS; Yth Salute Jrs; Acad Achvt; Syracuse U; Math.

CICCARELLA, JOE; Frontier SR HS; Lakeview, NY; (S); JA; Ski Clb; Spanish Clb; Varsity Clb; Var Ftbl; Hon Roll; NHS; GMI; Mech Engrng.

CICCARELLA, JOSEPH; Frontier SR HS; Lakeview, NY; (Y); JA; Ski Clb; Spanish Clb; Varsity Clb; Nwsp Stf; Var Ftbl; Var Golf; JV Trk; Hon Roll; NHS; Mechanical Engrng.

CICCARELLA, MARK; Maryvale SR HS; Depew, NY; (Y); Am Leg Boys St; Cmnty Wkr; French Clb; JA; Leo Clb; Library Aide; Mrchg Band; Vllybl; High Hon Roll; NHS; Acctg.

CICCARELLI, THERESA; Queen Of The Rosary Acad; Plainview, NY; (S); 5/44; Church Yth Grp; VP Math Clb; Church Choir; Yrbk Stf; Rep Soph Cls; Rep Jr Cls; JV Cheerleading; Im Sftbl; High Hon Roll; Hon Roll; Notre Dame; Engr.

CICCHILLO, RICHARD; W C Mepham HS; N Bellmore, NY; (Y); 2/385; Debate Tm; Acpl Chr; Church Choir; Ntl Merit SF; Sal; Am Leg Boys St; Boy Scts; French Clb; Quiz Bowl; Madrigals; All-State Mixed Chorus 84; Intl Rltns.

CICCI, JOSEPH; Fayetteville-Manlius HS; Fayetteville, NY; (Y); JV Var Bsbl; JV Var Ftbl; Hon Roll; NYS Regnts Schlrshp 84-85; Hobart Coll Geneva NY.

CICCIA, TINA; E Islip HS; E Islip, NY; (Y); Chess Clb; Girl Scts; Band.

CICCIMARRA, PAULA J; Westlake HS; Thornwood, NY; (Y); 11/154; Church Yth Grp; Ed Yrbk Stf; Stu Cncl; High Hon Roll; NHS; Italn Natl Hnr Socty 82-85; NY ST Regnts Schlrshp Wnnr 85; Siena; Lib Arts.

CICCONE, ROSA; Preston HS; Bronx, NY; (S); 4/76; Drama Clb; School Play; Stage Crew; Trs Sr Cls; Twrlr; NHS; Bus.

CICHANOWICZ, SARA; Mattituck HS; Cutchogue, NY; (Y); 14/118; French Clb; Pres German Clb; JV Var Fld Hcky; Hon Roll; NHS; Church Yth Grp; Cmnty Wkr; 4-H; JV Sftbl; Excel German 83; Delta Epsilon Phi German Ntl Hnr Soc 84; Cert Merit Frnch 85; Mrktng.

CICHELLO, MIKE; Weedsport Central HS; Weedsport, NY; (Y); 1/100; Yrbk Stf; VP Frsh Cls; Pres Soph Cls; Pres Jr Cls; Pres Sr Cls; L Ftbl; L Swmmng; High Hon Roll; NHS; Boy Scts; RPI Math, Aci Awd, W F Lampman Frnch Awd 85.

CICHON, MARIE; Mount Mercy Acad; Buffalo, NY; (Y); Cmnty Wkr; Yrbk Stf; Villa Maria; Comm Art.

CICHOSKI, JILL; Newburgh Free Acad; Newburgh, NY; (Y); Art Clb; Library Aide; Rgnts NYS Schlrshp 85; Philadelphia Coll Of Art; Art.

CICIOLA, DAWN M; Maria Regina HS; Bronx, NY; (Y); Key Clb; Church Choir; School Play; Nwsp Rptr; Rep Jr Cls; Stu Cncl; Hon Roll; Regnts Schlrshp 84-85; Schl Svc Awd; Hnrs Roll; St Bonaventure U; Prelaw.

CIECHANOWICZ, LISA S; Walt Whitman HS; South Huntington, NY; (Y); 82/625; Hon Roll; Jr NHS; Ntl Merit Schol; Outstndng Bus Stu Awd 82; Farmingdale Coll Sci Fair Hnrb Mntn 82; NY ST U Albany; Accntng.

CIECZKA, DIANE; Villa Maria Acad; Cheektowaga, NY; (Y); Computer Clb; French Clb; Yrbk Stf; Fll Schlrshp To VHA 82; Engr.

CIEHOMSKI, TODD; Kenmore East HS; Buffalo, NY; (Y); Varsity Clb; Variety Show; Bsbl; Ftbl; Ice Hcky; Wt Lftg; U Of Bufalo; Law.

CIERI, CINDY; Niagara Catholic HS; Niagara Falls, NY; (Y); 3/75; French Clb; Hosp Aide; Key Clb; Yrbk Stf; Var Capt Bowling; French Hon Soc; High Hon Roll; NHS; Niagara U; Nrs.

CIERVO, ALFONSO; Sewanhaka HS; Elmont, NY; (Y); 7/368; Math Clb; Chorus; School Musical; School Play; Crs Cntry; Socr; Trk; Cit Awd; High Hon Roll; NHS; March Dimes Hlth Awd 85; Math Dept Awd 85; Town Hempstead Citation 85; Stony Brook; Bio.

CIESLA, LYNN; Lackawanna HS; Lackawanna, NY; (Y); Am Leg Aux Girls St; Camp Fr Inc; Cmnty Wkr; FHA; Girl Scts; Hosp Aide; Radio Clb; Band; Yrbk Stf; High Hon Roll; Amer Awd 80; Miss United Tngr Fnlst 84.

CIESLAK, LYNN; St Marys HS; Cheektowaga, NY; (S); 1/205; Hosp Aide; Science Clb; Ski Clb; High Hon Roll; NHS; Awd Achvt Bio 84; Awd Achvt Engl 84; Awd Cert Achvt Music Recital 83; ST U Of NY; Pre-Med.

CIESLAK, MICHAEL; St Marys HS; Cheektowaga, NY; (S); 8/203; JV Bsbl; Var JV Bsktbl; High Hon Roll; Most Dedicated Player Awd Basbl 83; SUNY Buffalo; Biological.

CIESLEWITZ, STANLEY; Rome Free Acad; Rome, NY; (Y); Im Bsbl; Im Bsktbl; Var Bowling; Var Golf; Im Sftbl; Im Vllybl; Im Wt Lftg; Hon Roll; NHS; CPA.

CIFELLI, SCOTT; Alexander Central HS; Alexander, NY; (Y); Boy Scts; Math Clb; Ski Clb; Band; Concert Band; Jazz Band; Bsktbl; Tennis; Hon Roll; NHS; RIT; Mechncl Engrng.

CIFERRI, KIM; Pelham Memorial HS; Pelham, NY; (Y); Cmnty Wkr; Drama Clb; PAVAS; Band; Chorus; School Musical; Variety Show; Sftbl; Twrlr; Excllrtd Math Cours.

CIFONE, CHRISTINE; Glens Falls HS; Glen Falls, NY; (Y); AFS; Girl Scts; Ski Clb; Orch; Crs Cntry; Var Trk; High Hon Roll; Fashion Dsgn.

CIFUENTES, PATRICIA; Smithtown H S West; Smithtown, NY; (Y); Hosp Aide; Spanish Clb; Chorus; Stage Crew; Hon Roll; Spanish NHS; Bus Admin.

CILENTO, BEN; The Knox Schl; Miami Bch, FL; (Y); Computer Clb; FBLA; Math Tm; Spanish Clb; Varsity Clb; Yrbk Stf; Bsbl; Crs Cntry; Ftbl; Lcrss; 3rd-NY ST Wrstlng Chmp 85; Schlrshp-Trinity Coll 85; 1st Pl JR Orange Bowl Wrstlng Tourn 83; Trinity Coll; Ped-Med.

CILUFFO, DIANNE; Nazareth Acad; Rochester, NY; (Y); Church Yth Grp; Cmnty Wkr; Dance Clb; Exploring; French Clb; School Musical; Rep Jr Cls; Hon Roll; Boy Scts; Office Aide; 4 Awds Frnch; Danc Awds 83-85; Nrsng.

CIMASZEWSKI, GLORIA; Queen Of The Rosary Acad; Lindenhurst, NY; (S); 1/44; Church Yth Grp; Dance Clb; Math Clb; Yrbk Stf; High Hon Roll; NHS; NEDT Awd.

CIMATO, JASON; Lindenhurst HS; Lindenhurst, NY; (Y); Chess Clb; German Clb; Science Clb; Var L Bowling; Hon Roll; NHS; Bsktbl; Ntl Frgn Lang Hnr Soc German 83-84; Vet.

CIMBRICZ, JOHN R; Salamanca Central HS; Killbuck, NY; (Y); French Clb; Model UN; JV Bsbl; Var L Bsktbl; Im Socr; Var L Trk; Mst Imvprvd Bsktbl 85; Bus Adm.

CIMINELLI, SUZANNE; Floral Park Memorial JR SR HS; Bellerose, NY; (Y); Art Clb; Cmnty Wkr; Trs Dance Clb; Red Cross Aide; Variety Show; High Hon Roll; Hon Roll; Prfct Atten Awd; Hofstra U; Elem Educ.

CIMINI, DENISE; Sachem HS; Lk Ronkokoma, NY; (Y); Band; Color Guard; Drm & Bgl; Stat Bsktbl; Katherine Gibbs Schl; Exec Sec.

CIMINO, VINCENT; Washingtonville HS; Monroe, NY; (Y); 32/297; Ski Clb; Jazz Band; Pep Band; School Musical; Symp Band; Nwsp Stf; Pres Sr Cls; Rep Stu Cncl; NHS; Pres Schlr; Marist Coll; Cmnctns.

CIMMINO, DOMENICO; Mont Pleasant HS; Schenectady, NY; (Y); Cmnty Wkr; JA; Science Clb; Rep Jr Cls; Rep Sr Cls; Bsktbl; JV Var Socr; Capt Var Tennis; French Hon Soc; Hon Roll; Syracuse U; Bus Adm.

CINER, BARBARA; Yeshiva University HS For Girls; Far Rockaway, NY; (Y); Optmtry.

CINI, RICHARD A; Garden City SR HS; Garden City, NY; (Y); 39/320; Aud/Vis; French Clb; Political Wkr; Yrbk Bus Mgr; Rep Soph Cls; Rep Stu Cncl; Cit Awd; High Hon Roll; Ntl Jr Hnr Soc; St Johns Schlstc Exc Schlrshp 85; St Johns Comptv Schlrshp; St Johns U; Bkng.

CINIGLIO, MARIA; Christ The King Regional HS; Middle Village, NY; (Y); 3/385; Church Yth Grp; JA; High Hon Roll; Hon Roll; Cert Achvt Italian 84; Pace U; Bus.

CINITIEMPO, MARIA; St Catharine Acad; Bronx, NY; (Y); Dance Clb; Chorus; Church Choir; Hon Roll; NHS; Rgnts Schlrshp 85; Volunteer Svc 83; Fordham U; Frgn Lang.

CINQUE, TERESA ANN; Miller Place HS; Miller Place, NY; (Y); Aud/Vis; Church Yth Grp; Dance Clb; Sec FBLA; Varsity Clb; Nwsp Sprt Ed; Yrbk Stf; Var Bsktbl; Var Capt Vllybl; Hon Roll; Jrnlsm Awd 85; Bus Awd 85; Miller Pl Prnt Tchrs Org Schlrshp 85; Lemoyne Coll; Bus Admin.

CINQUEMANI, KELLY; Central Islip HS; Central Islip, NY; (Y); Church Yth Grp; Math Clb; Nwsp Rptr; Rep Jr Cls; Stat Sftbl; Var Swmmng; Hon Roll; NHS; NEDT Awd; Law.

CINTRON, CORINE; Grace Dodge V HS; Bronx, NY; (Y); 35/439; Hosp Aide; Teachers Aide; Sec Frsh Cls; Prfct Atten Awd; Hnr In Math, Global Hstry & Gen Sci 83; Nrsng.

CINTRON, NORMA Y; Jane Addams Vocational HS; Bronx, NY; (Y); 1/280; Church Yth Grp; Cmnty Wkr; Teachers Aide; Orch; Nwsp Stf; Yrbk Stf; High Hon Roll; Val; UFT Schlrshp 85; Regents 85; Alexander Medal 85; Mrymnt Trytwn Coll; Librl Arts.

CIOCH, LORETTA; Frankfort-Schuyler HS; Frankfort, NY; (S); Church Yth Grp; Cmnty Wkr; Hosp Aide; Library Aide; Office Aide; Spanish Clb; Chorus; High Hon Roll; Hon Roll; NHS; Nrs.

CIOFFI, ROBERT; Groton HS; Yonkers, NY; (Y); Nwsp Ed-Chief; Lit Mag; Var Crs Cntry; JV Ftbl; Var Lcrss; CC Awd; High Hon Roll; Hon Roll; NHS; Comp Sci.

CIOFFI, TERESA MARIE; Bishop Kearney HS; Brooklyn, NY; (Y); Church Yth Grp; Hosp Aide; VP JA; Service Clb; Spanish Clb; Rep Sr Cls; Capt Bowling; Hon Roll; NHS; High Series Bowling Trophy & 1st Pl Tm Trophy 85; 1st Hnrs For Reportcard 84-85; Pace U; Accntng.

CIORCIARI, JOHN; Regis HS; Rego Park, NY; (Y); Jr Cls; Bsktbl; Hon Roll; Ntl Merit Ltr; SAR Awd; Order Of The Owl 81; NY ST Regents Schlrshp 84; St Johns; Accntnt.

CIPERLEY, JAMIE LYNN; Columbia HS; Castleton, NY; (Y); VICA; Yrbk Stf; Var Mgr(s); Var Score Keeper; Ltrmn Ftbl Mgr 84-85; Vo Training LPN 84-86; JC Albany; Nrsng.

CIPOLLA, KIM; Union-Endicott HS; Endicott, NY; (Y); French Clb; Key Clb; Mathletes; Concert Band; Mrchg Band; Yrbk Stf; High Hon Roll; NHS; Var L Gym; Var L Trk; 1 Of 10 Chsen Marn Bio Stdy Prog 85; Trck All Div Tripl Jmp 85; Gftd Prog 81.

CIPOLLARI, JUDI; Columbia HS; E Greenbush, NY; (Y); 40/376; JA; Ski Clb; Nwsp Rptr; Nwsp Stf; Yrbk Stf; Lit Mag; Rep Sr Cls; Socr; High Hon Roll; NHS; Pres Acadmc Ftns Awd 85; Cum Laude Grad 85; Boston U; Fnanc.

CIPOLLONE, ROSA; Monsignor Scanlan HS; Bronx, NY; (Y); 35/265; Math Tm; Hon Roll; Prfct Atten Awd.

CIPOLLONE, TONI; Monsiggnor Scanlan HS; Bronx, NY; (Y); 1/265; Math Tm; High Hon Roll; NHS; Law.

CIPRIANO, GINA; East Syracuse Minoa HS; Minoa, NY; (Y); Science Clb; Variety Show; Var Capt Fld Hcky; JV Sftbl; Var Capt Vllybl; Hon Roll; MVP Awd Fld Hcky 84; Hnrbl Mntn All Cnty Fld Hcky 83; All Cnty 2nd Tm 84; NY St Elmers Awd Photo 2nd; Onon CC; Spec Ed.

CIPRIANO, PETER; Archbishop Stepinac HS; E White Plains, NY; (Y); 100/267; Stage Crew; Hon Roll; Rifle Clb Marksmn; Pace; Bus.

CIRANDO, LISA; Bishop Grimes HS; Syracuse, NY; (Y); Church Yth Grp; Political Wkr; Ski Clb; Band; Concert Band; Yrbk Stf; High Hon Roll; NHS; Hghst Avg Phys Sci; Sec NHS; Engl.

CIRELLA, TODD; Half Hollow Hills HS; Melville, NY; (Y); Boys Clb Am; Cmnty Wkr; Varsity Clb; Band; Concert Band; Mrchg Band; School Play; Variety Show; Rep Stu Cncl; Coach Actv; U Tampa; Hotel & Rest Mgmt.

CIRENZA, EMANUEL N; Cornwall Central HS; Cornwall, NY; (Y); 8/215; Am Leg Boys St; Variety Show; JV Capt Bsktbl; Coach Actv; Var Ftbl; Im Wt Lftg; Hon Roll; NHS; Rotary Yth Ldrshp Conf 84; Moderator Independence Day Ceremonies 84-85; Med.

CIRILLO, CHRISTINE; Cicero-North HS; Clay, NY; (S); 106/711; Vet Sci.

CIRILLO, DERON; Mount St Michael Acad; Bronx, NY; (Y); 41/270; Bsbl; NHS; Marist Coll; Comp Sci.

CIRILLO, DONNA; Cardinal Spellman HS; Bronx, NY; (Y); High Hon Roll.

CIRILLO, ELENA; Bishop Kearney HS; Brooklyn, NY; (Y); Off Frsh Cls; Off Soph Cls; Off Jr Cls; Sec Stu Cncl; NHS; Radio Brdcstr.

CIRILLO, MARGARET A; Newburgh Free Acad; Newburgh, NY; (Y); Var Crs Cntry; High Hon Roll; Hon Roll; Am Leg Aux Awd 83; Awd Excllnce Italian I & II 84 & 85; Elem Educ.

CIRINCIONE, RICHARD; St Francis Prep; Flushing, NY; (S); 69/690; Church Yth Grp; Im Bsktbl; Var Crs Cntry; Im Ftbl; Var Tennis; Var Trk; Im Vllybl; Hon Roll; NHS; Regents Schlrshp 85; Natl Hnr Roll 84; Acad All Amer 85.

CIRNIGLIARO, GIOVANNI; St Francis Prep; Flushing, NY; (S); 75/693; Hosp Aide; Ftbl; Trk; Wt Lftg; Opt Clb Awd; Bus.

CIRRITO, CHERYL; Tonawanda HS; Tonawanda, NY; (Y); 16/220; Church Yth Grp; Band; Trs Concert Band; Sec Lib Jazz Band; Mrchg Band; Orch; School Musical; Rep Stu Cncl; Rep High Hon Roll; Rep NHS; Qlty Stu 84-85; Louey Armstrong Awd 84-85; PTA Schl Scholar 84-85; Crane Schl Music Potsdam; Music.

CISCO, JENNIFER; Corning Painted Post West HS; Lindley, NY; (Y); 4-H; FBLA; Chorus; School Musical; School Play; Cit Awd; 4-H Awd; Hon Roll; NYS Beef Ambsdr 85; Bryantt & Stratton; Exec Secry.

CISEK, JULIUS; Carmel HS; Carmel, NY; (Y); Art Clb; Band; Chorus; Concert Band; Jazz Band; Mrchg Band; Rep Frsh Cls; High Hon Roll; Hon Roll; Poster Cont 1st Pl 79; Art Show 1st Prize Arch Drftng 85; Tlnt Show 1st Prize Accompnmnt 85; Syracuse U; Arch.

CISNEROS, MARY ELIZABETH C; Garden City HS; Garden City, NY; (Y); 33/320; Pres GAA; Key Clb; Sec Pep Clb; Spanish Clb; Nwsp Rptr; Lit Mag; Rep Frsh Cls; Rep Jr Cls; Var Bsktbl; JV Ice Hcky; Chrstn Sci Monitor Schlrshp 85; Amherst Coll; Bio.

CISYK, PETER; New Dorp HS; Staten Island, NY; (Y); Office Aide; Teachers Aide; Crs Cntry; Trk; Hon Roll; Ntl Merit Ltr; Bus Admin.

CISZAK, LYNN; Springville-Griffith Inst; Springville, NY; (Y); Sec Pres Church Yth Grp; Sec Trs 4-H; Co-Capt Yrbk Ed-Chief; JV Var Bsktbl; Var Powder Puff Ftbl; Timer; 4-H Awd; Hon Roll; Acctg.

CITERA, MARIA; Newfield HS; Selden, NY; (Y); Church Yth Grp; Band; Chorus; Concert Band; Mrchg Band; Sec Soph Cls; Rep Stu Cncl; JV Vllybl; Hon Roll; Sec Jr NHS; Stu Ctzn Mnth 82; Fpsych.

CITKOWITZ, CLAUDIA; Hunter Coll HS; New York, NY; (Y); Chess Clb; Pres Acpl Chr; Pres Madrigals; School Musical; Ntl Merit SF; Musicology.

CITRINITI, JOSEPH; Sauquoit Valley HS; Sauquoit, NY; (Y); Am Leg Boys St; Civic Clb; Service Clb; Hon Roll; NHS; Prfct Atten Awd; Stat Bsktbl; Im Bowling; JV Var Ftbl; Var Golf; Engr.

CIUDIN, CATALIN; Monroe HS; Webster, NY; (Y); Library Aide; Math Clb; Math Tm; Tennis; Vllybl; High Hon Roll; Hon Roll; NHS; Tennis Trphy 84; 11 Outstndng Certs 83-85; Clarkson U; Physics.

CIUFO, PAIGE; Greenville JR SR HS; Greenville, NY; (Y); Church Yth Grp; Band; Sec Frsh Cls; Rep Stu Cncl; JV Bsktbl; Excllnc Awd Music Fstvl 84.

CIVELLO, PATRICIA; Cicero-North Syracuse HS; N Syracuse, NY; (S); 33/622; Church Yth Grp; JA; Cheerleading; JV Socr; Hon Roll; JR Achvt Corp Secy 82-83; JR Prom Comm 84-85; Octagon Club 83-84; Bus.

CIVILETTO, CHRISTEN; La Salle SR HS; Niagara Falls, NY; (Y); Sec French Clb; Ed Yrbk Bus Mgr; VP Jr Cls; VP Sr Cls; Var Socr; Var Sftbl; Hon Roll; NHS; AFS; Church Yth Grp; Pre-Law.

CIVITA, FRAN C; White Plains HS; White Plains, NY; (Y); 42/545; Hosp Aide; Intnl Clb; Office Aide; Var L Cheerleading; Hon Roll; Kiwanis Awd; Pres Schlr; St Schlr; Local Schlrshp Awd 85; Princpls Awd 85; Suny; Nrsng.

CIZENSKI, DIANE; West Genesee SR HS; Syracuse, NY; (Y); Key Clb; Chorus; Color Guard; Mrchg Band; School Musical; Stage Crew; Variety Show; High Hon Roll; Hon Roll; Jr NHS; Elem Ed.

CIZMARIK, ANDRE K; Archbishop Molloy HS; Bayside, NY; (Y); 9/409; Rep Jr Cls; Var Crs Cntry; Var Trk; NHS; Ntl Merit SF; Fordham U; Law.

CLAIR, CHRYL; Waterloo SR HS; Waterloo, NY; (Y); FHA; Hon Roll; US Cerebral Palsey Awd 84-85; Awd For Getting Along W/Others 84-85; Diploma-2 Yrs In Chld Care 84-85; Cayuga Cmnty Coll; Home Ec.

CLAIRE, DEBORAH; Hornell SR HS; Hornell, NY; (S); 6/186; Var L Bsktbl; Var L Sftbl; Var Tennis; Var L Vllybl; High Hon Roll; NHS; SUNY Genesco; Acctng.

CLANCY, ALICIA; Portville Central HS; Portville, NY; (Y); FBLA; Ski Clb; Chorus; Hon Roll; Jamestown Bus Coll; Scrtrl.

CLANCY, DEBBIE J; East Meadow HS; East Meadow, NY; (S); Church Yth Grp; Girl Scts; Hosp Aide; Teachers Aide; Band; School Play; Nwsp Rptr; Crs Cntry; Trk; Hon Roll; Nrsng.

CLANCY, GERALDINE; John Jay HS; Katonah, NY; (Y); Chorus; Capt Tennis; Cit Awd; High Hon Roll; Trs NHS; Colgate U; Math.

CLANCY, KYLE; Mount Mercy Acad; Buffalo, NY; (Y); 2/200; Church Yth Grp; Cmnty Wkr; French Clb; Im Tennis; Hon Roll; 3rd Pl WNY Forgn Lang Fair Frnch 85; 1st Pl Easter Seals Vllybl Tourn 85; CYO VP 84-85; Canisius Coll; Engl.

CLANCY, LAUREN A; Carle Place HS; Westbury, NY; (Y); 23/116; Var L Cheerleading; Var Capt Fld Hcky; Var L Lcrss; Ski Clb; Rep Soph Cls; Boston U; Psychology.

CLANCY, MICHELE A; Oriskany HS; Oriskany, NY; (Y); 9/92; Varsity Clb; Nwsp Rptr; Var Capt Bsktbl; Var Capt Socr; Var Capt Trk; High Hon Roll; Jr NHS; NHS; Opt Clb Awd; Rgnts Schlrshp 85; Grtr Rltrs Yth Recog Day Hnr 85; Oswego ST; Comp Sci.

CLANCY, SHEILA A; Catholic Central HS; Menands, NY; (Y); 64/203; Church Yth Grp; German Clb; Math Clb; Yrbk Stf; Ntl Merit Ltr; Hudson Vlly CC; Trvl.

CLANCY, WILLIAM M; Salesian HS; Bronx, NY; (Y); 16/87; Am Leg Boys St; Boy Scts; Cmnty Wkr; Var L Swmmng; Pres Jr Vlntr Amblnc Crps 85-86; Slctd Fr Frdms Fndtn Yth Ldrshp Conf 85; NY ST Am Lgn Axlry Awd 85; Cmmrcl Plt.

CLARCQ, MATTHEW; Eastridge HS; Rochester, NY; (Y); 19/236; Boy Scts; Concert Band; Jazz Band; Mrchg Band; School Musical; Rep Stu Cncl; High Hon Roll; Hon Roll; NHS; Prfct Atten Awd; Teachng.

CLARE, CHRISTOPHER R; Northport HS; Northport, NY; (Y); 25/664; Boy Scts; Church Yth Grp; Computer Clb; Mathletes; Science Clb; Orch; Yrbk Stf; Hon Roll; Jr NHS; Lion Awd; Cooper Union; Arch.

CLAREY, MARELIZABETH; Westmoreland SR HS; Whitesboro, NY; (Y); Camera Clb; Girl Scts; Pep Clb; Band; Chorus; Church Choir; Color Guard; Nwsp Rptr; Nwsp Stf; Rep Frsh Cls; Utica Beauty Schl; Csmtlgst.

CLAREY, PAT; Chautaugua Central Schl; Mayville, NY; (Y); Scholastic Bowl; Ski Clb; Trs Soph Cls; Trs Jr Cls; Golf; High Hon Roll; Hon Roll; Jr NHS; Pre-Law.

CLARIDGE, EMILY; Fayetteville-Manlius HS; Manlius, NY; (Y); Model UN; PAVAS; Orch; Nwsp Rptr; Nwsp Stf; Hon Roll; NHS; U S Pony Clb Natl Dressg & Combnd Traing Tms 84-85; Cornell U; Sci.

CLARK, ANDRE; St Raymonds H S For Boys; Bronx, NY; (Y); 56/182; CAP; Drill Tm; Var Crs Cntry; Im Sftbl; Var Trk; 2nd Hnrs 83; Vrsty Ltr Trck-Crss Cntry 84-85; Militry.

CLARK, ANDREA; Palmyra-Macedon HS; Walworth, NY; (Y); Library Aide; Chorus; Church Choir; Yrbk Stf; Off Frsh Cls; Off Soph Cls; Stu Cncl; Interact; Wrestlerette; Press Clb; Travel.

CLARK, ANN; Canastota HS; Canastota, NY; (Y); Camera Clb; Dance Clb; Drama Clb; GAA; Cheerleading; Fld Hcky; Sftbl; Vllybl; Hon Roll; Spch Thrpy.

CLARK, BARBARA; Notre Dame HS; Batavia, NY; (S); 4/90; Drama Clb; Ski Clb; School Play; Sec Stu Cncl; Var JV Cheerleading; Var JV Sftbl; High Hon Roll; Prfct Atten Awd; Hghst Avg Spnsh 83-84; Perfct Attend Awd 82-83; Rochester Inst Tech; Comp Engr.

CLARK, BEVERLY; Kensington HS; Buffalo, NY; (Y); Hon Roll; Sec.

CLARK, CHRISTINE; Our Lady Of Mercy Acad; Northport, NY; (Y); Pres Computer Clb; Hosp Aide; Office Aide; Yrbk Stf; Var Badmtn; JV Mgr(s); Var Score Keeper; JV Sftbl; Im Vllybl; Hon Roll; Spnsh Awd 83; U Of Scranton; Math.

CLARK, DARBY A; Sachem HS North; Holtsville, NY; (Y); 213/1508; Church Yth Grp; Hosp Aide; Intnl Clb; Band; Chorus; ST Officer Rainbow Girls 85; Cherub Choir Dir; Nrsng.

CLARK, DEBBIE; Notre Dame HS; Le Roy, NY; (S); Ski Clb; JV Var Cheerleading; Var Socr; JV Sftbl; JV Var Vllybl; Hon Roll; NHS; Church Yth Grp; Drama Clb; 4-H; Stu Senate 83; Elem Educ.

CLARK, DIANE; Walton HS; Bronx, NY; (Y).

CLARK, ELAINE; Avon Central School; Avon, NY; (Y); 6/96; French Clb; Science Clb; Spanish Clb; Band; JV Capt Bsktbl; JV Var Socr; JV Var Sftbl; High Hon Roll; Jr NHS; NHS; Sci.

CLARK, ERIC; Gloversville HS; Gloversville, NY; (Y); 9/300; AFS; Am Leg Boys St; Math Tm; Band; Drm & Bgl; Jazz Band; Mrchg Band; School Musical; Variety Show; High Hon Roll; Area All ST Orchstra & Band 84-85.

CLARK, GREG; Skaneateles Central HS; Skaneateies, NY; (S); Var L Socr; Var L Tennis; Union Coll; Pre-Law.

CLARK, JENNIFER; Broadalhin Central HS; Broadalbin, NY; (Y); 15/74; French Clb; Office Aide; Chorus; Church Choir; Concert Band; Mrchg Band; Symp Band; Cheerleading; Socr; Jr NHS; Hgh Hnr Rll 82-83; Ntl Hnr Soc 85; Prfct Atten 82-85; Fulton-Montgomery CC.

CLARK, JENNIFER; Whitestone Acad; Beechhurst, NY; (S); Teachers Aide; Chorus; Church Choir; Hon Roll; Hnr In English & Sci 82-83; Trinity Coll; Bus Mngmnt.

CLARK, KATHLEEN; North Shore HS; Glen Head, NY; (Y); 6/220; Library Aide; Mathletes; Science Clb; Hon Roll; Jr NHS; NHS; Accptnc To Colubias Sci Hnrs Prog 84-85; Hnrbl Mntn In Great Amer Smoke-Out Essay Cont 83-84; Cornell; Vet Med.

CLARK, KATHY; Andover Central Schl; Andover, NY; (S); 6/30; Church Yth Grp; Chorus; Mrchg Band; School Play; Yrbk Stf; Socr; Sftbl; Vllybl; DAR Awd; Hon Roll; Hall Fame Cls 85; Brockport; Phy Ed.

CLARK, KELLY; Lockport SR HS; Lockport, NY; (Y); Drama Clb; Hosp Aide; Intnl Clb; JA; Chorus; Nwsp Rptr; Jr Cls; Hon Roll; Jr NHS; NHS; Dr.

CLARK, KIMBERLY; Pulaski JR SR HS; Pulaski, NY; (S); 3/99; GAA; Band; Chorus; Yrbk Phtg; Bsktbl; Socr; Sftbl; High Hon Roll; NHS; Ithaca Coll; PHYS Ther.

CLARK, KRISTEN; Auburn HS; Auburn, NY; (Y); Acpl Chr; Chorus; Church Choir; Color Guard; Madrigals; Mrchg Band; School Musical; Swing Chorus; High Hon Roll; NHS.

CLARK, KRISTINE; Elmira Free Acad; Elmira, NY; (Y); AFS; Key Clb; Ski Clb; Trs Spanish Clb; Varsity Clb; JV Cheerleading; Var L Tennis; High Hon Roll; Hon Roll; Jr NHS; Accntng.

CLARK, LEE; Gouverneur Central HS; Gouverneur, NY; (Y); Computer Clb; Pres 4-H; Pres FFA; JV Bsktbl; 4-H Awd; Hon Roll; Jr NHS; NHS; NY ST Star Frmr Awd In FFA 85; Agrcltr.

CLARK, LISA; Binghamton HS; Binghamton, NY; (Y); Camera Clb; Cmnty Wkr; GAA; Key Clb; Pep Clb; PAVAS; Chorus; Nwsp Phtg; Nwsp Stf; Yrbk Phtg; Nwspr Wrkshp Awd 85; Phtgrphy.

CLARK, MARCY; Elmira Free Acad; Elmira, NY; (Y); Church Yth Grp; JA; Chorus; Hon Roll; Corning CC; Bus Exectv.

CLARK, MARIBETH; John H Glenn HS; Greenlawn, NY; (Y); Church Yth Grp; Pep Clb; Teachers Aide; Varsity Clb; Chorus; Variety Show; Yrbk Phtg; Yrbk Rptr; Rep Frsh Cls; Rep Soph Cls; Psych.

CLARK, MATTHEW; Hudson HS; Hudson, NY; (Y); Speech Tm; Ski Clb; Stage Crew; Var JV Ftbl; Hon Roll; Bus Mngmnt.

CLARK, MELODY IRENE; Hutchinson Central Tech HS; Buffalo, NY; (Y); Temple Yth Grp; Chorus; Church Choir; Hon Roll; Medaille Coll; Comm.

CLARK, PATRICK J; Wayne Central HS; Macedon, NY; (Y); 54/205; Boy Scts; Math Tm; Ski Clb; Band; Jazz Band; School Musical; Var Capt Crs Cntry; JV Var Trk; Hon Roll; NHS; NYS Rgnts Schlrshp 85; Rochester Inst/Tech; Mech Engr.

CLARK, REBECCA; Cardinal Mooney HS; Rochester, NY; (Y); Band; Concert Band; Mrchg Band; Rep Frsh Cls; Var Swmmng; Stu SADD VP 84-85.

CLARK, REGINA; Spring Valley HS; Monsey, NY; (Y); Camera Clb; Church Yth Grp; Drama Clb; Girl Scts; Ski Clb; Chorus; School Play; Yrbk Stf; Srv Awd 83.

CLARK, RICK; Vestal SR HS; Vestal, NY; (Y); Bsbl; JV Bowling; Hon Roll; Broome CC; Acctnt.

CLARK, RICKY; G Ray Bodley HS; Fulton, NY; (Y); Chess Clb; Red Cross Aide; Bsbl; Ftbl; Wt Lftg; Wrstlng; U S Air Force; Elctrcn.

CLARK, SHARON E; Port Byron Central HS; Auburn, NY; (Y); 13/84; Girl Scts; Yrbk Phtg; Var JV Bsktbl; Var JV Fld Hcky; Var JV Sftbl; Hon Roll; NYS Regents Schlrshp 85; Jr Prom Queen 84; Am HS Athl 85; Cayuga CC; Elect Engrng.

CLARK, STEPHEN; St Francis Prep; Rockaway Bch, NY; (Y); Computer Clb; Band; Med.

CLARK, SUSAN; Franklin Acad; Constable, NY; (Y); 4-H; Hosp Aide; Ski Clb; Spanish Clb; Crs Cntry; Swmmng; Hon Roll; Elem Educ.

CLARK, THERESA; Gloversville HS; Johnstown, NY; (Y); 25/250; Teachers Aide; Band; Church Choir; Concert Band; Crs Cntry; Powder Puff Ftbl; Capt Trk; NHS; Mst Dedctd Trk 84; Prfct Trk Atten 84; Intl Friendshp Clb 81-85; Fulton Montgomery CC; Mth.

CLARK, TIA; Wantagh HS; Seaford, NY; (Y); Cmnty Wkr; Dance Clb; Girl Scts; JA; Concert Band; Rep Frsh Cls; JV Badmtn; Co-Capt Pom Pon; Var Trk; Outstndg Typst Cert 83-84; UCLA; Stk Brkr.

CLARK, TONYA; Murry Beratrawm HS; Rockaway Park, NY; (Y); Teachers Aide; Band; Mgr Trk; York Coll; Acctng.

CLARK, WENDI; Greenport HS; Greenport, NY; (Y); 7/56; Mathletes; Spanish Clb; School Musical; Nwsp Phtg; Yrbk Ed-Chief; Yrbk Phtg; Fld Hcky; Sftbl; High Hon Roll; Jr NHS; Strawberry Qn 85; Stu Of Mnth 85; Maire Worrell Awd 85; Greensboro Coll NC; Mth.

CLARK, WILLIAM; Elmira Southside HS; Elmira, NY; (Y); 5/333; Am Leg Boys St; Drama Clb; French Clb; VP Key Clb; Latin Clb; Quiz Bowl; Trs Radio Clb; Scholastic Bowl; Varsity Clb; School Musical; RIT Almn Schlrshp; Cheming Fndtn Harvey O Hutchinson Schlrshp; Park Chch Schlrshps; Rochester Inst Of Tech; Comp Sc.

CLARKE, ALISON; Holy Trinity HS; East Meadow, NY; (Y); 9/320; Math Clb; Stu Cncl; Var Badmtn; JV Capt Cheerleading; JV Gym; High Hon Roll; NHS; Ntl Merit Ltr; NEDT Awd; Hofstra; Fnnc.

CLARKE, AMY; Earl L Vandermeulen HS; Mt Sinai, NY; (Y); FBLA; Band; Mrchg Band; Yrbk Stf; Rep Frsh Cls; Rep Soph Cls; Stu Cncl; Cheerleading; Vllybl; High Hon Roll; Mst Outstndng Engl Stdnt; Stdnt Cncl Svc Awd; Bus.

CLARKE, BRENNA; Academy Of Mt St Ursula; Bronx, NY; (Y); Church Yth Grp; Cmnty Wkr; Drama Clb; Hosp Aide.

CLARKE, BROCKWAY; Little Falls JR SR HS; Little Falls, NY; (S); 15/120; Drama Clb; Spanish Clb; Varsity Clb; Nwsp Sprt Ed; Nwsp Stf; Lit Mag; Var Socr; Var Trk; Hon Roll; Great Books Pgm; Law.

CLARKE, CHARMAINE; Yonkers HS; Yonkers, NY; (Y); Nwsp Rptr; Nwsp Stf; Yrbk Stf; Rep Frsh Cls; Rep Soph Cls; Rep Jr Cls; Rep Sr Cls; Rep Stu Cncl; Var Capt Trk; Var Twrlr; Acad Achvt Awd 84-85; Stony Brook; Lib Arts.

CLARKE, CHRISTINA; Springfield Gardens HS; Springfield Gds, NY; (Y); 76/508; Camera Clb; Office Aide; Spanish Clb; Var L Tennis; Var L Vllybl; Prfct Atten Awd; Acad Awd 83; Elms Coll; Law.

CLARKE, DAVID; Alden Central HS; Elma, NY; (Y); 2/204; Am Leg Boys St; Quiz Bowl; Science Clb; Spanish Clb; High Hon Roll; Hon Roll; Lion Awd; Trs NHS; Sel To The Air Pistol JR Olympics 85; Sel To Rifle Natl Matches Camp Perry 84-85; Chem.

CLARKE, JEANNE; John F Kennedy HS; Utica, NY; (Y); 7/130; Cmnty Wkr; Hosp Aide; Yrbk Stf; Rep Stu Cncl; Fld Hcky; Cit Awd; DAR Awd; High Hon Roll; Kiwanis Awd; NHS; Carolyn Ellsworth Schlrshp 85; Daniel Goss Math Awd 85; Frank Nowak Awd Spec Ed 85; Utica Coll; Occuptnl Thrpy.

CLARKE, KARENA; Hillcrest HS; Kew Gardens, NY; (Y); FBLA; FNA; Hosp Aide; Red Cross Aide; Teachers Aide; Chorus; School Play; Gym; Sftbl; Tennis; Cert Of Merit For Art 82; Queensboro CC; Accntng.

CLARKE, KATHERINE; Greenwich Acad; Bedford, NY; (Y); Pres Art Clb; Church Yth Grp; Cmnty Wkr; Drama Clb; Hosp Aide; JA; Key Clb; Church Choir; School Musical; Nwsp Stf; Art Achvt Awd 82; Hnr Roll 84; Child Psy.

CLARKE, KELLY; Niskayuna HS; Clifton Park, NY; (Y); Hst Jr Cls; Stat Wrstlng; Hon Roll; Ntl Merit SF; NY ST Rgnts Schlrshp 85; ST U Of NY; Bus.

CLARKE, MARY; The Mary Louis Acad; Elmhurst, NY; (Y); Dance Clb; Girl Scts; Hosp Aide; Office Aide; Teachers Aide; Church Choir; Bsktbl; Bowling; Tennis.

CLARKE, MARY ANN; South Glens Falls Central HS; Wilton, NY; (Y); 5/235; Trs Pres Church Yth Grp; Key Clb; Band; Chorus; Church Choir; Nwsp Stf; Trs Soph Cls; Trs Jr Cls; Trs Sr Cls; Rep Stu Cncl; Glens Falls Found Schlrshp, Booster Clb Awd, Gurn Springs United Meth Chrch Schlrshp 85; Siena Coll; Dent.

CLARKE, NYLPHIA; Mount Vernon HS; Mount Vernon, NY; (Y); Girl Scts; Red Cross Aide; Band; Chorus; Church Choir; Color Guard; Concert Band; Mrchg Band; School Musical; High Hon Roll; Regnts Schlrshp 85; Sci.

CLARKE, PETER; Cicero North Syracuse HS; N Syracuse, NY; (S); #42 In Class; German Clb; Letterman Clb; Varsity Clb; Stu Cncl; Var JV Ftbl; Var Lcrss; Hon Roll; All Amer Athl 83; USMA; Engrng.

CLARKE, ROSEMARIE; Sacred Heart Acad; New Hyde Park, NY; (S); Sec Church Yth Grp; FTA; Math Clb; Church Choir; School Play; High Hon Roll; Hon Roll; NHS; Marketing.

CLARKE, SCOTT; Andover Central Schl; Andover, NY; (S); 2/30; Model UN; School Play; VP Jr Cls; Sec Trs Sr Cls; High Hon Roll; NHS; Val; Natl Chem Awd 84; Jim Karcanes Tina Norton Mem Awd 84; Am Hist Awd 84; Rochester Inst Tech; Comp Sci.

CLARKE, SUZANNE D; A Philip Randolph Campus HS; New York, NY; (Y); 1/154; Art Clb; Chess Clb; Computer Clb; Dance Clb; Debate Tm; Math Clb; Math Tm; Science Clb; Teachers Aide; Band; UFT Schlrshp 85; Minerva Awd 85; Congrssnl Cert Merit 85; NY U; Bio.

CLARMAN, CRUZ; James Monroe HS; Bronx, NY; (Y); Computer Clb; JA; Latin Clb; Math Tm; Teachers Aide; Jr Cls; Bsktbl; Swmmng; Hon Roll; Svc Awd 85; Arista Hnry Awd 85; CUNY Tech; Engrng.

CLARRETT, SHARON; Queen Of The Rosary Acad; Amityville, NY; (S); Math Clb; Spanish Clb; Trs Frsh Cls; Hon Roll; NHS; Pub Spkng Clb 84-85; Cndy Strpr 82-84; Recruit Clb 82-84; Psych.

CLARY, DENISE J; John C Birdlebough HS; Phoenix, NY; (Y); 7/200; 4-H; French Clb; Latin Clb; Model UN; Pres Jr Cls; Off Stu Cncl; Capt L Socr; L Trk; High Hon Roll; NHS; Clarkson U; Elect.

CLARY, JAMES; Cato-Meridian HS; Cato, NY; (Y); 3/70; Am Leg Boys St; Church Yth Grp; French Clb; Science Clb; Yrbk Stf; Var Bsktbl; Var Ftbl; High Hon Roll; NHS; Color Guard; Hon Men Ftbl Lg 83; Mech Engrng.

CLAUSEN, CAROLYN; John Jay HS; Hopewell Jct, NY; (Y); Dance Clb; Drama Clb; Stage Crew; Hon Roll; Bus.

CLAUSEN, KEITH; Fayetteville-Manlius HS; Manlius, NY; (Y); Trs Church Yth Grp; Rep Frsh Cls; Bsbl; Crs Cntry; JV Mgr(s); JV Socr; Trk; CA ST Poly U; Lndscp.

CLAUSON, LISA; Woodlands HS; White Plains, NY; (Y); Church Yth Grp; Girl Scts; Key Clb; Varsity Clb; Yrbk Rptr; Off Frsh Cls; Off Jr Cls; JV Fld Hcky; JV Var Socr; Sec Jr NHS; Pol Sci.

CLAUSON, MARK S; Odessa-Montour HS; Alpine, NY; (Y); Am Leg Boys St; Var JV Bsbl; Var JV Bsktbl; JV Var Ftbl; Hon Roll; Cobbleskill; Phys Educ.

CLAVELL, CARLOS M; Samuel Gompers Vocational Tech HS; Bronx, NY; (Y); High Hon Roll; NHS; Ntl Merit Ltr; Regents Schlrshp 85; Elec Engrng.

CLAVERIA, MARY ANN F; The Mary Louis Acad; Jamaica, NY; (Y); Church Yth Grp; Office Aide; Speech Tm; Nwsp Stf; Sec Frsh Cls; Sec Soph Cls; Stonybrook U; Med.

CLAXTON, COLLEEN; Grace H Dodge HS; Bronx, NY; (Y); 6/367; Debate Tm; Library Aide; Office Aide; Quiz Bowl; Scholastic Bowl; Teachers Aide; Chorus; Church Choir; Gym; Score Keeper; Untd Fed Tchrs Schlrshp 85; Regnts Schlrshp 85; Pace U White Plains; Accntg.

CLAY, JOSHUA H; Laurens Central HS; Otego, NY; (Y); 3/40; Am Leg Boys St; Drama Clb; French Clb; Key Clb; Ski Clb; Varsity Clb; School Play; Pres Stu Cncl; JV Bsktbl; Var Crs Cntry; Vet Med.

CLEARY, CYNTHIA M; Holy Trinity HS; Hicksville, NY; (S); Math Clb; Ski Clb; Stage Crew; Stu Cncl; Var Cheerleading; Capt Gym; High Hon Roll; NHS; Bus.

CLEARY, LINDA; The Mary Louis Acad; Bayside, NY; (Y); Art Clb; Red Cross Aide; Service Clb; Teachers Aide; Yrbk Stf; High Hon Roll; NHS; NEDT Awd; Cmnty Wkr; Bowling; Itln Clb 83-86; Amer Assn Tchrs Itln Awd 84; Alg I Cert Hnr 83; Math.

CLEARY, LISA; De Sales Catholic HS; Lockport, NY; (S); 3/45; Nwsp Stf; Gym; DAR Awd; Hon Roll; VP NHS; NEDT Awd.

CLEARY, PATRICIA; Woorheesville JR SR HS; Altamont, NY; (Y); Church Yth Grp; Drama Clb; 4-H; Intnl Clb; Key Clb; Spanish Clb; Drm Mjr(t); Yrbk Phtg; Stu Cncl; 4-H Awd; 4-H VP Hon Awd 83; Equine Awd 84; Bus Mngmnt.

CLEERE, STEPHANIE; Waterloo SR HS; Waterloo, NY; (Y); 28/161; FTA; Pep Clb; Chorus; Yrbk Stf; Rep Jr Cls; Var Trk; Mgr Vllybl; Suny Coll At Cortland; Pol Sci.

CLELAND, TARA; Notre Dame/Bishop Gibbons HS; Schenectady, NY; (S); 20/108; Church Yth Grp; GAA; Girl Scts; Hosp Aide; Y-Teens; Yrbk Stf; Crs Cntry; High Hon Roll; NHS; Civil Engr.

CLEMENS, MIKE P; Copiague HS; Copiague, NY; (Y); 32/350; Am Leg Boys St; Church Yth Grp; Drama Clb; French Clb; Political Wkr; School Musical; School Play; Var L Bsbl; Cit Awd; Suffolk Cnty All Leag Bsbl 85; Humanities Awd 85; Daniel B O Connel Memrl Awd-Outstndng Bsbl; Siena-Loudenville NY; Sci.

CLEMENZ, ANNE; East Hampton HS; Montauk, NY; (Y); 24/117; Girl Scts; Acpl Chr; Band; Chorus; Church Choir; Concert Band; Madrigals; Mrchg Band; School Musical; School Play; Best Actress 85; NY ST Music Fest-A Rtng 85; Suffolk Cnty Music Eductrs Assn 85; Theatre.

CLEMMER, DUANE E; Adlai E Stevenson HS; Bronx, NY; (Y); Chorus; Cit Awd; Hon Roll; Wilber Force; Law.

CLEMONS, TINA E; Pulaski JR SR HS; Pulaski, NY; (Y); 14/89; Drama Clb; GAA; Ski Clb; Band; Chorus; School Musical; Yrbk Stf; Vllybl; Hon Roll; Snow Incntv Awd 83; Bnd Awd 83-85; Daemen Coll; Physcl Therpy.

CLERICI, LISA; West Seneca East Senior HS; Cheektowaga, NY; (Y); German Clb; Stu Cncl; Var JV Sftbl; Hon Roll; JC Awd; Jr NHS; German Ntl Hnr Soc 85; Med.

CLEVELAND, BETSY; Odessa-Montour Central HS; Montour Falls, NY; (Y); 19/74; Ski Clb; Band; Pres Sr Cls; Var Capt Cheerleading; JV Sftbl; High Hon Roll; Drama Clb; Mrchg Band; School Play; Trs Frsh Cls; Albany Bus Coll Schlrshp 85; Odessa Clrcl Stff Schlrshp 85; Futur Sec Assn Awd 85; Albany Bus Coll.

CLEVELAND, WENDY; Sodus Central Schl; Sodus, NY; (Y); 3/97; Trs Science Clb; Trs Ski Clb; Teachers Aide; Var Capt Sftbl; Bausch & Lomb Sci Awd; Elks Awd; High Hon Roll; NHS; Rotary Awd; Var Capt Socr; Acadmc Schlrshp Clarkson; Sci Dept Schlrshp Clarkson; David M Richard Bio Awd; Clarkson U; Biochem.

CLIFFORD, ELIZABETH J; East HS; Rochester, NY; (Y); Am Leg Aux Girls St; Church Yth Grp; VP Pres Stu Cncl; Socr; High Hon Roll; NHS; Ntl Merit Ltr; Exploring; Yrbk Stf; Lit Mag; Rep Stud Advsry Bd 84-85; Stu Rep Budgt & Schl Envrmnt Comm 85; Dartmouth Bk Awd 85; Engl.

CLIFFORD, JERRY; West Genesee HS; Camillus, NY; (Y); Rep Frsh Cls; JV Crs Cntry; JV Socr; Hon Roll; Prfct Atten Awd.

CLIFFORD, MARY K; Mount Saint Mary Acad; Kenmore, NY; (Y); Cmnty Wkr; Service Clb; Church Yth Grp; FNA; Girl Scts; Hosp Aide; Church Choir; Variety Show; Rep Jr Cls; Hlth Assistant.

CLIFFORD, MAUREEN E; Copiague SR HS; Copiague, NY; (Y); 1/300; Nwsp Rptr; Yrbk Phtg; Yrbk Rptr; Ed Yrbk Stf; Trs Frsh Cls; Trs Soph Cls; Trs Jr Cls; Var Fld Hcky; Var Vllybl; High Hon Roll; Acctg.

CLIFFORD, NICOLE; Sachem North HS; Farmingville, NY; (Y); 215/1450; GAA; Hosp Aide; VP Soph Cls; VP Jr Cls; Stat Bsbl; Stat Bsktbl; Var Swmmng; Elem Educ.

CLIFFORD, PATTY; Cohoes HS; Cohoes, NY; (Y); 17/190; GAA; Key Clb; Math Clb; Crs Cntry; Trk; Vllybl; Hon Roll; NHS; Prfct Atten Awd; Schlrshp Awd 85; Stu Cncl Svc Awd 85; Math Awd 85; Geneseo; Acctg.

CLIFT, MICHELLE; Cathedral HS; New York, NY; (Y); 8/298; Intnl Clb; Library Aide; Nwsp Rptr; Nwsp Stf; Hon Roll; Prfct Atten Awd; JR Schlrs Prog 85; Hnbl Mntns Engl & Amer Hstry 85; Engl.

CLINA, MATTHEW J; Millbrook HS; Pleasant Valley, NY; (Y); 4/78; Pres Trs 4-H; Capt L Crs Cntry; Capt L Trk; High Hon Roll; Ntl Merit Ltr; Syracuse U; Mech Engr.

CLINE, LISA; Massena Central HS; Massena, NY; (Y); French Clb; Intnl Clb; Drm Mjr(t); Cheerleading; Twrlr; High Hon Roll; NHS; Ntl Merit Ltr; Prfct Atten Awd; Rotary Awd; Crouse Irving Mem; Nrs.

CLINE, SCOTT; Wellsville HS; Wellsville, NY; (Y); 28/130; Mrchg Band; Variety Show; Rotary Awd; Alfred ST Coll; Elec Engrng.

CLINERMAN, ANNE L; Mynderse Acad; Seneca Falls, NY; (Y); JV Var Sftbl; Var Vllybl; Bus.

CLINGER, ANGELA; Hilton Central HS; Rochester, NY; (Y); Exploring; Ski Clb; VICA; Yrbk Stf; JV Fld Hcky; High Hon Roll; Hon Roll.

CLINGER, CHERYL; Pittsford-Mendon HS; Pittsford, NY; (Y); Rep Frsh Cls; Sec Soph Cls; Sec Jr Cls; Sec Stu Cncl; Var JV Sftbl; Drama Clb; Chorus; School Musical; Var JV Fld Hcky; Powder Puff Ftbl; Elmira Coll Key Awd 85; Ldrshp Awd PTSA 83; Fclty Recog Awd 83; Cmmnctns.

CLOKE, AMY E; Notre Dame HS; Elmira, NY; (Y); 4/128; Scholastic Bowl; Nwsp Rptr; Yrbk Ed-Chief; Var L Crs Cntry; Var L Trk; Hon Roll; Ntl Merit Ltr; Regents State Schlrshp 85; Boston U; Aeronautical Engrng.

CLOKE, STEVE; Notre Dame HS; Elmira, NY; (Y); Boy Scts; Church Yth Grp; Pep Clb; Stage Crew; Ftbl; High Hon Roll; Hon Roll; Edward B Considine Schlrshp Awd 85; San Diego ST U; Small Bus Prop.

CLONTZ, KAREN; E J Wilson HS; Rochester, NY; (Y); Drama Clb; Trs Varsity Clb; Swing Chorus; VP Frsh Cls; VP Soph Cls; VP Jr Cls; VP Sr Cls; Var Capt Cheerleading; Var Capt Gym; High Hon Roll; Theatre.

CLOSE, JEAN; Berlin Central HS; Stephentown, NY; (Y); 18/63; Chorus; School Musical; Stage Crew; Ed Yrbk Sprt Ed; Cit Awd; Hon Roll; Prfct Atten Awd; STEP 82-83; Lydia Barkley Prfssnl Nrsng Memrl Awd 85; Lester T Russell Schlrshp 85; Hudson Vlly CC; Nrsng.

CLOSS, CATHERINE; Academy Of St Joseph; Kings Pk, NY; (Y); Church Yth Grp; FHA; Hosp Aide; Library Aide; Chorus; Church Choir; Hon Roll; Awd Applctn & Endeavr Sci 83-84.

CLOSS, JANET; Far Rockaway HS; Far Rockaway, NY; (Y); Band; Chorus; Drm & Bgl; School Musical; Nwsp Rptr; Yrbk Stf; Sr Cls; Swmmng; NHS; Capt Girls Swmmng Team 85-86.

CLOSS, WILLIAM P; Bainbridge-Guilford HS; Bainbridge, NY; (Y); 29/76; Yrbk Stf; French Clb; Band; Chorus; Jazz Band; Mrchg Band; Orch; Nwsp Stf; Trs Jr Cls; Regents Schlrshp 85fmost Imprvd Band 83; 3rd Pl Ntl French Cont 84; Hofotra U; Jrnlsm.

CLOTHIER, ROMIE; Parishville-Hopkinton Central Schl; Potsdam, NY; (Y); Computer Clb; Ski Clb; Art Clb; JV Bsbl; JV Var Socr; Hon Roll; Hgh Achvt, Exclnc Gym 82-83; Outstndng Stu 83-85; Sci.

CLOUGH, KIM; Guilderland Central HS; Schenectady, NY; (Y); Church Yth Grp; Pres Sec JA; Nwsp Rptr; Score Keeper; Capt Socr; Sftbl; 6th Pl Comp Litrcy Tst Cobleskll Coll 83; Achv Bus Math Schdy CC 85; SUNY Ag & Tech; Data Procsng.

CLOUSER, KIMBERLY; Niagara Wheatfield HS; Sanborn, NY; (Y); VP JA; Pres Latin Clb; Pres Band; Drm Mjr(t); School Musical; VP Stu Cncl; Var Swmmng; Capt JV Vllybl; High Hon Roll; VP NHS; Fstvl Prncss Rnnr-Up 83; Tri-M Music Hnr Soc 85; Math.

CLOW, LORI; L C Obourn HS; East Rochester, NY; (Y); 7/113; Exploring; JA; Yrbk Stf; Hon Roll; NHS; Prfct Atten Awd; Pres Schlr; Modern Lang Clb 84-85; St John Fisher Coll; Vet Med.

CLUM, KATHLEEN A; Germantown Central HS; Germantown, NY; (Y); 2/60; Am Leg Aux Girls St; Yrbk Stf; VP Soph Cls; VP Jr Cls; Cit Awd; High Hon Roll; NHS; Sal; Capt Cheerleading; NY ST Regnts Schlrshp 85; Math.

CLUM, SCOTT; Solvay HS; Syracuse, NY; (Y); Off Boy Scts; Off Exploring; Band; Chorus; Concert Band; Jazz Band; School Play; Stage Crew; Variety Show; JV Ftbl; Annapolis; Aviatn.

CLUTE, STEVEN; Vernon-Verona-Sherrill HS; Vernon, NY; (Y); Church Yth Grp; FFA; Mathletes; JV Ftbl; High Hon Roll; NHS; Law.

CO, MARY DAWN T; Vestal SR HS; Vestal, NY; (Y); 9/450; Cmnty Wkr; French Clb; Intnl Clb; Mathletes; High Hon Roll; NHS; Ntl Merit SF; Prfct Atten Awd; Cert Of Recgntn Vlntr Srv 84; Bus.

COADY, HOLLY; Hicksville HS; Hicksville, NY; (Y); Drama Clb; French Clb; School Play; French Hon Soc; High Hon Roll; Ntl Lang Arts Olympd 83; Hafstra U.

COAKLEY, KRISTINE; Lockport SR HS; Lockport, NY; (Y); Latin Clb; Pep Clb; Off Jr Cls; Cheerleading.

COAR, MARIE; Deer Park HS; Deer Park, NY; (Y); 76/422; Cmnty Wkr; Computer Clb; Dance Clb; Drama Clb; Intnl Clb; Spanish Clb; Chorus; School Play; Variety Show; Off Stu Cncl; Med.

COATES, CARRIANN; Ellenville HS; Ellenville, NY; (Y); Girl Scts; Chorus; JV Bsktbl; Wildlife Consrvtn.

COATES, DIANE; Churchville-Chili SR HS; Churchville, NY; (Y); FTA; Sec Girl Scts; JA; Model UN; Lit Mag; Bowling; High Hon Roll; NHS; YFU ATAD Japan 85; Math Teacher.

COATES, KIM A; John C Bridlebough HS; Fulton, NY; (Y); 27/200; AFS; Aud/Vis; Exploring; Ski Clb; Band; Concert Band; Mrchg Band; Stage Crew; Nwsp Phtg; Yrbk Phtg; NY ST Regents Scholar 85; SUNY Oswego.

COATS, JAYNE; Ursuline Schl; Stamford, CT; (Y); Hosp Aide; Concert Band; Crs Cntry; Trk; Hon Roll; Band; Chorus; NY ST Regent Schlrshp Nrs 85; Cert Exclnc Amer-Hst-Chem-Math II-COMM Svc; Cert Apprctn NW Hosp 84.

COATS, JENNIFER; Randolph Central Schl; E Randolph, NY; (Y); 3/90; Art Clb; Pres Drama Clb; English Clb; French Clb; Girl Scts; Quiz Bowl; Acpl Chr; Yrbk Sprt Ed; Lit Mag; NHS; AF Awd Sci Fair 84; Artwk Poetry Pub 84-85; Exc Pgm JCC 85; Geology.

COBB, CAROLINE B; Eldred Central Schl; Eldred, NY; (Y); 9/42; Ski Clb; Varsity Clb; Band; Chorus; Madrigals; Capt Var Cheerleading; Trk; Hon Roll; NHS; SUNY Oswego; Acctng.

COBB, JAMES A; Frontier SR HS; Blasdell, NY; (Y); Church Yth Grp; 4-H; Band; Jazz Band; Var L Socr; Trk; All Amer Hall Fame Band Hnrs 83-84; NYS Rgnts Schlrshp 84-85; Plattsburg ST U; Engrng.

COBB, JUDITH; Herman-Dekalb Central Schl; De Kalb Jct, NY; (S); 3/45; French Clb; Band; Chorus; Concert Band; Trs Mrchg Band; Stage Crew; Nwsp Rptr; Nwsp Stf; Yrbk Stf; High Hon Roll; Lcl Music Awd 84; Music.

COBB, TEDRA; Fairport HS; Fairport, NY; (Y); Church Yth Grp; Drama Clb; Chorus; School Musical; School Play; Swing Chorus; Stu Cncl; Socr; Hon Roll; NHS; Best Prfrmnc In Mjr Role 84; Miss NY Ntl Teen-Ager Pgnt 83; Miss Amer Coed Pgnt 85; Potsdam U; Msnry.

COCCA, MICHAEL; Tamorac HS; Troy, NY; (Y); German Clb; Math Tm; JV Ftbl; Ntl Merit Ltr; Mechncl Engrng.

COCCHIOLA, CHRISTINE; West Hempstead HS; West Hempstead, NY; (Y); 16/310; Orch; School Musical; Rep Sr Cls; Var Badmtn; Capt Pom Pon; Hon Roll; NHS; Eng,Math,Comp Awds 85; Pres Acad Ftns Awd 85; Comm Schlrshp 85; Suny Geneseo; Spcl Ed.

COCCHIOLA, JOANNE; West Hempstead HS; West Hempstead, NY; (Y); Trs Church Yth Grp; Orch; Var Badmtn; Var Pom Pon; Var Trk; Hon Roll; NHS; NY ST Yth Conf 84-85; Brd Diocesan Yth Cncl 84-85; Musical 85.

COCHRANE, CHERYL; De Sales Catholic HS; Lockport, NY; (Y); Cmnty Wkr; Hosp Aide; Hon Roll; Teachers Schlrshp 84; Helen Reichert Mem Schlrshp 85; Francis & Agnes Schimscheiner Mem Schlrshp 85.

COCKETT, BRIAN K; Midlakes HS; Phelps, NY; (Y); Var Bsktbl; Var Ftbl; Trk; Vllybl; Regnets Schlrshp 85; Bus.

COCKLE, JOEL; Fillmore Central HS; Fillmore, NY; (S); 3/60; FFA; High Hon Roll; Hon Roll; NHS; NYS Regents Scholar; Farm Supply Awd; Alfred ST Coll; Ag Sci.

COCO, GEOFFREY P; Binghamton HS; Binghamton, NY; (Y); 2/480; Am Leg Boys St; Computer Clb; Key Clb; Mathletes; Nwsp Rptr; Capt Var Crs Cntry; Var L Trk; High Hon Roll; NHS; ST Fin Olympic Of The Mind Tm 85; Grd Champ Delta X Math Cmptn 83; Grd 2nd Pl Delta X Math Cmptn 84; Comp Sci.

COCO, LORETTA; Southampton HS; Southampton, NY; (Y); 7/110; Rep GAA; Concert Band; Yrbk Ed-Chief; Ed Lit Mag; Rep Stu Cncl; Var Capt Cheerleading; Var Fld Hcky; Var Capt Sftbl; High Hon Roll; NHS; RI Schl Of Design; Advertising.

COCOZZO, MARGARET; Saratoga Springs HS; Saratoga, NY; (Y); Ski Clb; Nwsp Stf; Sec Trs Frsh Cls; Stu Cncl; JV Var Cheerleading; High Hon Roll; Law.

CODA, JOHN; Port Jerris HS; Sparrow Bush, NY; (Y); 10/196; Aud/Vis; Varsity Clb; Var Bsbl; Var Ftbl; Wt Lftg; Var Wrstlng; NHS; SCCC; Cmnctns.

CODDINGTON, DAVID E; Hornell SR HS; Hornell, NY; (Y); Exploring; JV Bsbl; JV Ftbl; Var Swmmng; Im Vllybl; Hon Roll.

CODELLA, JEFFREY; Warwick Valley HS; Warwick, NY; (Y); 60/200; Civic Clb; FFA; Chorus; Madrigals; Nwsp Rptr; Rep Soph Cls; Star Chapter Farmer Awd 83-84; Natl Sci Teacher Assoc Awd Environ Sci 84-85; Ag Educ.

CODERRE, MICHELLE; Smithtown High School East; Nesconset, NY; (Y); Spanish Clb; Var Bsktbl; Phy Thrpy.

CODY, CHRISTINE; Victor SR HS; Victor, NY; (Y); 20/230; Art Clb; Church Yth Grp; Model UN; Spanish Clb; School Musical; Stage Crew; Stu Cncl; High Hon Roll; Hon Roll; Educ.

COE, MICHELE; Caledonia Mumford Central Schl; Caledonia, NY; (Y); Pep Clb; Spanish Clb; Yrbk Stf; Stat Socr; Stat Trk; Hon Roll; Bus.

COELHO, AMY; Minisink Valley HS; Port Jervis, NY; (Y); Dance Clb; Drama Clb; 4-H; Chorus; School Play; Rep Frsh Cls; Stu Cncl; 4-H Awd; High Hon Roll; Hon Roll; JR Prom Prncss 84-85; All County Choir 84-85; Law.

COFFEY, BRIAN; Albertus Magnus HS; Pearl River, NY; (Y); Drama Clb; Leo Clb; Math Clb; Math Tm; Ski Clb; School Play; Golf; Ice Hcky; Mu Alp Tht; NHS; NY ST Regents Schlrshp; Manhattan; Engr.

COFFEY, BRIAN; Msgr Mc Clancy HS; Broad Channel, NY; (Y); Nwsp Bus Mgr; Yrbk Stf; Sec Soph Cls; Trs Jr Cls; St Francis Coll; Acctng.

COFFEY, JEANNE; Avoca Central HS; Avoca, NY; (Y); Political Wkr; Varsity Clb; Band; Chorus; Mrchg Band; Yrbk Phtg; Sec Frsh Cls; Hon Roll; Exploring; All-ST Orchestra 84.

COFFEY, MICHAEL W; St John The Baptist D HS; Bay Shore, NY; (Y); 80/600; Political Wkr; Rep Frsh Cls; Rep Soph Cls; Rep Jr Cls; JV Crs Cntry; JV Var Trk; Hon Roll; Mock Trial Team; Regents Schlrshp; CT Coll; Corp Law.

COFFTA, DAVID; Cardinal O Hara HS; Getzville, NY; (S); 14/173; Sec Trs Church Yth Grp; VP JA; Nwsp Stf; Hon Roll; 82-83 Schlrshp Cardinal O Hara 82; C Y O Outstndng Serv Awd 84; Bus.

COFFTA, JODIE; Cardinal O Hara HS; Getzville, NY; (S); 14/173; Cmnty Wkr; VP Sec JA; Library Aide; Red Cross Aide; Nwsp Rptr; Nwsp Stf; Hon Roll; Med.

COFRESI JR, MANUEL; Cardinal Spellman HS; Bronx, NY; (Y); Computer Clb; Math Clb; Math Tm; Band; 4-H Awd; Hon Roll; Cornell Schlrshp 85; Regnts Schlrshp 85; Polytech Schlrshp 85; Cornell U; Elec Engrng.

COGAN, BRIAN; Monignor Farrell HS; Staten Island, NY; (Y); Boy Scts; Church Yth Grp; Orch; Rptr Lit Mag; Ntl Merit SF; St Johns Comptv Schlrshp 84; Cert Merit 83; Sharpshootr NRA Cert 84; St Johns U; Cmmnctns.

COGAN, HOWARD; Monticello HS; Kiamesha Lake, NY; (Y); Cmnty Wkr; Sec Debate Tm; Pres Intnl Clb; Math Clb; Math Tm; NFL; Quiz Bowl; Sec Speech Tm; Pres Temple Yth Grp; Nwsp Rptr; Spkr Awd Brnx H S Fo Sci Tourn 84; Law.

COGHLAN, JOAN; Sacred Heart Academy; Garden City, NY; (S); 25/186; Var Math Tm; Yrbk Stf; Im Tennis; Hon Roll; NHS; Bus.

COGLIANO, BRENDA; Westfield Academy And Central Schl; Westfield, NY; (S); 11/74; School Play; VP Sr Cls; Rep Stu Cncl; Var L Bsktbl; Stat Ftbl; Var Sftbl; Capt L Vllybl; High Hon Roll; Hon Roll; NHS; NY ST Regnts Schlrshp Wnnr 85; Natl Hnr Roll 83; U Ctr SUNY; Comp Info Sci.

COHAN, TIMOTHY; Saratoga Springs HS; Saratoga Springs, NY; (Y); 5/465; Orch; Lit Mag; Wrstlng; High Hon Roll; NHS; Ntl Merit SF; Williams Bk Awd 84; AATF Frnch Cntst 84; Wrtng.

COHEN, ADAM; Sachem H S North; Holbrook, NY; (Y); 109/1383; Science Clb; Ski Clb; VP Temple Yth Grp; Jazz Band; Mrchg Band; Symp Band; Jr NHS; NHS; Band; Concert Band; 2nd Pl Sufflk Cnty Math Cont 85; 2nd Pl LI Sci Cngrs 83.

COHEN, ALAN J; Seaford HS; Seaford, NY; (Y); 5/241; Drama Clb; Band; Drm Mjr(t); Trs Jazz Band; School Musical; Yrbk Stf; Lit Mag; NHS; YFU Exchng Stu Jpn 82; Wesleyan U; Law.

COHEN, AMY R; G W Hewlett HS; Woodmere, NY; (Y); 34/278; Nwsp Stf; Hon Roll; NYS Regnts Schlrshp 84-85; U Of S CA; Bus.

COHEN, ANDREA M; Longwood HS; Coram, NY; (Y); 81/434; Cmnty Wkr; Temple Yth Grp; Drill Tm; Variety Show; Yrbk Stf; Rep Frsh Cls; Rep Soph Cls; Trs Jr Cls; Trs Sr Cls; Rep Stu Cncl; SUNY Oneonta; Elem Ed.

COHEN, AUSTIN B; West Islip SR HS; W Islip, NY; (Y); Computer Clb; Nwsp Phtg; Trs Soph Cls; Rep Stu Cncl; Var Swmmng; High Hon Roll; NHS; Ntl Merit Ltr; Jeffersn Awd 85; Math Awd 84; Engl Awd 84; Pre-Law.

COHEN, BILL; Edgemont HS; Hartsdale, NY; (S); CAP; Pres Computer Clb; Band; Nwsp Stf; Var Bsktbl; Var Crs Cntry; Var Trk; 1st Hnrs, Iona Coll Language Contest 84.

COHEN, BRADLEY J; Lafayette HS; Brooklyn, NY; (Y); 18/415; JA; Library Aide; Math Tm; Science Clb; Service Clb; Spanish Clb; Teachers Aide; Nwsp Ed-Chief; Nwsp Rptr; Yrbk Stf; NYS Regnts Schlrshp 84; Stonybrook; Hlth Sci.

COHEN, CHAD; Mahopac HS; Goldens Bridge, NY; (Y); 9/423; Am Leg Boys St; Math Tm; Temple Yth Grp; Stage Crew; Yrbk Stf; JV Bsktbl; Var Tennis; High Hon Roll; Hon Roll; Ntl Merit SF.

COHEN, CHARLES C; Amgerst Central HS; North Tonawanda, NY; (Y); 5/200; Boy Scts; Acpl Chr; Madrigals; School Musical; Rep Stu Cncl; NHS; NY ST Regents Schlrshp 85; 3rd Pl Ntl Sci Olympiad 84; 2nd Pl Schlwide Essay Cntst 85; Cornell U; Med.

COHEN, DAVID; Joseph C Wilson Magnet HS; Rochester, NY; (S); Church Yth Grp; Ski Clb; Diving; Socr; Swmmng; Tennis; High Hon Roll; NHS; Mst Valuable Plyr Swmng 83-84; High Hnr Trophy 83-84; Div II Swim Chmp Plaque 84-85; Cornell; Math.

COHEN, DAVID JONATHAN; Albany HS; Albany, NY; (Y); 4/600; Drama Clb; Latin Clb; Pres Temple Yth Grp; Chorus; Ed Nwsp Stf; Var Tennis; NHS; Ntl Merit SF; Gen Elec Hall Of Histry Fndtn Cntst Wnnr 84; Nyssma Mdl Lvl 6 83; Sol Kebel Awd Cong Ohev & Shelom 84; Chem.

COHEN, DREW; Riverdale Country Schl; New York, NY; (Y); Key Clb; Office Aide; Pres Nwsp Ed-Chief; Var L Bsbl; JV Socr; Var L Swmmng; Mst Vlubl Plyr-S Rvrdle Bsbl Leag 84; Bus.

COHEN, HARVEY; Corning-Painted Post West HS; Painted Post, NY; (Y); Cmnty Wkr; Key Clb; Ski Clb; Temple Yth Grp; Thesps; Varsity Clb; School Musical; JV Socr; Var L Tennis; High Hon Roll; Donovan Acad Sumr Schl Sci Schlrshp; 3rd Pl Tenns Sectnls.

COHEN, HOWARD; H S Truman HS; Bronx, NY; (Y); Service Clb; Chorus; Prfct Atten Awd; NYC Supr Yth Awd 84; Bus Dept Inc Tax Prep Awd 85; Intl Awd Radio Canada Intl 84; Comp Pgmmr.

COHEN, IRA; Half Hollow Hills H S West; Dix Hills, NY; (Y); 133/361; Drama Clb; Radio Clb; VP Band; VP Mrchg Band; VP Symp Band; Im Sftbl; Var Trk; High Hon Roll; NHS; Rotary Awd; SUNY Albany; Bus Law.

COHEN, JACOB; Forest Hills HS; Forest Hills, NY; (Y); 130/881; Pres Debate Tm; Trs Exploring; Science Clb; Teachers Aide; Orch; Nwsp Rptr; Ed Yrbk Phtg; NHS; Co-Capt Aud/Vis; Boy Scts; Attorney Gen Triple C Awd 83; Chancellors Rl Of Hon 83; Princpls Pride Of Yankees Awd 85; Boston U; Cardiolgst.

COHEN, JANE; Emma Willard HS; Menands, NY; (Y); Cmnty Wkr; Library Aide; Office Aide; Temple Yth Grp; Nwsp Rptr; Nwsp Stf; Lit Mag; Sec Soph Cls; Rep Stu Cncl; JV Sftbl; Global Ed Comm 84-86; Ind Study Piano 83-85; Law.

COHEN, JARED; White Plains HS; White Plains, NY; (Y); VP JA; Office Aide; Lit Mag; Rep Stu Cncl; Var Tennis; Hon Roll.

COHEN, JON; Lawrence HS; Woodmere, NY; (Y); Computer Clb; Debate Tm; Trs DECA; Radio Clb; Science Clb; Spanish Clb; Nwsp Rptr; Nwsp Stf; Im Bsktbl; Im Sftbl; DECA Achvt Awd 85; 2nd PBC Bsktbl Lge 85; Cmnctns.

COHEN, JONATHAN; Tappan Zee HS; Tappan, NY; (Y); 1/293; Capt Scholastic Bowl; VP Temple Yth Grp; NHS; Val; Yrbk Stf; Trk; Cit Awd; Ntl Merit Ltr; Rotary Awd; Amer Lgn-Outstndg Soc Stud Stu 85; A G Barone Awd-4 Yrs Svc To Stu, Schl & Cmnty 85; Engl Dept Awd 85; Columbia U; Polit Sci.

COHEN, KAREN; Bronx High School Of Science; Bronx, NY; (Y); Cmnty Wkr; English Clb; Library Aide; Office Aide; Temple Yth Grp; Y-Teens; Nwsp Ed-Chief; Nwsp Rptr; Nwsp Stf; Yrbk Stf; Awd Law Day 82; Jrnlsm.

COHEN, LAURIE L; Valley Central HS; Montgomery, NY; (Y); 3/255; Math Tm; Band; Lit Mag; Stu Cncl; NHS; Ntl Merit Ltr; Spanish NHS; Voice Dem Awd; Concert Band; Mrchg Band; Social Studies Honor Society 83-85; Regents Scholarship 85; SUNY Albany; Business Admin.

COHEN, LISA; Cold Spring Harbor HS; Laurel Hollow, NY; (Y); Chorus; School Musical; Symp Band; Variety Show; Cheerleading; Sftbl; Hon Roll; All Cnty Chorus 82; Law.

COHEN, LISA J; Tottenville HS; Staten Island, NY; (Y); 4/897; Math Tm; Office Aide; Scholastic Bowl; Variety Show; Ed Nwsp Rptr; Ed Yrbk Stf; High Hon Roll; NCTE Awd; NHS; Ntl Merit Ltr; Regnts Schlrshp Govs Comm Schlstc Achvt Schlrshp 85; Otto Burgdorf Mem Awd 85; Socl Studies Awds 84-85; Columbia U; Comp Sci.

COHEN, LISA M; Roy C Ketcham HS; Poughkeepsie, NY; (Y); 8/500; AFS; Pres VP Temple Yth Grp; Sec Soph Cls; Rep Sec Stu Cncl; Var Capt Cheerleading; JV Socr; High Hon Roll; Jr NHS; NHS; Ntl Merit SF.

COHEN, LORI; Cammack High Schl North; Commack, NY; (Y); Art Clb; Cmnty Wkr; English Clb; Intnl Clb; Service Clb; Nwsp Stf; Yrbk Stf; Lit Mag; Hon Roll; Temple Yth Grp; Ntl Art Hnr Soc 85-86; Fash Inst Tech.

COHEN, MARISA F; Jericho HS; Jericho, NY; (Y); 17/230; Drama Clb; Acpl Chr; Chorus; School Musical; School Play; Nwsp Sprt Ed; Lit Mag; Sec Sr Cls; NHS; Ntl Merit Ltr; Jap-Amer Exchng Stu 84; Wesleyan U; Writer.

COHEN, MARLENA; Rocky Point JR SR HS; Rocky Pt, NY; (Y); Bowling; Hon Roll; Dental Asst.

COHEN, MICHAEL; West Hempstead HS; W Hempstead, NY; (Y); Computer Clb; Letterman Clb; Ski Clb; Bsbl; JV Ice Hcky; JV Var Lcrss; Bsbl MIP 82-83; Boston Coll.

COHEN, MICHAEL A; Colonie Central HS; Loudonville, NY; (Y); Camera Clb; Drama Clb; Radio Clb; Ski Clb; Temple Yth Grp; School Musical; School Play; Variety Show; Yrbk Bus Mgr; Yrbk Stf; Hotel Mgmt.

COHEN, ROBERT; Calhoun HS; Merrick, NY; (Y); Aud/Vis; Camera Clb; Hon Roll.

COHEN, ROSALIND F; Comsewogue Senior HS; Pt Jefferson Sta, NY; (Y); 38/365; Pres Drama Clb; Chorus; School Play; Variety Show; Nwsp Stf; Ftbl; Outstndg Achvt Awd Engl & Htlh 83-84; Outstndg Achvt Awd Drama 84-85; Bio.

COHEN, SCOTT M; North Babylon HS; N Babylon, NY; (Y); 60/560; Church Yth Grp; JV Bsbl; Var Bowling; High Hon Roll; Hon Roll; Jr NHS; NHS; NY ST Regnts Schlrshp 84-85; SUNY Farmingdale; Acctng.

COHEN, SHARYN; Schem North HS; Farmingville, NY; (Y); Color Guard; Chld Educ.

COHEN, SHERRY L; Walt Whitman HS; Huntington Statn, NY; (Y); 5/625; Drama Clb; Key Clb; Chorus; School Musical; School Play; Lit Mag; Trs French Hon Soc; High Hon Roll; Jr NHS; NHS; Suffolk Cnty Inst Of Jewish Studies 85; Gold Medal Ntl Frnch Exam 85; NY ST Regents Schlrshp 85; Cornell U; Intl Relations.

COHEN, SHIRAH; Jamesville De Witt HS; Syracuse, NY; (Y); Cmnty Wkr; Temple Yth Grp; JV Crs Cntry; High Hon Roll; NHS; Band; Chorus; VP In JR Pro Art 85; Semi Fin In Yng Keybrd Artsts Assn 84; Acctpd To Chantaugua Schl Of Music 85; Music.

COHEN, STACEY B; Lawrence HS; Woodmere, NY; (Y); AFS; Cmnty Wkr; Spanish Clb; Orch; Hon Roll; NHS; Ntl Merit Schol; St U NY-ALBANY.

COHEN, STACY B; Great Neck South HS; Great Neck, NY; (Y); 5/218; Drama Clb; French Clb; School Play; Ed Nwsp Ed-Chief; Var L Bsktbl; Var L Sftbl; Cit Awd; Ntl Merit Schol; Prfct Atten Awd; Pres Schlr; Thomas J Watson Memrl Awd IBM Corp 85; Band Coll Essy Cntst 85; Deptmntl Awd Physcs 85; Harvard U; Intntl Reltns.

COHEN, TANYA; Moriah Central HS; Mineville, NY; (Y); 4/88; VP AFS; French Clb; GAA; Hosp Aide; Pres Frsh Cls; Trs Stu Cncl; Var Capt Cheerleading; Var Swmmng; High Hon Roll; VP NHS; SUNY Albany; Bus Mgt.

COHEN, VIVIAN; Manhattan Center For Science & Math; New York, NY; (Y); Capt VP Church Yth Grp; FNA; Hosp Aide; Math Clb; Red Cross Aide; Church Choir; Pres Frsh Cls; VP Jr Cls; High Hon Roll; Prfct Atten Awd; Acadmc All-Am 85; Howard; Med.

COHN, BARRIE; Plainview-Old Bethpage HS; Plainview, NY; (S); 83/194; Art Clb; Cmnty Wkr; DECA; Key Clb; Model UN; Band; Concert Band; Mrchg Band; School Musical; Symp Band; The American U; Bus.

COHN, JODY L; Lawrence HS; Inwood, NY; (Y); AFS; French Clb; Service Clb; Band; School Play; Mgr(s); Score Keeper; High Hon Roll; Jr NHS; NHS.

COKE, AUDREY M; John Jay HS; Brooklyn, NY; (Y); 69/537; JA; Library Aide; Teachers Aide; Yrbk Stf; Hon Roll; Sprts Awd Bst Athlt 83; Hnr Soc 83; Lwyr.

COKE, JEFF; Fairport HS; Fairport, NY; (Y); JV Bsktbl; Var L Ftbl; Var L Lcrss; 1st Tm All County Ftbl 84; Mst Valuable Def Back Ftbl 84; 2nd Tm All County Lcrss 84; Bus.

COLABELLA, FRANCINE; St Joseph Hill Acad; Staten Island, NY; (Y); 20/105; Cmnty Wkr; Exploring; FTA; VP JA; Math Tm; Yrbk Stf; VP Jr Cls; Regents Schlrshp 85; Stevens Inst; Electrical Engrng.

COLABELLO, BRIDGET; The Fransican Acad; N Syracuse, NY; (S); FBLA; GAA; Yrbk Stf; Sec Frsh Cls; VP Soph Cls; VP Jr Cls; Rep Stu Cncl; Var Tennis; High Hon Roll; NHS; Lemoyne Coll; Commercl Ad.

COLAIUTI, CARYN; Sewanhaka HS; Stewart Manor, NY; (Y); 30/300; Church Yth Grp; Orch; Rep Soph Cls; Rep Jr Cls; Hon Roll; NHS; JR Soc Womn Engrs 85; Engnrg.

COLANGELO, DAVID; Cicero North Syracuse HS; North Syracuse, NY; (S); 39/622; Boy Scts; Church Yth Grp; Math Tm; Jazz Band; Mrchg Band; Orch; Symp Band; VP Trk; Hon Roll; Syracuse Sym Youth Orch Awd 83-84; Clarkson U; Engrng.

COLANGELO, LYNN MARIE; Cardinal Spellman HS; Bronx, NY; (Y); Girl Scts; Service Clb; Color Guard; Yrbk Stf; Tennis; Var JV Twrlr; Im Vllybl; Hon Roll; 1st Hnrs-All 4 Yrs In H S; Regents Schlrshp; Fordham U; Fin.

COLAS, MAURICE; St Frances Prep; Elmont, NY; (Y); Ftbl; Sftbl; Wrstlng; Judo 1st Pl ST Champshps 84; Med.

COLASURDO, TERESA; Newark SR HS; Newark, NY; (Y); GAA; Service Clb; JV Var Bsktbl; Im Cheerleading; JV Tennis; Im JV Hon Roll; Nrsg.

COLAVITA, MARILINA; Henninger HS; Syracuse, NY; (Y); Itln Clb 84-85.

COLAVITO, JEANNE M; St Marys Girls HS; E Williston, NY; (Y); Cmnty Wkr; Pep Clb; Ski Clb; Chorus; Stage Crew; Hon Roll; NHS; Law.

COLBATH, MICHAEL R; Suffern HS; Suffern, NY; (Y); 86/497; Am Leg Boys St; Concert Band; JV Var Bsbl; JV Var Bsktbl; JV Var Ftbl; Hon Roll; All Conf Bsbl Awd 85; Engrng.

COLBERT, VIVA; George Woodland Wingate HS; Brooklyn, NY; (Y); Hosp Aide; Red Cross Aide; Chorus; Off Jr Cls; Trk; Hon Roll; Scl Sci Merit Excell 82; Sci Merit Excell 82; Law.

COLBURN, BILL A; Red Jacket Central HS; Manchester, NY; (Y); Am Leg Boys St; Varsity Clb; Concert Band; Jazz Band; Madrigals; School Musical; Yrbk Phtg; Rep Stu Cncl; Var L Ftbl; Var L Wrstlng; Graphic Dsgn.

COLBURN, LISA; Frewsburg Central HS; Frewsburg, NY; (Y); 3/85; Pres Church Yth Grp; Pres Sec 4-H; Rep Band; Concert Band; Jazz Band; Sec Stu Cncl; Bsktbl; Trk; Vllybl; Sec NHS; Jamestown CC; Mth.

COLBURN, MARY; Whitesboro SR HS; Whitesboro, NY; (Y); Cmnty Wkr; GAA; Hosp Aide; L Var Bsktbl; L Var Sftbl; Hon Roll; Sec Trs Church Yth Grp; Library Aide; Chorus; Hmn Svcs.

COLBY, KAREN; Wellsville HS; Wellsville, NY; (Y); 28/120; Debate Tm; Speech Tm; VP Chorus; Color Guard; Madrigals; School Musical; Stage Crew; Rep Jr Cls; Hon Roll; Yrbk Stf; Part In Natl Catholic Frnsc Leag Debates Lincoln-Douglas Debate; Plyr Mrs Pearce In My Fair Lady 85.

COLBY, KIM; Jamesville Dewitt HS; Dewitt, NY; (Y); 88/224; Church Yth Grp; Cmnty Wkr; Spanish Clb; Yrbk Stf; Socr; Sftbl; Hon Roll; Houghton Coll; Elem Ed.

COLBY, MAUREEN A; Amsterdam HS; Amsterdam, NY; (Y); 12/322; Cmnty Wkr; Drm Mjr(t); Yrbk Stf; Off Frsh Cls; Off Jr Cls; Off Sr Cls; Off Stu Cncl; Elks Awd; Hon Roll; NHS; Albany ST U; Math.

COLE, AMY; Gouverneur JR SR HS; Gouverneur, NY; (Y); 5/145; Church Yth Grp; 4-H; FFA; JA; Color Guard; Flag Corp; Mrchg Band; Orch; School Musical; 4-H Awd; 4 H Awds Arts Crfts 83-85; FFLA Sec; Pres Ldrshp Awd 83-85; Alfred St; Ag.

COLE, CAROL; Saint Catharines Acad; Bronx, NY; (Y); 127/205; Church Yth Grp; Hosp Aide; JA; Trk; Prfct Atten Awd; Nrsng.

COLE, DAVID M; Bronx H S Of Science; Flushing, NY; (Y); Cmnty Wkr; Debate Tm; Math Tm; Bowling; Hon Roll; NHS; Mth Awd; Bus.

COLE, DAVID P; Columbia HS; Nassau, NY; (Y); 4/353; School Musical; School Play; Var Socr; Ntl Merit SF; Symp Band; Nwsp Rptr; NHS.

COLE, DIANNA; Portville Central HS; Portville, NY; (Y); Cmnty Wkr; Band; Concert Band; Mrchg Band; High Hon Roll; JC Awd; Spnsh.

COLE, MELISSA; Trumansburg HS; Trumansburg, NY; (Y); Church Yth Grp; Trs Pres Drama Clb; Spanish Clb; Thesps; Chorus; School Play; Stage Crew; Variety Show; Yrbk Stf; PTO Rcgntn Awd 85; Bus Admn.

COLE, NELSON; The Knox Schl; Birmingham, AL; (S); Boy Scts; VP Computer Clb; Math Clb; PAVAS; Speech Tm; Thesps; Chorus; School Musical; School Play; Yrbk Rptr; Oxford-Emory; Mgmt.

COLE, PETER D; Stuyvesant HS; Flushing, NY; (Y); Cmnty Wkr; Var Capt Ftbl; Ntl Merit SF; Westinghse Sci Srch 85; Ntl Merit Fin 85; Cornell U; Med.

COLE, RICHARD D; Beach Channel HS; Rego Pk, NY; (Y); Science Clb; Teachers Aide; Rep Stu Cncl; Hon Roll; Prfct Atten Awd; Marine Bio.

COLE, ROBERT E; Oneida SR HS; Oneida Castle, NY; (Y); 3/180; Am Leg Boys St; Boy Scts; Concert Band; Jazz Band; Capt Var Bsbl; Capt Var Ftbl; Cit Awd; Dnfth Awd; God Cntry Awd; NHS; Am Yth Band-Eurpn Smmr Tour Recpnt 85; HS No 1 Clb 83; Cngrssnl Ctatn Frm Shrwd Boehlrt 85; US Academies; Med.

COLE, ROBYN KAYCIE; James E Sperry HS; Rochester, NY; (Y); Drama Clb; Thesps; Chorus; Madrigals; School Musical; School Play; JV Cheerleading; High Hon Roll; Hon Roll; NHS; Fashion Coordntng.

COLE, SEAN R; West Genesee HS; Camillus, NY; (Y); French Clb; Var Crs Cntry; Var Ftbl; Var Gym; Var Trk; High Hon Roll; Hon Roll; High Grde Math 83-84; Acctnt.

COLE, STEVEN T; East Syracuse-MINOA HS; East Syracuse, NY; (Y); Exploring; Science Clb; Im Bsktbl; JV Var Bowling; Im Vllybl; E Syracuse And Minoa High Schl Hnr Roll 83-84; MVP Varsity Bowling Team 84-85; NY ST Rgnt Schlrsp85; Potsdam College; Aeronautical.

COLE, WENDY S; Hilton HS; Hilton, NY; (Y); 5/276; Pres Church Yth Grp; Cmnty Wkr; Nwsp Rptr; Sec Jr Cls; Capt Var Bsktbl; Score Keeper; JV Socr; High Hon Roll; Sec NHS; NYS Regnts Schlrshp 85; Grove City Coll PA; Bus Adm.

COLE II, WILLIAM F; Paul V Moore HS; Central Square, NY; (Y); 28/315; AFS; Am Leg Boys St; Math Tm; VP Pres Band; Jazz Band; Mrchg Band; Symp Band; Bsktbl; JV Golf; JV Var Socr; Engrng.

COLECCHIA, CARLO; Clarkstown High Schl North; Congers, NY; (Y); Church Yth Grp; Pres Trs Intnl Clb; Office Aide; Chorus; JV Var Crs Cntry; Var Trk; Hon Roll; 3rd Pl Fordham U Poetry Cont 84-85; NY ST Schl Music Assoc Area All-ST 84; Iona Lang Cont 85; Chrprctcs.

COLEGROVE, CHERYL V; C P P West HS; Painted Post, NY; (Y); 50/254; Church Yth Grp; Exploring; Chorus; Church Choir; Orch; School Musical; Socr; High Hon Roll; Hon Roll; Regents Schlrshp 84-85; Dickinson Coll; Lang.

COLEGROVE, DAVID; Tonawanda JR SR HS; Tonawanda, NY; (Y); 5/225; Am Leg Boys St; ROTC; Varsity Clb; Rep Stu Cncl; JV Bsbl; JV Ftbl; L Swmmng; Hon Roll; VP NHS; NEDT Awd; Engrng.

COLEGROVE, KELLY; Tonawanda JR SR HS; Tonawanda, NY; (Y); 18/235; Office Aide; Stage Crew; Yrbk Stf; Rep Stu Cncl; Mgr(s); Hon Roll; NHS; NEDT Awd; Pres Schlr; Quality Stu 85; Elmira Coll; Secndry Ed.

COLELLA, CHARLES V; Archbishop Stepinac HS; E White Plains, NY; (Y); 27/206; VP Church Yth Grp; Church Choir; Rep Frsh Cls; Rep Soph Cls; Rep Jr Cls; Rep Sr Cls; Capt Ftbl; Wt Lftg; Hon Roll; NHS; Thomas Moore Ntl Hnrs Soc 84-85; Regnts Dip Math,Sci 81-85; Manhattan Coll; Engrng.

COLELLA, HELEN; South Shore HS; Brooklyn, NY; (Y); Girl Scts; Teachers Aide; Band; Bsktbl; Sftbl; Tennis; Hon Roll; Prfct Atten Awd; Bio.

COLEMAN, CAMILLE; August Martin HS; St Albans, NY; (Y); Computer Clb; Teachers Aide; Yrbk Rptr; Yrbk Stf; Cheerleading; Comp Sci.

COLEMAN, ELLEN; Longwood HS; Coram, NY; (S); 8/492; Am Leg Aux Girls St; Cmnty Wkr; Math Tm; Political Wkr; Pres Band; Orch; School Musical; Variety Show; High Hon Roll; NHS; NY ST Schl Music Assoc Fest 83-84; All-Amer Band 84; Pbl Rltns.

COLEMAN, JAMES; Hornell SR HS; Hornell, NY; (S); 10/198; VP 4-H; Math Clb; Ski Clb; Var Capt Swmmng; Bausch & Lomb Sci Awd; 4-H Awd; High Hon Roll; NHS; Boys St 84; Rennselaer Medal Math 84; U Rochester; Engrng.

COLEMAN, JOHN F; Middletown HS; Harrisburg, PA; (Y); Am Leg Boys St; Boy Scts; FCA; Key Clb; Letterman Clb; Rep Stu Cncl; Var L Bsktbl; Var Capt Ftbl; Var Wt Lftg; Hon Roll; Poli Sci.

COLEMAN, JOYCE; Tottenville HS; Staten Island, NY; (Y); 3/897; Stage Crew; Nwsp Stf; Yrbk Sprt Ed; Tennis; Bausch & Lomb Sci Awd; High Hon Roll; NHS; Renssealer Sci & Math Awd 85; SUNY-BINGHAMTON.

COLEMAN, KARI; Vestal SR HS; Vestal, NY; (Y); Mathletes; Co-Capt Mrchg Band; Orch; High Hon Roll; Hon Roll; Math.

COLEMAN, KRISTINE; Albertus Magnus HS; New City, NY; (Y); 45/190; Church Yth Grp; Math Clb; Service Clb; Teachers Aide; Hon Roll; Sci,Math Hnr Rl 83-84; Sci.

COLEMAN, LISA; Union Endicott HS; Owego, NY; (S); Band; Color Guard; Concert Band; Drill Tm; Flag Corp; Mrchg Band; Symp Band; Rep Jr Cls; Hon Roll; Rep Stu Cncl; Mbr U-E Wntrgrd Attndg Olympcs 85; Broome Tech; Nrsng.

COLEMAN, LISA M; Our Lady Of Mercy HS; Rochester, NY; (Y); French Clb; Hosp Aide; Science Clb; School Play; Stage Crew; Var L Swmmng; Hon Roll; Regnts Awd; Amer Chem Soc; PSAT; Dowling Coll; Mar Bio.

COLEMAN, MICHELE; Middletown SR HS; Middletown, NY; (Y); Teachers Aide; Symp Band; Yrbk Stf; Hon Roll; Orange County CC; Child Psych.

COLEMAN, TAMMY; Kensington HS; Buffalo, NY; (Y); 20/203; Church Yth Grp; Cmnty Wkr; FBLA; Church Choir; Yrbk Stf; Sftbl; Vllybl; Cit Awd; Hon Roll; Prfct Atten Awd; St Peter Claver Yth Schlrshp 85; D Youville Coll; Pre-Med.

COLERICK, KENNETH D; John F Kennedy HS; Utica, NY; (Y); 9/130; Hon Roll; NHS; Top 10 Awd 85; Pres Acad Fit Awd 85; P Newell Hamlin Awd 85; Elec Engrng.

COLERN, GERALD H; Maryvale HS; Cheektowaga, NY; (Y); 60/333; Drama Clb; Chorus; Var L Ftbl; Computer Clb; Leo Clb; Acpl Chr; Band; Concert Band; Jazz Band; Mrchg Band; Niagara U; Mgmt.

COLETTA, KRISTIN A; Walter Panas HS; Peekskill, NY; (Y); 1/213; Var Diving; Var Capt Gym; Var Sftbl; Var Swmmng; Var Capt Vllybl; High Hon Roll; Jr NHS; NHS; Ntl Merit SF; Val; St Johns Univ Comptv & Excllnc Schlrshp 85; Con Edison Schlrshp 85; Ciba-Geigy Awd 85; St Johns Univ; Pharm.

COLETTI, ANDREW; Archbishop Molloy HS; Whitesone, NY; (Y); 56/420; Bsktbl; Coach Actv; Score Keeper; Timer; High Hon Roll; Hon Roll; Bio.

COLF, LISA M; Le Roy Central HS; Le Roy, NY; (Y); Spanish Clb; Band; Chorus; Concert Band; Jazz Band; Mrchg Band; Pep Band; School Musical; Stage Crew; Hon Roll; Mike Ellingham Mem Awd 85; NY ST U Genesseo; Secndry Ed.

COLGAN, CHRISTIN; Longwood HS; Shirley, NY; (S); 10/493; Church Yth Grp; Chorus; High Hon Roll; NHS; Acadmc All-Amer 85.

COLGAN, TRACY; Sachem H S North; Holbrook, NY; (Y); 158/1509; Drama Clb; Ski Clb; Acpl Chr; Chorus; Madrigals; School Musical; Stage Crew; Score Keeper; Stat Socr; Hon Roll; Physcl Thrpy.

COLICCHIA, MARK; Kenmore West SR HS; Kenmore, NY; (Y); JA; Math Tm; Orch; High Hon Roll; 3rd Pl Erie Cnty Natl Spn I Comp 83; NYSSMA Drm Comp 84; 3rd Pl Schl Natl Mth Cont 85; Biol Sci.

COLIS, TOM D; Clarence Central HS; Clarence, NY; (Y); Am Leg Boys St; Church Yth Grp; Latin Clb; Trs Varsity Clb; School Play; Yrbk Bus Mgr; Trs Stu Cncl; Var Bsktbl; Var Capt Ftbl; Hon Roll; Comp Sci.

COLLADO, CARLOS MANUEL; Seward Park HS; New York, NY; (Y); Debate Tm; Drama Clb; Exploring; Latin Clb; Science Clb; Teachers Aide; Yrbk Phtg; Wt Lftg; Hon Roll; Spanish NHS; Dntstry.

COLLADO, EVELYN; Washington Irving HS; New York, NY; (Y); Teachers Aide; Chorus; Nwsp Rptr; Hon Roll; Nrs.

COLLADO, JUAN; La Salle Acad; New York City, NY; (Y); VP Frsh Cls; Capt Crs Cntry; Capt Trk; Hon Roll; Tck Schlrshp 85; Fordham U; Pre-Med.

COLLAR, EDWARD; Gloversville HS; Gloversville, NY; (Y); 8/224; Var JV Bsbl; Var JV Bsktbl; Coach Actv; High Hon Roll; NHS; Pres Schlr; Rgnts Schlrshp 85; FMCC Brd Of Trustees Schlrshp 85; GHS Sprts Boostr Clb Awd 85; Fulton Montgomery CC; Tchng.

COLLAZO, MICHAEL; Cathedral Preparatory Seminary; Brooklyn, NY; (Y); Church Yth Grp; Library Aide; NFL; Nwsp Stf; Hon Roll; Diocsn Schlrshp For HS 82; SUNY Buffalo; Jrnlsm.

COLLEGAN, SHELLY; Frontier Central HS; Hamburg, NY; (Y); FBLA; Pep Clb; Hon Roll; Hnbl Mntn Poetry Cntst 85; Gldn Poet Awd 85; Bus Mgmt.

COLLESANO, STANLEY; St Josephs Collegiate Inst; Buffalo, NY; (Y); Boys Clb Am; Teachers Aide; Var Capt Crs Cntry; Var Capt Trk; Hon Roll; SAR Awd; Most Val Rnnr Crss Cntry 84-85; Mostg Val Rnnr Trck 85; Coaches Awd Ldrshp Trck 84.

COLLETTE, TIMOTHY; Queensbury Central HS; Glens Falls, NY; (Y); Debate Tm; Ski Clb; Chorus; Crs Cntry; Im Lcrss; Trk; High Hon Roll; Hon Roll; Engnrng.

COLLIER, CHARISSE; Norman Thomas HS; Flushing, NY; (S); 71/677; Computer Clb; Hosp Aide; Office Aide; Band; Yrbk Stf; High Hon Roll; Hon Roll; Cert Awd Outstndng Achvt Alg 82; Baruch Coll; Comp Sci.

COLLIER, NICOLE; Chatham HS; Chatham, NY; (Y); 9/133; Band; Orch; School Musical; Rep Sec Stu Cncl; Crs Cntry; High Hon Roll; NHS; Ntl Merit SF; All-Cnty Band 84-85; All-Cnty Orchstr 85; Grievance Brd 85; SUNY Oneonta; Lbrl Arts.

COLLIGAN, MAUREEN; Dover JR SR HS; Dover Plains, NY; (S); Yrbk Stf; High Hon Roll; Hon Roll; Jr NHS; Voice Dem Awd; Math.

COLLIGAN, SHELLY; Frontier Central HS; Hamburg, NY; (Y); FBLA; Pep Clb; Hon Roll; Hon Men Wrld Poet Cont 85; Bus Adm.

COLLINS, ANDREW; Long Beach HS; Long Beach, NY; (S); 37/316; Yrbk Stf; JV Lcrss; Hon Roll; NHS; Moleclr Bio.

COLLINS, ANNE; Chester HS; Chester, NY; (Y); Girl Scts; Yrbk Phtg; Yrbk Stf; Pres Frsh Cls; Pres Soph Cls; Pres Jr Cls; Var Bsktbl; Var Socr; Var Vllybl; VFW Awd; Grl Sct Slvr Awd 84; Chester Sprts Assoc Sprtsmnshp Awd-Bsktbl 85; Sci Fld.

COLLINS, BECKY; Canton Hugh C Williams HS; Canton, NY; (Y); Dnfth Awd; High Hon Roll; NHS; Church Yth Grp; Stat Bsktbl; Stat Socr; Talntd JR Awd St Lawrence U 85; Clarkson Sci Day Awd 84; Treas CYO 85; Med.

COLLINS, BILL; Niagara Wheatfield SR HS; Sanborn, NY; (Y); Varsity Clb; Var Lcrss; Stat Score Keeper; JV Var Socr; Hon Roll; Niagara U; Mltry Sci.

COLLINS, CARRIE; James I O Neill HS; West Point, NY; (Y); 22/150; Church Yth Grp; Office Aide; Sec Pep Clb; Yrbk Stf; Trs Stu Cncl; Stat Bsbl; Capt Cheerleading; High Hon Roll; Dghtrs US Army Schlrshp 85; Estrn Seabrd Schlrshp 85; U Of KS; Jrnlsm.

COLLINS, CHRIS; Jamestown HS; Jamestown, NY; (Y); 8/380; Pres Frsh Cls; Rep Sr Cls; JV Var Bsktbl; Hon Roll; Jr NHS; NHS; Natl Ldrshp Awd 84-85; Regents Schlrsh& 85; USA Schlrshp 85; Jamestown CC; Med.

COLLINS, CHRISTINE; Mt Mercy Acad; Buffalo, NY; (Y); Spanish Clb; Var Cheerleading; Buffalo ST; Math.

COLLINS, DARREN; South Kortright Central Schl; Hobart, NY; (Y); 10/30; Varsity Clb; Band; Mrchg Band; Pres Frsh Cls; Rep Stu Cncl; Bsbl; Var Capt Bsktbl; Socr; Hon Roll; 1st Tm Sccr All Star Tm, MVP Sccr 84; J Zepka Mem Sccr Awd 85; Sci.

COLLINS, DAVE; Kenmore West SR HS; Tonawanda, NY; (Y); Math Tm; JV Bsbl; JV Var Bsktbl; Var Capt Vllybl; High Hon Roll; Hon Roll; Prfct Atten Awd; All Trny Tm Ken-Ton Intl Vllybl 84-85; All Niagara Frntr Leag 1st Tm Vllybl 84-85; Math.

COLLINS, DAVID J; Cardinal Mooney HS; Rochester, NY; (Y); 21/320; Boy Scts; Church Yth Grp; Exploring; Im Bowling; High Hon Roll; Hon Roll; APSL Natl Latn Hnr Socty 81-83; NY ST Regnts Schlrshp 85; Clarkson U; Elctrcl Engr.

COLLINS, FRED; Trumansburg Central HS; Ovid, NY; (Y); Church Yth Grp; Church Choir.

COLLINS, JACK; Tioga Central HS; Barton, NY; (Y); Library Aide; Ftbl; Wrstlng; Hon Roll; Broome Cmmnty; Crmnl Justice.

COLLINS, JAMES; Valley Central HS; Walden, NY; (Y); 104/400; Letterman Clb; Varsity Clb; Var Ftbl; Elec Engrng.

COLLINS, JENNIFER; E L Vandermeuten HS; Pt Jefferson, NY; (Y); Leo Clb; Thesps; Color Guard; Mrchg Band; School Musical; Stage Crew; Rep Jr Cls; Latin Clb; Red Cross Aide; Band; Nrsng.

COLLINS, JENNIFER A; Clarkstown High School North; Congers, NY; (Y); 106/500; French Clb; Band; Concert Band; Mrchg Band; Orch; School Musical; Stage Crew; Symp Band; Nwsp Rptr; Ed Lit Mag; Fclty Crtv Wrtng Awd; Ntl Merit Fndtn, Ntl Hnr Rll; Cert Awd Band; SUNY Albany; Psychlgy.

COLLINS, KAREN ANN; Nazareth Acad; Rochester, NY; (Y); 17/114; Spanish Clb; Stage Crew; Capt Var Bsktbl; JV Sftbl; Hon Roll; NHS; Ntl Honor Soc-Outstndng Student 85; Oswego Coll; Comptr Sci.

COLLINS, KEVIN P; Fordham Prep; New York, NY; (Y); Nwsp Rptr; Lit Mag; Bsktbl; Gen Excllnce Awd.

COLLINS, KIMBERLY A; Louis D Brandeis HS; Corona, NY; (Y); 1/716; Girl Scts; Science Clb; Service Clb; Rep Stu Cncl; Hon Roll; Sec NHS; Ntl Merit Ltr; Val; Nwsp Rptr; Manhattan Sci Fair Fnlst & 2nd 83; Winner Jr Acad Of Sci Awd NY Sci Fair 83; Med.

COLLINS, KRIS; Immaculate Heart Central HS; Black River, NY; (Y); Spanish Clb; Yrbk Stf; Sftbl; Jefferson CC.

COLLINS, MARGARET E; The Loyola Schl; Rockville Centre, NY; (Y); 7/52; Chorus; Church Choir; Madrigals; Mrchg Band; Orch; School Play; Stu Cncl; Var Bsktbl; Var Sftbl; JV Vllybl; Gld Medlst Bst Itln Lang Stdnt Schl 82 & 84; Brooklyn Prep Almn Schlrshp Loyda Schl 84; Smith Coll; Musc.

COLLINS, MARY; Brewster HS; Brewster, NY; (S); 16/150; Varsity Clb; Band; Mrchg Band; Pep Band; School Play; Var Capt Bsktbl; Var Capt Trk; Var Capt Vllybl; VP NHS; Vllybl All League MVP Bar 84; All ST Band 84-85; Spnish Hnr Rl 84; Accntng.

COLLINS, MICHAEL; St Marys HS; Lancaster, NY; (S); 2/200; Varsity Clb; Pres Jr Cls; Pres Stu Cncl; Var L Bsbl; Var L Ftbl; Var L Trk; NHS; Police Athltc Assn Schlrshp 85; Adminstrtv Bd 85; Var Ftbl All Star 85; Govt.

COLLINS, PAUL; Amherst Central HS; Snyder, NY; (Y); 71/311; Latin Clb; Quiz Bowl; Rep Frsh Cls; VP Soph Cls; Rep Jr Cls; Rep Sr Cls; Pres Stu Cncl; Im JV Bsbl; Im JV Bsktbl; JV Ftbl; ST U Of NY Buffalo; Chem Engr.

COLLINS, SARAH; Emma Willard Schl; Troy, NY; (Y); Aud/Vis; Cmnty Wkr; Political Wkr; Ski Clb; Band; Chorus; Stage Crew; Nwsp Stf; Yrbk Stf; Trs Frsh Cls; Earth Sci Rgnts Awd 83; Swarthmore Coll.

COLLINS, SEAN A; Bronx HS Of Science; Bronx, NY; (Y); Am Leg Boys St; Cmnty Wkr; Lit Mag; Ftbl; Sftbl; Prfct Atten Awd; OH ST; Envrnmntl Sci.

COLLINS, TIMOTHY; Susquehanna Valley HS; Binghamton, NY; (Y); Am Leg Boys St; Ski Clb; Spanish Clb; Bsktbl; JV Socr; Vllybl; Wt Lftg; Var Wrstlng; Med.

COLLINS, TRACY A; Elmira Free Acad; Elmira, NY; (Y); AFS; Drama Clb; Latin Clb; Quiz Bowl; Yrbk Stf; Var L Crs Cntry; Var L Swmmng; Var L Trk; Hon Roll; NHS; Chemung Cnty Womens Clb Schlrshp 85; U Fo Vermont; Bio Engnrng.

COLLINS, TRACY E; Sachem High School North; Holbrook, NY; (Y); 138/1500; Drama Clb; Political Wkr; Church Choir; Madrigals; School Musical; Lit Mag; NHS; Voice Dem Awd; Cmnty Wkr; Ski Clb; NYS Mock Trial Tm Attrny 85; Crmnl Jstc Awd NYS Bar Assoc 85; Outstndng Musicnshp 83-84; Law.

COLLINS, VALERIE; Spring Valley SR HS; Spring Vly, NY; (Y); German Clb; Office Aide; Mrchg Band; NHS; Outstndng Achvt German Awd 83; Bus.

COLLINS, VICTORIA A; Suffern HS; Suffern, NY; (Y); 52/400; Church Yth Grp; Computer Clb; Hosp Aide; Band; Chorus; Rep Stu Cncl; Vllybl; High Hon Roll; Hon Roll; Engrng.

COLLYMORE, KATHY; Far Rockaway HS; Far Rockaway, NY; (Y); Band; Chorus; Cit Awd; Phys Ed Hnr Roll 85; Comp Pgmmr.

COLMAN, MINDY; Fort Ann Central HS; Fort Ann, NY; (Y); 7/46; Church Yth Grp; French Clb; Math Tm; Pres Band; Yrbk Ed-Chief; Sec Sr Cls; Cheerleading; Fld Hcky; Capt Sftbl; NHS; Am Legn Nrsng Schlrshp 85; JR Prom Qn 84; SUNY-PLATTSBURGH; Nrsng.

COLMEAN, BRYAN; Jordan Elbridge HS; Elbidge, NY; (Y); 17/134; Am Leg Boys St; Cmnty Wkr; French Clb; Political Wkr; Church Choir; Drm & Bgl; Rep Sr Cls; Im Bsktbl; Var Golf; Im Socr; Son Of Veterns Resrv Awd 84; Senate Stdnt Policy Forum 85; Syracuse U; Chem Engr.

COLOMA, RALPH; Sacred Heart HS; Yonkers, NY; (Y); Cmnty Wkr; Hon Roll; Semi-Finlst Natl Hspanc Scholar Awds Prgm 85; 5000 Scholar Westchester Bus Inst 85; Fordham U; Bus Admin.

COLOMARA, CHRISTINE; Notre Dame Acad; Staten Island, NY; (Y); 3/96; Cmnty Wkr; Computer Clb; Girl Scts; Math Clb; Stage Crew; Nwsp Stf; Stu Cncl; High Hon Roll; NHS; Law.

COLOMBO, GREGORY; Longwood HS; Coram, NY; (Y); Boy Scts; Cmnty Wkr; Spanish Clb; Band; Var Capt Ftbl; Golf; Hon Roll; 1st Pl Awd Motocrs JR Standings All Round 84-85; JR Coram Fireman; Pres 1st Pl Phys Fit Awds; Bus.

COLOMBO, JOSEPHINE; Our Lady Of Perpetual Help; Brooklyn, NY; (Y); Girl Scts; Chorus; Church Choir; Sec Jr Cls; Hon Roll; NHS; Prfct Atten Awd; Bishop Mugaverop CYO Awd 82; Math.

COLOMBO, VITO; Archbishop Molloy HS; Middle Vlg, NY; (Y); 60/411; Intnl Clb; Var Capt Trk; No 1 Shotputter NY City 84; Med.

COLON, ANA; St Pius V HS; Bronx, NY; (Y); Hosp Aide; Jr Cls; VP NHS; Prfct Atten Awd; Mem Schlrshp 82; Bus Adm.

COLON, EDWIN; St John The Baptist D HS; Wyandanch, NY; (Y); 4/546; Chess Clb; Computer Clb; 4-H; Spanish Clb; Chorus; Stage Crew; Trk; Hon Roll; Jr NHS; NHS; Ntl Sci Olympd 83, 84; Engrng.

COLON, HERMINIO; E J Wilson HS; Spencerport, NY; (Y); 39/300; Church Yth Grp; Exploring; French Clb; Latin Clb; Math Clb; Varsity Clb; Yrbk Stf; JV Var Bsbl; Trk; Var Vllybl; Mst Dedicatd Sr Dedicatn Awd & Vrsty Vllybl 85; Alt Cand Naval Reserve Offcrs Traning Corps 85; U Of Rochester; Premed.

COLON, JOSE; Amsterdam HS; Amsterdam, NY; (Y); Boy Scts; Church Yth Grp; Rep Frsh Cls; Rep Soph Cls; Rep Stu Cncl; Var L Bsbl; Var L Socr; Hon Roll; 1st Tm Big Ten All-Star Tm Sccr & Bsebl 83-85; Elec Engrng.

COLON, MARITZA; Clara Barton HS; Brooklyn, NY; (Y); Cmnty Wkr; Hosp Aide; Teachers Aide; Chorus; Hon Roll; ST Gaudens Art Medal 84; NY Super Yth 84-85; Sci.

COLON, MARY; Bishop Ford C C HS; Brooklyn, NY; (Y); Intnl Clb; Pres JA; Science Clb; Yrbk Ed-Chief; Stu Cncl; Dnfth Awd; High Hon Roll; Hon Roll; Pres NHS; NYU Trustee Schlrshp 85; Brd Of Trustees Citatn Of Hnr 85; NY U; Librl Arts.

COLON, MIRIAM E; High School Of Fashion Industri; Bronx, NY; (Y); 21/365; Drama Clb; Exploring; Chorus; Stage Crew; Hon Roll; Prfct Atten Awd; Fashn Inst Tech; Fash Desgn.

COLONNA, CLAUDIA; Bishop Kearney HS; Brooklyn, NY; (Y); Service Clb; Teachers Aide; Chorus; Yrbk Ed-Chief; Yrbk Stf; Hon Roll; Princple Lst; Merit, Svc Awds; St Francis Coll; Bus Admin.

COLONNA, ROBERT M; Monsignor Farrell HS; Staten Island, NY; (Y); 53/297; Boy Scts; Teachers Aide; Yrbk Ed-Chief; Im Bsktbl; Im Bowling; JV Wrstlng; Hon Roll; Yrbk Stf; NYS Regents Schlrshp; Columbian Assoc Schlrshp; Manhattan Coll; Mech Engr.

COLOSA, ROBERT J; North Babylon SR HS; N Babylon, NY; (Y); 67/527; Boy Scts; Cmnty Wkr; Office Aide; Band; Mrchg Band; Bowling; High Hon Roll; Hon Roll; Jr NHS; Prfct Atten Awd; Prsdntl Acad Ftnss Awd 84-85; Hofstra U; Acctng.

COLOSI, SANTINA; Aquinas HS; Bronx, NY; (Y); 14/178; Computer Clb; Intnl Clb; JA; School Musical; School Play; High Hon Roll; Hon Roll; NHS; Prfct Atten Awd; Engl, Social Studies, Sci Fair, Attndnc Awd 83; 1st Hnr 84; Earth Sci; Iona Italian Cntst 2nd & 1st 85; Iona Coll; Accntng.

COLTON, ANNETTE; Niagara Wheatfield HS; Niagara Falls, NY; (Y); 135/315; Sec Frsh Cls; Sec Soph Cls; Sec Jr Cls; Sec Sr Cls; Rep Stu Cncl; Var Capt Bowling; JV Capt Sftbl; Prfct Atten Awd; Homecmng Qn & Miss Ntl Teenage Pgnt 85 & 83; Schlrshp Cert Of Hnr 85; MVP-BOWLING Awd 85; Associated Schls-Cruise Dirctr.

COLTON, CAROL; Vestal Central HS; Vestal, NY; (Y); 42/450; VP Trs Church Yth Grp; English Clb; French Clb; Ski Clb; Band; Mrchg Band; Orch; High Hon Roll; NHS; Prfct Atten Awd; NYSSMA Conf All State 84; Clarkson U; Mktg.

COLTON, CHRISTINE; Fayetteville-Manlius HS; Manlius, NY; (Y); Hosp Aide; VP Sec JA; Model UN; Chorus; Cit Awd; High Hon Roll; Ntl Merit Schol; Prfct Atten Awd; Cheerleading; Cert Exclnc Fr III A 85; Boston U; Pre-Med.

COLTON, MARK; Lockport SR HS; Lockport, NY; (Y); 5/525; Church Yth Grp; Latin Clb; Chorus; Stage Crew; JV Var Bsbl; High Hon Roll; Pres Jr NHS; NHS; Engrng.

COLUCCI, MARGARET; Herbert H Lehman HS; Bronx, NY; (Y); 17/444; Science Clb; Nwsp Ed-Chief; Nwsp Rptr; Hon Roll; NHS; Bronx Dist Atty Cittn Hon Awd 85; J G Bennett Meml Schlrshp 85; Outstndg Achvt Awds Engl, Math, Phy Ed; Fordham U.

COLUCCI, ROBERT; Cardinal O Hara HS; Kenmore, NY; (S); 14/145; Boy Scts; French Clb; Pres Frsh Cls; VP Soph Cls; Pres Jr Cls; Rep Stu Cncl; Var JV Bsbl; Var Capt Bsktbl; JV Ftbl; JV Socr; Cardinal O Hara Schlrshp 82; Fresh Baseball Most Dedicated 83; Baseball Most Val Plyr 84; Med.

COLUCCIO, ROSEMARY; St John Villa Acad; Staten Is, NY; (Y); Var Socr; Var Sftbl; Hon Roll; MIP Sftbl 83-85; Math.

COLVIN, JUDY; Harry S Truman HS; Bronx, NY; (Y); Hosp Aide; Math Tm; Teachers Aide; Chorus; Nwsp Rptr; Yrbk Phtg; Capt Tennis; NHS; NY U Med Schl; Med Doc.

COLYER, AMY; Schoharie Central Schl; Schoharie, NY; (S); Key Clb; Varsity Clb; Acpl Chr; Chorus; School Play; Stu Cncl; Co-Capt Cheerleading; Sftbl; High Hon Roll; NHS; Brigham Young U; Med.

COMAN, LAUREN J; Shenendehowa HS; Clifton Park, NY; (Y); Cmnty Wkr; Ski Clb; Varsity Clb; Yrbk Bus Mgr; Im Bsktbl; Im Fld Hcky; JV Powder Puff Ftbl; JV Socr; Im Trk; Im Vllybl; Cert Achvt Vlntry Svc Cmnty 84; Pres Phys Fit Awd 81-83; Worcester Polytech Inst; Engr.

COMBOY, PATRICIA; Desales Catholic HS; Sanborn, NY; (S); 2/47; Cmnty Wkr; Nwsp Stf; Yrbk Stf; High Hon Roll; NHS; Ntl Merit Ltr; NEDT Awd; Frshmn Yr Partial Schlrshp 82-83; Outstndng Frnch Stu; Pre-Med.

COMBS, CLAUDIA; Alden Central HS; Alden, NY; (Y); 4-H; VICA; Acctnt.

COMBS, DONALD; Freeport HS; Freeport, NY; (Y); 50/400; Church Yth Grp; Drm & Bgl; School Musical; Drm & Bgl; Variety Show; Var Crs Cntry; Var Trk; Hon Roll.

COMBS, DOREEN; Oceanside HS; Rockville Ctr, NY; (Y); Cmnty Wkr; Hosp Aide; Office Aide; Varsity Clb; Yrbk Sprt Ed; Bsktbl; Fld Hcky; Lcrss; Swmmng; Tennis; Sci, Art Awds 82; Nrsng.

COMERFORD, CATHY; Academy Of The Resurrection HS; Rye, NY; (Y); Drama Clb; Chorus; School Musical; Var Swmmng; Var Trk; Hon Roll; NHS; Cert Merit Schlstc Achvt 84; Awds Swmmng, Drama, Chrus 83-85; Lib Arts.

COMERFORD, KAREN; Jamesville-Dewitt HS; Fayetteville, NY; (Y); Church Yth Grp; Cmnty Wkr; French Clb; Key Clb; Pep Clb; Yrbk Stf; Sftbl; Vllybl; Hon Roll; Art Schltc Awds 85; Gold Key 85; Elem Ed.

COMITO, VINCENT; Seaford HS; Seaford, NY; (Y); Capt Aud/Vis; Drama Clb; Band; Concert Band; Jazz Band; Mrchg Band; Stage Crew; Hofstra U; Comp Sci.

COMMERATO, KIM; Smithtown High School East; St James, NY; (Y); Hosp Aide; Yrbk Stf; Stu Cncl; Var L Crs Cntry; Var L Trk; Vllybl; NHS; Italian Hnr Soc 84-86; Jrnlsm.

COMMERFORD, KELLEY; Rome Free Acad; Rome, NY; (Y); Church Yth Grp; Intnl Clb; Ski Clb; Yrbk Stf; Sec Soph Cls; Sec Jr Cls; Stat Bsbl; Var L Fld Hcky; JV L Sftbl; Var L Vllybl; All Star Fld Hcky 84; MVP Fld Hcky 84; Empire ST Games Fld Hcky 85; Comm.

COMMIKE, ALAN; Centereach HS; Farmingville, NY; (Y); 69/475; Computer Clb; Math Tm; Trk; High Hon Roll; Hon Roll; Suny At Buffalo; Comp Sci.

COMMISSO, MARIA; St Marys Girls HS; Floral Park, NY; (Y); 26/175; English Clb; Teachers Aide; Nwsp Rptr; High Hon Roll; Jr NHS; NHS; Manhattanville Coll Engl Awd 85; St Johns U; Phrmcy.

COMORA, JEANNIE; Lake George Central HS; Glens Falls, NY; (Y); Cmnty Wkr; Office Aide; Q&S; Teachers Aide; Band; Chorus; Concert Band; Mrchg Band; Lit Mag; Im Badmtn; Info Cnslng Elem Chldrn 85; Advncd Plcmnt Coll Eng, Psych & Sociology 86; Solo Mus Comp Awds 83-84; Corp Psych.

COMPANIE, MICHELE D; Laurens Central HS; W Oneonta, NY; (Y); 4/38; Drama Clb; Hosp Aide; Key Clb; Chorus; Color Guard; Drill Tm; Yrbk Ed-Chief; Yrbk Stf; High Hon Roll; Ntl Merit Ltr; National Ldrshp Organization 84-85; Regents Scholarship 85; Clark Foundation Scholarship 85; Lemoyne College; Political Sci.

COMSTOCK, JENNIFER; Randolph Central HS; Randolph, NY; (Y); 1/80; Am Leg Aux Girls St; Trs French Clb; Scholastic Bowl; Ski Clb; Acpl Chr; Sec Soph Cls; Rep Stu Cncl; JV Var Cheerleading; Hon Roll; Trs VP NHS; Acctng.

COMUNALE, CHRISTIE; Islip HS; Islip, NY; (Y); Var JV Cheerleading; High Hon Roll; Hon Roll; NHS; Achvt Math 83.

COMUNALE, TERRY; Kings Park SR HS; Ft Salonga, NY; (Y); 18/398; Band; Jr NHS; NHS; Church Yth Grp; NFL; Service Clb; Speech Tm; Varsity Clb; Pom Pon; Tennis; Ntl Forensic Leag Achvt Awd 83; NYSSMA All St Audtn-A/100% Rtng 85; Cathlc Leag Relgs/Cvl Rts Awd 85; Commnctns.

CONBOY, LISA; Cohoes HS; Cohoes, NY; (Y); Exploring; French Clb; GAA; Key Clb; Nwsp Sprt Ed; Pres Frsh Cls; Pres Soph Cls; Pres Jr Cls; Var Crs Cntry; Var Capt Trk; Cert Of Merit Fr I & II 83-84; MVP Crs Cntry & Trk 84-85; Oustndg Achvt Eng Hstry Hlth & Comp 83-85; Intl Affrs.

CONCANNON, CHRIS; Newfield HS; Centereach, NY; (Y); SADD Postr Cntst Awd 83; Dentstry.

CONCOLINO, MARIA ANN; Tottenville HS; Staten Island, NY; (Y); Variety Show; High Hon Roll; NHS; Schlstc Excell Schlrshp 85; Regents Schlrshp 85; Hnr Key 85; St Johns U; Bus.

CONDELLA, ROBERT; Horseheads SR HS; Horseheads, NY; (Y); Computer Clb; Drama Clb; French Clb; Ski Clb; Band; Concert Band; Mrchg Band; Orch; Hon Roll; Comp Sci.

CONDELLO, MARY; Glen Cove HS; Glen Cove, NY; (Y); 1/265; Debate Tm; Math Clb; Math Tm; Science Clb; Drm Mjr(t); Jazz Band; Mrchg Band; Symp Band; JV Bsktbl; Capt Var Swmmng; Brown U Bk Awd 84; George Washington U Eng Med 84; LI Cncl Soc Studs Cert 82-83; MA Inst Tech ; Bio.

CONDELLO, ROSANNA; Fairport HS; Fairport, NY; (Y); Drama Clb; Chorus; School Musical; School Play; Swing Chorus; Nwsp Ed-Chief; Rep Stu Cncl; High Hon Roll; Hon Roll; NHS; Brockport Alumni Schlrshp 85; St Marys Gld Vcl Music Awd 85; Presdntl Acadmc Ftnss Awd 85; SUNY-BROCKPORT; Eng.

CONDIT, ROBYN; Valley Stream Central HS; Valley Stream, NY; (Y); Chess Clb; Office Aide; Var Vllybl; NY ST U; Crim Jstc.

CONDLY, DIANE V; West Islip HS; West Islip, NY; (Y); 29/525; Chorus; School Play; Capt Cheerleading; High Hon Roll; NHS; Drama Clb; French Clb; Mathletes; Band; Hon Roll; Rgnts Schlrhsp Awd 85; MVP Kicline 85; Athltc Acadmc Achvt Awd 85; Fairfield U; Lib Arts.

CONDON, DEIRDRE; John Jay HS; Wappfalls, NY; (S); 165/360; Pres Civic Clb; DECA; Drama Clb; School Musical; Stage Crew; Var Mgr Crs Cntry; Mgr(s); Var Timer; Var Trk; Var Stat Vllybl; DECA Schlrshp 85; 2nd Pl Htl, Mtl Mgt Cmptn 85; Sullivan County CC; Htl Tech.

CONDON, DENISE MARIE; Clayton A Bouton HS; Voorheesville, NY; (Y); Church Yth Grp; Hosp Aide; Intnl Clb; Band; Pres Frsh Cls; Sec Jr Cls; Rep Stu Cncl; Cheerleading; Capt Fld Hcky; Mst Invlvd Stu Cncl 83; Clss Ldrshp 85; Nrsng.

CONDON, KATHLEEN; Seton Catholic Central HS; Endicott, NY; (Y); Key Clb; Varsity Clb; Yrbk Stf; Sec Frsh Cls; VP Soph Cls; VP Jr Cls; Stu Cncl; JV Var Cheerleading; Marywood; Soclgy.

CONDOS, PANAYOTA; H S Of Art & Design; Long Island City, NY; (S); 12/411; Church Yth Grp; French Clb; Library Aide; Teachers Aide; Orch; School Play; Nwsp Ed-Chief; Hon Roll; VP NHS; Prfct Atten Awd; Arista Pres 83; Supr Youth NYC Outstndg H S Stu 84; Concours Natl De Francais 85; Cooper Union; Arch.

CONE, ELIZABETH A; Smithtown HS West; Smithtown, NY; (Y); Thesps; Mrchg Band; School Musical; Nwsp Bus Mgr; Lit Mag; Stu Cncl; Hon Roll; NHS; Ntl Merit Ltr; Spanish NHS; Regents Schlrshp 85; SUNY Oswego; Comm.

CONERTY, MICHELLE; Mechanicville HS; Mechanicville, NY; (S); Computer Clb; Spanish Clb; Band; Concert Band; Mrchg Band; Pep Band; School Play; Trs Soph Cls; Var Capt Bsktbl; Stfbl; Math 10 Awd; Math.

CONERTY, SARAH J; Bolton Central HS; Bolton Landing, NY; (Y); 2/27; French Clb; Band; Concert Band; Mrchg Band; Nwsp Ed-Chief; Yrbk Ed-Chief; Var Bsktbl; Var Cheerleading; Score Keeper; Socr; Hamilton Coll; Engl Lit.

CONFORTI, STEPHANIE; St Joseph By The Sea; Staten Island, NY; (Y); High Hon Roll; Hon Roll; Math.

CONGDON, LISA; Granville Central HS; Wells, VT; (Y); Trs Frsh Cls; Var Capt Bsktbl; Var Sftbl; Hon Roll; Prfct Atten Awd; Coaches Sftbl Awd 85; All-Star In Bsktbl 85; Castleton ST Coll; Phy Ed Tchr.

CONGER, LISA; Warsaw Central Schl; Warsaw, NY; (S); 5/93; Sec French Clb; Mathletes; Band; Sec Jr Cls; JV Bsktbl; JV L Sftbl; JV Vllybl; 4-H Awd; NHS; Bus.

CONIGLARIO, CAROL TERESA; Commack High School South; Commack, NY; (Y); Camera Clb; Teachers Aide; Chorus; Rep Stu Cncl; JV Sftbl; Hon Roll; Bus Admin.

CONIGLIARO, CHARLES PETER; St Pauls Schl; Westbury, NY; (S); 3/30; Church Yth Grp; French Clb; Varsity Clb; Nwsp Ed-Chief; Nwsp Rptr; Rep Frsh Cls; Capt Bsbl; Bsktbl; Capt Var Socr; Wrstlng; Schlr/Athlt-US Army Resrv-Ntl Awd 84-85; Presdntl Acadmc Ftnss Awd 84-85; Vrsty Clb Trphy 81, 82 & 85; Georgetown U; Clsscs.

CONIGLIARO, REGINA; St Edmund HS; Brooklyn, NY; (S); 26/187; Nwsp Stf; Italian Awd, Hist Awd 82-83; Eng Awd 82-84; Pre Law.

CONIGLIO, MARIA; Herricks HS; Albertson, NY; (S); Pres DECA; Ed Yrbk Stf; DECA Pres 84-85; Yth Brd 84-85; Bus Admin.

CONKLIN, COLLEEN; Bishop Maginn HS; Albany, NY; (S); Church Yth Grp; Yrbk Stf; Var L Cheerleading; Var L Pom Pon; High Hon Roll; NHS; Comp.

CONKLIN, KAREN; Yonkers HS; Yonkers, NY; (Y); Key Clb; Office Aide; Nwsp Rptr; Nwsp Stf; Yrbk Rptr; Yrbk Stf; Lit Mag; Hon Roll; Spec Educ.

CONKLIN, KATHLEEN; Washingtonville HS; Campbell Hall, NY; (Y); VP Cmnty Wkr; Dance Clb; Pres French Clb; Ski Clb; Teachers Aide; Symp Band; Cheerleading; Gym; Trk; NHS; Amer Ath Trk, Chrldng 84-85.

CONKLIN, MARK; Churchville-Chili HS; Rochester, NY; (Y); 10/310; Boy Scts; Church Yth Grp; French Clb; Math Tm; School Play; Yrbk Stf; Tennis; High Hon Roll; NHS; Ntl Merit SF; Hamilton; Law.

CONKLIN, MICHELE; Oneida Senior HS; Munnsville, NY; (S); 3/225; Pres 4-H; Math Tm; Spanish Clb; Varsity Clb; Yrbk Stf; Pres Soph Cls; Var Capt Fld Hcky; Var Vllybl; Dnfth Awd; High Hon Roll; Madison Cnty Dairy Princess 84; Animal Sci.

CONKLIN, VANESSA; Bayshore HS; Bay Shore, NY; (Y); 71/425; Art Clb; Chorus; Stage Crew; Var Crs Cntry; Var Trk; High Hon Roll; Hon Roll; Prfct Atten Awd; Sci Awd 82-83; Soc Stds Awd 82-83; Syracuse U; Bus Adm.

CONKLING JR, DONALD L; St Joseph By The Sea HS; Staten Island, NY; (Y); Boy Scts; Church Yth Grp; Teachers Aide; Bowling; Crs Cntry; Trk; Wt Lftg; Wrstlng; Hon Roll; Altrnt AIM Pgm 85; Cert Awd Rakng 2nd Eng 84; Awd Trophy Most Sportsmn Like Plyr 83; Pol Sci.

CONLEY, KELLY; Frankfort Schuyler Central HS; Frankfort, NY; (S); Hosp Aide; Key Clb; Spanish Clb; Concert Band; Mrchg Band; Var JV Bowling; JV Tennis; Hon Roll; Hon Roll; NHS; Comp Sci.

CONLEY, KEVIN; Lansingburgh HS; Troy, NY; (S); 22/190; Varsity Clb; Trs Frsh Cls; Trs Soph Cls; Rep Sr Cls; JV Bsktbl; Var Capt Ftbl; Trk; High Hon Roll; Jr NHS; NHS; SUNY-OSWEGO; Phy Thrpy.

CONLEY, LAWRENCE; Scotia-Glenville HS; Schenectady, NY; (Y); Aud/Vis; JA; Band; Poli Sci.

CONLEY, MAUREEN; Irondequoit HS; Rochester, NY; (Y); Girl Scts; Hosp Aide; Latin Clb; Band; Pep Band; Nwsp Rptr; Rep Frsh Cls; Rep Soph Cls; Rep Jr Cls; JV Tennis; Soclgy.

CONLON, EDWARD; Bethpage HS; Bethpage, NY; (Y); 13/289; Var Bsktbl; High Hon Roll; NHS; Italian Soc 85; Engrng.

CONNELLY, CAROLYN; Garden City SR HS; Stewart Manor, NY; (S); 15/355; Drama Clb; School Musical; School Play; Rep Frsh Cls; Rep Jr Cls; JV Co-Capt Cheerleading; JV Gym; High Hon Roll; Jr NHS; Hon Roll; Nrthsr Cmmnty Arts Ctr Dance 83-84; Masquers Svc Awd 83-84.

CONNELLY, ERIN E; Scotia-Glenville HS; Scotia, NY; (Y); 14/255; Band; Jazz Band; Stat Bsktbl; Mgr(s); Var Capt Tennis; Var Capt Tennis; Var Capt Vllybl; High Hon Roll; Hon Roll; NHS; St Rose Coll; Pbl Cmnctns.

CONNELLY, JAMES; Newburgh Free Acad; Newburgh, NY; (Y); Var Trk; Jr NHS; NHS; Latin I & II Awds 83-84; NY ST Regnts Schlrshp 85; Fairfield U; Sprts Med.

CONNELLY, KATHLEEN; St Vincent Ferrer HS; Douglaston, NY; (Y); Drama Clb; Hosp Aide; Chorus; School Musical; School Play; Hon Roll; Amer Red Crss Adv First Aid Emer Care Crd 83; CPR Card Amer Red Cross 83; Vol Svc Beth Israel Med 85; Mt St Vincent; Nrsng.

CONNELLY, KELLI; North Rose-Wolcott HS; Wolcott, NY; (Y); 20/160; Ski Clb; Chorus; School Musical; Variety Show; Yrbk Stf; Rep Stu Cncl; 4-H Awd; Hon Roll; Church Yth Grp; Natl Hnr Socty Soc Stds Awd 85; Findlay Coll; Equestrn Stds.

CONNELLY, MATTHEW J; St Anthony HS; Brightwaters, NY; (Y); Art Clb; French Clb; Political Wkr; Nwsp Bus Mgr; Nwsp Rptr; Nwsp Stf; Lit Mag; JV Crs Cntry; Var Trk; French Hon Soc; Cngrsnl Arts Csomp 84; 1st Edtrl & 2nd Story Long Island Cath Jrnlsm Awd 85.

CONNERS, KIM; Hendrick Hudson HS; Montrose, NY; (Y); Aud/Vis; Library Aide; Red Cross Aide; Yrbk Stf; Hon Roll; NYS Sci Suprvrs Assoc Earth Sci Awd 85; Dsgn.

CONNERS, SCOTT D; Onondaga Central HS; Nedrow, NY; (Y); 8/76; German Clb; Trs Spanish Clb; Trs Band; Jazz Band; School Play; Yrbk Stf; Trs Stu Cncl; Tennis; High Hon Roll; Trs NHS; Regnts Schlrshp 85; Syracuse U; Pyschlgy.

CONNOLLY, BILL; Tonawanda HS; Tonawanda, NY; (Y); JV Ftbl; Hotstra U; Aviatn.

CONNOLLY, JOHN; Iona Prep Schl; Tuckahoe, NY; (Y); 65/200; Boy Scts; Im Bowling; JV Ftbl; Var Mgr(s); Var Wt Lftg; Var Hon Roll.

CONNOLLY, KEVIN; Little Falls JR SR; Little Falls, NY; (S); 1/90; VP Pres FBLA; Yrbk Rptr; Ed Lit Mag; Pres Soph Cls; Var L Bsbl; Pres NHS; Val; Voice Dem Awd; Am Leg Boys St; Drama Clb; RPI Mdl Math, Sci 83-84; Stu Rep Bd Educ 84-85; 4th ST FBLA Impro Spkng 84; Pre Med.

CONNOLLY, KRISTEN; Brentwood HS Ross; Brentwood, NY; (Y); 18/625; Color Guard; Capt Drill Tm; Mrchg Band; Sec Jr Cls; Sec Sr Cls; High Hon Roll; NHS; Regents Scintfc Endorsmnt 85; Presdntl Acadmc Ftns Awd 85; White Ltr Awd Vrsty Kickln 85; NY ST U Albany; Bus.

CONNOLLY, MICHAEL; Vestal Senior HS; Vestal, NY; (Y); ST U Of NY; Comp Sci.

CONNOLLY, MICHAEL J; John A Coleman HS; Woodstock, NY; (Y); Boy Scts; VP Exploring; Ski Clb; School Play; Stage Crew; Socr; Trk; Hon Roll; Natl Sci Olympiad Awd Bio 84; Comp Sci.

CONNOLLY, NANCY P; Albany HS; Albany, NY; (Y); 21/600; Church Yth Grp; Cmnty Wkr; Latin Clb; Red Cross Aide; Nwsp Stf; Lit Mag; Pres Stu Cncl; L Swmmng; High Hon Roll; NHS; NY ST Regents Schlrshp; Homecoming Queen Nominee; College Science Awd; Union College; Bio Medical Engr.

CONNOLLY, SEAN T; John F Kennedy HS; Bedford, NY; (Y); 5/185; Drama Clb; Hosp Aide; VP Pres JA; School Play; JV Var Socr; Var Tennis; High Hon Roll; NHS; CIBA-GIEGY Sci Awd 85; Colgate U.

CONNOLLY, SHANE; John C Birdlebough HS; Phoenix, NY; (Y); 1/185; Trs AFS; Band; School Musical; Nwsp Bus Mgr; Yrbk Ed-Chief; Yrbk Stf; Pres Jr Cls; High Hon Roll; NHS; Church Yth Grp; Outstndng Achvt Awd Germn II 84; Outstndng Achvt Awd Chem 85; Engrg.

CONNOLLY, SUE; Frontier Central HS; Lakeview, NY; (Y); Drama Clb; Pres FHA; Hosp Aide; Pep Clb; Red Cross Aide; Band; Concert Band; Mrchg Band; School Musical; School Play; Nrsg.

CONNOR, BRIAN O; Msgr Scanlan HS; Flushing, NY; (Y); Teachers Aide; Pres Soph Cls; Stu Cncl; JV Bsbl; Var Capt Bsktbl; Im Sftbl; Math Awd 83; Frshmn-SR Aid Awd 84-86; St Johns U; Acctnt.

CONNOR, SUE; Warrensburg JR-SR HS; Warrensburg, NY; (S); Sec 4-H; French Clb; Yrbk Stf; 4-H Awd; Hon Roll; NHS; Prfct Atten Awd; Acadmc All-Amer 84-85.

CONNOR, WILLIAM; Xaverian HS; Brooklyn, NY; (S); Model UN; NFL; Spanish Clb; Speech Tm; School Musical; School Play; Stage Crew; Frsh Cls; Pres Stu Cncl; Hon Roll; Ntl Frnsc Leag 83; Syracuse U; Comm.

CONNORS, HEATHER G; Middleburgh Central Schl; Middleburgh, NY; (Y); 18/76; Sec Church Yth Grp; 4-H; Band; Pres Chorus; Church Choir; Concert Band; Jazz Band; Madrigals; Mrchg Band; School Musical; Music Schlrshp To U Of Penn ST 84; NY Rgnts Schlrshp 85; Siena Coll; Lib Arts.

CONNORS, LINDA; Island Trees HS; Levittown, NY; (Y); 46/217; Camera Clb; Exploring; Concert Band; Yrbk Stf; Stu Cncl; Var Cheerleading; JV Trk; NY Fash Inst Tech; Merch.

CONNORS, MARCY; West Seneca West SR HS; Buffalo, NY; (Y); 15/520; Hosp Aide; Red Cross Aide; Band; Pres Jr Cls; Pres Sr Cls; JV Socr; Hon Roll; Pres Jr NHS; NHS; Church Yth Grp; Highest Av Latin IV Awd 85; Acad Achvt Rgnts Phys Awd 85; Awd Cnstnt Acad Achvt 84-85; Boston U; Pre-Med.

CONNORS, SHANNON; Mechanicville HS; Mechanicville, NY; (Y); 21/106; Cmnty Wkr; VP French Clb; Ski Clb; Camp Fr Inc; Nwsp Stf; Yrbk Bus Mgr; Yrbk Ed-Chief; Yrbk Phtg; Yrbk Rptr; Yrbk Sprt Ed; Yrbk Awd 85; SUNY Plattsburgh; Cmmnctns.

CONNORS, THOMAS J; Hamburg SR HS; Hamburg, NY; (Y); 42/406; Mgr Band; Concert Band; Jazz Band; Mrchg Band; Orch; School Musical; Symp Band; Var L Ftbl; High Hon Roll; Hon Roll; NY ST Regents Schlrshp 85; PA ST U; Pre-Vet Sci.

CONNORS, WILLIAM J; Syosset HS; Syosset, NY; (Y); 280/500; Boy Scts; Var Trk; NYS Rgnts Schlrshp 85; Manhattan Coll; Mech Engr.

CONOVER, JUDITH; Waterloo SR HS; Waterloo, NY; (Y); 32/178; FTA; Key Clb; Ski Clb; Band; Yrbk Ed-Chief; Sec Soph Cls; Sec Sr Cls; VP Sec Stu Cncl; Var Trk; Hon Roll; Gold Key Awd 85; Radford U; Spec Educ.

CONOVER, MICHAEL G; Akron Central HS; Akron, NY; (Y); 14/157; Boy Scts; Var Bsbl; Var Golf; High Hon Roll; Hon Roll; NHS; Regnts Schlrshp NY 85; Clemson U; Bus.

CONQUET, LISA; Jamaica HS; Jamaica, NY; (Y); 14/534; Ed Yrbk Stf; Ed Lit Mag; VP Stu Cncl; Jr NHS; NHS; Prfct Atten Awd; Intnl Clb; Band; School Musical; Variety Show; Cert Of Recog Amer Chem Soc 83; Semi-Fin Natl Hispnc Scholar Awd Prgm 85; NYS Regent Coll Scholar 85; Biol.

CONRAD, BONNIE; Victor Central SR HS; Victor, NY; (Y); FHA; Spanish Clb; High Hon Roll; Hon Roll; Spcl Ed Tchr.

CONRAD, CHAD; E J Wilson HS; Spencerport, NY; (Y); Boy Scts; Church Yth Grp; Varsity Clb; Var Mgr(s); Var Trk; Var Wrstlng; Hon Roll; Eagle Scout 84.

CONRAD, PAMELA; Faith Bible Acad; Fort Plain, NY; (Y); 1/5; Church Yth Grp; Drama Clb; Chorus; Church Choir; School Musical; Yrbk Ed-Chief; Yrbk Stf; Capt Vllybl; Cit Awd; Hon Roll; Voluntary Camp Cnslr For Mentally Handicapped 82-85; Cedarville Coll; Nursing.

CONRAD, PATRICK M; Lake Shore Central HS; Angola, NY; (Y); 3/259; Yrbk Phtg; Var Ftbl; Var Wrstlng; High Hon Roll; St Schlr; Best Stu Math 83; U Of TX Austin; Chem Engr.

CONROD, TRACEY LYNN; Farmingdale SR HS; Massapequa Park, NY; (Y); French Clb; Ski Clb; Sec Frsh Cls; Sec Jr Cls; Sec Sr Cls; JV Var Cheerleading; Sftbl; Ring Selection Comm; JR Prom Comm; Mktng.

CONROW, TRACY; Oneonta HS; Oneonta, NY; (Y); FBLA; Band; Color Guard; Mrchg Band; Bus.

CONROY, BRENDA; Pioneer Central HS; Java Center, NY; (Y); 16/170; French Clb; Band; Chorus; School Musical; Swing Chorus; Trs Jr Cls; Trs Sr Cls; JV Sftbl; Var Swmmng; JV Var Vllybl; Med.

CONROY, CHRISTIAN M; Cornwall Central HS; Cornwall, NY; (Y); 18/197; Boy Scts; Ski Clb; Nwsp Ed-Chief; Hon Roll; Pres Schlr; St Schlr; Eagle Scout 85; SUNY Albany; Econ.

CONROY, CHRISTOPHER J; Catholic Central HS; Clifton Park, NY; (Y); Chess Clb; Cmnty Wkr; Drama Clb; PAVAS; Thesps; Jazz Band; School Musical; School Play; Lit Mag; Var Golf; Comm Svc Awd, Athl Awf Glf 83; Actng.

CONROY, JOHN W; St Anthonys HS; Farmingville, NY; (Y); JV Var Ftbl; JV Lcrss; Bus Admin.

CONRY, DAWN; Bishop Kearney HS; Brooklyn, NY; (S); 3/344; Ski Clb; Rep Sr Cls; Capt Cheerleading; Var Crs Cntry; Var Trk; High Hon Roll; NHS; Ntl Merit Ltr; Fordham U Pres Scholar 85; John E & Noreen Mc Keen Scholar 85; Fordham U; Lawyr.

CONSER, DAN J; Wilson Central HS; Wilson, NY; (Y); 20/150; Boy Scts; Letterman Clb; Varsity Clb; Stage Crew; Yrbk Stf; Pres Soph Cls; Var L Bsktbl; Var L Ftbl; Hon Roll; FL Southern; Athl Training.

CONSIDINE, KATHLEEN L; Cornwall Central HS; Cornwall, NY; (Y); 17/198; Church Yth Grp; Drama Clb; Hosp Aide; Acpl Chr; Chorus; School Musical; School Play; High Hon Roll; Sec NHS; St Schlr; NY St Regnts Schlrshp 85; Pres Acad Ftns Awd 85; W Point Wives Clb Schlrshp 85; Syracuse U; Aerontcl.

CONSLER, CHRISTY; Honeoye Central Schl; Honeoye, NY; (S); Cmnty Wkr; French Clb; Rep Frsh Cls; VP Soph Cls; VP Stu Cncl; JV Capt Bsktbl; JV Capt Socr; High Hon Roll; NHS; Ski Clb; Bst Soph Term Paper 83-84; Intl Bus.

CONSORTE, MICHAEL; Ossining HS; Ossining, NY; (Y); French Clb; Math Tm; Nwsp Rptr; Ed Nwsp Stf; Yrbk Stf; Stu Cncl; High Hon Roll; Ossining HS French Awd 83-85; Jrnlsm.

CONSTABLE, GEORGE; Minisink Valley HS; Unionville, NY; (Y); Scholastic Bowl; Varsity Clb; Nwsp Rptr; Rep Jr Cls; Stu Cncl; Crs Cntry; Trk; High Hon Roll; NHS; Prfct Atten Awd; US Military Acad; Engrng.

CONSTABLE, JULIE F; St Stephens Schl; New York, NY; (Y); 3/54; Teachers Aide; Varsity Clb; Acpl Chr; Chorus; Church Choir; School Musical; School Play; Variety Show; Yrbk Stf; Lit Mag; Voice, Chorus Awd 83-84; Comp Awd 84; Yale; Frgn Svc.

CONSTANTINE, AMY; Gowanda Central Schl; Gowanda, NY; (Y); AFS; Church Yth Grp; Cmnty Wkr; Dance Clb; Drama Clb; 4-H; Hosp Aide; Ski Clb; Spanish Clb; Thesps; Phy Thrpst.

CONSTANTINO, MICHELE; York Centeral School; Leicester, NY; (Y); Pres Art Clb; Ski Clb; Band; Mrchg Band; School Musical; Nwsp Rptr; Yrbk Stf; Bsktbl.

CONSTANTINOU, ELIZABETH; Lindenhurst SR HS; Lindenhurst, NY; (Y); Sec French Clb; Spanish Clb; Church Yth Grp; Cheerleading; Hon Roll; NHS; Outstndng Achvt Italian Lang 83.

CONTA, JOSEPHINE; Bishop Kearney HS; Brooklyn, NY; (Y); Im Bowling; Hon Roll.

CONTE, JILL; Williamsbille South HS; Wmsvl, NY; (S); Cmnty Wkr; Hst DECA; Pep Clb; Ski Clb; Band; Yrbk Stf; Stu Cncl; Cheerleading; Distrbtv Ed Clbs Amer 4th NY ST Comptn Genl Mktg 85; Wk Exprnc Bermans Inc Top Sls East Cst 4 Wk 85; Erie CC; Ec.

CONTEH, MARGARET; New Rochelle HS; New Rochelle, NY; (Y); Dance Clb; Intnl Clb; Library Aide; Office Aide; School Play; Stage Crew; Var Trk; Var Vllybl; Prfct Atten Awd; Berkely Schl; Wrd Proc.

CONTENTO, DIANA J; Corning East HS; Corning, NY; (Y); Cmnty Wkr; Hosp Aide; Spanish Clb; Chorus; Drill Tm; Variety Show; JV Vllybl; Hon Roll; NHS; SOAR 85-86; Tourism.

CONTENTO, DONNA; Cathedral HS; Jackson Hts, NY; (Y); 137/298; Art Clb; Color Guard; Drm & Bgl; Yrbk Stf; Iona Coll; Acctg.

CONTI, ALICIA; Linton HS; Schenectady, NY; (Y); 32/326; Key Clb; Office Aide; Varsity Clb; Yrbk Phtg; Yrbk Stf; Jr Cls; Stu Cncl; Stat Bsbl; Var L Cheerleading; Var L Socr.

CONTI, DAVE; Trott Vocational HS; Niagara Falls, NY; (Y); Nwsp Rptr; Pres Jr Cls; Pres Sr Cls; JV Var Bsbl; Var Socr; JV Wrstlng; Hon Roll; Jr NHS; NHS.

CONTI, LISAMARIE; Amsterdam HS; Amsterdam, NY; (Y); 4-H; Girl Scts; Hosp Aide; Ski Clb; Bsktbl; Vllybl; Hon Roll; Prfct Atten Awd; Hudson Valley CC; Dntl Asst.

CONTI, MICHAEL; Union-Endicott HS; Endwell, NY; (Y); Boys Clb Am; JV Var Wrstlng; Hon Roll; Engnr.

CONTI, PHIL; Scotia-Glenville HS; Scotia, NY; (Y); Art Clb; Boy Scts; Cmnty Wkr; VP JA; Spanish Clb; JV Trk; Hon Roll; Regents Schlrshp 85; SUNY Albany; Crmnl Jstc.

CONTICCHIO, MICHAEL J; Blessed Sacrament HS; Mt Vernon, NY; (Y); Capt Debate Tm; NFL; Yrbk Ed-Chief; Hon Roll; NY ST Congrssnl Debate Champ 85; Crimnl Justc.

CONTINI, GRACE; John A Coleman HS; Bloomington, NY; (Y); Church Yth Grp; Drama Clb; JA; Key Clb; Service Clb; Var Cheerleading; Stat Crs Cntry; Engl, Mth, Religion, Hlth Hnrs 83-84; Art, Typng Hnrs 84-85; Mth, Engl, Sci Hnrs 82-83; Bus Adm.

CONTINO, ANTHONY; St Agnes HS; Long Island Cty, NY; (Y); 14/100; Hon Roll; Jr NHS; St Johns U; Pre Med.

CONTINO, NANCY; South Shore HS; Brooklyn, NY; (Y); 70/668; Office Aide; Spanish Clb; School Musical; Nwsp Rptr; High Hon Roll; Pres Schlr; Rcpnt Panamerican Scty US Awd 85; NY ST Regents Schlrshp 85; Hofstra U Fresh Schlrshp 85; Hofstra U; Pre-Law.

CONTRATTI, DAVID; Roy C Ketcham HS; Poughkeepsie, NY; (Y); 100/507; Ftbl; Hon Roll; Marist Coll Cmmtr Schlrshp 85; Pres Acadmc Ftnss Awd 85; Marist Coll; Comp Sci.

CONTRINO, JOSEPH R; Smithtown West HS; Smithtown, NY; (Y); Computer Clb; Bowling; Socr; Trk; Hon Roll; Clarkson U; Computer Engrng.

CONVERY, SUSAN K; Fox Lane HS; Mount Kisco, NY; (Y); #36 In Class; Hosp Aide; Nwsp Rptr; Nwsp Stf; JV Capt Bsktbl; Powder Puff Ftbl; Var Socr; High Hon Roll; NHS; NYS Rgnts Schlrshp Wnnr 85; Franklin/Marshall Coll; Pedtrcs.

CONWAY, DONNA; Pavilion Central HS; E Bethany, NY; (Y); Art Clb; FTA; Sec Soph Cls; Pres Jr Cls; Rep Stu Cncl; Var L Bsktbl; Var Capt Sftbl; Var Capt Vllybl; Cit Awd; NHS; St Nicholas Clb Scholar 85; Colonel Sanders Scholar 85; Berea Coll; Art.

CONWAY, JACQUELINE A; Cardinal Spellman HS; Bronx, NY; (Y); Church Yth Grp; Dance Clb; Girl Scts; Key Clb; Concert Band; Mrchg Band; High Hon Roll; Ntl Merit Ltr; NY St Regents Schlrshp 84-85; St U-NY; Pol Sci.

CONWAY, JOHN J; St Francis Prep; Bayside, NY; (Y); 322/690; Drama Clb; Hosp Aide; Model UN; Political Wkr; Thesps; School Musical; School Play; Stage Crew; Im Socr; Im Vllybl; Regents Schlrshp 85; Principals Schlrshp St Francis Coll 85; St Francis Coll; Hist.

CONWAY, LARRY; Mc Kee Vocational & Tech; Staten Is, NY; (Y); 40/238; Elec.

CONWAY, MICHELLE; Tamarac HS; Johnsonville, NY; (Y); Intnl Clb; Science Clb; Yrbk Stf; Off Jr Cls; Socr; Trk; Hon Roll; Bus Mgt.

CONWAY, MIKE; Xavier HS; Montclair, NJ; (Y); Church Yth Grp; Yrbk Phtg; Off Sr Cls; Bsktbl; Ftbl; Wt Lftg; Hon Roll.

CONWAY, PAUL; St Francis Prep; Astoria, NY; (Y); Art Clb; Boy Scts; Drama Clb; School Musical; School Play; Stage Crew; Tennis; Arch.

CONWAY, WILLIAM; Archbishop Molloy HS; Astoria, NY; (Y); 32/360; Church Yth Grp; Church Choir; Var JV Bsbl; JV Bsktbl; Im Ftbl; Im Sftbl; Im Tennis; Im Trk; Hon Roll; Jr NHS; Peer Grp Cnslng; Chldrns Hosp Vlntr; Fordham U; Mrktng.

COOK JR, ALLEN J; J C Bridlebough HS; Phoenix, NY; (Y); Hon Roll; Prfct Atten Awd; ST U Canton; Air Cond Engr.

COOK, BRIAN F; Oriskany Central HS; Oriskany, NY; (Y); 3/72; Band; Nwsp Ed-Chief; Yrbk Phtg; Rep Stu Cncl; Var L Bsbl; JV Capt Bsktbl; Cit Awd; High Hon Roll; Pres Jr NHS; VP NHS; Eng Awd 83-85; Soc Stu Awd 83-84; Outstndng Frshmn Awd Phys Ed 82-83; Med.

COOK, DANNY; Nazareth Regional HS; Brooklyn, NY; (Y); Exploring; Radio Clb; Yrbk Sprt Ed.

COOK, DARWYN; Altmar-Parish-Williamstown HS; Parish, NY; (Y); Band; Concert Band; Jazz Band; Mrchg Band; Pep Band; Var Wt Lftg; JV Var Wrstlng; NHS; High Hon Roll; Hon Roll; Math & Sci.

COOK III, GRANT W; Lockport Senior HS; Lockport, NY; (Y); 19/455; Drama Clb; Varsity Clb; Chorus; Jazz Band; Symp Band; Trs Jr Cls; Rep Stu Cncl; Var L Ftbl; NHS; Presdntl Acad Ftnss, Music, Drama, Navy Marine Clb Amer Awds 85; Heidelberg Coll; Music.

COOK, JENNIFER; Midwood HS; Brooklyn, NY; (Y); 2/500; Church Yth Grp; Girl Scts; Teachers Aide; Varsity Clb; Chorus; Church Choir; Madrigals; Var Socr; Lion Awd; Prfct Atten Awd; Doctor.

COOK, JESSICA; Cardinal Spellman HS; Bronx, NY; (Y); 2/580; Church Yth Grp; Computer Clb; Vllybl; Hon Roll; NHS; Ntl Merit Ltr.

COOK, JOHN; Saranac Central Schl; Cadyville, NY; (S); Church Yth Grp; Band; Church Choir; Concert Band; Jazz Band; Mrchg Band; Orch; School Musical; Stage Crew; Hon Roll; Coll Community Orch 84-85; NYSSMA Fall & Spg Fest 82-85; Ag.

COOK, KEVIN; Franklin Central HS; Franklin, NY; (Y); 1/21; Am Leg Boys St; 4-H; Jazz Band; Yrbk Ed-Chief; Bausch & Lomb Sci Awd; JP Sousa Awd; NHS; Val; Ski Clb; Band; Cornell U; Plnt Sci.

COOK, LARRY; Victor Central HS; Victor, NY; (Y); Model UN; High Hon Roll; Hon Roll; Elctrcl Engrng.

COOK, MARY A; Corning Painted Post East HS; Corning, NY; (Y); 26/230; Drama Clb; Hosp Aide; Thesps; Concert Band; Mrchg Band; School Musical; School Play; Off Stu Cncl; High Hon Roll; Hon Roll; Steuben All-Cnty Symphnc Band; Area All-ST Orch, Symphnc Band; Bio.

COOK, MARY B; Hoosick Falls Central HS; Eagle Bridge, NY; (Y); Computer Clb; 4-H; Pres FBLA; Pres Pep Clb; Chorus; Yrbk Ed-Chief; Yrbk Stf; Stu Cncl; Hon Roll; NHS; Edith Grace Craig Reynolds Schlrshp 85; Masonic Assn Schlrshp 85; Culinary Inst Of Am; Clnry Arts.

COOK, MATTHEW; Hendrick Hudson HS; Peekskill, NY; (Y); 13/200; Chess Clb; Trs Sr Cls; Rep Stu Cncl; Var Capt Crs Cntry; Var Capt Wrstlng; High Hon Roll; NHS; Pres Schlr; Hghst Avg Fr II 83; Hghst Mrk Fr Regnts 99 Prcnt 84; VA Polytech Inst; Comp Sci.

COOK, SCOTT A; Notre Dame HS; Clayville, NY; (Y); 9/174; Dance Clb; VP Drama Clb; Red Cross Aide; ROTC; Thesps; Capt Drill Tm; School Musical; Variety Show; Rep Frsh Cls; Rep Soph Cls; Regents Schlrshp 85; Acad All-Amer 85; Rhythm Lite Yr 82; Perf Arts.

COOK, SHANE; Groton Central HS; Groton, NY; (Y); Chess Clb; Computer Clb; Math Tm; Rep Sr Cls; Rep Stu Cncl; High Hon Roll; JETS Awd; SUNY; Elec Engrng.

COOK, SUSAN E; Jamesville-Dewitt HS; Dewitt, NY; (Y); Pres Key Clb; Ski Clb; Pres Spanish Clb; Sec Bsbl; Var Socr; Hon Roll; Regents Schlrshp 85; Ithaca Coll; Phy Therpy.

COOK, TRACY; Saugerties HS; Saugerties, NY; (Y); Cmnty Wkr; Hosp Aide; Pres JA; Band; Concert Band; Drill Tm; Mrchg Band; JV Bsktbl; Physcl Ftnss Awd 83; Marist Coll; Bio.

COOK, VICKI A; Herman-Dekalb Central HS; Hermon, NY; (Y); Church Yth Grp; Drama Clb; 4-H; Band; Mrchg Band; Nwsp Stf; Var Capt Bsktbl; Var Socr; 4-H Awd; Prfct Atten Awd; William Cooper Mem Schlrshp 85; St Lawrence Cnty Maple Queen 85-86; Frank & Katie Oaks Yng Mem Awd 85; Canton ATC; Bus Admin.

COOK, WILLY F; Owen D Young Central HS; Ft Plain, NY; (Y); Drm & Bgl; Var Bsbl; Var JV Bsktbl; Var Socr; Cit Awd; Jr NHS; NHS; Computer Clb; Drama Clb; Band; Mayflower Compact Awd 85; Siena; Comp Sci.

COOKE, KELLY J; Salmon River Central HS; Ft Covington, NY; (Y); 14/94; Church Yth Grp; Cmnty Wkr; Rep Soph Cls; VP Jr Cls; Pres Sr Cls; Rep Stu Cncl; Var Capt Bsbl; Var Capt Ice Hcky; Var Capt Socr; DAR Awd; MVP V Hcky 85; Salmon River Ctrl Stu Yr 85; Outstndng Athl 85; Elect Engr.

COOKE, STEPHEN; Saugerties HS; Saugerties, NY; (Y); Acpl Chr; Band; Chorus; Church Choir; Concert Band; Mrchg Band; School Musical; School Play; Var Ftbl; Var Trk; All St Vocal Solo 85; NYSMA Solo Exclnt 84; Plce Ofcr.

COOKHOUSE, FAYE; Fayetteville-Manlius HS; Manlius, NY; (Y); Aud/Vis; Thesps; School Musical; School Play; Mgr Stage Crew; Var Crs Cntry; Var L Trk; High Hon Roll; Hon Roll; Awd Excllnc Spnsh 85; Lang Arts.

COOLBAUGH, KEVIN; Chenango Forks HS; Binghamton, NY; (Y); 22/186; Ski Clb; Varsity Clb; High Hon Roll; Hon Roll; Var JV Lcrss; Hnr Rl 82, 83 & 84; Achvt Awds/Soc Stu, Bio & Span 83 & 84; Broome CC; Sci.

COOLEY, CANDACE; Remsen Central HS; Remsen, NY; (Y); French Clb; Pep Clb; Ski Clb; Varsity Clb; Jazz Band; Mrchg Band; Orch; Sftbl; Vllybl; High Hon Roll; SUNY-BINGHAMPTON; Bio.

COOMBS, KIMBERLY J; Addison Central HS; Addison, NY; (Y); 4/97; Am Leg Aux Girls St; GAA; Ski Clb; Yrbk Stf; Off Stu Cncl; Capt Var Bsktbl; Var Tennis; Var Capt Vllybl; High Hon Roll; NHS; NY ST Regnts Schlrshp 85; Twn Tier Schlrshp Alfred U 85; All Str Tm Regn Bsktbl 85; Alfred U; Cermc Engrng.

COON, ANDREA; Penn Yan Acad; Penn Yan, NY; (Y); 33/165; Quiz Bowl; Ski Clb; Nwsp Bus Mgr; Rep Sr Cls; JV Mgr Bsktbl; Capt JV Socr; JV Mgr Vllybl; High Hon Roll; Hon Roll; NYS Rgnts Schlrshp Awd 84-85; Beloit Coll; Soc Sci.

COON, DAVID; Westhampton Beach HS; Westhampton Bch, NY; (Y); 6/200; Computer Clb; Spanish Clb; Band; Chorus; Yrbk Phtg; Rep Soph Cls; Rep Jr Cls; JV Tennis; NHS; Aud/Vis; Presdntl Clsrm For Yng Amer; Engrng.

COON, SHELLEY; Our Lady Of Mercy HS; Fairport, NY; (Y); JA; Ski Clb; Spanish Clb; School Play; Rep Stu Cncl; Trk; Hon Roll; Psych.

COON, STACEY MARIE; Canastota JR SR HS; Canastota, NY; (Y); 15/135; Cmnty Wkr; Sec 4-H; GAA; Pres Intnl Clb; Library Aide; Science Clb; Teachers Aide; School Musical; JV Fld Hcky; Var Golf; Bryant & Stratton Powelson; Med.

COONEY, DIANE; Clarkstown High Schl South; New City, NY; (Y); Sec Church Yth Grp; Cmnty Wkr; Varsity Clb; Church Choir; Ed Yrbk Stf; Bsktbl; Lcrss; Powder Puff Ftbl.

COONEY, JAMES; Mt Upton Central HS; Mt Upton, NY; (Y); Church Yth Grp; Ski Clb; Var L Bsbl; JV L Bsktbl; Var L Socr; Hon Roll.

COONEY, LESLIE; Westhampton Beach HS; Westhamptn Bch, NY; (Y); Trk; Cosmetlgy.

COONEY, LISA; Jamesville-Dewitt HS; Syracuse, NY; (Y); GAA; Varsity Clb; Var L Bsktbl; Var L Sftbl; Acad Awd Phy Ed 85; All Cnty Bsktbll 85; Acctng.

COONRADT, KIMBERLY; Stissing Mt JR SR HS; Clinton Corners, NY; (Y); Cmnty Wkr; Pres 4-H; JV Var Bsktbl; Var Crs Cntry; JV Sftbl; Swmmng; Trk; 4-H Awd; Hon Roll; Oneonta Coll; Hme Econ Tchr.

COONS, DARLENE; Watkins Glen HS; Rock Stream, NY; (Y); 3/126; Am Leg Aux Girls St; Church Yth Grp; Band; School Play; VP Jr Cls; VP Stu Cncl; Var Bsktbl; High Hon Roll; Hon Roll; NHS; Engrng.

COONS, SHAWN; Lansingburgh HS; Troy, NY; (Y); French Clb; Rep Sr Cls; High Hon Roll; Jr NHS; 2nd Hghst Ave Ovrll 83; Air Force; Air Trffc Cntrllr.

COOPER, ANDREA JEAN; Warrensburg Central HS; Warrensburg, NY; (S); 2/68; Church Yth Grp; 4-H; French Clb; Varsity Clb; Var Fld Hcky; Hon Roll; NHS; Med.

COOPER, BRUCE; Bishop Grimes HS; Syracuse, NY; (Y); FBLA; Nwsp Phtg; Nwsp Rptr; Nwsp Stf; Yrbk Phtg; Yrbk Stf; Golf; OCC; Engrng.

COOPER, DARCI; Freeport HS; Freeport, NY; (Y); Key Clb; Letterman Clb; Sec Trs Ski Clb; Varsity Clb; Nwsp Rptr; Var Crs Cntry; Var Gym; Var Trk; High Hon Roll; Trs NHS.

COOPER, GAYLE; Hannibal HS; Hannibal, NY; (S); Varsity Clb; Rep Jr Cls; Rep Stu Cncl; Var Trk; Var Capt Vllybl; High Hon Roll; Hon Roll; NHS; SUNY Oswego; Acctng.

COOPER, JACQUELINE; Dewitt Clinton HS; Bronx, NY; (Y); Cmnty Wkr; Dance Clb; FNA; Hosp Aide; Chorus; UFT Awd 83; Ben Chancey Awd 83; Bus Admin.

COOPER, JILL; Bishop Scully HS; Amsterdam, NY; (Y); Church Yth Grp; JA; Political Wkr; Spanish Clb; Rep Stu Cncl; Tennis; Nrsng.

COOPER, MARSHALL; Rye Neck HS; Rye, NY; (Y); 11/96; AFS; Ski Clb; Pres Band; Jazz Band; Orch; Rep Stu Cncl; Socr; Tennis; Wrstlng; NHS; NYS Regnts Schlrshp 85; U Of MI.

COOPER, MELISSA; Dryden Central Schl; Dryden, NY; (Y); Dance Clb; GAA; Pep Clb; Chorus; Capt Var Cheerleading; Var Sftbl; Im Vllybl; High Hon Roll; Hon Roll; Bus.

COOPER, MELISSA; Henninger HS; Syracuse, NY; (Y); Church Yth Grp; French Clb; Intnl Clb; Pep Clb; Ski Clb; Yrbk Stf; Off Jr Cls; Off Sr Cls; Dnfth Awd; Hon Roll; Hofstra U; Engl.

COOPER, NANCY; Horseheads HS; Horseheads, NY; (Y); 74/370; Dance Clb; Latin Clb; Varsity Clb; Orch; Pres Jr Cls; Pres Sr Cls; Off Stu Cncl; Var Capt Cheerleading; Hon Roll; Miss Fngr Lks Tngr 84; Bucknell U; Law.

COOPER, ROBERT; Vestal SR HS; Vestal, NY; (Y); Prfct Atten Awd; Broome Cmnty Coll; Comp.

COOPER, SANDRA; Bishop Kearney HS; Brooklyn, NY; (Y); Spanish Clb; Hon Roll; NHS; Barouch City Col; Comp Syst.

COOPER, STACY; Tottenville HS; Staten Island, NY; (Y); Pres Temple Yth Grp; Concert Band; School Play; Stage Crew; Nwsp Rptr; Nwsp Stf; Yrbk Rptr; Rep Soph Cls; Communctns.

COOPER, THERESA; Gr Island HS; Gr Island, NY; (Y); Yrbk Stf; DAR Awd; NHS; Erie CC; Resp Thrpst.

COOPER, THERESA A; Hillcrest HS; S Ozone Pk, NY; (Y); 48/793; Cmnty Wkr; Hosp Aide; JA; Red Cross Aide; Chorus; Church Choir; Yrbk Stf; Hon Roll; Prfct Atten Awd; Natl Hnr Roll 83-84; Med.

COOPERMAN, TODD; Oceanside SR HS; Oceanside, NY; (Y); VP Computer Clb; Exploring; Model UN; Temple Yth Grp; Nwsp Stf; Hon Roll; Jr NHS; NHS; Ntl Merit Ltr; Spanish NHS; Amer Assn Tchrs Spnsh, Portgse Cntst; Chem.

COPELAND, MOLLY; Webster HS; Webster, NY; (Y); Camp Fr Inc; Church Yth Grp; Cmnty Wkr; Hosp Aide; Library Aide; Chorus; Swing Chorus; Variety Show; Lit Mag; Bsktbl; Cert Of Cmmndtn Distngshd Schl Citz Awd 84; Finley Coll; Anml Hsbndry.

COPP, BRENNAN; Mynderse Acad; Seneca Falls, NY; (S); 3/136; Boy Scts; Church Yth Grp; Ski Clb; Varsity Clb; Pres Frsh Cls; Bsbl; Bsktbl; Ftbl; DAR Awd; High Hon Roll; Natl Hnr Roll 84; Eagle Scout 84; USMA.

COPPETO, THOMAS J; Mt Vernon HS; Mount Vernon, NY; (Y); 1/590; Am Leg Boys St; Aud/Vis; Pres Key Clb; Math Clb; Science Clb; Nwsp Phtg; Sec Sr Cls; Capt Swmmng; Bausch & Lomb Sci Awd; High Hon Roll; Rensselaer Sci & Math Medal 84; NY ST Regents Schlrshp 84-85; Columbia U Sci Hnrs Pgm 84-85; MIT; Physics.

COPPINGER, TERENCE; Holy Cross HS; Bayside, NY; (Y); 100/460; Church Yth Grp; JV Trk; Hon Roll; Elec Engrng.

COPPOLA, ELIZABETH; North Babylon SR HS; N Babylon, NY; (Y); 58/556; High Hon Roll; Jr NHS; Prsdntl Acadmc Ftns Awd 85; Pace U; Accntn.

COPPOLA, MARIA; Linton HS; Schenectady, NY; (Y); 24/273; Intnl Clb; JA; Yrbk Phtg; Hon Roll; Sci Fair Proj Bacteria 1st Prz 81, Lungs 1st Prz 82; Achvt Awd Art 82; Accntnt.

COPPOLINO, DIANNA-MARIE; Somers HS; Yorktown Hghts, NY; (Y); 10/213; Teachers Aide; Chorus; High Hon Roll; Hon Roll; NHS; Spanish NHS; Cert Merit-Acctg II 85; Somers Falcty Assn-Acad Recog 85; Pace U Pleasantville; Bus.

CORASANITI, TONY; Henninger HS; Syracuse, NY; (Y); Im Bsktbl; Im Fld Hcky; Var Ftbl; JV Lcrss; Var JV Trk; Var JV Wt Lftg; Engr.

CORBETT, CHRISTINE; Franciscan HS; Peekskill, NY; (Y); Drama Clb; Chorus; Church Choir; School Musical; School Play; Variety Show; Nwsp Bus Mgr; Yrbk Bus Mgr; Rep Frsh Cls; French Hon Soc; Cmnctns.

CORBETT, JEAN MARIE; West Islip HS; West Islip, NY; (Y); 21/525; Ski Clb; Yrbk Stf; JV Bsktbl; Stat Lcrss; Var L Pom Pon; Hon Roll; NHS; Im Vllybl; Rgnts Schlrshp 85; Villanova U; Law.

CORBETT, KELLY; Soluay HS; Lakeland, NY; (Y); Math Clb; Trs Frsh Cls; Off Jr Cls; Var Bsktbl; Var JV Socr; Var Sftbl; Var Capt Vllybl; High Hon Roll; NHS; 2nd Tm All Cnty Vrsty Sftbl 85; JR Prom Queen 85; Spn Awd 84; Acctg.

CORBETT, MICHELLE; Onondaga Central HS; Syracuse, NY; (S); Art Clb; Trs GAA; Spanish Clb; Rep Frsh Cls; Stu Cncl; VP Crs Cntry; Socr; High Hon Roll; NHS; Prfct Atten Awd; Corp Law.

CORBI, CAROLINE; Cardinal Spellman HS; Bronx, NY; (Y); Cmnty Wkr; GAA; Yrbk Stf; Im Bsktbl; Coach Actv; Sftbl; High Hon Roll; Manhattan Coll; Engrng.

CORBIN, TRACY; Menninger HS; Syracuse, NY; (Y); 14/450; Church Yth Grp; Cmnty Wkr; Intnl Clb; Ski Clb; Yrbk Stf; Score Keeper; High Hon Roll; Hon Roll; NHS; Prfct Atten Awd; Natl Hnr Roll 83-84; ST U Af Buffalo; Engr.

CORCOARN, ROBERT F; Newfield HS; Selden, NY; (Y); 7/562; Church Yth Grp; Computer Clb; Drama Clb; VICA; School Play; Stage Crew; Trk; High Hon Roll; Hon Roll; Jr NHS; Stu Mnth 82; Carnegie; Elec Engr.

CORCORAN, BRIDGET; Frontier Central HS; Hamburg, NY; (S); Girl Scts; Library Aide; Office Aide; Hon Roll; NHS; NEDT Awd; Cosmetology.

CORCORAN, COLLEEN M; Shenendehowa HS; Clifton Park, NY; (Y); Church Yth Grp; Cmnty Wkr; Ski Clb; Off Soph Cls; Off Jr Cls; High Hon Roll; Ntl Frnch Cntst Cert Of Merit 85; Gregg Typng Awd 84; Schlstc Achvt Cert 82-85.

CORCORAN, JUSTIN; C A Bouton HS; Voorheesville, NY; (Y); Trs Key Clb; Nwsp Rptr; Trs Jr Cls; Rep Stu Cncl; Var Bsktbl; Var Capt Socr; VP NHS; Hon Roll; John Robert Larabee Mem Awd 85; Colonial Cncl All Star Soccer 84-85; St Matthews Chrch Cncl 85.

CORCORAN, KEVIN; Saint Anthonys HS; Kings Pk, NY; (Y); Church Yth Grp; Computer Clb; Intnl Clb; Red Cross Aide; Spanish Clb; High Hon Roll; Jr NHS; NHS; Spanish NHS; Pre-Med.

CORCORAN, MARK; Iona Prep Schl; New Rochelle, NY; (Y); 4/198; Ski Clb; Nwsp Stf; Yrbk Sprt Ed; JV Bsbl; Var L Golf; Wt Lftg; High Hon Roll; NHS; Ntl Merit Schol; Lib Arts.

CORCORAN, PAMELA; Bishop Grimes HS; Liverpool, NY; (Y); 9/150; Hosp Aide; Chorus; School Musical; Variety Show; Im Bowling; High Hon Roll; NHS; NEMA 85; Hrsbck Rdng & Show Rbbns 83-85; Alfred U; Bio.

CORCORAN, PATRICK J; Pine Bush HS; Walden, NY; (Y); 1/289; Math Tm; Ski Clb; Orch; Yrbk Phtg; VP Stu Cncl; Var Capt Socr; VP Capt Trk; Bausch & Lomb Sci Awd; High Hon Roll; NHS; RPI; Chem Engrng.

CORCORAN, ROBERT F; Newfield HS; Selden, NY; (S); 7/562; Church Yth Grp; Pres Trs Computer Clb; Drama Clb; VICA; Trk; Hon Roll; Jr NHS; NHS; Stu Of Mnth 81; Carnegi Mellon U; Elec Engrng.

CORCORAN, TOMMY J; West Isup HS; W Islip, NY; (Y); Var L Ftbl; Var Capt Lcrss; Var L Wrstlng; 2nd Tm All Lgu Suffolk Cnty NY 85; Physcl Thrpy.

CORCUERA, JIM; Amsterdam HS; Amsterdam, NY; (Y); Stage Crew; Rep Soph Cls; Rep Jr Cls; Rep Stu Cncl; High Hon Roll; Hon Roll; Fulton Montgomery Cmmnty.

CORDANI, LAURA; Half Hollow Hills HS East; Dix Hills, NY; (Y); FBLA; Hosp Aide; Leo Clb; Spanish Clb; Yrbk Stf; Cheerleading; High Hon Roll; Jr NHS; NHS; Spanish NHS; Engrng.

CORDARO, STEPHEN; St Francis Prep; Whitestone, NY; (S); 30/700; Church Yth Grp; Computer Clb; Ski Clb; Var L Tennis; Var L Trk; High Hon Roll; NHS; Pre-Med.

CORDELL, JOY; John Jay SR HS; Fishkill, NY; (Y); 31/560; Church Yth Grp; Cmnty Wkr; Office Aide; Lit Mag; L Co-Capt Gym; JV Socr; High Hon Roll; Sec NHS; Ntl Merit SF.

CORDELL, SHARI; Sandy Creek Central HS; Sandy Creek, NY; (Y); Art Clb; Ski Clb; Teachers Aide; Chorus; Color Guard; Mrchg Band; Stat Ftbl; Var Socr; JV Sftbl; JV Var Vllybl; Physical Educ Outstndng Ftnss Awd 82-85; AZ ST U; Crt Rptr.

CORDELLO, DENNIS; Gates-Chili HS; Rochester, NY; (S); 32/463; Chess Clb; Church Yth Grp; JA; Service Clb; Spanish Clb; JV Stat Bsbl; L Var Ftbl; Mgr(s); Var Wt Lftg; JV Wrstlng; Acctng.

CORDERO, BENITO JOSE; Yonkers HS; Yonkers, NY; (Y); Math Clb; Crs Cntry; JV Ftbl; Swmmng; Wt Lftg; Manhatten Coll; Elec Engr.

CORDERO, FRANK R; La Guardia HS Of Music & Art; Bronx, NY; (Y); 21/588; Science Clb; Hon Roll; Prfct Atten Awd; Art Hnr League 84; James Brody Art Awd 82; Gvrnrs Cmtee Schlstc Achvt 82; Syracuse U; Illstrtn.

CORDERO, PATRICIA; St Catherines Acad; Bronx, NY; (Y); 57/205; Dance Clb; Drill Tm; School Musical; School Play; Variety Show; Socr; Sftbl; Vllybl; Hon Roll; NHS; Mrktg.

CORECCIA, LORI; Clarkstown North HS; New City, NY; (Y); Ski Clb; Varsity Clb; JV Sftbl; Hon Roll; MVP Ski Team 85; Italian Club; Co-Capt Ski Team 85; ST Sectnls Ski Team 85; Bus.

CORENLL, CHARLENE; Broadalbin Central Schl; Broadalbin, NY; (Y); Church Yth Grp; Drama Clb; French Clb; Letterman Clb; Library Aide; Varsity Clb; Band; Church Choir; Concert Band; Mrchg Band; Mst Dedctd Chrldr 84-85.

CORIGLIANO, JACQUELINE; Immaculata Acad; W Seneca, NY; (Y); 6/45; Quiz Bowl; Chorus; Church Choir; Nwsp Rptr; VP Frsh Cls; Sec Stu Cncl; Cheerleading; Sftbl; Hon Roll; NHS; Testamur Latn Hnrs Socty Assn Prom Of Latn 85; Cert Mert MI Sftbl 2nd Tm All Str 85; Nws.

CORIGLIANO, ROSEMARIE; Franciscan HS; Fort Montgomery, NY; (Y); Office Aide; Red Cross Aide; Nrsg.

CORKERY, TODD E; Jamestown HS; Jamestown, NY; (Y); Church Yth Grp; Cmnty Wkr; JA; Political Wkr; Ski Clb; Spanish Clb; Cert Of Accomplishment Proj Bus 83; Merit Diploma Spanish/Engl Tutoring Proj 85; St Bonaventure U; Accntnt.

CORKHILL, NEIL; Lindenhurst SR HS; Lindenhurst, NY; (Y); Boy Scts; German Clb; Hon Roll; NHS; Stony Brook; Lbrl Arts.

CORLETTA, DEBORAHANN; Saint Johns Prep; Long Island City, NY; (Y); JV Var Cheerleading; High Hon Roll; NHS; St Johns U; Acctng.

CORLETTO, OLGA; Norman Thomas HS; West New York, NJ; (S); 86/671; JA; Hon Roll; Valedictorian 82.

CORMAN, AARON; Bethlehem Central HS; Glenmont, NY; (Y); 22/338; Soroptimist; Temple Yth Grp; Stu Cncl; JV Var Socr; Var Wrstlng; High Hon Roll; NHS; Pres Schlr; Excllnc Creatv Wrtg; ST U NY Albany; Finc.

CORN, MIKE G; Beach Channel HS; Belle Harb, NY; (Y); Math Tm; Quiz Bowl; Band; Ed Yrbk Rptr; Tennis; Jr NHS; Socl Stud Mdl; Law.

CORNACCHIO, SALLYANN; Moore Catholic HS; Staten Island, NY; (Y); 16/178; Cmnty Wkr; Math Tm; Chorus; Stage Crew; Yrbk Bus Mgr; Stu Cncl; Hon Roll; NHS; Library Aide; Science Clb; Acad All-Am Schlr Pgm 84-85; US Stu Cncl Awd 84-85; NY ST Regents Schlrsph 85; Rutgers U; Bio Sci.

CORNEAU, PATTI; Madrid Waddington HS; Madrid, NY; (Y); 5/65; Debate Tm; Drama Clb; French Clb; NFL; Spanish Clb; Speech Tm; School Musical; Socr; High Hon Roll; Hon Roll; 8th US Natl Cath Forn Lg 84; 8th NYS Spch Chmpshps 85; Nazareth Coll; Eng Tchr.

CORNEILLE, MICHELE; Tupper Lake HS; Tupper Lk, NY; (Y); 4/117; 4-H; Science Clb; Chorus; Stage Crew; 4-H Awd; High Hon Roll; NHS; Prfct Atten Awd; Math Awd 84; RI Schl Desgn; Arch.

CORNEILSON, CHRISTINE; Unatego JR SR HS; Bainbridge, NY; (Y); Church Yth Grp; Girl Scts; Letterman Clb; Spanish Clb; Varsity Clb; Chorus; Yrbk Stf; Stat Crs Cntry; Stat Trk; JV Var Vllybl; Cmnctns.

CORNELIUS, ANNE; Groton JR SR HS; Groton, NY; (Y); Church Yth Grp; Library Aide; Spanish Clb; Stat Bsbl; High Hon Roll; Hon Roll; Bus.

CORNELL, DEBORAH; Newfield HS; Selden, NY; (Y); #24 In Class; DECA; High Hon Roll; Hon Roll; Jr NHS; St Schlr; Stony Brook; Engl.

CORNELL, LORI; Jamestown HS; Jamestown, NY; (Y); Ski Clb; Chorus; Color Guard; Cheerleading; Swmmng; Sci.

CORNELL, REBECCA J; Pawling HS; Pawling, NY; (Y); 24/66; Church Yth Grp; Thesps; Varsity Clb; VP Chorus; School Play; Nwsp Stf; Yrbk Stf; Var Cheerleading; Rgnts Schlrshp 85; Sch Mascot 84-85; Plattsburgh ST U; Soclgy.

CORNEY, ANNEMARIE; St Edmunds HS; Brooklyn, NY; (Y); 43/187; Hosp Aide; Im Bowling; Sftbl; NHS; Nrsng.

CORNIEL, JOHN; Rice HS; New York, NY; (S); High Hon Roll; Hon Roll.

CORNISH, ANNE; Town Of Webb HS; Old Forge, NY; (S); 1/35; Spanish Clb; Chorus; Concert Band; Jazz Band; School Musical; Variety Show; Var Cheerleading; JV Vllybl; High Hon Roll; NHS; Math Teachr.

CORNISH, KAREN M; Thomas A Edison HS; Elmira Heights, NY; (Y); Cmnty Wkr; Drama Clb; Band; Chorus; Church Choir; Nwsp Stf; Stu Cncl; Mgr(s); Hon Roll; Church Yth Grp; Excllnt Ratgs NYSSMA; Capt A Sqd Clrgrd; Erly Chldhd Svcs.

CORNISH, REBECCA; North Rose Wolcott HS; Auburn, NY; (Y); 17/140; Office Aide; Spanish Clb; Teachers Aide; Chorus; Church Choir; School Musical; High Hon Roll; NHS; Bus Awd 84; Auburn; Sec.

CORNISH JR, RICHARD V; Rome Free Acad; Rome, NY; (Y); 24/512; Boy Scts; Church Yth Grp; VP Exploring; Intnl Clb; Red Cross Aide; Variety Show; High Hon Roll; Jr NHS; NHS; Voice Dem Awd; Eagle Scout 82; Rgnts Schlrshp 85; Vice Ldg Chf Ord Arrow 83-84; Rochester Inst Tech; Engrng.

CORNNELL, RICHARD; Holland Patent Central HS; Holland Patent, NY; (Y); Boy Scts; Band; Wrstlng; Hon Roll; Eagle Scout 84; Morrisville; Auto Body.

CORNUTE, ANTOINETTE R; Saratoga Springs HS; Saratoga Springs, NY; (Y); Pres Church Yth Grp; Drama Clb; GAA; Key Clb; Varsity Clb; Chorus; Var L Cheerleading; JV Gym; Var L Trk; Hon Roll; Syracuse; Math.

CORNWELL, PETER; Mineola HS; Albertson, NY; (Y); VP Church Yth Grp; Band; Chorus; Church Choir; Concert Band; Jazz Band; Mrchg Band; Pep Band; School Musical; St Johns U Pep Band 85; Fredonia ST U; Music Educ.

CORONA, IDA; St Barnabas HS; Bronx, NY; (Y); 58/187; Office Aide; Teachers Aide; Prfct Atten Awd; FIT; Fshn Merch.

CORONA, NICHOLAS; St Francis Prep; Queens Village, NY; (Y); 237/693; Am Leg Boys St; Debate Tm; W Point; Atty.

CORP, THOMAS; Liverpool HS; Liverpool, NY; (Y); JV Var Bsbl; JV Var Ftbl; Im Wt Lftg; JV Wrstlng; Bus.

CORPREW, AISHA; John Dewey HS; Brooklyn, NY; (Y); Concert Band; Wt Lftg; Barnard U; Civl Lwyr.

CORRA, LORI M; Grover Cleveland HS; Brooklyn, NY; (Y); 23/769; Computer Clb; Office Aide; Science Clb; Yrbk Stf; Lit Mag; High Hon Roll; Hon Roll; Prfct Atten Awd; Sci Wrtng Awd 82; Math Cert Awd 83; Regents ST Schlrshp 85; NY U; Comp Sci.

CORRADINI, ANDREA; Batavia HS; Batavia, NY; (Y); 17/228; Girl Scts; Band; Chorus; Concert Band; Mrchg Band; School Musical; Variety Show; Yrbk Phtg; Yrbk Rptr; Yrbk Stf; Syracuse U; Bus Mgmt.

CORRADINO, MICHELLE; Sachem North HS; Holbrook, NY; (Y); 103/1383; Teachers Aide; High Hon Roll; Cert Of Awd Chld Stds 85; 2nd Pl NY For Ntl Hstry Day 83; Cert Of Achvt Ntl Cntst Ntl Hstry Day 83; SUNY Stny Brk; Physcl Thrpst.

CORRADO, JOHN M; Marlboro HS; Marlboro, NY; (Y); 14/160; High Hon Roll; Drivrs Ed Awd 85; Dutchess CC; Elec Engrng.

CORRADO, JOSEPH; Marlboro Central HS; Marlboro, NY; (Y); 23/160; Dutchess CC; Comp Sci.

CORRARO, STEVE; Oneonia HS; Oneonta, NY; (Y); Boys Clb Am; Boy Scts; Church Yth Grp; Letterman Clb; Ski Clb; Varsity Clb; Band; Var L Bsbl; Var L Bsktbl; Var Golf.

CORREA, ANA MARIA; St Johns Prep; Elmhurst, NY; (S); 116/415; Dance Clb; Drama Clb; Ski Clb; Chorus; School Musical; School Play; Rep Stu Cncl; Hon Roll; VP Soph Cls; Rep Jr Cls; PS 89 2nd Grade Queens Art Awd; Queens Coll; Choreogrphy.

CORREA JR, ANTONIO; Cardinal Hayes HS; Bronx, NY; (Y); 27/264; Aud/Vis; Boys Clb Am; Stage Crew; Yrbk Stf; Stu Cncl; Prfct Atten Awd; 1st & 2nd Hnrs 83-84; 2nd Hnrs 82-85; NY U; Pre Med.

CORREA, LINA; Stella Maris HS; Brooklyn, NY; (Y); 10/250; French Clb; Hon Roll; NHS; Columbia U; Lang.

CORREA, LYNDA; Grover Cleveland HS; Maspeth, NY; (Y); 5/538; Debate Tm; Office Aide; Science Clb; High Hon Roll; Prfct Atten Awd; Regnts Schlrshp 85; Arista Hnr Soc Treas 84-85; Presdntl Schlrshp 85; Manhattan Coll; Comp Sci.

CORREIA, DEREK L; Northport HS; Northport, NY; (Y); 75/595; Cmnty Wkr; Mathletes; Rep Jr Cls; JV Im Lcrss; Im Wt Lftg; Hon Roll; Engrng.

CORREIA, EDDIE; Sacred Heart HS; Yonkers, NY; (Y); CAP; Intnl Clb; Library Aide; Hon Roll; Trs NHS; Prfct Atten Awd.

CORRENTE, MARY JO; Herbert H Lehman HS; Bronx, NY; (Y); 72/373; Bowling; Hon Roll; Accntng.

CORRICE, ANTHONY; Heavelton Central HS; Ogdensburg, NY; (S); Church Yth Grp; Latin Clb; Hon Roll; Jr NHS; NHS; Prfct Atten Awd; MA Inst Tech; Physics.

CORRICE, COLLEEN; Heuvelton Central HS; Ogdensburg, NY; (S); 4/52; Church Yth Grp; Cmnty Wkr; Debate Tm; GAA; Yrbk Stf; Socr; Vllybl; Lion Awd; NHS; Achvt Awd Ntl Hnrs Soc 82-83 & 83-84; Achvt Awd For Hlth 82-83; Plattsburgh ST U; Nrsng.

CORRIERI, DONNA LEE; Wall Kill HS; Wallkill, NY; (Y); 8/209; Church Choir; Mrchg Band; Nwsp Ed-Chief; Trs Frsh Cls; Rep Soph Cls; Tennis; Gov Hon Prg Awd; High Hon Roll; Hon Roll; NHS; Ithaca Coll; Cmmnctns.

CORRIGAN, JEANNINE; The Mary Louis Acad; Jackson Heights, NY; (Y); Church Yth Grp; French Clb; Library Aide; High Hon Roll; Nursing.

CORRIGAN, RICHARD; East Islip HS; East Islip, NY; (Y); Art Clb; FBLA; Chorus; Yrbk Phtg; Yrbk Stf; Lit Mag; Ftbl; Wt Lftg; Hon Roll; Syracuse U; Arch.

CORROON, COURTNEY T; Garden City SR HS; Garden City, NY; (Y); 100/319; Cmnty Wkr; Pres Pep Clb; School Musical; Var Lcrss; Var Socr; Jr NHS; Art Clb; Drama Clb; GAA; Key Clb; NY ST Regents Schlrshp; Georgetown U; Bus Admin.

CORRY, DEBRA A; Floral Park Memorial HS; Floral Park, NY; (Y); 13/189; Mathletes; Orch; School Play; Yrbk Phtg; JV Socr; Var Trk; JV Vllybl; Hon Roll; NHS; NYS Regnts Schlrshp 85; Comms.

CORSA, LAURA; Earl L Vandermeulen HS; Mt Sinai, NY; (Y); Art Clb; Girl Scts; High Hon Roll; Hon Roll; Advrtsng Dsgn.

CORSETTE, PATRICIA A; Paul V Moore HS; Constantia, NY; (Y); 74/350; VP GAA; Var Capt Bsktbl; Var Capt Socr; Var Capt Sftbl; Hon Roll; Rgnts Schlrshp 85; SUNY Oswego; Comp Sci.

CORSI, CHRISTINE; Maple Hill HS; Castleton, NY; (S); 10/80; French Clb; Sec Frsh Cls; VP Stu Cncl; Cheerleading; Fld Hcky; JV Capt Sftbl; Hon Roll; NHS; Rotary Awd; Boston; Finc.

CORSON, MICHELLE; Elmira Southside HS; Elmira, NY; (Y); Latin Clb; Pep Clb; Ski Clb; Chorus; Rep Stu Cncl; Hon Roll; Yth Cnty 85; Physcn Ass.

CORT, SHARON; Freeport HS; Freeport, NY; (Y); Band; VP Stu Cncl; Var Cheerleading; Stat JV Ftbl; Hon Roll; Rep Frsh Cls; Rep Soph Cls; Rep Jr Cls; Rep Sr Cls; Miss Black Teen Wrld & NY ST 85; Intl Yth Yr Achvt Awd 85; Long Is Yth Musical Theater Ensmbl; Boston U; Entrtnmnt Law.

CORTALE, MICHAEL; North Shore HS; Glen Head, NY; (Y); Tennis; U S Tennis Assn Rnkd 44 E Coast Boys 16 83-84; Rnkd Top 30 Boys 18 84-85; Bus.

CORTELLUCCI, ROBERT; Hutchinson Central Technical HS; Buffalo, NY; (Y); 40/262; Boy Scts; JA; Ski Clb; High Hon Roll; Hon Roll; NYS Regents Schlrshp Awd 85; SUNY At Buffalo; Engrng.

CORTES, CLAUDIA C; Holy Trinity HS; Plainview, NY; (S); 13/378; Drama Clb; Math Clb; Rep Frsh Cls; Rep Soph Cls; Rep Jr Cls; Rep Stu Cncl; High Hon Roll; Hon Roll; NEDT Awd; Math Awd Algebra 83; Psych.

CORTES, JULIA; Dodge Vocational HS; Bronx, NY; (Y); 6/34; Camera Clb; Church Yth Grp; Dance Clb; Office Aide; Chorus; Church Choir; Bsktbl; Socr; Vllybl; CC Awd; Art Cont Awd 83; Outstndg Achvt Acad & Extra-Curr 85; Catechst Frmatn Pgm 85; Grace Bible Coll; Theolgy.

CORTES, ROSANA; Rye HS; Rye, NY; (Y); 70/181; ROTC; Stat Bsktbl; Var L Socr; JV Sftbl; High Hon Roll; Hon Roll; SF Natl Hispanic Schlr Awds 85; Long Island U; Pharm.

CORTESE, STACY; Seton Catholic Central HS; Binghamton, NY; (Y); Key Clb; Band; Pep Band; Stu Cncl; Hon Roll; Broome CC; Math.

CORTEZ, RENEE; De Witt Clinton HS; New York, NY; (Y); Nrsg.

CORTI, LISA B; Curtis HS; Staten Island, NY; (Y); 2/328; Science Clb; Concert Band; Mrchg Band; Yrbk Phtg; Var L Tennis; NHS; NYS Schl Mus Assn All-St Bnd 83; NYS Regents Schlrshp 85; Acad Olym Tm Capt 85; Amherst Coll; Bio Sci.

CORTINA, MARIA; St Marys HS; New Hyde Pk, NY; (Y); 6/170; Cmnty Wkr; Library Aide; Math Clb; Chorus; High Hon Roll; Hon Roll; NHS; Ntl Merit Schol; Prfct Atten Awd; Sol Greene Schlrshp 85-86; St Johns U; Bus.

CORTRIGHT, BRENDA; Newark Valley HS; Newark Vly, NY; (Y); Dance Clb; 4-H; Color Guard; 4-H Awd; High Hon Roll; Hon Roll; Law.

CORVENE, ELISABETH; Lake George Central HS; Lake George, NY; (Y); School Musical; School Play; Pres Frsh Cls; Pres Soph Cls; VP Jr Cls; Var Cheerleading; Capt Var Fld Hcky; Var Pom Pon; Var Sftbl; Hon Roll.

CORY, ELISA; Walt Whitman HS; Melville, NY; (Y); 55/570; Sec Frsh Cls; High Hon Roll; Hon Roll; Jr NHS; Spanish NHS.

CORYEA, DEREK; Franklin Acad; Malone, NY; (S); 12/280; Drama Clb; French Clb; Math Clb; Math Tm; PAVAS; Ski Clb; Stage Crew; Yrbk Phtg; Off Sr Cls; High Hon Roll; Epsilon; Princeton; Pre Med.

CORYER, BRENDA; Honeoye Central HS; Honeoye, NY; (S); 17/65; Concert Band; Drm Mjr(t); Jazz Band; Cheerleading; Dnfth Awd; Hon Roll; French Clb; Band; Mrchg Band; Dirs Awd Band 83; Mc Donalds HS Band 84; All ST Band 84; Elem Ed.

COS, ALEXANDER; Pittsford Sutherland HS; Bethesda, MD; (Y); Ski Clb; Spanish Clb; Varsity Clb; L Crs Cntry; Ftbl; L Trk; Vllybl; Hon Roll; Aero-Sp Engrng.

COSADO, ANTHONY; Christopher Columbus HS; Bronx, NY; (Y); Chorus; Church Choir; School Musical; Bsbl; Wt Lftg; Advertiser.

COSCIA, DAWN K; John F Kennedy HS; Bronx, NY; (Y); 11/982; Dance Clb; Drama Clb; Office Aide; Y-Teens; Band; Orch; Hon Roll; NHS; Comm Arts Awd; SUNY Binghamton; Bus.

COSENTINO, APRIL R; Bronx High School Of Science; Bronx, NY; (Y); Church Yth Grp; Teachers Aide; St Prelmnts Modern Miss Pageant 85; Bio.

COSENTINO, CYNDI; Amsterdam HS; Amsterdam, NY; (Y); Hon Roll; SUNY; Bus Admn.

COSENTINO, PETER F; Fordham Preparatory Schl; Bronx, NY; (Y); Church Yth Grp; Computer Clb; Dance Clb; Math Clb; Math Tm; Var Bsbl; JV Var Ftbl; Excell Awds In Rlgs Stds, Latin & Alg 83; Brooklyn Prep Alumni Assn Schlrshp 85; Fordham Prep 82; Polytechnic Inst Of NY; Cmp Sc.

COSENZA, JODIE I; Dominican Acad; Brooklyn, NY; (Y); Computer Clb; Chorus; School Play; Rep Soph Cls; Rep Sr Cls; Hon Roll; NY ST Regents Schlrshp; Cum Laude Awd In Latin; Pace U.

COSGROVE, CASEY; West Genesee SR HS; Syracuse, NY; (Y); Key Clb; Rep Stu Cncl; High Hon Roll; Hon Roll; Languages.

COSGROVE, JILL; Nazareth Acad; Rochester, NY; (Y); VP 4-H; Spanish Clb; Varsity Clb; Bowling; Sftbl; Tennis; Hon Roll; Physcl Thrpy.

COSGROVE, NOREEN; Maria Regina HS; Crestwood, NY; (Y); 17/137; Trs Church Yth Grp; Debate Tm; Exploring; Key Clb; Model UN; Yrbk Rptr; Yrbk Stf; Swmmng; Hon Roll; Sec NHS; Law Bus.

COSGROVE, PATRICK B; St Peters Boys HS; Staten Island, NY; (Y); 7/194; Church Yth Grp; Cmnty Wkr; Var JV Bsktbl; High Hon Roll; NHS; Ntl Merit SF; St Schlr; Schlrshp Notre Dame U, Cornell & Manhattan Coll 85-89; Notre Dame U.

COSNER, CHRISTOPHER; Dryden HS; Dryden, NY; (Y); 13/160; Boy Scts; Chess Clb; Church Yth Grp; Chorus; Lit Mag; High Hon Roll; Hon Roll; Ntl Merit SF; 1st Pl Schl Wrtng Cont 85; Regents Scholar 85; Hnr Awd Acad Excllnce Engl 85; Grinnell; Engl.

COSNOWSKY, ANDREA; Ardsley HS; Ardsley, NY; (Y); French Clb; Varsity Clb; Chorus; Nwsp Stf; Yrbk Stf; Lit Mag; Rep Stu Cncl; JV Var Bsktbl; JV Socr; Var Swmmng; Citatn Muscular Distrphy Assoc 85; Intl Bus.

COSTA, CARLA; Herbert H Lehman HS; Bronx, NY; (Y); 9/420; Off Soph Cls; Bowling; Cheerleading; Hon Roll; Fordham U; Elem Tchng.

COSTA, LOREEN DENISE; Nyack HS; Valley Cottage, NY; (Y); 1/277; Drama Clb; Math Tm; Model UN; Spanish Clb; Mrchg Band; School Musical; School Play; Stage Crew; Yrbk Stf; Lit Mag; MIP La Crosse 85; Pre-Med.

COSTA, PETER R; John F Kennedy HS; Yorktown Heights, NY; (Y); 11/225; Am Leg Boys St; Boy Scts; Cmnty Wkr; Math Tm; Rep Soph Cls; Pres Jr Cls; Var L Ftbl; Var Wt Lftg; JV Var Wrstlng; High Hon Roll; Natl Sci Olympiad Wnnr-Chem 85; Schl Wghtlftng Rcrd Hldr 85; Rep To Micholean Yth In Govt 85; Rensselaer Polytechnical Inst.

COSTA, WILLIAM; North Babylon SR HS; North Babylon, NY; (Y); Cmnty Wkr; Intnl Clb; Spanish Clb; Chorus; Swing Chorus; L Im Socr; Im L Tennis; JV L Trk; Hon Roll; Jr NHS; NY Inst Tech; Engrng.

COSTANTINI, AMY; Solvay HS; Syracuse, NY; (Y); Sec French Clb; Chorus; Concert Band; School Play; Swing Chorus; Yrbk Rptr; High Hon Roll; NHS; Voice Dem Awd.

COSTANTINI, GENE; Waterford-Halfmoon HS; Waterford, NY; (Y); JV Bsktbl; JV Var Socr; Var Soccer Hnbl Mntn Awd 83; Var Soccer 2nd Tm All Colonial Cncl Tm 84; Psych.

COSTANZA, LISA; Whitesboro SR HS; Utica, NY; (Y); Drama Clb; Intnl Clb; Acpl Chr; Hst Orch; High Hon Roll; Hon Roll; Jr NHS; NHS; Chorus; Variety Show; Dr & Mrs Louis Spector Schlrshp To Estmn Schl Of Music 83-86; Dean L Harrington Schlrshp 84; Music Prfrmnc.

COSTANZO, DEBORAH LYNN; Dansville Central HS; Dansville, NY; (Y); 8/134; Ski Clb; Band; Chorus; Yrbk Stf; Pres Stu Cncl; Co-Capt Cheerleading; Hon Roll; Sec NHS; Livngstn Cntsy Jr Miss 84-85; Frgn Exch Stu Greece 84; Rochester Inst Tech; Comm Art.

COSTE, FRANCES MARIEL; Franklin Delano Roosevelt HS; Hyde Park, NY; (Y); Orch; Yrbk Bus Mgr; Yrbk Stf; NHS; Peer Tutr Spnsh, Soc Stds 84-85; Bus.

COSTELLO, JOANNE; Fayetteville-Manlius HS; Fayetteville, NY; (Y); JCL; Latin Clb; Color Guard; Flag Corp; Mrchg Band; Mrktng.

COSTELLO, JULIE A; Sauquoit Valley Central HS; Frankfort, NY; (Y); 1/118; Spanish Clb; Chorus; School Musical; Yrbk Stf; Rep Sr Cls; DAR Awd; VP NHS; Opt Clb Awd; Pres Schlr; Sal; Utica Coll; Acctng.

COSTELLO, KRISTIN; Catholic Central HS; Toy, NY; (Y); Church Yth Grp; French Clb; Math Clb; Math Tm; Variety Show; Off Soph Cls; Off Jr Cls; Var Pom Pon; High Hon Roll; Hon Roll; Co-Chrprsn Pilot Chaptr Of SADD 84-85; Law.

COSTELLO, MARY; Sacred Heart HS; Baldwin, NY; (S); 12/200; Debate Tm; Intnl Clb; Pep Clb; Stage Crew; Stu Cncl; Tennis; Trk; High Hon Roll; NHS; Debate 3rd Place 82; Math.

COSTELLO, MAUREEN; Plainedge HS; Bethpage, NY; (Y); Cmnty Wkr.

COSTELLO, MIRIAM; Williamsville North HS; E Amherst, NY; (Y); 18/312; Church Yth Grp; Cmnty Wkr; Sec French Clb; Rep Latin Clb; Nwsp Rptr; Nwsp Stf; French Hon Soc; High Hon Roll; Hon Roll; Sec NHS; NY ST U-Buffalo; Psych.

COSTELLO, MOLLY COLLEEN; Cardinal O Hara HS; Kenmore, NY; (Y); Drama Clb; VP French Clb; Quiz Bowl; School Musical; School Play; Stage Crew; Yrbk Rptr; Yrbk Stf; Jrnlsm.

COSTELLO, PATRICK; Oneida SR HS; Oneida, NY; (Y); 30/200; Church Yth Grp; Mathletes; Spanish Clb; Varsity Clb; Chorus; Yrbk Stf; Var L Ftbl; Var Capt Wrstlng; Hon Roll; Boy Scts; Mayors Yth Advsry Cncl 83-85; Math.

COSTELLO, THERESA; Our Lady Of Perpetual Help; Brooklyn, NY; (Y); Rep Stu Cncl; Coach Actv; Sftbl; High Hon Roll; Hon Roll; Princpls Lst 83-84 & 84-85; Iona Coll Lang Cont 85; Natl Sci Chem Tst 84; Nrsng.

COSTELLO, THOMAS E; St Anthonys HS; Dix Hills, NY; (Y); 5/225; Am Leg Boys St; Pres Frsh Cls; Rep Soph Cls; Stu Cncl; JV Bsktbl; Var Capt Ftbl; JV Lcrss; NHS; Hugh O Brian Yth Ldrshp Smnr 84; Newsdy Nwspapr Hnr Carir-Fnlst Carir Of Yr 85.

COSTENBADER, KAREN; Geneva HS; Geneva, NY; (S); 1/173; Cmnty Wkr; French Clb; Hosp Aide; Latin Clb; Model UN; Science Clb; Service Clb; Ski Clb; Spanish Clb; Varsity Clb; Intl Dir Of Distngshd Yng Ldrshp 84; Harvard Bk Awd 84; Roberts Wesleyan Coll H S Rsrch Schlrshp 83-84; Bio.

COSTIGAN, WAYNE; Bethpage HS; Plainview, NY; (Y); 32/290; Boy Scts; Computer Clb; French Clb; Nwsp Sprt Ed; Var Diving; JV Ftbl; JV Lcrss; Var Swmmng; High Hon Roll; Finance.

COSTON, LUANN E; Lakeland SR HS; Putnam Valley, NY; (Y); 7/400; Church Yth Grp; Dance Clb; French Clb; Girl Scts; Office Aide; Radio Clb; Band; Concert Band; Drm Mjr(t); Mrchg Band; SUNY Oswego; Psychology.

COTA, ARNOLD; Hugh C Williams HS; Hermon, NY; (Y); Boy Scts; Nwsp Stf; Var Ftbl; Hon Roll; Prfct Atten Awd; Comp Sci.

COTE, JOANNE E; Middletown HS; Middletown, NY; (Y); 26/380; Concert Band; Jazz Band; Mrchg Band; Orch; School Musical; Symp Band; Socr; NYS Regnts Schlrshp 85; Wellesley Coll; Vet.

COTE, LISA; Le Roy Central HS; Le Roy, NY; (Y); French Clb; Spanish Clb; Varsity Clb; Trs Frsh Cls; Trs Soph Cls; JV Var Sftbl; Var Twrlr; JV Var Vllybl; High Hon Roll; Jr NHS; Mgmt Info Sys.

COTES, TIMOTHY; East Meadow HS; Levittown, NY; (S); Chorus; Cit Awd; Hon Roll; Ntl Merit SF; Prfct Atten Awd; Law.

COTHRAN, TRACI; Onondaga Central HS; Nedrow, NY; (S); 1/73; German Clb; Spanish Clb; Varsity Clb; Sec Soph Cls; Rep Stu Cncl; Var Crs Cntry; Var Trk; High Hon Roll; NHS; Chorus; Hugh O Brien Yth Ldrshp Fndtn 83; Elem Ed.

COTON, WADE; Amsterdam HS; Amsterdam, NY; (Y); 12/320; Am Leg Boys St; 4-H; Varsity Clb; Var Bsbl; Var Bsktbl; Var Ftbl; High Hon Roll; Hon Roll; Trs NHS; Prfct Atten Awd; Engrng.

COTRONEO, PETER; Monsignor Farrell HS; Staten Island, NY; (Y); Chess Clb; Computer Clb; French Clb; Chorus; Im Bowling; French Hon Soc; High Hon Roll; VFW Awd; Mech Engr.

COTSALAS, ALEXIS; Garden City SR HS; Garden City, NY; (Y); 29/355; Church Yth Grp; Drama Clb; French Clb; German Clb; Hosp Aide; Chorus; School Play; Lit Mag; Var Badmtn; Var Tennis; JR Ntl Hnr Soc 83; Ntl Hnr Soc 85.

COTTA, JODIANNE; St Edmund HS; Brooklyn, NY; (Y); 90/200; Girl Scts; Hosp Aide; JA; Library Aide; Office Aide; School Play; Nwsp Rptr; Nwsp Stf; Sec Soph Cls; Bowling; Queens Coll; Med.

COTTER, KELLY; East Hampton HS; E Hampton, NY; (Y); 54/154; AFS; Chrmn Church Yth Grp; Teachers Aide; Chorus; Nwsp Ed-Chief; Pres Stu Cncl; Capt Cheerleading; DAR Awd; Swing Chorus; Nwsp Rptr; Prnt Tchr Cmnty Orgnztn Outstndng SR 85; Lds Vlg Imprvmnt Soc Bk Awd 85; Keene ST Coll NH; Scndry Educ.

COTTER, TOR; Middletown HS; Middletown, NY; (Y); Teachers Aide; Rep Soph Cls; Wt Lftg; Wrstlng; Electrncs.

COTTO, GEORGE W; James I O Neill HS; Highland Fls, NY; (Y); Pep Clb; Var Bsbl; Var Crs Cntry; Var Ice Hcky; Albany U NY; Poli Sci.

COTTONE, MICHELLE; Victor Central Schl; Victor, NY; (Y); 17/250; Sec 4-H; Model UN; Sec Spanish Clb; Varsity Clb; Chorus; School Musical; Rep Stu Cncl; Var Cheerleading; High Hon Roll; Prfct Atten Awd; Southampton Coll; Bus Mngmnt.

COTTRELL, JAMES; Hutchinson Central Tech; Buffalo, NY; (Y); JA; Ftbl; Trk; Hon Roll; Comp Sci.

COTUGNO, JOANNE; East Meadow HS; E Meadow, NY; (Y); FBLA; Band; Concert Band; Mrchg Band; Orch; Symp Band; Yrbk Phtg; Yrbk Stf; JV Var Cheerleading; Hon Roll; Perf Math Rgnts 82; Perf Mrchng Band Attd 84; Bus.

COUGHLAN, MARGARET; Cardinal Spellman HS; Bronx, NY; (Y); Church Yth Grp; Cmnty Wkr; Dance Clb; Service Clb; NHS; NEDT Awd; 1st Hnrs 83-85; Silver Medal Vol Split Rock Nrsng Hm 85; Bronze Medal Catholic Actn Corps Tutrng 85; Bio.

COULL, CHARMELLE; St Peters H S For Girls; Staten Isl, NY; (Y); Hosp Aide; Yrbk Stf; Lit Mag; Stu Cncl; Untd Cerbrl Palsy 85; Cornell U; Pedtrcn.

COULOMBE, KIMBERLY; Keveny Memorial Acad; Waterford, NY; (Y); 7/45; 4-H; Girl Scts; Color Guard; Crs Cntry; Score Keeper; Sftbl; Vllybl; Hon Roll; NHS; Prfct Atten Awd; Ntl Bus Hnr Soc 84 & 85; Maria Coll; Bus Mngmt.

COULOUMBIS, NIKKI D; Fallsburg Central HS; Woodbourne, NY; (Y); 4/57; Drama Clb; Quiz Bowl; Band; Stage Crew; Nwsp Stf; Rep Stu Cncl; Fld Hcky; Trk; Lion Awd; NHS; Gifted & Tlntd Scty 83-85; Balfour Schlr 85; All-Amer Schlr 84; Wheaton Coll; Econ.

COULTER, MICHAEL; Beacon HS; Beacon, NY; (S); Varsity Clb; Band; Concert Band; Mrchg Band; Pep Band; Ftbl; Var Tennis; Var JV Wrstlng; VP Jr NHS; Culinary Inst Of Am; Chef.

COUNTS, RAELINE; Dominican Commercial HS; Cambria Heights, NY; (Y); Pep Clb; Chorus; Bsktbl; Mgr(s); Score Keeper; Hon Roll; NHS; Air Force; Med Tech.

COURTER, SUSAN; Washingtonville HS; Washingtonville, NY; (Y); Q&S; Symp Band; Yrbk Phtg; Yrbk Rptr; Yrbk Stf; Rep Jr Cls; Stat Bsbl; JV Bsktbl; Var Socr; Var Trk.

COURTINES, MICHEL-ALEXIS R; Stuyvesant HS; Bayside, NY; (Y); Debate Tm; JA; Model UN; Science Clb; Rep Frsh Cls; Rep Soph Cls; Rep Jr Cls; Rep Sr Cls; Rep Stu Cncl; High Hon Roll; Chancllrs Hnr Rll 85; Westnghs Semi-Fnlst 85; Super Yth Awd 83; Georgetown U; Chem.

COURTNEY, MARGUERITA; Aquinas HS; Bronx, NY; (Y); 2/178; Computer Clb; French Clb; Teachers Aide; Nwsp Rptr; Nwsp Stf; Yrbk Stf; High Hon Roll; NHS; Prfct Atten Awd; Spanish NHS; Yth Ingrl Conf Schlrshp 85; Acad Excllnc Awd 85; 3rd Prz Sci Fair 83; Fordham U.

COUSINS, ANDREA; Bethlehem Central HS; Glenmont, NY; (Y); 89/338; Political Wkr; Nwsp Stf; Yrbk Stf; Hon Roll; Pres Acad Ftnss Awd 85; Ntl Achvt Pgm Outstndng Negro Stu 85; Williams Coll; Anthrplgy.

COUSINS, JOHN; South Park HS; Buffalo, NY; (Y); Cmnty Wkr; German Clb; National Guard.

COUTANT, STEVE; Marlboro HS; Marlboro, NY; (Y); Wt Lftg; Wrstlng; Engrng.

COUTINHO, ARMANDO; Christ The King Regional HS; Jamaica, NY; (Y); Computer Clb; English Clb; Varsity Clb; Bsbl; Coach Actv; Ftbl; Socr; Sftbl; Trk; Vllybl; St Johns U; English.

COUTTS, ANDREW; Vestal Central SR HS; Vestal, NY; (Y); 50/500; Trs Church Yth Grp; Varsity Clb; Var L Socr; Var L Tennis; Hon Roll; NHS; Prfct Atten Awd; Colgate U; Hstry.

COUTURE, BRIAN; West Valley Central HS; W Valley, NY; (Y); 7/45; Pres Church Yth Grp; Pres Drama Clb; Pres Sr Cls; Pres Stu Cncl; Var Bsktbl; Var Capt Trk; CC Awd; NHS; Pres 4-H; Pres Band; D Ford Mem Ldrshp, D W Mem Sprtsmnshp 85; Cornell; Engrng.

COUTURE, RICHARD; Newcomb Central HS; Newcomb, NY; (Y); 1/12; Chorus; Concert Band; Jazz Band; Pres Frsh Cls; Rep Soph Cls; Pres Jr Cls; Bsbl; Capt Bsktbl; Socr; High Hon Roll; Rensselaer Poly Inst; Biomdcl.

COVENEY, ALLISON; A E Stevenson HS; Bronx, NY; (Y); Church Yth Grp; Drama Clb; Math Clb; Orch; School Play; Stu Cncl; Bowling; NYS Regnts Schlrshp 85; Hampton Inst VA; Bus Mgt.

COVI, RENEE; Rocky Point JR/SR HS; Rocky Point, NY; (S); 5/250; Varsity Clb; Concert Band; Mrchg Band; Var Capt Crs Cntry; Var Capt Trk; Hon Roll; All League Track & Crosscty 83-84; Sci Med.

COVINGTON, EDITH J; John Bowne HS; Rego Park, NY; (Y); 80/656; Debate Tm; Intnl Clb; Variety Show; Yrbk Stf; Trk; NHS; Pres Acad Fit Awd 85; Century III Ldrs Cert Merit 85; Citation Hnr 1st Pl Essay Cont 84; U Of RI; Pol Sci.

COWAN, GREG; Northern Adirondack C S HS; Churubusco, NY; (Y); French Clb; Clinton Comm Plattsburgh; Math.

COWAN, KIMBERLY; John Jay SR HS; Hopewell Juncti, NY; (Y); Church Yth Grp; Var Cheerleading; Var Swmmng; High Hon Roll; Hon Roll; Psyclgy.

COWAN, KIMBERLY; New Rochelle HS; New Rochelle, NY; (Y); 167/595; Cmnty Wkr; Office Aide; Var Cheerleading; JV Coach Actv; Hon Roll; Howard A Spur Mem Awd 85; PACE U; Accntng.

COWAP, DANA; Plainedge HS; Massapequa, NY; (Y); Spanish Clb; Band; Yrbk Stf; VP Frsh Cls; JV Var Bsktbl; Var Sftbl; Var Tennis; High Hon Roll; NHS; Spanish NHS; Bus Adm.

COWDEN, MICHAEL A; Jordan-Elbridge JR SR HS; Elbridge, NY; (Y); Ski Clb; Band; Concert Band; Mrchg Band; Var L Ftbl; Var L Lcrss; High Hon Roll; NHS; Engr.

COWIN, JENNIFER L; Stillwater Central HS; Stillwater, NY; (Y); VP Jr Cls; Comm Arts.

COWLES, TRICIA; Corinth HS; Corinth, NY; (S); Art Clb; Church Yth Grp; Varsity Clb; Band; Chorus; Concert Band; Variety Show; Bsktbl; Fld Hcky; Sftbl; Tri-M 84; Crtnst.

COX, CARRIE; Albion HS; Albion, NY; (S); 10/178; Church Yth Grp; Rep Spanish Clb; Capt Color Guard; Hon Roll; Jr NHS; Merit Roll; Math.

COX, CRAIG; St Marys Boys HS; Garden City, NY; (S); 6/200; Church Yth Grp; Teachers Aide; Varsity Clb; Socr; Trk; High Hon Roll; Hon Roll; NHS.

COX, GEOFFREY; Nyack HS; Nyack, NY; (Y); 20/260; Jazz Band; School Musical; Ed Lit Mag; Rep Stu Cncl; JV Tennis; French Hon Soc; High Hon Roll; NHS; Computer Clb; Band; Frgn Exchng Stu-Japan 84; NY St Schl Music Assn-Jazz Sax-A Rtng 85; Comp Engrng.

COX, JAMES; Archbishop Molloy HS; Rockaway Bch, NY; (Y); 49/361; Bsktbl; Coach Actv; Ftbl; Sftbl; High Hon Roll; NHS; Pace U Trustees 85; Marcellin Champ Svc Awd 85; Schl Spirit Awd 85; Pace U-Pleasantville; Mgmt.

COX, JESSICA; Lynbrook HS; Lynbrook, NY; (Y); Church Yth Grp; Trs Pres Leo Clb; Pres Library Aide; Church Choir; Hon Roll; Trs NHS; Stu Mnth 84.

COX, JILL; Le Roy Central HS; Leroy, NY; (Y); Am Leg Boys St; Latin Clb; Ski Clb; Varsity Clb; Sec Jr Cls; Var Cheerleading; Var Trk; JV Vllybl; High Hon Roll; Jr NHS; Bus.

COX, JOANNE; Spackenkill HS; Poughkeepsie, NY; (Y); 9/167; Office Aide; Spanish Clb; Thesps; Flag Corp; Nwsp Rptr; NHS; Accntnt.

COX, KIM; Remsen Central Schl; Remsen, NY; (Y); Teachers Aide; Flag Corp; Yrbk Phtg; Yrbk Stf; Var Socr; Cit Awd; High Hon Roll; Hon Roll; Outstndg Acad Achvt Scl Stds 84-85; Nrs.

COX, PETER; Xavier HS; Brooklyn, NY; (Y); Dance Clb; Nwsp Rptr; NEDT Awd; Math.

COX, PHILIP J; Patchogue-Medford HS; E Patchogue, NY; (Y); 37/748; DECA; French Clb; Trs German Clb; Speech Tm; School Musical; Rep Frsh Cls; Rep Jr Cls; VP Sr Cls; Bsbl; Bsktbl; NY ST Regnts Scholar 85; George Washington U; Intl Rltns.

COXETER, RUTH; Albion HS; Albion, NY; (S); Latin Clb; Band; School Musical; Ed Lit Mag; Im Gym; NHS; JR Ms Fnlst, Perf Arts Awd 84; 1st Pl Inst Solo; Wheaton Coll Wheaton; Pre Med.

COY, DOUG L; Little Valley Central HS; Little Valley, NY; (Y); Pres Jr Cls; VP Sr Cls; Var Capt Bsbl; Var Ftbl; Var Trk; High Hon Roll; Hon Roll; Regnts Schlrshp 85; Jamestown CC; Lib Arts.

COY, LINDA J; Cardinal Spellman HS; Bronx, NY; (Y); Pres Church Yth Grp; Computer Clb; Debate Tm; Band; Church Choir; Mrchg Band; Hon Roll; 2nd Hnrs 83-85; Rgnts Schlrshp 84-85; U Rochester.

COYLE, EDWARD S; Glen Cove HS; Glen Cove, NY; (Y); Chess Clb; Computer Clb; Radio Clb; Socr; NHS; Ntl Merit SF; Ithaca Coll Schlrshp 85-86; Ithaca Coll; Tv Prdctn.

COYLE, JOHN; Geneseo Central Schl; Geneseo, NY; (Y); 3/97; French Clb; Intnl Clb; Letterman Clb; Mathletes; Varsity Clb; Pres Frsh Cls; Pres Soph Cls; Pres Jr Cls; Pres Sr Cls; Var L Bsbl; Georgetown; Bus.

COYLE, MICHAEL P; St Francis Prep; Flushing, NY; (Y); 190/670; Ski Clb; Im Ftbl; Im Sftbl; Im Wt Lftg; NY St Regents Schlrshp 85; Hnr Schlrshp Ny Inst Tech 85; US Air Force ROTC Schlrshp 85; NY Inst Technology.

COYLE, NANCY K; Lyons Central Schl; Lyons, NY; (Y); 2/94; Latin Clb; Varsity Clb; Band; Trs Frsh Cls; VP Jr Cls; Cheerleading; Socr; Hon Roll; NHS; Sal; Regents Schlrshp 85; SUNY Oswego; Physical Therapy.

COYLE, PATRICIA A; Bishop Kearney HS; Brooklyn, NY; (Y); 13/364; Art Clb; Church Yth Grp; FNA; Girl Scts; Ski Clb; Band; Yrbk Stf; Hon Roll; NYS Regents; Hunter Coll Schlrshp; Hunter Coll; Physcl Thrpy.

COYNE, CATHERINE; Avon Central Schl; Avon, NY; (Y); 15/106; Church Yth Grp; 4-H; GAA; Spanish Clb; Varsity Clb; Chorus; Yrbk Stf; Rep Stu Cncl; Var Capt Bsktbl; Var L Socr; MVP Vlybll 84; Most Imprvd Soccer 84; Desire, Dedctn Bsktbl 84-85; Cornell U Nazareth; Elem Ed.

COYNE, CHRISTOPHER A; Holy Trinity HS; N Massapequa, NY; (S); Math Clb; Var Crs Cntry; Var Trk; Hon Roll; NEDT Awd; Academic All-Amercn 84; Aero.

COYNE, JENNIFER; Smithtown HS East; Stony Brook, NY; (Y); GAA; Political Wkr; Radio Clb; Var L Crs Cntry; JV Capt Fld Hcky; Var L Trk; VP French Hon Soc; Hon Roll; NHS; Pres Schlr; All Leag Wntr Trk 84; Outstndng Scl Stds Achvt 85; Stony Brook U; Law.

COZOLINO, LAUREN; Walter Panas HS; Peekskill, NY; (Y); Ski Clb; Varsity Clb; Chorus; Rep Stu Cncl; Var Capt Cheerleading; Hon Roll; Pep Clb; Hmcmng Queen 83; Comm.

COZZIE, KAREN; Immaculate Heart Central; Watertown, NY; (Y); Variety Show; Yrbk Stf; Pres Frsh Cls; Pres Soph Cls; Stu Cncl; JV Var Socr; JV Sftbl; Hon Roll; Ntl Latin Ex 84; Elem Ed.

COZZOLINO, JOE; Gloversville HS; Gloversville, NY; (Y); 2/250; Cmnty Wkr; Nwsp Rptr; Off Soph Cls; Off Jr Cls; Stu Cncl; JV Var Bsbl; Fld Hcky; Var L Golf; Socr; Cit Awd; Med.

COZZOLINO, MELINDA; Hudson HS; Claverack, NY; (Y); Band; Chorus; Concert Band; Jazz Band; Mrchg Band; Orch; Pep Band; School Musical; Nwsp Rptr; Yrbk Stf; Chrmn YAC 84-86; Chsn Attnd Rotry Ldrshp Conf 84; Occptnl Thrpy.

CRABB, MARLENE; Carthage Central HS; Black River, NY; (Y); VP AFS; Trs French Clb; Key Clb; Varsity Clb; Band; Chorus; Concert Band; School Musical; JV Var Socr; Var JV Trk; Mth.

CRADDOCK, JOEL; E J Wilson HS; Spencerport, NY; (Y); Church Yth Grp; Exploring; Math Clb; Teachers Aide; Church Choir; Yrbk Stf; Im Bowling; Prfct Atten Awd; Math.

CRAFT JR, KENNETH D; Northport HS; Northport, NY; (Y); 248/643; Chess Clb; Church Yth Grp; FBLA; Pep Clb; Variety Show; Var L Lcrss; JV Socr; Hon Roll; FBL Amer Conf Awd 85; Cert Merit Wrk Stdy Prog 85; Oswego ST NY; Accntng.

CRAGER, JOHN C; West Islip HS; W Islip, NY; (Y); Hosp Aide; Mathletes; Ski Clb; Band; Pres Frsh Cls; Pres Soph Cls; Pres Jr Cls; Rep Stu Cncl; JV Bsktbl; Capt Lcrss; Intl Rel.

CRAGG, DEBORAH; Nazareth Acad; Churchville, NY; (S); Teachers Aide; Hon Roll.

CRAGNOLIN, MIKE; John F Kennedy HS; Utica, NY; (Y); Boy Scts; Computer Clb; Pres VP FBLA; Key Clb; Math Clb; Yrbk Bus Mgr; Yrbk Sprt Ed; Trs Stu Cncl; Var Socr; Var Vllybl; Comp Progmr.

CRAIB, CRISTI; Berlin Central HS; Berlin, NY; (S); #3 In Class; Ski Clb; Band; Chorus; Jazz Band; School Musical; Swing Chorus; JV Var Bsktbl; Var Socr; High Hon Roll; Stdnt Tutng 83; Volntr Actvty Teachg Convrsatn Frnch 4th Grd 85; 85 Clb Hnrs 83-85.

CRAIG, CORINNE; Onteora Central Schl; Bearsville, NY; (S); 14/245; Quiz Bowl; NHS; Am Coll Switzerland; Frgn Lang.

CRAIG, DEBORAH L; Harrison HS; White Plains, NY; (Y); 27/215; Rep Church Yth Grp; Ed Q&S; Sec Chorus; Color Guard; Variety Show; Var Socr; Cit Awd; NHS; Rotary Awd; St Schlr; SUNY Albany; Bus Mngr Mus.

CRAIG, FRASER; Iona Prep; Port Chester, NY; (Y); 114/196; Church Yth Grp; Cmnty Wkr; Library Aide; Ski Clb; Ice Hcky; Lcrss; Stonehill; Bus.

CRAIG, JENNIFER N; Pulaski JR SR HS; Pulaski, NY; (S); Drama Clb; French Clb; Ski Clb; Band; Chorus; Color Guard; Yrbk Ed-Chief; Stu Cncl; JV Socr; Snow Incntv Awd; Le Monye Coll; Bus.

CRAIGLOW, LISA ANNE; Williamsville East HS; East Amherst, NY; (Y); Church Yth Grp; Rep FBLA; Rep Pep Clb; Rep Soph Cls; Trs Jr Cls; Rep Stu Cncl; Var Fld Hcky; Im Powder Puff Ftbl; Im Swmmng; Var Trk; Fisher JR Coll; Bus.

CRAMER, MARY ANN; Minisink Valley HS; Westtown, NY; (Y); 2/250; Am Leg Aux Girls St; Band; Chorus; Yrbk Stf; VP Stu Cncl; Badmtn; Tennis; High Hon Roll; NHS; Ntl Merit Ltr; Catp USGF ST Gym Tm Champs 85; Area Sportsmn Clb Art Wnnr 85; Excllnt & Outstndng NYSSMA 83-85; Wildlife Bio.

CRAMER, MATTHEW; Williamsville East HS; E Amherst, NY; (Y); Varsity Clb; Var L Bsbl; Im Bsktbl; Var Capt Golf; Hon Roll; Prfct Atten Awd; Schl Glf Div II Co Chmps 84; Williamsville Cup Tm Chmpns 84; Amherst Auduborn JR Clb Chmpn 85; FL ST U; Glf Pro.

CRAMER, SHERRI; Cicer North Syracuse HS; Clay, NY; (S); 26/622; Church Yth Grp; Ski Clb; Concert Band; Mrchg Band; Symp Band; High Hon Roll; Hon Roll; Exploring; 4-H; Sci.

CRAMER, TERESA; Corning Painted Post West HS; Lindley, NY; (Y); Varsity Clb; Church Choir; Color Guard; Concert Band; Madrigals; Mrchg Band; Rep Jr Cls; Rep Stu Cncl; JV Var Cheerleading; High Hon Roll; All-Cnty Chorus 85; Liberty U; Music.

CRANDALL, AMY; Camden HS; Blossvale, NY; (Y); Varsity Clb; Yrbk Sprt Ed; Yrbk Stf; Sec Jr Cls; Sec Rep Stu Cncl; Var L Tennis; Var L Vllybl; NHS; Ski Clb; Empire ST Games Vllybl Tm 85; MVP Ten 84-85; Phys Thrpy.

CRANDALL, JOEL; Oxford Acad; Mcdonough, NY; (Y); 23/89; Am Leg Boys St; French Clb; Varsity Clb; VP Frsh Cls; Pres Soph Cls; VP Jr Cls; JV Bsbl; Var Capt Bsktbl; Var JV Ftbl; Bst Offensive Back Ftbl 85; All Trny Tm Norwich Trnmnt Bsktbl 85; Kiwanis Doubles Champ 84-85; Sports Trainer.

CRANDALL, LAURIE A; Pulaski JR SR HS; Pulaski, NY; (S); 2/114; Drama Clb; French Clb; GAA; Math Clb; Color Guard; JV Bsktbl; High Hon Roll; Hon Roll; NHS; Snow Schlrshp Awd Frnch Study 84; Hghst Mrk Sci Rgnts 84.

CRANDALL, MIKE; Granville Central HS; Hampton, NY; (Y); 15/119; AFS; Boy Scts; Church Yth Grp; Spanish Clb; Rep Frsh Cls; Im JV Bsktbl; Im Crs Cntry; Var Golf; Hon Roll; Siena Coll; Pol Sci.

CRANDALL, TINA; Massena Central HS; Massena, NY; (Y); Drama Clb; French Clb; Thesps; Chorus; Madrigals; School Play; Stage Crew; Music Awd 84; Lang.

CRANE, JUDY; Middletown HS; Middletown, NY; (Y); 15/367; Sec 4-H; Band; Symp Band; 4-H Awd; Hon Roll; Orange County CC; Engl.

CRANE, MICHELLE; Odessa-Montour HS; Montour Falls, NY; (Y); Drama Clb; FHA; Varsity Clb; Rep Frsh Cls; Rep Stu Cncl; Var Trk; High Hon Roll; NHS; Flagler Coll; Acctg.

CRANEY, BRENDA; Tamarac Britton Kill Cent; Troy, NY; (Y); Intnl Clb; Science Clb; Band; Chorus; Drill Tm; Variety Show; Capt Var Cheerleading; JV Sftbl; Hon Roll; Prfct Atten Awd; All Cnty Vcl Chrus, SADD Ntl Cncl 85; Trvl.

CRANNA, MICHAEL; Amherst Central HS; Amherst, NY; (Y); 7/300; Sec French Clb; Sec Latin Clb; Chorus; Yrbk Sprt Ed; Var Socr; High Hon Roll; NHS; Ntl Merit SF; Harvard Bk Awd 84; Dartmouth Coll; Chem Engr.

CRANSTON, LYNN; Springville Griffith Inst; Springville, NY; (Y); 60/197; Church Yth Grp; French Clb; GAA; Ski Clb; Yrbk Stf; Rep Frsh Cls; Rep Soph Cls; Rep Jr Cls; Rep Sr Cls; Sec Stu Cncl; Acad Ftnss Awds Pgm; Outstndng Acad Achvt 84-85; NY ST U-Fredonia; Psych.

CRANSTON, SEAN D; Bronx High School Of Science; Queens, NY; (Y); Band; Arista 84-85; Amer Inst Of Aero & Astro 84-85; MIT; Aeronautical Engrng.

CRAPARO, JOSEPH CHARLES; Seton Catholic Central HS; Binghamton, NY; (S); Church Yth Grp; Cmnty Wkr; Band; Concert Band; Jazz Band; Pep Band; Var JV Ftbl; NHS; Varsity Clb; Nwsp Rptr; Cathlc Yth Organztn Sec 84-85; JV &vrsty Bsktbl Cathlc Yth Organztn 83-85; Comp Engrng.

CRAPSER, KAREN; New Paltz HS; New Paltz, NY; (Y); Trs Church Yth Grp; Pres Trs 4-H; Chorus; Church Choir; High Hon Roll; Hon Roll; NHS; Awded Trip To Cooperstown 82; Htl Mgmt.

CRATER, JULIE; Salamonca Central HS; Salamanca, NY; (Y); 10/110; French Clb; Ski Clb; Varsity Clb; Band; Concert Band; Mrchg Band; Pep Band; Yrbk Stf; Var Swmmng; French Hon Soc; Varsity Ltr 84; Alfred Tech Coll; Acctg.

CRATSLEY, CYNTHIA RAE; Odessa Montour Central Schl; Odessa, NY; (Y); 21/86; Pres Art Clb; Cmnty Wkr; Hosp Aide; Varsity Clb; Yrbk Ed-Chief; Yrbk Stf; Lit Mag; Swmmng; Hon Roll; 4-H; NYS Schl Of Visual Arts 85; Schltc Art Awd 84-85; NY St Fair 1st Pl-Paintings 83-84; Fshn Inst Of Tech; Fshn Merch.

CRAVEDI, DIANE; St Catharine Acad; Bronx, NY; (Y); 14/225; Art Clb; Church Yth Grp; Drama Clb; English Clb; JA; Math Tm; Office Aide; Teachers Aide; Nwsp Rptr; Nwsp Stf; NYU; Pre-Med.

CRAVER, MIKE; Shenendehowa Central HS; Clifton Pk, NY; (Y); Band; Orch; Symp Band; Bsktbl; Hon Roll; Syracuse U; Archit.

CRAWFORD, ADRIENNE; Center Moriches HS; Ctr Moriches, NY; (Y); DECA; FBLA; FTA; Office Aide; School Play; Yrbk Stf; Sec Sr Cls; Capt Cheerleading; Hon Roll.

CRAWFORD, ALLYN; Port Richmond HS; Staten Isld, NY; (Y); Boys Clb Am; Band; School Musical; Variety Show.

CRAWFORD, ANGELENE; Avon Central HS; Avon, NY; (Y); 17/107; Trs FBLA; Library Aide; Rep Stu Cncl; Mgr(s); Var Swmmng; High Hon Roll; Hon Roll; Jr NHS; NHS; Bryant & Stratton; Bus.

CRAWFORD, CARLA E; Midwood Bedford & Glenwood HS; Brooklyn, NY; (Y); 113/626; Cmnty Wkr; Hosp Aide; Intnl Clb; Service Clb; Orch; Symp Band; Lit Mag; Var Bowling; NHS; Prfct Atten Awd; Thoughtful Ctzn Awd 84; Pre-Med.

CRAWFORD, CARRIE; Hilton Central HS; Hilton, NY; (Y); Model UN; Nwsp Stf; Yrbk Stf; JV Var Cheerleading; High Hon Roll; NHS.

CRAWFORD, CARRINGTON; Greene Central HS; Greene, NY; (Y); 18/100; Church Yth Grp; Band; Chorus; Concert Band; Swing Chorus; Hon Roll; Pres Schlr; Regents Scholar 85; Broome CC; Frgn Missionary Svc.

CRAWFORD, CRIS; Newark SR HS; Newark, NY; (Y); VP FHA; Band; Concert Band.

CRAWFORD, KIM MARIE; St John The Baptist HS; Deer Pk, NY; (Y); Art Clb; Hosp Aide; Service Clb; Chorus; Church Choir; JV Crs Cntry; Swng & Knttng Clb Ldr 83; Boston U; Pre-Med.

CRAWFORD, LYNDA; Gloversville HS; Glens Falls, NY; (Y); Drama Clb; Teachers Aide; School Play; Stage Crew; Var Tennis; High Hon Roll; Hon Roll; Jr NHS; Chem.

CRAWFORD, MICHAEL; Ossining HS; Ossining, NY; (Y); Church Yth Grp; Cmnty Wkr; JV Bsktbl; JV Var Socr; Var L Tennis; High Hon Roll; Hon Roll; NHS; Ntl Merit Schol; Cert Of Merit-Frnch 83 & 84; Comp Sci.

CRAWFORD, NATHALIE C; Bronxville HS; Bronxville, NY; (Y); 34/78; High Hon Roll; Hon Roll; NYS Regents Schlrshp 85; Westchester Bus Inst Bus Educ Awd 85; Mktg Awd 84; U Richmond; Bus.

CRAWFORD, STEPHEN; St Josephs Collegiate Inst; Kenmore, NY; (Y); 14/200; Sec Church Choir; School Musical; Pres Swing Chorus; Ed Lit Mag; Trs Sr Cls; Rep Stu Cncl; Bsbl; Crs Cntry; Hon Roll; NHS; Engl Lit.

CRAYTON, DENISE L; Greece Arcadia HS; Rochester, NY; (Y); 29/292; Church Yth Grp; Drama Clb; JA; Math Tm; High Hon Roll; Hon Roll; NHS; Regents Schlrshp 85; Pres Acad Fitness Awd 85; Acad Awd 84; Oswego ST Coll; Comp Sci.

CREA, NATINA; Christopher Columbus HS; Bronx, NY; (S); Cit Awd; High Hon Roll; Hon Roll; Jr NHS; NHS; Prfct Atten Awd.

CREANGE, RICHARD P; The Doane Stuart Schl; Paoli, PA; (Y); Ski Clb; Rep Sr Cls; Var L Socr; Stat Sftbl; Ntl Merit SF.

CREATO, ELIZABETH; Mattituck HS; Mattituck, NY; (Y); Yrbk Stf; Lit Mag; High Hon Roll; Hon Roll; Excell German 84-85; Buffalo U; Arch.

CREECH, RICHARD L; Liverpool HS; Liverpool, NY; (Y); 2/840; Pres Debate Tm; Political Wkr; Chorus; School Play; Trs Jr NHS; Pres NHS; Sal; Voice Dem Awd; Am Leg Boys St; Drama Clb; Natl Frnch Cont ST Wnnr 83-85; Nacel Cultrl Exch 85; Harvard Bk Awd 85; Pol Sci.

CREECH, SAMUEL; Windham Ashland Jewett C S HS; Lexington, NY; (S); 3/28; Drama Clb; Exploring; French Clb; Ski Clb; School Play; Nwsp Stf; Yrbk Stf; Pres Soph Cls; Pres Sr Cls; Rep Stu Cncl; Mst Impr Nordic Ski Racer Troph 82-83; Marist Coll; Pol Sci.

CREEDON, SUE; Villa Maria Acad; Warsaw, NY; (Y); Art Clb; French Clb; JA; Nwsp Stf; Bowling; Hon Roll; Prfct Attndnce; Erie CC; Secry.

CREGO, JANE; G R Bodley HS; Fulton, NY; (Y); Girl Scts; VP JA; Band; Concert Band; Drm & Bgl; Jazz Band; Mrchg Band.

CRENSHAW, GEORGE; Longwood HS; Medford, NY; (Y); 30/487; Boy Scts; Math Tm; Var Bowling; High Hon Roll; Hon Roll; NHS; Comp Pgmmg.

CREQUE, MICHELLE; Mt Vernon HS; Mt Vernon, NY; (Y); 130/600; Key Clb; Office Aide; Nwsp Rptr; Nwsp Stf; Yrbk Stf; Stu Cncl; Stat Bsbl; JV Var Cheerleading; Awd Otstndng Cmmnty Svc 85; LIU; Jrnlsm.

CREQUE, PATRICIA; Adlai E Stevenson HS; Bronx, NY; (Y); Hosp Aide; Office Aide; Teachers Aide; Capt Color Guard; Drm & Bgl; Drm Mjr(t); Capt Mrchg Band; Stage Crew; Yrbk Phtg; Cheerleading; Serv Mtl 83; Hunter Clg; Nrsg.

CRESCENZI, LISA; The Mary Louis Acad; Flushing, NY; (Y); Office Aide; Service Clb; Teachers Aide; Prfct Atten Awd; St Johns U; Mngmnt/ Mrktng.

CRESCI, ROGER; East Islip HS; E Islip, NY; (Y); 12/375; Band; Mrchg Band; JV Bsbl; Var Bsktbl; Capt Var Socr; High Hon Roll; NHS; FBLA; Im Sftbl; Hon Roll; All Leag & MVP Socr 84-85; EI All Tourn Tm Bsktbl Fest 84-85; Polytechnic Inst NY; Engrng.

CRESPO, DAISY; Norman Thomas HS; Brooklyn, NY; (S); 69/671; Library Aide; Teachers Aide; Band; Hon Roll; NHS; Golden Record Achvt Awd 82; Baruch Coll; Comp Systs.

CRESPO, ELENA C; The Bronx Hs Science; Bronx, NY; (Y); Cmnty Wkr; Latin Clb; Math Tm; Nwsp Bus Mgr; Nwsp Ed-Chief; Yrbk Stf; NHS; Ntl Merit Ltr; JA; Office Aide; Silver Mdlst Metro NY Math Fair 83; Wnnr Sci Haiku Cntst 82; Law.

CRESPO, FLOR; St Johns Prep Schl; Brooklyn, NY; (Y); Library Aide; High Hon Roll; Comm.

CRESPO, JOHN; St Marys Boys HS; Port Washington, NY; (S); 1/158; Cmnty Wkr; Nwsp Ed-Chief; Yrbk Sprt Ed; Var JV Trk; High Hon Roll; Ntl Merit Ltr; Mst Imprvd JV Trkmn 84; Engrng.

CREWS, ROBERTA; Fort Plain Central HS; Ft Plain, NY; (S); 8/81; Trs Church Yth Grp; Drama Clb; Rptr FFA; Math Clb; Office Aide; School Play; Yrbk Stf; High Hon Roll; Hon Roll; NHS; Lib Arts.

CRICHTON, CAMILLE; Bronx High School Of Science; Bronx, NY; (Y); Church Yth Grp; Teachers Aide; Church Choir; Yrbk Stf; Trk; Cert Compltn Engrng Careers 84; Coll Rep 84-85; Lib Arts.

CRIDDLE, AMY; Harpursville Central Schl; Harpursville, NY; (S); 1/85; Band; Sec Trs Soph Cls; Trs Jr Cls; Var L Bsktbl; Var L Fld Hcky; Var L Sftbl; High Hon Roll; NHS; Spanish Clb; Concert Band; Am Leg Oratorical Cntst 1st 83; Area Al-St Chorus 84; Suny Upstate Medical; Sprts Med.

CRIPPS, SCOTT; Hilton Central HS; Hilton, NY; (Y); 19/350; Var JV Bsbl; JV Tennis; High Hon Roll; NHS; Comp.

CRISAFULLI, SCOTT; Mexico HS; Oswego, NY; (Y); #13 In Class; Am Leg Boys St; Boy Scts; Church Yth Grp; German Clb; Rep Stu Cncl; Var L Ftbl; Wt Lftg; Co-Capt Wrstlng; DAR Awd; NHS; Sclr Athlte Awd; Sprtsmnshp Awd; St Lawrence U; Econ.

CRISCIONE, CHRISTOPHER; Florial Park Memorial HS; Floral Park, NY; (Y); 30/184; Sec Computer Clb; Mathletes; Sec Radio Clb; Variety Show; Nwsp Rptr; Yrbk Stf; L Trk; Hon Roll; NHS; Ntl Merit Ltr; NY ST Regents Schlrshp 85; Polytech Inst Of NY; Med Engrn.

CRISCO, RICHARD; Smithtown High School East; St James, NY; (Y); Ski Clb; Spanish Clb; Stu Cncl; Bsbl; Ftbl; Ice Hcky; Lcrss; Sftbl; Hon Roll.

CRISCUOLO, GAETANA; Aquinas HS; Bronx, NY; (Y); 1/178; Office Aide; Teachers Aide; Nwsp Rptr; Nwsp Stf; Yrbk Stf; VP Soph Cls; Off Jr Cls; High Hon Roll; NHS; Italian Ntlhnr Soc 85; Iona Coll Lang Cntst Awd 85; Schlrshp Yth Inaugural Conf 85; Fordham.

CRISOSTOMO, LUCIA I; G Westinghouse HS; Brooklyn, NY; (Y); 12/322; Church Yth Grp; Drama Clb; Office Aide; Chorus; Church Choir; Jr NHS; NHS; Prfct Atten Awd; Rgnts Schlrshp 85.

CRISS, TOM; Coto-Meridian HS; Cato, NY; (Y); Boy Scts; Church Yth Grp; Model UN; Varsity Clb; VICA; Rep Stu Cncl; JV Bsktbl; Var Ftbl; Stat Score Keeper; Var Trk; Cayuga CC; Electrnc Tech.

CRIST, APRIL; Salamanca Central HS; Salamanca, NY; (S); 21/129; FHA; Model UN; Band; Concert Band; Mrchg Band; Pep Band; Stat Sftbl; Hon Roll; All-Cnty Music Fest Outstndg 84-85; All-Cnty Band 85; Clarion U Of PA; Music.

CRIST, SANDY; Richfield Springs Central HS; Richfield Spgs, NY; (Y); GAA; Varsity Clb; Band; Chorus; Church Choir; Concert Band; Mrchg Band; School Musical; Yrbk Stf; Var Vllybl; Psych.

CRISTAL, JULIETA F; Harrison HS; New Rochelle, NY; (Y); 2/204; Math Tm; Band; Concert Band; Mrchg Band; Ed Nwsp Rptr; Rep Frsh Cls; Rep Soph Cls; Rep Sr Cls; JV Bsktbl; Var Sftbl; Acad Excl Achvt Awds 84-85; Rensselaer Awd; Math, Sci, Frnch Lang Awds 81-84; U Of PA Wharton; Intl Bus.

CRISTOFANO, RONNIE; Mt St Michael Acad; Bronx, NY; (S); 8/308; Church Yth Grp; Computer Clb; Stu Cncl; Im Bsktbl; Im Ftbl; Im CAP; High Hon Roll; Hon Roll; NHS; Spanish Clb; Pre-Med.

CRITCHELL, HEIDI; Hudson HS; Livingston, NY; (Y); AFS; 4-H; Model UN; Socr; Trk; High Hon Roll; NHS; Exch Stu Honduras 85.

CRITCHLOW, DAN; Palmyra-Macedon HS; Palmyra, NY; (Y); Trs 4-H; 4-H Awd; Prfct Atten Awd; Hnr For Mbrshp In Olymics Of The Mind 84; Math.

CROAN, LAURA; Bethpage HS; Bethpage, NY; (Y); 31/290; Sec 4-H; German Clb; Sec Girl Scts; MMM; Acpl Chr; Band; Concert Band; Mrchg Band; Chorus; Orch; Exch Stu Germany 83; Host Stu German Exch 83 & 84.

CROBAR, STEVEN L; Liverpool HS; Liverpool, NY; (S); 49/791; Exploring; VP Trk; Hon Roll; NHS; Lat Triple Jump Schlstc Div Empire ST Games 84; Comp Sci.

CROCE, MICHELE; Hay Shore HS; Bay Shore, NY; (Y); Art Clb; Cmnty Wkr; Pep Clb; Teachers Aide; Color Guard; Rep Frsh Cls; Rep Soph Cls; Rep Jr Cls; Rep Sr Cls; Rep Stu Cncl; York Coll Of PA; Psych.

CROCETTA, CHRISTOPHER; Gloversville HS; Gloversville, NY; (Y); Intnl Clb; Rep Stu Cncl; Bsbl; JV Bsktbl; JV Crs Cntry; Var JV Socr.

CROCKER, KIMBERLY; Granville Central HS; Granville, NY; (Y); GAA; Ski Clb; Chorus; Church Choir; School Musical; School Play; Im Badmtn; Im Bowling; Var Fld Hcky; Im Gym; Mst Imprvd 83-84; Delhi SUNY; Anml Tech.

CROCKER, LAURIE; Haverling Central HS; Bath, NY; (Y); Pres FTA; JCL; Latin Clb; Math Clb; Teachers Aide; Yrbk Stf; Stu Cncl; Cheerleading; Hnrbl Ment Lat 82-83; Stdnt Ldr 83-84; Yr Bk Stff 84-85; Dntl Hyg.

CROCKETT, GUENEVER; The Mary Louis Acad; Flushing, NY; (Y); Cmnty Wkr; Pres Drama Clb; Acpl Chr; Chorus; Madrigals; School Musical; School Play; Stage Crew; The Mary Louis Acad Music Schlrshp 82-86; Theatre.

CROGHAN, MICHAEL; Bronx H S Of Sceince; Bronx, NY; (Y); CAP; Science Clb; Rep Sr Cls; Rep Stu Cncl; L Var Diving; L Var Swmmng; US Air Force Acad Falcon Fndtn Schlrshp 85; Rgnts Schlrshp 85; Vly Forge Milt Acad Schlrshp 85; Vly Forge Mil Acad; Astro Engr.

CROMAS, FAITH; St Edmunds HS; Brooklyn, NY; (S); 7/187; Art Clb; Spanish Clb; Gym; Cit Awd; Hon Roll; Acadmc All Amer 85; Fashion Inst Of Tech; Fash Buyg.

CROMER, FRANCOISE; Mt Vernon HS; Mount Vernon, NY; (Y); Church Yth Grp; Trs Debate Tm; Drama Clb; VP Library Aide; Math Tm; Spanish Clb; Yrbk Stf; Sec Sr Cls; Var Cheerleading; Hon Roll; Cert Hnr NY ST Bar Assn 85; Awd Hal Jacksons Tlntd Teens Cntst 83; Awd 50 Hrs Vol Svc Sor 84-85; Econ.

CROMWELL, SHELLY; Corinth Central HS; Corinth, NY; (S); Drama Clb; Varsity Clb; Concert Band; Mrchg Band; Rep Stu Cncl; JV Var Fld Hcky; JV Var Sftbl; French Hon Soc; Hon Roll; NHS.

CRONE, ERIC; Haverling Central HS; Bath, NY; (S); Boy Scts; JCL; Pres Latin Clb; Math Clb; Var L Swmmng; Hon Roll; NHS; Regents Schlrshp 85; U Of Scranton; Pre-Med.

CRONE, MARK R; Pleasantville HS; Pleasantville, NY; (Y); 12/90; Aud/Vis; Yrbk Stf; Pres Jr Cls; JV Im Bsktbl; Var Capt Crs Cntry; Var Capt Trk; High Hon Roll; NHS; Ntl Merit Ltr; Im Socr; Regents Schlrshp 84-85; Mst Outstndng Bio Stu 82-83; Mst Outstndng Mech Drawing Stu 82-83; GA Inst Of Tech.

CRONIER, NICOLE; John C Birdlebough HS; Pennellville, NY; (Y); Art Clb; Exploring; Latin Clb; Yrbk Stf; Hon Roll; Masonic Awd; Regnl Schlstc Art Awd 85; Hnr Queen Frndshp Triangle Masonic Grp 84; Hnr Art Work 84-85; Irving Nursing Schl; Nurse.

CRONIN, ELIZABETH; Dominican Commercial HS; Bellerose, NY; (Y); Art Clb; Church Yth Grp; Library Aide; Pep Clb; Red Cross Aide; Hon Roll; Ntl Hnr Soc Probtnry 84-85; Educ.

CRONIN, ELIZABETH; Newfield HS; Selden, NY; (Y); Lit Mag; JV Var Cheerleading; JV Mgr(s); Cit Awd; French Hon Soc; High Hon Roll; NHS; Distgnsh Achvt Awd Litrtr 85; St Thomas U.

CRONIN, JAMES; Msgr Mc Clancy HS; Sunnyside, NY; (S); 38/228; Church Yth Grp; Crs Cntry; Trk; Hon Roll; Trs NHS; Spanish NHS; Embry-Riddle U; Aerontcl Engrng.

CRONIN, LOREEN; Cardinal Spellman HS; Bronx, NY; (Y); Church Yth Grp; Cmnty Wkr; Drama Clb; Key Clb; Pep Clb; Science Clb; School Musical; School Play; High Hon Roll; NHS; Mst Outstndng Soph Awd 83-84; Stony Brook; Psych.

CRONIN, MICHELLE; Lafayette HS; Nedrow, NY; (Y); Church Yth Grp; GAA; Sec Spanish Clb; Varsity Clb; Var Socr; Var Sftbl; Hon Roll; Asst & Captn Vly Girls Hcky Tm 83-85; All Star Apple Vly League Sftbl 82-84; Law.

CRONK, EDWARD; Liverpool HS; Liverpool, NY; (S); Trk; Hon Roll; NHS; JA; Im Vllybl; Im Wt Lftg; Rochester Inst Of Tech; Acctg.

CRONK, KRISTINE M; Averill Park HS; West Sand Lake, NY; (Y); 20/222; VP Pres Key Clb; Ski Clb; Variety Show; Nwsp Stf; Sec Sr Cls; Capt Crs Cntry; NHS; VP 4-H; Am Leg Boys St; Varsity Clb; Regents Schlrshp 85; Natl Bio Olympiad 85; Natl Chem Olympiad 85; Natl Chem Olympiad 85; Gold Awd 85; Cornell; Med.

CRONK II, RONALD L; East Syracuse-Minoa Central HS; Minoa, NY; (Y); 75/338; Drama Clb; VP JA; Thesps; Chorus; School Musical; School Play; Swing Chorus; Hon Roll; NHS; Church Choir; Regents Schlrshp; Mrsvl Ag & Tech Schl; Comp Repr.

CROOK, MIRJANA C; Brooklyn Friends Schl; Brooklyn, NY; (Y); Yrbk Bus Mgr; Regnts Schlrshp 85; Skidmore Coll; Bus.

CROOTE, LISA; Greenville JR SR HS; Dormansville, NY; (Y); 1/100; Church Yth Grp; Latin Clb; Concert Band; Symp Band; Rep Stu Cncl; Var L Sftbl; DAR Awd; High Hon Roll; Trs NHS; Voice Dem Awd; Amer Lgn Ortrcl Cont 85; AL; Forstry.

CROSBY, DAN; Chatham Central HS; Chatham, NY; (Y); 1/140; Am Leg Boys St; Stu Cncl; Crs Cntry; Trk; NHS; Math Tm; Jazz Band; Orch; School Musical; All ST Strng Orch 84; Rotry Yth Ldrshp Conf 84.

CROSBY, WILLARD M; Clarence Central SR HS; Clarence, NY; (Y); 46/264; Pres Drama Clb; PAVAS; Thesps; Chorus; School Musical; School Play; Nwsp Rptr; Yrbk Stf; Lit Mag; NHS; NY All St Chorus 84; Tuition Schlrshp Chautauqua Inst Theatre Schl 84; Drama Clb Schlrshp 83-84; Professional Actor.

CROSIER, DEBORA L; Owen D Young HS; Jordanville, NY; (S); FHA; Band; School Play; Yrbk Stf; Trs Jr Cls; High Hon Roll; Bus.

CROSLAND, TELITA; Hillcrest HS; St Albans, NY; (Y); 62/791; Hosp Aide; Capt Sftbl; Ntl Merit Ltr; Med.

CROSS, BILL; La Fayette HS; Jamesville, NY; (Y); Church Yth Grp; French Clb; VICA; Hon Roll; Embry-Riddle Aerontcl U; Pilot.

CROSS, KATHY; Immaculata Acad; Hamburg, NY; (Y); Cmnty Wkr; 4-H; Pres Girl Scts; JA; Library Aide; PAVAS; Orch; GSA Silver Awd 83; Prtl Schlrshp Immaculata Acad 82; Engrng.

CROSS, TRACEY; Ticonderoga HS; Ticonderoga, NY; (Y); 6/112; Drama Clb; FCA; Key Clb; Band; Chorus; Jazz Band; School Play; Trs Frsh Cls; Pres Soph Cls; Trs Stu Cncl; All Co Band 83-84; All Co Jazz Band 84-85.

CROSSETT, BETH; Lockport SR HS; Lockport, NY; (Y); 1/411; Am Leg Aux Girls St; Church Yth Grp; Yrbk Ed-Chief; Var Capt Bsktbl; Var Socr; High Hon Roll; NHS; Exploring; Intnl Clb; Church Choir; Rensselaer Polytechnic Inst Math & Sci Awd 85; Hugh O Brian Yth Fndtn Sem 84; Outstndng 9th Grde Stu; Engrng.

CROSSETT, M BETH; Lockport SR HS; Lockport, NY; (Y); 2/411; Am Leg Aux Girls St; Church Yth Grp; Yrbk Ed-Chief; Yrbk Sprt Ed; Capt Bsktbl; High Hon Roll; NHS; Exploring; Intnl Clb; Nwsp Stf; Hugh O Brian Yth Fndtn Smnr 84; Rensselaer Polytech Inst Math & Sci Awd 85; Roy B Kelly Outstndg Stu; Engrng.

CROSSON, KIM M; City Honors Schl; Buffalo, NY; (Y); 54/97; Pres Church Yth Grp; Dance Clb; Latin Clb; Red Cross Aide; VP Stu Cncl; Stat Socr; L Sftbl; Regnts & Amer Brd Fnrl Svc Ed Schlrshp 85; Canton Ag/Tech Coll; Mrtry Sci.

CROTEAU, ELLEN; Cardinal Mooney HS; Rochester, NY; (Y); 113/315; Intnl Clb; Service Clb; Ski Clb; Yrbk Stf; Rep Soph Cls; Pom Pon; Swmmng.

CROTHERS, VANESSA L; Churchville-Chili HS; North Chili, NY; (Y); 12/317; VP Church Yth Grp; Math Clb; Acpl Chr; Church Choir; School Play; Pres NHS; St Schlr; Rgnts Schlrshp Awd 85; Free Mthdst Futrs 85; Roberts Wesleyan Coll; Chem.

CROTHERS, WALTER; Newark HS; Newark, NY; (Y); 20/250; Am Leg Boys St; Church Yth Grp; French Clb; Letterman Clb; Service Clb; Varsity Clb; Nwsp Stf; Yrbk Stf; JV Var Bsbl; Var JV Socr; Comp Sci.

CROUCH, DIANA; Dryden Central HS; Freeville, NY; (Y); 63/160; Church Yth Grp; Cmnty Wkr; Library Aide; Teachers Aide; Church Choir; High Hon Roll; Hon Roll; Bus & Prof Women Awd 85; Tompkins Coll; Human Svcs.

CROUNSE, DAVID A; Shaker HS; Albany, NY; (Y); 85/410; JV Lcrss; Hon Roll; NY ST Regnts Schlrshp 85; U Of FL; Nuclr Engrng.

CROUSE, JEFF; Fort Plain Central Schl; Fort Plain, NY; (S); 2/59; Pres Church Yth Grp; Computer Clb; Trs Intnl Clb; Quiz Bowl; Pres Stu Cncl; Var Socr; L Trk; High Hon Roll; Trs NHS; Diplmtc Svc.

CROUSE, SAMANTHA C; Paul V Moore HS; Hastings, NY; (Y); 4/297; AFS; Nwsp Bus Mgr; Nwsp Ed-Chief; Nwsp Rptr; Rep Stu Cncl; High Hon Roll; Pres NHS; Ntl Merit Ltr; Locl Hnr Socty Soc Stds 84; Smmr Schlrs Prog Lemoyne Coll 84; Bst News Stry Syracuse Herald Journl 84; Syracuse U; Jrnlsm.

CROWDER, SCOTT W; Lakeland HS; Putnam Valley, NY; (Y); 1/330; Boy Scts; Rep Stu Cncl; Var Crs Cntry; Var Tennis; Var Trk; High Hon Roll; NHS; Ntl Merit Ltr; Val; Ciba Geigy Sci Awd 85; Bank Of NY Scholastic Achvt Dinner 85; Brown U.

CROWE, JON DAVID; James E Sperry HS; Henrietta, NY; (Y); Cmnty Wkr; JA; ROTC; JV Var Ftbl; JV Golf; Wt Lftg; Hon Roll; Jr NHS; NHS; Engrng.

CROWE, JOSEPH; Binghamton HS; Binghamton, NY; (Y); 41/478; Var Bsktbl; High Hon Roll; Hon Roll; SUNY Buffalo; Engr.

CROWELL, BRENDA; Cicero-North Syracuse HS; Clay, NY; (S); 34/622; Trs Church Yth Grp; Drill Tm; Mrchg Band; Twrlr; Hon Roll.

CROWELL, DAVID; Sodus Central HS; Sodus Pt, NY; (Y); Boy Scts; Model UN; Y-Teens; JV Var Bsbl; JV Var Bsktbl; High Hon Roll; Hon Roll; Socl.

CROWELL, KRISTIN; Forestville Central HS; Forestville, NY; (Y); 2/45; Am Leg Aux Girls St; Science Clb; Chorus; Color Guard; Mrchg Band; Stat Bsktbl; High Hon Roll; Hon Roll; NHS; Girl Scts; Outstndng Achvmnt Awd Spanish I II & III 83-85:AATSP Excllnc Frgn Lang Awd 85; Spain Hmsty Prog 84; Comp Sci.

CROWELL, THOMAS; Hugh C Williams HS; Canton, NY; (Y); Church Yth Grp; Quiz Bowl; Varsity Clb; Var Lcrss; High Hon Roll; NHS; Nwsp Stf; St Lawrence U Tlntd Jr 84; St Lawrence Co Art Show 85; HS Acdmc Ltr Awd 83, 84 & 85; Middlebury Coll.

CROWLEY, EILEEN; St Francis Prep; Flushing, NY; (Y); Art Clb; Church Yth Grp; Im Gym.

CROWLEY, KERRI J; Prattsburg Central HS; Branchport, NY; (Y); 11/33; Church Yth Grp; Varsity Clb; Band; School Play; Yrbk Ed-Chief; Cheerleading; DAR Awd; Hon Roll; JP Sousa Awd; Prattsburg Teachrs Assn Schlrshp 85; Houghton Coll; Communctns.

CROWLEY, MICHAEL J; Salamanca Central HS; Salamanca, NY; (Y); French Clb; Teachers Aide; Bowling; French Hon Soc; Church Yth Grp; Cmnty Wkr; Letterman Clb; Ski Clb; Crs Cntry; Ftbl; St Bonaventure; Elec Engr.

CROWLEY, RALENE; Norwood Norfolk Central HS; Norwood, NY; (Y); Art Clb; Pres Church Yth Grp; Dance Clb; 4-H; JCL; Latin Clb; Drm Mjr(t); Lit Mag; Hon Roll; JC Awd; Potsdam ST Coll; Pre-Law.

CROWLEY, SUSAN; Long Beach HS; Long Beach, NY; (S); 34/390; Church Yth Grp; Key Clb; Nwsp Rptr; Nwsp Stf; Yrbk Rptr; JV Cheerleading; JV Sftbl; JV Trk; Hon Roll; NHS.

CRUMBLEY, ERIC C; Cathedral Prep; New York, NY; (Y); Library Aide; Red Cross Aide; Pres Frsh Cls; Pres Soph Cls; Pres Jr Cls; Pres Stu Cncl; Capt Bsktbl; Capt Vllybl; Cit Awd; Sr Cls; Regents Schlrshp Nrsng; Sacrastan Awd Of Merit; MSP ISAL Bsktbl Lgu; Nrsng.

CRUMLISH, CHRISTINE; Geneva HS; Geneva, NY; (S); 7/170; French Clb; Latin Clb; Model UN; Band; Yrbk Rptr; NHS; Ntl Merit Ltr; Wellesly Bk Awd.

CRUPI, KEITH S; La Guardia H S Of Performing Arts; Rego Park Queens, NY; (Y); 322/588; Band; Concert Band; Jazz Band; Orch; School Musical; Symp Band; Ntl Merit Ltr; Schlrshp Manhattan Schl Of Music 85-86; 1st Prz Ithica HS Percssn Comptn 84; Manhattan Sch; Prof Percssnst.

CRUVER, TIM; Shenendehowa HS; Mechanicville, NY; (Y); Church Yth Grp; Off 4-H; Quiz Bowl; Band; Chorus; Church Choir; Swing Chorus; Cit Awd; 4-H Awd; Hon Roll; Mst Outstndng 4-H Ag 84; Stephen Mazzarella Awd Comm Svc, Ldrshp, Hmnty 83; Music Fest 81-83; Cobleskill; Anml Sci.

CRUZ, DEBRA; New Utrecht HS; Brooklyn, NY; (Y); 24/557; Sec Key Clb; GAA; Office Aide; Nwsp Rptr; Rptr Yrbk Stf; Im Bowling; Im Sftbl; Im Swmmng; Arista 84; NYS Regnts Schlrshp 85; Triple C Awd 83; Fordham U; Bus.

CRUZ, FRANKLIN; Christ The King Regional HS; Howard Beach, NY; (Y); 113/395; Computer Clb; Nwsp Sprt Ed; Var Coach Actv; Var Mgr(s); Timer; Hon Roll; Baruch Coll; Acctng.

CRUZ, GLORIA; Aquinas HS; Bronx, NY; (Y); 57/178; Camera Clb; Church Yth Grp; Computer Clb; Drama Clb; Key Clb; Library Aide; Office Aide; Hon Roll; CCD; Marid Regina Coll; Lgl Secy.

CRUZ, JEANNE M; St John Villa Acad; Staten Island, NY; (Y); Drama Clb; Hosp Aide; Math Tm; Scholar Sny U 85; NYU.

CRUZ, JENNIFER; Adali E Stevenson HS; Bronx, NY; (Y); Aud/Vis; Drama Clb; FNA; Hosp Aide; PAVAS; Band; Yrbk Stf; Capt Gym; Stat Twrlr; Cit Awd; Fordham U; Marine Bio.

CRUZ, LISA; St Johns Prep; Woodside, NY; (Y); High Hon Roll; Hon Roll; Jr NHS; NHS; Recmdtn Queens Bridge Med Pgm 85; Bus Adm.

CRUZ, PETER; Msgr Mc Clancy HS; Rego Pk, NY; (Y); Crs Cntry; Trk; Hon Roll; Mass Comm.

CRUZ, REIDAN; Saint Francis Prep; Astoria, NY; (Y); Boy Scts; Exploring; Leo Clb; Nwsp Ed-Chief; Yrbk Phtg; Sftbl; Vllybl; Accntng.

CRUZ, SEGUNDO; Eastern District HS; Brooklyn, NY; (Y); Cmnty Wkr; FNA; Hon Roll; NY City Coll; Elect Engr.

CRUZ, TINA; Central Islip HS; Central Islip, NY; (Y); 7/350; Stage Crew; Yrbk Stf; Lit Mag; Rep Soph Cls; VP Jr Cls; Hon Roll; Sec NHS; Engrng.

CSAKI, MICHELE; Colonie Central HS; Schenectady, NY; (Y); Church Yth Grp; Cmnty Wkr; Hosp Aide; Intnl Clb; Church Choir; Orch; High Hon Roll; Hon Roll; NHS; Sndy Schl Tchr 84-85; Socl Wk.

CSIZMAR, CHRISTOPHER; Cardinal O Hara HS; Tonawanda, NY; (Y); Music.

CTORIDES, CHRISTINA; William Cullen Bryant HS; New York, NY; (S); Library Aide; Teachers Aide; Band; Concert Band; Jazz Band; Ed Nwsp Rptr; French Hon Soc; Hon Roll; NHS; Lttr Acadmc Engl, Frnch, Greek, Geom, Bio 84; Pol Sci.

CUBAS JR, EDILBERTO MARTIN; Cardinal Hayes HS; New York, NY; (Y); 1/264; Chess Clb; Crs Cntry; JV Var Trk; Hon Roll; Prfct Atten Awd; Mnr Ltr Tutorng 85; USNA Smnr Smnr , Wrkshp 85; Gen Excel Medls 83-85; US Naval Acad; Aero Engr.

CUCCHIARA, JOSEPH; St Raymond H S For Boys; Bronx, NY; (Y); 19/189; Dance Clb; Science Clb; Hnr Awd; Baruch Coll; Bus Ed.

CUCCHIARA, PETER; H Frank Carey HS; Franklin Sq, NY; (Y); 53/222; Cmnty Wkr; Band; Concert Band; Jazz Band; Hon Roll.

CUCCIA, CATHERINE; Dover HS; Dover Plains, NY; (Y); Band; Concert Band; Drm Mjr(t); Mrchg Band; Church Yth Grp; Drama Clb; French Clb; Church Choir; Pep Band; School Musical; MUSIC.

CUCCIA, JOANNE; Roy C Ketcham HS; Wappingers Fall, NY; (Y); Art Clb; Drama Clb; Thesps; Chorus; Orch; School Musical; School Play; Stage Crew; Off Jr Cls; Hon Roll; Cnty Plyrs Nmntn Bst Spprtng Actress 85; Awds Mask Mime Drama Wrk 85; Law.

CUCCO, DEENA; Smithtown HS West; Smithtown, NY; (Y); Drama Clb; Intnl Clb; School Play; Stage Crew; JV Var Vllybl; Hon Roll; NHS; Regents Scholarship; Hofstar U; Math Teacher.

CUCCURULLO, LYNN; Colonie Central HS; Schenectady, NY; (Y); Dance Clb; Drama Clb; Chorus; School Play; Variety Show; JV Var Cheerleading; JV Sftbl; JV Vllybl; Fash Merch.

CUDDIHY, DONALD; Bishop Timon HS; Buffalo, NY; (Y); Boy Scts; Computer Clb; JA; Quiz Bowl; Chorus; Var Crs Cntry; Mgr(s); Score Keeper; Trk; High Hon Roll; St Bonaventure; Psych.

CUDDY, CASEY; Corning East HS; Bath, NY; (Y); 13/253; JA; Math Tm; Im Bsbl; JV Var Bsktbl; Im Ice Hcky; Lcrss; Hon Roll; NHS; Pres Schlr; Rgnts, RPI Schlrshps 85; Hnrs Mth, Sci; Rensselaer Polytech; Law.

CUDDY, MELINDA; Middletown HS; Middletown, NY; (Y); Yrbk Stf; Var L Swmmng; High Hon Roll; Hon Roll; NHS; Internatl Relatns.

CUDJOE, NIGEL; Franklin D Roosevelt HS; Brooklyn, NY; (Y); 107/530; Computer Clb; Yrbk Ed-Chief; Cncl Supv Adm Ldrshp Awd 85; Wagner Coll; Comp.

CUDNEY, JANET; South Park HS; Buffalo, NY; (Y); 40/360; Girl Scts; Hon Roll; Our Best Merit Awd 84-85; Acadmc Art.

CUEVAS, NELSON; St Agnes HS; New York, NY; (Y); JA; Rep Frsh Cls; Rep Soph Cls; Var L Bsbl; JV Crs Cntry; Im Vllybl; Hon Roll; NHS; Var L Bsktbl; NY St Regents Schlrshp 85; Pace U; Med.

CUFFARO, CATHERINE; Union-Endicott HS; Endicott, NY; (Y); Concert Band; Hon Roll; Med Asst.

CUFFE, JAMES F; Fox Lane HS; Mt Kisco, NY; (Y); 67/300; Cmnty Wkr; Band; Concert Band; Jazz Band; Mrchg Band; Sr Cls; Var Bowling; Var Ftbl; Var Trk; Im Wt Lftg; Outstndg Contrbtn Music Dept 83-85; NYS Regents Schlrshp 85; Syracuse U; Accntnt.

CUILLA, JOHN; Argyle Central Schl; Argyle, NY; (Y); Am Leg Boys St; Math Tm; Varsity Clb; Yrbk Sprt Ed; Var Bsbl; JV Var Bsktbl; Mgr(s); JV Var Socr; Hon Roll; French Clb; King Of Jr Prom 85; Phys Ed.

CUKROVANY, ROBIN; Hoosic Valley Central HS; Valley Falls, NY; (Y); Church Yth Grp; Band; Chorus; School Musical; School Play; Sec Soph Cls; Co-Capt Cheerleading; Socr; Co-Capt Vllybl; Hon Roll; Cosmtlgst.

CULBERT, CHRISTINA; Fillmore Central HS; Fillmore, NY; (S); 6/58; Am Leg Aux Girls St; 4-H; Sec Jr Cls; Score Keeper; Tennis; Vllybl; 4-H Awd; High Hon Roll; NHS; Ski Clb; NY City Career Awd Trp; Psych.

CULHANE, CHRISTOPHER; Mt St Michael Acad; Bronx, NY; (Y); #95 In Class; Church Yth Grp; Cmnty Wkr; Hon Roll; John Jay Coll; Polce Ofcr.

CULKIN, MICHAEL; Msgr Mc Clancy Memorial HS; Astoria, NY; (Y); Political Wkr; Spanish Clb; Im JV Bsktbl; Im Fld Hcky; Im Sftbl; Hon Roll; Aerontcl Engrng.

CULLEN, JENNIFER; Cattaraugus Central HS; Cattaraugus, NY; (Y); Ski Clb; Spanish Clb; Trs Y-Teens; Chorus; Jazz Band; Nwsp Stf; Trs Frsh Cls; Stat Bsktbl; Capt Cheerleading; Var Trk; PA Schl Press Assn-2nd Pl New Feature 82; Natl Guild Of Piano Awd; Presdntl Physcl Fitness Awd 80-83; Oswego; Busnss.

CULLEN, MOIRA ANN; Seton Catholic Central HS; Endicott, NY; (S); Pres Spanish Clb; Nwsp Rptr; Nwsp Stf; Var L Socr; Var Trk; High Hon Roll; Mgr NHS; Debate On Wndow On Wrld Prog 84; Attnd NYS Reg Journ Wrkshp 82-84; Med.

CULLEN, SUSAN; De Sales Catholic HS; Gasport, NY; (Y); 14/46; Hon Roll; Intl Frgn Lang Awd 83; Natl Hon Rl 85; Acad All Amer Awd 84; Yng Vlntrs Action 83-84; St Bonaventure U; Mth.

CULNANE, BETH; Mechanicville HS; Mechanicville, NY; (S); 8/110; French Clb; Nwsp Rptr; Rep Frsh Cls; Rep Stu Cncl; JV Bsktbl; VP Socr; VP Sftbl; High Hon Roll; Hon Roll; Bentley Coll; Bus.

CULP, DAVID RANDALL; Irondequoit HS; Rochester, NY; (Y); 80/397; Boy Scts; Church Yth Grp; Cmnty Wkr; Band; Concert Band; Mrchg Band; Orch; School Musical; Liberal Arts.

CULVER, DEBORAH; Frankfort-Schuyler Central HS; Frankfort, NY; (S); 13/99; Math Tm; Spanish Clb; Nwsp Stf; Yrbk Stf; Var Badmtn; Var Bowling; Var Fld Hcky; High Hon Roll; Hon Roll; NHS; Union Coll; Elec Engrng.

CULVER, KENNETH; Trumansburg HS; Trumansburg, NY; (Y); Am Leg Boys St; Orch; Stage Crew; Trs Frsh Cls; Socr; Tennis; Prfct Atten Awd; Mst Improved Ten Plyr 82; Biol.

CULVER, PHILIP; Trumansburg Central Schls; Mecklenburg, NY; (Y); 7/85; Boy Scts; French Clb; Band; Concert Band; Jazz Band; Mrchg Band; Var L Tennis; High Hon Roll; Hon Roll; Ntl Merit Ltr; Tompkins Cnty Yth Of Yr 83; Alt Boys ST 85; Stanford U; Intrptr.

CULZAC, CRESWELL; George Wingate HS; Brooklyn, NY; (S); 9/360; Hon Roll; Sal; Elec Engr.

CUMBERBATCH, MICHAEL; Bishop Loughlin Memorial HS; Brooklyn, NY; (Y); 15/215; Cmnty Wkr; Computer Clb; Hosp Aide; Teachers Aide; Im Stat Bsktbl; Mgr(s); High Hon Roll; Bishop Loughtins Silver L Awd 85; St Johns U; Psych.

CUMMING, LYNN; Notre Dame Acad; Staten Island, NY; (Y); Yrbk Phtg; Yrbk Stf; Bowling; Psych.

CUMMINGS, CAROL; Bishop Maginn HS; Albany, NY; (S); 9/118; Spanish Clb; Var Capt Bsktbl; JV Sftbl; Var Tennis; Var Capt Vllybl; High Hon Roll; Hon Roll; NHS; Law.

CUMMINGS, CAROL; General Brown HS; Dexter, NY; (Y); 38/125; Church Yth Grp; French Clb; Band; Chorus; Concert Band; Drill Tm; Flag Corp; Mrchg Band; Pep Band; Stage Crew; Plattsburg ST; Spcl Educ.

CUMMINGS, DEANNA; Keveny Memorial Acad; Watervliet, NY; (S); Church Yth Grp; Cmnty Wkr; Band; Concert Band; Mrchg Band; Trs Jr Cls; Rep Stu Cncl; Var Crs Cntry; High Hon Roll; Phy Thrpy.

CUMMINGS, DEBRA; Susquehanna Valley HS; Binghamton, NY; (Y); Art Clb; Chess Clb; Church Yth Grp; Cmnty Wkr; Drama Clb; Trs 4-H; Office Aide; Stage Crew; 4-H Awd; Sec.

CUMMINGS, GIZZELLE; De Witt Clinton HS; Bronx, NY; (Y); Pres Stu Cncl; Mgr Trk.

CUMMINGS, JANETTE; Attica SR HS; Attica, NY; (Y); Drama Clb; Pres 4-H; Hosp Aide; Chorus; Church Choir; School Play; Swing Chorus; 4-H Awd; Genesee CC.

CUMMINGS, JONATHON P; Attica SR HS; Attica, NY; (Y); 2/153; Boy Scts; Church Choir; JV Var Crs Cntry; Trk; High Hon Roll; Lion Awd; NHS; Sal; Acad All-Amer Frnch & Physics 84; Cornell U; Physics.

CUMMINGS, KATHLEEN; John Jay HS; Fishkill, NY; (Y); Church Yth Grp; Var Bsktbl; Var Vllybl; High Hon Roll; David G Bvrly Athlt Of Yr 82-83; Ntl Phy Ed Stu 84-85.

CUMMINGS, LAURIE; Berlin Central HS; Stephentown, NY; (S); 5/82; Pres Church Yth Grp; Ski Clb; Band; Chorus; Church Choir; Var Bsktbl; Var Socr; Var Sftbl; High Hon Roll; Rensselaer Cnty All Cnty Fest Band 82-83; Mssnry Nrs.

CUMMINGS, LORI; Oxford Acad; Oxford, NY; (Y); Church Yth Grp; 4-H; French Clb; JV Var Fld Hcky; JV Sftbl; All Tourny Team Fld Hcky 83; Occptnl Thrpy.

CUMMINGS, MARY; Oxford Acad HS; Oxford, NY; (Y); French Clb; FNA; Hosp Aide; Red Cross Aide; Badmtn; Capt Cheerleading; Socr; Sftbl; Tennis; Vllybl; Stu Fo Qrtr 84-85; Nrs Aid Astnt 84-85; Actvts Drctr.

CUMMINGS, MARY C; Keveny Memorial Acad; Watervliet, NY; (S); 5/39; Church Yth Grp; Cmnty Wkr; Teachers Aide; Band; Concert Band; Mrchg Band; Ed Yrbk Stf; High Hon Roll; NHS; Law.

CUMMINGS, MICH L; Caior-Durham HS; Acra, NY; (Y); Cmnty Wkr; GAA; Pep Clb; Political Wkr; Red Cross Aide; Varsity Clb; Stu Cncl; Socr; Sftbl; Hon Roll; SUNY Cobleskill; Fshr Mgmnt.

CUMMINGS, MICHAEL J; Pelham Memorial HS; Pelham, NY; (Y); 29/177; AFS; Stage Crew; Variety Show; Nwsp Rptr; Yrbk Ed-Chief; Hon Roll; NHS; NY St Regents Schlrshp 85; 2nd Short Story Cont 85; Kenyon Coll; Eng.

CUMMINGS, PATRICK C; Lansing HS; Ithaca, NY; (Y); 13/80; Spanish Clb; Var L Bsbl; Capt Ice Hcky; Var L Socr; High Hon Roll; Hon Roll; Engrng.

CUMMINGS, SCOTT D; Vestal SR HS; Vestal, NY; (Y); 23/450; Band; Concert Band; Jazz Band; Mrchg Band; Pep Band; School Musical; Hon Roll; NHS; Ntl Merit SF; Pres Schlr; SUNY-BINGHAMTON; Chem.

CUMMINGS, TERI; Alexander Central HS; Darien Center, NY; (S); 1/88; Math Tm; Varsity Clb; Drill Tm; Mrchg Band; Yrbk Ed-Chief; Yrbk Phtg; Yrbk Sprt Ed; Yrbk Stf; Rep Frsh Cls; Pres Soph Cls; NYS Regnts Schlrshp Wnnr 85; All-Star Leag Sccr, Vllybl & Sftbl; Recpnt Dept & Deans Schlrshp 85; Daemen Coll; Phys Thrpy.

CUMMINS, EILEEN; John A Coleman HS; Saugerties, NY; (Y); Dance Clb; Stage Crew; Bsktbl; Fld Hcky; Sftbl; Hon Roll; Ulster County CC.

CUMMISKEY, KRISTEN; Shennendehowa HS; Clifton Park, NY; (Y); 3/660; Hosp Aide; Key Clb; Chorus; Yrbk Sprt Ed; NHS; Ntl Merit Ltr; Pres Schlr; Philsphy Clb-Pres & Co-Foundr 84-85; U Of Notre Dame; Biomed Engrng.

CUMMO, CHRISTOPHER; Longwood HS; Middle Island, NY; (Y); 69/487; Var Bsbl; JV Ftbl; Var Golf; JV Trk; Hon Roll; Sci.

CUNNINGHAM, ANDREW; Mineola HS; Williston Park, NY; (Y); Key Clb; Var Capt Ftbl; Wt Lftg; Var Wrstlng; Hon Roll; Jr NHS; St Johns; CPA.

CUNNINGHAM, CHERYL; Bethpage HS; Old Bethpage, NY; (Y); 99/286; Boys Clb Am; Dance Clb; Girl Scts; Library Aide; Spanish Clb; Teachers Aide; School Play; Variety Show; Bsbl; Cheerleading; Best Costume Dsgn 85; Best Dsgn Of Baby Wear 85; Fshn Dsgn.

CUNNINGHAM, EILEEN J; Lindenhurst HS; Lindenhurst, NY; (Y); Key Clb; Spanish Clb; Nwsp Stf; Yrbk Stf; Var Bowling; Hon Roll; Jr NHS; NHS; Psychlgy.

CUNNINGHAM, GENE; St Francis Prep; Flushing, NY; (Y); 300/750; Var Bsbl; Ftbl; Phy Ed.

CUNNINGHAM, KARLA; Aquinas Inst; Rochester, NY; (Y); Drama Clb; Hosp Aide; School Musical; Stage Crew; Nwsp Rptr; Yrbk Stf; Var Bsktbl; Hon Roll; Volntr Svc Awd Cystc Fibrosis 83; Cty Rochster Recgntn-Sequicentnl Pgm 84; Bio.

CUNNINGHAM, LESLIE; Salmon River Central HS; Constable, NY; (Y); Band; Chorus; Concert Band; Mrchg Band; Yrbk Stf; Var Bsktbl; Var Socr; Var Trk; Hon Roll; 4-H; Elem Tchr.

CUNNINGHAM, MICHELLE A; Sachem High Schl North; Holbrook, NY; (Y); 134/1309; Drama Clb; Acpl Chr; Chorus; Madrigals; School Musical; School Play; Stage Crew; Swing Chorus; Variety Show; NHS; 100 Score Nyssma Solo Competitn 84-85; All County Chorus 84-85; SUNY Fredonia; Musical Theatre.

CUNNINGHAM, SEAN; Irondequoit HS; Rochester, NY; (Y); 1/337; Latin Clb; Radio Clb; Science Clb; Stu Cncl; JV Bsbl; Bsktbl; L Crs Cntry; JV Golf; High Hon Roll; Ntl Merit Schol; NY St Regnts Schl 85; SUNY; Chem Engrng.

CUNNINGHAM, STACEY; Salmon River Central HS; Bombay, NY; (S); 7/97; Sec Church Yth Grp; Sec Drama Clb; Pres VP 4-H; French Clb; Band; Chorus; Pres VP Church Choir; Concert Band; Mrchg Band; School Musical.

CUNNINGHAM, TODD; Liverpool HS; Liverpool, NY; (Y); Drama Clb; School Musical; School Play; Stage Crew; Ftbl; Trk; Wt Lftg; U Of MD; Comp Sci.

CUNY, LAURA; St Joseph By The Sea HS; Staten Island, NY; (Y); Art Clb; Computer Clb; Girl Scts; Yrbk Stf; JV Score Keeper; JV Timer; Hon Roll; NEDT Awd.

CUPP, ELEANOR; Dryden JR-SR HS; Dryden, NY; (Y); Hosp Aide; Band; Chorus; Jazz Band; School Musical; School Play; Stage Crew; Nwsp Sprt Ed; JV Bsktbl; Var Swmmng; Hme Econ Awd 84; U Of IL.

CURA, MONICA; Msgr Scanlan HS; Elmhurst, NY; (Y); 29/265; Intnl Clb; Art Clb; Church Choir; Yrbk Stf; Hon Roll; NHS; Prfct Atten Awd; Iona Lang Spnsh Cntst 85; Ntl Hnr Soc 84; Prnclpls Cert Of Merit 84; Villanova U; Accntng.

CURCILLO, TARA KRISTIN; Connetquot HS; Oakdale, NY; (Y); 34/700; Spanish Clb; Symp Band; VP Frsh Cls; VP Soph Cls; VP Jr Cls; Pres Sr Cls; Cheerleading; Trk; Cit Awd; High Hon Roll; Guy Lombardo Recgntn Awd 85; NYS Regnts Schlrshp 85; Most Outstndng Bus Law Stu 85; James Madison U; Eng.

CURCIO, DAWN; St Joseph By-The-Sea HS; Staten Island, NY; (Y); Art Clb; Computer Clb; Drama Clb; Chorus; School Musical; School Play; Hon Roll; NEDT Awd; Comp Sci.

CURCIO, GINA; Susquehanna Valley HS; Conklin, NY; (Y); French Clb; Varsity Clb; Band; Concert Band; Mrchg Band; Crs Cntry; Trk; Vllybl; STAC All Stars Vrsty Vlybll 84-85; Pres Phys Fit Awds; Ithica; Phys Ther.

CURCIO, NICOLE; The Masters Schl; Ocean City, NJ; (Y); Cmnty Wkr; VP Drama Clb; Acpl Chr; Stage Crew; Ed Yrbk Ed-Chief; VP Frsh Cls; High Hon Roll; Ntl Merit Ltr; Church Yth Grp; Rep Pep Clb; Excllnce Fr 83-84; Lib Art.

CURCIO, STEPHANIE A; Newfield HS; Selden, NY; (Y); 34/563; Church Yth Grp; Trs Yrbk Stf; Rep Frsh Cls; Stu Cncl; Stat Var Mgr(s); Cit Awd; High Hon Roll; Hon Roll; Jr NHS; NHS; Italian Hnr Scty 84-85; Regents Schlrshp 84-85; Girls Ldrs Club Vrsty Lttr 84-85; SUNY-STONY Brook; Phy Thrpy.

CURLEY, CATHI; Bainbridge Guilford Central Schl; Bainbridge, NY; (Y); VP Spanish Clb; Band; Color Guard; Concert Band; Orch; Co-Capt Cheerleading; Sftbl; Tennis; Prfct Atten Awd; Exec Secy.

CURLEY, KEVIN M; Suffern HS; Suffern, NY; (Y); 50/450; JV Var Bsbl; Im Bsktbl; Var Ftbl; JV Wrstlng; Hon Roll; NHS; Gtysbrg Coll; Physcl Ed.

CURLEY, MICHAEL D; Shenendehowa HS; Clifton Park, NY; (Y); Am Leg Boys St; JCL; Trs Latin Clb; Pres Leo Clb; Science Clb; Band; Rep Sr Cls; JV Trk; High Hon Roll; NHS; Magna Cum Laudi Ntl Latin Exm 84-85; Acad Achvt Cert 84-85; Aerospc Engrng.

CURR, LOUIE; Fabius Pompey Central Schl; Pompey, NY; (Y); 29/66; Computer Clb; Var Bsbl; JV Bsktbl; Var Socr; Cit Awd; Hon Roll; Morrisville Coll; Comp Info.

CURRAN, ANDREW B; John Jay HS; Katonah, NY; (Y); 1/290; Art Clb; Sr Cls; Swmmng; High Hon Roll; Jr NHS; NY ST Regents Schlrshp 85; Boy King Awd 85; U Of VA; Engrng.

CURRAN, CHRIS; West Hemstead HS; W Hempstead, NY; (Y); Aud/Vis; Computer Clb; Office Aide; Hon Roll; Prfct Atten Awd; Hnr Rl 84-85; Perf Atndnce Awd 84-85; Audio-Visual Awd 82-83; Hofstra U; Film Edtng.

CURRAN, CHRISTOPHER; Saranac Lake Central HS; Saranac Lk, NY; (Y); 18/127; AFS; Cmnty Wkr; Ski Clb; JV Golf; Var JV Socr; High Hon Roll; Hon Roll; NHS; Aldine Skng Tm 84-85; Marine Bio.

CURRAN, DEBORAH ANN; East Syracuse Minoa HS; E Syracuse, NY; (Y); 95/338; Hosp Aide; Ski Clb; Variety Show; Stat Lcrss; JV Var Socr; JV Vllybl; Hon Roll; Jr NHS; St Joseph Hosp; Nrsng.

CURRAN, ERIN; Lansingburgh HS; Troy, NY; (Y); 28/160; German Clb; Office Aide; Nwsp Stf; Stu Cncl; Cit Awd; Hon Roll; Jr NHS; NHS; Leland F Smith Memrl Schlrshp 85; Svc Schl Awd 85; Coll Of St Rose; Elem Ed.

CURRAN, JEANNE; Binghamton HS; Binghamton, NY; (Y); Art Clb; Lit Mag; Hon Roll; SUNY Binghamton; Zoolgy.

CURRAN, MARY P; St Francis Prep; Bayside, NY; (Y); 90/690; Church Yth Grp; Chorus; Stu Cncl; Hon Roll; NHS; NY St Regenst Awd 85; Manhattan Coll; Fin.

CURRAN, PATRICIA A; Garden City HS; Garden City, NY; (Y); 66/322; Key Clb; Office Aide; Spanish Clb; Stage Crew; Var Capt Swmmng; Var Trk; High Hon Roll; Jr NHS; Ntl Merit Ltr; Smith Coll; Span.

CURREN, TIMOTHY; Voorheesville HS; Altamont, NY; (Y); Church Yth Grp; Ski Clb; Bsktbl; Var Co-Capt Socr; Var Vllybl; Bus.

CURRIE, JILL K; Newfane HS; Newfane, NY; (S); 8/175; Church Yth Grp; Math Tm; Teachers Aide; Church Choir; School Musical; Symp Band; JV Var Bsktbl; JV Vllybl; Hon Roll; NHS; Math.

CURRIER, KAREN; Massena Cntrl Schl; Brasher Falls, NY; (Y); Rep Frsh Cls; Rep Soph Cls; Rep Jr Cls; Rep Stu Cncl; Powder Puff Ftbl; Hon Roll; Crmnl Justce.

CURRY, DANIEL; East Islip HS; Islip Terrace, NY; (Y); Political Wkr; Rep Soph Cls; Rep Jr Cls; JV Lcrss; Im Sftbl; Hon Roll; Babson Coll; Stckbrkr.

CURRY, JONATHAN; Edison Vo-Tech; Rochester, NY; (Y); Church Yth Grp; Band; Chorus; Church Choir; Drm & Bgl; Jazz Band; School Musical; High Hon Roll; Hon Roll; Prfct Atten Awd; Robert Weslyan; Music Ed.

CURRY, KARIN; Earl L Vandenmuelen HS; Mt Sinai, NY; (Y); Leo Clb; Pep Clb; Teachers Aide; Varsity Clb; Chorus; Cheerleading; Gym; High Hon Roll; Hon Roll; Qualfd ST Gym Comp 85; Ithaca; Acctg.

CURRY, LENISE; Buffalo Traditional Schl; Buffalo, NY; (S); #16 In Class; Chorus; Variety Show; Yrbk Phtg; Yrbk Stf; Hon Roll; NHS; Prfct Atten Awd; Merit Roll Awd; MUSIC.

CURRY, MIKE; H C Williams HS; Canton, NY; (Y); Cmnty Wkr; French Clb; Varsity Clb; Nwsp Stf; Yrbk Stf; Lit Mag; Im Bsbl; Im Bsktbl; JV Coach Actv; Var Crs Cntry; Trck Rcrds 84-85; Tchng.

CURRY, WILLIAM; Le Roy Central HS; Stafford, NY; (Y); AFS; Boy Scts; Spanish Clb; Varsity Clb; Socr.

CURTIN, AMY M; Mount Mercy Acad; West Seneca, NY; (Y); 4-H; French Clb; Chorus; School Musical; Rep Soph Cls; Ntl Merit Schol; Kent ST U; Vet.

CURTIN, BARBARA A; Mercy HS; Albany, NY; (Y); Library Aide; Chorus; Church Choir; Yrbk Stf; Rep Soph Cls; Rep Jr Cls; Rep Sr Cls; Bowling; High Hon Roll; Hon Roll; Martin Luther King Jr Schlrshp 85; Blck Hstry Mnth Essy Cont Wnnr 85; Cert Awd Hgh Achvt Relgn 85; Coll St Rose; Bio.

CURTIN II, R C KELLY; Orchard Park HS; Hamburg, NY; (Y); Drama Clb; Trs 4-H; Hosp Aide; Chorus; School Musical; School Play; Rep Stu Cncl; Ftbl; Lcrss; Hon Roll.

CURTIN, RAYMOND; Sachem HS; Farmingville, NY; (Y); 99/1600; Church Yth Grp; Varsity Clb; JV Var Ftbl; JV Var Lcrss; JV Var Wrstlng; NHS; Pres Schlr; Wrstlng & Ftbl All League 85; Mst Valuable Wrstlr 85; La Crosse All League 85; Cornell U; Bus.

CURTIN, SHANNON; Vernon-Verona-Sherrill Central Schl; Sherrill, NY; (Y); 70/240; AFS; Church Yth Grp; French Clb; GAA; Church Choir; JV Bsktbl; Golf; JV Sftbl; Am Field Svc Exc Stu 85; Bus Adm.

CURTIS, DEBORAH; Fayetteville Manlius HS; Fayetteville, NY; (Y); Dance Clb; Temple Yth Grp; Hon Roll; Isaiah Wolfson Schlrshp For Stdy In Israel 85; Ramah Semnr In Israel 6 Wk Stdy Tr 85; SADD 84-85; TV Post-Prodctn.

CURTIS, JIM; Hendrick Hudson HS; Montrose, NY; (Y); 1/150; Drama Clb; School Play; Nwsp Rptr; Rep Frsh Cls; Trs Soph Cls; Trs Jr Cls; Rep Stu Cncl; High Hon Roll; Highest Clss Avg; Oberlin Coll Bk Awd; Morton C Lindsey Mem Hstry Prize.

CURTIS, TIMOTHY; Watertown HS; Watertown, NY; (Y); Rep Soph Cls; Var L Lcrss; Var L Socr; JV Trk; Hon Roll; Dentistry.

CURTISS, BRIAN; Nottingham HS; Syracuse, NY; (Y); French Clb; Latin Clb; Ski Clb; Band; Jazz Band; Var Bsbl; Hon Roll; NHS; Lit Mag; Music Theory.

CURTO, MARK; Kenmore West SR HS; Kenmore, NY; (Y); High Hon Roll; Hon Roll; Prfct Atten Awd; Comp Sci.

CURZI, GARY W; Scotia-Glenville HS; Scotia, NY; (Y); 22/258; Aud/Vis; Library Aide; Orch; Stage Crew; Hon Roll; NHS; NYS Regents Schlrshp; Renssalear Polytech Inst; Math.

CUSATO, KRISTEN; Pine Bush HS; Pine Bush, NY; (Y); Political Wkr; Concert Band; Trs Stu Cncl; Bsktbl; Vllybl; Hon Roll; NHS; Voice Dem Awd; GAA; Office Aide; Brd Dir Pine Bush Arts Cncl 84-85; Spnsh Tutr Elem Schl Chldrn 84; Cmmnctns; Jrnlst.

CUSHMAN, HOWARD; North Rose-Wolcott HS; Red Creek, NY; (Y); Science Clb; Bsktbl; Hon Roll; Radio.

CUSICK, DANIEL; Seaford HS; Seaford, NY; (Y); Cmnty Wkr; Band; Debate Tm; Stu Cncl; Socr; Trk; Cit Awd; Lion Awd; Boys Clb Am; Boy Scts; Eagle Scout 84; Ad Altare Dei Awd 84; NYSSMA Awds 80-85; Arch.

CUSICK, PETER; Monsignor Farrell HS; Staten Island, NY; (Y); Am Leg Boys St; Pres Church Yth Grp; Math Tm; Rep Stu Cncl; Capt Var Crs Cntry; Var Trk; Pres NHS; Var X-Cntry MVP 83; Little League Bsbl Coach.

CUSIMANO, KELLIE; Jamestown HS; Jamestown, NY; (Y); Trs French Clb; Intnl Clb; Pres Latin Clb; French Hon Soc; High Hon Roll; Hon Roll; Jr NHS; NHS; Rotary Awd; JA; Natl Hnr Rl 84-85; Rtry Exch Stu 84; Stanford U; Intl Rltns.

CUSUMANO, FRANCINE; Walt Witman HS; Huntington Sta, NY; (Y); 36/540; GAA; Office Aide; JV Var Cheerleading; High Hon Roll; Hon Roll; Jr NHS; Yrbk Stf; Score Keeper; Awd Of Merit In Math, Span & Bus Dynmcs 83; Acctng.

CUSUMANO, LUISA; Bishop Grimes HS; Liverpool, NY; (Y); FBLA; Variety Show; Yrbk Stf; School Musical; Hon Roll; Italn Hnbr Soc 83-85.

CUTAJAR, PAUL O; St Anthonys HS; Huntington, NY; (Y); 1/282; Computer Clb; Ed Nwsp Rptr; Var Golf; High Hon Roll; NHS; Ntl Merit SF; Schlstc Yr Awd; Harvard Bk MGSR Peter J Nolan Schlrshp.

CUTHBERT, KAREN; Southside HS; Elmira, NY; (Y); Letterman Clb; Pep Clb; Varsity Clb; Rep Frsh Cls; Rep Soph Cls; Rep Jr Cls; Var L Crs Cntry; Var L Trk; Nwsp Stf; WENY Awd-Sprng Track 85; Bankng & Fnnc.

CUTIGNOLA, DIANE; Commack North HS; E Northport, NY; (Y); Stage Crew; Nwsp Rptr; Badmtn; Swmmng; High Hon Roll; Hon Roll; Gldn Quill Awd For Creative Wrtng 82; FL Atlantic U; Psychlgy.

CUTLER II, WILLIAM H; Jeffersonville-Youngsvle Ctrl Schl; Jeffersonville, NY; (S); 5/58; Sec Pres Science Clb; Hon Roll; Pres NHS; Bio.

CUTTING, HOPE ANNE T; Curtis HS; Staten Island, NY; (Y); 1/350; Art Clb; Church Yth Grp; Dance Clb; Sec Key Clb; Trs Math Clb; Math Tm; Science Clb; Teachers Aide; Stage Crew; Nwsp Stf; UFT Schlrshp 85; Super Yth Awd 84; Regents Schlrshp 85; St Johns U Schlrshp 85; St Johns U; Bus Fin.

CUTTING, REBECCA A; Moriah Central HS; Moriah Ctr, NY; (Y); Pres AFS; Church Yth Grp; Teachers Aide; Yrbk Phtg; Yrbk Stf; Pres Rep Stu Cncl; Hon Roll; Pastry Chef.

CUTTING, THOMAS E; Houghton Acad; Hume, NY; (Y); Chorus; Orch; VP Frsh Cls; Bsbl; Capt Bsktbl; Capt Socr; NHS; Houghton College.

CUZZUCOLI, AMY; Smithtown H S West; Hauppauge, NY; (Y); Hosp Aide; Symp Band; French Hon Soc; High Hon Roll; NHS; Political Wkr; Concert Band; Mrchg Band; Pep Band; Hon Roll; Pres Acad Fit Awd 85.

CWUDZINSKI, DONNA; Villa Maria Acad; Buffalo, NY; (Y); Computer Clb; Math Clb; Pep Clb; Hon Roll; Prfct Atten Awd; St Schlr; Hghst Scl Stds Avg 85; U Of Buffalo.

CWUDZINSKI, ELIZABETH; Villa Maria Acad; Buffalo, NY; (Y); Computer Clb; Math Clb; Ski Clb; Hon Roll; Prfct Atten Awd; Hghst Mth II Rgnts Avg Of Cls 84.

CYBRIWSKY, KRISTAN; Connetquot HS; Oakdale, NY; (Y); 39/800; Mrchg Band; Orch; School Musical; Nwsp Ed-Chief; Cheerleading; NHS; High Hon Roll; Jr NHS; All-ST Wind Ensmbl Flute 84-85; USDAN Ctr For Perf Arts Mrt Schrlshp 83; Julliard Pre-Coll & Orch; Oberlin; Music.

CYBULSKI, DINAMARIE; Villa Maria Acad; Buffalo, NY; (Y); Church Yth Grp; Spanish Clb; Gym; Hon Roll; Prfct Atten Awd; Political Wkr; Ski Clb; Sci.

CYLICH, LUZ D; Bronx High School Of Science; Bronx, NY; (Y); Yrbk Stf; Capt Var Swmmng; Hon Roll.

CYPHERS, PAMELA; Skaneateles HS; Skaneateles, NY; (S); 37/165; Drama Clb; Exploring; Hosp Aide; Orch; Stage Crew; Yrbk Stf; Socr; High Hon Roll; Hon Roll; Jr NHS; All Cnty Orchstr 82; A In Solo Comptn 82 Violin; ST Josephs Sch Nrsng; Nrse.

CYR, RITA; Queen Of The Rosary Acad; Westbury, NY; (S); Computer Clb; Girl Scts; Library Aide; Sec Frsh Cls; Sutton Sec Schl; Bus Admn.

CYRUS, CAROL; A E Stevenson HS; Bronx, NY; (Y); Church Yth Grp; JA; Office Aide; Chorus; Church Choir; Trk; Gradtd With Regnts Dplma 85; Union Coll; Psych.

CYRUS, TONYA; St Raymonds Academy For Girls; Bronx, NY; (Y); 1/68; Cmnty Wkr; Science Clb; Teachers Aide; Pep Band; Rep Jr Cls; VP Sr Cls; VP Stu Cncl; Hon Roll; Jr NHS; NHS; Awds Acadmc Excllnc 82-83; Awds Prfrmnc Hnr Rll 82-84; Med.

CZACHOR, LISA; Westlake HS; Thornwood, NY; (Y); Art Clb; FBLA; Stage Crew; Yrbk Stf; Stu Cncl; High Hon Roll; Hon Roll; Westchester Pulaski Assn Awd 85; Oneonta; Bus Ec.

CZAJKOWSKI, STAN; Haverling HS; Bath, NY; (Y); Chess Clb; VP French Clb; Math Clb; Stu Cncl; Bsbl; Bsktbl; High Hon Roll; NHS.

CZAJKOWSKI, STANLEY; Haverling Central HS; Bath, NY; (S); 2/185; Chess Clb; French Clb; Math Clb; Stu Cncl; Var Co-Capt Bsbl; Var Co-Capt Bsktbl; High Hon Roll; NHS; Prfct Atten Awd.

CZAPLA, DAWN M; Lancaster HS; Lancaster, NY; (Y); AFS; French Clb; VP JA; French Hon Soc; Hon Roll; 1st Pl Hnr Rl 85; U Buffalo; Acctng.

CZAPLICK, LINDA; Westhampton Beach HS; Westhampton, NY; (Y); 15/247; Church Yth Grp; French Clb; FBLA; Yrbk Phtg; Yrbk Stf; JV Cheerleading; Var Gym; Hon Roll; NHS; Suffolk Profssnl Phtgphrs Assoc 85; Pre-Med.

CZEBINIAK, DAN; Whitney Point HS; Binghamton, NY; (Y); Church Yth Grp; Hon Roll; Merit Achvt Awd 82; Broome CC; Comp Tech.

CZECHOWSKI, NANCY; Maryvale SR HS; Cheektowaga, NY; (Y); Church Yth Grp; Quiz Bowl; Sec Pres Spanish Clb; Acpl Chr; Chorus; School Musical; High Hon Roll; NHS; 2nd Ntl Spnsh Exm 85; Nrsg.

CZEKANSKI, LAURA; James E Sperry HS; Rochester, NY; (Y); 14/310; Spanish Clb; Thesps; Concert Band; School Musical; Sec Stu Cncl; Var JV Socr; Var JV Vllybl; Hon Roll; NHS; Spanish NHS; U Of San Diego; Poli Sci.

CZERWINSKI, STEFAN; Thomas A Edison HS; Elmira Hts, NY; (Y); Am Leg Boys St; French Clb; Quiz Bowl; Varsity Clb; Rep Stu Cncl; JV Bsktbl; JV Ftbl; Var Capt Tennis; High Hon Roll; Hon Roll; Chem Bwl Rep 84-85; Archeo.

CZUBA, PAULETTE; Frontier Central SR HS; Hamburg, NY; (S); Latin Clb; Library Aide; Office Aide; Chorus; School Musical; Hon Roll; NHS; Trocaire; Nrs.

CZUJKO, CYNTHIA; Mattituck HS; Mattituck, NY; (Y); 15/150; Church Yth Grp; 4-H; German Clb; Hosp Aide; Mathletes; Var Cheerleading; JV Sftbl; High Hon Roll; NHS; Germn Hnr Soc 85; Advncd Plcmnt Engl,Math; Nrsg.

D ADDARIO, JOHN; Cardinal Spellman HS; Bronx, NY; (Y); 3/525; Cmnty Wkr; Chorus; School Musical; Nwsp Ed-Chief; Rep Jr Cls; Rep Sr Cls; Bausch & Lomb Sci Awd; Gov Hon Prg Awd; NHS; Ntl Merit SF; Yale U; Psych.

D AGOSTINO, MARISA; Mahopac HS; Mahopac, NY; (Y); 26/385; Im Bsbl; Var JV Cheerleading; Im Sftbl; High Hon Roll; Hon Roll; NHS; Ladies Aux Italn Awd 85; Amer Assn Tchrs Italn Awd 84; Pres Acad Fit Awds Pgm 85; Fordham U; Law.

D AGOSTINO, TINA; Christopher Columbus HS; Bronx, NY; (S); 1/560; Cmnty Wkr; Math Tm; Teachers Aide; Band; Bsktbl; Swmmng; Vllybl; Gov Hon Prg Awd; High Hon Roll; Pres Schlr; Valdctrn 85; Hugh O Brian Schlr 83; NYU; Finance.

D ALBORA, LYNN; St John Villa Acad; Bklyn, NY; (Y); 14/120; Stage Crew; Nwsp Rptr; Yrbk Stf; Sec Trs Sr Cls; Bowling; Sftbl; Trk; Hon Roll; Merit List 84-85; Excllnce Italian II 83-84; Natl Hnr Rl; Nutrition.

D ALESSIO, DIANA; St Francis Boulevard HS; Richmond Hill, NY; (S); 103/693; Dance Clb; NFL; Political Wkr; Church Choir; Yrbk Phtg; Cheerleading; NHS.

D ALLAIRD, DANIEL P; Burnt Hills-Ballston HS; Scotia, NY; (Y); 50/330; Am Leg Boys St; Pres Stu Cncl; Var Capt Bsktbl; JV Var Ftbl; Var L Tennis; Hon Roll; Jr NHS; Church Yth Grp; Rep Soph Cls; Rep Jr Cls; Outstndng Jr Awd 85; Mark Howell Awd 80; Colgate U; Scl Wrk.

D AMATO, JOSETTE; Amherst Central HS; Snyder, NY; (Y); 41/310; Art Clb; Hosp Aide; Spanish Clb; Chorus; Church Choir; School Musical; Hon Roll; NHS; Outstndng Svc Awd 82; ST U NY Buffalo; Hlth.

D AMATO, LAURA; The Wheatley Schl; E Williston, NY; (Y); Exploring; Hosp Aide; Capt Mathletes; Chorus; Concert Band; Lit Mag; Cheerleading; NHS; Pep Band; Hon Roll; AATSP Spn Lvl III Cntst-2nd Pl 84; Slvr Pin-Math 84 & 85.

D AMATO, SALVATORE; Monsignor Farrell HS; Staten Island, NY; (Y); 93/296; Aud/Vis; JA; High Hon Roll; Hon Roll; Prfct Atten Awd; Cert Merit Italn; Regnts Schlrshp; ST U NY Albany.

D AMORE, FRANCINE J; Bishop Kearney HS; Brooklyn, NY; (Y); Ski Clb; High Hon Roll; NHS; Iona Lang Cntst-Itln II 2nd Hnrs 84; Accntng.

D ANDREA, MARY; Academy Of The Rsrctn; Larchmont, NY; (Y); Dance Clb; Drama Clb; Math Clb; School Musical; Stu Cncl; Jr NHS; NHS; NY ST Fin Of Natl Forensics Leag 84-85; Comm.

D ANGELO, FRANK; Mc Kee Technical HS; Staten Island, NY; (Y); 10/238; Seagull Soc 83-85; Engrng.

D ANGELO, JOHN JOSEPH; Saint Francis Prep; Flushing, NY; (Y); 81/693; Boy Scts; Ski Clb; Band; Concert Band; Im Fld Hcky; Golf; Im Wt Lftg; Hon Roll; Prfct Atten Awd; Bus.

D ANGELO, KIMBERLY; La Guardia HS Of Music & Art; Bayside, NY; (Y); Church Yth Grp; Office Aide; Teachers Aide; Boys Clb Am; Chorus; Church Choir; Nwsp Rptr; Ed Yrbk Stf; Ed Lit Mag; Hon Roll; Wrtng Awd 84; Oakley L Thorne Schlrshp 84; Fnlst NY Smmr Schl Arts 83; Thrtr.

D ANGELO, MARIA; Kenmore West HS; Kenmore, NY; (Y); 5/445; Church Yth Grp; Concert Band; Mrchg Band; School Musical; Variety Show; Diving; Capt Swmmng; High Hon Roll; NHS; Voice Dem Awd; Acadmc Schlrshp U Of Rochester 85-89; Roy G Freeman Schl Awd Hgh Acadmc & Ldrshp 85; U Of Rochester; Sci.

D ANNA, JANE M; St Edmunds HS; Brooklyn, NY; (Y); Rgnts Schlrshp 85; Brooklyn Coll; Pre-Law.

D ANNUNZIO, MARGARET MARY E; Tho Loyola Schl; Brooklyn, NY; (Y); 1/47; Drama Clb; Math Tm; NFL; Science Clb; Speech Tm; Nwsp Stf; Yrbk Ed-Chief; High Hon Roll; Ntl Merit Ltr; NEDT Awd; Columbia SHP 85-86; Gold Mdls Engl 84 & 85, Chem 85; 1st Pl Mth Lg 84-85; Mth.

D ARBANVILLE, STEPHANIE ANNE; Notre Dame Acadamy HS; Staten Island, NY; (Y); Church Yth Grp; Chorus; School Play; Yrbk Stf; Lit Mag; Widener U; Eng.

D ARCY, COLLEEN; Buffalo Academy Of The Sacred Heart; Williamsville, NY; (Y); Church Yth Grp; Girl Scts; Hosp Aide; JA; Red Cross Aide; Science Clb; Spanish Clb; Bowling; Hon Roll; Daeman Amherst NY; Phy Thrpy.

D ARIENZO, ANGELA; Smithtown H S East; St James, NY; (Y); Band; Mrchg Band; Stu Cncl; Bsktbl; Var Fld Hcky; Sftbl; JV Var Vllybl; Hon Roll; Jr NHS; NHS; Natl Italian Hon Soc 84-86; Girls Ldrs Clb 84-86; Phys Ther.

D ASCOLI, STEVEN A; Franklin K Lane HS; Glendale, NY; (Y); #7 In Class; Computer Clb; Band; Jazz Band; Hon Roll; Jr NHS; Queens Coll Awd For Achvt 82; U Of CA Berkeley; Physics.

D AURIA, CATHIE; West Hempstead HS; W Hempstead, NY; (Y); Church Yth Grp; Cmnty Wkr; Drama Clb; PAVAS; Chorus; School Musical; School Play; Var Trk; Schlrshp Theatre Brooklyn Coll 85; Mst Promising Actrss 82; Brooklyn Coll; Theatre.

D AVERSA, MIKE; East Meadow HS; East Meadow, NY; (Y); 100/400; Bsbl; Bsktbl; Ftbl; Hon Roll; SAT 85.

D DAS, KANITA; Monticello HS; Monticello, NY; (Y); 17/160; Band; Church Choir; Concert Band; Cheerleading; Tennis; Vllybl; High Hon Roll; Hon Roll; Ntl Hnr Socty Schlrshp 85.

D ERASMO, FRANCES; Mahopac HS; Mahopac, NY; (Y); 52/380; Art Clb; FBLA; VICA; Yrbk Stf; JV Sftbl; High Hon Roll; Hon Roll; NHS; Prfct Atten Awd; Exec Secy.

D EREDITA, LISA A; Solvay HS; Syracuse, NY; (Y); Hosp Aide; Spanish Clb; Chorus; Yrbk Ed-Chief; VP Soph Cls; Vllybl; Hon Roll; FNA; Off Jr Cls; Algebra Awd 82-83; Ldrshp Awd 83-84; Poli Sci.

D ONOFRIO, HARRY; Xaverian HS; Brooklyn, NY; (S); 150/427; Computer Clb; Dance Clb; JA; School Play; Stage Crew; Rep Jr Cls; Sr Cls; Sec Stu Cncl; Mgr(s); Hon Roll; Marine Corp Gym Ldr 83 & 85; St Johns U; Comp Sci.

D ONOFRIO, ROSEANN; Albertus Magnus HS; Spring Valley, NY; (Y); 20/190; Yrbk Stf; Hon Roll; Spsh & Natl Hnr Soctys 85; Math Hnr Socty 85; Ed.

D ONOFRIO, SANDRA D; Bishop Ludden HS; Syracuse, NY; (Y); High Hon Roll; Hon Roll; Acctg.

DA SILVA, ANNA C; La Guardia H S Of Music & Arts; New York, NY; (Y); Pep Band; Hosp Aide; Office Aide; Teachers Aide; Acpl Chr; Chorus; Variety Show; Photogrphy 84; Graphc 83; Parsons CA Inst Art; Fashn Art.

DA SILVA, MARIA FERNANDA; West Babylon SR HS; W Babylon, NY; (Y); High Hon Roll; Hon Roll; NHS; Psychlgy.

DA SILVA, MARK; Longwood HS; Coram, NY; (S); 17/500; Boy Scts; Math Tm; Yrbk Stf; High Hon Roll; Hon Roll; Jr NHS; Chem Engrng.

DA SILVA, MARY ANNE; Sacred Heart Acad; Franklin Sq, NY; (S); Church Yth Grp; Trs Chorus; Church Choir; School Musical; Spch Path.

DABNEY, HUGH; Elmira Southside HS; Elmira, NY; (Y); French Clb; Varsity Clb; JV Var Ftbl; Var Trk; High Hon Roll; Drftsmn.

DABY, DONNA; Lake Placid Central School; Lake Placid, NY; (Y); 8/41; Library Aide; Varsity Clb; Chorus; Yrbk Stf; Crs Cntry; Trk; Vllybl; High Hon Roll; Hon Roll; Prfct Atten Awd; Mst Imprvd Girl 83-84; Ed.

DABY, JENNIFER; Ticonderoga HS; Ticonderoga, NY; (Y); Church Yth Grp; Sec Key Clb; Varsity Clb; VP Band; Chorus; Rep Soph Cls; Var Cheerleading; High Hon Roll; Hon Roll; NHS; Amateur Athltc Union 85; Sec Sci.

DADDARIO, DARREN M; St Johns Prepatory Schl; Astoria, NY; (Y); Radio Clb; Teachers Aide; High Hon Roll; NHS; Queens Catholic Hs Schlrshp 85; St Johns U; Prof Wrestlng.

DADDAZIO, VINESSA; Churchville-Chili HS; Rochester, NY; (Y); Drama Clb; FTA; Acpl Chr; Chorus; Yrbk Rptr; Ed Yrbk Stf; Var JV Cheerleading; Dramatic Arts.

DADRAS, MONICA S; Art & Design HS; Douglaston, NY; (Y); Church Yth Grp; FTA; Office Aide; Church Choir; Yrbk Stf; Hon Roll; Prfct Atten Awd; Mst Enthusiastic Awd 85; Spec Stu Srv Awd 85; NY Inst Of Tech; Dsgn Grphcs.

DADY, JOELLA; Little Falls JR SR HS; Little Falls, NY; (S); 2/107; Drama Clb; VP GAA; Spanish Clb; Band; Orch; Var Capt Bsktbl; JV Var Cheerleading; Var L Fld Hcky; Var L Sftbl; Trs NHS; Hgh Excllnc Awd Engl & Soc Stds 82-83; Hgh Excllnc Awd Engl & Math 83-84; Sci.

DAGELE, DEBORAH; S S Seward Inst; Goshen, NY; (Y); 1/35; Trs FHA; VP Spanish Clb; Church Choir; Yrbk Stf; Trs Frsh Cls; VP Soph Cls; Trs Jr Cls; Cheerleading; Sftbl; High Hon Roll; Mst Outstndng Sc & Spnsh & Soc Stds 83-85; Bus Mgmt.

DAGEN, LOUIS; Ossining HS; Briarcliff, NY; (Y); 40/350; Computer Clb; Library Aide; Radio Clb; Temple Yth Grp; Concert Band; Mrchg Band; Hon Roll; Psych.

DAGOSTINO, MICHAEL; Mont Pleasant HS; Schenectady, NY; (Y); 14/205; Aud/Vis; Computer Clb; Spanish Clb; Var Golf; Var Tennis; Hon Roll; NHS; Spanish NHS; Elect Engr.

DAGOUNAKIS, EVA; Long Island City HS; New York, NY; (Y); 20/500; Church Yth Grp; Teachers Aide; Rep Trs Sr Cls; Rep Stu Cncl; Hon Roll; Mu Alp Thr; Prfct Atten Awd; Regents Schlrshp 85; Merit Awd 85; Arista Ofcr 85; NY U; Liberal Arts.

DAIGLE, GREGORY; Catholic Central HS; Clifton Pk, NY; (S); 2/203; Trs Church Yth Grp; Math Clb; School Musical; Yrbk Stf; Im Bsktbl; Var Socr; Var Trk; Pres NHS; Physics Awd; Notre Dame; Arch.

DAILEY, JENNIFER; Ogdensburg Free Acad; Ogdensburg, NY; (Y); 15/200; French Clb; Key Clb; Band; Mrchg Band; Pep Band; JV Var Crs Cntry; JV Var Trk; NHS; Russll Sage Coll & Ogdnsburg Educ Assn Schlrshps 85; Russell Sage Coll; Phys Thrpy.

DAILEY, JOY; Newark SR HS; Lyons, NY; (Y); 28/215; Church Yth Grp; Girl Scts; Math Tm; Teachers Aide; Band; Concert Band; Jazz Band; Mrchg Band; Orch; School Musical; Nyssma Medals 82-84; Gold Awd In Band 84-85; SUNY Brockport; Scndry Educ.

DAILEY, WILLIAM; Hornell HS; Hornell, NY; (Y); Rep Stu Cncl; Var L Bsbl; Var L Socr; High Hon Roll; Sprts Med.

DAILY, FRANCIS; La Salle Acad; New York, NY; (S); 91/237; Church Choir; School Musical; Nwsp Phtg; Nwsp Rptr; Pres Frsh Cls; Mgr(s); Hon Roll; Fordham U; Psych.

DAINO, JILL; West Genesee HS; Camillus, NY; (Y); Spanish Clb; Nwsp Ed-Chief; Off Jr Cls; Off Sr Cls; Var Cheerleading; High Hon Roll; Jr NHS; NHS; Wellesley Coll Bk Awd 85; Spnsh Hnrs Merit/Achvt Awd 85.

DAKA, JIMMY GZIM; Mount Saint Michael Acad; New York, NY; (Y); Socr; Empire ST Games 83-85; NY SST Dist Team 85; Csmpltn Leag All-Stars 85; Duke U; Bus.

DAKIN, BRIAN RICHARD; Fox Lane HS; Mt Kisco, NY; (Y); 30/300; Am Leg Boys St; Nwsp Sprt Ed; Var Bsktbl; Capt Trk; Cit Awd; NHS; SAR Awd; Concert Band; Mrchg Band; Rep Stu Cncl; Yth Crt 84-85; Hist Cmmtt 84-85; Ciba-Geigy Sci Awd 85; Lehigh U; Engr.

DALAL, RAGINI; Brighton HS; Rochester, NY; (Y); 73/315; Exploring; German Clb; Ski Clb; Rep Pres Spanish Clb; Nwsp Stf; Yrbk Stf; Fld Hcky; Spanish NHS; Spnsh Ntl Exm Wnnr 82-85; Lbrl Arts.

DALBERTH, MARK; Irondequoit HS; Rochester, NY; (Y); 3/387; Church Yth Grp; Ski Clb; Band; Jazz Band; Mrchg Band; Orch; Pep Band; Rep Sr Cls; Tennis; High Hon Roll; 2nd Pl Schl Am Chem Soc Test 84; Phsy.

DALCIN, BECKY; Fairport HS; E Rochester, NY; (Y); French Clb; Girl Scts; Math Clb; Band; Cheerleading; Coach Actv; Gym; Sftbl; Hon Roll; Geneseo ST; Acctng.

DALES, HOLLY-LYNNE; Onteora Central School; Woodstock, NY; (S); 26/245; French Clb; PAVAS; Yrbk Ed-Chief; High Hon Roll; NHS; Graphic Desgnr.

DALESANDRO, MARK; Lasalle HS; Niagara Falls, NY; (S); 10/278; Drama Clb; French Clb; Stage Crew; Yrbk Stf; Hon Roll; Jr NHS; NHS; Regents Schlrshp 84-85; Boston U; Aerosp.

DALEY, DANIEL V; Msgr Mc Clancy HS; Brooklyn, NY; (Y); Church Yth Grp; Math Tm; Varsity Clb; Lit Mag; Pres Jr Cls; JV Var Bsbl; Var Bsktbl; Im Coach Actv; Im Vllybl; Hon Roll; NYS Rgnts Schlrshp 85; Cathlc Daughtrs Awd 82-83; SUNY-STONYBROOK; Mech Engr.

DALEY, ERIN M; St Francis Prep HS; Woodhaven, NY; (Y); 261/690; Dance Clb; Intnl Clb; Office Aide; Service Clb; Band; Chorus; NY Regents Schlrshp 85; Hunter Coll; Math.

DALEY, MICHAEL F; Fayettevill - Manlius HS; Manlius, NY; (Y); 60/360; Church Yth Grp; Cmnty Wkr; Drama Clb; Thesps; School Musical; School Play; Swing Chorus; Nwsp Stf; NHS; JCL; Math Awd 82; Natl Latn Exm Max Cum Laude 82-83; Backstg Bckrs Drama Awd 85; Lamoyne Coll; Cmmnctns.

DALFIUME, LUKE; Tioga Central School; Nichols, NY; (S); 6/96; Church Yth Grp; Stage Crew; Variety Show; Var Bsbl; High Hon Roll; NHS.

DALIPI, MET; Mineola HS; Mineola, NY; (Y); Sec Computer Clb; FBLA; Key Clb; Spanish Clb; Yrbk Stf; Var Lcrss; JV Socr; High Hon Roll; Prfct Atten Awd; Comp Sci.

DALLURA, RUSS; St John The Baptist HS; Centereach, NY; (Y); Hon Roll; U Dytn; Bus Mngmnt.

DALRYMPLE, NICOLE-YANIQUE; Erasmus Hall HS; Brooklyn, NY; (Y); Lion Awd; Teachers Aide; School Musical; Variety Show; Nwsp Rptr; Nwsp Stf; Gym; Math Awd Soph; Math, Engl Tutr Awds Soph; MIT; Athl Trng.

DALY, ALISON; Hendrick Hudson HS; Montrose, NY; (Y); 30/210; Church Yth Grp; Letterman Clb; Varsity Clb; Var L Cheerleading; Var L Socr; Var Capt Swmmng; Hon Roll; NHS; All Cnty Swmr 85; Villanova U; Comp Sci.

DALY, JOEL; Bishop Scully HS; Amsterdam, NY; (S); 4/56; Math Clb; PAVAS; Political Wkr; JV Bsbl; Im Bsktbl; JV Ftbl; High Hon Roll; NHS; Ntl Merit Ltr; NY Smmr Schl Vsl Arts 84; Air Force Acad.

DALY, LAURA K; Amherst Central HS; Amherst, NY; (Y); 30/310; Quiz Bowl; Orch; School Musical; Nwsp Stf; High Hon Roll; NHS; Ntl Merit SF; Church Yth Grp; German Clb; GAA; Brown U Bk Awd 84; 6th Natl Sci 83; All St Orchestras 82-84; Bio Med Res.

DALY, LINDA RACHEL; Half Hollow Hills HS; Wheatley Hgts, NY; (Y); 3/566; Cmnty Wkr; Service Clb; Symp Band; Lit Mag; NHS; Pres Schlr; Spanish NHS; Leo Clb; Mathletes; Office Aide; Eng Dept Awd 85; NYS Regents Schlrshp 85; Pres Schlrshp-SUNY Stony Brook & SUNY Buffalo 85; Corp Law.

DALY, MARGARET A; Carle Place HS; Carle Place, NY; (Y); 19/116; AFS; Church Yth Grp; Debate Tm; Key Clb; Variety Show; Yrbk Stf; JV Fld Hcky; JV Lcrss; High Hon Roll; Hon Roll; Spnsh Acad Hnr Awd 81-82; Rgnts Schlrshp 85; Hofstra U; CPA.

DALY, MARK E; Tully Central Schl; Tully, NY; (Y); 3/80; Pres Church Yth Grp; Drama Clb; Spanish Clb; Trs Band; Chorus; School Musical; Rep Frsh Cls; Pres Soph Cls; Var Wrstlng; High Hon Roll; Onondaga Cnty Commnty Scholar Awd 85; Boys ST 85; Hugh O Brien Yth Semnr Delgt 84; SUNY-OSWEGO; Forgn Lang.

DALY, MARY E; St Marys HS; Manhasset, NY; (Y); Cmnty Wkr; Var GAA; Rep Frsh Cls; Rep Jr Cls; Rep Stu Cncl; Crs Cntry; Co-Capt Trk; Parsh Cncl St Marys Chrch 84-86; Fordham U; Comms.

DALY, MELISSA; Mt St Mary Acad; Buffalo, NY; (Y); VP Debate Tm; Off French Clb; VP NFL; School Musical; Nwsp Stf; Yrbk Stf; Rep Soph Cls; Pres Jr Cls; Var Gym; High Hon Roll; Canisius Coll.

DALY, MICHAEL W; New Hyde Park Memorial HS; New Hyde Park, NY; (Y); 18/267; Varsity Clb; Yrbk Sprt Ed; JV Bsbl; Var JV Ftbl; High Hon Roll; Jr NHS; NHS; Ntl Merit Ltr; PA ST Schlr Comptn 84; Carnegie-Mellon U; Elec.

DALY, NOREEN; Fontbonne Hall Acad; Brooklyn, NY; (Y); Cmnty Wkr; Office Aide; Service Clb; Teachers Aide; High Hon Roll; NHS; Prfct Atten Awd; Peer Ldrshp Trnng 85; Vllybl Sportsmnshp Awd-68th Pct Yth Cncl 84; Dentstry.

DALY, PHILIP; Archbishop Molloy HS; Jamaica Ests, NY; (Y); 193/409; Bsktbl; Ftbl; Sftbl; Hon Roll; Accntng.

DAMARA, MARK L; Westhampton Beach SR HS; East Moriches, NY; (Y); 40/190; Computer Clb; FBLA; Yrbk Stf; Lit Mag; Var L Socr; Var L Trk; Hon Roll; Creative Wrtng Cntst 3rd 83-84; U CO Boulder; Aerontcl Engrng.

DAMAS, MARGARETTE; Washington Irving HS; Brooklyn, NY; (Y); Hosp Aide; Vllybl; Hon Roll; Prfct Atten Awd; Arista Leag Awd 84; Intrfaith Med Ctr Merit Awd 85; Washington Irving Awd Lab Svc 84; Columbia U; Chem.

DAMASKINOS, TOM; Mc Kee Voc Tech HS; Staten Is, NY; (Y); 138/239; Math Clb; Teachers Aide; Hon Roll; Elec Engr.

DAMATO, ANNA M; Newtown HS; Elmhurst, NY; (Y); 14/603; Debate Tm; Math Tm; Service Clb; Band; Concert Band; School Play; Hon Roll; Prfct Atten Awd; Arista 82-85; Westinghse Semi Fin.

DAMES, MARK W; Monsignor Farrell HS; Staten Island, NY; (Y); Ed Yrbk Stf; JV Crs Cntry; Var Tennis; JV Trk; High Hon Roll; 2nd Hnrs Spnsh IV Iona Coll Lang Cntst 85; NY ST Regnts Schlrshp 85; Villanova U; Pre-Law.

DAMICO, JAMES C; Nazareth Regional HS; Brooklyn, NY; (Y); 17/300; School Play; Nwsp Rptr; Nwsp Stf; Hon Roll; NHS; Pres Schlr; Catholic Tchrs Assoc Schlrshp Awd 85; Regents Schlrshp 85; C W Post Acad Merit Schlrshp 85; Fordham U; Sci.

DAMON, CHRIS P; Rome Free Acad; Lee Center, NY; (Y); Boy Scts; Intnl Clb; Ski Clb; Marn Engrng.

DAMON, DANIEL J; Rushford Central HS; Cuba, NY; (Y); 2/30; 4-H; FFA; Band; Concert Band; Yrbk Stf; Cit Awd; 4-H Awd; High Hon Roll; NHS; Sal; FFA Empire Degree 84; Outstndng Stckmn Awd 80,82 & 84; NYS Swine Awd Wnr 84; Alfred Agri Tech; Comp Graph.

DAMON, JOY; Union Springs Acad; Norridgewock, ME; (S); 10/49; Church Yth Grp; Drama Clb; Teachers Aide; Varsity Clb; Chorus; Church Choir; School Play; Rep Stu Cncl; Gym; Hon Roll; Most Spiritual Girl 83-84; Atlantic Union Coll; Nrsng.

DAMON, SHERRY; General Brown HS; Watertown, NY; (Y); Camera Clb; Dance Clb; FHA; Cheerleading; Merit Achvt Rl 82-85; JVTC Voc Schl Cosmtlgy 84-85; Theatre.

DAMORE, PETER; Iona Prep; New Rochelle, NY; (Y); 57/196; Boy Scts; Crs Cntry; Ftbl; Trk; Ftbl, Trk, Crs Cntry Ltrs.

DAMOTA, RITA; Academy Of The Resurrec; Rye, NY; (Y); Dance Clb; Drama Clb; Hosp Aide; Chorus; School Musical; Hon Roll; NHS; Manhattanville Coll; Frnch.

DANAS, VASILIOS; Fort Hamilton HS; Brooklyn, NY; (Y); Church Yth Grp; Brooklyn Coll; Lawyer.

DANCA, GERIANNE; Sacred Heart Acad; Long Beach, NY; (S); 16/196; Aud/Vis; Church Yth Grp; Math Clb; Math Tm; Teachers Aide; School Musical; Sftbl; Hon Roll; NHS; Mth Regnts Awd 100 Prcnt 2 Consec Yrs 84; Comp Sci.

DANCE, CARRIE ANN; Farmingdale HS; Farmingdale, NY; (Y); Library Aide; Band; Mrchg Band; Symp Band; Nwsp Rptr; Hon Roll; NHS; Hofstra; Bio.

DANCESCU, ANDREW M; Newtown HS; New York, NY; (Y); 95/602; Chess Clb; Civic Clb; Computer Clb; Drama Clb; French Clb; Pres Key Clb; Math Clb; Office Aide; Science Clb; Teachers Aide; Arista Hnr Scty 84; Stony Brook; Bio Chem.

DANDREA, LISA; Sachem HS; Farmingville, NY; (Y); 72/1500; Hosp Aide; Spanish Clb; Band; Church Choir; Rep Frsh Cls; Rep Jr Cls; Rep Stu Cncl; High Hon Roll; Jr NHS; NHS; Stu Gov Awd For Svcs 85; Stonybrook ST U; Phy Thrpy.

DANDREA, PAYTON; Thomas A Edison HS; Elmira, NY; (Y); Church Yth Grp; Cmnty Wkr; Red Cross Aide; Nwsp Stf; Yrbk Stf; Hon Roll; Elmira Coll; Psych.

DANEHY, PAUL M; Hugh C Williams HS; Canton, NY; (Y); 6/135; Pres Church Yth Grp; French Clb; Trs Varsity Clb; School Musical; Nwsp Sprt Ed; Yrbk Phtg; Var Capt Bsktbl; Var L Ftbl; Var Golf; NHS; Acad Lttr Awd 82-84; NYS Regents Schlrshp 85; Natl Socl Stud Olympiad Awd 84; U Of NH; Mech Engrng.

DANGIM, MICHAEL; Freeport HS; Roosevelt, NY; (Y); Boy Scts; Varsity Clb; Chorus; JV Bsbl; Var Bsktbl; Phys Ed.

DANGLER, DAVID E; Irondequoit HS; Rochester, NY; (Y); 112/365; Capt Bowling; JV Wrstlng; NYS Regents Schlrshp 85; U Of Buffalo; Mech Engr.

DANIEL, ALFRED; Park West HS; New York, NY; (Y); Yrbk Stf; Hon Roll; Bio Sci Awd 85; De Vry; Elec Engr.

DANIEL, CHARLES; Truman HS; Bronx, NY; (Y); Drama Clb; Library Aide; Teachers Aide; Rep Frsh Cls; Rep Soph Cls; Rep Jr Cls; Var Bsktbl; Trk; Svc Credits 82-84; Boys St Champ Bsktbl 83; Barry U; Comp Sci.

DANIEL, FARAH; New Utrecht HS; Brooklyn, NY; (Y); Hosp Aide; Key Clb; Teachers Aide; Chorus; Nwsp Rptr; Yrbk Stf; Rep Stu Cncl; Var Co-Capt Gym; Hon Roll; Medl Arts Clb 84-85; NY U; Pre-Med.

DANIEL, LINDA M; Lawrence HS; Inwood, NY; (Y); 25/390; FTA; Science Clb; High Hon Roll; Hon Roll; NHS; Prfct Atten Awd; Spanish Clb; NYS Minority Schlrshp Achvmnt Awd 84; Cmmncmnt Awd Bus 85; PTA Lawrence Cncl Schlrshp 85; Rennsselaer Polytech Inst; Comp.

DANIEL, RONSARD; Nazareth Reginal HS; Brooklyn, NY; (Y); Trk; High Hon Roll; Hon Roll; Swarthmore Coll; Med.

DANIEL, SANDRA; Mt St Ursula Acad; Bronx, NY; (Y); Girl Scts; Science Clb; Chorus; Natl Lang Arts Olympiad Awd 83; Intl Rltns.

DANIELE, ROBERT J; Our Lady Of Lourdes HS; Millbrook, NY; (Y); 81/144; Im Bsktbl; Capt Tennis; MVP Tnns 85; Rochester Inst Tech; Elec Engr.

DANIELE, STACY; St Gabriel HS; New Rochelle, NY; (Y); 6/61; Church Yth Grp; Drama Clb; Library Aide; Chorus; Stage Crew; Yrbk Stf; Sec Jr Cls; High Hon Roll; Hon Roll; NHS; Ntl Olymp Soc Studies 84-85; Fnlst Citibk Essay Cntst 83; Nrsng.

DANIELLO, MICHELE; Saint Francis Prep; Howard Bch, NY; (Y); Dance Clb; Stage Crew; Accntng.

DANIELS, LAURA; Sacred Heart Academy HS; N Bellmore, NY; (S); 6/186; FHA; Math Clb; Math Tm; Chorus; Bowling; NHS; Ntl Merit Ltr.

DANIELS, LAURIE; Brockport HS; Brockport, NY; (Y); 47/300; Pres 4-H; Mathletes; Chorus; Swing Chorus; 4-H Awd; High Hon Roll; Hon Roll; St Schlr; 4-H Cnty Medl Wnnr Beef, Pltry 84; Cornell U; Vet Sci.

DANIELS, MICHAEL P; Cheektowaga Central HS; Cheektowaga, NY; (Y); 2/204; Concert Band; Mrchg Band; Bausch & Lomb Sci Awd; Hon Roll; Jr NHS; NHS; Sal; Rensselear Mdl Math & Sci 83-84; NYS Regents Schlrshp 84-85; Carr Parker Engrng Awd 84-85; SUNY Buffalo; Elect Engrng.

DANIELS, SANDRA E; Averill Park HS; Averill Park, NY; (Y); 32/222; Cmnty Wkr; Key Clb; Acpl Chr; Chorus; Stage Crew; Lit Mag; High Hon Roll; Lois C Smith Schlrshp Russell Sage Coll 84-85; Regnts Schlrshp 84-85; Rensselaer Polytechnc Inst; Bio.

DANIELS, SCHELISSA; Martin Van Buren HS; Queens, NY; (Y); Computer Clb; Math Tm; Office Aide; PAVAS; Teachers Aide; Cit Awd; Hon Roll; Comp Sci.

DANIELS, SHARON; Julia Richmand HS; New York, NY; (Y); Church Yth Grp; Hosp Aide; JA; Teachers Aide; Chorus; Church Choir; Badmtn; Score Keeper; Tennis; Vllybl; Hm Eco Occptnl Educ Awd 85; Comptitv Achvt Awd-Badmntn 85; La Guadia Coll; Phys Thrpst.

DANIELS, TYLENA; Bainbridge-Guilford HS; Bainbridge, NY; (Y); 5/72; Pres Spanish Clb; Band; Chorus; Mrchg Band; Orch; JV Var Vllybl; High Hon Roll; Pre-Law.

DANILOWICZ, BRET; Whitesboro SR HS; Whitesboro, NY; (Y); 2/384; Exploring; Science Clb; Ski Clb; Stu Cncl; Cit Awd; Jr NHS; NHS; Ntl Merit SF; Pres Schlr; High Hon Roll; Am Cntrct Bridge Lg Josephs Trophy 83; Utica Coll; Marine Bio.

DANISI, TINA; Newfield HS; Selden, NY; (Y); Var Pom Pon; Hon Roll; Jr NHS; Bus.

DANN, BRENDA L; G Ray Bodley HS; Fulton, NY; (Y); French Clb; Science Clb; Stat Bsktbl; High Hon Roll; NY ST Regents Schlrshp 85; SUNY Oswego; Comp Sci.

DANN, TRAVIS E; J C Birdlebough HS; Phoenix, NY; (Y); 4/198; Latin Clb; Var L Bsbl; Var L Ftbl; High Hon Roll; NHS; Ntl Merit Ltr; Teachers Aide; U S Army Resrv Natl Schlr Athl Awd; SUNY Geneseo; Comp Sci.

DANNELS, WENDY; St Marys School For The Deaf; Grand Island, NY; (Y); Yrbk Phtg; Yrbk Rptr; Pres Soph Cls; VP Sr Cls; L Capt Bsktbl; L Crs Cntry; L Capt Trk; L Capt Vllybl; Hon Roll; Lions Club Schlrshp Awd 85; MVP Track 82-85; MVP Crss Cntry 82-84; NTID; Engr.

DANNER, STACEY; Maple Hill HS; Castleton, NY; (Y); 11/94; Math Tm; Nwsp Stf; Yrbk Phtg; Var Capt Bsktbl; Var Capt Sftbl; High Hon Roll; JC Awd; NHS; Elmira Coll Key Awd 84; MVP Bsktbl 84 & 85; Elmira Coll; Acctng.

DANNER, WENDY; Villa Maria Acad; Buffalo, NY; (Y); Computer Clb; Math Clb; Pep Clb; Ski Clb; Prfct Atten Awd; ST U Buffalo; Psychlgy.

DANNEWITZ, KENNETH R; Hampton Bays HS; Hampton Bays, NY; (Y); 14/114; Aud/Vis; School Play; Stage Crew; Hon Roll; St Schlr; Fordham U; Public Accntnt.

DANSKIN, SUSAN A; New Paltz HS; New Paltz, NY; (Y); 1/160; Chess Clb; Rep Sr Cls; Var L Sftbl; L Capt Vllybl; High Hon Roll; Pres NHS; Ntl Merit Ltr; Val; Rep Jr Cls; Stat Bsktbl; Mid-Hudson Chap Ind Engrs Schlrshp 85; Hugh O Brian Ldrshp Sem Schl Rep 83; NY ST Rgnts Schlrshp 85; Cornell U; Chem Engrng.

DANTICAT, EDWIDGE; Clara Barton HS; Brooklyn, NY; (Y); Church Yth Grp; Hosp Aide; Chorus; Church Choir; Color Guard; Nwsp Rptr; Lit Mag; Hon Roll; Outstndg Stu 85; 1st Prz Brklyn Womans Poetry 85; 1st Prz NY Womans Poetry Cont 85; NY U; Psych.

DANTONIO, THERESA; Mount St Mary Acad; Buffalo, NY; (Y); Office Aide; Pep Clb; Service Clb; Teachers Aide; Stage Crew; Yrbk Stf; Rep Frsh Cls; Var Capt Cheerleading; Hon Roll; Cap Chrldng Vrsty Bkstbl & Ftbl 84-85; Miss NY Teenager Pgnt Fnlst 84; Natl Hnr Scty 85; U Of NY-BUFFALO; Chem.

DANTONOLI, THEODORE; Niagara Falls HS; Niagara Falls, NY; (Y); 16/257; Pres Chess Clb; Computer Clb; Ftbl; Tennis; Hon Roll; Jr NHS; Rochester Inst Tech; Micro Engr.

DANZGER, RAPHAEL A; Yeshiva University HS; Flushing, NY; (Y); Camera Clb; Computer Clb; Math Tm; St Schlr; Yeshiva Coll.

DAQUILA, MARIANNE T; Sachem H S North; Lake Ronkonkoma, NY; (Y); 131/1500; Church Yth Grp; Math Tm; Nwsp Rptr; Lit Mag; Socr; NHS; Pres Acadmc Fit Awd 85; Pres Schlrshp Manhattan Coll 85; Outstndng Yrbk Wrk Cert Awd 85; SUNY Buffalo; Engrng.

DARCH, CATHIE; Oakfield Alabama Central HS; Oakfield, NY; (Y); Library Aide; Ski Clb; Varsity Clb; VP Jr Cls; Stu Cncl; Capt Var Socr; Capt Var Sftbl; Vllybl.

DARCH, LYNN; Buffalo Academy Of The Sacred Heart; E Amherst, NY; (Y); Office Aide; Service Clb; Teachers Aide; Chorus; Church Choir; Orch; School Musical; JV Sftbl; Hon Roll; Church Yth Grp; Lucinda Yang Memrl Schlrshp 83; Schl Awd Excptnl Musicnshp 83; Music.

DARCY, MARY JAYNE; St John Villa Acad; Staten Is, NY; (Y); 9/130; Math Tm; Spanish Clb; Stage Crew; Nwsp Rptr; Yrbk Stf; Hon Roll; Gen Excell Phy Sci 82; Gen Excell Spnsh 84-85; Eurpn Stds Hnrs 84; Amer Stds Hnrs 85; Math Awd 85; Nrs.

DARCY, MARYANN; Nanuet SR HS; Nanuet, NY; (Y); Drama Clb; French Clb; Math Clb; Thesps; School Musical; School Play; Yrbk Stf; JV Var Cheerleading; Stat Lcrss; Stat Socr.

DARCY, PATRICIA; Bishop Kearney HS; Brooklyn, NY; (S); 48/350; Church Yth Grp; Library Aide; Hon Roll; NHS; Ntl Merit Ltr; Presdntl Schlrshp To St Josephs Coll Bklyn Ny 85-89; NY ST Regents Schlrsp 85; St Josephs Coll; Elem Educ.

DARDEN, JOHN K; St Johns Prep; Brooklyn, NY; (Y); Intnl Clb; PAVAS; Political Wkr; Speech Tm; Nwsp Rptr; Rep Sr Cls; Hon Roll; NHS; Val; LEAD Prgm Prtcpnt 84; U Of PA; Bus Adm.

DARGAN, JAMIE M; Skaneateles HS; Skaneateles, NY; (Y); JV Bsbl; JV Var Socr; Var Tennis; JV Trk; High Hon Roll; Hon Roll.

DARGATZ, ELKE; New Rochelle HS; New Rochelle, NY; (Y); Concert Band; Orch; Symp Band; Lit Mag; Diving; NHS; Ntl Merit Ltr; French Clb; Girl Scts; Mrchg Band; Outstndng Band, Mst Outstndng Dvr; Bus.

DARGUSTE, ELIZABETH; Bishop Kearney HS; Brooklyn, NY; (Y); NFL; Speech Tm; Band; Hon Roll; Pol Sci.

DARIENZO, STEPHANIE; Farmingdale HS; Farmingdale, NY; (Y); French Clb; FBLA; Sec Key Clb; Hon Roll; NHS; Engl.

DARLIN, SHERRI; Unatego JR SR HS; Wells Bridge, NY; (Y); Color Guard; Yrbk Phtg; Yrbk Stf; Sec Sr Cls; Sec Stu Cncl; JV Bsktbl; Var JV Bowling; JV Fld Hcky; Var JV Sftbl; CCBI; Sec Sci.

DARLING, BRIAN; Jordan-Elbridge HS; Jordan, NY; (Y); Art Clb; Crs Cntry; Lcrss; Wrstlng; High Hon Roll; Hon Roll; NHS; Arts.

DARLING, JEAN; Nazareth Acad; Rochester, NY; (Y); 4/110; Latin Clb; Pres Math Clb; Ed Lit Mag; Var L Bsktbl; Tennis; Var L Vllybl; Hon Roll; NHS; NEDT Awd; U Dallas Schlrshp 85; Pres Acadmc Fit Awd 85; Outstndng Schl Spirit Awd 85; U Dallas; Chem.

DARLING, JUDI; Gloversville HS; Gloversville, NY; (Y); 9/220; Church Yth Grp; Exploring; Hosp Aide; Office Aide; Band; Concert Band; Yrbk Stf; High Hon Roll; Masonic Awd; NHS; Mary Bachner Ury Awd 85; Park Terr Tchrs Awd 85; William St Thomas Sec Awd 85; Outstndng Bus Stu 85; Exec Sec.

DARLING, JULIE; Sodus Central HS; Sodus, NY; (Y); 5/118; AFS; Am Leg Aux Girls St; Church Yth Grp; Model UN; Pres Varsity Clb; Sec Jr Cls; Var Capt Bsktbl; Var Capt Crs Cntry; Var Capt Trk; NHS; Lions Clb Ctznshp Awd 85; Elmira Coll Key Awd 85.

DARLING, KELLY; South Lewis JR SR HS; Brantingham, NY; (Y); GAA; Band; Var Bsktbl; Var Golf; Var Socr; Var Sftbl; Var Trk; Var Vllybl; Hon Roll; Rep For Stu Cncl 83-85; Math.

DARLING, LAURA E; Le Roy HS; Batavia, NY; (Y); 9/120; AFS; French Clb; Math Tm; Varsity Clb; Capt Color Guard; Nwsp Phtg; Nwsp Rptr; Bsktbl; High Hon Roll; NHS; Rgnts Coll Schlrshp 85; Genesee Bus Awd 85; Genesee Comm Coll; Comp Sci.

DARLING, MICHELE A; Kingston HS; Hurley, NY; (Y); 60/511; Ski Clb; Chorus; School Musical; Capt Swmmng; Hon Roll; St Schlr; U Of Buffalo.

DARLING, NAOMI; Northville Central Schl; Northville, NY; (Y); Church Yth Grp; French Clb; Stu Cncl; High Hon Roll; Hon Roll; NHS; Syracuse U; Lndscp Arch.

DARLING, RAY L; Gloversville HS; Gloversville, NY; (Y); 50/250; Church Yth Grp; French Clb; Band; Church Choir; Concert Band; Jazz Band; Pep Band; Symp Band; JV L Bsktbl; Im JV Socr; Regnts Schlrshp Wnnr 85; Oneonta ST; Engrng.

DARMSTADT, CHARLES H; Sayville HS; Sayville, NY; (Y); 3/355; Church Yth Grp; Key Clb; Mathletes; Ski Clb; Yrbk Stf; Cit Awd; High Hon Roll; Trs NHS; Spnsh Deptmntl Awd 82; Haverford Coll; Pre-Med.

DARROCH, DANELLE M; Lockport SR HS; Lockport, NY; (Y); 4/411; German Clb; Hosp Aide; Intnl Clb; Latin Clb; Nwsp Rptr; Var Crs Cntry; Var Trk; Jr NHS; NHS; Prfct Atten Awd; Yng Peoples Inst At U Of CT 83; Art Awd 83; Intl Rltns.

DARROW, BRUCE; Woodlands HS; White Plains, NY; (Y); Capt Debate Tm; Key Clb; Math Tm; Chorus; Jazz Band; Yrbk Phtg; Rep Stu Cncl; High Hon Roll; NHS; Ntl Merit Ltr; Union Carbide Schlrshp-Washington Wrkshps Smnr 85; Columbia U Sci Hnrs Pgm 84-86; Physlgy.

DARROW, CAROLYN; Ithaca HS; Spencer, NY; (Y); Drama Clb; Ski Clb; Chorus; Madrigals; Orch; Variety Show; Lit Mag; Rep Frsh Cls; Rep Soph Cls; Rep Jr Cls; JR Music Clb Scholar Piano 84; Williams Coll.

DARWISH, DIANE; Great Neck South HS; Great Neck, NY; (Y); 27/560; Girl Scts; Temple Yth Grp; CSF 83 & 84.

DAS, SURJYA P; Guilderland Central HS; Guilderland, NY; (Y); 1/365; German Clb; Key Clb; Varsity Clb; Var JV Ftbl; Var JV Lcrss; High Hon Roll; Ntl Merit Schol; Val; Jr NHS; NHS; NY ST Minority Scholar Achvt Awd 84; Brd Ed Schltc Awd 82-85; H S Hghst Cumulative Avg Awd 83-85; Cornell U; Chem.

DASHNAW, ROBERT J; Walter Panas HS; Peekskill, NY; (Y); 35/250; Drama Clb; Chorus; Orch; School Musical; School Play; Swmmng; High Hon Roll; Hon Roll; Jr NHS; NHS; Arion Mus Awd; Natl Schl Orch Awd; Natl Schl Shrl Awd; Pace U Pleasantville; Mktg.

DASILVA, DENISE; West Hempstead HS; W Hempstead, NY; (Y); Church Yth Grp; Cmnty Wkr; Dance Clb; Girl Scts; Political Wkr; Chorus; Badmtn; Coach Actv; Sftbl; Vllybl; Sci.

DASILVA, TERESA; Dominican Commercial HS; Jamaica, NY; (Y); 5/293; Cmnty Wkr; Church Choir; School Play; Yrbk Stf; Rep Stu Cncl; NHS; 1st & 2nd Hnrs Span Iona Coll Lang Cntst 83-85; Phys Ther.

DASRATH, FLORETTA; Grove Cleveland HS; Brooklyn, NY; (Y); 110/659; Camera Clb; Church Yth Grp; English Clb; FNA; JA; Key Clb; Office Aide; Science Clb; Service Clb; Teachers Aide; Perfect Attndnc Hnr Scty 82-85; Regents Schlrshp Awd 85; Merit Achvt Wrtng 83; Hunter Coll; Nrs.

DASSAU, DIANE; H Frank Carey HS; Franklin Sq, NY; (Y); 66/222; FBLA; Capt Twrlr; High Hon Roll; Hon Roll; FBLA Dist 1 Nassau Compt 85; FBLA NY ST Comp 85; Bus.

DASTIN, GARY; Hicksville HS; Hicksville, NY; (Y); Ski Clb; Bsbl; JV Bsktbl; Fld Hcky; High Hon Roll; Hon Roll; Jr NHS; NHS; Trs Spanish NHS.

DATS, PAULA D; Ellicottville Central HS; Salamanca, NY; (Y); Ski Clb; Band; Chorus; Mrchg Band; Stu Cncl; JV Cheerleading; Sftbl; Hon Roll; JBC; Bus Mgmt.

DATTELKRAMER, SHARON; Hebrew Acad Of Nassau County; Valley Stream, NY; (S); Drama Clb; Hosp Aide; Office Aide; Symp Band; Ed Yrbk Stf; Vllybl; Gov Hon Prg Awd; Pres NHS; NEDT Awd; NY ST Regents Schlrshp 85; Barnard; Political Sci.

DATTILO, THERESA; Monsignor Scanlan HS; Bronx, NY; (Y); Intnl Clb; Math Tm; Yrbk Stf; JV L Bsktbl; JV Bowling; Var L Sftbl; Hon Roll; NHS; Top 10 Pct Cls; Math.

DATTOLO, JOSEPHINE; Lafayette HS; Brooklyn, NY; (Y); 26/407; Church Yth Grp; Intnl Clb; Yrbk Stf; Cit Awd; Hon Roll; Kiwanis Awd; Ntl Merit Schol; PACE U; Acctg.

DAU, PAUL; Bishop Ludden HS; Syracuse, NY; (S); Church Yth Grp; Math Tm; Socr; Hon Roll; NHS; Cornell U; Mech Engrng.

DAUPHIN, SCOTT; Red Creek Central HS; Fair Haven, NY; (Y); Am Leg Boys St; French Clb; Ski Clb; Spanish Clb; Yrbk Stf; Rep Stu Cncl; JV Socr; Voice Dem Awd; Pres Frsh Cls; Pres Soph Cls; Ldrshp Awd 83; Teenage Repbl Schl Poltcs, Rgffnts Task Force 84; Law.

DAUS, DOUGLAUS; Dover Plains JR/SR HS; Pawling, NY; (S); 13/94; Chess Clb; Ski Clb; Varsity Clb; Var Bsbl; Var Vllybl; Var Wt Lftg; High Hon Roll; NHS; US Math Awd 85; Dutchess CC; Mech Drwng.

DAUS, RUTH; Dover HS; Pawling, NY; (S); Ski Clb; Teachers Aide; Varsity Clb; Yrbk Stf; Stu Cncl; Trk; Vllybl; High Hon Roll; Hon Roll; NHS.

DAVENPORT, LIEN; Lansingburgh HS; Troy, NY; (Y); High Hon Roll; Hon Roll; Hghst Schlstc Achvt 85; Merit Achvt Awd 85; Advrtsg.

DAVERN, CONNIE; Commack North HS; Commack, NY; (Y); Dance Clb; MMM; PAVAS; Chorus; School Musical; Lit Mag; Stu Cncl; High Hon Roll; NHS; Nwsp Rptr; Lbrl Arts.

DAVI, MICHAEL; St John The Baptist D HS; Patchogue, NY; (Y); 6/617; Chess Clb; Debate Tm; JCL; Math Clb; Math Tm; Stage Crew; Nwsp Phtg; High Hon Roll; NHS; Ntl Merit Ltr; Pre-Law.

DAVID, AMY; Bishop Grimes HS; E Syracuse, NY; (Y); 60/155; Cmnty Wkr; Exploring; Political Wkr; Rep Frsh Cls; Sec Soph Cls; Var Crs Cntry; JV Sftbl; Var Trk; JV Vllybl; Hon Roll; Carried Torch For The Spec Olympcs 85; Spec Educ.

DAVID, DANA; Taconic Hills HS; Hillsdale, NY; (Y); 7/120; Am Leg Aux Girls St; Pres VP 4-H; Band; Nwsp Stf; Yrbk Stf; Stu Cncl; JV Var Cheerleading; Var Socr; Hon Roll; NHS; Mst Imprvd Plyr-Vrsty Soccr 84; Outstndng Achvt Awd-3 Yr Spn 85; Spn.

DAVID, EDSEL; Walton HS; Bronx, NY; (Y); 13/689; Debate Tm; Quiz Bowl; Variety Show; Yrbk Stf; VP Soph Cls; Pres Jr Cls; Var Tennis; Cit Awd; NHS; Pres Schlr; Mayor, Yankees, NY Daily News Outstndnt Stu 83-85; Ntl Merit Fndtn Awd 85; James K Hackett Spch Awd; Alfred U; Plctcl Sci.

DAVID, ISZELLYN ANN; Earl L Vandermeulen HS; Pt Jefferson, NY; (Y); 24/288; French Clb; Key Clb; Mathletes; Chorus; Mrchg Band; Orch; School Musical; Yrbk Stf; High Hon Roll; NHS; SUNY-STONY Brk.

DAVID, LAFLEUR; Sheepshead Bay HS; Brooklyn, NY; (Y); Church Yth Grp; JA; Teachers Aide; Band; Church Choir; Svc Cert Awd 83; Law.

DAVID, WILLIAM; Cicero-North Syracuse HS; N Syracuse, NY; (S); 54/711; JA; NHS; Comp Engr.

DAVIDE, SALVATORE J; Monsignor Farrell HS; Staten Island, NY; (Y); JA; Key Clb; Pep Clb; Sec Soph Cls; Bsktbl; Ftbl; High Hon Roll; NHS; St Schlr; Fordham U; Corp Law.

DAVIDSON, CAROLL; Oyster Bay HS; Oyster Bay, NY; (Y); Yrbk Stf; JV Bsktbl; Var Fld Hcky; Var Lcrss; Stat Vllybl; Bus Mgmt.

DAVIDSON, E DAVY; Camden Central HS; Camden, NY; (Y); Drama Clb; FBLA; Ski Clb; Varsity Clb; Stage Crew; Bsbl; Bsktbl; Lcrss; JV Var Socr; Timer; SUNY; Comp Engrg.

DAVIDSON, JENNIFER L; Delaware Acad; Delhi, NY; (Y); Chorus; Color Guard; Mrchg Band; School Musical; School Play; Yrbk Ed-Chief; Var L Cheerleading; Var L Fld Hcky; Hon Roll; Church Yth Grp; Regents Schlrshp 85; Jessie Burkett Awd 85; Pres Ftnss Awd 85; Russell Sage Coll; Intl Stud.

DAVIDSON, JOSEPH D; Clarkstown North HS; Congers, NY; (Y); Am Leg Boys St; German Clb; Orch; Bsktbl; Ftbl; Trk; A Avg 82-83; Bsktbl Won Boys ST Awd 85; West Point; Law.

DAVIDSON, JOSHUA; Great Neck South HS; Great Neck, NY; (Y); Cmnty Wkr; French Clb; Pres Temple Yth Grp; Band; Concert Band; Mrchg Band; Orch; School Musical; Symp Band; Crs Cntry; AATF Natl Frnch Cont 83; Outstndg Achvt Math 85; Charles E Blech Awd 84; Math.

DAVIDSON, LEA; Aquinas HS; Bronx, NY; (Y); Aud/Vis; Church Yth Grp; Political Wkr; Teachers Aide; Church Choir; School Musical; Stage Crew; Im Swmmng; Im Tennis; Hon Roll; Obstetrician.

DAVIDSON, MARC F; La Salle Acad; New York, NY; (S); 2/238; JA; VP Frsh Cls; Im Bsktbl; Mgr High Hon Roll; Mgr Hon Roll; Mgr Jr NHS; Mgr NHS; Mgr Ntl Merit SF; Baruch; Acctg.

DAVIE, KELLY; Port Richmond HS; Staten Isld, NY; (Y); #46 In Class; Church Yth Grp; Drama Clb; Hosp Aide; Library Aide; Pep Clb; Teachers Aide; Chorus; School Musical; Yrbk Stf; Cheerleading; TV Brdcstng.

DAVIES III, EARL; Granville Central HS; Wells, VT; (Y); 8/123; Am Leg Boys St; Ski Clb; JV Bsktbl; JV Crs Cntry; High Hon Roll; Hon Roll; Prfct Atten Awd; Mst Outstndng Schlstc Imrpvmnt 82-83; Math.

DAVIES, ELIZABETH; Brewster HS; Brewster, NY; (S); 7/200; Church Yth Grp; Var Gym; JV Socr; Hon Roll; Trs NHS; Chem & Phy Ed Achvt Awd 83-84; League Wmn Vtrs Essay Cont 84.

DAVIES, JEANNINE M; Pulaski Academy And Central; Pulaski, NY; (S); Art Clb; French Clb; GAA; Math Clb; PAVAS; Ski Clb; Yrbk Stf; Pres Soph Cls; Swmmng; Trk; Regnl Art Awd Wnnr 85; Ntl Art Awd Wnnr 85; Art.

DAVIES, JILL; Churchville-Chili SR HS; Churchville, NY; (Y); 13/308; Pres FTA; Math Tm; School Play; Nwsp Rptr; Lit Mag; Stu Cncl; Cit Awd; High Hon Roll; NHS; Pres Schlr; Faclty Awd 85; Coll Pres Schrlshp Awd 85; Outstdng Stu In Frnch 81; Westminster Coll; Educ.

DAVIES, MONICA; Academy Of The Resurrec; White Plains, NY; (Y); Church Yth Grp; Hosp Aide; Office Aide; Chorus; Pres Jr Cls; JV Var Coach Actv; Tennis; JV Vllybl; All Lge Vllybl 84.

DAVIES, PAT; E J Wilson HS; Spencerport, NY; (Y); French Clb; Letterman Clb; Varsity Clb; Var Golf; Ice Hcky; JV Socr; Vllybl; High Hon Roll; Hon Roll; Mst Imprvd Plyr Glf 85; Envr Sci.

DAVIES, TODD; Fayetteville-Manlius HS; Manlius, NY; (Y); Chess Clb; 4-H; Model UN; Ntl Merit Ltr; 2nd Pl Ntl Sci Olympiad-Bio 83-84; Physcs.

DAVILA, MARIA C; The Nichols Schl; Buffalo, NY; (Y); 2/125; Church Yth Grp; Chorus; Church Choir; Variety Show; Im Sftbl; Im Tennis; Im Vllybl; Hon Roll; Keiser Awd 81; Merit Awd 80; Cornell U; Pre-Med.

DAVINO, GEORGE; Richmond Hill HS; Ozone Park, NY; (Y); Computer Clb; Office Aide; Radio Clb; Teachers Aide; Band; Stage Crew; Nwsp Rptr; Yrbk Rptr; Comp Sci.

DAVIO, PETER; Franklin Acad; Malone, NY; (Y); 20/255; Am Leg Boys St; Ski Clb; Chorus; Swing Chorus; JV Crs Cntry; JV Trk; Hon Roll; Ntl Merit SF; Prfct Atten Awd; US Mltry Acad; Comp Sci.

DAVIS, ADAM; Greene Central HS; Greene, NY; (Y); 3/100; French Clb; VP Frsh Cls; Rep Jr Cls; Rep Sr Cls; Im Bsktbl; High Hon Roll; VP NHS; Bio Key Awd 84; Mbr Stu Cncl; Cornell; Vet.

DAVIS, AIMEE; New Rochelle HS; New Rochelle, NY; (Y); 117/597; Model UN; Ski Clb; Gym; JV Vllybl; NHS; Prfct Atten Awd; Model Cong Best Spkr Awd 84; IN U; Psych.

DAVIS, ALLAN E; W T Clarke HS; Westbury, NY; (Y); 10/193; MMM; Bausch & Lomb Sci Awd; NHS; Concert Band; Jazz Band; Mrchg Band; Orch; Stu Cncl; Hon Roll; NY ST Regents Schlrshp 85; Cntrl Commtt W T Clarke Model Congrss 84-85; SUNY-BINGHAMTON; Bio Sci.

DAVIS, ALLISON A; Hillcrest HS; New York, NY; (Y); 152/793; Church Yth Grp; VP JA; Radio Clb; School Musical; School Play; Yrbk Stf; Lit Mag; Rep Sr Cls; Rep Stu Cncl; Teachers Aide; Fnlst Miss Ntl Tngr Pgnt 84; NY ST Rgnts Schlrshp; Fash Merch.

DAVIS, ANN; Auburn HS; Auburn, NY; (S); 12/500; Cmnty Wkr; Teachers Aide; High Hon Roll; NHS; Mony Schlstc Art Awd 84; NY Poster Cntst 82; NYS Math Leag Cntst 82-83; Spec Educ.

DAVIS, APRIL L; Hutch Vo Tech; Buffalo, NY; (Y); #69 In Class; JA; Model UN; Nwsp Stf; Stu Cncl; DAR Awd; Hon Roll; Beta Sigma Phi Hnr Soc 82-85; Blck Enrchmnt Soc 83-85; Fredonia ST U; Coop Engrng.

DAVIS, BERTHA; Monticello HS; Monticello, NY; (Y); Sec Trs Church Yth Grp; Library Aide; High Hon Roll; NHS; Ntl Merit Ltr; Prfct Atten Awd; Nrs.

DAVIS, BETHANY S; Ilion JR-SR HS; Ilion, NY; (Y); 1/118; Model UN; Spanish Clb; Concert Band; Orch; Ed Yrbk Stf; Bausch & Lomb Sci Awd; Pres NHS; Ntl Merit Ltr; Val; God & Community Awd; 1st Class GSA; Outstndng Young New Yorker; Cornell U; Interior Dsgn.

DAVIS, BILL; Williamsville East; Williamsville, NY; (Y); FBLA; Latin Clb; Varsity Clb; JV Var Ftbl; Var Ice Hcky; Var Wt Lftg; Prfct Atten Awd; Bus Adm.

DAVIS, BRANDON; The Bronx H S Of Science; New York, NY; (Y); Church Yth Grp; Cmnty Wkr; Teachers Aide; Band; Nwsp Stf; Yrbk Phtg; Yrbk Stf; DAR Awd; Prfct Atten Awd; Cmmnctns.

DAVIS, CAROL; Washington Irving HS; Long Isld Cty, NY; (Y); FHA; Vllybl; Cert Merit Awd Bureau Of Hm Ec 85; Cert Achvt Borough Manhattn CC 85; Schl Cert Awd 84; Early Childhd Tchr.

DAVIS, CATHERINE; Mt St Ursula HS; Bronx, NY; (Y); NEDT Awd; Nrsng.

DAVIS, CYNTHIA; Albion HS; Albion, NY; (S); Lit Mag; Hon Roll; Soc Of Distngsd Am H S Stu 84-85.

DAVIS, DALE E; Cortland SR HS; Cortland, NY; (Y); 87/237; Church Yth Grp; Regents Schlrshp 85; Tompkins Crtlnd Comm Col; Acctn.

DAVIS, DEAN; Houghton Acad; Houghton, NY; (Y); Church Yth Grp; Varsity Clb; Im Badmtn; Var Bsktbl; Var Socr; Im Sftbl; Im Swmmng; Im Vllybl; JV Wrstlng; Houghton Coll; Hstry.

DAVIS, DENICE Y; Dominican Commercial HS; Jamaica Queens, NY; (Y); 138/300; Dance Clb; Spanish Clb; Chorus; Rep Frsh Cls; Hon Roll; Mgr Yr Trk 84-85; Miss NY ST Fin Miss Amer Co-Ed Pag 84-85; Siena Clb Acad Achvts 82-86; St Johns U; CPA.

DAVIS, DENNIS; Berne Knox Westerlo HS; Knox, NY; (Y); Trs Letterman Clb; Trs Varsity Clb; Band; Concert Band; Mrchg Band; Pep Band; Symp Band; Rep Frsh Cls; Rep Jr Cls; Sec Sr Cls; St Lawrence U; Pre Law.

DAVIS, DIANE; E Islip HS; E Islip, NY; (Y); High Hon Roll; Hon Roll; Frgn Lang Hnr Soc 85; Nrsng Home Vlntr 83; Med.

DAVIS, EMILIE M; Academy Of Mt Saint Ursula; Bronx, NY; (Y); Drama Clb; Church Choir; School Musical; VP Chorus; Stage Crew; Hon Roll; Karen Marsh Awd 84; Manhattan Coll; Bus Admin.

DAVIS, FREDRIC A; Jamaica HS; Jamaica, NY; (Y); BUS Admn.

DAVIS, GEORGIA LYNNE; Rome Free Acad; Blossvale, NY; (Y); Intnl Clb; Band; Concert Band; Mrchg Band; High Hon Roll; Hon Roll; Jr NHS; Lib Arts.

DAVIS, GLENN C; West Islip HS; W Islip, NY; (Y); Church Yth Grp; Church Choir; Stat Bsktbl; Var JV Diving; Stat Ftbl; JV Trk; E Stroudsburg; ; Hotel Mgmt.

DAVIS, GREG R; Horace Mann School; New York, NY; (Y); Ed Lit Mag; Rep Sr Cls; Rep Stu Cncl; Var L Bsbl; JV Socr; Im Wt Lftg; JV Wrstlng; Ntl Merit SF; Rep Frsh Cls; Rep Soph Cls; OTID Johns Hopkins Talnt 79; Med.

DAVIS, H CHRISTIAN; Dundee Central HS; Lakemont, NY; (Y); 4/65; Am Leg Boys St; Pres Science Clb; Ski Clb; Trs Sr Cls; High Hon Roll; NHS; Prfct Atten Awd; High Hon Roll; Centrl Western Sectn STANYS 1st Pl Sci Fic Stry 85; Dundee Tchrs Assn Awd Hghst Achvt Chem 84; Allegheny Coll; Bio.

DAVIS, JANET; Kendall JR SR HS; Kent, NY; (Y); 28/92; FHA; Pep Clb; Ski Clb; Chorus; Cheerleading; Pom Pon.

DAVIS, JIM; Wilson Magnet HS; Rochester, NY; (Y); Church Yth Grp; Teachers Aide; Sec Jr Cls; Rep Stu Cncl; Var Bsbl; Var Bsktbl; JV Ftbl; Var Socr; High Hon Roll; Hon Roll; Natl Sci Olympd 83 & 84; Achvt Awd Comp Sci 83 & 84; Sprts Awd Bsbll & Coaches Awd Outstndng Avg 85; Sec Educ.

DAVIS, JON; Greene Central HS; Greene, NY; (Y); VP Frsh Cls; VP Soph Cls; Ntl Merit Ltr; Army Res 84-85; ST U NY New Paltz; Elec Engnr.

DAVIS, KIMBERLY M; Vestal HS; Apalachin, NY; (Y); 49/450; Church Yth Grp; French Clb; Hosp Aide; Sec Ski Clb; Varsity Clb; Rep Frsh Cls; Rep Soph Cls; Rep Stu Cncl; JV Score Keeper; Var L Socr; Eldredge Schlrshp 85; Ithaca Coll Schlrshp 85; Ithaca Coll.

DAVIS, LASHAN; Newburgh Free Acad; New Windsor, NY; (Y); Library Aide; Varsity Clb; Church Choir; Yrbk Stf; Mgr(s); Vllybl; High Hon Roll; Hon Roll; Jr NHS; Val; Upwrd Bnd Prog 84-85; Co Ed Prog IBM 85-86; Comp.

DAVIS, MARLENE; Albion HS; Albion, NY; (S); 17/188; Pres Church Yth Grp; Pres Drama Clb; Pres 4-H; Chorus; School Musical; Swing Chorus; Trs Jr Cls; Trs Sr Cls; Trs NHS; NY ST Regents Schlrshp 85; Suny At Oswego; Acctng.

DAVIS, MATTHEW; Eden Central SR HS; Hamburg, NY; (Y); 2/193; Varsity Clb; Pres Concert Band; Jazz Band; Nwsp Ed-Chief; Trs Sr Cls; L Golf; L Tennis; Bausch & Lomb Sci Awd; Pres NHS; Sal; Swarthmore Coll Ntl Schlrshp 85; Arion Music Awd-Outstndng Musicl Achvt 85; Eden Cntrl Schlr-Athl Awd; Swartmore Coll; Pre-Med.

DAVIS, MELISSA ANNE; Newark SR HS; Newark, NY; (Y); 23/250; Church Yth Grp; Cmnty Wkr; Hosp Aide; Red Cross Aide; Band; Church Choir; Swing Chorus; Hon Roll; School Musical; Red Cross Yth Leadrshp Conf Delgt 84; Red Cross Yth Staff Stu 85; SUNY-OSWEGO; Zoolgy.

DAVIS, MICHAEL L; Midlakes HS; Clifton Springs, NY; (Y); 39/160; Am Leg Boys St; Aud/Vis; Stage Crew; Yrbk Sprt Ed; Sec Frsh Cls; Bsbl; JV Var Bsktbl; JV Var Ftbl; Golf; Hon Roll; Doug Blondell YMCA Awd Outstndg Ded 81; Oswego; Bus Adm.

DAVIS, MICHELLE; Canisteo Central Schl; Canisteo, NY; (Y); 5/71; Ski Clb; Orch; Yrbk Stf; Trs Soph Cls; Var L Sftbl; Var L Swmmng; Var L Vllybl; High Hon Roll; NHS; Bio.

DAVIS, MONICA; Hastings HS; Hastings On Hudsn, NY; (S); 1/117; AFS; Key Clb; Chorus; Madrigals; Orch; Ed Yrbk Stf; Sec Stu Cncl; Var Capt Crs Cntry; Var Capt Trk; Ntl Merit SF; Rensselaer Mdl For Math & Sci 84; All ST/All Cnty Orch 85.

DAVIS, PATRICIA; Whitestone Acad; Whitestone, NY; (S); Girl Scts; Math Clb; Bsktbl; Crs Cntry; Swmmng; Trk.

DAVIS, PAULA; Vernon-Verona-Sherrill Cntrl HS; Verona, NY; (Y); Pres Church Yth Grp; Chorus; Church Choir; School Musical; School Play; Yrbk Ed-Chief; Yrbk Sprt Ed; Rep Frsh Cls; High Hon Roll; Hon Roll; Elem Ed.

DAVIS, ROBERT S; Williamsville North HS; E Amherst, NY; (Y); 55/315; Am Leg Boys St; Church Yth Grp; Cmnty Wkr; JV Bsktbl; L Capt Golf; Hon Roll; NHS; St Schlr; Miami U OH; Acctng.

DAVIS, ROSE A; Dundee Central HS; Lakemont, NY; (Y); Trs Sec Church Yth Grp; Science Clb; Spanish Clb; Chorus; Church Choir; Off Frsh Cls; Off Soph Cls; Off Jr Cls; Nrsng.

DAVIS, SANDRA; Bishop Kearney HS; Brooklyn, NY; (Y); Dance Clb; Hosp Aide; Library Aide; Hon Roll; Pre-Med Rsrch & Educ Pgm 85-86; Schdl Cmmtte 84-85; Virginia Lee Schl Of Dance 82-84; Med.

DAVIS, SANDRA; Niagara Falls HS; Niagara Falls, NY; (Y); Cmnty Wkr; Drama Clb; Model UN; Office Aide; Thesps; Chorus; School Musical; Nwsp Stf; Rep Jr Cls; Cit Awd; Joseph Mansour Schlrhsp 85; SADD; Hnrs Clss 85; Volntr Porta-Niagara Girls Clb; Ctznshp Awds; Psych.

DAVIS, SARA; Lacuardia H S Of Music & The Arts; Jamaica, NY; (Y); Art Clb; Drama Clb; Political Wkr; Nwsp Stf; Lit Mag; NCTE Awd; Hon Mntn In City Coll HS Poetry Cntst 83-84; Hon Mntn PBS Pstr Cntst 81-82; Comprtve Lit.

DAVIS, SARA; Our Lady Of Mercy HS; Henrietta, NY; (Y); Pres Church Yth Grp; Cmnty Wkr; Girl Scts; JA; Model UN; Stage Crew; Var Score Keeper; Var Trk; Valparaiso U; Nrsng.

DAVIS, SCOTT; Corning-Painted Post West HS; Painted Post, NY; (Y); Ski Clb; Thesps; Varsity Clb; Acpl Chr; Chorus; Madrigals; School Musical; School Play; Var Golf; Var Capt Lcrss; Elec Engr.

DAVIS, SUSAN M; Beekmantown Central Schl; Plattsburgh, NY; (Y); 14/140; Ski Clb; School Play; Nwsp Phtg; Nwsp Stf; Ed Yrbk Phtg; High Hon Roll; NHS; Hon Roll; NYS Regnts Schlrshp 85; U Of NH; Bus Mgt.

DAVIS, SUZETTE; Queen Of The Rosary Acad; Westbury, NY; (Y); Pres Frsh Cls; Nassau CC; Chld Psych.

DAVIS, TAMMY; Dundee Central HS; Lakemont, NY; (Y); Church Yth Grp; 4-H; Library Aide; Quiz Bowl; Teachers Aide; Church Choir; Trk; JV Vllybl; Hon Roll; Nrsg.

DAVIS, TERESA; North Babylon SR HS; North Babylon, NY; (Y); Dance Clb; Intnl Clb; Spanish Clb; Chorus; Drill Tm; School Musical; Nwsp Stf; Var Cheerleading; JV Mgr(s); JV Score Keeper.

DAVIS, TERESA; Parishville-Hopkinton HS; Potsdam, NY; (Y); Chorus; School Musical; Yrbk Stf; Cheerleading; Socr; Child Psychlgy.

DAVIS, THOMAS; Bishop Cunningham HS; Fulton, NY; (Y); 1/50; Church Yth Grp; VP 4-H; French Clb; Yrbk Stf; Ftbl; Tennis; Dnfth Awd; 4-H Awd; High Hon Roll; NHS; Clarkson Schl; Med.

DAVIS, TINA; Horseheads SR HS; Pine Valley, NY; (Y); Varsity Clb; Var Capt Cheerleading; All Am Chrldr 85; Math.

DAVIS, TODD; Oneida HS; Canastota, NY; (Y); Boy Scts; Church Yth Grp; Band; Mrchg Band; Ftbl; Trk; Morrisville Coll; Htl Mgmt.

DAVIS, TONYA; Washington Irving HS; New York, NY; (Y); Church Yth Grp; Office Aide; Church Choir; Badmtn; Bsktbl; Gym; Trk; Vllybl; Wt Lftg; Prfct Atten Awd; Hnr Awd In Nrsng 84; Super Yth 85; Schlrshp From Mt Ida Coll 85-86; Mt Ida Coll; Comp Bus.

DAVIS, TORREY; Henninger HS; Syracuse, NY; (Y); 90/500; Church Yth Grp; Rep Frsh Cls; Rep Soph Cls; Rep Jr Cls; Rep Stu Cncl; Var JV Ftbl; Var JV Lcrss; Var Trk; JV Wrstlng; Hon Roll.

DAVIS, TRACY; Whitney Point Central HS; Lisle, NY; (S); 4-H; Trs JCL; Trs Latin Clb; Science Clb; Pres Soph Cls; Trs Stu Cncl; JV Var Cheerleading; DAR Awd; 4-H Awd; High Hon Roll; Cornell U; Vet.

DAVIS, VICKI; Perry Central HS; Perry, NY; (Y); 25/90; FHA; Girl Scts; Pep Clb; Varsity Clb; Band; Concert Band; Mrchg Band; Yrbk Stf; Cheerleading; Sftbl; Monroe CC:Dntl.

DAVIS, WENDY; La Guardia High Schl Of The Arts; Brooklyn, NY; (Y); Art Clb; Teachers Aide; Nwsp Rptr; Hon Roll; Art Directors Club Honor Award 82; Graphic Arts.

DAVISON, DONNA KAY; Liverpool HS; Liverpool, NY; (S); 56/792; Sec Exploring; VP JA; Ski Clb; Drm & Bgl; School Musical; Stu Cncl; High Hon Roll; Hon Roll; Jr NHS; NHS; Marine Biology.

DAVISON, KENNETH; Sodus Central Schl; Sodus, NY; (Y); Chess Clb; 4-H; Model UN; Science Clb; Bowling; 4-H Awd; High Hon Roll; 2nd Pl Bowling Sectn V; Chem Engnrng.

DAVISON, WAYNE K; Cicero-North Syracuse HS; Clay, NY; (Y); 240/766; Band; Concert Band; Jazz Band; Mrchg Band; Pep Band; School Musical; School Play; Symp Band; Trk; CC Awd; Rgnts Schlrshp 85; SUNY Fredonia; Music Educ.

DAVISSON, KARI; La Salle SR HS; Niagara Falls, NY; (S); 17/278; Office Aide; Lit Mag; Pom Pon; Hon Roll; NHS.

DAWES, DEBBIE; Whitesboro SR HS; Whitsboro, NY; (Y); 19/357; Intnl Clb; Yrbk Stf; Jr NHS; NHS; Pre Law.

DAWES, VICTORIA; Rye HS; Rye, NY; (Y); Church Yth Grp; Cmnty Wkr; Dance Clb; Church Choir; Fld Hcky; Lcrss; Mgr(s); Ldrshp Clb Chrprsn 85; Ldr Rye Christ Chrch Choir 84; Acholyte 81-85; Hartwick Coll; Fmly Thrpst.

DAWN, MILLER; Harpursville HS; Pt Crane, NY; (Y); Church Yth Grp; Girl Scts; Band; Chorus; Church Choir; Concert Band; Mrchg Band; Pep Band; School Play; Fld Hcky.

DAWSON, KRISTIN S; Shenendehowa HS; Clifton Park, NY; (Y); Church Yth Grp; Concert Band; Symp Band; JV Crs Cntry; High Hon Roll; NHS; Prfct Atten Awd; Presdntl Physcl Ftns Awd 80-82; Hnr Roll 80-83; Cert Of Merit Schlstc Achvt 84-85; Engr.

DAWSON, NATALIE R; Williamsville South HS; Williamsville, NY; (Y); 31/256; Drama Clb; Pep Clb; School Musical; Rep Frsh Cls; Var Capt Cheerleading; Var Capt Fld Hcky; L Trk; Hon Roll; Amhrt Jolly Boys Schlrshp Awd 85; Outstndng Dfns Fld Hockey 84; Smr Dnc Fstvl 84-85; Sprngfld Coll; Sprts Med.

DAWSON, STEVEN ALLEN; W T Sampson HS; Bevier, MO; (Y); 3/40; Church Yth Grp; Debate Tm; Drama Clb; Scholastic Bowl; Science Clb; Band; Jazz Band; Mrchg Band; Pep Band; School Play; Hugh O Brien Yth Fndtn Rep 83; U Of MO Columbia; Engrng.

DAWSON, TAMMY M; Copenhagen Central HS; Copenhagen, NY; (Y); 4/46; Drama Clb; French Clb; Quiz Bowl; Chorus; Stage Crew; Variety Show; Yrbk Stf; Hon Roll; NHS; School Play; Chechett Ballet 82-83 & 85; Psych.

DAY, DWAYNE; Greece Arcadia HS; Rochester, NY; (Y); Am Leg Boys St; Aud/Vis; Drama Clb; Library Aide; Nwsp Bus Mgr; Nwsp Rptr; Nwsp Stf; Hon Roll; NHS; Prfct Atten Awd; W Seneca Cert Merit Drg Cnslr 85; 2nd Pl W Senca Sci Olympd 83; Excptnl Wrk Frnch I 85; Poli Sci.

DAY, TIMOTHY; Kenmore East HS; Kenmore, NY; (Y); Boy Scts; VP Church Yth Grp; Radio Clb; Im Ice Hcky; Im Sftbl; Im Vllybl; Carrier Of Mnth 84; Sucny At Buffalo; Comm.

DAY, WANDA M; Union Springs Central Schl; Cayuga, NY; (Y); 10/105; Church Yth Grp; School Play; Yrbk Stf; Var JV Cheerleading; JV Fld Hcky; Sec Socr; Hon Roll; NHS; NYS Regnts Schlrshp 85; Cayuga Cty CC; Bus Adm.

DAYAL, VINAY; Flushing HS; Flushing, NY; (Y); 60/367; Nwsp Rptr; High Hon Roll; Hon Roll; Prfct Atten Awd; St Schlr; ST U NY Stony Brk; Biochem.

DAYBELL, R M; Averill Park HS; Averill Pk, NY; (Y); Art Clb; Aud/Vis; Political Wkr; Stage Crew; Nwsp Stf; Yrbk Phtg; Yrbk Stf; JV Socr; Var Tennis; Hon Roll; NY ST Smr Schl Or Arts 83.

DAYGER, CHRISTOPHER J; John Jay SR HS; Wappingers Fall, NY; (Y); Church Yth Grp; Ski Clb; Socr; High Hon Roll; 1st Schl Sci Fair 84; 1st County Sci Fair 84; Bio.

DAYTON, THOMAS; Cold Spring Harbor HS; Cold Spring Har, NY; (Y); 11/148; VP Pres Intnl Clb; Mathletes; Varsity Clb; Nwsp Rptr; Yrbk Sprt Ed; Lit Mag; Var L Bsbl; Var L Wrstlng; High Hon Roll; NHS; Pre-Med.

DAZIER, SIONETTE; Lafayette HS; Buffalo, NY; (Y); Bsktbl; Vllybl; Med.

DE ANGELIS JR, EDWARD; Saugerties HS; Saugert Ies, NY; (Y); Chess Clb; Church Yth Grp; FCA; JA; Stage Crew; Yrbk Phtg; Hon Roll; Dunwoody Inst Minneapls; Hm Ec.

DE ANGELIS, JODI; East Meadow HS; E Meadow, NY; (Y); Sec Key Clb; Concert Band; Orch; C W Post.

DE ANGELO, DONLYN; Scotia-Glenville SR HS; Scotia, NY; (Y); Art Clb; JA; Key Clb; Ski Clb; Stage Crew; Variety Show; JV Var Cheerleading; Cmrcl Art.

DE ANGELO, JEFFREY; Cicero N Syracuse HS; Mattydale, NY; (S); 31/711; Concert Band; Drm Mjr(t); Jazz Band; Orch; Pep Band; Symp Band; JP Sousa Awd; NHS; Opt Clb Awd; Cmnty Schlr Awd Onondaga Comm Coll 84; Schlrshp NY Inst Tech 84; SUNY; Aerosp Engrng.

DE ASLA, RICHARD; Sachem H S North; Ronkonkoma, NY; (Y); 159/1386; Jazz Band; Mrchg Band; Orch; Stage Crew; Symp Band; JV Var Tennis; VP NHS; Rotary Awd; Interact Clb Svc & Ldrshp Awd 85; 6th NYSSMA All ST Fest 85; Merit Awd Long Island Sci Congrss 84; Phys Sci.

DE AVEIRO, ROBERT; Lafayette HS; Brooklyn, NY; (Y); Computer Clb; JA; Math Clb; Math Tm; Hon Roll; Socr; Arista, Arkon Awds; Trig, Pre-Calc, Music, Sci, Engl, Socl Studies Hnr Certs; NYU; Comp Sci.

DE BAR, JODIE; Liverpool HS; Liverpool, NY; (S); Exploring; Hosp Aide; Sec JA; Ski Clb; Chorus; Drill Tm; Nwsp Stf; High Hon Roll; Hon Roll; Jr NHS; Pre Med.

DE BARTOLO, AMY; Cicero-North Syracuse HS; North Syracuse, NY; (S); 32/711; Sec German Clb; Mrchg Band; Nwsp Stf; Off Frsh Cls; Off Soph Cls; Hst Jr Cls; Stu Cncl; NHS; Sales.

DE BARTOLO, STEPHANIE; Mamaroneck HS; Larchmont, NY; (Y); FBLA; Service Clb; Spanish Clb; Hon Roll; NYS Cncl Soc Stds Cert Hnr 83; Cert Achvt Acctng I 84; Cert Dedctd Vlntr Svc 85.

DE BEASE, AMY J; Lakeland SR HS; Yorktown Hts, NY; (Y); 26/400; Trs German Clb; Trs Frsh Cls; Var Bsktbl; Im Lcrss; Socr; High Hon Roll; Hon Roll; NHS; Grmn-Amer Exch Stu 85; U AZ; Engnrng.

DE BENEDETTO, GINA; Fontbonne Hall Acad; Brooklyn, NY; (Y); Drama Clb; School Musical; School Play; Variety Show; Hon Roll; Prfct Atten Awd; Dyker Heights Awd Ldrshp & Svc 82; NY U; Drama.

DE BERNARDO, GAIL; Christopher Columbus HS; Bronx, NY; (S); 30/747; Band; Chorus; School Musical; Yrbk Stf; Swmmng; Hon Roll; NHS; Prfct Atten Awd; NY All ST Chorus 84; All Estrn Chrs 85; Fordham U; Psychlgy.

DE BETTA, JOSEPHINE; St John Villa Acad; Staten Is, NY; (Y); Dance Clb; Drama Clb; Chorus; School Musical; School Play; Variety Show; Spnsh Awd Hnrs; St John U; Bus Mgmnt.

DE BLASIS, MARIA R; Cardinal Mooney HS; Rochester, NY; (Y); 51/315; Am Leg Aux Girls St; Church Yth Grp; Exploring; Hosp Aide; Intnl Clb; Stage Crew; Yrbk Bus Mgr; Trs Stu Cncl; JV Vllybl; Hon Roll; Latin Hnr Soc 83084; Magna Cum Laude Ntl Latin Cntst Awd 84; Math.

DE BONIS, ERIN MARIE; Troy HS; Troy, NY; (Y); 25/450; Aud/Vis; Radio Clb; Ski Clb; Church Choir; Stage Crew; Rep Frsh Cls; High Hon Roll; NHS; Edith Grace Craig Reynolds Schlrshp 85; Princ Hnr Rl 85; MI ST U; Engrng.

DE BONO, MARY ELLEN; Northport HS; Northport, NY; (Y); Church Yth Grp; Pep Clb; Coach Actv; Var Socr; Var Trk; Hon Roll; NHS; NY ST Rgnts Schlrshp Awd 85; Holy Crss.

DE BRITO, MARGARIDA; Curtis HS; Staten Island, NY; (Y); 42/350; Hosp Aide; Mrchg Band; Orch; Yrbk Stf; Swmmng; Vllybl; Hon Roll; NHS; Office Aide; Intl Exch Stu Italy; ST U Coll Oneonta; Pol Sci.

DE BRITZ, JAMES; Fayetteville-Manlius HS; Manlius, NY; (Y); Church Yth Grp; Debate Tm; VP Jr Cls; VP Sr Cls; Rep Stu Cncl; Im Bsbl; JV Var Socr; Hon Roll; Mrn Blgy.

DE CANDIDO, KEITH A; Cardinal Spellman HS; Bronx, NY; (Y); Chess Clb; Debate Tm; Drama Clb; NFL; Speech Tm; Chorus; School Musical; Variety Show; Nwsp Rptr; High Hon Roll; Columbia U; Engl.

DE CANN, DWAYNE; Newark SR HS; Lyons, NY; (Y); 32/199; Am Leg Boys St; Church Yth Grp; Rep Band; Chorus; Concert Band; Jazz Band; Mrchg Band; Im Bsbl; High Hon Roll; Hon Roll; Air Force Acad; Pilot.

DE CARO, ADRIA; Commack HS North; Commack, NY; (Y); Rep Frsh Cls; Rep Soph Cls; Rep Jr Cls; Rep Sr Cls; Rep Stu Cncl; JV Var Cheerleading; High Hon Roll; Hon Roll; Grls Ldrs Corp Sec 84-85; Stu Faculty Advsry Comm 85-86.

DE CECCHIS, ELISA M; Briarcliff HS; Briarcliff Manor, NY; (Y); French Clb; Teachers Aide; Var Capt Cheerleading; Ntl Merit Schol; NY ST Rgnts Schlrshp 85; Pace U; Bus Mgmt.

DE CELESTINO, BLASE; Herbert Lehman HS; Bronx, NY; (Y); 44/473; Stage Crew; Yrbk Stf; Arista Hnr Soc 85; Comp Hnr Rll 85; Cert Achvt Prfct Atten 85; Comp Sci.

DE CESARE, KIM MARIE; Millbrook HS; Clinton Corners, NY; (Y); VICA; Im Badmtn; Rtlng Awd 85; Csmtly.

DE CICCO, MARK J; Sachem High School North Campus; Farmingville, NY; (Y); 65/1350; Church Yth Grp; Science Clb; Ski Clb; Concert Band; Off Frsh Cls; JV Tennis; Cit Awd; Zenith Clb-Hnr Soc Of Schl; Bio.

DE COSTANZO, DENISE; Bishop Kearney HS; Brooklyn, NY; (S); 2/345; Hosp Aide; Math Tm; Drama Clb; Gov Hon Prg Awd; High Hon Roll; NHS; Ntl Merit Ltr; Pres Schlr; Prsdntl Schlrshp To Manhattan Coll 85; Rgnts Schlrshp 85; 2nd Hnrs Frnch Cntst IA Coll 83; Manhattan Coll; Bio.

DE CRESCENZO, MIKE; Whitesboro SR HS; Whitesboro, NY; (Y); 47/313; Boy Scts; Trs Church Yth Grp; Rep Stu Cncl; Hon Roll; Potsdam Coll; Comp Sci.

DE CRISTOFARO, MICHAEL; Walt Whitman HS; Huntington, NY; (Y); 117/540; Aud/Vis; Computer Clb; Drama Clb; Mathletes; Band; Chorus; Concert Band; Drm Mjr(t); Flag Corp; Jazz Band; Duke U; Engrng.

DE DONA, ANNA; St Johns Prep; Woodside, NY; (S); 13/415; Hosp Aide; Yrbk Bus Mgr; Rep Sr Cls; Stu Cncl; High Hon Roll; Hon Roll; NHS; Prfct Atten Awd; Chem Awd 84; Pre-Med.

DE FABIO, DAN; Catholic Central HS; Clifton Park, NY; (Y); Concert Band; Jazz Band; Yrbk Stf; Off Sr Cls; High Hon Roll; NHS; Ntl Merit SF; Band; Pep Band; School Musical; All Am Hall Fame Band 85; Orig Awd Co-Authoring Cls Play Alexs Rest 85; Comp Graphics.

DE FANTI, LUCY; Preston HS; Bronx, NY; (S); Hosp Aide; Stage Crew; Nwsp Rptr; Nwsp Stf; Trs Frsh Cls; Im Vllybl; Hon Roll; NHS; NEDT Awd; Cornell U; Pre-Med.

DE FAZIO, CHRISTIAN; Lockport SR HS; Lockport, NY; (Y); 3/390; Latin Clb; Var Bsbl; Var Ice Hcky; JV Socr; NHS; Jr NHS; Genevieve H Smith Math Awd 83; Outstndng Ffrshmn Male Stu 83; NY Empire St Sec Ice Hcky Tm 85; Pre-Med.

DE FAZIO, TINA; Batavia HS; Batavia, NY; (Y); Band; Chorus; Concert Band; Drm Mjr(t); School Musical; Yrbk Stf; Rep Soph Cls; Var Cheerleading; Var Trk; Hon Roll; Most Outstdng Drum Majorette 85; Bus Admn.

DE FEO, MICHAEL J; Monticello HS; Rock Hill, NY; (Y); Church Yth Grp; French Clb; JA; Math Tm; JV Bsbl; High Hon Roll; Hon Roll; Gym; NHS; SE Ind Tchrs Assoc Achvt Awd Drftng 83; Awd Mech Drwng 83; U Tampa; Marine Bio.

DE FILIPPO, ELIZABETH; John Jay SR HS; Hopewell Junction, NY; (Y); Church Yth Grp; Drama Clb; Math Tm; Color Guard; High Hon Roll; Jr NHS; NHS; Cmnty Wkr; School Musical; School Play; 1st Pl WCAL Yamaha Elec Fest 84; Natl Sci Olympd 85; Bst Delg Livingston Model Congrss 85; Engrng.

DE FIO, ELENA M R; Fowler HS; Syracuse, NY; (Y); #4 In Class; Church Yth Grp; Nwsp Rptr; Yrbk Stf; Trs Sr Cls; Var Cheerleading; Score Keeper; Var Socr; Rotary Awd; Regnts & Fowler Fclty Schlrshps; St Rose Coll; Hist.

DE FOREST, ANDY; Unatego JR SR HS; Sidney, NY; (Y); Drama Clb; School Play; Stage Crew; Mechanic.

DE FOREST, ERIC; Tupper Lake HS; Tupper Lk, NY; (Y); 10/118; Pres VP Drama Clb; Pres Science Clb; Pres Chorus; School Musical; L Crs Cntry; High Hon Roll; NHS; Trs AFS; Band; Ntl Math Awd 83-84; Ortrcl Cntst 2nd Pl 83-84; All ST NYSSMA Choir 84-85; Lycoming U; Mus.

DE FOREST, SCOTT; Jordan Elbridge HS; Jordan, NY; (Y); 1/142; Am Leg Boys St; Red Cross Aide; Mrchg Band; Yrbk Ed-Chief; JV Var Bsktbl; JV Var Lcrss; Hon Roll; Jr NHS; NHS; NEDT Awd; Engrng.

DE FREES JR, BRUCE D; Rome Free Acad; Lee Center, NY; (Y); Camera Clb; Intnl Clb; Red Cross Aide; Ski Clb; Nwsp Sprt Ed; Hon Roll; Jr NHS; NHS; Syracuse U; Cmmnctns.

DE FREIDAS, SUZAN; Cardinal Spellman HS; Bronx, NY; (Y); Computer Clb; Girl Scts; Library Aide; Sec Science Clb; Church Choir; NEDT Awd; First Hnrs; Medal Sci/Med Art 85; Bronze And Silver Mdl Library Aid 84-85; Physics.

DE FREITAS, DAVID; East Syracuse Minoa HS; Kirkville, NY; (Y); German Clb; Golf; Tampa; Law.

DE GAETANI, PATRICIA; F D Roosevelt HS; Brooklyn, NY; (Y); 8/756; Office Aide; Teachers Aide; Chorus; Lit Mag; Bsktbl; Crs Cntry; Hon Roll; MVP Bsktbll 83; Future Studies Awd-High Achvt 83; Poetry Publctn In Schl Magzn & Yearbk 83 & 84; Bio.

DE GENNARO, ANTHONY; Msgr Mc Calncy Memorial HS; Jackson Heights, NY; (S); 55/229; Math Tm; Ski Clb; Stage Crew; Nwsp Rptr; Yrbk Rptr; Yrbk Stf; Rep Jr Cls; Rep Sr Cls; Rep Stu Cncl; JV Crs Cntry; NY Inst Tech; Comp Engrng.

DE HAAS, LAURIE; Horseheads HS; Pine Valley, NY; (Y); Girl Scts; JCL; Latin Clb; Swmmng; Hon Roll; Cntrl Cty Bus Inst; Exec Secrtr.

DE HART, ALEX; Hutch-Tech HS; Buffalo, NY; (Y); Archit.

DE HART, ANTHONY; Tioga Central Schl; Barton, NY; (Y); 3/105; Chess Clb; VP Computer Clb; Ski Clb; Trs Frsh Cls; Rep Soph Cls; Rep Jr Cls; Rep Stu Cncl; NHS; Comp Grhpcs.

DE JESUS, CASSANDRA; Babylon JR SR HS; Babylon, NY; (Y); Cmnty Wkr; Hosp Aide; Library Aide; Political Wkr; Yrbk Stf; Hon Roll; Stoney Brook; Pschy.

DE JESUS, DANIEL; Far Rockaway HS; Far Rockaway, NY; (Y); Var Bsbl; St Johns U; Acctg.

DE JESUS, DEBBIE; Canarsie HS; Brooklyn, NY; (Y); Band; Chorus; Concert Band; Drm Mjr(t); Jazz Band; Orch; School Musical; School Play; Symp Band; Hon Roll; St Johns U; Pre-Law.

DE JESUS, IRIS; Chara Barton HS; Brooklyn, NY; (Y); Church Yth Grp; Prfct Atten Awd; NYC Tech Coll; Dntl Lab.

DE JESUS, IVETTE; Grace Dodge Vo Tech; Bronx, NY; (Y); Dance Clb; FNA; Chorus; Yrbk Stf; Hon Roll; Regnts Schlrshp 85; Sci, Soc Stds, Math, Alg, Geom, Art Bio & Engl Awds 81-85; Marymount Coll; Premed.

DE JOHN, MARGARET; Mt St Mary Acad; Williamsville, NY; (Y); Pep Clb; Yrbk Phtg; Yrbk Rptr; Yrbk Stf; Erie Comm Coll; Dentl Hyg.

DE LA OSA CRUZ, STEVEN MARCO; Thomas A Edison HS; Elmira Hts, NY; (Y); Am Leg Boys St; Varsity Clb; Nwsp Stf; Yrbk Stf; Var L Bsbl; Var Ftbl; Hon Roll; Rotary Awd; IAC All-Star Shortstp 1st Tm Bsbl 85; Yth Cnty 85; Bus Ecnmcs.

DE LA TORRE, GERALDINE; Spring Valley SR HS; Monsey, NY; (Y); Hosp Aide; Key Clb; Spanish Clb; Orch; Lit Mag; Socr; Vllybl; Hon Roll; NHS; Spanish NHS; Vol Svc Good Samartn Hosp Cert Awd 83-84; Mst Imprvd Plyr Sprng Vly Var Socr 84; Rookie Yr Vllybl 84; Pre-Med.

DE LACERDA JR, ALBERTO G; North Babylon SR HS; North Babylon, NY; (Y); 29/601; Hosp Aide; Band; Yrbk Stf; JV Ftbl; Var Wrstlng; High Hon Roll; Jr NHS; NHS; Cardiology.

DE LAMARTER, MICHELLE; Waterloo SR HS; Waterloo, NY; (Y); Drama Clb; Pep Clb; Acpl Chr; Chorus; Stage Crew; Hon Roll; All Co Chrs; Var Ensemble Chrs; Med Secry.

DE LANNOY, HEATHER J; Garden City SR HS; Garden City, NY; (Y); 62/350; French Clb; German Clb; Sec Girl Scts; Band; Concert Band; Madrigals; Orch; Yrbk Stf; JV Socr; Jr NHS; Awd For Exc In Musiic 83; Grl Scout Slvr Awd 85; Fashion.

DE LILLO, DIANE; St Joseph Hill Acad; Staten Island, NY; (Y); 26/103; Drama Clb; Hosp Aide; JA; Political Wkr; Science Clb; Sec Spanish Clb; Cheerleading; Sftbl; Tennis; High Hon Roll; Spnsh Ltr Of Cmmndtn 84; Grad Hnrs 85; Fairfield U.

DE LOLA, BRIAN; Fairport HS; Fairport, NY; (Y); Var L Bsbl; JV L Bsktbl; Var L Ftbl; Hon Roll; Physcl Thrpy.

DE LONG, ME LINDA; South New Berlin Central HS; Norwich, NY; (Y); 10/40; Teachers Aide; Color Guard; Sec Frsh Cls; VP Soph Cls; Cheerleading; Hon Roll; Barbizon Modlg Schl 84-85; Travl.

DE LORA, DAWN; Newfield HS; Selden, NY; (Y); Dance Clb; Drama Clb; Pep Clb; PAVAS; Red Cross Aide; Chorus; Variety Show; Cheerleading; Trk; High Hon Roll; Math.

DE LORENZO, LORI; Johnstown HS; Gloversville, NY; (Y); Bus.

DE LOSH JR, WALTER M; Camden Central Schl; Taberg, NY; (Y); 24/231; Am Leg Boys St; Yrbk Stf; Hon Roll; Band.

DE LUCA, JEANNETTE; Academy Of The Resurrection HS; New Rochelle, NY; (Y); Art Clb; Chorus; Bsktbl; Cheerleading; High Hon Roll; Archdiocese NY 1st Pl Art Awd 84; Mktng.

DE LUCA, KEVIN; Amsterdam HS; Amsterdam, NY; (Y); 9/319; Computer Clb; Varsity Clb; Drm Mjr(t); Rep Frsh Cls; Trs Soph Cls; Trs Jr Cls; JV Capt Ftbl; High Hon Roll; Hon Roll; NHS; Comp Prgrmr.

DE LUCA, KRISTEN; Henninger HS; Syracuse, NY; (Y); GAA; Ski Clb; Off Soph Cls; Off Jr Cls; Stu Cncl; Var Capt Bsktbl; Var Capt Socr; Im Sftbl; Var Capt Trk; NHS; Steven W King Awd 85; ; Army MVP Sccr Awdd 85; Ldrshp Bsktbl Schlrshp 85; St Bonaventure U; Phy Ed.

DE LUCA, MICHAEL; The Kew-Forest Schl; Forest Hills, NY; (Y); 18/31; Spanish Clb; Sec Frsh Cls; Sec Soph Cls; VP Stu Cncl; Var Bsktbl; JV Mgr(s); Capt Sftbl; DAR Awd.

DE LUCA, RALPH; St Raymonds HS; Bronx, NY; (Y); 16/191; Computer Clb; Drama Clb; Math Tm; NFL; Speech Tm; School Play; Im Bsktbl; Im Ftbl; Hon Roll; NHS; Iona Coll; Comp Sci.

DE LUCIA, PETER J; Greece Athena HS; Rochester, NY; (Y); 30/282; DECA; Math Clb; Math Tm; Var Capt Socr; Hon Roll; NHS; Pres Schlr; Cty Soccr Leag 1st Tm 84; NYS Regnts Schlrshp 85; VA Tech; Engr.

DE MAILLE, GREGORY; St John The Baptist HS; W Babylon, NY; (Y); Church Yth Grp; Computer Clb; Math Clb; Var Ftbl; JV Wrstlng; High Hon Roll; Jr NHS; NHS; Spanish NHS; Metro Bowl Trophy Ftbl 84; Comp Engrng.

DE MARCHI, JASON; West Genesee SR HS; Camillus, NY; (Y); Aud/Vis; French Clb; Key Clb; Band; Concert Band; Mrchg Band; Pep Band; Variety Show; Soph Cls; Stu Cncl; DDA Pres 84; Accntnt.

DE MARIA, JACQUELINE M; Bishop Kearney HS; Brooklyn, NY; (Y); Girl Scts; Ski Clb; Yrbk Stf; Rep Soph Cls; Im Sftbl; Im Vllybl; St Johns U; Pol Sci.

DE MARINO, RENEE; Newfield HS; Selden, NY; (Y); Quiz Bowl; Variety Show; Trk; High Hon Roll; Hon Roll; Prfct Atten Awd; Bus Dynamcs Awd 83; Katherine Gibbs Bus; Wrd Prccsr.

DE MASI, OLYMPIA; Preston HS; Bronx, NY; (S); Drama Clb; Stage Crew; Nwsp Rptr; Hon Roll; NHS; Dntl Hygnst.

DE MECO, CHRIS; Churchville Chili SR HS; Rochester, NY; (Y); Math Tm; Concert Band; Yrbk Stf; Crs Cntry; Score Keeper; Wt Lftg; High Hon Roll; Hon Roll; Regents Schlrshp 85; Churchville-Chili Drkng Team 85; Rochester Inst Tech; Comp Engr.

DE METSENAERE, BILL; Churchville-Chili SR HS; Churchville, NY; (Y); Drama Clb; French Clb; Chorus; Madrigals; School Musical; School Play; Variety Show; Yrbk Stf; Stu Cncl; Hon Roll; Nazareth Coll Voice Comptn Wnnr 83; NYSSMA Conf 84; Ithaca; Music.

DE MICHELE, ANNA-MARIA; Bishop Ludden HS; Liverpool, NY; (S); 5/179; Exploring; Co-Capt Math Tm; High Hon Roll; Sec NHS; Smmr Schlr Lemoyne Coll 84; Schlrs Day Partcpnt SUNY 84; Lemoyne Coll; Pre Dentstry.

DE MOORS, TAMARA; Weedsport Central HS; Weedsport, NY; (Y); 7/95; Hosp Aide; Intnl Clb; Math Clb; Concert Band; Jazz Band; Mrchg Band; Fld Hcky; Trk; High Hon Roll; NHS; Elmira Coll Key Awd 85.

DE MOTT, MARK; Commack High School South; Commack, NY; (S); Office Aide; Teachers Aide; Acpl Chr; Chorus; School Musical; Variety Show; High Hon Roll; Hon Roll; Bus.

DE MUYNCK, DAVID A; Charles H Roth HS; Rush, NY; (Y); 1/210; Ski Clb; Im Bsbl; Var Crs Cntry; Var Capt Tennis; Bausch & Lomb Sci Awd; High Hon Roll; Jr NHS; NHS; Spanish NHS; Val; NYS Regnts Schlrshp 85; ACS Cntst Fnlst 84; Harvard Bk Awd 84; Rochester Inst Tech; Micro Elec.

DE NEUFVILLE, CAROL; Grand Island HS; Grand Island, NY; (Y); 12/325; Sec Church Yth Grp; Ski Clb; School Musical; Variety Show; Sec Trs Stu Cncl; Var Crs Cntry; JV Trk; High Hon Roll; NHS.

DE OLIVEIRA, WANDA; South Shore HS; Brooklyn, NY; (Y); Church Yth Grp; Dance Clb; School Musical; Htlh & Phy Educ 85; Pace U; Bus.

DE ORAZIO, DIANA; Seton Catholic Central HS; Binghamton, NY; (Y); Cmnty Wkr; Key Clb; Service Clb; Chorus; School Musical; Nwsp Stf; Yrbk Bus Mgr; Yrbk Phtg; Yrbk Stf; Art Clb; Awd For Excllnce In Vol Svc 85; Broome Cmnty Coll; Bus Mgt.

DE PALMA, KATHLEEN; St Edmund HS; Brooklyn, NY; (S); Hon Roll; Jr NHS; NHS; Scholar Soph Yr 83; Gen Merits Biol Eng II Chem & Soc Studies 83-84; NY U; Vet.

DE PALMA, PETER M; Pittsford Mendon HS; Pittsford, NY; (Y); VP Sr Cls; Rep Stu Cncl; Im Bsktbl; JV Ftbl; Var Golf; Hon Roll; Ntl Merit Ltr; St Schlr; SUNY Albany; Law.

DE PASQUALE, GINA; The Ursuline Schl; Eastchester, NY; (Y); 63/129; Dance Clb; Key Clb; Yrbk Stf; JV Bsktbl; JV Coach Actv; Im Socr; JV Sftbl; Im Swmmng; Im Trk; JV Vllybl; Natl Merit Fndtn 85; E Carolina U; Intr Dsgn.

DE PAULO, LEIGH ANN; Haverling Central HS; Bath, NY; (S); 9/140; Sec Exploring; French Clb; FTA; Mathletes; Chorus; Nwsp Ed-Chief; Yrbk Phtg; Rep Stu Cncl; High Hon Roll; NHS; Syracuse U; Lang Educ.

DE PELLEGRINI, LORRIE A; Holy Trinity HS; Levittown, NY; (S); 26/362; Camera Clb; Drama Clb; Math Clb; School Musical; School Play; Variety Show; Ed Nwsp Rptr; Ed Yrbk Phtg; Stu Cncl; High Hon Roll; Soc Dstngshd Amer HS Stu 83-84; St Johns; Engl.

DE PENA, JUAN; Nazareth Regional HS; Brooklyn, NY; (Y); Aud/Vis; CAP; Math Clb; Math Tm; Science Clb; Concert Band; JV Crs Cntry; JV Trk; Var Wrstlng; Embry-Riddle Aerntcl U; Engr.

DE PIETRO, JOHN; Cicero-North Syracuse HS; N Syracuse, NY; (Y); JV Golf; Im Socr; Psych.

DE PROSSINO, FRANCES; Bishop Kearney HS; Brooklyn, NY; (Y); Bowling; Trk; Prfct Atten Awd; Trvl.

DE PUY, ROBERT; Alexandria Bay Central HS; Alexandria Bay, NY; (Y); Bsbl; Bsktbl; Ftbl; Hon Roll; Prfct Atten Awd.

DE RIGGI, CATHERINE; Queen Of The Rosary Acad; Wantagh, NY; (Y); Art Clb; Computer Clb; Debate Tm; Drama Clb; Service Clb; School Musical; School Play; Nwsp Rptr; Nwsp Stf; Yrbk Stf; Niagara U; Htl, Rsrtrnt Mgmt.

DE RISO, ELLEN M; St Francis Prep; Howard Beach, NY; (Y); 47/690; Art Clb; Office Aide; PAVAS; Service Clb; Nwsp Rptr; Nwsp Stf; Im Sftbl; Im Vllybl; High Hon Roll; Hon Roll; Prospective Mem Of Natl Hnr Society; Italian Natl Hnr Society; BA.

DE RITIS, ANTHONY PAOLINO; Islip HS; Islip, NY; (Y); Art Clb; Chess Clb; Mathletes; Chorus; Jazz Band; Orch; School Musical; School Play; High Hon Roll; Jr NHS; Am Leg Cert Schl Awd 83; Long Island Trnng Orch Scholar 80-86; Lndscpe Archit.

DE ROBERTIS, ROSALBA; Half Houow Hills West HS; Dix Hls, NY; (Y); 129/361; Church Yth Grp; Spanish Clb; Chorus; School Play; Cheerleading; Socr; Twrlr; High Hon Roll; Hon Roll; Spanish NHS; Italian Hnr Soc; Italian Clb; Pol Sci.

DE ROBERTS, LYNN; Cicero North-Syracuse HS; Brewerton, NY; (S); 58/711; JV Capt Cheerleading; Capt Powder Puff Ftbl; Hon Roll; NHS; Albany ST U; Acctg.

DE ROSA, BETH; Gloversville HS; Gloversville, NY; (Y); French Clb; Yrbk Bus Mgr; Yrbk Stf; Rep Stu Cncl; Cheerleading; Powder Puff Ftbl; Vllybl; Hon Roll.

DE ROSA, KAREN M; Smithtown High School West; Smithtown, NY; (Y); 81/500; Yrbk Stf; Hon Roll; Pres Schlr; St Schlr; NY ST Regents Schlrshp 85; Suny At Oneonta; Engrng.

DE ROSA, MICHELLE; The Knox Schl; Port Jefferson, NY; (S); 5/28; Art Clb; Math Clb; Spanish Clb; Bowling; Gym; Socr; Sftbl; Swmmng; Tennis; High Hon Roll; Yale; Comp Sci.

DE RYCKE, KIM; Fairport HS; Fairport, NY; (Y); Chorus; Yrbk Stf; Capt Cheerleading; Var L Diving; Prfct Atten Awd; Accntng.

DE SANTIS, DANIEL; Bellport SR HS; Brookhaven, NY; (S); DECA; FBLA; Rep Frsh Cls; Sec Jr Cls; Rep Sr Cls; Stu Cncl; Suffolk Cnty DECA Winner 85; Art Exhib 83; Bus.

DE SANTIS, LORI; St Joseph By The Sea HS; Staten Island, NY; (Y); Teachers Aide; Rep Frsh Cls; Rep Soph Cls; Rep Stu Cncl; Hon Roll; Busnss Admin.

DE SILVA, JUDITH; New Dorp HS; Staten Island, NY; (Y); French Clb; VP Pres Intnl Clb; Office Aide; Yrbk Stf; French Hon Soc; Hon Roll; Prfct Atten Awd; NYU; Bus Adm.

DE SIMONE, LYNN; Mount St Joseph Acad; Buffalo, NY; (S); 3/60; Church Yth Grp; Chorus; School Musical; Stage Crew; Rep Stu Cncl; Score Keeper; Hon Roll; NHS; Ntl Merit Ltr; Regl Acad Awd 83; Canisius Coll; Med.

DE SOLA, MICHAEL; Fordham Preparatory Schl; Yonkers, NY; (Y); Key Clb; Rep Frsh Cls; Rep Soph Cls; Pres Sr Cls; JV Bsbl; JV Bsktbl; Var Golf; Var Tennis; Hon Roll; Ntl Ltn Exam Awd; Gen Excllnc.

DE SORBO, ANTONY; Haverling HS; Bath, NY; (S); French Clb; Math Clb; Red Cross Aide; Band; Concert Band; Mrchg Band; Symp Band; Pres Frsh Cls; Pres Soph Cls; Pres Jr Cls.

DE SORBO, MARY; Colonie Central HS; Albany, NY; (Y); 7/473; Cmnty Wkr; Hosp Aide; Intnl Clb; Variety Show; Yrbk Stf; High Hon Roll; Hon Roll; NHS; Cert Merit Childs Hosp Volun 83; Dentistry.

DE SOUSA, CHRISTINE; Mineola HS; Mineola, NY; (Y); 66/257; Cmnty Wkr; French Clb; Hosp Aide; JV Bowling; Socr; Rgnts Prof Ed Nrsng Schlrshp 85; Wmns Auxl Hlth Career Schlrshp 85; Nassau Comm Coll; Nrsng.

DE SOUSA, DIANE; Schoharie Central Schl; Schoharie, NY; (S); 4/82; Church Yth Grp; Hosp Aide; Band; Sec Frsh Cls; Sec Jr Cls; L Socr; L Trk; Stat Wrstlng; Hon Roll; Acad All-Amer 84; Nrs.

DE SOUSA, PATRICIA; Acad Of St Joseph; Kings Park, NY; (Y); Church Yth Grp; Hosp Aide; Band; Church Choir; High Hon Roll; Hon Roll; Applctn & Endeavor Awd Frnch 84-85; Child Study.

DE STEFANO, CHRISTOPHER A; Deer Park HS; Deer Park, NY; (Y); Am Leg Boys St; Art Clb; Boy Scts; Acpl Chr; Chorus; School Musical; Lit Mag; Bowling; High Hon Roll; NHS; Eagle Sct 85; Court Hnr 85; Frgn Lang Poster 1st Pl 83; Ordr Of Arrow BSA 83; Cooper Union; Comm Art.

DE STEFANO, JAMES; Valley Stream Central HS; Valley Stream, NY; (Y); Ski Clb; School Play; Variety Show; VP Frsh Cls; Var Bsbl; Var Capt Ftbl; JV Lcrss; High Hon Roll; Hon Roll; NHS.

DE STENO, DAVID; Highland HS; Highland, NY; (Y); 1/150; Dance Clb; Quiz Bowl; Spanish Clb; Yrbk Stf; High Hon Roll; Jr NHS; NHS; Ntl Merit Ltr; Spanish NHS; Bst Acad Achv Awd In Englsh 85; NE Rgnl Fin In Soph Fig 85; Natl Sci.

DE TOUCHE, AMELIA C; Dominican Commercial HS; Jamaica, NY; (Y); Art Clb; Church Yth Grp; Rep Soph Cls; Siena Clb Hnr 82-85; Sr Ftns USA AAHPERD Awd 85; Comp.

DE TRAGLIA, LORI; Lansingburgh HS; No Troy, NY; (Y); Camp Fr Inc; French Clb; JA; Yrbk Stf; Bowling; Hon Roll; Jr NHS; NHS; Local 452 Labor Un 85-86; V Ltr Plaque 85; Siena Coll; Comp Sci.

DE VANTIER, ROBERT; Niagara Wheatfield SR HS; Niagara Fls, NY; (Y); Church Yth Grp; Var L Bsbl; High Hon Roll; Hon Roll; NHS; 1st Annual Acd Convctn Acad Awd 85; Top 5 PSAT 84; All Star Bsbl Tm 85; U Of Buffalo; Accntng.

DE VAUL, VIRGINIA; East Syracuse-Minoa Central HS; Kirkville, NY; (Y); 50/338; DECA; Science Clb; Band; Concert Band; Mrchg Band; Variety Show; Hon Roll; NHS; Regents Schlrshp 85; SUNY-ALBANY; Hosp Admin.

DE VELASCO, GUSTAVO; Msgr Mc Clancy HS; Astoria, NY; (Y); Camera Clb; Nwsp Rptr; Yrbk Phtg; Pres Stu Cncl; NHS; Spanish NHS.

DE VERA, DAVID; La Salle Acad; New York, NY; (S); 3/250; Yrbk Stf; Rep Frsh Cls; Rep Soph Cls; Rep Jr Cls; Rep Sr Cls; Rep Stu Cncl; Hon Roll; Pres NHS; Incertive Awd 85; USAA 84-85; Usnmla 84-85; NY Y; Comp Sci.

DE VERNA, RAE; Wantagh HS; Wantagh, NY; (Y); 46/291; Library Aide; Scholastic Bowl; Bowling; High Hon Roll; NHS; Intnl Clb; Yrbk Stf; Hon Roll; Mechncl Drwg Awd 83; SR Awd Meritros Stu 85; Farmingdale U; Bus.

DE VINE, HOLLEY LYNN; Waverly JR SR HS; Waverly, NY; (Y); Band; Chorus; Concert Band; Madrigals; Mrchg Band; Stu Cncl; Elmira Bus Inst; Med Off Asst.

DE VIRGELES, KELLY; Tupper Lake Central HS; Tupper Lake, NY; (Y); 11/104; Pep Clb; Spanish Clb; Im Bsktbl; Var Socr; Hon Roll; NHS; Mercy Hlthcare Cntr Guild 85; Dennis J Palmer Mem Hgh Schltc Avg 85; Rena Proulx Frmr Mem Alt 85; SUNY Potsdam; Psych.

DE VITO, DAMON; La Salle Institute Of Troy HS; Troy, NY; (Y); 2/76; Church Yth Grp; ROTC; Service Clb; Nwsp Rptr; Yrbk Stf; Pres Sec Stu Cncl; Bsbl; Bsktbl; Coach Actv; Capt Golf; U Of PA; Bus.

DE VITO, SINA; Bishop Kearney HS; Brooklyn, NY; (Y); Hosp Aide; Library Aide; Political Wkr; Rep Jr Cls; Hon Roll; NHS; Cmmnctns.

DE VITO, WILLIAM; Saint Francis Prep; Bayside, NY; (S); 90/693; Drama Clb; Hon Roll; NHS; Am Leg Awd; Karate Clb; Weight Lftng; Med.

DE WATERS, LYNN; Churchville Chili SR HS; Spencerport, NY; (Y); Exploring; JCL; Yrbk Stf; Wrstlng; High Hon Roll; Hon Roll; Lab Technen.

DE WITT, JENNIFER; Moravia Central HS; Skaneateles, NY; (Y); Church Yth Grp; French Clb; Pep Clb; Service Clb; Church Choir; Trk; Hon Roll; Hotel Mgt.

DE WITT, JOHN; Alden Central HS; Alden, NY; (Y); 17/198; Science Clb; Hon Roll; Ntl Merit SF; NYS Regents Scholar 85; Alden Employees Assn Scholar; Rochester Inst Tech; Comp Engr.

DE WITT, MICHAEL; Alden Central HS; Alden, NY; (Y); Aud/Vis; French Clb; Teachers Aide; Hon Roll; Jr NHS; Pres Schlr; Amer Lgn Soc Studies Awd 85; George Washington U; Intl Rltns.

DE WYSOCKI, JACQUELINE; Fox Lane HS; Pound Ridge, NY; (Y); Cmnty Wkr; Church Choir; Concert Band; Jazz Band; Pep Band; School Musical; Hon Roll; Church Yth Grp; Drama Clb; Band; Feat Perf Cmmuty Play 83-84; Outstndng Muscal Ablty Awd 84-85; Engl.

DE YOUNG, DAWN NOEL; Shenendehowa HS; Clifton Pk, NY; (Y); Church Yth Grp; Drama Clb; Chorus; Church Choir; Orch; Swing Chorus; High Hon Roll; Hon Roll; NHS; Central Coll; Music Ed.

DE ZUTTER, CHARLES; Webster SR HS; Webster, NY; (Y); 51/537; French Clb; VP JA; Math Tm; Quiz Bowl; French Hon Soc; High Hon Roll; Jr NHS; Ntl Merit Ltr; Ntl Merit Spcl Schlrshp 85; Marshall Hahn Engrng Merit Schlrshp 85; VA Tech; Aerosp Engrng.

DEACONS, HEATHER; Solvay HS; Syracuse, NY; (Y); Exploring; Hosp Aide; Pres Soph Cls; Pres Jr Cls; Var Socr; Var Vllybl; Hon Roll; Mu Alp Tht; Chorus; Rep Frsh Cls; MVP Awd Vllybl Tourn 84-85; Shrthd Awd Ave Abov 90; ESG Vllybl 84; Sci.

DEAMER, JILL; Catholic Central HS; Troy, NY; (S); 25/203; Nwsp Rptr; Nwsp Stf; VP Stu Cncl; JV Var Cheerleading; Score Keeper; High Hon Roll; Hon Roll; Jr NHS; Trs NHS; Ntl Merit Schol; JC Of Albany; Nrs.

DEAN, APRIL; Herbert Lehman HS; Bronx, NY; (Y); Church Yth Grp; Yrbk Stf; Cheerleading; Ophelia De Vorer Schl Of Charm 85; Psych Club; Penn ST; Psych.

DEAN, CHARLES; A P W Centran HS; Williamstown, NY; (Y); Pres Church Yth Grp; Debate Tm; 4-H; Pres Quiz Bowl; Concert Band; Mrchg Band; Trk; Wt Lftg; Wrstlng; Rochester Bus Inst; Bus Mgmt.

DEAN, COLLEEN; Cooperstown HS; Cooperstown, NY; (Y); 8/100; GAA; Hosp Aide; Yrbk Bus Mgr; Yrbk Phtg; Off Soph Cls; Sec Jr Cls; Sec Sr Cls; Crs Cntry; Vllybl; NHS; Cross Mem Awd Engl 85; Clark Schlrshp 85; Regents Schlrshp 85; Cornell; Bio.

DEAN, DAWN M; Naples Central Schl; Naples, NY; (Y); 2/68; VP Concert Band; Mrchg Band; School Musical; School Play; Yrbk Ed-Chief; Yrbk Stf; Socr; Tennis; High Hon Roll; NHS; Tchr Of Yr Awd 85; Mth Awd 85; Pres Acad Fit Awd 85; Hamilton Coll; Psych.

DEAN, DONNA; Skaneateles Central HS; Skaneateles, NY; (Y); 19/165; Sec Church Yth Grp; Hosp Aide; Church Choir; Nwsp Rptr; Nwsp Stf; Ed Lit Mag; Tennis; High Hon Roll; Ntl Merit Ltr; Mony Schlstc Art Awds 82-85; Skaneateles Tchrs Assn Schlrshp 85; Houghton Coll; Math.

DEAN, MICHELLE; Vestal SR HS; Vestal, NY; (Y); Church Yth Grp; FBLA; German Clb; Hosp Aide; Off Jr Cls; Score Keeper; Swmmng; Hon Roll; 1st Pl Impromptu Spkng 85; Busnss.

DEAN, NADIA; Norman Thomas HS; Bronx, NY; (S); 13/676; Computer Clb; Trs FBLA; Math Tm; Hon Roll; NHS; 3rd Essay Cntst 84; 1st, 3rd Ctywid Comp 85.

DEAN, ROBIN; Webutuck Central HS; Millerton, NY; (Y); FBLA; Ski Clb; Spanish Clb; Chorus; Bsktbl; Gym; Twrlr; Vllybl; Lgl Sctry.

DEANGIOLETTI, STEPHEN; Smithtown West HS; Smithtown, NY; (Y); Art Clb; Boy Scts; Camera Clb; German Clb; Band; Nwsp Stf; Lit Mag; Var Crs Cntry; Hon Roll; NHS; Eagl Sct 85; Germn Hnr Socty 85; Sci.

DEAR, SUSAN JEANETTE; Midwood HS; Brooklyn, NY; (Y); 63/605; Church Yth Grp; Chorus; Church Choir; Madrigals; Variety Show; Lit Mag; Trk.

DEATON, HOLLY; Bishop Ludden HS; Liverpool, NY; (Y); Camp Fr Inc; Church Yth Grp; Cmnty Wkr; Office Aide; Chorus; Church Choir; Yrbk Stf; JV Bsktbl; CYO Schlrshp; Franciscan Grant; Maria Regina Coll.

DEATON, SHERRI; Bishop Ludden HS; Liverpool, NY; (Y); Church Yth Grp; Office Aide; Chorus; Boy Scts; Yrbk Stf; Hon Roll; Art Gold Key Awd Blue Ribbon 84-85; Folk Grp Dedication 83-84; CYO Schlrshp/Franciscan Grand 84-85; Maria Regina Coll; Liberal Arts.

DEAUGUSTINE, PHILIP; Fairport HS; Faiport, NY; (Y); Ski Clb; JV Bsbl; JV Ftbl; Prfct Atten Awd; Sprts Med.

DEAY, JODI; Bishop Scully HS; Amsterdam, NY; (Y); Cmnty Wkr; Computer Clb; Exploring; 4-H; JA; Ski Clb; Yrbk Stf; Gym; Sftbl; Vllybl; Fltn-Mntgmry CC; Erly Cldhd Ed.

DEBALD, ANDREA; St Francis Prep; Bayside, NY; (Y); 24/693; Hosp Aide; Office Aide; Yrbk Stf; High Hon Roll; Hon Roll; NHS; Bio Sci.

DEBELLIS, CLAUDIO; H F Ccarey HS; Franklin Sq, NY; (Y); 36/225; Boy Scts; Church Yth Grp; Cmnty Wkr; Computer Clb; Exploring; Hosp Aide; JA; NFL; Science Clb; Ski Clb; Med.

DEBIEN, DOUGLAS; Massena Central HS; Massena, NY; (Y); Band; Concert Band; Drm & Bgl; Jazz Band; Mrchg Band; Symp Band; David Houlihan Percussion Awd 85; MCHS Bnd Improvement Awd 85; Crane Schl Music; Music.

DEBNAR, TRACEY; Binghamton HS; Binghamton, NY; (Y); Drama Clb; Pep Clb; Chorus; School Musical; Booster Clb Awd Outstndg SR 85, Excllnc Drama 84; Drama Clb Awd Dedctn Schl Musicl 84; Allentown Coll; Actg.

DEBONO, DAN P; Northport HS; Northport, NY; (Y); 32/650; Variety Show; Nwsp Bus Mgr; Yrbk Stf; Rep Jr Cls; Lcrss; Socr; NHS; Church Yth Grp; Cmnty Wkr; Computer Clb; Civil Law Champ; Bus Comp Rnnr Up; US Naval Acad; Engrng.

DEBYAH, KELLY; Franklin Academy HS; Constable, NY; (Y); Church Yth Grp; 4-H; Hon Roll; Adv Keybrdng Stu Yr 84-85; Epsilon; Mdl Abv Avr Yr 84-85; Lgl Secy.

DEBYAH, MELISSA; Franklin Academy HS; N Bangor, NY; (Y); 9/277; Drama Clb; 4-H; French Clb; NFL; Speech Tm; Thesps; School Play; Hon Roll; Jr NHS; NHS; Franklin Cnty Dairy Princss 85; Mary Flanagan Memrl Schlrshp 85; CO Aero Tech; Aviatn.

DECARCIOFALO, PHILOMENA; Fowler HS; Syracuse, NY; (Y); French Clb; JA; Latin Clb; Office Aide; Pep Clb; Yrbk Stf; Cheerleading; NHS; Binghamton U; Nrs.

DECARLO, ERIC; Millbrook Center HS; Pleasant Valley, NY; (Y); Cmnty Wkr; Computer Clb; Drama Clb; Ski Clb; Chorus; Var Crs Cntry; Var Trk; Hon Roll; JC Awd; Natl Sci Olympiad Chem 85; Hghst Cls Avg Gen Sci 82-83; Comp Sci.

DECESARE, TERESA; De Sales HS; Lockport, NY; (Y); 9/47; Nwsp Rptr; Lit Mag; Var Capt Cheerleading; Capt Sftbl; High Hon Roll; Lion Awd; NHS; Ntl Merit Ltr; Rotary Awd; Francis & Agnes Schisheimer Memrl Schlrshp 84; U Of Buffalo; Pharm.

DECHICK, CAROLYN; Munderse Acad; Seneca Falls, NY; (Y); 39/140; Csmtlgy.

DECICCO, VINCENT L; Rocky Point HS; Rocky Point, NY; (Y); 21/189; Church Yth Grp; VP German Clb; JV Bsbl; Var L Trk; Hon Roll; De La Roche Schlrshp 85-86; Suffolk Cty Math Cont 84-85; Int Trck Rnng Clb 84-85; St Bonaventure U; Pre-Med.

DECINA, PETER DANIEL; Nyack HS; Valley Cottage, NY; (Y); 14/255; Spanish Clb; Lit Mag; Rep Sr Cls; JV Var Bsbl; Bsktbl; Ftbl; JV Var Wrstlng; High Hon Roll; NHS; Pres Schlr; Angel Del Rio Medl 85; J L Tillnghast Memrl Awd 85; Schlrsh Fund Awd 85; Iona Coll; Bus.

DECK, MARY M; Mt St Mary Acad; Williamsville, NY; (Y); Computer Clb; Chorus; High Hon Roll; Hon Roll; NEDT Awd; Its Academic Tm 82-85; Math.

DECKER, BRENDA LYNN; Mynderse Acad; Seneca Falls, NY; (Y); 43/140; Band; Concert Band; Jazz Band; Mrchg Band; Orch; Pep Band; School Musical; Yrbk Stf; Hon Roll; Outstndng NYSMA Awd 84; All Cty Jazz Concert Band 84-85; Most Imprvmnt Band 85.

DECKER, CHRISTIAN A; Pine Bush HS; Pine Bush, NY; (Y); VP Pres Church Yth Grp; NY ST Rgnts Schlrshp 84-85; Orange County CC; Socl Studies.

DECKER, DAWN; Prot Jervis HS; Huguenot, NY; (Y); 5/180; Cmnty Wkr; Key Clb; Varsity Clb; Trk; High Hon Roll; Hon Roll; Jr NHS; NHS; Crmnl Just.

DECKER, ELLEN; Keveny Memorial Acad; Wynantskill, NY; (S); Cmnty Wkr; JA; Service Clb; Pres Soph Cls; Sec Jr Cls; Score Keeper; High Hon Roll; U S Bus Ed Awd 85; Natl Bus Hnr Soc 84.

DECKER, EMILY S; Fairport HS; Fairport, NY; (Y); 60/600; Model UN; Pep Clb; Yrbk Phtg; Socr; Hon Roll; Sec Soph Cls; NYS Regents Schlrshp 85; Empire ST Games Alpine Skiing 83-85; All Cnty Soccer & Skiing 85; U Denver; Engrng.

DECKER, GINA M; East Aurora HS; West Falls, NY; (Y); 37/182; Stage Crew; Rep Frsh Cls; Rep Soph Cls; Rep Soph Cls; Rep Sr Cls; Hon Roll; JETS Awd; NYS Regents Schlrshp 85; Geneseo ST U; Comm.

DECKER, JAMES M; Eldred Central Schl; Barryville, NY; (Y); 2/43; Varsity Clb; Nwsp Ed-Chief; Pres Stu Cncl; Var L Bsbl; Var L Crs Cntry; Var L Trk; High Hon Roll; Trs NHS; Sal; Boy Scts; Hugh O Brian Yth Fndtn Outstndng Soph; Schlr Athlete Awd; Regnts Schlrshp; Lake Forest Coll; Engl.

DECKER, JIM; Portledge Schl; New Hyde Park, NY; (S); Pres Math Clb; School Play; Pres Jr Cls; Pres Sr Cls; Rep Stu Cncl; Var Capt Bsktbl; Var Lcrss; Var Socr; Hon Roll; Mu Alp Tht; Mat Excllnt Awd; Drama Awd; Schlrshp Hardwood Islnd Bio Stn ME; Bus.

DECKER, JOY; Warwick Valley Central HS; Warwick, NY; (Y); 48/201; FBLA; High Hon Roll; Hon Roll; FBLA Cert Apprectn 85; Tops Invest Cert Comptn 85; Sec.

DECKER, KARL; Valley Central HS; Montgomery, NY; (Y); 42/370; Boy Scts; Camera Clb; Church Yth Grp; Debate Tm; Var L Crs Cntry; Var L Trk; NHS; Beta Tau 84; Gold Medal Empire ST Games Javelin 85; Law.

DECKER, KATHLEEN; Queensbury HS; Glens Falls, NY; (Y); French Clb; Key Clb; Varsity Clb; Band; Yrbk Sprt Ed; Sec Stu Cncl; Var Swmmng; NHS; Ntl Merit Ltr; Math Clb; Zonta Clb Schlrshp 85; Clarkson U; Elec Engrng.

DECKER, KATHY; New Paltz HS; New Paltz, NY; (Y); 36/134; Yrbk Phtg; Yrbk Stf; Rep Soph Cls; Rep Sr Cls; Fld Hcky; Score Keeper; Oneonta; Jrnlst.

DECKER, MARLA; Salamanca Central HS; Salamanca, NY; (S); 23/127; Trs French Clb; GAA; Model UN; Ski Clb; Chorus; Rep Jr Cls; Trs Stu Cncl; Var L Bsktbl; Var L Cheerleading; Var Capt Crs Cntry; Grls Vrsty Trck & Crss-Cntry MVP 83 & 85; Pre-Law.

DECKER, MARY; Washingtonville HS; Washingtonville, NY; (Y); 4-H; Cheerleading; Ntl Merit Ltr; Aqwd Merit Pres Carter 82; Am Red Cross Hnry Awd 82; Acctng.

DECKER, SANDRA; Sherburne-Earlville HS; North Norwich, NY; (S); 6/138; Drama Clb; Band; Chorus; Concert Band; Mrchg Band; School Play; JV Capt Cheerleading; Var Capt Vllybl; Hon Roll; NHS; NYSSMA Music Awd 82; All-Cnty Band 82; Hartwick; Eng.

DECKER, TINA; Benjamin Franklin HS; Rochester, NY; (Y); FBLA; JA; Chorus; School Play; Swing Chorus; Variety Show; Nwsp Rptr; Nwsp Stf; Cheerleading; Gym; 4th Pl Comp At Greece Athena FBLA 85; Bus.

DECKMAN, CURTIS; Olean HS; Olean, NY; (Y); 28/192; Radio Clb; Ski Clb; Chorus; Yrbk Phtg; Var L Tennis; Hon Roll; NHS; Cmnctns.

DECOSTE, TRACY; Northeastern Clinton Central Schl; Mooers Forks, NY; (Y); Key Clb; Model UN; Bowling; Mth.

DECRESCENZO, VINCENT; Sachem HS; Lake Grove, NY; (Y); 55/1365; Jazz Band; Symp Band; Trk; NHS; NYS Regents Schlrshp; Colgate U.

DEDEE, MICHAEL; Bishop Karney HS; Rochester, NY; (Y); Letterman Clb; Varsity Clb; Rep Frsh Cls; Rep Soph Cls; Rep Jr Cls; Tennis; Vllybl; Hon Roll; Prfct Atten Awd; Aud/Vis; Mst Outstndng Athlte 85; Sctn V Vllybl & League Champs 83 & 85; Mgt.

DEDERER, JULIE A; F D Roosevelt HS; Hyde Park, NY; (Y); 25/325; Ski Clb; Band; Flag Corp; Ed Yrbk Stf; Var Socr; Capt Var Vllybl; Hon Roll; NHS; Homecoming Queen 84; NY ST Regents Schlrshp 85; Lehigh U; Business.

DEDRICK, AMY; Keveny Memorial Acad; Troy, NY; (S); Computer Clb; Spanish Clb; Band; Concert Band; Mrchg Band; School Musical; Yrbk Stf; High Hon Roll; Hon Roll; Jr NHS; NHS; St Rose Coll; Music Engr.

DEDYO, PAUL; Irvington HS; Irvington, NY; (Y); Ski Clb; Acpl Chr; Chorus; Bsktbl; Crs Cntry; Ftbl; Golf; Hon Roll; Area All ST Choir 85; Med.

DEEGAN, STACEY L; Huntington HS; Huntington, NY; (Y); 43/433; Church Yth Grp; Political Wkr; Chorus; Kiwanis Awd; NHS; Band; Church Choir; Hon Roll; Jr NHS; Presdntl Schlrshp For Lenoir Rhyn Coll 85; Belovd Queen Of Truth Triangle 83; ST Essay Cont For Tri; Lenoir-Rhyne Coll; Deaf Educ.

DEEGHAN, KATHY; Clinton Central HS; Clinton, NY; (Y); Church Yth Grp; Mrchg Band; Yrbk Stf; Trs Stu Cncl; Var Bsktbl; Var Socr; Var Sftbl; High Hon Roll; Hon Roll; Jr NHS; Outstndg Stu 84; MVP-ALL Star-Soccer 82-85; Most Impvd-Bsktbl-Vrsty 82; Math.

DEEKS, KIMBERLY A; West Senca West SR HS; West Seneca, NY; (Y); 1/543; Church Yth Grp; Mathletes; Q&S; Church Choir; Nwsp Ed-Chief; JC Awd; NHS; Ntl Merit Ltr; Prfct Atten Awd; Val; Rensselaer Awd 84; Taylor U; Comp Sci.

DEELY, GREGORY; Clarkstown South HS; New City, NY; (Y); Varsity Clb; Band; Concert Band; Jazz Band; Mrchg Band; Symp Band; Trk; Jr NHS; Pres Phys Ftns Awd 83-84; Elect Engrg.

DEERE, KELLY; Brentwood Sonderling HS; Brentwood, NY; (Y); 3/625; Debate Tm; Math Tm; Yrbk Stf; VP Soph Cls; VP Jr Cls; Pres Sr Cls; Rep Stu Cncl; Im Badmtn; High Hon Roll; NHS; Newsday High Hnrs Cmptn 85; Regnts Schlrshp 85; Mock Trl 85; Cornell U; Neurosci.

DEERKOSKI, JIM; Mattituck HS; Mattituck, NY; (Y); 6/120; 4-H; German Clb; Mathletes; Math Tm; Office Aide; Variety Show; High Hon Roll; Hon Roll; Jr NHS; NHS; Engrng.

DEERY, DARLENE; Thomas A Edison HS; Horseheads, NY; (Y); 25/84; Church Yth Grp; FNA; Hosp Aide; Church Choir; Drill Tm; Mrchg Band; Variety Show; Yrbk Stf; Var Trk; Capt Twrlr; Mst Imprvd Banner Twrlr 82; Outstndng Bann Twrlr 84-85; Med Sec.

DEETER, THERESA; Niagara Catholic HS; Niagara Falls, NY; (Y); Rep Soph Cls; Stat Badmtn; Var Bsktbl; Score Keeper; Var Sftbl; JV Var Vllybl; French Clb; Hosp Aide; Bus.

DEFALCO, SCOTT J; Lake George HS; Cleverdale, NY; (Y); 2/80; Am Leg Boys St; Math Tm; Lit Mag; Rep Frsh Cls; Rep Soph Cls; Rep Jr Cls; Rep Sr Cls; Rep Stu Cncl; Var Ftbl; Im Vllybl; Worcester Polytech Inst; Engrng.

DEFAYETTE, MELANIE; Saranac Central HS; Cadyville, NY; (S); 5/131; Var Capt Bsktbl; Var Capt Socr; Var Capt Sftbl; Pres NHS; SUNY; Data Proc.

DEFAZIO, JODY; Canastota HS; Canastota, NY; (Y); Cmnty Wkr; Drama Clb; Sec GAA; Girl Scts; Hosp Aide; Intnl Clb; Trs Leo Clb; Science Clb; Varsity Clb; Band; Commnctns.

DEFAZIO, MELANIE; St Peters High Schl For Girls; Staten Island, NY; (Y); Church Choir; Cheerleading; Gym; High Hon Roll.

DEFELICE, SUSAN M; Niagara Wheatfield HS; Niagara Falls, NY; (Y); 53/315; Drama Clb; French Clb; Pep Clb; PAVAS; Chorus; School Musical; Rep Stu Cncl; Hon Roll; NHS; Prfct Atten Awd; Niagara Wheatfield Acad Hnr Awd 82-85; NY ST Regents Schlrshp 85; NY ST Coll Fredonia; Bus Adm.

DEFENDORF, DARIN A; Moravia Central HS; Moravia, NY; (Y); 3/109; Am Leg Boys St; Ski Clb; Pres Sr Cls; Var Bsbl; Var Bsktbl; Var Ftbl; High Hon Roll; U S Air Force Adac; Pilot.

DEFILLIPO, NATALIE; West Hempstead HS; W Hempstead, NY; (Y); Key Clb; Sec Y-Teens; Rep Jr Cls; Var Badmtn; Var Bowling; Var Swmmng; Var Tennis; Hon Roll; Prfct Atten Awd; Psych.

DEFIO, GINA; West Genesee SR HS; Camillus, NY; (Y); Band; Concert Band; Jazz Band; Mrchg Band; Orch; Pep Band; School Musical; Symp Band; Var JV Mgr(s); Capt JV Swmmng; Syracuse Symph Yth Orch 84-85; All ST Wind Ensmbl 84; All Cnty; Music.

DEFONTE, CHRISTINE; Bishop Kearney HS; Brooklyn, NY; (Y); Library Aide; Hon Roll; 2nd Hnrs 83-84; Brooklyn Coll; Ed.

DEFOREST, LYNNE; Clarkstown H S South; New City, NY; (Y); Mrchg Band; Var Fld Hcky; Var Capt Lcrss; Coaches Awd La Crosse 84; Bus.

DEGMI, RICHARD; H Frank Carey HS; Franklin Sq, NY; (Y); 29/221; Art Clb; Yrbk Sprt Ed; Off Frsh Cls; VP Soph Cls; Pres Jr Cls; Pres Sr Cls; JV Bsktbl; Advrtsng.

DEGREGORY, DYANE; Shoreham-Wading River HS; Shoreham, NY; (Y); Art Clb; English Clb; Art Schl; Fash.

DEGUTIS, CHRISTOPHER; Amsterdam HS; Amsterdam, NY; (Y); 14/335; Concert Band; Jazz Band; Mrchg Band; Pep Band; Yrbk Stf; Rep Stu Cncl; Var Capt Swmmng; Var Capt Tennis; High Hon Roll; NHS; NY ST Rgnts Schlrshp 85; U S Military Acad; Elec Eng.

DEHAQUIZ, CLAUDINE; Tottenville HS; Staten Island, NY; (Y); Church Yth Grp; Library Aide; Teachers Aide; Orch; Socr; Timer; Hon Roll; Jr NHS; J L Hopkins Fndtn Potry/Art Awd 2nd Pl 83; Arch.

DEHAVEN, KARIN; Liverpool HS; Liverpool, NY; (S); Church Yth Grp; Exploring; German Clb; Library Aide; Teachers Aide; Concert Band; Stage Crew; Ed Lit Mag; Jr NHS; NHS; Syracuse U; Aero Engrng.

DEIBEL, ANN MARIE; St John The Baptist; Islip, NY; (Y); Church Yth Grp; Hosp Aide; Nrsng.

DEJESUS, AUDREY; Clara Barton HS; Brooklyn, NY; (Y); Dance Clb; FBLA; Office Aide; Variety Show; Yrbk Stf; Off Sr Cls; Stu Cncl; Prfct Atten Awd; School Play; United Hosp NY Vlntr Svc 85; Cprtn Gvrnmnt Cert Rcgntn 85; Mdcl Asst Cert 85; Borough Coll; Optmtst.

DEL BIANCO, JOHN; Beacon HS; Beacon, NY; (Y); 15/160; Nwsp Rptr; Hon Roll; NHS; Prfct Atten Awd; Frncs Mc Nair Schlrshp 85; Schell Athltc & Acadmc Ftns Awds 85; Dutchess CC; Comm.

DEL CARPINE, JOANNE; Sleepy Hollow HS; Tarrytown, NY; (Y); 16/166; Sec Drama Clb; Chorus; Orch; Var Capt Cheerleading; High Hon Roll; NHS; Ntl Merit Schol; Acpl Chr; School Musical; School Play; Mst Distngshd Musicn Awd 85; All Cnty ST Eastrn Chrs 84-85; Westchester Arts Prog 83-85; SUNY Purchase; Music.

DEL DUCO, STEVEN J; Somers Central HS; Yorktown Heights, NY; (Y); 25/213; Yrbk Sprt Ed; Off Stu Cncl; Bsktbl; JV Ftbl; Golf; JV Wrstlng; High Hon Roll; Hon Roll; St Schlr; Soc Stds Clb 82-84; Fairleigh Dickinson U, NYS Regnts Schlrshps 85; Villanova; Elec Engr.

DEL GAUDIO, CRAIG M; Shoreham Woding River HS; Wading River, NY; (Y); Am Leg Boys St; Camera Clb; Varsity Clb; Lit Mag; Var Socr; JV Tennis; Film Mkg.

DEL GROSSO, ANN MARIE; Commack HS; Commack, NY; (Y); Cmnty Wkr; Hosp Aide; Chorus; Yrbk Phtg; High Hon Roll; Hon Roll; Commack Dist Art Fest Cert Hnr Besc Photgrphy; Lib Arts.

DEL MONICO, MICHELE L; Linton HS; Schenectady, NY; (Y); 4/297; Ed Yrbk Stf; Capt L Socr; Capt L Sftbl; Hon Roll; NHS; Bucknell U.

DEL MONTE JR, EDWARD J; Port Chester SR HS; Port Chester, NY; (Y); #1 In Class; Am Leg Boys St; Key Clb; Spanish Clb; Thesps; School Play; Im JV Bsbl; Var Golf; Mu Alp Tht; NHS; Spanish NHS; HOBY Awd 83; Duracel Sci Fnlst 82; Engrng.

DEL NEGRO, CHRISTINE M; John Joy HS; Pound Ridge, NY; (Y); Church Yth Grp; Hosp Aide; Nwsp Stf; Cit Awd; Gov Hon Prg Awd; High Hon Roll; NHS; Ski Clb; Band; School Musical; NYS Rgnts Schlrshp 85; Outstndng Achvt Engl & Comptrs 82 & 84; Engl.

DEL NEGRO, SUSAN; Albertus Magnus HS; Garnerville, NY; (Y); 55/190; Drama Clb; Service Clb; School Musical; Var Socr; JV Capt Vllybl.

DEL ROSSO, ANTONIA; Northport HS; Northport, NY; (Y); 13/646; Cmnty Wkr; Political Wkr; Band; Drm & Bgl; Var L Fld Hcky; High Hon Roll; NHS; Ntl Merit SF; Cornell Natl Schlr 85; Hnrs Art Stu 85; Mech Drwng & Archit Des Awd 84-85; Cornell U; Archit.

DEL SIGNORE, CINDY; Cicero-North Syracuse HS; N Syracuse, NY; (S); 27/622; Church Yth Grp; JA; Trs Jr Cls; Rep Stu Cncl; Capt Cheerleading; Score Keeper; JV Var Socr; Hon Roll; Prfct Atten Awd; Bus Admin.

DEL SIGNORE, MARLA; Grand Island HS; Grand Is, NY; (Y); 14/280; Drama Clb; Hosp Aide; Trs Chorus; Madrigals; School Musical; Variety Show; L Swmmng; JP Sousa Awd; NHS; Ntl Merit Ltr; Grand Isl PTSA Acad Achvt Awd 81-85; U Chicago; Lib Arts.

DEL TORO, BRIAN J; Northport HS; East Northport, NY; (Y); 246/646; Yrbk Stf; Lit Mag; Frsh Cls; Stu Cncl; Arts Recgtn & Tlnt Srch 84; I Love NY Postr Cont 84; Congssnl Art Comp 83-84; Fine Arts.

DEL VALLE, ALEXANDRA; Aqinas HS; New York, NY; (Y); 13/178; Cmnty Wkr; Dance Clb; French Clb; Science Clb; Chorus; School Musical; School Play; Hon Roll; Jr NHS; NHS; Attndnc Awd 83; Home Rm Svc Awd 84; JR Acad Excell Awd 85; St Johns U; Pre-Med.

DEL VALLE, ANGEL; All Hallows HS; Bronx, NY; (Y); 6/33; Dance Clb; Math Clb; Stage Crew; Crs Cntry; Trk; Vllybl; High Hon Roll; Hon Roll; Ntl Merit Ltr; Prfct Atten Awd; Iona Coll; Teachr.

DEL VECCHIO, DIANE; Lafayette HS; Brooklyn, NY; (Y); Band; Yrbk Stf; Lit Mag; Hon Roll; Jr NHS; Arista Arkon 84-85; Sci.

DEL VECCHIO, ROSEMARY; East Syracuse-Minoa HS; Syracuse, NY; (Y); 98/360; Hon Roll; Prfct Attndnc Awd 81-84; Ntl Hnr Soc 82-85; Merit Hnr Rll 83-84; Canton ATC; Bus.

DELACEY, JAMES; Mt Pleasant HS; Schenectady, NY; (Y); Boy Scts; Cmnty Wkr; Drama Clb; School Musical; Wt Lftg; Wrstlng; Hon Roll; NHS; Ntl Merit Ltr; Peer Ldrshp Awd 84-85.

DELACORTE, MARK; Storm King HS; Cornwall, NY; (S); 3/29; Concert Band; High Hon Roll; Pres NHS.

DELAMATER, EDWARD; Connetquot HS; Ronkonkoma, NY; (Y); 52/726; Boy Scts; Exploring; Band; Concert Band; Mrchg Band; Symp Band; VP Jr Cls; Rep Sr Cls; Rep Stu Cncl; Bsbl; Engrng.

DELANCEY, HERBERT E; Bishop Ford Central Catholic HS; Newyork, NY; (Y); Boy Scts; Im Bsktbl; JV Var Socr; Hon Roll; Prfct Atten Awd; Hunter Coll; Comp Sci.

DELANEY, LORI; St Marys Academy; Troy, NY; (Y); 2/15; French Clb; Nwsp Stf; Yrbk Stf; Soph Cls; Cheerleading; Powder Puff Ftbl; High Hon Roll; Kiwanis Awd; NHS; Elem Ed.

DELANEY, SUZANNE; Baldwin SR HS; Baldwin, NY; (S); 36/503; Concert Band; Mrchg Band; Rptr Nwsp Stf; Rep Stu Cncl; High Hon Roll; Hon Roll; NHS; Schl Rep Wash Wrkshps 85; Awd Outstndng Yuth Proj 84; Band Awd 83; Tufts U; Pol Sci.

DELANS, W BRADLEY; Fayetteville-Manlius HS; Manlius, NY; (Y); Church Yth Grp; Political Wkr; Hon Roll; Cert Excllnc-Spnsh Awd 85; Syracuse U; Bus.

DELANY, MARK E; Skaneateles Central HS; Skaneateles, NY; (Y); Church Yth Grp; Cmnty Wkr; Red Cross Aide; Var Bsbl; Var Capt Bsktbl; Var Capt Ftbl; Var Lcrss; Wt Lftg; Hon Roll; All Lg Ftbl Awd 84-85; All Dist Awd Ftbl 84-85; All Lg Bsktbl Awd 84-85; Bus Adm.

DELARGY, GRETA; Wellington C Mepham HS; Merrick, NY; (Y); 46/385; Church Yth Grp; Lib Band; Concert Band; Mrchg Band; Orch; Badmtn; Bsktbl; Capt Vllybl; Hon Roll; NHS; US Army Rsrv Schlr/Athl Awd 85; Irving Leving Music Awd 85; Mepham PTA Math Awd 85; U Of SC; Crim Just.

DELAROSA, AWILDA; Nazareth Regional HS; Brooklyn, NY; (Y); Aud/Vis; JA; Latin Clb; Library Aide; Math Tm; Office Aide; Science Clb; Rep Stu Cncl; Capt Mgr(s); Sftbl; PA ST; Med.

DELCORVO, MARYELLEN; Cardinal Mooney HS; Rochester, NY; (Y); 112/293; Hon Roll; CCFL; Toursm.

DELEONARDO, GUY; Whitesboro Central Schl; Utica, NY; (Y); 3/315; Math Tm; High Hon Roll; Jr NHS; NHS; Opt Clb Awd; Rotary Awd; Regnts Schlrshp 85; Mohawk Valley CC; Engrng Sci.

DELEVAN, KELLY; Fredonia HS; Fredonia, NY; (Y); 20/188; GAA; Spanish Clb; Trs Frsh Cls; Var L Swmmng; High Hon Roll; Hon Roll; Spanish Exc Awd; Regents Schlrshp Wnnr; Law.

DELFOSSE, TRUDY; Walton HS; Bronx, NY; (Y); Regnts Schlrshp 85; Law.

DELGADO, CRISTINA; S T Gabriels HS; New Rochelle, NY; (Y); Drama Clb; Spanish Clb; Chorus; Yrbk Phtg; Yrbk Stf; Rep Frsh Cls; Hon Roll; Iona Coll; Med.

DELGADO, LISA; Bishop Kearney HS; Brooklyn, NY; (Y); Art Clb; Yrbk Stf; Hon Roll; Pace U; Mktng.

DELGADO, MARIA T; Beach Channel HS; Rockaway, NY; (Y); Cmnty Wkr; Computer Clb; FBLA; Chorus; Hon Roll; Sec Sci.

DELGADO, MARITZA; Cardinal Spellman HS; Bronx, NY; (Y); VP Church Yth Grp; Computer Clb; Latin Clb; Science Clb; Spanish Clb; 1st Hnrs, 2nd Hnrs; Acctng.

DELGAUDIO, ANNETTE; Cardinal Spellman HS; Bronx, NY; (Y); Computer Clb; JV Vllybl; Iona; Bus.

DELGIGANTE, ANTHONY; North Babylon HS; North Babylon, NY; (Y); FBLA; Spanish Clb; JV Bsbl; JV Ftbl; JV Var Ice Hcky; High Hon Roll; Hon Roll; Jr NHS; NHS; Med.

DELIA, CARMELA; Christ The King HS; Glendale, NY; (Y); Girl Scts; Red Cross Aide; School Play; Yrbk Stf; SUNY Stonybrook; Med.

DELINE, CHRISTINE; Wilson Central HS; Lockport, NY; (Y); FBLA; Girl Scts; Teachers Aide; VICA; Nwsp Rptr; Nwsp Stf; Pres Sr Cls; High Hon Roll; Hon Roll; Prfct Atten Awd; Occptnl Advsry Councl Outstndng Achvmnt Awd Data Prcssng 85; Cert Merit Assmbly ST NY 85; Bryant & Stratton Bus Inst; Sec.

DELL, KRISTI A; Bellport HS; East Patchogue, NY; (Y); 2/304; Church Yth Grp; Girl Scts; Orch; Nwsp Rptr; Var Tennis; Jr NHS; NHS; Sal; Var Bsktbl; Var Sftbl; Westnghs Sci Tlnt Srch 85; NY Regnts Schlrshp 85; Pre-Med.

DELL, MYRETTE; Far Rockaway HS; Far Rockaway, NY; (Y); 47/295; Church Yth Grp; 4-H; Hosp Aide; Library Aide; Chorus; Yrbk Stf; Trk; High Hon Roll; Hon Roll; NHS; SUNY Stonybrook; Med.

DELL OLIO, JAMES T; Garden City SR HS; Garden City, NY; (Y); 47/320; Am Leg Boys St; Church Yth Grp; Bsktbl; Var L Ftbl; Var L Lcrss; High Hon Roll; Jr NHS; NHS; La Crosse Tm NY ST Fnlst 85; Engrng.

DELLA MONICA, ANDREA; Bishop Kearney HS; Brooklyn, NY; (Y); 4/355; Nwsp Ed-Chief; Nwsp Rptr; Nwsp Stf; Lit Mag; Lion Awd; NHS; St Schlr; Cit Awd; High Hon Roll; Hon Roll; Thetablet Press Awd 84; Ntl Art Awd 84; Pres Acad Ftns Awd 85; LI U; Jrnlsm.

DELLA ROCCA, MICHELE; Bethpage HS; Bethpage, NY; (Y); 23/295; Teachers Aide; Var Fld Hcky; Var Trk; High Hon Roll; Pres NHS.

DELLA ROCCO, JEAN M; Mercy HS; Albany, NY; (Y); 7/65; Yrbk Stf; Lit Mag; JV Bsktbl; Var Sftbl; High Hon Roll; NHS; Coll St Rose Frshmn Acad Scholar 85; Coll St Rose; Art Ed.

DELLA-PERUTA, JOSEPH; Midwood High Schl Of Brooklyn College; Brooklyn, NY; (Y); 26/638; Am Leg Boys St; Boy Scts; Math Tm; Service Clb; Orch; Lit Mag; Arista Hnr Soc 85; Volntr Nrs Asst 85; Med.

DELLACAMERA, CHRISTOPHER; Roosevelt HS; Yonkers, NY; (Y); Camera Clb; Variety Show; Yrbk Stf; Pres Jr Cls; Pres Stu Cncl; Bsbl; Ftbl; Lcrss; Cit Awd; Gov Hon Prg Awd; Bus.

DELLAMORE, LESLIE; Liverpool HS; Liverpool, NY; (S); 131/873; AFS; VP Church Yth Grp; Girl Scts; JA; Coach Actv; Swmmng; Hon Roll; Jr NHS; NHS; Hnr Cert Vlntr Wk Comm 84.

DELLEA, LISA; Northeastern Clinton Central HS; W Chazy, NY; (Y); Art Clb; Pres Church Yth Grp; Girl Scts; Model UN; Teachers Aide; Chorus; School Musical; Stage Crew; High Hon Roll; Hon Roll; Hnr Cntrbtn Schl Thrgh Art Dept 84-85; Sunny Purchase; Art.

DELLER, MATTHEW J; Baldwin SR HS; Baldwin, NY; (Y); Am Leg Boys St; Aud/Vis; Pres Chess Clb; Drama Clb; Key Clb; Hon Roll; Ntl Merit SF; 1st VP Gen Org; Vrsty Archry, Riflry.

DELLERT, TODD; Charles O Dickerson HS; Trumansburg, NY; (Y); 3/90; Rptr Am Leg Boys St; Concert Band; Jazz Band; Mrchg Band; Pres Frsh Cls; Var L Bsbl; Var Capt Bsktbl; Var L Ftbl; High Hon Roll; NHS; Bio.

DELLES, LORRAINE; La Salle SR HS; Niagara Falls, NY; (S); 4/278; Church Yth Grp; Drama Clb; Thesps; Church Choir; School Musical; School Play; Stage Crew; Nwsp Stf; Hon Roll; NHS; Academic Achvmnt Awds 82-84; U Of Buffalo; Elec Engr.

DELLES, TAMMIE; Lawville Acad; Lowville, NY; (Y); 13/138; VP FTA; Spanish Clb; School Play; Yrbk Stf; Rep Jr Cls; Socr; Cit Awd; Hon Roll; NHS; Pres Schlr; ARC Chptr Of Chld Dvlmnt 85; SUNY Geneseo; Spec Ed.

DELMONTE, PAUL R; Pittsford-Mendon HS; Pittsford, NY; (Y); 31/285; Drama Clb; Nwsp Stf; Stu Cncl; Ftbl; Gym; Trk; High Hon Roll; NHS; VFW Awd; Air Force Acad; Military Pilot.

DELORENZO, MICHAEL D; Burnt Hills-Ballston Lake HS; Scotia, NY; (Y); 12/315; Aud/Vis; Political Wkr; Nwsp Rptr; Yrbk Stf; Lit Mag; High Hon Roll; Ntl Merit Ltr; Pres Schlr; Boy Scts; Engl Dept Medl Creatv Wrtng 85; 12 Vrsty Ltrs & 2 Vrsty Captnces Trk & Crs Cntry; Williams Coll; Pre-Med.

DELOZIER, JEANINE; Niskayuna HS; Scotia, NY; (Y); French Clb; Pep Clb; Mgr JV Bsktbl; Powder Puff Ftbl; Mgr Var Socr; JV Var Sftbl; NHS; Rensselaer Polytech; Bio Engr.

DELPRINCIPE, VICTORIA; St Catharine Acad; Bronx, NY; (Y); 9/205; Library Aide; Temple Yth Grp; Hon Roll; NHS; 2nd Hrs Iona Coll Lang Cntst Span 85; Trnsltr.

DELROSARIO, MARC; Valley Stream Central HS; Valley Stream, NY; (Y); Varsity Clb; Im Lcrss; Var Socr; All-Div Soccer Plyr 84-85; Engr.

DELUCA, CLAUDINE; Bishop Kearney HS; Brooklyn, NY; (Y); Hosp Aide; Speech Tm; Band; Orch; School Play; Off Frsh Cls; Off Soph Cls; Off Jr Cls; Stu Cncl; Hon Roll; All Borough Band & Orch 82-83; Publc Rltns.

DELUCA, GINA; Pelham Memorial HS; Pelham, NY; (Y); 51/177; Church Yth Grp; Cmnty Wkr; Dance Clb; Spanish Clb; Yrbk Stf; Pres Frsh Cls; Pres Soph Cls; Pres Jr Cls; Pres Sr Cls; Stu Cncl; Am Lgn Awd 85; Miss NY ST Teen Pgnt 3rd Rnnr Up 84; Rtry Clb Schlrshp-1st Pl Spch 85; Mnhttn Coll; Comm.

DELUCA, JOSEPH; Archbishop Molloy HS; Astoria, NY; (Y); 20/417; Bsktbl; NHS.

DELUCA, MICHELE; North Babylon SR HS; North Babylon, NY; (Y); Office Aide; Yrbk Sprt Ed; Var Sftbl; Hon Roll; Bus Admin.

DELVECCHIO, AMY; Aquinas Inst; Rochester, NY; (Y); 16/160; Church Yth Grp; Spanish Clb; Yrbk Stf; Rep Jr Cls; Stu Cncl; Im Capt Cheerleading; High Hon Roll; Hon Roll; Schlrshp Fres Yr 82; Schlrshp JR Yr 84; SUNY Fredonia; Tchg.

DELVECCHIO, ANTHONY E; Mount Saint Michael HS; New York, NY; (S); 21/308; High Hon Roll; Hon Roll; Engrng.

DELVECCHIO, GENNARO; John F Kennedy HS; Yorktown Heights, NY; (Y); Boy Scts; Camera Clb; Chess Clb; Computer Clb; JA; Science Clb; Stage Crew; Nwsp Stf; Wt Lftg; Hon Roll; Regnts Schlrshp; SUNY Binghamton; Comp Engr.

DELWO, KRISTI; Herkimer HS; Herkimer, NY; (Y); 1/128; Sec Drama Clb; School Musical; School Play; Yrbk Stf; VP Stu Cncl; Cheerleading; Gym; High Hon Roll; Trs NHS; Voice Dem Awd; Med.

DELY, CAROLE; West Hempstead HS; W Hempstead, NY; (Y); Library Aide; Ski Clb; Frsh Cls; Pom Pon; Hon Roll; Elem Ed.

DELZATTO, GLORIA M; St John The Baptist HS; Islip, NY; (Y); Church Yth Grp; Cmnty Wkr; Debate Tm; Hosp Aide; Library Aide; Office Aide; Service Clb; JV Var Tennis; High Hon Roll; Hon Roll; Bus Hnr Scty; Hofstra U; Comm.

DEMAIO, CHRISTINE G; Fontbonne Hall Acad; Brooklyn, NY; (Y); 44/140; Art Clb; Drama Clb; Library Aide; Stage Crew; Nwsp Rptr; Var Tennis; NHS; Schlrs Awd Hunter Coll; Fll Schlrshp Schl Visul Arts; Schlrshp NY U; Schl Visual Arts; Fine Arts.

DEMAIO, PATRICIA; St Edmund HS; Brooklyn, NY; (S); #21 In Class; Spanish Clb; NHS; Comrcl Art.

DEMAR, NINA; Westhampton Beach HS; E Quoque, NY; (Y); VP Latin Clb; Drill Tm; Yrbk Stf; Fld Hcky; Score Keeper.

DEMARCO, LAUREN; Bishop Kearney HS; Rochester, NY; (Y); Church Yth Grp; Ski Clb; Hon Roll; Rochester Inst Tech; Psych.

DEMARCO, THOMAS J; Bronx High School Of Science; Bronx, NY; (Y); Office Aide; Teachers Aide; NHS; Hstry.

DEMBECK, ANN MARIE; Warwick Valley HS; Pine Island, NY; (Y); 32/205; Sec Church Yth Grp; Cmnty Wkr; Trs 4-H; Church Choir; 4-H Awd; High Hon Roll; Hon Roll; Prfct Atten Awd; Girl Scts; Crtv Wrtng Awd; Church Serv Awds; Pace U; Soc Sci.

DEMBECK, JENNIFER; Washingtonvile HS; Rock Tavern, NY; (Y); Pres French Clb; Intnl Clb; Band; Concert Band; Pep Band; Yrbk Stf; Pres Stu Cncl; JV Socr; NHS; Bio.

DEMERS, KELLY; Skaneateles HS; Skaneateles, NY; (S); JV Var Bsktbl; Capt Var Socr; High Hon Roll; NHS; Band; Rep Frsh Cls; Rep Soph Cls; Rep Jr Cls; JV Sftbl; Var Trk; Soccer, Bsktbl & Track Awds 83-84; Ind Labr Rltns.

DEMESMIN, DOMINIQUE J; Sachem HS; Holbrook, NY; (Y); Yrbk Ed-Chief; Biol.

DEMETRIADES, RITSA; Archbishop Iakovos HS; Bayside, NY; (S); Church Yth Grp; Cmnty Wkr; Computer Clb; Girl Scts; Library Aide; Math Clb; Office Aide; Teachers Aide; Chorus; Church Choir; NY U.

DEMICK, DENISE; Berlin Central Schl; Stephentown, NY; (Y); 14/64; Ski Clb; Chorus; Yrbk Phtg; Mgr(s); Score Keeper; Socr; Vllybl; Lewis Memrl Schlrshp 85; Dykin Pond Envrnmntl Schlrshp 84; Plattsburgh St; Cmmnctns.

DEMICOLI, MARK; St John The Baptist HS; Massapequa, NY; (Y); 30/560; Boys Clb Am; Math Clb; Spanish Clb; Im Socr; High Hon Roll; Hon Roll; Spanish NHS; Villanova; Bus.

DEMIRJIAN, JANET; Christopher Columbus HS; Bronx, NY; (Y); Teachers Aide; Nwsp Rptr; Nwsp Stf; Cit Awd; Prfct Atten Awd; College; Comp Sci.

DEMMIN, DARLENE A; Wilson Central JR SR HS; Wilson, NY; (Y); 11/134; Am Leg Aux Girls St; 4-H; Science Clb; Band; School Play; Off Stu Cncl; Cheerleading; Hon Roll; Cntrl City Bus Inst, Regnts Schlrshps 85; Bus Mgt.

DEMONTE, JOANNE; Our Lady Of Perpetual Help HS; Brooklyn, NY; (Y); High Hon Roll; Hon Roll; St Johns U; Lawyer.

DEMORIZI, LIDIA R; Cardinal Spellman HS; Bronx, NY; (Y); Var L Swmmng; Var L Vllybl; French Clb; Girl Scts; Ski Clb; Teachers Aide; Church Choir; High Hon Roll; Hon Roll; St Schlr; Denison U; Bio.

DEMOURA, ANITA; Mt Vernon HS; Mount Vernon, NY; (Y); Spanish Clb; Teachers Aide; Hon Roll; Tchng.

DEMPSEY, JAMES W; St Anthonys HS; Kings Park, NY; (Y); Camera Clb; Cmnty Wkr; Chorus; Nwsp Rptr; Yrbk Phtg; Crs Cntry; Trk; NHS; Ntl Merit Ltr; Spanish NHS; AFROTC & Regnts Schlrshp 85-89; Tufts U; Elctrcl Engrng.

DEMPSTER, ZARIA M; Flushing HS; Flushing, NY; (Y); 75/364; Church Yth Grp; Color Guard; Orch; School Musical; Nwsp Stf; Yrbk Stf; Cheerleading; Socr; Vllybl; NHS; Natl Honor Roll 85; Luisa Uderhill Gold Medal-Physcl Fitness 85; MVP-SOCCER 85; St Johns U; Comptr Sci.

DEMSKE, PAULA; La Salle SR HS; Niagara Falls, NY; (S); 13/278; Sec Soph Cls; VP Jr Cls; Rep Stu Cncl; Hon Roll; NHS; Accntng.

DEMSKI, TANI; Hudson HS; Claverack, NY; (Y); Church Yth Grp; Band; Concert Band; Jazz Band; Mrchg Band; School Musical; Yrbk Stf; Tennis; Trk; Lion Awd; Columbia Greene CC; Music Ed.

DEMSKIE, ANDREW; Ellenville Central HS; Napanoch, NY; (Y); Cmnty Wkr; Stu Cncl; Var Ftbl; Var Trk; Hon Roll; Ulster Cnty CC; Acctg.

DEN BLEYKER II, NEIL; E Syracuse-Minca HS; E Syracuse, NY; (Y); Bsktbl; Im Vllybl; High Hon Roll; Hon Roll; Jr NHS; NHS; Dghtrs Clmbs Schlrshp Itln 3 Rgnts 85; Itln II Hnrs 84; Math.

DENAROSO, ENZO T; St Johns Prep; Greenpoint, NY; (Y); 83/415; Bsbl; Socr; Tennis; NHS; Queen Coll; Psych.

DENCENBURG, WHENDY; Dundee Central Schl; Tyrone, NY; (Y); Church Yth Grp; Chorus; High Hon Roll; Hon Roll; Gregg Typng Awd 84; Comp Oprtr.

DENEHAN, KIERAN; St Nickolas Of Tolentin; New York, NY; (Y); 9/139; Drama Clb; School Musical; School Play; Stage Crew; Capt Rep Frsh Cls; Pres Soph Cls; Capt Rep Jr Cls; Capt Rep Sr Cls; Capt Rep Stu Cncl; Im Bsktbl; Army ROTC Schlrshp 85; Alt Regnts Schlrshp 85; Partl Schlrshp-St Nicholas Of Tolentine 81; U Of Miami; Engr.

DENERO, JOSEPH A; Bishop Grimes HS; Syracuse, NY; (Y); Church Yth Grp; Band; Concert Band; Jazz Band; School Musical; NY Chiro Clg; Chiro.

DENESHA, STACY; Hermon De-Kalb Central HS; De Kalb Jct, NY; (S); 13/45; Drama Clb; Nwsp Rptr; Nwsp Stf; Yrbk Sprt Ed; VP Soph Cls; VP Jr Cls; Rep Stu Cncl; Var Bsktbl; Var Socr; Var Vllybl; Bus Admin.

DENHART, EVAN; Fox Lane HS; Bedford, NY; (Y); 130/280; Ski Clb; Nwsp Phtg; Yrbk Phtg; JV Var Bsktbl; JV Var Socr; Var Tennis; Vllybl; Empire ST Gms Vlybl 84-85.

DENICOURT, SCOTT; Potsdam HS; Potsdam, NY; (Y); 4/125; Pres French Clb; Letterman Clb; Rep Stu Cncl; JV Bsbl; JV Ftbl; Var L Ice Hcky; High Hon Roll; Hon Roll; CCT; Bio-Chem.

DENIS, MARCEL; Springfield Gardens HS; Laurelton, NY; (Y); 42/443; French Clb; Variety Show; Hon Roll; Prfct Atten Awd; (Y Polytchnc; Comp Sci.

DENISON, JODI; Madrid Waddington Central HS; Waddington, NY; (Y); 7/48; Drama Clb; French Clb; Spanish Clb; Chorus; Church Choir; School Musical; School Play; Yrbk Stf; Bsktbl; Mgr(s); St Lawrence Bank Of Madrid Schlrshp 85; Acadmc Achvt Awd; Canton ATC; Acctg.

DENK, ERIC; Seton Catholic Central HS; Binghamton, NY; (Y); Am Leg Boys St; Trs Service Clb; Band; School Musical; Crs Cntry; Mgr(s); Trk; Hugh O Brien Yuth Ldrshp Fdtn 84; CYO Bsktbl Cpt 84-85; Nespr Carier 81-83.

DENKENSOHN, SHERI N; Rondout Valley HS; Accord, NY; (Y); 5/199; 4-H; Band; School Musical; VP Soph Cls; JV Capt Bsktbl; Var Capt Fld Hcky; Stat Ftbl; Var Capt Trk; High Hon Roll; NHS; NYS Regents Schlrshp 85; Sunny Albany.

DENKEWITZ, PAUL; St Anthonys HS; Nesconset, NY; (Y); 22/282; Mrchg Band; High Hon Roll; Hon Roll; NHS; NY Inst Tech Scholar 85-86; NY Inst Tech; Arch.

DENKO, JULIE; Granville Central JR SR HS; Pawlet, VT; (S); 4/123; GAA; Var L Crs Cntry; Var L Trk; Elks Awd; High Hon Roll; NHS; Prfct Atten Awd; RPI Awd Math & Sci 85; VT ST Grange Ag Queen Rnnr Up 84; Psych.

DENMON, JOHN; Union Endicott HS; Endicott, NY; (Y); 40/420; Am Leg Boys St; Church Yth Grp; Rep Frsh Cls; Rep Soph Cls; JV Wrstlng; Hon Roll; Pres Schlr; SUNY Binghamton; Math.

DENNE, JODIE; North Collins Central HS; N Collins, NY; (Y); Girl Scts; Ski Clb; Chorus; Color Guard; School Musical; School Play; Stage Crew; Yrbk Phtg; Yrbk Stf; Stu Cncl; 1st Pl Hnrbl Ment Art Show 85; 2nd Pl Schl Art Show 85; Treas Yorker Clb 83-85; John Casa Blancas; Artist.

DENNEHY, TIM; Hilton Central HS; Rochester, NY; (Y); Church Yth Grp; JA; Ski Clb; Variety Show; Capt JV Bsktbl; Im Bowling; Var Ftbl; Im Socr; Im Sftbl; Im Swmmng.

DENNEY, LAURA; Eastridge HS; Rochester, NY; (Y); GAA; Chorus; School Musical; Hon Roll; Chem Engrng.

DENNEY, TAMMY; Canastota HS; Canastota, NY; (Y); VP Rptr FBLA; Color Guard; Mrchg Band; High Hon Roll; Hon Roll; Charles Kingsley Mem Awd 83-84; CCBI; Med Sec.

DENNIE, TREVOR; Gloversville HS; Gloversville, NY; (Y); 1/250; Math Tm; Nwsp Ed-Chief; JV Socr; Tennis; Ntl Merit Ltr; Brown U Area Alumni Awd; Ruth Craig Chem Awd; Writing.

DENNING, JULIE; Bolivar Central HS; Bolivar, NY; (Y); Chorus; Nwsp Rptr; Sec.

DENNIS, JODIE ANN; Roy C Ketcham HS; Poughkeepsie, NY; (Y); Art Clb; Spanish Clb; Hon Roll; Cheltenham Engl Art Coll; Art.

DENNIS JR, ROBERT A; Jericho HS; Jericho, NY; (Y); Ski Clb; Nwsp Rptr; Tennis; Var Trk; High Hon Roll; NCTE Awd; NHS; Ntl Merit Ltr; U Of PA Clb Of LI Awd For Outstndng Achvt 85; Bus.

DENNISON, CRAIG; Sutherland HS; Pittsford, NY; (Y); Boy Scts; Church Yth Grp; Exploring; Band; Mrchg Band; Stage Crew; Var Swmmng; Eagle Scout 84; Head Swim Team Assist 85; Hnr Carrier Of The Month & Hnr Carrier 84.

DENNISON, MICHELLE; Randolph Central HS; Randolph, NY; (Y); 3/69; VP Sec French Clb; Girl Scts; Trs Quiz Bowl; Ski Clb; Acpl Chr; Yrbk Stf; Var Cheerleading; Cit Awd; High Hon Roll; NHS; Ethel Matson Mem Schlrshp 85; Amer Legion Hist Awd 85; Enquirers Club Enlg Awd 83; Ithaca Coll; Law.

DENNY, CATHY; Alexandria Central HS; La Fargeville, NY; (Y); 6/50; FHA; Sec Frsh Cls; Sec Soph Cls; Var Bowling; Var L Socr; JV Sftbl; High Hon Roll; FHA; Mgr(s); Law.

DENNY, DARCINE A; Erasmus Hall HS; Brooklyn, NY; (Y); Math Clb; Math Tm; Bsktbl; Sftbl; Vllybl; Hon Roll; NY City Regnts Schlrshp; Arista, Sci Clb, Creatv Math & Sci; Cardlgst.

DENNY, DOUG; Holland Central Schl; Holland, NY; (Y); FFA; JV Bsktbl; JV Var Socr; JV Wrstlng; High Hon Roll; Jr NHS; NHS; 2nd Tm All Stars V Soccer 84-85; Math.

DENT, PETER; H S Of Fashion Industrs; Brooklyn, NY; (Y); 28/474; Capt Art Clb; Drama Clb; VP JA; School Play; Nwsp Stf; Yrbk Stf; Capt Vllybl; Hon Roll; Prfct Atten Awd; Alexander Mdl 85; United Fndtn Of Tchrs Awd 85; Josephine Lawrence Hopkins Fndtn Awd 85; PAL Awd 83; ST U Of NY; Psych.

DENTON, SUSAN; Mount Assumption Insti; Elizabethtown, NY; (Y); 27/84; Cmnty Wkr; Gym; Sftbl; High Hon Roll; Hon Roll; SUNY; Bus Adm.

DENTON, SUSAN E; Copiague HS; Lindenhurst, NY; (Y); 10/350; Computer Clb; FBLA; Sec German Clb; Hosp Aide; Math Tm; Yrbk Stf; NHS; Church Yth Grp; Math Clb; Band; Ntl Hnr Soc Serv Awd 85; Pres Acad Ftnss Awd 85; Geneva Coll Hnr Schlrshp 85; Geneva Coll; Accntng.

DENYSENKO, NINA; West Irondequoit HS; Rochester, NY; (Y); 47/300; Church Yth Grp; Cmnty Wkr; Girl Scts; Intnl Clb; Model UN; Acpl Chr; Chorus; Nwsp Rptr; Cit Awd; Hon Roll; Intl Reltns.

DENZ, MARY A; St Marys HS; Amherst, NY; (S); 14/185; Computer Clb; Political Wkr; Nwsp Rptr; Hon Roll; NHS; WNY BEAWNY Typg Cntst 1st Pl Elec 83-84; Awd Top Typg Stdnt 83-84; RIT; Comp Prog.

DENZLER, STEVEN; M S G R Farrell HS; Staten Island, NY; (Y); 50/294; Boy Scts; Computer Clb; JA; Science Clb; Yrbk Stf; Rep Soph Cls; Capt Bowling; Twrlr; Hon Roll; Prsdntl Acad Ftnss Awd 85; 1st Hnrs 82-85; SUNY Buffalo; Comp Engrng.

DEON, PAULA M; Brushton Moira Central HS; Moira, NY; (Y); #20 In Class; Hosp Aide; Band; Concert Band; Mrchg Band; School Play; Mgr(s); Score Keeper; Stat Sftbl; Stat Vllybl; Rgnts Schlrshp 85; Canton; Nrsng.

DEONARINE, MARINA M; Norman Thomas HS; Hollis, NY; (S); 10/671; Math Tm; Band; Hon Roll; NHS; Prfct Atten Awd; Gov Comm Schlstc Achvt Awd 82; Cert Perf Music 82; NY U; Acctng.

DEPALMA, KATHRYN; Southside HS; Rockville Ctr, NY; (Y); GAA; Hosp Aide; Key Clb; Varsity Clb; Chorus; Crs Cntry; Trk; Mrktng.

DEPESA, BARBARA; Herbet H Lehman HS; Bronx, NY; (Y); 7/473; Office Aide; Teachers Aide; Bowling; Sftbl; Cit Awd; Hon Roll; Educ.

DEPRA, DEBORA C; Rome Free Acad; Rome, NY; (Y); 11/532; VP Church Yth Grp; Intnl Clb; Office Aide; Pep Clb; Yrbk Ed-Chief; Rep Stu Cncl; Bsktbl; Cheerleading; Hon Roll; NHS; NCA All Amer Chrldr 84; Bsktbll Coachs Awd 83; NY U; Chem.

DEPRA, EMILY; Rome Free Acad; Rome, NY; (Y); Pres Church Yth Grp; Trs Drama Clb; Pep Clb; Teachers Aide; Drill Tm; Stage Crew; Yrbk Stf; Sec Frsh Cls; Rep Stu Cncl; Hon Roll; Tchng.

DEPTULA, CARYN; Bishop Grimes HS; Syracuse, NY; (Y); Hosp Aide; Band; Concert Band; Yrbk Ed-Chief; Var Cheerleading; Gym; Timer; Trk; Hon Roll; NHS; Music Awd 85; Ntl Hnr Soc 84-85; Chrldng 1st Cntywde Comptn 84-85; Lbrl Arts.

DEPUY, KELLY A; Holy Trinity HS; East Meadow, NY; (S); 7/315; Math Clb; Ski Clb; Varsity Clb; Nwsp Stf; Coach Actv; Var Socr; High Hon Roll; Ntl Merit Ltr; NEDT Awd; All Lg Socr; Adelphi; Med.

DERACO, CHRISTINE; Vestal Central SR HS; Vestal, NY; (Y); 47/450; Church Yth Grp; Cmnty Wkr; VP Spanish Clb; Teachers Aide; Rep Jr Cls; Rep Stu Cncl; High Hon Roll; Jr NHS; NHS; Ntl Merit Ltr; Jessie Baker & Margorie Perry Schlrshps 85; Natl Hnr Rll Yrbk 85; SUNY-CORTLAND; Erly Scndry Ed.

DERELLA, MICHAEL; Mohawk Central Schl; Mohawk, NY; (S); 11/102; Pres French Clb; Model UN; Mrchg Band; JV Var Bsktbl; JV Var Ftbl; High Hon Roll; Hon Roll; NHS; Acad M Awd 83-84; Jrnlsm.

DERHAM, SUZANNE; Skaneateles HS; Skaneateles, NY; (S); 31/165; Drama Clb; Orch; Yrbk Stf; Hon Roll; NHS; Broome Comm College; Dental Hyg.

DERITO, MICHAEL; Elmira Free Acad; Elmira, NY; (Y); Church Yth Grp; Spanish Clb; Rep Frsh Cls; Rep Soph Cls; Rep Jr Cls; Rep Sr Cls; Rep Stu Cncl; Bsktbl; Var Capt Socr; Var Capt Trk; Htl Mgmt.

DERK, JENNIFER K; Batavia SR HS; Batavia, NY; (Y); 23/245; Ski Clb; Teachers Aide; Yrbk Ed-Chief; Rep Soph Cls; Rep Jr Cls; Sec Stu Cncl; Score Keeper; Hon Roll; NHS; Gannett Rochester Yth Cares Awd 83-84; Acdmc All-Amer; Ntl Ldrshp Awd; Geneseo; Elem Ed.

DERKACH, DAWN M; St John Villa Acad; Staten Island, NY; (Y); 13/134; Cmnty Wkr; Chorus; School Musical; School Play; Variety Show; Yrbk Stf; DAR Awd; Hon Roll; Acad Schlrshp 85; Achvt Trig 84; Achvt Amer Hist 84; Wagner Coll.

DERKS, DEBRA; Newark SR HS; Newark, NY; (Y); Church Yth Grp; Latin Clb; Varsity Clb; Variety Show; L Var Crs Cntry; L Var Socr; L Var Trk; Hon Roll; Coachs Awd Outdr Trk 85; JR Olympcs Hgh Jmp Trk 85; Lat Natl Hnr Soc 83-85; Soc Wrk.

DERME, ERIN; Kenmore East SR HS; Tonawanda, NY; (Y); Drama Clb; Intnl Clb; PAVAS; Chorus; School Musical; School Play; Nwsp Rptr; Ed Yrbk Stf; JV Tennis; Theatre.

DERMODY, ELIZABETH; Bishop Ludden HS; Camillus, NY; (S); Church Yth Grp; Exploring; Intnl Clb; Spanish Clb; School Musical; Trk; Var Capt Vllybl; High Hon Roll; NHS; Spec Home Ec Awd; Cert Awd Spnsh; Vrsty Lttrs Vllybl; Nazareth Coll; Spch Path.

DEROSA, MARGARET; Hoosick Falls Central Schl; Hoosick Falls, NY; (Y); Church Yth Grp; Drama Clb; School Musical; School Play; Off Stu Cncl; Hon Roll; NHS; Yth Rep Parish Cncl 84-86.

DEROSA, ROBERT J; Patchoque-Medrod HS; E Patchogue, NY; (Y); 7/700; Rep Frsh Cls; Rep Soph Cls; Rep Jr Cls; Rep Sr Cls; Var Ftbl; Var Trk; Hon Roll; Jr NHS; NHS; Rotary Awd; Engrng Hnrs Schlrshp 85; George Wshngtn U; Engrng.

DEROSIER, KATHARINE; St Hildas & St Hughs HS; New York, NY; (Y); Cmnty Wkr; Dance Clb; Pep Clb; Chorus; School Play; Nwsp Rptr; Yrbk Stf; Lit Mag; Rep Jr Cls; Stu Cncl; 3rd Pl Cngrssnl Art Cntst 85; Jrnlsm.

DEROUCHIE, MARC; Massena Central HS; Massena, NY; (Y); Var Ice Hcky; Im Vllybl; All Trnmnt Team JV Hockey 84; Empire ST Hockey Team 85; Jr Select Hockey Camp Col Sprgs.

DEROY, DENISE; South Shore HS; Brooklyn, NY; (Y); Girl Scts; Office Aide; Hon Roll.

DERRENBACHER, JAMES R; Dansville Central HS; Dansville, NY; (Y); Am Leg Boys St; Letterman Clb; Band; Yrbk Stf; Ftbl; Swmmng; Trk; Wt Lftg; NHS; Ntl Merit Ltr; Phy Thrpy.

DERUSHIA, KELLY; Lisbon Central HS; Heuvelton, NY; (S); 3/50; Aud/Vis; Chess Clb; Computer Clb; Debate Tm; French Clb; Yrbk Stf; Trs Frsh Cls; Trs Soph Cls; High Hon Roll; NHS; Whiz Quiz Team 83-85; Aeronautical Engr.

DERYLAK, SUSAN M; East Aurora HS; E Aurora, NY; (Y); 2/182; AFS; Band; Jazz Band; Mrchg Band; Orch; Pep Band; School Musical; Ed Yrbk Stf; Hon Roll; Trs NHS; Elmira Coll Key Awd 84; U Rochester; Bio Chem.

DERZANOVICH, CHRISTINE; Seton Catholic Central HS; Binghamton, NY; (S); Church Yth Grp; Key Clb; Bsktbl; High Hon Roll; Jrnlsm.

DESAI, ANJALI; Roy C Ketcham SR HS; Wappingers Falls, NY; (Y); Drama Clb; Temple Yth Grp; Thesps; Yrbk Stf; High Hon Roll; Jr NHS; NHS; Sci Fair 3rd Pl 83; Bio Sci.

DESANCTIS, DAVID A; St Marys Boys HS; Manhasset, NY; (Y); Am Leg Boys St; Exploring; Letterman Clb; Ski Clb; Teachers Aide; Varsity Clb; Nwsp Rptr; Timer; Trk; Hon Roll; U S Naval Acad; Pilot.

DESANTO, FELICIA; St Catharines Acad; Bronx, NY; (Y); 105/205; Bsktbl; Sftbl; Acctng.

DESANTO, LISA; White Plains HS; White Plains, NY; (Y); Dance Clb; Drama Clb; Chorus; School Musical; Hon Roll; Dance Eductrs Of America-Ntl Dance Convntn; American Acad Of Dramatic Arts 84; Perfrmng Arts.

DESANTO, STEVEN; Newfield HS; Selden, NY; (Y); Sec Computer Clb; Science Clb; Ntl Merit SF; Sci.

DESCHAINES, SUZETTE; Franklin Delano Roosevelt HS; Staatsburg, NY; (Y); Hosp Aide; Office Aide; Dutchess CC; Bus.

DESEPOLI, KAREN; Smithtown High School East; Nesconset, NY; (Y); French Clb; Rep Soph Cls; Rep Jr Cls; Rep Stu Cncl; Var L Mgr(s); Var L Trk; French Hon Soc; High Hon Roll; NHS.

DESHANE, KRISTY; Norwood-Norfolk JR SR Centrl HS; Raymondville, NY; (Y); Church Yth Grp; Computer Clb; French Clb; Pep Clb; Chorus; School Musical; Powder Puff Ftbl; Twrlr; NCTE Awd; Hghst Av Soc II; Hghst Av Math 9; Canton ATC; Bus Admin.

DESIDERIO, RICIO I; Kings Park SR HS; Smithtown, NY; (Y); 31/445; Church Yth Grp; Dance Clb; Temple Yth Grp; Socr; Sftbl; High Hon Roll; Hon Roll; Jr NHS; St Schlr; Rgnts Schlrshp 85; Spnsh Awd 81; Renslr Schlrshp 85; Rensselaer Ply Inst; Comp Sci.

DESIR, JUDITH; Queen Of Rosary Acad; Freeport, NY; (S); Math Clb; Hon Roll; NHS; Chrstn Ldrshp Awd 81; Stu Svc Awd 81; Psych.

DESIR, TATIANA; Nazareth Regional HS; Brooklyn, NY; (Y); Church Yth Grp; Cmnty Wkr; GAA; Library Aide; Chorus; L Badmtn; Var Crs Cntry; Var Trk; Var Vllybl; Hon Roll; MVR Trck 83-85; U Of PA; Lwyr.

DESIRE, ZACHE; John Dewey HS; Brooklyn, NY; (Y); Church Yth Grp; French Clb; Math Clb; Service Clb; Teachers Aide; Band; Orch; Bsktbl; High Hon Roll; Val; 3rd Pl Mc Graw Hill Art Cont 84; Acad Of Finance 84-85; Daily New Supr Yth Of Yr Awd 84-85; Baruch; Fin.

DESJARDINS, MAURICE; West Seneca East SR HS; Cheektowaga, NY; (Y); Boy Scts; Cmnty Wkr; Exploring; Ski Clb; JV Var Ice Hcky; JV Var Socr; JV Trk; JC Awd; Jr NHS; Prfct Atten Awd; Archit.

DESLAURIER, COLLEEN M; Tottenville HS; Staten Island, NY; (Y); 53/843; Cmnty Wkr; Exploring; Key Clb; School Play; Nwsp Ed-Chief; Yrbk Stf; Lit Mag; High Hon Roll; Jr NHS; NHS; St Johns U Comp Schlrshp 85; St Johns U Schlstc Excell Schlrshp 85; Regents Schlrshp 85; SUNY-ALBANY; Bio.

DESMOINE, LUZ; Cathedral HS; Ny, NY; (Y); 61/298; Church Choir; Prfct Atten Awd; Concours De Francais Awd 85; Pre-Med.

DESORCIE, ALAINE M; Vestal SR HS; Apalachin, NY; (Y); 125/425; Church Yth Grp; Red Cross Aide; Color Guard; High Hon Roll; Hon Roll; Regents Schlrshp 85; St Josephs Schl Nrsng; Nrsng.

DESORCIE, MELINDA S; Au Sable Valley Central HS; Au Sable Forks, NY; (Y); 3/128; Church Yth Grp; Key Clb; VP Soph Cls; Trs Jr Cls; Pres Sr Cls; Sec Stu Cncl; Var Bsktbl; Var Socr; High Hon Roll; NHS; Siena Coll; Bio.

DESORMEAUX, MICHELLE; Berlin Central Schl; Stephentown, NY; (Y); GAA; Band; Chorus; School Musical; Swing Chorus; Yrbk Stf; Stu Cncl; Socr; Vllybl.

DESPOSITO, MARY L; Preston HS; Bronx, NY; (Y); #3 In Class; Yrbk Stf; High Hon Roll; Hon Roll; Berkley Bus Schl; Bus Mgmt.

DESSO, ALYSON L; Marcellus SR HS; Marcellus, NY; (Y); 11/164; Pres 4-H; School Musical; Off Sr Cls; Var Capt Vllybl; High Hon Roll; NHS; Church Yth Grp; Pres French Clb; Varsity Clb; Band; NY ST Regents Schlrshp 85; Cornell Tradition Frshmn Fllwshp 85; Cornell U; Clthng & Text Mgmt.

DESTEFANO, JOSEPH M; Valley Stream South HS; Valley Stream, NY; (Y); 14/178; AFS; Aud/Vis; Drama Clb; Science Clb; Ski Clb; Thesps; School Musical; School Play; Stage Crew; Yrbk Stf; NYS Regents Schlrshp 84-85; SUNY Binghamton; Psych.

DESTITO, MARIANNE; Rome Free Acad; Rome, NY; (Y); Church Yth Grp; Intnl Clb; School Play; Stat Bsktbl; Var JV Golf; Im Score Keeper; Im Timer; Im Capt Vllybl; NY ST Sctn III Golf Champ Tm Mbr 85; Mst Imprvd Awd For Rome Free Acad Grls Golf 84; Fine Arts.

DETEMPLE, DEIDREA; Glens Falls SR HS; Glen Falls, NY; (Y); Art Clb; Drama Clb; Chorus; School Musical; School Play; Stage Crew; Variety Show; Yrbk Ed-Chief; Yrbk Stf; Hon Roll; St Rose Coll Art Shw Excptnce 83-84; Prom Crt 84-85; Dsgnd Lk George Operata Clb Ckbk Covr 84-85; Parsons; Comm Art.

DETER, RAE ANN; Mynderse Acad; Seneca Falls, NY; (Y); 20/132; Band; Chorus; Concert Band; Drm Mjr(t); Jazz Band; Mrchg Band; Pep Band; School Musical; Rep Soph Cls; Stat Lcrss; Utica Coll; Occptnl Thrpy.

DETHOMASIS, ANNA; Rensselaer JR SR HS; Rensselaer, NY; (Y); DECA; Key Clb; Sftbl; Elem Tchr.

DETLEF, ALAN; Kenmore East SR HS; Tonawanda, NY; (Y); 81/350; Computer Clb; Math Clb; Im Bowling; Im Vllybl; Hon Roll; Jr NHS; NHS; NY ST U Buffalo; Comp Sci.

DETTMER, ROBERT; Mount Saint Michael Acad; Bronx, NY; (Y); 4/310; Pres Church Yth Grp; Rep Stu Cncl; Var L Bsbl; Var L Socr; High Hon Roll; Mt St Michael Acad Schlrshp 82-86; Pre Med.

DEVANE, CATHERINE; Preston HS; Bronx, NY; (S); 12/111; Cmnty Wkr; Drama Clb; English Clb; Chorus; School Musical; School Play; VP Jr Cls; Hon Roll; NHS; Ntl Merit Ltr; Cert Schvt Atngng Tona Coll 84; Ntl Soc Autisistic Child 83; Law.

DEVAY, SUSAN M; North Rose-Wolcott HS; N Rose, NY; (Y); 5/140; Cmnty Wkr; JA; Ski Clb; VP Spanish Clb; Teachers Aide; Chorus; Yrbk Stf; Rep Jr Cls; Sec Stu Cncl; Var Swmmng; Vrsty Ltr Swmmng 84; Elem Ed.

DEVER, DONALD J; Homer Central HS; Homer, NY; (Y); 75/200; Church Yth Grp; PAVAS; Band; Concert Band; Drm & Bgl; Mrchg Band; Stage Crew; Trk; Regents Schlrshp 85; Buffalo U; Physics.

DEVEREAUX, AMY; James L O-Neill HS; Highland Fls, NY; (Y); 15/121; Hosp Aide; Trs Jr Cls; Var Capt Crs Cntry; Var Capt Trk; High Hon Roll; Hon Roll; NHS; Church Yth Grp; Cmnty Wkr; French Clb; Mst Outstndng Bio Stu 83; Mst Outstndng Athl-Vrsty Trk 85; Pre-Med.

DEVIN, ERIN; Mount Mercy Acad; Orchard Pk, NY; (Y); Red Cross Aide; Ed Yrbk Ed-Chief; Rep Frsh Cls; Rep Soph Cls; Jr Cls; Trs Sr Cls; Var Socr; Var Tennis; Var Hon Roll; NHS.

DEVINE, EVA; St Agnes Cathedral HS; Massapequa, NY; (Y); 1/400; Orch; School Musical; Symp Band; Nwsp Rptr; High Hon Roll; NHS; NEDT Awd; Girl Scts; USDAN Cntr Prfrmng Arts Schlrshp 82 & 83; Psychlgy.

DEVINE, JAMES; Canastota HS; Canastota, NY; (Y); Church Yth Grp; Sec Trs Intnl Clb; VP Sec Leo Clb; Science Clb; Sec Trs Spanish Clb; Rep Frsh Cls; Var Trk; High Hon Roll; Hon Roll; Jr NHS; Phrmcy.

DEVITO, JOHN; John F Kennedy HS; Utica, NY; (Y); 3/130; Nwsp Sprt Ed; Nwsp Stf; JV Var Bsbl; Var Ftbl; High Hon Roll; Lion Awd; Varsity Clb; JV Var Bsktbl; Var Score Keeper; Hon Roll; Rookie Of Yr Awd-Am Legn Bsbll 84; Ntl Hnr Soc Inductns 84 & 85; Pre-Law.

DEVITO, MARYKATE; Mt Vernon HS; Mount Vernon, NY; (Y); Art Clb; Trs French Clb; Keywanettes; Spanish Clb; Band; Concert Band; Stage Crew; Lit Mag; Hon Roll; NHS; Boces Yng Author Conf; Mck Trl Tm Semifnlst 85; Ntl Hnr Soc 85.

DEVITO, MICHAEL; Machanicville HS; Mechanicville, NY; (S); 9/104; French Clb; Band; VP Frsh Cls; VP Jr Cls; Var Capt Bsktbl; High Hon Roll; NHS; Ski Clb; Rep Soph Cls; Rep Stu Cncl; Elec Engr.

DEVLIN, KAREN; Holy Trinity HS; Seaford, NY; (Y); 12/300; Drama Clb; School Musical; School Play; Pres Jr Cls; Twrlr; High Hon Roll; Hon Roll; NHS; NEDT Awd.

DEVLIN, LYNN; Lansingburgh HS; Troy, NY; (Y); French Clb; Hosp Aide; Sec Key Clb; Office Aide; Chorus; Yrbk Stf; Stu Cncl; High Hon Roll; Jr NHS; NHS.

DEVOE, JONATHAN J; Skaneateles Senior HS; Skaneateles, NY; (Y); Boy Scts; Drama Clb; Pres French Clb; Chorus; Orch; School Play; Swing Chorus; Rep Frsh Cls; Rep Soph Cls; JV Socr; NYSMA Solo A Rtng; Bus Mgmnt.

DEVOE III, ROBERT W; East Islip HS; E Islip, NY; (Y); Cmnty Wkr; Letterman Clb; Mathletes; Math Tm; Var JV Lcrss; Hon Roll; Prfct Atten Awd; 3rd Natl Labs Brdg Bldg Cntst 85; Bio Chem.

DEVOLE, LINDA; Wilson Central HS; Lockport, NY; (Y); Office Aide; Band; Chorus; Var L Trk; High Hon Roll; Hon Roll.

DEVONE, TRACY; Hempstead HS; Hempstead, NY; (S); 40/333; Church Yth Grp; Acpl Chr; Band; Chorus; Church Choir; Concert Band; Mrchg Band; School Musical; Rep Sr Cls; Hon Roll; Adephi U; Soc Wkr.

DEWEY, DAWN; Berne-Knox-Westerlo HS; Berne, NY; (Y); 4-H; Ski Clb; Stage Crew; Nwsp Rptr; Yrbk Stf; VP Soph Cls; Pres Jr Cls; Pres Sr Cls; Var Capt Bsktbl; Var Socr; MVP Vrsty Bsktbl Tm 84; JR Clss Prom Qn 85.

DEWEY, HELEN RUTH; Westhill SR HS; Syracuse, NY; (Y); 26/168; Capt Debate Tm; Sec Spanish Clb; Ed Yrbk Stf; JV L Cheerleading; Tennis; NHS; Spanish NHS; Dir General Bd Of Global Ministries 85-88; Dist Yth Cncl Pres 81-85; Conf Yth Cncl Secy, Treasr 81-85; CT Coll; Intl Affairs.

DEWEY, KATHERINE; Bishop Maginn HS; Albany, NY; (S); Latin Clb; Ski Clb; School Play; Nwsp Sprt Ed; Sec Jr Cls; Crs Cntry; Trk; NHS; Hugh O Brian Yth Fndtn Ldrshp Sem; Intl Frgn Lang Awd; Pre Med.

DEWEY, LISA ANNE; Fayetteville Manlius HS; Manlius, NY; (Y); 90/336; Swing Chorus; Trs Soph Cls; Capt Gym; Hon Roll; NHS; Pres Schlr; Cngrssnl Mdl Of Merit Awd Senator George Wortley 85; Cerebrl Palsy Dnce Marathn Chrprsn 84 & 85; UVM; Lib Art.

DEWEY, RICHARD; Bishop Maginn HS; Albany, NY; (S); 2/118; Latin Clb; Ski Clb; Pres Soph Cls; JV Bsbl; Var JV Ftbl; Var Tennis; High Hon Roll; NHS; Acad Al-Amer 83-84; Intl Frgn Lang Awd 83-84; Schl Latin Awd 83; Engr.

DEWITT, MARCIA J; Cairo-Durham HS; Leeds, NY; (Y); Ski Clb; Concert Band; Rep Sec Stu Cncl; Var Bsktbl; Var Sftbl; Var Tennis; Hon Roll; NHS; Church Yth Grp; Band; VP JR Natl Hnr Soc 82-83; Rep Greene Co Yth Bd Pres 84-85; Apptd NT ST Yth Cncl 85; Bio.

DEXTER, BRIAN; Holland Central HS; Strykersville, NY; (Y); Boy Scts; Sec Band; Jazz Band; Socr; Math.

DEY, DEBASTSH; George Washington HS; New York, NY; (Y); Science Clb; Hon Roll; NHS; SPICE 83; Entrnshp At The Columbia Presbytrn Med Chl 84-85; Cornell U; Engrng.

DEYETTE, MICHELLE; Shenedehowa HS; Round Lake, NY; (Y); Leo Clb; Varsity Clb; Chorus; Yrbk Stf; Rep Soph Cls; Jr Cls; Stat Bsktbl; Mgr(s); Score Keeper; Stat Sftbl; Citznshp & Vrsty Clb Awds 83 & 84; Ntl Hon Soc 85; Siena Coll; Acctng.

DEYLE, TRACY; Sperry HS; Henrietta, NY; (Y); Trs GAA; Sec Trs Ski Clb; Rep Soph Cls; Trs Jr Cls; Capt Socr; Sftbl; Capt Vllybl; Hon Roll.

DEYO, MARY E; Northern Adirondack Central; Altona, NY; (Y); Band; Chorus; Mrchg Band; Var Capt Cheerleading; Score Keeper; Var JV Vllybl; High Hon Roll; NHS.

DEZEEUW, MONIQUE M; Avon JR SR HS; Avon, NY; (Y); 10/102; Church Yth Grp; Drama Clb; Chorus; School Musical; School Play; Sec Frsh Cls; JV Cheerleading; Mgr(s); Score Keeper; Regents Schlrshp 85; Nazareth Col Rochester; Drama.

DEZSE, MARIA; Dominican Acad; New York, NY; (Y); Computer Clb; Latin Clb; Q&S; Science Clb; Ski Clb; Stage Crew; Nwsp Bus Mgr; Hon Roll; NHS; Prfct Atten Awd; Pre-Law.

DI BARI JR, PASQUALE; William Floyd HS; Mastic Beach, NY; (Y); 10/420; Am Leg Boys St; Church Yth Grp; Latin Clb; Concert Band; Lit Mag; Var L Crs Cntry; Var L Ftbl; Var L Trk; Var L Wrstlng; NHS; Sci.

DI BELLA, LORI A; H Frank Carey HS; Franklin Square, NY; (Y); 7/281; Church Yth Grp; Chorus; Concert Band; Pres Mrchg Band; Orch; Lit Mag; NHS; Ntl Merit SF; FBLA; Band; Gftd & Tlntd Prog 82-84; Forgn Lang Hnr Soc 83-84; Queens Coll; Music Ed.

DI BELLO, PAUL; Cicero-N Syracuse HS; N Syracuse, NY; (S); 1/622; Boy Scts; Exploring; Mathletes; Math Tm; VP Stu Cncl; JV Capt Bsktbl; Var Capt Ftbl; Var Capt Lcrss; High Hon Roll; Hon Roll; Acad All-Amer Ftbl 84-85; PA U; Chem.

DI BENEDELTO, KENNETH; V S Central HS; Valley Stream, NY; (Y); Hofstra; Accntng.

DI BERARDINO, LOUIS C; Rome Free Acad; Rome, NY; (Y); 129/536; Boy Scts; Debate Tm; Sec Speech Tm; Nwsp Rptr; Off Frsh Cls; Trk; Hon Roll; Jr NHS; NHS; Siena Coll; Intl Studies.

DI BLASIO, JEANNE; Ballston Spa HS; Ballston Spa, NY; (Y); 94/248; Ski Clb; Varsity Clb; Cheerleading; Gym; Hon Roll; Mt St Mary Coll; Nrsng.

DI CAIRANO, EMIDIO A; Mt Vernon HS; Mount Vernon, NY; (Y); Boys Clb Am; Boy Scts; Band; Concert Band; JV Var Socr; Hon Roll; Italian Awd 82; Merit Awd 82; Pres Phy Ftnss Awd 85; Sci.

DI CAPRIO, PATRICIA; Bishop Scully HS; Amsterdam, NY; (S); 6/75; French Clb; Math Clb; Yrbk Stf; Cheerleading; High Hon Roll; NHS; Russell Sage CollMATH.

DI CARLO, DEEANNE; Skaneateles HS; Skaneateles, NY; (S); 25/165; Drama Clb; School Musical; School Play; Stage Crew; Yrbk Stf; High Hon Roll; Hon Roll; NHS; Psych.

DI CARLO, MARGARET; Mt St Mary Acad; Buffalo, NY; (Y); 1/113; Hosp Aide; Pep Clb; Nwsp Rptr; VP Pres Stu Cncl; JV Capt Bsktbl; JV Capt Vllybl; High Hon Roll; NHS; Lit Mag; VP Soph Cls; Natl Sci Merit Awd 84; Wellsly Clg Ldrshp Schlrshp Awd 85; Amer Hist Awd Jr 85; Urbn Stud.

DI CESARE, DAVID; Eastridge HS; Rochester, NY; (Y); 24/250; Varsity Clb; Yrbk Stf; Bsbl; Socr; High Hon Roll; Hon Roll; Prfct Atten Awd; Comp Prog.

DI CESARE, NICOLE; Valley Central HS; Newburgh, NY; (Y); Church Yth Grp; Trs Debate Tm; Natl Beta Clb; Concert Band; Lit Mag; Stu Cncl; Capt Crs Cntry; Capt Trk; High Hon Roll; NHS; JR Olympc Natls Trk, Crs Cntry 82-84; NYSMA Awd Excllnt Flute 84; Natl Phys Fit Awd 82-83; SUNY Geneseo; Sec Ed.

DI CHRISTINA, MARIA; Frankfort-Schuyler Central School; Frankfort, NY; (S); 23/120; GAA; Spanish Clb; Rep Jr Cls; Sec Stu Cncl; Var Fld Hcky; Score Keeper; Var Sftbl; Var Capt Vllybl; High Hon Roll; Hon Roll; Winter Weekend Queen 85; Bus.

DI CICCO, SUSAN F; St Joseph-By-The Sea HS; Staten Island, NY; (Y); Nwsp Ed-Chief; Yrbk Stf; Rep Jr Cls; Rep Sr Cls; VP Stu Cncl; Stat Bsktbl; Var L Trk; Hon Roll; NHS; NEDT Awd; NY St Regnts Schlrshp 85; NY Gov Comm Schlstc Achvt Citatn 85; SUNY; Econ.

DI CIOCCIO, LINDA; Ossining HS; Ossining, NY; (Y); JV Bsktbl; Var L Sftbl; Hon Roll; Most Imprvd Spn Awd 85; All-Divsn Honrbl Mentn-Sftbl 85; Journlsm.

DI CLEMENTE, JEFFREY; Cicero N Syracuse HS; N Syracuse, NY; (S); 51/711; Boys Clb Am; Exploring; Mrchg Band; Nwsp Stf; Yrbk Phtg; Yrbk Stf; JV Score Keeper; L Swmmng; L Tennis; Hon Roll; Comp Engrng.

DI CUFFA JR, ALDO; Utica Free Acad; Utica, NY; (Y); Model UN; Spanish Clb; Nwsp Rptr; Stu Cncl; High Hon Roll; Hon Roll; NHS.

DI FIORE, ELENA; New Utrecht HS; Brooklyn, NY; (Y); JA; Key Clb; Math Tm; Science Clb; Nwsp Rptr; Nwsp Stf; Lit Mag; Cheerleading; High Hon Roll; NHS; Med Arts Clb 85; Arista 85; JR Acad 85; NY U; Jrnlsm.

DI FLAVIO, GINA; FrontierSR HS; Hamburg, NY; (S); #20 In Class; Church Yth Grp; French Clb; Varsity Clb; Jr Cls; Stu Cncl; Var Capt Bsktbl; Sftbl; High Hon Roll; Hon Roll; NHS.

DI FLORIO, VALERIE; Solvay HS; Solvay, NY; (Y); Varsity Clb; Yrbk Bus Mgr; Yrbk Sprt Ed; Yrbk Stf; Pres Frsh Cls; Rep Soph Cls; VP Jr Cls; Var Capt Socr; Var Sftbl; Var Vllybl; 1st Tm All-Cnty Vrsty Soccer & Vllybl 84; Mst Number Of Shut Outs-Soccer Cntrl Div 84; Bus Mgt.

DI FRANCO, DINA; Moore Catholic HS; Staten Isl, NY; (Y); Church Yth Grp; French Clb; Library Aide; Math Clb; Math Tm; Stage Crew; Stu Cncl; JV Sftbl; Hon Roll; Pace U; Accntnt.

DI FUSCO, THOMAS; Long Beach HS; Long Beach, NY; (S); 4/320; Church Yth Grp; Hosp Aide; Hon Roll; NHS; Futr Physcns Clb; Intrn Spnsr Pgm; Bio Sci.

DI GIANNO, JOHN; Msgr Mc Clancy HS; E Elmhurst, NY; (Y); Science Clb; Spanish Clb; Yrbk Bus Mgr; High Hon Roll; Hon Roll; NHS; Spanish NHS; Biolgcl Sci.

DI IOIA, STEVEN; Cortland SR HS; Dryden, NY; (Y); Am Leg Boys St; Yrbk Phtg; Ed Yrbk Stf; Pres Jr Cls; Pres Sr Cls; Rep Stu Cncl; Var L Socr; DAR Awd; High Hon Roll; NHS; Centrl NY Schl Newspaper Awd 1st Pl Photo 85; Aernautcl Engrng.

DI JOHN, DEANNA; Mohonasen HS; Schenectady, NY; (Y); 93/216; Pres DECA; FBLA; Sec Spanish Clb; VP Sr Cls; Rep Stu Cncl; Var Cheerleading; 1st Pl DECNY ST Conf Apprl/Access 85; Svdc Awd Chrldng 85; Franklin Pierce Coll; Psych.

DI LAPI, DONNA; Sacred Heart Acad; N Bellmore, NY; (S); 16/196; FTA; Hosp Aide; Math Clb; Math Tm; Spanish Clb; Hon Roll; NHS; Loyal Svc Awd 83; Mercy Hosp Vlntr Svc 83; Acctng.

DI LEO, MICHELLE; Farmingdale HS; Mass Park, NY; (Y); Dance Clb; Trs FBLA; Intnl Clb; Trs Key Clb; Trk; Hon Roll; NHS; Psych.

DI LIBERTO, LAURA; St Joseph Hill Acad; Staten Island, NY; (Y); 33/103; JA; Pep Clb; Service Clb; Spanish Clb; Varsity Clb; Crs Cntry; Trk; Vllybl; Hon Roll; Spanish NHS; NY St Regenst Schlrshp 85; 1st Pl Soc Stu Fair 82; NY St Champ Trck 85; Rutgers Coll; Pharm.

DI MAGGIO, JON D; Lockport SR HS; Lockport, NY; (Y); 114/455; Latin Clb; Ski Clb; Varsity Clb; Rep Soph Cls; Rep Jr Cls; Var Capt Crs Cntry; JV Swmmng; Capt Trk; Natl Hnr Rll 85; U Of S FL; Bus Mgmt.

DI MAGGIO, LISA; Tamarac HS; Hoosick Falls, NY; (Y); Intnl Clb; Ski Clb; Spanish Clb; VP Band; Pep Band; Yrbk Stf; Off Frsh Cls; Rep Soph Cls; Rep Jr Cls; Stu Cncl; Hudson Vlly CC; Bus Mgmt.

DI MAGGIO, MICHAEL; New Drop HS; Staten Island, NY; (Y); Var Bsbl; Score Keeper; Sftbl; Wt Lftg; Cit Awd; Gov Hon Prg Awd; High Hon Roll; Hon Roll; Ntl Merit Ltr; Pres Schlr; Baruch; Bus.

DI MAGGIO, ROSEMARIE; North Babylon SR HS; North Babylon, NY; (S); DECA; Intnl Clb; Library Aide; Office Aide; Chorus; Yrbk Stf; Socr; Sftbl; Trk; Itln Hnr Soc 83-84; DECA Parlmntrn 84-85; Bus Mgmt.

DI MARE, JOANNE; Tottenville HS; Staten Island, NY; (Y); 2/897; Tennis; High Hon Roll; Hon Roll; JETS Awd; NHS; Sal; St Schlr; Teachers Aide; Giusseppe A Nigro Awd Ordr Sons Italy Amer 85; Govnrs Comm Schlstc Achvmnt Citatn 85; Cooper Union; Eng.

DI MARE, JOSEPH G; Regis HS; Staten Island, NY; (Y); Cmnty Wkr; Hosp Aide; Orch; Im Bsktbl; Bowling; Im Tennis; Regis Schlrshp 81; Merit Stdnt 82; Adv Spnsh Clss 84; ST Regnl & Natl Accrdn Comptn Awds 81-84; U Of Rochester; Psych.

DI MARIA, SARA; Sheepshead Bay HS; Brooklyn, NY; (Y); Drama Clb; Office Aide; School Play; Nwsp Rptr; Nwsp Stf; Yrbk Stf; Prfct Atten Awd; Law Studys I, II, III, Itln & Engl Hnrs Cert 83-85; Law.

DI MEGLIO, LORI; Port Jervis HS; Port Jervis, NY; (Y); 22/198; VP Key Clb; Math Tm; Varsity Clb; Concert Band; Yrbk Phtg; Rep Stu Cncl; Var Tennis; JV Vllybl; Hon Roll; NHS; Pre-Law.

DI NALLO, LEAH; Mechanicville HS; Mechanicville, NY; (S); Nwsp Rptr; Yrbk Rptr; Rep Frsh Cls; Rep Soph Cls; Rep Jr Cls; Sec Sr Cls; Rep Stu Cncl; Cheerleading; Tmr; Marmount Coll; Elem Educ.

DI NAPOLI, GINA ANNE; Monsignor Scanlan HS; Bronx, NY; (Y); 34/265; Church Yth Grp; Intnl Clb; JA; Nwsp Rptr; Nwsp Stf; Hon Roll; Top 10% Of Frshmn Clss 82; Nom For Schlrshp For JR Achvrs 83; Elem Educ.

DI NARDO, KAREN; Lewiston-Potter HS; Lewiston, NY; (Y); 60/273; Spanish Clb; Var Capt Cheerleading; Powder Puff Ftbl; Hon Roll; Prfct Atten Awd; Spanish NHS; Rgnts Schlrshp 85; Geneseo ST U; Ec.

DI NOLFO, COLLEEN; Cardinal Mooney HS; Rochester, NY; (Y); 17/317; Exploring; Latin Clb; Variety Show; Yrbk Stf; Lit Mag; JV Socr; High Hon Roll; Hon Roll; NHS; Latn Merit Awd 84; Crtv Wrtg.

DI NONNO, DIANE; North Shore HS; Glen Head, NY; (Y); 12/225; AFS; Am Leg Aux Girls St; VP Drama Clb; Pres French Clb; Model UN; Thesps; Chorus; School Musical; School Play; Nwsp Rptr; Hstry.

DI PASQUALE, NADINE; Fontbonne Hall Acad; Brooklyn, NY; (Y); 22/137; Drama Clb; Hosp Aide; Office Aide; Teachers Aide; Chorus; School Musical; School Play; Hon Roll; NHS; Prfct Atten Awd; Regents Schlrshp 85; Pres Schlrshp 85; Brooklyn Coll Fresh Schlr 85; Bio.

DI PIERRO, GUS J; Chester HS; Chester, NY; (Y); 1/87; Drama Clb; Quiz Bowl; Band; Concert Band; Mrchg Band; School Play; Stage Crew; JV Bsktbl; JV Socr; High Hon Roll; Dr M I Gerner Awd Chem 84; VA Tech; Elec Engr.

DI PIERRO, PAUL; Chester JR SR HS; Chester, NY; (Y); Band; Jazz Band; School Musical; Stage Crew; Yrbk Stf; Rep Stu Cncl; High Hon Roll; Hon Roll; NHS; Rep Jr Cls; Arion Awd Outstndng JR Music 85; Middie Jazz Jmbree All Str Perfrmr 85; Outstndng Band Membr 84; SUNY Albany; Fed Law Enfrcmt.

DI PRETA, LARRY; Msgr Scanlan HS; New York, NY; (Y); 45/265; JV Var Bsbl; Dnfth Awd; Hon Roll; Prfct Atten Awd; Mth.

DI RADDO, STEVE; Jamesville De Witt HS; De Witt, NY; (Y); Cmnty Wkr; Bsbl; Wrstlng; Law.

DI RAGO, JOHN; Fox Lane HS; Bedford Hills, NY; (Y); Ski Clb; Var Bsbl; Im Mgr Coach Actv; JV Lcrss; JV Wrstlng; Hon Roll; Sprts Adm.

DI RUSSO, TOM; Sachem HS; Holbrook, NY; (Y); 151/1300; Boy Scts; German Clb; Ski Clb; Im Bowling; Stat Lcrss; JV Mgr(s); Stat Socr; Stat Wrstlng; Lawyer.

DI SANTO, DEANNA; Mynderse Acad; Seneca Falls, NY; (Y); Var Bsktbl; JV Cheerleading; JV Var Socr; JV Var Sftbl; High Hon Roll; Hon Roll.

DI SCIOSCIA, STEPHANIE; Gloversville HS; Gloversville, NY; (Y); Pres Sec Church Yth Grp; Exploring; French Clb; Hosp Aide; Church Choir; Concert Band; Symp Band; Yrbk Stf; High Hon Roll; Hon Roll; Cert & Candystriper Cap 83; Chrch Awd-Readng In Scrptrs 83-85; Chrch Awd-Compltng 12 Goals In Yr 83; Coll Of St Rose; Elem Educ.

DI SILVESTRI, GARY; Monsignor Farrell HS; Staten Island, NY; (Y); Boy Scts; Debate Tm; FBLA; Math Tm; Political Wkr; Varsity Clb; Orch; Nwsp Sprt Ed; Nwsp Stf; Pres Frsh Cls; Vrsty Clb Awd, Outstndng Stu Athlt 85; PAL Police Comm For Day 82; Interntl Exch Fnlst 84; Georgetown U; Intrntl Rel.

DI SISTO, LISA MARIA; Westlake HS; Hawthorne, NY; (Y); 3/147; Thesps; School Musical; School Play; Yrbk Ed-Chief; Var L Vllybl; High Hon Roll; NHS; Pres Schlr; Local 1-S Scholar 85; Knights Columbus Scholar Grant 85; Manhattan Coll; Engrng.

DI TULLIO, DENA; De Sales HS; Lockport, NY; (Y); 10/47; JV Var Bsktbl; JV Var Score Keeper; JV Var Sftbl; JV Var Vllybl; Law.

DIA PAUL, JOSEPH; Niagara Wheatfield SR HS; Sanborn, NY; (Y); 30/315; French Clb; High Hon Roll; Hon Roll; NHS; Niagara U Acad Schlrhsp 85-86; Niagra U Pres Schlrshp 85-86; Niagara U; Crmnl Just.

DIAGONALE, GREG; Fordham Prep; Bronxville, NY; (Y); Boy Scts; Drama Clb; Band; School Musical; Ftbl; Wt Lftg; Hon Roll; 1st Schlrshp Pin, Ntl Hnr Rl 83-84; U KS; Med.

DIAMOND, BARBARA; Southside HS; Rockville Ctr, NY; (Y); 10/300; Nwsp Ed-Chief; Band; Concert Band; Mrchg Band; Orch; Nwsp Stf; High Hon Roll; Jr NHS; Latin Hnr Soc 84-85.

DIAMOND, CATHERINE A; Mepham HS; Merrick, NY; (Y); 3/427; Drama Clb; Service Clb; Chorus; Nwsp Stf; Lit Mag; High Hon Roll; Ntl Merit SF; St Schlr; Union Coll; Med.

DIAMOND, DUANE; Schoharie Central HS; Esperance, NY; (S); 8/94; Boy Scts; Yrbk Stf; Hon Roll; NY ST Regents Scholar 85; Eagle Sct 85; Schl Ltr Acad 84; SUNY Cobleskill; Histotech.

DIAMOND, PETER G; Bishop Timon HS; Derby, NY; (Y); Boys Clb Am; Church Yth Grp; Civic Clb; Cmnty Wkr; Exploring; Varsity Clb; Bsbl; Var Bsktbl; Coach Actv; Var Ftbl; Hilbert Coll; Biochem.

DIAMOND, RACHEL; Columbus HS; Bronx, NY; (S); Math Tm; Office Aide; Band; School Musical; Hon Roll; Prfct Atten Awd; Ofcr Akiva/Jpsy Club; Chncllr Roll Hnr; Assoc Home Ec Tchrs NYC; Comp Sci.

DIANA, PATRICIA; Fayetteville Manlius HS; Manlius, NY; (Y); Church Yth Grp; VP Service Clb; Orch; Stage Crew; Variety Show; Yrbk Stf; Rep Stu Cncl; Var Capt Cheerleading; Hon Roll.

DIAS, MARVELYN E; St Francis Prep; Jackson Hts, NY; (Y); 286/690; Science Clb; Spanish Clb; Band; Concert Band; Mrchg Band; Pep Band; High Hon Roll; Hon Roll; Arista Hnr Soc; Manhattan Coll; Acctg.

DIAZ, ALTAGRACIA J; Middle College HS; Sunnyside, NY; (Y); Art Clb; Hosp Aide; Teachers Aide; Church Choir; High Hon Roll; Hon Roll; NHS; Queens Coll Pres Awd 84-85; Chem Tchrs Clb NY 84; Cert Merit Tchrs Soc Stud 84; Engrng.

DIAZ, DAVID; Herbert H Lehman HS; Bronx, NY; (Y); 40/444; Aud/Vis; Boys Clb Am; Dance Clb; Office Aide; Service Clb; Teachers Aide; Yrbk Stf; Rep Sr Cls; Rep Stu Cncl; Cit Awd; Arista Hnr Soc 84-85; Party Comm Chrpmn Awd 84-85; Pace U; Accntng.

DIAZ, EDGAR; Cardinal Haves HS; Bronx, NY; (Y); 56/267; Nwsp Stf; Yrbk Sprt Ed; Stu Cncl; JV L Bsbl; Var L Ftbl; Jrnlsm.

DIAZ, ERIC; Eastern District HS; Maspeth, NY; (Y); 33/400; Rep Stu Cncl; Im Ftbl; Elec Engrng.

DIAZ, EVELYN; Norman Thomas HS; Brooklyn, NY; (S); 7/671; JA; Hon Roll; NHS; Prfct Atten Awd; Acad All Amer 85; CPA.

DIAZ, FANNY; Norman Thomas HS; New York, NY; (Y); Church Yth Grp; Teachers Aide; Nwsp Stf; John Jay Coll; Crmnl Jstc.

DIAZ, HELEN; Our Lady Of Perpetual Help HS; Brooklyn, NY; (Y); Sftbl; Hon Roll; Prfct Atten Cert Awd 82-83; Prncpls Lst 82-84; Hnr Roll 84-85; Pace U; Bus.

DIAZ, JACQUELINE; St Vincent Ferrer HS; Astoria, NY; (Y); 40/102; Art Clb; Cmnty Wkr; Computer Clb; Dance Clb; Q&S; Spanish Clb; Variety Show; Yrbk Stf; Prfct Atten Awd; Spanish NHS; Pace U; Gen Bus.

DIAZ, JULIA; Yonkers HS; Yonkers, NY; (Y); Spanish Clb; Psychlgy.

DIAZ, LOURDES; James Monroe HS; Bronx, NY; (Y); Off Jr Cls; Tennis; Trk; Vllybl.

DIAZ, LUIS S; La Salle Acad; New York City, NY; (S); 19/250; Camera Clb; Pres Math Clb; Rptr Nwsp Stf; Yrbk Stf; High Hon Roll; Hon Roll; NHS; Camera Clb; Timer.

DIAZ, MARCELO; Cardinal Hayes HS; New York, NY; (Y); Church Yth Grp; Teachers Aide; Varsity Clb; Stage Crew; Frsh Cls; Soph Cls; Bsbl; Ftbl; Mgr(s); Trk; 2nd Hnrs 83; Bus Admin.

DIAZ, MARISOL; Stella Maris HS; Howard Beach, NY; (Y); 25/250; Library Aide; Spanish Clb; Teachers Aide; Rep Frsh Cls; Hon Roll; Prfct Atten Awd; Spanish NHS; Cmnty Wkr; Office Aide; Chorus; Schlstc Exclnce Awd 82-83; Acad Awds Span, Math, Sci & Hist 82-85; Second Hnr Awds 82-85; Bus.

DIAZ, SANDRA; St Johns Prep; Elmhurst, NY; (Y); Dance Clb; Chorus; Swmmng; DAR Awd; Hon Roll; Julliard; Dnc.

DIAZ, VIVIAN; Columbia HS; E Greenbush, NY; (Y); Math Clb; Varsity Clb; Trs Sec Stu Cncl; Fld Hcky; Powder Puff Ftbl; DAR Awd; NHS; Am Leg Aux Girls St; Cmnty Wkr; Drama Clb; NYS Empire St Math & Sci Tchr Awd; Siena Pres Scholar; Siena Coll; Math Tchr.

DIAZ, WILMA; Cardinal Spellman HS; New York, NY; (Y); Dance Clb; FCA; Science Clb; Ski Clb; Church Choir; School Play; Stage Crew; Yrbk Ed-Chief; Jr Cls; Var Cheerleading; Amer Lgn Cert Of Schl Awd 82; Cert Of Awd 82; 2nd Hnr Awd 83-85; Cornell; Pedtrcs.

DIBBLE, DIANNA; Liverpool HS; Liverpool, NY; (S); 65/800; DECA; Hon Roll; Outstndng Achvt Distrbtn II 84-85; Pres Acad Fit Awd 84-85; Regents Diploma Hnrs 85; SUNY Oswego; Bus Mngmnt.

DIBLBLE, DENISE; Connetquot HS; Ronkonkoma, NY; (Y); 150/694; Pres GAA; Rep Frsh Cls; Rep Jr Cls; JV Cheerleading; JV Var Sftbl; Hon Roll; Jr NHS; Prfct Atten Awd; Pre-Law.

DICERBO, CHERI; Manhasset HS; Manhasset, NY; (Y); Hosp Aide; Trs Soph Cls; Trs Jr Cls; Trs Sr Cls; Var Bsktbl; Var Capt Lcrss; JV Var Socr; High Hon Roll; Hon Roll; Bsbl; Lcrss Tm ST Champs All County 85; Lib Arts.

DICESARE, VALERIE M; Scotia-Glenville HS; Scotia, NY; (Y); Cmnty Wkr; Hosp Aide; Key Clb; Red Cross Aide; Ski Clb; Chorus; Sec Jr Cls; Rep Stu Cncl; Mgr Ftbl; JV Sftbl; Selective Creative Lab 84-85; Jrnslm.

DICHTER, ROBIN; Spackenkill HS; Poughkeepsie, NY; (Y); Leo Clb; Library Aide; VP Temple Yth Grp; Thesps; Chorus; Stage Crew; Nwsp Stf; Yrbk Stf; Lit Mag; Abraham Joshua Heschel Hnr Soc 84; Ed.

DICICCO, DONNA; Lindenhurst HS; Lindenhurst, NY; (Y); Sec Art Clb; Camera Clb; Church Yth Grp; Key Clb; PAVAS; Sftbl; Hon Roll; Jr NHS; Prfct Atten Awd; Adv.

DICIOCCIO, LINDA; Ossining HS; Ossining, NY; (Y); JV Bsktbl; Var L Sftbl; Hon Roll; All Div Hnrl Mntn Sftbl 85; Span II Awd 85; Phys Educ.

DICK, MARGARET; Washingtonville HS; Monroe, NY; (Y); Church Yth Grp; Computer Clb; French Clb; Ski Clb; Band; JV Bsktbl; Var Tennis; Hon Roll; DAR Awd.

DICK, STUART; Smithtown High School East; Nesconset, NY; (Y); Cmnty Wkr; Drama Clb; Radio Clb; Spanish Clb; Thesps; Hon Roll; NHS; Spanish NHS.

DICKENSON, KIMBERLY E; T R Proctor HS; Utica, NY; (Y); Rep Drama Clb; Library Aide; Pep Clb; Sec Spanish Clb; Nwsp Rptr; Rep Stu Cncl; Hon Roll; NHS; Govt Svcs.

DICKERSON, CRYSTAL L; Mt Vernon HS; Mt Vernon, NY; (Y); 121/628; Church Yth Grp; Political Wkr; Church Choir; Orch; School Musical; Stat Bsktbl; Cheerleading; Gym; Hon Roll; United Negro Wmn Westchester 85; ST U NY Albany; Comp Sci.

DICKERSON, LESLIE; Victor Central HS; Victor, NY; (Y); 11/200; Chorus; Pres Frsh Cls; Sec Jr Cls; VP Sr Cls; Rep Stu Cncl; NHS; Pres Schlr; Church Yth Grp; Ski Clb; Spanish Clb; Princeples Schl Svc Awd Victor Cntrl 85; Vera Brown Tchng Schlrshp 85; Ruth Mills Schlrshp 85; MI ST U; Spcl Ed.

DICKERSON, LYNN; Southside HS; Elmira, NY; (Y); 39/333; Hosp Aide; Pep Clb; Spanish Clb; Varsity Clb; Drill Tm; Rep Jr Cls; Rep Sr Cls; Var L Socr; Kiwanis Awd; Cmnty Wkr; Regnts Nrsng Schlrshp 85; Alfred ST Coll; Nrsng.

DICKERSON, SONDRA; Union Springs Acad; S Lancaster, MA; (S); 3/46; Ski Clb; Varsity Clb; Church Choir; VP Frsh Cls; Trs Soph Cls; VP Jr Cls; Rep Stu Cncl; Var Cheerleading; Gym; High Hon Roll; Schlrshp Teach Elem & Acdmy Gymnstcs 85-86; Loma Linda U; Engl.

DICKERSON, TRACY; Bishop Loughlin HS; Brooklyn, NY; (Y); 17/180; Church Yth Grp; Cmnty Wkr; Dance Clb; FBLA; Teachers Aide; Jazz Band; Hon Roll; NHS; 4-H; Musical Awd For Perf 85; Outstdng Cmnty Svc Wrkr 84; Jack & Jill Of Amer 84; Howard U; Phrmcy.

DICKERSON, WILLIAM; Notre Dame-Bishop Gibbons HS; Schenectady, NY; (S); 28/106; Aud/Vis; Nwsp Rptr; L Bsbl; L Bowling; Score Keeper; High Hon Roll; Hon Roll; NHS; NY ST Regnts Schlr 85; Siena Coll.

DICKEY, TOM; Tonawanda SR HS; Tonawanda, NY; (Y); #18 In Class; Church Yth Grp; French Clb; Rep Sr Cls; Rep Stu Cncl; Ftbl; Socr; Vllybl; Wrstlng; Hon Roll; Bio.

DICKINSON, DARLENE L; Harpursville Central HS; Harpursville, NY; (Y); VP 4-H; Quiz Bowl; Spanish Clb; Nwsp Rptr; 4-H Awd; Regnts Schlrshp 85; Horsemnshp Awds 84; Alfred U; Pol.

DICKINSON, DONNA; Cicero HS; Kirkville, NY; (Y); 136/680; German Clb; JV Cheerleading; Psych.

DICKINSON, HOLLY; Jamesville-Dewitt HS; Fayetteville, NY; (Y); 80/249; Church Yth Grp; Hosp Aide; Ski Clb; Capt Var Socr; High Hon Roll; Hon Roll; Key Clb; Trk; Bst Athl Awd 83; Empire ST Gms Gld Medl Slalm Skig 85; NY ST Ski Tm Eastrn Champ 85; Socl Wrk.

DICKINSON, KIMBERLY; Colonie Central HS; Albany, NY; (Y); Church Yth Grp; Band; Concert Band; Mrchg Band; Symp Band; Bowling; Mgr(s); Score Keeper; High Hon Roll; Hon Roll; Bus.

DICKMAN, ANITA MARIE; Shenendehowa HS; Ballston Lake, NY; (Y); 58/658; Drama Clb; Ski Clb; Varsity Clb; Chorus; Madrigals; Stage Crew; Pres Frsh Cls; Pres Soph Cls; Pres Jr Cls; Pres Sr Cls; Neil Hesson Awd 84; Jonesville Fire Dist Schlrshp 85; 2nd Rnnr Up Schlrshp Pag 85; Geneseo; Bio Chem.

DICKMAN, GLORIA I; Vestal SR HS; Binghamton, NY; (Y); 27/450; VP Temple Yth Grp; Rep Sr Cls; Rep Stu Cncl; JV Bsktbl; High Hon Roll; NHS; Cmnty Wkr; French Clb; School Play; Rep Frsh Cls; NY ST Regnts Schlrshp 85; Mock Trl-Stu Lawyer 84 & 85; Stu Rep To Brd Of Educ 84-85; SUNY Buffalo; Elem Educ.

DICKOUT, KATHLEEN; Lafayette HS; Buffalo, NY; (Y); Office Aide; Teachers Aide; Bowling; Comp.

DICKSON, JULIE; Thousand Islands HS; Clayton, NY; (Y); Varsity Clb; Chorus; Church Choir; Color Guard; School Musical; School Play; Stage Crew; Variety Show; Cheerleading; Hon Roll; Sectrl.

DICKSON, LAURIE; Warwick Valley HS; Warwick, NY; (Y); Varsity Clb; Color Guard; Drm & Bgl; Var Cheerleading; Socr; Hon Roll; Hghst Avg Spnsh Awd 84; Bus.

DICKSON, MICHAEL; Bay Shore HS; Bay Shore, NY; (Y); Drama Clb; Band; Concert Band; Drm & Bgl; Jazz Band; Mrchg Band; Orch; Pep Band; School Musical; School Play; Most Outstndg Stu Shop; Most Outstndg Stu Band; Elec Engr.

DICKSTEIN, STEVEN; Spring Valley SR HS; Monsey, NY; (Y); Key Clb; Temple Yth Grp; Band; Concert Band; Jazz Band; Symp Band; JV Var Tennis; High Hon Roll; Mu Alp Tht; NHS; Law.

DICOSTANZO, CHRISTOPHER; Freeport HS; Freeport, NY; (Y); Science Clb; Ski Clb; Teachers Aide; JV Var Bsbl; Var Bowling; High Hon Roll; Hon Roll; NHS; All Nassau Cnty Bwlng 83-84; Mth.

DICRUTTALO III, ALBERT; Gloversville HS; Gloversville, NY; (Y); 52/232; Drama Clb; Intnl Clb; School Musical; VP Frsh Cls; Capt Bsbl; Capt Bsktbl; Golf; Socr; Co-Capt Tennis; Hon Roll; NY ST Regnts Schlrshp 85; Hnbl Mntn Art Awd 85; Ithaca Coll; Explrtry.

DIDGET, GAY E; Allendale Columbia HS; Rochester, NY; (Y); Am Leg Aux Girls St; Drama Clb; Ski Clb; Acpl Chr; Chorus; Church Choir; Ed Yrbk Ed-Chief; Var Capt Vllybl; French Hon Soc; Girl Scts; Vocl Arts Awd 85; Drama Arts Awd 85; Hamilton Coll; Hstry.

DIDIO, BETH; Auburn HS; Auburn, NY; (Y); Debate Tm; Ski Clb; High Hon Roll; Hon Roll; Bus.

DIDZIULIS, JOHN; Bishop Scully HS; Amsterdam, NY; (Y); Drama Clb; Quiz Bowl; Pres Spanish Clb; School Play; Nwsp Stf; Yrbk Stf; VP Sr Cls; Capt Var Bowling; L Var Tennis; NYS Regents Scholar 85; SUC Brockport; Cmmnctns.

DIEBALL, LEE ANN; Sidney Central HS; Sidney, NY; (Y); 21/110; Church Yth Grp; School Musical; VP Jr Cls; Trs Sr Cls; Cheerleading; High Hon Roll; NHS; Prfct Atten Awd; Clark Art Awd 81-82; Acad All Amer 84-85; Syracuse U; Adv Dsgn.

DIEFENDORF, DONALD S; Cazenovia HS; Cazenovia, NY; (Y); 70/152; Cmnty Wkr; Drama Clb; Acpl Chr; Chorus; Jazz Band; Madrigals; Symp Band; Var Crs Cntry; Hon Roll; St Schlr; Oprtn Entrpr Bus Mngmnt Seminar 84; Stu Excel Awd 85; WA Coll; Pre-Med.

DIEFES, HEIDI A; Arlington HS; Poughkeepsie, NY; (Y); 27/597; 4-H; Band; Orch; School Musical; 4-H Awd; Ntl Merit Ltr; Civic Clb; German Clb; Hon Roll; NY ST Regents Schlrshp 85; Literary Soc Fndtn Inc Awd Germn II 84; Cornell; Food Sci.

DIEFES, RICHARD; Blind Brook HS; Pt Chester, NY; (Y); Hosp Aide; Math Tm; Band; Concert Band; Jazz Band; School Play; JV Var Crs Cntry.

DIEHL, JULIE; Mt Mercy Acad; Buffalo, NY; (Y); Church Yth Grp; FHA; Red Cross Aide; Hon Roll; Prfct Atten Awd; Sctry.

DIEHL, MATTHEW; Liverpool HS; Liverpool, NY; (S); 46/792; German Clb; Stage Crew; Stu Cncl; High Hon Roll; Hon Roll; Jr NHS; NHS; Crew Rwng Tm 80-84; Comm Vlntr Awd 83-84; Clarkson U; Mech Engrng.

DIEKOW, BETH E; Susquehanna Valley HS; Conklin, NY; (Y); 40/177; Church Yth Grp; French Clb; Pep Clb; Nwsp Stf; Yrbk Stf; Var Capt Fld Hcky; JV Var Sftbl; Hon Roll; NYS Regnts Schlrshp 85; Nrs.

DIEL, CYNTHIA; Island Trees HS; Bethpage, NY; (Y); Chorus; Capt Drm Mjr(t); Bowling; Socr; Twrlr; Cit Awd; High Hon Roll; Jr NHS; NHS; Bus Ed Schlrshp 85; Miss Teen Pagnt 85; Nassau Comm Coll; Legl Sec.

DIELE, MARIA N; Clarkstown HS North; Congers, NY; (Y); 91/540; Office Aide; Teachers Aide; Orch; Lit Mag; Cit Awd; Lang Cntst Awd 83-85; Itln Clb Schlrshp 85; Dantes Medl 85; Fordham U; Law.

DIENER, MICHAEL; Fairport HS; Faiport, NY; (Y); JV Socr; Wt Lftg; Wrstlng; Hon Roll; Sci Cittn 85; Wstrn NY Motcrss Comptn 85.

DIERINGER, JENNIFER K; G W Hewlett HS; Woodmere, NY; (Y); 25/278; Yrbk Rptr; Yrbk Sprt Ed; VP Jr Cls; Pres Sr Cls; L Var Crs Cntry; Var L Trk; NHS; Ntl Merit Ltr; Cmnty Wkr; Debate Tm; Jewish War Vet Awd 85; Twn Hempstd Citatn 85; Haverford Coll.

DIETZLER, DEBORAH ANN; Sachem HS; Holtsville, NY; (Y); 34/1400; Science Clb; Chorus; Sec School Musical; NHS; Dstngshd Acad, Beaumont, NYS Rgnts Schlrshps; Hofstra U; Pre Law.

DIETZMAN, BRIAN; Delaware Acad; Delhi, NY; (Y); Am Leg Boys St; Church Yth Grp; German Clb; Yrbk Stf; Var L Bsktbl; Var Crs Cntry; Var L Golf; JV Trk; Hon Roll; Engrng.

DIEZ, DOUGLAS S; Lewiston Porter HS; Ransomville, NY; (Y); 21/273; Exploring; Orch; Hon Roll; Trs NHS; Bucknell U; Chem Engrng.

DIEZ, LISA; Oceanside SR HS; Oceanside, NY; (S); Sec DECA; Capt Cheerleading; Socr; Hon Roll; Rotary Awd; Distrib Clbs Of Amer Fall Conf-Hnrb Mntn For Merch Info Manual 85; Nassua CC; Fash Byng.

DIEZ, MARY; Barker Central HS; Barker, NY; (Y); AFS; French Clb; VP Varsity Clb; Stat Bsktbl; Var L Fld Hcky; Var L Sftbl; Var L Vllybl; Hnrb Mntn Sftbl 85; Intr Dsgn.

DIFABIO, ANDREA; Emma Willard Schl; Loudonville, NY; (Y); Church Yth Grp; Ski Clb; JV Socr; Pre Law.

DIFEDE, CHRISTINE; Senior HS; Deer Park, NY; (Y); Hosp Aide; Library Aide; Drill Tm; Mrchg Band; Yrbk Stf; High Hon Roll; Jr NHS; NY St Physcl Ftnss Meet-3rd Pl Tm Medal 85; Med.

DIFFENDORF, MARY; Susquehanna Valley HS; Kirkwood, NY; (Y); Art Clb; Pep Clb; Varsity Clb; Chorus; Yrbk Rptr; Yrbk Stf; Rep Frsh Cls; Rep Soph Cls; Var Capt Bowling; Var Socr; Accntg.

DIFLORIO, THERESE; Henninger HS; Syracuse, NY; (Y); 7/450; Ski Clb; Band; Concert Band; Jazz Band; Madrigals; VP Jr Cls; VP Sr Cls; Stu Cncl; Socr; Swmmng; Pre-Med.

DIGANGI, ANGELO; Northport HS; Northport, NY; (Y); 25/595; DECA; Mathletes; Science Clb; Varsity Clb; Var Stat Bowling; Var Crs Cntry; Var Trk; High Hon Roll; Bike Clb-Grp Ldr 83-85; Matls Sci.

DIGGIN, MICHAEL D; Ward Melville HS; Stony Brook, NY; (Y); Am Leg Boys St; Aud/Vis; Church Yth Grp; Pres Debate Tm; Political Wkr; Nwsp Stf; Rep Sr Cls; Rep Stu Cncl.

DIGIAMBERDINE, CORINNA; Marlboro Central HS; Marlboro, NY; (Y); JV Sftbl; High Hon Roll; Hon Roll; Bio.

DIGIORGI, NICOLE; Lakeland SR HS; Yorktown Hts, NY; (Y); Radio Clb; Science Clb; Spanish Clb; Nwsp Stf; Rep Jr Cls; JV Sftbl; Hon Roll; Ntl Merit Ltr; Rep Stu Cncl; JV Lcrss; MVP Sftbl 83; Cert Hnr BAR Assoc 85; Cert Part Mock Trial 85; Law.

DIGIOVANNI, LAURA; West Irondequoit HS; Rochester, NY; (Y); 115/400; Var Cheerleading; JV Socr; Prfct Atten Awd; Bus.

DIGNAM, LYNN; St John The Baptist D H S; W Babylon, NY; (Y); 40/600; VP MMM; Chorus; Color Guard; School Musical; Nwsp Rptr; High Hon Roll; NHS; Spanish NHS; Modelng Cert-Barbizon Schls 83.

DIGREGORIO, ROB; Mattituck HS; Cutchoque, NY; (Y); German Clb; Service Clb; School Play; Variety Show; Rep Frsh Cls; Rep Soph Cls; VP Jr Cls; Var Bsbl; Var Bowling; Var Socr; Sccr Leag All-Star 83-84; Vrsty Sccr All-Leag Awd 84-85; Engr.

DIGRUCCIO, MARY; Christ The King R HS; Brooklyn, NY; (Y); 10/382; Cmnty Wkr; Library Aide; Math Clb; Teachers Aide; Church Choir; Nwsp Stf; Yrbk Stf; Hon Roll; NHS; Itln Achvt Awd 83; Psych.

DIKEMAN, GEORGE; Bethpage HS; Bethpage, NY; (Y); 2/291; Var Bsbl; Var Capt Swmmng; Hon Roll; NHS.

DILEO, ANNA; St Gabriel Blessed Scarament HS; Mt Vernon, NY; (Y); 27/61; Church Yth Grp; Service Clb; Bsbl; Sftbl; Vllybl; Hon Roll; Berkeley Schl.

DILEO, SALVATORE; Mt St Michael HS; Bronx, NY; (Y); 50/308; Camera Clb; Hon Roll; NHS; Spanish NHS; Spanish Clb; Jr NHS; St Johns U; Phrmcy.

DILGARD, ANGELA; Dominican Acad; Queens Village, NY; (Y); Latin Clb; Science Clb; School Musical; School Play; Prfct Atten Awd; Pre-Vet.

DILIBERTO, DAVID; East Ridge HS; Rochester, NY; (Y); Cmnty Wkr; Ski Clb; Varsity Clb; Var Capt Socr; Hon Roll.

DILIUS, MAUREEN; Cathedral HS; Ny, NY; (Y); 49/298; Chess Clb; Chorus; Church Choir; Nwsp Stf; Math 10 Hnrs; Choral Awd; Chess Clb Awd.

DILL, DAWN; Kenmore East HS; Tonawanda, NY; (Y); 20/352; Dance Clb; GAA; Drill Tm; Mrchg Band; High Hon Roll; Hon Roll; NHS; Prfct Atten Awd; Rochester Inst Tech; Acctnt.

DILL, KATHLEEN A; Millbrook Schl; Verbank, NY; (Y); Model UN; Yrbk Ed-Chief; Lit Mag; Rep Stu Cncl; Capt L Lcrss; Capt L Socr; High Hon Roll; Hon Roll; Trs Church Yth Grp; Cmnty Wkr; Mst Imprvd Plyr Vrsty Sccr 83-84; MVP Vrsty Sccr 84-85; Hstry.

DILLARD, LAY FOYA; August Martin HS; Jamaica, NY; (Y); 154/548; Debate Tm; Hst FBLA; Teachers Aide; Church Choir; Cheerleading; Trk; Hon Roll; Prfct Atten Awd; FBLA Awd 85; Howard U; Comp Sci.

DILLENBECK, ALICE; Oneida SR HS; Oneida, NY; (Y); Library Aide; SADD Pres; Exclint Emplymblty & Achvt Awd For Food Trds; Morrisville Coll; Rstrnt Mngmt.

DILLENBERGER, ROSE M; Moriah Central HS; Moriah, NY; (Y); Pres AFS; GAA; Spanish Clb; Stu Cncl; Bsktbl; Cheerleading; Hon Roll; Teaching.

DILLILLO, LINDA; Susan E Wagner HS; Staten Is, NY; (Y); Cit Awd; Hon Roll; Prfct Atten Awd; Acctnt & Bus Mngmnt Awds 84-85; Bernard M Baruch Coll; Acctng.

DILLMAN, ALAN; Sweet Home SR HS; North Tonawanda, NY; (Y); Chess Clb; 4-H; Church Choir; Orch; 4-H Awd; Vet.

DILLON, JEANETTE; Odessa-Montour HS; Montour Falls, NY; (Y); Drama Clb; Pres Varsity Clb; VP Jr Cls; VP Sr Cls; Stu Cncl; Var VP Bsktbl; Swmmng; Trk; Hon Roll; Sec NHS.

DILLON, KATHLEEN M; The Mary Louis Acad; Richmond Hill, NY; (Y); 53/283; Office Aide; Rgnts Schlrshp 85; Polytechnid Div Arts & Sci Schlrshp 85; Polytechnic Instit; Chem.

DILLON, MARK; Bishop Kearney HS; Rochester, NY; (S); Trs Church Yth Grp; Debate Tm; NFL; Nwsp Stf; Chrmn Jr Cls; Stat Vllybl.

DILLON, MAURA; Skaneateles HS; Skaneateles, NY; (S); Debate Tm; Model UN; Tennis; High Hon Roll; NHS; Hugh O Brian Ldrshp Conf 84; Olympics Of The Mind Renatra Fusca Awd 84.

DILLON, MICHAEL; Aquinas Institute Of Rochestr; Churchville, NY; (Y); 25/180; Ski Clb; Varsity Clb; Variety Show; Var L Ftbl; Var Trk; Wt Lftg; 4-H Awd; High Hon Roll; Hon Roll; Achvmnt Awd Amer Hist 85; Achvmnt Awd Theology 85; Prfct Schl Attndnc 83-85; Arch.

DILLON, THERESA; Onteora Central Schl; West Hurley, NY; (S); Church Yth Grp; Chorus; Ed Yrbk Stf; Pres Jr Cls; Stu Cncl; NHS; Hgh Hnr Awd 82-84; Engl.

DILLSWORTH, ANN MARIE; West Seneca West SR HS; W Seneca, NY; (Y); 57/550; Church Yth Grp; Drama Clb; Chorus; School Play; Hon Roll; Math Awd 81-82; Scl Awd 81-82; Sci Awd Gold Medal 82-83; SUNY-BUFFALO; Law.

DILORENZO, JOAN; Valley Central HS; Walden, NY; (Y); 23/300; Church Yth Grp; Debate Tm; Lit Mag; Rep Frsh Cls; Rep Soph Cls; Rep Jr Cls; Hon Roll; NHS; Spanish NHS; Prfct Atten Awd; Pre-Med.

DILWORTH, MAUREEN; Clyde-Savannah HS; Savannah, NY; (Y); Varsity Clb; Band; Jazz Band; Variety Show; Sec VP Stu Cncl; Var L Cheerleading; Trk; High Hon Roll; Hon Roll; 5th Pl Chrldng Partnr Comp 85.

DILWORTH, ROGER; Cold Spring Harbor HS; Huntington, NY; (Y); Boy Scts; Mathletes; Band; School Musical; Variety Show; Tennis; Wrstlng; High Hon Roll; Hon Roll; Ntl Merit Ltr; Cornell U; Law.

DIMACULANGAN, LISA M; St Jean Baptiste HS; New York, NY; (Y); 6/90; Intnl Clb; JA; Church Choir; Nwsp Bus Mgr; Nwsp Rptr; Hon Roll; NY ST Regents Coll Schlrshp 85; Advanced Math Awd 83-84; French Awd 82-83; Georgetown U; Nursing.

DIMARE, JOANNE C; Tottenville HS; Staten Island, NY; (Y); 2/900; Teachers Aide; Var Tennis; Gov Hon Prg Awd; High Hon Roll; Jr NHS; NHS; Sal; St Schlr; Church Yth Grp; Cmnty Wkr; Hnrbl Mntn For Italian Culture Week 82 & 84; Dante Awd; Cooper Union; Engrng.

DIMARTINO, LUCY; Yonkers HS; Yonkers, NY; (Y); Intnl Clb; Key Clb; Rep Jr Cls; Rep Sr Cls; Mgr(s); High Hon Roll; Hon Roll; NHS; Achvt Awds 82-85; Certs Of Excllnc 82-85.

DIMEGLIO, JOANNE; Bishop Ford CC HS; Brooklyn, NY; (Y); Fashion Inst Of Tech; Decrtng.

DIMEO, TIFFANY; John F Kennedy HS; Utica, NY; (Y); 23/146; Ed Yrbk Stf; Rep Soph Cls; VP Jr Cls; VP Sr Cls; JV Bsktbl; Var Capt Sftbl; Var Vllybl; Acad All Amer 85; U S Jrnlsm Awd 85; Utica Coll; Art.

DIMITROV, BARBARA; Bishop Kearney HS; Rochester, NY; (Y); Pres JA; Ski Clb; Mrchg Band; Capt Bowling; Pres Twrlr; Hon Roll; Vrsty Bwlng Hgh Series & Sec V Chmps NYS PHSAA 83-84; Dr.

DIMOCK, MICHAEL; Charles O Dickerson HS; Trumansburg, NY; (Y); 9/90; Drama Clb; Thesps; Stage Crew; Yrbk Stf; Pres Soph Cls; Rep Jr Cls; Stu Cncl; Var Tennis; NHS; Ntl Merit SF.

DIMOLA, JOHN; St Johns Prep HS; Astoria, NY; (Y); Im Trk; 2nd Hnrs Awd; CUNY; Intl Bus Adm.

DIMON, R THOMAS; Gouverneur HS; Gouverneur, NY; (Y); Church Yth Grp; Computer Clb; Pres 4-H; Crs Cntry; Socr; Trk; Hon Roll; Sec Jr NHS; Sec NHS; NY ST Regents Schlrshp Awd 85; Rochester Inst Tech; Mech Engr.

DIMOS, BILL; Cardinal Spellman HS; New York, NY; (S); 71/576; Camera Clb; Debate Tm; Drama Clb; VP Key Clb; Latin Clb; PAVAS; Chorus; School Musical; Nwsp Rptr; Nwsp Stf; Regents Schlrshp; NY U; Sci.

DIMOU, GEORGE; Yonkers HS; Yonkers, NY; (Y); Drama Clb; English Clb; French Clb; PAVAS; Sr Cls; Socr; Iona; Actng.

DINAPOLI, MIA; Commack H S South; Dix Hills, NY; (Y); Cmnty Wkr; Hosp Aide; Band; Mrchg Band; Orch; School Musical; Symp Band; Rep Stu Cncl; Pom Pon; Hon Roll; Ldrshp Awd 83-84; Vrsty Sport Awd 84-85; Comm Svc Awd 83-84.

DINARDO, DEBORAH; Union-Endicott HS; Owego, NY; (S); Band; Concert Band; Jazz Band; Mrchg Band; Orch; School Musical; Bsktbl; Sftbl; Hon Roll; U S Achvt Acad Natl Band Awd 84; Acadmc All Amer 84; Industrl Labor Reltns.

DINARDO, SANDY; S S Seward Inst; Newburgh, NY; (Y); Church Yth Grp; FFA; FHA; VICA; Yrbk Stf; Bowling; Sftbl; Hon Roll; Johnson; Culinary Foods.

DINATALE, ENRICO; Cardinal Hayes HS; Bronx, NY; (Y); 102/249; 3rd Hnrs Sr Yr 85; Borough Manhattan; Med.

DINEEN, KERRY; Guilderland Central HS; Guilderland, NY; (Y); 130/363; 4-H; Chorus; School Musical; 4-H Awd; High Hon Roll; Outstndng Chr Achvt 84; Siena-Cornell; Blgy.

DINEEN, LINDA; Frankfort-Schuyler HS; Frankfort, NY; (S); 16/97; Exploring; 4-H; High Hon Roll; NHS; 4th Contntl Math League 81-82; 3rd NY Math League 83-84; Mohawk Valley CC; Engrng Sci.

DINEEN, PATRICK; Mt St Michael Acad; Yonkers, NY; (Y); 32/308; Spanish Clb; Im Bsktbl; Var L Golf; Var L Ice Hcky; Var L Socr; Im Sftbl; Hon Roll; NHS; Spanish NHS.

DINGLE, JEFFREY MARK; West Hempstead HS; W Hempstead, NY; (Y); Church Yth Grp; Computer Clb; Yrbk Stf; Rep Frsh Cls; Rep Soph Cls; Rep Jr Cls; Rep Sr Cls; JV Bsbl; JV Bsktbl; Var Ftbl; All ST 400 & 300 Meter Rnnr 84-85; Comm.

DINGLE, KEVIN; Bronx H S Of Science; New York, NY; (Y); Church Yth Grp; Library Aide; Varsity Clb; Chorus; School Musical; Variety Show; Ftbl; Gym; JV Trk; Pres WIS 85-86; Engnr.

DINGMAN, ALAN; Hudson HS; Hudson, NY; (Y); Art Clb; PAVAS; Ski Clb; Spanish Clb; Var Trk; Pratt Inst; Illstrtr.

DINGMAN, MICHAEL D; G Ray Bodely HS; Fulton, NY; (Y); 56/267; Varsity Clb; Band; Concert Band; Mrchg Band; Orch; Pep Band; Var Bsbl; Var Capt Bowling; JV Ftbl; High Hon Roll.

DINGS, ALISON; Barker Central HS; Lockport, NY; (Y); 4/90; AFS; Church Yth Grp; French Clb; Band; Chorus; Concert Band; Mrchg Band; Orch; School Musical; Symp Band; Area All ST Bnd; Area All ST Studio Orch; Wrld Comp Odyssey Of Mnd; Northwestern; Music Prfrmnce.

DININ, PETER E; Irondequoit HS; Rochester, NY; (Y); 9/341; Math Tm; NHS; Chorus; Jazz Band; Orch; School Musical; Symp Band; All-State & All-Estrn States Mus Fstvl 85; John Phillip Sousa Ntl HS Hnrs Band 85; Cleveland Inst Of Mus; Mus.

DINITTO, PAUL; Gloversville HS; Gloversville, NY; (Y); 20/260; Intnl Clb; Mathletes; Chorus; Nwsp Rptr; Yrbk Sprt Ed; Yrbk Stf; JV Bsktbl; Var Capt Socr; Hon Roll; Pres NHS; Jrnlsm.

DINKEVITCH, MARINA; Spence HS; New York, NY; (Y); 3/37; Debate Tm; French Clb; Library Aide; Model UN; Office Aide; Teachers Aide; School Play; High Hon Roll; Hon Roll; Cert Merit Concours Ntl France 82; Smith COLL; French.

DINOLFO, JOSEPH; Bishop Kearney HS; Rochester, NY; (Y); Aud/Vis; Computer Clb; JA; Letterman Clb; Library Aide; Ski Clb; Varsity Clb; Stage Crew; Var L Bowling; Var Mgr(s); Rochester Inst Of Tech; Cmp Sci.

DINORCIA, NELLO; Archbishop Molloy HS; Sunnyside, NY; (Y); 157/409; 1st & 2nd Hnrs 82-85; Busn Mngmnt.

DIOLALLEVI, ANNA LISA; Christ The King Regional HS; Elmhurst, NY; (Y); 3/398; Office Aide; School Play; Nwsp Rptr; Rep Jr Cls; Sec Sr Cls; Trk; High Hon Roll; Lion Awd; VP NHS; Trustee Schlrshp Pace U 85; NYU Schlrshp 85; Italn Excllnc Awd 85; NYU; Lbrl Arts.

DION, DAVID; Northeastern Clinton Central HS; Rouses Pt, NY; (Y); Am Leg Boys St; Key Clb; Model UN; Ski Clb; Yrbk Phtg; Yrbk Stf; VP Jr Cls; Var Golf; Var Ice Hcky; Var Socr; Mst Well Round JR Athl, Acad, Clss Partcptn 84-85; All Str Hcky Frwrd Malone Tourn 84-85; Clarkson; Engrng.

DIONISIO, MARCY; Miller Place HS; Miller Pl, NY; (Y); Church Yth Grp; Pres Varsity Clb; Var Crs Cntry; Tennis; Var Trk; Hon Roll; Life Sci.

DIORIO, DAN; Union Endicott HS; Endicott, NY; (Y); Am Leg Boys St; Capt Church Yth Grp; Math Tm; VP Frsh Cls; Rep Soph Cls; Rep Jr Cls; Rep Sr Cls; Var JV Ftbl; Var Wt Lftg; Hon Roll; RIT; Elec Engrng.

DIORIO, JOSEPHINE; Bishop Ford CC HS; Brooklyn, NY; (Y); 1/250; Drama Clb; Science Clb; Chorus; School Play; Stage Crew; Nwsp Stf; Yrbk Stf; JV Tennis; High Hon Roll; NHS; Thtr Arts.

DIPASQUA, CRISTINA; Notre Dame HS; Sauquoit, NY; (Y); 15/175; Cmnty Wkr; Hosp Aide; Office Aide; Service Clb; Chorus; Church Choir; Yrbk Stf; Hon Roll; NHS; Utica Coll.

DIRAFFAELE, MARY M; Sachem HS; Lk Ronkonkoma, NY; (Y); Dance Clb; Band; Concert Band; Mrchg Band; Trk; Vllybl; Springfield MA; Sprts Dr.

DIRLAM, KARI; Hauppauge HS; Hauppauge, NY; (Y); Church Yth Grp; Concert Band; Mrchg Band; JV Capt Bsktbl; Var Socr; Var Sftbl; Vllybl; Hon Roll; NHS; Prfct Atten Awd; Aviation.

DIRNAGL, ANDREAS J; The Stony Brook Schl; Bay Shore, NY; (Y); 8/96; Church Yth Grp; Drama Clb; Quiz Bowl; Acpl Chr; Chorus; Church Choir; Madrigals; School Musical; School Play; Nwsp Rptr; Hnr Cert Natl Assn French Tchrs 82; Georgetown U; Intl Bus.

DIRR, MICHAEL; Cardinal O Hara HS; Buffalo, NY; (Y); Artist.

DIRUBBO, MARIA; Colonie Central HS; Albany, NY; (Y); Cmnty Wkr; Temple Yth Grp; Chorus; Hon Roll; Prfct Atten Awd; Comp.

DISALVO, BIANCA; New Rochelle HS; New Rochelle, NY; (Y); Church Yth Grp; Model UN; Chorus; Rep Jr Cls; JV Var Trk; Wooster Coll.

DISCENZA, DAVID; Queensbury HS; Glens Falls, NY; (Y); Drama Clb; Band; Chorus; Madrigals; School Musical; Diving; Ftbl; Golf; Swmmng; Paul Smiths Coll; Hotl Mgmt.

DISCIGLIO, JOHN; Newburgh Free Acad; Newburgh, NY; (Y); JV Bsbl; Comp Reprs.

DISMUKE, DEBORA; Midwood HS; Brooklyn, NY; (Y); Cmnty Wkr; Girl Scts; Office Aide; Coach Actv; Hon Roll; Prfct Atten Awd; Cert Dedicatd Svc 85; Good Conduct Awd 83; Baruch Coll; Corp Lwyr.

DISUNNO, LON; East Hampton HS; Amagansett, NY; (Y); Am Leg Boys St; Church Yth Grp; JV Var Bsbl; JV Bsktbl; Var Capt Ftbl; Var Wt Lftg; Cit Awd; Civil Engr.

DITCHER, JOHN G; Ellicottville Central HS; Ellicottville, NY; (Y); 4/49; Am Leg Boys St; Letterman Clb; Varsity Clb; Var Bsbl; Var Bsktbl; Var Ftbl; Im Ice Hcky; High Hon Roll; NHS; All Leag Mst Val Ofnsve Plyr Ftbl 84; Cattaraugus All Co Bsbl Tm 85; Econ.

DITE, CYNTHIA; Rome Catholic HS; Rome, NY; (Y); 33/82; Cmnty Wkr; School Musical; Yrbk Ed-Chief; Rep Sr Cls; Rep Stu Cncl; Var Capt Cheerleading; Var Capt Socr; Hon Roll; Church Yth Grp; Pep Clb; Presdntl Physical Ftnss Awd 83-85; St Pauls Coll Of St Rose Schlrshp 85; Coll Of St Rose; Secndry Eductn.

DIV, DY; New Utrecht HS; Bklyn, NY; (Y); Rep Sr Cls; Bsbl; Bsktbl; Gym; Capt Socr; Sftbl; Capt Vllybl; Wt Lftg; NCTE Awd; NEDT Awd; NY City Tech Coll; Accntng.

DIVER, MAUREEN; Bishop Kearney HS; Brooklyn, NY; (Y); Church Yth Grp; Service Clb; Ski Clb; Spanish Clb; Rep Sr Cls; Im Bsktbl; Im Bowling; Hon Roll; NYPD Holy Name Socty & Emerald Socty Schlrshps 82-83; Sci.

DIVERONICA, STEVE; Canastota HS; Canastota, NY; (Y); Am Leg Boys St; Church Yth Grp; Ski Clb; Yrbk Stf; VP Sr Cls; Rep Stu Cncl; Im Coach Actv; Im Ftbl; Im Swmmng; Var L Wrstlng; Boys ST Assmblymn 84-85; U Of Miami; Bus Mgmt.

DIVIRGILIO, SARAH; St Johns Prep; Astoria, NY; (Y); Debate Tm; Drama Clb; Speech Tm; School Play; Off Soph Cls; Off Jr Cls; High Hon Roll; NHS.

DIXEY, PATRICIA; John Jay SR HS; Hopewell Jct, NY; (Y); 92/560; Chorus; School Play; Var Swmmng; High Hon Roll; Hon Roll; IBM Awd For Excllnc In Data Processng 85; IBM Safety Awd 85; Marist Coll; Comp Sci.

DIXIT, CHIKIRSHA; Curtis HS; Staten Island, NY; (Y); Cmnty Wkr; Hosp Aide; Math Tm; School Musical; Lit Mag; Badmtn; Mgr(s); Trk; Hon Roll; Med.

DIXON, AMY; Kenmore West SR HS; Kenmore, NY; (Y); Dance Clb; GAA; Girl Scts; Pep Clb; Chorus; School Musical; School Play; Variety Show; Lit Mag; VP Frsh Cls; Schl Plnng Tm Awd 83-84; Ntl PTA Ltrrcy Awd 84-85; Wellesley Bk Awd 84-85; Secndry Eductn.

DIXON, ANASTASIA; Curtis HS; Stone Mountain, GA; (Y); Concert Band; Schl Intl Svc 82-83.

DIXON, BRIAN T; Camden Central HS; Camden, NY; (Y); 20/200; Church Yth Grp; Drama Clb; School Musical; School Play; Yrbk Phtg; Yrbk Stf; VP Frsh Cls; VP Soph Cls; Bsktbl; Tennis; ROTC Schlrshp 85; Clarkson U; Chem Engr.

DIXON, MARSHA H; Midwood HS; Brooklyn, NY; (Y); 153/605; Girl Scts; Mgr Bsktbl; Var Capt Socr; Var Vllybl; Cit Awd; NY ST Regents Schlrsp For Nrsg 85; Medical Sci Inst Prgm 81-85; Brooklyn Coll; Nrsng.

DIXON, MICHELLE; Norman Thomas HS; Bronx, NY; (S); 94/671; Church Yth Grp; JA; Band; Chorus; Pres Church Choir; Hon Roll; Lehman Coll; Nrs.

DIZON, MARIE DEANNA E; St Peters HS For Girls; Staten Isl, NY; (Y); Exploring; FNA; Library Aide; Mathletes; Math Clb; Math Tm; Red Cross Aide; Lit Mag; NHS; Nrsg.

DIZON, ROWENA FRANCESCA I; Sachem HS; Holbrook, NY; (Y); 35/1550; Cmnty Wkr; Dance Clb; Trs French Clb; Hosp Aide; Color Guard; Mrchg Band; Orch; Nwsp Rptr; Jr NHS; NHS; Wrtg Cont 1st Pl Prose 83; Jrnlsm.

DLHOPOLSKY, CHARLES; Holy Trinity HS; Lindenhurst, NY; (Y); Math Clb; Math Tm; Yrbk Ed-Chief; Pres Soph Cls; JV Bsbl; Im Ftbl; High Hon Roll; NHS; Hon Roll; 1st Pl Catholic Math Leag 85; MA Inst Tech; Comp Engr.

DLUGOSZ, PAUL; Bishop Timon HS; W Seneca, NY; (Y); Computer Clb; Quiz Bowl; Nwsp Stf; Lit Mag; Stu Cncl; Var Bsbl; Im Bsktbl; Im Ftbl; Hon Roll; VP NHS; Accntnt.

DMYTRENKO, ADRIAN R; New Hyde Park Memorial HS; New Hyde Park, NY; (Y); 15/269; Pres Camera Clb; Nwsp Sprt Ed; Var Tennis; Var Trk; NHS; Stdnt Mnth Art Dept Phtgrphy 84; NY ST Regnts Schlrshp 85; Div Champ Riflry Vrsty 83-85; SUNY Binghamton; Med.

DOAN, CHINH; Clarkstown HS; New City, NY; (Y); Math Tm; Science Clb; Mu Alp Tht; NHS; Nuc Physics.

DOANE, PATRICK; Canisteo Central HS; Canisteo, NY; (Y); Boy Scts; Varsity Clb; Band; Concert Band; Mrchg Band; Orch; Im Coach Actv; Var Wrstlng; DAR Awd; Hon Roll; Wrstlng Tm Sctn V Chmps 83; Orchstra Grad 85; SUNY Cobleskill; Comp Sci.

DOBBELAERE, CHRISTEN; Newark SR HS; Newark, NY; (Y); 109/179; Pep Clb; Yrbk Stf; Rep Jr Cls; Im Badmtn; Var Capt Cheerleading; Im Gym; Hon Roll; Bus.

DOBLE JR, WILLIAM T; Holland Patent Central Schl; Stittville, NY; (Y); 2/200; Mathletes; Band; Concert Band; Jazz Band; Orch; Pep Band; School Musical; Symp Band; High Hon Roll; NHS; Regnts Schlrshp 85; Utica Coll Of Syracuse U; Math.

DOBMEIER, CHERYL; Hamburg SR HS; Hamburg, NY; (Y); Church Yth Grp; Service Clb; Church Choir; Im Bsktbl; Im Gym; Im Socr; Im Swmmng; Im Tennis; Dyouville Coll; Nrsng.

DOBRAWSKY, MICHELLE L; Bethpage HS; Bethpage, NY; (Y); 2/295; Mathletes; Concert Band; Mrchg Band; Orch; Nwsp Rptr; NHS; Ntl Merit SF; Office Aide; Spanish Clb; Band; Rensselaer Poly Tech Inst Math & Sci Awd 84; AHSME Math Ex High Scorer 84; Rotary Clb Stu Month 84; Harvard U; Med.

DOBRIC, LAURA; St Johns Prep; Astoria, NY; (Y); Dance Clb; Ski Clb; 2nd Hnr 83; 1st Hnr 85; NY U; Tchr.

DOBSON, DAVID M; Chatham HS; Canaan, NY; (Y); 22/136; Latin Clb; Political Wkr; Chorus; School Musical; Nwsp Stf; Yrbk Stf; Var L Bsktbl; Var L Tennis; High Hon Roll; Earlham Coll; Pol Sci.

DOCCOLA, DONNA; St John Villa Acad; Staten Is, NY; (Y); Church Yth Grp; Civic Clb; Spanish Clb; Stage Crew; Nwsp Rptr; Yrbk Rptr; Tennis; Hon Roll; Nswpr Co-Edtr 85-86; Yrbk Copy Edtr 85-86; Jrnlsm.

DOCHERTY, MARILYN; Cardinal Spellman HS; Bronx, NY; (Y); Pep Clb; Service Clb; Ski Clb; Varsity Clb; Color Guard; School Musical; Yrbk Stf; Off Soph Cls; JV Var Cheerleading; Hon Roll; Pace U; Mktg.

DOCKUM, TOM; Warsaw Central Schl; Warsaw, NY; (S); 3/93; Varsity Clb; Var L Ftbl; Var L Tennis; Var L Trk; Var L Wrstlng; Hon Roll; Jr NHS; NHS; French Clb; Football All League Linebacker 84; Warsaw Cntrl Schltc Awd Math 84.

DODARO, DAVID; Salesian JR Seminary; Goshen, NY; (S); 2/5; Radio Clb; School Play; Yrbk Stf; Pres Jr Cls; Sec Stu Cncl; Stat Bsktbl; High Hon Roll; Voice Dem Awd; Villanova U; Philosophy.

DODARO, DAVID J; Salesian JR Seminary; Scottsdale, AZ; (Y); 2/5; Library Aide; Radio Clb; Band; School Play; Yrbk Ed-Chief; Pres Jr Cls; Sec Stu Cncl; Stat Bsktbl; High Hon Roll; Sal; Villanova U; Philosphy.

DODD, TIMOTHY; Unatego JR SR HS; Otego, NY; (Y); 9/81; Drama Clb; Varsity Clb; Band; School Musical; School Play; Bowling; Crs Cntry; Trk; NHS; Church Yth Grp; RYLA 85; Eng.

DODDS, MARIE; Heurelton Central HS; Heuvelton, NY; (Y); French Clb; JA; Chorus; School Play; Stage Crew; Swing Chorus; MI Vocl Music Awd 84-85; Helcptr Pilot.

DODDS, MICHELLE; Hudson HS; Hudson, NY; (Y); Pres Trs Science Clb; JV Gym; Var Pom Pon; Columbia Green CC; Comp Sci.

DODDS, PENNY L; Taconic Hills Central HS; Hillsdale, NY; (Y); 3/128; Band; Chorus; Yrbk Stf; Pres Sec Stu Cncl; JV Cheerleading; Capt Var Socr; DAR Awd; High Hon Roll; Hon Roll; NHS; Highest Avg Hist,Sci; NYS Regts Schlrshp; U VT; Animal Sci.

DODGE, DAN; Scotia-Glenville HS; Scotia, NY; (Y); JA; Key Clb; Yrbk Stf; Var Capt Ftbl; JV Var Trk; Hon Roll; Math.

DODGE, ERIC; Royalton Hartland Central HS; Middleport, NY; (Y); Boy Scts; Cmnty Wkr; French Clb; Stage Crew; Rep Stu Cncl; JV Ftbl; JV Trk; Hon Roll; Red Cross Aide; Amer Lgn Boys ST 85; Coll; Nrs.

DODGE, LAURICE; John F Kennedy HS; Utica, NY; (Y); 5/150; Key Clb; Spanish Clb; Hon Roll; Utica Coll; Math.

DODGE, LINDA M; Canastota HS; Canastota, NY; (Y); 13/135; Sec Church Yth Grp; Cmnty Wkr; Drama Clb; Trs Intnl Clb; Chorus; School Musical; Stage Crew; Variety Show; Yrbk Stf; NHS; R H Meyer Rainbow Girls Schlrshp 85; Ntl Hist & Gov Awd 85; SUNY Coll At Geneseo; Acctg.

DODGE, ROBERT; Tioga Central HS; Nichols, NY; (Y); 20/72; Computer Clb; Hosp Aide; Variety Show; Sec Frsh Cls; Trs Soph Cls; VP Jr Cls; Pres Sr Cls; Trs Stu Cncl; Crs Cntry; Trk; Ntl Sci Olym Chem 84, Physc 85; Mrch Dme Schlrshp 85; St Joseph Hlth Care; Nrsg.

DODMAN, LISA K; Nardin Acad; Orchard Park, NY; (Y); 9/85; Pres VP 4-H; Office Aide; Service Clb; Ski Clb; School Musical; Trs Frsh Cls; Rep Stu Cncl; JV Tennis; Hon Roll; NHS; Rgnts Schlrshp 85; Cert Excllnc-Latin III 84; Coll Of The Holy Cross; Math.

DOEBLER, DAVID; Newark SR HS; Newark, NY; (Y); 61/201; Aud/Vis; Trs Church Yth Grp; Ski Clb; Church Choir; School Musical; Stage Crew; Yrbk Stf; JV Tennis; Hon Roll; Grove City Coll; Bus Mgmt.

DOERMER, MARK; Grand Island HS; Grand Is, NY; (Y); Church Yth Grp; Band; Concert Band; Mrchg Band; Pep Band; School Musical; Stage Crew; Variety Show; JP Sousa Awd; Rgnts Schlrshp 85; SUNY-BUFFALO; Chem Engr.

DOETSCH, DEIRDRE; Delaware Valley Central HS; Callicoon, NY; (Y); 13/35; Church Choir; Rep Stu Cncl; JV Bsktbl; Hon Roll; NYS Rgnts Scholar Nrsg 85; Humanitarn Awd 85; Crouse; Nrsg.

DOGAS, TOM; Westlake HS; Hawthorne, NY; (Y); Church Yth Grp; Letterman Clb; Varsity Clb; Nwsp Rptr; Var JV Bsbl; Var Capt Socr; Hon Roll.

DOHERTY, ERIN ANNE; East Meadow HS; E Meadow, NY; (Y); Church Yth Grp; Cmnty Wkr; Debate Tm; Drama Clb; FBLA; Girl Scts; Key Clb; Concert Band; Flag Corp; Mrchg Band; NRA ST JR Olympc Shootg Champ 85; Key Clb East Meadw Actv Membr Awd 84; Nassau CC; Bus.

DOHERTY, LISE MARIE; Cedntral HS; Valley Stream, NY; (Y); AFS; Drama Clb; Band; Chorus; Concert Band; Madrigals; Mrchg Band; School Musical; School Play; Hon Roll; Msts Achvt SAT Scores 85; Cortland ST; Elem Ed.

DOHERTY, SHEILA M; Notre Dame Acad; Staten Island, NY; (Y); 34/91; Lit Mag; Ntl Merit Schlrshp Lttr; NYS Regnts Schlrshp 85.

DOHERTY, SHERRI; Villa Maria Acad; Buffalo, NY; (Y); 10/110; Computer Clb; Math Clb; Pep Clb; School Play; VP Stu Cncl; Gym; High Hon Roll; Prfct Atten Awd; Cum Laude Awd 82; Canisius Coll; Bio.

DOHRENWEND, TERRI A; Centereach HS; Centereach, NY; (Y); 28/481; Pres Church Yth Grp; Chorus; School Musical; Yrbk Ed-Chief; Yrbk Phtg; Var Vllybl; Hon Roll; Jr NHS; NHS; Rgnts Schlrshp 85; Stonybrook U; Occptnl Thrpy.

DOHT, ROBERT C; North Babylon HS; N Babylon, NY; (Y); 50/562; Church Yth Grp; Ski Clb; Chorus; Off Sr Cls; Var Bsbl; JV Ftbl; High Hon Roll; Hon Roll; NHS; Pres Schlr; SUNY-BINGHAMTON; Math.

DOLAN, BRIDGET; West Genesee SR HS; Syracuse, NY; (Y); Church Yth Grp; Hosp Aide; Pep Clb; Ski Clb; Color Guard; Off Jr Cls; Off Sr Cls; Var Cheerleading; Hon Roll; Prfct Atten Awd; Nice Kid Awd 82 & 83.

DOLAN, DEIRDRE; Maria Regina HS; Bronxville, NY; (Y); 5/127; Speech Tm; Nwsp Stf; Yrbk Ed-Chief; Yrbk Phtg; Rep Stu Cncl; Var Trk; NHS; Ntl Merit Ltr.

DOLAN, KERRY; Dobbs Ferry HS; Dobbs Ferry, NY; (S); 7/80; Key Clb; Band; Jazz Band; Mrchg Band; Yrbk Bus Mgr; Rep Soph Cls; Tennis; French Hon Soc; High Hon Roll; NHS; Louis Armstrong Jazz Awd 84.

DOLAN, KEVIN; Valhalla HS; Valhalla, NY; (Y); 28/120; Am Leg Boys St; Trs Jr Cls; Pres Sr Cls; Capt Ftbl; Trk; Cit Awd; High Hon Roll; Prfct Atten Awd; Phys Ftnss Awd 85; Presntl Acad Ftnss Awd 85; Pace U; Mktng.

DOLAN, LYNDA; Clifton-Fine Central Schl; Star Lake, NY; (S); 2/51; French Clb; Band; Chorus; School Play; JV Var Cheerleading; JV Var Socr; Var Capt Trk; High Hon Roll; NHS; Sal; Soccer MVP 84; Siena Coll; Bio.

DOLAN, PAUL T; Mc Quaid Jesuit HS; Pittsford, NY; (Y); 18/183; Church Yth Grp; School Play; Rep Frsh Cls; Var L Socr; Var L Vllybl; High Hon Roll; NEDT Awd; NY Regents Schlrshp 85; Pres Schlr 85; Natl Educ Dev Test Awd 83; U Of Tampa; Bus.

DOLAN, THOMAS; Cathedral Prep Sem; Brooklyn, NY; (Y); 7/15; Boy Scts; Sec Jr Cls; Swmmng.

DOLAN, WILLIAM; Mononasen SR HS; Schenectady, NY; (Y); Concert Band; Jazz Band; High Hon Roll; Berklee Schl Music; Music.

DOLATA, CAROLE; Commack High Schl North; Commack, NY; (Y); Church Yth Grp; Exploring; French Clb; Teachers Aide; Chorus; Nwsp Stf; Off Soph Cls; Off Jr Cls; Var Badmtn; High Hon Roll; Bus Admin.

DOLCE, JOHN; Christ The King R HS; Ridgewood, NY; (Y); 50/333; Camera Clb; Science Clb; Teachers Aide; Varsity Clb; Nwsp Phtg; Socr; Hon Roll; St Johns U; Law.

DOLCE, RICHARD; Kings Park HS; Kings Park, NY; (Y); 81/393; Debate Tm; Drama Clb; Band; Concert Band; Jazz Band; Mrchg Band; School Musical; Variety Show; Tennis; Law.

DOLDO, TODD J; Immaculate Heart Central HS; Watertown, NY; (Y); 16/82; Church Yth Grp; Cmnty Wkr; Yrbk Stf; Rep Jr Cls; VP Stu Cncl; JV Var Bsktbl; JV Var Ftbl; JV Var Lcrss; Hon Roll; All Star-All N Ftbl 82-84; 2nd Tm All Star La Crosse 84; 1st Tm All Star La Crosse 85; St Lawrence U; Pre-Law.

DOLE, GINA; Pioneer Central HS; Chaffee, NY; (Y); 42/203; French Clb; Band; Color Guard; Jazz Band; Mrchg Band; Stage Crew; Nwsp Phtg; Yrbk Stf; Rep Soph Cls; Rep Jr Cls; Comp.

DOLECKI, MARK A; Salamanca Central HS; Salamanca, NY; (Y); Am Leg Boys St; French Clb; Model UN; Band; Color Guard; Drm Mjr(t); Mrchg Band; French Hon Soc; NHS; Ntl Merit Ltr.

DOLGONOS, LISA; Kenmore West SR HS; Kenmore, NY; (Y); French Clb; Stage Crew; Variety Show; JV Trk; High Hon Roll; Hon Roll; Ntl French Cont Awd 84; Exc Atten Awd 84-85.

DOLICH, SCOTT; Rye HS; Rye, NY; (Y); 13/175; Ski Clb; Nwsp Phtg; Yrbk Ed-Chief; Yrbk Phtg; Yrbk Stf; Var Lcrss; Var Socr; High Hon Roll; Hon Roll; NHS.

DOLPH, LARRY; Bishop Cunningham HS; Oswego, NY; (S); Am Leg Boys St; French Clb; Yrbk Stf; VP Jr Cls; Capt Var Bsktbl; Var Capt Socr; Wt Lftg; Hon Roll; NHS; Ntl Phys Ed Awd 84-85; Bus.

DOLTON, EMILY C; Saratoga Springs SR HS; Saratoga Springs, NY; (Y); 14/465; Pres DECA; Trs Drama Clb; Girl Scts; High Hon Roll; NHS; 1st Pl DECA Adv Svcs 85; Regnts Schlrshp 85; Art Awds 83-84; SUNY Coll New Paltz; Art Dir.

DOMAGALA, PENNY; South Lewis Central HS; Glenfield, NY; (Y); Sec 4-H; Chorus; Church Choir; Score Keeper; JV Var Vllybl; 4-H Awd; Hon Roll; Sci Stu Rcgntn 85; Math Educ.

DOMALSKI, DEBORAH L; Lancaster Central HS; Depew, NY; (Y); Hosp Aide; Library Aide; Pep Clb; Yrbk Stf; Sec Sr Cls; Rep Stu Cncl; Im Bsktbl; Im Vllybl; Art Clb; Red Cross Aide; Rgnts Diploma Spcl Endrsmnt Grmn 85; Buffalo ST U.

DOMAN, JENNIFER M; Brooklyn Friends HS; Brooklyn, NY; (Y); Dance Clb; Exploring; Chorus; School Musical; Stage Crew; Nwsp Bus Mgr; Nwsp Ed-Chief; Pres Soph Cls; Pres Jr Cls; Pres Sr Cls; Theatre Critic.

DOMBEK, FRED; Lakeland HS; Mahopac, NY; (Y); Drama Clb; Ski Clb; Spanish Clb; Band; Concert Band; Jazz Band; Mrchg Band; Orch; School Musical; School Play; Mercy SUNY Purchase; Music.

DOMBROSKI, MARY; G Ray Bodley HS; Oswego, NY; (Y); Pep Clb; Yrbk Stf; Rep Frsh Cls; Trvlnd Trsm.

DOMBROW, RUSSELL W; Bishop Ludden HS; Syracuse, NY; (Y); Am Leg Boys St; French Clb; Political Wkr; Spanish Clb; Soph Cls; Var Ice Hcky; Var L Socr; High Hon Roll; Hon Roll; Pre-Law.

DOMBROWSKI, ANDREA R; Holy Trinity HS; Oyster Bay Cove, NY; (S); 15/360; Math Tm; Sec Sr Cls; Var Cheerleading; Var Gym; Capt Var Swmmng; Var Trk; High Hon Roll; NHS.

DOMBROWSKI, DENISE; Attica SR HS; Cowlesville, NY; (S); 10/150; VP AFS; Church Yth Grp; Sec Band; Trs Nwsp Stf; Trs Soph Cls; JV Cheerleading; Var Trk; Hon Roll; Intrnl Frng Lang Awd 85; Ed.

DOMBROWSKI, JILL M; West Seneca East SR HS; West Seneca, NY; (Y); 3/365; Dance Clb; Church Choir; Color Guard; Drm & Bgl; Flag Corp; Rep Chess Clb; Stu Cncl; Im Socr; Im Im Vllybl; JC Awd; Regnts Schlrshp 85; Cornell U Natl Schlr 85; Cornell U; Indstrl Rel.

DOMBROWSKI, LORI; Alden HS; Elma, NY; (Y); 26/203; Spanish Clb; School Musical; Pres Frsh Cls; Pres Soph Cls; Pres Jr Cls; Pres Sr Cls; Rep Stu Cncl; Hon Roll; Acdmc Awd; Chrch Wrk; Athlt Assn; U Of Buffalo; Physcl Thrpy.

DOMBROWSKI, LYNN; Alden HS; Alden, NY; (Y); 46/198; Church Yth Grp; Science Clb; Spanish Clb; School Musical; Nwsp Stf; Yrbk Phtg; Yrbk Rptr; Yrbk Sprt Ed; Yrbk Stf; Var Diving; SUNY; Phys Ed.

DOMBROWSKI, MARC; Saint Marys High Lancastr; Buffalo, NY; (S); Boy Scts; Science Clb; Ski Clb; Nwsp Rptr; Lit Mag; Socr; Bus Mgmt.

DOMENICO, ARWEN; Rome Free Acad; Rome, NY; (Y); 76/520; AFS; Drama Clb; Speech Tm; Stage Crew; Hon Roll; Jr NHS; Pres Schlr; Pres Acad Ftns Awd 85; SUNY-ALBANY; Hist.

DOMICO, KAREN; Alexander Central HS; Darien, NY; (Y); 17/87; FNA; Chorus; Color Guard; Nwsp Rptr; Nwsp Stf; NHS; Lector Church; Ed.

DOMILICI, MARIA; Bishop Kearney HS; Brooklyn, NY; (S); 53/343; Cmnty Wkr; Bsktbl; Coach Actv; Trk; Hon Roll; NHS; WA Square U Coll Schlrshp Ot NYU 85; U Trustee Shclrshp Of Pace U 85; Regents Shclrshp 85.

DOMINELLI, RICHARD A; Clarkstown South HS; Nyack, NY; (Y); 51/541; Boy Scts; Computer Clb; Band; Bowling; Jr NHS; Mu Alp Tht; NHS; Ntl Merit SF; NY Rgnts Bio Awd 81; Plattsburgh; Comp Sci.

DOMINGO, VANESSA; St Hildas HS; New York, NY; (Y); 4/20; Pep Clb; Chorus; School Play; Nwsp Stf; Yrbk Phtg; Yrbk Stf; Rep Soph Cls; VP Stu Cncl; Capt Bsktbl; Im Trk; Bus Adm.

DOMINGO, WILBERT; Sachem HS; Holbrook, NY; (Y); 212/1700; Art Clb; Chess Clb; Computer Clb; Hosp Aide; Yrbk Stf; Im Ftbl; JV Trk; JV Wrstlng; Jr NHS; NHS; Awd Paintg & Drwg I Art 84-85; Tanglaw Acadmc Awd 84; ST U Stonebrook; Pre-Med.

DOMINGUEZ, JULIO CESAR; Cardinal Hayes HS; New York, NY; (Y); Letterman Clb; Band; Chorus; School Musical; Stage Crew; Nwsp Rptr; Hon Roll; Prfct Atten Awd; Val; 2nd Hnrs 83; Columbia U; Pre-Med.

DOMINGUEZ, MARIA; Cathedral HS; Woodside, NY; (Y); 74/344; Art Clb; Intnl Clb; Latin Clb; Spanish Clb; Nwsp Phtg; Yrbk Phtg; Bsktbl; Socr; Sftbl; Vllybl; Prfct Attndnc Awd 81-83; Elec Engrng.

DOMINGUEZ, MARIA; H S Of Fashion Indstrys; New York, NY; (Y); 12/413; Sec Church Yth Grp; Chorus; Church Choir; Hon Roll; Awd Of Merit Sci; Trnsltr Spnsh Lang; SUNY; Fshn Dsgnr.

DOMINGUEZ, RODOLFO; Eastern District HS; Brooklyn, NY; (Y); Band; Ftbl; Vllybl; French Hon Soc; Hon Roll; Embry-Riddle Aero U; Cmrcl Plt.

DOMINIC, STACY; Northern Adirondack Central HS; Ellenburg, NY; (Y); Key Clb; Band; JV Var Bsbl; JV Var Bsktbl; JV Var Socr; Hon Roll.

DOMINIE, KIM; Tupper Lake HS; Tupper Lake, NY; (Y); 33/101; Hosp Aide; Off Frsh Cls; Off Soph Cls; Stu Cncl; Stat Bsktbl; JV Mgr Socr; Stat Vllybl; Hon Roll; NHS; Nrsg Schlrshp, Outstndng Stu Hlth Occup 85; Crouse Irving; RN.

DOMPKOWSKI, MARY; Hanburg SR HS; Hamburg, NY; (Y); 58/408; VP JCL; Service Clb; Orch; School Musical; Nwsp Rptr; Nwsp Stf; Sec Jr Cls; Sec Sr Cls; Stu Cncl; Var Cheerleading; Latin Achvt Awd 85; Helen Faux-Allen Mem Schlrshp; St Bonaventure U; Jrnlsm.

DOMURAD, JOHN; Susquehanna Valley HS; Kirkwood, NY; (Y); 17/174; Ski Clb; Spanish Clb; Rep Stu Cncl; Var JV Ftbl; Var JV Trk; JV Wrstlng; NHS.

DONACIK, ANDREW; Cardinal OHARA HS; Kenmore, NY; (S); 2/145; French Clb; Hosp Aide; Sec Frsh Cls; Sec Soph Cls; Sec Jr Cls; JV Bsktbl; Capt Crs Cntry; Trk; High Hon Roll; Wash Wrkshp Cngrssnl Smnr 85; Ntl Hnr Soc Schlrshp 84; Sch Ath Cross Cntry Awd 84; Econmcs.

DONAGHY, JOHN; James Sperry HS; Rochester, NY; (Y); Church Yth Grp; Math Tm; Thesps; School Play; Crs Cntry; Trk; Hon Roll; Jr NHS; NHS; Spanish NHS; Hmnts.

DONAHUE, KIM; Albion HS; Albion, NY; (Y); FNA; Girl Scts; Hosp Aide; JCL; Latin Clb; Spanish Clb; Teachers Aide; Nrsng Schlrshp.

DONAHUE, MICHAEL; De Sales HS; Geneva, NY; (Y); 9/29; French Clb; Letterman Clb; Political Wkr; Scholastic Bowl; Varsity Clb; Trs Rep Frsh Cls; Rep Soph Cls; Pres Jr Cls; Var Bsbl; JV Var Bsktbl; Engl.

DONAHUE, SUSAN M; Bronx High School Of Science; Bronx, NY; (Y).

DONALD, ROBERT; Washingtontonville SR HS; Washingtonville, NY; (Y); Boy Scts; Computer Clb; Ski Clb; Spanish Clb; Band; Rep Stu Cncl; JV Bsbl; Im Ice Hcky; Im Chrmn CAP; Hon Roll; Arch.

DONALDSON, JANE; Auburn HS; Auburn, NY; (Y); Ski Clb; Tennis; High Hon Roll; Hon Roll; VICA; Score Keeper; Trk; Ntl Merit Ltr.

DONALDSON, KIMBERLY B; Lyme Central HS; Chaumont, NY; (Y); Art Clb; GAA; Spanish Clb; Varsity Clb; Band; Church Choir; Concert Band; Mrchg Band; Pep Band; Trs Frsh Cls; Vrsty Socr MVP 85; Vrsty Socr All Star 83-85; Vrsty Sftbl All Star 84; Oswego; Bus.

DONALDSON, RONALD; Frontier Central HS; Hamburg, NY; (Y); French Clb; Varsity Clb; Bsktbl; Mgr(s); Score Keeper; Tennis; Hon Roll; Ntl Merit Ltr; Engrng.

DONATI, LISA; Henninger HS; Syracuse, NY; (Y); GAA; Intnl Clb; Key Clb; Library Aide; Pep Clb; Ski Clb; Yrbk Phtg; Yrbk Rptr; Yrbk Stf; Sec Frsh Cls; Librry Aid Awd 84.

DONATO, DAWN-MARIE; New Rochelle HS; Mamaroneck, NY; (Y); 116/600; JV Socr; NHS; U MA Amherst.

DONATO, EDWIN; Spackenkill HS; Poughkeepsie, NY; (Y); FCA; FBLA; PAVAS; Political Wkr; Science Clb; Spanish Clb; Variety Show; Nwsp Stf; Yrbk Rptr; Yrbk Stf.

DONATO, GINA; New Rochelle HS; New Rochelle, NY; (Y); Math Tm; Var Sftbl; High Hon Roll; Hon Roll; NHS; Biol Geom & Italian Awd 83; Smith Coll Bk Awd 85; Genetc Engr.

DONATO, RICK; Grand Island HS; Grand Island, NY; (Y); Teachers Aide; Var Capt Ice Hcky; Var L Socr; Hon Roll; Coaches Awd In Soccer 82; U Of NC Chrlt; Engrng.

DONATO, VINCENT; Bishop Maginn HS; Albany, NY; (S); Math Clb; Nwsp Stf; Trs Jr Cls; High Hon Roll; NHS; Wharton Sch Bus; Mgmt.

DONEGAN, COLLEEN; Academy Of St Joseph; Coram, NY; (Y); 3/121; Art Clb; Aud/Vis; Church Yth Grp; Cmnty Wkr; Science Clb; Yrbk Stf; Regnts Schlrshp; Ntl Art Hnr Soc; SUNY Stonybrook; Sec Ed.

DONELLA, STEPHEN P; Fayetteville-Manlius HS; Manlius, NY; (Y); Pres Debate Tm; NFL; Political Wkr; Pres Speech Tm; Nwsp Stf; Yrbk Stf; JV Socr; L Var Tennis; L Wrstlng; Hon Roll.

DONER, FRED; Watertown HS; Dexter, NY; (Y); Band; Ftbl; Wt Lftg; Wrstlng; Jefferson County Coll; Mgmt.

DONG, BETTY; Christopher Columbus HS; Bronx, NY; (S); 53/792; Chorus; Hon Roll; Science.

DONLEY, SEANNA; Auburn HS; Auburn, NY; (Y); Sec Drama Clb; Chorus; School Musical; School Play; Swing Chorus; High Hon Roll; Hist Clb VP 84-85; Telecomm.

DONNELL, CAROL O; Tonawanda JR SR HS; Tonawanda, NY; (Y); French Clb; Red Cross Aide; Chorus; Hon Roll; NHS; Bio Stu Yr 83-84; Vet.

DONNELLAN, KERRY ANN B; Bech Channel HS; Brooklyn, NY; (Y); Dance Clb; Yrbk Stf; Gym; Socr; Tennis; Comp.

DONNELLY, BRIAN; Sayville HS; Sayville, NY; (Y); 9/360; Am Leg Boys St; Key Clb; Church Choir; School Play; Nwsp Ed-Chief; Yrbk Sprt Ed; Socr; Cit Awd; High Hon Roll; Pres NHS; Advanced Placemnt Hist Awd 85; Hnr Soc Svc Awd 85; Notre Dame; Bio.

DONNELLY, COLLEEN; Odessa-Montour Central Schl; Odessa, NY; (Y); Aud/Vis; Trs Ski Clb; High Hon Roll; Neighbrhd Just Proj Mediatr 85; Giftd & Talntd Pgm 82-85; SUNY Albany; Mth.

DONNELLY, GERARD B; Sayville HS; Sayville, NY; (Y); 10/365; Am Leg Boys St; Key Clb; Church Choir; School Play; Nwsp Stf; Yrbk Sprt Ed; JV Socr; Im Vllybl; High Hon Roll; NHS; Pres NHS 84-85; Hnrs Natl Frnch Cntst 82-83 & 83-84; U Notre Dame; Pre-Med.

DONNELLY, JACQUELINE; Cardinal Mooney HS; Rochester, NY; (Y); 31/317; Library Aide; Spanish Clb; Teachers Aide; Rep Frsh Cls; JV Var Cheerleading; JV Pom Pon; Socr; Sftbl; Hon Roll; Spanish NHS; U Of Rochester; Pre-Med.

DONNELLY, JANET; Canisteo Central Schl; Canisteo, NY; (Y); 2/78; Church Yth Grp; Girl Scts; Ski Clb; Speech Tm; Yrbk Ed-Chief; Rep Soph Cls; Rep Jr Cls; High Hon Roll; NHS; Ntl Merit Ltr; 2nd Pl Spch Cntst 84; 3rd Pl Spch Cntst 85; Advrtsng.

DONNELLY, KEVIN; Chester HS; Chester, NY; (Y); Var L Bsbl; Var L Bsktbl; Hon Roll; Engrng.

DONNELLY, MARY P; Bishop Ludden HS; Auburn, NY; (S); Church Yth Grp; Intnl Clb; High Hon Roll; Hon Roll; Jr NHS; NHS; Hnr Roll; High Hnr Roll; Natl Hnr Scty; Nazareth Coll; Spec Educ.

DONNELLY, PETER J; St Josephs Colegiate Inst; Kenmore, NY; (Y); 11/201; Trk; High Hon Roll; NHS; Boy Scts; Nwsp Stf; Yrbk Stf; Ftbl; NROTC Schlrshp; Rochester Inst Of Tech; Engrng.

DONNELLY, TARA; St Agnes HS; Valley Stream, NY; (Y); 8/424; Drama Clb; Girl Scts; Spanish Clb; Teachers Aide; Chorus; School Musical; Nwsp Stf; Stu Cncl; High Hon Roll; NHS; Excllnc Spnsh Awd 85; Cum Laude 85; Amer Achvt Awd 84; Fordham Coll; Psych.

DONNER, LAURA; Nazareth Acad; Rochester, NY; (S); Math Clb; Math Tm; Ski Clb; Spanish Clb; Band; School Musical; Stage Crew; Var Capt Vllybl; Hon Roll; NHS; Natl Merit Excllnc Phy Ed 84; SUNY Buffalo; Comp.

DONNER, MITCHELL; Plainedge HS; Nmassapequa, NY; (Y); Aud/Vis; Mathletes; Quiz Bowl; Temple Yth Grp; Orch; Hon Roll; Rep Stu Cncl; Var Lcrss; JV Wrstlng; Law.

DONNO, FRANK; William Floyd HS; Shirley, NY; (Y); 6/428; Math Tm; MMM; Sec Thesps; Chorus; Orch; Swing Chorus; Nwsp Bus Mgr; NHS; 1st Forensic Tourny; Regents Schlrshp Wnnr; YMCA Yth & Govt Outstndng Atty Wnnr; NY U; Accntng.

DONOFRI, MICHELE; Our Lady Of Mercy Acad; Woodbury, NY; (Y); 16/116; Pres Camera Clb; Spanish Clb; Nwsp Phtg; Ed Yrbk Phtg; Yrbk Stf; Lit Mag; Ftbl; Sftbl; Hon Roll; Prfct Atten Awd; Chem Seminar Gifted HS Stu Adelphi U 83; Best Of Show Photo Religous Art Fest 84; NASSAU Comm Coll.

DONOFRIO, MICHAEL; Gloversville HS; Gloversville, NY; (Y); Band; Var Capt Bsbl; JV Im Ftbl.

DONOHUE, ADELE; South Side HS; Rockville Ctr, NY; (Y); 17/287; Exploring; Key Clb; Latin Clb; Science Clb; Cit Awd; High Hon Roll; Hon Roll; JETS Awd; Jr NHS; NHS; PTA Schlrshp 85; Tchrs Assoc Schlrsh& 85; Berkeley Bus Awd 85; Chem Tchr.

DONOHUE, BARBARA A; Holy Trinity HS; Bellmore, NY; (S); 26/362; Mathletes; Ski Clb; Spanish Clb; Bsktbl; Gym; Sftbl; Vllybl; NHS; Ntl Merit Ltr; NEDT Awd; Pre Med.

DONOHUE, BERNADETTE; Saratoga Central Catholic HS; Ballston Spa, NY; (Y); 1/51; Drama Clb; Rep Frsh Cls; Sec Soph Cls; Var L Bsktbl; Capt L Vllybl; Bausch & Lomb Sci Awd; JC Awd; Ntl Merit Ltr; St Schlr; Val; Lit Edtr Yrbk 84-85; Natl Hnr Socty 84-85; Hgh Hnr Rll 81-85; Cornell U; Nutr Sci.

DONOHUE, CATHERINE ANNE; Smithtown High School East; Smithtown, NY; (Y); Church Yth Grp; GAA; Band; Chorus; Drm & Bgl; Var L Fld Hcky; Sftbl; Var L Trk; NHS; Spanish NHS; Engr.

DONOHUE, EDWARD; C A Boynton Voorheesville HS; Voorheesville, NY; (Y); Boy Scts; Church Yth Grp; French Clb; Intnl Clb; Key Clb; Im Bsktbl; Var L Crs Cntry; Var L Trk; Im Wt Lftg; Hon Roll; Eagle Scout 85; Pre-Law.

DONOHUE, EILEEN; Saratoga Centera Catholic HS; Bronx, NY; (S); Drama Clb; GAA; Ski Clb; Varsity Clb; School Play; Yrbk Stf; Var L Bsktbl; JV Cheerleading; Var L Vllybl; Hon Roll; Outstndg SR Lfsvng Stu 83.

DONOHUE, GWYN M; Fairport HS; Fairport, NY; (Y); Debate Tm; Drama Clb; Yrbk Stf; Rep Stu Cncl; Stat Bsktbl; Var L Fld Hcky; Mgr(s); Hon Roll; Exploring; Ski Clb; NY ST Regents Schlrshp 85; NY ST Bar Assoc Awd 83; Miami U; Mrktng.

DONOHUE, JENNIE; Delaware Valley Central HS; Hortonville, NY; (Y); 3/44; Pres 4-H; Hosp Aide; Q&S; Sec Spanish Clb; Chorus; School Musical; School Play; Nwsp Ed-Chief; Nwsp Rptr; Yrbk Rptr; Journlsm.

DONOHUE, KELLEY; Buffalo Seminary HS; West Falls, NY; (Y); Pres Church Yth Grp; Sec 4-H; Red Cross Aide; Rep Frsh Cls; Rep Soph Cls; Rep Jr Cls; Chrmn Sr Cls; Rep Stu Cncl; Capt L Fld Hcky; Var L Lcrss; Fld Hockey MIP 82-83; Fld Hockey Unsung Hero Awd 83-84; U Rochester; Engrng.

DONOHUE, MARY LU; The Academy Of The Holy Angels; Pearl River, NY; (Y); 30/158; Church Yth Grp; Hosp Aide; Math Clb; Ski Clb; Teachers Aide; Nwsp Stf; Yrbk Stf; Rep Soph Cls; Var Vllybl; Hon Roll; Manhattan Coll Acadmc Awd 85; Manhattan Coll; Cvl Engrng.

DONOHUE, MEGAN F; Westhampton Beach HS; Southampton, NY; (Y); 3/199; Spanish Clb; Band; Chorus; Concert Band; Mrchg Band; Pep Band; Yrbk Stf; Trk; Bausch & Lomb Sci Awd; High Hon Roll; Boston Coll.

DONOHUE, PATRICIA A; Smithtown HS; Smithtown, NY; (Y); Church Yth Grp; GAA; Spanish Clb; Teachers Aide; Concert Band; Mrchg Band; JV Bsktbl; Var L Fld Hcky; JV Sftbl; High Hon Roll; Lafayette Coll; Engrng.

DONOHUE, RICHARD; Hicksville HS; Hicksville, NY; (Y); Cmnty Wkr; Spanish Clb; Chorus; Nwsp Rptr; Frsh Cls; Stu Cncl; Hon Roll; Bus.

DONOHUE, SCOTT; H Frank Carey HS; Garden City So, NY; (Y); 27/281; Aud/Vis; Drama Clb; Key Clb; Var Capt Bsbl; Bsktbl; Ftbl; Trk; High Hon Roll; Kiwanis Awd; Ntl Merit SF; NYS Regnts Schlrshp 85; Adelphi U Trustee Schlrshp 85; NYS Bldngs Schlrshp 85; Adelphi U; Bus.

DONOVAN, BRIEN; Smithtown High School West; Hauppauge, NY; (Y); Yrbk Phtg; JV Lcrss; JV Socr; Vllybl; Hon Roll; Grmn Natl Hnr Soc Delta Epsilon Phi 84-85; DECA Clb Rgnl Awd Wnnr 84-85; Ecology Clb 83-84; Phys Ther.

DONOVAN, CLAIRE; Our Lady Of Victory HS; Ossining, NY; (S); NHS; NEDT Awd; Schlrshp Pace Bus Schl; Schlrshp Simmons Bus Schl; Hstry Awd; Drama.

DONOVAN, JOHN; Alberto S Magnus HS; Pearl River, NY; (Y); 14/185; Cmnty Wkr; Hon Roll; Mu Alp Tht; NHS; US Bus Ed Awd 85; Ntl Hnr Roll 85; Math Hnr Roll 82-85; Rcklnd CC; Mngmnt.

DONOVAN, KRISTEN H; Ardsley HS; Ardsley, NY; (Y); Drama Clb; Hosp Aide; Key Clb; Service Clb; Chorus; Color Guard; School Play; French Hon Soc; Svc Awd 83-84; Binghamton; Intl Bus.

DONOVAN, MARK P; Fayetteville-Manlius HS; Manlius, NY; (Y); Model UN; Political Wkr; Jazz Band; Variety Show; Pres Frsh Cls; Stu Cncl; Bsktbl; JV Var Ftbl; JV Var Lcrss; Hon Roll; Engrng.

DONOVAN, MELISSA; Masters Schl; Rockville, MD; (Y); Drama Clb; Hosp Aide; Political Wkr; School Musical; School Play; Stage Crew; Rep Stu Cncl; Cheerleading; Gym; Church Yth Grp; MD Miss Ntl Tnagr Acad Excllcn Awd 83-84; Amer Coll In Paris; Pltcl Sci.

DONOVAN, NANCY; Oneida SR HS; Wampsville, NY; (S); Spanish Clb; Yrbk Stf; Sec Jr Cls; Sec Sr Cls; Var L Fld Hcky; High Hon Roll; Pres NHS; Varsity Clb; Sec Soph Cls; Pres Phys Fitness Awd 84; Reg Schlstc Art Awd 83; Bus.

DOOHER, KELLY A; East Syracuse Minoa HS; East Syracuse, NY; (Y); 9/338; Sec Drama Clb; Thesps; Chorus; School Musical; School Play; Stage Crew; Swing Chorus; Var L Tennis; High Hon Roll; Jr NHS; Regents Schlrshp 85; Suny Oswego; Bio.

DOOLEY, COLLEEN P; Islip HS; Islip, NY; (Y); 39/256; Chorus; Var Capt Bsktbl; Var Capt Tennis; JV Var Vllybl; Hon Roll; Jr NHS; NYS Schlrshp Ctznshp & PE Awd 84-85; Gld Key Awd 85; Pres Awd 85; Fairfield U; Lib Arts.

DOOLEY, EDWARD; St John The Baptist D HS; N Babylon, NY; (Y); MMM; Political Wkr; Chorus; Swmmng; Hon Roll; NHS; NYS U Albany; Acctng.

DOOLEY, KAREN L; N Rose-Wolcott HS; San Diego, CA; (Y); Ski Clb; Spanish Clb; Varsity Clb; Yrbk Stf; Socr; Swmmng; Tennis; Trk; High Hon Roll; Hon Roll; Psyclgy.

DOOLEY, KERRI; Farmingdale HS; Farmingdale, NY; (Y); Varsity Clb; Var Socr; Merchndsng.

DOOLEY, RICHARD; Morrisville-Eaton HS; Morrisville, NY; (Y); 3/55; Varsity Clb; Band; Concert Band; Var Tennis; High Hon Roll; NHS; Jeff Galbreath Memrl Awd 85; Morrisville Amer Legn 85; SUNY Coll Oswego; Mtrlgy.

DOOLITTLE, ANDREW; Holland Patent Central HS; Holland Patent, NY; (Y); 16/199; AFS; Church Yth Grp; Teachers Aide; Concert Band; Orch; Symp Band; JV Swmmng; Var Capt Tennis; NHS; Yrbk Phtg; NYS Regnts Schlrshp 85; U Of VA; Lbrl Arts.

DOOLITTLE JR, MARK A; Johnson City HS; Johnson City, NY; (Y); 63/212; Teachers Aide; Acpl Chr; School Musical; School Play; Swing Chorus; Yrbk Phtg; Var Bsbl; Var Socr; Hon Roll; St Schlr; Photo Cont 2 Ntl Awds, 2 Gold Keys, 2 Blue Rbbns & 2 Nmntns For Kodak Medlln 85; Rochester Inst Of Tech; Photogr.

DOORNBOS, TRINA; Vernon-Verona-Sherrill Central HS; Verona, NY; (Y); AFS; Yrbk Sprt Ed; Rep Frsh Cls; Rep Jr Cls; High Hon Roll; Hon Roll; Church Yth Grp; Girl Scts; Spanish Clb; Thesps.

DORANCY, PIERRE E; Brooklyn Tech; Brooklyn, NY; (Y); 314/1139; Church Yth Grp; Office Aide; Band; Concert Band; Var Crs Cntry; Var Trk; Hon Roll; Prfct Atten Awd; U PA; Bio.

DORB, MADELYN; Bethpage HS; Plainview, NY; (Y); 91/300; Cmnty Wkr; Office Aide; Temple Yth Grp; Y-Teens; Yrbk Stf; Rep Soph Cls; Rep Jr Cls; Stat Lcrss; Hon Roll; FBLA; Nal Soc Stu Olym 84; Pre-Dntl.

DORE, CATHERINE JOANNE; Holy Trinity HS; Bethpage, NY; (S); 21/432; High Hon Roll; Hon Roll; Ntl Merit Ltr; Non Regents Alg Achvt Awd 82; Non Regents Geom Scholar Awd 83; :Vet.

DOREMUS, CONSTANCE ANN; Riverhead HS; Riverhead, NY; (Y); German Clb; Hosp Aide; VP Intnl Clb; Trs Key Clb; Science Clb; Ski Clb; Chorus; Swing Chorus; Var Trk; Rotary Awd; Suffolk County CC; CPA.

DORESTANT, PAUL; Midwood HS; Brooklyn, NY; (Y); Drama Clb; French Clb; Intnl Clb; Math Tm; Chorus; School Play; Stage Crew; Stu Cncl; Lcrss; Hon Roll; Aerospc Engr.

DORETY, MICHELE; Duanesburg HS; Esperance, NY; (Y); Cmnty Wkr; Drama Clb; 4-H; French Clb; GAA; Girl Scts; Intnl Clb; Teachers Aide; Band; Chorus; MVP Soccr 85; Frgn Bus Cmmnctns.

DOREY, LISA; Plattsburgh HS; Plattsburgh AFB, NY; (Y); Church Yth Grp; Hosp Aide; Red Cross Aide; Ski Clb; Diving; Swmmng; High Hon Roll; Hon Roll; NHS; Soc Studs Achv Awd 84; Med Dr.

DORIAN, VANESSA; Clarkstown HS; New City, NY; (Y); Var Gym; Var Trk; Hon Roll; 25th Pl NYS Uneven Parall Bars 84; Bus.

DORIS, EILEEN; Sacred Heart HS; Yonkers, NY; (S); 6/240; Church Yth Grp; Intnl Clb; Yrbk Stf; Crs Cntry; Trk; High Hon Roll; NHS; NEDT Awd.

DORMADY, EDWARD J; Ithaca HS; Ithaca, NY; (Y); Political Wkr; Ski Clb; Band; Concert Band; Nwsp Bus Mgr; Cornell U.

DORMANN, BRIAN P; West Senecas SR HS; Cheektowaga, NY; (Y); 112/546; Yrbk Rptr; St Schlr; Syracuse U; Zoolgy.

DORN, TINA; Vernon-Verona-Sherrill HS; Vernon Ctr, NY; (Y); AFS; French Clb; VP JCL; Sec Latin Clb; Thesps; Chorus; Concert Band; Jazz Band; School Musical; School Play; Summer Music Prog Fredonia U 84; Music Camp Lake Luzerne 85; Musicology.

DORN, TOM; John F Kennedy HS; Utica, NY; (Y); Aud/Vis; Boy Scts; Church Yth Grp; Key Clb; Math Clb; Ski Clb; Nwsp Ed-Chief; Nwsp Rptr; Var Trk; JV Vllybl; Engrng.

DORR, D MICHAEL; The Doane Stewart Schl; W Sand Lake, NY; (Y); Boy Scts; Ski Clb; Socr; God Cntry Awd; Ntl Merit Schol; SUNY; Engrng.

DORRIES, JOANN MARIE; Deer Park HS; N Babylon, NY; (Y); 70/460; Art Clb; Cmnty Wkr; Drama Clb; FBLA; Intnl Clb; Library Aide; Political Wkr; Service Clb; School Play; Stage Crew; Secndry Ed.

DORSCHEL, KELLY; Whitney Point SR HS; Glen Aubrey, NY; (Y); French Clb; Teachers Aide; Chorus; School Play; Pres Frsh Cls; Rep Stu Cncl; Var Trk; Hon Roll; Im Vllybl; Chrs Awd 82; Outstndng Serv To Othrs 82 & & 83; Broome CC; Tchng.

DORSCHEL, WINONA; Harley Schl; Rochester, NY; (Y); Cmnty Wkr; Drama Clb; GAA; Key Clb; Varsity Clb; Chorus; School Musical; School Play; Variety Show; Yrbk Stf; Lilac Teen Pgnt Fnlst 85; Brghtn-Pttsfrd Post All-Star Sccr 83-84; Yth Rep Easter Seals Sccr Team 85; Bus.

DORSET, ERIK; Williamsville South HS; Williamsville, NY; (Y); Orch; School Musical; NHS.

DORSEY, BRYAN; Chester HS; Goshen, NY; (Y); 6/90; Band; Concert Band; Jazz Band; Mrchg Band; Swing Chorus; Symp Band; Stu Cncl; Hon Roll; NEDT Awd; Bus.

DORSEY, DAWN; William H Taft HS; Bronx, NY; (Y); Art Clb; Dance Clb; Office Aide; Chorus; Swmmng; Prfct Atten Awd; Engl Achvt Awd; Career Exploratns Achvt Awd 85; NYU.

DORTCH, KATRINA; H C Technical HS; Buffalo, NY; (Y); 10/270; Natl Beta Clb; Tennis; Hon Roll; Bus Admin.

DORVAL, CARLENE; Port Jervis HS; Huguenot, NY; (Y); Key Clb; Rep Stu Cncl; Mat Maids; Trk; Hon Roll; Navy.

DORVIL, MONIQUE; South Shore HS; Brooklyn, NY; (Y); Church Yth Grp; Debate Tm; French Clb; JA; OEA; Service Clb; Band; Stage Crew; Nwsp Stf; Cheerleading; Long Island U; Music.

DOS SANTOS, GEORGE; Sachem HS; Farmingville, NY; (Y); 254/1500; Intnl Clb; Red Cross Aide; Suffolk Cty Math Cont 2nd Pl 85; Rutgers Coll; Phrmcy.

DOSCHER, SUSAN; Spackenkill HS; Poughkeepsie, NY; (Y); Girl Scts; Concert Band; Pep Band; Yrbk Stf; Off Frsh Cls; Rep Jr Cls; Band; High Hon Roll; Hon Roll; St Fin NY Ntl Teenager Pagnt 84; Dutchess Cty Girls Scout Cncl Recg Cert 85; NY St Schl Music Assoc; Comp.

DOSS, CHERYL; Ohondaga Central HS; Syracuse, NY; (S); 10/80; Church Yth Grp; German Clb; Band; Chorus; Var Crs Cntry; Score Keeper; JV Socr; Var Trk; High Hon Roll; NHS; Math.

DOSTIE, DAWN; Amsterdam HS; Amsterdam, NY; (Y); 52/342; Pres JA; Rep Frsh Cls; Rep Soph Cls; Trs Jr Cls; Rep Sr Cls; Rep Stu Cncl; JV Var Cheerleading; Hon Roll; Coll St Rose Alumni Awd Schlrshp 85; NYS Regents Schlrshp 85-89; Coll St Rose; Bus Admin.

DOTO, VINCENT; Hudson HS; Hudson, NY; (Y); Camera Clb; Q&S; Band; Chorus; Concert Band; Jazz Band; Mrchg Band; Pep Band; Nwsp Stf; Yrbk Stf; Law.

DOTY, KELLY A; Curtis HS; Staten Island, NY; (Y); 12/328; Drama Clb; Girl Scts; Chorus; Jazz Band; School Musical; School Play; Nwsp Rptr; High Hon Roll; NHS; Wagner Coll Schlrshp 85; Wagner Coll; Math.

DOTY, VALERIE; Glens Falls SR HS; Glen Falls, NY; (Y); 9/225; Girl Scts; Pep Clb; High Hon Roll; NHS; Bio.

DOUCETT, JOSEPH T; Sayville HS; Sayville, NY; (Y); 27/363; Key Clb; Mathletes; Band; Mrchg Band; Yrbk Sprt Ed; JV Socr; Cit Awd; High Hon Roll; NHS; Pres Schlr; Regents Schlrshp 85; Pres Acad Ftns Awd 85; Polytech Of NY; Elec Engr.

DOUD JR, JOHN R; Pulaski JR SR HS; Pulaski, NY; (Y); Teachers Aide; Cit Awd; Snow Incentive Awd 85 & 83; Draftng.

DOUD, TIM; Massena Central HS; Massena, NY; (Y); Var Ftbl; JV Var Ice Hcky; Var Lcrss.

DOUGAN, CAMERON R; Green Meadow Waldorf Schl; Ho-Ho-Kus, NJ; (Y); Acpl Chr; Chorus; Orch; School Musical; School Play; Yrbk Stf; Lit Mag; Off Sr Cls; Off Stu Cncl; Bsktbl; Math Awd 84; Design Model Fountn Mosaic Plz 83; Math.

DOUGHERTY, CARRIE; Colton-Pierrepont Central; Colton, NY; (S); French Clb; Speech Tm; Pres Frsh Cls; Pres Soph Cls; Pres Jr Cls; VP Stu Cncl; Var Capt Socr; Var Sftbl; Hugh O Brien Awd 84; Coaches Awd 82; Nazareth; Spec Ed Tchr.

DOUGHERTY, JENNIFER; School Of The Holy Child; Rockville Ctr, NY; (Y); Hosp Aide; Nwsp Ed-Chief; Rep Frsh Cls; Rep Soph Cls; Pres Jr Cls; Pres Stu Cncl; Var Bsktbl; Var Socr; NHS; 4 Yr Acad Schrlshp To Schlof The Holy Child 82; Highst Avg Spnsh Ii 84; Hnrs Geo Hstry Englsh Bio 84.

DOUGHERTY, JILL; Tioga Central Schl; Candor, NY; (Y); 2/78; Church Yth Grp; Scholastic Bowl; Church Choir; Variety Show; Yrbk Stf; JV Cheerleading; JV Vllybl; High Hon Roll; NHS; Prfct Atten Awd; 1st Pl Splng Bee Lang Arts Fest Of Assoc 83; Comp Prog.

DOUGHERTY, KRISTIN; Morrisville-Eaton HS; Morrisville, NY; (Y); 3/60; Church Yth Grp; Drama Clb; Band; Rep Frsh Cls; Trs Soph Cls; Trs Jr Cls; Pres Stu Cncl; High Hon Roll; NHS; Ntl Merit Ltr; Math.

DOUGHERTY, MARY KAY; East Islip HS; E Islip, NY; (Y); 100/500; Art Clb; Mrchg Band; School Musical; Trs Sr Cls; Stu Cncl; Bsktbl; Fld Hcky; Pom Pon; Sftbl; High Hon Roll; Miss TEEN 85; Homecmg Atten 84; Vrsty Ltr Dnce Corp 85; Loyola Coll; Biol.

DOUGHERTY, PATRICK; Starpoint Ceantral HS; N Tonawanda, NY; (S); 22/200; Am Leg Boys St; VP Drama Clb; Sec Varsity Clb; School Musical; School Play; VP Soph Cls; L Bsbl; Capt Ftbl; Cit Awd; DAR Awd; Thomas Hewitt Athlete Awd 85; Stu Of Month 85; US Naval Acad; Physics.

DOUGHERTY, TRICIA; East Islip HS; East Islip, NY; (Y); FBLA; GAA; Letterman Clb; Pep Clb; Stage Crew; Yrbk Stf; Trs Jr Cls; Stat Bsbl; Var Fld Hcky; JV Var Sftbl; Bus.

DOUGHTY, JAMES P; Croton-Harmon HS; Croton-On-Hudson, NY; (Y); 3/105; Am Leg Boys St; Pres Debate Tm; French Clb; Pres Model UN; Nwsp Ed-Chief; Stu Cncl; Bsbl; NHS; Georgetown; Intl Rltns.

DOUGLAS, BARRY; Fondo-Fultonville Central HS; Amsterdam, NY; (Y); 23/109; Boy Scts; Dance Clb; 4-H; Yrbk Stf; High Hon Roll; Hon Roll; Kiwanis Awd; Schenectady Cnty Comm; Htl Tech.

DOUGLAS, COURTNEY; Mt Vernon HS; Mount Vernon, NY; (Y); Rep Stu Cncl; Var L Socr; Var L Trk; Hon Roll; Pres Schlr; Manhattan; Phys Ed.

DOUGLAS, COURTNEY C; Manhattan Center For Science & Math; Bronx, NY; (Y); Church Yth Grp; Computer Clb; Var Bsktbl; Hon Roll; Comp Tech.

DOUGLAS, DAVID; Niagara Falls HS; Niagara Falls, NY; (Y); Drama Clb; JA; Library Aide; Spanish Clb; Thesps; School Musical; School Play; Stage Crew; Comp.

DOUGLAS, GINGER; Sewanhaka HS; Elmont, NY; (Y); Rep Sec French Clb; Thesps; School Musical; School Play; Nwsp Stf; Yrbk Stf; Lit Mag; High Hon Roll; Hon Roll; Mst Imprvd Stu Awd Spn 85; Cazenovia; Artist.

DOUGLAS, KATHY; Saranac Lake HS; Saranac Lake, NY; (Y); Church Yth Grp; GAA; Ski Clb; Band; Chorus; Concert Band; Jazz Band; Mrchg Band; Var Crs Cntry; Var Swmmng; Outstndng Athlte Nrdc Skng 83-85; Brze Mdl Empire ST Wntr Gms Rly Tm 84-85; Cortland U; Sprts Med.

DOUGLAS, LISA S; Fashion Industries HS; Corona, NY; (Y); 102/473; Office Aide; Red Cross Aide; Teachers Aide; Stage Crew; Regents Schlrshp Awd 85; Cert Rec Executive Internships Pgm 85; NY Inst Of Tech; Communication.

DOUGLAS, LORENNE; Plattsburgh HS; Plattsburgh, NY; (Y); Service Clb; Engl.

DOUGLAS, MELISSA; Amsterdam HS; Ft Johnson, NY; (Y); 10/300; FBLA; Tennis; Hon Roll; NHS; SUNY-ALBANY; Pol Sci.

DOUGLAS, RICHARD W; Amsterdam HS; Amsterdam, NY; (Y); 40/350; Boy Scts; Letterman Clb; Ski Clb; Concert Band; Mrchg Band; JV Bsbl; Im JV Bsktbl; JV Var Ftbl; JV Socr; Hon Roll; John P Gomula Awd 85; Amstrdm Aides Assoc Awd 85; ST U Plattsburgh; Biolgcl Sci.

DOUGLAS, TANYA MARIE; Cardinal Spellman HS; Bronx, NY; (S); 15/568; Cmnty Wkr; Debate Tm; French Clb; NFL; Band; Concert Band; Mrchg Band; Hon Roll; NHS; Ntl Merit SF; Acad All-Amer Schlr 82-84; Cornell; Law.

DOUGLAS, TRACEY; Bishop Loughlin HS; Queens, NY; (S); 7/10; Computer Clb; Nwsp Rptr; 4-H Awd; High Hon Roll; NHS; Jrnlsm Awd 84; Polytechnic Int; Comp Sci.

DOUGLASS, JAMES; Gouverneur HS; Gouverneur, NY; (Y); Quiz Bowl; Varsity Clb; Var Golf; Var Capt Socr; Var Trk; High Hon Roll; Jr NHS; NHS; Spnsh I Awd 83; Spnsh II Awd 84.

DOUGLASS, KARIN; Canisteo Central Schl; Canisteo, NY; (S); 1/81; Band; Chorus; Co-Capt Color Guard; Orch; High Hon Roll; NHS; Ntl Merit Ltr; Nnr Ctznshp Awd 82-85.

DOUGLASS III, NORMAN E; Fayetteville-Manlius HS; Manlius, NY; (Y); Variety Show; Im Bsktbl; JV Socr; Hon Roll.

DOUNIAS, GEORGE J; Smithtown H S West; Smithtown, NY; (Y); Boys Clb Am; Computer Clb; Sec Jr Cls; Stu Cncl; L Crs Cntry; Trk; NY Regnts Schlrshp 85; SUNY Oswego; Comp Sci.

DOUNN, JACKIE; Christopher Columbua HS; Bronx, NY; (Y); 23/790; Office Aide; Band; Concert Band; Orch; School Musical; School Play; Yrbk Stf; Lit Mag; High Hon Roll; Hon Roll.

DOURDIS, KIKIE; Poughkeepsie HS; Poughkeepsie, NY; (Y); Hosp Aide; Office Aide; Chorus; Lit Mag; Var Socr; Krissler Bus Inst; Bus.

DOUTHARD, JON; August Martin HS; New York, NY; (Y); Church Yth Grp; Cmnty Wkr; Computer Clb; Math Clb; Church Choir; Drill Tm; Embry Rittle U; Airpln Pilot.

DOUTHIT, JACQUELYN; Cornwall Central HS; Cornwall-Huds, NY; (Y); 61/198; Church Yth Grp; Drama Clb; VP Library Aide; Stage Crew; JV Bsktbl; Var Powder Puff Ftbl; Stat Socr; JV Sftbl; Youth Govrnmnt Citizen Prty,Inernshp Radio Station WVSG AM 1170; U Of TX; Communctns.

DOW, MATTHEW J; Sweet Homes SR HS; Tonawanda, NY; (Y); Am Leg Boys St; Boy Scts; Science Clb; Chorus; Var Capt Crs Cntry; Var L Trk; High Hon Roll; NHS; Prfct Atten Awd; Italian Hnr Soc 85; Empire St Games 85; Sect VI 600 M Champ Indr Trk 84-85; Bio.

DOW, STEPHANIE; Weedsport Central HS; Weedsport, NY; (Y); French Clb; Intnl Clb; Math Tm; Yrbk Stf; Var Capt Fld Hcky; Sftbl; Stat Vllybl; Hnrb Mntn In Art 83; Mst Imprvd Sftbl 80; N Adams; Comp Prgmng.

DOWD, JAMES; Springfield Gardens HS; New York, NY; (Y); Computer Clb; JA; Off Jr Cls; Bsbl; Bsktbl; Bowling; Comp.

DOWD, PATRICK; Gloversville HS; Gloversville, NY; (Y); Rep Frsh Cls; Rep Soph Cls; JV Capt Bsktbl; JV Var Socr; Hon Roll; Pioneer Achiev Challenge; Intl Bus.

DOWD, PATRICK H; Johnstown HS; Johnstown, NY; (Y); 12/150; AFS; Boy Scts; Intnl Clb; Math Tm; Varsity Clb; Band; Chorus; Mrchg Band; Capt L Bsbl; Im Bsktbl; William Hladik Memrl Schlrshp 85; Lions Clb Schlrshp 85; Robert Mcfeeley Memrl Schlrshp 85; Hofstra U; Engrng.

DOWD, SHANNON; Northern Adironack Central HS; Lyon Mt, NY; (Y); French Clb; Hon Roll; Bus Mgt.

DOWD, THERESA; Clarkstown South SR HS; W Nyack, NY; (Y); Church Yth Grp; Var Capt Fld Hcky; JV Gym; Var Lcrss; Lion Awd; All Cty Fld Hcky 85; MVP Fld Fcky 85; All Conf, All Cty Lacrss 84; Siena Coll; Pol Sci.

DOWLEY, JEFF A; F D Roosevelt HS; Staatsburg, NY; (Y); 20/322; Drama Clb; French Clb; Math Tm; Stage Crew; Nwsp Phtg; Nwsp Rptr; Lit Mag; Hon Roll; NHS; Ntl Merit Ltr; NYS Regnts Schlrshp 85; Carnegie-Mellon U; Mech Engr.

DOWLING, CHRISTOPHER; Friends Acad; Westbury, NY; (Y); Church Yth Grp; Varsity Clb; Band; Concert Band; Jazz Band; Nwsp Sprt Ed; JV Bsbl; Var Capt Bsktbl; Var L Socr; NYS Regents Schlrshp Awd 85; Co MVP Friends Acad Bsktbl Tm 85; Brown U; Econ.

DOWLING, JOHN; Bishop Scully HS; Amsterdam, NY; (Y); #11 In Class; Math Clb; Math Tm; Rep Stu Cncl; Var Bsktbl; JV Ftbl; JV Golf; Var Tennis; Hon Roll; Mu Alp Tht; NHS; Elctrcl Engrng.

DOWLING, JOHN W; John F Kennedy HS; Carmel, NY; (Y); 40/200; Church Yth Grp; Pres Intnl Clb; Band; Jazz Band; Var JV Ftbl; Im Ice Hcky; Var JV Trk; Var Wt Lftg; Var Wrstlng; St Schlr; NY ST Chief Columbian Squire 84-85; Fordham; Pre-Med.

DOWLING, MICHAEL G; St Anthonys HS; E Northport, NY; (Y); Camera Clb; Ski Clb; Nwsp Phtg; Nwsp Rptr; Nwsp Stf; Yrbk Phtg; Yrbk Stf; Var L Lcrss; Var L Swmmng; Engrng.

DOWNER, THOMAS JOHN; Troy HS; Troy, NY; (Y); Boys Clb Am; JA; Y-Teens; JV Ftbl; High Hon Roll.

DOWNES, BRETT M; Homer Central HS; Cortland, NY; (Y); Church Yth Grp; Cmnty Wkr; Spanish Clb; Church Choir; Variety Show; Nwsp Stf; Cit Awd; Cmmnctns.

DOWNES, SUSAN; Commack High School North; Commack, NY; (Y); 3/100; Art Clb; Cmnty Wkr; Red Cross Aide; Nwsp Stf; Yrbk Stf; Cert Hnr Achvt Studio Art 83; St Josephs; Pre-Med.

DOWNEY, ELLEN M; Mt Mercy Acad; Buffalo, NY; (Y); JA; PAVAS; Spanish Clb; Acpl Chr; School Musical; School Play; Swing Chorus; Kiwanis Awd; Elected Miss Mercy Schl Yr 84-85; Theatre Arts.

DOWNEY, HALL E; Monroe HS; Rochester, NY; (Y); Hon Roll; NHS; Monroe CC; Data Proc.

DOWNEY, JOHN; John Jay SR HS; Hopewell Jct, NY; (Y); L Bsbl; Im Bsktbl; Im Ftbl; Im Ice Hcky; Syracuse U; Cmmnctns.

DOWNEY, MARK; Pittsford Sutherland HS; Rochester, NY; (Y); VP JA; Varsity Clb; Variety Show; VP Jr Cls; VP Sr Cls; Im Bsktbl; JV Var Golf; JV Var Score Keeper; Hon Roll; Stu Cncl Awd 84-85; Bus.

DOWNING, ROBIN; Corning-Painted Post West HS; Corning, NY; (Y); 70/241; JA; Varsity Clb; Off Jr Cls; Off Sr Cls; Sftbl; High Hon Roll; Hon Roll; Ntl Merit Ltr; Peer Ldrshp 84-85; Clss Svc Awd 85; Natl Mrt Fdn 85; Corning CC; Bus Adm.

DOWNS, NORA; Skaneateles Central HS; Skaneateles, NY; (Y); 11/165; Church Yth Grp; Drama Clb; Model UN; Rep Frsh Cls; Capt Crs Cntry; Capt Trk; High Hon Roll; NHS; Foundtn Schlrshp 85; Bucknell U; Comp Engrng.

DOXBECK, HEATHER; Kenmore West SR HS; Kenmore, NY; (Y); Church Yth Grp; Drama Clb; Pres Girl Scts; Hosp Aide; Math Tm; Concert Band; Stage Crew; Variety Show; High Hon Roll; NYS Sci Supr Assn Bio Awd 84; Rensselaer Poly Inst; Comp Sci.

DOXBECK, SHAWN; Bishop Mc Mahon HS; Buffalo, NY; (Y); Hon Roll; Cert Of Achvt Bookpng, Accntng 85 & Health 85; Prfct Conduct Awd 83-85.

DOYEN, ANNY; Niagara Wheatfield HS; Sanborn, NY; (Y); Pres Sec Church Yth Grp; FCA; Trs FBLA; Hst Sr Cls; Sec Stu Cncl; Cheerleading; High Hon Roll; Hon Roll; NHS; Acadmc Hnr Awds 83-85; Shrthd & Typg Awds 85; Acadmc Achvt Awd 85; Bus.

DOYEN, KURT C; Red Jacket Central HS; Palmyra, NY; (Y); 6/90; Am Leg Boys St; Church Yth Grp; Cmnty Wkr; Science Clb; Varsity Clb; Madrigals; School Musical; School Play; Rep Soph Cls; VP Stu Cncl; Athlte Of The Yr 83-85; Outstndng Wrstlr 83-85; Bsbl MVP 83-85; 1st Tm All Stars Bsbl 83-85; Engrng.

DOYKA, DEBORA LEE; Hamburg SR HS; Hamburg, NY; (Y); 47/398; Model UN; Concert Band; Mrchg Band; Ed Yrbk Ed-Chief; Yrbk Stf; DAR Awd; Hon Roll; Service Clb; Band; Nwsp Stf; Hamburg Tchrs Assoc Schlrshp 85; Clarkson U Schlrshp 85; Pres Acad Ftns Awd 85; Clarkson U; Mech Engr.

DOYLE, DENISE A; Palmyra-Macedon HS; Walworth, NY; (S); 12/220; Varsity Clb; Chorus; Rep Soph Cls; Rep Jr Cls; Crs Cntry; Socr; Capt Trk; Hon Roll; NHS; All Cnty Chrs 83 & 85; Binghamton; Nrsng.

DOYLE, ELIZABETH; Catholic Central HS; Troy, NY; (S); 22/203; Variety Show; Yrbk Stf; Rep Yrbk Phtg; Var Capt Bsktbl; Crs Cntry; Sftbl; High Hon Roll; Siena Coll; Acctng.

DOYLE, JEFFREY; Frontier Central HS; Hamburg, NY; (S); Var Socr; Var Trk; Var Wrstlng; Hon Roll; NHS; NEDT Awd.

DOYLE, JOHN; West Seneca West SR HS; Buffalo, NY; (Y); Key Clb; Spanish Clb; Var Capt Socr; Var Capt Swmmng; Hon Roll; JC Awd; Jr NHS; NHS.

DOYLE, JULIE A; Auburn HS; Auburn, NY; (Y); Church Yth Grp; Cmnty Wkr; Dance Clb; Chorus; Color Guard; Mrchg Band; DECA; JV Fld Hcky; Hon Roll; Elem Ed.

DOYLE, KIMBERLY A; Stissing Mt HS; Stanfordville, NY; (Y); 1/100; Pres AFS; Church Yth Grp; Band; Rep Jr Cls; Trs Stu Cncl; Var L Cheerleading; Var L Trk; High Hon Roll; NHS; AFS Turkey 85; Earth Sci.

DOYLE, LAURA; Saugerties HS; Saugerties, NY; (Y); VP German Clb; Key Clb; Library Aide; Nwsp Rptr; Ed Yrbk Stf; High Hon Roll; Hon Roll; Comm.

DOYLE, NOREEN; Bishop Maginn HS; Albany, NY; (Y); Art Clb; Latin Clb; Chorus; Yrbk Stf; Ftbl; Hon Roll; Cert Of Awd For Achvt Chmstry 85; Comp Sci.

DOYLE, PATRICIA; Mount Saint Mary Acad; Tonawanda, NY; (Y); Ski Clb; Spanish Clb; Chorus; Variety Show; Yrbk Rptr; Yrbk Stf; Rep Stu Cncl; Var Cheerleading.

DOYLE, SUSAN L; Charles W Baker HS; Baldwinsville, NY; (Y); 6/441; Exploring; Hosp Aide; Key Clb; Latin Clb; Cit Awd; High Hon Roll; Jr NHS; NHS; Natl Hnr Rll 85; Vol Svc Awd 84; Intl Multifds Schlrshp 85; Northeastern U; Pharm.

DOYLE, WILLIAM; Sachem HS; Lk Ronkonkoma, NY; (Y); 297/1400; Science Clb; Ski Clb; JV Ftbl; Hon Roll; Dowling Coll; Bus Admn.

DRABINSKI, DIANE; Webster HS; Webster, NY; (Y); 54/571; VP JA; Yrbk Stf; VP Sr Cls; Var Fld Hcky; Var Trk; High Hon Roll; NHS; Spanish NHS; Exploring; Office Aide; Homemcng Qn 84-85; Stu Rep Cncl 84-85; E W Spry Mem Schlrshp 85; Oswego ST; Zoolgy.

DRABO, DIANE; Susquehanna Valley HS; Conklin, NY; (Y); French Clb; Mathletes; Drm & Bgl; Nwsp Rptr; Ed Nwsp Stf; Rep Stu Cncl; Hon Roll; NHS; Clarkson; Engrng.

DRACHENBERG, DONALD; Oakfield Alabama Central HS; Batavia, NY; (Y); 30/77; Drama Clb; French Clb; Band; Concert Band; Mrchg Band; School Musical; Capt Bowling; JV Tennis; High Hon Roll; Hon Roll; Monroe Comm Coll; Radiolgc Tech.

DRAGONE, JOE; St Josephs Collegiale HS; N Tonawanda, NY; (Y); 52/701; Jazz Band; Orch; School Musical; Symp Band; Church Yth Grp; Mrchg Band; Swing Chorus; Im Ftbl; Im Sftbl; Hon Roll; NYSSMA Outstnand Ratng 83; All St Sectnl Band 83; Outstndng Mbr Awd 85; Music.

DRAHUSHUK, ADAM; Hudson HS; Hudson, NY; (Y); Band; Mrchg Band; JV Bsbl; JV Var Ftbl; JV Wrstlng; High Hon Roll; Rotary Awd; Tae Kwon Do Karate 2 Degr Blck Blt Instrctr & Judg; Comp Sci.

DRAINE, BRENDA; Yonkers HS; Yonkers, NY; (Y); Yrbk Stf; High Hon Roll; Hon Roll; Bus Adm.

DRAJEM, CHRISTOPHER R; St Josephs Collegiate Inst; Buffalo, NY; (Y); 26/200; Pres Church Yth Grp; Band; Chorus; School Musical; Nwsp Rptr; Nwsp Stf; Lit Mag; Swmmng; Hon Roll; Pres NHS; Psychlgy.

DRAJEM, MARK; St Josephs Collegiate Inst; Buffalo, NY; (Y); 15/201; Cmnty Wkr; Mathletes; Model UN; Pep Clb; Political Wkr; Service Clb; Nwsp Ed-Chief; Yrbk Stf; Crs Cntry; High Hon Roll; Svc Awd Diocese Of Buffalo 84; Poet.

DRAKE, DOUG R; John C Birdlebeughl HS; Phoenix, NY; (Y); 7/210; Latin Clb; Pres Frsh Cls; VP Soph Cls; Rep Stu Cncl; Var Capt Bsktbl; Var Capt Ftbl; Var Capt Golf; Cit Awd; High Hon Roll; Hon Roll; Empire ST Games In Handball Silver Medal 84-85; Math.

DRAKE, JENNIFER A; Elmira Southside HS; Pine City, NY; (Y); 6/333; Pres Latin Clb; Quiz Bowl; Red Cross Aide; Church Choir; Drm Mjr(t); School Musical; Yrbk Stf; High Hon Roll; Pres NHS; Spanish Clb; NY Telephone Co Schlrshp 85; Regents Schlrshp 85; Conf All-ST Band 84; Cornell U; Bio.

DRAKE, JONATHAN T; Notre Dame Bishop Gibbons HS; Schenectady, NY; (Y); 10/115; Ftbl; High Hon Roll; NHS; Horsemanship AHSA Medal 85; Maclay 82; Capital Dist Hunter/Jumper Council Medal; West Point.

DRAKERT, DONNA E; Valhalla HS; White Plains, NY; (Y); 19/120; French Clb; Math Tm; Band; Yrbk Stf; Trk; Hon Roll; NHS; Regents Schlrshp 85; Boston U; Hotel Mgmt.

DRALLE, MONIKA B; Greece Arcadia HS; Rochester, NY; (Y); 26/294; Drama Clb; Chorus; School Musical; School Play; High Hon Roll; Hon Roll; NHS; SF Congress Bundestag Schlrshp Pgm 84; AATG Hnbl Mntn German 83 84 & 85; Penn ST U; Intl Bus.

DRAZEN, BRADFORD; Binghamton HS; Binghamton, NY; (Y); Am Leg Boys St; Trs VP Key Clb; Pres Temple Yth Grp; School Musical; Rep Stu Cncl; Var L Golf; Var L Trk; High Hon Roll; NHS; Ntl Merit Ltr; Cnty Glf All Star 84; Cty Govmntl Intrnshp Prog 85; Regnl Pres Jwsh Ctr Yth 85-86; Med.

DREJAS, DOREEN J; Villa Maria Acad; Cheektowaga, NY; (Y); Computer Clb; FBLA; Pep Clb; Quiz Bowl; Ski Clb; Variety Show; VP Soph Cls; Hon Roll; Mrktng.

DRENGERS, ANDREW; St Agnes HS; Bayside, NY; (Y); 8/100; Hon Roll; Socl Stud.

DRESLER, YAEL; Shulamith HS For Girls; Brooklyn, NY; (S); Nwsp Stf; Hon Roll; Ntl Bible Cntst Awd 84; Effert Diligence & Attention Awd 83; LAW.

DRESLIN, KIM; Tioga Central HS; Smithboro, NY; (Y); 15/98; Am Leg Aux Girls St; Rep Church Yth Grp; Rep Stu Cncl; JV L Bsktbl; L Vllybl; High Hon Roll; Hon Roll; NHS; Ntl Sci Olymp Bio Earth Sci 83-84; Ntl Latin Ex 84; Broome CC; Biomed.

DREW, HARRY; Rocky Point HS; Rocky Pt, NY; (Y); 50/100; Teachers Aide; Sftbl; Var Wt Lftg; Cls Cmpstn Awds; Shrt Stry Wrtr.

DREWS II, LESLIE H O; Byron-Bergen Central Schl; Byron, NY; (Y); French Clb; Hon Roll; NYS Regnts Schlrshp 85; Niagara U NY; Sec Ed.

DREXELIUS, CAROL; Kenmore East SR HS; Tonawanda, NY; (Y); Office Aide; JV Bsktbl; JV Swmmng; Hon Roll; Ed.

DREXLER, JOE; Springville Griffith Inst; Glenwood, NY; (Y); Ski Clb; L Tennis; Hon Roll; NHS; NY ST Alpine Ski Rcng Team 82-85; Eastern Elite Ski Rcng Tm 85; Kssng Brdg Ski Area Rcr Yr 85; Sci.

DREXLER, PATTI; Charles H Roth HS; Rush, NY; (Y); Cmnty Wkr; Exploring; GAA; Rep Frsh Cls; Rep Soph Cls; Stat Bsktbl; Cheerleading; Powder Puff Ftbl; High Hon Roll; Hon Roll; Monroe CC; Bus Admin.

DRIBUSCH, CHRIS; Arlington SR HS; Poughkeepsie, NY; (Y); CAP; German Clb; JV Socr; Var Trk; Billy Mitchell Awd CAP 83; Cert Merit Amer Assn Tchrs Of Germ 2nd Lvl 83-84, 3rd Lvl 84-85; CPA.

DRIGGS, DAVID T; Vestal SR HS; Vestal, NY; (Y); Boy Scts; Trs Church Yth Grp; Computer Clb; French Clb; Mathletes; Ski Clb; Im Bsbl; Im Socr; High Hon Roll; NHS; NYS Regnts Schlrshp 85-89; Rensselaer Polytechnc; Engrng.

DRIGGS, STANLEY W; Vestal SR HS; Vestal, NY; (Y); 43/450; Boy Scts; VP Church Yth Grp; Ski Clb; High Hon Roll; NHS; Ntl Merit Ltr; Eagle Scout 82; PA ST; Elec Engrng.

DRILLINGS, JOEY; Monticello HS; Monticello, NY; (Y); NFL; Rep Soph Cls; Rep Jr Cls; Var Golf; High Hon Roll; Jr NHS; NHS; Rotary Awd; SUNY Binghamton; Pol Sci.

DRISCOLL, BENJAMIN; Whitney Point SR HS; Whitney Pt, NY; (Y); 3/100; Yrbk Stf; Stu Cncl; Crs Cntry; Mgr(s); Trk; High Hon Roll; Hon Roll; Elect Engr.

DRISCOLL, DAWN; Francis HS; Staten Island, NY; (S); Aud/Vis; Camera Clb; English Clb; Library Aide; Math Clb; Service Clb; Spanish Clb; Teachers Aide; Nwsp Rptr; Yrbk Ed-Chief; St Johns U; Sec Educ.

DRISCOLL, JOHN; Sholy Trinity HS; East Meadow, NY; (Y); 19/400; Church Yth Grp; Cmnty Wkr; Math Tm; Ski Clb; Ftbl; Lcrss; Hon Roll; NHS; Distgshd Soc Of Amer HS Stu 84-85; Acadmc All Amer 84-85; Ntl Hnr Soc 84-85; Engr.

DRISCOLL, JOHN; St Peters Boys HS; Staten Island, NY; (Y); 18/195; School Musical; School Play; Yrbk Stf; Im Bsktbl; JV Bowling; Im Sftbl; Hon Roll; NHS; St Johns U; Accntg.

DRISCOLL, PAUL; West Genesee SR HS; Syracuse, NY; (Y); Boy Scts; Drama Clb; JA; Political Wkr; Thesps; Band; School Musical; School Play; Yrbk Stf; Crs Cntry; Boys St Alt 85; Pol Sci.

DRISCOLL, SHARON; Saugerties HS; Saugerties, NY; (S); 2/250; Trs Church Yth Grp; Trs French Clb; Pres Chorus; Church Choir; Trs Yrbk Stf; Stat Sftbl; JV Var Vllybl; High Hon Roll; NHS; Sal; Brumbaugh-Ellis Pres Schlrshp 85; Boston U; Occp Thrpy.

DRISCOLL, SHEILA; St Peters HS For Girls; Staten Isl, NY; (Y); Exploring; Math Clb; JV Bsktbl; JV Sftbl; Timer; High Hon Roll; Trs Soph Cls; Metro Fin In Miss Natl Teen-Ager Pgnt 83.

DROGALIS, NORA; Sacred Heart Acad; Floral Park, NY; (S); 16/197; Math Clb; Math Tm; Pep Clb; Yrbk Stf; Rep Stu Cncl; Hon Roll; NHS; Georgetown; Crmml Law.

DROLLETTE, AMY; Saranac Central HS; Saranac, NY; (S); 12/106; Office Aide; Chorus; Im Bsktbl; Mgr(s); Im JV Socr; Im Sftbl; Var L Trk; Im Vllybl; Hon Roll; Navy; Med Lab Tech.

DROLLETTE, KRISTINA; Saranac Central Schl; Morrisonville, NY; (S); 34/106; Band; Ed Yrbk Stf; Trs Frsh Cls; Trs Soph Cls; Trs Jr Cls; JV Var Cheerleading; Hon Roll; Jacksonville U; Aviation Mgmt.

DRONS, DARCY; Our Lady Of Mercy; Rochester, NY; (Y); 77/210; Exploring; French Clb; JA; Q&S; Ski Clb; Nwsp Rptr; Rep Frsh Cls; Rep Jr Cls; Hon Roll; Schl Merit Roll; John Carroll U; Accntng.

DROP JR, JOSEPH M; Solvay HS; Lakeland, NY; (Y); Boy Scts; Church Yth Grp; Cmnty Wkr; Stage Crew; NHS; SUNY Delhi; Vet Sci.

DROWN, ELIZABETH; Nazareth Acad; Rochester, NY; (Y); Dance Clb; 4-H; Spanish Clb; Yrbk Stf; 4-H Awd; Hon Roll.

DROWN, MARY ELLEN; Bainbridge-Guilford HS; Masonville, NY; (Y); 13/77; French Clb; Hosp Aide; Hon Roll; Occptnl Therpy.

DROZ, ANTONIO; George W Fowler HS; Syracuse, NY; (S); 3/202; Sec Jr Cls; Sec Sr Cls; Var Co-Capt Ftbl; Var Trk; Var Capt Wrstlng; Sec NHS; MVP Wrestler Yr 83-84; St Lawrence U; Premed.

DROZD, SOPHIA; Aviation HS; Glendale, NY; (Y); 1/412; Debate Tm; Math Tm; Color Guard; Nwsp Stf; Rep Jr Cls; Capt Tennis; Ntl Merit Ltr; Prfct Atten Awd; Val; Schlrshp 5 Wk Smmr Comp Cours NYU 84; 2 1st Pl & 1 3rd Pl PAL Illus Poetry Cntst 83-85; Aerosp Engrng.

DRUBIN, RANDI; Kings Park SR HS; Kings Pk, NY; (Y); 114/393; Drama Clb; English Clb; Library Aide; Office Aide; Spanish Clb; Temple Yth Grp; Band; Chorus; Concert Band; Drm & Bgl; Mst Imprvd Musicn In 9th Grd 83; Cornell; Vet.

DRUCKENMILLER, DANIEL; Hoosic Valley Central HS; Valley Falls, NY; (Y); 2/100; Am Leg Boys St; 4-H; Chorus; Jazz Band; School Musical; School Play; Swing Chorus; JV Crs Cntry; JV Trk; NHS; U Rochester; Optcl Engrng.

DRUCKER, STACEY H; Valley Stream Central HS; Valley Stream, NY; (Y); Art Clb; Drama Clb; Mathletes; Math Tm; Teachers Aide; Temple Yth Grp; School Musical; School Play; Stage Crew; Ntl Merit Ltr; SUNY Albany; Psychlgy.

DRUCKMAN, DAVID; Long Beach HS; Long Beach, NY; (S); 12/319; Hosp Aide; Mathletes; Math Clb; Math Tm; High Hon Roll; Hon Roll; NHS; Rensselaer Polytchnc Inst Medal 84; Med.

DRURY, COLLEEN M; Bishop Ludden HS; Syracuse, NY; (Y); Church Yth Grp; VP Frsh Cls; Cheerleading; Pom Pon; MVP Chrldg 84-85; Buffalo ST; FBI Invstgtr.

DRURY, MICHELE; Lindenhurst HS; Lindenhurst, NY; (Y); Key Clb; Spanish Clb; Chorus; School Play; Stage Crew; Nwsp Rptr; Yrbk Phtg; Yrbk Stf; Fld Hcky; Score Keeper; 1st Pl Awd Engl Compstn On Arson 84.

DRURY, RICHARD; George W Hewlett HS; Valley Stream, NY; (Y); Aud/Vis; Varsity Clb; Bsbl; Bsktbl; Hoftstra U; Comp Sci.

DRUZIAK, DANIELLE; Asmsterdam HS; Amsterdam, NY; (Y); 42/319; Hosp Aide; Yrbk Stf; Var Socr; Geneseo; Educ.

DRY, MARGO; Salamanca HS; Salamanca, NY; (Y); Cmnty Wkr; DECA; Chorus; Yrbk Stf; Pres Jr Cls; Pres Sr Cls; Capt Trk; Hon Roll; Drama Clb; Office Aide; Girl Of Yr 85, Of Mnth 82; Capt All Guard Mrchng Band 83-84.

DRYGAS, JOHN; Nyack HS; Valley Cottage, NY; (Y); 10/257; Math Clb; Band; Concert Band; Jazz Band; Mrchg Band; Orch; Stat Boy Scts; Ski Clb; Spanish Clb; Rep Frsh Cls; Boston Coll; Biochem.

DRZEWIECKI, MICHELE; Sacred Heart Acad; Amherst, NY; (Y); 15/125; German Clb; Ski Clb; School Musical; Nwsp Rptr; High Hon Roll; Hon Roll.

DRZEWIECKI, PETER; St Joseph Collegiate Inst; Williamsville, NY; (Y); 7/202; Cmnty Wkr; Chorus; Stage Crew; Swing Chorus; Im Bsktbl; JV Crs Cntry; High Hon Roll; NHS; Prfct Atten Awd; U Notre Dame; Bio.

DU BICKI, JOANNE C; Smithtown H S East; Saint James, NY; (Y); French Clb; Office Aide; Orch; Nwsp Stf; Hon Roll; Dnce Ther.

DU BOIS, KAREN E; Orchard Park HS; Orchard Park, NY; (Y); 4/400; Am Leg Aux Girls St; Sec Church Yth Grp; Nwsp Ed-Chief; VP Frsh Cls; Sec Soph Cls; Sec Stu Cncl; JV Mgr(s); High Hon Roll; NHS; Minority Schlstc Achiev Awd 84; Ntl Achiev Schlrshp Pgm-Outstndg Negro Stu 84; BAP Assoc SR Awd 85; Yale U; Bio.

DU BREY, NANETTE; Saranac Central HS; Saranac, NY; (S); 12/136; Concert Band; School Musical; VP Frsh Cls; VP Soph Cls; VP Jr Cls; VP Sr Cls; NHS; Church Yth Grp; Drama Clb; French Clb; Area All ST Band 83-84; All Cnty Band & Orchestra; NYSSMA May Festival; Plattsburgh ST U; Elem Educ.

DU COTE, STEVE; Salmon River Central Schl; Bombay, NY; (S); 6/94; Math Clb; Science Clb; Bsktbl; Capt Swmmng; Trk; Hon Roll; VP NHS; Bio Sci.

DU PLESSIS, KATHLEEN; Monroe HS; Rochester, NY; (Y); Church Yth Grp; Pres French Clb; Office Aide; Red Cross Aide; School Musical; Yrbk Stf; Var Bsktbl; Var Swmmng; Var Tennis; High Hon Roll; Typing Awd 85; Brigham Young; Busnss Admin.

DU PONT, JOHN; St Marys Boys HS; E Williston, NY; (Y); 56/135; Cmnty Wkr; Service Clb; Ski Clb; Nwsp Sprt Ed; Yrbk Stf; Rep Sr Cls; Rep Stu Cncl; JV Crs Cntry; Score Keeper; JV Trk; Editor Paper 85; Contact Ofcr 85; Fredonia ST; Bus Sales.

DU PONT, SUE; Averill Park HS; Troy, NY; (Y); Varsity Clb; Var Bsktbl; Var Capt Socr; Var Trk; Hon Roll; Prfct Atten Awd; Schl Track Rcrds 85; Bus.

DU PUIS, JEAN; Bishop Maginn HS; Albany, NY; (Y); Boy Scts; Stage Crew; Bsktbl; Var Bowling; JV Var Crs Cntry; Score Keeper; Timer; JV Var Trk; Aerospace Engr.

DUA, RONIKA; Amherst SR HS; Amherst, NY; (Y); 28/310; Hosp Aide; Ski Clb; Spanish Clb; Chorus; Church Choir; School Musical; Lit Mag; Trk; High Hon Roll; NHS; Spanish Club Sec 84-85; Operetta Treasures 84-85; Pre Med.

DUBAY, SCOTT; Ravena Coeymans Selkirk HS; Selkirk, NY; (Y); Art Clb; Boy Scts; German Clb; Band; Sec Sr Cls; JV Bsktbl; JV Tennis; Capt Wt Lftg; Capt Wrstlng; Hon Roll; Hevywght Chmpnshp Gld Mdl 78; Columbia Green; Bus Adv.

DUBEY, AJAY K; George W Hewlett HS; Hewlett, NY; (Y); 4/278; Computer Clb; Debate Tm; Mathletes; Math Tm; MMM; NFL; Radio Clb; Science Clb; Speech Tm; Orch; 1st Pl Spkr 84; 9th Pl Spkr NY St 84.

DUBIEL, STEVEN R; Fox Land HS; Pound Ridge, NY; (Y); 80/300; Boy Scts; Ski Clb; Spanish Clb; Im Socr; Hon Roll; Regents Schlrshp 85; SR Camper Yr 81; U Of NH; Envrnmntl Affrs.

DUBILL, LAWRENCE; Kenmore East HS; Kenmore, NY; (Y); Band; Concert Band; Drm & Bgl; Jazz Band; Orch; Symp Band; Var Capt Ftbl; Var Trk; Hon Roll; MVP Ftbl 82-83; Mst Imprvd Plyr Jazz Band 84-85; Music.

DUBIN, LESLIE; Commack South HS; Commack, NY; (Y); 29/374; Cmnty Wkr; GAA; Key Clb; Teachers Aide; Variety Show; Var Capt Bsktbl; Var Capt Socr; Var Capt Sftbl; Vllybl; Cit Awd; Suffolk Zone NYSAHPR Hnrs 84; Girls Ldrs Corps 83-85; Yth Dvlpmnt Assn 83-85; Albany ST; Psych.

DUBIN, STEVEN S; Baldwin SR HS; Baldwin, NY; (Y); 82/502; Boy Scts; Chess Clb; Brnz Mdl Tm NY ST Empire Games In Engl Mtch Rflry 84; SUNY Maritime Coll; Elec Engr.

DUBOIS, DIANE L; Moriah Central HS; Port Henry, NY; (Y); AFS; Cmnty Wkr; Ski Clb; Band; Concert Band; Mrchg Band; Cheerleading; Score Keeper; Swmmng; High Hon Roll; Albany ST; Bus Adm.

DUBOIS, LISA; G Ray Bodley HS; Fulton, NY; (Y); Mat Maids; Stat Wrstlng; Hon Roll; Rgnts Dplma 85.

DUBRASKI JR, ROBERT J; Redhook Central HS; Tivoli, NY; (Y); JV Capt Ftbl; Var Wrstlng; High Hon Roll; Am Leg Boys ST 85; Mth.

DUCATTE, MELISSA; Saranac Central HS; Cadyville, NY; (S); 23/106; VP 4-H; Band; Yrbk Sprt Ed; JV Var Mgr(s); JV Var Score Keeper; 4-H Awd; Hon Roll; Prfct Atten Awd; Rochester Tech; Graph Arts.

DUCEY, KATHY; Bethpage HS; Bethpage, NY; (Y); 90/292; GAA; Spanish Clb; Varsity Clb; Trs Frsh Cls; Capt Var Fld Hcky; JV Lcrss; Var Trk.

DUCKERY, CYNTHIA; Newburgh Free Acad; Newburgh, NY; (Y); Chorus; Color Guard; Mrchg Band; Rep Frsh Cls; Sec Soph Cls; Bowling; JV Cheerleading; Twrlr; Hon Roll; Howard U.

DUCLOS, ANTOINE; Andrew Jackson HS; Queens Village, NY; (Y); 1/35; French Clb; Math Clb; Teachers Aide; Socr; French Hon Soc; High Hon Roll; Math Hnr Stu 85; Hghst Rgnt Score 85; Elec Engrng.

DUDASH, SHEILA; Bishop Ludden HS; Liverpool, NY; (S); Cmnty Wkr; Hosp Aide; Intnl Clb; Var MMM; Speech Tm; Band; Sec Chorus; Pep Band; School Musical; Rep Jr Cls; St Josephs Hosp Vlntr Awd 83; Span III Awd 84; Lumen Christi Hnr Soc 84-85.

DUDDLESTON, NANCY; Central HS; Valley Stream, NY; (Y); AFS; Art Clb; Ski Clb; Chorus; Yrbk Stf; Mgr(s); Hon Roll; Jr NHS; Score Keeper; Timer; SADD 84; Bus Hnr Scty 85.

DUDEWICZ, CAROLYN R; Jamesville-De Witt HS; De Witt, NY; (Y); 21/224; Exploring; Hosp Aide; Ski Clb; Jazz Band; Symp Band; Yrbk Stf; Var L Trk; High Hon Roll; Jr NHS; Roswell Pk Mem Inst Summer Resrch Prgrm For High-Ablty HS Stu 84; U Of Sthrn CA; Biochem.

DUDGEON, CHRISTINE; Washington HS; Washingtonville, NY; (Y); 1/290; Band; Symp Band; Yrbk Phtg; Yrbk Stf; Stu Cncl; Bsktbl; Socr; High Hon Roll; NHS; Siena Coll; Comp Sci.

DUDLEY, KRISTIN M; Lockport SR HS; Lockport, NY; (Y); AFS; Library Aide; Var L Swmmng; Hon Roll; Jr NHS; NHS; ST NY Regents Scholar 85; Friars Scholar St Bonaventure U 85; St Bonaventur U; Mass Cmmnctns.

DUDMAN, SUSAN; Cornwall Central HS; Cornwall, NY; (Y); Church Yth Grp; Drama Clb; Exploring; Girl Scts; Ski Clb; Spanish Clb; Acpl Chr; Chorus; School Play; Yrbk Stf.

DUERR, MICHELLE; The Acad Of St Joseph; Sayville, NY; (Y); Drama Clb; Orch; School Play; Engl.

DUERR, RENEE M; Iroquois Central HS; Elma, NY; (Y); 39/275; VP 4-H; French Clb; Pres Sec Model UN; Band; Color Guard; Mrchg Band; Yrbk Stf; Im Bowling; 4-H Awd; Hon Roll; NYS Regnts Schlrshp 85; Kiwanis Sr Recgntn 85; SUNY; Mgmt Sci.

DUERR, SUSAN ALEXANDRA; The Francisean Acad; Liverpool, NY; (Y); Drama Clb; Exploring; FBLA; GAA; NFL; Ski Clb; Yrbk Bus Mgr; Yrbk Stf; Rep Stu Cncl; Var Bsktbl; VP NY St Future Bus Ldrs Of Am 85-86; Lib Arts.

DUFAULT, CHERYL; West Seneca East SR HS; Vernon, CT; (Y); 10/365; Exploring; High Hon Roll; JC Awd; Jr NHS; NHS; Ntl Merit Ltr; NYS Rgnts Schlrshp 85; Outstndng Frnch & Spnsh Stu 85; Middlebury Coll; Frnch.

DUFAULT, SYLVIE; Catholic Central HS; Latham, NY; (S); 26/203; French Clb; German Clb; Math Clb; Pom Pon; Hon Roll; German Awd 82-83; French Awd 84; Acad Rollande; Hair Designer.

DUFF, CANDACE; Springfield Gardens HS; St Albans, NY; (S); 13/508; DECA; Trs FBLA; JA; Science Clb; Church Choir; School Musical; Nwsp Rptr; Nwsp Stf; High Hon Roll; Hon Roll; Natl Achvt Awd Outstndg Negro Stud Semifnlst 85; March Of Dimes Awd Svc 83; Extmprns Spkng 1st Pl 83; Cornell U; Econ.

DUFFALO, JANA F; Niskayuna HS; Schenectady, NY; (Y); Pep Clb; Spanish Clb; Variety Show; Ed Yrbk Sprt Ed; Stu Cncl; Capt Bsktbl; Coach Actv; Socr; Trk; U Of CT; Psych.

DUFFIN, ELIZABETH; Jamesville De Witt HS; Syracuse, NY; (Y); French Clb; Intnl Clb; Chorus; Orch; JV Socr; Coll St Rose Albany; Bus.

DUFFIN, MARGARET R; Jamesville-De Witt HS; De Witt, NY; (Y); 67/225; French Clb; Intnl Clb; Model UN; Band; Hon Roll; NY ST Regents Schlrshp 85; Canisius Coll; Hstry.

DUFFY, BRIGID EILEEN; Oneonta HS; Oneonta, NY; (Y); 17/185; Trs French Clb; Thesps; Concert Band; School Musical; Stage Crew; Nwsp Bus Mgr; Score Keeper; Stat Socr; Hon Roll; NHS; Acctg.

DUFFY, COLLEEN E; E Syracuse-Minoa HS; E Syracuse, NY; (Y); 83/338; Science Clb; Ski Clb; Variety Show; Var Bowling; NHS; NYS Rgnts Schlrshp 85; Le Moyne Coll; Bus Admn.

DUFFY, DANIEL M; F D Roosevelt HS; Hyde Park, NY; (Y); 23/325; Math Tm; Band; Mrchg Band; VP Frsh Cls; Sec Soph Cls; VP Jr Cls; VP Jr Cls; JV Bsbl; Var JV Bsktbl; Jr NHS; Villanova U; Bus Adm.

DUFFY, DAWN; Richburg HS; Bolivar, NY; (S); Concert Band; Mrchg Band; Nwsp Rptr; Yrbk Stf; Trs Jr Cls; Var Cheerleading; Var Socr; High Hon Roll; Jr NHS; NHS.

DUFFY, JANINE; St Francis Prep; Astoria, NY; (Y); 225/736; Var Boys Clb Am; Church Yth Grp; Cmnty Wkr; Rep Frsh Cls; Rep Soph Cls; Rep Jr Cls; Rep Stu Cncl; Capt Cheerleading; Coach Actv; Im Vllybl; Tchr Spec Ed.

DUFFY, KELLY; East Hampton HS; Montauk, NY; (Y); 1/130; Cmnty Wkr; Band; Chorus; Concert Band; Mrchg Band; School Play; Stage Crew; Lit Mag; Sec Stu Cncl; Var L Trk; Brown U Bk Awd Engl 85; LVIS Bk Awd Hghst Schltc Achvt 83-84; Long Island Cncl Soc Studs Achvt Awd 84; Med.

DUFFY, NANCY A; James I O Neill HS; Highland Falls, NY; (Y); 36/115; Civic Clb; Office Aide; Pep Clb; Teachers Aide; Yrbk Stf; JV Cheerleading; Sftbl; JV Vllybl; Hon Roll; Ofc Practice Awd 85; Genl Bus Awd 82; Adv Typing Awd 84; Highland Falls FD Schlrshp 85; USAA Schlrshp; Cobleskill ST Coll; Secry.

DUFORT, MICHELLE; Franklin Acad; Whippleville, NY; (Y); Church Yth Grp; French Clb; Ski Clb; Chorus; Nwsp Stf; Yrbk Stf; Off Stu Cncl; Var Bsktbl; Hon Roll; VP NHS; Cert Of Merit Fr 83-84; Epsilon VP 84-85; Siena Coll; Psych.

DUFRESNE, CHARLES; Sharon Springs Central Schl; Sharon Springs, NY; (S); 3/39; Am Leg Boys St; Trs Varsity Clb; Stage Crew; VP Frsh Cls; Pres Soph Cls; VP Sr Cls; Trs Stu Cncl; Capt L Socr; VP NHS; Trophy Awd Best Soccr Spirited Plyr 83; :Adv Design.

DUFRESNE, LYNDA; Bronx High School Of Science; New York, NY; (Y); Teachers Aide; Chorus; Rep Jr Cls; Rep Sr Cls; Off Stu Cncl; Cheerleading; Trk; Ntl Merit SF; Civil Engr.

DUGAN, ELAINE; Academy Fo The Holy Names; Delmar, NY; (Y); Church Yth Grp; Chorus; Nwsp Stf; Rep Stu Cncl; Acad All Amer 85; Spn Awd 83-85; Engl Awd 84-85; Chem 85; Psych.

DUGAN III, JOHN; Skaneateles Central HS; Skaneateles, NY; (S); Church Yth Grp; Rep Jr Cls; Var Bsbl; Var Crs Cntry; Capt Trk; Fire Sci.

DUGAN, LAURA; Cicero-N Syracuse HS; Clay, NY; (S); 83/622; Church Yth Grp; Exploring; Girl Scts; JA; Key Clb; Stage Crew; Powder Puff Ftbl; Hon Roll; Acctng.

DUGGAN, DONNA; Mexico Acad; Fulton, NY; (Y); Spanish Clb; Var Trk; Hon Roll; NHS; Prfct Atten Awd; Spanish NHS; Silver Medal Schlr Athl Awd 84; Acad Athletic Achvmnt Awd 85.

DUGGAN, LAURA A; Shaker HS; Latham, NY; (Y); Church Yth Grp; GAA; Crs Cntry; Trk; Hon Roll; NHS; Scholastic Athlete Awd 83-84; Bucknell U; Chem Engineering.

DUHAN, ROSE; Chatham HS; Old Chatham, NY; (Y); Math Tm; Ski Clb; Orch; School Play; Rep Stu Cncl; JV Var Crs Cntry; JV Var Trk; High Hon Roll; Hon Roll.

DUHOSKI, LEEANN; Bishop Ludden HS; Syracuse, NY; (S); Exploring; GAA; Bsktbl; Socr; High Hon Roll; NHS; Chem.

DUIGNAN, KATHLEEN; Uniondale HS; Uniondale, NY; (Y); 3/480; NFL; Band; Drm & Bgl; Orch; Yrbk Stf; VP Stu Cncl; Capt Cheerleading; Var JV Sftbl; Kiwanis Awd; NHS; NY ST Regnts Schlrshp 85; Outstndng SR Forgn Lang 85; UTA Schlrshp 85; U Of Miami; Pol Sci.

DUKETT, ANN L; Rome Free Acad; Rome, NY; (Y); 92/536; Chorus; Yrbk Stf; Hon Roll; Jr NHS; Ntl Merit Schol; Geneseo.

DULAK, CRAIG; West Seneca West HS; Buffalo, NY; (Y); Trk; Prfct Atten Awd; Bryant & Stratton; Accntnt.

DULANEY, DEBORAH; Cornwall Central HS; Cornwall, NY; (Y); Band; Drm & Bgl; Tennis; Hon Roll; Bus.

DULAY, RACHEL; Columbia HS; E Greenbush, NY; (Y); Art Clb; Church Yth Grp; Crs Cntry; Tennis; High Hon Roll; Hon Roll; NHS.

DUMA, JULIE; Lackawanna SR HS; Lackawanna, NY; (Y); Am Leg Aux Girls St; French Clb; GAA; Sftbl; Swmmng; High Hon Roll; Hon Roll; NHS; Wrnr Lmbrt Intl Schlrshp Awd 85; Bus.

DUMAIN, KIMBERLY; Eden Central SR HS; Eden, NY; (Y); 40/193; FTA; Band; Drm & Bgl; Orch; Pep Band; School Musical; Symp Band; Bowling; Vllybl; Pres Schlr; Mst Valuable SR Bowlng 85; St John Fisher Coll Rochester.

DUMBLETON, ELLEN; Dominican Commercial HS; Glendale, NY; (Y); Chess Clb; Hosp Aide; Sftbl; Swmmng; Vllybl; Hon Roll; Kiwanis Awd.

DUME, ADELINA; Hunter College HS; Woodside, NY; (Y); Cmnty Wkr; Teachers Aide; Var JV Bsktbl; Ntl Spanish Exam 83-85; NY U; Soc Wrk.

DUMIAN, DENISE; Susquehanna Valley HS; Binghamton, NY; (Y); Art Clb; French Clb; Band; Concert Band; Drill Tm; Mrchg Band; JV Bsktbl; JV Sftbl; JV Vllybl; High Hon Roll; Engr.

DUMOFF, MICHELE; Union Endicott HS; Endwell, NY; (Y); Key Clb; Temple Yth Grp; Band; Concert Band; Mrchg Band; NHS.

DUMONT, DOUG; Moriah Central HS; Witherbee, NY; (Y); Pres Stu Cncl; JV Var Ftbl; NY Inst Of Tech; Pol Sci.

DUMORNAY, WILCY; Samuel T Tilden HS; Brooklyn, NY; (Y); Dance Clb; DECA; Drama Clb; FBLA; Hosp Aide; Science Clb; Chorus; Drill Tm; School Play; Swing Chorus; UFT Schlrshp 83; Dly News Prncpls Pride Of Ynkees Awd 85; Bio.

DUNBAR, CYRELL; Benjamin Fanklin HS; Rochester, NY; (Y); Office Aide; Chorus; School Play; JV Gym; Hon Roll.

DUNBAR, DARNELL J; East HS; Rochester, NY; (Y); 27/267; Scholastic Bowl; Var L Ftbl; Var L Trk; Hon Roll; NHS; Prfct Atten Awd; Ntl Achvt Cmmnd Stu 84; MI ST U; Bus Admin.

DUNBAR, JENNIFER; The Buffalo Seminary; Buffalo, NY; (Y); 12/36; Political Wkr; Yrbk Phtg; Var Sftbl; Hon Roll; Rochester Inst Of Tech; Engrng.

DUNBAR, LANA; Canastota JR SR HS; Canastota, NY; (Y); Pres 4-H; Trs FBLA; Trs FFA; JV Var Bsktbl; Morgan Horse Assn Awd FFA 84-85; Equine Husbndry.

DUNCAN, GEORGINE; Villa Maria Acad; Buffalo, NY; (Y); Computer Clb; French Clb; Girl Scts; Chorus; Church Choir; Variety Show; Trs Soph Cls; Schlrshp To Cmnty Music Schl 85-86; Perform With Schlora Cantorum 85-86; M & T Bawk/Tst Buffalo Festvl; Music Vc.

DUNCAN, LISA; Lansingburgh HS; Troy, NY; (Y); 39/175; Spanish Clb; Varsity Clb; Capt Stu Cncl; JV Var Bsktbl; Score Keeper; Capt Socr; High Hon Roll; Hon Roll; Jr NHS; NHS; St Michaels Coll; Bus Admin.

DUNCAN, ROOSEVELT; Columbus Hitch HS; Bronx, NY; (S); Church Yth Grp; Debate Tm; English Clb; FCA; Political Wkr; Speech Tm; Teachers Aide; Mrchg Band; School Musical; School Play; Received A Hygiene Awd 85; A Merit Certificate In Government 85; City U; Liberal Arts.

DUNDON, CAITLIN; Honeoye Central HS; Livonia, NY; (S); 4/65; Pres Art Clb; Sec 4-H; French Clb; Jazz Band; Mrchg Band; Nwsp Rptr; Yrbk Ed-Chief; Rep Frsh Cls; Trs Soph Cls; Im Crs Cntry; All Star Pianist 84; 1st Ntl Essay Cmpttn 84; Cncl Intl Stu NYS 84; Syracuse U; Art.

DUNDON, COLLEEN; Mahopac HS; Mahopac, NY; (Y); 110/423; Camera Clb; Girl Scts; Science Clb; Yrbk Phtg; Yrbk Stf; JV Capt Fld Hcky; JV Var Socr; Im Vllybl; Hon Roll; Church Yth Grp; Camp Notre Dame Cullum Awd 83; Eng.

DUNDON, KELLEY L; Frontier Central HS; Lakeview, NY; (Y); 112/535; Cmnty Wkr; Drama Clb; French Clb; Letterman Clb; Pep Clb; Teachers Aide; Varsity Clb; School Play; Stage Crew; Nwsp Stf; Sprts Med.

DUNFORD, BETH; United Nations International Schl; New York, NY; (Y); Debate Tm; Model UN; Ski Clb; Off Stu Cncl; Crs Cntry; Vllybl; Georgetown; Pol Sci.

DUNGIE, CHRIS D; Mount Saint Michael Acad; Bronx, NY; (Y); 104/308; Chess Clb; Computer Clb; Hon Roll.

DUNHAM, BRIDGET; Henninger HS; Syracuse, NY; (Y); #48 In Class; Exploring; Concert Band; Jazz Band; Mrchg Band; Pep Band; Symp Band; Score Keeper; Timer; Hon Roll; Elec Engr.

DUNHAM, CHRISTOPHER J; Hudson Falls Central HS; Hudson Falls, NY; (Y); Acpl Chr; Band; School Musical; VP Stu Cncl; Var Socr; Tennis; Hon Roll; Ntl Merit Ltr; St Schlr; Navy ROTC Schlrshp 85-86; Rensselaer Polytech Inst; Engr.

DUNHAM, DIANA M; Hammond Central Schl; Hammond, NY; (Y); 2/26; VP Pres 4-H; French Clb; Pres Frsh Cls; Pres Soph Cls; JV Var Bsktbl; JV Var Socr; JV Var Sftbl; 4-H Awd; NHS; Sal; NYS Rgnts Schlrshp 85; St Lawrence U.

DUNHAM, LAURA; Waterloo Central HS; Waterloo, NY; (Y); 12/200; Color Guard; NHS; Law.

DUNHAM, VICKIE; Oakfield-Alabama HS; Batavia, NY; (Y); 23/83; Chorus; Trs Frsh Cls; Trs Soph Cls; Vllybl; Cit Awd; NHS; Prfct Atten Awd; Busnss Mgmt.

DUNICAN, MAUREEN; Maria Regina HS; N Tarrytown, NY; (Y); 61/127; Church Yth Grp; Church Choir; Rep Stu Cncl; Capt Swmmng; Yth Rep Movemnt Bettr Wrld U N 84-85; Elem Ed.

DUNKER, JUSTIN; August Martin HS; Bronx, NY; (Y); Aud/Vis; Library Aide; Office Aide; Band; Jazz Band; School Musical; Outstndg Achvt Comp Math 84-85; NY City Tech Coll; Elec Engr.

DUNKER, PATRICIA ANN; Our Lady Of Perpetual Hilp HS; Brooklyn, NY; (Y); Chorus; Hon Roll; Bus Adm.

DUNLAP, JAMES R; Ithaca HS; Ithaca, NY; (Y); Am Leg Boys St; Nwsp Stf; Rep Stu Cncl; Var Ftbl; Var Lcrss.

DUNLAP, RICHARD; Elmira Free Acad; Elmira, NY; (Y); Latin Clb; Ski Clb; Chorus; Yrbk Stf; Rep Frsh Cls; Rep Soph Cls; Rep Jr Cls; Rep Stu Cncl; Socr; High Hon Roll; Socr Lttrs 83-85; Law.

DUNLAP, TANYA; Clara Barton HS; Brooklyn, NY; (Y); Church Yth Grp; Dance Clb; Drama Clb; French Clb; Girl Scts; Chorus; School Play; Variety Show; Cheerleading; Prfct Atten Awd; Tlnt Show Recgntn Cert 84; Phys Fit Cert Awd 84; Crmnl Law.

DUNN, CINDY; La Webber JR SR HS; Lyndonville, NY; (Y); 35/60; Computer Clb; Prfct Atten Awd; Voctnl Indstr Clbs Of Amer 85; Genesee Comm Coll; Data Prcsng.

DUNN, DAVID; Haverling Central Schl; Bath, NY; (S); 15/146; French Clb; Math Clb; Ski Clb; Band; Mrchg Band; Orch; Symp Band; Nwsp Sprt Ed; Var Capt Socr; Var L Swmmng; U S Mltry Acad; Engr.

DUNN, DAVID; Horseheads Central Schls; Elmira, NY; (S); 28/407; Boy Scts; Hosp Aide; JCL; Latin Clb; Ski Clb; Band; Chorus; Concert Band; Jazz Band; Mrchg Band; Hopwood Smmr Scshlr Lynchburg Coll VA 84; Cum Laue Natl Latin Exam 82; Franklin & Marshall; Pre-Med.

DUNN, DAVONNIE; Harry S Truman HS; Bronx, NY; (Y); 32/544; NHS; SUNY Stonybrk; Pre-Med.

DUNN, DEIRDRE; Notre Dame Acad; Staten Island, NY; (Y); Art Clb; Computer Clb; Dance Clb; Drama Clb; GAA; Math Clb; Science Clb; School Musical; School Play; Nwsp Rptr; Villanova U; Bus.

DUNN, DIEDRE; E Aurora HS; East Aurora, NY; (S); 6/182; AFS; Varsity Clb; Trs Frsh Cls; Trs Soph Cls; Trs Jr Cls; Rep Sr Cls; Tennis; Hon Roll; NHS; GAA; Supr 7 Athl Wk 84; Sec VI Tnns Champ 84; Engrng.

DUNN, ERIKA; Jamestown HS; Jamestown, NY; (Y); Am Leg Aux Girls St; Quiz Bowl; Pres Acpl Chr; Madrigals; School Musical; VP Sr Cls; JV Var Tennis; High Hon Roll; Jr NHS; Pres NHS; Corp Law.

DUNN, GLORIOUS; De Witt Clinton HS; Bronx, NY; (Y); Debate Tm; Hosp Aide; Service Clb; Band; Orch; School Play; Vllybl; High Hon Roll; NHS; Prfct Atten Awd; Fr Awd; Achvt Awd; Cornell U; Psych.

DUNN, JEANNINE; Charles Damico HS; Albion, NY; (S); 21/180; Sec VP Church Yth Grp; Pres VP 4-H; Pres Spanish Clb; Chorus; Color Guard; Yrbk Stf; Pres Sr Cls; 4-H Awd; NHS; Merit Roll 83-84; SUNY-OSWEGO; Psych.

DUNN, JOHN; Smithtown East HS; St James, NY; (Y); Chess Clb; Office Aide; Science Clb; Pres Service Clb; Nwsp Ed-Chief; NHS; Ntl Merit Ltr; Stu Promtng Acadmc Medioctry 85; U Of DE; Civl Engrng.

DUNN, MICHAEL; St John The Baptist HS; Gt River, NY; (Y); 100/400; Church Yth Grp; Var Bsktbl; Var Golf; JV Lcrss; U Of Miami; Arch.

DUNN, MICHAEL; Voorheesville HS; Voorheesville, NY; (Y); Church Yth Grp; Computer Clb; Drama Clb; Intnl Clb; Chorus; School Play; Stage Crew; Var L Golf; Var L Trk; Hon Roll; Eng.

DUNN, NANCY; East Islip HS; Islip Terr, NY; (Y); Chess Clb; German Clb; Library Aide; Chorus; Var Tennis; Var Trk; Hon Roll; Paul Smiths Coll; Culinary.

DUNN, PHILIP; Commack HS; E Northport, NY; (Y); Varsity Clb; Var L Ftbl; Var L Trk; High Hon Roll.

DUNN, TOM; Smithtown HS West; Smithtown, NY; (Y); Hosp Aide; Science Clb; Spanish Clb; Concert Band; Jazz Band; Mrchg Band; Pep Band; Bsbl; Hon Roll; Spanish NHS; Sci.

DUNN, VICTORIA; Grand Island SR HS; Grand Island, NY; (Y); 27/325; Art Clb; Church Yth Grp; Cmnty Wkr; Church Choir; Hon Roll; Ltr Acad Excel 85; Comp Sci.

DUNNE, CHARLES G; Garden City SR HS; Garden City, NY; (Y); 136/365; Boy Scts; Yrbk Sprt Ed; Rep Stu Cncl; Lcrss; Hon Roll; NY ST Regents Schlrshp 85; Fairfield U; Liberal Arts.

DUNNE, EVAN; Bethpage HS; Bethpage, NY; (Y); 1/313; Boy Scts; Church Yth Grp; Cmnty Wkr; Library Aide; Spanish Clb; Chorus; God Cntry Awd; NHS; High Hon Roll; Fencing 83-85; Rensselaer Math,Sci Awd 84-85; Yth Gov Rep 84-85; Intl Aff.

DUNNE, JAMES; West Hempstead HS; W Hempstead, NY; (Y); Art Clb; Hon Roll; Art Hnr Soc 85-86; Commercl Art.

DUNNEWOLD, CHERYL L; Clymer Central HS; Clymer, NY; (Y); AFS; Library Aide; Chorus; School Play; Trs Frsh Cls; Var L Church Yth Grp; Var L Sftbl; High Hon Roll; VP NHS; NY ST Rgnts Schlrshp 85; Fredonia ST U; Bus Mgmnt.

DUNNING, JENNIFER; Parishville-Hopkinton Central HS; Potsdam, NY; (Y); Band; Mrchg Band; School Musical; VP Frsh Cls; VP Soph Cls; VP Jr Cls; VP Sr Cls; JV Var Socr; JV Var Vllybl; Bausch & Lomb Sci Awd; Army ROTC 85; Appt As Cadet-USCG Acad 85; USCG Acad; Comp Sci.

DUNPHY, KATHY; Sachem HS; Holbrook, NY; (Y); Dance Clb; Drama Clb; Hosp Aide; Ski Clb; Chorus; Stage Crew; Nwsp Stf; Off Jr Cls; Hon Roll; 2nd Pl Oral Presntn Natl Hstry Fair Sachem & Long Island & NY ST 83; Lib Arts.

DUNSCOMB, MARK; Ossining HS; Ossining, NY; (Y); Church Yth Grp; Varsity Clb; JV Var Lcrss; Hon Roll; Pre-Med.

DUNSTON, CHERYL; De Witt Clinton HS; Bronx, NY; (Y); Drama Clb; Girl Scts; Hosp Aide; Pres Key Clb; School Play; VP Sr Cls; 4-H Awd; Kiwanis Awd; Prfct Atten Awd; Kiwanis Awd 85; Wlk Amer Spcl Awd 85; Key Clb Pres Yr 84; U Of CA ST Lng Bch; Acctnt.

DUNTON, KIRSTEN; North Rose Wolcott HS; Wolcott, NY; (Y); 3/148; Am Leg Aux Girls St; Yrbk Stf; Pres Jr Cls; Pres Sr Cls; Rep Stu Cncl; Var Capt Swmmng; DAR Awd; VP NHS; Cit Awd; High Hon Roll; Hugh O Brien Ldrshp Awd 83; ST Senate Stu Polcy Forum 85; Clge Of William & Mary.

DUONG, TAI; Nyack HS; Valley Cottage, NY; (Y); Art Clb; Math Tm; High Hon Roll; Jr NHS; Stu Of The Week Nyack HS 85; Natl Sci Olympiad 85; WA Smmr Smnr/Amer U 85; Sci.

DUPLATRE, MICHELLE; St Francis Prep; Queens Vill, NY; (Y); Chorus; School Musical; Im Vllybl; Psychlgy.

DUPREE, ROSE; Northern Adirondack Central Schl; Churubusco, NY; (Y); Cmnty Wkr; French Clb; Library Aide; JV Bsktbl; Hon Roll; Phys Educ.

DUPREY, CHARMAIN; Crown Point Central HS; Crown Pt, NY; (S); Drama Clb; Hosp Aide; Band; Concert Band; Mrchg Band; School Play; Trs Jr Cls; Var Bsktbl; High Hon Roll; Hon Roll; Hghst Hrs In Moses Ludington Hosp For Cndy Strpng 84; US Navy; Med.

DUPUIS, MICHELLE; Cambridge Central Schl; Cambridge, NY; (Y); 11/83; GAA; Varsity Clb; Var Capt Bsktbl; Var Capt Fld Hcky; Var Capt Sftbl; High Hon Roll; Hon Roll; NHS; Don Cummings Fmly Awd Fld Hockey 85; Don Cummings Fmly Awd Sftbl 85; US Army Rsrve Schlr/Athl Awd 85; Albany Coll Pharm; Pharm.

DUQUE, ANDRES; William Nottingham HS; Syracuse, NY; (Y); Nwsp Stf; Yrbk Phtg; Yrbk Stf; Lit Mag; Hon Roll; NHS; Spec Achvmnt Awd 85; Cert Of Mrt 1 Gold Key For Art Piece Tres Sillas 85; Cert Of Merit 2 Gold Keys 83; Psychlgy.

DUQUE, KATIA D; Our Lady Of Mercy HS; Glen Cove, NY; (Y); 23/117; Computer Clb; Hosp Aide; Key Clb; Service Clb; Teachers Aide; Var Badmtn; NEDT Awd; Cmnty Wkr; High Hon Roll; Natl Assoc Of Wmn In Constrctn Schlrshp 85; NYS Rgnts Schlrshp 85; The Cooper Union; Civil Engr.

DUQUETTE, DIANE; Northeastern Clinton Central HS; Champlain, NY; (Y); Church Choir; Yrbk Stf; Clinton CC; Bus.

DURAND, MARCELLA C; Hunter College HS; New York, NY; (Y); Aud/Vis; Cmnty Wkr; Political Wkr; Chorus; School Musical; School Play; Stage Crew; Yrbk Stf; Mgr Jr Cls; Crs Cntry; Regents Schlrshp 85; Tulane U Shclrshp 85; Pell Grant 85; Envir.

DURANT, DIANNE; Potsdam Central HS; Potsdam, NY; (Y); Church Yth Grp; French Clb; Girl Scts; JA; Math Clb; Acpl Chr; Band; Chorus; Church Choir; Hon Roll; Microbio.

DURAWA, ANN MARIE; West Senecca West SR HS; Cheektowaga, NY; (Y); 31/543; Key Clb; Y-Teens; Trs Soph Cls; Off Jr Cls; Off Sr Cls; Stu Cncl; Hon Roll; Pres Jr NHS; Pres NHS; Drama Clb; NYS Regnts Schlrshp 84-85; Nazareth Coll Rochester; Law.

DURFEY, SUSAN M; John F Kennedy HS; Utica, NY; (Y); 12/140; Hon Roll; Jr NHS; Regents Schlrshp Awd 85; MVCC; Accntng.

DURHAM, JEANNE; Mineola HS; Mineola, NY; (Y); Church Yth Grp; Girl Scts; Key Clb; Office Aide; Band; Church Choir; Concert Band; Mrchg Band; Stu Cncl; High Hon Roll; Marchng Band Hnrs 83-85; Berkeley Coll; Sec.

DURKEE, SEAN; Lewiston-Porter Senior HS; Lewiston, NY; (Y); Boy Scts; Chorus; Var Swmmng; High Hon Roll; Lamp Learng Awd Sci 85; Eagle Scout 83; Sci.

DURKIN, MAUREEN; Bishop Kearney HS; Brooklyn, NY; (Y); Var Swmmng; Hon Roll; Nrsng.

DURLAK, ANDREA; Villa Maria Acad; Buffalo, NY; (S); 2/112; Computer Clb; JCL; Latin Clb; Math Clb; Chorus; Bowling; High Hon Roll; NHS; NEDT Awd; Rochester Inst Of Tech; Comp.

DURNIAK, KAREN J; Arlington HS; Hopewell Jct, NY; (Y); 59/572; Hosp Aide; Ski Clb; High Hon Roll; NHS; St Schlr; Acad Schlrshp; Nrs.

DUROCHER, JOHN F; Hugh C Williams HS; Canton, NY; (Y); 28/132; Varsity Clb; Yrbk Stf; Pres Jr Cls; Var Capt Bsbl; Var JV Bsktbl; Var Capt Socr; Var L Trk; High Hon Roll; Player Of Yr Var Soccer 84-85; Rookie Of Yr Var Trk 84-85; ROTC Army Schlrshp; RIT; Industrl Engrng.

DURR, AMY; Oakfield Alabama Central HS; Oakfield, NY; (Y); 11/83; Sec AFS; Church Yth Grp; Pres Drama Clb; Office Aide; Trs Chorus; Church Choir; School Musical; Swing Chorus; NHS; Am Leg Aux Girls St; Keyboardng/Cmmncntns Awd 83; Bus Dynamcs Awd 84; Word Of Life Intl Teens Vocl Solo 2nd Pl 83; Messiah Coll; Psych.

DURSI, CYNTHIA; Fox Lane HS; Bedford, NY; (Y); 57/270; Church Yth Grp; Ski Clb; Nwsp Rptr; Rep Jr Cls; French Clb; JV Lcrss; High Hon Roll; Hon Roll; Cmnty Wkr; Spanish Clb; Mary Jo Anderson Mem Awd-Outstndng In Schlrsp & Ctznshp 82-83; 3rd Prz-Photo Exchg Exhbt In CO 83-84.

DURSO, ANTHONY P; Rome Free Acad; Rome, NY; (Y); Hon Roll; NHS; Spnsh Hnrs 85; Mohawk Vly CC; Cartnst.

DURSO, JIM; Longwood HS; Yaphank, NY; (Y); High Hon Roll; Berkley Schl; Music.

DURWALD, MARK; Tonawanda JR SR HS; Tonawanda, NY; (Y); JV Ftbl.

DURYEA, SCOTT; New Rochelle HS; New Rochelle, NY; (Y); Boy Scts; Ski Clb; Y-Teens; JV Var Ice Hcky; Hon Roll; PTSA Awd Archit 85; Roger Williams; Archit.

DUSENBURY, CHARLOTTE; Johnstown HS; Gloversville, NY; (Y); Intnl Clb; Chorus; Variety Show; Hon Roll; Prfct Atten Awd; Acctng.

DUSINBERRE, RODNEY; Lockport SR HS; Lockport, NY; (Y); Church Yth Grp; French Clb; Latin Clb; Letterman Clb; School Play; Diving; Trk; SUNY Cobbleskill; Htl Mngmnt.

DUSING, VALERIE; Le Roy HS; Leroy, NY; (Y); AFS; Church Yth Grp; French Clb; Ski Clb; Chorus; Stage Crew; Yrbk Stf; Hon Roll; Floriculture.

DUSKAS, WILLIAM; Hugh C Williams HS; Canton, NY; (Y); 5/140; Pres Church Yth Grp; Varsity Clb; Trs Frsh Cls; Trs Soph Cls; Pres Jr Cls; VP Sr Cls; Rep Stu Cncl; Var Golf; Var Ice Hcky; Var Socr; Acad All-Northern Ice Hockey Tm 84-85; U S Naval Acad Summer Sem 85; U S Coast Guard Acad Proj Aim Wnr; U S Air Frc Acad; Aero Engrng.

DUSOVIC, ANTHONY; Mt Saint Michael Acad; New York, NY; (Y); 19/308; Hon Roll; Manhattan Coll; Engrng.

DUSSETSCHLEGER, JEFFREY; Half Hollow Hills High School East; Dix Hills, NY; (Y); 102/586; German Clb; Leo Clb; High Hon Roll; Jr NHS; NHS; Long Isl Sci Cngrss Blue Ribbon 82; SUNY Stony Brook.

DUSTIN, TERRI; Southwestern Central HS; Celoron, NY; (Y); French Clb; Hosp Aide; Chorus; Flag Corp; Hon Roll; Emphasis On Exc 85; French IV Lang Awd 85frnnr Up Girls St 85; Marine Bio.

DUTTA, SANJOY K; Stuyvesant HS; Queens Village, NY; (Y); Debate Tm; Library Aide; Science Clb; Lit Mag; Hon Roll; Chrmn NHS; Ntl Merit Schol; Wstnghs Semi-Fnst 85; Columiba U HS Sci Hnrs 84-85; Yale U.

DUVE, SUE; Saranac Central HS; Saranac, NY; (S); 25/135; Office Aide; Band; School Musical; Pres Frsh Cls; Pres Soph Cls; Im Mgr Bsktbl; Var Socr; Var Trk; JV Var Vllybl; High Hon Roll; MVP Ntl Sccr Coachs Assn Am 85; All Star Sccr MVP 84-85; 1st Tm All Star Sftbl 83-84; Siena; Comp Sci.

DUVILAIRE, NADIA; Martin Luther King Jr HS; Brooklyn, NY; (Y); Church Yth Grp; Intnl Clb; Teachers Aide; Chorus; Church Choir; Nwsp Rptr; Yrbk Ed-Chief; Hon Roll; Frgn Lang.

DVORAK, MICHELLE G; West Seneca E SR HS; West Seneca, NY; (Y); 33/365; Trs 4-H; Im Vllybl; Hon Roll; JC Awd; NHS; NY ST Regents Schlrshp 85; NY ST U Buffalo; Engrng.

DVOROCSIK, ANDREW J; Kingston HS; Kingston, NY; (Y); 16/520; Pres German Clb; Capt Quiz Bowl; Band; Jazz Band; VP Orch; Yrbk Stf; VP Capt Bsktbl; Var Crs Cntry; High Hon Roll; NHS; Le High U; Engr.

DWAILEEBE, JENNY; Olean HS; Olean, NY; (Y); Chorus; Color Guard; School Musical; Hon Roll; Art.

DWECK, CHARLES; Sephardic HS; Bewyork, NY; (S); Debate Tm; FBLA; Fld Hcky; Ice Hcky; Prfct Atten Awd; Brooklyn Coll.

DWORKEN, CORY; Locust Valley HS; Bayville, NY; (Y); #28 In Class; Am Leg Boys St; Boys Clb Am; Camera Clb; Cmnty Wkr; Library Aide; Ski Clb; Teachers Aide; Varsity Clb; Stage Crew; Yrbk Bus Mgr; Excel Eng 84-85; MVP V Tennis 84-85; NY St Regnts Schlrshp Wnnr 85; Carnegie Mellon U; Intl Fin.

DWULIT, YVONNE; St Vincent Ferrer HS; Woodside, NY; (Y); 21/114; Library Aide; Hon Roll; Cert Eductnl Dvlpmnt Ntl 84.

DWYER, DAWN M; Pawling HS; Pawling, NY; (Y); FBLA; Math Tm; Band; Off Sr Cls; Cheerleading; NY St Regnts Schlrshp 85; St U NY-ALBANY; Acctng.

DWYER, DOUGLAS W; Corning Painted Post West HS; Painted Post, NY; (Y); Art Clb; Boy Scts; Ski Clb; Orch; School Musical; Nwsp Phtg; Yrbk Phtg; Crs Cntry; High Hon Roll; Ntl Merit Ltr; Egl Sct 83; NY ST Media Arts Schl Awd 84; NY ST Vsl Arts Schl 85; Bus.

DWYER, JOHN; Ravena Coeymans Selkirk HS; Ravena, NY; (Y); 8/196; Var Tennis; Im Vllybl; High Hon Roll; NHS; NYS Regent Schlrshp; Clarkson U; Elec Engr.

DWYER, JONATHAN; Mahopac HS; Mahopac, NY; (Y); 33/423; Rep Stu Cncl; Bsktbl; JV Var Ftbl; JV Var Lcrss; High Hon Roll; Hon Roll; NHS; Amer Lgns Boys ST 85; Bus Admin.

DWYER, JOSEPH M; Clarkstown High School North; New City, NY; (Y); Var Capt Swmmng; Jr NHS; Ntl Merit Ltr; MVP Swmmr 83; Coaches Awd Swm 85.

DWYER, MICHAEL; Mount Vernon HS; Mount Vernon, NY; (Y); Church Yth Grp; Cmnty Wkr; Office Aide; Spanish Clb; Stu Cncl; High Hon Roll; Hon Roll; Jr NHS; NHS; Prfct Atten Awd; Prvt Invstgtr.

DYCHA, JOELLE; Kensington/Bflo Vo-Tech; Buffalo, NY; (Y); Cmnty Wkr; Exploring; Office Aide; Teachers Aide; Hon Roll; Villa Maria Coll; Bus Mgmt.

DYE, ANNETTE; Frankfort-Schuyler HS; Utica, NY; (S); Exploring; Library Aide; Spanish Clb; Teachers Aide; NHS; U C Brekley; Lawyer.

DYE, KATIE; Gowands Central Schl; Gowanda, NY; (Y); Ski Clb; Pres Spanish Clb; Trs Thesps; Band; Chorus; Rep Soph Cls; Rep Jr Cls; Rep Stu Cncl; Var Trk; JV Vllybl.

DYER, ANNE; Our Lady Of Victory HS; Bronx, NY; (Y); Art Clb; School Play; Yrbk Stf; Sftbl; Hon Roll; Spanish NHS; Regnts Schrlshp 85; Manhattan Coll; Bus.

DYER, BERNADETTE L; Springfield Gardens HS; Springfield Gdns, NY; (Y); 32/508; Girl Scts; Office Aide; Yrbk Bus Mgr; Yrbk Stf; Rep Jr Cls; Rep Sr Cls; High Hon Roll; Prfct Atten Awd; NYS Regents Schlrshp Wnnr 85; NC A&T U; Bus Admin.

DYER, MICHAEL; Lake Placid Central Schl; Lake Placid, NY; (Y); 6/45; Church Yth Grp; Varsity Clb; Var Bsbl; Capt Var Ice Hcky; Capt Var Socr; Cit Awd; Hon Roll; NHS; Lk Placid Ed Found Schrshp 85; John R Carnell Schrlshp 85; Bud Colby Mem Awd 85; MI St U; Comm.

DYETT, MICHELLE; Wingate HS; Brooklyn, NY; (Y); Church Yth Grp; Cmnty Wkr; Band; Church Choir; Sftbl; Swmmng; Tennis; Vllybl; High Hon Roll; Hon Roll; Hnr Awd Typng 83; Hnr Awd Eng & Socl Studies 83; Achvt Cert In Excllnc & Math 82; CPA.

DYGUS, KIMBERLIE; Connetquot HS; Bohemia, NY; (Y); 203/708; Church Yth Grp; FBLA; Chorus; Drill Tm; Stu Cncl; Fld Hcky; Hon Roll; Miss Bohemia Teen 84; Distingushed Serv Awd 85; OH Wesleyan.

DYKE, JENNIFER J; St Lawrence Central; Brasher Falls, NY; (Y); 2/100; Pres Church Yth Grp; Sec 4-H; Sec French Clb; Pep Clb; Band; Chorus; Concert Band; Drm Mjr(t); Mrchg Band; Pep Band; Gold Awd Girl Scouting 85; Clarkson Schl 85; Silver Awd 84; Mgmt.

DYKEMAN, TERESSA; Seton Catholic Central HS; Binghamton, NY; (S); Church Yth Grp; Varsity Clb; JV Var Cheerleading; DAR Awd; High Hon Roll; Tae Kwon Do Blck Blt; Math Adv Plcmnt; 3rd ST Dance; Scranton U; Math.

DYMEK, DANIELLE; Deer Park HS; Deer Park, NY; (Y); 131/422; Drama Clb; Pep Clb; Spanish Clb; Chorus; School Play; Variety Show; Yrbk Phtg; Rep Jr Cls; Gym; Score Keeper; Pre-Med.

DYRACK, KARA E; Hunter College HS; Staten Island, NY; (Y); AFS; VP Camp Fr Inc; Dance Clb; Intnl Clb; Math Clb; Chorus; School Musical; Stage Crew; Rotary Awd; 1st Pl Lvl IV AATSP Cncrs Nacn 84; Vldctrn Smmr Cls 83; Spnsh Heritage Pgm 83; U Of VA; Engr.

DYSARD, BARB; Albion HS; Albion, NY; (Y); Church Yth Grp; Teachers Aide; Y-Teens; Color Guard; Cheerleading; Gym; Pom Pon; Psych.

DYSINGER, BRIAN; Royalton Hartland HS; Lockport, NY; (Y); Boy Scts; Cmnty Wkr; 4-H; VICA; Var JV Ftbl; Var 4-H Awd; 2nd Pl Auto Mech Comptn 85; Alfred ST; Auto Mech.

DYSLIN, SANDRA; Chatham Central HS; Spencertown, NY; (Y); 23/150; Church Yth Grp; Dance Clb; Band; Jazz Band; Orch; School Musical; Yrbk Rptr; Score Keeper; Hon Roll; NHS; Rep JR Clss Stdnt Govt 85; Theatr Arts.

DYSON, APRIL; North Babylon SR HS; North Babylon, NY; (Y); French Clb; Intnl Clb; Cheerleading; French Hon Soc; High Hon Roll; Jr NHS; NHS; Secy.

DYSON, CORNELIUS; Freeport HS; Freeport, NY; (Y); Computer Clb; French Clb; Science Clb; Hon Roll; NHS; All Star Tutrng Mbr 85; Cornell U; Dent.

DYSON, NANCY; Attica Central Schl; Attica, NY; (Y); Sec Church Yth Grp; Chorus; Church Choir; Var Crs Cntry; Var Trk; NHS; Sign Lang 82; Yth Emplymnt Prep Pgm 84; Liberty Bapt Coll; Missions.

DZAAK, DWAYNE; Bishop Timon HS; West Seneca, NY; (Y); 8/140; English Clb; JA; Quiz Bowl; Spanish Clb; Varsity Clb; Church Choir; Nwsp Stf; Lit Mag; Rep Frsh Cls; Rep Soph Cls; St Bonaventure Schlrshp 85-89; St Bonaventure U; Pre-Med.

DZANOUCAKIS, GEORGE; William Cullen Bryant HS; Woodside, NY; (S); Boy Scts; French Clb; Orch; Nwsp Ed-Chief; Nwsp Rptr; French Hon Soc; Hon Roll; NHS.

DZIADIW, STENIA; Acad Of The Holy Names; Slingerlands, NY; (Y); Dance Clb; Debate Tm; Drama Clb; Girl Scts; JA; Latin Clb; Speech Tm; School Play; Lit Mag; Hon Roll; Ntl Fornscs Lgu Hnr Awd 84; Pre-Law.

DZIEKAN, CHERYL; Holland Central Schl; Holland, NY; (Y); Varsity Clb; Var Bsktbl; Var Capt Fld Hcky; Var Socr; Var JV Vllybl; Pres Awd 83; Ecie All Star Tm 84; Bus Adm.

DZIEL, ANDREW; Fowler HS; Syracuse, NY; (S); Boys Clb Am; Spanish Clb; Bsktbl; Socr; NHS; Bio Awd 85; Sccr, Engl Awd; Math.

DZIENIUS, LORRAINE; St Marys Girls; New Hyde Pk, NY; (Y); Drama Clb; Stage Crew; JV Score Keeper; JV Mgr Vllybl; High Hon Roll; Hon Roll; NHS; Gold Medal Bus; Adelphi Univ Trustee Schlrshp; Regent Schlrshp Diploma 85; Adelphi Univ; Elem Tchr.

DZIWIS, CHERYL; Whitesboro SR HS; Whitesboro, NY; (Y); 9/313; Church Yth Grp; Cmnty Wkr; GAA; Ski Clb; Bowling; Powder Puff Ftbl; High Hon Roll; Jr NHS; NHS; Case Wstrn Deans Hnr Awd 85; Rgnts Schlrshp 85; Pre-Prfsnl Schlrs Prgm 85; Case Wstrn Rsrv U; Pre-Law.

DZYGUN, DIANNE M; Kenmore West HS; Kenmore, NY; (Y); Church Yth Grp; Acpl Chr; Chorus; School Musical; Hon Roll; Prfct Atten Awd; Bus.

EADES JR, RICHARD E; Dansville SR HS; Dansville, NY; (Y); 7/150; Am Leg Boys St; Boy Scts; Band; Concert Band; Jazz Band; Mrchg Band; Golf; God Cntry Awd; High Hon Roll; NHS; U Of Rochester; Bus Mgmt.

EAGEN, KERRY; Notre Dame HS; Elmira, NY; (Y); Chess Clb; JA; Key Clb; Spanish Clb; Yrbk Stf; Hon Roll; Albany Coll Of Pharm; Phrmcy.

EAGLETON, MATTHEW; North Rose-Wolcott HS; Wolcott, NY; (Y); 1/180; Am Leg Boys St; Trs Stu Cncl; Var Crs Cntry; Var Swmmng; Var Trk; High Hon Roll; NHS; NY ST Stu Enrgy Rsrch Comp, Rensselaer Math, Sci Awd 85; Bio Chem.

EALLONARDO, SAMUEL J; Fayetteville-Manlius HS; Fayetteville, NY; (Y); 42/345; JCL; Im Bsktbl; Var Trk; Hon Roll; NHS; NROTC Schlrshp 85; Natl Latin Exam Awd 83; Spanish Exclnce Awd 83 & 84; SUNY Binghamton; Med.

EAMES, WENDY; Amsterdam HS; Amsterdam, NY; (Y); Drama Clb; FBLA; Yrbk Stf; JV Mgr(s); Hon Roll; Cazanovia; Fshn Merch.

EARL, CHRISTINA; Dryden HS; Harford, NY; (Y); Trs FHA; Chorus; Church Choir; Hon Roll; FHA Tresr Awd 83; Boces Hnr Exclnt Atten 85; Food Prep.

EARL, REGINA C; Alfred Almond Central Schl; Alfred Station, NY; (Y); 1/70; Ed Hst JCL; Thesps; Pres Stage Crew; Ed Yrbk Stf; Bausch & Lomb Sci Awd; NHS; Ntl Merit Ltr; Val; Latin Clb; Rotary Intl Exch Stu Japan 85-86; NYS Regents Schlrshp 85; Alumni Fac & Staff Schlrshp Clemson U 84; Clemson U; Physics.

EARLE, TAMMY; Hannibal Central HS; Hannibal, NY; (S); Sec Stu Cncl; Var Cheerleading; Var Socr; High Hon Roll; Hon Roll; Nurse.

EARLE, WENDY E; C W Baker HS; Baldwinsville, NY; (Y); 18/440; Church Yth Grp; Dance Clb; Sec Frsh Cls; Coach Actv; Powder Puff Ftbl; High Hon Roll; NHS; Smll Bus Schlrshp 85; Cazenovia Coll; Bus.

EARLEY, MAUREEN; The Mary Louis Acad; Bayside, NY; (Y); Church Yth Grp; Cmnty Wkr; Hosp Aide; Var Cheerleading; Coach Actv; Hon Roll; Acctg.

EARLL, DAWN; Peru Central HS; Elmendorf AFB, AK; (Y); 12/178; Math Tm; Model UN; Pres Science Clb; Band; Orch; Ed Nwsp Ed-Chief; High Hon Roll; NHS; Church Yth Grp; Library Aide; West Pt Invtnl Acadmc Wrkshp 85; Offcrs Wives Clb Schlrshp 85; Schlrs For Dollars 85; Harvard Model UN; AK U; Astronomy.

EARLY, JOHN D; Niskayuna HS; Schenectady, NY; (Y); French Clb; Stu Cncl; Var Vllybl; French Hon Soc; NHS; AATF Cont 3rd Pl 84, 2nd Pl 85; Chem Engrng.

EASON, MICHELLE; Sacred Heart HS; Yonkers, NY; (S); 31/238; Intnl Clb; Sftbl; Hon Roll; NHS; Lehman; Geolgy.

EASTMAN, JAMES; John H Glenn HS; E Northport, NY; (Y); 30/300; Am Leg Boys St; Boy Scts; Debate Tm; ROTC; Off Scholastic Bowl; Lcrss; Wrstlng; Hon Roll; NHS; Partcptd Coast Guard Acad AIM Prog 85; Recvd Retird Ofcr Assn Troa Awd 85; Annapolis; Areosp Engrng.

EASTMAN, KARI; Greenwich Central HS; Greenwich, NY; (Y); AFS; Chorus; School Musical; School Play; JV Var Sftbl; Drug/Alchl Rehab Counslr.

EASTMOND, DALENA M; Dominican Commercial HS; Springfield Gdns, NY; (Y); 7/273; Church Yth Grp; Cmnty Wkr; Intnl Clb; Spanish Clb; Church Choir; School Musical; Rep Stu Cncl; High Hon Roll; NHS; Iona Lang Cntst Wnnr Spnsh 1st Hnrs 84-85; NY ST Regnts Schlrshp 85; Frshmn Recog Schlrshp 85; Hofstra U; Bio Med Engrng.

EASTMOND, SHEILA L; Clara Barton HS; Brooklyn, NY; (Y); Pres FNA; Hon Roll; Prfct Atten Awd; Comp Sci.

EASTWOOD, BRUCE; Christ The King HS; Queens Village, NY; (Y); Varsity Clb; Bsktbl; Acctnt.

EASTWOOD, LORNA-MARIE; Commack High Schl South; Commack, NY; (Y); Church Yth Grp; Teachers Aide; Band; Concert Band; Mrchg Band; Pep Band; Symp Band; Lit Mag; Hon Roll; Golden Quill Awd 85; Engl Educ.

EATON, JACQUELYN; Greene Central Schl; Willet, NY; (Y); Swing Chorus; Sec Frsh Cls; Trs Sr Cls; Rep Stu Cncl; L Vllybl; High Hon Roll; Hon Roll; Prfct Atten Awd; MVP Vllybl Tourn Cortland 83; Phy Thrpy.

EATON, MICHAEL; Clinton Central HS; Clinton, NY; (Y); Art Clb; JV Bsbl; JV Ftbl; JV Golf; JV Trk; Hon Roll; Prfct Atten Awd; NY ST Art Olympcs-1st Pl Team 85; Graphc Art.

EATON, TIMOTHY J; New Hyde Park Memorial JR SR HS; New Hyde Park, NY; (Y); 32/270; Cmnty Wkr; Mathletes; Pres Spanish Clb; Nwsp Bus Mgr; Nwsp Phtg; Nwsp Rptr; Lit Mag; Tennis; High Hon Roll; Jr NHS; Bronz Acadmc Key 84; Teengr Yr Long Island 84; Regnts Schlrshp 84-85; C W Post; TV Prod.

EBANKS, KAREN; Andrew Jackson HS; Queens Village, NY; (Y); Pres Key Clb; Stage Crew; YOU Clb; Ldrshp Clb; MD.

EBERHARDT, MARY; Frontier Central HS; Lakeview, NY; (Y); Church Yth Grp; Pres Latin Clb; Capt Quiz Bowl; Ski Clb; Concert Band; Jazz Band; Yrbk Phtg; Mgr(s); High Hon Roll; Pres NHS; Sci Congress Gold Seal 83; Chem Engrng.

EBERLE, SUZANNE; St Marys HS; Depew, NY; (S); 10/196; Hosp Aide; Rep Frsh Cls; Rep Soph Cls; Rep Jr Cls; Pres Sr Cls; Var Sftbl; Var JV Trk; Hon Roll; NHS; Suny; Pre-Med.

EBERLING, EDWARD R; Earl L Vandermeulen HS; Port Jefferson, NY; (Y); Capt Chess Clb; Political Wkr; Science Clb; Concert Band; Mrchg Band; Nwsp Bus Mgr; Rep Stu Cncl; Ntl Merit Ltr; Pres Schlr; St Schlr; NYS Rgnts Schlrshp 85; Marist Coll; Brdcstng.

EBERT, MICHELLE L; Brockport HS; Brockport, NY; (Y); French Clb; Ski Clb; Color Guard; Drm & Bgl; Yrbk Phtg; Yrbk Stf; Rep Sr Cls; Earth Sci.

EBLING, BARBARA; Buffalo Seminary; Buffalo, NY; (Y); Quiz Bowl; Pres Science Clb; Sec Service Clb; Ski Clb; Rep Stu Cncl; JV Var Fld Hcky; NHS; Ntl Merit Schol; Cum Laude Soc 85; Harvard U; Bio.

EBNER, MICHAEL C; Clarkstown North HS; Congers, NY; (Y); German Clb; Ftbl; Ice Hcky; Jr NHS; Mercy Coll; Chirprctc.

ECHAN, CHERYL; Union-Endicott HS; Endicott, NY; (Y); Church Yth Grp; Cmnty Wkr; Hosp Aide; Pres Key Clb; Ski Clb; Off Yrbk Bus Mgr; Cheerleading; High Hon Roll; Hon Roll; NHS; Most Val Chrldr 84; Candystripping Pin 84; Liberal Arts.

ECHANIQUE, PETER; Curtis HS; Staten Island, NY; (Y); Band; Concert Band; Jazz Band; Mrchg Band; School Musical; Hon Roll; NHS; Regents Schlrshp Awd 85; Honor Key 85; SUNY Binghamton.

ECHOLS, EUGENIA; Buffalo Acad Of The Sacred Heart; Buffalo, NY; (Y); Church Yth Grp; Cmnty Wkr; Hosp Aide; Trs VP JA; Latin Clb; VP Model UN; Political Wkr; Red Cross Aide; Science Clb; Service Clb; Alpha Kappa Alpha Hnrs Schlrshp 84-85; MI ST U; Elec Engr.

ECK, KELLY; Unatego HS; Unadilla, NY; (Y); Chorus; Rep Stu Cncl; Sftbl; Vllybl; Hon Roll; Bus.

ECKARD, ROBERT T; G Ray Bodley HS; Fulton, NY; (Y); 4/266; French Clb; Science Clb; Stu Cncl; Ftbl; Elks Awd; High Hon Roll; NHS; Prfct Atten Awd; Outstndng Perf In Math 84-85; Outstndng Perf In Bio & Chem & Physics 82-85; Syracuse U; Pre-Med.

ECKART, GEORGE D; Pittsford Mendon HS; Pittsford, NY; (Y); Aud/Vis; Boy Scts; Radio Clb; Jr Cls; Im Bsktbl; Im Socr; Hon Roll; NHS; AFROTC 4 Yr Schlrshp 85-89; GA Inst Of Tech; Elec Engrng.

ECKENRODE, KATHERINE; Geneva HS; Geneva, NY; (S); 1/170; Latin Clb; Varsity Clb; Swmmng; High Hon Roll; NHS; Ntl Merit Ltr; Lat Awd; Cornell; Biol Sci.

ECKER, ANN MARIE; West Islip HS; West Islip, NY; (Y); 18/525; Library Aide; Nwsp Rptr; Yrbk Ed-Chief; Off Soph Cls; Off Jr Cls; Off Sr Cls; Stu Cncl; High Hon Roll; Hon Roll; Jr NHS; Bus Excell Awd, Svc Awds 85; Clss Of 1964 Schlrshp 85; W Islip H S Natl Hnr Soc Schlrshp 85; St Johns U; Fin.

ECKER, WESLEY S; Hudson Falls HS; Hudson Falls, NY; (Y); 4/225; Drama Clb; Acpl Chr; Concert Band; Jazz Band; Rep Sr Cls; Capt Socr; Var Trk; High Hon Roll; Pres NHS; NYSSMA All St Chorus,Orch 84; RPI; Comp Engrng.

ECKERT, GREG; Cuba Central HS; Cuba, NY; (Y); 8/60; French Clb; Model UN; Quiz Bowl; Varsity Clb; L Var Crs Cntry; Var L Golf; High Hon Roll; NHS; Church Yth Grp; Stage Crew; 1st Pl Allgny Intrshp Proj 85; Mnsfld U Wrtng Tm 85; 1st Pl Indstrl Arts Proj 83.

ECKERT, JOHN JEROME; Commack High School North; Commack, NY; (Y); Cmnty Wkr; Band; Nwsp Rptr; JV Bsktbl; Var L Ftbl; Var L Lcrss; Var L Trk; JV Wrstlng; High Hon Roll; Hon Roll; Regnl Empire ST Boxing-Silver 85.

ECKERT, TODD; Sunnyside Christian Acad; N Rose, NY; (Y); Church Yth Grp; FCA; 4-H; Ski Clb; Teachers Aide; Chorus; Church Choir; Nwsp Stf; Var Capt Bsktbl; Var JV Socr; NY ST Competitn 2nd Pl Hgh Jmp, Illstrtd Stroytllng, Discus, Wood Carvng, 3rd Pl Long Jmp 84; Chef.

ECKHOFF, JAMES; Archbishop Molloy HS; Williston Park, NY; (Y); 82/385; Political Wkr; NHS; Mahattan Coll; Engrng.

ECKLUND, DARYL L; Jamestown HS; Jamestown, NY; (Y); 79/375; Trs Church Yth Grp; Stage Crew.

ECKLUND, DAVID; Jamestown HS; Jamestown, NY; (Y); French Clb; Stage Crew; Yrbk Phtg; Comp Sci.

ECKMAN, JENNIFER; Frontier Central HS; Blasdell, NY; (Y); French Clb; Ski Clb; Im Bsktbl; Var Mgr(s); JV Var Sftbl; High Hon Roll; Hon Roll; NHS; Bus Adm.

ECKSTRAND, KYA; Chautauqua Central HS; Ashville, NY; (Y); 3/37; Ski Clb; Band; Chorus; JV Var Cheerleading; Var Trk; JV Vllybl; High Hon Roll; NHS.

ECONOMIDES, EDWARD; Vestal SR HS; Vestal, NY; (Y); Church Yth Grp; Capt Var Bsbl; Prfct Atten Awd; Bus.

ECROYD, KARIN; Washingtonville SR HS; Washingtonville, NY; (Y); Ski Clb; Pres Spanish Clb; Jazz Band; Pep Band; Symp Band; Var Bsktbl; Var L Sftbl; Hon Roll; NHS; SUNY; Bus Admin.

EDDY, DARLENE; Northeastern Clinton Central Schl; Champlain, NY; (Y); Church Yth Grp; CAP; Spanish Clb; Band; High Hon Roll; Hon Roll; Prfct Atten Awd; Geneseo; Bus Mgmt.

EDDY, JULIA; Alexander Central HS; Alexander, NY; (S); Church Yth Grp; Ski Clb; Chorus; Color Guard; Mrchg Band; Trk; High Hon Roll; Hon Roll; Jr NHS; Nrs.

EDDY, MARK; Clifton-Fine Central HS; Newton Falls, NY; (S); 8/51; French Clb; Band; Chorus; Trs Frsh Cls; Trs Soph Cls; Var JV Bsbl; Var JV Bsktbl; Ice Hcky; Var JV Socr; High Hon Roll; Achvt Awd Chem; Elec Engrng.

EDDY, MICHELE; Shenendehowa HS; Ballston Lake, NY; (Y); Cmnty Wkr; Pres 4-H; GAA; Spanish Clb; Pres Varsity Clb; Trs Frsh Cls; JV Var Crs Cntry; Var Trk; 4-H Awd; Hon Roll; Advrtsng & Dsgn.

EDDY, STEVEN D; East Syracuse-Minoa HS; E Syracuse, NY; (Y); 2/338; Yrbk Stf; Trs Stu Cncl; JV Bsbl; Var Capt Tennis; Dnfth Awd; High Hon Roll; Pres NHS; Ntl Merit Ltr; Pres Schlr; Sal; U Of Buffalo; Engrng.

EDELMAN, DIANE M; Rome Free Acad; Rome, NY; (Y); 29/536; Intnl Clb; Ski Clb; Yrbk Stf; Rep Frsh Cls; Var JV Golf; Jr NHS; NHS; Opt Clb Awd; Acad All-Amer Awd 84-85; Pres Acad Ftns Awd 84-85; Le Moyne Coll; Optmtry.

EDELMAN, PERI; Valley Stream S HS; Lynbrook, NY; (Y); 3/178; Sec AFS; Cmnty Wkr; Mathletes; VP Temple Yth Grp; Rep Frsh Cls; Rep Soph Cls; Rep Jr Cls; Rep Sr Cls; High Hon Roll; NHS; Rgnts Schlrshp 85; Mgmnt.

EDENS, JEANNE; Nazareth Academy; Rochester, NY; (Y); Dance Clb; Exploring; Chorus; High Hon Roll; Hon Roll; $100 Schlrshp During 8th Grd 82; Sci Awd 82; Achvmnt Awds In Clss-Shrthnd, Englsh 82-82.

EDGAR, DEBORAH S; Earl L Vandermeulen HS; Pt Jefferson, NY; (Y); FBLA; Pep Clb; Varsity Clb; Yrbk Stf; Trs Soph Cls; Trs Jr Cls; Trs Sr Cls; Rep Stu Cncl; Var Bsktbl; Var Fld Hcky; Suffolk Cnty Sftbl Cochs Assn-Al-Conf, Al-Leag Awd 85; Acctng.

EDGAR, JAMES; Bethlehem Central HS; Glenmont, NY; (Y); Boy Scts; Pres Exploring; Lit Mag; JV Golf; High Hon Roll; NHS; Prfct Atten Awd; Head Acolyte St Andrews Episcopal Chrch Albany 85-86; Silver Med Ntl Lation Ex 84; St NY Cert Merit; Engrng.

EDGE, WENDY L; La Guardia HS; Springfield Gdn, NY; (Y); 51/588; Teachers Aide; Variety Show; Rep Stu Cncl; Cheerleading; Jr NHS; Sec NHS; Super Yth Awd 84; Acctng.

EDGERTON, ELLEN; West Genesee HS; Syracuse, NY; (Y); Nwsp Rptr; Nwsp Stf; High Hon Roll; Hon Roll; Syracuse U; Jrnlsm.

EDGERTON, WENDY; Wilson Central HS; Wilson, NY; (Y); 91/144; Church Yth Grp; Y-Teens; Chorus; Church Choir; Nwsp Rptr; Nwsp Stf; Assocs Schls Inc; Trvl.

EDICK, ANTHONY W; Westmoreland Central HS; Clinton, NY; (Y); 12/87; Church Yth Grp; Church Choir; Trk; Wt Lftg; Wrstlng; PSAT Ltr Of Comm 83; NY ST Cert Of Merit 85; NY ST Rgnts Schlrshp 85; Mst Prmsng Yng Wrtr 83; Syracuse U; Psychlgy.

EDICK, SHARON M; Beaver River Central HS; Croghan, NY; (Y); 14/96; GAA; Girl Scts; Chorus; School Musical; Swmmng; High Hon Roll; Hon Roll; NHS; Regents Schlrshp 85.

EDINGER, HENRY F; Corcoran HS; Syracuse, NY; (Y); Am Leg Boys St; Chess Clb; French Clb; Hosp Aide; Key Clb; Science Clb; Yrbk Ed-Chief; VP Stu Cncl; Tennis; Hon Roll; Pltcl Sci.

EDINGER, NEHAMA; Yeshiva University H S For Girls; New York, NY; (Y); Art Clb; Nwsp Stf; Lit Mag; Ester Ben David Oratrcl Cntst 85; Egyptlgy.

EDISON, JANNETTE; Union Springs Acad; Whitehall, NY; (Y); Ski Clb; Band; Church Choir; Concert Band; Variety Show; Sec Soph Cls; VP Jr Cls; Pres Sr Cls; Stu Ldrshp Schlrshp 85; Greg Shrthnd Pnmnshp Awd 84-85; Greg Typng Prodctn Awd 84-85; Andrews U; Offc Adm.

EDISON, NANNETTE; Union Springs Acad; Whitehall, NY; (Y); Ski Clb; Spanish Clb; Band; Church Choir; Concert Band; Variety Show; Trs Soph Cls; Trs Jr Cls; Gregg Shrthd Penmnshp & Typg Prodctn Awds 84-85; Loma Linda U; Ornmntl Hortcltr.

EDLIN, AMY; The Wheatley Schl; Roslyn Hts, NY; (Y); Computer Clb; Drama Clb; Mathletes; VP Temple Yth Grp; Band; Var Swmmng; Hon Roll; Psych.

EDMISTON, DAWN M; John F Kennedy HS; Utica, NY; (Y); 9/140; Sec Pres Church Yth Grp; Pres Key Clb; Sec Trs Band; School Play; Sec Jr Cls; Var Capt Cheerleading; Sec Jr NHS; NHS; Cmnty Wkr; Drama Clb; Michael M D Auria Awd 84-85; Elmira Coll Key Awd & Scholar 84-85; All Star Sftbl Awd 83-84; Hamilton Coll; Socl Sci.

EDMOND, YANIQUE M; Cathedral HS; New York, NY; (Y); 75/325; Church Yth Grp; Dance Clb; Drama Clb; Intnl Clb; Library Aide; Hon Roll; Educ.

EDMONDS, TONY; Rensselaer JR SR HS; Rensselaer, NY; (Y); Boys Clb Am; Cmnty Wkr; Varsity Clb; JV Var Bsktbl; Bsktbl.

EDMONTSON, DENISE; Sacred Heart HS; Yonkers, NY; (S); Cmnty Wkr; Hosp Aide; Intnl Clb; Library Aide; Nwsp Rptr; Hon Roll; NHS; NEDT Awd; Cert Achvt Vlntry Comm Svc To City Of Yonkers 82; Cert Of Apprctn For Acad 84; 1st Hnrs Spnsh II 84; Med.

EDMUNDS, SUNJA E; Ward Melville HS; Stony Brook, NY; (Y); 8/765; GAA; Acpl Chr; Lit Mag; Var Capt Bsktbl; Var Lcrss; Var Capt Socr; NCTE Awd; NHS; Ntl Merit Ltr; Pres Schlr; Ntl Cornell Schlr 85; Three Vlg Schl Adminstr Assn Schlr/Athlt Awd 85; Three Vlg Tchrs Assn Svc Awd 85; Cornell U; Biolgcl Sci.

EDNEY, ROBERT; Horseheads HS; Horseheads, NY; (S); Am Leg Boys St; Church Yth Grp; Quiz Bowl; Science Clb; Band; Stu Cncl; Socr; Trk; NHS; Ntl Merit SF; Boys Track MVP 84.

EDSON, DEE; Massena Central HS; Massena, NY; (Y); Pres Trs 4-H; Rep Frsh Cls; 4-H Awd; High Hon Roll; NHS; Prfct Atten Awd; Top 10 Pct Cls 83, 84 & 85; Anml Sci.

EDSON, JOSEPH; Maple Hill HS; Castleton, NY; (S); 8/80; Debate Tm; Drama Clb; Band; Concert Band; School Musical; Variety Show; Stu Cncl; L Tennis; Hon Roll; NHS; Music.

EDWARD JR, STEVES; Fort Ann Central Schl; Ft Ann, NY; (Y); Boy Scts; Church Yth Grp; Ski Clb; Yrbk Stf; Var L Bsbl; Var L Bsktbl; Im Score Keeper; Var L Socr; Im Swmmng; Star Scout BSA 83; Jr Prom Committee 85; Aerontcl.

EDWARDS, BARBARA; New Dorp HS; Staten Island, NY; (Y); Church Yth Grp; Cmnty Wkr; Hosp Aide; Office Aide; Spanish Clb; Symp Band; Yrbk Stf; Rep Sr Cls; Rep Stu Cncl; Hon Roll; Early Educ Tchr.

EDWARDS, BOB; Union-Endicott HS; Endicott, NY; (S); 203/440; Letterman Clb; Nwsp Sprt Ed; Var Ftbl; Var Trk; Var Vllybl; All-Metro Team 84; Phys Therapy.

EDWARDS, CAROL D; Comsewogue HS; Pt Jefferson Sta, NY; (Y); 5/350; Nwsp Stf; Off Sr Cls; Stu Cncl; High Hon Roll; Hon Roll; Jr NHS; NCTE Awd; NHS; Church Yth Grp; Stu Svc Awd 84; Advncd Plcmnt Art Awd 84; Enrchd Engl Awd 83; Archtctr.

EDWARDS, CAROL LEE; New Dorp HS; Staten Island, NY; (Y); Exploring; Girl Scts; Intnl Clb; Teachers Aide; Chorus; School Musical; Var Cheerleading; Var Gym; Natl Spnsh Exam Cert 85; Merit Awds 82; Rutgers U; Early Chldhd Ed.

EDWARDS, DALE; Silver Creek Central HS; Silver Creek, NY; (Y); 7/80; VP Church Yth Grp; Cmnty Wkr; Math Clb; Red Cross Aide; Chorus; Madrigals; Var L Trk; Hon Roll; NYML Hghst Schl Scoreer 85; Fredonia ST Coll.

EDWARDS, DAVID; Maine Endwell HS; Endwell, NY; (Y); 79/250; Pep Clb; Varsity Clb; Var L Bsbl; Var L Bowling; Var Ftbl; JV Score Keeper; Hon Roll; Kiwanis Awd; Clarkson U; Elec Engrng.

EDWARDS, DAVID; New Rochelle HS; New Rochelle, NY; (Y); Boys Clb Am; Cmnty Wkr; FCA; Band; Stage Crew; Coach Actv; Capt L Socr; Wt Lftg; High Hon Roll; Hon Roll; Achvt Awd Mech Drwng 81; Mst Vlbl Def Plyr 83; Hofstra U; Engrng.

EDWARDS, DAVID LEE; Silver Creek Central HS; Silver Creek, NY; (Y); 2/125; Pres Spanish Clb; Trs Chorus; Pres Frsh Cls; Pres Soph Cls; Sec Stu Cncl; Var L Bsbl; Var L Bsktbl; Var L Crs Cntry; Var L Trk; Voice Dem Awd; Hntl Hnr Soc 84-85; Math Exmntn Awd 85; Randy Stull Vrsty Bsebl Sprtsmnshp Memorl Awd 85; Comm.

EDWARDS, DENNIS C; East Syracuse-Minoa HS; Minoa, NY; (Y); 60/350; Am Leg Boys St; Exploring; Im Bsktbl; L Ice Hcky; Var Capt Lcrss; Var L Socr; Im Vllybl; Hon Roll; Jr NHS; NHS.

EDWARDS, DOTTIE; Whitney Point HS; Lisle, NY; (Y); JCL; Latin Clb; Ski Clb; Yrbk Stf; High Hon Roll; Hon Roll; Excellnc Soc Stud 84; Pre-Med.

EDWARDS, EDEE; Unatego JR SR HS; Otego, NY; (Y); 1/88; Sec FNA; Pres FHA; Ski Clb; Yrbk Bus Mgr; Lit Mag; Vllybl; High Hon Roll; NHS; Val; Coll St Rose Albany Scholar 85; Fin Hartwick Poetry Cont 85; Corp Awd Achvt Sci & Mth 85; Coll St Rose Albany; Engl.

EDWARDS, ENRICO; Adlai E Stevenson HS; Bronx, NY; (Y); Service Clb; Teachers Aide; Concert Band; Jazz Band; Var Ftbl; Var Trk; Hon Roll; NHS; Prfct Atten Awd; Spanish NHS; Schlr JR Athl Awd 85; SR Band Awd 85; NY U; Med.

EDWARDS, EVELYN; Queen Of The Rosary Acad; Hempstead, NY; (Y); Cmnty Wkr; Girl Scts; Hosp Aide; Library Aide; Office Aide; Teachers Aide; Nwsp Rptr; Yrbk Stf; High Hon Roll; Hon Roll; Johnson & Wales; Mrktng.

EDWARDS, GAVIN; Scarsdale HS; Scarsdale, NY; (Y); Cmnty Wkr; Pres Drama Clb; School Play; Ed Lit Mag; Rep Stu Cncl; NHS.

EDWARDS, JENNIFER; Grand Island HS; Gr Island, NY; (Y); Red Cross Aide; Teachers Aide; High Hon Roll; Hon Roll; Cmnty Svc/Hm Eco Ntrtn Intrnshp 83; PTSA Awd Schltc Achvt 85; U Of Buffalo; Nrsng.

EDWARDS, KEITA; William Howard Taft HS; Bronx, NY; (Y); Pres Church Yth Grp; Teachers Aide; Trs Church Choir; Nwsp Ed-Chief; Rep Soph Cls; Rep Jr Cls; Bsktbl; Sftbl; Hon Roll; Prfct Atten Awd; Vrsty Awd 85; Prairie View A&M U; Pre-Med.

EDWARDS, KRISTIN M; Shenendehowa HS; Clifton Park, NY; (Y); 95/680; Am Leg Aux Girls St; Cmnty Wkr; Sec Varsity Clb; Rep Stu Cncl; Var Crs Cntry; Var Socr; Var Trk; High Hon Roll; NHS; Gld Mdl Empire St Games X-Cntry Ski Oreinteering 85; Accntng.

EDWARDS, LYNN; Newfield HS; Selden, NY; (Y); 97/600; Drama Clb; Chorus; School Musical; School Play; Swing Chorus; Mgr Socr; Hon Roll; Music Drama Awd 85; Asst Musicl Coord Schl Musicl 85; Chrs Secy 85; Adelphi U; Prfrmg Arts.

EDWARDS, MARY ANN; Springville-Griffith Inst; Springville, NY; (Y); Am Leg Aux Girls St; Sec Exploring; Band; Chorus; Orch; Trs Jr Cls; Stu Cncl; JV Var Cheerleading; God Cntry Awd; NHS; Stu Rep To Springvl Yth Bd 84-85.

EDWARDS, REGINA; Mexico Academy & Central HS; Mexico, NY; (Y); Exploring; VP Pres Spanish Clb; Band; Capt Color Guard; Jazz Band; Mrchg Band; Variety Show; Nwsp Ed-Chief; Yrbk Stf; Stu Cncl; Oswego Cnty Presss Clb Scholar Rnr-Up 85; Spn Clb Svc Awd 85; Am Legn Aux Awd 85; St Bonaventure U; Mass Comm.

EDWARDS, ROBERT; St Joseph By The Sea; Staten Island, NY; (Y); Nwsp Sprt Ed; Off Jr Cls; Capt Var Bsktbl; Hon Roll; NEDT Awd; JV Bsktbl MVP 83-84.

EDWARDS, SAMANTHA J; La Guardia HS Of Music & The Arts; Brooklyn, NY; (Y); 66/588; Office Aide; Service Clb; Yrbk Stf; CC Awd; Hon Roll; Rgnts Schlrshps Awd; Arch.

EDWARDS, SARAH; Paul D Schreiber HS; Port Washington, NY; (Y); 12/442; Drama Clb; Latin Clb; Chorus; Church Choir; Jazz Band; Madrigals; Orch; NHS; Ntl Merit SF; Pres Schlr; Pres Hnrs Schlrshp 85; Silver Medal Ntl Latin Ex 82-83; Suny; Music.

EDWARDS, SHARIN; Bishop Loughlin HS; Brooklyn, NY; (Y); Cmnty Wkr; Dance Clb; Drama Clb; Chorus; School Musical; School Play; Variety Show; Crs Cntry; Trk; Hon Roll; Phys Thrpy.

EDWIN, ANDREA; Saugerties HS; Saugerties, NY; (Y); 21/242; Girl Scts; Teachers Aide; Concert Band; Var L Crs Cntry; Var L Trk; Cit Awd; High Hon Roll; JP Sousa Awd; Sec NHS; Ithaca Coll; Phy Thrpy.

EFFINGER, ANDREW; Webster HS; Webster, NY; (Y); Drftg.

EFTHYMIOU, BARBARA; St Francis Prep; Bayside, NY; (S); 114/690; Church Yth Grp; JA; Var Bsktbl; Cheerleading; Trk; JV Var Vllybl; Hon Roll; NHS; Opt Clb Awd; Optimist Society 83-84; Ntl Hnr Society 83-85; St Johns U.

EGAN, AMANDA; City-As-School HS; Middle Vlge, NY; (Y); Church Yth Grp; Intnl Clb; Library Aide; Model UN; Teachers Aide; Church Choir; Stage Crew; Tennis; Trk; Lion Awd; Brooklyn Coll; Poli Sci.

EGAN, BARBARA; Columbia HS; E Greenbush, NY; (Y); Drama Clb; 4-H; Girl Scts; Ski Clb; School Play; Yrbk Stf; Crs Cntry; Socr; Hon Roll; Sec Exploring; Maria Coll; Ofc Mgmt.

EGAN, BETH; Columbia HS; E Greenbush, NY; (Y); Boy Scts; Exploring; 4-H; Girl Scts; Ski Clb; Sec Band; Jazz Band; Yrbk Stf; Crs Cntry; Socr; Dean JC; Crmnl Justc.

EGAN, KIMBERLY A; Sacred Heart HS; Bronx, NY; (Y); Church Yth Grp; Hosp Aide; Intnl Clb; Stage Crew; Cheerleading; Regents Schlrshp 85; Manhattan Coll; Phys Thrpst.

EGAN, MICHAEL; Mineola HS; Mineola, NY; (S); 7/250; 4-H; Political Wkr; Pres Concert Band; Jazz Band; Pres Mrchg Band; Pep Band; School Musical; Var Bowling; High Hon Roll; NHS; St Johns U New York; Math.

EGAN, MOIRA; Garden City HS; Garden City, NY; (S); 22/319; Boy Scts; Church Yth Grp; 4-H; JCL; Latin Clb; Mathletes; Chorus; Church Choir; Pres Stu Cncl; High Hon Roll; Ltin Achvt Awd Gold Medal 83-84; Frnch Achvt Awd 84; Amer Legion Essay Cont 84.

EGAN, PETER; Cold Spring Harbor HS; Cold Spring Har, NY; (Y); 60/120; Var L Lcrss; Var L Socr; Interact Clb Sec 84-85.

EGELER, JAMES D; Spring Valley SR HS; Spring Valley, NY; (Y); 12/435; Pres Church Yth Grp; Computer Clb; German Clb; Band; Church Choir; Concert Band; Drm & Bgl; Mrchg Band; Orch; Lit Mag; Frgn Lang, Math Hnr Soc 83; Kings Coll; Comp Math.

EGELSTON, MIKKI; Oakfield-Alabama Central HS; Oakfield, NY; (Y); 2/97; AFS; Pres Church Yth Grp; 4-H; French Clb; Chorus; Church Choir; Crs Cntry; Swmmng; Trk; God Cntry Awd; Untd Methdst Chrch & Roberts Wesleyan Acadmc Schlrshps 85-86; NY ST Rgnts Schlrshp 85-89; Roberts Wesleyan Coll; Physcs.

EGERT, AMY; Skaneateles Central HS; Skaneateles, NY; (S); Drama Clb; Band; Chorus; Stage Crew; Variety Show; Nwsp Rptr; Lit Mag; Crs Cntry; Trk; High Hon Roll; Hnr Mtn Art In Hrld Jrnl Annl Ptry Cont 84; Gold Key Sclstc Art Comp 82; NYSSAMA Duet Comp 82; Art.

EGERT, JENNIFER R; W C Mephan HS; Merrick, NY; (Y); Art Clb; Cmnty Wkr; Drama Clb; School Play; Ed Nwsp Stf; Ed Yrbk Stf; Lit Mag; Off Soph Cls; Hon Roll; NCTE Awd; Outstndng Thesbn Awd 83; Yale; Art.

EGGER, REGULA; Ossining HS; Briarcliff-Manor, NY; (Y); Church Yth Grp; Trs Sec Orch; High Hon Roll; NHS; All St Orch 84-85; All Cty Orch 82-85.

EGIZIANO, NOEL; Fox Lane HS; Bedford Hls, NY; (Y); #25 In Class; Dance Clb; Pep Clb; Teachers Aide; Variety Show; Rep Jr Cls; Stat Bsbl; Cit Awd; High Hon Roll; Hon Roll; NHS; Am Legn Auxlry Awd 82; Merit Awd Spnsh 84-85; Mktg Bus.

EGLAND, KEVIN J; Centereach HS; Centereach, NY; (Y); 8/479; Church Yth Grp; Math Tm; Concert Band; Jazz Band; Mrchg Band; Var L Socr; Var L Trk; High Hon Roll; Sec NHS; All Cnty Band 84; NY ST Regents Schlrshp 85; Suffolk Cnty Tchrs Assn Schlrshp; Messiah Coll.

EGLE, JEFFREY D; Arkport Central Schl; Arkport, NY; (Y); 9/46; Am Leg Boys St; Boy Scts; Ski Clb; Concert Band; Mrchg Band; JV Var Socr; Hon Roll; Off Frsh Cls; Var Trk; Var Wrstlng; Arkprot Alumni Assn Schlrshp 85; Amer Lgn Schlrshp 85; Royson N Whippel Schlrshp 85; SUNY Morrisville; Forestry.

EGLOFF II, NICHOLAS J; Lowville Acad; Lowville, NY; (Y); 2/132; Am Leg Boys St; French Clb; Band; Chorus; Jazz Band; Madrigals; Nwsp Ed-Chief; JV L Ftbl; Trs NHS; Ntl Merit Ltr; Elks Natl Found Schlrshp 85; Potsdam Coll Arts & Sci; Comp.

EGNACZYK, SANDRA; Scotia Glenville HS; Scotia, NY; (Y); Church Yth Grp; DECA; Orch; Peer Ldrshp Hnr Achvt Awd 85; Acctnt.

EGNER, DIONNE; Villa Maria Acad; Buffalo, NY; (Y); Computer Clb; FBLA; Swmmng; Pre Law.

EHBRECHT, WILLIAM; Fordham Preparatory Schl; Pound Ridge, NY; (Y); Boy Scts; Science Clb; Stage Crew; Crs Cntry; Socr; Trk; High Hon Roll; School Musical; School Play; Ntl Latin Awd.

EHLENFIELD II, ROBERT C; Attica HS; Cowlesville, NY; (Y); AFS; Am Leg Boys St; Computer Clb; Math Tm; Trk; NHS; Syracuse U; Law.

EHLERS, DONNA E; Half Hollow Hills H S East; Dix Hills, NY; (Y); 201/548; Hon Roll; NY ST Regents Schrlshp 85; ST U; Physcl Thrpst.

EHLERS, ELISABETH; Fayetteville Manlius HS; Manlius, NY; (Y); Church Yth Grp; Computer Clb; JA; Chorus; Church Choir; School Musical; Variety Show; Yrbk Rptr; Hon Roll; Ntl Chem Olympd 85; SADD 84-85; Cmnctns.

EHMANN, CHRISTINE E; Our Lady Of Mercy HS; Rochester, NY; (Y); 14/200; Sec Exploring; Girl Scts; JA; Sec Spanish Clb; Nwsp Rptr; Yrbk Rptr; High Hon Roll; NHS; NY ST Regents Schlrshp 85; Math Awd 82; U Of Rochester; Aero Space Engr.

EHRENPREIS, SANDRA; Martin Van Buren HS; Queens Village, NY; (Y); 26/580; Math Clb; Office Aide; Science Clb; Service Clb; Chorus; High Hon Roll; Hon Roll; NHS; Ntl Merit Schol; Arista 84-85; Alg Medal 83; Cornell; Bus.

EHRENREICH, LAURA M; Williamsville South HS; Williamsville, NY; (Y); 70/280; AFS; Church Yth Grp; Cmnty Wkr; GAA; Nwsp Bus Mgr; Yrbk Phtg; Yrbk Stf; Swmmng; DAR Awd; Hon Roll; Rgnts Schlrshp 85; Synchrnzd Swim Jr & Sr Natl Swim Meet; IN U; Sprts Med.

EHRHARDT JR, DANIEL R; Central Islip SR HS; Central Islip, NY; (Y); 29/325; Boy Scts; Church Yth Grp; Varsity Clb; Band; Concert Band; Drm Mjr(t); Mrchg Band; Stage Crew; Bowling; JV Lcrss; Eagle Scout 82; Tech Comp Awd 85; Vehicle Power Awd 85; Polytech NY; Aero Sp Engr.

EHRHART, DALE S; Le Roy Central HS; Le Roy, NY; (Y); Boy Scts; Exploring; Ctznshp Awd 85; Genesee CC; Acctg.

EHRLICH, GINNY; Longwood HS; Coram, NY; (S); 9/450; Speech Tm; Nwsp Bus Mgr; Nwsp Rptr; Nwsp Stf; Lit Mag; High Hon Roll; NHS; Hofstra U; Comp.

EICHE, CAROLYN J; St Francis Preparatory Schl; Glendale, NY; (Y); 100/690; Church Yth Grp; Drama Clb; Sec German Clb; Library Aide; Band; Concert Band; School Musical; School Play; Stage Crew; NHS; St Johns U Schltc Excllnc Awd & Cmptv Schlrshp 85; Rgnts Schlrshp 85; St Johns U; Comp Sci.

EICHENHOLZ, SCOTT R; Centereach HS; Centereach, NY; (Y); 9/489; Math Tm; Var Ftbl; Im Trk; Im Wrstlng; NHS; Gonen Soc Schlrshp 84; NYS Regents Schlrshp 85; Med.

EICHINGER, LAUREL; Hilton Central HS; Hilton, NY; (Y); 2/300; French Clb; VP Model UN; Ski Clb; Ed Yrbk Stf; Pres Frsh Cls; Var Capt Cheerleading; High Hon Roll; VP NHS; Frnch Exch 85.

EICHLER, KATIE; East Islip HS; E Islip, NY; (Y); DECA; Bsbl; Bsktbl; Var Tennis; Stu Part Day 85; Bus Mgmt.

EICHNER, JACKIE; Lawrence HS; Cedarhurst, NY; (Y); French Clb; FHA; Key Clb; Chorus; Yrbk Stf; High Hon Roll; NHS; Ntl Merit Schol; Soc Hnr De Francais 85; Bus.

EICHWALD, KENNETH B; Harrison HS; Harrison, NY; (Y); 33/218; Boy Scts; Debate Tm; Exploring; Trk; Wrstlng; St Schlr; Lehigh U; Bus.

EICK, JULIE; Royalton-Hartland Central HS; Middleport, NY; (Y); 9/150; Sec Trs Church Yth Grp; Drama Clb; Spanish Clb; Chorus; Church Choir; Yrbk Stf; High Hon Roll; Hon Roll; NHS.

EIDENWEIL, JOHN C; Wantagh HS; Wantagh, NY; (Y); 24/300; Mathletes; L Bsktbl; L Var Ftbl; Var Capt Lcrss; Cit Awd; NHS; Nassau Cnty Interschlstc Math Leag 83; Wantagh Bd Of Ed Merit Schlrshp 85; Rochester Inst Of Tech; Engrng.

EIHOLZER, KARL D; Jamesville-Dewitt HS; Jamesville, NY; (Y); Boy Scts; Church Yth Grp; VP Model UN; Acpl Chr; Chorus; School Musical; Stage Crew; Swing Chorus; Hon Roll; Frgn Svc.

EILERTSEN, MARJORIE A; Acad Of The Holy Names; Delmar, NY; (Y); 2/62; NFL; Nwsp Ed-Chief; Nwsp Rptr; Yrbk Bus Mgr; Bsktbl; Sftbl; Tennis; Vllybl; Pres Schlr; Sal; Pres Schlrshps Marist & Ithaca 85-89; Acad, Tnns Schlrshp St Rose 85-89; Ithaca Coll; Jrnlsm.

EILL, JULIE; Westhampton Beach HS; Remsenburg, NY; (Y); 5/250; Dance Clb; Hosp Aide; Spanish Clb; Varsity Clb; Chorus; School Musical; Yrbk Stf; Fld Hcky; Score Keeper; High Hon Roll; Hampshire Coll.

EIMBINDER, RICHARD A; Half Hollow Hills HS; Melville, NY; (Y); 20/568; Drm Mjr(t); Orch; Symp Band; Ed Yrbk Ed-Chief; High Hon Roll; NHS; NY ST Sen Prg; Yth Govt; Cornell U Schlrshp; Cornell U; Bus Admin.

EINSEL III, CARLTON E; Harborfields HS; Huntington Sta, NY; (Y); 29/335; Nwsp Stf; Var JV Bsbl; JV Ftbl; Var JV Wrstlng; Hon Roll; Jr NHS; NHS; Pres Schlr; Hghst Achvt Scl Stds 85; ROTC 4 Yr Schlrshp 85; Fordham U; Eco.

EINSETLER, FRANK E; West Babylon HS; W Babylon, NY; (Y); 15/467; Boy Scts; Computer Clb; Band; Concert Band; Drm & Bgl; Jazz Band; Mrchg Band; Pep Band; Variety Show; Pres Sr Cls; US Air Force Acad; Aerosp Engr.

EISCH, AMELIA J; Vestal SR HS; Vestal, NY; (Y); Am Leg Aux Girls St; Nwsp Sprt Ed; Pres Soph Cls; Pres Stu Cncl; JV Cheerleading; Var Capt Fld Hcky; Trs NHS; Lib Orch; Binghamton Yth Symphony 82; Asst Editor In Chf Stu Nwspaper 85-86; Pres SADD 85-86; Pol Sci.

EISEN, HOWARD JAY; Hunter College HS; Staten Island, NY; (Y); Computer Clb; Nwsp Rptr; Nwsp Stf; Rep Sec Stu Cncl; JV Tennis; Mu Alp Tht; Math Tm; Yrbk Stf; NYS Rgnl Dir Of NYS Secndry Schl Stu Orgnztn 84-85; MA Inst Of Tech; Engrng.

EISENBACH, DEBRA E; High School Of Art Design; Maspeth, NY; (Y); 2/439; Math Tm; Teachers Aide; Hon Roll; NHS; Sal; Church Yth Grp; Computer Clb; Drama Clb; Variety Show; Nwsp Rptr; Ntl Art Hnr Soc; Pratt Instit; Illust.

EISENBERG, HEIDI; G W Hewlett HS; Hewlett, NY; (Y); 70/278; Pep Clb; Nwsp Sprt Ed; Nwsp Stf; Ed Yrbk Stf; JV Bsktbl; Coach Actv; Var Gym; Var Capt Trk; Var Capt Vllybl; Achvt Awd Ldrs Corps 85; Pres Acad Fitnss Awd 85; U Of FL; Phys Thrpy.

EISENBERG, OSMAN; Newfield Central HS; Newfield, NY; (Y); Boy Scts; Varsity Clb; Band; Concert Band; Jazz Band; Mrchg Band; Var L Ftbl; Var Trk; Var Wrstlng; Hon Roll; Envrnmntl Sci.

EISENBERG, WARREN M; Newfield HS; Coram, NY; (Y); #56 In Class; Computer Clb; Band; Concert Band; Jazz Band; Mrchg Band; School Musical; Regnets Schlrshp 85; SUNY Albany; Neurology.

EISENHARDT, TERI; Valley Central HS; Newburgh, NY; (Y); 67/305; Yrbk Stf; Off Frsh Cls; Off Soph Cls; Off Jr Cls; Off Stu Cncl; Vllybl; Sec French Hon Soc; Hon Roll.

EISENHART, CHRISTINE; Pittsford Sutherland HS; Pittsford, NY; (Y); Exploring; French Clb; JA; Im Bsktbl; Hon Roll; Psych.

EISENHAUER, JOHN; Immaculate Heart Central HS; Watertown, NY; (Y); 3/81; Am Leg Boys St; Boy Scts; Mrchg Band; Pres Stu Cncl; Var L Bsktbl; Var L Ftbl; Var L Lcrss; NHS; Church Yth Grp; Debate Tm; HOBY Ldrshp Awd 84; Summa Cum Laude Natl Lat Exam LAT II 84; West Point; Engrng.

EISENMESSER, LEE J; Smithtown HS West; Smithtown, NY; (Y); Jazz Band; Mrchg Band; Orch; Pep Band; School Musical; Symp Band; JV Var Socr; JV Var Trk; NHS; Spanish NHS; All ST Band 84-85; All Cnty Bands 82-85; Emory U; Bus Admn.

EISENSTEIN, JONI; Long Beach HS; Long Beach, NY; (S); 13/316; Key Clb; Office Aide; Sec Stu Cncl; JV Cheerleading; JV Mgr(s); Var Swmmng; Hon Roll; NHS; 2nd Pl Bio Sci Fair; Pres Clsrm Young Am; SUNY; Intl Rel.

EISER, CATHY JOANNE; Our Lady Of Mercy HS; Rochester, NY; (Y); 4/200; Church Yth Grp; Exploring; Church Choir; JV Sftbl; Var JV Tennis; High Hon Roll; NHS; Mxwl Ctznshp & Plb Afrs Schlrshp Awd 85; NY ST Rgnts Schlrshp 85; Ntl Sci Merit Awd 83; Syrcuse U; Elec Engrng.

EISNER, DENNIS A; Camden HS; Camden, NY; (Y); Yrbk Sprt Ed; JV Bsbl; JV Bsktbl; JV Bowling; JV Ftbl; Wt Lftg; High Hon Roll; NHS; Prfct Atten Awd; Rotary Awd; Bus Admin.

EISNER, SARA; Commack High School North; E Northport, NY; (Y); VP Temple Yth Grp; Varsity Clb; Orch; Nwsp Rptr; Yrbk Stf; Ed Lit Mag; Var Trk; French Hon Soc; High Hon Roll; NCTE Awd; Outstndng Jr Ramettis 84-85; Sci.

EITEL, KATHRYN M; Johnson City SR HS; Johnson City, NY; (Y); 5/212; Mathletes; Band; Concert Band; Mrchg Band; Orch; Nwsp Ed-Chief; Nwsp Rptr; Nwsp Stf; High Hon Roll; Hon Roll; Acad Achvt Awd; Bio.

EK, KIRSTEN; Horseheads HS; Horseheads, NY; (Y); Spanish Clb; Varsity Clb; Color Guard; Concert Band; Mrchg Band; Rep Stu Cncl; Var L Gym; High Hon Roll; NHS; Ntl Merit SF; Spnsh Achvt Awd 83; NY St Gymnstcs Chmp 84; Schlstc Art Awd 81; Lbrl Arts.

EKLUND, JOSHUA; Smithtown High School East; St James, NY; (Y); Pres Art Clb; Church Yth Grp; Var Trk; FIT; Fshn Dsgn.

ELAM, DARRYL; Albion HS; Waterport, NY; (Y); Spanish Clb; High Hon Roll; Hon Roll; NHS; Brockport ST; Bus Comm.

ELDRED, ANN; Liverpool HS; Liverpool, NY; (S); 21/789; Exploring; Varsity Clb; Chorus; Rep Stu Cncl; JV Var Socr; JV Var Trk; Hon Roll; NHS; Ntl Merit Ltr; Most Likely To Succeed 85; Med.

ELDREDGE, JANINE M; Columbia HS; Castleton, NY; (Y); 5/353; Ski Clb; Band; School Musical; Symp Band; Nwsp Rptr; High Hon Roll; JP Sousa Awd; NHS; Summa Cum Laude Grad 85; Rensselaer Polytech; Engrng.

ELDRIDGE, ALLAN; Smithtown High School East; St James, NY; (Y); 20/550; Art Clb; Drama Clb; French Clb; PAVAS; Radio Clb; Ski Clb; Thesps; Chorus; School Musical; School Play; New York U; Librl Arts.

ELDRIDGE, JANINE; Chenango Forks Central HS; Binghamton, NY; (Y); Debate Tm; French Clb; Ski Clb; Drm Mjr(t); Mrchg Band; Variety Show; Var L Tennis; High Hon Roll; NHS; Prfct Atten Awd; SUNY Binghamton; Pre-Law.

ELDRIDGE, TERRI; Westmoreland Central HS; Rome, NY; (Y); Church Yth Grp; Dance Clb; GAA; Model UN; Ski Clb; Color Guard; Yrbk Stf; VP Soph Cls; Trs Jr Cls; Trs Stu Cncl; Cazanovia Coll; Accntnt.

ELECZKO, TAMMY; Depew HS; Depew, NY; (Y); French Clb; Office Aide; Drm Mjr(t); Mrchg Band; Stat Bowling; Hon Roll; Merit Rll; Recptnst.

ELFAST, DAWN; North Babylon SR HS; North Babylon, NY; (Y); Office Aide; Chorus; Intr Dsgnr.

ELFLEIN, KAREN; Kenmore East SR HS; Tonawanda, NY; (Y); GAA; Orch; Var L Tennis; Hon Roll; Human Rltns Peer Tm; Hstry Prof.

ELGART, JEFFREY; Midwood HS; Brooklyn, NY; (Y); 118/605; Drama Clb; Math Tm; Office Aide; Political Wkr; Temple Yth Grp; Band; Concert Band; Mrchg Band; School Musical; School Play; NYS Rgnts Coll Schlrshp, Cert Merit 85; Brooklyn Coll; Pol Sci.

ELIA, JAMES M; East Meadow HS; East Meadow, NY; (S); 3/414; Computer Clb; Mathletes; Mrchg Band; Symp Band; Ed Nwsp Stf; Ed Lit Mag; L Trk; Bausch & Lomb Sci Awd; High Hon Roll; NHS; Frnch Profcncy Awd, Erth Sci Lab Asst, Music Lttrs 82; Nassau Cnty Math Awd & Mrchg Band Attdc Ltr 84; Cornell U; Med.

ELIAS, MELISSA; Whitesboro SR HS; Utica, NY; (Y); 4-H; Off Stu Cncl; DAR Awd; 4-H Awd; Hon Roll; Syracuse U; Law.

ELICIER, MICHELLE; St Peters HS For Girls; Staten Island, NY; (Y); FNA; Math Tm; Hon Roll; Fordham U; Bio.

ELIOPOULOS, ELIAS; Blind Brook HS; Rye Brook, NY; (Y); Pres Church Yth Grp; Math Tm; Model UN; Nwsp Stf; Var L Bsbl; Var L Socr; Ntl Merit Ltr; Brown U.

ELIOT, JONATHAN K; Germantown Central HS; Germantown, NY; (Y); 1/60; Sec Pres Varsity Clb; Rep Stu Cncl; JV Var Bsbl; Var Capt Bsktbl; Var Capt Socr; Bausch & Lomb Sci Awd; NHS; Val; Voice Dem Awd; PA ST U.

ELKIN, LISA; Brighton HS; Rochester, NY; (Y); 133/315; Temple Yth Grp; Rep Soph Cls; Rep Jr Cls; Trs Sr Cls; JV Cheerleading; Psych.

ELKIN, PAUL; Ellenville HS; Ellenville, NY; (Y); Drama Clb; Yrbk Sprt Ed; Pres Frsh Cls; VP Soph Cls; Stu Cncl; Var Bsktbl; Var Ftbl; Var Tennis; High Hon Roll; Pres NHS; Natl Educ Merit Achvmnt Awd Sci & Engl 83 & 84; Dntstry.

ELLENBERG, LAWRENCE; James Madison HS; Brooklyn, NY; (S); Office Aide; Teachers Aide; High Hon Roll; Ntl Hnr Roll 84; Arista 82-85; Sing Ldr; Law.

ELLER, ROBERT; Bishop Grimes HS; Syracuse, NY; (Y); FBLA; NFL; Sec Jr Cls; Trs Sr Cls; Var JV Socr; High Hon Roll; NHS; Debate Tm; Drama Clb; Model UN; NEMA 85; Natl Merit Scholar Crp Applcnt 85; Italn Hnr Soc, Attestato Di Lodge 83-85; Phys Ther.

ELLIA, MELISSA; Eastridge HS; Rochester, NY; (Y); Exploring; Varsity Clb; Band; Rep Stu Cncl; Var Bsktbl; JV Fld Hcky; Var JV Sftbl; JV Var Vllybl; Hon Roll; NHS.

ELLINGHAUS, DAVID M; Fox Lane HS; Bedford, NY; (Y); Ski Clb; Soph Cls; Jr Cls; Sr Cls; Trs Stu Cncl; Ftbl; Swmmng; Trk; High Hon Roll; Ntl Hnr Roll-Ntl Merit Fndtn 85; Pre Law.

ELLIOT, LAUREN J; Rye HS; Rye, NY; (Y); 9/200; Trs AFS; Model UN; Spanish Clb; Pres Temple Yth Grp; Nwsp Rptr; Ed Nwsp Stf; Yrbk Stf; Lit Mag; Sec Stu Cncl; JV Sftbl; Regents Schlrshp 85; Brown U; Law.

ELLIOTT, ALLAN; George W Wingate HS; Brooklyn, NY; (Y); Camera Clb; Church Yth Grp; 4-H; Church Choir; Nwsp Rptr; Nwsp Sprt Ed; Nwsp Stf; Var Bsbl; Var Bsktbl; Var Ftbl; Hnrs Awd-Sci Cls 83; Cmnctns.

ELLIOTT, ANGIE M; Copiague SR HS; Copiague, NY; (Y); Computer Clb; FBLA; Spanish Clb; Variety Show; Farmingdale Coll; Sec Sci.

ELLIOTT, BARRY; Bolivar Central HS; Bolivar, NY; (Y); Aud/Vis; Library Aide; Spanish Clb; Chorus; School Musical; School Play; Stage Crew; Variety Show; Ftbl; Trk.

ELLIOTT, BEVERLY; Amherst Central HS; Amherst, NY; (Y); 35/312; Ski Clb; Chorus; Orch; School Musical; Var L Swmmng; High Hon Roll; Hon Roll; NHS; Ntl Merit Ltr; NYS Regents Schlrshp 85; U MI Ann Arbor; Intl Bus.

ELLIOTT, DARIS; Vernon Verona Sherrill Central HS; Verona, NY; (Y); GAA; JV Bsktbl; Var Crs Cntry; JV Sftbl; JV Var Trk; Hon Roll; Bryant & Stratton; Travl.

ELLIOTT, DAVID; Hastings HS; Hastings-Hudson, NY; (Y); 33/127; Boy Scts; Drama Clb; Acpl Chr; Band; Chorus; Madrigals; Orch; School Play; Stage Crew; Aud/Vis; Columbia Sci Hnrs Pgm; U Of Rochester; Bio.

ELLIOTT, DONALD E; Brewster HS; Patterson, NY; (Y); Boy Scts; Stu Cncl; JV Var Bsbl; JV Bsktbl; Coach Actv; JV Var Ftbl; Mgr(s); Spnsh Achvt 82-83; Fordham; Journlsm.

ELLIOTT, GINALYN; Sachem North HS; Holtsville, NY; (Y); Radio Clb; Chorus; Hon Roll; Comp Math.

ELLIOTT II, LEWIS; Lisbon Central HS; Lisbon, NY; (S); 4/48; Computer Clb; Quiz Bowl; Sec Jr Cls; Var Socr; Hon Roll; Jr NHS.

ELLIOTT, LINDA S; Fontbonne Hall Acad; Brooklyn, NY; (Y); Cmnty Wkr; Teachers Aide; School Play; Variety Show; Nwsp Stf; Rep Frsh Cls; Rep Stu Cncl; Var Cheerleading; Hon Roll; Ntl Merit Schol; Awd Cnslr Retarded/Deaf 82; Acad Hnr Lang Arts Awd 83; Mrktng.

ELLIOTT, MOLLY; Fayetteville Manlius HS; Fayetteville, NY; (Y); VP Church Yth Grp; JCL; Var Bsktbl; Var Capt Swmmng; High Hon Roll; Hon Roll; NHS.

ELLIOTT, PAMELA M; Brushton-Moira Central HS; Brushton, NY; (Y); Band; Mrchg Band; School Play; Stage Crew; Yrbk Stf; JV Bsktbl; JV Mgr Vllybl; Tlntd Jr Prgm St Lawrence U 84; Potsdam; Psych.

ELLIOTT, SANDRA; Fort Plain HS; Ft Plain, NY; (Y); Drama Clb; French Clb; Varsity Clb; Stage Crew; Yrbk Stf; Stu Cncl; Var Capt Bsktbl; Var Cheerleading; JV Var Socr; L Sftbl; Mst Imprvd Soccer Awd 85; Engl Awd 85; Trvl.

ELLIOTT, SUSANNAH J; Paul V Moore HS; Cleveland, NY; (Y); 24/298; AFS; Drama Clb; German Clb; Q&S; Radio Clb; Chorus; School Musical; School Play; Stage Crew; Nwsp Rptr; Regents Schlrshp 85; Oswego Coll.

ELLIS, CHARISSE; Midwood HS; Brooklyn, NY; (Y); Church Yth Grp; Office Aide; Teachers Aide; Church Choir; Var Crs Cntry; Var Trk; Cit Awd; Prfct Atten Awd; Mech Engrng.

ELLIS, CHRISTOPHER K; Sandy Creek Central Schl; Lacona, NY; (Y); 10/60; Computer Clb; Band; Chorus; VP Frsh Cls; Stu Cncl; Capt Bsbl; Capt Bsktbl; Ftbl; Hon Roll; NHS; NY ST Regents Scholarship Awd 85; Syracuse U; Computer Science.

ELLIS, DENISE; Union Endicott HS; Endicott, NY; (Y); French Clb; Key Clb; Yrbk Phtg; Yrbk Stf; Lit Mag; Engl.

ELLIS JR, JAMES; Bishop Timon HS; Buffalo, NY; (S); Merit Awd Soph 83-84; Merit Awd JR 84; Comp Maint.

ELLIS, JANET; Cohoes HS; Cohoes, NY; (Y); Church Yth Grp; Cmnty Wkr; Girl Scts; Chorus; Color Guard; Mrchg Band; School Play; Hon Roll; Phys Ther.

ELLIS, JOHN MITCHELL; Midwood HS; Brooklyn, NY; (Y); 156/605; Boy Scts; Church Yth Grp; Science Clb; Teachers Aide; Varsity Clb; School Play; Ftbl; Lcrss; Sal; St Schlr; NY ST Rgnts Schlrshp 85; SUNY Stony Brook; Econ.

ELLIS, KATHLEEN; La Salle SR HS; Niagara Falls, NY; (Y); Jrnlsm.

ELLIS, KEMBERLEA; Jordan Elbridge Central HS; Jordan, NY; (Y); Drama Clb; Girl Scts; Band; Chorus; Mrchg Band; School Musical; Tennis; Wentworth Inst Of Tech; Dntl.

ELLIS, KIM; Berlin Central HS; Stephentown, NY; (S); Church Yth Grp; Ski Clb; Chorus; Church Choir; School Musical; JV Bsktbl; High Hon Roll; U S Army Resv Stu Athlete Awd 84; Lang Arts Olympiad Awd 82.

ELLIS, KIMBERLY; Glens Falls HS; Glens Falls, NY; (Y); 40/236; French Clb; Pep Clb; Chorus; JV Powder Puff Ftbl; JV Vllybl; Hon Roll; Engl.

ELLIS, LISA; Plattsburgh HS; Plattsburgh, NY; (Y); Drama Clb; Sec French Clb; Model UN; Quiz Bowl; Pres Band; Chorus; Orch; Variety Show; High Hon Roll; NHS; Dptmntl Awds In Sci,Soc Stds,Mthmtcs,Music 85; Dptmntl Awds Mthmtcs,Engl,Sci 84; Animal Bio.

ELLIS, PAUL; Hilton Central HS; Hilton, NY; (Y); Exploring; Ski Clb; Spanish Clb; High Hon Roll; NHS; Engrng.

ELLISON, ANGELA; Churchville Chili HS; Rochester, NY; (Y); Drama Clb; JCL; Latin Clb; Acpl Chr; Chorus; Yrbk Stf; Hon Roll; NYSSMA Solo Voice 83-85; Ntnl Latin Exam Silver Mdl 84; Boston U; Oceanography.

ELLISON, MELISSA; Southside HS; Elmira, NY; (Y); JA; Key Clb; Ski Clb; Spanish Clb; Band; Concert Band; Jazz Band; Trk; Hon Roll; Bus Sec.

ELLISON, SALLY; Kensington HS; Buffalo, NY; (Y); Church Yth Grp; Hosp Aide; Church Choir; Stage Crew; Rep Stu Cncl; Capt Cheerleading; Hon Roll; NHS; Prfct Atten Awd; SUNY; Sec Sci.

ELLISON, TESSA; Stuyvesant HS; Brooklyn, NY; (Y); Chrmn Aud/Vis; Boy Scts; Church Yth Grp; Dance Clb; Pres Exploring; German Clb; Library Aide; Office Aide; Teachers Aide; School Musical; Math & Engl Hnrs 83; Bio & Engl Hnrs 84; German & Engl Hnrs 85; LIU Schlrs Pgm 85; Pre-Med.

ELLMAN, CANDACE E; Sachem North HS; Lake Ronkonkoma, NY; (Y); 12/1400; Mrchg Band; Orch; School Musical; Stage Crew; Symp Band; Variety Show; Jr NHS; NHS; Drama Clb; Girl Scts; Scholar Aid Assn Luthrns 85; 2 Scholar Parnts Wthout Prtnrs Inc 85; Oberlin Coll.

ELLOR, CHRIS; Ticonderoga HS; Ticondderoga, NY; (Y); Boy Scts; Church Yth Grp; Ski Clb; Mgr Bsbl; JV Ftbl; Mgr(s); U Of Bridgeport; Engrng.

ELLWANGER, JAMES F; Monroe JR SR HS; Rochester, NY; (Y); 20/178; Chess Clb; Pres Church Yth Grp; Cmnty Wkr; VP 4-H; Ski Clb; Drm & Bgl; Trk; Hon Roll; NHS; Hofstra U; Psych.

ELLWANGER, JON; Iona Preparatory Schl; New Rochelle, NY; (Y); 55/198; Stu Cncl; JV Var Bsktbl; JV Var Ftbl; Var Lcrss; JV Var Tennis; Hon Roll; NHS.

ELMAN, ANDREW; Roy L Ketcham HS; Wappinger Falls, NY; (Y); Drama Clb; Red Cross Aide; Thesps; School Play; Stage Crew; Var Crs Cntry; Lcrss; Var Socr; Hon Roll; Stage Dsgn.

ELMER, ALLISON; Hugh C Williams HS; Pompano Bch, FL; (Y); French Clb; JV Cheerleading; Im Tennis; Southern Methodist U; Bus.

ELMER, KATHLEEN M; Copenhagen Central HS; Carthage, NY; (Y); #4 In Class; Yrbk Stf; VP Soph Cls; Rep Jr Cls; Rep Sr Cls; Trs Stu Cncl; Var L Socr; Var L Sftbl; Hon Roll; Sec NHS; Voice Dem Awd; Jefferson Comm; Physical Therpy.

ELMES, RHONDA; Notre Dame Acad; Staten Island, NY; (Y); Var Crs Cntry; Var Trk; Cert-Natl Spnsh Exm 85; Comp Sci.

ELMORE JR, JOSEPH; Mc Kinley HS; Buffalo, NY; (Y); Art Clb; Chess Clb; French Clb; Spanish Clb; Variety Show; Nwsp Stf; Yrbk Phtg; Yrbk Stf; Capt L Bsktbl; Tennis; Psych.

ELMORE JR, MATTHEW; White Plains HS; White Plains, NY; (Y); 15/454; Math Tm; Nwsp Rptr; Nwsp Stf; Hon Roll; NHS; Ntl Merit Ltr; Iona Language Comp Cert Spnsh 3rd Yr 83; Engrng.

ELSEN, MARY K; Salamanca City Central HS; Salamanca, NY; (S); 3/130; Am Leg Aux Girls St; VP Concert Band; Pres Stu Cncl; Bsktbl; Crs Cntry; Tennis; Vllybl; Sec French Hon Soc; NHS; Spanish NHS; Lang.

ELSENHEIMER, JAMES A; Marathon Central HS; Marathon, NY; (Y); 8/63; Am Leg Boys St; Drama Clb; Band; Chorus; VP Jr Cls; Pres Sr Cls; Var Bsbl; Var Socr; Var Wrstlng; DAR Awd; NYS Regnts Schlrshp 85; Natl Hnr Socty; Allegheny Coll; Pol Sci.

ELSTON, BARBARA; Notre Dame HS; Elmira, NY; (Y); Key Clb; Band; Church Choir; Concert Band; Sftbl.

ELWOOD, CANDACE; Horseheads HS; Millport, NY; (S); 44/407; Library Aide; Spanish Clb; Hon Roll; Corning CC; Spnsh Tchr.

ELWOOD, JACQUELYN; Unatego SR HS; Unadilla, NY; (Y); 37/90; Church Yth Grp; FCA; Var Bsktbl; Var Fld Hcky; Var Sftbl; Prfct Atten Awd; MIP Fld Hcky 84; All Star Tm Fld Hcky 84; Vrsty Bsktbl Tm Sctn IV Champs 85.

EMANUEL, CHRISTOPHER A; Mt St Michael Acad; Bronx, NY; (Y); 21/286; Church Yth Grp; Capt Bsbl; NHS; Spanish NHS; CHSAA All League 3rd Baseman 84; NY ST Regents Schlrshp 85; Catholic High Schl Schlrshp 85; St Johns U; Hotel Mgr.

EMANUELE, DANIEL; Albion HS; Albion, NY; (S); 20/200; Cmnty Wkr; Latin Clb; Band; Drm Mjr(t); Jazz Band; JV Var Bsbl; NHS; Political Wkr; Law.

EMBLER, JILL; Valley Central HS; Walden, NY; (Y); 25/300; Stu Cncl; High Hon Roll; Hon Roll; NHS; Spanish NHS; Church Yth Grp; Girl Scts; Varsity Clb; Acpl Chr; Church Choir; Pace U; Pre-Law.

EMENS, CHERYL; West Seneca East SR HS; Cheektowaga, NY; (Y); Church Yth Grp; VP German Clb; JA; Key Clb; Library Aide; Orch; JV Socr; JC Awd; NHS; German Ntl Hnr Soc; Bio.

EMENS, SHELLY; Romulus Central HS; Romulus, NY; (S); 1/52; Ski Clb; Trs Varsity Clb; Chorus; Capt Color Guard; VP Stu Cncl; Var Cheerleading; Capt Var Socr; Capt Var Sftbl; High Hon Roll; NHS; Bus Admin.

EMERLING, MICHELLE; Springville Griffith Inst; Springville, NY; (Y); French Clb; FBLA; Sec Sr Cls; JV Var Sftbl; Hon Roll; Grls Vrsty Sftbl Awd & Lttr 85; Shrthnd Awds 85; Bus Mgmt.

EMERSON, DAWN; Cuba Central HS; Black Crk, NY; (Y); 1/60; Church Yth Grp; Spanish Clb; Varsity Clb; Yrbk Stf; Sec Soph Cls; Trs Jr Cls; Sec Sr Cls; Socr; High Hon Roll; NHS; Wnnr Stdnt Engry Rsrch Comp 85; Hghst Clss Avr 83-85; Ntl Hnr Soc Hghst Avr Plq 84; Stckbrkr.

EMERSON, DAWN; Tonawanda SR HS; Tonawanda, NY; (Y); Aud/Vis; Church Yth Grp; Spanish Clb; Band; Boy Scts; Concert Band; Jazz Band; Mrchg Band; School Musical; Var Bowling; Early Child Ed.

EMERSON, JILL; Geneva HS; Penn Yan, NY; (Y); 40/180; Latin Clb; Varsity Clb; Chorus; Var Bsktbl; Var Socr; Var Sftbl; JV Vllybl; Hon Roll; Madrigals; School Musical; Acad Achvt Lists 82-85; Frgn Exch Stu Italy 83-84; FL E All-Star Team Sccr Hon Ment Sftbl 84-85; Med.

EMERSON, LORI; Auburn HS; Auburn, NY; (Y); Chorus; Yrbk Stf; High Hon Roll; Intl Bus.

EMERSON, MARIE; Lakeland HS; Shrub Oak, NY; (Y); Drama Clb; French Clb; Chorus; School Play; Var Fld Hcky; High Hon Roll; Hon Roll; Intl Cmmnctns.

EMERSON, PAMELA; Belmont Central HS; Belmont, NY; (Y); Sec Pres FNA; Chorus; Rep Frsh Cls; Rep Soph Cls; Rep Jr Cls; Pres Sr Cls; Sec Stu Cncl; Var Cheerleading; Var Sftbl; Hon Roll; Dghtrs Amer Rvltn 81-82; Vrsty Letter Sccr 82; Crmnl Jstc.

EMERY, JOEL; Salmon River Crntral School; Bombay, NY; (S); French Clb; Band; Concert Band; Jazz Band; Mrchg Band; Pep Band; Rep Stu Cncl; JV Bsktbl; Var Golf; Stat Ice Hcky; JR Achvmnt Band Awd 83-84; Area All-State Band 83-84; Comp Pgmng.

EMILIO, ALESSANDRA; Bishop Kearney HS; Staten Island, NY; (S); 21/380; Library Aide; Science Clb; Band; Nwsp Rptr; Var Trk; Hon Roll; NHS; NEDT Awd; NY ST Regnts Schlrshp 85; Cornell U; Bio Sci.

EMILIO, LAURA; Smithtown H S West; Smithtown, NY; (Y); French Clb; Library Aide; Office Aide; French Hon Soc; High Hon Roll; Hon Roll; Comp Sci.

EMKEN, JANET; Bethpage HS; Bethpage, NY; (Y); 34/270; Pres Girl Scts; MMM; Band; Chorus; Concert Band; Mrchg Band; Orch; Fld Hcky; Hon Roll; GSA Slvr Awd 84; Nassau CC; Engrng.

EMLEN, ANNE A; Rome Free Acad HS; Rome, NY; (Y); 147/536; Intnl Clb; Band; Concert Band; Mrchg Band; Pep Band; High Hon Roll; Hon Roll; NHS; Prfct Atten Awd; Rgnts Schlrshp 85; NY ST U Geneseo; Comp Sci.

EMLEY, GREG; Pine Valley Central HS; Conewango Vlley, NY; (Y); 8/60; FFA; Var JV Bsktbl; Hon Roll; Lion Awd; Bsktbl Div 3 All Star Tm 83-85; Hghst Cls Avg Hstry Awd.

EMMERT, TINA; Notre Dame HS; Attica, NY; (S); Church Yth Grp; Library Aide; Socr; Sftbl; Swmmng; Hon Roll; Amer Legion Aux Awd 82; Psych.

EMMETT, LAURA A; Saint Joseph Hill Acad; Staten Island, NY; (Y); 42/103; Cmnty Wkr; Hosp Aide; Yrbk Stf; Rep Stu Cncl; Cheerleading; Mgr(s); Trk; NEDT Lttr Of Cmmndtn 83; SUNY Binghamton; Med.

EMMI, CHRISTINE; Canastota Central HS; Canastota, NY; (Y); Cmnty Wkr; Drama Clb; GAA; Intnl Clb; Science Clb; Chorus; Yrbk Stf; JV Capt Bsktbl; Score Keeper; Var Tennis; Comm.

EMPIE, PAUL; Johnstown HS; Johnstown, NY; (Y); Radio Clb; Wt Lftg; Paul Smiths; Forest Ranger.

EMPIE, SCOTT; Hendrick Hudson HS; Montrose, NY; (Y); Stage Crew; Golf; Mgr(s); Swmmng; High Hon Roll; NHS; Math Course I Regents Exam Awd 83; Swmmng Pin 85; Bryant; Bus Admin.

EMPIE, TERI; Scotia-Glenville HS; Scotia, NY; (Y); JV Trk; Pol Sci.

EMRICH, SUSAN; St Francis Prep; Glendale, NY; (S); Cmnty Wkr; Teachers Aide; JV Var Bsktbl; JV Var Sftbl; JV Var Vllybl; NHS; Scty Dist Amer HS Stus; Natl Merit; Regents Schlrshp; Bus Admin.

EMSING, COLLEEN; Bethlehem Central HS; Selkirk, NY; (Y); Church Yth Grp; Girl Scts; Hosp Aide; Office Aide; Red Cross Aide; Ski Clb; Cheerleading; Score Keeper; High Hon Roll; NHS; Grl Sct Slvr Awd 83; Bus.

ENCALADA, CARLOS F; Cardinal Spellman HS; Bronx, NY; (Y); Science Clb; Spanish Clb; Yrbk Stf; Im Bsbl; Im Vllybl; Hon Roll; NY ST Rgnts Schlrshp 85; Manhattan Coll; Accntnt.

ENCARNACION, CLEO; Walton HS; Bronx, NY; (S); 14/575; French Clb; Teachers Aide; NHS; Computer Clb; Quiz Bowl; French Hon Soc; Hstry, Engl, Frnch Awd 83; Pol Sci.

ENCK, GRETEL; Bainbridge-Guilford HS; Bainbridge, NY; (Y); 2/77; Pres 4-H; Trs French Clb; Band; Chorus; Orch; Yrbk Ed-Chief; Trs Jr Cls; JV Bsktbl; Trk; 4-H Awd.

ENDE, ERIC; Jericho HS; Jericho, NY; (Y); Cmnty Wkr; Office Aide; Temple Yth Grp; Chorus; Bsktbl; Var Ftbl; JV L Socr; Sftbl; Wt Lftg; NHS; Med.

ENDERS, COLLEEN; Cazenovia HS; Cazenovia, NY; (Y); Church Yth Grp; Dance Clb; Drama Clb; Exploring; GAA; Girl Scts; Chorus; Orch; School Musical; Variety Show; Mst Imprvd Frnch Stu 83; Cobleskill; Bus Admin.

ENDRESS, CAROLYN; Ripley Central Schl; Ripley, NY; (S); 2/28; Nwsp Rptr; Yrbk Stf; JV Bsktbl; Var Sftbl; JV Vllybl; High Hon Roll.

ENDRESS, WENDY; Laurens Central HS; Laurens, NY; (Y); 1/36; Pres VP Drama Clb; Pres Key Clb; Ski Clb; Color Guard; VP Soph Cls; Rep Jr Cls; Pres Stu Cncl; Socr; Cit Awd; DAR Awd; Clark Schlrshp 85; Regents Schrshp 85; Cong Medal Merit 85; Union Coll; Mgr Econ.

ENEA, ROSA; Preston HS; Bronx, NY; (S); 3/100; High Hon Roll; Hon Roll; NHS; Ntl Merit Ltr; Prfct Atten Awd; Ntl Merit Awd 84; Hnr Roll Cert 81-84; Sci Awd For Bio 83-84; NY U; Pre-Law.

ENERSON, DAWN; Tonawanda JR SR HS; Tonawanda, NY; (Y); Aud/Vis; Church Yth Grp; Girl Scts; Spanish Clb; Band; Chorus; Church Choir; Jazz Band; Mrchg Band; Pep Band; Chldhd Educ.

ENG, DONNA; St Johns Prep; Elmhurst, NY; (Y); Intnl Clb; Science Clb; NHS; Prfct Atten Awd; Med Tech.

ENG, FELIX L; Hillcrest HS; Queens Village, NY; (Y); 121/793; Church Yth Grp; Hosp Aide; JA; Office Aide; Science Clb; Teachers Aide; Im Badmtn; Im Bsktbl; Im Ftbl; Im Gym; NY ST Regents Schlrshp 85; Citation For Outstndng Prdctvty From JR Achvt 83; RPI; Engrng.

ENG, JOAN; Hicksville HS; Hicksville, NY; (Y); Am Leg Aux Girls St; Church Yth Grp; Chorus; Church Choir; Variety Show; Hon Roll; Awd For Wrtng Best Essay On Schl Spirit 84; Aeronautics.

ENGEL, CHRIS; Jamestown HS; Jamestown, NY; (Y); French Clb; Latin Clb; Spanish Clb; Chorus; Nwsp Rptr; Hon Roll; NHS; Spnsh,Latin Oratrcl Awd 83-84; Salem.

ENGEL, FAITH ANN; Elmont Memorial HS; Elmont, NY; (Y); 20/247; FBLA; Girl Scts; Office Aide; Political Wkr; Service Clb; Spanish Clb; Teachers Aide; Temple Yth Grp; Orch; Variety Show; Ind Arts Awd 85; PTSA Inda Arts Awd 85; Offc Francis T Purcell Awd 85; Nassau CC; Hnrs Librl Arts.

ENGEL, JEANNE M; Sanford H Calhoun HS; Merrick, NY; (Y); 8/336; Pres Church Yth Grp; Trs Band; Orch; Yrbk Stf; Off Jr Cls; Var Badmtn; High Hon Roll; Hon Roll; NHS; St Schlr; NY ST Rgnts Schlrshp 85; St Johns U Schlrshp 85; St Johns U; Phrmcy.

ENGEL, SUE; Chatham HS; Spencertown, NY; (Y); Hosp Aide; Latin Clb; Chorus; Yrbk Stf; Hon Roll; Aviation.

ENGELBERG, ILENE; Hauppauge HS; Hauppauge, NY; (Y); Dance Clb; Ski Clb; VP Temple Yth Grp; Y-Teens; Orch; Stage Crew; Stu Cncl; JV Tennis; Hon Roll; Bus.

ENGELBERG, YOCHEVED; Torah Academy For Girls; Far Rockaway, NY; (Y); 1/27; Cmnty Wkr; Stage Crew; Yrbk Rptr; Yrbk Stf; High Hon Roll; Jr NHS; NHS; Ntl Merit SF; Math, Sci Awd.

ENGERT, MARI; Charles D Amico HS; Albion, NY; (S); 3/187; Church Yth Grp; FFA; Trs FNA; Hosp Aide; Teachers Aide; High Hon Roll; NHS; Pres Schlr.

ENGLANDER, MERIDITH; Ca Bouton JR SR HS; Voorheesville, NY; (Y); Drama Clb; Band; School Play; High Hon Roll; NHS; Hosp Aide; Intnl Clb; Temple Yth Grp; Stage Crew; Yrbk Stf; Med.

ENGLE, CARL S; Elba Central Schl; Elba, NY; (Y); Am Leg Boys St; Math Clb; Science Clb; Varsity Clb; Rep Stu Cncl; Var Bsbl; Var Bsktbl; Var Capt Ftbl; High Hon Roll; Hon Roll; Dedctd Athl Awd 85; Ftbl All Leag Hnrb Mntn 84; Elec Engr.

ENGLE, CATHERINE; Highland HS; Clintondale, NY; (Y); 18/120; Pres 4-H; Varsity Clb; Concert Band; Mrchg Band; Orch; Yrbk Stf; Var L Trk; 4-H Awd; NHS; Spanish NHS; Ag.

ENGLE, DAVID F; Wellsville HS; Wellsville, NY; (Y); 26/130; JV Socr; Capt Trk; NYS Rgnts Schlrshp 85; Fredonia ST U New York; Comm.

ENGLE, ERIC; Thousand Islands Central HS; Clayton, NY; (Y); 10/71; Boy Scts; Wrstlng; Ntl Merit SF; Stu Cncl Awd Outstndng Achvt Eng 85; Marguerite Ewster Mem Schlrshp 85; Hnrs Grad 85; Queens U Kingston ON Can; Eng.

ENGLE, KENNETH T; Islip HS; Islip, NY; (Y); 50/250; School Play; Yrbk Phtg; VP Stu Cncl; JV Bsbl; Coach Actv; JV Var Ftbl; JV Lcrss; Im Wt Lftg; Var Wrstlng; Hon Roll; NYS Rgnts Schlrshp 85; Amvets Dodge Driver Exclince Prgm NYS Champ 85; AFROTC Schlrshp 85; Aerosp Engrng.

ENGLE, LISA; North Warren Central HS; Chestertown, NY; (S); 10/50; Chorus; Drm Mjr(t); Nwsp Rptr; Var Cheerleading; Hon Roll; CPA.

ENGLE, MARCELLA; Kenmore West SR HS; Bowling Green, KY; (Y); Drama Clb; Girl Scts; Science Clb; Mrchg Band; Hon Roll; Western KY U; Sci.

ENGLE, PHIL; Amsterdam HS; Amsterdam, NY; (Y); 4-H; Concert Band; Embry Riddle; Aviatn.

ENGLER, ALEXANDRA; Unatego Central HS; Otego, NY; (Y); 5/80; Ski Clb; Spanish Clb; Band; Chorus; Mrchg Band; Pep Band; School Play; Crs Cntry; Trk; High Hon Roll; Bio.

ENGLERT, JOHN; Aquinas Inst; N Chili, NY; (S); 3/168; Church Yth Grp; JA; Math Clb; Office Aide; Stage Crew; High Hon Roll; Prfct Atten Awd; Partl Schlrshp To Aquinas 82-86; Hortcltr.

ENGLERT, SARAH; Mount Saint Mary Acad; Grand Island, NY; (Y); 9/120; Church Yth Grp; Hosp Aide; School Play; Rep Soph Cls; Rep Jr Cls; Sec Stu Cncl; Var Badmtn; Var Gym; Hon Roll; NHS; Med.

ENGLESBERG, BARI SUE; Newfield HS; Coram, NY; (Y); Girl Scts; Trs Temple Yth Grp; Chorus; Variety Show; Yrbk Stf; Stu Cncl; Swmmng; High Hon Roll; Hon Roll; Jr NHS; NHS; Top 10 Swmmrs NY ST 82-85; Swm Tm Capt 84-86; LI Newsday Publctns 81-82; Psych.

ENGLISH, DAVID; Bishop Loughlin M HS; Brooklyn, NY; (Y); Boy Scts; CAP; Exploring; Hosp Aide; Color Guard; Drill Tm; Im Var Crs Cntry; Capt Gym; Trk; Hon Roll; Gen Wm B Mitchell Awd Schlrshp 85; Med.

ENGSTROM, ANNA; James L O Neill HS; Garrison, NY; (Y); French Clb; Pep Clb; Yrbk Stf; Hon Roll; Psych.

ENNIS, KRISTIN S; Amherst Central HS; Amherst, NY; (Y); 17/35; AFS; Cmnty Wkr; VP French Clb; Latin Clb; Library Aide; Political Wkr; Service Clb; Rep Stu Cncl; High Hon Roll; NHS; Boston College Schlrshp 85-86; Boston Coll; Foreign Studies.

ENRIGHT, BETH; Acad Of The Resrrctn; New Rochelle, NY; (Y); Church Yth Grp; GAA; Science Clb; Rep Stu Cncl; Trk; Hon Roll; NHS; Varsity Clb; Stage Crew; Lit Mag; Leheigh; Comp.

ENRIGHT, DEANA; Notre-Dame Bishop Gibbons HS; Schenectady, NY; (S); 13/140; JA; High Hon Roll; Hon Roll; Geo Awd 84; Hudson Valley; Dntstry.

ENRIGHT, MATTHEW; Aquinas Inst; Rochester, NY; (Y); 12/165; Church Yth Grp; Computer Clb; Drama Clb; Stage Crew; Yrbk Ed-Chief; Yrbk Phtg; Yrbk Sprt Ed; Yrbk Stf; High Hon Roll; Hon Roll; Acadmc Schlrshps 83 84 & 85; Mechncl Engrng.

ENRIQUEZ, GABRIEL; New Dorp HS; Staten Island, NY; (Y); Cmnty Wkr; Orch; Im Gym; JV Socr; Hon Roll; CSI; Engr.

ENSER, MICHELLE; Frontier HS; Hamburg, NY; (Y); 14/502; Sec Drama Clb; Math Clb; Concert Band; Var Swmmng; Var High Hon Roll; Jr NHS; NHS; English Clb; German Clb; Pep Clb; SAT Regents Schlrshp 85; Varsity Rifle Team 84-85; 2nd In Sci Cngrs Of Wstn NY 82; U Of NY Buffalo; Engrng.

ENSMENGER, PETER; Xavier HS; Brooklyn, NY; (Y); Church Yth Grp; Ski Clb; Y-Teens; NYS Regents Scholar 85; Springfield Coll Scholar 85-86; Springfield Coll; Bus.

ENSMINGER, KAREN; Grand Island HS; Grand Island, NY; (Y); Pres 4-H; Hosp Aide; Church Choir; Concert Band; Drill Tm; Variety Show; JV Tennis; JV Trk; 4-H Awd; Hon Roll.

ENTERLEIN, DAWN; Fox Lane HS; Bedford, NY; (Y); 66/300; Intnl Clb; Rep Frsh Cls; Rep Soph Cls; Pres Jr Cls; JV Bsktbl; JV Gym; Hon Roll; Crs Cntry; Trk; Hnrbl Ment All St Cross Cty 84; All Cty Cross Cty 80-84; All Cty Track 83-85; Psych Ed.

ENTIN, ELYSE; Smithtown East HS; Smithtown, NY; (Y); Hosp Aide; Temple Yth Grp; Thesps; School Play; Stu Cncl; Hon Roll; Spanish NHS; Bnai Brith Chptr VP 83-84.

ENTRESS, SHARON; Gates Chili HS; Rochester, NY; (Y); Church Yth Grp; Spanish Clb; School Play; Sci.

ENTWISTLE, PAUL; Royalton-Hartland Central HS; Gasport, NY; (Y); Cmnty Wkr; JV Wrstlng; Hon Roll; Bus.

EPISCOPIO, LEONARD G; Lafayette HS; Brooklyn, NY; (Y); 13/407; Debate Tm; Math Tm; Nwsp Sprt Ed; JV Ftbl; Regents Schlrshp 85; Arista Hnr Scty 83-85; Akron Hnr Scty 83-85; Stony Brook Coll; Pre-Med.

EPOLITO, LAWRENCE WILLIAM; Anthony A Henninger HS; Syracuse, NY; (Y); Am Leg Boys St; Yrbk Ed-Chief; Yrbk Phtg; Rep Frsh Cls; Rep Soph Cls; Rep Jr Cls; Pres Sr Cls; Rep Stu Cncl; Bowling; Im Socr; Publc Rltns Offcr 85-86; Graphc Arts.

EPPEL, BECKY; Union Springs Academy; Scipio Center, NY; (S); 4/48; VP Frsh Cls; VP Soph Cls; Sec Jr Cls; Rep Stu Cncl; Ski Clb; Varsity Clb; Band; Church Choir; Concert Band; High Hon Roll; Cornell U; Bio.

EPPEL, DIETER; Union Springs Acad; Scipio Center, NY; (S); 7/44; Ski Clb; Band; Off Frsh Cls; Off Jr Cls; High Hon Roll; Hon Roll.

EPPERSON, LAURA; Greece Athena HS; Rochester, NY; (Y); 7/281; Church Yth Grp; Drama Clb; Ski Clb; Band; Chorus; Church Choir; Concert Band; School Musical; High Hon Roll; Hon Roll; Allegheny Schlr Schlrshp 85; Allegheny; Biochem.

EPPICH, GREGORY; St Marys Acad; Glens Falls, NY; (S); 7/45; Boy Scts; French Clb; ROTC; Pres Ski Clb; Band; Nwsp Rptr; Nwsp Sprt Ed; Nwsp Stf; Yrbk Bus Mgr; Yrbk Stf; Comp Sci.

EPPS, KIMBERLY D; August Martin HS; Jamaica, NY; (Y); 35/375; Math Tm; Office Aide; Science Clb; Teachers Aide; Nwsp Rptr; Yrbk Rptr; Lit Mag; NHS; Albany ST U; Accntng.

EPSTEIN, DYANE; Commack HS South; Commack, NY; (Y); Art Clb; Cmnty Wkr; Hosp Aide; Office Aide; Teachers Aide; Temple Yth Grp; Nwsp Sprt Ed; Nwsp Stf; Var Bsktbl; Im Fld Hcky; Vol Awd 82-83; Art Show; Stu Recgntn Awd 83-84; Most Imprvd Plyr V Sports Awd 84-85; Elem Ed.

EPSTEIN, MILES Z; Pleasantville HS; Pleasantville, NY; (Y); VP Model UN; Band; Mrchg Band; Nwsp Bus Mgr; Nwsp Rptr; Lit Mag; Hon Roll; 1st WPRPGA Essay, Soc Stds Awd 84; Newspr Jrnlsm Awd 85; Gov Svc.

ER, FISUN; Fontbonne Hall HS; Brooklyn, NY; (Y); Computer Clb; Dance Clb; Science Clb; Chorus; School Play; Bsktbl; Gym; Swmmng; Vllybl; Swmng Awd 81; Chld Psych.

ERDMAN, KATHY; Buffalo Acad Of Sacred Heart; Williamsville, NY; (Y); Church Yth Grp; Cmnty Wkr; Dance Clb; Service Clb; Spanish Clb; School Musical; Stage Crew; Variety Show; Rep Stu Cncl; Hon Roll; Canisus Coll; Advrtsng.

ERICKSON, BRIAN; Long Island Lutheran HS; Plainview, NY; (S); Chorus; School Musical; School Play; Lit Mag; Sec Jr Cls; Bowling; Var Crs Cntry; Var Tennis; High Hon Roll; Jr NHS; Engrng.

ERICKSON, KATHRYN; Vernon-Verona-Sherrill Central HS; Vernon, NY; (Y); Pres 4-H; Pres Trs Latin Clb; Mathletes; Thesps; Yrbk Bus Mgr; VP Frsh Cls; High Hon Roll; NHS; Church Yth Grp; Natl Latin Exam Cum Laude; Natl Latin Exam Slvr Mdl; SUNY; Chem Engrng.

ERICKSON, LANCE M; Garden City HS; Garden City, NY; (Y); 27/355; Church Yth Grp; VP Spanish Clb; Stage Crew; Var Bowling; Im Vllybl; High Hon Roll; NHS; Excllnt Achvt Spn Awd 84; Bus.

ERICKSON, RAYMOND; Jamestown HS; Jamestown, NY; (Y); Church Yth Grp; French Clb; Ski Clb; Rep Jr Cls; Ftbl; Socr; Swmmng; Trk; Hon Roll.

ERIE, ROMISHE; Springfield Gardens HS; Springfield, NY; (Y); 131/443; FNA; Teachers Aide; Fld Hcky; Gym; Socr; Vllybl; Hon Roll; Prfct Atten Awd; Perf Attndnc 83-84; Caribbean Clb 83-84; Columbia U; Midwf.

ERKLENZ, MICHELLE; Canisteo Central Schl; Hornell, NY; (Y); 20/82; Trs GAA; Girl Scts; School Play; Sec Frsh Cls; Sec Soph Cls; Sec Jr Cls; Pres Sr Cls; Var Capt Bsktbl; Var Capt Socr; Var Capt Sftbl; Schlr Athlt Army Resrv Awd 85; Delta Kappa Gamma Grnt 85; Nazareth Alumni Schlrshp S Tier 85; Nazareth; Spec Educ.

ERLE, BRIAN; Union Endicott HS; Endicott, NY; (Y); 129/450; Am Leg Boys St; Boys Clb Am; Letterman Clb; Ski Clb; Varsity Clb; Bsbl; Bsktbl; Golf; Lcrss; Sftbl; Boys Amer Lgn Capt Awd 84; Amer Lgn Dugie Evans Sprtsmnshp Awd 84; Suny Morrisville; Comp Sci.

ERLICH, LORI; Sheepshead Bay HS; Brooklyn, NY; (Y); Off Office Aide; Spanish Clb; Band; School Musical; Recvd 99 Law Stds & Cncrt Bnd 85; Bus.

ERMANOVICS, BURTON WIDMARK; Minisink Valley HS; Otisville, NY; (Y); Boy Scts; Chorus; JV Coach Actv; Swmmng; Wt Lftg; Hon Roll; Orange Cnty CC; Bus Admin.

ERNDL, MICHELE; Domminican Commercial HS; Glendale, NY; (Y); 2/250; Church Yth Grp; Hosp Aide; Teachers Aide; Sftbl; Hon Roll; NHS; Steuban Awd Citation Of Mrt In Stdy Of Grmn Lang 84.

ERNENWEIN, LAURIE A; Vernon Verona Sherrill HS; Rome, NY; (Y); 60/245; Church Yth Grp; Girl Scts; High Hon Roll; Hon Roll; Prfct Atten Awd; Dollars For Schlrs Schlrshp 85; Cert Achvt-Boces-Fd Trds 83-85; SUNY Morrisville; Rstrnt Mgmt.

ERNISSE, KELLY; Franklin Delano Roosevelt HS; Hyde Park, NY; (Y); DECA; Culinary Inst Of Amer; Chef.

ERNST, BETH; Poland Central Schl; Poland, NY; (Y); 15/56; Ski Clb; Varsity Clb; Yrbk Stf; VP Frsh Cls; Rep Stu Cncl; JV Var Cheerleading; Cit Awd; High Hon Roll; Hon Roll; Prfct Atten Awd; Math II High Honor Awd 84; American Legn Schlrshp 8k; Russell Sage Coll; Physcl Thrpy.

ERNST, DEBBIE; Chenengo Forks HS; Chenango Forks, NY; (Y); Trs Church Yth Grp; Ski Clb; Spanish Clb; JV Var Cheerleading; Hon Roll; Prfct Atten Awd; Surry Binghamton; Comp Sci.

ERNST, DEBORAH; Sayville HS; Sayville, NY; (Y); 7/337; Trs Key Clb; Chorus; Orch; Nwsp Stf; Yrbk Sprt Ed; JV Sftbl; Var Tennis; JV Vllybl; High Hon Roll; NHS; Mbr Of All-Cnty Orchstra Violin; Acctng.

ERNST, LORI; Liverpool HS; Liverpool, NY; (S); 54/972; Ski Clb; Spanish Clb; Yrbk Ed-Chief; Rep Frsh Cls; Rep Soph Cls; Rep Jr Cls; Rep Stu Cncl; JV Var Cheerleading; High Hon Roll; NHS; Mkrtng.

ERNST, PATRICIA; Saratoga Central Catholic HS; Gansevoort, NY; (S); Drama Clb; JV Cheerleading; JV Vllybl; High Hon Roll; NHS; Acadmc Excllnc Skidmore Coll Saratoigian Top 10 Pct Clss 84.

ERNSTHAUSEN, MARK; E J Wilson HS; Spencerport, NY; (Y); Church Yth Grp; Exploring; Jazz Band; Symp Band; Var Swmmng; Var Tennis; Timer; Hon Roll.

ERNSTHAUSEN, MARY; E J Wilson HS; Spencerport, NY; (Y); VP Church Yth Grp; VP Math Clb; Band; School Musical; Symp Band; Swmmng; Tennis; High Hon Roll; Hon Roll; Frshmn Soph & Jr Music Awds 82 83 & 84; Prncpl Horn Rochester Philharmonic Yth Orchstr 83-85; Penn ST U; Engrng.

EROL, ERDAL; Eastridge HS; Rochester, NY; (Y); Church Yth Grp; Cmnty Wkr; Computer Clb; German Clb; Science Clb; Teachers Aide; JV Var Socr; High Hon Roll; Ec I Cert Of Merit 83; Ntl Sci Olympd Dist Awd 83; Outstndng Cntrbtn Ind Comp Conf 84; RIT; Bus Admin.

ERRICO, DEANNA MAE; Maple Grove JR SR HS; Bemus Point, NY; (Y); 5/80; Am Leg Aux Girls St; Var L Bsktbl; Capt Mat Maids; Var L Trk; Var L Vllybl; Stat Wrstlng; NHS; Prfct Atten Awd; Church Yth Grp; Cmnty Wkr; Hugh Brian Yth Fndtn Ldrshp Smnr 84; Smi-Fnlst Cngrss-Bndstag Stu Exchng Pgm 85; Phys Thrpy.

ERTEL, RICHARD C; South Side HS; Rockville Ctr, NY; (Y); 72/292; FCA; Model UN; Var JV Bsbl; Var JV Ftbl; Hon Roll; Aclyte Chrch 80-85; Archlgy.

ERVIN, ANTHONY; Williamsville North HS; Williamsville, NY; (Y); JV Bsbl; Im Bsktbl; JV Var Ftbl; Var Trk; Accntng.

ERWAY, VICTOR M; Cherry Valley HS; Cherry Valley, NY; (Y); 4/36; Am Leg Boys St; Varsity Clb; VP Soph Cls; Pres Jr Cls; Pres Sr Cls; Var Bsbl; Var Bsktbl; Var Socr; High Hon Roll; NHS; Bus Mngmnt.

ESBRI, LUIS; Adley Stevenson HS; Bronx, NY; (Y); Church Yth Grp; Hon Roll; Art, Spnsh, & Engl Awd 85; Engrng.

ESCOTTO, SANTOS; Bishop Loughlin HS; Brooklyn, NY; (Y); Spanish Clb; Capt Varsity Clb; Rep Frsh Cls; Sec Soph Cls; VP Jr Cls; Var Capt Bsktbl; Hon Roll; Comp Pgm.

ESDENKOTTER, TINA; Islip HS; Islip, NY; (Y); Mathletes; Concert Band; Orch; School Musical; Nwsp Stf; Var Capt Bsktbl; Var Capt Socr; Var Sftbl; Jr NHS; NHS; 8th Pl Suffolk Cty French Test 83; Bio.

ESGRO, MARY ELLEN; Johnson City HS; Johnson City, NY; (Y); 14/251; Am Leg Aux Girls St; Hosp Aide; Varsity Clb; Sec Soph Cls; Stu Cncl; Var L Socr; Var L Trk; Var L Vllybl; High Hon Roll; NHS; St Bonaventure.

ESKEDAL, SANDRA PATRICIA; Scotia-Glenville HS; Scotia, NY; (Y); Church Yth Grp; Red Cross Aide; Im Stat Bsktbl; Im Mgr(s); Im Capt Powder Puff Ftbl; JV Var Score Keeper; Im Sftbl; JV Var Timer; JA; Spanish Clb; U Miami; Law.

ESOLA, VINNIE; Northern Adirondack Central HS; Ellenburg Depot, NY; (Y); Chess Clb; JA; Pep Clb; Ski Clb; Drm Mjr(t); Nwsp Stf; Pres Jr Cls; Bsbl; Bsktbl; Crs Cntry.

ESPERTO, GEORGE; East Meadow HS; East Meadow, NY; (S); 45/414; Math Tm; Bsbl; Socr; Trk; Wrstlng; Hon Roll.

ESPINEL, TAMMY; St Vincent Ferrer HS; Astoria, NY; (Y); 23/114; Library Aide; Science Clb; Hon Roll; Hstry Awd Excllnc 83-84; Sci Olympd Awd Bio 83-84; Med.

ESPOSITO, ANNE; Dundee Central HS; Rock Stream, NY; (Y); 3/70; Trs AFS; Varsity Clb; Chorus; JV L Sftbl; Var L Tennis; Var L Trk; High Hon Roll; Trs NHS; Hghst Achvt Amer Stds 83-84; Hghst Achvt Engl 9 81-82; Regents Schlrshp; Law.

ESPOSITO, BERNADETTE; Bishop Kearney HS; Brooklyn, NY; (Y); Aud/Vis; Dance Clb; Teachers Aide; Hon Roll; Jr NHS; NHS; Bio.

ESPOSITO, FORTUNE; Midwood HS; Brooklyn, NY; (Y); Brooklyn Coll; Bus Mgmt.

ESPOSITO, FRAN D; Preston HS; Bronx, NY; (Y); 3/50; Yrbk Stf; High Hon Roll; Hon Roll; NHS; Berkley Bus Schl; Med Sec.

ESPOSITO, GINA; Newfield HS; Selden, NY; (Y); Trs Computer Clb; Girl Scts; Quiz Bowl; Yrbk Stf; Var Bowling; ROTC; Jr NHS; NHS.

ESPOSITO, GRANT J; Hunter College HS; New York, NY; (Y); Drama Clb; Political Wkr; School Play; Var Co-Capt Bsktbl; Var L Tennis; High Hon Roll; Mu Alp Tht; Regnts Schlrshp 85; Cornell Arts & Sci; Govt.

ESPOSITO, JOHN; John F Kennedy HS; Shenorock, NY; (Y); 14/187; High Hon Roll; Hon Roll; Ntl Merit SF; Hofstra U.

ESPOSITO, JOSEPH A; St Anthonys HS; Central Islip, NY; (Y); Spanish Clb; Teachers Aide; Nwsp Stf; Ice Hcky; High Hon Roll; NHS; Spanish NHS; St Champ Ice Hockey Tm 84.

ESPOSITO, KELLY ANN; Roy C Ketcham HS; Wappingers Falls, NY; (Y); AFS; Band; Nwsp Stf; High Hon Roll; Hon Roll; Spch Thrpy.

ESPOSITO, LAURA; Garden City HS; Garden City, NY; (S).

ESPOSITO, PATRICIA; Bishop Kearney HS; Brooklyn, NY; (Y); Bowling; Albany Sci Fair Comp Hnrbl Mntn; Schl Sci Fair 2nd Pl; SEER Comp Various Przs; Pre-Law.

ESPOSITO, RICHARD; Onteora Central HS; Woodstock, NY; (S); Am Leg Boys St; Math Tm; Orch; Var Bsbl; Var Socr; High Hon Roll; NHS; High Hnrs The Yr 83-84; Engrng.

ESPOSITO, RICHARD; Tottenville HS; Staten Island, NY; (Y); St Johns U; Air Piolot.

ESPOSITO, SCOTT; Kenmore East HS; Kenmore, NY; (Y); 2/330; Math Tm; School Musical; School Play; Var Bsktbl; Var Tennis; Sal; Drama Clb; German Clb; Mathletes; Math Clb; Notre Dame Schlr 85; Moore Fmly Awd 85; U Of Notre Dame.

ESQUIVEL, MICHELLE; Clarkstown South HS; New City, NY; (Y); Office Aide; Nwsp Stf; Yrbk Stf; Lit Mag; Jr NHS; NHS; 2nd Hnrs Iona Lang Cont Fr III 85; Fshn Dsgn.

ESSENBURG, HANNA; Comsewogue HS; Po Jefferson St, NY; (Y); 24/346; Chorus; Nwsp Rptr; Nwsp Stf; Yrbk Stf; Im Badmtn; High Hon Roll; Jr NHS; NHS; St Jude Chldrns Rsrch Hosp Math-A-Thon,Dance-A-Thon,Walk-A-Thon 82-84; Rgnts Schlrshp 85; Suffolk CC; Gntc Engrng.

ESTABROOK, NANCY; Greene Central Schl; Oxford, NY; (Y); Band; Chorus; Concert Band; Drm Mjr(t); Jazz Band; Mrchg Band; Var L Fld Hcky; Var L Sftbl; Var L Vllybl; Hon All Star Crtlnd Vlybl Tourny 84-85; SUNY Cortland; Phys Educ.

ESTEBAN, JOSEFINA; Cathedral HS; Ny, NY; (Y); Art Clb; Church Yth Grp; Cmnty Wkr; Dance Clb; FNA; Hosp Aide; Intnl Clb; Alcala De Henares-Spain; Med.

ESTENOZ, MARIA; Grand Island HS; Grand Island, NY; (Y); Church Yth Grp; Chrmn Cmnty Wkr; Hosp Aide; Political Wkr; Stu Cncl; High Hon Roll; Hon Roll; Im Badmtn; Natl Hisp Schlrshp Awd 85; Acad Achvt Awd 82; Rgnts Schlrshp Awd 85; Boston U; Pre-Med.

ESTERLINE, MARK; Athena HS; Rochester, NY; (S); Church Yth Grp; DECA; Nwsp Phtg; Nwsp Rptr; Bsbl; Bsktbl; High Hon Roll; Hon Roll; Distrib Ed Clbs Of Amer-1st Rgnl In Real Est, 2nd ST In Real Est 85; Kings Coll; Bus.

ESTEVES, ISIS; Pelham Memorial HS; Pelham, NY; (Y); AFS; Drama Clb; Model UN; School Musical; Nwsp Stf; Lit Mag; Capt Twrlr; Hon Roll; NHS.

ESTEVEZ, CYNTHIA; Academy Mount St Ursula HS; New York, NY; (Y); Dance Clb; Girl Scts; Variety Show; Yrbk Stf; Prfct Atten Awd; Ntl Piano Plyng Aud Awd 78-80; Comp.

ESTILO, MAGNOLIA; Springfield Gardens HS; Rosedale, NY; (S); 11/508; Concert Band; Orch; School Musical; Symp Band; High Hon Roll; Hon Roll; Pres NHS; Mbm Of Queensborough Symph Band 82-85; Church Pianist/Organ 83-85; Acad Olymp 84-85; Pianist.

ESTIN, BETH; Sachem High School North Campus; Lake Grove, NY; (Y); 78/1509; French Clb; Science Clb; Teachers Aide; Temple Yth Grp; Band; Concert Band; Drm & Bgl; Mrchg Band; Orch; Child Psych.

ESTRADA, FERNANDO; La Salle Acad; New York, NY; (Y); Chess Clb; Band; Concert Band; Drm Mjr(t); Mrchg Band; Crs Cntry; Hon Roll; NY Inst Tech; Audio Rcrdng.

ESTRADA, FRED; Island Trees HS; Levittown, NY; (Y); 16/212; Debate Tm; Intnl Clb; Im Badmtn; JV Bsbl; Bowling; Ftbl; Im Wt Lftg; High Hon Roll; Hon Roll; NHS; NY ST Regents Schlrshp 85; NY U; Pre-Med.

ESTRADA, NANCY; Mamaroneck HS; Mamaroneck, NY; (Y); Girl Scts; Bsbl; Bsktbl; Swmmng; Tennis; Vllybl; Kiwanis Awd; Rotary Awd; Stu Aid-Found; United Hosp; Radialogy.

ESTREICHER, CAROLYN; Susan E Wagner HS; Staten Island, NY; (Y); 10/500; School Musical; Yrbk Stf; Rep Jr Cls; Rep Sr Cls; Trs Stu Cncl; High Hon Roll; NHS; Rep Soph Cls; Acadmc Olymps Sqd 84-85; Frshmn Orientr 83-85; Bus.

ESTRELLA, CLARIBEL; Edward R Murrow HS; Brooklyn, NY; (Y); 182/725; Trs Church Yth Grp; FHA; Hosp Aide; Office Aide; School Musical; Variety Show; Yrbk Stf; Cheerleading; Vllybl; Am Assoc Tchrs Of Spnsh-Awd Excllnc Spnsh 84; St Francis Coll; Med.

ESTRELLA, LISSETTE; Far Rockaway HS; Far Rockaway, NY; (Y); Office Aide; Teachers Aide; Chorus; Church Choir; Capt Drm Mjr(t); Stage Crew; Wt Lftg; Mgr Wrstlng; Hon Roll; Pace U Westchester; Mktg.

ETKIN, EDWARD; Solomon Schechter HS; Brooklyn, NY; (Y); 2/40; Art Clb; Science Clb; Nwsp Stf; Yrbk Stf; Ntl Merit Ltr; Achvt Acad Awd; Biolmed Engrng.

ETKIN, JONATHAN; Minisink Valley HS; Middletown, NY; (Y); Ski Clb; JV Bsbl; Im Capt Bsktbl; Var Capt Ftbl; Var Trk; High Hon Roll; Hon Roll; NHS; Duke U; Bus.

ETWARU, KUMARIE; Hillcrest HS; Jamaica, NY; (Y); 34/793; Hosp Aide; Office Aide; Teachers Aide; VICA; High Hon Roll; NHS; NYS Regnts Schlrhsp 85; Hunter Col Merit Awd 84-85; NY U.

EURILLO, DON; Bainbridge Guilford Central HS; Bainbridge, NY; (Y); 15/80; Boy Scts; Quiz Bowl; Orch; Ice Hcky; Lcrss; Trk; Wt Lftg; Wrstlng; Ntl Merit Ltr; NYSSMA Music Awd 84; Mock Trl Awd 2nd 85.

EVANGELISTA, CARMEN; Longwood HS; Coram, NY; (S); 5/450; Capt Math Tm; Sec NHS; Hosp Aide; Nwsp Stf; Yrbk Ed-Chief; Yrbk Sprt Ed; High Hon Roll.

EVANGELISTA, SUSAN A; Sachem North HS; Lake Ronkonkoma, NY; (Y); 14/1628; Orch; Rep Sr Cls; Mst Outstndng Spnsh Stdnt 83-84; Albright Coll; Acctng.

EVANS, ANNE; Mt Mercy HS; Buffalo, NY; (Y); 16/166; VP Latin Clb; Off Jr Cls; Sec Stu Cncl; Var Badmtn; Bsktbl; Var JV Vllybl; DAR Awd; Hon Roll; Cmnty Wkr; JCL; Brnz Mdl In Empire ST Games For Crew 85; Hnrbl Mntn In Sci Fair 85; Top 10% Of Clss 85; SUNY.

EVANS, BRIAN S; Hartford Central Schl; Argyle, NY; (Y); 6/42; Sec Trs 4-H; Math Tm; Science Clb; 4-H Awd; Hon Roll; New York State Regents Schlrshp; Adirondack Comm; Electrnc Engrn.

EVANS, CAMILLE; Holy Trinity HS; Uniondale, NY; (Y); Civic Clb; Hosp Aide; Math Clb; Concert Band; Yrbk Stf; Rep Soph Cls; Rep Church Yth Grp; Stu Cncl; JV Crs Cntry; Var Trk; Nassau Cnty Med Ctr Volunteer Svc Awd 85; U Of Rochester; Bio.

EVANS, CASSIE; Camden HS; College Station, TX; (Y); 2/208; Nwsp Stf; High Hon Roll; NHS; Sal; Pres Acad Ftns Awd 85; NY ST Regnts Coll Schlrshp 85; TX A & M; Math.

EVANS, ERIC; Fashion Industries HS; Bronx, NY; (Y); 72/430; Boys Clb Am; Camera Clb; Yrbk Phtg; Yrbk Stf; Rep Stu Cncl; Tennis; Vllybl; Cit Awd; Gov Hon Prg Awd.

EVANS, GEORGE; Bishop Timon HS; Buffalo, NY; (S); 2/180; Scholastic Bowl; Chorus; Camp Fr Inc; Nwsp Rptr; Yrbk Stf; Lit Mag; Rep Frsh Cls; Rep Soph Cls; Rep Jr Cls; Im Bsktbl.

EVANS, HEATHER; Greene Central HS; Greene, NY; (Y); 3/105; Pres Church Yth Grp; French Clb; Ski Clb; Chorus; Color Guard; Mrchg Band; JV Sftbl; Var Tennis; High Hon Roll; NHS; Hghst Frnch Rgnts 85; Semfnlst Oprtn Entrprse 85; Cert & Ltr Mrchng Band 85; Occuptnl Thrpy.

EVANS, JOAN M; Frankfort Schuyler Central Schl; Frankfort, NY; (Y); Trs GAA; Girl Scts; Spanish Clb; Yrbk Stf; JV Var Bsktbl; Var Capt Sftbl; High Hon Roll; Hon Roll; Albany St U; Bus Admin.

EVANS, JONATHAN SCOTT; Freeport HS; Freeport, NY; (Y); 90/500; Debate Tm; DECA; French Clb; Latin Clb; Scholastic Bowl; Ski Clb; Rep Frsh Cls; Rep Soph Cls; Wrstlng; SUNY Albany; Corp Law.

EVANS, KARLTON ALLEN; Buffalo Traditional School; Buffalo, NY; (Y); Dance Clb; Spanish Clb; Chorus; Drill Tm; Yrbk Stf; Var Swmmng; SAR Awd; NAACP Natl Act-So Comptn 85; Arch.

EVANS, KATHLEEN; Altmar Parish Williamstown HS; Parish, NY; (Y); Church Yth Grp; Girl Scts; Mathletes; Varsity Clb; Yrbk Stf; JV Socr; Vllybl; Hon Roll; Sftbl; SUNY Potsdam; Elem Educ.

EVANS, KELLY; Rensselaer JR SR HS; Rensselaer, NY; (S); DECA; Pres Key Clb; Q&S; Nwsp Ed-Chief; Yrbk Ed-Chief; VP Frsh Cls; Timer; High Hon Roll; Trs NHS; Score Keeper; Rensselaerr Yth Yr Awd 84; Maria Coll; Med.

EVANS, LAURIE; Hilton HS; Hilton, NY; (Y); Ski Clb; Varsity Clb; Jazz Band; Mrchg Band; Symp Band; Tennis; High Hon Roll; Rep Stu Cncl; Score Keeper; Hon Roll.

EVANS, LISA; Riverside HS; Buffalo, NY; (Y); Girl Scts; Key Clb; Office Aide; Ed Lit Mag; Rep Stu Cncl; Bowling; Hon Roll; NHS; Sec.

EVANS, LISA A; Tonawanda HS; Tonawanda, NY; (Y); 40/270; Hosp Aide; Pres Band; Pres Concert Band; VP Jazz Band; Pres Mrchg Band; Pres Orch; Pres Pep Band; School Musical; Trk; Hon Roll; Tonawanda Jazz Rennisance 85; Niagara U; Nrsng.

EVANS, MATTHEW; Wilson Central HS; Wilson, NY; (Y); Aud/Vis; Teachers Aide; Stage Crew; JV Var Bsktbl; Var Golf; Var Trk; MVP Golf; Drafting.

EVANS, MAUREEN; Mount Mercy Acad; Buffalo, NY; (Y); 8/205; Hosp Aide; Model UN; Quiz Bowl; Ski Clb; Spanish Clb; Chorus; Rep Soph Cls; Rep Stu Cncl; Hon Roll; Pres NHS; Regents Scholar NY; U Of Buffalo; Phrmcy.

EVANS, PATRICE A; Skaneateles Central HS; Skaneateles, NY; (Y); Ski Clb; Lit Mag; Trs Soph Cls; Var Tennis; Var Vllybl; High Hon Roll; Jr NHS; NHS; Math.

EVANS, SCOTT; Whitesboro Central Schl; Whitesboro, NY; (Y); Church Yth Grp; Varsity Clb; Acpl Chr; Chorus; JV Golf; L Var Ice Hcky; L Var Socr; Hon Roll.

EVANS, STACY; Edison Technical & Occupationl HS; Rochester, NY; (Y); Exploring; Chorus; Variety Show; Rep Frsh Cls; Rep Soph Cls; Rep Jr Cls; Score Keeper; JV Vllybl; Srv Aide Awd 83-85; Hnr Roll 84-85; UCLA; Drama.

EVANS, TIM R; Newburgh Free Acad; Newburgh, NY; (Y); Boy Scts; Key Clb; Political Wkr; Ski Clb; Varsity Clb; Stu Cncl; Crs Cntry; Trk; High Hon Roll; Hon Roll; Arch.

EVANSON, THERESE F; Cardinal Spellman HS; New York, NY; (Y); Sec Camera Clb; Cmnty Wkr; Hosp Aide; JA; Office Aide; Science Clb; Church Choir; High Hon Roll; Hon Roll; Regnts Schlrshp; Math Awd; Bio.

EVERETT, ANDREA; Faith Bible Acad; Sharon Springs, NY; (Y); Church Yth Grp; Drama Clb; Radio Clb; Chorus; Church Choir; School Musical; Stage Crew; Sec Trs Yrbk Stf; Vllybl; Schl Spirit 85; Music Awd 85; Yrbk Awd 85; Bapt Bible Coll; Erly Chldhd Ed.

EVERETT, JEFFREY L; Watkins Glen HS; Watkins Glen, NY; (Y); 27/126; Am Leg Boys St; 4-H; Hon Roll; Arch.

EVERETT, KORRIE; Smithtown H S West; Hauppauge, NY; (Y); Hosp Aide; Chorus; Color Guard; Orch; School Musical; Stage Crew; Hon Roll; Rotary Awd; Orchstra Schl Ltr 85; SUNY Potsdam; Music.

EVERETT, STEVEN; Albion HS; Albion, NY; (S); 12/180; Pres Latin Clb; Band; Concert Band; Jazz Band; Mrchg Band; L Ftbl; NHS; NYS Regents Schlrshp 85; NYS Mus Awds 82 & 83; U MO Rolla; Elect Engrng.

EVERLETH, REBECCA; Lockport SR HS; Lockport, NY; (Y); 47/475; Church Yth Grp; Computer Clb; Stat GAA; Intnl Clb; Library Aide; Math Clb; Spanish Clb; Teachers Aide; Varsity Clb; Y-Teens; Spanish Tip To Spain With Spanish Clb 85; Criminal Justice.

EVERLY, WILLIAM; Cambridge Central Schl; Buskirk, NY; (Y); 37/82; Boy Scts; Cmnty Wkr; FBLA; Band; Chorus; Yrbk Stf; Rep Frsh Cls; Sec Soph Cls; Rep Jr Cls; Rep Sr Cls; Egl Sct Awd 85; Cmmnty Schlrshp 85; Cls Serv & All Cnty Chrs Awds 85; Castleton ST Coll; Bus Admin.

EVERTS, PAMELA; Hudson HS; Hudson, NY; (Y); 7/170; AFS; Hosp Aide; Orch; School Musical; Nwsp Rptr; Var Bowling; High Hon Roll; Hon Roll; NHS; Jrnlsm.

EVERY, VICKI; Chatham HS; Ghent, NY; (Y); 25/140; Band; Flag Corp; Pep Band; Pres Frsh Cls; Pres Soph Cls; Pres Jr Cls; Sec Stu Cncl; Socr; Hon Roll; NHS; Htl Admn.

EWALD, BRETT M; Wilson Central HS; Ransomville, NY; (Y); 3/134; Camera Clb; Red Cross Aide; Var L Tennis; High Hon Roll; NHS; Pres Schlr; Yrbk Phtg; Im Vllybl; Prfct Atten Awd; NY ST Regnts Schlrshp 85; Paulien Weiller Mem Awd 85; Odyssy Of Mind 7th Pl 84; SUNY Coll Buffalo; Bio.

EWANOW, ROB; Eastridge HS; Rochester, NY; (S); 49/209; DECA; Var Swmmng; Timer; CC Awd; Hon Roll; Ntl Fnls DECA 85; Nazareth Coll; Chem.

EWART, PETER; Northeastern Clinton Central Schl; Rouses Point, NY; (Y); Church Yth Grp; Cmnty Wkr; French Clb; Model UN; Pres Jr Cls; Var Bsktbl; Var Socr; Var Tennis; High Hon Roll; NHS; Mst Outstndng Frnch Stu 84-85; Outstndng Dlgt Awd At Hrvd Mdl UN Conf 84; Amer Lgn Ortrcl Cntst 85; Indstrl Distrib.

EWEST, RONALD; Mc Kee Vo Tech; Staten Is, NY; (Y); 38/238; Teachers Aide; Rep Soph Cls; Cit Awd; Prfct Atten Awd; PA ST U; Arch.

EWING, JEFF; Shenendehowa HS; Ballston Lake, NY; (Y); Church Yth Grp; Var Bsbl; Var Bowling; High Hon Roll; Bus Admin.

EXNER, KRISTINE; Cicero-North Syracuse HS; Clay, NY; (S); 78/622; Church Yth Grp; Church Choir; Merit Roll 83-84; Bryant & Stratton Bus Schl; Bus.

EYDELMAN, VICTORIA; Midwood HS; Brooklyn, NY; (Y); 67/605; Chorus; School Musical; School Play; Yrbk Stf; Cit Awd; Hon Roll; NY U; Law.

EYFA, YANINA; Christopher Columbus HS; Bronx, NY; (S); 55/767; High Hon Roll; Hon Roll; NCTE Awd; NHS; Regents Schlrshp 85; Pratt Inst; Arch.

EYGNOR, KELLY J; North Rose-Wolcott HS; Wolcott, NY; (Y); FBLA; Office Aide; Ski Clb; Varsity Clb; JV Socr; Var Swmmng; High Hon Roll; Hon Roll; Ntl Merit Ltr; Daytona Beach CC; Legal Sectry.

EYTINA, SARENDA; Bronx H S Of Science; New York, NY; (Y); Math Tm; Chorus; Var Cheerleading; Mgr Crs Cntry; Var Cheerleading; Swmmng; Mgr Trk; Ntl Merit SF; Chem Engrng.

EZZO, BARBARA; Cairo-Durham JR & SR HS; Purling, NY; (Y); Girl Scts; Hosp Aide; Trs Soph Cls; JV L Cheerleading; JV Sftbl; Var Tennis; High Hon Roll; Hon Roll; Comp Sci.

FABER, ROSALIE; Schoharie Central HS; Schoharie, NY; (Y); Hosp Aide; Key Clb; Teachers Aide; Chorus; Concert Band; School Musical; Yrbk Stf; Rep Stu Cncl; Math.

FABER, TONNI; Delaware Acad; Bovina Ctr, NY; (Y); Sec 4-H; German Clb; Office Aide; Ski Clb; JV Var Sftbl; Var L Trk; 4-H Awd; Hon Roll; Vet.

FABERY, MICHEAL; Cicero North Syracuse HS; N Syracuse, NY; (S); 75/750; Im Bowling; Var Golf; Clarkson U; Elec Engrng.

FABIANO, ELIZABETH; Niagara Catholic HS; Sanborn, NY; (Y); 16/75; Drama Clb; Key Clb; Science Clb; Spanish Clb; Yrbk Stf; Stat Var Bsktbl; Crs Cntry; Hon Roll; NHS; NEDT Awd; HS Schlrshp Marks Entrnc Exm 83.

FABICH, DEREK; Lansing HS; Ithaca, NY; (Y); Cmnty Wkr; Debate Tm; German Clb; School Musical; School Play; Var Diving; Var Ftbl; JV Gym; Var Swmmng; Var Trk; Doctor.

FABISH, DAVID Z; F D Roosevelt HS; Staatsburg, NY; (Y); 41/325; Hosp Aide; Math Tm; L Mrchg Band; Nwsp Phtg; Ed Nwsp Stf; NHS; Ntl Merit SF; Chess Clb; Computer Clb; Math Tm; Proj Stdy Acad Precty 81; Rensselaer Awd Sci, Math 84; Vltnr Yr Nrthrn Dutchess Hosp 84; Northwestern; Med.

FABISH, LYNNE; Goshen Central HS; Goshen, NY; (Y); 5/200; Church Yth Grp; Pres Cmnty Wkr; Chorus; Church Choir; School Musical; Variety Show; Rep Trs Stu Cncl; Var Capt Crs Cntry; Var L Trk; NHS; Stu Senate Scholar 85; Rutgers Coll; Bus.

FABRYKANT, ADRIANA J; Hillcrest HS; Kew Gardens, NY; (Y); Dance Clb; Teachers Aide; Temple Yth Grp; Y-Teens; Hon Roll; Outstndng Achvt Awds In Engl & Recgntn Of Perfrmnce 83 & 84; St Johns U; Lwyr.

FACCI, MARIA; Linton HS; Schenectady, NY; (Y); Yrbk Stf; Off Soph Cls; Off Jr Cls; Off Sr Cls; Stat Bsktbl; JV Var Socr; High Hon Roll; Sec NHS; Lintonians Serv Clb; Suksdorf Inv Art Exh; Bio.

FACE, DINA; L A Webber Schl; Lyndonville, NY; (S); 4/67; French Clb; Band; Mrchg Band; Nwsp Ed-Chief; Lit Mag; High Hon Roll; NHS; JR Clss Awd; Stu-Faclty Rev Brd Rep; SUNY Brockport; Jrnlsm.

FACEY, ERIKA; Long Island Lutheran HS; Freeport, NY; (S); Spanish Clb; Orch; Pep Band; Cheerleading; Sftbl; High Hon Roll; Hon Roll; NHS; Acdmc All-Amer 84-85; Ntl Engl Merit Awd 84-85; MD.

FACHKO, ELIZABETH; Attica Central HS; Darien Center, NY; (S); 8/135; Church Yth Grp; Band; Mrchg Band; JV Socr; JV Sftbl; JV Vllybl; Hon Roll; NHS; Miss JR ACRY 83; Medcl Lab Tech.

FACINELLI, LISA; Dominican Commercial HS; Ozone Park, NY; (Y); 1/300; High Hon Roll; Hon Roll.

FACTOR, ROBIN; Oyster Bay HS; Oyster Bay, NY; (Y); Camera Clb; German Clb; Nwsp Phtg; Nwsp Stf; Yrbk Phtg; Yrbk Stf; Lit Mag; Mgr(s); Score Keeper; Journlsm.

FADIAN, CAROLINE; Bishop Grimes HS; Syracuse, NY; (Y); Hon Roll; SADD Pgm 85; Comm Art.

FADUSKI, CHARLES; Liverpool HS; Liverpool, NY; (S); 78/798; Am Leg Boys St; JA; Thesps; Orch; Symp Band; Socr; High Hon Roll; NHS; Ntl Merit Ltr; Athl Actvty Crew.

FAGAN, KARA; West Hempstead HS; W Hempstead, NY; (Y); Key Clb; Nwsp Rptr; Yrbk Stf; Stat Bsktbl; Var Tennis; Hon Roll; NHS; VP Frsh Cls; Pres Soph Cls; Pres Jr Cls; Outstndng Achvt Bio 84; Ntl Olympd Stds Fnlst 85; Schlrshp Ntl Conf Chrstns & Jews 85; U Of MA; Comm.

FAGAN, MAUREEN K; St Francis Preparatory Schl; Flushing, NY; (Y); Cmnty Wkr; Hosp Aide; Library Aide; Science Clb; Chorus; Hon Roll; Chess Clb; Ntl Merit Ltr; Cert Hnr Eng 85; Acad Excel Schlrshp 85; St Johns U; Phrmcy.

FAGAN, STACEY; Valley Central HS; Montgomery, NY; (Y); Church Yth Grp; Cmnty Wkr; Pres VP 4-H; Office Aide; Service Clb; Spanish Clb; Chorus; Hon Roll; Spanish NHS; Elem Ed.

FAGAN, TIMOTHY; Mount Saint Michael Acad; Yonkers, NY; (Y); 11/286; Im Ice Hcky; NHS; Spanish NHS.

FAGELLO, WILLIAM; La Salle Acad; New York, NY; (Y); Rep Jr Cls; Im Bsbl; JV Var Bsktbl; Im Sftbl; NHS; Psych.

FAGGELLA, DENISE M; John F Kennedy HS; Yorktown Heights, NY; (Y); 1/184; VP JA; Pres Jr Cls; Capt Var Cheerleading; Bausch & Lomb Sci Awd; NHS; Val; Archdiocesan Schlrshp 85; Bk Of NY Schlstc Achvt Awd 85; Catholic U Of Amer; Engr.

FAGNANI, THOMAS; Schoharie Central HS; Schoharie, NY; (S); 19/94; JV Ftbl; Var Mgr(s); Var Socr; Var Trk; Capt Wrstlng; Hon Roll; Hmcmng King 84; Mst Imprvd Wrstlng 84; Clarkson; Engrng.

FAHEY, DAN; Fox Lane HS; Bedford, NY; (Y); 18/275; Am Leg Boys St; Trs Key Clb; Spanish Clb; Capt Var Crs Cntry; Capt Var Trk; High Hon Roll; NHS; US Nvl Acad.

FAHEY, KATHRYN; St Edmund HS; Brooklyn, NY; (S); 11/187; Art Clb; Spanish Clb; Yrbk Stf; Hon Roll; Accntng.

FAHRENKRUG, CARL; Fayetteville/Manlius HS; Manlius, NY; (Y); Trs Chess Clb; Computer Clb; Math Clb; Var Crs Cntry; Var Trk; Hon Roll; NHS; 300 Clb Awd Math Regnts Exms 85; Outstndng Achvt Math 83; Clarkson U; Engrng.

FAHS, TRACEY; Lockport SR HS; Lockport, NY; (Y); VICA; JV Sftbl; Prfct Atten Awd; Medaille Coll; Lib Arts.

FAIGNANT, PAULA MARIE; Mont Pleasant HS; Schenectady, NY; (Y); JA; Office Aide; Chorus; Color Guard; JV Socr; JV Sftbl; Peer Ldrshp Awd 85; Smmr Yth Emplymnt Trning Pgm 84; Grls JV Sccr Awd 83-84; Psych.

FAILING, TIM; Fort Plain HS; Ft Plain, NY; (Y); Art Clb; Math Clb; Varsity Clb; Coach Actv; Ftbl; Socr; Trk; Wrstlng; Most Outstndng Undrclsmn 84-85; Most Imprvd Athl 83; ST Wrstly Qualif 1st Sectnls,2nd Champ 84-85; Springfield Coll; Pre-Med.

FAILING, TIMOTHY; Fort Plain HS; Fort Plain, NY; (Y); Varsity Clb; Bsktbl; Coach Actv; Ftbl; Capt Socr; Trk; Wt Lftg; Capt Wrstlng; Hon Roll; Outstndng Underclsmn 83-85; Most Imprvd Athl 83-84; ST Wrstlng Tourn 84-85; Springfield Coll; Pre-Med.

FAILLA, FRANCES; Preston HS; Bronx, NY; (S); 2/104; Church Yth Grp; Church Choir; School Musical; Nwsp Ed-Chief; Sftbl; Vllybl; Hon Roll; NHS; Pres Schlr; Scholar 82-83.

FAILLA, FRANK; Msgr Mc Clancy HS; Long Island Cy, NY; (Y); High Hon Roll; Hon Roll; Pace; Accntng.

FAILLE, MIKE; James E Sperry HS; Rochester, NY; (Y); Exploring; High Hon Roll; Jr NHS; NHS; Spanish NHS; Modified Midget Auto Racng 2nd 83; Modified Midget Auto Racng 4th Pl 84; Mech Engrng.

FAINA, LORAINE; Mynderse Acad; Seneca Falls, NY; (Y); GAA; Band; Chorus; Concert Band; Jazz Band; Mrchg Band; Pep Band; School Musical; Swing Chorus; Rep Jr Cls; Cert Awd Ensem Perf 82; All Cty Jazz Band 84; NYS PHSAA Sectn Soccer 83.

FAIR, JOCELYN; Hendrick Hudson HS; Buchanan, NY; (Y); Debate Tm; Exploring; Science Clb; Yrbk Stf; Pres Frsh Cls; Rep Soph Cls; Rep Jr Cls; VP Sr Cls; Rep Stu Cncl; Stat Stu Cncl; U Of VT; Biochem.

FAIR, MIKE; Spackenkill HS; Poughkeepsie, NY; (Y); 50/177; Var Trk; Elec Engrng.

FAIRBANKS, CARIN A; Roy C Ketcham HS; Poughkeepsie, NY; (Y); Band; School Play; Hon Roll; Horsemnshp Awds 82-85; Anthroplgy.

FAIRBANKS, JENNIFER; Olean SR HS; Olean, NY; (Y); Hosp Aide; Red Cross Aide; Service Clb; Chorus; Church Choir; Color Guard; School Musical; School Play; Cheerleading; Im Vllybl.

FAIRBANKS, JOHN DANIEL; Union Springs Acad; Jamestown, NY; (S); Drama Clb; Ski Clb; Band; Concert Band; Yrbk Stf; High Hon Roll; Hon Roll; Sci.

FAIRBANKS, LAURI A; John C Birdlebough HS; Phoenix, NY; (Y); 3/198; Hosp Aide; Trs Latin Clb; Red Cross Aide; Band; Yrbk Phtg; Stat Bsktbl; Score Keeper; High Hon Roll; NHS; Prfct Atten Awd; Hamilton Coll; Pre-Med.

FAIRBANKS, MARK; J C Birdlebough HS; Phoenix, NY; (Y); 2/182; Latin Clb; Teachers Aide; Band; Concert Band; Pep Band; Yrbk Phtg; JV Var Bsktbl; High Hon Roll; Hon Roll; Aerosp Engrng.

FAIRBANKS, REBECCA; Union Springs Acad; Jamestown, NY; (S); 4/53; Drama Clb; Ski Clb; Church Choir; Concert Band; School Musical; Yrbk Ed-Chief; Yrbk Stf; Pres Frsh Cls; Jr Cls; Sr Cls; Schl Lttr Yrbk Edtr 84-85; Andrews U; Cmmnctv Disordrs.

FAISON, MICHELLE; Newburgh Free Acad; Newburgh, NY; (Y); Girl Scts; Library Aide; Office Aide; Chorus; Sec Sr Cls; Var Cheerleading; High Hon Roll; Hon Roll; Hi-Tech Pgm Marist Coll 84; Keystone JC; Pediatrician.

FAKHOURI, FARIS; Yonkers HS; Yonkers, NY; (Y); Boy Scts; Off Frsh Cls; Vllybl; Mercey; Dr.

FAKLER, PAUL; Ward Melville HS; Stony Brook, NY; (Y); 110/789; Pres Aud/Vis; Computer Clb; Debate Tm; NFL; Political Wkr; Radio Clb; Jazz Band; Nwsp Ed-Chief; Jr NHS; NHS; MI ST U; Mech Engr.

FALABELLA, CAROL; Notre Dame Academy HS; Staten Island, NY; (Y); Science Clb; Yrbk Stf; JV Capt Cheerleading; NHS; JV Chrldng Sportsmnshp Awd 83; Concours Natl Frnch Cont Excllnce Awd 83; Concours Frnch Cont 83-85; Med Tech.

FALCH, DOUGLAS; Iona Preparatory Schl; New Rochelle, NY; (Y); Computer Clb; Dance Clb; NFL; Y-Teens; VP Stu Cncl; Bsktbl; Crs Cntry; Var Socr; Var Trk; Hon Roll; Pre-Law.

FALCHI, JENNIFER; Rome Catholic HS; Rome, NY; (Y); 7/90; Library Aide; Nwsp Ed-Chief; Ed Yrbk Stf; Rep Soph Cls; High Hon Roll; NHS; Prfct Atten Awd; 2nd Pl Itln Amer Essay Cntst 83; SR Merit Awd Phy-Ed 85; Presdntl Awd Phy-Ed 84; Bio.

FALCONE, HEATHER A; Norwood Norfolk Central Schl; Norwood, NY; (Y); 10/123; Yrbk Stf; VP Frsh Cls; VP Sr Cls; Rep Stu Cncl; Var Capt Cheerleading; VP NHS; Ntl Merit Ltr; Drama Clb; Girl Scts; Prom Queen 84-85; Rutgers U; Comms.

FALICK, JENNIFER; Middletown HS; Middletown, NY; (Y); Key Clb; Band; Concert Band; Symp Band; Nwsp Stf; Yrbk Stf; Var L Cheerleading; Var Swmmng; Hon Roll; NHS; Acad Achvt Top 15 Stu 82-85; Orthdntst.

FALIK, SANDY; Roy C Ketcham HS; Poughkeepsie, NY; (Y); Pres Drama Clb; Pres Thesps; School Musical; School Play; Nwsp Bus Mgr; Yrbk Stf; JV Socr; Hon Roll; NHS; Ntl Merit Ltr; Med.

FALINSKI, NATALIA K; Thomas R Proctor HS; Utica, NY; (Y); 2/200; Chorus; Yrbk Stf; VP Soph Cls; VP Jr Cls; Pres Sr Cls; Rep Stu Cncl; High Hon Roll; NHS; Prfct Atten Awd; Sal; NYS Rgnts Schlrshp 85; Clarkson U; Elec Engr.

FALIS, NEIL D; Clarkstown H S North; New City, NY; (Y); Cmnty Wkr; Exploring; French Clb; Mathletes; Math Clb; Math Tm; Band; Nwsp Rptr; Nwsp Stf; Yrbk Stf.

FALKENBERG, PAT; Susquehanna Valley HS; Binghamton, NY; (Y); Sec Pep Clb; Pres Spanish Clb; Nwsp Stf; Yrbk Sprt Ed; Rep Sr Cls; JV Var Bsktbl; Var Capt Fld Hcky; JV Var Sftbl; Hon Roll; SR Of Mnth 85; MVP SR Sftbl 83; SUNY-BROCKPORT; Elem Educ.

FALKOWSKI, AGATHA; Ichabod Crane HS; Valatie, NY; (Y); 49/183; High Hon Roll; Hon Roll; NHS; Prfct Atten Awd; Effort & Achvt Awd Hlth, Mth, Bus 82, 84 & 85; Yrbk Staff Awd 82; All County Chorus 80; Acctng.

FALLAT, MICHAEL; Auburn HS; Auburn, NY; (Y); 11/444; German Clb; Jazz Band; School Musical; Symp Band; High Hon Roll; NHS; Pres Schlr; Exploring; Band; Mrchg Band; Auburn Jazz Awd 85; Regnts Schlrshp 85; Auburn High Chem Awd 85; Rochester Inst Tech; Microelec.

FALLS, BRENDAN; Mineola HS; Mineola, NY; (Y); Acctng.

FALSONE, KAREN; St Francis Prep; Whitestone, NY; (S); 57/690; Art Clb; Library Aide; Office Aide; Science Clb; Chorus; Hon Roll; NHS; Opt Clb Awd; Teacher.

FALTER, SARAH; Irondequoit HS; Rochester, NY; (Y); #17 In Class; Girl Scts; Hosp Aide; Ski Clb; Varsity Clb; Score Keeper; JV Var Socr; Timer; Hon Roll; Prfct Atten Awd; U CA-LONG Beach; Physcl Thrpy.

FALTYN, JENNIFER; Alden Central HS; Alden, NY; (Y); Church Yth Grp; Hon Roll; 3rd Pl Schl Spnsred Writng Cont 83; Jrnslm.

FALTYN, JOSEPH; South Park HS; Buffalo, NY; (Y); German Clb; Science Clb; Sci.

FALVO, FRANK; Wilson Central HS; Lockport, NY; (Y); 7/134; Am Leg Boys St; Science Clb; Ski Clb; Teachers Aide; JV Var Ftbl; High Hon Roll; Hon Roll; Prfct Atten Awd; St Schlr; Im Bsktbl; NY ST Regents Scholarship 85; Rochester Inst; Elect Engrng.

FALZARANO, JAMES; Greece Olympia HS; Rochester, NY; (Y); Yrbk Stf; JV Bsbl; Var Bowling; Var Trk; High Hon Roll; Hon Roll; Rochester Inst Tech; Accntnt.

FALZARINE, MARY BETH; Utica Free Acad; Utica, NY; (Y); 9/258; Cmnty Wkr; Drama Clb; Sec French Clb; Political Wkr; Service Clb; Sec Acpl Chr; High Hon Roll; Jr NHS; NHS; Pres Schlr; Mary Mount Coll; Eng.

FALZOI, JILL; Nazareth Acad; Rochester, NY; (Y); Church Yth Grp; Pres Debate Tm; Drama Clb; Band; School Musical; Nwsp Stf; Lit Mag; Rep Stu Cncl; Hon Roll; NHS; Presdntl Acad Fitness Awd 85; Suny Geneseo; Engl.

FAMULARE, MICHAEL; Fayetteville-Manius HS; Fayetteville, NY; (Y); Cmnty Wkr; Rep Soph Cls; Bsktbl; Cornell; Restrnt Ownr.

FANALE, KAREN; Aquinas Inst; Rochester, NY; (S); 18/161; Pres Drama Clb; Spanish Clb; Speech Tm; School Musical; Nwsp Rptr; Yrbk Stf; Rep Stu Cncl; High Hon Roll; Intl Frgn Lang Awd 85.

FANCH, KRISTIN; Gloversville HS; Gloversville, NY; (Y); 23/190; French Clb; Key Clb; Band; Chorus; Concert Band; Jazz Band; Mrchg Band; Yrbk Phtg; Yrbk Stf; High Hon Roll; Sci.

FANCHER, BARB; Portville HS; Portville, NY; (Y); Teachers Aide; Band; Concert Band; Mrchg Band; Stat Trk; Vllybl; High Hon Roll; Pres NHS; Prfct Atten Awd; Stat Ftbl; All Star Tm Vlybl 84; Crinmnlgy.

FANCHER, LORI; Walton Central HS; Walton, NY; (Y); 10/100; Pres Sec 4-H; Girl Scts; Key Clb; Trs Model UN; Orch; Rep Stu Cncl; JV Var Bsktbl; Var Trk; Voice Dem Awd; Intrntl Fin.

FANCHER, MARK; Nottingham HS; Syracuse, NY; (Y); 57/220; Camera Clb; French Clb; Ski Clb; Var Golf; JV Socr; Vllybl; Hon Roll; NHS; Syracuse U; Mech Engr.

FANNING, KAREN; Stella Maris HS; Rockaway Beach, NY; (Y); 4/230; Am Leg Aux Girls St; French Clb; NFL; Drm Mjr(t); School Play; Nwsp Rptr; Rep Stu Cncl; Cheerleading; High Hon Roll; NHS.

FANNING, SHANNON; Academy Of St Joseph; St James, NY; (Y); Library Aide; Science Clb; Teachers Aide; Church Choir; Yrbk Ed-Chief; Yrbk Stf; NHS; NEDT Awd.

FANNING, THOMAS; Earl L Vandermeulen HS; Mt Sinai, NY; (Y); Exploring; Ftbl; Wt Lftg; Hon Roll; NHS; Wrstlng; Mt Sinai Tchr Assoc Schlrshp 85; U Of NH; Chem Engr.

FANNUCCI, DARCIE; Keveny Memorial Acad; Ballston Lake, NY; (S); 3/43; Cmnty Wkr; Math Clb; Math Tm; Sec Spanish Clb; Color Guard; Rep Soph Cls; VP Jr Cls; Stu Cncl; JV Var Cheerleading; High Hon Roll; Natl Business Honor Society 84-85; Elementary Educ.

FANT, MELINDA G; Columbia HS; Rensselaer, NY; (Y); 74/353; Trs Church Yth Grp; Hosp Aide; VP Concert Band; Orch; Nwsp Rptr; Nwsp Stf; Rep Frsh Cls; Rep Sr Cls; Hon Roll; NHS; Regnts Schlrshp 85; NYS Mus Assn Cmptn Awd 83-84; U Of ME Orono; Pol Sci.

FANTINATO, TRICIA; East Syracuse-Minoa HS; E Syracuse, NY; (Y); Latin Clb; Chorus; Var Tennis; Var Trk; Hon Roll; Jr NHS; NHS; Acpl Chr; Nyssma Concert Choir Mdl 85; High Hnr Hist 84; High Hnr Biology 84; ND; Bio Chem.

FANTINI, SUE; Clarkstown North HS; New City, NY; (Y); Cmnty Wkr; Band; Concert Band; Mrchg Band; Orch; School Musical; Stage Crew; Gym; Hon Roll.

FANTON, KATHY A; Wellsville HS; Wellsville, NY; (Y); 6/130; FBLA; Nwsp Stf; Stat Bsktbl; High Hon Roll; Hon Roll; St Schlr; NY ST Regents Schlrshp 85; Fox & Company Schlrshp 85; Alfred ST Coll; Accntng.

FANTOZZI, REGINA; Rocky Point JR SR HS; Sound Bch, NY; (Y); Chorus; Badmtn; Bowling; Socr; Sftbl; Tennis; Vllybl; Incarnate Word Col6; Sociolgy.

FARAGE, REGINA; Bishop Kearney HS; Brooklyn, NY; (S); 15/327; Girl Scts; Political Wkr; Ski Clb; Church Choir; Bowling; High Hon Roll; Lion Awd; NHS; Rochester Inst Technlgy; Engr.

FARAGUNA, MARIELAINA; Connetquot HS; Bohemia, NY; (Y); Trs Art Clb; Camera Clb; Drama Clb; Stage Crew; JV Diving; JV Gym; JV Trk; High Hon Roll; Jr NHS; NHS; Regnts Schlrshp NY St 85; Suffolk Cty Math Cont 83-84; Orbba 82-84; Child Psych.

FARAH, ANN MARIE; Farmingdale HS; Massapequa Pk, NY; (Y); Key Clb; Jazz Band; Orch; School Musical; Yrbk Rptr; Yrbk Stf; Acctng.

FARANELLO, GREGORY; Valley Stream Central HS; Valley Stream, NY; (Y); 18/351; Debate Tm; Drama Clb; School Musical; School Play; Variety Show; Pres Soph Cls; Pres Jr Cls; Stu Cncl; Bsbl; Capt Bsktbl; West Point; Law.

FARBER, LEONARD; Bronx High Schl Of Science; Queens Village, NY; (Y); Cmnty Wkr; Teachers Aide; Trs Temple Yth Grp; Chorus; Jazz Band; Tennis; Wt Lftg; Med.

FARDINK, KELLY J; Clymer Central HS; North Clymer, NY; (Y); 2/38; Library Aide; Band; Church Choir; School Play; Pres Frsh Cls; VP Sr Cls; High Hon Roll; Trs NHS; NYS Rgnts Schlrshp 85; Ithaca Coll; Bio.

FARELLA, MARIE M; Central HS; Valley Stream, NY; (Y); AFS; Church Yth Grp; Service Clb; Sftbl; Jr NHS; Mu Alp Tht; NHS; Spanish NHS; Girl Scts; Nwsp Stf; Child Psychlgy.

FARES, CHRISTINA; Glens Falls SR HS; Glen Falls, NY; (Y); 63/240; Pep Clb; Teachers Aide; Powder Puff Ftbl.

FARGIS, SHEILA M; Academy Of The Resurrection HS; Larchmont, NY; (Y); 3/62; Sec Church Yth Grp; Math Tm; NFL; Pep Clb; Chorus; Trs Soph Cls; Trs Sr Cls; High Hon Roll; NHS; Ntl Merit Ltr; Local 1262 Union Schlrshp 85; Bowdoin Coll.

FARINA, KAREN; Smithtown High School East; Smithtown, NY; (Y); Church Yth Grp; Hosp Aide; Ski Clb; Im Sftbl; Hon Roll; Katherine Gibbs; Secy.

FARINA, PAULA; Baldwin SR HS; Baldwin, NY; (Y); 127/503; Cmnty Wkr; GAA; Ski Clb; Yrbk Stf; JV Var Cheerleading; Capt Var Gym; Hon Roll; St Schlr; Regents ST Schlrshp Wnnr 85; Mistress Cermns Sportsnite 85; Choreogrphr Sportsnite 85; Bucknell U; Bio.

FARINHA, NIGEL I; Xavier HS; Hollis Queens, NY; (Y); 24/222; Math Clb; ROTC; Concert Band; Drm Mjr(t); Mrchg Band; Nwsp Stf; Pres Stu Cncl; Hon Roll; NHS; NEDT Awd; Schlrshp 81; Fresh & SR Tutor Yr 81-82; Gold & Slvr Ldrshp Medals JROTC; Law.

FARKAS, ILENE; Lynbrook HS; Lynbrook, NY; (Y); FBLA; VP Mathletes; Spanish Clb; Temple Yth Grp; Varsity Clb; Nwsp Rptr; Yrbk Stf; Var L Sftbl; Socr; Sftbl; Mathelete Commentn 85; Bsktbl Trnmnt All Str 85; Bus.

FARKAS, LESLIE ATTILA; Ithaca HS; Ithaca, NY; (Y); Boy Scts; Chess Clb; German Clb; Math Clb; Science Clb; NHS; Ntl Merit Ltr; Isabella Sherman HS Schltc Awd 85; Cornell U; Elec Engrng.

FARKOUH, LISA J; Notre Dame Academy HS; Staten Island, NY; (Y); 1/92; Hosp Aide; Pres Latin Clb; Science Clb; Chorus; School Musical; Yrbk Ed-Chief; Capt L Tennis; NHS; School Play; Yrbk Bus Mgr; USAA Merit Awd In Sci 83; Pre-Med.

FARLEY, CARA; Port Richmond HS; Staten Isld, NY; (Y); AFS; Trk; Hon Roll; Afs Stu To Chile.

FARLEY, SEAN; Horseheads HS; Horseheads, NY; (S); Am Leg Boys St; Political Wkr; Science Clb; Stu Cncl; JV Bsbl; Im Bsktbl; JV Socr; Vllybl; Hon Roll; NHS; Joe Colucci Mem Awd 83.

FARMAN, GARRETT; Medina Senior HS; Medina, NY; (Y); 30/156; Am Leg Boys St; Boy Scts; Red Cross Aide; Ski Clb; Acpl Chr; Chorus; Ftbl; Lcrss; Cit Awd; High Hon Roll; Honorati 85; Engrng.

FARNAN, WILLIAM; Saratoga Central Catholic HS; Ballston Spa, NY; (S); 16/51; Boy Scts; Drama Clb; Varsity Clb; School Play; Variety Show; Yrbk Rptr; Yrbk Stf; Var Capt Golf; Var JV Score Keeper; High Hon Roll; Buffalo ST; Cartgrphy.

FARNELL, SANDY; Little Falls JR SR HS; Little Falls, NY; (Y); 7/110; Church Yth Grp; 4-H; FBLA; Band; Church Choir; Concert Band; Jazz Band; Mrchg Band; Orch; Pep Band; 4-H Pres, VP & Dairy Supt 84-85; Herkimer Cnty Dairy Maid 84-85; NYS Dairy Jdgng Tm 84; Math.

FARNELLA, HILARY J; Jamestown HS; Jamestown, NY; (Y); Ski Clb; Chorus; Trs Frsh Cls; Trs Soph Cls; Trs Jr Cls; Trs Sr Cls; Rep Stu Cncl; JV Cheerleading; L Var Tennis; Hon Roll; Nrsng.

FARNEY, MICHAEL A; Beaver River Central Schl; New Bremen, NY; (Y); 25/90; Boy Scts; Church Yth Grp; Varsity Clb; Var Diving; Var Golf; Var Swmmng; Hon Roll; Most Outstndng SR Athlete Awd-Swmmng 85; Frontier Leag All-Star Golf 84; Adv Electrncs.

FARNEY, PETER W; South Lewis Central Schl; Lyons Falls, NY; (Y); 3/103; Boy Scts; Band; Rep Stu Cncl; Var L Crs Cntry; Var L Golf; High Hon Roll; NHS; Ntl Merit Ltr; Century III Ldrs Comp - 1st Alt NYS 84; Air Force ROTC Schlrshp 85; U Of VA; Elec Engr.

FARR, MARY E; Corinth HS; Corinth, NY; (S); Drama Clb; Trs French Clb; Pres Key Clb; Pres Library Aide; Var Bsktbl; Mgr Sftbl; Jr NHS; Trs NHS; Voice Dem Awd; Gannet Nwsp Awd, Top 10 Pct Jr Cls 84.

FARR, MICHELLE; Whitney Point HS; Whitney Point, NY; (Y); 16/119; French Clb; JV Sftbl; Var Capt Vllybl; Cit Awd; High Hon Roll; Hon Roll; Masonic Awd; Clute Memrl Schlrshp 85; Good Ctznshp Awd 85; Hgh Hnr Roll 85; Wilkes Coll; Phy Thrpy.

FARR, SAMARA; Horseheads HS; Big Flats, NY; (Y); 37/405; Cmnty Wkr; Drama Clb; Concert Band; Mrchg Band; Orch; Variety Show; VP Stu Cncl; NHS; Band; Symp Band; Elmira Symphny Cncrto Comptn Sol Wnr 84-85; 1st Frnch Hrn Crng Phlhrmnc Yth Orchstra 84-86; Music Prfrmnc.

FARR, STACEY; Whitney Point Central HS; Maine, NY; (Y); French Clb; Ski Clb; Chorus; Yrbk Stf; Off Soph Cls; Stu Cncl; Cheerleading; NHS; Cazenovia Coll; Fash Merch.

FARRELL, ANDREA MARIE; John Jay SR HS; Pittstown, NJ; (Y); 1/495; AFS; Church Yth Grp; Drama Clb; Teachers Aide; Color Guard; School Play; Nwsp Rptr; High Hon Roll; Jr NHS; NHS; Rgnts Schlrshp 85; Bcknl U Dean List 84 & 85; Phi Eta Sigma Hnry 85; Alpha Lambda Delta Hnr Scty 85; Bucknell U; Pltcl Sci.

FARRELL, CLARE; St Vincent Ferrer HS; Rego Park, NY; (Y); 11/114; Art Clb; Church Yth Grp; Math Tm; Pep Clb; Yrbk Ed-Chief; Hon Roll; Crmnl Justc.

FARRELL, COLLEEN; Sachem HS; Holbrook, NY; (Y); 42/1700; Ger Merit 83; Ger IV & Spn I-Outstndng Achvt 86; Langs.

FARRELL, KEVIN; West Genesee SR HS; Syracuse, NY; (Y); 9/500; Exploring; VP Math Tm; Ski Clb; Rep Jr Cls; Rep Sr Cls; Rep Stu Cncl; Bsktbl; Ice Hcky; High Hon Roll; NHS; Regents Scholar 85; Outstndng Stu Mth & Engl 85; Commncmnt Spkr 85; U Rochester; Med.

FARRELL, MICHAEL C; St Josephs Collegiate Inst; Williamsville, NY; (Y); Nwsp Sprt Ed; Nwsp Stf; Yrbk Stf; Ice Hcky; Hon Roll; ST U Of NY; Fin.

FARRELL, MOIRA E; Mount Mercy Acad; Buffalo, NY; (Y); 26/200; Debate Tm; Hosp Aide; JCL; Latin Clb; Model UN; Service Clb; Im Badmtn; Im Fld Hcky; Hon Roll; NYS Rgnts Schlrshp 85; Fordham U; Corp Law.

FARRELL, SHAUN M; Lewiston-Porter HS; Youngstown, NY; (Y); 1/273; JV Var Socr; JV Var Tennis; JV Var Trk; High Hon Roll; NHS; Ntl Merit Ltr; Lamp Of Learnng 83-85; Police Athltc Leag 85; Rensselaer Polytech Inst; Engng.

FARRELL, SUSAN; Sodus Central HS; Williamson, NY; (Y); 19/125; Am Leg Aux Girls St; Model UN; VP Science Clb; Pres Spanish Clb; School Play; VP Jr Cls; Sec Stu Cncl; Bsktbl; Socr; Prfct Atten Awd; Monroe CC; Dntl Hygnst.

FARRELL, TRACY LYNN; Division Avenue HS; Levittown, NY; (Y); Church Yth Grp; Cmnty Wkr; German Clb; Girl Scts; Varsity Clb; Chorus; Stage Crew; Variety Show; Frsh Cls; Soph Cls; SUNY; Elem Educ.

FARRELL, WILLIAM G; La Salle Acad; Brooklyn, NY; (Y); Hon Roll; NHS; Ntl Merit Ltr; NY ST Regnts Schlrshp 85; Brooklyn Coll; Engrng.

FARRELLY, TARA A; Our Lady Of Mercy Acad; Williston Park, NY; (Y); 1/115; Art Clb; Debate Tm; Pep Clb; Pres Service Clb; Yrbk Stf; Lit Mag; High Hon Roll; Pres NHS; NEDT Awd; 1st Hnrs 81-85; Yng Comm Ldrs Amer 85; U Notre Dame; Acctng.

FARRINGTON, ABBY A; Covent Of The Sacred Heart HS; Sea Bright, NJ; (Y); Cmnty Wkr; Key Clb; Model UN; Yrbk Stf; Lit Mag; Pres Frsh Cls; Var Capt Fld Hcky; Lcrss; Tennis; High Hon Roll; Latin Achvt Awd 82; Magnu Cum Laude Ntl Latin Exam 82; Engl Achvt Awd 84; Hamilton; Law.

FARRINGTON, ROBERT M; La Salle Acad; New York, NY; (Y); Cmnty Wkr; JA; Band; Concert Band; JV Im Bsktbl; JV Crs Cntry; Im Fld Hcky; JV Trk; Im Vllybl; Wt Lftg; Hist Awd 81-82; Span & Sci Awds 82-83; St Johns U; Accntng.

FARROW, LEE; Cornwall Central HS; Cornwall On Hudsn, NY; (Y); Chess Clb; Math Tm; Ski Clb; Yrbk Stf; Ftbl; Socr; Tennis; Hon Roll; Law.

FARRUGIA, MICHAEL; De Sales Catholic HS; Lockport, NY; (Y); Boy Scts; Church Yth Grp; Cmnty Wkr; Computer Clb; Teachers Aide; Varsity Clb; Nwsp Stf; Yrbk Stf; Rep Stu Cncl; Bsbl; Explorer Post Intro To Comp 84; Buffalo ST.

FARRY, SHEILA; Mount Mercy Acad; Buffalo, NY; (Y); Church Yth Grp; Dance Clb; Sec Spanish Clb; Yrbk Bus Mgr; Lit Mag; Rep Frsh Cls; Off Soph Cls; Capt Cheerleading; Im Vllybl; Hon Roll; Shrthnd Outstndng Recgntn 84-85; Hilbert Coll; Lawyers Asst.

FARTHING, BILL; Niagara Wheatfield HS; Niagara Falls, NY; (Y); JA; Varsity Clb; Band; Jazz Band; Capt Var Ftbl; High Hon Roll; NHS; Niagara Gazette All Area Ftbl All Stars Tm 84; Hnbl Mntn Western NY HS Ftbl 84; Math.

FARTHING, JENNIFER A; Chenango Valley HS; Binghamton, NY; (Y); Drama Clb; French Clb; Ski Clb; Varsity Clb; School Musical; Nwsp Stf; Yrbk Stf; Sr Cls; Stu Cncl; Var Crs Cntry; NY ST Regnts Schlrshp 85; SUNY Geneseo; Cmmnctns.

FARZAN, DAVID J; Williamsville South HS; Williamsville, NY; (Y); Band; Concert Band; Mrchg Band; Pep Band; Hon Roll; Regents Schlrshp 85; Comp Sci.

FASANELLE, JOAN MARIE; Fontbonne Hall Acad; Brooklyn, NY; (Y); 20/130; Civic Clb; Cmnty Wkr; Drama Clb; Teachers Aide; School Play; Nwsp Rptr; Yrbk Stf; Pres Jr Cls; Pres Stu Cncl; NHS; Harold Jensen Awd Ldrshp Schl & Comm 85; Nation Ntl Ed Dev Test Svc Awd 84; Schl Stu Cncl Pres 86.

FASANO, MARIA; Notre Dame HS; Batavia, NY; (S); 8/67; Yrbk Stf; Lit Mag; Hon Roll; NHS; NEDT Awd.

FASCIGLIONE, JOSEPH; Mount St Michael HS; Bronx, NY; (Y); 90/350; Iona Coll; Psych.

FASCIO, YVETTE; Cathedral HS; Newyork, NY; (Y); 152/298; Church Yth Grp; Intnl Clb; Stage Crew.

FASCO, KELLY; Averill Park HS; Averill Pk, NY; (Y); 3/216; Church Yth Grp; Teachers Aide; Yrbk Ed-Chief; Stat Bsktbl; Var Tennis; Sec NHS; Pres Schlr; Outstndng Rec Frnch Spnsh 85; Hgst Cumulctive Awd 85; Trinity Coll; Elem Ed.

FASOLDT, JEFFREY C; Liverpool HS; Liverpool, NY; (Y); 175/791; Exploring; JA; Art Clb; JV Wrstlng; Ntl Merit Ltr; Regents Schlrshp 85; Pres Acad Ftns Awd 85; ST U-Geneseo; Comp Sci.

FASON, TAANEE; Sheepshead Bay HS; Brooklyn, NY; (Y); 123/465; Church Yth Grp; Hosp Aide; JA; Library Aide; Office Aide; Church Choir; Cheerleading; NHS; Outstndng Svc Awd 85; Cmnty Svc Awd 85; Med.

FASSL, SHEILA; Williamsville East HS; East Amherst, NY; (Y); Church Yth Grp; JV Capt Socr; Hon Roll; Empire ST Games Sccr Silver Medal 85; Bus.

FASSLER, ANITA; Greece Athena HS; Rochester, NY; (Y); DECA; Drama Clb; Science Clb; Chorus; School Musical; School Play; Crs Cntry; Trk; Vllybl; Hon Roll; 1st Pl Sllng Awd DECA ST Wide 85; 1st Pl Grls Ensmbl Comptn 84; 1st Pl Chrl Comptn Ntn Wide 83; Math.

FASSNACHT, TINA; Valley Central HS; Montgomery, NY; (Y); Spanish Clb; Varsity Clb; JV Bsktbl; Var Tennis; Hon Roll; NHS; Pres Spanish NHS; Cert Merit Partcptn Amer HS Math Exm 85; Bus.

FASTENBERG, JILL; Jericho HS; Jericho, NY; (Y); GAA; Key Clb; Office Aide; Varsity Clb; Yrbk Stf; Sec Frsh Cls; Sec Soph Cls; Sec Jr Cls; Stu Cncl; JV Var Socr.

FATTAH, SURAIA; Christopher Columbus HS; Bronx, NY; (S); 2/576; Cmnty Wkr; Hosp Aide; Band; Bsktbl; Gov Hon Prg Awd; High Hon Roll; NHS; NY U; Pre-Med.

FAUBERT, GISELE M; Franklin Acad; Malone, NY; (Y); Church Yth Grp; Drama Clb; French Clb; Hosp Aide; NFL; Varsity Clb; Chorus; School Play; Diving; Gym.

FAUCHER, KIMBERLIE F; Cicero-North Syracuse HS; Brewerton, NY; (S); DECA; Ski Clb; Rep Frsh Cls; Rep Soph Cls; Stu Cncl; Var Capt Cheerleading; Hon Roll; Merit Roll 83-84; Bus Admin.

FAUCHER, PATRICK; Massena Central HS; Massena, NY; (Y); 12/300; Concert Band; Jazz Band; Mrchg Band; School Musical; Rep Jr Cls; Rep Sr Cls; JV Socr; High Hon Roll; Hon Roll; NHS; Louis Armstrong Jazz Awd 85; NY ST Regents Schlrshp Awd 85; Pres Acad Fitns Awd 85; GM Inst; Elec Engnrng.

FAULISE, TRACY LYNN; John C Birdlebough HS; Pennellville, NY; (Y); 38/186; Sec Trs Church Yth Grp; German Clb; Band; Concert Band; Mrchg Band; Var Mgr(s); Var Score Keeper; Stat Tennis; JV Trk; JV Stat Vllybl; Delhi Coll; Animal Husbndry.

FAULK, JULIUS; Andrew Jackson HS; E Elmhurst, NY; (Y); Band; Orch; School Musical; Hon Roll; Law Enfrcmnt.

FAULKNER, ANDREA; A Philip Randolph Campus HS; Bronx, NY; (Y); 44/166; Church Yth Grp; Girl Scts; Office Aide; Teachers Aide; Chorus; Church Choir; Variety Show; Var Trk; Mst Imprvd Trck 83; Bio-Med Engr.

FAULKNER, DENISE; Clymer Central Schl; Clymer, NY; (Y); Pres Soph Cls; Sec Jr Cls; Pres Sr Cls; Var Capt Cheerleading; JV Var Vllybl; High Hon Roll; NHS; FFA; Trs Library Aide; Trs Pres Ski Clb; 3rd Pl Coll Jmstwn Bus Coll Annual Accntng Cntst 85; Brnz Schlrshp/Ldrshp Awd 85; Cmnctns.

FAULKNER, GARY; Shenendehowa HS; Waterford, NY; (Y); 138/650; JA; Im Bsbl; Var Capt Bowling; High Hon Roll; Hon Roll; No 1 JR Bowler Capital Dist 84-85; No 1 Suburban Cncl Bwlr 84-85; Mst Hnrd Plyr Awd Co-Ed Bwlng 84-85; Vincennes U; Bowling Mngmnt.

FAULKNER, PRESTON; Richburg Central HS; Bolivar, NY; (S); 1/16; Am Leg Boys St; Spanish Clb; Band; Concert Band; Mrchg Band; Nwsp Ed-Chief; Nwsp Rptr; Yrbk Ed-Chief; Pres Frsh Cls; Pres Soph Cls; Aero Engr.

FAULKNOR, TIMOTHY A; Earl L Vandermeulen HS; Mt Sinai, NY; (Y); 41/286; Boy Scts; Mathletes; Varsity Clb; Band; JV Bsktbl; Var Capt Socr; Hon Roll; Cum Laude Grad 85; Albright Coll; Bus.

FAULS, BRIAN; Smithtown H S West; Smithtown, NY; (Y); Boy Scts; Trs Chess Clb; Exploring; Thesps; Chorus; School Play; Stage Crew; Hon Roll.

FAUPEL, MARK; H Frank Carey HS; Garden City So, NY; (Y); #3 In Class; Church Yth Grp; Trs Debate Tm; VP German Clb; Mathletes; Thesps; School Musical; High Hon Roll; Hon Roll; Jr NHS; NHS; Comp Engr.

FAUST, JEFFREY E; Archbishop Walsh HS; Bolivar, NY; (Y); 10/66; Boy Scts; Drama Clb; School Musical; School Play; Yrbk Stf; High Hon Roll; Ntl Merit SF; Acceptnce NY ST Summer Schl Of Art 84; NY ST Regents Scholar Awd 85; Rochester Inst Tech; Graph Desg.

FAUSTIN, ALISON; Murry Bergtraum HS; Jamaica, NY; (Y); Girl Scts; Hosp Aide; Prfct Attndnc 83-84; Comp Anlyst.

FAUSTINI, DIANE; St Catharine Acad; Bronx, NY; (Y); Art Clb; Service Clb; Teachers Aide; Yrbk Stf; Stu Cncl; Cert Awd Exclince & Achvt Art 83 & 85; Cert Awd Theater Arts 85; Cert Awd Outstndng Svc Drama 84; Fash Inst Tech; Fashn Desgnr.

FAVA, MARCO; Elmira Free Acad; S River, NJ; (Y); AFS; Computer Clb; Rep Intnl Clb; Math Clb; Math Tm; MMM; Pres Science Clb; Ski Clb; Rptr Nwsp Rptr; Rep Frsh Cls; Comp Course Tchng Awd 83; U Of Bologna Italy; Elec Engrng.

FAVARO, JENNIFER; Saranac Central HS; Cadyville, NY; (S); 14/106; Sec Church Yth Grp; Pres Drama Clb; Rptr Trs French Clb; Chorus; School Musical; Yrbk Stf; Rep Soph Cls; Rep Jr Cls; VP Stu Cncl; Hon Roll; Cornell; Psych.

FAVATA, SUZANNE; Cornwall Central HS; Cornwall, NY; (Y); Drama Clb; Hosp Aide; Model UN; Ski Clb; Thesps; Varsity Clb; Stage Crew; Sec Stu Cncl; Var L Swmmng; Var L Trk; Ntl Hugh O Brien Yth Ldrshp Smnr 84; Poltcl Sci.

FAWER, DAVID; George W Hewlett HS; Hewlett, NY; (Y); FBLA; Political Wkr; Temple Yth Grp; Off Sr Cls; Swmmng; Hon Roll; NHS; Law.

FAY, DANIEL; Massena Central HS; Massena, NY; (Y); 10/300; Am Leg Boys St; Church Yth Grp; Debate Tm; Key Clb; Radio Clb; Var Lcrss; Var Socr; JV Var Wrstlng; High Hon Roll; Hon Roll; USMA At West Pt; Mltry Sci.

FAY, JASON; Watkins Glen Central HS; Watkins Glen, NY; (S); 2/130; Aud/Vis; French Clb; Math Clb; Nwsp Bus Mgr; Yrbk Bus Mgr; L Crs Cntry; L Trk; Bausch & Lomb Sci Awd; High Hon Roll; NHS; Elmira Coll Key Awd 85; Info Sys Mgmt.

FAY, MARGARET; Liverpool HS; North Syracuse, NY; (Y); 116/875; VP Stu Cncl; JV Var Cheerleading; Powder Puff Ftbl; JV Socr; Hon Roll; Jr NHS; Lemoyne Summer Schlr 85; NY ST Stu Senate Rep 85; NY Miss Amer Co-Ed Pageant St Finlst Top 20 85; Syracuse U; Vet.

FAY, MARYELLEN; Commack High School South; Commack, NY; (Y); Office Aide; Teachers Aide; Varsity Clb; Nwsp Ed-Chief; Nwsp Rptr; Nwsp Stf; JV Var Bsktbl; Stat Ftbl; Mgr(s); Score Keeper.

FAY, MAUREEN; Half Hollow Hills High School East; Dix Hills, NY; (Y); Church Yth Grp; Leo Clb; Office Aide; Service Clb; Band; Yrbk Stf; Trk; High Hon Roll; Jr NHS; NHS.

FAY, MAUREEN; John A Coleman HS; Tillson, NY; (S); 1/66; Church Yth Grp; Varsity Clb; School Play; Co-Capt Yrbk Stf; Sec Jr Cls; Var L Crs Cntry; Var L Trk; High Hon Roll; NHS; Ntl Merit Ltr; PTA Awd For Acad Excel & Spirit; Gnrl Excel Awd; Ntl Sci Olympd Awd In Chmstry; Math.

FAY, SEAN; Mynderse Acad; Seneca Falls, NY; (S); Church Yth Grp; Wrstlng; Hon Roll; Bio.

FAZACKERLEY, JOHN S; Livonia HS; Lakeville, NY; (Y); Drama Clb; Ski Clb; Varsity Clb; School Play; Nwsp Rptr; Yrbk Stf; Rep Stu Cncl; Var Trk; Mgr(s); Regents Schlrshp; U Miami; Marine Bio.

FAZIO, MARY; The Franciscan Acad; Syracuse, NY; (Y); NFL; Chorus; School Musical; Frsh Cls; Jr Cls; Stu Cncl; Hon Roll; Jr NHS; NHS; Hugh O Brien Yth Fndtn 83-84.

FAZIO, ROY; Cazenovia HS; Cazenovia, NY; (Y); Church Yth Grp; Letterman Clb; JV Bsktbl; Coach Actv; Var Capt Ftbl; Mgr(s); Var L Trk; Wt Lftg; Hon Roll; Empire ST Games European Tm Hndball 85; Mech Engr.

FEAGLES, JUDY; St Johnsville Central Schl; St Johnsville, NY; (Y); 6/30; English Clb; 4-H; French Clb; Band; Chorus; Dnfth Awd; 4-H Awd; Hon Roll; Quiz Bowl; Mrchg Band; OHM Jr Hlstn Clb Dstngshd Jr 84; 4-H Ctznshp Shrtcrs Washington DC 84; VP Yth Advsry Cncl 84; ANML Sci.

FEATHER, AMY; Nyack HS; Nyack, NY; (Y); 36/277; Church Yth Grp; Hosp Aide; School Play; Lit Mag; Rep Stu Cncl; High Hon Roll; NHS; Pres Schlr; Artwork Dsplyd Cngrsmns Exhibit 84; GO Rec Hmcmng Decor Comm 85; Nyack Coll.

FEATHER, DAVID S; St Anthonys HS; Oakdale, NY; (Y); Jazz Band; Symp Band; Im Bsktbl; High Hon Roll; NHS; Psych.

FEATHERS, NEIL; New Pebanon Central HS; Hancock, MA; (Y); Church Yth Grp; Band; Chorus; School Play; Yrbk Phtg; Stu Cncl; Socr; Trk; Hon Roll; Acad All Amer Schlr Prog 83-84; Natl Ledrshp & Svc Awds 84-85; All Cnty Band & Choir 84-85; Arch.

FEATHERSTON, PAUL; Poughkeepsie HS; Queens Village, NY; (Y); 46/195; French Clb; Nwsp Stf; Rep Frsh Cls; Var Capt Bsktbl; JV Var Ftbl; Hon Roll; VFW Awd; Voice Dem Awd; Outstndng Sportsmnshp Awd 85; Alpha Phi Alpha Acadmc Excllnc 85; Citznshp & Schl Srvc Awd 85; Fredonia ST U; Crmnl Justc.

FEATHERSTONE, STEVE; Onondaga Central HS; Nedrow, NY; (Y); Art Clb; German Clb; Yrbk Ed-Chief; Var Tennis; Hon Roll; Syracuse U; Bus.

FEBEL, JOHN; Elmira Free Acad; Elmira, NY; (Y); Ski Clb; Spanish Clb; Stage Crew; Socr; Hon Roll; Gen Bus Mgmt.

FEBERT, KARINA; Rocky Point HS; Miller Pl, NY; (Y); JV Mgr(s); JV Score Keeper; Hon Roll; Stonybrook; Nrsng.

FEBLES, ROSEMARIE; Maria Regina HS; Yonkers, NY; (Y); 28/130; Sec Church Yth Grp; Cmnty Wkr; Nwsp Rptr; Lit Mag; Vllybl; NHS; Cert Of Appreciation For Mission Actvts 82-84; IONA Leadershp Workshop 83-84; Eductn.

FECICA, WALTER; Saunders HS; Yonkers, NY; (Y); 23/198; VICA; Yrbk Bus Mgr; Yrbk Stf; High Hon Roll; Hon Roll; NHS; Crftsmn Awd Chem 85; Manhattan Coll; Chem.

FECURA, MICHELLE; Hoosic Valley Central HS; Melrose, NY; (Y); Band; Chorus; Mrchg Band; JV Fld Hcky; Var Mgr(s); Var Score Keeper; Var Sftbl; Prfct Atten Awd.

FEDDER, PATRICK H; Starpoint Central HS; Sanborn, NY; (Y); 8/198; Band; Mrchg Band; Pep Band; Nwsp Stf; Hon Roll; Jr NHS; Clarkson U; Elec Engr.

FEDDO, THOMAS P; North Tonawanda SR HS; N Tonawanda, NY; (Y); Am Leg Boys St; Boy Scts; Jazz Band; Symp Band; Var L Ftbl; Var L Swmmng; Jr NHS; Trs NHS; Eagl Sct Brnz Palm 85; Rensselaer Plytchnc Inst Math & Sci Awd 85; U S Naval Acad; Aerosp Engrng.

FEDELE, ELIZABETH; Nazareth Acad; Rochester, NY; (Y); Church Yth Grp; Spanish Clb; Chorus; Yrbk Stf; Pres Sr Cls; Rep Stu Cncl; Sftbl; Pre-Law.

FEDKIW, RON; Newfane SR HS; Newfane, NY; (S); 5/175; Varsity Clb; Crs Cntry; Trk; Wrstlng; High Hon Roll; Hon Roll; Mu Alp Tht; Pre-Med.

FEDUNIEC, DENYS A; Sachem HS North; Lake Grove, NY; (Y); 55/1542; Mrchg Band; Orch; School Musical; Var Trk; Jr NHS; NHS; Pres Schlr; Cmnty Wkr; French Clb; Science Clb; NY All ST Mus Cmptn Awd 83-84; Engl Achvt Awd 83; Regnts Schlrshp 85; ST U Binghamton; Gynclgy.

FEDYSZEN, PETER J; Massapequa HS; Massapequa, NY; (Y); 20/450; Am Leg Boys St; Cmnty Wkr; German Clb; Key Clb; Political Wkr; Varsity Clb; Variety Show; Rep Jr Cls; Bsktbl; Var L Lcrss; Spnsh Hnrs 83-85; Comp Awd 84; Union Coll; Bio.

FEE, ANN M; John S Burke Catholic HS; Monroe, NY; (Y); Teachers Aide; Varsity Clb; Color Guard; Nwsp Rptr; Yrbk Stf; JV Var Cheerleading; JV Socr; Hon Roll; Coll Of Mt St Vincent; Comm.

FEELEY, KATHLEEN; Utica Free Acad; Utica, NY; (Y); Model UN; Thesps; Acpl Chr; Nwsp Bus Mgr; Yrbk Stf; VP Soph Cls; DAR Awd; High Hon Roll; NHS; Debate Tm; Wellesley Coll Clb Prz 85; Hstry.

FEELEY, WILLIAM A; Bishop Timon HS; W Seneca, NY; (Y); Computer Clb; Quiz Bowl; Varsity Clb; Chorus; JV L Crs Cntry; Var L Socr; Var L Trk; Hon Roll; NHS; Engl Awd 83; Acctng.

FEELY, AMY E; Cohocton Central HS; Cohocton, NY; (Y); 2/26; Pres Church Yth Grp; Pres 4-H; French Clb; Sec Band; Sec Chorus; JV Var Cheerleading; Var Sftbl; Var Tennis; High Hon Roll; Trs NHS; SUNY Geneseo; Elem Ed.

FEENAGHTY, MARIAN; Washingtonville HS; Monroe, NY; (Y); JA; Varsity Clb; Yrbk Stf; Stu Cncl; Var Socr; Var Trk; SUNY Albany; Eco.

FEENER, KIMBERLY L; Lake Placid HS; Lake Placid, NY; (Y); 4/45; AFS; French Clb; Key Clb; Varsity Clb; School Musical; Yrbk Stf; Sec Stu Cncl; JV Var Socr; High Hon Roll; Hon Roll; Regents Schlrshp 85; Stony Brook; Engl.

FEENEY, BARBARA JEAN; Massena Central HS; Massena, NY; (Y); Church Yth Grp; Cmnty Wkr; French Clb; Rep Frsh Cls; Gym; Im Powder Puff Ftbl; Var Score Keeper; JV Capt Sftbl; Hon Roll; NHS; Top Ten Pct Of Cls 83-85; Acctg.

FEENEY, MARY; St Patricks Central Catholic HS; Coxsackie, NY; (Y); 2/30; Dance Clb; Drama Clb; Color Guard; Drill Tm; School Play; Pres Jr Cls; Elks Awd; High Hon Roll; Hon Roll; Jr NHS; Sea Cadt USN Yr 85; Membr U S Navl Sea Cadt Corps 84-85; U S Naval Acad; Ofcr.

FEENY, SEAN; Saratoga Central Catholic HS; Saratoga Springs, NY; (S); High Hon Roll; Hon Roll; Engineering.

FEENY, SHARON; Saratoga Central Catholic HS; Saratoga Springs, NY; (S); 10/50; French Clb; Radio Clb; High Hon Roll; Hon Roll; St Rose; Spch.

FEERICK, DEIRDRE; Dominica Acad; Sunnyside, NY; (Y); Church Yth Grp; FCA; Political Wkr; Q&S; Nwsp Rptr; Nwsp Stf; Pres Frsh Cls; Pres Trs Stu Cncl; Sftbl; Hon Roll; Fred Huber Stu Athlt Awd 82; Emerald Soc & Knghts Of Colmbus Schlrshp 82; JR Editor Of Domican Acad; Law.

FEES, PATRICIA; Nazareth Acad; Rochester, NY; (Y); JA; Latin Clb; Library Aide; Chorus; Var Bowling; Var Tennis; Hon Roll; Ntl Latin Exam Magna Cum Laude 83; Monroe CC; Comp Tech.

FEGAN, ANDREW; Wilson Magnet HS; Rochester, NY; (S); Boy Scts; Church Yth Grp; Latin Clb; Temple Yth Grp; Stu Cncl; Trk; Hugh O Brien Yth Fndtn Ldrshp Awd 82-83; Marine Corps; Psych.

FEGAN, PETER; Albertus Maguns HS; Blauvelt, NY; (Y); Fld Hcky; Lcrss; Pace U; Acctg.

FEGLEY, MATTHEW; Geneva HS; Geneva, NY; (S); 24/170; Varsity Clb; Var Bsbl; Var Bsktbl; Hon Roll; NHS; Ntl Merit Ltr; Law.

FEGLEY, SHARON; Waterloo SR HS; Waterloo, NY; (Y); 68/175; French Clb; FTA; Teachers Aide; Varsity Clb; Capt Var Bsktbl; Capt Var Socr; Capt Var Sftbl; Capt Var Vllybl; Most Athl Girl Coaches Awd 85; MVP Sftbl 85; MV Offensive Plyr Soccer 85; SUNY; Physcl Thrpy.

FEHLMAN, BILL; Falconer Central Schl; Falconer, NY; (Y); Am Leg Boys St; Var L Bsbl; Var L Ftbl; Hon Roll; NHS; All Confr Bsbl Var 84-85; Hnrb Mntn Ftbl Var 83-84; Meritorious Awd Bsbl & Ftbl Var & JV 82-85; Air Force; Engrng.

FEHR, AMY; Depew HS; Depew, NY; (Y); GAA; Capt Cheerleading; JV Socr; Math.

FEINBERG, MICHAEL; Commack High Schl North; Commack, NY; (Y); Church Yth Grp; GAA; Rep Stu Cncl; JV Socr; Var Sftbl; Hon Roll; NHS; Mdcl Sci.

FEINSON, ANDREA; Long Beach HS; Long Beach, NY; (S); 19/320; DECA; Band; Yrbk Bus Mgr; Yrbk Phtg; Yrbk Stf; Tennis; Hon Roll; NHS; Arista Awd 84; Vrsty Athl Awd 83-84; Hnrbl Ment Sci Fair 82; Bio.

FEIST, NICOLE F; Hunter College HS; New York, NY; (Y); Political Wkr; School Play; Nwsp Stf; Lit Mag; VP Stu Cncl; Ntl Merit SF; AFS; Cmnty Wkr; Drama Clb; French Clb; Leopold Schepp Fndtn Schlr 85; Regents Schlr 85; Wesleyan U; Law.

FEIWEL, NANCY; Wantagh HS; Wantagh, NY; (Y); Key Clb; Spanish Clb; Temple Yth Grp; Orch; Rep Jr Cls; Var L Badmtn; Var L Tennis; Hon Roll; NHS; Yrbk Stf; Yth Incntv Awd 84 & 85.

FELBERBAUM, NANCY; John F Kennedy HS; Riverdale, NY; (Y); 116/982; Hosp Aide; Scholastic Bowl; Science Clb; Chorus; School Play; Nwsp Rptr; JV Socr; Regents Schlrshp; 2nd Pl Acad Olym; Hnr Ment Sci Fair; SUNY-ALBANY; Psych.

FELDMAN, ALAN; Bronx HS Of Science; Bronx, NY; (S); Nwsp Phtg; Nwsp Rptr; Nwsp Stf; Yrbk Phtg; Yrbk Stf; Lit Mag; Ntl Merit Ltr; Econ.

FELDMAN, BARBARA; Cicero North Syracuse HS; Liverpool, NY; (S); 87/711; Pep Clb; Drill Tm; Stat Lcrss; Powder Puff Ftbl; Score Keeper; Stat Socr; French Hon Soc; Hon Roll; NHS; Air Frce; Nrs.

FELDMAN, JAIME; Roosevelt HS; Scarsdale, NY; (Y); 67/287; Girl Scts; Hosp Aide; School Play; Variety Show; Rep Frsh Cls; Rep Soph Cls; Rep Sr Cls; JV Var Cheerleading; Hon Roll; Chrldng Awd 81-85; Hmcmng Prncss 85; Cortland ST.

FELDMAN, JESSICA; Mont Pleasant HS; Schenectady, NY; (Y); 27/300; Drama Clb; Spanish Clb; Concert Band; Jazz Band; Mrchg Band; School Play; Yrbk Ed-Chief; Yrbk Stf; French Hon Soc; Prfct Atten Awd; 1st Pl Amer Lung Assn Poster Cont Prize $200 85; Natl Frnch Exam 7th Pl 84-85; Natl Frnch Exam 9th Pl; Frgn Lang.

FELDMAN, LYNN R; Harrison HS; Harrison, NY; (Y); 7/215; Chorus; Ed Yrbk Stf; Rep Frsh Cls; Rep Soph Cls; Rep Jr Cls; Rep Sr Cls; JV Socr; Var Tennis; French Hon Soc; NHS.

FELDMAN, NICOLE; Broadalbin Central HS; Johnstown, NY; (Y); 4-H; French Clb; Library Aide; Chorus; Yrbk Bus Mgr; Cit Awd; 4-H Awd; Church Yth Grp; Pep Clb; Hon Roll; Outstndg SR Girl Fulton Co 4-H 83; Ldrshp Awd 4-H 84; Outstnd SR Girl 4-H Clb 83 & 83-84; Cobleskill U; Acctnt.

FELDMAN, STEPHEN M; Scarsdale HS; Scarsdale, NY; (Y); Cmnty Wkr; Ski Clb; Varsity Clb; Stage Crew; Im Bsktbl; Im Ftbl; Var Lcrss; Var Socr; Im Sftbl; Hon Roll; NY St Regents Schlrshp Awd 85; MVP Jr Var Lacrosse 84; Brown U.

FELDMAN, WENDY; South Shore HS; Brooklyn, NY; (Y); Dance Clb; Girl Scts; Teachers Aide; Twrlr; Hon Roll; Prfct Atten Awd; Eng Awd 83; Typing Schlrshp 85; Typing Awd 85; Stenotype Acad; Court Steno.

FELIANO, JAMES; St Agnes HS; New York, NY; (Y); Rep Cmnty Wkr; Model UN; NHS; Teachers Aide; Myrs Vlntr Yth Awds 85; Engl Ltratr.

FELIBERTY JR, AURELIO; Rice HS; New York, NY; (S); Hon Roll; ASCENT Prog 85; John Jay Coll; Govt Agncy.

FELICETTI, LAURA; Saint John The Baptist HS; Lindenhurst, NY; (Y); Model UN; Red Cross Aide; Teachers Aide; Ed Nwsp Bus Mgr; Lit Mag; Frsh Cls; Crs Cntry; Trk; Jr NHS; Drama Clb; 2nd Pl-Vndlsm Essy Cntst; Cert Of Merit-Natl Essy/Poetry Prs; Farifield U; Psych.

FELICETTI, VALERIE; St Francis Prep; Fresh Meadows, NY; (S); 86/700; Drama Clb; Band; Concert Band; Jazz Band; Mrchg Band; School Musical; Im Vllybl; Var Hon Roll.

FELICIANO, FELIX; Aviation HS; Bronx, NY; (Y); 10/417; CAP; Exploring; JA; Stu Cncl; Hon Roll; Prfct Atten Awd; Pegasus Soc 85; Aeronutcl Engr.

FELICIANO, NELSON; Manhattan Center For Science Math; New York, NY; (Y); Boys Clb Am; Cmnty Wkr; Cit Awd; Hon Roll; Elec Engr.

FELIX, DALE L; Norwood-Norfolk Central HS; Norfolk, NY; (Y); 4/117; JCL; Latin Clb; School Play; High Hon Roll; Hon Roll; NHS; Regents Schlrshp 85; SUNY Binghamton; Comp Sci.

FELIX, JUDITH; South Shore HS; Brooklyn, NY; (Y); Dance Clb; Girl Scts; L Socr; Prfct Atten Awd; Pictr Hung Metro Museum Modrn Art 83; John Jay Coll Criminal Justice.

FELIX, KEVIN; De Sales Catholic HS; Lockport, NY; (Y); Boy Scts; JV Bsktbl; Capt Golf; JV Var Wrstlng; Hon Roll; Eagle Scout Awd 85; Elec Engrng.

FELIX, LISA; Warsaw Central Schl; Warsaw, NY; (S); 2/93; Church Yth Grp; French Clb; Chorus; Yrbk Ed-Chief; Trs Jr Cls; Trs Sr Cls; Capt Var Socr; Var Trk; NHS; Sal; Amherst Coll.

FELIX, MARTHA; Eastern Dist HS; Brooklyn, NY; (Y); 4/386; Office Aide; Nwsp Rptr; Cit Awd; French Hon Soc; Hon Roll; City Coll; Med.

FELIZ, AIDA; Cathedral HS; Ny, NY; (Y); Dance Clb; FNA; Hosp Aide; Office Aide; Teachers Aide; Gym; Hon Roll; Prfct Atten Awd; Mst Versatile Stu Awd 82; NY U; Nrsng.

FELIZ, LUIS; Westbury SR HS; Westbury, NY; (Y); 6/250; Boy Scts; Computer Clb; Varsity Clb; Yrbk Phtg; Var Golf; High Hon Roll; Hon Roll; NHS; Semi-Fnlst Ntl Hspnc Schlr Awds 84-85; NY Inst Of Tech; Comp Sci.

FELL, PATRICIA; Beacon HS; Beacon, NY; (Y); Church Yth Grp; Math Tm; Chorus; School Musical; Variety Show; Soph Cls; Stu Cncl; Hon Roll; Acctng.

FELLER, KATHERIN E; St Hildas And St Hughs HS; New York City, NY; (Y); 7/26; Church Yth Grp; Cmnty Wkr; Drama Clb; Chorus; Stage Crew; Ed Lit Mag; Rep Sr Cls; NHS; Ntl Merit Schol; NY U; Theatre.

FELLER, LYNNE CAROL; Churchville-Chili SR HS; Rochester, NY; (Y); 26/324; FTA; JCL; Orch; VP Symp Band; Nwsp Rptr; Lit Mag; Stu Cncl; High Hon Roll; NHS; Music Excllnc Awd 85; Outstndng Svc Awd 85; Presdntl Acadmc Ftns Awd 85; Crane Schl Of Music; Music.

FELLER, RICHARD S; Half Hollow Hills East HS; Melville, NY; (Y); 7/559; Mathletes; Nwsp Stf; High Hon Roll; Jr NHS; Ntl Merit Schol; Pres Schlr; St Schlr; Deans Schlrshp 85; Pres Schlr U Of CA-BERKELEY 85; Pres Schlr SUNY-BUFFALO 85; Cornell U; Mech Engr.

FELLION, LORI; Franklin Acad; Malone, NY; (Y); Drama Clb; Model UN; Pres Spanish Clb; Chorus; School Play; Swing Chorus; Pres Stu Cncl; Hon Roll; NHS; Acad All Amer 83-84; Biochmstry.

FELLOWS, GEORGE W; Rome Free Acad; Rome, NY; (Y); 111/512; Var Tennis; Var Wrstlng; Jr NHS; NHS; Pres Schlr; Highest Acadmc Avg-Art 82; Albany ST U; Bio.

FELLOWS, REBECCA; Granville Central HS; Wells, VT; (S); 9/128; Math Tm; Band; Chorus; Pep Band; Rep Stu Cncl; Fld Hcky; Pom Pon; Hon Roll; French Clb; Peer Counclng Drug, Achol Abuse; Intl Ord Rainbow; U MA Amherst; Ind Engrng.

FELLOWS, WILLIAM C; Argyle Central HS; Argyle, NY; (Y); Boy Scts; Camera Clb; French Clb; Math Clb; Political Wkr; Ski Clb; Yrbk Phtg; Yrbk Stf; Soph Cls; Jr Cls; Teresa Edder Awd Achvt 77; Soc Studies Achvt Awd 84; Physcl Sci.

FELTON, MARK; Rockland Country Day Schl; Palisades, NY; (S); Camera Clb; Computer Clb; Drama Clb; Math Tm; Quiz Bowl; Scholastic Bowl; Ski Clb; Chorus; School Musical; School Play; Headmasters Awd 83-84; Brown; Med.

FELTON, TYWANNA; Woodlands HS; White Plains, NY; (Y); Church Yth Grp; Spanish Clb; Trk; Lane Coll; Surgeon.

FELTRE, ANTHONY; Hendrick Hudson HS; Croton, NY; (Y); 23/191; Science Clb; Spanish Clb; Rep Soph Cls; Var Bsbl; JV Capt Bsktbl; Var Ftbl; Var Trk; Im Wt Lftg; High Hon Roll; Pres Schlr; Frat Dunderberg Lodge Awd 85; Highest Av Span 81 & 82; Drew U; Doctor.

FELTS, RENE L; Mercy HS; Rensselaer, NY; (Y); Var Capt Bsktbl; Var Sftbl; Var Capt Vllybl; High Hon Roll; NHS; Varsity Clb; Rep Frsh Cls; Rep Soph Cls; Rep Jr Cls; Rep Sr Cls; Schlrshp K Of C Rensselaer 85; Albany Coll Pharm; Pharm.

FEMINELLA, JOHN; St John The Baptist HS; Deer Pk, NY; (Y); Boy Scts; Cmnty Wkr; Band; Chorus; Jazz Band; School Musical; Variety Show; Bsktbl; Socr; Swmmng; Brentwood Yuth Dev Corp, BACCA Awds 84; Sts Cyril, Methodius Sccr Leag Awd 83; St Johns U Queens; Law.

FENLON, EDWARD E; South Jefferson Central HS; Adams Center, NY; (Y); 4/135; Am Leg Boys St; FCA; Concert Band; Mrchg Band; Pres Stu Cncl; Var Capt Crs Cntry; Var Capt Trk; Jr NHS; NHS; Prfct Atten Awd.

FENN, TYLER; Webutuck Central HS; Millerton, NY; (Y); 3/65; Drama Clb; Quiz Bowl; Ski Clb; Thesps; Band; Chorus; School Musical; School Play; Off Frsh Cls; Off Soph Cls; 1st Art Show 83 & 84; Cornell; Arch.

FENNELL, LAURA; West Babylon SR HS; W Babylon, NY; (Y); 14/149; Cmnty Wkr; Church Choir; Yrbk Stf; Cit Awd; High Hon Roll; NHS; Ntl Merit Ltr; SUNY Stony Brook; Med Doc.

FENNELL, RAQUEL G; Uniondale HS; Hempstead, NY; (Y); Key Clb; Office Aide; Yrbk Stf; Lit Mag; Cheerleading; Swmmng; High Hon Roll; Dnstry.

FENNESSY, MARY BETH; Auburn HS; Auburn, NY; (Y); Cmnty Wkr; Girl Scts; Letterman Clb; Varsity Clb; Bsktbl; Var Socr; Var Sftbl; Var Trk; Hon Roll; Radlgic Tech.

FENSTER, DAVID; Francis HS; Staten Island, NY; (S); 1/20; Yrbk Stf; High Hon Roll; NHS; Hosp Volunteer Certificate 83-84; SCIENCE Research.

FENSTERER, BRIAN; Hauppauge HS; Hauppauge, NY; (Y); Church Yth Grp; Ski Clb; Prfct Atten Awd; Culinary Arts Inst; Culnry Arts.

FENSTERMADNER, SARA ANN; E L Vandermeulen HS; Pt Jefferson, NY; (Y); Var JV Bsktbl; Var Mgr(s); JV Tennis; Hon Roll; Outstndng Achvt In Adver & Dsgn Awd; Lynchburg Coll; Eng.

FENTON, TODD; Granville Central HS; Wells, VT; (Y); 10/160; Math Clb; Hon Roll; Prfct Atten Awd; Saratoga Vo-Tech; Hvy Eqpt Main.

FENTON, ZANITA; Union Endicott HS; Endicott, NY; (S); Debate Tm; Key Clb; Color Guard; Concert Band; Flag Corp; Mrchg Band; Nwsp Rptr; High Hon Roll; Hon Roll; Harvard; Hist.

FEOLA, CECILIA; Mynderse Acad; Seneca Falls, NY; (S); 22/140; Intnl Clb; Band; Color Guard; Concert Band; Mrchg Band; Var Bowling; JV Var Socr; JV Var Sftbl; Var Vllybl; High Hon Roll; Physcn Asst.

FERA, RENEE; Holy Angels Acad; Cheektowaga, NY; (S); 2/30; French Clb; Chorus; Church Choir; School Musical; Nwsp Rptr; Pres Stu Cncl; High Hon Roll; NHS; Prfct Atten Awd; Schlrshp To Holy Angels Acad 81; SUNY Ab; Frnch.

FERALDI, COREY S; Pioneer Central HS; Chaffee, NY; (Y); JV Var Bsbl; Var Golf; JV Var Socr; Lib Arts.

FERBER, THOMAS; Baldwin SR HS; Baldwin, NY; (Y); 111/502; Boy Scts; Chess Clb; VP Exploring; Library Aide; Mathletes; Am Leg Boys St; Im Bowling; Im Sftbl; Regnts Schlrshp 85; SUNY Albany; Acctng.

FERCHEN, RICHARD A; Niagara Wheatfield HS; Sanborn, NY; (Y); 98/313; Boy Scts; Church Yth Grp; Civic Clb; Pep Clb; Church Choir; Hon Roll; Regents Schlrshp Wnnr 85; Full Tuition Pastoral Schlrshp 85; Liberty U; Christian Music.

FERCHLAND, PATRICIA; St Johns Prep; Broad Chnl, NY; (Y); Letterman Clb; Varsity Clb; Band; Chorus; Church Choir; Mrchg Band; Nwsp Stf; Rep Frsh Cls; Sec Soph Cls; Off Jr Cls; Eng.

FERENCE, REBECCA A; Marathon Central HS; Marathon, NY; (Y); 16/60; Chorus; Nwsp Stf; Yrbk Stf; Hon Roll; Rgnts Schlrshp Nrsng 85; St Joseph; Nrsng.

FERENCZ, NICOLE; Yeshiva Univ High Schl For Girls; Flushing, NY; (Y); Cmnty Wkr; Teachers Aide; Temple Yth Grp; Chorus; Sci.

FERGERSON, JODY L; John C Birdlebough HS; Clay, NY; (Y); 1/200; AFS; Ski Clb; Spanish Clb; Jazz Band; High Hon Roll; Ntl Merit SF; Val; Cmnty Wkr; Drama Clb; Exploring; Outstndng Achvt Latin 82-85, Spn 84-85, Chem 84; Mt Holyoke Coll; Frgn Lang.

FERGUS, JILL; St Vincent Ferrer HS; New York, NY; (Y); 20/128; French Clb; Library Aide; Chorus; Church Choir; Madrigals; School Musical; Yrbk Stf; Tennis; Athlt Awd Phy Ftnss 84-85; NY U; Music.

FERGUSON, ALICE L; Great Neck South SR HS; Great Neck, NY; (Y); 19/218; Cmnty Wkr; French Clb; GAA; Nwsp Rptr; Yrbk Phtg; Yrbk Stf; Crs Cntry; Trk; Var Ltrs Trk, Winter Trk, Crs Cntry; Zimbalist Humanitarn Awd 85; NY Merit Scholar 84; U MA Amherst.

FERGUSON, DAVID; Bishop Grimes HS; N Syracuse, NY; (Y); Art Clb; Church Yth Grp; Ski Clb; Lit Mag; Tennis; Hon Roll; NHS; Syracuse U Credt Art Courses 85; Cmmrcl Artst.

FERGUSON, JILL; Thousand Islands Central HS; Clayton, NY; (Y); Varsity Clb; Variety Show; JV Var Bsktbl; Hon Roll; NNYSAS Awd Cert Merit; Fshn.

FERGUSON, JULIE; Sacred Heart Acad; Rockville Centre, NY; (S); 12/186; Library Aide; Pres Science Clb; Teachers Aide; Yrbk Stf; Rep Soph Cls; Rep Stu Cncl; Tennis; High Hon Roll; NHS; Mission Clb Rep 84-85; Manhattan; Engr.

FERGUSON, KARA MARIE; St John The Baptist D H S HS; Babylon, NY; (Y); 10/601; Church Yth Grp; Latin Clb; Service Clb; Rep Frsh Cls; Stu Cncl; Var Cheerleading; Var Gym; NHS; NY St Regnts Schlrshp 85; Manhattan Pres Sch Schlrshp; U Scranton; Bus.

FERGUSON, KIMBERLY; Sodus Central Schl; Sodus Pt, NY; (Y); FBLA; Office Aide; Pep Clb; Chorus; Color Guard; Var Cheerleading; Mgr(s); Morrisville Coll; Exc Bus Trng.

FERGUSON, LETTIE ANN; Union Springs Acad; Middletown, NY; (Y); Church Yth Grp; Ski Clb; Varsity Clb; Acpl Chr; Band; Chorus; Church Choir; Concert Band; School Musical; Yrbk Stf; Orange Cnty CC; Physcl Thrpy.

FERGUSON, LORI; Carthage Central HS; Carthage, NY; (Y); Varsity Clb; Chorus; Mrchg Band; Im Badmtn; JV Bsbl; JV Bsktbl; JV Var Swmmng; Im Vllybl; Vet.

FERGUSON, MARVIN; Burgard Vo-Tech; Buffalo, NY; (Y); Capt Bsktbl; HS Athltc Awd-Bsktbl 85; CAO Achvt-Trpy Bsktbl 85; Wstrn NY All Star Slctns-Bsktbl 85; Niagara CC; Data Proc.

FERGUSON, MICHAEL; La Salle Senior HS; Niagara Falls, NY; (S); 8/278; Ski Clb; Trs Varsity Clb; Rep Frsh Cls; Var Crs Cntry; Capt Trk; Hon Roll; NHS; Top Ten 84; U Of Buffalo; Med.

FERGUSON, SEAN; Notre Dame HS; Utica, NY; (Y); Bsktbl; Accountng.

FERGUSON, SHANNON L; Bishop Ford Central HS; Brooklyn, NY; (Y); JA; Math Tm; Lit Mag; Stu Cncl; Im JV Bsktbl; Im Capt Ftbl; Hon Roll; USAA Ntl Awds 84-85; Acad All Amer 84-85; Syracuse U; Pol Sci.

FERGUSON, SHARI; Broadalbin HS; Broadalbin, NY; (Y); 8/55; French Clb; Intnl Clb; Letterman Clb; Teachers Aide; Varsity Clb; Band; Chorus; Color Guard; Cheerleading; Sftbl; Hnr Rl & Hi Hnr Rl; Rochester Inst; Deaf Intrptn.

FERLO, DESIREE; Rome Catholic HS; Rome, NY; (Y); Library Aide; Yrbk Stf; Rep Frsh Cls; JV Cheerleading; Mgr(s); Im Powder Puff Ftbl; Hon Roll; Pres VP Rotary Awd; Eng.

FERLO JR, LEO; Rome Free Acad; Rome, NY; (Y); Intnl Clb; Chorus; Concert Band; Mrchg Band; Variety Show; JV Wrstlng; Music.

FERLONI, ANGELINA P; Maria Regina HS; Pleasantville, NY; (Y); 8/144; Rep Model UN; Service Clb; Capt Bsktbl; Capt Vllybl; High Hon Roll; NHS; Eileen Martin Schlrshp 85; Regents Coll Schlrshp 85; Boston Coll; Bus.

FERMIN, DALINDA; Mabel Dean Bacon Voc HS; Brooklyn, NY; (S); Hon Roll; Regents Geo & Bio 84; Crim Law.

FERMO, CAROLYN; Academy Of St Joseph; Kings Pk, NY; (Y); Cmnty Wkr; Hosp Aide; Library Aide; Science Clb; Spanish Clb; Chorus; Stu Cncl; NHS; Sec Jr Cls; Holy Crss Bk Prze 85; Spnsh Awd 84.

FERNANDES, DONNA; Brewster HS; Brewster, NY; (S); 19/176; Trs Chorus; Color Guard; Rep Soph Cls; Rep Jr Cls; Trk; Hon Roll; NHS; Sect.

FERNANDES JR, MANUEL D; Iona Prep HS; Yonkers, NY; (Y); 94/196; Boy Scts; JV Crs Cntry; JV Trk; Wt Lftg; Hon Roll; Prfct Atten Awd; Westchester Yth Golden Apple 83; Boy Scout Gov Day Golden Apple 85; Ad altare dei-Medal 83; Iona Coll; Psych.

FERNANDEZ, AMY; John Dewey HS; Brooklyn, NY; (Y); Church Yth Grp; JA; Office Aide; Teachers Aide; Band; Concert Band; Mrchg Band; Prfct Atten Awd; Secy.

FERNANDEZ, CARLOS; Bishop Scully HS; Amsterdam, NY; (Y); Art Clb; PAVAS; Var Bowling; Ntl Art Hnr Soc 83; Art.

FERNANDEZ, CARMEN; William H Taft HS; Bronx, NY; (Y); Debate Tm; Library Aide; Office Aide; Teachers Aide; Band; Church Choir; Orch; Stage Crew; Cheerleading; Vllybl; SUNY New Paitz; Psych.

FERNANDEZ, CAROLINE; St Edmund HS; Brooklyn, NY; (Y); 35/40; Spanish Clb; Hon Roll; Outstndg Wrk Soc Stud 83-84; Outstndg Wrk Spnsh I, II, III 81-85; Brooklyn Coll; Nrsry Schl Tchr.

FERNANDEZ, CHRISTINE L; Claybon A Bouron JR SR HS; Voorheesville, NY; (Y); 7/127; VP Spanish Clb; Chorus; Church Choir; Jazz Band; Rep Stu Cncl; Var Capt Fld Hcky; Var L Trk; DAR Awd; High Hon Roll; NHS; Hghst Ave Spnsh Ovr 3 Yrs 84; 1600 Mtr Wlk Schl Recrd 83; SUNY Buffalo; Humnts.

FERNANDEZ, DAVID; Aviation HS; Woodside, NY; (Y); 68/417; Debate Tm; Office Aide; VP Sr Cls; VP Stu Cncl; High Hon Roll; Hon Roll; IL Inst Of Tech; Mech Engr.

FERNANDEZ, EVETTE; Our Lady Perpetual Help HS; Brooklyn, NY; (Y); Art Clb; Church Yth Grp; Prfct Atten Awd; Brooklyn Coll; Psych.

FERNANDEZ, FRANCINE; High School Of Art & Design; Astoria, NY; (Y); 76/412; Office Aide; Teachers Aide; Band; Twrlr; Hon Roll; Prfct Atten Awd; Exec Intrnshp Prgm 85-86; Advrtsng.

FERNANDEZ, JOSETTE; Christ The King R HS; Brooklyn, NY; (Y); Rep Stu Cncl; JV Cheerleading; JV Gym; Prfct Atten Awd; St Vincients Hosp Schl Nrsg.

FERNANDEZ, MARINO; Archbishop Molloy HS; Flushing, NY; (Y); 4/409; Crs Cntry; Trk; High Hon Roll; Hon Roll; NHS; Schl Mdl Rank 7 On 454 83; Schl Mdl Rank 7 On 446 84; Schl Mdl Rank 4 On 409 85; NY U; Bus Admin.

FERNANDEZ, MICHAEL R; Scarsdale HS; Scarsdale, NY; (Y); Aud/Vis; Drama Clb; Chorus; School Musical; School Play; Stage Crew; Ntl Merit Ltr; Syracuse U; Arch.

FERNANDEZ, VICKY; St Francis Prep; College Point, NY; (Y); 250/698; Dance Clb; GAA; Hosp Aide; Service Clb; Varsity Clb; Band; Concert Band; Orch; Var Socr; JV Trk.

FERNEZ, LISA M; Cardinal Spellman HS; Bronx, NY; (Y); 11/564; Stage Crew; Nwsp Rptr; Chess Clb; Var Bsktbl; Var Capt Sftbl; High Hon Roll; NHS; NYS Regnts Schlrshp 85; CMSV Foul Shootg Champ 82-84; Acadmc Athl Harlem Tourn Vrsty Levl 81-82; Fordham U; Jrnlsm.

FERNSEBNER, KAREN; Depew HS; Cheektowaga, NY; (Y); VP French Clb; Band; Chorus; Drill Tm; Mrchg Band; School Musical; Yrbk Stf; Rep Stu Cncl; Hon Roll; NHS; Chldhd Ed.

FERRAGOSTO, BIANCA; St Patricks CC HS; Hudson, NY; (Y); Aud/Vis; Drama Clb; School Play; Nwsp Rptr; Rep Stu Cncl; JV Cheerleading.

FERRAIOLI, KIM MARIE; Washingtonville HS; Salisbury Mills, NY; (Y); Hst FBLA; Band; JV Var Socr; Var Sftbl; Hon Roll; Oprtn Entrprs Amer Mgmt Assn 85; Comp Prgmmng.

FERRAIUOLO, KRISTI A; Sachem HS; Holtsville, NY; (Y); 116/1600; GAA; Girl Scts; Science Clb; Orch; Yrbk Stf; Fld Hcky; Hon Roll; Jr NHS; NHS; Silver Awd Girl Scts, Silver Ldrshp Pin 84; Engrng.

FERRANDINO, MARIA; Colonie Central HS; Albany, NY; (Y); Art Clb; Pres FBLA; Hosp Aide; Band; Socr; JV Sftbl; Hon Roll; Bus Adm.

FERRANTE, ANGELA; West Hempstead HS; West Hempstead, NY; (Y); Rep Variety Show; Rep Stu Cncl; Var Trk; Var Vllybl; Hon Roll; Bio Achvmnt 83-84; Italy Sons Awd 84-85; Nursing.

FERRANTE, RAFFAELINA; High Schl Of Art & Design; Maspeth, NY; (S); 9/411; FTA; Teachers Aide; Color Guard; Nwsp Stf; Pres Frsh Cls; VP Rep Soph Cls; Rep Stu Cncl; Hon Roll; Kiwanis Awd; NHS; Arista 83; Manhatan Super Yth Awd 84; Ntl Art Hnr Scty 85; NY U; Intl Bus.

FERRARA, MARIANN; Perry Central HS; Perry, NY; (Y); Church Yth Grp; Key Clb; Spanish Clb; Band; Chorus; Concert Band; Mrchg Band; Sec Jr Cls; High Hon Roll; Hon Roll; Roberts Wesleyan Coll; Nrs.

FERRARA, MICHAEL C; Pittsford Mendon HS; Pittsford, NY; (Y); 127/270; Trs Sr Cls; Socr; NY ST Regents Coll Schlrshp 85; U Of Rochester; Med.

FERRARA, ROBERT; Nazareth Regional HS; Belle Hrbr, NY; (Y); Boy Scts; JA; Office Aide; Concert Band; Stu Cncl; Fld Hcky; Ftbl; Wt Lftg; Wrstlng; Hon Roll; Top 10 Scr Hcky 83-86; Stu Cncl Awd 85; Blood Donor 85; Bus.

FERRARA, SAMUEL; Victor Central SR HS; Victor, NY; (Y); 8/270; Art Clb; Quiz Bowl; Science Clb; Spanish Clb; Varsity Clb; Frsh Cls; Soph Cls; Jr Cls; Stu Cncl; Socr; Law.

FERRARI, ERIC; Johnstown HS; Johnstown, NY; (Y); Im JV Bsktbl; Var L Ftbl; Hon Roll; NHS; Bio Sci.

FERRARO, DONNA; Smithtown H S West; Smithtown, NY; (Y); Church Yth Grp; Dance Clb; Office Aide; Off Soph Cls; Mgr(s); Score Keeper; Timer; Hon Roll; Italian Hon Soc 84; Bus.

FERRARO, JOHN J; Little Falls JR SR HS; Little Falls, NY; (Y); 26/100; Am Leg Boys St; Boy Scts; Ski Clb; Band; Concert Band; Pep Band; Vllybl; High Hon Roll; Syracuse U; Bus Adm.

FERRARO, JOHNEEN; Southwestern Central HS; Lakewood, NY; (Y); French Clb; Girl Scts; Pep Clb; Ski Clb; Chorus; School Musical; School Play; Var JV Cheerleading; Var Sftbl; Var Trk; Pres Phys Fit Awd 83; Trk Sectnls 83; Elem Ed.

FERRARO, JOSEPH; Lindenhurst HS; Lindenhurst, NY; (Y); FCA; JV Socr; Hon Roll; Stony Brook; Dntst.

FERRARO, ROSALIA; Stella Maris HS; Ozone Park, NY; (Y); Girl Scts; Y-Teens; St Johns U; Ed.

FERRAROTTO, LOUISE; Bishop Ford C C HS; Brooklyn, NY; (Y); 50/375; Nwsp Rptr; Pres Soph Cls; Rep Stu Cncl; Mgr Bsktbl; Mgr(s); Var Trk; Im Vllybl; Hon Roll; NHS; Stony Brook; Pre-Med.

FERREIRA, ANTONIO M; Mohawk Central Schl; Mohawk, NY; (Y); Chrmn Am Leg Boys St; Church Yth Grp; Cmnty Wkr; Concert Band; Rep Orch; JV Bsktbl; Hon Roll; JETS Awd; NHS; Aud/Vis; NY Acad Sci Stu Rsrch Pgm 85; 2nd Pl Comp Lit Cobleskill Coll Day 85; NYSSMA Solo Comp 84; Aero Engrng.

FERREIRA, EVELYN; Cathedral HS; Nyc, NY; (Y); 35/298.

FERREIRA, MARK; N Babylon HS; North Babylon, NY; (Y); Aud/Vis; Church Yth Grp; Civic Clb; Computer Clb; Drama Clb; Intnl Clb; Library Aide; Spanish Clb; Varsity Clb; Orch; Bio Sci.

FERRERO, DEBBIE; Brewster HS; Brewster, NY; (S); 59/179; Church Yth Grp; Var Cheerleading; Score Keeper; Hon Roll; Mst Imprvd Chrldr 83; Accntng.

FERRETTI, THERESA; Shenendehowa HS; Clifton Park, NY; (Y); DECA; GAA; Varsity Clb; Chorus; Capt Powder Puff Ftbl; Var Capt Sftbl; Stat Wrstlng; High Hon Roll; Hon Roll; Bus Mngmnt.

FERRIGNO, MARY ANN; St Joseph By The Sea HS; Staten Island, NY; (Y); Computer Clb; Library Aide; Nwsp Stf; Rep Stu Cncl; High Hon Roll; NHS; Slippery Rock U; Acctng.

FERRIS, DEBORAH; Winddon Ashland Jewett HS; Ashland, NY; (Y); Trs Church Yth Grp; Drama Clb; Church Choir; School Play; Score Keeper; Hon Roll; Siena; Comp Sci.

FERRIS, DEBRA; Greene Central HS; Chenango Forks, NY; (Y); 13/103; French Clb; Red Cross Aide; Yrbk Stf; JV Var Fld Hcky; Var Tennis; High Hon Roll; Hon Roll; Sidney Fed Credit Union Schlrshp 85; SUNY Genesco; Comp Sci.

FERRIS, LEE; Fonda-Fultonville Central HS; Fultonville, NY; (Y); 13/100; Boy Scts; Church Yth Grp; Band; Chorus; Church Choir; Concert Band; Mrchg Band; Swmmng; Hon Roll; Boy Scts Ord Of Arrow 83; Boy Scts Ntl Jamboree Schlrhsp 85; SUNY Maritime; Naval Arch.

FERRIS, SYLVIA; Heuvelton Central HS; Ogdensburg, NY; (S); Dance Clb; Girl Scts; Latin Clb; JV Var Cheerleading; JV Socr; High Hon Roll; Lion Awd; NHS.

FERRIS, THERESA L; G Ray Bodley HS; Fulton, NY; (Y); English Clb; French Clb; Science Clb; Variety Show; Yrbk Stf; Trs Frsh Cls; Mat Maids; JV Vllybl; High Hon Roll; Hon Roll; NY ST Regents Schlrshp 85; Cobleskill A&T Coll; Wldlf Tec.

FERRUFINO, RUBEN; St Raymond High School For Boys; Bronx, NY; (Y); 21/240; Computer Clb; JV Var Trk; Schltc Intramrls Sftbl; Astrnmy.

FERRUGIO, JOSETTA; St Edmund HS; Brooklyn, NY; (S); 16/190; Hon Roll; NHS; Boston U; Law.

FERRUZZA, JEFFREY; Aquinas Inst; Rochester, NY; (Y); 8/166; Exploring; Spanish Clb; Stage Crew; Yrbk Stf; JV Var Socr; Var JV Trk; Hon Roll; Prfct Atten Awd; Acad All Amer 85; Med.

FERRY, AMY; Gowanda Central HS; Perrysburg, NY; (Y); 3/127; Am Leg Aux Girls St; Drama Clb; Pres VP 4-H; Var French Clb; Thesps; School Musical; School Play; Nwsp Ed-Chief; Stu Cncl; NHS; Med.

FERRY, LAURA; Kenmore W SR HS; Kenmore, NY; (Y); French Clb; Rep Frsh Cls; Trs Soph Cls; Rep Jr Cls; VP Sr Cls; Stu Cncl; JV Capt Bsktbl; JV Var Vllybl; High Hon Roll; Prfct Atten Awd; Bio Awd 84; Repsntd Schl WA DC Wrkshp Smr 85; Outstndng Ldrshp & Perfrmnce Awd 83; Harvard; Med.

FERRY, PATTY; John A Coleman HS; Tillson, NY; (Y); Sec Church Yth Grp; 4-H; JV Capt Bsktbl; Sftbl; 4-H Awd; Hnrs Eng II,Relgn 83-85.

FESTA, CAROL; Richmond Hill HS; Howard Beach, NY; (Y); English Clb; Math Clb; Office Aide; Spanish Clb; Teachers Aide; Nwsp Rptr; Yrbk Phtg; High Hon Roll; NHS; Hofstra; Intl Bus.

FESTA, SUSAN; Saint Francis Prep; Middle Village, NY; (S); 12/693; Math Tm; Office Aide; Rep Soph Cls; Rep Jr Cls; High Hon Roll; NHS; Acadmc All-Am 85; Nrsng.

FETLER, KAREN; F D Roosevelt HS; Staatsburg, NY; (Y); 71/325; Sec 4-H; French Clb; Cheerleading; 4-H Awd; Hon Roll; Rochester Inst; Mech Engrng.

FETTERLY, MICHELE A; Batavia SR HS; Batavia, NY; (Y); 6/247; Church Yth Grp; Chorus; Church Choir; School Musical; High Hon Roll; NHS; SUNY-GENESEO.

FETTEROLF, ROBERT; Union-Endicott HS; Endicott, NY; (Y); Boys Clb Am; Church Yth Grp; Key Clb; Concert Band; Jazz Band; Mrchg Band; Pep Band; Symp Band; Trk; Wrstlng; Bus Admin.

FEUER, SCOTT; John Dewey HS; Brooklyn, NY; (Y); FBLA; Nwsp Stf; JV Bsktbl; High Hon Roll; Daily News Super Yth Wnnr 84; Law.

FEUERMAN, MARY; Riverhead HS; Riverhead, NY; (Y); Hst FBLA; JA; VICA; Parlimentary Procedure Team Treas 84-85; Peer Group 84-85; Mngmnt.

FEUZ, LISA; Springville-Griffith Inst; Springville, NY; (Y); Church Yth Grp; French Clb; Yrbk Stf; High Hon Roll; Hon Roll; NHS; Aerontcs.

FEYERABEND, BOB; Bishop Ludden HS; Syracuse, NY; (Y); Stage Crew; Variety Show; Yrbk Stf; VP Stu Cncl; Var Bsbl; Var Bsktbl; JV Ftbl; Var Socr; Var Tennis; Hon Roll; Acadmc Schlrshp Syracuse U 85; Ntl Merit Awd Ldrshp; Syracuse U; Jrnlsm.

FEYNMAN, DEBBIE J; Forest Hills HS; Forest Hills, NY; (Y); 58/881; Computer Clb; English Clb; Model UN; Office Aide; Teachers Aide; Yrbk Stf; High Hon Roll; Hon Roll; Jr NHS; NHS; Bus.

FIALA, THOMAS C; Brewster HS; Brewster, NY; (Y); 1/176; Spanish Clb; Nwsp Stf; Yrbk Stf; Sec Stu Cncl; High Hon Roll; Hon Roll; Ntl Merit SF; Hnrs English 10 Pre-Calculus & Spanish Iii 83-84; Electrical Engrng.

FIANDACH, MICHELLE; Penfield HS; Penfield, NY; (Y); Exploring; Chorus; Im Socr; Im Sftbl; Im Vllybl; Chld Care.

FIATO, KIMBERLY; Herkimer SR HS; Herkimer, NY; (Y); 32/114; Drama Clb; School Play; Stage Crew; Var Capt Bsktbl; Var Capt Fld Hcky; Var Capt Sftbl; Hon H Acad 85; Coaches Apprctn Awd 85; Cls Ath 85; Ematrude Watson Outstndng SR Bus Stu Awd 85; Oakland CC MI; Comp Sci.

FICETOLA, NEVI; St Vincent Ferrer HS; Astoria, NY; (Y); 33/114; Service Clb; Busnss.

FICHERA, SENTA; Nazareth Regional HS; Brooklyn, NY; (Y); JA; Hon Roll; Italian Gold Mdl Awd 84; Italian Supr Achvt Awd 85.

FICK, WILLIAM; Connetquot HS; Bohemia, NY; (Y); Boy Scts; Exploring; Math Tm; Nwsp Rptr; Nwsp Stf; Yrbk Stf; High Hon Roll; Hon Roll; Physcs.

FICKBOHM, ANDREA I; Smithtown HS East; St James, NY; (Y); Church Yth Grp; Exploring; German Clb; Capt Hosp Aide; Symp Band; High Hon Roll; Hon Roll; NHS; Ntl Merit Ltr; Regnts Schlrshp Wnnr 85; Oral Roberts U; Nrsng.

FICKES, JENNIFER A; Nanvet SR HS; Nanuet, NY; (Y); 56/180; Church Yth Grp; Drama Clb; Girl Scts; Math Tm; Teachers Aide; School Play; Mgr Stage Crew; Hon Roll; Rcklnd CC Hnrs Schlrshp 85; Rockland CC; Bus.

FICO, KIM; Hicksville HS; Hicksville, NY; (Y); Spanish Clb; Yrbk Sprt Ed; Stat Ftbl; Stat Lcrss; Hon Roll; Jr NHS; NHS; Spanish NHS; Bus.

FIDLER, ANNETTE M; Central HS; Valley Stream, NY; (Y); 44/360; AFS; Church Yth Grp; Teachers Aide; Pres Band; Chorus; Church Choir; Concert Band; Madrigals; Mrchg Band; Orch; Dist Music Fstvl Schlrshp 85; Tempo Music Hnr Soc VP 84-85; Natl Choral Awd 85; SUW; Elem Ed.

FIDLER, PHILIP; Walter Panas HS; Peekskill, NY; (Y); Church Yth Grp; FBLA; Spanish Clb; Y-Teens; Im Ftbl; Var Tennis; Var Wrstlng; High Hon Roll; NHS; Optmtry.

FIEDLER, CHARLOTT R; John C Birdlebough HS; Phoenix, NY; (Y); 77/200; Church Yth Grp; Drama Clb; Office Aide; Red Cross Aide; Ski Clb; School Musical; School Play; Hon Roll; NYS Regents Nrsng Schlrshp 85; Crouse Irving Hosp; Nrsng.

FIEDOROWICZ, LISA; St John The Baptist DHS; Lk Ronkonkoma, NY; (Y); Rep Jr Cls; Stat Socr; Hon Roll; NHS; Spanish NHS; Church Yth Grp; Band; Church Choir; Mrchg Band; Adelphi; Acctg.

FIEGE, ANDREA; Churchville-Chili HS; Rochester, NY; (Y); Sec Church Yth Grp; Pres FTA; GAA; Pep Clb; Symp Band; Yrbk Sprt Ed; Sec Sr Cls; Coach Actv; Var L Socr; Var Trk; Am Muscl Found Band Hnrs 82-84; Area All St Band 82-83; Ed.

FIEGL, WADE; Fillmore Central HS; Fillmore, NY; (S); Church Yth Grp; JV Bsbl; Var Socr; Var Trk; High Hon Roll; NHS; French Clb; Varsity Clb; Drill Tm; Yrbk Stf; Standrd Bearer Awd 85; Mst Valbl Athl Awd Trck 85; Sci.

FIELD, KATHLEEN A; Marcellus HS; Marcellus, NY; (Y); VP Church Yth Grp; Ski Clb; Symp Band; Sec Rep Stu Cncl; Co-Capt Cheerleading; JV Socr; Var Trk; High Hon Roll; Hon Roll; NHS; St Bonaventure U; Pre-Med.

FIELDS, HELENE L; Benjamin N Cardozo HS; Bayside, NY; (Y); 42/476; Cmnty Wkr; Exploring; Science Clb; Nwsp Ed-Chief; Cit Awd; NHS; Library Aide; Service Clb; Teachers Aide; Lit Mag; Westinghouse Sci Hnrs 85; JR Acad Sci HS Coord 83-84; Queens Coll; Law.

FIELDS, MARK; Northeastern Acad; Brooklyn, NY; (S); Stu Cncl; NHS; Prfct Atten Awd; Ntl Engl Merit Awd 85; Pace U; Bus Admin.

FIELDS, MICHELE; Eastridge HS; Rochester, NY; (Y); 23/201; Color Guard; Mrchg Band; Yrbk Stf; High Hon Roll; Hon Roll; NHS; E Irndequt Tchrs Assn Schlrshp 85; Cert Merit 85; Ldrshp Awd-Music 85; Monroe CC; Accntng.

FIELDS, SHELIA; Julia Richman HS; Brooklyn, NY; (Y); Church Yth Grp; JA; ROTC; Med Lab Svc Awd 85; VA ST U; Doctor.

FIELLO, JEFFREY; West Genesee SR HS; Syracuse, NY; (Y); French Clb; Stage Crew; High Hon Roll; Hon Roll; Bio.

FIERO, SUZANNE; General Douglas Mac Arthur HS; Levittown, NY; (Y); 30/319; JA; Model UN; Office Aide; Rep Frsh Cls; VP Stu Cncl; Var Cheerleading; Var Score Keeper; High Hon Roll; Hon Roll; Jr NHS; Scholar Awd Hofstra U 85; Scholar Awd C W Post Coll 85; Hofstra U; Acctg.

FIERRO, ANTHONY; St Francis Preparatory HS; Howard Bch, NY; (Y); 110/750; Boy Scts; Spanish Clb; Band; Concert Band; Mrchg Band; Im Fld Hcky; Golf; Im Ice Hcky; High Hon Roll; Hon Roll; NY U; Pre-Law.

FIERRO, DOREEN L; Academy Of The Resurrection HS; Port Chester, NY; (Y); 1/86; Art Clb; Aud/Vis; Church Yth Grp; Math Clb; Service Clb; Yrbk Ed-Chief; High Hon Roll; NHS; Hugh O Brien Ldrshp Awd For Outstdng Soph 84; Manhattanville Coll Awd For Outstdng Achvmnt Englsh 85; SCI.

FIERRO, LISA; Mercy HS; Lk Ronkonoma, NY; (Y); Church Yth Grp; Cheerleading; Mgr(s); Law.

FIFIELD, RICHARD; Lindenhurst HS; Lindenhurst, NY; (Y); 30/540; Boy Scts; Church Yth Grp; Ski Clb; Varsity Clb; Nwsp Stf; Yrbk Stf; Bsktbl; Socr; Hon Roll.

FIFIELD, SUSAN MARJORIE; Shenedehowa HS; Clifton Pk, NY; (Y); Aud/Vis; Pres Church Yth Grp; 4-H; Hosp Aide; Church Choir; Mgr Trk; 4-H Awd; High Hon Roll; Southrn Saratoga Cnty Womens Clb Awds 83-85; Campus Life Stu Ldr 81-84; Chamberlayne JR Coll; Fshn Dsn.

FIGIEL, DARIUSZ; Comoes HS; Cohoes, NY; (Y); Dance Clb; FTA; Key Clb; Varsity Clb; Band; Mrchg Band; Orch; Var Socr; Var Trk; Hon Roll; Hudson Valley CC.

FIGO, AMY M; Churchville-Chili SR HS; Rochester, NY; (Y); Math Tm; Mrchg Band; Symp Band; High Hon Roll; Hon Roll; NHS; NY ST Regents Schlrshp 85; NY ST U Brockport; Comp Sci.

FIGUARDA, IRENE; St Raymond Acad; Bronx, NY; (Y); Comp Sci.

FIGUEROA, ADAM; Manhattan Ctr For Science & Math; New York, NY; (Y); 15/400; Camera Clb; Computer Clb; JA; JV Bsbl; JV Ftbl; High Hon Roll; Hon Roll; Acad Chem Scholar Polytech Inst NY 85.

FIGUEROA, CAMILLE; Manhattan Center For Science & Math; New York, NY; (Y); 9/31; Camera Clb; School Musical; School Play; Variety Show; Social Wrkr.

FIGUEROA, IRENE; St Raymond Acad; Bronx, NY; (Y); Camera Clb; Library Aide; Comp Sci.

FIGUEROA, JAIME; James Monroe HS; Bronx, NY; (Y); Art Clb; Boys Clb Am; Computer Clb; Drama Clb; Rep Jr Cls; Capt Bsktbl; Var Ftbl; St Johns U; Comp Sci.

FIGUEROA, MARY; Christ The King RHS HS; Maspeth, NY; (Y); 8/385; Rep Frsh Cls; Rep Soph Cls; Rep Jr Cls; VP Stu Cncl; JV Sftbl; High Hon Roll; Pres NHS; Principals Hnr 82-85; Relign Awd 82; Queens Coll Pres Achvt Awd 84; St Johns U; Psych.

FIGUEROA, NELSON; Cathedral Prep; Brooklyn, NY; (Y); Chorus; Church Choir; Yrbk Stf; Hon Roll; 2nd Highest In Cls Honor 83.

FIGUEROA, SHARON; Preston HS; Bronx, NY; (S); High Hon Roll; NHS; Fordham U; Lingst.

FIGUEROA, STEVEN; Cardinal Hayes HS; New York, NY; (Y); 6/40; Boy Scts; Pres Frsh Cls; VP Jr Cls; JV Ftbl; Trk; High Hon Roll; Hon Roll; 1st Hnrs/4 Tms Yr; 1st, 2nd Hnrs; VA; Law.

FILASKY, JULIE; Rocky Point JR SR HS; Rocky Point, NY; (S); 11/180; French Clb; Chorus; Madrigals; Mrchg Band; School Musical; Nwsp Rptr; Fld Hcky; Capt Vllybl; Hon Roll.

FILICIA, EDITH; Pulaski JR SR HS; Pulaski, NY; (Y); Art Clb; Exploring; School Play; Trk; Encentive Awd 84; Oswego Coll; Artist.

FILINGERI, ANDREA; Frankfort-Schuyler Central HS; Frankfort, NY; (S); Sec Trs GAA; Rep Frsh Cls; Rep Soph Cls; Rep Jr Cls; JV Var Bsktbl; JV Var Fld Hcky; Var L Trk; High Hon Roll; NHS; Visual Art.

FILIPOWSKI, KATHLEE ANN; Minisink Valley HS; Middletown, NY; (Y); 17/232; VP JA; Key Clb; Math Tm; Office Aide; Teachers Aide; Cit Awd; High Hon Roll; Kiwanis Awd; Lion Awd; NHS; Chrprsn Ctzns Prty-Yth Govt Chrprsn 81-84; Rifl Clb 82-83; Cert Ldrshp Trng Conf 83; Orange County CC; Acctg.

FILIPPINI, JAYME E; Stissing Mt JR & SR HS; Stanfordville, NY; (Y); 4/87; AFS; Band; Yrbk Stf; Pres Frsh Cls; Pres Soph Cls; VP Sr Cls; JV Bsktbl; JV Var Fld Hcky; Var Trk; Hon Roll; Regents Schlrshp 85; Boston U; Art.

FILIPPON, BRIDGET; West Hempstead HS; W Hempstead, NY; (Y); 31/310; Chrmn Key Clb; NHS; Pres Schlr; W Hempstead Comm Schlrshp 85; Outstndng Svc Eng Dept 85; NY ST Regnts Schlrshp 85; Fairfield U; Accntng.

FILIPSKI, DORIE; Springville Griffith Inst; Colden, NY; (Y); 14/197; GAA; Spanish Clb; JV Var Cheerleading; Var Swmmng; Var Tennis; High Hon Roll; NHS; U Of VA; Psych.

FILIPSKI, JENNIFER; Kenmore West SR HS; Kenmore, NY; (Y); 47/445; Band; Mrchg Band; Yrbk Ed-Chief; Hon Roll; NHS; Regnts Schlrshp 85; U NY Buffalo; Law.

FILKINS, JULIE; Berne-Knox-Westerlo Central Schl; East Berne, NY; (Y); Office Aide; Hon Roll; Albany Bus Coll; Sec.

FILKORN, EMIL J; Hamburg SR HS; Hamburg, NY; (Y); 27/391; CAP; Exploring; German Clb; Model UN; Var Tennis; Var Trk; Var Vllybl; High Hon Roll; NHS; Grmn Awd Outstndng Prfmnce Schl Yr 82-83 & 84-85; Astrnmy.

FILLINGER, ERIC; Irondequoit HS; Rochester, NY; (Y); 9/325; Church Yth Grp; Varsity Clb; Church Choir; Orch; Stu Cncl; Var Capt Crs Cntry; Var Trk; NHS; German Clb; Latin Clb; Elmira Key Schlrshp 85; Med.

FILLMORE, MARIE; Argyle Central HS; Argyle, NY; (Y); 1/30; Math Tm; Chorus; Concert Band; Yrbk Rptr; Trs Sr Cls; Cit Awd; DAR Awd; JP Sousa Awd; NHS; Val; J Prindl Mem Schlrshp 84-85; Bennington Chrl Soc Schlrshp 85; Amer Legn Oratcl Cntst Wnr 85; SUNY Potsdam.

FILOSA, JENNIFER ANNE; Sachem North HS; Farmingville, NY; (Y); 50/1509; Drama Clb; Science Clb; Spanish Clb; Varsity Clb; Chorus; School Play; Yrbk Stf; Var Bowling; Jr NHS; NHS; Mst Valuable Bwlr Var Bwlng 83-85; Soc Stud Fair Wnnr 83; Acctng.

FILOSA, SUSAN; Port Richmond HS; Staten Isld, NY; (Y); 8/500; AFS; Cmnty Wkr; PAVAS; Temple Yth Grp; School Musical; Nwsp Rptr; Yrbk Stf; High Hon Roll; Jr NHS; Trs NHS; Columbia Assn Fir Dept Schlrshp Awd 2nd Pl 82; Bio.

FILPO, LIZETTE; Hillcrest HS; Corona, NY; (Y); 151/792; Intnl Clb; JA; VICA; Yrbk Rptr; Rep Soph Cls; Gov Hon Prg Awd; High Hon Roll; Spanish NHS; Hosp Aide; Office Aide; Sec De Amigos Unidas 83; Stonybrook; Lib Arts.

FILSAIME, ARNELLE; Fashion Industries HS; Brooklyn, NY; (Y); 27/473; Johnsn & Wales Schlrshp 85; Johnson Wales Clg; Fashn Merch.

FILSON, DAVID H; Troy HS; Troy, NY; (Y); 25/450; Exploring; German Clb; Rep Stu Cncl; Hon Roll; NHS; NYS Rgnts Schlrshp 85-86; U Of Rochester Schlrshp; Hnr Stu 85; U Of Rochester; Bio-Chmstry.

FINCH, ANGELA M; Washington Irving HS; New York, NY; (Y); 36/370; Service Clb; Band; Church Choir; Drm & Bgl; Drm Mjr(t); Yrbk Stf; High Hon Roll; Bnai Brith 85; Ntrtnst.

FINCH, JANICE; Murry Bergtraum HS; Bronx, NY; (Y); JA; Red Cross Aide; Hon Roll; Accntnt.

FINCH, MARC; Camden HS; Camden, NY; (Y); AFS; Ski Clb; Varsity Clb; Var L Bowling; JV L Ftbl; Var Capt Golf; High Hon Roll; NHS; Elec Engrng.

FINCK, NANCY; Spackenkill HS; Poughkeepsie, NY; (Y); Church Yth Grp; Yrbk Stf; Capt Var Bsktbl; Var Trk.

FINCK, WILLIAM J; Archbishop Stepinac HS; Bronxville, NY; (Y); Church Choir; Socr; Tennis; Trk; Hon Roll; Widener U; Bus.

FINE, BRIAN; Hendrick Hudson HS; Montrose, NY; (Y); Bsbl; Var Bowling; Acctg.

FINEL, BERNARD I; The Kew Forest Schl; Forest Hills, NY; (Y); Pres Chess Clb; Computer Clb; Debate Tm; Nwsp Stf; VP CAP; Rep Stu Cncl; Var Score Keeper; JV Socr; Var L Sftbl; Timer; Comp Pgm.

FINELLI, MICHAEL; Monsignor Farrell HS; Staten Island, NY; (Y); 17/295; Drama Clb; School Play; Yrbk Stf; Stu Cncl; Bsktbl; Ftbl; High Hon Roll; NHS; Pres Schlr; Manhattan Coll; Elec Engrng.

FINGER, ANDREA; Monsignor Scanlan HS; Bronx, NY; (Y); Computer Clb; Nwsp Stf; Yrbk Stf; Geometry-Highest Avg 84-85; Typing 85-86; Spnsh 84-85; Accntng.

FINGER, JULIE; Mc Kinley HS; Buffalo, NY; (Y); FFA; Girl Scts; Library Aide; Pep Clb; Brdcstng.

FINGERHUT, LORI; Longwood HS; Coram, NY; (Y); 25/525; Yrbk Stf; JV Cheerleading; High Hon Roll; Hon Roll; NHS; Acad All Amer 84-85; Acctng.

FINGERLING, MARYELLEN; Academy Of St Joseph; Northport, NY; (Y); Church Yth Grp; Cmnty Wkr; Orch; School Musical; Nwsp Rptr; Nwsp Stf; Yrbk Stf; JV Var Bsktbl; Var Capt Socr; NEDT Awd.

FINGUERRA, MARK; St Pauls Schl; Westbury, NY; (S); 2/29; Chess Clb; Church Yth Grp; Cmnty Wkr; Drama Clb; Trs Exploring; Pres Pep Clb; Varsity Clb; Nwsp Ed-Chief; Nwsp Rptr; Pres Frsh Cls; Latin Awd 83-85.

FINI, TOM; St Francis Preparatory Schl; Douglaston, NY; (S); 41/693; Chess Clb; Computer Clb; Debate Tm; Model UN; NFL; Office Aide; Socr; Tennis; Optimate Soc; Law.

FINK, CAROL; Fonda-Fultonville Central HS; Tribes Hill, NY; (Y); Key Clb; Nwsp Ed-Chief; Nwsp Stf; Sec Sr Cls; JV Capt Socr; JV Sftbl; Var L Vllybl; Cit Awd; Hon Roll; Prfct Atten Awd; High Awd GS 84; High Avg Hlth 84-85; Pre Med.

FINK, DAWN MARIE; Islip HS; Islip, NY; (Y); Mathletes; Chorus; Color Guard; School Musical; Variety Show; Nwsp Stf; Cheerleading; High Hon Roll; Jr NHS; VP NHS; Sci Awd 83; Key Awd 85; Vocl Music Schlrshp 85.

FINK, HILLARY; Harborfields HS; Greenlawn, NY; (Y); 50/335; Drama Clb; Sec Key Clb; VP Temple Yth Grp; Band; Co-Capt Pep Band; School Play; Nwsp Stf; Yrbk Stf; Camera Clb; Mathletes; PTA Cncl Schlrshp 85; Schl Actvty Fnd Schlrshp 85; Intl Thespn Soc 84-85; SUNY Albany; Spcl Educ.

FINK, JILL; Fayetteville Manlius HS; Manlius, NY; (Y); Hosp Aide; Model UN; Ski Clb; Temple Yth Grp; Yrbk Stf; Hon Roll; JA; Acadmc Achv Photo 83-84; Pian Suzki Hnr 82-83; Spnsh Humants Fair Awd 84-85; Psychlgy.

FINK, TRACY A; Amherst Central HS; Amherst, NY; (Y); DAR Awd; Hon Roll; Boston U.

FINKBEINER, PAUL G; Jamestown HS; Jamestown, NY; (Y); 30/374; Church Yth Grp; German Clb; Acpl Chr; School Musical; Nwsp Rptr; Hon Roll; Jr NHS; Ntl Merit SF; Regents Schlrshp Cert 85; Commdtn Achvt PSAT 84; Founders Schlrshp Newbery Coll 85; Newberry Coll; Bus Adm.

FINKE, MARTINA; Smithtown High School East; Nesconset, NY; (Y); Church Yth Grp; Thesps; Church Choir; Orch; Stage Crew; Rep Frsh Cls; Rep Soph Cls; Rep Jr Cls; Var Badmtn; Hon Roll; Intl Bus.

FINKELSTEIN, BRYNA G; Shulamith HS; Brooklyn, NY; (Y); Acpl Chr; School Musical; School Play; Yrbk Stf; Hon Roll; Faculty Recgntn Awd 82-84; Stern Coll.

FINKELSTEIN, CHAIM; Mesiutha Tipereth Jerusalem HS; New York, NY; (Y); Cmnty Wkr; Computer Clb; English Clb; Latin Clb; Chorus; Nwsp Ed-Chief; Nwsp Rptr; Yrbk Ed-Chief; Rep Sr Cls; Bsktbl; Regents Schlrshp 85; Crtv Wrtng Awd 84; Poetry Awd 85; Wrtng.

FINKELSTEIN, ELLIOT; Middletown HS; Middletown, NY; (Y); Math Tm; Acpl Chr; Jazz Band; Symp Band; Capt Rep Stu Cncl; Trk; High Hon Roll; NHS; Temple Yth Grp; Chorus; Chem,Eng,Hist Achvt Awd 84-85; Comp.

FINKELSTEIN, MARTIN; Middletown HS; Middletown, NY; (Y); Teachers Aide; Trk; High Hon Roll; Hon Roll; NHS; Toxiclgst.

FINKELSTEIN, STUART; Middletown HS; Middletown, NY; (Y); Temple Yth Grp; Acpl Chr; Jazz Band; School Musical; Lit Mag; NHS; Ntl Merit Ltr; Drama Clb; Math Tm; Mrchg Band; Chem Achvt Awd 84; Eng Achvt Awd 85; NY St Math Tm Meet 85; Engrng.

FINLAYSON, JOHN M; South Glens Falls Central HS; South Glens Falls, NY; (Y); 4/237; Am Leg Boys St; Boy Scts; Ski Clb; Concert Band; Mrchg Band; Var Crs Cntry; JV Trk; High Hon Roll; NHS; Ntl Merit Ltr; Empire ST Games Archery & Mens Schltc 85; Michael Kay Mem Cross Cntry Awd; Clarkson U; Math.

FINN, CINDY; Lindenhurst HS; Lindenhurst, NY; (Y); Church Yth Grp; French Clb; Varsity Clb; Yrbk Stf; Var Capt Cheerleading; Var Trk; French Hon Soc; Hon Roll; Jr NHS; NHS; USCAA Ntl Chrldng Awd 85; USCAA Ntl Frnch Awd 83; Pre-Med.

FINN, MICHAEL; Lindenhurst HS; W Babylon, NY; (Y); Boy Scts; French Clb; ROTC; Yrbk Stf; Hon Roll; NHS; CPA.

FINNEN, MAUREEN C; Holy Trinity HS; Bellmore, NY; (Y); Hosp Aide; Math Clb; Ski Clb; Spanish Clb; VP Stu Cncl; Var Twrlr; Ntl Hnr Roll 85; Nassau CC; Htl Mngmnt.

FINNERTY II, GARY H; Altmar-Parish-Williamstown Ctl HS; Williamstown, NY; (Y); 5/110; Am Leg Boys St; French Clb; Varsity Clb; Mrchg Band; Pres Jr Cls; Trs Stu Cncl; Var Bsbl; Var Capt Bsktbl; Hon Roll; Prfct Atten Awd; 1st Tm-All Leag Bsbl 84-85; 2nd Tm All Leag Bsktbl 85; Pre-Med.

FINNERTY, JAMES M; North Rose-Wolcott HS; N Rose, NY; (Y); Ski Clb; Varsity Clb; Socr; Tennis; Hon Roll; Pol Sci.

FINNERTY, PAUL E; Trinity-Pawling Schl; Holmes, NY; (Y); Chess Clb; Computer Clb; School Play; Stage Crew; Rep Sr Cls; Stu Cncl; Mgr Ftbl; Lcrss; Im Socr; Im Tennis; Regnts Schlrshp 85; U Of Rochester; Psychlgy.

FINNERTY, PAULA A; Altmar-Parish-Williamstown HS; Williamstown, NY; (Y); 1/90; Church Yth Grp; Pres Trs French Clb; Nwsp Rptr; High Hon Roll; Hon Roll; Pres NHS; Prfct Atten Awd; Val; NY ST Regents Schlrshp 85; Walter Kling Mem Schlrshp 85; SUNY-GENESEO; Comp Sci.

FINNIN, MICHAEL; St Francis Preparitory Schl; Bayside, NY; (S); 44/703; Math Clb; Im Bowling; Optimate Socty 83-84; NY U; Med.

FINO, MICHAEL; Marlboro HS; Highland, NY; (Y); 21/170; Varsity Clb; Stu Cncl; JV Var Bsbl; JV Bsktbl; JV Var Ftbl; Hon Roll; NHS.

FIODELISO, JAMES J; Cardinal Mooney HS; Rochester, NY; (Y); 33/327; Bsktbl; L Var Bowling; Hon Roll; Latn Hnr Soc 81-82; Rit Schlrshp 85; Rgnts Schlrshp 85; Rochester Inst Of Tech; Phrmclg.

FIORATTI, ARIANNA C; The Chapin Schl; New York, NY; (Y); Pres Art Clb; Church Yth Grp; JCL; Sec Latin Clb; Ski Clb; Nwsp Rptr; Ed Yrbk Stf; Rep Frsh Cls; Rep Jr Cls; Rep Stu Cncl; John Jay Shclr At Columiba U 85; Regents Schlrshp 85; Harvard Radcliffe; Art History.

FIORAVANTI, CLAYTON L; Ithaca HS; Ithaca, NY; (Y); Am Leg Boys St; Cmnty Wkr; Office Aide; Political Wkr; Pres Spanish Clb; Off Frsh Cls; Rep Soph Cls; Rep Jr Cls; Rep Stu Cncl; Stu Aide Middle STS Coordntr 85; Chamber Commerce Yth Adv Cncl; U Buffalo; Pol Sci.

FIORE, CARMINE M; HS Of Fashion Indstrs; Brooklyn, NY; (Y); 1/473; Art Clb; Office Aide; Soroptimist; Stage Crew; Yrbk Ed-Chief; Rep Frsh Cls; Rep Soph Cls; VP Jr Cls; VP Sr Cls; Rep Stu Cncl; Regnts Schlrshp 85-86; Fashion Inst Of Tech; Fshn Merc.

FIORE, CHRISTINE; Sachem HS; Farmingville, NY; (Y); 21/1400; Color Guard; Nwsp Ed-Chief; Nwsp Phtg; Nwsp Rptr; Score Keeper; Jr NHS; NHS; L I Sci Cong High Hnrs 83; Best Feture Writr 83; Hofstra U; Bus Mgmt.

FIORE, PAT; John D Kennedy HS; Utica, NY; (Y); Art Clb; Cmnty Wkr; Nwsp Sprt Ed; Nwsp Stf; Rep Stu Cncl; Var Bsbl; JV Bsktbl; Var L Ftbl; Wt Lftg; Hon Roll; Bus Mgmt.

FIORELLO, STACIE; Midwood HS; Brooklyn, NY; (Y); 95/638; Dance Clb; Math Tm; Office Aide; Teachers Aide; Variety Show; Yrbk Stf; Capt Cheerleading; Gym; Prfct Atten Awd; Archon 85; Modl Cngrss 85; Pschlgy.

FIORENTINO, ANNETTE; Lakeland HS; Putnam Valley, NY; (Y); Spanish Clb; Yrbk Stf; Rep Stu Cncl; Bsbl; Bsktbl; Socr; Sftbl; Tennis; Hon Roll; NHS; Coachs Awd; All Leag Hnrbl Ment Sccr; Fengl.

FIORENTINO, CAROLYN JO; Mt St Josephs Acad; Buffalo, NY; (S); 1/60; Spanish Clb; Church Choir; Nwsp Stf; Yrbk Bus Mgr; Yrbk Stf; Sec Rep Soph Cls; Sec Rep Jr Cls; Hon Roll; Sec NHS; Ntl Merit SF; Hnr Awds In Span, Math, Music 81-82; Hnr Awds In Span, Engl, Soc Stud, Sci 81-84; St John Fisher; Pharmacy.

FIORESE, PETER; Beacon HS; Beacon, NY; (S); 6/170; Chess Clb; Math Clb; Math Tm; Science Clb; Chorus; Church Choir; High Hon Roll; Hon Roll; NHS; Ntl Merit Ltr; Sienna; Comp Sci.

FIORETTI, THOMAS; Mc Kee Vocational HS; Staten Island, NY; (Y); Teachers Aide; Ftbl; Golf; Wt Lftg; CSI; Bus Admin.

FIORILLO, TRACY J; Smithtown H S East; St James, NY; (Y); Yrbk Stf; Stu Cncl; Var Capt Badmtn; Var Capt Tennis; Hon Roll; NHS; Off Frsh Cls; Off Soph Cls; Off Jr Cls; Off Sr Cls; Presntl Acad Ftnss Awd 85; US Army Rsrve Natl Schlr/Athlte Awd 84-85; Italian Hnr Soc Secy 84-85; U Of Richmond; Bus.

FIORINI, ANGELA; St Patricks CCHS HS; Catskill, NY; (Y); 11/40; Cmnty Wkr; Drama Clb; Girl Scts; Ski Clb; School Play; Yrbk Stf; VP Frsh Cls; VP Soph Cls; Sec Jr Cls; Sec Sr Cls; Regents Schlrshp 85; JC Of Albany; Grphc Art.

FIORINO, STEVE; Churchville Chili SR HS; Rochester, NY; (Y); 39/330; Church Yth Grp; Yrbk Phtg; Trk; Wt Lftg; Hon Roll; Holland Exc Stu.

FIORITO, JOHN; Iona Prep HS; White Plains, NY; (Y); 81/196; Boy Scts; Debate Tm; Chorus; Capt Var Ice Hcky; Hon Roll; Bus Mgmt.

FIRRINCIELI, VINCENT; Archbishop Stepinac HS; N Tarrytown, NY; (Y); 32/204; Church Yth Grp; Cmnty Wkr; Rep Frsh Cls; Rep Jr Cls; Var Ftbl; Hon Roll; NHS; Iona; Math.

FIRST, LISA; Hudson HS; Hudson, NY; (Y); Ski Clb; Lib Band; Concert Band; Jazz Band; Mrchg Band; Orch; Pep Band; Yrbk Stf; Tennis; Hon Roll; Med Asst.

FISCH, PETER J; C A Bouton JR & SR HS; Voorheesville, NY; (Y); 17/122; French Clb; Var Swmmng; Nwsp Ed-Chief; Var Jr Cls; Pres Stu Cncl; JV Var Bsbl; JV Var Ftbl; Var L Socr; Var L Vllybl; JV Var Wrstlng; St John Fisher Coll; Jrnlsm.

FISCHANG, RONALD; Kingston HS; Kingston, NY; (Y); Cmnty Wkr; Computer Clb; Spanish Clb; RIT Alumni Schlrshp 85-86; Rochester Inst Of Tech; Math.

FISCHER, CATHLEEN; School Of The Holy Child; Millwood, NY; (Y); 7/40; Service Clb; Mgr Stage Crew; Nwsp Rptr; Nwsp Stf; Yrbk Stf; High Hon Roll; Hon Roll; NEDT Awd; Ntl Merit SF; NY ST Rgnts Schlrshp; Mdlbry Coll; Lawyer.

FISCHER, KASEY; Olean HS; Olean, NY; (Y); FHA; Spanish Clb; Diving; Gym; Sftbl; Swmmng; Hon Roll; Fd Svc.

FISCHER, KATHLEEN; Dominican Commercial HS; Woodside, NY; (Y); Intnl Clb; Teachers Aide; Concert Band; Drm & Bgl; High Hon Roll; Hon Roll; Jr NHS; NHS; Siena Clb 82; Prin List 82; NY U; Jrnlsm.

FISCHER, KELLY E; Auburn HS; Auburn, NY; (Y); Church Yth Grp; Pres 4-H; German Clb; Teachers Aide; Hon Roll; Spec Ed Vlntr Awd 85; Cayuga County CC.

FISCHER, KRISTIN; E Hampton HS; E Hampton, NY; (Y); 15/150; Nwsp Ed-Chief; Yrbk Rptr; VP Stu Cncl; Nwsp Rptr; Yrbk Stf; Rep Frsh Cls; Rep Soph Cls; Rep Jr Cls; VP Sr Cls; Bsktbl; Gold Medal Jrnlsm 84-85; Outstndng SR Awd, Prsdntl Acadmc & Ftns Awd 85; CA U Berkelay; Jrnlsm.

FISCHER, KRISTIN; Mexico HS; New Haven, NY; (Y); Band; Hon Roll; Johnson & Wales; Hotl Rest Mgmt.

FISCHER, LAURIE; Hicksville HS; Westbury, NY; (Y); 91/535; AFS; Sec Pres Service Clb; Pres Temple Yth Grp; Trk; High Hon Roll; NHS; Boston U; Intl Rel.

FISCHER, RHONDA A; Allegany Central HS; Allegany, NY; (Y); 8/91; Art Clb; Camp Fr Inc; Drama Clb; School Play; Nwsp Rptr; Yrbk Ed-Chief; Trs Stu Cncl; Stat Sftbl; High Hon Roll; NHS; St Bonaventure U Scholar 85-86; C Felt Mth Awd 85; Pres Acad Fitnss Awd; St Bonaventure U; Acctng.

FISCHETTI, GINA; Bishop Kearney HS; Brooklyn, NY; (Y); Hon Roll.

FISCINA, EVELYN; Stella Maris HS; Maspeth, NY; (Y); Girl Scts; Band; High Hon Roll; Hon Roll; 1st Hnrs 83; 2nd Hnrs 83; Prncpls List 82; Pre-Law.

FISH, LAURA; Vestal Central SR HS; Binghamton, NY; (Y); Varsity Clb; Stu Cncl; JV Bsktbl; Var Capt Socr; Trk; High Hon Roll; NHS; Empire ST Gms 83-85; Cptn Empire ST Gms 85; Cptn Vrsty Sccr Tm 85; Law.

FISH, LISA O; North Warren Central Schl; North Creek, NY; (Y); 2/41; Church Yth Grp; Math Tm; Band; Chorus; Church Choir; Jazz Band; Mrchg Band; School Play; Yrbk Bus Mgr; Sal; SUNY-POTSDAM; Math Eductn.

FISH, MARY; Onondaga Central HS; Marietta, NY; (S); 39/72; VP Art Clb; Yrbk Bus Mgr; Hon Roll; Teachers Aide; Chorus; Var JV Score Keeper; Trk; Art.

FISH, MELISSA; Newfield HS; Newfield, NY; (Y); Stage Crew; Vllybl; Bus Achv 85; Bus Mgmt.

FISH, ROSE MARY; Franklin Academy SR HS; Malone, NY; (Y); High Hon Roll; Hon Roll; Ntl Merit Ltr; Outstndng Stu Of Yr/Bus Law 85; US Ntl Math Awd 83; Canton Coll; Scrtrl & Accntng.

FISHBECK, VICKI; Heuvelton Central HS; Heuvelton, NY; (S); 9/55; Sec Church Yth Grp; Trs 4-H; Yrbk Stf; JV Socr; 4-H Awd; Hon Roll; NHS; Math Achvt Awd 84; Canton ATC; Bus Admin.

FISHER, AMY; Oxford Acad; Oxford, NY; (Y); 3/100; French Clb; Varsity Clb; Sec Concert Band; Yrbk Ed-Chief; Sec Stu Cncl; Fld Hcky; High Hon Roll; Pres NHS; Prfct Atten Awd; Church Yth Grp; Operation Enterprise AMA 85; Schlrs Day Cortland U NY 85; Yrbk Sem Cazenovia Coll 85; Ithaca; Mktg.

FISHER, AMY; Plattsburgh HS; Plattsburgh, NY; (Y); Pres Church Yth Grp; Hosp Aide; Model UN; Band; Jazz Band; Orch; Cheerleading; Crs Cntry; High Hon Roll; NHS; Elec Engrng.

FISHER, CAROLE; Vernon Verona Sherrill Central Schl; Rome, NY; (Y); Ed Exploring; Ski Clb; Band; Concert Band; Drm & Bgl; Jazz Band; Mrchg Band; Nwsp Stf; Var Socr; NEDT Awd; Intr Desgn.

FISHER, ELENA; Hutchinson Central Tech HS; Buffalo, NY; (S); 29/262; Pres Jr Cls; Rep Sr Cls; Rep Stu Cncl; Capt English Clb; Hon Roll; Pottsdam Coll; Comp Sci.

FISHER, ELIZABETH; Little Falls JR SR HS; Little Falls, NY; (S); 9/109; GAA; Acpl Chr; Band; Chorus; Concert Band; Mrchg Band; Symp Band; Yrbk Phtg; Var L Badmtn; NHS; Bio.

FISHER, GRETCHEN; The Masters Schl; Factoryville, PA; (Y); GAA; Acpl Chr; Pres Chorus; VP Sr Cls; Var L Fld Hcky; Var L Lcrss; Var L Sftbl; Cum Laude 85; Ciba Geigy Sci Awd 85; Most Outstndng Stu 84; Case Western Reserve U; Chem.

FISHER, JANE M; Fairport HS; Fairport, NY; (Y); 9/600; Ski Clb; Varsity Clb; Concert Band; Mrchg Band; Var Crs Cntry; Var Trk; Hon Roll; NHS; Ntl Merit Ltr; NY ST Regents Schlrshp 85; MA Inst Of Tech; Mech Engrng.

FISHER, JANTHI E; Lindenhurst HS; Lindenhurst, NY; (Y); 3/594; Church Yth Grp; Nwsp Ed-Chief; High Hon Roll; NHS; Pres Schlr; Rotary Awd; Spanish NHS; St Schlr; Art Clb; Girl Scts; TAL Mth Awd 85; Sci Olympd West Point 85; PTA Frgn Lang Awd 85; Wake Forest U; Vet.

FISHER, JENNIFER; West Canada Valley HS; Newport, NY; (Y); Church Yth Grp; Drama Clb; French Clb; Pep Clb; Ski Clb; Band; Chorus; Church Choir; Color Guard; Concert Band; Mohawk Vly Rvw Publ 85; Jrnlsm.

FISHER, JILL; Delaware Valley Central HS; Callicoon, NY; (S); 6/38; Drama Clb; Ski Clb; Chorus; Yrbk Stf; JV Var Cheerleading; Var L Sftbl; High Hon Roll; NHS; Prfct Atten Awd; Awd Of Excllnce Chrldng 14th Pl Natl Comp 83; Engrng.

FISHER, KIMBERLY; Amsterdam HS; Amsterdam, NY; (Y); 65/294; Church Yth Grp; Cmnty Wkr; Hosp Aide; Ski Clb; Teachers Aide; Church Choir; Drm Mjr(t); Yrbk Stf; High Hon Roll; Prfct Atten Awd; Prfct Attndnc Awd 82-85; Hnr Roll Awd 82-83; Suny; Tchr.

FISHER, LIESEL; John S Burke Catholic HS; Westbrookville, NY; (Y); 50/150; Church Yth Grp; Pep Clb; Ski Clb; Yrbk Stf; Var L Cheerleading; Var Tennis; High Hon Roll; Debate Tm; Sec 4-H; GAA; Miss Teen 84; Ramapo Tchrs Assoc Schlrshp 85; NY ST Regnts Schlrshp 85; U Of Scanton; TV Nwscstr.

FISHER, MICHELE K; Eastchester HS; Eastchester, NY; (Y); 24/163; Key Clb; Ski Clb; Band; Concert Band; Mrchg Band; School Musical; School Play; Yrbk Stf; Var Tennis; Var Trk; Regents Schlrshp 85; Tufts U.

FISHER, MONICA; Notre Dame HS; Wyoming, NY; (S); 3/82; 4-H Awd; High Hon Roll; NHS; 4-H; Bsktbl; Cheerleading; Tennis; Vllybl; Accntnt.

FISHER, NANCY; Akron Central HS; Akron, NY; (Y); 3/159; Drama Clb; Ski Clb; Band; Mrchg Band; School Musical; High Hon Roll; NHS; Ntl Merit SF; Cornell U; Bio-Chem.

FISHER, SALLY J; Sanford H Calhoun HS; Merrick, NY; (Y); 9/336; Drm & Bgl; Nwsp Stf; Rep Frsh Cls; Pres Soph Cls; Rep Jr Cls; Pres Sr Cls; Rep Stu Cncl; Var Capt Socr; JV Sftbl; Church Yth Grp; Rep Natl Ldrshp Trng Ctr At La Salle Mil Acad 83 & 84; Cornell U; Govt.

FISHER, SHELLY; C-Ns HS; Clay, NY; (S); 49/711; Hosp Aide; Capt Bowling; Hon Roll; NHS; Bryant Stratton; Acctg.

FISHER, TAMMY; Franklin Acad; Malone, NY; (Y); Hon Roll; Merchndsng.

FISHER, WILLIAM SCOTT; Lyndonville Central Schl; Waterport, NY; (Y); 6/60; Var Am Leg Boys St; Var Varsity Clb; Var Concert Band; Pres Soph Cls; Pres Jr Cls; Var Capt Trk; High Hon Roll; NHS; Prfct Atten Awd; Math.

FISHER, WYNNIE; Alden Central HS; Alden, NY; (Y); Church Yth Grp; FTA; Sec Science Clb; Spanish Clb; Concert Band; Hon Roll; Prfct Atten Awd; Cmnty Wkr; 4-H; Mrchg Band; Erie County Fair Marchng Band 85; Pres Acad Fit Awd 85; Acad Ltr 83-85; Buffalo ST Coll; Secndry Ed.

FISHMAN, ANDREW; South Shore HS; Brooklyn, NY; (Y); French Clb; School Musical; Var Tennis; JV Gym; NY ST Regents Schrlshp 85; Hofstra U; Bio.

FISK, DAVE; Richburg Central HS; Friendship, NY; (S); Yrbk Stf; VP Jr Cls; Bsktbl; Socr; High Hon Roll; Hon Roll; Jr NHS; NHS; Archlgy.

FISKE, BARRY; Irondeqoit HS; Rochester, NY; (Y); Boy Scts; Church Yth Grp; Computer Clb; Drama Clb; Latin Clb; Radio Clb; Ski Clb; Varsity Clb; Orch; School Musical; Life Scout Awd 84; Cmmnctns.

FITCH, AL; Greenwich Central HS; Greenwich, NY; (Y).

FITCH, ALLICIA; Mont Pleasant HS; Schenectady, NY; (Y); French Clb; JA; Spanish Clb; Chorus; Color Guard; French Hon Soc; Intl Brotherhood Of Magicians 85; JR Exec Cmmtt 85; Frgn Lang.

FITCH, CHUCK; Greenwich Central HS; Greenwich, NY; (Y); Boy Scts; Exploring; Nwsp Stf; Yrbk Stf; High Hon Roll; Hon Roll.

FITCH, DORIS T; Rome Free Acad; Rome, NY; (Y); 216/536; Church Yth Grp; Hosp Aide; Office Aide; Chorus; Nwsp Stf; Pres Sr Cls; Im Sftbl; Im Trk; Hon Roll; Rome Free Acad Nrs Schlrshp 85; Dr H A Zutruen Mem Awd 85; Mohawk Vly CC; Nrs.

FITCH, LAURA; East Rochester HS; Pittsford, NY; (Y); 14/112; Drama Clb; Acpl Chr; Band; Chorus; Church Choir; School Musical; School Play; Yrbk Rptr; Trs NHS; Allegheny Clg.

FITCH, TED; Clyde Savannah HS; Lyons, NY; (Y); Im Bsktbl; Var Golf; Hon Roll; Prfct Atten Awd; St Schlr; Regents Schlrshp; Internshp For Assemblymn Nozzolio; SUNY-OSWEGO; Math Teachr.

FITE, DEIDREA L; Wheatland-Chili HS; Scottsville, NY; (Y); 1/85; VP Ski Clb; Stage Crew; Pres Frsh Cls; VP Jr Cls; Rep Stu Cncl; Var Socr; JV Sftbl; High Hon Roll; NHS; Hghst Avg Eng 84-85; Excllnce Spn 84-85fhghst Avg 83-84; Cornell; Hotl Mgmt.

FITTS, ANITA; Port Chester SR HS; Port Chester, NY; (Y); VP Church Yth Grp; Color Guard; Hon Roll; NC Ag & Tech St U; Bus Adm.

FITTS, GREGORY; Starpoint Central HS; Sanborn, NY; (S); 24/198; Mrchg Band; Pep Band; Nwsp Ed-Chief; Nwsp Rptr; VP Co-Capt Golf; Co-Capt Tennis; Jr NHS; NHS; Pep Clb; Varsity Clb; Starpoint Stu Of Mnth 85; All-Cnty, All-St Bnds 80-85; All NE HS Concert Bnds 83-85; MI ST U; Communications.

FITTS, LANDON T; Saunders Trades & Tech HS; Yonkers, NY; (Y); 33/198; VICA; Ftbl; Hon Roll; U Of New Haven Acadmc Schlrshp 85; YAMSE Schlrshp 85; Highest Avg-Techncl Electrcty 12 85; U Of New Haven; Electrcl Engrng.

FITZ-GORDON, HEATHER; St Francis Prep; Queens Village, NY; (S); 168/700; Drama Clb; Hosp Aide; Band; Concert Band; Drill Tm; Mrchg Band; Orch; Pep Band; Stage Crew; Law.

FITZGERALD, AMY; Henninger HS; Syracuse, NY; (Y); Am Leg Aux Girls St; GAA; Band; Mrchg Band; Yrbk Sprt Ed; Rep Frsh Cls; Rep Soph Cls; Rep Jr Cls; Trs Sr Cls; Rep Stu Cncl.

FITZGERALD, BERNADETTE T; Homer Central HS; Cortland, NY; (Y); French Clb; German Clb; Girl Scts; Library Aide; Ski Clb; Nwsp Rptr; Nwsp Stf; St Lawrence U; Engl.

FITZGERALD, BRIAN; Elmira Free Acad; Elmira, NY; (Y); German Clb; Band; Mrchg Band; Symp Band; JV Var Socr; Var Trk; High Hon Roll; Hon Roll; Mktg.

FITZGERALD, BRIAN; Iona Preparatory Schl; New Rochelle, NY; (Y); 40/200; Hosp Aide; Nwsp Rptr; Crs Cntry; Trk; Hon Roll; NHS; Bus.

FITZGERALD, KERRY; East Islip HS; Islip Terrace, NY; (Y); 18/485; Cmnty Wkr; Math Tm; Political Wkr; Nwsp Rptr; Stu Cncl; Var L Tennis; High Hon Roll; Hon Roll; Jr NHS; NHS; Scty Distngshd Amer Stus 85; SUNY-BINGHAMTON; Econ.

FITZGERALD, KIM; Bishop Ludden HS; Camillus, NY; (S); Ski Clb; Variety Show; Trs Jr Cls; Score Keeper; NHS; Frnch Awd 81-82; Math.

FITZGERALD, PATRICIA H; St Barnabas HS; Yonkers, NY; (Y); 5/136; NFL; Office Aide; Nwsp Rptr; Sec Twrlr; High Hon Roll; Hon Roll; NHS; Prfct Atten Awd; Scholar Iona Coll & Manhattan 85; Pres Acad Fit Awd 85; Natl Sci Olympiad Physics 85; Fordham U; Law.

FITZGERALD, REGINA; St Edmund HS; Brooklyn, NY; (Y); 53/187; Sec Trs Stu Cncl; Sftbl; Vllybl; Hon Roll; Elem Educ.

FITZGERALD, SHEILA; Academy Of The Holy Names; Albany, NY; (Y); Drama Clb; NFL; Sec Speech Tm; Orch; School Play; Nwsp Stf; Lit Mag; Pres Stu Cncl; Var Bsktbl; Var Sftbl; Acadmc Schlrshp Basd Entrnc Exm 82-86; Degr Excllnc Natl Fornsc Leag 85.

FITZGERALD, THERESA; Holy Trinity HS; West Hempstead, NY; (Y); Cmnty Wkr; Hon Roll; Cert Of Achv In Sequntl Math Crs I 83; Adelphi U; Lbrl Arts.

FITZGERALD, TROY; Somers HS; Katonah, NY; (Y); 31/212; Boy Scts; Jazz Band; Symp Band; Var Tennis; Cit Awd; Hon Roll; Ntl Merit SF; OM 1st Regn 83-85; PTSA Serv Awd 85; Brigham Young U; Law.

FITZGIBBONS, MARY JUDE; Bishop Grimes HS; Syracuse, NY; (Y); FBLA; Hosp Aide; NFL; Ski Clb; Variety Show; Trk; Hon Roll; Spec Ed.

FITZPATRICK, ANNE; Whitesboro SR HS; Whitesboro, NY; (Y); 38/350; Drama Clb; GAA; Chorus; Rep Stu Cncl; Var Fld Hcky; Var Trk; Hon Roll; Jr NHS; Vrsty Ski Tm 84-85; Engrng.

FITZPATRICK, ERIC; Watertown HS; Watertown, NY; (Y); Key Clb; Concert Band; Mrchg Band; Jefferson CC; Bio.

FITZPATRICK, KEITH; St Francis Prep; Flushing, NY; (S); Crs Cntry; Swmmng; Trk; NHS; Opt Clb Awd.

FITZPATRICK, SHAWN M; Kensington HS; Buffalo, NY; (Y); 10/197; French Clb; Girl Scts; Pep Clb; Chorus; Hon Roll; Erie CC; Reg Surgcl Nrs.

FITZPATRICK, TARA; Irvington HS; Irvington, NY; (Y); 15/115; Pep Clb; Acpl Chr; Yrbk Ed-Chief; Pres Soph Cls; Var Capt Bsktbl; Var Capt Crs Cntry; Var Capt Trk; Elks Awd; Hon Roll; Key Clb.

FITZSIMMONS, ANDREA; Longwood HS; Ridge, NY; (S); 13/500; Nwsp Stf; Var Capt Crs Cntry; Var Capt Trk; High Hon Roll; Jr NHS; NHS; Scnt XI Gold Key Awd 85; All-Leag Crss Cnty 81-85; All-Leag Trck 81-85; U Of SD; Phy Educ.

FITZSIMMONS, DIANA; Washingtonville HS; Washingtonville, NY; (Y); 1/209; Symp Band; Yrbk Stf; Var Socr; NHS; NY Regents Schlrshp 85; Acad All-Amer 85; Binghampton; Intl Bus.

FITZSIMMONS, KIMBERLY A; Central Islip HS; Central Islip, NY; (Y); Church Yth Grp; Ski Clb; Stat Ftbl; Stat Lcrss; Var Score Keeper; JV Socr; JV Var Sftbl; Var Timer; Home Ec Awd For Child Care 85; SUNY Coll-Brockport; Psych.

FITZSIMMONS, PATRICIA; Churchville-Chili SR HS; Churchville, NY; (Y); GAA; Ski Clb; Acpl Chr; Madrigals; School Musical; Sec Soph Cls; Sec Jr Cls; Sec Sr Cls; Stu Cncl; JV Var Cheerleading; De Varian Awd Top Female Voclst Rochester Philhrmc Lg 84; Syracuse U; Music Prfrmnce.

FIUTAK, GEOFFREY; Christian Brothers Acad; Liverpool, NY; (Y); 3/93; Church Yth Grp; Exploring; Ski Clb; Nwsp Rptr; JV Var Tennis; JV Trk; High Hon Roll; Hon Roll; NHS.

FIX, MARY; Cleveland Hill HS; Cheektowaga, NY; (Y); 4-H; GAA; JCL; Var Capt Vllybl; Hon Roll; MIP JV 82-83, Vrsty 83-84; Acctng.

FLAGG, RON; Greece Olympia HS; Rochester, NY; (Y); 15/314; Church Yth Grp; FBLA; Varsity Clb; Var JV Socr; Var Capt Wrstlng; High Hon Roll; Hon Roll; NHS; Prfct Atten Awd; Brockport; Bus Admin.

FLAGLER, MICHAEL J; Niagara Wheatfield SR HS; Niagara Falls, NY; (Y); 67/315; Church Yth Grp; Key Clb; Rep Stu Cncl; Var Trk; Var Vllybl; Var Wrstlng; Hon Roll; Jr NHS; NHS; St Schlr; Hofstra U; Pol Sci.

FLAHERTY, MARY; Mt Mercy Acad; Buffalo, NY; (Y); Church Yth Grp; Computer Clb; Spanish Clb; School Play; Stage Crew; Rep Stu Cncl; Im JV Bowling; Im Vllybl; Tchr VBS 85; MVP JV Bwlng 84; 3rd Pl Frgn Lang Fair 85; U Notre Dame; Chld Care.

FLAHERTY, SUE M; West Islip HS; W Islip, NY; (Y); Var Bsktbl; Var Socr; Var Vllybl; High Hon Roll; Hon Roll; NHS; Im Badmtn; Sci Excllnc Awd 83; All Leag Vllybl 84; All Leag, Cnty & Conf Vllybl 85.

FLAHERTY, SUSAN; Roy C Ketcham HS; Wappingers Fall, NY; (Y); Drama Clb; Thesps; Chorus; School Musical; School Play; Stage Crew; Pres Frsh Cls; Stu Cncl; Bsktbl; Score Keeper; Indctd Intl Thespn Socty 85; Theatr Arts.

FLAHERTY, SUSAN M; Our Lady Of Mercy HS; New Hyde Pk, NY; (Y); 8/114; Dance Clb; Hosp Aide; Key Clb; Varsity Clb; Rep Jr Cls; Rep Sr Cls; Rep Stu Cncl; Gym; Socr; Sftbl; Fairfield U; Math.

FLAIM, JOHN; Saint Francis Prep; Middle Village, NY; (S); 218/724; Art Clb; Math Clb; Ski Clb; Im Ftbl; Im Ice Hcky; Im Socr; Hon Roll; Italian Merit Cert 83; NY ST Regents Schlrshp; Manhattan Coll; Elec Engrng.

FLAMENBAUM, MINDY; Sachem H S North; Holbrook, NY; (Y); 58/1300; Cmnty Wkr; FBLA; JA; Temple Yth Grp; Nwsp Rptr; Nwsp Stf; Lit Mag; Hon Roll; Jr NHS; NHS.

FLANAGAN, BRIAN; Hicksville HS; Hicksvl, NY; (Y); Ski Clb; Lcrss; Var Wrstlng; Am Legn Cert Schl Awd.

FLANAGAN, CARRIE E; Canisteo Central Schl; Hornell, NY; (Y); 9/80; JV Stat Bsktbl; High Hon Roll; NHS; Acad All Stars 85; Local Hnr Soc 84-85; Geneseo; Comp Sci.

FLANAGAN, DEAN M; Bishop Scully HS; Broadalbin, NY; (Y); 15/69; Pres Stu Cncl; Bsbl; Capt Bsktbl; Capt Ftbl; Hon Roll; NHS; NY ST Regnts Schlrshp 85; Tri Vlly Leag 1st Tm Southrn Div All Str 85; Union Coll; Lwyr.

FLANAGAN, MIKE; Aquinas Inst; Rochester, NY; (Y); 42/171; Boy Scts; Church Yth Grp; Var Capt Bsbl; Var Capt Ftbl; Var JV Wt Lftg; Hon Roll; Eagle Scout Awd 82; Theolgy IX Achvt Awd 82; Amer Hstry Achvt Awd 85; Math.

FLANAGAN, RICHARD; St John The Baptist HS; Bayshore, NY; (Y); 50/550; Debate Tm; Model UN; Nwsp Rptr; Lit Mag; Var Bowling.

FLANAGAN, VICTOR L; Angelica Central HS; Angelica, NY; (Y); 11/24; Camera Clb; 4-H; French Clb; Science Clb; Yrbk Ed-Chief; Yrbk Stf; Var Bsbl; JV Ftbl; JV Lcrss; NY ST Regnts Schlrshp 85; USMC; Nrsg.

FLANDER, PENNY; Whitesboro SR HS; Utica, NY; (Y); Boys Clb Am; Church Yth Grp; Exploring; Girl Scts; Hon Roll; Edward Kuth Memrl Schlrshp 85; Utica Schl Of Commerce; Med Sec.

FLANDERS, ALLISON M; Penfield HS; Penfield, NY; (Y); Spanish Clb; Yrbk Ed-Chief; Sec Stu Cncl; Var Capt Fld Hcky; Var Trk; High Hon Roll; NHS; Penfld HS Serv Awd 84-85; Rochester Sesqisentnnl Art Awd 84; Pres Physcl Ftns Awd 85; Psych.

FLANDERS, T PATRICK; Canajoharie Central HS; Canajoharie, NY; (Y); 11/101; Am Leg Boys St; Boy Scts; FCA; Varsity Clb; Yrbk Stf; Capt Wrstlng; NHS; ROTC Schlrshp 85; Clarkson U; Engnrng.

FLANIGAN, ANN; Hudson Falls SR HS; Hudson Falls, NY; (Y); 42/237; Church Yth Grp; Cmnty Wkr; Drama Clb; 4-H; Key Clb; Quiz Bowl; Science Clb; Spanish Clb; Chorus; School Musical; WA Cnty Dairy Prncss 85; Bio.

FLANNERY, RAYMOND L; Canisius HS; Orchard Pk, NY; (Y); 20/169; Church Yth Grp; JA; Math Clb; Nwsp Sprt Ed; Var L Bsktbl; Var L Trk; High Hon Roll; Mu Alp Tht; NHS; VP Prodtn JR Achvt 82-83; All Cathlc 2 Trck Evnts 83-84; Bst Defns Plyr Wnng Bsktbl Tm Leag 84-85; U Of Notre Dame; Math.

FLANSBURG, KELLI; Germantown Central HS; Germantown, NY; (Y); 2/50; Chorus; School Musical; Yrbk Stf; Pres Soph Cls; Pres Jr Cls; Pres Sr Cls; Rep Stu Cncl; Var Bsktbl; Var Fld Hcky; Var Sftbl; Stu Exchng Ambssdr 85; Part In Rgnl Lvl Of Oratorical Cont Spnsrd By Amer Lgn 85.

FLASHBURG, SANDRA; Sheepshead Bay HS; Brooklyn, NY; (Y); School Play; Yrbk Bus Mgr; Stu Cncl; Bnai Brith Holocaust Cntst 85; NYS Bar Assn For Mock Trl 85; Dailey News/NY Yankees Super Yth 85; Advrtsng.

FLEARY, NOCOLE B; James Madison HS; Brooklyn, NY; (Y); 33/812; Office Aide; School Musical; Nwsp Rptr; Yrbk Stf; Rep Stu Cncl; High Hon Roll; Hon Roll; NY St Regents Schlrshp 85; Baruch Coll Incentv Awd 85; Baruch Coll; Acctng.

FLECK, LAURIE A; Kingston HS; Kingston, NY; (Y); 21/520; Pres Sec AFS; Girl Scts; Hosp Aide; Rep Stu Cncl; Var Twrlr; God Cntry Awd; High Hon Roll; NHS; Spanish NHS; Grl Sct Gld Awd 84; U Of VT; Physcl Thrpy.

FLECKEN, ERIC; Depew HS; Cheektowaga, NY; (Y); 25/295; VP Computer Clb; Quiz Bowl; Teachers Aide; Lit Mag; Hon Roll; NHS; Adv Placemnt Exam Engl Top Rankng 85; Egan Scholar 85; Pres Scholar 85; Mercy Hurst Coll; Psych.

FLEET, MICHELLE M; Rome Free Acad; Rome, NY; (Y); 3/536; Intnl Clb; Letterman Clb; Varsity Clb; Yrbk Stf; Stu Cncl; Var Trk; Var Twrlr; Hon Roll; NHS; Opt Clb Awd; Miss NY State Fair 82; Miss Senior NY State Intermdt Solo Baton Champ 83; Miss Oneida Cnty Batn Twrl; Clarkson U; Accounting.

FLEICHER, TOMILYNN; Greene Central HS; Chenango Forks, NY; (Y); French Clb; JV Sftbl; Im Vllybl; High Hon Roll; NHS; Sci.

FLEIGNER, JAMES; Newfield HS; Selden, NY; (S); 4/547; Boy Scts; Drama Clb; Chorus; School Musical; Cit Awd; Hon Roll; Jr NHS; NHS; Swarthmore Coll; Mech Engrng.

FLEISCHER, LEON; Mahopac HS; Mahopac, NY; (Y); 23/450; Trk; NHS.

FLEISCHUT, MICHAEL; Gloversville HS; Gloversville, NY; (Y); 12/236; AFS; French Clb; Ski Clb; VP Stu Cncl; Capt Crs Cntry; Hon Roll; NHS; Pres Schlr; Clarkson U; Chem Engrng.

FLEMING, AVALON; John Dewey HS; Brooklyn, NY; (Y); Im Gym; Im Tennis; Im Vllybl; Hon Roll.

FLEMING, BARBARA; Eastern District HS; Brooklyn, NY; (Y); 87/331; Church Yth Grp; Cmnty Wkr; FNA; Hosp Aide; Library Aide; Office Aide; Red Cross Aide; Teachers Aide; Church Choir; Rep Frsh Cls; Mdl & Cert Excllnce Hlth Careers 85; Nrsg.

FLEMING, COLLEEN; Albany HS; Albany, NY; (Y); Church Yth Grp; Office Aide; Chorus; Orch; School Musical; Var Bowling; Prfct Atten Awd; Mst Musical 84-85; Bst Sect Ldr 84-85; Mst Cmtt To Music 84-85; Vocal Music.

FLEMING, LAURA; Grand Island HS; Grand Island, NY; (Y); Church Yth Grp; Cmnty Wkr; Dance Clb; French Clb; Math Clb; Ski Clb; Pres Stu Cncl; Im Badmtn; Hon Roll; NHS; Engnrng.

FLEMING, MARGARET; Acad Of The Holy Names; Loudonville, NY; (Y); Cmnty Wkr; Drama Clb; Hosp Aide; Speech Tm; School Play; Nwsp Stf; Yrbk Ed-Chief; Lit Mag; Natl Sci Olympd 85; Mst Dedctd Fund Rsr Nwspapr 85; Finance.

FLEMING, TERESA M; Houghton Acad; Angelica, NY; (Y); 3/28; Chess Clb; French Clb; Science Clb; Ski Clb; Chorus; Sec Sr Cls; Bsktbl; Cheerleading; Socr; High Hon Roll; NY ST Rgnts Schrlshp 85; Nazareth Coll Rochester; Frnch.

FLETCHER, CHRISTINE M; Schoharie Central HS; Schoharie, NY; (Y); GAA; Library Aide; Pep Clb; Teachers Aide; Chorus; Church Choir; Pres Jr Cls; JV Var Socr; Nrsg.

FLETCHER, DREW; Stissing Mountain JR SR HS; Pine Plains, NY; (Y); Pres FFA; Rep Stu Cncl; Sec FFA 84-85; VP NY Assn FFA 85-86; SUNY-COBLESKILL; Ag Educ.

FLETCHER, JEFF; Naples Central HS; Naples, NY; (Y); JV Var Score Keeper; Hon Roll; BOCES Mst Imprvd 85; Tulsa JR Coll; Elec.

FLETH, EDWARD; Churchville Chili HS; Rochester, NY; (Y); Church Yth Grp; Drama Clb; Math Tm; Trk; Vllybl; Hon Roll; NHS; Houghton Coll.

FLEURY, AMY; Franklin Acad; Burke, NY; (Y); FBLA; Our Lady Of Victory; Sec.

FLEURY, CHRISTINE; Guilderland Central HS; Schenectady, NY; (Y); Rep Sr Cls; JV Var Bsktbl; Var Diving; Var Capt Swmmng; High Hon Roll; Hon Roll; Ntl Merit Schol; Med.

FLICK, VICKI L; La Fargeville Central HS; Clayton, NY; (Y); 1/26; Quiz Bowl; Pres Band; Pres Sec Chorus; Pres Sr Cls; L Cheerleading; NHS; Ntl Merit Ltr; Val; Pres French Clb; GAA; Outstndng Stu Awd; Frontier Leag-All Star Scr; St Lawrence U; Math.

FLICKINGER, HAL; Liverpool HS; Liverpool, NY; (S); 127/792; Church Yth Grp; ROTC; Band; Color Guard; Drill Tm; Var Stat Bsktbl; Im Vllybl; Hon Roll; Jr NHS; NHS; Ntl Wnnr Vly Forge Hnr Awd 84; Outstndng Cadet Awd 84; Resv Off Assoc Awd 83; Syracuse U; US Marine.

FLICKINGER, THOMAS; Liverpool HS; Liverpool, NY; (S); 133/792; Church Yth Grp; ROTC; Band; Rep Stu Cncl; JV Im Bsktbl; Ftbl; Hon Roll; Jr NHS; NHS; Reserve Offcrs Assoc Awd 82; Natl Sojurners Awd 82; Syracuse U; Bus Admin.

FLIEGEL, KAREN S; Nanuet SR HS; Nanuet, NY; (Y); 1/160; Debate Tm; Math Clb; Temple Yth Grp; Band; Concert Band; Mrchg Band; Nwsp Ed-Chief; Nwsp Rptr; Nwsp Stf; Yrbk Stf; Music & Math Actvtys; Ntl Hnr Scty; Princeton; Law.

FLIEGLER, ROBERT J; Commack South HS; Commack, NY; (Y); 12/420; Cmnty Wkr; Nwsp Stf; Yrbk Sprt Ed; JV Bsktbl; Var L Socr; Var L Trk; High Hon Roll; NHS; Stu Ldrshp Awd 84-85; Pres Acad Fitnss Awd 85; Regents Scholar 85; Franklin & Marshall Coll; Bio.

FLINT, GARY; Ballston Spa HS; Ballston Spa, NY; (Y); 24/117; Trs Church Yth Grp; VP Service Clb; High Hon Roll; Hon Roll; NHS; ST U Of NY; Comp Sci.

FLINT, LAURA; Berlin Central HS; Petersburg, NY; (S); 4-H; GAA; Ski Clb; Band; Chorus; JV Bsktbl; Var Socr; Var Sftbl; High Hon Roll; Prfct Atten Awd.

FLOOD, BRIAN; St Marys Boys HS; Muttontown, NY; (Y); Cmnty Wkr; VP Ski Clb; Nwsp Phtg; Nwsp Rptr; Nwsp Stf; Yrbk Phtg; Yrbk Rptr; Lit Mag; Rep Stu Cncl; Var Golf; Outstndng Yrbk,Newspr 84; Acadmc Perfrmnc Schlrshp 85; LIC; Pre Law.

FLOOD, EILEEN; The Mary Louis Acad; Richmond Hill, NY; (Y); Church Yth Grp; Girl Scts; Library Aide; Political Wkr; Teachers Aide; Im Bsktbl; Im Ftbl; JV Score Keeper; NEDT Awd; VP Law Clb 84-85.

FLOOD, JENNIFER; Academy Of St Joseph; Northport, NY; (Y); Church Yth Grp; Pep Clb; Teachers Aide; Socr; Kiwanis Awd; Math Imprvmnt Awd 85; Priv Schl St Champ Soccer 83; Penn ST U; Radiologist.

FLOOD, SCOTT; Minisink Valley HS; Middletown, NY; (Y); 10/225; Quiz Bowl; Scholastic Bowl; Band; Concert Band; Jazz Band; Mrchg Band; Pep Band; Symp Band; Bsktbl; Ftbl; Wrld Fnls Olympc Of Mnd 84; U Of MD; Aero Engnrg.

FLORA, KENT P; North Rose Wolcott HS; Wolcott, NY; (Y); Art Clb; Cmnty Wkr; Spanish Clb; Yrbk Stf; Var Golf; Spnsh Achvt Awd 83; Hole In One Awd 82-83; Golf Sectnl Qual 84-85; Bradley U; Comm Art.

FLORCZYK, RAY M; Paul V Moore HS; Central Sq, NY; (Y); 49/297; Boy Scts; ROTC; Hon Roll; NHS; Pres Schlr; Regents Schlrshp; ST U NY Oswego; Med.

FLORENDO, JAMES; Bishop Scully HS; Amsterdam, NY; (S); 2/75; Am Leg Boys St; Math Clb; VP Stu Cncl; Var Golf; Var Tennis; Bausch & Lomb Sci Awd; VP NHS; Engrng.

FLORES, ALMA; Bushwick HS; Brooklyn, NY; (Y); 2/208; Teachers Aide; Church Choir; School Play; Nwsp Ed-Chief; Nwsp Rptr; Yrbk Stf; Lit Mag; Trs Stu Cncl; Mgr(s); Swmmng; Randolph Evans Mem & Roothbert Fellow Schlrshps 85; Smith Coll; Pre Med.

FLORES, CHRISTEL; Brooklyn Technical HS; Jamaica, NY; (Y); Pres Science Clb; Sec Service Clb; Rep Jr Cls; Hon Roll; NHS; Mathletes; Stu Of The Mnth Material Sci 83; Bronz Mdl Bio 84; Natl Sci Olympiad-Patrtcptd With Distnctn 85.

FLORES, DIANA; Christopher Columbus HS; Bronx, NY; (Y); Dance Clb; Drama Clb; Girl Scts; NFL; Spanish Clb; Speech Tm; Band; Concert Band; School Play; Pres Church Yth Grp; Relgn Hnrs 82; John Jay Coll; Crmnl Law.

FLORES, JAVIER; Fordham Preparatory Schl; Yonkers, NY; (Y); Spanish Clb; Var Capt Ftbl; Capt Wt Lftg; Spanish NHS; CHSFL SR Bwl & 1st Tm All Leag 84; Daily Nws 2nd Tm All City 84; Fordham U; Econ.

FLORES, JENNY; Medina HS; Medina, NY; (Y); #23 In Class; AFS; Debate Tm; Pep Clb; Spanish Clb; Acpl Chr; Chorus; Var Cheerleading; Var Pom Pon; Hon Roll; NHS; Daisy Chain 85; Honorati 84-85; Bus.

FLORES, KAREN; Columbia HS; Menands, NY; (Y); 10/353; Key Clb; Math Tm; Ski Clb; Speech Tm; Varsity Clb; Crs Cntry; Trk; High Hon Roll; NHS; Pres Schlr; Menands Rotry Schlrshp; Ntl Hnr Soc; Clarkson U; Engrng.

FLORES, MARIE MARDI S; John S Burke Catholic HS; Middletown, NY; (Y); Cmnty Wkr; Office Aide; Spanish Clb; Im Bowling; Vllybl; High Hon Roll; Hon Roll; English Clb; Rep Frsh Cls; Var Trk; ROTC U Of Tampa 85; WSVC Schlrshp 85; U Of CA; Pre-Med.

FLORES, PAULA; Cathedral HS; Corona, NY; (Y); 19/298; JA; Color Guard; Mrchg Band; Hon Roll; Prfct Atten Awd; Acctnt.

FLORESKA, KATIA; Springfield Gardens HS; Rosedale, NY; (Y); 118/443; Dance Clb; Debate Tm; JA; Chorus; School Musical; School Play; Vllybl; Cit Awd; Hon Roll; Prfct Atten Awd; RN.

FLORIA, CAROL; St John The Bapitst D HS; Selden, NY; (Y); Math Clb; Math Tm; Pom Pon; Twrlr; Mu Alp Tht.

FLORIE, PHILIP; A G Berner HS; Massapequa Park, NY; (Y); JV Socr; Var L Wrstlng; All Cnty Wrestler 6th Pl 84-85; Arch.

FLOSS, AMY TAYLOR; Nardin Acad; Buffalo, NY; (Y); Service Clb; Stage Crew; Yrbk Phtg; Yrbk Stf; Trs Sr Cls; Hon Roll; 1st Pl Sci Fair & Art Show; Outstndg Awd Alg; SUNY Buffalo.

FLOWER, KRISTINE; Glens Falls HS; Glen Falls, NY; (Y); Girl Scts; Yrbk Stf; Stat Fld Hcky; Mgr(s); Score Keeper; High Hon Roll; Hon Roll.

FLOWERS, AMY; Romulus Central HS; Waterloo, NY; (S); 3/40; Chorus; Capt Color Guard; School Musical; Variety Show; Pres Frsh Cls; Pres Soph Cls; Pres Jr Cls; JV Var Cheerleading; High Hon Roll; NHS; Sociolgy.

FLOYD, DARWIN E; The Bronx High School Of Science; Bronx, NY; (Y); Debate Tm; Teachers Aide; Band; Color Guard; Orch; Var Capt Bsktbl; Prfct Atten Awd; Princpls Awd 83; Math Awd 83; Law.

FLOYD, DAVID; Fort Ann Central HS; W Ft Ann, NY; (Y); Boy Scts; French Clb; Math Clb; Yrbk Stf; Bsbl; High Hon Roll; Hon Roll; ACC.

FLOYD, MARNITA Y; Christopher Columbus HS; Bronx, NY; (Y); 33/792; Key Clb; Nwsp Rptr; Cheerleading; Hon Roll; Merit Chem Awd 85farista 85.

FLOYD, REMONIA; Andrew Jackson HS; Cambria Hgts, NY; (Y); Dance Clb; Girl Scts; Chorus; Church Choir; Cheerleading; Vllybl; Hon Roll; Jr NHS; NHS; Pre-Med.

FLUSCHE, PAMELA; F D Roosevelt HS; Hyde Park, NY; (Y); Ski Clb; Band; Concert Band; Mrchg Band; Var L Socr; Var L Trk; JV Var Vllybl; Hon Roll; NHS; Ntl Merit Ltr; Notre Dame; Engr.

FLYNN, ANDREW L; Fordham Prep; Scarsdale, NY; (Y); Hosp Aide; Key Clb; Service Clb; Ski Clb; Yrbk Ed-Chief; Yrbk Stf; Capt Var Golf; Var Swmmng; NHS; Ntl Merit SF; Jesuit Pres Schlr-Fordham Prep 82-86; Genl Exclnc Awd 83-85; Clsscs Comptn; Hstry.

FLYNN, ANNE MARIE; Our Lady Of Mercy Acad; Plainview, NY; (Y); Powder Puff Ftbl; Trk; 2nd Hnrs 3rd Qrtr 82-85; St Johns U; Acctg.

FLYNN, CHRIS; Massena Central HS; Massena, NY; (Y); Church Yth Grp; Computer Clb; Bsbl; Cit Awd; Hon Roll; Prfct Atten Awd; Bus.

FLYNN, DEBORAH; Newark Valley HS; Owego, NY; (Y); 11/130; Church Yth Grp; Library Aide; Ski Clb; Stu Cncl; Stat Socr; Var Trk; High Hon Roll; Hon Roll; NHS; Salute To Yth 85; Elec Engr.

FLYNN, FRANCIS J; Penn Yan Acad; Penn Yan, NY; (Y); 41/189; Am Leg Boys St; VP Jr Cls; VP Sr Cls; JV Ftbl; Var Lcrss; Bus Admin.

FLYNN, KAREN; Port Jervis SR HS; Westbrookvl, NY; (Y); Key Clb; Spanish Clb; Varsity Clb; Band; Capt Color Guard; Capt Drm Mjr(t); Mrchg Band; Pep Band; Yrbk Stf; Var Capt Mat Maids; Miss Orange Cnty Fair 85; Law.

FLYNN, MARGARET; Binghamton HS; Binghamton, NY; (Y); 4/560; Art Clb; Key Clb; Ski Clb; Jazz Band; High Hon Roll; NHS; Ntl Merit SF; Gld Mdl Natl Schltc Art Awd 83; Arch.

FLYNN, MARY; Solvay HS; Solvay, NY; (Y); Key Clb; Math Clb; Ski Clb; Spanish Clb; Band; Concert Band; Jr Cls; Sr Cls; Hon Roll; Acctng.

FLYNN, MARY A; Red Creek JR-SR HS; Red Creek, NY; (Y); VP French Clb; Girl Scts; Sec Ski Clb; Band; JV Socr; High Hon Roll; NHS; Bio.

FLYNN, NICOLE; Sacred Heart HS; Yonkers, NY; (Y); High Hon Roll; Hon Roll; 1st & 2nd Semstr HS Schlrshp 83-85; Engl.

FLYNN, PATRICIA; Smithtown High School East; Smithtown, NY; (Y); GAA; Spanish Clb; Varsity Clb; Off Frsh Cls; Off Soph Cls; Off Jr Cls; Var Bsktbl; Var L Fld Hcky; Sftbl; Var L Vllybl; Girls Ldrs Clb Sec 83-85; Psych.

FLYNN, TARA A; Notre Dame HS; Jackson Heights, NY; (Y); Chess Clb; Girl Scts; Hosp Aide; Chorus; Yrbk Phtg; Yrbk Stf; Mgr Bsktbl; Tennis; High Hon Roll; Hon Roll; 1st Hnrs All Subj H S 81-85; Fll Schlrshp To H S; NY Regnts Schlrshp; Williams Coll; Bio.

FLYNN, TARA M; Guilderland Central HS; Albany, NY; (Y); 16/369; Drama Clb; Varsity Clb; Chorus; School Musical; School Play; Stage Crew; Lit Mag; Trk; High Hon Roll; NHS; C J Ciaccio Schlrshp Awd PTSA 85; Alum Assn Awd Exclnc Engl 85; U Of Rochester; Poli Sci.

FLYNN, TIMOTHY; Bishop Timon HS; Hamburg, NY; (Y); Bus.

FLYNN, TIMOTHY; Cardinal Mooney HS; Rochester, NY; (Y); Aud/Vis; Church Yth Grp; Library Aide; Chorus; School Musical; Trs Frsh Cls; Trs Jr Cls; JV Bsbl; Im Bsktbl; JV Wrstlng; U Of TN Knoxville; Cmmnctns.

FLYNN, TINA; Acad Of The Holy Names; Schenectady, NY; (Y); Church Yth Grp; Nwsp Stf; Ed Lit Mag; Western Civilization Awd 84; Alg II Awd 85; Adv Plcmnt Am Hist Awd 85; Lit Mag Wrtng Fiction Awd 85; Sienas; Bus.

FODROWSKI, ELIZABETH A; Smithtown West HS; Smithtown, NY; (Y); Yrbk Stf; Stu Cncl; Stat Ftbl; Hon Roll; NY St Regents Schlrshp 85; SUNY-GENESEO; Acctng.

FOELS, PATRICIA; Tonawanda SR HS; Tonawanda, NY; (Y); #1 In Class; Church Yth Grp; Cmnty Wkr; French Clb; Acpl Chr; Jazz Band; School Musical; Stu Cncl; Cheerleading; High Hon Roll; Jr NHS; Rotary Clb Essay Awd 84; Elmira Key Awd 85; Kiwanis Ctznshp Awd 83; Tulane LA; Lang.

FOGARTY, MAUREEN P; Cardinal Spellman HS; Bronx, NY; (Y); 124/525; L Var Crs Cntry; L Var Trk; Hon Roll; Iona Coll; Accntg.

FOGEL, ROBERT; The Bronx High School Of Science; Bronx, NY; (Y); Office Aide; Bausch & Lomb Sci Awd; High Hon Roll; NHS; Ntl Merit Ltr; Knights Pythias Awd Acadmc Excllnc 85; Awd Excllnc Forgn Lang 85; Cornell U; Bio.

FOGLE, TROY; Corning-Painted Post West HS; Corning, NY; (Y); Key Clb; Varsity Clb; School Play; Var JV Ftbl; Var JV Lcrss; High Hon Roll; Hon Roll; Binghamton SUNY; Math.

FOLAND, PENNY; Faith Heritage HS; Brewerton, NY; (Y); 3/27; Church Yth Grp; Chorus; Nwsp Stf; Var L Socr; Var L Trk; Var Capt Vllybl; Cit Awd; Hon Roll; Pres NHS; Hdmstrs Awd; Natl Sci Merit Awd; Med.

FOLCK, BRIAN D; Kenmore West SR HS; Tonawanda, NY; (Y); Band; Concert Band; Mrchg Band; Variety Show; Hon Roll; Spanish NHS; Natl Spnsh Exam 83; Engrng.

FOLEY, ANN; Ripley Central Schl; Ripley, NY; (S); 3/27; Pep Clb; VP Frsh Cls; Sec Jr Cls; Vllybl; Hon Roll; NHS; Comp Tech; Comp Tech.

FOLEY, DEBORAH; Nanuet HS; Nanuet, NY; (Y); 22/173; Debate Tm; Intnl Clb; Model UN; Quiz Bowl; Scholastic Bowl; Nwsp Rptr; Nwsp Stf; Stat Fld Hcky; High Hon Roll; Hon Roll; SUNY Albny; Bus.

FOLEY, DIANE; Bishop Magunn HS; Albany, NY; (S); 13/118; Am Leg Aux Girls St; Nwsp Rptr; Yrbk Stf; VP Jr Cls; Stu Cncl; Capt Cheerleading; Sftbl; High Hon Roll; NHS; Ntl Merit Ldrshp Awd 83-84; ST U Of Albany; Psych.

FOLEY, EILEEN; Gates-Chili HS; Rochester, NY; (Y); 9/463; French Clb; Math Clb; Math Tm; Rep Jr Cls; Var Capt Cheerleading; Var Capt Pom Pon; High Hon Roll; NHS; Merit Scholar Clarkson U 85-86; NYS Regents Scholar 85; Pres Acad Fit Awd 85; VA Polytech; Biomed.

FOLEY, ELIZABETH; Sacred Heart HS; Yonkers, NY; (S); Church Yth Grp; 4-H; Hosp Aide; Intnl Clb; Nwsp Rptr; Trk; Vllybl; 4-H Awd; Hon Roll; NHS; Citation Of Merit 84; Svc Awd 84.

FOLEY, KEVIN; Washingtonville HS; Blooming Grove, NY; (Y); Chess Clb; 4-H; Ski Clb; Spanish Clb; Bsktbl; Golf; Tennis; Church Yth Grp; Cmnty Wkr; Varsity Clb; Regnts Schlrshp 85; MVP Glf 84; Boston U; Bus Mgt.

FOLEY, KIERAN; Academy Of The Resurrection HS; Rye, NY; (Y); Dance Clb; Math Clb; Chorus; Pres Soph Cls; Rep Stu Cncl; Var Swmmng; Var Trk; Var Vllybl; High Hon Roll; NHS; Bus.

FOLEY, MAUREEN; General Douglas Mac Arthur HS; Levittown, NY; (Y); Computer Clb; Science Clb; Yrbk Stf; JV Bsktbl; Cheerleading; Socr; Trk; High Hon Roll; Hon Roll; Jr NHS; Bio.

FOLEY, VINCE; Clayton A Bouton HS; Voorheesville, NY; (Y); Church Yth Grp; Cmnty Wkr; Key Clb; Spanish Clb; Stage Crew; Variety Show; Nwsp Stf; Rep Trs Stu Cncl; Var L Bsbl; Var Capt Bsktbl; Comp Sci.

FONDA, KRISTEN; Hudson HS; Hudson, NY; (Y); Pres Church Yth Grp; Hosp Aide; Church Choir; Yrbk Stf; VP Frsh Cls; VP Soph Cls; Var Capt Bsktbl; JV Cheerleading; Var Capt Sftbl; Var Tennis; MVP-VRSTY Bsktbl 83-84, Vrsty Sftbl 84-85; Most Impvd Plyr Vrsty Tennis 84; Chld Psych.

FONDACARO, MICHAEL; Shenendehowa HS; Clifton Pk, NY; (Y); 205/650; Band; Chorus; Orch; Pep Band; School Musical; Swing Chorus; High Hon Roll; Hon Roll; Outstndng Acad Achvt 83-84; Top Rated HS Band/ST 84-85; Coll Of St Rose; Comm.

FONDY, SUSAN R E; Jamesville-De Witt HS; Syracuse, NY; (Y); 16/224; Math Tm; Model UN; Crs Cntry; Gym; Trk; High Hon Roll; NHS; Ntl Merit Ltr; Church Yth Grp; French Clb; Bristol-Myers Corp Schlrshp 85; NYS Regnts Schlrshp 85; NYS U Binghamton; Chem.

FONG, DAVID; Norman Thomas HS; Brooklyn, NY; (S); 48/667; JA; Hon Roll; Mock Election 84; Regents Schlrshp 85; System Analyst.

FONG, MING Y; Hunter College HS; Brooklyn, NY; (Y); Hosp Aide; Math Clb; Math Tm; Model UN; Swing Chorus; Yrbk Stf; Trs Jr Cls; Var Vllybl; Im Wrstlng; Mu Alp Tht; Yale U; Chem.

FONSECA, PATRICIA; Saratoga Springs HS; Greenfield Center, NY; (Y); 3/465; Key Clb; Orch; Fld Hcky; High Hon Roll; NHS; Ntl Merit Ltr; Colby Coll Bk Awd; Eng Dept Essay Awd; Skidmore Coll; Law.

FONTAINE, JULIE; Galway HS; Middle Grove, NY; (Y); 4/78; Drama Clb; GAA; Yrbk Stf; Socr; Capt Trk; Vllybl; High Hon Roll; Hon Roll; NHS; Galway Tchrs Assoc Schlrshp 85; Siera Clg; Math.

FONTANA, DAVID; Hauppauge HS; Smithtown, NY; (Y); Camera Clb; Nwsp Rptr; Nwsp Sprt Ed; Nwsp Stf; Badmtn; Bsktbl; Ftbl; Golf; Wt Lftg; Hon Roll; Law.

FONTANA, FRANK; Bronx H S Of Science; Bronx, NY; (Y); Chess Clb; Cmnty Wkr; Political Wkr; Nwsp Stf; Var Bsbl; Jr NHS; Prfct Atten Awd; U VA; Arch.

FONTANA, JEAN; Commack H S North; Commack, NY; (Y); Hon Roll; Gdnc Aid 82-85; Accntng.

FONTANA, THERESA; Bishop Ford C C HS; Brooklyn, NY; (Y); JA; Math Tm; Speech Tm; Rep Stu Cncl; Im Bowling; High Hon Roll; NHS; Acad Schlrshp Johnson & Wales 85-86; Johnson & Wales Coll; Mgmt.

FOOTE, DEBORAH; Altmar-Parish-Williamstown HS; Parish, NY; (Y); Church Yth Grp; Drama Clb; VP French Clb; Ski Clb; Varsity Clb; Band; Concert Band; Mrchg Band; School Play; Yrbk Rptr; Jrnlsm.

FOOTE, HEATHER; John Marshall HS; Rochester, NY; (Y); 5/178; Aud/Vis; Math Tm; Service Clb; Ski Clb; Yrbk Stf; VP Sr Cls; Mgr(s); NHS; VFW Awd; Pep Clb; Yth Cares Awd 84; Rgnts Schlrshp NY ST 85; U Of MI; Polt Sci.

FORBES, CARL A; Yonkers HS; Yonkers, NY; (Y); 9/378; Debate Tm; Drama Clb; Math Tm; Variety Show; Lit Mag; Hon Roll; NY ST Regnts Schlrshp 85; Afro-Amrcn Cltrl Soc Pres 85; Athln Soc 85; Le Moyne Coll; Poltcl Sci.

FORBES, MICHELLE; Auburn HS; Auburn, NY; (Y); 6/500; Drama Clb; School Musical; Stage Crew; Stat Score Keeper; High Hon Roll; NHS; Prfct Atten Awd; Comp Sci.

FORD, COURTNEY; City Honors Schl; Buffalo, NY; (Y); 7/98; French Clb; Latin Clb; Nwsp Stf; Yrbk Stf; Var Capt Drama Clb; L Mgr Socr; Var L Vllybl; High Hon Roll; Prfct Atten Awd; St Schlr; Semi Fin 85; Mt Holyoke Bk Awd 84; Rochester Inst Tech; Comp Math.

FORD, HELEN L; St Johns Acad; Plattsburgh, NY; (Y); 3/45; Sec Jr Cls; Rep Stu Cncl; Var L Cheerleading; Var L Socr; Var L Sftbl; High Hon Roll; Ntl Merit Ltr; 4 Year Air Force ROTC Schlrshp 85; Clarkson U; Electrical Engnrg.

FORD, JACQUELINE E; Aquinas HS; Bronx, NY; (Y); 51/178; Cmnty Wkr; Dance Clb; Drama Clb; Office Aide; Chorus; Church Choir; School Musical; School Play; Hon Roll; Prfct Atten Awd; Prfct Atten Awd 82-85; Hrn Roll 82-85; Schl Musicl & Plys 82-85; Pdtrcn.

FORD, JENNIFER M; Massena Central HS; Massena, NY; (Y); 6/309; Cmnty Wkr; Yrbk Stf; JV Var Cheerleading; Mgr(s); JV Var Socr; High Hon Roll; NHS; Pres Schlr; St Schlr; Acad Banq Schltc Awd 85; Top SR Female Acad Banq 85; Hnr Stu Awd 85; Potsdam ST; Pre-Med.

FORD, JUDY; Andrew Jackson HS; Richmond Hill, NY; (Y); #1 In Class; Hosp Aide; Science Clb; Service Clb; Church Choir; Trs Sr Cls; Var Trk; High Hon Roll; NHS; Ntl Merit SF; Prfct Atten Awd; Qns Clg Pres Awd Acadmc Achvt 83-85; 1st Pl Schl Sci Fair 85; SUNY Stonybrook; Bio.

FORD, MARIA; Hillcrest HS; Cambria Hts, NY; (Y); Church Yth Grp; Cmnty Wkr; Drama Clb; Office Aide; Thesps; Church Choir; School Play; Lit Mag; Hon Roll; Queens Coll Presdntl Awd For Achvt 83; Spelman Coll; Chldhd Ed.

FORD, SEAN CRISPIN; Archbishop Walsh HS; Olean, NY; (Y); 19/60; Am Leg Boys St; Nwsp Sprt Ed; Rep Stu Cncl; JV Capt Bsbl; Var Capt Bsktbl; Var Capt Ftbl; Hon Roll; Letterman Clb; Ski Clb; Varsity Clb; Cty Yth Brd 84; MVP JV Bsktbl Tm 84; Mst Sprtd Ftbl Plyr Awd 83; Mktng.

FORDE, ANN P; Sacred Heart Acad; Massapequa, NY; (Y); Cmnty Wkr; Debate Tm; Hosp Aide; Political Wkr; Red Cross Aide; School Play; Yrbk Stf; Hon Roll; NHS; Pres Futr Physcns 84-85; NY ST Regnts Schlrshp 85; Fordham U Grnt 85; Fordham U; Jrnlsm.

FORDE, LAURA K; Pinecrest Christian HS; Salisbury Center, NY; (S); 1/22; Church Yth Grp; Teachers Aide; Acpl Chr; Chorus; Church Choir; School Musical; VP Stu Cncl; Var L Bsktbl; Var Score Keeper; Var Sftbl; Outstndng Serv In Music 83; Highest Over All Average 84; Messiah.

FORDE, TRACEY; Central Islip HS; Central Islip, NY; (Y); 4/350; Mrchg Band; Nwsp Rptr; Yrbk Stf; Lit Mag; Sec Frsh Cls; Sec Soph Cls; Rep Jr Cls; Pres Sr Cls; Rep Stu Cncl; VP NHS; Med.

FORELLA, JANET; St Joseph By The Sea; Staten Island, NY; (Y); Art Clb; Church Yth Grp; Drama Clb; School Play; Yrbk Stf; 1st Rnkng Art JR Yr Awd 85; Fshn Inst Tech; Comm Art.

FOREMAN, TRACY; Rome Free Acad; Rome, NY; (Y); 37/536; Cmnty Wkr; Key Clb; Band; Church Choir; Jazz Band; Mrchg Band; Pep Band; JV Golf; JV Tennis; NHS; NYS Regents Schlrshp 85; Amer Assoc U Women Schlrshp 85; Pres Acad Ftns Awd 85; SUNY-ALBANY; Bus.

FORGET, TRACEY; Plattsburgh HS; Plattsburgh, NY; (Y); VP Service Clb; Hon Roll; Acad Awd Alg 83; Plattsburgh ST U; Math.

FORGIONE, DIANE; North Babylon SR HS; North Babylon, NY; (Y); Girl Scts; Library Aide; VICA; Chorus; High Hon Roll; Hon Roll; Jr NHS; NHS; Grl Scout Slvr Awd 85; Frmngdl Coll; Dntl Hygn.

FORMICA, JOSEPHINE; Bishop Kearney HS; Brooklyn, NY; (Y); VP Dance Clb; School Play; Stage Crew; Variety Show; Prncpls List 82-83; 1st Hnrs 83-84; 2nd Hnrs 84-85; St Vincents Med Ctr; Nrs.

FORNEFELD, MICHELLE; Eastridge HS; Rochester, NY; (Y); 11/210; German Clb; Office Aide; Red Cross Aide; Concert Band; Mrchg Band; School Musical; Nwsp Stf; Yrbk Stf; High Hon Roll; Hon Roll; Rochester Sueuben Soc 85; Htl Mgmt.

FORNES, MARY LEE; Springville Griffith Inst; Springville, NY; (Y); 2/201; Trs Key Clb; Band; Chorus; Orch; JV Var Bsktbl; JV Diving; Var Swmmng; JV Vllybl; French Hon Soc; High Hon Roll; U Of NC Chpl Hl; Vtrnry Med.

FORNESS, RICHARD J; Lyme Central Schl; Chaumont, NY; (Y); 5/33; Yrbk Ed-Chief; L Bsbl; L Bsktbl; L Socr; High Hon Roll; Hon Roll; NHS; Aud/Vis; Boy Scts; Exploring; Blue Rbbn & Bst Show NNY Art Show 84; Gold Key Awds Art Shows 85; Eagle Scout BSA 85; U VT; Civil Engr.

FORNEY, JIM; Ogdensburg Free Acad; Ogdensburg, NY; (Y); 30/200; Math Clb; Band; Jazz Band; Mrchg Band; JP Sousa Awd; Semper Fidelis Awd 85; Natl Merit Fndtn Natl Hnr Rl 85; All ST Concrt Band 84; SUNY; Music Ed.

FORRESTER, DANIEL B; Newburgh Free Acad; Newburgh, NY; (Y); 25/720; Ski Clb; Temple Yth Grp; Acpl Chr; Chorus; School Musical; JV Bsbl; Im Bsktbl; Var Tennis; High Hon Roll; NHS; Regents Schlrshp Awd 85.

FORRESTER, JEANNE; Cairo-Durham HS; Cairo, NY; (Y); 2/92; School Play; Yrbk Bus Mgr; Yrbk Stf; Trs Sr Cls; Trs Stu Cncl; Var L Cheerleading; Var L Socr; Var L Trk; Ntl Merit Ltr; Sal; Rgnts Schlsrhp; Bstn U; Math.

FORRETT, KELLEY; Northern Adirondack HS; Ellenburg, NY; (Y); Church Yth Grp; Key Clb; Ski Clb; JV Bsktbl; Swmmng; High Hon Roll; Hon Roll; NHS; Monroe Clinton Comm; Fld Svc.

FORSBERG, JULIE; Jamestown HS; Jamestown, NY; (Y); Church Yth Grp; French Clb; Acpl Chr; Band; Chorus; Concert Band; Madrigals; Mrchg Band; School Musical; Symp Band; NYSSMA Awd Music 81-85; Eng.

FORSEY, GREGORY J; Newfane SR HS; Lockport, NY; (S); 7/170; Am Leg Boys St; Boy Scts; Math Clb; Ski Clb; Pres Varsity Clb; Band; Jazz Band; Symp Band; Yrbk Sprt Ed; Yrbk Stf; All Cnty Band 83; Naval Acad; Engr.

FORSEY, JANICE; Northville Central Schl; Northville, NY; (Y); Church Yth Grp; GAA; Church Choir; Yrbk Stf; Bsktbl; Socr; Hon Roll; Fulton Montgomery CC; Elem Ed.

FORSTER, LATISHA; H S Fashions Industrs; New York, NY; (Y); 119/365; Dance Clb; Debate Tm; Drama Clb; Chorus; School Musical; School Play; Capt Cheerleading; Hon Roll; Jr NHS; NHS; Adelphi U; Psych.

FORSTER, MARK; St Josephs Collegiate Inst; Cheektowaga, NY; (Y); 16/200; Hon Roll; NHS; Dist Carrier Of Mnth 84; ST U NY Buffalo; Comp Engrng.

FORSTER, MIKE; Liverpool HS; Liverpool, NY; (Y); Varsity Clb; Wrstlng.

FORSTER, ROBERT; Oceanside SR HS; Oceanside, NY; (Y); Cmnty Wkr; Hosp Aide; Y-Teens; Concert Band; Nwsp Sprt Ed; High Hon Roll; Jr NHS; Mathletes; Math Tm; Temple Yth Grp; Afro-Asian Scl Stds, Spnsh & Math 2nd Pl Awds 83-84; Med.

FORSTNER, ANDREAS J; Xaverian HS; Brooklyn, NY; (Y); 2/347; Pres Chess Clb; VP French Clb; Var Math Tm; Variety Show; Im Bsktbl; Im Ftbl; High Hon Roll; Trs NHS; Ntl Merit SF; Comp Sci.

FORSYTH, JOHN; St John The Baptist HS; W Babylon, NY; (Y); Church Yth Grp; Cmnty Wkr; Teachers Aide; Aerosp Sci.

FORTE, DONNA; Smithtown H S HS; Saint James, NY; (Y); Art Clb; German Clb; Hosp Aide; Hon Roll; Pre-Law.

FORTE, MARK; Horseheads HS; Horseheads, NY; (Y); Pres Sec 4-H; JCL; Trs Latin Clb; Band; Concert Band; Mrchg Band; High Hon Roll; Hon Roll; Accntg.

FORTE, VICTORIA; Preston HS; Bronx, NY; (Y); Hon Roll; 2nd Hnrs Awd 84; Comp Sales.

FORTH, CATHERINE M; Mont Pleasant HS; Schenectady, NY; (Y); 2/230; Ski Clb; Spanish Clb; Yrbk Ed-Chief; JV VP Civic Clb; DAR Awd; Hon Roll; NHS; Sal; Spanish NHS; Schenectady Profssnl Engrs Soc 85; Union Coll; Mech Engr.

FORTI, RENE; St Johns Prep; Astoria, NY; (S); 1/415; Hosp Aide; Ski Clb; Teachers Aide; School Musical; School Play; Nwsp Stf; Yrbk Stf; High Hon Roll; VP NHS; Ntl Merit Ltr; Acad All Amer Awd 84; Tablet Awd 85; Natl Ldrshp & Svc Awd 85; Pre-Med.

FORTINO, HENRY; Jamesville-Dewitt HS; Syracuse, NY; (Y); Church Yth Grp; Bsbl; High Hon Roll; Hon Roll; Jamesville-Dewitt Hgh Schl Acadmc Awd Bus 84-85; Acctg.

FORTNA, VIRGINIA; Arlington HS; Poughkeepsie, NY; (Y); Intnl Clb.

FORTON, KENNETH; Grand Island HS; Grand Island, NY; (Y); 29/325; Boy Scts; Pres Trs Church Yth Grp; JA; Mathletes; Variety Show; Rep Stu Cncl; High Hon Roll; NHS; Ntl Merit Ltr; Political Wkr; Pro Deo Et Patria Rlgs Embl 84; Schl Ltr Acad Excell 85; Cert Acad Excell 84; Sls & Adv.

FORTSCH, JERILYN; Smithtown H S West; Smithtown, NY; (Y); Church Yth Grp; Hosp Aide; Band; Concert Band; Mrchg Band; Symp Band; Lit Mag; Trk; Hon Roll; Opt Clb Awd; Psych.

FORTUNATE, ROBERT; Iona Preparatory Schl; White Plains, NY; (Y); 49/196; Church Yth Grp; Debate Tm; NFL; Red Cross Aide; Science Clb; School Musical; Trk; Pol Sci.

FORTUNATO, JAY; Farmingdale SR HS; Farmingdale, NY; (Y); 18/600; Boy Scts; Mgr Ed Yrbk Stf; Tennis; High Hon Roll; Ntl Merit Ltr; Elec Engnr.

FORYS, ALBERT; Bishop Kearney HS; Rochester, NY; (Y); Im Var Bowling; Im Score Keeper; Im Sftbl; Hon Roll; NHS; Cert Of Merit Coaches Awd Bowlng 85; Rochester Inst Of Tech; Bus.

FOSS, DENISE M; Holland Central Schl; South Wales, NY; (Y); 1/116; Varsity Clb; Var Co-Capt Bsktbl; Var L Fld Hcky; Var Co-Capt Sftbl; JV L Vllybl; Bausch & Lomb Sci Awd; High Hon Roll; Jr NHS; Pres NHS; Val; Rgnts Schlrshp 85; Rensselaer Poly Inst; Chmcl Eng.

FOSS, KIRSTEN; Fairport HS; Fairport, NY; (Y); Exploring; German Clb; Science Clb; Ski Clb; JV Var Fld Hcky; Hon Roll; Germ Amer Prtnrshp Pgm 83-85; Bio Sci.

FOSS, RANDY L; Pioneer Senior HS; Chaffee, NY; (Y); Art Clb; Boy Scts; Cmnty Wkr; Drama Clb; JA; Key Clb; Latin Clb; Math Clb; Science Clb; Band; Olympics Of Mind 83 & 84; ST U Buffalo; Aerospace Engrng.

FOSSETT, MICHELLE E; New Rochelle HS; New Rochelle, NY; (Y); French Clb; Hosp Aide; Intnl Clb; Spanish Clb; Chorus; Bowling; Sftbl; French Hon Soc; High Hon Roll; Hon Roll.

FOSTER, ADRIAN RENEE; Nazareth Regional HS; Brooklyn, NY; (Y); Church Yth Grp; Dance Clb; Acpl Chr; Chorus; Church Choir; Hon Roll; Eng Awd 84; Kingsmen Singer Mdl 85; Cncrt Chrs Mdl 84; St Johns U; Accntng.

FOSTER, D THORP; Fairport HS; Fairport, NY; (Y); Yrbk Phtg; Capt Tennis; Hon Roll; NHS; Ntl Merit SF; Eastrn Ten Assn Ranking 28 84; Eastrn Ten Assn Ranking 45 83; Bus.

FOSTER, JASON W; Mohawk Central HS; Ilion, NY; (Y); JA; Math Tm; Varsity Clb; Var L Bsktbl; Var L Crs Cntry; Var L Tennis; Hon Roll; Regents Schlrshp 85.

FOSTER, JODI; Sanford H Calhoun HS; N Merrick, NY; (Y); Key Clb; Chorus; Church Choir; JV Cheerleading; Stat Ftbl; Gym; Hon Roll; Jr NHS; NHS; Soc Stds Achvt Awd 85; Pres Phy Fit 83-85; Radlgc Tech.

FOSTER, KIM S; Massena Central HS; Norfolk, NY; (Y); 8/250; 4-H; Band; Concert Band; Mrchg Band; Pep Band; Var Capt Bsktbl; Hon Roll; NHS; Vrsty Bsktbl Awd-Mst Rebnds 85; St Lawrence Vly Hrsmns Assn-Hgh Pt Rdr 84; Horse Trnr.

FOSTER, KRISTINA; Southampton HS; Southampton, NY; (Y); 42/98; Drama Clb; Exploring; GAA; Chorus; Jazz Band; School Musical; School Play; Var Capt Cheerleading; Var Capt Vllybl; DAR Awd; USMC; Trsnprtn.

FOSTER, LORI JEAN; Fairport HS; Fairport, NY; (Y); 100/623; Drama Clb; Pres Exploring; Pres VP Model UN; Sec Chorus; School Play; Swing Chorus; Lit Mag; Rep Stu Cncl; Hon Roll; NHS; Ldrshp Awd Frrstl Equstrn Camp 82; Rsrv Champ Strlng Eqstrn Ctr Indr Champ 84; Purdue U; Pre-Vet.

FOSTER, LORI R; Cuba Central Schl; Cuba, NY; (Y); 6/65; Sec Pres French Clb; Ski Clb; Varsity Clb; Chorus; Yrbk Stf; Pres Frsh Cls; Trs Stu Cncl; Var L Socr; Var Trk; NY ST Regents Schlrshp 85; U Of Buffalo; Pre-Optometry.

FOSTER, MICHAEL; Elmira Southside HS; Pine City, NY; (Y); Cmnty Wkr; Latin Clb; Hon Roll; Elec Engrng.

FOSTER, MICHAEL; Ossining HS; Ossining, NY; (Y); Var Socr; Var Trk; Var Wt Lftg; Hon Roll; Air Force; Math.

FOSTER, MONIQUE M; H S Of Fashion Industrs; New York, NY; (Y); 57/365; Aud/Vis; Church Yth Grp; Drama Clb; Political Wkr; Teachers Aide; Yrbk Phtg; Tennis; PA ST; Advrtsng.

FOSTER, PAULINE; Clara Barton HS; Brooklyn, NY; (Y); Dance Clb; Variety Show; Yrbk Stf; Hon Roll; Cert Of Svc 85; Macy Hnr Soc; Phys Fit; Nrsng.

FOSTER, THOMAS; Amsterdam HS; Amsterdam, NY; (Y); Cmnty Wkr; Yrbk Stf; Soph Cls; JV Swmmng; Hon Roll; Art Director.

FOSTVEIT, EDGAR M; De Ruyter Central Schl; De Ruyter, NY; (Y); 1/43; Am Leg Boys St; Varsity Clb; Band; Mrchg Band; Yrbk Stf; Pres Frsh Cls; Pres Sr Cls; Stu Cncl; Var Bsktbl; Var Socr; Regenst Schlrshp 85; Pres Alfred U 85; Corning Glass Schlr 85; Alfred U; Engrng.

FOTI, BRIAN; Fairport HS; Fairport, NY; (Y); Camera Clb; Drama Clb; French Clb; Chorus; School Play; Swing Chorus; Variety Show; Yrbk Stf; Hon Roll.

FOTINO, GIA; Warwick Valley Central Schl; Warwick, NY; (Y); 22/200; Ski Clb; Band; Jazz Band; Mrchg Band; Pep Band; Diving; Golf; Sftbl; Swmmng; High Hon Roll; Ampr ST Games-Alpine Skiing 85; Educ.

FOUCART, JEFFREY S; E W Baker HS; Baldwinsville, NY; (Y); 20/441; Band; Chorus; Church Choir; Jazz Band; Mrchg Band; Symp Band; Nwsp Stf; High Hon Roll; NHS; All Around Talent 84; Chrs Accomp 83-85; 2 Logos Schl Orgnzatn Print 84-85; U Of TX; Archit.

FOUCHIE, RENEE M; Hutchingson Technical HS; Buffalo, NY; (Y); 32/265; Hosp Aide; JA; Yrbk Stf; Stu Cncl; Socr; Sftbl; Cit Awd; NHS; Pres Schlr; ST U Of NY; Srgcl Nrs.

FOUCHT, CRAIG D; Victor Central SR HS; Victor, NY; (Y); French Clb; Varsity Clb; Orch; School Musical; School Play; Stu Cncl; Var L Swmmng; Cit Awd; High Hon Roll; Hon Roll; Actor.

FOULKE, BRYAN; Susquehanna Valley HS; Conklin, NY; (Y); Boy Scts; Ski Clb; Spanish Clb; Rep Frsh Cls; Rep Soph Cls; Rep Jr Cls; VP Stu Cncl; JV Var Ftbl; JV Var Trk; Hon Roll; FL Inst Tech; Aerosp Engr.

FOUNTAIN, ALAN; Niagara Wheatfield SR HS; Sanborn, NY; (Y); 10/300; German Clb; Math Clb; PAVAS; Concert Band; Mrchg Band; JV Var Tennis; High Hon Roll; Hon Roll; NHS; Prfct Atten Awd; Natl Hon Soc 85-86; Hgh Hon Roll 82-86; Prfct Atten Awd 85; Rochestr Inst Of Tech; Elec Eng.

FOUNTAIN, CRYSTAL; Canisteo Central HS; Bath, NY; (S); 6/88; Model UN; Band; Concert Band; Mrchg Band; High Hon Roll; Hon Roll; NHS; Ntl Merit Ltr; Voice Dem Awd; US Achvt Awd 83; Lcl Hnr Soc 84-85; Geneseo SUNY; Psychlgy.

FOUNTAIN, JIM; Massena Central HS; Massena, NY; (Y); Variety Show; JV Ftbl; Im Vllybl; Im Wt Lftg; Music.

FOUNTAS, GEORGIA; Oyster Bay HS; Oyster Bay, NY; (Y); 10/175; AFS; Art Clb; Nwsp Stf; Var Capt Fld Hcky; Var Mgr Sftbl; Hon Roll; NY U; Psychtrst.

FOURACRE, DOUGLAS; Geneva HS; Geneva, NY; (S); 19/170; Am Leg Boys St; Boy Scts; Latin Clb; Band; Jazz Band; Socr; Tennis; Hon Roll; NHS; Eagle Scout Awd 84; Church Fellowship 84; Bio.

FOURNIER, MONIQUE; Brushton Moira Central HS; Brushton, NY; (Y); 9/58; Yrbk Stf; JV Var Vllybl; Bausch & Lomb Sci Awd; Hon Roll; NHS; Regnts Schlrshp 85; Albany Coll; Phrmcyst.

FOUS, CHERYL; William Cullen Bryant HS; Astoria, NY; (Y); 1/579; Band; Yrbk Stf; Hon Roll; NHS; Val; Acad Letter & Pins 82-85; Regents Hnr 81-85; Sci Medal & Spnsh Cert 82; Pace U; Cert Pbl Accntnt.

FOWKES, ANNEMARIE; Port Jefferson HS; Port Jeff, NY; (Y); Swmmng; Art Clb; French Clb; Pep Clb; Crs Cntry; Most Impvd Swmmr 83-84; U Of Southern FL; Polit Sci.

FOWLER, JOHN K; Wilson Central Schl; Wilson, NY; (Y); Band; Chorus; School Musical; School Play; Swing Chorus; Variety Show; Nwsp Stf; JV Ftbl; Var Tennis; Hon Roll; ST Chmp Olympics Of Th Mind 82-85; Highest ST Mus Awd Solo & Grp 82-85; Westminster Choir Coll; Mus.

FOWLER, KAREN; Hempstead HS; Hempstead, NY; (S); 12/333; Boy Scts; Office Aide; Nwsp Rptr; Nwsp Stf; Yrbk Bus Mgr; Yrbk Stf; Cit Awd; High Hon Roll; NHS; FL Inst Techlgy; Engrng.

FOWLER, KAREN; Wilson Central HS; Wilson, NY; (Y); 2/120; Am Leg Aux Girls St; Chorus; School Musical; Nwsp Stf; Yrbk Stf; Rep Stu Cncl; NHS; Sal; NSMA Ntl Sci Merit Awd 83-84; Bio.

FOWLER, LISA A; General Brown HS; Brownville, NY; (Y); 20/132; JCL; Key Clb; Var Socr; Hon Roll; Sec NHS; Regnts Schlrshp 85; Natl Latn Exm Cum Laude 82; Natl Latn Exm Magna Cum Laude 83; Jefferson CC; Bio.

FOWLER, MARK; Clyde-Savannah Central Schl; Clyde, NY; (Y); JV Bsbl; Var JV Bsktbl; Var JV Ftbl; Hon Roll; Prfct Atten Awd; Buffalo ST U; Engrng.

FOWLER, PAULA K; Argyle Central Schl; Argyle, NY; (Y); Trs French Clb; Teachers Aide; Yrbk Bus Mgr; Sec Frsh Cls; Pres Jr Cls; JV Var Sftbl; JV Var Vllybl; Hon Roll; Church Yth Grp; Cmnty Wkr; MVP Vllybl 82-83; Coll Of St Rose; Tchg.

FOWLES, DONNA; Washington Irving HS; Brooklyn, NY; (Y); Art Clb; Debate Tm; JA; Science Clb; Chorus; Bsktbl; Swmmng; Cit Awd; Hon Roll; Prfct Atten Awd; Cty Cncls Stu Svc Hnr Prclmtn 83; Rebecca Nelson Lang Arts Mem Awd 83; Irwin Tobin Phy Ed Awd 83; Pre Med.

FOX, ANDREA R; Maple Grove HS; Bemus Point, NY; (Y); Drama Clb; French Clb; Chorus; Nwsp Rptr; Yrbk Stf; Pres Schlrshp 85; NYS Rgnts Schlrshp 85; Ntl Hnr Soc 84-85; Lake Erie Coll.

FOX, ANN; Villa Maria Acad; Depew, NY; (S); JCL; Nwsp Ed-Chief; Yrbk Stf; Hon Roll; NHS; NEDT Awd; Voice Dem Awd; Pres Computer Clb; Drama Clb; Sistrhd Yth Awd Natl Conf Christn & Jews 85; Volntr Mnth 84; 1st Pl Villa Maria Acad Voice.

FOX, DAVID; Holy Trinity HS; Roosevelt, NY; (Y); Art Clb; Camera Clb; French Clb; Math Clb; Office Aide; Ski Clb; Stage Crew; Variety Show; Nwsp Rptr; Yrbk Sprt Ed; Vassar Coll; Pre-Med.

FOX, DAWN M; Avoca Central HS; Wallace, NY; (Y); 2/50; JCL; School Play; Yrbk Ed-Chief; Trs Sr Cls; Socr; Sftbl; High Hon Roll; NHS; Prfct Atten Awd; Ski Clb; Psych.

FOX, HOWARD; Commack North HS; Smithtown, NY; (Y); Chess Clb; Debate Tm; Speech Tm; Nwsp Rptr; Nwsp Stf; High Hon Roll; Hon Roll; Hofstra Fornsc Tourn Ltr Merit 84-85; Bus.

FOX, JEFFREY; Gloversville HS; Gloversville, NY; (Y); 17/250; JV Var Bsktbl; JV Var Crs Cntry; Trk; Hon Roll; NHS; Pres Schlr; Pres Scholar Siena Coll 85; Alfred E Johnson Scholar 85; NYS Regents Scholar 85; Siena Coll; Acctng.

FOX, JONATHAN; Attica Central HS; Cowlesville, NY; (Y); Quiz Bowl; Band; Concert Band; Jazz Band; Mrchg Band; Coach Actv; Mgr(s); Hon Roll; Bio.

FOX, KATHLEEN E; Brocton Central Schl; Fredonia, NY; (Y); Drama Clb; French Clb; Madrigals; School Musical; Nwsp Bus Mgr; Yrbk Stf; Sec Frsh Cls; Pres Stu Cncl; Hon Roll; NHS; NYS Regnts Schlrshp 85; SUNY Fredonia; Comm.

FOX, KIMBERLY; Cleveland Hill HS; Cheektowaga, NY; (Y); 1/109; Pres AFS; GAA; Hosp Aide; JCL; Yrbk Stf; Rep Stu Cncl; Crs Cntry; Var Trk; JV Var Vllybl; NHS; Cornell; Sci.

FOX, KRISTIN E; Wahingonville SR HS; Campbell Hall, NY; (Y); Ski Clb; Symp Band; Nwsp Rptr; Pres Jr Cls; Pres Stu Cncl; Crs Cntry; Trk; NHS; Rotary Awd; Cornell U; Cmmnctns.

FOX, MICHAEL; Milford Central HS; Maryland, NY; (S); 10/23; Am Leg Boys St; Acpl Chr; Chorus; Jazz Band; School Musical; Stu Cncl; Trk; Hon Roll; Crs Cntry; Stu Of Mnth Awd 84; SUNY; Elec Tech.

FOX, NANCY; De Ruyter Central Schl; De Ruyter, NY; (S); 2/37; Drama Clb; Yrbk Stf; Pres Frsh Cls; Rep Soph Cls; Rep Sr Cls; Sec Stu Cncl; Var Capt Cheerleading; Gym; Var JV Socr; Var Trk; Fresh Schlrshp Cup Hghst Aver 83; Mst Omprvd Trck 83; Morrisville Tech; Phy Thrpst.

FOX, ROBERT; St John The Baptist HS; Lindenhurst, NY; (Y); Boy Scts; Mathletes; Math Tm; Red Cross Aide; Science Clb; Nwsp Stf; High Hon Roll; Ithaca Coll Scshlrshp 85; 2nd Natl Sci Olympiad Chem 84; NYS Regents Schlrshp 85; Ithaca Coll; Physics.

FOX, SHARON; Mount Assumption Inst; Champlain, NY; (Y); 1/66; Drama Clb; Math Clb; Band; Nwsp Stf; Yrbk Ed-Chief; Gym; High Hon Roll; NHS; NEDT Awd; MA Inst Of Tech; Astrophysics.

FOX, THOMAS; Catholic Central HS; Troy, NY; (S); 16/203; Cmnty Wkr; JA; Yrbk Stf; JV Im Bsktbl; VP L Crs Cntry; VP L Trk; High Hon Roll; NHS; Prfct Atten Awd; Comm Svc Awd Vlntrng Retarded 84; Spnsh Awd 82; Rensselaer Polytec; Engr.

FOX JR, WALTER LOUIS; A P Randolph Campus HS; New York, NY; (Y); Aud/Vis; Band; Color Guard; School Play; Yrbk Stf; Bsktbl; Cit Awd; Ntl Merit Ltr; Stu Svc Hnr Citatn 83; Cty Cncl Citatn 83; Am Inst Sci & Tech 82; Engrng.

FOX, WILLIAM; Jericho HS; Jericho, NY; (Y); Var Ftbl; JV Trk; Accntng.

FOXWORTH, HOPE; La Salle SR HS; Niagara Falls, NY; (Y); Hon Roll; NHS; Acad Merit Awd 84-85; Bio.

FRACCALVIERI, CRISTINA; St John The Baptist Diocesan HS; W Bayshore, NY; (Y); 1/650; Hosp Aide; Chrmn Math Tm; Model UN; Nwsp Sprt Ed; Ed Lit Mag; French Hon Soc; Mu Alp Tht; NHS; Ntl Merit SF; Nwsp Phtg; Accptd Into Columbia U Sci Hnrs Prog 85; Harvard; Med.

FRACCALVIERI, PAUL; Ward Melville HS; Stony Brook, NY; (Y); 114/760; Cmnty Wkr; Drama Clb; Chorus; School Musical; Tennis; Cit Awd; Jr NHS; Kiwanis Awd; NHS; ROTC Army Scholar 85; Century III Ldrshp Awd 85; Republcn Clb Cmnty Svc Scholar 85; St Bonaventure; Frgn Lang.

FRACENTESE, MARY; Bishop Kearney Catholic HS; Brooklyn, NY; (Y); Spanish Clb; Bowling; Amer Hstry Advnce Plcmnt Exam 85; Nrsg.

FRACHETTI, ROBERT; Solvay HS; Solvay, NY; (Y); Boy Scts; Math Clb; Ski Clb; Off Frsh Cls; Off Soph Cls; Off Jr Cls; High Hon Roll; Hon Roll; NHS; Eagle Scout 85; Engrng.

FRACHETTI, SUZANNE; Solvay HS; Solvay, NY; (Y); 5/167; Church Yth Grp; Math Clb; Ski Clb; School Musical; Yrbk Stf; Sr Cls; Var Cheerleading; High Hon Roll; Pres NHS; Civic Center Drama Awd 84; Schlrshp Oper Entrprs 83; Solvay Bk Awd & Schlrshp 85; Le Moyne Col6; Bus.

FRACHT, HARVEY; Bronx High School Of Science; Bronx, NY; (Y); Cmnty Wkr; Science Clb; Teachers Aide; Temple Yth Grp; Varsity Clb; Elks Awd; NHS; Bnai Brith Bershad Schlrshp 85; Exclnc Calculus Awd Brnx HS Of Sci 85; Golden Ayin Awd Excel Hebrew; Dartmouth Coll; Pre-Med.

FRADENBURG, JIM; Canastota HS; Canastota, NY; (Y); Boy Scts; Church Yth Grp; FTA; Science Clb; Teachers Aide; JV Bsktbl; Var Ftbl; Im Mgr Vllybl; Im Mgr Wt Lftg; Hon Roll; Dollars Schlrs Org; Ed.

FRADENBURG, SEAN; Oneida HS; Oneida, NY; (Y); 50/220; Letterman Clb; Varsity Clb; Yrbk Phtg; Yrbk Stf; JV Var Ftbl; JV Var Socr; Var Trk; Im Vllybl; Rotary Awd; SR Privlg & Rghts Cmmttee 84-85; OH U; Sprts Sci.

FRAEHMKE, THOMAS W; Valley Stream Central HS; Malverne, NY; (Y); 24/365; AFS; Church Yth Grp; Computer Clb; Yrbk Phtg; Var Bsktbl; Mu Alp Tht; NHS; Regents Schlrshp; Arch.

FRAGALE, ELIZABETH V; St Catherine Acad; Bronx, NY; (Y); Service Clb; Teachers Aide; Variety Show; Hon Roll; NHS; Regnts NYS 85; Fordham U.

FRAGOMEN, DEBORA MARIA ANN; Spring Valley SR HS; Spring Valley, NY; (Y); 94/435; Church Yth Grp; Key Clb; Library Aide; Ski Clb; Teachers Aide; Band; Church Choir; Concert Band; Mrchg Band; Var Cheerleading; Italn Hnr Soc 82-83; Pace U Pleasantville Cmps; Math.

FRAIOLI, CHRIS; Iona Prep; Larchmont, NY; (Y); 23/198; Capt JV Lcrss; Hon Roll; William & Mary Coll; Bus Mgmt.

FRAMENT, MARY G; Scotia-Glenville HS; Scotia, NY; (Y); 9/255; Exploring; Hosp Aide; Red Cross Aide; Chorus; Pres Stu Cncl; Var Fld Hcky; JV Gym; High Hon Roll; NHS; Pres Pres Schlr; Acadmc Excllnc Awd Top 5 Pct Clss 85; Kay Sturdy Schlrshp & Francis W Zapf Memrl Awd 85; Russell Sage Coll; Phy Thrpy.

FRANASIAK, KEN; Niagara Wheatfield HS; Niagara Fls, NY; (Y); Varsity Clb; Ice Hcky; Capt Lcrss; Hon Roll; Acad Achvt Awd 85; Bus.

FRANCE, DIANE; Mynderse Acad; Seneca Falls, NY; (S); 39/132; GAA; Var Capt Bsktbl; Var Capt Socr; Var Capt Sftbl; Hon Roll.

FRANCE, RAMONA; Canaseraga Central HS; Canaseraga, NY; (Y); Varsity Clb; Chorus; Color Guard; Stage Crew; Yrbk Phtg; Yrbk Stf; Stu Cncl; Var JV Cheerleading; Var Socr; Var Sftbl.

FRANCIA, JOANNE; G W Hewlett HS; Valley Stream, NY; (Y); Dance Clb; GAA; Girl Scts; Var Capt Bsktbl; Var Sftbl; Var Vllybl; Comp.

FRANCIA, LISA; Norwood Norfolk Central HS; Norfolk, NY; (Y); French Clb; Pep Clb; Teachers Aide; Bsktbl; Sftbl; Hon Roll; Law Enfrcmnt.

FRANCIAMORE, SERGIO; New Rochelle HS; Scarsdale, NY; (Y); Church Yth Grp; Computer Clb; Off FBLA; Intnl Clb; Model UN; JV Ftbl; JV Lcrss; Wt Lftg; Corp Intl Schlrhsp Awd 85; Intl Bus.

FRANCIS JR, ANTHONY D; John F Kennedy HS; New York, NY; (Y); Var Bsktbl; Cit Awd; 4-Yr Bsktbl Schlrshp Niagara U 85; PSAL Medl Bsktbl Rnnr-Up 85; Bsktbl Medl 85; Niagara U; Comp Sci.

FRANCIS, AVEMARIA M; Bishop Ford Central Catholic HS; Brooklyn, NY; (Y); 106/366; Yrbk Stf; Wt Lftg; Wrstlng; Regents Schlrshp 85; MD U; Psych.

FRANCIS, FEMI; Sheepshead Bay HS; New York, NY; (Y); Intnl Clb; Math Tm; Chorus; School Musical; School Play; Variety Show; High Hon Roll; Hon Roll; Prfct Atten Awd; Amer Legn Cert Achvt; Schlrshp & Gd Ctznshp Certs; Med.

FRANCIS, JIM; Roy C Ketcham HS; Poughkeepsie, NY; (Y); Band; Concert Band; Jazz Band; Symp Band; Var Crs Cntry; Var Swmmng; Var Trk; Hon Roll; Htl Mngmnt.

FRANCIS, JOHN; Hendrick Hudson HS; Peekskill, NY; (Y); Boy Scts; JV Bsbl; Capt Var Lcrss; Capt Var Socr; Trk; Wrstlng; Morisville Coll; Elect Engr.

FRANCIS, PATRICK; Pioneer Central HS; Arcade, NY; (Y); 12/209; Latin Clb; Rep Sr Cls; Pres Stu Cncl; Wrstlng; Jr NHS; NHS; Pres Schlr; Cnty Gov Stu Intern Partcptn Awd 85; St Bonaventure U NY; Bio.

FRANCIS, SCOTT J; Paul V Moore HS; Brewerton, NY; (Y); Trs Varsity Clb; Var L Bsbl; Var L Ftbl; Var L Socr; Hon Roll; NHS; Pres Schlr; JV Bsktbl; St Lawrence U; Econ.

FRANCIS, VICKI; Milford Central Schl; Cooperstown, NY; (S); 3/30; Chorus; Concert Band; Jazz Band; Mrchg Band; Pep Band; School Musical; Nwsp Stf; Score Keeper; Jr NHS; NHS; Engl, Bio Hgh Awd 83-84; Engl.

FRANCISCO, BETHANY; Fonda-Fultonville Central HS; Amsterdam, NY; (Y); Church Yth Grp; Band; Chorus; Church Choir; Concert Band; Mrchg Band; Trk; SUNY Cobleskill; Anmal Hsbndry.

FRANCISCO, DANIEL; Tupper Lake Central Schl; Tupper Lk, NY; (Y); 16/100; Pres 4-H; 4-H Awd; Hon Roll; Delg WA DC Ctznshp Short Course 85; 4-H Safety Awd 82-84; ST Fair Blue Ribbn Awd 83; Paul Smiths Forstry; Forstry.

FRANCO, JOE; Moore Catholic HS; Staten Island, NY; (Y); Boy Scts; Bowling; Hon Roll; Prfct Atten Awd; Penn ST; Meteorology.

FRANCO, TONI; Bishop Kearney HS; Brooklyn, NY; (Y); Hosp Aide; Office Aide; Yrbk Stf; Off Jr Cls; Hon Roll; NHS; Comm.

FRANCO, ZOILA A; St Michaels Acad; Southgate, CA; (Y); 10/127; Sec Church Yth Grp; Cmnty Wkr; Pres JA; Office Aide; Church Choir; Rep Jr Cls; Sec Stu Cncl; Mgr Bsktbl; Im Gym; Score Keeper; ST U LA; Chld Psychtrst.

FRANCOIS, DANIAH JEAN; Dominican Commercial HS; Elmhurst, NY; (Y); 84/273; Hosp Aide; Library Aide; Office Aide; Teachers Aide; Rep Sr Cls; Sr Cls; Pres Schlr; Pricipals List 82-83 & 84-85; Presdntl Acad Fitness Awd; Sienna Clb Awd; Hunter Coll; Lbrl Arts.

FRANGIPANE, DENISE; Monticello HS; Kauneonga Lake, NY; (Y); Church Yth Grp; Girl Scts; Intnl Clb; ROTC; Band; Chorus; Yrbk Stf; Fash Inst Of Tech; Fash Dsgn.

FRANGO, ANDREA; Sheepshead Bat HS; Brooklyn, NY; (Y); Library Aide; Spanish Clb; School Musical; Stage Crew; Rep Stu Cncl; NY Inst Tech; Hotel Mgmt.

FRANGOS, STEPHANIE; The Norman Howard Schl; Rochester, NY; (Y); 1/15; Art Clb; Cmnty Wkr; Ski Clb; Varsity Clb; Yrbk Stf; Stu Cncl; Cheerleading; Coach Actv; Golf; Hon Roll; Hon Mntn Monroe Cnty Schlstc Art Show; Mbr NYS Comm Blind & Vslly Hndcppd Of The SLB 84-86; U Of CO; Dance.

FRANICH, RACHEL; Harry S Truman HS; Bronx, NY; (Y); Lit Mag; Hon Roll; Outstndng Achvt Yr Englsh Awd 85; Brown U Bk Awd 85.

FRANK, AMY; Oppenheim-Ephratah Central Schl; Johnstown, NY; (S); 1/26; Band; Rep Stu Cncl; Var Socr; Var Sftbl; Var Vllybl; High Hon Roll; VP Jr NHS; Pres NHS; Spanish NHS; Engr.

FRANK, BRADLEY; Martin Van Buren HS; Queens Village, NY; (Y); 14/600; Math Tm; Scholastic Bowl; Science Clb; School Play; Hon Roll; Jr NHS; NHS; Teachers Aide; Temple Yth Grp; 2nd Pl Queens Borough Sci Fair 84; 1st Pl HS Sci Fair 84; 2nd Pl HS Sci Fair 85.

FRANK, DEBBIE; Shenedehowa HS; Waterford, NY; (Y); Hon Roll; Greg Typng Awd For Achv 85; Hudson Vlly CC; Adv.

FRANK, JEFF; Mayfield JR SR HS; Mayfield, NY; (Y); 2/80; Church Yth Grp; Cmnty Wkr; Nwsp Rptr; Nwsp Stf; High Hon Roll; NHS; Prfct Atten Awd; Cls Cncl 82-83 & 84-85; Lcl Hstrcl Soc 83-85; Psych.

FRANK, JENNIFER A; Copiague HS; Lindenhurst, NY; (Y); 12/348; Pres German Clb; Chorus; Concert Band; Drm Mjr(t); Jazz Band; School Musical; Yrbk Phtg; Var Fld Hcky; Var Capt Sftbl; Sec NHS; Germn Natl Hon Soc 83-85; Schlr Athl Awd 85; Pres Acad Ftnss Awd 85; Fredonia; Music Educ.

FRANK, LISA; Bishop Ludden HS; Syracuse, NY; (S); Church Yth Grp; Exploring; Trk; High Hon Roll; Pres NHS; Hghst Grd Awd Medls Latn, Soc Std 82-83; Highst Grd Awd Cert Engl, Frnch 82-84; OCC; Humnities.

FRANK, MATTHEW; Cardinal Mooney HS; Hilton, NY; (Y); Church Yth Grp; Cmnty Wkr; Exploring; School Musical; Stage Crew; Variety Show; Hon Roll; Comp Sci.

FRANK, MICHAEL; Clifton-Fine Central Schl; Star Lake, NY; (S); French Clb; Band; Stage Crew; VP Frsh Cls; Rep Soph Cls; Var Capt Bsbl; Var Capt Bsktbl; Var Capt Socr; High Hon Roll; Hon Roll; SUNY Plattsburgh; Bus Econ.

FRANK, ROBIN; Hilton Central HS; Hilton, NY; (Y); 6/310; French Clb; JA; Math Clb; Var Sftbl; JV Capt Vllybl; High Hon Roll; NHS; Church Yth Grp; Hon Roll; 3rd Pl Awd Monroe Cnty Bus Tchrs Assoc 84; 1st Rnd Wnnr Greece Athena HS Spllng Bee 83; Accntng.

FRANK, SCOTT LARRY; Springville-Griffith Inst; Springville, NY; (Y); 2/200; VP NHS; Soc Mayflower Descndts Awd 85; Spn Sh Hgst Schlstc Avg 84-85.

FRANK, SYLVIA; Fonda-Fultonvills C S HS; Esperance, NY; (Y); 1/120; VP Intnl Clb; Key Clb; Band; Mrchg Band; High Hon Roll; Trs NHS; Ntl Merit Ltr; Hghst Acad Avg 83-85; Pre-Med.

FRANK, TRACEY; Alexander Central HS; Batavia, NY; (Y); Dance Clb; 4-H; French Clb; Girl Scts; Band; Sec Chorus; Concert Band; Jazz Band; Mrchg Band; Variety Show; Bst Sectn Marchng Band 83; Bst Sectn Concert Band 85; Excllnt Ratng Solo Fest Band 84; Spec Ed.

FRANKE, JUDY; Wilson Central Schl; Wilson, NY; (Y); Teachers Aide; Rep Stu Cncl; Hon Roll; Bryant & Stratton Bus; Accntnt.

FRANKEL, DEBBY S; Prospect Park Yeshiva HS; Brooklyn, NY; (Y); 15/68; English Clb; French Clb; Math Clb; Chorus; Stage Crew; Cheerleading; High Hon Roll; SAT Schlrshp 85; Touro Coll; Phy Thrpy.

FRANKEL, JASON; Guilderland Central HS; Albany, NY; (Y); 14/369; Church Yth Grp; Rep Stu Cncl; High Hon Roll; NHS; Regnts Schlrshp 85; Grad Hghst Hnrs 82-85; Regnts Diplm 85; Clarkson U; Engrng.

FRANKEL, JEFFREY S; Sachem North HS; Farmingville, NY; (Y); 63/1468; Cmnty Wkr; Drama Clb; Temple Yth Grp; Chorus; School Musical; School Play; Variety Show; Nwsp Ed-Chief; Trs Frsh Cls; NHS; NYS Regnts Schlrshp 85; Acadmc All Amer Schlr Prog; Emory U; Acctng.

FRANKEL, LAWRENCE M; Lawrence HS; Woodmere, NY; (Y); 1/379; Math Tm; Orch; Ed Nwsp Stf; NHS; Ntl Merit Schol; Val; Science Clb; Spanish Clb; Teachers Aide; High Hon Roll; Grumman Awd & Hghst Hnrs 83; Rensselaer Medal 84; Cornell U; History.

FRANKEL, SERENA; JLM Great Neck North SR HS; Great Neck, NY; (Y); 124/275; French Clb; Latin Clb; Political Wkr; Ski Clb; Spanish Clb; Temple Yth Grp; Pres Schlr; St Schlr; Figure Skatng Awd; George Washington U; Pre-Med.

FRANKINO, NANCY; St Marys HS; Buffalo, NY; (S); 8/171; Camp Fr Inc; Computer Clb; Trs Sec Exploring; Science Clb; Church Choir; Nwsp Stf; Mgr(s); Var Sftbl; High Hon Roll; NHS; ST U Of NY; Accntng.

FRANKLIN, PATRICIA A; Westislip HS; W Islip, NY; (Y); Library Aide; Office Aide; Hon Roll; NHS; Schl Svc Awds 84-85, Hgh Hnrs Awds 83-85; Soc Stds Excel Awd 85; CPA.

FRANKLIN, REBECCA D; Norwich HS; Norwich, NY; (Y); 19/174; Pres French Clb; Chorus; Yrbk Ed-Chief; Var Cheerleading; Var Fld Hcky; JV Capt Vllybl; High Hon Roll; Hon Roll; NHS; Math Clb; Regnts Schlrshp 85; Stdnt Rotrn 85; Rotry Interact Clb 84-85; SUNY Albany; Pol Sci.

FRANKLYN, PHILLIP; Mt St Michaels Acad; Bronx, NY; (Y); 102/339; Computer Clb; JV Bsktbl; Hon Roll; Comp Sci.

FRANQUI, ALICIA; Aquinas HS; Bronx, NY; (Y); 34/178; Debate Tm; Office Aide; Stage Crew; Variety Show; Hon Roll; Chorus; Sec Rep Frsh Cls; Lona Coll Frgn Lang Cont Spn Natve 1st Hnrs 84-85; Mar Sci.

FRANTA, CHERIE; Greene Central HS; Greene, NY; (Y); 1/110; Art Clb; French Clb; Math Tm; Pres Sr Cls; JV Capt Bsktbl; Var Socr; Im Vllybl; High Hon Roll; Pres NHS; Prfct Atten Awd; Gld Key & Blue Rbn S Cntrl NY Rgnl Art Exhbtn 82 & 84; 1st Pl Prnt Mkng 83; Archtctr.

FRANTONO, MICHAEL J; Mt St Michael Acad; Bronx, NY; (Y); 39/308; Bsktbl; Fld Hcky; Ftbl; Sftbl; NHS; 1st 2nd Hnrs 82-85; Bus Mgmt.

FRANTZ, SUSAN; Bishop Grimes HS; N Syracuse, NY; (Y); Church Yth Grp; FBLA; NFL; Ski Clb; Nwsp Rptr; Rep Soph Cls; Trs Jr Cls; Cheerleading; Piano Music Mrt 83, 85 & 86; U Of VT; Englsh.

FRANZ IV, JOHN C; Waterford-Halfmoon HS; Waterford, NY; (Y); 19/92; Math Clb; Yrbk Stf; Var JV Bsbl; Var JV Bowling; Hon Roll; Elmira Coll Key Awd 85; Engrng.

FRANZ IV, PHILIP; John Jay HS; Katonah, NY; (Y); Church Yth Grp; Intnl Clb; Ski Clb; Var Lcrss; Var Socr; Law.

FRANZEK, JAMES; St Josephis Collegiate Inst; Snyder, NY; (Y); 50/196; Ski Clb; Im Bowling; JV Ice Hcky; JV Trk; High Hon Roll; Hon Roll; Engrng.

FRANZEN, KEITH M; Whitesboro Central Schl; Whitesboro, NY; (Y); Boy Scts; Ski Clb; Var Bowling; JV Golf; High Hon Roll; Hon Roll; NHS; Elec Mech Engrng.

FRANZESE, DEBRA; Bethpage HS; Plainview, NY; (Y); 44/277; FBLA; Rep Soph Cls; Rep Jr Cls; Var Co-Capt Cheerleading; Stat Ftbl; Var Sftbl; High Hon Roll; Hon Roll; Jr NHS; Hofstra; Accntng.

FRANZITTA, DONNA; Valley Stream Central HS; Valley Stream, NY; (Y); 96/365; Chess Clb; Drill Tm; Variety Show; Off Soph Cls; Off Jr Cls; Off Sr Cls; Bowling; Capt Pom Pon; Hon Roll; Jr NHS; Kickline Capt 82-85; Talent Troupe 83-85; Spnsh Tutor; FIT; Fshn.

FRAS, ANDREW I; Binghamton HS; Binghamton, NY; (Y); 1/500; Pres Debate Tm; German Clb; Ski Clb; Bausch & Lomb Sci Awd; High Hon Roll; Masonic Awd; NHS; Ntl Merit SF; Chess Clb; Drama Clb; NASA NSTA SSIP 82-83; Stu Advsry Cmmtt 83-84; Schlstc Achvt Awds Sci, Engl, Frnch, Germn, Soc Stds; Med.

FRASCA, DANIELLE; Riverhead HS; Manorville, NY; (Y); Church Yth Grp; Cmnty Wkr; ROTC; Flag Corp; Var Trk; Hon Roll; NJROTC Meritrous Achvt Awd 85; JR Rotry Clb Interact; Polish Twn Cvc Assn Inc; Radlgy.

FRASCATORE, MARCO; Cicero-North Syracuse HS; North Syracuse, NY; (S); 82/600; Church Yth Grp; Bsbl; Bsktbl; Var Bowling; Hon Roll; Perfect Attndnce 82; Daemen Coll; Accntng.

FRASER, DANIEL; Cicero-No Syracuse HS; Clay, NY; (Y); 250/777; Aud/Vis; Church Yth Grp; Drama Clb; Ski Clb; School Musical; School Play; Stage Crew; Rep Sr Cls; Var Socr; Trk; Empire Games Trck 85.

FRASER, DANIEL; Liberty HS; Ferndale, NY; (Y); 6/85; Latin Clb; Var L Bsbl; Var L Socr; High Hon Roll; NHS; NY ST Regnts Schlrshp 85; Liberty Facity Assn Schlrshp 85; SUNY Binghamton; Comp Sci.

FRASER, JANE; Sweethome SR HS; Town Of Tonawanda, NY; (Y); 128/425; Church Yth Grp; German Clb; Yrbk Stf; Off Soph Cls; Socr; Tennis; NCTE Awd; German Hnr Scty Awd 83; Outstndng Vlntr Awd 84; Outstndng Vlntr Awd 83.

FRASER, MELODYE; Union Springs Acad; Collins, NY; (Y); Church Yth Grp; Band; Church Choir; Concert Band; Hon Roll; Secy Sci.

FRASER, MEREDITH; L C O Bourn HS; East Rochester, NY; (Y); 4/111; Mathletes; Math Tm; Model UN; Band; Nwsp Rptr; Hon Roll; NHS; Rotary Awd; NY State Regents Schlrshp 85; Presidntl Acadmc Fitness Awd 85; Nazareth Coll Of Rochester; Art.

FRASER, SHAWNA; Saratoga Springs HS; Saratoga Springs, NY; (Y); Dance Clb; Sec Ski Clb; Nwsp Stf; Cheerleading; Stat Score Keeper; High Hon Roll; Hon Roll; Aerontcl Engr.

FRASER, STUART; Eden Central HS; Eden, NY; (Y); 37/193; Church Yth Grp; Band; Chorus; Concert Band; Drm & Bgl; Jazz Band; Orch; Pep Band; School Musical; Symp Band; St Bonaventure Outstndg Musicn Awd Jass Fstvl 85; Alfred ST Coll; Comp Grphcs.

FRASIER, CAROL; Johnstown HS; Johnstown, NY; (Y); Timer; JV Var Vllybl; High Hon Roll; Hon Roll; Var NHS; Prfct Atten Awd; Busn.

FRASIER, CELESTE; Northville Central HS; Northville, NY; (Y); Am Leg Aux Girls St; Cmnty Wkr; Teachers Aide; Band; Chorus; School Musical; School Play; Yrbk Stf; High Hon Roll; NHS; Bennington Coll; Theatre.

FRASIER, GARY; Gloversville HS; Gloversville, NY; (Y); Church Yth Grp; Med.

FRATANGELO, JOHN; Holy Cross HS; College Point, NY; (S); 114/385; Cmnty Wkr; Service Clb; Varsity Clb; Var Capt Ftbl; Trk; Wt Lftg; Phys Educ.

FRATARCANGELO, CATHERINE; Haverling Central Schl; Bath, NY; (S); French Clb; Latin Clb; Math Clb; Yrbk Stf; Sec Frsh Cls; Sec Soph Cls; Cheerleading; Tennis; High Hon Roll; NHS; Intl Rel.

FRATE, ERIC P; Shendehova HS; Ballston Lake, NY; (Y); Ski Clb; Varsity Clb; Var Capt Swmmng; JV Trk; High Hon Roll; Ntl Merit SF; MVP Swim 85; Engrng.

FRATELLO, CARMELA; Lehman HS; Ridgewood, NJ; (Y); Library Aide; Office Aide; Teachers Aide; School Musical; Yrbk Ed-Chief; Yrbk Stf; Hon Roll; Jr NHS; NHS; Prfct Atten Awd; Arista 84-85; Med.

FRATERRIGO, LISA; Notre Dame HS; Batavia, NY; (S); 18/85; Teachers Aide; Mat Maids; Hon Roll; NHS; Alfred ST; Crt Rprtng.

FRATESCHI, RACHEL; Solvay HS; Syracuse, NY; (Y); FNA; Hosp Aide; Concert Band; Yrbk Ed-Chief; Yrbk Phtg; Sec Soph Cls; Hon Roll; Ldrshp Awd 83-84; Awd Excel Music 84-85; Svc Awd 83-84; Crouse Irving Schl; Nrsng.

FRATESCHI, THOMAS; Fayetteville Manlius HS; Manlius, NY; (Y); Boy Scts; Camera Clb; Bsbl; Score Keeper; Timer; Wt Lftg; JV Wrstlng; Onodoga CC; Arch.

FRATTIN, CHRISTINE JACQUELINE; Islip HS; Islip, NY; (Y); Color Guard; Drill Tm; Mrchg Band; Yrbk Rptr; Yrbk Stf; Rep Jr Cls; JV Var Mgr(s); JV Var Sftbl; High Hon Roll; Hon Roll; AATF Natl Cntst 82; 1st Suffolk Cnty 1st Regn 5th US 83; 1st Suffolk 5th Rgn 84; 2nd Suffolk Cnty 85; Teaching.

FRATTO, ADAM; Manlius Pebble Hill HS; Syracuse, NY; (S); Cmnty Wkr; Computer Clb; Model UN; Office Aide; Political Wkr; Quiz Bowl; Acpl Chr; Band; Chorus; Madrigals.

FRAUENHEIM IV, EDWARD E; Amherst Central SR HS; Snyder, NY; (Y); 2/310; Drama Clb; Model UN; Quiz Bowl; Nwsp Sprt Ed; Trs Sr Cls; JV Var Socr; Dnfth Awd; High Hon Roll; NHS; Ntl Merit SF; 2nd Pl Canisius Coll Math II Cntst 83-84; Chem Rsrch.

FRAWLEY, PATRICK M; Babylon JR & SR HS; Babylon, NY; (Y); 24/155; Boy Scts; Variety Show; Rep Soph Cls; Rep Jr Cls; JV Capt Ftbl; Rgnts Schlrshp 85; Stony Brook SUNY; Comp Sci.

FRAZEE, LEANNE; Harrisville Central HS; Harrisville, NY; (Y); GAA; Chorus; School Musical; School Play; Trs Frsh Cls; Trs Jr Cls; Trs Sr Cls; Var Capt Bsktbl; Var Capt Vllybl; NHS; Canton ATC; Pre-Vet Sci Tech.

FRAZIER, ALTONE; Bishop Loughlin M HS; Rockaway Bch, NY; (Y); Band; School Musical; JV Var Bsktbl; Hon Roll; Bio Sci.

FRAZZETTA, EDWARD; John A Coleman HS; Stone Ridge, NY; (S); 3/72; Drama Clb; School Musical; Yrbk Stf; Off Frsh Cls; Off Soph Cls; Off Jr Cls; Var Capt Socr; Trk; High Hon Roll; NHS; Bio Olymp Awd 84; Schl Spirit Awd 84.

FRECHETTE, ELAINE; Mercy HS; Menands, NY; (Y); 3/44; Church Yth Grp; Dance Clb; Drama Clb; French Clb; Church Choir; School Play; Lit Mag; Rep Soph Cls; Rep Jr Cls; Rep Sr Cls; Ntl Merit Sci Awd 85; HS Schlrshp 82; Amer Bar Assoc Cert 85; Engrng.

FREDENBURGH, STEPHANIE; Roy C Ketcham SR HS; Poughkeepsie, NY; (Y); Church Yth Grp; Drama Clb; Acpl Chr; Chorus; L Orch; School Musical; School Play; Symp Band; Nwsp Stf; High Hon Roll; Ldrstein Mem Schlrshp 85; Hnr Musicn Awd 84; Downe Chambr Music Ctr Schlrshp 85; Music.

FREDERICK, PAUL; Scotia-Glenville HS; Scotia, NY; (Y); Church Yth Grp; Key Clb; Concert Band; Jazz Band; Mrchg Band; Orch; School Musical; Im JV Ftbl; Hon Roll; NHS; Ec.

FREDERICK, SUSAN A; Johnstown HS; Johnstown, NY; (Y); Church Yth Grp; Intnl Clb; Nwsp Rptr; Nwsp Stf; Stu Cncl; Score Keeper; Socr; Timer; High Hon Roll; NHS; Platlsburgh U; Soclgy.

FREDERICKS, CHERYL; Monohasen SR HS; Schenectady, NY; (Y); 35/177; Church Yth Grp; Spanish Clb; Concert Band; Flag Corp; Mrchg Band; Pep Band; Rep Jr Cls; Rep Stu Cncl; VP Mgr Socr; NHS; Secndry Ed.

FREE, ROBERT A; Hamburg SR HS; Boston, NY; (Y); 39/411; Model UN; Service Clb; Symp Band; Stu Cncl; Im JV Bsktbl; Hon Roll; NHS; Ntl Merit SF; Im Socr; Amer H S Athl Awd; Boston Coll; Mrktg.

FREE, THOMAS A; Hamburg SR HS; Boston, NY; (Y); 3/409; Boy Scts; Computer Clb; JCL; Thesps; Variety Show; Yrbk Bus Mgr; Capt Badmtn; Powder Puff Ftbl; High Hon Roll; Opt Clb Awd; Gardener Of Yr 84; Stu Of Yr 82; Harvard; Law.

FREED, JULIE; Monticello HS; Monticello, NY; (Y); 1/160; Debate Tm; Intnl Clb; NFL; Yrbk Phtg; Tennis; High Hon Roll; NHS; Pres Schlr; Val; NY ST Rgnts Schlrshp 85; Northstar Bank Schlrshp 85; NY ST Stu Snt Polcy Forum Partcpt 85; Cornell U; Food Sci.

FREED, STEVE; Ticonderoga HS; Putnam Station, NY; (Y); Church Yth Grp; JV Var Ftbl; High Hon Roll; Hon Roll; NHS.

FREEDBERG, DOUGLAS B; Middletown HS; Middletown, NY; (Y); 1/396; Capt Scholastic Bowl; Capt Golf; High Hon Roll; Pres NHS; Ntl Merit Ltr; Val; Boy Scts; Yrbk Stf; Rep Stu Cncl; Rgnts Schlrshp NY 85; Acad Achvt Awds Math, Hist & Englsh 83 84; U Of AZ; Pre-Med.

FREEDMAN, ALISA; Jamesville-De Witt HS; Jamesville, NY; (Y); JA; Key Clb; Pep Clb; Spanish Clb; Band; Yrbk Stf; JV Sftbl; JV Capt Vllybl.

FREELUND, ELIZABETH; North Shore HS; Glen Cove, NY; (Y); AFS; Drama Clb; Q&S; Temple Yth Grp; School Play; Nwsp Rptr; Yrbk Stf; Rep Stu Cncl; Ntl Merit Ltr; Quill & Scrll Awd 84; Mktg Mgmt.

FREEMAN, CINNAMON J; Royalton-Hartland Central HS; Middleport, NY; (Y); 5/127; Am Leg Aux Girls St; French Clb; Varsity Clb; Chorus; Pres Soph Cls; Var Capt Bsktbl; Trk; Var JV Vllybl; Hon Roll; Regents Schlrshp 85; Full-Time Frshman Brockport Coll 84-85; SUNY Coll Brockport; Accntng.

FREEMAN, DAVID M; Jamestown HS; Jamestown, NY; (Y); 43/400; Church Yth Grp; Drama Clb; Pres Acpl Chr; Band; Madrigals; Mrchg Band; Pres Symp Band; Nwsp Stf; Regents Schlrshp Awd NY ST Regents 85; US Asst Awd Tuition Schlrshp 85; Jamestown CC; Broadcasting.

FREEMAN, GAIL; South Side HS; Rockville Ctr, NY; (Y); #22 In Class; Drama Clb; Key Clb; Latin Clb; Thesps; Madrigals; School Play; Var Crs Cntry; Var Trk; High Hon Roll; NHS; Hnrbl Thspn Stu Awd; Humnts.

FREEMAN, ROBERT; Ossining HS; Briarcliff, NY; (Y); Ski Clb; Temple Yth Grp; Varsity Clb; Nwsp Rptr; Yrbk Stf; JV Var Bsbl; JV Bsktbl; JV L Ftbl; French Hon Soc; High Hon Roll; IN Awd Best Rnng Back 84; All Leag All Sectn Hnr Ment Ftbl 84; Bus.

FREEMIRE, STEVE; Vernon Verona Sherrill Central HS; Vernon Ctr, NY; (Y); 17/234; Boy Scts; Computer Clb; Varsity Clb; Golf; High Hon Roll.

FREER, CARRIE; Massena Central HS; Massena, NY; (Y); Church Yth Grp; Sec French Clb; Radio Clb; Off Stu Cncl; Stat Bsktbl; Powder Puff Ftbl; Stat Socr; Capt Var Vllybl; Hon Roll.

FREEZER, NICOLE J; Ramaz HS; New York, NY; (Y); Art Clb; Drama Clb; Temple Yth Grp; Chorus; Stage Crew; Yrbk Stf; Lit Mag; Tennis; Brandeis U.

FREGOE, LEE; Massena Central HS; Massena, NY; (Y); Key Clb; Rep Stu Cncl; JV Bsbl; JV Var Ice Hcky; JV Var Socr; Var Trk; Hon Roll; Church Yth Grp; French Clb; Quiz Bowl; Mst Imprvd Plyr Sccr Cmp; All Trnmnet JV Hcky, 2nd Tm All Nrthrn V Sccr 84; Engrng.

FREGOE, LISA; Saranac Central HS; Morrisonville, NY; (Y); 44/118; Girl Scts; Chorus; Yrbk Stf; Hon Roll; Arch.

FREID, JAMES; Cicero-N Syracuse HS; Clay, NY; (S); 99/771; Cmnty Wkr; Math Tm; Ski Clb; Band; Concert Band; Mrchg Band; Pep Band; Symp Band; Trk; Hon Roll; Fnlst AFROTC Schlrshp 84-85; Syracuse U; Comp Sci.

FREIDHOFF, LYNNETTE; Pittsford Sutherland HS; Pittsford, NY; (Y); Engrng.

FREIERT, ROBERT C; Cleveland Hill HS; Cheektowaga, NY; (Y); JCL; Yrbk Stf; Var Vllybl; Hon Roll; NYS Regents Schlrshp 85; Clarkson U; Engrng.

FREIS, SYLVIA; Longwood HS; Yaphank, NY; (Y); 13/487; Capt Pep Clb; Capt Drill Tm; Mgr Stage Crew; Yrbk Bus Mgr; Yrbk Ed-Chief; Bsktbl; Capt Pom Pon; Sftbl; High Hon Roll; NHS; Treas Of Yaphank Fire Dept 84-85; Stu Of The Yr 83; White Lttr In Sprt Linette-Kickline; U Of TX; Engrng.

FREITAS, JULIE; Bishop Kearney HS; Rochester, NY; (Y); Hosp Aide; Pres JA; Color Guard; Mrchg Band; Rep Frsh Cls; Twrlr; Monroe CC; Lib Arts.

FRENCH, CHARLES R; Moriah Central HS; Witherbee, NY; (Y); JV Bsktbl; Im Var Ftbl; Hon Roll; Oswego; Indstrl Arts Tchr.

FRENCH, KELLY; Knox Memorial Central Schl; Russell, NY; (S); 1/22; Sec Band; Drm Mjr(t); School Play; Yrbk Bus Mgr; Pres Stu Cncl; Capt Var Cheerleading; Var Socr; High Hon Roll; VP NHS; Prsdntl Schlr 85; St Lawrence U; Bio.

FRENCH, MATTHEW; Sherburne-Earlville Central HS; Sherburne, NY; (S); #3 In Class; Boy Scts; Church Yth Grp; Stage Crew; JV Crs Cntry; Var Swmmng; JV Trk; Hon Roll; NHS; Prfct Atten Awd; Aerospc Engrng.

FRENCH, MECHELLE; Hudson Falls HS; Hudson Falls, NY; (Y); 69/231; Drama Clb; 4-H; Hosp Aide; VP Key Clb; Spanish Clb; Varsity Clb; Stage Crew; Rep Frsh Cls; Rep Soph Cls; Rep Jr Cls; Elem Educ.

FRENCH, STEPHEN; Shenendehowa SR HS; Ballston Lake, NY; (Y); 38/647; Key Clb; Varsity Clb; Trk; Wrstlng; High Hon Roll; NHS; Yrbk Stf; Rep Jr Cls; Rep Sr Cls; Navy ROTC Schlrshp RPI 85; AIR Forc & Army ROTC 85; Regnts Schlrshp 85; Vrsty 3-D Ltr; RPI Troy NY; Engnrng.

FRENCH, SUE ANN; Haverling Central HS; Bath, NY; (Y); Exploring; JCL; Trs Latin Clb; Math Clb; Band; Concert Band; Mrchg Band; Symp Band; Yrbk Stf; Stu Cncl; Natl Lat Exam Cum Laude 83; Law.

FRENIA, MELISSA; Liverpool HS; Liverpool, NY; (S); 152/792; Pres Church Yth Grp; Off Exploring; Hosp Aide; Rep Stu Cncl; Stat Bsktbl; Powder Puff Ftbl; High Hon Roll; Hon Roll; Jr NHS; YMCA Cert Volunteer Svc 82; ST Josephs Hosp Volunteer Pin 82; SUNY Geneseo; Acctng.

FRENZ, MARCIA; Irondequoit HS; Rochester, NY; (Y); 17/391; Camp Fr Inc; Ski Clb; Varsity Clb; Orch; School Musical; Rep Soph Cls; Var Capt Crs Cntry; Var Trk; Hon Roll; NHS; Hist.

FRERICHS, KIM DENEEN; Niagara Wheatfield SR HS; Niagara Falls, NY; (Y); 48/313; Pres Church Yth Grp; FHA; Pep Clb; PAVAS; Yrbk Stf; Cheerleading; High Hon Roll; NHS; Art Dept Awd Medl 85; Art Inst Pittsburgh; Fashn Illu.

FRESHMAN, MICHELLE E; Shaker HS; Menands, NY; (Y); Drama Clb; Pres VP French Clb; Sec JA; Temple Yth Grp; Yrbk Bus Mgr; Lit Mag; Stu Cncl; Elks Awd; NHS; Ntl Merit Schol; Wellesley Coll; Polt Sci.

FREUNDLICH, ROBERT S; East Syracuse-Minor HS; E Syracuse, NY; (Y); 4/338; Pres Latin Clb; Ski Clb; School Musical; Variety Show; Var L Gym; High Hon Roll; NHS; Ntl Merit SF; Boy Scts; Computer Clb; RPI Math/Sci Mdl 83-84; Wesleyan U; Genetics.

FREVELE, TERRY; St John The Baptist HS; Ronkonkoma, NY; (Y); Church Yth Grp; Dance Clb; Hosp Aide; Chorus; Science Clb; School Musical; School Play; Stage Crew; Crs Cntry; Trk; Stony Brook U; Psych.

FREY, CATHERINE; Bishop Ludden HS; Baldwinsville, NY; (S); 6/280; L Tennis; High Hon Roll; Hon Roll; Awds Spn & Fr 83-84; Intl Bus.

FREY, CHRISTINE; St Dominic HS; Huntington, NY; (Y); 5/119; Nwsp Rptr; Sec Soph Cls; Trs Sr Cls; Rep Stu Cncl; Var Cheerleading; JV Var Sftbl; Var Tennis; Im Vllybl; High Hon Roll; Pres NHS; Amercnsm Awd 85; Hmcmng Queen 84; Memrl Schlrshp 85; Stonehill Coll; Psych.

FREY, EVELYN; Dominican Commercial HS; Brooklyn, NY; (Y); Hosp Aide; Rep Frsh Cls; Bus.

FREY, NORMAN; Columbia HS; W Sand Lk, NY; (Y); Aud/Vis; Church Yth Grp; Cmnty Wkr; Computer Clb; Drama Clb; Intnl Clb; JA; Trs Key Clb; Service Clb; School Musical; Acctg.

FREY, SUE; Vestal SR HS; Vestal, NY; (Y); 4-H; Hon Roll; Prfct Atten 82-83; Findlay Coll Grant 84-85; Findlay Coll; Equestrian Studs.

FREYTAG, CHRISTINE; Whitesboro SR HS; Utica, NY; (Y); Church Yth Grp; Dance Clb; Band; Church Choir; Concert Band; Mrchg Band; Orch; Var JV Cheerleading; Mgr(s); Bus Mngmnt.

FRICHNER, JASON M; Bronx HS Of Sci; New York, NY; (Y); Library Aide; Lit Mag; NHS; Staff Blck Annotated Bibliogrphy 84-85; Ownr Wrd Proc Comp Co; Med.

FRIED, ALISON A; Great Neck South HS; Great Neck, NY; (Y); 2/218; French Clb; Hosp Aide; Drill Tm; Nwsp Stf; Yrbk Stf; Pres Schlr; Sal; Charles Evan Hughes & L I Cncl Achvt Awds 85; Nwsdy Hgh Hnrs Fnlst 85; U Of PA.

FRIED, ELIZABETH; The Ursaline Schl; New Rochelle, NY; (Y); 29/129; French Clb; Girl Scts; Chorus; Yrbk Phtg; Badmtn; Var Trk; High Hon Roll; NHS; Westchester Bus Inst Awd 84; Trk Coaches Awd 84; Roger Williams Coll; Marine Bio.

FRIED, ROBIN; Sheepshead Bay HS; Brooklyn, NY; (Y); Drama Clb; Office Aide; PAVAS; Teachers Aide; Chorus; School Musical; Yrbk Stf; Trs Sr Cls; Rep Stu Cncl; Cit Awd; Hnr Cittn City Cncl NY 82; Bus Mgmt.

FRIEDLAND, DONNA; New Paltz HS; New Paltz, NY; (Y); 1/131; French Clb; Hosp Aide; Math Clb; Temple Yth Grp; Yrbk Stf; High Hon Roll; NHS; Physcn.

FRIEDLE, DAVID; James I O Neill HS; Highland Fls, NY; (Y); Boy Scts; Church Yth Grp; Computer Clb; Drama Clb; Chorus; School Musical; Hon Roll.

FRIEDLY, STACEY; Maryvale SR HS; Cheektowaga, NY; (Y); 40/400; Letterman Clb; Bsbl; JV Capt Ftbl; Hon Roll; Bus Adm.

FRIEDMAN, ANDREA; Dominican Commercial HS; Richmond Hill, NY; (Y); 16/253; Art Clb; Church Yth Grp; Cmnty Wkr; Dance Clb; PAVAS; Service Clb; Spanish Clb; Teachers Aide; Yrbk Stf; High Hon Roll; Danc Awd 82; Art Hnr 83; Danc Schlrshp 82; Danc.

FRIEDMAN, ANDREW J; Doane Stuart School; Slingerlands, NY; (Y); 1/30; Ski Clb; Yrbk Phtg; Bsbl; Rep Jr Cls; Sr Cls; Var Co-Capt Bsbl; Var Bsktbl; Var Socr; High Hon Roll; Ntl Merit SF; Parents Assn Stu Of The Yr Awd 83; Brown Univ Bk Awd 84; Amherst Coll; Sci Resrch.

FRIEDMAN, ARIC; John Ahams HS; Howard Beach, NY; (Y); 22/591; Office Aide; Science Clb; Ski Clb; Teachers Aide; Band; Concert Band; Jazz Band; Mrchg Band; Orch; Symp Band; UCLA; Engr.

FRIEDMAN, BARNABY; East Hampton HS; Wainscott, NY; (Y); Aud/Vis; Lit Mag; Var Tennis; High Hon Roll; Hon Roll; Jr NHS.

FRIEDMAN, BRIAN; Longwood HS; Coram, NY; (Y); Church Yth Grp; Nwsp Stf; JV Var Bsbl; JV Var Ftbl; Wt Lftg.

FRIEDMAN, DANA S; Valley Stream South HS; Lynbrook, NY; (Y); 43/180; Sec AFS; VP Temple Yth Grp; Rep Frsh Cls; Rep Soph Cls; Rep Jr Cls; Rep Sr Cls; Var Trk; JV Vllybl; Regents Schlrshp 85; SUNY Albany; Hist.

FRIEDMAN, DEREK; Spackenkill HS; Poughkeepsie, NY; (Y); Var Bsbl; Stat Bsktbl; Var Ftbl; Var Score Keeper; Occidental Coll; Vet.

FRIEDMAN, JEANNETTE; Gowanda Central HS; Gowanda, NY; (Y); 92/124; Spanish Clb; Yrbk Stf; JV Bsktbl; Im Trk; Prfct Atten Awd; RN.

FRIEDMAN, JENNIFER; Irondequoit HS; Rochester, NY; (Y); 41/390; Dance Clb; Exploring; Latin Clb; Model UN; Ski Clb; Temple Yth Grp; Chorus; Hon Roll.

FRIEDMAN, JILL S; Brighton HS; Rochester, NY; (Y); 108/340; French Clb; Hosp Aide; VP Temple Yth Grp; Rep Frsh Cls; Rep Soph Cls; Rep Jr Cls; Rep Sr Cls; AM U; Child Psych.

FRIEDMAN, LAWRENCE M; Alfred G Berner HS; Massapequa Park, NY; (Y); 11/426; Sec Ski Clb; NHS; Ntl Merit Ltr; CT Coll; Law.

FRIEDMAN, LEE ANN; William Floyd HS; Mastic, NY; (Y); 32/428; Debate Tm; Key Clb; MMM; Chorus; Orch; School Musical; Ed Nwsp Rptr; Hon Roll; NHS; Regents Schlrshp 85; SUNY At Binghmtn; Pre-Law.

FRIEDMAN, LILI; Niskayuna HS; Schdy, NY; (Y); Sec Church Yth Grp; Cmnty Wkr; 4-H; Girl Scts; Key Clb; Pep Clb; Spanish Clb; Rep Jr Cls; Var Fld Hcky; Var Trk; Intl Bus.

FRIEDMAN, MARK; Far Rockaway HS; Far Rockaway, NY; (Y); Cmnty Wkr; Office Aide; Temple Yth Grp; Var Capt Bowling; Var Capt Tennis; Var L Wrstlng; Hon Roll; Prfct Atten Awd; Gary Rosen Memrl Awd-Hartmn Y 83; NY Daly Nws Spr Yth Awd 85; Bus Adm.

FRIEDMAN, MICHAEL; Stuyvesant HS; Brooklyn, NY; (Y); Computer Clb; Debate Tm; Math Clb; Capt Math Tm; Science Clb; Ntl Merit SF; Political Wkr; Lit Mag; Hon Roll; Certfct Of Achv Math Assn Of Amer 82-85; Natl Cncl Of Tchrs Of Math Awd 82; Mcgraw Hill Awd 82; M I T; Comp Sci.

FRIEDMAN, MICHAEL J; Scarsdale HS; Scarsdale, NY; (Y); Red Cross Aide; Teachers Aide; Yrbk Stf; Im Bsktbl; JV Golf; Im Sftbl; NY ST Regents Schlrshp 85; U Of MI; Pre-Med.

FRIEDMAN, RICHARD B; James Madison HS; Brooklyn, NY; (Y); 34/801; JV Var Bsbl; Var Capt Bsktbl; Hon Roll; Jr NHS; Prfct Atten Awd; NY ST Regent Schlrshp 85; Brooklyn Coll.

FRIEDMAN, SUZANNE; Valley Stream Central HS; Valley Stream, NY; (Y); Debate Tm; Temple Yth Grp; Band; Chorus; Concert Band; Mrchg Band; Orch; Crs Cntry; Socr; Sftbl; Music Hnr Soc 84; Acctg.

FRIEDMAN, VICKI; John F Kennedy HS; Bronx, NY; (Y); Aud/Vis; Office Aide; Teachers Aide; Chorus; Yrbk Stf; High Hon Roll; NHS; Val; Regents Schlrshp 84-85; UFT Schlrshp 85; Suny Albany; Bus.

FRIEDRICHS, DONNA; Smithtown High School East; Nesconset, NY; (Y); GAA; Rep Frsh Cls; Rep Soph Cls; Rep Soph Cls; Rep Sr Cls; Stu Cncl; Var Socr; Vllybl; Hon Roll; Chrmn Of JR & SR Prom 85; Htl Tech.

FRIEND, ADAM; Tottenville HS; Staten Island, NY; (Y); 7/815; Science Clb; Concert Band; Var Stat Bsbl; Gov Hon Prg Awd; High Hon Roll; NHS; Ntl Merit Ltr; Daily Nws Supr Yth 84; NYS Rgnts Scshlrshp 85; Var Bsbl Stu Athl 85; Brown U.

FRIENDS II, RICHARD L; Hornell SR HS; Hornell, NY; (Y); 35/198; Computer Clb; Varsity Clb; Bsbl; Bsktbl; Mgr(s); Score Keeper; Trk; Wrstlng; Hon Roll; Cert Merit Achvt Bio 83, Reading 85; Cert Merit Assmbly ST NY 85; Natl Tech Inst Deaf; Accntnt.

FRIENDS, SCOTT; Jasper Central HS; Woodhull, NY; (Y); 2/30; French Clb; Band; Yrbk Stf; Pres Jr Cls; Pres Sr Cls; JV Capt Bsktbl; JV Var Socr; Var JV Trk; High Hon Roll; NHS; Elmira Coll Key Awd 85; Varsty Clb 83-85.

FRIES, CINDIE A; Schl Of Performing Arts; New York, NY; (Y); Teachers Aide; Thesps; Chorus; School Musical; School Play; Stage Crew; Sftbl; Hon Roll; Dance Awd 81; Actng.

FRIES, SYLVIA; Longwood HS; Yaphank, NY; (S); 19/490; Math Tm; Capt Pep Clb; Chorus; Stage Crew; Yrbk Bus Mgr; Yrbk Ed-Chief; Bsktbl; Var Capt Pom Pon; Sftbl; High Hon Roll; White Letter Awd 85; Schlrshp To C W Post Jrnlsm Cnfrnc 85; Stu Of Year 81; U Of PA; Engrng.

FRIETSCH, BARBARA; Dominican Commercial HS; Glendale, NY; (Y); Art Clb; Girl Scts; Swmmng; Timer; Hon Roll; Spanish NHS; Principals List 83-85; Siena Clb 83-85.

FRIGULETTO, MICHAEL; Notre Dame Bishop Gibbons HS; Schenectady, NY; (S); 12/120; Computer Clb; Nwsp Stf; Lit Mag; Var Golf; Comp.

FRIND, AMIE; Mount Vernon HS; Mount Vernon, NY; (Y); Sec Church Yth Grp; Sec French Clb; Key Clb; Latin Clb; Nwsp Stf; High Hon Roll; Jr NHS.

FRINK, LISA; Norwich SR HS; Norwich, NY; (Y); Church Yth Grp; Computer Clb; Chorus; Yrbk Phtg; Yrbk Stf; Cheerleading; Hon Roll; United Church Christ Scholar 85; CCBI Schl Scholar 85; Mst Outstndng Chrldr & Ltr 84-85; CCBI; Retail Mechndsng.

FRINKS, DONNA; Bishop Maginn HS; Albany, NY; (S); 10/118; Spanish Clb; Nwsp Rptr; Nwsp Stf; Var Bsktbl; Var Sftbl; Var Tennis; High Hon Roll; NHS; Sftbl MVP; Cptn Of Bsktbl Team; SUNY Geneseo; Acctng.

FRINTZILAS, JULIE; Harborfields HS; Greenlawn, NY; (Y); Church Yth Grp; VICA; Art.

FRISCIA, JOHN; South Shore HS; Brooklyn, NY; (Y); Ftbl; Wt Lftg; St Johns U; Sprts Admin.

FRISCIC, MARINA; U N International Schl; New York, NY; (Y); Chorus; School Musical; Rep Frsh Cls; Rep Soph Cls; Rep Jr Cls; Rep Sr Cls; Rep Stu Cncl; Im Cheerleading; Var Sftbl; Var Vllybl; Barnard Coll; Lwyr.

FRISINA, CHARLES; Oceanside HS; Oceanside, NY; (Y); U Of MA; Bus.

FRISONE, LISA ANN; Cardinal Mooney HS; Rochester, NY; (Y); 75/317; Cmnty Wkr; Intnl Clb; Concert Band; School Musical; Nwsp Stf; Lit Mag; Hon Roll; Spcl Awd Cncrt Band 85; Syracuse U; Law.

FRITTON JR, JOSEPH E; Trott Vocational HS; Niagara Falls, NY; (Y); 2/139; Stage Crew; Pres Soph Cls; Var Ice Hcky; Cit Awd; Hon Roll; NHS; Prfct Atten Awd; Sal; Friends Niagara Falls Pub Lib Awd 85; PAL Schlrshp Fin 85; Schug Mem Schlrshp Awd 85; Niagara Cty Comm; Micro Elect E.

FRITTON, RHONDA A; Newfane SR HS; Lockport, NY; (S); 5/172; Drama Clb; Sec Frsh Cls; JV Bsktbl; JV Sftbl; Hon Roll; NHS; GMC/BOCES Coop Ed Pgm 84; Clarkson; Ind Engrng.

FRITZ, FRANCINE; Warwick Valley HS; Warwick, NY; (Y); 69/200; Office Aide; Color Guard; JV Cheerleading; JV Sftbl; Swmmng; Hon Roll; Acctng.

FRITZ, GRETCHEN; Lockport SR HS; Lockport, NY; (Y); 85/455; Cmnty Wkr; Drama Clb; Latin Clb; Chorus; Jazz Band; School Musical; Symp Band; Hon Roll; NY All-ST Chorus 84-85; All-Eastern Chorus 84-85; Sound Of Amer European Concrt Tour-Hnr Chorus 85; Potsdams Crane Schl/Music; Msc.

FRITZ, MARY; Westfield Central HS; Westfield, NY; (S); 6/79; Pres Trs Church Yth Grp; Girl Scts; Hosp Aide; Radio Clb; Service Clb; Ed Yrbk Stf; Trs Stu Cncl; High Hon Roll; NHS; Stu Of Month 84; Buffalo News Carrier Of The Month 84; Presbyterian Schlrshp 85; Grove City; Accounting.

FRITZEN, KATRINA; Duanesburg Central Schl; Quaker St, NY; (Y); Art Clb; Drama Clb; Hosp Aide; Pep Clb; Drill Tm; Rep Frsh Cls; Sec Soph Cls; Cheerleading; Socr; Capt Twrlr; Ft Lauderdale; Art.

FRLAN, KARMEN; Washington Irving HS; Astoria, NY; (Y); Computer Clb; Debate Tm; Library Aide; Office Aide; Teachers Aide; Nwsp Rptr; Off Jr Cls; Gym; Hon Roll; Ntl Merit Ltr; Acadmc Olympcs 85; Daily News Prncpls Prid Of Yankees 84; Lincoln Douglas Debate 85; Comptr Engrng.

FROELICH, LAURA J; The Spence Schl; New York, NY; (Y); Debate Tm; Drama Clb; Spanish Clb; Rep Stu Cncl; High Hon Roll; Ntl Merit Ltr; Schl Yr Abrd Prog 83-84; Brown U.

FROESE, KENNETH; New Dorp HS; Staten Island, NY; (Y); French Clb; Ski Clb; Ftbl; Wt Lftg.

FROGOLA, ANITA; Watkins Glen Central HS; Watkins Glen, NY; (S); 1/146; Am Leg Aux Girls St; Letterman Clb; Band; Jazz Band; Yrbk Stf; Var Capt Swmmng; French Hon Soc; Pres NHS; Val; Church Yth Grp; Mansfield ST Coll Ready Writng Cont 2nd Pl 82; BPW Ldrshp Conf 83; Math.

FROMAGET, KIMBERLY; Washingtonville SR HS; Monroe, NY; (Y); French Clb; Ski Clb; Symp Band; Yrbk Rptr; Off Frsh Cls; Off Soph Cls; Off Jr Cls; Tennis; Trk; Cit Awd; Orange Cty Yth Bur Teen Vol Awd 85; Rotary Clb Ldrshp Conf 84; Siena Coll; Acctng.

FROMBERG, PAMELA; Sheepshead Bay HS; Brooklyn, NY; (Y); Aud/Vis; PAVAS; Chorus; School Musical; School Play; Good Schlstc 79; Field Day Awd 79; Acctg.

FROMBGEN, DIANE; Barker Central HS; Barker, NY; (Y); 4/100; AFS; Pres Spanish Clb; Concert Band; Pres Frsh Cls; Var JV Fld Hcky; Var JV Trk; Hon Roll; Church Yth Grp; Varsity Clb; Band; Elmira Key Awd 85; Ntl Hnr Soc 85; Rantra Fusca Creatvty Awd-Odyssy Of Mind 84 & 85.

FROMMATER, SANDRA; Bay Shore HS; Bay Shore, NY; (Y); Girl Scts; Office Aide; Yrbk Stf; Cit Awd; Beach Proj 84-85; Suffolk Cnty CC; Sec.

FROMMER, ROBERT; Mamareneck HS; Larchmont, NY; (Y).

FRONCZAK, MARK; Niagara Wheatfield HS; Niagara Falls, NY; (Y); Pres Latin Clb; Math Clb; Math Tm; Spanish Clb; Var Ftbl; Hon Roll; NHS; Boys St Fnl 85; Niagara Cty Leg Intern 85; Biochem.

FRONCZEK, LAURA; Mount Mercy Acad; E Aurora, NY; (S); 33/200; Cmnty Wkr; 4-H; French Clb; FHA; Model UN; Nwsp Rptr; Nwsp Stf; Im Badmtn; 4-H Awd; Hon Roll; 4-H Grnd Chmpn Engl Hunt Seat Hrshmshp 83; Natl Frnch Exam Cert Of Merit 82; Librl Arts.

FROSOLONE, TINA; Niagara Catholic HS; Niagara Falls, NY; (Y); 14/79; Dance Clb; Drama Clb; Key Clb; Ski Clb; Trs Spanish Clb; School Play; Yrbk Stf; Vllybl; Hon Roll; Kiwanis Awd; Niagara County CC.

FROST, ART; Keveny Memorial Acad; Troy, NY; (Y); Chess Clb; Computer Clb; Letterman Clb; Math Clb; Math Tm; Ski Clb; Spanish Clb; Bsbl; Bsktbl; Socr.

FROST, SARAH S; Pittsford Sutherland HS; Pittsford, NY; (Y); Drama Clb; Science Clb; NHS; Ntl Merit Ltr; Church Yth Grp; Model UN; Yrbk Ed-Chief; Yrbk Stf; High Hon Roll; Hon Roll; 1 Man Exhbt Albright Knox Gallery 84-85; Prtfolio In Schlstc Art Shw 85; Hnbl Mntn Natl Arts Recog 85; Fine Art.

FROUXIDES, VIVIAN; Farmingdale HS; Farmingdale, NY; (Y); Sec Church Yth Grp; Pres Debate Tm; French Clb; FBLA; Key Clb; Flag Corp; Variety Show; Nwsp Stf; Yrbk Stf; Mgr(s); Bus.

FRUEHAN, LEONORE; Jamesville Dewitt HS; Dewitt, NY; (Y); 17/240; German Clb; Hosp Aide; Chorus; Orch; School Musical; Symp Band; Yrbk Stf; Trs Jr Cls; Trs Sr Cls; Ntl Merit Ltr; Natrl Sci.

FRY, DANA; Oakfield Alabama HS; Basom, NY; (Y); 9/93; Art Clb; Church Yth Grp; French Clb; Natl Beta Clb; High Hon Roll; Hon Roll; NHS; Fr Awd 83-85; Drwg Awd 84-85; Paintng Awd 84-85; Chld Psych.

FRY, J ALEXANDER; Northport HS; Northport, NY; (Y); 81/661; Cmnty Wkr; Concert Band; Mrchg Band; Symp Band; Var Crs Cntry; JV Lcrss; JV Tennis; Var Trk; Hon Roll; NHS; Crs Cntry Medals 83-84; Interact VP 84-85; Arch Awd 85; Notre Dame; Arch.

FRYDMAN, YAEL; Shulamith High School For Girls; Brooklyn, NY; (S); Art Clb; Library Aide; Office Aide; Teachers Aide; Temple Yth Grp; Chorus; School Musical; Lit Mag; Stu Cncl; Bsbl; Bus Mgmt.

FRYE, DONALD; Broadalbin Central HS; Broadalbin, NY; (Y); 18/75; Am Leg Boys St; Drama Clb; Library Aide; Mathletes; Math Tm; Varsity Clb; School Play; Variety Show; Yrbk Ed-Chief; Yrbk Phtg; Natl Hnr Soc 82-85; Am Leg Boys ST 85; Clarkson; Comp Sci.

FRYE, TAMMY ANISSA; Cleveland Hill HS; Cheektowaga, NY; (Y); AFS; Drama Clb; JCL; Library Aide; Band; Chorus; Color Guard; School Musical; Lit Mag; Hon Roll; Awd Cheektowaga Patrtc Cmmsn 82; Exclint NY ST Schl Music Assn Comp 84; Psychlgy.

FRZIER, MONALISA; Farmingdale HS; Amityville, NY; (Y); Chrmn Church Yth Grp; VP Church Choir; Rep Stu Cncl; Grad Cert From Barbyon Schl Of Modeling 82-83; Educ For Deaf.

FUCA, GLORIA; Christopher Columbus HS; Bronx, NY; (Y); 157/792; Dance Clb; Library Aide; Teachers Aide; Nwsp Rptr; Nwsp Stf; Cit Awd; Prfct Atten Awd; Pltcl Sci.

FUCCI, ANTHONY J; Mt St Michael Acad; Bronx, NY; (S); 14/308; Church Yth Grp; Teachers Aide; NHS; Fordham U; Psych.

FUCHEK, CAROLYN; Walter Panas HS; Peekskill, NY; (Y); Hosp Aide; Orch; Music.

FUCITO, THERESA; Germantown Central HS; Hudson, NY; (Y); 8/45; Church Yth Grp; Band; Chorus; Concert Band; School Musical; Swing Chorus; Yrbk Stf; Var Fld Hcky; High Hon Roll; NHS; Alma Roger Music Awd 83; NYSSMA Solo Comptn 85; Otstndg Perfmc Math 85; SUNY; Bus Admin.

FUDAL, THOM; Sachem HS; Holbrook, NY; (Y); 78/1160; Church Yth Grp; Pres Science Clb; Ski Clb; Acpl Chr; Chorus; Madrigals; School Musical; School Play; Stage Crew; Hon Roll; Drama Clb Ldrshp Awd 85; Merit Awd Sci Fair 83; Soc Stds Fair Merit Awd 83; Theatre Arts.

FUDGE, PATRICIA; Chenango Valley HS; Binghamton, NY; (Y); Chrmn Church Yth Grp; Teachers Aide; Pres Sec Band; Pres Concert Band; Jazz Band; Mrchg Band; Orch; Pep Band; Symp Band; Hon Roll; Supr Achv-Excllnc Ldrshp Schlrshp/Ctznshp, Charctr 83; Hghst GPA Typwrtng II 84; Al-Rgn Band 82-85; Broome CC; Bus.

FUDGER, ELIZABETH; Johnstown HS; Johnstown, NY; (Y); Yrbk Bus Mgr; Yrbk Ed-Chief; Stu Cncl; Var Crs Cntry; JV Sftbl; JV Trk; Hon Roll; Trvl.

FUEGLISTER, VALERIE; Hicksville HS; Hicksville, NY; (Y); Cmnty Wkr; French Clb; German Clb; Hosp Aide; Lit Mag; French Hon Soc; 1st Pl Orgnl Frnch Poetry Cntst 83; Ltn Hnr Soc 85; 3 Poems Pblshd In Anthlgs; Pre Med.

FUENTES, DANNY; Susan E Wagner HS; Staten Is, NY; (Y); JA; VP Jr Cls; Gym; Trk; Hon Roll.

FUENTES, DENNIS; Albertus Magnus HS; Nanuet, NY; (Y); Drama Clb; Math Tm; Service Clb; School Musical; Yrbk Phtg; Yrbk Stf; Lit Mag; Crs Cntry; Hon Roll; Coll Mt St Vincent; Cmmnctn Art.

FUENTES, MICHELLE; Kings Park SR HS; Kings Pk, NY; (Y); Concert Band; Mrchg Band; Nwsp Phtg; Nwsp Rptr; Nwsp Stf; Rep Stu Cncl; Var JV Sftbl; Hon Roll; Band; Im JV Mgr(s); Jump Rope Awd 83-84; Outstndng Achvt Kings Herald Awd 85; Cerbrl Palsy Tag Day Rep Awd 84; Hofstra U; Comm.

FUERST, ROBERT C; Lakeshore Central HS; Angola, NY; (Y); Am Leg Boys St; 4-H; Trs Frsh Cls; Mgr(s); Swmmng; Hon Roll; Sci Olympd Awd 82-83 & 83-84; Cornell; Mech Engrng.

FUERTES, GEORGE; Kings Park HS; Kings Pk, NY; (Y); 32/392; Var Lcrss; Hon Roll; Engrng.

FUERTES, MONICA; Kings Park SR HS; Kings Park, NY; (Y); 1/446; VP Cmnty Wkr; Band; Mrchg Band; Ed Yrbk Stf; Var L Crs Cntry; Var L Trk; High Hon Roll; NHS; Ntl Merit Ltr; Val; Brown U; Biochem.

FUGALLI, CLAUDIA; North Shore HS; Glen Head, NY; (Y); 30/200; Drama Clb; Political Wkr; Thesps; Chorus; School Musical; School Play; Stage Crew; Variety Show; Nwsp Stf; Hon Roll.

FUHRMAN, JASON K; Arsdley HS; Dobbs Ferry, NY; (Y); Aud/Vis; Math Tm; Temple Yth Grp; School Play; Nwsp Stf; Yrbk Stf; JV Var Socr; JV Wrstlng; French Hon Soc; Ntl Merit Ltr; NYS Regnts Schlrshp 84-85; 1st Pl Chem Cntst 83; Cornell U; Ind Lbr Rels.

FUHST JR, ROBERT F; Mt St Michael Acad; Bronx, NY; (S); 20/308; Spanish Clb; Var Bsbl; Im DECA; Im Ftbl; High Hon Roll; Hon Roll; NHS; Spanish NHS; Cmmnctns.

FULLER, APRIL; Hempstead HS; Hempstead, NY; (S); 26/333; Pres Church Yth Grp; French Clb; Office Aide; Teachers Aide; Var L Crs Cntry; L Capt Trk; Hon Roll; NHS; Stonybrook U; Engl.

FULLER, BARBARA; Gouverneur HS; Gouverneur, NY; (Y); Trs Church Yth Grp; Trs Girl Scts; Band; Concert Band; Mrchg Band; Orch; Pep Band; Girl Sct Gold Ldrshp Awd 84; Girl Sct Gold Awd 85; Sec.

FULLER, BRENDA; Vestal SR HS; Vestal, NY; (Y); Cmnty Wkr; Red Cross Aide; Wrk Wth Spcl Olympc 85-86; Tch Gymnstcs At Grls Clb 84-86; Pyscl Thrpy.

FULLER, DEIDRE; De Sales Catholic HS; Newfane, NY; (Y); Ski Clb; Nwsp Stf; Yrbk Stf; Rep Stu Cncl; Var L Cheerleading; Var L Tennis; Bus Adm.

FULLER, DONNA FAYE; Mt Vernon HS; Mount Vernon, NY; (Y); Cmnty Wkr; Girl Scts; VP Band; Concert Band; Drm Mjr(t); Mrchg Band; Pep Band; Stage Crew; Hon Roll; Fshn Illstrtn.

FULLER, ERIC; St Francis Prep Schl; Brooklyn, NY; (S); 100/700; Ski Clb; Hon Roll; NHS; Opt Clb Awd; Pres Schlr; St Francis Coll; Bus Mktg.

FULLER, HUGH L; Edison Tech & Occupational Ctr; Spencerport, NY; (Y); 2/271; Boy Scts; Math Tm; Pres Science Clb; Varsity Clb; Var L Swmmng; Bausch & Lomb Sci Awd; NHS; Exploring; Math Clb; Model UN; Ntl Shclr Athl 84; L R Klepper Schlrshp Athl Awd 83; L R Klepper Most Promising Stu Athl Awd 84; Rensselaer Polytech Inst; Engr.

FULLER, KIMMO; Berlin Central HS; Berlin, NY; (S); 6/82; Trs Soph Cls; JV Bsbl; L Socr; Capt L Wrstlng; Engr.

FULLER, LAURIE; Coxsackie-Athens Central HS; Catskill, NY; (Y); 9/94; 4-H; Red Cross Aide; Spanish Clb; Yrbk Bus Mgr; Yrbk Stf; High Hon Roll; Hon Roll; U Of AL-TUSCALOOSA; Accntng.

FULLER, LISA; Slamanca HS; Killbuck, NY; (Y); Drama Clb; French Clb; Ski Clb; Hon Roll; Hon Roll; Ftbl Hmcmng Attndnt 83; Attndnce Awd 84; 3rd Highest Avrge Native Amer 85; Hotel Mgt.

FULLER, PATRICIA L; Scotia-Glenville SR HS; Scotia, NY; (Y); Church Yth Grp; Cmnty Wkr; Exploring; Girl Scts; Red Cross Aide; Chorus; Sec Soph Cls; Ntl Merit SF; Library Aide; Stage Crew; Regents Schlrshp Awd 85; SUNY Geneseo; Hlth Fld.

FULLER, STEVE; Mt St Joseph HS; Buffalo, NY; (Y); German Clb; Pep Clb; Var Bsbl; Var Bsktbl; Var Socr; SAR Awd; Bus Admin.

FULLER, WILLIAM L; Homer Central HS; Homer, NY; (Y); 71/203; Trs Church Yth Grp; German Clb; Thesps; School Musical; School Play; Nwsp Stf; JV Bsbl; Socr; NY ST Regents Schlrshp 85; Oral Roberts U; Telecomm.

FULOP, JACKIE; Seaford HS; Seaford, NY; (Y); Exploring; GAA; Varsity Clb.

FULTON, BEATE; Washingtonville HS; Washingtonville, NY; (Y); Ski Clb; Spanish Clb; Pep Band; Symp Band; Fld Hcky; Socr; Vllybl; High Hon Roll; Lion Awd; NHS; ST Class B Rnnup Soccer 84-85; Engr.

FULTON, MARLON; Long Beach SR HS; Long Beach, NY; (Y); Aud/Vis; Church Yth Grp; Computer Clb; Chorus; Church Choir; School Musical; Yrbk Stf; Crs Cntry; Mgr(s); Hon Roll; NC Central U; Bus Adm.

FUNDIS, MARK; Cooperstown Central HS; Cooperstown, NY; (Y); Church Yth Grp; English Clb; Varsity Clb; Chorus; Nwsp Stf; Rep Sr Cls; Stu Cncl; Var L Bsktbl; Var L Socr; Var L Trk; Hartwick Coll Poetry Cont Fin 84; Schl Hgh Jmp Rcrd 85; Ctr ST All Star Trck & Bsktbl 84-85; PSYCH.

FUNDIS, STACEY; Cooperstown Central HS; Cooperstown, NY; (Y); Church Yth Grp; English Clb; GAA; Nwsp Stf; Yrbk Stf; JV Bsktbl; Var Socr; Var Tennis; Comm.

FUNG, BEN; Bayside HS; Whitestone, NY; (Y); Prfct Atten Awd; Office Aide; Band; School Musical; Nwsp Ed-Chief; Nwsp Rptr; Yrbk Stf; Im Vllybl; High Hon Roll; Hon Roll; Cert Excell Math 85; SUNY-STONY Brook; Dntst.

FUNK, LESTER; Stissing Mt JR SR HS; Pine Plains, NY; (Y); Boy Scts; Church Yth Grp; ROTC; Yrbk Stf; Var Capt Bsbl; Var Capt Bsktbl; Im Coach Actv; Var Capt Socr; Hon Roll; Yrbk Phtg; Hnr Rl 83-84; Most Impvd Var Bsktbl 84-85 All Confnce Bsbl 85; ROTC; Sci.

FUNK, SHARON; St Peters HS For Girls; Staten Island, NY; (Y); Church Yth Grp; Girl Scts; Hosp Aide; Teachers Aide; Nwsp Ed-Chief; Bowling; St Johns U; Bus Adm.

FUNSCH, CHRISTY B; West Genesee SR HS; Syracuse, NY; (Y); 14/500; Dance Clb; Ski Clb; High Hon Roll; NYS Rgnts Schlrshp 85; OUTSTNDNG Stu Eng Awd 85; Mst Orig Choreography 82; Hamilton Coll; Eng.

FURA, JEAN; Amsterdam HS; Amsterdam, NY; (Y); DECA; Girl Scts; Band; Concert Band; Mrchg Band; Stu Cncl; Hon Roll; Ntl Hnr Rl 84; ST U NY; Acctng.

FURCI, MARIA; East Islip HS; Islip Ter, NY; (Y); FBLA; Yrbk Stf; Pres Soph Cls; Pres Jr Cls; Tennis; Vllybl; High Hon Roll; Hon Roll.

FUREY, DANIEL; Rhinebeck HS; Rhinecliff, NY; (Y); AFS; Boy Scts; Church Yth Grp; CAP; Ski Clb; Band; Concert Band; Stage Crew; Yrbk Phtg; Yrbk Stf; Comp Grphscs.

FUREY, JOAN; John A Coleman HS; Tillson, NY; (S); Pres 4-H; French Clb; Hosp Aide; Key Clb; Yrbk Stf; JV Capt Bsktbl; Cit Awd; High Hon Roll; Jr NHS; Safety Awd 4-H 84; Clothing Awd 4-H 83.

FURGAL, JEFF; Whitesboro SR HS; Whitesboro, NY; (Y); 80/380; Sec Church Yth Grp; Varsity Clb; Var L Bsktbl; JV Ftbl; Var L Lcrss; Hon Roll.

FURGAL, KAREN; Hugh C Williams HS; Canton, NY; (Y); Church Yth Grp; 4-H; GAA; Chorus; Yrbk Bus Mgr; Rep Frsh Cls; Rep Soph Cls; Stu Cncl; Var Capt Bsktbl; JV Var Socr; Niagara U; Nrsng.

FURIA, JOHN; Wayland Central HS; Wayland, NY; (Y); FFA; Var Capt Wrstlng; Machnst.

FURINO, GAVIN; Byron-Bergen HS; Bergen, NY; (Y); Church Yth Grp; Variety Show; Socr; Trk; Wrstlng; Hon Roll; Jr NHS; Prfct Atten Awd; MVP Wrstlng 83; Genesee Regn All Star Wrstlng 83 & 84; Genesee Regn Socr All Star84; Regnl Trk 85.

FURMAN, BYRON; Delaware Acad; Delhi, NY; (Y); Spanish Clb; JV Trk; Hon Roll; Wrtng.

FURMAN, JOEL S; Shaarei Torah Of Rockland HS; Suffern, NY; (Y); Temple Yth Grp; Nwsp Rptr; Lit Mag; High Hon Roll; Hon Roll; NY ST Regnts Schlrshp 85; Yeshira U; Law.

FURMAN, ROB; Pittsford Sutherland HS; Pittsford, NY; (Y); Ski Clb; Var Ftbl; Hon Roll; NHS; PTSA Ldrshp Awd; 2nd Pl Firemns Essay Cont; Law.

FURNARI, MARIA; Mercy HS; Albany, NY; (Y); 15/60; Church Yth Grp; Stage Crew; Rep Soph Cls; Rep Sr Cls; Bowling; High Hon Roll; Hon Roll; Geometry Awd 82-83; Gnrl Chem, Soc Stud, & Rlgn Awds 83-84; Accntng Awd 84-85; Le Moyne Coll; Bus Admin.

FURST, MICHAEL; Oceanside HS; Oceanside, NY; (Y); Church Yth Grp; Computer Clb; French Clb; Nwsp Ed-Chief; Dele To Hugh O Brien Yth Fndtn 84; NY ST Squire Of The Yr 84; NY ST Offcr Of The Columbian Sqrs; Comp Sci.

FURTEK, JOEL F; Notre Dame HS; Utica, NY; (Y); Boy Scts; Chrmn Model UN; ROTC; Drill Tm; School Musical; Pres Jr Cls; Var Capt Socr; JETS Awd; Lion Awd; NHS.

FUSCO, ANGELA; Kings Park SR HS; Kings Park, NY; (Y); 125/400; Church Yth Grp; Teachers Aide; VICA; Church Choir; Mgr(s); Trk; Vllybl; Hon Roll; Chem.

FUSCO, LAURA; New Utrecht HS; Brooklyn, NY; (Y); Key Clb; Yrbk Stf; Arista Hnr Soc 85-86; Art.

FUSCO, MICHELE; Dover JR SR HS; Wingdale, NY; (S); 21/94; Band; Sftbl; High Hon Roll; Hon Roll; Jr NHS; Acctng.

FUSINA, ANDREW C; Cardinal Spellman HS; Bronx, NY; (Y); 22/568; Cmnty Wkr; Sec Computer Clb; High Hon Roll; NY ST Rgnts 85; Manhattan Coll.

FUSS, LISA; Milton Central HS; Hamlin, NY; (Y); 6/310; Cmnty Wkr; Drama Clb; Exploring; 4-H; Math Clb; Var Crs Cntry; Timer; Var Trk; 4-H Awd; High Hon Roll; Comp.

FUSS, SUSAN; Hannibal Central HS; Hannibal, NY; (S); Church Yth Grp; French Clb; Key Clb; Varsity Clb; Chorus; School Play; Yrbk Stf; JV Var Bsktbl; Var Sftbl; High Hon Roll.

FUSSELL, BETH; Le Roy Central Schl; Leroy, NY; (Y); Latin Clb; Ski Clb; Varsity Clb; Chorus; School Musical; School Play; Variety Show; Yrbk Bus Mgr; Stu Cncl; Cheerleading; Locl Govt Pgm 85.

FUST, LISBETH; Fayetteville Manlius HS; Fayetteville, NY; (Y); Model UN; Science Clb; Var Crs Cntry; Var L Trk; Hon Roll; Mock Trl Comp-Wnng Tm 84; Hist.

FUTTERMAN, MICHELLE L; Lawrence HS; N Woodmere, NY; (Y); VP French Clb; Model UN; Pres Temple Yth Grp; Sec Band; Chorus; Mrchg Band; School Musical; Rep Stu Cncl; High Hon Roll; NHS; Entrtnmnt Law.

FYE, VIANNA; Cicero North Syracuse HS; Clay, NY; (S); 63/622; Exploring; FBLA; JA; Var Fld Hcky; JV Sftbl; Jr NHS; Math.

GABALSKI, RONALD; Alden SR HS; Alden, NY; (Y); Aud/Vis; Stage Crew; Spanish Clb; Band; Concert Band; Jazz Band; Mrchg Band; Pep Band; Timer; Hon Roll; Natl Sci Olympd Eart & Sci 7th Pl 83; Bio 8th Pl 84; Audo Vsul.

GABEL, CAROLEE R; Wallkill SR HS; Wallkill, NY; (Y); 6/209; Drama Clb; Lit Mag; Im Tennis; Hon Roll; NHS; Secy SADD 84-85; Tlntd & Gftd 84-85; JR Grt Bks 82-83; Morehead ST U KY; Cmmnctns.

GABEL, LISA A; Gowanda JR SR HS; Gowanda, NY; (Y); Drama Clb; French Clb; Thesps; Band; Chorus; Concert Band; Mrchg Band; School Musical; School Play; Variety Show; Syracuse U; Law.

GABEL, MICHAEL P; Northport HS; Northport, NY; (Y); 81/595; Am Leg Boys St; Cmnty Wkr; Drama Clb; Chorus; Pep Band; School Musical; School Play; Crs Cntry; Trk; Hon Roll.

GABELMAN, DEBRA B; East Meadow HS; E Meadow, NY; (Y); FBLA; Orch; Yrbk Ed-Chief; Yrbk Stf; Rep Soph Cls; Sec Jr Cls; Cheerleading; Lcrss; Hon Roll; NHS.

GABERLAVAGE, WILLIAM; Farmingdale HS; N Massapequa, NY; (Y); Boy Scts; Var L Ftbl; Im Wt Lftg; Var L Wrstlng; Prfct Atten Awd; Engrng.

GABERMAN, MARK D; John Jay SR HS; South Salem, NY; (Y); Intnl Clb; Nwsp Stf; Yrbk Stf; Lit Mag; JV Socr; High Hon Roll; Hon Roll; NHS; Regnts Schlrshp 85; Bus.

GABOR, MARY; Mineola HS; Mineola, NY; (Y); 4-H; Girl Scts; Key Clb; Teachers Aide; Chorus; Church Choir; Vllybl; 4-H Awd; Gov Hon Prg Awd; Hon Roll; Medcl Rsrch.

GABRIEL, ANDREA; Connetquot HS; Ronkonkoma, NY; (Y); 258/694; Cmnty Wkr; Concert Band; Mgr(s); Pom Pon; Socr; Sftbl; Trk; Mgr Stat Wrstlng; Wrkd At 2 Day Camps For Chldrn 84-85; Outstdng Art Awd 83; U Of DE; Psych.

GABRIEL, ANDREW; Rome Free Acad; Rome, NY; (Y); Exploring; Science Clb; Chem Engrng.

GABRIEL, BEVERLEY E; Sarah J Hale HS; Brooklyn, NY; (Y); 1/268; Computer Clb; Mathletes; Math Tm; Office Aide; Teachers Aide; Hon Roll; Jr NHS; NHS; Prfct Atten Awd; Val; U Fed Teachers Schlrshp 85; Regents Schlrshp 85; St U-New York; Bio Sci.

GABRIEL JR, MICHAEL J; Huntington HS; Huntington Sta, NY; (Y); 30/400; Am Leg Boys St; Pres Computer Clb; Key Clb; Mathletes; Mrchg Band; Rep Stu Cncl; Var L Socr; Var L Trk; NHS; Band; Long Island Mth Fair Bronze Mdlst 85; Physics.

GABRIELE, CATHERINE A; Mercy HS; Bridgehampton, NY; (Y); 7/108; Church Yth Grp; Ski Clb; Variety Show; Rep Jr Cls; VP Stu Cncl; JV Capt Fld Hcky; High Hon Roll; Trs NHS; Spn Intl Law.

GABRIELLI, ANDREA L; Huntington HS; Huntington, NY; (Y); 96/433; Sec Church Yth Grp; Chorus; Capt Flag Corp; Mrchg Band; Orch; Trk; Hon Roll; St Schlr; NY Schlrshp 85; Miami U Oxford OH; Intl Stds.

GABRINOWITZ, WALTER; Bethpage HS; Bethpage, NY; (Y); 85/290; Ftbl; Lcrss; Wt Lftg.

GADAWSKI, ROBERT; Niagara Catholic HS; Lewiston, NY; (Y); 2/80; Am Leg Boys St; Quiz Bowl; Science Clb; Trs Spanish Clb; Var JV Bsbl; Im Bsktbl; Im Ftbl; Im Vllybl; High Hon Roll; Sec NHS; Hnrbl Mntnfthr Kroupa Awd 85; Coach Yr Lewiston Bsbll League 84; Niagara U; Pre Med.

GADSON, MELISSA; Eli Whitney Voc HS; Brooklyn, NY; (Y); GAA; Math Tm; Stage Crew; Cheerleading; Gym; Trk; Hnr Soc Trphy 81; Comp Pgm.

GADWAY, JULIE A; Northeastern Clinton Cen Schl; Mooers Forks, NY; (Y); 11/146; Mgr Scrkpr Socr; Var Sftbl; Var Vllybl; Hon Roll; 2nd Team All-Star Vrsty Vlybl 83-84; Dfnsv Plyr Yr All-Star Vrsty Vlybl 84-85; Regents Schlrshp 85; Plattsburgh ST; Accntnt.

GADWAY, REBECCA; Saranac Central HS; Saranac, NY; (S); Trs Church Yth Grp; French Clb; Chorus; Concert Band; Mrchg Band; French Hon Soc; Hon Roll; NY ST Schl Music Assoc Awd 84; Loma Linda Coll; Archlgy.

GAEBEL, RICHARD; Immaculate Heart Central HS; Watertown, NY; (Y); NFL; Nwsp Rptr; Var Ftbl; Var Golf; High Hon Roll; Hon Roll; NHS; Rtry Crtcl Issues Smnr 85; Augsbury N Cntry Schlr 85; Cert Of Hnrb Mntn Latin Exam; St Lawrence U; Mech Engr.

GAETA, ANTHONY; Bethpage HS; Bethpage, NY; (Y); Var Ice Hcky; Rfrgrtn & Engr Dsgn.

GAETA, MICHAEL; Archbishop Molloy HS; Glendale, NY; (Y); 173/409; Chess Clb; Off Science Clb; Band; Church Choir; Rep Jr Cls; Stu Cncl; Psychlgy.

GAETE, ADRIANA; Longwood HS; Coram, NY; (Y); Red Cross Aide; Var Socr; JV Trk; Hon Roll; Music.

GAFFNEY, KELLY; West Genesee SR HS; Syracuse, NY; (Y); Band; Concert Band; Mrchg Band; Pep Band.

GAFFNEY, MICHAEL P; Mc Quaid Jesuit HS; Rochester, NY; (Y); 7/180; Cmnty Wkr; Exploring; Varsity Clb; Yrbk Stf; JV Var Crs Cntry; Var Vllybl; High Hon Roll; NHS; Ntl Merit Ltr; Harvard Prz Bk Awd 84; Rgnts, J & M Boyle Dailey Mem Schlrshps 85; U Notre Dame; Engrng.

GAGE, ALLEN; Hebrew Academy Of Nassau County; W Hempstead, NY; (S); Computer Clb; Math Tm; Service Clb; Teachers Aide; Temple Yth Grp; Fld Hcky; Tennis; Hon Roll; NHS; NEDT Awd.

GAGE, DEMIAN; Dryden HS; Freeville, NY; (Y); 5/150; Am Leg Boys St; Church Yth Grp; Quiz Bowl; Spanish Clb; JV Var Bsbl; JV Var Bsktbl; Var Socr; High Hon Roll; NHS; Camera Clb; Sci Awd 83; Soc Studs Awd 84 & 85.

GAGE, JENNIFER; Bishop Scully HS; Fultonville, NY; (Y); Art Clb; Drama Clb; Trs Rep 4-H; Ski Clb; Stage Crew; Yrbk Ed-Chief; Var Crs Cntry; Tennis; 4-H Awd; Hon Roll; Skidmore; Vet.

GAGE, KELLY; John Jay HS; Hopewell Juncti, NY; (Y); Ski Clb; Var Soph Cls; Var Jr Cls; JV Capt Bsktbl; Rotary Awd; Quinnipac; Physcl Thrpy.

GAGE, ROBERT A; Wayne Central HS; Ontario, NY; (Y); 20/200; Mathletes; Art Clb; Math Tm; Ski Clb; Im Bsktbl; Hon Roll; NHS; Regents Schlrshp Awd 85; SUNY Geneseo; Physics.

GAGLIANO, CHRISTINA; Curtis HS; Staten Island, NY; (Y); #15 In Class; Church Yth Grp; Cmnty Wkr; Hosp Aide; Key Clb; Sec Science Clb; Varsity Clb; Yrbk Stf; Sftbl; Tennis; NHS; Mth Awd 85; Jrnlsm Awd 85; Skidmore Coll; Engr.

GAGLIO, MICHELE; Moore Catholic HS; Staten Island, NY; (Y); Church Yth Grp; Teachers Aide; Bowling; Hon Roll; NHS.

GAGLIO, PAULA MARIE; Moore Catholic HS; Staten Island, NY; (Y); 26/180; Church Yth Grp; Math Tm; Bowling; High Hon Roll; Hon Roll; NHS; Prfct Atten Awd; Empire ST Math Sci Tchr Schl 85; Regnts Schlrshp 85; Wagner Coll; Math.

GAGNE, MARTHA; The Doanestuart Schl; Saratoga Spgs, NY; (Y); Drama Clb; Pres 4-H; Political Wkr; Pres Spanish Clb; School Play; Nwsp Rptr; Crs Cntry; 4-H Awd; Hon Roll; Spanish NHS; Shelia M Keasby Memrl Drma Awd 85; Spnsh Dept Hgh Hnrs Awd 85; 4-H Anml Train Awd 82; Pace U; Poli Sci.

GAH, ANDREW; Coxsackie Athens HS; W Coxsackie, NY; (Y); 1/104; Boy Scts; Math Clb; Quiz Bowl; Pep Band; Nwsp Ed-Chief; Pres Stu Cncl; Capt Ice Hcky; Capt Lcrss; Ntl Merit Schol; Prfct Atten Awd; Congrssnl Medl Hnr 84; Mensa 85; Mega Socty 85; CA Tech; Nuclr Engrng.

GAHR, THOMAS; Notre Dame HS; Batavia, NY; (S); 3/65; Chess Clb; Ski Clb; Trs Jr Cls; Var Ftbl; JV Capt Wrstlng; Hon Roll; NHS; Mst Vlble Plyr JV Wrstlng; Math Awd; Sci Awd; Math.

GAIEWSKI, DAVID; Smithtown H S East; Smithtown, NY; (Y); Yrbk Stf; Off Soph Cls; Off Jr Cls; Off Sr Cls; JV Bsbl; Hon Roll; NHS; Pres Of Italian Hnr Soc 85-86; NYSMA-PIANO 83; Engrng.

GAINDH, SAVITA; John F Kennedy HS; Riverdale, NY; (Y); 6/982; Teachers Aide; Rep Sr Cls; NHS; Amer Legn Awd; Sci Hnrs Soc; JR Acad Of Sci; Cooper Union; Engr.

GAINES, DAVID; Groton Central Schl; Groton, NY; (Y); 5/65; Am Leg Boys St; Computer Clb; Spanish Clb; Var Capt Bsktbl; Var Ftbl; Var Trk; High Hon Roll; Hon Roll; NHS; PA ST; Mech Engr.

GAINEY, LAURA; Lackawanna SR HS; Lackawanna, NY; (Y); GAA; Hosp Aide; Red Cross Aide; Spanish Clb; Var Crs Cntry; Var Capt Trk; High Hon Roll; NHS; Stat Wrstlng; Empire Glrs ST 85; Crs Cntry ST Mt 82; Boston Coll; Pre-Law.

GAITTEN, CHRISTINA; John A Coleman HS; Stone Ridge, NY; (Y); 16/75; Church Yth Grp; 4-H; French Clb; JA; Spanish Clb; Varsity Clb; Yrbk Stf; JV Fld Hcky; Var Sftbl; JV Trk; Empire ST Games Fld Hcky 85.

GAJER, LORI; Tonawanda HS; Tonawanda, NY; (Y); Church Yth Grp; Cmnty Wkr; French Clb; GAA; Im Bsktbl; Coach Actv; Powder Puff Ftbl; Sftbl; Swmmng; Vllybl; U Of NY-BUFFALO; Grtcs.

GAJEWSKI, SANDRA A; Moriah Central HS; Port Henry, NY; (Y); 4/83; GAA; Ski Clb; Cheerleading; Socr; High Hon Roll; NHS; Physical Fitness Awd 84-85; Regents Schlrshp 85; President Of Natl Hnr Society Moriah Central 85; SUNY Plattsbrugh; Chemistry.

GAJKOWSKI, ANTHONY R; Kensington/Bflo Voc Tec Ctr; Buffalo, NY; (Y); Computer Clb; FBLA; Yrbk Stf; Var Bsbl; Var Crs Cntry; Var Ftbl; Var Swmmng; Chess Clb; VP Frsh Cls; Bflo Bd Of Ed Sherman Feyler Awd & Awd Of Excllnc 85; Gen Pulaski Assoc Niagara Frntr Cratv Art Awd; NY ST U Buffalo; Arch.

GALANAKIS, ALEXA; Stony Brook Prep School; Stony Brook, NY; (Y); 2/84; Art Clb; Church Yth Grp; Cmnty Wkr; Drama Clb; Hosp Aide; Latin Clb; Teachers Aide; Thesps; School Play; Yrbk Stf; Kings Awd Emergng Artist 85; Cum Laude 83-85; Bio.

GALANEK, CHARLENE; Academy Of The Resrrctn; New Rochelle, NY; (Y); Art Clb; Camera Clb; Math Clb; NFL; Stage Crew; Yrbk Phtg; Trs Soph Cls; Var Sftbl; NHS; Carrier Of Mnth Stndrd Star 85; Law.

GALANTE, BONINA; Bishop Kearney HS; Brooklyn, NY; (Y); Office Aide; Teachers Aide; Hon Roll; NHS; Natl Cmmrtv Cert 83; Pace U; Acctg.

GALANTE, DAVID NGUYEN; Eastmeadow HS; Eastmeadow, NY; (S); Camera Clb; Yrbk Phtg; Yrbk Sprt Ed; Socr; Var Tennis; Hon Roll; NYU; Bus.

GALANTUCCI, EVELYN A; Bishop Kearney HS; Brooklyn, NY; (S); Church Yth Grp; Office Aide; Hon Roll; NHS; St Francis Coll; Law.

GALARNEAU, LISA; Mohonasen HS; Schenectady, NY; (Y); 59/215; VP DECA; Mgr Drama Clb; Exploring; Trs JA; Mrchg Band; Swing Chorus; Yrbk Stf; Rep Stu Cncl; Var L Sftbl; Art Clb; Paul Smiths Schlrshp 85; Paul Smiths Coll; Htl/Rest Mgmt.

GALARNEAU, LYDIA LEILA ROSE; Pembroke HS; Williamsville, NY; (Y); 1/110; Art Clb; Cmnty Wkr; Debate Tm; Church Choir; Sec Stu Cncl; Capt Var Socr; Bausch & Lomb Sci Awd; NHS; Val; Exploring; German Hgh Avg 81-85; Wellesley Coll; Gyneclgst.

GALARZA, VICKY; Brewster HS; Brewster, NY; (S); 36/167; Debate Tm; Pep Clb; Chorus; School Play; Trs Frsh Cls; Trs Soph Cls; Trs Jr Cls; Trs Sr Cls; Var Crs Cntry; Trk; Spn II Hnrs 81; Eng Achvt 81; Plattsburg U; Acctg.

GALAS, TAMMY; Tonawanda SR HS; Tonawanda, NY; (Y); Varsity Clb; Yrbk Stf; Pres Jr Cls; Pres Sr Cls; Sec Stu Cncl; Bsktbl; Sftbl; Swmmng; Vllybl; Hon Roll; Stu Advsry Comm 84-86; Girls ST Rnnrup; Bio.

GALASSO, CHRISTINE E; Lakeland SR HS; Yorktown Hts, NY; (Y); Cmnty Wkr; Drama Clb; Thesps; Chorus; Church Choir; School Musical; Trs Sr Cls; NHS; Ntl Merit SF; Anml Bhvr.

GALASSO, MARY LAUREN; Acad Of St Joseph HS; Greenlawn, NY; (Y); 11/120; Church Yth Grp; Girl Scts; Hosp Aide; Mathletes; Band; School Play; Socr; High Hon Roll; Jr NHS; NHS; Regents Nrsng Schlrshp 85; Spnsh IV Excell Awd 84; 350 Hr Svc Awd 84; Georgetown U; Ped.

GALATI, PATRICIA; St John The Baptist HS; St James, NY; (Y); Church Yth Grp; Cmnty Wkr; Dance Clb; Hosp Aide; Chorus; Ed Lit Mag; Rep Jr Cls; French Hon Soc; High Hon Roll; NHS; SCMEA 82; Pre-Med.

GALATIOTO, LILLIAN; Mc Mahon HS; Buffalo, NY; (Y); Hon Roll; Jr NHS; NHS; Prfct Atten Awd; Merit Roll 81-82; Pefect Conduct 81-85; Bus.

GALATSOS, MARY; Kenmore East SR HS; Tonawanda, NY; (Y); Aud/Vis; Camera Clb; Drama Clb; Trs GAA; Pep Clb; Var Bsktbl; Var Sftbl; JV Capt Vllybl; Office Aide; Stage Crew; Sftbl Rookieyr 85; MVP Vlybl 83; Bsktbl Most Imprvd Plyr 82; Wrtng.

GALBI, DWIGHT E; Maine-Endwell SR HS; Endwell, NY; (Y); 5/253; Pres Trs French Clb; Ed Yrbk Phtg; Rep Jr Cls; Trs Stu Cncl; Var Capt Crs Cntry; Var L Trk; Bausch & Lomb Sci Awd; NHS; Hon Roll; IBM Watson Schlrshp 85; Mock Trial Tm 82-85; Duke U; Elec Engrng.

GALBRAITH, DIANE; Dryden Central HS; Freeville, NY; (Y); Ski Clb; Spanish Clb; Var Swmmng; Var Capt Trk; High Hon Roll; NHS; Acadmc Achvt Awd Bio 84; IAC Girls Div I Trck Champ 2nd Pl 84; Acadmc Achvt Awd Spnsh 85; Cornell; Bio.

GALE, BRENDA LYNN; Westhill HS; Syracuse, NY; (Y); 7/168; AFS; Debate Tm; French Clb; Pres FBLA; Ski Clb; Spanish Clb; Yrbk Bus Mgr; Cheerleading; Hon Roll; NHS; Regents Scholar NYS 85; AFS Exch Stu Colombia 84; Svc Clbs Amer Outstndng SR Soc Stud 85; Cornell U; Htl Admin.

GALEANO, ANA MARIA; Roy C Ketcham HS; Poughkeepsie, NY; (Y); Ski Clb; Chorus; Pres Frsh Cls; Rep Soph Cls; VP Jr Cls; Rep Stu Cncl; Capt Cheerleading; High Hon Roll; Hon Roll; Jr NHS; Law.

GALEK, DAWN; Sodus Central HS; Sodus, NY; (Y); 9/98; French Clb; Pres Model UN; VP Science Clb; Stu Cncl; Cit Awd; High Hon Roll; St Schlr; Prfct Atten Awd; Hon Roll; AFS; Acdmc Lttr; Stu Cncl Svc Schlrshp; Untd Ntns Clb Svc Awd; SUNY Geneseo; Bio Chem.

GALEOTA, DAWN; Coplague HS; Lindenhurst, NY; (Y); Civic Clb; Cmnty Wkr; Girl Scts; Varsity Clb; Yrbk Stf; Var Fld Hcky; Var Sftbl; Tennis; Var Vllybl; High Hon Roll; Thrpy.

GALETTE, FRITZ A; Xaverian HS; Brooklyn, NY; (Y); Am Leg Boys St; Nwsp Stf; JV Var Cheerleading; JV Vllybl; Pre-Med.

GALGANSKI, MICHELE; Alexander Central Schl; Alexander, NY; (S); 1/88; AFS; Varsity Clb; Concert Band; Mrchg Band; Rep Soph Cls; Stu Cncl; Var Socr; Var Capt Trk; High Hon Roll; NHS; NJHS 82-83; Outstndng Schlr-Ath Awd 83-84; TAC Natl Jr Olympic Trck & Fld 84; Math.

GALGOUL, RACHEL; Potsdam HS; Potsdam, NY; (Y); AFS; French Clb; JA; Math Clb; Band; Nwsp Stf; JV Var Cheerleading; High Hon Roll; Ntl Merit Ltr; Natl Achvt Acad; UC San Diego; Math.

GALIK, CYNTHIA; Sacred Heart HS; Yonkers, NY; (Y); VP Church Yth Grp; Hosp Aide; Hon Roll; Sacred Hearts Annl Sprng Wrtng Cont 83; Intl League Of Wmn Peace Wrtng Cont 84; Bio Sci.

GALLACCHI, BRIAN; Albany HS; Albany, NY; (Y); 174/600; Church Yth Grp; JV Var Bsbl; JV Var Bowling; Bridgeport; Graphic Comm.

GALLACHER, JOHN; Westampton Beach HS; Remsenburg, NY; (Y); 12/232; Church Yth Grp; Spanish Clb; Band; Chorus; Concert Band; Pep Band; Variety Show; Yrbk Stf; Stu Cncl; Tennis; Sailng Awds 82-85; Sprtsmn Of Yr Ten 82-85; Phys Sci.

GALLAGHER, AMANDA; Pelham Memorial HS; Pelham Manor, NY; (Y); AFS; Church Yth Grp; Ski Clb; Nwsp Bus Mgr; Nwsp Ed-Chief; Nwsp Stf; Lit Mag; Var Crs Cntry; JV Lcrss; JV Trk.

GALLAGHER, JAMES; Washingtonville HS; Campbell Hall, NY; (Y); Rep Stu Cncl; Var L Bsbl; VP Ftbl; Hon Roll; Prof Basebl.

GALLAGHER, JIM; Wantagh HS; Wantagh, NY; (Y); Aud/Vis; Boy Scts; Church Yth Grp; Cmnty Wkr; Ski Clb; Drm & Bgl; Mrchg Band; Yrbk Stf; Hon Roll; Culinary Arts.

GALLAGHER, JOHN; Albertus Magnus HS; Blauvelt, NY; (Y); 64/196; Drama Clb; Varsity Clb; Pres Soph Cls; Trs Sr Cls; Stu Cncl; Bsktbl; Lcrss; Var Capt Socr; Hon Roll; Ntl Merit Ltr; Outstndng Athlt Ntl Awd 84; Bus.

GALLAGHER, JOHN; Archbishop Molloy HS; Whitestone, NY; (Y); Math Tm; Speech Tm; Hon Roll; Sec NHS; Pres Schlr; Charles Johnson JR Mem Scholar 85; Archbishop Molloy Alumni Mdl Outstndng Qualits, Succss Studs 85; Manhattan Coll; Mth.

GALLAGHER JR, JOHN; Irondequoit HS; Rochester, NY; (Y); 41/383; Church Yth Grp; Latin Clb; Scholastic Bowl; Varsity Clb; Rep Jr Cls; Var L Bsktbl; JV Golf; Hon Roll; Med Tech.

GALLAGHER, ROD; Marlboro Central HS; Marlboro, NY; (Y); 1/180; Art Clb; Varsity Clb; Concert Band; Mrchg Band; Var Bsbl; Var Bsktbl; High Hon Roll; NHS; Rensselaer Polytech Inst Math Sci Awd 85; Elmira Coll Key Awd 85; Engr.

GALLAGHER, TAMMY; Queensbury HS; Glens Falls, NY; (Y); 40/226; Ski Clb; Spanish Clb; Varsity Clb; Crs Cntry; Trk; Hon Roll; Outstndng Achvt Home Ec 85; Cortland; Phys Educ.

GALLANT, CANDACE; Cardinal O Hara HS; Buffalo, NY; (S); 5/145; Art Clb; Quiz Bowl; Band; Church Choir; Orch; School Musical; School Play; Stage Crew; High Hon Roll; Youth Artistic Achvmnt Awd 84; Art Inst Of Chgo; Fash Design.

GALLELLO, ANGELA; St Gabriel HS; New Rochelle, NY; (Y); 2/61; Teachers Aide; Yrbk Stf; Stu Cncl; Hon Roll; Amer Studys Ntl Cntst Awd 85.

GALLI, NICOLE; Sacred Heart Acedemy; Massapequa Park, NY; (S); 2/186; Trs Debate Tm; Math Tm; NFL; Trs Speech Tm; High Hon Roll; NHS; Ntl Merit Ltr; Hugh Obrien Yth Ldrshp Fndtn Rep 82; Math.

GALLIPOLI, MARIANNE J; St Angnes Cathedral HS; Elmont, NY; (Y); Spanish Clb; Off Frsh Cls; Off Soph Cls; Off Jr Cls; High Hon Roll; NHS; NEDT Awd; Rgnts, St Johns Comptve & Schlstc Excel Schlrshps 85; St Johns U.

GALLIVAN, ERIN; Byron Bergen JR SR HS; Bergen, NY; (Y); Band; Color Guard; Drill Tm; Drm Mjr(t); Mrchg Band; Frsh Cls; Trs Jr Cls; Rep Stu Cncl; JV Var Cheerleading; JV Var Socr.

GALLIVAN, SHANNON; Byron-Bergen HS; Bergen, NY; (Y); 3/90; Math Tm; Spanish Clb; Trs Band; Var L Diving; Var L Socr; Var L Swmmng; Var L Trk; High Hon Roll; NHS; Cornell U; Med.

GALLIVAN, TIMOTHY; Bishop Timon HS; Buffalo, NY; (S); 10/160; Math Clb; Spanish Clb; Chorus; Bausch & Lomb Sci Awd; Dartmouth; Psych.

GALLO III, FERDINAND J; Mercy HS; Riverhead, NY; (Y); 1/128; Church Yth Grp; Rep Key Clb; Math Tm; Ski Clb; Rep Frsh Cls; Rep Soph Cls; High Hon Roll; NHS; Ntl Merit Ltr; Law.

GALLO, FRANCES; Mahopac HS; Mahopac, NY; (Y); 62/423; Rep Sr Cls; Var Bsktbl; Var Socr; Var Capt Vllybl; High Hon Roll; NHS; Yrbk Stf; Hon Roll; All County Hnrb Mntn Var Socr 85; Nwsp Spotlight Ath 84; Voluntr Cmnty Svc Wrk 83; Psychtry.

GALLO, LAURA; Bishop Kearney HS; Brooklyn, NY; (Y); Girl Scts; Nwsp Stf; Bowling; Bus Adm.

GALLO, LEIGH; Nyack HS; Upper Nyack, NY; (Y); 5/167; Am Leg Aux Girls St; French Clb; Math Tm; Band; School Play; Rep Stu Cncl; Var Capt Vllybl; French Hon Soc; High Hon Roll; NHS.

GALLOWAY, TONYA; Mt Vernon HS; Mount Vernon, NY; (Y); #94 In Class; Camera Clb; Hosp Aide; Band; Concert Band; Mrchg Band; School Musical; Stage Crew; Variety Show; Yrbk Phtg; Long Is U C W Post.

GALLUCCIO, KENNETH; Lindenhurst HS; Lindenhurst, NY; (Y); 16/625; Boy Scts; Ski Clb; Varsity Clb; Rep Sr Cls; Var L Ftbl; Var L Lcrss; Var L Wrstlng; Hon Roll; NHS; USAF Acad; Comp.

GALLUCH, PETER; Bishop Timon HS; Lackawanna, NY; (S); 6/180; Quiz Bowl; Chorus; Nwsp Stf; Rep Soph Cls; Rep Stu Cncl; Var Ftbl; High Hon Roll; US Naval Acad; Arspc Engr.

GALLUP, CATHI; Rochester Christian HS; Rochester, NY; (S); 2/5; Church Yth Grp; Drama Clb; Band; Chorus; Concert Band; Orch; Yrbk Bus Mgr; VP Stu Cncl; Var Capt Cheerleading; High Hon Roll; Dist Chrstn HS Stu 83-84; Muskingum Coll; Spec Ed.

GALLUZZO, DIANNE M; Plainview Old Bethpage HS; Plainview, NY; (Y); 73/196; Church Yth Grp; Cmnty Wkr; Spanish Clb; Band; Church Choir; Concert Band; Mrchg Band; Orch; Pep Band; School Musical; Outstndng Band Awd 84; Outstndng Wind Emsemble Awd 83; Outstndng 7th Grade Chorus Awd 80; Music Ed.

GALLWEY, STEVE L; Harley HS; Rochester, NY; (Y); VP Sr Cls; Var L Bsktbl; Socr; Var L Trk; Ntl Merit Ltr; Aero.

GALOSIC, JANE; St Johns Prep; Astoria, NY; (Y); Dance Clb; Hon Roll; NHS; 1st Hnrs Acadmc Awd 85; Pace U; Acctg.

GALPIN, LYNN; Elmira Southside HS; Elmira, NY; (Y); Key Clb; Y-Teens; Chorus; Rep Soph Cls; Rep Jr Cls; Rep Sr Cls; Hon Roll; YWCA-Y-TN Recgntn Svcs Cmnty 82; SADD; Paul Smith; Toursm/Trvl.

GALUNAS, CYNTHIA; East Hampton HS; E Hampton, NY; (Y); Church Yth Grp; FBLA; Orch; School Musical; Ed Lit Mag; High Hon Roll; Jr NHS; NHS; Sec Educ.

GALUNAS, LAURIE; East Hamptonm HS; E Hampton, NY; (Y); FBLA; Chorus; Church Choir; School Musical; JV Cheerleading; Hon Roll.

GALURA, DONNA; Sacred Heart HS; Yonkers, NY; (Y); Var Capt Crs Cntry; Var Capt Trk; High Hon Roll; NHS.

GALVIN, BRIDGET; Berne Knox Westerlo Central HS; Delanson, NY; (Y); Band; Color Guard; Mrchg Band; Co-Capt Twrlr; Lgl Sec.

GALVIN, JEFFREY M B; Westhill HS; Syracuse, NY; (Y); 24/168; Ski Clb; Teachers Aide; School Play; VP Frsh Cls; VP Stu Cncl; Var Trk; Hon Roll; NHS; Camera Clb; Church Yth Grp; NY ST Rgnts Schlrshp 85; AF ROTC Schlrshp 85; 99 Per Cnt Ntl Ed Dvlpmt Test 83; SUNY Binghamton; Pre-Med.

GALVIN, MAUREEN; Corning West HS; Painted Post, NY; (Y); 15/242; Thesps; Acpl Chr; Color Guard; Mrchg Band; School Musical; School Play; VP Jr Cls; NHS; NY ST Regnts Schlrshp 85; Corning Tchrs Assn Schlrshp Awd 85; Corning CC; Comm.

GAMACHE, VALERIE; Glens Falls HS; Glen Falls, NY; (Y); AFS; Key Clb; Band; Chorus; Yrbk Phtg; Rep Jr Cls; JV Var Bsktbl; JV VP Fld Hcky; High Hon Roll; Bio.

GAMBA, JASON; St Francis Prep; Middle Village, NY; (S); 73/693; Ftbl; Hon Roll; NHS; Academic All American 85; Business.

GAMBACORTA, MARIA; Sacred Heart Acad; Buffalo, NY; (Y); Trs Church Yth Grp; Cmnty Wkr; Hosp Aide; Red Cross Aide; VP Service Clb; Sec Spanish Clb; Stage Crew; Nwsp Rptr; Tennis; Hon Roll; Phy Thrpy.

GAMBALE, MAEANNA; St Edmunds HS; Brooklyn, NY; (Y); Church Yth Grp; Cmnty Wkr; Computer Clb; Spanish Clb; Nwsp Rptr; Capt Bowling; Hon Roll; Jr NHS; Pace U; Acctng.

GAMBARDELLA, LISA A; Garden City HS; Garden City, NY; (Y); 4/319; French Clb; Pep Clb; Capt Rep Sr Cls; JV Bsktbl; JV Var Lcrss; NHS; Ntl Merit Ltr; Pres Schlr; Key Clb; Lit Mag; Columbia Assn Schlrshp Awd 85; Am Legn Aux Awd 84; U Of PA; Ecnmcs.

GAMBARO, KARIN; Island Trees HS; Levittown, NY; (Y); 13/200; Library Aide; Concert Band; Mrchg Band; Swing Chorus; Nwsp Rptr; High Hon Roll; Jr NHS; Pres Acdmc Ftns Awd 85; Geneva N Gallow Schlrshp 85; Islnd Trees Schlrshp 85; Nassau CC; Englsh.

GAMBINO, ANTHONY; Nazareth Regional HS; Brooklyn, NY; (Y); Var Ftbl; Bld Donor 85; Accntng.

GAMBINO, JAYNE; Bishop Kearney HS; Brooklyn, NY; (Y); Art Clb; Girl Scts; Office Aide; Band; Bowling; Trk; Hon Roll; Sociology.

GAMBINO, LUCRECIA; Bishop Kearney HS; Brooklyn, NY; (Y); Art Clb; Cmnty Wkr; Chorus; Yrbk Stf; Hon Roll; Golden Recrd Achvt Awd 79; 1st 2nd Hnr Awds Iona Lang Cntst 84-85; Arista Hnr Awd 83; Law.

GAMBINO, MARY ANN; John Adams HS; Ozone Park, NY; (Y); Intnl Clb; Hon Roll; Queensborough CC; Bus Mgmt.

GAMBINO, MIKE; Walt Whitman HS; Huntington Stat, NY; (Y); 329/540; JV Bsbl; JV Ftbl; Hon Roll; Spanish NHS; AZ ST U; Busnss.

GAMBLE, MICHELLE MARIE; Honeoye Falls-Lima HS; Honeoye Falls, NY; (Y); 1/159; Church Yth Grp; Math Clb; Pres Frsh Cls; Rep Stu Cncl; Var Bsktbl; Var Capt Socr; JV Sftbl; JV Vllybl; High Hon Roll; Pres NHS; All Cnty Soccer Tm I 83 & 84; Bio Med Engrng.

GAMBOLI, JENNIFER; Sayoille HS; Sayville, NY; (Y); 9/363; Church Yth Grp; Key Clb; Mathletes; Ski Clb; Chorus; Stat Ftbl; JV Var Tennis; Vllybl; High Hon Roll; NHS; Expository Wrtng Awd 85; Bucknell; Lbrl Arts.

GAMERMAN, ELLEN; Mamaroneck HS; Larchmont, NY; (Y); Cmnty Wkr; Dance Clb; Drama Clb; School Play; Stage Crew; Cit Awd; High Hon Roll; NHS; Wellesley Bk Awd 85; Librl Arts.

GAMLEN, FRED; Cazenovia HS; Cazenovia, NY; (Y); Church Yth Grp; 4-H; FBLA; Hon Roll; Pblc Spkng Cntst Awd 84-85; ST Fr Trctr Drvng Comp 82-83.

GAMZON, SCOTT; Woodlands HS; Hartsdale, NY; (Y); Math Tm; School Musical; School Play; Stage Crew; Nwsp Rptr; Ed Lit Mag; Crs Cntry; Trk; High Hon Roll; NHS; Columbia Bk Awd 85; Washington Wrkshps Partcpnt 85; English.

GANCILA, DEBORAH A; St John Villa Acad; Brooklyn, NY; (Y); 3/124; Math Tm; Pres Pep Clb; Nwsp Ed-Chief; Yrbk Rptr; VP Soph Cls; Var Sftbl; High Hon Roll; Sec Trs NHS; NEDT Awd; Pres Schlr; NY ST Regnts Schlrshp 85; Deans Schlrshp Fordham U; Fordham U; Chem.

GANDHI, AASHISH; Bronx H S Of Science; Jackson Heights, NY; (Y); Office Aide; Teachers Aide; Hon Roll; Semi Fnlst Wstnghse Sci Tlnt Srch 84-85; Rgnts Schlrshp 85; NY City Mayrs & Bd Of Educ 85; Cornell U; Biochmstry.

GANDHI, SAMIR; Edgemont HS; Scarsdale, NY; (S); Debate Tm; Intnl Clb; NFL; Speech Tm; Nwsp Rptr; Nwsp Stf; Lit Mag; Bus.

GANDINI, CHRISTINE; East Meadow HS; E Meadow, NY; (Y); Church Yth Grp; FBLA; Chorus; Concert Band; Mrchg Band; School Musical; Symp Band; JV Cheerleading; Var Sftbl; Hon Roll; Nassau CC; Bus.

GANDOLFO, ANGELA; Dominican Commercial HS; Glendale, NY; (Y); Sec Church Yth Grp; Hon Roll; Prin List 82-85; Natl Bus Hnr Soc 84-85; Secry.

GANDY, INDRA N; Bishop Ford Central HS; Brooklyn, NY; (Y); Church Yth Grp; Cmnty Wkr; Computer Clb; Dance Clb; Chorus; Church Choir; Variety Show; Stu Cncl; Var Tennis; Hon Roll; Ntl Sci Olympiad 85; 2nd Major Tennis Awd 85; Pace U; Bus Mngmnt.

GANDY, TERI LYNN; Spring Valley SR HS; Spring Valley, NY; (Y); 67/435; French Clb; Pep Clb; Band; Yrbk Rptr; Yrbk Stf; Var Capt Cheerleading; Vllybl; High Hon Roll; Hon Roll; VP Sr Cls; 2nd Rnr Up Miss Afro Scholar Comp 85; Outstndg Achvt Art Awds 82 84 & 85; Cooper Union; Archit.

GANELES, ANDREW; Yeshiva HS; Far Rockaway, NY; (Y); 2/10; Temple Yth Grp; Yrbk Stf; NYS Regent Schlrshp 85; Queens Coll; Music.

GANEY, CHRISTINE; Frontier Central HS; Hamburg, NY; (Y); Church Yth Grp; Drama Clb; Girl Scts; Pep Clb; Spanish Clb; Chorus; Church Choir; School Musical; Rep Soph Cls; Rep Jr Cls; Erie Cty Chors 79; Sci Fair Awd 82; Bus Adm.

GANGI, CHRISTINE; New Dorp HS; Staten Island, NY; (Y); Art Clb; Key Clb; School Play; Yrbk Phtg; Yrbk Stf; Stu Cncl; Hon Roll; NHS; Spanish NHS; Haney Art Awd 84; Honor Key 85; FIT; Commrcl Art.

GANGITANO, GREG; Farmingdale S HS; S Farmngdale, NY; (Y); Aud/Vis; FBLA; Math Clb; Pep Clb; Radio Clb; Science Clb; Ski Clb; Tennis; Vllybl; Wt Lftg; Engrng.

GANNETT, SARAH; Newark HS; Newark, NY; (Y); 18/206; Church Yth Grp; Hosp Aide; Varsity Clb; Rep Jr Cls; Cheerleading; Swmmng; Trk; French Hon Soc; High Hon Roll; Mth.

GANNON, COLLEEN; Skaneateles HS; Skaneateles, NY; (S); Church Yth Grp; Ski Clb; Variety Show; Nwsp Rptr; Yrbk Stf; Powder Puff Ftbl; High Hon Roll; NHS; Susquehanna U Wrtng Hnr 84; Comp Dsgn.

GANNON, DENISE; Preston HS; Bronx, NY; (Y); 3/25; Drama Clb; VP Frsh Cls; Jr Cls; 1st & 2nd Hnrs 82-85; Tobe-Coburn; Fshn.

GANNON, EILEEN; Moore Catholic HS; Staten Island, NY; (Y); Ski Clb; Yrbk Stf; Rep Stu Cncl; Jr Cls; Frsh Cls; High Hon Roll; Bus Adm.

GANNON, EILEEN M; Lackawanna SR HS; Lackawanna, NY; (Y); Drama Clb; French Clb; Ski Clb; Band; Concert Band; Mrchg Band; School Play; Stage Crew; Symp Band; Bsktbl; Awd Excel Frnch, Amer Hist Awd 85; Pre Med.

GANNON, LISA A; Suffern HS; Sloatsburg, NY; (Y); 12/410; Church Yth Grp; Hosp Aide; Flag Corp; Var Capt Twrlr; High Hon Roll; NHS; VP English Clb; Service Clb; Concert Band; Yrbk Stf; Chem,Sci Awd 82-85.

GANNON, RENE D; Shenendehowa HS; Greenfield Ctr, NY; (Y); Exploring; VP FFA; Chorus; Swing Chorus; Hon Roll; Awd For Excllnce Horticultre George T Smith 85; Cruise Dir.

GANNON, THERESA C; Lewiston-PORTER HS; Lewiston, NY; (Y); 36/276; Pres Girl Scts; Mgr Concert Band; Jazz Band; Orch; Sec Trs Stage Crew; High Hon Roll; NHS; Ntl Merit SF; Drama Clb; Library Aide; Gold Awd 84; Marian Religious Awd 85; Niagara U.

GANNON, THOMAS M; John S Burke HS; Washingtonville, NY; (Y); 5/150; Boy Scts; Cmnty Wkr; JV Bsbl; Var Socr; Var Trk; High Hon Roll; NHS; Fairfield U; Pre-Med.

GANOTT, GAIL D; Chazy Central Rural HS; Chazy, NY; (Y); 2/48; Sec Trs Church Yth Grp; Model UN; Sec Pep Clb; Chorus; Church Choir; School Play; Nwsp Rptr; Yrbk Stf; Rep Jr Cls; Im Bsktbl; Pres Schlrshp 85; ROTC Schlrshp 85; Lyndon ST Coll; Metrlgy.

GANSHAW, JOEL; Marlboro HS; Milton, NY; (Y); 23/150; Band; Concert Band; Mrchg Band; Crs Cntry; Trk; High Hon Roll; Hon Roll; NHS.

GANSLE, KATHLEEN; Rocky Point HS; Rocky Point, NY; (S); 9/300; German Clb; GAA; Mathletes; Thesps; Acpl Chr; Concert Band; Mrchg Band; School Musical; Yrbk Stf; Vllybl; Educ.

GANTT, SANDRA; La Salle SR HS; Niagara Falls, NY; (Y); Sec Church Yth Grp; VP Pres French Clb; Hon Roll; Jr NHS; NHS; Comp.

GANTZ, PAULA A; Minisink Valley HS; New Hampton, NY; (Y); 12/232; High Hon Roll; Prfct Atten Awd; Rgnts Schlrshp 85; New Paltz; Speech Hrng Handi Ed.

GANZ, BETH; Blind Brook HS; Rye Brook, NY; (Y); Political Wkr; Spanish Clb; Chorus; School Play; Nwsp Rptr; Var Sftbl; JV Tennis; Duke U; Fashion Design.

GANZ, DAVID; Longwood HS; Shoreham, NY; (Y); Math Clb; Math Tm; Stage Crew; Socr; High Hon Roll; Hon Roll; Binghamton; Pre-Med.

GANZELL, ERICA; Edward R Murrow HS; Brooklyn, NY; (Y); 1/725; Computer Clb; Math Tm; Quiz Bowl; Science Clb; Ski Clb; Orch; Lit Mag; Sftbl; Swmmng; Val; Renselaer Polytechnic Inst Medal-Excllnc In Math & Sci 85; Acadmc Excllnc Plaque-Edward R Murrow 85; Brown U; Bio Resrch.

GAPINSKI, KEITH; Archbishop Molloy HS; Brooklyn, NY; (Y); Computer Clb; Lit Mag; Creative Writng.

GARA, STEVE; Greatr Neck North SR HS; Great Neck, NY; (Y); Thesps; Varsity Clb; Band; Concert Band; Drm Mjr(t); Orch; Stage Crew; Nwsp Rptr; Nwsp Stf; Rep Jr Cls; Pharm.

GARASZ, KIM; Maryvale SR HS; Cheektowaga, NY; (Y); Spanish Clb; Var L Crs Cntry; JV Gym; Hon Roll; Para-Lgl.

GARAVUSO, THOMAS; Aviation HS; Brooklyn, NY; (Y); 188/417; Boy Scts; JA; Drm & Bgl; Hon Roll; Cert Excllnce Physics 85; Attndnce Awds 83-85; Cmndtn Hnsty & Cncrn Property Others 85; USAF; Air Frame Mech.

GARAYUA, JOSE; St Nicholas Of Tolentine HS; Bronx, NY; (S); 19/141; Stage Crew; Rep Frsh Cls; Stu Cncl; Prfct Atten Awd; No Detention; Pace U; Systm Anlyst.

GARBARINO, ELLEN; St Johns Prep Schl; Flushing, NY; (Y); Hosp Aide; Chorus; Nwsp Rptr; JV Var Cheerleading; Coach Actv; Hon Roll; Queens Coll; Elem Schl Tchr.

GARBARINO, JOHN MICHAEL; Regis HS; Scarsdale, NY; (Y); Chess Clb; Church Yth Grp; Cmnty Wkr; Teachers Aide; Church Choir; Nwsp Stf; Yrbk Rptr; Yrbk Stf; Im Bsbl; Im Bsktbl; Genl Excl 83-85; Cornell U; Cvl Engr.

GARBER, CATHERIN L; Vestal HS; Vestal, NY; (Y); 13/450; FBLA; Band; Concert Band; Mrchg Band; Symp Band; Rep Stu Cncl; Cheerleading; Trk; High Hon Roll; NHS; SUNY Binghamton; Math.

GARBEROGLIO, KIMBERLY; Frontier Central HS; Buffalo, NY; (Y); 50/500; FBLA; Ski Clb; Nwsp Phtg; Yrbk Phtg; Stu Cncl; Socr; Swmmng; Trk; Hon Roll; NHS; Regents Schlrshp Nrsng 85; D Youville Coll; Nrsng.

GARBOWSKI, JOSEPH A; Pierson HS; Sag Harbor, NY; (Y); 1/55; Church Yth Grp; Nwsp Rptr; Crs Cntry; Bausch & Lomb Sci Awd; High Hon Roll; NHS; NY Regents Schlrshp 85; U Of MA; Microbio.

GARBUTT, KIM; Massena Central HS; Massena, NY; (Y); Church Yth Grp; JA; Yrbk Stf; Cheerleading; Gym; Trk; Hon Roll; Jr NHS; NHS; Frnch Comptn Awd 84-85; Acad Banqt 84-85; Tintd JR 84-85.

GARCES, JAVIER R; Sacred Heart HS; Yonkers, NY; (S); 5/214; Boy Scts; Nwsp Rptr; Nwsp Stf; Var Crs Cntry; Trk; Hon Roll; NHS; Sacred Heart Schlrshp 82; Harvard; Comp Sci.

GARCIA, CHARLES; Richmond Hill HS; Richmond Hill, NY; (Y); Boys Clb Am; Church Yth Grp; Cmnty Wkr; JA; Math Clb; High Hon Roll; Hon Roll; NHS; Prfct Atten Awd; Spanish NHS; Arista 85; Math Awd 85; Schlstc Achvt 84; St Johns U; Bus Mgmt.

GARCIA, COLETTE A; St Catharine Acad; Bronx, NY; (Y); Rep Stu Cncl; Trk; Prfct Atten Awd; NYS Regents Schlrshp 85; NYS Letter Of Mrt 85; NYS Certfct Of Mrt 85; St Johns U; Med.

GARCIA, DAVID; All Hallows Inst; New York, NY; (Y); 2/100; Bowling; High Hon Roll; Hon Roll; Natl Merit Schlrshp 85; NY City Coll; Mech Engrng.

GARCIA, EVELYN; St Nicholas Of Tolentine HS; New York, NY; (Y); 36/141; Yrbk Stf; Vllybl; Prfct Atten Awd; No Detentions 83, 84 & 85; Top Stu Hist 83; Top Stu Art 82; Manhattan Coll; Bus Admin.

GARCIA, FRANCISCO; Bolivar Central HS; Bolivar, NY; (Y); Ski Clb; Var JV Ftbl; Var Trk; Var JV Wrstlng; Hon Roll; Med.

GARCIA, GERALDINE; Franciscan HS; Mohegan Lake, NY; (Y); Hosp Aide; School Musical; Pres Rep Soph Cls; VP Rep Jr Cls; Rep Stu Cncl; Var L Vllybl; Hon Roll; NHS; Spanish NHS; Church Choir; 1st Pl Bnd Talnt Show 85; Ldrshp,Hnr Roll Awd 84-85; 3rd Pl Schl Bnd Talnt Show 84.

GARCIA, GINA; Franklin Delano Roosevelt HS; Brooklyn, NY; (Y); Math Tm; Chorus; School Musical; Lit Mag; Hon Roll; Arista 83; Chem 84-85; Laureate Schlrs 84-85; Hofstra U; Busnss Admin.

GARCIA, JANET; Bishop Loughlin HS; Brooklyn, NY; (S); Spanish Clb; High Hon Roll; Prfct Atten Awd; Teach Communion 82-85; Bus.

GARCIA, JEANNY; St Vincent Ferrer HS; Jackson Hts, NY; (Y); 4/115; Library Aide; Math Tm; Hon Roll; NHS; Iona Lang Cont 1st Hnrs 85; Acctng.

GARCIA, JOSE; Mount Saint Michael HS; Bronx, NY; (Y); Chess Clb; Exploring; French Clb; Intnl Clb; Latin Clb; Capt Powder Puff Ftbl; Var Socr; French Hon Soc; Hon Roll; NHS.

GARCIA, LISA A; Fontbonne Hall Acad; Brooklyn, NY; (Y); 20/138; Math Tm; Variety Show; Nwsp Rptr; Rep Stu Cncl; High Hon Roll; NHS; NEDT Awd; Office Aide; Teachers Aide; Rep Sr Cls; NY ST Regents Schlrshp 85; Iona Coll Language Cntst Hnrs 82-85; NY U.

GARCIA, MARANGELLIE; Bishop Loughlin HS; Ny, NY; (Y); John Jay Coll; Law.

GARCIA, MARY; North Babylon SR HS; North Babylon, NY; (Y); Drama Clb; VP Intnl Clb; JV Fld Hcky; Hon Roll; NHS; Band; Mrchg Band; School Musical; School Play; Nwsp Phtg; Elem Ed.

GARCIA, SORAYA; St Raymonds Academy For Girls; Bronx, NY; (Y); 25/68; Computer Clb; Library Aide; Office Aide; Science Clb; VP Soph Cls; Rep Stu Cncl; Hon Roll.

GARCILAZO, ESTHER; Cathedral HS; Ny, NY; (Y); 109/304; Hon Roll; Prfct Atten Awd; Accntnt.

GARCZYNSKI, JUDITH; Farmingdale HS; Farmingdale, NY; (Y); Church Yth Grp; Cmnty Wkr; Girl Scts; Concert Band; Mrchg Band; Symp Band; Yrbk Stf; High Hon Roll; Sec NHS; Ntl Merit Ltr.

GARDEPE, PAULA; Stockbridge Valley Central Schl; Pratts Hollow, NY; (S); 3/48; Church Yth Grp; 4-H; French Clb; GAA; Math Clb; Pep Clb; Science Clb; Spanish Clb; Varsity Clb; Color Guard; Trvl Agnt.

GARDINA, RACHEL; Frontier Central HS; Blasdell, NY; (S); Church Yth Grp; German Clb; Chorus; Hon Roll; NHS; Bus Mgmnt.

GARDINIER, LORI A; East Syracuse Minoa HS; Fayetteville, NY; (Y); Office Aide; Hon Roll; Jr NHS; Cncl Svc Awd For Scl Stds 85; Ononadaga CC; Comp Oper.

GARDINIER, TIMOTHY; Amsterdam HS; Amsterdam, NY; (Y); 88/294; Church Yth Grp; 4-H; Church Choir; Hon Roll; JV Bsbl; JV Var Bsktbl; JV Var Ftbl; Happy Sportsmnshp Awd 83; Engrng.

GARDINIER, WILLIAM; Little Falls JR SR HS; Little Falls, NY; (S); 13/109; Am Leg Boys St; French Clb; FBLA; Hosp Aide; Ski Clb; Nwsp Rptr; Nwsp Stf; Yrbk Stf; Badmtn; Crs Cntry; Sci.

GARDNER, BARRY C; Chenango Valley HS; Binghamton, NY; (Y); Church Yth Grp; French Clb; Ski Clb; Yrbk Phtg; Yrbk Stf; Var Trk; Jr NHS; NYS Rgnts Schlrshp 85; Broome Comm Coll; Eng Sci.

GARDNER, BEVERLY R; Eastern Districk HS; Brooklyn, NY; (Y); 22/415; Hon Roll; Regnts Schlrshp 85; Engl, Bus Ed, Gym Hnrs 83-85; Baruch; Comp Sci.

GARDNER, DANA; Andes Central Schl; Andes, NY; (Y); GAA; Band; Chorus; Drm Mjr(t); Pres Frsh Cls; VP Sr Cls; VP Jr Cls; Var Bsktbl; High Hon Roll; NHS; Phy Thrpy.

GARDNER, DANA; Horseheads HS; Newtown, PA; (Y); 73/407; Drama Clb; French Clb; JCL; Latin Clb; Ski Clb; Varsity Clb; Nwsp Rptr; Yrbk Rptr; Trk; Hon Roll; Mansfield Ready-Wrtg Cntst 1st Pl 85; Modrn Myth Cntst ST Levl 1st Pl 84; Regnts Schlrshp 85; U Of Richmond; Jrnlsm.

GARDNER, DAVID; Binghamton HS; Binghamton, NY; (Y); Debate Tm; Drama Clb; Varsity Clb; Var Capt Bsbl; Var Capt Bsktbl; Var Powder Puff Ftbl; High Hon Roll.

GARDNER, ELYSA S; Clarkstown HS North; New City, NY; (Y); 26/480; Off Drama Clb; Chorus; School Musical; School Play; Variety Show; Mu Alp Tht; NHS; NY St Schl Music 83; All St Choir 84-85; Comm Theater Prod 83-85; Wesleyan U; Brdcst Comm.

GARDNER, HEATHER; Rye HS; Rye, NY; (Y); Model UN; Rep Stu Cncl; JV Lcrss; High Hon Roll; Hon Roll.

GARDNER, JEFF M; Pine Valley Central HS; Gerry, NY; (Y); Am Leg Boys St; Drama Clb; Band; Chorus; Mrchg Band; School Play; Trk; Hon Roll; NHS; Voice Dem Awd; Avg Bowl 85; Fredonia ST; Eng.

GARDNER, KIMBERLEE; Greece Athena HS; Rochester, NY; (Y); Church Yth Grp; Band; Concert Band; Symp Band; High Hon Roll; Hon Roll; Law.

GARDNER, LARRY; North Rose-Wolcott HS; Wolcott, NY; (Y); Boy Scts; Varsity Clb; Crs Cntry; Mgr(s); Trk; Wt Lftg; Wrstlng; Hon Roll; Ntl Merit Ltr; Prfct Atten Awd; JUDSO.

GARDNER, LYNDA; Chatham HS; Ghent, NY; (Y); 9/130; French Clb; Hosp Aide; Math Tm; VP Ski Clb; Yrbk Ed-Chief; VP Jr Cls; VP Sr Cls; Rep Stu Cncl; VP Capt Socr; High Hon Roll; NY ST Regent Schlrshp 85-86; SUNY Potsdam; Biology.

GARDNER, ROBERT; Chester HS; Chester, NY; (Y); Var Bsktbl; High Hon Roll; NEDT Awd; Prfct Atten Awd.

GARDNER JR, ROBERT W; Bethpage HS; Bethpage, NY; (Y); Aud/Vis; CAP; Band; Concert Band; Pep Band; Stu Cncl; Hon Roll; NY Inst Tech.

GARDNER, SCOTT; Franklin Acad; Constable, NY; (Y); Band; Jazz Band; Franklin Acad Schlrshp 84; Med.

GARDNER, THOMAS H; Loneisland Lutheran HS; Garden City, NY; (S); German Clb; Jazz Band; School Musical; VP Jr Cls; Var Ftbl; Trk; JV Var Wrstlng; Hon Roll; NHS; Sci.

GARDNER, WANDA; Hannibal Central HS; Martville, NY; (Y); Pres Rptr 4-H; FFA; Key Clb; VICA; Hon Roll; Girl Scts; School Play; Variety Show; Capt Vllybl; Morrisville Coll; Floriculture.

GAREE, WARD K; Herkimer SR HS; Herkimer, NY; (Y); Model UN; Hon Roll; Rgnts Schlrshp 85; Nazareth Coll; Bio Chem.

GARFINKEL, ANDREW; Port Jervis HS; Port Jervis, NY; (Y); 28/200; Boy Scts; Temple Yth Grp; Var Ftbl; Var Trk; Var Wrstlng; Hon Roll; Socr; Eagle Sct 85; Temple Beth-El Sistrhd Helen Zeger Awd 85; Yeshiva U; Rbbncl.

GARFINKEL, ROCHELLE A; E Hampton HS; Amagansett, NY; (Y); French Clb; Nwsp Phtg; Nwsp Rptr; Ed Yrbk Phtg; Yrbk Rptr; Capt Var Sftbl; JV Var Tennis; Regents Schlrshp 85; Clarkson U; Computer Sci.

GARGAN, NICK; Au Burn HS; Auburn, NY; (Y); Var Tennis.

GARGAN, RUTH; Lindenhurst HS; Lindenhurst, NY; (Y); Chorus; JV Socr; Psych.

GARGIULO, ALBERT; Msgr Mc Clancy HS; Jamaica, NY; (Y); 8/250; Library Aide; Rep Jr Cls; Rep Sr Cls; Stu Cncl; High Hon Roll; Hon Roll; Merit Awd Sci Fair 84-85; Activty Awd Stu Cncl 84-85; Acctng.

GARGIULO, ALETHA; Rocky Point HS; Rocky Point, NY; (Y); 18/186; Hon Roll; NHS; Ntl Merit Ltr; Mark Twain Literary Contest Honorable Mention 84; Academic All American 85; ST U Of NY; Psyciatry.

GARGUILO, MICHAEL G; Oriskany Central HS; Oriskany, NY; (Y); Am Leg Boys St; Varsity Clb; School Play; JV Bsbl; JV Var Bsktbl; Var Ftbl; Var Trk; High Hon Roll; VP Jr NHS; Trs NHS; Boston Coll; Comp Sci.

GARIBOLDI, JOHN; Commack South HS; Dix Hills, NY; (Y); JA; Red Cross Aide; Varsity Clb; Bsbl; Ftbl; Wt Lftg; Wrstlng; Cit Awd; Hon Roll; MVP Ftbll 83-84; Farmingdale; HVAC.

GARITE, JANINE; Sachem HS; Lake Grove, NY; (Y); Church Yth Grp; Cmnty Wkr; Var Trk; NHS; U Center; Comp Sci.

GARLAND, RANDY G; Centereach HS; Centereach, NY; (Y); 1/489; Math Tm; Band; Jazz Band; School Musical; Socr; Trk; Bausch & Lomb Sci Awd; Cit Awd; Ntl Merit Ltr; Val; All NY ST Band 84; 1st Pl Troph ST FBLA Comptn 85; Publctn Prose Prz Prism Magzn Natl 85; YALE U; Mech Engrng.

GARLICK, LOU ANNE; Clarkstown High School South; New City, NY; (Y); Twrlr; Vllybl; Photo.

GARLO, MARIE E; Saint Joseph Acad; Amityville, NY; (Y); Science Clb; Yrbk Rptr; Yrbk Stf; Jr NHS; Ntl Merit SF; NEDT Awd; NJCL Natl Latin Exam Maxima Cum Laude 82; Studnt Coordntr ASJ 83-85; CYO Swim Team 74-84; Pre Vet Med.

GARMIRE, LAURA; Union Endicott HS; Endicott, NY; (Y); Varsity Clb; Rep Stu Cncl; Var Vllybl; High Hon Roll; Hon Roll; NHS; Elem Ed.

GARMONE, ANTHONY; Mayvale HS; Cheektowaga, NY; (Y); Boy Scts; Letterman Clb; Pep Clb; Ski Clb; School Musical; Bsbl; Ftbl; Ice Hcky; Trk; Wrstlng.

GARNEAU, GREGG; Pelham Memorial HS; Pelham, NY; (Y); Ice Hcky; High Hon Roll; NHS; NY U; Busnss.

GARNES, GREG; Hillcrest HS; Queens, NY; (Y); Cmnty Wkr; Computer Clb; Hosp Aide; Math Tm; Science Clb; Sftbl; Cit Awd; Hon Roll; Ntl Merit Schol; Prfct Atten Awd; Syracuse U; Med.

GARNETT, BETH M; Lawrence HS; Atlantic Beach, NY; (Y); 84/379; Debate Tm; Science Clb; Temple Yth Grp; Variety Show; Nwsp Rptr; Yrbk Stf; Rep Jr Cls; High Hon Roll; NHS; Ntl Art Hnr Soc 83-85; JR Art Awd 84; Archon Hnr Soc 85; Stony Brook; Art.

GARNETT, ROBERT; August Martin HS; Queens, NY; (Y); Aud/Vis; Boy Scts; Camera Clb; Office Aide; Teachers Aide; Chorus; Church Choir; Lit Mag; Wt Lftg; Cit Awd; Elec Engr.

GARNIER, ROSEMARIE; West Hempstead HS; Island Pk, NY; (Y); JV Badmtn; JV Swmmng; Hon Roll; NHS.

GAROFALO, DANA MARIE; Frankfort-Schuyler HS; Frankfort, NY; (Y); 32/98; FBLA; GAA; Key Clb; Trs Soph Cls; Rep Jr Cls; Sec Sr Cls; Stu Cncl; Hon Roll; 1st Pl Ofc Procedures For FBLA In Dist 85; Herhimer CC; Travel.

GAROFALO, ROSEMARIE; Bishop Kearney HS; Brooklyn, NY; (Y); Ski Clb; High Hon Roll; NHS; St Johns U; Bus.

GAROFALO, SHARI; Cicero-North Syracuse HS; Clay, NY; (S); 64/622; Church Yth Grp; Powder Puff Ftbl; Hon Roll; Spec Ed.

GAROFOLO, LISA; Nazareth Acad; Rochester, NY; (Y); Rep Frsh Cls; Hon Roll; John Steinbeck Awd 85; Cert Of Merit Advncd Keybdg 85; Achvt Awds Exclnce Amer Studies 85; Rochester Inst Tech; Htl Admin.

GARRETT, BRENDA; Liverpool HS; Liverpool, NY; (Y); 193/820; Exploring; JA; Ski Clb; Sftbl; Cert De Merite Frnch Cntst 84; Acctg.

GARRETT, DERRICK; Archbishop Molloy HS; Queens Vlg, NY; (Y); 6/409; Computer Clb; Bsktbl; Ftbl; Sftbl; High Hon Roll; NHS; Comptr Sci.

GARRETT, JANICE; Connetquot HS; Ronkonkoma, NY; (S); 12/671; Church Yth Grp; Key Clb; Concert Band; Mrchg Band; Yrbk Stf; Var Crs Cntry; Capt Trk; Var Vllybl; NHS; Ntl Merit Ltr; Ambassador Coll; Elem Ed.

GARRETT, KEITH R; Lyme Central HS; Chaumont, NY; (Y); Church Yth Grp; ROTC; VICA; Score Keeper; Socr; Wrstlng; Prfct Atten Awd; 1st Pl Trphy Voc Ind Clbs Of Amer 84; 1st Pl Trphy UICA Regnt Comp 85; Schltcs Awd Mach Tech 84 & 85; Mach Tech.

GARRETT, KELLY; Linton HS; Schenectady, NY; (Y); Dance Clb; Variety Show; Rep Soph Cls; Rep Jr Cls; Var Cheerleading; JV Socr; Chld Psychlgy.

GARRETT, MELANIE; Walton HS; Bronx, NY; (Y); Church Yth Grp; Cmnty Wkr; Computer Clb; Hosp Aide; School Play; Variety Show; Fshn Mrchndsng.

GARRETT, NELL K; Albany Academy For Girls; Albany, NY; (Y); Nwsp Stf; Yrbk Stf; Ntl Merit SF; Cum Laude Soc 85; Wells Coll; Engl.

GARRICK, CATHERINE; Lindenhurst SR HS; Lindenhurst, NY; (Y); Band; Concert Band; Mrchg Band; ST U Of NYMED Lab Tech.

GARRISON, BLAKE; St Patricks Cc HS; Palenville, NY; (Y); Drama Clb; Ski Clb; School Play; Trs VP Stu Cncl; Var L Bsbl; Var L Bowling; Var L Socr; Church Yth Grp; Bsbl Athlt Wk 85; NASTAR-SKI Slalom Gld Medl 83; Stu Landbk Revisn Comm Rep 84; Cmnctns.

GARRISON, DAN; Springville Griffith Inst; Collins, NY; (Y); 41/192; VP 4-H; L Golf; FFA; ST U Buffalo; Mech Engr.

GARRISON, LINDA; Beacon HS; Beacon, NY; (S); 4/190; Math Clb; Math Tm; Science Clb; Rep Jr Cls; Hon Roll; Jr NHS; NHS; Bio & Amer Hstry Awd 83-84; SPC Educ.

GARRISON, NAOMI; Penn Yan Acad; Penn Yan, NY; (Y); Trs 4-H; GAA; Service Clb; Chorus; Rep Frsh Cls; Var Bowling; 4-H Awd; High Hon Roll; Hon Roll; NHS; Acctng.

GARRISON, SHENA; Nazareth Regional HS; Brooklyn, NY; (Y); Chorus; Church Choir; Cheerleading; Gym; Hon Roll; Psych.

GARRISON, THERESA; John C Birdlebough HS; Phoenix, NY; (Y); Church Yth Grp; Temple Yth Grp; Color Guard; Crouse Irving Hosp Schl; Nrsng.

GARRITY, DAVID G; Corning-Painted Post W HS; Painted Post, NY; (Y); 15/252; Boy Scts; Key Clb; Varsity Clb; Rep Jr Cls; Rep Stu Cncl; JV Bsbl; JV Var Bsktbl; High Hon Roll; VP NHS; Prfct Atten Awd; Eagle Sct Awd 83; Parnt Tchr Stu Assn VP 84; Dent.

GARRITY, KATHRYN; St Vincent Ferrer HS; Astoria, NY; (S); 18/117; Church Yth Grp; Library Aide; Q&S; Church Choir; Nwsp Sprt Ed; Cheerleading; Sftbl; Tennis; Hon Roll; NEDT Awd.

GARSON, JULIET; Laguardia HS; New York, NY; (Y); Cmnty Wkr; Thesps; School Play; Hon Roll; Governors Committee Schlstc Achvt Citation 82.

GARTANI, CAMILLE; Roy C Ketcham SR HS; Poughkeepsie, NY; (Y); Science Clb; Spanish Clb; Yrbk Stf; Hon Roll.

GARVER, CARRIE; Lockport SR HS; Lockport, NY; (Y); 54/451; Girl Scts; Intnl Clb; Sec VICA; Ed Nwsp Ed-Chief; Stu Cncl; CC Awd; Hon Roll; Jr NHS; Prfct Atten Awd; Camera Clb; Girl Scout Silvr Awd 84, 1st Cls 83; Comp Prgmr.

GARVEY, CHRISTINE I; Flushing HS; Flushing, NY; (Y); Color Guard; School Musical; School Play; Variety Show; Yrbk Stf; Rep Frsh Cls; Rep Soph Cls; Rep Jr Cls; Rep Sr Cls; L Cheerleading; Atrny Gnrls Trpl C Awd 82; Srv League Awd 85; Fshn Inst Of Tech; Fshn Buying.

GARVEY, PAUL; Williamsville South HS; Williamsville, NY; (Y); Boy Scts; Church Yth Grp; Cmnty Wkr; Computer Clb; Ski Clb; Vllybl; Wt Lftg; Yth Engaged In Svc Awd-Outstndng Vlntr 83; Twn Of Amhrst Yth Bd-Cert Of Apprctn 84.

GARVIN, DIANE; Frontier Central HS; Blasdell, NY; (S); Pep Clb; Spanish Clb; Chorus; High Hon Roll; Hon Roll; NHS; Ntl Merit Ltr; NEDT Awd; Creative Writing.

GARY, KATHLEEN; Walt Whitman HS; Huntington, NY; (Y); 51/631; Church Yth Grp; Hosp Aide; Chorus; Nwsp Stf; JV L Socr; High Hon Roll; Jr NHS; NHS; Italn Natl Hnr Socty 83-85; NY ST Regnts Schlrshp 85; Ithaca Coll; Lwyr.

GARY, KEVIN; Catholic Central HS; Troy, NY; (S); 12/203; Chess Clb; French Clb; Pres Math Clb; Var Bsbl; Var Bsktbl; Var Golf; JV Socr; High Hon Roll; NHS; Math & Frnch Awd; RPI; Comp Pgmr.

GASBARRA, DINA; Walter Panas HS; Peekskill, NY; (Y); Sftbl; Swmmng; High Hon Roll; Hon Roll.

GASIOROWSKI, SCOTT; Bishop Ludden HS; Syracuse, NY; (Y); JV Var Bsktbl; Bus Mgmt.

GASNER, KELLY; Broadalbin Central HS; Gloversville, NY; (Y); 2/90; Art Clb; Drama Clb; Spanish Clb; Variety Show; Yrbk Stf; Sec Frsh Cls; Trs Jr Cls; Rep Stu Cncl; High Hon Roll; Jr NHS; Schl & Cnty Seat Belt Postr Contst 85; Chem Achvt Awd 85; Miami U; Grphc Arts.

GASPARINI, FRANCIS M; Calasanctius Preparatory Schl; Williamsville, NY; (Y); Math Tm; Ski Clb; Yrbk Stf; Rep Soph Cls; Var L Socr; NEDT Awd; Outstndg Achvt 83-84; MVP Soccr 83-84; Cornell U; Engr.

GASSLER, JOHN P; Pelham Memorial HS; Pelham, NY; (Y); 7/160; Am Leg Boys St; Aud/Vis; Computer Clb; JV Var Bsbl; Var Ftbl; High Hon Roll; NHS; Ntl Merit Ltr; Pre-Med.

GASTON, LASHON; Martin Luther King HS; Bklyn, NY; (Y); Church Yth Grp; Cmnty Wkr; Hosp Aide; JA; Office Aide; Band; School Musical; Rep Stu Cncl; Cit Awd; Hon Roll; Psych.

GASTON, MURIELLE; Cathedral HS; Rego Pk, NY; (Y); 46/298; Intnl Clb; Office Aide; Hon Roll; Ntl Merit Ltr; Rotary Awd; St Johns U; Bus Adm.

GATCHALIAN, JOSEPH P; MSGR Farrell HS; Staten Island, NY; (Y); 47/296; Boy Scts; Camera Clb; Church Yth Grp; Exploring; JA; Pep Clb; Science Clb; Church Choir; Pep Band; Hon Roll; Bio.

GATES, ANDREW; Byron-Bergen Central Schl; Bergen, NY; (Y); Model UN; Trs Frsh Cls; Trs Stu Cncl; Var Golf; Var L Socr; Var L Swmmng; NHS.

GATES, JOLENE; Binghamton HS; Binghamton, NY; (Y); Key Clb; Nwsp Rptr; Nwsp Stf; Var Trk; Broome CC; Phys Thrpy.

GATES, KATHRYN; Horseheads SR HS; Horseheads, NY; (S); 17/409; Ski Clb; Spanish Clb; Chorus; High Hon Roll; Hon Roll; NHS; AATSP Spnsh Tst Awd 84; Engrng.

GATES, KEN; Mt Markham Central HS; W Winfield, NY; (Y); 12/120; Intnl Clb; Ski Clb; Varsity Clb; VP Jr Cls; Bsktbl; L Ftbl; L Capt Trk; High Hon Roll; Hon Roll; Ntl Merit Ltr; Cntr St Conf All Star Trk Tm; NYS Rgnts Schlrshp; Hartwick Coll; Med.

GATES, MARY; Whitesboro SR HS; Whitesboro, NY; (Y); Church Yth Grp; GAA; Chorus; JV Var Fld Hcky; Powder Puff Ftbl; Score Keeper; Var Sftbl; Hon Roll; Geneseo ST; Accntng.

GATES, MICHAEL; Bishop Kearney HS; Rochester, NY; (S); 12/144; Am Leg Boys St; Exploring; NFL; Band; School Musical; School Play; Nwsp Rptr; High Hon Roll; NHS; Iona Coll; Teachr.

GATES, STEPHEN M; Morrisville-Eaton Central Schl; Morrisville, NY; (Y); 6/57; Am Leg Boys St; Band; Jazz Band; Var Tennis; High Hon Roll; Hon Roll; NHS; Church Yth Grp; Drama Clb; Chorus; Congress-Bundestag Yth Exch Pgm 85; Mdsn Cnty Schlrshp 85; Natl Sci Olympiad 83-84; Pre-Med.

GATES, THOMAS; Westport Central HS; Westport, NY; (Y); 5/21; Var Capt Bsbl; Capt Bsktbl; Var Coach Actv; Golf; Var Socr; Hon Roll; NHS; Ntl Merit Ltr; MVP Bsbl,Bsktbl,Soccer 85; U NC-CHARLOTTE; Bus.

GATHERS, SANDRA; Mabel Dean Bacon Vocational HS; Bronx, NY; (S); 22/299; Camera Clb; Church Yth Grp; Drama Clb; JA; Pres Church Choir; Vllybl; Hon Roll; Ntl Merit Schol; Prfct Atten Awd; Bus.

GATT, ANDREW; Coxsackie Athens HS; W Coxsackie, NY; (Y); 3/104; VP German Clb; Math Clb; Quiz Bowl; Trs Soph Cls; Var L Bsktbl; Var L Socr; Var L Trk; High Hon Roll; NHS; Mensa Soc Mbr 85.

GATT, SANDRA; Newfield SR HS; Selden, NY; (S); 3/563; Hosp Aide; Band; Jazz Band; Rep Frsh Cls; Rep Soph Cls; Rep Jr Cls; Rep Sr Cls; Stat Bsktbl; Var Capt Fld Hcky; Cit Awd; Outstndng Frshmn Schlrshp Comptn 84-85; Cornell U; Math.

GATTEAU III, JAMES V; W Tresper Clarke HS; Westbury, NY; (Y); 2/230; Drama Clb; 4-H; Capt Mathletes; Mgr School Musical; Nwsp Ed-Chief; Yrbk Bus Mgr; Var Tennis; NHS; Pres Schlr; Sal; Rensselaer Math, Sci Mdl 84; U Notre Dame; Math.

GATTI, EILEEN C; Seward Park HS; New York, NY; (Y); 28/760; Library Aide; Office Aide; Nwsp Stf; Lit Mag; Hon Roll; Hon Mntn Bk Awd, Amer Pen Women 83; Rgnts Schlrshp 85; Soc Stud Wall Of Fame 84; CA Coll Of Arts & Crafts; Art.

GATTO, VINCENT; Tottenville HS; Staten Island, NY; (Y); Cmnty Wkr; FNA; Hosp Aide; Service Clb; Boy Scts; Key Clb; Office Aide; Ski Clb; Teachers Aide; School Play; Tottenville Alumni Assoc Schlrshp 85; Svc Awd 85; CSI; Nrsng.

GAU, ELIZABETH; Bishop Kearney HS; Rochester, NY; (Y); Ski Clb; Concert Band; Drm Mjr(t); Mrchg Band; School Musical; Nwsp Stf; Rep Frsh Cls; Tennis; Vllybl; NHS; Hugh O Brian Yuth Fdtn Amb, Acad All Amercn 84; Hnr Nwsp Crrer 83.

GAUDELLI, RENEE; Lindenhurst HS; Millville, NJ; (Y); Varsity Clb; Fld Hcky; JV Var Sftbl; Hon Roll; Vindland Beauty Schl; Beautcn.

GAUDETTE, ANNA MARIE; Canastota JR SR HS; Canastota, NY; (Y); 28/136; Ski Clb; JV Var Cheerleading; Im Gym; JV Sftbl; JV Vllybl; Cit Awd; High Hon Roll; Jr NHS; Merit Awd Senator John Mc Cann 85; Morrisville Ag & Tech; Bus.

GAUDIO, FLAVIO; Archbishop Molloy HS; S Ozone Pk, NY; (Y); 1/361; Service Clb; Band; Yrbk Phtg; Trk; Bausch & Lomb Sci Awd; NHS; Sal; St Schlr; Intnl Clb; High Hon Roll; ILGWU Ntl Schlrshp Fund Awd 85; Queens Coll Pres Awd Achvt 84; Iona Coll Lang Comptn 1st Pl Italian I; Cornell U; Psych.

GAUDIO, SUSAN L; Clarkstown North HS; New City, NY; (Y); Drama Clb; Hosp Aide; Band; Chorus; School Musical; School Play; Yrbk Phtg; Hon Roll; Fine Art.

GAUGER, NANCY; Fontbonne Hall Acad; Brooklyn, NY; (Y); Var Cheerleading; 1st Hnrs 82-83; Hnbl Mntn Chem & Span 3 84-85; NY U; Law.

GAUGHAN, BRIAN C; Lakeland HS; Mohegan Lake, NY; (Y); 96/350; Boy Scts; Pres JA; L Ftbl; NY ST Regents Schlrshp 85; Army ROTC Schlrshp 85; Law.

GAUGHAN, JOHN E; Norwich SR HS; Norwich, NY; (Y); 31/208; Church Yth Grp; Bsktbl; Score Keeper; Timer; High Hon Roll; Hon Roll; VFW Awd; Colgate; Pediatrics.

GAUGHRAN, CATHERINE A; Holy Trinity D H S; W Hempstead, NY; (S); Math Clb; Math Tm; Ski Clb; Chorus; School Play; Nwsp Stf; Yrbk Ed-Chief; Hon Roll; NEDT Awd; Engl.

GAUGLER, WAYNE; East Hampton HS; Montauk, NY; (Y); Band; JV Ftbl; Wt Lftg; Hon Roll; Mech Drawing Awd, Boatbldng Indu Arts Awd, Engr Drawng Awd 83-85; Engr Drawing.

GAUL, SUSAN K; West Seneca Christian HS; Lackawanna, NY; (Y); Sec Trs Church Yth Grp; Band; Concert Band; School Play; Stage Crew; Cheerleading; Vllybl; Merit Rll 82-85; Typng Awd 84; Erie CC; Lwyr.

GAULRAPP, JENNIFER; Lindenhurst SR HS; Lindenhurst, NY; (Y); Key Clb; Yrbk Stf; Off Soph Cls; Off Jr Cls; Off Sr Cls; Var Cheerleading; Var Sftbl; Var Swmmng; Hon Roll; NHS; Cornell; Mrktg.

GAUSS, SUSAN; Scotia-Glenville HS; Scotia, NY; (Y); VP German Clb; Key Clb; Varsity Clb; Orch; Var Swmmng; High Hon Roll; Ntl Merit SF; German Awd.

GAUTAVE, SANDRA; Bishio Kearney HS; Brooklyn, NY; (Y); Library Aide; 1, 2 Hnrs; Law.

GAUTHIER, JEANNINE M; Owen D Young Central Schl; Mohawk, NY; (S); 1/22; Sec Trs French Clb; Varsity Clb; Chorus; Nwsp Stf; Yrbk Stf; Pres Jr Cls; Var Capt Cheerleading; Im Socr; High Hon Roll; NHS; Lang Awd & Hm Ec 81; Trvl.

GAVAZZI, JENNIFER E; Newfane HS; Lockport, NY; (S); 10/176; Church Yth Grp; Band; Church Choir; School Musical; High Hon Roll; Hon Roll; NHS; Nurse.

GAVEY, BARBARA C; Albertus Magnus HS; Spring Valley, NY; (Y); 14/181; Latin Clb; Math Tm; Hon Roll; Math Hnr Rl; Sci Hnr Rl; Natl Lat Exm; Ivy Lague; Entrepnrshp.

GAVIGAN, SHANNON M; Hilton Central HS; Hilton, NY; (Y); 73/299; Spanish Clb; Teachers Aide; Band; Concert Band; Var Bsktbl; Var Crs Cntry; Hon Roll; St John Fisher Grant Schlrshp 85-86; Hon Roll 81-85; Best Defnsv Plyr-Most Impvr Plyr Bsktbl 83-85; St John Fisher Coll; Math.

GAVIGAN, THOMAS; Hilton Central HS; Hilton, NY; (Y); 20/355; Computer Clb; Var Crs Cntry; Var Mgr(s); Var L Trk; High Hon Roll; Prfct Atten Awd; Comp Pgmr.

GAVNEY, ELIZABETH A; Sachem HS North Campus; Holbrook, NY; (Y); 23/1428; Church Yth Grp; French Clb; Math Tm; Scholastic Bowl; Service Clb; Madrigals; Orch; School Musical; NHS; Ntl Merit SF; NENC All-Eastern Orch 85; Outstndng Muscn In Orch 83; Meritorious Math Stu 82; Mus Ed.

GAWLAK, MARY; Frontier SR HS; Blasdell, NY; (S); Varsity Clb; Jazz Band; VP Pres Stu Cncl; Var Capt Bsktbl; JV Var Sftbl; JV Capt Vllybl; High Hon Roll; JP Sousa Awd; NHS; NEDT Awd; Ntl Hist, Govt Awds 85; Bsktbl, Vllybll 84-85.

GAWRONSKI, GLENN; Canisius HS; Buffalo, NY; (Y); 21/148; Im Bsktbl; Im Ftbl; Hon Roll; Prfct Atten Awd; Canisius Coll.

GAWRONSKY, DEBRA F; Berner HS; Massapequa Park, NY; (Y); 36/426; Acpl Chr; Madrigals; Orch; School Musical; Variety Show; Hon Roll; NHS; Chorus; Flag Corp; Stage Crew; NY All ST Chors 83-84; Eastman Merit Schlrshp 85; All Cty Orch Chors 82-85; Eastman Schl Of Mus; Mus.

GAY, DOUGLAS E; Seton Catholic Central HS; Endicott, NY; (Y); 14/150; Key Clb; Var L Socr; Var Capt Trk; NHS; Ntl Merit Ltr; NY ST Rgnts Schlrshp 85; Boston U; Environmntl Engrng.

GAY, KATHY; Greece Athena HS; Rochester, NY; (Y); Cmnty Wkr; JA; Office Aide; Nwsp Rptr; Nwsp Stf; Hon Roll; Bus.

GAY, ROBERT; Greenwich Central Schl; Greenwich, NY; (Y); Am Leg Boys St; Pres Band; Chorus; Church Choir; Jazz Band; School Musical; Var L Golf; Var L Tennis; High Hon Roll; NHS; Elec Engrng.

GAYDOS, STEPHEN; West Seneca East SR HS; Buffalo, NY; (Y); Band; Concert Band; Jazz Band; Mrchg Band; School Musical; Hst Symp Band; Ftbl; Boy Scts; Drama Clb; Pep Band.

GAYDUSEK, KELLY ANN; Broadalbin Central HS; Broadalbin, NY; (Y); 1/59; Am Leg Aux Girls St; Intnl Clb; Library Aide; Pep Clb; Spanish Clb; Yrbk Stf; VP Jr Cls; DAR Awd; High Hon Roll; VP NHS; St Lawrence U; Psych.

GAYLE, DIONNE M; Bronx High School Of Science; New York, NY; (Y); Yrbk Stf; Lit Mag; Var L Bsktbl; Coach Actv; Var L Sftbl; Dailynews Hs Softball All-Star 84; Awd For Most Improved Plyr Softball 84.

GAYLE, SHIRLENE R; Thomas Jefferson HS; Brooklyn, NY; (Y); 5/278; Math Clb; Nwsp Stf; Hon Roll; Regnts Schlrshp 85; UFT Coll Schlrshp Fnd 85; Alfred U; Psych.

GAYLES, PAULA; Buffalo Traditional HS; Buffalo, NY; (Y); Aud/Vis; Church Yth Grp; Intnl Clb; Library Aide; Red Cross Aide; Spanish Clb; Acpl Chr; Chorus; Church Choir; Stage Crew; Afro Acad Cltrl Tech Sci Olympcs 85; Excll Eng 85; Panhellenic Awd 85; Howard U; Phy Thrpy.

GAYLO, CHRIS; Fairport HS; Fairport, NY; (Y); JA; Varsity Clb; Var Crs Cntry; Var Trk; Hon Roll; Engrng.

GAYOSO, TONY A; Holy Trinity HS; Bellmore, NY; (S); 20/265; Drama Clb; Math Clb; Ski Clb; Concert Band; School Musical; School Play; Ftbl; High Hon Roll; NHS; NY Polytech; Engr.

GAYTON, HARRY; Olean HS; Olean, NY; (Y); FFA; Trk; Hon Roll.

GAZIANO, DARLENE; Eastridge HS; Rochester, NY; (Y); French Clb; VP Red Cross Aide; Varsity Clb; Band; Mrchg Band; School Musical; VP Yrbk Stf; JV Fld Hcky; Var Vllybl; NHS; Arch.

GAZZALEY, ADAM; Bronx H S Of Science; Howard Beach, NY; (Y); Debate Tm; Key Clb; NFL; Teachers Aide; Lit Mag; Rep Soph Cls; Rep Jr Cls; Rep Sr Cls; Prfct Atten Awd; Med.

GAZZOLA, KRISTINE; East Islip HS; East Islip, NY; (S); 124/475; Hosp Aide; Varsity Clb; Rep Jr Cls; Rep Jr Cls; Rep Stu Cncl; Cheerleading; Coach Actv; Gym; Trk; Hon Roll; Confrnc Ii All Around Chmpn Gymnstcs 83; MVP Gymnstcs 83-84; Capt Of Gymnstcs Tm 84; Northern IL; Nrsng.

GBUR, MARIA; St George Acad; New York, NY; (Y); 1/33; Dance Clb; Hosp Aide; Yrbk Ed-Chief; VP Frsh Cls; Pres Jr Cls; L Vllybl; High Hon Roll; NHS; Val; NYS Regnts Schlrshp 85; NYC Cmptrllrs Awd 85; Natl HS Awd Excllnc 85; SUNY Stonybrook; Pre-Med.

GEARD, MARCUS J; Dobbs Ferry HS; Dobbs Ferry, NY; (Y); Pres Computer Clb; Key Clb; Math Tm; Model UN; Nwsp Ed-Chief; French Hon Soc; High Hon Roll; French Clb; Regents Schlrshp 85; Vassar Coll; Psych.

GEARHART, WARRIE; Gowanda Central HS; Gowanda, NY; (Y); Thesps; Chorus; Color Guard; School Musical; School Play; Rep Soph Cls; Stat Bsktbl; Stat Ftbl; Mgr Lcrss; AFS; All Cnty Chorus 82-83; Scl Wrkr.

GEARY, ROY; York Central HS; York, NY; (Y); 3/86; Am Leg Boys St; Pres Key Clb; Pres Band; Concert Band; High Hon Roll; Hon Roll; Jr NHS; NHS; Chorus; Church Choir; Anthony M Lariton JA Awd Scholar 85; Clsrm Hnrs Bnd, Spn 85; Law.

GEATRAKAS, PATRICIA; Mexico HS; Mexico, NY; (Y); Exploring; Science Clb; Spanish Clb; Varsity Clb; Band; Color Guard; Concert Band; Mrchg Band; Symp Band; Yrbk Phtg; SADD Pres & Treas 84-85; Chrldng MVP 84-85; Psych.

GEBAUER, LINDA; Ithaca HS; Ithaca, NY; (Y); 45/430; German Clb; Girl Scts; JA; Ski Clb; Sec Concert Band; Jazz Band; Mrchg Band; Orch; Jr NHS; NHS; Per Atten Awd 82; Ithaca Coll Yuth Orch, Prncpl Fltst 83-84; M J Craig Awd, F Wilcox Mem Awd 85; Cornell U; Bus.

GEBER, STUART; Long Beach HS; Lido Beach, NY; (S); 10/291; DECA; Hosp Aide; Key Clb; School Musical; Tennis; Hon Roll; NHS; 2nd-Sci Fair, 2nd-Long Isl Sci Congress 82; Bronze & Gold Mdl Hegren Culture Exam 83 & 84; Vp NHS 84; Bsns Admin.

GEDDES, ANTHONY; Union Springs Acad; Fort Fairfield, ME; (S); 6/52; Drama Clb; FCA; Ski Clb; Varsity Clb; Acpl Chr; Band; Chorus; Church Choir; Jazz Band; Mrchg Band; Bst Sprtsmnshp Awd 83; His.

GEDEN, MICHELLE; Waterford-Halfman HS; Waterford, NY; (Y); 12/90; English Clb; Chorus; Madrigals; Swing Chorus; Yrbk Stf; Lit Mag; VP Soph Cls; High Hon Roll; Hon Roll; NEDT Awd; Librl Arts.

GEDEON, CARINE; Catherine Mc Auley HS; Brooklyn, NY; (Y); Debate Tm; Pres French Clb; Rep Service Clb; Chorus; Nwsp Rptr; Rep Stu Cncl; Vllybl; French Hon Soc; Hon Roll; MDA Merit 83-84; Yth Fit Achvt Awd 81-82; Cert Dance Achvt 84; Pace U; Intl Mngmnt.

GEDEON, MARIE; John Dewey HS; Brooklyn, NY; (Y); Yrbk Stf; VA ST U; Jrnlsm.

GEE, ANNIE; Midwood HS; Brooklyn, NY; (Y); 150/605; Cmnty Wkr; Intnl Clb; Office Aide; Service Clb; Teachers Aide; Chorus; Orch; School Play; Hon Roll; Merit Awd 82; Exc Attndnc Awd 84; NY U; Bus.

GEE, BRIAN; Alden Central HS; Alden, NY; (Y); 59/203; Church Yth Grp; Library Aide; Comp.

GEE, PAMELA; Hornell HS; Hornell, NY; (Y); 25/180; Art Clb; Girl Scts; Hosp Aide; Spanish Clb; Chorus; Im Bowling; Im Vllybl; High Hon Roll; Hon Roll.

GEE, WENDY; Wellsville HS; Wellsville, NY; (Y); 30/130; Concert Band; Mrchg Band; Orch; School Musical; Nwsp Stf; Socr; Sftbl; Swmmng; High Hon Roll; Hon Roll; Arion Awd Band 85; Alfred ST Coll; Acctng.

GEER, LISA; Gloversville HS; Gloversville, NY; (Y); Dance Clb; Var Cheerleading; JV Trk; Var Hon Roll; Ed.

GEER, LORI; Colonie Central HS; Albany, NY; (Y); Rptr FBLA; Yrbk Stf; Socr; Child Psych.

GEFFNER, MIKE; Commack HS South; Commack, NY; (Y); Cmnty Wkr; Hosp Aide; Office Aide; Teachers Aide; Trs Temple Yth Grp; Variety Show; Nwsp Stf; Stu Cncl; Ftbl; Cit Awd; Pres Hocus Pocus Entrtnmnt Co 83-86; Med Explrs Pgm 84-85; Vol Ambulance Corp 85; Pre-Med.

GEGA, KIM; Lindenhurst HS; Lindenhurst, NY; (Y); Church Yth Grp; German Clb; Science Clb; Band; Concert Band; Mrchg Band; Hon Roll; NHS; Nrsng.

GEHL, DAN; Albion HS; Albion, NY; (Y); Boy Scts; Church Yth Grp; Cmnty Wkr; JV Var Ftbl; Var Capt Trk; Prfct Atten Awd; MVP Track 85; Yth Ldrshp Awd BSA 85; NY Inst; Arch.

GEHRMANN, ROBIN; Midwood HS; Brooklyn, NY; (Y); 148/605; School Musical; School Play; Stu Cncl; St Schlr; Boy Scts; Temple Yth Grp; Student Of Year 84; NY U; Pre-Med.

GEIGER, KEVIN R; Hamburg HS; Hamburg, NY; (Y); Ski Clb; JV Var Coach Actv; JV Var Ice Hcky; Var L Socr; Var L Tennis; JR ST Chmpn Hcky Tm 84-85; NH Ntl Chmpnshp; Alfred ST Ag & Tech; Cvl Engr.

GEIGER, KIMBERLY; North Collins Central HS; N Collins, NY; (Y); 3/79; 4-H; Science Clb; Ski Clb; Band; Concert Band; Drm Mjr(t); Mrchg Band; School Musical; Variety Show; Nwsp Stf; All Star Vlybl,Sftbl,Soccer 83-85; Rochester Inst Tech.

GEIGER, LINDA J; Calamanca Central HS; Kill Buck, NY; (Y); Church Yth Grp; Drama Clb; French Clb; Hosp Aide; Red Cross Aide; Sec Spanish Clb; Stu Cncl; Cheerleading; Coach Actv; French Hon Soc; Frgn Lang Educ.

GEIL, PATRICIA; Our Lady Of Victory Acad; Mt Vernon, NY; (S); 6/150; Computer Clb; Science Clb; Nwsp Stf; Rep Stu Cncl; High Hon Roll; NHS; NEDT Awd; Spanish NHS; Sci Medal 84; Engl Medal 83; Pediatrician.

GEIMAN, TRACEY; Connetquot HS; Ronkonkoma, NY; (S); 8/671; Hosp Aide; Temple Yth Grp; Y-Teens; Stu Cncl; JV Cheerleading; Jr NHS; NHS; Medallion Awd Candy Striping 84; Merit Awd-Tn Ldrshp 83; Athltc Aaawwwwd Chrldng 82.

GEISER, JOSEPH; Seton Catholic Central HS; Apalachin, NY; (S); Boys Clb Am; Sec Church Yth Grp; Nwsp Rptr; Var L Ftbl; Im Vllybl; High Hon Roll; NHS; Cath Fmly Life Insur Schlrshp 82 & 84; Sci.

GEISERT, ANDREW; Archbishop Molloy HS; Glendale, NY; (Y); 42/411; Computer Clb; French Clb; German Clb; Im Sftbl; High Hon Roll; Stoney Brook; Engrng.

GEISLER, TRACI; Stockbridge Valley Central HS; Munnsville, NY; (S); 5/36; Am Leg Aux Girls St; GAA; Mathletes; Math Clb; Pep Clb; Science Clb; Spanish Clb; Pres Band; Concert Band; Mrchg Band; Phys Ftnss Awd 80-85; Dnce Awds; Acad Awds; Comms.

GEIST, LAURA; Benjamin N Cardozo HS; Bayside, NY; (Y); 31/476; Cmnty Wkr; Exploring; School Musical; Nwsp Stf; Yrbk Stf; Lit Mag; Trk; Ntl Merit SF; Hosp Aide; Key Clb; Arista Scty 84-85; Stu Sci Trng Pgm 84.

GEITNER, MATTHEW; G Ray Bodley HS; Fulton, NY; (Y); VP Pres Latin Clb; Var L Bsktbl; Var L Trk; Cit Awd; Dnfth Awd; High Hon Roll; Hon Roll; NHS; Police Benvlnt Asc Awd 82-83; Oper Enterp 85; Polit Sci.

GELBER, LISA B; Scarsdale HS; Scarsdale, NY; (Y); Drm Mjr(t); Jazz Band; Orch; Symp Band; Pres NHS; Hosp Aide; Sec Temple Yth Grp; Nwsp Rptr; Bnai Brith Schlrshp Awd 85; Philip Morriscoll Schlrshp 85; Hnr Rll MAA 84-85; Amherst Coll; Relgn.

GELFAND, BORIS Y; Bronx H S Of Science; New York, NY; (Y); Chess Clb; Computer Clb; Math Tm; Nwsp Ed-Chief; Ntl Merit Schol; Math Assoc Am Ntl Merit Rl 84; NY Cty Math Fair Gold Medl 84; Westinghse Talent Srch 85; MIT; Phys.

GELFAND, DOUGLAS M; Commack H S North; E Northport, NY; (Y); Computer Clb; Hosp Aide; MMM; Office Aide; Teachers Aide; Band; Concert Band; Mrchg Band; Pep Band; School Musical; SADD.

GELFUSO, TOM; Frankfort Schuyler Central HS; Frankfort, NY; (S); Var Golf; Var Vllybl; Hon Roll; NHS; Mohawk Vly Comm Coll; Elect Mai.

GELIN, JOHN C; Bishop Ford Central Catholic HS; Brooklyn, NY; (Y); Art Clb; Computer Clb; Lit Mag; Stu Cncl; Im Bsktbl; Im Ftbl; Im Wt Lftg; Hon Roll; Ntl Merit Ltr; Syracuse U; Sci.

GELLER, AMY; Yeshiva University HS For Girls; Flushing, NY; (Y); 1/150; English Clb; Ntl Cncl Of Yng Israel Acdmc Achvt Schlrshp 85; Bus Mngmnt.

GELLER, ANDREA; Oyster Bay HS; E Norwich, NY; (Y); Chorus; School Musical; Yrbk Stf; Trs Jr Cls; Trs Sr Cls; Rep Stu Cncl; Cheerleading; Tennis; High Hon Roll; NHS.

GELLER, ROBIN M; Patchogue-Medford HS; East Patchogue, NY; (Y); 13/765; Hosp Aide; Leo Clb; School Musical; Yrbk Rptr; Lit Mag; Trs Frsh Cls; Mgr Trk; NHS; St Schlr; Cmnty Wkr; Patchogue Medford Arts Cncl Photo Awd 2nd Pl 82; Cmmnctns.

GELLERSON JR, GARY A; Hutchinson Central Technical HS; Buffalo, NY; (Y); 6/264; Nwsp Stf; Rep Stu Cncl; Var Socr; High Hon Roll; Kappa Sigma Phi Frtrnty Schlrshp 85; Past Prncpls Awd Comp Sci 85; SUNY Buffalo; Comp Sci.

GELLINEAU, CYRIL; St John The Baptist HS; N Amityville, NY; (Y); Church Yth Grp; Computer Clb; Off Frsh Cls; ROTC; Comp.

GELLING, EDWARD P; La Salle Acad; Brooklyn, NY; (Y); 13/237; Rifle Tm; Hnr Roll; Pace U; Info Syst.

GELLMAN, RYAN L; Nichols Schl; Williamsville, NY; (Y); Nwsp Rptr; Im Ice Hcky; Im Tennis; Var Trk; Regions Schlrshp; Soph Hist Paper Rnnr Up; Head Of Schl Soup Kitchen Cmte; U Of PA; Law.

GELOSO, ANTIONETTE; Fonda Fultonville Central S HS; Fonda, NY; (Y); FBLA; Intnl Clb; Key Clb; Teachers Aide; VICA; Color Guard; Drill Tm; Flag Corp; Mrchg Band; Capt Twrlr; Englsh Awd Hghst Avg 82; Mst Crteous Stu 85; Frendlst Prson 82; Johnson & Walse RI; Bus Mgmt.

GELSEY, ALEX; Niagara Falls HS; Niagara Falls, NY; (Y); 18/230; Ski Clb; Spanish Clb; Hon Roll; Bus.

GELSI, ANGELA; Dobbs Ferry HS; Dobbs Ferry, NY; (S); 7/102; Pres Chorus; Capt Color Guard; Concert Band; Jazz Band; School Musical; Sec Frsh Cls; Sec Soph Cls; Swmmng; Var Tennis; JV Trk; USNBA 83 & 84.

GEMMATI, MATTHEW; West Seneca West SR HS; West Seneca, NY; (Y); Rep Stu Cncl; JV Var Coach Actv; JV Var Score Keeper; Ldrshp Awd Red Cross 84; Rent-A-Kid 82; Air Frc; Air Pln Mech.

GENDEBIEN, MICHELLE; Lisbon Central Schl; Ogdensburg, NY; (S); 1/37; Sec 4-H; Pres Girl Scts; Trs Library Aide; Pres Chorus; VP Swing Chorus; Var JV Cheerleading; Var L Socr; High Hon Roll; NHS; Prfct Atten Awd; NYSSMA Excell Sng 84; St Lawrence All-Cnty Shw Choir 84-85; Vly Leag Chorus 84-85.

GENDRON, JOSEPH J; Holy Trinity HS; Bethpage, NY; (S); 52/362; Church Yth Grp; Math Clb; Math Tm; Ski Clb; Nwsp Stf; High Hon Roll; Cert NEDT 81; Merit Awd Cathlc Dtrs Amer Poetry 84; Hofstra; Comp Sci.

GENEROUS, DONNA; John C Birdlebough HS; Phoenix, NY; (Y); 35/180; Sec FBLA; Band; Concert Band; Mrchg Band; JV Socr; JV Var Trk; Stat Wrstlng; 1st Pl All Leag Awd Trck 100 M Hrdls 85; 2nd Pl NYSPHSAA Sectn III Awd Trck 100 M Hrdls 85.

GENGE II, CLIFTON K; Corning Painted Post West HS; Painted Post, NY; (Y); 36/254; Key Clb; Letterman Clb; Varsity Clb; School Musical; Variety Show; Rep Sr Cls; L Bsktbl; L Ftbl; Capt Trk; High Hon Roll; Hnr Grad Mth 85; Ath Of Mnth 85; All Sthrn Trails Conf Div II 2nd Tm Grd 85; Union Coll.

GENGENBACH JR, RICHARD L; Clarkstown North HS; New City, NY; (Y); Pres German Clb; Art Clb; VP VICA; Nwsp Stf; Yrbk Phtg; Yrbk Sprt Ed; JV Bsbl; Var Ftbl; JV Golf; High Hon Roll; Biomdcl Engrng.

GENGLER, MATTHEW G; Shoreham Wading River HS; Shoreham, NY; (Y); Chess Clb; Church Yth Grp; Varsity Clb; Socr; Tennis; Wrstlng; NHS; Campbell U; Pre-Law.

GENIE, LISA M; Moriah Central Schl; Mineville, NY; (Y); 5/83; Ski Clb; Band; Variety Show; Yrbk Stf; VP Jr Cls; VP Sr Cls; High Hon Roll; NHS; Regents Schlrshp Awd 85; Schlrs For Dollars 83-85; Lnguage Culture Club 83-85; SUNY Oneonta; Pltcl Sci.

GENIER, RICHARD L; Hudson Falls SR HS; Hudson Falls, NY; (Y); 7/246; Camera Clb; JV Var Ftbl; Im Socr; Var Swmmng; JV Trk; Im Wt Lftg; Hon Roll; NHS; Sci Semnr 83-84; NY Regnts Schlrshp 84-85; Stdnt Qrtr Soc Stds Dept 82-83; Air Force; Engrng.

GENIER, TERESA; Glens Falls HS; Glens Falls, NY; (Y); Fld Hcky; Sftbl; Vllybl; Hon Roll; Jr NHS; NHS; Potsdam Coll; Engrng.

GENNA, CARL; Somers HS; Katonah, NY; (Y); Yrbk Stf; Var Ftbl; Var Wrstlng; Hon Roll; German Hnr Soc 83-84; Bus.

GENOVA, ANDREW; Bishop Kearney HS; Rochester, NY; (Y); Aud/Vis; Boy Scts; Church Yth Grp; Computer Clb; Band; Concert Band; Mrchg Band; School Musical; Im Bowling.

GENOVA, KIMBERLY; Southampton HS; Southampton, NY; (Y); GAA; Spanish Clb; Yrbk Stf; Off Stu Cncl; JV Var Fld Hcky; Var Trk; High Hon Roll; Hon Roll; Jr NHS; NHS; Med.

GENSHEIMER, HEIDI L; Averill Park HS; W Sand Lk, NY; (Y); 50/220; Ski Clb; School Play; High Hon Roll; Art Awd; U Of Boulder CO; Liberal Arts.

GENSLER, BILLIE; Oyster Bay HS; Oyster Bay, NY; (Y); Trs Model UN; Spanish Clb; Nwsp Stf; Yrbk Stf; Var Badmtn; Var Bowling; High Hon Roll; Jr NHS; NHS; Ntl Merit Ltr; Sci.

GENSON, RAYMOND; Mc Graw HS; Blodgett Mills, NY; (Y); Socr.

GENTILE JR, JOSEPH B; Oswego HS; Oswego, NY; (Y); Am Leg Boys St; Variety Show; JV Bsbl; JV Coach Actv; Var Capt Ftbl; Var Trk; Wt Lftg; High Hon Roll; NEDT Top 10 Pcnt 83; U Notre Dame; Sports Law.

GENTILE, LORI; Mt Mercy Acad; Lackawanna, NY; (S); 6/200; Church Yth Grp; Computer Clb; Model UN; Spanish Clb; Nwsp Stf; High Hon Roll; Hon Roll; NHS; Engineering.

GENTILE, NANCY; Onondaga HS; Nedrow, NY; (S); 2/73; VP Exploring; Sec German Clb; Hosp Aide; Concert Band; Jazz Band; School Play; Yrbk Ed-Chief; Cheerleading; High Hon Roll; NHS; Wellesly Book Awd 84; Engrng.

GENTILE, WENDY; Roosevelt HS; Yonkers, NY; (S); Band; Concert Band; Mrchg Band; School Musical; School Play; Stage Crew; Variety Show; Yrbk Stf; Var Sftbl; Red Cross Aide; All-City HS Band 85; Coll; Music.

GENTNER, TIMOTHY; Westfield Central HS; Westfield, NY; (S); 4/100; Church Yth Grp; Cmnty Wkr; Hosp Aide; Quiz Bowl; Band; School Musical; Var L Bsktbl; Var L Ftbl; Var L Tennis; Bausch & Lomb Sci Awd; U Of Miami; Physician.

GENTRY, CASSANDRA; North Babylon HS; N Babylon, NY; (Y); French Clb; Intnl Clb; Trk; Hon Roll; Jr NHS; NHS; Pres Schlr; Trk 83; Ntl Hnr Soc 84; Presdntl Schlr 85; Tusgegee U; Engrng.

GENUNG, JEFFREY; Oxford Acad; Oxford, NY; (Y); Am Leg Boys St; Drama Clb; French Clb; Mrchg Band; Nwsp Stf; Hon Roll; NHS; 1st Am Legn Oratrcl Cntst 83; Mock Trial Comptn 83-86; Acadmc Chllng Tm 84-8l; Comm.

GENUNG, SCOTT; South New Berlin Central HS; Norwich, NY; (Y); Concert Band; Jazz Band; Mrchg Band; Bsbl; Bsktbl; Ftbl; Hon Roll; Prfct Atten Awd; Mst Imprvd Mrchng Band Stu 82; Cnty Cmptn Prblm Slvng Cntst Schl Dlgt 83-84; Bus Mgmt.

GEOBEL, STEPHANIE; Christopher Columbus HS; Bronx, NY; (S); Cit Awd; High Hon Roll; Hon Roll; NHS; Prfct Atten Awd; SOC Wrk.

GEORGALAS, DESPINA; Long Island City HS; Long Island City, NY; (S); Office Aide; Teachers Aide; Nwsp Rptr; Hon Roll; Grk Clb 85; Ed Schl Nwspr 84-85; Hunter Coll.

GEORGE, CHERYLANN; Dominican Commercial HS; Middle Vlge, NY; (Y); Art Clb; Pep Clb; Stu Cncl; Sftbl; Hofsta U; Psych.

GEORGE, CRAIG; Kenmore East HS; Tonawanda, NY; (Y); Varsity Clb; Ftbl; Pol Secrty.

GEORGE, EILEEN; Attica SR HS; Strykersville, NY; (S); 8/152; Math Tm; Nwsp Rptr; Yrbk Bus Mgr; Yrbk Ed-Chief; Yrbk Stf; Rep Stu Cncl; Hon Roll; Jr NHS; NHS; Bernice Blom Incentv Awd 84; Rochester Inst Of Tech; Sci.

GEORGE, ELIZABETH; The Mary Louis Acad; Jamaica, NY; (Y); Camera Clb; Church Yth Grp; Cmnty Wkr; Hosp Aide; Office Aide; Spanish Clb; Svc Awd 83.

GEORGE, JACQUELINE; Thomas R Proctor HS; Utica, NY; (Y); Dance Clb; Drama Clb; Key Clb; Capt Color Guard; School Musical; School Play; Variety Show; High Hon Roll; NHS; Prfct Atten Awd; Scholar Elmira Coll 85; Syracuse U; Biol.

GEORGE, JEFFREY; Haverling Central HS; Bath, NY; (Y); Computer Clb; French Clb; Latin Clb; Math Clb; Math Tm; Quiz Bowl; Scholastic Bowl; JV Socr; J V Sccr Pin & Cert 82-83; Acadmc All-ST Pin 84-85; Recrdng Eqpmnt.

GEORGE, JEFFREY; Silver Creek Central HS; Silver Creek, NY; (Y); 34/92; Aud/Vis; Church Yth Grp; Key Clb; Ski Clb; Varsity Clb; Chorus; School Play; Stage Crew; Yrbk Stf; JV Capt Ftbl; Hudson Valley CC; Machnst Tech.

GEORGE, JEREMY; M V HS; Mt Vernon, NY; (Y); JV Gym; Var Trk; Act-So Comptn 85; Cazenovia Coll; Art.

GEORGE, LISA A; West Hempstead HS; W Hempstead, NY; (Y); 7/310; Sec Key Clb; Trs Spanish Clb; Stu Cncl; Stat Lcrss; Var L Tennis; Hon Roll; NHS; Stu Mnth, Amer Leg Awd, Cert Hnr Soc Wmn Engrs 85; SUNY; Pre Med.

GEORGE, LYNNE; Alexander Central HS; Alexander, NY; (S); 6/89; Color Guard; Yrbk Phtg; Var JV Bsktbl; Var Cheerleading; Score Keeper; Var JV Vllybl; Hon Roll; Jr NHS; Lion Awd; NHS; Geneseo; Acctng.

GEORGE, MARIANN; York Central HS; Wadsworth, NY; (Y); Sec Key Clb; Ski Clb; Band; Jazz Band; Mrchg Band; Pep Band; Ed Yrbk Stf; Sec Frsh Cls; Cheerleading; Sec NHS; Paralgl.

GEORGE, PATRICIA; Notre Dame HS; Batavia, NY; (S); 2/82; Drama Clb; School Musical; School Play; Nwsp Rptr; Yrbk Ed-Chief; High Hon Roll; Kiwanis Awd; NHS; Prfct Atten Awd; Lbrl Arts.

GEORGE, RICHELLE; Lincon HS; Yonkers, NY; (Y); 4/306; Drama Clb; Chorus; Ed Lit Mag; Rep Stu Cncl; Var Swmmng; Var Tennis; NHS; Natl Achvt Schlrshp 85; Natl Art Hnr Soc Pres 85; Nwspapr Art Edtr 85; Harvard U; Engl.

GEORGE, THOMAS; St Francis Prep; Floral Park, NY; (Y); Aud/Vis; Camera Clb; Chess Clb; Computer Clb; JA; PAVAS; Science Clb; Service Clb; School Play; Yrbk Stf; SUNY Stonybrook; Engrng.

GEORGIADES, ISMINI; Long Island City HS; Long Island City, NY; (S); 5/565; Church Yth Grp; Cmnty Wkr; Trs Debate Tm; Hosp Aide; Math Tm; Variety Show; Nwsp Ed-Chief; Nwsp Rptr; Yrbk Rptr; Lit Mag.

GEORGIANIS, MARIA; St Francis Prep; Flushing, NY; (S); 2/693; Cmnty Wkr; Library Aide; Science Clb; Chorus; Hon Roll; Jr NHS; Principals List; NYU Stonybrook; Premed.

GEPPI, SARAH; Keveny Memorial Acad; Watervliet, NY; (S); Art Clb; Spanish Clb; Yrbk Stf; JV Bsktbl; Var JV Sftbl; Var Capt Vllybl; Hon Roll; NHS.

GEPPI JR, THOMAS A; La Salle Inst; Watervliet, NY; (Y); 11/77; Art Clb; Nwsp Rptr; Lit Mag; Bsktbl; Ftbl; High Hon Roll; NHS; Pres & Acadmc Schlrshp Niagara U 85; Acadmc Schlrshp Siena Coll 85; Niagara U; Cmmnctns.

GERACE, JAMES P; Moutn Asumption Inst; Plattsburgh, NY; (Y); 1/90; Math Tm; Model UN; Scholastic Bowl; School Play; Symp Band; Nwsp Ed-Chief; Yrbk Ed-Chief; Dnfth Awd; NHS; Ntl Merit SF; Bst Actr Awd; Engrng.

GERACE, JOSEPH S; Frontier Central HS; Hamburg, NY; (Y); Art Clb; Aud/Vis; JA; Nwsp Rptr; Yrbk Phtg; Yrbk Rptr; Rep Jr Cls; High Hon Roll; Hon Roll; Prfct Atten Awd; Intrnshp Buffalo ST Coll 85; Natl Merit Awd 85; Wake Forest U; Archlgy.

GERACI, GIOVANNA; Nazareth Regional HS; Brooklyn, NY; (Y); 17/300; Yrbk Rptr; Hon Roll; NHS; NY St Regents Schlrshp 85; Brooklyn Coll Schlrs Awd 85; Pres Acad Ftns Awd 85; Brooklyn Coll; Psych.

GERACI, MARGARET A; T R Proctor HS; Utica, NY; (Y); Art Clb; Pep Clb; Stage Crew; Yrbk Stf; Hon Roll; Prfct Atten Awd; Italian Clb 82-84; Bus Mgt.

GERALDINE, KISH; Fox Lane HS; Mt Kisco, NY; (Y); 50/273; Drama Clb; Concert Band; Mrchg Band; JV Vllybl; Hon Roll; Cert Of Acad Merit Frch 84; Scientific Journalism.

GERARD, DAVID B; Elmont Memorial HS; Flushing, NY; (Y); 11/247; FBLA; Pres Key Clb; Math Tm; Model UN; Temple Yth Grp; Band; Orch; School Play; Trs Stu Cncl; Var Trk; U Of PA; Pre-Med.

GERARD, JOSEPH; Copiague SR HS; Amityville, NY; (Y); Computer Clb; DECA; FBLA; Yrbk Phtg; Yrbk Stf; Var Capt Socr; Var Trk; DECA Chptr Proj Awd 84-85; Span Clb Cert Of Apprctn 83-84; Marine Corps; Bus.

GERARD, KATHLEEN F; Walter Panas HS; Peekskill, NY; (Y); 2/211; FBLA; Stat Sftbl; Stat Vllybl; High Hon Roll; NHS; Ntl Merit Ltr; Sal; St Schlr; NY ST Regnts Schlrshp 85; Albany; Bus Adm Finc.

GERARD, SANDRA R; Greece Arcadia HS; Rochester, NY; (Y); 2/287; Cmnty Wkr; Math Tm; Ski Clb; Stu Cncl; High Hon Roll; Ntl Merit Schol; Sal; Church Yth Grp; FBLA; JA; U S Ldrshp & Svc Awd 84; Amer Chem Assoc Cntst Fnlst 84; Regnt Schlrshp Wnnr; U Of PA; Intl Bus Mgmt.

GERASIMCZYK, LEE; Richmond Hill HS; Richmond Hill, NY; (Y); Drama Clb; English Clb; Radio Clb; Church Choir; School Musical; School Play; Nwsp Stf; VP Soph Cls; Jr Cls; Sr Cls; Super Yuth Awd 84-85; NY U; Chld Psych.

GERATY, ALICIA L; East HS; Rochester, NY; (Y); 18/270; Church Yth Grp; Cmnty Wkr; Office Aide; Yrbk Sprt Ed; Swmmng; High Hon Roll; NHS; Prfct Atten Awd; Pres Schlr; Exploring; JR Of Yr 83-84; NY ST Rgnts Schlrshp Wnr 84-85; Bible Quiz Hgh Scr 84-85; Rochester Bus Instit.

GERAZOUNIS, PETER; Holy Cross HS; Woodside, NY; (Y); 4/320; Chess Clb; Church Yth Grp; Computer Clb; Library Aide; JV Var Trk; High Hon Roll; NHS; Ntl Merit SF; Prfct Atten Awd; Partial Schl Schlrshp; Engnrng.

GERBASIO, VINCENT; St Francis Prep; Rosedale, NY; (Y); 270/700; Math Tm; JV Var Bsbl; JV Var Ftbl; Var Trk; Var Wt Lftg; Amherst; Math.

GERBE, GINA M; Sachem HS; Lake Ronkonkoma, NY; (Y); 1/1600; Dance Clb; VP French Clb; Socr; Pres Jr NHS; NHS; Ntl Merit SF; Val; Hdmaster Schlr 84-85; Math Awd 83; French Awd 83; U PA; Engnrg.

GERBER, LISA B; Cazenovia HS; Manlius, NY; (Y); 45/164; Sec AFS; Band; Mrchg Band; Symp Band; Nwsp Stf; Yrbk Phtg; Rep Jr Cls; JV Tennis; Var Trk; Hon Roll; U S Band Awd 84; Rgnts Schlrshp 85; Skidmore Coll; Frnch.

GERBER, LON; Ward Melville HS; Centereach, NY; (Y); 140/760; Im Bsbl; Im Bsktbl; High Hon Roll; Regenst Schlrshp 85; Suny Binghamton; Law.

GERBER, MARY A; William Nottingham HS; Syracuse, NY; (Y); 50/220; Church Yth Grp; French Clb; Latin Clb; Band; Chorus; Concert Band; Var Capt Socr; Var Capt Sftbl; Var Vllybl; Hon Roll; Mony Schlstc Art Awd Hnrb Mntn 82; Syracuse U.

GERBER, RONALD; Clarkstown High School South; Nanuet, NY; (Y); 20/540; Chess Clb; Computer Clb; Math Tm; Science Clb; JV Trk; Hon Roll; Jr NHS; Mu Alp Tht; NHS; Awd From The Amer Chem Soc 85; 8th Annl H S Physcs Cont At Iona Coll 2nd Pl Trphy 85; Math.

GERBER, SUE; Hamburg SR HS; Hamburg, NY; (Y); 2/360; Spanish Clb; Concert Band; Mrchg Band; High Hon Roll; NHS; Ntl Merit Ltr; Pres Schlr; Sal; Rgnts Scshlrshp 85; RPI Mdl Math & Sci 84; U Buffalo; Elect Engrng.

GERDING, CINDY M; Mohonasen HS; Schenectady, NY; (Y); 1/215; Am Leg Aux Girls St; Co-Capt Color Guard; Yrbk Stf; Sec Frsh Cls; Pres Soph Cls; Pres Jr Cls; Pres Sr Cls; Capt Sftbl; Vllybl; Val; SUNY Genseo Alum Fellws Schlrshp 85; Artemes Awd Mst Outstndng Femal Schlr/Athlt 85; Sci Awd 85; SUNY Geneseo; Biomedcl Tech.

GERE, KELLY; Le Roy Central Schl; Stafford, NY; (Y); AFS; 4-H; Church Choir; Score Keeper; 4-H Awd; High Hon Roll; Church Yth Grp; Girl Scts; Chorus; Color Guard; Legal Secretary.

GEREMIA, PETER; Bishop Kearney HS; Webster, NY; (Y); Var L Tennis; Ed Adm.

GERENCSER, ANNA; Nyack HS; Vly Cottage, NY; (Y); 5/254; Trs Exploring; Girl Scts; Var Tennis; French Hon Soc; High Hon Roll; NHS; Pres Schlr; NY St Regnts Schlrshp 85; Italian Am Schlrshp 85; Nyack Rotary Clb Schlrshp 85; Le Moyne Coll; Bio.

GERENCSER, MARY; Nyach HS; Valley Cottage, NY; (Y); 49/257; Band; Concert Band; Mrchg Band; School Musical; Rep Soph Cls; JV Var Fld Hcky; Stat Ice Hcky; JV VP Sftbl; French Hon Soc; High Hon Roll; Hon Men All Conf Sftbl 85.

GERENTINE JR, JOE; Beacon HS; Beacon, NY; (Y); 36/250; Key Clb; Math Tm; Spanish Clb; Hon Roll; NHS; Spn II Awd 85; Spn I Awd 84; Comp Sci.

GERES, CARRIE; Spring Valley SR HS; Monsey, NY; (Y); 151/448; Church Yth Grp; German Clb; Band; Drm Mjr(t); Yrbk Stf; Swmmng; Twrlr; Hon Roll; Trvl/Trsm.

GERKEN, SUZANNE; Eden Central HS; Eden, NY; (Y); 4-H; GAA; Girl Scts; Chorus; School Musical; 4-H Awd; Var L Cheerleading; JV Stat Tennis; Alfred; Rtl Bus Mgmt.

GERLACH, PETER; Niagara Wheatfield HS; North Tonawanda, NY; (Y); Trs Pep Clb; PAVAS; Trs Chorus; Pep Band; School Musical; School Play; Stage Crew; Swing Chorus; Capt Socr; JV Wrstlng; All-Cnty Chr 84-85; All-ST Chr 84-85; Nyssma Fstvl 84-85; U Of Rochester; Phy Sci.

GERMAINE, JOELLE; Catholic Central HS; Pleasant Dale, NY; (S); 21/230; Trs German Clb; Math Tm; Chorus; Church Choir; School Musical; Yrbk Stf; High Hon Roll; NHS; Lois C Smith Chem Schlrshp 83-84; Arch Engrng.

GERMAN, GORDON; South Park HS; Buffalo, NY; (Y); Boys Clb Am; Camera Clb; Bsktbl; Crs Cntry; Bus.

GERMAN, TIMOTHY; Gates Chili HS; Rochester, NY; (S); 30/469; Boy Scts; Camera Clb; Computer Clb; Exploring; 4-H; Pres German Clb; Mgr JA; Math Clb; Ski Clb; Band; Elec Engrng.

GERMANO, MICHELE; Bishop Kearney HS; Rochester, NY; (Y); JA; Stat Bsktbl; Var Bowling; Var Mgr(s); Stat Sftbl; Hon Roll; Church Yth Grp; Tght-Bus Basics-To 5th & 6th Grdrs 84-85; VP Finc JR Achv 84-85.

GERMILLER, JANICE M; Arlington Senior HS; Poughkeepsie, NY; (Y); Debate Tm; Drama Clb; Intnl Clb; Chorus; Orch; Lit Mag; Ntl Merit SF; Williams Coll; Eng.

GERMILLER, JOHN A; Arlington HS; Poughkeepsie, NY; (Y); 7/587; Debate Tm; Intnl Clb; Ski Clb; Yrbk Stf; High Hon Roll; Ntl Merit SF; Rensselaer Inst; Mech Engrng.

GERO, DEBBIE; Commack High School North; Commack, NY; (Y); Cmnty Wkr; Concert Band; Mrchg Band; Nwsp Rptr; Off Frsh Cls; Off Soph Cls; Off Jr Cls; Off Sr Cls; Stu Cncl; High Hon Roll; Ntl Hon Soc 85-86; Outstndng Sci Stu 83-84; Law.

GEROUX, GREG; Glens Falls HS; Glen Falls, NY; (Y); Drama Clb; Varsity Clb; School Musical; Stage Crew; Yrbk Phtg; Yrbk Rptr; Yrbk Sprt Ed; VP L Socr; High Hon Roll; Cmmctns.

GEROW, ANNE; Liverpool HS; Liverpool, NY; (S); 70/792; Church Yth Grp; Exploring; Concert Band; Stat Lcrss; Im Powder Puff Ftbl; JV Socr; Var L Swmmng; High Hon Roll; Hon Roll; Jr NHS; Psych.

GERRINGER, KELLY; Chenango Forks HS; Chenango Forks, NY; (Y); Cmnty Wkr; Band; Concert Band; Mrchg Band; High Hon Roll; NHS; Engrng.

GERRISH, CYNTHIA; Oakfield-Alabama Central Schl; Oakfield, NY; (Y); Church Yth Grp; Drama Clb; Hosp Aide; Chorus; Capt Color Guard; School Musical; Teams; Timer; Trk; Capt Twrlr; NRS.

GERS, LIA; Barker Central Schl; Barker, NY; (Y); 31/95; Girl Scts; Acpl Chr; Chorus; Capt Fld Hcky; High Hon Roll; Hon Roll; Tennis; Lifegrd Cert 83; Barbizor Schl Of Modelng Grad 84; Yth For Undrstndng Frgn Stu Hostss 83; Alfred ST Coll; Medcl Lab Tech.

GERSCH, ALAN M; Ramaz Schl; New York, NY; (Y); Art Clb; Chess Clb; Debate Tm; Math Tm; Stage Crew; Nwsp Stf; Ntl Merit SF; All Amer Schlr Awd 84; Physics.

GERSH, MICHAEL; Smithtown High Schl East; Nesconset, NY; (Y); FBLA; Math Clb; Spanish Clb; Temple Yth Grp; Stu Cncl; Hon Roll; Jr NHS; NHS; Spanish NHS; Bus Mgmt.

GERSHOWITZ, STEVEN; Jericho HS; Jericho, NY; (Y); Temple Yth Grp; Yrbk Stf; Pres Frsh Cls; Pres Jr Cls; VP Sr Cls; Pres Stu Cncl; Var Capt Socr; Var Trk; Hon Roll; NHS; Cert Of Merit-Spnsh 84-85; Law.

GERSTEL, DEBRA; Roslyn HS; Roslyn, NY; (Y); AFS; Key Clb; Yrbk Phtg; Yrbk Stf; Stu Cncl; NHS; Cornell U; Bus.

GERSTENFELD, STEVEN E; Holy Trinity HS; Roosevelt, NY; (S); Math Clb; Math Tm; Bsktbl; Ftbl; High Hon Roll; Hon Roll; Mu Alp Tht; NHS; Intl Bus.

GERSTMAN, CARYN; Port Richmond HS; Staten Isld, NY; (Y); Art Clb; Debate Tm; Drama Clb; Hosp Aide; VP JA; Math Clb; Math Tm; Red Cross Aide; VP Ski Clb; Pres Temple Yth Grp; Jr Achvt Merit Awd 83; Daily News Super Yth 85; Bus.

GERSTUNG, GREG; Lockport SR HS; Lockport, NY; (Y); 28/411; Camera Clb; Exploring; High Hon Roll; Hon Roll; Jr NHS; NHS; Roy B Kelly Awd-Outstndng Mal Stu 82-83; Chemcl Engr.

GERVAIS, JO ANNE M; Brushton Moira Central HS; Mora, NY; (Y); 12/57; French Clb; Capt Bsktbl; Capt Crs Cntry; Var Sftbl; Babe Ruth Awd; Potsdam Coll; Comp Sci.

GERVASE, LOREL; Batavia HS; Batavia, NY; (Y); Office Aide; Chorus; Nwsp Stf; Yrbk Phtg; Yrbk Stf; Im Bowling; Im Golf; Im Wt Lftg; Hon Roll; Mgmt.

GESCHWENDER, PAULA; Grand Island HS; Gr Island, NY; (Y); GAA; Yrbk Stf; JV L Swmmng; High Hon Roll; Ntl Merit Ltr.

GESMUNDO JR, JOSEPH D; St Anthonys HS; Smithtown, NY; (Y); Church Yth Grp; Drama Clb; Library Aide; Chorus; Church Choir; School Musical; Nwsp Rptr; High Hon Roll; NHS; NEDT Awd; Italian NHS 84-85; NYS Regents Schlrshp 85; Outstndng Achvt Physics Awd 84; Boston Coll; Bio.

GESSELLI, TERESA; Mahopac HS; Mahopac, NY; (Y); 120/423; Chorus; School Musical; School Play; High Hon Roll; Hon Roll; Prfct Atten Awd; Fshn Coor.

GESSO, JIM; Valley Central HS; Maybrook, NY; (Y); Church Yth Grp; Stu Cncl; Hon Roll; Embry-Riddle Aero U; Cmmrcl Plt.

GETSIOS, DESPINA; St Francis Prep Schl; Bayside, NY; (Y); 216/693; Church Yth Grp; Dance Clb; Office Aide; Church Choir; Concert Band; Orch; School Musical; Hon Roll.

GEYFMAN, VADIM; Liverpool HS; Liverpool, NY; (Y); Hon Roll; Regents Schlrshp 85; Presdntl Acad Ftns Awd 85; SUNY-OSWEGO; Comp Sci.

GHENT, GINA; St Joseph By The Sea HS; Staten Island, NY; (Y); 10/245; Aud/Vis; Nwsp Stf; Var Capt Bsktbl; Var Sftbl; Var Tennis; High Hon Roll; NHS; NEDT Awd; Pol Sci.

GHERSI, LINDA; North Shore HS; Glen Head, NY; (Y); Cmnty Wkr; French Clb; Model UN; Varsity Clb; Var Capt Cheerleading; Var Pom Pon; Trk; Schlr Mnth Sci 85; Typng Awd 84; Bus.

GHEZZI, ROXANNE M; Solvay HS; Solvay, NY; (Y); 16/167; Stage Crew; Rep Sr Cls; Var Socr; Var Capt Sftbl; Var Vllybl; High Hon Roll; NHS; Church Yth Grp; Chorus; Rgnts Schlrshp Wnnr 85; Union Coll; Bio Sci.

GHORISHI, ZAHRA; Williamsville South HS; Williamsville, NY; (Y); 93/245; Chess Clb; Church Yth Grp; Computer Clb; Hosp Aide; Intnl Clb; Math Clb; Quiz Bowl; Scholastic Bowl; Science Clb; Nwsp Rptr; Effrt & Attitde Awd 81; Mst Intllgnt 84; U Of NY-BUFFALO; Bio.

GHOSTLAW, PAUL; Salmon River Central HS; Fort Covington, NY; (S); Church Yth Grp; Band; Concert Band; Pres Frsh Cls; Pres Jr Cls; Rep Stu Cncl; Var Bsbl; Var Capt Bsktbl; Var Socr; Hon Roll; Phys Ed.

GIACINTO, MARIA; Cardinal Spellman HS; Bronx, NY; (Y); Art Clb; Cmnty Wkr; Hosp Aide; Library Aide; Pep Clb; Teachers Aide; Stage Crew; Nwsp Stf; Coach Actv; High Hon Roll; Ntl Hnr Soc 84-85; NY U; Law.

GIACOBBE, J MICHAEL; Farmingdale HS; N Massapequa, NY; (Y); Varsity Clb; School Musical; Trs Frsh Cls; Pres Soph Cls; Trs Jr Cls; Trs Sr Cls; JV Var Lcrss; JV Var Socr; Hon Roll; NHS; U PA; Arch.

GIACOBBI, JAMES; Christian Brothers Academy; Fayetteville, NY; (Y); 33/109; Cmnty Wkr; VP JA; Ski Clb; Rep Stu Cncl; Var L Crs Cntry; Var L Trk; Hon Roll; NY ST Regents Schlrshp 84-85; Rochester Inst Tech; Engrng.

GIACONE, PETER A; Regis HS; Elmhurst Corona, NY; (Y); Speech Tm; Lit Mag; Ntl Merit Ltr; Hly Crss Coll Bk Awd 84; Georgetown; Bus.

GIAMARINO, JOHN; Connetquet HS; Oakdale, NY; (Y); 21/694; Camera Clb; Cmnty Wkr; Chorus; JV Socr; Hon Roll; Jr NHS; Arspc Engrng.

GIAMBALVO, GINA; Bishop Kearney HS; Brooklyn, NY; (S); 8/340; Math Tm; Bowling; Jr NHS; NHS; Full Tuition Scholar Pace U 85; Pace U; Acctg.

GIAMBO, DEBRA A; Guilderland Central HS; Altamont, NY; (Y); 13/369; Chorus; Concert Band; Orch; School Musical; Swmmng; High Hon Roll; NHS; Pres Church Yth Grp; Madrigals; Swing Chorus; Brd Educ Hghst Achvt Awd 85; NYSSMA Conf All-ST Wmns Chorus Mbr 83; Regents Schlrshp 84; Dickinson Coll; Math.

GIAMBRA, RENEE; Niagara Wheatfield SR HS; North Tonawanda, NY; (Y); Hosp Aide; Chorus; School Play; High Hon Roll; Hon Roll; NHS; Prfct Atten Awd; Schl Ply Hnrbl Ment Trphy 83-84; Outstndng Achvmnt Math Awd 82-84; RN.

GIAMMATTEI, ANDREA; Marlboro HS; Marlboro, NY; (Y); 24/165; Pres Church Yth Grp; Drama Clb; Pres Trs 4-H; Thesps; Chorus; School Musical; School Play; Rep Jr Cls; Rep Stu Cncl; Stat Bsktbl; Cardinal Spellman Awd 84-85; Miss United Teenager Cert 84; 4-H Awds & Hnrs Fshn, Cmmtng Demo 82-84; Theatre.

GIAMMONA, STEVE; Holy Cross HS; Bayside, NY; (Y); 14/312; Nwsp Stf; Sec Jr Cls; JV Var Bsbl; JV Var Ftbl; JV Var Trk; Wt Lftg; Hon Roll; Sec NHS; Engrng.

GIAMPIETRO, MARYANN; Commack North HS; Commack, NY; (Y); Lit Mag; Hon Roll; Cmnty Wkr; Teachers Aide; Bus.

GIANGIOBBE, ADRIENNE; West Genesee SR HS; Syracuse, NY; (Y); Art Clb; Cmnty Wkr; Hosp Aide; MMM; Color Guard; Crs Cntry; Swmmng; Hon Roll; Syracuse U; Nrsg.

GIANNAKIS, ANNA; Archbishop Iakovos HS; Bayside, NY; (S); Cmnty Wkr; Computer Clb; French Clb; Math Clb; Science Clb; Teachers Aide; Bsktbl; Vllybl; High Hon Roll; Queens Coll Pres Scholar 82-83; MA Inst Of Tech; Comp Sci.

GIANNAKOS, GUS; Monsignor Mc Claney Memorial HS; New York, NY; (S); 51/225; Boy Scts; Cmnty Wkr; Hosp Aide; School Play; Stage Crew; Nwsp Ed-Chief; Nwsp Rptr; Pres Sr Cls; Im Bsbl; Im Bsktbl; Lttr Nwspapr Wrtng 84; 2nd Pl Schl Sci Fair 82; NY U; Pre-Dntstry.

GIANNANTONIO, CINDY; Ward Melville HS; Stony Brook, NY; (Y); 4-H; Chorus; Yrbk Stf; JV Fld Hcky; JV Sftbl; 4-H Awd; High Hon Roll; Hon Roll; NHS; Pres Acadmc Ftns Awd 85; Oneonta Coll NY; Engl.

GIANNETTA, MATTHEW J; Archbishop Stepinac HS; Yonkers, NY; (Y); 81/207; Nwsp Rptr; Lit Mag; Im Fld Hcky; Camp Fr Inc; SUNY Oswego; Bio.

GIANNICCHI, ANNEMARIE; West Seneca West SR HS; West Seneca, NY; (Y); 56/543; Cmnty Wkr; FBLA; Hosp Aide; Trs JA; Concert Band; Mrchg Band; Rep Jr Cls; Rep Stu Cncl; Im Bowling; Hon Roll; Trocaire Merit Schlrshp 85; 1st Gen Bus Awd 83; 2nd Typng Awd 83; Trocaire Coll; Med Assist.

GIANNICO, DENISE; Valley Stream Central HS; Valley Stream, NY; (Y); AFS; Mgr(s); Score Keeper; Timer; Hon Roll; Natl Bus Hnr Soc 84-85; SADD 83-84; Sci.

GIANNINO, ANTHONY R; St Anthony HS; East Northport, NY; (Y); Chess Clb; Computer Clb; Ski Clb; Chorus; Bowling; Hon Roll; NY ST Rgnts Schlrshp 85; Dun Scotus Cert 82 & 83; Oneonta; Pilot.

GIANNONE, MONICA; Fox Lane HS; Bedford Hills, NY; (Y); Church Yth Grp; Ski Clb; Chorus; JV Crs Cntry; JV Fld Hcky; JV Lcrss; Hon Roll; Soc Stds Commndtn Achvmnt 82-83; Diploma De Merito 82-85; Dermatology.

GIANNUZZI, VEYA MAUREEN GULIA; Seton Catholic Central HS; Vestal, NY; (Y); 25/160; Key Clb; Varsity Clb; Yrbk Stf; Var Trk; High Hon Roll; Hon Roll; NHS; U Of VT; Bio.

GIANSANTE, DIANNE; De Sales Catholic HS; Lockport, NY; (Y); 1/46; Ed Nwsp Ed-Chief; Yrbk Stf; Stu Cncl; Var Vllybl; Pres NHS; Ntl Merit Ltr; NEDT Awd; Val; Francis & Agnes Schimscheiner Memrl Scholar 84-85; Intl Frgn Lang Awd Spn 83-84; Natl Sci Merit Awd; Syracuse U; Biol.

GIARDINA, ESTHER MARIE; Bishop Ford Central Catholic HS; Brooklyn, NY; (Y); Dance Clb; Variety Show; High Hon Roll; Prfct Atten Awd; Med.

GIARDINA, JULIE A; Queen Of The Rosary Acad; Wantagh, NY; (Y); 15/52; Church Yth Grp; Hosp Aide; Speech Tm; Varsity Clb; School Musical; Nwsp Sprt Ed; Pres Stu Cncl; Capt Gym; Hon Roll; Pres Stu Cncl 85-86; Leadrs Clb 84-86; St Johns U Jamaica; Spch Path.

GIARDINA, LAURA; Farmingdale HS; Farmingdale, NY; (Y); Church Yth Grp; GAA; Hosp Aide; Intnl Clb; Key Clb; Ski Clb; Varsity Clb; Chorus; Nwsp Stf; Mgr(s).

GIARDINA, MICHAEL; Bethpage HS; Plainview, NY; (Y); 50/280; Latin Clb; Wt Lftg; High Hon Roll; Hon Roll; Ntl Merit Schol; Regents Schlrshp 85; SS Olympiad Cert 84; Trustee Achvt Awd 85; Adelphi U; Fin.

GIARDINI, LISA; Allegany Central Schl; Allegany, NY; (Y); Camp Fr Inc; Church Yth Grp; High Hon Roll; Hon Roll; Prfct Atten Awd; Best Pen & Ink Art Awd 84; Law.

GIATZIKIS, VICKY; Our Lady Of Perpetual Help HS; Brooklyn, NY; (Y); Badmtn; Tennis; Trk; Vllybl; Wt Lftg; Hon Roll; Hon Roll; Brooklyn Coll; Bio-Chem.

GIBBONS, CECILE; Hempstead HS; Uniondale, NY; (S); 46/333; Dance Clb; Badmtn; High Hon Roll; Hon Roll; Adelphi U; Nrsng.

GIBBONS II, JAMES; West Seneca East HS; W Seneca, NY; (Y); Aud/Vis; CAP; Stage Crew; Hon Roll; Spnsh Hnrs 83-84; Cert Of Mrt 85; Pol Sci.

GIBBONS, KENNETH W; Scotia-Glenville HS; Scotia, NY; (Y); 45/255; Computer Clb; Science Clb; Yrbk Stf; Hon Roll; Pres Schlr; Renesselaer Polytech; Mgmt Engr.

GIBBONS, MELISSA; St Edmund HS; Brooklyn, NY; (Y); 23/187; Church Yth Grp; English Clb; Pres Spanish Clb; Hon Roll; Awd For Chrstn Srv 82-84; Hnr Cert For Religion8 English & Spnsh 83-85; Cert Awd Of Exc Soc Stds 83-84; Spec Ed.

GIBBONS, NOREEN; John A Coleman HS; Kingston, NY; (S); French Clb; Rep Jr Cls; Var Bsktbl; Var Sftbl; Hon Roll; NHS; Prfct Atten Awd; Geom, Bio Awd 83; Harvard; Law.

GIBBONS, SUSAN A; Middletown HS; Middletown, NY; (Y); 15/380; Key Clb; Office Aide; Teachers Aide; Hon Roll; NHS; Ntl Merit SF; NY Regents Schlrshp 85; NY U Trustee Schlrshp 85; NY U Schlrs Program 85; NY U; Mus Rcrdng Tech.

GIBBONS, VANESSA; A Philip Randolph Campus HS; New York, NY; (Y); Church Yth Grp; Dance Clb; Hosp Aide; Office Aide; Service Clb; Teachers Aide; Chorus; Church Choir; Cheerleading; Tennis; Most Imprvd Plyr Vlybl 85; Comp Tech.

GIBBS JR, ARNOLD; Longwood HS; Coram, NY; (Y); Boy Scts; Key Clb; Band; Chorus; Mrchg Band; Orch; JV Bsbl; JV Ftbl; Hon Roll.

GIBBS JR, DONALD; Our Savior Lutheran HS; Bronx, NY; (Y); Boys Clb Am; Church Yth Grp; Lib Office Aide; Rep Jr Cls; Pres Stu Cncl; Bsktbl; Gym; Cit Awd; Hon Roll; Archit Enr.

GIBBS, EVELYN T; Richmond Hills HS; Jamaica, NY; (Y); 33/298; Church Yth Grp; English Clb; Girl Scts; Hosp Aide; Math Clb; Spanish Clb; School Play; Hon Roll; Prfct Atten Awd; Banking.

GIBBS, GLENDON; Richmond Hill HS; Queens Village, NY; (Y).

GIBBS, LISA; Keveny Memorial Acad; Troy, NY; (Y); 18/40; Art Clb; Ski Clb; School Play; VP Soph Cls; Rep Jr Cls; VP Sr Cls; Rep Stu Cncl; L Var Sftbl; L Var Tennis; Hon Roll; NYS Paper Carrier Yr 84-85; Phys Thrpy.

GIBBS, LISA; Murry Bergtraum HS; Brooklyn, NY; (Y); Accntnt.

GIBBS, RENAE; Linton HS; Schenectady, NY; (Y); Key Clb; Red Cross Aide; Ski Clb; Off Jr Cls; Var Bowling; Var Tennis; Hudson Vly CC; Bus Admin.

GIBBS, ROBYN; Harry S Truman HS; Bronx, NY; (Y); 18/544; Cmnty Wkr; Hosp Aide; Office Aide; Service Clb; Temple Yth Grp; Yrbk Stf; Hon Roll; Pres Schlr; Spnsh Awd; Rgnts Schlrshp; Colgate U.

GIBBS, WENDI; Vestal SR HS; Vestal, NY; (Y); Drama Clb; French Clb; Varsity Clb; Var Trk; Acctng.

GIBILORO, GEORGE; John F Kennedy HS; Utica, NY; (Y); Bsktbl; Bowling; Ftbl; Sftbl; Swmmng; Trk; Chorus; Delhi; Bldg Cntrctr.

GIBNEY, DANIELLE; James I O Neill HS; Fort Montgomery, NY; (Y); Am Leg Aux Girls St; Church Yth Grp; Pep Clb; Sec Jr Cls; Rep Stu Cncl; Capt Var Cheerleading; Var Trk; Hon Roll; NHS.

GIBSON, BRUCE; West Seneca East HS; Buffalo, NY; (Y); Church Yth Grp; CAP; FCA; French Clb; Latin Clb; Pep Clb; Ski Clb; Varsity Clb; Band; Concert Band; Cornell; Htl Rest Mgt.

GIBSON, DOUGLAS B; Irondequoit HS; Rochester, NY; (Y); 18/396; Boy Scts; Computer Clb; Math Clb; Stage Crew; Im Vllybl; High Hon Roll; Hon Roll; NHS; Prfct Atten Awd; ACS Chem Cont 1st Schl,Fnlst Hnrs 84; Engr.

GIBSON, JEANETTE; Hempstead HS; Hempstead, NY; (S); 23/333; Church Yth Grp; Civic Clb; Girl Scts; Spanish Clb; Speech Tm; Sec Nwsp Rptr; Hon Roll; NY ST Musc Tchrs Assn Awd 83; Alpha Kappa Alpha Srrty Monetry Awd 84; Long Isl Sci Cngrss Awd 81; Howard U; Jrnlsm.

GIBSON, LAURA; Seton Catholic Central HS; Binghamton, NY; (Y); Church Yth Grp; GAA; Key Clb; Office Aide; JV Var Bsktbl; JV Cheerleading; Var Sftbl; Hon Roll; NHS; Exec Sec.

GIBSON, LORRI JO; Bishop Kearney HS; Pittsford, NY; (Y); Band; Concert Band; Jazz Band; Mrchg Band; Pep Band; School Musical; High Hon Roll; Jr NHS; NHS; All-Amer Schlr 85; Engr.

GIBSON, LYNDA; Sachem North HS; Farmingdale, NY; (Y); 30/1383; Cmnty Wkr; Science Clb; Nwsp Stf; Hon Roll; Jr NHS; NHS; Clarkson U; Bus.

GIBSON, MARIN E; Lockport SR HS; Lockport, NY; (Y); AFS; Intnl Clb; Political Wkr; Ski Clb; Symp Band; VP Frsh Cls; JV Capt Swmmng; Var Trk; Jr NHS; Trinity Coll; Intrntl Rltns.

GIBSON, PETER C; Canton HS; Canton, NY; (Y); Church Yth Grp; Quiz Bowl; Thesps; Chorus; School Musical; School Play; Stage Crew; Swing Chorus; Lit Mag; Sec Sr Cls; Regents Scholarship 85; Colgate U.

GIBSON, RENEE; Liberty HS; Liberty, NY; (Y); Ski Clb; Yrbk Stf; Var Bsktbl; Capt L Socr; Sftbl; Hon Roll; Soccer MVP & All Star Tm 85; Sullivan Co CC; Hotel Tech.

GIBSON, SANDRA; Livingston Manor Central Schl; Livingston Manor, NY; (Y); 4/34; Pres Varsity Clb; Chorus; Concert Band; Yrbk Stf; Pres Frsh Cls; Pres Soph Cls; Pres Jr Cls; Capt Var Bsktbl; Capt L Socr; Capt Var Sftbl; Tchrs Assoc Awd Hghr Ed 85; Nancy Foster Mem Awd Grls Athltcs 85; Cortland ST; Phy Ed.

GIBSON, SHARMIN; Bishop Loughlin HS; Brooklyn, NY; (Y); PAVAS; Science Clb; Band; Chorus; School Musical; School Play; Stage Crew; NYU; Med.

GIBSON, WILLIAM; Park West HS; Bronx, NY; (Y); 83/515; Art Clb; Aud/Vis; Library Aide; Office Aide; Red Cross Aide; Spanish Clb; Hon Roll; Spanish NHS; Prfct Atten Awd 85; Top 85 Pcnt Hygiene Cls 85; Intl Frgn Lang Awd 85.

GICZKOWSKI, KIM; Depew HS; Depew, NY; (Y); 25/254; Church Yth Grp; Dance Clb; Trs GAA; Spanish Clb; Band; Concert Band; Mrchg Band; Im Bsktbl; Im Sftbl; Im Tennis; Fredonia ST Coll; Elem Educ.

GIDDINGS, ANNE M; Paul V Moore HS; Central Square, NY; (Y); 39/297; Var Hon Roll; Regents Schlrshp 85-86; Ecol Sci.

GIDDINGS, GEOFFREY; Fort Hamilton HS; Brooklyn, NY; (Y); 38/567; Church Yth Grp; Nwsp Stf; Yrbk Stf; Co-Capt Tennis; Cit Awd; Hon Roll; Chrmn NHS; Ft Hamilton Awd Excel Careers 85; Cathloic Trchrs Assoc Outstndng Charctr Citznshp 85; Physicn.

GIELLA, LAURA; Holy Trinity HS; East Meadow, NY; (Y); 50/319; JV Var Vllybl; Sports Night 82-86; Kickline 84-85 & 85-86; Mission Clb 83-86; Nrsng.

GIERER, MICHAEL R; Mount St Michael HS; Bronx, NY; (Y); 102/300; Bsbl; Bsktbl; Hon Roll; St Schlr; Iona Coll; Corp Lawr.

GIESIN, PETER; Gilboa-Conesville Central Schl; North Blenheim, NY; (S); 1/28; 4-H; Pres Frsh Cls; VP Soph Cls; Rep Stu Cncl; Var Capt Bsktbl; High Hon Roll; NHS; Air Force Acad; Engrng.

GIFAS, JIMMY; Lincoln HS; Yonkers, NY; (S); 55/306; Church Yth Grp; FBLA; Nwsp Rptr; Nwsp Stf; Yrbk Stf; Rep Stu Cncl; Internshp Legislative Offs 85; Travel Club 84-85; Greek Orthodox Yth Assoc 83; Bus.

GIFF, ALICE P; Elmont Memorial HS; Weston, CT; (Y); 6/247; DECA; NCTE Awd; Key Clb; Variety Show; Yrbk Stf; Co-Capt Cheerleading; Co-Capt Sftbl; High Hon Roll; Sec Jr NHS; Sec NHS; Regnts Schlrshp 85; Fairfield U CT; Accntg.

GIFFIN, ROSEMARY; Riverhead HS; Riverhead, NY; (Y); Latin Clb; Library Aide; Chorus; Nwsp Ed-Chief; Nwsp Rptr; Nwsp Stf; Prjct Life Cert Awd 85; Spcl Educ.

GIFFORD, DARLYN; Mayfield Central HS; Mayfield, NY; (Y); 1/77; Pres Girl Scts; Varsity Clb; Var Co-Capt Bsktbl; Var Co-Capt Socr; Var Co-Capt Vllybl; Bausch & Lomb Sci awd; Sec NHS; Val; Union Coll Schlrshp 85; Myfld Tchrs Assn Schlrshp 85; Union Coll; Chmcl Engrng.

GIFFORD, MICHAEL; Mayfield JR SR HS; Mayfield, NY; (Y); Drama Clb; Varsity Clb; Chorus; School Play; Variety Show; Pres Stu Cncl; Var Capt Socr; Trk; Hon Roll; Ldrshp Conf; AF Acad.

GIFFORD, NANCY; Innaculata Acad; W Seneca, NY; (Y); Dance Clb; Nwsp Stf; Trs Sr Cls; JV Cheerleading; Hon Roll; Med.

GIGLIELLO, LOUIS J; Corning East HS; Cornng, NY; (Y); Ski Clb; Varsity Clb; Coach Actv; Var L Ftbl; Var L Lcrss; Var Wrstlng; NHS; Engrng.

GIGLIO, ALEXANDRA; Golden Heights Christian Schl; Hilton, NY; (Y); 1/5; Church Yth Grp; Drama Clb; Ski Clb; Concert Band; Socr; High Hon Roll; Ntl Merit Ltr; NY ST Regents Schlrshp 85; Bio.

GIGLIO, ANTHONY J; Sherburne-Earlville HS; Sherburne, NY; (Y); Trs Frsh Cls; Trs Soph Cls; VP Jr Cls; Rep Sr Cls; Hon Roll; Var Bsbl; Var Bsktbl; Geneseo; Bus Admn.

GIGLIO, JEANINE M; Mahopac HS; Mahopac, NY; (Y); 24/423; Am Leg Aux Girls St; Leo Clb; Political Wkr; Concert Band; Mrchg Band; Orch; Yrbk Stf; High Hon Roll; NHS; Advcd Sumr Stdy U Of Madrid Spn 84; Govt.

GIGLIOTTI, JENNI; Gates Chili HS; Rochester, NY; (Y); 6/464; Church Yth Grp; Exploring; JA; Service Clb; Ski Clb; Band; High Hon Roll; Hon Roll; NHS; NY ST Regents Schlrshp 85; U Of Rochester; Pre-Med.

GIGLIOTTI, SAMUEL S; Waterloo SR HS; Waterloo, NY; (Y); 1/200; Am Leg Boys St; Band; Concert Band; Jazz Band; Mrchg Band; Pres Frsh Cls; Pres Stu Cncl; Var Golf; High Hon Roll; NHS; Jzz Bnd Awd-Paul Shaffer Awd 85; Masons Essy Cntst Wnnr 85; Engrng.

GILADY, ELIZABETH I; Francis Lewis HS; Flushing, NY; (Y); 42/527; Cmnty Wkr; VP JA; Office Aide; Science Clb; Teachers Aide; Chorus; Nwsp Phtg; Nwsp Rptr; Cit Awd; High Hon Roll; Cert Of Hon Westinghouse Sci Talnt Srch 85; Citation Of Merit By Mayor 85; Nathan Quinones Roll Of Hnr; NY U; Jrnlsm.

GILBERT, CATHERINE H; Ellicottville Central HS; E Otto, NY; (Y); Bryant & Stratton; Bus.

GILBERT, DAVID; North Babylon SR HS; North Babylon, NY; (Y); Drama Clb; Concert Band; Mrchg Band; School Musical; School Play; Stage Crew; High Hon Roll; NHS; Med.

GILBERT, JAMES; Rocky Point JR SR HS; Rocky Point, NY; (S); 15/220; Ski Clb; Varsity Clb; Yrbk Stf; Var Capt Bsktbl; Golf; Hon Roll; All League Golf; Bus Mgmt.

GILBERT, KEVIN; G Ray Bodley HS; Fulton, NY; (Y); 130/256; JA; Hon Roll; Regens Dipplm 85; Sls Mgr.

GILBERT, LLOYD H; New Rochelle HS; New Rochelle, NY; (Y); Chess Clb; Var L Bsktbl; NHS; Ntl Merit Ltr; Spanish NHS; Johns Hopkins; Polt Sci.

GILBERT, MARTIN S; Hutchnson Central Technical HS; Buffalo, NY; (Y); 55/262; Regents Coll Schlrshp 85-89; ST U NY Buffalo; Elect Engrng.

GILBERT, MICHAEL; Immaculate Heart Central HS; Watertown, NY; (Y); 1/85; Quiz Bowl; JV Var Bsbl; JV Var Bsktbl; Cmnty Wkr; High Hon Roll; NHS; Val; Frontier Lg All Star Bsbl 85.

GILBERT, MICHAEL; St Josephs Collegiate Inst; Tonawanda, NY; (Y); 61/193; Church Yth Grp; Mathletes; Math Clb; Math Tm; Pep Clb; Ski Clb; Spanish Clb; Varsity Clb; Chorus; Nwsp Stf; MVP Bsbl Tm 83; Unsung Hero Awd Hcky 85; Mst Sprtd Awd Ftbl 84; Canisus Coll; Pre Law.

GILBERT, RICHARD S; Scarsdale HS; Scarsdale, NY; (Y); Cmnty Wkr; Ski Clb; Temple Yth Grp; Nwsp Phtg; Yrbk Phtg; JV Lcrss; Regents Schlrshp 85; Johns Hopkins U; Med.

GILBERT, SERENA C; Newburgh Free Acad; Newburgh, NY; (Y); Church Yth Grp; Drama Clb; Acpl Chr; School Play; High Hon Roll; Debate Tm; 4-H; Girl Scts; Pep Clb; Chorus; Dorthy C Gale Meml Schlrshp 85; Orange Cnty Ballet Theatre 79-85; Fnlst Miss United Teenager Pgnt 84; SUNY Purchase; Dance.

GILBERT, VICKI; Canaseraga Central HS; Canaseraga, NY; (Y); 6/24; Varsity Clb; Band; Chorus; Color Guard; Concert Band; Drm Mjr(t); Jazz Band; Mrchg Band; School Play; Swing Chorus; Athletic Awd For Most Athletic Female 85; Mary Kay Awd 85; Alfred ST; Floriculture Merch.

GILBERT, VICTORIA; Liverpool HS; Liverpool, NY; (S); 25/1000; Church Yth Grp; Exploring; Nwsp Phtg; Nwsp Rptr; JV Bsktbl; High Hon Roll; NHS; Chess Clb; Cmnty Wkr; Computer Clb; Adv & Art Awd 84; ROTC Schlrshp 84-85; Photgrphy & Drwng Awd 84; Cornell U; Arch.

GILBERTI, JIMMY; Holy Trinity HS; Uniondale, NY; (Y).

GILCHICK, STACEY; North Babylon Sr HS; North Babylon, NY; (Y); 18/592; Girl Scts; Intnl Clb; Yrbk Stf; Rep Jr Cls; Var Mgr(s); Pom Pon; French Hon Soc; High Hon Roll; Jr NHS; NHS; Acctg.

GILCHRIST, DEBORAH L; Vestal HS; Binghamton, NY; (Y); Ntl Merit Ltr; NY ST Regents Schlrshp 85; Comp.

GILDAY, JOSEPH F; Kingston HS; Kingston, NY; (Y); 50/511; Nwsp Rptr; Nwsp Stf; Lit Mag; French Hon Soc; High Hon Roll; Hon Roll; VP Jr NHS; NY ST Regnts Schlrshp 85; Siena Coll; Bio.

GILDE RUBIO, DAVID M; Sonderling HS; Bayshore, NY; (Y); 51/629; Spanish Clb; Band; Nwsp Stf; Socr; Trk; Hon Roll; NHS; Spnsh Awd 82; NYS Regnts Schlrshp 85; Hofstra U; Comms.

GILES, NANCY L; Vestal HS; Vestal, NY; (Y); 14/450; Sec Church Yth Grp; Drama Clb; Concert Band; School Play; Im Bsktbl; High Hon Roll; Masonic Awd; NHS; Ntl Merit Ltr; Dean Schlrshp Canisius College 85; Canisius Buffalo; Marketing.

GILHOOLY, CAROL; Mount Mercy Acad; Buffalo, NY; (Y); Art Clb; Church Yth Grp; Cmnty Wkr; 4-H; Red Cross Aide; Nwsp Stf; Yrbk Stf; Lit Mag; 4-H Awd; Hon Roll; Villa Maria Coll; Grphc Art.

GILHULEY, MICHAEL; Bethpage HS; Bethpage, NY; (Y); 44/290; Latin Clb; Spanish Clb; Im Crs Cntry; JV Var Ftbl; Var Ice Hcky; JV Var Lcrss; Hon Roll; Math.

GILL, EILEEN; Cathedral HS; Maspeth, NY; (Y); Art Clb; Bsktbl; Gym; Sftbl; Hon Roll; NHS; Pace U; Accntng.

GILL, KAREN; Chester HS; Chester, NY; (Y); Band; Color Guard; Mrchg Band; Yrbk Phtg; Yrbk Stf; Score Keeper; Jrnlsm.

GILL, KELLIE; Victor SR HS; Victor, NY; (Y); Church Yth Grp; Ski Clb; Band; Mrchg Band; Htl & Rest Mgt.

GILL, ROGER; Salesian HS; New Rochelle, NY; (Y); 3/90; Yrbk Stf; Pres Soph Cls; Trs VP Stu Cncl; Var Capt Bsbl; Var Bsktbl; High Hon Roll; NHS; Outstndng Bsbl Plyr-MVP 85; Math Awd 81-85; Knghts Of Pythias Awd 85; Manhattan Coll; Engrng.

GILL, SCOTT D; Starpoint Central HS; Sanborn, NY; (Y); 27/187; Computer Clb; Exploring; Math Tm; Varsity Clb; JV Var Bsbl; Im Bsktbl; Var Ftbl; Hon Roll; Jr NHS; U Of Buffalo; Aero Engr.

GILLAN, LAURA; Farming Dale HS; Farmingdale, NY; (Y); German Clb; Political Wkr; Drill Tm; Nwsp Bus Mgr; L Cheerleading; Jr NHS; St Schlr; Church Yth Grp; Dance Clb; Flag Corp; Wnnr US Cngrs W Grmn Bundestag Schlrshp 85; Pol Sci.

GILLARD, MARGUERITE; Smithtown High School West; Smithtown, NY; (Y); Spanish Clb; Sec Thesps; Chorus; School Play; Hon Roll; Spanish NHS; Acctng.

GILLEECE, FRANCIS; E L Vandermuelen HS; Pt Jefferson, NY; (Y); 70/300; FBLA; Latin Clb; Leo Clb; Ski Clb; Acpl Chr; Chorus; School Musical; School Play; Frsh Cls; JV Var Ftbl; Geo Washington U; Acctg.

GILLEN, COLLEEN; Frontier Central HS; Hamburg, NY; (Y); 90/540; Hosp Aide; Latin Clb; Office Aide; Pep Clb; VP Ski Clb; Stu Cncl; Swmmng; Tennis; Hon Roll; NHS; Pres Ftns Awd 85; St Bnvntr U.

GILLEN, GLEN E; St Anthonys HS; Pt Jeff Station, NY; (Y); French Clb; Stage Crew; Bowling; French Hon Soc; NHS; Duns Scotus Hnr Awd; NY U; Bus.

GILLEN, PATRICIA A; Stella Maris HS; Brooklyn, NY; (Y); Var Math Tm; JV Cheerleading; High Hon Roll; Hon Roll; Sec NHS; NY ST Regents Schlrshp 85; 1/2 Yr Schlrshp Of Free Tuition 83; BMT Holy Name Society Schlrshp 82; The Wood Schl; Bus.

GILLESPIE, ALLISON; The Mary Louis Acad; Flushing, NY; (Y); Church Yth Grp; Yrbk Stf; Acctng.

GILLESPIE, AUDREA; Christopher Columbus HS; Bronx, NY; (Y).

GILLESPIE, PATRICIA; Lindenhurst HS; Lindenhurst, NY; (Y); Girl Scts; Varsity Clb; Yrbk Stf; Stu Cncl; Capt Var Crs Cntry; Var Fld Hcky; Var Capt Trk; Hon Roll; Jr NHS; NHS; 2nd Pl Firemans Essay Awd 84-85; Pre-Med.

GILLESPIE, SHANNON MARY; Holy Trinity Diocesan HS; Westhemp, NY; (S); 3/302; Church Yth Grp; Drama Clb; Chorus; School Musical; School Play; High Hon Roll; Hon Roll; NEDT Awd; Iona Lang Competition 2nd Hnrs 84; NY ST Music Teachers Assoc Auditions 2nd Pl 84; Music.

GILLETT, DOROTHY; Midwood HS; Brooklyn, NY; (Y); Sci.

GILLETT, GLENN; Beach Channel HS; Glendale, NY; (Y); Aud/Vis; Boy Scts; Teachers Aide; Varsity Clb; Rep Stu Cncl; 4-H Awd; Var Crew Most Wins 84-85; Cert For Attndc 85; Htl Mgmt.

GILLETT, JOSEPH; Byron Bergen Central HS; S Byron, NY; (Y); Boy Scts; Church Yth Grp; Var Socr; Var Swmmng; Var Trk; NHS; Law.

GILLETT, MIKE; Plattsburgh HS; Plattsburgh, NY; (Y); JV Socr; Var Tennis; Comp Sci.

GILLETT, TERESA ANN; North Rose-Wolcott HS; Wolcott, NY; (Y); Pres FFA; GAA; VP Chorus; School Musical; Pres Stu Cncl; Capt Socr; JV Cit Awd; High Hon Roll; Hon Roll; Am Leg Aux Girls St; Sec V Cls A Bwlng Chmpn 82-83; SADD 84-85; Canton ATC; Vet Med.

GILLETTE, CARRIE M; Corning East HS; Corning, NY; (Y); Exploring; French Clb; Hosp Aide; Chorus; Drill Tm; High Hon Roll; Hon Roll; Natl Ldrshp & Svc Awds 85; Nrsng.

GILLETTE, GARY; Fillmore Central Schl; Fillmore, NY; (S); VP Computer Clb; Var Mgr(s); High Hon Roll; Hon Roll; NHS; Prfct Atten Awd; Olean Times Herald Outstndng Carrier For Allegany Cnty 85; Rgnl Hnr Carrier Of Jan 85.

GILLETTE, JACKIE; Susquehanna Valley HS; Conklin, NY; (Y); Nwsp Rptr; Nwsp Sprt Ed; Rep Frsh Cls; Trs Soph Cls; Trs Jr Cls; Rep Stu Cncl; JV Var Bsktbl; Var Fld Hcky; JV Var Sftbl; Trs Jr NHS; Pre-Med.

GILLETTE, STEPHEN; Ellenville Central Schl; Ellenville, NY; (Y); AFS; Spanish Clb; Variety Show; Yrbk Stf; Pres Frsh Cls; Rep Soph Cls; Rep Jr Cls; Rep Sr Cls; Stu Cncl; JV Var Bsbl; All Tri Cnty Puntr 84; Bus Mgmt.

GILLIG, LAURA; Mt Mercy Acad; Buffalo, NY; (Y); French Clb; JA; Off Jr Cls; VP Sr Cls; Im Vllybl; Hon Roll; Jr NHS; NHS; W NY Frgn Lang Fair 84 & 85; Aeros Engnrng.

GILLIGAN, MARYBETH; Glens Falls HS; Glen Falls, NY; (Y); 36/222; AFS; Band; Mrchg Band; Trs Jr Cls; Rep Stu Cncl; L Var Bsktbl; Capt Powder Puff Ftbl; High Hon Roll; Hon Roll; L Var Sftbl; Mbr Fthls All Star Sftbl Tm 84-85; Elem Ed.

GILLILAND, GREGG; Berlin Central HS; E Nassau, NY; (Y); Chorus; Stage Crew; Yrbk Stf; Stu Cncl; Bsktbl; Socr; Vllybl; Boy Scts; Teachers Aide; Wrstlng.

GILLIN, ELIZABETH; The Ursuline Schl; Scarsdale, NY; (Y); 27/129; Cmnty Wkr; Nwsp Rptr; Ed Yrbk Ed-Chief; Yrbk Stf; Stu Cncl; Var Fld Hcky; Var Trk; Cit Awd; Hon Roll; Jr NHS; Outstndng Ctzn Awd 84; Alumni Key Awd 85; Fairfield U; Engl.

GILLINGHAM, CONNIE; Unatego Central JR SR HS; Unadilla, NY; (Y); French Clb; Yrbk Stf; Lit Mag; High Hon Roll; John Tama Mem Awd 84; Navy Reserves.

GILLINGS, KAREN C; Schroon Lake Central Schl; Schroon Lake, NY; (S); 1/30; Cmnty Wkr; Model UN; Varsity Clb; Orch; School Musical; Variety Show; Trs Jr Cls; Rep Stu Cncl; Co-Capt Cheerleading; Socr; I Care Awd 82-84; Writer Of Mnth 84-85; Engl.

GILLMAN, MARTIN B; John F Kennedy HS; Plainview, NY; (Y); 49/275; Math Tm; Variety Show; Yrbk Stf; JV Var Bsktbl; Var Im Socr; Hon Roll; Am Leg Boys St; Im Sftbl; Im Vllybl; NYS Rgnts Schrlshp; SUNY Albany; Chriprctor.

GILLS, KAREN; Bishop Loughlin Memorial HS; Brooklyn, NY; (Y); Cheerleading; Crs Cntry; Trk; High Hon Roll; Hon Roll; Gld & Slvr L 82-83; Purple L 83-84; John Jay Coll; Law.

GILMAN, CATHY; Mount Assumption Inst; Plattsburgh, NY; (Y); Cmnty Wkr; Varsity Clb; Nwsp Stf; Yrbk Phtg; Yrbk Stf; JV Var Bsktbl; Ftbl; JV Mgr(s); Var Mgr(s); JV Score Keeper; Bio.

GILMAN, KURT; South Glens Falls SR HS; S Glens Falls, NY; (Y); 2/249; Am Leg Boys St; Boy Scts; Church Yth Grp; Key Clb; Ski Clb; Stu Cncl; High Hon Roll; NHS; Rensselaer Polytechnic Inst Math & Sci Awd 85; Outstdng Svc Awd 85; Aerosp Engr.

GILMAN, TIMOTHY; Kendall JR SR HS; Holley, NY; (Y); 4-H; FFA; Hon Roll; NHS; FFA Empire Dgr 85; Schltc Lttr & Bar 83-84; Alfred Coll; Anml Hsbndry.

GILMARTIN, ANNE M; Cardinal Spellman HS; Bronx, NY; (Y); Dance Clb; Twrlr; Hon Roll; NHS; Deans Scholarship Fordham U 85; Fordham U; Biology.

GILMARTIN, JAMES J; Holy Trinity HS; Bellmore, NY; (Y); 44/469; Pres Latin Clb; Pres Frsh Cls; Pres Soph Cls; Var Crs Cntry; Hon Roll; Regent Schlrshp 84; Baruch Cuny; Bus.

GILMORE, FATIMA H; Beach Charonel HS; Rockaway, NY; (Y); IN Tech U; Aerospc Engrng.

GILMORE JR, LOUIS D; Oswego HS; Oswego, NY; (Y); Aud/Vis; Church Yth Grp; JA; Library Aide; Soph Cls; Jr Cls; Crs Cntry; Tennis; Hon Roll; NEDT Awd.

GILMORE, MARY; Holy Trinity HS; Syosset, NY; (Y); JV Bsktbl; JV Sftbl; Hon Roll; Coachs Awd-Sftbl 84; Most Imprvd-Sftbl 85; Accntng.

GILMORE, RICK; Northern Adirondack Central HS; Ellenburg Ctr N, NY; (Y); Church Yth Grp; 4-H; FFA; Key Clb; JV Var Bsktbl; JV Var Socr; Hon Roll; Won 1st Ping Pong Tourn Schl 84.

GILMORE, SUSAN; Coxsackie-Athens HS; Earlton, NY; (Y); 16/94; Nwsp Rptr; Nwsp Stf; Yrbk Stf; Stu Cncl; High Hon Roll; Hon Roll; SUNY Cobleskill; Hotel Tech.

GILMOUR, TRICIA; Freeport HS; Freeport, NY; (Y); Cmnty Wkr; Key Clb; Ski Clb; Nwsp Rptr; Var Gym; JV Lcrss; Var Socr; Sec NHS; Phys Ther.

GILPIN, LAURICE; Cathedral HS; New York, NY; (Y); Computer Clb; Office Aide; Yrbk Stf; Lit Mag; VP Frsh Cls; Vllybl; Hon Roll; Jr NHS; NHS; Prfct Atten Awd; Vllybll 82-85; Hnr Rll 76-82; Natl Hnr Soc 83-85; Mercy; Comp Engnr.

GILREATH, JANICE; La Salle SR HS; Niagara Falls, NY; (S); 12/278; Debate Tm; Hon Roll; NHS; Spnsh.

GILROY, GAIL; St Vincent Ferrer HS; Glendale, NY; (Y); 17/115; Hosp Aide; Pep Clb; Chorus; Yrbk Stf; Rep Frsh Cls; Rep Soph Cls; Rep Jr Cls; Stu Cncl; Hon Roll; NEDT Awd; Hlth.

GILROY, JENNIFER M; St Francis Preparatory Schl; Glendale, NY; (Y); 209/690; Dance Clb; Spanish NHS; Pres Schlrshp St Francis Coll 85; Rgnts Schlrshp NY ST 85; St Francis Coll; Law.

GILSON, KRISTIN E; Hunter College HS; New York, NY; (Y); Math Clb; Y-Teens; Stage Crew; Var Vllybl; Mu Alp Tht; Trinity Coll.

GIMBRONE, BETH; Salamanca Central HS; Salamanca, NY; (S); 17/120; Band; Concert Band; Jazz Band; Mrchg Band; Pep Band; Bowling; High Hon Roll; Hon Roll; NHS; Spanish NHS; ST U Of NY Fredonia; Elem Edu.

GIMPEL, KATHLEEN; Earl L Vandermeulen HS; Pt Jefferson, NY; (Y); 15/287; Mathletes; Varsity Clb; Pres Sr Cls; Var JV Bsktbl; Var JV Fld Hcky; Var JV Sftbl; High Hon Roll; NHS; Hanger Awd Athlt Schlr Awd 85; Hstry.

GINGERICH, DEBRA; Indian River Central HS; Philadelphia, NY; (Y); 13/128; AFS; Chorus; School Musical; School Play; Yrbk Stf; Off Jr Cls; Stu Cncl; Cheerleading; Trk; Hon Roll; Area All ST Chrs 83-84; JR Hgh Bi-Cnty Chrs 83; SR Hgh Bi-Cnty Chrs 84; Math.

GINGOLD, MICHAEL K; Croton-Harmon HS; Croton-On-Hudson, NY; (Y); 5/104; Drama Clb; School Play; Nwsp Rptr; Nwsp Stf; Yrbk Stf; Lit Mag; L Crs Cntry; Hon Roll; NHS; Ntl Merit SF; Jr Gold Hnr Key; NY U; Filmmaking.

GINQUITTI, DONNA; Valley Central HS; Maybrook, NY; (Y); Office Aide; Hon Roll; Spanish NHS; Orange Cnty CC; Nrsg.

GINTER, WENDY; Northville Central HS; Northville, NY; (Y); 4-H; Library Aide; Rep Stu Cncl; NHS; Rdng Club VP 84-85; Med Explr 2nd VP 83-84.

GIOBBIE, ALBERT E; Monsignor Farrell HS; Staten Island, NY; (Y); 22/298; French Clb; Office Aide; Science Clb; Chorus; Im Bowling; High Hon Roll; Jr NHS; NHS; 2nd & 3rd Pl Ntl French Cntst 82-83; Boston U; Brdcstng.

GIOELI, JOSETTE; North Tionawanda SR HS; N Tonawanda, NY; (Y); 169/470; Drama Clb; Trs FBLA; JA; Spanish Clb; Varsity Clb; Rep Sr Cls; Rep Stu Cncl; Capt Bsktbl; Capt L Sftbl; AFS; Lcl Schlrshp Sthrlnd Ldge 85; Niagara U; Bus Mgmt.

GIOENI, LORA JEAN; Saint Edmund HS; Brooklyn, NY; (Y); 60/210; Hosp Aide; Church Choir; Var Bsktbl; JV Score Keeper; Var Sftbl; Var Vllybl; A Tunic & A Medex Ptch Coney Islnd Hosp 83; Hstry.

GIOIA, FRANCA; Grover Cleveland HS; Ridgewood, NY; (Y); 15/659; Key Clb; Band; Pres Sr Cls; Stu Cncl; Hon Roll; NYS Regents Schlrshp 85; SUNY Stony Brook; Pre-Med.

GIOIA, JEANINE; Nazareth Regional HS; Brooklyn, NY; (Y); 59/261; Drama Clb; Band; Hon Roll; Frnch I Cert; Hofstra U; Pre-Med.

GIOMENTO, SUZETTE; Jamestown HS; Jamestown, NY; (Y); Church Yth Grp; French Clb; Intnl Clb; JA; Band; Chorus; Concert Band; Mrchg Band; Hon Roll; Jr NHS; Lab Tech.

GIORANDINO, ANTHONY; H Frank Carey HS; Franklin Sq, NY; (Y); 70/222; Pres Science Clb; Band; Var Capt Lcrss; High Hon Roll; Hon Roll; Lit Mag; Nassau Industrl Arts Teachers Assn-2nd Pl 83-84; Adelphi; Bio.

GIORDANI, CHRISTINA; Copiague HS; Copiague, NY; (Y); Gym; Wlk Ethopia 85; Type A Thon Mrch Dimes 85; Farmingdale U; Sci.

GIORDANO, DOMINIC A; Mahopacc HS; Mahopac, NY; (Y); Office Aide; Stu Cncl; Var Bsbl; Socr; Wt Lftg; Pace U; Bus Mgmt.

GIORDANO, FRANK G; St Anthonys HS; Hauppauge, NY; (Y); Spanish Clb; JV Crs Cntry; Im Ftbl; Var Swmmng; JV Trk; Cit Awd; Hon Roll; Spanish NHS; Duns Scotus Acad Hnr 83-85; Fin.

GIORDANO, JOE; Earl L Vandermuellen HS; Mt Sinai, NY; (Y); Chess Clb; Cmnty Wkr; Math Tm; Band; Jazz Band; Nwsp Phtg; Yrbk Phtg; Bsbl; Ftbl; Hon Roll; NYSSMA-CLARINET Solo 83; Syracuse U; Engrng.

GIORDANO, JOSEPH H; Earl L Vandermeulen HS; Mt Sinai, NY; (Y); 63/257; Red Cross Aide; Band; Nwsp Phtg; Yrbk Phtg; Rep Frsh Cls; Bsbl; Ftbl; Chess Clb; High Hon Roll; Hon Roll; Syracuse U; Engrng.

GIORDANO, LILY; Great Neck South SR HS; New Hyde Park, NY; (Y); Church Yth Grp; Cmnty Wkr; Drama Clb; Chorus; School Musical; Ed Lit Mag; JV Vllybl; Sec Rotary Awd; French Clb; Mathletes; Gold Mdl Natl Lat Exam Amer Clsscl Leg/Natl JR Cls Lg 84; A Grade NY ST Schl Music Assn Vocl 85; Intl Rel.

GIORDANO, LOUIS; Lindenhurst HS; Lindenhurst, NY; (Y); 5/540; Debate Tm; Pres German Clb; Mathletes; Spanish Clb; Nwsp Stf; Var Tennis; Jr NHS; NHS; Mst Inprvd In Tennis; Frgn Lng Essay Cntst Wnr; Cornell U; Attorny.

GIORDANO, MICHELLE; La Salle SR HS; Niagara Falls, NY; (Y); Cmnty Wkr; Teachers Aide; Pres Stu Cncl; Var Bowling; Mgr(s); Var Sftbl; JV Trk; Cit Awd; Hon Roll; Lion Awd; Pnmnshp & Bst Drssd Awds 83; Vrsty Ltr & Pins 85; Bus.

GIORDANO, NANCY L; Beaver River Central HS; Beaver Falls, NY; (Y); 7/90; FBLA; Pres GAA; Band; Jazz Band; VP Pres Stu Cncl; Var Bsktbl; Var Trk; High Hon Roll; NHS; Var Tennis; U Of Rochester; Mech Engr.

GIORGIO, JEANNE M; Acad Of The Resrrctn; New Rochelle, NY; (Y); Yrbk Stf; Coach Actv; Sftbl; JV Var Vllybl; Hon Roll; Acctg.

GIORLANDINO, CARMELO; Abraham Lincoln HS; Brooklyn, NY; (Y); Chess Clb; Intnl Clb; Math Tm; Science Clb; Nwsp Ed-Chief; Nwsp Rptr; Nwsp Stf; Rep Jr Cls; Rep Sr Cls; High Hon Roll; Chem Engrng.

GIOVANNETTI, MARY BETH; Auburn HS; Auburn, NY; (Y); Church Yth Grp; Cmnty Wkr; Drm & Bgl; Sftbl; High Hon Roll; Hon Roll.

GIOVE, JENNY B; Smithtown HS East; Nesconset, NY; (Y); Yrbk Stf; Off Soph Cls; Off Jr Cls; Off Sr Cls; Cheerleading; Gym; Hon Roll.

GIOVO, RONALD; Mexico Acad; Mexico, NY; (Y); Boy Scts; Church Yth Grp; Spanish Clb; JV Var Bsbl; VFW Awd; BYU; Elec Engrng.

GIPPLE, MICHELLE; Williamsville South HS; Williamsville, NY; (Y); AFS; Sec French Clb; High Hon Roll; Hon Roll; Ntl Merit SF; Bus Mngmnt.

GIRAGE, DARI; Buffalo Sacred Heart Acad; Buffalo, NY; (Y); #40 In Class; Church Yth Grp; Service Clb; Spanish Clb; Chorus; Hon Roll; Dedictd Outstndg Svc Clb 84; Canisus; Psychlgy.

GIRALDEZ, DENISE; Minisink Valley HS; Westtown, NY; (Y); 2/234; Drama Clb; VP Band; Chorus; Drm Mjr(t); Sec Trs Stu Cncl; Var L Tennis; NHS; Sal; Voice Dem Awd; Minority Schlstc Achvt Awd 84; C W Post; Brdcstng.

GIRALDO, JOHN; Holy Cross HS; Bayside, NY; (Y); 8/326; Church Yth Grp; Service Clb; Nwsp Rptr; Var L Socr; Hon Roll; NHS; 1st Hnrs-Each Period 83-85; Schlr Of Yr Awd 83-85; Fr Awd-Hghst Avg 83-85; Engrng.

GIRALDO, MARIA I; Holy Trinity Diocesan HS; Plainview, NY; (Y); 115/362; French Clb; Chorus; School Musical; School Play; Stage Crew; Yrbk Stf; Im Bsktbl; Hon Roll; Natl Hnr Rll 84-85; Hofstra U; Med.

GIRARD, DAVID; Mexico HS; Oswego, NY; (Y); 9/189; Am Leg Boys St; Ski Clb; VP Chorus; Drm Mjr(t); School Musical; Variety Show; Pres Stu Cncl; Capt Trk; VP NHS; Clarkson U; Elec Engrng.

GIRARD, MICHELE; Mexico H S & Acad; Central Square, NY; (Y); German Clb; Ski Clb; JV Capt Bsktbl; JV Var Socr; Hon Roll; German Hnr Soc; Psych.

GIRARDI, JOSEPH; Mineola HS; Mineola, NY; (Y); Am Leg Boys St; VP Sr Cls; Var L Bsbl; Im Bsktbl; Im Fld Hcky; JV Var Ftbl; Im Wt Lftg; High Hon Roll; Hon Roll; Engrng.

GIRGENTI, DOUG; H Frank Carey HS; Franklin Sq, NY; (Y); #6 In Class; Boy Scts; Var Socr; JV Wrstlng; High Hon Roll; Jr NHS; NHS; Spanish NHS; Voice Dem Awd; Brown U Bk Awd 85; Tlntd & Gftd Prog 83-85; Comp Prgrmg.

GIRGENTI, PATRICK; Franklin D Roosevelt HS; Brooklyn, NY; (Y); Chorus; Swmmng; Hon Roll; Marine Bio.

GIRMUS, ANNETTE; Cato Meridian HS; Cato, NY; (Y); Drama Clb; French Clb; GAA; Girl Scts; Ski Clb; Band; Chorus; Concert Band; Jazz Band; School Play; Law.

GIRONDA, SUZANNE; Westlake HS; Hawthorne, NY; (Y); Drama Clb; English Clb; French Clb; Science Clb; School Musical; School Play; Stage Crew; Trk; AFS; Library Aide; Elem Ed.

GIROUX, THOMAS J; Trinity-Pawling Schl; Wapp Fls, NY; (Y); 3/87; Church Yth Grp; Computer Clb; French Clb; Quiz Bowl; Nwsp Stf; Rep Frsh Cls; Rep Jr Cls; Var L Bsbl; Var L Bsktbl; Var L Socr; Twn Wappngr Sr Lge All Star Tm 83; Elec Engrng.

GIRRBACH, BONNIE; Jeffersonvle-Youngsvle Cntrl HS; Kenoza Lake, NY; (S); 4/58; Church Yth Grp; Church Choir; Socr; Trk; High Hon Roll; Sec NHS; Sal; Busi Admin.

GIRSKY, JEFF O; Half Hollow Hills H S East; Dix Hills, NY; (Y); Debate Tm; Drama Clb; Pres Political Wkr; Speech Tm; School Play; Nwsp Rptr; VP Sr Cls; Crs Cntry; Ftbl; Capt Lcrss; 1st Pl Intl Dance, Lang Fair 85; Intern To 2 Cngrssmn 85; Clark; Law.

GIRVEN, KENNETH; Lincoln HS; Yonkers, NY; (S); 20/400; Art Clb; Nwsp Phtg; Nwsp Rptr; Nwsp Stf; Yrbk Phtg; Yrbk Rptr; Yrbk Stf; Badmtn; Hon Roll; Acadmc Achvt Awd Schlstc 83-84; Fordham U; Law.

GIRVIN, DAVID C; East Aurora HS; East Aurora, NY; (Y); 50/182; Pres Church Yth Grp; Key Clb; Varsity Clb; L Band; Jazz Band; Mrchg Band; Pep Band; L Ftbl; Var Ice Hcky; L Wrstlng; SUNY-OSWEGO.

GISEL, KAREN; Maryvale HS; Cheektowaga, NY; (Y); Church Yth Grp; Cmnty Wkr; Dance Clb; Office Aide; Chorus; School Musical; Jr Cls; Cheerleading; Hon Roll; NHS.

GISIANO, JOHN D; Roy C Ketcham HS; Wapp Fls, NY; (Y); Var Coach Actv; Var Capt Socr; Proj Advntr 82-83; Ntl Latn Cntst 3rd Pl 81-84; Sci Smnr Prog 84-85; Ind Engr.

GISONDA, ANGELINA; Our Lady Of Perpetual Help HS; Brooklyn, NY; (Y); Art Clb; Stage Crew; JV Vllybl; High Hon Roll; Italian Regents 85; Siology Regents 83; Vet.

GITTLITZ, LEAH; Spring Valley SR HS; Spring Valley, NY; (Y); Cmnty Wkr; Math Tm; Pres Temple Yth Grp; Thesps; Mrchg Band; Nwsp Ed-Chief; Var Twrlr; High Hon Roll; Mu Alp Tht; NHS; Outstndng Svc Theater Arts 84-85; Bio.

GIUFFRIDA, LISA ANNE; Corning East HS; Corning, NY; (Y); 17/250; Drama Clb; Sec Radio Clb; Pres Spanish Clb; Thesps; Chorus; Trs Sr Cls; Cheerleading; Capt Crs Cntry; Trk; NHS; Regents Scholar 84-85; Edward C Schneider Mem Awd 85; Mth Hnrs Gold Cord 85; Corning CC; Lib Arts.

GIUFFRIDA, MICHELLE L; East HS; Corning, NY; (Y); Drama Clb; Thesps; Varsity Clb; School Musical; Yrbk Stf; Cheerleading; Tennis; High Hon Roll; NHS; French Clb; Tnns Ltrs & Bars.

GIUGLIANO, VIRGINIA; Mynderse Acad; Seneca Falls, NY; (Y); 1/129; Am Leg Aux Girls St; Pres Model UN; Chorus; Concert Band; Drm Mjr(t); Jazz Band; Mrchg Band; School Musical; Bausch & Lomb Sci Awd; JP Sousa Awd; Internshp W/Assblymn Michael F Nozzolio 84-85; Mbr Sound Of Amer Hnr Band 85; Union Coll; Med.

GIULIANI, FRANCA; Moore Catholic HS; Staten Island, NY; (Y); Art Clb; Drama Clb; Chorus; School Musical; School Play; Rep Soph Cls; Rep Jr Cls; Rep Sr Cls; Rep Stu Cncl; NHS; Fash Desgn.

GIUNTA, JOANNE; Marlboro Central HS; Marlboro, NY; (Y); VP Camera Clb; Church Yth Grp; Cmnty Wkr; 4-H; FTA; Nwsp Phtg; Nwsp Stf; Score Keeper; Timer; 4-H Awd; Dutchess CC; Tchr.

GIURA, MARIA; Bishop Kearney HS; Brooklyn, NY; (S); Camera Clb; FTA; Ski Clb; Nwsp Rptr; High Hon Roll; Sec FTA Clb; Hnrbl Mntn Awd Merit Cert Poerty; SAV Prg; Tchr.

GIVENS, CHRISTINE; Sacred Heart Acad; Westbury, NY; (Y); 54/196; Civic Clb; Dance Clb; Debate Tm; French Clb; NFL; Speech Tm; Lit Mag; Hon Roll; NHS; Ntl Hgh Hnr Rll 84; Spelman Coll Acadmc Schlrshp 85; Spelman Coll; Lbrl Arts.

GIVENS, COURTNEY BROOKE; Elmira Free Acad; Elmira, NY; (Y); 57/254; Church Yth Grp; VP Library Aide; Y-Teens; Nwsp Rptr; Frsh Cls; Trs Soph Cls; Trs Jr Cls; Cheerleading; Trk; High Hon Roll; Bk Schlrshp Cosmopolitan Women & NAACP 85; Wells Coll; Pol Sci.

GIVENS, TANYA; Cathedral HS; Ny, NY; (Y); Church Yth Grp; Cmnty Wkr; Exploring; Library Aide; Office Aide; Teachers Aide; School Play; Cit Awd; Temple U.

GJELAJ, GEORGE; Cardinal Spellman HS; Bronx, NY; (Y); High Hon Roll; Hon Roll; Fordham U; Fnc.

GJURICH, STEVEN; Frontier HS; Blasdell, NY; (Y); 46/525; Sec Drama Clb; JA; Latin Clb; Church Yth Grp; Dance Clb; Ski Clb; Concert Band; Crs Cntry; Hon Roll; NHS; Canisius Coll Grant 85-86; Canisius Coll; Mrktng.

GLACY, KURT; South Glens Falls SR HS; S Glens Falls, NY; (Y); Aud/Vis; Church Yth Grp; Key Clb; Chorus; Church Choir; Variety Show; High Hon Roll; Hon Roll; Pres NHS; Bus.

GLADITSCH, AUDREY; H Frank Carey HS; Franklin Sq, NY; (Y); 23/250; Dance Clb; French Clb; High Hon Roll; Hon Roll; NHS; Frgn Lang Hnr Soc 84-85; Bus.

GLANTZ, KARYNN; Corning Painted Post West HS; Painted Post, NY; (Y); 70/246; Drama Clb; Pres Ski Clb; Sec Temple Yth Grp; Thesps; Varsity Clb; Band; Concert Band; School Musical; School Play; Stage Crew; Best Thespian; Holfstra U; Marketing.

GLANZEL, LYNN; Avon Central HS; Avon, NY; (Y); JV Sftbl; JV Vllybl; Hon Roll; Jr NHS; Banking.

GLASCO, CASAUNDRA; Edison Vo Tech; Rochester, NY; (Y); Church Yth Grp; Office Aide; Church Choir; JV Var Cheerleading; Hon Roll; Prfct Atten Awd; Comp Prgrmng.

GLASCOCK, AARON F; Northeastern Clinton Central Schl; Mooers Forks, NY; (Y); 4/146; High Hon Roll; NHS; Ntl Merit Ltr; Pres Schlr; Regnts Schlrshp NY 85; Plattsburgh ST U; Comp Sci.

GLASER, LAUREN; Christopher Columbus HS; Bronx, NY; (S); 18/792; Concert Band; Lit Mag; High Hon Roll; Jr NHS; NHS; Spanish NHS; Office Aide; Teachers Aide; Temple Yth Grp; School Musical; Adv Span 85; Engl 84; Globl Hstry 83; Amer Hstry 85; Pre Law.

GLASER, ROBERT; Columbus HS; Bronx, NY; (Y); Prfct Atten Awd; Sci Awd Hgst Cls 83; Soc Studies Awd 84; Math Awd 84; John Jay.

GLASGOW, WAYNE A; Archbishop Molloy HS; Rosedale, NY; (Y); 172/371; Church Yth Grp; Intnl Clb; Stage Crew; JV Crs Cntry; Im Ftbl; JV Sftbl; JV Trk; Hon Roll; Ntl Merit Schol; Comp Sci.

GLASS, ALLISON; Centereach HS; Centereach, NY; (Y); 35/475; Math Tm; Temple Yth Grp; Variety Show; Stat Bsktbl; Var Crs Cntry; Var Trk; Wt Lftg; Hon Roll; Prfct Atten Awd; Regents Schlrshp 85; Suny At Stonybrook; Med.

GLASS, DEBRA; Waterford-Halfmoon HS; Waterford, NY; (Y); 9/83; Dance Clb; Math Clb; Chorus; Yrbk Stf; Var Fld Hcky; High Hon Roll; VP NHS; Church Yth Grp; French Clb; Lit Mag; Skidmore Coll Acad Achvmnt Awd 84; Englsh.

GLASS, EVAN R; Glen Cove HS; Glen Cove, NY; (Y); 16/270; Nwsp Phtg; Rep Stu Cncl; Var Lcrss; Var Socr; Hon Roll; NHS; Ntl Merit Ltr; Tufts U.

GLASS, JESSICA K; Nightingale-Bamford HS; New York, NY; (Y); Model UN; Mgr Chorus; Nwsp Phtg; Nwsp Rptr; Yrbk Phtg; Yrbk Stf; Ed Lit Mag; Var Socr; Var Sftbl; Var Vllybl; Wesleyan U; Fine Arts.

GLASS, JOSEPH; Skaneateles Central HS; Skaneateles, NY; (S); Model UN; Band; Jazz Band; Orch; Pep Band; Socr; L Tennis; Cit Awd; High Hon Roll; NHS; Sci.

GLASS, MATTHEW; Patchogue-Medford HS; Patchogue, NY; (Y); 61/708; Am Leg Boys St; Drama Clb; Band; Concert Band; Mrchg Band; School Musical; School Play; Rep Stu Cncl; Capt Socr; Var Capt Tennis; Faculty Awd 83.

GLASSER, AMY; Sachem High Schl North; Lk Ronkonkoma, NY; (Y); 223/1400; Cmnty Wkr; Girl Scts; Science Clb; Ski Clb; Spanish Clb; Temple Yth Grp; Band; Sci Hnrs 82-84; NYSMA Awd 83.

GLASSFORD, KIM; Alexander Hamilton HS; Elmsford, NY; (S); 6/54; Sec VP Key Clb; Yrbk Stf; Rep Soph Cls; Sec Trs Stu Cncl; Var Capt Cheerleading; Var Sftbl; High Hon Roll; Hon Roll; Rotary Awd; Bus Educ Awd 84; Fairfield U; Nrs.

GLASSFORD, MIMI; Alexander Hamilton HS; Elmsford, NY; (S); 3/50; Key Clb; Yrbk Stf; Rep Soph Cls; Rep Jr Cls; JV Var Cheerleading; Var Sftbl; High Hon Roll; Rotary Awd; Sci.

GLATZ, CHRISTINE; Rensselaer HS; Rensselaer, NY; (S); Hst DECA; Key Clb; Math Tm; Varsity Clb; Rep Stu Cncl; Var Fld Hcky; JV Sftbl; Capt JV Vllybl; NHS; Siena Coll; Comp Sci.

GLAVAS, HARITINI; Gates-Chili HS; Rochester, NY; (Y); Church Yth Grp; Sec Exploring; French Clb; JA; Model UN; Office Aide; Yrbk Phtg; Yrbk Stf; High Hon Roll; Hon Roll; Comp.

GLAVIN, HELENE E; Keveny Memorial Acad; Waterford, NY; (S); #1 In Class; Girl Scts; Bsktbl; Sftbl; Vllybl; High Hon Roll; Acdmc All-Amer 84; Amer H S Athlt 85; Albany Cnty Lgsltv Intrn 84-85; Educ.

GLAVIN, KATHLEEN A; Maple Hill HS; Castleton, NY; (Y); 14/94; Exploring; French Clb; Math Tm; Yrbk Ed-Chief; Rep Stu Cncl; Co-Capt L Crs Cntry; Var L Trk; Var JV Vllybl; Hon Roll; St Schlr; Albany Coll Pharm; Pharm.

GLAZIER, CHRIS; Whitney Point HS; Whitney Pt, NY; (Y); Boy Scts; French Clb; Ski Clb; Church Choir; Off Soph Cls; Crs Cntry; Socr; Trk; Syracuse U; Sci.

GLAZIER, DANIEL; Sandy Creek Central HS; Lacona, NY; (Y); 31/110; Church Yth Grp; Drama Clb; Band; Chorus; Church Choir; Concert Band; Jazz Band; Mrchg Band; School Musical; Variety Show; Grd 6 Vocl Solo-Prfct Score 85; Hnr Soc Tlnt Shw-1st Pl 85; VFW Voice Of Demcrcy Cntst-2nd Pl 84; Canton ATC; Mortry Sci.

GLAZIER, LAURA; Franklin Acad; Malone, NY; (Y); French Clb; Ski Clb; Nwsp Rptr; Ed Yrbk Stf; Rep Stu Cncl; Hon Roll; NHS; Bus Exec.

GLEASON, BETH; Waterloo SR HS; Waterloo, NY; (Y); 11/178; Pres VP Exploring; Stat Wrstlng; Hon Roll; NHS; Voice Dem Awd; Ella M B Pease Schlrshp 85; Mbr Finger Lks Cncl Cub Sct Day Cmp Stff 85; Daemen Coll; Phy Thrpy.

GLEASON II, CHARLES F; Oneonta SR HS; Oneonta, NY; (S); Art Clb; Nwsp Stf; Yrbk Stf; ST Awd Hghst Avg SR Gen Biol Cls 84; Cartoon Art.

GLEASON, CHERYL; Newfield HS; Port Jeff Sta, NY; (Y); 179/542; Hosp Aide; Service Clb; Ski Clb; VICA; Hon Roll; Kathleen Reilly Mem Awd 85; Pres Awd; Suffolk CC; Nrsng.

GLEASON, DEBRA; Cuba Cenral Schl; Cuba, NY; (Y); Ski Clb; Band; Chorus; Concert Band; Yrbk Stf; Golf; Score Keeper; Sftbl; High Hon Roll; Hon Roll; All County Band; Jamestown CC; Acctng.

GLEASON, JAMES; Horsehead SR HS; Horseheads, NY; (Y); 1/400; German Clb; Natl Beta Clb; Var Tennis; Hon Roll; Pres NHS; Gld Mdl NY ST Sci Olympd 85; Rensselaer Sci Awd 85; Magna Cun Laude Ntl Latn Exm 83; Engnrng.

GLEASON, JEFF; Thomas A Edison HS; Elmira Hts, NY; (Y); Computer Clb; Drama Clb; French Clb; Band; Mrchg Band; School Play; JV Bsbl; JV Var Bsktbl; JV Ftbl; Hon Roll; De Vry Inst Of Tech; Comptr Pgm.

GLEASON, KAREN; Brentwood HS; Brentwood, NY; (Y); 16/625; Chorus; Concert Band; Orch; School Musical; Hon Roll; JP Sousa Awd; VP NHS; Ntl Merit SF; Regents Schrlshp 85; Hallmrk Music Awd 85; Regents Sci Hnrs Dip 85; Kings Coll; Music.

GLEASON, SUSAN M; Ravena Coeymans Selkirk HS; Glenmont, NY; (Y); 2/200; Church Yth Grp; Pres Key Clb; Yrbk Ed-Chief; Rptr Lit Mag; Capt Var Tennis; DAR Awd; Elks Awd; NHS; Ntl Merit Ltr; Sal; Colgate Mem Schlrshp 85; NY ST Rgnts Schlrshp 85; Colgate U; Doctor.

GLEASON, TAMMY; Granville Central Schl; Granville, NY; (S); 13/122; Math Tm; Yrbk Phtg; Hon Roll; Math.

GLEBA, MICHAEL C; Bronx High School Of Science; Bronx, NY; (Y).

GLEBA, SCOTT J; Cardinal Spellman HS; Bronx, NY; (Y); Church Yth Grp; JV L Bsktbl; Var L Socr; Hon Roll; ST U NY Buffalo.

GLEISSNER, ROBERT; Wantagh HS; Wantagh, NY; (Y); Boy Scts; Computer Clb; Mathletes; Ski Clb; Silver Math Awd 84; Best HS Math Awd 84; Comp Sci.

GLEN, BENILDA V; Clara Barton HS; Brooklyn, NY; (Y); 46/469; Church Yth Grp; Dance Clb; Drama Clb; Girl Scts; Office Aide; Teachers Aide; Church Choir; Yrbk Stf; Rep Frsh Cls; Hon Roll; UCLA; Pedtrcn.

GLENN, NICOLE; Adlai E Stevenson HS; Bronx, NY; (Y); Cmnty Wkr; Dance Clb; Political Wkr; Band; Concert Band; Nwsp Stf; Spec Hnr & Rec For ST Wd Mock Trial Partcptn Awd 85; Merit Outstndng Achvt Spnsh 85; Law.

GLENNON, ANDREW L; Mac Arthur HS; Wantagh, NY; (Y); 8/319; Computer Clb; Socr; Tennis; Hon Roll; NHS; Regnts Schlrshp 85; Engr.

GLEUSSNER, MARGARET; Morris Central Schl; Morris, NY; (Y); 2/37; Ski Clb; Rep Stu Cncl; Vllybl; Cit Awd; High Hon Roll; NHS; Sal; Am Leg Aux Girls St; Drama Clb; German Clb; Wshngtn Cngrsnl Wrkshps 85; Rotary Schlrshp; Scty Of Myflwr Dscntnts Ed Awd; St Bonaventure U; Pre-Law.

GLICK, TRIESHA J; Pine Bush HS; Middletown, NY; (Y); 8/289; Chorus; Capt Drill Tm; School Musical; School Play; Stage Crew; Variety Show; Pom Pon; Powder Puff Ftbl; High Hon Roll; Hon Roll; Hofstra U.

GLICKMAN, AMY; Southside HS; Rockville Ctr, NY; (Y); 141/320; Computer Clb; Debate Tm; Drama Clb; Latin Clb; Science Clb; Spanish Clb; Pres VP Temple Yth Grp; Band; Cit Awd; Hon Roll; Psych.

GLICKMAN, DAVID; Yeshiua University HS For Boys; Flushing, NY; (Y); 37/110; Math Tm; Band; Yrbk Phtg; Yrbk Stf; Sftbl; Wrstlng; Yeshiva U; Bio.

GLICKMAN, JENNIFER; Packer Collegiate Inst; Brooklyn, NY; (Y); Church Yth Grp; Dance Clb; Drama Clb; Temple Yth Grp; Thesps; School Musical; School Play; Stage Crew; Lit Mag; Off Frsh Cls; NY ST Smr Schl Of Arts For Theatre 84; Enl Spkng Union Semi Fnlst 84; Psychology.

GLICKMAN, MARK M; Half Hollow Hills HS; Melville, NY; (Y); 2/548; Quiz Bowl; Service Clb; Nwsp Stf; Lit Mag; Capt Crs Cntry; Var Trk; High Hon Roll; NHS; Ntl Merit SF; Sal; Brown U Book Awd 84; Adelphi U Lang Awd Spanish 84; 1st Pl Schl Suffolk Cty Math 82; Math.

GLIDDEN, AMY; Thomas A Edison HS; Elmira Hts, NY; (Y); Church Yth Grp; Dance Clb; French Clb; Quiz Bowl; Color Guard; VP Jr Cls; Rep Stu Cncl; Bsbl; High Hon Roll; Hon Roll; RIT; Engnrng.

GLIDDEN, SUSAN; Hugh C Williams HS; Canton, NY; (Y); Chorus; Orch; Sec Frsh Cls; Sec Soph Cls; VP Jr Cls; Pres Sr Cls; Im Lcrss; JV Var Socr; High Hon Roll; NHS.

GLINKA, DARRA; Roy C Ketcham HS; Poughkeepsie, NY; (Y); Church Yth Grp; Band; Chorus; JV Bsktbl; Trk; Cit Awd; Dutchess CC; Engrng.

GLITCH, CHERYL; Victor Central HS; Victor, NY; (Y); Varsity Clb; VP Soph Cls; Rep Stu Cncl; Var Bsktbl; Var Socr; JV Sftbl; Var Trk; Cit Awd; Hon Roll.

GLOAK, GEOFFREY T; Keveny Memorial Acad; Waterford, NY; (S); 1/37; Drama Clb; Band; Concert Band; Jazz Band; Mrchg Band; School Play; VP Jr Cls; High Hon Roll; Ntl Merit Ltr; Val; RPI Math & Sci Awds 84; Marlboro Coll; Envir Sci.

GLOBENFELT, SARAH; Garden City HS; Garden City, NY; (Y); 55/320; Dance Clb; Concert Band; Jazz Band; Mrchg Band; Variety Show; High Hon Roll; Jr NHS; Exploring; French Clb; Mathletes; Hnry Mntn Adelphi Frnch Poet Cntst 84; Outstndg Ntl Hnr Soc 82; Regnts Schlrshp 85; U Of S CA; Bus.

GLODOWSKI, PAUL; Farmingdale HS; N Massapequa, NY; (Y); Boy Scts; Dance Clb; FBLA; JA; Mathletes; Model UN; Pres Spanish Clb; Chorus; Color Guard; School Musical; UCLA; Bus Adm.

GLOGOWSKI, KIMBERLY A; Hamburg Senior High; Hamburg, NY; (Y); 33/406; Girl Scts; Hosp Aide; Band; Cheerleading; Mgr(s); Hon Roll; Regents Schlrshp 85; Pharm.

GLOMSKI, MATTHEW J; Amhurst Central HS; Amherst, NY; (Y); 13/310; Math Tm; Pres Quiz Bowl; Btty Crckr Awd; High Hon Roll; Hon Roll; NHS; Aud/Vis; Boy Scts; Debate Tm; French Clb; Euchre Clb Of Amer 85; Mbr Hnr Petition Clb 85; Cliff Diving Clb 84; Columbia Coll; Physics.

GLOVER, HOLLY; Alexander HS; Alexander, NY; (Y); Band; Concert Band; Mrchg Band; JV Var Cheerleading; Genesee CC; Travl & Toursm.

GLOW, KATHLEEN; Morrisville-Eaton Central Schl; Morrisville, NY; (Y); 11/60; 4-H; GAA; Math Tm; Band; Chorus; Concert Band; Mrchg Band; JV Bsktbl; Var Cheerleading; Var Crs Cntry; Fashn Dsgn.

GLOW, RONALD H; North Collins Central HS; Lawtons, NY; (Y); 13/74; Church Yth Grp; Drama Clb; Band; Chorus; Church Choir; Concert Band; Mrchg Band; School Musical; School Play; Nwsp Ed-Chief; Regents Schlrshp 85; Fredonia; Theatre Arts.

GLOWACKI II, MICHAEL J; Weedsport JR SR HS; Weedsport, NY; (Y); 3/65; Yrbk Stf; Pres Frsh Cls; Pres Soph Cls; Pres Jr Cls; Pres Sr Cls; Var Bsbl; JP Sousa Awd; Lion Awd; Cmnty Wkr; Math Clb; Hugh O Brien Intl Ambssdr 83; Congrssnl Mdl Merit 85; Union Coll; Pre-Med.

GLOWNY, LISA M; M-Dunt Mercy Acad; Buffalo, NY; (Y); Church Yth Grp; Computer Clb; French Clb; Hosp Aide; Model UN; Church Choir; Nwsp Stf; Rep Stu Cncl; Im Bowling; Math Clb; NYS Regents Scshlrshp 85; U NY Buffalo; Comp Pgm.

GLUCK, LORI; Jericho HS; Syosset, NY; (Y); Varsity Clb; Band; Trs Jr Cls; Sec Sr Cls; Var Capt Socr; Var JV Sftbl; JV Trk; JV Vllybl; Hon Roll; Spanish NHS; MVP & All Leag Sccr JR; Long Isl Selct Sccr Tm.

GLYNN, DONNA; Stella Maris HS; Rockaway Point, NY; (Y); Church Yth Grp; Math Tm; Pep Clb; Chorus; Yrbk Stf; VP Frsh Cls; Pres Soph Cls; Coach Actv; Accntng.

GLYNN, PATRICIA E; Nardin Acad; Lewiston, NY; (Y); Hosp Aide; Chorus; Nwsp Rptr; Nwsp Stf; Ed Lit Mag; Rep Stu Cncl; Hon Roll; NYS Regnts Schlrshp 85; Niagara U; Engl.

GOATSEAY, DENISE; Cardinal O Hara HS; Tonawanda, NY; (S); 2/140; Art Clb; Girl Scts; Color Guard; Drm & Bgl; Mrchg Band; Stage Crew; Im Badmtn; Im Bowling; High Hon Roll; Hon Roll; 1st & 2nd Hnrs; SUNY Geneseo; Acctng.

GOBLE, PATRICIA ANNE; Middletown HS; Middletown, NY; (Y); 25/369; Hon Roll; NY ST Regnts Schlrshp 85; Ag & Tech Coll; Vet.

GOCHA, ANTHONY S; Riverhead HS; Riverhead, NY; (Y); 19/204; Acpl Chr; Drm & Bgl; Orch; School Musical; School Play; NHS; Pres Schlr; Aud/Vis; Drama Clb; German Clb; Amer Choral Dirctrs Awd; NYSSMA All ST Band; Craig Hallock Mem Scholar; Crane Schl Music; Music Ed.

GODBOUT, KATHLEEN; Seton Catholic Central HS; Johnson City, NY; (Y); 12/152; Church Yth Grp; GAA; Key Clb; Var L Bsktbl; Var L Socr; Var L Sftbl; High Hon Roll; Trs NHS; Prfct Atten Awd; Natl Schlrshp Athl Awd 85; Sftbl All Str 83-85; Sccr All Str 85; Regnts Hnrs 85; Le Moyne Coll.

GODDARD, LAUREEN A; East Islip HS; Islip Terrace, NY; (Y); 21/475; Art Clb; Computer Clb; Math Tm; Band; Concert Band; Mrchg Band; Orch; Pep Band; School Play; Nwsp Stf; Awds Sci Fair; Phy Ftnss Awds; Pre Med.

GODDEAU, REBECCA; Saranac Central HS; Morrisonville, NY; (Y); French Clb; Yrbk Stf; Sec Frsh Cls; Sec Soph Cls; Sec Jr Cls; JV Var Socr; Hon Roll; Clinton CC; Nrsng.

GODFREY, DONALD; Candor HS; Candor, NY; (Y); 17/88; Aud/Vis; Varsity Clb; Var L Bsbl; Var Capt Ftbl; Rotary Awd; US Navy; Air Traf Ctrl.

GODFREY, RICHARD; Francis Lewis HS; Northport, FL; (Y); Art Clb; Church Yth Grp; Cmnty Wkr; Computer Clb; Debate Tm; DECA; Lit Mag; Rep Stu Cncl; Var Bsktbl; Cit Awd; Acadmc Excllnce Consumer Law 85; Air Force; Law.

GODFRYD, DEBORAH; Kenmore West HS; Tonawanda, NY; (Y); CAP; Debate Tm; JA; Political Wkr; Thesps; Color Guard; Stage Crew; High Hon Roll; Cert Achvt Outstndng Perfrmnc Mth Exam 85; Excllnt Atten Awds 82-84; Law.

GODLEWSKI, CHRIS S; Au Sable Valley Central HS; Au Sable Forks, NY; (Y); 5/128; Church Yth Grp; Key Clb; Model UN; Ski Clb; Band; Jazz Band; School Play; Variety Show; VP Jr Cls; Trs Stu Cncl; Regents Scholarshp; Union College; Pre Med.

GODOY, PEDRO; Mcc Kee Technical HS; Staten Island, NY; (Y); 7/286; Rep Soph Cls; Rep Stu Cncl; Cit Awd; High Hon Roll; Hon Roll; NHS; Supr Yth Awd 84; Seagl Soc Mc Kee 85; Arch Engrng.

GODSIL, ELIZABETH; Bishop Grimes HS; Syracuse, NY; (Y); Exploring; FBLA; Girl Scts; JA; Ski Clb; Variety Show; Rep Jr Cls; Timer; Trk; Hon Roll; Higst Awd Girl Scouting Gold Awd 84; Mt Olive Coll; Bus Mgmt.

GOEBEL, DONNA; Warwick Valley HS; Warwick, NY; (Y); 10/205; French Clb; Pres Band; Concert Band; Drm Mjr(t); Jazz Band; Symp Band; Trk; High Hon Roll; Sec NHS; Amer Muscl Fndtn Band Hnrs 85; Natl Sec Educ Cncl Acadmc All Amer 85.

GOEBEL, HOWARD; Broadalbin Central HS; Gloversville, NY; (Y); 7/63; Drama Clb; Letterman Clb; Spanish Clb; Varsity Clb; Mrchg Band; Pep Band; School Play; Var L Bsktbl; Var L Ftbl; Pres Schlr; Advncd Comp Math Course-Ithaca Coll 84; FMCC Presidents Schlrshp 85; Fulton-Montgomery CC; Engr.

GOECKEL, KELLY; Williamsville North HS; E Amherst, NY; (S); Church Yth Grp; DECA; Off Drama Clb; Girl Scts; Teachers Aide; Chorus; School Musical; Off Jr Cls; Off Stu Cncl; JV Socr; Bus.

GOEI, WALTER; Pelham Memorial HS; Pelham, NY; (Y); Band; Concert Band; Jazz Band; Mrchg Band; Pep Band; VP Frsh Cls; JV Socr; 2nd Pl Greenbelt Forms Div-All Amer Open 85; Karate, Kung Fu, Taekwon Do Chmpnshps 85; Embry-Riddle; Aeronaut.

GOELLER, DEIRDRE; Palmyra-Macedon HS; Macedon, NY; (Y); Church Yth Grp; Ski Clb; Chorus; School Play; JV Socr; Var Trk; Med.

GOETCHIUS, KAREN; Faith Heritage Schl; Jamesville, NY; (Y); 1/27; Church Yth Grp; Drama Clb; Ski Clb; School Play; Nwsp Stf; Off Soph Cls; VP Stu Cncl; Var L Trk; NHS; Elem Ed.

GOETHERT, CHRIS; Rome Free Acad; Rome, NY; (Y); 25/500; Art Clb; Intnl Clb; Ski Clb; Var Socr; Var Tennis; Hon Roll; NHS; Ntl Merit SF; Chess Clb; Church Yth Grp; Poly Sci.

GOETTEL, MICHAEL; Vestal HS; Vestal, NY; (Y); Church Yth Grp; Cmnty Wkr; Bsktbl; Coach Actv; Engrng.

GOHIL, PENELOPE; John Dewey HS; Brooklyn, NY; (Y); Church Yth Grp; Hosp Aide; JA; Science Clb; Nwsp Rptr; Nwsp Stf; Badmtn; Tennis; Vllybl; Hlth Careers Bureau Cert Awd 85; PAL Art & Ptry Awd 85; United Hosp Fund Of NY Vol Svc Awd 85; Med.

GOHO JR, GERALD G; Keshequa Central HS; Nunda, NY; (Y); 6/100; Am Leg Boys St; Pres Varsity Clb; Band; Var Golf; Var JV Socr; High Hon Roll; NHS; Ski Clb; Chorus; JV Bsbl; Gleason Mem Schlrshp 85; Ormond Scism Mem Sci Awd 85; Amer Assn Of Physics Tchrs Stu Of Yr 85; Rochester Inst Tech; Elec Engr.

GOKEY, LINDA; Franklin Acad; Whippleville, NY; (Y); High Hon Roll; Ernest Barletta Mem Schlrshp 85; North Country CC; Bus Adm.

GOLANKA, LAURIE A; Niagara-Wheatfield SR HS; Niagara Falls, NY; (Y); 55/313; Sec Office Aide; High Hon Roll; Hon Roll; Prfct Atten Awd; Attitude Achvmnt Schlrshp 85; Outstndng Achvmnt Awd For Acdmc Excllnc 85; Regnts Dplma Endrsd In Bus; Central Cty Bus Inst; Ct Rprtng.

GOLASZEWSKI, DAVID A; Niagara Wheatfield HS; North Tonawanda, NY; (Y); 31/315; Am Leg Boys St; Stu Cncl; Var Capt Crs Cntry; Var Capt Trk; Hon Roll; NHS; Prfct Atten Awd; Church Yth Grp; JA; Pep Clb; NY ST Rgnts Schlrshp Wnnr 85; Niagara Cnty CC Distngshd Stu 85; Elec Engrng.

GOLBOIS, VIVYAN L; Lawrence HS; N Woodmere, NY; (Y); 63/379; Cmnty Wkr; French Clb; Mathletes; Math Clb; Math Tm; Temple Yth Grp; Orch; Stu Cncl; High Hon Roll; NHS; Ltr Merit Spch Tourn 83-84; Regents Schlrshp 85; Valedictorian Hebrew HS 84; Bausch & Lomb Sci Awd 85; U Rochester; Elec Engrng.

GOLCZEWSKI, MARIE; Westlake HS; Thornwood, NY; (Y); 17/154; Art Clb; French Clb; Stu Cncl; High Hon Roll; Hon Roll; NHS; Art Awd 82; Pace U Schlrshp 85; Pace U Pleasantvl; Bus Adm.

GOLD, JOHN D; Hunter College HS; Jackson Heights, NY; (Y); Math Tm; Lit Mag; Mu Alp Tht; Ntl Merit SF; NY ST Rgnts Schlr 84; Math Stu 82; Gym Team 81-84; MA Inst Tech; Aero Engr.

GOLD, SETH; Hendrick Hudson HS; Croton, NY; (Y); 8/191; VP Debate Tm; Spanish Clb; Band; Concert Band; Jazz Band; Mrchg Band; Orch; Symp Band; Rptr Yrbk Stf; High Hon Roll; Cornell U; Frnsc Med.

GOLD, STEVEN; Long Beacvh HS; Lido Beach, NY; (S); 35/316; Hosp Aide; Key Clb; Ski Clb; Temple Yth Grp; Band; Mrchg Band; School Musical; Bsktbl; Tennis; NHS; Silvr Medl Hebrw Cultr Test 83; Gold Medl Hebrw Cultr Test 84.

GOLDBERG, ADRIANNE; Ramaz HS; Riverdale, NY; (Y); Cmnty Wkr; Hosp Aide; Ed Science Clb; Service Clb; Temple Yth Grp; Chorus; School Play; Lit Mag; St Schlr; Service Awd Riverdale Jewish Ctr 81; All Around Camper; Regents Schlrshp; Sophie Davis Bio Med; Medicine.

GOLDBERG, ANDREA; Sanford H Calhoun HS; Merrick, NY; (Y); Drama Clb; Chrmn Key Clb; Pres Mathletes; Pres Math Clb; Pres Math Tm; School Play; Hon Roll; NHS; Exploring; Quiz Bowl; Elmira Coll Key Awd For Outstdng Acvh-JR 85; Overall Excell In Spnsh Awd 85; NY Dist Key Clb Conv 85; Bio.

GOLDBERG, BETH; Hebrew Academy Of Nassau County; Great Neck, NY; (S); Service Clb; Temple Yth Grp; Nwsp Stf; High Hon Roll; NHS; NEDT Awd; Pre-Law.

GOLDBERG, CHARLES; Sheepshead Bay HS; Brooklyn, NY; (Y); Capt Aud/Vis; Boy Scts; Pres Computer Clb; Math Tm; Office Aide; Stage Crew; VP Sr Cls; Stu Cncl; Bowling; NHS.

GOLDBERG, DAVID; Nottingham HS; Syracuse, NY; (Y); 12/220; Pres Exploring; French Clb; Hosp Aide; Latin Clb; Math Tm; Capt Quiz Bowl; Ski Clb; Capt Socr; Var Tennis; High Hon Roll; Oswego Lang Fair 1st, 2nd Pl 83-84; Natl Frnch Cont Regnl Wnnr 80-85; NY ST Regnts Schlrshp 85; Cornell U; Bio.

GOLDBERG, ELISABETH; Fashion Industries HS; New York, NY; (Y); 59/366; Church Yth Grp; Drama Clb; Office Aide; PAVAS; Chorus; School Musical; Yrbk Stf; Sftbl; Hon Roll; Parsons Schl Of Dsgn; Arch.

GOLDBERG, LAURA B; Half Hollow Hills H S East; Dix Hills, NY; (Y); School Play; Stage Crew; Nwsp Stf; Cit Awd; High Hon Roll; Ntl Merit Ltr; St Schlr; Eductnl Commnctns Schlrshp Semi-Fnlst 85; Audra Feinstein Memrl Schlrshp 85; MD Ctr For Arts Intrn 85; Clark U; Filmmaker.

GOLDBERG, MELINDA L; Saunders Trades & Technical HS; Yonkers, NY; (Y); 6/190; Computer Clb; VICA; Nwsp Rptr; Yrbk Stf; Ed Lit Mag; Rep Frsh Cls; High Hon Roll; NHS; Suprndnt Schls Achvt Awed 81-85; Awd Wrtg 84; Pres Acad Ftnss Awd 85; Manhattan Coll; Chem.

GOLDBERG, WARREN; Bethpage HS; Plainview, NY; (Y); 49/290; High Hon Roll; Hon Roll; Comp Sci.

GOLDBLATT, DAVID L; Harborfields HS; Greenlawn, NY; (Y); 49/335; Aud/Vis; Computer Clb; Math Clb; Science Clb; Teachers Aide; Temple Yth Grp; Ed Nwsp Ed-Chief; Nwsp Rptr; High Hon Roll; Ntl Merit SF; Elec Engrng.

GOLDEN, ALLISON S; Saugerties HS; Saugerties, NY; (Y); 17/237; French Clb; JA; Office Aide; High Hon Roll; Hon Roll; NHS; Ntl Merit SF; Ulster County CC; Comp Sci.

GOLDEN, ANDREW H; Woodmere Acad; Oceanside, NY; (Y); Chess Clb; Hosp Aide; Library Aide; Ski Clb; Temple Yth Grp; Varsity Clb; Nwsp Rptr; Bsktbl; Capt Socr; Capt Tennis; Emory U; Med.

GOLDEN, DEBBIE; Christopher Columbus HS; Bronx, NY; (Y); 94/492; Drama Clb; Office Aide; Band; Chorus; Concert Band; JV Bsktbl; JV Vllybl; Hon Roll; Humantorism 83; Comp Sci.

GOLDEN, ERICA; Commack HS North; E Northport, NY; (Y); Intnl Clb; Math Tm; Temple Yth Grp; Chorus; Lit Mag; Off Frsh Cls; Off Soph Cls; Off Jr Cls; Off Sr Cls; Stu Cncl; NYS Sci Supvs Assn Gen Sci Awd 83.

GOLDEN, JAMES; North Babylon HS; North Babylon, NY; (Y); 34/600; Cmnty Wkr; Band; Variety Show; Yrbk Stf; JV Bsbl; Var Socr; JV Tennis; Jr NHS; NHS; Pres Stu Gov 85-86.

GOLDEN, JANICE; Grand Island SR HS; Grand Island, NY; (Y); 25/325; Dance Clb; French Clb; JA; Variety Show; Rep Stu Cncl; Hon Roll; Acadmc Achvt Awd 84; Acadmc Achvt Lttr 85; Math.

GOLDEN, JENNIFER; Cicero North Syracuse HS; Clay, NY; (S); 7/771; Church Yth Grp; Hosp Aide; Color Guard; Tennis; High Hon Roll; Hon Roll; Jr NHS; NHS; Bio Sci.

GOLDEN, JOY; Auburn HS; Auburn, NY; (S); School Musical; Nwsp Stf; High Hon Roll; Hon Roll; Jrnlsm.

GOLDEN, MARY ELIZABETH; Acad Of The Holy Names; Loudonville, NY; (Y); Church Yth Grp; Cmnty Wkr; Hosp Aide; NFL; Speech Tm; School Play; Yrbk Phtg; Lit Mag; Stu Cncl; Drama Clb; Comprtv Anatomy Awd 83-84; Ntl Frnsc Lgu Degr Of Merit 83-84; Ntl Frnsc Lgu Degr Hnr & Excllnc 84-85; Occptnl Thrpy.

GOLDEN, MICHAEL; Geneva HS; Geneva, NY; (S); 23/175; Spanish Clb; Varsity Clb; Yrbk Rptr; Stu Cncl; Ice Hcky; Lcrss; High Hon Roll; Hon Roll; NHS.

GOLDENBERG, JOEL; Bronx High Schl Of Sci; Jackson Heights, NY; (Y); Drama Clb; Office Aide; Teachers Aide; Temple Yth Grp; Cert Cmmndtn Police Dept 82; Rutgers U; Dentstry.

GOLDFARB, BRUCE; Smithtown High School East; Nesconset, NY; (Y); Pres Key Clb; Ski Clb; Temple Yth Grp; Trs Frsh Cls; Trs Soph Cls; Im Bsktbl; JV Var Tennis; NHS; Spanish NHS; Accntng.

GOLDGEWERT, RONALD; Brookdale H S Of Hanc; Greenlawn, NY; (S); 1/75; Chess Clb; Hosp Aide; Teachers Aide; Temple Yth Grp; Nwsp Stf; Bsbl; Sftbl; High Hon Roll; NHS; NEDT Awd.

GOLDHIRSCH, ANN; Hebrew Acad; Valley Stream, NY; (S); 5/67; Hosp Aide; Math Tm; Yrbk Ed-Chief; Bsktbl; NHS; Ntl Merit SF; NEDT Awd; Nwsp Rptr; Hon Roll; NY Regents Schlrshp 85; Deans List 84 & 85; Barnard Coll; Sci.

GOLDKRAND, JUDITH ELLEN; Albany HS; Albany, NY; (Y); 2/600; Cmnty Wkr; Hosp Aide; Pres Spanish Clb; Temple Yth Grp; Nwsp Stf; Capt Swmmng; Cit Awd; High Hon Roll; NHS; Sal; MI U Merit Schlrshp; Spinoza Awd; Yale; Pre-Med.

GOLDMAN, BRUCE; Woodlands HS; Elmsford, NY; (Y); Computer Clb; Capt Debate Tm; Math Tm; NFL; Concert Band; Jazz Band; Var Crs Cntry; High Hon Roll; NHS; Undefeated Debate Tm Mid Westchester Div Bi Weekly Debates 84-85; 3rd Woodlands HS Sci Fair 84-85.

GOLDMAN, DANA; Kings Park SR HS; Kings Park, NY; (Y); 15/446; Drama Clb; NFL; Q&S; Science Clb; Sec Speech Tm; Band; Chorus; School Play; Lit Mag; Stu Cncl; SADD Stu Pres 82-85; Syracuse U; Comm.

GOLDMAN, DEBORAH; Hebrew Academy Of Nassau County; Lake Success, NY; (S); 1/70; Math Tm; Nwsp Rptr; Yrbk Stf; High Hon Roll; VP NHS; Ntl Merit Ltr; Val; Band; Rep Stu Cncl; Intl Yth Achvt 84; Regents Schlrshp 85; Cornell U; Bio.

GOLDMAN, MARC; Farmingdale HS; S Farmingdale, NY; (Y); Service Clb; Thesps; Jazz Band; Mrchg Band; Orch; School Musical; Stage Crew; Var L Swmmng; High Hon Roll; VP NHS; Voic Demcrcy 84-85; Band 82-85; Dentstry.

GOLDMAN, VICTOR; Hicksville HS; Hicksville, NY; (Y); 2/400; Boy Scts; VP Exploring; Mathletes; Wrstlng; French Hon Soc; High Hon Roll; Hon Roll; Jr NHS; NHS; Ntl Merit Schol; Ind Engrng.

GOLDSCHMIDT, JEAN; Spackenkill HS; Poughkeepsie, NY; (Y); German Clb; School Play; Yrbk Bus Mgr; Yrbk Stf; Trk; Physcs.

GOLDSCHMIDT, LINDA; School Of The Holy Child; Scarborough, NY; (S); Hosp Aide; Key Clb; Service Clb; Rep Frsh Cls; Rep Stu Cncl; Var Capt Fld Hcky; Var Capt Swmmng; Cit Awd; Hon Roll; NHS; U Of Notre Dame; Bus.

GOLDSTEIN, ARLENE; Oceanside HS; Oceanside, NY; (Y); 3/600; Hosp Aide; Key Clb; Spanish Clb; Temple Yth Grp; High Hon Roll; Hon Roll; Jr NHS; NHS; Spnsh Acadmc Awd 84; PTA Schlstc Achvt Awd 84; S Taylor Johnson Schlrshp Key 85; Med.

GOLDSTEIN, AVRAM F; Yeshiva University HS; Flushing, NY; (Y); 6/101; Math Clb; Nwsp Ed-Chief; Nwsp Rptr; Yrbk Ed-Chief; NHS; Ntl Merit Ltr; NY ST Regents Schlrshp 85; Political Sci.

GOLDSTEIN, CYNTHIA M; Sachem High School North; Lk Ronkonkoma, NY; (Y); 129/1383; Spanish Clb; Orch; Yrbk Phtg; Yrbk Stf; Lit Mag; Rep Soph Cls; Trs Jr Cls; Stat Lcrss; Jr NHS; Dedctn & Svc 85; Sachem SR Hgh Sce Cngrss 3rd Pl 84; Cert Of Mrt Spnsh 84; Blackburn Coll; Bus Adm.

GOLDSTEIN, DEBORA; John Dewey HS; Brooklyn, NY; (Y); Computer Clb; Math Tm; Science Clb; Yrbk Stf; Hon Roll; Jr NHS; Ntl Merit Ltr; Engl, Scholar Medal Mark Twain 83; Sci.

GOLDSTEIN, GREGORY M; Mc Kiss Vocational Technical HS; Staten Island, NY; (Y); 11/238; Yrbk Stf; Var Bsbl; Mgr Bsktbl; Capt L Bowling; Mgr Ftbl; Hon Roll; Stu Athlt 84-86; Seagull Scty 83-86; Elec Engrng.

GOLDSTEIN, HAL L; Spring Valley HS; Monsey, NY; (Y); 37/438; Key Clb; VP Ski Clb; Band; Yrbk Phtg; Yrbk Stf; JV Bsbl; Var Golf; High Hon Roll; Hon Roll; NHS; Regnt Schlrshp 85; William Lightfoot Shultz Fndtn Schlrshp 85; Cornell U; Arch.

GOLDSTEIN, HOWARD J; Newburgh Free Acad; New Windsor, NY; (Y); 1/720; Service Clb; Pres Temple Yth Grp; Var JV Bsbl; High Hon Roll; Jr NHS; NHS; Spanish NHS; Val; U Of PA; Liberal Arts.

GOLDSTEIN, JEFFREY D; Niskayuna SR HS; Schenectady, NY; (Y); Am Leg Boys St; Chess Clb; Cmnty Wkr; Spanish Clb; Stu Cncl; JV Trk; NHS; Quiz Bowl; Yrbk Stf; JV Crs Cntry; Century III Ldrshp Cont 84-85; PTO Exec Brd Votng 84-85; SADD Local Chptr Fndr 84-85; Cornell; Pol Sci.

GOLDSTEIN, JOANNE; Onteora HS; Shandaken, NY; (S); 12/245; Girl Scts; PAVAS; Temple Yth Grp; Chorus; Mrchg Band; Hon Roll; NHS; Ntl Merit Ltr; Concert Band; Nwsp Stf; Girl Scout Slvr Ldrshp Awd 83; Girl Scout Wider Opportuniy 82; Regnts Schlrshp 84; Suny Potsdam; Drama.

GOLDSTEIN, KAREN; Half Hollow Hills High Schl East; Melville, NY; (Y); Cmnty Wkr; Hosp Aide; Leo Clb; Teachers Aide; Orch; Stage Crew; Yrbk Stf; Lit Mag; Hon Roll; NHS.

GOLDSTEIN, MARCIE; Smithtown H S East; Nesconset, NY; (Y); Var Trk; Hnrs Rgnts Diploma 85; IN U; Law.

GOLDSTEIN, MICHAEL; Mineola HS; Williston Park, NY; (Y); High Hon Roll; Exploring; French Clb; Hst Key Clb; Nwsp Rptr; Lit Mag; 3rd Pl Lng Awd 85; Law.

GOLDSTEIN, SHERRI; W C Mepham HS; North Bellmore, NY; (Y); 82/400; Nwsp Stf; Yrbk Stf; Off Soph Cls; Off Jr Cls; Off Sr Cls; Var Bowling; Hon Roll; Pres Acadmc Ftns Awd 85; Dinkelmeyer PTA Awd 85; Hofstra U; Bio.

GOLDSTONE, JEFF; Aquinas Inst; Rochester, NY; (Y); 5/166; St Thomas Clb 82-84; St John Fisher.

GOLDWIRE, JOSETTE; Murry Bergtraum HS; Brooklyn, NY; (Y); Cmnty Wkr; Chorus; Color Guard; Yrbk Stf; Cheerleading; Hon Roll; Comp Engrng.

GOLEBIEWSKI, BETH; Mount Mercy Acad; W Seneca, NY; (S); French Clb; Ski Clb; Nwsp Stf; High Hon Roll; Hon Roll; Opt Clb Awd; Recgntn Awd 84; Zoo Aide Pgm Awd 83; Le Moyne U; Bio.

GOLIA, THERESA; East Meadow HS; East Meadow, NY; (S); 25/414; Hosp Aide; Chorus; Var Fld Hcky; Var Lcrss; JV Var Vllybl; Cit Awd; Hon Roll; NHS; SUNY Stony Brook; Phy Thrpy.

GOLIN, PAUL; Susan E Wagner HS; Staten Island, NY; (Y); Ski Clb; Concert Band; School Musical; Symp Band; Nwsp Rptr; Rep Stu Cncl; High Hon Roll; NHS; Enrgy Dept Awd; Borough Wide Sci Fair Wnnr.

GOLINO, SUSAN; The Academy Of The Resurrec; New Rochelle, NY; (Y); Math Tm; NFL; Chorus; Yrbk Ed-Chief; JV Var Cheerleading; Swmmng; High Hon Roll; Hon Roll; SUNY Albany.

GOLLNITZ, SHARON; Westfield Acad; Westfield, NY; (S); 10/77; PAVAS; Teachers Aide; Stu Cncl; Stat Bsbl; Stat Bsktbl; Stat Ftbl; High Hon Roll; NHS; ST U Of NY Fredonia.

GOLUB, ALAN S; Midwood H S At Brooklyn College; Brooklyn, NY; (Y); 43/720; Math Tm; Service Clb; Concert Band; School Musical; Lit Mag; Capt Swmmng; Cit Awd; High Hon Roll; Syracuse U Ctznshp Ed Schlrshp 85; Newhouse Coll; Tele Cmnctn Mgmn.

GOLUBOFF, BRYAN; John F Kennedy HS; Merrick, NY; (Y); Cmnty Wkr; Drama Clb; Temple Yth Grp; School Play; Nwsp Ed-Chief; Nwsp Sprt Ed; Ed Lit Mag; Pres Frsh Cls; Var Bsbl; Wrtng.

GOMAN, KATHY; Stillwater Central HS; Mechanicville, NY; (Y); 10/86; French Clb; VP Girl Scts; Hon Roll; NHS; Drama Clb; School Play; Silver Ldrshp Awd 83; Comp Sci.

GOMEZ, CANDICE; U S Central HS; Valley Stream, NY; (Y); Chorus; Nwsp Rptr; Cheerleading; Crs Cntry; French Hon Soc; High Hon Roll; Mu Alp Tht; Psych.

GOMEZ, CARLOS; Xavier HS; Jackson Hts, NY; (Y); 25/250; Boy Scts; French Clb; Intnl Clb; Spanish Clb; Yrbk Rptr; Var Socr; French Hon Soc; Hon Roll; Ntl Merit Ltr; Phy.

GOMEZ, DIANA M; Sacred Heart Acad; Oceanside, NY; (Y); 35/186; Off Art Clb; School Musical; Ed Nwsp Rptr; Ed Nwsp Stf; Rep Jr Cls; Stu Cncl; Hon Roll; NCTE Awd; NHS; Fordham U Deans Schlrshp 85; Fordham U; Jrnlsm.

GOMEZ, ELISSA; St Joseph By The Sea HS; Staten Island, NY; (Y); 74/284; Art Clb; Aud/Vis; Girl Scts; Chorus; Yrbk Stf; Bowling; Hnrb Plcmt Cert-NY Lng Assn 83.

GOMEZ, FRANCYS; Bishop Kearney HS; Brooklyn, NY; (Y); Church Yth Grp; Key Clb; Spanish Clb; Church Choir; Bowling; Spnsh Lang Cntst Iona Coll-1st Hnrs 85; Law.

GOMEZ, GUADALUPE; Cathedral HS; Bronx, NY; (Y); 83/298; FNA; French Hon Soc; Hlth.

GOMEZ, JANIS MARY; Peekskill HS; Peekskill, NY; (S); 1/157; Concert Band; Nwsp Sprt Ed; Trs Stu Cncl; Stat Ftbl; JV Capt Sftbl; Var L Vllybl; Stat Wrstlng; High Hon Roll; NHS; Mrchg Band; Schlrshp Pins 83-85; Rensselaer Mdl Math & Sci 85; Engl.

GOMMEL, ERIC; Fairport HS; Fairport, NY; (Y); Science Clb; Yrbk Phtg; Rep Stu Cncl; JV Wrstlng; High Hon Roll; Hon Roll; JETS Awd; NHS; Prfct Atten Awd; Bio.

GOMPPER, DANIEL; Nyack HS; Valley Cottage, NY; (Y); 12/277; FBLA; Ski Clb; Stage Crew; Yrbk Ed-Chief; Trs Stu Cncl; Var Capt Crs Cntry; Var Trk; JV Wrstlng; 4-H Awd; NHS; Crs Cntry MVP 84; Crs Cntry All Conf 85; Engrng.

GONCALVES, PAULA; Fower SR HS; Syracuse, NY; (S); 85/225; Church Yth Grp; Spanish Clb; VICA; Nwsp Phtg; Rep Soph Cls; Var Cheerleading; Var Sftbl; Var Swmmng; Cosmetlgy.

GONCALVES, ROD; Susan E Wagner HS; Staten Island, NY; (Y); 1/497; Chess Clb; Hosp Aide; Office Aide; Scholastic Bowl; Spanish Clb; Teachers Aide; School Play; Pres Soph Cls; Pres Jr Cls; Pres Sr Cls; Amer Chem Socty Awd 83; Grad Dept Awds Bio, Chem, Physcs, Math, Soc Stds, Spnsh, Sci 85; Northwestern U; Physcn.

GONDRE, MARJORIE; Cathedral HS; Bkly, NY; (Y); Chess Clb; Church Yth Grp; French Clb; Girl Scts; Intnl Clb; Chorus; Church Choir; Yrbk Stf; Hon Roll; 2nd Hnrs Frnch-Iona Coll Lang Contst 83 & 84; Med.

GONG, STEPHEN M; La Salle Acad; New York, NY; (S); 22/252; Computer Clb; Math Clb; Orch; Im Bsktbl; Im Bowling; Im Sftbl; Hon Roll; Cardinal Hayes Hnr Scty 81-85; Comp Sci.

GONGORA, GERALDINE; Attica SR HS; Attica, NY; (Y); Stage Crew; Nwsp Rptr; Yrbk Stf; Stu Cncl; Hon Roll; NHS.

GONSALVES, CHIQUITA; North Shore HS; Glen Head, NY; (Y); AFS; Mathletes; Nwsp Sprt Ed; Yrbk Stf; Hon Roll; NHS; Rookie Of Yr Math 83; Schlr Of Mnth 83-84; Engr.

GONYO, TIMOTHY; Northeastern Clinton Central HS; Mooers, NY; (Y); Am Leg Boys St; Model UN; VP Band; Concert Band; Mrchg Band; Yrbk Stf; High Hon Roll; NHS; Ntl Merit Ltr; CAP; Pol Sci.

GONZALES, GENE VINCENT; Cicero North Syracuse HS; Clay, NY; (S); 47/622; Boy Scts; Debate Tm; Exploring; Pres JA; Model UN; Q&S; Nwsp Ed-Chief; Nwsp Rptr; Nwsp Stf; Lit Mag; Empire St Press Assn Wrtg Awd 84; Schl Pres Inst-Syracuse U 83-84; Pres-Cicero-N Syracuse Gm Clb 82-84; Syracuse U; Journalism.

GONZALES, KARYL; Springville Griffith Inst; Colden, NY; (Y); AFS; Church Yth Grp; Ski Clb; Chorus; Var L Swmmng; JC Awd; Pres Schlr; ST U Of NY Buffalo; Pre-Med.

GONZALES, KEVIN; La Salle HS; Niagara Falls, NY; (Y); Im Bsbl; Var Ftbl; JV Trk; JV Wt Lftg; Hon Roll; Sertoma Essay Awd 82; Wnr Svgs Bnd; Cert Merit Asmblymn 82; U Bflo; Comp Sci.

GONZALES, MELINDA; Lawrence SR HS; Lawrence, NY; (Y); French Clb; Math Clb; Pres PAVAS; Sec Science Clb; Ed Nwsp Stf; Yrbk Stf; Ed Lit Mag; French Hon Soc; High Hon Roll; NHS; Art Awd 82; Regnts Schlrshp 85; Barnard Coll; Bio.

GONZALEZ, CARL; Earl L Vandermuelen HS; Mt Sinai, NY; (Y); Math Tm; Chorus; School Play; Yrbk Stf; Rep Frsh Cls; JV Ftbl; Mgr(s); Score Keeper; Hon Roll; Prfct Atten Awd; Bus.

GONZALEZ, CARMEN; Glens Falls SR HS; Glen Falls, NY; (Y); 35/227; AFS; Girl Scts; Chorus; Sftbl; Vllybl; Mohawk Vly; Legal Sec L.

GONZALEZ, CLAUDIA; Dominican Commercial HS; Laurelton, NY; (Y); Church Yth Grp; Office Aide; Spanish Clb; Teachers Aide; Church Choir; Publc Rltns.

GONZALEZ, DAVID; Valley Stream Central HS; Valley Stream, NY; (Y); AFS; Computer Clb; Mathletes; Ski Clb; School Play; Nwsp Phtg; Yrbk Phtg; Var Capt Lcrss; Jr NHS; Mu Alp Tht; Med.

GONZALEZ, DIANA; Hunter College HS; New York, NY; (Y); Cmnty Wkr; Var Capt Crs Cntry; Var Sftbl; Timer; Var Trk; Mu Alp Tht; Sec Athletic Assn; Ntl Hispaic Schlr Awds; Pomona Coll; Bio.

GONZALEZ, DOUGLAS PETER; Bronx High School Of Sci; New York, NY; (Y); Rptr Lit Mag; NYC Dstrct Cncl Of Crpntrs Schlrshp 85; Cooper Union; Cvl Engrng.

GONZALEZ, DWIGHT; Lasalle Acad; Brooklyn, NY; (S); 4/240; CAP; Off Stu Cncl; Im Bsktbl; NHS; Ntl Merit Ltr; Incntv Awds Mnths Jan & June 84; Vol Tutrng 84-85; St Francis Coll; Crim Just.

GONZALEZ, ELIZABETH; Grace Dodge HS; Bronx, NY; (Y); Dance Clb; Band; Chorus; Color Guard; School Play; Nwsp Rptr; Sftbl; Wt Lftg; NCTE Awd; Spanish NHS; Aws Sooper Grad Awd Englsh 83; Spllng Awd; Englsh Awd; Obstrcn.

GONZALEZ, EVELYN; A Philip Randolph Campus HS; Brooklyn, NY; (Y); Dance Clb; Math Tm; Wt Lftg; Hon Roll; Pres Schlr; Cert Apprctn 83; Cert Achv Math; Cert Merit Lang Arts 83; Bus Adm.

GONZALEZ, FLAVIO A; Hillcrest HS; Briarwood, NY; (Y); 35/793; Computer Clb; Teachers Aide; Hon Roll; Rgnts Coll Schlrshp 85; SUNY Stony Brook; Med.

GONZALEZ, FRENANDO; La Salle Acad; Brooklyn, NY; (S); 16/237; Church Yth Grp; Office Aide; VP Sr Cls; VP Stu Cncl; Var NHS; Prfct Atten Awd; St Josephs Coll; Intl Law.

GONZALEZ, GABRIELA; St Johns Prep; Astoria, NY; (Y); Art Clb; Camera Clb; Dance Clb; Science Clb; School Play; Variety Show; Lit Mag; Hon Roll; NHS; Natl Sci Olympd Phys Sci 83; Queens Bridge Pgm Med 85; Psychtrst.

GONZALEZ, GINA; Niagara Catholic HS; Niagara Falls, NY; (Y); French Clb; Hosp Aide; Key Clb; Political Wkr; Teachers Aide; Yrbk Ed-Chief; Hon Roll; Trs NHS; Church Yth Grp; Cmnty Wkr; Fr Kroupa Awd Rnnr Up 85; Ballet Schlrshp 84; Intl Rltns.

GONZALEZ, GRICEL; Christopher Columbus HS; Bronx, NY; (S); 19/792; Hosp Aide; Math Tm; Teachers Aide; Chorus; Hon Roll; Arista 83-85; Spnsh, Bio Awds 84-85; Pre-Med.

GONZALEZ, HAYDEE; Clara Barton HS; Brooklyn, NY; (Y); Church Yth Grp; French Clb; Spanish Clb; Church Choir; Variety Show; Yrbk Stf; Hon Roll; Prfct Atten Awd; Amer Inst Sci & Tech NY City Awd 83; Pride Yankees Awd 84; Pre-Med.

GONZALEZ, IVAN; Walton HS; Bronx, NY; (Y); Church Yth Grp; Cmnty Wkr; Computer Clb; Latin Clb; Spanish Clb; Church Choir; School Musical; Jr Cls; Ftbl; Gym; Perf Atten Awd 84; Acad Aeronautics; Comm Pilot.

GONZALEZ, JEANETTE; Stella Maris HS; Far Rockaway, NY; (Y); Church Yth Grp; French Clb; Library Aide; Var JV Sftbl; Hon Roll; Merit Awd Math 84; Med.

GONZALEZ, JOANNE; Dominican Commercial HS; Brooklyn, NY; (Y); Spanish Clb; JV Bsktbl; Fnrl Drctr.

GONZALEZ, JOSE; Saint Agnes HS; New York, NY; (Y); 15/100; Hon Roll; NHS; 1st 2nd Hnr 85; St Johns U; Phrmcy.

GONZALEZ, LESLIE; Cathedral HS; Ny, NY; (Y); 27/298; VP Church Yth Grp; Cmnty Wkr; JA; Library Aide; Pep Clb; Political Wkr; Rep Jr Cls; Rep Stu Cncl; Prfct Atten Awd; VP Temple Yth Grp; Vet.

GONZALEZ, LILLIAN ANN; Eastern District HS; Brooklyn, NY; (Y); 5/432; Art Clb; Library Aide; Math Tm; Red Cross Aide; Service Clb; Teachers Aide; Pres Soph Cls; Rep Sr Cls; Rep Stu Cncl; High Hon Roll; Arturo Schomburg Schlrshp 85-86; Edwin Gould Schlrshp 85; Yth Dplmt Stu Exch Prog 84-85; Hampshire Coll; Pol Sci.

GONZALEZ, LUIS; Sachem HS North Campus; Holtsville, NY; (Y); 422/1383; Pres Science Clb; Socr; Var Trk; Air Frc Acad; Art.

GONZALEZ, MARCIAL; Sachem HS; Holtsville, NY; (Y); 44/1428; Science Clb; Service Clb; Acpl Chr; Pres Madrigals; Mgr Mrchg Band; School Musical; Swing Chorus; Mgr(s); Jr NHS; NHS; St Lvl Ntl Hstry Day 2nd Pl 83; Lbrl Arts.

GONZALEZ, MICHELE; Union Endicott HS; Endicott, NY; (Y); Church Yth Grp; Drama Clb; Hosp Aide; Pres VICA; Band; Chorus; Concert Band; Mrchg Band; School Musical; School Play; Area All ST Chrs 83; NYS Delg VICA 85; Ntl Delg VICA 85; Albany Schl Of Nrsng; Reg Nrse.

GONZALEZ, MORIS; Freeport HS; Freeport, NY; (Y); Art Clb; Spanish Clb; Teachers Aide; Socr; Dntl Tech.

GONZALEZ, MYRA; Cathedral HS; Brkyn, NY; (Y); 44/298; FNA; Intnl Clb; School Play; Variety Show; Yrbk Stf; Aerontcs.

GONZALEZ, ROLANDO; Mount St Michael Acad; Bronx, NY; (Y); 36/318; Im Fld Hcky; Im Ftbl; Spanish NHS; Cardinals Ldrshp Prjct 85; Brdcst Jrnlsm.

GONZALEZ, ROSITA; Bishop Laughlin Memorial HS; Brooklyn, NY; (Y); Church Yth Grp; Office Aide; Hon Roll; Gold L Hgh Hnrs 83-84; NY City Tech; Ex Secy.

GONZALEZ, STEVEN; Cardinal Hayes HS; New York, NY; (Y); Hosp Aide; Chorus; School Musical; School Play; Nwsp Rptr; 2nd Hnrs; Schl Lttr; Manhattan Coll; Jrnlsm.

GONZALEZ, VICTORIA; John Jay HS; Brooklyn, NY; (Y); Church Yth Grp; Drama Clb; Church Choir; Variety Show; Nwsp Stf; Yrbk Stf; Cit Awd; Hon Roll; Prfct Atten Awd; Eng Crmnlgy & Amer His Awd; Jrnlst.

GONZALEZ, YOLANDA; Aquinas HS; New York, NY; (Y); 31/178; Chorus; School Musical; School Play; Pres Soph Cls; Hon Roll; Prfct Atten Awd; Spanish NHS; Treble Clef Spring & Christmas Concerts 84-85; Comp Sci.

GOOD, ANDREW; Horseheads HS; Horseheads, NY; (S); 20/407; Pres Chess Clb; Pres JCL; Pres Letterman Clb; Quiz Bowl; Pres Varsity Clb; Rep Stu Cncl; Var L Golf; Var L Socr; Var L Trk; Ntl Merit SF; Century III Ldrshp Awd Schlrshp 85; Tompkins-Cortland CC Chall 1st 84; Corning Chem Bowl 1st 84; Engr.

GOOD, WILLIAM; Grand Island HS; Grand Island, NY; (Y); Boy Scts; Chess Clb; Mathletes; Var Ftbl; JV Socr; Var Trk; Hon Roll; Sr Patrol Ldr Troop 425 Scouting 82-84; Air Force ROTC; Electrical.

GOODACRE, DAWN M; St Agnes Acad; College Point, NY; (Y); 8/302; Teachers Aide; JV Var Crs Cntry; Capt Trk; High Hon Roll; NHS; Ntl Merit Ltr; NY ST Regents Schlrshp 85; Schlstc Exc Schlrshp 85; St John Su; Bus Mngmnt.

GOODBERRY, ANDREA; La Salle SR HS; Niagara Falls, NY; (Y); Var Cheerleading; Hon Roll; NHS; Gentcs.

GOODE, PATRICIA; Jamesville-De Witt HS; Fayetteville, NY; (Y); Church Yth Grp; Cmnty Wkr; Hosp Aide; Key Clb; Nwsp Ed-Chief; Yrbk Stf; Var Capt Socr; Var Capt Sftbl; Cit Awd; Hon Roll; Cmnty Awd 85; Volunteer Awd 84-85; Med.

GOODELL, KATHY A; Averill Park HS; Averill Pk, NY; (Y); Band; Concert Band; Jazz Band; Yrbk Stf; Powder Puff Ftbl; Hon Roll; JR Coll St Albany; Law.

GOODELLE, KATHLEEN A; Auburn HS; Auburn, NY; (Y); Dance Clb; Var Capt Swmmng; Var Timer; Cayuga CC; Med Tech.

GOODEN, GREGG; Newfield HS; Selden, NY; (Y); Chess Clb; Computer Clb; Quiz Bowl; Science Clb; Var Golf; High Hon Roll; Hon Roll; Comp Sci.

GOODEN, ILALE; Baldwin SR HS; Baldwin, NY; (Y); 110/502; Lit Mag; Rep Stu Cncl; Var L Fld Hcky; Var L Trk; Im Wt Lftg; High Hon Roll; Hon Roll; Regnts Schlrshp NY ST 84-85; Spnsh Diploma Of Merit 83-84; Merit Schlr For Outstndng Negro Stu 84-85; U Of PA; Cvl Engrng.

GOODENOUGH, JOHN; Whitney Point Central Schl; Lisle, NY; (Y); Cmnty Wkr; VP Jr Cls; JV Var Bsktbl; JV Var Crs Cntry; Var Trk; Hon Roll; Church Yth Grp; Rep Frsh Cls; JV Ftbl; Var Tennis; Excllnc Adv Wood 85; Excllnc Phy Educ 85; Marine Bio.

GOODENOUGH, JULIE; Whitney Point HS; Lisle, NY; (Y); 14/114; French Clb; Bsktbl; Crs Cntry; Trk; High Hon Roll; NHS; Salute To Yth 84; Bsktbl Scholar 85; Ithaca Coll; Sprts Med.

GOODERMOTE, PATRICIA A; Chatham HS; Chatham, NY; (Y); 13/150; Drama Clb; Pres Latin Clb; Library Aide; Orch; School Musical; Yrbk Stf; Trk; High Hon Roll; NHS; Music Ed.

GOODHART, CHRISTINE; Port Chester SR HS; Port Chester, NY; (Y); 12/226; Sec Band; Jazz Band; Mrchg Band; Tennis; High Hon Roll; Hon Roll; Jr NHS; NHS; Pres Schlr; Wmns Clb & PTA Schlrshps 85; Geneseo; Vet.

GOODIS, MICHELLE M; Brentwood Ross HS; Brentwood, NY; (Y); 30/625; Co-Capt Mrchg Band; Pres Orch; School Musical; High Hon Roll; NHS; Prfct Atten Awd; French Clb; Mathletes; Math Tm; Concert Band; Ntl Hnr Soc Nwsltr-Edtr 84-85; Rotry Clb Awd 85; Presdntl Acadmc Ftnss Awd 85; Stonybrook U; Bio.

GOODLOE, PAUL; Archbishop Stepinac HS; New Rochelle, NY; (Y); 80/201; JA; Yrbk Stf; Rep Frsh Cls; Rep Jr Cls; Im Bsktbl; JV Var Ftbl; DAR Awd; Pre Med.

GOODMAN, ANDREW S; Scarsdale HS; Scarsdale, NY; (Y); Debate Tm; Political Wkr; VP Band; Concert Band; VP Jazz Band; VP Mrchg Band; School Musical; Symp Band; Nwsp Rptr; Nwsp Stf; Pol Sci.

GOODMAN, BONNIE B; Spring Valley SR HS; Spring Vly, NY; (Y); Cmnty Wkr; Girl Scts; Library Aide; Red Cross Aide; Teachers Aide; Chorus; School Musical; School Play; Stage Crew; Cit Awd.

GOODNIGHT, THOMAS; Wilson Central HS; Wilson, NY; (Y); Aud/Vis; Church Yth Grp; Band; Concert Band; Jazz Band; Mrchg Band; Pep Band; Var Golf; Im Bsktbl; 2nd Pl ST Cmptn In Asmbl Of God Teen Tlnt 85; JR All Amer Hall Of Fame Band Hnrs 85; Bus Adm.

GOODNOUGH, CATHERINE A; St Barnabas HS; Bronx, NY; (Y); 5/136; Office Aide; Yrbk Ed-Chief; VP Soph Cls; Rep Stu Cncl; High Hon Roll; NHS; Prfct Atten Awd; Spanish NHS; Pep Clb; NYS Regnts Schlrshp Nrsng 85; Math & Engl Medl 83; Coll New Rochelle; Nrsng.

GOODRICH, AMY; Fabius-Pompey Central Schl; Fabius, NY; (Y); Varsity Clb; Pres Stu Cncl; Var L Cheerleading; JV Vllybl; Pres Schlr; Onondaga Cnty Dairy Princess 85; Suny Morrisville; Ag.

GOODRIDGE, BONNIE; Andover Central HS; Andover, NY; (Y); 5/14; Pres FCA; Off FHA; Girl Scts; Model UN; Chorus; Color Guard; Mgr Yrbk Stf; L Socr; 4-H Awd; High Hon Roll; Trvl.

GOODRIDGE, SHARON; Samuel J Tilden HS; Brooklyn, NY; (Y); DECA; Hosp Aide; Teachers Aide; School Play; Schltc Credit Cert 83; Hnr Cards-French, Math & Psych 84; Hnr Card-Word Processng 85; Nrsng.

GOODRUM, PHILIP E; William Nottingham HS; Syracuse, NY; (Y); 20/22; Latin Clb; Ski Clb; Orch; Yrbk Ed-Chief; Trs Jr Cls; Var VP Bsbl; Var JV Socr; Var Trk; Hon Roll; NHS; Congrssnl Awd Of Hnr 85; Regents Sclrshp 84; Magna Cum Laude For Natl Latin Exam 84; Cornell U; Bio.

GOODSMITH, BETH R; Clarkstown HS South; New City, NY; (Y); 66/541; Exploring; Quiz Bowl; Teachers Aide; Temple Yth Grp; Stage Crew; JV Swmmng; Hon Roll; NHS; NY Regnts Schlrshp 85; Union Coll; Pre-Med.

GOODWIN, DEBORAH A; Pittsford Mendon HS; Pittsford, NY; (Y); Math Clb; Math Tm; Pep Clb; Varsity Clb; Cheerleading; Fld Hcky; Cit Awd; DAR Awd; High Hon Roll; Hon Roll; NY Regents Schlrshp 85; Bucknell; Math.

GOODWIN, WENDY; Tioga Central HS; Nichols, NY; (S); 29/72; Varsity Clb; Variety Show; Nwsp Sprt Ed; Nwsp Stf; Rep Stu Cncl; Cheerleading; Capt Fld Hcky; Sftbl; Hon Roll; Most Improved Cheerleader 83; Presidential Physical Fitness Awd 84.

GOODWINE, JOLENE; Long Island Lutheran HS; Roosevelt, NY; (S); 7/55; Sec Church Yth Grp; Band; Church Choir; School Musical; Yrbk Sprt Ed; VP Sr Cls; Rep Stu Cncl; Var JV Bsktbl; Var Btty Crckr Awd; Cit Awd; Yth Recogntn Awd 83; School Service Awd 84; Chem.

GOODWINE, ROCHELLE; John Dewey HS; Brooklyn, NY; (Y); Boys Clb Am; Church Yth Grp; Dance Clb; Girl Scts; Drill Tm; Yrbk Stf; Rep Stu Cncl; Wt Lftg; Hon Roll; Prfct Atten Awd; Achvt Awd Math 83; Law.

GOOLDEN, ANDREW; Madrid-Waddington HS; Madrid, NY; (Y); 11/48; AFS; Trs Varsity Clb; VP Jr Cls; Golf; Var L Socr; Var L Wrstlng; High Hon Roll; NHS; Boy Scts; Church Yth Grp; Sec X All Nrthrn Hon Men Socr 83-84; Bus Scholar 84-85; Ihaca Coll; Bus.

GOOLEY, JODY; Newark Valley HS; Owego, NY; (Y); 2/120; Boy Scts; Computer Clb; Varsity Clb; Var Bsktbl; Var Ftbl; Var Golf; High Hon Roll; Hon Roll; Engrng.

GOON, MATTHEW; Tottenville HS; Staten Island, NY; (Y); Am Leg Boys St; Church Yth Grp; Model UN; Concert Band; Orch; School Musical; Yrbk Stf; Sec Sr Cls; Crs Cntry; VP NHS; Eng Awd 83; Pre-Med.

GOON, SHUE MEI; Brooklyn Technical HS; New York, NY; (Y); Church Yth Grp; Debate Tm; Library Aide; Office Aide; Teachers Aide; Chorus; Vllybl; Hon Roll; NHS; Vlybl Trophy 4th City 85; CCNY Sophie Davis; Med.

GOPAL, SUNIL; Half Hollow Hills High Schl East; Dix Hills, NY; (Y); Hosp Aide; Var Crs Cntry; Var Socr; Var Trk; High Hon Roll; Hon Roll; Jr NHS; NHS; TIPS Treas 84-85; Med.

GORCZYCA, SHERRI; Grand Island HS; Grand Island, NY; (Y); Church Yth Grp; Variety Show; Hon Roll; Acad Ltr 85; Math.

GORCZYNSKI, ANGELA; S S Seward Inst; Florida, NY; (Y); Dance Clb; FFA; FHA; Ski Clb; Spanish Clb; Band; Variety Show; Yrbk Stf; JV Bsktbl; JV Sftbl; Orange County CC; Bus Mngmnt.

GORCZYNSKI, CATHERINE; Warwick HS; Pine Isld, NY; (Y); #38 In Class; Church Yth Grp; Ski Clb; Teachers Aide; Chorus; Church Choir; Trk; High Hon Roll; Hon Roll; NHS; Prfct Atten Awd; Bus Admin.

GORDNER, BRIAN; Waterloo SR HS; Waterloo, NY; (Y); Aud/Vis; 4-H; Letterman Clb; Science Clb; Spanish Clb.

GORDON, ANTHONY J; Bronx HS Science; Bronx, NY; (Y); Church Yth Grp; JA; Teachers Aide; Im Bsktbl; Awd Hist Stud 85; Creation Annotated Blck Bibliography 85; U MD; Anml Sci.

GORDON, ASHAWNTAY SHAWN; Nazareth Acad; Rochester, NY; (Y); Church Yth Grp; Cmnty Wkr; Hosp Aide; Church Choir; Hon Roll; Bst Prsn Awd 83-84; Rcrd Kpng High Grade 84-85; Byrant Straton Inst; Acctng.

GORDON, AUDREY L; Mercy HS; Rensselaer, NY; (Y); 19/69; Dance Clb; Stage Crew; Variety Show; Yrbk Stf; High Hon Roll; Eng Awd 82; Eng & Bio Awd 83; Accntng Awd 84; New York U; Cmnctns.

GORDON, ELIZABETH; Madison Central Schl; Madison, NY; (Y); 12/44; Band; Chorus; Drm Mjr(t); Jazz Band; Yrbk Sprt Ed; Sec Stu Cncl; Cheerleading; Socr; Sftbl; Hon Roll; Herkimer Cnty CC; Bus.

GORDON, FLOYD; Saint Agnes HS; Far Rockaway, NY; (Y); Rep Chess Clb; Rep Yrbk Phtg; Rep Yrbk Stf; Rep Soph Cls; Rep Sr Cls; Trk; Hon Roll; NHS; Natl Hnr Soc; SUNY Binghamton; Bio.

GORDON, JULIA E; City Honors Schl; Buffalo, NY; (Y); 26/97; French Clb; Red Cross Aide; Ski Clb; Temple Yth Grp; Chorus; School Play; Yrbk Stf; Lit Mag; Trs Soph Cls; VP Jr Cls; Joseph Manch Creative Achvt Awd 84; Tufts U.

GORDON, MARJI L; Half Hollow Hills East HS; Wheatley Hts, NY; (Y); Leo Clb; Variety Show; Sr Cls; Var JV Cheerleading; Sftbl; Trk; JV Vllybl; High Hon Roll; Jr NHS; NHS; MI U; Bus Mgmt.

GORDON, MICHAEL; St Raymonds Boys HS; Bronx, NY; (Y); Bsktbl; Crs Cntry; Mgr(s); Ntl Merit Ltr; 2nd Hnrs 83; Pace U; Comp Prgrmmng.

GORDON, SABRINA S; Midwood HS; Brooklyn, NY; (Y); Chorus; School Musical; Variety Show; VP Sr Cls; Med.

GORDON, SCOTT A; Franklin Acad; Malone, NY; (Y); 35/252; Varsity Clb; JV Var Bsbl; Var L Crs Cntry; Var L Swmmng; Cortland ST; Biology.

GORDON, SETH D; Newburgh Free Acad; New Windsor, NY; (Y); 33/720; French Clb; Library Aide; Temple Yth Grp; Nwsp Bus Mgr; Nwsp Rptr; Yrbk Bus Mgr; High Hon Roll; Jr NHS; NHS; Orange Cnty Liquor Dealrs Assn Schlrshp 85; NY ST Regnts Schlrshp 85; Boston U; Bus Mgmt.

GORDON, TAMMY; Fort Ann Central Schl; Fort Ann, NY; (Y); 4/43; Dance Clb; French Clb; Math Clb; Math Tm; Band; Yrbk Stf; Var L Cheerleading; Var L Fld Hcky; High Hon Roll; NHS; Jostens Natl Ring Disply Cntst Natl Wnnr 83; Albany Coll Of Pharm; Pharm.

GORELCZENKO, WALTER; St Francis Prep; Elmhurst, NY; (Y); Cmnty Wkr; Political Wkr; Var JV Tennis; Var JV Trk; Pol Sci.

GORGOGLIONE, DARLENE; Herbert H Lehman HS; Bronx, NY; (Y); 51/400; Dance Clb; Hon Roll; Fshn Dsgnr.

GORGOL, TIMOTHY W; Johnson City SR HS; Johnson City, NY; (Y); Pres Drama Clb; Pres Band; Pres Concert Band; Jazz Band; Mrchg Band; School Musical; Symp Band; Yrbk Ed-Chief; High Hon Roll; NHS; Regents Schlrshp 85; Penn ST U; Bus Admin.

GORHAM, ANNE; Ichabod Crane Central HS; Valatie, NY; (Y); 8/189; Drama Clb; Office Aide; School Play; Yrbk Ed-Chief; Yrbk Stf; Lit Mag; High Hon Roll; Hon Roll; NHS; Rotary Awd; Schl Svc Awd 85; 90 Pct Or Bettr Regnts Exm 84-85; Effrt & Achvt Soc Stds 84; Marn Bio.

GORIS, EVELYN TERESA; Cathedral HS; New York, NY; (Y); 30/298; Hon Roll; Iona Lang Cntst 1st Hnrs Cert Spnsh 3 85; Bus Adm.

GORMAN, ALLISON; New Rochelle HS; New Rochelle, NY; (Y); Chorus; Hon Roll; NHS; Comp Sci.

GORMAN, CYNTHIA J; Grand Island SR HS; Grand Isl, NY; (Y); 32/280; French Clb; Mathletes; Ski Clb; Chorus; School Musical; School Play; Stage Crew; Variety Show; Ntl Merit Ltr; Fin In Wells Coll Poetry Cont 84; Playwrtng Crs With Emanual Fried 84; Regents Schlrshp 85; SUNYAB; Novelst.

GORMAN, DAVID J; Greece Arcadia HS; Rochester, NY; (Y); 66/293; Boy Scts; CAP; Exploring; Hon Roll; NYS Regents Schlrshp 85; AFROTC Schlrshp 85; Rochester Inst Of Tech; Engrng.

GORMAN, DOUGLAS M; Starpoint Central HS; Sanborn, NY; (Y); 9/250; Am Leg Boys St; Church Yth Grp; Letterman Clb; Ski Clb; Varsity Clb; Var L Crs Cntry; Var L Trk; Hon Roll; Jr NHS; NHS; Engrng.

GORMAN, FIONA M; St Barnabas HS; Yonkers, NY; (Y); 15/147; Yrbk Ed-Chief; Yrbk Phtg; Yrbk Stf; Rep Sr Cls; Hon Roll; NHS; Prfct Atten Awd; Pres Acad Fit Awd 85; N H Sci Olympiad Physics; Fordham U; Econ.

GORMAN, JOANN; Our Lady Of Perpetual Help HS; Brooklyn, NY; (Y); Exploring; Rep Stu Cncl; Mandel; Dntl Asst.

GORMAN, JOHN; Maple Hill HS; Castleton, NY; (S); Boy Scts; Church Yth Grp; Ski Clb; Spanish Clb; Bsbl; Socr; Hon Roll; Aviator.

GORMAN, KELLI; Horseheads HS; Horseheads, NY; (S); 51/407; Church Yth Grp; Cmnty Wkr; Spanish Clb; Teachers Aide; Varsity Clb; Yrbk Stf; Rep Stu Cncl; JV Var Sftbl; JV Var Vllybl; Hon Roll; Rookie Yr Sftbl 83; All STC Tem Sftbl, Vllybl 83-84; Ambassdr Pgm 84; Elem Ed.

GORMAN, LISA; Nazareth Acad; Rochester, NY; (Y); Church Yth Grp; Exploring; Girl Scts; JA; Chorus; JV Bsktbl; Var Bowling; JV Socr; JV Sftbl; Hon Roll; Girl Sct Slvr Awd 83; Envmt Sci.

GORMAN, MAUREEN C; Williamsville East HS; Williamsville, NY; (Y); FBLA; GAA; VP JA; Pep Clb; Band; Trs Symp Band; Rep Stu Cncl; Var L Socr; High Hon Roll; NHS; Case Western Reserve U; Finc Mg.

GORMAN, SHARON; Hoosick Falls Central HS; Hoosick Falls, NY; (Y); Church Yth Grp; Cmnty Wkr; Hosp Aide; Band; Chorus; Mrchg Band; Ntl Merit Ltr; Medcl Fld.

GORMAN, SHARON E; Smithtown East HS; Nesconset, NY; (Y); Hosp Aide; Math Tm; Ski Clb; Concert Band; Mrchg Band; Stu Cncl; Sftbl; NHS; Ntl Merit Ltr; Spanish NHS; Regents Schlrshp NY St 85; St U-New York; Comp Sci.

GORSKI, WENDY A; West Seneca East SR HS; Cheektowaga, NY; (Y); 1/365; Trs GAA; Lit Mag; Var JV Sftbl; Var L Tennis; Im Vllybl; High Hon Roll; JC Awd; NHS; Sal; VFW Awd; Resselaer Polytechnic Inst Math & Sci Mdl 83-84; Canisius Acad Mrt Schlrshp 85; Canisius Coll; Bio.

GORTON, ANN MARIE; Valley Central HS; Montgomery, NY; (Y); Spanish Clb; Yrbk Stf; Off Sr Cls; Stu Cncl; Vllybl; Spanish NHS; Orange Cnty CC; Bus.

GORTON, CHRIS; Mexico Acad; Fulton, NY; (Y); Exploring; German Clb; Ski Clb; Concert Band; Mrchg Band; Stage Crew; Yrbk Stf; Rep Stu Cncl; Var Socr; Var Trk.

GOSKOWSKI, RAYMOND M; Seton Catholic Central HS; Binghamton, NY; (Y); Am Leg Aux Girls St; Boy Scts; Church Yth Grp; Key Clb; Mathletes; Science Clb; Ski Clb; Band; Concert Band; Socr; Clarkson U; Engrng.

GOSMAN, DIANE M; E Hampton HS; Montauk, NY; (Y); 1/145; Trs FBLA; Chorus; Concert Band; Lit Mag; Sec Sr Cls; JV Var Fld Hcky; Lion Awd; VP NHS; Val; NYS Regents Schlrshp 84-85; Williams Coll; Poli Sci.

GOSNELL, HOWARD; Charles H Roth HS; W Henrietta, NY; (Y); 30/212; Boy Scts; Letterman Clb; Red Cross Aide; Ski Clb; Varsity Clb; Trs Frsh Cls; Trs Soph Cls; JV Var Bsbl; JV Bsktbl; JV Var Ftbl; Police Sci.

GOSS, PAMELA JANE; Kenmore West HS; Kenmore, NY; (Y); 40/445; Yrbk Stf; Trk; High Hon Roll; Hon Roll; NHS; Prfct Atten Awd; Mbr Of Hnr Clb 85; U Of Buffalo; Civil Engr.

GOSS, PATRICK; Garden City SR HS; Garden City, NY; (Y); FCA; German Clb; Latin Clb; Nwsp Rptr; Nwsp Stf; Yrbk Stf; JV Bsktbl; Im Sftbl; High Hon Roll; Ntl Merit Ltr; Lttr Exclnc Littl Leag Asstnc 84; Engrng.

GOSS, TIMOTHY W; Amherst Central SR HS; Amherst, NY; (Y); 35/310; German Clb; Math Tm; Political Wkr; Capt Quiz Bowl; School Play; Math Tm; Political Wkr; Badmtn; Bsktbl; Ftbl.

GOSSMAN, BARBARA; Southwestern Central HS; Lakewood, NY; (Y); French Clb; Ski Clb; Band; Concert Band; Mrchg Band; High Hon Roll; Hon Roll; NHS; Lang Awd Fr 82-83; Soc Stud Awd Wstrn Civl Natn 83-84; Jamestown CC; Acctg.

GOSSMANN, LAURA; St Johns Preparatory HS; Woodside, NY; (Y); 91/500; Church Yth Grp; GAA; Letterman Clb; Office Aide; Varsity Clb; Concert Band; Rep Stu Cncl; Var Bsktbl; JV Sftbl; Hon Roll; MVP Sftbl 84; Coaches Awd Bsktbl 84; Frnch Trnsltr.

GOSSOO, MARK; Onteora HS; Shandaken, NY; (S); 14/245; Am Leg Boys St; Pres Church Yth Grp; Concert Band; Drm Mjr(t); Jazz Band; Mrchg Band; High Hon Roll; Hon Roll; NHS; Ntl Merit SF; Brown U; Comp Sci.

GOTHARD, SHEILA; Lockport SR HS; Lockport, NY; (Y); Latin Clb; Rep Frsh Cls; Rep Soph Cls; Rep Stu Cncl; Sftbl; Vllybl; Crmnl Jstc.

GOTLIEB, BRIAN LANCE; Midwood HS At Brooklyn Coll; Brooklyn, NY; (Y); 162/604; Chess Clb; Cmnty Wkr; Library Aide; Math Clb; Office Aide; Y-Teens; School Play; Bowling; Score Keeper; Lehigh U; Med.

GOTTBETTER, ADAM S; Irvington HS; Irvington, NY; (Y); 24/122; French Clb; Key Clb; Ski Clb; Varsity Clb; Nwsp Ed-Chief; Yrbk Bus Mgr; Sec Frsh Cls; Rep Soph Cls; Rep Jr Cls; Capt Crs Cntry; NY ST Regents Schlrshp 85; All-Leag Cross Cntry 84; Lehigh U; Bus Law.

GOTTEFELD, JON; Port Richmond HS; Staten Isld, NY; (Y); School Play; Nwsp Rptr; Nwsp Sprt Ed; Sec Pres Frsh Cls; Sec Pres Soph Cls; Trs Jr Cls; JV Bsbl; Var Bsktbl; Var Trk; Hon Roll; Daily News Super Yth 84; Regents Scholar 85.

GOTTERT, MICHAEL J; Wm Floyd HS; Shirley, NY; (Y); 114/418; Aud/Vis; Band; Concert Band; Jazz Band; Mrchg Band; NY ST Regents Schlrshp 85; American U; Polt Sci.

GOTTESFELD, SANDY; James I Oneill HS; Putnam Vly, NY; (Y); Temple Yth Grp; Yrbk Phtg; Yrbk Stf; Arts.

GOTTESMAN, RUTH; Sheepshead Bay HS; Brooklyn, NY; (Y); Intnl Clb; Math Tm; Quiz Bowl; Science Clb; Service Clb; School Musical; Yrbk Ed-Chief; Trs Stu Cncl; NHS; Ntl Merit SF; Daily News Super Yth 83-84; Harvard U; Educ.

GOTTFRIED, MARK; Smithtown H S West; Smithtown, NY; (Y); Ski Clb; Off Jr Cls; Stu Cncl; Engrng.

GOTTMAN, MARJORIE; Lockport SR HS; Lockport, NY; (Y); 32/411; AFS; Drama Clb; Hosp Aide; Flag Corp; Mrchg Band; School Musical; Symp Band; Swmmng; Hon Roll; NHS; Co Chrprsn Lckprt Intrfth Grp 85-86; Math.

GOTTMANN, MICHELLE; Cleveland Hill HS; Cheektowaga, NY; (Y); GAA; Ski Clb; Band; VP Stu Cncl; Capt Var Cheerleading; Powder Puff Ftbl; JV Var Vllybl; Hon Roll; Varsity Clb.

GOTTSCHALL, DAVE; Irondequoit HS; Rochester, NY; (Y); JV Ftbl; Var L Lcrss; Mech Engrng.

GOTTSCHALL, MICHELLE; Mynderse Acad; Seneca Falls, NY; (Y); Mrchg Band; Yrbk Stf; Twrlr; Mst Outstndng Mjrt 82-83; Bryant & Stratton; Med Recptnst.

GOTTSHALL, SUSAN; Millbrook HS; Millbrook, NY; (Y); Church Yth Grp; Sec Sr Cls; JV Cheerleading; High Hon Roll; Hon Roll; Top Natl Sci Olympd 84; 1st Natn Sci Olympd 85; Vet Sci.

GOTTSTEIN, AMY; Colonie Central HS; Albany, NY; (Y); 4-H; Girl Scts; Chorus; Hon Roll; Mar Biol.

GOUGH, PHILLIP; Cardinal Mooney HS; Rochester, NY; (Y); Cmnty Wkr; School Musical; School Play; Stage Crew; Off Stu Cncl; Bsktbl; Bus.

GOULD, BRENDA; Albion HS; Albion, NY; (Y); Art Clb; Sec 4-H; Sec FFA; Teachers Aide; Bsktbl; Sftbl; Vllybl; 4-H Awd; Hon Roll; Brockport; Police.

GOULD, ELISA; Laguardia HS Of Music And The Arts; Brooklyn, NY; (Y); 84/588; Hon Roll; NHS; Spnsh Awd 81; Adelphi U; Dance.

GOULD, ELIZABETH; Tioga Central HS; Nichols, NY; (S); 7/96; Chess Clb; High Hon Roll; NHS; Ntl Latn Exam Awd 84.

GOULD, KEVIN; Granville Central HS; Granville, NY; (Y); AFS; Math Tm; Sec Sr Cls; Stu Cncl; Ftbl; Wt Lftg; Bio Achv 81-82; Hnrs Chem 82-83; Physcs Acclrtd 83-84; SUNY Plattsburgh; Bio.

GOULD, MICHAEL; Cornwall Central HS; Mountainville, NY; (Y); 12/198; Church Yth Grp; Drama Clb; Acpl Chr; Chorus; School Musical; School Play; Hon Roll; NHS; Opt Clb Awd; St Schlr; NYS Rgnts Schlrshp 85; Presdntl Acadmc Ftns Awd 85; Mntnvl Engn Co Schlrshp Awd 85; Albany Phrmcy Coll; Pharmcy.

GOULT, LISA; Bishop Ludden HS; Syracuse, NY; (Y); Art Clb; Church Yth Grp; Cmnty Wkr; Hosp Aide; Library Aide; Office Aide; Acpl Chr; Yrbk Phtg; Yrbk Stf; Chorus; Green Belt; Folk Group; Maria Regina; Occup Therpy.

GOURLAY, WILLIAM; Bishop Timon HS; Cheektowaga, NY; (S); 15/163; Quiz Bowl; Chorus; Nwsp Sprt Ed; Yrbk Stf; Lit Mag; Im Bsktbl; Var Crs Cntry; Var Socr; Hon Roll; U Of Buffalo; Law.

GOVENER, PAMELA; North Rose-Wolcott HS; Wolcott, NY; (Y); Pres Sec Church Yth Grp; Sec Ski Clb; Band; Chorus; Madrigals; Var Sftbl; Var Swmmng; High Hon Roll; NHS; NYSMA Vocal & Inst Comp; Childrens Dentistry.

GOVIA, CLIFFORD; North Eastern Acad; Brooklyn, NY; (S); 4/50; Church Yth Grp; Cmnty Wkr; Debate Tm; 4-H; FTA; Scholastic Bowl; Church Choir; Yrbk Bus Mgr; Yrbk Ed-Chief; Yrbk Phtg; Schlrshp Awd 84; Afro Amer Awd 84; Bible Awd 84.

GOW, KATHLEEN M; Batavia SR HS; Batavia, NY; (Y); 4/240; Pres Sec Church Yth Grp; Band; Chorus; Church Choir; Concert Band; Mrchg Band; Orch; Rep Stu Cncl; NHS; Regnts Schlrshp & Yth Salute 85; Genesee CC Merit Tuitn Schlrshp 85; Acadmc All Amer 85; Genesee CC; Humn Svcs.

GOWAN, BARBARA JO; Saranac Lake HS; Saranac Lake, NY; (Y); 4/134; Trs AFS; JV Var Socr; Var Trk; Bausch & Lomb Sci Awd; High Hon Roll; Hon Roll; Pres NHS; GAA; Band; Mrchg Band; Katherine B Lynch Schlrshp 85; Mary E Dicks Mem Schlrshp 85; NY St Phys Ftnss Awd 83; Clarkson U; Scndry Math Ed.

GOWIE, AMY; Columbia HS; Rensselaer, NY; (Y); Church Yth Grp; Teachers Aide; Stage Crew; Mgr(s); Score Keeper; Special Educ.

GOYAL, NAVEEN; Bronx High School Of Science; Flushing, NY; (Y); Drama Clb; Orch; School Play; Nwsp Rptr; NHS; Library Aide; Prfct Atten Awd; Westnghse Sci Talent Srch 85; Biomed Prgm 85; Bio Jrnl 85; Rensselaer Plythech; Med.

GOZ, LISA; Commach H S South; Dix Hills, NY; (S); Drama Clb; Math Tm; Chorus; School Musical; School Play; Nwsp Rptr; Rep Stu Cncl; High Hon Roll; Cmnty Wkr; Library Aide; Ntl Sci Merit Awd 83; Varsity Athltc Awd 84; Child Psychtrst.

GOZINSKY, STEVEN; Commack HS South; Commack, NY; (Y); Math Tm; Spanish Clb; Teachers Aide; Temple Yth Grp; Chorus; Nwsp Stf; JV Tennis; High Hon Roll; NHS; Golden Quill Awd Crtve Wrtng 84; Stonybrook U; Law.

GRABB, CYNTHIA J; South Lewis JR Sr HS; Glenfield, NY; (Y); 24/104; 4-H; GAA; Band; Jazz Band; School Musical; Cheerleading; Golf; 4-H Awd; Hon Roll; St John Fisher; Tchng.

GRABB, MARGARET C; Churchville-Chili SR HS; Rochester, NY; (Y); 22/300; Pres GAA; Sec JCL; Yrbk Sprt Ed; JV Var Bsktbl; JV Var Vllybl; High Hon Roll; NHS; JV Socr; Var Swmmng; Var Trk; Smr Exch Stu 84; Murial Dsgn For Gym Wall 84; Hon Mntn Schlstc Art Exhib 82-84; U Of Buffalo; Pre Med.

GRABDA, MARK; Solvay HS; Solvay, NY; (Y); Aud/Vis; Hon Roll; Boy Scts; Key Clb; Frsh Cls; Var Ftbl; Var Ice Hcky; Hnrble Mntn All-Cntry Footbl 84; Ecnmcs.

GRABER, MARK T; Averill Park HS; West Sand Lake, NY; (Y); Drama Clb; Ski Clb; School Musical; School Play; Nwsp Stf; JV Var Tennis; Computer Clb; Math Tm; Quiz Bowl; Teachers Aide; RPI High School Summer Program 84; NY ST Regents Schlrshp 85; Rensselaer Poly Tech; Comp Sci.

GRABER, PETER; Cardinal O Harra HS; Kenmore, NY; (Y); Ski Clb; JV Socr; Hon Roll; SUNYAB.

GRABER, ROBIN; Commack High School North; Commack, NY; (Y); Office Aide; Service Clb; Spanish Clb; Teachers Aide; Off Frsh Cls; Off Soph Cls; Off Jr Cls; Stu Cncl; High Hon Roll; NHS.

GRABIEC, JOHN M; Islip HS; Islip, NY; (Y); 27/256; Boy Scts; Band; Jazz Band; School Musical; JV Var Ftbl; Hon Roll; NHS; Church Yth Grp; Concert Band; Mrchg Band; Inst Of Gftd & Tlntd Stu 83; Robotics Inst 83; NYS Regnts Scholar 85; Rochester Inst; Comp Engrng.

GRABLE, COREY; John Dewey HS; Brooklyn, NY; (Y); Art Clb; Boy Scts; Church Yth Grp; Cmnty Wkr; JA; Church Choir; Josephine Lawrence Hopkins Fndtn; Police Athl Leag Art Awd 3rd 84; HS Cert Law Inst 85; Law.

GRABLER, TERESA; Stella Maris HS; Woodside, NY; (Y); French Clb; Math Tm; Science Clb; Band.

GRABOSKI, RAYMOND J; Notre Dame HS; Elmira, NY; (Y); 8/129; Latin Clb; Nwsp Ed-Chief; Var Tennis; High Hon Roll; NHS; Pep Clb; Teachers Aide; Nwsp Stf; Yrbk Stf; JV Bsbl; Red Crs Yth Ldrshp Prog; PAL Prog; U Of Scranton; Ec.

GRABOW, DOUGLAS E; Babylon HS; Babylon, NY; (Y); 2/150; Boy Scts; French Clb; Math Tm; Yrbk Stf; JV Var Crs Cntry; High Hon Roll; NHS; Ntl Merit Ltr; Sal; NY ST Rgnts Schlrshp 85; Polytechnic Inst Of NY; Engr.

GRABOWSKI, KATHLEEN; Bishop Grimes HS; Liverpool, NY; (Y); Church Yth Grp; Debate Tm; Hosp Aide; Capt Speech Tm; Chorus; JV Var Cheerleading; Hon Roll; NHS; Onondaga Cnty CC Schlr 85; Cmmnctns.

GRABOWSKI, KATHLEEN; The Franciscan Acad; Syracuse, NY; (Y); FBLA; GAA; Ski Clb; Speech Tm; Chorus; Pres Frsh Cls; Pres Jr Cls; Pres Sr Cls; Rep Stu Cncl; Bsktbl; Math Schlrshp 85-86; Incentive Schlrshp 80-81.

GRACE, AMANDA J; Franklin Delano Roosevelt HS; Hyde Park, NY; (Y); 40/325; Pres AFS; Cmnty Wkr; Drama Clb; French Clb; Church Choir; Hon Roll; Am Fld Svc Exchg Stu Belgium 83-84; NY ST Rgnts Schlrshp 85; Mount Holyoke Coll; Englsh.

GRACE, HILARY; Manhasset HS; Manhasset, NY; (Y); Cmnty Wkr; GAA; Hosp Aide; Library Aide; Office Aide; Nwsp Rptr; Lit Mag; Stu Cncl; JV Lcrss; Hon Roll; 100 Hnrs Awd Vlntr Awd; Psychtrst.

GRACEY, DAVE; Iona Prep; New Rochelle, NY; (Y); 62/196; Church Yth Grp; Var L Ftbl; Var L Trk; Var Wt Lftg; Camp Cnslr 83; Big Bros 85; Tchrs Aid Relg Prog Chrch 85; Bus Admin.

GRACH, KURT; Biship Ford HS; Brooklyn, NY; (Y); Band; Mrchg Band; Orch; Stage Crew; Art Clb; JV Lcrss; JV Socr; JV Wrstlng; Comp Sci.

GRACIA, BARBARA; Bishop Ford Central Catholic HS; Brooklyn, NY; (Y); Camera Clb; Church Yth Grp; Girl Scts; Hosp Aide; Speech Tm; Cheerleading; Engl.

GRADY, DEBRA; Man-Center For Sci & Math; Bronx, NY; (Y); JA; Math Clb; Office Aide; School Musical; Stage Crew; Nwsp Stf; Tennis; Hon Roll; Med.

GRADY JR, RICHARD; Hicksville HS; Hicksville, NY; (Y); Computer Clb; Latin Clb; Science Clb; Ski Clb; Rep Jr Cls; Var Tennis; JV Trk; Hon Roll; Jr NHS; NHS; Chmcl Sci.

GRADY, SUZANNE R; Buffalo Acad Of The Sacred Heart; Port Clinton, OH; (Y); Church Yth Grp; Pres JA; Sec Latin Clb; Scholastic Bowl; School Musical; Nwsp Stf; Rep Stu Cncl; Hon Roll; Dance Clb; Girl Scts; Amer Hosp Awd For Svc 84; Buffalo Cncl On Wrld Affairs Cert Of Merit 85; Med.

GRAF, DINA JO; Holley JR SR HS; Holley, NY; (Y); 4/85; Band; Chorus; Concert Band; Mrchg Band; Swing Chorus; Rep Frsh Cls; Rep Soph Cls; Rep Jr Cls; Stu Cncl; Co-Capt Cheerleading; Bogue Fndtn & NY ST Regnts Schlrshps 85; Delhi Ag & Tech; Vet Sci.

GRAF, JENNIFER A; Paul D Schreiber HS; Port Washington, NY; (Y); 95/432; Chorus; Madrigals; School Musical; School Play; Stage Crew; Nwsp Stf; Rep Stu Cncl; JV Gym; NHS; Regents Schlrshp 85; Pres Acdmc Ftns Awd 85; L I Cncl Soc Stud Achvt Awd 83 & 85; U CT; Bio.

GRAF, LISA; Bishop Kearney HS; Brooklyn, NY; (Y); Spanish Clb; Teachers Aide; Bowling; Gov Hon Prg Awd; NHS; Howard Golden Awd 82; Pre-Dental.

GRAF, MELANIE; Grand Island HS; Grand Is, NY; (Y); 34/281; Church Yth Grp; Cmnty Wkr; Dance Clb; English Clb; French Clb; Ski Clb; Powder Puff Ftbl; Hon Roll; NYS Regents Schlrshp 85; Clarkson U; Civil Engr.

GRAFF, KATHLEEN; Forestville Central HS; Forestville, NY; (Y); Mgr Yrbk Stf; Trs Jr Cls; JV Bsktbl; JV Crs Cntry; Im Vllybl; Schlrshp Of Stu Cncl 85; SUNY Fredonia; Socl Wk.

GRAFSTEIN, RICH; Clarkstown H S North; New City, NY; (Y); Comm.

GRAHAM, ALISTAIR; Springfield Gardens HS; Queens, NY; (Y); Boy Scts; Camera Clb; Camp Fr Inc; Exploring; Red Cross Aide; Color Guard; Drill Tm; School Play; Hon Roll; Rgnts Endrsmnt Merit; Manhattan Coll; Elec Engrng.

GRAHAM, COURTNEY; Middletown HS; Middletown, NY; (Y); Sec Church Yth Grp; Acpl Chr; Band; Chorus; Concert Band; Madrigals; School Musical; Swing Chorus; Symp Band; Yrbk Stf; Eaglet 85-86; Fred Waring Choreogrphy Wrkshp 85; Penn ST U; Elem Educ.

GRAHAM, CYNTHIA; James I O Neill HS; West Point, NY; (Y); Pres Church Yth Grp; Debate Tm; French Clb; Pep Clb; School Musical; JV Socr; JV Var Vllybl; High Hon Roll; Hon Roll; NHS; Brigham Young U; Chld Psych.

GRAHAM, DEANNA; Hartford Central HS; Hartford, NY; (S); Drama Clb; 4-H; GAA; Math Tm; OEA; Ski Clb; Varsity Clb; Acpl Chr; Band; Concert Band; 1985 Washngton Cnty Alt Dairy Prncss 85; Stu Rep Forum Of Senate 85; Bus.

GRAHAM, ELIZABETH A; East HS; Corning, NY; (Y); Dance Clb; Ski Clb; Yrbk Stf; Off Frsh Cls; Off Jr Cls; High Hon Roll; Hon Roll; Bus.

GRAHAM, HEATHER; Mt Mercy Acad; Buffalo, NY; (Y); FHA; JA; Latin Clb; Teachers Aide; Chorus; Church Choir; Yrbk Bus Mgr; 2nd Pl Latin Jr Clsscl Lge; 1st Pl Latin Frgn Lang Fair; Chld Dvlpmnt.

GRAHAM, IAN; Great Neck South HS; Great Neck, NY; (Y); Debate Tm; Model UN; NFL; Political Wkr; Speech Tm; School Play; Nwsp Ed-Chief; JV Tennis; Cit Awd; George Washington U Engr Medal 85; Amer Legion Cert Schl Awd 83; Polt Sci.

GRAHAM, KIEVE; De Witt Clinton HS; Bronx, NY; (Y); Art Clb; Church Yth Grp; Office Aide; JV Im Bsktbl; Cit Awd; Hon Roll; Prfct Atten Awd; Spec Mth Awd; Arista Awd & Pin; Engl, Sci, Soc Stud Awd; Fordam U; Acctng.

GRAHAM, KIMBERLY L; Honeoye Central Schl; Honeoye, NY; (S); Church Yth Grp; Spanish Clb; Teachers Aide; Chorus; School Musical; Swing Chorus; Yrbk Stf; High Hon Roll.

GRAHAM, MARK; City Honors HS; Buffalo, NY; (Y); German Clb; Ski Clb; School Play; Yrbk Phtg; Var Crs Cntry; Var Trk; Hon Roll.

GRAHAM, MARTHA S; St Raymonds Acad; Bronx, NY; (Y); 38/91; Intnl Clb; Spanish Clb; Chorus; 2nd Hnrs 85; Hunter Coll; Psych.

GRAHAM, MARY; Lowville Acad; Lowville, NY; (Y); AFS; Sec FTA; Teachers Aide; Varsity Clb; Var L Bsktbl; Var L Socr; Var L Sftbl; High Hon Roll; NHS; Prfct Atten Awd; Nomntd N Country Schlr Awd 85; Clarkson U Sci Awd 85; AFS Pad Way France 85; St Lawrence U; French Tchr.

GRAHAM, SHARON; Skaneateles HS; Skaneateles, NY; (S); Sec Band; Chorus; Jazz Band; Var Cheerleading; Tennis; High Hon Roll; NHS; Math.

GRAHAM, SONIA; Bishop Grimes HS; Syracuse, NY; (Y); Church Yth Grp; Library Aide; Chorus; Church Choir; School Play; Sec Jr Cls; Hon Roll; Parlmntrn Lamda Kappa Mu Xi Kopelle Sororty 84-85; Bishop Grimes Chrs Awds 82-85; Syracuse U; RN.

GRAHAM, THERESA A; Washingtonville HS; New Windsor, NY; (Y); JA; Spanish Clb; School Play; Symp Band; Nwsp Stf; Stu Cncl; Vllybl; NHS; NY ST Regents Schlrshp 85; Natl Hnr Soc Svc Awd 85; Fordham U; Comm.

GRAHAM, TODD; Albion SR HS; Albion, NY; (S); 19/170; Band; Chorus; Concert Band; Jazz Band; Mrchg Band; Pep Band; Symp Band; Fredonia ST U; Mus Sound Tech.

GRAINER, MELISSA; Little Falls HS; Little Falls, NY; (Y); 20/109; French Clb; Band; Concert Band; Mrchg Band; Orch; Yrbk Stf; JV Bsktbl; Pom Pon; Hon Roll; Highest Avg Math Algebra 82-83; Med Tech.

GRAJKO, CARI; Skaneateles HS; Skaneateles, NY; (S); GAA; Yrbk Phtg; Stu Cncl; Bsktbl; Golf; Powder Puff Ftbl; Socr; Sftbl; High Hon Roll; Hon Roll; Schltc Art Awds Cert Of Merit 84; Blu Ribbn Regnl Schltc Art Awd 84; Natl Schltc Awd Achvt Art 84; Psych.

GRAKOWSKY, MICHAEL; Charles H Roth HS; W Henrietta, NY; (Y); 52/210; German Clb; JA; High Hon Roll; Hon Roll; NYS Rgnts Schlrshp 85; U Of Rochester; Bus Admin.

GRAM, ALISA; Earl L Vandermeulen HS; Pt Jefferson Stat, NY; (Y); 32/280; FBLA; Yrbk Stf; Sec Sr Cls; High Hon Roll; Hon Roll; NHS; Pep Clb; Spanish Clb; Stage Crew; Rep Frsh Cls; Scl Sci.

GRAMAROSSA, NORA; Depew HS; Depew, NY; (Y); 113/254; Church Yth Grp; Cmnty Wkr; Girl Scts; Spanish Clb; Teachers Aide; Band; Concert Band; Mrchg Band; Rep Stu Cncl; Southwestern NY Schlrshp 84-85; U Pittsburgh; Phys Ther.

GRAMILA, PATRICIA A; Holy Trinity HS; Bethpage, NY; (Y); Ski Clb; Stage Crew; Hon Roll; NY ST Regnts Schlrshp 85; Nassau CC; Bus Adm.

GRAMZA, NANCYANN; Emerson Vocational HS; Buffalo, NY; (Y); Nwsp Stf; Yrbk Stf; Bowling; Socr; Tennis; Vllybl; Culnry Svc.

GRANADO, EDDIE; George Washington HS; New York, NY; (Y); 79/315; Teachers Aide; Im Bsbl; Im Fld Hcky; Im Ice Hcky; Capt Vllybl; Hunter Coll; Mass Media.

GRANADOS, LISA; Christopher Columbus HS; Bronx, NY; (Y); 79/792; Church Yth Grp; Drama Clb; Office Aide; Spanish Clb; Chorus; School Musical; School Play; Hon Roll; SR Chorus 85; Hnr Rll 84; Sagrado Corazon; Trsm.

GRANBOIS, TOM; Weedsport Central HS; Weedsport, NY; (Y); 4/100; Math Clb; Spanish Clb; Ftbl; Var L Trk; Im Vllybl; Im Wrstlng; Cit Awd; High Hon Roll; Prfct Atten Awd.

GRAND, BETH A; Warsaw Central Schl; Warsaw, NY; (Y); 17/93; Debate Tm; Drama Clb; French Clb; Science Clb; Band; Chorus; School Musical; School Play; Variety Show; Rep Stu Cncl; Alumni Schlrshp 85; Knox Coll; Pre-Law.

GRAND, EMILY; Edward R Murrow HS; Brooklyn, NY; (Y); 11/725; Library Aide; Math Tm; Office Aide; Scholastic Bowl; Ski Clb; Teachers Aide; School Musical; Gov Hon Prg Awd; Ntl Merit Ltr; E R Murrow Acadmc Excllnc Plaque 85; Prnts Assc Awd Exmplry Svc 85; Princeton U.

GRANDE, HALLIE E C; The Buffalo Seminary; Orchard Pk, NY; (Y); Yrbk Phtg; Sec Frsh Cls; Trs Soph Cls; Sec Sr Cls; JV Var Fld Hcky; JV Var Lcrss; Hon Roll; NHS; AFS; Cmnty Wkr; 1/2 Schlrshp Seminary; MIP Lacrosse 81-82; Chem Lab Aide Cert, Smmr Intrnshp Buffalo ST Coll 85; U Toronto; Eng.

GRANDEL, KIM; Romulus Central Schl; Romulus, NY; (S); Spanish Clb; JV Socr; JV Capt Sftbl; JV Capt Vllybl; High Hon Roll; Hon Roll; Natl Phy Ed Awd 84-85; Lingst.

GRANDINETTI, THOMAS; Hudson HS; Hudson, NY; (Y); Boys Clb Am; Church Yth Grp; Varsity Clb; Var L Bsbl; Var L Ftbl; Hon Roll; Bus Admin.

GRANEY, JOHN; Iona Preparatory Schl; Hartsdale, NY; (Y); 50/200; Church Yth Grp; Debate Tm; Quiz Bowl; Service Clb; Speech Tm; VP Frsh Cls; Frsh Hnrs & Soph 2nd Hnrs; Psych.

GRANEY, JOSEPH; Auburn HS; Auburn, NY; (Y); 1/420; Hosp Aide; Model UN; Golf; High Hon Roll; NHS.

GRANGER, ALLAN J; Twin Tiers Baptist HS; Elmira, NY; (Y); 1/23; Chess Clb; Debate Tm; Quiz Bowl; Chorus; Off Sr Cls; Mgr Wrstlng; High Hon Roll; Hon Roll; Val; Christian Spirit Awd 84; Mark Twain Cnty Acad Achvr 85; Hstry Awd 82 & 84; OK Bptst Coll; Bible.

GRANGER, JUDY; Wellsville HS; Wellsville, NY; (Y); 13/130; Pres Frsh Cls; Pres Sr Cls; Rep Stu Cncl; High Hon Roll; Hon Roll; NHS; Ntl Merit SF; Pres Schlr; FHA; Hosp Aide; NYS Regents Schlrshp; Natl Hnr Soc Schlrshp; Buffalo U; Engl.

GRANT, AGNES; John Dewey HS; Brooklyn, NY; (Y); Church Yth Grp; Cmnty Wkr; Church Choir; Corp Law.

GRANT, ANJALI; The Bronx H S Of Science; Riverdale, NY; (Y); JA; Office Aide; Spanish Clb; Teachers Aide; Socr; High Hon Roll; Hon Roll; Ntl Merit Ltr; Arch.

GRANT, BETSY; Massena Central HS; Massena, NY; (Y); French Clb; Girl Scts; Band; Concert Band; Mrchg Band; Pep Band; Rep Stu Cncl; Var Bsktbl; Var Sftbl; Prfct Atten Awd; SADD 84-85; Yth Cncl 84-85; Bus Mngmnt.

GRANT, BRIAN; Cornwall Central HS; Newburgh, NY; (Y); Ski Clb; Yrbk Phtg; Sec Jr Cls; VP Sr Cls; Rep Stu Cncl; Var Trk; Hon Roll; Med.

GRANT, CHRISTINE E; Gilboa-Conesville Central HS; Gilboa, NY; (Y); Drama Clb; GAA; Pep Clb; Concert Band; Jazz Band; Swing Chorus; Yrbk Phtg; Var Capt Cheerleading; Var Socr; Pres Schlr; Miss Loves Baby Soft Intrl Bty Const 84; Miss Empr ST Buty Cont 84; Pres Phy Ftns Awd 84; Fash Inst Tech; Appr Prod.

GRANT, DOUGLAS; Cardinal Spellman HS; Bronx, NY; (Y); Boy Scts; Church Yth Grp; Mrchg Band; Hon Roll; 2nd Hnrs 83-85; Syracuse; Accntnt.

GRANT, JACQUALINE; Bishop Kearney HS; Rochester, NY; (Y); Library Aide; Nwsp Phtg; Yrbk Stf; High Hon Roll; Hon Roll; NHS; Ntl Merit Ltr; Schlrshp 82-86; Hopwood Smmr Schlrshp Prgm-Lynchburg 85; Bioengr.

GRANT, JODI; Oyster Bay HS; Oyster Bay, NY; (Y); AFS; Drama Clb; Mathletes; Political Wkr; Chorus; School Musical; Nwsp Ed-Chief; Nwsp Rptr; Yrbk Rptr; Yrbk Stf.

GRANT, KATHLEEN M; Williamsville North HS; E Amherst, NY; (Y); 67/315; Trs Spanish Clb; JV Sftbl; Hon Roll; Rgnts Schlrshp 85; U Of Buffalo; Bus Admin.

GRANT, MARC; Cardinal Spellman HS; Bronx, NY; (Y); Bsktbl; Trk; Rad Tech.

GRANT, MARGARET; Caledonia-Mumford HS; Caledonia, NY; (Y); Science Clb; VP Spanish Clb; Chorus; Concert Band; Mrchg Band; Yrbk Stf; Var Crs Cntry; Var Trk; NHS.

GRANT, MELISSA; Little Falls JR SR HS; Little Falls, NY; (S); 14/89; Exploring; Girl Scts; Band; Concert Band; Jazz Band; Mrchg Band; Orch; Pep Band; Yrbk Stf; Hon Roll; Music Awd 84; Acctg.

GRANT, MICHAEL J; Alden Central HS; Alden, NY; (Y); Boy Scts; 4-H; FFA; Letterman Clb; Rep Jr Cls; Rep Sr Cls; Var L Bsbl; Var Capt Ftbl; Var Capt Wrstlng; Arch.

GRANT, MICHELE; Le Roy HS; Clearwater, FL; (Y); Spanish Clb; Varsity Clb; Chorus; School Musical; Yrbk Phtg; Yrbk Stf; JV Bsktbl; Var Socr; Var Sftbl; Var Vllybl; All Trnmnt Sftbl Awd 85; Livingston County All Stars Sftbl Awd 85; U Sthrn FL; Bio Tchr.

GRANT, PETAL; Sheepshead Bay HS; Brooklyn, NY; (Y); Drama Clb; Math Clb; Teachers Aide; Chorus; School Musical; Jr Cls; Sftbl; Tennis; Vllybl; Cert Merit Sci Hortcltr 85; Cert Achvt Hghst Stndng Rcrdkpng 85; Borough Of Manhattan CC; Nrsng.

GRANT, ROBERT; Bishop Ford C C HS; Brooklyn, NY; (Y); 15/375; Computer Clb; Drama Clb; Teachers Aide; Church Choir; School Play; Yrbk Phtg; High Hon Roll; NHS; Dist Atty Citation Hnr 85; Intl Yth Achvt Awd; Allegheny Coll; Pre-Law.

GRANTO, GINA ALICIA; Niagara Falls HS; Niagara Falls, NY; (Y); Church Yth Grp; Library Aide; Nwsp Phtg; Nwsp Rptr; Yrbk Stf; Stu Cncl; CC Awd; Cit Awd; Miss Rainbow Queen 84; Niagara U; Comm.

GRAPES, LYNETTE; Niagara Wheatfield HS; North Tonawanda, NY; (Y); Church Yth Grp; Hosp Aide; Chorus; Pres Frsh Cls; Pres Soph Cls; Pres Jr Cls; Pres Sr Cls; Pres Stu Cncl; Var JV Socr; Var Hon Roll; D Youville; RN.

GRASIER, ROBERT E; Niskayuna HS; Schenectady, NY; (Y); Chorus; Church Choir; Jazz Band; Orch; School Musical; Symp Band; NHS; Ntl Merit Ltr; Cert Of Merit Music 84; Comp Sci.

GRASING, ANNE; Oceanside HS; Oceanside, NY; (Y); Key Clb; Service Clb; Spanish Clb; Chorus; Yrbk Stf; Var Crs Cntry; Var Trk; Hon Roll; Trck Pins, Metals 83-84; Stony Brook; Pre Law.

GRASSI, DENISE J; Gorton HS; Yonkers, NY; (Y); Spanish Clb; Nwsp Rptr; Nwsp Stf; Lit Mag; Rep Church Yth Grp; JV Var Cheerleading; Cert Excel Westchester Cty 84-85; Bus Ed Assoc; Bus Mgmt.

GRASSMANN, ROBERT J; Cicero North Syracuse HS; Clay, NY; (Y); Am Leg Boys St; Ski Clb; Var Gym; JV Socr; Var Trk; Jr NHS; NHS.

GRASSO, CATHY; Valley Stream North HS; Franklin Sq, NY; (Y); 8/164; Debate Tm; Drama Clb; NFL; Chorus; School Musical; Nwsp Rptr; Yrbk Phtg; Pres Frsh Cls; Hst Soph Cls; Capt Socr; Parnt Tchr Stu Assoc Acadmc Schlrshp 85; St Johns U; Comm.

GRASSO, LAUREL; Bainbridge Guilford HS; Guilford, NY; (Y); 3/73; Ski Clb; Spanish Clb; Chorus; Var Bowling; Var Cheerleading; Var Tennis; Var Trk; High Hon Roll; Jr NHS; NHS; MVP Tnns Plyr 84-85; Mst Imprvd Tnns Plyr 82-83; Hghst Engl Rgnts 84-85; Cornell; Psych.

GRATZON, PATRICIA; The Ursuline Schl; Yonkers, NY; (Y); 51/129; Hosp Aide; Political Wkr; Yrbk Stf; Var JV Fld Hcky; Var Trk; Hon Roll; NY U Prtl Schlrhsp 85; MIP Field Hocky 84; NY U; Pre-Med.

GRAU, BARBRA; East Meadow HS; East Meadow, NY; (S); 60/414; Debate Tm; FBLA; Key Clb; Model UN; Temple Yth Grp; Nwsp Stf; Yrbk Stf; Var L Score Keeper; JV Sftbl; Hon Roll; Accntng.

GRAU, JENNFER; Newfield HS; Selden, NY; (Y); Service Clb; Varsity Clb; Rep Stu Cncl; Var Fld Hcky; Var Sftbl; Var Vllybl; High Hon Roll; Hon Roll; NHS; Athlt Schlr & Socl Stud Awd 82-83; Pre Law.

GRAUE, MARY LOU; The Mary Louis Acad; S Ozone Park, NY; (Y); 5/283; Girl Scts; Office Aide; School Play; Sr Cls; Im Bowling; Im Vllybl; High Hon Roll; Hon Roll; NHS; Spain Schlrshp 84; St Johns U NY; Chmstry.

GRAUER, ALLAN; Martin Van Buren HS; Hollis Hills, NY; (Y); 31/650; JA; Math Clb; Science Clb; Temple Yth Grp; School Play; Yrbk Stf; Tennis; Hon Roll.

GRAUMENZ, CATHY; Paul V Moore HS; Bernhards Bay, NY; (Y); 20/297; Trs Church Yth Grp; Trs German Clb; Concert Band; Mrchg Band; Symp Band; Stu Cncl; High Hon Roll; Hon Roll; NHS; Prfct Atten Awd; NY ST Regents Schlrshp; Onodaga CC; Accntnt.

GRAUPMAN, MARK; Edison Tech & Occupational Ed Ctr; Rochester, NY; (Y); Var Bsbl; 9th Yr Math Awd 83; Mst Imprvd Plyr Awd Bsbl 85; Elec Drftng.

GRAVELLE, NORBERT; E J Wilson HS; Spencerport, NY; (Y); 7/280; Am Leg Boys St; Boy Scts; Exploring; JCL; Latin Clb; Pres Model UN; JV Capt Swmmng; JV Tennis; High Hon Roll; Hon Roll; Latin Achvt Awd; Rochester Inst Tech; Elec Engr.

GRAVES, DARREN N G; Kings Park SR HS; Kings Pk, NY; (Y); 196/393; Twn Spnsrd Sccr Leag; Jiu Jitsu; Hofstra; Robtcs.

GRAVES, SUSAN; John S Burke Catholic HS; Chester, NY; (Y); Cmnty Wkr; 4-H; GAA; Ski Clb; Rep Sr Cls; Rep Stu Cncl; JV Cheerleading; Var Crs Cntry; JV Var Socr; Var Sftbl; Sportsmnshp Awd, Lay Fac Assoc Schlrshp,Dist Council 82, Schlrshp Awd 85; Scranton U; Acctng.

GRAVES, TJADE; Bishop Loughlin M H S; Brooklyn, NY; (Y); Var Crs Cntry; Var Trk; Syracuse U.

GRAY, CAROL; Sacred Heart HS; Bronx, NY; (S); 10/236; Pres Church Yth Grp; Intnl Clb; NHS; Acad Perfrmnc Hnrs 83; High Hnrs 84; Regents Schlrshp 84; Bus.

GRAY, CHARMAINE; Holy Trinity HS; Hempstead, NY; (S); 21/318; Yrbk Stf; Off Stu Cncl; Hon Roll; NEDT Awd; Math Awd 84; Georgetown U; Crdlgst.

GRAY, DAVID; Westlake HS; Thornwood, NY; (Y); Computer Clb; Science Clb; School Play; Cit Awd; Mech Engrng.

GRAY, ELIZABETH; Bethlehem Central HS; Delmar, NY; (Y); GAA; Ski Clb; Band; Concert Band; Sec Frsh Cls; Stu Cncl; JV Var Bsktbl; JV Var Fld Hcky; Hon Roll; SUNY Advncd Spnsh 85; Librl Arts.

GRAY, FAITHLYN; Washington Irving HS; Brooklyn, NY; (Y); Hon Roll; Prfct Atten Awd; Church Yth Grp; Church Choir; Exec Secy.

GRAY, JANICE; Pulaski HS; Pulaski, NY; (S); 4-H; French Clb; Math Clb; Ski Clb; Chorus; Concert Band; Mrchg Band; School Musical; Yrbk Phtg; Yrbk Stf; Snow Incentive Awd 81 & 83; Psychlgy.

GRAY JR, LEON; Cardinal Spellman HS; Bronx, NY; (Y); Cmnty Wkr; Band; Concert Band; Jazz Band; Mrchg Band; Pep Band; Variety Show; Trk; Elctrcl Engrng.

GRAY, MICHELLE; Immaculata HS; New York, NY; (Y); Trs Church Yth Grp; Chorus; Color Guard; Drill Tm; Sec Soph Cls; VP Jr Cls; Sec Trs Stu Cncl; Capt Bowling; Swmmng; Hon Roll; Hgh Gme Bwlng Grls; Prmtd Hghr Belt Judo; Adelphi U; Law.

GRAY, PETER; Fox Lane HS; Mt Kisco, NY; (Y); 8/279; Drama Clb; VP French Clb; Trs Pres Intnl Clb; Ski Clb; Temple Yth Grp; Madrigals; School Play; French Hon Soc; High Hon Roll; NHS; NCCJ 3 Day Ldrshp Conf 84; Polit Sci.

GRAY, ROBERT; Lake George Central HS; Lake George, NY; (Y); Computer Clb; Var Ftbl; Im Wt Lftg; Aud/Vis; JV Bsktbl; Hon Roll; Comp Sci.

GRAY, SABRINA; Boys & Girls HS; Brooklyn, NY; (Y); Computer Clb; Dance Clb; JA; Office Aide; Chorus; Sec Jr Cls; High Hon Roll; Hon Roll; Prfct Atten Awd; Val; Legal Secry.

GRAY, SHARON; Whitesboro SR HS; Whitesboro, NY; (Y); 87/350; Church Yth Grp; Spanish Clb; Band; Chorus; Concert Band; Mrchg Band; Orch; School Musical; JV Var Bowling; Im Sftbl; Daemen Coll; Phy Thrpy.

GRAY, STEVE; Shenendehowa HS; Clifton Park, NY; (Y); Church Yth Grp; German Clb; Ski Clb; Band; Socr; High Hon Roll; Hon Roll; Sci.

GRAY, TAMMY; Niagara Falls HS; Niagara Falls, NY; (Y); Church Yth Grp; Office Aide; Teachers Aide; Yrbk Stf; JV Vllybl; Hon Roll; NHS; Aud/Vis; Spanish Clb; Varsity Clb; Ntl Hist Day Awd 85; Niagara U; Comp Prgrmr.

GRAY, TAMMY; Sodus Central HS; Sodus, NY; (Y); 16/112; French Clb; Varsity Clb; Band; Concert Band; Mrchg Band; JV Var Cheerleading; JV Var Tennis; High Hon Roll; Hon Roll; Prfct Atten Awd; Comm.

GRAY, TRACEY R; Jericho HS; Jericho, NY; (Y); 37/228; Cmnty Wkr; Service Clb; JV Var Vllybl; Hon Roll; NHS; Vlybl MVP 84; Rgnts ST Schlrshp 85; U Of MI.

GRAY, WESLEY; Ripley Central HS; Ripley, NY; (Y); Church Yth Grp; Band; Church Choir; Concert Band; Mrchg Band; Bsktbl; Golf; Mgr(s); Hon Roll; Art Shw Awds 1st Pl 83-85; Golf-MVP 83-85; Chld Dev.

GRAYS, ANITA DOREEN; Sidney HS; Sidney, NY; (Y); 40/104; Sec Trs FFA; GAA; Math Clb; Sec Spanish Clb; Pres Soph Cls; Var L Bsktbl; NHS; Church Yth Grp; 4-H; Chorus; Sidney Rotary Clb Schlrshp 85; Rgnts Schlrshp Rcpnt 85; HS Cncl Schlrshp 85; Broome CC; Phys Ther.

GRAYSON, ADAM; Onteora HS; West Hurley, NY; (S); Temple Yth Grp; Chorus; Nwsp Rptr; Nwsp Stf; Yrbk Stf; Trs Frsh Cls; Trs Soph Cls; Trs Jr Cls; Trs Sr Cls; Stu Cncl; Tufts; Lawyer.

GRAYSON, NANETTE; South Park HS; Buffalo, NY; (Y); Nwsp Stf; Lgl Secy.

GRAYSON, RICHARD HARRY; Mount Vernon HS; Mount Vernon, NY; (Y); Aud/Vis; Chess Clb; Key Clb; Spanish Clb; Yrbk Stf; Var Capt Bsbl; Wt Lftg; Hon Roll; Jr NHS; Stu Of Mnth Spn 84; Sci.

GRAZIADEI, DANIEL; Cardinal Spellman HS; Bronx, NY; (Y); Camera Clb; Church Yth Grp; Nwsp Stf; High Hon Roll; Hon Roll; MIT; Mech Engrng.

GRAZIANO, CHRIS; Vestal SR HS; Apalachin, NY; (Y); Nwsp Rptr; JV Bsbl; Var Wrstlng; High Hon Roll; Hon Roll; Lawyer.

GRAZIANO, LAURA B; Bronx High Schl Of Science; Flushing, NY; (Y); Church Yth Grp; Office Aide; Church Choir; Drm & Bgl; Lit Mag; Hon Roll; Ntl Merit SF; Hnrb Mntn Citywide Poetry Cont 85; Schlrshp Boston U Tanglewood Inst 85.

GRAZIANO, MICHAEL S; City Honors HS; Buffalo, NY; (Y); #8 In Class; English Clb; Math Tm; Chorus; Orch; Ntl Merit SF; Opt Clb Awd; PSAT Semi Fnlst; Physics.

GRAZIANO, PAMELA; Commack High School North; Commack, NY; (Y); 74/440; Chorus; Yrbk Stf; Var Socr; High Hon Roll; Hon Roll; NHS; Pres Schlr; Rgnts Schlrshp 85; SUNY-GENESEO; Acctng.

GRAZIANO, VINCE; East Islip HS; Islip Terrace, NY; (Y); Varsity Clb; Band; Var Crs Cntry; JV Trk; Hon Roll; Vrsty Lttrs Trck 83-85; MVP Vrsty Trck 85; Accntnt.

GRECO, CARMINE J; Sachem North HS; Holbrook, NY; (Y); 151/1340; Computer Clb; Science Clb; Bsbl; Wt Lftg; Hon Roll; Ecnmcs.

GRECO, CLAUDINE; Bishop Kearney HS; Brooklyn, NY; (Y); 18/350; Spanish Clb; Yrbk Stf; Hon Roll; NHS; 2nd Hnrs Iona Coll Lang Cont 84; Comm Art.

GRECO, JIM; Mahopac HS; Mahopac, NY; (Y); 35/425; Ntl Hnr Soc 85; Engrng.

GRECO, LARA; Fairport HS; Fairport, NY; (Y); Ski Clb; Varsity Clb; Concert Band; Flag Corp; Mrchg Band; Var Crs Cntry; Var Swmmng; Hon Roll; Fairport Area Swm Tm Ldrshp Awd 85; Ped Hematology.

GRECO, LORI; Clinton HS; Clinton, NY; (Y); Girl Scts; Yrbk Stf; JV Sftbl; Hon Roll; Toursm.

GRECO, LUISA; St Catharines Acad; Bronx, NY; (Y); 20/220; Teachers Aide; Hon Roll; NHS; Iona Lang Cntst 2nd Hnrs Itln; Hist Merit Awd; All-Amer Schlr; Med.

GRECO, MICHAEL; Kenmore West SR HS; Kenmore, NY; (Y); Am Leg Boys St; Church Yth Grp; Letterman Clb; Ski Clb; Varsity Clb; Chorus; Var Capt Bsbl; JV Bsktbl; Var JV Ftbl; Im Tennis; MVP Bsbl,Ftbl 83-84; Ldrshp Awd 84; Ashand Coll; Hist.

GRECO, VICTORIA; Smithtown High Schl East; Nesconset, NY; (Y); Cmnty Wkr; GAA; Orch; Off Soph Cls; Off Jr Cls; Var Badmtn; Var Mgr(s); Var Score Keeper; Hon Roll; Acctng.

GRECO, VITO J; Rome Free Acad; Rome, NY; (Y); JV Socr; High Hon Roll; JETS Awd; Jr NHS; NHS; Highst Avg Scholar Math Awd 83; Scholar Soc Studies Awd 83; Clarkson Potsdam NY; Elec Engr.

GREDISH, GERARD P; Mount St Michael HS; Yonkers, NY; (Y); 75/309; Concert Band; Stage Crew; Nwsp Phtg; Nwsp Sprt Ed; Yrbk Phtg; Yrbk Sprt Ed; Schl Hnrs 85.

GREELEY, CHRISTINA; The Ursuline Schl; Mt Vernon, NY; (Y); 45/140; Dance Clb; Ski Clb; Stu Cncl; Var Fld Hcky; Var Trk; Hon Roll; HS Schlrshp 82-85; MVP Vrsty Fld Hcky 84-85; Villanova U; Pre-Med.

GREELEY, WILLIAM; Hoosick Falls Central Schl; Buskirk, NY; (Y); 80/106; Aud/Vis; Computer Clb; Radio Clb; Rep Stu Cncl; Kiwanis Awd; Svc Awd Clss Duty 85; Herkimer County CC; Rado Brdcs.

GREEN, AMY; Warwick Valley HS; Warwick, NY; (Y); 20/200; Art Clb; Camera Clb; Church Yth Grp; Cmnty Wkr; Hosp Aide; Yrbk Stf; JV Var Bsktbl; Tennis; Trk; Hon Roll; AZ ST U; Busnss Mgmt.

GREEN, ANDREW W; Palmyra-Macedon Central HS; Palmyra, NY; (Y); 23/185; Varsity Clb; Acpl Chr; Chorus; School Musical; School Play; Var Capt Bsktbl; Var Capt Golf; Var JV Socr; Ember-Riddl Aerontcl U; Aerntcl.

GREEN, BENJAMIN; Harry S Truman HS; Bronx, NY; (Y); Math Tm; Hon Roll; Tp Jr In Mth & Sci; Ntwrthy Achvt & Sustnd Exllc In Mth & Engl.

GREEN, BETH; West Genesee SR HS; Camillus, NY; (Y); Mathletes; Math Tm; Ski Clb; Spanish Clb; Temple Yth Grp; Chorus; Mrchg Band; School Musical; Yrbk Phtg; Yrbk Stf; Math League 83-84; Spcl Ed.

GREEN, CATHERINE A; The Dalton Schl; New York, NY; (Y); Library Aide; Var L Bsktbl; Var Capt Socr; Var Capt Sftbl; Ntl Merit Ltr; Harvard.

GREEN, CHERYL; Amsterdam HS; Amsterdam, NY; (Y); Trs Church Yth Grp; FBLA; Yrbk Stf; Cheerleading; Tennis; Hon Roll; Cmptr Sci.

GREEN, DANIEL; James I O Neill HS; West Point, NY; (Y); French Clb; School Musical; Nwsp Rptr; Frnch I III Acad Awd 84-85; Liberal Arts Coll; Frgn Lang.

GREEN, DONALD; Bishop Kearney HS; Rochester, NY; (Y); Rep Frsh Cls; JV Var Ftbl; Im Wt Lftg; JV Wrstlng; Hon Roll; RIT; Tool & Die.

GREEN, GERARD; Archbishop Molloy HS; Whitestone, NY; (Y); Service Clb; Im Bsktbl; Im Ftbl; JV L Socr; Im Capt Sftbl; Hon Roll; Coach Parish Trk Tm 83-84; Altarboy 82-83.

GREEN, JEFF; Niskayuna HS; Schdy, NY; (Y); Boy Scts; Exploring; JV Var Bsktbl; Var Ftbl; Bus.

GREEN, JENNIFER; Marlboro HS; Milton, NY; (Y); 8/150; Church Yth Grp; Drama Clb; Pres Sec 4-H; Chorus; Church Choir; School Musical; Yrbk Stf; 4-H Awd; High Hon Roll; NHS; Hghst Grd Fr Rgnts Exm 84; Hghst Engl Rgnts Exm 85; Hghst Soc Stud Rgnts Exm 85; Psych.

GREEN, KENNETH J; Central Islip HS; Central Islip, NY; (Y); Drama Clb; School Musical; School Play; Stage Crew; Lit Mag; NHS; NEDT Awd; Band; Concert Band; Mrchg Band; Central Islip Tchrs Assn Humntrn Awd 84; Advnc Mech Drwg Awd 85; Milwaukee Schl Engrng; Arch.

GREEN, KRISTINE; Liverpool HS; Clay, NY; (S); 45/794; Ski Clb; Spanish Clb; School Musical; Rep Stu Cncl; Var L Fld Hcky; Var L God Cntry Awd; JV Trk; High Hon Roll; Jr NHS; NHS; Outstndng Data Processng Stu Of Yr 84; SUNY U Buffalo; Computer Sci.

GREEN, LISA M; Walter Panas HS; Peekskill, NY; (Y); 4/211; Debate Tm; Drama Clb; NFL; Temple Yth Grp; Chorus; School Musical; High Hon Roll; NHS; Ntl Merit Ltr; St Schlr; Clark U; Clinical Psychologist.

GREEN, MARGARET; Grand Island HS; Grand Island, NY; (Y); Im Crs Cntry; U Of Buffalo-SUNY; Phrmcst.

GREEN, MARLENE; Edward R Murrow HS; Brooklyn, NY; (Y); 28/725; Cmnty Wkr; Library Aide; Teachers Aide; Chorus; Variety Show; Rep Sr Cls; Off Stu Cncl; Cit Awd; High Hon Roll; Ntl Merit Schol; Untd Fdrtn Tchrs Schlrshp 85; Rectent Schlrshp 85; Chncllrs Hnr Roll 85; NY U; Human Resrcs Admin.

GREEN, MICHELLE; Cicero North Syracuse HS; Clay, NY; (S); 143/622; CAP; Library Aide; Lit Mag; Accntnt.

GREEN, MICHELLE Y; Valley Central HS; Walden, NY; (Y); Camera Clb; Trs Church Yth Grp; Trs 4-H; Spanish Clb; Band; Concert Band; Mrchg Band; Im Bsktbl; Var Crs Cntry; JV Socr; Gladys E Boleman Awd 85; Vly Cntrl Schlrshp Cncl 85; Loleta S Mons Nrsng Schlrshp 85; Hope Coll; Psych.

GREEN, PAMELA; Ft Ann Central HS; Ft Ann, NY; (Y); 17/57; VICA; Band; Concert Band; Mrchg Band; Yrbk Stf; JV Cheerleading; Stat Score Keeper; Hon Roll; Csmtlgy.

GREEN, ROSEANN; Saint John The Baptist HS; Brentwood, NY; (Y); Office Aide; Teachers Aide; Mrchg Band; JV Var Pom Pon; JV Powder Puff Ftbl; Hon Roll; Manhattan; Psych.

GREEN, SETH; Rocky Point HS; Rocky Point, NY; (Y); 65/190; Chess Clb; Temple Yth Grp; Chorus; Bsbl; Tennis; Regnets Schlrshp; Merit & Challenge Schlrshp; NY Inst Of Tech; Chiropractor.

GREEN, SHAWN; Torrejon American HS; San Angelo, TX; (Y); ROTC; Band; Color Guard; Concert Band; Drill Tm; Jazz Band; School Musical; DAR Awd; Hon Roll; Carr ROTC Schlrshp 85; Amer Legion Gen Military Excllnce Awd 85; Retired Offcrs Assn Awd 84; Angelo ST U; Tchr.

GREEN, WENDY; John C Birdlebough HS; Phoenix, NY; (Y); 17/200; Dance Clb; Sec French Clb; Band; Mrchg Band; Nwsp Stf; JV Var Cheerleading; Var L Sftbl; Var L Trk; High Hon Roll; FBLA; Bus Awd 82; High Acad Achvt Awd Sftbl 85; Grad Hnrs; Dean JC; Dance.

GREEN, WENDY SOPHIA; Mount Vernon HS; Mount Vernon, NY; (Y); Aud/Vis; Key Clb; Library Aide; Office Aide; Spanish Clb; Hon Roll; Jr NHS; Engl.

GREENAKER, JAMES; Byron-Bergen Schl; Bergen, NY; (Y); Debate Tm; Model UN; Yrbk Stf; Rep Stu Cncl; Var Bsktbl; Var Socr; Var Trk; Coach Jesse Owens Trk Tm 85; Coach Elem Bsktbl 80-81 & 83-85; Mock Trials 85; Chem Engrng.

GREENAWAY, ANDREA; Northeastern Acad; Jamaica, NY; (Y); Church Yth Grp; Cmnty Wkr; Girl Scts; Church Choir; Drill Tm; Lit Mag; Stu Cncl; Cheerleading; Ntl Merit Schol; Art Awd 82-83; Spn Awd 84-85; Columbia Union Coll; Eng.

GREENAWAY, FOUSTINA; Walton HS; Bronx, NY; (Y); Office Aide; Chorus; Prfct Atten Awd; All City Chrs 84; Cert Peer Cnslng 85; Math Awd 83; John Jay Schl Perf Art; Pre-Law.

GREENBERG, BRIGITTE; Connetquot SR HS; Oakdale, NY; (S); 5/723; Nwsp Ed-Chief; Nwsp Rptr; Soph Cls; Cheerleading; Trk; High Hon Roll; Trs Jr NHS; Trs NHS; Connetquot Teachers Assn Outstndng Achvt Awd 82; Outstndng Achvt Awd Spanish 82; Academic Awd 82; Journalism.

GREENBERG, JEFFREY; Green Meadow Waldorf Schl; Woodcliff Lake, NJ; (Y); Chorus; Orch; Yrbk Phtg; Yrbk Stf; Lit Mag; Var Bsktbl; Var Lcrss; Capt Var Socr; NHS; Colgate U; Pol Sci.

GREENBERG, JULIE E; Laguardia HS Of Music & Arts; New York, NY; (Y); 80/590; Dance Clb; Drama Clb; French Clb; PAVAS; Y-Teens; Jr NHS; NHS; Dncr.

GREENBERG, ROBERT J; Lawrence HS; Atlantic Bch, NY; (Y); Pres Aud/Vis; Boy Scts; Capt Chess Clb; Pres Computer Clb; Capt Math Clb; Pres Science Clb; Trs VICA; Ed Nwsp Bus Mgr; High Hon Roll; NHS; Natl Sci Olympd Awd Physcs 85; Schl Engrng & Appld Sci Awd 85; RITEC Awd Brkhvn Natl Labs 85; Bio-Med Engrng.

GREENBERG, SHARON B; John F Kennedy HS; Bronx, NY; (Y); 15/982; Band; School Musical; Wt Lftg; Hon Roll; Ntl Merit SF; St Schlr; UFT Schlrshp 85-89; Schl Cert Exc Math 82; U CA-BERKELEY; Lang.

GREENBERG, STEVEN M; Baldwin HS; Baldwin, NY; (Y); 18/503; Capt Mathletes; High Hon Roll; NHS; Ntl Merit Ltr; Hi Hnrs LI Sci Cngrs 84 & 85; Bronze Mdl LI Math Fair 83; Spcl Rec UC Davis SSTP 84; Cooper Union; Elect Engrng.

GREENBLATT, JASON DOV; Yeshira University S H Tmsta; Forest Hills, NY; (Y); Yrbk Ed-Chief; Hon Roll.

GREENE, ANDREA; Jamesville-Dewitt HS; Fayetteville, NY; (Y); 93/246; German Clb; Key Clb; Pep Clb; High Hon Roll; Hon Roll; Psych.

GREENE, BONNIE L; New Rochelle HS; New Rochelle, NY; (Y); Key Clb; Nwsp Stf; Yrbk Ed-Chief; Lit Mag; Rep Stu Cncl; NHS; Spanish NHS; Schl Serv & Drama Awd 82; NYS Rgnts Schlrshp 85.

GREENE JR, JEROME A; General Brown HS; Dexter, NY; (Y); Am Leg Boys St; French Clb; Trs Key Clb; Rep Frsh Cls; Rep Jr Cls; Sec Stu Cncl; Var L Bsktbl; Var L Lcrss; High Hon Roll; Hon Roll; Canton ATC; Busnss Admin.

GREENE, JODI M; Wellsville HS; Wellsville, NY; (Y); 18/130; Art Clb; School Musical; School Play; Stage Crew; Yrbk Stf; Rep Stu Cncl; Var Capt Cheerleading; Var JV Pom Pon; Hon Roll; Alfred ST Coll; Human Svcs.

GREENE, KATHRYN F; Kings Park HS; Kings Park, NY; (Y); 97/446; Chorus; Sftbl; High Hon Roll; NY ST Rgnts Schlrshp 85; SUNY Stonybrook; Bio Sci.

GREENE, MARIA; North Babylon SR HS; N Babylon, NY; (Y); Art Clb; Church Yth Grp; French Clb; Intnl Clb; Office Aide; Teachers Aide; Chorus; Church Choir; Nwsp Stf; Rep Sr Cls; Hofstra; Corp Law.

GREENE, MICHELE; Horseheads SR HS; Horseheads, NY; (S); 13/407; German Clb; Varsity Clb; Concert Band; Drm Mjr(t); Jazz Band; Mrchg Band; Var Sftbl; Var Vllybl; High Hon Roll; Advt.

GREENE, PATRICIA A; Holy Trinity Diocesan HS; Levittown, NY; (S); 5/362; Teachers Aide; Stu Cncl; Bowling; Cheerleading; High Hon Roll; Hon Roll; NHS; Math Awd 83-84; Intl Bus.

GREENE, PAULA; Holy Angels Acad; Buffalo, NY; (Y); French Clb; Chorus; Church Choir; School Musical; School Play; Vllybl; Hon Roll; Math Clb; Teachers Aide; Natl Math Cntst 85; Excllnc In Chorus & Folk Group 83-85; Buffalo ST Coll; Comp Sci.

GREENE, RAQUEL G; The Bronx High Schl Of Science; Bronx, NY; (Y); Church Yth Grp; Teachers Aide; Band; Church Choir; Concert Band; Yrbk Stf; Cit Awd; Hon Roll; Prfct Atten Awd; Trnsltr.

GREENE, RHONDA; Clara Barton HS; Brooklyn, NY; (Y); Church Yth Grp; Office Aide; Teachers Aide; Church Choir; Vllybl; High Hon Roll; Sal; Hnr Roll Awd 82; Cert Of Recgntn Schlrshp 82-83; Accntnt.

GREENEBAUM, WENDY M; Marlboro Central HS; Marlboro, NY; (Y); 21/145; Girl Scts; Band; VP Concert Band; VP Mrchg Band; Pep Band; Cit Awd; High Hon Roll; Hon Roll; Jr NHS; NHS; Dutchess Cnty CC; DP.

GREENFIELD, BARAK J; Hebrew Academy Of Nassau County; Great Neck, NY; (S); 5/70; Computer Clb; Capt Debate Tm; Math Tm; Political Wkr; Orch; Nwsp Rptr; Stu Cncl; High Hon Roll; NHS; Frnscs Tourn Fnlst 83 & 84; Belkin Schlrshp, Rgnts Schlrshp 85; Yeshiva U; Med.

GREENFIELD, CAREN; Port Richmond HS; Staten Island, NY; (Y); 5/565; Capt Debate Tm; Math Tm; Office Aide; Teachers Aide; Nwsp Stf; Yrbk Stf; Cit Awd; DAR Awd; French Hon Soc; Gov Hon Prg Awd; Assoc Of Tchrs Math NYC 85; James C Hackett Awd Excel 85; Rutgers U; Math.

GREENFIELD, DANIEL; Watkins Glen HS; Watkins Glen, NY; (S); Aud/Vis; High Hon Roll; Hon Roll; NHS; Prfct Atten Awd; 2nd Pl A-V Awd-Video 84-85; 2nd Pl Woodshp Constrctn Awd 82-83; Data Procssng.

GREENFIELD, ERIC; Delaware Academy And Central Schl; Delhi, NY; (Y); Am Leg Boys St; German Clb; Yrbk Stf; Pres Jr Cls; Var Golf; Var Wrstlng; Hon Roll; Jr NHS; NHS; Boy Scts; AMA Camp 85; Clarkson; Engrng.

GREENFIELD, MICHAEL; Fairport HS; Fairport, NY; (Y); Trs Math Tm; Sec Model UN; Temple Yth Grp; Lib Concert Band; Soroptimist; Mrchg Band; High Hon Roll; NHS; Ntl Merit Ltr; Rep Stu Cncl; Monroe Cnty Math Leag Top 84-85; Al-Cnty Band 82-85; Chase Lincoln Math Awd 85; Engrng.

GREENIER, KEEGAN D; Chazy Central Rural Schl; Chazy, NY; (Y); 2/48; School Play; Yrbk Stf; High Hon Roll; NHS; Ntl Merit Schol; $1000 Sci Awd & $3500 Trustee Awd Clarkson U 85; NYS Math/Sci Tchrs Schlrshp 85; NYS Rgnts Scshlrshp; Clarkson U Potsdam; Sec Educ.

GREENLEAF, KIMBERLY; Whitesboro SR HS; Utica, NY; (Y); Hosp Aide; Orch; Yrbk Stf; Rep Stu Cncl; Var Cheerleading; Powder Puff Ftbl; Trk; Var JV Vllybl; Hon Roll; Ltr Vlybl 85; 3 Blue Rbbns 1st Pl Trk Field Evnts 83; Med.

GREENMAN, C RONALD; Byron Bergen JR SR HS; Bergen, NY; (Y); Church Yth Grp; Cmnty Wkr; Spanish Clb; JV Var Bsbl; High Hon Roll; Hon Roll; Jr NHS; NHS; Prfct Atten Awd; ST Bonaventure U; Accntnt.

GREENMAN, SAM; Copiaque HS; Amityville, NY; (Y); Computer Clb; Spanish Clb; Variety Show; Nwsp Rptr; Yrbk Stf; JV Socr; Hon Roll; Gftd & Tlntd Smmr Mrn Bio Cls 84; Vet Med.

GREENOUGH, LAURA; St Johns Prep; Astoria, NY; (Y); 47/525; Teachers Aide; Chorus; Drm & Bgl; School Musical; Hon Roll; Pres NHS.

GREENSPAN, MIREET; Yeshiva University HS For Girls; Flushing, NY; (Y); Nwsp Ed-Chief; Lit Mag; Max Stern Schlrshp 85; Queens Coll Schlrs Prog 85; Stern Coll; Law.

GREENSTEIN, JESSICA; Watkins Glen HS; Watkins Glen, NY; (S); 4/126; 4-H; Math Clb; Chorus; Concert Band; Drm & Bgl; Jazz Band; Mrchg Band; French Hon Soc; Hon Roll; NHS; Med.

GREENWALD, DANIEL; Barker Central Schl; Barker, NY; (Y); Cmnty Wkr; 4-H; French Clb; Varsity Clb; Pres Jr Cls; Pres Sr Cls; Bsbl; Bsktbl; Ftbl; Swmmng; MVP Swmr & Mst Imprvd Ftbl Plyr 84; All League Swmr, All League Ftbl 84-85; Alfred; Anmnl Sci.

GREENWALD, JEFF; Mt Vernon HS; Mount Vernon, NY; (Y); Aud/Vis; Key Clb; Var Socr; Var Capt Tennis; Hon Roll; Bio Stu/Mnth 84; Outstndng Athl/Mnth 83-84; Marine Bio.

GREENWICH, GRACE; Mount Vernon HS; Mount Vernon, NY; (Y); Church Yth Grp; Dance Clb; Chorus; Church Choir; Orch; School Musical; Cheerleading; Crs Cntry; Trk; Jr NHS; Cert Awd Trk, Hghst Avr Keybrdng, Ltr Orch 84; Prsdntl Phy Ftnss Awd 85; Hlth.

GREENWOOD, JODIE; Frewsburg Central HS; Jamestown, NY; (Y); 1/90; Am Leg Aux Girls St; 4-H; Spanish Clb; Band; Mrchg Band; JV Sftbl; Capt Swmmng; Var Trk; NHS; Medcl Prfssn.

GREER JR, KENNETH; Mynderse Acad; Seneca Falls, NY; (S); Var JV Lcrss; Hon Roll; JV Lttr 83; Vrsty Lttr 84; Army.

GREER, LORI S; Avon Central Schl; Avon, NY; (Y); 2/105; Pres Church Yth Grp; Pres 4-H; Spanish Clb; VP Band; Chorus; Jazz Band; School Musical; High Hon Roll; NHS; Sal; NY ST Rgnts Schlrshp 85; Ithaca Coll Schlrshp 85; Squires Schlrshp 85; Ithaca Coll; Comp Sci.

GREER, MARK; Hannibal Central HS; Sterling, NY; (S); Key Clb; Math Clb; High Hon Roll; Hon Roll; Prfct Atten Awd; Bus.

GREER, STEVEN; Cicero North Syracuse HS; Clay, NY; (S); 7/652; Ski Clb; Swmmng; High Hon Roll; Jr NHS.

GREGG, LATAJI; Susan E Wagner HS; Staten Island, NY; (Y); Cmnty Wkr; Hosp Aide; JA; Model UN; Office Aide; Radio Clb; Hon Roll; Prfct Atten Awd; Bus.

GREGG, ROBIN; Samuel J Tilden HS; Brooklyn, NY; (Y); Art Clb; Dance Clb; Drama Clb; Teachers Aide; Chorus; School Play; Stage Crew; Off Sr Cls; Cheerleading; Sftbl; Drake Inst; Sec Sci.

GREGO, MAUREEN; St Dominic HS; Syosset, NY; (Y); 11/119; Church Yth Grp; Quiz Bowl; School Musical; Nwsp Stf; Trs Frsh Cls; VP Stu Cncl; High Hon Roll; NHS; NEDT Awd; St Francis Coll Endwd Schlrshp 85; St Francis Coll; Dntstry.

GREGOIRE, ANNE; Mt Mercy HS; Buffalo, NY; (Y); 25/160; Spanish Clb; Cheerleading; Hon Roll; MI Chrldr 82-83; U Of Buffalo; Nrsg.

GREGOIRE, CHRISTINE; Romulus HS; Romulus, NY; (S); Office Aide; Ski Clb; Chorus; School Musical; Yrbk Stf; VP Sr Cls; Rep Stu Cncl; JV L Bsktbl; Var L Socr; DAR Awd; Lib Arts.

GREGOIRE JR, JAMES P; Romulus Central HS; Romulus, NY; (Y); Am Leg Boys St; Aud/Vis; Office Aide; Ski Clb; Spanish Clb; Yrbk Stf; Rep Jr Cls; Stat Bsbl; Crs Cntry; Hon Roll; Spnsh.

GREGOR, ERIC C; Kenmore East SR HS; Tonawanda, NY; (Y); 317/1200; Church Yth Grp; Scholastic Bowl; Letterman Clb; Varsity Clb; Hon Roll; JV Bsbl; Bsktbl; Bowling; Ftbl; Socr; All Star Tm-Sectnl IV Vllybl 85; MVP-VRSTY Tennis-Sectnls Finals 85; St U Coll; Bio.

GREGORIO, LAURA; Half Hollow Hills East HS; Dix Hills, NY; (S); Church Yth Grp; Hst FBLA; Service Clb; Orch; Nwsp Ed-Chief; Lit Mag; JV Trk; High Hon Roll; Jr NHS; Spanish NHS; Outstndng Achvt Hnr Awd Home Ec 83; Guidance Aide; County Winner Rotary Intnal Writing Contest.

GREGORY, DAPHNE; Pulaski JR SR HS; Pulaski, NY; (Y); Cmnty Wkr; Girl Scts; Chorus; Sftbl; Trk; Snow Incntve Awd 85; Ftnss USA AAHPER Sr Awd 84; CCBI; Secy.

GREGORY, DARCY; Northern Adirondack Central HS; Ellenburg Depot, NY; (Y); 3/105; Key Clb; Library Aide; Pep Clb; Trs Band; Concert Band; Mrchg Band; Trs Frsh Cls; Trs Soph Cls; Trs Jr Cls; High Hon Roll; Capt Chrng Squad 85-86; Math.

GREGORY, DAVID; Chenango Valley HS; Binghamton, NY; (Y); Political Wkr; Var L Bsktbl; Var L Tennis; Jr NHS; NHS; Fin.

GREGORY, JOYCE; Cathedral HS; Brkn, NY; (Y); 78/298; Chess Clb; Library Aide; Chorus; Hon Roll; Prfct Atten Awd; Piano Achvt Awd 85; Med.

GREGORY, LAURA; New Berlin Central HS; S New Berlin, NY; (Y); 7/50; Debate Tm; Sec Trs 4-H; Yrbk Ed-Chief; VP Frsh Cls; Pres Soph Cls; Var L Socr; 4-H Awd; High Hon Roll; Jr NHS; Lion Awd; Stan Home Scholar 85; Natl Chem Soc Awd Sci Proj 84; Rep New Berlin NYS Stu Senate 84; St John Fisher Coll; Econ.

GREGORY, LYNNE; St Francis Prep; Flushing, NY; (S); 50/693; Church Yth Grp; Dance Clb; Hosp Aide; Math Clb; Lit Mag; Twrlr; High Hon Roll; Jr NHS; NHS; Ntl Merit Ltr.

GREGORY, MARY; Nanuet HS; Nanuet, NY; (Y); Church Yth Grp; Variety Show; Sec Soph Cls; Sec Jr Cls; Sec Sr Cls; Rep Stu Cncl; JV Capt Bsktbl; JV Capt Socr; Hon Roll; NHS; Advrtsng.

GREINER, CATHERINE; Sacred Heart Acad; Garden City, NY; (S); 23/190; Chorus; School Musical; School Play; Stage Crew; Yrbk Stf; High Hon Roll; Hon Roll; NHS; Trig Hnrs Course; Hnrs Engl Course; Holy Cross; Bus Admin.

GREINER, DINA; Marlboro HS; Marlboro, NY; (Y); #6 In Class; Church Yth Grp; Band; Chorus; Concert Band; Mrchg Band; Var Trk; High Hon Roll; NHS; Mariest Coll; Bus Mgmt.

GREINER, MICHAEL; Skaneateles HS; Skaneateles, NY; (Y); 25/165; Socr; Wrstlng; High Hon Roll; Hon Roll; NHS; CCC; Math.

GRELL, TRACEY; North Shore HS; Glenwood Landing, NY; (Y); Exploring; Girl Scts; Varsity Clb; JV Bsktbl; Var Fld Hcky; Score Keeper; Sctn VIII-NASSAU Cnty Fld Hcky Chmpns 82-83; AA Div Flr Hcky Chmpns 85.

GRELLA, ALBERICO; North Shore HS; Glen Cove, NY; (Y).

GRELLA, MARC J; Monsignor Farrell HS; Staten Island, NY; (Y); 67/300; Nwsp Stf; Yrbk Stf; Rep Sr Cls; Rep Stu Cncl; Im Bsktbl; Crs Cntry; Var Trk; Hon Roll; NHS; Ntl Merit SF; Pre-Med.

GRELLA, SUSAN M; John Adams HS; Howard Beach, NY; (Y); 26/598; Library Aide; Office Aide; Nwsp Rptr; Stu Cncl; High Hon Roll; NHS; NY ST Regents Schlrshp Awd 85; St Johns U Schlst Excel Awd 85; SUNY Queen Coll; Accntng.

GREMILLION, PATRICIA; Longwood HS; Ridge, NY; (Y); 178/472; Girl Scts; Nwsp Stf; Yrbk Phtg; Lit Mag; Stu Cncl; Crs Cntry; Sftbl; Trk; Hon Roll; Jr NHS; St Marys Of MD Albany; Pre Law.

GRENDAHL, MICHELLE A; Saratoga Springs HS; Wilton, NY; (Y); 23/465; Girl Scts; Variety Show; High Hon Roll; Jr NHS; NHS; Germn Merit Awd; Regnts Schlrshp; SADD; Regnts Hnrs Diplm; Mt Holyoke Coll; Sci.

GRENNILLE, SHERI; Port Jervis HS; Montague, NJ; (Y); 1/180; Hosp Aide; Math Tm; Scholastic Bowl; High Hon Roll; NHS; Ntl Merit Ltr; Val; Rensselaer Polytech Inst Math & Sci Medal 84; Bucknell U; Chem Engr.

GRESALFI, CHARLES R; Lynbrook HS; E Rockaway, NY; (Y); 78/265; Boy Scts; Varsity Clb; Lit Mag; Var Capt Ftbl; L Var Lcrss; Var Capt Wrstlng; Hon Roll.

GRESKO, JOYCE; South Park HS; Buffalo, NY; (Y); Chorus; Pres Jr Cls; Hon Roll; Prfct Atten Awd; Outstndng Grds, Atten 84-85; Hnr Clss 82-85; Lgl Secy.

GRESOCK, GREGORY; Horseheads SR HS; Horseheads, NY; (Y); 7/405; Boy Scts; Model UN; Mrchg Band; Var Crs Cntry; High Hon Roll; NHS; Eagle Awd 85; 1st Pl Mnsfld Math Cmptn 85; Sci.

GRESS, DARREN; Grand Island SR HS; Gr Island, NY; (Y); Red Cross Aide; Ski Clb; Band; Concert Band; Jazz Band; Mrchg Band; Pep Band; School Musical; Variety Show; JV Golf; Acad Awd Ltr 84-85; Potsdam; Data Proc.

GRESSLER, KATHRYN; Mohawk Central HS; Mohawk, NY; (S); Art Clb; Teachers Aide; Mrchg Band; Variety Show; Sec Soph Cls; Rep Stu Cncl; Bsktbl; Jr NHS; NHS; Spanish Clb; Academic Awd 83-84; Educ.

GREUBEL, KIRK; Stamford H Calhoun HS; Merrick, NY; (Y); Boy Scts; Church Yth Grp; Var Lcrss; Var Swmmng; Ord Arrow, Lifeguard Cert 85; Slippery Rock U PA.

GREY, ORVILLE; Andrew Jackson HS; Jamaica, NY; (Y); Leo Clb; Office Aide; Teachers Aide; Score Keeper; Socr; High Hon Roll; Chmpnshp Soccer Trnmnt 85.

GRIDLEY, SHARON; West Genesee SR HS; Camillus, NY; (Y); 5/500; Cmnty Wkr; Hosp Aide; Capt Var Swmmng; High Hon Roll; NHS; Med.

GRIEB, KIMBERLY; Hilton Central HS; Hilton, NY; (Y); L Chorus; School Musical; High Hon Roll; Hon Roll.

GRIER JR, DAVID E; E L Vandermeulen HS; Mt Sinai, NY; (Y); 21/286; Cmnty Wkr; Computer Clb; Math Clb; Var Ftbl; Var Trk; JV Wrstlng; Cit Awd; High Hon Roll; Hon Roll; NHS; Aero Engrng.

GRIESBACH, ELIZABETH; Our Lady Of Victory Acad; Bronx, NY; (S); 11/159; French Clb; PAVAS; Lit Mag; Tennis; French Hon Soc; NHS.

GRIESE, LAURI; Morrisville Eaton Central HS; Morrisville, NY; (Y); VP 4-H; Band; Mrchg Band; Vllybl; 4-H Awd; Hon Roll; Comm.

GRIESEMER, KRISTY; Hoosick Falls Central HS; Hoosick Falls, NY; (Y); 5/104; Pres 4-H; French Clb; Ski Clb; Varsity Clb; Stu Cncl; Var Cheerleading; 4-H Awd; High Hon Roll; NHS; ST Comptr Publ Presntns 83-85; Engrng.

GRIFFATON, MICHAEL C; St Anthonys HS; Central Islip, NY; (Y); Art Clb; Chess Clb; Concert Band; Yrbk Stf; High Hon Roll; NHS; Spanish NHS; Pblc Rltns Clb-VP 84-85; Pre Med.

GRIFFIN, ANDRE; John Dewey HS; Brooklyn, NY; (Y); Boys Clb Am; Cmnty Wkr; 4-H; JA; Band; Im Bsktbl; Im Ftbl; Im Gym; Im Trk; Im Wt Lftg; Bryant Coll; Busnss Admin.

GRIFFIN, BILL; Chruchville-Chili SR HS; Rochester, NY; (Y); Boys Clb Am; Computer Clb; Varsity Clb; Var Capt Bsktbl; Ftbl; JV Var Mgr(s); JV Var Score Keeper; Pepsi NBA Hot Shot Bsktbl Gld Medlst 83; St Pius X JR Hgh Asst Coach Bsktbl 84-85; Potsdam SUNY; Physcs.

GRIFFIN, BRENDAN M; Yorktown HS; Yorktown Hts, NY; (Y); Pres Sr Cls; Var Bsbl; Var Capt Bsktbl; Var Capt Ftbl; High Hon Roll; Hon Roll; Accntng.

GRIFFIN, CHARLES; Freeport HS; Freeport, NY; (Y); Pres Acpl Chr; Pres Band; Chorus; Jazz Band; Pres Mrchg Band; School Musical; School Play; Variety Show; Nwsp Phtg; Yrbk Phtg; Music.

GRIFFIN, CORA; Monroe SR JR HS; Rochester, NY; (Y); Library Aide; Math Tm; Office Aide; Red Cross Aide; Teachers Aide; Chorus; Bsktbl; Coach Actv; Fld Hcky; Mgr(s); All Star Tm Vlybl & Sccr 84-85; MVP Vlybl 82-84; FL ST; Acctng.

GRIFFIN, DONALD; Greenwich Central HS; Cambridge, NY; (Y); Church Yth Grp; FFA; Varsity Clb; Var Crs Cntry; Var Trk; Im Wt Lftg; Hon Roll; Prfct Atten Awd; FFA 84; Outstndg Ldrshp FFA 85; Ofcr De Moly Sr Cnclr 85; Cornell Clg; Mech Engrng.

GRIFFIN, KERRY; St John The Baptist HS; Lk Ronkonkoma, NY; (Y); 17/550; Dance Clb; Office Aide; Varsity Clb; Variety Show; Yrbk Stf; Rep Frsh Cls; Co-Capt Pom Pon; High Hon Roll; Chnnl 13 Art Cntst Fnlst 85; Schl Ldrshp Awd 83.

GRIFFIN, KIM; Warrensburg Central Schl; Warrensburg, NY; (S); 1/76; Pres French Clb; Varsity Clb; Sec Jr Cls; Var JV Bsktbl; Var JV Fld Hcky; Var JV Vllybl; Hon Roll; NHS; Pres Schlr; Amer Legion Awd 82; Mltry Acad; Engrng.

GRIFFIN, MARY JEAN; Salamanca Central HS; Salamanca, NY; (Y); Camera Clb; Drama Clb; French Clb; Girl Scts; Spanish Clb; Band; Concert Band; Jazz Band; Mrchg Band; Pep Band; Math & Sci Awd Mst Outstndng 83; MVP Var Rifle Tm 84; Dstngshd Expert Rifle Awd 84; Bio.

GRIFFIN, MAUREEN; Bishop Kearney HS; Brooklyn, NY; (S); Church Yth Grp; Ski Clb; Capt Bowling; NHS; Regents Schlrshp 85; St Johns U; Bus Admin.

GRIFFIN, MIKE; Manlius Pebble Hill HS; Cazenovia, NY; (Y); Coach Actv; Var L Socr; Var L Trk; Hon Roll; 2nd Team All Star Soccer 84-85; 3rd Leag Meet In Mile Relay Track 84-85; Springfield Coll; Health Fitnss.

GRIFFIN, THERESE; Notre Dame Acad; Staten Island, NY; (Y); Computer Clb; French Clb; Intnl Clb; Math Clb; Science Clb; Hydro Quebec Frnch Hnr Cert 85; Lawyer.

GRIFFIN, TODD; Sayville HS; Sayville, NY; (Y); 5/365; VP Key Clb; Concert Band; Orch; Var Capt Socr; Cit Awd; High Hon Roll; NHS; Pres Schlr; Var Capt Tennis; David M Jones Memrl, Harvey Case Memrl & Sayville Tchrs Assoc Schlrshps 85; U Of Rochester; Bio.

GRIFFING, ALEXANDRA E; The Bronx High School Of Science; New York, NY; (Y); JA; Concert Band; Orch; Nwsp Stf; Psychtry.

GRIFFING, AMY L; Bayport Blue Point HS; Blue Point, NY; (Y); 5/222; Church Yth Grp; Key Clb; Mathletes; Band; Jazz Band; Orch; School Musical; Sftbl; Jr NHS; NHS; Regents Coll Schlrshp 85; SUNY-ONEONTA; Math.

GRIFFING, GEOFFREY; Longwood HS; Coram, NY; (Y); 28/500; Aud/Vis; Drama Clb; Math Tm; Chorus; School Musical; School Play; Stage Crew; Yrbk Stf; High Hon Roll; NHS; Pre-Med.

GRIFFITH, DAVID A; Skaneateles HS; Skaneateles, NY; (Y); 56/165; CAP; Drama Clb; School Musical; School Play; Stage Crew; Mgr(s); JETS Awd; Ntl Merit Ltr; NYS Rgnts Schlrshp; Onondaga CC; Engr.

GRIFFITH, KAREN; Bay Shore HS; Bay Shore, NY; (Y); 3/386; Drama Clb; Thesps; Chorus; Color Guard; Orch; School Musical; School Play; Stage Crew; Nwsp Rptr; VP Frsh Cls; Tom Shrt Awd Mst Outstndng Stu 82; Ntl Mnrty Achvt Awd 84; Jean T Flynn Awd 85; Vassar Coll; Pre Med.

GRIFFITH, KATHRYN; Bishop Loughlin HS; Brooklyn, NY; (Y); Cmnty Wkr; Girl Scts; Office Aide; Teachers Aide; High Hon Roll; Hon Roll; Bus Admin.

GRIFFITH, PAUL; Amsterdam HS; Ft Johnson, NY; (S); 5/319; Band; Drm Mjr(t); Jazz Band; Mrchg Band; High Hon Roll; NHS; Comp Engrng.

GRIFFITH, ROBERT; Garden City HS; Garden City, NY; (S); 15/325; Spanish Clb; Rep Frsh Cls; Rep Soph Cls; Rep Jr Cls; Var L Bsktbl; Var Capt Ftbl; Var Capt Lcrss; High Hon Roll; Jr NHS; NHS; Hnrb Mntn Ftbl All Cnfrnc 84; All Cnfrnc Nassau Cnty Empire ST Team 84; Ivy League Schl.

GRIFFITH, ROD; Walter Panas HS; Peekskill, NY; (Y); Aud/Vis; FBLA; Office Aide; Teachers Aide; Nwsp Stf; Stu Of Mnth Spn, Engl 85; Cmmnctns.

GRIFFITHS, ANN MARIE; Susquehanna Valley HS; Conklin, NY; (Y); Chorus; Concert Band; Jazz Band; Mrchg Band; Orch; School Musical; Pres Frsh Cls; NHS; Spanish NHS.

GRIFFITHS, JEFF; Milford Central HS; Milford, NY; (S); 1/30; Am Leg Boys St; VP Computer Clb; Trs Spanish Clb; Jazz Band; Mrchg Band; Var L Bsbl; Var JV Bsktbl; Var L Socr; Jr NHS; NHS; Elec Engr.

GRIFFO, LORI; Solvay HS; Solvay, NY; (Y); Off Soph Cls; Off Jr Cls; JV Sftbl; High Hon Roll; Hon Roll; NHS; Intl Frgn Lang Awd 84-85; Acad All Amer 84-85; Syracuse U.

GRIGER, KATHLEEN; Horseheads Senior HS; Horseheads, NY; (S); 19/407; Varsity Clb; Chorus; Concert Band; Mrchg Band; Rep Stu Cncl; Capt Var Cheerleading; High Hon Roll; NHS; Church Yth Grp; Spanish Clb; Chemung Cnty JR Mss Schlstc Achvt Awd 85; U DE; Fin Mgr.

GRIGOLI, JOHN; Oneonta SR HS; Oneonta, NY; (Y); Camera Clb; Computer Clb; JV Bsbl; Hon Roll; Spanish Clb; Yrbk Phtg; :Comp Prog.

GRIGONIS, AMY; Mattituck HS; Cutchoque, NY; (Y); Sec 4-H; German Clb; Chorus; School Play; Variety Show; Hon Roll; Elem Ed.

GRILLI, BARBARA; Spackenkill HS; Poughkeepsie, NY; (Y); 42/176; Leo Clb; Temple Yth Grp; Yrbk Stf; VP Tennis; Bus.

GRILLO, DOMINICK J; Tottenville HS; Staten Island, NY; (Y); 42/895; Cmnty Wkr; Debate Tm; Office Aide; Teachers Aide; NHS; Ntl Merit SF; School Play; Acad Olympics 82-85; NY Cty Theo Roosevelt Dclmtn Cntst 83; Brooklyn Coll Fndtn Hnrs Schlr; Williams Coll; Math.

GRILLO, JOHN M; Sachem HS; Lk Grove, NY; (Y); 137/1206; Art Clb; Ski Clb; Spanish Clb; Yrbk Stf; Rep Jr Cls; Tennis; Wrstlng; Jr NHS; NHS; Cornell; Architect.

GRIMALDI, MARIA; West Seneca East SR HS; W Seneca, NY; (Y); DECA; French Clb; German Clb; JA; Spanish Clb; Hon Roll; NHS; Ntl Merit Ltr; Prfct Atten Awd; Certs Awd Frnch Spnsh, Grmn 82-85; Cert Honnr Francais Ntl Frnch Cntst 83-85; U Of Buffalo; Intntl Bus.

GRIMALDI, MIRELLA; St Catharine Acad; Bronx, NY; (Y); 5/205; Teachers Aide; Stu Cncl; NHS; Natl Hstry & Govt & Natl Engl Merit & Acadmc All Amer Awds 84-85.

GRIMBERG, ADDA; Oceanside HS; Oceanside, NY; (Y); 1/556; Pres French Clb; Key Clb; Pres Orch; High Hon Roll; Jr NHS; NHS; Ntl Merit SF; Val; Long Island String Fstvl 84; AATF Natl Fr Cont-Levl 4 1st Pl Nassau 84; Med.

GRIMES, JAMES; Bishop Maginn HS; Albany, NY; (Y); Letterman Clb; Swing Chorus; Nwsp Stf; JV Var Bsbl; JV Capt Bsktbl; Var Capt Ftbl; Var Capt Trk; Pres Schlr; JV MVP 83-85; U N ME; Bus Adm.

GRIMES, JILL; Greenwich Centgral HS; Greenwich, NY; (Y); AFS; Girl Scts; Hosp Aide; Pep Clb; JV Sftbl; High Hon Roll; Hon Roll; NHS; Maria Coll Albany; Occu Ther.

GRIMES, PAMELA; Medina HS; Medina, NY; (Y); 5/156; VP Church Yth Grp; Acpl Chr; Chorus; Rep Stu Cncl; Var L Sftbl; Stat Swmmng; Var L Vllybl; High Hon Roll; NHS; Prfct Atten Awd; Phy Educ.

GRIMINS, STACY; C-PP West HS; Corning, NY; (Y); Exploring; Chorus; Hon Roll; Geneso; Educ Tchng.

GRIMM, CYNTHIA S; Saint Edmund HS; Brooklyn, NY; (Y); French Clb; Gym; Vllybl; Cit Awd; Hon Roll; Prfct Atten Awd; Frnch Lang Fair 2nd & 3rd 83; Sci Fair 3rd 84; St Johns Coll; Law.

GRIMM, JOHN W; Charles H Roth HS; Industry, NY; (Y); 9/195; Am Leg Boys St; Boy Scts; Church Yth Grp; Pres Soph Cls; Stu Cncl; Coach Actv; Var Capt Ftbl; Var Capt Lcrss; God Cntry Awd; NHS; Henrietta Yth Hall Of Fame 85; Eagle Scout Awd 85; Librl Arts.

GRIMM, KRISTEN T; Scotia Glenville HS; Scotia, NY; (Y); French Clb; Spanish Clb; Lit Mag; High Hon Roll; Hon Roll; NCTE Awd; Russell Sage Annl Poetry Celebrtn 1st Prz 85; 1st Stdnt Judg Scotias 10th Annl Mock Trl 85; St John Fisher Coll; Prof Wrtg.

GRIMMER, MARY E; Notre Dame HS; Utica, NY; (Y); 8/174; Cmnty Wkr; Mathletes; Spanish Clb; Nwsp Rptr; Capt Bsktbl; Trk; Vllybl; High Hon Roll; Hon Roll; VP NHS; Recipient Of Garnett Newspaper Carrier Schlrshp 85; Candidate For Utica Optimists Yth Of Mnth 85; Elementary Education.

GRIMSHAW, JOE; Northeastern Clinton Central Schl; Champlain, NY; (Y); Art Clb; Model UN; Yrbk Ed-Chief; Cert Of Awd Outstndng Accmplshmnts In Art 84-85; Cert Of Apprctn Outstndng Art Contrbtn To Schl 84-85; Cmmrcl Art.

GRINDER, ANN MARIE; Frontier Central HS; Blasdell, NY; (Y); French Clb; Concert Band; Crs Cntry; Tennis; Trk; French Hon Soc; High Hon Roll; Hon Roll; NHS; NEDT Awd; Bio.

GRINE, MARY EILEEN; Nordin Acad; Kenmore, NY; (S); 22/92; Service Clb; Chorus; School Musical; Hon Roll; NHS; Certfd Peer Mnstr 84-85; Stdnt Asst Campus Mnstr 85; Theatr.

GRINNELL, HEATHER L; Waterville Central HS; Waterville, NY; (Y); Varsity Clb; Band; Chorus; School Musical; Swing Chorus; Yrbk Stf; Rep Stu Cncl; Cheerleading; Score Keeper; Trk; Regents Schlrshp 85; All St Choir Chrldng Captain; Cazenovia Coll; Lib Arts.

GRINNELL, STEVE M; Corning East HS; Corning, NY; (Y); Boy Scts; Chorus; Madrigals; Var L Socr; High Hon Roll; Hon Roll; NHS; Ntl Merit Ltr; Drama Clb; Exploring; Eagle Rank 85; William B Tomb Scholar 84; U S Miltry Acad Invtnl Acad Wrkshp 85; Comp Sci.

GRINNELL, TERESA; Tully Central HS; Tully, NY; (Y); Cmnty Wkr; Exploring; GAA; Spanish Clb; Varsity Clb; VP Frsh Cls; VP Soph Cls; VP Jr Cls; VP Sr Cls; Rep Stu Cncl; Cert Rec Duties Chrch 85; Amer Inst Frgn Stud 85; SUNY Geneseo; Accntng.

GRINSTED, STEVEN; East Islip SR HS; East Islip, NY; (Y); Church Yth Grp; Letterman Clb; Varsity Clb; JV Var Bsktbl; Im Sftbl; Wt Lftg; 2nd Long Isl Brdg Bldng Cont 85; 8th Ntl Brdg Bldng Cont 85; 3rd Pl Arch Dsgn Ntl Brdg Bldng Cont 85; Arch.

GRIPPE, CHANDRA MICHAELE; Middletown HS; Middletown, NY; (Y); Church Yth Grp; Hosp Aide; Key Clb; Church Choir; Var Score Keeper; Trk; OCBT Dance Schlrshp 79-80; Vrsty Soccer Plyrs & Soc Studies Studnts To Mexico 84; C Irving Schl; Nrsng.

GRIPPIN, JOSEPH W; Gilboa Conesville HS; North Blenheim, NY; (Y); Band; Chorus; Church Choir; Mrchg Band; School Musical; School Play; Swing Chorus; Variety Show; Yrbk Stf; Church Yth Grp; Accompainist Awd 84; Cert Commendation Summer Schl Of Arts 83; Vocal Perf.

GRIST, LORI; Cicero North Syracuse HS; Clay, NY; (S); 65/711; Yrbk Stf; Hon Roll; Pre-Law.

GRISWOLD, APRIL; Brushton-Moira Central Schl; Brushton, NY; (Y); 14/59; 4-H; French Clb; Hosp Aide; School Play; Stu Cncl; Hon Roll; D Youville Coll; Nursing.

GRITZKE, TINA; Maryvale HS; Cheektowaga, NY; (Y); DECA; GAA; Varsity Clb; Chorus; Yrbk Sprt Ed; Rep Jr Cls; Rep Stu Cncl; Im Socr; Stat Trk; Hon Roll; Bus Mngmnt.

GROBARCIK, CHRISTINA; Sheepshead Bay HS; Brooklyn, NY; (Y); Mgr Yrbk Bus Mgr; Yrbk Stf; Sec Frsh Cls; Hon Roll; 3rd Pl Sci Fair 83; Schlshp Character 83; NYU; Bus Mgmt.

GROBMAN, WILLIAM; Herricks HS; New Hyde Park, NY; (Y); 4/306; Cmnty Wkr; Key Clb; Quiz Bowl; JV Bsbl; NCTE Awd; NHS; Ntl Merit Ltr; Bio.

GROCHOWSKI, SANDY; West Seneca East SR HS; W Seneca, NY; (Y); DECA; JA; Concert Band; Mrchg Band; Nwsp Stf; JV Swmmng; Var Trk; Hon Roll; NHS; Ntl Merit Ltr; SUNY At Buffalo; Business Admi.

GROENING, BRUCE; Jamesville-Dewitt HS; Dewitt, NY; (Y); AFS; Church Yth Grp; Cmnty Wkr; Ski Clb; Concert Band; Jazz Band; Pep Band; Im Crs Cntry; Im Socr; High Hon Roll; Psych.

GROFF, DAVID D; L C Obourn HS; E Rochester, NY; (Y); Church Yth Grp; Exploring; Band; Mrchg Band; Pres Soph Cls; JV Ftbl; JV Trk; Hon Roll; Monroe CC; Bus Econ.

GROGAN, ELIZABETH; Bishop Kearney HS; Brooklyn, NY; (Y); Cmnty Wkr; Library Aide; Bowling; Secy.

GROLL, CHRISTINA; West Hempstead HS; Island Park, NY; (Y); 3/310; Am Leg Aux Girls St; Ski Clb; Yrbk Stf; Rep Sr Cls; Var Capt Badmtn; High Hon Roll; NHS; Ntl Merit Ltr; Excllnce Spn; Hnrb Mntn AATSP Exam; Dartmouth Coll; Frgn Lang.

GRONEMEIER, DARRELL F; Cortland SR HS; Cortland, NY; (Y); 44/243; Camera Clb; Band; Concert Band; Jazz Band; Mrchg Band; Var L Ice Hcky; NHS; NY ST Regnts Schlrshp 85-86; Univ Dayton OH; Phtgrphy.

GRONO, ANDREA; Our Lady Of Victory Academy; Yonkers, NY; (S); 12/137; Church Yth Grp; Mgr Spanish Clb; Mgr Yrbk Stf; Mgr Frsh Cls; Var Capt Bsktbl; Var Capt Sftbl; Var Vllybl; Mgr High Hon Roll; VP NHS; SR Cls Queen 84; Intl Frgn Lang Awd 84; Bst Defnsv Ply Vrsty Bsktbl 84; Adelphi U; Ob.

GROOM, MADONNA N; Frontier Central HS; Blasdell, NY; (Y); 23/524; Drama Clb; French Clb; Girl Scts; Pep Clb; Chorus; Color Guard; Drm & Bgl; School Musical; Nwsp Rptr; Nwsp Stf; Pres Awd For Acad Fitnss & Achvt 85; Chffrng.

GROOME, KATHLEEN M; The Mary Louis Acad; Flushing, NY; (Y); 6/283; Hosp Aide; Teachers Aide; Chorus; High Hon Roll; Jr NHS; NHS; Music Schlrshp To Mary Louis Acad 81-85; St Johns U Schlrshp 85-89; Boston Coll Schlrshp 85-89; Boston Coll; Bio.

GROSBAUM, LAURENCE J; Sherburne-Earlville HS; Poolville, NY; (S); Math Tm; Ski Clb; Yrbk Sprt Ed; JV Bsbl; Hon Roll; NHS; Natl Hnr Socty 84; Natl Sci Merit Awd 84; Chem Engrng.

GROSPIN, ANDY; Chenango Forks HS; Binghamton, NY; (Y); Ski Clb; Ftbl; High Hon Roll; Boy Scts; 4-H; Hon Roll; Indust Arts Awd 85; Stu Yr Indus Arts 84; Mech Engr.

GROSS, ALLISON; Onteora Central HS; West Hurley, NY; (S); Church Yth Grp; Band; Concert Band; Mrchg Band; Var Bsktbl; Var Capt Fld Hcky; Var Sftbl; High Hon Roll; NHS.

GROSS, DEBORAH; Commack HS; Commack, NY; (Y); Cmnty Wkr; Nwsp Ed-Chief; Nwsp Stf; Lit Mag; JV Bsktbl; JV Var Sftbl; High Hon Roll; Hon Roll; NHS; Stat Ftbl; Martial Arts 84-85; Sprts Phy Thrpst.

GROSS, KARANN B; Huntington HS; Huntington Sta, NY; (Y); 37/433; Drama Clb; Chorus; School Musical; Symp Band; Yrbk Stf; Trs Stu Cncl; Var Vllybl; Hon Roll; NHS; Bst Dir Awd 84; SUNY Binghamton.

GROSS, LINDA; The Brearley Schl; New York, NY; (Y); Art Clb; Debate Tm; Math Clb; Service Clb; Concert Band; Nwsp Rptr; Lit Mag; Var Badmtn; Ntl Merit Schol; Pres Schlr; Yale U; Molecular Bio.

GROSS, MATTHEW; Ellsworth J Wilson HS; Spencerport, NY; (Y); Exploring; JCL; Trs Latin Clb; Math Tm; Model UN; Ski Clb; JV Golf; L Tennis; High Hon Roll; NHS; U Of Rochester Ntl Schlrshp 85; NY ST Rgnts Schlrshp 85; Spncrprt Ladies Axlry Schlrshp For Med 85; U Of Rochester; Pre-Med.

GROSS, SUSAN L; Niagara Falls HS; Niagara Falls, NY; (Y); 17/250; JA; Key Clb; Band; Yrbk Stf; Crs Cntry; Co-Capt Trk; Jr NHS; Sec NHS; Amer Legn Awd 82; NY ST Regnts Schlrshp 85; Hofstra U; Ind Engr.

GROSS, TRINA; Eastridge HS; Rochester, NY; (Y); 51/216; Band; Concert Band; Drill Tm; Hon Roll; Eisenhart Awd 85; All ST Band 85; Chautauqua Yth Orch; Orch.

GROSSBERG, PENINA; Albany HS; Albany, NY; (Y); 8/600; Cmnty Wkr; Dance Clb; Latin Clb; VP Temple Yth Grp; Nwsp Stf; Yrbk Rptr; Yrbk Stf; Lit Mag; Hon Roll; NHS; Elmira Coll Key Awd Schlrshp 84; U Of PA.

GROSSE, CARLA J; Stuyvesant HS; Brooklyn, NY; (Y); Girl Scts; Office Aide; Chorus; School Musical; Variety Show; Nwsp Stf; NHS; Ntl Merit Ltr; Prfct Atten Awd; Hghst Hnrs In Italian Gold Mdl 85; Arista Hnr Soc 83-85; Cornell U.

GROSSFELD, SCOTT; Commack H S South; Commack, NY; (Y); Band; Mrchg Band; Symp Band; Nwsp Phtg; Nwsp Rptr; Yrbk Phtg; Yrbk Stf; High Hon Roll; Hon Roll; NHS; Acctg.

GROSSI, SUSAN; Valley Stream North; Malverne, NY; (Y); Cmnty Wkr; Pep Clb; Ski Clb; Varsity Clb; Variety Show; Hst Frsh Cls; Var Badmtn; Var Capt Cheerleading; Var Capt Gym; Var Sftbl; Outstndng Var Athl 81-85; MVP Gynnstcs 84-85; Var Chrldng Trophy 81-85; Cortland; Phys Educ.

GROSSMAN, ADRIANNE; North Shore HS; Sea Cliff, NY; (Y); Church Yth Grp; Sec Key Clb; Orch; French Clb; Mathletes; PAVAS; Chorus; School Musical; Rep Soph Cls; Rep Jr Cls; (Y All St Orch 83; NY Regnts Schlrshp 85; Colgate U; Med.

GROSSMAN, BETH A; Mineola HS; Mineola, NY; (Y); 2/257; Trs Pres French Clb; Temple Yth Grp; Concert Band; Yrbk Ed-Chief; Rep Stu Cncl; Score Keeper; JV Capt Vllybl; NHS; Ntl Merit Ltr; Sal; ST Chem Comp Awd; Rgnt Schlrshp; Outstndg Fresh Extracur Actvts; Princeton U; Mrktg.

GROSSMAN, CAROLYN; Saint Francis Prep; Bayside, NY; (Y); Tennis; 1st Pl Photgrphy Cntst For Poor Soc Areas 82; Bus Mngmnt.

GROSSMAN, JILL; Lafayette HS; Brooklyn, NY; (Y); 25/407; Service Clb; Temple Yth Grp; Bsktbl; Capt Tennis; Kiwanis Awd; NHS; Regnts Schlrshp 85; PTA Schlrshp 85; SUNY; Acctng.

GROSSMAN, ROBERT J; West Islip HS; W Islip, NY; (Y); Var Ftbl; MVP Rifle 83-84; 1st Pl Rifle Prone & Hgh Avg, 2nd Pl Stndg Positn 82-83; Rep Suffolk Cnty ST Fnls; Law Enfrcmnt.

GROSSMAN, SHERI; Oceanside HS; Oceanside, NY; (S); Pres DECA; Var Bsktbl; Var Tennis; Var Vllybl; Hon Roll; Merch Awd ST 85; Syracuse; Fshn Merch.

GROSSO, CATHLEEN; Saint Francis Prep; Kew Gardens, NY; (Y); 187/693; Drama Clb; Thesps; School Musical; School Play; JV Im Bowling; Church Yth Grp; Service Clb; Chorus; NYU; Psych.

GROSSO, DINA; Smithtown H S West; Smithtown, NY; (Y); Church Yth Grp; Exploring; Im Mgr(s); Im Trk; Hon Roll; NHS; Italian Hnr Scty 83-85; Pace U; Bio.

GROSSO, ED; Washingtonville HS; Monroe, NY; (Y); Boy Scts; Ski Clb; Socr; Trk; Hon Roll; Mst Imprvd Triple Jmp Awd 84; Mst Vlbl Triple Jmp Awd 85; Orange Cty Coaches Tm Var Sccr 85; Engrng.

GROSSO, FRANCINE; Liverpool HS; Syracuse, NY; (S); 17/794; Church Yth Grp; Drama Clb; FBLA; GAA; Teachers Aide; Chorus; School Musical; School Play; Stage Crew; Yrbk Stf; NY ST Rgnts Schlrshp; Rice U; Biomed Engrng.

GROSZ, GERALD; Roy C Ketcham SR HS; Poughkeepsie, NY; (Y); Computer Clb; Math Clb; Math Tm; Jazz Band; Orch; Symp Band; High Hon Roll; NHS; Math.

GROTH, MIKE; Jamesville-De Witt HS; Jamesville, NY; (Y); #47 In Class; Church Yth Grp; Cmnty Wkr; Pres JA; Red Cross Aide; School Play; Bsktbl; Coach Actv; JV Lcrss; JV Socr; High Hon Roll.

GROUDAS, PETER; Chatham HS; E Chatham, NY; (Y); 12/135; Latin Clb; Band; Concert Band; Jazz Band; Mrchg Band; Pep Band; JV Socr; NHS; NY ST Regents Schlrshp 85; SUNY U Stonybrook; Elec Engrng.

GROUP, KRISTIN; Mayville Central HS; Mayville, NY; (S); 3/50; Hosp Aide; Mrchg Band; Pres Sr Cls; Bsktbl; Coach Actv; Sftbl; Tennis; Dnfth Awd; NHS; 4-H; Eta Nu Chapt Of Beta Sigma Phi 85; Athlt Of Yr 84; Allegheny Coll; Sprts Med.

GROVER, KIM; Newfield Central HS; Newfield, NY; (Y); Varsity Clb; Jazz Band; Pres Jr Cls; Var Fld Hcky; Var Trk; Var Vllybl; Band; Mrchg Band; School Play; Rep Stu Cncl; Radio.

GROW, JOHN L; Bishop Kearney HS; Ontario, NY; (Y); Am Leg Boys St; Computer Clb; Rep Frsh Cls; Rep Soph Cls; Rep Stu Cncl; Im Bsbl; Im Bsktbl; JV Var Coach Actv; Var L Ftbl; Var L Lcrss; History.

GRUBE, JOSEPH; Cattaraugus HS; Cattaraugus, NY; (Y); 2/55; Boy Scts; Debate Tm; VP 4-H; Letterman Clb; Pep Clb; Spanish Clb; Varsity Clb; Band; Concert Band; Drm & Bgl; Elec Engr.

GRUBE, MARK S; Honeoye Central HS; Canandaigua, NY; (Y); 10/80; Art Clb; Aud/Vis; French Clb; Stage Crew; Yrbk Stf; JV Crs Cntry; Hon Roll; Pres Schlr; NY ST Summer School Visual Arts 84; Finalist Sch Of Visual Arts 85; Scholastic Art Show Participant; Schl Of Visual Arts.

GRUBE, MARYANN B; Brewster HS; Brewster, NY; (S); 38/176; VICA; School Play; Bowling; Score Keeper; Wt Lftg; High Hon Roll; Hon Roll; NHS; Hnrb Mntn Bread Disp 84; Felisitations Awd Weddng Cake 84; Dunwoodie Inst; Pstry Chef.

GRUBER, BRENDA; Allegany Central HS; Allegany, NY; (Y); 10/90; Church Yth Grp; Church Choir; Concert Band; Mrchg Band; School Play; Nwsp Stf; Capt Cheerleading; Elks Awd; High Hon Roll; NHS; Royson Whipple Scholar 85; Dresser Clark Spec Recgntn Scholar 85; Home Ec Awd 85; Morrisville Coll; Diet Tech.

GRUBER, KARL GREGG; Walton HS; Bronx, NY; (Y); Computer Clb; Office Aide; Science Clb; Teachers Aide; Band; Chorus; VP Frsh Cls; JV Bsbl; Sftbl; Swmmng; Scomp Sci.

GRUBER, MICHAEL; Spring Valley HS; Spring Valley, NY; (Y); VP Cmnty Wkr; Key Clb; Spanish Clb; Rep Frsh Cls; Var Tennis; High Hon Roll; Hon Roll; Mu Alp Tht; NHS; Spanish NHS; AP Outstndng Accomplshmnt Awd 84; Outstndng Svc & Devtn Awd 85; Sthwstrn Ath Conf Tenns Awd 85; Bus.

GRUDZINSKI, JULIANNE; Farmingdale SR HS; Farmingdale, NY; (Y); Drama Clb; Thesps; Sec Chorus; Sec Madrigals; School Musical; School Play; Variety Show; Yrbk Stf; Stu Cncl; Mgr(s); Binghamton Coll; Engl.

GRUDZINSKI JR, WALTER; Berlin American HS; Apo New York, NY; (S); 1/90; Art Clb; Capt Bsbl; Var Capt Golf; High Hon Roll; Trs Jr NHS; NHS; Ntl Merit Ltr; Boy Scts; Chess Clb; Church Yth Grp; DODDS Golf Chmpshp 3rd Pl 83, 2nd Pl 84; DODDS Sci Smnr; Math.

GRUMER, ELISA H; The Bronx H S Of Science; Bronx, NY; (Y); Office Aide; Science Clb; Teachers Aide; Temple Yth Grp; Lit Mag; Hon Roll; Jr NHS; Prfct Atten Awd.

GRUND, ELLEN M; Clarisstown So HS; New City, NY; (Y); Church Yth Grp; Cmnty Wkr; Stage Crew; Lit Mag; Fld Hcky; Swmmng; St Schlr.

GRUNERT, FRED; Cazenovia Central HS; Cazenovia, NY; (Y); Ski Clb; Var L Socr; High Hon Roll; Hon Roll; Estrn Jr Olympc Team Skiing Alpine 82&84; Empire ST Games 83-84.

GRUPP, THOMAS; Kenmore East SR HS; Tonawanda, NY; (Y); Boy Scts; Varsity Clb; JV Ftbl; Var Capt Swmmng; Var Capt Trk; Sci.

GRUZZON, CESAR A; All Hallows Inst; Bronx, NY; (Y); 3/90; Aud/Vis; Drama Clb; Math Clb; School Play; Rep Stu Cncl; Var Bsbl; JV Var Bowling; JV Var Ice Hcky; High Hon Roll; NHS; Stu Achvt Awds 83-85; Outstndng Achvt Math 85; Pre-Med.

GRYCZON, ANNE; Mineola HS; Mineola, NY; (Y); Sec Art Clb; Key Clb; Service Clb; Variety Show; Nwsp Stf; Hon Roll; Awd Stu Spnsr 85; Intl Stud.

GRZANKOWSKI, SUSAN; Villa Maria Acad; Buffalo, NY; (S); 5/118; Computer Clb; JCL; Latin Clb; Ski Clb; Pres Jr Cls; High Hon Roll; Bowling; Prfct Atten Awd; NEDT Merit Cert 83; Cert High Engl Avg 83; Reg Cert Merit Gannon U 85; Med.

GRZEGORCZAK, JILL; Immaculata Acad; Orchard Pk, NY; (Y); 1/50; Church Yth Grp; French Clb; Hosp Aide; Teachers Aide; Nwsp Stf; Trs Stu Cncl; High Hon Roll; NHS; NEDT Awd; Psych Inrnshp SUNY Coll Buffalo 85; Elem Spec Ed.

GUALTIERI, EUGENE; Anthony A Henninger HS; Syracuse, NY; (Y); 2/400; Intnl Clb; Key Clb; Science Clb; Var Capt Crs Cntry; Var Capt Trk; High Hon Roll; NHS; Ntl Merit SF; Oper Enterprs Schlrshp 85; Physics.

GUALTIERI, THOMAS P; Fayetteville-Manlius HS; Manlius, NY; (Y); Rep Frsh Cls; Pres Soph Cls; Pres Jr Cls; Pres Sr Cls; Rep Stu Cncl; Crs Cntry; JV Lcrss; Cit Awd; High Hon Roll; Hon Roll; Onondaga CC Schlr 85; Recgntn-Apprectn Cert Stu Assn 84; Apprctn Cert Crebrl Plsy 84 & 85.

GUANU, SETH R; Cherry Valley Central HS; Cherry Valley, NY; (Y); Am Leg Boys St; Drama Clb; Quiz Bowl; Band; School Musical; Rep Stu Cncl; Var Bsktbl; Var Socr; High Hon Roll; NHS; Clark Schlrshp 85; Potsdam ST Coll; Comp Engr.

GUARDADO, EDWIN; Freeport HS; Freeport, NY; (Y); VP Church Yth Grp; Letterman Clb; Varsity Clb; Church Choir; Concert Band; Var Capt Socr; Var Trk; High Hon Roll; NHS; MITE Awd Cornell U 85; Engrng.

GUARDINO, STACEY; Bishop Kearney HS; Brooklyn, NY; (Y); Key Clb; Math Tm; Office Aide; Spanish Clb; High Hon Roll; NHS; Prfct Atten Awd; 5th Pl Jr V Math Tm 84-85; Acctng.

GUARINI, MARK; Rome Free Acad; Rome, NY; (Y); Intnl Clb; Ski Clb; Band; Mrchg Band; Pep Band; Var Golf; Pre-Dntstry.

GUARINO, ANN; Nanuet SR HS; Nanuet, NY; (Y); Church Yth Grp; Church Choir; Nwsp Rptr; Nwsp Stf; Socr; Acctng.

GUARINO, DIANA; Unatego Centraal HS; Otego, NY; (Y); 14/83; French Clb; Spanish Clb; JV Var Cheerleading; Stat Trk; High Hon Roll; Ntl Merit Ltr; Hosp Aide; Acad All Amer; Intl Frgn Lang Awd; Intl Ldrshp, Svc Awd; Cornell U; Psytry.

GUARNIERI, MARY; Saratoga Central Catholic; Greenfield Center, NY; (S); Drama Clb; Varsity Clb; School Play; JV Var Cheerleading; JV Var Pom Pon; Hon Roll; Sienna Coll; Math.

GUARRERA, MARGARET; G Ray Bodley HS; Fulton, NY; (Y); Exploring; French Clb; Science Clb; Color Guard; Mrchg Band; Yrbk Stf; Rep Frsh Cls; Rep Soph Cls; Rep Jr Cls; Rep Stu Cncl; Dntl Hygnst.

GUASTELLA, ANGELA; Bishop Kearney HS; Brooklyn, NY; (Y); 120/400; Art Clb; Library Aide; Rep Sr Cls; JV Bowling; JV Trk; Hon Roll; Riding Club 82-83; 2nd Pl-Math Cntst 85; Brooklyn; Elem Eductn.

GUAY, GARY; Plattsburgh HS; Plattsburgh, NY; (Y); Model UN; Ski Clb; Ftbl; ST U NY Plattsburgh.

GUAY, HEATHER A; Northeastern Clinton HS; Rouses Point, NY; (Y); 25/142; Model UN; Ski Clb; Yrbk Stf; VP Stu Cncl; Capt L Bsktbl; Var L Crs Cntry; Capt L Socr; Var L Tennis; High Hon Roll; NHS; Regnts Schlrshp 85; St Micheals; Dntst.

GUAY, STEPHEN; Mount Assumption Inst; Plattsburgh, NY; (Y); Var JV Bsbl; JV Bsktbl; Var JV Ftbl; Hon Roll; Law.

GUAY, WAYNE R; Northeastern Clinton Central; Rouses Point, NY; (Y); 7/146; Chess Clb; Model UN; Quiz Bowl; Chorus; Var Bsbl; L Bowling; Capt Tennis; High Hon Roll; NHS; Pres Schlr; Clarkson U; Indstrl Dist.

GUBBINS, DAWN; Notre Dame HS; Whitesboro, NY; (Y); 5/170; Pres VP Church Yth Grp; Mathletes; ROTC; Var Stat Bsktbl; Stat Sftbl; High Hon Roll; NHS; Spanish Clb; Speech Tm; Powder Puff Ftbl; Acad All Amer 83-84 & 84-85; Regents Scholar 85; Mini Boot Camp Hnr Grad 83; Clarkson U; Comp Sci.

GUBERMAN, RICH; The Dwight Schl; New York, NY; (Y); Boy Scts; Key Clb; Political Wkr; Service Clb; Nwsp Rptr; Yrbk Stf; Lit Mag; VP Frsh Cls; Stu Cncl; JV Socr; NYS Regents Schlrshp 85; Hnr Schlr Two Ten Schrlshp 85; Franklin And Marshall; Law.

GUCCIARDI, SCOTT P; Auburn HS; Auburn, NY; (Y); 25/430; Am Leg Boys St; ROTC; Chorus; Var Swmmng; High Hon Roll; NHS; SAR Awd; School Musical; Mltry Ordr Wrld Wars Mdl 84; Air Frc Assn Awd 85; 1st Prvt Pilt Flght Solo 84; Aero Engrng.

GUDAS, TIMOTHY; Horseheads HS; Horseheads, NY; (S); 3/407; Ski Clb; Spanish Clb; Varsity Clb; Rep Jr Cls; L Capt Socr; NHS; Ntl Merit SF; French Clb; Intnl Clb; All Leag Soccer; All Leag Hnrbl Mntn Lacrosse; Econ.

GUELI, MARY; North Babylon SR HS; N Babylon, NY; (Y); Sec DECA; Sec Stu Cncl; JV Cheerleading; JV Gym; Jr NHS; CW Post Ctr Acadmc Schlrshp 85; DECA Awd-1st Pl Finnc & Credt 84; CW Post Ctr; Econmcs.

GUELLI, MARY; North Babylon HS; N Babylon, NY; (Y); DECA; Sec Stu Cncl; Cheerleading; Gym; Jr NHS; C W Post Acad Schlrshp 85; DECA-1ST Pl Bnkg & Fin Awd 84; C W Post Center NY; Econ.

GUELLY, GABRIELE; The Mary Louis Acad; Middle Village, NY; (Y); German Clb; GAA; Girl Scts; Ski Clb; Bsktbl; St Johns U; Real Est.

GUENTHER, DAVID; Kensington HS; Buffalo, NY; (Y); Boy Scts; Chess Clb; Computer Clb; German Clb; JA; Science Clb; Stu Cncl; Crs Cntry; Cit Awd.

GUERCIO, MICHAEL; Sachem HS; Holbrook, NY; (Y); Science Clb; Hon Roll; Jr NHS; NHS; Cmnty Wkr; Im Crs Cntry; Im Swmmng; Im Wt Lftg; Bus Mngmnt.

GUERIN, JAMES; Valley Stream Central HS; Valley Stream, NY; (Y); Red Cross Aide; Yrbk Stf; Var JV Bsbl; Var JV Bsktbl; Var JV Ftbl; High Hon Roll; Jr NHS; Mu Alp Tht; NHS; Spanish NHS; Harold Earl Awd-Bst Stu Athlt 83; Hnr Usher-Top Achvt JR Cls 85; Great Bks Clb.

GUERNELLI, GIANILEIA F; Cardinal Spellman HS; New York, NY; (Y); Camera Clb; Church Yth Grp; Cmnty Wkr; Computer Clb; Library Aide; Radio Clb; Spanish Clb; Concert Band; Lit Mag; Swmmng; Hgh Hnr Roll 82-85; VFW Awd 85; Manhattan Coll; Med.

GUERNSEY, JOEY; Mc Graw HS; Mcgraw, NY; (Y); Pep Clb; Science Clb; Varsity Clb; Band; Chorus; Concert Band; Jazz Band; Mrchg Band; Pep Band; Swing Chorus; Stu Mth 82-83; Outstndng Bnd 83-84; Fabius Pompey Al-Trnmnt Tm Bsktbl Trphy 84-85; USAF; Secrty Polic.

GUERRA, ANNE; Utica Free Acad; Utica, NY; (Y); Sec Drama Clb; Latin Clb; Sec Service Clb; Speech Tm; Thesps; Acpl Chr; School Play; Nwsp Rptr; Nwsp Stf; Yrbk Rptr; Natl Latin Exam Magna Cum Lauda 83 & 85; Jr B-Sharp Mus Clb Piano 84-86; Harrison Cline Mem Acting Awd; Optometry.

GUERRA, LOUIS J; Locust Valley HS; Bayville, NY; (Y); Am Leg Boys St; Intnl Clb; Chorus; Madrigals; School Musical; School Play; Nwsp Rptr; JV Bsbl; Var Bowling; High Hon Roll; Film Director.

GUERRERO, LUIS; James Monroe HS; Bronx, NY; (Y); Cmnty Wkr; Exploring; JA; Latin Clb; Spanish Clb; School Musical; School Play; Yrbk Phtg; Yrbk Sprt Ed; Off Frsh Cls; Acad Aerontcs; Dsgn.

GUERRERO, SYLVANA; Mabel Dean Bacon Vhs; Brooklyn, NY; (S); 1/299; Hosp Aide; Hon Roll; Prfct Atten Awd; Hunter Coll; Obstrcl Nrs.

GUERRIER, FLORENCE; John Dewey HS; Brooklyn, NY; (Y); Girl Scts; Library Aide; Aud/Vis; Office Aide; Teachers Aide; Band; Yrbk Stf; High Hon Roll.

GUERRIER, REGINE; Midwood HS; Brooklyn, NY; (Y); 112/605; Hosp Aide; PAVAS; Band; School Musical; Variety Show; Yrbk Stf; Rep Stu Cncl; Var Bowling; Capt Trk; Hon Roll; Sol Greene Schlrshp 85; Ariston Archon Soc; Brandeis U; Biochem.

GUERRINO, CLAUDIA; Our Lady Of Victory Acad; Yonkers, NY; (S); 9/160; Yrbk Stf; Off Sr Cls; High Hon Roll; Comp Sic Awd 83-84; Fordham U; Law.

GUERRY, AMY; Horseheads HS; Horseheads, NY; (S); 27/407; French Clb; Trs NFL; Spanish Clb; Varsity Clb; Chorus; Trs Jr Cls; Trs Stu Cncl; Var Co-Capt Cheerleading; High Hon Roll; NHS; Bus.

GUEVARA, ROSA; Aquinas HS; Bronx, NY; (Y); 38/178; Cmnty Wkr; Exploring; Hosp Aide; Science Clb; Prfct Atten Awd; Boys Clb Am; Chess Clb; Math Awd; Nrs.

GUGGEMOS, KIMBERLY A; Kenmore East HS; Tonawanda, NY; (Y); Trs Math Clb; Concert Band; Drill Tm; Swing Chorus; JV Var Pom Pon; JV Tennis; Stat Wrstlng; High Hon Roll; NHS; Poem Publshd 84.

GUGLIELMO, STEVEN; St Francis Prep Schl; Floral Park, NY; (Y); Boy Scts; Drm & Bgl; Trk; Sci Fictn Soc Pres 84-85; Opertn FUN Vlntr Cnslr 83-84; U Sthrn CA; Film.

GUGLUIZZA, JOSEPH E; Cortland JR SR HS; Cortland, NY; (Y); Pres Am Leg Boys St; Varsity Clb; Band; Mrchg Band; Yrbk Stf; Rep Stu Cncl; High Hon Roll; NHS; JV Bsktbl; Var L Ftbl; MVP JR Vrsty La Crosse 84; Naval Acad; Elec Engr.

GUGSA, EMEYE; Martin Van Buren HS; Queens Village, NY; (Y); English Clb; French Clb; GAA; Math Clb; Math Tm; Science Clb; Socr; Vllybl; High Hon Roll; Hon Roll; Cert Schlrshp 83-84; Cert Merit Excllnc Globl Hstry 83; Cert Merit Excllnc Bio 84.

GUIDA, GEORGE MARIO; Malverne HS; Lynbrook, NY; (Y); 4/159; VP Computer Clb; Exploring; Key Clb; Capt Quiz Bowl; Service Clb; Ski Clb; School Musical; Nwsp Ed-Chief; Yrbk Stf; Ed Lit Mag; Century III Rep; Dept Eng Awd; Columbia U; Jrnlsm.

GUIDI, DENISE M K; New Paltz HS; New Paltz, NY; (Y); 48/169; Girl Scts; Sec Band; Chorus; School Play; Ed Yrbk Phtg; Off Frsh Cls; Sec Soph Cls; Sec Jr Cls; Sec Sr Cls; Sec Stu Cncl; Dennis Moore Assn Art Schlrshp 85; Rchstr Inst Of Tech; Phtgrphy.

GUIDIE, STEPHAN; Alden Central HS; Alden, NY; (Y); Aud/Vis; French Clb; Science Clb; Band; Chorus; School Musical; Rep Stu Cncl; Var L Crs Cntry; Hon Roll; Prfct Atten Awd; Acad Ltr Awds; Rochester Inst Tech; Comp Sci.

GUIDO, GINA M; Newfare SR HS; Burt, NY; (Y); Church Yth Grp; Exploring; Sec 4-H; Political Wkr; Yrbk Sprt Ed; Score Keeper; Var JV Sftbl; JV Vllybl; Hon Roll; Ntl Merit Ltr; Ntl Competiave Shclrshp U Of Dallas 85; Regence Schlrshp 85; ST U Of NY Genesco; Pltcl Sci.

GUIGLOTTO, MICHAEL; Mahopac HS; Mahopac, NY; (Y); 10/400; Math Clb; Math Tm; Science Clb; Var Golf; Var Wrstlng; Cit Awd; DAR Awd; High Hon Roll; NHS; U Of MI Ann Arbor; Comp Engrng.

GUILBAULT, MATTHEW F; Averill Park HS; W Sand Lk, NY; (Y); 4-H; Ski Clb; Var Capt Socr; High Hon Roll; Hon Roll; Prfct Atten Awd; Syracuse U; Aerospace Engrng.

GUILBERT, REBECCA; Msgr Scanlan HS; Bronx, NY; (Y); 4/265; Intnl Clb; Service Clb; Nwsp Stf; High Hon Roll; NHS; Engl, Hstry, Sci, Math, & Spnsh Acad Cmmndtn; Attndnc Cert; Prin List 1st Hnrs Schltc Achvt 84; Sci.

GUILE, DANIEL; Jamesville-Dewitt HS; Jamesville, NY; (Y); 27/270; Variety Show; JV Ftbl; JV Lcrss; Dnfth Awd; High Hon Roll; NHS.

GUILE, THERESA; Hoosick Falls Central Schl; Hoosick Falls, NY; (Y); Church Yth Grp; Trs Drama Clb; Girl Scts; Band; Chorus; Concert Band; Orch; School Musical; School Play; Stage Crew.

GUILI, JOANN; Cardinal O Hara HS; Tonawanda, NY; (Y); Church Yth Grp; French Clb; GAA; Girl Scts; Chorus; Rep Frsh Cls; JV Var Bsktbl; Im Bowling; JV Cheerleading; Var Sftbl; Niagra U; Bus.

GUILLEN JR, JOSUE PERICLES; Hunter College Campus Schl; New York, NY; (Y); Concert Band; Nwsp Phtg; Yrbk Phtg; Capt Tennis; Ham Radio Oper Call Ltrs WB2KVG; Wesleyan U; Engr.

GUINTA, ANTHONY J; Elmira Free Acad; Elmira, NY; (Y); 10/250; Band; Concert Band; JV Bsbl; JV Bsktbl; Var L Tennis; High Hon Roll; NHS; ST John Fisher Coll; Bio.

GUINTI, JOHN A; Tottenville HS; Staten Island, NY; (Y); Church Yth Grp; Boy Scts; Ski Clb; Soroptimist; Symp Band; Rep Frsh Cls; Pres Jr Cls; Pres Stu Cncl; Bsktbl; Cit Awd; Dly News Msc Exc Awd 85; Dly News Prncl Prd Of Ynks 85; Stn Islnd Spr Yth 85; Pdrtcn.

GUINYARD, MELANIE; Queen Of The Rosary Acad; Roosevelt, NY; (S); Pres Math Clb; Nwsp Rptr; VP Soph Cls; Sec Jr Cls; NHS; NEDT Awd; Pre-Law.

GUIRY, SUZANNE; Smithtown High School East; Nesconset, NY; (Y); French Clb; Hosp Aide; Office Aide; Frsh Cls; Soph Cls; Jr Cls; French Hon Soc; NHS; Natl Hnr Soc 84; French Natl Hnr Soc 85; Bio.

GULA, KAJA C; Loyola Schl; New York, NY; (Y); 1/52; Art Clb; Service Clb; Ski Clb; School Play; Yrbk Stf; JV Mgr(s); Var Vllybl; High Hon Roll; NEDT Awd; St Schlr; Vet Med.

GULCYNSKI, RAYMOND; Bishop Timon HS; Buffalo, NY; (S); 18/132; Computer Clb; Var Tennis; NHS; Unsung Plyr Awd Tennis 83; Rlgn Dept Awd Cndct Soc 84; Erie Commumity N; Engrng.

GULICK, DAVID G; Corning-Painted Post West HS; Painted Post, NY; (Y); 39/254; Varsity Clb; Rep Frsh Cls; L Socr; NY ST Regnts Schlrshp 85; SUNY Buffalo; Bus Adm.

GULISANO, JUNE; Eastridge HS; Rochester, NY; (Y); Chorus; School Musical; Hon Roll; Clearwater Christian Coll; Law.

GULKER, HOLLY; New Rochelle HS; New Rochelle, NY; (Y); Political Wkr; Temple Yth Grp; Chorus; Lit Mag; Hon Roll; NHS; Modl Cngrss; Spnsh Hnr Soc; Dnc & Gymnstcs; NY U.

GULKIS, AMY; Bethpage HS; Plainview, NY; (Y); 24/293; French Clb; FBLA; Spanish Clb; Temple Yth Grp; Rep Soph Cls; Rep Jr Cls; JV L Bsktbl; Var L Fld Hcky; High Hon Roll; NHS; SUNY Albany; Intl Bus.

GULLA, JERRY; Rome Free Acad; Rome, NY; (Y); 46/512; Computer Clb; Exploring; Science Clb; Nwsp Stf; High Hon Roll; Hon Roll; Jr NHS; NHS; St Schlr; NY ST Regents Schlrshp 85; Natl Deans List 85; Clarkson U; Engr.

GULLA, LEANNE; Cardinal Spellman HS; Bronx, NY; (Y); 125/535; Church Yth Grp; Girl Scts; Chorus; Off Soph Cls; Sr Cls; Off Stu Cncl; Capt Bowling; Gym; Trk; Fordham U Schl Bus.

GULLICKSEN, AMY; Saranac Lake HS; Saranac Lk, NY; (Y); FBLA; Bus.

GULLO, CHRISTINA; West Seneca East SR HS; Buffalo, NY; (Y); Aud/Vis; DECA; Office Aide; Stage Crew; Tennis; Trk; Hon Roll; JC Awd; NHS; DECA Rgnl Trophy 85; U Buffalo; Mrktng.

GULLO, JOSEPH; Lafayette HS; Brooklyn, NY; (Y); Art Clb; Aud/Vis; Computer Clb; Teachers Aide; Nwsp Ed-Chief; Nwsp Rptr; Yrbk Stf; Var Bsbl; Sftbl; High Hon Roll; Arista 84-86; Archon 84-86; Boy Ldr Arista 85-86; NYU; Bus Adm.

GULLY, MARY; Lansing Beach HS; Troy, NY; (Y); Band; Chorus; School Play; Capt Bowling; High Hon Roll; Jr NHS; NHS; Bus.

GULOTTY, ERIC S; Chatham Central HS; East Chatham, NY; (Y); 25/128; Drama Clb; Latin Clb; Chorus; Orch; School Musical; School Play; Bowling; Socr; NHS; Voice Dem Awd; Thtre.

GUMBS, COLIN; Freeport HS; Freeport, NY; (Y); Mathletes; Band; Concert Band; Mrchg Band; Nwsp Rptr; High Hon Roll; Hon Roll; NHS; Mth.

GUMINA, STEPHANI; Greece Olympia HS; Rochester, NY; (Y); 53/316; DECA; Exploring; FBLA; Math Clb; Math Tm; Science Clb; Tennis; Hon Roll; 1st Pl Dist FBLA Bus Math, Gen Bus 82; Regnts Schlrshp 85; Geneseo; Chem.

GUNDELMAN, PATRICK; Salamanca City Central HS; Killbuck, NY; (Y); #2 In Class; Am Leg Boys St; Drama Clb; Thesps; Rep Soph Cls; Im Socr; Var Swmmng; French Hon Soc; High Hon Roll; NHS; Amer Lgn Schlr & Ldrshp Awd.

GUNDERMAN, KIMBERLY LEE; Thomas A Edison HS; Horseheads, NY; (Y); 6/89; Varsity Clb; School Musical; Nwsp Stf; Yrbk Stf; Sec Jr Cls; Sec Sr Cls; Rep Stu Cncl; Var Cheerleading; Chorus; Stage Crew; Mrch Dimes Schlrshp 85; David A Kooley Hstrns Awd 85; Bus Awd Elmira Hghts Bus & Prof Womns Clb 85; Arnot Ogden Hosp Schl Nrsg; RN.

GUNDERMAN, TERRY J; Horseheads HS; Horseheads, NY; (Y); 80/409; French Clb; Letterman Clb; Science Clb; Spanish Clb; Varsity Clb; Var L Golf; JV Socr; Var L Tennis; Hon Roll; NYS Rgnts Schlrshp 84-85; SUNY-STONEYBROOK; Indstrl Engr.

GUNDERSON, EDWARD; Archbishop Molloy HS; Elmont, NY; (Y); 30/409; Science Clb; Hon Roll; NHS; Ntl Merit SF; Rensselaer Polytech; Comp Engr.

GUNDERUD, LASZLO; Roy C Ketcham HS; Wappinger Falls, NY; (Y); Aud/Vis; Boy Scts; Drama Clb; Library Aide; Church Choir; Orch; High Hon Roll; Hon Roll; Astrphysc.

GUNN, ALLISON R; Amherst Central SR HS; Amherst, NY; (Y); 32/310; French Clb; JCL; Latin Clb; Pres Chorus; Madrigals; Trs School Musical; Co-Capt Swmmng; NHS; 2nd In WNY Regn Natl Frnch Exm 85; U Of New Hampshire; Vet.

GUNN, KIMBERLY S; New Rochelle HS; New Rochelle, NY; (Y); French Clb; Chorus; Church Choir; Trk; Cit Awd; French Hon Soc; Hon Roll; NHS; Med.

GUNN, MELANIE; Curtis HS; Staten Island, NY; (Y); Church Yth Grp; GAA; Key Clb; OEA; Church Choir; School Play; Nwsp Rptr; Nwsp Stf; VP Frsh Cls; Pres Soph Cls; Supr Crt Judge.

GUNNING, STACIE M; Notre Dame HS; Gillett, PA; (Y); 11/124; Art Clb; Boy Scts; Hosp Aide; JA; Latin Clb; Library Aide; Ski Clb; Band; Nwsp Stf; High Hon Roll; Keuka Coll; Nrsng.

GUNTHER, HEIDI; Oneonta HS; Oneonta, NY; (Y); 50/185; 4-H; French Clb; Varsity Clb; Im Bsktbl; Im Score Keeper; Im Var Vllybl; 4-H Awd; Hon Roll; Chorus; Madrigals; Outstndng Chorus Mbr 83-84; Clnry Arts Inst Amer; Pro Chf.

GUNTHER, JENNIFER; Central HS; Valley Stream, NY; (Y); Church Yth Grp; Ski Clb; Badmtn; Cheerleading; Capt Socr; Vllybl; High Hon Roll; Jr NHS; NHS; Mth.

GUNTHER, KRISTINE; Bishop Kearney HS; Brooklyn, NY; (Y); 3/355; Church Yth Grp; Library Aide; Math Tm; Spanish Clb; JV Cheerleading; Var L Swmmng; High Hon Roll; Trs NHS; Amer Chem Soc Awd Chem 84; Mth Merit Awd Mth Lg 85; Mth Achvt Awd 2nd Calc & 1st Mth Wrtgs 85; Elec Engrng.

GUNTHEP, RANDALL; Gilboa Conesville HS; Gilboa, NY; (S); Boy Scts; Spanish Clb; Band; Bsktbl; Bowling; Crs Cntry; Golf; Wt Lftg; High Hon Roll; Hon Roll; Mst Valuable Plyr Awd 83-84.

GUNTHERT, DENNIS; Vestal SR HS; Apalachin, NY; (Y); Ski Clb; Var L Ice Hcky; High Hon Roll; Ntl Merit SF; Prfct Atten Awd; Cornell; Law.

GUPTA, ANURAG W; Hunter College HS; Elmhurst S, NY; (Y); Trs Chess Clb; Computer Clb; Library Aide; Math Tm; Science Clb; VP Stat Bowling; DAR Awd; Mu Alp Tht; Ntl Merit SF; Secy-Treas Schl Bwlng Leag 84-85; MIT; Elec Engr.

GUPTA, EVA; Beacon HS; Beacon, NY; (S); Rptr Nwsp Ed-Chief; Var Crs Cntry; Var Trk; Wt Lftg; High Hon Roll; NHS; Ntl Merit Ltr; Soc Of Dstngshd Am HS Stu Awd 84; Eng & Math Awd 83; Comp Sci.

GUPTA, NEENA; Vestal SR HS; Binghamton, NY; (Y); English Clb; Sec French Clb; Hosp Aide; Intnl Clb; High Hon Roll; NHS; Ind Awarness Co Op IBM 84-85; Regents Schlrshp 85; U TX-AUSTIN; Engrng.

GURALNY, JENNIFER S; Pulaski JR SR HS; Pulaski, NY; (S); Church Yth Grp; Drama Clb; GAA; Math Clb; Chorus; School Musical; Yrbk Phtg; Powder Puff Ftbl; Sftbl; Hon Roll; Snow Enrchmnt Awd 83.

GURBACKI, EDWARD; West Seneca East SR HS; Cheektowaga, NY; (Y); 40/365; Ftbl; Trk; Wt Lftg; Wrstlng; Rgnts, RIT Schlrshp 85; Rochester Inst Tech; Mech Engr.

GURDIN, STEVEN; Easthchester HS; Scarsdale, NY; (Y); Pres Ski Clb; VP Jr Cls; Pres Sr Cls; Rep Stu Cncl; Var Crs Cntry; JV Socr; Capt Var Tennis; NHS; Latin Clb; Spanish Clb; All-Leag Tnns 84-85; MVP Var Tnns Tm 84-85.

GURLEY, JENNIFER A; Notre Dame HS; Whitesboro, NY; (Y); 26/174; Church Yth Grp; Drama Clb; Service Clb; School Musical; Yrbk Bus Mgr; Cheerleading; Powder Puff Ftbl; Tennis; High Hon Roll; Sec Frsh Cls; American U; Intl Rel.

GURMAN, BONNIE; Wantagh HS; Wantagh, NY; (Y); Drama Clb; Pres Library Aide; Pres Temple Yth Grp; Nwsp Stf; Bowling; Long Island Industrial Arts Comp 84; Long Island Industrial Arts Comp 2nd Pl 85; Arch.

GURNETT, PAUL; Royalton-Hartland HS; Gasport, NY; (Y); 37/134; Boy Scts; Bowling; Var Crs Cntry; Var Score Keeper; Var Trk; Hon Roll; Bus Adm.

GURTOWSKI, STEPHANIE; Solvay HS; Syracuse, NY; (Y); Sec Spanish Clb; Yrbk Stf; Off Soph Cls; Sec Jr Cls; Stu Cncl; Capt Var Cheerleading; High Hon Roll; Hon Roll; NHS; Am Hist Awd 85; Adv Keybrdng Awd 85; Elem Ed.

GURWITZ, DEBORAH; Onteora HS; West Hurley, NY; (S); Band; Mrchg Band; Hon Roll; NHS.

GUSAKOV, SCOTT; East Aurora HS; East Aurora, NY; (S); AFS; Computer Clb; Model UN; Radio Clb; Science Clb; Concert Band; Jazz Band; School Musical; Hon Roll; NHS; All High Mrchng Band Erie Cty Fair 83-84; MI U; Mech Engr.

GUSICK, NED; Riverdale Country Schl; New York, NY; (Y); School Play; Nwsp Stf; Yrbk Stf; Lit Mag; Rep Jr Cls; Rep Sr Cls; Mgr(s); Var Swmmng; Hon Roll; Ntl Merit Ltr; Excllnce Hstry 85; Poetry Readng Hon Men Cont 84; Bk Collectn Cont Semi-Fin 84.

GUST, CHRISTOPHER; Alden Central HS; Alden, NY; (Y); 5/215; Cmnty Wkr; Quiz Bowl; Science Clb; Nwsp Rptr; High Hon Roll; NHS; Acadmc Lttr 84-85.

GUSTAVSON, ERIC; Churchville-Chili SR HS; Churchville, NY; (Y); JCL; Math Clb; Math Tm; Ntl Merit Ltr; Psych.

GUSZCZA, JIM; Jordan-Elbridge HS; Jordan, NY; (Y); 10/135; FBLA; God Cntry Awd; JETS Awd; SAR Awd; Spiro T Agnew Awd 85; Stu Nrcssts Cmmndtn 85; JR Nihilists Amer Awd 84; Horatio Alger Schl Bus.

GUTBERLET, DARREN; Bishop Kearney HS; Webster, NY; (Y); Boy Scts; JA; Model UN; Ski Clb; Var Crs Cntry; Var Trk; Hon Roll; NHS.

GUTER, MARLENE; Rochester Christian HS; Webster, NY; (S); 2/14; Church Yth Grp; Spanish Clb; Chorus; Orch; Yrbk Stf; Bsktbl; Socr; Sftbl; Hon Roll; Drama Clb; Calvin Coll; Engr.

GUTH, BRAD; Cold Springs Harbor HS; Cold Spring Har, NY; (Y); Intnl Clb; Mathletes; Band; Jazz Band; Nwsp Stf; Yrbk Sprt Ed; Lit Mag; Trs Stu Cncl; JV Bsbl; Var Golf; Rotary Stu Of Mnth.

GUTHRIE, ANDREW; Ravena-Loeymans-Selkirk HS; New Baltimore, NY; (Y); #3 In Class; French Clb; Trs Key Clb; Var Socr; Var Tennis; Vllybl; High Hon Roll; NHS; Ntl Merit SF; Math Comp 82-84; Tnns Achvt Awd 84; Engr.

GUTIERREZ, GERALD; Abp Walsh HS; Salamanca, NY; (Y); Computer Clb; Spanish Clb; Yrbk Phtg; JV Var Bsktbl; Regents Schlr 85; Natl Hispnc Awds 85; Sccr 81-85; Biomed Engr.

GUTIERREZ, GIOVANNI; William Cullen Bryant HS; Jackson Hts, NY; (Y); Teachers Aide; NHS; Prfct Atten Awd; Hnr Mark NY ST Frnch Regents 85; Frgn Lang Hnr Scty 83-84; US Naval Acad; Aerosp Engr.

GUTIERREZ, KATHLEEN; Stissing Mountian HS; Red Hook, NY; (Y); Aud/Vis; Pep Clb; Band; Yrbk Stf; Var Cheerleading; JV Sftbl.

GUTIERREZ, MARIA; Bishop Ford CC HS; Brooklyn, NY; (Y); Art Clb; Ski Clb; Var Tennis; High Hon Roll; Archit Engr.

GUTIERREZZ, RONALD; Stuyvesant HS; Hollisworth, NY; (Y); Boy Scts; Nwsp Stf; Jr Cls; Sr Cls.

GUTMAN, STUART; Suffern HS; Suffern, NY; (Y); 2/400; Cmnty Wkr; Math Tm; Symp Band; Mgr Lit Mag; Pres Stu Cncl; Var Tennis; High Hon Roll; Jr NHS; NHS; Math Clb; Pltcl Sci.

GUTMANN, AMY; New Rochelle HS; New Rochelle, NY; (Y); Hosp Aide; MMM; Temple Yth Grp; Varsity Clb; Chorus; Var L Vllybl; Natl Music Hnr Soc 85; Downst Vllybl Tm 85; Physiothrpy.

GUTOWSKI, ROBERT J; Roy C Ketcham HS; Wappinger Fls, NY; (Y); 10/550; Church Yth Grp; Thesps; Jazz Band; Orch; School Play; Symp Band; Mrchg Band; Yrbk Bus Mgr; Pres NHS; Drama Clb; All-Cnty Chorus & Band 84-85; Cardinal Spellman Awd 84-85; Duke Of St Marys 83-84; Liberal Arts.

GUTOWSKI, TRACY; Amsterdam HS; Amsterdam, NY; (Y); DECA; Concert Band; Mrchg Band; Yrbk Stf; Hon Roll; Herkimer CC; Trvl.

GUTOWSKI, WENDY; West Seneca East SR HS; W Seneca, NY; (Y); DECA; Spanish Clb; Var Capt Bowling; High Hon Roll; Hon Roll; Jr NHS; NHS; Camp Fr Inc; Dance Clb; Key Clb; MVP Bowling 82-83 & 84-85; Jayncees Awd Bowling 84-85; Var Ltr Chorus 84-85.

GUTTENBERG, MICHAEL; Commack N HS; East Northport, NY; (S); 61/440; Cmnty Wkr; Temple Yth Grp; Nwsp Ed-Chief; Nwsp Rptr; Rep Frsh Cls; Off Soph Cls; Rep Jr Cls; Rep Sr Cls; Rep Stu Cncl; Wt Lftg; Unsung Hero 85; Washington U; Law.

GUTZMORE, NORBERT; Bushwick HS; Brooklyn, NY; (Y); 29/208; Church Yth Grp; Madrigals; Trs Sr Cls; Trk; Bausch & Lomb Sci Awd; Hon Roll; Otto P Burgdorf Awd 85; Hnr Cert Assoc Of Tchr Of Math 85; NY ST Series Regnts Schlrshp 85-89; SUNY New Paltz; Comp Sci.

GUY, LARRY; Park West HS; Brooklyn, NY; (Y); Office Aide; Teachers Aide; Nwsp Ed-Chief; Nwsp Rptr; Nwsp Stf; Off Sr Cls; Off Stu Cncl; Law.

GUYER, JOLYNN; Mexico HS; Fulton, NY; (Y); Pres 4-H; Spanish Clb; Color Guard; Mgr(s); Mat Maids; Score Keeper; 4-H Awd; Hon Roll; Psychlgy.

GUYTON, SHARON; Fashion Industries HS; Queens, NY; (Y); Church Yth Grp; Cmnty Wkr; Dance Clb; Hosp Aide; JA; Library Aide; Service Clb; Teachers Aide; Church Choir; Rep Frsh Cls; Atten Awds 85; Citatn Awd 85; Norfolk U; Med Tech.

GUYTON, TRACIE; Carthage Central HS; Carthage, NY; (Y); French Clb; High Hon Roll; Hon Roll; Var Tennis; JV Vllybl; Stu Of SADD 84-85; Jefferson CC; Soclgy.

GUZIK, PATRICK R; Berlin American HS; Apo, NY; (S); 2/90; Computer Clb; English Clb; Spanish Clb; Nwsp Rptr; Yrbk Rptr; JV Bsbl; JV Bsktbl; Var Socr; High Hon Roll; Hon Roll; 3rd Pl Regnl Splng Cntst 83; US Military Acad; Math Engrng.

GUZINSKI, AMY A; Villa Maria Acad; Buffalo, NY; (Y); Church Yth Grp; Computer Clb; Math Clb; Pep Clb; Ski Clb; Spanish Clb; Nwsp Rptr; Sec Soph Cls; Rep Stu Cncl; High Hon Roll; NY ST Regents Schlrshp 85; St Bonavenuture Friar Schlrshp 85; St Bonaventure U; Accntng.

GUZMAN, BRUNILDA; St Nicholas Of Tolentine HS; Bronx, NY; (S); 1/12; Hosp Aide; Spanish Clb; Teachers Aide; Stat Gym; High Hon Roll; Hon Roll; 3 1st Hnrs 84-85; 2 Awds For Art & Rcrd Kpng 84; Hnr & Pendnt 84; Bus.

GUZMAN, CLARIBEL; Mabel Dean Baron HS; New York, NY; (S); 26/299; Dance Clb; Band; Hon Roll; Prfct Atten Awd; Comp Sci.

GUZMAN, LORIANN; Walton HS; Bronx, NY; (S); 8/679; Dance Clb; Office Aide; Service Clb; Teachers Aide; Chorus; Variety Show; Pres NHS; Daily News Super Yth 83-84; Natl Hist & Govt Awd 85; Bus Admin.

GUZMAN, LYN; Buffalo Academy Of Sacred Heart; Williamsville, NY; (Y); Pres Church Yth Grp; Cmnty Wkr; Model UN; Ski Clb; Teachers Aide; Stage Crew; St Gregory The Great CYO Sargent At Arms & Pres 84-86; ST Univ Of NY; Accntng.

GUZMAN, MARIA; Norman Thomas HS; New York, NY; (S); 9/584; FBLA; Office Aide; Chorus; Vllybl; Cit Awd; Hon Roll; Jr NHS; NHS; Prfct Atten Awd; UFT Coll Schlrshp 85; Bio Sci.

GUZSKI, DENISE; John F Kennedy HS; Utica, NY; (Y); 16/139; Pep Clb; Camp Fr Inc; Yrbk Ed-Chief; Sec Frsh Cls; Sec Trs Soph Cls; Sec Stu Cncl; Var Capt Badmtn; Var Fld Hcky; JV Sftbl; Jr NHS; Phys Thrpy.

GUZZO, JEANNE; Sachem High School North Campus; Lk Ronkonkoma, NY; (Y); Band; Concert Band; Orch; Pep Band; Symp Band; Accntnt.

GWINN, CLAIRE; Smithtown H S West; Smithtown, NY; (Y); Sec DECA; Exploring; Hosp Aide; Pres Leo Clb; Spanish Clb; Teachers Aide; Chorus; School Play; Yrbk Stf; Lit Mag.

GWINN, LINDA; Smithtown High School West; Smithtown, NY; (Y); Exploring; Leo Clb; Teachers Aide; Chorus; Nwsp Stf; Lit Mag; Var Badmtn; JV Var Fld Hcky; Var Trk; Hon Roll; SCMEA Suffolk Cnty Music Educ Assoc, Select Chorus 82.

GWITT, CHRIS; Frontier Central HS; Hamburg, NY; (Y); #34 In Class; Hon Roll; NHS; Bus Adm.

GWON, JOANNE; Roosevelt HS; Yonkers, NY; (S); 6/287; Band; Concert Band; Mrchg Band; Stage Crew; Yrbk Stf; Lit Mag; Sec Sr Cls; Cheerleading; CC Awd; High Hon Roll; E Yonkers Rtry Clb & Yonkers Fed Chrs Schlrshps 85; Suprntndt Awd 90 Clb 84-85; SUNY Binghamton; Bus.

GWYDIR, CRAIG; L I Lutheran HS; Huntington, NY; (S); 1/57; Pres Computer Clb; Mathletes; Symp Band; Trs Sr Cls; Trs Stu Cncl; Var Bsbl; Var Socr; Kiwanis Awd; Trs NHS; Val; 1T Pl Hnrs LI Sci Congrs-Comp Catgry 81-84; LILCO Tchrs CU Awd Sci Achvt 82; Cntry III Ldrshp Awd; Polytech Inst Of NY; Aero Engr.

GYORE, TRACY; Lowville Academy & Central Schl; Lowville, NY; (Y); Letterman Clb; Spanish Clb; Varsity Clb; Swmmng; Prfct Atten Awd; Oceanography.

HA, THUY; Dover JR & SR HS; Dover Plains, NY; (S); FNA; Sr Cls; Badmtn; High Hon Roll; Voice Dem Awd; Art Awd 82; Dutchess Comm Coll; Nrs.

HAAF, KIRSTEN; Voorheesville HS; Voorheesville, NY; (Y); 2/103; Key Clb; Band; Chorus; Mrchg Band; Symp Band; Nwsp Rptr; Rep Frsh Cls; JV Sftbl; High Hon Roll; NHS; RPI Math,Sci Awd 85; Highst Avg Hist 84; 2nd Hgst Avd Cls 85; Chem.

HAAG, GREGORY; Eden SR HS; Eden, NY; (Y); FFA; Lion Awd; Prfct Atten Awd; Pres Schlr; Regents Schlrshp 85; Geneseo ST U; Cvl Engrng.

HAAK, JENNIFER; Fairport HS; Fairport, NY; (Y); Political Wkr; Yrbk Bus Mgr; Stu Cncl; Var Capt Sftbl; Var Capt Tennis; High Hon Roll; Pres NHS; JCL; Chorus; Yrbk Stf; Univ Rochester Pada Awd 85; Ltn Dept Awd 85; Stdnt Rep NY ST Snte Stdnt Plcy Frm 85; Law.

HAAKMAT, DANIELLE; Notre Dame Acad HS; Staten Island, NY; (Y); Civic Clb; Cmnty Wkr; Hosp Aide; Intnl Clb; Library Aide; JV Swmmng; NHS; Ntl Merit SF; Bus Admin.

HAAS, AMY; James I O Neill HS; West Point, NY; (Y); Aud/Vis; Camera Clb; Church Yth Grp; Drama Clb; French Clb; Pep Clb; Chorus; Church Choir; School Musical; School Play; Hghst Grd Pt Avg Frnch Level 4 85; Bus Admin.

HAAS, BARBARA ANN; Seton Catholic Central HS; Endicott, NY; (S); French Clb; Nwsp Rptr; Nwsp Stf; Rep Jr Cls; Rep Stu Cncl; High Hon Roll; NHS; Natl Piano Playing Auditions 84; Law.

HAAS, ERIK; Bishop Kearney HS; Ontario, NY; (Y); JA; Ski Clb; Bsktbl; JV Lcrss; Var Capt Socr; Sftbl; JA Co Yr 84; Empire St Games Qlfr NYS Fnlst 83-84; Bus Mgt.

HAAS, ERIKA; Emma Willard HS; Troy, NY; (Y); AFS; German Clb; Intnl Clb; Nwsp Rptr; Yrbk Stf; Ntl Merit Ltr; Readers Dig Schlrshp 84-85; Cong-Bundestag Schlrshp 84-85; Cum Laude Soc 84-85.

HAAS, ROLFE D; Chenango Valley Jr HS; Binghamton, NY; (Y); #1 In Class; Cmnty Wkr; Political Wkr; Pres Spanish Clb; Hst School Musical; Nwsp Rptr; High Hon Roll; Pres Jr NHS; NHS; St Schlr; Val; Hugh Obrian Yth Ldrshp Fndtn Outstndng Soph 83-84; Natl Merit Pgm 86; Soc Sci.

HABER, EDWARD; Bishop-Ford CC HS; Brooklyn, NY; (Y); Cmnty Wkr; Varsity Clb; Color Guard; Stu Cncl; Crs Cntry; Swmmng; Tennis; Trk.

HABER, JEANNE; New Lebanon Central HS; Old Chatham, NY; (Y); 2/55; Sec Church Yth Grp; Sec Spanish Clb; Band; Chorus; Concert Band; Mrchg Band; Swing Chorus; Rep Frsh Cls; Rep Soph Cls; Mgr(s); Natl Hnr Socty 85; NYSSMA Grd 6 Music B 85; Russell Sage Coll; Bus.

HABER, MELISSA; Half Hollow Hills High School East; Dix Hills, NY; (Y); 35/499; FBLA; Leo Clb; Office Aide; Yrbk Stf; High Hon Roll; Jr NHS; NHS; Spanish NHS; Bus.

HABER, MICHAEL I; Ramaz Upper Schl; New York, NY; (Y); Aud/Vis; Capt Camera Clb; School Play; Ed Nwsp Phtg; Ed Yrbk Phtg; Yrbk Stf; Lit Mag; Bsktbl; Capt Ftbl; Sftbl; NYC Rgnts Schlrshp Awd 85; All-Star Team Bsktbl 83-84; Bus.

HABICHT, DOUGLAS; Alden HS; Alden, NY; (Y); Var Ftbl; Hon Roll.

HACHE, ABRAHAM ALEXIS; St Agnes HS; New York, NY; (Y); 16/100; Leo Clb; Chorus; Gym; Trk; Wt Lftg; Cit Awd; Hon Roll; 2nd Hnrs 84-85; Bus Admin.

HACHIGIAN, NINA L; Scarsdale HS; Scarsdale, NY; (Y); Chrmn Church Yth Grp; Pres Debate Tm; Pres French Clb; Sec Church Choir; Pres Stu Cncl; NHS; Ntl Merit SF; Pres Clsrm For Yng Amer 84; Comp Sci.

HACHTEN, MICHAEL; North Collins Central HS; N Collins, NY; (Y); 2/78; Band; Concert Band; Mrchg Band; School Musical; School Play; Yrbk Stf; Var L Tennis; Hon Roll; Prfct Atten Awd; Pres Schlr; MI Plyr Tennis 84; Erie Cnty Fair All Hgh Band 84-85; Regnts Schlrshp 85; Rochester Inst Of Tech; Sci.

HACIC, CAROL; Frontier Central HS; Blasdell, NY; (S); French Clb; Pep Clb; Ski Clb; Chorus; Var L Socr; High Hon Roll; Hon Roll; NHS; NEDT Awd; Am HS Math Exam 85; Accntng.

HACK, JUDY A; Schuylerville Central HS; Schuylerville, NY; (Y); 1/99; Church Yth Grp; Cmnty Wkr; French Clb; Chorus; Bausch & Lomb Sci Awd; High Hon Roll; Jr NHS; NHS; Val; Rgnts Schlrshp 85; C Mortimer Mem, Friars Schlrshp 85; St Bonaventure U; Engl.

HACK, TRACIE L; Palmyraa-Macedon Central HS; Palmyra, NY; (Y); 49/205; Sec AFS; Sec VP Church Yth Grp; Sec VP Ski Clb; Varsity Clb; Rep Soph Cls; Rep Jr Cls; JV Var Socr; Var Sftbl; Var Capt Trk; Prfct Atten Awd; NYS Rgnts Schlrshp 85; Oneonta; Phys Thrpy.

HACKETT, LAURIE; Plattsburgh HS; Plattsburgh, NY; (Y); Var Capt Cheerleading; Yrbk Stf; Hon Roll; Math.

HADDAD, GEORGE; Kenmore West HS; Kenmore, NY; (Y); Boy Scts; Computer Clb; Pres JA; Pres Math Tm; Model UN; Quiz Bowl; High Hon Roll; Prfct Atten Awd; Voice Dem Awd; Gld Medlst Wrld Fnls Olympcs Mind 81; Hghst Hnr ST Sci Cngrss 85; Voic Demcrcy Spch Wrtg Cntst Win 84; Cornell U; Med Rsrch.

HADDEN, SCOTT; Lake Placid Central HS; Lake Placid, NY; (Y); 2/48; Am Leg Boys St; Boy Scts; Computer Clb; Varsity Clb; Pres Jr Cls; Rep Stu Cncl; L Crs Cntry; L Socr; L Trk; Cit Awd; Crs Cntry Ski Tm 82-86.

HADDLETON, CINDY; Gates-Chili SR HS; Rochester, NY; (S); Cmnty Wkr; Office Aide; Service Clb; Spanish Clb; Nwsp Ed-Chief; Ed Yrbk Stf; High Hon Roll; NHS; Prfct Atten Awd; Journalism.

HADLOCK, JUDY; South New Berlin Central HS; Norwich, NY; (Y); Teachers Aide; VICA; Color Guard; Nwsp Rptr; Stu Cncl; Hon Roll; Altrnt Dairy Prncss Chenango Cnty 85-86; Stdnt Qrtr Adv Keybrdg 2 Qrtrs 85; CCBI; Secy.

HAEFFNER, KIMBERLY; Rocky Point HS; Rocky Point, NY; (S); 8/180; Chorus; Church Choir; Concert Band; Madrigals; Mrchg Band; School Musical; Var Vllybl; Hon Roll; Sec NHS; Ntl Merit Ltr; Spch Pathlgy.

HAEGELAND, MICHELLE; Smithtown High School East; St James, NY; (Y); Rep Church Yth Grp; Chorus; High Hon Roll; Hon Roll; Algeb Awd 82-83; Geom Awd 83-84; Fr Awd 83-84; NY ST U Stony Brook; Bus Mgmt.

HAENLE, MARK; Royalton Hartland Cent HS; Middleport, NY; (Y); 33/130; 4-H; Temple Yth Grp; Art Awd 82; Paper Carrier Mnth 83; Air Force.

HAERR, HOLLI; E L Vandermeulen HS; Port Jefferson, NY; (Y); 10/264; Acpl Chr; Chorus; Madrigals; School Musical; Symp Band; JV Trs Vllybl; Cit Awd; NHS; Ntl Merit Ltr; French Clb; Brown Bk Eng Awd 85; All ST Bassoonst 84-85; Suffolk Cnty Vllybl Clb-USVBA 84-85.

HAFELE, ROBERT W; Downsville Central Schl; Downsville, NY; (Y); 3/26; Band; Chorus; Drm Mjr(t); Jazz Band; School Musical; Pres Sr Cls; Pres Stu Cncl; Var Bsktbl; Trs NHS; St Schlr; NY ST U Potsdam; Music.

HAFNER, JEAN-PAUL; Mc Graw HS; E Freetown, NY; (Y); 1/45; Am Leg Boys St; Drama Clb; Trs French Clb; Capt Quiz Bowl; Varsity Clb; Nwsp Stf; Trs Stu Cncl; Var Bsbl; High Hon Roll; NHS; Cornell; Pre-Med.

HAGBERG, KURTIS; Southwestern Centrail HS; Ashville, NY; (Y); Letterman Clb; VICA; Band; Concert Band; Mrchg Band; Mgr(s); Rifle Tm 82-83, 83-84, & 84-85; Schl Awd In Woodworking 84-85.

HAGELSTEIN, DAWN; John Adams HS; Ozone Pk, NY; (Y); Service Clb; Teachers Aide; NHS; Cert 1st Hnrs 84; Cert 1st & 2nd Hnrs 85; Data Proc.

HAGENAH, BETTY ANN; Maria Regina HS; Whiteplains, NY; (Y); 41/127; Yrbk Stf; Rep Sr Cls; Stu Cncl; Math.

HAGENBERGER, ROBERT; Sachem HS; Lk Ronkonkoma, NY; (Y); 286/1394; Ski Clb; Varsity Clb; Golf; Accntng.

HAGER, CHARLES; Msgr Mc Clancy Memorial HS; Forest Hills, NY; (Y); Boy Scts; Cmnty Wkr; Band; Variety Show; Hon Roll; Recpnt Of Bread For Wrld Awd 82-83; Fthr Edward Troike Ldrshp Prog Volntr Aid 84-85; Hlth Care.

HAGERMAN, DIANE; St Vincent Ferrer HS; Sunnyside, NY; (Y); 35/114; Church Yth Grp; Pep Clb.

HAGERTY, MARJORIE T; Lakeland HS; Yorktown Heights, NY; (Y); 10/450; Debate Tm; Thesps; Chorus; School Musical; School Play; Sec Sr Cls; Stat Bsbl; High Hon Roll; NHS; Pres Schlr; NY ST Regents Schlrshp 85; New Rochelle Coll; Psychlgst.

HAGGERTY, MAURA; Pelham Memorial HS; Pelham, NY; (Y); Church Yth Grp; Cmnty Wkr; Nwsp Rptr; Nwsp Stf; Yrbk Stf; Sec Frsh Cls; VP Soph Cls; JV Lcrss; Hon Roll; NHS; Eng,Jrnlsm.

HAGGERTY, MAUREEN P; Our Lady Of Perpetual Help HS; Brooklyn, NY; (Y); 4/162; Office Aide; NHS; NYC Regents Schlrshp 85; Principals List 81-85; NY Inst Of Tech; Architect.

HAGLER, JAMES K; West Seneca East SR HS; W Seneca, NY; (Y); 8/365; Aud/Vis; German Clb; Var JV Socr; Var JV Tennis; High Hon Roll; Hon Roll; JC Awd; NHS; German Hnr Scty; Heidelberg Coll; Math.

HAGLUND, SUZIE; Rh Sperry HS; Rochester, NY; (Y); 15/311; GAA; School Musical; Nwsp Ed-Chief; Nwsp Rptr; Sec Jr Cls; Rep Sr Cls; JV Var Socr; Var Tennis; Pres NHS; Spanish NHS; SUNY Geneseo; Spec Ed Tchr.

HAGO, JAIME; Walton HS; New York, NY; (Y); Boys Clb Am; Office Aide; Hon Roll; Syracuse U; Aerospc Engrng.

HAGO, JOHN R; La Salle Acad; Woodside, NY; (S); Boy Scts; Church Yth Grp; Spanish Clb; School Musical; Sec Jr Cls; Bowling; Im Socr; Spanish NHS; Med.

HAGUES, BRIAN; Whitesboro HS; Utica, NY; (Y); 45/370; Varsity Clb; Band; Concert Band; Jazz Band; Mrchg Band; Orch; Var L Socr; Var L Tennis; Hon Roll; Jr NHS; Amer Legion Essay Cont 3rd Pl 83; Aerosp Engr.

HAHER, DONALD R; Oneonta HS; Oneonta, NY; (Y); 31/172; German Clb; Var Ftbl; Art Clb; Regents Schlrshp; SUNY Buffalo; Engrng.

HAHM, JUNG-SUK; The Knox Schl; St James, NY; (S); 1/38; Camera Clb; French Clb; Math Clb; Nwsp Ed-Chief; Nwsp Rptr; Nwsp Stf; Yrbk Rptr; Stu Cncl; Im Bowling; Var Crs Cntry; Bancroft Phinney Awd 83-84; Amer Hstry Awd Soc Mayflwr Descend NY 84; Physics.

HAHN, BELINDA; Jamesville-De Witt HS; Syracuse, NY; (Y); Art Clb; German Clb; Chorus; Crs Cntry; Trk; High Hon Roll; NHS; Blue Ribbon Art 84.

HAHN, BRIAN; Cicero-North Syracuse HS; Clay, NY; (S); 96/711; Boy Scts; Ski Clb; Concert Band; Mrchg Band; Orch; Pep Band; Symp Band; Var Tennis; VP NHS; Ntl Merit Ltr; Aerospace Engrng.

HAHN, LORI; Byron-Bergen HS; Bergen, NY; (Y); Church Yth Grp; Band; Concert Band; Mrchg Band; Trk; Genesee CC.

HAHN, MICHAEL; Saint Marys HS; Cheektowaga, NY; (S); 15/185; Boy Scts; Drm & Bgl; School Musical; Sec Jr Cls; JV Bsbl; Hon Roll; NHS; Eagle Scout 85.

HAIGH JR, RICHARD; Lakeland HS; Putnam Vly, NY; (Y); Boy Scts; Cmnty Wkr; Nwsp Ed-Chief; JV Socr; High Hon Roll; NHS; Prfct Atten Awd; Outstndg Achvt-Hghst Avg Overall 83; Hghst Achvt-Math & Frgn Lang 83; Israel Ben Schreiber Awd 83; Fnnc.

HAIGNEY, CHRISTINE; Walter Panas HS; Bronx, NY; (Y); Math Tm; Chorus; Soph Cls; Jr Cls; Twrlr; High Hon Roll; Ntl Merit SF; Physcs.

HAILE, MONICA; Dominican Commercial HS; Jamaica, NY; (Y); Computer Clb; Dance Clb; Pep Clb; Teachers Aide; Rep Frsh Cls; Rep Soph Cls; Stu Cncl; L Cheerleading; Hon Roll; NY Inst Tech; Sys Anlyst.

HAILSTON, DENNIS D; Owen D Young Central HS; Richfield Springs, NY; (S); 3/30; VP Jr Cls; Var Bsbl; Var JV Bsktbl; Cit Awd; High Hon Roll; Hon Roll; Jr NHS; NHS; Boy Scts; Mst Impr Plyr Vrsty Bsbl 84; Rgnts Awd Course III Math 83-84; All League Awd 84; Prof Bsbl Plyr.

HAINES, PHILLIP; Skaneateles HS; Skaneateles, NY; (S); Church Yth Grp; Chorus; Church Choir; Hon Roll; NHS; Peer Shrng 84-85; Pop Chr, Boys Ensemble 84-85; All Cnty 84-85; Engrng.

HAINES, RAE; G Ray Bodley HS; Fulton, NY; (Y); Sec Latin Clb; Math Clb; Ski Clb; Varsity Clb; Rep Soph Cls; Rep Jr Cls; Stu Cncl; Coach Actv; Mat Maids; Var Socr; Awd Good Grade Pnt Avg 83; Travel.

HAIRR, MARY D; Huntington HS; Huntington, NY; (Y); 26/433; AFS; Key Clb; Sec Varsity Clb; Jazz Band; Variety Show; Capt Var Crs Cntry; Capt Var Trk; Hon Roll; Lion Awd; Pres NHS; Bronze Mdl Math Fair 84; U Of NC Chapel Hill; Pre-Med.

HAJDUK, THERESA M; Tonawanda JR SR HS; Tonawanda, NY; (Y); 10/235; Sec Church Yth Grp; Stage Crew; Yrbk Stf; Mgr(s); Timer; Hon Roll; NHS; Ntl Merit SF; Regents Schlrshp 85; Quality Stu Awd 85; Geneseo.

HAKIEL, ANGELIQUE; Lindenhurst HS; Lindenhurst, NY; (Y); Orch; School Musical; Variety Show; Yrbk Stf; Rep Sr Cls; Trs Rep Stu Cncl; Hon Roll; Jr NHS; NHS; Music Awds NYSSMA 82-84; Bus.

HALABY, JUDY A; Fontbonne Hall HS; Brooklyn, NY; (Y); Church Yth Grp; Teachers Aide; Stage Crew; Variety Show; Sftbl; Swmmng; NY ST Regnts Schlrshp 85; Red Cross Blood Donr Prog 85; Psych.

HALABY, MICHAELLE; Bishop Ford C C HS; Brooklyn, NY; (Y); Dance Clb; French Clb; JA; Math Tm; Science Clb; Chorus; Yrbk Stf; Hon Roll; NHS; Ntl Merit Ltr; Medicine.

HALADY, CHRISTINE; Mount Mercy Acad; Blasdell, NY; (S); Sec Church Yth Grp; VP French Clb; Trs Girl Scts; JA; Chorus; Madrigals; Nwsp Stf; Capt Sftbl; Im Capt Vllybl; Hon Roll; Wstrn NY Frgn Lang Fair 2nd Pl 83; Class Delg 84-85; Piano Lssns 83.

HALAMANDARIS, ANNETTE; Curtis HS; Staten Island, NY; (Y); 50/328; CAP; Cheerleading; SUNY Coll Geneseo; Bus.

HALBEISEN, PETER; South Lewis Central HS; Boonville, NY; (Y); Varsity Clb; JV Trk; Hon Roll; Sec Trs NHS; Prfct Atten Awd; Mohawk Valley CC; Engrng Sci.

HALBERT, CHRISTINE; Acad Of The Resrrctn; Scarsdale, NY; (Y); Aud/Vis; Dance Clb; Drama Clb; Math Clb; School Play; Yrbk Phtg; Yrbk Stf; VP Soph Cls; Hon Roll; NHS; Catholic Yth Orgnztn Art Shw 1st & 3rd Pl 83, 3rd Pl 85; Iona Coll; Bus.

HALBFINGER, DAVID; Baldwin SR HS; Freeport, NY; (S); Debate Tm; Mathletes; VP Quiz Bowl; Thesps; Chorus; Orch; Nwsp Rptr; French Hon Soc; Chess Clb; Drama Clb; Asst Cncrtmstr Lng Islnd Strng Fstvl H S Orch 85; Semi-Fnlst Princeton Bk Awd; Lng Isl Mth Fr Slvr Mdl.

HALDEMAN, KRISTIN; Catholic Central HS; Troy, NY; (S); 1/203; French Clb; German Clb; Yrbk Stf; Pres Stu Cncl; VP Capt Cheerleading; Score Keeper; Bausch & Lomb Sci Awd; High Hon Roll; NHS; Rensselaer Polytechnic Inst Medal For Excellence In Math-Sci 84; Georgetown U; Foreign Lang.

HALE, JOSEPH B; Lockport SR HS; Lockport, NY; (Y); 8/455; Exploring; JA; Library Aide; Var Bowling; Var Crs Cntry; JV Trk; Hon Roll; Jr NHS; NHS; Prfct Atten Awd; Regnts Schlrshp 85; Rensselaer Medal 84; Gen Mtrs Inst; Elec Engrng.

HALE, MARGARET ANN; Chittenango HS; Bridgeport, NY; (Y); Am Leg Aux Girls St; Band; Concert Band; Jazz Band; Orch; School Musical; School Play; Tennis; High Hon Roll; NHS.

HALE, NANCY; Knox Memorial Central HS; Russell, NY; (S); Varsity Clb; Band; Concert Band; Mrchg Band; Yrbk Stf; Bsktbl; Socr; Vllybl; High Hon Roll; NHS; Nurse.

HALE, NATALIE; Villa Maria Acad; Kenmore, NY; (Y); Computer Clb; JCL; Latin Clb; Drm & Bgl; Swing Chorus; Hon Roll; Rep Jr Cls; Canisius Coll; Psych.

HALE JR, ROBERT; Living Word Acad; Canastota, NY; (S); 6/12; Trs Sr Cls; Var L Bsbl; Var L Bsktbl; Var L Socr; Im Wrstlng; SUNY-MRRSVL; Natrl Rsrcs.

HALEY, KOLLEEN; Geneseo Central HS; Geneseo, NY; (Y); Spanish Clb; Rep Stu Cncl; Var Socr; Var Trk; JV Vllybl; Hon Roll; Nrs.

HALEY, THERESA A; Salamanca Central HS; Killbuck, NY; (Y); Am Leg Aux Girls St; Cmnty Wkr; French Clb; Red Cross Aide; High Hon Roll; Hon Roll; Acctg.

HALFIN, MARCIA; Colonie Central HS; Albany, NY; (Y); 6/511; Art Clb; Office Aide; Red Cross Aide; Teachers Aide; High Hon Roll; NHS; Phys Fit Mert Awd NY Picture Nwspaper 82-83; Grd Ldge Pythias ST NY Awd Essay Cont 82-83.

HALFON, SAUL E; Niskayuna HS; Schenectady, NY; (Y); Trs Drama Clb; School Musical; School Play; Stage Crew; Variety Show; NCTE Awd; NHS; Ntl Merit Ltr; St Schlr; Brown U Bk Awd 84; Nisk Art Prose Hnrbl Mntn 84; Chem.

HALIMA, SARA; Sephardic HS; Brooklyn, NY; (S); 3/30; Nwsp Stf; Yrbk Stf; NHS; Sal; Brooklyn Coll; Psych.

HALKO, NICHOLAS J; Keveny Memorial Acad; Watervliet, NY; (S); 7/40; Rep Stu Cncl; Hon Roll; NHS; Natl Bus Hnr Soc 84; Acctng.

HALL, ALLISON; Spackenkill HS; Poughkeepsie, NY; (Y); Stage Crew; Var Trk; JV Var Vllybl; Trk Awd 4th, All Conf 85; Emp ST Swm Leag Chmpshp Meet 4th 85, 6th 83.

HALL, ANDREA S; Oxford Acad; Oxford, NY; (Y); 11/78; Church Yth Grp; Ski Clb; Band; Chorus; Concert Band; Jazz Band; Orch; Symp Band; Yrbk Stf; Sec Soph Cls; Rtry Schlrshp 85; Exch Stu To Peru 85-86; Clark U Worcester MA; Law.

HALL, AVIAN; Camden SR HS; Blossvale, NY; (Y); Drama Clb; 4-H; Hosp Aide; Acpl Chr; Chorus; School Musical; School Play; Stage Crew; Hon Roll; Psych.

HALL, BRIAN; Massena HS; Massena, NY; (Y); 12/294; High Hon Roll; Prfct Atten Awd; Bio Awd 82-83; Elden Browne 85; Pres Acad Ftns Awd 85; Clarion U; Opto.

HALL, COLLEEN M; Johnson City SR HS; Johnson City, NY; (Y); Pep Clb; Varsity Clb; Color Guard; Yrbk Stf; Stu Cncl; Stat Var Ftbl; Var Socr; Var L Trk; Hon Roll; Church Yth Grp; Natl Spnsh Test Lvl 2 Accmplshmnt Cert 85; NY ST Art Cont Hnrbl Ment Awd 82; Bio.

HALL, CRAIG; Delaware Academy & Central Schl; Delhi, NY; (Y); Boy Scts; Church Yth Grp; 4-H; Library Aide; Spanish Clb; Golf; Hon Roll; NHS; Elec Engrng.

HALL, DAVID; Hannibal Central School; Hannibal, NY; (S); Band; Concert Band; Mrchg Band; Yrbk Stf; Hon Roll; NHS; Ag.

HALL, DONNA; St Johns Prep HS; Middle Vlg, NY; (Y); Church Yth Grp; Band; JV Sftbl; Bus Mgmt.

HALL, GABRIELA Y; Saint Barnabas HS; Bronx, NY; (Y); Dance Clb; Hosp Aide; Library Aide; Teachers Aide; Chorus; Nwsp Rptr; High Hon Roll; Hon Roll; NHS; Spanish NHS; NY ST Regnts Schlrshp 85; Natl Sci Olympd Awd 81; NY U; Behvrl Bio.

HALL, JEAN M; H C Williams HS; Canton, NY; (Y); 49/132; VP Capt 4-H; Chorus; Drm Mjr(t); Swing Chorus; Ed Yrbk Phtg; Yrbk Stf; 4-H Awd; Church Yth Grp; Acpl Chr; Color Guard; Regents Schlrshp 85; Potsdam ST U; Bio.

HALL, JEFFREY C; Newfane Central Schl; Lockport, NY; (S); Varsity Clb; Var Bsbl; Var Ftbl; Hon Roll; NHS; Comp Prog.

HALL, JOHN; Horseheads HS; Elmira, NY; (S); 6/406; French Clb; JCL; Latin Clb; Ski Clb; Lit Mag; High Hon Roll; NHS; Ntl Merit Ltr; Prfct Atten Awd; Yth Cnty 84; Ntnl Sci Olympiad 83; Red Cross Ldrshp Conf 84; U Of Rochester; Elec.

HALL, JULIE; Lockport SR HS; Lockport, NY; (Y); 9/411; AFS; Girl Scts; Intnl Clb; Stu Cncl; L Swmmng; Var Trk; Jr NHS; NHS; Hon Roll; 1st Cls Grl Scts 83; Slvr Awd Grl Scts 84; Engrng.

HALL, KAREN; Smithtown High School East; Nesconset, NY; (Y); Dance Clb; Spanish Clb; Band; Concert Band; Mrchg Band; School Musical; Symp Band; Hon Roll; Off Frsh Cls; Smithtown Coll Aid Fund Schlrshp 85; Exchng Stu Japan 82; NYSSMA 84; Suny Geneseo; Elem Ed.

HALL, KRISTOPH G; Gates-Chili HS; Rochester, NY; (Y); 70/463; Drama Clb; Ski Clb; School Musical; Rep Soph Cls; Rep Jr Cls; VP Sr Cls; Capt Crs Cntry; Var JV Ftbl; Var Swmmng; Var JV Trk; Regents Schlrshp 84-85; Purdue; Sci.

HALL, LARRY; Waverly LR SR HS; Lockwood, NY; (Y); Cmnty Wkr; Ski Clb; Bsktbl; Hon Roll; Cert Of Merit DEC 83; West Schlrshp Awd 85; Tompkins Cortland CC; Mec Engr.

HALL, LARRY J; Hadley Luzerne HS; Hadley, NY; (Y); 10/70; Var Bowling; Var Golf; Var Socr; Hon Roll; NHS; NY Regents Shclrshp 85; Marine Bio.

HALL, SANDRA; Uniondale HS; Uniondale, NY; (Y); Sec Church Yth Grp; Church Choir; Badmtn; High Hon Roll; Hon Roll; Jr NHS; 2 Cert After Entering Teen Tlnt Cmptn-Bible & Plaque 83; 1T Dist Lvl, 1st ST & 1ST Rnnr Intl Cmptn; Long Island Hosp Schl/Nrsng; Nr.

HALL, THOMAS C; New Hartford Central HS; New Hartford, NY; (Y); 70/300; Capt Chess Clb; FTA; Teachers Aide; Bsktbl; Hon Roll; St Schlr; Regnts Schlrshp 85; Syracuse U; Tchr.

HALL, WENDY LYNN; Canastota HS; Canastota, NY; (Y); Pres 4-H; High Hon Roll; Hon Roll; Law Enfrcmnt.

HALLADAY, CHERYL; Groton Central Schl; Groton, NY; (Y); 10/80; Church Yth Grp; Yrbk Stf; Bowling; JV L Vllybl; High Hon Roll; NHS; Library Aide; Mary Evelyn Dempsey Awd 85; Pres Acdmc Ftns Awd 85; Freedom Choice Schlrshp 85; Rochester Inst Tech; Elec Engr.

HALLADAY, CRAIG; Henninger HS; Liverpool, NY; (Y); 23/583; Church Yth Grp; School Musical; School Play; Rep Jr Cls; Bsbl; Var L Ftbl; Var L Lcrss; Vllybl; Wt Lftg; Hon Roll; Cardiologist.

HALLAHAN, SEAN; Lake George HS; Lk George, NY; (Y); School Play; Yrbk Stf; Lit Mag; High Hon Roll; Hon Roll; Artist.

HALLERUD, NOELLE; Tioga Central HS; Owego, NY; (Y); Church Yth Grp; Girl Scts; VP Chorus; Variety Show; JV Bsktbl; Var Trk; JV Vllybl; NYSSMA Solo Festvl Awd 84-85; Selctd NYSSMA All Cty Festvl 84-85; Photo.

HALLETT, NANCY; Candor Central HS; Willseyville, NY; (Y); Church Yth Grp; Band; Chorus; Church Choir; Mrchg Band; Rep Stu Cncl; JV Cheerleading; Capt Pom Pon; Im Sftbl; Hon Roll; Music.

HALLETT, SHERI L; Canandaigua Acad; Canandaigua, NY; (Y); 9/277; German Clb; Band; Concert Band; Drm Mjr(t); Mrchg Band; Pep Band; JV Var Bsktbl; Var Sftbl; High Hon Roll; Hon Roll; Oswego ST U; Comp Sci.

HALLGREN, CRIS; Corning P P West HS; Painted Post, NY; (Y); Church Yth Grp; Band; Concert Band; Mrchg Band; Yrbk Phtg; Yrbk Stf; Hon Roll; Math.

HALLIDAY, JAMES; Mamaroneck HS; Larchmont, NY; (Y); Church Yth Grp; Capt Math Tm; Concert Band; Jazz Band; Var L Lcrss; Var L Socr; High Hon Roll; Sec NHS; Math Clb; Ski Clb; Harvard Bk Awd; All Lg Socr 2 Yrs; Natlchem Soc Tm; Engrng.

HALLIFAX, DARCY; Haverling Central HS; Kanona, NY; (S); 10/150; AFS; French Clb; Math Clb; Math Tm; School Musical; Yrbk Stf; Lit Mag; High Hon Roll; NHS; Regnts Schlrshp 85; NY ST U Geneseo; Comp Sci.

HALLINAN, RENEE; Fayetteville-Manlius SR HS; Manlius, NY; (Y); Hon Roll; Prfct Atten Awd; Cerebral Palsy Dance Marathon Rcgntn 85; Accntng.

HALLINGER, CAROL ANNE; St Francis Prep; Glendale, NY; (S); 45/693; Math Clb; Trk; Hon Roll; Optimate Soc 84.

HALLISSY, MARIA; St Francis Preparatory Schl; Flushing, NY; (S); 20/693; Dance Clb; Teachers Aide; Chorus; School Play; High Hon Roll; NHS; Math.

HALLIT, ANN; Coxsackie-Athens HS; Coxsackie, NY; (Y); Spanish Clb; Trs Band; Jazz Band; Pep Band; Rep Frsh Cls; Rep Soph Cls; Trs Jr Cls; JV Cheerleading; High Hon Roll; NHS; Mdcl Tchnlgst.

HALLOCK, JOHN; Pittsford Sutherland HS; Pittsford, NY; (Y); Var JV Socr; Var Trk.

HALLOCK, ROBERT; Paul D Schreiber HS; Port Washington, NY; (Y); 72/423; Madrigals; School Musical; School Play; Nwsp Stf; JV Crs Cntry; Cit Awd; DAR Awd; NHS; Ntl Merit Ltr; Val; Pt Washington Play Trp Awd; Karen Joy Borus Humntrian Awd; Nassau Cnty Exec Acad Awd; Wesleyan U; Polticl Sci.

HALLORAN, MARY B; Williamsville East HS; East Amherst, NY; (Y); Pres Exploring; Trs French Clb; Model UN; Trs Concert Band; School Musical; Var Swmmng; High Hon Roll; Cert Svc Hosp Wrk 84; Outstndng Volntr Awd 82; Law.

HALLOWELL, LISA; Liperpool HS; Liverpool, NY; (S); 50/750; Church Yth Grp; 4-H; Band; Concert Band; Mrchg Band; Hon Roll; Jr NHS; NHS; Cosmetology Prctl Merit Awd 84; U Of Geneseo; Educ.

HALPERIN, KENNETH J; Bayside HS; Fresh Meadows, NY; (Y); 65/679; DECA; JA; Office Aide; Service Clb; Teachers Aide; Varsity Clb; Nwsp Rptr; Var Tennis; Hon Roll; SUNY-ALBANY; Accntnt.

HALPERN, MICHAEL; Longwood HS; Coram, NY; (Y); Nwsp Rptr; Nwsp Stf; NHS.

HALPERN, MITCHELL; Richmond Hill HS; Ozone Pk, NY; (Y); Art Clb; Boys Clb Am; Church Yth Grp; JV Bsbl; Var Wrstlng; Chncllrs Hnr Rll Excl & Achvt Engl 85; Schl Of Visual Arts; Comm Art.

HALSDORF, AARON; Bethlehem Central HS; Clarksville, NY; (Y); 28/330; Chess Clb; Model UN; Socr; Swmmng; Vllybl; High Hon Roll; Hon Roll; NHS; Ntl Merit Ltr; Prfct Atten Awd; Schlrshp JR Coll Albanys Inst Russn Studs 85.

HALSE, BETH; Tamarac HS; Troy, NY; (Y); 28/112; Church Yth Grp; Varsity Clb; Yrbk Stf; Off Frsh Cls; Off Soph Cls; Off Jr Cls; Off Sr Cls; Pres Stu Cncl; JV Var Socr; Hon Roll; Art Sbjct Awd 85; Cls 85 Awd, Tamarac Schlrshp 85; Brd Ed Dist Pres Awd 85; HVCC; Retl Mktng.

HALSE, RICHARD E; Troy HS; Troy, NY; (Y); 12/450; Computer Clb; Pres JA; Nwsp Stf; High Hon Roll; Hon Roll; Jr NHS; NHS; Prfct Atten Awd; Regnts Schlrshp 85; RPI; Elctrcl Tech.

HALSEY, TERESA J; Evander Childs HS; Bronx, NY; (Y); 4/503; Office Aide; Acpl Chr; Chorus; Lit Mag; Tennis; Cit Awd; Hon Roll; Jr NHS; NHS; Ntl Merit Ltr; Regnts Schlrshp 85; UFT Schlrshp 85; SUNY Binghamton.

HALSTEAD, KIM; Cato Meridian HS; Martville, NY; (Y); Drama Clb; Yrbk Stf; Var Bsktbl; Var Fld Hcky; Var Trk; Im Vllybl; Hon Roll; Prfct Atten Awd; Hghst Achvt Bus Educ 84-85; Fshn Merch.

HALSTEAD, SHERRI; Oato-Meridian HS; Martville, NY; (Y); Church Yth Grp; GAA; Varsity Clb; Bsktbl; Fld Hcky; Trk; MI Track 84-85; Perf Attndnc Schl 84-85; Bryant & Straton; Bus Secy.

HALTERMANN, LISA; Granville Central HS; Granville, NY; (Y); Chorus; Yrbk Sprt Ed; Yrbk Stf; Rep Frsh Cls; Var L Crs Cntry; Var L Trk; MIP Outdoor Trk 83; MVP X-Cntry 85; Prin Awd Slf Imprvmnt 85; Champlain Coll; Bus Admin.

HAMAD, GISELLE; Garden City HS; Garden City, NY; (Y); 7/320; Drama Clb; Pres French Clb; Chorus; Concert Band; School Musical; School Play; Ed Yrbk Phtg; Pres Jr NHS; NHS; Ntl Merit SF; Little Theatre Awd 85; AATF Poetry Hon Men 85; Choral Dept Awd 85; MIT; Med.

HAMALAK, DANIEL; Johnstown HS; Johnstown, NY; (Y); Red Cross Aide; Variety Show; Im JV Bsktbl; Im JV Ftbl; Sml Bus Mgt.

HAMALUDIN, ALISANDE; Hillcrest HS; Brooklyn, NY; (Y); 106/793; Drama Clb; Hosp Aide; JA; Band; School Play; Yrbk Rptr; Yrbk Stf; Sftbl; Prfct Atten Awd; Regents Schlrshp Awd 85; St Thoams Schlrshp Awd 85; St Thoams Of Villanova; Bus.

HAMAN, LESLIE; Whitesboro SR HS; Utica, NY; (Y); Hon Roll; Mohawk Valley; Law.

HAMAN, THERESA; Remsen Central HS; Remsen, NY; (Y); Mathletes; Ski Clb; Yrbk Stf; VP Soph Cls; Pres Jr Cls; JV Var Cheerleading; Var Socr; Var Sftbl; High Hon Roll; Hst NHS; Physcs, Trignmtry, & Frnch III Excllnc Awds 85; Math.

HAMBLIN, BARB; Fort Ann Central HS; Ft Ann, NY; (Y); 7/55; School Play; Yrbk Stf; Score Keeper; Sftbl; Hon Roll; NHS; Bus.

HAMBLIN, CHERIE; Fayetteville-Manlius HS; Fayetteville, NY; (Y); Cmnty Wkr; Drama Clb; French Clb; Trs JCL; Political Wkr; Chorus; School Musical; Variety Show; Lit Mag; Pres Frsh Cls; Congress-Bundestag Scholar Ger 85-86; 1st Pl County Natl Frnch Cont 82; Columbia U; Intl Reltns.

HAMBLIN, MECHELE; South Shore HS; Brooklyn, NY; (Y); Long Islnd U; Psych.

HAMELIN, SUSAN; Madrid-Waddington Central HS; Waddington, NY; (Y); #3 In Class; Drama Clb; French Clb; Girl Scts; Spanish Clb; L Band; Mrchg Band; L Trk; Capt Twrlr; NHS; Yrbk Lay-Out Editor 84-85; Donald J Connor Schlrshp 85; Madrid Amer Legion Aux Awd 85; SUNY-POTSDAM; Elec Educ.

HAMELIN, TAMI-LYN; Franklin Acad; Constable, NY; (Y); 12/135; Sec Church Yth Grp; Pres 4-H; VP Speech Tm; Band; Swing Chorus; Ed Nwsp Stf; Ed Yrbk Stf; L Trk; Hon Roll; Miss Amer Co-Ed ST Fin 85; Pres Phi Sigma 85-86; ST Fin Natl Catholic Forn Lg 83-85; Syracuse U; Spch Thrpy.

HAMER, LILLIAN; Dominican Commercial HS; S Ozone Park, NY; (Y); Church Yth Grp; JA; Hon Roll; NHS; Engr.

HAMERNIK, MARC; Nottingham HS; Syracuse, NY; (Y); Ski Clb; Var JV Ftbl; Var JV Lcrss; JV Trk; Hon Roll; Bio Sci.

HAMILL, JACQUELINE; Mahopac HS; Mahopac, NY; (Y); 93/420; JV Sftbl; High Hon Roll; Hon Roll; Vol Hosp Work; Hlth.

HAMILTON, ALLEN; Rochester School For The Deaf; Rochester, NY; (S); 2/23; School Play; Nwsp Stf; Pres Sr Cls; L Bsbl; Capt Bsktbl; L Socr; Hon Roll; Outstndngn Acad Stdnt 83-84; Ntl Tech Inst; Comp Prgmr.

HAMILTON, CHRISTOPHER M; Oxford Academy HS; Oxford, NY; (Y); 6/81; Pres Church Yth Grp; Pres French Clb; Ski Clb; Rep Stu Cncl; JV Var Bsbl; JV Var Ftbl; High Hon Roll; Hon Roll; NHS; Pres Schlr; NYS Regents Schrlshp 85; Rochester Inst Tech Schlrshp 85; Knights Pythias Awd 85; Rochester Inst Tech; Elec Engrn.

HAMILTON, DAVE; Shenendehowa Central HS; Clifton Park, NY; (Y); 330/660; Ski Clb; JV Var Lcrss; Hon Roll; Pre-Med.

HAMILTON, DAVID B; Gouverneur Central HS; Gouverneur, NY; (Y); Hon Roll; ATC Canton; Elec Engr.

HAMILTON, GREGORY A; Palmyra Macedon Central HS; Macedon, NY; (S); 10/200; AFS; Church Yth Grp; ROTC; School Musical; JV Var Ftbl; JV Var Trk; Cit Awd; High Hon Roll; NHS.

HAMILTON, LARRY; Waterloo HS; Waterloo, NY; (Y); 30/178; Debate Tm; Pep Clb; Ski Clb; Varsity Clb; Bsktbl; Coach Actv; L Lcrss; Rgnts Schlrshp Wnnr 85; MVP Vrsty La Crosse 85; U Of MA; Chmstry.

HAMILTON, LAURA; St Agnes Cathedral HS; Levittown, NY; (Y); Art Clb; Rep Soph Cls; High Hon Roll; NHS; NEDT Awd; Miss Ann G Taylor Cum Laude Awd 85; Monsignor Quealy Awd For Rlgn 85; Art Awd 85; Nassau CC; Adv Art.

HAMILTON, LISA; Savona Central HS; Savona, NY; (Y); 3/22; AFS; Teachers Aide; Chorus; Drm Mjr(t); Mrchg Band; School Play; Yrbk Ed-Chief; Yrbk Stf; Pres Jr Cls; Stu Cncl; Iue Local Un Schrlshp 85; St U New York; Engrng.

HAMILTON, MARTIN; Pulaski JR SR HS; Pulaski, NY; (Y); Boys Clb Am; Church Yth Grp; Math Clb; Varsity Clb; JV Var Bsktbl; L Ftbl; JV Trk; Prfct Atten Awd; Hobart & William Smith; Bus.

HAMILTON, MONTRESE; Niagara Falls HS; Niagara Falls, NY; (Y); Computer Clb; Model UN; Spanish Clb; Yrbk Stf; Cheerleading; Hon Roll; NHS; Ntl Merit Ltr; Prfct Atten Awd; Trs Pep Clb; Mbr Niagara Fls Youth Brd 85; WA Congr Wrkshp 85; American U; Fin.

HAMIRWASIA, RAJESH; Jamesville Dewitt HS; Fayetteville, NY; (Y); Aud/Vis; Key Clb; JV Trk; Hon Roll; RIT; Elec Engrng.

HAMLET, TALETHIA; Mabel Dean Bacon V HS; Brooklyn, NY; (S); Computer Clb; Dance Clb; JA; Bowling; Cheerleading; Hon Roll; Dentist.

HAMLETT, SANDRA G; Cardinal Spellman HS; Bronx, NY; (Y); Sec VP Debate Tm; French Clb; Sec VP NFL; Sec Speech Tm; NHS; Church Yth Grp; Science Clb; Hon Roll; 3rd Pl Trphy NYC NFL Dist 84; Commnded Status Ntnl Achvmnt Schlrshp Prog 84-85; Syracuse U; Pub Rel.

HAMLIN, LISA; Hudson Falls HS; Hudson Falls, NY; (Y); 22/206; Key Clb; Band; Concert Band; Jazz Band; Mrchg Band; Clrksn; Comp Engrng.

HAMM, ELLEN; Mount Mercy Acad; Buffalo, NY; (Y); 25/200; Drama Clb; Hosp Aide; JA; Model UN; Political Wkr; School Play; Nwsp Stf; Rep Jr Cls; Trs Sr Cls; Rep Stu Cncl.

HAMM, JOEL; Oakfield Alabama Central HS; Oakfield, NY; (Y); Church Yth Grp; Band; Jazz Band; Mrchg Band; Trs Jr Cls; JV Capt Bsktbl; JV Var Ftbl; JV Var Trk; Wt Lftg; NY ST Phy Ftns Awds; Bus.

HAMM, KATHY; Coxsackie-Athens Central HS; Coxsackie, NY; (Y); Spanish Clb; 4-H Awd; 4-H; Variety Show; Nwsp Stf; Yrbk Stf; Cosmtlgy.

HAMMEL, BARBARA; St Francis Prep; Flushing, NY; (S); 14/693; Cmnty Wkr; Library Aide; Math Clb; Ski Clb; Drm & Bgl; Var Twrlr; Hon Roll; NHS; Acad All-Amer 85; Law.

HAMMEL, DONNA L; Islip HS; Islip, NY; (Y); 20/250; Vllybl; Hon Roll; Jr NHS; Rgnts Schlrshp 85; Southampton Coll Schlrshp 85; Hnrs & Achvt Schlrshp 85; Long Island U.

HAMMEL, STEVE; Attica Central HS; Attica, NY; (S); 3/150; Math Clb; Math Tm; VP Frsh Cls; Var L Socr; Var L Tennis; Tnns Mst Vlbl Plyer 83-84, Soccer 83; Colgate; :Biochem.

HAMMER, MARC; Lynbrook HS; Hewlett Harbor, NY; (Y); Debate Tm; FBLA; Mathletes; Science Clb; Spanish Clb; Nwsp Phtg; Nwsp Rptr; Nwsp Stf; High Hon Roll; NHS; Pre-Med.

HAMMER, MICHELE; St Francis Prep; Ozone Park, NY; (S); 116/693; Hosp Aide; Math Tm; Spanish Clb; Teachers Aide; Hon Roll; NHS; Math.

HAMMETT, FRED; Grand Island HS; Grand Island, NY; (Y); Mathletes; Varsity Clb; Ftbl; Trk; Hon Roll; Elec Engrng.

HAMMOND, CHERRY; Avoca Central Schl; Cohocton, NY; (Y); Trs French Clb; FBLA; Band; School Play; Nwsp Stf; Ed Yrbk Ed-Chief; Sec Jr Cls; JV Capt Cheerleading; Var Sftbl; Hon Roll; Avoca Physcl Ftns Awd 83-84; Bryant Stratton Inst; Acctng.

HAMMOND, ELIZABETH; Canisteo Central HS; Canisteo, NY; (S); 4/80; Color Guard; Concert Band; Orch; School Play; Capt Swmmng; Var Tennis; Cit Awd; High Hon Roll; Hosp Aide; Band; All Cnty Band; Russell Sage; Phy Thrpy.

HAMMOND, ERIC; Tioga Central HS; Owego, NY; (S); 12/75; Aud/Vis; Latin Clb; Ski Clb; Crs Cntry; Golf; Hon Roll; NHS; Prfct Atten Awd; Broome CC; Comp Sci.

HAMMOND, GARY; Heuvelton HS; Heuvelton, NY; (S); 3/45; VP Latin Clb; Band; Chorus; VP Soph Cls; VP Jr Cls; Var Bsbl; Stat Bsktbl; Var Socr; NHS; Natl Sci Merit Awd 84; Accntnt.

HAMMOND, MICHELLE; Tioga Central HS; Owego, NY; (S); 9/96; Dance Clb; Ski Clb; Varsity Clb; JV Var Bsktbl; JV Crs Cntry; JV Var Fld Hcky; JV Sftbl; High Hon Roll; NHS; Ntl Lat Awd Gld Mdl 1st 84; Med.

HAMMOND, ROBERT G; Southwestern Cenral HS; W E Jamestown, NY; (Y); Am Leg Boys St; Drama Clb; VP JA; Ski Clb; Band; Chorus; Var JV Socr; Var JV Tennis; Hon Roll; NHS; Acctng.

HAMMOND, TIMOTHY J; New Hartford SR HS; New Hartford, NY; (Y); VP Exploring; Chorus; JV Bsbl; JV Var Ftbl; Hon Roll; Jr NHS; Regnts Schlrshp 85; Mohawk Valley CC; Mech Engr.

HAMPSON, ARTHUR W; East Islip HS; E Islip, NY; (Y); 65/475; Boy Scts; Church Yth Grp; Math Tm; Var L Socr; St Schlr; Internshp Brookhaven Natl Lab 84; Hofstra U; Engrng.

HAMPSTON, ED; Voorheesville JR SR HS; Voorheesville, NY; (Y); Math Tm; Red Cross Aide; Nwsp Stf; Yrbk Bus Mgr; Var Crs Cntry; Var Swmmng; Var Trk; High Hon Roll; NHS; Mem Empire ST Wtr Polo Tm 85; Engrng.

HAMPTON, JANET; Midwood HS; Brooklyn, NY; (Y); VP Boy Scts; Trs FHA; Chorus; School Musical; Nrsg.

HAMUKA, JOHN; Newfield HS; Selden, NY; (Y); 23/579; Band; Concert Band; Mrchg Band; Var Crs Cntry; Var Trk; NYS Regents Schlrshp 85; Polytechnic Inst NY; Aerontcl.

HAN, MEI F; Mabel Dean Bacon V HS; New York, NY; (S); 8/299; Teachers Aide; Chorus; Hon Roll; NY Super Yth Awd 84; Dntl Tech.

HAN, TAI; Seward Park HS; New York, NY; (Y); Art Clb; Camera Clb; Computer Clb; Library Aide; Math Clb; Science Clb; Teachers Aide; Sftbl; Vllybl; High Hon Roll; Coll; Engr US Dfnc.

HAN, WILLIAM; La Salle Acad; New York, NY; (S); 1/260; Math Clb; Yrbk Stf; Pres Soph Cls; Capt Bowling; High Hon Roll; Hon Roll; NHS; Cand Coll Hnr Schlrshp 84-85; Engrng.

HAN, YOUNG MI; Brooklyn Technical HS; Flushing, NY; (Y); Church Yth Grp; Library Aide; Office Aide; Service Clb; Teachers Aide; Chorus; Yrbk Stf; Hon Roll; NHS; Prfct Atten Awd.

HANAU, MICHAEL S; Blind Brook HS; Rye Brook, NY; (Y); Math Tm; Nwsp Bus Mgr; Nwsp Ed-Chief; Rep Frsh Cls; Trs Jr Cls; Ntl Merit Ltr; PA U; Bus.

HANBURY, DON; Tioga Central HS; Owego, NY; (Y); 15/100; Yrbk Stf; Hon Roll; NHS; Bus.

HANBURY, MARI J; Mount Assumption Inst; Plattsburgh, NY; (Y); Hosp Aide; Math Clb; Ed Yrbk Stf; Var Powder Puff Ftbl; JV Socr; Regents Schlrshp 85; Alfred U; Vet-Med.

HANCHUK, WALTER; Regis HS; Astoria, NY; (Y); Camera Clb; Co-Capt Chess Clb; Computer Clb; Nwsp Phtg; Yrbk Phtg; Im Bsktbl; Bowling; Cheerleading; NYS, Cooper Union Schlrshps 85; The Cooper Union; Mech Engr.

HANCOCK, DAVID B; Thomas A Edison HS; Elmira, NY; (Y); 4/89; Boy Scts; CAP; Letterman Clb; Acpl Chr; Band; Chorus; Church Choir; Concert Band; Jazz Band; Mrchg Band; ROTC Schlrshp 85; NYS Regnts Schlrshp 85; Chem Bow 84; RIT; Comp Tech.

HANCOCK, DEBRA A; Holt Trinity Diocesan HS; West Hempstead, NY; (S); 1/356; Mathletes; Capt Math Tm; Nwsp Ed-Chief; Rep Frsh Cls; Stu Cncl; High Hon Roll; NHS; Ntl Merit Ltr; NEDT Awd; Schlrshp To Study Abrd 83; Phi Beta Kappa 84; Pol Sci.

HANCOCK, EMILY; Victor Central HS; Victor, NY; (Y); 3/230; French Clb; Quiz Bowl; Teachers Aide; Varsity Clb; Band; Concert Band; Mrchg Band; Var JV Bsktbl; Var Capt Crs Cntry; Stat Score Keeper; MVP Cathy Rush Smr Bsktbl Cmp 83; MVP Crss Cntry 84; MVP Trk 85; Empire ST Gms Fnls 85.

HAND, TANYA; Beacon HS; Wappingers Falls, NY; (Y); 14/165; Dance Clb; JV Cheerleading; Gym; High Hon Roll; Hon Roll; Jr NHS; NHS; Sal; Natl Bus Hnr Socty 84-85; Montclair ST Coll; Comp Sci.

HANDLEY, JAMES; Patchague-Medford HS; Patchogue, NY; (Y); 120/975; Boy Scts; Key Clb; Im Bsbl; Socr; Im Sftbl; Hon Roll.

HANDLEY, RICHARD; Arlington High-North Campus; Poughkeepsie, NY; (Y); Cmnty Wkr; Computer Clb; Thesps; School Musical; School Play; Stage Crew; Variety Show; Nwsp Rptr; Ed Lit Mag; Jrnlsm.

HANEKE, MARK D; Cairo-Durham HS; Oak Hill, NY; (Y); 4/81; Church Yth Grp; 4-H; Pep Clb; Band; Chorus; Concert Band; Pep Band; School Musical; Yrbk Stf; Rep Stu Cncl; U Of CO Boulder; Air Flght Pln.

HANER, WENDY M; Chatham HS; Chatham, NY; (Y); Hosp Aide; Latin Clb; Library Aide; Ski Clb; Chorus; Drm & Bgl; Madrigals; Var JV Vllybl; Hon Roll; Prfct Atten Awd; Hudson Vlly CC; Rsprtry Thrpy.

HANESIAN, LAUREL ANN; Niagara Wheatfield HS; Lewiston, NY; (Y); Latin Clb; Pep Clb; PAVAS; Lib Band; Jazz Band; Madrigals; Mrchg Band; Pep Band; School Musical; JV Var Socr; Sectnl All ST Orch 82; 3 Acadmc Hnr Awds 82-85; Music Ltr 84; Music.

HANEY, JENNIFER; Cardinal Ohara HS; Kenmore, NY; (Y); Pres French Clb; Stage Crew; Trs Pres Jr Cls; Pres Rep Sr Cls; Rep Stu Cncl; JV Badmtn; JV Bsktbl; JV Sftbl; Hon Roll; Guidnc Cnslr.

HANEY, MICHELLE; Cardinal O Hara HS; Kenmore, NY; (Y); 12/180; French Clb; U Of NY Buffalo; Tchr.

HANEY, SHEILA; Preston HS; Bronx, NY; (S); 11/104; Church Yth Grp; Pep Clb; Yrbk Ed-Chief; Sec Sr Cls; Swmmng; High Hon Roll; Hon Roll; NHS; NEDT Awd; Hrsbck Rdng Clb 81-83; Bus Mgmnt.

HANEY, STEPHEN; Franklin Delano Roosevelt HS; Brooklyn, NY; (Y); Computer Clb; Dance Clb; Science Clb; Ftbl; Hon Roll; Mrt Achvmnt Awd Form The NY ST Enrgy Rsrch & Dev Auth & The ST Enrgy Offc 84; NY ST Sen Achv Awd; Stony Brook; Sci.

HANG, SALLY; H S Of Fashion Indstrs; New York, NY; (Y); Service Clb; Prfct Atten Awd; Math Clb; Yrbk Stf; Hon Roll; GO Svc Awd 83; Fash Desgnr.

HANKIN, LAURA K; Hackley Schl; Purchase, NY; (Y); Pres Debate Tm; Hosp Aide; Model UN; NFL; Band; Nwsp Stf; Off Sr Cls; Stu Cncl; Var Capt Socr; Hon Roll; Awds In Debate 81-83; NY ST Regents Schlrshp Awd 85; Emory U.

HANLEY, KATHLEEN; Southside HS; Rockville Ctr, NY; (Y); 60/250; Church Yth Grp; Key Clb; Chorus; Trk; High Hon Roll; Hon Roll; St Johns U; Accntng.

HANLEY, KATHY J; Hackley Schl; Congers, NY; (Y); 48/93; Church Yth Grp; Concert Band; Mrchg Band; JV Socr; JV Twrlr; Jr NHS; Mu Alp Tht; NHS; Ntl Merit Ltr; Engrng.

HANLON, ELLIE; The Ursuline Schl; White Plains, NY; (Y); Drama Clb; Ski Clb; School Musical; School Play; Nwsp Stf; Yrbk Stf; Tennis; Tennis Champ Awd; Psych.

HANLON, ERIN; Cicero-North Syracuse HS; Clay, NY; (S); 73/711; Ski Clb; Powder Puff Ftbl; Hon Roll; Ithaca Coll; Hlth Admin.

HANLON, FRANCES; Longwood HS; Middle Isl, NY; (Y); 19/392; Sec Band; Concert Band; Mrchg Band; School Musical; High Hon Roll; Jr NHS; NHS; Acad All-Am Schlr 85; Gld Mdl LI Mus Tchrs Assn Piano Solo 85; BOCES Sum Inst Gftd & Tlntd 83; Mus Educ.

HANNA, ROSEMARY; Sacred Heart Acad; Tonawanda, NY; (Y); French Clb; Stage Crew; Nwsp Stf; JV Badmtn; Bowling; Var Socr; JV Sftbl.

HANNAHAM, JAMES; Roosevelt HS; Yonkers, NY; (S); Band; Concert Band; Lit Mag; High Hon Roll; NHS; NAACP ACT-SO Awd 84.

HANNAY, DOUGLAS C; Greenville Central HS; Westerlo, NY; (Y); Church Yth Grp; Radio Clb; Band; Chorus; Concert Band; Jazz Band; Mrchg Band; School Musical; Symp Band; Hon Roll; NY ST Rgnts Schlrshp; Berklee Coll Of Music; Music.

HANNEL, BRAD; Frontier Central HS; Lakeview, NY; (Y); Trs Aud/Vis; Boy Scts; Church Yth Grp; Drama Clb; Mgr JA; Latin Clb; Stage Crew.

HANNIE, KAREN; Pittsford Sutherland HS; Pittsford, NY; (Y); Church Yth Grp; Computer Clb; Debate Tm; FBLA; Library Aide; Model UN; Office Aide; Ski Clb; Teachers Aide; Band; 1st Tm All Stars Sect Sftbll 85; Bst Del Model UN 84; U Dayton; Bus.

HANNIS, ERIC R; Chenango Valley HS; Binghamton, NY; (Y); Rep Am Leg Boys St; Art Clb; Boy Scts; Church Yth Grp; Drama Clb; Exploring; Latin Clb; Varsity Clb; School Musical; Ed Nwsp Sprt Ed; Hgh Hon Grad BOCES-SCOPE 84; Asst Dirctr Cmnty Yth Summr Schl Pgm 85; Pre-Law.

HANNON, CHRISTINE; Thomas A Edison JR SR HS; Elmira Hts, NY; (Y); Church Yth Grp; French Clb; Girl Scts; Concert Band; Drm Mjr(t); Jazz Band; Hon Roll; Most Outstndg Musician 85; Elmira Coll Key Awd 85; Frnch.

HANNON, FREDRICK; Theodore Roosevelt HS; Bronx, NY; (Y); 29/595; Cmnty Wkr; Political Wkr; Service Clb; Orch; Off Church Yth Grp; Off Jr Cls; Pres Sr Cls; Rep Stu Cncl; Rgnts Schlrshp 85; Awd Outstndg Achvt 82; Hamilton Coll; Bus Mktg.

HANNON, LISA; Highland HS; Highland, NY; (Y); Drama Clb; French Clb; School Musical; School Play; Stage Crew; Rep Stu Cncl; Score Keeper; Socr; Trk; French Hon Soc; Htl/Rest Mngmnt.

HANON, DIANE M; Holy Trinity HS; E Meadow, NY; (S); 2/380; French Clb; Math Clb; Math Tm; Ski Clb; Stage Crew; Stu Cncl; High Hon Roll; JC Awd; Jr NHS; Mu Alp Tht; Mollay; Nursing.

HANON, MICHELE; Holy Trinity HS; East Meadow, NY; (Y); English Clb; French Clb; Library Aide; Math Clb; Ski Clb; Stage Crew; Cheerleading; Socr; Trk; Aldephi; Ec.

HANOVER, LAURIE; Fairport HS; Fairport, NY; (Y); 3/600; Math Tm; Model UN; Mrchg Band; Symp Band; High Hon Roll; NHS; Ntl Merit Ltr; Rotary Awd; Top 10 Hnr Stu 85; Cornell U; Med.

HANRAHAN, JOSEPH G; Roxbury Central HS; Roxbury, NY; (Y); Am Leg Boys St; Band; Chorus; Church Choir; Jazz Band; Mrchg Band; School Musical; Capt L Bsbl; L Bsktbl; Hon Roll; Tech Elec.

HANRAHAN, JULIE ANNE; Smithtown H S East; St James, NY; (Y); Am Leg Aux Girls St; Church Yth Grp; GAA; Pres Frsh Cls; Pres Jr Cls; Var Capt Vllybl; High Hon Roll; Jr NHS; NHS; Spanish NHS; Hugh O Brian Yuth Ldrshp, NYSSSSO 84; Stu Mnth 85.

HANRATTY, KERRY; Academy Of St Joseph; Yaphank, NY; (Y); Art Clb; Science Clb; Dance Clb; Chorus; Drm & Bgl; Sec Stu Cncl; Twrlr; NHS; NEDT Awd; NYS Ed Dept Stu Adv Committe 84-86; Boston Coll.

HANS JR, PETER D; Cortland HS; Cortland, NY; (Y); 56/237; Boy Scts; Church Yth Grp; Ski Clb; Stage Crew; Yrbk Phtg; Yrbk Stf; Var Golf; NHS; Regents Schlrshp 85; St U Coll-Cortland; Law.

HANSEN, EVE; Corning-Painted Post East HS; Corning, NY; (Y); Girl Scts; Ski Clb; Chorus; Yrbk Stf; JV Var Bsktbl; JV Var Swmmng; Var Trk; JV Vllybl; High Hon Roll; Hon Roll; SUNY; Sci.

HANSEN, GREG; Smithtown West HS; Hauppauge, NY; (Y); Ski Clb; Golf; Socr; High Hon Roll; Hon Roll; Spanish NHS; Law.

HANSEN, MICHAEL; Hicksville HS; Hicksville, NY; (Y); 3/750; Computer Clb; Drama Clb; Thesps; Orch; Stage Crew; Variety Show; High Hon Roll; Hon Roll; Jr NHS; NHS; Italian Ntl Hnr Soc 84; Exc Itaian Awd Assoc Tchrs 85; Pre-Med.

HANSEN, ROBT; Alden Central HS; Marilla, NY; (Y); Prfct Atten Awd; Mech.

HANSON, CHRISTINA; Shenedehowa HS; Clifton Park, NY; (Y); AFS; Church Yth Grp; Hosp Aide; Intnl Clb; Chorus; Church Choir; JV Trk; ST U Of NY; Occptnl Thrpy.

HANSON, CINDY; Potsdam HS; Potsdam, NY; (Y); French Clb; Varsity Clb; Nwsp Stf; JV Var Cheerleading; High Hon Roll.

HANSON, CURT; Geneseo Central HS; Geneseo, NY; (Y); 7/96; Band; Var L Bsbl; Var L Bsktbl; Var L Ftbl; High Hon Roll; NHS; Boostr Clb Awd Bsktbl & Cnty All Str Bsbl 84-85; Engrng.

HANSON, JACALYN; Trott Vo-Tech; Niagara Falls, NY; (Y); Girl Scts; Library Aide; Office Aide; Band; Chorus; Stat Bsktbl; Stat Ftbl; Comp.

HANSON, JOHN; Shape American HS; APO, NY; (Y); High Hon Roll; Dance Clb; Pres Exploring; ROTC; Scholastic Bowl; Ski Clb; Chorus; L Mgr(s); St Schlr; Outstndng Cdt-ROTC 84; U Of KS; Med.

HANSON, KEN; Fonda-Fultonville Central Schl; Tribes Hill, NY; (Y); Var Bsbl; Var Ftbl; Wt Lftg; Var Wrstlng; Hon Roll; NHS; Arch.

HANSON, WAYNE; Bishop Loughlin HS; Brooklyn, NY; (S); Chess Clb; Computer Clb; Drama Clb; Science Clb; High Hon Roll; NHS; Prfct Atten Awd.

HANSRAJ, SADHVEE; Dominican Acad; Brooklyn, NY; (Y); Computer Clb; Dance Clb; Latin Clb; Office Aide; Science Clb; School Musical; School Play; Lit Mag; Trs Jr Cls; French Hon Soc; Pre Med.

HANTMAN, H MATTHEW; Sayville HS; Bayport, NY; (Y); 14/370; Temple Yth Grp; Band; Yrbk Bus Mgr; Tennis; High Hon Roll; NHS; Natl Frnch Exam Cont 84-85; Natl Span Cont 84-85; Trinity Coll; Engl.

HANTMAN, PATTI LISA; Bethpage HS; Bethpage, NY; (Y); Office Aide; Spanish Clb; Temple Yth Grp; Yrbk Stf; Rep Frsh Cls; Rep Soph Cls; Var Cheerleading; Var Tennis; High Hon Roll; Law.

HAPANOWICZ, SHAWN; Whitesboro SR HS; Whitesboro, NY; (Y); Church Yth Grp; Varsity Clb; Var Ftbl; Var Lcrss; Im Wt Lftg; Acctng.

HAPPELL, CAROL; Silver Creek Central HS; Silver Creek, NY; (Y); Girl Scts; Varsity Clb; Band; JV Var Bsktbl; Bowling; Cobleskill; Profssnl Chef.

HARAVON, LESLIE D; Pleasantville HS; Pleasantville, NY; (Y); 3/86; Cmnty Wkr; Drama Clb; Girl Scts; Hosp Aide; Band; Chorus; Mrchg Band; Pep Band; School Musical; Nwsp Rptr; All ST All Eastern Choruses 84-85; Acad Excllnc Awd 84; Most Outstndng Frnch Stu 82-83; Philosophy.

HARBAUGH, MARK; Cicero North Syracuse HS; Clay, NY; (S); 18/711; Computer Clb; Mathletes; Ski Clb; Pres Frsh Cls; Rep Soph Cls; Rep Jr Cls; Rep Stu Cncl; Var Bsbl; Var Bsktbl; Var Ftbl; Buffalo U; Aerosp Engr.

HARBERT, TERENCE; Nottingham HS; Syracuse, NY; (Y); Boys Clb Am; Exploring; JA; Cornell U; Engrng.

HARD, SUZANNE; Unatego JR SR HS; Unadilla, NY; (Y); FBLA; OEA; Color Guard; Yrbk Stf; Crs Cntry; Gym; Swmmng; Hon Roll; Bus Sec.

HARDENSTINE, TAMMY; Rome Free Acad; Rome, NY; (Y); Church Yth Grp; Chorus; Church Choir; Flag Corp; Nwsp Stf; Hon Roll; Jr NHS; Stetson U; Sec Ed.

HARDER, BRADLEY; Jeffersonvlle-Youngsvlle Cntrl Schl; Youngsville, NY; (S); 2/58; Varsity Clb; Band; Nwsp Ed-Chief; Yrbk Sprt Ed; Trs Jr Cls; Trs Sr Cls; Var L Crs Cntry; Var L Trk; High Hon Roll; Trs NHS; Top Cross Ctry Rnnr Schl & League 84; Engrng.

HARDER, CHERYL H; Homer Central HS; Homer, NY; (Y); Band; Concert Band; Jazz Band; Mrchg Band; Symp Band; Yrbk Stf; High Hon Roll; Hon Roll; NHS; Tompkins Cortland CC; Bus Adm.

HARDER, GABRIELLE; Haverling Central HS; Bath, NY; (S); 27/150; Sec AFS; French Clb; Math Clb; Nwsp Ed-Chief; Yrbk Ed-Chief; Rep Jr Cls; Rep Sr Cls; NHS; Hosp Aide; High Hon Roll; Natl Soc Stud Olymp; Stdnt Cncl Spec Achvt.

HARDER, WENDY S; Taconic Hills Central HS; Hudson, NY; (Y); 4/130; Pres Intnl Clb; Varsity Clb; Band; Yrbk Stf; Var Fld Hcky; Trk; Bausch & Lomb Sci Awd; NHS; Church Choir; Mgr(s); Teenager Of Mnth 84-85; MI Tech U; Chem Engrng.

HARDERS, JAMES R; Jamesville De Witt HS; Jamesville, NY; (Y); 19/224; Boy Scts; Model UN; Ski Clb; Chorus; Stage Crew; Var L Socr; High Hon Roll; NHS; Regents Schlrshp 85; MIP Vrsty Sccr Team 84; Clarkson U; Mech Engr.

HARDIMAN, PAMELA; Farmingdale HS; N Massapequa, NY; (Y); Drama Clb; French Clb; School Musical; Stu Cncl; Cheerleading; Gym; Hon Roll; Lion Awd; Pub Rel.

HARDIN, JEFF S; Rome Free Acad; Rome, NY; (Y); Ski Clb; Band; Concert Band; Mrchg Band; Swmmng; High Hon Roll; Hon Roll; Aeronautical Schlng.

HARDIN, KIMBERLY N; St Joseph HS; Brooklyn, NY; (Y); Church Yth Grp; French Clb; Hosp Aide; Pep Clb; Political Wkr; Science Clb; Y-Teens; Chorus; Church Choir; School Musical; Hon Men Sci Sympo; Hnrs Grad Recvd Medl; Outstndg Bsktbl Plyr Awd; St Johns U; Phrmcy.

HARDING JR, ROGER LEWIS; Hornell HS; Hornell, NY; (Y); Pres Church Yth Grp; French Clb; Im Bowling; Var Trk; Hon Roll; Prfct Atten Awd; Arch.

HARDING, RONDA; Adeli E Stevenson HS; Bronx, NY; (Y); Dance Clb; Girl Scts; Hosp Aide; Office Aide; PAVAS; Band; Orch; Variety Show; Cheerleading; Gym; Uppard Bound Pgm 85; Awd Vol Local Hosp 84-85; Vet.

HARDING, SALLY A; St Johns The Baptist HS; Amityville, NY; (Y); Church Yth Grp; Cmnty Wkr; Dance Clb; Nwsp Stf; Ed Yrbk Bus Mgr; Lit Mag; Hon Roll; Bst Stu, Cncl Lay Tchrs 85; Isl Drftng & Tech Schl Schlrshp 85; Engl.

HARDTER, LAUREN; Liverpool HS; Liverpool, NY; (S); 117/856; Ski Clb; Band; Mrchg Band; Symp Band; High Hon Roll; Hon Roll; Jr NHS; NHS; Opt Clb Awd; All-County Band; Area-All-State Band; Lifesaving Cert; Elem Educ.

HARDY, CRAIG; Union-Endicott HS; Endwell, NY; (Y); Boy Scts; French Clb; Varsity Clb; Stu Cncl; Var Capt Bsktbl; JV Var Golf; Var Tennis; Bus.

HARDY, KAREN; Prospect Heights HS; Brooklyn, NY; (Y); 3/250; VP FBLA; Math Tm; Red Cross Aide; Stage Crew; Pres Sr Cls; Cit Awd; High Hon Roll; NHS; Spanish NHS; Church Yth Grp; Yth Ldrshp Awd 85; MIT; Mech Engrng.

HARDY, LAURA; Leroy Central Schl; Leroy, NY; (Y); French Clb; Band; Chorus; Mrchg Band; School Musical; Nwsp Ed-Chief; High Hon Roll; NHS; Church Choir; Concert Band; NACEL Smmr Cultural Exch France 85; Syracuse U; Jrnlsm.

HARDY, SEBASTIAN G; Collegiate Schl; New York, NY; (Y); Chess Clb; Debate Tm; Math Clb; Math Tm; Model UN; NFL; Political Wkr; Acpl Chr; Chorus; Nwsp Ed-Chief.

HARDY, WILLIAM JAMES; Dryden Central HS; Freeville, NY; (Y); #24 In Class; 4-H; Band; Chorus; Mrchg Band; Lit Mag; VP Stu Cncl; Trk; Wrstlng; Dnfth Awd; 4-H Awd; Socl Studies Awd 82; FHA-HERO Awd 83; Socl Studies Awd 84; Hiriam Coll; Bio.

HARGETT, CANDY; South Glens Falls HS; Gansevoort, NY; (Y); FBLA; Office Aide; Band; Trs Chorus; Rep Stu Cncl; JV Fld Hcky; Powder Puff Ftbl; Score Keeper; Hon Roll; VP Jr NHS; Persnl Lttr Of Congrtlns From Sen Joseph Bruno 84; Soc Stds Awd 83; Cert Of Apprctn For Offc Aid 82-83; Pol Sci.

HARGETT, LORI; Grace Dodge Vocational HS; New York, NY; (Y); Cmnty Wkr; Computer Clb; Drama Clb; Girl Scts; Office Aide; Band; Concert Band; School Play; Nwsp Rptr; Nwsp Stf; OH U; Bio Sci.

HARGIS, BRIAN; Massena Central HS; Massena, NY; (Y); Sec FFA; Thesps; Chorus; Madrigals; School Musical; School Play; Stage Crew; Variety Show; JV Tennis; Hon Roll; TX A&M.

HARGRAVE, KEITH A; Mexico HS; Mexico, NY; (Y); 10/180; Exploring; Trs Band; Concert Band; Jazz Band; Mrchg Band; School Musical; Rep Stu Cncl; Bausch & Lomb Sci Awd; High Hon Roll; Hon Roll; NY ST Rgnts Schlrshp 85; FA Smedley Mem Chmstry Awd 84; NYSMMA Trmpt Solo Exc Rtng 84; Canton Ag & Tech; Engrng.

HARGRAVE, KEVIN; Mexico Acad & Central Schl; Mexico, NY; (Y); Pres FFA; Mrchg Band; Var Bowling; NHS; Canton; Elec.

HARGROVE, PAUL; La Salle Acad; Brooklyn, NY; (Y); 3/245; Am Leg Boys St; Nwsp Rptr; Rptr Yrbk Stf; Pres Frsh Cls; Pres Jr Cls; Stu Cncl; Crs Cntry; Trk; NHS; Church Yth Grp; Accntng.

HARGROVE, SOPHIE; Rooserelt JR SR HS; Freeport, NY; (Y); 3/215; Band; Concert Band; Mrchg Band; Orch; High Hon Roll; Hon Roll; Jr NHS; NHS; Bus Adm.

HARGROVE, TINA C; Half Hollow Hills East; Melville, NY; (Y); Chess Clb; Computer Clb; Debate Tm; FBLA; Leo Clb; Speech Tm; Chorus; Variety Show; Yrbk Stf; Tennis; Acctng.

HARIPRASHAD, JUNE; Bronx High School Of Science; Bronx, NY; (Y); Church Yth Grp; Cmnty Wkr; Library Aide; Rep Sr Cls; NHS; Presdntl Acadmc & Hlth Ftnss Awd 85; Bryn Mawr Coll; Med.

HARKAVY, ELLIOT G; Midwood HS; Brooklyn, NY; (Y); 23/630; Capt Math Tm; Nwsp Phtg; Yrbk Bus Mgr; Var Swmmng; NHS; Ntl Merit SF; Chrmn City-Wide Mdl Cong 85; Pres Untd Syng Yth Chptr 85; Comp Sys Anlyst.

HARKE, DOUGLAS J; Geneseo Central Schl; Geneseo, NY; (Y); 4/75; Boy Scts; Capt Mathletes; Math Clb; Math Tm; Trs Sr Cls; Trs Stu Cncl; Var Capt Ice Hcky; Var Capt Socr; Var Trk; Bausch & Lomb Sci Awd; NYS Regents Schlrshp 85; Campbell Mem Schlrshp 84; Purdue; Engrng.

HARKENRIDER, CHRISTINE M; Hornell SR HS; Hornell, NY; (Y); 21/198; Trs Art Clb; Church Yth Grp; Exploring; Spanish Clb; VICA; Chorus; High Hon Roll; Hon Roll; Outstndng Stu Hm Hlth Aide Awd 85; Hornell Fire Fghtrs Assn Scholar 85; Achvt Home/Hlth Svcs 85; Alfred ST Coll; Nrsng.

HARKINS, KAREN; Buffalo Seminary; Amherst, NY; (Y); 2/35; Rep AFS; Trs Jr Cls; Var Lcrss; VP NHS; Ntl Merit Ltr; Dance Clb; French Clb; Ski Clb; Grad Cum Laude; Natl Hnr Roll; Outstndg Achvt Awd Fr 84-85; Niagara Mohawk Sys Scholar Wnr Coll; WA U In St Louis; Biochem.

HARKINS, VINCENT J; Polytechnic Prep Country Day Schl; Rockaway Point, NY; (Y); Church Yth Grp; Intnl Clb; Letterman Clb; Pep Clb; Spanish Clb; Varsity Clb; Nwsp Rptr; Bsbl; Capt Bsktbl; Co-Capt Ftbl; NYS Regnts Schlrshp 85; US Merchant Marine; Ntcl Engr.

HARLEY, JANET; George W Wingate HS; Canada; (Y); Sftbl; Hon Roll; Prfct Atten Awd; Med Doctor.

HARLEY, NICOLE; Cardinal Spellman HS; New York, NY; (Y); 71/500; Hosp Aide; Latin Clb; Spanish Clb; Variety Show; Yrbk Stf; Hon Roll; Business.

HARLOW, LOUISE; Clyde-Savannah Central Schl; Savannah, NY; (Y); Jazz Band; Pres Jr Cls; Pres Sr Cls; High Hon Roll; NHS; VFW Awd; Voice Dem Awd; Drama Clb; 4-H; Band; Outstndng Svc Cls Contributing Mbr 84; Meritorious Awd In Schlrshp 84; Wayne Co Select Bnd Fest 83; SUNY Oswego; Engl.

HARM, MICHELE; West Seneca West SR HS; W Seneca, NY; (Y); 62/543; Pres Church Yth Grp; GAA; Yrbk Rptr; Yrbk Stf; Rep Stu Cncl; Trk; Jr NHS; NHS; Cmnty Wkr; Regents Schlrshp 85; O Youville Hnrs Schlrshp 85; O Youville Coll; Nrsng.

HARMER, TERRY; Spackenkill HS; Poughkeepsie, NY; (Y); Boy Scts; Sec Church Yth Grp; Church Choir; Var Trk; Var Wrstlng; Hon Roll; Ntl Merit Ltr; Rotary Awd; On My Hnr Awd,Boy Scts Relgs Awd 82; Brigham Young U; Med.

HARMETZ, JOYCE; South Shore HS; Brooklyn, NY; (Y); 138/668; Exploring; Hosp Aide; Temple Yth Grp; Ntl Merit Schol; Pres Schlr; Cert Of Achvt Hghst Stndng Advncd Typwrtng 85; George Fagin Memrl Awd 85; Brooklyn Coll.

HARMON, DAVID J; Saratoga Springs HS; Ballston Spa, NY; (Y); 34/465; Key Clb; Varsity Clb; VP Jr Cls; VP Sr Cls; Stu Cncl; Golf; Wt Lftg; High Hon Roll; NHS; Ntl Merit SF; Prom Commitee 84-85; Hmcmng Court 84-85; Skidmore Coll; Archtr.

HARMON, LISA; Hillcrest HS; Jamaica, NY; (Y); Computer Clb; Library Aide; Chorus; Swmmng; Cit Awd; Hon Roll; NY Schl; Med Asst.

HARMON, NATALIE; Tioga Central HS; Smithboro, NY; (Y); Church Yth Grp; Girl Scts; Ski Clb; Spanish Clb; Teachers Aide; Band; Church Choir; Color Guard; Flag Corp; Mrchg Band; Mrchng Band Schl Ltrs 83-84; NYS Tchrs Coll; Tchr Educ.

HARMON, SUZETTE; Longwood HS; Ridge, NY; (Y); Church Yth Grp; CAP; Key Clb; Flag Corp; JV Var Vllybl; High Hon Roll; Hon Roll; NHS; Rgnts Schlrshp 85; Cornell; Metrlgst.

HARMON, TRACEY L; Byron-Bergen JR SR HS; S Byron, NY; (Y); 17/90; Church Yth Grp; VP Frsh Cls; Trs Sr Cls; Var L Cheerleading; JV Socr; JV Sftbl; Jr NHS; Kiwanis Awd; Bryant; Busn Mngmnt.

HARMON, TRINA; Midlakes HS; Clifton Spgs, NY; (Y); 9/154; Church Yth Grp; Trs Debate Tm; Trs English Clb; Pres Girl Scts; Trs Model UN; Spanish Clb; Lit Mag; High Hon Roll; Hon Roll; Ntl Merit SF; Rgnts Schlrshp 84-85.

HARMS, MICHELE G; Cassadaha Valley Central HS; Gerry, NY; (Y); 3/105; Church Yth Grp; Pres Science Clb; Trs Spanish Clb; Band; Chorus; School Musical; Lit Mag; High Hon Roll; NHS; Ntl Merit Ltr; Regnts Schlrshp 85; Presdntl Acadmc Ftns Awd 85; Schlrshp Jamestwn Coll 85; Jamestown Comm Coll; Med Tech.

HARN, RUBY; John Bowne HS; Flushing, NY; (Y); Ctywde Ind Arts Kings Plz Exhbt 85.

HARNES, DEBORAH; Naples American HS; FPO, NY; (Y); Chorus; Orch; Symp Band; Rep Frsh Cls; Sec Stu Cncl; Var Cheerleading; Hon Roll; Church Yth Grp; Band; Church Choir; NASH Acad Excell Awd 85; Var Lttry In Symphonic Bnd 83-85; Var Lttr In Chrldng 85; Music Educ.

HARNETT, PETER; Oswego HS; Oswego, NY; (Y); Chess Clb; VP JA; VP Of Yr 84; Comp Sci.

HARNETT, SUSAN; Moore Catholic HS; Staten Island, NY; (Y); Math Tm; Science Clb; Spanish Clb; Var Bsktbl; High Hon Roll; NHS; Parade Mag Girls All Am Bsktbl Tm 85; Adidas All Am Bsktbl Tm 85.

HARNEY, MARGARET; Valley Stream Central HS; Malverne, NY; (Y); 21/365; AFS; Debate Tm; Drama Clb; 4-H; French Clb; Service Clb; Ski Clb; Nwsp Stf; Stu Cncl; French Hon Soc; Long Isl Fed Of Womens Clb 85; Adelphi Awd Manhatten Coll Awd 85; Fairfld Schlrshp 85; Pres Acad Fitnss; Fairfield U; Acctng.

HAROLD, CHRISTINE; Preston HS; New York, NY; (S); 9/76; Trs Stu Cncl; Cheerleading; Im Vllybl; High Hon Roll; VP NHS; Partial Schlrshp To Preston H S 81; Pace U; Nursing.

HARP, KIMBERLY; Cicero-North Syracuse HS; Clay, NY; (S); 131/622; 4-H; Ski Clb; Color Guard; Drill Tm; Mth.

HARP, SABRINA; Cicero North Syracuse HS; Cicero, NY; (S); 34/771; Church Yth Grp; Acpl Chr; Chorus; Lit Mag; Capt Bsktbl; Var Cheerleading; Powder Puff Ftbl; Var Capt Socr; Var Sftbl; Var JV Vllybl; Vrsty Soccer Most Improved Plyr 84; Vrsty All County Team Hnrbl Mntn 84; Excep Srs Gm Vrsty Soccer 84; Bryant; Stewardess.

HARPAZ, IZ HAR; Richmond Hill HS; Kew Gardens, NY; (Y); #2 In Class; JA; Math Clb; Radio Clb; Science Clb; Varsity Clb; School Musical; School Play; Swmmng; High Hon Roll; Hon Roll; MVP Swmmr 85; Comp Sci.

HARPAZ, IZHAR; Richmond Hill HS; Kew Gardens, NY; (Y); #2 In Class; Computer Clb; JA; Math Clb; School Musical; Nwsp Rptr; VP Capt Swmmng; High Hon Roll; NHS; Ivy League Coll; Comp Math.

HARPER, CATHY; Cathy Harper HS; Savannah, NY; (Y); Band; JV Cheerleading; High Hon Roll; Hon Roll; Cayuga CC; Comp Sci.

HARPER, PATRICIA; Bishop Maginn HS; Albany, NY; (S); 12/118; Spanish Clb; Yrbk Stf; JV Var Cheerleading; JV Var Pom Pon; Var Trk; High Hon Roll; NHS; Red Cross Aide; Nwsp Stf; Theology Awd; Siera Coll; Math.

HARPER, PATTI; Rome Free Acad; Rome, NY; (Y); Sec Co-Capt Ski Clb; Yrbk Rptr; Yrbk Stf; Rep Stu Cncl; Capt Var Crs Cntry; Var Trk; Hon Roll; NHS; Secy Sci.

HARPER, TAMMY; Newfield Central Schl; Newfield, NY; (Y); Math Clb; Spanish Clb; Varsity Clb; Chorus; Stu Cncl; Cheerleading; Twrlr; Vllybl; Hon Roll; NHS; Acctnt.

HARPER, VIRGINIA; St John The Baptist HS; Lindenhurst, NY; (Y); Church Yth Grp; Drama Clb; Hosp Aide; JV Bsktbl; Var Socr; Jr NHS; Law.

HARRADINE, MARK A; E J Wilson HS; Spencerport, NY; (Y); Mathletes; Pres Model UN; Ski Clb; Varsity Clb; Pres Stu Cncl; Var L Crs Cntry; Var L Tennis; Bausch & Lomb Sci Awd; Ntl Merit SF; High Hon Roll; Rensselaer Mdl 84; Econ.

HARRAH, STEPHANIE; Colonie Central HS; Albany, NY; (Y); 77/511; Camera Clb; Hst FBLA; Variety Show; Capt Cheerleading; Score Keeper; High Hon Roll; Hon Roll; Bus.

HARRALSON, BETH; Saquoit Valley Central HS; Sauquoit, NY; (S); 17/90; Church Yth Grp; Acpl Chr; Chorus; School Musical; Sec Trs Frsh Cls; Trs Soph Cls; Sec Stu Cncl; JV Fld Hcky; Interact 83-85; Syracuse U; Engr.

HARRELL, LAURIE; Amsterdam HS; Amsterdam, NY; (Y); 12/294; Cmnty Wkr; Hosp Aide; Mrchg Band; Pres Soph Cls; High Hon Roll; Hon Roll; NHS; Pre-Law.

HARRIGAN, AMY S; West Genesee SR HS; Syracuse, NY; (Y); 133/460; Pres Church Yth Grp; Hosp Aide; VP JA; Band; Church Choir; Concert Band; Mrchg Band; Orch; School Musical; Yrbk Stf; Regents Schlrshp 85; Fllschlrshp Crouse Irving Schl 85; Crouse Irving Schl/Nrsng; Nrsng.

HARRIGAN, ANNMARIE; Rensselaer JR SR HS; Rensselaer, NY; (Y); Church Yth Grp; DECA; Hosp Aide; Key Clb; Yrbk Stf; Score Keeper; Socl Wrkr.

HARRIGAN, DAVID; Elmira Free Acad; Elmira, NY; (Y); Church Yth Grp; Spanish Clb; Rep Soph Cls; JV Var Bsbl; JV Var Ftbl; Im Wt Lftg; Hon Roll; All Leag Ftbl All-Str Awd 84; Yth Cnty 85; Bus Mngmnt.

HARRIGAN, MAUREEN F; Moore Catholic HS; Staten Island, NY; (Y); 1/189; Art Clb; Hosp Aide; Math Tm; Spanish Clb; Nwsp Stf; Yrbk Stf; JV Sftbl; High Hon Roll; Regents Schlrshp 85; St Johns Schlrshp 85; St Johns U; Education.

HARRIGAN, NOREEN C; Newfield HS; Selden, NY; (Y); 58/542; Hosp Aide; Service Clb; Chorus; School Musical; Trs Frsh Cls; Trs Jr Cls; Var JV Cheerleading; JV Gym; Hon Roll; Jr NHS; Regents Schlrshp 85; Outstndng Soc Studies Awd 82; St Josephs Coll; CPA.

HARRIGAN, SCOTT D; Northern Adirondack Central HS; Chateaugay, NY; (Y); 2/96; VP 4-H; Pres VP FFA; Key Clb; Rep Stu Cncl; Var Socr; 4-H Awd; High Hon Roll; Pres NHS; Regents Schlrshp 85; Dstngshd Schlr Awd 82-85; Cornell U; Engrng.

HARRINGTON, BRIAN; Columbia HS; E Greenbush, NY; (Y); Church Yth Grp; Drama Clb; Key Clb; Trs Spanish Clb; Chorus; School Musical; School Play; Psych.

HARRINGTON JR, BRUCE E; Canastota HS; Canastota, NY; (Y); Am Leg Boys St; Pres FBLA; Intnl Clb; Pres Leo Clb; Science Clb; Nwsp Stf; Yrbk Stf; Ftbl; Wrstlng; High Hon Roll; Excllnc Wrttn Exprssn Awd 85; 3rd Pl Colmn Wrtng HS Prss Day 85; 3rd Pl Publc Spkng FBLA Dist Cnf 85; Corprt Law.

HARRINGTON, CINDY; Colonie Central HS; Albany, NY; (Y); Sec Church Yth Grp; Dance Clb; 4-H; Intnl Clb; Ski Clb; Spanish Clb; Orch; 4-H Awd; Hon Roll; All-Subrbn Cncl JR Hgh 83; NY ST Danc Fstvl-Blue Rbbn 84; Hudson Valley.

HARRINGTON, DAWN; Bishop Ludden HS; Bridgeport, NY; (Y); Church Yth Grp; Teachers Aide; Church Choir; Yrbk Stf; High Hon Roll; Hon Roll; NHS; Stdnt Mnth Chldcare BOCES 84; Onondaga CC; Humnts.

HARRINGTON, KATIE; Bishop Scully HS; Amsterdam, NY; (Y); 24/69; Drama Clb; French Clb; Math Clb; School Play; Bowling; Sftbl; Elks Awd; High Hon Roll; Hon Roll; NHS; All Cnty Schlrshp 85-86; Irish Amer Club Schlrshp 85-86; John P Gomulka Schlrshp 85-86; Fulton Mntgmry CC; Psych.

HARRINGTON, KELLY; Camden HS; Camden, NY; (Y); AFS; Exploring; 4-H; Ski Clb; Chorus; School Musical; Stu Cncl; 4-H Awd; High Hon Roll; Hon Roll; Cmmnctns.

HARRINGTON, ROBYN; Charles O Dickerson HS; Trumansburg, NY; (Y); 14/85; French Clb; Varsity Clb; Concert Band; Jazz Band; Mrchg Band; Yrbk Stf; Sec Soph Cls; JV Var Vllybl; Hon Roll; NHS; Spec Capt Awd JV Vlybl 83-84; Math.

HARRINGTON JR, WILLIAM J; Saratoga Springs HS; Middle Grove, NY; (Y); 63/465; Cmnty Wkr; Computer Clb; Library Aide; Science Clb; High Hon Roll; Hon Roll; NHS; Regnts Schlrshp 85; Acad Achvt Awd 84; Nclr Techn.

HARRIS, ALDRENA; Hempstead HS; Hempstead, NY; (S); 22/333; Church Yth Grp; Dance Clb; 4-H; FHA; Pep Clb; Church Choir; Yrbk Stf; Rep Jr Cls; Var Cheerleading; Hon Roll; Air Force; Acctng.

HARRIS, ALFONSO B; Kensington HS; Buffalo, NY; (Y); Computer Clb; Band; JV Var Bsktbl; Var Trk; Hon Roll; Comp Pgmr.

HARRIS, ANDREA M; La Guardia H S Of The Arts; Bronx, NY; (Y); 85/588; Art Clb; Cmnty Wkr; PAVAS; Y-Teens; Nwsp Rptr; NHS; Fash Design.

HARRIS, ANDREW M; Archbishop Walsh HS; Olean, NY; (Y); 6/250; Am Leg Boys St; NFL; Political Wkr; Red Cross Aide; Yrbk Stf; VP Jr Cls; Pres Stu Cncl; Tennis; Capt Wrstlng; High Hon Roll; NY ST Regnst Schlrsh P85; Army ROTC Schlrshp 85; Am Leg Boys Nation 84; Boston U; Pre-Law.

HARRIS, BONNI; Hornell HS; Hornell, NY; (Y); Drama Clb; German Clb; Library Aide; Chorus; Crs Cntry; Socr; Sftbl; Swmmng; Trk; Alfred Tech; Acct.

HARRIS, CAROLYN; Scotia-Glenville HS; Scotia, NY; (Y); AFS; Church Yth Grp; Trs German Clb; Key Clb; Church Choir; Rep Frsh Cls; Socr; High Hon Roll; NHS; NY ST Comm Advisory Councl-Gifted Educ 84.

HARRIS, CHERYL; St Michael Acad; New York, NY; (Y); Pres Church Yth Grp; Dance Clb; Variety Show; Yrbk Stf; Pres Stu Cncl; Var JV Cheerleading; Hon Roll; NHS; Gold Seal Of Acad Excell 85; Rochester Inst/Tech; Bus Mgmt.

HARRIS, CLIFTON F; Malverne HS; W Hempstead, NY; (Y); 44/148; Chess Clb; Church Yth Grp; Q&S; Nwsp Rptr; Nwsp Stf; Yrbk Rptr; Yrbk Stf; Lit Mag; JV Var Ftbl; Var Trk; Wrtrs Clb Svc Awd 83-84; Jrnlsm Svc Awd 83-84; Coaches Awd-Indr Trck 83-84; NY U; Wrtng.

HARRIS, DAVE; Sparkenkill HS; Poughkeepsie, NY; (Y); PAVAS; Thesps; School Musical; Symp Band; Bsktbl; Ftbl; Trk; Elec Engrng.

HARRIS, DAVID; New York Military Acad; Cornwall On Hudsn, NY; (S); Computer Clb; ROTC; Drill Tm; Nwsp Stf; Yrbk Stf; Capt Var Crs Cntry; Var Lcrss; Var Trk; High Hon Roll; Hon Roll; Military Ordr Wrld Wars Awd Merit 83-84; Mc Gill; Engr.

HARRIS, ELLEN; Irondequoit HS; Rochester, NY; (Y); 50/350; Ski Clb; VP Varsity Clb; Variety Show; Nwsp Rptr; Var L Bsktbl; Mgr(s); Var L Socr; Var L Trk; Stat Vllybl; Prfct Atten Awd; Math.

HARRIS, GEORGE; Liverpool HS; Liverpool, NY; (S); 162/790; Nwsp Sprt Ed; Stu Cncl; Var L Ice Hcky; Var L Lcrss; Var L Socr; Hon Roll; Accntng.

HARRIS, IAN J; Baldwin SR HS; S Hempstead, NY; (Y); 47/502; Aud/Vis; Computer Clb; Key Clb; Science Clb; Temple Yth Grp; Nwsp Bus Mgr; Nwsp Rptr; Hon Roll; Rgnts Schlrshp 85; SUNY Stonybrook; Comp Engrng.

HARRIS, JAMES; Rice HS; Bronx, NY; (Y); Dance Clb; Chorus; Rep Jr Cls; Pres Stu Cncl; Hon Roll; SUNY Purchase; Dance.

HARRIS, JENISE A; John Dewey HS; Brooklyn, NY; (Y); Church Yth Grp; Band; Jazz Band; School Musical; School Play; Rep Soph Cls; Math Clb; Teachers Aide; Chorus; Concert Band.

HARRIS, JILL; Albion HS; Waterport, NY; (S); 27/178; Pres Church Yth Grp; Ski Clb; Trs Spanish Clb; Color Guard; JV Socr; Comp Sci.

HARRIS, JONATHAN; Mount Vernon HS; Mount Vernon, NY; (Y); Boys Clb Am; Church Yth Grp; Cmnty Wkr; FCA; Math Clb; Office Aide; Church Choir; Bsbl; Ftbl; Hon Roll; Hnr Rll; Church Yth Grp; Bys Clb Amer; Bus Admn.

HARRIS, JOY; Highland HS; Highland, NY; (Y); 16/120; French Clb; Trs Yrbk Stf; Stat Socr; Var Trk; French Hon Soc; High Hon Roll; NHS; Best Acadmc Achvt Regnts Englsh 84-85; Hotel Mgmt.

HARRIS, JULIE; Salamanca Central HS; Salamanca, NY; (S); 16/129; French Clb; Model UN; Nwsp Rptr; Nwsp Stf; Yrbk Stf; French Hon Soc; High Hon Roll; Hon Roll; NHS; Acad Achvt Awds; Cnty Gov Intrnshp Pgm; NYS Regents Schlrshp; Cornell U; Comp Sci.

HARRIS, KAREN A; Nyack HS; Valley Cottage, NY; (Y); 50/256; Drm Mjr(t); Yrbk Stf; Sec Sr Cls; Stu Cncl; JV Bsktbl; Coach Actv; Var Lcrss; High Hon Roll; Hon Roll; NHS; Occptnl Thrpy.

HARRIS, KATHERINE; Shenendehowa HS; Ballston Lake, NY; (Y); Drama Clb; Ski Clb; Varsity Clb; Band; School Play; Trs Jr Cls; Fld Hcky; High Hon Roll; Hon Roll; NHS.

HARRIS, KENERSON; Tonawanda HS; Tonawanda, NY; (Y); 7/250; French Clb; Band; Concert Band; Jazz Band; Mrchg Band; School Musical; Socr; Hon Roll; NHS; Math Stu Yr 82-83.

HARRIS, KIMBERLY; Salamanca Central HS; Little Valley, NY; (Y); 4-H; French Clb; Varsity Clb; Color Guard; Var Trk; Cit Awd; 4-H Awd; High Hon Roll; NHS; Nrsng.

HARRIS, LAURA; Hudson Falls Central HS; Hudson Falls, NY; (Y); 32/230; 4-H; Key Clb; Spanish Clb; Varsity Clb; Score Keeper; Sftbl; Tennis; Vllybl; 4-H Awd; Spanish NHS; Suny At Cortland; Health Educ.

HARRIS, MARCIA; Herbert H Lehman HS; Bronx, NY; (Y); 19/473; Girl Scts; Band; Concert Band; Orch; School Play; Tennis; Cit Awd; High Hon Roll; Hon Roll; Pol Sci.

HARRIS, MARY; Newfield HS; Coram, NY; (Y); Cmnty Wkr; Drama Clb; Chorus; Church Choir; School Musical; School Play; Pres VP Stu Cncl; Var Fld Hcky; Var Trk; Pres Jr NHS; Ctznshp Awd 82-83; Theatre.

HARRIS, OTIS L; Mannheim American HS; Apo New York, NY; (Y); 10/127; Am Leg Boys St; Debate Tm; Model UN; Nwsp Rptr; High Hon Roll; Hon Roll; NHS; Church Yth Grp; Cmnty Wkr; JA; Schlrshp Omega Psi Phi Frat Inc 85; Schlrshp Mannheim/Worms Comm 85; Top 10 Per Cent Sr Clss 85; IA ST U; Mass Comm.

HARRIS, PAMELA J; Poughkeepsie HS; Poughkeepsie, NY; (Y); 10/195; Computer Clb; Nwsp Stf; Rep Jr Cls; JV Bsktbl; Var L Sftbl; Hon Roll; Jr NHS; NHS; Cert Awd Acadmc Excllnc 84-85; Presdntl Acadmc Ftnss Awd 84-85; Majorie Gunther Memrl Libry Awd 84-85; Dutchess CC; Comp Sci.

HARRIS, RICH; Saugerties HS; Saugerties, NY; (Y); Ski Clb; Varsity Clb; Band; Symp Band; Var L Socr; Var L Wrstlng; High Hon Roll; Hon Roll; NHS; Bio.

HARRIS, ROY C; James E Sperry HS; Pittsford, NY; (Y); 6/311; Spanish Clb; Pres Band; Trs Church Choir; Orch; Var Trk; VP NHS; Ntl Merit Schol; Spanish NHS; Scholastic Bowl; Concert Band; Rochester Harvard Clb Bk 84; Carl S Ell Schlshp NE U 85; James E Sperry Alumni Awd 85; Northeastern U; Elect Engr.

HARRIS, SCOTT; Lyndonville HS; Lyndonville, NY; (Y); Church Yth Grp; Computer Clb; Yrbk Stf; Trs Soph Cls; Rep Stu Cncl; JV Bsbl; Math.

HARRIS, STACEY; Spring Valley HS; Pearl River, NY; (Y); 50/500; Spanish Clb; Spanish NHS; Science Clb; Law.

HARRIS, STEFANIE; Great Neck North SR HS; New York, NY; (Y); 117/300; Cmnty Wkr; Drama Clb; Hosp Aide; PAVAS; Teachers Aide; School Musical; School Play; JV Cheerleading; Peer Cnslr 85; NY U; Thetr.

HARRIS, SUSAN; Maryvale HS; Cheektowaga, NY; (Y); French Clb; High Hon Roll; Hon Roll; Roswell Parks Smmr Res Pgm 85; Physcn.

HARRIS, SUSAN M; Schuylerville Ceantral HS; Schuylerville, NY; (Y); 7/99; Pres 4-H; Band; Nwsp Ed-Chief; Nwsp Rptr; Var Capt Bsktbl; Var Capt Fld Hcky; High Hon Roll; Hon Roll; Jr NHS; NHS; NY St Regents Schlrshp 85; NYS Cons Ed Del Ntl Congress 84; Stu Cncl Ltr 84; Suny Coll; English.

HARRIS, TAIJA LANE; Ogdensburg Free Acad; Ogdensburg, NY; (Y); 17/200; Band; Color Guard; Concert Band; Mrchg Band; Yrbk Stf; Var L Cheerleading; Var L Crs Cntry; Var L Trk; NHS; Ntl Merit Ltr; Regents Schrlshp 85; U CA-DAVIS; Bio.

HARRIS, TRACEY S; Norman Thomas HS; New York, NY; (S); 79/677; Dance Clb; JA; Math Clb; Office Aide; Vllybl; Hon Roll; Jr NHS; Prfct Atten Awd; Pace; Pub Acctg.

HARRIS, VICK; Springfields Gardens HS; Rosedale, NY; (Y); Boys Clb Am; Computer Clb; FBLA; Math Clb; Crs Cntry; Diving; Gym; Sftbl; Swmmng; Trk; Machnst.

HARRIS, YOLANDA; Kensington Academic HS; East Providence, RI; (Y); 10/225; Church Yth Grp; VP Drama Clb; VP French Clb; Hosp Aide; Office Aide; Teachers Aide; Capt Drill Tm; Sec Soph Cls; Var Trk; Rep Frsh Cls; High Grde Amer Stud Regnts 85; Hosp Admin.

HARRISINGH, MELANIE; New Rochelle HS; New Rochelle, NY; (Y); Camera Clb; Church Yth Grp; Yrbk Phtg; Cotillion Natl Assn Negro Bus & Prof Wmns Clbs Inc 85; Trk Mgr; Psych.

HARRISON, CHRISTINE; Richmond Hill HS; Ozone Pk, NY; (Y); Church Yth Grp; Sec Cmnty Wkr; Key Clb; Spanish Clb; Chorus; School Musical; Frgn Lang Hnr Soc 82-83; Profncy Spnsh Awd 83-85; Hunter; Frgn Lang.

HARRISON, KAREN; Cardinal Spellman HS; Bronx, NY; (Y); Capt Flag Corp; Girl Scts; Hosp Aide; School Musical; Variety Show; Yrbk Stf; High Hon Roll; NHS; Ignatius Loyola; Pre Med.

HARRISON, KATHLEEN L; Hudson Falls Central HS; Hudson Falls, NY; (Y); 25/211; Am Leg Aux Girls St; 4-H; Spanish Clb; Varsity Clb; Acpl Chr; Band; Chorus; Concert Band; Mrchg Band; School Musical; 4 H Jr Ldrshp Awd 83; Regnts Schlrshp 85; Pres Acad Ftns Awd 85; Le Moyne Coll; Econ.

HARRISON, KEVIN; Warwick Valley HS; Warwick, NY; (Y); 27/204; Boy Scts; Church Yth Grp; FFA; Science Clb; Var Capt Swmmng; Var Trk; Hon Roll; 4th Pl Fnlsts Empire ST Gms 100 Mtr Brststrk 84 & 85; Engrng.

HARRISON, MARK W; Fairport HS; Fairport, NY; (Y); 120/600; Aud/Vis; Boy Scts; German Clb; Math Tm; Model UN; Concert Band; Mrchg Band; Orch; Symp Band; Computer Clb; NY ST Regents Schlrshp; Eagle Scout; Grove City Coll; Engr.

HARRISON, MAUREEN; Cardinal Spellman HS; Bronx, NY; (Y); Church Yth Grp; Cmnty Wkr; Intnl Clb; Service Clb; High Hon Roll; NHS; NEDT Awd; Lawyer.

HARRISON, SHERRY; Bradford Central HS; Beaver Dams, NY; (S); 2/32; FBLA; Yrbk Bus Mgr; Sec Sr Cls; Sec Stu Cncl; Capt Cheerleading; Var Socr; Var Sftbl; High Hon Roll; NHS; Acad All Amer; Bryant & Stratton Bus; Bus Mgmt.

HARRNACKER, MICHAEL B; Mynderse Acad; Seneca Falls, NY; (Y); 28/136; 4-H; Band; Chorus; Concert Band; Jazz Band; Mrchg Band; Pep Band; School Musical; School Play; Swing Chorus; Engr.

HARRSCH, CYNTHIA; Clyde-Savannah HS; Clyde, NY; (Y); Sec Jr Cls; Trs Rep Stu Cncl; Sec NHS; 4-H; 4-H Awd; High Hon Roll; Harvard Prz Bk 85; Cert Of Profcncy In Accntg 85; Acctng.

HARRY, JUANITA M; Frontier Central HS; Randallstown, MD; (Y); Latin Clb; Acpl Chr; Chorus; Church Choir; School Musical; Crs Cntry; Trk; NHS; Musicn.

HARRY, VIRGINIA PAIGE; Warwick Valley HS; Georgetown, TX; (Y); 3/200; Church Yth Grp; 4-H; Math Tm; Band; Crs Cntry; Trk; High Hon Roll; NHS; Hgst Avg Math Awd 85; U TX; Math.

HART, BETH M; Oriskany Central HS; Oriskany, NY; (Y); #5 In Class; Trs Varsity Clb; Band; Nwsp Phtg; Var Capt Bsktbl; Var Capt Crs Cntry; Var Trk; High Hon Roll; Hon Roll; Jr NHS; Trs NHS; Regents Schlrshp 85; Mohawk Valley CC; Engrng.

HART, CARA LYNN; West Seneca Christian Schl; W Falls, NY; (Y); Church Yth Grp; Drama Clb; Library Aide; Chorus; Yrbk Stf; Jrnlsm.

HART, CHRISTOPHER W; Horace Mann HS; Englewood, NJ; (Y); Cmnty Wkr; French Clb; Library Aide; Nwsp Rptr; Ftbl; Golf; Bsbl; Clark U; Hist.

HART, DARREN; Linton HS; Schenectady, NY; (Y); 33/273; Capt Var Golf; Var Tennis; Hon Roll; Fnlst For NROTC Schlrshp 85; Astro Physcs.

HART, DIANNA; Glens Falls SR HS; Glens Falls, NY; (Y); AFS; Key Clb; Band; Pep Band; High Hon Roll; Hon Roll; NHS; Ntl Merit Schol; Regents Nursing Schlrshp 85; SUNY At Plattsburgh; Nrsng.

HART, RAYMOND L; Peekskill HS; Peekskill, NY; (Y); 49/146; Am Leg Boys St; Band; Concert Band; Jazz Band; Mrchg Band; Rep VP Stu Cncl; Stat Bsktbl; Var L Ftbl; Var Capt Lcrss; Hon Roll; Sullivan County Coll; Comp Sci.

HART, THERESA; Gowanda Central HS; Gowanda, NY; (Y); 2/121; Thesps; Band; Chorus; Mrchg Band; School Musical; School Play; Nwsp Rptr; Trs Sec Stu Cncl; High Hon Roll; Jr NHS; St Marys Coll IN; Spec Ed.

HART, YONYETTA; John Jay HS; Brooklyn, NY; (Y); 115/537; JA; Church Choir; Cheerleading; Prfct Atten Awd; Outstndng Schlrshp Engl, Bkkpng & Soc Studys 85; US Air Force; Comp Engr.

HARTE, KATHLEEN; St Joh The Baptist HS; Lk Grove, NY; (Y); Dance Clb; Service Clb; Yrbk Stf; Rep Frsh Cls; Sec Soph Cls; VP Jr Cls; Pres Stu Cncl; Pom Pon; Girl Scts; Nwsp Stf; Cert Achvt Yth Gov; Cert Prof Typng; Cath Leag Rlgs & Civil Rghts; St Johns U; Bus.

HARTELL, MARK; Susan E Wagner HS; Staten Is, NY; (Y); Hosp Aide; Office Aide; Red Cross Aide; Science Clb; School Musical; Hon Roll; Jr NHS; NHS; 1st Pl Cty Wd Sci Fair 83; Hnbl Mntn Cty Wd Sci Fair 84; 2nd Pl Metl Cty Wd Indstrl Arts Exhib 84; Med Tech.

HARTER, GLEN; Brockport Central HS; Brockport, NY; (Y); Latin Clb; Yrbk Stf; Rep Stu Cncl; Stat Bsktbl; High Hon Roll; NHS; NY ST Regnts Schlrshp 85; 3-1-3 Prog Attnd Coll Frshmn Yr While H S SR 84-85; Astrnmy Lab SUNY 85; Suny Brockport; PHD.

HARTGENS, AMBER; Louis D Brandeis HS; New York, NY; (Y); 43/747; Office Aide; Nwsp Rptr; Yrbk Phtg; Stu Cncl; Chrmn Bsktbl; Im Sftbl; Var Tennis; Hon Roll; NHS.

HARTIGAN, MARGARET E; Huntington HS; Huntington, NY; (Y); 18/433; Cmnty Wkr; Office Aide; Pep Clb; Red Cross Aide; Stage Crew; Yrbk Rptr; Stu Cncl; Var Capt Swmmng; High Hon Roll; NHS; Holy Cross; Librl Arts.

HARTLEY, MICHELLE; Jamaica HS; Flushing, NY; (Y); Church Yth Grp; Hosp Aide; Teachers Aide; Chorus; Church Choir; Rep Jr Cls; Prfct Atten Awd; Med.

HARTMAN, DANIEL L; Westmoreland Central Schl; Rome, NY; (Y); 4/88; French Clb; Im JV Bsbl; Im JV Ftbl; Im JV Wrstlng; High Hon Roll; Hon Roll; Trs NHS; Regents Schlrshp 84-85; Leag All Star Ftbl 84-85; Leag All Star Wrestlng 83-85; Alfred ST Coll; Elec Engr.

HARTMAN, EVELYN M VIVI; Roy C Ketcham HS; N Hamburg, NY; (Y); Aud/Vis; Computer Clb; Library Aide; Chorus; High Hon Roll; Hon Roll; NHS; Comp.

HARTMAN, LYNN; Buffalo Academy For Visual & Perf Art; Buffalo, NY; (Y); 2/98; Boy Scts; Church Yth Grp; Exploring; Library Aide; Teachers Aide; Stage Crew; Yrbk Stf; Var Capt Bowling; Bausch & Lomb Sci Awd; High Hon Roll; Telecomm Schlrshp 84-85; Hgst Avg Hist,Sci,Comm 84-85; Hnr Rl; SUNY; Comm.

HARTMAN, MARK; Spring Valley SR HS; Monsey, NY; (Y); Cmnty Wkr; Computer Clb; FBLA; Office Aide; Political Wkr; Ski Clb; Temple Yth Grp; Stage Crew; Bsbl; Fld Hcky; Bus.

HARTMAN, MORGAN; Susquehanna Valley HS; Conklin, NY; (Y); Hosp Aide; Spanish Clb; Varsity Clb; Lit Mag; Rep Frsh Cls; Rep Stu Cncl; Var L Ftbl; Var L Trk; Var L Wrstlng; Hon Roll; Pres Physcl Ftns Awd 82-84; Syracuse U; Comm.

HARTMAN, PATRICK THOMAS; Aquinas Inst; Rochester, NY; (Y); 46/153; Church Yth Grp; Computer Clb; Nwsp Sprt Ed; Nwsp Stf; Yrbk Phtg; Yrbk Sprt Ed; Var Capt Swmmng; Var Tennis; Var Trk; Hon Roll; James V Stillwell Scholar 85; U Of Dayton; Elec Engrng.

HARTMANN, DEAN; St Francis Prep; Woodhaven, NY; (Y); 340/693; Band; Concert Band; Mrchg Band; Pep Band; Golf.

HARTMANN, SARAH K; Oneonta SR HS; Oneonta, NY; (S); 7/190; Drama Clb; German Clb; Thesps; Chorus; Madrigals; School Musical; Nwsp Stf; Stu Cncl; Hon Roll; Bst Actress Awd 84; NYSSA For Bio 84; Northwestern U; Actng.

HARTNAGEL, LINDA; East Meadow HS; E Meadow, NY; (Y); Drama Clb; FBLA; Key Clb; Latin Clb; School Play; Cheerleading; Var Tennis; Hon Roll; Prfct Atten Awd; Art Clb.

HARTNETT, MICHAEL J; West Genesee HS; Syracuse, NY; (Y); Church Yth Grp; Key Clb; Band; Concert Band; Jazz Band; Mrchg Band; Orch; Pep Band; Crs Cntry; Wrstlng; Natl Champ Fld & Cncrt Band-W Genesee Wldct Band 84; NY ST Mrchng Fld Band Champ 82-84; Genesee; Ed.

HARTNEY, LYNN; Salem Central HS; Salem, NY; (Y); Aud/Vis; GAA; Yrbk Rptr; Yrbk Stf; Var L Bsktbl; Var L Crs Cntry; Var L Trk; Hon Roll; All Amer Ath 84-85; Bio.

HARTRICH, LAURA A; Buff Acad Of The Sacred Heart; Tonawanda, NY; (Y); Sec French Clb; Pres Red Cross Aide; Sec Science Clb; Ed Nwsp Stf; Stu Cncl; High Hon Roll; Hon Roll; Pres Schlr; NY ST Regents Schlrshp 85; Pre-Med.

HARTS, MELISSA; St Francis Prep; Hollis, NY; (S); Dance Clb; Library Aide; Service Clb; Church Choir; Drm & Bgl; Nwsp Rptr; Hon Roll; Church Yth Grp; Dance Achvts 82-83; Queens Talntd Yth Comp Awd 83; Cornell U; Comm.

HARTSAGH, NORA; Victor SR HS; Macedon, NY; (Y); Church Yth Grp; Chorus; Jazz Band; Mrchg Band; School Musical; Var Trk; High Hon Roll; NHS; Ntl Merit Ltr; Prfct Atten Awd; Bio.

HARTSOUGH, NORA; Victor SR HS; Macedon, NY; (S); 2/250; Church Yth Grp; Chorus; Jazz Band; Mrchg Band; School Musical; Trk; High Hon Roll; NHS; Ntl Merit Ltr; Prfct Atten Awd; Bio.

HARTUNG, CHRISTOPHER; Fayetteville-Manlius HS; Manlius, NY; (Y); Church Yth Grp; Pres Debate Tm; Model UN; Political Wkr; Pres Speech Tm; Socr; High Hon Roll; Hon Roll; NHS; Bus Adm.

HARTZ, JENNIFER; Byron Bergen Central; Churchville, NY; (Y); Drama Clb; FTA; Hon Roll; Cert Of Rcgntn From Byron Bergen 83; Travel.

HARVEY, ANDY; Massena Central HS; Norfolk, NY; (Y); Canton ATC; Engr.

HARVEY, DEANIE LYNN; Bradford Central Schl; Beaver Dams, NY; (Y); 8/28; Exploring; Speech Tm; Yrbk Sprt Ed; Capt Bsbl; Capt Socr; Capt Sftbl; Capt Vllybl; John Reed Mem Schlrshp 85; Corning CC; Cosmetology.

HARVEY, DENNIS; Herbert H Lehman HS; Bronx, NY; (Y); 183/473; Art Clb; Bowling; Cit Awd; Hon Roll; Ntl Merit Ltr; Prfct Atten Awd; Bond For Brthrhd 82; Engrng.

HARVEY, JACQUELINE; Cortland JR SR HS; Cortland, NY; (Y); Church Yth Grp; French Clb; Girl Scts; Cheerleading; Swmmng; High Hon Roll; Hon Roll; Trvl.

HARVEY, JEANINE; Cicero-North Syracuse HS; Clay, NY; (S); 37/722; Mathletes; Math Tm; Ski Clb; Varsity Clb; Rep Jr Cls; Powder Puff Ftbl; Var Socr; Var Sftbl; Hon Roll; NHS.

HARVEY, JEFFREY P; Gowanda Central HS; Gowanda, NY; (Y); 20/159; FCA; Spanish Clb; School Play; Var JV Bsbl; JV Bsktbl; JV Var Ftbl; Var Wt Lftg; JV Var High Hon Roll; JV Var Hon Roll; Var NHS; Navy; Electrical Engineer.

HARVEY, JERILYNN; Indian River HS; Antwerp, NY; (Y); 10/140; Sec Latin Clb; Pres Jr Cls; Pres Sr Cls; Rep Stu Cncl; Var Bsktbl; Var Socr; Var Capt Sftbl; NHS; NEDT Awd; Pres Schlr; Sports Phys Thrpst.

HARVEY, JULIE; Victor Central SR HS; Sterling, VA; (Y); Church Yth Grp; Exploring; Hosp Aide; Color Guard; Concert Band; Mrchg Band; Yrbk Stf; USA Fitness Awd 85; Brigham Young U; Physical Thrpy.

HARVEY, TODD; Union-Endicott HS; Endicott, NY; (Y); Am Leg Boys St; Church Yth Grp; Band; Concert Band; Jazz Band; Mrchg Band; Orch; School Musical; Symp Band; Hon Roll; Engrng.

HARZEWSKI, JILL; Maryvale SR HS; Cheektowaga, NY; (Y); GAA; Trs Orch; School Musical; Yrbk Stf; Rep Jr Cls; Rep Stu Cncl; Var Mgr(s); Powder Puff Ftbl; Var L Trk; Hon Roll; Gerontology.

HASAN, CANDY S; Hutchinson Central Technical HS; Buffalo, NY; (Y); 5/256; NHS; Math Tm; Natl Beta Clb; High Hon Roll; Hon Roll; Regents Schlrshp 85; SUNY-BUFFALO; Comp Pgrmr.

HASDAY, MARLENA; South Shore HS; Brooklyn, NY; (Y); 75/500; Dance Clb; Scholastic Bowl; Spanish Clb; Varsity Clb; Stage Crew; Yrbk Stf; Lit Mag; Gym; Regents Schlrshp 85-92; Baruch Coll; Ind Psych.

HASELEY, LAURIE; Niagara Wheatfield HS; Sanborn, NY; (Y); Hosp Aide; Latin Clb; Library Aide; Pep Clb; PAVAS; Chorus; Capt Color Guard; School Musical; JV Trk; NHS; Med.

HASELHOFF, OTTO; St Francis Prep; Flushing, NY; (S); 99/700; JV Im Tennis; High Hon Roll; Hon Roll; AATG Germn Awd; Bus.

HASELL, SANDRA DANITA; Mabel Dean Bacon HS; Brooklyn, NY; (S); 2/299; Church Yth Grp; Dance Clb; Girl Scts; Math Tm; Church Choir; Rep Stu Cncl; Cheerleading; Hon Roll; NHS; Prfct Atten Awd; Dist Atty Eliz Holtzman Cit Hnr 82; City NY Super Yth Awd 84; Cont Math League Comp 82; Nrs.

HASEMANN, SUZANNE; Rocky Point JR SR HS; Rocky Pt, NY; (Y); Church Yth Grp; Comptd Adv Shrthd 120 WPM Long Island Bus Ed Cntst 85; Suffolk CC; Secy Sci.

HASENAUER, JOSEPH; Whitesboro SR HS; Whitesboro, NY; (Y); 44/360; Varsity Clb; Bsbl; Capt Bsktbl; Ftbl; Hon Roll; Mr & Mrs Joseph A Furgal Mem At Awd 85; Gold Key Schltc Art Awd 85; Art Inst Pitsburge; Comm Art.

HASKELL, TODD; Cold Spring Harbor HS; Huntington, NY; (Y); Debate Tm; Intnl Clb; Political Wkr; Acpl Chr; Band; Chorus; Nwsp Ed-Chief; Nwsp Rptr; Nwsp Stf; Lit Mag; Poli Sci.

HASKINS, KIMBERLY Y; The Mary Louis Acad; Laurelton, NY; (Y); 9/283; Art Clb; Variety Show; Lit Mag; Rep Stu Cncl; High Hon Roll; NHS; Ntl Merit SF; NEDT Awd; 2nd Hnrs Spanish III, Iona Coll Lang Contest 84; Elec Engrng.

HASKINS, PAMELA GAIL; Portledge Schl; Oyster Bay, NY; (Y); Math Tm; Lit Mag; VP Frsh Cls; VP Sr Cls; Var Capt Bsktbl; Var Crs Cntry; Var L Fld Hcky; Var L Lcrss; Sftbl; Hon Roll; Mst Imprvd Fld Hcky 84-85; Davidson Memrl Bk Schlrshp 84-85; Athltc Hnr Roll 81-85; U Of CT; Bus.

HASLAUER, CHRISTINE; Whitesboro SR HS; Utica, NY; (Y); 100/312; Church Yth Grp; Cmnty Wkr; Drama Clb; 4-H; Trs Intnl Clb; Library Aide; Hon Roll; Acpl Chr; Chorus; Church Choir; NACEL Exch Stu France 83; SADD Sec 84 & 85; Daniel Olmstead Kern Awd; Wells Coll; Lib Art.

HASLER, KAREN; York Central Schl; Leicester, NY; (Y); AFS; Boy Scts; Cmnty Wkr; 4-H; Chorus; 4-H Awd; Hon Roll; NHS; EMT.

HASLER, MARCIA; York Central HS; Piffard, NY; (Y); Art Clb; Church Yth Grp; 4-H; Chorus; Church Choir; School Musical; School Play; Swing Chorus; Variety Show; Yrbk Rptr; ST Trck Meet Hgh Jmp 83 & 85; Bus Awd 84; Fredonia ST Coll; Cmmnctns.

HASSELL, ANITA; Warwick Valley HS; Pine Isld, NY; (Y); 30/200; Church Yth Grp; Pep Clb; Yrbk Bus Mgr; Yrbk Stf; Var Trk; Var Wt Lftg; High Hon Roll; Hon Roll; Hghst Avr, Grtst Undrstndg Spnsh 1st 84; St Bonaventure; Prsnll Mgr.

HASSENFRATZ, DEBORAH; Alden Central HS; Lancaster, NY; (Y); Art Clb; Aud/Vis; Sec Church Yth Grp; English Clb; 4-H; Hosp Aide; Nwsp Stf; Mgr(s); JV Tennis; Var Trk; Mngmnt.

HASSETT, KATHLEEN; Churchville-Chili SR HS; Rochester, NY; (Y); Church Yth Grp; JCL; Latin Clb; Chorus; School Play; Ntl Merit Ltr.

HASSLER, DARRYL; Northstar Christia Acad; N Chili, NY; (Y); Ski Clb; Band; Chorus; School Play; Yrbk Phtg; JV Bsktbl; Hon Roll; New Life Bible Schl; Radio.

HASTEE, LORI; Oakfield-Alabama HS; Alabama, NY; (Y); Dance Clb; Hosp Aide; Ski Clb; Band; Chorus; Concert Band; Drm Mjr(t); Mrchg Band; Sec Stu Cncl; Cheerleading; Sci.

HASTINGS, SCOTT W; Vestal SR HS; Vestal, NY; (Y); 159/450; FBLA; Key Clb; JV Bowling; L Golf; Hon Roll; NY ST Regnts Schlrshp Awd 85; Broome CC; Bus Mgmt.

HASTY, KEVIN; Wyandanch Memorial HS; Wyandanch, NY; (Y); Var JV Bsbl; Bsktbl; Ftbl; Gym; Trk; Wt Lftg; Milton L Olive PTA Inctv Awd 85; Old Westbury; Law.

HATCH, DOREEN; Sachem HS; Holtsville, NY; (Y); 158/1463; Pres Church Yth Grp; Sec Drama Clb; Chorus; Church Choir; Madrigals; School Musical; Stage Crew; Swing Chorus; NHS; Outstndg Stu Chorus; C W Post U; Music Educ.

HATCH, KAREN J; Chatham HS; Canaan, NY; (Y); 10/135; Church Yth Grp; 4-H; 4-H Awd; High Hon Roll; NHS; Window Paintg Cntst 83; Nwsp Ad Cntst 85; Berkshire Christn Clg; Elem Edu.

HATFIELD, LINDA; Patchoque-Medford HS; Patchogue, NY; (S); 188/740; Sec Band; Sec Concert Band; Mrchg Band; School Musical; Stage Crew; Symp Band; Var Badmtn; JV Tennis; Prfct Atten Awd; Elem Educ.

HATKI, ANDREW; Richmond Hill HS; Ozone Park, NY; (Y); 7/285; English Clb; Office Aide; Radio Clb; Spanish Clb; School Musical; Nwsp Rptr; Rep Frsh Cls; Rep Soph Cls; Rep Jr Cls; Var Capt Bsbl; Regnts Schlrshp; U S Army Resrv Athl & Schlr Awd; PTA Athl Schlr Awd; Cornell U; Med.

HATSIOS, GEORGE J; Roy C Ketcham HS; Poughkeepsie, NY; (Y); Drama Clb; Mathletes; Q&S; Science Clb; School Play; Stage Crew; Nwsp Rptr; Yrbk Stf; Lit Mag; Im Bsktbl; 2nd Dist Sci Fair 1st Cnty Sci Fair Physics 85; Pre Med.

HATTAR, MARLENE; Yonkers HS; Yonkers, NY; (Y); FBLA; Key Clb; Spanish Clb; Varsity Clb; Nwsp Rptr; Nwsp Stf; Yrbk Stf; Lit Mag; Rep Stu Cncl; Var Vllybl; Manhatten.

HATTON, EILEEN; St Edmund HS; Brooklyn, NY; (S); 1/187; Dance Clb; Church Choir; Nwsp Ed-Chief; Yrbk Stf; Sec Jr Cls; High Hon Roll; NHS; Prfct Atten Awd; Val; Wrld Peace Essay Cntst 1st Pl 83; Partial Schlarshp Awd 82-84; Engl Awd 82-84; Wrtng.

HATTON, ELIZABETH A; Geneseo Central HS; Geneseo, NY; (Y); Ski Clb; JV Var Sftbl; Hon Roll; NYS Regnts Schlrshp 85; Marymount Coll Tarrytown.

HATTRICK, ELLEN; Southampton HS; Southampton, NY; (Y); Spanish Clb; School Play; Yrbk Sprt Ed; Tennis; Vllybl; Trs Frsh Cls; MVP Vllybl 85; Spnsh.

HAU, BONNIE; St Johns Prep; Astoria, NY; (S); 25/548; Pres Camera Clb; Cmnty Wkr; Chorus; Pep Band; Nwsp Rptr; Rep Soph Cls; Rep Jr Cls; Rep Stu Cncl; Capt Var Cheerleading; High Hon Roll; 2nd Hnrs Acadmc Awd 85; SUNY-BINGHAMTON; Bus Commnctns.

HAUCK, JUNE MARIE; H Frank Carey HS; Garden City S, NY; (Y); 5/222; Hosp Aide; Band; Yrbk Bus Mgr; Sec Soph Cls; Sec Jr Cls; High Hon Roll; Hon Roll; Sec Jr NHS; Sec NHS; Cmnty Wkr; Frgn Lang Hnr Soc Treas 84.

HAUCK, LINDA; Chruchville-Chili HS; Rochester, NY; (Y); GAA; JCL; Latin Clb; Var Sftbl; JV Var Swmmng; JV Vllybl; Hon Roll; Monroe CC; Med Tech.

HAUGEN, MARY; St Peters HS For Girls; Staten Island, NY; (Y); 2/107; Hosp Aide; Math Tm; Nwsp Rptr; Yrbk Ed-Chief; Yrbk Sprt Ed; Stu Cncl; Capt Cheerleading; Coach Actv; NHS; Regents Schlrshp 85; Excell Awd; Hnr Awd; St Johns U; Math.

HAUGHNEY, MICHAEL; Lansingburg HS; Troy, NY; (Y); Cmnty Wkr; High Hon Roll; Hon Roll; Mechncl Drwng I 82-83.

HAUGHTON, JUDITH; John Dewey HS; Brooklyn, NY; (Y); Church Yth Grp; JA; MMM; PAVAS; Teachers Aide; Acpl Chr; Chorus; Church Choir; School Musical; School Play; Bible Schlrshp Exam Awd 80; Math Awd 81; Berkeley; Music.

HAUK, MARIE J; Wallkill SR HS; Newburgh, NY; (Y); 7/200; Drama Clb; Girl Scts; Band; Concert Band; Mrchg Band; School Play; Rep Jr Cls; High Hon Roll; NHS; SUNY Binghamton; Nrsng.

HAUK, MARY; Kenmore East HS; Tonawanda, NY; (Y); Hst Band; Chorus; Hst Color Guard; Hst Jazz Band; Hst Mrchg Band; Orch; High Hon Roll; NHS; Pres Schlr; St Schlr; MVP Marching Band 85; Regnts Schlrshp 85; NY ST Field Band Conf Schlrshp 85; U Buffalo; Bio Sci.

HAULTON, ROBERT; South Park HS; Buffalo, NY; (Y); Boys Clb Am; Debate Tm; Chorus; School Play; Stage Crew; Swmmng; Hon Roll; US Army; Engrng.

HAUNSS, KAREN; St Francis Prep; Flushing, NY; (S); 5/693; German Clb; Library Aide; Math Clb; Ski Clb; Im Tennis; Im Vllybl; High Hon Roll; NHS; Ntl Merit Ltr; Brown U; Med.

HAUPT, DAWN; Roy C Ketcham HS; Wappngers Fls, NY; (Y); Church Yth Grp; Cmnty Wkr; Teachers Aide; High Hon Roll; Hon Roll; Dutches CC; Chld Care.

HAURI, KRIS; Forestville Central HS; Forestville, NY; (Y); Church Yth Grp; 4-H; Girl Scts; Band; Chorus; Yrbk Ed-Chief; Yrbk Stf; Bsktbl; Vllybl; 4-H Awd; Air Force.

HAURY, MADALYN; Paul V Moore HS; W Monroe, NY; (Y); 10/276; Pres Church Yth Grp; Math Tm; Church Choir; Stu Cncl; Var Gym; High Hon Roll; NHS; Rotary Awd; Chorus; Le Moyne Coll Accpntce 85; Le Moyne Coll; Bus.

HAUSER, DENISE; Fox Lane HS; Pound Ridge, NY; (Y); 89/275; Pep Clb; Ski Clb; Spanish Clb; JV Fld Hcky; Stat Lcrss; Stat Socr; Hon Roll; Pre-Med.

HAUSER, ELLEN; Bronx H S Of Science; New York, NY; (Y); Debate Tm; Drama Clb; Teachers Aide; Lib Arts.

HAUSER, MICHAEL; Gloversville HS; Gloversville, NY; (Y); Boy Scts; Golf; Hon Roll; Accntng.

HAUSLE, EDWARD; Archbishop Molloy HS; Flushing, NY; (Y); 305/409; Church Yth Grp; Computer Clb; Pep Clb; Band; Nwsp Stf; Rep Frsh Cls; Rep Soph Cls; Rep Jr Cls; Var L Trk; Var Wt Lftg; Pre-Med.

HAUSMAN, ALICIA T; John F Kennedy HS; Plainview, NY; (Y); 8/275; Pres Cmnty Wkr; Sec Ed Yrbk Stf; Sec Stu Cncl; Mgr Mgr(s); Hon Roll; NHS; Exploring; Kickline Capt 84-85; Outstndg NYSSMA 84; Coord Neighbrhd Watch Pgm 84-85; Brandeis U; Bio.

HAUSNER, JOYCE; Sachem North HS; Lk Ronkonkoma, NY; (Y); 190/1383; Color Guard; Concert Band; Jazz Band; Mrchg Band; Orch; Symp Band; Yrbk Stf.

HAUSNER, SONYA; Notre Dame Bishop Gibbons HS; Scotia, NY; (S); Ski Clb; Bsktbl; Socr; L Var Swmmng; High Hon Roll; NHS.

HAUTMANN, STACEY; Westhampton Beach HS; Quogue, NY; (Y); 22/247; Hst Trs FBLA; Spanish Clb; Drill Tm; Yrbk Stf; Rep Stu Cncl; Score Keeper; Trk; High Hon Roll; NHS; Most Imprvd Plyr Awd Girls Trk; Lawyer.

HAVEN, KYLE; Unatego HS; Otego, NY; (Y); Boy Scts; Ski Clb; Band; Ftbl; Trk; High Hon Roll; Boys Clb Am; Church Yth Grp; French Clb; Varsity Clb; Engr.

HAVENS, JOHN A; Niagara Falls HS; Niagara Falls, NY; (Y); Church Yth Grp; Cmnty Wkr; Computer Clb; Key Clb; Library Aide; Model UN; Quiz Bowl; Spanish Clb; Yrbk Phtg; Cit Awd; U Buffalo; Med.

HAVENS, KELLI; Waterloo SR HS; Waterloo, NY; (Y); 19/175; FTA; Model UN; Pres Spanish Clb; Chorus; Capt Color Guard; School Musical; Swing Chorus; JV Cheerleading; Var L Trk; JV Vllybl; Tchng.

HAVENS, KENNETH; Poland Central HS; Poland, NY; (Y); 2/56; French Clb; L Vllybl; Hon Roll; NHS; Prfct Atten Awd; Sal; Hghst Avg Engl 85, Frnch II 83, Accntng 85; Herkimer Cnty CC; Accntnt.

HAVENS, TERRY; Olean HS; Olean, NY; (Y); Art Clb; Aud/Vis; Camera Clb; Latin Clb; Library Aide; Red Cross Aide; Chorus; Crs Cntry; Ftbl; High Hon Roll; Math.

HAVENS, TODD L; Niagara Falls HS; Niagara Falls, NY; (Y); Church Yth Grp; Cmnty Wkr; Computer Clb; Key Clb; Library Aide; Model UN; Quiz Bowl; Spanish Clb; Yrbk Phtg; Cit Awd; U Buffalo; Sci.

HAVILAND, BRIAN; Walter Panas HS; Peekskill, NY; (Y); 18/221; VP Church Yth Grp; Band; Chorus; Mrchg Band; Orch; School Musical; School Play; Var Trk; NHS; St Schlr; Pres Acad Ftnss Awd 85; Cornell U; Cnslng.

HAVLIR, TANYA; Sidney HS; Sidney Center, NY; (Y); 2/110; Math Clb; Math Tm; Spanish Clb; DAR Awd; High Hon Roll; Prfct Atten Awd; Natl Social Studies Olympied 83; Natl Sci Olympiad 4th 84; Regents Schlrshp 85; Broome Comm ; Chem Engrng.

HAWK, BRIAN; Cortland JR SR HS; Cortland, NY; (Y); VICA; Bowling; Coach Actv; Golf; Swmmng; Vllybl; Ski Clb; Varsity Clb; Var Crs Cntry; Var Trk; Most Imprvd Math,Cross Cty 83-85; Alfred.

HAWK, KATHY; Weedsport Central HS; Pt Byron, NY; (Y); 7/85; Church Yth Grp; Sec French Clb; Spanish Clb; Var L Bsktbl; Var L Fld Hcky; Var L Sftbl; High Hon Roll; Jr NHS; Sec NHS; Prfct Atten Awd; Envrnmtl Sci.

HAWK, STEVE; Rye Neck HS; Rye, NY; (Y); 5/98; VP Jr Cls; Sec Sr Cls; Stu Cncl; Bsktbl; Capt Crs Cntry; Capt Golf; VP NHS; Key Clb; Nwsp Ed-Chief; Harvard U Bk Awd Schrshp 84; Oberlin Coll Bk Awd 83; Georgtown U; Bus Adm.

HAWKER, BRIAN; Fonda Fultonville Central HS; Tribes Hill, NY; (Y); Aud/Vis; Cmnty Wkr; Computer Clb; Letterman Clb; Teachers Aide; Varsity Clb; Yrbk Phtg; JV Var Crs Cntry; Var Trk; Mst Vlbl Rnnr/Crss-Cntry 84; Adv.

HAWKINS, CRAIG; Vestal SR HS; Vestal, NY; (Y); Chorus; Jazz Band; Orch; School Musical; Prfct Atten Awd; Music Educ.

HAWKINS, JAMES; Wilson Magnet HS; Rochester, NY; (Y); Boy Scts; Computer Clb; Chorus; Yrbk Stf; Sec Jr Cls; Rep Stu Cncl; Var Bsbl; Var Ftbl; Co-Capt Vllybl; Hon Roll; NY ST Acad Decthln 85; Recmmd For Natl Hnrs Scty 85; Ctznshp 82; Comp Sci.

HAWKINS, JENIFER; Minisink Valley HS; Otisville, NY; (Y); FBLA; Nwsp Rptr; Hon Roll; FBLA Outstndng Awd 84-85; Orange Cnty CC; Psych.

HAWKINS, SALLY; Naples Central HS; Naples, NY; (Y); 4/70; French Clb; Girl Scts; Ski Clb; Band; Chorus; Color Guard; Concert Band; Drm Mjr(t); Jazz Band; Mrchg Band; Yth Cares Awd 84; Cornell U; Bus Mgmt.

HAWKINS, VANESSA; Lindenhurst SR HS; Lindenhurst, NY; (Y); Church Yth Grp; Dance Clb; Office Aide; ROTC; Color Guard; Drill Tm; School Musical; School Play; JV Capt Vllybl; Hon Roll; Nrsg Admin.

HAWLEY, KATHLEEN L; Auburn HS; Auburn, NY; (Y); 23/444; Church Yth Grp; Girl Scts; Church Choir; High Hon Roll; Jr NHS; NHS; Wrd Lfe Bible Clb Schlrshp 84 & 85; Pres Acdmc Ftns Awd 85; Peter Bauxbaum Awd 85; Wrd Life Bible Inst.

HAWRYLUK, NATALIE M; Rondout Valley Central HS; Cottekill, NY; (Y); 1/199; Am Leg Aux Girls St; Girl Scts; Math Tm; Var JV Bsktbl; Var Capt Trk; Var L Vllybl; DAR Awd; High Hon Roll; NHS; Ntl Merit SF; Stu Of The Month 83.

HAWTHORNE, BRIAN W; G Ray Bodley HS; Fulton, NY; (Y); Am Leg Boys St; Acpl Chr; Chorus; School Musical; Var L Tennis; High Hon Roll; Hon Roll; NHS; Cert Excel Math,Physcl Ed; Math.

HAY, BRUCE; F D Roosevelt HS; Hyde Park, NY; (Y); Am Leg Boys St; Boy Scts; Mrchg Band; School Musical; Stage Crew; VP Jr Cls; VP Sr Cls; Var Trk; NHS; Hugh Obrien Ldrshp Conf 84; Med.

HAYAKAWA, GEORGE; Sperry HS; Henrietta, NY; (Y); 3/278; Chorus; Trk; High Hon Roll; Jr NHS; NHS; Spanish NHS; Renssalear Medal Sci,Math 85; Friendshp Amb 83; MIT; Physcl Sci.

HAYASHI, YOICHI; Scarsdale HS; Scarsdale, NY; (Y); Sec Chess Clb; Hosp Aide; JV Crs Cntry; Var Swmmng; NHS; NYS Regnts Schlrshp 85; Columbia U; Med.

HAYDEN, MARY; De Sales HS; Lockport, NY; (Y); Girl Scts; Nwsp Phtg; Ed Yrbk Ed-Chief; Kiwanis Awd; Ntl Merit Ltr; VFW Awd; Rep Frsh Cls; Rep Soph Cls; Rep Jr Cls; Rep Sr Cls; St Josephs Acad Alumni Awd 84-85; Francis Agnes Sehimschienel Mem Grant 83-84; St Bonarenture U; Elem Ed.

HAYEK, KAREN; Kenmore West SR HS; Kenmore, NY; (Y); Church Yth Grp; GAA; Varsity Clb; Var L Bsktbl; Var L Socr; Var L Sftbl; MVP Vrsty Socr Tm 84-85; Canisins Coll; Acctg.

HAYES, CHRISTINE A; West Senecca East SR HS; West Seneca, NY; (Y); Church Yth Grp; GAA; JA; Ski Clb; JV Bsktbl; Im Vllybl; Prfct Atten Awd.

HAYES, CLAIRE; Mayfield Central HS; Mayfield, NY; (Y); 6/77; Drama Clb; Band; Chorus; Concert Band; Mrchg Band; School Play; Nwsp Stf; Ed Yrbk Ed-Chief; NHS; Pres Acad Fit Awd 85; Allen Brown Schlrshp 85; Potsdam Coll; Math Tchr.

HAYES, DALE; Lake Placid Central HS; Lake Placid, NY; (Y); VP Stu Cncl; Var Ice Hcky; Var Tennis.

HAYES, DARRELL; Valley Central HS; Walden, NY; (Y); 15/315; Band; Concert Band; Mrchg Band; Socr; Hon Roll; Prfct Atten Awd; Ski Tm 83-85; Elec.

HAYES, JANE; Sacred Heart HS; Yonkers, NY; (Y); 34/213; Art Clb; Church Yth Grp; Model UN; Variety Show; Rptr Sec Stu Cncl; Capt Var Cheerleading; Var Sftbl; Hon Roll; Accntng.

HAYES, JENNIFER; Jamesville-Dewitt HS; Jamesville, NY; (Y); Church Yth Grp; Key Clb; Math Tm; JV Bsktbl; Var Crs Cntry; Var Trk; Le Moyne Coll; Ed.

HAYES, KAREN; St Edmund HS; Brooklyn, NY; (S); 1/190; Cmnty Wkr; Spanish Clb; Off Stu Cncl; Var Bsktbl; JV Sftbl; High Hon Roll; NHS; Partial Schlrshp 1st In Class 83-85; Spec Ed.

HAYES, KELLY; East Seneca SR HS; Cheektowaga, NY; (Y); DECA; French Clb; JA; Trs Key Clb; Radio Clb; Yrbk Stf; Alfred ST Coll; Med Lab Tech.

HAYES, KEVIN; Parishville-Hopkinton HS; Parishville, NY; (Y); Varsity Clb; Yrbk Stf; Pres Soph Cls; Stu Cncl; Bsktbl; Socr; Canton; Bus Mgmt.

HAYES, KIMBERLY; St Edmund HS; Brooklyn, NY; (S); 4/190; Am Leg Aux Girls St; Girl Scts; Science Clb; Spanish Clb; Nwsp Rptr; Ed Nwsp Stf; Yrbk Stf; Rep Jr Cls; High Hon Roll; Hon Roll; Ntl Hnr Roll 83; St Johns U; Bio.

HAYES, LAURA; Jasper Central Schl; Cameron, NY; (Y); 1/27; Drama Clb; Pres French Clb; Varsity Clb; Chorus; Yrbk Ed-Chief; Trk; Cit Awd; High Hon Roll; NHS; Bsktbl; Elmira Key Awd 85; Pres Physcl Ftns Awd 83-84; Bucknell U; Biolgy.

HAYES, LISA; High School Of Fashion Industri; Brooklyn, NY; (Y); 62/473; Church Yth Grp; Cmnty Wkr; Pres Frsh Cls; Rep Stu Cncl; Vllybl; Hon Roll; Prfct Atten Awd; Cert Of Rcgntn Awd By Exec Intrnshp Prog 85; Morgan ST U; Bus Mgmt.

HAYES, MARC; Hermon-Dekalb HS; Richville, NY; (S); Boy Scts; Pres 4-H; Quiz Bowl; Concert Band; Nwsp Ed-Chief; Yrbk Sprt Ed; Var Bsbl; Var Capt Bsktbl; NHS; French Clb; Ping Pong Champ 83 & 85; Jrnlsm.

HAYES, MATTHEW J; Paul V Moore HS; West Monroe, NY; (Y); Drama Clb; German Clb; Radio Clb; Science Clb; Varsity Clb; School Play; Stage Crew; Nwsp Rptr; Nwsp Stf; Var Capt Trk; Regents Schlrshp 85; SUNY Potsdam; Chem Engrng.

HAYES, MICHAEL; Johnstown HS; Caroga Lake, NY; (Y); Am Leg Boys St; Boy Scts; Church Yth Grp; Intnl Clb; JV Bsktbl; Var Capt Crs Cntry; JV Ftbl; Stat Timer; Var Capt Trk; High Hon Roll; Mth 9 Algebra Awd 83; Latin Awd 84 & 85; Bio.

HAYES, RICH; Shenendehowa HS; Clifton Park, NY; (Y); Socr; Bus.

HAYES, SALLY; Mt Mercy Acad; Buffalo, NY; (Y); Art Clb; Church Yth Grp; Drama Clb; Latin Clb; Teachers Aide; Chorus; School Play; Nwsp Stf; Yrbk Stf; JV Bsktbl; Graphics.

HAYES, TAMARA K; Holland Patent Central HS; Rome, NY; (Y); 5/198; Pep Clb; Drm Mjr(t); Variety Show; Cheerleading; Pom Pon; Powder Puff Ftbl; Twrlr; High Hon Roll; NHS; NYS Regents Schlrshp 85; Stu Cncl Hnr Point Pin & Ltr 82 & 83; Hamilton Coll; Child Psych.

HAYES, TRACEY A; Canandaigua Acad; Canandaigua, NY; (Y); 29/277; FNA; Sec Political Wkr; Sec Spanish Clb; Rep Yrbk Stf; Rep Frsh Cls; Rep Soph Cls; Rep Jr Cls; Rep Sr Cls; Sec Stu Cncl; High Hon Roll; NYS Regnts Nrs Schlrshp 85-89; Niagara U; Nrs.

HAYLE, BRIAN W; Mont Pleasant HS; Schenectady, NY; (Y); 23/225; Aud/Vis; Cmnty Wkr; Key Clb; Ski Clb; Mrchg Band; Orch; Golf; French Hon Soc; High Hon Roll; NHS; Natl Fr Cont Awd 82; Catholic U Of Amer; Law.

HAYMON, KRIS; Lehman HS; Bronx, NY; (Y); 1/473; Church Yth Grp; Computer Clb; Mathletes; Science Clb; Teachers Aide; High Hon Roll; NHS; Prfct Atten Awd; Salutatorian 81; Acad Olympics 84; Comp Sci.

HAYNAL, RICHARD; Riverhead HS; Riverhead, NY; (Y); Church Yth Grp; Latin Clb; Mathletes; Math Clb; Ski Clb; Nwsp Rptr; Nwsp Stf; Crs Cntry; Tennis; Hon Roll.

HAYNER, BRIAN P; Tamarac HS; Troy, NY; (Y); 13/110; Cmnty Wkr; Varsity Clb; JV Var Bsbl; JV Var Bsktbl; JV Var Ftbl; Cit Awd; Elks Awd; Hon Roll; NHS; Church Yth Grp; H S Sportsmnshp Awd 84-85; Rochester Inst Of Tech; Comptr.

HAYNER, KELLY L; BainBRIDGE-GUILFORD HS; Bainbridge, NY; (Y); 2/78; Trs Church Yth Grp; Pres Spanish Clb; Orch; Nwsp Stf; Bsktbl; Cit Awd; High Hon Roll; NHS; Sal; Span I, II, III Awds 82-84; Susquehanna U.

HAYNER, TARA; Sharon Springs Central HS; Cherry Valley, NY; (S); Ski Clb; Spanish Clb; Varsity Clb; Chorus; Concert Band; Drm Mjr(t); School Musical; Rep Stu Cncl; JV Var Cheerleading; Var Socr; Tchng.

HAYNES, ARIEL; August Martin HS; Brooklyn, NY; (Y); 220/700; Boy Scts; CAP; Computer Clb; Exploring; ROTC; JV Var Ftbl; Socr; Cert Merit Genrl Excllnc Sci Fair 84; Cert Awd Bio Regnts 84; Cadt Mnth Cvl Air Patrl 83; St Johns U; Comp Prgrmr.

HAYNESWORTH, ELAINE; John Dewey HS; Brooklyn, NY; (Y); FHA; Teachers Aide; Im Badmtn; Im Tennis; NHS; Home Ec Spec Recogntn 84; Philadelphia Coll; Fashn Desgnr.

HAYS, DAVID; Fairport HS; Fairport, NY; (Y); Pres Church Yth Grp; Jazz Band; Orch; Sec Stu Cncl; Hon Roll; NHS; Ntl Merit SF; Intract Pres Treas; Stu Cncl Monroe Cty Sec,Pres; Assoc Teen Age Dipl 85.

HAYS, ROB; Lansing HS; Ithaca, NY; (Y); 5/80; Church Yth Grp; Spanish Clb; Stage Crew; JV Crs Cntry; Var Capt Socr; Var Trk; High Hon Roll; Ntl Merit Ltr.

HAYWOOD, DAWN; Northeastern Acad; Brooklyn, NY; (Y); Church Yth Grp; Quiz Bowl; Chorus; Church Choir; School Play; Hon Roll; Eng, Relgn, Music Awds 83; Hlth Awd 85; Ny U; Pre-Med.

HAYWOOD, KANARI; La Guardia HS; Queens Village, NY; (Y); 196/588; Service Clb; Chorus; School Musical; 3rd Pl Wnnr Delta Sigma Theta Jabberwock Catillion 83; Awd Phy Fit 82; Vocl.

HAZELL, JULIE; Victor SR HS; Victor, NY; (Y); Ski Clb; Varsity Clb; Stu Cncl; Var Coach Actv; Var Score Keeper; Var Socr; Var Capt Trk; Nrse.

HAZELTINE, VALERIE A; Pioneer Central HS; Sardinia, NY; (Y); 52/209; Aud/Vis; English Clb; Key Clb; Latin Clb; Band; Chorus; Color Guard; Concert Band; Drm Mjr(t); Flag Corp; 2nd & 3rd Yr Music Awds 84-85; D Youville Coll; Med Tech.

HAZEN, CYNTHIA; Kendall Central HS; Kendall, NY; (Y); 18/90; Trs Church Yth Grp; Pep Clb; Spanish Clb; Chorus; Color Guard; School Musical; Rep Stu Cncl; JV Var Cheerleading; JV Socr; High Hon Roll; Brockport; Jrnlsm.

HAZEN, ELLEN K; Hilton Central HS; Hilton, NY; (Y); 3/310; Math Tm; Ski Clb; Mrchg Band; Symp Band; Nwsp Stf; Var L Crs Cntry; Var L Trk; High Hon Roll; NHS; Ntl Merit SF; Fnlst Jr Yr Alumni Notre Dame 85; Comp Fld.

HAZEN, ROBERT; Rye HS; Rye, NY; (Y); Aud/Vis; Band; Concert Band; Mrchg Band; Orch; Pep Band; Stage Crew; Hon Roll.

HAZLEHURST, TANYA; Aquinas HS; Bronx, NY; (Y); 32/178; Church Yth Grp; Dance Clb; Debate Tm; Teachers Aide; Church Choir; School Play; VP Soph Cls; High Hon Roll; Hon Roll; Georgetown U; Pol Sci.

HAZLETT, RYAN; Chenango Valley JR SR HS; Binghamton, NY; (Y); 28/201; Church Yth Grp; Stage Crew; Pres Frsh Cls; Rep Soph Cls; VP Jr Cls; Rep Sr Cls; Rep Stu Cncl; JV Bsbl; Var Bowling; Wt Lftg; Broome CC; Comp Sci.

HEACOCK, KIMBERLY; G Ray Bodley HS; Fulton, NY; (Y); French Clb; Trk; Hotel Rest Mgmt.

HEAD, ANNE; Notre Dame HS; Utica, NY; (Y); Hosp Aide; Key Clb; Ski Clb; Concert Band; Stu Cncl; Var JV Cheerleading; High Hon Roll; NHS; Rep Frsh Cls; Rep Soph Cls; Gettysburg Coll; Child Psych.

HEADY, LEEANN; Dover JR SR HS; Dover Plains, NY; (S); Church Yth Grp; 4-H; Yrbk Stf; VP Jr Cls; Rep Stu Cncl; JV Fld Hcky; High Hon Roll; Hon Roll; NHS; Voice Dem Awd; Psych.

HEALD, JOHN R; Rome Free Academy HS; Rome, NY; (Y); 16/536; Intnl Clb; JV Crs Cntry; Var Trk; Hon Roll; Jr NHS; NHS; NYS Regnts Schlrshp; Colgate U Smnrs.

HEALE, JULIE; Byron-Bergen Central HS; Bergen, NY; (Y); Hosp Aide; Band; Socr; Vllybl; Hon Roll; NHS; Art Clb; Girl Scts; Teachers Aide; Chorus; Genesee CC; Hmn Serv.

HEALEY JR, PATRICK; Niagara Falls HS; Niagara Falls, NY; (Y); Computer Clb; Var Bsbl; Var Capt Bowling; Cit Awd; Hon Roll; Prfct Atten Awd; Computer Clb; Bus Adm.

HEALING, SHERRY; Johnstown HS; Gloversville, NY; (Y); Intnl Clb; Chorus; Color Guard; School Musical; Bus Mgt.

HEALY, JAMES A; Maple Grove JR-SR HS; Maple Springs, NY; (Y); 2/80; Computer Clb; Scholastic Bowl; Band; Nwsp Rptr; JV Trk; High Hon Roll; Sal; Boy Scts; Quiz Bowl; Cit Awd; Hnrs Schlstc Pgm 81-85; Boy Sct Eagle Awd 82; NY ST Rgnts Schlrshp Wnnr 85; Carnegie-Mellon U; Comp Info Sy.

HEALY, JOHN; Archbishop Molloy HS; Jackson Hts, NY; (Y); 170/450; Intnl Clb; Im Bsktbl; Im Bowling; Im Socr; DAR Awd; U Of Dallas; Law.

HEALY, MARK; Mahopac HS; Carmel, NY; (Y); 180/485; Boy Scts; Church Yth Grp; Chorus; Stage Crew; JV Crs Cntry; JV Trk; JV Var Wrstlng; Comp Sci.

HEALY, PATRICK; Seaford HS; Seaford, NY; (Y); Am Leg Boys St; Boy Scts; Concert Band; Jazz Band; Mrchg Band; School Play; High Hon Roll; NHS; Socr; Drama Clb; Ntl Sci Olympd 85; Ntl Soc Stds Olympd 85; All Cnty Band 83; Engrng Mgmt.

HEANEY, ELIZABETH; Henninger SR HS; Syracuse, NY; (Y); Crs Cntry; Mgr(s); Score Keeper; Timer; Trk; Hon Roll; Physcl Thrpy.

HEANEY, ELLEN MARIE; Grover Cleveland HS; Ridgewood, NY; (Y); 105/700; Key Clb; St Johns U.

HEANEY, MARK D; Garden City HS; Garden City, NY; (Y); 35/320; Camera Clb; Church Yth Grp; Key Clb; Office Aide; Varsity Clb; School Play; Yrbk Phtg; Lit Mag; Coach Actv; Capt Socr; Mc Coy Schlrshp 85; Colgate U; Law.

HEAPHY, JEANINE; Cardinal Spellman HS; Bronx, NY; (Y); Cmnty Wkr; Lit Mag; Im Bsktbl; Hon Roll; Ntl Merit Ltr; Spec Ed.

HEARD, PETER; Mattituck HS; Mattituck, NY; (Y); German Clb; JA; VICA; School Play; Stage Crew; Variety Show; Yrbk Stf; Frsh Cls; Stu Cncl; Socr; Crpntry.

HEARLE, KORY; Walter Panas HS; Peekskill, NY; (Y); 13/230; Ski Clb; Yrbk Stf; Off Frsh Cls; Off Soph Cls; VP Jr Cls; Off Sr Cls; Cheerleading; High Hon Roll; NHS; Pres Acad Ftns Awd 85; Cty Typng Awd 83; Stu Cncl Awd 84; Oneonta; Bus Econ.

HEARN, DAVID T; Waterloo SR HS; Waterloo, NY; (Y); Am Leg Boys St; JA; Letterman Clb; Pep Clb; Varsity Clb; Var L Bsbl; Var L Ftbl; Var L Golf; Rotary Awd; St Schlr; U Of Buffalo; Chem Engr.

HEARN, LEAH T; E Syracuse Minoa HS; Kirkville, NY; (Y); 136/338; Exploring; French Clb; Science Clb; Variety Show; Yrbk Stf; Var Bowling; Stat Ftbl; JV Socr; Im Trk; Stat Wrstlng; NY St Rgents Schlrshp 85; Sci.

HEARTY, PATRICK; Bethpage HS; Bethpage, NY; (Y); 30/290; Var L Ftbl; Var L Ice Hcky; High Hon Roll; Hon Roll; Best Defnsmn Ice Hockey 85; Lawyr.

HEARTY, TIMOTHY; Bethpage HS; Bethpage, NY; (Y); 129/290; Art Clb; Ftbl; Ice Hcky; Hon Roll; Coach Awd Sprtsmnshp Ice Hcky; Law.

HEATER, MATTHEW J; Port Jervis SR HS; Sparrowbush, NY; (Y); 3/200; Boy Scts; Math Tm; Co-Capt Scholastic Bowl; Rep Stu Cncl; Var Bowling; Var Ftbl; Var Golf; High Hon Roll; NHS; Ntl Merit Ltr; Bucknell U; Mech Engr.

HEATH, CAROLE; Oyster Bay HS; Oyster Bay, NY; (Y); AFS; Trs Sec German Clb; Science Clb; Yrbk Stf; Stu Cncl; JV Var Cheerleading; High Hon Roll; Cold Spg Harbor Currclm Study 85.

HEATH, CHRIS; Berne-Knox-Westrlo HS; Delanson, NY; (Y); VICA; JV Bsbl; Bus.

HEATH, DAVID; Ithaca HS; Ithaca, NY; (Y); Boy Scts; Church Yth Grp; Ski Clb; Church Choir; Im Bowling; Im Socr; Jr NHS; NHS; Ithaca Jrnl Carrier Yr 84; Sherman Univ Schlrshp 85; Deacons Schlrshp 85; Cornell U; Agri Eng.

HEATH, SUE; Northville Central HS; Mayfield, NY; (Y); Church Yth Grp; GAA; Yrbk Phtg; Yrbk Stf; VP Soph Cls; VP Jr Cls; Rep Stu Cncl; Var L Bsktbl; Var Mgr(s); Var Mgr(s); Best Defnsv Plyr Scr,Sftbl 85.

HEATON, DAVID; Hendrick Hudson HS; Peekskill, NY; (Y); 4/196; Cmnty Wkr; Political Wkr; Band; Yrbk Stf; Var L Bsktbl; Var L Socr; High Hon Roll; Pres NHS; Ntl Merit Ltr; Pres Acad Ftnss Awd 85; AAA Drvrs Educ Awd 85; Merit Schlrshp Recog Lttr 84; Duke U; Econ.

HEATON, ERIC; Hendrick Hudson HS; Peekskill, NY; (Y); 2/196; Band; Yrbk Stf; Var L Bsktbl; Var L Socr; Ntl Merit SF; Sal; Concert Band; Mrchg Band; Orch; Pep Band; GA Pac Schlrshp, Prsdntl Acad Ftnss Awd 85; Hghst Gr Math I, II, III 81-83; Merit Schlrshp 84; Dartmouth Coll; Econ.

HEAVENS, FAITH A; Midwood HS; Brooklyn, NY; (Y); 81/600; Boy Scts; Church Yth Grp; Cmnty Wkr; Exploring; Hosp Aide; Library Aide; Math Tm; Office Aide; Acpl Chr; Chorus; Midwood Med Sci Inst 81-85; Mt Sinai Med Ctr Scndry Educ Hlth Pgm 84-85.

HEAVEY, VICTORIA; Garden City SR HS; Garden City, NY; (Y); 57/350; Church Yth Grp; Cmnty Wkr; Office Aide; Teachers Aide; Pres Frsh Cls; Rep Soph Cls; Rep Jr Cls; Off Sr Cls; Var Tnk; JV Vllybl; Bus.

HEAVLOW, RENE; A Philip Randolph C HS; Rosedale, NY; (Y); 25/166; Church Yth Grp; Math Tm; Office Aide; Teachers Aide; Chorus; Church Choir; Madrigals; Orch; Nwsp Bus Mgr; High Hon Roll; Acad Olympcs Tm 83-84; Vassar; Elec Engrng.

HEBBARD, CAROL M; Cambridge Central HS; Eagle Bridge, NY; (Y); Sec Trs French Clb; Chorus; Yrbk Stf; Lit Mag; JV Cheerleading; High Hon Roll; Hon Roll; NHS; Regents Schlrshp 85; Ithaca Coll; Comm.

HEBERT, DAWN; West Genesee HS; Warners, NY; (Y); French Clb; Acpl Chr; Chorus; Church Choir; School Musical; School Play; Stage Crew; Im Swmmng; High Hon Roll; Hon Roll; Music Dedictn 84; Hghst Avg Grade Coll Algebra 84; Succssfl Compltn Modlng Schl 81; Engrng.

HEBERT, KRISTIN; Acad Of The Holy Names; Troy, NY; (Y); Drama Clb; Varsity Clb; Ed Yrbk Stf; Ed Lit Mag; VP Frsh Cls; Sec Sr Cls; Var JV Socr; Theol Awd 83 & 85; Lit Awd 85; Chem Awd 85; Comm.

HEBERT, RICHARD B; Schalmont HS; Duanesburg, NY; (Y); 27/188; Hon Roll; 3rd Pl Chem Comptn Cobleskill Coll 84; Regnts Schlrshp 85; ST Cert Merit Regnts Schlrshp; SUNY Albany; Comp Sci.

HEBERT, SUSAN; Akron Central Schl; Akron, NY; (Y); Pep Clb; Chorus; Swing Chorus; Var Cheerleading; Crs Cntry; Sftbl; Swmmng; Capt Vllybl; Genesee CC; Trvl.

HEBERT, TERRY; Cohoes HS; Cohoes, NY; (Y); French Clb; Var Bowling; JV Var Cheerleading; French Hon Soc; High Hon Roll; Hon Roll; Accntng.

HECHT, RICHARD S; Collegiate HS; New York, NY; (Y); 6/42; Art Clb; Exploring; Hosp Aide; Stage Crew; Nwsp Rptr; Nwsp Stf; Var Socr; Sftbl; Var Trk; Cit Awd; Regents Schlrshp Awd 85; Columbia U; Bus Law.

HECK, CARRIE A; Rocky Point JR SR HS; Rocky Point, NY; (Y); Dance Clb; French Clb; Girl Scts; Hosp Aide; Yrbk Stf; Hon Roll; NY Regents Schlrshp Nrsng 85; SUNY-STONY Brook; Pre-Med.

HECK, ROBERT E; Union-Endicott HS; Endicott, NY; (Y); 69/430; Boy Scts; French Clb; Varsity Clb; Var L Crs Cntry; Var L Trk; NY St Regenst Schlrshp 85; Catholic Yth Org Bsktbl Var 83-85; Univ Of NC; Pre-Dentistry.

HECKMAN, NANCY; Schoharie Central HS; Esperance, NY; (Y); Church Yth Grp; Drama Clb; French Clb; Key Clb; Band; Chorus; Church Choir; Pep Band; School Musical; Swing Chorus; Jrnlsm.

HECKMANN, JILL A; Lakeland SR HS; Shrub Oak, NY; (Y); 65/385; Ski Clb; Capt Bowling; JV Socr; Var Capt Vllybl; High Hon Roll; Hon Roll; NHS; SUNY Albany; Comp Sci.

HECTOR, ANESTINE E; George W Wingate HS; Brooklyn, NY; (Y); Bsktbl; Socr; Vllybl; Prfct Atten Awd; Mst Outstndng Netbal Plyr 81; Schl Scholar 81; Stoney Brook Coll; Dr.

HECTOR JR, THEODORE E; Saratoga Central Catholic HS; Schuylerville, NY; (Y); Pres Aud/Vis; Church Yth Grp; Chorus; Stage Crew; Stat Ftbl; Var Score Keeper; Var Wt Lftg; Ntl Merit Ltr; Hotel Mgt.

HEDDING, MICHELLE ANN; Edison Techinical & Occu Educ Center; Rochester, NY; (Y); 4/271; VP Exploring; Hosp Aide; VP JA; Math Tm; Model UN; Political Wkr; Sec NHS; Regents Schlrshp 84-85; Syracuse U; Physician.

HEDGES, LISA; Gowanda Central Schl; Perrysburg, NY; (Y); Church Yth Grp; 4-H; Spanish Clb; Thesps; Chorus; Rep Frsh Cls; Rep Soph Cls; Rep Jr Cls; JV Bsktbl; Var Trk; Telecmmnctns.

HEDGES, WENDY; Kings Park HS; Northport, NY; (Y); Church Yth Grp; Hon Roll; Tvl.

HEDQUIST, MARC THOMAS; Floral Park Memorial HS; Floral Pk, NY; (Y); 73/180; Chess Clb; Varsity Clb; Var Bsbl; Var Bsktbl; Var Crs Cntry; Var Ftbl; Prfct Atten Awd; Bsbl-MVP 85; Bsbl-All Conf Nassau Cnty Natl Leag 85; Stony Brook; Pre-Law.

HEDRICK, LISA; Mt Saint Joseph HS; Sloan, NY; (S); 11/60; Yrbk Stf; VP Soph Cls; JV Badmtn; Var Capt Bsktbl; Var L Sftbl; Var L Vllybl; Hon Roll; NHS; All Cath Vlybl; 1st Tm Cath In Bsktbl; Phys Ther.

HEDRICK, YVONNE; Cicero HS; Mattydale, NY; (S); 45/622; Hon Roll; NHS; Art.

HEDSTROM, SANDY; Falconer Central HS; Falconer, NY; (Y); VP Church Yth Grp; French Clb; Band; Mrchg Band; JV Cheerleading; Trk; Hon Roll.

HEE, WALTER M; Bronx H S Of Science; Flushing, NY; (Y); Computer Clb; Library Aide; Science Clb; Prfct Atten Awd; Space Shuttle Stu Invlvmnt Proj Cert Awd 83; Engrng.

HEENAN, KATHLEEN; The Mary Louis Acad; Flushing, NY; (Y); Drama Clb; Art Clb; Chorus; School Musical; School Play; NY U; Theatr.

HEETER, SHAWN A; Hamburg HS; Hamburg, NY; (Y); 34/400; Coach Actv; JV Var Socr; JV Trk; Hon Roll; NHS; Ntl Merit Ltr; Pres Schlr; Regnts Clg Schlrshp 85; UAW Schlrshp 85; U Of Buffalo; Mech Engrng.

HEFFELFINGER, SYRENA; Hornell SR HS; Hornell, NY; (Y); Band; Color Guard; Concert Band; Flag Corp; Mrchg Band; Symp Band; Hon Roll; Alfred ST Coll; Bus.

HEFFEREN, CAROLYN; Seaford HS; New York, NY; (Y); Computer Clb; Teachers Aide; Nwsp Stf; Yrbk Ed-Chief; Yrbk Stf; VP Jr Cls; Pres Sr Cls; Vllybl; High Hon Roll; Hon Roll; Herff Jones Yrbk Awd 85; Acctg.

HEFFLER, MARGARET; Richmond Hill HS; Richmond Hill, NY; (Y); Girl Scts; Teachers Aide; Variety Show; Hon Roll; NHS; Englsh Hnr Soc 85.

HEFFNER, HONORA; Buffalo Seminary HS; Hamburg, NY; (Y); 1/140; Hosp Aide; Orch; School Play; Yrbk Stf; Trs Sr Cls; NHS; Val; Cum Laude 85; Colgate U; Chem.

HEGENER, KARA; Roy C Ketcham HS; Wappingers Fall, NY; (Y); Church Yth Grp; Concert Band; Stage Crew; Yrbk Stf; Stu Cncl; Stat Ftbl; High Hon Roll; Drama Clb; Ski Clb; Band; U Of NC-CHAPEL Hill; Accntng.

HEICK, DANIEL; Bishop Grimes HS; Syracuse, NY; (Y); Ski Clb; Stage Crew; Trs Frsh Cls; Bsktbl; JV Var Ftbl; JV Golf; Wt Lftg; Hon Roll; Cert Prfcncy 85.

HEICK, PATRICK; Bishop Grimes HS; Syracuse, NY; (Y); Boy Scts; Ski Clb; Stage Crew; Variety Show; Bsktbl; JV Var Ftbl; Pre-Law.

HEID, JAMES; Mynderse Acad; Seneca Falls, NY; (S); 38/140; Am Leg Boys St; JV L Bsbl; JV Var Bsktbl; Var Capt Golf; High Hon Roll; Hon Roll; Rotary Awd; MVP Golf Team 83; NE U; Bus.

HEIDE, KEVIN; Carmel HS; Lk Carmel, NY; (Y); Exploring; Ski Clb; Boy Scts; Bsbl; Bowling; Diving; Ice Hcky; Swmmng; Hon Roll; Westchester CC; Engr.

HEIDELBERGER, SUZANNE; Garden City SR HS; Garden City, NY; (Y); 89/355; French Clb; German Clb; Intnl Clb; Pep Clb; Chorus; Color Guard; School Play; Hon Roll; Rep Soph Cls; Rep Jr Cls; Sailng Awds 83; Htl Mgmnt.

HEIDRICH, KATHLEEN; Holy Trinity HS; Hicksville, NY; (Y); Hon Roll; IFLA Awd 85; Languages.

HEIER, ELAINE; Chenango Forks HS; Chenango Forks, NY; (Y); Teachers Aide; Tennis; Hon Roll; Prfct Atten Awd; BOCES Tchr Assn Awd 84-85; Outstndng Achvt Hm Ec 83-85; Achvt Awd Engl 83-85; Broome CC; Secy.

HEIGES, ANDREW C; Lasalle Military Academy HS; East Islip, NY; (S); 15/97; Drama Clb; ROTC; School Play; Stage Crew; Yrbk Rptr; Bsbl; Var Crs Cntry; High Hon Roll; NHS; Sup Cadet J ROTC; Mgmnt.

HEIGLE, KATHLEEN; The Francciscan Academy; Syracuse, NY; (S); 2/24; Drama Clb; FBLA; Hosp Aide; NFL; Teachers Aide; Chorus; Yrbk Bus Mgr; Tennis; Trk; High Hon Roll; MONY Reg Schltc Art Awd 84; Cert Achvt Svc Cmnty 84; Astro.

HEIL, CHRISTOPHER; Bainbridge-Guilford HS; Bainbridge, NY; (Y); 11/80; Band; Orch; Var Tennis; Cit Awd; High Hon Roll; Hon Roll; Mocktrl Tm 85; Partcpnt Confcr 84; NROTC; Comp Sci.

HEILIGENSTADT, NOREEN; Northport HS; East Northport, NY; (Y); 3/651; Service Clb; Var Socr; Capt Trk; Hon Roll; NHS; Sal; Cornell U; Comp Sci.

HEILMAN, CATHY A; Immaculate Heart Central HS; Evans Mills, NY; (Y); 5/81; Cmnty Wkr; Spanish Clb; Nwsp Rptr; Yrbk Bus Mgr; Hon Roll; NHS; Prfct Atten Awd; Pres Schlr; Jefferson CC; Journ.

HEIM, LAUREN; East Meadow HS; Eastmeadow, NY; (S); FBLA; Yrbk Stf; Vllybl; Accntng.

HEIMERL, SUSAN; Williamsville East HS; Williamsville, NY; (Y); 34/300; Church Yth Grp; Drama Clb; Girl Scts; JA; Latin Clb; School Musical; High Hon Roll; Hon Roll; Hnr Carrier Awd 83; Latn Awd 85; SUNY; Biolgcl.

HEIN, CAROLYN; St Joseph By-The-Sea HS; Staten Island, NY; (Y); Aud/Vis; Cmnty Wkr; Computer Clb; Nwsp Stf; Yrbk Stf; Im Bowling; Var Tennis; High Hon Roll; Hon Roll; Grls Tnns Mst Imprvd Plyr 83; Var Tnns Coaches Awd 84-85; Bus.

HEINEMANN, MARK; Lockport SR HS; Lockport, NY; (Y); Boy Scts; Drama Clb; French Clb; Intnl Clb; Yrbk Phtg; Rep Frsh Cls; Off Stu Cncl; Cit Awd; Hon Roll; Jr NHS; Bus Admin.

HEINEMEIER, RACHEL; Dur Saviour Lutheran HS; Bronx, NY; (S); 2/22; Church Yth Grp; Church Choir; School Play; Sec Stu Cncl; Var Trk; Var Vllybl; High Hon Roll; Jr NHS; NHS; Alpine Days Qn; DECA ST Comp; Hmcmng Royalty; U Of WA; Bus Admin.

HEINEMEIER, SARAH; Bronx Science HS; Bronx, NY; (Y); Math Clb; Spanish Clb; Band; Bio.

HEINEN, MARK; Fairport HS; Fairport, NY; (Y); Ski Clb; Varsity Clb; Var L Bsbl; Im Wt Lftg; Hon Roll; NY ST Regents Schlrshp 85; Miami U; Bus Admin.

HEININGER, JON; Franklin Acad; Constable, NY; (Y); 1/252; Varsity Clb; JV Bsktbl; Var Trk; High Hon Roll; NHS; Malone Fed Tchrs Awd Hghst Avg; 1 Ltr Ea Bsktbl, Indr & Outdr Trck; Natl Hnr Socty Epsln Hnr Socty; Acctg.

HEINS, JAMES; Bishop Grimes HS; E Syracuse, NY; (Y); Boy Scts; Church Yth Grp; Ftbl; Golf; Hon Roll; Jr NHS; Schlstcs Art Awd 83; Art.

HEINTZ, ANDREW; Monsignor Farrell HS; Staten Island, NY; (Y); Aud/Vis; Church Yth Grp; Cmnty Wkr; Debate Tm; English Clb; JA; Pres Sr Cls; Trk; Hon Roll; Manresa Schlrshp 81; Mock Trial Team 85; US Merch Marine Acad; Law.

HEINTZ, JAMES; Plattsburgh HS; Plattsburgh, NY; (Y); Drama Clb; Model UN; Band; Jazz Band; Mrchg Band; Orch; Hon Roll; Acad Awd Excel Grmn 85; 1st & 2nd Pl Div Intrschlstc Progmng Cntst 85; Bio.

HEINTZ, JOB; Skaneateles HS; Skaneateles, NY; (S); Ice Hcky; Lcrss; NHS; Syracuse U; Physics.

HEINTZ, KATHRYN C; Union Springs Central HS; Cayuga, NY; (Y); 5/100; Chorus; Concert Band; Jazz Band; Swing Chorus; Sec Sr Cls; JV Socr; JV Vllybl; High Hon Roll; NHS; German Clb; Prom Court 84; Syracuse U; Mngmnt.

HEINZ, DON J; Houghton Acad; Houghton, NY; (Y); Aud/Vis; Church Yth Grp; Civic Clb; Computer Clb; Dance Clb; Library Aide; Mathletes; OEA; ROTC; Orch; Emerg Med Tech Certfctn 84; Lions Clb Hearng Imprd Rcpnt 83; Adv 1st Aid Amblnc Persnnl Fire Dpt 82-85; Rochester Inst Of Tech; Comm.

HEINZ, INGRID; Ossining HS; Ossining, NY; (Y); 25/267; Church Yth Grp; Computer Clb; Girl Scts; Off Jr Cls; Stu Cncl; High Hon Roll; Hon Roll; NHS; Pres Schlr; Outstndg Achvt Italian 83-85; Westchestr Bus Inst Outstndg Achvt Awd 84 & 85; Rgnts Schlrshp 85; PA ST U; Hotl Mgmt.

HEINZELMAN, STACY; Minisink Valley HS; Otisville, NY; (Y); Pep Clb; Ski Clb; Band; Concert Band; Mrchg Band; Pep Band; Symp Band; Yrbk Stf; High Hon Roll; NHS; Sci.

HEINZMAN, TODD; Newark SR HS; Newark, NY; (Y); 80/210; German Clb; Band; Concert Band; Mrchg Band; Variety Show; JV Var Lcrss; Hon Roll.

HEISLER, JACQUELYN M; W Seneca East SR HS; W Seneca, NY; (Y); 108/365; DECA; French Clb; JA; Pep Clb; Chorus; Drm Mjr(t); School Musical; Yrbk Stf; Mgr Stu Cncl; Var Cheerleading; Vrsty Chrldng Outstndng Awd 83-84; 1st Pl Apprl & Accsr 84-85; Cert Of Merit For Peer Cnslng 84-85; Buffalo ST Coll; Comm Dsrdrs.

HEISLER, JOHN R; Watertown HS; Watertown, NY; (Y); 4/290; Am Leg Boys St; Church Yth Grp; Intnl Clb; Nwsp Sprt Ed; VP Stu Cncl; Im Bsktbl; Im Vllybl; High Hon Roll; NHS; Pres Clsrm Yng Am 85; Engrng.

HELANDER, LORI; Cicero-North Syracuse HS; Liverpool, NY; (S); 48/711; Rep Stu Cncl; Hon Roll; NHS; Comp.

HELDMAN, MARY; Holland Patent HS; Rome, NY; (Y); Rep Jr Cls; Cheerleading; Fld Hcky; Trk; Hon Roll; Excllnt Wnnr 84; 1st Pl Partner Comb 85.

HELENBROOK, ROBERT S; Grand Island SR HS; Grand Is, NY; (Y); 13/281; Varsity Clb; Pres Soph Cls; Trs Jr Cls; Trs Sr Cls; Rep Stu Cncl; Var L Socr; NHS; Pres Schlr; St Schlr; Im Badmtn; NFL Sccr Tm 84; PTSA Ltr Acdmc Achvt & Achvt Bar 84-85; MC Sr Cls Night 85; Notre Dame U; Mech Engrng.

HELFER, ROBERT; Honeoye Central Schl; Honeoye, NY; (S); 1/65; Hosp Aide; VP JA; Symp Band; VP Jr Cls; VP Stu Cncl; Var Capt Bsktbl; Var Capt Trk; Hon Roll; VP NHS; Century III Lcl Schlrshp Wnnr 84; Bd Educ Excel Awd 82-84; Ithaca/Dreyfus Coll Rsch Pgm 84; William; Bus.

HELFNER, BONNIE; Commack South HS; Commack, NY; (S); Temple Yth Grp; Chorus; School Musical; Variety Show; Nwsp Stf; Yrbk Stf; Cit Awd; High Hon Roll; Ldrshp Day Awd 84; Med.

HELFTER, CELESTE; Parishville-Hopkinton Central HS; Potsdam, NY; (S); 2/39; 4-H; Ski Clb; Spanish Clb; Band; Var Capt Vllybl; High Hon Roll; NHS; Sal; NY ST Regnts Schlrshp Wnnr 85; Utica Coll Syracuse; Med Tech.

HELION, JOHN; Mont Pleasant HS; Schenectady, NY; (Y); Yrbk Stf; Hon Roll; 4th Seton Coll Drwng, Hnrbl Ment Art Womns Clb 85; Comm Art.

HELLDORFER, SUSAN; Our Lady Of Mercy Acad; Bethpage, NY; (Y); 2/111; Computer Clb; Hosp Aide; Trs Q&S; Chorus; Yrbk Bus Mgr; Yrbk Stf; Var Badmtn; High Hon Roll; NHS.

HELLEIS, LISA; Longwood HS; Coram, NY; (S); 4/500; Hosp Aide; Key Clb; Office Aide; Q&S; Chorus; Color Guard; Variety Show; Nwsp Stf; Lit Mag; NHS; Acad All Amer Awd 85; Middle Islnd PTA Councl Scholar For Art 82.

HELLENBACH, PEGGY; Maryvale HS; Cheektowaga, NY; (Y); 5/220; Cmnty Wkr; French Clb; German Clb; Hosp Aide; Band; Church Choir; Jazz Band; Pep Band; Maryvale U-Crest Fire Prevntn Essay 2nd Rnnr-Up 84; Bio.

HELLER, ADAM H; Rye HS; Rye, NY; (Y); Cmnty Wkr; Model UN; Hon Roll; St Schlr; Econ.

HELLER, CHRISTOPHER SCOTT; Colonie Central HS; Schenectady, NY; (Y); 18/420; Boy Scts; JA; Band; Concert Band; Orch; Crs Cntry; Trk; High Hon Roll; NHS; Ntl Merit Ltr; Natl Hnr Rll 84; NYS Regnts Schlrshp 85; ST U Of NY Albany; Comp Engr.

HELLER, DAVID; Jamesville Dewitt HS; Jamesville, NY; (Y); Model UN; Nwsp Stf; High Hon Roll; Hon Roll; Ctzn Fndtn Prjct Entrprs 85; Latin Awd 83; Explrs Prgm Data Prcsng 84-85; Brdcstng.

HELLER, JAMIE G; Harrison HS; Purchase, NY; (Y); 1/200; Cmnty Wkr; Pres Soph Cls; VP Pres Stu Cncl; Var Tennis; Pres NHS; Ntl Merit Ltr; Rotary Awd; Spanish NHS; Val; Ski Clb; Harvard Bk Awd 84; Dartmouth Coll.

HELLER, MATTHEW; Hauppauge HS; Hauppauge, NY; (Y); 4/498; Symp Band; Nwsp Stf; Var Mgr Bsbl; Var Ftbl; Var Wrstlng; NHS; Ntl Merit SF; Varsity Clb; Orch; Yrbk Stf; Boces II G/T Summr Inst 83; Princeton U Bk Awd 85; Adelphi U Smmr Acad Intl Stds 85; Duke; Polt Sci.

HELLER, TODD A; Greece Arcadia HS; Rochester, NY; (Y); 5/292; Band; Jazz Band; School Musical; Symp Band; Bsbl; Ftbl; High Hon Roll; NHS; Louis Armstrng Jazz Awd 85; Admssn Distnctn AZ ST 85; Pres Acad Ftns Awd 85; AZ ST; Accntnt.

HELLER, VALERIE A; Pittsford Sutherland HS; Pittsford, NY; (S); 52/234; Church Yth Grp; DECA; Drama Clb; Nwsp Bus Mgr; Hon Roll; Ski Clb; Variety Show; Nwsp Stf; Yrbk Stf; Powder Puff Ftbl; Var Awds DECA ST Comps 84-85; James W Burdett Sr Awd 85; PTSA Mrktng Awd 84; MI ST U; Hotl Mgmt.

HELLERMAN, MARY; Leroy Central HS; Leroy, NY; (Y); AFS; French Clb; Spanish Clb; Teachers Aide; Varsity Clb; Drm Mjr(t); Mrchg Band; Pres Frsh Cls; Pres Soph Cls; Stu Cncl; Nrsg.

HELLERT, TODD; Medina HS; Medina, NY; (Y); 27/160; Church Yth Grp; Computer Clb; 4-H; Im Ftbl; Var L Socr; Cit Awd; 4-H Awd; High Hon Roll; Hon Roll; Exploring; AYSO Yth Sccr Orgnztn Referee 84-85; Engrng.

HELMER, ROBERT; Newfield HS; Centereach, NY; (S); 6/568; Pres Varsity Clb; Rep Stu Cncl; Var Capt Bsktbl; Var Socr; Var Trk; Jr NHS; NHS; All-League Bsktbl 84 & 85; All-League Soccer 84; Stu-Athl Of Mnth-Preview Mag 85; Mech Engrng.

HELMKE JR, WILLIAM G; Nanvet SR HS; Spring Valley, NY; (Y); Math Tm; Varsity Clb; Var Capt Crs Cntry; Var Trk; Hon Roll; Mu Alp Tht; NHS; Mech Engrng.

HELMS, LINDA; Baldwin SR HS; Baldwin, NY; (Y); 45/502; Church Yth Grp; Var Sec Fld Hcky; JV Socr; Var L Trk; High Hon Roll; Hon Roll; U Of VT; Phy Therpy.

HELMUTH, BRIAN S; Elmira Southside HS; Pine City, NY; (Y); 14/380; Boy Scts; Ski Clb; Chorus; Jazz Band; Symp Band; Yrbk Phtg; Var Tennis; Var Trk; VP NHS; Computer Clb; BSA Brnz Palm 84; Cornell U; Marn Bio.

HELTMAN, KRISTIN; East Aurora HS; East Aurora, NY; (S); 10/182; Key Clb; Red Cross Aide; School Musical; Rep Frsh Cls; Rep Soph Cls; Sec Jr Cls; Pres Sr Cls; Rep Stu Cncl; Swmmng; Hon Roll; Done Most Of East Aurora 84-85; ST Mbr Antl Piano Plyng Audtns 82; Engr.

HELVOIGT, HEIDI; Sherburne-Earlville Central Schl; Earlville, NY; (S); 9/138; Drama Clb; Pres VP 4-H; Band; Chorus; Jazz Band; Mrchg Band; School Musical; Cit Awd; 4-H Awd; NHS; Pol Sci.

HEMMER, KENNETH A; Susan E Wagner HS; Staten Island, NY; (Y); 72/497; L Var Bsbl; L JV Bsktbl; L Var Ftbl; Hon Roll; St Schlr; Lehigh U; Ec.

HEMMER, VINCENT; Fayetteville Manlius HS; Manlius, NY; (Y); JCL; Pres Model UN; NFL; Political Wkr; Pres Speech Tm; Nwsp Ed-Chief; Stu Cncl; NHS; 2nd Pl NYS Extmprns Spkng 85; Orondaga Cnty Comm Serv Awd 83; Engl & Scl Stds Awds 83-85; Polt Sci.

HEMMERICK, CHRISTINE; St John The Baptist DHS; E Islip, NY; (Y); 90/551; Church Yth Grp; Cmnty Wkr; Hosp Aide; Teachers Aide; Chorus; Drm & Bgl; Hon Roll; Fairleigh Dickinson U; Accntng.

HEMPLING, JOANN; Mount Mercy Acad; Buffalo, NY; (Y); 20/180; Sec Spanish Clb; Im Vllybl; Hon Roll; Jr NHS.

HEMPSON, SCOTT; Deer Park HS; Deer Park, NY; (Y); 113/442; Boy Scts; Band; Jazz Band; Mrchg Band; Stage Crew; Variety Show; JV Lcrss; Var Socr; High Hon Roll; Biochemst.

HEMSING, ROBERT; Hendrick Hudson HS; Montrose, NY; (Y); Church Yth Grp; French Clb; Swmmng; Tennis; High Hon Roll; Hon Roll; Jr NHS; NHS; Bus Admin.

HEMSWORTH, AUDRA; Notre Dame Acad; Staten Island, NY; (Y); Church Yth Grp; Drama Clb; Hosp Aide; Tennis.

HENCHEY, JOSEPH P; Msgr Farrell HS; Staten Island, NY; (Y); 10/295; Yrbk Stf; VP Frsh Cls; VP Soph Cls; Hon Roll; Ntl Merit Ltr; NYS Regnts Schlrshp 85; PACE U; Bio.

HENCHY, DEIDRE; Washingtonville HS; Monroe, NY; (Y); Cmnty Wkr; Political Wkr; Band; Jazz Band; Symp Band; Yrbk Stf; Rep Stu Cncl; Stat Ftbl; Var Capt Tennis; Capt Var Vllybl; NY ST Ntl Msc Clb Gld Cup Awd For Piano 84; All Cnty Bnd Clarinet 83; Pltcl Sci.

HENCI, DARDANE; Long Island City HS; Astoria Li, NY; (Y); 115/549; Boys Clb Am; Computer Clb; Office Aide; Teachers Aide; Chorus; Cit Awd; Hnrbl Mntn Outstndg Ctznshp 85; NY U; Phrmclgy.

HENDEE, CHRISTOPHER; Medina HS; Medina, NY; (Y); Band; Concert Band; Mrchg Band; Var Bsbl; Var Socr; Var Capt Swmmng; Hon Roll; MVP Awd-Swmmg, Stu Of Mnth-Athl 85; Awd Elecrncs, Stu Of Mnth-Boeces 85; All Leag-1st Pl Bckstrk 85; Elec.

HENDERSON, DEBRA; Geneva HS; Geneva, NY; (S); 16/170; VP Church Yth Grp; Ski Clb; Varsity Clb; School Play; Rep Stu Cncl; JV Var Sftbl; JV Tennis; High Hon Roll; Hon Roll; NHS.

HENDERSON, DONALD; Johnstown HS; Johnstown, NY; (Y); 25/220; Exploring; Ski Clb; Variety Show; JV Ftbl; JV Trk; Hon Roll; Prince Prm; U Of Miami; Accntnt.

HENDERSON, JAMIE; Livonia Central Schl; Conesus, NY; (Y); 24/155; Church Yth Grp; Spanish Clb; Band; Concert Band; Mrchg Band; Sec Frsh Cls; Sec Soph Cls; Var L Bsktbl; Var L Socr; JV Vllybl; Cortland; Phy Ed Instrc.

HENDERSON, LEE ROGER; Henninger HS; Syracuse, NY; (Y); Exploring; Spanish Clb; Band; Concert Band; Mrchg Band; Pep Band; Variety Show; Nwsp Rptr; High Hon Roll; Ntl Merit Ltr.

HENDERSON, MARILYN; Mexico & Central Acad; Parish, NY; (Y); Art Clb; German Clb; Hon Roll; Delta Epsilon Phi Outstndng Germn Stu Awd 83; Photogrphr.

HENDERSON, MICHAEL; Palmyra Macedon HS; Macedon, NY; (Y); Pres Jr Cls; Var Capt Socr; Im Wt Lftg; Var Capt Wrstlng; Assocd Schls Inc; Trvl Agnt.

HENDERSON, REGGIE; Cardinal Hayes HS; New York, NY; (Y); 17/285; Boy Scts; JV Mgr(s); JV Score Keeper; Hon Roll; U Bridgeport; Bus.

HENDERSON, SUE; Tully Central Schl; Tully, NY; (Y); Church Yth Grp; Drama Clb; French Clb; Hosp Aide; Library Aide; Chorus; Church Choir; School Musical; Hon Roll; NHS; Area All ST Chorus 83; All County Chorus 82; Mth.

HENDRICK, VIEONICA L; Red Creek JR SR HS; Sterling, NY; (Y); 10/72; French Clb; Office Aide; Band; Chorus; Stage Crew; Yrbk Stf; JV Var Score Keeper; JV Socr; Hon Roll; Paul Smiths Coll; Trvl/Trsm.

HENDRICKS, DARIAN CHRISTOPHER; Cardinal Spellman HS; Bronx, NY; (S); 8/568; Debate Tm; Pres French Clb; NFL; School Play; Rep Frsh Cls; Rep Soph Cls; Gov Hon Prg Awd; High Hon Roll; Jr NHS; NHS; Excel Frnch 81-84; Columbia; Engr Mgmt.

HENDRICKS, JENNIFER; Hudson HS; Hudson, NY; (Y); AFS; Pres VP Church Yth Grp; Model UN; Chorus; Var L Socr; Var L Trk; High Hon Roll; NHS; Acctng.

HENDRICKS, SIMONE CLAIR; St Catharine Acad; Bronx, NY; (Y); 87/202; Church Yth Grp; Sec Chorus; School Musical; School Play; Mgr Stage Crew; Rep Jr Cls; Rep Stu Cncl; Prfct Atten Awd; Drama Clb; Girl Scts; Outstndng Prfrmnce Drama 83, Music & Drama 84 & 85; Pre-Med.

HENDRICKSON, LINDA; Plainedge HS; Massapogua, NY; (S); 131/325; Pres VP DECA; Library Aide; Chorus; School Play; Yrbk Phtg; DECA 3rd Pl ST, Natls 85, 1st Pl Cnty 84; Excell Mrktng Awd 85; Mt St Mary Coll; Comm.

HENDRIX, DIANE L; Ilion Central HS; Ilion, NY; (Y); 16/118; Model UN; Spanish Clb; Varsity Clb; Orch; Yrbk Stf; Vllybl; High Hon Roll; Jr NHS; NHS; Regnts Schlrshp 85; Natl Hnr Socty Schlrshp; Herkimer County CC; Bio.

HENDRIX, ELIZABETH; Gowanda Central Schl; Gowanda, NY; (Y); 1/150; AFS; Pres Church Yth Grp; Concert Band; School Musical; Yrbk Phtg; Rep Stu Cncl; Stat Wrstlng; High Hon Roll; NHS; Cmnty Wkr; Rensselaer Mth & Sci Medl 85; Renselaer Polytech Inst; Engrng.

HENESEY, MAURA M; G W Fowler HS; Syracuse, NY; (Y); 16/200; Pres Church Yth Grp; Nwsp Rptr; VP Jr Cls; VP Sr Cls; Stu Cncl; Hon Roll; Medals Trophies Comptv Irish Step Dancing 84; St John Fisher Coll; Pol Sci.

HENGELSBERG, THOMAS; Perry Central HS; Perry, NY; (Y); AFS; Am Leg Boys St; Art Clb; Aud/Vis; Ski Clb; Stage Crew; Var JV Socr; JV Tennis; High Hon Roll; Hon Roll; B Arch.

HENKE, MICHAEL JOHN; Kenmore West HS; Buffalo, NY; (Y); Boy Scts; SUNY At Buffalo; Elec Engnr.

HENKIND, HILARY M; Scarsdale HS; Scarsdale, NY; (Y); Sec Exploring; French Clb; Pep Clb; Varsity Clb; Orch; School Play; Var Crs Cntry; JV Sftbl; JV Tennis; Var Trk; Regents Schlrshp 85; Unin Coll; Bio.

HENN, KATHY A; Sachem HS; Holbrook, NY; (Y); 318/1500; Var GAA; Chorus; Var Capt Bsktbl; Im Stat Sftbl; JV Trk; JV Vllybl; All Leag Bsktbl 85; NY Cls A Tourn Tm 85.

HENNEBERG, STACY; Attica Central HS; Attica, NY; (Y); Church Yth Grp; Nwsp Rptr; Yrbk Stf; 50 Dlr Awd-Jr Cls Advsrs 85; Geneseo SUNY; Dent.

HENNEDY, DEAN; Susan E Wagner HS; Staten Island, NY; (Y); French Clb; ROTC; Science Clb; Chorus; School Play; Ftbl; Wt Lftg; Hon Roll; Prfct Atten Awd; Astrnmy.

HENNEMAN, TAMARA; Tioga Central HS; Owego, NY; (Y); Ski Clb; Teachers Aide; Varsity Clb; Band; Mrchg Band; Variety Show; Yrbk Stf; Frsh Cls; Sftbl; Var Capt Vllybl; SUNY Fredonia; Bus Adm.

HENNESSY, ELISABETH; Walt Whitman HS; Melville, NY; (Y); 52/550; Church Yth Grp; Concert Band; School Musical; Var Cheerleading; Socr; Hon Roll; Spanish NHS; Girls Ldrs Clb 84-85; Capt Sprts Night Chrldr 85; Boston Coll; Lib Arts.

HENNESSY, PATRICK; Arch Bishop Molloy HS; Richmond Hill, NY; (Y); Lit Mag; Im Bsktbl; Im Ftbl; Im Sftbl; Regents Schlrshp 85; Natl Hispanic Schlr Awd 85; Champ In Ftbl 84; Queens Coll; Lbrl Arts.

HENNIGAN, MAGGIE; Fayetteville Manlius HS; Manlius, NY; (Y); Teachers Aide; Coach Actv; Var Capt Swmmng; JV Var Vllybl; Hon Roll; MVP Swmg 84; Vllybl 1st Tm All Cnty All Str 85; Spec Ed.

HENNIGAN, SHEILA; Liverpool HS; Liverpool, NY; (S); #58 In Class; Church Yth Grp; Drama Clb; Ski Clb; Concert Band; School Play; Stage Crew; Stu Cncl; JV Sftbl; Hon Roll; Jr NHS; Mech Engrng.

HENNING, CHRISTINE; Manhasset HS; Manhasset, NY; (Y); VP Church Yth Grp; Trs GAA; Concert Band; School Musical; Yrbk Bus Mgr; Var Fld Hcky; Var Trk; NHS; Mrchg Band; Orch; Smmr Stdy Awd 85; LI Math Fair-Brnz Mdl 85.

HENNING, ROBERT A; Lewiston Porter HS; Lewiston, NY; (Y); 79/279; Ski Clb; Golf; Regnts Schlrshp 85; Cobleskill Coll; Hortcltr.

HENNING, TAMMY; Honeoye Central HS; Honeoye, NY; (Y); 11/63; Drama Clb; Ski Clb; School Musical; Stu Cncl; Mgr(s); Hon Roll; Law.

HENNINGER, MARY; Royalton-Hartland HS; Gasport, NY; (Y); 5/140; VP Varsity Clb; Chorus; Church Choir; Stu Cncl; Var Capt Bsktbl; Var Capt Fld Hcky; Var Capt Sftbl; Hon Roll; NHS; Physcl Therpy.

HENRICE, JAMES; Cardinal Hayes HS; Bronx, NY; (Y); 70/264; Chess Clb; Acpl Chr; Chorus; Engrng.

HENRICKS, ELISE; Vestal HS; Vestal, NY; (Y); Church Yth Grp; French Clb; Hosp Aide; Service Clb; Concert Band; Mrchg Band; Symp Band; Stat Bsktbl; High Hon Roll; VP NHS; Natl Yth Ldrshp Awd 85; Chem.

HENRICKSON, LINDA; Cicero-North Syracuse HS; N Syracuse, NY; (S); 97/711; Girl Scts; Acctng.

HENRIQUEZ, WILLS S; St Anthonys HS; Massapequa, NY; (Y); Chess Clb; Drama Clb; Varsity Clb; School Play; Lit Mag; Sec Jr Cls; Stu Cncl; Crs Cntry; Socr; Trk; Lousi & Irene Simon Schlrshp Fund 85; NY U Schlrshp 85; Dun Scotus 85; NY U; Pre-Med.

HENRY, CHRISTOPHER P; Wallkill SR HS; Wallkill, NY; (Y); Am Leg Boys St; Boy Scts; Church Yth Grp; Drama Clb; School Play; Rep Frsh Cls; JV Socr; Var Wrstlng; Hon Roll; Boy Scts Eagle Awd; Rgnts Schlrshp; Amer Lgn Ntl HS Oritcl Cntst; Suny; Bus.

HENRY, DAWN; John Jay HS; Fishkill, NY; (Y); 50/550; VP Church Yth Grp; Drama Clb; Band; Church Choir; School Musical; School Play; Stage Crew; Yrbk Stf; High Hon Roll; Jr NHS; NHS; Intl Bus.

HENRY, HOWARD; Cardinal Spellman HS; Bronx, NY; (Y); Bsktbl; Var Trk; Hon Roll.

HENRY, KELLY; Academy Of The Holy Names; Schenectady, NY; (Y); JV Socr; Var Trk; Spnsh I, II, & III Outstndng Achvt 82-85.

HENRY, KEVIN A; Westbury SR HS; E Norwich, NY; (Y); 15/259; Cmnty Wkr; FBLA; VP Varsity Clb; Band; Trs Soph Cls; Rep Stu Cncl; Var Bsbl; Var Swmmng; NHS; Ntl Merit Schol; Cornell; Bus.

HENRY, MARION; De Witt Clinton HS; Bronx, NY; (Y); Office Aide; Concert Band; Nwsp Rptr; Prfct Atten Awd; Math 85; Accntng.

HENRY, MICHAEL; John H Glenn HS; E Northport, NY; (Y); Bsbl; Capt Ftbl; High Hon Roll; Hon Roll; Jr NHS; Pres NHS; Sec Spanish NHS.

HENRY, MICHAEL; Mt Vernon HS; Mount Vernon, NY; (Y); Boys Clb Am; Boy Scts; Chess Clb; Computer Clb; Hst FBLA; Intnl Clb; Office Aide; Crs Cntry; Wt Lftg; Hon Roll; Miami-Dade Med Ctr; Doctor.

HENRY, MICHAEL; Olean HS; Olean, NY; (Y); 19/210; Trs AFS; Band; Concert Band; Jazz Band; Mrchg Band; Trs Orch; School Musical; Hon Roll; NHS; French Clb; 20 Point Ltr Awd 85; Law.

HENS, SAMANTHA; Mc Kinley HS; Buffalo, NY; (Y); Yrbk Phtg; Yrbk Stf; Hon Roll; ST U-New York; Engrng.

HENSEL, KENNETH; Salamanca Central HS; Salamanca, NY; (S); Spanish NHS; Comp Sci.

HENSEL, SUE; Alexander Central HS; Batavia, NY; (Y); Drama Clb; 4-H; FTA; JV Tennis; 4-H Holstein & All Breed Grnd Champ 80 & 83-84; 4-H Bst Uddr & Dairy Prodctn Awd 84; OCC; Sprts Adm.

HENSEN, CHERYL; Liverpool HS; Liverpool, NY; (S); 158/792; Exploring; Var Capt Bsktbl; Var Capt Socr; Var Sftbl; Hon Roll; 1st Tm All Cnty Sccr 82-84; Sccr MVP 84; Empire ST Gm Sccr 84; Hnrb Mntn Bsktbl & Sftbl MVP Sftbl 83; Albany; Pre-Law.

HENSINGER, ROBIN ANNE; Half Hollow Hills East HS; Wheatley Hts, NY; (Y); Pres Sec Service Clb; Chorus; Orch; School Musical; High Hon Roll; Jr NHS; NHS; Church Yth Grp; German Clb; Hosp Aide; Natl Germ Hnr Soc; A NYSSMA; Georgetown; Law.

HENSON, JEAN MARIE; St Marys Girls HS; E Williston, NY; (Y); Teachers Aide; School Play; Stage Crew; Im Coach Actv; Im Sftbl.

HENTSCHEL, KAREN; Cardinal Spellman HS; Bronx, NY; (Y); German Clb; Hosp Aide; Pep Clb; Rep Soph Cls; Rep Jr Cls; Rep Sr Cls; Hon Roll; Ntl Merit Ltr; 1st Hnrs 82-84; 2nd Hnrs 84-85; Ntl Merit 85; Physcl Therpy.

HENZEL JR, ROBERT E; West Canada Valley Central HS; Newport, NY; (S); Aud/Vis; Cmnty Wkr; Debate Tm; Drama Clb; Yrbk Stf; Var L Diving; Bausch & Lomb Sci Awd; NHS; Chess Clb; French Clb; 1st Pl Rgnl Comptn Olympics Of The Mnd 84; Cert De Merite Ntl Frnch Exam 84; 1st Pl Mdl UN Debate 84; Rensselaer Polytech; Nuc Engr.

HEPBURN, SARAH; School Of The Holy Child; Bronx, NY; (Y); Church Yth Grp; French Clb; Sec Key Clb; Teachers Aide; Chorus; School Play; Yrbk Stf; Hon Roll; Hghst Hnrs Engl 83; Latin Hnrs 83.

HEPPEL, TAMMY; Mc Mahon HS; Buffalo, NY; (Y); Dance Clb; Yrbk Stf; Hon Roll; Prfct Atten Awd; Bus.

HERBERT, CANDACE; Turner/Carroll HS; Buffalo, NY; (Y); 15/105; Trs Soph Cls; Trs Sr Cls; Var Co-Capt Cheerleading; Hon Roll; NHS; Prfct Atten Awd; Cert Of Hnr Math 85; Serv Awd Recrtmnt 85; Canisius Clg; Bus.

HERBERT, CARLA; Fairport HS; Fairport, NY; (Y); Intnl Clb; Mrchg Band; Symp Band; Hon Roll; Prfct Atten Awd; Accntng.

HERBERT, JACQUELINE; Lindenhurst SR HS; Lindenhurst, NY; (Y); Spanish Clb; Nwsp Stf; Yrbk Stf; Var Trk; Hon Roll; NHS.

HERBERT, SOPHIA; St Francis Prep; Cambria Hts, NY; (S); 26/693; Church Yth Grp; Dance Clb; Library Aide; High Hon Roll; Hon Roll; NHS; Ntl Merit Ltr; Karate Trophies 83-84; NY U; Law.

HERBST, MIKE; Maryvale HS; Cheektowaga, NY; (Y); Orch; School Musical; JV Vllybl; Hon Roll; NHS; Prfct Atten Awd; Med.

HERCZ, ZAMIRA; Solomon Schechter HS; Brooklyn, NY; (Y); 6/48; Chess Clb; Hosp Aide; Office Aide; Science Clb; Teachers Aide; Chorus; School Musical; School Play; Variety Show; Nwsp Rptr; Parade Wrk Rlly Soc 82-85; Brooklyn Coll; Med.

HERD, VICTORIA L; Miller Place HS; Miller Pl, NY; (Y); 81/191; Cmnty Wkr; Drama Clb; FBLA; Office Aide; School Musical; School Play; Rotry Intl Exch Stu Finland 83-84; Dncr Commty Prfrmncs 80-85; U Of OR; Dnce Tchr.

HEREDIA, TINA; Franklin Acad; Burke, NY; (Y); Church Yth Grp; FBLA; Hon Roll; Epsilon Hnr Soc 83; Sec.

HERGER, ANNA; Carthage Central HS; Carthage, NY; (Y); Church Yth Grp; Drama Clb; Key Clb; Chorus; Church Choir; School Musical; School Play; Swing Chorus; High Hon Roll; NHS; CPR Instrctr 85; All Conf Mixed Chorus 85; All Eastern Mixed Chorus 85; Psych.

HERING, PAULA E; Mohonasen SR HS; Schenectady, NY; (Y); 3/215; Trs Church Yth Grp; Sec 4-H; Trs Key Clb; Orch; Nwsp Stf; Yrbk Ed-Chief; High Hon Roll; NHS; Pres Schlr; Nwsp Rptr; E Corbitt Schlrshp 85; NY ST Regnts Schlrshp 85; A H Erbacher Schlrshp 85; E B Morgan Schlstc Awd 85; Muhlenberg Coll; Engl.

HERINGTON, GARY A; Monroe HS; Rochester, NY; (Y); 3/190; Math Tm; Var Bsbl; Var Capt Ftbl; Var Capt Wrstlng; High Hon Roll; NHS; Pres Schlr; St Schlr; S Stiller Ath Acad Schlrshp Awd, All Cty Bsbl, Hawley-Sheehan -Befman Schlrshp Awd 85; Rochester Inst Tech; Comp Math.

HERINGTON, LORIE; Canisteo Central HS; Wilmington, NC; (Y); 3/80; Debate Tm; Quiz Bowl; Ski Clb; Spanish Clb; Varsity Clb; Band; Concert Band; Mrchg Band; Symp Band; Bsktbl; Hnr Soc 83-85; Acad Allstars 85; Gov Intrnshp 85; Furman U; Pre-Law.

HERKERT, CAROL ANN; Cardinal O Hara HS; Kenmore, NY; (Y); French Clb; Nwsp Rptr; Nwsp Stf; JV Badmtn; Stat Bsktbl; Stat Sftbl; Hon Roll; NHS; NHS Scholar 83; Phrmcy.

HERKEY, LEANNE; Alden Central HS; Alden, NY; (Y); GAA; VP Bsktbl; VP Capt Crs Cntry; VP Capt Trk; JV Vllybl; Hon Roll; Hosp Aide; Letterman Clb; Varsity Clb; Empire ST Games Trk 85; Phys Ed.

HERL, LYNNE; Lockport SR HS; Lockport, NY; (Y); Dance Clb; Drama Clb; 4-H; Color Guard; Mrchg Band; Symp Band; Off Jr Cls; Sftbl; NHS; Concert Band; Gold Music Awd 83; Psych.

HERLIHY, MARGARET; Centereach HS; Centereach, NY; (Y); 113/475; Pres Drama Clb; Sec Thesps; Acpl Chr; Chorus; Church Choir; Madrigals; School Musical; Stage Crew; Swing Chorus; Variety Show; James Truscello Music Awd 85; U Of Hartford; Music Ed.

HERLIHY, MAUREEN B; Sayville HS; Bayport, NY; (Y); 38/350; Key Clb; Rep Frsh Cls; Rep Soph Cls; Trs Jr Cls; Pres Sr Cls; Var JV Fld Hcky; High Hon Roll; Hon Roll; NHS; Albany Suny; Math.

HERMAN, AUDREY; Albion HS; Albion, NY; (S); 15/175; English Clb; Office Aide; Spanish Clb; Teachers Aide; School Musical; School Play; Stage Crew; Lit Mag; Rep Frsh Cls; Rep Soph Cls; Niagara U; Spanish.

HERMAN, BETSY; Perry Central HS; Perry, NY; (Y); #23 In Class; French Clb; Band; Mrchg Band; Score Keeper; Hon Roll; Bryant & Stratton Bus; Secy Sci.

HERMAN, JOHN; Gowanda Central HS; Perrysburg, NY; (Y); Am Leg Boys St; Boy Scts; Spanish Clb; Frsh Cls; Var Bsktbl; Var Capt Ftbl; Var Trk; High Hon Roll; NHS; Prfct Atten Awd; Engrng.

HERMAN, PAULA; Mount Mercy Acad; Buffalo, NY; (Y); Church Yth Grp; Sec Computer Clb; French Clb; JA; Hon Roll; Hnrbl Ment U Onf NY Lang Fair 85; 2nd Pl Intllst Alg II 84.

HERMAN, TERRI A; G W Hewlett HS; Hewlett, NY; (Y); 38/278; Var L Gym; Hon Roll; Crmnl Jstc Awd; Colmnst Locl Papr; PTA Schlrshp; Emory U; Atty.

HERMANN, KIMBERLY; East Meadow HS; E Meadow, NY; (Y); 88/414; FBLA; Girl Scts; Key Clb; Band; Chorus; Concert Band; Mrchg Band; Trs Soph Cls; Var JV Lcrss; Pom Pon; Houston U; Hotel Adm.

HERNANDEZ, CARLA; General Douglas Mac Arthur HS; Levittown, NY; (Y); 96/319; 4-H; GAA; Varsity Clb; Chorus; Nwsp Stf; Var Badmtn; Var Tennis; 4-H Awd; Hon Roll; Jr NHS; Amer Lgn Ctznshp Awd; Nassau CC; Scndry Educ.

HERNANDEZ, DANIEL; Christopher Columbus HS; Bronx, NY; (Y); 76/792; Boy Scts; Exploring; Office Aide; Teachers Aide; Chorus; Pres Frsh Cls; Pres Soph Cls; VP Jr Cls; Hon Roll; Prfct Atten Awd; Accntnt.

HERNANDEZ, DANIEL; North Rockland HS; West Haverstraw, NY; (Y); 151/560; Church Yth Grp; Golf; Gym; Adv Plcmnt Calculus 84-85; SUNY-BUFFALO; Mech Engr.

HERNANDEZ, DENISE; St Catharine Acad; Bronx, NY; (Y); Hon Roll; Inter Am U; Soc Wrk.

HERNANDEZ, HIMILCE; Norman Thomas HS; Bronx, NY; (S); 61/671; FBLA; Math Tm; Trs Sr Cls; Cit Awd; Hon Roll; NY U; Accntnt.

HERNANDEZ, JANET; John Dewey HS; Brooklyn, NY; (Y); Bus.

HERNANDEZ, LUCY; John Dewey HS; Brooklyn, NY; (Y); Church Yth Grp; Dance Clb; Drama Clb; Church Choir; Rep Soph Cls; Rep Jr Cls; Bsbl; Score Keeper; Sftbl; Hon Roll; Phys Thrpy.

HERNANDEZ, NANCY; Cardinal Spellman HS; Bronx, NY; (Y); Camera Clb; Cmnty Wkr; Latin Clb; Spanish Clb; Chorus; Variety Show; Hon Roll; Brnz Medl Recog Latn Amer Clb 85; Medl Ld Sngr Chrs 85; NY U; Psych.

HERNANDEZ, VANESSA; Washington Irving HS; Brooklyn, NY; (Y); Girl Scts; Service Clb; Spanish Clb; Teachers Aide; Varsity Clb; Chorus; Concert Band; JV Gym; Pom Pon; Hon Roll; John Jay Coll; Crmnl Law.

HERNDON, RODNEY; Mount Vernon HS; Mount Vernon, NY; (Y); Boys Clb Am; Computer Clb; Key Clb; Band; Concert Band; Mrchg Band; Var Capt Crs Cntry; Hon Roll; NHS; Boy Of Yr 85; Sir Thomas J Diptem Sprtsmnshp Awd 85; Comp Sci.

HERNE, JEFF J; Franklin Academy HS; Constable, NY; (Y); Debate Tm; NFL; Ski Clb; Speech Tm; Rep Frsh Cls; Rep Stu Cncl; Plattsboro ST U; Comptr Pgmmng.

HEROLD, ETTA; Onondaga HS; Nedrow, NY; (Y); 9/90; Church Yth Grp; German Clb; Band; Jazz Band; Yrbk Phtg; Rep Stu Cncl; JV Tennis; Var Vllybl; Hon Roll; Geneseo; CPA.

HERON, SUSAN; Far Rockaway HS; Far Rockaway, NY; (Y); Computer Clb; Key Clb; Office Aide; Teachers Aide; Y-Teens; Cheerleading; Hon Roll; NHS; Bus.

HEROTH, TONIA; Fort Plain HS; Ft Plain, NY; (Y); Computer Clb; Office Aide; Varsity Clb; Yrbk Rptr; Yrbk Stf; Stu Cncl; Bsktbl; Sftbl; Hon Roll; Peer Ldr Ship Grp 84-85; Bryant & Stratton; Fshn Merch.

HEROUX JR, BERNARD B; E J Wilson HS; Rochester, NY; (Y); Church Yth Grp; Ski Clb; JV Bsktbl; Var Crs Cntry; Hon Roll; Schlstc Achvt Soc; Outstndng Achvt Awd Woodwrkng; Prsdntl Physcl Ftns Awd; Messiah Coll; Comp Sci.

HEROUX, JOE; Cohoes HS; Cohoes, NY; (Y); French Clb; JV Bsbl; Hon Roll; Bus.

HEROUX, KIMBERLY; Lansingburgh HS; Troy, NY; (Y); French Clb; JV Bsktbl; JV Var Cheerleading; JV Var Score Keeper; High Hon Roll; Hon Roll; Sec Sci.

HERR, CINDY; Long Island Lutheran HS; E Northport, NY; (S); Pres German Clb; Trs Mathletes; Quiz Bowl; Spanish Clb; School Musical; Stat Bsktbl; Var Vllybl; High Hon Roll; NHS; NYSMA Awd For Piano & Voice 83; Engrng.

HERR, COLLEEN; Frontier Crntral HS; Blasdell, NY; (Y); Church Yth Grp; VP FBLA; Science Clb; VP VICA; Chorus; Color Guard; Nwsp Stf; Yrbk Stf; Off Jr Cls; Off Sr Cls; Legl Secy.

HERR, ROBERT M; Frontier Central HS; Blasdell, NY; (Y); Aud/Vis; German Clb; Science Clb; Yrbk Stf; Bsktbl; Sftbl; JV Var Trk; Vllybl; Hon Roll; NHS; 3 Yr Pin Yrbk Stf 80-83; 3 Yr Pin Audio-Visual 80-83; Var & JV Ltrs Trck 82-84; Erie CC; Auto Mech.

HERRADOR, HELEN; Academy Of St Joseph; Bay Shore, NY; (Y); Drama Clb; Hosp Aide; Library Aide; Stage Crew; Yrbk Stf; NHS; Acad Achvt Awd 2nd 84; Christian Courtesy Mdl 84; Fnlst Commissioners Stu Adv Comm 84; Med.

HERRERA JR, MIGUEL A; Brooklyn Technical HS; Brooklyn, NY; (Y); 5/1139; Cmnty Wkr; Hosp Aide; Office Aide; Political Wkr; Teachers Aide; JV Bsbl; Im Sftbl; Im Vllybl; French Hon Soc; Gov Hon Prg Awd; Assn Electrcl Contrctrs Scholar 85; NYC Assn Tchrs Eng Cert Outstndg Eng Achvt 85; Soc Std Gld Mdl 85; Harvard U; Engrng.

HERRICK, CHRIS; Rome Free Acad; Rome, NY; (Y); 234/530; Church Yth Grp; Hon Roll; Jr NHS; Mohawk Valley CC; Acctg.

HERRICK, DIANE; Randolph Central Schl; Little Valley, NY; (Y); 3/74; Pres Sec 4-H; Speech Tm; Spanish Clb; Sec Band; Yrbk Stf; High Hon Roll; NHS; Concert Band; Mrchg Band; Hon Roll; Excell Schlrshp 85; Hnrbl Ment PTA Sci Fair 85; Girls ST 85; Srgcl Nrs.

HERRICK, JOHNNA; Granville HS; Pawlet, VT; (Y); 14/117; Quiz Bowl; Band; Chorus; Concert Band; Drm & Bgl; Jazz Band; Mrchg Band; Orch; Pep Band; School Musical; Semper Fidelis & Robert Garrity Music Awds 85; WA Cnty Music Tchrs Awd 85; Shenandoah Coll; Music Ed.

HERRICK, LESLIE; Frewsburg Central HS; Frewsburg, NY; (Y); Church Yth Grp; Pep Clb; Band; Rep Soph Cls; Rep Stu Cncl; Var Cheerleading; High Hon Roll; Hon Roll; Jamestown CC; Mth.

HERRICK, RICHARD; C-PP West HS; Corning, NY; (Y); 130/300; Computer Clb; Exploring; High Hon Roll; Hon Roll; Comp Sci Awd 85; Mst Imprvd 4 Yr HS Yrs 85; Corning CC; Comp Sci.

HERRICK JR, RONALD; Corning Painted Post West HS; Corning, NY; (Y); Hon Roll; Prfct Atten Awd; Auto Mech.

HERRING, KATHLEEN; Cardinal Mooney HS; Hilton, NY; (Y); 143/317; Church Yth Grp; Var Fld Hcky; Hon Roll; Catholic Womens Clb Schlrshp 84-85; Bus Admin.

HERRING, MICHAEL; Christian Brothers Acad; Baldwinsville, NY; (Y); 12/93; Pep Clb; Varsity Clb; JV Var Bsktbl; JV Var Lcrss; High Hon Roll; Jr NHS; NHS; Ldrshp Educ & Devlpmnt Pro 84; Columbia U; Dartmouth Clg; Ecnmcs.

HERRINGTON, MATTHEW; Nottingham HS; Syracuse, NY; (Y); 24/220; Drama Clb; Latin Clb; Political Wkr; Ski Clb; Thesps; School Play; Lit Mag; Tennis; NHS; Ntl Merit SF; Syracuse U; Intl Rel.

HERRITY, KAREN; Chester HS; Chester, NY; (Y); Concert Band; Drm Mjr(t); Jazz Band; Mrchg Band; Yrbk Stf; Sec Jr Cls; Var Score Keeper; Var Socr; Var Capt Vllybl; Hon Roll; Cortland; Pre Phy Thrpy.

HERRMANN, DANIEL J; Westhill HS; Syracuse, NY; (Y); 10/168; Math Tm; Ski Clb; Symp Band; Yrbk Stf; JV Var Bsbl; JV Stat Bsktbl; Im Var Socr; Hon Roll; NHS; NEDT Awd; NY ST Regents Schlrshp 85; 5th Pl Onondaga Cnty Math Exam 85; Le Moyne Coll Poi Mu Epsilon Math Awd; Clarkson U; Elec Engr.

HERRON, DAVID M; Owen O Young HS; Mohawk, NY; (Y); Chorus; Drm & Bgl; Yrbk Stf; Var Bsbl; JV Var Bsktbl; Var Socr; Hon Roll; Govrs Trphy-Recog; Munson Wms Proctor Inst; Artst.

HERRON, EILEEN M; Valley Stream Central HS; Valley Stream, NY; (Y); 1/370; Pres Leo Clb; Yrbk Ed-Chief; Off Stu Cncl; Vllybl; Bausch & Lomb Sci Awd; Cit Awd; Lion Awd; Mu Alp Tht; NHS; Ntl Merit Ltr; Phi Betta Kappa 85-89; NY ST Rgnts Schlrshp, VS Cntrls H W Gross Awd 85; Adelphi U; Bio.

HERRSCHAFT, JAMES J; West Hampton Beach HS; E Quogue, NY; (Y); 16/190; Teachers Aide; Concert Band; Jazz Band; Pep Band; Variety Show; Var Tennis; High Hon Roll; Trs NHS; Prfct Atten Awd; 1st Pl Schl Talent Show 84; NY ST Regents Schlrshp 85; U Of Notre Dame; Bus Admin.

HERSCH, JONATHAN; Commack H S North; Commack, NY; (Y); Exploring; MMM; Pres Temple Yth Grp; Mrchg Band; School Musical; Nwsp Rptr; JV Bsbl; French Hon Soc; High Hon Roll; Pres NHS; Med.

HERSCOVICI, STEVEN; Horace Greeley HS; Chappaqua, NY; (Y); 45/272; Math Tm; Rep Frsh Cls; Rep Soph Cls; Trs Jr Cls; Trs Sr Cls; JV Bsbl; Im Bsktbl; Ntl Merit Ltr; U Of Chicago.

HERSHMAN, KARYN; Lawrence HS; Cedarhurst, NY; (Y); Drama Clb; Science Clb; School Play; Yrbk Stf; Cit Awd; Marine Biolgst.

HERSTEIN, ROBERT; Spring Valley HS; Spring Vsalley, NY; (Y); Computer Clb; Math Clb; Math Tm; Orch; Var Tennis; High Hon Roll; Hon Roll; Jr NHS; Mu Alp Tht; Spanish NHS; Sci Achvt Awd 83; SE Athl Conf All Cnty 85; NYS Athl Conf Cls A Rnnr-Up,Dbls 3rd Pl 85; Sci.

HERTE, BRIAN G; St Anthonys HS; E Northport, NY; (Y); JV Var Bsktbl; VP Coach Actv; Duns Scotus Awd-Acadmc Hnrs 83-84; Hofstra; Accntng.

HERTEL, MARK; Mount Saint Michael Acad; Bronx, NY; (Y); 25/308; Camera Clb; Ski Clb; Lit Mag; Var Bsbl; Stat Bsktbl; Mgr(s); High Hon Roll; NHS; Fairfield U; Bus.

HERTER, KENNETH; Alden HS; Alden, NY; (Y); 55/200; Pres Rptr FFA; Pres Letterman Clb; Varsity Clb; Stu Cncl; JV Var Ftbl; Ice Hcky; High Hon Roll; Hon Roll; Wt Lftg; Erie Cnty Fair Schlrshp 85; FFA Schlrshp 85; Alfred ST; Animal Husbandry.

HERTLEIN, PAUL; St Marys Boys HS; Glen Head, NY; (Y); 3/162; Nwsp Stf; Yrbk Stf; Rep Soph Cls; Var Trk; High Hon Roll; Ntl Merit SF.

HERTZ, EUGENE STEVEN; S H Calhoun HS; Merrick, NY; (Y); 45/360; Computer Clb; Band; Chorus; Concert Band; Jazz Band; Madrigals; School Musical; Capt Tennis; Hon Roll; Bl Rbbn Excllnc-Long Is Sci Congrss 83; Presdntl Acadmc Ftnss Awd 85; NY St Regnts Schlrshp 85; U Of MA; Comp Sci Engrng.

HERTZ, KORINNE; Liverpool HS; Liverpool, NY; (S); 87/792; Church Yth Grp; Dance Clb; Drama Clb; Hon Roll; Jr NHS; NHS; Onondaga Cnty JR Miss 2nd Rnnr Up 85; Syracuse U; Spch Pathlgy.

HERUBIN, COLLEEN; John F Kennedy HS; Utica, NY; (Y); 8/139; Ski Clb; Yrbk Ed-Chief; Yrbk Stf; Rep Stu Cncl; Badmtn; Var Sftbl; Hon Roll; Nuclr Med.

HERZ, NICOLE S; La Guardia HS Of Music & The Arts; New York, NY; (Y); Band; Orch; Nwsp Phtg; Yrbk Phtg; Art Hnr League 84; Art Exhib Cert 82, 83 & 84; Arts.

HERZ, SETH JEREMY; Binghamton HS; Binghamton, NY; (Y); Math Tm; Sec Trs Spanish Clb; Temple Yth Grp; Trk; High Hon Roll; NHS; Prfct Atten Awd; Salute To Yth Pgm 84-85; MVP-BSBL 83; Coachs Awd-Bsbl Team 84; CYO Bsktbl-Most Imprvd 83-85.

HERZIG, BRYIN; Cazenovia Central HS; Cazenovia, NY; (Y); Band; Chorus; Concert Band; Mrchg Band; Symp Band; Nwsp Rptr; Bsbl; Mgr(s); Score Keeper; Wrstlng; Bst Atttitde Wrstlng 83; Bst Attitde Bsbl 85; Oper Entrprse AMA 85; Bus Mgmt.

HERZOG, ELAINE; Academy Of St Joseph HS; Hauppauge, NY; (Y); 10/128; Church Yth Grp; Girl Scts; Hosp Aide; Math Clb; Office Aide; Band; Orch; Var Badmtn; Var Co-Capt Bsktbl; Coach Actv; Stu Advisory Committee Semi Fin 83-84; Mst Outstndng Awd Music 84-85; Vrsty Bsktbl MVP 84-85; Nrsng.

HERZOG, KAREN; Mt St Mary Acad; Kenmore, NY; (Y); Pep Clb; Chorus; School Musical; Nwsp Rptr; Ed Yrbk Stf; Lit Mag; Rep Soph Cls; Sec Jr Cls; Rep Stu Cncl; JV Bsktbl; Eng.

HESKIN, KEERSTEN; Solvay HS; Solvay, NY; (Y); 25/170; Yrbk Stf; Var Capt Cheerleading; Var Capt Pom Pon; L Trk; Hon Roll; NHS; Pres Schlr; NY ST Regnts Schlrshp Wnnr 85; Clara Hill Murphy Schlrshp Wnnr 85; SUNY Oswego.

HESS, LORI; Horseheads HS; Horseheads, NY; (Y); Latin Clb; Chorus; JV Sftbl; Var Trk; High Hon Roll; Hon Roll; Russell Sage Coll; Physcl Thrpy.

HESS, MELANI; Walter Panas HS; Peekskill, NY; (Y); Rep Jr Cls; JV Var Cheerleading; High Hon Roll; Hon Roll; Jr NHS; NHS; Stu Of Month Spanish, Engl & Sci 82-85; Spanish.

HESSE, ANITA K; Grover Cleveland HS; Middle Village, NY; (Y); 46/750; VP Camera Clb; Science Clb; Ntl Merit Ltr; Wnr Womens Hist Essay Cmptn 85; Fnlst NY ST Media Arts Cmptn 85; NY ST Regents Schlrshp 85; Culinary Inst Of Amer; Arts.

HESSELBIRG, FRANCES; Queen Of The Rosary Acad; Hauppauge, NY; (S); 3/80; Church Yth Grp; Cmnty Wkr; Letterman Clb; Library Aide; Varsity Clb; School Play; High Hon Roll; NHS; Drama Clb; Physical Fitness Awd 82-83; Chemistry.

HESSION, DEBBIE; Kings Park HS; Kings Park, NY; (Y); #79 In Class; Church Yth Grp; 4-H Awd; Bus.

HESSLINK, TRACEY KATHLEEN; Clarence Central HS; Clarence Ctr, NY; (Y); 7/282; Am Leg Aux Girls St; Teachers Aide; Tennis; Cit Awd; NHS; Drama Clb; Latin Clb; Nwsp Bus Mgr; Mgr(s); Hon Roll; Buffalo Wellsley Clb Awd 85; Peer Guide 84-85; Med Adm.

HESTER, ANDREW; Bishop Ford HS; Brooklyn, NY; (Y); 9/370; Chess Clb; Math Tm; Var Bowling; Hon Roll; Comptrollers Awd 85; Polytech Inst Of NY Scholar 85; Polytech Inst NY; Aerospc Engr.

HESTER, PETER W; Garden City HS; Garden City, NY; (Y); Church Yth Grp; Cmnty Wkr; German Clb; Hosp Aide; Nwsp Sprt Ed; Lcrss; Capt Socr; Jr NHS; NHS; Regents Schlrshp Awd 85; Bio.

HETRICK, KATRIN; Jamestown HS; Jamestown, NY; (Y); Sec Trs Church Yth Grp; JA; Spanish Clb; Nwsp Ed-Chief; Nwsp Rptr; Nwsp Stf; Hon Roll; Jr NHS; NHS; SUNY-FREDONIA; Med.

HETTENBACH, JAMES F; St Anthonys HS; Centerport, NY; (Y); Chess Clb; Lit Mag; Var Im Bsktbl; JV Var Lcrss; Hon Roll; Jr NHS; Ntl Merit Ltr; Bio.

HETTIG, NICOLE; Liverpool HS; Liverpool, NY; (S); Nwsp Rptr; Nwsp Sprt Ed; Nwsp Stf; Rep Frsh Cls; Rep Soph Cls; Rep Sr Cls; JV Diving; JV Socr; Hon Roll; Jr NHS; Rgnts Nrsng Schlrshp 85; Geneseo Coll; Bio.

HETZEL, DANIEL A; Mercy HS; Center Moriches, NY; (Y); 14/124; Drama Clb; MMM; Quiz Bowl; Chorus; School Musical; Stage Crew; Variety Show; Hon Roll; NHS; NY ST Regents Schlrshp; Fredonia ST U; Snd Rcrdng Tech.

HETZLER, DAVID H; Livonia HS; Livonia, NY; (Y); 3/130; Computer Clb; Math Clb; Science Clb; Ski Clb; High Hon Roll; Jr NHS; Mathletes; Math Tm; Stu Cncl; JV Socr; Ntl Soc Prof Engr, Regnts Schlrshps 85; Carnegie-Mellon U; Elec Engr.

HEVERLY, GAYLE A; East Aurora HS; E Aurora, NY; (Y); 35/182; Band; Chorus; Orch; School Musical; Yrbk Stf; Rep Stu Cncl; Hon Roll; Jr NHS; Regnts Schlrshp 85; ST U Coll Fredonia; Bus Admin.

HEWES, GINA; Charles O Dickerson HS; Trumansburg, NY; (Y); 1/87; French Clb; Science Clb; Sec Jr Cls; VP Stu Cncl; L Trk; High Hon Roll; NHS; Prfct Atten Awd; L Socr; Val; Coachs Awd 85; SAT Score 85; Cornell U; Archlgy.

HEWITT, KELLI; Brooklyn Technical HS; Brooklyn, NY; (Y); 73/1200; Band; High Hon Roll; NHS; Prfct Atten Awd; Bus Admin.

HEWITT, MICHAEL; Weedsport Central HS; Auburn, NY; (Y); 5/64; 4-H; French Clb; Math Clb; Ski Clb; Band; Jazz Band; Yrbk Phtg; Crs Cntry; Trk; Hon Roll; Hazel M Tryor Awd 84-85; Nrthestrn U; Civil Engnrng.

HEWITT, PATRICK; Msgr Mc Clancy HS; Bayside, NY; (S); 71/225; Church Yth Grp; Cmnty Wkr; Teachers Aide; Soph Cls; Stu Cncl; Educ Incntv Awd 81; Queens Coll; Phy Ed.

HEWITT, THERESA; Vernon Verona Sherrill Central HS; Verona, NY; (Y); Sec Church Yth Grp; Thesps; Band; Capt Color Guard; Drm & Bgl; Mrchg Band; School Musical; School Play; Hon Roll; Elem Ed.

HEWLETT, JAMES A; Webster HS; Webster, NY; (Y); 23/550; Am Leg Boys St; JA; Pres Jr Cls; Pres Sr Cls; Pres Stu Cncl; JV Var Socr; High Hon Roll; Hon Roll; Jr NHS; NHS; Comp.

HEWLETT, URSELA; Academy Of Mt St Ursula; Bronx, NY; (Y); Church Yth Grp; Drama Clb; Library Aide; Teachers Aide; Varsity Clb; Chorus; School Play; Stage Crew; Pres Soph Cls; Rep Stu Cncl; Iona Coll; Comp Sci.

HEXIMER, DAVID; Kenmore East HS; Tonawanda, NY; (Y); 49/330; Pres German Clb; Varsity Clb; Var JV Bsbl; Var Im Bowling; High Hon Roll; Hon Roll; NHS; U Of NY; Accntng.

HEY, ERIC; Olean HS; Erie, PA; (Y); Boy Scts; Church Yth Grp; Varsity Clb; Var Golf; JV Wrstlng; Hon Roll; Edward Cashimere Awd For Hstry 85; Aviation.

HEY, KRISTEN; Oyster Bay HS; Oyster Bay, NY; (Y); Pres Church Yth Grp; Hosp Aide; Chorus; Yrbk Bus Mgr; Lit Mag; VP Frsh Cls; VP Soph Cls; VP Jr Cls; Capt Badmtn; NHS.

HEYMAN, WILLIAM; Poughkeepsie HS; Poughkeepsie, NY; (Y); Chess Clb; Church Yth Grp; Debate Tm; Chorus; Hon Roll; NHS; Prfct Atten Awd; 1st Pl Sci Fair 85; 1st Pl Amer Hstry Div U S Soc Stds Olympd 85; Sci Dept Stdnt Semstr 85; Bio.

HEYWARD, MARILYN RUTH; Andrew Jackson HS; Queens, NY; (Y); Church Yth Grp; Hosp Aide; Science Clb; Band; Church Choir; Pace U; Psych.

HIBBARD, JACQUELYN; Albion HS; Albion, NY; (S); 18/168; Pres Church Yth Grp; Band; Chorus; Swing Chorus; JV Sftbl; Hon Roll; NHS; Pres 4-H; Wmns Chorale; SUNY Geneseo; Elem Educ.

HIBBERT, SETH L; Liverpool HS; Liverpool, NY; (Y); 31/874; Am Leg Boys St; Socr; High Hon Roll; Hon Roll; Jr NHS; NHS; Outstndng Hlth Eductn Student 84-85; Cert Of Honrbl Merit-Magna Cum Laude-Natl Latin Exam 83-84; Intelligence Srvc.

HICKEY, ELIZABETH; St Marys Lancaster HS; Depew, NY; (S); #15 In Class; Hosp Aide; Spanish Clb; Speech Tm; Varsity Clb; Badmtn; Var Capt Cheerleading; Trk; NHS; Phy.

HICKEY, ELLEN; Olean HS; Olean, NY; (Y); 7/200; AFS; Church Yth Grp; Hosp Aide; Pres Science Clb; VP Varsity Clb; Orch; JV Var Cheerleading; Var Swmmng; Hon Roll; NHS; 20 Point Awd 85; RN.

HICKEY JR, JAMES P; Farmingdale HS; Farmingdale, NY; (Y); 29/625; Cmnty Wkr; Key Clb; Variety Show; JV Var Bsbl; JV Var Socr; Hon Roll; Jr NHS; NHS; Ntl Merit Schol; Acad Schlrshp Hofstra U 85; Hofstra U; Acctng.

HICKEY, JENNIFER A; Catholic Central HS; Troy, NY; (Y); 37/200; Dance Clb; French Clb; Math Clb; Math Tm; Ski Clb; Yrbk Phtg; Yrbk Stf; JV Var Bsktbl; Var Tennis; Var Trk; Socl Studs Awd & Math Awd 82-83 & 84-85; St Francis Coll; Bus Mgt.

HICKEY, JOHN; Archbishop Molloy HS; Richmond Hl, NY; (Y); 110/409; Church Yth Grp; Capt JV Socr; Trk; Hon Roll; Gaelic Ftbl Titles 83 & 84; Bus Admin.

HICKEY, KAREN ANN E; Cohoes HS; Cohoes, NY; (Y); Camera Clb; Office Aide; Yrbk Phtg; Cheerleading; Ftbl; Sftbl; Wt Lftg; Ntl Merit Schol; Sal; Val; Hudson Valley; Sec.

HICKEY, KEVIN D; Oneonta HS; Oneonta, NY; (Y); 97/181; Church Yth Grp; Cmnty Wkr; Computer Clb; French Clb; Library Aide; JV Bowling; Mgr(s); Math.

HICKEY, MICHAEL J; Mt St Michael HS; Bronx, NY; (Y); Ftbl; 4-H Awd; High Hon Roll; Hon Roll; JETS Awd; Jr NHS; NHS; Ntl Merit SF; Computer Clb; 4-H; NY ST Regnts Schlrshp 85-86; Manhattan Coll; Engrng.

HICKEY, MICHAEL P; Webster HS; Penfield, NY; (Y); 120/540; Exploring; Band; Chorus; Concert Band; Jazz Band; Swing Chorus; Hon Roll; Ntl Merit SF; Bio & Geomtry Awds 84; Sci Olympd Chmstry Tm 85; Maestro Please Comptn Gld Wnng Cncrt Band 85; Astrnmy.

HICKEY, PATRICIA; Herbert H Lehman HS; Bronx, NY; (Y); 14/454; Math Tm; Science Clb; Nwsp Rptr; Nwsp Stf; Lit Mag; Hon Roll; NHS; Ntl Merit Ltr; St Schlr; Iona Clg.

HICKEY, VINCENT G; Stissing Mt HS; Elizavle, NY; (Y); 3/79; AFS; Aud/Vis; Camera Clb; Computer Clb; Drama Clb; Library Aide; Yrbk Stf; High Hon Roll; NHS; Rotary Awd; NEMA 84; Siena; Comp Sci.

HICKOK JR, ROY KEITH; Massena Central HS; Massena, NY; (Y); AFS; French Clb; Band; Concert Band; Mrchg Band; Rep Frsh Cls; Var JV Socr; Var Trk; Var Capt Wrstlng; Prfct Atten Awd; Most Team Points-JV Wrestlng Team 84; Med.

HICKOX, TRACY; Cicero-North Syracuse HS; Bridgeport, NY; (Y); Church Yth Grp; Cmnty Wkr; GAA; Teachers Aide; School Play; VP Jr Cls; Pres Stu Cncl; Im Stat Bsktbl; Stat Fld Hcky; JV Var Score Keeper; Natl Hstry & Govt Awd 85; SUNY Oneonta; Fash Desgn.

HICKS, ANAYANSI; South Shore HS; Brooklyn, NY; (Y); Brooklyn Coll; Jrnlsm.

HICKS, ANNE; Haverling Central School Bath; Bath, NY; (Y); JCL; Latin Clb; Math Clb; Chorus; School Play; Yrbk Bus Mgr; Rep Sr Cls; Tennis; Hon Roll; Comp Pgmr.

HICKS, CINDY; Amherst Central SR HS; Amherst, NY; (Y); 16/310; Church Yth Grp; Cmnty Wkr; JCL; Latin Clb; Trs Radio Clb; School Musical; Var Fld Hcky; Var Trk; High Hon Roll; NHS; Coaches Awd Trk 84; Crss Cntry Sect 84; :Neurosci.

HICKS, KEVIN; Dryden Central HS; Freeville, NY; (Y); Church Yth Grp; Drama Clb; Spanish Clb; Band; Chorus; School Musical; School Play; JV Bsktbl; NHS; Compse Music Schl Chrs; Adv.

HICKS, LILA; Onteora HS; Woodstock, NY; (S); 13/245; Pres AFS; Orch; Pres Soph Cls; Pres Jr Cls; Pres Sr Cls; Rep Stu Cncl; Crs Cntry; Trk; NHS; Chorus; DECA Good Ctznshp Awd 83; Band Coll Consttn In Yr 2000 Smmr Prog 84; Political.

HICKS, STEPHEN; Longwood HS; Coram, NY; (Y); Am Leg Boys St; Pres Key Clb; Science Clb; Orch; Pres Soph Cls; Pres Sr Cls; Rep Stu Cncl; Var L Bsbl; Var Ftbl; Hon Roll; Outstndng Achvt Acad Gvn By Gordon Heigts Cmmnty Affrs Assoc Inc 83; Med.

HIDALGO, JULES; Mountainside Christian Acad; Schroon Lake, NY; (Y); Church Yth Grp; Chorus; School Play; Yrbk Sprt Ed; Pres Stu Cncl; Var Capt Bsbl; Var Bsktbl; Var Socr; High Hon Roll; MVP Bsbl; Word Lif Bibl Inst; Math.

HIDALGO, MICHELLE; Mountainside Christian Acad; Schroon Lake, NY; (Y); Church Yth Grp; Quiz Bowl; Chorus; School Play; Bowling; Hon Roll; Scripture Memary Awd 83-85; MIP Bowler 80-81; Word Of Life Teens Intl 84; 1st Pl Chorus 84; Word Of Life Bible Inst; Histry.

HIGBEE, JAMES; Kenmore West SR HS; Kenmore, NY; (Y); Boy Scts; JA; Band; Mrchg Band; Hon Roll; Elec Engr.

HIGBIE, TIMOTHY J; Ft Hamilton HS; Brooklyn, NY; (Y); 244/600; Aud/Vis; Office Aide; Teachers Aide; Band; Chorus; Concert Band; Rep Stu Cncl; Hon Roll; NY ST Rgnts Schlrshp 85; St Johns U; Finance.

HIGBY, CINDY L; Carthage Central HS; Black River, NY; (Y); 13/203; Drama Clb; Library Aide; Spanish Clb; School Play; Nwsp Rptr; High Hon Roll; Hon Roll; NHS; Prfct Atten Awd; Carol Reno Mem Schlrhsp 85; Presndtl Acadmc Ftns Awd 85; Jefferson Coll Clb; Mgmt.

HIGGINS, FAITH; Whitesboro SR HS; Whitesboro, NY; (Y); Intnl Clb; Library Aide; Chorus; School Musical; Variety Show; Nwsp Rptr; Nwsp Stf; Lit Mag; Rep Stu Cncl; High Hon Roll; Syracuse U; Intl Studies.

HIGGINS, JAMES F; Rome Free Acad; Rome, NY; (Y); 166/478; AFS; Am Leg Boys St; Debate Tm; Intnl Clb; Key Clb; NFL; Speech Tm; Nwsp Rptr; Rep Sr Cls; DAR Awd; Voice Dem Nrthrn NY Dist Wnnr 85; Rep NYS Senate Stu Polcy Forum 85; NY ST Regents Scholar 84-85; Utica Coll; Lib Arts.

HIGGINS, KELLY; Stella Maris HS; Belle Harbor, NY; (Y); Nwsp Stf; Yrbk Stf; VP Frsh Cls; Rep Jr Cls; Rep Stu Cncl; Chld Psychlgy.

HIGGINS, SALLY; Thousand Islands HS; Alexandria Bay, NY; (Y); Varsity Clb; School Play; Variety Show; Nwsp Rptr; Nwsp Stf; VP Jr Cls; VP Sr Cls; JV Var Socr; JV Var Sftbl; JV Capt Vllybl; Psych.

HIGGINS, THERESE; De Sales Catholic HS; N Tonawanda, NY; (S); 6/48; Nwsp Stf; Yrbk Stf; VP Stu Cncl; Var Badmtn; Var Capt Bsktbl; Score Keeper; Var Sftbl; Var Capt Vllybl; High Hon Roll; NHS; Ntl Sci Merit Awd 83; Outstndng HS Athlts In Amer 83-84; US Achvt Acad 84; Bio.

HIGGINS, WILLIAM; Cathedral Prep Seminary; Ridgewood, NY; (Y); Church Yth Grp; Drama Clb; Library Aide; NFL; Thesps; Chorus; School Play; Variety Show; Ed Nwsp Stf; Score Keeper; Cathedral Coll; Prsthd.

HIGHMORE, SARAJANE E; St John The Baptist DHS HS; Sayville, NY; (Y); 36/600; Cmnty Wkr; French Clb; Nwsp Rptr; Yrbk Stf; Rep Frsh Cls; Var Cheerleading; Stat Wrstlng; Hon Roll; NHS; Ntl Merit Ltr; IN U Bloomington; Bus.

HIGHSMITH, DAVID EARL; Blessed Sacrament HS; Mt Vernon, NY; (Y); 6/100; Rep Stu Cncl; JV Bsbl; JV Var Bsktbl; NHS; Schlrshp Blssed Sacramnt 82-86; Math Awd 83-84; Comp Sci.

HIGHT, RONALD; Gouverneur JR SR HS; Gouverneur, NY; (Y); Sec Boy Scts; 4-H; FFA; JV Bsbl; JV Wrstlng; Canton ATC; Ag.

HIGHTOWER, FELICE; John Dewey HS; Brooklyn, NY; (Y); Cmnty Wkr; Dance Clb; Debate Tm; Chorus; School Musical; School Play; Yrbk Stf; Tennis; Wt Lftg; Ntl Merit Ltr; Service Awd 83; Law.

HIGLEY, DARLENE; Onteora Central HS; West Shokan, NY; (S); Band; Concert Band; Mrchg Band; High Hon Roll; Hon Roll; NHS; Hgh Hnr Rll Rec Awd 83-84; Spnsh Hgh Hnr Rec Cert 83-84; Math Rec Cert 83; Tchng.

HIGLEY, MEGAN M; Norwich HS; Norwich, NY; (Y); 4/186; Pres Chorus; Drm Mjr(t); Jazz Band; School Musical; Symp Band; NHS; Church Yth Grp; Band; Church Choir; Concert Band; Oprtn Entrpse Schlrshp Wnnr 84; Pianst 74-85; Bucknell U; Music.

HILBERT, LISA A; East Aurora HS; East Aurora, NY; (Y); 1/182; Church Yth Grp; Teachers Aide; Hon Roll; NHS; Ntl Merit SF; Val; Band; Drm & Bgl; Orch; Classicl Assn Of Westrn NY Hnr Cert 83; Cornell U; Nutrtnl Sci.

HILDES, ELIZABETH; Earl V Vandermuelen HS; Pt Jefferson, NY; (Y); 15/280; Pres Spanish Clb; Band; Nwsp Stf; Yrbk Rptr; Yrbk Stf; Lit Mag; JV Fld Hcky; Hon Roll; NHS; St Schlr; FFA Scholar 85; Bucknell U; Anml Behavr.

HILDRETH, KIRSTEN M; Charles H Roth SR HS; Henrietta, NY; (Y); French Clb; Latin Clb; Library Aide; Thesps; Stage Crew; Ed Lit Mag; French Hon Soc; Minerva B Cambell Lit Awd 80, 81, 83 & 84; Wells Coll Poetry Cntst Fnlst 83 & 84; Schlstc Ltr Awd 84.

HILE, MARY MICHELLE; Newburgh Free Acad; Newburgh, NY; (Y); 49/655; Girl Scts; Natl Beta Clb; Spanish Clb; Yrbk Stf; Var L Bsktbl; High Hon Roll; Hon Roll; NHS; Opt Clb Awd; Stu Ctzn Mnth 85; U Of TN-CHATTANOOGA; Psychlgy.

HILKEN, DAWN; Alexander HS; Alexander, NY; (S); Ski Clb; High Hon Roll; Hon Roll; Jr NHS; NHS; Cosmtlgy.

HILL, BENJAMIN W; Mount Vernon HS; Mt Vernon, NY; (Y); 28/549; Cmnty Wkr; Computer Clb; FTA; Sec Key Clb; Math Tm; Nwsp Stf; Yrbk Sprt Ed; Pres Stu Cncl; Wrstlng; NHS; Wmns Welfare Clb Scholar 85; Omega Psi Phi Scholar 85; Hugh G Stewart Awd 85; Rochester Inst Tech; Comp Sci.

HILL, CASSANDRA; Hempstead HS; Hempstead, NY; (S); 25/333; Sec Church Yth Grp; VP Church Choir; Mrchg Band; Nwsp Stf; Sec Soph Cls; Stu Cncl; JV Bowling; Hon Roll; Embry-Riddle; Pilot.

HILL, CHRISTINE; Chenago Valley HS; Binghamton, NY; (Y); Sec Art Clb; French Clb; Yrbk Stf; JV Cheerleading; Var L Tennis; Var Trk; Var L Vllybl; High Hon Roll; Jr NHS; NHS; Syracuse; Intr Dsgn.

HILL, CYNTHIA; Maryvale Senior HS; Depew, NY; (Y); 11/320; Trs Acpl Chr; Pres Chorus; Concert Band; Pres Jr Cls; Pres Sr Cls; Var L Cheerleading; Var L Trk; NHS; French Clb; GAA; NY ST Rep Hugh O Brien Intl Ldrshp Sem 84; Freedms Fndtn Rep 85; Cop Law.

HILL, DANIEL; Frewsburg Central HS; Frewsburg, NY; (Y); Boy Scts; Church Yth Grp; Im Bsbl; Stat Bsktbl; Var L Ftbl; Im Ice Hcky; JV Var Score Keeper; Im Wt Lftg; Hon Roll; Mst Imprvd Vrsty Ftbl Plyr Awd 84.

HILL, DAVID; South Lewis HS; Turin, NY; (Y); Varsity Clb; Ftbl; Wt Lftg; Hon Roll.

HILL, DONALD; Delaware Valley Central HS; North Branch, NY; (Y); JV Bsktbl; JV Ftbl; Kautz Schlrshp 85; Orange Cnty CC; Law.

HILL, DOUGLAS; Cader Cantral Schl; Willseyville, NY; (Y); Church Yth Grp; 4-H; Library Aide; Band; Chorus; Nwsp Rptr; Trs Sec Soph Cls; Var L Trk; High Hon Roll; Hon Roll; Comp Sci.

HILL, JEFFREY A; Forest Hills HS; Rego Park, NY; (Y); 7/881; Nwsp Rptr; Nwsp Sprt Ed; High Hon Roll; Hon Roll; NHS; Ntl Merit Schol; Daily News Princpls Pride Yankees Awd 84; Cornell U; Radio.

HILL, JOHN; Cardinal O Hara HS; Tonawanda, NY; (S); 10/145; Boys Clb Am; French Clb; Rep Jr Cls; Rep Stu Cncl; Var Bsktbl; Coach Actv; Var Socr; High Hon Roll; Hon Roll; Cardinal O Hara Schlrshp; Engr.

HILL, JUDITH L; Clarence Central SR HS; Willimsville, NY; (Y); #3 In Class; Drama Clb; Hosp Aide; Thesps; Acpl Chr; Chorus; Church Choir; Concert Band; Jazz Band; Orch; School Musical; Buffalo Wellesley Clb Awd, Elmira Coll Key Aws & Schlrshp, Westminster Chr Coll Voice Schlrshp 83-84; Duke U; Poli Sci.

HILL, KELLY; Frewsburg Central Schl; Frewsburg, NY; (Y); 15/96; Church Yth Grp; Cmnty Wkr; Pres Hosp Aide; Hon Roll; NHS; Opt Clb Awd; Voice Dem Awd; 4-H; Library Aide; Trs Pep Clb; Lions Clb, Jamestwn Gen Hsp Aux Schlrshps 85; R H Jackson Schlrshp Awd 84; Jamestown CC; Nrsg.

HILL, KELLY; Remsen Central HS; Remsen, NY; (Y); Mathletes; Ski Clb; Trs Band; Drm Mjr(t); Jazz Band; Yrbk Stf; Sec Soph Cls; Sec Jr Cls; Cheerleading; VP NHS; Mth.

HILL, LAURA; Pierson HS; Sag Harbor, NY; (Y); 14/45; Spanish Clb; Band; Chorus; School Musical; School Play; Nwsp Stf; Yrbk Stf; Lit Mag; Fld Hcky; Cheerleading; Perf Music.

HILL, LORRAINE; Sachem HS; Ronkonkoma, NY; (Y); 163/1463; Church Yth Grp; Hosp Aide; Ski Clb; SUNY-NEW Paltz; Bus Admin.

HILL, MARK; Averill Park HS; Sand Lake, NY; (Y); 6/200; Pres 4-H; 4-H Awd; Hon Roll; Kiwanis Awd; NHS; Ntl Merit SF.

HILL, MICHAEL S; Forest Hills HS; Rego Park, NY; (Y); 117/881; Debate Tm; Drama Clb; VP Exploring; Letterman Clb; VP Science Clb; Varsity Clb; Concert Band; Orch; High Hon Roll; Hon Roll; Ltr, Capt Var Fncng Tm 83-85; 2nd Pl Borough Sci Fair 84; Aerospc Engrng.

HILL, MIKE; Carmel HS; Lk Carmel, NY; (Y); French Clb; Band; Concert Band; Mrchg Band; JV Var Ftbl; Trk; Wt Lftg; High Hon Roll; Hon Roll; NHS; Offnsv Coachs Awd 83; NE Bass Drum Champ 84; Hudson Vly Bass Drm Champ 85; Biochem.

HILL, NATHAN; Liverpool HS; N Syracuse, NY; (S); 74/791; Exploring; Varsity Clb; Stage Crew; Nwsp Rptr; Var Socr; Hon Roll; Jr NHS; NHS; Magna Cum Lauda Natl Latin Exam 84; Bio Sci.

HILL, NICOLE; Mt St Ursula HS; Bronx, NY; (Y); Library Aide; Flag Corp; Yrbk Stf; JV Trk; Psych.

HILL, RANDOLPH A; Cardinal Hayes HS; Bronx, NY; (Y); 15/250; Boys Clb Am; Band; Mrchg Band; Var JV Ftbl; Hon Roll; Diamond H Pin 82; Hayes Tutoring 85; Wagner Coll; Law.

HILL, ROBERT E; Suffern HS; Suffern, NY; (Y); Am Leg Boys St; Cmnty Wkr; Trs Stu Cncl; Trk; Hon Roll; NHS; Bus.

HILL, STEVEN; Poland Central HS; Poland, NY; (Y); 1/56; Band; Concert Band; Jazz Band; Rep Frsh Cls; Rep Jr Cls; Rep Sr Cls; Hon Roll; NHS; Ntl Merit Ltr; Val; PAT Schlrshp 85; Rotary Schlrshp 85; Regents Schlrshp 85; Clarkson U; Elec.

HILL, THOMAS C; Marcellus SR HS; Syracuse, NY; (Y); 10/164; Am Leg Boys St; Church Yth Grp; Quiz Bowl; Rep Jr Cls; Sr Cls; Im Civic Clb; High Hon Roll; NHS; Psych.

HILLABUSH, TAMARA; Byron-Bergen Central HS; Byron, NY; (Y); French Clb; Band; Concert Band; Nwsp Ed-Chief; Ed Lit Mag; Pres Jr Cls; High Hon Roll; Jr NHS; NHS; U Rochester Padeia Awd 84-85; Comm.

HILLAGE, FREDERICK; Westmoreland HS; Westmoreland, NY; (Y); DECA; Model UN; Varsity Clb; School Play; Nwsp Rptr; Nwsp Stf; Yrbk Stf; Bsbl; Var Wrstlng; Hon Roll; USMC; Polcmn.

HILLEBRAND, RANDAL K; Delaware Academy & Central Schl; Delhi, NY; (Y); 4/87; AFS; Nwsp Ed-Chief; Yrbk Ed-Chief; Var L Bsktbl; Var L Crs Cntry; L Var Trk; High Hon Roll; NHS; Prfct Atten Awd; Pres Schlr.

HILLENBRAND, MARY; Sacred Heart Acad; North Floral Park, NY; (Y); Church Yth Grp; Girl Scts; Math Clb; Service Clb; Chorus; Church Choir; Hon Roll; NHS; Acctg.

HILLMAN, DENISE; Wilson Central Schl; Wilson, NY; (Y); 60/146; Church Yth Grp; 4-H; Band; Chorus; Church Choir; School Musical; Swing Chorus; Variety Show; Stu Cncl; Hon Roll; Keoka Coll; Bio Chem.

HILLS, ADRIENNE; Charles E Gorton HS; Yonkers, NY; (Y); 3/209; FBLA; Hosp Aide; Yrbk Stf; Rep Stu Cncl; Var Cheerleading; High Hon Roll; Hon Roll; NHS; Church Yth Grp; Pep Clb; Natl Cncl Negro Wmn Awd Schltc Achvt 84-85; Suptd Awd Schltc Exlnce 85; Berkeley Schl; Word Prcsng.

HILLY, NAGHAM; Edward R Murrow HS; Brooklyn, NY; (Y); 90/729; Im Gym; Im Wt Lftg; Gov Hon Prg Awd; Hon Roll; Sal; Engrvng Svc Gold Medal 85; Govt Awd 85; Pace U; Mgmt Sci.

HILPL, KIMBERLY; Alexandria Central Schl; Alexandria Bay, NY; (Y); 1/60; French Clb; Band; Concert Band; Mrchg Band; Trs Frsh Cls; VP Jr Cls; Var Bowling; Var JV Socr; Hon Roll; NHS; Augsbury North Cntry Schlr 85.

HILSER, SUZANNE; The Masters Schl; Rhinebeck, NY; (Y); Cmnty Wkr; Hosp Aide; Key Clb; Nwsp Stf; JV Bsktbl; JV Capt Fld Hcky; JV Sftbl; Hon Roll; Psychlgy.

HILTON, BRIAN; New Covenant Christian Schl; Rochester, NY; (S); Church Yth Grp; Band; Chorus; Yrbk Ed-Chief; Var Bsktbl; Var Socr; Var Sftbl; HS Quartet.

HILTON, MONICA; Altmar Parish Williamstown HS; Altmar, NY; (Y); JV Vllybl; High Hon Roll; Hon Roll; Elem Ed.

HILTON, RICK; Whitesboro SR HS; Marcy, NY; (Y); 32/358; Boy Scts; Exploring; Jr NHS; Eagl Sct 84.

HILTON, ROBERT; Clinton HS; Clinton, NY; (Y); 24/134; Cmnty Wkr; Varsity Clb; Yrbk Stf; Stat Bsktbl; Mgr(s); JV Var Socr; JV Var Tennis; High Hon Roll; Hon Roll; Jr NHS; NY ST Regents Schlrshp 85; Bsktbl Mgr Of The Yr 83; Hobart Coll; Englsh.

HILTS, BARBARA; Morrisville-Eaton Central HS; Eaton, NY; (Y); Office Aide; Chorus; Concert Band; Mrchg Band; Nwsp Stf; JV Var Cheerleading.

HIMBURY, WENDI; Buffalo Traditional HS; Buffalo, NY; (S); 1/120; Church Yth Grp; Debate Tm; Math Tm; Spanish Clb; Yrbk Phtg; Yrbk Stf; Hon Roll; NHS; Prfct Atten Awd; Val; Hear Hndcp Ed.

HIMELFELT, HEIDI; Bronx High School Of Sci; Bronx, NY; (Y); JA; Office Aide; Science Clb; Teachers Aide; Stu Cncl; NHS; Regents Schlrshp 85; Calculus Awd 85; Englsh Awd 85; Columbia U; Math.

HIMES, LARA; Lewiston-Porter HS; Youngstown, NY; (Y); 1/273; Church Yth Grp; High Hon Roll; NHS; Ehret Schlrshp 85-86; Coll Wooster; Jrnlsm.

HINCHMAN, JOHN; Marlboro HS; Marlboro, NY; (Y); 32/170; Var Tennis; Syracuse U; Bus Adm.

HINCKSON, CORANE; Acad Of Mt St Ursula; New York, NY; (Y); 13/167; Dance Clb; VP Library Aide; Chorus; Hon Roll; NHS; Ntl Merit Ltr; 1st Hnr Iona Coll Spnsh Lang 84-85; U Cntr Binghamton; Law.

HINDS, CHELLYANNE; John Dewey HS; Brooklyn, NY; (Y); Hosp Aide; Science Clb; Teachers Aide; Nwsp Rptr; Lit Mag; Rep Jr Cls; Pride Yankees Super Yth Awd; Ntl Lge Amer Pen Wm; Cert Recgntn; Excllnce Perf Hlth Asstng Sklls 85; Georgetown U; Bio.

HINDS, ESTHER; Susan E Wagner HS; Staten Island, NY; (Y); High Hon Roll; Hon Roll; Loma Linda U; Pedtrcn.

HINDS, SHARON R; Dansville SR HS; Dansville, NY; (Y); 23/145; Sec Church Yth Grp; Varsity Clb; Capt Color Guard; Yrbk Ed-Chief; Sec Stu Cncl; Var Capt Cheerleading; Hon Roll; Ntl Merit Ltr; Rgnts Schlrshp 85; JR MISS Pgnt 84; Alfred ST Coll; Ret Bus Mgmnt.

HINE, WENDY; Fredonia HS; Fredonia, NY; (Y); 12/181; French Clb; Science Clb; Band; Chorus; School Musical; Nwsp Stf; Var L Swmmng; Hon Roll; Art Clb; Ski Clb; NY ST Schl Music Assn Cmptn 83-85; Frnch Exc Awd 85; Mst Imprvd In Band Cndctrs Awd 83; Psychlgy.

HINES, BRIAN; Hamburg SR HS; Hamburg, NY; (Y); Band; Concert Band; Jazz Band; Mrchg Band; Orch; Symp Band; Ftbl; Hon Roll; NHS; Mercyhurst Coll; Hotl-Rest Mgt.

HINES, CHERYL; Emma Willard Schl; Freeville, NY; (Y); Dance Clb; Chem Rsrch.

HINES, MICHAEL; Xavier HS; New York City, NY; (Y); Nwsp Rptr; Off Sr Cls; Trs Stu Cncl; Swmmng; Tennis; Secnd Hnrs 84-85; Thrd Hnrs 85; Bus.

HINKELMAN, JEANNE; Nazareth Acad; Rochester, NY; (Y); Exploring; Ski Clb; Spanish Clb; Band; Rep Soph Cls; High Hon Roll; NHS; Girl Scts; Hon Roll; Riding Clb 82-85; Acad Achv In Spnsh 84-85; Yth Ministry 83; SCI.

HINKLE, SHARON; Johnstown HS; Johnstown, NY; (Y); Chorus; School Musical; School Play; Nwsp Stf; Yrbk Stf; JV Cheerleading; Timer; High Hon Roll; Prfct Atten Awd; Home Ec Awd 85; Gillen Schlrshp 85; Better Averge 4 Yrs 85; SUNY Plattsburgh; Elem Educ.

HINKLEY, JODI; Susquehanna Valley HS; Kirkwood, NY; (Y); French Clb; Girl Scts; Service Clb; Chorus; Rep Frsh Cls; Rep Soph Cls; Rep Jr Cls; Rep Stu Cncl; JV Bowling; JV Tennis; Bryant & Stratton; Fshn Mrch.

HINKSON, PAUL; Centereach HS; Centereach, NY; (Y); 54/482; Math Tm; Quiz Bowl; Band; Concert Band; Jazz Band; Mrchg Band; School Musical; Var L Socr; NHS; St Schlr; Messiah Coll; Phys.

HINNERS, EUGENE; SAUGERTIES HS; Saugerties, NY; (Y); Exploring; German Clb; Band; Chorus; Mrchg Band; Var Trk; Rochester Inst Of Tech; Comp.

HINTON, ALYSON E; Westbury HS; Westbury, NY; (Y); 15/220; Drama Clb; FBLA; Sec Key Clb; Varsity Clb; Band; Yrbk Ed-Chief; Stu Cncl; Var Cheerleading; Var Vllybl; NHS; CCSBE Awd 85; Schl Svc Awd 85; Yrbk Awd 85; MI U; Bus.

HINTZ, ANJANETTE; Jordan-Elbridge Central Schl; Memphis, NY; (Y); Ski Clb; Aud/Vis; Tennis; Hon Roll; Med.

HIRALALL, SHARON; Freeport HS; Freeport, NY; (Y); Girl Scts; Hosp Aide; Band; Chorus; Coach Actv; Sftbl; Tennis; Prfct Atten Awd; NY Mus Awd 82 & 83; Cert Hnr NYS Bar Assoc 84; Hofstra U; Accntng.

HIRANO, YOKO; Irvington HS; Irvington, NY; (Y); Church Yth Grp; Key Clb; Chorus; Swing Chorus; Yrbk Stf; Lit Mag; Jr Cls; Crs Cntry; Trk; High Hon Roll; Hon Roll; Hugh O Brien Ldrshp Awd 84; Comm Ambssdr George Washington Schl Engrng 85.

HIRSCH, JULIE; Bayside HS; Bayside, NY; (Y); 64/677; Pep Clb; Ski Clb; Teachers Aide; Bsktbl; Socr; Hon Roll; U Of WI-PSYCH.

HIRSCH, MITCHELL; Freeport HS; Freeport, NY; (Y); 85/450; Aud/Vis; Boy Scts; French Clb; Ski Clb; Band; Concert Band; Mrchg Band; Nwsp Phtg; Nwsp Rptr; Wrstlng; Adelphi U; Pre-Med.

HIRSCH, SUSAN; Nazareth Acad; Rochester, NY; (Y); Var Intnl Clb; Chorus; Var Hon Roll; Bst Crtcl Wrtng Awd 85; Ofcr Fidlty Tringl #4 83-84.

HIRSCHBERG, ROBERT; Sheepshead Bay HS; Brooklyn, NY; (Y); Cmnty Wkr; Library Aide; Office Aide; Spanish Clb; Drm Mjr(t); Nwsp Stf; Cit Awd; High Hon Roll; NHS; Prfct Atten Awd; Arista 85; Cornell; Vet.

HIRSCHL, ANN R; The Masters Schl; Washington, MO; (Y); Band; Concert Band; Mrchg Band; Orch; Symp Band; St Louis Sympny Yth Orch 80-83; MO ST Music Fest I Ratng 82-83; MO All ST Orch 82-83; Music.

HIRSCHL, CYNTHIA R; Seton Catholic Central HS; Binghamton, NY; (Y); 19/156; Art Clb; French Clb; Hosp Aide; Ski Clb; NHS; Grinnell Coll.

HIRSHAUT, AVIVA C; Torah Academy For Girls; Lawrence, NY; (Y); 1/17; Art Clb; Debate Tm; Drama Clb; Service Clb; Y-Teens; School Musical; Ntl Merit Ltr; St Schlr; Stern Coll For Women; Math.

HIRSHBEIN, PERETZ; Hunter College HS; New York, NY; (Y); Model UN; Temple Yth Grp; Pres Band; Orch; Yrbk Phtg; Mu Alp Tht; Ntl Merit SF; Pol Sci.

HIRSHON, GLENN D; Port Richmond HS; Staten Island, NY; (Y); 9/581; Math Tm; Sec Science Clb; Service Clb; Band; Concert Band; Orch; School Musical; Symp Band; 1st Pl Sci NY Amer Inst Sci & Tech; Recgn Achvt Mus 83-84; Apprectn Awd; NY Acad Sci Cert Merit; Phys.

HIRTH, REBECCA; Hendrick Hudson HS; Peekskill, NY; (Y); Drama Clb; Orch; School Play; Yrbk Stf; JV Stat Fld Hcky; Hon Roll; NHS; Spec Ed.

HIRTH, TODD; Christian Brothers Acad; Cazenovia, NY; (Y); 29/96; Church Yth Grp; Cmnty Wkr; Exploring; Red Cross Aide; Prfct Atten Awd; Brother Adolphus Hnr Soc 82-85; Hartwick Coll; Bio.

HITCHCOCK, CELINA; Mt Merry Acad; Buffalo, NY; (Y); Drama Clb; Science Clb; Stage Crew; Yrbk Ed-Chief; Yrbk Stf; Hon Roll; Exec Secy.

HITCHCOCK, DALE; Walton JR SR HS; Walton, NY; (Y); 7/100; Boy Scts; Church Yth Grp; Computer Clb; Trs Frsh Cls; Tennis; High Hon Roll; Hon Roll; Voice Dem Awd; Cert Awd Mbr SUS 85; Lg Champ Tennis Tm 82-83; High Hnr Rl Awd 83-84; Elec Engrng.

HITCHCOCK, PATTY; Union Springs Acad; Tonawanda, NY; (S); Chorus; Concert Band; School Musical; Variety Show; Stu Cncl; Hon Roll; NHS; Atlantic Union Coll; Medcl Admn.

HITCHCOCK, STACEY L; Pulaski Academy & Central Schl; Pulaski, NY; (S); Am Leg Aux Girls St; Church Yth Grp; Drama Clb; French Clb; GAA; Math Clb; Chorus; Color Guard; School Musical; Nwsp Stf; Acad All Amer 85; Tchr Of Hrng.

HITE, PAULA; Avon Central HS; Avon, NY; (Y); 19/106; Ski Clb; Spanish Clb; Chorus; Yrbk Stf; Stat Socr; JV Sftbl; Var Tennis; Var Trk; Stat Vllybl; Hon Roll; Pre-Law.

HITT, CHRISTOPHER; Bay Shore HS; Bay Shore, NY; (Y); Computer Clb; Yrbk Sprt Ed; Gym; Hon Roll; LEAD 85; SADD 83; Bus.

HITT, HEIDI; South Kortright Central HS; E Meredith, NY; (Y); 4/33; Band; School Play; Sec Sr Cls; Sec Stu Cncl; Bsktbl; Socr; Sftbl; High Hon Roll; NHS; Regents Scholar 84-85; Delhi Ag Ttech Coll; Psych.

HITT, JULIE; Walton Central HS; Walton, NY; (Y); Key Clb; Varsity Clb; VICA; Sec Soph Cls; Var Crs Cntry; Var Trk; JV Var Vllybl; Hon Roll; Mst Desire Excell Awd Trk & Crs Cntry 84-85; JR Prom Prncss 85; Mohawk Vly CC; Social Wrkr.

HITTNER, BARRIE; Sachem HS; Farmingville, NY; (Y); 60/1400; Drama Clb; Radio Clb; Chorus; School Musical; School Play; Stage Crew; Mgr Lit Mag; Sr Cls; Jr NHS; NHS; Ithaca Coll Schlrshp 85-86; Ithaca Coll.

HLADIK, TINA; Queensbury HS; Glens Falls, NY; (Y); Key Clb; Varsity Clb; Band; JV Var Fld Hcky; JV Var Trk; High Hon Roll; NHS; Prfct Atten Awd; Bus Admn.

HLAVATY, DAWN; Lake George HS; Lake George, NY; (Y); Dance Clb; Ski Clb; Var JV Bsktbl; Var Powder Puff Ftbl; Var JV Vllybl; Hon Roll; Western New Engl Coll; Psych.

HNELOSUB, MARIA; T R Proctor HS; Utica, NY; (Y); 9/175; Drama Clb; Chorus; School Musical; Stu Cncl; High Hon Roll; Hon Roll; Jr NHS; Kiwanis Awd; NHS; Prfct Atten Awd; Dr John P Sheehan Schlrhsp Trst Fnd 85-86; Boyd Golder Utica Kiwanis Schlrshp 85-86; Utica Coll; Comp Sci.

HO, STANLEY Y; Bronx HS Of Science; Briarwood, NY; (Y); Hosp Aide; Intnl Clb; Teachers Aide; Band; Nwsp Stf; Hon Roll; Med.

HO, WINSTON; Bronx H S Of Science; New York, NY; (Y); JA; Office Aide; Teachers Aide; Svc Awd-Holcst Stds Ctr 85; Poly Inst Brooklyn; Elec Engrng.

HOAG, DARLENE; Cato-Meridian Central HS; Cato, NY; (Y); Ski Clb; Yrbk Stf; Im Vllybl; Hon Roll; NHS; Bus.

HOAGLAND, JASON C; Whitehall JR SR HS; Whitehall, NY; (Y); 10/84; Var Bsbl; Hon Roll; Art Clb; Cmnty Wkr; French Clb; Letterman Clb; Varsity Clb; Var Bsktbl; Im Coach Actv; JV Crs Cntry; Part Drug Cnslng Prog 82-85; Plyd On NY ST Champ Bsbl Tm CC-DD Div 83-84; Phy Ed.

HOAGLAND, KIM; Kenmore West HS; Kenmore, NY; (Y); GAA; Varsity Clb; Color Guard; Stage Crew; Capt Tennis; Vllybl; Hon Roll; Hnrb Mntn Ten 84; All Star Hon Ten 83; Aviatn.

HOARE, MARLO J; Caniseo Central Schl; Canisteo, NY; (Y); 27/80; Church Yth Grp; Girl Scts; Orch; Yrbk Stf; Rep Stu Cncl; Var Bsktbl; High Hon Roll; NYS Regents Nrsng Schlrshp 85; Alfred Ag & Tech Coll; Nrs.

HOBAICA II, JOSEPH B; T R Proctor HS; Utica, NY; (Y); Am Leg Boys St; Pep Clb; Yrbk Stf; Trs Soph Cls; Trs Jr Cls; Trs Sr Cls; Rep Stu Cncl; Var L Crs Cntry; Lion Awd; Pres NHS; Cross Cnty Lgu All Star 83-84; Wrkshp Ldrshp 83-84; Colgate U Semnr 84; Suny Albany; Pre-Law.

HOBBINS, MICHAEL; St Marys Acad; Whitehall, NY; (S); 7/43; Boy Scts; French Clb; ROTC; Varsity Clb; Concert Band; Mrchg Band; Yrbk Stf; VP Sr Cls; Var L Ftbl; Var L Golf; Regnts & Navy ROTC Schlrshps; U S Naval Acad; Nuclr Engrng.

HOBBS, LISA; Far Rockaway HS; Brooklyn, NY; (Y); Church Yth Grp; VP Key Clb; Quiz Bowl; Teachers Aide; VP Stu Cncl; Hon Roll; Prfct Atten Awd; Queens Coll Pres Awd For Achv 84; Daily News Princpls Pride Of The Yankees Awd 84; Arista 85; Engrng.

HOCH, HEIDI A; Greece Athena HS; Rochester, NY; (Y); 60/306; DECA; Yrbk Ed-Chief; Yrbk Sprt Ed; Trs Pres Stu Cncl; Var Capt Bsktbl; Var L Socr; Var L Trk; Var Capt Vllybl; FBLA; VP Varsity Clb; Lilac Teen Pgnt Fnlst 84; All Cnty Vlybl Team 85; All Cnty Bsktbl Team 85; Intl Bus.

HOCHFELD, ERIC; Oceanside HS; Oceanside, NY; (Y); Intnl Clb; Library Aide; Model UN; Temple Yth Grp; JV Bsktbl; JV Socr; Im Sftbl; Hon Roll.

HOCHMAN, CARYN; Yeshira Univ HS For Girls; Brooklyn, NY; (Y); 13/80; Temple Yth Grp; Nwsp Rptr; Rep Stu Cncl; Prophets Awd, Acadmc Excellence Awd 85; Rgnts Schlrshp 85; Awd Excellence Frgn Plcy 85; Binghamton SUNY.

HOCHSTEIN, ALLISON; The Bronx High Schl Of Science; Bronx, NY; (Y); Drama Clb; Teachers Aide; Off Frsh Cls; Off Soph Cls; Off Jr Cls; Stu Cncl; Var L Socr; High Hon Roll; Prfct Atten Awd; Arista 85.

HOCHSTER, HOWARD J; Bayside HS; Bayside, NY; (Y); 15/700; Boy Scts; Ed Nwsp Phtg; Ed Yrbk Phtg; Swmmng; Tennis; Cit Awd; High Hon Roll; Jr NHS; Pres NHS; Aud/Vis; Benjamin Chancy Citation Of Honor 82; Yeshiva U; Biology.

HOCHULSKI, TOM; West Seneca East SR HS; Cheektowaga, NY; (Y); Hon Roll; Engrng.

HOCKER, NANCY J; Southold HS; Southold, NY; (Y); 7/56; Drama Clb; Off ROTC; Ski Clb; Spanish Clb; Drill Tm; School Play; Sec Stu Cncl; Co-Capt Cheerleading; Trk; Hon Roll; NY ST Rgnts Schlrshp 85; Creatve Wrtng Cntst Wnnr 84; Penn ST U; Bio.

HOCKEY, DAVID; West Genessee SR HS; Syracuse, NY; (Y); Ski Clb; Trk; High Hon Roll; Hon Roll; Prfct Atten Awd; Engrng.

HOCKING, KIM; Whitesboro SR HS; Whitesboro, NY; (Y); 17/358; Intnl Clb; Band; Nwsp Stf; Yrbk Stf; Lit Mag; Hon Roll; Jr NHS; NHS; Ntl Merit SF; Ed.

HODAPP, PATRICIA M; Mria Regina HS; White Plains, NY; (Y); 16/144; Church Yth Grp; Cmnty Wkr; Girl Scts; Service Clb; Teachers Aide; Chorus; Nwsp Rptr; High Hon Roll; NHS; Pres Schlr; Regents Schlrshp 85; Natl Hnr Scty 83-85; Pres Schlrshp 85; Manhattan Coll; Elec Engr.

HODELIN, FRANK; St Francis Preparatory Schl; Jamaica, NY; (Y); Art Clb; School Musical; Variety Show; Yrbk Stf; Hon Roll; Optimate Soc 82-83; Parsons Schl Art-Dsgn; Comm Art.

HODGE, ANDREA M; Paul V Moore HS; Brewerton, NY; (Y); Dance Clb; PAVAS; High Hon Roll; Hon Roll; Dance County Schl; Ballet.

HODGES, ERIC; Greece Athena HS; Rochester, NY; (Y); Q&S; Radio Clb; Nwsp Ed-Chief; Nwsp Sprt Ed; Yrbk Rptr; Lit Mag; Var Tennis; Hon Roll; Jnrlst Of The Yr 85; All-Cnty Tnns 83 & 85; Pres Of SADD 85; St Bonaventure U; Jrnlsm.

HODGES, MICHELLE; Whitney Point Central HS; Whitney Pt, NY; (Y); 33/115; Latin Clb; Ski Clb; Chorus; Swing Chorus; Cheerleading; Natl Ldrshp Awd 83; Spec Awds Dance 83-85; Amer Teen Miss Charm 85; Cortland; Guid Cnslr.

HODGSON, MELISSA; Nazareth Regional HS; Brooklyn, NY; (Y); Dance Clb; Chorus; School Musical; Yrbk Stf; Cheerleading; VA ST U; Secndry Educ.

HODNETT, CALVIN; Rice HS; New York, NY; (S); 11/101; Boy Scts; Chorus; Church Choir; Nwsp Rptr; Yrbk Ed-Chief; Yrbk Phtg; Stu Cncl; Var Bsktbl; L Trk; Hon Roll; Comp.

HODNETT, EVE L; Jamestown HS; Jamestown, NY; (Y); 113/409; Boys Clb Am; Pres JA; Ski Clb; Acpl Chr; Chorus; Church Choir; Bsktbl; Swmmng; Teach.

HODOS, JEROME; Albany HS; Albany, NY; (Y); 3/600; Cmnty Wkr; Debate Tm; Pres English Clb; Latin Clb; Teachers Aide; Concert Band; Nwsp Stf; Ed Lit Mag; Trk; Chess Clb; Harvard Book Prz 84; Malcolm Bump Mem Debate Tourn 1st Pl Novice 83; William D Goewey Mem Latin Prz 84; Harvard; Philsphy.

HOECKH, BARBARA; Mount Mercy Acad; Buffalo, NY; (S); 12/199; JA; JCL; Model UN; Nwsp Sprt Ed; Nwsp Stf; Im Ice Hcky; Im Vllybl; High Hon Roll; Hon Roll; NHS; Awd Merit Modl Un; 3rd Pl Natl Jr Cls League Exam; Hon Men Regnl Jr Cls League Exam; Canisius Coll; Med.

HOEFFNER, DONNA; Valley Central HS; Montgomery, NY; (Y); 20/300; Natl Beta Clb; Frsh Cls; Soph Cls; Jr Cls; Sr Cls; Var Bsktbl; Var Socr; Var Sftbl; Hon Roll; Spanish NHS; Engrng.

HOEFFNER, STEVE; Hornell SR HS; Hornell, NY; (Y); Boy Scts; Ski Clb; Pres Soph Cls; Hon Roll; Cert Mert Phy Sci; Ag.

HOEFLICH, LAUREN A; Woodmere Acad; Woodmere, NY; (Y); School Musical; School Play; Variety Show; Lit Mag; Rep Soph Cls; Rep Sr Cls; Var Socr; JV Vllybl; Brown Univ Book Awd 84; Outsndng Achvt Englsh 84; Cum Laude Soc 84; Cornell U; Bus.

HOEFLICH, MICHAEL; St Marys Dioceson HS; Lancaster, NY; (S); 7/192; Varsity Clb; Pres Jr Cls; Bsktbl; Crs Cntry; Ftbl; Tennis; Trk; High Hon Roll; Hon Roll; NHS; Intl Stu Ldrshp Inst Notre Dame 84-85; Acctng.

HOELER, DAVID; Copiague SR HS; Copiague, NY; (Y); 15/365; VP German Clb; Band; Concert Band; Jazz Band; Mrchg Band; Bsbl; Socr; Trk; Hon Roll; Prfct Atten Awd; German Natl Hon Soc 83-85; SUNY Farmingdale; Engrng.

HOEN, CYD; Bishop Maginn HS; Rensselaer, NY; (Y); GAA; Spanish Clb; School Play; JV Cheerleading; JV Score Keeper; Var Sftbl; Var Vllybl; High Hon Roll; Hon Roll; Cortland ST; Math.

HOENIG, DEBBIE; John Jay HS; Hopewell Jct, NY; (Y); Church Yth Grp; Teachers Aide; Wappingers Centrl Schls Tchrs Awd 85; Gordon Coll; Tchr.

HOENISCH, IAN; Rome Free Acad; Lee Center, NY; (Y); Computer Clb; Ski Clb; Varsity Clb; Scr; 4-H Awd; High Hon Roll; Hon Roll; Comp.

HOEPELMAN, WILLIAM J; Newtown HS; New York City, NY; (Y); Art Clb; Aud/Vis; PAVAS; School Play; Stage Crew; Ed Yrbk Ed-Chief; Yrbk Stf; Vllybl; German Clb; Intnl Clb; Spring Art Show Awd 84; Channel 13 Art Awd 84.

HOERBELT, MARK D; Batavia HS; Batavia, NY; (Y); 30/210; 4-H; Chorus; Church Choir; Orch; School Musical; Swing Chorus; Im Bsbl; Var JV Bsktbl; Im Bowling; Im Coach Actv; Orch Awd 83-85; Monroe Cty Tnns All Star 85; Choral Awd 84-85; Music.

HOERNER, JAMES G; Gates Chili HS; Rochester, NY; (Y); 24/463; Band; Chorus; Concert Band; Mrchg Band; School Musical; JV Socr; High Hon Roll; NHS; Ntl Merit Ltr; Pep Band; All ST Band Stu 82-84; Rochester Inst; Elec Engrng.

HOFER, BETH; General Douglas Mac Arthur HS; Wantagh, NY; (Y); 3/325; Cmnty Wkr; Sec Model UN; Science Clb; VP Temple Yth Grp; Orch; School Musical; Nwsp Stf; Yrbk Ed-Chief; Sec Stu Cncl; High Hon Roll; SUNY Stony Brook; Phys Thrpy.

HOFF, KRISTINE; Roy C Ketcham HS; Wappingers Falls, NY; (Y); AFS; DECA; Drama Clb; FBLA; Ski Clb; Color Guard; Mrchg Band; Stage Crew; Gym; Swmmng; Boston U; Bus.

HOFFBERG, AMY; Wantagh HS; Wantagh, NY; (Y); Drama Clb; Mathletes; Math Clb; Math Tm; Ski Clb; School Musical; School Play; Stage Crew; Boston U; Law.

HOFFELDER, CAROLYN; Garden City HS; Garden City, NY; (Y); Church Yth Grp; GAA; Hosp Aide; Office Aide; Pep Clb; Teachers Aide; JV Bsktbl; Var Fld Hcky; Var Lcrss; Hon Roll; Intl Fin.

HOFFERT, LINDA JEAN; Northville Central HS; Hadley, NY; (Y); 4/59; Am Leg Aux Girls St; Cmnty Wkr; Exploring; GAA; Sec Frsh Cls; Var Sftbl; JV Vllybl; Hon Roll; NHS; Natl Schltc Ftns Awd 85.

HOFFMAN, AMY; Victor SR HS; Macedon, NY; (Y); Am Leg Aux Girls St; Ski Clb; Spanish Clb; Concert Band; Mrchg Band; Yrbk Bus Mgr; Sec Pres Stu Cncl; High Hon Roll; Hon Roll; Boston Coll; Tchg Eng.

HOFFMAN, BRENDA; Corinth Central HS; Corinth, NY; (S); 22/98; Key Clb; MMM; Band; Chorus; Concert Band; Mrchg Band; Stat Fld Hcky; Htl Teh.

HOFFMAN, DAVID A; Kenmore West SR HS; Kenmore, NY; (Y); Boy Scts; JA; Capt Math Tm; Scholastic Bowl; Band; Orch; Im Bsktbl; Hon Roll; Trs Church Yth Grp; Civic Clb; 3rd Wrld Olymp Mind Comp 85; Outstndng Yuth Yr Awd 85; Law.

HOFFMAN, DEBBIE E; Bronx High School Of Science; New York, NY; (Y); Cmnty Wkr; JA; Library Aide; Political Wkr; Teachers Aide; Nwsp Ed-Chief; Nwsp Rptr; Nwsp Stf; Hon Roll.

HOFFMAN, ELLEN; Berlin Central HS; Petersburg, NY; (Y); 2/57; GAA; Nwsp Ed-Chief; Yrbk Ed-Chief; Cit Awd; High Hon Roll; NHS; Sal; Var Socr; JV Vllybl; Hon Roll; Irving Flaumenbaum Mem Schlrshp Awd 85; Edith Grace Craig Reynolds Schlrshp 85; NY ST Rgnts Schlrsh; SUNY Plattsburgh; Bus Mgmt.

HOFFMAN, HEATHER; Susan E Wagner HS; Staten Island, NY; (Y); Dance Clb; JA; Chorus; Variety Show; Nwsp Stf; Cit Awd; Hon Roll; Prfct Atten Awd; Wagner Coll; Soclgy.

HOFFMAN, JENNIFER; Sweet Home SR HS; North Tonawanda, NY; (Y); Trs Church Yth Grp; French Clb; Service Clb; Off Frsh Cls; Off Soph Cls; French Hon Soc; High Hon Roll; Hon Roll; Outstndng Volntr Awd 83-84.

HOFFMAN, JOHN P; Marcus Whitman Central HS; Gorham, NY; (Y); Am Leg Boys St; Boy Scts; Band; Concert Band; Mrchg Band; Bsbl; Bsktbl; Socr; High Hon Roll; NHS; Poltcl Sci.

HOFFMAN, JULIE; Barker Central HS; Barker, NY; (Y); Sec AFS; Am Leg Aux Girls St; Pres Church Yth Grp; French Clb; Varsity Clb; School Musical; Sec Stu Cncl; Var Capt Fld Hcky; Var L Trk; NHS; William & Mary; Frgn Lang.

HOFFMAN, KELLY A; Newfane Central HS; Newfane, NY; (Y); 18/162; AFS; Latin Clb; Ski Clb; Varsity Clb; Band; Concert Band; School Musical; Symp Band; Yrbk Rptr; Yrbk Sprt Ed; MI ST U; Frgn Lang.

HOFFMAN, KURT; Williamsville East HS; East Amherst, NY; (Y); Hon Roll; Prfct Atten Awd; Prfct Attndnc Awd 82-85; Mltry.

HOFFMAN, LAURA; Albertus Magnus HS; Suffern, NY; (Y); 30/200; Church Yth Grp; Cmnty Wkr; Letterman Clb; Varsity Clb; Y-Teens; Stage Crew; Yrbk Stf; Soc Studies Hnrs Pgm 83-84; Math,Sci Awd 82-85.

HOFFMAN, MARY M; Cardinal Spellman HS; Bronx, NY; (Y); Pres Civic Clb; Girl Scts; Drm Mjr(t); Mrchg Band; Stage Crew; Hon Roll; NYS Regnts Schlrshp 85; Ithaca Coll; Chem.

HOFFMAN, MEG; Our Lady Of Mercy HS; Rochester, NY; (Y); Girl Scts; Spanish Clb; Varsity Clb; Band; Stage Crew; JV Var Sftbl; Hon Roll; Grl Scout Slvr Awd 84; Technel Theatre.

HOFFMAN, MICHAEL J; Hamburg SR HS; Hamburg, NY; (Y); AFS; Am Leg Boys St; French Clb; Rep Jr Cls; Rep Stu Cncl; JV Bsbl; JV Var Bsktbl; Law.

HOFFMAN, MICHELLE; Mount Mercy Acad; Buffalo, NY; (S); 33/161; Computer Clb; JA; Nwsp Stf; Lit Mag; JV Bowling; Hon Roll; Valdctrn 82; Richmond Spkng Cntst Wnnr 81-82; Treas 82; SUNYAB; Nsrg.

HOFFMAN, PHILIP; Hillcrest HS; Rosedale, NY; (Y); Debate Tm; VP JA; Temple Yth Grp; Rep Stu Cncl; Im Gym; Ldrshp Trnng & JR Achvt 83; SUNY-ALBANY; Engl.

HOFFMAN, PHILIP S; Fairport HS; Fairport, NY; (Y); DECA; Drama Clb; School Play; VP Sr Cls; Bsbl; JV Wrstlng; Hon Roll; Boy Scts; Church Yth Grp; 4-H; NY ST Schl Acting 84; Best Actor Awd 84; 1st Pl Regnls DECA Radio Adv 83; Theatre.

HOFFMAN JR, ROBERT; Northville Central HS; Speculator, NY; (Y); Drama Clb; French Clb; Band; School Musical; School Play; JV Socr; High Hon Roll; Val; Boy Scts; Church Yth Grp; Babe Ruth Awd; Alg Awd Hghst Scr On Regents; Fulton Montgomery CC; Elec Tch.

HOFFMAN, SAMUEL; United Nations International Schl; Forest Hills, NY; (Y); Model UN; PAVAS; Nwsp Stf; Lit Mag; Var Tennis; Hon Roll; Estrn Tennis Assoc 83-84; Ldr Nuclear Issue Grp 84-85; Econ.

HOFFMAN, SUZANNE; Mount Saint Mary HS; Kenmore, NY; (Y); 4/115; Pep Clb; Ski Clb; Spanish Clb; Teachers Aide; Nwsp Ed-Chief; Nwsp Rptr; Nwsp Stf; Yrbk Stf; Lit Mag; Var Badmtn; Erie County Rnr Up Doubles Badmitton 83; MVP Var Ten 84; Logo Cont Wnnr 84.

HOFFMANN, ANN; Albetus Magnus HS; Stony Point, NY; (Y); 10/190; Drama Clb; Math Tm; Stage Crew; Nwsp Stf; Im Bsktbl; Var Crs Cntry; Var Trk; High Hon Roll; Hon Roll; NHS; Latin, Math & Sci Hnr Soc; Comm.

HOFFMANN, BARBARA L; Locust Valley HS; Bayville, NY; (Y); 1/186; Art Clb; Cmnty Wkr; Hosp Aide; Spanish Clb; Yrbk Stf; Lit Mag; Tennis; High Hon Roll; NHS; Val; Excel Expositry Wrtng,Am Hist; Acad Excel; Wesleyan U; Bio.

HOFFMANN, KENNETH A; La Salle Military Acad; Stony Brook, NY; (Y); 10/100; Am Leg Boys St; Cmnty Wkr; ROTC; Chorus; Drill Tm; Ed Nwsp Stf; Var L Socr; NHS; Mst Dedicated La Salle Rifles Drill Tm Awd 84-85; Pre-Law.

HOFFMANN, LAURA; Newfield HS; Centereach, NY; (Y); Hosp Aide; VICA; Var L Crs Cntry; Var L Trk; Hon Roll; Prfct Atten Awd; Pres Schlr; Presdntl Awd Phy Ed 85; Nrsng.

HOFFOWER, KATE B; Fairport HS; Fairport, NY; (Y); Drama Clb; German Clb; Y-Teens; School Play; Yrbk Stf; Fld Hcky; Hon Roll; Yth Yr Awd 82; Best Actrss Trphy 84; Vrsty Ltr Field Hockey 83; Acting.

HOFMANN, CANDANCE; Schoharie Central Schl; Howes Cave, NY; (Y); Band; Color Guard; Concert Band; Co-Capt Flag Corp; Mrchg Band; Prfct Atten Awd; Bus.

HOFMANN, ELEANOR; The Mary Louis Acad; Jamaica, NY; (Y); Chorus; Recognition-Svcs Mendered At Schl 84; Librl Arts.

HOFMANN, GREGORY; Attica Central HS; Attica, NY; (S); 6/150; JV Bsbl; JV Var Bsktbl; Var Socr; Hon Roll.

HOGAN, ELLEN; Smithtown H S East; Nesconset, NY; (Y); Cit Awd; Hon Roll; Regents Nursing Schlrshp 85; Suffolk CC; Nrsng.

HOGAN, ELLIE F; Columbia HS; E Greenbush, NY; (Y); Cosmetology.

HOGAN JR, JOHN F; Mt St Michael Acad; Bronx, NY; (Y); 46/308; Nwsp Stf; Im Bsktbl; Im Fld Hcky; Im Ftbl; Hon Roll; Manhattan Coll; Engrng.

HOGAN, KELLY; Cardinal Mooney HS; Rochester, NY; (Y); Church Yth Grp; Library Aide; Varsity Clb; Stage Crew; Variety Show; Yrbk Stf; Socr; Niagra; Trvl.

HOGAN, KEVIN; Elmira Free Acad; Elmira, NY; (Y); Church Yth Grp; Ski Clb; Spanish Clb; Stu Cncl; Var Ftbl; Var Trk; Citznshp Awd 79; Optmtrst.

HOGAN, MATTHEW J; La Salle Inst; Troy, NY; (Y); 10/85; Am Leg Boys St; ROTC; VP Ski Clb; Nwsp Stf; Bsbl; Hon Roll; NHS; Ntl Merit Ltr; Siena Coll; Pol Sci.

HOGAN, MICHELE; Westmoreland Central HS; Clinton, NY; (Y); GAA; Chorus; Nwsp Rptr; Var JV Bsktbl; Var JV Socr; Sftbl; High Hon Roll; Bsktbl All Star Ltr 83-85; Sftbl Capt MVP MIP & All Star 85; Data Proc.

HOGAN, SUZANNE M; C W Baker HS; Baldwinsville, NY; (Y); Philip Morris Intl Stu Exch Schlrshp 85; U Buffalo; Engrng.

HOGAN, THOMAS; Lehman HS; New York, NY; (Y); 69/444; Hon Roll; St Schlr; Comp Tech Awd; Iona Coll; Bus.

HOGANCAMP, REBECCA A; Southside HS; Pine City, NY; (Y); 2/333; Model UN; Pres Spanish Clb; Swing Chorus; Symp Band; Yrbk Ed-Chief; Stu Cncl; High Hon Roll; NHS; Sal; NYS Regnts Schlrshp 85; Ntl Merit Schlrshp 84; VA Poly Tech; Physcs.

HOGENKAMP, EILEEN; Buffalo Academy Of The Sacred Heart; Williamsville, NY; (Y); Church Yth Grp; Cmnty Wkr; Drama Clb; French Clb; Hosp Aide; Key Clb; Pep Clb; Service Clb; Ski Clb; Stage Crew; Canisius Coll; Accntnt.

HOGG, FRED; Silver Creek Central HS; Silver Creek, NY; (Y); Church Yth Grp; Spanish Clb; Varsity Clb; Nwsp Rptr; Nwsp Stf; Yrbk Rptr; Var Bsbl; Var Bsktbl; Var Ftbl; Var Trk; NYS Phys Ftns Awd 84 & 85; Syracuse U; Sci.

HOGG, WILLIAM C; Uniondale HS; Uniondale, NY; (Y); 52/480; Mathletes; JV Bsktbl; JV Ftbl; High Hon Roll; Hon Roll; NHS; Elec Engr.

HOGLE, KAREN; Knox Memorial Central HS; Hermon, NY; (S); French Clb; Concert Band; Mrchg Band; Yrbk Ed-Chief; Sec Jr Cls; Stat Score Keeper; Var Socr; Var Vllybl; High Hon Roll; Sci Stu Awd 85; Whiz Quiz Tm Mbr 85; St John Fisher Coll; Gerontlgy.

HOGREWE, KYLE; Crand Island HS; Gr Island, NY; (Y); GAA; Variety Show; Nwsp Rptr; Nwsp Stf; Yrbk Stf; Sec Frsh Cls; Sec Sr Cls; Rep Stu Cncl; JV Cheerleading; Hon Roll; SADD Awd; Mst Schl Spirit Awd; Involvmnt Cls Bus Awd; Criminal Justice.

HOGUE, KRISTEN; Shenendehowa HS; Clifton Park, NY; (Y); 160/800; AFS; Church Yth Grp; FBLA; Leo Clb; Temple Yth Grp; High Hon Roll; Hon Roll; Accptd NY ST Smmr Schl Arts 85; Arts.

HOHL, ROD; Somers HS; Katonah, NY; (Y); Hon Roll; Regnts Schlrshp 84; Compsg Muscn.

HOHLOWSKI, SEAN; E L Vandermuellen HS; Port Jefferson, NY; (Y); Camp Fr Inc; Computer Clb; Science Clb; Im Bsktbl; Var Golf; Im Ice Hcky; Im Tennis; Var Trk; Hon Roll; Outdoor Clb 83-84; Engr.

HOINICKI, LESA; West Seneca East SR Ny; Buffalo, NY; (Y); 7/365; GAA; Pep Clb; Var L Crs Cntry; Var Capt Trk; Stat Vllybl; High Hon Roll; JC Awd; NHS; U Of Rochester Alumni Regnl Scholar 85; NYS Regnts Scholar 85; MVP Girls Vrsty Trk Tm 84 & 85; U Of Rochester; Psych.

HOJNACKI, KAREN; Smithtown High School East; St James, NY; (Y); Hosp Aide; Key Clb; Pres Spanish Clb; Nwsp Phtg; Yrbk Phtg; Sr Cls; Cit Awd; High Hon Roll; NHS; Pres Schlr; Knights Of Columbus Commnty Ldr 84-85; Coll William & Mary; Intl Rltns.

HOJNICKI, LESA M; W Seneca East SR HS; Cheektowaga, NY; (Y); 7/365; GAA; Yrbk Rptr; Yrbk Stf; Var Crs Cntry; Var Capt Trk; High Hon Roll; NHS; NYS Regnts Schlrshp 85; U Rochester Almni Reg Schlrshp 85; Psychlgy.

HOKE, HEATHER-MARIE; Owen D Young Central Schl; Jordanville, NY; (Y); Band; School Play; Nwsp Stf; Trs Sec Stu Cncl; JV Capt Cheerleading; JV Var Vllybl; High Hon Roll; Jr NHS; Church Yth Grp; Q&S; Spec Awd In Govrnrs Trphy Rsrch Cont 85; Mst Imprvd Awd In Sccr 85; Bus Mgmt.

HOKE, MICHAEL; La Fayette HS; Jamesville, NY; (Y); VP FFA; Var Capt Bsktbl; Var L Lcrss; Hon Roll; Polc Sci.

HOKENSON, HEIDI; Farmingdale HS; Farmingdale, NY; (Y); 4/625; Key Clb; Sec Band; Mrchg Band; School Musical; Yrbk Ed-Chief; Var Capt Badmtn; Var Socr; Var Capt Tennis; Pres Sec NHS; Brd Of Ed Awd 85; Farmingdale PTA Schlrshp 85; Abigail E Leonard Awd 85; Cornell U; Labor Rltns.

HOLBEN, AMY P; Lake Shore Central HS; Angola, NY; (Y); 13/259; Church Yth Grp; Ski Clb; Nwsp Ed-Chief; Nwsp Rptr; Yrbk Stf; Trk; Hon Roll; NHS; NYS Regnts Schlrshp 85; Alfred U; Cermc Engr.

HOLCK, LYNN MARIE; Pittsford Mendon HS; Pittsford, NY; (Y); Church Yth Grp; Math Clb; Model UN; Pep Clb; Band; Orch; Trk; High Hon Roll; Hon Roll; NHS; Law.

HOLCOMB JR, JOHN; Pioneer HS; Arcade, NY; (Y); 1/208; Concert Band; Drm Mjr(t); Ed Lit Mag; Capt Diving; Tennis; Bausch & Lomb Sci Awd; JP Sousa Awd; Ntl Merit Ltr; Pres Schlr; Val; St Bonaventure U; Math.

HOLDEN, AMY E; Hackley Schl; Rye Brook, NY; (Y); 4/89; AFS; Model UN; Yrbk Stf; JV Lcrss; High Hon Roll; Ntl Merit SF; Rotary Awd; Hgh Hnrs Cert 83-84; Nacel Cltrl Exch Frnc 83; Scl Sci.

HOLDER, FRANCINE; South Shore HS; Brooklyn, NY; (Y); #600 In Class; Church Yth Grp; Dance Clb; Church Choir; Concert Band; School Play; Rep Sr Cls; Trk; Irwin Tobin Phys Ed Awd 85; Music Svc Awd 85; SR Cls Rep Awd 85; La Guardia Coll; Bus Mgmt.

HOLDER, MICHAEL A; Mt St Michael Acad; Bronx, NY; (Y); JV Var Bsktbl; MVP In Irland 85; All Str Boys Yesteryr Smmr Leag 83; Plyd Vrsty 84; Pro Bsktbl.

HOLDER, ROCHELLE; Kenmore East SR HS; Tonawanda, NY; (Y); Trs Pres GAA; Rep Frsh Cls; Rep Stu Cncl; Capt L Bsktbl; Var L Trk; High Hon Roll; Hon Roll; NHS; Ntl Merit Ltr; Prfct Atten Awd; U Of Notre Dame; Intl Bus Adm.

HOLDSWORTH, GEORGE M; The Stony Brook Schl; Mt Sinai, NY; (Y); 1/96; Yrbk Phtg; Yrbk Sprt Ed; L Capt Bsbl; Coach Actv; Var L Ftbl; High Hon Roll; Ntl Merit Schol; Val; Rensselaer Mdl Math & Sci 84; Strong Awd Chem 83; Cum Laude Soc 85; Rensselaer Polytech Inst; Comp.

HOLLAND, STANLEY; Horseheads HS; Horseheads, NY; (S); 37/409; Hon Roll; Engrng.

HOLLAND, WANDA; The Chapin Schl; Brooklyn, NY; (Y); Church Yth Grp; Teachers Aide; Chorus; Church Choir; Sec Stu Cncl; Im Bsktbl; Im Vllybl; Regents Schlrshp Awd 85; Columbia U; Eng Prof.

HOLLENBECK, KAREN; Candar HS; Candor, NY; (Y); Varsity Clb; Chorus; Trs Frsh Cls; Im Badmtn; Var L Bsktbl; Powder Puff Ftbl; Var L Sftbl; Var L Vllybl; Hon Roll; Prfct Atten Awd; Comptr.

HOLLENBECK, LAURA S; Hamburg HS; Hamburg, NY; (Y); 37/387; Church Yth Grp; Dance Clb; French Clb; Hosp Aide; Varsity Clb; Church Choir; Rep Soph Cls; Rep Jr Cls; Var Capt Cheerleading; JV Var Socr; Cornell; Surgeon.

HOLLER, KATHLEEN; De Sales Catholic HS; Lockport, NY; (Y); Church Yth Grp; Cmnty Wkr; GAA; Varsity Clb; Var Bsktbl; Var Sftbl; Capt Var Vllybl; Niagara; Nrsng.

HOLLERAN, PAT; Elmira Southside HS; Elmira, NY; (Y); Church Yth Grp; FCA; Letterman Clb; Political Wkr; Spanish Clb; Varsity Clb; Socr; Cit Awd; Hon Roll; Star Gazette Carrier Mnth 83; Citznshp Awd 82; Math.

HOLLEY, PATRICK; East Islip HS; East Islip, NY; (Y); JV Var Bsbl; Var L Ftbl; Im Sftbl; Im Vllybl; Im Wt Lftg; All Legue Bsbl Jr 85; Chef.

HOLLEY, VINCENT K; Hornell HS; Harnell, NY; (S); 11/198; CAP; Computer Clb; High Hon Roll; NHS; Prfct Atten Awd; Alfred U; Finance.

HOLLIDAY, MARGARET; Fairport HS; Fairport, NY; (Y); Office Aide; Varsity Clb; Var Capt Cheerleading; Hon Roll; NHS; Ldrshp Awd 85; Pre-Med.

HOLLIDAY, PAUL; George Washington HS; New York, NY; (Y); Im Bsktbl; Var Bowling; Var Ftbl; Im Swmmng; Im Vllybl; Outstndng Achv Data Prcssng & Coll Bound 83-85; Manhattan Coll; Bus Mgmt.

HOLLIS, PHILISSE; Wyandanch JR SR HS; Wyandanch, NY; (Y); 15/98; Rep Church Yth Grp; Rep Drama Clb; VP French Clb; Rep Girl Scts; VP JA; Sec Trs Key Clb; Rep Stage Crew; Pres Nwsp Sprt Ed; Pres Nwsp Stf; Sec Soph Cls; Cornell U NY; Mth.

HOLLISTER, KATHY; Pittsford Sutherland HS; Pittsford, NY; (Y); Trs Church Yth Grp; School Musical; Yrbk Ed-Chief; Fld Hcky; Trk; High Hon Roll; NHS; Art Clb; French Clb; Stage Crew; Natl Frnch Test 5th Pl Natl 83; Colby Coll; Bio.

HOLLISTER, KIM; Tioga Central HS; Barton, NY; (S); 3/72; Varsity Clb; Nwsp Ed-Chief; Pres Frsh Cls; Pres Soph Cls; Capt Cheerleading; High Hon Roll; Pres NHS; Lib Clb Pres; Outstndng Chrldr; Geneseo; Engr.

HOLLISTER, WALTER; Seaford HS; Seaford, NY; (Y); Chess Clb; Chorus; Hon Roll; Farmingdale; Elec Technlgy.

HOLLMAN, JOAN; Hicksville HS; Hicksville, NY; (Y); Drm & Bgl; Mrchg Band; School Play; Pom Pon; Jr NHS; NHS; Am Leg 85; AZ ST U; Mrktng.

HOLLOWAY, SYBIL; Our Lady Of Mercy Acad; Westbury, NY; (Y); VP Computer Clb; Pres Dance Clb; Sec Girl Scts; Pres Science Clb; Sec Spanish Clb; Masonic Awd; Prfct Atten Awd; Mrch Of Dimes Dstngshd Stu Hlth Career Awd 85; Grl Sct 5-Yr Awd 83; Hnt Merit Fndtns Ntl Hnr Roll 85; Smith Coll; Bio.

HOLLOWAY, VICTORIA; Woodlands HS; White Plains, NY; (Y); 1/200; Hosp Aide; Math Tm; Concert Band; Orch; Rep Stu Cncl; High Hon Roll; NHS; VP Exploring; Symp Band; Mst Outstndng Acad Hon Natl Cncl Negro Wmn 85; Columbia U Sci Hnrs Pgm 84-86; Amer Musicl Fndtn Awd 85; Med.

HOLLWEDEL, DEBRA; Islip HS; Islip, NY; (Y); Church Yth Grp; Band; Drill Tm; School Musical; Stage Crew; Yrbk Stf; Jr NHS; NHS; Elem Educ.

HOLLY, LISA; John Dewey HS; Brooklyn, NY; (Y); Chorus; Jrnlsm.

HOLM, DAWN; Bishop Kearney HS; Brooklyn, NY; (Y); FNA; Hosp Aide; Rep Jr Cls; NHS; Church Yth Grp; Bowling; Cheerleading; Hon Roll; Pace U; RN.

HOLM, VANESSA; Torreton American HS; Oildale, CA; (Y); Red Cross Aide; School Musical; Nwsp Bus Mgr; Nwsp Ed-Chief; Nwsp Rptr; Nwsp Sprt Ed; Nwsp Stf; Yrbk Phtg; Yrbk Stf; Rep Frsh Cls; Outstndng JR, SR; Bus Mgmnt.

HOLMAN, ERIC; Jordan-Elbridge HS; Jordan, NY; (Y); Church Yth Grp; Varsity Clb; Church Choir; Rep Frsh Cls; JV Var Bsbl; JV Var Bsktbl; Im Fld Hcky; JV Var Ftbl; JV Lcrss; Im Vllybl.

HOLMES, ANN MARY; St Patricks CC HS; Hudson, NY; (Y); 6/40; Ski Clb; Nwsp Stf; Yrbk Stf; Rep Frsh Cls; Bowling; NHS; Regents Schlrshp 85; Ct Saint Vncnt Coll; Comm.

HOLMES, HEIDI MARGARET; John C Birdlebough HS; Phoenix, NY; (Y); 24/200; Trs German Clb; High Hon Roll; Hon Roll; NHS; SUNY-OSWEGO; Comp Sci.

HOLMES, JIMMY; Seaford HS; Seaford, NY; (Y); Band; Mrchg Band; School Musical; Stage Crew; Rep Frsh Cls; Stat Bsktbl; Stat Score Keeper; Im Vllybl; Bus Mgmnt.

HOLMES, KESHIA R; St Francis Prep; Brooklyn, NY; (Y); #110 In Class; Library Aide; NFL; Science Clb; Band; Concert Band; Nwsp Rptr; Nwsp Stf; Off Jr Cls; Off Sr Cls; Hon Roll; Schlrshp Duke 84-85; Ntl Spch Fnls 85; Duke U Durham; Pre Med.

HOLMES, KIMBERLY; Royalton Hartland Central HS; Middleport, NY; (Y); Cmnty Wkr; French Clb; VP Orch; Nwsp Rptr; Hon Roll; NHS; All Cnty Orchstr; Annoucers Clb; Elem Ed.

HOLMES, LAURA M; Smithtown H S West; Smithtown, NY; (Y); Church Yth Grp; Band; Concert Band; Mrchg Band; Hon Roll; NHS; Italian Hnr Soc 84; NY Regents Schlrshp 85; Rensselaer Polytechnic; Engrng.

HOLMES, NICHOLAS M; Pittsford Mendon HS; Pittsford, NY; (Y); Church Yth Grp; Cmnty Wkr; Drama Clb; Math Clb; Model UN; Chorus; School Musical; School Play; Rep Stu Cncl; JV Tennis; Black Schlrs 84-85; Mnrty Stu Lab Apprntcshp 84; Georgetown U; Biology.

HOLMES, ROBIN; Hartford Central HS; Fort Ann, NY; (S); Church Yth Grp; 4-H; French Clb; Math Tm; Pep Clb; Science Clb; Ski Clb; Band; Chorus; Church Choir; Comp Sci.

HOLMES, TONIA VICTORIA; Norman Thomas HS; Brooklyn, NY; (S); 59/671; Girl Scts; JA; Temple Yth Grp; Chorus; Yrbk Stf; Cheerleading; Hon Roll; SUNY Old Westbury; Accntng.

HOLMSTROM, GAIL; Clymer Central HS; Clymer, NY; (Y); AFS; Church Yth Grp; 4-H; Chorus; Church Choir; Yrbk Ed-Chief; Yrbk Stf; JV Cheerleading; High Hon Roll; NHS; Bus Coll; Secr.

HOLNESS, CHRISTINA; Cardinal Spellman HS; Bronx, NY; (Y); Cmnty Wkr; Spanish Clb; Nwsp Rptr; Lit Mag; Syracuse U; Jrnlsm.

HOLODAK, THERESA; Sacred Heart HS; Yonkers, NY; (S); 8/240; Sec Am Leg Aux Girls St; Drama Clb; Intnl Clb; Rep Jr Cls; Var Trk; Var Vllybl; High Hon Roll; NHS; Jr Pres Slovak Cath Sch 84-85; Iona Coll; Mrkg.

HOLOHAN, RAYMOND; St Marys Boys HS; Bellmore, NY; (Y); 16/158; Nwsp Rptr; Yrbk Stf; Im Bowling; JV Golf; Hon Roll; Ntl Merit Ltr; Engrng.

HOLSEY, MICHAEL; Herbert H Lehman HS; Bronx, NY; (Y); Boy Scts; Cmnty Wkr; Rep Frsh Cls; Bsbl; Bsktbl; Ftbl; Socr; Wt Lftg; Hon Roll; Prfct Atten Awd; Life Sci 84.

HOLSINGER, PAUL; Rocky Point JR SR HS; Rocky Pt, NY; (Y); 24/207; Am Leg Boys St; Boy Scts; Church Yth Grp; Computer Clb; German Clb; Science Clb; JV Wrstlng; Hon Roll; Arntcl Engrng.

HOLSTEAD, CATHY; Central HS; Valley Stream, NY; (Y); Ski Clb; Band; Concert Band; Mrchg Band; School Play; Var Socr; Sftbl; High Hon Roll; Jr NHS; NHS; Phy Ther.

HOLSTEIN, RICH; Jamesville De Witt HS; Syracuse, NY; (Y); Temple Yth Grp; Band; Concert Band; Pep Band; JV Bsbl; Var Bowling; Ftbl; Var Swmmng; High Hon Roll; Socl Studies Awd 85; Svc Awd 85; VA U; Bio Chem.

HOLT, BECKY; Fort Ann Central HS; Ft Ann, NY; (Y); 3/57; Drama Clb; Red Cross Aide; Teachers Aide; High Hon Roll; NHS; Dicksonson; Author.

HOLT, KERRIE A; Catskill SR HS; Catskill, NY; (Y); 23/139; Church Yth Grp; Chorus; Church Choir; School Musical; Yrbk Stf; Rep Stu Cncl; Hon Roll; Jr NHS; Regents Schlrshp 85; Marguerite Young Awd Outstndng Stu 83; SUNY Plattsburg; Elem Ed.

HOLT, RAYMOND R; G Ray Bodley HS; Fulton, NY; (Y); 7/268; Exploring; VP German Clb; Pres Science Clb; Capt L Gym; Capt L Trk; Hon Roll; NHS; Chorus; School Musical; Variety Show; All Onondaga Leag Gymnstcs Awd 83; Pres Acad Awd 85; Sox Stuber Sprtsmnshp Meml Awd 85; Syracuse U; Bio Sci.

HOLTHOUSE, BETHANN; Clymer Central HS; N Clymer, NY; (Y); Church Yth Grp; Sec 4-H; Library Aide; Chorus; Church Choir; Yrbk Bus Mgr; 4-H Awd; High Hon Roll; NHS; Dietitics.

HOLTON, DENISE E; Valley Steam Central HS; Valley Stream, NY; (Y); Drama Clb; Chorus; Orch; School Musical; School Play; Lit Mag; NHS; Ntl Merit Ltr; Madrigals; Variety Show; NY ST Rgnts Schlrshp; Music Hnr Soc 84-85; Hofstra U; Law.

HOLTZ, DONNA L; Akron Central Schl; Akron, NY; (Y); 18/157; French Clb; Concert Band; Mrchg Band; Swmmng; NHS; U Of Scranton; Phy Thrpy.

HOLVIK, SHARON; Huntington HS; Huntington Sta, NY; (Y); Sec Church Yth Grp; Hosp Aide; Band; Church Choir; JV Cheerleading; Var L Fld Hcky; High Hon Roll; Hon Roll; Jr NHS; NHS; Nrsng.

HOLWAY, KELLY; Grand Island HS; Grand Island, NY; (Y); 5/325; GAA; Varsity Clb; Hst Jr Cls; Hst Sr Cls; Var Stat Bsktbl; Var L Socr; Var L Sftbl; High Hon Roll; NHS; Ntl Merit Ltr; Spec Educ.

HOLZ, LARRY; Commack High School South; Dix Hills, NY; (S); Church Yth Grp; Math Tm; Teachers Aide; Chorus; Variety Show; Var JV Ftbl; L Var Trk; High Hon Roll; Hon Roll; BOCES Summer Pgm For Gifted & Talented 84.

HOLZMAN, KAREN; Connetquot HS; Bohemia, NY; (Y); Church Yth Grp; Chorus; Church Choir; Off Frsh Cls; Off Soph Cls; Off Jr Cls; Off Sr Cls; Stu Cncl; 4-H; JA; Music Awd Chrs 83; Outstndg Achvt 82; Nysoma Medls 82-85; Chld Ed.

HOLZWEISS, ROBERT; Franciscan HS; Peekskill, NY; (Y); Yrbk Stf; Sec Jr Cls; Stu Cncl; Bsbl; Bsktbl; Capt Var Socr; Hon Roll; NHS; Spanish NHS; NEDT Achvt Awd 83; Cvl Engr.

HOM, BILL; Monsignor Mc Clancy Memorial HS; Woodside, NY; (Y); 30/229; Camera Clb; French Clb; JA; Library Aide; Math Clb; Science Clb; Yrbk Phtg; Yrbk Stf; High Hon Roll; Hon Roll; NY U Schlrshp 85; Principals List 83; 1st & 2nd Hnr Listing 83-84; NY U; Bus.

HOM, DANNY W; La Salle Academy HS; Long Island City, NY; (S); Camera Clb; Chess Clb; Hosp Aide; Im Bowling; MA Inst Of Tech; Chemcl Engr.

HOM, JUDITH; Sachem HS North Campus; Holbrook, NY; (Y); 15/1383; French Clb; Math Tm; Im Badmtn; Stat Sftbl; Im Vllybl; Hon Roll; Jr NHS; NHS; Prfct Atten Awd; Best Bio 82; Long Isl Sci Congrss Merit 82 & 84; Med.

HOM, XENIA B; Hillcrest HS; Jamaica, NY; (Y); 9/793; Church Yth Grp; Hosp Aide; JA; Band; Church Choir; Orch; Yrbk Stf; Lit Mag; NHS; St Schlr; Chancy Citation Music 82; NYU Trustee Schlrshp 85; NYU-CORNELL; Bio Sci.

HOMAN, LAUREN J; Sachem HS North; Farmingville, NY; (Y); 502/1508; Dance Clb; Girl Scts; Ski Clb; Chorus; Concert Band; Mrchg Band; Dance & Flag Tm; Dance Out Musclar Dystrphy; Towson ST U; Dance.

HOMENICK, JENNIFER; Schenectady Christian HS; Clifton Park, NY; (Y); Church Yth Grp; Hosp Aide; Key Clb; Chorus; Church Choir; School Musical; Yrbk Stf; Cheerleading; High Hon Roll.

HOMER, CHRISTOPHER M; Cortland JR SR HS; Cortland, NY; (Y); 40/244; Stage Crew; Var L Socr; Hon Roll; NHS; NY ST Regents Schlrshp 84-85; Hobart Coll; Vet.

HOMER, CLAUDIA; Queensbury HS; Glen Falls, NY; (Y); 39/230; Church Yth Grp; 4-H; French Clb; Girl Scts; Key Clb; Cheerleading; Socr; Tennis; Trk; Albany ST; Mktg.

HOMICK, BARBARA; Auburn HS; Auburn, NY; (Y); 20/444; Church Yth Grp; French Clb; Political Wkr; Nwsp Ed-Chief; Lit Mag; High Hon Roll; NHS; VFW Awd; Model UN; Teachers Aide; Regnts Schlrshp Awd 85; Joseph Malyaso Memrl Schlrshp 85; Geneseo ST Coll; Engl.

HOMICZ, BETH J; Shenendehowa HS; Ballston Lake, NY; (Y); 5/710; Art Clb; Cmnty Wkr; Drama Clb; Sec Intnl Clb; Nwsp Rptr; Nwsp Stf; High Hon Roll; NHS; Rotary Awd; Plcd In Ntl Frnch Cntst 84; Hghst Achvt In Frnch I 83; SADD Pres 84-86; Mdlbry Grgtwn; Frnch.

HONAN, STEPHAN; St John The Baptist HS; Brentwood, NY; (Y); Var Crs Cntry; Ftbl; Var Trk; Hon Roll; Vrsty Trk Awd 85; VA Poly Tech Inst; Arch.

HONEY, MARK; Falloner Central HS; Kennedy, NY; (Y); 3/105; FBLA; Bsktbl; Crs Cntry; Trk; Hon Roll; NHS; Regents Scholar 85; Frshmn Merit Awd Fredonia 85; Fredonia; Bus Admin.

HONEYWELL, NADJA; Sheepshead Bay HS; Brooklyn, NY; (Y); Art Clb; Church Yth Grp; Church Choir; Gym; Hon Roll; Prfct Atten Awd; Frnch, Art & Daily Nws Artstc Awds 84-85; Columbia U; Med.

HONG, GENE K; Williamsville South HS; Williamsville, NY; (Y); 12/245; Church Yth Grp; Computer Clb; Math Clb; Math Tm; Ski Clb; Concert Band; Jazz Band; Orch; Pep Band; Yrbk Stf.

HONG, HIEN C; Edison Vo Tech; Rochester, NY; (Y); 8/271; Math Clb; Math Tm; JV Ftbl; Hon Roll; Regent Schlrshp 85; JETS Team Comp 85; RIT; Elec Engr.

HONG, KATHERINE M; Academy Of The Holy Names; Loudonville, NY; (Y); Math Tm; NFL; Chorus; Nwsp Bus Mgr; Yrbk Bus Mgr; Lit Mag; Office Aide; Variety Show; Nwsp Stf; Natl Sci Merit Awds Chem 85; Olympd Awd Chem 85; Outstndng Achvt Math 85; Pharm.

HONG, MAY; Jamaica HS; Jamaica, NY; (Y); Intnl Clb; Lit Mag; Vllybl; Hon Roll; NYCC; Bio.

HONG, PATRICIA M; Scarsdale HS; Scarsdale, NY; (Y); Church Yth Grp; Teachers Aide; Ed Lit Mag; NHS; Sftbl; Regents Schlrshp 85; U PA.

HONG, PAULA; Dominican Acad; Jackson Hts, NY; (Y); 12/53; Science Clb; School Musical; Yrbk Stf; Hon Roll; NHS; Ntl Merit Ltr; NEDT Awd; Bucknell U; Phys.

HONG, SUSANNA; Dominican Acad; Jackson Hts, NY; (Y); Nwsp Rptr; Trs Jr Cls; Stu Cncl; Hon Roll; U Of VA; Frgn Affrs.

HONGO, LARA; Watertown HS; Watertown, NY; (Y); Chorus; Yrbk Stf; Sec Frsh Cls; Rep Soph Cls; Rep Stu Cncl; JV Var Fld Hcky; JV Tennis; Capt Var Vllybl; Hon Roll; Jr NHS; Kathy Haggerty Mem Awd 82; MVP JV Vlybl 83; Law.

HONIG, DEBRA; Wantagh HS; Wantagh, NY; (Y); Political Wkr; Spanish Clb; Temple Yth Grp; Variety Show; Nwsp Ed-Chief; Yrbk Rptr; Rep Jr Cls; Hon Roll; NHS; Prfct Atten Awd; Columbia Schlstc Press Assn-1st Pl Cert-Featr Wrtng 84; Achvt & Excllnc Cert-Spn & Frnch 85; Commnctns.

HONIGMANN, GLORIA MARIE; Bethpage HS; Bethpage, NY; (Y); 66/290; French Clb; Girl Scts; Yrbk Stf; Swmmng; High Hon Roll; Hon Roll; Cvl Engr.

HONS, DEBORAH; Central Islip HS; Central Islip, NY; (Y); 32/400; Church Yth Grp; Dance Clb; Color Guard; Flag Corp; Yrbk Phtg; Yrbk Stf; Sec Jr Cls; Sec Sr Cls; Bus.

HONSBERGER, JAMES; Clarence Central HS; Clarence Ctr, NY; (Y); 87/263; Church Yth Grp; Latin Clb; Letterman Clb; Varsity Clb; Var Capt Bsbl; Var Capt Bsktbl; Im Ftbl; High Hon Roll; Hon Roll; MVP Bsbl 85; All Trnmnt Tm Bsktbl, Bsbl 85; Fredonia ST Coll; Bus Mngmnt.

HOOD, ERICA; Granville HS; Granville, NY; (Y); Drama Clb; French Clb; Intnl Clb; Chorus; School Musical; School Play; Variety Show; Vllybl; Hon Roll; SUNY-DELHI; Vetrnrn Tech.

HOOD, HAROLYN L; Bishop Maginn HS; Albany, NY; (Y); 5/118; Civic Clb; Hon Roll; NHS; Intl Frgn Lang Awd 84; Rochester Inst Of Tech; Chem.

HOOD, IRENE; Malverne HS; Malverne, NY; (S); 15/157; High Hon Roll; Hon Roll; NHS; 7 Merit Certs; 3 Excllnc Awds; Bus Mgmt.

HOOGS, ANTHONY J; Jamesville Dewitt HS; Fayetteville, NY; (Y); 5/224; Quiz Bowl; Jazz Band; School Musical; Variety Show; Diving; Im Diving; Var Socr; High Hon Roll; NHS; Ntl Merit SF; Outstndng Achvt Awds In Ltn, Engl, & Math 83; Physics.

HOOK, DANIEL; Kenmore West SR HS; Kenmore, NY; (Y); Var Capt Swmmng; JV Trk; High Hon Roll; NHS; Physio.

HOOLIHAN, MAUREEN; Kenmore West Senior HS; Kenmore, NY; (Y); 53/445; Math Tm; School Musical; High Hon Roll; Hon Roll; NHS; Prfct Atten Awd; Regents Schlrshp 85; 7th NY Natl Span Exam Lvl 3 83; 17th Western NY Natl Span Exas Lvl 4 & 5 84; U Buffalo.

HOOPER, CHRISTOPHER P; Norwood-Norfolk Central HS; Norwood, NY; (Y); French Clb; Chorus; Church Choir; School Musical; Swing Chorus; Coach Actv; Var L Socr; Var Trk; Hon Roll; Outstndng Perfrmnce In Chorus 82-85; Elec Engrng.

HOOPER, HELEN; Midwood HS; Brooklyn, NY; (Y); Yrbk Stf; Capt Twrlr; Prfct Atten Awd; Prin Prd Awd 85; Law.

HOOPER, STEPHEN; Iona Preparatory Schl; Rye, NY; (Y); 1/196; Ed Nwsp Stf; Ed Lit Mag; JV Crs Cntry; JV Var Trk; High Hon Roll; Hon Roll; NHS; Prfct Atten Awd; Genl Exclnce 83-85; French Mdl 82-85; Sci Mdl 83-84; Engrng.

HOOVEN, BARBARA; Buffalo Academy Of The Sacred Heart; Snyder, NY; (Y); 25/116; Trs Latin Clb; Model UN; Service Clb; Nwsp Rptr; High Hon Roll; Hon Roll; NHS; Cmnty Wkr; Local Schlrshp 85; Canisius Coll.

HOPE, ROBIN; G Ray Bodley HS; Fulton, NY; (Y); Color Guard; Mrchg Band; Yrbk Sprt Ed; Rep Jr Cls; JV Var Mat Maids; Var Trk; SADD Hlth Awd 84-85; Apprctn Awd Yrbk 84-85; Distngshd Svc Awd Video Prod 84-85; Cntrl City Bus Inst; Ct Reportr.

HOPKINS, AARON; Bishop Cunningham HS; Oswego, NY; (S); Boy Scts; Latin Clb; Spanish Clb; Varsity Clb; JV Bsbl; Var Ftbl; Sftbl; Im Swmmng; Prfct Atten Awd; FL Inst Tech; Pre-Med.

HOPKINS, BRUCE; Amsterdam HS; Amsterdam, NY; (Y); 19/330; Var Capt Golf; High Hon Roll; NHS; Pres Schlr; JV Bsktbl; Regents Schlrshp 85; Raphael J Mcnulty Awd 85; Union Coll; Comp Sci.

HOPKINS, CHRISTOPHER; Cazenovia Central Schl; Cazenovia, NY; (Y); Am Leg Boys St; Boy Scts; Nwsp Ed-Chief; Trs Stu Cncl; Score Keeper; Timer; God Cntry Awd; Mst Imprvd In Soc Stds 11r 85; Scoutings Hghst Ideals 85; Stu Excell Awd From Cazenova Cntrl Schl 85; Salem Coll; Yth Agncy Adm.

HOPKINS, JAMES R; Angelica Central Schl; Angelica, NY; (Y); Am Leg Boys St; 4-H; French Clb; Pres Frsh Cls; Trs Soph Cls; Trs Jr Cls; Stu Cncl; High Hon Roll; Hon Roll; NHS; SUNY; Sci.

HOPKINS, JEANETTE; Preston HS; Bronx, NY; (Y); Sec Church Yth Grp; Teachers Aide; School Musical; Stage Crew; Twrlr; Hon Roll.

HOPKINS, JONATHAN; Bishop Cunningham HS; Oswego, NY; (S); Boy Scts; Latin Clb; Spanish Clb; Jr Cls; Bsbl; Bsktbl; Ftbl; San Diego U; Law.

HOPKINS, KATHLEEN; G Ray Bodley HS; Fulton, NY; (Y); 18/257; Letterman Clb; Varsity Clb; Yrbk Bus Mgr; Rep Frsh Cls; Rep Soph Cls; Rep Jr Cls; Rep Sr Cls; Rep Stu Cncl; Var Cheerleading; High Hon Roll; Best All Around Bus Major 84-85; Superior Achvt In Bus 83; Schlrshp 83-85; Onondaga CC; Exec Sec.

HOPKINS, LAURA; Auburn HS; Auburn, NY; (Y); Church Yth Grp; Cmnty Wkr; Hon Roll; Cazenovia Coll; Fash Desgn.

HOPKINS, LINDA E; Vestal SR HS; Vestal, NY; (Y); Church Yth Grp; Sec Drama Clb; Hosp Aide; Sec Service Clb; Teachers Aide; School Play; Ed Yrbk Stf; Cmnty Wkr; Exploring; French Clb; Regents Schlrshp 85; 1st Pl Suny Cortland Drama Cmptn 84-85; Ithaca Coll; Ed.

HOPLIGHT, LISA MARIE; Niagara Wheatfield HS; Niagara Fls, NY; (Y); Pres Church Yth Grp; Girl Scts; Pep Clb; Color Guard; JV Capt Bsktbl; Social Studies.

HOPPENTHALER, SANDRA; Coxsackie Athens JR SR HS; W Coxsackie, NY; (Y); 4-H; German Clb; Band; Concert Band; Rep Stu Cncl; JV Cheerleading; Var Gym; 4-H Awd; Hon Roll; Trvl.

HOPPER, DAWN; Connetquot HS; Ronkonkoma, NY; (Y); 9/750; Art Clb; JA; School Play; Trs Stu Cncl; Mgr(s); High Hon Roll; Hon Roll; NHS; ORBA Art Awd 83; Purdue U; Aerosp Engrng.

HOPSEKER, VICKI; Watertown HS; Watertown, NY; (Y); GAA; Var L Bsktbl; Var L Fld Hcky; Var L Sftbl; Hon Roll; Jr NHS; NHS; Band; Concert Band; Mrchg Band; Vrsty Sftbl All-Star 83-85; Vrsty Fld Hcky Hnrb Mntn All Star 83; Vrsty Bktbl Hnrb Mntn All Star 84-85; Med.

HORAN, BETH; Bishop Ford Central Catholic HS; Brooklyn, NY; (Y); Church Yth Grp; Dance Clb; Speech Tm; Prfct Atten Awd; St Josephs NY; Psychlgy.

HORAN, CHRISTOPHER; Valhalla HS; N White Plains, NY; (Y); 29/120; Church Yth Grp; Cmnty Wkr; Political Wkr; Teachers Aide; Varsity Clb; Band; Concert Band; Mrchg Band; Orch; Stage Crew; SUNY Oneonta; Acctng.

HORAN, DONALD; Andover Central Schl; Andover, NY; (Y); 12/60; Am Leg Boys St; Letterman Clb; School Play; Yrbk Sprt Ed; Var L Bsbl; Capt Var Swmmng; High Hon Roll; Church Yth Grp; Computer Clb; Model UN; Allegany Cnty Mus Assoc Chrs 85; US Army Natl Sccr Coaches Assoc Am MVP 85; Murlyn Conde Awd 85; Alfred ST Coll; Acctg.

HORAN, ERIN; Edward R Murrow HS; Brooklyn, NY; (Y); 215/735; Drama Clb; Chorus; School Play; Yrbk Stf; Rep Soph Cls; Rep Sr Cls; Rep Stu Cncl; Capt Cheerleading; Gym; John F Kennedy Awd Chractr 85; Regnts Endrsmnt Merit 85; Runr E R Murrows Anl 85; Rochester Inst; Hotl Mgmt.

HORAN, GRACE E; Walt Whitman HS; Huntington, NY; (Y); 60/625; PAVAS; Yrbk Stf; French Hon Soc; High Hon Roll; Jr NHS; NHS; Gifted & Talented Smmr Pgm 82; NY ST Smmr Schl Arts 83; Schlrshp Huntington Fine Arts Wrkshp 84-85; Art.

HORAN, THOMAS; Massapequa HS; Massapequa, NY; (Y); French Clb; Variety Show; Nwsp Stf; Hon Roll; NYS Regents Scholar 84-85; ST U NY Albany; Intl Bus.

HORDINES JR, JOHN C; Mt St Michael Acad; Bronx, NY; (Y); 27/300; Boy Scts; Hon Roll; NHS; Spanish NHS; SUNY Binghampton; Bio.

HORDLOW, KARA; Garden City HS; Garden City, NY; (Y); 23/355; Church Yth Grp; GAA; Nwsp Ed-Chief; Yrbk Sprt Ed; Var Capt Fld Hcky; Var Capt Sftbl; High Hon Roll; Pres Jr NHS; NHS; Ntl Merit Ltr; Jrnlsm.

HORIOGLU, ROGER; The Bronx H S Of Science; Flushing, NY; (Y); Art Clb; Church Yth Grp; Mathletes; Math Tm; Science Clb; Band; Jazz Band; Lit Mag; JV Var Socr; High Hon Roll; Silvr Mdl NYC Mth Fair 84 & 85; 2nd Prz Sci Fair 85; Gld Mdl Brd Jmp 82; Med.

HORMANN, BARBRA A; Fontbonne Hall Academy; Brooklyn, NY; (Y); Church Yth Grp; Service Clb; Teachers Aide; Chorus; Church Choir; School Play; Nwsp Stf; Hon Roll; Prfct Atten Awd; NY ST Nrsng Schlrshp 85; Valparaiso U; Nrs.

HORN, ANDREA; Dover JR-SR HS; Dover Plains, NY; (S); 3/70; Pres Jr Cls; JV Bsktbl; JV Var Fld Hcky; High Hon Roll; NHS; Voice Dem Awd.

HORN, ELISABETH A; Fayetteville-Manlius HS; Manlius, NY; (Y); 160/335; Church Yth Grp; Dance Clb; Hosp Aide; Spanish Clb; Teachers Aide; Varsity Clb; Acpl Chr; Chorus; Church Choir; Madrigals; NYSSMA ST & Eastern 84-85; Ctznsp Awd 85; Green Mountain Coll; Cmmnctns.

HORN, JOHN G; City Honors HS; Buffalo, NY; (Y); 14/97; Church Yth Grp; French Clb; Ski Clb; Speech Tm; Chorus; Jazz Band; Madrigals; Mrchg Band; School Musical; School Play; NY Regents Schlrshp 84; U Of Rochester; Music Prfrmnc.

HORN, KEVIN; Albion SR HS; Albion, NY; (Y); Boy Scts; Camera Clb; Computer Clb; VICA; Mgr Stage Crew; Amer Coll Muscns Gld Wnr 83-85; Prfct Atten Awd 85; FL Inst Of Vo Tech; Bus Mgr.

HORN, LISA; Fayetteville Manlius SR HS; Manlius, NY; (Y); 165/335; Church Yth Grp; Civic Clb; Cmnty Wkr; Dance Clb; Hosp Aide; Spanish Clb; Teachers Aide; Varsity Clb; Acpl Chr; Chorus; Music Awd 80-81; All ST All Estrn Voice NYSSMA 84-85; Wrk Schlrshp Clg Grntd Me 85-86; Green Mountain Coll; Cmmnctns.

HORN, MARY R A; Shaker HS; Latham, NY; (Y); Debate Tm; Drama Clb; Chorus; School Musical; School Play; Stage Crew; Nwsp Rptr; Rep Frsh Cls; Hon Roll; NHS; Shakr Theatr Dedictn & Svc Bckstge 83-84; Natl Hnr Roll 84-85; Law.

HORN, TRAVIS; Union Endicott HS; Endicott, NY; (Y); CAP; Rep Frsh Cls; Rep Soph Cls; Rep Jr Cls; Rep Stu Cncl; Var Ftbl; Var Trk; Var Wrstlng; Civil Air Patrol Billy Mitchell Awd 82; Capt MVP Fresh Ftbl Squad 82.

HORNAUER, MICHELE LEE; Sharon Springs Central Schl; Sharon Springs, NY; (S); 3/32; Varsity Clb; School Musical; Trs Soph Cls; Var Socr; Cit Awd; Hon Roll; NHS; Prfct Atten Awd; Computer Clb; FHA; Am Leg Aux Essy Awd 84; Stu Cncl R L Fitch Ldrshp Awd 84; Suny:Cert Pub Accntnt.

HORNBECK, CAMIELLE; Southside HS; Wellsburg, NY; (Y); German Clb; VICA; Chorus; Elmira Coll; Lib Arts.

HORNBERGER, CATHERINE E; Bronx High School Of Science; New York, NY; (Y); Key Clb; Jr Cls.

HORNEDO, EDITH; St Pius V HS; Bronx, NY; (Y); Dance Clb; Latin Clb; Service Clb; Chorus; Variety Show; Nwsp Stf; Yrbk Stf; NHS; Guitar Clb 83; Cert Of Hnr 85; The Wood Schl; Resrvtnst.

HOROSZEWSKI, DEBORAH; Bainbridge-Guilford HS; Bainbridge, NY; (Y); GAA; Office Aide; Yrbk Stf; Var Capt Bsktbl; Sftbl; Hon Roll; Prfct Atten Awd; Church Yth Grp; VICA; Band; Cathy Rush Bsktbl Cmp All Str Tm Vrsty 84; Mst Imprvd Vrsty Plyr Athl Achvt Awd 83-85; Trvl.

HOROWITZ, AMY; Lynbbrook HS; Lynbrook, NY; (Y); Debate Tm; Drama Clb; French Clb; NFL; Speech Tm; Thesps; Chorus; Madrigals; School Musical; School Play; Humn Rltns Cmte 84-85.

HORSTMANN, STACEY M; Bayport-Blue Point HS; Bayport, NY; (Y); 3/246; Church Yth Grp; Mathletes; Political Wkr; Chorus; School Musical; School Play; Hon Roll; NHS; Yrbk Stf; JV Crs Cntry; NY ST Regnts Schlrshp Wnnr 85; Long Island Cncl Soc Stds Achvt Awd 83-84; Hamilton Coll; Hstry.

HORTA, JACQUELINE; Midwood HS; Brooklyn, NY; (Y); Drama Clb; Hosp Aide; Office Aide; Political Wkr; Red Cross Aide; Orch; Stu Cncl; Prfct Atten Awd; Supr Yth Prncpls Prde Dly News & Ynks Awd 85; Cert Hon Mock Trl Team 85; Pltcs.

HORTON, CYNTHIA; F D Roosevelt HS; Hyde Park, NY; (Y); JV Var Cheerleading; JV Sftbl; NY ST Chmpns Ntl Chrldng 84-85.

HORTON, MICHELLE; Sherburne-Earlville HS; Sherburne, NY; (S); 12/142; Drama Clb; Band; Concert Band; Jazz Band; Mrchg Band; Var Cheerleading; Var Trk; Hon Roll; NHS; Mock Trl 85; SUNY Geneseo; Spch Path.

HORTON, TERESA M; Northville Central HS; Northville, NY; (Y); 2/60; Church Yth Grp; Dance Clb; Pres GAA; VP Sec Band; Yrbk Stf; Var Cheerleading; Var Socr; Var Trk; Capt Twrlr; VP NHS; NY ST Regnts Schlrshp 85; Natl Hnr Socty Awd 82; Alfred U; Bus.

HORTON, WILLIAM F; Newburgh Free Acad; New Windsor, NY; (Y); 88/725; Key Clb; Var Vllybl; Hon Roll; NHS; NY ST Regents Schlrshp Wnnr 85; ST U Of NY Buffalo; Aero Engr.

HORUCY, SCOTT; Frontier Central HS; Hamburg, NY; (Y); 100/480; Varsity Clb; Var JV Socr; JV Trk; Comp Sci.

HORVATH, JEFFREY; Kenmore West SR HS; Tonawanda, NY; (Y); 11/450; Computer Clb; Math Tm; Science Clb; High Hon Roll; NHS; Its Acad Tm 82-85; Philip S Eggleton Awd Top Phycs Stu 85; Sir Isaac Newton Awd Outstndng Math Tm Achv; CA Inst Of Tech; Aetrophyscs.

HORVATH, KELLY; Kenmore West HS; Tonawanda, NY; (Y); Girl Scts; Library Aide; Math Tm; Variety Show; High Hon Roll; Tv Quiz Show Tm 83-86; Horsebck Rdng Clb 83-86; U Of Buffalo; Bio.

HORVATH, KRISTY M; Rye Country Day School; Ryebrook, NY; (Y); Cmnty Wkr; Model UN; Political Wkr; Chorus; Madrigals; Stage Crew; Nwsp Ed-Chief; Nwsp Stf; Var Capt Cheerleading; Var Socr; Brown U Bk Awd Engl Excllnc 85; Bio, Chem Olympds Top 10 84-85; Natl Frnch Cont 6th 84; Biochem.

HORVATH, VICTORIA; Frontier Central HS; Blasdell, NY; (Y); Debate Tm; German Clb; JCL; Chorus; Concert Band; Mrchg Band; School Musical; Var Socr; High Hon Roll; NHS; Canadian-Am Hungarian Folk Dance Cmptn Fnlst 83; Bnd Cncl Sr Rep 84-85; Bio-Chem.

HORVATH, WADE R; Mattituck HS; Cutchogue, NY; (Y); Pres Civic Clb; Cmnty Wkr; Ski Clb; NY ST Rgnts Schlrshp 85-86; SUNY Potsdam; Anthrplgy.

HOSEY, ROBERT; Skaneateles Central HS; Skaneateles, NY; (S); 17/165; Exploring; Hosp Aide; Capt Bsbl; JV Ftbl; High Hon Roll; NHS; Hlth Sci.

HOSFORD JR, MICHAEL MURPHY; Richfield Springs Central Schl; Richfield Spgs, NY; (Y); 10/65; Boy Scts; JV Bsbl; JV Var Bsktbl; Var Crs Cntry; Var Ftbl; Var Trk; Hon Roll.

HOSIER, WENDE; Webutuck Central Schl; Amenia, NY; (Y); 10/74; Rptr 4-H; Band; Chorus; Madrigals; Var Fld Hcky; Score Keeper; Hon Roll; VFW Awd; TAP Awd 85-86; Dutchess Comm Coll NY; Nrs.

HOSLEY III, MORRISON J; Long Lake Central HS; Long Lake, NY; (Y); 3/15; Am Leg Boys St; Church Yth Grp; Chorus; Stu Cncl; Stat Bsbl; Socr; High Hon Roll; NHS; Presdntl Clsrm For Yng Amers 85; Exchng Stu To Japan 85-86; Engrng.

HOSNER, PAUL; Cicero-North Syracuse HS; Clay, NY; (S); 90/710; Debate Tm; Exploring; JA; Spanish Clb; Im Bsktbl; Im Bowling; Hon Roll; NHS; Natl Hstry & Govt Awd 83-84; Syracuse U; Radio & TV.

HOSP, R DAVID; Rye Country Day Schl; Rye, NY; (Y); Drama Clb; Model UN; Madrigals; School Play; Pres Jr Cls; Pres Sr Cls; Pres Stu Cncl; Var Ice Hcky; Lcrss; Chorus; Poltcl Nwspr, Opns Edtr & Asst Ed.

HOTALING, KEN; Germantown Central HS; Germantown, NY; (Y); 8/44; Chorus; School Musical; Swing Chorus; Yrbk Bus Mgr; Yrbk Phtg; Rep Stu Cncl; Var Vllybl; Hon Roll; Pres NHS; Am Leg Boys St; Stu Exch Alt Ambsdr 84-85.

HOTALING, THOMAS; Ichabod Crane Central HS; Niverville, NY; (Y); 11/186; Am Leg Boys St; Varsity Clb; Band; Mrchg Band; Nwsp Sprt Ed; High Hon Roll; Hon Roll; Pres NHS; Var L Bsbl; Var L Bsktbl.

HOTCHKISS, AMY; Houghton Acd; Belmont, NY; (Y); Church Yth Grp; Debate Tm; Drama Clb; Speech Tm; Chorus; School Play; Im Badmtn; Im Bsbl; Im Bsktbl; Im Swmmng; Houghton Coll; Psyclgy.

HOTCHKISS, PETER R; Cicero-North Syracuse HS; N Syracuse, NY; (S); 97/622; Political Wkr; JV Bsbl; Var L Socr; Hon Roll; Engr.

HOTCHKISS, TERESA; Randolph Central HS; Kennedy, NY; (Y); Art Clb; Church Yth Grp; Ski Clb; Varsity Clb; Rep Stu Cncl; Var Crs Cntry; Var Trk; Hon Roll; Summer Adv Ldrshp Trng Pgm 85; Houghton; Bus.

HOTH, DANIEL; Bishop Timon HS; Buffalo, NY; (Y); Computer Clb; Ski Clb; Spanish Clb; Chorus; Bsbl; Bsktbl; Ftbl; Golf; Hon Roll.

HOTH, MELINDA; Aquinas Inst; Scottsville, NY; (Y); 56/167; Band; Chorus; Concert Band; Drill Tm; Mrchg Band; School Musical; Stage Crew; Yrbk Stf; Hon Roll; Prfct Atten Awd.

HOTSKO, JOHN; Union Endicott HS; Endwell, NY; (Y); Key Clb; Mathletes; JV Bowling; Var L Tennis; High Hon Roll; Ntl Merit Ltr; STAC Div 1 All Star Tnns 84; Genetc Engr.

HOTZELT, DIANE JOY; Uniondale HS; Uniondale, NY; (Y); Am Leg Aux Girls St; Debate Tm; Trs Drama Clb; NFL; Mgr Speech Tm; Acpl Chr; Drm & Bgl; Nwsp Ed-Chief; NHS; Band; Brown U Bk Awd 85; Cmmnctns.

HOUGHTALING, BECKY; Oxford Acad; Oxford, NY; (Y); Church Yth Grp; Chorus; Yrbk Phtg; Yrbk Stf; JV Fld Hcky; Ridley Lowell; Trvl.

HOULIHAN, MICHAEL; Eastridge HS; Rochester, NY; (Y); Jazz Band; Mrchg Band; School Musical; Wrstlng; Hon Roll; NHS; Bio Sci.

HOUPT, KRISTEN; Niagara Wheatfield HS; Niagara Falls, NY; (Y); Am Leg Aux Girls St; French Clb; Hosp Aide; Pep Clb; Chorus; Swing Chorus; JV Cheerleading; Var Tennis; Hon Roll; NHS; Hghst Avg Frnch III Awd 84-85; Spch Pathlgy.

HOURY, CORINE C; Glen Cove HS; Glen Cove, NY; (Y); 74/265; French Clb; PAVAS; Lit Mag; Hon Roll; Regents Schlrshp 85; Fnlst Schl Of Vis Arts Schlrshp 85; ST U Oswego; Brdcstng.

HOUSE, MICHELLE; Canisteo HS; Canisteo, NY; (Y); Ski Clb; Band; VP Frsh Cls; VP Soph Cls; Var Cheerleading; Stat Crs Cntry; Stat Ftbl; Var Trk; High Hon Roll; NHS; Acad Achvt Awd 84-85; Local Hnr Soc 83-85.

HOUSEL, BRIAN; Lyndonville Central HS; Lyndonville, NY; (S); 2/60; Computer Clb; Varsity Clb; Yrbk Phtg; Pres Frsh Cls; Rep Stu Cncl; Socr; Var Capt Trk; Bausch & Lomb Sci Awd; Sal; Clarkson U; Electrical Engr.

HOUSEL, MARY; James E Sperry HS; Rochester, NY; (Y); GAA; Trs Jr Cls; Trs Sr Cls; Var Diving; JV Var Socr; JV Sftbl; Var Swmmng; NHS; Church Yth Grp; Exploring; Monroe Cmnty Coll Schlr Awd 85-86; Jake Awd Outstndng Ctznshp 85; Monroe CC; Lbrl Arts.

HOUSEL, SCOTT; Marion Central Schl; Marion, NY; (Y); Church Yth Grp; Stage Crew; Var Bsktbl; Var Trk; Ntl Merit Ltr; Crombach Mem Schlrshp 85; Navy; Comp.

HOUSER, YEVETTE; Henninger High SR; Syracuse, NY; (Y); Church Yth Grp; Dance Clb; 4-H; Girl Scts; Intnl Clb; Church Choir; Drm Mjr(t); Bsktbl; Var Trk; Var Twrlr; Bus Adm.

HOVER, CHRISTINA; Cathedral HS; Brooklyn, NY; (Y); Library Aide; Band; Accntg.

HOVER, TRACY; Hudson HS; Hudson, NY; (Y); Drama Clb; Band; Sec Chorus; Concert Band; Mrchg Band; Pep Band; School Musical; Socr; Sftbl; Hon Roll; Rookie Vocalist 83.

HOVEY, PAM; E J Wilson HS; Spencerport, NY; (Y); 2/250; Church Yth Grp; Drama Clb; Girl Scts; Math Clb; Ski Clb; Bowling; Hon Roll; NHS; Home Ec; Daytona Bch; Trvl & Trsm.

HOWARD, CHARISSE; H C Technical HS; Buffalo, NY; (Y); Exploring; Girl Scts; JA; Teachers Aide; Chorus; Hon Roll; Merit Roll; Engrng.

HOWARD, DEBRA; Roslyn HS; Roslyn, NY; (Y); 1/200; Trs Varsity Clb; Nwsp Ed-Chief; Nwsp Sprt Ed; Var Tennis; Var Trk; NHS; Var Sprng Trck Capt & Sprtsmnshp Awd; Frshmen Crss-Cntry Tm Capt; Bio Sci.

HOWARD, ERIC M; Prattsburg Central HS; Prattsburg, NY; (Y); 1/35; Am Leg Boys St; Band; Jazz Band; Yrbk Bus Mgr; Bausch & Lomb Sci Awd; High Hon Roll; Pres NHS; Val; Concert Band; Mrchg Band; Most Conscientious Pupil 83-85; Out Of St Tuition Waiver 85; Highest 4 Yr Avrge Math 85; U Of S FL; Comp Sci.

HOWARD, HENRY; Victor Central HS; Fairport, NY; (Y); Aud/Vis; Quiz Bowl; Spanish Clb; Im Bsktbl; Im Ice Hcky; Im Socr; JV Var Wrstlng; Hon Roll; Victor Flm Socty 1st Pl 84-85; 2nd 83-84; Cmmnctns.

HOWARD, JOHN; West Genesee SR HS; Camillus, NY; (Y); Im Bsbl; Stat Bsktbl; Im Ftbl; Im Trk; High Hon Roll; Hon Roll; Prfct Atten Awd; Rnkd 3-Rsng Money For Cls Of 86 Dine-A-Mate Sale 85; Acctg.

HOWARD, KATHLEEN; Manhasset HS; Manhasset, NY; (Y); 1/200; Church Yth Grp; Hosp Aide; Mrchg Band; Ed Nwsp Stf; Ed Lit Mag; Trs Stu Cncl; Var Fld Hcky; Var Gym; High Hon Roll; NHS; Most Outstndng Jr In Math/Sci-G Washington U 85; Summer Study Awd 85; Sports Awd GAC 83; Sci.

HOWARD, KEARY J; Maple Grove JR SR HS; Bemus Point, NY; (Y); 1/80; French Clb; Pep Clb; Quiz Bowl; Band; Concert Band; Jazz Band; Mrchg Band; Pep Band; Variety Show; Nwsp Ed-Chief; NYS Regnts Awd Wnnr 85; Hugh O Brian Yth Ldrshp Wnnr 83; U Rochester Schlrshp 85; U Of Rochester; Mech Engr.

HOWARD, KELLY; Cooperstown Central HS; Cooperstown, NY; (Y); 15/99; GAA; Yrbk Ed-Chief; Trs Soph Cls; Trs Stu Cncl; JV Bsktbl; Var Cheerleading; Capt Var Fld Hcky; Capt Var Trk; Hon Roll; NHS; Rotary Yth Ldrshp Conf 85; Jr Olympics Fld Hcky 84; Empire ST Games Fld Hcky 84.

HOWARD, KELLY LYNN; West Genesee SR HS; Camillus, NY; (Y); Church Yth Grp; Hosp Aide; Chorus; Mrchg Band; Stage Crew; Yrbk Stf; Rep Chrmn Sr Cls; Hon Roll; NHS; Aud/Vis; IN U; Med.

HOWARD, KELLY M; Hugh C Williams HS; Canton, NY; (Y); 25/140; Church Yth Grp; Chorus; Color Guard; Nwsp Rptr; Yrbk Stf; Var JV Cheerleading; Stat Socr; Stat Sftbl; High Hon Roll; NHS; Svc Awd-Young Vol In Action 84; Svc Awd-St Lawrence Co Head Start 84; Canton ATC; Accntng.

HOWARD, L SCOTT; G Ray Badley HS; Fulton, NY; (Y); 26/250; Band; Concert Band; Jazz Band; Mrchg Band; Orch; Pep Band; School Musical; Cit Awd; Dnfth Awd; Hon Roll; Rochester Inst Of Tech; Chem.

HOWARD, LOHANNE; Thousand Islands HS; Clayton, NY; (Y); Band; Chorus; Concert Band; Mrchg Band; High Hon Roll; Lion Awd; NHS; AFS; School Musical; School Play; Jrnlsm.

HOWARD, RICHARD; Cicero-North Syracuse HS; North Syracuse, NY; (S); 76/764; Cmnty Wkr; German Clb; NHS; Brockport U; Metrlgy.

HOWARD, RICHARD P; Kenmore West SR HS; Kenmore, NY; (Y); Boy Scts; Computer Clb; Varsity Clb; Im Bsktbl; Ftbl; Var Socr; Var Trk; Im Vllybl; Hon Roll; Excllnt Attndnc Awd 82-85; Comp Sci.

HOWARD, SCOTT; G Ray Bodley HS; Fulton, NY; (S); Exploring; Science Clb; Band; Concert Band; Drm & Bgl; Jazz Band; Mrchg Band; Orch; Pep Band; School Musical; Rochester Inst Tech; Chem.

HOWARD, SCOTT; Henninger HS; Syracuse, NY; (Y); 10/525; Church Choir; Concert Band; Mrchg Band; High Hon Roll.

HOWARD, TINA D; Wyandanch Memorial HS; Wyandanch, NY; (Y); Dance Clb; Trs DECA; Girl Scts; Key Clb; Library Aide; Flag Corp; Yrbk Stf; Rep Stu Cncl; Hon Roll; Ntl Merit Ltr; Incntv Awd 85; Crprt Law.

HOWARD, WILLIAM BRADLEY; Randolph Central Schl; Randolph, NY; (Y); Am Leg Boys St; Var L Bsbl; Var L Ftbl; Var L Wrstlng; Hon Roll; NHS; Southern Tier Div II Wrestling Champ 84-85; Hnrbl Mntn All Conf Selection Ftbl 84.

HOWE, BRADLEY; East Islip HS; East Islip, NY; (Y); Computer Clb; Math Tm; Nwsp Bus Mgr; Rep Stu Cncl; Var Tennis; Var Trk; NHS; Med.

HOWE, LISA M; Johnson City HS; Endicott, NY; (Y); 8/212; Drama Clb; French Clb; Key Clb; Pep Clb; Political Wkr; Ski Clb; Yrbk Stf; VP Frsh Cls; Rep Trs Stu Cncl; Stat Bsktbl; NYS Regents Scshlrshp 84-85; U DE; Intl Rel.

HOWE, NANCY; Niskayuna HS; Schdy, NY; (Y); Latin Clb; Symp Band; Rep Frsh Cls; Rep Soph Cls; Rep Jr Cls; NHS.

HOWE, ROBERT A; Deleware Acad; Delhi, NY; (Y); Yrbk Stf; VP Sr Cls; Capt Bsbl; Bsktbl; Cobleskill Coll; Tchr.

HOWE, STEPHANIE L; Hamilton HS; Hamilton, NY; (Y); 2/52; Concert Band; Orch; Yrbk Stf; Sec Sr Cls; Var Fld Hcky; Var Capt Tennis; Sal; Band; Chorus; Mrchg Band; Sctn III Tennis Champ 82; Conf All-Star Tennis 83; French Prz; Hobart-William Smith; Lbrl Arts.

HOWE, TIM J; Westhill SR HS; Syracuse, NY; (Y); 19/168; French Clb; Math Tm; Var Capt Bowling; JV L Ftbl; Im Wt Lftg; Hon Roll; NHS; Boy Scts; Rgnts Schlrshp 85; Schl Math Cont Wnr 83; SUNY Buffalo; Engr.

HOWELL, DAVID; West Hempstead HS; W Hempstead, NY; (Y); Church Yth Grp; Band; Stage Crew; Hon Roll.

HOWELL JR, PETER B; New Paltz HS; New Paltz, NY; (Y); Am Leg Boys St; Church Yth Grp; Computer Clb; Rep Jr Cls; Crs Cntry; Diving; Trk; High Hon Roll; Hon Roll; Summr Sci Inst SUNY 84; Cornell; DNA Tech.

HOWELL, SANDRA JEANNE; Samuel T Tilden HS; Brooklyn, NY; (Y); 24/502; Church Yth Grp; DECA; Chorus; Church Choir; Rptr Nwsp Stf; Yrbk Rptr; VP Sr Cls; NHS; Library Aide; Teachers Aide; Vocal Music Plaque & Medal 82; SUNY; Bus.

HOWELL, WANDA A; Queen Qut Reach HS; New York City, NY; (Y); Church Yth Grp; Cmnty Wkr; Computer Clb; Dance Clb; FFA; FHA; FNA; Model UN; Office Aide; PAVAS; Hnr Awd 80.

HOWENSTEIN, MATTHEW; Amsterdam HS; Amsterdam, NY; (Y); Rep Stu Cncl; Var Tennis; Hon Roll; Rensselaer Polytech Inst; Arch.

HOWES JR, BANNING B; North Salem HS; Brewster, NY; (Y); 3/82; Nwsp Ed-Chief; Pres Stu Cncl; Var Bsktbl; Capt Socr; Dnfth Awd; High Hon Roll; Var Pres NHS; Ntl Merit Ltr; Air Force ROTC Schlrshp 85; NYS Regents Schlrshp 84-85; Rennselaer Polytech Inst; Engr.

HOWLAND, ALANA; Irondequoit HS; Rochester, NY; (Y); Cmnty Wkr; Red Cross Aide; Service Clb; Teachers Aide; Cit Awd; Hon Roll; NHS; Prfct Atten Awd; Pres Schlr; U Of Dayton; Elem Educ.

HOWLAND, CAJSA; Immaculate Heart Central HS; Watertown, NY; (Y); FBLA; GAA; Band; Chorus; Maria Regina Coll; Chld Dvlpmnt.

HOWLAND, JANNA; Moravia Central Schl; Locke, NY; (Y); Am Leg Aux Girls St; GAA; Color Guard; Mrchg Band; Yrbk Stf; Trs Soph Cls; Rep Stu Cncl; JV Var Fld Hcky; JV Var Vllybl; Hon Roll; Marine Bio.

HOWLAND, KAREN; Horseheads SR HS; Horseheads, NY; (S); 16/407; Drama Clb; Hst JCL; VP Hst Latin Clb; Chorus; Stage Crew; Lit Mag; Hon Roll; NHS; Ntl Merit Ltr; German Clb; Gftd & Tlntd Pgm 81-85; Ped.

HOWLETT, CHRISTINE E; Our Lady Of Lourdes HS; Poughkeepsie, NY; (Y); 66/144; Drama Clb; Exploring; Hosp Aide; Pep Clb; Color Guard; Mrchg Band; Bowling; High Hon Roll; Marist Commtr Schlrshp 85; Hosp Vlntr Awd 84 & 85; Marist Coll; Comm.

HOWLEY, CHRISTOPHER A; Regis HS; White Plains, NY; (Y); VP Sr Cls; Var L Bsbl; Im Bsktbl; Im Bowling; NY ST Schlrshp 85; Boyle Dailey Memrl Schlrshp 85; Hospital Volunteer Awds 82-83; U Of Notre Dame; Pre Med.

HOWLEY, JOHN; Auburn HS; Auburn, NY; (Y); Intnl Clb; JA; Varsity Clb; JV Crs Cntry; Var Ice Hcky; Var Trk; Hon Roll.

HOWZE, ANGEL; Anthony A Henniger HS; Syracuse, NY; (Y); 285/400; Drama Clb; Band; Color Guard; Concert Band; VP Sr Cls; Trk; Outstndng Minrty Stu Awd-Peace Inc 85; Outstndng Wood-Wnd Sctn/N E Music Fstvl 85; Comm.

HOYEN III, HARRY; Webster SR HS; Webster, NY; (Y); 4/560; Symp Band; Trs Sr Cls; Pres Stu Cncl; Var Capt Ice Hcky; Var Capt Tennis; High Hon Roll; JETS Awd; NHS; German Clb; Hosp Aide; Grmn Ntl Hnr Scty 83; Ldrshp Fndtn Rep & Awd Rcpnt 83-85; Med.

HOYT, DAVID; Commack H S North; E Northport, NY; (Y); Math Tm; Nwsp Rptr; Lit Mag; Rep Soph Cls; Rep Jr Cls; High Hon Roll; NHS; Ntl Merit SF; Var Golf; Capt Vrsty Fncng Tm 85; Hghst Suffolk Cnty Math Cntst 85; Mgmt.

HOYT, LAURENCE E; Smithtown High School West; Smithtown, NY; (Y); Ski Clb; Varsity Clb; Var JV Bsktbl; Regents Schlrshp 85; Rochester Inst Of Tech; Bio.

HOYT, SHELLY; Ripley Central HS; Ripley, NY; (Y); 7/30; Church Yth Grp; Pep Clb; Ski Clb; Chorus; Yrbk Stf; Var Capt Bowling; Var Capt Cheerleading; Var Sftbl; Var Capt Vllybl; Hon Roll; Gannon U; Parlgl.

HOYT, THERESA; East Islip SR HS; Islip Terrace, NY; (Y); 63/475; Political Wkr; Teachers Aide; Crs Cntry; Trk; Hon Roll; Ntl Merit Schol; Hofstra U; Intl Bus.

HOYT, WENDY; Columbia HS; Castleton, NY; (Y); Church Yth Grp; Cmnty Wkr; VP 4-H; Chorus; Church Choir; Mrchg Band; Orch; School Musical; Symp Band; Hon Roll; Music Educ.

HOYTE, CLAIRE; Brooklyn Tech HS; Brooklyn, NY; (Y); Church Yth Grp; Church Choir; Cheerleading; Hon Roll; Gold Cup Natl Fed Music Clbs 83; Bible Quiz Awd 84; Cert Perfrmnce Brooklyn Music Tchrs Guild 85; Pre-Med.

HRANEK, MATTHEW; Binghamton HS; Binghamton, NY; (Y); 51/400; French Clb; Key Clb; Nwsp Phtg; Yrbk Phtg; Yrbk Stf; VP Jr Cls; Socr; Hon Roll; Key Clb Awd 85; Educ Schlrshp Awd 85; Rochester Inst; Phtgrphy.

HRAZDINA, GEZA; Romulus Schl; Romulus, NY; (S); 3/44; Am Leg Boys St; Ski Clb; Band; Jazz Band; Yrbk Ed-Chief; VP Pres Stu Cncl; Var Bowling; NHS; Music Awd 82; Olympcs Of Mind 84-85; Cornell U; Biol.

HRESHCHYSHYN, ADRIAN V; Calasanctius HS; Buffalo, NY; (Y); Lit Mag; Sec Stu Cncl; Var Bsktbl; Var L Socr; School Play; NYS Rgnts Schlrshp 85; Slvr Mdl Skng & Vllybl 81 & 82; U Of Rochester; Bio.

HRONCICH, THOMAS J; Sayville HS; Sayville, NY; (Y); 43/368; Pres Drama Clb; Key Clb; School Musical; School Play; Var Capt Tennis; NHS; Boy Scts; Mathletes; Band; Chorus; NY ST Rgnts Schlrshp 85; Hobart Coll; Pre-Law.

HRUBES, MICHAEL; S H Calhoun HS; Merrick, NY; (Y); Computer Clb; Band; Var JV Lcrss; Sci Fair Hnrb Mntn 83; Hnr Awd Carrier 84; Bus.

HRYCYN, CHRISTINA; St Francis Prep Schl; Woodside, NY; (S); 156/690; Am Leg Aux Girls St; Girl Scts; Library Aide; Science Clb; Service Clb; Im Gym; Jr NHS; NHS; Optimate Soc; CUNY Hunter; Hlth Sci.

HSIAO, LIANGHSU; Jamaica HS; Long Island Cty, NY; (Y); 116/534; Cmnty Wkr; Math Tm; Swmmng; Math Clb; Achvt Speed Wrtng, Typng, Swmmng 85; NY Mth Lg Merit Awd 85; Silver Medal Mth 85; U CA Berkeley; Physics.

HSIEH, FRANK; Mineola HS; Mineola, NY; (Y); Computer Clb; FBLA; Letterman Clb; Service Clb; Varsity Clb; Var L Bsbl; Tennis; Wt Lftg; Hon Roll; Hofstra; Bus Mngmnt.

HSU, PATTY; E L Vandermeulan HS; Pt Jefferson, NY; (Y); Hst FBLA; Mrchg Band; Orch; School Musical; Lit Mag; Hon Roll; 2nd Rnnr Up NYS Modern Miss Tenn Schlrshp Pgnt 85; 1st FBLA Dist Bus Comp 85; Cmmnctns.

HSU, YVONNE; Bronx High School Of Science; Corona, NY; (Y); Intnl Clb; NY U; Bus Admin.

HU, CHIMING; Newtown HS; Elmhurst, NY; (Y); 23/772; Exploring; Mathletes; Math Tm; Chorus; Lit Mag; High Hon Roll; Hon Roll; Prfct Atten Awd; Cooper Union; Engrng.

HU, LISA P; John Jay HS; Hopewell Jct, NY; (Y); 1/563; AFS; Jazz Band; Orch; L Tennis; NHS; Ntl Merit SF; Math Clb; Chorus; Nwsp Stf; Swmmng; Schl Rep Intl Youth Day 84; All State Full Orchestra 84-85; Engl Stu Week 83-84; Med.

HUANG, JEFFERSON P; New Paltz HS; New Paltz, NY; (Y); Dance Clb; FHA; Drm & Bgl; Capt Cheerleading; Lcrss; Btty Crckr Awd; Val; Nw Brunwck Inst; Hd Chef.

HUANG, SHERMAN; Avoca Central Schl; Avoca, NY; (S); 1/45; JCL; Math Clb; Concert Band; Mrchg Band; Rep Stu Cncl; Tennis; High Hon Roll; NHS; Prfct Atten Awd; 1st Pl NY ST JCL Acad Cntst 84; 1st Saunders Schlrshp Comptn 84; 2nd Pl W Nevin III HS Math Compt; Engrng.

HUBBARD, JOHN; Nottingham HS; Syracuse, NY; (Y); French Clb; Latin Clb; Jazz Band; Nwsp Rptr; Crs Cntry; Trk; NHS; MVP Crss Cntry Ski Tm; Queens U; Engr.

HUBBARD, JULIA; Walton Central Schl; Walton, NY; (Y); 4-H; Key Clb; Model UN; Orch; Rep Stu Cncl; JV Fld Hcky; JV Sftbl; 4-H Awd; Voice Dem Awd; 4-H Hnr Secy 83; Jrnlsm.

HUBBARD, LAURIE; Thomas A Edison JR SR HS; Horseheads, NY; (Y); Teachers Aide; Nwsp Stf; High Hon Roll; Legl Sec.

HUBBARD, STACEY; Horseheads SR HS; Elmira, NY; (Y); DECA; Hon Roll; Prfct Atten Awd; DECA Club-Gen Mktg 1st Pl 85; Corning Comm Coll; Bus Adm.

HUBELL, DINA; Saddle River Day Schl; Spring Valley, NY; (Y); Key Clb; Math Tm; JV Cheerleading; Var Tennis; JV Vllybl; Hon Roll; Spanish NHS; Cum Laude Soc 85-86; Spanish Hnr Soc; Math.

HUBENY, LISA; Liverpool HS; Liverpool, NY; (S); 29/800; Pres Church Yth Grp; Exploring; JA; Concert Band; Mrchg Band; Rep Stu Cncl; Hon Roll; Jr NHS; NHS; Pre-Med.

HUBER, CHRISTINE; Centereach HS; Centereach, NY; (Y); 34/475; Hosp Aide; Variety Show; Yrbk Sprt Ed; Rep Jr Cls; Trs Sr Cls; Var Cheerleading; JV Crs Cntry; Pom Pon; Vllybl; NHS; U Of CT Acad Grnt 85; NHS Svc Awd 85; U Of CT; Hlth Mngmnt Systms.

HUBER, LISA; Preston HS; Bronx, NY; (Y); Drama Clb; Teachers Aide; Stage Crew; Swmmng; High Hon Roll; Fordham U; Comp Sci.

HUBER, NANCY; South Sick HS; Rockville Ctr, NY; (Y); 119/291; Church Yth Grp; Girl Scts; Key Clb; Diving; Swmmng; Hon Roll; Elem Educ.

HUBERT, JEFFREY T; Queensbury HS; Glens Falls, NY; (Y); 10/235; Am Leg Boys St; Key Clb; Band; Concert Band; Ftbl; Trk; Wrstlng; High Hon Roll; NHS; Prfct Atten Awd; Chem Engr.

HUBERT, LAURA; Delaware Valley Central Schl; Fremont Cntr, NY; (Y); 7/42; VP 4-H; Band; Chorus; Concert Band; School Musical; Yrbk Stf; JV Var Cheerleading; Hon Roll; Dance Clb; Acpl Chr; Broome Cnty CC; Dntl Hyg.

HUBERT, STEVEN L; Blind Brook HS; Ryebrook, NY; (Y); French Clb; Math Tm; Chorus; School Musical; Trs Sr Cls; Stu Cncl; Var Capt Bsktbl; Var Tennis; Ntl Merit SF.

HUBNER, SUSANNAH; Cazenovia HS; Cazenovia, NY; (Y); Hon Roll; Design.

HUCK, KRISTEN T; W Genesee SR HS; Camillus, NY; (Y); 132/500; Church Yth Grp; Debate Tm; Pres Spanish Clb; Yrbk Ed-Chief; Yrbk Stf; Off Sr Cls; Kiwanis Awd; Off Jr Cls; Stu Cncl; Hon Roll; Sr Class Senate Schlrshp 85; Sr Mnth Nov 84; Outstndg Sr Awd 85; Nazareth Coll; Scl Wrkr.

HUCK, TERESA; Mercy HS; Wading River, NY; (Y); Service Clb; Nwsp Ed-Chief; Nwsp Rptr; Var Bsktbl; High Hon Roll; Lion Awd; NHS; Natl Hnr Socty 85; Bus Adm.

HUCKABONE, KELLIE; Dundee Central Schl; Dundee, NY; (Y); Trs DECA; Varsity Clb; Trs Soph Cls; Sec Jr Cls; Sec Sr Cls; Stat Bsktbl; Score Keeper; Socr; Vllybl; High Hon Roll; Bus.

HUDAK, MARYBETH; Saint Francis Prep; Flushing, NY; (Y); Drama Clb; Ski Clb; Color Guard; School Musical; School Play; Im Ftbl; Im Sftbl; Im Vllybl; Lwyr.

HUDAK, PETER; St John The Baptist D HS; Central Islip, NY; (Y); Teachers Aide; Hon Roll; Acctng.

HUDD, BARBARA ANN; Maria Regina HS; White Plains, NY; (Y); 30/130; Key Clb; Service Clb; Chorus; Nwsp Stf; Yrbk Ed-Chief; Yrbk Stf; Rep Stu Cncl; Fld Hcky; High Hon Roll; NHS; Comm.

HUDDERS, WAYNE; Williamsville South HS; Williamsville, NY; (Y); 19/246; Cmnty Wkr; Quiz Bowl; Chorus; Concert Band; Orch; School Musical; Var L Tennis; NHS; Prfct Atten Awd; Math Clb; Outstndng Vltnr Awd Cmnty Svc 85; Engrng.

HUDDLESTON, JAMES; Kings Park SR HS; Northport, NY; (Y); 12/393; VP Computer Clb; High Hon Roll; NHS; Elec Engrng.

HUDSON, CAROLYN; Bishop Hearney HS; Rochester, NY; (Y); Ski Clb; Off Frsh Cls; Off Jr Cls; Stu Cncl; Var L Cheerleading; Var Coach Actv; Var L Gym; Var L Pom Pon; High Hon Roll; Hon Roll; Chrldng JV & Vrsty Champ; Modern Miss Pagent NYS Fin.

HUDSON, JENNIFER; The Chapin Schl; New York, NY; (Y); VP Model UN; Pres Science Clb; Teachers Aide; Chorus; Variety Show; Nwsp Stf; Var L Fld Hcky; Ntl Merit Ltr; St Schlr; Pacific NW Bell Scholar 85; Fnlst Miss Co-Ed WA ST 84; Pres Fine Art Pgm NEWS 84-85; Georgetown U; Psych.

HUDSON, LYNNE; Maple Hill HS; Castleton, NY; (S); 6/72; VP Exploring; Girl Scts; Math Clb; Ski Clb; Spanish Clb; Nwsp Rptr; Fld Hcky; Trk; NHS; Girl Scout Slvr Awd 83.

HUEHN, WENDE; Alden SR HS; Alden, NY; (Y); 50/200; Boy Scts; Church Yth Grp; Cmnty Wkr; Exploring; Letterman Clb; Science Clb; Varsity Clb; Band; Jazz Band; Mrchg Band; Music Awd 81; Sports Awd 84; U Of NY Buffalo; Engrng.

HUESKES, TERI A; Pearl River HS; Pearl River, NY; (Y); 21/241; Church Yth Grp; Office Aide; Red Cross Aide; Teachers Aide; Twrlr; High Hon Roll; Masonic Awd; NHS; Ntl Merit Ltr; Pres Schlr; Spcl Extra Svc Awd Intl Ord Rnbw Grls 85; St Rep NY-GRMNY Ord Rnbw Grls 85; Ofcr Ord Rnbw Grls 83-84; E Carolina U; Phys Ther.

HUESTIS, AMY; Ticonderoga HS; Ticonderoga, NY; (Y); Varsity Clb; Rep Soph Cls; VP Jr Cls; Var Bsktbl; Coach Actv; Var Socr; Var Trk; High Hon Roll; NHS; Prfct Atten Awd; CVAC All-Star Bsktbl Team 85; CVAC Sccr Team 84; Arch.

HUEY, CHITUNG; Franklin D Roosevelt HS; Brooklyn, NY; (Y); 5/750; Math Tm; Chorus; Cit Awd; Hon Roll; Arista 83-85; Bus Mgmt.

HUFF, DOREEN E; Seaford HS; Seaford, NY; (Y); 36/271; Drama Clb; Girl Scts; School Musical; NHS; Acting.

HUFFMAN, JENNIFER; Royalton-Hartland Central HS; Gasport, NY; (Y); CAP; Band; Pep Band; Nwsp Ed-Chief; School Musical; Yrbk Stf; Var Bsktbl; Var Trk; Hstry.

HUFNAGEL, GEORGE; Lockport SR HS; Lockport, NY; (Y); 69/411; Latin Clb; Hon Roll; Jr NHS; Comp Sci.

HUG, VICKIE; Monroe Woodbury SR HS; Monroe, NY; (Y); 16/385; Church Yth Grp; VP Service Clb; Chorus; Church Choir; High Hon Roll; Sec NHS; Ntl Merit SF; NYS Regents Schlrshp 85; Hamilton Coll.

HUGGARD, CAROL C; Holy Trinity Diocesan HS; Jericho, NY; (S); 33/375; Math Clb; Accntnt.

HUGGINS, DARCY; Gilbertsville Central HS; Morris, NY; (Y); 5/25; Church Yth Grp; Chorus; Church Choir; Concert Band; Jazz Band; Mrchg Band; Var L Socr; Hon Roll; NHS; Ntl Merit Ltr; Area-Al ST Band-Flut 84; Al-Cnty Band-Flut 84 & 85; Lnguist.

HUGGINS, ROGER A; Pittsford Mendon HS; Pittsford, NY; (Y); Aud/Vis; Exploring; Radio Clb; Chorus; School Musical; Stage Crew; Swing Chorus; Hon Roll; Ntl Merit Ltr; Chess Clb; NY ST Regnts Schlrshp 85; U Of MN Twin Cities; Physcs.

HUGGLER, SCOTT; Liberty Central HS; Liberty, NY; (Y); Boy Scts; Cmnty Wkr; Band; Chorus; Concert Band; Jazz Band; Mrchg Band; Pep Band; School Musical; Swing Chorus.

HUGHES, ALAN; Indian River Central HS; Evans Mills, NY; (Y); 2/125; FFA; Latin Clb; School Play; Rep Stu Cncl; Hon Roll; NHS; NEDT Awd; Prfct Atten Awd; Natl Latin Exam Awd Maxima Cul Laude & Magna Cum Laude 83-85; Ag.

HUGHES, ALISSA; Frontier SR HS; Hamburg, NY; (S); Hosp Aide; Pep Clb; Red Cross Aide; Frsh Cls; High Hon Roll; Hon Roll; NHS; NEDT Awd; Sci.

HUGHES, BRENDA; Schuylerville Central HS; Schuylerville, NY; (Y); Pres FBLA; Girl Scts; Library Aide; Office Aide; Pep Clb; Red Cross Aide; Band; Chorus; Nwsp Stf; Sftbl; Hudson Vlly Cmnty Coll; Wrd Prc.

HUGHES, BRIDGET; Bethlehem Central HS; Delmar, NY; (Y); GAA; Girl Scts; Key Clb; Ski Clb; Yrbk Stf; Rep Frsh Cls; Rep Soph Cls; Rep Jr Cls; JV Socr; JV Sftbl.

HUGHES, CHRISTINE; St Francis Prep; Little Neck, NY; (S); 19/693; Library Aide; Math Clb; Lit Mag; High Hon Roll.

HUGHES, DEBORAHANN V; St Anns Schl; Brooklyn, NY; (Y); Chorus; Hon Roll; ABC Schrl 81; Fnlst Wells Coll Poetry Cntst 84; Fnlst Hollins Poetry Cntst 85; NASP Cmmndtn Wnnr 84; Jrnlsm.

HUGHES, DUNCAN; Desales Catholic HS; Lockport, NY; (S); Boy Scts; Ftbl; Wrstlng; Arch.

HUGHES, ERIC; Clinton HS; Clinton, NY; (Y); Art Clb; Aud/Vis; Stage Crew; Variety Show; Nwsp Bus Mgr; Nwsp Rptr; Lit Mag; Rep Frsh Cls; Rep Soph Cls; Rep Stu Cncl; SUNY; Comp Sci.

HUGHES, JAMES; Hudson HS; Hudson, NY; (Y); Boys Clb Am; Church Yth Grp; JV Bsbl; Var Bsktbl; Score Keeper; JV Timer; Hon Roll; Engrng Sci.

HUGHES, JULIE; Massena Central HS; Massena, NY; (Y); Church Yth Grp; French Clb; Sec Soph Cls; Sec Jr Cls; Rep Stu Cncl; JV Capt Bsktbl; JV Capt Vllybl; High Hon Roll; Hon Roll; NHS; Acad Banq Top 10 Pcnt Cls 83 & 84; Rotary Exch Pgm 85; Elec Engr.

HUGHES, KAREN C; Tully HS; Tully, NY; (Y); 5/75; Trs Library Aide; Math Tm; Quiz Bowl; Service Clb; Teachers Aide; Trs Stu Cncl; NHS; St Schlr; JV Score Keeper; Onondaga Cnty Cmmnty Schlr 84; Amer Mgmt Assn Ed Bus Wknd 84; ST U NY Binghamton; Acctng.

HUGHES, KATHLEEN; Sacred Heart Acad; New Hyde Park, NY; (S); Yrbk Stf; Crs Cntry; Trk; Hon Roll; NHS; Adopt A Grndprnt VP; Soc Justice Clb; Med.

HUGHES, KELLY; Long Island Lutheran HS; Melville, NY; (S); Ski Clb; Yrbk Stf; Pres Frsh Cls; Mgr(s); DAR Awd; Hon Roll; NHS; SUNY Fredonia; Law.

HUGHES, LISA; Springfield Gardens HS; Laurelton, NY; (Y); 49/443; Acctnt.

HUGHES, LOLENE; Jordan-Elbridge Central HS; Elbridge, NY; (Y); Church Yth Grp; Cmnty Wkr; Quiz Bowl; Red Cross Aide; Band; Chorus; Church Choir; Concert Band; Drm Mjr(t); Jazz Band; Elmira Key Awd 85; Math Sympsm 82-83; All Cnty Band Chorus & Jazz 82-85; Bio.

HUGHES, MELISSA A; Scotia-Glenville HS; Scotia, NY; (Y); Key Clb; Assoctd Schl Trvl; Trvl Agnt.

HUGHES, NANCY; Cardinal O Hara HS; Kenmore, NY; (Y); Cmnty Wkr; French Clb; Hosp Aide; Varsity Clb; Im Bowling; Stat Ftbl; Var JV Score Keeper; L Vllybl; Hon Roll; Serv Volntr Awd 82; Canisius Coll; Bus.

HUGHES, PATRICK; Christian Brothers Acad; Liverpool, NY; (Y); 20/94; Cmnty Wkr; JA; Ski Clb; Im Bsktbl; JV Socr; Timer; Trk; High Hon Roll; Hon Roll; Bros Basilian Indr Trk Awd Svc & Loyalty 85; Onondaga CC; Elec Engrng.

HUGHES, TAMAR; Gilbertsville Central HS; Morris, NY; (Y); 2/27; Dance Clb; Drama Clb; Varsity Clb; Chorus; Rep VP Stu Cncl; Var Capt Bsktbl; NHS; Sal; Band; Mrchg Band; Elmira Coll Key Awd 84; Cngrssmn Boehlert Awd 85; Stu Cncl Ldrshp Awd 85; ST U Coll NY Fredonia; Genetc.

HUGHS, CHRIS; Sandy Creek Central Schl; Sandy Creek, NY; (Y); 9/102; French Clb; Chorus; School Musical; JV Var Bsbl; JV Var Bsktbl; Var Ftbl; High Hon Roll; Hon Roll; Drama Clb; Frontier Leag Acad All Star Bsktbl 85; Bus.

HUGHSON, SANDRA; West Seneca East SR HS; Buffalo, NY; (Y); DECA; 4-H; German Clb; Chorus; Orch; Yrbk Stf; Bowling; 4-H Awd; Natl German Hnr Soc 84; Genrl Busnss.

HUGICK, RHONDA JO; Richfield Springs Central HS; Richfield Spg, NY; (Y); Band; Chorus; Mrchg Band; Swing Chorus; Stu Cncl; Cheerleading; Trk; Vllybl; Hon Roll; Jr NHS; Trk MVP; Russell Sage; Bio.

HUGUS, ROBERT; Saranac Central HS; Cadyville, NY; (S); 18/106; JV Var Bsbl; Im JV Bsktbl; JV Var Ftbl; Im Socr; Im JV Trk; JV Wrstlng; Hon Roll; Law.

HUHJUNGSUN, DAVID; Midwood HS; Brooklyn, NY; (Y); 55/650; VP Church Yth Grp; Intnl Clb; Math Tm; Science Clb; Orch; Yrbk Stf; Ed Lit Mag; NHS; Prfct Atten Awd; Archon Natl Svc Socty 84; Music Schlrshp Brooklyn Coll 81; Colgate U; Comp Sci.

HUIE, JOY SUE; John Dewey HS; Brooklyn, NY; (Y); Intnl Clb; Library Aide; Math Clb; Math Tm; Office Aide; Teachers Aide; High Hon Roll; Hon Roll; Prfct Atten Awd; Princ List 82; Baruch Coll; Acctg.

HUIZENGA, NOLAN; Houghton Acad; Houghton, NY; (Y); Chorus; Yrbk Phtg; VP Jr Cls; Pres Sr Cls; Trs Stu Cncl; Var L Socr; High Hon Roll; Hon Roll; NHS; Ntl Merit Ltr; Houghton; Science.

HUIZINGA, FLORIA; Candor Central Schl; Willseyville, NY; (Y); Boys Clb Am; Var Sftbl; Hon Roll; Sec.

HULBERT, KEVIN; Sandy Creek Central Schl; Lacona, NY; (Y); 15/80; Drama Clb; French Clb; Band; Chorus; Concert Band; Mrchg Band; JV Var Bsbl; JV Var Bsktbl; NHS; Voice Dem Awd; Brockport; H S Soc Stds Tchr.

HULBERT, TODD; Minisink Valley HS; Middletown, NY; (Y); 7/235; Chess Clb; Scholastic Bowl; Varsity Clb; Nwsp Stf; Var L Bsbl; Var L Socr; High Hon Roll; NHS; Prfct Atten Awd.

HULL, CATHY; Saugerties HS; Malden, NY; (Y); French Clb; Chorus; Hon Roll; NHS; Physcl Thrpst.

HULL, CLARISSA; Beacon HS; Glenham, NY; (Y); 47/154; JA; Spanish Clb; Church Choir; Sec Sr Cls; Hon Roll; NHS; Top Schlrshp Awd 85; Mt Lebanon Bapt Chrch Awd 85; Les Souers Schlrshp Awd 85; Marist Coll; Bus Admin.

HULL, JAMES; Ellenville HS; Ellenville, NY; (Y); 7/115; Church Yth Grp; Pres Computer Clb; Drama Clb; School Play; Stage Crew; Rep Frsh Cls; JV Var Socr; Var L Trk; High Hon Roll; NHS; Hnrb Mntn Ntl Sci Olympd 81-85; Mst Imprvd Vrsty Trk 85; Comp Tech.

HULL RYDE, BETSY; Charlotte Valley Central HS; Davenport Center, NY; (S); Drama Clb; Varsity Clb; Sec Frsh Cls; VP Soph Cls; Stu Cncl; Var Bsktbl; Var Socr; High Hon Roll; Hon Roll; NHS; Spanish II, Soc Stu Exc Awd 84; Teaching.

HULLENDER, CARRIE; The Masters Schl; Altus, OK; (Y); Church Yth Grp; Dance Clb; Debate Tm; FCA; French Clb; Key Clb; Letterman Clb; Pep Clb; Political Wkr; Red Cross Aide; U OK; Psych.

HULLSTRUNG, LYNDA J; Plainedge HS; Seaford, NY; (Y); 3/313; School Play; Stage Crew; Nwsp Rptr; Yrbk Stf; Lit Mag; Mgr(s); Bausch & Lomb Sci Awd; High Hon Roll; NHS; Sec Spanish NHS; Jewsh War Vet Brthrhood Awd; Regnl Ind Tech Ed Awd; Pace U Pleasantville; Pbl Accnt.

HULPIAU, CHRIS; Tonawanda SR HS; Tonawanda, NY; (Y); 14/230; French Clb; Yrbk Stf; Rep Stu Cncl; JV Socr; Hon Roll; U Buffalo.

HULS, TANYA; New Lebanon Central HS; Stephentown, NY; (Y); 14/56; GAA; Yrbk Stf; Trs Frsh Cls; JV Var Score Keeper; High Hon Roll; Hon Roll; NHS; Sculpture Awd 84; Hudson Vly CC; Accntng.

HULSANDER, BONNIE; Dryden JR SR HS; Dryden, NY; (Y); Mgr(s); Score Keeper; Hon Roll; Bus Math Awd 85; Guidnc Offc Awd 85; Alfred ST; Bus Adm.

HULSE, LORI; Riverhead HS; Calverton, NY; (Y); 36/245; Key Clb; Latin Clb; Ski Clb; Jazz Band; Yrbk Phtg; Trs Jr Cls; Capt Cheerleading; Sftbl; Vllybl; Hon Roll; RCFA Essay Cntst 1st Pl 85; St John Fisher; Comm.

HULSE, TERRI; Whitney Point C S; Maine, NY; (Y); 4-H; French Clb; Chorus; Trk; 4-H Awd; Hon Roll; Paul Smithes Coll; Srvyng.

HULSE, WILLIAM J; Riverhead HS; Calverton, NY; (Y); Boy Scts; Key Clb; Ski Clb; Bowling; Ftbl; Wrstlng; Cit Awd; Superior Performance In Afro Asian Studies 82; 2nd In Excellent Drivers Prog 84; NY ST Regnt Schl 85; Clarkson U; Accounting.

HULSEAPPLE, PAUL; Minisink Valley HS; Middletown, NY; (Y); Boy Scts; Pres Church Yth Grp; Socr; Tennis; High Hon Roll; Hon Roll; Prfct Atten Awd; Frank W Jackson Mem Awd 84; Kiwanis Spnsh III Awd 85; Math.

HULTGEN, PATRICK T; Hutchinson Central Technical HS; Buffalo, NY; (Y); Debate Tm; Math Clb; Math Tm; Nwsp Stf; High Hon Roll; Hon Roll; SAR Awd.

HULTS, LORIE; Albion HS; Albion, NY; (Y); 12/175; Church Yth Grp; Girl Scts; Spanish Clb; Y-Teens; Color Guard; JV Sftbl; Stat Swmmng; Cit Awd; Jr NHS; NHS; Crmnl Just.

HUMANN, JULIE; Saint John The Baptist D HS; Islip Ter, NY; (Y); Civic Clb; Im Socr; Hon Roll; Grand Champ Of Horse Show 84; Equitation.

HUMBACH, THOMAS; Mount Vernon HS; Mount Vernon, NY; (Y); Boy Scts; Band; Jazz Band; Mrchg Band; JV Ftbl; Hon Roll; Engnrng.

HUMBERT, SHERI; North Rose-Wolcott HS; Clyde, NY; (Y); Sec Church Yth Grp; Sec 4-H; Band; Church Choir; Var Vllybl; 4-H Awd; High Hon Roll; NHS; FFA; NYSSMA Solo Comp Music Awd 82-83; Cornell U; Vet Med.

HUMBERT, STEPHEN M; North Rose-Wokott HS; Clyde, NY; (Y); Am Leg Aux Girls St; Church Yth Grp; VP Frsh Cls; VP Sr Cls; Rep Stu Cncl; JV Var Bsbl; JV Var Bsktbl; Var Crs Cntry; High Hon Roll; Hon Roll; NYS Regents Schlrshp 84-85; SUNY-GENESEO; Psych.

HUME, MAUREEN; Keveny Memorial Acad; Cohoes, NY; (S); 3/50; Hosp Aide; Math Clb; Band; Concert Band; Jazz Band; Mrchg Band; Var Capt Cheerleading; Score Keeper; High Hon Roll; Ortho.

HUME, ROBERT M; Vestal SR HS; Vestal, NY; (Y); 126/500; Varsity Clb; Swmmng; French Clb; FBLA; Ski Clb; Trk; High Hon Roll; Hon Roll; NYS Rgnts Schlrshp; Clarkson; Cvl Engrng.

HUMMER, LISA; Williamsville East HS; East Amherst, NY; (Y); 32/299; Drama Clb; French Clb; JA; Band; Church Choir; VP Sr Cls; High Hon Roll; NHS; Physcn.

HUMPHREY, KENDREA; Churchville-Chili SR HS; Rochester, NY; (Y); Orch; Sftbl; Swmmng; Trk; Vllybl; NHS; Persevrnc Rsrch Awd 83; Comp Sci.

HUMPHREY, LUCINDA; Berlin Central HS; Petersburg, NY; (Y); 10/65; Art Clb; Cmnty Wkr; Drama Clb; Spanish Clb; Teachers Aide; School Musical; Stage Crew; Swing Chorus; JV Sftbl; Hon Roll; Cert Achvt 85; Dramatics Key 85; Austine Beauty Schl; Art.

HUMPHREY, LYNNE A; Fayetteville-Manlius HS; Fayetteville, NY; (Y); 9/335; Chorus; Var Capt Socr; Var Capt Vllybl; Cit Awd; DAR Awd; High Hon Roll; Pres NHS; Model UN; Church Choir; Rep Stu Cncl; Balfour Key Awd 85; Italian-Amer Ath Clb Awd 85; Cornell Natl Scholar 85; U Of VA.

HUMPHREY, RENA; Hoosick Falls Central HS; Hoosick Falls, NY; (Y); Church Yth Grp; Drama Clb; 4-H; French Clb; Band; Chorus; Mrchg Band; School Musical; School Play; Hon Roll; Scl Wrkr.

HUMPHREY, SUSAN; Liverpool HS; Liverpool, NY; (S); 190/790; Church Yth Grp; Dance Clb; DECA; Ski Clb; Mrchg Band; Variety Show; Nwsp Stf; Sr Cls; Stu Cncl; Powder Puff Ftbl; DECA 3rd Region 9 Comp; :Bus Admin.

HUMPHREYS, MATTHEW; Whitesboro SR HS; Whitesboro, NY; (Y); Exploring; Math Tm; Teachers Aide; JV Bsktbl; JV Var Lcrss; Elmira Key Clb Schlrshp 85; RPI Merit Awd Math,Sci 85; RPI; Engr.

HUMPHREYS, SUSAN; East Hampton HS; E Hampton, NY; (Y); Yrbk Stf; Var Sftbl; JV Tennis; High Hon Roll; Hon Roll; Jr NHS; Arch Drawng Awd 84-85.

HUMPHRIES, ALEXIS; Brooklyn Tech HS; Roosevlt Is, NY; (Y); L Diving; 11th NYC Diving Chmpnshps 85; U PA; Vet Med.

HUNDLEY, CARLA; Kensington HS; Buffalo, NY; (Y); Church Yth Grp; Computer Clb; Dance Clb; English Clb; FBLA; GAA; Math Tm; Science Clb; Spanish Clb; Varsity Clb; U OF NY-BUFFALO; Accntnt.

HUNDT, LAURA; Lindenhurst HS; Lindenhurst, NY; (Y); Spanish Clb; Varsity Clb; Orch; Stage Crew; Yrbk Phtg; Yrbk Stf; VP Frsh Cls; Sec Soph Cls; Cheerleading; Cheerleading; Comm.

HUNDT, NANCY L; Our Lady Of Mercy Acad; Hicksville, NY; (Y); 9/118; Girl Scts; VP Spanish Clb; Badmtn; Mgr Var Bsktbl; Mgr Var Sftbl; Mgr Var Vllybl; NHS; Camera Clb; NY ST Regents Schlrshp 85; Bio.

HUNG, ELLEN; Brooklyn Technical HS; New York, NY; (Y); 15/1200; Library Aide; Math Clb; Math Tm; Office Aide; VP Science Clb; Service Clb; Teachers Aide; Orch; Yrbk Stf; Rep Stu Cncl; Pre-Med.

HUNG, JAMES L; Port Richmond HS; Staten Island, NY; (Y); 8/581; Pres Trs Church Yth Grp; JA; Math Tm; Pres Science Clb; Sec Service Clb; Orch; Pres Frsh Cls; Pres Soph Cls; Pres Jr Cls; Pres Stu Cncl; Cert Of Merit Ntl Frnch Cntst 82-84; NY ST Rgnts Schlrshp 85; Ntl Hnr Soc Schlrshp 85; Hnr Roll Awd; Cooper Union; Elect Engr.

HUNGER, ELIZABETH; Cardinal Mooney HS; Hilton, NY; (Y); 63/357; VP Sec 4-H; Yrbk Stf; 4-H Awd; Hon Roll; NHS; Equasterian Awds-Horsemanshp-Reg & Ntl 83-85; Bus Adm.

HUNGERFORD, SHERI; Fayetteville-Manlius HS; Manlius, NY; (Y); Art Clb; 4-H; Girl Scts; Pep Clb; Variety Show; Yrbk Stf; Fld Hcky; Sftbl; Vllybl; 4-H Awd; Potsdam Coll.

HUNSINGER, CHARLES; Newfield Central HS; Newfield, NY; (Y); French Clb; Varsity Clb; Band; Chorus; Jazz Band; Mrchg Band; Variety Show; Var Bsktbl; Var Ftbl; Var Trk; Band Awd 84-85; All County Band; Music Camp 83-85; Music Ltr 84-85; TC3; Lang.

HUNSINGER, LORIE; Randolph Central Schl; Randolph, NY; (Y); 1/68; 4-H; Var Trk; Bausch & Lomb Sci Awd; Dnfth Awd; NHS; Pres Schlr; Val; Drama Clb; Ski Clb; Spanish Clb; Rgnts Schlrshp 85; Cummins Engine Sons & Dau Schlrshp 85; Frshmn Merit Schlrshp SUNY Fredonia 85; St U Coll Fredonia; Tech.

HUNSINGER, SCOTT; St Regis Falls Central Schl; Dickinson Center, NY; (S); Boy Scts; Church Yth Grp; Ski Clb; Band; Chorus; Yrbk Phtg; VP Soph Cls; Ftbl; Socr; Var Wrstlng; Engrng.

HUNT, CANDEE; Southwestern Central HS; Jamestown, NY; (Y); French Clb; Hosp Aide; Pep Clb; Ski Clb; Sec Chorus; Nwsp Stf; Yrbk Stf; Var L Cheerleading; Bus.

HUNT, CHRISANN; Auburn HS; Auburn, NY; (Y); Dance Clb; Girl Scts; Sec JA; Hon Roll.

HUNT, DAVID; Saugerties HS; Saugerties, NY; (Y); Hon Roll; NHS.

HUNT, DAWN A; Dover JR SR HS; Dover Plains, NY; (S); 36/94; High Hon Roll; Hon Roll; Acctng.

HUNT, DONNA M; Catholic Central HS; Wynantskill, NY; (Y); 79/203; Cmnty Wkr; Hosp Aide; Math Clb; Red Cross Aide; Service Clb; Chorus; Yrbk Stf; Hon Roll; Regnts Schlrshp Nrsng 85; Jean M Coon Humntrn Awd 85; St Marys Amsterdam; Nrsng.

HUNT, ELIZA P; Northport HS; Northport, NY; (Y); 96/661; VP Spanish Clb; Band; Mrchg Band; Symp Band; Crs Cntry; Trk; Hon Roll; NHS; Spanish NHS; NASA Hghst Achvt Frgn Langs 85; Advncd Spnsh Clb Awd 85; Earlham Coll; Spanish.

HUNT, ERIC; Lafayette HS; Brooklyn, NY; (Y); Church Yth Grp; FCA; JA; Office Aide; ROTC; Teachers Aide; Church Choir; Color Guard; Hon Roll; Prfct Atten Awd; Comp Pgmmr.

HUNT, ERIKA J; Patchogue-Medford HS; Patchogue, NY; (Y); 29/711; Aud/Vis; Cmnty Wkr; Key Clb; Math Tm; Chorus; Nwsp Ed-Chief; Lit Mag; High Hon Roll; Jr NHS; NHS; Regents NY Schlrshp Awd 85; SCMEA Fest,Nyssma Comp 81-83; Peer Ldr; Stonybrook U; Med.

HUNT, HOLLY L; Walter Panas HS; Crompond, NY; (Y); Pres Church Yth Grp; Stu Cncl; JV Socr; VP L Tennis; High Hon Roll; Hon Roll; Sec Jr NHS; NHS; Sci.

HUNT, KAREN; Herbert H Lehman HS; Bronx, NY; (Y); Church Yth Grp; Girl Scts; Political Wkr; Vllybl; Hon Roll; NHS; Howard U Georgetwn; Law.

HUNT, KATHY; Platsburgh SR HS; Plattsburgh, NY; (Y); Church Yth Grp; Library Aide; Office Aide; Chorus; Secry.

HUNT, KERRI; Moore Catholic HS; Staten Island, NY; (Y); Cmnty Wkr; French Clb; Math Tm; Yrbk Stf; Bowling; JV Var Sftbl; NHS; Bus.

HUNT, MARY ALICE; Niskayuna HS; Niskayuna, NY; (S); AFS; Church Yth Grp; German Clb; High Hon Roll; Hon Roll; Var Ltr Acad Exclnc 84-85; Tlntd, Gftd Pgm ST MD 82-84.

HUNT, WILLIAM R; Nichols HS; Buffalo, NY; (Y); 3/110; Pres Pep Clb; Chorus; Pres Sr Cls; JV Crs Cntry; Capt Trk; Hon Roll; Elec Engr.

HUNTE, NOEL L; La Salle Acad; New York, NY; (S); 1/29; Church Yth Grp; Hosp Aide; Math Clb; Math Tm; Nwsp Rptr; Nwsp Stf; Yrbk Stf; Trk; Hon Roll; Incentive Awd 84; Pre-Med.

HUNTER, ALLISON; Peekskill HS; Dayton, OH; (S); 17/168; Church Yth Grp; Capt Pep Clb; School Play; Pres Sr Cls; Rep Stu Cncl; Stat Bsktbl; JV Vllybl; High Hon Roll; Hon Roll; NHS; Schlstc Aptitude Awd 81-84; Miami U Mnrty Schlrshp 85; Miami U Oxford OH; Brdcstng.

HUNTER, ANDREW J; Solvay HS; Syracuse, NY; (Y); 25/170; Pres Church Yth Grp; Nwsp Ed-Chief; Nwsp Rptr; Nwsp Stf; Trk; High Hon Roll; Hon Roll; VFW Awd; Voice Dem Awd; Congrssmns Medal Of Merit 85; Faculty Leadrshp Awd 85; Presdntl Acadmc Fitness Awd 85; Le Moyne Coll; Govt.

HUNTER, DAVETTE MICHELLE; Notre Dame HS; Bath, NY; (Y); 34/127; French Clb; Quiz Bowl; Red Cross Aide; School Musical; Rep Stu Cncl; Capt Bsktbl; Cheerleading; Capt Sftbl; Vllybl; Hon Roll; Hmcmg Qn 84-85; IUE Locl 313 Schlrshp 85; Seton Hill Coll; Biochem.

HUNTER, DOUGLAS M; Bronx High School Of Science; New York, NY; (Y); Trk; Westinghouse Semi-Fnlst 84-85; Gentc Engr.

HUNTER, JERROD; Grand Island SR HS; Garden City, KS; (Y); 22/281; Church Yth Grp; Mathletes; Math Tm; Stu Cncl; Crs Cntry; Vllybl; Hon Roll; Ntl Merit SF; Amer Mensa Ltd 85; Rsrch Fllwshp Roswell Park Memrl Inst Buffalo NY 85; Chem.

HUNTER, JULIE; Gilboa-Conesville Central HS; Gilboa, NY; (S); Girl Scts; Spanish Clb; Band; Nwsp Stf; Yrbk Ed-Chief; Bowling; Score Keeper; Sftbl; High Hon Roll; NHS; Siena Coll; English.

HUNTER, KAREN L; Odessa Montour Central Schl; Montour Fls, NY; (Y); 28/80; Church Yth Grp; Teachers Aide; Band; Mrchg Band; Rep Stu Cncl; Cheerleading; High Hon Roll; Hon Roll; Church Choir; Concert Band; Futr Secys Amer 84-85; Alfred ST Coll; Bus Adm.

HUNTER, MATTHEW J; Notre Dame HS; Bath, NY; (Y); Am Leg Boys St; Cmnty Wkr; School Musical; School Play; Rep Stu Cncl; Var JV Bsbl; Var JV Ftbl; Var L Wrstlng; Hon Roll; NHS; Natl Socl Studies Olympd W/Distnctn 83; US Naval Acad; Math.

HUNTINGTON, REBECCA SUE; York Central HS; Mt Morris, NY; (Y); FTA; Girl Scts; Key Clb; Teachers Aide; Color Guard; James A Cooney Awd 85; Wntrgrd Co Capt 84; Stengrphr.

HUNTINGTON, STACEY; Barker Central HS; Barker, NY; (Y); AFS; Church Yth Grp; Sec Trs 4-H; VP French Clb; FBLA; Varsity Clb; Chorus; Yrbk Stf; JV Bsktbl; Trk; Roberts Wesleyan Coll; Elem Ed.

HUNTLEY, LINDA; Greene Central HS; Greene, NY; (Y); 26/105; Ski Clb; Band; Chorus; Color Guard; Concert Band; Mrchg Band; Symp Band; Var Golf; Var Tennis; Hon Roll; Tnns Certf 85; Golf Certf 83; Operatn Enterprs 85; Bus Adm.

HUNTLEY, NADIA; Dominican Commercial HS; Jamaica, NY; (Y); Service Clb; School Play; Stage Crew; JV Bsktbl; Sftbl; Outstndng Achvt For SQPA Yth Cncl 84-85; Engl Tchr.

HUNTRESS, THOMAS; Union Springs Acad; Merrimac, MA; (Y); 13/50; VP Soph Cls; Hon Roll; NHS; Prfct Atten Awd; Schl Letter-Ldrshp 85; Educ.

HUNTRESS, TOM; Union Springs Acad; Merrimac, MA; (S); 13/50; FCA; Off Frsh Cls; VP Soph Cls; Ftbl; Trk; Hon Roll; NHS; Engl.

HUPKA, LISA; Port Jervis HS; Sparrowbush, NY; (Y); French Clb; Varsity Clb; Chorus; Yrbk Stf; L Trk; Hon Roll; Nwsp Stf; Law.

HURD, JAMES D; South Side HS; Elmira, NY; (Y); Carpentr.

HURD, JANET; Jordan-Elbridge HS; Elbridge, NY; (Y); English Clb; FNA; Hosp Aide; Nwsp Stf; Cheerleading; Socr; Yrbk Stf; Peace Corps; Nrsg.

HURD, PATTI; Gloversville HS; Glovesville, NY; (Y); 52/260; Pep Clb; Concert Band; Mrchg Band; Pep Band; School Musical; Stage Crew; Symp Band; Nwsp Rptr; Nwsp Sprt Ed; Hon Roll; Pionr Achvt Chlng 83-85; Med.

HURLBURT, DEREK C; Warsaw Central HS; Warsaw, NY; (Y); Am Leg Boys St; Mathletes; Var Capt Bsbl; Var L Bsktbl; JV Socr; High Hon Roll; Jr NHS; NHS; Boy Scts; Varsity Clb; Cls Hnr Bearer 85; Career Mntrshp Prgm 85; Acdmc Achvt Awd For Acdmc Stndrds 85; Accntng.

HURLEY, ALICE L; Buffalo Sem; Buffalo, NY; (Y); Pres AFS; Rep Stu Cncl; Fld Hcky; Var Capt Tennis; Var Vllybl; Hon Roll; NHS; Ntl Merit SF; Natl Prz Maritime Essay Cntst; Highest All Sch Score Natl Math Cntst; Stanford; Foreign Svc.

HURLEY, CHRIS; Mahopac HS; Carmel, NY; (Y); 75/425; Church Yth Grp; JV L Bsktbl; Hon Roll; Comp Engrng.

HURLEY, COLLEEN; Alden Central HS; Alden, NY; (Y); French Clb; Rep Chess Clb; JV Var Cheerleading; Hon Roll; NHS; Ntl Earth Sci Olympiad.

HURLEY, KEN; Carmel HS; Carmel, NY; (Y); JV Socr; Var Trk; Photography Awd 85; Alfred ST; Comp Grphcs.

HURLEY, MICHAEL J; Lake Placid Central Schl; Lake Placid, NY; (Y); 4/45; Key Clb; Yrbk Stf; Sec Soph Cls; Pres Jr Cls; Pres Sr Cls; Var L Golf; Var Capt Ice Hcky; NHS; Computer Clb; Quiz Bowl; Regents Diploma 85; Regents Schlrshp 85; Hamilton Coll; Bus Mngmnt.

HURNY, BETH; West Irondequoit HS; Rochester, NY; (Y); 4/367; Church Yth Grp; Cmnty Wkr; Hosp Aide; Office Aide; Rep Soph Cls; Var Swmmng; Cit Awd; High Hon Roll; Hon Roll; NHS; Bio Sci.

HURSH, DAVID; Corning East HS; Corning, NY; (Y); 36/250; Band; Jazz Band; School Musical; Bsbl; NHS; Church Yth Grp; Concert Band; Symp Band; Coach Actv; Hon Roll; AFSCME Union Scholar 85; Truman Jacoby Mem Scholar 85; NY ST Regents Scholar 85; Mansfield U; Secndry Ed.

HURST, PATRICIA; Fillmore Central HS; Fillmore, NY; (S); 5/53; Sec 4-H; High Hon Roll; Hon Roll; NHS; O Lean Business Inst; Accntnt.

HURTUBISE, CHRISTINE; Monsignor Scanlan HS; Flushing, NY; (Y); 76/265; Church Yth Grp; Cmnty Wkr; Intnl Clb; Church Choir; Yrbk Ed-Chief; Im Gym; Hon Roll; Prfct Atten Awd 85; Frsh Aide Pgm Awd 85; Eng Hnrs 84; Spec Ed.

HURWITZ, MARK; Fayetteville-Manlius HS; Manlius, NY; (Y); Hosp Aide; VP Temple Yth Grp; Yrbk Phtg; Stu Cncl; JV Var Crs Cntry; JV Lcrss; High Hon Roll; NHS; Ntl Merit SF; Exploring; Outstdng Socl Stds Stu 81-82; NYS Regents Schlrshp 85; Meet The Teens Clmn Ftr-Syracuse Hrld Jrnl 85; Franklin; Bio.

HURXTHAL, MARIE; John Jay SR HS; Fishkill, NY; (Y); 75/560; FBLA; School Musical; Pres Soph Cls; JV Var Cheerleading; High Hon Roll; Jr NHS; Mc Donalds Schlrshp Acadmc Excllnc 85; Pres Acadmc Fit Awd 85; Natl Merit Fndtn Natl Hnr Rll 85; Marist Coll; Corp Acctg.

HURYSZ, BRIAN J; Wayne Central HS; Walworth, NY; (Y); 5/215; Computer Clb; JA; Math Clb; Math Tm; Ski Clb; High Hon Roll; NHS; Ntl Merit Ltr; Boy Scts; Church Yth Grp; Acad Exclnc In Math 83-84; Rgnts Schlrshp 85; JA Mgmnt Awd 82-83; Plattsburgh; Phys Engr.

HUSAIN, RUMANA; Colonie Central HS; Albany, NY; (Y); Intnl Clb; Ski Clb; Socr; Comp Sci.

HUSE, JENNIFER; Gouverneur JR SR HS; Richville, NY; (Y); Church Yth Grp; 4-H; Varsity Clb; Sec Jr Cls; VP Sr Cls; Var Capt Cheerleading; Var L Socr; Var L Trk; High Hon Roll; Hon Roll; Acadmc Ltr Awd 84-85; Colgate.

HUSHIN, MICHAEL; East Islip HS; Islip Terrace, NY; (Y); Aud/Vis; Boy Scts; Stage Crew; Nwsp Phtg; Hon Roll; E Islip Sci Fair 3rd Pl Wnnr 83; Elctrcl Engrng.

HUSSEIN, ZAKEYA; John Dewey HS; Brooklyn, NY; (Y); Prfct Atten Awd; Mc Calls Pattern Awd 85; Carol Gersten Awd 85; Fash Des.

HUSSEY, COLETTE MARIE; Acad Of The Rsrrctn; New Rochelle, NY; (Y); Drama Clb; NFL; Speech Tm; Chorus; School Play; Cheerleading; Tennis; NHS; VP Frsh Cls; Pres Soph Cls; Eddy Awd Outstndng Achvt Brdcst Jrnlsm News & Views 85; Engl.

HUSSEY, KATHLEEN; Monticello HS; Monticello, NY; (Y); Var Capt Vllybl; Sullivan Cnty CC; Spnsh.

HUSSEY, KIMBERLY J; Fairport HS; Fairport, NY; (Y); Math Tm; Science Clb; Concert Band; Jazz Band; Mrchg Band; Var L Swmmng; High Hon Roll; NHS; VFW Awd; Voice Dem Awd; Aerosp Engr.

HUSSEY, ROBERT M; Dansville SR HS; Dansville, NY; (Y); 6/169; Am Leg Boys St; Computer Clb; Drama Clb; Ski Clb; Varsity Clb; Band; Chorus; Jazz Band; Crs Cntry; Trk; Outstndng Perfrmnce Awd Jazz Ensmble 85; County All Stars Crs Cntry 84; Area All ST Band 81; Engrng.

HUSTED, REBECCA; Barker Central Schl; Gasport, NY; (Y); AFS; 4-H; French Clb; Hon Roll; NHS.

HUSTIS, HARRIET E; Haldane Central Schl; Cold Spring, NY; (Y); 1/70; Band; Jazz Band; Lit Mag; Rep Stu Cncl; High Hon Roll; Jr NHS; NHS; Prfct Atten Awd; Val; NY ST Regents Schlrshp 85; Early Grad; Middlebury Coll; English.

HUTCHESON, GRACE A; Brighton HS; Rochester, NY; (Y); 1/320; Church Yth Grp; Cmnty Wkr; Varsity Clb; Band; Orch; Yrbk Ed-Chief; Var Capt Crs Cntry; Var JV Socr; Var Trk; NHS; Assoc Amer Tchrs German Achvt Awds 81-85; Steuben Scty Schlrshp Rnnr-Up 85; Yth Cares Awd 84; Rice U; Biochem.

HUTCHESON, MARK; Horseheads SR HS; Horseheads, NY; (Y); Boy Scts; Exploring; German Clb; Band; Chorus; Jazz Band; Mrchg Band; School Musical; Variety Show; Hon Roll; Engr.

HUTCHINGS, LISA; Webster SR HS; Webster, NY; (Y); 174/540; Hosp Aide; Office Aide; Chorus; Color Guard; VP Drill Tm; JV Var Swmmng; Mst Vlbl Swmnng 84; 3rd Yr Var Awd 85; Cert Of Hnr In Englsh 85; Bus.

HUTCHINGS, VIDA; Royalton Hartland Central HS; Gasport, NY; (Y); 18/136; VP French Clb; Girl Scts; Pres Spanish Clb; Varsity Clb; Yrbk Stf; Rep Stu Cncl; Var Capt Bsktbl; Var Fld Hcky; Var Vllybl; Hon Roll; Educ.

HUTCHINSON, JENNETTE; Corning-Painted Post West HS; Scottdale, PA; (Y); 52/251; Pres Church Yth Grp; Hosp Aide; Letterman Clb; Thesps; Varsity Clb; Band; Mrchg Band; School Musical; Rep Jr Cls; Rep Sr Cls; CA U; Elem Ed.

HUTCHINSON, KERRY; Fayetteville-Manlius HS; Fayetteville, NY; (Y); Church Yth Grp; Exploring; Var Swmmng; Var L Vllybl; High Hon Roll; Hon Roll.

HUTCHINSON, SHANE; Chenango Forks Central HS; Binghamton, NY; (Y); Rep Frsh Cls; Var Ice Hcky; Var Lcrss; Var Socr; Hon Roll; Broome Cnty H S Hockey All-Star Team 84-85; MVP Sherburne-Earlville Lacrosse Tourn 85; Art Awd 83; Archit.

HUTCHINSON, THOMAS; Kenmore East SR HS; Kenmore, NY; (Y); 14/330; Varsity Clb; Variety Show; Nwsp Rptr; Yrbk Sprt Ed; L Bsbl; L Bsktbl; High Hon Roll; Hon Roll; VP NHS; Ntl Merit Ltr; NY ST Regnts & Karr Parker Engrng Schlrshps 85; Rochester Inst Of Tech; Ind Eng.

HUTCHINSON, TIMOTHY; Archbishop Molloy HS; Glendale, NY; (Y); 87/410; Boy Scts; Church Yth Grp; Church Choir; Im Ftbl; Im Sftbl; Hon Roll; Engr.

HUTCHINSON, WENDY; Fairport HS; Fairport, NY; (Y); 86/600; Dance Clb; DECA; French Clb; JA; Ski Clb; Teachers Aide; Drill Tm; Hon Roll; NY ST Regents Schlrshp 85; DECA Regnl Comp 83; MI ST U; Merch Mgmt.

HUTLEY, MELISSA; Falconer Central HS; Jamestown, NY; (Y); 10/126; 4-H; FBLA; GAA; Chorus; School Musical; Cheerleading; Score Keeper; High Hon Roll; Hon Roll; Accntnt.

HUTTENLOCKER, DOUGLAS; Kenmore West SR HS; Kenmore, NY; (Y); JA; Yrbk Sprt Ed; Socr; Comp.

HUTTER, DEBBIE; St Johns Prep; Maspeth, NY; (Y); GAA; Letterman Clb; Library Aide; Office Aide; Ski Clb; Teachers Aide; Var Capt Crs Cntry; Var Capt Trk; MVP Crss Cntry 83-85; Coachs Awd 84 & 85; MVP Indoor & Outdr 84 & 85; Vet.

HUTTNER, ROSS; South Shore HS; Brooklyn, NY; (Y); 6/668; Teachers Aide; Chorus; Pres Schlr; Regents Scholar 85; Brooklyn Coll; Comp Sci.

HUTTON, CLIFFORD; Union Endicott HS; Endicott, NY; (Y); Art Clb; Key Clb; Band; Concert Band; Jazz Band; Mrchg Band; Symp Band; Acad All Amer 85; Aerontcl Engr.

HUVANE, PATRICK; Cardinal Spellman HS; Bronx, NY; (Y); Church Yth Grp; Ski Clb; Im Bsbl; JV Var Bsktbl; JV Var Ftbl; Im Socr; Im Wt Lftg; Hon Roll; Engrng.

HUYNH, HOAN; Christopher Columbus HS; Bronx, NY; (S); Hon Roll; SUNY Stonybrook; Med Lab Tech.

HUYNH, HUY; John Dewey HS; Brooklyn, NY; (Y); Math Tm; Science Clb; Engrng.

HUYNH, JANNE M; Forest Hills HS; Long Island, NY; (Y); Church Yth Grp; Exploring; Math Clb; Science Clb; Church Choir; Jr NHS; NHS; 1st Pl Queens Borough Sci Fair 84; Bus Ed Advsry Commssn Medal 83; United Fed Tchrs Medal & Cert 83; Med.

HVAL, NINA; Portledge Schl; Little Neck, NY; (Y); Library Aide; Nwsp Ed-Chief; Fld Hcky; Lcrss; Hon Roll; Regnts Schlrshp 85; Duke U; Hstry.

HWANG, VICTOR; Hauppauge HS; Smithtown, NY; (Y); Exploring; Hosp Aide; Symp Band; Rep Frsh Cls; VP Soph Cls; Off Jr Cls; Crs Cntry; Trk; Pres NHS; High Hon Roll; Med.

HYATT, JENNIFER; Skaneateles SR HS; Skaneateles, NY; (S); Intnl Clb; Band; Orch; Lit Mag; Var Co-Capt Cheerleading; VP Tennis; VP Trk; High Hon Roll; NHS; Tennis, Track, Chrldng Vrsty Athltc Awds 83-84; Tennis, Chrldng Vrsty Athltc Awds 84-85; Secondary Educ.

HYDE, MELISSA; Le Roy Central Schl; Leroy, NY; (Y); Varsity Clb; Yrbk Phtg; Yrbk Stf; Var Trk; Var High Hon Roll; Var Hon Roll; Jr NHS; Cazenovia Coll; Fshn Merch.

HYDE, MICHELLE L; Churchville Chili SR HS; Rochester, NY; (Y); 47/324; Church Yth Grp; Cmnty Wkr; Exploring; French Clb; FTA; Ski Clb; Chorus; JV Swmmng; High Hon Roll; Sec NHS; ST U Of NY; Spch Pthlgy.

HYDE, PATRICE; Deer Park HS; Deer Park, NY; (Y); Hosp Aide; Office Aide; Band; Drill Tm; Drm & Bgl; Mrchg Band; Capt Bsktbl; Hon Roll; Bio.

HYDE JR, TUCKER; Immaculata HS; New York, NY; (Y); Church Yth Grp; Cmnty Wkr; Band; Color Guard; Drill Tm; Mrchg Band; Im Bsktbl; Var Socr; Im Vllybl; Var Hon Roll.

HYDE, VIVIENNE; Brooklyn Tech HS; Jamaica, NY; (Y); Computer Clb; Drama Clb; Math Tm; Spanish Clb; Band; Church Choir; Concert Band; Yrbk Stf; Vllybl; Hon Roll; Ntl Fed Music Clbs; Syracuse U; Nrsng.

HYER, MICHAEL; East Islip HS; East Islip, NY; (Y); JV Var Bsktbl; Var Tennis; High Hon Roll; Hon Roll; Pres Phy Fit Awd 85; SADD 84-85; Engrng.

HYLA, MICHELLE L; Arlington HS; La Grangeville, NY; (Y); 70/518; Drama Clb; Girl Scts; School Musical; JV Sftbl; Hon Roll; NY ST Regents Schlrshp 85; Hnr Key 85; Siena Coll; Biomed Engr.

HYLAND, CHRISTINE; Haverling JR SR HS; Bath, NY; (S); 18/150; Math Clb; Mrchg Band; Yrbk Ed-Chief; Sec Jr Cls; Sec Sr Cls; L Var Cheerleading; Im Gym; Var L Swmmng; High Hon Roll; NHS; Binghamton U; Surg Nrsg.

HYLTON, TRACEY; Mount Version HS; Mt Vernon, NY; (Y); 32/597; Key Clb; Science Clb; Yrbk Phtg; High Hon Roll; Hon Roll; Alpha Kappa Alpha Sorority Awd 85; Ntl Cncl Of Negro Women Awd 85; Boston Coll; Pre-Med.

HYMAN, JANICE A; Cardinal Spellman HS; Bronx, NY; (Y); 8/535; Computer Clb; VP Science Clb; Im Tennis; High Hon Roll; Ntl Merit Ltr; Brnz Medl Rnkg 8 Of 535 83-84; Brnz Medl Rnkg 10 Of 575 82-83; Gold Medl Rudimnts Calculus 83-84; Columbia U; Sci.

HYMAN, JILL R; Jericho HS; Jericho, NY; (Y); 44/230; Dance Clb; School Play; Cheerleading; Tennis; NHS; This Weeks Music 84-85.

HYMAN, LINDA; Holland Central HS; Strykersville, NY; (Y); 12/102; Pres 4-H; Sec GAA; Varsity Clb; Rep Jr Cls; JV Var Cheerleading; 4-H Awd; High Hon Roll; Hon Roll; Jr NHS; NHS; Genesee; Word Proc.

HYNES, CHRISTOPHER S; Greenville JR SR HS; Greenville, NY; (Y); 9/91; Am Leg Boys St; Boy Scts; Key Clb; Spanish Clb; Trs Jr Cls; JV Bsbl; JV Var Bsktbl; NHS; Eagle Scout 84; Rotary Intl Exch Stu 84-85; Lttr.

HYNES, JODI; Seton Catholic Central HS; Vestal, NY; (Y); Church Yth Grp; VP French Clb; Key Clb; Ski Clb; Teachers Aide; Ed Yrbk Stf; Rep Stu Cncl; Hon Roll; NHS; Lemoyne Coll; Eng.

HYNES, JULIE; Ogdensburg Free Acad; Ogdensburg, NY; (Y); 50/289; Sec Key Clb; Yrbk Stf; Sec Frsh Cls; Sec Sr Cls; Stu Cncl; Var Socr; Var Timer; Var Trk; Var Vllybl; 1st Tm All Northern Trk 80-85, Socr 84; Marilyn Ferguson Awd 85; SUNY Oswego.

HYNES, TINA M; Our Lady Of Mercy HS; Fairport, NY; (Y); Church Yth Grp; Chorus; Yrbk Stf; Hon Roll; NY ST Rgnts Nrsng Schlrshp 85; Dnce Stu Of Yr 83; Oswego ST U; Crmnl Just.

HYSLOP, LUCI A; Briarcliff Public HS; Briarcliff Mnr, NY; (Y); Lit Mag; Library Aide; Yrbk Phtg; Hon Roll; NY ST Smmr Schl Arts 84; Westchstr Arts Pgm 83-85; Arts Reg & Tlnt Srch 84; Fine Arts.

IACOBELLI, CAROL M; Mt St Marys Acad; Tonawanda, NY; (Y); Church Yth Grp; Cmnty Wkr; Model UN; Hon Roll; Ntl Merit Ltr; St John Fisher Coll; Comm.

IACOBELLI, LOUIS A; Monsignor Farrell HS; Staten Island, NY; (Y); Band; Concert Band; Mrchg Band; Var Bsktbl; Var Bowling; Hon Roll; NYS Regents Schlrshp 84-85; St Johns U; Comm.

IACOBELLIS, JOHN; Holy Trinity HS; Island Park, NY; (Y); Cmnty Wkr; Chorus; Yrbk Rptr; Yrbk Stf; Hon Roll; Bus Mngmnt.

IACOBUCCI, CONNIE; Colonle Central HS; Albany, NY; (Y); Ski Clb; Orch; Socr; Hon Roll; Perf Atten 83-84.

IACOBUCCI, KRISTEE; Waterford Halfmoon HS; Waterford, NY; (Y); 5/86; Math Clb; Yrbk Ed-Chief; Yrbk Phtg; Yrbk Rptr; Yrbk Stf; Stu Cncl; High Hon Roll; Hon Roll; NHS; Camera Clb; Natl Ed Developmnt Tst Awd 84; Skidmore Coll Acad Excllnce Awd 85; Hudson Valley Cmnty; Bus Adm.

IACOVETTA, ANA; Cardinal Spellman HS; Bronx, NY; (Y); Church Yth Grp; Pres Debate Tm; French Clb; NFL; Science Clb; Pres Speech Tm; Hon Roll; Gold Mdl Forensics 83-85; Regents Schlrshp 84-85; Degree Dist Ruby 83; Boston U; Intl Bus Law.

IADAROLA, CHRISTINE M; Our Lady Of Victory Acad; Yonkers, NY; (S); Computer Clb; Science Clb; VP Pres Service Clb; Yrbk Stf; Hon Roll; NHS; Pace-Iona; Acctng.

IADELUCA, LUISA; Aquinas HS; Bronx, NY; (Y); 98/178; Church Yth Grp; Cmnty Wkr; Intnl Clb; Service Clb; Acpl Chr; Chorus; Church Choir; School Musical; School Play; Variety Show; Italian Hnr Soc 85; Amer Assn Italian Tchrs Awd 84; Fordham U; Trvl Agnt.

IADICICCO, AUGIE J; Niagara-Wheatfield SR HS; Niagara Falls, NY; (Y); 1/315; Am Leg Boys St; Exploring; Pres JA; Pres Math Clb; School Musical; Co-Capt Vllybl; Bausch & Lomb Sci Awd; Val; Trs French Clb; NYS Rgnts Schlrshp 85; Altrt Schlrshp Coll Clb 85; Resselaer Ply Inst; Physics.

IAMAIO JR, ANTHONY J; G Ray Bodley HS; Fulton, NY; (Y); 41/266; Science Clb; Variety Show; Capt L Swmmng; Var L Trk; Hon Roll; Prfct Atten Awd; NY ST Regents Schlrshp 85; Syracuse U Schlrshp 85; Syracuse U; Chemistry.

IAMICELI, NANCY A; St Barnabas HS; Yonkers, NY; (Y); 85/187; Drama Clb; Office Aide; School Play; Prfct Atten Awd; Second Honors 84&85; Wood Schl Berkley; Bus.

IANDOLO, RACHELLE; Christopher Columbus HS; Bronx, NY; (Y).

IANNACCI, THERESA; Stella Maris HS; Ozone Park, NY; (Y); Cmnty Wkr; FNA; Hosp Aide; Science Clb; Yrbk Stf; Comm Svc; Effort Chem; Nursing Coll; RN.

IANNARELLI, SABINA; St Johns Prep HS; Jackson Hts, NY; (Y); Hon Roll; NHS; Outstndng Acad Achvt 1st Hnrs Awd; Fordham U; Bus.

IANNITTI JR, MICHAEL R; St Anthonys HS; Scottsdale, AZ; (Y); 85/285; Art Clb; Library Aide; Teachers Aide; Nwsp Stf; Wt Lftg; Wrstlng; High Hon Roll; Hon Roll; NHS; Ntl Merit Ltr; Dun Scotus Awd 83, 84 & 85; AZ ST U; Chem Engr.

IANNO, CATHERINE; Liverpool HS; Liverpool, NY; (S); 10/792; Ski Clb; Band; Chorus; Jazz Band; School Musical; Rep Stu Cncl; Var Golf; Sftbl; High Hon Roll; NHS; Comm Schlr Awd 84; Mst Imprvd Ply Awd-Glf 83; Latin II Awd 84; Math II Awd 83; Psych.

IANNOLI, PASQUALE; Aquinas Inst; Rochester, NY; (S); 1/180; Computer Clb; Drama Clb; Nwsp Ed-Chief; Yrbk Stf; Rep Jr Cls; Rep Sr Cls; JV Var Socr; Bausch & Lomb Sci Awd; High Hon Roll; Jr NHS; Rennselaer Math & Sci Awd 84; Phi Beta Dappa Awd 85; Rochester U; Premed.

IANNONE, LOUIS; St Josephs Collegiate Inst; E Amherst, NY; (Y); 44/193; Church Yth Grp; French Clb; Quiz Bowl; Nwsp Rptr; Yrbk Rptr; Im Bowling; Var L Trk; High Hon Roll; NHS; Ntl Merit Ltr.

IANNUCCI, LOUIS; South Shore HS; Brooklyn, NY; (Y); 85/660; Pres Computer Clb; Res Acad Awd 85; Chem Mdl 85; Math Cert 85; Polytechnic Inst Of NY; Elec E.

IANNUZZI, JESSICA; Miller Place HS; Miller Pl, NY; (Y); FBLA; Varsity Clb; Nwsp Phtg; Nwsp Stf; Yrbk Phtg; Yrbk Stf; Bsktbl; Sftbl; Tennis; High Hon Roll.

IANSON, ERIC; Sachem HS; Holbrook, NY; (Y); 121/1300; Boy Scts; Band; Bowling; Jr NHS; NHS; Cystic Fibrosis Fndtn Spec Svc Awd 85; Interact Club Ldrshp & Svc Awd 85; Most Imprvd Band Mbr 84; Physics.

IBANEZ, ELINOR ROSE; Dominican Commercial HS; Brooklyn, NY; (Y); 15/296; Spanish Clb; Chorus; Rep Stu Cncl; Capt Var Cheerleading; High Hon Roll; Hon Roll; Jr NHS; Rcvd Var Chrldng Ltrs 84; St Johns U; Jrnlsm.

IBRAHIM, RICHARD; F D Roosevelt HS; Brooklyn, NY; (Y); Art Clb; Computer Clb; French Clb; Math Clb; Science Clb; Chorus; Bsktbl; Sftbl; Wt Lftg; Wrstlng.

ICOCHEA, HELEN; St Peters HS For Girls; Staten Island, NY; (Y); Exploring; FNA; GAA; Hosp Aide; Library Aide; Math Clb; Math Tm; Chorus; Nwsp Rptr; Tennis; Biochem.

IDEMAN, CATHERINE; Corning-Painted Post West HS; Painted Post, NY; (Y); Church Yth Grp; Hon Roll; Bus.

IDICULLA, SAJI; Geneseo Central Schl; Geneseo, NY; (Y); 9/99; Political Wkr; Red Cross Aide; Yrbk Ed-Chief; JV Var Sftbl; Var L Tennis; High Hon Roll; Jr NHS; NHS; Prfct Atten Awd; Camera Clb; 1st JR Yrbk Editr 84-85; 5th Natl Soc Stud Olympd Tst 85; St Lawrence U; Bus Lwyr.

IERVASI, ROSEMARY; Fontbonne Hall Acad; Brooklyn, NY; (Y); 7/130; Cmnty Wkr; Drama Clb; Teachers Aide; School Play; Stage Crew; Rep Frsh Cls; Rep Soph Cls; Off Sr Cls; Mgr(s); Score Keeper; Harold Jensen Mem Awd 82; 2nd Hnrs Iona Lang Test 84; Latin Clsscl Leag Cum Laude 85; Intl Studies.

IEVINS, ERIK L; Johnson City HS; Binghamton, NY; (Y); 3/212; Church Yth Grp; Mathletes; Chorus; Orch; Aud/Vis; Band; Church Choir; Symp Band; High Hon Roll; Hon Roll; NYSSMA Solo Comp 82-84; Rotary Clb Awd Outstndng Musician 84; Harmony Clb Schlrshp 85; Engrng Sci.

IGLESIAS, NIEVES; Hendrick Hudson HS; Peekskill, NY; (Y); 26/191; Exploring; Spanish Clb; Color Guard; Mrchg Band; Pep Band; Co-Capt Twrlr; Cit Awd; Hon Roll; NHS; Natl Ldrshp & Svc Awd 85; Albany ST U; Pol Sci.

IGNATOWSKI, KIMBERLY; West Seneca East SR HS; Cheektowaga, NY; (Y); Church Yth Grp; Jr NHS; Prfct Atten Awd; Latn I Awd Magna Cum Laude 84-85; Frnch II-III-IV Abov 90 Ave 82-85; Daemen Coll; Phy Thrpy.

IGO, MICHAEL; Cornwall Central HS; Cornwall, NY; (Y); 92/198; Yrbk Sprt Ed; Yrbk Stf; Rep Stu Cncl; Hon Roll; Mt St Mary Clg; Acctg.

IHLEN, MICHAEL J; St Anthonys HS; Smithtown, NY; (Y); Nwsp Rptr; Im Bowling; French Hon Soc; High Hon Roll; St Schlr; Pres Schlrshp Manhattan Coll 85; Manhattan Coll; Elect Engrng.

IKELER, RONALD; Letchworth Central HS; Arcade, NY; (Y); Pres 4-H; FFA; Varsity Clb; Rep Jr Cls; JV Bsbl; Var L Wrstlng; 4-H Awd; High Hon Roll; Hon Roll; Mckormick Farms Schlrshp 85; Alfred ST Coll; Agric.

ILAN, AARON; Bethpage HS; Plainview, NY; (Y); 20/290; FBLA; Var Trk; High Hon Roll; Hon Roll; NHS; Ntl Merit SF; Sec Ed.

ILARDI, JAMES; St Raymond High School For Boys; Bronx, NY; (Y); 13/182; Art Clb; Computer Clb; Math Tm; Science Clb; Yrbk Stf; Hon Roll; NHS; Italian Clb; Activity Awd; Bus.

ILG, HELGA; Manhasset HS; Manhasset, NY; (Y); Dance Clb; VP French Clb; VP German Clb; Drill Tm; Nwsp Stf; Badmtn; Cheerleading; High Hon Roll; Hon Roll; Hofstra U; Chrprctr.

ILLERBRUN, AMY; Letchworth HS; Bliss, NY; (Y); 13/83; 4-H; FHA; Library Aide; Chorus; 4-H Awd; High Hon Roll; Hon Roll; Outstndng Stu Awd Trade Schl 85; Cosmetologist.

ILLIG, TRACI; Kenmore West SR HS; Kenmore, NY; (Y); Girl Scts; Band; Concert Band; Mrchg Band; School Musical; JV Var Sftbl; Im Var Vllybl; High Hon Roll; Hon Roll.

ILLOVSKY, PETER; Msgr Mcclancy HS; Floral Park, NY; (Y); Camera Clb; Library Aide; VP Science Clb; Yrbk Phtg; Cngrsnl Rcgntn Awd 85; SUNY Stny Brk; Pre-Med.

IM, DAVID; Brooklyn Vo Tech; Flushing, NY; (Y); Church Yth Grp; Church Choir; Orch; Yrbk Phtg; Yrbk Stf; Hon Roll; Prfct Atten Awd; Elec Engrng.

IMBESI, FORTUNATO; Cicero North Syracuse HS; Clay, NY; (S); 23/622; Capt Tennis; High Hon Roll; Hon Roll; Jr NHS; NHS; Prfct Atten Awd; Accntnt.

IMBRIANO, MATTHEW; Beach Channel HS; Howard Beach, NY; (Y); 5/485; Debate Tm; Library Aide; Math Tm; Scholastic Bowl; Yrbk Stf; High Hon Roll; NHS; Ntl Merit Ltr; Pride Of Yankees Awd 83; NY ST Regents Schlrshp 85; Cooper Union; Aerospace Engrng.

IMHOF, MEG; Portledge HS; Bayville, NY; (S); Church Yth Grp; Math Clb; School Play; Nwsp Rptr; Yrbk Rptr; Bsktbl; Fld Hcky; Lcrss; Sftbl; Hon Roll; Empire ST Games Fld Hcky Team 85; Acad All-Amer 85; Amer HS Athl 84-85; Math.

IMIOLO, DEBORAH ANN; Maryvale SR HS; Cheektowaga, NY; (Y); Pres Drama Clb; Acpl Chr; Band; Chorus; Concert Band; Jazz Band; Mrchg Band; Orch; Variety Show; NHS; Eastman Schl Mus; Mus.

IMMEDIATO, MARIE; Mount Vernon HS; Mount Vernon, NY; (Y); 32/600; FTA; Office Aide; Teachers Aide; Hon Roll; Jr NHS; Elem Ed.

IMPELLIZZERI, JOHN A; Jamesville-Dewitt HS; Jamesville, NY; (Y); Chess Clb; Exploring; Mathletes; Math Tm; Hon Roll; Comp Engrng.

IMPERATO, MARY; Saint Joseph By The Sea HS; Staten Island, NY; (Y); Drama Clb; School Musical; School Play; Variety Show; Stat Bsktbl; Bowling; Score Keeper; High Hon Roll; Hon Roll; NHS; Bus.

IMPERATO, STEPHANIE; Bishop Kearney HS; Brooklyn, NY; (Y); Girl Scts; Capt Bowling; Mth.

IMS, STEVE; Webster HS; Webster, NY; (Y); 2/560; German Clb; Math Tm; Capt Crs Cntry; Capt Trk; Vllybl; JETS Awd; Pres NHS; Sal; Full Tuitn Schlrshp Case Westrn Resrv U 85; Gannett Newsppr Schlrshp 85; Mst Lkly Sccd 85; Case Western Resrv U; Mech Engr.

INDELICATO, GINA; Monsignor Scanlan HS; Bayside, NY; (Y); 10/259; Intnl Clb; Yrbk Ed-Chief; Yrbk Stf; NHS; Prfct Atten Awd; Prin Lst 83; Itln Hnrs 83-85; NY U; Bus.

INDERMILL, ALICIA; Spackenkill HS; Poughkeepsie, NY; (Y); 51/170; JV Bsktbl; Var Socr.

INFANTE, BRIDGID; John S Burke Catholic HS; New Windsor, NY; (Y); Drama Clb; Pres 4-H; Model UN; School Play; Stage Crew; Variety Show; 4-H Awd; High Hon Roll; Hon Roll; NEDT Awd; Theron Crawford Vet Sci Awd 83; Teen Amb St 4 H Pgm 82-85; NY St Pub Spkng Fin 84-85.

INFANTE, CINDY; Islip HS; Islip, NY; (Y); 45/250; Rep Sr Cls; Rep Stu Cncl; Var Capt Cheerleading; Stat Ftbl; Var Vllybl; High Hon Roll; Hon Roll; NHS; Chorus; Mrchg Band; Pres Acad Achvt Awd 85; Ntl JR Hnr Soc 81-83; Suny-Farmingdale; Acctng.

INFANTE, JOSE; Mamaroneck HS; Larchmont, NY; (Y); Latin Clb; Chorus; Lit Mag; JV Var Socr; Wt Lftg; Empire ST Game 84-85; All Cty Chorus 85; Roger Williams; Writer.

INFANTINO, ANTHONY; Archbishop Molloy HS; Howard Bch, NY; (Y); 110/470; Art Clb; Boy Scts; Math Clb; Math Tm; NY ST Rgnt Schlrshp 85.

ING, CHANNARITH; New Utrecht HS; Brooklyn, NY; (Y); Church Yth Grp; Cmnty Wkr; Arista 85.

INGENITO, STEVEN MICHAEL; Richmond Hill HS; Richmond, NY; (Y); Audio Engr.

INGERICK, RENEE; Dolgeville Central HS; Dolgeville, NY; (S); 40/82; GAA; Jazz Band; School Musical; Yrbk Ed-Chief; VP Sr Cls; VP Trs Stu Cncl; Capt Var Cheerleading; Church Yth Grp; Cmnty Wkr; 4-H; Most Congenial Bsktbl Chrldng 84; Realtors Awd 85; Hmcmng & Prom Queen; Cobleskill; Home Ec Educ.

INGERSOLL, JILL; Owego Free Acad; Owego, NY; (Y); Hosp Aide; Ski Clb; Varsity Clb; Band; Mrchg Band; Bsktbl; Fld Hcky; Trk; Hon Roll; Clb Athl Awd 82-85; Alfred ST Coll; Med Assist.

INGERSOLL, SUZANNE L; Watervill Central Schl; Waterville, NY; (Y); 5/93; GAA; Band; Pres Stu Cncl; Capt Cheerleading; Fld Hcky; Score Keeper; Var Capt Trk; Hon Roll; Ntl Merit Ltr; NYS Rgnts Schlrshp 85; Wells Coll E B Morgan Awd 85; Wells Coll; Law.

INGHAM, MARY; Bainbridge-Guilford HS; Bainbridge, NY; (Y); Church Yth Grp; Teachers Aide; VICA; Chorus; Hon Roll; Suco Oneota; Elem Educ.

INGHAM, STACEY; Cicero-North Syracuse HS; N Syracuse, NY; (S); 113/622; Exploring; Pres JA; Var Golf; Vet.

INGHER, STACY; Commack High School South; Commack, NY; (Y); Letterman Clb; Varsity Clb; Y-Teens; Nwsp Stf; Var L Badmtn; JV Tennis; Hon Roll; Vet Med.

INGKAVET, STEPHEN; Commack High School South; Commack, NY; (Y); Art Clb; Boy Scts; Exploring; Jazz Band; Orch; Symp Band; Yrbk Stf; Lit Mag; High Hon Roll; Hon Roll; Natl Sci Oly Cert Bio 83; Art.

INGLESE, STEVEN; Nazareth Regional HS; Brooklyn, NY; (Y); 2/280; Math Tm; Trk; Cit Awd; Gov Hon Prg Awd; Hon Roll; NHS; Pres Schlr; Regents Scholar 85; Comp Sci Hnr Cert 85; Chem Medl 85; St Johns U; Bus Mngmnt.

INGLIS, LEA; Our Lady Of Mercy HS; Penfield, NY; (Y); 38/200; Church Yth Grp; Spanish Clb; Teachers Aide; Church Choir; School Musical; Nwsp Stf; Yrbk Stf; Hon Roll; Oustndng Fresh Engl Achvt Awd; Prsdntl Acad Ftnss Awd 85; JR Yr Awd 84; Le Moyne Coll Syracuse; Acctng.

INGRAM, EILEEN; St John The Baptist HS; Farmingdale, NY; (Y); 23/601; Girl Scts; Hosp Aide; Service Clb; Spanish Clb; Chorus; Nwsp Ed-Chief; Rep Church Yth Grp; Elks Awd; High Hon Roll; Jr NHS; Fairfield U.

INGRAM, KIMBERLY; Niagara Falls HS; Niagara Falls, NY; (Y); Psychlgy.

INGRAM, STEPHEN; Kings Park SR HS; Kings Park, NY; (Y); 79/463; Art Clb; Drama Clb; Science Clb; Varsity Clb; Stage Crew; Lit Mag; Ftbl; Wt Lftg; Wrstlng; NHS; 1st Pl Smithtown E Wrstlng Tourn 85; 2nd Leag Iv Wrstlng; Washington & Lee U.

INGRAO, JENNIFER; Franklin D Roosevelt HS; Salt Point, NY; (Y); AFS; Band; Concert Band; Mrchg Band; Symp Band; Socr; Engrng.

INGRASSIA III, JOHN R; Monsignor Farrell HS; Staten Island, NY; (Y); Art Clb; Aud/Vis; Boy Scts; Chess Clb; Computer Clb; Dance Clb; JA; Ski Clb; Symp Band; Yrbk Stf; Pace U; Finc.

INGRAVALLO, KATHERINE; Fontbonne Hall Acad; Brooklyn, NY; (Y); 12/138; Drama Clb; Hosp Aide; Office Aide; School Play; Hon Roll; NHS; Prfct Atten Awd; NY ST Regnts Schlrshp 85; 1st Hnrs Iona Coll Lang Cntst 84; NY U; Sci.

INGULLI, FRANK; Monsignor Scanlan HS; Bronx, NY; (Y); 5/236; Math Tm; Im Bsktbl; Im Ftbl; Im Sftbl; Hon Roll; Math Hnrs Italain I II III Hnrs 82-85; Med.

INKS, MICHELE; Notre Dame Acad; Staten Island, NY; (Y); Church Yth Grp; Cmnty Wkr; Computer Clb; Math Clb; Y-Teens; Yrbk Stf; Bsktbl; Score Keeper; Sftbl; NHS; Med.

INNEO, JOAN; Williamsville East HS; Williamsville, NY; (Y); 116/288; Cmnty Wkr; FBLA; Ski Clb; Rep Frsh Cls; Rep Soph Cls; Rep Stu Cncl; St Schlr; Canisius Coll; Bus.

INNES, KAREN; Hillcrest HS; Rosedale, NY; (Y); Intnl Clb; JA; Teachers Aide; Gold Medal Schl Sci Fair 84-85; Med.

INNIS, NIGER R; Brooklyn Tech; New York, NY; (Y); Cmnty Wkr; Debate Tm; Political Wkr; VP Stu Cncl; JV Ftbl; Drama Clb; FBLA; Speech Tm; Teachers Aide; School Play; Stu Cncl Awd 85; Rcl Justice Dmstc Cncl Schlrshp 85; Pro Athl Actn Schlrshp 85; Yale; Law.

INSERRA, BARBARA; Bishop Kearney HS; Brooklyn, NY; (Y); Art Clb; Camera Clb; Church Yth Grp; Hosp Aide; Office Aide; Service Clb; Ski Clb; Hon Roll; St Johns U; Engrng.

INSETTA, JENNIFER; Oneonta SR HS; Oneonta, NY; (Y); Church Yth Grp; Drama Clb; French Clb; Key Clb; Q&S; Thesps; Varsity Clb; Chorus; Church Choir; Nwsp Rptr; Exclnce Socl Stud 82; Qull & Scroll 85; St Bonaventure U.

INSLER, TODD; Mount Vernon HS; Mount Vernon, NY; (Y); Aud/Vis; Trs Pres Key Clb; Concert Band; Yrbk Phtg; Stat Diving; Stat Swmmng; Im Wt Lftg; JV Wrstlng; Hon Roll; Kiwanis Awd; Embry-Riddle Aeron U; Aeron Sci.

INTERMONT, MICHELE; Sacred Heart Acad; Rockville Centre, NY; (S); 1/186; Church Yth Grp; FTA; Library Aide; Math Tm; Yrbk Stf; Lit Mag; JV Swmmng; NHS; Cath Daughters Of Amer Poetry Con 1st 2nd Locl Lev 3rd ST Lev 84; Princetn Bk Awd82-84; Intl Forgn Lan.

INZERILLO, ANGELA; Oyster Bay HS; Oyster Bay, NY; (Y); Model UN; Spanish Clb; Nwsp Rptr; Yrbk Bus Mgr; Yrbk Stf; Rep Soph Cls; Rep Jr Cls; Rep Stu Cncl; Var Badmtn; Var Bowling; Bus.

INZERILLO, WILLIAM B; Commack H S North; Commack, NY; (Y); Am Leg Boys St; Dance Clb; Varsity Clb; Acpl Chr; Chorus; School Play; Stage Crew; Swing Chorus; Variety Show; JV Crs Cntry; Regnts Schlrshp-ACT; Dramatcs.

IOBST, LAURIE; Union-Endicott HS; Endicott, NY; (S); 90/430; Church Yth Grp; Band; Church Choir; Color Guard; Pres Concert Band; Jazz Band; Pres Mrchg Band; Orch; Hon Roll; Outstnd Marchng Band 83-84; JR All-Amer Band Hall Of Fame 84; Acad All-Amer 84; Messiah Coll; Elem Ed.

IOCOLANO, EVELYN K; Fontbonne Hall Acad; Brooklyn, NY; (Y); USGF Gymnastic Comp 79-83; Trustee Schlrshp Pace U; Regents Coll Schlrshp; Pace U.

IOVINE, DANIELLE; Bishop Kearney HS; Brooklyn, NY; (Y); 5/365; Math Clb; Math Tm; Gym; NHS; Chem Awd 84; Bio.

IOVINO, MICHELE; Stella Maris HS; Ozone Park, NY; (Y); Library Aide; Science Clb; Nwsp Rptr; Nwsp Stf; Hon Roll; Queens Coll; Bus.

IPPOLITO, CYNTHIA; Avon Central HS; Caledonia, NY; (Y); Church Yth Grp; Dance Clb; French Clb; Trs Girl Scts; Band; Concert Band; Drm Mjr(t); Mrchg Band; Pep Band; Variety Show; Niagara U; Travel/Tourism.

IPPOLITO, JOHN; St Johns Prep; Astoria, NY; (S); Boy Scts; Hosp Aide; Nwsp Stf; Ftbl; Tennis; Trk; High Hon Roll; Hon Roll; Natl Sci Olympliad Awd Biology 83; Queens Coll Pres Awd 84; Pre-Med.

IPPOLITO, JOSEPHINE; St Johns Prep; Astoria, NY; (Y); 35/415; Teachers Aide; Chorus; Hon Roll; NHS; Prfct Atten Awd; Pace U; Comp Prog.

IRA, JOANNE C; Academy Of The Holy Names; Delmar, NY; (Y); Hosp Aide; JA; Nwsp Rptr; Yrbk Stf; Var Capt Socr; Var Sftbl; Var Vllybl; Engl Awd 84; Chem, Bio Awds 83-84; Bio.

IRAM, STEPHEN; Vernon-Verona-Sherrill HS; Verona, NY; (Y); Am Leg Boys St; Drama Clb; JCL; Latin Clb; Thesps; Varsity Clb; Band; Concert Band; Drm & Bgl; Mrchg Band; Engrng.

IRBY, LEIGH; Lawrence HS; Inwood, NY; (S); 50/450; Pres Church Yth Grp; Sec Exploring; VP FTA; Pres Pep Clb; Band; Orch; Ed Lit Mag; High Hon Roll; NHS; AFS; NYSSMA Awd 82-84; Ophthlmlgy.

IRIZARRY, GILBERT; Patchogue Medford HS; Medford, NY; (Y); 1/748; Computer Clb; Debate Tm; Math Tm; Nwsp Stf; Yrbk Phtg; Rep Sr Cls; High Hon Roll; Jr NHS; NHS; Val; NYS Sci Congrss Awd 82; American Nuclear Socty Awd 83; RITEC Awd 85; Cornell U; Comp Engrng.

IRIZARRY JR, RAYMOND; Sheepshead Bay HS; Brooklyn, NY; (Y); Spanish Clb; JV Var Ftbl; Prfct Atten Awd; Exploring; Hnr Math & Spnsh 85; Avg 92 Bio Lab Technqs II 85; Accntng.

IRLAND, KEVIN; Mynderse Acad; Seneca Falls, NY; (Y); 8/134; Am Leg Boys St; Boy Scts; Church Yth Grp; Cmnty Wkr; Drama Clb; Intnl Clb; JA; Trs Model UN; Political Wkr; Band; Elmira Coll Key Awd; Outstndng Stu 84; Senera Cnty Tngr Of Yr 85; Gould Rumps Schlrshp 85; Union Coll; Pltcl Sci.

IRONS, GERALD D; Springville Griffith Inst; Springville, NY; (Y); 9/201; Exploring; Capt Ice Hcky; High Hon Roll; Hon Roll; NHS; Regents Schlrshp 85; ST U NY Buffalo; Pharm.

IRONS, MICHAEL; Lake George HS; Pilot Knob, NY; (Y); 1/78; Church Yth Grp; Varsity Clb; Var Bsbl; Capt Bsktbl; Capt Socr; Bausch & Lomb Sci Awd; High Hon Roll; NHS; Val; Renssalaer Mdl RPI Mdl 84; Holy Cross; Math.

IRVINE, LAURIE; Grand Island HS; Grand Island, NY; (Y); 22/320; Variety Show; Var L Cheerleading; Ftbl; Var L Gym; NHS; Spcl Olym Coach; Camp Cnslr Mently Retrd Children; Physcl Thrpy.

IRVING, ATHENA; Newburgh Free Acad; New Windsor, NY; (Y); 89/720; French Clb; Girl Scts; Band; Chorus; Mrchg Band; Yrbk Stf; High Hon Roll; Hon Roll; Pres Schlr; Ilalian Clb 84-85; Marine Mdlnd Bnk Awd Lcl Hstry 84-85; Niagara U; Trvl Mgmt.

IRWIN, RAE; Saranac Central HS; Morrisonville, NY; (S); 2/130; Library Aide; ROTC; Yrbk Ed-Chief; Yrbk Stf; Stu Cncl; Var L Cheerleading; Var Trk; High Hon Roll; Ntl Hnr Roll; Rensselaer Poly I; Arch.

ISAAC, TRACEY L; Clarkstown North HS; New City, NY; (Y); Cmnty Wkr; French Clb; Var Twrlr; Home Room Rep 85; Yth Againtt Cancer 84; Stu Exchnge Prgm 85; SADD 83-85; Pol Sci.

ISAACS, ASHER; Kenmore East SR HS; Kenmore, NY; (Y); Math Clb; Varsity Clb; Pres Band; Pres Frsh Cls; Var Tennis; Var Capt Vllybl; High Hon Roll; NHS; Intnl Clb; Concert Band; Empire St Vlybl Tm 85; A Ratng NY St Solo Music Assoc 84-85; Pol Sci.

ISAACS, RHONDA; Beach Channel HS; Rockaway, NY; (Y); Cmnty Wkr; Service Clb; Yrbk Stf; Lit Mag; Trs Stu Cncl; Hon Roll; Arista 82-85; Bus.

ISAACSON, MAXINE HYLA; James E Sperry HS; Rochester, NY; (Y); 20/311; Nwsp Rptr; French Hon Soc; Hon Roll; NHS; Cmnty Wkr; Debate Tm; Drama Clb; French Clb; Library Aide; Temple Yth Grp; WEIU, Regents, RIT Alumni, Am Legn Ely Fagen & Frederick Douglas Schlrshps 85; Schltc Lttr 84; Rochester Inst Of Tech; Accntnt.

ISAACSON, MICHELLE; Christopher Columbus HS; Bronx, NY; (S); 6/792; Office Aide; Band; Nwsp Stf; Yrbk Stf; Hon Roll; Jr NHS; Pres NHS.

ISABELLA, TODD; Saranac Lake Central HS; Saranac Lk, NY; (Y); Rep Stu Cncl; JV Bsbl; Var Ftbl; Cantonatc; Lib Arts.

ISABELLE, AIMEE; Catholic Central HS; Watervliet, NY; (S); 10/203; Church Yth Grp; French Clb; Math Clb; Chorus; Church Choir; School Musical; Yrbk Stf; High Hon Roll; NHS; Nrsg.

ISAKSSON, KIMBERLY; Sachem High School North; Holbrook, NY; (Y); 89/1400; Drama Clb; Band; Color Guard; Mrchg Band; School Musical; Nwsp Rptr; Ed Lit Mag; Ntl Merit SF; 1st Pl Poetry 85; Schl Rep Interact Clb 85; Eng.

ISBELL, JOHN; Mercy HS; Moriches, NY; (Y); 16/102; Math Tm; High Hon Roll; Hon Roll; NHS.

ISERNIA, JAMES; Sachem HS; Lake Ronkonkoma, NY; (Y); 7/1483; Science Clb; Ski Clb; Varsity Clb; Rep Sr Cls; JV Capt Ftbl; Wrstlng; Jr NHS; Pres NHS; Schlr Athlt 85; Spagnoli Ftbl Awd Schlrshp 85; PTA Schlrshp Acad Awd 85; Cornell; Pre-Med.

ISHAM, CHRISTINA; Tioga Central HS; Barton, NY; (Y); Art Clb; 4-H; Band; Church Choir; Variety Show; Sec Jr Cls; Capt Var Cheerleading; 4-H Awd; Hon Roll; Cmnty Wkr; 2 Blue Rbns & Metals For Muscl Myssma Solo 82-83; Athltc Awds Chrldng 82-85; Ridley-Lowell Schl; Trlv Agnt.

ISHAM, JOSEPH R; Lancaster HS; Lancaster, NY; (Y); Church Yth Grp; Cmnty Wkr; Ftbl; Ice Hcky; Hon Roll.

ISIDORE, SHIRLEY; Dominican Commercial HS; Laurelton, NY; (Y); Pres Church Yth Grp; Dance Clb; Hosp Aide; Chorus; School Musical; Yrbk Stf; Prncpls List 83-85; Siennas Clb 83-84; Awd Extrcrclr Actvts 84-85; Med.

ISLAS, KRISTEN; Saramac Central HS; Saranac, NY; (S); 7/103; Pres French Clb; Yrbk Stf; Pres Frsh Cls; Pres Soph Cls; Pres Jr Cls; JV Var Socr; High Hon Roll; Hon Roll; NHS; Soccer All Star Tm 84; Med.

ISMAIL, DEEMA; Fontbonne Hall Acad; Brooklyn, NY; (Y); 27/130; Cmnty Wkr; Drama Clb; Office Aide; Variety Show; Hon Roll; Prfct Atten Awd; NY ST Regents Scholar 85; Hnrb Mntn World Civilizatn 83, Lang Arts II 84, Latin I 85, Gen Music 83; NY U; Accntnt.

ISOLA, DANIELLE M; Moore Catholic HS; Staten Island, NY; (Y); 20/180; French Clb; Service Clb; Yrbk Rptr; Rep Frsh Cls; Rep Soph Cls; Rep Jr Cls; Rep Sr Cls; Pres Stu Cncl; Cheerleading; NHS; Regnts Schlrshp 85; U Of Scranton; Pre-Law.

ISOLDI, CONRAD; Xavier HS; Staten Island, NY; (Y); Cmnty Wkr; Soph Cls; NEDT Awd; Bus Adm.

ISRAEL, ANDREW J; Xavier HS; Brooklyn, NY; (Y); Ski Clb; Var L Bsktbl; Var L Ftbl; Var L Trk; Im Wt Lftg; Pres Schlr; St Schlr; 1st Tm All Leag Ftbl 84; Shtptt Awds 82-83; Rugby E Cst Chmps 84-85; Marist Coll; Accntg.

ISRAEL, LEE A; Half Hollow Hills High School East; Dix Hills, NY; (Y); Art Clb; Camera Clb; Civic Clb; Cmnty Wkr; FBLA; JA; Key Clb; Leo Clb; Ski Clb; Teachers Aide; Brandeis; Bus.

ISRAEL, SHARON G; Jericho HS; Jericho, NY; (Y); Key Clb; Teachers Aide; Pres Temple Yth Grp; Chorus; Hon Roll; NHS; Cornell U; Humn Dvlpmnt.

ISRAELOFF, BONNIE L; Baldwin SR HS; Baldwin Harbor, NY; (Y); 87/502; Y-Teens; Var Badmtn; Var Tennis; Regnts Schlrshp 85; Tnns Indiv Cntys 85; Badmntn Indiv Cntys 84; U Of WI Madison; Advrtsg.

ISSER, REBECCA S; Shaker HS; Loudonville, NY; (Y); Spanish Clb; Temple Yth Grp; Yrbk Sprt Ed; Fld Hcky; Gym; High Hon Roll; NHS; Tufts U; Liberal Arts.

ITOH, MIKI; Academy Of The Resurrec; Larchmont, NY; (Y); 2/63; Math Clb; Yrbk Rptr; Sec Frsh Cls; Sec Church Yth Grp; L Tennis; High Hon Roll; NHS; Ntl Merit Ltr; Sal; Art Clb.

IVANENOK, JOSEPH F; Homer Central HS; Homer, NY; (Y); 10/210; Am Leg Boys St; Political Wkr; Band; Chorus; School Play; Stage Crew; Bsktbl; Crs Cntry; Lcrss; High Hon Roll; Aero Engr.

IVANOV, KERANA; St Catherine Acad; Bronx, NY; (Y); 19/205; Stu Cncl; NHS; Spnsh III 85; Law.

IVES, JEFF C; Cairo-Durham HS; Durham, NY; (Y); 4-H; JV L Bsbl; JV L Socr; 4-H Awd; High Hon Roll; Hon Roll; Comp Sci.

IVISON, JOHN; Byron-Bergen Central JR SR HS; Byron, NY; (Y); Am Leg Boys St; Boy Scts; Math Tm; Model UN; Trs Soph Cls; VP Jr Cls; Pres Stu Cncl; Var Swmmng; Ntl Jr Hortcltul Assoc 83-86; Cornell U; Ag.

IZEN, BETH; John H Glenn HS; E Northport, NY; (Y); Girl Scts; Hosp Aide; ROTC; Sec Science Clb; Sec Temple Yth Grp; Rep Jr Cls; DAR Awd; Key Clb; Color Guard; Drill Tm; NJROTC Meritors Achvt Awd 85; Dstngshd Cadet Awd 85; Biomdcl Engrng.

IZHAKY, DANNY; James Madison HS; Brooklyn, NY; (S); Aud/Vis; Computer Clb; Debate Tm; Office Aide; Science Clb; Stage Crew; High Hon Roll; Theodore Meyerwitz Awd 82; Math, Sci Achvt Awd 84; Achvt Awd Grant For Sci Proj 84.

IZYDORCZAK, JERRY; Alden Central HS; Alden, NY; (Y); Cmnty Wkr; Letterman Clb; Bsbl; Bsktbl; Ftbl; Cansius Coll.

IZZI, PATTI; Hicksville Senior HS; Hicksville, NY; (Y); Church Yth Grp; Dance Clb; Church Choir; Variety Show; Var L Gym; Hon Roll; NHS; Phys Ed.

IZZO, DARCY; Northville Central HS; Northville, NY; (Y); GAA; Color Guard; School Musical; Yrbk Sprt Ed; Yrbk Stf; Score Keeper; JV Var Socr; Var Sftbl; Library Aide; Rep Frsh Cls; Ldrshp Conf Rep 85; Drama.

IZZO, JENNIFER; Mickayuna HS; Schenectady, NY; (Y); AFS; Sec French Clb; Pep Clb; Service Clb; School Musical; Pres Soph Cls; Pres Jr Cls; Pres Sr Cls; Var Capt Cheerleading; Socr; Union Coll; Lbrl Arts.

JABLON, KYLE S; Lawrence HS; Cedarhurst, NY; (Y); 57/379; Political Wkr; Temple Yth Grp; Band; Jazz Band; Orch; Im Ftbl; High Hon Roll; NHS; Concert Band; Nwsp Phtg; NY ST Regent Schlrshp 85; Amer Legion Certfct Of Schl Awd 82; U Ctr At Binghamton; Med.

JABS, STACEY; Saugerties HS; Saugerties, NY; (Y); 20/240; Pres French Clb; Math Tm; Yrbk Ed-Chief; Ed Yrbk Phtg; Capt Trk; High Hon Roll; NHS; GAA; Math Clb; Office Aide; Max Salkind Awd 85; Intl Bus.

JACK JR, CHARLES; Hutchinson Central Technical HS; Buffalo, NY; (Y); 15/262; JA; Hon Roll; NHS; SAR Awd; Rgents Schlrshp; Rochester Inst Alumni Schlrshp; St U NY; Pre-Med.

JACK, DOUGLAS W; Kenmore West HS; Kenmore, NY; (Y); 33/445; Red Cross Aide; Ski Clb; Thesps; Church Choir; Rep Stu Cncl; High Hon Roll; NHS; VFW Awd; NY ST Schl Music Assoc Conf 84; Music Edctrs Natl Conf 85; NY ST Regents Schlrshp 85; Carnegie-Mellon U; Ind Mgmt.

JACKEMUK, GARY; West Genesee SR HS; Camillus, NY; (Y); 5/500; Exploring; Ski Clb; School Play; Rep Soph Cls; Rep Jr Cls; Im Vllybl; High Hon Roll; Hon Roll; NHS; UCLA; Comp Sci.

JACKINO, JENNIFER; Pelham Memorial HS; Pelham Manor, NY; (Y); Church Yth Grp; Cmnty Wkr; Off Jr Cls; Off Sr Cls; JV Var Bsktbl; JV Cheerleading; JV Var Lcrss; Hon Roll; NHS; Spanish NHS; Rnnr Up-Natl Spansh Hnrs Exam 84; Pres-March Of Dimes Stu Rep 84-85; Miss Teen Grtr New York 84-85; Intl Lang.

JACKMAN, MARK; New Rochelle HS; New Rochelle, NY; (Y); 1/700; Pres Computer Clb; Capt Math Tm; Model UN; Lit Mag; High Hon Roll; Hon Roll; NHS; Ranked 1st Westchester Interschlstic Math 84-85; 3rd Pl IA Coll Phys Comp 85; MIT; Comp Sci.

JACKMAN, STEPHEN; Lewis C Obourn HS; East Rochester, NY; (Y); 1/111; Drama Clb; VP Model UN; Varsity Clb; Jazz Band; Madrigals; Var Capt Swmmng; Bausch & Lomb Sci Awd; Pres NHS; Val; Yorker Clb Treas; Wesleyan U; Sci.

JACKMORE, JANE; Acad Of St Joseph; St James, NY; (Y); Church Yth Grp; Cmnty Wkr; Debate Tm; Drama Clb; Model UN; School Play; Yrbk Stf; Ntl Merit Ltr; NEDT Merit Cmmndatn 83; Dartmouth; Law.

JACKOB, RICHARD; Lincoln HS; Yonkers, NY; (S); Art Clb; Drama Clb; School Play; Stage Crew; Nwsp Stf; Crs Cntry; Trk; Comp.

JACKOWITZ, LANCE; Susan E Wagner HS; Staten Is, NY; (Y); Dance Clb; Drama Clb; JA; Temple Yth Grp; School Musical; School Play; Stage Crew; Bowling; Swmmng; Hon Roll; Accntng.

JACKOWSKI, CHARLES; Franklin Delano Roosevelt HS; Hyde Park, NY; (Y); JV Bsbl; JV Var Wrstlng; Ntl Phy Ed Awds 84-85; Engrng Comp Sci.

JACKSON, AMY LOUISE; C W Baker HS; Baldwinsville, NY; (Y); 97/441; Art Clb; Math Clb; Math Tm; Ski Clb; Color Guard; School Musical; Lit Mag; Hon Roll; NYS Rgnts Schlrshp 85; MONY Schlstc Art Awd Gld Key 85; HS Fest Arts 2nd Pl Ribbon Pncl/Overall 85; The Cooper Union; Arch.

JACKSON, ANTHONY M; Cardinal Spellman HS; Bronx, NY; (Y); 123/568; Church Yth Grp; Computer Clb; Band; Church Choir; Concert Band; Jazz Band; Mrchg Band; Pep Band; Hon Roll; U FL; Aerospace Engrng.

JACKSON, AUDRA E; Midwood HS; Brooklyn, NY; (Y); Church Yth Grp; Office Aide; Teachers Aide; School Musical; School Play; Yrbk Stf; Jr NHS; Modl Congrss Rnnr & Rep 81-82; Mock Trial Lwyr 84-85; Psych.

JACKSON, CAROL; St Francis Prep; Middle Village, NY; (S); 132/693; Var Bsktbl; JV Sftbl; JV Vllybl; Molloy Coll; Nrsng.

JACKSON, CHERYL; Penn Van Acad; Penn Yan, NY; (Y); 5/167; Church Yth Grp; VP Drama Clb; 4-H; GAA; Intnl Clb; Model UN; Pep Clb; Ski Clb; Band; Church Choir; Cornell U Nalt Schlr 85; Lewis Armstrong Awd In Jazz 85; Inst Magzn Mrt Awd 84; Cornell U; Agri Econ.

JACKSON, DAVE L; Mount Vewrnon HS; Mount Vernon, NY; (Y); Intnl Clb; Hon Roll; Westchester Bus Inst; Comp Pgm.

JACKSON, DAVID; Millbrook HS; Millbrook, NY; (Y); JV Var Bsbl; JV Var Bsktbl; JV Var Ftbl; Var L Trk; Com Sci.

JACKSON, DEBORAH; Southside HS; Channelview, TX; (Y); 42/333; Girl Scts; JA; Latin Clb; Varsity Clb; Chorus; Church Choir; Var Sftbl; Hon Roll; Vol For Handicap Swim 84; Med Explr 84; Arnot-Ogden Schl/Nrsgn; RN.

JACKSON, DIANNE E; C A Bouton JR SR HS; Voorheesville, NY; (Y); 4/122; Drama Clb; Concert Band; Jazz Band; School Play; Symp Band; High Hon Roll; NHS; Pres Schlr; Cmnty Wkr; French Clb; Colonl Cncl Math Cont; Regenst Schlrshp Wnnr NY St; Utica Coll; Psych.

JACKSON, HOWARD; Far Rockaway HS; Far Rockaway, NY; (Y); Math Clb; Chorus; Bsktbl; Tennis; Var Wrstlng; City U-New York; Engr.

JACKSON, JEANETTE; Gandor Central HS; Candor, NY; (Y); 5/88; Varsity Clb; Yrbk Stf; VP Frsh Cls; VP Soph Cls; VP Sr Cls; Var Capt Cheerleading; Var Powder Puff Ftbl; High Hon Roll; Pres Schlr; Suny; Sec Sci.

JACKSON, JENNIFER; Niagara Wheatfield SR HS; Niagara Falls, NY; (Y); French Clb; PAVAS; Band; Jazz Band; Mrchg Band; Stu Cncl; Var Tennis; Cit Awd; Hon Roll; V Ltr Tennis 84; Acad Hnr Awds 83-85; V Ltr Hnrs Music 84-85; Niagara U; Phrmcy.

JACKSON, JEUANITA; South Park HS; Buffalo, NY; (Y); Church Yth Grp; Drama Clb; Teachers Aide; School Musical; Jr NHS; Awd Best Persnlty 85.

JACKSON, JILL; Mynderse Acad; Seneca Falls, NY; (Y); 4/133; Concert Band; Mrchg Band; School Musical; High Hon Roll; NHS; Pres Schlr; St Schlr; JA; Science Clb; Navy Sci Awd Meritrs Achvt 83; Regents Scholar 85; Colgate U; Chem.

JACKSON, JIM; St Francis Prep; Middle Vlg, NY; (Y); Capt Ftbl.

JACKSON, KRISTINE MARIE; Johnstown HS; Johnstown, NY; (Y); Trs Intnl Clb; Varsity Clb; Mrchg Band; Nwsp Stf; Var Bsktbl; Hon Roll; NHS; Color Guard; Nwsp Rptr; JV Fld Hcky; Robt Mc Feeley Mem Schlrshp 85; Porf Wilcox Mem Awd 85; Bugle Awd Schl Nswpr 85; Syracuse U; Dietitian.

JACKSON, LEE ANNA; Curtis HS; Staten Island, NY; (Y); 43/327; Key Clb; Office Aide; Teachers Aide; Nwsp Rptr; Yrbk Stf; JV Var Cheerleading; Pom Pon; Hon Roll; Publishd Poem Search Inside 82; Cert Svc Def Contract Adm Svcs Regn 84; Jewish Fndtn Ed Wmn Scholar 85; Syracuse U; Cmmnctns.

JACKSON, LESLIE; Marlboro HS; Newburgh, NY; (Y); 36/166; Yrbk Phtg; Yrbk Rptr; Yrbk Stf; Hon Roll; JV Bsktbl; JV Var Mgr(s); JV Var Score Keeper; Var Trk; New Paltz; Psych.

JACKSON, LISA; Sacred Heart Acad; S Floral Park, NY; (S); 12/186; Math Tm; Chorus; Rptr Yrbk Phtg; Hon Roll; NHS; Engrng.

JACKSON, MARIA A; Saint Jean Baptiste HS; Bronx, NY; (Y); 28/88; Cmnty Wkr; JA; Teachers Aide; Stage Crew; Nwsp Rptr; Nwsp Stf; Yrbk Ed-Chief; Yrbk Stf; Rep Stu Cncl; Hon Roll; 1st Hnr Awd Spnsh 84; Spec Rcgntn Yrbk Edtr 85; Spec Rcgntn Nwsprs Wrtr 85; Hunter Coll; Elem Ed.

JACKSON, MARILYN J; Spring Valley SR HS; Spring Valley, NY; (Y); 13/535; Church Yth Grp; Cmnty Wkr; Drama Clb; German Clb; Library Aide; Thesps; Band; Church Choir; Mrchg Band; School Musical; German Hnr Scty 83; Vassar Coll; Frgn Lang.

JACKSON, MATTHEW; Pelham Memorial HS; Pelham, NY; (Y); Church Yth Grp; MMM; Concert Band; Jazz Band; Mrchg Band; Nwsp Ed-Chief; Rep Frsh Cls; High Hon Roll; Hon Roll; Pres-Tri M/Modern Music 85-86; Hist.

JACKSON, MEREDITH; Fonda Fultonville Central HS; Fonda, NY; (Y); Church Yth Grp; Band; Chorus; Mrchg Band; VP Frsh Cls; Coach Actv; Var Capt Swmmng; JV Trk; Hon Roll; MVP Swmmng 85; Marist.

JACKSON, MICHAEL J; Albany HS; Albany, NY; (Y); 12/600; Nwsp Rptr; L Capt Swmmng; Stat Timer; High Hon Roll; NHS; Ntl Merit Ltr; Mst Val Frshmn Swmmng 82; SUNY-ALBANY; Acctng.

JACKSON, PAMELA ELIZABETH; Music & Art HS; New York, NY; (Y); 127/620; AFS; Art Clb; Dance Clb; Hosp Aide; Teachers Aide; Yrbk Bus Mgr; Bsktbl; Prfct Atten Awd; Intl Livng Schlrshp Smmr In France 84; Ntl Recgntn, Achvt Schlrshp Prgo 84; Med.

JACKSON, PAULA; Boys And Girls HS; Brooklyn, NY; (Y); Teachers Aide.

JACKSON, RODNEY; Mayfield Central HS; Mayfield, NY; (Y); Exploring; Varsity Clb; Crs Cntry; Trk; Hon Roll; Kiwanis Awd; Mst Improv Crss Cntry 83; Mst Valbl Crss Cntry 84; Mst Vlbl Trck 85.

JACKSON, SHEZ; Mount Vernon HS; Mt Vernon, NY; (Y); 70/590; Church Yth Grp; FBLA; Off Sr Cls; Rep Stu Cncl; Hon Roll; Natl Bus & Profssnl Womens Leag 85; NAACP Schlrshp 85; Excllnc In Art & Keyboarding 83-84; Long Is U; Bus Admin.

JACKSON, TRACIE; Boys & Girls HS; Brooklyn, NY; (Y); Drama Clb; FNA; Hosp Aide; Nwsp Sprt Ed; Yrbk Phtg; Bsbl; Bowling; Gym; Swmmng; Vllybl.

JACKSON, TRACY; Walton HS; Bronx, NY; (Y); Boys Clb Am; Computer Clb; FBLA; Office Aide; Chorus; Tennis; Prfct Atten Awd; Outstndng Achvt Acadmc & Extr Currclr 85; Cert Of Merit Schlstc Achvt 84; Fordham U; Bus Adm.

JACKSON, VALERIE E; St Lawrence Central HS; Winthrop, NY; (Y); 10/106; Computer Clb; French Clb; Yrbk Stf; Pres Frsh Cls; Pres Jr Cls; Pres Sr Cls; JV Var Cheerleading; CC Awd; NHS; Alcoa Fndtn Schlrshp 85; NY ST U Pstdm; Math.

JACKSON, YOLANDA R; Hillcrest HS; Cambria Hts, NY; (Y); 70/793; Exploring; Girl Scts; Hosp Aide; Chorus; Yrbk Stf; Lit Mag; Hon Roll; Jr NHS; Cmnty Wkr; Ski Clb; Natl Hon Roll 84; Pre-Med Pgm 81-85; Adelphi; Pre-Med.

JACOB, JOHN J; Tonawanda JR SR HS; Tonawanda, NY; (Y); 20/235; Math Clb; Var L Bowling; Hon Roll; NHS; Rgnts Schlrshp 85; Qlty Stu Awd 85; ST U Of NY At Bflo; Acctg.

JACOB, JOSEPH; Tonawanda SR HS; Tonawanda, NY; (Y); 1/223; Am Leg Boys St; Teachers Aide; Var L Bowling; Wrstlng; Hon Roll; NHS; Rensselaer Mdl 85; Elmira Coll Key Awd 85; Outstdng Math Stu Awds 83-85; Outstdng Sci Stu Awd 85; U Of Buffalo; CPA.

JACOB, SARAH L; Nightingale Bamford HS; New York, NY; (Y); Art Clb; Cmnty Wkr; Drama Clb; Stage Crew; Nwsp Rptr; Yrbk Stf; Var Badmtn; JV Bsktbl; Mgr(s); Awd Latin 81-2; Awd Imprvmnt All Areas 82-83; Awd Achvt Final Exams 83-84; Oberlin Coll.

JACOBS, BONNIE; Chenango Forks Central HS; Binghamton, NY; (Y); Hon Roll; Achvt Awd-Accntng 84-85; Achvt Awd-Shrthnd 84-85; Achvt Awd-Math 84-85; Ridle Lowell; Accntng.

JACOBS, CINDY; Evander Childs HS; Bronx, NY; (Y); 5/503; Girl Scts; Hosp Aide; JV Vllybl; High Hon Roll; Prfct Atten Awd; Pride Of Yankees Outstndng Achvt Awd 84-85; Mind-Bldrs Aftrschl Pgm Cert Awd 84; Cty Coll Partcptn Awd; Cornell; Med.

JACOBS, DINA; Tappan Zee HS; Orangeburg, NY; (Y); Math Tm; Spanish Clb; Nwsp Stf; Rep Frsh Cls; Rep Soph Cls; Rep Jr Cls; Rep Sr Cls; Var Swmmng; Var L Tennis; NHS; Math Hnr Soc Treas 85-86; Yrbk Undrclsmn Sect Ed 83-84; Yrbk Layout Ed 84-86; Sci.

JACOBS, GREGG; Earl L Vandermeulen HS; Mt Sinai, NY; (Y); Computer Clb; Mathletes; Nwsp Ed-Chief; Nwsp Rptr; Var Bowling; JV Crs Cntry; High Hon Roll; NHS; Outstndng Mth Stu 83; Comp Sci.

JACOBS, JENNIFER; Long Island Lutheran HS; Wantagh, NY; (S); Ski Clb; Chorus; Variety Show; Rep Frsh Cls; Var Socr; JV Sftbl; Var Trk; Mgr Wrstlng; High Hon Roll; NHS; Schlrshp Tst 82-84; Schlrshp Top 10 Pct JR Hgh Clss 82; Engl.

JACOBS III, JOHN A; Amsterdam HS; Amsterdam, NY; (Y); 5/319; Trs 4-H; Varsity Clb; JV Ftbl; 4-H Awd; High Hon Roll; NHS; Engrng.

JACOBS, MARIA E; Schalmont HS; Schenectady, NY; (Y); Church Yth Grp; Capt Color Guard; Mrchg Band; JV Bsktbl; Score Keeper; Stat Socr; Var Vllybl; High Hon Roll; Hon Roll; Math.

JACOBS, MARK; Pelham Memorial HS; Pelham, NY; (Y); Band; Concert Band; Jazz Band; Mrchg Band; Golf; Merit Schlrshp 85-86; Clarkson Schl; Math.

JACOBS, MISTY; Groton Central HS; Groton, NY; (Y); Scrkpr 4-H; VP Ski Clb; Concert Band; Mrchg Band; Nwsp Sprt Ed; Yrbk Ed-Chief; Stu Cncl; Trk; High Hon Roll; Hon Roll; Gold Key - Blue Ribbon In Art; RIT; Graphic Design.

JACOBS, TRACY L; Frontier Central HS; Hamburg, NY; (Y); Latin Clb; Science Clb; Band; Chorus; JV Var Bsktbl; Im Var Socr; Im JV Sftbl; JV Var Vllybl; High Hon Roll; Hon Roll.

JACOBSEN, KATHRYN; John F Kennedy HS; Bedford, NY; (Y); 82/184; Church Yth Grp; Girl Scts; Service Clb; Chorus; Var L Crs Cntry; Var L Socr; Var L Trk; Hon Roll; Educ.

JACOBSON, ADAM; The Gow Schl; Huntington, WV; (Y); Key Clb; Temple Yth Grp; Varsity Clb; Nwsp Sprt Ed; Yrbk Sprt Ed; Bsktbl; Crs Cntry; Lcrss; Cit Awd; Hon Roll; Mst Imprvd Lacrosse Plyr 85; WV U Weslyan; Comm.

JACOBSON, JEFFREY; Springfield Gardens HS; Rosedale, NY; (S); Computer Clb; Yrbk Stf; Rep Stu Cncl; Stat Bsktbl; Var Bowling; Sftbl; Vllybl; NHS; Chiropractor.

JACOBSON, KIRK; Falconer Central Schl; Falconer, NY; (Y); 18/105; Computer Clb; VP JA; Chorus; High Hon Roll; NHS; St Schlr; JA Prgrsve Awd 83; JA Mgt Awd 84; SUNY Coll Fredonia; Comp Sci.

JACOBSON, VIRGINIA; Dryden HS; Dryden, NY; (Y); Ski Clb; Spanish Clb; Band; Chorus; Jazz Band; School Musical; High Hon Roll; Drama Clb; 4-H; Pep Clb; Sound Amer Hon Band & Chorus 84; Alto Sax Jazz Solo Awd 83-84; Sax & Vocal Solo Awds 81-85; Cornell U; Intl Studs.

JACOBUS, LYNETTE; Addison Central HS; Addison, NY; (S); 8/98; Church Yth Grp; JCL; Latin Clb; Science Clb; Ski Clb; Varsity Clb; Color Guard; Yrbk Ed-Chief; Rep Stu Cncl; Bsktbl; Cornell; Chld Psych.

JACOPELLE, JILL A; East Syracuse Minoa HS; E Syracuse, NY; (Y); Math Tm; Concert Band; Stage Crew; Variety Show; Lit Mag; Pres Jr Cls; Pres Stu Cncl; Var Gym; Hon Roll; NHS; Onandaga CC; Med Tech.

JACOX, MICHELLE; South Glens Falls SR HS; Ft Edward, NY; (Y); Office Aide; Yrbk Stf; JV Fld Hcky; Var Score Keeper; Hon Roll; RN.

JACQUELINE, PERRIN; West Irondequoit HS; Rochester, NY; (Y); 53/337; Exploring; Library Aide; Hon Roll; NHS; Pres Schlr; Monroe CC; Medcl Secy.

JACQUES, JAMEY M; Broadalbin Central HS; Gloversville, NY; (Y); Library Aide; Band; Concert Band; Jazz Band; Mrchg Band; Symp Band; Var Bsbl; JV Bsktbl; Var Bowling; Var Socr; Comp.

JACQUES, SUSAN B; Homer SR HS; Homer, NY; (Y); 2/199; Church Yth Grp; Soph Cls; Jr Cls; Mgr Trk; High Hon Roll; NHS; Sal; Hgh Avg Frnch I; Johns Hopkins U; Psychlgy.

JACZYNSKI, MARY; Byron-Bergen HS; S Byron, NY; (Y); AFS; FTA; Model UN; Teachers Aide; Variety Show; Nwsp Rptr; Nwsp Stf; Yrbk Stf; Ed Lit Mag; Sec Sr Cls; Hnbl Mntn 3rd Pl Sci Fair 83; Partcptn Clg Credt Adv Plcmt Amer Hstry Course 85; Med Tech.

JADLICKYJ, MARIA; Francis Lewis HS; Flushing, NY; (Y); 73/526; Church Yth Grp; Dance Clb; Natl Beta Clb; Office Aide; Science Clb; Teachers Aide; Chorus; Church Choir; School Musical; Variety Show; Summer Sci Inst Awd IN U 84; REAP 84; JR Acad Of NY Acad Of Sci 84; City Coll Of NY; Sci.

JAECKLE, MARK R; West Seneca East Senior HS; West Seneca, NY; (Y); 6/365; Letterman Clb; Ski Clb; Varsity Clb; Yrbk Sprt Ed; Capt L Ftbl; Var JV Swmmng; Var JV Trk; High Hon Roll; Jr NHS; NHS; Regents Schlrshp 85; Ithaca Coll; Phys Ther.

JAEGER, BARBARA J; Baldwin SR HS; Baldwin, NY; (Y); 17/502; Hosp Aide; VP Mathletes; Chorus; Concert Band; Mrchg Band; NHS; Ntl Merit Ltr; St Schlr; Church Yth Grp; Service Clb; Jostens Fndtn Schlrshp 85; Grmn Ntl Hon Soc 84; WA U; Physcl Thrpy.

JAEGER, DAVID; Farmingdale HS; South Farmingdale, NY; (Y); Aud/Vis; Cmnty Wkr; Debate Tm; Drama Clb; School Play; Rep Frsh Cls; Hon Roll; Jr NHS; NHS; Rotary Awd; Bio.

JAEGER, MEG; Freeport HS; Freeport, NY; (Y); Cmnty Wkr; DECA; Letterman Clb; Ski Clb; Concert Band; Nwsp Ed-Chief; Crs Cntry; Swmmng; Trk; Hon Roll.

JAEGER, TYRONE; Gilboa-Conesville Central HS; Prattsville, NY; (S); Yrbk Stf; Stu Cncl; JV Capt Bsktbl; High Hon Roll; NHS; Crs Cntry; Math 9 Regents 83.

JAFARIAN, JACLYN; Lockport SR HS; Lockport, NY; (Y); #15 In Class; French Clb; Intnl Clb; Ski Clb; Jr Cls; Sr Cls; Stat Bsktbl; Var Tennis; Hon Roll; Jr NHS; NHS; Comp.

JAFFE, ARI B; Edgemont HS; Scarsdale, NY; (Y); Computer Clb; Ed Nwsp Rptr; Nwsp Stf; Ed Lit Mag; Ntl Merit SF; Cum Laude Soc 84; Natl Assn Of Tchrs Of Spnsh & Portuguese 2nd Pl 83; Amer Comptr Sci Leag Top Score; Bio.

JAFFEE, DARA; Bethpage HS; Plainview, NY; (Y); 23/300; Pres French Clb; Capt Drill Tm; Var Gym; High Hon Roll; Pres NHS; Spanish Clb; Yrbk Stf; Rep Frsh Cls; Rep Soph Cls; Rep Jr Cls.

JAFFESS, SHARI L; Hillcrest HS; Floral Park, NY; (Y); 2/793; Debate Tm; Office Aide; Chorus; Var L Vllybl; Pres NHS; Ntl Merit Ltr; Sal; Math Tm; Nwsp Rptr; Rep Stu Cncl; Queens Coll Pres Awd 83; Daily News Super Yth 83; Yng Ambassador Israeli & French Forgein Exch 83-85; Cornell U.

JAGER, CRISTIAN R; Forest-Hills HS; Forest Hills, NY; (Y); Pres Debate Tm; Math Tm; Variety Show; Mgr(s); JV Socr; Tennis; High Hon Roll; Jr NHS; NHS; Prfct Atten Awd; Pre Med.

JAGER, DAVID; St Josephs Collegiate Inst; Kenmore, NY; (Y); 51/210; Am Leg Boys St; Boys Clb Am; Var Bsbl; JV Bsktbl; High Hon Roll; NHS; Ntl Hnr Soc; Bst Httr Awd; Bsbl.

JAGER, ERIK; Queensbury HS; Glens Falls, NY; (Y); Boy Scts; Church Yth Grp; JV Bsktbl; High Hon Roll; Eagle Scout 85; Brown Belt Karate 85; Order Arrow 83; Lib Art.

JAGODZINSKI, ANDREW J; Brockport SR HS; Hamlin, NY; (Y); Ski Clb; Socr; Swmmng; Stu Pilot 84-85; Camp Pathfndr-Cnslr 85; Aviatn.

JAGODZINSKI, KIMBERLY M; Nardin Acad; Buffalo, NY; (Y); 24/89; Model UN; Office Aide; Ski Clb; Speech Tm; Chorus; Stage Crew; Lit Mag; Rep Sr Cls; Regnts Schlrshp 84-85; SUNY Albany; Poly Sci.

JAIME, DAREN; Rice HS; New York, NY; (Y); Computer Clb; Color Guard; Drill Tm; Nwsp Stf; Pres Frsh Cls; Rep Stu Cncl; Im Var Bsktbl; Im Var Coach Actv; DAR Awd; Im Var Mgr(s); St Johns; Ref.

JAIN, ASTRID; Irvington HS; Irvington, NY; (Y); 2/122; Key Clb; Chorus; Ed Yrbk Bus Mgr; L Var Tennis; High Hon Roll; Ntl Merit Ltr; Sal; March Dimes Hlth Career Awd; P Ludington Mth Awd; Columbia Sci Hnrs Pgm; Wellesly Book Awd; Brown U; Med.

JAISON, DENA; Shulamith HS; Brooklyn, NY; (S); 5/28; Temple Yth Grp; Chorus; School Musical; Ed Nwsp Stf; Yrbk Stf; NHS; Brooklyn Coll.

JAKLITSCH, LISA; Christ The King Regional HS; Ridgewood, NY; (Y); 28/385; Yrbk Stf; Var Bowling; Var Swmmng; Var Tennis; High Hon Roll; Hon Roll; Psych.

JAKOBY, KENNETH; Kings Park HS; Smithtown, NY; (Y); 34/393; Chess Clb; Sec Computer Clb; Science Clb; Spanish Clb; Hon Roll; NHS; Inst Gftd & Tlntd Stdnts Aerontcs ST U Farmingdale 83; 3rd Pl Sci Fair 85; Natl Sci Olympd 83; Elctrcl Engrng.

JAKUBACK, JOAN M; Alfred G Berner HS; Massapequa Park, NY; (Y); 22/429; Drama Clb; Pep Clb; Stage Crew; Yrbk Stf; JV Var Cheerleading; Im Gym; Hon Roll; NHS; New York State Regents Scholarship 85.

JAKUBEK, RON; Nyack HS; Valley Cottage, NY; (Y); 27/270; Math Clb; School Play; Lit Mag; Rep Frsh Cls; Rep Soph Cls; Rep Jr Cls; L Var Bsbl; L Var Ftbl; High Hon Roll; NHS; MVP For JV Bsbl 84; Alter Svcs Awd 82; Math.

JAKUBOWSKI, KATHY E; Yorktown HS; Yorktown Hts, NY; (Y); Church Yth Grp; Hon Roll; Schlstc Achvt Awd 83; Acctng.

JAKUC, CHRISTINA LYNN; Shenendehowa Central HS; Clifton Park, NY; (Y); Am Leg Aux Girls St; GAA; Leo Clb; VP Varsity Clb; Rep Soph Cls; Rep Jr Cls; Sec Stu Cncl; Var Bsktbl; JV Crs Cntry; JV Socr; Shenendehowa Rtry Clb Awd 84; Fin.

JAMADAR, CHARMAINE S; Norman Thomas HS; New York, NY; (S); 79/671; Band; Concert Band; Yrbk Stf; Cit Awd; Hon Roll; Baruch Coll; CPA.

JAMES, BETH ANNE; Vernon-Verona Sherrill HS; Verona, NY; (Y); 5/294; AFS; 4-H; Latin Clb; Math Tm; Red Cross Aide; Thesps; Band; Orch; Yrbk Stf; Rep Stu Cncl; Dollars For Schlrs Schlrshp 85; Clarkson U; Indust Distr.

JAMES, CAROLINE; Lindenhurst SR HS; Lindenhurst, NY; (Y); Trs Key Clb; Trs Frsh Cls; Trs Soph Cls; Trs Jr Cls; Trs Sr Cls; Var Capt Cheerleading; Hon Roll; Jr NHS; Trs NHS; German Clb; Mst Outstndng Chrldr; Educ.

JAMES, CLAUDIA; Saranac Central HS; Morrisonville, NY; (S); 25/106; French Clb; Hosp Aide; Red Cross Aide; Chorus; Yrbk Stf; Hon Roll; Nrsng.

JAMES, DONALD; Groton Central HS; Groton, NY; (Y); 25/65; Art Clb; Chess Clb; Bsbl; Wrstlng.

JAMES, DONOVAN; Bronx HS Of Science; Brooklyn, NY; (Y); Boy Scts; JA; Band; Jazz Band; School Musical; Lit Mag; Rep Frsh Cls; Rep Stu Cncl; Capt Crs Cntry; Capt Trk; JFK Athltc Awd 85; IN U; Surgeon.

JAMES, FAITH A; Midwood High; Brooklyn, NY; (Y); 157/605; Church Choir; Variety Show; Cheerleading; Prfct Atten Awd; Regents Nrsng Schlrshp 85; Hunter Coll; Nrs.

JAMES, IAN R; James I O Neill HS; West Point, NY; (Y); Boy Scts; Computer Clb; Mrchg Band; School Musical; Nwsp Rptr; Nwsp Stf; JV Socr; High Hon Roll; NHS; Engrng.

JAMES, JEANETTE; New Utrecht HS; Brooklyn, NY; (Y); Church Yth Grp; Church Choir; High Hon Roll; Arista 85; OH Wesleyan Coll; Comp Sci.

JAMES, JOCKLIN; Copiague SR HS; Amityville, NY; (Y); Dance Clb; GAA; Girl Scts; Pep Clb; Band; Chorus; Pep Band; JV Var Bsktbl; Crs Cntry; Var Trk; MVP Bsktbl 84-85; All-Leag Bsktbl 84-85; All-Tourn Plaque Bsktbl 84-85; UWV; Bus Admin.

JAMES, JOHN H; Poland Central Schl; Poland, NY; (Y); Am Leg Boys St; French Clb; Varsity Clb; Concert Band; Jazz Band; Var Badmtn; Capt Var Tennis.

JAMES, JULIE; Nottingham HS; Syracuse, NY; (Y); French Clb; Latin Clb; JV Var Sftbl; JV Trk; High Hon Roll; NHS; Summa Cum Laude-Natl Latin Exam 85; Maxima Cum Laude-Natl Latin Exam 83-84; Cert De Merite 83; Bio.

JAMES, RICHARD; Chenango Forks HS; Binghamton, NY; (Y); Ski Clb; Var Ftbl; Var Lcrss; Var Trk; High Hon Roll; NHS; Rtry Yth Cnfrnc 85; All-League Ftbl Team 83 & 84; Math.

JAMES, SHERRIE; Barker Central HS; Barker, NY; (Y); AFS; French Clb; Sec Frsh Cls; Sec Soph Cls; Sec Jr Cls; Sec Sr Cls; Var L Fld Hcky; Var Capt Sftbl; Var L Vllybl; MVP Grls Vrsy Sftbl 85; Niagara-Orlns All Lg Sftbl 84; Erie CC Nrth; Dntl Hyg.

JAMES, STEPHANIE; Copiague SR HS; Copiague, NY; (Y); Debate Tm; Band; Concert Band; Mrchg Band; Yrbk Stf; Lit Mag; Im Bowling; Hon Roll; 2 Cert Hnrs NYS Bar Assn 85; John Jay Crminal Law; Engl.

JAMES, TRAVIS L; Gowanda Central HS; Collins, NY; (Y); 2/156; VP Church Yth Grp; Cmnty Wkr; Math Tm; JV L Ftbl; High Hon Roll; Jr NHS; NHS; Ntl Merit Schol; Sal; Prfct Atten Awd; Ftbl Awds 82; Rochester Inst Of Tech; Ele Eng.

JAMES, ZENOBIA; Holy Trinity HS; Roosevelt, NY; (Y); Yrbk Stf; Trk; Stonybrook Coll.

JAMIESON, DONNIE D; Newburgh Free Acad; Newburgh, NY; (Y); Camera Clb; Library Aide; Political Wkr; ROTC; Color Guard; Nwsp Phtg; Hon Roll; AF Assn Awd, Ldrshp Awd 85; Cadet Crps Commndr 85-86; Cornell U; Arch.

JAMIN, MERIDITH J; The Maskers Schl; Scarsdale, NY; (Y); Hosp Aide; Spanish Clb; Nwsp Phtg; Yrbk Phtg; Hon Roll; Northwestern U; Econmcs.

JAMINDAR, SWATI; Central HS; Valley Stream, NY; (Y); AFS; Ski Clb; Nwsp Rptr; JV Var Socr; JV Var Sftbl; JV Var Vllybl; Hon Roll; NHS; NY U; Law.

JAMISON, MICHELE A; Pittsford Mendon HS; Pittsford, NY; (Y); Church Yth Grp; Cmnty Wkr; Math Clb; Yrbk Stf; Powder Puff Ftbl; JV Vllybl; High Hon Roll; NHS; Pres Schlr; St Schlr; NY ST Womns Bowling Assn Schlrshp 85; PTSA Awd Phys Ed 84; U Of Rochester; Opthalmologist.

JAMISON, PAUL C; Locust Valley HS; Locust Valley, NY; (Y); 10/200; Am Leg Boys St; Boy Scts; Church Yth Grp; Computer Clb; Jazz Band; Yrbk Phtg; Var Socr; Var Tennis; High Hon Roll; Jr NHS; NHS; Burknell U; Sci.

JANACK, AMY; Solvay HS; Syracuse, NY; (Y); 11/168; Art Clb; Yrbk Stf; Jr Cls; Sr Cls; Hon Roll; NHS; MONY Art Awds 85; Regents Scholar 85; Geddes Vets Cash Awd 85; Alfred U; Fine Arts.

JANCEVSKI, VALENTINA; Lackawanna SR HS; Lackawanna, NY; (Y); Church Yth Grp; Dance Clb; Scholastic Bowl; High Hon Roll; NHS; Rgnts Awd For Excllnc-Bio & Chem 83-84; Hghst Schltc Achvt 84.

JANDREAU, CHRISTINE; Niagara Wheatfield HS; Niagara Falls, NY; (Y); Hosp Aide; Pep Clb; PAVAS; Chorus; Swing Chorus; Yrbk Ed-Chief; Var Tennis; Hon Roll; NHS; Prfct Atten Awd; Bus Mngmnt.

JANES, MARY; Attica SR HS; Attica, NY; (S); 2/150; Color Guard; Rep Stu Cncl; Var L Cheerleading; JV Capt Sftbl; L Swmmng; Floor Hockey; Phy Thrpy.

JANGRO, RHONDA; Schoharie Central HS; Schoharie, NY; (S); 11/77; Sec 4-H; VICA; Var Bowling; 4-H Awd; Hon Roll; Coca Cola Jr Ntl Champ Bowling 84; Stratford Schl; Dir.

JANICEK, MARGARET; St Francis Prep Schl; Flushing, NY; (Y); JA; Im Sftbl; Bio, Math Hnrs; Queens Coll; Psych.

JANICIJEVIC, MELANIE; Roy C Ketcham HS; Wappingers Fls, NY; (Y); Science Clb; Chorus; Orch; School Musical; High Hon Roll; Hon Roll; Music Camp Scholar Awd 83-84; NY ST Music Camp Scholar Awd 84-85; Natl Exam Le Grand Councours 83-84; Elem Ed.

JANICKI, CHRIS; Utica Free Acad; Utica, NY; (Y); Pres Church Yth Grp; Sec Computer Clb; Model UN; Spanish Clb; Im Bsbl; JV Bsktbl; NHS; Exploring; Mathletes; Service Clb; Intrnshp NY Acad Sci 84; Notre Dame J V Tourn-All Tourney 84 Bskbl 84; Engrng.

JANISZEWSKI, KRISTIN; Delaware Acad; Delhi, NY; (Y); AFS; Hosp Aide; Intnl Clb; Spanish Clb; Chorus; Color Guard; Mrchg Band; School Musical; School Play; Yrbk Stf; Syracuse U; Cmnctns.

JANISZEWSKI, MARK; Seneca Vocational HS; Buffalo, NY; (Y); 2/300; Hon Roll; NHS; U Buffalo; Engrng.

JANKOWIAK, JACQUELYN; Turner/Carroll HS; Buffalo, NY; (Y); 1/90; French Clb; Office Aide; Nwsp Sprt Ed; Nwsp Stf; Yrbk Ed-Chief; Yrbk Stf; Lit Mag; High Hon Roll; NHS; Prfct Atten Awd; H S Schlrshp 82; 1st Pl PSAT 84; NY ST Earth Sci Awd 83; Nrsng.

JANKOWIAK, LISA; Grand Island HS; Grand Is, NY; (Y); Hon Roll; NY ST Regnts Schlrshp 85; U Of NY Buffalo; Pol Sci.

JANKOWSKI, BONNIE; Kensington HS; Buffalo, NY; (Y); Bowling; Sftbl; High Hon Roll; Hon Roll; Prncpls Hnr Roll Lst 85; Wrk Exprnce Pgm 85; Buffalo ST U; Bus.

JANKOWSKI, DONNA; St Marys HS; Depew, NY; (S); 13/220; Drm & Bgl; Drm Mjr(t); Variety Show; Hon Roll; Math Awd; Sci Awd; SUNY-BUFFALO; Phy Thrpy.

JANKOWSKI, MELISSA; West Seneca East SR HS; Cheektowaga, NY; (Y); VP French Clb; Hosp Aide; JA; Science Clb; French Hon Soc; Hon Roll; Prfct Atten Awd; Natl Frnch Cont Awd 83-85; ST U Coll Buffalo; Soc Wrk.

JANKOWSKI, MICHELE; St Francis Prep; Kew Gardens, NY; (Y); Cmnty Wkr; Drama Clb; Pep Clb; Chorus; School Musical; School Play; Stage Crew; Rep Soph Cls; Stu Cncl; Gym; Arch.

JANKOWSKI, ROBERT; Rhinebeck Central HS; Rhinebeck, NY; (Y); 7/96; Quiz Bowl; Band; Yrbk Phtg; Yrbk Sprt Ed; Rep Stu Cncl; Var L Bsktbl; Var L Golf; Var L Tennis; Elks Awd; NHS; MVP Tennis Tm 85; USMA West Point; Elec Engrng.

JANNE, PASI A; United Nations International Schl; New York, NY; (Y); Computer Clb; Yrbk Stf; Wnnr Anual Westinghse Sci Srch 85; Bio.

JANSEN, LORI; Chenango Valley HS; Binghamton, NY; (Y); Drama Clb; Band; Color Guard; Concert Band; Drill Tm; Mrchg Band; School Musical; Symp Band; Tennis; Trk; NYSSMA Blue Mdl & Red Mdl 83 & 85; NY Jr Miss St Pagnt Wnnr 84; Miss Teen USA NY St Pag Fnlst 84; Broome CC; Psych.

JANSMA, KRISTI; Delaware Acad; E Meredith, NY; (Y); Church Yth Grp; Concert Band; Mrchg Band; Orch; School Musical; School Play; Yrbk Stf; L Capt Cheerleading; High Hon Roll; Prfct Atten Awd; Lbrl Arts.

JANSSON, DAVID R; Miller Place HS; Miller Place, NY; (Y); 9/201; Jazz Band; JV Bsbl; Var Bsktbl; Socr; Trk; High Hon Roll; NCTE Awd; NHS; Church Yth Grp; Varsity Clb; Cornell U Frsh Fellowship 85; Empire ST Games Long Island Vllybl Tm 84; Cornell U; Mth.

JANTSON, ANDREA; Glens Falls HS; Glens Falls, NY; (Y); 14/222; Band; Orch; Sec Sr Cls; Rep Stu Cncl; Powder Puff Ftbl; Sftbl; Swmmng; High Hon Roll; NHS; Pres Schlr; Zonta Clb Schlrshp 85; Cliff Bosworth Sci Schlrshp 85; Fairfield U; Bio.

JANUCHOWSKI, DENNIS; Grand Island SR HS; Grand Island, NY; (Y); 43/325; Boy Scts; Exploring; Mathletes; Ski Clb; Band; Mrchg Band; JV Tennis; Hon Roll; Masonic Awd; Del Molay Awd 84; Schlstc Achvt Awds 84-85; Cert Dist Cndn Math Comp 83; Law.

JANUSZ, DANIELLE; Bishop Kearney HS; Brooklyn, NY; (Y); Church Yth Grp; Cmnty Wkr; Hosp Aide; Key Clb; Math Tm; Ski Clb; Gym; Hon Roll; NHS; St Saviors HS Partial Schlrshp 82; Pre Med.

JANUSZ, WILLIAM F; Valley Stream Central HS; Valley Stream, NY; (Y); Boy Scts; Church Yth Grp; Leo Clb; Band; Chorus; Church Choir; Madrigals; Mrchg Band; Concert Band; Orch; Elec Engrng.

JAQUAYS, COLIN P; Mohawk Central HS; Mohawk, NY; (Y); 24/99; Am Leg Boys St; Math Tm; JV Var Bowling; Hon Roll; 6th Pl Complit Cntst 84; Physcis.

JARACZ, JOSEPH; H C Technical HS; Buffalo, NY; (Y); Chess Clb; Church Yth Grp; Hon Roll; NHS; Rochester Inst Of Tech; Archtrl.

JARAMILLO, GEORGE; La Salle Acad; New York, NY; (Y); Crs Cntry; Trk; Hon Roll.

JARASHOW, JONATHAN; Hebrew Academy Nassau County; Massapequa Pk, NY; (S); Debate Tm; Quiz Bowl; Pres Temple Yth Grp; Bsktbl; Capt Socr; High Hon Roll; NHS; Stu Crt Jdg 85; Hofstra U Forensics Comptn Fnlst 85; Ntl Soc Of Dstngshd H S Stu 84; Med.

JARCZYK, WENDY; West Seneca East SR HS; Buffalo, NY; (Y); Rep Frsh Cls; Rep Soph Cls; Rep Jr Cls; Trocaire; Sec Sci.

JARCZYNSKI, MARY; Byron-Bergen HS; S Byron, NY; (Y); AFS; FTA; Model UN; Teachers Aide; Variety Show; Nwsp Rptr; Nwsp Stf; Yrbk Stf; Ed Lit Mag; Sec Sr Cls; Hnbl Mntn 3rd Pl Sci Fair 83; Partcptn & Clg Crdt Adv Plcmt Amer Hstry Course 85; Med Tech.

JARDINE, JACKI; Valley Central HS; Maybrook, NY; (Y); 22/260; Sec Stu Cncl; Cheerleading; Hon Roll; NHS; Mary Wilkinson Bedford Awd Math 82-83; Walden Womans Clb Hm Ec Achvt Awd 82-83; Nrsg.

JARDINE, MICHELLE M; Shaker HS; Latham, NY; (Y); Dance Clb; Key Clb; School Musical; Cheerleading; Gym; Powder Puff Ftbl; High Hon Roll; Prfct Atten Awd; Regents Schlrshp 85; Ithaca Coll Schlrshp 85; Ithaca Coll; Bus Admin.

JARMACZ, JUDI-LYNNE; East Syracuse-Minoa HS; Minoa, NY; (Y); Dance Clb; JV Cheerleading; High Hon Roll; Hon Roll; Jr NHS; NHS; Phys Ed Awd 83-84; Bookkeeping & Acctn II Awd 84-85; Prof Dance.

JARMAN, JUNE A; South Side HS; Rockville Centre, NY; (Y); 23/284; Cmnty Wkr; Chorus; High Hon Roll; Hon Roll; Jr NHS; NHS; Spnsh Exch Prog 85; Harvard Holy Cross; Psych.

JARNOT, JAMES M; Lancaster Central HS; Lancaster, NY; (Y); 76/435; Key Clb; Pep Clb; Ski Clb; Variety Show; Nwsp Stf; Yrbk Stf; Hon Roll; ST U Buffalo; Art Comm.

JAROMIN, PATRICK K; Lake Shore Central HS; Derby, NY; (Y); Am Leg Boys St; Boy Scts; Church Yth Grp; Drama Clb; Madrigals; School Musical; School Play; Yrbk Stf; NHS; Ntl Merit SF; Capt Its Acad Tm 84; Summr Music Theatr Pgm Plattsburg ST 85; Elec Engrng.

JARRETT, GERI; Webutuck Central HS; Millerton, NY; (Y); Am Leg Aux Girls St; Quiz Bowl; Sec Chorus; School Musical; Variety Show; VP Frsh Cls; Trs Soph Cls; Rep Jr Cls; Rep Stu Cncl; JV Var Bsktbl; Coach Watkins Awd 84-85; Cmmrcl Pilot.

JARRETT, JEAN; Newtown HS; East Elmhurst, NY; (Y); 292/695; Art Clb; Church Yth Grp; Dance Clb; French Clb; Chorus; School Play; Stage Crew; Yrbk Stf; Var Cheerleading; L Trk; Fest Arts Cert 85; Grphc Arts.

JARRETT, JEFFREY; Mynderse SR HS; Seneca Falls, NY; (S); 5/140; Boy Scts; Quiz Bowl; Band; Concert Band; Jazz Band; Mrchg Band; Pep Band; Score Keeper; Trk; High Hon Roll.

JARVELA, JENNIFER A; Roy C Ketcham SR HS; Wappinger Fls, NY; (Y); 4-H; Math Clb; Band; Church Choir; School Musical; JV Var Bsbl; JV Var Cheerleading; Hon Roll; Hon Roll; Jr NHS; Excllnt Rtng NYSSMA Solo 83; Bio.

JARVIS, KEVIN; Massena Central HS; Massena, NY; (Y); 24/320; Pres Church Yth Grp; Cmnty Wkr; Varsity Clb; Rep Frsh Cls; Rep Sr Cls; Rep Stu Cncl; Var Bsbl; JV Var Socr; Var Trk; Cit Awd; Frnch Alumni Schlrshp Awd 85; GM Inst; Mech Engr.

JARVIS, LOUIS; Hilton Central HS; Hilton, NY; (Y); Im JV Ftbl; Var JV Trk; High Hon Roll; Hon Roll; 2 1st & 3rd Pl Monroe Cnty Ind Arts Exhbt 83-85; Rochester Inst Tech; Prntr.

JARVIS, STEVEN; Northville Central HS; Northville, NY; (Y); Am Leg Boys St; Boy Scts; Band; Yrbk Stf; Stu Cncl; Var Bsbl; JV Var Bsktbl; Comp Sci.

JARVIS, TAMMY L; Massena Central HS; Massena, NY; (Y); Church Yth Grp; French Clb; Off Stu Cncl; Powder Puff Ftbl; Sftbl; Swmmng; Vllybl; Hon Roll; Prfct Atten Awd; David Locy Awd 80; 1T Team All-Nrthrn Swmng 83; Elem Ed.

JARZABEK, S PAUL; Bishop Scully HS; Amsterdam, NY; (S); JA; Math Clb; Spanish Clb; Cornell; Vet Med.

JASINSKI, DEBORAH; West Seneca East SR HS; Buffalo, NY; (Y); Church Yth Grp; DECA; 4-H; German Clb; German Ntl Hrn Soc 84; Comm.

JASKOLKOWSKI, LORI ANN; Lincoln HS; Yonkers, NY; (S); 6/424; Church Yth Grp; Cmnty Wkr; Nwsp Sprt Ed; Trs Stu Cncl; JV Bsktbl; JV Capt Vllybl; High Hon Roll; NHS; Frgn Lang.

JASKOWIAK JR, RAYMOND; Cardinal O Hara HS; Buffalo, NY; (S); 18/158; Art Clb; Church Yth Grp; French Clb; JV Bsbl; Var Bowling; High Hon Roll; Hon Roll; Ed Argy Awd 84; Knights Of Altar Bishops Awd 82; Canisius; Art.

JASKOWSKI, LYNN MARIE; Frontier Central HS; Hamburg, NY; (Y); French Clb; Yrbk Stf; Var Socr; Hon Roll; NHS; Sci.

JASON, KAREN J; New Rochelle HS; New York, NY; (Y); 1/597; Nwsp Rptr; Pres French Hon Soc; VP NHS; Val; Iona Coll Forgn Lang Cntst 2nd Pl; Wellesley Coll Bk Awd; Brown U; Intl Bus.

JASPER, KAREN; Acad Of The Holy Names; Albany, NY; (Y); Dance Clb; Drama Clb; School Play; Nwsp Rptr; Nwsp Stf; Lit Mag; Hon Roll; H S Art Awd 84; Art.

JASPER, MARY; Niagara Wheatfield SR HS; Niagara Falls, NY; (Y); 86/313; Church Yth Grp; Hosp Aide; Latin Clb; VICA; Church Choir; Im Var Bowling; Hon Roll; Vrsty Bowling Athltc Awd 85; Schlrshp-Peter N Whitchner Trst 85-86; Roberts Wesleyan Coll; Psychlgy.

JASSAL, MANMEET K; Cortland JR SR HS; Cortland, NY; (Y); Latin Clb; Ski Clb; Spanish Clb; Lit Mag; High Hon Roll; NHS; Prfct Atten Awd; 20th Century Clb Awd 85; Pres Acad Ftns Awd 85; Summa Cum Laude-Latin 85; SUNY Binghamton; Bio.

JASTRAB, DAVID; Whitesboro SR HS; Whitesboro, NY; (Y); Aud/Vis; Jr NHS; NHS; Cmmnctns.

JASTREMSKI, KIMBERLY; Fayetteville-Manlius HS; Chittenango, NY; (Y); Model UN; Thesps; Chorus; School Musical; School Play; Swing Chorus; Variety Show; Rep Stu Cncl; High Hon Roll; NHS; Frgn Lang.

JASTRZEMBSKI, JULIE C; St Francis Preparatory HS; College Point, NY; (Y); Art Clb; Cmnty Wkr; Teachers Aide; Im Vllybl; Im Wt Lftg; Hon Roll; NHS; C W Post.

JAUCH, PAMELA; Williamsville East HS; Williamsville, NY; (Y); 119/280; Church Yth Grp; Cmnty Wkr; GAA; Pep Clb; Ski Clb; Varsity Clb; JV Powder Puff Ftbl; Var Sftbl; Var Vllybl; High Hon Roll; Bus Mgmt.

JAVARONE, PAULA; Mayfield Central Schl; Mayfield, NY; (Y); Drama Clb; Hosp Aide; Band; Chorus; Jazz Band; School Play; Rep Soph Cls; JV Capt Bsktbl; Var Socr; Hon Roll; Mst Imprvd Awd In Jv Bsktbl 83-84; Schlstc Athlc Awd 85; Syrcs U Pre-Coll Smr Prgm 85; Archtctr.

JAVELINE, BARRY J; Comsewogue SR HS; Prt Jefferson Stn, NY; (Y); 2/338; Nwsp Stf; Rep Jr Cls; Capt Tennis; Jr NHS; NHS; Prfct Atten Awd; Pres Schlr; Sal; St Schlr; Pres Acad Ftns Awd 85; SUNY Binghamton; Pol Sci.

JAVINETT, VINCENT; Wallkill SR HS; Wallkill, NY; (Y); Cmnty Wkr; English Clb; FCA; Soroptimist; Band; School Play; Yrbk Stf; Rep Stu Cncl; JV Ftbl; Capt Socr; Bsktbl MIP 85; Soccer Coaches Awd 85; Regents Schlrshp 85; SUNY Morrisville; Bus Admin.

JAWORSKI, MARK; West Seneca West SR HS; Buffalo, NY; (Y); Aud/Vis; DECA; Ftbl; Army.

JAWORSKI, PATRICIA; Mc Kinley HS; Buffalo, NY; (Y); Rptr FFA; Rep Stu Cncl; Var Tennis; High Hon Roll; NHS; Buffalo Brd Of Ed Exc Awd 85; Envrnmntl Bio.

JAYCARD, MARTIN; Hicksville HS; Hicksville, NY; (Y); Ice Hcky; High Hon Roll; Hon Roll; Manhattan Coll; Comp Sys Analst.

JAYNE, JEFFREY; Jordan-Elbridge JR SR HS; Jordan, NY; (Y); Spanish Clb; Crs Cntry; JV Var Lcrss; Var Capt Wrstlng; Wildlife & Fishery.

JEAN, CRYSTAL; Sacred Heart HS; Bronx, NY; (S); 16/238; Hosp Aide; Office Aide; Yrbk Stf; Pres Soph Cls; Pres Jr Cls; Var Trk; High Hon Roll; Hon Roll; NHS; Tennis Schlrshp 81-84; ATA Tennis Trophies 80-84; 2nd Schl Sci Fair 82; Amherst Coll; Bio.

JEAN, LINDA; Copiague HS; Copiague, NY; (Y); Yrbk Phtg; Lit Mag; Hon Roll; Bus.

JEAN, ROLAND Y; La Salle Acad; Brooklyn, NY; (S); 57/237; Nwsp Rptr; VP Crs Cntry; VP Trk; Comp Sci.

JEAN, SMITH; Harry S Truman HS; New York, NY; (Y); 3/544; Cmnty Wkr; English Clb; French Clb; Math Tm; Nwsp Sprt Ed; Lit Mag; Vllybl; Gov Hon Prg Awd; High Hon Roll; NHS; Pres Acdmc Ftns Awd 85; Gov Comm Scshlstc Achvt Citation 85; Bronx Dist Attys Citation Hnr 85; SUNY Binghamton; Pre-Med.

JEAN-FRANCOIS, FARAH; Dominican Commercial HS; Elmhurst, NY; (Y); 73/273; Hosp Aide; Teachers Aide; Cheerleading; Prncpls Lst 81-85; Prsnnl Typg; Pres Acadmc Fit Awd 85; Hunter Coll; Nrsg.

JEAN-LOUIS, MAGDA; Christ The King HS; Jamaica, NY; (Y); 12/385; Art Clb; Computer Clb; Library Aide; Speech Tm; Stage Crew; Yrbk Stf; High Hon Roll; ROTC; NHS; Engrng.

JEDLICKA, GEORGE E; Hillcrest HS; Richmond Hill, NY; (Y); 23/793; Drama Clb; Office Aide; Teachers Aide; JV Trk; NHS; Comp Prgmng Awd 82; SUNY New Paltz; Comp Sci.

JEDREICICH, STEVEN; St Johns Prep; Woodside, NY; (S); Am Leg Boys St; Church Yth Grp; Band; Church Choir; Concert Band; Jazz Band; Orch; Nwsp Stf; Hon Roll; NHS; Full HS Tuition Schlrship 83; Schl Of Engrng; Engrng.

JEDRICH, CHRISTOPHER; South Lewis Central HS; Constableville, NY; (Y); 11/87; Varsity Clb; Var L Bsktbl; Var Capt Golf; High Hon Roll; Hon Roll; NHS; Arch Engrng.

JEDZINIAK, DAVE; Warwick Valley Central HS; Warwick, NY; (Y); 8/200; JV Bsbl; JV Bsktbl; Ftbl; High Hon Roll; Hon Roll; Regents Bio Schlrshp 84; Ntl Sci Olympd Chem Cntst Top 10 85; Warwick Vrsty MVP-BSBL 84.

JEFFORDS, MARCIA; Niagara Falls HS; Niagara Falls, NY; (Y); Church Yth Grp; Computer Clb; Dance Clb; Drama Clb; Hosp Aide; Spanish Clb; JV Cheerleading; Gov Hon Prg Awd; Kiwanis Awd; Ntl Yorker Excllc Awd 85; St John Fisher; Comp Sci.

JEFFRIES, JOAN; Rensselaer JR SR HS; Rensselaer, NY; (S); 4/80; Key Clb; Ed Yrbk Stf; Stat Ftbl; Score Keeper; Stat Sftbl; Sec NHS; Maria Coll Albany; Legal Ofc.

JEFFRIES, JOHN A; Holland Patent Central Schl; Holland Patent, NY; (Y); 9/190; Boy Scts; Chess Clb; Mathletes; Math Tm; Spanish Clb; L Trk; High Hon Roll; NHS; Ntl Merit Ltr; Ski Tm Lttrs 83,85; Acad Lttrs 83-85; Cornel Coll Of Engrng; Aero Eng.

JEFFRIES, NICK; Long Island City HS; Astoria, NY; (Y); 27/579; Math Tm; Rep Sr Cls; Sec Stu Cncl; High Hon Roll; Mu Alp Tht; Regnts Schlrshp Awd 85; Arista 83-85; Polytechnic Inst NY; Engrng.

JELINEK, CYNTHIA A; Smithtown West HS; Smithtown, NY; (Y); 93/500; Cmnty Wkr; Off Stu Cncl; Var Capt Badmtn; French Hon Soc; High Hon Roll; Hon Roll; NHS; Regnts Schrlshp NYS; Villanova; Bus.

JELLINEK, DANIEL; Mamaroneck HS; Larchmont, NY; (Y); Key Clb; Latin Clb; Ski Clb; Nwsp Stf; JV Bsktbl; Var Tennis; Model Lgsltr 85; Bus.

JELLINEK, MARK; Rockland Country Day HS; Palisades, NY; (S); Debate Tm; Drama Clb; Math Tm; Yrbk Phtg; Yrbk Stf; Var Bsbl; Var Socr; Hon Roll; Asst Dir Of Stage Lghtg 84-86; Cptn Of Var Soccer Tm 85-86; Brown U; Sci.

JEMETZ, BOHDAN; West Genesee SR HS; Warners, NY; (Y); Boy Scts; Exploring; Acpl Chr; Chorus; School Musical; High Hon Roll; Hon Roll; Aud/Vis; Outstndng Stu Frgn Lang Awd 85; Ntl Sci Olypd Chem 85; Ukrainian Bandurists Soc 84; Syracuse U; Chem.

JEN, WENDY K; Williamsville North HS; Williamsville, NY; (Y); 29/315; Concert Band; Pep Band; School Musical; School Play; VP Sec Symp Band; Bsktbl; Var Capt Socr; Var Capt Tennis; NHS; Varsity Soccer Rookie Awd 83; Varsity Soccer Most Valuable Fullback 84; Interscholstc Conf Sects 84; OH ST U; Electrical Engnrg.

JENAL, WILLIAM L; New Hyde Park Memorial HS; New Hyde Park, NY; (Y); 43/267; Drama Clb; Thesps; School Play; Nwsp Rptr; Yrbk Stf; Lit Mag; JV Var Bsbl; JV Var Bsktbl; JV Socr; Regents Schlrshp 85; St Johns Competitive Schlrshp 85; St Johns; Pre-Law.

JENDRAS, DOUGLAS; Mahopac HS; Mahopac, NY; (Y); 37/398; Cmnty Wkr; Bsbl; JV Bsktbl; JV Var Ftbl; Var Trk; High Hon Roll; NHS; Im Wt Lftg; Pres Acdmc Fit Awd 84-85; Brd Regnts Endrsmnt 84-85; Albany ST U; Pre-Med.

JENG, HAWFENG; F D Roosevelt HS; Brooklyn, NY; (Y); Math Tm; Columbia U; Elec Engr.

JENKINS, DANIEL; Altmar Parish Williamstown HS; Parish, NY; (Y); Boy Scts; Band; Concert Band; Jazz Band; Mrchg Band; Pep Band; Golf; High Hon Roll; Hon Roll; NHS; Siena Coll; Accntng.

JENKINS, JAMES; Fairport HS; Fairport, NY; (Y); JV Bsktbl; Im Ftbl; Var Lcrss; High Hon Roll; Hon Roll; CCFL Sci Olympcs; Bucknell U; Elec Engr.

JENKINS, JOHN; Riverside HS; Buffalo, NY; (S); 24/210.

JENKINS, JOSEPH; Roosevelt JR SR HS; Roosevelt, NY; (Y); FTA; Trs Intnl Clb; Mathletes; Nwsp Rptr; Yrbk Stf; Trs Jr Cls; Bowling; Trk; Hon Roll; NHS; Natl Hnr Rll 84-85; U Of SC; Elec Engr.

JENKINS, MICHAEL; Maple Hill HS; Castleton, NY; (S); Aud/Vis; Boy Scts; Trs Church Yth Grp; French Clb; Band; God Cntry Awd; NHS; Math Clb; Math Tm; JV Socr; NY Wnnr Sons Of Amer Revltn Egl Sct Comptn 83; Math.

JENKINS, PATRICK B; August Martin HS; Jamaica, NY; (Y); Boy Scts; Pres Computer Clb; Library Aide; Drm & Bgl; Rep Stu Cncl; Var Ftbl; St Schlr; Comp Sci.

JENKINS, SHAUNTEL; Bronx H S Of Science; Bronx, NY; (Y); Dance Clb; Service Clb; Chorus; Rep Sr Cls; Rep Stu Cncl; Ntl Merit Ltr; Spanish NHS; Poly Tech Inst; Engrng.

JENKS, CATHERINE; Colton Pierreport Central Schl; Colton, NY; (S); 2/32; 4-H; French Clb; Office Aide; Stage Crew; Yrbk Stf; Bsktbl; High Hon Roll; Hon Roll; Jr NHS; NHS; Regnts Schlrshp; Conway Schlrshp; Potsam St; Ed.

JENNE, LISA; Knox Memorial Central HS; Russell, NY; (S); 3/22; Yrbk Sprt Ed; Sec Soph Cls; Sec Trs Stu Cncl; Var Capt Bsktbl; Var Score Keeper; Var Capt Socr; Var Sftbl; Var Capt Vllybl; High Hon Roll; NHS; MVP Sccr 84; Frst Tm All Nrthn Sftbl & Sccr 83-85; Secnd Tm All Nrthn Bsktbl Vllybl 83-85; Jefferson CC; Phy Thrpst.

JENNEVE, JEFFREY; Niagara Wheatfield HS; Sanborn, NY; (Y); 7/350; Church Yth Grp; Math Tm; Im Var Bsktbl; High Hon Roll; NHS; Ntl Merit SF; Clarkson U Trustee Schlrshp; Clarkson U; Comp.

JENNINGS, ANDREW; Chenango Forks HS; Binghamton, NY; (Y); 9/176; Pres Church Yth Grp; Exploring; French Clb; Pres Jr Cls; Var Capt Ice Hcky; Var Capt Lcrss; Var JV Val; High Hon Roll; Pres NHS; Stu Yr-Pre-Calcls; U Of VA; Civl Engrng.

JENNINGS, LISA; Marlboro Central HS; Marlboro, NY; (Y); 10/100; Church Yth Grp; Yrbk Phtg; Rep Jr Cls; Bsktbl; Var Capt Crs Cntry; Var Capt Trk; High Hon Roll; NHS; Sprts Mdls 82-84; Bio Regnts Awd 84; Shrthnd Schl Awd 84; Bio.

JENNINGS, MELISSA; Cicero-North Syracuse HS; Brewerton, NY; (S); 78/622; Political Wkr; Adv.

JENNINGS JR, STANLEY; Chenango Forks Central Schl; Binghamton, NY; (Y); Debate Tm; Ski Clb; Band; Mrchg Band; School Musical; School Play; Trs Stu Cncl; JV Var Socr; Masonic Awd; NHS; Soc Studies Stu Yr 83; Frnch Stu Yr 85; Yth Salute Recgntn 85; U VA; Pre-Law.

JENNINGS, SUZANNE; Attica Central HS; Attica, NY; (S); 12/165; Nwsp Sprt Ed; Stu Cncl; Var L Socr; Var L Sftbl; Var L Vllybl; High Hon Roll; Hon Roll; NHS; Church Yth Grp; Regnts Schlrshp; Nazareth Coll; Psych.

JENNINGS, WILLIAM; Fort Ann Central HS; Ft Ann, NY; (Y); Am Leg Boys St; French Clb; Math Clb; Math Tm; Red Cross Aide; Scholastic Bowl; Yrbk Stf; Im Bsbl; Var L Golf; High Hon Roll; Answers Please Tm 85; Frstry.

JENSEN, BOB; Frontier Central HS; Lakeview, NY; (Y); Spanish Clb; JV Bsbl; JV Var Ice Hcky; Var Capt Socr; Hon Roll.

JENSEN, CARL L; Longwood HS; Beachwood, NJ; (Y); Boy Scts; Drama Clb; Latin Clb; Q&S; Mrchg Band; Stage Crew; Lit Mag; Trk; NY Regnt Schlrshp; U Of Charleston; Sci Engrng.

JENSEN, ROCHELLE; John F Kennedy HS; Utica, NY; (Y); Church Yth Grp; Band; Yrbk Phtg; Yrbk Stf; JV Bsbl; Cobelskill U; Flrcltr.

JENSEN, SANDRA; Waterloo SR HS; Waterloo, NY; (Y); 7/178; Pres VP Church Yth Grp; Sec Trs Model UN; VP Science Clb; Nwsp Ed-Chief; Sftbl; Vllybl; Cit Awd; DAR Awd; NHS; Regents Schlrshp 84-85; Cornell U; Natrl Rsrcs.

JENSIS, DIANNE; Maple Hill HS; Castleton, NY; (Y); 18/94; Church Yth Grp; Spanish Clb; Nwsp Stf; Yrbk Stf; L Cheerleading; Stat Socr; Trk; Hon Roll; Syracuse U; Telecomm Prod.

JEON, YONG M; Schomarie Central HS; Delanson, NY; (S); Math Clb; Varsity Clb; Yrbk Stf; Var Socr; Var Tennis; Hon Roll; NHS; Rpi; Mech Engr.

JERABEK, JEFFREY J; Lackawanna SR HS; Lackawanna, NY; (Y); 2/500; Am Leg Boys St; Varsity Clb; JV Var Bsbl; Var Bowling; High Hon Roll; Hon Roll; Pres NHS; Pres Of The Natl Hnr Scty 85-86; Boys ST Rep 85; Chem Engr.

JERGE, JEANNE M; Grand Island SR HS; Grand Island, NY; (Y); 53/325; Cmnty Wkr; Drama Clb; Girl Scts; Chorus; School Musical; Stage Crew; Im Vllybl; NHS; Art Clb; Ski Clb; Grl Sct Slvr Ldrshp & Slvr Awds 83 & 84; ST U Of NY; Elem Educ.

JERGE, JON; Grand Island HS; Grand Is, NY; (Y); 14/281; Boy Scts; Chorus; Pres Concert Band; Jazz Band; School Musical; Hon Roll; JP Sousa Awd; NHS; GR ISL H S Outstndng Bandsmn 84-85; NROTC Schlrshp 85; Appt U S Navl Acad; U S Naval Acad; Physcs Engrng.

JERMAN, JOHN; Mount Vernon HS; Mount Vernon, NY; (Y); Chess Clb; Yrbk Stf; Soph Cls; High Hon Roll; NHS; Law.

JERRY, RHONDA; Saranac Central HS; Cadyville, NY; (S); 6/106; 4-H; Yrbk Stf; VP Jr Cls; Off Stu Cncl; Var Capt Bsktbl; Var Capt Socr; JV Sftbl; Var JV Vllybl; High Hon Roll; NHS; Cornell U; Vet.

JESENSKI, CHRISTINE; Bishop Scully HS; Amsterdam, NY; (Y); 32/69; VP JA; Spanish Clb; Nwsp Rptr; Hon Roll; Natl Hnr Rl 84-85; Schenectady Cnty CC; Hotl Tech.

JESSUP, JOEL; Elmira Southside HS; Elmira, NY; (Y); 20/330; Chess Clb; High Hon Roll; Schlrshp Acctng 85; Bryant & Stratton; Acctng.

JESSUP, MARY; Attica Central HS; Attica, NY; (Y); Art Clb; Library Aide; Teachers Aide; Hon Roll; Outstndng Achvt Awd-Art 82-83; Art.

JESTER, AMY; Oneonta SR HS; Oneonta, NY; (Y); Bowling; Bus Acctg.

JESTER, DAN; Huntington Christian Schl; Wantagh, NY; (Y); 4/27; Church Yth Grp; Varsity Clb; Band; Chorus; Concert Band; Var Capt Bsbl; Var L Bsktbl; Var L Socr; High Hon Roll; Hon Roll; Messiah Coll; Acct.

JESTER, WENDY J; W C Mepham HS; N Bellmore, NY; (Y); Concert Band; Symp Band; Yrbk Ed-Chief; Rep Jr Cls; Rep Sr Cls; L Var Bsktbl; L Var Socr; Hon Roll; NHS; French Clb; LI Cncl Soc Stud Achvt Awd 85.

JETER JR, THOMAS; South Park HS; Buffalo, NY; (Y); Art Clb; Camera Clb; Chess Clb; DECA; JA; Ftbl; Tennis; Cit Awd; SAR Awd; Grphc Arts.

JETHANI, TARUN; Mineola HS; Williston Park, NY; (Y); Cmnty Wkr; JA; Library Aide; Mathletes; Math Clb; Math Tm; Office Aide; OEA; Q&S; Teachers Aide; Achvd Hghst Avg Polical For 1st 2 Qtrs 83-84; 1st In Keybrdng In Nassau Cnty & 3rd In Long Isl 84-85; Pre-Med.

JETTER, LISA; Kenmore West Senior HS; Kenmore, NY; (Y); Church Yth Grp; Political Wkr; Orch; School Musical; Var Tennis; High Hon Roll; Hon Roll; NYS Sci Supvrs Assn Bio Awd 84; NYS Mus Comp Awd Flute Solo 83; NFL Tm Tennis 84-85; Med.

JEUDY, ISBEN; South Shore HS; Brooklyn, NY; (Y); French Clb; Math Clb; Math Tm; Science Clb; School Play; Nwsp Stf; Lit Mag; Socr; Wt Lftg; French Hon Soc; Brooklyn Coll; Pre-Med.

JEW, KERRI; Sanford H Calhoun HS; Merrick, NY; (Y); 3/300; Drama Clb; Hosp Aide; Key Clb; Math Tm; Chorus; Stage Crew; Variety Show; Nwsp Ed-Chief; Nwsp Rptr; Nwsp Stf; Georgetown U Schlrshp Smmr Prog 85; Sanford H Calhoun PTSA Svc Awd 85; Vlntr Mth Lydia E Hall Hosp 85; Med.

JEWELL, JENNIE; Cato-Meridian Central HS; Cato, NY; (Y); Church Yth Grp; French Clb; Yrbk Stf; Hon Roll; Mst Imprvd Soc Stu 83-84; JR Ambulance Corp 85; Bryant & Stratton; Sec Asst.

JEWETT, KELLEY; Geneva HS; Geneva, NY; (S); 20/170; Pres Ski Clb; Varsity Clb; Yrbk Stf; Rep Stu Cncl; Var L Socr; Var L Sftbl; Var L Trk; Var L Vllybl; NHS; Mst Outstndng Spnsh I Stu; Yth Ldrshp Awd; Bio.

JEZIORO, SHANE; Gowanda Central HS; Irving, NY; (Y); Rep Stu Cncl; Var Ftbl; Var Lcrss; Hon Roll; Syracuse ST U; Engrng.

JHA, BHUVDUTT BUNTY; John Bowne HS; Yonkers, NY; (Y); 3/912; Computer Clb; Library Aide; Math Clb; Math Tm; Ed Q&S; Pres Science Clb; Nwsp Rptr; Vllybl; Gov Hon Prg Awd; High Hon Roll; Westnghse Sci Tlnt Srch Awd 85; JR Acad NY Acad Sci Rsrch Comp Awd 85; JR Sci Humnts Syposm Awd 85; City Coll NY; Engrng.

JIAMPIETRO, JEFFREY D; New York Mills JR SR HS; New Hartford, NY; (Y); 3/45; Am Leg Boys St; Boy Scts; Varsity Clb; Var JV Bsktbl; Var Tennis; Bausch & Lomb Sci Awd; High Hon Roll; Hon Roll; Opt Clb Awd; VP Soph Cls; Schrlshp Awd Hgst Acad Avg; V Ltr; Union Coll.

JILSON, ROXANNE; Nazareth Acad; Rochester, NY; (Y); Spanish Clb; Monroe CC; Mech Tech.

JIM, SULLIVAN; Fredonia HS; Fredonia, NY; (Y); Boy Scts; Church Yth Grp; Ski Clb; Spanish Clb; Band; Symp Band; Nwsp Rptr; Var L Bsbl; Fld Hcky; Var L Socr; Hnr Roll 84-86; Engrng.

JIMENEZ, GUADALUPE; John Jay HS; Brooklyn, NY; (Y); Cmnty Wkr; Spnsh Cert Awd 84; Cert Achvt, Cert Vlntrng 85; Bus.

JIMENEZ, JOSE; Far Rockaway HS; Far Rockaway, NY; (Y); Am Leg Boys St; Camera Clb; Church Yth Grp; Cmnty Wkr; Drama Clb; Key Clb; School Play; Nwsp Rptr; Yrbk Rptr; Capt Swmmng; Tchg.

JIMENEZ, JUNIOR E; Wyandanch Memorial HS; Weatley Hts, NY; (Y); Camera Clb; Cmnty Wkr; Drill Tm; Nwsp Phtg; Yrbk Stf; Stu Cncl; Socr; Swmmng; Wrstlng; Prfct Atten Awd; USMC; Psych.

JIMENEZ, RAFAEL; Cardinal Spellman HS; Bronx, NY; (Y); Church Yth Grp; Latin Clb; Band; School Musical; School Play; Lion Awd; Fordham U; Psych.

JIMENEZ JR, RAFAEL; Cardinal Hayes HS; New York, NY; (Y); 60/264; Computer Clb; Hosp Aide; JV Bsbl; Awd HEOP Bus Pgm 84-85; Bus Fin.

JIMENEZ, RICHARD A; Cardinal Hayes HS; New York, NY; (Y); 5/249; Church Yth Grp; Chorus; Jazz Band; School Musical; Nwsp Rptr; Im Vllybl; NHS; Prfct Atten Awd; Chess Clb; Dance Clb; Band Pin; Diamond H; Vlybl Capt Mdl; Skidmore Coll; Music.

JIMENEZ, SERENA; Cathedral HS; Bx, NY; (Y); 38/298; Hon Roll; Pre Med.

JIMENEZ, WYONA; Immaculata HS; New York, NY; (Y); Drama Clb; Drm Mjr(t); Swmmng; Hon Roll; Fordham U; Lwyr.

JIMENEZ LAVERGNE, LISETTE; Bronx HS Of Science; New York, NY; (Y); Girl Scts; Latin Clb; Chorus; Aspira Pin 84; Drama.

JIMENZ, GEORGIANA; St Pius V HS; Bronx, NY; (Y); Schl Awds 80-85; Bus Adm.

JIMERSON, GERALD; Senior HS; Verdailles, NY; (Y); Band; Jazz Band; Mrchg Band; JV Lcrss; Seneca Nation Johnson O Malley Awd 85; Mech Engr.

JIMINEZ, CHARISSE; Preston HS; Bronx, NY; (Y); Dance Clb; Service Clb; Variety Show; Pres Soph Cls; Pres Jr Cls; Rep Stu Cncl; Hon Roll.

JIMROGLOU, STEPHANIE; Hicksville HS; Hicksvl, NY; (Y); Church Yth Grp; GAA; Letterman Clb; Math Clb; Var Capt Bsktbl; Var Sftbl; Var Vllybl; High Hon Roll; Hon Roll; Jr NHS; MVP Bsktbl Tm 83; Excllnc Spnsh Awd 83; Hofstra U; Acctg.

JINVIT, KANDAPA; Acad Mount St Ursula; Bronx, NY; (Y); 24/167; Camera Clb; Church Yth Grp; Intnl Clb; Office Aide; Service Clb; Rep Soph Cls; Pres Jr Cls; Pres Sr Cls; High Hon Roll; Hon Roll; Yth Ministry Svc Awd 85; Manhattan Coll Schlrshp 85; Manhattan Coll Riverdale; Accnt.

JIRANEK, KATHRYN; Miller Place HS; Miller Pl, NY; (Y); Church Yth Grp; Drama Clb; FBLA; Ski Clb; School Musical; School Play; Stage Crew; Yrbk Stf; Hon Roll; Math I & III Awds 82-85; Hghst Awd Math III 84-85; Acctng.

JIRAS, JONATHAN; Southampton HS; Southampton, NY; (Y); Boy Scts; Pol Sci.

JOBMANN, KARL; Union Endicott HS; Endicott, NY; (Y); Computer Clb; Band; Comp Sci.

JOBSON, CAROLINE; Albertus Magnus HS; Valley Cottage, NY; (Y); 16/190; Sec Church Yth Grp; Math Tm; Ski Clb; Nwsp Rptr; JV Crs Cntry; Var Trk; High Hon Roll; NHS; Math Hnr Soc 85; Bio.

JOCK, CHRIS; Salmon River Central HS; Bombay, NY; (Y); 23/87; Church Yth Grp; FFA; Knights Of Columbus Schlrshp 85; Canton Atc; Elec Engnrng.

JOCK, DANIEL; Massena Central HS; Bombay, NY; (Y); Camera Clb; Cmnty Wkr; Computer Clb; Ski Clb; Yrbk Phtg; Mgr(s); Score Keeper; L Trk; RCC; Electr Tech.

JOCK, KIM; Saranac Central HS; Morrisonville, NY; (S); 9/106; Cmnty Wkr; Hosp Aide; Model UN; Spanish Clb; Teachers Aide; Trs Band; Color Guard; Concert Band; Cheerleading; High Hon Roll; Outstndg Grade Woodwnd Quintet 83; Cornell U; Vet.

JOCK, TODD M; Remsen Central HS; Remsen, NY; (Y); FFA; VP Band; Concert Band; Jazz Band; Mrchg Band; Var Bsktbl; Var Socr; Var Trk; Cit Awd; Hon Roll; Sci.

JOE, DENNIS; Far Rockaway HS; Far Rockaway, NY; (Y); Key Clb; Stat Ftbl; Pres Awd Achvt 83-85; Pride Yankees Awd 84.

JOENSEN, MOLLY PATRICIA; Lockport SR HS; Lockport, NY; (Y); 91/413; Hosp Aide; Latin Clb; School Musical; Swing Chorus; VP Frsh Cls; Trk; Hon Roll; Jr NHS; Prfct Atten Awd; Cmnty Wkr; Niagara Cnty Spirit JR Ms Schlrshp 84-85; Niagara Cnty CC; Rehab Svcs.

JOHANSON, GREG; W C Mepham HS; Bellmore, NY; (Y); Old Westbury Coll; Sound Engr.

JOHN, BURTON; Sachem North HS; Farmingville, NY; (Y); 30/1509; French Clb; Math Tm; Science Clb; Var JV Ftbl; Im JV Lcrss; Im JV Wrstlng; High Hon Roll; NHS; 8th Pl Chem Bio Olypiad 84-85; Intl Hocky Champ 84; Engrng.

JOHN, JOYLENE I; Midwood HS; Brooklyn, NY; (Y); 73/603; Church Yth Grp; Hosp Aide; Math Tm; Lit Mag; Socr; NHS; Ntl Merit SF; Med.

JOHN, LINDA; Notre Dame Acad; Staten Island, NY; (Y); Computer Clb; Library Aide; Chorus; NHS; Ntl Frnch Cntst 85, Cert Concours De Francais 85; Awd Sundy Schl Tchr 84-85.

JOHN, PAUL; Yonkers HS; Yonkers, NY; (Y); Church Yth Grp; Math Clb; Church Choir; Vllybl; High Hon Roll; Edwin G Michaelian Yth Govt Pgm Cert Partcptn 85; Elec Engrng.

JOHN, RAJEEV C; Mt St Michael Acad; Bronx, NY; (Y); JA; Library Aide; Mrchg Band; Nwsp Stf; Yrbk Stf; Sec Frsh Cls; VP Soph Cls; Var Badmtn; Var Coach Actv; Capt Fld Hcky; KS Inst Tech; Comp Tech.

JOHN, SUSAMMA; Dominican Commercial HS; Jamaica, NY; (Y); Church Yth Grp; Hosp Aide; Service Clb; Teachers Aide; WA Congrssnl Semnr Schlrshp 85; Psych.

JOHN, SUSAN; Long Island City HS; Long Island City, NY; (S); 1/570; Church Yth Grp; Debate Tm; Teachers Aide; Nwsp Rptr; Nwsp Stf; Lit Mag; Cit Awd; High Hon Roll; Hon Roll; Mu Alp Tht; Law.

JOHN, VINNIE; Wellsville HS; Wellsville, NY; (Y); Library Aide; Quiz Bowl; Varsity Clb; Church Choir; Drill Tm; Var L Socr; Var L Trk; Var Capt Vllybl; Hon Roll; Most Imprvd Plyr Soccer 84-85; Piloting.

JOHNSEN, CAROL; Bishopkearney HS; Brooklyn, NY; (Y); FNA; Intnl Clb; Key Clb; Library Aide; Ski Clb; Library Awd 84-85; NY U; Pre-Law.

JOHNSEN, KRISTINE A; West Islip HS; W Islip, NY; (Y); Cmnty Wkr; Mathletes; Varsity Clb; Var Church Choir; Concert Band; Orch; Yrbk Stf; Stat Swmmng; Var L Trk; Hon Roll; C W Post; Elem Educ.

JOHNSON, ANN; Byron-Bergen Central Schl; Bergen, NY; (Y); French Clb; Concert Band; Mrchg Band; Orch; Hon Roll; Roberts Wesleyan Music Scholar 85; Doris Sands Cook Mem Music Scholar 85; NYS Sumr Schl Orch Stud 85; Roberts Wesleyan Coll; Music.

JOHNSON, ANNA; Washington Irving HS; New York, NY; (Y); 74/500; Computer Clb; FBLA; Hosp Aide; JA; Office Aide; Chorus; Church Choir; School Play; Nwsp Bus Mgr; Yrbk Rptr; Cert Awd Vocl Tlnt 82; Borough Manhattan Chorus Awd Vocl Tlnt 82; Borough Of Manhattan; Nrs.

JOHNSON, AVA YVONNE; George Washington HS; New York, NY; (Y); 32/1105; Sec Church Yth Grp; Civic Clb; Exploring; 4-H; French Clb; Girl Scts; Flag Corp; Capt Trk; French Hon Soc; 4-H Awd; Fnlst Modern Mis Teenager Pgnt 84; Peru Bus Schl; Bus Admin.

JOHNSON, CAREY P; Boys And Girls HS; Buffalo, NY; (Y); Band; Yrbk Phtg; Gym; Silver L Avg Maintainence Awd 82-84; U Buffalo; Bio.

JOHNSON, CHERIE; Buffalo Traditional HS; Buffalo, NY; (S); 15/150; Debate Tm; FNA; Hosp Aide; Red Cross Aide; Crs Cntry; Trk; Cit Awd; 4-H Awd; NHS; Prfct Atten Awd; Canisius; Law.

JOHNSON, CURT M; Brewster HS; Brewster, NY; (S); 44/176; Sec Church Yth Grp; Yrbk Stf; Rep Jr Cls; Var Tennis; Hon Roll; Hst NHS; Shlrshp Arch Design 84; Arch.

JOHNSON, CYNTHIA A; Camden HS; Westdale, NY; (Y); Red Cross Aide; High Hon Roll; Hon Roll; Exec Sec.

JOHNSON, DANIEL; Bishop Kearney HS; Rochester, NY; (S); Concert Band; Jazz Band; Mrchg Band; Pep Band; School Musical; School Play; Stage Crew; Socr; Cit Awd; Hon Roll.

JOHNSON, DAVE; Schoharie Central Schl; Esperance, NY; (Y); 4-H; FFA; Cobleskill Ag & Tech; Ag Bus.

JOHNSON, DAVID; SHAPE American HS; A P O New York, NY; (Y); 12/68; Boy Scts; Letterman Clb; Model UN; Varsity Clb; Yrbk Bus Mgr; Yrbk Sprt Ed; Var Ftbl; Var Socr; Var Capt Wrstlng; Cit Awd.

JOHNSON, DAVID; Waverly HS; Waverly, NY; (Y); 1/140; VP Computer Clb; Capt Math Tm; Capt Jazz Band; Capt Mrchg Band; Var L Tennis; Ntl Merit Schol; Val; Am Leg Boys St; Cmnty Wkr; Exploring; Rensselaer Med Math & Sci 84; VA Polytech Inst U Schlrshp 85; Marshall Hahn Schlrshp Engr 85; VA Polytech Inst; Aero Engr.

JOHNSON III, DAVID E; Sidney HS; Unadilla, NY; (Y); 5/108; Art Clb; Boy Scts; Pres Varsity Clb; Band; Yrbk Sprt Ed; Stu Cncl; Var Capt Diving; Var L Trk; NHS; Physician.

JOHNSON, DEANNE; Canisteo Central HS; Canisteo, NY; (S); 7/81; Band; Color Guard; Concert Band; Drm Mjr(t); Mrchg Band; Var L Bsktbl; High Hon Roll; Hon Roll; NHS; Phy Thrpy.

JOHNSON, DENA L; Hillcrest HS; Jamaica, NY; (Y); 18/793; Hosp Aide; High Hon Roll; 2nd School Science Fair 83; NY U; Dentist.

JOHNSON, DERRICK K; Akron Central HS; Akron, NY; (Y); 7/159; Am Leg Boys St; Cmnty Wkr; Band; Off Sr Cls; Bsbl; Bsktbl; Coach Actv; Ftbl; Socr; High Hon Roll; Boys ST Rep 84; Case Inst Of Tech Merit Schlrshp 85-86; Case Wstrn Resrve U; Elec Engrg.

JOHNSON, DERRIN; Hutchinson Central Technical HS; Buffalo, NY; (Y); JA; Band; Concert Band; Jazz Band; Mrchg Band; Ftbl; Mgr(s); UCSD; Engr.

JOHNSON, DOLORES; Walton HS; Bronx, NY; (Y); English Clb; FBLA; Concert Band; Gym; Hosp Aide; Library Aide; Mathletes; Swmmng; Prfct Atten Awd; Accntng.

JOHNSON, EARL; St John The Baptist HS; E Massapequa, NY; (Y); Computer Clb; Debate Tm; Band; Nwsp Bus Mgr; Yrbk Bus Mgr; VP Frsh Cls; JV Capt Bsktbl; Georgetown U; Bus.

JOHNSON, EILEEN; Saugerties HS; Saugerties, NY; (Y); French Clb; Math Clb; Math Tm; Ski Clb; Mrchg Band; Powder Puff Ftbl; Hon Roll; NHS; Mngmnt Inf Sys.

JOHNSON, ERIC R; Keveny Memorial Acad; Cohoes, NY; (S); Cmnty Wkr; Computer Clb; French Clb; Math Clb; Political Wkr; Red Cross Aide; Im Bsktbl; Im Vllybl; Hon Roll; Prfct Atten Awd; Bio.

JOHNSON, GREGORY; Richmond Hill HS; Queens, NY; (Y); Boys Clb Am; Teachers Aide; Varsity Clb; Var Wrstlng; CPA.

JOHNSON, GREGORY LLOYD; Iona Prep; Bronx, NY; (Y); 50/194; Ftbl; Capt Trk; Hon Roll; Sec Trs NHS; Fndr & Pres Of Afro Cult Clb; Wesleyan U; Bio.

JOHNSON, HOLLY B; Troupsburg Central Schl; Troupsburg, NY; (Y); Computer Clb; Sec 4-H; Teachers Aide; Var L Bsktbl; Score Keeper; 4-H Awd; Hon Roll; Math.

JOHNSON, IVAN; Buffalo Traditional HS; Buffalo, NY; (S); 5/116; Chess Clb; Intnl Clb; Math Tm; Spanish Clb; Cit Awd; Hon Roll; NHS; Prfct Atten Awd; Gov Commndtn Human Rel Essay; Blck Wrtng Cntst Awd; Mech Engrng.

JOHNSON, JAMES P; Niagara Falls HS; Niagara Falls, NY; (Y); Boys Clb Am; Boy Scts; Ftbl; Trk; GA ST U; Bus Admin.

JOHNSON, JAMES R; Canandaigua Acad; Canandaigua, NY; (Y); 5/277; Ntl Merit Ltr; St Schlr; NY ST U-Buffalo.

JOHNSON, JEFFREY; Liverpool HS; Liverpool, NY; (S); 179/792; Stu Cncl; Var Ftbl; Var Trk; Im Var Wt Lftg; High Hon Roll; Hon Roll; Reasearch & Dvlpmnt Electrncs 84; WPI; Elec Engrng.

JOHNSON, JENNIFER; Notre Dame Bishop Gibbons HS; Schenectady, NY; (S); 22/108; Band; Concert Band; Jazz Band; School Musical; Variety Show; High Hon Roll; Hon Roll; NHS; Music Awd 81; Psych.

JOHNSON, JOANNE; Catholic Central HS; Averill Park, NY; (Y); 21/179; French Clb; Math Clb; Score Keeper; Sftbl; High Hon Roll; Hon Roll; High Hnr Rl; Hnr Rl; Physcl Thrpy.

JOHNSON, JOSEPH; Lewiston Porter HS; Youngstown, NY; (Y); 27/277; Church Yth Grp; Cmnty Wkr; Ftbl; Tennis; Wrstlng; Hon Roll; NHS; Lamp Lrng 83; Natl Hnr Rll 84-85; U S Tnns Assoc Rnkd 8th 84; Tnns Rnkd 7th 85; Yth Grp 79-84; Rochester Inst Of Tech; Mico El.

JOHNSON, JOSEPHINE; Stella Mares HS; Arverne, NY; (Y); Cmnty Wkr; Library Aide; Spanish Clb; Teachers Aide; Voice Dem Awd; Europn Studys Hnr Cls 83-84; Bus.

JOHNSON, JUDY; Morigh Central HS; Port Henry, NY; (Y); Var Bsktbl; Var Score Keeper; Var Socr; Var Sftbl; Var Swmmng; Comp Pgmr.

JOHNSON, JULIA; Longwood Central HS; Ridge, NY; (Y); Cmnty Wkr; Drama Clb; Pres Acpl Chr; Chorus; School Musical; School Play; Hon Roll; Rotrn Stdnt Mnth 85; Southampton; Chirop.

JOHNSON, JULIE; New Lebanon Central HS; Williamstown, MA; (Y); Sec Frsh Cls; Var JV Socr; High Hon Roll; Hon Roll; NHS; Hstry.

JOHNSON, JULIE A; Queensbury HS; Glens Falls, NY; (Y); 25/227; Lit Mag; Bsktbl; Fld Hcky; Mgr(s); Sftbl; Vllybl; High Hon Roll; Hon Roll; Regents Schlrshp 85; Dalmen Coll Amherst; Advrtsng.

JOHNSON, KALIE; Victor Central SR HS; Victor, NY; (Y); 26/205; Art Clb; Church Yth Grp; GAA; Coach Actv; Var Mgr(s); Var Score Keeper; Capt Sftbl; Timer; High Hon Roll; Hon Roll.

JOHNSON, KAREN; Center Moriches HS; C Moriches, NY; (Y); 10/97; Ski Clb; JV Bsktbl; JV Socr; JV Sftbl; Hon Roll; Leaders Clb; Fashion Rtl.

JOHNSON, KATHY; Ossining HS; Ossining, NY; (Y); Spanish Clb; Yrbk Stf; Hon Roll; Spanish NHS; H S Schlrshp Awd 85; Sectrl.

JOHNSON, KEMPTHORNE; Albany HS; Albany, NY; (Y); Computer Clb; Hosp Aide; JA; Church Choir; Yrbk Stf; Bsktbl; Wt Lftg; High Hon Roll; Engrng.

JOHNSON, KERSTIN; The Stony Brook Schl; Setauket, NY; (Y); 5/84; JV Fld Hcky; Var Mgr(s); High Hon Roll; Cum Laude 83-85; Slvr Mdl Frnch 84; Gld Mdl Bible 85.

JOHNSON, KIM; Dundee Central HS; Penn Yan, NY; (Y); 30/77; Cmnty Wkr; FHA; Varsity Clb; Chorus; Cheerleading; Socr; Trk; High Hon Roll; Hon Roll.

JOHNSON, KIM-MONIQUE; Holy Trinity HS; Wyandanch, NY; (S); 5/302; Math Clb; Variety Show; Nwsp Rptr; Yrbk Stf; JV Bsktbl; High Hon Roll; NEDT Awd; Jrnlsm.

JOHNSON, KRISTEN N; Ballston Spa HS; El Paso, TX; (Y); 21/248; Concert Band; Yrbk Stf; Rep Stu Cncl; JV Var Bsktbl; JV Fld Hcky; High Hon Roll; Hon Roll; NHS; Pres Schlr; Church Yth Grp; Gen Proprty Schlrshp 85; Lib Arts.

JOHNSON, KRISTIN; Waterloo SR HS; Waterloo, NY; (S); 28/178; Sec Ed FTA; VP Varsity Clb; Band; Yrbk Sprt Ed; Sec Stu Cncl; Var L Socr; JV Var Vllybl; High Hon Roll; Church Yth Grp; Concert Band; Wolg Key Awd 84; Law.

JOHNSON, LAURA; Schuylerville Central HS; Victory Mills, NY; (Y); Church Yth Grp; Cmnty Wkr; FBLA; JV Crs Cntry; JV Sftbl; Hon Roll; Pub Serv.

JOHNSON, LISA; Byron-Bergen HS; Bergen, NY; (Y); Church Yth Grp; FCA; Spanish Clb; Band; Color Guard; Mrchg Band; Trs Sr Cls; Var Cheerleading; Hon Roll; Mst Valuable Chrldng Awd 83; Houghton Coll; Bus Admin.

JOHNSON, LISA; St Marys Girls HS; Williston Park, NY; (Y); Cmnty Wkr; Trs Service Clb; Variety Show; Rep Stu Cncl; High Hon Roll; NHS.

JOHNSON, LISA A; Warwick Valley HS; Warwick, NY; (Y); 39/205; Drama Clb; Hosp Aide; Office Aide; Drm & Bgl; School Play; Stage Crew; Trs Frsh Cls; Trs Soph Cls; Trs Jr Cls; JV Socr; St Anthny Cmnty Hosp Auxlry Nrsng, Sal Troup & Polc Benvlnt Assn Schlrshps 85; SUNY Brockport; Nrsng.

JOHNSON, LYNETTE; Dolgeville Central School; Stratford, NY; (Y); 35/81; Church Yth Grp; Band; Sec Soph Cls; Sec Jr Cls; Cheerleading; Sftbl; Swmmng; Vllybl; Cit Awd; NHS; Ntl Hnr Roll 83; Cbleskil Ag & Tech; Hm Econ Tch.

JOHNSON, LYNN; Jamestown HS; Jamestown, NY; (Y); 18/375; Cmnty Wkr; Acpl Chr; Concert Band; Madrigals; Nwsp Rptr; Rep Sr Cls; VP Jr NHS; NHS; Church Yth Grp; German Clb; Amer Legion Aux Awd 82; Acad Schlrshp Houghton Coll 85; Houghton Coll; Chem Tchr.

JOHNSON, MARIA A; Jane Addams Vocational HS; New York, NY; (Y); Capt Trk; High Hon Roll; Hon Roll; Regents Scholarship 85; St Johns U; Public Admin.

JOHNSON, MARK; Woodlands HS; White Plains, NY; (Y); Church Yth Grp; FBLA; Letterman Clb; ROTC; Varsity Clb; Band; Yrbk Rptr; Var Bsbl; Var Bsktbl; Elec Engrng.

JOHNSON, MARTIN; Vestal HS; Binghamton, NY; (Y); Varsity Clb; Yrbk Stf; JV Var Bsbl; JV Var Ftbl; Var Ice Hcky; Schlstt Art Awds 82-84; Bus Adm.

JOHNSON, MARV; Rome Free Acad; Rome, NY; (Y); Var JV Bsbl; JV Socr; Hon Roll; Jr NHS; NHS; Grphc Art.

JOHNSON, MARY BETH; Johnstown HS; Johnstown, NY; (Y); Civic Clb; VP Intnl Clb; School Musical; Nwsp Sprt Ed; Yrbk Stf; Pres Stu Cncl; Var L Tennis; High Hon Roll; NHS; Ntl Merit Ltr; Hist Awd 85; Rep NY ST Stu Senate 85; Schl Rep St Rose 85.

JOHNSON, MELANIE; Aquinas HS; Bronx, NY; (Y); 59/178; French Clb; Hon Roll; Girl Scts; Westchester Bus Inst Awd Outstndng Determntn Hgh Bus Studs 85; Pace U; Bus Mngmnt.

JOHNSON, MELISSA; Eli Whitney Voc HS; Brooklyn, NY; (Y); Computer Clb; GAA; JA; Model UN; Office Aide; Teachers Aide; Yrbk Stf; Bsktbl; Wt Lftg; Prfct Atten Awd; Fashion Inst Tech; Fshn.

JOHNSON JR, MELVIN; Roosevelt JR SR HS; Roosevelt, NY; (Y); Art Clb; Boy Scts; Band; Chorus; Concert Band; Jazz Band; Mrchg Band; Orch; School Play; Variety Show.

JOHNSON, MICHAEL C; North Babylon HS; North Babylon, NY; (Y); 32/688; ROTC; Bowling; L Golf; L Socr; Cit Awd; Hon Roll; Jr NHS; NHS; Pres Schlr; St Schlr; Patriot Socr Clb Scholar 85; N Babylon PTA Scholar 85; Notre Dame; Navl Aviatr.

JOHNSON, MICHELLE; Horseheads HS; Horseheads, NY; (Y); Dance Clb; French Clb; JA; Corning CC.

JOHNSON, MICKEY; Edison Tech; Rochester, NY; (Y); Elctrnc Tech.

JOHNSON, NICHELLE; Midwood HS; Brooklyn, NY; (Y); Computer Clb; Hosp Aide; Math Tm; Band; Color Guard; Concert Band; Orch; Twrlr; Med.

JOHNSON, ORLANDO; James Monroe HS; Bronx, NY; (Y).

JOHNSON, PATRICIA A; Naples Central HS; Naples, NY; (Y); 24/95; GAA; Girl Scts; Varsity Clb; Stage Crew; VP Frsh Cls; Var Capt Bsktbl; Var Capt Socr; Var Sftbl; High Hon Roll; Hon Roll; 1st Tm All Stars Sccr 84; Hon Mntn Sccr, Bsktbl & Sftbl 82-85; Wilmingtron-Boyd Schl; Trvl Agt.

JOHNSON, PHYLLIS; Dundee Central HS; Himrod, NY; (Y); 38/78; FHA; Chorus; JV Coach Actv; Var Trk; Mst Imprvd Stu Engl 82-83; Mst Imprvd Stu Cosmtlgy 84-85; Brok 2 Trk Rcrds 82-84; Cosmtlgy.

JOHNSON, RAE; Allegany Central Schl; Allegany, NY; (Y); 12/109; Band; Yrbk Stf; Im Vllybl; High Hon Roll; NHS; Boston U; Occupational Thrpy.

JOHNSON, REBECCA; Oneonta HS; Oneonta, NY; (Y); 6/180; Drama Clb; Ski Clb; Thesps; Varsity Clb; School Musical; Stage Crew; Socr; French Clb; Hosp Aide; Spanish Clb; Pre Med.

JOHNSON, REBECCA L; Bay Ridge HS; Brooklyn, NY; (Y); 31/266; Girl Scts; Teachers Aide; Chorus; Nwsp Rptr; VP Sr Cls; Trk; Hon Roll; Super Yth Awd 84; Cert Merit 85; NY ST Regents Schlrshp 85; Enviromntl Awrnss Awd 84-85; Marymount Coll; Educ.

JOHNSON, RONALD E; Mount St Michael Acad; Yonkers, NY; (Y); 30/300; Church Yth Grp; Service Clb; Church Choir; Im Bsktbl; JV Golf; Hon Roll; NHS; Prfct Atten Awd; Ushr, Bell Rngr St Marks Chrch 84-85; Pre-Law.

JOHNSON, ROSEMARIE; Christopher Columbus HS; Bronx, NY; (Y); Dance Clb; Chorus; Vllybl; Math.

JOHNSON JR, RUSSELL D; Rome Free Acad; Rome, NY; (Y); 123/577; Varsity Clb; JV Var Bowling; Jr NHS; Prfct Atten Awd; Regents Schlrshp 85; Rome Jr Bowling Schlrshp 85; 7th Tnl Coca-Cola Singles Chmpnshp Bowling Tourn 82; SUNY-BUFFALO; Arch.

JOHNSON, SANDRA L; Westhill HS; Syracuse, NY; (Y); Pres FBLA; Band; Chorus; Trs Stu Cncl; JV Var Socr; JV Var Vllybl; Hon Roll; Sprtsmnshp Awd Sftbl83; Outstndng Athlte In Cmmnty 85; NYS Music Assoc Awds 82-84; Oswego; Bus.

JOHNSON, SHARA; Jamesville-De Witt HS; Syracuse, NY; (Y); French Clb; Band; Chorus; Im Cheerleading; Im Socr; Hon Roll; Cert Apprectn Vol 84-85; Bus Adm.

JOHNSON, SHAWN; Franklin Acad; Burke, NY; (Y); 13/260; Varsity Clb; Band; Var Capt Ftbl; Var L Trk; Hon Roll; NHS; Ntl Merit SF; Prfct Atten Awd; Engrng.

JOHNSON, SHERRY L; Flushing HS; E Elmhurst, NY; (Y); Var Bsktbl; Music Bus.

JOHNSON, STEVEN E; Marion JR SR HS; Marion, NY; (Y); 3/105; Am Leg Boys St; Boy Scts; Model UN; Band; Color Guard; Mrchg Band; Bsbl; Trk; Hon Roll; Pres NHS; 100 Pct Sequential Math I Regents 83; 100 Pct Bio Regents 84; Aeronautical Engnrng.

JOHNSON, THERESA; Glens Falls HS; Glen Falls, NY; (Y); Dance Clb; Spanish Clb; Gym; Powder Puff Ftbl; Hon Roll; Prfct Atten Awd.

JOHNSON, TIRZA; Adlai E St Evenson HS; Bronx, NY; (Y); 1/500; Cmnty Wkr; Hon Roll; NHS; Val; Japan-U S Exch Stu Scholar 85; Pre-Med.

JOHNSON, TISHA; St Pius V HS; New York, NY; (Y); Camera Clb; Teachers Aide; Hon Roll; Frnch I Bst Imprv Awd 83; Hlth Cours Awd Bst Imprv 83; Jrnlsm.

JOHNSON, TRACY LEA; Arlington HS; Poughkeepsie, NY; (Y); 124/596; Intnl Clb; Var L Socr; Sec L Trk; Hon Roll; Gen Excel Off Procdres 85; Hnr Key 85; U Buffalo; Acctng.

JOHNSON, WAYNE W; Cicero-North Syracuse HS; Syracuse, NY; (Y); 65/622; Am Leg Boys St; Var Socr; NHS; Sci.

JOHNSON, ZACHARY; Kensington HS; Buffalo, NY; (Y).

JOHNSTON, COLIN; West Babylon SR HS; W Babylon, NY; (Y); Church Yth Grp; Cmnty Wkr; JA; Leo Clb; Q&S; Band; Ftbl; High Hon Roll; Hon Roll; Jr NHS; Orthodntst.

JOHNSTON, DAVID L; Holy Trinity HS; Hicksville, NY; (S); Math Clb; Math Tm; Ski Clb; Rep Stu Cncl; Crs Cntry; JV Lcrss; Trk; JV Wrstlng; High Hon Roll; Hon Roll; Cornell.

JOHNSTON, JOSEPH; Cardinal Mooney HS; Rochester, NY; (Y); 80/350; Church Yth Grp; JV Bsbl; Var Capt Ftbl; Wt Lftg; Hon Roll; Spanish NHS; Accntnt.

JOHNSTON, KIM; Allegany Central HS; Allegany, NY; (Y); Debate Tm; Drama Clb; Key Clb; Band; Concert Band; Jazz Band; Mrchg Band; Orch; Pep Band; School Musical; Bnd Schrlshp; Math.

JOHNSTON, LORI; Curtis HS; Staten Island, NY; (Y); Dance Clb; French Clb; Intnl Clb; Drill Tm; Flag Corp; Mrchg Band; Yrbk Stf; JV Var Cheerleading; Intl Bus.

JOHNSTON, MICHAEL F; Elmira Notre Dame HS; Elmira, NY; (Y); 26/88; Am Leg Boys St; Pres Frsh Cls; Pres Soph Cls; Rep Stu Cncl; JV Var Bsbl; JV Var Bsktbl; JV Var Ftbl; High Hon Roll; Hon Roll; NHS; Bus Adm.

JOHNSTON, MIKE R; Shenendehowa Central HS; Clifton Park, NY; (Y); Prfct Atten Awd; Psych.

JOHNSTON, PAUL; Fairport HS; Fairport, NY; (Y); Church Yth Grp; Ski Clb; Yrbk Stf; Rep Stu Cncl; Var L Socr; Engrng.

JOHNSTON, ROBERT J; Waterville Central Schl; Waterville, NY; (Y); 1/100; Am Leg Boys St; Drama Clb; Mathletes; Chorus; School Musical; Swing Chorus; Capt L Crs Cntry; L Trk; High Hon Roll; NHS; All ST Chrs 85; MI Crss Cntry Troph 84; Williams Coll.

JOHNSTON, SCOTT D; Indian River Central HS; Theresa, NY; (Y); 3/130; AFS; VP Key Clb; Chorus; Concert Band; Drm & Bgl; Orch; School Musical; Crs Cntry; Tennis; DAR Awd; RIT; Comp Sci.

JOHNSTON, TERI; Colonie Central HS; Loudonville, NY; (Y); 186/511; Band; Variety Show; Cheerleading; Natl Physical Ed Awd 84-85; Sociologist.

JOHNSTONE, CHRISTOPHER; Saratoga Springs SR HS; Saratoga Sprgs, NY; (Y); 15/473; Orch; Var Tennis; VP NHS; Prfct Atten Awd; Confrmtn Bethsda Espcpl Chrch 82; Hd Chrstr Bethsda Epscpl 82; Poltic Sci.

JOHNSTONE, RITA; St Edmund HS; Brooklyn, NY; (S); 10/187; Girl Scts; JV Sftbl; Hon Roll; Phy Thrpst.

JOINSON, MARISSA; Great Neck South HS; Great Neck, NY; (Y); Varsity Clb; School Musical; Lit Mag; JV Lcrss; Var Swmmng; Var Twrlr; Phtgrphy.

JOLES, JEFFREY; Hermon De Kalb Central Schl; Hermon, NY; (S); 11/45; Boy Scts; Drama Clb; School Play; Nwsp Stf; Var Bsbl; JV Var Wrstlng; Hon Roll; Navy; Law Enfrcmnt.

JOLY, MIKE; Saint Josephs Collegiate Inst; Williamsville, NY; (Y); 98/200; Church Yth Grp; Band.

JONES, ANDREW H; Hamburg SR HS; Hamburg, NY; (Y); Jazz Band; School Musical; Yrbk Rptr; High Hon Roll; NHS; Regents Schlrshp; U Of Buffalo; Anthropology.

JONES, BARBARA L; Greece Olympia HS; Rochester, NY; (Y); Cmnty Wkr; Exploring; Hosp Aide; Nwsp Phtg; Nwsp Rptr; Nwsp Stf; Yrbk Phtg; Sec Frsh Cls; Hon Roll; Regnts Schlrshp; Intl Bus Mgmt.

JONES, BRIAN W; Holland Patent Central HS; Barneveld, NY; (Y); 7/200; Math Tm; Model UN; Chorus; School Musical; NHS; Rotary Awd; Rotary Yth Exch Stu 85-86; Hamilton Coll; Intl Stds.

JONES, CAROL A; Norman Thomas HS; Brooklyn, NY; (S); 42/670; FBLA; Chorus; Church Choir; Cit Awd; High Hon Roll; Hon Roll; Jr NHS; Ntl Merit Schol; Baruch; Accounting.

JONES, CHARI; Schoharie Central HS; Howes Cave, NY; (S); 16/78; Key Clb; Library Aide; Chorus; Stu Cncl; Hon Roll; Georgetown U; Psych.

JONES, CHARLES; St Hildas And St Hughs HS; New York, NY; (Y); Chorus; Yrbk Stf; Var Capt Bsktbl; Var Capt Socr; Hon Roll; NCTE Achvt Awd Wrtng; Acad Lat, Elem Ed; Caesar Sght Trnsltn; Mech Engrng.

JONES, CHRISTINE; Albion HS; Albion, NY; (Y); Trs 4-H; Trs Sec Spanish Clb; Teachers Aide; 4-H Awd; Hon Roll; Ntl Merit Schol; Sec.

JONES, CHRISTINE; Sauquoit Valley Central HS; Sauquoit, NY; (Y); GAA; Girl Scts; Band; Chorus; Concert Band; Drm & Bgl; Jazz Band; Mrchg Band; School Play; Stage Crew; Morisville Ag Tech Coll; Bus.

JONES, CHRISTOPHER; Binghamton HS; Binghamton, NY; (Y); Art Clb; Church Yth Grp; Computer Clb; High Hon Roll; NHS; Dstngshd Expert Awd Natl Rifle Assn 85; Schl Ltr Comp Pgmmg Achvt 85; Rochester Inst Tech; Comp Engrg.

JONES, CYNDEE; Olean HS; Apple Valley, MN; (Y); 8/212; Ski Clb; Varsity Clb; Yrbk Stf; Bsktbl; Score Keeper; Sftbl; Hon Roll; NHS.

JONES, DAVID; West Genesee HS; Syracyse, NY; (Y); Boy Scts; Church Yth Grp; Natl Beta Clb; Band; Yrbk Stf; Rep Frsh Cls; Hon Roll; GA Tech; Sci.

JONES JR, DAVID J; Greene Central HS; Greene, NY; (Y); Spanish Clb; Varsity Clb; Trs Soph Cls; L Capt Bsbl; L Capt Bsktbl; L Ftbl; Hon Roll; MVP Var Bsbl, 2nd All Cnty & Lg 83-84; 1st All Cnty Ftbl, Hnbl Mntn All Lg 84-85; 2nd All Co Bsktbl; Lbr Rel.

JONES, DAWN; Sauquoit Valley HS; Sauquoit, NY; (Y); Art Clb; GAA; Girl Scts; VICA; Color Guard; Bowling; JV Var Cheerleading; Sftbl; Hon Roll; Prfct Atten Awd; Maintnd Ovr 90 Prcnt Socl Stud, Wrd Prcssng 84-85; MVP Ftbl Chrldng 84-85; Mst Imprvd Bwlng 84; Bus.

JONES, DENISE MARIE; Onondaga HS; Syracuse, NY; (Y); German Clb; Chorus; IN U; Psych.

JONES, DEREK H; Onondaga Central HS; Syracuse, NY; (S); Exploring; Spanish Clb; Trs Jr Cls; High Hon Roll; Bus.

JONES, DOUGLAS; John Dewey HS; Brooklyn, NY; (Y); Boy Scts; Church Yth Grp; Orch; Swmmng; Bnkg.

JONES, ERIC; Saratoga Central Catholic HS; Ballston Spa, NY; (S); Drama Clb; Ski Clb; Mech Engr.

JONES, FRANK CURTIS; Chenango Valley HS; Binghamton, NY; (Y); 5/186; Am Leg Boys St; Drama Clb; Ski Clb; Jazz Band; Mrchg Band; School Musical; Yrbk Bus Mgr; Im Ice Hcky; Capt Var Socr; Var Tennis; Nvl Air Frce & Army ROTC Schlrshp Offrs 85; Natl Yth Slte 84; MA Inst Tech; Nclr Phycs.

JONES III, FRANK L; Nottingham HS; Syracuse, NY; (Y); FBLA; Ntl Merit Ltr; Indstrl Admin.

JONES, FREDERICK; Hempstead HS; Hempstead, NY; (Y); Am Leg Boys St; Computer Clb; Science Clb; Var Crs Cntry; Var Trk; Hon Roll; Prfct Atten Awd; Hnrb Mntn Long Island Sci Congrss 83; NY Tech Engrng Pgm Awds 83-85; Rutgers; Elec Engrng.

JONES, GREGORY; Albion HS; Albion, NY; (S); 16/175; Spanish Clb; Band; Concert Band; Mrchg Band; Pep Band; Var L Golf; Hon Roll; Jr NHS; Bus Admin.

JONES, GREGORY R; De Witt Clinton HS; Bronx, NY; (Y); Boy Scts; Acpl Chr; Concert Band; Yrbk Rptr; Hon Roll; NHS; US Military Acad; Mech Eng.

JONES, GREGORY SCOTT; Pine Valley Central Schl; South Dayton, NY; (S); 1/60; Am Leg Boys St; Quiz Bowl; Var JV Bsktbl; Var JV Ftbl; Hon Roll; NCTE Awd; NHS; Ntl Merit Ltr; Val; VFW Awd; Ntl Hnr Roll 84 & 85; NY Rgnts Schlrshp; West Point; Engr.

JONES, HARRY; Walton HS; Bronx, NY; (S); Computer Clb; Office Aide; NHS; Prfct Atten Awd; Comp Sci.

JONES, INGRID RAMONA; St Raymond Academy For Girls; Bronx, NY; (Y); 26/68; Debate Tm; Drama Clb; FBLA; Library Aide; Office Aide; Teachers Aide; Band; School Play; Yrbk Stf; Var L Twrlr; Westchester Bus Inst Bus Ed 85; The Berkley Schl; Fashn Dsgnr.

JONES, JACKIE; Niagara Wheatfield HS; Sanborn, NY; (Y); Pres Church Yth Grp; French Clb; Pep Clb; Var Swmmng; Buffalo ST; Elem Ed.

JONES, JEFFREY J; Saugerties HS; Saugerties, NY; (Y); 15/250; Church Yth Grp; Math Tm; Chorus; Church Choir; Socr; High Hon Roll; NHS; All County Chorus 83-85; Juggling Club 85; NYS Regents Schlrshp Winner 85; Clarkson U; Mechanical Engnrg.

JONES, JOCELYN A; Marcellus SR HS; Marcellus, NY; (Y); 24/164; Hosp Aide; Ski Clb; Symp Band; Trs Frsh Cls; Sec Soph Cls; Var Im Socr; Var Capt Sftbl; Var Capt Vllybl; High Hon Roll; NHS; NY ST Regents Schlrshp 85; Empire ST Vlybl Games-Alt 84; 1st Tm All-Cnty Sccr/Vlybl Athl Awds 83-85; Ithacca Coll; Bio.

JONES, JULIE; South Lewis Central HS; Boonville, NY; (Y); GAA; Color Guard; L Var Tennis; Var Capt Vllybl; Hon Roll; Psych.

JONES, KAREN; Bishop Kearney HS; Brooklyn, NY; (Y); Girl Scts; Service Clb; Chorus; Bsbl; Bsktbl; Cheerleading; Gym; Socr; Swmmng; Trk; 2nd Hnrs Fresh Year 81; Ranked Top 7 Percent PSATS Among Negro Stu 84; VA St U; Comp.

JONES, KAREN; The Mary Louis Acad; Glendale, NY; (Y); Church Yth Grp; Cmnty Wkr; Speech Tm; Church Choir; Stage Crew; Math 1st Hnrs 84-85.

JONES, KATHLEEN; Pelham Memorial HS; Pelham, NY; (Y); Sec AFS; Sec 4-H; VP Girl Scts; Teachers Aide; Spcl Ed Tchr.

JONES, KENDRICK; Hempstead HS; Hempstead, NY; (Y); Computer Clb; Var Science Clb; Var Crs Cntry; Var Trk; Hon Roll; Prfct Atten Awd; Honrbl Mentn Awd-Sci Congrss 83; NY Inst Of Technlgy/Engrng Awds 83-85; Villvanova; Electrcl Engrng.

JONES, KENRICK; Bishop Loughlin HS; Brooklyn, NY; (S); #5 In Class; Science Clb; High Hon Roll; NHS; Med.

JONES, KEVIN; Depew HS; Depew, NY; (Y); 60/258; Band; Chorus; Jazz Band; Mrchg Band; School Musical; Stage Crew; Swing Chorus; Variety Show; Var L Ftbl; Var L Tennis; Regnts Schlrshp & Diplm 85; Outstndng Credit Achvt 85; SUNY Fredonia; Music.

JONES, KIM; Clarkstown South HS; Nanuet, NY; (Y); Art Clb; Church Yth Grp; Cmnty Wkr; Dance Clb; GAA; PAVAS; Var Capt Fld Hcky; Var Lcrss; Sftbl; Pre-Med.

JONES, KIM; Mt Vernon HS; Mt Vernon, NY; (Y); 34/500; Spanish Clb; Band; Mrchg Band; Pep Band; Stage Crew; Symp Band; Variety Show; Yrbk Stf; Hon Roll; Mst Imprvd Musician 82-83; Mt Vernon Womens League 85; SUNY; Law.

JONES, KIM; Woodlands HS; White Plains, NY; (Y); FBLA; Math Tm; Rep Jr Cls; Var Cheerleading; Var Trk; Hon Roll; NHS; Bkng.

JONES, LAURA; New Rochelle HS; New Rochelle, NY; (Y); Girl Scts; Political Wkr; Spanish Clb; Nwsp Stf; Mgr(s); Score Keeper; Mgr Trk; NHS; Spanish NHS; Commnctns.

JONES, LAURIE; Holland HS; Holland, NY; (Y); AFS; GAA; Pres Varsity Clb; Rep Stu Cncl; Var Capt Bsktbl; Var Capt Fld Hcky; Var Capt Trk; Var Capt Vllybl; High Hon Roll; Hon Roll; Ath Yr 83-84 & 84-85; Wmns Sports Fndtn Top Female Ath Awd 84-85; ECIC Field Hockey & Bsktbl 83-85; Ath Trainer.

JONES, LISA; Union Endicott HS; Endicott, NY; (S); #201 In Class; Pres Church Yth Grp; Girl Scts; Ski Clb; Band; Church Choir; Concert Band; Jazz Band; Mrchg Band; Symp Band; Coach Actv; Med Tech.

JONES, LORALEE; John C Birdlebough HS; Phoenix, NY; (Y); Drama Clb; Latin Clb; Chorus; School Musical; JV Bsktbl; JV Socr; JV Var Sftbl; Var L Trk; Elem Educ.

JONES, LYTRESE; Freeport HS; Freeport, NY; (Y); 35/450; Concert Band; Variety Show; Capt Var Socr; JV Var Sftbl; Hon Roll; NHS; Prfct Atten Awd; Blck Ed Schlrshp; U NC Charlotte; Comp Sci.

JONES, MARCI; Potsdam Central HS; Potsdam, NY; (Y); Varsity Clb; Yrbk Phtg; JV L Bsktbl; Capt Coach Actv; Stat Mgr(s); Socr; Var L Trk; JV Var Vllybl; Hon Roll; Stage Crew; Bus.

JONES, MARGUERITE; John Dewey HS; Brooklyn, NY; (Y); Cmnty Wkr; Dance Clb; JA; Office Aide; Service Clb; Teachers Aide; Band; Stage Crew; Rep Soph Cls; Score Keeper; Cert Grt Achvt 67th Precient 83-84; Baruch; Acctnt.

JONES, MARK; Fairport HS; Fairport, NY; (Y); Hon Roll; Physcs.

JONES, MATTHEW; Scotia-Glenville HS; Scotia, NY; (Y); 9/226; Key Clb; Chorus; VP Stu Cncl; Var L Ftbl; JV Capt Vllybl; High Hon Roll; NHS; Ntl Merit Ltr; Acpl Chr; Im Ice Hcky; Grmn Bk Awd Achvt In Grmn Lang; Chmcl Engrng.

JONES, MELANIE; Edward R Murrow HS; Brooklyn, NY; (Y); 4-H; Girl Scts; Latin Clb; USC Smmr 84; Vet.

JONES, MELANIE J; Lyme Central Schl; Chaumont, NY; (Y); Jazz Band; Var Bsktbl; Var Socr; Var Sftbl; Band; Chorus; Concert Band; Mrchg Band; Yrbk Stf; Sec Jr Cls; Bsktbl All Star 84-85; Soccer All Star 83-84; Sftbl Hnrb Mntn 84-85; Jfrsn CC; Sprts Med.

JONES, MICHAEL; Woodlands HS; White Plains, NY; (Y); 52/180; Semi-Fin Natl Merit Achvt Scholar 84; Semi-Fin T J Watson IBM Scholar 84; Comp Sci.

JONES, MICHELLE; South New Berlin Central HS; S New Berlin, NY; (Y); Church Yth Grp; Office Aide; VICA; Jazz Band; Variety Show; Sec Soph Cls; Var Bsktbl; Var Socr; Hon Roll; Cmnty Wkr; Mst Outstdg Female Ath 85; Mst Impvd Plyr Bsktbl 85; Ridley-Lowell; Exec Sec.

JONES, MONIQUE; Kensington HS; Buffalo, NY; (Y); 67/197; FBLA; Model UN; Teachers Aide; Sec Chorus; Pres Church Choir; Variety Show; Rep Stu Cncl; Rep Trk; Buffalo Schl Cnslrs Assn Awd 85; Past Prncpls Schlrshp 85; Edinbor U PA; Soclgy.

JONES, NICOLE D; Frontier Central HS; Lake View, NY; (Y); 36/504; Trs Intnl Clb; VP Latin Clb; Ski Clb; School Play; VP Soph Cls; Var Capt Socr; High Hon Roll; NHS; NEDT Awd; 4-H; Regents Schlrshp 85; U Of Buffalo; Pharmcy.

JONES, PAMELA L; Kenmore West SR HS; Kenmore, NY; (Y); 1/445; Hosp Aide; Mathletes; Math Tm; School Musical; DAR Awd; NHS; Val; High Hon Roll; Ntl Sci Merit Awd In Biology 85; Wellesley Col Book Awd 84; St John Fisher Coll Pres Schlrshp 85; St John Fisher; Pre-Med.

JONES, PAUL; Unatego Central HS; Otego, NY; (Y); Air Force; Data Procssng.

JONES, PETER; Auburn HS; Auburn, NY; (Y); 2/400; Latin Clb; Letterman Clb; Math Tm; Lit Mag; Bsktbl; Socr; Tennis; Elks Awd; High Hon Roll; NHS; Regnts Scholar 85; Tchrs Scholar 85; Pinkney Scholar 85; Cornell; Law.

JONES, PETER; Beacon HS; Beacon, NY; (Y); 33/206; Pres Trs French Clb; School Play; Nwsp Rptr; Nwsp Stf; French Hon Soc; Office Aide; Offc Aide Awd; Mrktng.

JONES, PETER; Fox Lane HS; Pound Ridge, NY; (Y); 86/283; AFS; Pep Clb; Ski Clb; Varsity Clb; Lit Mag; Rep Frsh Cls; Rep Soph Cls; JV Var Bsktbl; Im Crs Cntry; Capt Var Ftbl; Bus.

JONES, RANDY; North Rose-Wolcott HS; Wolcott, NY; (Y); 7/142; Var Capt Bsbl; Var L Bsktbl; High Hon Roll; NHS; NY ST Rgnts Schlrshp 84-85; DAR Hstry Awd 84-85; Oneonta ST U; Accntng.

JONES, REBECCA; Oneonta SR HS; Oneonta, NY; (Y); 33/184; 4-H; French Clb; Key Clb; Band; Chorus; Concert Band; Jazz Band; Madrigals; Mrchg Band; Pep Band; Outstndng Chr,Band 82-84; Clemson U; Anml Sci.

JONES, ROGER M; Vestal Central HS; Apalachin, NY; (Y); 75/450; Chorus; School Play; JV Bsbl; Var L Bsktbl; Var L Ftbl; Var L Golf; High Hon Roll; Hon Roll; NHS; Gridirion Cmt Schlr/Athlt Awd 84-85; Math Awd; Hnrs Awd; Blmsbrg U PA; Accntng.

JONES, RUFUS; Manlius Pebble Hill HS; Syracuse, NY; (S); Church Yth Grp; Model UN; Office Aide; Quiz Bowl; Acpl Chr; Chorus; Madrigals; Orch; School Musical; Yrbk Stf; David E Lauffer Music Schlrshp 83; Mst Imprvd Tennis Plyr 84; Pre Med.

JONES, SANDRA; Frankfort-Schuyler HS; Frankfort, NY; (S); Computer Clb; DAR Awd; High Hon Roll; NHS; Natl Hnr Soc 84-85; Mohawk Valley CC; Bus Adm.

JONES, SARA; Frontier HS; Hamburg, NY; (Y); Cmnty Wkr; 4-H; JA; Latin Clb; Ski Clb; Nwsp Stf; Rep Jr Cls; Mgr(s); High Hon Roll; Hon Roll; Intl Rltns.

JONES, SCOTT; Hamburg SR HS; Hamburg, NY; (Y); 20/355; Church Yth Grp; Band; Concert Band; Jazz Band; Mrchg Band; Orch; School Musical; Symp Band; JV Socr; NHS; Music Schlrshp 85-86; Eric Cty Music Awd 81-85; Oral Roberts U; Music.

JONES, SCOTT A; Archbishop Stepinac HS; White Plains, NY; (Y); 3/206; Church Yth Grp; Computer Clb; Exploring; JA; Key Clb; Nwsp Rptr; Trk; High Hon Roll; NHS; Ntl Merit Ltr; NY ST Regents Scholar 85; Alumni Scholar Rochester Inst Of Tech 85-86; Acad Scholar Cornell U 85-86; Rochestr Inst Tech; Biomed Comp.

JONES, SULIN; Webutuck Central HS; Wassaic, NY; (Y); Drama Clb; Political Wkr; Quiz Bowl; Thesps; Chorus; Church Choir; School Musical; School Play; Hon Roll; Bst Actress Awd 84 & 85; Actress.

JONES, SUSAN; Cicerio-N Syracuse HS; N Syracuse, NY; (S); 55/622; Color Guard; Drill Tm; Mrchg Band; Var Pom Pon; Powder Puff Ftbl; Hon Roll; Cornell; Bio.

JONES, TARA; Cardinal Spellman HS; Bronx, NY; (Y); Church Yth Grp; Latin Clb; Variety Show; Yrbk Stf; Stu Cncl; Im Bsktbl; JV Trk; Im Vllybl; Hon Roll; Communctns.

JONES, TOM; Guilderland HS; Altamont, NY; (Y); 110/369; ROTC; Var Wrstlng; 1st Pl Capitol Dist Inds Arts Assn Colonte Exhibit 85; Rocheste Inst Of Tech; Elec Eng.

JONES, TRACEY; Bishop Ford Central Catholic HS; Brooklyn, NY; (Y); Computer Clb; GAA; JA; Nwsp Phtg; Nwsp Stf; Yrbk Phtg; Yrbk Stf; Cheerleading; Crs Cntry; Trk; NY U; Prelaw.

JONES, TYLER; Lowville Academy Central HS; Lowville, NY; (Y); Trs Church Yth Grp; Bsbl; Capt Wrstlng; Hon Roll; Prfct Atten Awd; Jefferson CC.

JONES, WANDA; Murry Bergtraum HS; Bronx, NY; (S); 60/576; JA; Stage Crew; Variety Show; Rep Sr Cls; Trs Stu Cncl; Accntnt.

JONES, WANDA; Niagara Wheatfield HS; Niagara Falls, NY; (Y); 146/315; Church Yth Grp; FBLA; Girl Scts; Office Aide; Teachers Aide; Chorus; Church Choir; Hon Roll; Prfct Atten Awd; Acad Excell Awd 85.

JONES, WARREN; Cardinal Hayes HS; Bronx, NY; (Y); Church Yth Grp; Cmnty Wkr; Dance Clb; Office Aide; Teachers Aide; Acpl Chr; Band; Church Choir; Concert Band; Mrchg Band; Syracuse; CPA.

JONES, WILLIAM; Corning West HS; Coopers Plains, NY; (Y); French Clb; Key Clb; Letterman Clb; Varsity Clb; Var L Bsbl; JV Var Bsktbl; High Hon Roll; Kiwanis Awd; NHS; Hon Roll.

JONGEN, AMIE J; Naples Central Schl; Naples, NY; (Y); 11/83; Yrbk Ed-Chief; Yrbk Stf; Sec Sr Cls; Rep Stu Cncl; Bsktbl; Socr; Sftbl; Vllybl; High Hon Roll; NHS; Phy Ther.

JORDAN, AMY; Candor Central Schl; Candor, NY; (Y); GAA; Drill Tm; Varsity Clb; JV Capt Bsktbl; Powder Puff Ftbl; JV Var Sftbl; JV Var Vllybl; High Hon Roll; NHS; Prfct Atten Awd; All-Star Vlybl Awd 84; All-Star Bskbl Awd 84-85; All-Star Sftbl Awd 85; Comp Sci.

JORDAN, ANTHONY; Warwick Valley HS; Warwick, NY; (Y); 2/200; Band; Concert Band; Jazz Band; Mrchg Band; Symp Band; Nwsp Stf; Var Capt Crs Cntry; Var L Trk; Hon Roll; Mst Imprvd Crss Cntry Rnnr 84; Anthroplgy.

JORDAN, CATHERINE; Dover JR SR HS; Wingdale, NY; (S); 1/94; Am Leg Aux Girls St; Varsity Clb; Band; Jazz Band; Sec Sr Cls; Var JV Bsktbl; Co-Capt Var Fld Hcky; Var JV Sftbl; High Hon Roll; Val; Fld Hcky All-Star Team 83-84; Fld Hcky All-Cnty Awd 84; Chem Engrng.

JORDAN, JAMIE; Broadalbin Central HS; Broadalbin, NY; (Y); 2/90; French Clb; Letterman Clb; Concert Band; Mrchg Band; Rep Frsh Cls; Bowling; Capt Sftbl; High Hon Roll; NHS; Mst Vlbl Plyr Bwlng, Sftbl 85; Ed.

JORDAN, JULIE; Johnstown HS; Johnstown, NY; (Y); Intnl Clb; Stu Cncl; JV Bsktbl; Var Fld Hcky; Trk; Undefeated ST Champ Fld Hcky Tm 84; St Champ Fld Hcky Tm 85; MIP Fld Hcky 85.

JORDAN, KIMBERLY; Liverpool HS; Liverpool, NY; (S); 60/800; Church Yth Grp; Drama Clb; JA; Letterman Clb; Varsity Clb; Rep Stu Cncl; Var Fld Hcky; High Hon Roll; Hon Roll; Jr NHS; Ntl JR Rowing Tm Alt 84; Bus Law Achvmnt Awd 83; Empire ST Games For Crew Gold Mdl 83; Pol Sci.

JORDAN, KIMBERLY; Lyons Central Schl; Lyons, NY; (Y); 17/96; French Clb; JCL; Latin Clb; Varsity Clb; Yrbk Stf; Trs Stu Cncl; Var Capt Cheerleading; Var L Socr; Var L Trk; Cit Awd; Ithaca Coll.

JORDAN, MARIA; Dodge Vocational HS; Bronx, NY; (Y); Computer Clb; Dance Clb; Drama Clb; Off Jr Cls; Trvl.

JORDAN, MARK J; Hackley HS; Ossining, NY; (Y); Nwsp Phtg; Yrbk Phtg; Var Bsbl; JV Var Socr; Lehigh U; Bus.

JORDAN, MICHELE; Moore Catholic HS; Staten Island, NY; (Y); Art Clb; Dance Clb; French Clb; Yrbk Stf; Rep Frsh Cls; Hon Roll; Schl Sci Fair Awd; Fshn Byng.

JORDAN, SHIRLEY; Hermon De Kalb Central Schl; Hermon, NY; (S); 3/45; Drama Clb; French Clb; Stage Crew; Yrbk Bus Mgr; Pres Jr Cls; Var Bsktbl; Var Socr; Var Sftbl; High Hon Roll; NHS; Engr.

JORDAN, SONYA; Saratoga Springs SR HS; Porter Corners, NY; (S); 53/473; Art Clb; DECA; Rep Frsh Cls; JV Trk; High Hon Roll; NHS; FBLA; Key Clb; Vllybl; Prfct Atten Awd; Cert Achv Bus Dynmcs 83; Cert Achv Art 85; Prjct Mgr 1st Pl NY ST Pepsi Lern-Ern 85; Bus.

JORDAN, STEPHANIE; Highland HS; Highland, NY; (Y); 24/140; Stage Crew; Variety Show; JV Stat Sftbl; Advancd Typng Prodctn 85; Dutchess CC; Para-Legal Stu.

JORDAN, THOMAS; Bishp Loughlin Memorial HS; Brooklyn, NY; (Y); Cmnty Wkr; Dance Clb; Drama Clb; Jazz Band; School Musical; Prfct Atten Awd; Citation Svc 85; Semper Fidelis Awd Musical Exclince 85; Pace U; Drama Arts.

JORDAN, WENDY; Pelham Memorial HS; Pelham Manor, NY; (Y); Church Yth Grp; Cmnty Wkr; Dance Clb; Girl Scts; Teachers Aide; Church Choir; Hon Roll; Comp Acctng.

JORDAN, YVETTE; A Philip Randolph HS; Brook, NY; (Y); Church Yth Grp; Civic Clb; Cmnty Wkr; Library Aide; Math Tm; Office Aide; Political Wkr; Teachers Aide; Church Choir; Pres Frsh Cls; Miss Crown Hts Schlrshp Awd 85; Dnstry.

JORGE, MALDONADO; Seaford HS; Seaford, NY; (Y); Boys Clb Am; Boy Scts; Computer Clb; Chorus; JV Capt Socr; Trk; Hon Roll; Hofstra U; Bus Mngmnt.

JOROLEMON, MICHAEL; Auburn HS; Auburn, NY; (S); 37/500; Band; Chorus; Concert Band; Jazz Band; Mrchg Band; Pep Band; School Musical; Symp Band; Trk; High Hon Roll; Physics/Computer Based Lab; Natl Sci Fndtn Sponsored Program 84; Chem Engrng.

JORQUERA, MARIANELA; St Johns Prep; Brooklyn, NY; (Y); Chorus; Socr; Vllybl; Wt Lftg; Hon Roll; NHS; Coaches Awd Vlby; Vrsty Athlt Awd Soccer; NY U; Math.

JOSE, E DANIELLE; Mechanicville HS; Mechanicville, NY; (S); 1/106; Cmnty Wkr; VP Exploring; Math Tm; Trs Ski Clb; Spanish Clb; Band; Mrchg Band; Nwsp Rptr; Var Bsktbl; Score Keeper; Mary Mastroianni Awd 83; Earth Sci Awd 83; Aerosp Engr.

JOSEPH, ANGELA; Fox Lane HS; Pound Ridge, NY; (Y); 22/260; Stat Var Bsktbl; Stat JV Ftbl; Var Mgr(s); Stat Var Trk; High Hon Roll; NHS; Tutorl Awd 83; Outstndng Achvt Awd-Spn 83 & 85; Latin Hnr Soc 85; Accntnt.

JOSEPH, DALE; Brooklyn Tech HS; Flushing, NY; (Y); Office Aide; Trk; Hon Roll; Cert Of Exc In Spnsh I & II & Englsh II 83; Cert Of Exc In Chmsry II 84; Nrs.

JOSEPH, GUERSCHOM; Nyack HS; Nyack, NY; (Y); Church Yth Grp; Church Choir; Rep Jr Cls; Minister.

JOSEPH, JONATHAN K; Shaker HS; Loudonville, NY; (Y); Nwsp Stf; Capt Var Ftbl; Var Lcrss; 1st Tm All Cnty Lacrosse 84; Physics.

JOSINSKY, STEVEN A; Francis Lewis HS; Flushing, NY; (Y); 32/527; Office Aide; Ski Clb; L Concert Band; Var L Socr; Hon Roll; Jr NHS; NHS; NY ST Regnts Schlrshp 85; Joe Louis Athl Schlr Schlrshp 85; Tri-M Music Hnr Socty 85; Alfred U; Cermc Engrng.

JOU, PETER; St Agnes HS; New York, NY; (Y); 5/100; Church Yth Grp; High Hon Roll; NHS; Vol Children Assoc 84-85; MIT; Chem.

JOUBEN, LISA; Richfield Springs Central HS; Richfield Spgs, NY; (Y); 2/58; Church Yth Grp; Pres Debate Tm; GAA; JCL; VP Latin Clb; NFL; Pres Speech Tm; Band; Concert Band; Mrchg Band; DAR Amer Hstry Prz 85; Rotary Yth Ldrs Conf 85; Nalt Sci Olympiad 85; Amer Lgn Pst Oratorcl Cont 84; Med.

JOWDY, LYNNE; Wilson Central HS; Lockport, NY; (Y); High Hon Roll; Hon Roll; NHS; Bus.

JOY, JENNIFER; St Marys HS; Lancaster, NY; (S); Yrbk Stf; Rep Frsh Cls; Rep Soph Cls; Rep Jr Cls; Rep Stu Cncl; High Hon Roll; NHS; Accntnt.

JOY, MYER; Chautauqua Central HS; Chautauqua, NY; (Y); 1/38; Quiz Bowl; Scholastic Bowl; Trs Chorus; School Musical; VP Rep Stu Cncl; Var Capt Bsktbl; Var Crs Cntry; Var Capt Golf; Im Socr; High Hon Roll; Cert Outstndg Achvt Amer Chem Soc 85; Pres Acad Fit Awd 85; Ind Engrng.

JOY, SUSAN; Fayetteville Manlius SR HS; Fayetteville, NY; (Y); Church Yth Grp; Chorus; Church Choir; Orch; Swing Chorus; Drama Clb; 4-H; Hosp Aide; Choir Awd Bst Sopran 84; Musicl Carer.

JOYCE, CHRISTOPHER; Plattsburgh SR HS; Plattsburgh, NY; (Y); Cmnty Wkr; Ski Clb; Trs Concert Band; Jazz Band; Mrchg Band; Trs Orch; Var L Golf; Hon Roll; NHS; Math Acadmc Awd 83; NYSMA Area All ST Concert Band 83-84; NYSMA Hnrs Rectl Saxphn Qurlt 84; Penn ST; Engr.

JOYCE, JOANNE; St Vincent Ferrer HS; Sunnyside, NY; (S); Q&S; Nwsp Rptr; Quill & Scroll Awd 84-85; Comm.

JOYCE, MARY K; Palmyra Macedon HS; Palmyra, NY; (S); 6/205; Service Clb; Chorus; School Musical; School Play; Rep Stu Cncl; JV Var Tennis; NHS; Ntl Merit Ltr; AFS; Church Yth Grp; Hugh O Brien Yth Ldrshp Awd 83; Econ.

JOYCE, ROBERT; Hannibal HS; Hannibal, NY; (S); 3/117; Am Leg Boys St; Pres Computer Clb; Ed Yrbk Phtg; Var L Bsktbl; Var L Crs Cntry; Var L Golf; High Hon Roll; Pres NHS; Ntl Merit Ltr; Comp Engrng.

JOYCE, SHEILA T; Albany HS; Albany, NY; (Y); Aud/Vis; Rgnts Schlrshp; Russell Sage Coll; Nrsng Comp.

JOYCE, STEVEN; Newark HS; Newark, NY; (Y); 88/201; Service Clb; Ski Clb; Varsity Clb; Var Diving; JV Var Ftbl; Var L Lcrss; Var Swmmng; Var Trk; Hon Roll.

JOYMANGAL, SHANTA; Franklin D Roosevelt HS; Brooklyn, NY; (Y); Brooklyn Coll; Accntng.

JOYNER JR, CHARLES G; Cardinal Spellman HS; Bronx, NY; (Y); Bsktbl; Hon Roll; Law.

JOYNER, ROBIN; Altmar-Parish-Williamstown HS; Williamstown, NY; (Y); Pep Clb; Concert Band; Mrchg Band; Pep Band; VP L Bowling; Var L Cheerleading; Var Pom Pon; Var Trk; Hon Roll; Prfct Atten Awd; Secry.

JOYNER, SHIRELL; Central Islip SR HS; Central Islip, NY; (Y); Band; Drm Mjr(t); Yrbk Phtg; Sec Frsh Cls; Rep Stu Cncl; Var L Cheerleading; Var L Trk; Letterman Clb; Varsity Clb; Concert Band; Music Hnrs Soc 85; Al-ST Music Awd 85; Asst Ed Yrbk; Pre-Med.

JOZWICK, TAMMY; Dover JR SR HS; Wingdale, NY; (S); Drama Clb; Mathletes; Chorus; School Musical; Swing Chorus; Jr NHS; Comm Art.

JUBIN, ANNOICA; Sidney SR HS; Unadilla, NY; (Y); Church Yth Grp; Teachers Aide; Chorus; Flag Corp; Stage Crew; VP Socr; Hon Roll; Hnr Rl 84-85; Vrsty Sccr 82-83; U TX Austin; Med.

JUDD, ERIC; Roy C Ketcham HS; Poughkeepsie, NY; (Y); 70/480; Church Yth Grp; Var Crs Cntry; Var Tennis; Var Trk; High Hon Roll; Hon Roll; NHS; Engrg.

JUDD, KIMBERLY A; Riverhead HS; Riverhead, NY; (Y); Cmnty Wkr; ROTC; Color Guard; Drill Tm; Flag Corp; Im Gym; Rotary Awd; Rtrd Ofcrs Assn Awd 84; NJROTC Asprng Twrd Excllnc Awd & Dstngshd Cadet 84; Hnr Cadet Acad Avg 85; Mltry.

JUDGE, DIANE E; Baldwin SR HS; Baldwin, NY; (Y); 32/503; Concert Band; Mrchg Band; Orch; Pep Band; Nwsp Ed-Chief; Nwsp Rptr; Nwsp Sprt Ed; Score Keeper; Hon Roll; NHS.

JUDGE, SHERYL; Dominican Commercial HS; Far Rockaway, NY; (Y); Aud/Vis; Hosp Aide; Office Aide; Teachers Aide; Prfct Atten Awd; Prncpls List 82-84; Siena Clb 83; Comp Analyst.

JUDON, LA NESHIA R; Lakenheath American HS; APO, NY; (Y); Church Yth Grp; Cmnty Wkr; FCA; GAA; JA; Political Wkr; Variety Show; Var JV Bsktbl; High Hon Roll; Jr NHS; MVP Bsktbl 84; Fstst Typst Awd 83-84; Coll Crse Scholar Mth Stdies 83-84; NYC; Lwyr.

JUDSKI, KATHY-JOY; Seton Catholic HS; Binghamton, NY; (Y); Key Clb; Ski Clb; Yrbk Stf; Rep Stu Cncl; Sftbl; Tennis; Hon Roll; Mock Trial Lawyer 84-85; Stu Brd Class Rep 82-84; Law.

JUDSON, KATHRYN; Ichabod Crane HS; Niverville, NY; (Y); 12/180; Sec Church Yth Grp; Pres 4-H; French Clb; Color Guard; Yrbk Stf; Rep Jr Cls; 4-H Awd; High Hon Roll; Sec NHS; Ed.

JUDYCKI, KATHLEEN; Liverpool HS; Liverpool, NY; (S); 23/800; Church Yth Grp; Chorus; Church Choir; School Musical; School Play; Symp Band; Stu Cncl; Var Capt Cheerleading; High Hon Roll; NHS; Lib Arts.

JUENGERKES, WENDY; East Islip HS; E Islip, NY; (Y); Church Yth Grp; Cmnty Wkr; Girl Scts; Chorus; Church Choir; Stage Crew; Nwsp Rptr; Nwsp Stf; Rep Frsh Cls; Rep Jr Cls; Psych.

JUERGENS, PAMELA M; John Jay SR HS; Fishkill, NY; (Y); 329/560; Ski Clb; Var L Socr; Var L Vllybl; Keystone JC; Phy Thrphy.

JUGO, PATRICIA; Lindenhurst SR HS; Lindenhurst, NY; (Y); French Clb; Ski Clb; Orch; Hon Roll.

JUHRE, ALEXANDRA; Albany HS; Albany, NY; (Y); 37/600; French Clb; Latin Clb; Ed Lit Mag; Hon Roll; NHS; Ntl Merit Ltr; Regents Schlrshp 85; Swarthmore Coll; Lingstcs.

JULCH, PAUL; Spring Valley HS; Monsey, NY; (Y); 7/450; Computer Clb; Hosp Aide; VP Pres Spanish Clb; Nwsp Rptr; Nwsp Stf; Yrbk Stf; Jr NHS; Mu Alp Tht; NHS; Spanish NHS; Soc Stds Acad Awd; Bus Mgmt.

JULES, MICHELE; St Edmund HS; Brooklyn, NY; (S); 6/190; French Clb; Girl Scts; Hosp Aide; Church Choir; School Musical; Var Cheerleading; High Hon Roll; Jr NHS; NHS; :Med.

JULIAN, MATTHEW; Union Endicott HS; Endicott, NY; (Y); Boy Scts; Vllybl Co Capt 85; Broome CC; Elec Engrng.

JULIANO, CHRISTINE; Notre Dame-Bishop Gibbons HS; Scotia, NY; (S); 6/108; French Clb; Chorus; School Musical; Nwsp Stf; Yrbk Phtg; Rep Frsh Cls; Rep Soph Cls; Rep Jr Cls; Rep Sr Cls; Rep Stu Cncl; Engl Creatvty Awd; Genl Elec-Steinmetz Awd; Holy Cross Coll; Chemstry.

JULIANO, VIRGINIA M; Christ The King HS; Brooklyn, NY; (Y); 13/500; Girl Scts; Nwsp Rptr; Nwsp Stf; High Hon Roll; Hon Roll; Jr NHS; NHS; Regents Schlrshp 85; Schlstc Excell Schlrshp 85; St Johns U Comp Schlrshp 85; St Johns U; Comm.

JULIAS, KELLY; Wilson Central HS; Ransomville, NY; (Y); VP Church Yth Grp; Chorus; School Play; Yrbk Rptr; VP Jr Cls; Var L Bsktbl; Var L Fld Hcky; Var L Trk; NHS; JV, Var, Ltr & Coaches Vlybl Awd 84; Moving Up Day Duchess 84; Hmcmng Prin 84; Fash Merch.

JUNG, JOE; Holland Central Schl; Holland, NY; (Y); 7/125; AFS; Church Yth Grp; French Clb; Library Aide; Red Cross Aide; Varsity Clb; Stage Crew; Rep Stu Cncl; Coach Actv; Mgr(s); U NY Gftd Math Prog 80-84; Amer Lgn Schlrshp Awd 83; Advtsg Dsgn.

JUNG, MARISA; Williamsville East HS; E Amhurst, NY; (Y); Church Yth Grp; Aud/Vis; Chorus; Rep Soph Cls; Var Capt Cheerleading; Var Capt Pom Pon; Var L Vllybl; High Hon Roll; Hon Roll; Prfct Atten Awd; Wilson Comptn Chrldng 83; Var Chlrldng Comptn,Most Sprtd 84; UCLA; Bus.

JUNN, GINA; Kenmore West HS; Tonawanda, NY; (Y); Church Yth Grp; Girl Scts; Rep Stu Cncl; JV Capt Bsktbl; JV Var Vllybl; Hon Roll; Med.

JUNNELLI, LYNDA A; Sachem HS; Holbrook, NY; (Y); 551/1383; Chorus; Bus.

JUNZ, DAVID; Lindenhurst HS; Lindenhurst, NY; (Y); Boy Scts; Ski Clb; Yrbk Phtg; Yrbk Stf; Var Bsktbl; Var Trk; Masonic Awd; Suffolk Dist Mastr Cnclr Ordr De Molay 84-85; Mastr Amityvl De Molay 82-83; VP Meth Yth Fllwshp 81-82; Travl.

JUREWICZ, CHRISTINA; Olean HS; Olean, NY; (Y); Varsity Clb; Yrbk Stf; Var JV Bsktbl; Var Sftbl; Im Vllybl; Hon Roll; NHS; IAABO All Trny Tm Vrsty Bsktbl 84; Chautauqua Cnty Div I All Str Vrsty Sftbl 85; Bus Adm.

JURISTA, JAMES; Vestal HS; Vestal, NY; (Y); Boys Clb Am; Im Bsktbl; Ftbl; Im Lcrss; Im Sftbl; Im Vllybl; Im Wt Lftg; Var Wrstlng; Law.

JURMAN, LAURENCE; Half Hollow Hills High Schl West; Dix Hills, NY; (Y); 43/375; Cmnty Wkr; Hosp Aide; Pres MMM; Service Clb; Chorus; Mrchg Band; Orch; Sec Symp Band; Trk; NHS; Natl Choral Awd 85; Bnd Slvr Mdl 85; Tri-M Svc Awd 85; Chorus Slvr Mdl 85; Brandeis U; Med.

JUSTIAN, ERIC; Hauppauge HS; Smithtown, NY; (Y); 70/450; Drama Clb; Mrchg Band; Orch; Stage Crew; Swing Chorus; Symp Band; Spanish Clb; Thesps; Band; Chorus; Spch Arts Clb Awd 84-86; NYSSMA Mdls 83-86; NJ Jazz Fstvls Soloist Awd 85; Theatre.

JUSTICE, JOHN; Kenmore West SR HS; Kenmore, NY; (Y); Boys Clb Am; Debate Tm; Math Tm; Quiz Bowl; Im Bowling; Im Socr; High Hon Roll; Atty Kenmore Yth Court 83-85; Achvt Awd Math 83-85; NY Sci Supvrs Awd Bio 84; Rensselaer Polytech Inst; Chem.

JUSTICH, FRANK; Msgr Mc Clancy HS; Corona, NY; (Y); Boy Scts; Church Yth Grp; FCA; JV Bsktbl; JV Coach Actv; Hnd Ball Spec Achvt Awd; Hnr Awd Imprvg All Clss 10 Pts; Syracuse; Engrng.

JUSTINO, GAIL; Lyons JR SR HS; Lyons, NY; (Y); 19/92; Pres AFS; Latin Clb; School Musical; Nwsp Rptr; Sec Frsh Cls; Capt Cheerleading; Capt Socr; Trs NHS; Voice Dem Awd; Acadmc All Amer 84-85; Natl Hnr Socty Awd 85; Hoffman Fndtn Hstry Schlrshp Hnbl Mntn 85; SUNY Geneseo; Cmmnctns.

JUZWICK, DAVID R; Williamsville East HS; Williamsville, NY; (Y); Boy Scts; Church Yth Grp; Ski Clb; Spanish Clb; Stage Crew; Bsbl; Fld Hcky; High Hon Roll; Hon Roll; Lou Gehrig Bsbl All-Star; Coll; Corp Law.

KA KOYIANNIS, THEODORE M; Garden City HS; Garden City, NY; (Y); 50/360; Pres Church Yth Grp; Key Clb; Im Bsktbl; JV Var Wrstlng; High Hon Roll; JC Awd; Jr NHS; Boy Scts; Rep Frsh Cls; Rep Soph Cls; Mchl J Gurilides Awd Outstndng Ctznshp 85.

KABATCHNIK, EDAN; Horseheads HS; Elmira, NY; (S); 2/407; Computer Clb; Debate Tm; JCL; Latin Clb; Quiz Bowl; Ski Clb; Temple Yth Grp; Concert Band; Drm Mjr(t); Mrchg Band; Physics.

KABEL, JEFFREY M; Orchard Park HS; Orchard Park, NY; (Y); 30/450; Am Leg Boys St; Church Yth Grp; Intnl Clb; Yrbk Ed-Chief; Rep Stu Cncl; Var Tennis; NHS; Spanish NHS; Hon Roll; Law.

KABORYCHA, VINCENT; St John The Baptist HS; Central Islip, NY; (Y); Bowling; Socr; Hon Roll; Vet Med.

KACER, ROBERT; New Hyde Park Memorial HS; New Hyde Park, NY; (S); 29/269; Camera Clb; Church Yth Grp; DECA; Spanish Clb; Varsity Clb; Nwsp Stf; Capt Var Crs Cntry; Capt Var Trk; NHS; NY ST Rgnts Schlrshp 85; MVP And All-Cnty Rifle Tm 83-85; 3 Slvr Mdls In Empire ST Gms 83-84; U Of PA; Engrng.

KACHAYLO, ANDY M; Rome Free Acad; Rome, NY; (Y); Intnl Clb; Key Clb; Ski Clb; Bus.

KACHEJIAN, KAREN; Smithtown H S East; Nesconset, NY; (Y); Stu Cncl; Var L Bsktbl; Var L Fld Hcky; Var L Sftbl; Vllybl; Hon Roll; All League Fld Hcky Awds 83-84; MVP Offnse Fld Hcky Awd 84; Bus Adm.

KACZMARCZYK, CHRISTINE; Schenectady Christian Schl; Burnt Hills, NY; (Y); 2/11; School Play; Yrbk Ed-Chief; Sec Stu Cncl; Var L Cheerleading; Var Capt Socr; High Hon Roll; Sal; Church Yth Grp; Cmnty Wkr; NY ST Music Comptn Hgh Awds 83-85; Messiah Coll; Art.

KACZMARCZYK, DANUTA; Uniondale HS; Uniondale, NY; (Y); 46/480; Art Clb; Pres Church Yth Grp; Dance Clb; NFL; Speech Tm; Orch; Yrbk Stf; Pres Stu Cncl; High Hon Roll; Jr NHS; Eng Achvt Awd 83; Hofstra U; Bus.

KACZMARCZYK, ERIC J; Lancaster Central HS; Depew, NY; (Y); Church Yth Grp; Office Aide; PAVAS; Band; Chorus; School Musical; Variety Show; Var L Socr; :Radio & TV Brdcstng.

KACZMAREK, JOY; St Marys Acad; Glens Falls, NY; (S); 2/47; Art Clb; Drama Clb; French Clb; Chorus; Church Choir; School Musical; Nwsp Phtg; Nwsp Rptr; High Hon Roll; Bst Supptng Actress-Lk George Yth Thtr 84; Outstndng Perfrmnc-Lk George Yth Thtr 83; Am Leg Awd 82; Actress.

KACZOROWSKI, JULIE L; West Seneca East HS; Cheektowaga, NY; (Y); 5/365; Yrbk Stf; Off Soph Cls; Off Jr Cls; Bsktbl; Trk; Vllybl; NHS; NYS Regents Schlrshp 85; Pres Schlrshp Alfred U 85; Alfred U; Elem Educ.

KACZOROWSKI, KEVIN; West Seneca East SR HS; Buffalo, NY; (Y); Varsity Clb; Nwsp Stf; Yrbk Sprt Ed; Capt Var Bsktbl; Var JV Trk; Var Capt Vllybl; High Hon Roll; JC Awd; NHS; Prfct Atten Awd; Frgn Lang Awds Ltn 83 & 84; Acctng.

KADEHJIAN, LISA; Loyola Schl; Long Island City, NY; (Y); 4/52; Art Clb; Drama Clb; Service Clb; Ski Clb; Chorus; School Musical; School Play; Variety Show; Yrbk Stf; Hon Roll; New York U; Bio.

KADELL, NADINE; Maryvale SR HS; Cheektowaga, NY; (Y); Sec French Clb; Spanish Clb; Varsity Clb; Yrbk Stf; Rep Jr Cls; Rep Stu Cncl; Var Trk; High Hon Roll; Hon Roll; Jr NHS; NY ST U Bflo; Math.

KADTKE, STEFANIE; William Nottingham HS; Syracuse, NY; (Y); Var Capt Vllybl; Hon Roll; MVP Vlybl 83-84; John Jay Schl Crmnl Jstc.

KAELIN, JANICE; Notre Dame-Bishop Gibbons HS; Schenectady, NY; (S); 20/108; Nwsp Stf; Lit Mag; Rep Stu Cncl; Var Cheerleading; Var Tennis; High Hon Roll; NHS; Amer Inst For Frgn Study Awd 84; Mst Artstc 84; U Of MA-AMHERST; Jrnlsm.

KAELIN, KARIN SUE; Valley Stream Central HS; Orlando, FL; (Y); 99/345; AFS; Trs Church Yth Grp; Red Cross Aide; Band; Chorus; Church Choir; School Musical; Hon Roll; Camera Clb; Pres Dance Clb; Tempo Music Hnr Soc 84-85; David Gould Schlrshp, Bst Creatvty, 2nd Grup Improv Fest Arts 85; Lenoir Rhyne Coll; Comm.

KAFEL, MARIA; John A Coleman Catholic HS; Kingston, NY; (Y); French Clb; Key Clb; Stage Crew; Gym; Trk; Vllybl; Hon Roll; NHS; Prfct Atten Awd; Sr Mary Eileen Mc Manus Awd 85; Comp Sci.

KAFLOWITZ, ALAN; Roy C Ketcham HS; Poughkeepsie, NY; (Y); Boy Scts; JV Trk; JV Wt Lftg; Hon Roll; Cnty Dutchs Dept Pks Recrtn, Consrvtn Awd Trffc Cntrl 83; Dutchess CC; Polc Sci.

KAGAN, ERRAN; Herricks SR HS; Searingtown, NY; (S); DECA; Radio Clb; Quill Pen Awd 84; Archry Tm 83; 3rd Civic Conciousns Awd; Albany U; Med.

KAGAN, JILL; Kings Park SR HS; Kings Park, NY; (Y); Am Leg Aux Girls St; Pres Art Clb; Pres Civic Clb; Drama Clb; NFL; Office Aide; Sec Radio Clb; Trs Speech Tm; Chorus; School Musical; IONY Art Cntst Wnnr 83; Syracuse U; Advtsng Dsgn.

KAGELS, PETER; Lockport SR HS; Lockport, NY; (Y); Intnl Clb; Hon Roll; NHS; Boston U; Acctng.

KAGER, CHRIS; Coxsackie-Athens Central HS; Coxsackie, NY; (Y); 1/104; Capt Quiz Bowl; Ski Clb; Trs Spanish Clb; Trs Frsh Cls; Off Jr Cls; Im Bowling; L Var Ftbl; L Var Socr; High Hon Roll; NHS; Med.

KAHAN, MICHAEL; Walter Panas HS; Peekskill, NY; (Y); Debate Tm; NFL; Band; Mrchg Band; School Play; Rep Frsh Cls; Rep Soph Cls; Rep Jr Cls; Var Tennis; NHS; Fnlst Lincoln Douglas Debate 85.

KAHL, KRISTIN A; Port Chester SR HS; Port Chester, NY; (Y); 9/250; VP Drama Clb; Ski Clb; VP Spanish Clb; VP Thesps; Color Guard; School Musical; School Play; Yrbk Stf; Var Cheerleading; Ntl Merit Ltr; Regents Schlrshp 85; William & Mary.

KAHLER, CHRISTOPHER; Smithtown High School East; Nesconset, NY; (Y); Boy Scts; JV Bsbl; Var Crs Cntry; High Hon Roll; Hon Roll; Jr NHS; NHS; Spanish NHS; Aerontcl Engrng.

KAHLER, TRACY; Rome Free Acad; Rome, NY; (Y); Varsity Clb; Fld Hcky; Score Keeper; Vllybl; High Hon Roll; Hon Roll; Jr NHS; NHS; Math.

KAHN, CYNTHIA; Music And Art; Riverdale, NY; (Y); 96/551; Office Aide; Teachers Aide; Hon Roll; Advrtsng.

KAHN, DEBORAH N; Great Neck North SR HS; Great Neck, NY; (Y); Debate Tm; Library Aide; Temple Yth Grp; Chorus; Concert Band; Orch; School Musical; Symp Band; Nwsp Bus Mgr; Nwsp Rptr; Bnai Brith Of Grt Nck Awd 85; Journ Awd Guide Post-Nwspr 85; Commndtn Form Grt Nck Brd Of Ed 85; Med.

KAHN, DONALD R; Carmel HS; Carmel, NY; (Y); 60/370; Boy Scts; Church Yth Grp; Hosp Aide; Leo Clb; Nwsp Rptr; JV Ftbl; Trk; Hon Roll; Lion Awd; Eagle Scout 85; Alfred U; Hist.

KAHN, LISA; Earl L Vandermeulen HS; Mt Sinai, NY; (Y); 7/259; FBLA; Leo Clb; Pep Clb; Spanish Clb; Temple Yth Grp; Nwsp Stf; Yrbk Stf; Rep Frsh Cls; Rep Soph Cls; Rep Jr Cls; Stu Cncl Awd 83; Rgnts Schlrshp 85; Soc Stud Awd 83; Muhlenberg Coll; Pre Med.

KAHNE, BRUCE; Abraham Lincoln HS; Brooklyn, NY; (Y); 18/489; Capt Debate Tm; Orch; School Play; Nwsp Ed-Chief; Rep Stu Cncl; Var Capt Bsbl; Hon Roll; NHS; SUNY Binghamton.

KAIDEN, ROBERT; South Side HS; Rockville Centre, NY; (S); 13/284; JCL; Trs Latin Clb; Science Clb; Spanish Clb; High Hon Roll; JETS Awd; NHS; First Long Island Science Congress 84; Merit Schlrshp Reciepient 85; Hamilton; Political Science.

KAISER, RONI JO; Kenmore East SR HS; Kenmore, NY; (Y); Camp Fr Inc; GAA; Pep Clb; Sec Temple Yth Grp; JV Socr; Sci.

KAISER, TRICIA; Notre Dame-Bishop Gibbons HS; Schenectady, NY; (S); 22/108; Cmnty Wkr; GAA; Hosp Aide; Red Cross Aide; Coach Actv; Capt Diving; Capt Swmmng; High Hon Roll; NHS; Adv Math Awd; Empire ST Games; Math.

KAISERMAN, JEFFREY; Smithtown HS East; Saint James, NY; (Y); Computer Clb; Drm & Bgl; Drm Mjr(t); Jazz Band; Mrchg Band; Orch; School Musical; Symp Band; Variety Show; Hon Roll; Sftwr Engrng.

KAKAREKA, SHERI; Gloversville HS; Gloversville, NY; (Y); 70/230; Dance Clb; FCA; GAA; Intnl Clb; Chorus; Gym; High Hon Roll; Hon Roll; Ntl Merit Ltr; NYS Gms 2nd Pl Vlt Fnls 84; U Of MD; Lbrl Arts.

KALAFARSKI, CAROL; G Ray Bodley HS; Fulton, NY; (Y); Hosp Aide; Yrbk Bus Mgr; Sec Jr Cls; Var Socr; JV Capt Sftbl; Var Vllybl; Phy Thrpy.

KALAFARSKI, EDWARD M; G Ray Bodley HS; Fulton, NY; (Y); 57/247; Am Leg Boys St; Drama Clb; Spanish Clb; School Musical; School Play; Stage Crew; Variety Show; Hon Roll; NYS Rgnts Schlrshp 85; Fulton Polish Home 4 Yr Schlrshp 85; Syracuse U; Comm.

KALATA, JULIE; Lockport SR HS; Lockport, NY; (Y); 40/411; Church Yth Grp; Drama Clb; English Clb; 4-H; Intnl Clb; Nwsp Stf; Lit Mag; Rep Frsh Cls; Rep Soph Cls; Rep Jr Cls; Cmmnctns.

KALB, JOHN; Bishopford Central Catholic HS; Brooklyn, NY; (Y); 10/375; Church Yth Grp; VP JA; Math Clb; Math Tm; Science Clb; Spanish Clb; Im Bowling; High Hon Roll; NHS; NY ST Regents Schlrshp 85; Acad Excell; Cooper Union; Comp Engr.

KALBFLEISCH, KATHRYN; James E Sperry HS; Rochester, NY; (Y); German Clb; Chorus; Church Choir; Hon Roll; NHS; Natl Germn Hon Soc 84; Schlrshp Intl Stud Assn Germn 85; Germn.

KALDOR, EDITH; High School For The Humants; New York, NY; (Y); Aud/Vis; German Clb; Intnl Clb; Yrbk Phtg; Var Bsktbl; JV Crs Cntry; JV Trk; Gov Hon Prg Awd; Rider Coll Lang Comptn 84; Coll NY; Bio Med Pgm.

KALEC JR, DONALD; Notre Dame HS; Elmira, NY; (Y); Science Clb; Ski Clb; Trs Band; Trs Concert Band; Trs Jazz Band; Trs Pep Band; Stage Crew; Yrbk Stf; Hon Roll; SUNY Canton; Funrl Dir.

KALENDER, ERIC; Clarkstown H S North; New City, NY; (Y); Cmnty Wkr; Library Aide; Nwsp Stf; High Hon Roll; Mu Alp Tht; NHS; SUNY Binghamton; Medcl Doc.

KALFA, PAUL; Long Island City HS; Astoria, NY; (Y); Teachers Aide; Var L Socr; Var L Trk; JV Wrstlng; Cit Awd; Hon Roll; NCTE Awd; Prfct Atten Awd; Young Plywrghts Assn Awd 84; Bus Hnr Soc 85; Hunter Coll; Psychtry.

KALFELZ, SUE; Lansing HS; Ithaca, NY; (Y); 1/80; Am Leg Aux Girls St; Sec Trs 4-H; VP French Clb; Band; Jazz Band; Orch; School Musical; Sec Frsh Cls; Cheerleading; Diving; Pres SADD 84-85; Pres Ntl Hon Soc 85-86.

KALIK, NOREEN S; James Madison HS; Brooklyn, NY; (Y); 50/900; Spanish Clb; Chorus; Color Guard; School Musical; Bsktbl; Cheerleading; Vllybl; Prfct Atten Awd; Baruch Schlrshp 85-89; Regents Schlrshp 85-89; Baruch Coll; Spansh.

KALIKSTEIN, RUTH; Shevach HS; Flushing, NY; (Y); 4/21; Dance Clb; Drama Clb; Q&S; Chorus; Hon Roll; SAT 84-85; Yrbk Art Editor 84-85.

KALL, JACQUELYN; Fayetteville-Manlius HS; Fayetteville, NY; (Y); Temple Yth Grp; Var L Gym; Var Capt Tennis; High Hon Roll; Hon Roll; NHS; Natl Ldrshp & Svc Awd 84; STPA Phys Ed Awd 85; Clarance E Gaffey Mem Tnns Awd 85; SUNY Albany; Bus.

KALLFELZ, KRISTEN; Bishop Ludden HS; Syracuse, NY; (S); Church Yth Grp; Hosp Aide; High Hon Roll; Jr NHS; NHS; Opt Clb Awd; Home Ec Awd 84; Ithaca Coll; Physcl Thrpy.

KALOCSAI, CHARLEEN; Corning Painted Post East HS; Corning, NY; (Y); Drama Clb; Exploring; French Clb; Sec Band; Concert Band; Mrchg Band; School Musical; School Play; Stage Crew; High Hon Roll; SUNY-BUFFALO; Phrmcy.

KALOS, VALERIE J; Woodmere Acad; Far Rockaway, NY; (Y); Var Bsktbl; Var Socr; Regnts Schlrshp 85; Grinnell Coll.

KALTEN, SUZANNE M; Plainedge HS; Seaford, NY; (Y); 18/311; Church Yth Grp; Cmnty Wkr; Latin Clb; Stage Crew; Nwsp Stf; Lit Mag; Trk; NHS; Pres Schlr; St Schlr; Acad Schlrshp To Hofstra U NY 85; Hnrbl Mntn Natnwd Poetry Cont 85; Sr English Award 85; Hofstr U; Social Sci.

KALWEIT, KIMBERLY A; West Irondequoit HS; Rochester, NY; (Y); 46/337; Hosp Aide; Model UN; Ski Clb; Im Golf; Im Sftbl; Hon Roll; NHS; Regnts Schlrshp 85; U Of Roch Almni Schlrshp 85; Awd A Avg 2 Yr Period Spnsh 81; Boston U; Pre-Med.

KAMEN, DAVID; Hillcrest HS; Forest Hills, NY; (Y); Boy Scts; Office Aide; Band; Stu Cncl; UF & Srv Awd 83; Culinary Inst Of Amer; Chef.

KAMENECKA, TED; Spackenkinn HS; Poughkeepsie, NY; (Y); 24/175; Boys Clb Am; Cmnty Wkr; Temple Yth Grp; Rep Jr Cls; Var Capt Socr; Tennis; Hon Roll; NHS; Ten All Lg All Cnty 83-84; Ten 1st Pl DCSL Dbls 83-84; Pre-Med.

KAMENS, MARK; Kenmore East SR HS; Tonawanda, NY; (Y); Church Yth Grp; Varsity Clb; Ftbl; Wt Lftg; Hon Roll; Bus Mgt.

KAMERY, BRIAN; Forestville HS; Fredonia, NY; (Y); 4/43; Varsity Clb; Var Bsbl; Im Bsktbl; Im Coach Actv; JV Var Ftbl; Im Wt Lftg; Hon Roll; Engrng.

KAMIN, BERNADETTE; St Francis Prep; Middle Village, NY; (S); 140/704; Dance Clb; GAA; Red Cross Aide; Ski Clb; Teachers Aide; Varsity Clb; Rep Stu Cncl; Coach Actv; Gym; Hon Roll.

KAMIN, RACHELLE N; Torah Academy For Girls; Far Rockaway, NY; (Y); 2/27; Debate Tm; Temple Yth Grp; Gov Hon Prg Awd; Hon Roll; Trs NHS; Brkln Coll Frshmn Schlrshp 85; NY Regnts Schlrshp 85; Brooklyn Coll.

KAMINSKI, KATHLEEN; Cardinal O Hara HS; Buffalo, NY; (S); 3/139; Sec Drama Clb; French Clb; Quiz Bowl; Thesps; School Musical; School Play; Nwsp Rptr; Var Golf; High Hon Roll; Acad Tm; Niagara U; Theatr.

KAMINSKY, LEAH; Commack High School South; Dix Hls, NY; (Y); Teachers Aide; Concert Band; Mrchg Band; Trs Symp Band; Var Badmtn; High Hon Roll; Hon Roll; Vrsty Athlt Awd 83-84; Bio.

KAMPEL, DEBRA; Commack HS; E Northport, NY; (Y); 29/440; Drill Tm; Nwsp Stf; Lit Mag; Off Frsh Cls; Off Soph Cls; Off Jr Cls; Off Sr Cls; French Hon Soc; High Hon Roll; NHS; Smith Coll; Lib Arts.

KAMPF, ROBYN; Commack North HS; E Northport, NY; (Y); Cmnty Wkr; Intnl Clb; Office Aide; Temple Yth Grp; Jr Cls; Chrmn Stu Cncl; Var Badmtn; French Hon Soc; High Hon Roll; NHS; Gftd Stu Schlrshp 84-85; Hnrs In Englsh & Sci 83; Med.

KAMPMEIER, STEPHEN FREDERICK; Pittsford Sutherland HS; Pittsford, NY; (Y); 12/235; AFS; French Clb; Model UN; Orch; School Play; Cit Awd; Hon Roll; Pres NHS; Rotary Awd; St Schlr; Steuben Awd For Prfncy In German Language 84; Hnrs Natl Frnch & German Exams 84-85; Amherst Coll; History.

KAMROWSKI, KIM; Maryvale HS; Cheektowaga, NY; (Y); French Clb; Med.

KAMVOSOULIS, GEORGIA; Mahopac HS; Mahopac, NY; (Y); 2/378; Church Yth Grp; Math Tm; Lit Mag; Rep Sr Cls; Rep Stu Cncl; High Hon Roll; NHS; Prfct Atten Awd; Sal; Ntl Eng Merit Awd 82; Stu Month French,Hist 85; Regents Schlrshp 85; Vassar Coll; Math.

KANCHES, DARCY; Galway HS; Amsterdam, NY; (Y); Drama Clb; Pres French Clb; Trs Chorus; Swing Chorus; Trs Frsh Cls; VP Soph Cls; Pres Jr Cls; Rep Stu Cncl; JV Capt Cheerleading; High Hon Roll.

KANDALL, MARLENE H; Professional Childrens Schl; New York, NY; (Y); Cmnty Wkr; Dance Clb; Yrbk Stf; Joffrey Ballet Sch Schlrshp 82-85; Merit Awd Arts Recgntn Tlnt Srch 85; Regents Schlrshp.

KANDILAKIS, DEAN; Ossining HS; Ossining, NY; (Y); Trs Exploring; High Hon Roll; Hon Roll; Mod & Clsscl Lang Dept Recgntn Frnch Awd 85; Lang.

KANE, BRUCE; Oyster Bay HS; East Norwich, NY; (Y); 20/120; Computer Clb; Library Aide; Nwsp Rptr; Lit Mag; Hon Roll; Comp Sci.

KANE, CHRIS; Greenville Central Schl; S Westerlo, NY; (Y); Radio Clb; VP Spanish Clb; JV Bsktbl; JV Socr.

KANE, DAVID; Corning-Painted Post West HS; Corning, NY; (Y); 10/250; Key Clb; Varsity Clb; Stat Bsktbl; JV Ftbl; Var Lcrss; High Hon Roll; NHS; Elec Engrng.

KANE, ELIZABETH; Elmira Free Acad; Elmira, NY; (Y); Sec Latin Clb; Concert Band; Mrchg Band; Stage Crew; Symp Band; Yrbk Sprt Ed; Rep Stu Cncl; Var JV Bsktbl; Var Tennis; Hon Roll; Phys Thrpst.

KANE, GERALD; H C Technical HS; Buffalo, NY; (Y); French Clb; Rep Soph Cls; Rep Stu Cncl; Crs Cntry; Swmmng; SAR Awd; Kappa Sigma Phi Scholar Awd 85; Harvard; Bus Adm.

KANE, GERALD; Nyack HS; Valley Cottage, NY; (Y); Capt Math Tm; Scholastic Bowl; Off Jr Cls; Off Sr Cls; Var L Bsbl; Var L Golf; Var L Socr; Lion Awd; NHS; VP Spanish NHS; RPI; Law.

KANE, JAQUELINE; Villa Maria Acad; Buffalo, NY; (Y); Sec Spanish Clb; Hon Roll; Erly Chldhd Educ.

KANE, JENNIFER; Bishop Kearney HS; Rochester, NY; (Y); Church Yth Grp; Cmnty Wkr; Church Choir; School Musical; School Play; Nwsp Rptr; Yrbk Stf; Lit Mag; Hon Roll; NHS; Harvard Bk Awd 85; Med.

KANE, KATHLEEN E; Elmira Southside HS; Elmira, NY; (Y); 4/333; VP Key Clb; Sec Latin Clb; Model UN; Chorus; Trs Stu Cncl; Capt Crs Cntry; Var Swmmng; Capt Trk; NHS; Cmnty Wkr; Southside HS Athl Of Yr 84; SUNY Plattsburgh; Intl Bus.

KANE, MICHAEL J; Ithaca HS; Ithaca, NY; (Y); Am Leg Boys St; Intnl Clb; Bsktbl; Var JV Lcrss; Im Sftbl; Jr NHS; NHS.

KANE, RYAN; Rome Catholic HS; Rome, NY; (Y); Drama Clb; Chorus; School Musical; Var Ftbl; Hon Roll; Aerosp Engr.

KANFOUSH, SHARON; Sauquoit Vly Cntrl HS; Sauquoit, NY; (Y); 2/100; Am Leg Aux Girls St; Yrbk Stf; Rep Frsh Cls; Rep Soph Cls; Trs Jr Cls; Sec Sr Cls; Fld Hcky; High Hon Roll; Hon Roll; NHS; Marine Arch.

KANIA, MICHAEL; S S Seward Inst; Florida, NY; (Y); Art Clb; Camera Clb; FFA; Yrbk Stf; Var Capt Bsktbl; Capt Var Socr; Hon Roll; Mst Imprvd H S Art Awd 85; MVP Marist Coll Summr Bsktbl Cmp 85; 1st Tm Westrn Sullivan Bsktbl Lg 85; Elec Tech.

KANITZ, CARON; Hermon-De Kalb Central HS; De Kalb Jct, NY; (S); Church Yth Grp; Drama Clb; Sec Trs 4-H; French Clb; Band; Yrbk Stf; Var L Vllybl; 4-H Awd; Hon Roll; NHS; Diry Princess Alter Schlrshp 85; Kings Coll; Bus.

KANOUS, KAREN; Lasalle Senior HS; Niagara Falls, NY; (S); 7/278; Hon Roll; NHS; Exec Secy.

KANSLER, ADAM; Cold Spring Harbor HS; Huntington, NY; (Y); 17/152; Intnl Clb; Mathletes; Science Clb; Yrbk Phtg; Yrbk Sprt Ed; Var Bsbl; JV Bsktbl; JV Var Lcrss; High Hon Roll.

KANTAK, MELANIE; West Genesee HS; Camillus, NY; (Y); 26/500; Exploring; Mathletes; Sr Cls; Im Bsktbl; JV Socr; Stat Vllybl; High Hon Roll; Im Sftbl; Im Tennis; NY ST Rgnts Schlrshp 85; Aldersn Brds Acad Schlrshp 85; Camls Fire Dept Schlrshp 85; Alderson Broaddus Clg; Tchr.

KANTHA, SHIVANTHI; Smithtown East HS; Nesconset, NY; (Y); Chorus; Var L Badmtn; VP French Hon Soc; Pres NHS; French Clb; Hosp Aide; Teachers Aide; Orch; High Hon Roll; Hon Roll; All Cnty Chrs 84; Binghampton; Bio.

KANTOR, ANDREW; Kings Park HS; Kings Pk, NY; (Y); 33/393; Im Bsktbl; Var Crs Cntry; Var Trk; High Hon Roll.

KAPA, SUZANNE; Linton HS; Schenectady, NY; (Y); Drama Clb; Orch; Hon Roll.

KAPALA, MARY; Little Falls JR SR HS; Fort Plain, NY; (S); 1/109; Sec Nwsp Stf; Pres Frsh Cls; Pres Soph Cls; Rep Sr Cls; JV Fld Hcky; VP NHS; Drama Clb; Spanish Clb; Band; Concert Band; RIT Math/Sci Awd 85; Yorkers Govrnrs Trphy 84; Stu Rep Brd Of Ed 85-86; Bnkng.

KAPELA, LISA; Ellenville HS; Wawarsing, NY; (Y); 6/122; English Clb; Science Clb; Teachers Aide; Rptr Lit Mag; Stu Cncl; High Hon Roll; NHS; Rgnts Schlrshp 85; Bio-Pre Med.

KAPELL, LEWIS A; Christian Brothers Acad; Syracuse, NY; (Y); 1/103; Speech Tm; NHS; Ntl Merit SF; Math Tm; Nwsp Rptr; Nwsp Stf; Yrbk Rptr; Yrbk Stf; Stu Cncl; High Hon Roll.

KAPLAN, AUDREY H; East Islip HS; Islip Terrace, NY; (Y); 3/475; Math Tm; Temple Yth Grp; Band; Concert Band; Mrchg Band; Nwsp Rptr; JV Tennis; High Hon Roll; Hon Roll; VP Jr NHS; Bronze Med Cnty Math Fair 83; 3rd Pl EIHS Sci Fair 83; Cert Outstndng Sch Svc 84; Rensselaer Poly Inst; Comp Sci.

KAPLAN, ELISE M; Half Hollow Hills High School East; Dix Hills, NY; (Y); 52/548; FBLA; Leo Clb; Office Aide; Mrchg Band; Symp Band; Sftbl; Var Tennis; French Hon Soc; High Hon Roll; Jr NHS; NY ST Regnts Schlrshp 85; U Of MI.

KAPLAN, ERIC; Smithtown High School East; Nesconset, NY; (Y); French Clb; Key Clb; Scholastic Bowl; Pres Sr Cls; Stu Cncl; Var Bsktbl; French Hon Soc; Jr NHS; NHS; Pres SAAD 85-86; Med.

KAPLAN, ERIC L; Hunter College HS; Brooklyn, NY; (Y); Capt Debate Tm; Drama Clb; School Play; Ed Lit Mag; Ntl Merit SF; Telluride Assn Summer Pgm 84; Hnrb Mntn NYC Young Playwrites 84; Silver Mdl NYC Math Fair 84.

KAPLAN, HOLLY; Smithtown HS East; Nesconset, NY; (Y); FBLA; Temple Yth Grp; Nwsp Rptr; Off Frsh Cls; Off Soph Cls; Off Jr Cls; Off Sr Cls; Stu Cncl; High Hon Roll; Hon Roll; Bus.

KAPLAN, JONATHAN; Wartagh HS; Wantagh, NY; (Y); Computer Clb; Mathletes; Math Clb; Math Tm; Temple Yth Grp; Band; Nwsp Phtg; Nwsp Stf; Yrbk Phtg; Yrbk Stf; 1st Pl-Sci Fair; L I Math Fair-Brnz Medl Of Hnr 83; Vrsty Lttrmn-Swmmng 83-85; Hgh Scorer Mathlts 84-85; U Of PA-WHARTON; Bus Mgmt.

KAPLAN, KEITH B; Hunter College HS; Staten Island, NY; (Y); Cmnty Wkr; Trs Computer Clb; Hosp Aide; Library Aide; Math Clb; Var L Bowling; Ntl Merit SF; Gftd & Tlntd Stu; Med.

KAPLAN, LORI; Brighton HS; Rochester, NY; (Y); 27/315; Spanish Clb; VP Temple Yth Grp; Chorus; JV Swmmng; Var Trk; Spnsh Hnr Awd 83; Acctng.

KAPLAN, RENEE; Bishop Kearney HS; Brooklyn, NY; (Y); Girl Scts; Ski Clb; Band; Bus Mgt.

KAPNER, PETER M; Woodmere Acad; Woodmere, NY; (Y); Chess Clb; Math Clb; Band; Concert Band; St Schlr; Regents Schlrshp 85; Boston U; Bus.

KAPOGIANNIS, MARIA T; Arlington HS; Poughkeepsie, NY; (Y); 28/572; Church Yth Grp; Cmnty Wkr; Dance Clb; Drama Clb; French Clb; Church Choir; Yrbk Phtg; Yrbk Stf; Hon Roll; Order Of Ahepa Medal For Excel In Greek Language 81; Union Coll; Engrng.

KAPPEL, MELISSA; Webutuck HS; Millerton, NY; (Y); Chorus; Yrbk Stf; Rep Frsh Cls; Sec Jr Cls; Rep Stu Cncl; Var L Fld Hcky; Var Trk; All County Hnrb Mntn Field Hockey 84-85; Fashn Merchndsng.

KAPPESSER, JILL; St Francis Prep; Middle Village, NY; (Y); 41/693; Cmnty Wkr; Dance Clb; JV Tennis; Optimate Soc.

KAPPS, SUSAN; St Ohn The Baptist Diocesan HS; Babylon, NY; (Y); Model UN; Church Choir; Ed Nwsp Stf; Ed Lit Mag; Rep Jr Cls; Stu Cncl; French Hon Soc; Hon Roll.

KAPRAL, VINCENT; Corning East HS; Corning, NY; (Y); 27/249; Am Leg Boys St; Model UN; Political Wkr; VP Sr Cls; VP Stu Cncl; Bsbl; Ftbl; NHS; Pres Schlr; Rotary Awd; Gftd & Tlntd; Amer Lgn Post Model Ctzn Awd Lcl; Outstdng Delg Model Un; The American U; Rssn Area.

KAPSACK, CLAUDIA; The Hartsdale Schl; New City, NY; (Y); Girl Scts; Pep Clb; Temple Yth Grp; Chorus; Rehab Phsyc.

KAPSHO, LYNDA; Vernon Verona Sherrill Central HS; Sherrill, NY; (Y); Yrbk Phtg; Yrbk Stf; Var JV Cheerleading; Var JV Fld Hcky; Var L Trk; Fash Dsgn.

KAPUR, NAMRITA; Pittsford-Mendon HS; Pittsford, NY; (Y); VP JA; Pres Model UN; Y-Teens; Concert Band; Gym; High Hon Roll; NHS; Exploring; Math Clb; Math Tm; PTSA Math Awd 84; Commtt Chrprsn Awd 84; Princeton; Biochem.

KAPUSTEIN, HOWARD; East Meadow HS; East Meadow, NY; (S); 21/414; Aud/Vis; VP Pres Computer Clb; Drama Clb; Key Clb; Math Tm; Stage Crew; Nwsp Stf; Lit Mag; Hon Roll; NHS; Rensselaer Plytch Inst; Cmp Sci.

KARAFANDA, DIANE M; Shaker HS; Latham, NY; (Y); GAA; Trs Service Clb; Stage Crew; Ed Yrbk Stf; Rep CAP; Var Score Keeper; Im JV Socr; NEDT Awd; Dance Clb; French Clb; NY ST Regents Schlrshp 85; Al Tech Corp Sons & Dghtrs Schlrshp 85; Rensselaer Polytech; Biomed.

KARALIS, MARIA; Forest Hills HS; Middle Village, NY; (Y); 66/881; Science Clb; Chorus; Stage Crew; High Hon Roll; Hon Roll; Svc Leag 83; Queens Coll; Comp Sci.

KARALUS, RICHARD J; Depew HS; Cheektowaga, NY; (Y); 20/254; Pres French Clb; Rep Stu Cncl; Capt Swmmng; Im Trk; High Hon Roll; Hon Roll; Rep NHS; St Schlr; Swmng Mdls 82-85; Prncpls Awd For Ldrshp 85; Rgnts Schlrshp 85; Rochester Inst Of Tech; Bio.

KARAM, MARY LOU; St John Villa Acad; Bklyn, NY; (Y); 22/160; Art Clb; Church Yth Grp; Hosp Aide; JA; Office Aide; Hon Roll; Europen Hist,Spnsh II,Eng Achvt Awd 84; Nutrtnst.

KARAMANLIS, CATHERINE; Lansingburgh HS; Troy, NY; (Y); Sec French Clb; Sec Frsh Cls; Sec Jr Cls; Var JV Cheerleading; Var Tennis; Var Trk; Hon Roll; Jr NHS; NHS; Chorus.

KARANDY, DAVID; Notre Dame-Bishop Gibbons HS; Schenectady, NY; (S); 1/108; Red Cross Aide; Nwsp Stf; Lit Mag; Rep Frsh Cls; Rep Soph Cls; Rep Jr Cls; Var L Crs Cntry; Ntl Merit Ltr; Sci, Engl, Math, RPI Awds.

KARAS, STAN; Utica Free Acad; Utica, NY; (Y); Computer Clb; Mathletes; Model UN; Trk; High Hon Roll.

KARCHER, EDWARD J; Garden City HS; Garden City, NY; (Y); 115/320; Sec Key Clb; Rep Sr Cls; Rep Stu Cncl; Var Ice Hcky; JV Lcrss; Im Socr; Im Sftbl; Im Vllybl; Var Wrstlng; Hon Roll; Pres Acad Fit Awd 85; Villanova U; Prof Sldr.

KARCHER, REBECCA J; Akron Central Schl; Akron, NY; (Y); 13/157; VP Church Yth Grp; French Clb; Ski Clb; Chorus; School Musical; Swing Chorus; Ed Yrbk Ed-Chief; Yrbk Phtg; NHS; Regents Schlrshp; Grove City Coll; Bus Admin.

KARCHNER, KEITH; Monticelo HS; Monticello, NY; (Y); Debate Tm; Library Aide; Office Aide; Speech Tm; Yrbk Stf; Score Keeper; High Hon Roll; Hon Roll; NHS; Olympics Mind Team 83-84; Eng Lit Teacher.

KARCIC, DORIS; Msgr Scanlan HS; College Pt, NY; (Y); Cmnty Wkr; Trk; Hon Roll; Prfct Atten Awd; 2nd Hnrs 83-84; Sci Awd 83-84; Italn Awd 83-84; Queens Clg; Soc Workr.

KARET, GAIL B; Nichols Schl; Kenmore, NY; (Y); AFS; Dance Clb; Ski Clb; Temple Yth Grp; JV Swmmng; Hon Roll; Ntl Merit SF; Austin Fox Awd 84; Sci Fair 3rd Pl 83; Psych.

KARIM, SANGITA; Hilcrest HS; Woodside, NY; (Y); Dance Clb; Church Choir; Socr; Tennis; Hon Roll.

KARIM, SHAHNAZ; Farmingdale HS; Farmingdale, NY; (Y); Hosp Aide; Nwsp Stf; Bsktbl; Tennis.

KARIM, SHUJA; Earl L Vandermelven HS; Mt Sinai, NY; (Y); FBLA; Var L Trk; Hon Roll; Engr.

KARIRA, RAJ; St Francis Prep; Woodside, NY; (Y); 177/693; Frsh Cls; Trk; Opt Clb Awd; Prfct Atten Awd; Bus.

KARL, LISA A; William Floyd HS; Shirley, NY; (Y); 1/428; MMM; Trs Thesps; Chorus; Orch; School Musical; Nwsp Ed-Chief; Trs NHS; Val; Alumni Memrl Schlrshp; Thorndike Schlrshp; Colgate U.

KARL, REBECCA; Allegany Central Schl; Olean, NY; (Y); Art Clb; Church Yth Grp; Stat Bsktbl; JV Var Cheerleading; Crs Cntry; Im Socr; JV Tennis; Stat Trk; Im Vllybl; High Hon Roll; Word Life 1st Cls Schlrshp 84; Word Life Clbs Teen Invlvd Comptn 82-85; Math.

KARLESKI, ED; Solvay HS; Solvay, NY; (Y); Mgr Yrbk Bus Mgr; Yrbk Stf; Off Frsh Cls; Off Jr Cls; JV Bsbl; Bsktbl; Socr; Hon Roll; Mgt.

KARLOWICZ, LYDIA M; Immaculata Acad; Blasdell, NY; (Y); 4/77; French Clb; Quiz Bowl; Trs Sec Service Clb; Lit Mag; Hon Roll; NHS; Immaculata Acad Schlrshp 81-82; NY ST Regents Coll Schlrshp 85; Hilbert Coll; Accntnt.

KAROGLANIAN, MATTHEW; Mahopac HS; Baldwin Pl, NY; (Y); 177/423; Cmnty Wkr; Library Aide; Political Wkr; Variety Show; Var L Ftbl; Var L Lcrss; JV Trk; Wt Lftg; Hon Roll; Syracuse U; Arch.

KARON, MICAHEL; F D Roosevelt HS; Ny, NY; (Y); 128/800; Socr; Vllybl; Stoney Brook; Comp.

KAROUNA, NATALIE; Hunter College HS; Flushing, NY; (Y); Chorus; Church Choir; Orch; Var Capt Sftbl; Var L Vllybl; St Schlr; Church Yth Grp; Yrbk Stf; JV L Bsktbl; Pblc Schl Athl Lgu Awd 85; Colgate U; Bio.

KAROUSSIS, ALEXANDER CLEVELAND; Southampton HS; Southampton, NY; (Y); Drama Clb; French Clb; Ski Clb; School Play; Stage Crew; Hon Roll; Pol Sci.

KARP, JASON; Riverhead HS; Wading River, NY; (Y); 3/250; Cmnty Wkr; Drama Clb; JCL; Latin Clb; Science Clb; Ski Clb; Acpl Chr; Band; Chorus; Concert Band; Josfens Schlrshp 85; Duke U; Elec Engrng.

KARP, SAMUEL; Germantown Central HS; Hudson, NY; (Y); 4/60; Am Leg Boys St; Quiz Bowl; Scholastic Bowl; Varsity Clb; School Play; Yrbk Stf; Rep Frsh Cls; Rep Soph Cls; Rep Jr Cls; Rep Sr Cls; Ithaca Coll; Math.

KARPELES, CHRISTINE; St Peters HS For Girls; Staten Isl, NY; (Y); Teachers Aide; Pres Stu Cncl; Bsktbl; Sftbl; Trs Frsh Cls; Soph Cls; Pres Jr Cls; Co-Capt Cheerleading; Coach Actv; JV St Champ Chrldng Co-Capt 84; Comm MDA Dance-A-Thon 85; Cortland U; Stckbrkr.

KARPENKO, CHRISTOPHER J; Royalton Hartland Cent HS; Middleport, NY; (Y); 3/130; Am Leg Boys St; Pres 4-H; Spanish Clb; Var Stat Bsbl; High Hon Roll; Hon Roll; Trs NHS; Rotary Awd; Rensselaer Polytech Inst Math & Sci Awd 84; NY ST Regents Schlrshp 85; Physics Awd,Scl Stds Awd 85; OH U; Chem Engr.

KARPF, JEFFREY D; Smithtown East HS; Smithtown, NY; (Y); Var L Math Tm; Ed Temple Yth Grp; Jazz Band; Nwsp Ed-Chief; Pres Trs Stu Cncl; Pres French Hon Soc; NHS; Ntl Merit SF; Cmnty Wkr; Model UN; Town Of Smithtown Traffic & Safety Brd Apptmnt 83-85; Yth For Understndg,Natl Cncl Of Soc Stds 84; Intl Reltns.

KARPINOS, TRACY; Half Hollow Hills East HS; Dix Hills, NY; (S); 129/548; Model UN; MMM; Acpl Chr; Chorus; Madrigals; School Musical; Swing Chorus; Nwsp Rptr; Mgr(s); French Hon Soc; NYSSMA All-State Conf Mxd Chr 83-85; Stu Of The Mnth 81-82; BOCES Cltrl Arts Ctr 82-85; Musical Thtr.

KARPINSKI, CHERYL; New Hyde Park Memorial HS; New Hyde Park, NY; (S); Cmnty Wkr; DECA; Lit Mag; Twrlr; High Hon Roll; Hon Roll; Camera Clb; Office Aide; Band; Sftbl; Itln Clb Mbr 84-85; Prom Comm 85; 2nd Pl Poetry Cont 84; Chief Justice.

KARSKI, PATRICK M; Notre Dame HS; Pine City, NY; (Y); 48/128; Library Aide; Pep Clb; Spanish Clb; School Play; Stage Crew; Nwsp Stf; Hon Roll; SUNY Brckprt; Pre-Law.

KARTALIAN, KARYN A; Lewiston-Porter HS; Lewiston, NY; (Y); 11/273; Ski Clb; VP Frsh Cls; VP Soph Cls; VP Jr Cls; VP Sr Cls; Rep Stu Cncl; Var L Socr; Var L Swmmng; Hon Roll; NHS; Regnts Schlrshp 85; Engl, Math, Sci & Frnch Awds; U Of Rochester; Bio.

KARTON, BARBARA; Wheatley HS; Mineola, NY; (Y); Varsity Clb; Stu Cncl; JV Var Bsktbl; JV Var Fld Hcky; Var Lcrss; All Conf Fld Hocky 83-84; Empire States Plyr 83.

KARUKAKALAM, MATTHEW; Hicksville HS; Westbury, NY; (Y); 114/500; Church Yth Grp; Trs Computer Clb; French Clb; Intnl Clb; Ski Clb; Im Tennis; Im Wrstlng; Hon Roll; MI ST U; Intl Bus.

KASABRI, INAM; Fox Lane HS; Mt Kisco, NY; (Y); Hon Roll; NHS; Ntl Merit Ltr; Bus Adm.

KASEGUMA, RICK; Unatego HS; Unadilla, NY; (Y); 1/90; Computer Clb; Political Wkr; Ski Clb; Spanish Clb; Trs Band; School Musical; Pres VP Stu Cncl; Cit Awd; NHS; WCTU High Avg Sci Chem 83-85; Harvard; Comp Sci.

KASH, SHERA; Geneva HS; Geneva, NY; (S); 1/176; Model UN; Pres Science Clb; Ski Clb; Spanish Clb; Yrbk Rptr; Lit Mag; Cit Awd; High Hon Roll; NHS; Ntl Merit Ltr; RPI Mdl Exec Math & Sci; Spnsh Clb Awd Outstndg Achvt; Hnr Mtn Poster Cont; Bio.

KASHMER, KIMBERLY; Horseheads HS; Horseheads, NY; (S); 25/410; Am Leg Aux Girls St; Latin Clb; Science Clb; Stu Cncl; Bsktbl; Crs Cntry; Score Keeper; Sftbl; Trk; High Hon Roll; NYS Regnts Schlrshp 85; Med.

KASOLD, MICHAEL; St Marys Acad; Gansevoort, NY; (S); 11/42; Ski Clb; Yrbk Ed-Chief; Yrbk Phtg; Im JV Bsktbl; Var L Ftbl; Hon Roll; Elec Engrng.

KASPROWICZ, SUSAN; John F Kejnnedy JR SR HS; Cheektowaga, NY; (Y); 7/146; Band; Church Choir; School Play; Variety Show; Trs Sr Cls; Bowling; Hon Roll; Jr NHS; VP NHS; NY ST Regents Schlrshp 85; SUNY-BUFFALO; Elec Engr.

KASPRZYK, THERESA; Holland HS; Holland, NY; (Y); Trs AFS; JA; Trs Band; Concert Band; Jazz Band; Mrchg Band; Yrbk Phtg; Score Keeper; JV Vllybl; Hon Roll; Phtgrphy.

KASSABASIAN, VICKI; Colonie Central HS; Albany, NY; (Y); 68/510; Church Yth Grp; Band; Mrchg Band; JV Crs Cntry; Var Trk; Ntl Phy Ed Awd Wnnr 85.

KASSAS, CHRISTOPHER; Archbishop Stepinac HS; Port Chester, NY; (Y); Church Yth Grp; JA; Acpl Chr; Band; Church Choir; Drill Tm; Orch; Pep Band; School Musical; Variety Show; Band Ltrs 82-86; Mus.

KASSEBAUM, PATRICIA; St Edmund HS; Brooklyn, NY; (S); 5/190; Pres Church Yth Grp; English Clb; Pres French Clb; Rep Stu Cncl; Capt Bowling; High Hon Roll; NHS; Prfct Atten Awd; Yth Rep Chrch Lit Comm 84; Spec Ed.

KASSIN, MYLES S; Clarkstown High School North; New City, NY; (Y); French Clb; Quiz Bowl; Temple Yth Grp; Y-Teens; Nwsp Bus Mgr; Nwsp Sprt Ed; Socr; NHS; Intl Bnkg/Law.

KASSMAN, DONNA; Southside HS; Rockville Centr, NY; (Y); 19/284; FBLA; Key Clb; Latin Clb; Yrbk Stf; JV Var Cheerleading; Socr; JV Tennis; High Hon Roll; Jr NHS; NHS; U MI; Bus Mngmnt.

KASSNER, CAROLYN; East Islip HS; East Islip, NY; (Y); Church Yth Grp; Math Tm; Teachers Aide; Bsktbl; Var Vllybl; High Hon Roll; Hon Roll; Jr NHS; Masonic Awd; NHS; Cortland ST U; Tchr.

KASSNER, HEIDI; Pierson HS; Sag Harbor, NY; (Y); 3/50; Spanish Clb; Chorus; School Play; Yrbk Stf; Trs Stu Cncl; Capt Cheerleading; Fld Hcky; High Hon Roll; NHS; Pres Schlr; Sag Harbor Chamber Of Commerc Awd 85; Rutgers Coll; Pre-Law.

KASSOFF, SHANA; Albany HS; Albany, NY; (Y); 10/600; Temple Yth Grp; Nwsp Phtg; Yrbk Ed-Chief; Yrbk Phtg; High Hon Roll; NHS; U Of PA.

KAST, MELISSA; Martin Van Buren HS; Jamaica, NY; (Y); Math Tm; Concert Band; School Musical; Symp Band; Variety Show; Yrbk Stf; L Gym; Hon Roll; ARISTA 83-85; Accntng.

KASTENBAUM, STEVEN; James Madison HS; Brooklyn, NY; (S); Aud/Vis; Cmnty Wkr; Band; Concert Band; Stage Crew; Variety Show; Nwsp Bus Mgr; Nwsp Phtg; Nwsp Rptr; Hon Roll; Outstndng Achvt Acad Ex Cur Act 84; Photo Gold Metalist 83; Arch Eng.

KASTENS, STACY E; Spring Valley SR HS; Spring Valley, NY; (Y); 89/435; Cmnty Wkr; Hosp Aide; Key Clb; Yrbk Phtg; High Hon Roll; Hon Roll; Rgnts Nrsng Schlrshp 85; Binghamton ST U; Nrsng.

KASTNER, DIANA L; Alfred G Berner HS; Massapequa Park, NY; (Y); 40/426; Church Yth Grp; Pep Clb; Stage Crew; Variety Show; Yrbk Stf; Twrlr; Hon Roll; NHS; NY ST Rgnts Schlrshp 85; Suny New Paltz; Studio Art.

KATASKAS, ERIK M; North Rose-Wolcott HS; N Rose, NY; (Y); Aud/Vis; Boy Scts; Ski Clb; Swmmng; Rochester Inst Tech; Arch Engr.

KATAYAMA, URSULA; New Rochelle HS; New Rochelle, NY; (Y); Model UN; Symp Band; Nwsp Stf; Lit Mag; Var L Swmmng; French Hon Soc; NHS; French Clb; Math Tm; Mrchg Band; Band Awd; Coll New Rochelle Bk Awd; Soc Stud Awd.

KATKIN, ELIZABETH; Williamsville North HS; Williamsville, NY; (Y); 2/312; Ski Clb; School Musical; Sec Symp Band; CAP; Trs Soph Cls; Var Tennis; Pres NHS; Ntl Merit Ltr; Sal; U MI Schlrshp 85; Yale U; Soc Sci.

KATOPIS, CHRIS J; Bronx High School Of Science; Hollis Hills, NY; (Y); Boy Scts; Church Yth Grp; Computer Clb; French Clb; Drm & Bgl; Lit Mag; Ntl Merit Ltr; Prfct Atten Awd; Grtr Metropltn NY Math Fair Merit Cert 85; Bio-Med Engrng.

KATTA, DEBORAH E; Dunkirk HS; Dunkirk, NY; (Y); 23/220; Trs Frsh Cls; Rep Soph Cls; Rep Jr Cls; Pres Sr Cls; Rep Stu Cncl; Cheerleading; Stat Trk; High Hon Roll; NHS; M Belden Mem Schlrshp, Cert Achvt Frnch 85; Fredonia ST U; Math.

KATYL, DONALD J; Vestal HS; Vestal, NY; (Y); 54/485; Mathletes; Hon Roll; NY Regents Schlrshp 85; Broome CC; Engrng Sci.

KATZ, ALISA; Shulamith HS; Brooklyn, NY; (S); 2/32; Dance Clb; School Musical; Nwsp Stf; Yrbk Ed-Chief; NHS; Ntl Merit Ltr; Val; Stern Coll; Med Fld.

KATZ, ALLAN; Bronx High School Of Science; Bronx, NY; (Y); JA; Teachers Aide; JV Bowling; Ntl Merit Schol; Natl Spn Exam 85; Tutor Schl Stu 83-85; Mth.

KATZ, DEBRA A; Walt Whitman HS; Hunt Sta, NY; (Y); 26/625; High Hon Roll; Jr NHS; Regents Schlrshp 85; Berkeley Schl Awd Outstndng Achvt Bus Ed 85; SUNY Albany; Bus.

KATZ, ERIC; Clarkstown South HS; W Nyack, NY; (Y); Hosp Aide; Capt Math Tm; Quiz Bowl; Science Clb; Speech Tm; Temple Yth Grp; Jazz Band; School Play; Tennis; Pres Mu Alp Tht; All Conf Tns Tm 84-86; Colmba Sci Hnrs Prog 84-86; SADD Vice Pres 85-86; Northwestern; Med.

KATZ, JENNIFER; John F Kennedy HS; Riverdale, NY; (Y); Debate Tm; Drama Clb; JA; School Musical; School Play; Hon Roll; NHS; Mock Trial Tm 84-85; Mth Awd; Engl Awd; Northwestern U; Drama.

KATZ, JOSHUA A; Roslyn HS; Roslyn Hts, NY; (Y); Science Clb; Teachers Aide; Nwsp Stf; Var L Crs Cntry; JV Jr NHS; NCTE Awd; Ntl Merit SF; Hnr Roll 81-84; Wnnr Round I NY ST ERDA Stu Energy Research Comp & Recipient Of $500 Grant 82; Medicine.

KATZ, LILACH; H Frank Carey HS; West Hempstead, NY; (Y); 12/281; Debate Tm; Model UN; Temple Yth Grp; Rep Stu Cncl; Cit Awd; French Hon Soc; High Hon Roll; Hst NHS; VFW Awd; Voice Dem Awd; Outstndng Social Studies Deptmnt Stu 85; Century III Ledrs Schlrshp Fin 85; Frgn Lang Hnr Soc 83-85; Duke U; Psych.

KATZ, LISA; Clarkstown South HS; New City, NY; (Y); 60/505; Cmnty Wkr; Temple Yth Grp; Yrbk Sprt Ed; Yrbk Stf; JV Cheerleading; Var Capt Fld Hcky; Stat Ice Hcky; Powder Puff Ftbl; Im Sftbl; Jr NHS; UNC; Occptnl Thrpst.

KATZ, MARC; Van Buren HS; Queens Village, NY; (Y); 5/579; Math Tm; Nwsp Rptr; Ed Yrbk Stf; VP Frsh Cls; VP Soph Cls; VP Sr Cls; Stu Cncl; Var L Tennis; High Hon Roll; NHS; Law Tm NY Mock Trial Trnmnt 84-85; Hist Hnr Soc; Bus Admin.

KATZ, MELISSA; Commack High School North; E Northport, NY; (Y); Band; Concert Band; Capt Flag Corp; Jazz Band; Stage Crew; Symp Band; Off Frsh Cls; Var Badmtn; High Hon Roll; NHS; SADD Pres 82-86.

KATZ, MELISSA; John F Kennedy HS; Plainview, NY; (Y); 3/275; Yrbk Stf; High Hon Roll; VP NHS; Ntl Merit Ltr; SUNY Albny Pierce Schlrshp 85; Rgnts Ashlrshp 85; SUNY Albny; Med.

KATZ, NANCY; Clarkstown South HS; W Nyack, NY; (Y); #31 In Class; Capt Math Tm; NHS; Ntl Merit SF; Aud/Vis; Letterman Clb; Quiz Bowl; Yrbk Stf; High Hon Roll; Rep Frsh Cls; Rep Soph Cls; STU Agnst Drunk Drvng Pres 84-85; Vrsty Ski Tm Capt 83-84; MVP Coaches Awd 81-83; Ofcr Mu Alpha Theta; Vet Med.

KATZ, PAMELA S; The Wheatley Schl; Old Westbury, NY; (Y); 5/136; Cmnty Wkr; Drama Clb; Pres Key Clb; Service Clb; Teachers Aide; Temple Yth Grp; Chorus; Nwsp Rptr; Yrbk Bus Mgr; Yrbk Rptr; Hofetra U Spnsh Poetry Cntst 1st Pl 84; U Of PA; Ec.

KATZMAN, VAN S; Herricks HS; Roslyn, NY; (Y); 13/306; Am Leg Boys St; School Play; Yrbk Sprt Ed; Capt Socr; Cit Awd; NHS; Ntl Merit Ltr; Scholastic Bowl; Rep Stu Cncl; JV Bsktbl; Outstndng Scl Stds Stu Awd 85; SR Actor Awd 85; Yth Ctznshp Awd 85; Yale Coll; Amer Hist.

KAUFFMAN, MICHAEL; North Warren Central HS; Chestertown, NY; (S); 5/50; Church Yth Grp; Chorus; Nwsp Rptr; Socr; Tennis.

KAUFMAN, ADAM; Ward Melville HS; Stony Brook, NY; (Y); 29/769; Temple Yth Grp; Jazz Band; Nwsp Phtg; Nwsp Rptr; Nwsp Stf; Lit Mag; High Hon Roll; NHS; Pres Of North Shore Jewish Ctr Chaptr United Synagogue Yth 84-85; ST U NY Albany; Intl Diplomcy.

KAUFMAN, BARBARA; Villa Maria Acad; Buffalo, NY; (S); 13/118; Pres Church Yth Grp; Computer Clb; French Clb; Church Choir; Bowling; Swmmng; NHS; Math.

KAUFMAN, BRIAN; Skaneateles Central HS; Skaneateles, NY; (S); Boy Scts; High Hon Roll; Hon Roll; NHS; Law Enfrcmnt.

KAUFMAN, IRA; East Meadow HS; East Meadow, NY; (S); 6/414; Aud/Vis; Drama Clb; Key Clb; Science Clb; School Play; Var Capt Tennis; High Hon Roll; NHS; Ntl Merit Ltr; NY Regnts Schlrshp 85; Med.

KAUFMAN, JEFF S; Shenendehowa Central HS; Clifton Park, NY; (Y); 24/650; AFS; Pres Intnl Clb; Trs Temple Yth Grp; Trs Stu Cncl; High Hon Roll; NHS; Acad Achvt Awds 84; Psych.

KAUFMAN, JOHN R; The Collegiate Schl; New York, NY; (Y); Chess Clb; French Clb; Math Tm; Model UN; Speech Tm; Yrbk Bus Mgr; Conrell U; Bus.

KAUFMAN, MATTHEW L; Rome Free Acad; Rome, NY; (Y); 148/542; Boy Scts; German Clb; Intnl Clb; Pep Clb; Ski Clb; Nwsp Phtg; Yrbk Phtg; Rep Stu Cncl; JV Crs Cntry; Citadel; Polt Sci.

KAUFMAN, PETER A; Valley Stream North HS; Malyerne, NY; (Y); 11/160; Debate Tm; Concert Band; Drm Mjr(t); Jazz Band; Var Bsktbl; Mu Alp Tht; NHS; Earlhan Coll; Pol Sci.

KAUFMAN, SARA; Mepham HS; N Bellmore, NY; (Y); French Clb; GAA; Service Clb; Ski Clb; Band; Nwsp Stf; Yrbk Stf; Rep Frsh Cls; Off Soph Cls; Off Jr Cls; Bus.

KAUFMAN, STEVEN; New Rochelle HS; New Rochelle, NY; (Y); Model UN; Off Frsh Cls; Off Soph Cls; Off Jr Cls; Capt Swmmng; NHS; Spanish NHS; Yale U; Pre-Med.

KAUFMAN, SUZANNE; Roy C Ketcham HS; Wappingers Falls, NY; (S); CAP; Pres FBLA; Yrbk Stf; Stu Cncl; Stat Bsktbl; Score Keeper; Vllybl; High Hon Roll; Jr NHS; Civil Air Patrol-Mst Actv Cdt 82; Acctng.

KAUFMAN, SVETLANA; Solomon Schechter HS; Brooklyn, NY; (Y); Vllybl; Elec Engrng.

KAUFMANN, NANCY C; New Rochelle HS; Scarsdale, NY; (Y); 15/650; Trs Computer Clb; French Clb; Chorus; Ed Lit Mag; Rep Sr Cls; Rep Stu Cncl; French Hon Soc; NHS; Temple Yth Grp; Hon Roll; Stu Mnth 85; French Hnr Soc Awd 85; U Of PA.

KAUP, LISA; Pual D Schreiber HS; Pt Washington, NY; (Y); 152/435; GAA; Var Capt Bsktbl; Var Lcrss; Var Socr; Var Capt Sftbl; Joseph Augustino Mem Athl Awd 85; Outstndng Stu Awd 85; F Lee Warble Mem Schlrshp Awd 85; Slippery Rock U; Athl Trngn.

KAUPER, RICHARD; Olean HS; Olean, NY; (Y); 12/206; Varsity Clb; Var Crs Cntry; JV Var Trk; Hon Roll; NHS; Awd Excllnc Latn I; Boston U; Phy Thrpst.

KAUS, ROBERT; Mahopac HS; Mahopac, NY; (Y); 17/423; Var Capt Crs Cntry; JV Trk; High Hon Roll; Hon Roll; NHS; Engrng.

KAUSCH, KURT; Bishop Kearney HS; Rochester, NY; (Y); Hosp Aide; Model UN; Mrchg Band; Rep Frsh Cls; Rep Soph Cls; Rep Jr Cls; Im Bowling; High Hon Roll; Hon Roll; Rochester Inst Tech; Biochem.

KAUTZKY, LISA M; Cardinal Mooney HS; Rochester, NY; (Y); 14/320; Service Clb; Chorus; School Musical; Yrbk Stf; Soph Cls; Swmmng; French Hon Soc; NHS; St Schlr; Regents Chem Awd 84; John Carroll Pres Hnr Awd 85-86; John Carroll U Amer Values Schlrshp 85-86; John Carroll U; Comp Sci.

KAUTZMAN, MARK; Notre Dame Bishop Gibbons HS; Schenectady, NY; (S); 3/108; Art Clb; Boy Scts; Computer Clb; Teachers Aide; High Hon Roll; NHS; Hall Hstry Fndtn Essy Cntst Cert Mrt 84; Carnegie; Elec Engrg.

KAVAN, BILL; Westhampton Beach HS; Westhampton Bea, NY; (Y); 62/236; Pres Church Yth Grp; Computer Clb; FBLA; Yrbk Stf; Bus Admn.

KAVAN JR, H RICHARD; Hauppauge HS; Hauppauge, NY; (Y); 96/500; FBLA; Science Clb; Ski Clb; High Hon Roll; NHS; 1st Pl Addng/Calcltng FBLA Dist I-Suffk Cty 84-85; Engrng.

KAVANAGH, MARK; Nyack HS; Nyack, NY; (Y); 34/277; Drama Clb; Quiz Bowl; Band; School Musical; School Play; High Hon Roll; Lion Awd; NHS; Pres Schlr; Spanish NHS; NY Regnts Scholar 85; Drama Angels Awd 85; Dr Harry Barnes Awd 85; Manhattan Coll; Cvl Engrng.

KAVANAUGH, MICHAEL; Northern Adirondack HS; Ellenburg Depot, NY; (Y); French Clb; Pres Key Clb; Library Aide; Stu Cncl; JV Bsbl; JV Var Bsktbl; Mgr(s); Hon Roll; NHS; Socr; Bus.

KAVANAUGH, PATRICK; Cornwall Central HS; Newburgh, NY; (Y); Church Yth Grp; Rep Political Wkr; Ski Clb; VP Jr Cls; Pres Sr Cls; Rep Stu Cncl; L Capt Crs Cntry; L Capt Trk; Hon Roll; Bst Frshmn Athlt 83; Mst Vlbl Rnr 84; SUNY Albany; Bus.

KAVATHAS, KATINA; Kenmore West SR HS; Kenmore, NY; (Y); Church Yth Grp; Dance Clb; VP Trs Exploring; GAA; Office Aide; Pom Pon; 3 Regents Crdts For Taking The Greek Regents Exam 84; Grad From Greek Schl 81; U Of NY Buffalo; Dentl Hygn.

KAVNER, ABBY; Arlington HS; Poughkeepsie, NY; (Y); 47/585; Debate Tm; Orch; School Musical; Yrbk Stf; Ntl Merit SF; Sci.

KAWANISHI, RIKA J; Northport HS; Northport, NY; (Y); French Clb; Orch; Capt Var Tennis; Hon Roll; NHS; Most Orignl Halloween Costume 81; Suny; Bio.

KAY, CINDY; Smithtown High School West; Smithtown, NY; (Y); Hon Roll; Jr NHS; Spanish NHS; Italian Natl Hnr Soc 85-86; Lang.

KAY, DEBORAH L; St Barnabas HS; Bronx, NY; (Y); 44/187; Dance Clb; Drama Clb; Girl Scts; Hosp Aide; Library Aide; Office Aide; Service Clb; School Musical; Yrbk Phtg; Hon Roll; 2nd Hnrs 82-85; Mt St Vincent; Comp Sci.

KAY, DIANE; Fort Hamilton HS; Brooklyn, NY; (Y); Girl Scts; Band; Off Frsh Cls; Bowling; Cit Awd; Bus.

KAY, ELYSIA M; H Frank Carey HS; Garden City, NY; (Y); 26/281; Cmnty Wkr; Temple Yth Grp; Concert Band; Mrchg Band; Var L Tennis; High Hon Roll; NHS; Spanish NHS; St Schlr; Hnrs Regents Diploma Math 85; Clncl Psych.

KAY, JOSEPH; St Josephs Colligate Inst; Amherst, NY; (Y); 24/198; Chorus; Im Bsktbl; Im Bowling; JV Socr; Im Tennis; Im Trk; High Hon Roll; Trs NHS; Pre-Med.

KAYASTHA, RAJIV; Jamesville-De Witt HS; Syracuse, NY; (Y); Cmnty Wkr; Computer Clb; Exploring; JA; Var L Tennis; Hon Roll; Pre-Med.

KAYE, JILL MARIE KATHLEEN; Nardin Acad; Buffalo, NY; (Y); Hosp Aide; JA; Yrbk Stf; Hon Roll; Regents Schlrshp 85; Buffalo St Coll; Int Design.

KAYES, KATHLEEN; Portville Central HS; Portville, NY; (Y); 1/114; Drama Clb; Model UN; Capt Color Guard; Pres Mrchg Band; School Musical; School Play; JV Bsktbl; Stat Ftbl; Mgr(s); Var Trk; County Govt 85-86; Olympics Mind 84 & 85; Mntrshp Olean Genl Hosp 85; Manhattan Coll; Pre-Med.

KAZDA, MICHAEL; Schalmont Central HS; Schenectady, NY; (Y); 8/188; Church Yth Grp; Var Capt Tennis; High Hon Roll; Hon Roll; Masonic Awd; Prfct Atten Awd; Pres Schlr; Outstndng Acad Achvt Pres Pgm 84-85; NYS Rgnts Schlrshp Awd 85; Rensselaer Polytech Inst Schlrshp 85; Rensselaer Polytech Inst; Comp.

KAZENOFF, SUZANNE; Rocky Point JR SR HS; Rocky Point, NY; (S); 15/238; Exploring; French Clb; Mathletes; Thesps; Chorus; Madrigals; School Musical; Hon Roll; NHS; Voice Dem Awd; Mark Twain Awds Creative Wrtng 83 & 85; Frnch Clb & Chorus Pres 85; Law.

KAZES, JANET; Our Lady Of Victory Acad; Buchanan, NY; (S); 11/137; French Clb; Girl Scts; Hosp Aide; French Hon Soc; High Hon Roll; NHS; NEDT Awd; Schlrshp Smmr Stdy France 83-84; Relgn Awd 82-83.

KAZLO, LAURI; Crown Point Central HS; Crown Pt, NY; (S); Trs Varsity Clb; Trs Stu Cncl; Var Bsktbl; Var Cheerleading; Var Socr; Var Sftbl; Hon Roll; VP NHS; Nwsp Stf; Yrbk Stf.

KAZMIERCZAK, MICHAEL; Hutchison Central Technical HS; Buffalo, NY; (Y); Chess Clb; Math Clb; Math Tm; Nwsp Rptr; Nwsp Stf; Lit Mag; Mgr(s); Var Tennis; High Hon Roll; Hon Roll; Geology.

KEANE, KELLY A; Cazenovia HS; Cazenovia, NY; (Y); 10/150; Cmnty Wkr; Ski Clb; Nwsp Stf; Yrbk Stf; Rep Stu Cncl; VP Socr; High Hon Roll; NHS; Rgnts Schlrshp; Rochester Inst Tech; Engrng.

KEANE, PATRICIA MARIE; Orchard Park HS; Orchard Park, NY; (Y); 17/410; Am Leg Aux Girls St; Sec 4-H; Hosp Aide; Pres Stu Cncl; Var Capt Swmmng; High Hon Roll; NHS; Trs Ski Clb; SADD Fndr & Pres 84-85; Hugh O Brien Yth Fndtn 84; Intl Stu Ldrshp Pgm 85; Polt Sci.

KEANE, THOMAS M; Mineola HS; Mineola, NY; (Y); 4/257; VP 4-H; Political Wkr; Concert Band; Mrchg Band; School Play; Ed Nwsp Stf; Lit Mag; Rep Stu Cncl; NHS; Ntl Merit SF; NY ST Yth Cncl 83-85; Most Intllgnt, Most Likely Succeed 84; Yale; Polt Sci.

KEARNEY, AMY; Smithtown HS East; Smithtown, NY; (Y); Ski Clb; Chorus; Church Choir; Yrbk Stf; Off Jr Cls; Off Sr Cls; Bsktbl; Hon Roll.

KEARNEY, COLLEEN; Union Springs Acad; Clay, NY; (Y); Church Yth Grp; Hosp Aide; Teachers Aide; Church Choir; Concert Band; Englsh.

KEARNEY, LISA; Schoharie Central HS; Schoharie, NY; (Y); Pres Church Yth Grp; VP Drama Clb; Hosp Aide; Spanish Clb; Band; Chorus; Rep Stu Cncl; Score Keeper; Acad All Amer 85; Elem Educ.

KEARNEY, SUSAN; Bay Shore HS; Bay Shore, NY; (Y); 18/367; Hosp Aide; School Play; Nwsp Ed-Chief; Ed Yrbk Stf; Tennis; Sec NHS; Pres Schlr; Outstndng Stdnt Jrnlsm 85; Regnts Schlrshp 85; Magna Cum Laude Natl Latn Exm 82; PA ST U; Sci.

KEARNEY, WILLIAM; Horseheads HS; Big Flats, NY; (Y); 156/410; Boy Scts; Computer Clb; French Clb; Pep Clb; Ski Clb; Varsity Clb; Badmtn; JV Var Lcrss; Vllybl; Hon Roll; Mansfield U; Geological Engr.

KEARNS, PATRICIA; Fonda-Fultonville Central HS; Fultonville, NY; (Y); Chorus; Bsktbl; Socr; Sftbl; Cazenovia Coll; Bus.

KEARNS, PATRICK; Port Jervis HS; Port Jervis, NY; (Y); 2/225; Chess Clb; Math Tm; Scholastic Bowl; Rep Stu Cncl; JV Golf; High Hon Roll; Pres Chess Clb; Ntl Merit SF; Engrng.

KEARSE, BRADLEY; L I Lutheran HS; Hempstead, NY; (S); Nwsp Rptr; Pres Frsh Cls; Bowling; Ftbl; Swmmng; High Hon Roll; Hon Roll; Jr NHS; NHS; Prfct Atten Awd; U VA; Engrng.

KEARY, KEVIN; Newfield HS; Selden, NY; (Y); Computer Clb; Band; Stage Crew; High Hon Roll; Hon Roll; ST U Of NY Stony Brook; Pharm.

KEATING, DEIRDRE; Lindenhurst HS; Lindenhurst, NY; (Y); French Clb; Key Clb; Ski Clb; Varsity Clb; Nwsp Rptr; Sec Stu Cncl; Tennis; French Hon Soc; High Hon Roll; High Hon Roll; 1st Pl Drunk Driving Essay; Binginton; Law.

KEATING, EILEEN; The Mary Louis Acad; Flushing, NY; (Y); Church Yth Grp; Cmnty Wkr; Sec Soph Cls; Sec Jr Cls; Socr; Sftbl; Trk; High Hon Roll; Hon Roll; NHS; Soc Sci.

KEATING, SHARI; Cicero-N Syracuse HS; N Syracuse, NY; (S); 67/711; Chorus; Mrchg Band; School Musical; Symp Band; NHS; Band; Orch; All-State Bank 84; Syracuse Symphony Yth Orch Principal Clarinetist 84-85; Music.

KEATS, JOELLE; Orchard Park HS; Orchard Park, NY; (Y); 18/435; Church Yth Grp; Varsity Clb; Mgr Bsktbl; Var Fld Hcky; Var Capt Sftbl; Var Vllybl; Cit Awd; Hon Roll; NHS; 7th In Wstrn NY-NATL Spnsh Exam 85; Natl Merit High Scorer Semi-Fnlst 85; Pol Sci.

KEAVENEY, EILEEN; Holy Trinity HS; Seaford, NY; (Y); Girl Scts; Teachers Aide; Band; Swmmng; Hon Roll; B Hnr Roll; Accntng CPA.

KEEBLER, SUSAN; Waterloo SR HS; Waterloo, NY; (Y); 4-H; FHA; Band; Concert Band; Mrchg Band; Yrbk Phtg; Hon Roll; JR Prom Decor Cmmtt Chrprsn 85; Daisy Chain 85.

KEEFE, DANIEL; Elmire Free Acad; Elmira, NY; (Y); Church Yth Grp; Spanish Clb; JV Var Socr; High Hon Roll; Hon Roll; Law.

KEEFNER, JEFF; Chatham HS; Spencertown, NY; (Y); 42/130; Church Yth Grp; Library Aide; High Hon Roll; Hon Roll; ST U Of NY; Chem Tech.

KEEGAN, CHRISTINE; Earl L Vandermeulen HS; Mt Sinai, NY; (Y); 101/286; Church Yth Grp; FBLA; Leo Clb; Pep Clb; Spanish Clb; Band; Rep Stu Cncl; Var Cheerleading; Fld Hcky; JV Trk; Econmcs.

KEEGAN, COLLEEN; Immaculate Heart Central HS; Watertown, NY; (Y); French Clb; Sec Frsh Cls; Sec Sr Cls; JV Cheerleading; Stat Lcrss; JV Socr; Hon Roll; NHS; Lemoyne; Psych.

KEEGAN, JOHN J; Northport HS; E Northport, NY; (Y); 18/595; Cmnty Wkr; ROTC; Rep Stu Cncl; Var L Bsktbl; Hon Roll; Elec Engnrng.

KEEHAN, DAWN; Bishop Scully HS; Fonda, NY; (Y); 1/60; 4-H; 4-H Awd; High Hon Roll; NHS; RPI; Math.

KEELY, MARY; Queen Of The Rosary Acad; Wantagh, NY; (S); 6/45; Math Clb; Sec Frsh Cls; Pres Jr Cls; VP Badmtn; JV Bsktbl; Capt Var Socr; Var Vllybl; High Hon Roll; Mu Alp Tht; Pres NHS; Phy Ftnss Awd; Ntl Hnr Soc; Acctng.

KEENAN, ANN MARIE; Albertus Magnus HS; New City, NY; (Y); 23/200; Church Yth Grp; Math Tm; Sec Jr Cls; JV Bsktbl; JV Crs Cntry; JV Sftbl; Hon Roll; NHS; NYC Police Dept Holy Nm Soc 82; NYC Emerald Soc Scholar 82; Comm.

KEENAN, BRIAN; Bishop Kearney HS; Rochester, NY; (Y); Church Yth Grp; Letterman Clb; Ski Clb; Varsity Clb; Var Bsbl; Capt L Ftbl; JV Wrstlng; Hon Roll; Penn ST; Archit.

KEENAN, KATHRYN; Oneida HS; Oneida, NY; (Y); FBLA; Ski Clb; Spanish Clb; Pom Pon; Vllybl; High Hon Roll; Hon Roll; Johnson & Vales; Accntng.

KEENAN, KEITH; Tamarac HS; Cropseyville, NY; (Y); Sec Computer Clb; Rep Frsh Cls; JV Bsbl; JV Ftbl; JV Wrstlng; Hon Roll; NHS; Cornell; Bio Chem.

KEENAN, PATRICE; Holy Trinity HS; Massapequa, NY; (Y); Church Yth Grp; Var Capt Pom Pon; Hofstra U; Acctng.

KEENAN JR, PAUL J; Jamesville Dewitt HS; Dewitt, NY; (Y); Pres Church Yth Grp; JCL; Latin Clb; Var L Crs Cntry; Var L Trk; High Hon Roll; NHS; Jamesville-De Witt Svc Awd 85; Elec Engrng.

KEENAN, THOMAS A; Sayville HS; Sayville, NY; (Y); 82/365; Key Clb; Concert Band; Mrchg Band; JV Swmmng; Var Tennis; ST U Oneonta; Elec Engrng.

KEENE, CAROL J; Gilbertsville Central HS; Gilbertsville, NY; (Y); 3/25; Am Leg Aux Girls St; Church Yth Grp; 4-H; GAA; Band; Chorus; Pres Civic Clb; Cit Awd; 4-H Awd; NHS; Elmira Key Awd 85; Mst Dedctd Frshman Athl 83; Rotary & Exch Stu.

KEENE, KELLY; Hoosick Falls Cental HS; Hoosick Falls, NY; (Y); VP 4-H; French Clb; Band; 4-H Awd; Hon Roll; NHS; Trvl.

KEENEHAN, JIM; Cardinal Mooney HS; Rochester, NY; (Y); Var Tennis; Scl Stds Awd 84; Monroe CC; Bus.

KEENEY, CANI; Batavia HS; Batavia, NY; (Y); Band; Concert Band; Mrchg Band; Yrbk Phtg; Yrbk Rptr; Yrbk Stf; Toursm.

KEENEY, MARY; Christ The King HS; Ridgewood, NY; (Y); 27/405; Office Aide; Political Wkr; Teachers Aide; Band; Chorus; Church Choir; School Play; Var Swmmng; Hon Roll; NHS; Relgn Awd 1st Hnrs 85; Phys Ed 2nd Hnrs 85; Stonehill Coll; Bus.

KEHL, WENDY; Attica SR HS; Cowlesville, NY; (S); 4/151; Pres VP 4-H; Chorus; Capt Color Guard; Yrbk Ed-Chief; Yrbk Stf; Hon Roll; VP NHS; AFS; Church Choir; 4-H Awd; Ntl Merti Sci Awd 84-85; St Joeshps; Nrsng.

KEICHER, LISA; Villa Maria Acad; Buffalo, NY; (S); Computer Clb; French Clb; Hosp Aide; JCL; Pres Latin Clb; Math Clb; Nwsp Rptr; Hon Roll; NHS; Pre-Med.

KEIL, DAVID A; Fayetteville-Manlius HS; Manlius, NY; (Y); Church Yth Grp; Pep Clb; Im Bsktbl; JV Golf; St Schlr; Im Ftbl; Rgnts Schlrshp 85; Syracuse U; Bio.

KEILITZ, KATHLEEN; Lindenhurst SR HS; Lindenhurst, NY; (Y); French Clb; Band; Concert Band; Mrchg Band; Nwsp Rptr; Yrbk Stf; French Hon Soc; High Hon Roll; NHS; Natl Hnr Socty Secy 85-86; Intl Mktg.

KEIPPER, CAROL; West Seneca East SR HS; W Seneca, NY; (Y); VP Church Yth Grp; DECA; Im GAA; Church Choir; Rep Soph Cls; Stat Bsktbl; Var JV Mgr(s); Var JV Socr; Stat Vllybl; JC Awd.

KEITEL, VANESSA; Guilderland Central HS; Albany, NY; (Y); 6/360; Band; Jazz Band; Orch; Pep Band; School Musical; Stage Crew; Symp Band; Lit Mag; High Hon Roll; Ntl Merit Ltr; Bio.

KEITH, MARY; Mineola HS; Mineola, NY; (Y); Key Clb; Variety Show; High Hon Roll; Hon Roll; Bus Law.

KEITH, SHERRY L; Niagara Wheatfield SR HS; Niagara Falls, NY; (Y); 6/313; Pep Clb; PAVAS; Band; Mrchg Band; School Musical; High Hon Roll; NHS; All ST Conf Band 84; All Estrn Band 85; Hamilton Coll; Lib Art.

KEITT, ALICE; Springfield HS; New York, NY; (Y); Cit Awd; Hon Roll.

KEKKE, TOMOKO; Paul D Schreiber HS; Port Washington, NY; (Y); Chorus; Orch; New Englnd Consrvtry Schlrshp 85-86; Port Sngrs Schlrshp 85-86; Hartt Schl Of Music Schlrshp 85-86; New England Consrvtry.

KELBLEY, JAY; Pittsford Sutherland HS; Brighton, NY; (Y); Aud/Vis; Computer Clb; Debate Tm; German Clb; Model UN; Stage Crew; Lit Mag; JV Ftbl; Var Trk.

KELLAR, CINDY; Berlin Central Schl; Cherry Plain, NY; (S); 12/85; Pep Clb; Cheerleading; High Hon Roll; Hon Roll; Prfct Atten Awd.

KELLEHER, AMY; Frontier Central HS; Hamburg, NY; (Y); 17/500; Cmnty Wkr; Hosp Aide; Trs JA; Band; School Musical; NHS; Pres Schlr; VFW Awd; Latin Clb; Library Aide; All Am Hall Fame Band Hnrs 84; Hamburg Quota Clb Schlrshp 85; NY ST Regnts Schlrshp 85; Villa Maria Coll; Nrsng.

KELLEHER, CRAIG; Archbishop Molloy HS; Maspeth, NY; (Y); Pres Aud/Vis; Chess Clb; Computer Clb; Political Wkr; Lit Mag; DAR Awd; Hon Roll; Ntl Merit Ltr; Law.

KELLEHER, JOHN J; St Anthonys HS; Commack, NY; (Y); Art Clb; Computer Clb; Math Tm; Radio Clb; Stage Crew; Nwsp Sprt Ed; JV Socr; Hon Roll; NHS; Im Bowling; Duns Scotus Cert; Engrng.

KELLEHER, MICHAEL J; St Francis Prep; Jamaica, NY; (Y); Cmnty Wkr; VP Debate Tm; Drama Clb; Model UN; Political Wkr; Im Ftbl; Im Socr; Im Sftbl; Ltr Pol Sci 83-85; Ltr Debate 83-85; American U; Pol Sci.

KELLER, DAVID B; Fairport HS; Fairport, NY; (Y); German Clb; JA; Y-Teens; Band; Concert Band; Mrchg Band; Bsbl; Diving; Timer; Wt Lftg; Regents Scholarship 85; Northeastern U; Civil Engnrng.

KELLER, DEAN; Fairport HS; Fairport, NY; (Y); Art Clb; Varsity Clb; Band; Concert Band; Sec Jazz Band; Mrchg Band; Lit Mag; Crs Cntry; Capt Swmmng; NHS; All St Wind Ens Solo Chair 84; 1st Pl Schlstc Art Show 85.

KELLER, INGRID GRACE; Valley Stream North HS; Malvern, NY; (Y); 36/168; Church Choir; Yrbk Stf; Vllybl; Hon Roll; Mst Outstndng Stu Awd Nrsng 85; Nassau Cmnty; Nrsng.

KELLER, KATHLEEN M; St Catharine Acad; Bronx, NY; (Y); Office Aide; Teachers Aide; Chorus; Rep Stu Cncl; Hon Roll; Ntl Merit Ltr; NEDT Awd; Church Yth Grp; Cmnty Wkr; Im Swmmng; Full Academic Schlrshp St Catharine Acad 81-85; Regents Schlrshp & Diplma 85; Fordham U; Comm Arts.

KELLER, LORI; Henninger HS; Syracuse, NY; (Y); Off Jr Cls; Rep Sr Cls; Off Stu Cncl; High Hon Roll; NHS; Regents Schlrshp 85; Geneseo; Spec Educ.

KELLER, MARLA J; New Dorp HS; Staten Island, NY; (Y); #3 In Class; Am Leg Aux Girls St; Key Clb; Varsity Clb; Capt Var Sftbl; Pep Clb; Gov Hon Prg Awd; NHS; French Clb; GAA; Math Tm; David M Winfield Fndtn Schlrshp 85; Staten Island Fdrtn Of PTA Schlrshp 85; Cornell U; Law.

KELLER, MELANIE; Groton Central HS; Groton, NY; (Y); Church Yth Grp; Girl Scts; Band; Chorus; Drm Mjr(t); Yrbk Stf; Socr; Trk; High Hon Roll; Ithaca Coll; Phy Thrpy.

KELLER, RUTH; Fort Ann Central HS; Fort Ann, NY; (Y); 8/42; French Clb; Mathletes; Math Tm; Band; Drm & Bgl; JV Cheerleading; JV Var Sftbl; Hon Roll; NHS; Willits Fdtn Schlrshp 85; Norwich U; Engrng.

KELLER, STEPHANIE K; Gowanda Central HS; Perrysburg, NY; (Y); 5/163; Sec Church Yth Grp; Chrmn Red Cross Aide; Capt Scholastic Bowl; Pres Spanish Clb; Rep Jr Cls; Rep Sr Cls; VP NHS; St Schlr; Camera Clb; Chorus; Newspaper Managing Editor; PA Announcer; Newspaper Special Features Editor; Syracuse U; Engineering.

KELLER, SUE; West Seneca East HS; Cheektowaga, NY; (S); 93/365; Sec DECA; French Clb; Key Clb; Color Guard; Drm Mjr(t); Nwsp Stf; Hon Roll; JC Awd; Outstndng DECA SVC Awd 83-84; Southtown Dance Cls Awd 84; Exec Sec.

KELLEY, CHERYL L; Cicero North Syracuse HS; Clay, NY; (S); 42/622; Girl Scts; Library Aide; Lit Mag; Stu Cncl; Hon Roll; N Area Teenage Vlntr Rnnr-Up 84; Girl Scout Awd 84; US Naval Sea Cadet Corp.

KELLEY, CHRIS; Alden Central HS; Alden, NY; (Y); 16/210; Church Yth Grp; Var JV Bsbl; Var JV Bsktbl; Ftbl; Var Mgr(s); JV Var Score Keeper; Var JV Timer; Hon Roll; NHS; St U NY; Arch.

KELLEY, CYNTHIA; Lowville Acad & Central Schl; Lowville, NY; (Y); FFA; Score Keeper; JV Var Sftbl; Elks Awd; Hon Roll; Med Lat Tech.

KELLEY, KAREN; Camden Central HS; Camden, NY; (Y); Sec Trs AFS; Am Leg Boys St; Am Leg Aux Girls St; Drama Clb; Varsity Clb; Stage Crew; Yrbk Stf; Var Golf; High Hon Roll; Hon Roll.

KELLEY, KATHY; Frontier Senior HS; Hamburg, NY; (Y); Dance Clb; Drama Clb; Pep Clb; Spanish Clb; Chorus; School Musical; School Play; Var Cheerleading; High Hon Roll; Hon Roll; Math.

KELLEY, KRISTINE; Wheatland-Chili HS; Scottsville, NY; (Y); Girl Scts; Library Aide; Nwsp Sprt Ed; Sec Trs Nwsp Stf; Stat Bsktbl; Stat Sftbl; Hon Roll; Prfct Atten Awd; Church Yth Grp; GAA; Ltr Mgr Of Var Bsktbl Tm 85; High Avrg Stenoscrpt 85; Tickt Chrmn Schl Ply; Polc Offcr.

KELLEY, LISA; Saugerties HS; Saugerties, NY; (Y); 90/270; 4-H; Girl Scts; Library Aide; Office Aide; Varsity Clb; Var Sftbl; JV Trk; Var JV Vllybl; Hon Roll; 1st & 2nd Tm All Star Frstbsmn 85; MVP Sftbl 85; Krsslr Bus Inst Cert Merit 85; Bus.

KELLEY, LORI; Pineview Christian Acad; Troy, NY; (Y); 3/9; Church Yth Grp; JA; Spanish Clb; Chorus; Church Choir; Trk; Vllybl; High Hon Roll; Hon Roll; Regnts Diplma 85; 1st & 2nd Prz Home Ec Fair 84; Nyack Coll; Elem Ed.

KELLEY, PATRICK; Ogdensburg Free Acad; Ogdensburg, NY; (Y); 31/196; Cmnty Wkr; Quiz Bowl; School Play; Nwsp Rptr; Yrbk Sprt Ed; Trs Frsh Cls; Trs Soph Cls; Rep Stu Cncl; JV Var Trk; JV Vllybl; Regents Schlrshp 85; Cynthia Deloney Schlrshp 85; Suny Genese; Bio.

KELLEY JR, ROBERT A; Saratoga Springs SR HS; Saratoga Sprgs, NY; (Y); JV Var Trk; Albany JC; Cmrcl Art.

KELLEY, TERESA; Pulaski JR SR HS; Pulaski, NY; (Y); Drama Clb; Sec Trs 4-H; GAA; Pres VP Girl Scts; Math Tm; Band; Chorus; Concert Band; Mrchg Band; School Musical; Grl Sct 10 Yr Awd 84; Hrsbck Rdng Fr Hndcppd.

KELLEY, ZACK; Hornell SR HS; Hornell, NY; (Y); Band; Concert Band; Mrchg Band; Stu Cncl; Var L Bsbl; Var L Bsktbl; Var L Tennis; Hon Roll; NHS; Eng Excel Awd 84-85; Bio Excel Awd 84.

KELLMAN, DEBRA; Dominican Commercial HS; Jamaica, NY; (Y); Art Clb; Dance Clb; Letterman Clb; Office Aide; Science Clb; Spanish Clb; Teachers Aide; Varsity Clb; Church Choir; Yrbk Stf; PACE U; Bus.

KELLNER, SARA A; Calasanctius Schl For Th Gifted; Hamburg, NY; (Y); Art Clb; Drama Clb; 4-H; Political Wkr; Chorus; School Play; Yrbk Stf; PTA Awd Acad Achvt 80-81; Calasanctius Art Awd 81-83; Art.

KELLOGG, HOLLY; John Jay HS; Katonah, NY; (Y); 3/290; Band; Yrbk Phtg; JV Lcrss; Hon Roll; Regents Schlrshp 85; U S Natl Art Awd 85; Suny Geneseo; Art.

KELLOGG, RICH; Frontier SR HS; Hamburg, NY; (Y); Boy Scts; Chess Clb; Computer Clb; Teachers Aide; School Play; Im Bsbl; Im Bsktbl; Hon Roll; Navy; Comp Sci.

KELLOGG, SUSAN; Byron-Bergen HS; Batavia, NY; (Y); 4-H; Band; Concert Band; Mrchg Band; Yrbk Stf; Hon Roll; Genesee CC; Bus Mgmt.

KELLY, ALICIA; Moravia Central HS; Moravia, NY; (Y); GAA; Chorus; Stage Crew; Yrbk Stf; Stu Cncl; JV Bsktbl; JV Fld Hcky; JV Sftbl; Hon Roll; Intr Dsgn.

KELLY, ALTHEA; Delaware Acad; Hamden, NY; (Y); Intnl Clb; Library Aide; Spanish Clb; Hon Roll; Air Force; Comp Elec.

KELLY, AMY; Livonia HS; Conesus, NY; (Y); 14/140; Girl Scts; Ski Clb; Chorus; Color Guard; Yrbk Stf; Rep Stu Cncl; High Hon Roll; Hon Roll; NHS; Rotary Awd; Exchng Stu-Brazil 83-84; CC Of Finger Lakes; Police Sci.

KELLY, BRENDAN P; Rye HS; Rye, NY; (Y); 17/180; Capt Ski Clb; Pres Concert Band; Jazz Band; School Musical; Pres Stu Cncl; JV Bsbl; JV Bsktbl; NHS; Leo Clb; Orch; Arion Foundation Awd 84; Lcl Wnnr Century Iii Ldrshp Awd 84; Schl Wnnr Hearst Fndtn Schlrshp Awd 84; Swarthmore Coll; Bio.

KELLY, BRIAN; Hendrick Hudson HS; Montrose, NY; (Y); Cmnty Wkr; Bsbl; Bsktbl; Ftbl; Score Keeper; Hon Roll; Bus.

KELLY, CATHY; Madrid Waddington HS; Madrid, NY; (Y); Drama Clb; French Clb; Spanish Clb; Band; Chorus; Var JV Bsktbl; Var JV Socr; Var Trk; Var JV Vllybl; Hon Roll; MIP JV Soccer 82-83; MIP JV Bsktbl 83-84.

KELLY, CHARMAINE L; Naples Central HS; Naples, NY; (Y); Cmnty Wkr; Trs Band; Chorus; Concert Band; Mrchg Band; Nwsp Ed-Chief; Yrbk Ed-Chief; Yrbk Stf; High Hon Roll; NHS; Law.

KELLY, CHRISTINE; Madrio Waddington HS; Madrid, NY; (Y); AFS; Debate Tm; GAA; Spanish Clb; School Play; Cheerleading; Socr; Hon Roll; Band; Chorus; Engl.

KELLY, CHRISTINE; Valhalla HS; Valhalla, NY; (Y); 3/120; Drama Clb; School Musical; VP Jr Cls; VP Sr Cls; Sec Stu Cncl; Var Cheerleading; Hon Roll; NHS; Ntl Merit SF; Pres Schlr; Regents Schlrshp 85; Bucknell U; Liberal Arts.

KELLY, CHRISTINE RUTH; The Mary Louis Acad; Forest Hills, NY; (Y); Cmnty Wkr; Library Aide; Service Clb; Church Choir; Yrbk Stf; Engr.

KELLY, CHRISTOPHER; Archbishop Molloy HS; Woodside, NY; (Y); 194/409; Hon Roll.

KELLY, CINDY; Plainedge HS; N Massapequa, NY; (Y); High Hon Roll; Hon Roll; Spanish NHS; Engl Awd 83; Frnch Awd 85; C W Post; Intl Bus.

KELLY, CYDNEY; Buffalo Traditional HS; Buffalo, NY; (S); 10/120; Debate Tm; Pres French Clb; Math Tm; Nwsp Stf; Yrbk Stf; Sftbl; Capt Swmmng; Vllybl; Hon Roll; NHS; Econ.

KELLY, DEIRDRE; North Babylon SR HS; North Babylon, NY; (Y); Hosp Aide; Spanish Clb; Yrbk Sprt Ed; Stu Cncl; Var Capt Fld Hcky; Var Capt Gym; Var Mat Maids; Var Sftbl; High Hon Roll; NHS; Mt St Vincent; Spec Educ.

KELLY, DELYNN; West Irondequoit HS; Rochester, NY; (Y); 95/337; Church Yth Grp; Chorus; Var Trk; Hon Roll; Prfct Atten Awd; Madrigals; Swing Chorus; Variety Show; Blck Schlr 85; Englsh Spcl Rprt Of Exc 84; Cert Of Rcgntn For Acdmc Achvt 85; St John Fisher Coll; Corp Law.

KELLY, DOUGLAS A; Bronx High School Of Science; Bronx, NY; (Y); Nwsp Rptr; Lit Mag; Ntl Merit SF; Wnnr NYC Mag Fic Cntst May 84; Hldr 2 Cpyrghts On 2 Shrt Nvls 81; NY U; Finc.

KELLY, EDWARD; Valley Stream Central HS; Valley Stream, NY; (Y); Chorus; Hon Roll; Mu Alp Tht; Math.

KELLY, EILEEN; North Rockland HS; Garnerville, NY; (Y); 25/561; Trs Church Yth Grp; Spanish Clb; Band; Chorus; Mrchg Band; Yrbk Stf; Hon Roll; NHS; Pres Schlr; NYS Rgnts Scholar 85; CYO Yth Archdcsn Awd 85; Le Moyne Coll; Biol.

KELLY, ELIZABETH; Albion HS; Albion, NY; (Y); 19/168; Cmnty Wkr; Latin Clb; Spanish Clb; Variety Show; Hon Roll; NHS; Niagara U; Travl.

KELLY, GARY; Christian Brothers Acad; Bridgeport, NY; (Y); FCA; JV Capt Bsbl; Var Capt Ftbl; Var Trk; Var Capt Wrstlng; Cortland U; Law Enfrcmnt.

KELLY, JAMES; Hornell SR HS; Harnell, NY; (S); 2/198; Aud/Vis; Math Clb; Var L Crs Cntry; Var L Socr; Var Trk; High Hon Roll; NHS; Prfct Atten Awd; Sal; Ntl Hstry/Gvrnmnt Awd 85; Elec Engrng.

KELLY, JANINE; Saint Francis Prep; Middle Village, NY; (Y); Dance Clb; Rep Frsh Cls; Rep Soph Cls; Var Gym; St Francis Prep Athltc Gym Svc 84-86; Svc Internshp 84-85; Phy Ed.

KELLY, JOHN; Candor Central Schl; Willseyville, NY; (Y); Boy Scts; Computer Clb; Varsity Clb; JV Bsbl; Var Crs Cntry; Var Trk; Hon Roll; Aud/Vis; Chess Clb; Wrstlng; Tompkins Cortlnd Coll; Crim Jus.

KELLY, KAREN; Binghamton HS; Binghampton, NY; (Y); 47/548; Key Clb; Var L Sftbl; Var L Vllybl; High Hon Roll; Hon Roll; Prfct Atten Awd; All ST Hnrs Catchr Schltc Sftbl Vrsty Tm; Pre-Coll Elec Engrng Course; Penn ST; Elec Engrng.

KELLY, KATHERINE; Seton Catholic Central HS; Binghamton, NY; (Y); 11/152; Church Yth Grp; French Clb; Key Clb; Yrbk Stf; Rep Stu Cncl; Var Trk; Sec NHS; NY ST Regnts Schlrshp 85; CYO Le Moyne Coll Schlrshp 85; Claire C Burns Schlrshp 85; Le Moyne Coll; Bio.

KELLY, KATHLEEN; East Aurora HS; East Aurora, NY; (S); 7/182; Girl Scts; School Musical; Rep Frsh Cls; Rep Soph Cls; Rep Jr Cls; Sec Sr Cls; Var JV Vllybl; Hon Roll; Jr NHS; NHS; Girl Scout; U Of Rochester; Pre Med.

KELLY, KATHLEEN; Frontier HS; Hamburg, NY; (Y); 28/500; German Clb; Latin Clb; Pep Clb; Stu Cncl; Bsktbl; Socr; Vllybl; Hon Roll; NHS; Pres Schlr; Canisius; Pre-Med.

KELLY, KATHLEEN; Stella Maris HS; Breezy Point, NY; (Y); Var Capt Bsktbl; Var Swmmng; Var Tennis; Var Capt Vllybl; Athlete Of Yr 85; Athletic Cert Awd 81-85; Mvpvrsty Vllybl 85; Pace U; Comm.

KELLY, KATHLEEN M; Longwood HS; Ridge, NY; (Y); 131/545; Hon Roll; Regents Schlrshp 85; Suffolk County Comm; Lib Arts.

KELLY, KATHLEEN P; Sachem HS; Holbrook, NY; (Y); Am Leg Aux Girls St; Cmnty Wkr; 4-H; Office Aide; Chorus; 4-H Awd; VFW Awd; E Stroudsburg; Elem Educ.

KELLY, KATHY; G Ray Bodley HS; Fulton, NY; (Y); Hosp Aide; Latin Clb; Science Clb; JV Var Socr; Var Trk; High Hon Roll; NHS; Phrmcy.

KELLY, KATHY M; Southside HS; Rockville Ctr, NY; (Y); 90/300; Church Yth Grp; Debate Tm; Drama Clb; Latin Clb; Nwsp Stf; Yrbk Stf; Pres Frsh Cls; Rep Soph Cls; Rep Jr Cls; Rep Sr Cls; Parents Teachers Assoc Schlrshp 85; Latin Club Awd 85; IN U; Econ.

KELLY, KEVIN; Miller Place HS; Miller Pl, NY; (Y); 37/205; Varsity Clb; Band; Concert Band; Jazz Band; Pres Frsh Cls; Pres Soph Cls; JV Bsktbl; JV Socr; Var Trk; Vllybl; Math & Scl Stds Awd 85; Math.

KELLY, KIM; Wellsville HS; Genesee, PA; (Y); Art Clb; French Clb; Ski Clb; Varsity Clb; Var L Bsktbl; Var L Cheerleading; Var L Sftbl; High Hon Roll; NHS; Zoolgy.

KELLY, LANCE; Union Springs Acad; Ashville, NY; (Y); Church Yth Grp; Drama Clb; FCA; Ski Clb; Church Choir; Off Soph Cls; Off Jr Cls; Ftbl; Gym; Sftbl; Ktrng Coll Med Arts; Ultr Snd.

KELLY, LEANNE; Lansingburgh HS; Troy, NY; (Y); French Clb; Chorus; Bsktbl; High Hon Roll; Hon Roll; Hdsn Vly CC.

KELLY, MARGARET; Academy Of Saint Joseph; Lindenhurst, NY; (Y); Hosp Aide; Library Aide; Science Clb; Yrbk Stf.

KELLY, MARGARET; Alfred G Berner HS; Massapequa Park, NY; (Y); 56/410; Church Yth Grp; Dance Clb; French Clb; GAA; JV Capt Vllybl; Hon Roll; Mdcl.

KELLY, MARGARET; Skaneateles HS; Skaneateles, NY; (S); Church Yth Grp; Hosp Aide; Pres Frsh Cls; Pres Soph Cls; Pres Jr Cls; Rep Stu Cncl; Var Bsktbl; Var Socr; High Hon Roll; Jr NHS; George Dowley Sailing Trophy 81-82; Vrsty Soccer Team All-Leag 83-85; Estrn Reg Soccer Camp 83; Math.

KELLY, MARY CATHERINE; Mt Mercy Acad; Buffalo, NY; (S); Computer Clb; JCL; Model UN; Q&S; Ed Nwsp Ed-Chief; Ed Nwsp Stf; Hon Roll; Ntl Merit SF; Cit Awd; Column Fredonia Awd 84; Classcl Lang.

KELLY, MELISSA; Geneva HS; Geneva, NY; (S); 13/170; VP Pres Latin Clb; Model UN; Ski Clb; Varsity Clb; Yrbk Stf; Sec Frsh Cls; Var Swmmng; JV Tennis; Hon Roll; NHS; Outstndng Art Stu 84; Art Hstry.

KELLY, MICHAEL; Mannheim American HS; Apo, NY; (Y); 15/130; Church Yth Grp; Model UN; Varsity Clb; Var Ftbl; Var Trk; Var Wrstlng; NHS; Outstndg Achvts Awd Math 84-85; 1st Pl Annl HS Math Exam 84-85; Shrt Stry Pblshd Sketches 84-85; Civil Engr.

KELLY, MICHELE M; W C Mepham HS; Bellmore, NY; (Y); French Clb; Band; Concert Band; Yrbk Stf; Off Soph Cls; Off Sr Cls; Stu Cncl; French Hon Soc; Hon Roll; NHS; Vrsty Bnd Ltr 83-84; Lwyr.

KELLY, PATRICIA L; Northport HS; E Northport, NY; (Y); 58/585; Camera Clb; Service Clb; Yrbk Phtg; Yrbk Stf; Rep Stu Cncl; Hon Roll; Excel In Media 83.

KELLY, PATRICK J; Dansville Central HS; Dansville, NY; (Y); 1/135; Concert Band; Mrchg Band; School Musical; Trs Stu Cncl; Var Socr; Var Tennis; Pres NHS; Val; Am Leg Boys St; Frgn Exchng Stu Spain 84; NY ST Lions Yth Band 84-85; Outstndng Physcs Stu Yr/Physcs Awd 85; Yale U; Econmcs.

KELLY, PATTI J; Onteora HS; Pine Hill, NY; (Y); 55/245; Chorus; Orch; School Play; High Hon Roll; Hon Roll; Chess Clb; Computer Clb; Girl Scts; Nwsp Bus Mgr; Cheerleading; Regents Schlrshp 84-85; Ulster Cnty CC; Comp Sci.

KELLY, SHARON; Nazareth Acad; Rochester, NY; (Y); Boys Clb Am; Cmnty Wkr; Office Aide; Spanish Clb; Chorus; Yrbk Stf; Lit Mag; Best Imprvd Wrtng 85; Creatv Wrtng 84; Paine Coll; Jrnlsm.

KELLY, SUSAN; Caledonia Mumford HS; Churchville, NY; (Y); Pep Clb; Spanish Clb; Band; Chorus; Concert Band; Mrchg Band; JV Socr; Stat Vllybl; High Hon Roll; Hon Roll; Monroe CC; Sec.

KELLY, TAMI; Auburn HS; Auburn, NY; (Y); Drama Clb; Ski Clb; Var Fld Hcky; Stat Lcrss; High Hon Roll; Hon Roll; Chrprsn Ethiopia Fund Dr 84; Prfct Atndnc 84-85; U Rochester; Bio.

KELLY, TAMMY; Camden HS; Camden, NY; (Y); Drama Clb; Chorus; Orch; School Musical; School Play; Var JV Cheerleading; JV Tennis; High Hon Roll; Hon Roll; Sec.

KELLY, WASSON; Monroe HS; Rochester, NY; (Y); Boy Scts; Cmnty Wkr; Latin Clb; Ski Clb; Band; Concert Band; Mrchg Band; Symp Band; Socr; Hon Roll; Eagl Scout 85; Med.

KELLY, WILLIAM; St Marys Boys HS; Williston Park, NY; (Y); 27/130; Church Yth Grp; Ski Clb; Nwsp Phtg; Yrbk Stf; Capt Bowling; Diving; Golf; Trk; NY Inst Tech; Mech Engr.

KELSCH, ROBERT D; Plainedge HS; N Massapequa, NY; (Y); 5/311; Computer Clb; French Clb; School Play; Lit Mag; French Hon Soc; High Hon Roll; Jr NHS; NHS; Pres Schlr; Regnts Schlrshp 85; Ntl Hist Day Wnnr 82; Hnrbl Mntn Frnch Poet Cntst 82; Adelphi U; Bio.

KELSEY, DARLENE P; Hunter-Tannersville Central HS; Lexington, NY; (Y); 6/33; Chorus; Church Choir; Cit Awd; DAR Awd; Hon Roll; Ntl Merit Schol; Clarkson U; Chem Engrng.

KELSEY, DAVID; Utica Free Acad; Utica, NY; (Y); Debate Tm; Intnl Clb; Ski Clb; Nwsp Stf; Tennis; Wrstlng; Rotary Awd; Rotry Intl Schlrshp 85-86; Intl Stu Exch; Lawrence & Robert Crade Memrl Prze Mst Imprvd Stu 85; Ind Labr Rltns.

KELSEY, DONNA; Midlakes HS; Clifton Springs, NY; (Y); 9/150; Cmnty Wkr; Debate Tm; French Clb; Intnl Clb; Model UN; Service Clb; Thesps; School Musical; School Play; Stage Crew; Regnts Schlrshp 85; Maria Regina Frshmn Schlrshp 85; Natl Hnr Rll 84; Maria Regina Coll; Bus Mgmt.

KELSH, M EILEEN; Garden City HS; Garden City, NY; (Y); 14/355; French Clb; German Clb; Latin Clb; Yrbk Stf; Var Badmtn; High Hon Roll; Jr NHS; NHS; Church Yth Grp; Intnl Clb; Intl Stu Exchng Ambssdr/ Spain 84; Ntl Merit Schlrshp Cmptn Cmmnded Stu 85.

KELSO, KELLY; Allegany Central HS; Allegany, NY; (Y); Ski Clb; Spanish Clb; Thesps; Chorus; School Musical; School Play; Nwsp Ed-Chief; Yrbk Stf; High Hon Roll; NHS; Adm Schlrshp Soc 85.

KELTON, RIVA K; Garden Schl; Whitestone, NY; (Y); 1/25; NFL; Temple Yth Grp; School Play; Nwsp Rptr; Rep Frsh Cls; Tennis; High Hon Roll; Jr NHS; NHS; Val; Regents Schlrshp 85; Barnard Coll; Law.

KEMMERER, RICHARD; Victor SR HS; Victor, NY; (Y); 26/250; Church Yth Grp; Varsity Clb; Rep Stu Cncl; Var Crs Cntry; Var Swmmng; Var Trk; High Hon Roll; Hon Roll; VP NHS; Med.

KEMNITZER, JOHN; Stissing Mtn JR SR HS; Stanfordville, NY; (Y); Band; Var Bsbl; Var Bsktbl; Var Crs Cntry; Hon Roll; NHS; Sprts Med.

KEMNITZER, VALERIE; Stissing Mtn JR SR HS; Stanfordville, NY; (Y); Pep Clb; Band; Yrbk Stf; Var Capt Bsktbl; Var Crs Cntry; Var Trk; Var Capt Vllybl; Hon Roll; Nrsg.

KEMP, STEVEN; Grand Island HS; Gr Island, NY; (Y); Church Yth Grp; Band; Concert Band; Mrchg Band; Pep Band; Hon Roll; PTSA Hnrs Acad Achvt 83; Engrng.

KEMPF, NORMA; Miller Place HS; Sound Beach, NY; (Y); Church Yth Grp; Varsity Clb; JV Var Bsktbl; Tennis; Vllybl; All League & All Confrnce-Vllybl 85.

KEMPTON, DAWN; St John The Baptist HS; Lindenhurst, NY; (Y); 100/600; Var JV Bsbl; Var Vllybl; Hon Roll; St Johns U; Phrmcy.

KENCH, NATHAN; Fairport HS; Fairport, NY; (Y); 115/600; Church Yth Grp; Cmnty Wkr; FBLA; Key Clb; Pep Clb; Church Choir; Variety Show; Var L Socr; Hon Roll; Mst Imprv Plyr Vrsty Sccr 84; NY ST Regnts Schlrshp 85; ST U Oswego.

KENDALL, ALAN; Potsdam Central HS; Hannawa Falls, NY; (Y); 11/126; JA; Varsity Clb; Rep Frsh Cls; Rep Soph Cls; Rep Stu Cncl; Var Socr; L Trk; High Hon Roll; Hon Roll; NHS; Outstndg Sci Stu Awd 85; Rensselaer Polytech; Engrng.

KENDALL, DOUGLAS J; Vestal HS; Binghamton, NY; (Y); Boy Scts; Church Yth Grp; FBLA; Varsity Clb; Im JV Bsbl; Im Bsktbl; JV L Socr; High Hon Roll; Hon Roll; Prfct Atten Awd; SUNY Albany; Bus Mgmt.

KENDALL, KRISTINE; Alexander Central Schl; Attica, NY; (S); 7/88; Spanish Clb; Hon Roll; Jr NHS; NHS; GCC; Wrd Prcsng.

KENDRICK, LOUISA; St Catherine Acad; Bronx, NY; (Y); 69/205; Church Yth Grp; Dance Clb; Teachers Aide; Chorus; Church Choir; School Musical; School Play; Variety Show; Rep Frsh Cls; Rep Soph Cls; Excell In Chem Mrt Awd 85; Comp Sci.

KENEFICK, CHRISTINE LYNN; Notre Dame HS; Horseheads, NY; (Y); Am Leg Aux Girls St; Drama Clb; School Musical; School Play; Nwsp Ed-Chief; Sec Jr Cls; Cheerleading; Hon Roll; NHS; Cmnty Wkr; Rep Yth For Yth Conf Hld In Albany 85; Intl Law.

KENEFICK, DEBORA A; Holy Trinity HS; Hicksville, NY; (Y); 3/340; Math Clb; Spanish Clb; Nwsp Sprt Ed; Rep Stu Cncl; Capt Socr; Trk; High Hon Roll; NHS; St Schlr; U Of Scranton; Bio.

KENEHAN, MAURA; Maine-Endwell SR HS; Endwell, NY; (Y); 51/250; French Clb; Sec Chrmn Key Clb; School Musical; School Play; Nwsp Stf; Sec Stu Cncl; Var Capt Cheerleading; Hon Roll; NHS; Rotary Awd; Mst Spirited Chrldr Awd 84; Spartan Spirit Awd 83-85; U Scranton; Mktng.

KENIRY, MARYMARGARET; Shenendehowa HS; Mechanicville, NY; (Y); Am Leg Aux Girls St; Capt Hosp Aide; Concert Band; Orch; Pep Band; Rep Soph Cls; Rep Jr Cls; Rep Sr Cls; Pres Stu Cncl; Cit Awd; Century III Ldr 84-85; Jaycees Outstdng Yng New Yrkr 84-85; Shenendehowa PTSA Neil Hesson Awd Ctznsh; Union Coll; Bio.

KENNA, JENNIFER; Colonie Central HS; Albany, NY; (Y); Band; Rep Frsh Cls; Socr; Marist Coll; RN.

KENNEALY, SUZANNE; Williamsville East HS; Buffalo, NY; (Y); 77/299; Cmnty Wkr; Office Aide; Var Vllybl; High Hon Roll; Hon Roll; Vrsty Vlybl Coaches Awd; Actn Lrng Intrnshp Prgm; AZ ST U; Nrs.

KENNEDY, BETSEY; Cooperstown Central HS; Mt Vison, NY; (Y); GAA; Chorus; Yrbk Bus Mgr; Yrbk Phtg; Yrbk Stf; Off Frsh Cls; Off Soph Cls; Off Jr Cls; Off Stu Cncl; Fld Hcky; Nrs.

KENNEDY, BILL; Spackenkill HS; Poughkeepsie, NY; (Y); 14/167; Boy Scts; Concert Band; Jazz Band; Pep Band; School Musical; Yrbk Stf; Capt Bsktbl; Var L Golf; High Hon Roll; NHS; Bsktbl MVP 84-85; Bsktbl MIP 84-85; Var Ltr 83-84; Pol Sci.

KENNEDY, CHRISTINE; Spackenkill HS; Poughkeepsie, NY; (Y); 32/135; Hosp Aide; Concert Band; Pep Band; School Musical; Stage Crew; Yrbk Stf; Var L Bsktbl; Var L Fld Hcky; Hon Roll; NHS; Oswego; Accntng.

KENNEDY, DANA; Immaculata Acad; Hamburg, NY; (Y); French Clb; Pres Soph Cls; Pres Jr Cls; VP Stu Cncl; JV Var Bsktbl; Trk; Hon Roll; Hugh O Brian Yth Found Ldrshp Smnr 84; Golden Bear Awd Bsktbll 85; Bus.

KENNEDY, DEBORAH; Fort Plain Central HS; Ft Plain, NY; (Y); Church Yth Grp; Chorus; Yrbk Ed-Chief; VP Frsh Cls; VP Soph Cls; VP Jr Cls; VP Sr Cls; Cit Awd; Hon Roll; NH Manchester; Adm Asst.

KENNEDY, DENNIS E; Tullyu Central Schl; Tully, NY; (Y); Am Leg Boys St; Varsity Clb; Band; Chorus; School Play; Stage Crew; Stu Cncl; Bsktbl; Crs Cntry; Lcrss.

KENNEDY, DOUGLAS B; Rome Free Acad; Rome, NY; (Y); 44/544; Am Leg Boys St; Boy Scts; VP Computer Clb; Drama Clb; German Clb; Letterman Clb; Model UN; Pep Clb; Ski Clb; Speech Tm; Regnets NY ST Schlrshp 85; ROTC Schlrshp 85; Colgate Smnr 84-85; Eagle Awd 84; US Air Force Acad; Aerosp Engr.

KENNEDY, FRANCES J; Mt Mercy Acad; West Seneca, NY; (Y); 9/198; French Clb; Sftbl; Hon Roll; NHS; Ntl Merit Ltr; Schlrshp To St Bonaventure 85; Schlrshps From Canisius College 85; St John Fischer And U Of Dayton 85; St Bonaventure U.

KENNEDY, JEFFREY S; John Marshall HS; Rochester, NY; (Y); 4/200; Pres French Clb; Math Tm; Pep Clb; Stu Cncl; Ftbl; Var L Tennis; Var L Vllybl; High Hon Roll; U Rochester Schlrshp 85; NYS Regnts Schlrshp; Rochester Inst Of Tech; Ele Eng.

KENNEDY, JOHN; Mt St Michael HS; Bronx, NY; (Y); 43/308; Boys Clb Am; VP Church Yth Grp; Stu Cncl; JV Var Bsktbl; Hon Roll; NHS; Spanish NHS; Comp.

KENNEDY, KAREN ANN; Bishop Kearney HS; Brooklyn, NY; (Y); Art Clb; Church Yth Grp; Girl Scts; Hosp Aide; Ski Clb; Teachers Aide; Rep Soph Cls; Trk; Hon Roll; Cooking Clb 83-84; Accntnt.

KENNEDY, MARGARET M; Cooperstown Central Schl; Mt Vision, NY; (Y); 5/100; Trs GAA; Chorus; School Play; Pres Soph Cls; Pres Jr Cls; Pres Stu Cncl; Var Capt Fld Hcky; Var Capt Vllybl; NHS; Ntl Merit Ltr; Cornell U.

KENNEDY, RUSELL L; North Salem HS; Purdys, NY; (Y); Am Leg Boys St; Boy Scts; Yrbk Bus Mgr; Yrbk Phtg; Yrbk Stf; Stu Cncl; Hon Roll; Nwsp Phtg; Nwsp Stf; God Cntry Awd; Lions Clb Scholar; Bus.

KENNEDY, THERESA; Horseheads HS; Horseheads, NY; (Y); JCL; Latin Clb; Band; Color Guard; Mrchg Band; Hon Roll; Bus Adm.

KENNEDY, THOMAS; Lansingburgh HS; Troy, NY; (Y); German Clb; JV Var Bsbl; JV Var Socr; High Hon Roll; Hon Roll; Jr NHS; Sr Athl Awd 85; Hudson Valley CC; Civil Tech.

KENNEDY, WILLIAM; Archbishop Stepinac HS; Yorktown Heights, NY; (Y); 72/220; JA; Key Clb; Nwsp Rptr; Yrbk Rptr; L Tennis; L Trk; Hon Roll; NHS; TOP Cnslr 83-85; Cathlc U Of Amer; Bio-Med.

KENNEDY, WILLIAM M; Fillmore Central Schl; Fillmore, NY; (Y); Spanish Clb; Chorus; Orch; Trk; Hon Roll; NHS; Prfct Atten Awd; Regnts Schlrshp 85; SUNY Geneseo; Aero Engr.

KENNELLY, PATRICK; Iona Prep; Larchmont, NY; (Y); 100/200; Dance Clb; Ski Clb; Rep Frsh Cls; Var Capt Crs Cntry; Var Tennis; Var Capt Trk; All Cnty Trck; All State Crs Cntry; Law.

KENNERSON, SHAWN; Honeoye Central HS; Honeoye, NY; (S); Boy Scts; French Clb; Var L Bsbl; Var L Bsktbl; Var Capt Socr; Prfct Atten Awd; Elec Engrng.

KENNEY, ANTHONY; Westhampton Beach HS; E Moriches, NY; (Y); 28/178; Church Yth Grp; Red Cross Aide; JV Bsktbl; Lcrss; Var Capt Socr; Var Tennis; Trk; Vllybl; Hon Roll; NHS; Empire ST Vllybl 85; Cert Ocean Lifeguard 83-85; Engrng.

KENNEY, CHRISTOPHER J; Lockport SR HS; Lockport, NY; (Y); 21/455; Pres Band; Concert Band; Mrchg Band; School Musical; Symp Band; JP Sousa Awd; Jr NHS; NHS; Pres Schlr; Knghts Of Clmbs Schlrshp 85; NY ST Rgnts Dplma 85; NY ST Rgnts Schlrshp 85; NY ST U Frdna; Comp Sci.

KENNEY, KATHLEEN; Hoosick Falls Central HS; Hoosick Falls, NY; (Y); Hosp Aide; Band; Yrbk Ed-Chief; Rep Stu Cncl; Var L Bsktbl; Var L Fld Hcky; Var L Sftbl; NHS; Empr ST Gms-Fld Hcky-Slvr Mdl 85-86; Outstndng Stu JR Cls-Schlr/Athl 85; Sprts Med.

KENNEY, REBEKAH A; Gowanda Central HS; Perrysburg, NY; (Y); Pres Church Yth Grp; Hosp Aide; Capt Aud/Vis; VICA; Church Choir; Yrbk Stf; St Josephs Schl Nrsng; Nrsg.

KENNEY, TAMMY; South Shore HS; Brooklyn, NY; (Y); School Play; Yrbk Stf; Pom Pon; JV Sftbl; Trk; Phy Fit Achvt Awd 82-84.

KENNISON, DIANA; Salamanca HS; Salamanca, NY; (Y); 34/120; Band; Chorus; Color Guard; High Hon Roll; Hon Roll; Prfct Atten Awd; Acctng.

KENNY, MARY; Brewster HS; Brewster, NY; (Y); Office Aide; Bus.

KENNY, STEPHEN; Grand Island HS; Grand Island, NY; (Y); JA; Variety Show; JV Swmmng; Im Wt Lftg; Hon Roll; Cert Awd Schlstc Achvt; Pre-Med.

KENNY, VIRGINIA A; Fontbonne Hall Acad; Brooklyn, NY; (Y); Church Yth Grp; School Play; Stage Crew; Chrmn Stu Cncl; Var Bsktbl; VP Sftbl; NYS Regents Schlrshp; Mr Jenson Awd; Cath Char Hnbl Mntn; Marist Coll; Psych.

KENT, LANITA; Jasper Central Schl; Jasper, NY; (Y); French Clb; FFA; Teachers Aide; Varsity Clb; Chorus; JV Var Bsktbl; JV Var Socr; Var Trk; Var Vllybl; Hon Roll; Pres Phy Fit Awd 82-85; Ag Tchr.

KENT, SEAN; Fairport HS; Fairport, NY; (Y); Chorus; Church Choir; Trs Jr Cls; Trs Sr Cls; Rep Stu Cncl; Var Capt Swmmng; High Hon Roll; Hon Roll; NHS; Dartmouth Bk Awd 85; Ldrshp Awd 85; All Co Swim 85.

KENTON, EDWARD; Sspringfield Gardens HS; Rosedale, NY; (Y); 8/508; Trs Church Choir; Bsktbl; Score Keeper; Tennis; Vllybl; Arista Awds 84-85; Queens Coll; Med.

KENTOR, DAVID S; Nanuet HS; Pearl River, NY; (Y); 10/160; Math Tm; Teachers Aide; Temple Yth Grp; Nwsp Rptr; Socr; Trk; Hon Roll; Mu Alp Tht; NHS; Ntl Merit Ltr.

KENVILLE, BRYAN; Caledonia-Mumford HS; Scottsville, NY; (Y); 2/85; Boy Scts; Church Yth Grp; Math Tm; Chorus; Church Choir; Concert Band; Jazz Band; Mrchg Band; Swing Chorus; NHS; JR Of Yr Awd 84-85; Career Mntrshp Prgm 84-85; Mansfld U Ready Wrtg Cont 84-85; Astrophyscst.

KENYON, JODY; Canaseraga Central Schl; Canaseraga, NY; (Y); 5/20; Am Leg Boys St; Varsity Clb; Band; Chorus; Concert Band; Jazz Band; Mrchg Band; Rep Frsh Cls; Rep Jr Cls; Rep Sr Cls.

KENYON, PAMELA; St Anthonys HS; Huntington, NY; (Y); 29/282; Drama Clb; Hosp Aide; Chorus; School Musical; School Play; Nwsp Stf; Yrbk Stf; Hon Roll; NHS; Cortland ST U; Elem Eductn.

KENYON, PATRICIA; Lockport SR HS; Lockport, NY; (Y); 117/411; French Clb; Intnl Clb; Var Socr; JV Var Sftbl; Hon Roll; Jr NHS; Intl Bus.

KEOLAMPHU, JOSEPH; Pelham Memorial HS; Pelham, NY; (Y); Boy Scts; Church Yth Grp; JV Var Bsktbl; Aud/Vis; Library Aide; Radio Clb; Chorus; Orch; Stage Crew; Rep Frsh Cls; Penn ST; Bio.

KEOUGH, TINA; Chenango Valley HS; Binghamton, NY; (Y); Church Yth Grp; Cmnty Wkr; French Clb; Hosp Aide; Nwsp Rptr; Yrbk Rptr; Var JV Cheerleading; Var Tennis; Jr NHS; Ntl Merit Ltr; Jrnlsm.

KERBS, KEVIN; Hicksville HS; Hicksville, NY; (Y); High Hon Roll; Comp.

KEREKES, ALLYSON T; Pine Plains HS; Clinton Corners, NY; (Y); AFS; Church Yth Grp; Math Clb; Pep Clb; Teachers Aide; Chorus; Nwsp Stf; Yrbk Stf; Score Keeper; Hon Roll; Tutrl Srvc Awd 85; TV Commnctns.

KERIN, JOHN P; Rome Free Acad; Rome, NY; (Y); 22/534; Boy Scts; Nwsp Ed-Chief; Var Trk; High Hon Roll; Trs NHS; Ntl Merit Ltr; Pres Schlr; NY ST Regents Scholar 85; U Rochester; Elec Engrng.

KERKAM, SCOTT; Smithtown H S West; Hauppauge, NY; (Y); Church Yth Grp; VP DECA; German Clb; Yrbk Stf; French Hon Soc.

KERKER, BONNIE; Clarkstown North HS; New City, NY; (Y); 28/425; Cmnty Wkr; Temple Yth Grp; Ed Yrbk Stf; Rep Jr Cls; High Hon Roll; Mu Alp Tht; NHS; Spanish Clb; Band; JV Tennis.

KERN, JOSEPH; Smithtown H S West; Smithtown, NY; (Y); Var Trk; Itln Hnr Soc 84-85; Metrlgy.

KERN, ROBERT G; East JR SR HS; Rochester, NY; (Y); 21/265; Library Aide; Rep Sr Cls; Rep Stu Cncl; Hon Roll; NHS; Prfct Atten Awd; A H Wilcox Memrl Schlrshp 85; Admsns Schlrshp St John Fisher Coll 85; Presdntl Acadmc Ftnss Awd 85; St John Fisher Coll; Cmnctns.

KERNAGHAN, DONNA; Deer Park HS; Deer Park, NY; (Y); Art Clb; Intnl Clb; Math Clb; Math Tm; Service Clb; Lit Mag; High Hon Roll; Jr NHS; NHS; Ntl Merit Schol; Home Ec Awd Child Care 82; Rep Deer Pk 85; Engnr.

KERNAGHAN, KELLY; Mont Pleasant HS; Schenectady, NY; (Y); 34/205; Boy Scts; German Clb; Yrbk Stf; JV Socr; Var Trk; High Hon Roll; Hon Roll; Drama Clb; Ski Clb; School Play; Grmn Achv Awd 82-83; Grmn Hnr Scty 84-85; Jr Upwrd Achvrs 84-85; Engrng.

KERNER, LAURAINNE; Sacred Heart Acad; Wantagh, NY; (S); Art Clb; French Clb; Science Clb; Band; Chorus; School Musical; Hon Roll; NHS; Co-Pres Fine Arts Culture Clb 84-85; Sacred Heart Acad Rprtry Co 83-85; Folk Grp 82-85; VA Poly Tech; Vetrnry Med.

KERR, CARLA; Springfield Gardens HS; Springfield Grdns, NY; (Y); English Clb; Chorus; Swing Chorus; Off Sr Cls; Vllybl; Hon Roll; Pres Schlr; Schlstc Awd 85; Englsh 85; Hnr Roll 82; La Urardia; Sec.

KERR, CAROL A; Clifton-Fine Central Schl; Fine, NY; (Y); French Clb; Band; Chorus; JV Bsktbl; Var Capt Socr; Var Capt Sftbl; High Hon Roll.

KERR, JAMES D; Sandy Creek Central HS; Lacona, NY; (Y); Trs Church Yth Grp; Computer Clb; Sec JCL; Ski Clb; Chorus; Concert Band; Mrchg Band; Nwsp Ed-Chief; Hon Roll; NHS; Magha Cum Laude Ntl Latin Exam 83; Regents Dplm Schlrshp ,5; Potsdam Coll; English.

KERR, JENNIFER M; Chittenango HS; Bridgeport, NY; (Y); 26/200; French Clb; Varsity Clb; Band; Var Cheerleading; Var Socr; Hon Roll; Jr NHS; NY ST Rgnts Schlrshp Awd 85; SUNY Geneseo; Elem Educ.

KERR, KEITH; Bishop Timon HS; Buffalo, NY; (Y); Am Leg Boys St; Aud/Vis; Boys Clb Am; Camera Clb; Computer Clb; Quiz Bowl; Science Clb; Rep Frsh Cls; Stat Bsktbl; High Hon Roll.

KERR, TAMMY; Frontier Central HS; Lake View, NY; (S); Pep Clb; Ski Clb; Cheerleading; High Hon Roll; Hon Roll; NHS; 1st Pl Advrtsg Art Layout Ad In Hamburg Sun 84; Sprtsmnshp Awds Lkvw Sccr & Sftbl 83-84; Fredonia; Art.

KERSCHBAUMER, LISA; H Frank Carey HS; Garden City S, NY; (Y); 38/222; German Clb; High Hon Roll; Frgn Lang Dept Outstndng Achv 85; Frgn Lang Hnr Soc 85; Hofstra; Accntnt.

KERSCHENBAUM, RISA P; Newfield HS; Coram, NY; (Y); 49/563; Art Clb; Cmnty Wkr; DECA; Library Aide; Office Aide; Service Clb; Lit Mag; High Hon Roll; Hon Roll; Jr NHS; NY ST Regnts Schlrshp 85; DECA Regnl Fnlst Apprl Accssrs 85; Ithaca Coll; Bus.

KERSHAW, JAMES; Maine-Endwell SR HS; Endwell, NY; (Y); 1/247; VP Mathletes; Mrchg Band; School Musical; Ed Yrbk Stf; Stu Cncl; Var L Trk; Pres NHS; Ntl Merit Ltr; Rotary Awd; Val; Jostens Fndtn Schlrshp 85; Watson Schlrshp 85; Dartmouth Coll; Math.

KERST, CHRISTINE; Wheatland Chili Central Schl; Scottsville, NY; (Y); Church Yth Grp; Library Aide; Model UN; Ski Clb; Nwsp Stf; Yrbk Stf; High Hon Roll; NHS; Prfct Atten Awd; Hon Roll; 1st Pl Rochester Bus Inst Basic Prgmng Cont 83; Highest Avrge 83; Sci.

KERSTMAN, HOPE M; Flushing HS; Flushing, NY; (Y); 4/364; Office Aide; School Musical; Nwsp Ed-Chief; Yrbk Rptr; Cheerleading; Tennis; Gov Hon Prg Awd; High Hon Roll; NHS; Exclnce Editorials 85; Tchrs Awd Outstndng Achvt Hist 85; Tchrs Cert Span 85; Cornell U; Jrnlsm.

KERVIN, SUSAN M; Scio Central Schl; Allentown, NY; (S); 2/44; Pres Spanish Clb; Yrbk Stf; VP Frsh Cls; Var Tennis; Var Trk; High Hon Roll; NHS; NEDT Awd; Natl Sci Olympiad 82; Pre Law.

KERWIN, MELISSA; Frankfort-Schuyler HS; Ilion, NY; (Y); 45/97; GAA; VP Spanish Clb; Yrbk Phtg; Yrbk Stf; Rep Frsh Cls; Rep Stu Cncl; Bsktbl; Fld Hcky; Socr; Vllybl; Stacey Weston Athl Awd; Nrsng Rgnts Schlrshp Altrnt; Niagara U; Nrsng.

KERWIN, WILLIAM S; Greece Athena HS; Rochester, NY; (Y); 1/283; Cmnty Wkr; Math Tm; Quiz Bowl; Ski Clb; JV Var Golf; JV Socr; Im Vllybl; Bausch & Lomb Sci Awd; High Hon Roll; JETS Awd; Pres & ROTC Schlrshps 85; Carnegie-Mellon U; Elec Engr.

KESEL, BRIAN; Cicero N Syracuse HS; Cicero, NY; (S); 18/650; Church Yth Grp; Math Tm; Model UN; Band; Chorus; School Musical; Pres Soph Cls; Pres Jr Cls; Pres Sr Cls; NHS; Math 10 Awd 83; Scout Of The Yr 83; SUNY; Sci.

KESINGER, AMY L; Skaneateles HS; Skaneateles, NY; (Y); Trs Church Yth Grp; Orch; Vllybl; High Hon Roll; NHS; Ntl Merit Ltr; Nrsg.

KESINGER, LISA; Skaneateles Central HS; Skaneateles, NY; (S); 2/165; VP Church Yth Grp; Acpl Chr; Chorus; Church Choir; High Hon Roll; Jr NHS; NHS; Math.

KESLER, CHERIE; Notre Dame HS; Corning, NY; (Y); Church Yth Grp; Library Aide; Mansfield; Mth Schl Tchr.

KESSENICH, QUINT; Lynbrook HS; Lynbrook, NY; (Y); 38/240; Var Capt Lcrss; JV Var Socr; Var Capt Wrstlng; Hon Roll; NHS; La Crosse All Amer All Conf 85; All Div Socr 84; Cnty Chmp & Div Chmp Wrstlg 85; Bst Goalie Awd 85.

KESSLER, MARK; Sanford H Calhoun HS; Merrick, NY; (S); DECA; Exploring; Key Clb; School Play; Nwsp Phtg; Var Golf; Im Wt Lftg; Hosp Aide; 4th Pl Intl Comp Cont UW 83; Hgh Achvt Amer Comp Sci Lg 83.

KESSLER, RENEE M; Camden Central HS; Camden, NY; (Y); AFS; Cmnty Wkr; Hosp Aide; Band; Concert Band; Orch; School Musical; Yrbk Phtg; Yrbk Stf; Hon Roll; Langs.

KESSLER, TODD; Port Richmond HS; Staten Isld, NY; (Y); 17/605; Library Aide; Bsbl; Ftbl; Trk; Wt Lftg; High Hon Roll; NHS; Acadmc All Amer 85; Med.

KESTER, KEVIN T; Pittsford Mendon HS; Pittsford, NY; (Y); 2/270; Chess Clb; Im Bsktbl; JV Golf; Var L Socr; Hon Roll; NY St Reg Schlrshp 85; NY St Sect V Soccr Champ 83-84; Hamilton Coll; Bus.

KESTLER, PAMELA; Rhinebeck Central HS; Rhinebeck, NY; (Y); 20/98; Pres AFS; Pres Church Yth Grp; Drama Clb; Chorus; School Musical; School Play; Yrbk Stf; Cheerleading; High Hon Roll; Hon Roll; PTSO Svc Awd 85; Suny Oneonta; Math.

KETCHAM, KINDRA; Pittsford Sutherland HS; Pittsford, NY; (Y); Church Yth Grp; English Clb; French Clb; Girl Scts; JA; Chorus; Church Choir; Socr; Swmmng; Cit Awd; Faclty Ldrshp Awd 83.

KETCHAM, LAURA L; William Nottingham HS; Syracuse, NY; (Y); 9/220; Chorus; School Musical; Swing Chorus; Nwsp Ed-Chief; Crs Cntry; Trk; High Hon Roll; Trs NHS; Sec Church Yth Grp; French Clb; Harvard Book Wad 84; Nwspr Awd 85; Sprtsmnshp Awd Crscntry 83; Brown U; Liberal Arts.

KETCHAM, YVONNE M; Canandaigua Acad; Canandaigua, NY; (Y); 37/270; Color Guard; High Hon Roll; Regents Schlrshp 85; Niagara U Pres Schlrshp 85; Niagara U; Nrs.

KETCHEN, MICHAEL; Schenectady Christian Schl; Duanesburg, NY; (S); Band; Church Choir; Mrchg Band; Socr; Hon Roll; RPI; Comp Sci.

KETCHMERE, MICHAEL E; Gates-Chili HS; Rochester, NY; (Y); 4/464; Chess Clb; Church Yth Grp; JA; Mathletes; Math Clb; Math Tm; Band; Rep Frsh Cls; Rep Soph Cls; Tennis; Resselaer Poly Inst; Chem Engrn.

KETCHNER, KAREN; Horseheads HS; Big Flats, NY; (Y); Art Clb; Spanish Clb; Color Guard; Hon Roll; USGF Cls Comptr Gym At St 85; Outstndng Spnsh,Art Stu 83-85; Coach.

KETCHNER, LAURIE; Olean HS; Olean, NY; (Y); Pres Church Yth Grp; FCA; Varsity Clb; Chorus; Church Choir; Trs Sr Cls; Stu Cncl; Var Cheerleading; Sftbl; Hon Roll; 1st Bptst Church Yth Pastor 85; JR Cls Hmcmng Attndnt 84; JR Cls Prom Commt 85; Psychlgy.

KEYES, LESLIE; Freeport HS; Freeport, NY; (Y); Cmnty Wkr; Mathletes; Teachers Aide; Band; Concert Band; Mrchg Band; School Musical; Rep Frsh Cls; Rep Soph Cls; Sec Jr Cls; Pre-Law.

KEYES, SHEILA; Seton Catholic Central HS; Binghamton, NY; (Y); Church Yth Grp; Cmnty Wkr; Drama Clb; German Clb; Key Clb; Service Clb; Ski Clb; Chorus; Church Choir; Drill Tm; Rotry Exch Schlrshp 85-86.

KEYS, DANIEL G; Bloomfield Central HS; Holcomb, NY; (Y); 3/92; Am Leg Boys St; Boy Scts; Drm Mjr(t); VP Soph Cls; Trs Stu Cncl; Var L Socr; Bausch & Lomb Sci Awd; High Hon Roll; NHS; Chess Clb; Rgnts Schlrshp 85; Eagle Awd 83; Yuth Cares Awd 84; Hamilton Coll; Physc.

KEYSER, MICHAEL; Franklin Acad; Constalbe, NY; (Y); French Clb; Model UN; Nwsp Stf; Yrbk Stf; Ntl Soc Stud Olympd 84; Law Enfrcmnt.

KHAGHAN, MOJDEH; The Wheatley Schl; East Hills, NY; (Y); 3/92; Sec Debate Tm; Model UN; Temple Yth Grp; Nwsp Rptr; AFS; Lit Mag; Socr; Sftbl; NHS; St Schlr; Berman Cup-Exclnce Latin 82; AATF Frnch Cntst 1st & 3rd 83-84; Natl Cncl Tchrs Engl Part 84; Columbia Coll; Intl Aff.

KHALAK, HANIF; Kenmore East SR HS; Kenmore, NY; (Y); Boy Scts; Computer Clb; Exploring; JA; Math Tm; Orch; JV Capt Crs Cntry; JV Trk; Rensselaer Polytech Inst Awd 85; Erly Admssn Natl Hnr Scty 85; Engr.

KHAMSI, BITA; Scarsdale HS; Scarsdale, NY; (Y); VP Church Yth Grp; School Musical; Rep Frsh Cls; Rep Soph Cls; Capt Jr Cls; Lib Sr Cls; Var Trk; Ntl Merit Ltr; Lcrss; NY St Regence Schlrshp 85; Rep At NY ST Secndry Schl Stu Orgnztn 84; Mem Of Wstchstr Cnty Brd Mdl L; Bio.

KHAN, ARIF; Jericho SR HS; Jericho, NY; (Y); 2/230; Spanish Clb; Var Capt Crs Cntry; Var Capt Trk; High Hon Roll; Hon Roll; NHS; Ntl Merit Ltr; Sal; Spanish NHS; Mst Vlubl Rnnr Crss Cntry 83-84; Mst Dedctd Indr Trck 82-83; All Cnty Crss Cntry 84-85; Yale U; Bio Sci.

KHAN, CHARLENE; Cathedral HS; Brooklyn, NY; (Y); 39/302; Art Clb; Nwsp Rptr; Future Nurses; Library Aid.

KHAN, GAUHER; Herbert H Lehman HS; Bronx, NY; (Y); 60/444; Math Tm; Socr; Trk; Vllybl; Wt Lftg; Hon Roll; Prfct Atten Awd; Attnmnt Awd; Polytechnic Inst; Aero Sp Engr.

KHAN, RUBAB A; Immaculate Heart Central HS; Carthage, NY; (Y); Intnl Clb; NFL; Band; Nwsp Stf; Yrbk Stf; Hon Roll; NHS; Pres Schlr; Regents Schlrshp Awd 84-85; Mt Holyoke Coll; Bio.

KHANNA, ARUNA; Dominican Acad; New York, NY; (Y); Hosp Aide; Latin Clb; Variety Show; Rep Frsh Cls; Rep Stu Cncl; Hon Roll; Prfct Atten Awd; Natl Poetry Press Natl Essay Mrt Awd 82; Natl Latin Exam Cert Of Hnrbl Mrt 84.

KHERA, SAMIRA; Corning-Painted Post West HS; Painted Post, NY; (Y); JA; Chorus; School Musical; Nwsp Phtg; Nwsp Rptr; Nwsp Stf; Dnfth Awd; NHS; Cmnty Wkr; Exploring; Intl Sci & Engrng Fair 85; Radcliffe Summr Pgm Sci 85; NY ST Summr Schl Arts Fil/Media 84; Med.

KHODADADIAN, DAVID K; John Fitzgerald Kennedy HS; Plainview, NY; (Y); Math Tm; Socr; High Hon Roll; Hon Roll; Jewish Stu 82-84; Chem Awds 85; Med.

KHUU, LE; Martin Luther King HS; Bklyn, NY; (Y); FBLA; FNA; Hosp Aide; Office Aide; OEA; Radio Clb; Red Cross Aide; Science Clb; Nwsp Bus Mgr; Yrbk Phtg.

KHUU, PHILIP; Martin Luther King HS; Bklyn, NY; (Y); Mathletes; Math Clb; Math Tm; Science Clb; Nwsp Sprt Ed; JETS Awd.

KIANG, DAVID; Hackley Schl; Peekskill, NY; (Y); 21/86; Church Yth Grp; Computer Clb; Drama Clb; Math Tm; Orch; Nwsp Rptr; Lit Mag; Var Lcrss; High Hon Roll; Ntl Merit Ltr; Cnty Piano Comp 83; Rice U; Mech Engrng.

KIBBY, JENNIFER; Williamsville South HS; Williamsville, NY; (Y); 24/245; Band; Nwsp Bus Mgr; AFS; Church Yth Grp; Chorus; Orch; Nwsp Rptr; High Hon Roll; NHS; Bryn Mawr; Psyco Bio.

KIBLER, KEITH; Attica Central HS; N Java, NY; (Y); 22/140; Am Leg Boys St; Church Yth Grp; Capt Ice Hcky; High Hon Roll; NHS; Prfct Atten Awd.

KIDD, CHRIS N; Brewster HS; Brewster, NY; (Y); Cmnty Wkr; Ski Clb; JV Lib Socr; JV Var Trk; Hon Roll; NHS; Mechncl Drwng Hnrs; MIP Sophm Track & MVP Track JR; Arch.

KIDDER, KEITH; St Marys Of Lancaster HS; Alden, NY; (Y); 15/199; VP Trs Chess Clb; Quiz Bowl; Science Clb; Badmtn; Bsktbl; Var L Golf; Stat Vllybl; NHS; Deans Grant Canisius Coll 85; Canisius Coll; Math.

KIDNEY, MICHAEL; Eldred HS; Eldred, NY; (Y); German Clb; Ski Clb; VICA; Wrstlng.

KIEDEL, JENNIFER; Villa Maria Acad; Cheektowaga, NY; (Y); Computer Clb; Variety Show; Hon Roll; Prfct Atten Awd; Acadmc All-Amer 85; Polish Clb Sec 85; Cathlc Yth Orgnztion 84-85; Bryant & Stratton Inst; Sec.

KIEDERER, GLENN M; Mahopac HS; Mahopac, NY; (Y); 83/378; Nwsp Rptr; Rep Sr Cls; JV Var Ftbl; JV Var Wrstlng; High Hon Roll; Hon Roll; NY ST Rgnts Schlrshp 85; SUNY Buffalo; Elec Engrng.

KIEGLE, CHRISTOPHER J; Kingston HS; Woodstock, NY; (Y); 2/510; Band; Chorus; Orch; School Musical; Nwsp Phtg; Nwsp Rptr; Nwsp Sprt Ed; Yrbk Phtg; Yrbk Stf; Sal; Area All St Bnd 84; Area All St Choir 83; Rensselaer Polytech; Elect Engr.

KIEN, THAI-BAO H; Southampton HS; Southampton, NY; (Y); Math Tm; High Hon Roll; NHS; Cornell U; Phys.

KIENER, KAREN; Sacred Heart Acad; Cheektowaga, NY; (Y); Church Yth Grp; Hosp Aide; Sftbl; Vllybl; Hon Roll; Pre-Vet.

KIENTZLER, MARK; Warwick Valley HS; Warwick, NY; (Y); Church Yth Grp; Drama Clb; French Clb; Band; Chorus; Church Choir; Jazz Band; Madrigals; School Musical; JV Socr; Culinary Inst Of Amer; Chef.

KIER, STEPHEN; E J Wilson HS; Rochester, NY; (Y); Model UN; Outstndng Achvt Amer Stds III 84-85; GMI; Elect Engr.

KIERAN, ELLEN; Mohonasen SR HS; Schenectady, NY; (Y); Sec Exploring; Band; Chorus; Pep Band; Rep Jr Cls; Var Crs Cntry; Mgr(s); Var Trk; High Hon Roll; NHS; Civil Engr.

KIERNAN, LISA; Beacon HS; Beacon, NY; (Y); 76/166; French Clb; VP German Clb; Var Office Aide; Teachers Aide; Var French Hon Soc; Ntl Merit Schol; Bus Admin.

KIERNAN, THERESA; Southampton HS; Southampton, NY; (Y); Church Yth Grp; GAA; Math Tm; Scholastic Bowl; Spanish Clb; Yrbk Stf; Sftbl; Tennis; High Hon Roll; NHS.

KIEY, SUZANNE; Scheiber HS; Port Washington, NY; (Y); 52/420; GAA; Nwsp Rptr; Rep Soph Cls; Rep Jr Cls; Var Socr; L Sftbl; Jr NHS.

KIFFER, STEVEN; Copliague HS; Copiague, NY; (Y); 8/300; Church Yth Grp; Cmnty Wkr; FBLA; School Play; High Hon Roll; Prfct Atten Awd; Rotary Awd; VFW Awd; Hghst Acadmc Achv Spnsh 85; Sailbt Racng Awds; SUNY; Navl Arch.

KILBOURN, ANDREA; James E Sperry HS; Henrietta, NY; (Y); Pres Church Yth Grp; Spanish Clb; Concert Band; Jazz Band; Hon Roll; Jr NHS; NHS; Spanish NHS; School Musical; Intern Carnegie Grant Smmr Prog Educ 84; Tchng.

KILBURN, MICHELLE; Scotia-Glenville HS; Schenectady, NY; (Y); Drama Clb; JA; Spanish Clb; Chorus; Variety Show; Rep Frsh Cls; Var JV Cheerleading; JV Gym; Amer Tlnt Of Yr Awds; Athlt Awd In Bsktbl Chrldng 85; 2nd Model Of Tomorrow Pgnt 84; ST U NY Albny; Spnsh.

KILBURN, SHERRIE; Kenmore West HS; Kenmore, NY; (Y); GAA; Political Wkr; JV Stat Bsktbl; Mgr(s); Score Keeper; Var Socr; High Hon Roll; Hon Roll.

KILBY, CHARLES W; Fox Lane HS; Pound Ridge, NY; (Y); 70/300; Hon Roll; Ntl Merit SF; NY ST Regents Schlrshp 85; Hobart; Histry.

KILCHER, STEPHEN; Guilderland HS; Guilderland, NY; (Y); Exploring; Ski Clb; Stage Crew; Rep Jr Cls; Im Bowling; Var Crs Cntry; Im Ftbl; JV Golf; JV Capt Lcrss; JV Wrstlng; Albany Bus Coll; Acctng.

KILCOMMONS, GERALDINE A; Wantagh HS; Wantagh, NY; (Y); 4-H; FBLA; Hosp Aide; Chorus; Rep Soph Cls; Rep Jr Cls; JV Cheerleading; Capt Var Socr; Capt Var Trk; Capt Vllybl; Vet Med.

KILCOYNE JR, JOHN; Lake Shore Central HS; Angola, NY; (Y); 21/259; Band; Concert Band; Jazz Band; Orch; Im JV Ftbl; Var Vllybl; Hon Roll; Jr NHS; NY ST Regents Schlrshp 8k; CornellAGRI.

KILE, LEONARD; Cathedral Prep Sem; Glendale, NY; (Y); NFL; JV Var Crs Cntry; Sftbl; JV Var Trk; Hon Roll; NHS; NEDT Awd; Cntntl Math Leag 82-83; Jrnlsm.

KILIAN, GINA; Bishop Scully HS; Scotia, NY; (S); 9/68; Cmnty Wkr; French Clb; GAA; Varsity Clb; Nwsp Ed-Chief; Yrbk Stf; Var Capt Bsktbl; High Hon Roll; NHS; Brown U; Eng.

KILIAN, JAMES R; Ichabod Crane HS; Stuyvesant, NY; (Y); 8/170; Church Yth Grp; Trs Computer Clb; Hon Roll; NHS; Regents Schlrshp 85; Clarkson U; Comp Sci.

KILIAN, RICHARD J; Ichabod Crane HS; Stuyvesant, NY; (Y); 41/170; Sec Computer Clb; Drama Clb; School Musical; School Play; Nwsp Rptr; Lit Mag; Stu Cncl; Regents Schlrshp 85; Plattsburgh ST U; Comp Sci.

KILKENNY, TOM; Smithtown High Schl East; Saint James, NY; (Y); Key Clb; Ski Clb; Mrchg Band; Symp Band; Stu Cncl; Swmmng; Im Vllybl; Var Wrstlng; High Hon Roll; Jr NHS; Pres Challenge 83; Bus.

KILKER, BOB M; Churchville-Chili HS; Rochester, NY; (Y); 9/313; Im Bsbl; Im Bsktbl; Im Bowling; Var L Socr; Var Trk; Im Vllybl; Im Wt Lftg; Im Wrstlng; High Hon Roll; Hon Roll; Schlr Ath Army Rsrv Awd, All Cnty Sccr Awd 85; GMI; Elec Engrng.

KILLEEN, KATHLEEN; Linton HS; Schenectady, NY; (Y); 22/312; VP Exploring; Hon Roll; Chem.

KILLEEN, KELLY; Ichabod Crane HS; Nassau, NY; (Y); Drama Clb; Pres Girl Scts; Library Aide; Office Aide; Ski Clb; Flag Corp; School Play; Nwsp Rptr; Trs Lit Mag; High Hon Roll.

KILLEEN, PATRICIA; Our Lady Of Mercy HS; Pittsford, NY; (Y); 56/197; JA; Service Clb; Varsity Clb; Chorus; Var Swmmng; JV Trk; Hon Roll; St Lawrence U; Econ.

KILLIAN, CHRISTINE; Albertus Magnus HS; Blauvelt, NY; (Y); 12/190; Church Yth Grp; Math Clb; French Hon Soc; NHS; Math & Sci Hon Sco 85-86.

KILLIAN, LORI; Saranac Central HS; Cadyville, NY; (S); Office Aide; L Cheerleading; Hon Roll.

KILLOCK, TABATHA; Kenmore West HS; Buffalo, NY; (Y); Girl Scts; Sec Math Tm; Hon Roll; Comp Sci.

KILMER, BRENDA; Walton Central HS; Walton, NY; (Y); Sec 4-H; Sec FFA; Hon Roll; Prfct Atten Awd; Hrtcltr.

KILROY, LISA; Haverling Central HS; Bath, NY; (S); 17/147; Church Yth Grp; French Clb; GAA; JCL; Latin Clb; Math Clb; Math Tm; Ski Clb; Band; Concert Band; Carrier Of Month 82; College Academic Schlrshp 85; 1S Coast Guard Acad; Marine Bi.

KIM, CHARLES C; Professional Childrens Schl; Bronxville, NY; (Y); PAVAS; Orch; Ntl Merit SF; Stone Fndtn Schlrshp.

KIM, CHONG; Bronx H S Of Science; Bronx, NY; (Y); Church Yth Grp; Computer Clb; Key Clb; Math Clb; Math Tm; Teachers Aide; Church Choir; Pep Band; Capt Bsktbl; Swmmng; Cornell; Pre-Med.

KIM, CHONG; Churchville-Chili SR HS; Rochester, NY; (Y); Math Clb; Model UN; Chorus; Nwsp Stf; Ed Lit Mag; Trs Frsh Cls; Trs Stu Cncl; Tennis; NHS; Psych.

KIM, ENOCH; Salmon River Central HS; Constable, NY; (S); Church Yth Grp; Var Socr; Var Swmmng; Var Trk; NHS.

KIM, JANE C; Bronx High School Of Science; Elmhurst, NY; (Y); French Clb; Key Clb; Math Tm; Teachers Aide; Church Choir; Yrbk Stf; Prfct Atten Awd; VP Chrh Yth Grp 84-85; Ntl Frnch Cont 83-85; Merit Serv Cert 84; Cornell U; Optomtry.

KIM, JEAN; St Hildos & St Hughs HS; New York, NY; (Y); Cmnty Wkr; Pres Dance Clb; Chorus; Rptr Nwsp Rptr; Yrbk Stf; Rep Jr Cls; Rep Stu Cncl; Var Vllybl; NHS; Schlrshp 82-84; Spanish Awrd 84; Bio.

KIM, JULIA; Stuyvesant HS; Briarwood, NY; (Y); Capt Debate Tm; Model UN; Chorus; NHS; Ntl Merit Ltr; Cert Excllnc Engl, Hstry & Spnsh 83-84; Schlrshp Awd-Gld & Slvr 82-85; Hcktt Awd 85; Cornell U; Art.

KIM, JUNG-A; Bronx H S Of Science; Arlington, VA; (Y); Cmnty Wkr; JA; Library Aide; Teachers Aide; Varsity Clb; Band; Concert Band; Yrbk Stf; Var L Trk; NHS; Outstndng Acadmc Achvt Pres Fit Awd 85; Outstndng Achvt 2 Forgn Lang 85; SUNY Binghamton; Biochem.

KIM, KELLY; Fayetteville-Manlius HS; Manlius, NY; (Y); Pres Chess Clb; Cmnty Wkr; JCL; Math Tm; Model UN; Political Wkr; Var L Tennis; High Hon Roll; NHS; Computer Clb; Lat I Natl Lat Exam Gold Medl 83; Lat II Natl Lat Exam Gold Medl 84; Lat Schl Awd 83-85; Med.

KIM, LISA; Franklin D Roosevelt HS; Brooklyn, NY; (Y); Intnl Clb; Model UN; Science Clb; Yrbk Stf; Hon Roll; Prfct Atten Awd; Cert Of Distnctn-Excllnc In Schlrshp 84; Cert Of Distnctn-Excllnc In Sci, Chem & Physics 83-84; Pharmcy.

KIM, MARGARET M; Dansvile SR HS; Dansville, NY; (Y); 3/145; Chorus; Concert Band; Jazz Band; Mrchg Band; School Musical; Yrbk Ed-Chief; JV Var Socr; JV Var Tennis; Trs NHS; NY St Reg Schlrshp 85; Albany Coll; Pharmcy.

KIM, MYONG; F D Roosevelt HS; Hyde Park, NY; (Y); Church Yth Grp; Church Choir; Golf; Socr; Hon Roll; NHS; D F P Awd For Fine Acad Perfmnce & Attndnce 84-85; May Wk Clbrtn Excllnce 84-85; Comp & Elec Engnrng.

KIM, NANCY E; Maria Regina HS; Hartsdale, NY; (Y); 30/127; Church Yth Grp; Library Aide; Chorus; Church Choir; Hon Roll; NHS; Bus Mgmt.

KIM, RAYMOND J; Onteora Central JR SR HS; Woodstock, NY; (Y); 41/245; Boy Scts; Math Tm; Concert Band; Jazz Band; Mrchg Band; High Hon Roll; JP Sousa Awd; Hosp Aide; Mathletes; Band; All Cty Concrt Band 82-85; Mus Awds 82-85; NYS Regnts Schlrshp 85; Syracuse U; Comp Sci.

KIM, ROBERT; Irvington HS; Irvington, NY; (Y); 22/120; Church Yth Grp; Key Clb; Band; Chorus; School Musical; Yrbk Stf; Sec Sr Cls; Var L Ftbl; Var L Trk; Hon Roll; NY ST Rgnts Schlrshp 85; SOG Schlrshp 85; Tufts Librl Arts Schlrshp 85; Tufts U; Economics.

KIM, TAE Y; Benjamin Cardozo HS; Bayside, NY; (Y); Math Clb; Math Tm; Service Clb; Var Tennis; Var Vllybl; Hon Roll; NHS; Brstl Meyer Pol Athl Lge Stry Tllng Cntst 1st Pl 84; Time Ed Prog Wrtng Cnsts Fnlst 85; NY U.

KIMBALL, ANGELA; Sandy Creek Central HS; Sandy Creek, NY; (Y); 6/98; Computer Clb; Drama Clb; French Clb; Trs JCL; Trs Latin Clb; Ski Clb; Teachers Aide; Band; Chorus; Church Choir; All ST, Conf Vcl 84-86; Phy Ftnss 83-84; Lang Fair 1st 84; Eastman Schl Music; Perf Arts.

KIMBALL, CHRISTINE E; Hilton Central HS; Hilton, NY; (Y); 35/297; Sec Trs Exploring; JA; Office Aide; Nwsp Rptr; Yrbk Ed-Chief; Trs Sr Cls; Stu Cncl; Stat Mgr Sftbl; Var L Tennis; NHS; Bernard Whelehan Schlrshp 85; Cazenovia; Fshn Merch.

KIMBALL, DONNA-ANN; Solvay HS; Liverpool, NY; (Y); Exploring; Chorus; Concert Band; Yrbk Stf; Sec Stu Cncl; Capt Bowling; High Hon Roll; NHS; Church Yth Grp; Onadoga CC Cmnty Schlr Prog 85; Balfour Awd Human Eclgy 85; Med Tech.

KIMBALL, LAURA; Jamestown HS; Jamestown, NY; (Y); 1/405; Pres French Clb; Trs Concert Band; Trs Mrchg Band; School Musical; Rep Frsh Cls; Rep Soph Cls; Rep Jr Cls; VP Sr Cls; NHS; Val; 1st Pl Lakewood Area JR Miss Schlrshp Pgnt 84; NY ST JR Miss Fnlst 85; Colgate U; Appld Math.

KIMBER, THOMAS W; Geneseo Central Schl; Geneseo, NY; (Y); 10/65; Boy Scts; Math Tm; VP Jr Cls; VP Sr Cls; Rep Stu Cncl; Socr; High Hon Roll; NHS; Ntl Merit Ltr; Ski Clb; Clarkson U; Comp Sci.

KIMBLE JR, EDWARD LEE; Odessa-Montour Central HS; Millport, NY; (Y); Computer Clb; High Hon Roll; Hon Roll; NHS; Olympcs Of The Minds 82-85; Engrng.

KIMBROUGH, CELESTINE; Newfield HS; Selden, NY; (Y); 109/576; High Hon Roll; Hon Roll; NHS; Textile Engrng.

KIMMEL, JOHN D; Newfane SR HS; Lockport, NY; (Y); Drama Clb; Exploring; School Play; Hon Roll; Ntl Merit Ltr; St Schlr.

KIMMEL, MICHAEL; Baldwin SR HS; Baldwin, NY; (Y); Boy Scts; Mathletes; Band; Concert Band; Jazz Band; Mrchg Band; Orch; School Musical; Im Bsbl; NHS; Math.

KIMMEL, MICHAEL; Wayland Central HS; Wayland, NY; (Y); Art Clb; Church Yth Grp; Red Cross Aide; Varsity Clb; Swmmng; Tennis; 1st Pl Tnns Cnty Div 85; 1st Pl Relay Sectnls 85; Gd Kid Awd 85.

KIMMEL, NOEL J; The Nichols Schl; Buffalo, NY; (Y); Pep Clb; Political Wkr; Ski Clb; School Musical; School Play; Nwsp Bus Mgr; Nwsp Rptr; Yrbk Stf; JV Ftbl; Mgr(s); NYS Regnts Schlrshp; Colgate U; Ecnmcs.

KIMMERLY, DONNA LYNN; Northstar Christian Acad; Hilton, NY; (S); 9/30; Church Yth Grp; JA; Chorus; Church Choir; Yrbk Bus Mgr; Yrbk Stf; Sec Frsh Cls; Sec Soph Cls; Sec Jr Cls; JV Cheerleading; Recptnst.

KIMPTON, TODD; Canastota HS; Canastota, NY; (Y); Aud/Vis; Pres Church Yth Grp; Var JV Bsktbl; Im Coach Actv; Var JV Golf; High Hon Roll; Hon Roll; Prfct Atten Awd; Bus.

KIMURA, SHIN; Bronx H S Of Science; Elmhurst, NY; (Y); Computer Clb; Office Aide; Teachers Aide; Lit Mag; Off Sr Cls; Bsktbl; Coach Actv; Hon Roll; Prfct Atten Awd; 2nd Pl Se Kendo Fed Tourn Jap Fncg 83; 1st Pl Ken-Zen Dojo Tourn 84.

KINAHAN, KATRINA; West Genesee SR HS; Camillus, NY; (Y); Church Yth Grp; Exploring; Yrbk Stf; Im Bsktbl; Var Cheerleading; Im Vllybl; High Hon Roll; Ntl Sci Olympiad Chmstry 85; Nice Kid Awd 83; Phrmcy.

KINCH, RUSSELL; Gates-Chili SR HS; Rochester, NY; (Y); 48/463; Boy Scts; Church Yth Grp; Band; Orch; High Hon Roll; Hon Roll; NHS; NYS Regnts Schlrshp 85; Hofstra U; Bus Adm.

KINCH, STACY; Walton Central HS; Walton, NY; (Y); 3/99; Library Aide; Chorus; Orch; Yrbk Stf; High Hon Roll; Jr NHS; Regnts Schlrshp 85; Music Ltr & Orch, Chrs, Instrmnt Pins & Awd Outstndng Wrk Cello; ST U Coll NY Oneonta; Psych.

KINDBERG, MARK; Jamestown HS; Jamestown, NY; (Y); Am Leg Boys St; Church Yth Grp; Spanish Clb; Var L Bsktbl; High Hon Roll; Jr NHS; NHS; Stckbrkr.

KING, AMY; Pulaski JR & SR HS; Pulaski, NY; (S); 12/91; Office Aide; Band; Chorus; Mrchg Band; Hon Roll; NHS; Jefferson CC; Sec Sci.

KING, ANDREA L; Owen D Young Central HS; Jordanville, NY; (S); 1/14; Q&S; Pres Varsity Clb; Capt Var Socr; Capt Var Vllybl; Cit Awd; DAR Awd; Pres NHS; Val; 4-H; Frm Bur Ctznshp Awd 84; Herkimer Cnty Dairy Prncss 84; All-Str Sftbl Tm Awd 83; Cornell U; Vet Coll.

KING, BETSY M; Hoosick Falls Central Schl; Hoosick Fls, NY; (Y); 14/102; French Clb; Trs FBLA; VP Pep Clb; Yrbk Stf; Stu Cncl; Cit Awd; High Hon Roll; NHS; Amer Lgn Awd; PTA Schlrshp Awd; Samaritan Schl Nrsng; RN.

KING, BILL; Bishop Ludden HS; Syracuse, NY; (Y); Pres Aud/Vis; Church Yth Grp; School Play; Stage Crew; Msgr Martin J Watley Awd Svc 85; Rgnts Schlrshp 85; Le Moyne Coll; Comp Sci.

KING, CARRIE; Franklin Acad; Burke, NY; (Y); French Clb; Hon Roll; Schl Scholar 83-85; Natl Merit Mth Awd 83-84; Natl Sci Tst Awd 82-83; Comp.

KING, CATHERINE; Saint Francis Prep; Bayside, NY; (S); 78/690; Dance Clb; Variety Show; Hon Roll; Opt Clb Awd; Acad All Amer 85.

KING, DANIEL; O Lean HS; Olean, NY; (Y); 2/200; Math Tm; JV Var Bsktbl; High Hon Roll; NHS; Clsscl Assn Wstrn NY, Latn Awd 83.

KING, DAVID; Hartford HS; Granville, NY; (S); Church Yth Grp; FFA; Pep Clb; Socr; Hon Roll.

KING, DIANNE C; West Hempstead HS; W Hempstead, NY; (Y); 47/310; Church Yth Grp; Hon Roll; NHS; Bus Educ Excllncy LIBEC Awd 85; Pres Acad Ftnss Awd 85; Bus Mchns Awd 84; C W Post; Bus Mgmt.

KING, DIEDRE; Herbert H Lehman HS; New York, NY; (Y); Teachers Aide; Hon Roll; Bus Admin.

KING, ELIZABETH; Colg Spring Harbor HS; Huntington, NY; (Y); 38/140; Drama Clb; Hosp Aide; Intnl Clb; Chorus; School Musical; Nwsp Stf; Off Soph Cls; Off Jr Cls; Var Sftbl; Hon Roll; Outstndg Achvmt French Awd 85; French.

KING, JACKIE; Susquehanna Valley HS; Conklin, NY; (Y); Church Yth Grp; Pres 4-H; Library Aide; Ski Clb; Sec Spanish Clb; Sec Frsh Cls; VP Soph Cls; Rep Jr Cls; Trs Stu Cncl; Socr; 1st Pl Blue Rbbn Awds 4-H 82-84; NYSMA Soloist Awds 82-83; Canton Tech; Vet Sci.

KING, JACQUELINE M; Glens Falls HS; Glens Falls, NY; (Y); 5/250; Sftbl; Vllybl; High Hon Roll; Jr NHS; NHS; Prfct Atten Awd; St Schlr; SUNY Potsdam; Comp Sci.

KING, JAN; Schuylerville HS; Schuylerville, NY; (Y); Church Yth Grp; Computer Clb; Debate Tm; 4-H; Trs Rep FFA; Math Clb; Trs Stu Cncl; Ftbl; Cit Awd; Hon Roll; 4-H Awd-Went Natls Chgo 84; Ctznshp Awd 85; Semi-St Fnlst Extemporaneous Spkng 85; Cornell; Ag.

KING, JOSEPH P; St Anthonys HS; Kings Pk, NY; (Y); 50/350; Spanish Clb; Nwsp Stf; Rep Frsh Cls; Im Bsktbl; Var Golf; Im Ice Hcky; Var Trk; NHS; Spanish NHS; Prncpls List; Boston Coll; Law.

KING, KATHY; Fashion Industries HS; Brooklyn, NY; (Y); 25/365; Yrbk Stf; Hon Roll; Fash Desgnr.

KING, KELLY; Niagara Wheatfield SR HS; Niagara Falls, NY; (Y); 40/327; German Clb; Pep Clb; Chorus; Yrbk Stf; Var L Bowling; High Hon Roll; Hon Roll; NHS; Bryant; Accntng.

KING, KEVIN M; Wilson Central HS; Newfane, NY; (Y); 33/134; Church Yth Grp; JV Var Crs Cntry; JV Var Ftbl; Var L Trk; High Hon Roll; Hon Roll; Var Masonic Awd; Olympics Of Mind Omonautst 82; Odyssey Of Mind Ecology Dozer 85; Tri ST; Mechanical Engrng.

KING, KIMBERLY; New Berlin Central HS; New Berlin, NY; (Y); Sec Church Yth Grp; French Clb; GAA; Trs Band; Concert Band; Mrchg Band; Pep Band; Var Sftbl; JV Vllybl; Hon Roll; All Cnty Choir 85; Nrsng.

KING, LINDA; Berlin Central HS; Cropseyville, NY; (Y); Church Yth Grp; 4-H; GAA; Band; Chorus; Church Choir; School Musical; Nwsp Rptr; Bsktbl; Socr; Pre-Law.

KING, MARIE; Newfield HS; Selden, NY; (Y); Church Yth Grp; Library Aide; Pep Clb; Spanish Clb; Cheerleading; Mgr(s); Trk; NHS; Lwyr.

KING, PETER; William Nottingham HS; Syracuse, NY; (Y); Cmnty Wkr; Exploring; Red Cross Aide; Ski Clb; Pres Spanish Clb; Band; Chorus; Stage Crew; Yrbk Phtg; Yrbk Sprt Ed; Sprtsmnshp Scholar Marhus Pebble Hill 83; Colgate; Invstmnt Bnkr.

KING, RICHARD; Copiague SR HS; Amityville, NY; (Y); FBLA; VP Spanish Clb; Ed Nwsp Ed-Chief; VP Frsh Cls; Var Crs Cntry; Var L Trk; Var Wrstlng; Computer Clb; Yrbk Rptr; Yrbk Stf; Natl Confrnce Of Chrstns & Jews 83-84; Humanitarian Awd 83-84; Schlrshp-Boces III 82-85; Bus Adm.

KING, ROBERT J; Churchville Chili HS; Rochester, NY; (Y); 24/324; Math Tm; JV Var Crs Cntry; Var Capt Trk; Im Vllybl; Im Wt Lftg; Im Wrstlng; Hon Roll; NHS; St Schlr; Rgnts Schlrshp 85; Cornell U; Pre-Med.

KING, SARAH; Auburn HS; Auburn, NY; (Y); Varsity Clb; Coach Actv; Socr; Sftbl; Vllybl; High Hon Roll; NHS; U Of Rochester.

KING, SHELLEY; Bishop Kearney HS; Brooklyn, NY; (S); Hosp Aide; Math Tm; Science Clb; Ski Clb; Rep Frsh Cls; Trk; Hon Roll; NHS; Ntl Merit Awd Wnnr Bio 83; City Coll Of NY; Med.

KING, STACEY E; John Jay HS; Katonah, NY; (Y); 6/290; French Clb; Sec German Clb; Intnl Clb; Ed Lit Mag; Cit Awd; High Hon Roll; Jr NHS; NHS; Frnch III, Grmn II, Bio, Drwng, Painting Awd 83; Grmn III Engl Oil Pntng 84; Brown U; Bio.

KING, STEPHEN; Camden Central Schl; Camden, NY; (Y); 1/220; AFS; Mathletes; Varsity Clb; Yrbk Stf; Var Bsktbl; Var Ftbl; Var Trk; High Hon Roll; NHS; Ntl Merit SF; Navl Acad Smmr Smnr 85; Biochem Rsrch.

KING, STEVEN; Mynderse Acad; Seneca Falls, NY; (S); 12/141; Aud/Vis; Boy Scts; Science Clb; Yrbk Ed-Chief; Yrbk Phtg; Yrbk Stf; High Hon Roll; Hon Roll; Clarkson; Engnrng Field.

KING, SUSAN; Cicero-North Syracuse HS; North Syracuse, NY; (S); 38/711; Color Guard; Mrchg Band; Rep Frsh Cls; Rep Soph Cls; Rep Stu Cncl; Hon Roll; NHS; 4th Runner Up Miss N Syracuse Cont 84; Instrctr For 2 Color Guards 85; Model In Guild Fashionata 84-85; Onondage CC; Guidance Cnslng.

KING, SUZANNE; Lake George HS; Lake George, NY; (Y); Chorus; School Play; Trs Soph Cls; Trs Jr Cls; Hon Roll; Jr NHS; Prom Ct 85; Psych.

KING, VONDA; Altmar Parish Williamstown HS; Williamstown, NY; (Y); Church Yth Grp; Girl Scts; Library Aide; Bryant Strtn Bus Schl; Scrtrl.

KING, YVETTE; The Mary Louis Acad; Jamaica, NY; (Y); Hosp Aide; Office Aide; Pres VP Spanish Clb; Teachers Aide; Yrbk Stf; Sec Jr Cls; Nrsng.

KINGMA, ALFRED; St Agnes HS; Ny, NY; (Y); 12/100; Model UN; Hon Roll; NHS; U Scranton.

KINGSLEY, KELLI C; Greene Arcadia HS; Rochester, NY; (Y); 10/292; Exploring; Math Tm; Nwsp Stf; Lit Mag; Var Trk; High Hon Roll; Hon Roll; NHS; NY St Regents Schlrshp 85-86; Pres Acad Awd 85; Rochester Inst Technology; Comp.

KINGSLEY, SUE; Thomas A Edison JR SR HS; Horseheads, NY; (Y); Church Yth Grp; VICA; Church Choir; Hon Roll; Chldhd Educ.

KINGSTON, SHARON; St Francis Prep; Woodside, NY; (S); 94/690; Drama Clb; Yrbk Stf; High Hon Roll; Ntl Merit Ltr; Schlrshp To Hunter Coll 85; Prtl Schlrshp NY U 85; Psychology.

KINGSTON, TINA; Massena Central HS; Massena, NY; (Y); French Clb; Chorus; Gym; Sftbl; Hon Roll; Plattsburg ST; Lab Techncn.

KINLEN, WILLIAM G; Lehman HS; Bronx, NY; (Y); Am Leg Boys St; Boys Clb Am; Church Yth Grp; Y-Teens; Stage Crew; Prfct Atten Awd; Ten Trophy, Ltr, Gold Medal 83-85; Farmingdale CC; Air Con/Refrig.

KINMARTIN JR, PAUL; Bishop Timon HS; West Seneca, NY; (S); 20/132; Pep Clb; Quiz Bowl; Red Cross Aide; Chorus; Pres Jr Cls; Stu Cncl; Var JV Ftbl; Hon Roll; NHS; Most Outstndng Stu; Serv Awd; Syracuse U; Bus.

KINNE, LAURA; Vernon-Verona-Sherrill HS; Blossvale, NY; (Y); Church Yth Grp; Sec Computer Clb; Exploring; Girl Scts; Teachers Aide; Concert Band; Mrchg Band; Yrbk Stf; High Hon Roll; Hon Roll; Arch.

KINNEY, CHRISTINE; Cicero N Syracuse HS; N Syracuse, NY; (S); 43/622; Ed Lit Mag; 1st Pl US Army Rsrv Ntl Essay Cntst 84; 1st Pl Bst Feature Stry HS Pressday 84; Hmrm Rep 84; St John Fisher Coll; Clncl Soc.

KINNEY, DARLENE; Midlakes HS; Clifton Springs, NY; (Y); Chess Clb; Computer Clb; Dance Clb; Drama Clb; Chorus; Church Choir; Variety Show; Hon Roll; FHA; Girl Scts; Mst Imprvd Stu BOCES D P 84-85; Mus Ltr 84-85; CCFL; Comp Oper.

KINNEY, JEANNE M; Pittsford Mendor HS; Pittsford, NY; (Y); Debate Tm; Nwsp Rptr; Yrbk Stf; Stu Cncl; Var Capt Socr; Var Sftbl; NHS; Ntl Merit SF; Latin Clb; High Hon Roll; All-Cnty Sccr 84; 2nd Tm All-Grtr Rchstr Sccr Tm 84; Liberal Arts.

KINNEY, REGINA; St Francis Prep; Bayside, NY; (S); 57/395; Math Clb; Chorus; Lit Mag; Hon Roll; NHS; Bus.

KINNEY, ROBERT B; Pittsford Mendon HS; Pittsford, NY; (Y); Aud/Vis; Varsity Clb; Acpl Chr; Chorus; Swing Chorus; Trk; Wt Lftg; Wrstlng; Hon Roll; Penn ST; Aernonaut Engrng.

KINNEY, ZOE B; William Nottingham HS; Syracuse, NY; (Y); 22/250; Drama Clb; French Clb; Sec Latin Clb; Ski Clb; Acpl Chr; Chorus; Madrigals; Orch; School Musical; Nwsp Rptr; Slvr Mdl Natl Latin Exam 84; 4th St Concours Natl De Francais 83; 3rd St Concours Natl De Francais 82; Skidmore Coll.

KINOSHITA, ALTHEA; Somes HS; Katohah, NY; (Y); 7/220; Am Leg Aux Girls St; Drama Clb; Chorus; Nwsp Rptr; French Hon Soc; High Hon Roll; NHS; Ntl Merit Ltr; Boy Scts; Madrigals; Amer Legn Oratorical Cont Dept Fnlst 84; Scl Stds Stu Mnth 81; Frnch Stu Yr 84; Vassar Coll; Anthrplgy.

KINSELLA, JEANNE; Sacred Heart Acad; New Hyde Park, NY; (S); Church Yth Grp; Library Aide; Chorus; Church Choir; Madrigals; School Musical; School Play; Music Hnr Soc 82-85; Music Ther.

KINTNER, LAURA; Scio Central Schl; Scio, NY; (S); 5/44; FBLA; Color Guard; Var Tennis; Var Trk; High Hon Roll; Jr NHS; NHS; U S Bus Ed Awd 83; Natl Ldrshp & Svc Awd 84; Alfred Ag & Tech.

KIPP, KELLY; Saranac Central HS; Cadyville, NY; (S); 3/106; Trs Drama Clb; French Clb; Band; Concert Band; Jazz Band; Mrchg Band; Pep Band; School Musical; High Hon Roll; NHS.

KIPP, WILLIAM; Immaculata HS; New York, NY; (Y); Sec Soph Cls; Sec Jr Cls; Im Sftbl; Hon Roll; Regnts Mth 85; Regns Frgn Lang 85; Fordham U; Bnkg.

KIRBY, BRIAN; Kenmore West SR HS; Kenmore, NY; (Y); 15/489; Boy Scts; Math Clb; Math Tm; Var L Bowling; High Hon Roll; Ntl Merit Ltr; ST U Of NY Buffalo; Arch.

KIRBY, BYRON; Holy Cross HS; Jamaica, NY; (Y); Hosp Aide; JV Crs Cntry; Var JV Trk; Hon Roll; NHS; U Of SC; CPA.

KIRBY, JOSEPH; Cardinal Spellman HS; Bronx, NY; (Y); German Clb; Hon Roll; Columbia; Jrnlsm.

KIRBY, PHILLIP; Mount Vernon HS; Mt Vernon, NY; (Y); Aud/Vis; Church Yth Grp; Office Aide; Rep Soph Cls; Rep Jr Cls; Rep Sr Cls; Rep Stu Cncl; JV Var Bsktbl; JV Ftbl; Hon Roll; Accntng.

KIRBY, TINA; Edison Tech HS; Rochester, NY; (Y); Church Yth Grp; Varsity Clb; Yrbk Stf; Rep Stu Cncl; Sftbl; Swmmng; Hon Roll; Hair Stylst.

KIRCHBERGER, DAVID R; West Seneca East SR HS; W Seneca, NY; (Y); Computer Clb; French Clb; Im Bsktbl; JV Var Ftbl; Im Wt Lftg; Marine Bio.

KIRCHDORFER, DEBORAH; Connetquot HS; Oakdale, NY; (S); 14/671; Stat Lcrss; Var JV Trk; High Hon Roll; Jr NHS; NHS; Ntl Merit Ltr; Church Yth Grp; French Clb; Library Aide; Math Clb; Leaders Club; Student Exchange; Bus.

KIRCHNER, ANN MARIE; New Hyde Park Memorial HS; New Hyde Park, NY; (Y); Church Yth Grp; Girl Scts; Varsity Clb; Yrbk Sprt Ed; JV Fld Hcky; JV Lcrss; Trs Capt Twrlr; High Hon Roll; Hon Roll; Jr NHS; Acad Achvt Brz Mdl 84, Slvr Mdl 85.

KIRIMCA, IRFAN; Lafayette HS; Brooklyn, NY; (Y); VP JA; Var JV Ftbl; VP NHS; Super Yth Awd 84 & 85; Bus Mngmnt.

KIRINCICH, JOSEPH C; St Francis Prep; Whitestone, NY; (Y); 100/690; JA; Math Clb; Ski Clb; Bsbl; Bowling; Charles Johnson JR Mem Schlrhsp 85; Manhattan Coll Acadmc Schlrshp 85; Manhattan Coll; Engr.

KIRISITS, SUE; Tonawanda SR HS; Tonawanda, NY; (Y); Spanish Clb; JV Cheerleading; Sftbl; L Var Swmmng; Acctg.

KIRK, KEVIN P; Herkimer Central HS; Herkimer, NY; (Y); 3/130; Am Leg Boys St; Pres French Clb; VP Model UN; Pres Band; Pres Frsh Cls; VP Soph Cls; Pres Jr Cls; L Var Crs Cntry; NHS; CVC Crs Cntry All Star 83-84; Ldrshp Sem Coll St Rose 82; Pre-Med.

KIRK, PETER; Bishop Timon HS; W Seneca, NY; (Y); Am Leg Boys St; VP French Clb; Chorus; Nwsp Rptr; Nwsp Stf; Yrbk Stf; Rep Jr Cls; Var Ftbl; Var Capt Swmmng; Var JV Trk; Frnch Hnr Awd; Ftbl All Cathlc; Swmg MVP.

KIRK, ROBERT J; Greenwick Central HS; Greenwich, NY; (Y); AFS; Art Clb; Pres Church Yth Grp; Computer Clb; Letterman Clb; Varsity Clb; Chorus; Concert Band; Jazz Band; School Play; Demolay Mbr.

KIRK, SANDRA; West Hampton Beach HS; Manorville, NY; (Y); Ski Clb; Spanish Clb; School Musical; Yrbk Stf; Co-Capt Bsktbl; Score Keeper; Socr; Sftbl; Vllybl; Hon Roll; Chem.

KIRKER, BETSEY L; Downsville Central Schl; Downsville, NY; (Y); Spanish Clb; School Play; Yrbk Stf; Rep Frsh Cls; Stu Cncl; Cheerleading; Socr; Hon Roll; Prfct Atten Awd; USBEA; Dentl Hygiene.

KIRKEY, TONI; Groton Central HS; Cortland, NY; (Y); FHA; Chorus; Vllybl; Wt Lftg; Hon Roll; Tompkins-Cortland CC; Htl Mgmt.

KIRKHUS, ROY P; F D Roosevelt HS; Salt Point, NY; (Y); 13/325; Am Leg Boys St; Pres Church Yth Grp; Capt L Ftbl; DAR Awd; High Hon Roll; NCTE Awd; Rowing Crew 81-85; Outstndg Young NY Nomn 84; Best Liked; Bus Admin.

KIRKPATRICK, ELIZABETH; Rome Free Acad; Rome, NY; (Y); Church Yth Grp; Church Choir; Orch; Var Diving; Hon Roll; Jr NHS; NHS; All ST Orch 83-84; Med.

KIRKPATRICK, LESLEY; Commack High School South; Dix Hills, NY; (Y); Service Clb; Nwsp Phtg; Nwsp Rptr; Yrbk Stf; Rep Frsh Cls; Rep Soph Cls; Rep Stu Cncl; Var JV Vllybl; High Hon Roll; NHS; Gldn Quill Awd 85.

KIRKPATRICK, TERESE; Nardin Acad; Kenmore, NY; (S); 25/88; Art Clb; VP JA; VP Service Clb; School Musical; Stage Crew; Ed Nwsp Ed-Chief; Socr; Swmmng; Hon Roll; NHS; JR Achvmnt Shclrshp 85; Alfred U; Ceramic Engrng.

KIRKWOOD, RICHARD T; Saint Francis HS; Lackawanna, NY; (Y); 24/143; Boy Scts; Pres Church Yth Grp; Nwsp Phtg; Yrbk Phtg; Yrbk Stf; Lit Mag; Hon Roll; NY ST Regents Coll Schlrshp 85; Cath Yth Org One Act Play Comp 82; Rochester Inst Tech Schlrshp 85; Rochester Inst Tech; Prof Photo.

KIRNON, AUDREY; Cardinal Spellman HS; Bronx, NY; (Y); Sec Church Yth Grp; Office Aide; Chorus; Church Choir; Nwsp Rptr; Nwsp Stf; Yrbk Rptr; Yrbk Stf; Lit Mag; Im Sftbl; NYC Assn Tchrs Engl 83; Comms.

KIROL, KEITH A; Lockport SR HS; Lockport, NY; (Y); 4/433; Am Leg Aux Girls St; Aud/Vis; Church Yth Grp; Latin Clb; Varsity Clb; Church Choir; Stu Cncl; Var Capt Swmmng; High Hon Roll; NHS; KOFC Soc Stud, Math, & Stud Cncl Awd 85; Navy-Marine Athltc Schlst Achvt 85; NY St Reg Schlrshp 85; US Naval Acad; Engnrng.

KIRSCH, MARY; Holland Central HS; Holland, NY; (Y); Am Leg Aux Girls St; Nwsp Rptr; Stu Cncl; High Hon Roll; Hon Roll; Jr NHS; NHS; Prfct Atten Awd; Helen Piedmont Mem Awd; Pres Acad Ftns Awd; Delta Kappa Gamna Scty Awd; John Roberts Powers; Fshn Merch.

KIRSCH, SHARON; Bishop Ludden HS; Syracuse, NY; (S); Church Yth Grp; Cmnty Wkr; Trs Soph Cls; Trs Jr Cls; Hon Roll; Piano Lessons 81-85.

KIRSCHENHEITER, PAMELA; The Franciscan Acad; Syracuse, NY; (S); 10/24; VP MMM; VP NFL; Ski Clb; Trs Chorus; School Musical; School Play; Variety Show; Stu Cncl; Cheerleading; Socr.

KIRSCHNER, WENDY S; Lancaster HS; Depew, NY; (Y); 64/454; Trs German Clb; Office Aide; Hon Roll; Ntl Merit Ltr; Psych.

KIRSCHNER, WILLIAM A; Valley Stream Central HS; Valley Stream, NY; (Y); 15/350; Computer Clb; Mathletes; Ski Clb; Nwsp Stf; Yrbk Stf; Mu Alp Tht; NHS; Ntl Merit Ltr; German Hnr Scty 85; Aircrft Dsgn.

KIRWAN, JENNIFER; Villa Maria Acad; Tonawanda, NY; (Y); Ski Clb; Hon Roll; Hghst Avg Math & Engl Awds 85; Nrsng.

KISCH, WENDY J; Fox Lane HS; Mt Kisco, NY; (Y); 40/300; Mathletes; Ski Clb; Band; Chorus; Yrbk Stf; JV Fld Hcky; JV Lcrss; High Hon Roll; Hon Roll; NHS; Regnts Schlrshp 85; SUNY Binghamton.

KISH, KATHERINE; Albion HS; Albion, NY; (S); 9/180; Spanish Clb; Bsktbl; Score Keeper; High Hon Roll; Hon Roll; NHS; Hnr Grad 85; Signor Prz Spkng Cont 84; SUNY-FREDONIA; Lang Educ.

KISIEL, ALLISON D; Clinton Central HS; Clinton, NY; (Y); 16/134; Key Clb; Band; Concert Band; Yrbk Stf; Sec Soph Cls; Sec Jr Cls; Sec Sr Cls; Sec Stu Cncl; Var Capt Socr; Var L Sftbl; Regents Scholar 85; Mst Versatile SR Awd 85; Dollars For Schlrs Scholar 85; Ithaca Coll; Phys Thrpy.

KISS, AMY; Kenmore West HS; Kenmore, NY; (Y); Church Yth Grp; Exploring; Hosp Aide; Ski Clb; Band; Concert Band; Mrchg Band; Stage Crew; JV Capt Swmmng; Trk; Med.

KISS, EVA; F D Roosevelt HS; Staatsburg, NY; (Y); 8/325; French Clb; Orch; School Musical; Nwsp Stf; Hon Roll; NHS; St Schlr; Asst Prncpl Violnst-NY ST All ST Orch 83-84; Prncpl Violnst NY ST Area All ST Orch 83-84; Hofstra U.

KISSAME, KATHLEEN A; Jamesville-Dewitt HS; Dewitt, NY; (Y); 35/224; French Clb; Yrbk Stf; Capt Crs Cntry; Trk; High Hon Roll; NHS; NYS Regnts Schlrshp 85; Elmira Coll Schlrshp 84.

KISSANE, CAROLYN; Cardinal Spellman HS; Bronx, NY; (Y); Church Yth Grp; Dance Clb; Key Clb; Pep Clb; School Play; Rep Frsh Cls; Rep Soph Cls; Rep Jr Cls; Pres Sr Cls; Pres Stu Cncl; Hugh O Brien Ambsdr Outstndng Soph 84.

KISSANE, JENNIFER; Jamesville-De Witt HS; Dewitt, NY; (Y); Church Yth Grp; Cmnty Wkr; French Clb; Key Clb; Var Capt Crs Cntry; Var L Trk; High Hon Roll; NHS.

KISSILEFF, BETH P; Horace Mann Schl; Teaneck, NJ; (Y); Intnl Clb; Nwsp Stf; Lit Mag; Crs Cntry; Trk; Ntl Merit SF; Alt Telluride Asoc Smmr Pgms 84.

KISSINGER, JOHN F; Huntington HS; Huntington Bay, NY; (Y); 3/433; Boy Scts; Church Yth Grp; Mathletes; Quiz Bowl; Service Clb; Acpl Chr; Chorus; Pres Orch; School Musical; Ed Nwsp Stf; Eagle Scout 85; Englsh Awd 85; Amer Studies Awd 85; Prncton U.

KISSINGER, MARK; New Paltz HS; New Paltz, NY; (Y); 14/130; Boy Scts; Var Crs Cntry; Var Trk; God Cntry Awd; High Hon Roll; Hon Roll; NHS; MHAL 1st Tm 3200 M Relay 84; Engrng.

KISSINGER, PAUL A; New Paltz HS; New Paltz, NY; (Y); Boy Scts; Chorus; Flag Corp; School Musical; Golf; Trk; Eagl Sct 84; SUNY Cobleskill; Data Proc.

KISZAK, TAMMY; Alexander Central HS; Darien Center, NY; (S); 12/88; FNA; Yrbk Stf; Stu Cncl; Socr; Sftbl; Trk; High Hon Roll; Hon Roll; Jr NHS; Sec NHS; Daemen Coll; Phys Thrpy.

KITCHEN, WILLIAM; Vernon-Verona-Sherrill HS; Vernon Ctr, NY; (Y); Am Leg Boys St; Mathletes; Math Tm; Concert Band; School Musical; Pres Frsh Cls; Ftbl; Cit Awd; High Hon Roll; NHS; Slvr Cty Math Awd 85; NYS Math Actuarial Awd 85; Chem Engrng.

KITEVSKI, JOHN; Holy Cross HS; Bayside, NY; (Y); 46/319; Art Clb; Hosp Aide; Science Clb; Yrbk Stf; Stat Socr; Hon Roll; NHS; Ntl Merit Ltr; Elec Engnrng.

KITLER, DEBORAH; Schoharie Central HS; W Berne, NY; (Y); Church Yth Grp; FHA; Chorus; School Musical; School Play; Nwsp Stf; Yrbk Stf; Cheerleading; Vllybl; Cobleskill Coll; Chldhd Devlpmt.

KITSOS, STACEY; Sacred Heart Acad; Elmont, NY; (S); 9/196; FTA; Girl Scts; Math Tm; Chorus; School Musical; Hon Roll; NHS; Edctn.

KITT, LORI; Cardinal Mooney HS; Rochester, NY; (Y); 155/356; Merit Awd 83-85; Chaminade HI; Intr Dsgn.

KIVLEHAN, BRIAN; Tappan Zee HS; Blauvelt, NY; (Y); Bsbl; Bsktbl; Golf; Socr; St Catharines Little League Bsktbll Coach Of Yr 83-84; Manhattan Coll; Bus.

KLABEN, GREGORY; Monsingor Farrell HS; Staten Island, NY; (Y); 200/296; Boy Scts; Chess Clb; Hosp Aide; JA; Red Cross Aide; Service Clb; Band; Stage Crew; VP Frsh Cls; Im Bsktbl; NY ST Regnts Schlrshp 85; Wittenberg U; Pre-Med.

KLAFEHN, DAVID; Kendall Central HS; Kendall, NY; (Y); 14/83; AFS; Church Yth Grp; Sec FFA; Pep Clb; Nwsp Phtg; Yrbk Phtg; Cit Awd; Hon Roll; NHS; Prfct Atten Awd; FFA Empire Deg Awd 85; Alfred Tech; Frmng.

KLAFFKA, ERIC; Seneca Vocational HS; Lancaster, NY; (Y); 3/172; Math Clb; Math Tm; Mgr(s); Score Keeper; Var Tennis; NHS; Pres Acad Ftns Awd 84-85; Ethnic Hist Cclub 83-85; Promotional Rd Show 84-85.

KLAGGES, CHARLES; Lindenhurst HS; Lindenhurst, NY; (Y); Boy Scts; Chorus; Comp Pgmr.

KLAISS, JACQUELINE; G Ray Bodley HS; Fulton, NY; (S); Hosp Aide; Pres JA; Latin Clb; Concert Band; Orch; Cit Awd; Elks Awd; High Hon Roll; NHS; Century III Ldr Awd 84-85; All Cnty Music Schlrshp 84-85; Biochem.

KLAJBOR, JEFFREY; Dunkirk HS; Dunkirk, NY; (Y); 39/220; Var L Bsktbl; JV Trk; High Hon Roll; Hon Roll; NHS; Joyce Campese Memrl Awd 85; Fredonia ST.

KLANG, TINA; Wellsville HS; Wellsville, NY; (Y); Church Yth Grp; Rep Jr Cls; Var Tennis; High Hon Roll; NHS; Prfct Atten Awd; Mst Imprvd Tnns Plyr Vrsty 83; Hmcmng Queen 82; U Of Buffalo; Phrmcy.

KLAYBOR, KELLY; West Seneca West SR HS; W Seneca, NY; (Y); GAA; Chorus; Nwsp Stf; Yrbk Stf; Rep Frsh Cls; Rep Soph Cls; Rep Jr Cls; Stu Cncl; Cnsistnt Acad Achvt & Outstndng Wrk In Rgnts Bio Awds 83-85; Cansuis; Bus Adm.

KLEEFIELD, JACQUELINE B; Riverdale Country Schl; New York City, NY; (Y); Dance Clb; French Clb; School Play; Yrbk Ed-Chief; Tennis; Vllybl; Hon Roll; Semi-Fnlst NY ST Shkspr Recttn Comptn/Anglo-Am Schl 82-83; Bio Sci.

KLEHR, THOMAS J; Milford Central Schl; Milford, NY; (Y); 1/25; Computer Clb; Math Tm; VP Sr Cls; Bausch & Lomb Sci Awd; High Hon Roll; NHS; Val; School Play; Nwsp Stf; Yrbk Stf; 1st Pl Sci Fair; NYS Regnts & Clarkson Schlrshps; Clarkson U; Comp Engr.

KLEIMAN, TAMMY A; Cicero-North Syracuse HS; N Syracuse, NY; (Y); Hon Roll; Merit Roll 83-85; Advocate 83; Cosmotlgy.

KLEIN, CHRISTINE; St Frances Prep; Glendale, NY; (S); 81/695; Math Clb; Speech Tm; Church Choir; High Hon Roll; Ntl Merit SF; Opt Clb Awd; Bus.

KLEIN, COREY; Long Beach HS; Long Beach, NY; (S); 25/400; Aud/Vis; Pres Camera Clb; Chess Clb; Pres Temple Yth Grp; Ed Nwsp Phtg; Yrbk Phtg; Var Bsktbl; Var Tennis; NHS; Med.

KLEIN, ERIC A; Cicero-North Syracuse Central HS; N Syracuse, NY; (Y); Am Leg Boys St; Church Yth Grp; Exploring; Key Clb; Ski Clb; School Play; Var Diving; JV Lcrss; Var Swmmng; Wheaton Coll; Pltcl Sci.

KLEIN, ERIK; Berlin Central HS; Berlin, NY; (S); 9/82; Boy Scts; School Musical; Pres Frsh Cls; Trs Jr Cls; Stu Cncl; Var L Bsbl; Var L Bsktbl; Var L Socr; Hon Roll; 2nd Team Lgue All Star Soccer Tm 84.

KLEIN, KAREN; St Marys HS; Williamsville, NY; (S); 36/194; Teachers Aide; Varsity Clb; Lit Mag; Rep Soph Cls; Rep Jr Cls; VP Sr Cls; Im Badmtn; JV Co-Capt Cheerleading; Var JV Trk; Im Vllybl; St Bonaventure U; Mktg.

KLEIN, KEITH; Sachem North HS; Centerach, NY; (Y); 7/1300; Math Tm; Temple Yth Grp; Chorus; School Musical; Stage Crew; Var Mgr(s); JV Socr; Var Trk; NHS; Slvr Mdl Long Is Math Fair 84; Outstndg Math Stu 83-84; Outstndg Span IV Stu 84-85.

KLEIN, LISA M; Arlington HS; Salt Pt, NY; (Y); 47/572; Cmnty Wkr; Drama Clb; German Clb; Hosp Aide; Orch; School Musical; Hnr Key 85; Slava Russian Hnr Socty 84-85; Silvr Medl Russn Olympd Wrttn Essy 84-85; Wells; Lang.

KLEIN, MARC D; Blind Brook HS; Rye Brook, NY; (Y); Acpl Chr; Chorus; Yrbk Stf; JV Bsktbl; JV Socr; JV Tennis; Ntl Merit Ltr; French Clb; Regnts Schlrshp 85; Mus Tours 83-85; U Of MI Ann Arbor; Dntstry.

KLEIN, MARK N; Yeshiva Univ HS; Forest Hills, NY; (Y); #16 In Class; Natl Beta Clb; Nwsp Ed-Chief; Nwsp Rptr; Yrbk Stf; Im Fld Hcky; NHS.

KLEIN, PAUL R; Northport HS; East Northport, NY; (Y); 16/661; Key Clb; Mathletes; Chorus; Cit Awd; Hon Roll; NHS; Ntl Merit Ltr; Drew U.

KLEIN, ROBERT; James E Sperry HS; Pittsford, NY; (Y); Radio Clb; Yrbk Rptr; Var JV Diving; Var JV Swmmng; Jr NHS; Notre Dame U; Law.

KLEIN, SHARON; Buffalo Academy Of The Sacared Heart; Williamsville, NY; (Y); Church Yth Grp; Service Clb; Badmtn; Intl Assn Machinsts Essay Cont 85.

KLEIN, STACY S; Huntington HS; Huntington, NY; (Y); 9/433; Sec AFS; Band; Concert Band; Lit Mag; Rep Stu Cncl; Var Gym; DAR Awd; High Hon Roll; NHS; Ntl Merit Cmmnd Semi-Fnlst 85; Dartmouth Coll; Engl.

KLEIN, TODD M; Roosevelt HS; Yonkers, NY; (Y); 11/287; Trk; High Hon Roll; NHS; Superintndnts Achvt Awd 84; Club 90 Exelc Awd 84; SUNY-BUFFALO; Elec Engrng.

KLEINCLAUS, HOLLY; Kenmore East HS; Buffalo, NY; (Y); Cmnty Wkr; Exploring; FHA; German Clb; Math Clb; Hon Roll; ASPCA Explr Pgm Awd 84-85; ST U NY; Animal Hlth.

KLEINER, SONIA; Clarkstown High School North; New City, NY; (Y); Math Clb; Office Aide; Spanish Clb; Temple Yth Grp; Lit Mag; High Hon Roll; Mu Alp Tht; NHS; SADD Sec 84-86; Gdnc Offc Aid 82-85.

KLEINHANS, JULIE; Bishop Ludden HS; Camillus, NY; (S); 1/180; Band; School Musical; Swing Chorus; Pres Jr Cls; Vllybl; NHS; Ntl Merit Ltr; Val; JR Ntl Hnr Soc 84; Ntl Band Awd 83-84; Rgnts Schlrshp 85; Cornell U; Pre Vet.

KLEINMAN, HAL; Ellenville Central Schl; Ellenville, NY; (Y); 5/85; Chorus; Madrigals; School Musical; VP Frsh Cls; Var Mgr(s); High Hon Roll; NHS; Sci Olympd; All ST Chrs Audtn A-; Area All ST Chrs; Corp Law.

KLEINMAN, SHERI A; V S Central HS; N Valley Stream, NY; (Y); 51/357; AFS; Art Clb; Cmnty Wkr; French Clb; Hosp Aide; Ski Clb; French Hon Soc; High Hon Roll; NHS; Ntl Merit Ltr; Regnts Schlrshp; Delphi U Trstee Schlrshp; Adolphi U; Intl Law.

KLEMASZEWSKI, JAMES E; Alfred-Almond Central HS; Almond, NY; (Y); 7/74; Am Leg Boys St; Aud/Vis; Computer Clb; Trs FFA; JCL; Yrbk Stf; Swmmng; Tennis; High Hon Roll; NHS; SUNY Schlrshp 85; Ntl Hnr Soc Schlrshp 85; SUNY; Comp Sci.

KLEMCZYK, CHRISTOPHER P; Columbia HS; Rensselaer, NY; (Y); 22/380; Key Clb; Var L Lcrss; JV L Socr; NHS; Ntl Merit SF; Engrng.

KLEMENKO, KIM; New York Military Acad; Stony Brook, NY; (S); 2/70; ROTC; Chorus; Nwsp Ed-Chief; Var Socr; Var Sftbl; Var Swmmng; Sec NHS; Math Tm; Yrbk Stf; George Washington U Engrng Medal 84; Retired Officers Assn ROTC Medal 84; Distngshd Cdt Stts 83-84.

KLEMENT, ORNA; White Plains HS; White Plains, NY; (Y); Dance Clb; Pres Drama Clb; French Clb; Acpl Chr; Chorus; School Musical; School Play; Ed Nwsp Stf; Ed Yrbk Stf; Schlrshp Study Voice Westcherster Arts Prg 83-85; Theatre.

KLEMPA, KAREN A; Johnstown HS; Johnstown, NY; (Y); Teachers Aide; Stu Cncl; Bryon & Stratton Bus Coll.

KLEMPA, VERONICA; Minisink Valley HS; New Hampton, NY; (Y); Drama Clb; Chorus; Flag Corp; Mrchg Band; Stage Crew; High Hon Roll; Hon Roll; Kiwanis Awd; Pre-Med.

KLEMZ, THERESA; Cardinal Mooney HS; Rochester, NY; (Y); 49/317; Var Cheerleading; High Hon Roll; Hon Roll; Spanish NHS; St John Fisher Coll; Math Tchr.

KLENK, KATY; Nazareth Acad; Rochester, NY; (S); Hosp Aide; Latin Clb; Yrbk Rptr; Yrbk Stf; Trs Stu Cncl; Hon Roll; Pre-Med.

KLICK, SUSANNE; South Glens Falls SR HS; S Glens Falls, NY; (Y); 38/238; Accntng.

KLIER, MAUREEN; Mount Mercy Acad; Colden, NY; (Y); #3 In Class; JCL; Pres Latin Clb; Ski Clb; Chorus; School Play; Yrbk Stf; JV Badmtn; Var Tennis; High Hon Roll.

KLIESCH, ELIZABETH; St Peters HS For Girls; Staten Isl, NY; (Y); Teachers Aide; Chorus; Sftbl; Hon Roll; Ntl Hnr Soc 84-85.

KLIMECK, HELEN; Solvay HS; Solvay, NY; (Y); 3/170; VP Key Clb; French Clb; Pres Math Clb; Chorus; Color Guard; Yrbk Stf; Off Frsh Cls; Off Soph Cls; Off Jr Cls; Off Sr Cls; Pres Scholar RIT 85; Am Leg Scholar 85; Solvay Tigers Scholar 85; Rochester Inst Tech; Med Tech.

KLIMEHUCK, PATTY; Union-Endicott HS; Endicott, NY; (Y); Church Yth Grp; Cmnty Wkr; Dance Clb; Fashn Merchndsng.

KLIMEK, SUE; Skaneateies Central HS; Mottville, NY; (S); Var Crs Cntry; JV Socr; Var Trk; Var Vllybl; High Hon Roll; Hon Roll; NHS; Data Proc.

KLINDT, DEBRA L; Sidney HS; Sidney Center, NY; (Y); 20/110; GAA; Math Clb; Math Tm; Office Aide; Rep Stu Cncl; Bsktbl; Sftbl; High Hon Roll; NHS; Prfct Atten Awd; Oprtn Entrprse Schlrshp 84; Rgnts Schlrshp 85; Achvt Awd 83-84; Paul Smiths Coll; Trvl.

KLINE, DAVID T; Millbrook Prep Schl; Norristown, PA; (Y); Model UN; Quiz Bowl; Jazz Band; School Musical; School Play; JV Bsktbl; Var Crs Cntry; Hon Roll; Excellence In Algebra 82; NY Regents Schlrshp 85; U Of Vermont; Veterinary Sci.

KLINE, E; Broadalbin HS; Broadalbin, NY; (Y); French Clb; Girl Scts; Hosp Aide; Pep Clb; Varsity Clb; Chorus; Sec Jr Cls; JV Socr; High Hon Roll; NHS; Elem Educ.

KLINE, MICHAEL; Churchille-Chili SR HS; N Chili, NY; (Y); Boy Scts; Math Tm; Ski Clb; Concert Band; Jazz Band; Mrchg Band; Symp Band; Tennis; High Hon Roll; NHS; Eagle Scout Awd 84; Engrng.

KLINE, MITCHELL; Minisink Valley HS; Middletown, NY; (Y); Math Tm; Ski Clb; Temple Yth Grp; Pres Band; Jazz Band; Orch; Rep Stu Cncl; JV Socr; High Hon Roll; Hon Roll; Cert Of Hnr Recgntn Of Excel Schlrshp 83; Outstndng Musician 83 & 85.

KLINE, PAUL; St Marys HS; West Seneca, NY; (S); 2/210; Ski Clb; Varsity Clb; Rep Soph Cls; Rep Jr Cls; Rep Sr Cls; Rep Stu Cncl; JV Bsbl; Im Bsktbl; JV Var Ftbl; JV Trk; All Cath Ftbl 83-85; Comm Cards Grades 81-85; U Of Buffalo; Polt Sci.

KLINETOB, NADYA; Broadalbin Central HS; Broadalbin, NY; (Y); 1/90; Sec Trs French Clb; Varsity Clb; Chorus; Sec Stu Cncl; JV Var Cheerleading; JV Var Socr; God Cntry Awd; High Hon Roll; Jr NHS; NHS; Ntl Sci Merit Awd 83-85; Prncpls List 83-85; Schlrshp-Smmr Excllnc Pgm Fulton-Montmgry CC; Stanford; Psych.

KLING, KATHERINE; West Irondequoit HS; Rochester, NY; (Y); 48/365; Church Yth Grp; Red Cross Aide; Sec Frsh Cls; Sec Stu Cncl; DAR Awd; Hon Roll; NHS; Pres Schlr; Richard Thompson Mem Awd 85; Hazel Lalonde Mem Awd 85; CP Malone Mem Awd 85; William Smith Coll; Psych.

KLING, WALTER; Pulaski JR SR HS; Pulaski, NY; (Y); Varsity Clb; VICA; JV Ftbl; JV Wrstlng; BOCES Weldng 84-85; Completn Weldng Course 85-86; Weldng.

KLINGENBERGER, TIMOTHY; Churchville-Chili HS; Rochester, NY; (Y); Hosp Aide; JCL; Band; School Musical; Pres Frsh Cls; Pres Stu Cncl; Crs Cntry; Trk; Hon Roll; NHS; Scott M Trainor Awd 83-84; Cornell; Med.

KLINGLER, ARTHUR; Edmeston Central HS; Edmeston, NY; (Y); 7/36; Quiz Bowl; Band; Chorus; Church Choir; School Musical; School Play; Yrbk Bus Mgr; Cit Awd; High Hon Roll; JP Sousa Awd; Gvg All Out Effrt Schl & Sprts Charles Rider Memrl Awd 85; Mohawk Valley CC; Acctg.

KLINKOWIZE, LAURA; Pelham Meemorial HS; Pelham, NY; (Y); Ski Clb; Nwsp Stf; Lit Mag; Rep Soph Cls; Var Fld Hcky; Var Gym; JV Lcrss; High Hon Roll; NHS; Engrng.

KLIRONOMOS, ANTONIA; Lindenhurst SR HS; Lindenhurst, NY; (Y); VP Church Yth Grp; Yrbk Stf; Rep Frsh Cls; Sec Soph Cls; Rep Jr Cls; Rep Sr Cls; Rep Stu Cncl; Var Tennis; Hon Roll; Jr NHS; Achvt Awd In Hlth 85; Bus.

KLISIWECZ, WALTER P; Hamilton Central Schl; Hubbardsville, NY; (Y); 14/54; 4-H; Stage Crew; Rep Jr Cls; Hon Roll; NHS; Regnts Schlrshp NY ST 85; SUNY Albany; Bus Adm.

KLOCK, BRIAN; Grand Island HS; Gr Island, NY; (Y); Varsity Clb; JV Var Bsbl; JV Var Bsktbl; JV Ftbl; Im Vllybl; Hon Roll; Acctg.

KLOCK, DEBORAH; Little Falls JR SR HS; Little Falls, NY; (Y); Exploring; 4-H; FBLA; Girl Scts; Spanish Clb; Band; Orch; Nwsp Stf; 4-H Awd; Hon Roll; SUNY-COBLESKILL; Anml Hsbndry.

KLOCK, JENNIFER; Grand Island SR HS; Gr Island, NY; (Y); Band; NHS; Civic Clb; Cmnty Wkr; Girl Scts; Latin Clb; Pep Clb; PAVAS; Concert Band; Mrchg Band; Band Pres 85-86; Spcl Olymp 82-84; Comm.

KLOCKOWSKI, CHRISTINE; Bainbridge-Guilford HS; Guilford, NY; (Y); 16/75; Red Cross Aide; Ski Clb; Spanish Clb; Chorus; Color Guard; Mrchg Band; Orch; Rep Stu Cncl; JV Sftbl; JV Vllybl; Most Enthuiasm In Learning The Spanish Lang 85; Spec & Elem Educ.

KLODASKI, MARYANN; Mercy HS; Riverhead, NY; (Y); 43/123; Key Clb; Yrbk Phtg; Yrbk Sprt Ed; Bsktbl; Hon Roll; Rotary Awd; Kiwanis Schlrshp 84-85; SUNY Cblskl; Bio Tech.

KLOEPFER, CURTIS P; Islip HS; Islip, NY; (Y); 5/278; Model UN; Yrbk Bus Mgr; Var Bowling; Trk; High Hon Roll; Jr NHS; VP NHS; NY St Regents Schrlshp 85; U Dallas Schlrshp 85; Johns Hopkins; Pol Econ.

KLOIBER, WENDY; Cicero-North Syracuse HS; N Syracuse, NY; (S); 4/622; Office Aide; Teachers Aide; JV Vllybl; Hon Roll; Hstry Prof.

KLOPFENSTEIN, DEANNA; Arlington HS; Hopewell Jct, NY; (Y); Church Yth Grp; Cmnty Wkr; Girl Scts; Intnl Clb; Ski Clb; Teachers Aide; Mgr(s); Hotl Mgr.

KLOS, DARRYL; Lackawanna SR HS; Lackawanna, NY; (Y); 17/312; French Clb; Var Socr; Wt Lftg; High Hon Roll; Hon Roll; NHS; St Bonaventure U; Math.

KLOS, LYNN; Lackawanna SR HS; Lackawanna, NY; (Y); Yrbk Bus Mgr; Yrbk Stf.

KLOSSNER, MICHAEL A; Holland Patent Central HS; Stittville, NY; (Y); Art Clb; VP Varsity Clb; Chorus; School Play; Yrbk Sprt Ed; Var Golf; Var Swmmng; St Schlr; Royson Whipple Schlrshp 85; NY ST Regents Schlrshp 85; SUNY Morrisville; Auto Engrng.

KLOTZ, ADAM; Dobbs Ferry HS; Dobbs Ferry, NY; (S); 1/102; Temple Yth Grp; Concert Band; Jazz Band; Mrchg Band; Rep Stu Cncl; Capt Tennis; NHS; Ntl Merit Ltr; Spanish NHS; AFS; Engrng.

KLUBEK, KATHLEEN; Lackawanna SR HS; Lackawanna, NY; (Y); 9/288; Band; Jazz Band; Tennis; NHS; Mary Ann D Amore Mc Manus Awd 85; U Buffalo; Bio.

KLUEPFEL, DAVID F; Connetquot HS; Ronkonkoma, NY; (Y); 28/765; Am Leg Boys St; Yrbk Stf; VP Sr Cls; JV Bsbl; JV Var Ftbl; JV Var Trk; Wt Lftg; High Hon Roll; NHS; Law.

KLUEPFEL, JUDITH A; Mahopac HS; Mahopac, NY; (Y); 54/357; Cmnty Wkr; Teachers Aide; Band; Concert Band; Mrchg Band; Nwsp Rptr; Trs Soph Cls; Trs Jr Cls; Stu Cncl; High Hon Roll; Fordham U; Hist.

KLUG, ANJA; Narrowsburg Central Schl; Narrowsburg, NY; (Y); Church Yth Grp; Ski Clb; Chorus; School Play; VP Stu Cncl; JV Bsktbl; Var Capt Socr; Var Sftbl; Hon Roll; NHS; Canton Coll; Vet.

KLUG, DAVID; Seneca Voc HS; Buffalo, NY; (Y); Chess Clb; Band; Concert Band; Jazz Band; Yrbk Stf; Off Jr Cls; Ftbl; Ice Hcky; Wt Lftg; Ntl Merit Ltr; NC Opertr.

KLUGE, NANCY LYNN; Groton Central Schl; Groton, NY; (Y); VP 4-H; Girl Scts; Rep Chorus; Yrbk Phtg; Yrbk Sprt Ed; Var Capt Cheerleading; Var Socr; Var Stat Trk; 4-H Awd; Hon Roll; Phys Ther.

KNAPIK, RAYLENE A; Amsterdam HS; Amsterdam, NY; (Y); FBLA; Teachers Aide; Elks Awd; Hon Roll; Jr NHS; NHS; Pres Schlr; St Schlr; St Rose; Bus Adm.

KNAPP, ALLEN; Mahopac HS; Mahopac, NY; (Y); 34/423; Pres Trs Church Yth Grp; German Clb; Trs Orch; JV Capt Socr; High Hon Roll; Hon Roll; NHS; Prfct Atten Awd; Red Crs SR Lfsvg Cert; Engrng.

KNAPP, ANDREA P; Laurens Central Schl; Laurens, NY; (Y); 8/37; Am Leg Aux Girls St; Drama Clb; Key Clb; Rep VP Sr Cls; Rep Stu Cncl; Var Bsktbl; Var Capt Cheerleading; Var Capt Socr; NHS; Ski Clb; Clark Schlrshp 85-86; St Marys Cthlc Comm Awd 85-83; Presdntl Acadmc Ftns Awd 85; Springfield Coll; Hlth Ftns.

KNAPP, CHERYL A; Warwick Valley HS; Chester, NY; (Y); 17/210; Church Yth Grp; Office Aide; Teachers Aide; Var Coach Actv; Stat Var Crs Cntry; Var Trk; High Hon Roll; Hon Roll; Sec NHS; NY Regents Schlrshp 84-85; Susquehanna U; Accntnt.

KNAPP, ELIZABETH ANN; St John Villa Acad; Staten Island, NY; (Y); Pres Church Yth Grp; Dance Clb; Math Clb; Mrchg Band; Nwsp Phtg; Nwsp Stf; Yrbk Phtg; Yrbk Stf; Swmmng; Twrlr; 1st Pl-Metropolitan Twirling Assoc 84; Cath Youth Organ Teenage Fed Comm Svc Awd 85; Classical Ballet.

KNAPP, MARY; Elmira Southside HS; Wellsburg, NY; (Y); French Clb; JA; Hon Roll; Prfct Atten Awd; Accntng.

KNAPP, PAULA; F D Roosevelt HS; Hyde Park, NY; (Y); 118/365; Drama Clb; 4-H; Quiz Bowl; School Musical; Stu Cncl; 4-H Awd; Hon Roll; 1st Pl 4-H Dairy Bwl Tm 84; NYS Regents Scholar Awd 85; NYS Regents Diploma 85; SUNY Cobleskill; Animal Sci.

KNAPP, ROBERT W; Madison Central HS; Madison, NY; (Y); 5/39; Am Leg Boys St; Varsity Clb; Jazz Band; High Hon Roll; Boy Scts; Band; Concert Band; Mrchg Band; Var Bsktbl; Rgnts Schlrshp 85; MVCC; Engrng.

KNAUS, CHRISTOPHER; Union-Endicott HS; Endwell, NY; (Y); Exploring; Key Clb; Band; Concert Band; Jazz Band; Mrchg Band; Orch; High Hon Roll; NHS; Natl Yth Ldrshp Cncl 85; Engrng.

KNAUS, JENNIFER; West Seneca SR HS; Cheektowaga, NY; (Y); Bryant & Stratton; Bus.

KNAUS, KRISTIN; J A Coleman HS; Stone Ridge, NY; (Y); Cmnty Wkr; 4-H; Girl Scts; Cheerleading; Gym; Score Keeper; 4-H Awd; Med.

KNAUST, STEPHANIE; Coxsackie Athens HS; Coxsackie, NY; (Y); Band; Drm & Bgl; Drm Mjr(t); Mgr(s); Score Keeper; High Hon Roll; Hon Roll; NHS; Sci.

KNAUTH, DANIEL; John A Coleman HS; Kingston, NY; (Y); Chess Clb; Key Clb; School Play; Yrbk Stf; Rep Frsh Cls; Rep Jr Cls; JV Socr; Var Trk; Hon Roll; Ntl Merit Ltr.

KNEALE, AMY; Onondaga HS; Syracuse, NY; (S); 9/73; Trs GAA; Spanish Clb; Chorus; Var Capt Crs Cntry; Socr; Var Capt Trk; High Hon Roll; NHS; Most Outstndng Underclsmn Athlete 82-84; V Ltr Clb Co Pres 84-85; Lib Arts.

KNEBEL, MAURICE; West Irondequoit HS; Rochester, NY; (Y); Church Yth Grp; Computer Clb; Latin Clb; Math Clb; Math Tm; Model UN; Nwsp Stf; Yrbk Stf; High Hon Roll; Hon Roll; Latin Awd 84; GMI Engrng & Mgmt; Elec Engrng.

KNECHTEL, JOANNE M; South Jefferson HS; Mannsville, NY; (Y); 1/134; VP FFA; Pres German Clb; School Musical; Yrbk Ed-Chief; Pres Soph Cls; Trs Jr Cls; Var Sr Cls; Stat Ftbl; Var Trk; Bausch & Lomb Sci Awd.

KNECHTEL, JUDITH ANNE; Liverpool HS; Liverpool, NY; (S); Church Yth Grp; Cmnty Wkr; JA; Ski Clb; Chorus; High Hon Roll; Hon Roll; Jr NHS; NHS; Cert Achvt & Cert Of Apprctn 81-82; Syracuse U; Bus Mgmt.

KNEE, BRADLEY; Onteora HS; Woodstock, NY; (S); 10/245; Math Tm; Stage Crew; Trs Jr Cls; Trs Sr Cls; Tennis; High Hon Roll; Hon Roll; VP NHS; Brown U; Bio.

KNESPLER, DONNA; Salem Central Schl; W Babylon, NY; (Y); 9/54; FHA; Yrbk Stf; Lit Mag; Hon Roll; NHS; Thomas Yushak Mem Awd 85; Tabatha Bauer Awd 85; Tri County Branch Wmns Natl Farm/Gdn Assn Schlar 85; SUNY; Vet Sci Tech.

KNETTEL, KAREN; Half Hollow Hills H S West; Dix Hills, NY; (Y); Art Clb; Debate Tm; French Clb; Hosp Aide; Leo Clb; Nwsp Stf; Yrbk Stf; High Hon Roll; Jr NHS; NHS; Bus Mgmt.

KNIBBS, BRENDA; Minisink Valley HS; Slate Hill, NY; (Y); Pres Acpl Chr; Band; Pres Chorus; Church Choir; Concert Band; Mrchg Band; Swing Chorus; Symp Band; High Hon Roll; Hon Roll; Most Outstndng JR In Music 85; Most Dedctd Soph In Music 84; Area All-ST Choir 84; Music Eductn.

KNICKERBOCKER, JANE; Uork Central HS; Leicester, NY; (Y); Trs Key Clb; Concert Band; Mrchg Band; Yrbk Ed-Chief; JV Sftbl; Hon Roll; Jr NHS; NHS; Ski Clb; Jazz Band; Eng Clsrm Hnrs 83-85; Yth Fit Achvt Awd 83-84.

KNICKERBOCKER, SELENA; Southside HS; Wellsburg, NY; (Y); Church Yth Grp; Cmnty Wkr; Girl Scts; Teachers Aide; Chorus; Church Choir; Stu Cncl; Corning CC; Hndcpd Chldrn Tchr.

KNICKERBOCKER, SUSAN K; George W Fowler HS; Syracuse, NY; (Y); Church Yth Grp; Cmnty Wkr; Pep Clb; Chorus; Church Choir; Nwsp Stf; Yrbk Stf; Stu Cncl; Hon Roll; St Schlr; Regents Schlrshp 85; Houghton Coll.

KNIER, WENDY; Holland Central HS; Strykersville, NY; (Y); Pres AFS; VP Church Yth Grp; Sec 4-H; Church Choir; Stat Bsktbl; Scrkpr Fld Hcky; AFS Exch Stu Australia 84; Fern Leaf Clb Awd Highest Grade Eng II Regents 85; Jeanne Blair Awd Eng; Elem Educ.

KNIFFIN, ANDREA; Valley Central HS; Montgomery, NY; (Y); Debate Tm; Chorus; Yrbk Stf; Soph Cls; Jr Cls; Sr Cls; Cheerleading; Hon Roll; NHS; Spanish NHS; Psychlgy.

KNIGHT, ANNELIES; Warwick Valley HS; Warwick, NY; (Y); Ski Clb; High Hon Roll; Astrmny.

KNIGHT, ELIZABETH; Chatham HS; Chatham, NY; (Y); Math Tm; Flag Corp; Rep Stu Cncl; JV Var Cheerleading; Elks Awd; NHS; Rotary Awd; Church Yth Grp; Letterman Clb; Library Aide; All League Math Tm; Clarkson U; Engrng.

KNIGHT, EVELYN; Bishop Loughlin Memorial HS; Brooklyn, NY; (Y); 23/180; Church Yth Grp; Chorus; Church Choir; High Hon Roll; Hon Roll; Ntl Merit Ltr; Hunter Coll; Med.

KNIGHT, GEORGE; Aviation HS; Flushing, NY; (Y); 13/417; Hon Roll; Prfct Atten Awd; Peagasus Soc Awd 85; Rules Pegasus Soc Cncl 85; Commercial Airline Pilot.

KNIGHT, KRISTINE M; Irondequoit HS; Rochester, NY; (Y); 33/334; Ski Clb; Varsity Clb; Band; Yrbk Stf; JV Socr; Var Trk; Var Vllybl; Hon Roll; NHS; Prfct Atten Awd; Regents Schlrshp 85; Nazareth Coll; Advrtsng.

KNIGHT, MICHELLE; Warwick Valley HS; Warwick, NY; (Y); 2/200; Church Yth Grp; Pres Sec 4-H; Trs French Clb; Hosp Aide; Capt Science Clb; Yrbk Ed-Chief; Var Capt Tennis; 4-H Awd; High Hon Roll; NHS; Bus Econ.

KNIGHT, PATRICIA; Bishop Grimes HS; Syracuse, NY; (Y); 47/207; Church Yth Grp; FBLA; Political Wkr; Yrbk Bus Mgr; Yrbk Stf; High Hon Roll; Hon Roll; NHS; Nazareth Coll; Pol Sci.

KNIGHT, SUZANNE M; Bishop Grimes HS; Syracuse, NY; (Y); 50/203; FBLA; Political Wkr; Yrbk Stf; DAR Awd; High Hon Roll; NHS; Canisius Coll; Pol Sci.

KNIGHTON, SANDRA; Moore Catholic HS; Staten Island, NY; (Y); Church Yth Grp; Hosp Aide; Chorus; School Musical; Bowling; NHS; Acad All Am Hnr Math 85; Med.

KNIGHTS, MELISSA; Medina SR HS; Medina, NY; (Y); AFS; VP Church Yth Grp; Dance Clb; Pep Clb; Ski Clb; Spanish Clb; Chorus; Stu Cncl; Cheerleading; Fld Hcky; Skinner Mem Awd-Ldrshp & Ctznshp, Overall Att & GPA; Bus Admin.

KNIPES JR, JOSEPH F; Granville Central HS; Wells, VT; (S); AFS; Math Tm; Ski Clb; Band; Mrchg Band; High Hon Roll; NHS.

KNIPPLE, ROBERT; Union Springs Acad; Jamestown, NY; (Y); Church Yth Grp; Ski Clb; Band; Church Choir; Concert Band; School Musical; School Play; Stage Crew; Variety Show; Score Keeper; Andrews U; Med Sci.

KNIRSCH, DAWN; Our Lady Of Victory; Yonkers, NY; (Y); Art Clb; Cmnty Wkr; Service Clb; Spanish Clb; Stage Crew; Nwsp Rptr; Yrbk Stf; Lit Mag; Off Frsh Cls; Off Soph Cls; Schl Spirit Awd; Manhattan Coll; Tchr.

KNITTWEIS, GWEN; Newfield HS; Selden, NY; (Y); Letterman Clb; Band; Chorus; Concert Band; Jazz Band; Mrchg Band; Var Fld Hcky; French Hon Soc; NHS; All-Lge All-Conf Plyr Awd 84-85; Awd Outstndng Achvmnt Bio 83-84; Engr.

KNOBLOCH, MARIE C; Warwick Valley HS; Warwick, NY; (Y); 5/200; Hosp Aide; Math Tm; Yrbk Phtg; Rep Soph Cls; Rep Jr Cls; Rep Sr Cls; French Hon Soc; High Hon Roll; NHS; Georgetown U; Med.

KNOCK, RACHEL E; Hunter College HS; New York, NY; (Y); Dance Clb; Drama Clb; Chorus; School Musical; School Play; Stage Crew; VP Jr Cls; Stu Cncl; Ntl Merit SF; Yth Undrstndng Germn Stdnt 84-85.

KNOEDLER, SHERRI; Riverhead HS; Wading River, NY; (Y); FBLA; VICA; Prnts, Alumni & Frnds Asrng Twrd Exc Awd 84; Lgl Scrtry.

KNOELL, CHRISTOPHER TODD; North Tonawanda SR HS; N Tonawanda, NY; (Y); 23/479; Chess Clb; Computer Clb; Teachers Aide; Hon Roll; NHS; Pres Schlr; Quality Stu Awd 85; Frgn Lang Hnr Scty 83-85; Cmpltn Cert For Roswell Pk Mem Inst Smmr Rsrch Part Prog; Boston U; Bio.

KNOPE, SHARON; Cardinal Mooney HS; Rochester, NY; (Y); 98/317; Office Aide; Teachers Aide; Cit Awd; French Hon Soc; Hon Roll; Cert Achvt Bus Math & Bus Dynmcs 84; Recog Svc Main Ofc Wrk 83-84; Bus.

KNORR, PAUL O; Munich American HS; Apo, NY; (Y); 10/110; Boy Scts; ROTC; Jazz Band; Pep Band; Sec Stu Cncl; Hon Roll; NHS; Ntl Merit Schol; Cmnty Wkr; Band; 4 Yr Army ROTC Schlrshp 85; Presdntl Acadmc Ftnss Awd 85; FL Inst Of Tech; E Engrng.

KNOTT, KATHLEEN A; New Hyde Park Memorial HS; New Hyde Park, NY; (Y); 29/269; Cmnty Wkr; Drama Clb; Leo Clb; Band; Yrbk Stf; Rep Sr Cls; Cit Awd; High Hon Roll; Lion Awd; NHS; NYS Regents Schlrshp 85; Samarateen Of Yr Awd 84; Stanley Marcus Hum Awd 85; Bostonu; Spec Ed.

KNOTT, KRISTEN; Kings Park SR HS; Kings Pk, NY; (Y); 8/390; Office Aide; Teachers Aide; Varsity Clb; Nwsp Rptr; Yrbk Phtg; Yrbk Sprt Ed; Yrbk Stf; Coach Actv; Mgr(s); Var Socr; Magna Cum Laude Natl Latin Exam 83.

KNOTT, SCOTT A; Cassadaga Valley HS; Gerry, NY; (Y); 1/79; Am Leg Boys St; Computer Clb; FFA; Quiz Bowl; JV Var Bsbl; JV Var Ftbl; Hon Roll; NHS; Engrng.

KNOWLES, LINDA; Copiague HS; Copiague, NY; (Y); Yrbk Stf; JV Capt Fld Hcky; Score Keeper; Ger NHS 83-86; Hofstra U; Lang.

KNOX, JACQUELINE J; Aquinas HS; Bronx, NY; (Y); Church Yth Grp; Debate Tm; Hosp Aide; Office Aide; Teachers Aide; Stage Crew; Nwsp Rptr; Pres Frsh Cls; High Hon Roll; Cmnty Wkr; NY ST Regents Schlrshp 85; Marymount.

KNOX, KIA; Sleepy Hollow HS; Tarrytown, NY; (Y); VP Art Clb; Sec Church Yth Grp; Drama Clb; Pres JA; Spanish Clb; Church Choir; Color Guard; Cheerleading; Capt Pom Pon; Hon Roll; Anne V Nixon Schlrshp Awd 85; Cazenovia Coll; Fash Merch.

KNUDSEN, JOHN; Smithtown HS East; Nesconset, NY; (Y); Var Mgr(s); High Hon Roll; Hon Roll; Jr NHS; NHS.

KNUDSEN, RANDY; Lindenhurst HS; Lindenhurst, NY; (S); 93/635; Pres Band; Chorus; Pres Concert Band; Jazz Band; Mrchg Band; Swing Chorus; Pres Symp Band; Yrbk Phtg; Yrbk Stf; Hon Roll; E Coast 1st Pl Div I Percussion; Berklee Coll Of Music Jazz Ensmbl Smmr Schlrshp 84; U Of Hartford; Music.

KNUTSON, DEBRA; Union Springs Acad; Barre, VT; (S); 5/50; Chorus; Church Choir; School Musical; Variety Show; Nwsp Ed-Chief; Sec Soph Cls; Sec Jr Cls; Sec Sr Cls; Rep Stu Cncl; NHS; Atlantic Union Coll; Elem Ed.

KO, CHRISTINA; Brooklyn Technical HS; New York, NY; (Y); Office Aide; Chorus; Yrbk Stf; Hon Roll; NHS; Prfct Atten Awd.

KO, JAMES; Hillcrest HS; Elmhurst, NY; (Y); 8/794; Pres Church Yth Grp; Math Tm; Service Clb; Church Choir; Orch; Var Sftbl; Cit Awd; Hon Roll; NHS; Val; Trustees Schlrshp NY U 85; Regents Coll Schlrshp 85; Arista 85; NY U; Bus Adm.

KO, JOHN; Stuyvesant HS; Elmhurst, NY; (Y); Pres Computer Clb; Hosp Aide; Pres Lit Mag; Stu Cncl; Bowling; NHS; Ntl Merit SF; Office Aide; Science Clb; Rockwell Intl 1st Pl Wnr Ind Art 83; JR Acad Sci Rsrch Comp 85; Kiwanis Clb Maspeth Scholar Awd 85; MA Inst Of Vo Tech; Med.

KO, KWANG WOO; Brooklyn Technical HS; Woodside, NY; (Y); Sec Church Yth Grp; Math Clb; Math Tm; Service Clb; Teachers Aide; Rep Jr Cls; Hon Roll; NHS; Sci Plymp Awd 85; Incentive Awd 83; MIT; Aero Sp.

KO, SIN KUEN; Corning-Painted-Post East HS; Corning, NY; (Y); 2/240; VP Art Clb; Drama Clb; French Clb; Quiz Bowl; Varsity Clb; Var L Trk; Bausch & Lomb Sci Awd; High Hon Roll; VP NHS; RPI Math & Sci Mdl 84; Wms Math Awd 85; NY ST Rgnts Schlsp 85; Bongs Prize 85; AAUW Schlsp 85; Cornell U; Engr.

KOAN, SIMON; Susan E Wagner HS; Staten Island, NY; (Y); Band; Elec Engrng.

KOBASKY, BARBARA; La Guardia H S Of Music & The Arts; Brooklyn, NY; (Y); 70/598; Church Yth Grp; Teachers Aide; Band; Chorus; Concert Band; Orch; Stage Crew; Symp Band; Nwsp Rptr; Nwsp Stf; Prncpls Awd Outstndng Svc 85; UFT Awd/Acadmc Excllnc & Schl Svc 85; Outstndng Instrmntl Music Awd 82; Wagner Coll; Psych.

KOBLAND, ELIZABETH; Cicero N Syracuse HS; N Syracuse, NY; (S); 83/711; Band; Concert Band; Mrchg Band; Orch; Pep Band; School Musical; Symp Band; Nwsp Stf; Yrbk Stf; Rep Frsh Cls; Oswego; Comm.

KOBLEROWSKI, PHIL; Ossinging HS; Briarcliff, NY; (Y); Aud/Vis; Off Computer Clb; Exploring; Model UN; Golf; High Hon Roll; Hon Roll; NHS.

KOBRIN, DANIEL; Fallsburg HS; Mt Dale, NY; (Y); Boy Scts; Library Aide; Quiz Bowl; Teachers Aide; VICA; Nwsp Stf; Yrbk Stf; Rep Soph Cls; Hon Roll; Johnson/Wales; Pastry-Clnry Art.

KOCH, DEANNE; Frontier Central HS; Hamburg, NY; (S); DECA; FBLA; Band; Yrbk Phtg; Yrbk Stf; Rep Soph Cls; JV Bsktbl; Hon Roll; NHS; Top 10 Fnlsts Miss Teen Wstrn NY Pgnt 84.

KOCH, GLEN D; Little Valley Central HS; Gowanda, NY; (Y); 1/22; Am Leg Boys St; VP Soph Cls; Pres Sr Cls; Rep Stu Cncl; Var L Bsbl; Var Capt Bsktbl; Bausch & Lomb Sci Awd; High Hon Roll; Pres NHS; Val; NY ST Rgnts Schlrshp 85; U Of Rochester; Mech Engr.

KOCH, LAURIE; Schl Of The Holy Child HS; Yonkers, NY; (Y); Church Yth Grp; French Clb; Girl Scts; Key Clb; Chorus; Yrbk Stf; Stat Bsktbl; Hon Roll; Office Aide; School Play; Bst Actress Ldg Role 83; Bst Spprtng Actress 84; Latin I Awd 83.

KOCH, MELISSA; Hillcrest HS; Rosedale, NY; (Y); Temple Yth Grp; Orch; Hon Roll; Ntl Merit Ltr; Hnrb Mntn-Cert Of Excellnce In Hebrew 84; Stu Bar Cert 85; Hnr Roll 83-85; Psych.

KOCH, TODD; Fairport HS; Fairport, NY; (Y); Var Bsbl; JV Bsktbl; Var Ftbl; Bus Adm.

KOCHEM, HEATHER E; Schalmont HS; Schenectady, NY; (Y); Church Yth Grp; Cmnty Wkr; Drama Clb; German Clb; Thesps; School Musical; School Play; Stage Crew; Hon Roll; Exploring; Perf Arts Prod Wrkshp 81-86; SCC Act Play Comp 2nd Pl 84; Theatre.

KOCHER, JENNIFER; Glens Falls HS; Glens Falls, NY; (Y); 4/250; Band; Chorus; JV Cheerleading; Var Trk; High Hon Roll; JP Sousa Awd.

KOCHER, MININDER S; Mcquaid Jesuit HS; Penfield, NY; (Y); 9/186; Boys Clb Am; Sec Church Yth Grp; Cmnty Wkr; Exploring; French Clb; VP JA; Model UN; Political Wkr; Scholastic Bowl; Varsity Clb; Albert Einstein Awd 85; All-Leag Triple Jump 84-85; All-Clb League Lacrosse 84-85; Med.

KOCHES, RUSSELL; Monsignor Mc Clancy HS; Jackson Heights, NY; (Y); 2/210; Var Bowling; Hon Roll; Coaches Awd 85; St Johns U; Bus Adm.

KOCHIAN, JEFFREY L; East Syracuse Minoa HS; East Syracuse, NY; (Y); 35/350; Am Leg Boys St; JA; Latin Clb; Trs Stu Cncl; Var Socr; Hon Roll; NHS; Selctd Natl JA Conf Deleg 84-85.

KOCK, DARRYL; Attica Central HS; Attica, NY; (S); 12/160; Ski Clb; VP Band; Drm Mjr(t); Stu Cncl; Var Crs Cntry; Swmmng; Hon Roll; NHS; Ntl Merit Ltr; Distngshed Soc Am HS Stu 85; Health.

KOCOUREK, ANN; St Francis Prep; Woodside, NY; (S); 64/690; Hon Roll; Peer Cnslr 84; Syracuse U; Bus.

KOCSIS, MARK; Massena Central HS; Massena, NY; (Y); Spanish Clb; Yrbk Stf; Rep Frsh Cls; JV Bsktbl; JV Crs Cntry; Var Trk; Hon Roll; Acadmc Bnqt 83; Ind Mgmt.

KOEDDING, KAREN; St Francis Prep; Whitestone, NY; (Y); 285/693; Cmnty Wkr; Math Tm; Ski Clb; Chorus; Nwsp Stf; Im Sftbl; Im Vllybl; Hon Roll.

KOEHLER, ANDREW; Fox Lane HS; Bedford, NY; (Y); 77/300; JV Var Socr; Tennis; Hon Roll; Spnsh Diplma Of Merit 84 & 85.

KOEHLER, JODY L; Greenwood Central HS; Andover, NY; (Y); 1/20; Band; Mrchg Band; Symp Band; DAR Awd; High Hon Roll; NHS; Val; Spanish Clb; Yrbk Stf; Sec Frsh Cls; Greenwood Mem Schlrshp 85; Cornell Frshmn Schlrshp 85; Ctznshp Awd Canisteo Rotry Clb 85; Cornell U; Appld Econ.

KOEHNKE, ANDREW; Long Island Lutheran HS; Farmingdale, NY; (S); VP German Clb; Ski Clb; Jazz Band; VP Soph Cls; Sec Jr Cls; Var Capt Crs Cntry; Var Capt Trk; High Hon Roll; NHS; Aerontcl Engrng.

KOELLER, STEVE; Moore Catholic HS; Staten Island, NY; (Y); Math Tm; Im Bowling; Hon Roll; U CA-SAN Diego; Comp Sci.

KOELSCH, KEVIN; Cicero-N Syracuse HS; N Syracuse, NY; (S); 29/622; Boy Scts; Church Yth Grp; Math Tm; Ski Clb; Hon Roll; Rep Stu Cncl; Var Capt Lcrss; Var Capt Socr; Bus.

KOENEN, MICHELLE M; The Hewitt Schl; New York, NY; (Y); French Clb; Key Clb; Model UN; Teachers Aide; Ed Lit Mag; Stu Cncl; Coach Actv; Swmmng; High Hon Roll; Hon Roll; NY ST Rgnts Schlrshp 85; Cert De Merite Concours Natl De Francais 83; Mt Holyoke; Frnch.

KOENIG, BETH; Brighton HS; Rochester, NY; (Y); 153/315; Girl Scts; Spanish Clb; Pres Temple Yth Grp; Chorus; Nwsp Stf; Rep Jr Cls; Rep Sr Cls; Var Capt Fld Hcky; JV Swmmng; All Cnty, 1st Tm-Fld Hockey 84; Athl.

KOENIG, CHRISTOPHER; St Francis Prep; College Pt, NY; (Y); 140/702; Math Clb; JV Bowling; Hon Roll; Engrng.

KOENIG, JACLYN J; Williamsville South HS; Williamsville, NY; (Y); 62/245; Art Clb; Church Yth Grp; French Clb; Hosp Aide; Pep Clb; Ski Clb; Nwsp Bus Mgr; Nwsp Sprt Ed; Sec Sr Cls; Stu Cncl; Pharm.

KOENIG, JON GREGORY; Fairport HS; Fairport, NY; (Y); Trs Intnl Clb; Orch; Rep Stu Cncl; Im Bsktbl; Var Trk; Im Vllybl; God Cntry Awd; Hon Roll; NHS; Boy Scts; Eagle Scout Awd 81; Air Force ROTC Schlrshp 85; Babbitt Schlrshp Awd 85; NY ST Rgnts Schlrshp 85; NC ST U; Elec Engr.

KOENIG, LYLE; Newfield HS; Coram, NY; (Y); Albany U; Law.

KOENIG, MARK; Carmel HS; Carmel, NY; (Y); Boy Scts; Church Yth Grp; Im Ftbl; Var Trk; High Hon Roll; Hon Roll; NHS; DECA; Eagle Scout 84; Landmrks Cmnty Citation 83; Engrng.

KOENIG, MONICA S; Canisteo Central Schl; Canisteo, NY; (Y); 12/81; Cmnty Wkr; Girl Scts; Concert Band; Mrchg Band; Stat Bsktbl; JV Socr; Var Tennis; High Hon Roll; NHS; Rutgers U; Engrng.

KOEPF, LIANNE; Cleveland Hill HS; Cheektowaga, NY; (Y); 3/100; FHA; Band; Chorus; School Musical; Swmmng; Trk; Hon Roll; NHS; Voice Dem Awd; Regents Dipl & Schlrshp 85; Firemans Schlrshp 85; Buffalo ST Coll; Elem Educ.

KOERNER, JOHN F; Mexico HS; Mexico, NY; (Y); 2/200; Var Capt Bsktbl; Var Capt Socr; Var Capt Trk; Bausch & Lomb Sci Awd; Ntl Merit Ltr; Pres Schlr; Sal; St Schlr; Ntl Schlr Athlt 85; SUNY-ALBANY; Pre-Med.

KOERPER, KATHLEEN; Churchville-Chili HS; Rochester, NY; (Y); Church Yth Grp; Nwsp Stf; Stu Cncl; Swmmng; Top 3 Bckstrk JR Olympics 83; Evangel Coll; Nrs.

KOFERL, ROGER S; Sachem HS; Lake Rowkonkoma, NY; (Y); 231/1500; Varsity Clb; Rep Sr Cls; Var JV Bsbl; Var JV Ftbl; Var JV Wt Lftg; Hon Roll; Letterman Clb; Ski Clb; Band; Nwsp Rptr; NYS Regents Schlrshp 85; Outstndng Defense JV Bsbl 83; SUNY; Political Sci.

KOFFLER, ALAN R; George W Hewlett HS; Woodmere, NY; (Y); 35/276; Camera Clb; Temple Yth Grp; Band; Mrchg Band; Symp Band; Nwsp Stf; Regent Schlrshp 85; Law.

KOGON, S MARNY; Columbia HS; Castleton, NY; (Y); 89/353; Math Tm; JV Bsktbl; JV Fld Hcky; Var Sftbl; Hon Roll; NHS; NY ST Regnts Schlrshp 85; U Of MA Amherst; Bus.

KOGUT, GAIL; Bishop Ludden HS; Syracuse, NY; (S); Church Yth Grp; Political Wkr; Nwsp Rptr; Nwsp Stf; Cheerleading; High Hon Roll; NHS.

KOHL, KEVIN R; Southwestern HS; Lakewood, NY; (Y); Am Leg Boys St; German Clb; VP Band; Concert Band; Drm Mjr(t); Jazz Band; Mrchg Band; Var L Vllybl; Hon Roll; NHS; Aerosp Engr.

KOHLBRENNER, KAREN M; Tully Central HS; Tully, NY; (Y); 1/71; French Clb; Varsity Clb; Rep Jr Cls; Rep Sr Cls; Rep Stu Cncl; Var L Trk; NHS; Pres Schlr; Val; Sumr Rsrch Prog Chem 84; NY Tele Co Schlrshp 85-89; Clarkson U; Engrg.

KOHLER, HEATHER; Patchohue-Medford HS; N Patchogue, NY; (Y); 10/708; Acpl Chr; Chorus; Nwsp Rptr; Nwsp Stf; High Hon Roll; Hon Roll; Jr NHS; NHS; Computer Clb; German Clb; Dowling Coll Acad Hnr Scholar 85; PWP IYEA Chptr & Regnl Wnnr, 1st, 2nd & 3rd Pl 83; Dowling Coll; Cmmnctns.

KOHLMAN, DIANE; Churchville-Chili HS; Churchville, NY; (Y); Cmnty Wkr; GAA; Nwsp Rptr; Var Bsktbl; Var Coach Actv; Var Capt Socr; Var Sftbl; Cit Awd; Hon Roll; Bsktbl MIP & Demcrt & Chrncl All Grtr Rochester Hnbl Mntn; Sftbl 1st Tm All Cnty 84; Nazareth Coll; Ed.

KOHLMEIER, KEVIN; Frontier Central HS; Hamburg, NY; (Y); 1/500; Sec Chess Clb; French Clb; Math Tm; JV Golf; High Hon Roll; Hon Roll; NHS; NEDT Awd; Val; VFW Awd; Schlrshp Study France 83-84; U MI Mag Schrlshp 84-85; MI St U Schlrshp84-85; MI St U; Acctng.

KOHLMETZ, ANDREW M; Horace Greeley HS; Chappaqua, NY; (Y); Boy Scts; Church Yth Grp; Computer Clb; School Musical; School Play; Stage Crew; Variety Show; JV Crs Cntry; Var L Tennis; U Of Richmond.

KOHLROSER, WILLIAM R; West Islip HS; West Islip, NY; (Y); 7/525; Boy Scts; Church Yth Grp; Computer Clb; Drama Clb; Service Clb; Nwsp Rptr; Yrbk Stf; JV Ftbl; Jr NHS; NHS; Bkkpng, Chem Excl Awds; U Of VA; Engr.

KOHN, DAVID; E L Vanderneulen HS; Port Jefferson, NY; (Y); 36/260; Cmnty Wkr; Pres Computer Clb; Math Tm; Science Clb; Band; Concert Band; Wt Lftg; High Hon Roll; Hon Roll; NHS; Sci Man Of Yr 82; NY ST Rgnts Schlrshp 85; Stevens Inst Of Tech; Doctor.

KOHNBERG, STEWART JASON; Martin Van Buren HS; Bayside, NY; (Y); 75/625; Computer Clb; Debate Tm; JA; Office Aide; Science Clb; Service Clb; Temple Yth Grp; School Musical; Yrbk Phtg; Westinghouse Semi-Finlst 85; Bus Mgmt.

KOHR, SUSAN; Nottingham HS; Syracuse, NY; (Y); 10/230; French Clb; Nwsp Stf; Var Capt Socr; Hon Roll; NHS; 1st Pl Ntl Frnch Cntst 84.

KOKASCH, THERESA; Dominican Commercial HS; Glendale, NY; (Y); Dance Clb; German Clb; Girl Scts; Intnl Clb; Pep Clb; Church Choir; Cit Awd; Jr NHS; NHS; Slvr & Gld Awds In Grl Scouts 84 & 85; Farmingdale; Vtrnrn.

KOKESCH, ANNA L; St Marys Acad; Ft Edward, NY; (Y); 8/42; Cmnty Wkr; Hosp Aide; Key Clb; Nwsp Rptr; Yrbk Stf; High Hon Roll; Pres Schlr; French Clb; Library Aide; Pep Clb; Marymount Grant 85-86; Cath Dgtrs Awd 85; Cmnty & Socl Invlvmnt Schlrshp 85; Marymount Coll Tarrytwn; Psych.

KOKKINIS, ANNAMARIA; Arlington HS; Poughkeepsie, NY; (Y); 148/572; Church Yth Grp; Dance Clb; Hosp Aide; Variety Show; Nwsp Stf; Yrbk Stf; Rep Jr Cls; German Clb; Intnl Clb; Ski Clb; ASO Schlrshp Wnnr 85; Miss NY Charm Rnnr Up 85; Miss Teen NY Cntstnt 85; Dutchess CC; Law.

KOKOCINSKI, MIKE; Dunkirk SR HS; Dunkirk, NY; (Y); Key Clb; Letterman Clb; Q&S; Radio Clb; Service Clb; Pres Spanish Clb; Nwsp Ed-Chief; Yrbk Stf; L Bowling; Tennis; Excllnc Cert-Course I Math, Spn II & Earth Sci 83; Excllnc Cert-Eng Hnrs, Bio & Course II 84; USC; Trvl.

KOLACKI, ELIZABETH; Broadalbin Central HS; Broadalbin, NY; (Y); Varsity Clb; Band; Chorus; Var L Bowling; Var L Socr; Var L Trk; Var L Vllybl; NHS; French Clb; Girl Scts; Girl Scout Gold Awd 85; MVP Trck 85; Engr.

KOLANDA, JOSEPHINE; Owego Free Acad; Owego, NY; (Y); 8/242; Church Yth Grp; Key Clb; Rep Stu Cncl; Var Capt Bsktbl; Var L Socr; NHS; Pres Schlr; Boy Scts; 4-H; Varsity Clb; Weiss Scholar 85; All STAC Div All Star Var Socr 83, Var Bsktbl 85; U FL; Phrmcy.

KOLARICK, VICTORIA A; St Barnabas HS; Bronx, NY; (Y); 7/136; Hosp Aide; Office Aide; Pep Clb; Chorus; VP Jr Cls; Stu Cncl; High Hon Roll; Hon Roll; Sec NHS; Spanish NHS; Regents Nrs Schlrshp 85; Mt St Vincent Coll; Nrs.

KOLBE, GEORGE S; Minisink Valley HS; Middletown, NY; (Y); Cmnty Wkr; Ski Clb; Varsity Clb; Var JV Bsbl; Var Capt Ftbl; High Hon Roll; Hon Roll; NHS; Med.

KOLBE, JEFFREY; Barker Central HS; Gasport, NY; (Y); AFS; Varsity Clb; Band; Var L Bsbl; L Capt Ftbl; Hon Roll; Crim Justce.

KOLBERT, MICHELLE; Maryvale HS; Depew, NY; (Y); French Clb; German Clb; GAA; Hosp Aide; Pres JA; Mrchg Band; Symp Band; Cheerleading; Hon Roll; NHS; Nrsg.

KOLCH, KIMBERLY; Rome Free Acad; Rome, NY; (Y); Church Yth Grp; Exploring; Intnl Clb; Pep Clb; Nwsp Stf; Lit Mag; High Hon Roll; Jr NHS; NHS.

KOLENDRA, CAROLYN; St John Villa Acad; Staten Is, NY; (Y); 11/105; Hosp Aide; Band; Color Guard; Flag Corp; Yrbk Phtg; Hon Roll; Phy Ftnss Awd 84-85; Natl Sci Olympiad 83-84; Pre Calculus Mrt 84-85; Rutgers Schl Of Pharmacy; Prmcy.

KOLENOVIC, AJSHA; F D Roosevelt HS; Brooklyn, NY; (Y); 28/716; Band; Chorus; Hon Roll; Comptrllrs Awd 83; Library Aide Awd 83; Atten Awd 83; Med Tech.

KOLIAS, NICK; Vestal Central SR HS; Vestal, NY; (Y); Am Leg Boys St; Church Yth Grp; Mathletes; Orch; Var Trk; High Hon Roll; NHS; Natl Sci Olympiad Tm 85; Russian Clb 83-84.

KOLINSKI, JOE; Manlius-Pebble-Hill HS; Manlius, NY; (Y); Model UN; Chorus; Concert Band; Jazz Band; School Musical; School Play; Stage Crew; Variety Show; Yrbk Phtg; Var L Golf; Notre Dame; Bus Admin.

KOLLAR, JEFF; Wantagh HS; Wantagh, NY; (Y); Boy Scts; Church Yth Grp; Computer Clb; Drama Clb; Chorus; Church Choir; School Musical; Mgr(s); Swmmng; VFW Awd; Comp Sci.

KOLLAR, PATRICIA; Mercy HS; Albany, NY; (Y); Drama Clb; Yrbk Ed-Chief; JV Capt Bsktbl; High Hon Roll; Hon Roll; NHS; Powder Puff Ftbl; Trk; Church Yth Grp; Cmnty Wkr; Phrmcy.

KOLLGAARD, LISA; Laurens Central HS; Laurens, NY; (Y); 2/36; Drama Clb; Key Clb; Spanish Clb; Varsity Clb; Pres Sr Cls; VP Stu Cncl; Var Capt Socr; Var Capt Vllybl; Pres NHS; Ntl Merit Ltr; Cortland ST; Phys Ed.

KOLLMER, ANDREW; St John The Baptist HS; Bohemia, NY; (Y); 42/556; Church Yth Grp; Var Capt Bowling; Jr NHS; Envrnmntl Sci.

KOLOZSVARY, LINDA; Henninger HS; Syracuse, NY; (Y); Ski Clb; Band; Concert Band; Jazz Band; Mrchg Band; Pep Band; High Hon Roll; Hon Roll; Ntl Assn Of Jazz Ed Ctn For Outstndng Musicnshp 85.

KOMIN, CHAYA S; Shulamith Girls Schl; Brooklyn, NY; (Y); Art Clb; Camera Clb; Cmnty Wkr; Computer Clb; Math Clb; Science Clb; Y-Teens; Hon Roll; Regents Schlrshp Awd 85; Brooklyn Coll; Comp Math.

KOMOROWSKI, KAREN; Harpursville Central HS; Harpursville, NY; (Y); 5/67; Cmnty Wkr; French Clb; Political Wkr; Spanish Clb; Mgr(s); Var L Vllybl; High Hon Roll; NHS; Voice Dem Awd; Natl Salute Yth Awd 84; Miss Teen NY Acad Nmntn 84; SUNY-BINGHAMTON; Lbrl Arts.

KOMOROWSKI, SHERYL; Villa Maria Acad; Buffalo, NY; (S); 7/116; Computer Clb; JCL; Latin Clb; Pep Clb; Var JV Bowling; Var Capt Cheerleading; Im Gym; Im Swmmng; NHS; Magna Cum Laude 82-83; Vlntr Villa Maria Infmry 83-84; Canisius; Phrmcy.

KOMOROWSKI, STEFANIE; Unatego JR SR HS; Unadilla, NY; (Y); 7/81; Band; Concert Band; Mrchg Band; Pep Band; Yrbk Stf; Var Bsktbl; Cit Awd; High Hon Roll; NHS; Josten Key Awd Exc Physcl Ed 85; Math.

KOMSA, LORRAINE; S S Seward Inst; Florida, NY; (Y); FHA; Hosp Aide; Ski Clb; Spanish Clb; Yrbk Stf; Sftbl; Hon Roll; Cortland Coll; Elem Tchr.

KON FONG, MAY LYNN; St Francis Prep; Corona, NY; (S); 52/693; JA; Band; Drm & Bgl; Jazz Band; Mrchg Band; Hon Roll; NHS; Cornell; Med.

KON-FONG, MAY LYNN; St Francis Prep; Corona, NY; (S); 52/706; JA; Band; Concert Band; Drm & Bgl; Jazz Band; Hon Roll; NHS; Colombia U; Neurosrgn.

KONDRAR, IRINA; Christopher Columbus HS; Bronx, NY; (S); 4/400; Office Aide; Teachers Aide; Cit Awd; Hon Roll; NHS; Prfct Atten Awd; Acad All Amer 84; Regents Schlrshp; SUNY Stonybrook; Comp Sci.

KONDZELA, THOMAS; Cornwall Central HS; Cornwall-On-Hudsn, NY; (Y); 23/208; Var L Ftbl; Var L Wrstlng; NHS; Wt Lftg.

KONDZIELA, CAROL A; Springville-GRIFFITH Inst; Colden, NY; (Y); 3/225; Spanish Clb; Yrbk Ed-Chief; Rep Frsh Cls; Var Tennis; High Hon Roll; NHS; Prfct Atten Awd; NY ST Regents Schlrshp; Presidential Schlrshp; Most Artistic JR SR; U Of Pittsburgh; Occuptnl Thrpy.

KONECKY, KAREN; Union-Endicott HS; Endicott, NY; (Y); Church Yth Grp; Hosp Aide; Ski Clb; Band; Chorus; Jazz Band; Mrchg Band; School Play; Symp Band; Hon Roll; Clarkson U; Chem Engr.

KONGSVIK, JOHN; Hoosick Falls Central Schl; Hoosick Falls, NY; (Y); Church Yth Grp; CAP; Computer Clb; Drama Clb; French Clb; Chorus; School Musical; School Play; Wrstlng; Hon Roll; Theater.

KONIECZNY, EILEEN; Broadalbin HS; Broadalbin, NY; (Y); 5/58; French Clb; Intnl Clb; Letterman Clb; Library Aide; Office Aide; Chorus; Church Choir; Drill Tm; Mrchg Band; Yrbk Stf; All Amer Chrldr 83; Civic Clb Queen 83; Coldeskill Coll; Bus Admin.

KONIK, MARY; Little Falls JR SR HS; Little Falls, NY; (Y); FHA; Girl Scts; Spanish Clb; Concert Band; Mrchg Band; Orch; JV Var Badmtn; Im Pom Pon; Elem Ed.

KONING, JEFF; Bishop Kearney HS; Penfield, NY; (Y); Boy Scts; JA; Ski Clb; Stage Crew; Hon Roll; Cornell Vet Schl; Pre-Vet.

KONLIAN, LISA; Clarkstown South HS; New City, NY; (Y); Office Aide; Service Clb; Pres Frsh Cls; JV Socr; Var L Vllybl; Hersheys Ntl Trck & Fld-5th In NY Sftbll Throw 82; Physcl Ftnss Awd 83-85; Accntng.

KONNO, KATTIE V; Art & Design HS; Woodside, NY; (Y); 45/411; VP Pres Art Clb; Library Aide; Office Aide; Teachers Aide; Yrbk Stf; Trs Stu Cncl; Hon Roll; Trs NHS; Prfct Atten Awd; Tchrs Bst Art Stu Awd 84; NY Inst Of Tech; Comp Grphcs.

KONOPKA, STANLEY; Union-Endicott HS; Endicott, NY; (Y); Key Clb; Mathletes; Rep Soph Cls; Optometry.

KONTOGIANNIS, CONSTANTINE; Albany HS; Albany, NY; (Y); 24/600; Computer Clb; Sec Key Clb; Science Clb; Yrbk Phtg; JV Ice Hcky; Hon Roll; NHS; Regents Schlrshp Wnnr NYS 85; Rensseller Plytchnc Inst; Aeros.

KONTRABECKI, AMY; Hambrurg Central HS; Hamburg, NY; (Y); 4-H; Spanish Clb; Band; Chorus; Color Guard; Concert Band; Mrchg Band; Orch; School Musical; Yrbk Stf; Regents Schlrshp 85; Oberlin Consvtry Music Schlrshp 85; Suny Music Schlrshp 85; Oberlin Conservatory; Music.

KONZ, SHARON R; Fillmore Central HS; Houghton, NY; (Y); 4/50; Trs Church Yth Grp; Trs Spanish Clb; Chorus; School Play; Yrbk Stf; Hon Roll; NHS; NY ST Rgnts Schlrshp 85; Menno Simons Schlrshp 85; Eastern Mennonite; Hstry.

KOOCH, MICHELLE; Greene Central Schl; Greene, NY; (Y); 14/112; Band; Chorus; Color Guard; Mrchg Band; Symp Band; Yrbk Stf; Var L Vllybl; High Hon Roll; Accntng.

KOONZ II, WILLIAM; Colonie Central HS; Schenectady, NY; (Y); Church Yth Grp; Computer Clb; Var JV Socr; High Hon Roll; Hon Roll; Capital Dist Ind Arts Assn 2nd Pl, Hnrbl Mntn 85; Archit.

KOOP, KELLY; Hicksville HS; Hicksville, NY; (Y); Library Aide; Yrbk Stf; Hon Roll; Jr NHS; Spcl Ed.

KOOP, RONALD; Lockport SR HS; Lockport, NY; (Y); 90/450; Latin Clb; Varsity Clb; Yrbk Ed-Chief; Yrbk Stf; VP Frsh Cls; Rep Stu Cncl; Var Ice Hcky; Prfct Atten Awd; SUNY Buffalo; Comp Sci.

KOOPMANN, REBECCA; Middleburgh Central Schl; Fultonham, NY; (S); 2/77; Teachers Aide; DAR Awd; High Hon Roll; Jr NHS; NHS; Ntl Merit SF; Sal; German Clb; Acpl Chr; Jared Van Wagenen Latin III Awd 83; Middleburg Lodge 663 F & A M Soc Stu 81; Bob Jones U; Comp Sci.

KOOS, ALINA; Bronx H S Of Science; New York, NY; (Y); French Clb; Yrbk Phtg; Im Vllybl; Hon Roll; Prfct Atten Awd; Layout Editor Of Math Mag 85-86; Editor-In-Chief Photographic Mag 85-86; Math.

KOPACZ, SUSAN; West Seneca West SR HS; West Seneca, NY; (Y); 109/560; Cmnty Wkr; Hosp Aide; Office Aide; Red Cross Aide; Hon Roll; Prfct Atten Awd; 2-Yth Engagd In Svc Awds 82 & 83; Ltn Cum Laude Awd 82-83; 2 Awds Frm Mercy & OLV Hosp 83 & 85; ST U Of NY Buffalo; Phys Thrp.

KOPEC, COURTNEY M; Fordham Prep; Tareytown, NY; (Y); Church Yth Grp; JV Bsktbl; Var Trk; Malcolm Wilson Schlrshp 83-84; John Giamarco Greek Schlrshp 84-85; Engr.

KOPEC, KATHERINE B; Sachem HS; Farmingville, NY; (Y); 315/1407; VP Drama Clb; Radio Clb; Acpl Chr; Chorus; Madrigals; School Musical; School Play; Swing Chorus; Variety Show; Lit Mag; NYS Regents Schlrshp 85; Most Imprvd Vocalist 82; Potsdam Coll; Music Ed.

KOPEC, KATHLEEN; Mynderse Acad; Seneca Falls, NY; (Y); Am Leg Aux Girls St; Cheerleading; Coach Actv; Trk; Hon Roll.

KOPECKY, DEREK; Massena Central HS; Massena, NY; (Y); Key Clb; Var JV Bsktbl; 1st Pl Frgn Lang Day Potsdam ST Coll 84-85; Math.

KOPEK, STEVEN; Whitesboro SR HS; Whitesboro, NY; (Y); 8/350; Ski Clb; Pres Varsity Clb; Var L Ftbl; Var L Golf; High Hon Roll; Jr NHS; Polit Sci.

KOPLIK, JOE; Union Endicott HS; Endicott, NY; (Y); Boys Clb Am; Computer Clb; Comp Sci.

KOPP, STEPHEN; Hungington HS; Huntington, NY; (Y); 7/433; Acpl Chr; Band; Chorus; Nwsp Ed-Chief; Sec Lit Mag; Hon Roll; NHS; Concert Band; Jazz Band; Mrchg Band; Tufts U.

KOPPLIN, CONSTANCE L; Monticello HS; Monticello, NY; (Y); 1/160; Key Clb; Concert Band; Yrbk Ed-Chief; Var Capt Crs Cntry; Var Capt Socr; Var L Trk; High Hon Roll; NHS; Ntl Merit Ltr; Pres Schlr; Renssalaer Medal 84; Regents Schlrshp 85; U Tampa; Marine Bio.

KOPS, MITCH; E L Vandermevlen HS; Pt Jefferson, NY; (Y); 1/280; Aud/Vis; Spanish Clb; Varsity Clb; JV Socr; Var Tennis; Hon Roll; NHS.

KORALEWSKI, KIM; Frontier HS; Hamburg, NY; (Y); French Clb; Pep Clb; Chorus; School Play; Stu Cncl; High Hon Roll; Hon Roll; NHS; Exec Brd Stu Govt 84-85; Ed.

KORDYJAK, MICHELE; Amsterdam HS; Amsterdam, NY; (Y); 9/360; 4-H; Concert Band; Mrchg Band; Yrbk Stf; Hon Roll; NHS; Vet.

KOREMAN, DONNA; Bishop Maginn HS; Albany, NY; (Y); JV Bsktbl; JV Var Sftbl; High Hon Roll; NHS; Bookkpng/Acctg Achvt Awd 84-85; Advncd Keybrdg Achvt Awd 84-85; Acctnt.

KORENMAN, ERIC; Riverdale Country Schl; New York, NY; (Y); Math Clb; Science Clb; Chorus; Orch; School Play; Dartmouth Coll; Sci.

KORMACKI, KURT A; Eden Central HS; Eden, NY; (Y); School Musical; Hon Roll; NHS; Regnts Schlrshp 85; 3rd Pl Poetry Cntst 85; Carnegie-Mellon U; Fine Arts.

KORNACKI, FLORENCE; West Valley Central Schl; W Valley, NY; (Y); 11/45; Sec Trs Church Yth Grp; Math Tm; Teachers Aide; VICA; Band; Chorus; Church Choir; Mrchg Band; Stage Crew; Trk; Regnts Schlrshp 85; Pres Acad Ftnss Awd 85; U Pittsburgh; Comp Sci.

KORNFELD, GLENN; Shaarei Torah HS; Rockaway, NJ; (Y); 3/15; Chess Clb; Lit Mag; Cert Merit Outstndng Achvt 85; Pres Acadmc Fit Awd Prog & Outstndng Acadmc Achvt 84-85; Montclair ST Coll; Acctg.

KORNFELD, STEVEN A; Rye Country Day Schl; White Plains, NY; (Y); Nwsp Ed-Chief; Nwsp Rptr; Nwsp Stf; VP Rep Soph Cls; VP Rep Jr Cls; Stu Cncl; Var Capt Bsktbl; Var Capt Lcrss; Var Capt Socr; All Lge Sccr, Bsktbk, Lacrosse; Cmnty Svc Awd; Harvard Alumni Bk Awd; U Of PA; Lib Arts.

KOROLOV, MARIA; Wm Nottingham HS; Syracuse, NY; (Y); Math Tm; Teachers Aide; Lit Mag; High Hon Roll; Hon Roll; NHS; Ntl Merit Ltr; Outstndg Stdnt Year Comp Sci Centrl Tech 83-85; Comp Pgmr Centrl Tech Voc 83-85; Asst Tchr Cntrl Tech; Cornell; Computer Engr.

KORONOWSKI, EDWARD; Whitesboro SR HS; Marcy, NY; (Y); 70/312; Am Leg Boys St; Boy Scts; 4-H; VP Band; Concert Band; Jazz Band; VP Mrchg Band; Pres Sr Cls; Var L Bsktbl; Opt Clb Awd; Whitesbord Alumni, Genetaska Clb Scholars 85; Greater Utica Brd Realtors Awd 85; Cornell U; Vet.

KOROTKIN, ALEXANDER; George Washington HS; Bronx, NY; (Y); 3/315; Computer Clb; Math Clb; Swmmng; Gov Hon Prg Awd; High Hon Roll; Hon Roll; NHS; Union College; Electrical Engr.

KORPI, ROBERT; Sachem High School North; Lake Ronkonkama, NY; (Y); 143/1468; Var Bowling; Math II Top Stu Awd 83-84; Regents Schlrshp 84-85; Presdntl Acad Fitness Awd 85; NYIT; Mech Engnrng.

KORSH, ROGER; Kenmore West SR HS; Kenmore, NY; (Y); Boy Scts; JA; Orch; JV L Swmmng; Excllnt Attndnc Awd 84; Engrng.

KORTKAMP, KRISTA; Liverpool HS; Liverpool, NY; (S); 80/791; Church Yth Grp; Concert Band; Mrchg Band; Hon Roll; Jr NHS; NHS; Buffalo U; Elec Engrng.

KOSAKOWSKI, MARK E; Solvay HS; Syracuse, NY; (Y); Aud/Vis; French Clb; Trs Key Clb; Trs Ski Clb; Nwsp Rptr; Trs Nwsp Stf; JV Ftbl; Hon Roll; Ntl Merit SF; NYS Regents Schlrshp 85-86; Syracuse U; Comm.

KOSARA, CATHY; Warwick Valley HS; Warwick, NY; (Y); 10/200; Church Yth Grp; Band; Concert Band; Jazz Band; Capt Bsktbl; Capt Socr; Trk; High Hon Roll; NHS; NYS Sci Supvs Assn Chem Awd 84-85; Natl Sci Merit Awd 84-85; Engrng.

KOSAROVICH, EUGENE W; Cohoes HS; Cohoes, NY; (Y); 3/175; Aud/Vis; Pres Math Clb; Pres Science Clb; Ski Clb; School Musical; Bausch & Lomb Sci Awd; High Hon Roll; NHS; Ntl Merit SF; Prfct Atten Awd; Rensselaer Mth, Sci Mdl; Rensselaer Poly Inst; Comp Engr.

KOSIOR, MATTHEW; West Hampton Beach HS; Center Moriches, NY; (Y); 6/200; Hosp Aide; Band; Concert Band; Mrchg Band; Yrbk Stf; L Socr; NHS; Case Western; Med.

KOSLOR, CATHERINE; Warwick Valley HS; Warwick, NY; (Y); Girl Scts; Library Aide; Band; Chorus; Cheerleading; Trk; Hon Roll; Orange County CC; Med Sec.

KOSLOSKI JR, JAMES J; Floral Park Memorial HS; Floral Park, NY; (Y); 2/184; Aud/Vis; VP Computer Clb; VP Mathletes; VP Radio Clb; Ed Nwsp Stf; Rptr Yrbk Stf; Var Ftbl; Bausch & Lomb Sci Awd; High Hon Roll; NCTE Awd; George Washington U Brnz Mdl 84; Columbia U Sci Hnrs Pgm 83-84; Brnz Mdl L I Math Fair 84; Engr.

KOSLOSKI, KRISTIN M; Center Moriches HS; Manorville, NY; (Y); 5/85; Drama Clb; Band; Chorus; School Musical; School Play; Hon Roll; NHS; Ntl Merit Ltr; French Clb; Ski Clb; Interact Club 81-82; All Suffolk County Chorus 83-84; All NY ST Mixed Choir 84; Goucher College; Political Sci.

KOSMINOFF, LYNN; Fox Lane HS; Bedford Vlg, NY; (Y); 9/275; Key Clb; Pep Clb; Spanish Clb; Off Frsh Cls; Off Soph Cls; Off Jr Cls; Lcrss; Vllybl; High Hon Roll; Soc Sci Outstndng Achvt Awd 82-84; Spnsh Excllnc Merit Dplma 82-84; Engl Hnrs 84-85; Pltcl Sci.

KOSNIK, SUSAN; Maryvale SR HS; Depew, NY; (Y); Spanish Clb; Bowling; Var Socr; Trk; Hon Roll; Perfect Attendance 82-85; Accntnt.

KOSSOW, GRACE J; Honcoye Central Schl; Holcomb, NY; (Y); 26/61; French Clb; Library Aide; Red Cross Aide; Band; Color Guard; Concert Band; Flag Corp; Jazz Band; Mrchg Band; Pep Band; NYS Regents Schlrshp 85; CC Finger Lakes; Accntng.

KOSTBAR, LYNN; Notre Dame Acad; Staten Island, NY; (Y); Church Yth Grp; Varsity Clb; Var Bsktbl; NHS.

KOSTER, CONSTANCE; Eli Whitney Voc HS; Brooklyn, NY; (S); 2/279; NHS; Acadmc Olymp Math & Sci Tm 84; Lib Arts.

KOSTNER, CINDY; St Johns Prep; Long Isld Cty, NY; (Y); Computer Clb; High Hon Roll; Hon Roll; NHS; Queens Coll; Comp Sci.

KOSZALKA, JOAN; Copiague HS; Lindenhurst, NY; (Y); Church Yth Grp; Cmnty Wkr; German Clb; Teachers Aide; Im Bowling; JV Fld Hcky; Im Gym; JV Sftbl; Hon Roll; Early Chldhd Educ.

KOSZELA, ROBERT E; Hilton Central HS; Hilton, NY; (Y); Boy Scts; German Clb; Nwsp Phtg; High Hon Roll; Hon Roll; Principles List Acad Awd; Rocherter Inst Of Tech; Bio.

KOT, RAYMOND; Grand Island HS; Gr Island, NY; (Y); Treas Solar Greenhouse Soc 83-85; Canisius Coll; Pre-Med.

KOTAS, ANDREW; Martin Luther HS; Brooklyn, NY; (Y); Letterman Clb; Ski Clb; JV Var Socr; NHS; NY City Tech Coll; Civil Engr.

KOTAS, HENRY; Richmond Hill HS; Woodhaven, NY; (Y); Police Sci.

KOTHA, SUDHA; Ogdensburg Free Acd; Ogdensburg, NY; (Y); 7/207; Art Clb; Cmnty Wkr; Dance Clb; French Clb; Hosp Aide; Key Clb; Pres Temple Yth Grp; Band; Chorus; VP Soph Cls; Acdmc Achvt Awd 85; JR Medil Awd 84; Art Awd 85; Cornell; Doctor.

KOUBEK, MICHAEL; Archbishop Molloy HS; Flushing, NY; (Y); 175/409; Boy Scts; Cmnty Wkr; Exploring; Pep Clb; Yrbk Phtg; Mgr(s); Trk; Cit Awd; High Hon Roll; Prfct Atten Awd; Scout Yr 82 & 84; JR Ldrshp Boy Scouts Awd 81 & 82; Scout Spirit Awd 85; Eagle Scout 85; St Johns U; Pre-Law.

KOUROFSKY, JODI; Northern Adirondack Central Schl; Lyon Mt, NY; (Y); Key Clb; Library Aide; Band; Yrbk Stf; Var Capt Bsktbl; Var L Socr; Var L Sftbl; Var L Vllybl; High Hon Roll; NHS.

KOUTSIS, PHILIP; Eastchester HS; Eastchester, NY; (Y); Church Yth Grp; Ski Clb; Socr; Tennis; Hon Roll.

KOVAC, ANDREA; Seton Catholic Centrl HS; Binghamton, NY; (Y); Church Yth Grp; French Clb; Ski Clb; Y-Teens; JV Socr; Var Trk; Hon Roll; Psych.

KOVAC, BEATA; Bishop Ford C C HS; Brooklyn, NY; (Y); Art Clb; Computer Clb; Ski Clb; Service Clb; 1st, 2nd Hnrs 82-83; Frnch Awd Merit 83; Columbia U; Med.

KOVACS, EVA; Ellsworth J Wilson HS; Rochester, NY; (Y); Girl Scts; Latin Clb; Concert Band; High Hon Roll; Hon Roll; NHS; Cert Of Accmplshmnt In Proj Bus 81; Hotel Mngmnt.

KOVACS, PETE; Kings Park HS; Kings Pk, NY; (Y); 10/400; Boy Scts; Cmnty Wkr; Computer Clb; Debate Tm; DECA; NFL; Science Clb; High Hon Roll; Jr NHS; NHS; Yng Schlrs Pgm Storybrook SUNY 84-85; NYS Fnlst DECA 84; Vice Chrmn Schl Beautifcatn Pgm 85; Engrng.

KOVAL, EDWARD B; Commack HS South; Commack, NY; (Y); 30/374; Pres Computer Clb; Math Tm; MMM; Mrchg Band; School Musical; Symp Band; High Hon Roll; NHS; NY ST Rgnts Schlrshp 85; All ST Band 84; Union Coll; Comp Sci.

KOVAL, MARIE; Mayfield Central Schl; Mayfield, NY; (Y); 13/77; Drama Clb; Chorus; School Musical; School Play; Stage Crew; Variety Show; Score Keeper; Timer; High Hon Roll; Fulton Montgomery CC; CPA.

KOVAL, STEPHEN C; Schuylerville HS; Stillwater, NY; (Y); 3/101; French Clb; VP FFA; Pres Soph Cls; VP Sr Cls; JV Var Bsbl; JV Bsktbl; Var Capt Ftbl; Cit Awd; Hon Roll; Jr NHS; Harvard Bk Awd 84; FFA Empire ST Degree 84; SUNY Cobleskill; Ag.

KOVALICH, KAREN; Hudson HS; Hudson, NY; (Y); Church Yth Grp; Band; School Musical; Yrbk Stf; Rep Stu Cncl; JV L Bsktbl; Var L Trk; Var Vllybl; High Hon Roll; NHS; Rookie Instrumntlst Yr 82-83; Phrmcst.

KOVARICK, PAUL; Union Endicott HS; Endicott, NY; (S); 103/430; Church Yth Grp; Varsity Clb; Rep Frsh Cls; JV Var Bsbl; JV Var Bsktbl; Var Ftbl; Var Capt Vllybl; Hon Roll; Engrng Sci.

KOVEN, BETH E; Huntington HS; Huntington, NY; (Y); 39/339; Key Clb; Temple Yth Grp; Band; Concert Band; Mrchg Band; JV Fld Hcky; Hon Roll; Jr NHS; NHS; Pres Acad Ftns Awd 85; Rgnts Scholar 85; SUNY Binghamton; Sci.

KOVNER, SCOTT; Sheepshead Bay HS; Brooklyn, NY; (Y); 1/510; Computer Clb; Library Aide; Math Tm; Scholastic Bowl; Science Clb; Ed Yrbk Stf; High Hon Roll; Trs NHS; Ntl Merit Ltr; Val; Engrng.

KOWAL, DONNA; Tottenville HS; Staten Island, NY; (Y); 136/897; Dance Clb; Drama Clb; Thesps; School Musical; School Play; Stage Crew; Yrbk Stf; Ski Clb; Variety Show; Hon Roll; SUNY-BRCKPRT; Comm.

KOWAL, JULIE; Warwick Valley HS; Goshen, NY; (Y); 41/200; Trs FBLA; Vllybl; Hon Roll; Accntnt.

KOWALCHIK, LORI; Islip HS; Islip, NY; (Y); Cmnty Wkr; Hosp Aide; Library Aide; Chorus; Yrbk Stf; Hon Roll; Jr NHS; Soc Wrk.

KOWALCZEWSKI, EDWARD A; Maryvale SR HS; Cheektowaga, NY; (Y); 34/333; Cmnty Wkr; Computer Clb; Sec Drama Clb; VP French Clb; Varsity Clb; School Play; Variety Show; Nwsp Rptr; Nwsp Stf; Yrbk Rptr; SUNY Buffalo; Bio Sci.

KOWALCZYK, BARBARA; Gloversville HS; Gloversville, NY; (Y); 10/275; Church Yth Grp; Drama Clb; Band; Chorus; Church Choir; Concert Band; Mrchg Band; School Musical; Swing Chorus; Cit Awd; Shenandoah Conservatory; Dance.

KOWALCZYK, NOELLE; Villa Maria Acad; Cheektowaga, NY; (S); Church Yth Grp; Computer Clb; Math Clb; Bowling; Swmmng; CC Awd; High Hon Roll; Hon Roll; NHS; Prfct Atten Awd; Bryant & Stratton; Fash Merch.

KOWALEWSKI, JOHN; Greece Athena HS; Rochester, NY; (Y); 9/300; Science Clb; Jazz Band; Symp Band; High Hon Roll; Hon Roll; Pres NHS; Ntl Merit Ltr; Splng Bee Chmp Soph Cls; Brdcstng.

KOWALEWSKI, JOHN; Vestal SR HS; Apalachin, NY; (Y); VP Church Yth Grp; Nwsp Stf; Im Bsbl; Im Bsktbl; Hon Roll; Ntl Merit Ltr; Church Choir; NYS Rgnts Schlrshp 85; Broome CC; Comp Sci.

KOWALEWSKI, KIMBERLY; Liverpool HS; Liverpool, NY; (S); 87/792; Church Yth Grp; Pep Clb; High Hon Roll; Jr NHS; NHS; Opt Clb Awd; B C; Mktng.

KOWALL, THOMAS; Owen D Young C S HS; Mohawk, NY; (Y); Boy Scts; 4-H; Band; Chorus; Nwsp Stf; Var Capt Bsbl; Var Capt Bsktbl; Var Coach Actv; Socr; DAR Awd; Oneonta ST; Phys Ed Tchr.

KOWALOWSKI, LAURA; Northern Adirondack Central HS; Ellenburg Depot, NY; (Y); Sec Trs Key Clb; Speech Tm; Yrbk Sprt Ed; Pres Frsh Cls; Pres Soph Cls; Score Keeper; Swmmng; High Hon Roll; NHS; French Clb; Barbizon Schl Of Modeling Grad 83-84; St U Of NY; Comp Sci Engrng.

KOWALSKI, BRIAN M; Amsterdam HS; Amsterdam, NY; (Y); Band; Concert Band; Mrchg Band; Orch; Hon Roll; Prfct Atten Awd; Reg Art Awd; Ellistrator.

KOWALSKI, DAVID; Solvay HS; Syracuse, NY; (Y); Nwsp Rptr; Golf; High Hon Roll; Bryant & Stratton; Acctg.

KOWALSKI, JENNIFER; Corland SR HS; Cortland, NY; (Y); Cmnty Wkr; Orch; School Musical; Yrbk Stf; Stu Cncl; Hon Roll; NHS; Latin Awd 82-83; Vet.

KOWALSKI, LAURA; Earl L Vandermeulen HS; Mt Sinai, NY; (Y); 20/280; Trs FBLA; Latin Clb; Nwsp Stf; Yrbk Stf; Socr; Stat Sftbl; Trk; High Hon Roll; NHS; Excel Bus Awd 83; Intl Bus.

KOWALSKI, THOMAS P; Solvay HS; Syracuse, NY; (Y); 1/167; Pres Church Yth Grp; Key Clb; Math Clb; Chorus; School Musical; Bausch & Lomb Sci Awd; High Hon Roll; Val; Off Jr Cls; Syracuse U; Doctor.

KOZAK, ANDREW; Smithtown H S West; Smithtown, NY; (Y); Camera Clb; Chess Clb; Science Clb; Crs Cntry; Trk; Hon Roll; Hghst Mark On Earth Sci Regnts 85; Engrng.

KOZERA, TERESE; Mount Mercy Acad; Lackawanna, NY; (S); Speech Tm; Nwsp Stf; Yrbk Phtg; Hon Roll; Natl Hnr Scty Latin Hnr 83; 3rd Pl Ortaory Comp Awd 83; Boston U; Comm.

KOZIEL, MARK; Maryvale SR HS; Depew, NY; (Y); Drama Clb; Varsity Clb; Band; VP Chorus; Bsktbl; Ftbl; Trk; Hon Roll; Acctg.

KOZINSKI, DAVID J; Depew HS; Cheektowaga, NY; (Y); 28/254; Computer Clb; Lit Mag; Var Tennis; Hon Roll; NHS; Ntl Merit Ltr; Regnts Schlrshp 85; ST U Of NY Buffalo; Arch.

KOZLOSKI, GREGORY; Farmingdale HS; Farmingdale, NY; (Y); Nwsp Stf; Crs Cntry; Trk; Hon Roll; Mst Imprvd Plyr Crs Cntry 83-84, Trk 84-85; Forestry.

KOZLOWSKI, FRED; Union Endicott HS; Endwell, NY; (Y); Boys Clb Am; Church Yth Grp; Spanish Clb; Yrbk Stf; JV Golf; Mgr(s); Var Socr; Hon Roll; VP Med Explorers Clb 84-85; Hist Clb; Scranton U; Pre Med.

KOZLOWSKI, LAURA K; Dunkirk HS; Dunkirk, NY; (Y); 28/220; French Clb; Hosp Aide; Key Clb; Letterman Clb; Varsity Clb; Band; Yrbk Phtg; Var Capt Bsktbl; Var Capt Sftbl; Hon Roll; NY ST Rgnts Schlrshp Nrsng 85; Sisters Of Charity Hosp Sch; Rn.

KOZLOWSKI, MARISA; Liverpool HS; Liverpool, NY; (Y); 3/792; Drama Clb; Trs German Clb; Math Tm; Mgr Stage Crew; Rep Stu Cncl; NCTE Awd; NHS; Ntl Merit SF; AFS; Exploring; Cornell Bk Awd 84; Soc Of Mayflwr Descndnts Awd 84; Ntl Latin Exam Awd 84; Chem.

KOZLOWSKI, MICHELE; Westmorland Central HS; Rome, NY; (Y); 27/87; Camera Clb; Drama Clb; Exploring; Model UN; Chorus; Nwsp Stf; Yrbk Stf; Hon Roll; Polish Indepndnt Clb Inc Schlrshp Awd 85; Music Certs 81-84; Herkimer Cnty CC; Medcl Recrds.

KOZMA, DEANNA M; Riverside HS; Buffalo, NY; (Y); 1/205; Am Leg Aux Girls St; Sec Church Yth Grp; Debate Tm; French Clb; Library Aide; Math Tm; Variety Show; Hon Roll; Kiwanis Awd; NHS; Home Ec Stu Of The Yr; Charles Whitney Awd For Val; ST U Of NY Buffalo; Comp Engr.

KOZODOY, JULIA A; St Francis Prep; Woodhaven, NY, (Y), 255/690, Drm & Bgl; School Play; Im Gym; Im Powder Puff Ftbl; Optimates List; Regents Schlrshp; Spnsh Cert Of Merit.

KOZOWER, MAX J; Williamsville North HS; Getzville, NY; (Y); Am Leg Boys St; Math Tm; Var Capt Ftbl; Var Capt Tennis; High Hon Roll; VP NHS; Ntl Merit Ltr; Amer Legn Boys Nation 85; Western NY Dist 14 Tennis Champnshp-Rnnr Up 85; JV Ftbl Outstndng Back 83.

KOZYRA, KIMBERLY A; Whitesboro SR HS; Marcy, NY; (Y); Church Yth Grp; Exploring; Girl Scts; Chorus; Church Choir; School Musical; School Play; Variety Show; Nwsp Rptr; Nwsp Stf; Eng.

KRACH, KIMBERLY A; Chatham HS; Old Chatham, NY; (Y); Church Yth Grp; Drama Clb; Girl Scts; Chorus; School Musical; School Play; JV Crs Cntry; JV Socr; Var Sftbl; Var Tennis; Mst Outstndng Vrsty Vllybl 84; Mst Imprvd Vrsty Tnns 84; Make-Up Artst.

KRAEGER, AMY; South Lewis Central HS; Constableville, NY; (Y); GAA; Chorus; Mrchg Band; Yrbk Stf; Sec Frsh Cls; Rep Stu Cncl; JV Var Socr; Var Trk; Prfct Atten Awd; Alpine Schl Ski Race Team 83-85.

KRAEGER, HANS; Watertown HS; Watertown, NY; (Y); Intnl Clb; Chorus; School Musical; School Play; Stage Crew; Im Bsktbl; Var Ftbl; JV Var Lcrss; Wt Lftg; Key Awd 85; Stu Tech Dirctr 85; Syracuse; Med Spec.

KRAEMER, PAMELA; Warwick Valley Central HS; Warwick, NY; (Y); #119 In Class; Drama Clb; FBLA; Chorus; Madrigals; School Musical; Cazenovia Coll; Special Ed.

KRAFT, ANDREW F; Homell SR HS; Hornell, NY; (Y); 75/200; Var L Bsbl; Hon Roll; MVP Bsbl 85; 1st Tm All Star Sullivan Trls Conf Bsbl 85; Suny Brockport; Hstry.

KRAFT, HEIDI MARIE; Bishop Kearney HS; Rochester, NY; (Y); 31/126; Ski Clb; Band; Concert Band; Jazz Band; Mrchg Band; Orch; School Musical; Symp Band; High Hon Roll; Hon Roll; NYSMA Outstndng Woodwind/Flute 82-83; St John Fisher Coll; Med.

KRAFT, TARA; Earl L Vandermeulen HS; Mt Sinai, NY; (Y); Art Clb; FBLA; Pep Clb; Spanish Clb; Yrbk Stf; VP Frsh Cls; Stu Cncl; Bsktbl; Capt Cheerleading; Fld Hcky; Chem Awd 84; Med.

KRAIS, MARIA; Red Creek HS; Red Creek, NY; (Y); 2/75; French Clb; Yrbk Ed-Chief; Yrbk Phtg; Trs Jr Cls; VP Sr Cls; Bausch & Lomb Sci Awd; High Hon Roll; NHS; Prfct Atten Awd; Sal; Amer Lgn Schl Awd 85; Rotary Clb Sci Awd 85; Alumni Achvt Awd 85; St John Fisher Coll; Bus Mngmnt.

KRAJEWSKI, LISA; Mechanicville HS; Mechanicville, NY; (S); 3/104; Math Tm; Ski Clb; Spanish Clb; Yrbk Stf; Sec Jr Cls; Var JV Cheerleading; High Hon Roll; Hon Roll; NHS; Jr Usher 84; Top 6 Dinner; Union Coll; Econ.

KRAK, KRISTINE LEE; Marcellus Central HS; Marcellus, NY; (Y); 21/164; Computer Clb; Girl Scts; Science Clb; Ski Clb; Band; Chorus; Concert Band; Mrchg Band; School Musical; School Play; Binghamton U; Bio-Chem.

KRAKOWSKI, TRACEY; Frontier Central HS; Hamburg, NY; (S); French Clb; Pep Clb; Hon Roll; NHS; Engrng.

KRAL, ALEX; Mamaroneck HS; Larchmont, NY; (Y); Computer Clb; Pres French Clb; German Clb; Math Clb; Math Tm; Ski Clb; Yrbk Stf; JV Socr; JV Tennis; JV Trk; Outstndng Achvt Soc Stds 83; Westchester Cnty Intl Math Leag Hnr 84-85; Caprice SR Advsr 85-86; Math.

KRALJIC, HELEN; St John Villa HS; Staten Island, NY; (Y); Cmnty Wkr; Hosp Aide; Letterman Clb; Stage Crew; Yrbk Phtg; Yrbk Stf; Crs Cntry; Mgr(s); Swmmng; Trk; Hnrs Intro & Studio Art 83-84; Coachs Awd Trck 84; Ed.

KRALL, MICHAEL; Horace Greeley HS; Chappaqua, NY; (Y); Chess Clb; Concert Band; Jazz Band; Orch; Pep Band; School Musical; Outstndng JR Concert Band 84-85; Chess Excllnce 83-84; Music.

KRALL, RICHARD R; West Seneca West Senior HS; West Seneca, NY; (Y); 5/543; Math Tm; Nwsp Stf; Var Capt Tennis; High Hon Roll; NHS; Bio, Chem Awds 83-84; SUNY Buffalo; Engr.

KRAMEISEN, CHERYL; Peekskill HS; Peekskill, NY; (S); 6/168; French Clb; Girl Scts; Yrbk Stf; Stu Cncl; Bowling; Tennis; High Hon Roll; NHS.

KRAMER, BEN; Watkins Glen HS; Montour Falls, NY; (S); 1/100; Am Leg Boys St; Letterman Clb; Math Clb; Var L Swmmng; Var L Tennis; French Hon Soc; High Hon Roll; NHS; Ntl Merit Ltr; Bio Regnt Awd 84.

KRAMER, DARCI; Tupper Lake Central HS; Tupper Lk, NY; (Y); 21/102; ROTC; Nwsp Stf; Capt Rep Frsh Cls; Capt Rep Soph Cls; Capt Rep Stu Cncl; Var Bsktbl; Var Capt Crs Cntry; Var Gym; Var Capt Trk; Hon Roll; All Northern Awd Athl 84 & 85; Clarkson U; Indstrl Distr.

KRAMER, DAVID H; Blind Brook HS; Rye Brook, NY; (Y); Nwsp Sprt Ed; Ntl Merit Ltr; School Musical; Var L Bsbl; Capt L Bsktbl; Var Crs Cntry; Dartmouth Coll; Radio/TV.

KRAMER, DENNIS J; Springville-Griffith Inst; Boston, NY; (Y); 12/197; JV Var Bsbl; Var Golf; High Hon Roll; NHS; Jim O Neal Mem Sprtsmnshp Awd Bsbl 84; NYS Rgnts Schlrshp 85; Rochester Inst Of Tech; Elec En.

KRAMER, FELICE; Half Hollow Hills High School East; Huntington, NY; (Y); Trs GAA; Hosp Aide; Leo Clb; Nwsp Stf; Lit Mag; Var Crs Cntry; Var Trk; High Hon Roll; NHS; Spanish NHS; Ntl JR Hon Soc 82; Frnch Hnr Soc 85.

KRAMER, HOWARD; Yorktown HS; Yorktown Hts, NY; (Y); Drama Clb; Pep Clb; Quiz Bowl; Acpl Chr; Pres Chorus; School Musical; School Play; Variety Show; Hon Roll; Cmnty Wkr; Tenor In Area All St Chorus 85; Arch.

KRAMER, MICHAEL; Farmingdale HS; N Massapequa, NY; (Y); Chorus; School Musical; School Play; Yrbk Sprt Ed; Bowling; Var JV Socr; Hon Roll; Jr NHS; NHS; Coca-Cola NY St Sctnl Fnlst-Bowling 84-85; Nassau Cnty Bar Assc-Essay Cont-Hnrb Mntn 85; Jrnlsm.

KRAMER, MIKE; Smithtown High School East; Saint James, NY; (Y); French Clb; Off Frsh Cls; Off Soph Cls; Off Sr Cls; Stu Cncl; JV Var Bsktbl; JV Ftbl; Var L Trk; French Hon Soc; High Hon Roll.

KRAMER, RACHEL; Hunter College HS; New York City, NY; (Y); School Musical; School Play; Stage Crew; Debate Tm; Speech Tm; Temple Yth Grp; Chorus; Nwsp Rptr; Yrbk Phtg; Yrbk Stf; Pepsi Chllng Grls Dstnc Awd Cyclng 83; Actng.

KRAMER, SCOTT A; Depew HS; Depew, NY; (Y); 8/254; French Clb; Ski Clb; Band; Chorus; Concert Band; Mrchg Band; School Musical; Trk; Vllybl; NHS; Rnnr Up Hugh O Brien Ldrshp Cntst 83fnatl Hnr Rl 84; Cornell U; Vet Sci.

KRAMER, TODD; Saugerties HS; Malden Hudson, NY; (Y); 17/236; Ski Clb; Varsity Clb; Var Bsktbl; Var Golf; High Hon Roll; NHS; 1st Alt Boys ST 85; Golf Sctn Champ,Qualf Big I & NY ST Champ 85; Ulsler Cnty JR Golf Champ 83; Golf Crs Arch.

KRAMP, RHONDA S; Newfane SR HS; Lockport, NY; (S); 9/166; Varsity Clb; Band; Var Bsktbl; Var JV Fld Hcky; Var JV Sftbl; Hon Roll; Mu Alp Tht; NHS; Radio.

KRANBUHL, MICHAEL; Vernon-Verona-Sherill HS; Blossvale, NY; (Y); Band; JV Ftbl; High Hon Roll; Hon Roll; Cvl Engrng.

KRANIAK, CHRISTINE; Sachem HS; Holbrook, NY; (Y); Dance Clb; Girl Scts; Library Aide; Math Tm; Office Aide; Chorus; Bowling; Sftbl; Tennis; Suffolk CC; Tchng.

KRANJAC, GISELLE; The Mary Louis Acad; Jackson Heights, NY; (Y); Hosp Aide; Intnl Clb; Hon Roll; NHS; Gld Medls Piano Cntsts 83-85; Hrbl Mntn Ntl HS Itln Cntst 85; 13 Yr Awd Dncng 85; Fordham U; Accntng.

KRANSON, ALEX; Tamarac HS; Troy, NY; (Y); Computer Clb; Varsity Clb; Var Tennis; Hon Roll; NHS; U CA Davis; Comp Sci.

KRANTZ, DAVID L; Sidney HS; Sidney, NY; (Y); 7/104; Am Leg Boys St; Boy Scts; Church Yth Grp; Jazz Band; JV Bsktbl; L Golf; Cit Awd; God Cntry Awd; High Hon Roll; Pres NHS; Rotry Clb & Spengler Fund Engr & Regnts Schlrshps 85; Clarkson U; Chem Engr.

KRANZLE, JENNIFER; Sachem North HS; Farmingville, NY; (Y); Drama Clb; German Clb; Girl Scts; Library Aide; Ski Clb; Band; Chorus; Church Choir; Madrigals; School Musical.

KRASE, JOHN; Cardinal Spellman HS; Bronx, NY; (Y); Boys Clb Am; Boy Scts; Church Yth Grp; Dance Clb; Pep Clb; Service Clb; Off Jr Cls; Capt Swmmng; Coaching Awd Swwng 83-84 & 84-85; Metro NYC Cath HS Athl Assoc Swmmng All Str Tm 84-85; Comp Sci.

KRASINSKI, RICHARD; St Francis Prep; Whitestone, NY; (S); 32/693; Civic Clb; Math Clb; Bowling; Ftbl; High Hon Roll; Acdmc All-American 85; Engrng.

KRASNIEWICZ, CATHY; Warwick Valley HS; Warwick, NY; (Y); 9/200; VP Pres Church Yth Grp; Drama Clb; Ski Clb; School Play; Rep Soph Cls; Rep Stu Cncl; Var Diving; Var Swmmng; Var Vllybl; High Hon Roll; Natl Sci Olympd Chem Fnlst 84; 2nd Pl Physcs 85.

KRASSNER, AMY L; Clarkstown South HS; New City, NY; (Y); 30/556; Ed Yrbk Stf; Capt Gym; Lcrss; Socr; Jr NHS; Mu Alp Tht; NHS; Regents Schlrshp 85; U Of New Hampshire; Intl Lawyer.

KRATZ, JOHN A; C W Baker HS; Baldwinsville, NY; (Y); 20/400; Am Leg Boys St; Church Yth Grp; Jazz Band; Mrchg Band; Symp Band; Yrbk Stf; Rep Stu Cncl; High Hon Roll; NHS; Ntl Merit Ltr; Acad All Amer 85; Pre-Law.

KRATZKE, TODD; Alden Central HS; Alden, NY; (Y); 40/200; Church Yth Grp; French Clb; Var JV Ftbl; Var JV Trk; Var L Wrstlng; NYS Regnts Schlrshp 85; 4 Yr Schlrshp-USAF Acad 85; USAF Acad; Attrny.

KRAUS, CATHY L; Plainedge HS; Bethpage, NY; (Y); 35/311; French Clb; FNA; Hosp Aide; School Play; Crs Cntry; Trk; Hon Roll; NY STA Regents Schlrshp 85; Villahova U; Nursing.

KRAUS, KATHLEEN; Honeoye Central Schl; Springwater, NY; (S); 3/64; Spanish Clb; Color Guard; School Musical; VP Frsh Cls; Trs Stu Cncl; JV Capt Cheerleading; High Hon Roll; Rotary Awd; Chorus; Hnr Ment Wrld Poerty Mag 84; Olymp Of Mind 82; Ivy League; Psych.

KRAUSE, JODY L; Palmyra Macedon HS; Palmyra, NY; (Y); Aud/Vis; German Clb; Ski Clb; Varsity Clb; Mrchg Band; Symp Band; Var Sftbl; Var Capt Vllybl; Hon Roll; NY St Regents Schlrshp 85; Suny Cortland; Med.

KRAUSE, KARL E; Deposit Central HS; Deposit, NY; (Y); 5/79; Varsity Clb; Var Bsbl; Var Bsktbl; Capt Var Ftbl; Hon Roll; NHS; Homecmg Def Back Of Game 84; Rotary Yth Ldrshp Conf 85; E All Starm Tm Ftbl Lnebackr 84; Colgate; Pre-Dntl.

KRAUSE, PAUL; Fillmore Central Schl; Fillmore, NY; (S); 4/50; Am Leg Boys St; Varsity Clb; VP Jr Cls; VP Sr Cls; Rep Stu Cncl; Var Bsbl; Var Capt Socr; Var Trk; Var Capt Wrstlng; NHS; SUNY-GENESEO; Math.

KRAUSE, WILLIAM A; New York Mills HS; New Hartford, NY; (Y); Am Leg Boys St; Church Yth Grp; Spanish Clb; Varsity Clb; Band; Jazz Band; Var Capt Bsktbl; Var L Ftbl; Var L Tennis; Hon Roll; EMT.

KRAUSS, DEBORAH J; Blind Brook HS; Rye Brook, NY; (Y); 1/89; French Clb; Temple Yth Grp; Jazz Band; Symp Band; Nwsp Stf; Rep Sr Cls; Var Crs Cntry; Ntl Merit SF; Cmnty Wkr; Natl French Contest 80-84; Iona Coll Language Contest 83-84; Century Iii Leadership Schlrshp 84.

KRAUSS, ERIC; Ardsley HS; Ardsley, NY; (Y); Drama Clb; Temple Yth Grp; Varsity Clb; Rep Frsh Cls; Rep Soph Cls; Rep Jr Cls; Rep Sr Cls; Stu Cncl; Capt Ftbl; Trk; Ldr Corp 81; Century 3 Ldrshp Pgm 83, 84 & 85; SUNY Binghamton; Bus.

KRAUSS, ERIC C; St John The Baptist HS; Smithtown, NY; (Y); 201/600; Mathletes; Math Clb; Math Tm; Political Wkr; Nwsp Rptr; Nwsp Stf; JV Crs Cntry; JV Trk; Hon Roll; NY ST Regnts Schlrshp 85; Iona Coll Merit Awd 85; SUNY Albany; CPA.

KRAUSS, KAREN L; Warsaw Central Schl; Warsaw, NY; (Y); 20/93; Debate Tm; Trs Drama Clb; Yrbk Stf; Rep Stu Cncl; Var Capt Cheerleading; Var Socr; Var JV Sftbl; Cit Awd; Jr NHS; Regents Schlrshp Awd 84-85; Pltcl Sci.

KRAUSS, RIVKA; Shulamith HS; Flushing, NY; (S); 1/32; Cmnty Wkr; Quiz Bowl; Temple Yth Grp; School Play; Ed Yrbk Stf; Lit Mag; Hon Roll; NHS; Val; Queens Coll; Spch Thrpy.

KRAUTH, MARLENE; Brocton Central HS; Brocton, NY; (Y); Letterman Clb; Ski Clb; Varsity Clb; Band; Trs Sr Cls; VP Stu Cncl; JV Var Bsktbl; Var L Sftbl; High Hon Roll; Rgnts Schlrshp 85; Rochester Inst Tech; Chem.

KRAVAT, JENNIFER M; Laguavdia HS; New York, NY; (Y); 78/588; Dance Clb; Drama Clb; Office Aide; PAVAS; Teachers Aide; Thesps; School Musical; School Play; Stage Crew; NHS; Theatre.

KRAVETZKY, LESLIE; Commack High Schl North; E Northport, NY; (Y); MMM; Spanish Clb; Teachers Aide; Chorus; School Musical; School Play; Swing Chorus; Jr Cls; High Hon Roll; NHS; Frgn Lang.

KRAWIECKI, JAMES A; Amsterdam HS; Fort Johnson, NY; (Y); 21/335; Cmnty Wkr; Yrbk Stf; Hon Roll; NHS; NY ST Regents Schlrshp 85; Fulton Montgomery; Engineering.

KREACIC, HELEN; Moravia Central Schl; Locke, NY; (Y); Ski Clb; Stage Crew; Pres Sr Cls; Trs Stu Cncl; High Hon Roll; Pres French Clb; JV Crs Cntry; Crmnl Jstc.

KREBS, CHARITY; Holy Angels Acad; Williamsville, NY; (Y); 4/38; Chorus; School Musical; Nwsp Stf; Lit Mag; Pres Soph Cls; Rep Jr Cls; VP Stu Cncl; Var Badmtn; High Hon Roll; NHS; Canisius Coll; Jrnlsm.

KREGER, LORI; Oneonta SR HS; Oneonta, NY; (Y); 6/141; Drama Clb; Key Clb; Spanish Clb; Varsity Clb; Stage Crew; Yrbk Stf; Var Capt Sftbl; High Hon Roll; NHS; NY ST Regents Schlrshp 85.

KREHBIEL, DOUGLAS M; Hunter College HS; Kew Gardens, NY; (Y); Chess Clb; Computer Clb; Pres Math Clb; Math Tm; Chorus; Var L Bsbl; Capt Bowling; Mu Alp Tht; Ntl Merit Ltr; German Clb; NYS Rgnts Schlrshp 85; Rensselaer Poly Inst; Comp Engr.

KREIN, TIMOTHY P; Vestal SR HS; Appalachin, NY; (Y); 7/450; Mathletes; Im Bsktbl; JV Ftbl; High Hon Roll; NY ST Sci Olympiad West Pnt 85; Ntl Merit Hnrb Mntn 84; IBM Watson Schlrshp Semi-Fnlst 85; Broome CC; Comp Sci.

KREIS, CATHY A; East Syracuse Minoa HS; East Syracuse, NY; (Y); 12/338; Cmnty Wkr; Exploring; Latin Clb; Science Clb; Variety Show; Var Capt Cheerleading; Im Lcrss; High Hon Roll; Hon Roll; NHS; NYS Regents Schlrshp 85; Achvmnt Awd In Bio 83; St Lawrence U; Bio.

KREMBS, MARY; Onteora HS; West Hurley, NY; (S); 16/250; Drama Clb; Math Tm; Color Guard; Stage Crew; High Hon Roll; Hon Roll; NHS; Ntl Merit Ltr; Church Yth Grp; Acpl Chr; Bst Color Guard Capt Novice Div EMBA 84; Rifle Instrctr Mrchg Bnd 84; RIT; Comp Mthmtcs.

KREMPA, STEVEN M; Niskayuna HS; Schdy, NY; (Y); German Clb; Lit Mag; NHS; Grmn Natl Hnr Scty 85.

KRENITSKY, DARIA; Solvay HS; Syracuse, NY; (Y); Spanish Clb; Trs Concert Band; Ed Yrbk Rptr; Yrbk Stf; Off Soph Cls; Off Jr Cls; High Hon Roll; NHS; Mu Alpha Theta; Cornell U; Sci.

KRENZER, DAWN; Caledoria Mumford Central School; Caledonia, NY; (Y); 3/95; Pres 4-H; French Clb; Math Tm; Science Clb; Band; School Musical; Stat Bsbl; High Hon Roll; Pres NHS; Am Leg Aux Girls St; Regnts & Salvatn Army Schlrshps 85; Keuka Coll; Socl Wrk.

KRENZER, DEBORAH; Caledonia-Mumford Central Schl; Caledonia, NY; (Y); 3/88; Sec Church Yth Grp; Pres VP 4-H; Pres French Clb; Math Tm; Science Clb; Band; Stat Socr; 4-H Awd; High Hon Roll; NHS; Natl Lagn Arts Olympd 83; All-Star Smmr Sftbl 83-84; Elem Educ.

KRENZER, KATHLEEN; Wheatland-Chili HS; Scottsville, NY; (Y); Chorus; School Play; Yrbk Ed-Chief; Yrbk Stf; Stu Cncl; Stat Bsktbl; Stat Socr; Hon Roll; Mgmt.

KREPPEIN, KIMBERLY; Valley Central HS; Walden, NY; (Y); 33/281; Off Frsh Cls; Sec Soph Cls; Off Jr Cls; Rep Stu Cncl; Stat Bsbl; Capt Cheerleading; Hon Roll; NHS; Spanish NHS; Chrldr Of Yr Awd 85; Chirprctr.

KRESGE, BETH ANN; C W Baker HS; Baldwinsville, NY; (Y); JA; Band; Chorus; Nwsp Phtg; Yrbk Phtg; Yrbk Stf; Lit Mag; Var L Swmmng; Var Timer; Var L Trk; Bldwnsvll Comm Schlrshp $500 85; Mnylschlstc Art Awd Cert Of Merit 85; Yth Ftnss Achvmnt Awd 84-85; Art Inst Of Philadelphia; Photo.

KRESS, BRIAN T; Lockport SR HS; Lockport, NY; (Y); 111/411; Boy Scts; Red Cross Aide; Band; Concert Band; Mrchg Band; Symp Band; JV Var Wrstlng; Vet.

KRETSER, BRENDA; Johnstown HS; Ft Palin, NY; (Y); Color Guard; Mrchg Band; Vllybl; Hon Roll; Cazenovia; Bus.

KRETZ, CHRISTOPHER; Archbishop Molloy HS; Bayside, NY; (Y); 23/409; Lit Mag; JV Crs Cntry; Var Trk; NHS; Ntl Merit SF; Lit.

KREZMIEN, BRIAN; Springville Griffith Inst; Springville, NY; (Y); Exploring; Band; Chorus; Rep Frsh Cls; Rep Soph Cls; Rep Jr Cls; Rep Sr Cls; Rep Stu Cncl; JV Var Bsbl; JV Var Bsktbl; Marine Corps; Aviation.

KRICHMAR, TODD A; Baldwin SR HS; Baldwin, NY; (Y); 24/503; Am Leg Boys St; Political Wkr; Jazz Band; Variety Show; Nwsp Stf; Lit Mag; God Cntry Awd; High Hon Roll; NHS; Spanish NHS; Columbia Jrnlsm Awd 85; Spnsh Merit Awd 82; Hgh Hnr Grad 82 & 85.

KRIEGER, CHRIS; Port Jervis HS; Godeffroy, NY; (Y); Cmnty Wkr; Varsity Clb; Var L Bsktbl; Var L Ftbl; Var Trk; High Hon Roll; Hon Roll; Rotry Clb Outstndng Stu Ath 83-85; Mst Imprvd Ftbl Plyr 82-83; Engrng.

KRIEGER, DAVE; De Sales HS; Lockport, NY; (Y); Varsity Clb; VP Bsbl; JV Capt Bsktbl; Var Capt Ftbl; Wt Lftg; Bus.

KRIEGER, KEITH; Skaneateles HS; Skaneateles, NY; (S); Var Ice Hcky; Var Lcrss; Var Socr; Hon Roll; NHS; Bus.

KRIEGER, LYNETTE; Alden Central HS; Alden, NY; (Y); 19/192; Pres Trs Exploring; Letterman Clb; Office Aide; Science Clb; Varsity Clb; Nwsp Stf; Yrbk Stf; Hon Roll; Kiwanis Awd; Alden Fire Dept Schlrshp 85; Rifle Letter 83-85; Acad Letter Winner 83-85; Canisius Coll; Accntng.

KRIESEL, LAURA; Lierpool HS; Liverpool, NY; (S); 524/829; Church Yth Grp; DECA; Hosp Aide; JA; Office Aide; Church Choir; Cheerleading; Swmmng; Stu Of The Mnth 85; 3rd Pl In St Comp 85; Crouse-Irving Schl Of Nrsng.

KRINSKY, DARLENE; Kings Park HS; Kings Park, NY; (Y); 39/465; Art Clb; Office Aide; Spanish Clb; Chorus; Nwsp Ed-Chief; Nwsp Stf; Lit Mag; High Hon Roll; Jr NHS; NHS; Adelphi U.

KRINSKY, LAURA; Smithtown High Schl West; Smithtown, NY; (Y); Hosp Aide; Temple Yth Grp; School Musical; Stage Crew; Var Mgr(s); Var Score Keeper; JV Sftbl; High Hon Roll; NHS; Spanish NHS; SCI.

KRISHER, KIM; Lyndonville HS; Medina, NY; (S); 3/65; Am Leg Aux Girls St; Church Yth Grp; Varsity Clb; Trs Band; Var Bsktbl; Var Socr; Var Capt Sftbl; DAR Awd; NHS; Farm Bureau Ctznshp Schlrshp Awd 85; All Cnty Band 83-85; Region Bsktbl, Sftbl All Leag Teams 84-85; U Of Rochester; Engrng.

KRISHNAPPA, NANDINI; Shenendehowa HS; Clifton Park, NY; (Y); 1/650; Drama Clb; Temple Yth Grp; Yrbk Sprt Ed; Rep Stu Cncl; Var Capt Tennis; NCTE Awd; VP NHS; Ntl Merit Ltr; Val; Key Clb; Pres Fitness Awd 81-82; Acadmc Excllnt Comm 83-85; Engrng Mgmt.

KRISTEL, KRISTINE; Linton HS; Schenectady, NY; (Y); Dance Clb; Key Clb; Red Cross Aide; VP Service Clb; Ski Clb; Teachers Aide; Rep Soph Cls; Rep Jr Cls; Sr Cls; JV Cheerleading; Lwyr.

KRITAS, ALEXIOS T; The Waldorf Schl; Woodmere, NY; (Y); Church Yth Grp; Cmnty Wkr; Chorus; Madrigals; Orch; School Musical; School Play; Yrbk Stf; Pres Jr Cls; Crs Cntry; Regents State Schlrshp 85; Williams Coll; Pol Sci.

KRITZLER, ROBERT; Whitesboro SR HS; Marcy, NY; (Y); 15/325; Boy Scts; Concert Band; Jazz Band; Mrchg Band; Orch; Var L Trk; Jr NHS; NHS; Eagle Scout Awd 84; Cornell U; Vet.

KRIVICICH, KRISTINE; New Field HS; Selden, NY; (Y); Pres Church Yth Grp; Chorus; Church Choir; Jazz Band; High Hon Roll; Hon Roll; Variety Show; NYSSMA Outstndng Awd Level 4 82-83, Level 5 83-84, Level 6 84-85; Engrng.

KRMENEC, ANNE M; Union-Endicott HS; Endicott, NY; (Y); 161/430; Computer Clb; Spanish Clb; Band; Color Guard; Flag Corp; Jazz Band; Mrchg Band; Pep Band; Symp Band; Yrbk Stf; Regnts Schlrsph 85; Broome Cmnty Coll; Med Lab.

KROHN, RALPH; Bishop Timon HS; Buffalo, NY; (Y); Aud/Vis; Church Yth Grp; Library Aide; Nwsp Rptr; Score Keeper; Timer; Hon Roll; Awd Hgst Mark Voc Cls.

KROL, ANGELA; Emerson V H S HS; Buffalo, NY; (Y); Yrbk Phtg; Yrbk Stf; Var Capt Bowling; Var Mgr(s); Stat Socr; Var Tennis; Hon Roll.

KROLIKOWSKI, EILEEN; Floral Park Memorial HS; Floral Park, NY; (Y); 3/184; Trs Mathletes; Orch; School Musical; Variety Show; Nwsp Ed-Chief; Yrbk Stf; NHS; Ntl Merit Ltr; MIT; Bio.

KROLL, MARY; Williamsville East HS; Williamsville, NY; (Y); 27/389; Girl Scts; Yrbk Stf; JV Stat Trk; Hon Roll; Rgnts Schlrshp 85; 1st Cls 81; Amherst YES Outstndng Vlntr 83; ST U Coll At Geneseo; Spec Ed.

KROMER, SUSAN M; A G Berner HS; Massapequa, NY; (Y); 14/478; Girl Scts; Teachers Aide; Acpl Chr; Band; Orch; Cheerleading; Hon Roll; NHS; Ntl Merit Schol; SUNY Farmingdale; Bus Admin.

KRON, ERIC J; Susquehanna Valley SR HS; Binghamton, NY; (Y); 13/177; Ski Clb; Nwsp Stf; Yrbk Phtg; Var Golf; High Hon Roll; Hon Roll; Jr NHS; NHS; Ntl Merit SF; Penn ST U; Biochem.

KRONE, STACEY J; Glen Cove HS; Glen Cove, NY; (Y); Pep Clb; Pres Spanish Clb; Trs Temple Yth Grp; Nwsp Rptr; Yrbk Stf; Rep Stu Cncl; Mgr Lcrss; Mgr Socr; Mgr Wrstlng; Hon Roll; Regents Schlrshp 85; 10th Yr Eng Awd 83; SUNY Albany; Corp Law.

KRONER, JILL; Eastridge HS; Rochester, NY; (Y); 1/200; French Clb; Varsity Clb; Color Guard; School Musical; Var JV Bsktbl; Var Fld Hcky; Var JV Vllybl; High Hon Roll; NHS; GAA; Harvard Book Awd; Mth.

KRONER, KEVIN T; Columbia HS; Rennselaer, NY; (Y); Am Leg Boys St; Ski Clb; Nwsp Rptr; Ed Nwsp Stf; Wt Lftg; High Hon Roll; Hon Roll; Catholic U Of Amer; Lawyr.

KROOG, JOHN; Lindenhurst HS; Lindenhurst, NY; (Y); Varsity Clb; VP Jr Cls; VP Capt Bsbl; JV Var Ftbl; La Crosse MIP 84; Bsbl JV Lindy Pride 85; Ftbl JV Ironman 83; Engrng.

KROPP, DARREN D; North Babylon SR HS; North Babylon, NY; (Y); 20/560; Computer Clb; Mathletes; Capt Bowling; Trk; High Hon Roll; NHS; NY Poly Tech; Elec Engr.

KROSLOW, MICHELE; The Stoney Brook Schl; Stony Brook, NY; (Y); 42/84; Church Yth Grp; Office Aide; Teachers Aide; Im Bsktbl; Im Fld Hcky; JV Var Sftbl; Hon Roll; Merit Achvt Awd 83 & 85; Messiah Coll PA; Elem Educ.

KROUSE, DEBORAH; Mohawk Central Schl; Mohawk, NY; (S); 4/77; Church Yth Grp; Cmnty Wkr; French Clb; Spanish Clb; Teachers Aide; Varsity Clb; Bsktbl; Tennis; Vllybl; Sec NHS; Hnr Smnar; Hnr Rll; JR Ntl Hnr Soc; Utica Coll; Nrsg.

KROUZIL, DENISE; Sachem HS; Holbrook, NY; (Y); 39/1383; German Clb; Math Tm; Concert Band; Mrchg Band; Yrbk Sprt Ed; Yrbk Stf; Jr NHS; NHS; 2nd Pl Schl Sci Fair 84; Hnr Ment Grmn 83; Recgntn LI Sci Cngrss 84; Phy Thrpy.

KRUEGER, ARTHUR; Hicksville HS; Hicksville, NY; (Y); Im Stat Bsktbl; JV Ftbl; Var L Trk.

KRUEGER, DAWN M; Mc Mahon HS; Buffalo, NY; (Y); Sec Jr Cls; Stu Cncl; Merit Awds; Wnnr Schl Essay Cont 83-84; Srgcl Nrs.

KRUEGER, JC; York Central Schl; Leicester, NY; (Y); Drama Clb; Ski Clb; VICA; VP Jr Cls; Pres Sr Cls; Var Crs Cntry; JV Wrstlng; High Hon Roll; NHS; Sci Clsrm Hnrs 83; VIA Statemn Awd 84; 2nd Pl Machine Draftng NYS VICA Skill Olympcs 85; Engr.

KRUFT, DAVID; Floral Park Memorial HS; Floral Park, NY; (Y); 21/188; Church Yth Grp; Orch; School Musical; Nwsp Rptr; Yrbk Ed-Chief; High Hon Roll; Hon Roll; VP NHS; Pres Schlr; Mathletes; Regents Schlrshp 85; Messiah Coll.

KRUGER, CHRIS; Riverhead HS; Manorville, NY; (Y); 40/250; Church Yth Grp; Exploring; Chorus; Swing Chorus; Var L Ftbl; Var L Trk; Var L Wrstlng; All Lge Ftbll Nwsdy; Mnrvlle Athltcs Assn; All Lge Wrstlng; Bus.

KRUGER, DAVE; Amsterdam HS; Ft Johnson, NY; (Y); Bsbl; Alfred; Carpentry.

KRUGER, JOHN; Archbishop Molloy HS; Richmond Hill, NY; (Y); 137/361; NY ST Regents Schrlshp 85; Hofstra U; Engrng.

KRUK, JACKIE; Mont Pleasnat HS; Schenectady, NY; (Y); 12/258; French Clb; Key Clb; Pep Clb; Cheerleading; Sec French Hon Soc; High Hon Roll; VP NHS; Frnch Hon Soc Scholar 85; Pres Acad Fit Cert 85; Civil Engrng.

KRUK, JANE; W Seneca W SR HS; Buffalo, NY; (S); 146/532; VP DECA; JA; Rep Frsh Cls; Rep Soph Cls; Rep Jr Cls; Rep Sr Cls; Rep Stu Cncl; JC Awd; Bus Admin.

KRUK, JEFFREY; Haverling Central HS; Bath, NY; (Y); French Clb; Math Clb; Ski Clb; Yrbk Phtg; Bsbl; Hon Roll; Bio Sci.

KRUKONIS, MARY; John F Kennedy HS; Utica, NY; (Y); Church Yth Grp; Drama Clb; Hosp Aide; Teachers Aide; Church Choir; Orch; School Play; Stage Crew; Nwsp Rptr; Nwsp Stf; Ntl Honor Soc 85; Cert Of Apprectn-Volntry Serv Faxton 84; Nursng.

KRULL, TIMOTHY R; West Seneca West SR HS; West Seneca, NY; (Y); 36/543; Church Yth Grp; Nwsp Stf; Hon Roll; Pres Schlr; NYS Rgnts Schlrshp 85; Alfred U; Elec Engrng.

KRUMBHOLZ, KAREN J; Holy Trinity HS; Freeport, NY; (S).

KRUPA, MICHAEL; Cardinal Mooney HS; Rochester, NY; (Y); 59/316; Var Bowling; Hon Roll; Best Acctg Avg 85; 2nd Pl Coca-Cola ST Bowling Champ 85; Acctg.

KRUPKE, BECKY; Pulaski HS; Pulaski, NY; (Y); French Clb; Ski Clb; Band; Mrchg Band; School Play; Yrbk Bus Mgr; Yrbk Stf; Var Socr; Swmmng; Tennis; Typhng Cont JCC 85; Schl Press Inst Yrbk 85; Tourism.

KRUPKIN, ILONA; Ezra Acad Of Queens; College Point, NY; (Y); 1/40; Art Clb; Cmnty Wkr; Dance Clb; Library Aide; Science Clb; Chorus; Yrbk Stf; Hon Roll; Val; Pres Queens Coll Awd 82-84; NHS 85; NY Inst Tech Awd 83-84; Pace U; Bus Admin.

KRUPSKI, ANTHONY; Cardinal Ohara HS; Cheektowaga, NY; (S); 1/140; Rep Frsh Cls; Rep Soph Cls; VP Jr Cls; VP Sr Cls; Rep Stu Cncl; Var Capt Bsbl; Var Capt Bsktbl; Hon Roll; VP NHS; All-Cthlc Bsktbl; 3-Time All-Cthlc Bsebl; Prtl Schlrshp; Pharm.

KRUPSKI, JAMES; Mattituck HS; Peconic, NY; (Y); 10/110; Mathletes; Math Tm; Spanish Clb; Jazz Band; School Play; Variety Show; Hon Roll; NHS; Suffolk Cnty All Star Mth Tm 85; NY ST All Star Mth Tm 85; Comp Pgmmg.

KRUSKA, GINA MARIE; Hempstead HS; Hempstead, NY; (Y); Office Aide; Varsity Clb; Flag Corp; Mrchg Band; Sec Sr Cls; Var Tennis; High Hon Roll; Hon Roll; NHS; Bus Admin.

KRUTCHEN, MELISSA; Pittsford Mendon HS; Pittsford, NY; (Y); AFS; Cmnty Wkr; Band; Mrchg Band; Yrbk Stf; Var JV Fld Hcky; JV Swmmng; High Hon Roll; Hon Roll; NHS; Vrsty Ltr Skng 84-85; Intntl Bus.

KRYM, HOLLIS; Pittsford-Mendon HS; Pittsford, NY; (Y); AFS; Cmnty Wkr; Math Tm; Socr; Hon Roll; NHS; Rep HS In Albany NY Senate Stu Plcy Forum 84-55; 2 YMCA Yth & Govt Conf 84-85.

KRYMAN, LORI; Notre Dame HS; Batavia, NY; (S); 4/81; Yrbk Bus Mgr; Capt Soph Cls; Stu Cncl; Var Trk; DAR Awd; High Hon Roll; NHS; Prfct Atten Awd; Computer Clb; Office Aide; NYS Cncl On Yth Ldrshp 84-85; Vet Sci.

KRZEMIENSKI, ELLEN; Lindenhurst SR HS; Lindenhurst, NY; (Y); Spanish Clb; Band; Concert Band; Mrchg Band; Nwsp Ed-Chief; Nwsp Rptr; Yrbk Phtg; NHS; Bus Admin.

KRZYMINSKI, JOHN; St John The Baptist HS; Seaford, NY; (Y); Boy Scts; Bowling; Hon Roll.

KRZYWICKI, CHERYL; Turner Carroll HS; Buffalo, NY; (Y); 2/125; Cmnty Wkr; French Clb; Pep Clb; Service Clb; Nwsp Stf; Yrbk Stf; JV Var Sftbl; High Hon Roll; Hon Roll; NHS; Prfct Atten 83-85; Frnch Awd 83-85; Carrier Mnth Nwsp 84; Canisius Coll; Pre-Law.

KRZYZEWSKI, DAVE; Union-Endicott HS; Endicott, NY; (S); 35/450; Church Yth Grp; Key Clb; Band; Concert Band; Jazz Band; Mrchg Band; Symp Band; High Hon Roll; Hon Roll; NHS; Rochester Inst Of Tech; Comp.

KRZYZYKOWSKI, GAIL; Maryvale HS; Cheektowaga, NY; (Y); Drama Clb; Acpl Chr; Band; Chorus; Church Choir; Concert Band; Jazz Band; Mrchg Band; Orch; Symp Band; MI Musicn 83-84; Music Tchr.

KUAN, CHIEN HUA; Seward Park HS; New York, NY; (Y); Teachers Aide; Chorus; Nwsp Stf; Yrbk Stf; Meritorious Svc Cert 85; Sci Hon Cert 84; Cert Merit Exclint Atten 84; Biomed Engrng.

KUBA, RONALD; Queensbury HS; Glen Falls, NY; (Y); 72/226; Ski Clb; Band; Concert Band; Orch; Symp Band; JV Crs Cntry; Hon Roll; Prfct Atten Awd; Warren Cnty Musci Ed Awd 85; Southampton U.

KUBERA, MICHAEL T; Dunkirk HS; Dunkirk, NY; (Y); Am Leg Boys St; Varsity Clb; Rep Stu Cncl; Capt JV Ftbl; High Hon Roll; Hon Roll; NHS; Achvt Awds Soc St, Math I & II & Rgnts Bio 83-85; Vet Med.

KUBES, ANISSA; Mohonasen HS; Schenectady, NY; (Y); Drama Clb; Band; Concert Band; Flag Corp; Mrchg Band; Pep Band; Swing Chorus; Rep Frsh Cls; JV Cheerleading; Hon Roll; Sectrl.

KUBIAK, DAVE; Frontier Central HS; Hamburg, NY; (Y); Aud/Vis; Drama Clb; Ski Clb; School Play; Nwsp Rptr; Nwsp Stf; Yrbk Ed-Chief; Yrbk Stf; Rep Stu Cncl; Hon Roll; Law Enfrcmnt.

KUBIAK, JAMES; Maryvale SR HS; Cheektowaga, NY; (Y); Church Yth Grp; French Clb; Varsity Clb; Stage Crew; JV Bsbl; JV Var Ftbl; Var L Trk; JV Wrstlng; Outstndng & Offnsv Prep Ftbl Plyr Of Yr 84; Southhampton U; Marine Bio.

KUBIAK, SHELIE; Shenendehowa HS; Clifton Park, NY; (Y); Church Yth Grp; Chorus; Church Choir; Yrbk Stf; Rep Soph Cls; Rep Jr Cls; Rep Stu Cncl; High Hon Roll; NHS; Schltc Achvt Awd 83-85; Cert Merit NY ST Sntr Joe Bruno 85; Union U; Bio.

KUBIK, ANTHONY S; Johnson City SR HS; Binghamton, NY; (Y); 11/221; Boy Scts; Computer Clb; Var L Socr; Var L Trk; High Hon Roll; Hon Roll; NHS; St Schlr; Eagl Sct; Marshl Hahn Engrng Merit Schlrshp; VA Tech Blacksburg VA; Engrng.

KUBLER, KEVIN; Christ The King R HS; Maspeth, NY; (Y); 26/387; Computer Clb; Bsbl; Fld Hcky; Golf; Vllybl.

KUBLER, ROBERT; Curtis HS; Staten Island, NY; (Y); Teachers Aide; VP Socr; Hnr Key 85; Theodore Huebener Memorl Grmn Exclinc Awd 85; Bus Mgmt.

KUBOW, STEPHEN A; City Honors Schl; Buffalo, NY; (Y); 5/97; Math Tm; Pres Band; Concert Band; Jazz Band; Mrchg Band; VP Soph Cls; VP Jr Cls; VP Sr Cls; ST U NY Buffalo Adv Coll Cred Pgm 84-85; NYS Regents Schlrsph Wnnr 85; Hnrs Pgm SUNY Buffalo 85; Chem.

KUCHAR, NATALIE A; Shenendehowa HS; Canton, MI; (Y); Debate Tm; DECA; FBLA; Hosp Aide; Leo Clb; Pres Speech Tm; Powder Puff Ftbl; JV Sftbl; High Hon Roll; NY U; Bus.

KUCHERA, MARK; Oriskany Central Schl; Oriskany, NY; (Y); Varsity Clb; Band; Pres Sr Cls; Var L Crs Cntry; Var L Trk; Sec NHS; Exploring; Spanish Clb; Engrng.

KUCHTA, TRACY; Sweethome SR HS; Tonawanda, NY; (Y); 24/425; Church Yth Grp; Cmnty Wkr; Girl Scts; Stat Bsktbl; JV Socr; Hon Roll; NHS; Prfct Atten Awd; Spanish NHS; Grl Sct 10 Yr Pin & Silvr Awd 84; SUNY Oneonta; Ststcs.

KUCINSKI, DANIELLE; Union-Endicott HS; Endicott, NY; (Y); Drama Clb; School Play; Yrbk Phtg; Ed Lit Mag; Hon Roll; Kodak Mdln Of Exc In Phtgrphy 84-85; Gld Key Blue Rbn Schlstc Phtgrphy Art Cmptn 84-85; Phtgrphy.

KUCK, BARBARA; Rye Neck HS; Mamaroneck, NY; (Y); 4/98; Pres VP Key Clb; Pres Frsh Cls; Pres Jr Cls; Pres Sr Cls; Rep Stu Cncl; Var Capt Fld Hcky; DAR Awd; Trs NHS; Church Yth Grp; School Play; Holy Crs Bk Prz Outstndg Scholar 84; Key Clb Spec Svc Awd 83-85; Tm Awd 82 & 84; Dartmouth Coll.

KUDER, STEVEN; Lintoin HS; Schenectady, NY; (Y); Intnl Clb; Math Clb; Spanish Clb; Varsity Clb; Rptr VICA; JV Ftbl; L Trk; Wt Lftg; Hon Roll; IL Inst Of Tech; Mech Engrg.

KUDLA, ANNE; De Sales HS; N Tonawanda, NY; (S); 3/40; Varsity Clb; Yrbk Stf; Rep Stu Cncl; Var Capt Bsktbl; Var Sftbl; Var Vllybl; Hon Roll; NHS; Spanish NHS.

KUEBLER, KAREN E; Lake Shore Central HS; Derby, NY; (Y); 5/259; Church Choir; Orch; School Musical; School Play; Ed Yrbk Ed-Chief; Cit Awd; DAR Awd; NHS; Church Yth Grp; Drama Clb; Ntl Sci Bio Awd; NYS Sci Supvrs Assn Bio Awd; Girl Sct Gold Awd; U Acad Schlrshp-Slippery Rock U; Slippery Rock U; Music Therapy.

KUEFFNER, KRIS M; New Hyde Park Memorial HS; New Hyde Park, NY; (Y); 24/269; Drama Clb; Mathletes; Varsity Clb; Chorus; Madrigals; School Musical; School Play; Nwsp Stf; Yrbk Stf; Var Capt Crs Cntry; All-Cnty Cross Cntry 81-85; Dist Choir 80-83 & 85; U Of PA; Math.

KUEHNEL, KRISTA K; Lindenhurst SR HS; Lindenhurst, NY; (Y); 5/594; Church Yth Grp; Thesps; School Musical; Jr NHS; Vetrnry Sci.

KUERZDOERFER, BETH; West Seneca East SR HS; Buffalo, NY; (Y); Sec Church Yth Grp; Nwsp Stf; JC Awd; Jr NHS; Ntl Grmn Hnr Scty 84; Bus.

KUGAL, PETER M; Oceanside HS; Oceanside, NY; (Y); 9/532; Key Clb; Mathletes; Office Aide; VP Science Clb; VP Temple Yth Grp; High Hon Roll; Jr NHS; NHS; Math Achvt Awd 81-82; Cert Merit 83, 85; M J Orzano Math Awd 85; NY ST U Buffalo; Elec Engrng.

KUGLER, ELIZABETH; Schroon Lake Central HS; Schroon Lake, NY; (Y); 1/24; Trs Varsity Clb; Yrbk Bus Mgr; Trs Frsh Cls; Trs Soph Cls; Trs Jr Cls; Trs Sr Cls; Co-Capt Bsktbl; Socr; Bausch & Lomb Sci Awd; Pres NHS; Pres Schlrshp Hartwick Coll 85; US Army Rsrve Schlr/Athlte Mdl 85; Hartwick Coll; Nrsg.

KUHL, HEIDI C; Scotia-Glenville HS; Scotia, NY; (Y); 18/255; VP JA; Concert Band; Yrbk Bus Mgr; Ed Yrbk Stf; Pres Frsh Cls; Rep Stu Cncl; NHS; FBLA; German Clb; Band; Hlth Physcs Socty Radiation Essay Cont 1st; Dale Carnegie Yth Schlrshp; JR Achvmnt Area Pres Of Yr 85; Suny Binghamton.

KUHL, JOE; St John The Baptist D HS; Lindenhurst, NY; (Y); Hon Roll; Wrtg Music.

KUHL, LAURA M; Beaver River Central Schl; Croghan, NY; (Y); 5/90; Cmnty Wkr; GAA; VP Spanish Clb; Teachers Aide; Yrbk Stf; Rep Stu Cncl; Var L Cheerleading; Var L Trk; High Hon Roll; Sec NHS; Regents Schlrshp 85; Am H S Math Awd 84; Sci Stu Recgntn Day 84; Herkimer County Comm Coll; Sci.

KUHLMAN, MARIE; Tioga Central HS; Nichols, NY; (Y); Church Yth Grp; Ski Clb; Varsity Clb; Variety Show; Vllybl; Sunny Binghamton; Bus.

KUHN, ERIC; Southside HS; Pine City, NY; (Y); French Clb; Latin Clb; Chorus; Hon Roll; Yth Cnty 85; Engrng Day 85.

KUHN, JANICE M; Wayne Central HS; Macedon, NY; (Y); 25/200; Girl Scts; L Math Tm; Ski Clb; Teachers Aide; Mgr(s); Var L Tennis; Var L Trk; Hon Roll; NHS; Chorus; GSUSA Gold Awd 82; Clarkson U; Math.

KUHN, PHILIP S; Oyster Bay HS; Oyster Bay, NY; (Y); 2/140; Trs Pres Computer Clb; Concert Band; Ed Nwsp Rptr; JV Stat Bsbl; Var L Socr; Trs NHS; Ntl Merit SF; Sal; Mathletes; Temple Yth Grp; Penn ST Schlr 84; Mdl For Piano & Clarnt ST Music Cont 82-84; All County Band 85; Comp Sci.

KUHN, THOMAS; Greece Athena HS; Rochester, NY; (S); 5/281; Church Yth Grp; Science Clb; Ski Clb; Pres VP Band; Concert Band; Jazz Band; School Musical; Stage Crew; High Hon Roll; NHS; Outstndg Cncrt Bnd Mbr 82; Law.

KUILAN JR, ALFREDO; Mt St Michaels Acad; Bronx, NY; (Y); Am Leg Boys St; Church Yth Grp; Cmnty Wkr; Nwsp Rptr; Lit Mag; Off Stu Cncl; Ftbl; Drill Tm; Auxlry Pol Schlstc Achvt Awd NY City 85; Auxlry Pol Svc Awd Mdl; Norwich U; Intl Rel.

KUJAN, DENISE; Scotia Glenville HS; Scotia, NY; (Y); 4-H; German Clb; Hosp Aide; Office Aide; Teachers Aide; Church Choir; JV Fld Hcky; 4-H Awd; High Hon Roll; Hon Roll; Physcl Thrpy.

KUJAWSKI, GAIL; Victor SR HS; Victor, NY; (Y); 96/248; Trs Sec 4-H; Ski Clb; JV Var Socr; Var Trk; High Hon Roll; Hon Roll; Mendon Pony Clb D-3 Tstng Compltn 84; Grphc Art.

KUKLEWICZ, BRIAN; Seneca Vocational HS; Buffalo, NY; (Y); 1/180; Computer Clb; Math Clb; Math Tm; Tennis; High Hon Roll; Hon Roll; Kiwanis Awd; NHS; Pres Schlr; Val; Schlstc Achvt Awd 85; Schl Msk Socty 84; Comp.

KUKODA, KAREN; Buffalo Acad Fo The Sacred Heart; Kenmore, NY; (Y); Church Yth Grp; Red Cross Aide; Ski Clb; Chorus; School Musical; School Play; Stu Cncl; Socr; Sftbl; Bus Mgmt.

KULASZEWSKI, TODD; Cleveland Hill HS; Buffalo, NY; (Y); Boy Scts; Chess Clb; School Musical; Symp Band; Tennis; Solo Music Awd NYSMA 79-84; Duet Music Awd NYSMA 84; Rochester Inst Tech; Arch.

KULERS, LAURA; Mahopac HS; Mahopac, NY; (Y); 13/423; High Hon Roll; Comp Sci.

KULICH, CHRISTINA; Ichabod Crane HS; Kinderhook, NY; (Y); Debate Tm; Drama Clb; Ski Clb; School Musical; School Play; Yrbk Stf; JV Var Fld Hcky; High Hon Roll; NHS; Ntl Merit Ltr; Mst Imprvd Plyr Fld Hcky 84; Johns Hopkins U.

KULICHIK, JEFF; Tully Central Schl; Tully, NY; (Y); 1/80; French Clb; Varsity Clb; Yrbk Stf; Rep Jr Cls; Pres Sr Cls; Var L Bsktbl; Var L Ftbl; Var L Lcrss; French Hon Soc; High Hon Roll; Cortland St Schlrs Day 86.

KULINOWSKI, KAREN; West Seneca East SR HS; W Seneca, NY; (S); 44/365; DECA; Trs Frsh Cls; Trs Soph Cls; Rep Jr Cls; Pres Sr Cls; Sec Stu Cncl; High Hon Roll; Hon Roll; NHS; JA; Hilbert Acad Schlrshp 85; Natl Fnlst DECA 85; Buffalo ST Col6; Scl Wrk.

KULINOWSKI, KRISTEN; West Seneca East SR HS; West Seneca, NY; (Y); Drama Clb; Chorus; School Musical; School Play; Nwsp Ed-Chief; Capt Tennis; NHS; Ntl Merit SF; Var Socr; Hon Roll; Clscl Assn Westrn NY Tst 1st Pl Latn IV 85; Jaycee Awds Music, Math, Latn IV & Spnsh II 85; Psych.

KULINSKI, ELISABETH; Poughkeepsie HS; Poughkeepsie, NY; (Y); School Play; Hon Roll; Look Amer Hstry AP 84-85; Envrnmntl Sci.

KUMBATOVIC, NICHOLAS; Msgr Mcclancy HS; Astoria, NY; (S); 2/229; Cmnty Wkr; Math Tm; Spanish Clb; High Hon Roll; NHS; Spanish NHS; Queens Coll Pres Awd For Achievement 82; Academic All-American Directory 83; Electrical Engrng.

KUMMER, MICHAEL J; Archbishop Molloy HS; Middle Village, NY; (Y); 145/410; Dance Clb; Teachers Aide; Yrbk Phtg; Yrbk Sprt Ed; L JV Bsktbl; L Var Crs Cntry; Im Capt Sftbl; L Var Trk; High Hon Roll; Hon Roll; Villanova; Bus Adm.

KUMP, AUDREY; St Francis Prep; Middle Vill, NY; (Y); 365/696; Dance Clb; Service Clb; Ski Clb; Chorus; Regnt Schlrshp 85; Bus.

KUMP, LISA M; The Mary Louis Acad; Ridgewood, NY; (Y); 2/298; Drama Clb; Orch; School Musical; Pres Frsh Cls; Var Cheerleading; High Hon Roll; Hon Roll; NHS; NEDT Awd; Pres Schlr; Mary Louis Acad Schlrshp 81-82; St Josephs Coll Pres Schlr 85; St Josephs Coll; Chemistry.

KUMPEL, JAMES J; West Hempstead HS; W Hempstead, NY; (Y); 1/335; Am Leg Boys St; Computer Clb; Mathletes; Quiz Bowl; Radio Clb; Nwsp Stf; Stu Cncl; Bsktbl; Var L Tennis; Cit Awd; Princeton Bk Awd Rcptnt 85; 1st Pl Ntl Soc Stds Olympd Am Hstry 85; Rensslr Mdlst RPI Math & Sci 85; Princeton; Engr.

KUMPON, KAREN; Binghamton HS; Binghamton, NY; (Y); 15/548; Am Leg Aux Girls St; Church Yth Grp; VP Spanish Clb; Concert Band; Mrchg Band; Bsktbl; Cheerleading; Vllybl; High Hon Roll; NHS; Comp.

KUNEN, JULIE; New Rochelle HS; New Rochelle, NY; (Y); Model UN; Temple Yth Grp; Orch; Nwsp Rptr; Nwsp Stf; Lit Mag; Rep Jr Cls; High Hon Roll; NHS; Ntl Merit SF; Brown U Alumni Engl Awd; 3rd Pl Cnty Ltn II Cntst; Schl Serv Awd.

KUNKEL, ROBERT J; Greece Arcadia HS; Rochester, NY; (Y); 8/292; Boy Scts; Ski Clb; Pres Jazz Band; Pres Symp Band; Pres Frsh Cls; JV Socr; High Hon Roll; NHS; Exploring; Chorus; Outstndng Muscn 82-84; Regnts Schlrshp 85; SUNY Fredonia; Engrng.

KUNKEL, TRACY A; Guilderland Central HS; Guilderland, NY; (Y); 29/369; Band; Stage Crew; Stu Cncl; High Hon Roll; Ntl Merit Ltr; SUNY Geneseo Alumni Flw Schlrshp 85; NYS Rgnts Schlrshp 85; Exclnce Genl Lat 85; SUNY Geneseo; Bio.

KUNZ, CHARLES; Sachem High School North; Holbrook, NY; (Y); 86/1383; Chorus; NYSSMA 83-84; Comp Sci.

KUNZ, ELIZABETH; Bethlehem Central HS; Delmar, NY; (Y); Hosp Aide; Pres Key Clb; Ski Clb; Rep Frsh Cls; Rep Soph Cls; Rep Jr Cls; JV Socr; Im Vllybl; Hon Roll; Natl Socl Stud Olympd 84; Bus.

KUNZE, LISA; Kenmore East HS; Tonawanda, NY; (Y); French Clb; Hon Roll; Prtl Schlrshp Cardinal O Hara 82; Phy.

KUO, DAVID; Pearl River HS; Tappan, NY; (Y); 2/239; Am Leg Boys St; Pres French Clb; Math Tm; Co-Capt Scholastic Bowl; Orch; Yrbk Stf; Bausch & Lomb Sci Awd; NCTE Awd; Ntl Merit Schol; Sal; Brown U; Med.

KUO, HSIAO; Newtown HS; Elmhurst, NY; (Y); 30/603; Computer Clb; Math Tm; Office Aide; Teachers Aide; Orch; Hon Roll; Prfct Atten Awd; Regents Schlrshp 85; Polytech Inst NY; Elec Engr.

KUO, JOHN S; Bronx High School Of Science HS; Whitestone, NY; (Y); Hosp Aide; Math Tm; Science Clb; Orch; Lit Mag; VP NHS; Ntl Merit SF; Church Yth Grp; Office Aide; Prfct Atten Awd; RPI Mdl Encllnt Math & Sci 84; ACS Chem Exam 84; Bronze Mdl NY Math Fair 83; Bio.

KUO, MARK HUAN FU; The Bronx High School Of Science; Queens, NY; (S); Hosp Aide; Math Tm; Orch; Rep Jr Cls; JV Crs Cntry; Var Trk; Med Dr.

KUO, YUN G; Ellenville HS; Ellenville, NY; (Y); Rep Computer Clb; Var L Trk; Rep Jr Cls; Mth Computer Awd 83-84; Comp.

KUPIEC, MICHAEL; Utica Free Acad; Utica, NY; (Y); JA; Key Clb; Bsbl; Bsktbl; Bowling; Ftbl; High Hon Roll; Hon Roll; NHS.

KURDZIEL, KEVIN; Emerson Vocational HS; Buffalo, NY; (Y); Hon Roll; Poltcl Sci.

KURDZIEL, LORI ANNE; Alden Central HS; Alden, NY; (Y); 101/203; Pres Trs Church Yth Grp; GAA; Letterman Clb; Varsity Clb; Stu Cncl; Var Cheerleading; Var Capt Trk; Art Clb; Camp Fr Inc; Sec Pres 4-H; Mst Sprtd In Ftbl 85; Niagara U; Nrs.

KUREK, CATHERINE A; Lewiston-Porter SR HS; Ransomville, NY; (Y); 18/273; Church Yth Grp; 4-H; Nwsp Rptr; Nwsp Stf; Yrbk Ed-Chief; Yrbk Phtg; Yrbk Rptr; Yrbk Sprt Ed; Yrbk Stf; Rep Soph Cls; Deans Schlrshp 85; Regents Schlrshp 85; Canisius Coll; Mgmt Info Systms.

KUREK, CATHY; Lewiston-Porter SR HS; Ransomville, NY; (Y); 18/275; Church Yth Grp; Debate Tm; 4-H; Nwsp Rptr; Nwsp Stf; Yrbk Ed-Chief; Yrbk Phtg; Yrbk Rptr; Yrbk Sprt Ed; Yrbk Stf; Deans Schlrshp-Canisius Coll 85; NY ST Rgnts Schlrshp 85; Canisius Coll Hnrs Pgm 85; Canisius Coll; Mngmt Info Systm.

KUREK, LORI A; Saint Marys HS; Lancaster, NY; (S); VP Girl Scts; Hosp Aide; Library Aide; Trs Science Clb; Church Choir; Lit Mag; Hon Roll; NHS; Bus.

KUREK, TERESA; Niagara Catholic HS; Niagara Falls, NY; (Y); 25/80; Church Yth Grp; Hosp Aide; Trs JA; Key Clb; Nwsp Stf; Yrbk Stf; JV Capt Badmtn; JV Bowling; Var Cheerleading; Hon Roll; Vlybl Trophy 84; Hnr Rl Cert 83-84; Law.

KURKJIAN, JENNIFER; Clayton A Bouton JR SR HS; Voorheesville, NY; (Y); Math Tm; Varsity Clb; Band; Concert Band; Variety Show; Nwsp Rptr; Yrbk Rptr; Im Powder Puff Ftbl; Var Tennis; Var JV Vllybl; Intl Affairs.

KURLOWICZ, WENDY; Solvay HS; Solvay, NY; (Y); Boys Clb Am; Exploring; Hosp Aide; Ski Clb; Off Soph Cls; Off Jr Cls; Hon Roll; Keybrd Awd 85; Mgmt.

KURTZ, GREGORY; Archbishop Molloy HS; Glendale, NY; (Y); German Clb; Trk; Wt Lftg; NY U; Jrnlsm.

KURTZ, JENNIFER M; Cortland JR SR HS; Cortland, NY; (Y); 17/240; Trs Temple Yth Grp; Thesps; School Musical; Yrbk Stf; Stu Cncl; Gym; Hon Roll; NHS; MVP Vrsty Gymntcs 82; Frshmn Reeecgntn Schlrshp 85; Hon Mntn Joseph C Mack Memrl Awd 85; Hofstra U; Acctng.

KURTZ, KATHY A; Gowanda Central Schl; Gowanda, NY; (Y); 5/156; Sec French Clb; School Musical; Trs Nwsp Bus Mgr; High Hon Roll; Sec NHS; Prfct Atten Awd; Regents Schlrshp 85; Union College.

KURUC, LISA; Liverpool HS; Liverpool, NY; (S); Chorus; School Musical; School Play; Swing Chorus; High Hon Roll; Hon Roll; NHS; Niagara U; Trvl.

KURUVILLA, SELWYN; East Meadow HS; E Meadow, NY; (S); Math Tm; Spanish Clb; Nwsp Phtg; Nwsp Rptr; Yrbk Phtg; Socr; NHS; Spanish NHS; US Dept Of Enrgy Awd 83; Mc Graw Hill Bk Awd 83; Med.

KURYLA, JEFFREY; Cicero-N Syracuse HS; Mattydale, NY; (Y); Hon Roll; Ntl Merit SF; St Schlr; NYS Regents Scholar 85-89; Onondaga CC; Jrnlsm.

KURYLO, MARY; Charles E Gorton HS; Yonker, NY; (Y); 20/209; Church Yth Grp; Im Trk; High Hon Roll; Mercy Coll; Accntng.

KURYLO, NATALIE; Spackenkill HS; Poughkeepsie, NY; (Y); 35/170; Sec Thesps; Stage Crew; Ed Nwsp Stf; High Hon Roll; Yrbk Stf; Var Bowling; Var Tennis; Cert Of Merit Natl Fr Exam 84; 3 Thespn Stars 83-85.

KURZ, SUSAN; Preston HS; New York, NY; (Y); Nwsp Stf; NHS; Bio Chmst.

KURZIK, DANA; Webster HS; Rochester, NY; (Y); 14/550; Yrbk Stf; Rep Frsh Cls; Rep Soph Cls; Rep Jr Cls; Rep Sr Cls; JV Var Socr; JV Vllybl; High Hon Roll; Jr NHS; NHS; NY ST Rgnts Schlrshp; SUNY Binghamton; Bus Mgmt.

KURZYNA, PETER; St Johns Prep; Woodhaven, NY; (Y); Chorus; Im Bsbl; Im Ftbl; Hon Roll; NHS.

KUSHNER, ADAM; Mepham HS; N Bellmore, NY; (Y); Computer Clb; Mathletes; Math Clb; Math Tm; Chorus; Var Crs Cntry; JV Trk; Quiz Bowl; Y-Teens; Im Fld Hcky; Amer Schltc Math 85; NY Math League 85; Natl Sci Olympad 85; Comp Systms Anlys.

KUSHNER, DEBORAH; Commack High School North; Commack, NY; (Y); MMM; Temple Yth Grp; Chorus; School Musical; Swing Chorus; Hon Roll; Hon Roll; Deaf Educ.

KUSKOWSKI, LEONARD J; St Anthonys HS; E Northport, NY; (Y); 9/201; Drama Clb; Chorus; Madrigals; School Musical; Nwsp Rptr; Var Mgr(s); Var Capt Swmmng; High Hon Roll; NHS; Art Clb; YMCA Intl Swmmng Hl Of Fm Mst Outstndng 85; Empire ST Games Wtr Polo Slvr Mdl 84; Duke U; Engrng.

KUSMIERZ, DAWN; Mount Mercy Acad; Buffalo, NY; (Y); Church Yth Grp; Latin Clb; Var Bsktbl; JV Bowling; Hon Roll; VFW Awd.

KUSMISS, STEFANIE; Roy C Ketcham HS; Wappingers Fls, NY; (Y); Drama Clb; Chorus; School Play; Sec Frsh Cls; Var L Trk; Hon Roll; Prfct Atten Awd; Wntr Trk All Star 55 Mtr Hrdls In Lcl Nespapr 85; Hnrb Mntn Wntr Trk All Star Hrdls 84; Educ.

KUSTERA, DAN; H Frank Carey HS; Franklin Sq, NY; (Y); 24/222; Church Yth Grp; JV Ftbl; Hon Roll; Jr NHS; NHS; Polytech Inst NY; Elec Engr.

KUSZNIR, ROMA; St Francis Prep; Flushing, NY; (S); 2/700; Math Tm; Science Clb; Capt Var Swmmng; Im Vllybl; Bausch & Lomb Sci Awd; High Hon Roll; NHS; Sal; Spanish NHS; Renssalaer Mth & Sci Awd 84; Rgnts Schlrshp 85; Soc For Distgshd H S Stu 85; Columbia U; Biomed.

KUTER, PATRICK J; Williamson HS; Williamson, NY; (Y); Am Leg Boys St; Camera Clb; Church Yth Grp; Computer Clb; French Clb; FBLA; Letterman Clb; Science Clb; Chorus; Stage Crew; Syracuse U; Legal.

KUTSCHERA, SONDRA; Delaware Valley Central HS; Callicoon, NY; (Y); Teachers Aide; Chorus; Church Choir; Yrbk Stf; Rep Frsh Cls; Rep Jr Cls; Var JV Cheerleading; Var Trk; Rifle Clb-Marksmn, 1st Cls-Marskmn, Pro-Marksmn 83-84; Psych.

KUTSCHERA, VALERIE A; Comack H S North; Commack, NY; (Y); 11/440; Yrbk Stf; Frsh Cls; Var Trk; High Hon Roll; NHS; Rgnts Schlrshp 85; Pres Schlrshp Marist Coll 85; Engnrng Hnrs Schlrshp G Washington U 85; Marist Coll; Comp Sci.

KUTTAMPEROOR, THOMAS; Spring Valley SR HS; Spring Valley, NY; (Y); Church Yth Grp; Cmnty Wkr; Library Aide; Model UN; Band; Church Choir; Wrstlng; Cit Awd; Kiwanis Awd; Prfct Atten Awd; Sci Fair Awd 82-83; Bus Adm.

KUTZBACH, JENNIFER; Cleveland Hill HS; Cheektowaga, NY; (Y); AFS; Church Yth Grp; FHA; Teachers Aide; Band; Concert Band; Powder Puff Ftbl; Swmmng; Hon Roll; Elem Tchg.

KUTZER, CHRISTINE M; Hilton Central HS; Hilton, NY; (Y); Pres 4-H; Girl Scts; Office Aide; Teachers Aide; Mrchg Band; 4-H Awd; Hon Roll; Amer Legn Cert Medl For Amercnsm 85; Monroe CC; Secy Sci.

KUTZER, STEFANIE; Catholic Central HS; Troy, NY; (Y); Church Yth Grp; Computer Clb; Sec German Clb; Pep Clb; Sec Stu Cncl; JV Cheerleading; Var Pom Pon; High Hon Roll; Hon Roll; Cert Of Awd In German I 83; Phrmcy.

KUZMICKI, JOHN W; Monsignor Farrell HS; Staten Island, NY; (Y); Boy Scts; Chess Clb; VP Computer Clb; Pres Science Clb; Pres Frsh Cls; Pres Soph Cls; Pres Jr Cls; Im Bsktbl; Im Bowling; Var Ftbl; NYS Rgnts Schlrshp 85; Case Western Reserve; Pre-Med.

KUZNICKI, LISA; Kensington HS; Buffalo, NY; (Y); Computer Clb; Science Clb; Nwsp Rptr; Yrbk Ed-Chief; Yrbk Rptr; Yrbk Stf; Bowling; Sftbl; Prfct Atten Awd; Air Force; Cmmnctns.

KWAN, SUSAN M; Elmont Memorial HS; Elmont, NY; (Y); 8/248; Orch; Yrbk Stf; Var Sftbl; Var Capt Vllybl; Jr NHS; Trs NHS; Frgn Lang Hnr Soc 82-85.

KWARTA, SCOTT R; St John The Baptist HS; Islip Terrace, NY; (Y); 1/601; Church Yth Grp; Pres MMM; Chorus; NHS; Spanish NHS; Science Clb; Service Clb; Jr NHS; NY St Regents Schlrshp 85; Local 3 Ibew Schlrshp 85; Fordham U; Acctng.

KWAS, KEITH A; Lake Shore Central HS; Derby, NY; (Y); Chess Clb; Church Yth Grp; JA; Yrbk Phtg; High Hon Roll; Hon Roll; Jr NHS; NHS; Band; Natl Sci Olympiad 83 & 85; Ocngrphr.

KWASNIEWSKI, DIANNE; Immaculata Acad; W Seneca, NY; (Y); French Clb; PAVAS; Chorus; School Musical; Nwsp Stf; Yrbk Ed-Chief; Hon Roll; Natl Sci Merit Awd 85; Natl Ldrshp Orgnztn 84; Pres Acadmc Fit Awd 85; Niagara U; Frnch.

KWIATKOWSKI, HELENE; Bishop Scully HS; Amsterdam, NY; (Y); 29/69; Drama Clb; JA; Pep Clb; Spanish Clb; Trs Soph Cls; Hon Roll; Mu Alp Tht; NHS; Rotary Awd; Frgn Exch Stu; Engrng.

KWIATKOWSKI, LYNN A; Amherst Central HS; Snyder, NY; (Y); 12/269; Church Yth Grp; French Clb; GAA; Trs Model UN; Ski Clb; Trs Sr Cls; Var Tennis; Var Trk; High Hon Roll; NHS; Law.

KWIECINSKI, JEANNE; Hauppauge HS; Hauppauge, NY; (Y); Cmnty Wkr; GAA; Varsity Clb; Rep Sr Cls; Capt Var Swmmng; Hon Roll; Volntr Hndcppd Awd 85; MVP Grls Vrsty Swm 84-85; Empire ST Games Qualfr 84; Springfield Coll MA.

KWIECINSKI, KARON; Walton Central Schl; E Branch, NY; (Y); AFS; Key Clb; Model UN; Nwsp Stf; Sec Jr Cls; Fld Hcky; Vllybl; Band; Concert Band; Mrchg Band; Fld Hcky Vrsty Ltr 85; Occptnl Thrpst.

KWITEK, LAURA; St Marys HS; Alden, NY; (S); Church Yth Grp; Cmnty Wkr; 4-H; Science Clb; Varsity Clb; Chorus; School Musical; Rep Stu Cncl; Var Trk; NHS; Pres Hlth Prof Clb 84-85; Comm.

KWOK WAI, STEVE CHU; Seward Park HS; New York, NY; (Y); 25/760; JA; Band; Hon Roll; NHS; Prfct Atten Awd; Regents Schlrshp 85; NY U; Doctor.

KWON, NANCY; Oneida HS; Oneida, NY; (S); Computer Clb; Hosp Aide; Latin Clb; Math Tm; Spanish Clb; Yrbk Ed-Chief; Yrbk Sprt Ed; Yrbk Stf; Tennis; High Hon Roll.

KWON, SOONAE; George W Hewlett HS; Hewlett, NY; (Y); Rardee Lewis Mem Fund 85; St Johns U.

KWONG, DAVID; Lafayette HS; Brooklyn, NY; (Y); Acctg.

KWONG, HENRY; Newtown HS; Elmhurst, NY; (Y); 12/603; Cmnty Wkr; Rep Stu Cncl; JV Crs Cntry; Var L Tennis; Gov Hon Prg Awd; Hon Roll; Ntl Merit Ltr; Office Aide; Ntl Schlr/Athl 85; Untd Fdrtn Of Tchrs Schlrshp 85; Brown U; Bus.

KY, JENNY M; The Stony Brook Schl; Central Islip, NY; (Y); 3/97; Art Clb; Dance Clb; Intnl Clb; Spanish Clb; Chorus; Drm Mjr(t); Orch; Sec Soph Cls; Pres Jr Cls; Pres Sr Cls; Readr Dgst Schlrshp Natl Music Guild Tchrs Forum Piano 82-83; Readr Dgst Schlrshp Hgh Hnr Medl 83-84.

KYI, DAVID; St Agnes HS; New York, NY; (Y); 28/100; Church Yth Grp; Cmnty Wkr; Teachers Aide; Im Bsktbl; Im Trk; High Hon Roll; Hon Roll; Jr NHS; NHS; Prfct Atten Awd; Columbia; Med Lab Tech.

KYLE, NANCY L; Hannibal Central HS; Hannibal, NY; (Y); Trs French Clb; Hosp Aide; Ed Yrbk Stf; High Hon Roll; NHS; Prfct Atten Awd; Exploring; 4-H Awd; Rgnts Schlrshp 85; Pres Acad Fitnss Awd 85; Allee Memrl Hosp Axlry Schlrshp 85; Brockport ST U; Nrsng.

KYRIAZIS, KAREN; Hendrick Hudson HS; Peekskill, NY; (Y); 21/192; Concert Band; Jazz Band; Mrchg Band; Ed Yrbk Stf; VP Stu Cncl; Var Socr; High Hon Roll; NHS; Pres Schlr; Rgnts Schlrshp 85; Leroy Lucy Awd 85; St Pauls Scty Schlrshp 85; Oneonta ST; Pltcl Sci.

L AMOREAUX, LAURIE; Corning-Painted Post West HS; Painted Post, NY; (Y); Sec Ski Clb; Varsity Clb; Capt Color Guard; Concert Band; Mrchg Band; School Musical; Stu Cncl; Var Capt Sftbl; Var Capt Vllybl; Sec NHS; Psych.

LA BARCA, LAURA; St Francis Prep; Ridgewood, NY; (S); 30/747; GAA; JA; Capt Coach Actv; Var Sftbl; High Hon Roll; Ntl Merit SF; US Ntl Figure Sktng Champ 82; Brnz Mdlst Sktng 83; Free Sktng Champ 84; Fordham U; Sprts Med.

LA BARGE, DENNIS; Northern Adirondack HS; Altona, NY; (Y); Key Clb; Var L Bsbl; Var L Bsktbl; Var L Socr; Hon Roll; CVAC Bsbl 1st All ST 3rd Bs 84; CVAC Bsktbl 1st Tm All ST Grd 85.

LA BARGE, EDMUND; Cohoes HS; Cohoes, NY; (Y); Art Clb; Boy Scts; Varsity Clb; JV Var Socr; Var Wrstlng; Cohoes Middle Schl Art Awd 82; Engrng.

LA BARRON, POLLY; Greenwich Central HS; Greenwich, NY; (Y); 2/85; AFS; Church Yth Grp; 4-H; Band; Chorus; Jazz Band; Yrbk Ed-Chief; Yrbk Stf; JV Fld Hcky; Bus Mgmnt.

LA BELLA, CYNTHIA; Bishop Kearney HS; Rochester, NY; (Y); Ski Clb; Concert Band; Mrchg Band; Var Gym; Sftbl; High Hon Roll; NHS; Natl Merit Sci Awd 84; Marine Bio.

LA BIANCA, VINCENT; Freeport HS; Freeport, NY; (Y); Computer Clb; Exploring; Mathletes; Science Clb; Band; Concert Band; Jazz Band; Mrchg Band; Nwsp Rptr; High Hon Roll; Cmptr Pgm.

LA BOMBARD, LORI; Northern Adirondack Central HS; Ellenburg Depot, NY; (Y); Yrbk Stf; JV Var Cheerleading; Var Socr; Var Sftbl; Hon Roll; Bus Clb & Booster Clb Treas; Our Lady Of Victory; Exec Secy.

LA BRAKE, JAMES; Massena Central HS; Massena, NY; (Y); Civic Clb; Lit Mag; Im Wt Lftg; Hon Roll; NHS; Acad Banquet 83-85; Awd For Bio 84; Cytlgy.

LA BUZ, TAMMY; John F Kennedy HS; Utica, NY; (Y); Church Yth Grp; 4-H; Chorus; 4-H Awd; Hon Roll; St Elizabeth Schl; Nrsng.

LA CASCIA, ANNE; St Francis Preparatory Schl; Richmond Hill, NY; (Y); Girl Scts; Church Choir; Variety Show; Hon Roll; Grl Scout Slvr Awd 85; Arch.

LA CASSE, DANE E; Shenendehowa HS; Clifton Park, NY; (Y); Boy Scts; JCL; Latin Clb; Symp Band; Im JV Ftbl; JV Capt Vllybl; Hon Roll; Prfct Atten Awd; Ntl Latin Exam Magna Cum Laude 84-85; Siena Coll; Pre-Med.

LA CAVERA, GINA; Schoharie Central HS; Schoharie, NY; (S); 13/96; Key Clb; Ski Clb; School Musical; Yrbk Stf; Trs Stu Cncl; Capt Vllybl; High Hon Roll; Hon Roll; St U At Oneonta; Comm.

LA CHAPELLE, MICHAEL; Niskayuna HS; Scotia, NY; (Y); Am Leg Boys St; Drama Clb; Spanish Clb; School Musical; Variety Show; Nwsp Stf; Hon Roll; NHS; Pres Schlr; Panhellenic Schlrshp 85; Cornell U.

LA CLAIR, DANIELLE; Tupper Lake JR SR HS; Tupper Lake, NY; (Y); SUNY; Mass Cmmnctns.

LA CLAIR, JAMES; Amherst SR HS; Buffalo, NY; (Y); Computer Clb; Orch; High Hon Roll; Hon Roll; NHS; Chem Lab Asst 84-85; UB; Chem.

LA COMBE, AMY; Jamesville-De Witt HS; Dewitt, NY; (Y); 35/250; Yrbk Sprt Ed; Stu Cncl; Var Capt Bsktbl; Var Capt Sftbl; Var L Swmmng; Dnfth Awd; High Hon Roll; Jr NHS; NHS; All-Conty Grls Bskbl 82-85; All-State Empire State Games.

LA COPPOLA, LORINE; St Johnsville Central Schl; St Johnsville, NY; (Y); 3/39; School Play; Yrbk Stf; Pres Sr Cls; JV Var Bsbl; JV Cheerleading; Coach Actv; Var Capt Score Keeper; JV Sftbl; Cit Awd; Jr NHS; Rgnts Schlrshp 85; Peer Ldr Cathlc Svc Bettr Your Body Prog 83-85; ST U Oneonta; Phy Thrpy.

LA COUR, JEAN-PIERRE A; Ossining HS; Ossining, NY; (Y); Cmnty Wkr; JV Bsbl; Bsktbl; Ftbl; Golf; Score Keeper; Hon Roll; All Div Hon Men Ftbl 84; Syracuse U; Elec Engrng.

LA COURCIERE, JACQUELINE; Our Lady Of Lourdes HS; Poughkeepsie, NY; (Y); Am Leg Aux Girls St; Church Yth Grp; Drama Clb; Ski Clb; Nwsp Rptr; Rptr Nwsp Stf; Yrbk Phtg; Yrbk Stf; VP Soph Cls; Rep Jr Cls; Holy Cross Bk Prz 85; Spch.

LA CROIX, BETHANY; E J Wilson HS; Spencerport, NY; (Y); Exploring; Sec Math Clb; Symp Band; Yrbk Stf; Var L Trk; Hon Roll; Prfct Atten Awd; Solo Fest NY St; MI Plyr Trk Tm.

LA DOUCE, CHRISTINE; Auburn HS; Auburn, NY; (Y); Church Yth Grp; Ski Clb; Varsity Clb; Sec Sr Cls; Var L Golf; Var Capt Tennis; Var L Trk; Prsdntl Acadmc Ftnss Awds Prog 85; MIP Tennis 84; Mary Washington Coll; Lbrl Arts.

LA DUC, SAMANTHA; Plattsburgh SR HS; Plattsburgh, NY; (Y); Trs Cmnty Wkr; Debate Tm; Hosp Aide; JA; Model UN; Sec Office Aide; Ski Clb; Drm Mjr(t); Mgr(s); Score Keeper; Yng Tns Actn-40 Hr Svc 82-83; Cert Achv Engl 85; Bus Adm.

LA DUCA JR, ROBERT; Cathedral Preparatory Seminary; Ozone Park, NY; (Y); 1/25; Debate Tm; NFL; Political Wkr; Variety Show; Nwsp Stf; Sec Stu Cncl; NHS; Ntl Merit Ltr; Val; Gld Mdl 4 Yrs; Math, Sci, Lat Mdl; Yale U; Chem.

LA DUE, KARYN B; Amsterdam HS; Amsterdam, NY; (Y); 24/335; Cmnty Wkr; 4-H; Hosp Aide; Quiz Bowl; Yrbk Stf; Hon Roll; NHS; Pres Schlr; Rgnts Schlrshp; Albany Coll; Phrmcst.

LA FACE, MARIA; Bishop Grimes HS; Clay, NY; (Y); Debate Tm; Girl Scts; Hosp Aide; JA; Hon Roll; Prom Comm 85; South Eastern Acad; Ticket Agnt.

LA FARNARA, KIM; Oakfield-Alabama Central HS; Oakfield, NY; (Y); Art Clb; Drama Clb; Capt Color Guard; Capt Flag Corp; School Musical; School Play; Bowling; Redesign Tm-Paint Mural In Genesee Cntry Mall 85; Actress.

LA FARO, LAURA L; Weedsport Central Schl; Weedsport, NY; (Y); Pres Church Yth Grp; Math Clb; Spanish Clb; Pres Trs Chorus; Yrbk Ed-Chief; High Hon Roll; Sec NHS; Outstndng Chorus Mbr 81-85; Dir Awd For Chorus 84; Royson N Whipple Schlrshp 85; Morrisville; Food Prcssng Tech.

LA FAVE, LISA M; Frontier Central HS; Blasdell, NY; (Y); Church Yth Grp; Varsity Clb; Church Choir; Concert Band; Mrchg Band; Yrbk Stf; Var JV Bsktbl; Var L Socr; JV L Sftbl; Hon Roll; Chch Sftbl Leag All Str 81-83; Phy Ed.

LA FEVER, RANDY; Richburg Central HS; Bolivar, NY; (Y); Nwsp Rptr; Nwsp Stf; High Hon Roll; Hon Roll; Jr NHS; NHS; Ntl Merit Ltr; Rdo Brdcstng.

LA FONTAINE, SHELLY; Fairport HS; Fairport, NY; (Y); French Clb; FBLA; Hon Roll; Bus Adm.

LA FORGIA, LAURA; St Agnes HS; East Meadow, NY; (Y); 12/425; Art Clb; Teachers Aide; High Hon Roll; Hon Roll; NHS; Ntl Merit Ltr; Ann G Taylor Awd 85; Italian Club 84; Adelphi; Accntnt.

LA FUZE, MAURICE; Union-Endicott HS; Endicott, NY; (S); 11/430; Key Clb; Varsity Clb; Var Capt Ftbl; Var L Trk; Hon Roll; Ntl Merit Ltr; VA Tech; Engrng.

LA GRECA, STEVEN T; Plainedge HS; N Massapequa, NY; (Y); 2/311; Pres French Clb; MMM; Orch; School Musical; Lit Mag; French Hon Soc; NHS; Ntl Merit Ltr; Sal; St Schlr; Ribbn Merit Long Island Sci Cngrss 83; 2nd Pl Cnty Lvl Cncours Natl De Francais 83; Hofstra U; Cmmnctns.

LA GUERRE, JEAN; Saint Agnes HS; Corona, NY; (Y); 11/100; NHS; Hon Roll; Nwsp Stf; Lit Mag; NY U; Optmtry.

LA HART, REBECCA; Saranac Lake HS; Saranac Lake, NY; (Y); Yrbk Stf; Regnts Bus Math Awd 83-84; Bus.

LA JOIE, SANDRA; Half Hollow Hills High Schl East; Dix Hills, NY; (Y); Office Aide; Spanish Clb; Teachers Aide; Band; Concert Band; Co-Capt Trs Drill Tm; Mrchg Band; Symp Band; Variety Show; Nwsp Stf; NYSSMA Awds 83-85; Hum Rel Awd 84; All Amer Drll Tm Awd Excel 83; Corp Law.

LA LONDE, JACQUELINE; Charles H Roth HS; Honeoye Falls, NY; (Y); VP Pres French Clb; Intnl Clb; VP Pres Thesps; School Musical; School Play; Yrbk Stf; Var L Tennis; French Hon Soc; NHS; Pres Schlr; Chptr Wnnr NHS Schlrshp Fnls 85; Pres Acdmc Ftns Awd 85; Outstndng NYSSMA Comp 85; Old Dominion U; Bio-Chem.

LA MAINA, THERESA; Sacred Heart Acad; E Meadow, NY; (S); Var Church Yth Grp; Math Clb; Service Clb; Chorus; School Musical; Hon Roll; NHS; St Johns U; Law.

LA MARE, MICHELLE; Saranac Central HS; Morrisonville, NY; (S); 5/130; Library Aide; Yrbk Stf; High Hon Roll; Hon Roll; Sec NHS; Economics.

LA MONICA, ADAM; Freeport HS; Freeport, NY; (Y); 50/450; Key Clb; Bsbl; Bsktbl; Bowling; Fld Hcky; Ftbl; CC Awd; Cit Awd; Hon Roll; U Miami.

LA MORTE, DEBBIE; Washingtonville HS; Campbell Hall, NY; (Y); Sec 4-H; Girl Scts; Teachers Aide; Chorus; 4-H Awd; Hon Roll; Silver Ldrshp Awd Girl Scouts 83; Comp Sci.

LA MOY, JAMES; Niagara Falls HS; Niagara Falls, NY; (Y); Hon Roll; Lion Awd; Cert Excllnc Ntl Hstry Day 85; Top 10 Concrs Ntl-Frnch 82-84; Law.

LA NASA, PIA; Sacred Heart Acad; Williamsville, NY; (Y); Red Cross Aide; Acpl Chr; School Musical; Nwsp Rptr; Rep Frsh Cls; Rep Soph Cls; Pres Jr Cls; Hon Roll; NHS; Prfct Atten Awd.

LA NEVE, BARBARA; Henninger HS; Syracuse, NY; (Y); Girl Scts; Library Aide; Science Clb; Concert Band; Stu Cncl; Tennis; High Hon Roll; NHS; Dance Lessons; Engl.

LA PAGE, C ANDREW; Bishop Kearney HS; Rochester, NY; (Y); Cmnty Wkr; Model UN; High Hon Roll; Hon Roll; Law.

LA PAGE, MARIE R; Massena Central HS; Massena, NY; (Y); Hon Roll; Clercl.

LA PLACA, ANDREW; Bishop Kearney HS; Rochester, NY; (Y); Ski Clb; School Musical; Rep Soph Cls; Pres Sr Cls; Im Bsbl; Var Wrstlng; Hon Roll; St John Fisher; Pre-Dnstry.

LA PLANTE, DAVID; Franklin Acad; Malone, NY; (Y); French Clb; Varsity Clb; Band; Stage Crew; Nwsp Phtg; Nwsp Stf; Yrbk Phtg; Yrbk Stf; JV L Crs Cntry; Var L Golf; Natl Sci Olympd 82-83; AZ ST U; Bus.

LA POLT, COLLEEN; Laurens Central Schl; Mt Vision, NY; (Y); 6/36; Drama Clb; Sec Key Clb; VP Spanish Clb; Chorus; Stage Crew; Sec Sr Cls; SUNY Potsdam; Comp Info Sci.

LA PORT, ROSEMARIE; South Park HS; Buffalo, NY; (Y); Capt Debate Tm; Library Aide; Band; Concert Band; Mrchg Band; Nwsp Stf; Stu Cncl; Capt Swmmng; Tennis; NHS; OH ST U; Bio.

LA PORTE, KENNA; Northeastern Clinton Central HS; Mooers, NY; (Y); Model UN; Chorus; Concert Band; Symp Band; Yrbk Stf; Trs Soph Cls; Stu Cncl; Var Bsktbl; Var Sftbl; Hon Roll; Potsdam; Psych.

LA PORTE, MARIBETH; Harpersville Central HS; Harpersville, NY; (Y); Quiz Bowl; Scholastic Bowl; Spanish Clb; Color Guard; Hon Roll; Prfct Atten Awd; Sci Awd 83; Elmira Coll; Eng Lit.

LA PORTE, MICHELLE; Smithtown High School East; Nesconset, NY; (Y); Teachers Aide; Mrchg Band; Orch; School Musical; Symp Band; Off Frsh Cls; Sec Soph Cls; Var Badmtn; High Hon Roll; Hon Roll; Hnrb Mntn Lng Islnd Flute Clb 85; NY ST Schl Music Assn 85; Hadassah Srv Awd 85; Music Prfrmnc.

LA PRADE, KATHRINE; Massena Central HS; Massena, NY; (Y); Stu Cncl; Crs Cntry; Socr; Trk; Hon Roll; Typng Cntst 84 & 85; CCBI; Lgl Sec.

LA QUAY, LISA; Pine Valley Central HS; South Dayton, NY; (S); 4/65; Pres Trs AFS; Sec Church Yth Grp; Trs Chorus; Madrigals; JV Var Bsktbl; Hon Roll; Jr NHS; NHS; Voice Dem Awd; Chautauqua Cnty Music Tchrs Assn Musicn Of Wk Feb 85; Physcl Thrpy.

LA ROCCA, LISA; Richmond Hill HS; Richmond Hill, NY; (Y); 1/300; Girl Scts; Math Tm; Scholastic Bowl; Nwsp Rptr; Trs Jr Cls; Jr NHS; NHS; Pres Schlr; Val; Church Yth Grp; Spr Yth Pgm 85; Accntng.

LA ROCCA, RICHARD; Wantagh HS; Wantagh, NY; (Y); Var Bsbl; Hon Roll; Bsbl Vrsty-Leag Hnrb Mntn 85; Pol Sci.

LA ROCCA, VINCENT; Somers HS; Mahopac, NY; (Y); Yrbk Stf; Rep Stu Cncl; Var Bsktbl; Capt Ftbl; Var Golf; Powder Puff Ftbl; Sprts Awds 85; Safe Rides Co-Fndr, Treas 85; Villanova U; Pro-Ball Mgt.

LA ROCQUE, RICHARD W; Oneida HS; Sylvan Beach, NY; (Y); 14/240; French Clb; Im Bsktbl; Im Vllybl; High Hon Roll; Hon Roll; Regents Schlrshp 85; Pres Schlrshp For Alfred U 85; Pres Acad Fitness Awd 85; Alfred U; Engrng.

LA ROSA, LISA; Bishop Kearney HS; Brooklyn, NY; (Y); Capt Church Yth Grp; Cmnty Wkr; Band; Hon Roll; NHS; Coaches Awd St Dominics Sftbl Tm 84; Musc.

LA ROSE, JOHN C; Franklin Academy HS; Malone, NY; (Y); Boy Scts; Church Yth Grp; Teachers Aide; JV Ftbl; N Country CC; Law Enfrcmnt.

LA ROSE, LISA; Clifton-Fine Central HS; Newton Falls, NY; (S); 7/52; French Clb; Chorus; Capt Bsktbl; Capt Socr; High Hon Roll; NHS; Talented Jrs Computers 83; All-Northern Bsktbl 2nd Team 84; Soccer Hnrbl Mntn 84; Albany Med Ctr; RN.

LA ROSE, MICHELLE L; Seton Catholic Central HS; Endwell, NY; (Y); 4/132; Am Leg Aux Girls St; Church Yth Grp; Pres Key Clb; Mathletes; Varsity Clb; School Musical; Yrbk Ed-Chief; Yrbk Stf; Trs Soph Cls; Stu Cncl; Jaycees Outstndng Yth Ldr 84; Yth Salute 84; Notre Dame; Bio.

LA ROSE, STUART; Christian Brothers Acad; Liverpool, NY; (Y); Exploring; NFL; Red Cross Aide; Speech Tm; Nwsp Bus Mgr; Yrbk Ed-Chief; Stu Cncl; Hon Roll; Le Moyne Coll Syracuse; Crp Law.

LA RUSSA, MICHELE; Christ The King HS; Howard Beach, NY; (Y); 12/370; Hon Roll; 1st Hnrs Rank Cert 83-85; 2nd Hnrs Rank Cert 82-83; Med.

LA SARSO, MATTHEW G; Fort Edward HS; Fort Edward, NY; (Y); 2/60; Drama Clb; Varsity Clb; Band; Mrchg Band; Pres Jr Cls; JV Var Ftbl; Var L Trk; Hon Roll; Blgcl Engr.

LA SELVA, DONNA; Central Islip HS; Central Islip, NY; (Y); 13/300; Girl Scts; Band; Drm Mjr(t); Mrchg Band; JV Bsktbl; Mgr(s); Score Keeper; Sftbl; Swmmng; Hon Roll; Mst Val Swmmr 82-84; Natl Schlr/Ath Awd 85; Cornell U; Pre-Med.

LA VARNWAY, ANNETTE; Warrensburg Central HS; Warrensburg, NY; (Y); 9/71; 4-H; Band; Concert Band; Mrchg Band; School Play; Stage Crew; 4-H Awd; High Hon Roll; Hon Roll; NHS; Rochester Inst Of Tech; Dietcs.

LA VENIA, DEBORAH; Bishop Kearney HS; Brooklyn, NY; (S); Pres Dance Clb; Office Aide; Rep Frsh Cls; Off Soph Cls; Rep Jr Cls; Rep Sr Cls; Hon Roll; NHS; ST U Stonybrook; Sci.

LA VIGNE, KEVIN MICHAEL; Mechanicville HS; Mechanicville, NY; (Y); 26/104; VP Spanish Clb; Yrbk Stf; JV Bowling; JV Ftbl; Hudson Vlly Cmnty Coll; Auto.

LABAN, JEFFREY; Gilboa Conesville Central HS; Gilboa, NY; (S); 4-H; Var Bsbl; Var Bowling; Var Golf; Var Socr; Var Swmmng; Var High Hon Roll; Var Hon Roll; Var Prfct Atten Awd; Oneonta ST; Sci.

LABAN, WENDI; Gilboa Conesville Central Schl; Gilboa, NY; (S); 5/25; Varsity Clb; Chorus; JV Var Bsktbl; Var Bowling; Coach Actv; Var Socr; High Hon Roll; Hon Roll; GAA; Band; Stdnt Edtrl 84; Dsgnd Report Cards 84; Arch.

LABARBERA, MARY; St Johns Prep; Jackson Heights, NY; (Y); Dance Clb; Chorus; Variety Show; Wt Lftg; High Hon Roll; Prfct Atten Awd; Med.

LABARBERA, PATTI; Hauppauge HS; Hauppauge, NY; (Y); FBLA; Library Aide; Rep Frsh Cls; Rep Soph Cls; Rep Jr Cls; Stu Cncl; High Hon Roll; Hon Roll; NHS; Law.

LABASH, PAUL; Eastridge HS; Rochester, NY; (Y); 9/260; Varsity Clb; JV Var Socr; High Hon Roll; Hon Roll; Sci.

LABATE, STEPHEN; John Adams HS; S Ozone Pk, NY; (Y); Prfct Atten Awd; Polit Sci.

LABELLA, VICTORIA J; T R Proctor HS; Utica, NY; (Y); Pep Clb; Yrbk Stf; JV Cheerleading; Var Sftbl; Hon Roll; Engrng.

LABOMBARDA, FRANK; Nazareth HS; Brooklyn, NY; (Y); Var Bsbl; Im Bsktbl; Im Ftbl; Im Sftbl; Hon Roll; Math.

LABOSSIERE, CHANTAL J; Francis Lewis HS; Bayside, NY; (Y); 5/527; Office Aide; Teachers Aide; Yrbk Stf; High Hon Roll; NHS; Ntl Merit SF; Georgetown U; Med.

LABOY, ZULEIKA; Mabel Dean Bacon Vocational HS; New York City, NY; (S); 30/299; Hosp Aide; Teachers Aide; Chorus; School Play; Hon Roll; Nrsng.

LABRIE III, JOSEPH; Scotia-Glenville HS; Schenectady, NY; (Y); Chess Clb; JA; Red Cross Aide; Trs Pres Ski Clb; Spanish Clb; Concert Band; Mrchg Band; High Hon Roll; Hon Roll; Prfct Atten Awd; Marine Sci.

LABROUSSE, SORAYA; Dominican Commercial HS; Queens Vlge, NY; (Y); NHS; Siena Clb 82-85; Princpls List 82-85; Combintn Stu Bus,Acad 84-85.

LACEY, DIANE; Chenango Valley HS; Pt Crane, NY; (Y); Art Clb; French Clb; Hosp Aide; Color Guard; Mrchg Band; Nwsp Stf; Yrbk Bus Mgr; Jr NHS; NHS; Cert Volntry Apprctn 84; Presdntl Achv Awd 85; Brdcstng.

LACEY, JONATHAN R; Williamsville South HS; Williamsville, NY; (Y); 29/245; AFS; CAP; Exploring; JA; JV Trk; High Hon Roll; Hon Roll; NHS; Ntl Merit SF; Cornell U; Govnmt.

LACH, AMY; Barker Central HS; Barker, NY; (Y); AFS; Church Yth Grp; French Clb; Teachers Aide; Sec Soph Cls; Sec Jr Cls; Swmmng; Esprit Pgm Gifted & Talented 83-84 & 84-85; Hmcmng Princess 83-84.

LACHER, KIM; John Glenn HS; E Northport, NY; (Y); Dance Clb; Temple Yth Grp; Rep Stu Cncl; Var Tennis; High Hon Roll; Hon Roll; Jr NHS; Spanish NHS; Intl Bus.

LACHER, LAWRENCE C; Walt Whitman HS; Melville, NY; (Y); 38/625; Computer Clb; French Clb; Key Clb; JV Bsktbl; Var Bowling; French Hon Soc; High Hon Roll; Hon Roll; NHS; NYS Regents Schlrshp 85; Mfg Hanover Qtr Century Schlrshp 85; U VA; Aerospace Engrng.

LACHMANN, MATTHEW P; Saugerties HS; Saugerties, NY; (Y); 8/242; German Clb; Quiz Bowl; Ski Clb; Varsity Clb; Crs Cntry; Trk; Wrstlng; High Hon Roll; Hon Roll; SUNY Albany; Acctng.

LACHS, WENDY; Walter Panas HS; Peekskill, NY; (Y); 3/211; Cmnty Wkr; Debate Tm; Drama Clb; Chorus; School Musical; Nwsp Ed-Chief; Yrbk Stf; NHS; Ntl Merit Ltr; Full Tuitn Schlrshp Brdcst Jrnlsm Schl Visl Arts 85; Rep NYS Hugh O Brien Yth Ldrshp Semnr 83; Schl Visl Arts; Brdcst Jrnlsm.

LACINSKI, PAUL; Hauppauge HS; Hauppauge, NY; (Y); 3/510; Boy Scts; Rep Church Yth Grp; FBLA; Speech Tm; Yrbk Rptr; Var JV Ftbl; JV Trk; High Hon Roll; Pres NHS; Ntl Merit Ltr; Hauppauge Scholar 85; Vincent J Trinkwald Mem Awd 85; Regents Scholar 85; Amherst Coll; Pol Sci.

LACKEY, KEVIN; Geneseo Central HS; Geneseo, NY; (Y); Boy Scts; Ski Clb; Spanish Clb; Lit Mag; VP Frsh Cls; VP Soph Cls; VP Sr Cls; VP Stu Cncl; JV Var Bsbl; JV Bsktbl; Natl Socl Stud Olympd 85.

LACKEY, STEPHEN; Glens Falls SR HS; Glens Falls, NY; (Y); JV Trk; High Hon Roll; Hon Roll.

LACLAIR, MARCIE; Indian River Central HS; Antwerp, NY; (Y); 7/130; Pres AFS; VP Key Clb; Trs Latin Clb; Color Guard; Mrchg Band; School Musical; School Play; Trs Frsh Cls; Trs Soph Cls; Rep Jr Cls; Elmira Coll Key Awd; Med Fld.

LACOMB, WILLIAM S; Holland Patene Central HS; Hinckley, NY; (Y); 76/199; Cmnty Wkr; Exploring; Library Aide; High Hon Roll; Hon Roll; Delhi ST U; Acctng.

LACOMIS, LYNNE; Binghamton HS; Binghamton, NY; (Y); #10 In Class; Key Clb; Band; Concert Band; Mrchg Band; High Hon Roll; NHS; Rotary Awd; Med Career Schlrshp 85; Awd Excll Ltn 85; Pres Acad Ftnss Awd 85; SUNY Binghamton; Pre Med.

LACON, THOMAS S; H Frank Carey HS; Franklin Sq, NY; (Y); 46/267; Boy Scts; Church Yth Grp; Debate Tm; Library Aide; Office Aide; Church Choir; Hst Soph Cls; Rep Jr Cls; Hon Roll; Eagle Scout 85; Pre-Med.

LACOURSE, LISA; Massena Central HS; Massena, NY; (Y); French Clb; Yrbk Stf; Im Powder Puff Ftbl; Ptsdm Coll; Elem Ed.

LACRAIX, MICHAEL; Hoosick Falls Central HS; Eagle Bridge, NY; (Y); French Clb; Red Cross Aide; Pres Ski Clb; Stage Crew; Yrbk Stf; VP Frsh Cls; Pres Soph Cls; Rep Stu Cncl; Hon Roll; Outstndng Stu Of Yr 83; Svc Awd 84; Merit Awd 85; Phrmcy.

LACY, MARK; Cattaraugus Central HS; Cattaraugus, NY; (Y); 2/66; Am Leg Boys St; Pep Clb; Spanish Clb; Band; Jazz Band; Mrchg Band; Rep Jr Cls; VP Stu Cncl; Var Bsbl; Coach Actv; Rensselaer Medal 85; US Air Force Acad; Engr.

LADDISON, KEVIN; Hugh C Williams Canton Central HS; Hermon, NY; (Y); Boy Scts; Letterman Clb; Varsity Clb; School Play; Crs Cntry; Timer; Trk; Hon Roll; Prfct Atten Awd; Upward Bound 83 & 85; Marine Biol.

LADOUCEUR, ROBERT; Ogdensburg Free Acad; Ogdensburg, NY; (Y); 35/195; Pres Church Yth Grp; Cmnty Wkr; Drama Clb; Math Clb; PAVAS; School Play; Monseignor A D Charbaneau Schlrshp 85; Plattsburgh ST U; Mass Media.

LAFACE, MARIA; Bishop Grimes HS; Syracuse, NY; (Y); Exploring; FBLA; Yrbk Stf; Tutoring; Music.

LAFALCE, CARMEN A; Lafayette HS; Buffalo, NY; (Y); 11/237; Pres French Clb; Math Tm; Red Cross Aide; Pres Ski Clb; Teachers Aide; Swmmng; Hon Roll; Key Clb; Library Aide; Math Clb; NY ST Regents Scholarship 84-85; Rochester Inst Of Tech; Computr.

LAFAVE, MATTHEW; John F Kennedy HS; Utica, NY; (Y); Aud/Vis; Drama Clb; Library Aide; Mathletes; Band; Chorus; Concert Band; Jazz Band; Mrchg Band; Pep Band; Accntng.

LAFEMINA, STACY; Sanford H Calhoun HS; Merrick, NY; (Y); Nwsp Stf; Yrbk Stf; Rep Frsh Cls; Rep Soph Cls; Sec Jr Cls; Var Capt Cheerleading; Var Diving; JV Sftbl; Var Trk; Pres Fit Awd; MVP Chrldng; Frgn Lang.

LAFFER, HILARY; Fayetteville-Manlius HS; Manlius, NY; (Y); GAA; Temple Yth Grp; Yrbk Stf; Stu Cncl; Bsktbl; Cheerleading; Socr; Hon Roll; NHS; Delta Kappa Beta Sorority-Pldg Pres Corresp Sec 83-86; Humanities Clb-Fair Chrmn, VP For PR 84-86; Comp Sci.

LAFFERTY, CHRIS; Olean SR HS; Cuba, NY; (Y); Chess Clb; French Clb; Key Clb; Ski Clb; Varsity Clb; Off Frsh Cls; Off Soph Cls; Off Jr Cls; Stu Cncl; Bsktbl; Geology.

LAFFERTY, PEGGY; Hilton Central HS; Hilton, NY; (Y); Girl Scts; Model UN; Ski Clb; Med.

LAFFEY, CRAIG P; Sachem High School North; Holbrook, NY; (Y); 50/1678; Science Clb; Ski Clb; Wt Lftg; Jr NHS; Ntl Merit SF; Regents Schlrshp 85; Suny Buffalo; Aero Engr.

LAFFMAN, KELLY; Kings Park SR HS; Kings Pk, NY; (Y); 47/393; Church Yth Grp; Cmnty Wkr; Var Debate Tm; Pres Spanish Clb; Teachers Aide; Ed Nwsp Ed-Chief; Nwsp Rptr; Lit Mag; High Hon Roll; Hon Roll; Hnbl Mntn Wrld Poetry Cntst Natl 84; Medl Excllnc Spnsh 85; UCLA; Jrnlsm.

LAFLEUR, RONALD; Jordan-Elbridge HS; Memphis, NY; (Y); Church Yth Grp; Ski Clb; JV Bsktbl; JV Var Ftbl; Im Sftbl; Im Tennis; Im Wt Lftg; Hon Roll; Onondaga CC; Acctg.

LAFOLLETTE, GINA; Cleveland Hill HS; Cheektowaga, NY; (Y); GAA; JCL; Latin Clb; Ski Clb; Stu Cncl; Powder Puff Ftbl; Var Trk; Hon Roll; Prfct Atten Awd; Pharm.

LAFONTANT, NERLANDE; Cardinal Spellman HS; Bronx, NY; (Y); Rep Sr Cls; Trk; French Clb; Corp Lwyr.

LAFORCE, SHARI; Hilton Central HS; Hilton, NY; (Y); Model UN; Ski Clb; Nwsp Stf; Yrbk Stf; VP Frsh Cls; VP Soph Cls; Rep Jr Cls; Rep Sr Cls; Rep Stu Cncl; Var Cheerleading; Hnr Rl; Var Trk; Fredonia ST Coll; Bio.

LAFOUNTAIN, JEFFREY J; Newfane SR HS; Newfane, NY; (Y); 34/162; Camera Clb; School Musical; Stage Crew; Yrbk Phtg; Hon Roll; Alfred Ag & Tech; Comp Graph.

LAFUENTE, CYNTHIA I; Poughkeepsie HS; Poughkeepsie, NY; (Y); 45/193; AFS; Math Clb; Math Tm; Radio Clb; Variety Show; Yrbk Stf; Watson Schlrshp 85; Regents Schlrshp Wnnr 85; Rensselaer Polytech; Elec Engng.

LAGAMI, MARIA; St Joseph By The Sea HS; Staten Isalnd, NY; (Y); Yrbk Stf; Hon Roll; NEDT Awd; Rutgers U.

LAGAN, COLLEEN; North Babylon SR HS; North Babylon, NY; (Y); Hosp Aide; Intnl Clb; Spanish Clb; Concert Band; Mrchg Band; Nwsp Stf; Var L Tennis; High Hon Roll; Jr NHS; NHS; Bus Law.

LAGATTA, JULIA J; Islip HS; Bayshore, NY; (Y); Hosp Aide; Mathletes; Concert Band; Mrchg Band; Orch; Yrbk Stf; VP Stu Cncl; Var Bowling; JV Cheerleading; JV Socr; Nrsng.

LAGATTUTA, LUCILLE; Holy Trinity HS; East Meadow, NY; (Y); Spanish Clb; Yrbk Sprt Ed; Yrbk Stf; Stu Cncl; Var Socr; 1st Pl Arch Design House 85; Arch.

LAGERAAEN, PAUL; Farmingdale HS; Farmingdale, NY; (Y); Boys Clb Am; Band; Lcrss; Swmmng; Hon Roll; Var Ltr Swmmng 83-84 & 84-85; Chem Engrng.

LAGOY, CRAIG; West Genesee HS; Camillus, NY; (Y); Dance Clb; French Clb; Varsity Clb; JV Var Bsbl; JV Var Bsktbl; Bowling; Wt Lftg; High Hon Roll; Hon Roll; Clarkson Coll; Engrng.

LAGUA, BELINDA T; Jamesville-De Witt HS; Jamesville, NY; (Y); 25/227; Sec French Clb; Model UN; Ski Clb; Band; Stage Crew; Yrbk Stf; Socr; Capt Vllybl; High Hon Roll; NHS; MONY Schlstc Art Awd 83; MVP Sccr Team 84; U Of VT; Phy Thrpy.

LAGUERRE, MARIE-LAURENCE N; The Mary Louis Acad; Cambria Heights, NY; (Y); 126/283; Church Yth Grp; Chorus; Yrbk Stf; Rep Sr Cls; Im Bsktbl; Trk; Ntl Merit Ltr; NEDT Awd; Pre-Law.

LAGUERRE, VLADIMIR; Archbishop Molloy HS; Queens Vlg, NY; (Y); 28/409; Pres French Clb; Ed Yrbk Stf; L Crs Cntry; L Trk; Hon Roll; NHS; Tutrng Clb 82-85; Summr HS Rsrch Prog 85; MIT; Phys.

LAGUZZA, JENNIFER L; Arlington HS; Pleasant Valley, NY; (Y); 103/600; Drama Clb; Ski Clb; Chorus; Variety Show; Nwsp Stf; Yrbk Stf; Pres Jr Cls; Gym; Hon Roll; Lion Awd; U Of Rochester; Psych.

LAGUZZA, LISA; Vernon Verona Sherrill Central Schl; Sherrill, NY; (Y); Church Yth Grp; Cmnty Wkr; Rep Frsh Cls; Rep Soph Cls; Rep Jr Cls; Rep Stu Cncl; JV Var Cheerleading; JV Var Fld Hcky; JV Var Trk; High Hon Roll; MVP Fld Hcky JV 83; Regnts Scholar 85; Sci.

LAHRS, MARGARET; Immaculata Acad; W Seneca, NY; (Y); 4-H; Hosp Aide; Nwsp Stf; Hon Roll; Prfct Atten Awd; Nrsng.

LAI, KAREN; Flushing HS; Corona, NY; (Y); Intnl Clb; Library Aide; Office Aide; Teachers Aide; Nwsp Bus Mgr; High Hon Roll; Hon Roll; Prfct Atten Awd; PTA Schlrshp; Baruch; Acctng.

LAI, MICHAEL; Midwood HS; Brooklyn, NY; (Y); Chess Clb; Computer Clb; Ski Clb; Teachers Aide; Var Bsbl; Comp Sci.

LAI, MICHELLE A; Shaker HS; Latham, NY; (Y); Jazz Band; Orch; Nwsp Bus Mgr; Nwsp Rptr; Nwsp Stf; Elks Awd; NHS; Natl Schl Orch Assn Awd 84; NYS Mus Assn Winter Conf All St Orch 83 & 84; SADD Treas; Columbia U; Engrng.

LAI, WILLIAM; Fort Hamilton HS; Brooklyn, NY; (Y); 4/567; Scholastic Bowl; Science Clb; Ed Yrbk Stf; Lit Mag; Hon Roll; NHS; Chorus; Bausch & Lomb Sci Awd; Prfct Atten Awd; Chancellors Rl Hnr 85; Mayors Citation Merit 85; Gov Schlstc Achvt Awd 84-85; Mech Engr.

LAIETA, CHRISTINE; Academy Of St Joseph; Holbrook, NY; (Y); Art Clb; Dance Clb; Drama Clb; Chorus; Sftbl; Liberal Arts.

LAIKHRAM, SHARMILA; Walton HS; New York, NY; (S); 15/653; Hosp Aide; Library Aide; Cit Awd; Hon Roll; NHS; Prfct Atten Awd; Adhoc Cmmtt Mbr; Hnr Engl Awd 84; Econ Awd 84; Pace U; Psych.

LAIRD, SEAN; Pelham Memorial HS; Pelham, NY; (Y); Var Bsbl; Var Bsktbl; Var Ftbl; Cbl TV Dfnsv Ftbl Tm 84 & 85; OH ST U; Ag.

LAIS JR, CHARLES J; Catholic Central HS; Troy, NY; (Y); German Clb; School Musical; Variety Show; Nwsp Stf; Hon Roll; Exploring; Math Clb; Yrbk Stf; Im Bowling; Prfct Atten Awd; NYS Regents Schrlshp 85; ST U NY Albany; Creat Wrtng.

LAITNER, URSULA; Cicero North Syracuse HS; Liverpool, NY; (S); 22/602; German Clb; Capt Color Guard; Capt Mrchg Band; Sec Soph Cls; Sec Jr Cls; Rep Stu Cncl; Stat Ftbl; JV Capt Powder Puff Ftbl; Crim Just.

LAJAM, CLAUDETTE; Manhasset HS; Manhasset, NY; (Y); Debate Tm; GAA; NFL; Yrbk Stf; JV Var Socr; NHS; Ntl Merit Ltr; Spanish Clb; Chorus; Nwsp Rptr; 1st Pl Hofstra U Spn Poetry Cont 84; 2nd Pl Natl Physcs Olympd 85; NYS Bar Assn Mock Trial Tourn 85; Polit Sci.

LAKATOS, JOSEPH; St Francis Prep; Flushing, NY; (S); 37/694; Civic Clb; Office Aide; Var Bowling; High Hon Roll; NHS; Opt Clb Awd; Intramural Sports 82-85; Stock Market Club 84-85; Law.

LAKE, CHRIS; Johnstown HS; Caroga, NY; (Y); AFS; Intnl Clb; Variety Show; JV Bsktbl; JV Var Ftbl; JV Trk; High Hon Roll; Pre Law.

LAKE, MICHAEL; Port Richmond HS; Staten Isld, NY; (Y); 3/500; Debate Tm; Math Tm; Yrbk Sprt Ed; Pres Stu Cncl; JV Ftbl; Var Wt Lftg; Hon Roll; JETS Awd; NHS; Ntl Merit Ltr; Chem Awd-American Chemical Soc 84; Med.

LAKE JR, NORBERT G; Mount Markham HS; W Winfield, NY; (Y); 30/120; Pres Service Clb; Band; Chorus; Concert Band; Jazz Band; School Musical; Swing Chorus; Hon Roll; NHS; Aud/Vis; Louis T Groab Annual Awd For Serv 83; SUNY-POTSDAM; Music.

LAKE, RHONDA; St Barnabas HS; Bronx, NY; (Y); Cmnty Wkr; Dance Clb; Office Aide; Pres Frsh Cls; Var Bowling; Var Cheerleading; Im Sftbl; JV Swmmng; Camera Clb; Library Aide; Pace U; Acctng.

LAKEMAN, CAROLYN; Niagara Wheatfield SR HS; N Tonawanda, NY; (Y); Am Leg Aux Girls St; French Clb; Pep Clb; Varsity Clb; Chorus; JV Var Mat Maids; Capt Var Socr; JV Var Sftbl; Jr NHS; SUNY; Bus Adm.

LAKHAN, GILLIAN; Brooklyn Technical HS; Brooklyn, NY; (Y); Cmnty Wkr; Rep Frsh Cls; Rep Soph Cls; Rep Jr Cls; Prfct Atten Awd; Operation Crossrds Africa W Indies Schlrshp 85; Rsrch & Wrtng Sklls Awd 84; Comp Sci.

LAKOMY, KIMBERLY; Heuve Hon Central Schl; Ogdensburg, NY; (Y); French Clb; Girl Scts; Chorus; Drm Mjr(t); Mrchg Band; School Musical; Yrbk Stf; Var Capt Cheerleading; JV Socr; Twrlr; Univ Miami FL; Comm.

LALA, PATRICE; Manhassett HS; Manhasset, NY; (Y); 20/197; Church Yth Grp; Hosp Aide; Mathletes; Service Clb; Orch; Yrbk Stf; JV Fld Hcky; Sftbl; NHS; U Of Rochester; Math.

LALIWALA, SHEELA; Connetquot HS; Ronkonkoma, NY; (Y); Band; Color Guard; Mrchg Band; Symp Band; Yrbk Stf; JV Cheerleading; High Hon Roll; Hon Roll; Jr NHS; NHS; Med Dr.

LALLEY, NOELLE M; Jamesville-De Witt HS; Dewitt, NY; (Y); 70/250; Art Clb; German Clb; Intnl Clb; Key Clb; Chorus; JV Cheerleading; High Hon Roll; Hon Roll; Syracuse U; Chld & Fmly Studies.

LALLIER, DEBRA; Seaford HS; Seaford, NY; (Y); Band; Concert Band; Drill Tm; Mrchg Band; Vllybl; High Hon Roll; Hon Roll; NY Polytech Inst; Aerontcs Eng.

LALLIER, LISA; Sauquoit Valley HS; Sauquoit, NY; (Y); Church Yth Grp; Civic Clb; Dance Clb; GAA; Girl Scts; Hosp Aide; Pep Clb; Band; Pep Band; Stage Crew; MIP Awd Ftbll Chrldng 84; MVCC; Nrsng.

LALLY, CHRISTINE; St Marys Girls HS; Roslyn Heights, NY; (Y); Church Yth Grp; Hon Roll; Jr NHS; NHS; Cert Of Mrt For Outstdng Schlstc Achv-NY ST Senate 84; Med.

LAM, CELIA; Murry Bergtraum HS; Brooklyn, NY; (Y); #10 In Class; Hosp Aide; Math Tm; Office Aide; Science Clb; Varsity Clb; Band; VP Powder Puff Ftbl; VP Stu Cncl; Capt Tennis; Hon Roll; VFT Schlrshp; Physc Clb NY Awd, Outstndng Svc Awd 85; NY U; Sys Anlyst.

LAM, HEUNG W; Aviation HS; New York, NY; (Y); 49/417; JA; Hon Roll; NY U; Med.

LAM, LESLIE Y; Norman Thomas HS; New York, NY; (S); 37/671; FBLA; Math Tm; Cit Awd; High Hon Roll; Hon Roll; Prfct Atten Awd; 2nd Pl Acctng FBLA Comptn Citywd 85; Acctnt.

LAM, MEE YEE; Norman Thomas HS; New York, NY; (S); 50/671; Sec FBLA; Band; Hon Roll; NHS; Prfct Atten Awd; Suny Binghamton; Comp Sci.

LAM, MUNG-MAN; Cathedral HS; New York, NY; (Y); 5/325; Intnl Clb; Library Aide; Chorus; Nwsp Stf; Gym; High Hon Roll; Prfct Atten Awd; NY U; Bus Adm.

LAMANCHE, STEVE; G Ray Bodley HS; Fulton, NY; (Y); Band; Concert Band; Jazz Band; Mrchg Band; Orch; Pep Band; School Musical; Variety Show; Bsbl; All-Cnty Bnd 82-85; Area All-ST Bnd 83-85; Music.

LAMB, JAMES; Bayside HS; Whitestone, NY; (Y); Am Leg Boys St; Aud/Vis; Service Clb; Chorus; Madrigals; School Play; Stdnt Svc Hnr Citatn Cty Cncl 83; Gld Drama & Brnz Chrs Awds 83; Law.

LAMB, PATRICIA; Mexico HS; Mexico, NY; (Y); Dance Clb; German Clb; Band; Chorus; Madrigals; Mrchg Band; School Musical; School Play; Swing Chorus; Variety Show; Germn Club Srvc Awd 85; Most Imprvd Alto 82; Albany Medcl Schl Of Nursing.

LAMB, TODD; Newark Valley HS; Newark Vly, NY; (Y); Church Yth Grp; Stu Cncl; JV Var Bsbl; JV Var Bsktbl; Var Socr; High Hon Roll; NHS; Prfct Atten Awd; Bucknell U; Elctrcl Engrng.

LAMBERSON, NANCY; Geneva HS; Geneva, NY; (S); 10/170; Band; Concert Band; Mrchg Band; Pep Band; Ed Yrbk Stf; High Hon Roll; NHS; Ntl Merit SF; Acad All-Amer Schlr 83-84; Syracuse U; Bus Mgmt.

LAMBERT, ERIC; Lake George HS; Lake George, NY; (Y); Varsity Clb; Band; Mrchg Band; JV Bsktbl; Var Socr; High Hon Roll; VP Jr NHS; NHS; Sprtsmnshp Awd Vrsty Sccr 84.

LAMBERT, LARRY; Saranac HS; Morrisonville, NY; (Y); Wrstlng; Plattsburgh ST; Comp Sci.

LAMBERT, MARY A; Canaseraga Central HS; Hornell, NY; (Y); 8/26; Pres DECA; Chorus; Color Guard; Mrchg Band; School Musical; Yrbk Stf; Capt Vllybl; High Hon Roll; Hon Roll; Trk; Outstndng Stu Sales & Mrktg 84-85.

LAMBERT, MICHAEL G; Stillwater Central HS; Stillwater, NY; (Y); 10/100; Am Leg Boys St; Pres Key Clb; Math Tm; VP Varsity Clb; JV Bsbl; Var Capt Ftbl; Var L Wt Lftg; Var L Wrstlng; High Hon Roll; Hon Roll; NYS Regents Schlrshp 85; SUNY Cortland; Phys Ed.

LAMBERT, PRISCILLA; Holy Child HS; Scarsdale, NY; (Y); Art Clb; Key Clb; Stage Crew; Yrbk Stf; Gym; Hon Roll; Ntl Merit Ltr; 2nd Hnrs 82-84; 2nd Hnrs 85; Bus.

LAMBERT, ROBIN; Elmira Free Acad; Elmira, NY; (Y); Cmnty Wkr; French Clb; High Hon Roll; Hon Roll; Ntl Schlstc Art Awd Gld Mdl 82-83; Rchster Inst Of Tech; Advt Exec.

LAMBERT, WILLIAM; Skaneateles HS; Skaneateles, NY; (S); 4/167; Church Yth Grp; Drama Clb; Model UN; Nwsp Rptr; Var Crs Cntry; High Hon Roll; Rotary Awd; Am H S Math Exam 1st 83; 3rd Pl CNY Branch Ntl Leag Penwomen 83; Scholar Merit 83.

LAMIA, MICHAEL; Albertus Magnus HS; Nyack, NY; (Y); 60/196; JV Bsbl; JV Ftbl; Var Golf; Hon Roll; U Of MI; Busnss Admin.

LAMITIE, LYNN; Franklin Acad; Malone, NY; (S); 9/252; Pres Trs 4-H; Band; Concert Band; Dnfth Awd; 4-H Awd; Hon Roll; NHS; Ntl Merit Ltr; Natl Sci Olympiad Sci Merit Awd & Acad All Amer Stu 84; Potsdam ST U; Chem.

LAMKIN, SHARI; Byron Bergen HS; Byron, NY; (Y); 1/117; Debate Tm; Concert Band; VP Stu Cncl; Var Bsktbl; Var Capt Cheerleading; Var Capt Trk; NHS; Ntl Merit Ltr; AFS; C Hiller Mem Svc, Music 85; Pre Law.

LAMMERTZ, JOHN; New Rochelle HS; New Rochelle, NY; (Y); Boys Clb Am; Var Bsbl; Var Bsktbl; Coach Actv; JV Ftbl; Var Wt Lftg; NHS; Bus Mgmt.

LAMONICA, STEPHANIE; Oneonta SR HS; Oneonta, NY; (Y); 9/180; Art Clb; Drama Clb; Sec French Clb; Letterman Clb; Ski Clb; Spanish Clb; Varsity Clb; Yrbk Sprt Ed; L Var Socr; Trk; Hghst Ave Germn I 85; All Arnd Plyr Sccr Sthrn Tier Athltc Assn 84; Frnch.

LAMONT, MICHELE DAWN; Shenendehowa HS; Clifton Park, NY; (Y); Hosp Aide; Sec Pres Key Clb; Sec Latin Clb; Church Choir; Symp Band; Kiwanis Awd; NHS; JCL; Concert Band; Jazz Band; Skidmore Coll & Saratogian Acad Excllnc Awd 83-84; Rgnts Schlrshp Awd 85; Presdntl Acadmc Ftns Awd 85; Canisius Coll; Med.

LAMOREE, JEFFREY; Beacon HS; Beacon, NY; (S); 1/160; Boy Scts; French Clb; Math Clb; Math Tm; Science Clb; Varsity Clb; Var Capt Socr; High Hon Roll; VP Jr NHS; NHS; Math, Sci, Soc Studies Awds 83-84; :Elec Engr.

LAMOS, BARBARA; Stony Brook Schl; Stony Brook, NY; (Y); Chorus; Church Choir; Orch; School Musical; Pres Frsh Cls; Off Soph Cls; Off Jr Cls; Var L Fld Hcky; Mgr(s); Var L Trk; Houghton Coll; Elem Educ.

LAMOUR, TIFFANY; St Jean Baptists HS; New York, NY; (S); Ski Clb; School Play; Yrbk Phtg; Lit Mag; Bsktbl; Lib Cheerleading; Coll; Art.

LAMOUREUX, EDWARD; Horseheads HS; Horseheads, NY; (S); 18/407; Am Leg Boys St; Science Clb; Varsity Clb; Chorus; Concert Band; Mrchg Band; JV Var Bsktbl; Var Tennis; Hon Roll; VP NHS; Biology.

LAMPARELLA, SUSAN; Vestal HS; Vestal, NY; (Y); 60/460; Church Yth Grp; Girl Scts; Ski Clb; Varsity Clb; School Play; Rep Sr Cls; Var L Cheerleading; Im Socr; High Hon Roll; NHS; Bst All Arnd Chrldr Awd 85; 1st Pl Grls Pres Phy Fit Awd 83; PTA Dist Cncl Schlrshp 85; SUNY Geneseo; Spch Pathlgy.

LAMPAZZI, CHRISTINE; Warwick Valley HS; Warwick, NY; (Y); 80/200; French Clb; Varsity Clb; Yrbk Stf; Tennis; SPEC Ed Tchr.

LAMPE, JEFFREY D; City Honors Schl; Buffalo, NY; (Y); 10/97; Pres Church Yth Grp; Sec French Clb; Math Tm; Nwsp Stf; Trs Stu Cncl; Var Capt Socr; Ntl Merit SF; Yale Book Awd Wnnr; NFL Man Of The Yr Awd; Cornell U; Ind.

LAMPERSBERGER, AMY; Carmel HS; Carmel, NY; (Y); 12/370; Pres Service Clb; Orch; School Musical; Yrbk Ed-Chief; Trs Stu Cncl; JC Awd; JP Sousa Awd; NHS; March Dimes Hlth Career Scholar 85; Roland Bartlett Mem Scholar 85; Northeastern U; Phys Thrpy.

LAMPURI, ANTHONY; Christian Brothers Acad; Liverpool, NY; (Y); 51/103; FCA; JA; Pep Clb; Ski Clb; Varsity Clb; Chorus; Variety Show; Yrbk Stf; Bsbl; Ftbl; All Leag & MVP-FTBL 84-85; Alfred ST; Air Condtng/Refrgtn.

LAMURAGLIA, JAMES; Bishop Kearney HS; Webster, NY; (Y); Church Yth Grp; Ski Clb; Concert Band; Jazz Band; Mrchg Band; Pep Band; Stage Crew; NHS; Alfred Tech; Mech Engnrng.

LANCE, LISA; Sweet Home SR HS; N Tonawanda, NY; (Y); 16/425; GAA; Science Clb; Var Capt Socr; Trs French Hon Soc; High Hon Roll; Hon Roll; NHS; MVP Awd Grls Vrsty Sccr 83-85; NY ST Regnts Schlrshp 84-85; Syracuse U; Aerosp Engrng.

LANCE, SUE; Nazareth Acad; Rochester, NY; (Y); Latin Clb; Library Aide; Quiz Bowl; Ski Clb; Spanish Clb; Teachers Aide; Band; School Musical; School Play; Score Keeper; Bio.

LANCER, PATRICIA; Bishop Kearney HS; Rochester, NY; (S); 33/128; NFL; Ski Clb; Band; Color Guard; Drm & Bgl; Mrchg Band; Yrbk Stf; Cheerleading; Niagria U; Nrsng.

LANCI, VINCENT; St Marys Boys HS; Roslyn, NY; (Y); Nwsp Stf; Var Tennis; Hon Roll; Hofstra; Bus Mgmt.

LANCTON, JEFF; Mahopac HS; Mahopac, NY; (Y); 97/398; Computer Clb; Library Aide; Nwsp Rptr; Nwsp Stf; High Hon Roll; Hon Roll; NY ST Rgnts Schlrshp; Clarkson U; Comp Sci.

LANDAU, CLAUDIA; Colonie Central HS; Albany, NY; (Y); Church Yth Grp; Intnl Clb; Nwsp Phtg; Nwsp Stf; Rep Frsh Cls; Rep Jr Cls; Sec Sr Cls; Trk; High Hon Roll; NHS; Harvard Bk Prz 85; Psych.

LANDAU, LISA R; Wellington C Mepham HS; N Bellmore, NY; (Y); Nwsp Rptr; Ed Nwsp Stf; Yrbk Rptr; Yrbk Stf; Off Soph Cls; Off Jr Cls; Var Capt Sftbl; Var Capt Vllybl; High Hon Roll; NHS; Boston U; Phys Occu.

LANDAU, MELISSA; Mamaroneck HS; Larchmont, NY; (Y); PAVAS; Spanish Clb; Teachers Aide; Temple Yth Grp; Chorus; School Musical; School Play; Lit Mag; High Hon Roll; Spanish NHS; PACE Drama Awd 84; NY ST Cncl For Scl Stds Cert Of Hnr 83; Med.

LANDEL, JOHN; Naples Central HS; Naples, NY; (Y); Church Yth Grp; Hon Roll; Prfct Atten Awd; Auto Mech.

LANDER, DEBRA; W C Mepham HS; N Bellmore, NY; (Y); Debate Tm; Temple Yth Grp; Band; Yrbk Stf; Rep Soph Cls; Rep Jr Cls; Sec Sr Cls; Rep Stu Cncl; Hon Roll; NHS; Bus.

LANDER, JEFF; Le Roy HS; Leroy, NY; (Y); Boy Scts; Latin Clb; Varsity Clb; Chorus; School Musical; Var Golf; Var Socr; JV Wrstlng; Hon Roll.

LANDER, RENEE M; Le Roy HS; Leroy, NY; (Y); 33/117; Office Aide; Chorus; Mrchg Band; School Musical; Score Keeper; Twrlr; High Hon Roll; J E T Awd 85; Raymond J Branton Mem 85; Suny Cortland; Elem Ed.

LANDERS, KIM; Royalton-Hartland HS; Gasport, NY; (Y); VICA; Var Sftbl; Hon Roll; Cosmtlgy.

LANDERS, TERI; Cicero-N Syracuse HS; Clay, NY; (S); 36/711; Rep Jr Cls; Rep Sr Cls; Powder Puff Ftbl; Var Socr; Var Sftbl; Capt Vllybl; Cit Awd; Hon Roll; NHS; Albany; Comp Sci.

LANDESBERG, LEONARD J; South Side HS; Rockville Ctr, NY; (Y); 1/270; Boy Scts; Band; Concert Band; Pep Band; High Hon Roll; Jr NHS; NHS; Var JV Socr; Harvard Book Awd 85; Silvr Medl Natl Latn Exam 85; 96th Pct JETS NEAS Exam 85.

LANDRIO, MARK; Notre Dame-Bishop Gibbons HS; Delanson, NY; (S); 11/108; Computer Clb; Nwsp Stf; Var Tennis; High Hon Roll; NHS; Ntl Merit Ltr; Schl Chem Awd 84; Union Coll; Med.

LANDRY, TAMARA; Franklin Acad; Malone, NY; (Y); 4-H; French Clb; Trs Model UN; VP Pep Clb; Varsity Clb; Nwsp Stf; Yrbk Stf; Swmmng; High Hon Roll; NHS; Schl Schlrshp 85; High French Hnr Awd 84.

LANDSBERG, RUTH E; Great Neck South HS; Great Neck, NY; (Y); Cmnty Wkr; Hosp Aide; Teachers Aide; Pres Temple Yth Grp; Pres Jr Cls; Pres Stu Cncl; NY ST Regents Schlrshp 85; English.

LANE, DAVID; Woodmere Acad; Hewlett, NY; (Y); 2/50; Model UN; VP Science Clb; Nwsp Stf; Yrbk Stf; Pres Jr Cls; Rep Stu Cncl; Golf; Var Capt Socr; Var Swmmng; Sal; Regnts Schlrshp 85; Cum Laude 84; U Of PA; Bus.

LANE, KIMBERLY; Bethlehem Central HS; Delmar, NY; (Y); Cmnty Wkr; Hon Roll; Cum Laude Cert Hnrbl Merit 85; Am Classcl League; Ec.

LANE, RICHARD; Cardinal Spellman HS; Yonkers, NY; (Y); Boy Scts; Camera Clb; Iona Coll; Accntng.

LANE, ROBIN; Hoosick Falls Central Schl; Hoosick Falls, NY; (Y); Drama Clb; French Clb; Girl Scts; Acpl Chr; School Musical; School Play; Stage Crew; JV Var Cheerleading; Hon Roll; NHS; USC Coastal Carolina; Acctng.

LANE, SANDRA; Gilboa Conesville Central HS; Prattsville, NY; (S); 3/36; Cmnty Wkr; GAA; Yrbk Ed-Chief; Sec Frsh Cls; Sec Soph Cls; Sec Jr Cls; Sec Sr Cls; Sec Stu Cncl; NHS; Cobleskill; Bus Mgmt.

LANE, SETH; Shoreham Wading River HS; Shoreham, NY; (Y); Mathletes; Capt Crs Cntry; Capt Trk; Psych.

LANE, TRACEY; Waterloo SR HS; Waterloo, NY; (Y); Pres 4-H; Chorus; 4-H Awd; Hon Roll; Hvy Equip Oprtn.

LANFAIR, JEFFREY; South New Berlin Central Schl; Norwich, NY; (Y); Wt Lftg; High Hon Roll; Hon Roll; Lion Awd; NHS.

LANFEAR, MONICA; Fort Ann Central HS; Comstock, NY; (Y); Drama Clb; Office Aide; VP VICA; School Play; Yrbk Stf; JV Sftbl; High Hon Roll; Hon Roll; Adirondack CC; Cosmtlgy.

LANG, ANNE; Sacred Heart Acad; Floral Park, NY; (Y); Cmnty Wkr; Dance Clb; Variety Show; Nwsp Rptr; Nwsp Stf; Bsktbl; Gym; Hon Roll; NHS; March Dimes Distgushd Stu Hlth Carer Awd 85; NYS Nrsng Reg Schlrshp 85; Merit Awd Dancng 85; SUNY; Nrsng.

LANG, BARBARA; Schoharie Cendral HS; Sloansville, NY; (Y); Key Clb; Latin Clb; Hon Roll; 1st Rnnr Up Prom Ct 85; Stoney Brook.

LANG, BRIEN F; Mc Quaid Jesuit HS; Fairport, NY; (Y); 38/200; Varsity Clb; Acpl Chr; School Musical; Nwsp Stf; Ed Yrbk Stf; Sec Stu Cncl; Cit Awd; NHS; Ntl Merit Ltr; Pres Schlr; Democrat & Chronicle Student Appeal-Editrl Cartoon 1st Pl 84; Boston Coll; Eng.

LANG, CHRISTINE E; Holy Trinity HS; East Meadow, NY; (S); 5/380; Mathletes; Math Clb; Hon Roll; Stoneybrook U; Med.

LANG, CHRISTINE M; Frontier Central HS; Hamburg, NY; (S); Drama Clb; Library Aide; Pep Clb; Red Cross Aide; Ski Clb; Chorus; School Musical; Stage Crew; Yrbk Stf; Var Mgr(s); NEDT Merit Awd 84; Yth Emplymnt-Wrkr Of Yr 85; Fredonia; Math.

LANG, HEIDI A; Hamburg SR HS; Hamburg, NY; (Y); 67/400; Pres Church Yth Grp; VP JA; School Musical; Sec Soph Cls; Rep Jr Cls; Rep Sr Cls; Stu Cncl; JV Var Cheerleading; Hon Roll; NHS; Salute Ldr 85; Wittenberg U; Finc.

LANG, LORI; Walton Central HS; Walton, NY; (Y); AFS; Library Aide; Chorus; Color Guard; Mrchg Band; Sec Frsh Cls; Rep Soph Cls; Twrlr; High Hon Roll; Hon Roll; Regnts Schlrshp 85; Cazenovia Coll; Spec Ed.

LANG, MARCELLA; Upper Room Christian Schl; Fountain Hills, AZ; (Y); Church Yth Grp; Office Aide; Hon Roll; Jr NHS; Distngshed Christian H S Stu ACSI 84; AZ ST U; Law.

LANG, STEPHANIE; Lindenhurst HS; Lindenhurst, NY; (Y); 4/800; Chorus; Jazz Band; Mrchg Band; School Musical; Variety Show; Hon Roll; Ntl Merit Ltr; 2 Mdls Outstndng Grd Nyssma 83 & 85; Grmn Hnr Soc 84; Suny Binghamton; Bio.

LANG, STEPHEN; Bishop Timon HS; Buffalo, NY; (Y); Boys Clb Am; Boy Scts; Drama Clb; Ski Clb; Spanish Clb; Chorus; Stage Crew; Yrbk Stf; Ftbl; Vllybl; Engrng.

LANGAN, DAN; Farmingdale HS; N Mass, NY; (Y); Var L Gym; Var Trk; Hon Roll; NHS; Mech Engrng.

LANGAN, MARY; Franciscan HS; Lake Peekskill, NY; (Y); Girl Scts; Stage Crew; Var Capt Bsktbl; Var JV Vllybl; Hon Roll; Hugh O Brien Yth Fndtn Smnr 84.

LANGDON, GEORGE B; Franklin Acad; Malone, NY; (Y); 1/253; AFS; Boy Scts; French Clb; VP Intnl Clb; Ski Clb; Rep Stu Cncl; JV Crs Cntry; High Hon Roll; NHS; Val; Engrng.

LANGDON, KAREN E; Batavia HS; Batavia, NY; (Y); 21/234; Cmnty Wkr; Yrbk Stf; JV Tennis; High Hon Roll; NHS; Genesee Bus Scholar Awd 85; MA Coll Pharm & Hlth; Pharm.

LANGDON, KEVIN; Lynbrook HS; Lynbrook, NY; (Y); FCA; Wrstlng; Acctnt.

LANGDON, MICHAEL; Albion HS; Albion, NY; (S); Boy Scts; Latin Clb; Concert Band; Mrchg Band; Pep Band; Trk; NHS; Mt Union Coll; Astrophysics.

LANGE, ANDREW; Kenmore West SR HS; Kenmore, NY; (Y); Church Yth Grp; Orch; School Musical; Variety Show; Im Mgr Socr; High Hon Roll; Hon Roll; Prfct Atten Awd; NY ST U.

LANGE, DAVID; John F Kennedy HS; Utica, NY; (Y); 23/130; Im Ice Hcky; SUNY; Law.

LANGE, KATHLEEN; Dryden Central HS; Dryden, NY; (Y); Pep Clb; Band; Cheerleading; Swmmng; Trk; Hon Roll; Engl Awd 84-85; Marine Bio.

LANGE, LISA; Poland Central HS; Utica, NY; (Y); 4/60; Am Leg Aux Girls St; Church Yth Grp; Pres Sec 4-H; FHA; Teachers Aide; Varsity Clb; Yrbk Ed-Chief; Yrbk Phtg; Yrbk Stf; Rep Soph Cls; Business Exclnce Aeds 82-84; Soc Stu Exclnce Awds 83-84; Bus.

LANGELOTTI, KIMBERLY; Greece Athena HS; Rochester, NY; (S); 107/295; Church Yth Grp; DECA; Teachers Aide; Rep Jr Cls; Rep Sr Cls; Rep Stu Cncl; Hon Roll; Distributv Ed Clbs Amer Regnl & ST Wnnr 85; Nrsng.

LANGER, LORETTA J; Mineola HS; Mineola, NY; (Y); 71/256; Church Yth Grp; Key Clb; Thesps; Acpl Chr; Chorus; Church Choir; School Musical; Stage Crew; Gym; Trk.

LANGFORD, ADAM; Salem Central HS; Salem, NY; (Y); Am Leg Boys St; Var Bsbl; Var Bsktbl; Acctng.

LANGHAM, BARBARA; Auburn HS; Auburn, NY; (Y); Ski Clb; Rep Soph Cls; Rep Jr Cls; Rep Sr Cls; High Hon Roll; Hon Roll; Niagara U.

LANGHAM, BETH; Auburn HS; Auburn, NY; (Y); 32/440; Ski Clb; Rep Frsh Cls; Rep Soph Cls; Rep Jr Cls; Off Sr Cls; Off Stu Cncl; Capt Sftbl; High Hon Roll; Hon Roll; NHS; Ithaca Coll; Lbrl Arts.

LANGIE, MATT B; Pittsford Mendon HS; Pittsford, NY; (Y); 2/265; Ski Clb; Yrbk Stf; JV Var Lcrss; High Hon Roll; Hon Roll; U Va; Engrng.

LANGL, GREGORY; Maryvale HS; Cheektowaga, NY; (Y); Boy Scts; Church Yth Grp; Cmnty Wkr; German Clb; Varsity Clb; Im Bowling; Im Socr; Im Sftbl; Var Trk; Var Vllybl; Boy Scts Of Am 84; Canisius Clg; Bus Admin.

LANGLEY, JODY; Romulus Central Schl; Romulus, NY; (S); 4/50; Pres Spanish Clb; Chorus; Color Guard; School Musical; Variety Show; Sec Jr Cls; Sec Stu Cncl; Capt L Cheerleading; Var L Socr; Var L Sftbl; SUNY Oswego; Psych.

LANGLEY, SCOTT; Millbrook HS; Millbrook, NY; (Y); Boy Scts; Math Clb; VP Soph Cls; Pres Jr Cls; Trs Stu Cncl; Var Capt Bsbl; Var JV Bsktbl; Var Ftbl; High Hon Roll; VP NHS; Outstndng JR Stdnt 85; USAF; Mech Engrng.

LANGMANN, PHIL W; Spencer-Van Etten HS; Spencer, NY; (Y); 3/105; Computer Clb; Debate Tm; French Clb; JA; Letterman Clb; Math Clb; Pep Clb; Ski Clb; Varsity Clb; Acpl Chr; Alfred U; Bus.

LANGONE, VERNA; St Edmunds HS; Brooklyn, NY; (Y); 28/180; Spanish Clb; Bowling; Sftbl; Hon Roll; NHS; Spanish NHS; Law.

LANGOWSKI III, JOHN F; James I O Neill HS; West Point, NY; (Y); Boy Scts; Church Yth Grp; Computer Clb; German Clb; Yrbk Stf; JV Var Ftbl; Var L Trk; Hon Roll; NHS; Norwich U; Gen Sci.

LANGWORTHY, AMANDA J; Hammondsport Central Schl; Hammondsport, NY; (Y); 21/73; Church Yth Grp; Teachers Aide; Band; Chorus; Church Choir; Pep Band; Nwsp Stf; Yrbk Stf; Regents Schlrshp 85; Corning CC; Human Svcs.

LANKA, KAREN; Niskayuna HS; Schdy, NY; (Y); Art Clb; Church Yth Grp; French Clb; GAA; Key Clb; Pep Clb; JV Capt Bsktbl; JV Socr; Var JV Sftbl; Art Awd 83-85; Scr Chmpnshp 84; Engrng.

LANKAU, DENISE M; Shoreham Wading River HS; Shoreham, NY; (Y); 80/170; Church Yth Grp; FBLA; Mathletes; Math Tm; Service Clb; Acctng Awd 84; Math Assn 3rd Pl Lcl Cntst 82; Regnts Schlrshp 85; Oswego SUNY; Acctng.

LANN, VANESSA; Mamaroneck HS; Mamaroneck, NY; (Y); 1/400; Drama Clb; Pres French Clb; Math Clb; Math Tm; School Play; Nwsp Rptr; Nwsp Stf; High Hon Roll; Pres NHS; Val; Paideia Awd 85; 1st Pl Cnty Yng Wrtrs Comp Poetry 85; Natl Cncl Music Tchrs Assoc Comp 83-84; Yale; Pianist.

LANNING, CATHIE; Oxford Academy HS; Oxford, NY; (Y); French Clb; Varsity Clb; Band; Concert Band; Jazz Band; Trs Jr Cls; JV Var Bsktbl; JV Var Sftbl; Hon Roll; NHS.

LANNING JR, DAVID C; Spencer-Van Etten Central Schl; Spencer, NY; (Y); 20/102; Boy Scts; Civic Clb; Cmnty Wkr; Computer Clb; Library Aide; Band; Concert Band; Jazz Band; Mrchg Band; Rep Stu Cncl; Hstry Awd 82; Engl Awd 83; Spncr Alum Assn Schlrshp 85; Alfred ST Coll; Elec Engrng.

LANNING MURRAY, MICHELLE; Union Endicott HS; Endicott, NY; (Y); 38/417; French Clb; Key Clb; Spanish Clb; NHS; ST U NY Binghamton; Lwyr.

LANOS, IVORY B; Wilson Magnet HS; Rochester, NY; (Y); Church Yth Grp; Cmnty Wkr; VP Sr Cls; Cit Awd; High Hon Roll; Hon Roll; NHS; 4-H; Library Aide; Office Aide; Monroe Cnty Cmmnty Svc Wrkr Awd 85; Monroe CC; Brdcstg.

LANOT JR, ANDRE; East Meadow HS; E Meadow, NY; (Y); French Clb; School Play; Lcrss; Wt Lftg; Five Towns Coll; Music.

LANOU, FREDERICK J; East Islip SR HS; E Islip, NY; (Y); 96/475; Trs Stu Cncl; JV Var Lcrss; JV Socr; Hon Roll; Prfct Atten Awd; Regents Schlrshp 85; Maritime Coll; Engrng.

LANPHEAR, KATHY; Waterloo HS; Waterloo, NY; (Y); 24/161; Pep Clb; Chorus; Rep Frsh Cls; Rep Soph Cls; Rep Jr Cls; Rep Sr Cls; Hon Roll; Ntl Merit Ltr; Diane R Faiola Awd 85; Seneca Falls Bus Prfssnl Wmns Clb Awd 85; Arcadia Schl Commerce; Med Sec.

LANPHERE, TAMMY; Ripley Central Schl; Ripley, NY; (S); 2/28; Band; Rep Frsh Cls; VP Soph Cls; Bsktbl; Sftbl; Tennis; Hon Roll; NHS; Ntl Merit Ltr.

LANSING, BRIAN C; Connetquot HS; Sayville, NY; (Y); 39/723; Boy Scts; Jazz Band; Mrchg Band; School Play; Lit Mag; Trk; Ntl Merit Ltr; NYS Regnts Schlrshp 85; NYS Mus Tchr Assn Awd; Tri-M Mus Hnr Soc 85; U Of Richmond; Pre-Law.

LANSING, KRISTA; Whitesboro SR HS; Whitesboro, NY; (Y); 70/358; Sec Church Yth Grp; Variety Show; Capt Cheerleading; Hon Roll; Outstndng Awd For St Pauls CYO 82-84; Sprt Awd For St Pauls CYO 84-85; Chld Psych.

LANSKY, JUDITH E; The Nichols Schl; Amherst, NY; (Y); 10/110; Cmnty Wkr; Drama Clb; Hosp Aide; Yrbk Stf; Var Sftbl; JV Var Tennis; Var Trk; JV Vllybl; Hon Roll; Nrthwstrn U; Bus.

LANZA, ALEXANDRA; Center Moriches HS; Center Moriches, NY; (Y); Cmnty Wkr; Girl Scts; Hosp Aide; Latin Clb; Office Aide; Service Clb; Nwsp Bus Mgr; Lit Mag; Trs Frsh Cls; Trs Soph Cls; Springfield Coll Humncs Awd 84; 1st Cls Grl Scouts 82; Suffolk Cnty CC Menthln Bus 1st Pl 85; Bentley Coll MA; Intl Finance.

LANZA, ROBERT; Far Rockaway HS; Far Rockaway, NY; (Y); Computer Clb; Key Clb; Political Wkr; Jazz Band; High Hon Roll; Cpt Fncng Tm 84; Arista Leag 95; Engrng.

LANZENDORF, DONNA L; Mohonasen SR HS; Schenectady, NY; (Y); 11/215; Band; Yrbk Stf; Pres Frsh Cls; Pres Stu Cncl; Capt Im Bsktbl; Capt JV Socr; High Hon Roll; NHS; Ntl Merit Ltr; Mrchg Band; Elmira Key Awd 84; Foundr & Pres SADD 85; Steinmitz Memrl Awd; Union Coll; Jrnlsm.

LANZISERA, DOMINICK; Locust Valley HS; Bayville, NY; (Y); Boys Clb Am; Cmnty Wkr; Mathletes; Service Clb; Spanish Clb; Nwsp Sprt Ed; Jr NHS; NY Math Leag Cert Of Merit 85; Harvard Prz Bk 85; Pre Med.

LANZISERA, JOSEPH; Roy C Ketcham HS; Poughkeepsie, NY; (Y); Civic Clb; Math Clb; Political Wkr; High Hon Roll; Hon Roll; Jr NHS; NHS; Engrng.

LAO, DANIRA; Our Lady Of Perpetual Help HS; Brooklyn, NY; (Y); Hosp Aide; School Musical; School Play; Variety Show; Hon Roll; Med.

LAO, ROGER S; Riverhead HS; Aquebogue, NY; (Y); 6/255; Pres Ski Clb; Pres Band; Jazz Band; Trs Frsh Cls; Var Golf; Var Capt Socr; Var Capt Tennis; NHS; Regents Schlrshp 85; Hamilton Coll; Physics.

LAPERUTA, NANCY T; Stissing Mountain HS; Stafordsville, NY; (Y); Yrbk Stf; Hnr Key 83-84; Cosmotlgy.

LAPESA, ANNA; Bishop Frd C C H HS; Brooklyn, NY; (Y).

LAPHAM, JEFF; Tamarac HS; Troy, NY; (Y); Varsity Clb; Var Capt Bsbl; Var Capt Bsktbl; Var Capt Ftbl; Hon Roll; Ntl Merit Ltr; Wasaran Leag All Star Tm Bsbl 85; Bus Admin.

LAPIETRA, JOSEPH; Cardinal Mooney HS; Rochester, NY; (Y); Civic Clb; Library Aide; Stage Crew; Nwsp Sprt Ed; Rep Jr Cls; Im Bsktbl; Im Bowling; JV Socr; JV Timer; Cit Awd; Rochester Inst Of Tech; Htl Mgr.

LAPINE, CARMEN; Beacon HS; Beacon, NY; (S); Math Clb; Math Tm; Varsity Clb; Trs Frsh Cls; Var JV Bsbl; Var JV Bsktbl; Var JV Ftbl; Hon Roll; Hghst Scre In Schl On Annl Amer HS Math Math Exam 84.

LAPKIN, JOANNA B; Mamaroneck HS; Larchmont, NY; (Y); 15/379; Drama Clb; School Play; High Hon Roll; NHS; English Clb; French Clb; Latin Clb; Service Clb; Teachers Aide; Thesps; Columbia Coll NY.

LAPLANTE, JANE; Norwood-Norfolk Central HS; Norfolk, NY; (Y); French Clb; FTA; Pres Girl Scts; Band; Chorus; School Musical; Lit Mag; Capt Trk; Hon Roll; SUNY Potsdam; Elem Ed.

LAPLANTE, SANDI M; Saranac Lake Central HS; Saranac Lk, NY; (Y); 16/132; Hosp Aide; Band; Concert Band; Soroptimist; Sec Sr Cls; Stu Cncl; JV Var Bsktbl; Var Capt Crs Cntry; Trk; Vllybl; Most Imprv Bsktbl; All Cty Hnr Band 84-85; Coachs Awd Trk; MVP Bsktbl; Rel Ltr Trk 85; Suny Potsdam; Bio.

LAPLATNEY, DAVID P; Hugh C Williams HS; Canton, NY; (Y); Capt Quiz Bowl; Band; Concert Band; Jazz Band; School Musical; High Hon Roll; Pres NHS; Ntl Merit SF; Chess Clb; NY ST Schl Music Assn Blue Mdlst 83-84; Natl Soc Studies Olympiad Awd 84; Cornell U; Engrng.

LAPOINTE, ADRIANNE; Mary Louis Acad; Flushing, NY; (Y); Dance Clb; Drama Clb; Sftbl; Pulski Assn HS Schlrshp 82; Hunter Coll; Nrsng.

LAPP, MICHELLE; Vestal SR HS; Vestal, NY; (Y); Church Yth Grp; Church Choir; High Hon Roll; Prfct Atten Awd; Spanish NHS; Ridley Lowell Bus Inst; Sec.

LAPP, PATRICE-MICHELLE; Lindenhurst SR HS; Lindenhurst, NY; (Y); 8/580; Cmnty Wkr; Dance Clb; German Clb; Math Tm; Teachers Aide; Var L Badmtn; Var L Swmmng; High Hon Roll; NHS; NYS PTA Jenkins Memrl Schlrshp 85; Grmn Clb Awd 85; PTA Schlrshp For Tchng 85; SUNY-ALBANY; Secndry Educ.

LAPUMA, ALFONSO; Notre Dame HS; Frankfort, NY; (Y); 7/175; Am Leg Boys St; Boy Scts; ROTC; Yrbk Stf; Stu Cncl; Socr; Trk; NHS; Acad All Amer Awd 84; Natl Sci Merit Awd Wnnr 84; Clarkson U; Engr.

LARAGY, MOLLY; Bishop Kearney HS; Rochester, NY; (S); NFL; Speech Tm; Concert Band; Jazz Band; Mrchg Band; School Musical; School Play; Nwsp Rptr; Jrnlsm.

LARAIA, MICHAEL; Bethpage HS; Bethpage, NY; (Y); Am Leg Boys St; Boy Scts; Varsity Clb; Nwsp Rptr; Yrbk Stf; Rep Frsh Cls; Rep Soph Cls; Rep Jr Cls; Diving; Lcrss; Eagle Scout 82; St Michaels; Phys Thrpy.

LARAMIE, MARK; Northeastern Clinton Central Schl; Champlain, NY; (Y); 36/153; Boy Scts; Computer Clb; Model UN; JV Var Bsktbl; Var Golf; JV Var Socr; Hon Roll; Ag.

LARAWAY, WESLEY D; Middleburgh Central HS; Middleburgh, NY; (Y); Am Leg Boys St; Boy Scts; Band; Chorus; School Musical; Trs Jr Cls; Pres Stu Cncl; Trk; Hon Roll; Prfct Atten Awd; All Cnty Swng Chr Stu 84; Amer Legn Gd Citznshp Citn 83.

LARIOS, STEFFANI; Plattsburgh HS; Plattsburgh, NY; (Y); 6/160; Drama Clb; French Clb; Hosp Aide; Sec Band; Capt Bsktbl; Trk; French Hon Soc; High Hon Roll; Masonic Awd; Pres NHS; Thomas Armstrong Schlrshp 85-86; Physics & Chem Acad Awd 84-85; Union Coll; Pre-Med.

LARKIN, GRETA C; Notre Dame HS; Utica, NY; (Y); 9/175; Boy Scts; Hosp Aide; Math Tm; Spanish Clb; Rep Frsh Cls; Var Bowling; Var Crs Cntry; Timer; Var Trk; High Hon Roll; NY Regents Schlrshp 85; Acad All-Amer 85; Siena Coll; Pre-Law.

LARKIN, KATHLEEN E; Holy Trinity HS; Bellmore, NY; (S); 5/404; Hosp Aide; Mathletes; Math Clb; Math Tm; Ski Clb; Spanish Clb; Yrbk Stf; Stu Cncl; Twrlr; Gov Hon Prg Awd; Pre Med.

LARNER, KIM; Palmyra-Macedon Central HS; Palmyra, NY; (Y); Dance Clb; Debate Tm; Drama Clb; Girl Scts; Math Clb; Chorus; Color Guard; School Play; Rep Soph Cls; Im Vllybl; Buffalo U; Spclzd Nrsng.

LAROQUE, EDDIE; James Madison HS; Brooklyn, NY; (Y); Chorus; School Play; Cheerleading; Gym; Trk; Hon Roll; Prfct Atten Awd; Engl Achvt Awd 85; Outstndng Achvt Engl Awd 85; Regents Awd 85; CCNY; Pre-Med.

LARRABEE, JUDY; Union Springs Acad; Phoenix, AZ; (S); Varsity Clb; Chorus; Church Choir; Yrbk Stf; Soph Cls; High Hon Roll; Apollo Coll; Dntl Hygnst.

LARRABEE, MARK; John C Birdlebough HS; Fulton, NY; (Y); 2/250; Computer Clb; High Hon Roll; Elctrcl Engrng.

LARRAURI, ELIZABETH M; Bishop Ford C C HS; Brooklyn, NY; (Y); 10/398; JA; Math Tm; Science Clb; Spanish Clb; Stat Sftbl; Hon Roll; NHS; Pres Schlr; SR Ldr 84-85; St Francis Coll; Law.

LARREA, GIOVANNI; St Franics Prep; Jamaica, NY; (Y); 270/695; Cmnty Wkr; Hosp Aide; Var Capt Crs Cntry; Var Capt Trk; Prfct Atten Awd; CHSAA 1st Tm Trck-N-Fld All Star 82-85; Cathlc Leag A Mdl For Todays Yth Essay Cont 81-82; Villanova; Engrng.

LARRIER, CARRIE; Sheepshead Bay HS; Brooklyn, NY; (Y); Intl Clb; Libry Aid; Offc Aid; Hndbl Tm Var; Nwspr Sprts Edtr; Yrbk Sprts Edtr; Hnrs Int Prog Sheepshd Bay; Bernard M Baruch Coll; Bus.

LARSEN, AMY S; John Bowne HS; Richmond Hill, NY; (Y); 6/656; FFA; Library Aide; Var L Vllybl; NHS; NY ST Regnts & Rockefeller Grp Schlrshps 85; Grad Hnrs 85; VA Polytechnic Inst; Anml Sci.

LARSEN, BOB; Westmoreland Central HS; Rome, NY; (Y); 3/89; Church Yth Grp; Rep Sr Cls; Rep Stu Cncl; High Hon Roll; VP NHS; Prfct Atten Awd; Pres Schlr; Rotary Awd; Cmnty Wkr; 4-H; Fed Jr Fellowshp Pgm Awd 85; Mohawk Vly CC; Engr Sci.

LARSON, DENISE R; Spencer Van Etten JR SR HS; Spencer, NY; (Y); 2/100; French Clb; Sec Trs Radio Clb; Science Clb; JV Vllybl; Bausch & Lomb Sci Awd; High Hon Roll; NHS; Sal; Richard Wells Math II Awd 84; NY ST Regents Schlrshp 85; SUNY Stony Brook; Physics.

LARSON, ED; Smithtown East HS; Ronkonkoma, NY; (Y); Ski Clb; Band; Concert Band; Mrchg Band; Wrstlng; Hon Roll; Engr.

LARSON, ELIZABETH A; Fairport HS; Fairport, NY; (Y); Church Yth Grp; Math Tm; Concert Band; Jazz Band; Orch; Lit Mag; NHS; All ST & All Cnty Bnds & Orchstr 82-85; Hgh Scr Amer Natl HS Math Exam 83-84; Wellesley Bk Awd 85; Engnrng Physics.

LARSON, KIMBERLY; Jamestown HS; Jamestown, NY; (Y); Spanish Clb; Color Guard; Mrchg Band; Trs Frsh Cls; Rep Soph Cls; Rep Jr Cls; Hon Roll; Jr NHS; NHS; Church Yth Grp; Wntgrd Bi ST Champ 83-84; Math.

LARSON, MICHELLE; Ralph R Mc Kee Vo-Tech; Staten Islan, NY; (Y); 53/238; Sec Office Aide; Ed Lit Mag; Seagull Soc 85; Rep Clg Fair 84; 1st Hon Mntn NYC Ptry Cntst & Hon Roll 85; Archt Engr.

LARSON, PETER; Lansing Central HS; Groton, NY; (Y); 1/80; Am Leg Boys St; School Musical; Nwsp Rptr; Yrbk Phtg; Yrbk Rptr; Ftbl; Capt Swmmng; High Hon Roll; NHS; Ntl Merit SF; JETS Schl Tm 4th Regn 84; 3rd Pl Sthrn Tier Regnl Spn Exam 85; Citznshp Awd 85; Syracuse U; Archit.

LARSON, ROBERT; Mattituck HS; Mattituck, NY; (Y); 40/120; Church Yth Grp; German Clb; Variety Show; Messiah Coll; Compt Sci.

LARSON, WENDY; Jamestown HS; Jamestown, NY; (Y); 17/405; Church Yth Grp; French Clb; Sec Yrbk Rptr; Rep Stu Cncl; High Hon Roll; Jr NHS; NHS; Intnl Clb; Chorus; Drill Tm; NYS Rgnts Coll Schlrshp 85; Unif Stu Asst Schlrshp 85; Vikings Schlrhsp 85; Jamestown CC; Eng.

LARSSON, ALAN; Palmyra Macedon HS; Palmyra, NY; (Y); Aud/Vis; Camera Clb; Yrbk Phtg; Ntl Merit SF; Elec Engrng.

LASHER, BRIAN J; Lockport SR HS; Lockport, NY; (Y); 3/383; Drm Mjr(t); Jazz Band; Symp Band; Var L Swmmng; Bausch & Lomb Sci Awd; Hon Roll; NHS; Ntl Merit Ltr; MA Inst Of Tech; Engrng.

LASHER, CHRISTINE A; Fairport HS; Fairport, NY; (Y); Pres Chorus; School Musical; Swing Chorus; Yrbk Stf; Trs Jr Cls; Rep Stu Cncl; Capt Socr; High Hon Roll; NHS; Rotary Awd; All-Conf Choir 84; Lilac Teen Pgnt Fnlst 84; Natl Frnch Exam Cert Merit 82; Colgate U; Pre-Law.

LASHER, EVAN H; Valley Stream South HS; Valley Stream, NY; (Y); 32/178; AFS; Math Clb; Ski Clb; Temple Yth Grp; Yrbk Stf; Golf; Wrstlng; NHS; U Of MD Coll Park; Tax Lwyr.

LASHER, JAMES L; St Johnsville Central HS; Fort Plain, NY; (Y); 5/22; Am Leg Boys St; Trs Yrbk Stf; Trs Frsh Cls; Trs Soph Cls; Trs Jr Cls; Trs Sr Cls; Mgr(s); Hon Roll; Comp Sci.

LASHER, MICHELE; Dolgeville Central Schl; Dolgeville, NY; (S); 11/80; Art Clb; Church Yth Grp; Cmnty Wkr; German Clb; Color Guard; School Musical; Yrbk Stf; Hon Roll; Jr NHS; NHS; Herkimer Cnty CC; Crmnl Jstc.

LASHOMB, JEFFREY WAYNE; Massena Central HS; Massena, NY; (Y); Church Yth Grp; Nwsp Phtg; Hon Roll; Prfct Atten Awd; Perfect Atten Awd 84; Clarkson Coll; Mech Engnrng.

LASHOMB, JENNIFER; Franklin Acad; Malone, NY; (Y); Church Yth Grp; French Clb; Varsity Clb; Var Swmmng; Hon Roll; Prfct Atten Awd; Art.

LASKER, JOANNE; Alden Central HS; Alden, NY; (Y); Cmnty Wkr; Library Aide; Hon Roll.

LASKI, ANN; Mount St Mary Acad; Kenmore, NY; (Y); 105/125; Church Yth Grp; French Clb; Ski Clb; Chorus; Var Vllybl; Hon Roll; Excep Perf Math 83; Spec Mnstr Holy Comm 84; Vet.

LASKIN, HYUNJA F; The Bronx High School Of Science; New York, NY; (Y); Church Yth Grp; Cmnty Wkr; Pres French Clb; Hosp Aide; JA; Yrbk Ed-Chief; Ed Lit Mag; Rep Stu Cncl; NHS; Ntl Merit Ltr; NY ST Energy & Rsrch Comp 82; Most Imprvd Westhampton Yatch Squad 82; Molecular Bio.

LASKODY, LEE; Longwood HS; Coram, NY; (Y); Key Clb; Math Tm; Band; Nwsp Sprt Ed; Yrbk Stf; Im Socr; NHS.

LASKOW, JOHN A; St Francis Preparatory Schl; Woodside, NY; (Y); 415/690; Computer Clb; Trk; Wrstlng; St Schlr; St Johns U; Law.

LASKY, ERIC; Lynbrook HS; Lynbrook, NY; (Y); FBLA; Spanish Clb; Temple Yth Grp; Yrbk Bus Mgr; Var JV Bsktbl; Var JV Lcrss; Var JV Socr; Hnr Roll 83-85; Bus.

LASORSA, ANNE MARIE; Herricks HS; Williston Park, NY; (S); 135/306; Church Yth Grp; Cmnty Wkr; DECA; Ed Nwsp Phtg; VFW Awd; Voice Dem Awd; St Johns U; Accntnt.

LASSEN, DIANE; New Dorp HS; Staten Island, NY; (Y); Twrlr; Hon Roll; FIT; Fshn Merch.

LASSEN, FREDERICK; Avon Central Schl; Avon, NY; (Y); 2/90; Pres Church Yth Grp; Band; Chorus; Jazz Band; School Musical; School Play; Variety Show; NHS; Ntl Merit Ltr; U Of R Paideia Cert 85; Jr Yr Fin Notre Dame Clb Rochester 85; Oberlin Conservatoy; Music.

LATAILLE, PATRICIA; Sacred Heart Acad; Valley Stream, NY; (Y); School Musical; Var Socr; Hon Roll; NHS; Phy Ed.

LATANYSHYN, MARYANNE; Auburn HS; Auburn, NY; (Y); Var Fld Hcky; Var Stat Score Keeper; JV Var Timer; High Hon Roll; Hon Roll; NHS; Corp Law.

LATCHA, SHERON; St Francis Prep; Queens Village, NY; (S); 8/693; Church Yth Grp; Cmnty Wkr; Library Aide; Math Clb; Teachers Aide; Prncpls List 83-84; USNLMA 85; Cornell U; Bio.

LATER, KRISTINE E; Penfield HS; Rochester, NY; (Y); 7/365; Drama Clb; 4-H; French Clb; VP JA; Math Tm; Spanish Clb; Stage Crew; Nwsp Rptr; Yrbk Stf; Trs Lit Mag; Gleason Mem Schlrshp Wnnr 85; Co Ed Forgn Lang Nwspapr 84-85; Regents Schlrshp Wnnr 85; U Rochester; Bus.

LATHAM, WILLIAM H; Garden City SR HS; Garden City, NY; (Y); 73/319; Boy Scts; Church Yth Grp; French Clb; Trs Science Clb; Concert Band; Mrchg Band; Ed Lit Mag; Trk; Vllybl; Cit Awd; Webb Inst Of Arch; Naval Arch.

LATIMER, DONNA; Deposit Central HS; Deposit, NY; (Y); 2/68; Cmnty Wkr; School Play; Sec Frsh Cls; Sec Soph Cls; VP Jr Cls; Stu Cncl; Var Capt Cheerleading; Pres NHS; Sal; Rgnts Schlrshp 85; Marist Coll; Bus Admn.

LATIMER, STEVE; Fredonia HS; Fredonia, NY; (Y); Spanish Clb; Orch; Symp Band; Nwsp Rptr; Var Tennis; Hon Roll; Church Yth Grp; Ski Clb; Band; Mst Imprvd Vrsty Tnns Plyr 83-85; NY Schl Mus Assn Excllnt Soloist 83-85; Law.

LATKO, WENDI; Caledonia-Mumford HS; Mumford, NY; (Y); 2/95; Science Clb; Trs Band; Stu Cncl; Var L Bsktbl; Var L Crs Cntry; Var L Trk; NHS; Ntl Merit Schol; Sal; French Clb; Frederick M Hinsdale Schlr Athl Awd 85; Comp Ex Schlrshp 85; Allegheny Coll.

LATON, ROGER B; Mamaroneck HS; Larchmont, NY; (Y); Library Aide; Math Tm; Service Clb; Orch; Nwsp Stf; Yrbk Stf; DAR Awd; NHS; VFW Awd; Boston U; Bio.

LATONA, MICHELLE; Buffalo Academy Of The Sacred Heart; Williamsville, NY; (Y); Spanish Clb; Hon Roll; Math.

LATORA, DENISE C; Moore Catholic HS; Staten Island, NY; (Y); 3/170; Art Clb; Drama Clb; Library Aide; Stage Crew; Nwsp Rptr; High Hon Roll; NHS; Ntl Merit Ltr; Comp Schlrshp Exam St Johns U 84; Acad Schlrshp St Johns U 85; Regents Schlrshp 85; St Johns U; Math.

LATORELLA, MARC D; Geneseo Central Schl; Geneseo, NY; (Y); 3/70; Drama Clb; Mathletes; Yrbk Stf; Trs Jr Cls; Crs Cntry; High Hon Roll; Jr NHS; NHS; Ntl Merit Ltr; T B Sear Engr Schlrshp 85; Cornell U; Mech Engr.

LATORRE, MARY CATHERINE; Marymount Schl Of New York; Woodside, NY; (Y); Drama Clb; Intnl Clb; Model UN; Pres NFL; VP Chorus; School Play; French Hon Soc; Regnts Schlrshp 85; Ntl Hspnc Schlrshp Awds Prog 85; Pol Sci.

LATTEY, ERIK; Brooklyn Vo Tech; Brooklyn, NY; (Y); 16/912; Cmnty Wkr; Teachers Aide; Yrbk Phtg; Var L Ftbl; Hon Roll; NHS; Rgnts Schlrhsp Awd 85; Grvnrs Citation 85; Rensselaer Polytech; Arch.

LATTIMER, CAROLYN; Minisink Valley HS; Slate Hill, NY; (Y); Cmnty Wkr; Dance Clb; Yrbk Stf; High Hon Roll; Hon Roll; Hotl Mgmt.

LAU, KIN HUNG; Bronx High Schl Of Science; New York, NY; (Y); Prfct Atten Awd; Law.

LAU, KITTY KIT-YEE; H S Of Fashion Indst; Brooklyn, NY; (Y); 49/365; JA; Office Aide; Teachers Aide; Variety Show; Hon Roll; Prfct Atten Awd; Baruch Coll; Bus Admin.

LAU, MICHAEL; Sachem HS; Holbrook, NY; (Y); 228/1300; MMM; Varsity Clb; Jazz Band; Mrchg Band; Gym; Band; Chorus; Concert Band; Madrigals; Nwsp Rptr; All Amer Gymnst 84-85; NY ST Still Rings Champ 84-85; USGF Champ Cls II Awds 84-85; Sprts Med.

LAUDADIO, DANIELA; Sachem North HS; Holbrook, NY; (Y); 106/1600; Ski Clb; Sftbl; Math.

LAUDE, KYLE; Mynderse Acad; Seneca Falls, NY; (S); 34/132; Band; Concert Band; Jazz Band; Mrchg Band; Pep Band; Stage Crew; High Hon Roll.

LAUER, DANIEL; Niagara Wheatfield HS; Sanborn, NY; (Y); PAVAS; Im Ftbl; JV Socr; JV Tennis; Art.

LAUFER, LISA; Lockport SR HS; Lockport, NY; (Y); Church Yth Grp; VP VICA; Drm & Bgl; VP Frsh Cls; Rep Soph Cls; Rep Stu Cncl; Bryant & Straton; Bkkpr.

LAUFFER, JENNIFER D; Niagara Wheatfield SR HS; N Tona, NY; (Y); 12/315; Pres Church Yth Grp; Hosp Aide; VP Latin Clb; Library Aide; Pep Clb; PAVAS; VICA; High Hon Roll; NHS; Rgnts Schlrshp Awd 85; Dstngshd Stu Merit Tuition Schlrshp 85; Houghton Coll Adv Ldrshp Trng Prog 83; Niagara Cnty CC; Nrsng.

LAUGHLIN, JODIE; Mount St Mary Acad; Tonawanda, NY; (Y); 11/110; Church Yth Grp; Office Aide; Ski Clb; Spanish Clb; Nwsp Rptr; Yrbk Ed-Chief; Rep Stu Cncl; JV Cheerleading; High Hon Roll; NHS; Ec.

LAUGHNEY, GEORGE K; Union-Endicott HS; Endicott, NY; (Y); Key Clb; Political Wkr; Rep Jr Cls; Rep Sr Cls; Rep Stu Cncl; Var L Crs Cntry; Var L Trk; St Schlr; Mock Trl 85; Pre Law.

LAUGHTON, JULIE; Fayetteville-Manlius HS; Manlius, NY; (Y); Cmnty Wkr; 4-H; MMM; Ed Yrbk Phtg; JV Socr; Var Trk; 4-H Awd; High Hon Roll; Hon Roll; Chem Awd 85; Erth Sci Awd 83; NYS Ski Tm 82-85; Engr.

LAUKAITIS, JAMES; Smithtown West HS; Smithtown, NY; (Y); German Clb; Var Vllybl; Grmn Hon Soc 84-85; Empre ST Gms Mns Vllybll 84-85; US Vllybl Assc 84-85; Physics.

LAUNDREE, JOHN; Ticonderoga HS; Ticonderoga, NY; (Y); Am Leg Boys St; Drama Clb; 4-H; French Clb; Yrbk Sprt Ed; Crs Cntry; NHS; CAP; Exploring; Key Clb; Comp Engr.

LAURIA, KRISTEN; Kenmore West HS; Kenmore, NY; (Y); Church Yth Grp; Drama Clb; Math Tm; Band; Concert Band; Mrchg Band; Orch; School Musical; Symp Band; Stu Cncl; Roswells Summr Resrch Pgm 85; Schl Yth Court 83-84; U Of Buffalo; Med.

LAURIELLO, JOHN; Amsterdam HS; Amsterdam, NY; (Y); 18/300; Jazz Band; Mrchg Band; Symp Band; Hon Roll; NHS; USCG Acad; Marine Engrng.

LAURIN, MICHELLE; Clifton-Fine Central HS; Star Lake, NY; (S); French Clb; School Play; Yrbk Stf; Rep Soph Cls; JV Var Cheerleading; Trk; Hon Roll; NHS; Figure Skating; Mazareth Coll Rochester; Psych.

LAURITO, MIKE; Tioga Central HS; Barton, NY; (Y); Rep Stu Cncl; Var L Bsbl; JV Bsktbl; Hon Roll; Prfct Atten Awd; Math.

LAUTERBACH, KAREN A; New Hartford HS; New Hartford, NY; (Y); 24/264; Art Clb; Cmnty Wkr; Drama Clb; German Clb; Teachers Aide; Yrbk Stf; Im Bsbl; JV Var Cheerleading; Powder Puff Ftbl; Hon Roll; NYS Regents Schlrshp 85; Nazareth Coll Schlrshp 85; Nazareth Coll Rochester; Art.

LAUZON, CLAUDETTE; Salmon River Central HS; Fort Covington, NY; (S); 2/90; Capt Var Bsktbl; Capt Var Socr; Var Capt Trk; Hon Roll; NHS; Prfct Atten Awd; Sal; FFA; VP Band; 2nd Tm All-Northern Bsktbl 84; 1st Tm Al-Northern-Track 83; 1st Tm All-Northern Soccer 84; Phy Ed.

LAUZON, MARCELLA; Salmon River Central HS; Ft Covington, NY; (S); 1/96; Church Yth Grp; French Clb; Pres Pep Clb; Chorus; Church Choir; Yrbk Stf; French Hon Soc; High Hon Roll; Hon Roll; Sec NHS; Bausch & Lomb Medal 84; Potsdam ST; Elem Ed.

LAUZZE, KRIS L; Wellsville HS; Wellsville, NY; (Y); 8/132; Nwsp Ed-Chief; Yrbk Stf; Rep Stu Cncl; Stat Bsktbl; Cheerleading; Var Socr; Var Capt Trk; Hon Roll; NY ST Regents Schlrshp 85; Geneseo ST; Math.

LAVALLEY, ROBERTA; Lansingburgh HS; Troy, NY; (Y); Camp Fr Inc; FBLA; JA; Ski Clb; VICA; Band; Chorus; Concert Band; Mrchg Band; Stage Crew; Achvt Awd In Data & Word Prcssng I 85; ST U Of NY; Bus.

LAVELLE, PATRICIA; Bishop Kearney HS; Brooklyn, NY; (Y); Service Clb; Ski Clb; Spanish Clb; Rep Jr Cls; Hon Roll; NHS; Prfct Atten Awd; Hnrbl Mntn In A Poetry Cont 85.

LAVERY, BETH; Springville Griffith Instit; Springville, NY; (S); 4-H; FFA; Speech Tm; Varsity Clb; Nwsp Rptr; Stu Cncl; Cheerleading; Trk; 4-H Awd; Kiwanis Awd; FFA Ldrshp Awd At Oswegatchie Cmp 84; FFA Fndtn Awd In Floriclutre 84; FFA Fdntn Awd Pblc Spkng 84; Cornell U; Floriculture.

LAVERY, CATHRYN; Pelham Memorial HS; Pelham, NY; (Y); Drama Clb; School Musical; School Play; Variety Show; Nwsp Stf; Lit Mag; Political Wkr; Chorus; Off Frsh Cls; Off Soph Cls; Engl.

LAVIGNA, DIANE; Mechanicville HS; Mechanicville, NY; (S); Spanish Clb; Band; Yrbk Stf; Var Capt Bsktbl; High Hon Roll; Hon Roll; NHS; Skidmore Awd 83; Marist Coll; Communications.

LAVIGNE, DANIELLE; Queensbury HS; Glens Falls, NY; (Y); 6/226; Key Clb; Math Clb; Varsity Clb; Var L Bsktbl; Var L Fld Hcky; Mgr(s); Var L Sftbl; Stat Vllybl; High Hon Roll; Pres NHS; Pres Acad Ftns Awd 85; US Army Res Ntl Schlr 85; Union Coll; Math.

LAVIGNE, SUSAN; Johnstown HS; Johnstown, NY; (Y); 1/200; Civic Clb; Trs Intnl Clb; Nwsp Bus Mgr; Yrbk Stf; VP Stu Cncl; Var Tennis; Var JV Vllybl; AFS; 4-H; Math Tm; RPI Mdl 84-85; Balfour Awd 84-85; Pres NY ST CAR 84-85.

LAVIN, MICHAEL; Cathedral Prep; New York, NY; (Y); Drama Clb; Library Aide; Lit Mag; NHS; NEDT Awd; Schlrshp Cathedrl Prep 82.

LAVINE, STEFANIE; Farmingdale HS; Farmingdale, NY; (Y); Am Leg Aux Girls St; Cmnty Wkr; Drama Clb; Girl Scts; Chorus; School Musical; Yrbk Stf; Hon Roll; Jr NHS; Altrnt Amer Legn Aux Grls ST 85; Theatr Arts.

LAVINO, DINA; New Dorp HS; Staten Island, NY; (Y); Art Clb; Hosp Aide; Latin Clb; Sec Office Aide; Stage Crew; Yrbk Stf; Cheerleading; High Hon Roll; Hon Roll; NHS; Fash Inst Tech; Advrtsng.

LAVINSKY, COREY; South Side HS; Rockville Ctr, NY; (Y); 51/293; DECA; FBLA; JV Var Socr; Var JV Wrstlng; Hon Roll; Distributv Ed Clbs Am Reg Fnslt 84-85; Bus Mgmt.

LAVIOLETTE, MARK; Mont Pleasant HS; Schenectady, NY; (Y); 57/200; Church Yth Grp; Office Aide; Ski Clb; Ed.

LAVIS, LAURA; Mount Mercy Acad; Buffalo, NY; (Y); 50/200; Art Clb; Computer Clb; FHA; Girl Scts; JA; Science Clb; School Play; Hon Roll; Rgnts Schlrshp; Perfrmnc AM Schlstc Math Assoc Test & Intll Test.

LAVOIE, LISA; G Ray Bodley HS; Fulton, NY; (Y); French Clb; Hosp Aide; Band; Concert Band; Mrchg Band; Orch; Pep Band; School Musical; School Play; Symp Band; Nrsng.

LAVOPA, SUSAN; Miller Place HS; Miller Pl, NY; (Y); 101/201; FBLA; Yrbk Stf; Crs Cntry; Trk; Spnsh Awd 83-84; Crss Cntry & Trck Awds 84-85; Psych.

LAW, DENISE; Cortland JR SR HS; Cortland, NY; (Y); Church Yth Grp; GAA; Girl Scts; Y-Teens; Band; Color Guard; Mrchg Band; Capt Cheerleading; Crs Cntry; Hon Roll.

LAW, GEORGE; George W Fowler HS; Syracuse, NY; (Y); Church Yth Grp; NHS.

LAW, JAMES P; Saranac Lake HS; Saranac Lake, NY; (Y); Church Yth Grp; Yrbk Bus Mgr; VP Frsh Cls; Pres Soph Cls; VP Jr Cls; VP Trs Stu Cncl; Crs Cntry; Trk; Prfct Atten Awd; Am Leg Boys St; Diocsn Yth Cncl 82-85; Prsh Yth Retreat Team 83-85; Prsh Yth Mnstry Team 84-85; Law.

LAW, JULIE; South Lewis HS; Lyons Fls, NY; (Y); 4-H; GAA; Var Socr; Var Trk; Hon Roll; Empire St Games Skiing 85; Hnbl Mntn All Str Sccr 84.

LAW, LESLIE; Parishville Hopkinton HS; Colton, NY; (Y); Spanish Clb; Band; Chorus; Concert Band; School Musical; School Play; Stage Crew; Variety Show; Hon Roll; Music Excllnc 84-85; Potsdam ST U; Perf Arts.

LAW, MARNI R; Sherburne Earlville HS; Sherburne, NY; (S); 10/138; Drama Clb; Band; Chorus; Concert Band; Mrchg Band; School Musical; School Play; Variety Show; Hon Roll; NHS; Anml Study.

LAW, MELISSA; Stissing Mountain JR SR HS; Pine Plains, NY; (Y); Church Yth Grp; Cmnty Wkr; Band; Bsktbl; Fld Hcky; Trk; Hon Roll; NHS; Dutchess Cnty Music Edctrs Assn Music Feest 83; Selctd Trck & Fld Sectn I Conf C All Str Tm 85; Dntl Hyg.

LAW, TAMMY; Gilbertsville Central HS; S Berlin, NY; (Y); 6/26; Band; Chorus; Color Guard; School Play; Yrbk Stf; Sec Stu Cncl; Cheerleading; Socr; Sftbl; High Hon Roll; Cobleskill; Acctg.

LAWERNCE, AMY M; Franklin Acad; Malone, NY; (Y); 48/250; French Clb; Varsity Clb; Band; Church Choir; Concert Band; Hon Roll; St Schlr; Acad All Amer 85; SUNY Potsdam; Math.

LAWLER, MARLENE M; Auburn HS; Auburn, NY; (Y); 78/444; Drama Clb; Model UN; Trs Sr Cls; Bsktbl; Hon Roll; Hstry Clb; Cayuga Cnty CC Trstee Schlrshp 85; Cayuga Cnty CC; Phtgrphy.

LAWLER, SEAN; Auburn HS; Auburn, NY; (Y); German Clb; JA; Ski Clb; Ftbl; Lcrss; Wt Lftg; High Hon Roll; Hon Roll; Chrmn Of Mdl 85; Hist Clb 85; Poltics.

LAWLESS, MIKE; Saranac Lake HS; Saranac Lk, NY; (Y); Computer Clb; Spanish Clb; Varsity Clb; School Play; Nwsp Stf; Pres Sr Cls; Ftbl; Timer; Wt Lftg; Capt Vrsty Ftbl 85; Siena; Doc.

LAWLOR, KEVIN; St Marys Boys HS; Old Bethpage, NY; (S); 8/162; Rep Soph Cls; Var Capt Tennis; Service Clb; Yrbk Stf; High Hon Roll; Dentstry.

LAWRENCE, AMY B; Franklin Acad; Malone, NY; (Y); 36/253; Pres Church Yth Grp; Band; Church Choir; Crs Cntry; Trk; NHS; AFS; Houghton Coll; Teachng.

LAWRENCE, ANDREA; Mynderse Acad; Seneca Falls, NY; (S); 29/132; Band; Color Guard; Concert Band; Jazz Band; Mrchg Band; School Musical; High Hon Roll; Hon Roll; Dstngshd H S Amern Stdnt 83-84; Natl Hnr Rll 84-85; Oswego; Frnch Trnsltr.

LAWRENCE, CHARISE; Abraham Lincoln HS; Brooklyn, NY; (Y); 40/489; Band; School Musical; Nwsp Ed-Chief; VP Sr Cls; Co-Capt Cheerleading; Hon Roll; Jr NHS; NHS; Prfct Atten Awd; Gov Comm Schltc Achvt Citation 85; Daily News Super Yth Awd 84 & 85; Chancellors Hon Rl Jrnlsm 85; NY U; Cmmnctns.

LAWRENCE, JEAN; Stella Maris HS; Brooklyn, NY; (Y); Hosp Aide; Library Aide; Nwsp Rptr; Hon Roll; Publcty Cmmte; Clercl Wrk; Psychlgy.

LAWRENCE, LALISA; Longwood HS; Medford, NY; (S); 22/545; Mgr Church Yth Grp; Chorus; Church Choir; JV Var Vllybl; High Hon Roll; Hon Roll; Jr NHS; NHS; Acad All Amer 85; Outstndng Acad Achvts 83; Mth Awd 82; Carnegie-Mellon U; Engr Mtllrgc.

LAWRENCE, LESLIE; Islip HS; Islip, NY; (Y); Sec Frsh Cls; Var Bowling; Suffolk Cnty Wmn Bwlng Assn Kappy Queripel Awd 84-85; U Of PA; Acctng.

LAWRENCE, MICHELE M; Fairport HS; Fairport, NY; (Y); 13/620; Sec Church Yth Grp; Pres Ski Clb; Church Choir; Concert Band; Jazz Band; School Play; Yrbk Bus Mgr; Hon Roll; NHS; Nwsp Ed-Chief; Semifnlst Lilac Teen Pgnt 84; Inter-Club Cncl 85; Regents Schlrshp Wnnr 85; U Of WI-MADISON; Gentc Engr.

LAWRENCE, MICHELLE; Mohawk Central Schl; Mohawk, NY; (S); 7/77; Varsity Clb; Concert Band; Mrchg Band; Yrbk Stf; Sec Jr Cls; Sec Sr Cls; Sec Stu Cncl; Capt Powder Puff Ftbl; Hon Roll; NHS; Albany Coll Of Pharmacy; Pharm.

LAWRENCE, MITZI; Mabel Dean Bacon V H S; Brooklyn, NY; (S); 28/299; JA; Library Aide; Teachers Aide; Hnr Scty 84; Bus Admin.

LAWRENCE, PAUL; Clara Barton HS; Brooklyn, NY; (Y); 1/500; Cmnty Wkr; Computer Clb; Drama Clb; Exploring; JA; Math Tm; School Play; Stu Cncl; Hon Roll; Prfct Atten Awd; NYC Super Yth 84-85; Bost U Smmr 85; Acad Olympics 85; Pre-Med.

LAWRENCE, RHONDA JOAN; Waterloo SR HS; Waterloo, NY; (Y); 60/173; Am Leg Aux Girls St; Drama Clb; FTA; Chorus; Capt Color Guard; School Musical; School Play; Swing Chorus; Yrbk Stf; High Hon Roll; Arcadia Schl Comm; Secr.

LAWRENCE, STACEY; John Jay HS; Brooklyn, NY; (Y); 42/537; Math Tm; Capt Chorus; Color Guard; Jr NHS; Ntl Merit Ltr.

LAWRIE, LINDA; Oneida SR HS; Canastota, NY; (S); Computer Clb; Varsity Clb; Rep Soph Cls; Rep Sr Cls; Var L Fld Hcky; High Hon Roll; Jr NHS; NHS; Math.

LAWSON, ELAINE; Sacred Heart HS; Yonkers, NY; (S); 19/238; Hosp Aide; Twrlr; Hon Roll; NHS; Ntl Ldrshp Awd & Service Awd 83; Ntl Honor Roll Awd 83; Manattan Coll; Acctng.

LAWTON, CYNTHIA A; Immaculata Acad; Orchard Park, NY; (Y); 1/77; Cmnty Wkr; Girl Scts; Quiz Bowl; Ed Yrbk Stf; Hon Roll; VP NHS; Ntl Merit Ltr; NEDT Awd; Pres Schlr; Val; GSA Slvr Awd 84; Outstndng Vol Awd Yth Engaged In Svc 83; Western NY Sci Cngrs 1st 83; St Bonaventure U; Math.

LAWTON, DEBBIE; Gloversville HS; Gloversville, NY; (Y); DECA; Pep Clb; Pres Varsity Clb; Yrbk Stf; Pres Frsh Cls; Pres Soph Cls; Var Capt Crs Cntry; Var Crs Cntry; Var Powder Puff Ftbl; Var Capt Trk; Track Schlrshp 85; Track Athlt Of Yr 84-85; Bst Track & Fld Prfrmr 83-85; Fltn/Mntgmry CC; Comp Sci.

LAWTON, EDWIN D; Springville Griffith Inst; Collins, NY; (Y); 9/201; Pres Band; Chorus; Jazz Band; Orch; Var L Bsktbl; Var L Ftbl; Hon Roll; NHS; Gftd Tlntd Prog 84-85; Messiah Coll Acad Schlrshp 85; Messiah Coll; Bus.

LAWTON, LYNNORE S; La Guardia Hs Of Musci & The Arts; Brooklyn, NY; (Y); 231/541; Church Yth Grp; Library Aide; Chorus; Church Choir; Nwsp Stf; Yrbk Stf; Rep Sr Cls; Hon Roll; NY ST Regents Schlrshp 85; 1st Pl Beginners Trophy Tnns 83; Ithaca Coll; Comm.

LAWTON, WENDY KAY; Silver Creek Central HS; Irving, NY; (Y); Girl Scts; Library Aide; Spanish Clb; Yrbk Stf; Im Badmtn; Capt Bowling; Im Fld Hcky; Im Golf; Im Gym; Stat Score Keeper; SUNY Morrisvl; Nrsng.

LAWYER, BRADFORD JAY; Schoharie HS; Schoharie, NY; (S); 7/85; Boy Scts; Band; Bowling; High Hon Roll; Bowling Achievement Awards 84; Comp Sci.

LAX, HOPE; Peekskill HS; Peekskill, NY; (S); Concert Band; Mrchg Band; School Play; Nwsp Rptr; Rep Stu Cncl; Capt Tennis; High Hon Roll; NHS; Drama Clb; Acpl Chr; All Lg Ten Tm 83-84; All Conf Ten Tm 84-85; Comm.

LAX, JENNIFER; Lawrence HS; Cedarhurst, NY; (Y); AFS; Drama Clb; French Clb; Key Clb; Red Cross Aide; Stage Crew; Nwsp Rptr; High Hon Roll; VP Sec NHS; Fannie Monham Awd 83; Newman Awd 83; Med.

LAY, DAWN; Pine Bush HS; Pine Bush, NY; (Y); GAA; Ski Clb; Band; Concert Band; Mrchg Band; Sec Jr Cls; Var Im Cheerleading; JV Im Fld Hcky; Score Keeper; Stat Vllybl; Natl Chrldrs Assn Supr Str Sqd 85; Orange Cnty CC.

LAYFIELD, TERESA; Canisteo Central HS; Canisteo, NY; (Y); Trs 4-H; German Clb; Pep Clb; Teachers Aide; Color Guard; Stage Crew; Var Tennis; Hon Roll; Elmira Coll Key Awd-Schlrshp 85; Wildlife Cnsrvtn.

LAYO, MICHELLE A; Massena Central HS; Massena, NY; (Y); French Clb; Gym; Hon Roll; Acctng.

LAZAR, ELLYN H; Spring Valley SR HS; New City, NY; (Y); 28/440; Key Clb; Ski Clb; Temple Yth Grp; Nwsp Stf; Yrbk Stf; Trs Stu Cncl; High Hon Roll; NHS; Ntl Merit Schol; Tufts U.

LAZARO, MATTHEW J; North JR SR HS; Franklin Sq, NY; (Y); 15/160; Debate Tm; 4-H; Spanish Clb; Nwsp Rptr; Nwsp Sprt Ed; Var Capt Crs Cntry; Var Trk; 4-H Awd; High Hon Roll; NHS; NY Regents Schlrshp 85; Hofstra Dist Acad Schlrshp 85; Hofstra U; Engr.

LAZARUS, JARROD A; Tottenville HS; Staten Island, NY; (Y); 32/830; Cmnty Wkr; Model UN; Quiz Bowl; Concert Band; Pres Stu Cncl; High Hon Roll; NHS; JV Bowling; Cornell Natl Scholar 85; Ruth Saronson Scholar 85; Snys Rgnts Scholar 85; Cornell U; Vet.

LAZORE, LAURA; Massena Central HS; Massena, NY; (Y); Church Yth Grp; Pep Clb; Teachers Aide; Flag Corp; Miss IBEW 83; Miss Labor Day 84; Barbizon Grad 83; Miss VFW 83-84; Prom Dcrtng Commtt 85; Spec Ed.

LAZZARO, JOSEPH; Williamsville South HS; Williamsville, NY; (Y); Cmnty Wkr; DECA; FBLA; Ski Clb; JV Var Ftbl; Var Ice Hcky; Var Wt Lftg; Hon Roll; MVP Ice Hockey 84; Jr All Star Ice Hcky Team 84; ST U Of NY-BUFFALO; Bio.

LAZZARO, RANDALL C; Xavier HS; Brooklyn, NY; (Y); Cmnty Wkr; Intnl Clb; Trs Leo Clb; Rep Frsh Cls; Rep Soph Cls; Rep Jr Cls; Wt Lftg; NY ST Rgnts Schlrshp 85; Leo Clb Mbrshp Dir 83; U Of FL; Jrnlsm.

LE, DINH Q; Canarsie HS; Brooklyn, NY; (Y); 16/561; Computer Clb; Math Tm; High Hon Roll; Hon Roll; NHS; NY U; Chem Engrng.

LE, LANH; Linton HS; Schenectady, NY; (Y); #1 In Class; Intnl Clb; Chorus; Rep Frsh Cls; Rep Soph Cls; Rep Jr Cls; Rep Stu Cncl; Var Tennis; High Hon Roll; NHS; RPI Medl Mth & Sci Awd 85.

LE, LONG; Union-Endicott HS; Endwell, NY; (Y); Cmnty Wkr; NFL; Var Socr; Var Tennis; Var Vllybl; High Hon Roll; Hon Roll; Jr NHS; U Of Scranton; Doc.

LE, VUONG; Dover JR SR HS; Wingdale, NY; (Y); 15/96; FNA; Socr; Vllybl; High Hon Roll; Hon Roll; Dutchess CC; Nrs.

LE BAR, DENISE ANNE; Gowanda Central HS; Gowanda, NY; (Y); 7/160; Am Leg Aux Girls St; Trs French Clb; Sec Trs Chorus; Sec Frsh Cls; Sec Soph Cls; Stu Cncl; Var Capt Cheerleading; Cit Awd; High Hon Roll; Pres NHS; Regents Schlrshp Wnnr 85; Fredonia ST U; Bus Admin.

LE BARON, KANDIS; Jamestown HS; Jamestown, NY; (Y); Art Clb; Drama Clb; French Clb; JA; Political Wkr; Chorus; School Musical; School Play; Rep Frsh Cls; Rep Soph Cls; Jamestown High Arts Festvl 82-85; Fine Arts.

LE BLANC, GESS; Mount Saint Michael Acad; Bronx, NY; (Y); 6/300; Church Yth Grp; Stu Cncl; Im JV Crs Cntry; Im JV Ftbl; Im JV Trk; Hon Roll; Pres NHS; Spanish NHS; Penn Relays 1st Pl Medley Relay 85; Athl Awd 84-85; Cornell U; Pre-Med.

LE BLANC, JENNIFER L; Ballston Spa HS; Ballston Spa, NY; (Y); 20/217; French Clb; VP FBLA; Drill Tm; Rep Jr Cls; Rep Sr Cls; Var JV Fld Hcky; High Hon Roll; Hon Roll; NHS; Acadmc Achvt Awd Skidmore Coll 84; Fincl Mgmt.

LE BLANC, MATTHEW; Linton HS; Schenectady, NY; (Y); 14/300; Am Leg Boys St; Var Ftbl; Hon Roll; NHS; Ntl Merit Ltr; St Georges Ldg #6 Free & Accptd Masons Yth Awd 85; Engrng.

LE BLANC, MATTHEW; Salamanca HS; Salamanca, NY; (Y); 23/150; French Clb; Letterman Clb; Varsity Clb; Concert Band; Jazz Band; Pep Band; JV Capt Ftbl; L Var Trk; Im Vllybl; Hon Roll; MVP Ftbl 84-85; Petro Engr.

LE BLANC, RONA; Cardinal Spellman HS; Bronx, NY; (Y); Dance Clb; French Clb; Science Clb; Rep Soph Cls; Rep Stu Cncl; JV Capt Cheerleading; JV Var Pom Pon; JV Trk; Hon Roll; NHS; CYO Overall Chrldng Chmp 85; Micro Bio.

LE BOWITZ, SHERI; Smithtown H S East; Smithtown, NY; (Y); Model UN; Office Aide; Political Wkr; Spanish Clb; Pres Temple Yth Grp; Nwsp Stf; Frsh Cls; Hon Roll; Jr NHS; Spanish NHS; Yth Of Yr Fnlst 85; YMCA Yth Of Yr 85; Regnts Schlrshp 85; Brandeis U; Pol Sci.

LE BRITON, JEFF; Fairport HS; Fairport, NY; (Y); DECA; Exploring; Ski Clb; Yrbk Bus Mgr; Yrbk Stf; Rgnl DECA Treas 85-86; 3rd Pl At Rgnl DECA Cmptn 85; 2nd Pl ST DECA Cmptn 86; Bus Adm.

LE BRON, ANTHONY VICTOR; Bishop Timon HS; Buffalo, NY; (S); 4/167; Computer Clb; Library Aide; Spanish Clb; Church Choir; Nwsp Rptr; Nwsp Stf; Stu Cncl; High Hon Roll; Hon Roll; Comp Sci.

LE CLAIR, AMANDA; Northern Adirondark Central HS; Ellenburg Depot, NY; (Y); CAP; Pres 4-H; French Clb; Key Clb; Yrbk Stf; JV Capt Bsktbl; Var Socr; JV Capt Sftbl; Var Capt Vllybl; Hon Roll; Castleton Coll; Athltc Trnr.

LE CLAIR, BETH; Keene Central HS; Keene, NY; (S); Varsity Clb; Band; Rep Stu Cncl; Var Capt Socr; Var Sftbl; Var Capt Vllybl; High Hon Roll; Hon Roll; NHS; Sal; Excllnt Eng, Hist 84, Phy Ed 83; Courtland SUNY; Ath Trng.

LE CLAIR, PAM; Franklin Acad; Burke, NY; (Y); Pep Clb; Cheerleading; Trk; Epsilon Soc 82-85.

LE DOUX, PAULA JEAN; Kingston HS; Tillson, NY; (Y); Am Leg Aux Girls St; Hosp Aide; Sec Spanish Clb; Nwsp Stf; Yrbk Stf; Rep Stu Cncl; Var Swmmng; Pres NHS; Spanish NHS.

LE DUC, ANNETTE; Saranac Central HS; Cadyville, NY; (S); 17/140; Hosp Aide; Office Aide; Chorus; Yrbk Stf; Cheerleading; Hon Roll; Prfct Atten Awd; SUNY Plattsburg; Nrsng.

LE GRO, CHERRI; Haverling Central Schl; Bath, NY; (S); 6/148; Pres Sec 4-H; Trs French Clb; Math Clb; Ski Clb; Pres Chorus; Trs Yrbk Stf; Var L Swmmng; High Hon Roll; NHS; Varsity Clb; Outstndng 4-Her Cnty Awds Clthng, Pblc Spkng, Dog Care, Cnsrvtn 81-82 & 84; Clarkson U; Chem Engrng.

LE JUEZ, KIM; Cathedral HS; Bx, NY; (Y); 140/299; Aud/Vis; Intnl Clb; Library Aide; School Play; Sullivan Cnty CC; Trvl.

LE MAY, SCOTT; Canastota HS; Canastota, NY; (S); Church Yth Grp; Science Clb; Var JV Bsbl; Var Capt Bsktbl; Var Golf; Var Capt Socr; Im Vllybl; High Hon Roll; Hon Roll; Jr NHS; Hnrbl Mention All Lge Soccer 83; All Lge All Star Soccer 84; Rookie Of Yr Bsbl 84; Chemcl Engrng.

LE MOLE, JACQUELINE; Moore Catholic HS; Staten Island, NY; (Y); 2/250; Sec Church Yth Grp; French Clb; Math Tm; Speech Tm; Pres Chorus; Nwsp Rptr; Yrbk Stf; Chrmn Tennis; NHS; Voice Dem Awd.

LE PAGE, MICHELLE; Massena Central HS; Massena, NY; (Y); French Clb; Hosp Aide; Var Cheerleading; Stat Lcrss; Var Mgr(s); Var Score Keeper; Stat Wrstlng; NHS; Church Yth Grp; Thesps; Engrng.

LE PINE, KAREN; Franklin Acad; Malone, NY; (S); 10/253; French Clb; Pep Clb; Band; Hon Roll; SUNY-POTSDAM; Math.

LE PORE, JACQUELINE; St Francis Prep HS; Bay Terrace, NY; (S); 112/693; Band; Mrchg Band; Variety Show; Yrbk Stf; Rep Stu Cncl; Trk; Hon Roll; Jr NHS; Ntl Merit Ltr.

LE ROY, MARIE; Jeffersonville-Youngsville HS; Jeffersonville, NY; (Y); 18/60; Art Clb; Computer Clb; Spanish Clb; Varsity Clb; Chorus; Yrbk Stf; Pres Sr Cls; Var Capt Bsktbl; Var L Sftbl; Hon Roll.

LE ROY, MONA D; Fashion Industries HS; Brooklyn, NY; (Y); 2/365; Art Clb; Yrbk Ed-Chief; Pres Jr Cls; Hon Roll; Schlrshp HS 83-85; Textile Dsgn.

LE STYNE, SANDRA MONA LISA; Lehman HS; Bronx, NY; (Y); JA; Teachers Aide; Chorus; Pres Frsh Cls; Cit Awd; Prfct Atten Awd; Engl, Sci Ctznshp 84; Engl, Ctznshp, Svc 85; Engl, Atten, Sci, Ctznshp, Soc Studs 83; Pre-Med.

LEA, DEBORAH; Kings Park HS; Kings Park, NY; (Y); 90/395; Church Yth Grp; Girl Scts; Church Choir; Drm & Bgl; Mrchg Band; Nwsp Rptr; Nwsp Stf; Yrbk Stf; Hon Roll; 1st Cls Girl Sct Awd 83; Rif Awd 85; Stony Brook U; Sci.

LEACH, CHRIS; Murry Bergtraum HS; Bronx, NY; (Y); 28/576; JA; Crs Cntry; Trk; Prfct Atten Awd; Cornell U; Engrng.

LEACH, JOHN W; Catholic Central HS; Troy, NY; (Y); 38/203; Church Yth Grp; German Clb; Math Clb; Variety Show; Hon Roll; NYS Regnts Schlrshp 85; Hudson Valley CC; Med Lab Tech.

LEACH, KAREN; Jordon-Elbridge HS; Jordan, NY; (Y); Band; Concert Band; Mrchg Band; School Play; Nwsp Rptr; JV Bsktbl; Var Tennis; Hon Roll; Jr NHS; NHS; Onondaga CC Schlrshp 85; Carnegie Fdn Tutoring Schlrshp 84-85; Jrnlsm.

LEACH, KATHY; Jordan-Elbridge Central HS; Jordan, NY; (Y); Band; Concert Band; Mrchg Band; JV Bsktbl; JV Mgr(s); JV Var Score Keeper; Var Tennis; Hon Roll; Jr NHS; Accntng.

LEACH, MICHAEL; Grand Island HS; Grand Island, NY; (Y); Boy Scts; Church Yth Grp; Cmnty Wkr; Varsity Clb; Concert Band; Var L Bsktbl; Im Vllybl; God Cntry Awd; Hon Roll; NHS; Eagle Scout 84; Order Of The Arrow 82; Schlstc Lttr 85; Aeron Engrng.

LEACH, MICHELE; George W Hewlett HS; Valley Stream, NY; (Y); Drama Clb; Thesps; School Musical; School Play; Stage Crew; Nwsp Rptr; Nwsp Stf; Yrbk Stf; Lit Mag; Stu Cncl; Drama Club 85.

LEACH, PATRICIA; Sodus Central HS; Alton, NY; (Y); Pres Church Yth Grp; Band; Church Choir; High Hon Roll; Sec NHS; NYSSMA Solos Flute 83-85; Med.

LEACH, SEAN; Alden Central HS; Alden, NY; (Y); Rep Jr Cls; Rep Sr Cls; Im JV Bsktbl; Im JV Ftbl; Mth.

LEACH, TROY; Grand Island SR HS; Grand Isl, NY; (Y); Art Clb; Variety Show; June Glassman PTA Schlrshp 85; NY ST Regnts Schlrshp 85; U NY-BUFFALO; Arch.

LEAF, LISA; Bishop Grimes HS; N Syracuse, NY; (Y); Vet Med.

LEAL, KAREN A; North Shore SR HS; Glenwood Landing, NY; (Y); 3/205; VP Sec Latin Clb; Math Clb; Political Wkr; NCTE Awd; VP NHS; Chorus; Hon Roll; Ntl Merit Ltr; Maxima Cum Laude Ntl Ltn Exm 82; Slvr Mdl Math Fr 83; Nov Stu Mnth Awd 84; Radcliffe COLL; Classics.

LEARNED, CHRISTOPHER J; Northport HS; Northport, NY; (Y); Computer Clb; Mathletes; School Musical; Nwsp Stf; Hon Roll; Comp Sci.

LEARY, BRIAN; Pulaski JR SR HS; Pulaski, NY; (Y); Math Clb; Varsity Clb; Var Bsktbl; Var Ftbl; Var Trk; Hon Roll; Envrnmntl Sci.

LEARY, KATHLEEN; Mt Mercy Acad; West Seneca, NY; (S); 4-H; French Clb; Hosp Aide; Chorus; Yrbk Rptr; Yrbk Stf; Hon Roll; NHS; Nrsng.

LEASURE, TONI; Canisteo Central Schl; Andover, NY; (Y); DECA; Ski Clb; Trs Jr Cls; Score Keeper; Outstndng DECA Prjct 85; 1st Pl Gnrl Mktng Suprvsry Lvl 85; Cert Mertrous Awd Trk Scrkpng 84; Alfred ST Coll; Sales.

LEATBERS, SUZANNE; Greece Athena HS; Rochester, NY; (Y); 69/256; Sec Church Yth Grp; Pres Girl Scts; Chorus; School Musical; Symp Band; Yrbk Stf; JV Socr; JV Tennis; JV Vllybl; Hon Roll; Volenteer Srv Awd 85; Miss Amer Coed Pgnt 85; Gld Ldrshp Awd 84.

LEATHERBARROW, MARK; Bishop Timon HS; Buffalo, NY; (Y); Boy Scts; Exploring; Ski Clb; Spanish Clb; Chorus; School Musical; School Play; Stage Crew; Nwsp Phtg; Nwsp Rptr; RIT.

LEATHERLAND, TAMMY LEE; Massena Central HS; Massena, NY; (Y); Church Yth Grp; VP Spanish Clb; Band; Concert Band; Mrchg Band; Pep Band; JV Capt Sftbl; Stat Var Score Keeper; Var L Sftbl; NHS; Acadmc Banqt Top 10 Pct Clss 83-84; Albany Coll Pharmacy; Pharm.

LEAVITT, DAVID; Christopher Columbus HS; Bronx, NY; (S); 16/792; Debate Tm; Office Aide; Hon Roll; NHS; Law.

LEAVITT, GARY W; East Hampton HS; E Hampton, NY; (Y); 15/148; Madrigals; Orch; School Musical; School Play; Yrbk Stf; Lit Mag; Var Trk; Ntl Merit Ltr; Pres Schlr; Rep Frsh Cls; NY All ST Solo Chrs 83; New England Conservatory.

LEAVY, KAREN; Stella Maris HS; Rosedale, NY; (Y); 1/215; Hosp Aide; Library Aide; Red Cross Aide; Science Clb; Yrbk Stf; High Hon Roll; NHS; Prfct Atten Awd; Queens Coll Pres Achvt Awd 83 & 84; Police Athltc Lg Essay Cont 84; Med.

LEBEAU, COLLETTE; Mexico HS; Parish, NY; (Y); Spanish Clb; Varsity Clb; Var Crs Cntry; Var Trk; Spanish NHS; Span Folk Dance & Perf Concorde Hotel Sapn Drama 84; Nrsng.

LEBEAU, LISA; Pulaski HS; Pulaski, NY; (Y); JV Bsktbl; Cit Awd; Trvl & Toursm.

LEBEN, JENNIFER; Sheepshead Bay HS; Brooklyn, NY; (Y); 8/465; Math Tm; School Play; Nwsp Stf; Hon Roll; Aud/Vis; Drama Clb; Office Aide; Service Clb; School Musical; NHS; Rgnts Schlrshp 85; U Of Binghamton; Mgmt.

LEBITZ, ELLEN; Fontbonne Hall Acad; Brooklyn, NY; (Y); 27/133; Cmnty Wkr; Drama Clb; Math Tm; Stage Crew; Yrbk Phtg; Hon Roll; NEDT Awd; Prfct Atten Awd; Brooklyn/Queens Catholic Charities Offc For Disable-Apprectn Cert 84-85; Outstndng Achvt Cert-Bio 84; Special Eductn.

LEBOFSKY, BENJAMIN V; Clarkstown H S South; New City, NY; (Y); 57/525; Math Tm; Yrbk Stf; Var Stat Trk; Bausch & Lomb Sci Awd; NHS; Ntl Merit Ltr; Pres Schlr; Strawtown Elem PTA Scholar 85; Clarkstown Tchrs Assn Scholar 85; NYS Regnts Scholar 85; UNY Bingamton; Pre-Med.

LEBOV, BETH; Sheepshead Bay HS; Brooklyn, NY; (Y); FTA; Library Aide; Mathletes; Math Clb; Math Tm; Office Aide; Teachers Aide; School Musical; Yrbk Stf; Hon Roll; Cert Of Schlrshp In LOWI 84; Cert Of Schlrshp In Math Resrch 85; Cert Of Schlrshp In Englsh 83; Math Tchr.

LEBOVIC, KENNETH; Hebrew Academy Of Nassau County; W Hempstead, NY; (S); 2/90; Computer Clb; Debate Tm; Drama Clb; Math Tm; Rep Jr Cls; JV Tennis; High Hon Roll; NHS; Rep Stu Cncl; Fnlst Forensic Comp 85.

LEBRON, LIZETTE; Grace Dodge HS; Bronx, NY; (Y); 107/385; Church Yth Grp; Computer Clb; Dance Clb; Capt FCA; Model UN; Political Wkr; Service Clb; Chorus; Sec Jr Cls; Hon Roll; Soc Stds Hnr 84; Sci Awd 83; Englsh Awd 83; Hunter Coll; Socl Wrk.

LEBRON, SUSAN; Acad Of Mount St Ursula; Bronx, NY; (Y); 75/105; Church Yth Grp; Intnl Clb; Sec Spanish Clb; Variety Show; Yrbk Stf; NY U; Gynclgy.

LECCESE, CAROL; Richmond Hill HS; New York, NY; (Y); Teachers Aide; Chorus; Cheerleading; Elem Ed Tchr.

LECHNER, MICHELLE; West Seneca West SR HS; West Seneca, NY; (Y); 18/543; Key Clb; Office Aide; Spanish Clb; Rep Frsh Cls; Rep Soph Cls; Rep Jr Cls; Rep Sr Cls; Rep Stu Cncl; Stat Vllybl; NHS; Rgnts Schlrshp, Prncpl Awd Acad Achvt 85; Canisius Coll; Sec Ed.

LECLAIR, KERRY; Moriah Central HS; Pt Henry, NY; (Y); Boy Scts; Stu Cncl; JV Var Bsbl; JV Var Bsktbl; JV Var Ftbl; Im Wt Lftg; High Hon Roll; Hon Roll; NHS; Law.

LECRAW, JOSEPHINE; Pelham Memorial HS; Pelham, NY; (Y); 6/177; AFS; Political Wkr; Chorus; Lit Mag; JV Var Cheerleading; Pres NHS; Cmnty Wkr; Debate Tm; Nwsp Stf; Yrbk Stf; Tarah Lentner Awd 84; Schl Cmte Of Philsphy 84; Chorus Awd 83-84; Georgetown U; Pol Sci.

LEDDY, ARLENE; Delaware Acad; Delhi, NY; (Y); German Clb; Girl Scts; Yrbk Stf; Rep Frsh Cls; Rep Soph Cls; JV Capt Fld Hcky; Var JV Sftbl; Var Twrlr; Var Capt Vllybl; Hon Roll; German Clb Conv 2nd Prz Oral Declamatn 82-83; 1st Prz Essay German 82-83; Art Wrk Displyd Exh 85.

LEDEE, RICHARD; E Meadow HS; E Meadow, NY; (S); 19/414; Cmnty Wkr; Concert Band; Jazz Band; Mrchg Band; Rep Sr Cls; Var Ftbl; Var Lcrss; Capt Wrstlng; Hon Roll; NHS; Natl Hispanic Schlr Awds Pgm Semi-Fin 85.

LEDESMA, JOHN P; Our Savior Lutheran HS; Bronx, NY; (S); Hon Roll.

LEDWITH, DENISE A; South Shore HS; Brooklyn, NY; (Y); Chorus; Ntl Hnr Roll 85; Hofstra U; Bus.

LEDYARD, DEBBIE; Lake Placid Central HS; Wilmington, NY; (Y); Yrbk Ed-Chief; Yrbk Stf; Var JV Cheerleading; High Hon Roll; Hon Roll; Comm.

LEE, A; Henninger HS; Syracuse, NY; (Y); Socr; High Hon Roll; NHS; Prfct Atten Awd; Onondaga County Mth Tchrs Assn Cert Merit 84; Natl Ldrshp Orgnztn 84-85; Engrng.

LEE, ANDREA; F D Roosevelt HS; Staatsburg, NY; (Y); Concert Band; Mrchg Band; Orch; School Musical; Socr; Hon Roll; Sec NHS; Natl Merit Schlrshp Hgh Scorer 85; NYSSMA Area All ST Band 84; Animal Psych.

LEE, ANITA C; Arlington HS; Poughkeepsie, NY; (Y); 1/596; Cmnty Wkr; Debate Tm; French Clb; Math Tm; Chorus; Yrbk Ed-Chief; Lit Mag; Trs Stu Cncl; Var Trk.

LEE, ANN MARIE; Bainbridge Guilford Central HS; Bainbridge, NY; (Y); 8/74; French Clb; Band; Concert Band; Jazz Band; Orch; Variety Show; Ntl Merit Ltr; Rotary Awd; Prsdntl Acdmc Fitness Awd 85; Rgnts Schlrshp 85.

LEE, BEN C; Bronx H S Of Science; New York, NY; (Y); Computer Clb; Orch; Nwsp Rptr; Yrbk Stf; Trs Frsh Cls; Gentcs.

LEE, BENIN ANTINI; Senior HS; Brooklyn, NY; (Y); Church Yth Grp; Intnl Clb; Office Aide; Church Choir; Concert Band; Nwsp Rptr; Loma Linda U; Med Rsrch.

LEE, BONNIE; St Michaels HS; New York, NY; (Y); Drama Clb; Intnl Clb; Stage Crew; Nwsp Ed-Chief; Ed Nwsp Phtg; Nwsp Stf; Ed Yrbk Phtg; Yrbk Stf; Bowling; Syracuse U, Boston Coll & NY U Schlrshps 85; Perfct Attendnc Awd 85; Hofstra Mid Income Awd 85; NY U; Comptr Sci.

LEE, CHARLES A; Abraham Lincoln HS; Brooklyn, NY; (Y); 39/489; Hosp Aide; Teachers Aide; School Musical; Nwsp Rptr; Nwsp Stf; VP Sr Cls; NHS; Church Yth Grp; Science Clb; Chorus; Interntl Schlrshp Camp Schlrshp 83-84; Commended Negro Stu Ntnl Merit Schlrshp Corp 84; Med.

LEE, CHARLOTTE C; East HS; Corning, NY; (Y); Drama Clb; French Clb; Thesps; Band; Concert Band; Jazz Band; Mrchg Band; School Musical; School Play; Stage Crew; Lib Arts.

LEE, CHRISTINE; Walton HS; Bronx, NY; (Y); 165/565; Cmnty Wkr; Variety Show; Nwsp Stf; Yrbk Stf; Pres Jr Cls; Pres Stu Cncl; Cheerleading; Swmmng; Prfct Atten Awd; Frnch Awd 82-85; Bus Mchn 82-83; Pepperdine U; Comp Pgmr.

LEE, CLARA; Benjamin N Cardozo HS; Bayside, NY; (Y); 52/475; Science Clb; Chorus; Church Choir; School Musical; Lit Mag; NHS; Ntl Merit Schol; Church Yth Grp; Office Aide; Service Clb; Queens Coll; Optometry.

LEE, DAVID; Archbishop Molloy HS; Forest Hl, NY; (Y); 170/409; Chess Clb; Computer Clb; Math Tm; Hon Roll; Columbia U; Med.

LEE, DAVID; Aviation HS; Astoria, NY; (Y); 72/417; Aud/Vis; JA; Library Aide; Stage Crew; Yrbk Stf; Hon Roll; Jr NHS; NHS; Prfct Atten Awd; Elec Engrng.

LEE, DOROTHY; Andrew Jackson HS; St Albans, NY; (Y); Girl Scts; Band; Chorus; Church Choir; Color Guard; School Play; Bsktbl; Hon Roll; Prfct Atten Awd; Tchr.

LEE, EDNA; Brooklyn Technical HS; New York, NY; (Y); 27/1139; Computer Clb; Office Aide; Teachers Aide; Yrbk Stf; High Hon Roll; ST Regents Schlrshp 84-85; U Cntr At Stonybrook.

LEE, ELIZABETH; Walton HS; Bronx, NY; (S); 32/672; Hosp Aide; Nwsp Rptr; Sec Yrbk Stf; Sec Stu Cncl; Cheerleading; NHS; Prfct Atten Awd; Bio, Engl, Hstry, Frnch, Math, Chem 82-84; Coll Notre Dame MD; Law.

LEE, FELICIA; 135th Convent Avenue HS; Jamaica, NY; (Y); Computer Clb; Math Tm; Science Clb; Cit Awd; High Hon Roll; Hon Roll; NHS; USAA Math 83; USAA Citznship 84; Sci Medal; Princeton U; Surgeon.

LEE, GEORGE; La Salle Acad; New York, NY; (S); Chess Clb; Computer Clb; Science Clb; Nwsp Stf; Gov Hon Prg Awd; NHS; NY U; Dentstry.

LEE, GREGORY; Bronx HS Of Science; New York, NY; (Y); Key Clb; Math Tm; Office Aide; Teachers Aide; Band; Concert Band; Orch; Columbia; Chem.

LEE, GREGORY; Hastings HS; Hastings-On-Hudso, NY; (S); 13/117; Rptr Key Clb; Pres Latin Clb; Orch; School Musical; Nwsp Rptr; Stu Cncl; JV Trk; High Hon Roll; NHS; Ntl Merit Ltr.

LEE, HONGJOO P; Francis Lewis HS; Flushing, NY; (Y); 100/547; Pres Church Yth Grp; Hosp Aide; JA; Math Tm; VP Y-Teens; Ed Lit Mag; Socr; Hon Roll; Ntl Merit Schol; Art Awd 82; SPISE Cert 83; U Of NY Binghamton; Bio Sci.

LEE, ISAAC; Freeport HS; Freeport, NY; (Y); Off Stu Cncl; Trk; Selct Chorale 85.

LEE, JAMES; St Francis Prep HS; Bayside, NY; (Y); Tennis; Arch.

LEE, JEEHIUN; Union-Endicott HS; Endicott, NY; (Y); 1/460; Debate Tm; French Clb; Hosp Aide; Key Clb; Mathletes; Ski Clb; Orch; High Hon Roll; NHS; Ntl Merit Ltr.

LEE, JONATHAN; Tuckahoe HS; Tuckahoe, NY; (Y); 1/45; Church Yth Grp; JV Bsbl; Var Ftbl; Var Socr; High Hon Roll; Hon Roll; Hon Awd Chem Regents 85; Hon Awd Comp Progmmng II 85; Rensselaer Polytech Inst; Mech.

LEE, JUDY; Norman Thomas HS; New York, NY; (S); 60/671; FBLA; Band; Hon Roll; NHS; Prfct Atten Awd; Bus Adm.

LEE, JULIA; Wheatley HS; Old Westbury, NY; (Y); Hosp Aide; Teachers Aide; Orch; Yrbk Phtg; Yrbk Stf; Lit Mag; JV Bsktbl; Cheerleading; JV Fld Hcky; NHS; Ntl Hnr Roll 84; NYS Schl Music Assn Awd 85; Cornell U; Orthdntstry.

LEE, JULIE; Northport HS; Northport, NY; (Y); 11/595; Hosp Aide; Acpl Chr; Orch; School Musical; Variety Show; Sec Stu Cncl; Var Im Fld Hcky; Hon Roll; Prfct Atten Awd; School Play; Musicn Of Yr 83; All Estrn & All ST Orch 84-85.

LEE, KAREN; Brooklyn Technical HS; Flushing, NY; (Y); VP Church Yth Grp; FCA; Hosp Aide; Sec Church Choir; Nwsp Rptr; Nwsp Stf; Sec Frsh Cls; Bowling; Hon Roll; Prfct Atten Awd; Cert Achvt Engl 84; Svc Awd In G O 83; Sci Fair Awd 83; Cornell; Arch.

LEE, KATHERINE; Flushing HS; Flushing, NY; (Y); Intnl Clb; Library Aide; Math Tm; Office Aide; Band; Church Choir; Variety Show; High Hon Roll; Hon Roll; Prfct Atten Awd; UFT Schlrshp 85; Regents Schlrshp 85; Parsons Hosp Schlrshp 85; St Johns U; Pharm.

LEE, KATHERINE M; Shenendehowa Central HS; Ballston Lake, NY; (Y); 5/650; Am Leg Aux Girls St; GAA; Key Clb; Varsity Clb; Chorus; Rep Stu Cncl; Fld Hcky; Trk; Computer Clb; Pres NHS; Skidmore Coll Acad Excllnce 83; PTSA Scholar 85; Norstar Savings Bank Awd 85; Wharton Coll; Intl Bus.

LEE, KATHY; H S Of Art And Design; Staten Island, NY; (Y); 7/411; Church Yth Grp; FTA; Church Choir; Nwsp Stf; Rep Jr Cls; Var L Vllybl; French Hon Soc; High Hon Roll; NHS; Frnch Cont Cert 83, 85; Cooper Union; Fine Art.

LEE, KAUKLEE; Seward Park HS; Brooklyn, NY; (Y); 9/760; Pres Computer Clb; Stage Crew; Lit Mag; Hon Roll; NHS; Prfct Atten Awd; Chess Clb; Regnts Coll Schlrshp 85; Untd Fed Tchrs Schlrshp 85; Polytechnic Inst NY; Elctcl En.

LEE, KEVIN S; Benjamin Cardozo HS; Little Neck, NY; (Y); 34/476; Math Clb; Office Aide; Im Vllybl; Hon Roll; NHS; Regenis Scholarship 85; New York U; Optometry.

LEE, LEONARD; Liverpool HS; Liverpool, NY; (Y); Exploring; Hon Roll; NHS; Ntl Merit SF; Amer Industrial Arts Stu Assn Tech Writing 83; Electrical Engrng.

LEE, LILLIAN; John Dewey HS; Brooklyn, NY; (Y); Math Tm; Office Aide; Science Clb; Teachers Aide; Nwsp Stf; VP Stu Cncl; Hon Roll; Prfct Atten Awd; Princpl Lst 83; Marlane Ellen Nussbaum Mem Awd 83; Mth Awd Cert 83; NYU; Bus Admin.

LEE, LILY; Liverpool HS; Liverpool, NY; (Y); Art Clb; Lit Mag; Var Vllybl; High Hon Roll; Jr NHS; Mu Alp Tht; NHS; Pres Schlr; Church Yth Grp; Computer Clb; 2nd Regnl, 1st ST & 2nd Ntl Art Comptn 83; Sci Schl Comptn 3rd Pl 83; Delg PA Outstndng Yng Amer 84; Dntst.

LEE, MARIE; H S Of Fashion Industrs; Staten Island, NY; (Y); 15/365; Hosp Aide; Office Aide; Teachers Aide; Chorus; Stage Crew; Engl Hnrs 85; Cmmrcl Photo.

LEE, MENCILY; Sheepshead Bay HS; Brooklyn, NY; (Y); 4/465; Church Yth Grp; Intnl Clb; Library Aide; Math Tm; Science Clb; Cert Spec Congrssnl Recog Greetgs 84-85; Awd Excllnc Crmnlgy 84-85; Awd Outstndng Achvt Math 84-85.

LEE, MICHELLE; Notre Dame Academy HS; Staten Island, NY; (Y); Church Yth Grp; Computer Clb; Drama Clb; Yrbk Phtg; Yrbk Stf; Var Swmmng; Var Tennis; Ntl Merit Ltr.

LEE, MON; Seward Park HS; New York, NY; (Y); JA; Teachers Aide; School Play; Swing Chorus; Hon Roll; Regents Schlrshp 85; Syracuse U; Engrng.

LEE, NANCY A; Queensbury HS; Glens Falls, NY; (Y); 11/236; Church Yth Grp; French Clb; GAA; Hosp Aide; Key Clb; Math Clb; Ski Clb; Varsity Clb; Band; VP Frsh Cls; NY ST Regents Schlrshp 85; Bucknell U; Intnl Bus.

LEE, NOELE; Gorton HS; Yonkers, NY; (Y); Yrbk Ed-Chief; Lit Mag; Pres Jr Cls; Pres Stu Cncl; Var Cheerleading; Var Tennis; High Hon Roll; NHS; Hosp Aide; Q&S; Supt Awd Clb 90 84-85; Rensselaer Medal 85.

LEE, PATRICK; Hunter College HS; New York, NY; (Y); Math Clb; Science Clb; Var Bsbl; Var Bowling; Rensselaer Polytechnic.

LEE, PENNY; Broadalbin Central HS; Braoadalbin, NY; (Y); Intnl Clb; Letterman Clb; Varsity Clb; Color Guard; Mrchg Band; Yrbk Stf; Rep Stu Cncl; Var JV Socr; Var L Trk; Art Clb; Chldhd Dev.

LEE, PETER; La Salle HS; New York, NY; (S); Camera Clb; Hon Roll; NHS; Computer Sci.

LEE, REBECCA; Hilton Central Schl; Hilton, NY; (Y); Sec Church Yth Grp; Chorus; Church Choir; School Musical; Symp Band; Variety Show; Rep Stu Cncl; High Hon Roll; NHS; Prfct Atten Awd; All ST Cmptn 85; NYS Music Tchr Assoc Piano 85; Tchng Flute & Piano Lssns Chldrn 83-85; Music.

LEE, RICHARD; Lindenhurst HS; Lindenhurst, NY; (Y); Science Clb; Golf; Aero Sp Engrng.

LEE JR, RICHARD; Dover HS; Pawling, NY; (S); 8/94; Chess Clb; Math Tm; Rep Stu Cncl; High Hon Roll; Ntl Merit Schol; Prfct Atten Awd; Buffalo U; Math.

LEE, STEPHEN; Archbishop Molloy HS; Howard Beach, NY; (Y); 52/409; Church Yth Grp; French Clb; Im Bsktbl; Im Ftbl; Im Lcrss; Im Sftbl; Var L Trk; High Hon Roll; NHS; Wt Lftg; Pre-Med.

LEE, SUE; Liverpool HS; Liverpool, NY; (S); 16/792; Ski Clb; Orch; School Musical; Yrbk Stf; Rep Stu Cncl; Var JV Cheerleading; Hon Roll; NHS; Engl 10 Wrtng Awd 83; SUNY Schlrs Incntv Pgm Stonybrook 84; Cornell; Arch.

LEE, SUE; Stuyvesant HS; Flushing, NY; (Y); Cornell U; Comm Art.

LEE, SUNG; Christopher Columbus HS; New York, NY; (Y); Church Yth Grp; Science Clb; Church Choir; Debate Tm; Service Clb; Speech Tm; Teachers Aide; Trk; Wt Lftg; Hon Roll; POLY Schlrshp Mtchng Rgnts Pell Grant Tap Rgnts Schl 85; Achvmnt Rcgntn Awd NDSL 85; Chm I Mrt 84; Polytechnic Inst NY; Elec Engr.

LEE, SUNHEE; Northport HS; Northport, NY; (Y); 12/585; Church Yth Grp; French Clb; Mathletes; Science Clb; Acpl Chr; Orch; School Musical; Variety Show; Nwsp Phtg; Nwsp Rptr; Cld Sprng Hrbr Lab Asst 85-86; Amer Lgn Awd Schlrshp 83.

LEE, SUSAN; Stuyvesant HS; Little Neck, NY; (Y); Sec Church Yth Grp; Acpl Chr; Chorus; Church Choir; School Musical; School Play; Lit Mag; Rep Jr Cls; Office Aide; Madrigals; Cert Of Excllnc Spnsh 84; Christian Clb Pres 84-85; 1st Pl Teen Tlnt Comptn Vocal Ensmbl 84; Music.

LEE, TERESA; Cathedral HS; Queens Village, NY; (Y); 56/298; Band; Mrchg Band; Albany; Bus.

LEE, TIM; Liverpool HS; Liverpool, NY; (Y); 3/874; Church Yth Grp; Exploring; ROTC; Rep Jr Cls; DAR Awd; High Hon Roll; Jr NHS; NHS; Cornell Bk Awd 85; Am Leg Schlstc Exc Medal 85; Studio Art Awd 85; Aero Engrng.

LEE, TODD; Ossining HS; Ossining, NY; (Y); Church Yth Grp; Cmnty Wkr; Model UN; Rep Stu Cncl; JV Lcrss; Var Socr; High Hon Roll; Hon Roll; Pres NHS; Econ.

LEE, VERONICA; Webster HS; Webster, NY; (Y); 118/560; Church Yth Grp; Model UN; School Musical; Ed Yrbk Stf; Var Tennis; Hon Roll; NHS; Natl Guild Audtns 82-84; NY ST Music Tchrs Assn 82-83; 2nd Pl In Monroe Cnty Typng Cont 83; Purdue U; Phrmcy.

LEE, VIVIAN; Bronx High Schl Sci; Bronx, NY; (Y); Office Aide; Yrbk Phtg; Rep Jr Cls; Gym; NHS; Pres Schlr; Regnts Schlrshp 85; Syracuse U; Comm.

LEE, WAI-FONG; Norman Thomas HS; New York, NY; (S); 23/671; FBLA; Cit Awd; Hon Roll; Trs NHS; Prfct Atten Awd; NY U; Acctg.

LEE, WENDY; Williamsville East HS; Clarence, NY; (Y); Church Yth Grp; Drama Clb; French Clb; Ski Clb; Church Choir; Hon Roll; Law.

LEE, WILLIAM; La Salle Acad; New York, NY; (S); 73/249; Chess Clb; Math Clb; Math Tm; Nwsp Rptr; Nwsp Stf; Yrbk Stf; Vllybl; Hon Roll; Elec Engr.

LEE, WILLIAM; Westbury HS; Westbury, NY; (Y); 4/225; Computer Clb; Mathletes; Yrbk Phtg; Yrbk Stf; JV Bowling; Im Ftbl; Mgr(s); Var Trk; Hon Roll; NHS; Woodmen Awd Achvt Am Hist 84; Polytechnic Inst NY; Elec Engr.

LEE, WING WAH; Seward Park HS; New York, NY; (Y); Drama Clb; Radio Clb; School Musical; Gym; Swmmng.

LEE, YUK PING; Franklin Delano Roosevelt HS; Brooklyn, NY; (Y); 19/530; Pres Schlr; Baruch Coll; Mgmt.

LEEHR, JOHN N; Curtis HS; Staten Island, NY; (Y); 100/356; Am Leg Boys St; ROTC; Drill Tm; Var L Swmmng; ROTC; Naval Aviatr.

LEEPER, JONATHAN; Jamestown HS; Jamestown, NY; (Y); Im Bsktbl; Var JV Ftbl; Im Wt Lftg; Hon Roll; Mechncl Engrng.

LEES, SONIA E; Martin Van Buren HS; Bayside, NY; (Y); 17/596; School Musical; Rep Frsh Cls; Pres Soph Cls; VP Pres Stu Cncl; Var Tennis; High Hon Roll; Hon Roll; NHS; JA; Key Clb; Hstry, Mth, Sci Hon Soc 84-85; Ldrs & Ldr Exec Brd; Hugh O Brien Ldrshp Awd; Adolescent Psych.

LEES, VICTORIA A; Pittsford Mendon HS; Pittsford, NY; (Y); Aud/Vis; Church Yth Grp; Drama Clb; Nwsp Stf; Lit Mag; Rep Soph Cls; Rep Jr Cls; Sec Sr Cls; Hon Roll; Pres Schlr; Schlrshp Carnegie Mellon U 85; Rochester Schlstc Art Awds 85; Hnbl Mntn Natl Judging Schlstc Art Awds; Carnegie Mellon U; Art.

LEFCOURT, LORI; Paul D Schreiber HS; Pt Washington, NY; (Y); 16/448; GAA; Latin Clb; Yrbk Ed-Chief; Pres Frsh Cls; Pres Soph Cls; Pres Jr Cls; Pres Sr Cls; Rep Stu Cncl; Var Badmtn; Bsbl; Contrbtn To Schl Cmmnty Awd 85; Physcl Eductn Awd 85; Duke U; Math.

LEFEBVRE, DANIEL J; Altmar-Parish-Williamstown HS; Parish, NY; (Y); Am Leg Boys St; Drama Clb; Trs French Clb; Concert Band; Jazz Band; School Play; Pres NHS; Lbrl Arts.

LEFF, DANIEL; Hunter Colege HS; Bronx, NY; (Y); Ntl Merit Schol; SUNY.

LEFF, LILA M; Syosset HS; Syosset, NY; (Y); 100/518; Civic Clb; Cmnty Wkr; Debate Tm; Drama Clb; NFL; Political Wkr; Radio Clb; Band; Nwsp Ed-Chief; Lit Mag.

LEFF, SHERRIE; Smithtown East HS; Smithtown, NY; (Y); Cmnty Wkr; GAA; Spanish Clb; Teachers Aide; Temple Yth Grp; Nwsp Rptr; Rep Frsh Cls; Rep Soph Cls; High Hon Roll; Hon Roll; Cert Apprctn Typeathon Cerebral Palsy 83; Hofstra U; Bus Mngmnt.

LEFFLER, JAMES M; New Lebanon Central HS; East Nassau, NY; (Y); Variety Show; Albany JC; Comm Art.

LEFFLER, JENNY; Fox Lane HS; Bedford, NY; (Y); 31/275; Intnl Clb; Ski Clb; Rep Frsh Cls; Rep Jr Cls; Rep Stu Cncl; JV Var Bsktbl; JV Fld Hcky; JV Var Lcrss; High Hon Roll; Hon Roll.

LEFFORD, MARA; Spring Valley SR HS; Monsey, NY; (Y); Latin Clb; Thesps; Hon Roll.

LEFKOWITZ, ROBERT A; Ardsley HS; Hartsdale, NY; (Y); Aud/Vis; Computer Clb; Drama Clb; Exploring; Math Tm; Science Clb; School Play; Westnghse Sci Talent Srch 85; Computer Comp 84-84; Elec Engrng.

LEFORT, MICHAEL R; Holland Central HS; Strykersville, NY; (Y); Am Leg Boys St; Church Yth Grp; Pres Trs 4-H; VICA; Stage Crew; 4-H Awd; High Hon Roll; Hon Roll; Jr NHS; Kiwanis Awd; VICA ST Comptn 84; NYS Regnts Schlrshp Wnnr 85; Amer Allsafe Awd 84; Syracuse U; Aerosp Engrng.

LEFORT, MICHELLE; Holland Central Schl; Strykersville, NY; (Y); 3/120; Church Yth Grp; 4-H; Varsity Clb; Color Guard; JV Var Cheerleading; JV Var Score Keeper; Var Socr; 4-H Awd; High Hon Roll; Hon Roll; Med.

LEFSYK, MARK; Linton HS; Schenectady, NY; (Y); JV Bsbl; Var Bsktbl; Lib Art.

LEGARRETA, ANN MARIE; Islip HS; Bayshore, NY; (Y); 24/256; Yrbk Stf; Rep Jr Cls; Rep Sr Cls; Rep Stu Cncl; Var JV Cheerleading; High Hon Roll; Hon Roll; Jr NHS; NHS; Ntl Merit Ltr; Spnsh Awd 82; Pres Acadmc Ftns Awd 85; SUNY Geneseo:Acctg.

LEGAS, HELENE; St Francis Prep; Jackson Heights, NY; (S); 101/704; Church Yth Grp; Opt Clb Awd; Mrktng.

LEGER, SHARON; Mont Pleasant HS; Schenectady, NY; (Y); Spanish Clb; Spnsh Awd 82-83; Spnsh Awd 83-84; Spnsh Awd & Intro Spnsh Hnr Soc 84-85; RPI; Arch.

LEGG, ANDREW; Scotia-Glenville HS; Schenectady, NY; (Y); Boy Scts; Ski Clb; Trk; Wrstlng; Engrng.

LEGGETT, DAN; North Warren Central Schl; Chestertown, NY; (S); 5/48; Math Tm; Pres Jr Cls; Pres Sr Cls; Var Golf; Var Socr; High Hon Roll; Hon Roll; NY ST Regents Schlrshp 85; Clarkson U; Engrng.

LEGGIADRO, DANIELA; Blind Brook HS; Rye Brook, NY; (Y); Spanish Clb; Band; Tennis; Med.

LEGGIO, LYNNANNE; Sachem HS; Lk Ronkonkoma, NY; (Y); 121/1509; Hosp Aide; Spanish Clb; Band; Concert Band; Mrchg Band; Orch; Yrbk Stf; High Hon Roll; Hon Roll; Jr NHS; SUNY-BINGHAMTON; Psych.

LEGOFF, PATRICIA; Dominican Acad; Middle Village, NY; (Y); 2/45; Latin Clb; Science Clb; School Play; Nwsp Bus Mgr; Nwsp Stf; VP Jr Cls; High Hon Roll; NHS; Prfct Atten Awd; Latn Awd.

LEGUILLOU, MICHELE; Commack HS North; East Northport, NY; (Y); Cmnty Wkr; Teachers Aide; Nwsp Stf; Yrbk Phtg; Yrbk Stf; Mgr Fld Hcky; Hon Roll; Childhd Ed.

LEHMAN, DAVID; Wantagh HS; Wantagh, NY; (Y); Chess Clb; FBLA; Band; Concert Band; Mrchg Band; Orch; Pep Band; Rep Frsh Cls; Rep Soph Cls; VP Rep Jr Cls; Bus.

LEHMANN, EILEEN; Connetquot HS; Ronkonkoma, NY; (S); 1/671; VP Church Yth Grp; Rptr FBLA; Quiz Bowl; Chorus; Nwsp Sprt Ed; Ed Lit Mag; Swmmng; NHS; Ntl Merit Ltr; Renselaer Medal 84; Valdectorian; Engr.

LEHMANN, KRISTINA M; Byron-Bergen HS; Byron, NY; (Y); Sec Spanish Clb; Nwsp Rptr; Rep Stu Cncl; Cit Awd; DAR Awd; NCTE Awd; VP NHS; AFS; FTA; Band; Ntl Hnr Rl 84; Peer Cnslr 85; Syracuse U; Spch Pthlgy.

LEHMANN, STEVEN; Wellington C Mepham HS; N Bellmore, NY; (Y); 9/385; Church Yth Grp; Var L Bowling; Var Capt Socr; Var L Tennis; Im Wt Lftg; JV Wrstlng; Cit Awd; Hon Roll; Sec NHS; Prfct Atten Awd; Navy ROTC Schlrhp 85; Presdntl Acadmc Tns Awd 85; Long Island Benevdent Fnd Schlrshp 85; U Of N Carolina; Bus Adm.

LEHNER, ERIC; Ej Wilson/Spencerport HS; Spencerport, NY; (Y); Am Leg Boys St; Church Yth Grp; Model UN; Concert Band; Jazz Band; Mrchg Band; Symp Band; High Hon Roll; Hon Roll; NHS; U Of Rochester Paideia Cert 85; Elec Engr.

LEHNER, KENNETH R; Canisius HS; Buffalo, NY; (Y); 20/160; Cmnty Wkr; Spanish Clb; Capt Bsbl; High Hon Roll; Hon Roll; NHS; Spanish NHS; Political Wkr; Pub Rel Buff Bisons AAA Amer Assn Bsbl 83-85; Phil Scafidi Mem Bsbl Awd 83; Chldrns Hosp Aid 82-85; Fordham U NY; Bus Adm.

LEHNERT, KIM LYNN; North Babylon HS; North Babylon, NY; (Y); 5/601; Hosp Aide; Spanish Clb; Orch; Nwsp Stf; Yrbk Stf; Var Tennis; High Hon Roll; Jr NHS; NHS; Chld Psych.

LEHR, DARRIN; Msgr Mc Clancy HS; Long Island City, NY; (S); 25/225; Nwsp Sprt Ed; Nwsp Stf; JV Var Bsbl; Jr NHS; NHS; Spanish NHS; J V Bsbl Coachs Awd 82-83; Vrsty Bsbl Hnrbl Mntn As JR Brooklyn Tablet 83-84; Comp.

LEHR, SHERRY; Manlius Pebble Hill Schl; Tully, NY; (S); Drama Clb; Model UN; Quiz Bowl; Chorus; Madrigals; School Musical; School Play; Ed Lit Mag; Var Socr; JV Tennis; Goodyr Burlingame Awd 84.

LEHRER, RICHARD; Clarkstown HS South; West Nyack, NY; (Y); 64/541; Drama Clb; Math Clb; Temple Yth Grp; Thesps; School Musical; School Play; Var Trk; NHS; Ntl Merit Ltr; The Cooper Union; Engrng.

LEIBMAN, MARTIN; Bronx HS Of Science; Floral Pk, NY; (Y); Hon Roll; Prfct Atten Awd; Bronze Mdl Excllnce Algebra 82; Artistic Merit Awd 85; Regents Scholar 84-85; SUNY Binghamton; Psych.

LEIBOLD, DEBBIE; John S Burke Catholic HS; Goshen, NY; (Y); French Clb; Science Clb; Rep Soph Cls; JV Vllybl; High Hon Roll; Gen Excllnce Awd 85; Pre-Med.

LEIBOLD, GINA; Moore Catholic HS; Staten Island, NY; (Y); 10/180; Cmnty Wkr; French Clb; Math Tm; Chorus; Rep Stu Cncl; Capt Crs Cntry; Trk; Hon Roll; Natl Hnr Roll 85; Natl Sci Merit Awd 85; SI Cross Cntry 1st Team All-Star 84; Biochem.

LEIBOLD, JAMES; John S Burke HS; Goshen, NY; (Y); Model UN; Science Clb; Rep Frsh Cls; Rep Soph Cls; JV Bsktbl; Var Capt Socr; Var L Tennis; High Hon Roll; Hon Roll; 3rd Pl Hstry Olympd Awd 85; Asian Stud.

LEIBRING, CAREY; Royalton-Hartland Central Schl; Gasport, NY; (Y); 9/200; VP Spanish Clb; Hon Roll; Awd Proj Adept 82-85.

LEIDICH, RAYMOND; Union Springs Acad; Middletown, NY; (Y); Church Yth Grp; Ski Clb; Band; Concert Band; Jazz Band; Cit Awd; Bio Tech.

LEIDKA, CARRIE; Cicero-North Syracuse HS; Mattydale, NY; (S); 30/622; Stage Crew; Nwsp Rptr; Lit Mag; Hon Roll; Comp Prog.

LEIGH, COURTNEY; Dominican Commercial HS; Jamaica, NY; (Y); Church Yth Grp; Cmnty Wkr; Hosp Aide; Chorus; Rep Stu Cncl; Prncpls List; Fin.

LEIN, CHERYL; Bethpage HS; Plainview, NY; (Y); 31/269; Art Clb; French Clb; Spanish Clb; Band; Concert Band; Mrchg Band; Orch; High Hon Roll; Hon Roll; Jr NHS; Tri M Music Hnr Soc 84-85; Bsh Frnch Awd 85; Art Awds 81-85; Farmingdale; Law.

LEIN, CHRISTOPHER; Starpoint Central HS; Lockport, NY; (S); 1/200; Varsity Clb; Yrbk Ed-Chief; Var L Bsktbl; Trk; Bausch & Lomb Sci Awd; VP Jr NHS; NHS; Val; Its Acdmc Tm Capt 84; Pre-Med.

LEINING, CHRISTINE; Hoosic Valley Central HS; Schagticoke, NY; (Y); Pres VP 4-H; Yrbk Stf; Hon Roll; Paier Coll Of Art; Grphc Dsgn.

LEIREY, JAMES E; Kingston HS; Kingston, NY; (Y); Am Leg Boys St; Church Yth Grp; Y-Teens; JV Var Bsktbl; Var Golf; Hon Roll; Ulster Cnty Cmnty Coll; Comp.

LEISENFELDER, NOREEN; Mercy HS; Albany, NY; (Y); Church Yth Grp; School Play; Stage Crew; Rep Soph Cls; VP Jr Cls; Stu Cncl; Var Bsktbl; Var Vllybl; High Hon Roll; NHS; Math Sci & Bsktbl Awds 83; Sci Engl & Bsktbl Awds 84; Socl Frnch Bsktbl & Vlybl Awds 85; Nrs.

LEISNER, WILLIAM J; Cardinal Mooney HS; Rochester, NY; (Y); 11/318; School Musical; High Hon Roll; Hon Roll; Ntl Merit Ltr; Spanish NHS; Church Yth Grp; Cmnty Wkr; Exploring; Variety Show; Lit Mag; NYS Rgnts Schlrshp 85; Ithaca Coll; Cmmnctns.

LEITH, ELIZABETH; Mercy HS; Albany, NY; (Y); 4/48; Q&S; Chorus; School Play; Nwsp Rptr; Rep Soph Cls; Rep Stu Cncl; JV Var Bsktbl; High Hon Roll; Schlrshp 82; Cert Of Awd All Subjcts 83-85; Bsktbl Awd 84-85; Lbrl Arts.

LEIUS, JOY; Mamaroneck HS; Mamaroneck, NY; (Y); Key Clb; Chorus; Bowling; Cheerleading; Fld Hcky; Gym; Pom Pon; Score Keeper; Sftbl; Hon Roll; Pysch.

LELEONNEC, MARC; Archbishop Stepinac HS; White Plains, NY; (Y); 3/201; VP Key Clb; Yrbk Stf; JV Var Crs Cntry; JV Socr; JV Swmmng; JV Var Trk; Hon Roll; Jr NHS; NHS.

LELIS, AUSRA T; Cardinal Mooney HS; Rochester, NY; (Y); Am Leg Aux Girls St; Cmnty Wkr; Girl Scts; Rep Frsh Cls; Rep Soph Cls; Rep Jr Cls; Var Trk; High Hon Roll; Hon Roll; Spanish NHS; Law.

LEM, GEORGE; W C Bryant HS; Jackson Hts, NY; (Y); 6/579; Lib Debate Tm; Teachers Aide; Hon Roll; NHS; Pres Schlr; NY U Trustee Schlrshp 85; John W Gracik Alumni Schlrshp 85; NY U; Pre-Med.

LEMANSKY, RICHARD; Tottenville HS; Staten Island, NY; (Y); Computer Clb; Office Aide; JV Socr; Hon Roll; Jr NHS; Air Force Acad; Aerosp Tech.

LEMBECK, LORI; Smithtown H S West; Smithtown, NY; (Y); Var Sftbl; JV Vllybl; NHS; Spanish NHS.

LEMBESIS, VASILIOS S; Albany HS; Albany, NY; (Y); 39/600; Church Yth Grp; Cmnty Wkr; French Clb; Var Socr; JV Trk; NHS; Regents Schlrshp 85; Columbia U; Aerontcl Engr.

LEMBKE, TODD M; Medina SR HS; Medina, NY; (Y); 85/156; Boy Scts; Pres FFA; School Play; Lit Mag; Rep Jr Cls; Var Ftbl; JV Var Lcrss; JV Socr; FFA Natl Fndtn Awd Pub Spkg 85; FFA Dist II Pub Spkg 3rd Pl 85; KS ST U; Ag.

LEMBO, CHARLES; Bethpage HS; Bethpage, NY; (Y); 62/310; Capt Aud/Vis; Boy Scts; Yrbk Stf; Var Socr; Hon Roll; Arch.

LEMBO, RINO; Mount Vernon HS; Mount Vernon, NY; (Y); Key Clb; Hon Roll; Jr NHS; JV Bsbl; Cert Of Awd In Math 83-85.

LEMCKE, MARY; Hilton Central HS; Hilton, NY; (Y); Library Aide; Office Aide; Badmtn; Socr; Hon Roll; Bus Adm.

LEMEN, BETH; Whitesboro SR HS; Whitesboro, NY; (Y); 4/392; GAA; Model UN; Nwsp Ed-Chief; Yrbk Sprt Ed; Ed Lit Mag; Var Capt Trk; High Hon Roll; Jr NHS; Sec NHS; Var Crs Cntry; Wellesley Clb Awd, MVP Trck 85; MVP Crss Cntry 84; Engrng.

LEMIRE, CHRISTOPHER R; St Anthonys HS; Kings Park, NY; (Y); 27/227; Pres Church Yth Grp; Ski Clb; Nwsp Rptr; Rep Stu Cncl; Var Capt Ftbl; Wt Lftg; High Hon Roll; Hon Roll; Jr NHS; NHS; Regents Schlrshp ST NY 85; Acad Excell Awd 85-86; U Of Dallas Schlrshp 85; C W Post Coll; Polt Sci.

LEMKE, JILL M; Alden Central HS; Alden, NY; (Y); 5/198; Art Clb; Girl Scts; Ski Clb; Yrbk Bus Mgr; Yrbk Phtg; Yrbk Stf; Im Fld Hcky; Rgnts Schlrshp 85; Pres Acad Ftnss Awd 85; Acad Lttr 85; SUNY Brockport; Bus Admin.

LEMMA, MESFIN; New Rochelle HS; New Rochelle, NY; (Y); Camera Clb; Chess Clb; Computer Clb; Model UN; Yrbk Phtg; Hon Roll; NHS; Art Awd 83; Bio-Chem Engrng.

LEMON, SHERRY; Allegany Central HS; Allegany, NY; (Y); Art Clb; Library Aide; Hon Roll; Alfred ST Coll; Med.

LENAHAN, AILEEN M; Mahopac HS; Mahopac, NY; (Y); 38/390; JV Fld Hcky; Stat Var Sftbl; High Hon Roll; Hon Roll; NHS; Regnts Schlrshp 85; Siena Coll; Comp Sci.

LENANE, EDWARD; Mont Pleasant HS; Schenectady, NY; (Y); French Clb; Key Clb; Pep Clb; Varsity Clb; Yrbk Stf; Rep Jr Cls; Rep Sr Cls; Var Capt Crs Cntry; Var Trk; French Hon Soc; MV Rnnr Trk 83-85; Engrng.

LENARD, HELEN ANNE; Frontier Central HS; Hamburg, NY; (S); French Clb; Chorus; JV Bsktbl; Var Mgr(s); Var JV Sftbl; Tennis; Hon Roll; NHS; Accntng.

LENCZEWSKI, VINCENT; Archbishop Molloy HS; Middle Vlg, NY; (Y); 23/408; Chess Clb; Cmnty Wkr; Hosp Aide; Intnl Clb; Science Clb; Im Ftbl; Im Sftbl; JV Trk; High Hon Roll; Jr NHS; NY ST Rgnts Schlrshp 86; ST U Stony Brook; Med.

LENER, ED; Charles O Dickerson HS; Ithaca, NY; (Y); Church Yth Grp; Computer Clb; High Hon Roll; VA Tech; Geolgy.

LENIHAN, KATHLEEN; Dominican Commercial HS; Middle Vlge, NY; (Y); Girl Scts; Chorus; Drm & Bgl; Mrchg Band; Variety Show; Bowling; Tennis; Prfct Atten Awd; Principals List 82-84; CUNY Baruch; Accntng.

LENNANE, TRACY; Port Jervis HS; Port Jervis, NY; (Y); 27/250; Church Yth Grp; Pres Key Clb; Math Tm; Spanish Clb; Varsity Clb; Band; Mrchg Band; Yrbk Phtg; Yrbk Stf; Var Socr; A Rtngs In NY ST Band 83-84; Achvt Awd Math Team 85; Marywood Coll; Bus Adm.

LENNON, DAVID; G Ray Bodley HS; Fulton, NY; (Y); Science Clb; Ski Clb; Spanish Clb; Symp Band; JV Bsbl; JV Var Bsktbl; Var Golf; Oper Entrprse Miller Brewng Co 85.

LENNON, STACEY; Washingtonville HS; Monroe, NY; (Y); French Clb; Rep Frsh Cls; Rep Jr Cls; Rep Stu Cncl; Capt Crs Cntry; Var Trk; NHS; MIP Var X-Cntry 82-83; MVP Var X-Cntry & Co-Capt 83-84; MVP Var X-Cntry & Co-Capt, MIP Indoor Trck.

LENNOX, BRIAN; Caledonia-Mumford C S; Caledonia, NY; (Y); Church Yth Grp; Drama Clb; VP French Clb; Band; Chorus; Mrchg Band; School Musical; School Play; Swing Chorus; Masonic Awd; Vrty Club Drama Awd 85; Baldwin-Wallace Coll; Theatre.

LENNOX, MIKE; Edwards Central Schl; Edwards, NY; (Y); Computer Clb; Debate Tm; French Clb; JA; Quiz Bowl; Varsity Clb; School Play; Yrbk Sprt Ed; VP Frsh Cls; VP Frsh Cls; Baby Ruth Awd 85; Natl Schlr/ Athlte Awd 85; Cortland U; Sprts Med.

LENO, CHRISTINA; Holy Trinity HS; Plainview, NY; (Y); 42/368; School Play; Stage Crew; Nwsp Rptr; Nwsp Stf; Yrbk Stf; Var Stu Cncl; High Hon Roll; Hon Roll; NHS; Math Schlrhsp Awd; Math Schlrhsp Awd; Teaching.

LENTZ, KAREN; Mt Mercy Acad; W Seneca, NY; (Y); Computer Clb; 4-H; Hosp Aide; JA; Quiz Bowl; Nwsp Stf; Hon Roll; NHS; Vet.

LENZ, ALISON; Mynderse Acad; Seneca Falls, NY; (S); GAA; Ski Clb; JV Var Bsktbl; Var Capt Crs Cntry; Var Capt Trk; Hon Roll; MIP, MVP, All Leag Cross Cntry 84; MPV ST Qualif 3000 M Trck 84; Patricia Hurley Mem Awd 82; Athl Trng.

LEO, KIM; Islip HS; Islip, NY; (Y); Pres Trs Church Yth Grp; VP Concert Band; Mrchg Band; School Musical; Rep Jr Cls; Stat Bsbl; Var Cheerleading; Coach Actv; Mgr(s); Wrstlng; Pre-Vet.

LEOMBRUNO, TAMMY; S Glens Falls SR HS; S Glens Falls, NY; (Y); 53/200; Sec Frsh Cls; VP Soph Cls; JV Var Bsktbl; JV Var Fld Hcky; Var Sftbl; JV Vllybl; Eng Dept 81; Psych.

LEON, ANA; Norman Thomas HS; New York, NY; (S); 24/671; FBLA; Hosp Aide; VP JA; Orch; Nwsp Rptr; Cit Awd; Hon Roll; NHS; Prfct Atten Awd; Recgntn Outstndg Serv To JHS 82; Awd For Abiding Love & Interest Music 82; Engl Stu Of Month 84-85; Cornell U; Psychologist.

LEON, GRACELYN; Cardinal Spellman HS; Bronx, NY; (S); Chess Clb; Dance Clb; NFL; Science Clb; Spanish Clb; Speech Tm; Yrbk Stf; Im Vllybl; High Hon Roll; NHS; Natl Hispanic Schlrshp Awds Pgm 84; Law.

LEON, LISA; Valley Stream Central HS; Valley Stream, NY; (Y); JV Bsktbl; Var Socr; JV Sftbl; Var JV Vllybl; Hon Roll; Jr NHS; NHS; Spanish NHS.

LEON, PRISCILA; Dominican Acad; New York, NY; (Y); Latin Clb; Science Clb; Church Choir; School Musical; School Play; Hon Roll; NEDT Awd; Prfct Atten Awd; Magna Cum Laude Natl Latn Exm 83-84; Merit Cert Natl Frnch Cntst 85; Biochem.

LEON, RACHEL; Mont Pleasant HS; Schenectady, NY; (Y); 29/243; Civic Clb; Cmnty Wkr; Drama Clb; French Clb; Chorus; School Play; Variety Show; Yrbk Ed-Chief; Yrbk Rptr; Rep Stu Cncl; Cert Achvt Rcgntn Vol Svc Cmmnty 85; Geneseo; Engl.

LEON, STEVEN; St Francis Preparatory HS; Little Neck, NY; (S); 59/ 690; Computer Clb; Office Aide; Rep Soph Cls; Coach Actv; Var Crs Cntry; Im Ftbl; Var Trk; Im Vllybl; NHS; Spanish NHS; Prncpls List 83; Chem.

LEONARD, COLLEEN; Catholic Central HS; Troy, NY; (Y); Church Yth Grp; French Clb; Math Clb; Math Tm; Rep Jr Cls.

LEONARD, GARY; Wheatland-Chili Central Schl; Scottsville, NY; (Y); 4/80; Am Leg Boys St; Band; Jazz Band; Mrchg Band; Sec Jr Cls; Var L Bsbl; Var L Bsktbl; Var L Socr; Hon Roll; NHS; Notre Dame; Engrng.

LEONARD, PATRICIA M; Whitney Point Central HS; Endwell, NY; (Y); JCL; Latin Clb; Chorus; Hon Roll; NHS; Ntl Fed Stu Musicans 83-85; Engr.

LEONARD, SANTINA E; Stissing Mtn JR SR HS; Stanfordvle, NY; (Y); 7/80; AFS; Cmnty Wkr; Concert Band; Yrbk Stf; JV Var Bsktbl; JV Fld Hcky; Var L Vllybl; Hon Roll; NHS; Natl Eng Mrt Awd 84-85; Rensselaer Poly Inst; Engnrng.

LEONARD, VALERIE A; John Jay HS; Hopewell Jct, NY; (Y); 222/560; Stat Bsktbl; Mt St Mary Coll Schlrshp 85; Eng Stu Wk 84; Mt St Mary Coll Newburgh; Nrsng.

LEONARDI, DOUGLAS; Sachem HS; Farmingville, NY; (Y); 225/1350; Boys Clb Am; CAP; German Clb; Science Clb; Band; Concert Band; Nwsp Rptr; Lit Mag; Ntl Merit SF; Pysics Rsrch.

LEONARDO, JOSEPH; Beacon HS; Beacon, NY; (S); JA; Cit Awd; High Hon Roll; Jr NHS; NHS; Hstry Awd & Ind Arts Awd 84; Engrng.

LEONE, MARIA; Bishop Ford C C HS; Brooklyn, NY; (Y); Art Clb; Computer Clb; Red Cross Aide; Ski Clb; Yrbk Stf; Crs Cntry; Trk; Acctng.

LEONE, MARIA; Mynderse Acad; Seneca Falls, NY; (Y); 18/133; GAA; JA; Yrbk Stf; JV L Bsktbl; Var L Crs Cntry; Var L Socr; High Hon Roll; Hon Roll; NHS; Natl Hnr Rll; Marcia Regina Coll; Secy Sci.

LEONE, RAYMOND; Dundee Central HS; Dundee, NY; (Y); 18/66; Boy Scts; Computer Clb; Math Clb; Varsity Clb; Crs Cntry; Ftbl; Trk; Hon Roll; NYS Regnts Schlrshp 85.

LEONE, ROBERT; Sachen High School North; Holtsville, NY; (Y); 9/ 1432; French Clb; Hosp Aide; Math Tm; Pres MMM; Rep Concert Band; Pres Jazz Band; Rep Mrchg Band; Pres Symp Band; Trs NHS; Ntl Merit Ltr; Berkelee Schl Of Music Grant 84; Mc Donalds All-Am Mrchng/Jzz Bnd 84-85; NY All-St Jazz Ensmbl 83-85; Harvard U; Chem.

LEONETTI, PETER; Catholic Central HS; Troy, NY; (Y); Math Clb; Spanish Clb; High Hon Roll; Hon Roll; Prfct Atten Awd; Rensselaer Cnty Mock Trial Trnmnt 85; Economics.

LEONG, EDWIN; Brooklyn Technical HS; Brooklyn, NY; (Y); Camera Clb; Cmnty Wkr; Office Aide; Service Clb; Teachers Aide; Elec Engrng.

LEONHARDT, MARCE; Rensselaer HS; Rensselaer, NY; (Y); VP Sec Computer Clb; Varsity Clb; Nwsp Rptr; Yrbk Phtg; Var Fld Hcky; Trk; JV Vllybl; Oustdng Sls Awd 84; 3rd Plc Radio Advrtsng 85; Photo.

LEPITSCH, BARBARA; Smithtown High School West; Smithtown, NY; (Y); Ski Clb; Rep Jr Cls; Rep Sr Cls; Var Capt Tennis; Var Trk; JV Var Vllybl; NHS; Church Yth Grp; Drama Clb; Hosp Aide; German Hnr Scty 83-85; Pres Acad Ftns Awd 85; Gold Key Athl Achvt Awd 85; SUNY-ONEONTA; Phy Thrpy.

LEPKOWSKI, KIM MARIE; Mt Mercy Acad; Lackawanna, NY; (Y); 9/ 202; Am Leg Aux Girls St; Model UN; Nwsp Sprt Ed; Var Capt Bowling; High Hon Roll; NHS; Pres Schlr; Cmnty Wkr; Hosp Aide; JA; Acad Tm Capt 84-85; Tu Appearance 83-85; Monsignor Martin Bwlng MVP 83-84, 2nd Tm All-Cath 82-85; Trocair Coll; Law.

LEPORE, JACQUELINE; St Francis Prep HS; Bayside, NY; (Y); 112/ 693; Yrbk Stf; Rep Stu Cncl; Trk; Hon Roll; Jr NHS; Ntl Merit Ltr; Optimates List 84-85; Pre-Dent.

LEPP, TRACI; Greece Olympia HS; Rochester, NY; (Y); 36/376; Drama Clb; Red Cross Aide; Chorus; School Musical; Stage Crew; Rep Frsh Cls; Rep Soph Cls; Rep Stu Cncl; Hon Roll; NHS; Wmns Ed, Ind Un Schlrshp 85; Rochester Inst Tech; Purchsng.

LERCH, BRIAN; Lockport SR HS; Lockport, NY; (Y); VP AFS; Church Yth Grp; Drama Clb; Latin Clb; School Musical; Stage Crew; Stu Cncl; Tcrk; Camera Clb; Band; Karate-Brown Belt 84; Chrmn Lockport Inter Faith 85; Alfred Tech; Arch.

LERCH, TERENCE; East Aurora HS; East Aurora, NY; (S); 8/182; Rep Soph Cls; Rep Jr Cls; Rep Sr Cls; JV Bsktbl; Var Golf; JV Trk; Hon Roll; Jr NHS; NHS; Regents Schlrshp 85; Rochester Inst Tech; Comp Engr.

LERNER, ALISA; Tottenville HS; Staten Island, NY; (Y); 16/897; Math Tm; Office Aide; Quiz Bowl; School Play; Nwsp Stf; Hon Roll; Jr NHS; NHS; Ntl Hnr Roll Yrbk 83-85; SUNY Stony Brook; Nrsng.

LERNER, ERIC; Farmingdale SR HS; S Farmingdale, NY; (Y); Pres FBLA; Nwsp Ed-Chief; Nwsp Stf; Lit Mag; Ntl Merit Ltr; Outstdng Achv 84-85; Nassau Bar Asn Essay Cont 2nd Pl 84-85; H S Corrspndnt To Town Nwspr-OBSERVER 84; U Of MI; Englsh.

LEROUX, MELANEY ANN; Massena Central HS; Rooseveltown, NY; (Y); 60/296; French Clb; Var Socr; Hon Roll; NHS; Prfct Atten Awd; Pres Fitness Awd 85; Alcoa Schlrshp 85; Canton Ag & Tech Coll; Engrng.

LEROUX, PAULA; Salmon River Central HS; Ft Covington, NY; (Y); 18/87; Church Yth Grp; Drama Clb; Girl Scts; Band; Church Choir; School Play; L Mgr(s); L Swmmng; Ann Merkel Grl Sct Schlrshp 85; Knigts Oc Columbs Cncl Schlrshp 85; Cobleskill Clg; Hotel Tech.

LES PIERRE, KAREN F; Horace Mann HS; Bronx, NY; (Y); Teachers Aide; Var L Fld Hcky; Karen Les Piere Medal 82; All Ivy Team Fld Hcky 83-84; Prep For Pref Prog 82; Psych.

LESEFSKE, MICHELLE; Gowanda Central HS; Gowanda, NY; (Y); Mrchg Band; Pep Band; School Musical; School Play; Yrbk Bus Mgr; Yrbk Stf; Rep Jr Cls; Rep Stu Cncl; Var Trk; Hon Roll; 1st Pl Awd Wstrn NY Schl Press Assn 85; Thespn Soc 84; Fash Dsgn.

LESHKOWICH, ANN MARIE; Garden City SR HS; Garden City, NY; (Y); 1/319; French Clb; Pres Latin Clb; Teachers Aide; Nwsp Stf; Ed Yrbk Stf; High Hon Roll; Jr NHS; NHS; Ntl Merit SF; Val.

LESHOWITZ, KAREN; John Adams HS; Howard Beach, NY; (Y); 8/590; Library Aide; Math Tm; Nwsp Stf; Yrbk Stf; Var Sftbl; Cit Awd; High Hon Roll; NCTE Awd; Sec NHS; Pres Schlr; Chnclrs Hon Rll 85; Amer Assoc Tchrs Spnsh & Portgse Awd85; NYS Rgnts Schlrshp 85; Cornell U; Law.

LESICA, DIANE L; St Johns Prep; Astoria, NY; (Y); 57/415; Office Aide; Teachers Aide; Yrbk Stf; Lit Mag; High Hon Roll; Regents Schlrshp 85; Cert Merit Regents Schlrshp 85; Baruch; Comp.

LESINSKI, BONNIE; Grand Island SR HS; Grand Island, NY; (Y); 19/ 325; French Clb; GAA; Hosp Aide; Variety Show; Nwsp Rptr; Rep Stu Cncl; Bsktbl; Var JV Mgr(s); Var JV Score Keeper; Sftbl; Phrmcy.

LESKIW, LISA; G Ray Bodley HS; Fulton, NY; (S); Church Yth Grp; Sec Latin Clb; Science Clb; Orch; School Musical; Hon Roll; Prfct Atten Awd; Concert Mistress All-County Orch 82 & 83; U Buffalo; Sci.

LESLIE, ANITA; Buffalo Acad Of The Sacred Heart; Williamsville, NY; (Y); 10/126; Science Clb; Spanish Clb; Var Crs Cntry; NHS; Natl Precision Figure Skating Champ 84-85; Hugh O Brian Yth Ledrshp Seminar Rep 84; Amherst YES 85; Advertising.

LESLIE, JENNIFER; Sheepshead Bay HS; New York, NY; (Y); 4-H; Bsktbl; Socr; Bus Adm.

LESNIAK, CHRISTINE; North Collins Central HS; N Collins, NY; (Y); Camp Fr Inc; Cmnty Wkr; Girl Scts; Nwsp Stf; Drftng.

LESNIAK, LAURIE ANN; West Canada Valley HS; Utica, NY; (Y); 12/ 78; Church Yth Grp; GAA; Band; Chorus; School Play; Off Sr Cls; Cheerleading; Trk; High Hon Roll; NHS; Le Moyne Coll; Chld Psych.

LESPERANCE, DANIELLE M; Ogdensburg Free Acad; Ogdensburg, NY; (Y); 3/197; French Clb; Sec Key Clb; Color Guard; Mrchg Band; Yrbk Ed-Chief; Rep Stu Cncl; Co-Capt Crs Cntry; High Hon Roll; NHS; Ntl Merit SF.

LESSER, JANE; Smithtown West HS; Smithtown, NY; (Y); 80/500; Lit Mag; Capt Var Socr; Hon Roll; Regents Schlrshp 85; Vrsty Swtr Sccr 83; All-Cnty Sccr 83; Dowling Coll; Accntnt.

LESSNER, DONNA; Roy C Ketcham HS; Wappinger Falls, NY; (Y); Girl Scts; Temple Yth Grp; Concert Band; Stage Crew; Var Capt Gym; French Hon Soc; High Hon Roll; Jr NHS; NHS; Drama Clb; Girl Schout Wider Opportunity Sport Spree 83.

LESTER, CARL A; Rice HS; New York, NY; (S); 9/74; Boy Scts; Cmnty Wkr; Computer Clb; Library Aide; Office Aide; Rep Soph Cls; Rep Stu Cncl; High Hon Roll; Childrens Aid Soc Outstndng Svcs Awd 84; Sport Fndtn Swmmng Medals 79-82; NY Inst Of Tech; Comp Sci.

LESTER, CHRISTOPHER; St Josephs Collegiate Inst; Buffalo, NY; (Y); 44/193; Camera Clb; Church Yth Grp; Cmnty Wkr; Prtl Schlrshp SJCI 82-86.

LESTER, DEREK M; St Johns Prep; Brooklyn, NY; (Y); JV Var Ice Hcky; Regents Schlrshp 85; Baruch Coll; Bus Adm.

LETO, PAULINA; Mary Louis Acad; Richmond Hill, NY; (Y); Italian Clb; Awd Svc Cert; Comp.

LETO, TAMMY; Christ The King HS; Woodside, NY; (Y); 14/386; Red Cross Aide; High Hon Roll; Jr NHS; NHS; Library Aide; Cert Hnr Stdnt Athl Trainr 84; Awd Spnsh Proj 81 Postr 1st Pl 81; Pre-Med.

LETSCHER, STEPHEN L; St Anthonys HS; Ronkonkoma, NY; (Y); Boy Scts; Computer Clb; Spanish Clb; Chorus; Im Bowling; Var Trk; Var Wt Lftg; Hon Roll; Jr NHS; Spanish NHS; Prelaw.

LETTERI, JEANNE; Millb Rook HS; Salt Point, NY; (Y); 4-H; Var Bsktbl; JV Fld Hcky; 4-H Awd; High Hon Roll; Hon Roll; JC Awd.

LETTERIELLO, DINA; Bishop Kearney HS; Brooklyn, NY; (Y); Church Yth Grp; Cmnty Wkr; Teachers Aide; Nwsp Stf; Hon Roll; Chrch Lector 83-85; Katherine Gibbs; Bus.

LETTIERI, MARY ANN; Center Moriches HS; Ctr Moriches, NY; (Y); Spanish Clb; Varsity Clb; Var Bsktbl; Var Socr; Var Sftbl; Hon Roll; NHS; Phys Ther.

LETTKO, KEVIN X; Troy HS; Troy, NY; (Y); 31/400; Band; Concert Band; Jazz Band; Mrchg Band; VP NHS; NY ST Rngts Schlrshp 85-86; Suny-Albany NY; Math.

LETTON, SARINA R; Saugerties HS; Saugerties, NY; (Y); 16/242; Varsity Clb; Variety Show; Nwsp Rptr; Nwsp Stf; Yrbk Stf; High Hon Roll; Hon Roll; Jr NHS; NHS; Stu Contributd Mst To JR Cls 84; Psych.

LEUNG, ALEXANDER T C; Bronx HS Of Science; New York, NY; (Y); Capt Math Tm; Teachers Aide; High Hon Roll; Hon Roll; Ntl Merit Ltr; Wstnghse Tlnt Srch Semi Fnlst 85; NY City Math Tm Mbr 81-85; 12th Pl Chem Comp NT Cty 84; Math Professor.

LEUNG, HANG LEI; Murry Bergtraum HS; New York, NY; (Y); Intnl Clb; Stage Crew; Yrbk Phtg; Bsktbl; Swmmng; Hon Roll; Rest Mgmt.

LEUNG, JEANIE; Farmingdale HS; Massapequa Park, NY; (Y); French Clb; VP Pres FBLA; Intnl Clb; Library Aide; Rep Chorus; Rep Stu Cncl; Hon Roll; NHS; FBLA Dist 2nd Pl Bus Math I 84; Pres Interact Clb 85; Bus.

LEUNG, KAREN; F D R HS; Brooklyn, NY; (Y); Church Yth Grp; FCA; Intnl Clb; Office Aide; Nyu; Cmmntn.

LEVANDUSKI, JOSEPH; Horseheads SR HS; Horseheads, NY; (S); 55/ 407; JV Var Bsbl; JV Var Bsktbl; JV Var Ftbl; JV Wrstlng; Mansfield U PA; Bus Admin.

LEVEILLE, BARBARA J; Newtown HS; E Elmhurst, NY; (Y); Cit Awd; Prfct Atten Awd; Sienna Clb Awd 82-84; Prncpls Lst 82-84; Ctzns Schlrshp 85; Queensborough Coll; Psych.

LEVENSOHN, BETSY; Bethlehem Central HS; Delmar, NY; (Y); Am Leg Aux Girls St; Pres Drama Clb; Hosp Aide; Temple Yth Grp; Chorus; School Play; Rep Frsh Cls; Rep Soph Cls; JV Fld Hcky; High Hon Roll; Pre-Med.

LEVENSON, BRUCE; Sheepshead Bay HS; Brookly, NY; (Y); 5/500; Hosp Aide; Quiz Bowl; Red Cross Aide; Science Clb; Service Clb; Var Nwsp Ed-Chief; Off Jr Cls; Tennis; Vol Svc Awd 85; Bio.

LEVENSTEIN, JOSEPH; Broup HS Of Science; Bronx, NY; (Y); JA; Prfct Atten Awd; Regnts Schlrshp 85; Partcptn Natl Spnsh Cntst 83; Fordham U; Math.

LEVENTERIS, MARIA; St Johns Prep HS; Astoria, NY; (Y); Camera Clb; High Hon Roll; NHS.

LEVENTHAL, BETH; Stuyvesant HS; Brooklyn, NY; (Y); Cmnty Wkr; Hosp Aide; NHS; Ntl Merit Ltr; Spanish NHS; Cert Stu Athlt Trnr 83; 3rd Prz Cndn Studies Essy Cntst 85; Princeton U; Sprts Med.

LEVENTHAL, MARA; New Rochelle HS; New Rochelle, NY; (Y); Cmnty Wkr; Hosp Aide; Model UN; Nwsp Stf; Stu Cncl; Trs NHS; Spanish NHS; Welleshey Bk Awd 85; 17th Pl Intl Bible Cntst 83; 1st Pl Ntl Bible Cntst 83.

LEVERNOIS, MICKEY; Guilderland Central HS; Altamont, NY; (Y); Var Im Socr; Outstndng Acadmc Achvt 83; Engrng.

LEVESQUE, LISA; Mercy HS; Riverhead, NY; (Y); 14/123; JV Var Cheerleading; JV Var Sftbl; Hon Roll; NHS; Additive Prdcts Div Schlrshp Awd 85; Knights Of Columbus Schlrshp 85; SR Awd Sftbl & Chrldng 85; C W Post; Elem Educ.

LEVESQUE, NICOLE S; Pittsford Mendon HS; Pittsford, NY; (Y); Drama Clb; School Play; Sec Stu Cncl; Cheerleading; Gym; Powder Puff Ftbl; Hon Roll; NYS Regnts Schlrshp 85; U Of MI Ann Arbor; Pol Sci.

LEVETZ, LONNY; James Madison HS; Brooklyn, NY; (S); 4/802; Debate Tm; JA; Lit Mag; Bsbl; Bsktbl; Gov Hon Prg Awd; High Hon Roll; Acad Olympics 85; Arista 82-85; Cornell; Law.

LEVEY, SHARI; Clarkstown H S North; New City, NY; (Y); Cmnty Wkr; Spanish Clb; Temple Yth Grp; Chorus; JV Sftbl; Im Trk; Psych.

LEVI, JULIE; Town Of Webb Schl; Inlet, NY; (S); Am Leg Aux Girls St; Dance Clb; Chorus; School Play; Variety Show; Yrbk Stf; Cheerleading; Sftbl; High Hon Roll.

LEVI, MICHELE; Long Beach HS; Lido Beach, NY; (S); 2/350; Hosp Aide; Math Tm; Band; Chorus; Mrchg Band; School Musical; Yrbk Stf; NHS; Ntl Merit Ltr; Sal; Bst Mathlete 82-83; Phi Beta Kappa Alumi Citatn Awd 84-85; It's Acad Tm 83; Cornell U; Bio Sci.

LEVIKER, CAROL; Lowville Academy & Central Schl; Lowville, NY; (Y); French Clb; Chorus; School Musical; Pres Frsh Cls; Rep Soph Cls; Sec Jr Cls; Sec Sr Cls; Rep Stu Cncl; JV Var Cheerleading; Var Swmmng; Bryant; Trvl Mgmt.

LEVIN, AARON; Sachem HS; Holtsville, NY; (Y); 33/1350; Band; Concert Band; Capt Mrchg Band; Orch; Capt Bsbl; Capt Bsktbl; Wt Lftg; High Hon Roll; Jr NHS; NHS; Hnrbl Ment Sci Fair 82-84.

LEVIN, CLAUDIA J; Bethpage HS; Plainview, NY; (Y); 23/280; Drama Clb; Spanish Clb; Temple Yth Grp; School Musical; Yrbk Phtg; High Hon Roll; NHS; Pres, VP & Treas Temple Yth Grp 83-85; Accntng Awd 85; Clark U Worchester.

LEVIN, DAVID A; Bayside HS; Bayside, NY; (Y); 6/687; Math Tm; Quiz Bowl; Scholastic Bowl; Science Clb; Spanish Clb; Varsity Clb; Yrbk Sprt Ed; Tennis; High Hon Roll; Hon Roll; NY U; Pre Med.

LEVIN, LISA A; Newburgh Free Acad; Newburgh, NY; (Y); Temple Yth Grp; Acpl Chr; Orch; Nwsp Stf; Rep Soph Cls; Trs Jr Cls; Trs Stu Cncl; Trk; High Hon Roll; Jr NHS; Am HS Math Ex 85; NYSMA Olym Sci Cntst 83; Neburgh Yth Ct 85.

LEVIN, NAOMI; Forest Hills HS; Forest Hills, NY; (Y); 19/881; Dance Clb; Science Clb; Temple Yth Grp; Band; School Musical; Variety Show; High Hon Roll; Hon Roll; Jr NHS; NHS; Ntl Cncl Jewsh Wmn Essy Cntst Wnnr 85; Bus Dept Hon Roll; Med.

LEVINE, BRIAN; Earl L Vandermeulen HS; Mt Sinai, NY; (Y); 30/280; Concert Band; Jazz Band; JV Var Bsbl; JV Var Ftbl; High Hon Roll; NHS; Prfct Atten Awd.

LEVINE, BRUCE; Tottenville HS; Staten Island, NY; (Y); 220/980; Boy Scts; Drama Clb; Library Aide; Sec Ski Clb; School Play; Rep Sr Cls; Var Bowling; Var Crs Cntry; Var Trk; Ntl Merit Ltr; SUNY U Buffalo; Pol Sci.

LEVINE, DAVID L; Horace Mann-Barnard Schl; New York, NY; (Y); Trs Temple Yth Grp; School Musical; School Play; Stage Crew; Nwsp Phtg; Yrbk Phtg; Ntl Merit Ltr.

LEVINE, EDWARD S; Yorktown HS; Yorktown Hts, NY; (Y); Aud/Vis; FBLA; JA; Hon Roll; Cmmnctns.

LEVINE, GRETCHEN; Columbia HS; E Greenbush, NY; (Y); 49/353; Chorus; JV Var Tennis; Hon Roll; NYS Regents Schlrshp Awd; Hudson Vlly CC.

LEVINE, JOSHUA M; Rye Country Day Schl; New Rochelle, NY; (Y); Chess Clb; Pres Computer Clb; Drama Clb; Math Tm; Model UN; Pres Science Clb; Y-Teens; School Play; Stage Crew; Variety Show; Columbia U Sci Hnrs Prog 84-85; Ruth Schwab Vlntr Svc Awd 83-84; Natl Sci Olympiad Chem 84; Carnegie Mellon U; Elec Engnrng.

LEVINE, KIMBERLY A; General Douglas Mac Arthur HS; Wantagh, NY; (Y); 16/319; Pres VP Aud/Vis; Debate Tm; Trs French Clb; Model UN; School Musical; Nwsp Sprt Ed; JV Var Bsktbl; JV Var Sftbl; Var Capt Tennis; High Hon Roll; Nassau Cnty Tns All Star 83; NY ST Rgnts Schlrshp 85; Cornell U; Ind Labor Rltns.

LEVINE, MITCHELL J; Sutherland HS; Pittsford, NY; (Y); Debate Tm; English Clb; Model UN; Jazz Band; School Play; Yrbk Stf; JV Bsktbl; Hon Roll; Ntl Merit SF; Ntl Lat Awd 82-84; Mdl UN Awd 81-82; Physic.

LEVINE, NAOMI R; Half Hollow Hills High School East; Dix Hills, NY; (Y); 1/550; Cmnty Wkr; Hosp Aide; Church Choir; Nwsp Sprt Ed; Bausch & Lomb Sci Awd; NHS; Val; Science Clb; Nwsp Rptr; High Hon Roll; Westnghs Sci Tlnt Srch; Rensselaer Polytnc Inst Awd Math & Sci; NY ST Sci Congress; MA Inst Of Techlgy; Med.

LEVINE, PATTI J; Edward R Murrow HS; Brooklyn, NY; (Y); 6/725; Math Tm; Lit Mag; Stu Cncl; Gym; Intl Sci & Engr Fair Fin-4th Pl Awd 83-84; Daily News Super Yth 83; Westinghouse Hnrs Grp 85; Rsrch Sci.

LEVINE, PETER L; Nottingham HS; Syracuse, NY; (Y); 4/230; French Clb; Latin Clb; Math Tm; Madrigals; Nwsp Stf; Lit Mag; Var Bsktbl; High Hon Roll; NHS; Ntl Merit SF; Telluride Assn Smmr Pgm Schlrshp 84; Century III Ldrs ST Fnlst; Lit.

LEVINE, ROBERT; John F Kennedy HS; Plainview, NY; (Y); 11/275; Radio Clb; Band; Jazz Band; Orch; Stage Crew; Symp Band; JP Sousa Awd; Ntl Merit SF; DOWNBEAT Magzn Schlrshp 83; NY ST Schl Music Assoc-All Cnty Jazz Bnd & Orch 82-83; NY U; Bus.

LEVINE, SHERYL H; Oceanside HS; Oceanside, NY; (Y); 7/530; Trs Computer Clb; Sec Mathletes; Trs Science Clb; Pres Spanish Clb; Lib Concert Band; Mrchg Band; High Hon Roll; Jr NHS; NHS; Ntl Merit Ltr; Regents Schlrshp 85; NYSSMA Retng 84; U PA; Engrng.

LEVINSKY, DAVID M; Clarkstown H S North; New City, NY; (Y); Chess Clb; Computer Clb; Library Aide; High Hon Roll; Jr NHS; Mu Alp Tht; NHS; Jrnl News Div II Carrier Of Yr 85; Elec Engrng.

LEVINSON, SHOSHANA A; Performing Arts At Laguardia HS; Brooklyn, NY; (Y); Band; Concert Band; Jazz Band; Orch; School Musical; Variety Show; Benjamin Chancy Awd; NY ST Regents Scoll Schlrshp; Stony Brook; Music.

LEVISON, MARRA; Francis Lewis HS; Flushing, NY; (Y); 55/527; Drama Clb; FBLA; Office Aide; Orch; School Play; Var Tennis; Hon Roll; NHS; Library Aide; Teachers Aide; Westinghse Semi Finlst Sociology 85; FBLA City Wide Comp,1st Place Business Comm 85; 3rd Pl Business; Social Science.

LEVITSKY, MELISSA; Marion JR/SR HS; Marion, NY; (Y); 16/117; Band; Chorus; Church Choir; Color Guard; Concert Band; Drm Mjr(t); Mrchg Band; School Musical; School Play; Yrbk Stf; Marion Mem Scholar 85; Anne Kumuks/Newark Plyrs Scholar 85; SUNY Oswego; Cmmnctns.

LEVO III, ANTHONY F; Saratoga Springs HS; Greenfield Ctr, NY; (Y); 115/450; Boy Scts; Pres Church Yth Grp; Political Wkr; Band; Pep Band; Yrbk Ed-Chief; Hon Roll; St Schlr; Frank Sullvn Jrnlsm Awd 85; Twn Greenfld Hstrns Awd 85; Siena Coll Loudonvl NY; Bus.

LEVY, ALICIA; Lawrence HS; Inwood L I, NY; (Y); 114/379; Trs AFS; Band; Concert Band; Mrchg Band; Nwsp Stf; Yrbk Stf; Trk; Hon Roll; Inwood Civics Jesse Cestari Mem Awd 85; Lawrence Cncl Jesse Cestari Mem Awd 85; Hofstra U; Accntng.

LEVY, ERIC T; Kingston HS; Lake Katrine, NY; (Y); 70/530; Aud/Vis; Pep Clb; Spanish Clb; Pres Temple Yth Grp; Stu Cncl; Var L Bsbl; Var Bsktbl; Var Capt Socr; Hon Roll; Spanish NHS; All ST Sccr Tm 84; Cornell U; Ind & Labr Rel.

LEVY, IRA SAMUEL; Woodlands HS; White Plains, NY; (Y); 4/180; Debate Tm; Pres FBLA; Trs Jr Cls; Pres Sr Cls; Rep Stu Cncl; Swmmng; Tennis; Temple Yth Grp; Nwsp Rptr; Washington Wrkshps I & II 84-85; SUNY-BINGHAMTON; Econ.

LEVY, JONATHAN; The Gow Schl; Pt Washington, NY; (Y); Ski Clb; Band; Yrbk Phtg; Yrbk Stf; Var Bsbl; Var Bsktbl; JV Lcrss; JV Socr; High Hon Roll; U Of Buffalo; Arch.

LEVY, KIRK; Plainedge HS; N Massapequa, NY; (Y); 1/311; Capt Scholastic Bowl; Trs Temple Yth Grp; Lit Mag; Rep Soph Cls; Trs French Hon Soc; NHS; Ntl Merit Ltr; Val; Renssalaer Polytech Inst Mdl Of Valor Math & Sci; Dakin Memrl Stu Awd; Emory U; Pre-Med.

LEVY, MARC; Hunter Coll HS; Brooklyn, NY; (Y); Acpl Chr; Chorus; Madrigals; School Musical; Swing Chorus; Ntl Merit SF; Psych.

LEVY, STELLA; Mt Vernon HS; Mount Vernon, NY; (Y); Drama Clb; French Clb; FTA; Rep Key Clb; Teachers Aide; School Musical; Yrbk Stf; Pres Jr Cls; High Hon Roll; Jr NHS.

LEWANDOWSKI, DANETTE R; Mount Mercy Acad; Buffalo, NY; (Y); JCL; Pres Latin Clb; Yrbk Phtg; JA; Science Clb; Chorus; Im Bowling; NY ST Regents Spec Ed Schlrshp 85; 1st Latin Audio Visual Frgn Lng Fair 84; U Of NY Buffalo; Nrs.

LEWANDOWSKI, DARREN; Hutchinson Central Technical HS; Buffalo, NY; (Y); Boy Scts; Band; Concert Band; Jazz Band; Rep Jr Cls; Comp Sci.

LEWANDOWSKI, ED; Liverpool HS; Liverpool, NY; (S); Chess Clb; Varsity Clb; Swmmng; Psych.

LEWANDOWSKI, GERALD; St Marys HS; Depew, NY; (S); Camera Clb; Pres Chess Clb; Computer Clb; Yrbk Stf; Im Bowling; High Hon Roll; Hon Roll; NHS; Comp Prgrmr.

LEWANDOWSKI, KEVIN; Canisus HS, E Aurora, NY; (Y); 35/169; Math Clb; Spanish Clb; Stage Crew; Yrbk Stf; JV Crs Cntry; JV Ice Hcky; Hon Roll; Mu Alp Tht; Engrng.

LEWANDOWSKI, LIANA S; Hamburg SR HS; Hamburg, NY; (Y); 130/400; Sec DECA; Ski Clb; Color Guard; Trs Jr Cls; Rep Stu Cncl; High Hon Roll; Hon Roll; Ntl Merit Ltr; 1st Awd Gen Merch 83-84; Ntl Hnr Rll 85; Canisius Coll; Bus.

LEWIS, ANGELICA; Earl L Vandermeulen HS; Pt Jefferson, NY; (Y); Latin Clb; Color Guard; Madrigals; Orch; School Musical; Crs Cntry; High Hon Roll; NHS; Band; Color Guard; All County Band; Mid-Island Band; Frgn Lang.

LEWIS, CHEENA; Walton HS; Bronx, NY; (Y); Dance Clb; Drama Clb; Library Aide; School Play; Swmmng; Prfct Atten Awd; Columbia U; Comp Pgmr.

LEWIS, CHERYL; Springville Griffith Inst; Springville, NY; (Y); Church Yth Grp; Spanish Clb; Hon Roll; Cmmrcl Art.

LEWIS, CHISTOPHER; Beacon HS; Beacon, NY; (Y); 46/212; Church Yth Grp; Pres Civic Clb; Key Clb; Varsity Clb; Var Capt Bsktbl; Capt JV Ftbl; Cit Awd; Hon Roll; Dutchess Comm; Civil Engr.

LEWIS, CHRISTOPHER; Beacon HS; Beacon, NY; (Y); 46/214; Church Yth Grp; Pres Civic Clb; Key Clb; Var L Bsktbl; JV Capt Ftbl; Cit Awd; Hon Roll; Dutchess CC; Civl Engrng.

LEWIS, CORNELIUS; Cardinal Spellman HS; Bronx, NY; (Y); Church Yth Grp; Bsktbl; Ftbl; Hon Roll; U Of NC-CHAPEL Hill; Law.

LEWIS, DANIEL; Smithtown East HS; Smithtown, NY; (Y); Boy Scts; Chess Clb; Church Yth Grp; Radio Clb; Var Crs Cntry; JV Tennis; Hon Roll.

LEWIS, DAVID C; Prattsburg Central HS; Bath, NY; (Y); Am Leg Boys St; Cmnty Wkr; FFA; Teachers Aide; Nwsp Rptr; Trs Nwsp Stf; Trs Jr Cls; High Hon Roll; Hon Roll; NHS; Assoc Parnts-Tchrs Stu Tutr Awd 85; Prattsburg Hardwr Ag-Bus Awd 85; Corning CC; Elem Ed.

LEWIS, DAWNETTE; Bronx HS Of Sci; Bronx, NY; (Y); Library Aide; Office Aide; Service Clb; Spanish Clb; Teachers Aide; Yrbk Stf; Im Bsktbl; Bus Admin.

LEWIS, DONNA; Central Islip SR HS; Central Islip, NY; (Y); Sec Aud/Vis; Hon Roll; Ntl Merit Ltr; Htl Mgmt.

LEWIS, ERIC; Freeport HS; New York, NY; (Y); Letterman Clb; Teachers Aide; Varsity Clb; Variety Show; Rep Stu Cncl; Var Crs Cntry; Var Capt Trk; Hon Roll; Ntl Merit Ltr; Prfct Atten Awd; MVP All Cnty & Wall Of Fame Awd Sprng Trck 85; Accntng.

LEWIS, JEFF; Cornwall Central HS; Highland Mls, NY; (Y); 22/200; Church Yth Grp; Cmnty Wkr; Math Tm; Band; Concert Band; Hon Roll; Embry-Riddle; Engr.

LEWIS, JEFF; Niagara Wheatfield HS; Niagara Falls, NY; (Y); Latin Clb; JV Bsbl; Var Golf; Hon Roll; Lwyr.

LEWIS, JEFFREY; Smithtown H S East; Nesconset, NY; (Y); 87/545; Boys Clb Am; Rep Jr Cls; Rep Sr Cls; Im Bsktbl; JV Var Tennis; Hon Roll; NHS; Binghamton; Pre-Hlth.

LEWIS, JODI; Central Islip SR HS; Central Islip, NY; (Y); 2/400; Drama Clb; School Musical; Stage Crew; Nwsp Phtg; Lit Mag; VP Stu Cncl; Hon Roll; Pres NHS; Office Aide; Chorus; 2nd Highest Av Jr Cls 85; Cntrl Islip Tchrs Assoc Humanitarian Awd 85; Advrtsng Art.

LEWIS, JOHN; Clarkstown HS North; Congers, NY; (Y); 75/400; Boy Scts; Math Tm; JV Bsbl; JV Ftbl; Hon Roll; Mu Alp Tht; Tutoring Squad; Mech Engr.

LEWIS, JOHN; Ithaca HS; Ithaca, NY; (Y); Ski Clb; Nwsp Phtg; Nwsp Stf; Yrbk Phtg; Yrbk Rptr; JV Var Lcrss; Im Socr; David L Dunlap Outstndng Photgrphy Awd 85; Bucknell U; Pre Med.

LEWIS, JONATHAN; Jamestown HS; Jamestown, NY; (Y); 185/380; Church Yth Grp; Red Cross Aide; Band; Mrchg Band; JV L Bsbl; Capt Var Crs Cntry; Var L Ftbl; Var L Trk; MVP Trck 85; Coach Awd 83; JCC; Art.

LEWIS, JULIE; Greenville Central Schl; Rensselaerville, NY; (Y); 1/70; French Clb; Sec Science Clb; Spanish Clb; School Musical; Hon Roll; NHS; Rotary Awd; Art Clb; Cmnty Wkr; Latin Clb; Catherine Carleson Chem Awd 85; Schlrshp & Svc Spartan Awd 84-85; Outstndng Nyssma Solost Comp; Pre-Med.

LEWIS, KENNETH A; Brooklyn Technical HS; Bronx, NY; (Y); Aud/Vis; Computer Clb; Math Clb; Band; Concert Band; School Musical; JV Bsktbl; Hon Roll; JP Sousa Awd; NHS; Elec Tech.

LEWIS, LISA; Holy Trinity HS; Hempstead, NY; (Y); Church Yth Grp; Drama Clb; JA; Chorus; School Musical; School Play; Stage Crew; Busnss Mgmt.

LEWIS, LYNDON EARL; Nottingham HS; Fayetteville, NY; (Y); French Clb; Chorus; Trs Jr Cls; Var JV Crs Cntry; Var Trk; Hon Roll; 3rd Pl Rgnl In Natl Frnch Cont 85; 1st Pl Proctor Invtnl JV Crss-Cntry Race 85; 1T Pl Sectnl Chmpshp; Acctng.

LEWIS, LYNN; North Warren HS; Chestertown, NY; (S); VP Frsh Cls; VP Soph Cls; VP Jr Cls; Var L Bsktbl; Var L Fld Hcky; Var L Tennis; Var L Vllybl; Hon Roll.

LEWIS, MARC; Prospect Heights HS; Brooklyn, NY; (Y); #3 In Class; Church Yth Grp; Debate Tm; Off Frsh Cls; Trk; Hawthorne Coll; Bus Adm.

LEWIS, MEGAN; Smithtown High School West; Smithtown, NY; (Y); Exploring; French Clb; Leo Clb; JV Capt Bsktbl; Var Fld Hcky; Im Socr; JV Var Vllybl; French Hon Soc; Hon Roll; Varsity Lets 84-85; Booster Clb Awds 84-85; All Star Team, Leag & All Conf In Field Hockey 84-85; Physical Therapy.

LEWIS, MICHAEL; Odessa-Montour Central Schl; Montour Falls, NY; (Y); Am Leg Boys St; Art Clb; Aud/Vis; Lit Mag; VP Frsh Cls; Rep Stu Cncl; Var L Bsktbl; Stat Ftbl; High Hon Roll; Hon Roll; Eng.

LEWIS, MICHELLE; Corning Painted Post East HS; Corning, NY; (Y); Church Yth Grp; High Hon Roll; Hon Roll; Harry M Blodgett Awd 84-85.

LEWIS, MINDY; Hilton Central HS; Hilton, NY; (Y); JA; Yrbk Stf; Fld Hcky; High Hon Roll; Hon Roll; Best Offnsv Fld Hcky 84-85; Hnrb Mntn Wrld Poetry 85; Golden Poet Awd 85; Monroe CC; Lwyr.

LEWIS, NADENE C; Clara Barton For Health Prof; Brooklyn, NY; (Y); Church Yth Grp; Debate Tm; Hosp Aide; Chorus; Church Choir; Variety Show; Nwsp Stf; Yrbk Stf; Hon Outstndng Perfrmr Mock Trial Tm 85; St Thomas U; Bio.

LEWIS, PAULA; Mount Vernon HS; Mt Vernon, NY; (Y); Library Aide; Office Aide; Nwsp Rptr; Nwsp Stf; Pom Pon; Pol Sci.

LEWIS, SHERRI; North Rose Walcott HS; Wolcott, NY; (Y); Varsity Clb; VP Band; Sec Chorus; Jazz Band; Pres Jr Cls; Bsktbl; Socr; Capt Sftbl; Vllybl; Hon Roll; Fredonia Nazareth; Music.

LEWIS, STACY; Islip HS; Islip, NY; (Y); Church Yth Grp; Office Aide; Church Choir; Drill Tm; Rep Jr Cls; Rep Stu Cncl; Stat Bsktbl; Var JV Cheerleading; High Hon Roll; Jr NHS.

LEWIS, TERENCE; Roosevelt HS; Roosevelt, NY; (Y); Chess Clb; FTA; Mathletes; Nwsp Stf; Yrbk Phtg; Trs Soph Cls; Pres Stu Cncl; Bowling; Crs Cntry; NHS; Engr.

LEWIS, TIMOTHY A; Hunter College HS; New York, NY; (Y); Science Clb; Chorus; Camera Clb; Swing Chorus; Nwsp Phtg; Yrbk Ed-Chief; Yrbk Phtg; Yrbk Stf; Lit Mag; St Schlr.

LEWIS, TRACIE; Mt St Joseph Acad; Buffalo, NY; (Y); Church Yth Grp; JA; Library Aide; Spanish Clb; Church Choir; School Musical; Variety Show; Sec Rep Jr Cls; Rep Stu Cncl; Vactn Bible Schl Tchg Awd 84; Piano Awd 84; Bus Awd 85; Music.

LEWIS, TRACY M; Mc Mahon HS; Cheektowaga, NY; (Y); Girl Scts; Latin Clb; Office Aide; Chorus; Canisius Coll; Accntg.

LEWIS, VINCENT C; Mount Saint Michael Acad; Bronx, NY; (Y); 59/298; Boy Scts; Church Yth Grp; Cmnty Wkr; Church Choir; Var Crs Cntry; Var L Ftbl; Var L Trk; C W Post; Comp Sci.

LEWITAS, DAVID; East Meadow HS; East Meadow, NY; (S); Computer Clb; Math Clb; Crs Cntry; Trk; Wrstlng; NHS; Econ.

LEWTON, KAREN C; Saratoga Springs SR HS; Greenfield Ctr, NY; (Y); 10/450; Chorus; Sec Frsh Cls; High Hon Roll; Hon Roll; NHS; Prfct Atten Awd; Subrbn Cncl Ldrshp Conf 83; Saratoga High Awd Nght 84; Skidmore Clg Awds Dnr 85; Bus Admin.

LEY, ERIC; St Johns Prep; Astoria, NY; (Y); Coach Actv.

LEYSATH, BRIAN; Naples Central HS; Naples, NY; (Y); 9/86; Concert Band; Jazz Band; Mrchg Band; School Musical; Rep Jr Cls; VP Stu Cncl; JV Var Socr; Var L Swmmng; JV L Tennis; High Hon Roll; Brown U; Comp Sci.

LEZCANO JR, CONRADO; Monsignor Scanlan HS; Bronx, NY; (Y); 86/265; JV Var Bsbl; Var Trk; Comp Pgm.

LEZCANO, KARINA D; Msgr Scanlan HS; Jackson Heights, NY; (Y); 65/265; Church Yth Grp; Dance Clb; VP Intnl Clb; Variety Show; Yrbk Stf; Trk; Hon Roll; Iona Coll Hnrs Italn III Cont 85; Dancng Trophies 83-84; Med.

LI, BONNIE P; Newtown HS; Elmhurst, NY; (Y); 1/603; Chess Clb; Computer Clb; 4-H; JA; Key Clb; Math Clb; Math Tm; Office Aide; Science Clb; Teachers Aide; Regents Coll Schlrshp U Of NY 85; Wstnghs Sci Tlnt Srch Semi-Fnlst High Hnrs 85; Coll; Med.

LI, CHRISTINE; Edgemont HS; Scarsdale, NY; (Y); Dance Clb; Debate Tm; Nwsp Ed-Chief; Nwsp Stf; Ntl Merit SF; Art Clb; French Clb; Latin Clb; NFL; Stage Crew; Latin Cicero Clscl Clb Cont 83; Frnch II Iona Coll Lang Cont 84; NYS Novice Team Debate 83; Princeton; Intl Rel.

LI, EUGENE; Roosevelt HS; Yonkers, NY; (S); 26/287; Pres Church Yth Grp; Capt Band; Mrchg Band; Capt Lcrss; Capt Socr; JP Sousa Awd; Lacrosse All Div All Conf 85; Chaminade Music Schlrshp 85; U MA.

LI, JIAYUAN; Richmond Hill HS; Richmond Hill, NY; (Y); #4 In Class; Chess Clb; Debate Tm; Math Clb; Rep Stu Cncl; Var Tennis; Hon Roll; Jr NHS; NHS; PA Soc Stds Cncl Awd 82-83; Regnts Schlrshp 84-85; NY U; Engrng.

LI, JOSEPH; Bronx H S Of Science; New York, NY; (Y); Computer Clb; Intnl Clb; Library Aide; Math Tm; Chorus; High Hon Roll; Hon Roll; NCTE Awd; Prfct Atten Awd; Achvt Mth, Sci, Soc Stud 83; Comp Sci.

LI, KWOKTUNG; Flushing HS; Flushing, NY; (Y); 11/364; Chess Clb; Library Aide; Math Clb; Math Tm; Science Clb; Swmmng; High Hon Roll; Rep Frsh Cls; Rep Soph Cls; United Fedrtn Of Tchrs Schlrshp 85; Stony Brook; Elec Engrng.

LI CAUSI, MICHELE; John A Coleman HS; Ulster Park, NY; (Y); 16/74; Key Clb; Varsity Clb; Yrbk Rptr; Rep Jr Cls; Stu Cncl; Var Cheerleading; High Hon Roll; Hon Roll; NHS; JV Fld Hcky; NYSMA Music Hnr 86; Pre-Law.

LIANG, CHRISTINA; Alexander Hamilton HS; White Plains, NY; (Y); 3/54; Church Yth Grp; Key Clb; Yrbk Stf; Rep Sr Cls; Capt JV Cheerleading; High Hon Roll; Jr NHS; NHS; Ntl Merit Ltr; Pres Schlr; Regents Schlrshp 84-85; Presdntl Schlrshp 84-85; Frsh Recog Schlrshp 84-85; Boston Coll; Bus.

LIANG, MARILYN; Brighton HS; Rochester, NY; (Y); 22/315; Hosp Aide; Ski Clb; Varsity Clb; Yrbk Bus Mgr; Rep Sr Cls; Var Co-Capt Cheerleading; French Clb; Latin Clb; Stu Cncl; NHS; Brighton Pittsford Post All Star Cheerldng 2nd Tm 85; Best Frnch Stu 83; Sci.

LIAO, EDWARD; Sheepshead Bay HS; Brooklyn, NY; (Y); Camera Clb; Computer Clb; Yrbk Bus Mgr; Capt Swmmng; Cmnty Wkr; Library Aide; Math Tm; Office Aide; Science Clb; Teachers Aide; Hnr Sch 82-85; Engr.

LIBBY, BONNIE L; New Covenant Christian Schl; Rochester, NY; (Y); Church Yth Grp; Rptr Spanish Clb; Yrbk Stf; JV Var Bsktbl; Var L Sftbl; High Hon Roll; Val; NYS Regents Schlrshp 85; Deans Schlrshp 85; Oral Roberts U; Educ.

LIBERATORE, ANGELA; Fowler HS; Syracuse, NY; (Y); Dance Clb; FTA; PAVAS; Church Choir; Concert Band; Orch; School Musical; Art Clb; Camera Clb; Cmnty Wkr; Bst Occptnl Stu Awd 84; Fash Illust.

LIBERATORE, GREGORY; Schalmont HS; Schenectady, NY; (Y); Am Leg Boys St; Off Stu Cncl; JV Capt Bsktbl; Var Capt Socr; Trk; Hon Roll; Masonic Awd; Elmira Ky Awd 85; CPR Certfd, BLS Certfd 85; Eucharistc Minstr Chrch 85; Bio.

LIBERATORE, LISA; Cicero-North Syracuse HS; Clay, NY; (Y); 177/622; Exploring; JV Bsktbl; SUNY; Law.

LIBERTINO, STACY; Academy Of The Resurrection HS; New Rochelle, NY; (Y); Church Yth Grp; NFL; Off Frsh Cls; Trs Jr Cls; Stu Cncl; Var Cheerleading; Swmmng; NHS; Mst Spirited Chrldr 84-85; Sci.

LIBMAN, MICHELE F; Baldwin SR HS; Baldwin, NY; (Y); 22/502; Cmnty Wkr; Key Clb; Yrbk Stf; Rep Stu Cncl; Co-Capt JV Fld Hcky; High Hon Roll; Spanish NHS; Regents Schlrshp 85; NHR 85; Housewarers Clb NY Schlrshp Wnnr 85; Vet Med.

LICARI, JODEE; Oneonta HS; Oneonta, NY; (Y); Art Clb; French Clb; SUNY Purchase; Art Hstry.

LICATA, CHRISTOPHER; Bishop Timo HS; W Seneca, NY; (Y); Art Clb; Boy Scts; Chorus; Yrbk Stf; Capt Ftbl; Var Trk; Ftbl Al-Leag MVP Trck Al-Leag; Ftbl Al-Cathlc MVP Al-Wstrn NY, Trck Al-Leag MVP; Trck Al-Leag; Colgate; Law.

LICHORWIC, DOUG; VVS HS; Vernon, NY; (Y); Stu Cncl; JV Var Bsbl; Im Bsktbl; Im Bsktbl; JV Var Ftbl; Im Wt Lftg; High Hon Roll; Hon Roll; NHS.

LICHT, DARLENE; Star Point Central Schl; N Tonawanda, NY; (Y); 36/196; Church Yth Grp; Varsity Clb; Trs Stu Cncl; Var Capt Bsktbl; Var L Fld Hcky; Var L Sftbl; Var Capt Vllybl; Hon Roll; Jr NHS; Pres Schlr.

LICHTENBERG, N GAIL; Ramapo SR HS; Spring Valley, NY; (Y); 1/519; Aud/Vis; German Clb; Math Tm; Nwsp Rptr; Yrbk Stf; Bausch & Lomb Sci Awd; Elks Awd; High Hon Roll; Jr NHS; Mu Alp Tht; Lederle Labs Sci Awd 85; Ciba Geigy Suffern Site Schlrshp 85; 4 Yr Hnry Schlrshp UC Berkeley 85; U CA Berkeley; Comp Sci.

LICHTENBERGER, RANDY; Monticello HS; Smallwood, NY; (Y); Math Tm; Quiz Bowl; Stage Crew; Nwsp Bus Mgr; Nwsp Ed-Chief; Nwsp Phtg; Yrbk Stf; High Hon Roll; NHS; Prfct Atten Awd; MEP 82; Olympics Of Mind 2nd Pl 84-85; Stage Crew Ltr; MIT; Geolgy.

LICHTENSTEIN, SHARON; Ramapo SR HS; Monsey, NY; (Y); Key Clb; Yrbk Sprt Ed; Sec Jr Cls; Pres Sr Cls; JV Sftbl; High Hon Roll; VP Jr NHS; Mu Alp Tht; NHS; Spanish NHS; Cert Comm Svc Jr Cls 85; Wrtng Schl Newspaper 83; Inv Spnsh Lit Clb 85; Bus.

LICHTENTHAL, DONNA; Notre Dame HS; Corfu, NY; (S); 10/81; Pres Church Yth Grp; Debate Tm; 4-H; Pep Clb; Ski Clb; School Play; Ed Yrbk Phtg; Pres Stu Cncl; Capt Cheerleading; Trk; Finance.

LICHTMAN, CHRISTINE BENJAMINA; Hicksville HS; Hicksville, NY; (Y); Dance Clb; Mgr Drama Clb; Office Aide; Ski Clb; Orch; Mgr Stage Crew; Yrbk Ed-Chief; Mgr Crs Cntry; Mgr Trk; Teachers Aide; Vltnr Clb 84, Pres 85-86; NY Inst Tech; Htl Admn.

LICTUS, AMY; Clymer Central Schl; Clymer, NY; (Y); Church Yth Grp; Girl Scts; Library Aide; Office Aide; Teachers Aide; Chorus; Church Choir; Yrbk Stf; Trs Sr Cls; Capt Cheerleading.

LICURSI, NANCY; Farmingdale HS; Farmingdale, NY; (Y); Intnl Clb; Var Diving; Var Capt Gym; Mgr(s); Trk; NHS; Physical Thrpy.

LIDDELL, ROBERT; Ballston Spa HS; Ballston Spa, NY; (Y); 50/240; Am Leg Boys St; Varsity Clb; Rep Sr Cls; Var L Bsbl; JV Capt Bsktbl; Var L Socr; Hon Roll; 2nd Tm Socr All Star Foothills Cncl 84-85; Med.

LIDDIARD, DONNA; Jordan-Elbridge JR SR HS; Elbridge, NY; (Y); 17/150; Drill Tm; Mrchg Band; Stage Crew; Nwsp Stf; Im Sftbl; Var Tennis; Var Twrlr; Hon Roll; Jr NHS; NHS; Mst Sprtd Awd Mrchng Bnd; Mst Imprvd Mrchng Bnd; Sally Pert Mem Schlrshp 85; SUNY Oswego; Acct.

LIDDLE, HEATHER R; Lyon JR & SR HS; Newark, NY; (Y); 5/92; Pres Church Yth Grp; Pres 4-H; French Clb; Model UN; Yrbk Rptr; Sec Sr Cls; High Hon Roll; NHS; NYS Regnts Schlrshp 85; Hoffman Hist Essy 1st Pl 85; Roberts Wesleyan Coll; Bus Adm.

LIDDLE, JULIE; Bethlehem Central HS; Delmar, NY; (Y); 60/338; Pres GAA; Capt Bsktbl; Capt Var Sftbl; Vllybl; Hon Roll; Martha C Stafford Memrl Schlrshp 85; Outstndng Feml Athl 85; Pres Acadmc Fit Awd 85; SUNY Stony Brook; Bio.

LIDDLE, MARK; Grand Island SR HS; Gr Island, NY; (Y); Varsity Clb; JV Golf; JV Var Ice Hcky; JV Lcrss; U Of Buffalo; Engr.

LIDDLE, MELANIE A; Naples Central HS; Naples, NY; (Y); FHA; Band; Chorus; Concert Band; Jazz Band; Mrchg Band; Eastman Schl Music Horizons Stu 85; All Cnty,ST Band 83-84; Music.

LIDDLE, THOMAS; Charlotte Valley Central HS; Oneonta, NY; (S); Varsity Clb; Bsktbl; Socr; Wt Lftg; High Hon Roll; Hon Roll; NHS; Acad Excellence In Art 82; Perfect Attndce 82.

LIDDY, DONALD; Camden Central Schl; Camden, NY; (Y); Ski Clb; Band; Chorus; Concert Band; Drm & Bgl; Orch; JV Trk; JV Var Wrstlng; Hon Roll; Cableskill; Forstry.

LIEB, DAVID J; Albany HS; Albany, NY; (Y); 33/600; Pres Drama Clb; French Clb; School Play; Lit Mag; Hon Roll; NHS; Ntl Merit Ltr; St Schlr; Exploring; Stage Crew; Mary Morgan Prz Creatv Wrtg 81; Florence Ward Sci Exam 81; Cornell U; Bio.

LIEBERFARB, MARSHAL; Wantagh HS; Wantagh, NY; (Y); Am Leg Boys St; Debate Tm; Mathletes; Off Jr Cls; Sec Sr Cls; Rep Stu Cncl; Golf; NHS; NASA Launch & Lnd Exprmnt Prtcptnt 85; Med.

LIEBERMAN, MATTHEW; The Wheatley Schl; Albertson, NY; (Y); Drama Clb; Hosp Aide; School Musical; School Play; Trs Soph Cls; Trs Jr Cls; Ntl Merit Ltr; PAVAS; Thesps; Chorus; AATF Natl Fr Cont Fnlst 83; Contntl Mth Lg Cert Hnrs 83; Outstndng Achvt Drama 85.

LIEBIG, DOUGLAS C; Granville Central HS; Granville, NY; (Y); 28/148; Yrbk Phtg; Hon Roll; NY ST Regents Schlrshp 85-86; Elec Engr.

LIEBMAN, DAVID; Brouxs Science HS; Java, NY; (Y); Ed Nwsp Phtg; Yrbk Phtg; Video Jrnlsm.

LIEBSON, DEANA; Sachem North; Holbrook, NY; (Y); 135/1500; Dance Clb; Nwsp Rptr; Yrbk Rptr; Hon Roll; Psych.

LIEDY, GEORGETTE; Lackawanna SR HS; Lackawanna, NY; (S); 56/288; Church Yth Grp; GAA; Office Aide; Ski Clb; Spanish Clb; Band; Jazz Band; Orch; Pep Band; Symp Band; Pre-Law.

LIFTON, JUDIE B; Friends Acad; Old Westbury, NY; (Y); Var Tennis; Cmnty Wkr; Debate Tm; French Clb; Political Wkr; Nwsp Ed-Chief; Yrbk Phtg; Yrbk Rptr; High Hon Roll; Ntl Merit Schol; Cum Laude Society 84; U Of PA.

LIGGIO, MARC A; Garden City HS; Garden City, NY; (Y); 48/320; Chess Clb; Political Wkr; High Hon Roll; Ntl Merit SF; Bus.

LIGGIO, VALERIE ANN; Kenmore East HS; Tonawanda, NY; (Y); 6/330; French Clb; Pep Clb; Nwsp Rptr; Rep Frsh Cls; JV Trk; High Hon Roll; NHS; Ntl Merit Ltr; Rgnts Schlrshp 85; Pres Acad Fitnss Awd 85; SUNY-BINGHAMTON; Intl Fin.

LIGHTENFIELD, GEORGE; Schuylerville Central HS; Schuylerville, NY; (Y); Police Sci.

LIGHTFOOT, JOSEPH C; Ogdensburg Free Acad; Ogdensburg, NY; (Y); 15/200; Am Leg Boys St; Key Clb; JV Var Ftbl; JV Ice Hcky; Var Trk; Im Vllybl; Im Wt Lftg; Hon Roll; NHS; Clarkson U; Engrng.

LIGHTHALL, SANDRA; Holland Patent HS; Prospect, NY; (Y); Boys Clb Am; Chess Clb; Chorus; Bsktbl; Powder Puff Ftbl; Swmmng; Trk; Sullivan CC; Drama.

LIGHTHALL, WILLIAM; Stockbridge Valley HS; Munnsville, NY; (S); 3/54; Church Yth Grp; FFA; Varsity Clb; JV Var Bsbl; JV Var Cheerleading; JV Var Socr; High Hon Roll; Hon Roll; Chrldng Mst Enthstc 84; 1st Pl Lnd Jdgng At Mrrsvlle Coll 83; Navy; Nursing.

LIGOCI, TAMMY; Cicero-North Syracuse HS; N Syracuse, NY; (S); 24/700; German Clb; Color Guard; Mrchg Band; Hon Roll.

LIGUORI, DEBRA S; Ithaca HS; Ithaca, NY; (Y); Ski Clb; Yrbk Stf; Sec Stu Cncl; Hon Roll; Jr NHS; Southern Methodst U; Bus.

LIJEWSKI, JULIE; South Park HS; Buffalo, NY; (Y); 14/375; Church Yth Grp; Hosp Aide; Band; Chorus; Concert Band; Mrchg Band; School Musical; Trk; Hon Roll; Mrt Scholar Trocaire Coll 85; Trocaire Coll; Nrsng.

LIKUS, DAWN; West Seneca East SR HS; West Seneca, NY; (S); 36/365; Pres DECA; Variety Show; Nwsp Stf; Socr; CC Awd; High Hon Roll; NHS; Finance & Crdt Competition Regnl 1st St 2nd 84; DECA Hstrn 84-85; Fordham U; Intl Mgmt.

LILAVOIS, SHIRLEY; The Mary Louis Acad; Jamaica, NY; (Y); Church Yth Grp; Hosp Aide; Office Aide; Spanish Clb; Teachers Aide; Stage Crew; Variety Show; Hon Roll; Prfct Atten Awd; Nrsg.

LILLARD, ANDRE; Riverside HS; Buffalo, NY; (S); Church Yth Grp; Debate Tm; Stage Crew; Nwsp Rptr; Nwsp Sprt Ed; Nwsp Stf; Yrbk Stf; Lit Mag; Rep Stu Cncl; Tennis; Cornell U; Hotel Admn.

LILLENSTEIN, DAVID J; Pioneer Central HS; Delevan, NY; (Y); 40/220; Boy Scts; French Clb; Latin Clb; Temple Yth Grp; Stage Crew; Nwsp Rptr; Nwsp Stf; Rep Frsh Cls; Rep Soph Cls; Rep Jr Cls; Bus Adm.

LILLIBRIDGE, GAIL L; Shenendehowa Central Schl; Clifton Park, NY; (Y); 21/710; Church Yth Grp; Computer Clb; Office Aide; Stu Cncl; High Hon Roll; NHS; SADD Rep 84-85; Peer Drug Cnslg Elem Stdnts 83-85; Mech Engrng.

LILLIBRIDGE, MARK D; Saratoga Springs SR HS; Saratoga Springs, NY; (Y); Computer Clb; Math Tm; Science Clb; Band; Bausch & Lomb Sci Awd; High Hon Roll; NHS; Ntl Merit SF; Prfct Atten Awd; RPI Mdl Excel Math & Sci 84; Comp Sci.

LILLIS, TERRI; Catholic Central HS; Latham, NY; (Y); Church Yth Grp; French Clb; Math Tm; Office Aide; Variety Show; Pom Pon; High Hon Roll; NHS; Soc Stud, Frnch I & II, Mth II Hnr Awd 83-85; Cornell-Vassar; Psychlgy.

LILLIS, TIMOTHY J; Bishop Timon HS; Buffalo, NY; (Y); Camera Clb; Ski Clb; Pres Spanish Clb; Stage Crew; Ed Yrbk Phtg; Ed Lit Mag; Rep Stu Cncl; Var L Bowling; Cmnty Wkr; Variety Show; Service & Photo Awd; Canisius Coll; Actng.

LIM, ELAINE; Norman Thomas HS; Flushing, NY; (S); 6/671; Church Yth Grp; FBLA; Math Clb; Band; Hon Roll; Prfct Atten Awd; Val; Regents Schlrshp; NY U; Acctng.

LIMA, EDUARDO F; Yonkers HS; Yonkers, NY; (Y); Boy Scts; Yrbk Stf; JV Bsktbl; JV Var Ftbl; Hon Roll; Air Force Acad; Elctrncs.

LIMBRICK, NANCY; Glen Cove HS; Glen Cove, NY; (S); Hosp Aide; Spanish Clb; Varsity Clb; JV Bsktbl; Score Keeper; Var Socr; Var Trk; Hon Roll; DECA; Hnr Soc 85; Adelph U; Med.

LIMERICK, MELISSA; Tioga Central HS; Barton, NY; (S); 25/96; Debate Tm; Ski Clb; Ed Nwsp Stf; VP Frsh Cls; VP Soph Cls; VP Jr Cls; VP Stu Cncl; Var Fld Hcky; Var Golf; High Hon Roll; Spnsh Awd 84; Paul Smiths; Rest Mgnt.

LIMITONE, KEITH; New Rochelle HS; New Rochelle, NY; (Y); Chorus; School Musical; Hon Roll; NY Cty Coll; Math.

LIMNER, JULIA M; Rome Free Acad; Rome, NY; (Y); Intnl Clb; Ski Clb; Yrbk Phtg; Rep Frsh Cls; Rep Soph Cls; Rep Jr Cls; Rep Sr Cls; Rep Stu Cncl; Var Trk; Hon Roll; NY Schl Of Dog Grmng; Spcl Med.

LIN, ANNA; Potsdam Central HS; Potsdam, NY; (Y); AFS; Am Leg Aux Girls St; Exploring; French Clb; Math Tm; Nwsp Ed-Chief; Yrbk Phtg; JV Cheerleading; Trk; NHS; Indoor Trk Fld Sportsmnshp Awd 84-85.

LIN, EDWARD; Hillcrest HS; Fresh Meadows, NY; (Y); 45/759; Chess Clb; Chrmn Church Yth Grp; Math Tm; Church Choir; Orch; Nwsp Rptr; Hon Roll; Jr NHS; NHS; Benjamin Chancey Music Citation 82; Union College; Chemistry.

LIN, EUGENE; Archbishop Holloy HS; Elmhurst, NY; (Y); 10/450; Art Clb; Chess Clb; Church Yth Grp; German Clb; Math Clb; Yrbk Stf; NHS.

LIN, HOWARD C; Nanuet SR HS; Nanuet, NY; (Y); French Clb; Capt Math Tm; Capt Quiz Bowl; Nwsp Rptr; Stu Cncl; Tennis; High Hon Roll; NHS; Columbia U Sci Hnrs Pgm 85-86; Roswll Pk Memrl Inst Resrch Pgm 85; Pearl Rvr Tnns Dbls Chmpn Div B 85; Pre-Med.

LINARES, MARIALISA; Saint Pius V HS; Bronx, NY; (Y); Cmnty Wkr; Hosp Aide; Chorus; Twrlr; Natl Hon Soc 83-85; Awds Math 83-84; Hunter; RN.

LINCOLN, BRENDA; Newfield Central HS; Newfield, NY; (Y); 7/55; VP Varsity Clb; Band; Jazz Band; Yrbk Stf; Pres Sr Cls; Rep Stu Cncl; Var Cheerleading; Cit Awd; Hon Roll; NHS; PA ST; Htl Mngmnt.

LINCOLN, DONNA; Hilton Central HS; Hilton, NY; (Y); 7/300; Exploring; German Clb; Math Clb; Church Choir; Concert Band; Symp Band; Var JV Bsktbl; High Hon Roll; Hon Roll; Jr NHS; Ntl Hnr Rl 85; Clarkson; Physics.

LINDAHL, WILLIAM C; Seaford SR HS; Seaford, NY; (Y); 45/246; Pres Church Yth Grp; Drama Clb; Library Aide; Chorus; School Play; Hon Roll; NHS; NY ST Regents Schlrshp 85; Clarkson U; Comp Sci.

LINDBERG, LAURA; Nottingham HS; Syracuse, NY; (Y); Pres Church Yth Grp; Yrbk Stf; Stat Lcrss; Var JV Vllybl; Hon Roll; NHS; Spanish NHS; Spanish Clb; Chorus.

LINDELL, DARLENE M; Averill Park HS; Averlill Park, NY; (Y); 13/225; Cmnty Wkr; Computer Clb; 4-H; Band; Concert Band; Mrchg Band; Vllybl; High Hon Roll; Hon Roll; NHS; Edith Grace Craig Reynolds Schlrshp 85; Leo Doherty Schlrshp 85; 85 Clb 85; Hudson Vlly CC; Data Proc.

LINDENBAUM, SETH M; Midwood HS; Brooklyn, NY; (Y); 193/605; Drama Clb; Math Tm; Service Clb; Temple Yth Grp; Pt Guard Vrsty Bsktbl 81-85; 20th Century Fox Movie Audition 85; SUNY-ALBANY.

LINDERMAN, JENNIFER; Commack North HS; E Northport, NY; (Y); Hosp Aide; Office Aide; Rep Frsh Cls; Rep Soph Cls; Rep Jr Cls; Rep Stu Cncl; Mgr(s); High Hon Roll; NHS; Acad All Am 84-85; Huntington Fine Arts Wrkshp Schlrshp 85; Arch.

LINDLAU, JOSEPH; Greenville Central Schl; Greenville, NY; (Y); 5/82; School Play; Trk; NHS; St Regenst Schrlshp 84-85; Culnry Arts.

LINDMAN, JENNIFER J; Shenendehowa SR HS; Clifton Park, NY; (Y); 79/650; Church Yth Grp; Cmnty Wkr; JCL; Latin Clb; Natl Beta Clb; Yrbk Sprt Ed; Var Tennis; High Hon Roll; NHS; Pres Acad Fit Awds Pgm 85; Miami U; Bus.

LINDO, CESAR; Christ Of King HS; Ozone Park, NY; (Y); 42/385; Math Tm; Var Socr; NHS; 2nd Hnrs Awd 82-85; Polytechnic Inst NY; Aersp Eng.

LINDQUIST, KRIS; Bolivar Central HS; Bolivar, NY; (Y); Church Yth Grp; Drama Clb; Spanish Clb; Color Guard; Yrbk Stf; Pres Soph Cls; Socr; Trk; Var Vllybl; Hon Roll.

LINDQUIST, KRISTIN; Pavilion Central HS; Pavilion, NY; (Y); 6/69; AFS; Church Yth Grp; Nwsp Ed-Chief; VP Sr Cls; Capt Cheerleading; Crs Cntry; Trk; Cit Awd; DAR Awd; NHS; Gannett Rchstr Nwsppr Yth Cares Awd 84; Genesee Cnty Jr Miss 85; Mt Union Coll Ntl Essay Cntst 85; St Lawrence U.

LINDSAY, DAVID; Riverhead HS; Riverhead, NY; (Y); French Clb; Latin Clb; Band; Concert Band; Drm & Bgl; Variety Show; Wt Lftg; JV Var Wrstlng; SUNY-CORTLAND; Chem.

LINDSAY, KIM M; Scotia-Glenville HS; Scotia, NY; (Y); Key Clb; Ski Clb; VP Jr Cls; Trs Sr Cls; Rep Stu Cncl; Stat Bsktbl; Marine Bio.

LINEKIN, MAURENE; Sachem North HS; Holbrook, NY; (Y); 200/1509; Hosp Aide; Radio Clb; Ski Clb; Band; Concert Band; Lcrss; Score Keeper; Socr; JV Tennis; Hon Roll; NYSSMA In Flute 82-84; Syrcus U; Musis Mngmnt.

LINELL, ERIK; Broadalbin Central HS; Broadalbin, NY; (Y); 3/54; Am Leg Boys St; Church Yth Grp; Drama Clb; Library Aide; Spanish Clb; School Play; Trs Sr Cls; Socr; Bausch & Lomb Sci Awd; Pres NHS; Rgnts Schlrshp 85; Hugh O Brian Ldrshp Smnr 83; Yrbk Layout Editor; Purdue U; Aero Engrng.

LING, EDWARD; Norman Thomas HS; Brooklyn, NY; (Y); Computer Clb; JA; Office Aide; Quiz Bowl; Teachers Aide; Band; Nwsp Stf; Yrbk Stf; Badmtn; Tennis; NY U; Pre Med.

LINGE, ELIZABETH; St Anthonys HS; Commack, NY; (Y); 1/300; Drama Clb; Nwsp Ed-Chief; Im Lcrss; High Hon Roll; NHS; Ntl Merit SF; NEDT Awd; Sal; Pres Spanish NHS; Model Congress 84-85; Cathloic U; Pol Sci.

LINGNER, VICKI; Sachem HS; Lk Ronkonkoma, NY; (Y); Chorus; Color Guard; Mrchg Band; Yrbk Stf; Comm Art.

LINK, GAIL ANN; Bishop Kearney HS; Webster, NY; (Y); Church Yth Grp; JA; Ski Clb; School Play; Im Sftbl; High Hon Roll; Hon Roll; Lion Awd; NHS.

LINKER, KERRIE L; Arlington HS; Poughkeepsie, NY; (Y); 48/572; Capt Color Guard; Concert Band; Jazz Band; Mrchg Band; Symp Band; Rep Soph Cls; Hon Roll; Lion Awd; Honor Key 85; Winter Guard 81-85; Susquehanna U; Comp Sci.

LINO, JOSETTE; Margaretville Central HS; Arkville, NY; (Y); French Clb; Sec Hosp Aide; Teachers Aide; Chorus; Sec Jr Cls; Sec Sr Cls; Capt JV Cheerleading; Var Socr; Trk; Hon Roll; Mst Imprvd Plyr Socr 82-83; Air Force.

LINTS, KELLY; Oneonta JR SR HS; West Oneonta, NY; (Y); 102/141; Art Clb; Church Yth Grp; FBLA; Chorus; Color Guard; Hon Roll; Charles & Charlotte Bissell Smith Schlrshp 85; ST U; Elem Schl Teach.

LIONBERGER, MARGARET; Emma Willard HS; Dedham, MA; (Y); Art Clb; Drama Clb; Ski Clb; Varsity Clb; Band; Chorus; Orch; School Play; Lit Mag; Lcrss.

LIOTTA, CHRISTOPHER; Archbishop Molby HS; Rosedale, NY; (Y); 106/450; Chess Clb; Church Yth Grp; Math Clb; Math Tm; Science Clb; Band; Drm & Bgl; Capt Bowling; Sftbl; Hon Roll; AJBC Schlrshp 82-83; St Johns U; Lawyer.

LIPARI, ANNA MARIE; Unatego JR SR HS; Wells Bridge, NY; (Y); French Clb; Chorus; VP Bowling; JV VP Sftbl; Becker JC; Animal Care.

LIPKA, WILLIAM; Catholic Central HS; Cohoes, NY; (Y); German Clb; JV Ftbl; Wt Lftg; Hon Roll; Natl Endowment For Th Humanities Russian Studies 85; Hartwick Coll Smmr Art Prog For H S Stu 84; Lang.

LIPKIN, BERYL; Croton Harmon HS; Croton-On-Hudson, NY; (Y); 23/111; AFS; Drama Clb; Temple Yth Grp; Thesps; Band; Mrchg Band; School Musical; School Play; NHS; Regents Schrlshp 85; Gold Hnr Key 84; SUNY.

LIPP, DAVID; Maryvale SR HS; Cheektowaga, NY; (Y); Boy Scts; Chorus; Im JV Bsktbl; Im JV Ftbl; JV Var Trk; Engrng.

LIPPERT, DEBORAH; Ten Broeck Acad; Franklinville, NY; (Y); 4/64; Church Yth Grp; Cmnty Wkr; Drama Clb; French Clb; Hosp Aide; Office Aide; Spanish Clb; Varsity Clb; School Musical; Variety Show; Cornell U; Consumer Econ.

LIPPOLIS, CHARLES A; Fordham Preparatory Schl; Bronx, NY; (Y); Cmnty Wkr; Computer Clb; Latin Clb; Rep Jr Cls; Sec Stu Cncl; Var Bowling; High Hon Roll; Lat Awd, Magna Cum Laude Perf Ntl Lat Ex 82-83; 1st Fordham Prep Sci Fair 84-85; A O Krautter Mem Awd; Pre Med.

LIPPOTH, JEANNE; Acad Of The Rsrctn; New Rochelle, NY; (Y); GAA; Yrbk Stf; Pres Frsh Cls; VP Jr Cls; JV Cheerleading; Var Swmmng; Var L Trk; Hon Roll; SUNY Stony Brook; Phy Thrpst.

LIPSCOMB, KARLA; Anthony A Henninger HS; Syracuse, NY; (Y); Boys Clb Am; Sec Church Yth Grp; Sec JA; Chorus; Church Choir; School Musical; Variety Show; Rep Jr Cls; Cmnty Wkr; Library Aide; Cert Of Awd Herald Jrnl 85; Boys Clb Keystne Awd/Pres 84-85; Syracuse U; Math.

LIPSKI, CHRISTOPHER; Copiayue SR HS; Lindenhurst, NY; (Y); Computer Clb; Yrbk Stf; Stu Cncl; Hon Roll; Outstndng Acdmc Achvt In Crmnl Law & Prntng 85; Printer.

LIPTAK, DIANA L; C W Baker HS; Syracuse, NY; (Y); 9/441; Key Clb; Ski Clb; Spanish Clb; VP Frsh Cls; Pres Jr Cls; Rep Stu Cncl; JV Var Vllybl; High Hon Roll; Pres Jr NHS; Pres NHS; Alfred U Pres Schlrshp 85; NYS Elk Assoc Schlrshp 85; NYS Regents Schlrshp 85; Alfred U; Bio.

LIPTON, ROBIN; Commack HS North; E Northport, NY; (Y); Chorus; Lit Mag; High Hon Roll; Hon Roll; Poem Pub Lit Mag 84; Bus Adm.

LIQUORI, DENISE; Cardinal Spellman HS; Bronx, NY; (Y); Pep Clb; Variety Show; Nwsp Sprt Ed; Nwsp Stf; Im Bsktbl; Coach Actv; Score Keeper; High Hon Roll; NHS; NEDT Awd; Scaragalla Awd 83; Theater Arts.

LIQUORIE, CRISTINA; Mount Vernon HS; Mount Vernon, NY; (Y); Drama Clb; French Clb; VP Keywanettes; School Musical; Lit Mag; Capt Pom Pon; Swmmng; Hon Roll; Kiwanis Awd; Art Stu Of Mnth 84; Studio Art.

LIRAIANO, MAYRA; Cathedral HS; Newyok, NY; (Y); 109/298; Chorus; Church Yth Grp; Intnl Clb; Church Choir; Cheerleading; Albany ST; Bus Adm.

LISCOMB, KERRY; Indian River Central HS; Antwerp, NY; (Y); AFS; Church Yth Grp; Dance Clb; Ski Clb; Off Soph Cls; Off Jr Cls; JV Var Cheerleading; JV Socr; Var Trk; JV Vllybl; Jefferson Comm Coll; Bus Adm.

LISCUM, KRISTEN; Hugh C Williams HS; Canton, NY; (Y); 4-H; Thesps; Chorus; School Musical; School Play; Stage Crew; Cheerleading; Gym; Score Keeper; Socr; Cazenovia Coll; Spec Educ.

LISI, MICHELLE; Lindenhurst SR HS; Lindenhurst, NY; (Y); 1/600; Debate Tm; Drama Clb; Pres Mathletes; Jazz Band; Symp Band; NHS; Ntl Merit Ltr; Pres Schlr; Val; Joan Rizzo Mem Scholar 85; Am Leg Awd 85; Phi Beta Kappa Long Island 85; Hofstra U; Mth.

LISIECKI, MARK; St Josephs Collegiate Inst; Amherst, NY; (Y); 36/201; Church Yth Grp; Var German Clb; Nwsp Rptr; Nwsp Stf; High Hon Roll; NHS; Prfct Atten Awd; Art Clb; Library Aide; Office Aide; Deans Schlrshp Canisius Coll Buffalo NY 85; Hnbl Mntn St Joseph Collegt Inst Art Shw 83; Canisius Coll; Pre-Med.

LISNOFF, LAWRENCE; Commack High Schl HS; Smithtown, NY; (Y); Math Tm; Nwsp Rptr; French Hon Soc; High Hon Roll; Ntl Merit SF; Columbia Sci Hnrs Pgm 85; Elec Engrng.

LISSAK, SHERYL D; James Madison HS; Brooklyn, NY; (Y); 36/812; Hosp Aide; Ski Clb; School Play; Nwsp Rptr; Yrbk Phtg; Yrbk Stf; Co-Capt Cheerleading; Hon Roll; Ntl Merit Schol; Prfct Atten Awd; CSA Awd Ldrshp 82; Spec Merit Awd Assn Asst Princpls 82; United Hosp Fnd JR Svc Awd 83-84; Hunter Coll.

LITMAN, CRAIG S; John Dewey HS; Brooklyn, NY; (Y); JA; Capt Math Tm; Science Clb; Orch; Nwsp Ed-Chief; Im Tennis; Im Vllybl; NY St Regents Schlrshp 85; SUNY; Pre-Med.

LITTLE, BRENDA R; St Francis Prep; Hollis, NY; (Y); 123/690; Church Yth Grp; JA; Opt Clb Awd; Pre Med.

LITTLE, CYNTHIA ANN; Rondout Valley HS; Kingston, NY; (Y); Am Leg Aux Girls St; JA; Trs Spanish Clb; Aud/Vis; Church Choir; Pres VP Stu Cncl; JV Bsktbl; Capt Trk; High Hon Roll; NHS; Psych.

LITTLE, DAVID P; St Marys Acad; Glens Falls, NY; (S); 11/47; Drama Clb; Pres 4-H; ROTC; Ski Clb; Speech Tm; Varsity Clb; Chorus; Color Guard; Drill Tm; School Musical; NY ST Tm Dmnstrtng Tm Chmpn 84; 4-H Ntl Tm Dmnstrtng Tm 1st Rnr Up 84; 4-H Pblc Spkg Awd 84; US Naval Acad.

LITTLE JR, EDWARD; Long Island Lutheran JR SR HS; W Hempstead, NY; (S); Church Yth Grp; French Clb; Pep Band; Symp Band; Var Wrstlng; Hon Roll; NHS; 3rd Pl NY Private Schl Invit 84; Boston U; Pre-Med.

LITTLE, ELIZABETH; ST Marys Acad; Glens Falls, NY; (S); 13/42; 4-H; Varsity Clb; Yrbk Stf; Pres Stu Cncl; Capt Var Bsktbl; Capt Var Crs Cntry; Capt Var Sftbl; 4-H Ntl Pblc Spkng Awd 83; Amer Athlete Awd In Bsktbl 85; Le Moyne Coll; Law.

LITTLEBEAR, MICHAEL; Midwood HS; Brooklyn, NY; (Y); Aud/Vis; JV Var Ftbl; Comm.

LITTLEFIELD, DEVON; Hoosick Falls Central HS; Hoosick Falls, NY; (Y); Drama Clb; Ski Clb; Stage Crew; Stu Cncl; Var Bsbl; L Var Crs Cntry; JV Tennis; JV Trk; Union Coll; Polit Sci.

LITTLETON, ANGELA; Kingston HS; Kingston, NY; (Y); 85/520; French Clb; Chorus; School Musical; School Play; Yrbk Stf; Lit Mag; French Hon Soc; Hon Roll; Library Aide; Outstndg Ratng NYSSMA Comp 82-83; A Ratng All-State NYSSMA Comp 83-84; Fordham Coll; Psych.

LITTMAN, MARC J; Northport HS; Northport, NY; (Y); 24/659; Cmnty Wkr; Stu Cncl; Crs Cntry; Lcrss; Trk; High Hon Roll; NHS; Lehigh U; Math.

LITUCHY, TODD; Commack HS North; Commack, NY; (Y); Chess Clb; Debate Tm; Math Tm; Nwsp Phtg; Nwsp Rptr; Yrbk Phtg; Bowling; High Hon Roll; NHS; Harvard U Smmr Schl Pgm 85; Hofstra U Fornsc Trnmnt 84-86; Bus.

LITVACK, JEFFREY S; Commack High School South; Dix Hills, NY; (Y); Cmnty Wkr; Computer Clb; Hosp Aide; Math Tm; Office Aide; Sec Temple Yth Grp; Mrchg Band; Nwsp Ed-Chief; Nwsp Stf; Yrbk Rptr; Outstndg Soph Awd 84; Hugh O Brien Yth Orgnztn 84-85; NY ST Yth Cncl 85; Pre-Med.

LITVACK, STEVEN; Commack H S South; Dix Hills, NY; (S); Cmnty Wkr; Computer Clb; Math Clb; Math Tm; VP Temple Yth Grp; Mrchg Band; Nwsp Rptr; Yrbk Rptr; Yrbk Stf; VP Stu Cncl; Mgmt.

LITVIN, STAN; James Madison HS; Brooklyn, NY; (Y); Var Chess Clb; Var Intnl Clb; Var Math Clb; JV Var Socr; Var Hon Roll; St Schlr; NYU; Bus Mngmnt.

LIU, DIANA; Bronx H S Of Science; Jamaica, NY; (Y); Church Yth Grp; Library Aide; Teachers Aide; Varsity Clb; Yrbk Bus Mgr; Var Socr; Ntl Merit SF; H S Wrtg Proj Lehman Coll Scholar 85; Vet Med.

LIU, ELAINE; Clarkstown SR H S South; West Nyack, NY; (Y); Drama Clb; Orch; School Musical; Centerstage Schlrshp 85; Muscn Of Yr Orch Plaque 85; Piano Gold Rbbn Cert 84; U Pittsburgh; Mus.

LIU, FAYE; Liverpool HS; Liverpool, NY; (S); 79/792; VP Sec JA; Orch; Hon Roll; Jr NHS; NHS; Phy Thrpy.

LIU, FENG X; Erasmus Hall HS; Brooklyn, NY; (Y); #6 In Class; Math Tm; Prfct Atten Awd; Regnts Schlrshp 85; Elec Engr.

LIU, JEAN; Clarkstown South HS; W Nyack, NY; (Y); Math Tm; Orch; School Musical; Stage Crew; Nwsp Ed-Chief; Mu Alp Tht; NHS; NJ Sci Leag 84-85; Rockland Suburban Symph 85; NY Acad Sci Rsrch Trng Pgm 85.

LIU, JOHN C; Bronx High Schl Of Science; Bayside, NY; (Y); Hosp Aide; Math Tm; Var Crs Cntry; Var L Trk; NHS; Ntl Merit Ltr; Math Exms Merit Cert 83; Outstndng Stu Geo,Meteor,Ocengrphy 85; Physcs Cntst Hnrs Cert 84; SUNY Binghamton; Biophy.

LIU, LISA; Niskayuna HS; Scotia, NY; (Y); Cmnty Wkr; French Clb; Mathletes; Rep Frsh Cls; Rep Soph Cls; Rep Jr Cls; JV Trk; French Hon Soc; Pep Clb; Ski Clb; Presndtl Awd Physcl Ftns Awd 83; Music Comp Piano 83; Cert Of Merit French 85; Math.

LIU, MARIA; Hillcrest HS; Brooklyn, NY; (Y); Church Yth Grp; Dance Clb; FCA; Intnl Clb; Library Aide; Math Clb; PAVAS; Service Clb; Teachers Aide; Chorus; Cert Music Achvt Awd 85; Queens Coll; Music.

LIU, WEICHEE; Clara Barton HS; Brooklyn, NY; (Y); Computer Clb; Hosp Aide; Office Aide; Teachers Aide; Stu Cncl; Stony Brook; Mechncl Engnrng.

LIU, WEIYU; Clara Barton HS; Brooklyn, NY; (Y); Church Yth Grp; Cmnty Wkr; Computer Clb; Hosp Aide; Teachers Aide; Yrbk Stf; Tennis; Polytech; Comp Sci.

LIUBA, ARABELLA J; Hackley Schl; Scarsdale, NY; (Y); 15/87; Drama Clb; Chorus; Jazz Band; Variety Show; Nwsp Rptr; Nwsp Stf; Yrbk Stf; Lit Mag; High Hon Roll; Rgnts Schlrshp 85; Hoff-Barthelson Music Schl 85; 1st Priz Fordham U Comp Italn Poetry 84; Vassar Coll; Communctns.

LIVANIS, ATHANASIOS; St Johns Prep; Astoria, NY; (Y); French Clb; High Hon Roll; Hon Roll; NTL Sci Olympiad Chem 83, Physcs 84 With Dstnctn; NYS Rgnts Schlrshp; Erly Admssn Coll 84; St John U; Govt.

LIVERMORE, DAVID; Churchville-Chili SR HS; Spencerport, NY; (Y); 35/317; Pres Church Yth Grp; FTA; Band; Chorus; Orch; Symp Band; Dnfth Awd; High Hon Roll; NHS; Tlnts Chrst,Natl Awd Brass Div 84; Bkstr Awd,Ctznshp & Ldrshp 85; NY ST All ST Choir 84; Grand Rapids Bapt Coll; Tchng.

LIVERPOOL, GRACE; Springfield Gardens HS; Rosedale, NY; (Y); 140/525; Dance Clb; Office Aide; Hon Roll; NHS; Prfct Atten Awd; Chorus; NY City Coll; Nrs.

LIVINGSTON, BECKY; Perry Central HS; Perry, NY; (Y); 8/92; Drama Clb; Yrbk Stf; JV Var Cheerleading; JV Socr; Var Trk; Pres Micro Spprt Comm Sr; Vol Fire Dept Awd Sr; Comp.

LIVINGSTON, CHERYL; Liverpool HS; Liverpool, NY; (S); 239/792; Ski Clb; Rep Stu Cncl; Jr NHS; Variety Show; Nwsp Stf; Rep Frsh Cls; Rep Soph Cls; Rep Jr Cls; Rep Sr Cls; Im Gym; Daemen Coll; Travl.

LIVINGSTON, EMILY; Pawling HS; Patterson, NY; (Y); 6/66; Church Yth Grp; Spanish Clb; Varsity Clb; Chorus; Church Choir; Variety Show; Trs Sr Cls; JV Cheerleading; Gym; Mgr(s); NY ST Regents Schlrshp 85; NY Sahperd S Eastern Zone Phy Fitness Awd 85; SUNY Geneseo; Frgn Svc.

LIVINGSTON, HELEN; New Rochelle HS; New Rochelle, NY; (Y); Church Yth Grp; Cmnty Wkr; Yrbk Stf; Crs Cntry; Socr; Trk; Cortland.

LIVINGSTON, MARY; Cardinal Ohara HS; N Tonawanda, NY; (Y); Church Yth Grp; Drama Clb; French Clb; School Musical; Hon Roll; UNY Geneseo; Pub Rel.

LIVOTE, JOANNE; Kings Park SR HS; Kings Pk, NY; (Y); 1/393; Office Aide; Red Cross Aide; Varsity Clb; Jazz Band; Nwsp Stf; Var Bsktbl; Var Socr; Var Sftbl; NHS; Val; Francis J Carlucci Memrl Sci Awd 83; Hugh O Brien Schlrshp Contst Finlst 84; Sci.

LIVOTI, JOHN; G Ray Bodley HS; Fulton, NY; (Y); 106/256; Church Yth Grp; Drama Clb; JA; Red Cross Aide; School Musical; Stage Crew; Variety Show; JV Bsktbl; Var Bowling; Hon Roll; Suny Coll; Comp Prgmr.

LIZEWSKI, JOHN JOSEPH; Mattituck-Cutchogue HS; Cutchoque, NY; (Y); 44/118; 4-H; Pep Clb; Ski Clb; Varsity Clb; School Musical; School Play; Variety Show; Rep Frsh Cls; Pres Jr Cls; VP Stu Cncl; Fairfield; Accntng.

LIZZUL, MARINA; St John The Baptist HS; Ronkonkoma, NY; (Y); Drama Clb; School Play; Hon Roll; Psychlgy.

LLAGUNO, MONICA A; St Saviour HS; Brooklyn, NY; (Y); 8/79; Church Yth Grp; French Clb; Hosp Aide; VP Jr Cls; VP Sr Cls; Pom Pon; French Hon Soc; High Hon Roll; NHS; NY U Schlrshp 85-86; NY ST Regents Schlrshp 85-86; NY U; Bio.

LLANO, FRANCES; St Johns Prep; Elmhurst, NY; (Y); Dance Clb; French Clb; Bsktbl; Cheerleading; Hon Roll; 2nd Hnrs Awd Acadmc 85; Pre-Med.

LLOREDA, LINDA; Saranac Lake Central HS; Saranac Lk, NY; (Y); Church Yth Grp; Cmnty Wkr; Concert Band; Jazz Band; Yrbk Stf; Sec Soph Cls; Rep Stu Cncl; Trk; Hon Roll; NHS; Elmira Key Awd 85; SUNY-ALBANY; Bus Admin.

LLOYD, JOHN; Holy Trinity HS; Massapequa, NY; (Y); Band; Jazz Band; Mrchg Band; JV Ftbl; JV Wrstlng.

LLOYD, LAURIE J; Smithtown West HS; Smithtown, NY; (Y); Spanish Clb; Mrchg Band; Symp Band; Rep Sr Cls; Rep Stu Cncl; Bsktbl; Var Capt Socr; Sftbl; Var Capt Vllybl; Hon Roll; Regnts Schlrshp 85; Spnsh Hnr Socty 83-85; Hnr Rll 81-85; SUNY Albany; Bus Adm.

LLOYD, MEREDITH; Smithtown H S West; Smithtown, NY; (Y); NHS; Spanish NHS; NY ST Coll; Psych.

LLOYD, RICHARD; Northern Adirondack Central S HS; Plattsburgh, NY; (Y); 1/105; Am Leg Boys St; Computer Clb; Rep Stu Cncl; Var L Bsktbl; Capt Diving; Capt Swmmng; High Hon Roll; NHS; Engrng.

LLOYD, SHARON; C A Bouton JR SR HS; Voorheesville, NY; (Y); Church Yth Grp; Drama Clb; Intnl Clb; Key Clb; Red Cross Aide; Ski Clb; Spanish Clb; Variety Show; Nwsp Rptr; Yrbk Stf; Adv.

LLOYD, WANDA; Norman Thomas HS; New York, NY; (S); Dance Clb; JA; Band; Concert Band; School Musical; Variety Show; Nwsp Stf; High Hon Roll; Hon Roll; Prfct Atten Awd; Sec.

LO, GEORGE; La Salle Acad; New York, NY; (Y); Camera Clb; Trs Math Clb; Math Tm; Teachers Aide; Yrbk Stf; Crs Cntry; Im Sftbl; Hon Roll; NHS; Lab Rsrch Sci.

LO, GIM W; Grover Cleveland HS; Ridgewood, NY; (Y); Am Leg Boys St; Hon Roll; Acctng, Phy Ed 85; Soc Stds 83; Mech Engr.

LO, JOHN; La Salle Acad; New York, NY; (S); Art Clb; Camera Clb; Math Clb; Nwsp Stf; Yrbk Sprt Ed; Var Trk; Hon Roll.

LO, OLIVIA T; Kingston HS; Kingston, NY; (Y); 19/525; Art Clb; Lit Mag; Hon Roll; Rgnts Schlrshp 85; German Hnr Soc 82-85; Expnd Horizons Pgm 85; SUNY Albany; Psychlgy.

LO, PUI-KWAN; Mabel Dean Bacon Vocational HS; New York, NY; (S); 3/299; Hon Roll; NHS; Irwin Price Mem Awd 82; Sci.

LO, WINSON; La Salle Acad; New York, NY; (S); 2/250; Math Tm; Nwsp Rptr; Yrbk Stf; Trk; Gov Hon Prg Awd; NHS.

LO CASCIO, KEITH W; Commack High School South; Commack, NY; (Y); Aud/Vis; Church Yth Grp; Office Aide; Varsity Clb; JV Var Bsbl; Hon Roll; Bio Awd 84; Acctng.

LO CASCIO, PHYLLIS; Bishop Kearney HS; Brooklyn, NY; (Y); Math Clb; Math Tm; Yrbk Phtg; Yrbk Stf; Hon Roll; Prfct Atten Awd; Pace U; Acctg.

LO DESTRO, DENEAN; Alexander Central HS; Darien Center, NY; (S); Band; Chorus; Var L Crs Cntry; Var L Trk; Hon Roll; Jr NHS; NHS; Prfct Atten Awd; AFS; Spanish Clb; Coaches Awd Crs Cntry 84; Amer Musicl Fndtn Band Hons 84; All Star Tm Trk 83-84; Biol.

LO FASO, JOANN; St Johns Prep; S Ozone Park, NY; (S); Chorus; St Johns U; Law.

LO GATTO, JEANNE MARIE; Hicksville HS; Hicksville, NY; (Y); German Clb.

LO GIUDICE, FRANCESCA ANGELA; Mercy HS; Albany, NY; (Y); 4/70; Ed Yrbk Stf; Lit Mag; High Hon Roll; NHS; Most Likely To Succeed; Most Intelligent; St Rose; Elem Educ.

LO MACCHIO, LISA; Liverpool HS; Liverpool, NY; (S); 75/792; Art Clb; Ski Clb; Mrchg Band; Orch; School Musical; Rep Stu Cncl; Crs Cntry; Jr NHS; NHS; Opt Clb Awd; Outstdng Stu TV Intrvw 84.

LO PRESTI, LAVINIA; New Utrecht HS; Brooklyn, NY; (Y); 1/548; Science Clb; Rep Frsh Cls; Gov Hon Prg Awd; High Hon Roll; Hon Roll; NHS; St Schlr; Val; United Fdntn Tchrs Scholar 85; Gld Mdl Exclnce Italian 85; Marymount Manhattan; Intrprtr.

LO VULLO, STEVEN; Kenmore West SR HS; Tonawanda, NY; (Y); Varsity Clb; Rep Frsh Cls; Rep Soph Cls; Rep Jr Cls; JV Bsbl; Var Diving; JV Ice Hcky; Var Capt Swmmng; Law.

LOADWICK, COURTNEY; Thousand Islands HS; Clayton, NY; (Y); Am Leg Aux Girls St; Band; Chorus; Concert Band; Mrchg Band; School Musical; School Play; Variety Show; JV Socr; Hon Roll; Lions Clb Schlrshp 85; Jefferson Comm Coll; Bus.

LOATMAN, LEWIS; Riverhea SR HS; Riverhead, NY; (Y); Church Yth Grp; ROTC; Spanish Clb; Color Guard; Drill Tm; Var Ftbl; Var Trk; U S Navy NJROTC Cadet Mnth Awd 84; MC Natl Yth Phys Fit Awd 85; Cert Merit Achvt Prfct Atten 84-85; Pre-Law.

LOBACCARO, JACK; H Frank Carey HS; Franklin Sq, NY; (Y); 15/225; Key Clb; Mathletes; Var Bsbl; High Hon Roll; Jr NHS; NHS; Forgn Lang Hnr Socty Itln 84-85; Bus.

LOBBAN, JACQUELINE Y; New Rochelle HS; New Rochelle, NY; (Y); Hosp Aide; Spanish Clb; Church Choir; NHS; Prfct Atten Awd; Spanish NHS; Data Proc.

LOBERT, MICHELLE; Walton HS; Bronx, NY; (Y); 6/32; Office Aide; Swmmng; Vllybl; Cit Awd; Stanley Simon Awd 84; Merit Awd Attndnce 84; Nrse.

LOBMEYER, MICHAEL; St John The Baptist D HS; Brentwood, NY; (Y); Library Aide; Red Cross Aide; JV Crs Cntry; JV Trk; JV Wrstlng; St Johns U; Acctg.

LOBO, PAUL A; The Loyola Schl; New York, NY; (Y); 16/52; Boy Scts; Service Clb; Bsbl; Bsktbl; Socr; NEDT Awd; Prfct Atten Awd; Political Wkr; Ski Clb; School Play; Class 85 Alumni Rep; Colgate U; Polt Econ.

LOBOS, JACQUELINE; St Johns Prep; Elmhurst, NY; (Y); Cmnty Wkr; Dance Clb; Drama Clb; School Play; Stu Cncl; Wt Lftg; Hon Roll.

LOCAPUTO, DAVID; Solvay HS; Syracuse, NY; (Y); 53/167; Boy Scts; Church Yth Grp; JV Var Bsbl; Cit Awd; High Hon Roll; Hon Roll; VFW Awd; Voice Dem Awd; Onondaga CC; Psych.

LOCASTRO, ANTHONY; Manhasset HS; Manhasset, NY; (Y); Ski Clb; Rep Frsh Cls; Ftbl; Lcrss; Wrstlng; Hon Roll.

LOCCISANO, INEZ; Our Lady Of Perpetual Help HS; Brooklyn, NY; (Y); Dance Clb; Library Aide; Cheerleading; High Hon Roll; Hon Roll; Chrstn Ldrshp Awd 82; Cert Of Merit Maria Rgna Chrch 82; Chrldng Athlt Awd 82; Sociolgy.

LOCEY, LINDA; James Sperry HS; Rochester, NY; (Y); Spanish Clb; Band; Concert Band; Sec Trs Sr Cls; Rep Stu Cncl; JV Sftbl; Jr NHS; NHS; Spanish NHS; Schlstc Ltrs 85.

LOCICERO, DAWN; St Johsn Prep; Corona, NY; (Y); High Hon Roll; Hon Roll; Prfct Atten Awd; St Johns U; Bus.

LOCKE, BRIAN; Union-Endicott HS; Endicott, NY; (Y); Concert Band; Mrchg Band; Symp Band; Hon Roll.

LOCKE, HEIDI K; Saratoga Springs HS; Saratoga Springs, NY; (Y); 11/465; Pres Church Yth Grp; Key Clb; Chorus; Var JV Cheerleading; Coach Actv; High Hon Roll; NHS; AATF Natl Frnch Exam Awds 80-84; NYSSMA Music Comptn 82-83; Horseback Rdng 82-84; Middlebury Coll; Frgn Lang.

LOCKE, NADINE A; Sheepshead Bay HS; Brooklyn, NY; (Y); 55/465; Church Yth Grp; JA; Nwsp Stf; Hon Roll; Lib Arts Schlrshp 85; Rgnts Coll Schlrshp 85; Polytechnic Inst NY; Tech Wrtg.

LOCKE, RENEE H; Brockport Central HS; Spencerport, NY; (Y); 9/300; Cmnty Wkr; VP Mathletes; Trs Band; Yrbk Stf; Twrlr; High Hon Roll; Jr NHS; NHS; Mrchg Band; NYS Rgnts Schlrshp 85; Schlrshp GM Inst 85; GM Inst; Mech Engrng.

LOCKE, TIMOTHY; Thousand Islands HS; Clayton, NY; (Y); Boy Scts; Cmnty Wkr; Library Aide; School Play; Variety Show; Bsbl; Ftbl; Ice Hcky; Sftbl; Hon Roll; Elect Engr.

LOCKER, DAVID M; Hillcrest HS; Forest Hills, NY; (Y); 394/633; Boy Scts; Church Yth Grp; German Clb; Rgnts Coll Schlrshp 85; Adelphi U; Acctng.

LOCKWOOD, BRENDA; Hartford Central Schl; Hartford, NY; (S); 5/43; 4-H; French Clb; Math Tm; Varsity Clb; Yrbk Stf; Pres Soph Cls; Pres Jr Cls; Fld Hcky; NHS; NY ST U; Bus.

LOCKWOOD, CINDY; Pine Bush HS; Pine Bush, NY; (Y); 51/276; FBLA; Hon Roll; Paula M Desco Awd 84-85; Orange Cnty CC; Sec Sci.

LOCKWOOD, DANIEL C; Pittsford-Mendon HS; Fairport, NY; (Y); 1/300; Model UN; Service Clb; Varsity Clb; Var L Crs Cntry; Var Capt Lcrss; Im Sftbl; Im Wt Lftg; High Hon Roll; Hon Roll; NHS; Scty Quality Cntrl Engr Mtg 84; Wrote Amer Chem Scty Exam 83; Mdl Untd Ntns Club; Mock Trl Tm; La Crosse; Princeton U; Elec Engr.

LOCKWOOD, LOUISE M; Hamburg SR HS; Hamburg, NY; (Y); 10/389; Pres Church Yth Grp; VP Band; Chorus; Madrigals; Mrchg Band; School Musical; Symp Band; Capt Gym; NHS; NYS Regnts Schlrshp 85; Math Awd 82; Bus Adm.

LOCKWOOD, MICHELLE; Letchworth Central HS; Castile, NY; (Y); Art Clb; Band; Chorus; VP School Musical; Yrbk Stf; Capt Cheerleading; Vllybl; Cit Awd; High Hon Roll; Pres Schlr; Memrl Schlrshp 85; NYSSMA Awd-Al-Cnty Bnd 85; Graphc Dsgn.

LOCKWOOD, ROBERT M; New Rochelle HS; New Rochelle, NY; (Y); 158/529; Church Yth Grp; Cmnty Wkr; Var Wrstlng; NHS; Ntl Merit Ltr; Pres Role Plyng Games Clb 85; Most Pins Awd Wrstlng 84; Sailor,Nav East Coast; US Naval; Pilot.

LOCKWOOD II, THEODORE; Pulaski JR SR HS; Pulaski, NY; (S); 6/100; Drama Clb; French Clb; Band; Chorus; Mrchg Band; VP Jr Cls; Var Ftbl; Var Tennis; NHS; Area All State Chorus 82-83; Chemistry.

LOCKYER, MARY JO; Fox Lane HS; Bedford Vlg, NY; (Y); Cmnty Wkr; Pres Key Clb; Political Wkr; Trs Radio Clb; Concert Band; Jazz Band; Mrchg Band; Ed Nwsp Ed-Chief; Cit Awd; Bedford Vlg C & M Clb 85; Pace U.

LODERER, KIRSTEN; St Francis Preparatory HS; Middle Village, NY; (Y); Im JV Gym; Jr NHS; Psychlgy.

LODGE, KIRSTEN; New Paltz HS; New Paltz, NY; (Y); 3/134; AFS; Cmnty Wkr; Hosp Aide; Lit Mag; High Hon Roll; Hon Roll; NHS; Ntl Merit Ltr; 2 Poems Pblshd 85; Georgetown; Frgn Lang.

LOECHNER, MERRILL; Island Trees HS; Levittown, NY; (Y); 44/212; Camera Clb; Cmnty Wkr; Library Aide; ROTC; Band; Chorus; Stage Crew; Nwsp Phtg; Yrbk Phtg; Hon Roll; Band Ltr; Drama Pin; New England Coll; Aquatic Cinem.

LOESBERG, NOAH; Half Hollow Hills H S East; Dix Hills, NY; (Y); Drama Clb; School Musical; School Play; Lit Mag; Var Crs Cntry; JV Trk; High Hon Roll; Hon Roll; Jr NHS; $100 Bond Awd For Essay Cntst 83-84; Hnrbl Mntn For French Poem 82-83; Performing Arts.

LOESCH, CAROL ANN; Deer Park HS; Deer Park, NY; (Y); 3/570; Cmnty Wkr; Intnl Clb; Sec Mathletes; Pres Math Clb; Pres Math Tm; Science Clb; Orch; High Hon Roll; Jr NHS; NHS; Math Fair Slvr Mdl Brnz Mdl; Nyssma Mdl; Accptnc By Adelphi In The Intl Stds Prog; Pre-Med.

LOESCH, TAMMI; Oakfield Alabama Central HS; Oakfield, NY; (Y); Drama Clb; French Clb; GAA; Office Aide; Ski Clb; Varsity Clb; School Musical; School Play; Bsktbl; NHS; Fash Merch.

LOETMAN, SCOTT; Mepham HS; N Bellmore, NY; (Y); Chess Clb; Computer Clb; Pres Math Tm; Science Clb; Var Trk; Hon Roll; NHS; Medl Hghst Bio Scor Natl Sci Olympd 85; Silvr Medl Comp Div Long Island Math Fair 85; Comp.

LOEW, DAVID H; Fonda-Fultonville Central HS; Fonda, NY; (Y); Nwsp Rptr; Ed Nwsp Stf; JV Var Bsbl; High Hon Roll; Hon Roll; NHS; Ntl Merit Ltr; Yrbk Stf; Rep NY ST Stu Senate Policy Forum 85; Dedication Awd Varsity Baseball 85; Economics.

LOFARO, TAMI J; St Francis Prep; Beechhurst, NY; (Y); Hosp Aide; JA; Ski Clb; Camp Fr Inc; Stage Crew; Nwsp Ed-Chief; Opt Clb Awd; Pace U; Bus.

LOFFREDO, JANINE M; Charles W Baker HS; Baldwinsville, NY; (Y); 11/441; Orch; JV Cheerleading; JV Var Socr; Vllybl; High Hon Roll; Jr NHS; NHS; Daniel Stevens Mem Schlrshp 85; Baldwinsville Comm Schlrshp 85-86; Comm Svc Awd 85; Ithaca Coll; Phy Thrpy.

LOFFREDO, MICHELE; Cardinal O Hara HS; Buffalo, NY; (S); Yrbk Stf; Im Badmtn.

LOFSTROM, ERIC; Fairport HS; Fairport, NY; (Y); Church Yth Grp; Ski Clb; JV Ftbl; Hnrb Mntn In Sibleys Art Show 85; Lake Frst Syracuse; Cmrcl Art.

LOFTUS, DOUGLAS P; Springville Griffith Inst; Boston, NY; (Y); 10/197; FBLA; Teachers Aide; Thesps; Rep Stu Cncl; Hon Roll; NHS; Rotary Awd; St Schlr; SUNY-ONEONTA; Accntnt.

LOFTUS, JOHN; Sweet Home Central HS; Tonawanda, NY; (Y); 75/425; Ski Clb; Chorus; Nwsp Rptr; Nwsp Stf; JV Var Ice Hcky; JV Var Lcrss; JV Var Vllybl; High Hon Roll; Hon Roll; Athlt Schlrshp To OH ST For Vlybl 85; Empire ST Games Sld Mdl Wnr Vlybl 83 & 84; OH ST; Pre-Med.

LOFTUS, KEVIN; Bishop Cunningham HS; Oswego, NY; (Y); Chess Clb; German Clb; JA; Library Aide; School Play; Crs Cntry; Hon Roll; Engr.

LOFTUS, MARK J; Skan HS; Skaneateles, NY; (Y); 67/155; Var L Lcrss; Var L Socr; Hon Roll; Pre-Law.

LOGAN, EILEEN; Holy Trinity HS; East Meadow, NY; (S); 64/369; Math Clb; Stage Crew; Socr; High Hon Roll; Hon Roll; Rgnts Prfssnl Educ In Nrsng Schlrshp 85; Cardiology.

LOGAN, ERICA; James Sperry HS; Pittsford, NY; (Y); Nwsp Stf; High Hon Roll; NHS; Schlstc Ltr 85; US Mltry Acad; Engrng.

LOGAN, KHALDA D; La Guardia Music & The Arts HS; Queens New York, NY; (Y); 150/500; Church Yth Grp; Dance Clb; Drama Clb; Office Aide; Teachers Aide; Church Choir; School Musical; School Play; Variety Show; Rep Sr Cls; Scholar Alvin Ailey 83; Arts Recog & Talent Search Semi-Finlst 85; Biol.

LOGAN, LAURIE; Mamaroneck HS; Larchmont, NY; (Y); AFS; Aud/Vis; Boy Scts; Church Yth Grp; Dance Clb; Latin Clb; Pres Service Clb; Ski Clb; Sec Spanish Clb; Nwsp Stf; 1st Hnrs Spn 4 Iona Coll Lang Cont 85; Excllnce Spn 3 Hnrs 84; DAR & Tchrs Awd Soc Stud 84; Law.

LOGAN, SHEILA; Mercy HS; Hampton Bays, NY; (Y); 12/104; Library Aide; Math Tm; Office Aide; Service Clb; Chorus; School Musical; Stage Crew; Trk; Hon Roll; NHS; Music Hnr Soc 85; Suffolk County Comm Coll; Bus.

LOGAN, TAMARA M; Oriskany Central Schl; Rome, NY; (Y); 14/90; Drama Clb; Key Clb; Band; Chorus; Var Stu Cncl; Bowling; Vllybl; Jr NHS; NHS; Ithaca Coll; Music Educ.

LOGIUDICE, MICHAEL; Arlington HS; Poughheepsie, NY; (Y); 179/600; Boy Scts; Ftbl; SUNY Albany; Acctng.

LOGSDON, SCOTT; Notre Dame HS; Pavilion, NY; (S); Ski Clb; Spanish Clb; Var Bsbl; Var Bsktbl; Var Ftbl; Im Sftbl; High Hon Roll; NHS; Lawyer.

LOGUE, SHERRI; South Side HS; Elmira, NY; (Y); Pep Clb; Concert Band; Mrchg Band; Symp Band; Hon Roll.

LOGUZZO, DIANA; St John Villa Acad; Bklyn, NY; (Y); 11/109; Math Clb; Math Tm; Service Clb; Teachers Aide; Chorus; School Musical; School Play; Nwsp Stf; Yrbk Stf; VP Frsh Cls; Hugh O Brian Awd 84; Georgetown U; Lang.

LOH, ALEXANDRA; New Rochelle HS; New Rochelle, NY; (Y); Drama Clb; French Clb; Model UN; Am Leg Aux Girls St; School Musical; Nwsp Stf; Lit Mag; VP French Hon Soc; Hon Roll; NHS; Lewis Lyman Awd 83; Frnch II Excllnc Awd 83; Schl Svc Awd 83; Intl Affairs.

LOH, ELAINE; William Cullen Bryant HS; Jackson Hts, NY; (S); 5/580; Math Tm; Nwsp Ed-Chief; Nwsp Rptr; Nwsp Stf; Yrbk Stf; Capt Bowling; Gov Hon Prg Awd; Hon Roll; Trs NHS; Governors Citation 84; Qns Coll Pres Awd 84; Mktg.

LOHER, SUSAN H; Locust Valley HS; Locust Valley, NY; (Y); 15/186; Church Yth Grp; VP Spanish Clb; Nwsp Ed-Chief; Rep Jr Cls; Tennis; Trk; High Hon Roll; Jr NHS; NHS; 3rd Best News Stry 84; Exclnc German 84; Exclnc Jrnlsm Awd 85; SUNY Binghamton.

LOHMAN, JON; Irvington HS; Irvington, NY; (Y); Key Clb; Ski Clb; Chorus; School Play; Bsktbl; Coach Actv; Socr; Hon Roll; Area All-ST Chorus 85; Wrtng.

LOHNAU, DEBORAH; Farmingdale SR HS; Farmingdale, NY; (Y); 27/625; Girl Scts; Varsity Clb; Nwsp Stf; Swmmng; Jr NHS; NHS; Marion Awd GSA; Bryn Mawr Coll; Math.

LOHSE, CAROL A; Sachem High School North Campus; Holtsville, NY; (Y); 33/1453; German Clb; Trs Science Clb; Chorus; Lit Mag; Jr NHS; NHS; Ntl Merit Ltr; Drama Clb; Exploring; Bst In Studio In Art Awd 84; 3rd Pl Intl Music Long Islnd Lang Fair 83; Rochester Inst Of Tech; Med Ill.

LOIACANO, DAVID D; Frankfort-Schuyler Central HS; Frankfort, NY; (Y); Boy Scts; Church Yth Grp; Library Aide; Math Tm; Spanish Clb; Band; Church Choir; Concert Band; Jazz Band; Mrchg Band; U S Navy; Nuclr Tech.

LOINAZ, WILLIAM; Lisbon Central Schl; Ogdensburg, NY; (S); 1/48; Pres Aud/Vis; Pres Chess Clb; NFL; VP Spanish Clb; VP Speech Tm; Chorus; Yrbk Stf; Trs Jr Cls; Trs Sr Cls; Hon Roll; Medicine.

LOIS, JENNIFER; Hendrick Hudson HS; Peekskill, NY; (Y); 8/191; Office Aide; Spanish Clb; Varsity Clb; Yrbk Stf; JV Var Cheerleading; Var Golf; Var Capt Swmmng; High Hon Roll; NHS; Ntl Merit Ltr; Rgnts Schlrshp 85; Hghst Avg Spnsh 85; Dartmouth Coll.

LOMANTO, DORENE; Curtis HS; Staten Island, NY; (Y); 4/325; Trs Key Clb; Scholastic Bowl; Nwsp Ed-Chief; Nwsp Phtg; Nwsp Rptr; Ed Yrbk Phtg; Ed Lit Mag; Cheerleading; High Hon Roll; Hon Roll; Dow Jones Newsppr Fund & Untd Fed Tchrs & Generoso Pope Schlrshps; NY U; Jrnlsm.

LOMANTO, MARIA; Gloversville HS; Gloversville, NY; (Y); 11/248; Am Leg Aux Girls St; Trs Drama Clb; Intnl Clb; School Musical; Nwsp Stf; Yrbk Stf; Pres Trs Stu Cncl; Var Stat Ftbl; High Hon Roll; NHS; Lib Arts.

LOMBARD, LORI; Wellsville HS; Wellsville, NY; (Y); Key Clb; Office Aide; Jazz Band; Orch; VP Frsh Cls; Rep Soph Cls; Rep Jr Cls; Sec Sr Cls; Stat Bsktbl; Var Socr; Maple Fest Queen 85; Mbr Yth Amer European Cncrt Tour 84; Spch Path.

LOMBARDI, CELESTE; Ramapo HS; Pomona, NY; (Y); Cmnty Wkr; Hosp Aide; VP Intnl Clb; Science Clb; Spanish Clb; Nwsp Rptr; Off Soph Cls; Off Jr Cls; VP Stu Cncl; High Hon Roll; Cert Cmmndtn-Law Career Grp 84 & 85; Cert Merit 85; Cert Achvt-Mock Trial 84 & 85; Cert Hon, Cmmndtn 85; Pre-Med.

LOMBARDI, DONNA; John S Burke Catholic HS; Warwick, NY; (Y); Dance Clb; Varsity Clb; Cheerleading; Socr; Vllybl; High Hon Roll; Hon Roll; NHS; Ltn Awd 83-84; Art Awd 82-83; Acdmc Cmndtn Bio, Eng, Hist 82-84; Cornell NY U; Med.

LOMBARDI, FILOMENA; Saschem HS; Ronkonkoma, NY; (Y); 288/1463; Art Clb; Camera Clb; Chorus; Yrbk Stf; Pres Frsh Cls; Pres Stu Cncl; Bsktbl; Cheerleading; Sftbl; Hon Roll; Dowling Coll; Acctnt.

LOMBARDI, JENNIFER; Walt Whitman HS; Melville, NY; (Y); Church Yth Grp; Hosp Aide; Key Clb; Band; School Play; JV Var Cheerleading; French Hon Soc; High Hon Roll; Hon Roll; Jr NHS; Grls Ldrs Clb; NY ST Schl Music Assoc; Bus.

LOMBARDI, LOUIS; John Adams HS; Ozone Pk, NY; (Y); Boy Scts; Teachers Aide; Band; Mrchg Band; School Play; Stage Crew; Awd 2nd Hnrs 84-85.

LOMBARDI, MARIANNE; The Franciscan Acad; Syracuse, NY; (S); 4/24; Pres MMM; Political Wkr; Chorus; Yrbk Stf; Sec Frsh Cls; Pres Sr Cls; DAR Awd; High Hon Roll; JC Awd; NHS; Soc Distgshd Amer H S Stu 83-84; JR Natl Hnr Soc 80-82; Law.

LOMBARDI, MARK; Elmont Memorial HS; Elmont, NY; (Y); Key Clb.

LOMBARDO, JOHN; Newfield HS; Selden, NY; (Y); Computer Clb; Science Clb; Golf; Prfct Atten Awd; Comp Prgmr.

LOMBARDO, SHAWN; Commach High School South; Commack, NY; (Y); Math Tm; Stage Crew; Nwsp Rptr; Var Co-Capt Badmtn; Socr; JV Tennis; High Hon Roll; NHS; Ntl Merit Ltr; Attrny.

LOMBINO, JUDY A; Rome Catholic HS; Rome, NY; (Y); Cmnty Wkr; School Musical; School Play; Variety Show; Yrbk Stf; Sec Sr Cls; Hon Roll; St Schlr; St Rose; Bus Admin.

LOMENA, JEANNETTE; St Joseph Acad; Deer Pk, NY; (Y); Dance Clb; Girl Scts; Hosp Aide; Math Tm; Spanish Clb; School Play; Variety Show; Capt Cheerleading; Im Gym; Library Aide; Silver Awd Girl Sct 85; Stonybrook; Psych.

LOMTEVAS, PAUL; Kew Forest HS; Forest Hills, NY; (Y); 7/30; Spanish Clb; Nwsp Sprt Ed; Lit Mag; Var Capt Bsktbl; Ftbl; Var Socr; Sftbl; Hon Roll; Ntl Merit Ltr; NY Regents Schlrshp; JV Bsktbl Coach; JV Sftbl Coach; West Point; Engrng.

LONCAR, MICHAEL G; St Francis HS; West Seneca, NY; (Y); 2/146; Trs Boy Scts; Bowling; Lion Awd; NHS; Lttr Hgh Avg; Eagl Scout; Air Force Acad; Chem Engr.

LONCHER, JEFFREY; Frontier Central HS; Lakeview, NY; (Y); Boys Clb Am; Boy Scts; French Clb; Teachers Aide; Varsity Clb; Bsktbl; Ftbl; Trk; Vllybl; Wt Lftg; Draftng.

LONG, BLAKE A; Kenmore East SR HS; Kenmore, NY; (Y); Church Yth Grp; Stage Crew; Ice Hcky; Sftbl; Vllybl; Mechncl Engr.

LONG, BRIDGET; John A Coleman HS; Kingston, NY; (S); 9/67; Rep Soph Cls; Hon Roll; Hnrs European Hist, Hnrs Algebra II, Hnrs Bus Comm & Typing 83-84.

LONG, COLLEEN M; Skaneateles HS; Skaneateles, NY; (Y); Church Yth Grp; Cmnty Wkr; Office Aide; Hon Roll; Tarrant Cnty JC; Chld Psych.

LONG, CORRIN; Notre Dame Acad; Staten Island, NY; (Y); Drama Clb; Math Clb; Math Tm; Science Clb; Nwsp Stf; Var Tennis; Natl Fr Cont 84-85; Otstndg Achvt JR Vrsty Math League 84; Busd.

LONG, GINA; Bishop Grimes HS; Liverpool, NY; (Y); School Musical; School Play; Rep Soph Cls; Pres Jr Cls; Bowling; Hon Roll; NHS.

LONG, HEATHER; Onteora Central Schl; Boiceville, NY; (S); 6/245; Drama Clb; Speech Tm; Color Guard; Mrchg Band; Trs Frsh Cls; Var Bsktbl; High Hon Roll; NHS; Letter Of Commendation Natl Merit Schlrshp; General Business Awd; Biology And Society.

LONG, JACQUELINE; Frewsburg Central HS; Frewsburg, NY; (Y); 3/96; Drama Clb; Girl Scts; Band; Chorus; School Musical; School Play; Nwsp Ed-Chief; Hon Roll; NHS; Ntl Merit Ltr; Syracuse U; Erly Chldhd Educ.

LONG, JERI LYNN; Longwood HS; Middle Island, NY; (Y); 99/492; Stage Crew; Variety Show; VP Soph Cls; Rep Jr Cls; VP Sr Cls; Rep Stu Cncl; Capt Cheerleading; Vllybl; Hon Roll; Prfct Atten Awd; Amer Poetry Poem Pblctn 85; Wrld Of Poetry Cntnst Hnrb Mntn 85; Wrld Of Poetrys Gldn Poet Awd 85; NC U; Bus.

LONG, KATRINA; Lafayette HS; Buffalo, NY; (Y); Church Yth Grp; Cmnty Wkr; Church Choir; Drill Tm; Yrbk Stf; Sec Jr Cls; Capt Bowling; Rochester Inst Tech; Data Proc.

LONG, KELLEY; North Warren Central HS; Pottersville, NY; (S); 8/48; Girl Scts; Band; Chorus; School Play; Nwsp Stf; Yrbk Stf; VP Jr Cls; VP Sr Cls; Rep Stu Cncl; Var Cheerleading; Hugh O Brien Ldrshp Awd; Hartwick Coll; Lbrl Arts.

LONG, LAURA ROSALIE; Fredonia HS; Fredonia, NY; (Y); 47/185; Art Clb; Cmnty Wkr; FTA; Chorus; School Musical; School Play; Stage Crew; Ed Nwsp Stf; Rep Stu Cncl; DAR Awd; NYSSMA Solo Comptn 85; Ganon U Wrtg Awd Featr Ctgry 4th Pl 84; Our Town Plyd Louella Soames 85; Fredonia ST Coll; Elem Ed Tchr.

LONG, PATRICK J; The Nichols Schl; Buffalo, NY; (Y); School Musical; School Play; Nwsp Ed-Chief; VP Jr Cls; Var Capt Ftbl; Var Lcrss; Var Capt Wrstlng; Jr NHS; NHS; Ntl Merit SF; Irwin Awd 84; Austin Fox Awd Bst JR Eng Paper 84; W Point Acad Wrkshp 84; Eng.

LONG, REBECCA M; Gates Chili SR HS; Rochester, NY; (Y); 36/463; Library Aide; Office Aide; High Hon Roll; NHS; NY ST Regnts Nrsng Schlrsph 85; Wegmans Food Mrkts Schlrshp 85; Suny Coll Brockprt; Nrs.

LONG, RICHARD; Irondequoit HS; Rochester, NY; (Y); 90/360; Exploring; Ski Clb; Band; Concert Band; Mrchg Band; JV Socr; Hon Roll; Prfct Atten Awd; Bus Mgmt.

LONGHANY, PATTY; Le Roy Central HS; Stafford, NY; (Y); French Clb; FBLA; Intnl Clb; Letterman Clb; NFL; Office Aide; OEA; Varsity Clb; Pres Sec 4-H; Bsktbl; Ofc Wrk.

LONGO, DAWN; West Lake HS; Hawthorne, NY; (Y); 22/154; Dance Clb; Debate Tm; NHS; Debate Tm Pres 83-85; Hawthorne Ladies Aux Schlrshp 85; Grad High Hnrs 85; SUNY Albany; Acctg.

LONGO, ROBIN REGINA; Valley Stream Central HS; Valley Stream, NY; (Y); 17/365; AFS; Art Clb; Church Yth Grp; Cmnty Wkr; Dance Clb; Drama Clb; Girl Scts; Hosp Aide; Intnl Clb; Band; Recog Awd Hofstra U 85; Dept Forgn Lang Excllnc In Itln 85; Pres Acadmc Fit Awds 85; Villanova U; Elctrcl Engrng.

LONGSHORE, KRISTINE; Madrid Waddington HS; Madrid, NY; (Y); 1/55; GAA; NFL; Speech Tm; School Musical; Yrbk Stf; Var Crs Cntry; Var Trk; NHS; AFS; Church Yth Grp; WNPI TV; Amer HS Athl; Dartmouth; Pre Med.

LOOBY, ERIC R; Chelsea HS; New York, NY; (Y); 3/201; Church Yth Grp; Cmnty Wkr; Band; Church Choir; Sr Cls; Capt Trk; Hon Roll; Jr NHS; Regents Schlrshp 85; Elect Engrng.

LOOKER, SUZANNE; Indian River Central HS; Calcium, NY; (Y); Nwsp Stf; Yrbk Stf; Coach Actv; Prfct Atten Awd; Excllnt Schlrshp 85; Accntng.

LOOMIS, CRAIG R; Gowanda Central HS; Perrysburg, NY; (Y); 13/158; Am Leg Boys St; French Clb; Ski Clb; Thesps; Stu Cncl; Ftbl; Trk; Wrstlng; NHS; Hrdst Wrkr JV Ftbl 82; 3rd Pl Dunkirk Trnmnt Wrstlng 85; 3rd Pl Randolf Leag Trnmnt Wrstln 85; RIT; Comp Engrng.

LOOMIS, EILEEN; Bishop Maginn HS; Albany, NY; (Y); Drama Clb; JA; Red Cross Aide; Service Clb; Band; Chorus; School Musical; School Play; Var Tennis; Hon Roll; 1st Pl Greek Hrtg Essay Cntst 83; Marion Awd 83; St Rose; Spec Educ.

LOONEY, JOHN; Whitesboro SR HS; Whitesboro, NY; (Y); 49/359; Church Yth Grp; Varsity Clb; VP Stu Cncl; Var L Bsktbl; Var L Lcrss; Cit Awd; JV Ftbl; Cert Merit Boys ST 85; Pol Sci.

LOONIE, LOREEN; Cornwall Central HS; Cornwall, NY; (Y); Acpl Chr; Chorus; Variety Show; Rep Frsh Cls; Rep Soph Cls; Rep Jr Cls; Sec Sr Cls; JV Bsktbl; JV Socr; JV Vllybl; Chrs 82-83; Comms.

LOOTENS, STEVEN; Aquinas Inst; Rochester, NY; (Y); 39/185; Crs Cntry; Trk; Hon Roll; Mech Engrng.

LOPANE, CATHERINE; St Gabriel HS; New Rochelle, NY; (Y); 7/61; Yrbk Stf; Natl Soc Stds Olympd Medl; Natl Soc Stds Olympd Awd; Secdry Schl Tchr.

LOPARCO, LORI; Rome Free Acad; Rome, NY; (Y); Pep Clb; Yrbk Stf; Sec Stu Cncl; Var Cheerleading; JV Capt Vllybl; Hon Roll; Sec Jr NHS; NHS; Prncpls Awd 82-83; Outstndng Perfrmnc Frnch 82-83; 100 Clb Algbr 82-83.

LOPATER, STEVEN J; Great Neck South HS; Glen Cove, NY; (Y); Exploring; Math Tm; Quiz Bowl; Science Clb; Temple Yth Grp; Yrbk Stf; Hon Roll; Pres Schlr; Spanish Clb; Regnts Schlrshp 85; U Of MI; Pre-Med.

LOPES, ELIZABETH; Newfield HS; Selden, NY; (Y); Computer Clb; Dance Clb; Intnl Clb; Latin Clb; Math Clb; Spanish Clb; Chorus; Variety Show; Cit Awd; High Hon Roll; Hofstra; Psych.

LOPEZ, ALEX; Newtown HS; Elmhurst, NY; (Y); 51/603; Aud/Vis; Cmnty Wkr; Office Aide; Teachers Aide; Rep Soph Cls; Rep Sr Cls; Hon Roll; Regents Coll Schlrshp 85; Natl Hspnc Schlr Awds 85; JR Engr Tech Scty 85; Pratt Inst; Arch.

LOPEZ, ANNA; Mount Vernon HS; Mt Vernon, NY; (Y); Church Yth Grp; Cmnty Wkr; Dance Clb; Hosp Aide; Office Aide; Political Wkr; Teachers Aide; Church Choir; Vllybl; Hon Roll; Admin Med Sec.

LOPEZ, ANNETTE; Manhattan Center For Sci & Math; Bronx, NY; (Y); Sec Church Yth Grp; Drama Clb; Library Aide; School Musical; Nwsp Stf; High Hon Roll; Hon Roll; Cardinal Spellman Yth Awd 85; Elec Engr.

LOPEZ, BLANCA; Cathedral HS; Ny, NY; (Y); 141/298; Church Yth Grp; Library Aide; Cert Awd For Library Aid 85; Bilingual Exec Sec.

LOPEZ, CHRISTINE; Solvay HS; Solvay, NY; (Y); 4-H; VP Spanish Clb; Chorus; Variety Show; Yrbk Stf; Frsh Cls; Soph Cls; Jr Cls; High Hon Roll; Hon Roll; Med Tech.

LOPEZ, DANIEL; Fort Hamilton HS; Brooklyn, NY; (Y); Hosp Aide; Office Aide; Varsity Clb; Color Guard; Off Frsh Cls; Bsbl; Hnr Cert Spnsh Achvt 84-85; Nrs.

LOPEZ, GLADYS JANET; Benjamin Franklin HS; Rochester, NY; (Y); JA; Latin Clb; Model UN; Office Aide; Pep Clb; Nwsp Rptr; Yrbk Stf; Off Jr Cls; Gym; High Hon Roll; RIT; Bus.

LOPEZ, JOHN; C W Baker HS; Baldwinsville, NY; (Y); Boy Scts; Chess Clb; Church Yth Grp; Drama Clb; Science Clb; Var Capt Tennis; MVP Tnns; Messiah Coll Grantham; Chem.

LOPEZ, LAWRENCE A; St Anthonys HS; Holbrook, NY; (Y); Dance Clb; Ftbl; Spanish NHS; Elec Engnrng.

LOPEZ, MAURICIO; Lindenhurst HS; Lindenhurst, NY; (Y); Ftbl; Psych.

LOPEZ, NOELLE DENISE; Adlai E Stevenson HS; Bronx, NY; (Y); Church Yth Grp; Dance Clb; Debate Tm; Office Aide; Service Clb; Teachers Aide; Band; Concert Band; Jazz Band; Mrchg Band; Queens Coll; Law.

LOPEZ, NORMA; Sacred Heart HS; New York, NY; (Y); Hon Roll; Bus Admin.

LOPEZ, ROBERT; Sheepshead Bay HS; Brooklyn, NY; (Y); Church Yth Grp; Computer Clb; Ftbl; Dentst.

LOPITZ, AMANDA; Canastota HS; Canastota, NY; (Y); Drama Clb; Band; Chorus; Color Guard; Concert Band; Mrchg Band; School Play; Stage Crew; High Hon Roll; Hon Roll; SUNY Geneseo; Bio.

LOPOUKHINE, LYDIA; Nyack HS; Nyack, NY; (Y); Church Yth Grp; Drama Clb; Math Clb; Radio Clb; Orch; School Musical; School Play; Stage Crew; Yrbk Stf; Lit Mag;)ngr.

LORD, JANETTE; Alexander HS; Attica, NY; (Y); 17/88; Chorus; Capt Color Guard; School Musical; Rep Frsh Cls; Sec Soph Cls; VP Jr Cls; Pres Sr Cls; Capt Cheerleading; Ntl Merit Schol; Yrbk Stf; Futr Tchrs Awd 85; Sprit Awd 85; Genesee CC; Spec Ed.

LORD, KIM M; Bishop Loughlin HS; Brooklyn, NY; (Y); 17/180; Cmnty Wkr; Office Aide; High Hon Roll; Hon Roll; Svc Citation 85; Bishop Loughlin Silver L Cert 85; St Johns U; Liberal Arts.

LORD, LEIGHANN; St Francis Prep; Jamaica Queens, NY; (S); 184/690; Church Yth Grp; Cmnty Wkr; Color Guard; Drm & Bgl; Mrchg Band; Spanish NHS; Penn ST Blck Achvt Awd 85; Ntl Hnr Rll 85; Baruch Coll; Finance.

LORD, MICHELLE; Camden HS; Cleveland, NY; (Y); Acpl Chr; Band; Chorus; Concert Band; Sec Stu Cncl; JV Bsktbl; Capt JV Fld Hcky; High Hon Roll; NHS; Camden Rotary Club Acad/Athl Awd 85; Syracuse U; Phy Thrpst.

LOREN, HEATHER; New Rochelle HS; New Rochelle, NY; (Y); Mgr Drama Clb; Intnl Clb; Math Tm; Temple Yth Grp; Nwsp Rptr; Yrbk Stf; Rep Jr Cls; Stu Cncl; Sec French Hon Soc; NHS; Bus Admin.

LORENTZEN, ELIZABETH; W C Mepham HS; N Bellmore, NY; (Y); 27/385; High Hon Roll; NHS; Prfct Atten Awd; Cmnty Wkr; Science Clb; Hon Roll; Jr NHS; Molloy Schlrs Prgm 85; Molloy Coll; Psychlgy.

LORENZ, KAREN; Franciscan HS; Garrison, NY; (Y); Debate Tm; Drama Clb; School Musical; Variety Show; Nwsp Ed-Chief; Nwsp Rptr; Stu Cncl; French Hon Soc; Hon Roll; NHS; Pre Law.

LORENZ, KATHLEEN; St Joseph By The Sea HS; Staten Island, NY; (Y); Girl Scts; Pres Frsh Cls; Pres Soph Cls; VP Jr Cls; Stu Cncl; Bsktbl; Sr Helen Flynn Schlrshp 85; St Johns U; Bus.

LORENZ, KURT; Whitesboro SR HS; Marcy, NY; (Y); Varsity Clb; Pep Band; JV Bsbl; Var L Ftbl; Im Golf; Im Ftbl; Var L Lcrss; JV Socr; Im Wt Lftg; Var L Wrstlng; Manhattan Co; Aero Ntcl Engr.

LORENZATTO, NILDA; St Agnes Acad; Elmhurst, NY; (Y); Yrbk Phtg; Rep Soph Cls; Rep Jr Cls; Rep Sr Cls; Hunter Coll NY.

LORENZEN, JAN; Liberty Central HS; Liberty, NY; (Y); Chess Clb; Band; Church Choir; NHS; Comp Sci.

LORENZO, ANDREA; Penfield HS; Penfield, NY; (Y); 1/371; Model UN; Spanish Clb; Swing Chorus; Lit Mag; Sec Pres Stu Cncl; JV L Tennis; Ntl Merit SF; Val; Art Clb; Drama Clb; Harvard Bk Awd 84; Phi Beta Kappa Awd Acadmc Exclnc 85; Law.

LORENZO, THOMAS; Walt Whitman HS; Huntington, NY; (Y); 55/540; Boy Scts; Chorus; JV Var Lcrss; Im Var Socr; Jr NHS; Finc.

LORETTO III, CONIO; North Collins Central HS; N Collins, NY; (Y); Drama Clb; Band; Concert Band; Mrchg Band; School Musical; School Play; Variety Show; Nwsp Rptr; Rep Jr Cls; Rep Sr Cls; Eden Corn Fest Tlnt Show 1st Pl 83; Music Therapy.

LORIE, CRAIG; East Meadow HS; E Meadow, NY; (S); Computer Clb; Key Clb; Math Clb; Math Tm; Cheerleading; Hon Roll; Jr NHS; NHS; Acad All Amer; Comp Sci.

LORIMER, CATHRYN; Fayetteville Manlius HS; Fayetteville, NY; (Y); Church Yth Grp; Cmnty Wkr; Key Clb; Ski Clb; Chorus; Church Choir; School Musical; Rep Frsh Cls; Rep Soph Cls; Hon Roll; Psychlgy.

LORZ, ROBERT; Williamsville East HS; Buffalo, NY; (Y); Art Clb; Capt Gym; Hon Roll; 5th Pl Sect IV Mens Gymstcs 84; Hnrb Mntn Damean All High Art Compt 85; Buffalo ST; Comm.

LOSHIGIAN, PETER; Hauppauge HS; Hauppauge, NY; (Y); Trs Pres Church Yth Grp; Mgr Trk; Hon Roll; NHS; Asst Sndy Schl Tchr 86; Bio Mech.

LOSITO, JOHN; Elmira Free Acad; Elmira, NY; (Y); Civic Clb; JA; Political Wkr; Ski Clb; Chorus; School Play; Trs Jr Cls; Trs Sr Cls; Wrstlng; Bowling; JR Bowler Of Yr 84-85; Penn ST ; Bus Adm.

LOTATARO, KAREN; St Edmund HS; Brooklyn, NY; (S); 16/187; Art Clb; Cmnty Wkr; Hosp Aide; Science Clb; Art Awd 84; Christian Svc Awd 84; Pre-Med.

LOTITO, CHRISTOPHER J; Edward R Murrow HS; Brooklyn, NY; (Y); 63/725; Boy Scts; Exploring; VP Jr Cls; Capt Bowling; NY ST Regents & LIU Schlrshp 85; Var Sci Awds 83-84; Westinghouse Sci Tlnt Srch 85; Arnold & Marie Schwartz; Pharm.

LOTT, ERRIKA; Bishop Loughlin Memorial HS; Brooklyn, NY; (S); 11/254; Cmnty Wkr; Science Clb; Vllybl; High Hon Roll; NHS; Prfct Atten Awd; Bus.

LOTT, KARINA M; Newtown HS; Elmhurst, NY; (Y); 244/800; Art Clb; Office Aide; School Musical; School Play; Stage Crew; Variety Show; Outstndng Achvt Awd Costume Design 84; NY U; Theatre Design.

LOU, JANICE; Franklin Delano Roosevelt HS; Brooklyn, NY; (Y); Cit Awd; Hon Roll; Hnrs Math Cls 85; Schlstc Awd Eng 85.

LOUCKS, DANA; Oneida SR HS; Canastota, NY; (Y); Letterman Clb; Varsity Clb; Concert Band; Jazz Band; Symp Band; Bsbl; Bsktbl; Ftbl; High Hon Roll; Jr NHS; Ftbl 2nd Tm All Leag 84; All Star Jazz Band 84-85; Ins Brkr.

LOUCKS, JILL A; East Syracuse-Minoa HS; E Syracuse, NY; (Y); 68/338; Drama Clb; Thesps; Chorus; School Musical; School Play; Stage Crew; Swing Chorus; Yrbk Stf; Crs Cntry; Regents Schlrshp 85; SUNY-ALBANY; Bio.

LOUCKS, LEE ANN; Mynderse Acad; Seneca Falls, NY; (Y); 24/140; Am Leg Aux Girls St; GAA; Var L Bsktbl; Var L Socr; Var L Sftbl; Cit Awd; Hon Roll; NHS; Ldrshp Awd 82-83; 1st Tm All Leag Sftbl 84-85; All-Tournmnt Tm-Bsktbl 84-85; Comp Mgmt.

LOUCKS, MARCY; Haverling Central HS; Bath, NY; (S); 13/114; French Clb; JCL; Latin Clb; Math Clb; Ski Clb; Band; Color Guard; Yrbk Stf; Rep Jr Cls; NHS.

LOUCKS, ROBERTEEN; Mayfield HS; Mayfield, NY; (Y); 22/74; Drama Clb; Teachers Aide; Stage Crew; Nwsp Stf; Timer; Hon Roll; Hm Ec & Gregg Typg Awds 84-85; Regnts Diplm NY ST 85; FMCC; Erly Ed.

LOUCKS, WILLIAM; Mayfield Central HS; Mayfield, NY; (Y); 42/71; Art Clb; Drama Clb; VICA; School Play; Stage Crew; Yrbk Phtg; Yrbk Stf; High Hon Roll; Hon Roll; Brurer Goulet Mem Awd 85; FMCC Schlrshp 85; Hghst Avg Voc Awd 85; Futon Coll; Grphc Artst.

LOUDEN, COLEEN; Notre Dame Acad; Staten Island, NY; (Y); Church Yth Grp; Drama Clb; School Musical; School Play; Var Cheerleading; NHS; Lib Art.

LOUGH, LISA; Sayville HS; Sayville, NY; (Y); 63/373; French Clb; Hosp Aide; Nwsp Phtg; Nwsp Rptr; Nwsp Stf; Var Trk; Hon Roll; Regnts Schlrshp 85; Rutgers Coll; Cmmnctns.

LOUGHEED, MICHAEL S; Stissing Mt HS; Pine Plains, NY; (Y); Boy Scts; Church Yth Grp; FFA; Varsity Clb; Nwsp Stf; Pres Sr Cls; JV Var Bsktbl; JV Var Ftbl; JV Socr; Dutchess CC; Bus.

LOUIE, ELAINE; Bronx Science HS; Flushing, NY; (Y); Church Yth Grp; Cmnty Wkr; FCA; Hosp Aide; Library Aide; Office Aide; Service Clb; Teachers Aide; Church Choir; Sec Frsh Cls; Regents Schlrshp; Barnard Coll; Math.

LOUIE, KERRY; Xaverian HS; Brooklyn, NY; (S); 3/347; Math Tm; Nwsp Sprt Ed; Rep Jr Cls; Rep Sr Cls; Var L Crs Cntry; Var L Trk; NHS; Ntl Merit Ltr; Prfct Atten Awd; Spanish NHS; MIT; Civil Engrng.

LOUIE, RICHARD; Bronx High Schl Sci; Flushing, NY; (Y); Math Tm; Ntl Spn Exam-15th Pl 85; Iona Coll Physcs Comptn-1st Hnrs 85; ARML Contst 85; Pre-Med.

LOUIE, RON; Bethpage HS; Plainview, NY; (Y); 22/286; Art Clb; Band; Jazz Band; Mrchg Band; School Play; Yrbk Stf; High Hon Roll; NHS; Concert Band; Nwsp Stf; Regents Scholar 84-85; Top 10 Amer H S Mth Exam 84; Tri-Mc Music Hon Soc 84-85; CW Post U; Grphic Design.

LOUIS, JILLAN; Andrew Jackson HS; Queens Village, NY; (Y); #4 In Class; Science Clb; Variety Show; Trk; High Hon Roll; Hon Roll; NHS; Advanced Plcmnt Engl; Arista Girl Ldr 85-86; John Jay; Law.

LOUIS, JIMMY; The Bronx High School Of Science; Bronx, NY; (Y); JA; Teachers Aide; Chorus; School Play; Full Scholar Deerfield Acad 81; Comp Engrng.

LOUIS, LINDA PIERRE; St Joseph HS; Brooklyn, NY; (Y); 1/114; Church Yth Grp; Dance Clb; Drama Clb; Hosp Aide; Red Cross Aide; Variety Show; Yrbk Stf; Bsktbl; High Hon Roll; Sal; Brooklyn Cathlc Intrrcl Cncl Schlrshp 81-85; Govrnr Cmmttee Schlstc Achvt Citatn 85; Long Island U; Pharm.

LOUIS JACQUES, FREDERIQUE; St Frances Prep; Queens Village, NY; (S); 118/690; JA; Band; Chorus; Drm & Bgl; Hon Roll; NHS; Opt Clb Awd; Spanish NHS; Cmnty Wkr; Stus Act Awd 84; Rgnts Schlrshp 84-85; Penn ST Schlrshp 84-85; Syracuse U; Engrng.

LOUIS-JACQUES, FREDERIQUE; St Francis Prep; Queens Village, NY; (Y); 118/690; JA; Library Aide; Rep Drm & Bgl; Mrchg Band; Hon Roll; NHS; Opt Clb Awd; Spanish NHS; Syracuse U; Chem Engrng.

LOUISON, CAROLYN L; Midwood HS; Brooklyn, NY; (Y); 61/605; Math Tm; Mgr Orch; Ed Nwsp Stf; Ed Lit Mag; City Coll Schlr Awd 85; Arista & Archon Hnr Scty Awds 84; Regents Coll Schlrshp 85; City Coll; Ccomp Sci.

LOUIT, ANNE; Mamaroneck HS; Larchmont, NY; (Y); French Clb; Pres German Clb; Math Clb; Math Tm; Nwsp Rptr; Nwsp Stf; Ed Lit Mag; Var Crs Cntry; Var Trk; Spanish NHS; MVP Indoor Trk 85; 1st Hnrs Iona Lang Cntst 85; Copier SR Or Advsry 85; Spanish Natl Hnr Soc 85.

LOURDEL, PETER; Tonawanda JR SR HS; Tonawanda, NY; (Y); Church Yth Grp; Church Choir; JV Bsbl; Var Socr; Hon Roll; Prfct Atten Awd; Grace Coll; Nrsng.

LOVE, DAVID ANDREW; Francis Lewis HS; Laurelton, NY; (Y); Math Tm; Teachers Aide; Band; Nwsp Ed-Chief; Debate Tm; Office Aide; Scholastic Bowl; Queens Coll Acad Achvt Awd 82-83; Arista Pres 84-85; YFU US-JAPAN Schlrshp 84; Wstnghse Sci SF 84; Harvard; Engrng.

LOVE, DENNIS; Gouverneur HS; Gouverneur, NY; (Y); Varsity Clb; Var Capt Bsbl; Var Capt Bsktbl; Var Capt Ftbl; Hon Roll; NHS; Canton ATC.

LOVE, DERRICK; Wilson Magnet HS; Rochester, NY; (Y); Aud/Vis; Cmnty Wkr; Radio Clb; Stu Cncl; Bsktbl; Cit Awd; High Hon Roll; Chess Clb; Intnl Clb; Office Aide; Most Imprvd 84-85; Athl Awds 83-85; Syracuse U; Comm.

LOVE, MARY ANN; Williamsville South HS; Williamsville, NY; (Y); 8/245; Drama Clb; School Musical; High Hon Roll; Pres NHS; Ntl Merit Ltr; Regnts Schlrshp 85; Alumni Schlrshp ST U Coll Geneseo NY 85; Unique Dnc Co; ST U Coll Geneseo NY; Bus.

LOVE, TRACIE; Haverling Central HS; Bath, NY; (S); 22/150; French Clb; FBLA; Latin Clb; School Play; Yrbk Stf; Stu Cncl; Cheerleading; Swmmng; Hon Roll; NHS; Bus.

LOVELACE, CINDY; Bethlehem Central HS; Delmar, NY; (Y); GAA; Varsity Clb; Rep Soph Cls; Rep Stu Cncl; JV Bsktbl; Var Score Keeper; Score Keeper; Var Sftbl; Var Trk; Hon Roll; Elem Ed.

LOVELL, CHARLENE; Norman Thomas HS; Long Island City, NY; (S); Hosp Aide; JA; Orch; School Play; VP Soph Cls; Im Gym; Trk; Cit Awd; Hon Roll; Future Secretaries Assoc 84; Medicine.

LOVELL, ROBBI; Watkins Glen HS; Watkins Glen, NY; (Y); 45/125; Church Yth Grp; Cmnty Wkr; Drama Clb; 4-H; Girl Scts; Hosp Aide; Letterman Clb; Math Clb; Red Cross Aide; Ski Clb; Kissimmee Acad; Trvl Training.

LOVELLO, ADRIENNE; The Mary Louis Acad; Maspeth, NY; (Y); Office Aide; Yrbk Phtg; High Hon Roll; Hon Roll; NHS; Knighs Columbus Essay Cont 82.

LOVERO, LISA; Roosevelt HS; Yonkers, NY; (S); Civic Clb; Drama Clb; Political Wkr; Band; Lit Mag; Trs Soph Cls; NHS; Church Yth Grp; Chorus; Mrchg Band; Al-Amer Hll Fm Bnd Hnrs 85; US Collegt Bnds 84; N Amer Hnrs Bnd 85; Law.

LOVETT, MICHELE; John Dewey HS; Brooklyn, NY; (Y); Math Tm; Service Clb; Concert Band; JV Bsktbl; Im Vllybl; Hon Roll; Jr NHS; JR Rep; Serv SR Class Usher; Bernard Buruch Coll; Bus Adm.

LOVRIA, LAURA; Notre Dame HS; Batavia, NY; (S); 1/60; Drama Clb; School Musical; School Play; Rep Stu Cncl; Var Socr; JV Tennis; Hon Roll; Jr NHS; NHS; Class Awd 84.

LOW, ROBERT C; High School Of The Performing Arts; New York City, NY; (Y); Boy Scts; JA; Band; Concert Band; Drm & Bgl; Orch; School Musical; Symp Band; Ice Hcky; Trk; DCI World Champions 83-84; P Lewis Silver Scholarship 83-84; Music Performance.

LOWE, HEIDI M; Campbell Central Schl; Campbell, NY; (Y); 2/46; French Clb; Varsity Clb; Chorus; Var L Sftbl; Bausch & Lomb Sci Awd; High Hon Roll; NHS; Sal; NYS Regents Schlrshp 85; Amer Assoc U Women Schlrshp 85; Pathlgy.

LOWE, JAMES R; Batavia HS; Batavia, NY; (Y); 8/249; Band; Chorus; Concert Band; Jazz Band; Mrchg Band; School Musical; Pres Frsh Cls; Hon Roll; NHS; Ntl Merit Ltr; Ittaca Coll HS Music Comp 1st Pl Piano 84; Howard Hanson Cert Merit 85; Eastman Schl Music; Music.

LOWE, PAUL G; St Josephs Collegate Inst; Kenmore, NY; (Y); 19/200; Pres Church Yth Grp; Cmnty Wkr; Var Ftbl; Var Trk; Hon Roll; Chrmn Yth Engaged Svc 85; Outstndg Yth Of Yr Cmmndtn 85; Outstndg Volntr 84 & 85; Notre Dame; Engrng.

LOWELL, AMY E; Mahopac HS; Mahopac, NY; (Y); 39/378; Var JV Mgr(s); Var Capt Socr; High Hon Roll; Hon Roll; VP Sal; Prfct Atten Awd; Regents Schlrshp 85; SUNY Albany; Intl Bus.

LOWELL, LISA ANNE; Maple Grove HS; Jamestown, NY; (Y); 12/80; Am Leg Aux Girls St; Aud/Vis; Church Yth Grp; Pep Clb; Chorus; School Play; Stage Crew; Var Capt Cheerleading; Var Capt Trk; NHS; Allegheny Coll; Pre-Med.

LOWELL, SHARON; Mohawk Central HS; Mohawk, NY; (Y); 53/98; Drama Clb; Library Aide; Office Aide; Teachers Aide; Color Guard; Mrchg Band; School Play; Yrbk Stf; Stu Cncl; Hon Roll; Herkimer Cnty CC; Child Care.

LOWENBERG, ROBYN; Town Of Webb HS; Old Forge, NY; (S); Spanish Clb; Teachers Aide; Varsity Clb; Band; Chorus; School Play; Yrbk Phtg; Yrbk Stf; Stu Cncl; Golf; Plattsburgh; Elem Ed.

LOWENGUTH, JEFFREY; Bishop Kearney HS; Ontario, NY; (Y); Jazz Band; Mrchg Band; Orch; Pep Band; School Musical; Crs Cntry; Trk; Hon Roll; Band; Concert Band; Acad All Am 85; Ntl Hnry Concert Band 85.

LOWES, LAUREL; Cortland JR SR HS; Walden, NY; (Y); French Clb; Hosp Aide; MMM; Band; Chorus; Concert Band; Orch; School Musical; Rotary Awd; Church Yth Grp; SUNY-NEW Paltz; Langs.

LOWNE, YVONNE; Huntington Christian Schl; Greenlawn, NY; (S); Hosp Aide; Varsity Clb; Band; Chorus; Pres Frsh Cls; Sec Jr Cls; Stu Cncl; Mgr Bsktbl; Socr; NHS; Sci Awd 83-84; High Hnr Roll 83-85; Houghton Coll; Pre-Med.

LOY, CHARLES; West Babylon SR HS; West Islip, NY; (Y); DECA; Nwsp Sprt Ed; Yrbk Stf; High Hon Roll; Jr NHS; NHS; Ntl Merit Ltr; Gftd & Tlntd Yth Smmr Prog 82-83; Outstndng Math & Sci Stdnt 84-85; Entrprnr.

LOZADA, ANTHONY; Pearl River HS; Orangeburg, NY; (Y); 11/239; Chess Clb; Computer Clb; Math Tm; Quiz Bowl; Jazz Band; Orch; School Musical; Nwsp Phtg; Nwsp Rptr; Yrbk Phtg; Ciba Geigy Sci Awd, Comm Arts Awd Music, Prsdntl Acad Ftnss Awd 85; Boston U; Med.

LOZADA, LORIE; Herbert H Lehman HS; Bronx, NY; (Y); 55/444; Church Yth Grp; Office Aide; Church Choir; Orch; Yrbk Stf; Rep Stu Cncl; Bowling; Tennis; Hon Roll; NHS; Comp Awd 83-84; Psych Awd 82-83; Baruch Coll; Bus.

LOZADA, RICARDO; Amsterdam HS; Amsterdam, NY; (Y); Band; Concert Band; Mrchg Band; Symp Band; JV Trk; Prfct Atten Awd; Culinary Arts.

LOZINA, JOSEPH P; Niagara Catholic HS; Lewiston, NY; (Y); 11/80; Letterman Clb; Spanish Clb; Varsity Clb; Var Bsbl; Var Bsktbl; Var Capt Golf; Hon Roll; JC Awd; NHS; Sprts Med.

LUBA, LOUIS J; St Francis HS; Blasdell, NY; (Y); 45/155; Drama Clb; PAVAS; Chorus; Pres Stu Cncl; Var L Lcrss; Var Capt Socr; Var Capt Wrstlng; NHS; Red Cross Aide; Acpl Chr; Natl Ldrshp Develpmnt Corp 84; West Point; Crmnlgy.

LUBANSKI, JOHN; Auburn HS; Auburn, NY; (Y); Ski Clb; Varsity Clb; Nwsp Stf; Var L Socr; Var L Trk; Arch.

LUBART, ANN D; Kingston HS; Kingston, NY; (Y); 3/580; Cmnty Wkr; Nwsp Stf; Ed Lit Mag; French Hon Soc; God Cntry Awd; NHS; VP French Clb; Civic Clb; Temple Yth Grp; Jr NHS; Vanderbilt Mansion Tour Guide 85; Hartwick Coll Poetry Cont Fin 84; Bst Poem Awd & Bst Prose Awd 83-84; Vassar Coll.

LUBELL, JEFFREY; Ossining HS; Briarcliff Mnr, NY; (Y); 1/267; Model UN; Temple Yth Grp; Band; Nwsp Bus Mgr; Nwsp Ed-Chief; NHS; RPI Sci Medal 85; Harvard Bk Awd 85.

LUBETSKY, CARY A; George W Hewlett HS; Woodmere, NY; (Y); 12/278; Nwsp Bus Mgr; Yrbk Sprt Ed; Rep Frsh Cls; Capt Var Swmmng; Hon Roll; NHS; Ntl Merit Ltr; Cornell U; Engrng.

LUBEY, WILLIAM PAUL; Utica Free Acad; Utica, NY; (Y); Church Yth Grp; Key Clb; Spanish Clb; DAR Awd; Hon Roll; NHS; Prfct Atten Awd; CYO Pstrs Recgntn Awd 83; Prfct Attndnc 85; Deans, Natrl Sci Schlrshps 85; Pres Acad Ftns Awd 85; Daemen Coll; Phy Thrpy.

LUBIN, SANDRA; Connetquot HS; Ronkonkoma, NY; (S); 15/728; Band; Sec Frsh Cls; Sec Soph Cls; Sec Jr Cls; Off Stu Cncl; Fld Hcky; Sftbl; Vllybl; Hon Roll; Pres Jr NHS; CW Post; Bus Admin.

LUBMAN, ANDREW J; Lawrence HS; N Woodmere, NY; (Y); 101/376; Drama Clb; Pres Band; Pres Chorus; Jazz Band; Mrchg Band; Orch; School Musical; Band Awd 82; Music Awd Music & Art Fndtn 84; Berklee Coll Of Music Boston.

LUCA, SARA; Bishop Kearney HS; Brooklyn, NY; (S); 4/336; Art Clb; Drama Clb; Yrbk Stf; Hon Roll; NHS; 2nd Pl Cntst Amer Assn Tchrs 84; Acad All-Amer Awd 84.

LUCARELLI, LEONARD; Commack High School South; Commack, NY; (Y); 10/400; Math Clb; Math Tm; Teachers Aide; Rep Frsh Cls; Rep Stu Cncl; Im Bowling; JV Socr; High Hon Roll; Prfct Atten Awd; Sons Italy Schlsrhp Awd 84; Law.

LUCARELLI, STEVE; Lackawanna SR HS; Lackawanna, NY; (S); 5/283; Trs Varsity Clb; Pres Band; Concert Band; Mrchg Band; JV Var Bsbl; Capt Ice Hcky; Vllybl; Bausch & Lomb Sci Awd; High Hon Roll; Hon Roll; Engrng.

LUCARELLI, TAMMY; T R Proctor HS; Utica, NY; (Y); Church Yth Grp; Drama Clb; Pep Clb; High Hon Roll; Hon Roll; Colgate Sem 84-85; Bus Admin.

LUCAS, CAROLYN; Fox Lane HS; Bedford, NY; (Y); Intnl Clb; Ski Clb; Chorus; Rep Frsh Cls; Rep Soph Cls; Rep Jr Cls; JV Fld Hcky; Stat Ftbl; Var Lcrss; JV Powder Puff Ftbl; All Cnty Chorus; U Of VT; Soc Sci.

LUCAS, DAWN; Andrew Jackson HS; Jamaica, NY; (Y); Dance Clb; Office Aide; Teachers Aide; Cit Awd; Hon Roll; Prfct Atten Awd; Crmnl Law.

LUCAS, DEBRA; Mc Kinley HS; Buffalo, NY; (Y); JA; Library Aide; Stu Cncl; Merit Rll; Make Up Artistry.

LUCAS, EDWARD W; Roy C Ketcham HS; Wappinger Fls, NY; (Y); Computer Clb; Pres Drama Clb; Science Clb; VP Thesps; Chorus; School Musical; School Play; High Hon Roll; NHS; Crftsmn Yr Awd Electrcty 85; Comp Sci.

LUCAS, ELIZABETH NOREEN; Stella Maris HS; Ozone Park, NY; (Y); Am Leg Aux Girls St; Drama Clb; Pres French Clb; School Musical; School Play; Nwsp Rptr; Tablet Nwspr All Schlstt Team 85; Englsh Awd 85; Frnch Slb Awd 85; St Johns U; Bus Mrktng.

LUCAS, KATHLEEN; Fredonia HS; Fredonia, NY; (Y); FTA; GAA; Hosp Aide; Chorus; School Musical; VP Jr Cls; Rep Stu Cncl; Var Capt Bsktbl; Var Capt Cheerleading; Hon Roll; Elem Ed.

LUCAS, TONYA T; Walton HS; Bronx, NY; (Y); 244/679; Hosp Aide; Chorus; Church Choir; Nwsp Rptr; Nwsp Stf; Yrbk Stf; Rep Stu Cncl; Gym; Prfct Atten Awd; SUNY Oswego; Pre-Med.

LUCCA, TOM; Half Hollow Hills East HS; Dix Hills, NY; (Y); Church Yth Grp; Computer Clb; Math Clb; Service Clb; Mrchg Band; Nwsp Stf; Swmmng; Engrng.

LUCCHESE, ANGELA; Hillcrest HS; Flushing, NY; (Y); FCA; GAA; Chorus; Capt Var Sftbl; Jr NHS; Adelphi U; Phy Thrpy.

LUCE III, DOMINICK; Walter Panas HS; Peekskill, NY; (Y); High Hon Roll; Hon Roll; Engl Stu Mnth 84; Columbia U; Archit.

LUCENA, AMY C; Academy Of Saint Joseph; Brentwood, NY; (Y); 2/121; Art Clb; Church Yth Grp; Service Clb; Spanish Clb; Chorus; Variety Show; Yrbk Stf; NHS; Regnts Schlrshp 85; Art Achvt Awd 84; UCLA Gym Schlrshp 85; UCLA.

LUCERI, DAVID; Lindenhurst HS; Lindenhurst, NY; (Y); Boy Scts; German Clb; Varsity Clb; Band; Concert Band; Mrchg Band; Ftbl; Lcrss; Socr; Wt Lftg; Eagle Sct Boy Scts Amer 86; SUNY; Engrng.

LUCIA, CARI; Northern Adirondack HS; Altona, NY; (Y); Computer Clb; French Clb; Key Clb; Band; Concert Band; Mrchg Band; JV Sftbl; High Hon Roll; Hon Roll; Admin.

LUCIANO, DANA M; New Rochelle HS; New Rochelle, NY; (Y); 35/597; Church Yth Grp; Computer Clb; Model UN; Lit Mag; NCTE Awd; NHS; Ntl Merit SF; Sec Spanish NHS; Iona Coll Lang Contest Spnsh 1st Hnrs 84; Philosophy.

LUCIANO, JOHN J; East Hampton HS; E Hampton, NY; (Y); Am Leg Boys St; Aud/Vis; Band; Chorus; Concert Band; Drm Mjr(t); Jazz Band; Mrchg Band; Pep Band; School Musical; LVIS Achvt Awd 85; Music.

LUCIANO, MICHELLE; Jeffersonvl-Youngsvl Central Schl; Jeffersonville, NY; (S); 5/60; Church Yth Grp; Drama Clb; Chorus; Church Choir; School Musical; Sec Stu Cncl; Var L Trk; Hon Roll; NHS; Cardinal Spln Yth Awd 84; U Of Stevbenville; Bio.

LUCICH, JEANNE L; A G Berner HS; Massapequa Park, NY; (Y); 2/426; Orch; Nwsp Rptr; Yrbk Sprt Ed; Var L JA; Var L Trk; Bausch & Lomb Sci Awd; NHS; Ntl Merit Ltr; Sal; Rensselaer Plytchnc Math, Sci Awd & Schlrshp 84; Amer H S Athl 85; Dartmouth Coll; Sprts Med.

LUCIOUS, SONYIA A; Andrew Jackson HS; Jamaica, NY; (Y); Church Yth Grp; Cmnty Wkr; Girl Scts; Library Aide; Office Aide; Pres OEA; Service Clb; Teachers Aide; Church Choir; Rep Frsh Cls; Hnry HS Achvt Alpha Kappa Alpha Srty 85; U Of Monevallo; Pblc Admin.

LUCITT, JEANNE M; Bennett HS; Buffalo, NY; (Y); Ski Clb; Spanish Clb; Nwsp Rptr; Im Socr; Im Wt Lftg; Regnts Schlrshp 85; Buffalo ST Coll; Law.

LUCKEN, LYNN; Kenmore East SR HS; Buffalo, NY; (Y); 42/300; Church Yth Grp; Band; Mrchg Band; Pep Band; Off Frsh Cls; Soph Cls; Im Cheerleading; Im Pom Pon; High Hon Roll; Hon Roll; Typng Awd 81-82; Regents Schrlshp 84-85; U NY-BUFFALO; Nrsng.

LUCKMAN, JAMES; Barker Central HS; Gasport, NY; (S); 5/94; AFS; Pres Church Yth Grp; Debate Tm; VP French Clb; Varsity Clb; Pres Concert Band; Stu Cncl; Cit Awd; 4-H Awd; Hon Roll; Outstndng FFA Awd 84; Empire Frmr Deg 84; FFA 1st Pl Swine Frmng 85; SUNY-GENESEO; Bus Admin.

LUCY, CELESTE; Beacon HS; Beacon, NY; (S); 16/175; Key Clb; JV Cheerleading; Sftbl; NHS; Biology.

LUCZAK, LYNN; Frontier Central HS; Hamburg, NY; (Y); 52/500; French Clb; Varsity Clb; Band; Mrchg Band; VP Soph Cls; Diving; Sftbl; Hon Roll; NHS; Rep Frsh Cls; Diving Conf Champ 83-84, Rcrd Hldr 83-85; Empire ST Games Fin 83-84; VA Commonwlth U Richmond.

LUDDEN, JOHN; Hornell SR HS; Hornell, NY; (S); 4/198; Math Clb; Band; Mrchg Band; Pep Band; Symp Band; Rep Sr Cls; Rep Stu Cncl; Var L Tennis; High Hon Roll; NHS; Rochester Inst; Elect Engrng.

LUDDEN, THERESA; Welsville HS; Wellsville, NY; (Y); 21/133; School Musical; Nwsp Stf; Yrbk Stf; Bsktbl; JV Socr; Profssnl Bus Wmns Schlrshp 85; Wellsville Alumni Assn Schlrshp 85; Alfred ST Coll; Ct Rprtg.

LUDLAM, JOYCE M; Johnson City HS; Johnson City, NY; (Y); 19/212; Sec Latin Clb; Color Guard; Rep Stu Cncl; Stat Bsktbl; JV Score Keeper; Var L Tennis; Hon Roll; NHS; NY ST Regnts Schlrshp Wnr 84-85; NY ST U Cortland; Math.

LUDT, KATHY; Skaneatcles HS; Skaneatcles, NY; (S); Variety Show; Trs Frsh Cls; Trs Soph Cls; Trs Jr Cls; Rep Stu Cncl; L Tennis; L Trk; High Hon Roll; Psychology.

LUDWICK, DAVE; Minisink Valley HS; Unionville, NY; (Y); 10/250; Quiz Bowl; Scholastic Bowl; Nwsp Ed-Chief; Rep Stu Cncl; Var Tennis; High Hon Roll; Hon Roll; NHS; Outstndng Soph Boy 84; Jrnlsm.

LUDWIG, DALE R; Geneseo Central Schl; Geneseo, NY; (Y); 23/74; Am Leg Boys St; Boy Scts; Ski Clb; Pres Stu Cncl; JV Var Bsktbl; Capt Var Socr; Capt Var Trk; Hon Roll; Livingston Cnty All Str Sccr Tm 82 & 84; Olympcs Mind 2nd Pl Wrld Fnls 85; Fredonia.

LUDWIG, JILL M; Keshequa Central Schl; Nunda, NY; (Y); 1/96; AFS; Drama Clb; Band; Stage Crew; Nwsp Stf; Yrbk Stf; VP Pres Stu Cncl; High Hon Roll; NHS; Math Tm; Ntl Merit Schlrshp Semi-Fnlst 84-85; U Of Rochester,Bio.

LUDWIG, KRISTA M; Carthage Central HS; Black River, NY; (Y); 4/203; Pres Church Yth Grp; Rep Drama Clb; French Clb; Hosp Aide; Key Clb; Library Aide; Color Guard; Flag Corp; School Play; Nwsp Rptr; Nrsng.

LUDWIG, LISA A; Byron Bergen HS; Byron, NY; (Y); 8/88; Church Yth Grp; FTA; Teachers Aide; Yrbk Stf; 4-H Awd; Hon Roll; Jr NHS; NHS; Prfct Atten Awd; Civic Clb; Regence Schlrshp 85; Geneso ST.

LUDWIG, TRACEY; Nardin Acad; East Amherst, NY; (S); Dance Clb; Hosp Aide; Ski Clb; School Musical; Nwsp Stf; Lit Mag; Sec Jr Cls; Stu Cncl; Hon Roll; NHS; Acadmc All-Amer Awd 85; Yamaha Music Awds 83-84; Accntng.

LUDWIN, DAWN; Longwood HS; Shirley, NY; (S); 12/480; Intnl Clb; Key Clb; Math Tm; Q&S; Lit Mag; High Hon Roll; NHS; Nacels Smmr Cultrl Exch Franc 85; Art Hstry.

LUEBKERT, KATHY; Deer Park HS; N Babylon, NY; (Y); Mrchg Band; Variety Show; Var Pom Pon; U Of Tampa; Busnss Admin.

LUFT, DANIEL K; Notre Dame HS; Athens, PA; (Y); Art Clb; Lit Mag; Hon Roll; Boston U.

LUGBAUER, JOHN P; East Islip HS; East Islip, NY; (Y); 22/475; Boy Scts; Math Tm; Nwsp Rptr; Bowling; Hon Roll; Grumman Engrng Schlrshp 85; Marshall Hahn Engrng Schlrshp 85; Long Islnd Sci Cong Hgh Hnrs 85; VA Polytechnic; Aerospc Engr.

LUGO, DAMARIS; William Howard Taft HS; Bronx, NY; (Y); Sec Jr Cls; Hon Roll; Prfct Atten Awd; Cert Of Apprctn 85; Cert Of Awd 84; Iona Coll; Comp Pgmmr.

LUGO, MYRNA IRIS; H S Of Fashion Ind; Bronx, NY; (Y); 154/486; Office Aide; Teachers Aide; Hon Roll; Navy; Yeoman.

LUGO, YOLANDA; Norman Thomas HS; New York, NY; (S); 54/671; Teachers Aide; Chorus; Church Choir; Nwsp Stf; Hon Roll; Wood Schl Schlrshp Comp 85; Future Secys Assoc 83-85; Wood Schl; Exec Secy.

LUI, DAVID; Norman Thomas HS; New York, NY; (S); 2/671; Debate Tm; FBLA; Math Tm; Yrbk Ed-Chief; Cit Awd; High Hon Roll; Hon Roll; Pres NHS; Manhattan Borough Pres Cert Of Citznshp & Scholar 82; NY U; Comp Info Systms.

LUI, ROBERT; Bishop Ford C C HS; Brooklyn, NY; (Y); Computer Clb; Hon Roll; Cert Rcgntn Part JR Math Leag 85; Cert Rcgntn Part Natl Sci Olympiad 84; Engr.

LUIS, FRANK; Ossining HS; Ossining, NY; (Y); Boy Scts; Im JV Ftbl; Pre-Med.

LUISA, EDWARD M; Franciscan HS; Yorktown Hts, NY; (Y); 10/57; Boy Scts; Trs Church Yth Grp; Varsity Clb; VP Soph Cls; JV Bsbl; JV Var Bsktbl; Var Socr; Hon Roll; Spanish NHS; Bsktbl Coachs Awd 83; Bsktbl Vrsty MVP 84; Bsktbl & Sccr All Leag Hnrb Mntn 83-84; George Washington U; Engr.

LUISI, MARIA R; Bishop Grimes HS; Syracuse, NY; (Y); 36/207; Exploring; Hosp Aide; Speech Tm; Chorus; Variety Show; Yrbk Stf; Hon Roll; NHS; Italian Hnrs Awd 85; Cert Merit Ctznshp Awd 85; Natl Soc Stud Olympiad 85; Le Moyne Coll; Hstry.

LUK, NGA MAN; Richmond Hill HS; Richmond, NY; (Y); 52/300; Chess Clb; Key Clb; Math Clb; Teachers Aide; Band; Stage Crew; Tennis; Hon Roll; Prfct Atten Awd; Schl Hnr Rll 85; Bus Mgt.

LUKAS, CHRISTINE; Waverly HS; S Waverly, PA; (Y); 20/140; Sec VP Church Yth Grp; Spanish Clb; Variety Show; Yrbk Sprt Ed; Rep Stu Cncl; Var L Bsktbl; Var L Crs Cntry; Var L Sftbl; Var L Vllybl; Pres Schlr; Bus & Prof Womn Clb Awd West Schlrshp 85; All Str Selctn Bsktbl & Sftbl 85; Mansfield U; Bus Adm.

LUKASIEWICZ, TIMOTHY; West Seneca West HS; Buffalo, NY; (Y); Boy Scts; Cmnty Wkr; Spanish Clb; Rep Frsh Cls; Rep Soph Cls; Rep Jr Cls; JV Wrstlng; Hon Roll; Supr Achvt & Excllnc Chem 85; U Of Buffalo; Arch Eng.

LUKASZEWICZ, SUSAN; Notre Dame HS; Batavia, NY; (S); 4/67; Yrbk Stf; Lit Mag; JV Vllybl; Hon Roll; NHS; Phys Thrpy.

LUKASZEWSKI, GLEN; Beacon HS; Beacon, NY; (Y); 56/206; JV Ftbl; Comp.

LUKAWSKI, JOLANTA E; St Joseph Hill Acad; Brooklyn, NY; (Y); 17/103; Church Yth Grp; VP French Clb; FTA; Hosp Aide; NFL; Science Clb; Yrbk Phtg; Rep Frsh Cls; Rep Jr Cls; Hon Roll; Regents Schlrshp 85; Concours Natl De Francais Certificat De Merite 85; City U Of NY Med Schl; Phys.

LUKE, CAROL; Ripley Central HS; Ripley, NY; (Y); Church Yth Grp; Pep Clb; Band; Chorus; Mrchg Band; School Musical; Sec Frsh Cls; Sec Soph Cls; Pres Jr Cls; Rep Stu Cncl; Elem Tchr.

LUKE, DANIELLE; Connetquot HS; Ronkonkoma, NY; (Y); 15/697; FBLA; Nwsp Ed-Chief; Cheerleading; Gym; Sftbl; Tennis; 4-H Awd; High Hon Roll; Jr NHS; NHS; Gymnstc Awd; Civic Assn Creative Wrtng; Cornell U; Math.

LUKEMAN, MICHELLE; Southside HS; Elmira, NY; (Y); Pep Clb; Spanish Clb; Chorus; Nwsp Stf; Yrbk Stf; Hon Roll; Yth Cnty 85; Med Asst.

LUKIN, SUZANA; St Johns Prep; Astoria, NY; (S); Chorus; Church Choir; Variety Show; High Hon Roll; Hon Roll; NHS; St Johns U.

LULKIN, SHAWN; Central Islip HS; Central Islip, NY; (Y); 14/270; Boy Scts; Chess Clb; Varsity Clb; Band; Jazz Band; Mrchg Band; Lcrss; Swmmng; High Hon Roll; Hon Roll; Billy Masi Band Scholar Awd; Mst Valble Swmmr Awd; Bst Frsh Swmmr; U Of AZ; Crimnl Justc.

LULO, ABDOH; East Meadow HS; East Meadow, NY; (Y); AFS; Aud/Vis; Boy Scts; Cmnty Wkr; Dance Clb; Drama Clb; Exploring; FBLA; FHA; Intnl Clb; Automtv Mech Awds 83-84; Metl Shp Awd Attitude 83-84; Auto Mech.

LUM, EVA; Herricks HS; Roslyn, NY; (Y); 1/306; Am Leg Aux Girls St; Key Clb; Nwsp Ed-Chief; Rep Sr Cls; Cit Awd; NHS; Ntl Merit Ltr; Val; George Washignton U Engrng Mdl 84; Grumman Engrng/Sci Scholar 85; Harvard U; Comp Sci.

LUM, JENNIFER; West Islip HS; W Islip, NY; (Y); Drama Clb; Teachers Aide; Chorus; School Play; Stage Crew; JV Stat Lcrss; Hon Roll; Hon Roll; NHS; Pre-Med.

LUM, SAU KING; Norman Thomas HS; Brooklyn, NY; (S); 75/671; Art Clb; JA; Math Clb; Math Tm; Office Aide; Chorus; Cit Awd; High Hon Roll; Hon Roll; Prfct Atten Awd; Acctnt.

LUMAN, AMBER J; Lewiston Porter HS; Lewiston, NY; (Y); Cmnty Wkr; Spanish Clb; Pres Chorus; School Play; Nwsp Ed-Chief; Trs Stu Cncl; Var Capt Cheerleading; Var JV Trk; Var Capt Vllybl; NHS; Lamp Lrng Awds 83-85; 2nd Team All-Leag Vrsty Vlybl 85; Chld Psych.

LUNA, MAX E; M S G R Mc Claney HS; Queens Vlg, NY; (Y); Varsity Clb; Pres Trk; Pres Wt Lftg; Long Island U; Arch.

LUNA, ZULMA; Manhattan Center For Math & Science; New York, NY; (Y); Camera Clb; Cmnty Wkr; JA; Office Aide; Teachers Aide; Chorus; High Hon Roll; Hon Roll; Arista 83-85; Comp Sci.

LUNDBERG, CHRISTOPHER; Ossining HS; Ossining, NY; (Y); JA; Lit Mag; Capt Var Lcrss; JV Wrstlng; High Hon Roll; Hon Roll; NHS; NCTE Achvt SF Local Wnnr 85; All Conf Hnbl Mntn La Crosse A III 85; Gftd & Tlntd Wrtrs Sem 84; Arch.

LUNDE, LISA; Smithtown H S West; Smithtown, NY; (Y); Ski Clb; Stu Cncl; Var L Mgr(s); Hon Roll; U Of DE; Acctng.

LUNDGREN, LAURA LYNN; Huntington Christian Schl; St James, NY; (S); 5/22; Teachers Aide; Band; Chorus; Yrbk Bus Mgr; Trs Jr Cls; Mgr Socr; Capt Sftbl; Hon Roll; NHS; U S Achievement Awd 84-85; Society Of Distinguished Amer High Sch Stu 84-85; Acad All American 85; Messiah College; History Educ.

LUNDQUIST, MONA E; Garden City HS; Garden City, NY; (Y); Church Yth Grp; Hosp Aide; Key Clb; Red Cross Aide; Band; Mrchg Band; Nwsp Stf; Yrbk Stf; JV Cheerleading; Hon Roll; Hartwick Coll; Nrsng.

LUNDRIGAN, TAMARA; Camden HS; Camden, NY; (Y); 24/206; Ski Clb; Varsity Clb; Yrbk Stf; Stu Cncl; Im Cheerleading; JV Sftbl; JV Var Tennis; High Hon Roll; Hon Roll; Rotary Awd; Eleanor Isciah Memrl Schlrshp 85; Acadmc All Amer 85; Oswego; Acctg.

LUNDY, KATHY; Liverpool HS; Liverpool, NY; (S); Trs Hst DECA; JA; Ski Clb; Variety Show; Nwsp Stf; Trs Stu Cncl; Stat Var Lcrss; Powder Puff Ftbl; Score Keeper; Anti Shoplftng Proj-4th Pl 84; Apparel & Acces Region-3rd Pl 84; Johnson & Wales Coll; Trsm.

LUNDY, NOREEN T; Holy Trinity Diocesan HS; Bethpage, NY; (S); 15/362; Capt Debate Tm; Drama Clb; Pres French Clb; Teachers Aide; Chorus; School Musical; School Play; Sec Frsh Cls; Fld Hcky; French Hon Soc; Intl Frgn Lang Awd 82; Harvard; Intl Frgn Law.

LUNNY, PEGGY ANN; Bishop Kearney HS; Brooklyn, NY; (Y); Art Clb; Dance Clb; Bsktbl; Cheerleading; Crs Cntry; Capt Trk; Hon Roll; Fine Arts.

LUNTZ, BARBARA; Fredonia Central Schl; Fredonia, NY; (Y); 10/200; Off French Clb; GAA; Key Clb; Science Clb; Ski Clb; Orch; Symp Band; Nwsp Stf; Yrbk Stf; Var L Tennis.

LUONGO, ANDREA; Cardinal Spellman HS; Bronx, NY; (Y); 19/370; Church Yth Grp; Computer Clb; Ski Clb; VICA; Y-Teens; Off Jr Cls; Stu Cncl; Sftbl; NHS; High Hon Roll; Minr Ltr Sftbl; St Catherines Acad Scholar; Hnry Recogntn NEDT Tsts; Cornell; Arch.

LUPIA, CARMELA M A; Waterville Central HS; Oriskany Falls, NY; (Y); 9/89; Am Leg Aux Girls St; Band; Nwsp Stf; Ed Yrbk Stf; Pres Frsh Cls; Sec Soph Cls; Var Socr; High Hon Roll; Hon Roll; NHS; Bus.

LUPINI, LORI; Whitesboro SR HS; Whitesboro, NY; (Y); 58/320; Church Yth Grp; GAA; Hst Acpl Chr; Var L Bsktbl; Var L Fld Hcky; Var L Trk; Var L Trk; Hon Roll; Track All Star Tm 85; NY ST U; Physcl Ed.

LUPKIN, JONATHAN; Benjamin N Cardozo HS; Bayside, NY; (Y); 8/476; Acpl Chr; School Musical; Nwsp Stf; Pres Stu Cncl; High Hon Roll; NHS; St Schlr; Quiz Bowl; Chorus; Nwsp Rptr; Var Fncng Tm Capt 84-85; 1985 Law Inst Achvt Awd Exclnce 84-85; Columbia Coll.

LUPO, DAWN; Commack H S North; Commack, NY; (Y); GAA; Teachers Aide; Coach Actv; Im Gym; Var Ice Hcky; Hon Roll; Dntstry.

LUPO, LAURIE; Bishop Kearney HS; Rochester, NY; (Y); 9/128; GAA; Hosp Aide; Sec Stu Cncl; JV Capt Cheerleading; Var Im Socr; JV Var Sftbl; JV Tennis; High Hon Roll; Hon Roll; Pres Schlr; ST U Of NY Geneseo.

LUPO, SALVATORE; Msgr Mc Clancy Memorial HS; Woodside, NY; (Y); Exploring; Intnl Clb; Im Bowling; Im Ftbl; Im Timer; Hon Roll; Natl Sci Olympiad/Physics Cntst 85; Schl Scie Fair Merit Awd 85; Cath Lg Religious & Civil Rights 82.

LUPO, SALVATORE; Newfield HS; Selden, NY; (Y); Band; Concert Band; Mrchg Band; High Hon Roll; Hon Roll; Jr NHS; NYSSMA Solo Awd 83; Indstrl Arts Awd 83; Electrcty/Electrncs Awd 84; Aerontcs.

LUPO, THOMAS; Richmond Hill HS; Richmond Hill, NY; (Y); 2/298; Boys Clb Am; Boy Scts; FBLA; Math Clb; Rep Soph Cls; Rep Jr Cls; VP Sr Cls; NHS; Ntl Merit Ltr; Sal; Rensselaer Medal Math,Sci 84; Queens Coll Pres Awd Achvt 82-84; Super Yth 84.

LUPTON, THEODORE NICHOLS; Northport HS; East Northport, NY; (Y); 54/650; Pres Aud/Vis; JV Socr; Var Trk; Hon Roll; Ntl Merit SF; Army ROTC Schlrshp 84; Moore Schlrshp 85; Natl Merit Fnlst 85; Citadel Charleston; Hstry.

LURIE, PETER S; New Rochelle HS; New Rochelle, NY; (Y); 32/600; Chrmn Y-Teens; Ed Lit Mag; Tennis; NCTE Awd; NHS; Ntl Merit SF; Engl.

LURKER, KAREN; Curtis HS; Staten Island, NY; (Y); 3/328; Key Clb; Nwsp Rptr; Var Tennis; Var Co-Capt Vllybl; Hon Roll; Jr NHS; Sec NHS; Exch Stu Japan 83; Bryn Mawr Coll; Intl Bus.

LUSAKA, PATRICK J; Roosevelt HS; Scarsdale, NY; (Y); 13/287; Key Clb; Office Aide; Varsity Clb; Yrbk Stf; Capt Var Socr; High Hon Roll; Hon Roll; NHS; Engrng.

LUSCHER, ARLENE; Christ The King Regional HS; Ridgewood, NY; (Y); 44/385; 2nd Hnr Cert 84.

LUSCHWITZ, BRIAN S; Vestal HS; Apalachin, NY; (Y); 16/450; FBLA; Mathletes; Math Tm; Var Capt Ice Hcky; JV Lcrss; High Hon Roll; NHS; Ntl Merit SF; AATSEEL Excellence In Russian Awd 82; Vestal Hockey Sportsmanshp Trophy 84; VMVP Awd Best Def 85; MIT; Biomedical Engineering.

LUSK, YVONNE D; Marathon Central HS; Marathon, NY; (Y); 2/60; Sec Church Yth Grp; Drama Clb; Pres Sec 4-H; Quiz Bowl; Concert Band; Mrchg Band; Yrbk Ed-Chief; Rep Stu Cncl; NHS; Sal; Regnts Schlrshp 85; Tlnts For Christ Music Comptn 2nd Pl ST 84; Amer Lgn Aux Grls ST Alt 84; SUNY Potsdam Coll.

LUSS, KEVIN; Southampton HS; Water Mill, NY; (Y); 10/120; Church Yth Grp; Spanish Clb; Yrbk Rptr; Yrbk Stf; Pres Soph Cls; Pres Jr Cls; Stu Cncl; JV Bsbl; Var Capt Socr; Hon Roll; Bus.

LUTHER, DEBBIE; Unions Springs Acad; Norridgewock, ME; (S); 11/50; Drama Clb; Chorus; Drill Tm; School Musical; Yrbk Phtg; Rep Sr Cls; Gym; Hon Roll; NHS; Voice Dem Awd; Typng II Awd 84-85; Psych.

LUTHER, KATRINA; Canastota HS; Canastota, NY; (S); 2/150; Service Clb; Band; Mrchg Band; School Musical; JV Cheerleading; Var Golf; High Hon Roll; Sec NHS.

LUTOMSKE, REBECCA C; Watkins Glen HS; Watkins Glen, NY; (Y); Letterman Clb; Pres Library Aide; Model UN; Thesps; School Play; Stage Crew; Mgr(s); Score Keeper; Hon Roll; Ntl Merit SF; 1st Superia Awd In AZ ST Fair Art Cmptn 81; Regents Schlrshp 85; SUNY Oswego; Psychology.

LUTZ, REBECCA; Oneonta HS; Oneonta, NY; (Y); 3/200; Church Yth Grp; Drama Clb; 4-H; Girl Scts; Q&S; Thesps; Band; Chorus; Church Choir; Concert Band.

LUTZ, TAMARA; Notre Dame Acad; Staten Island, NY; (Y); Computer Clb; Nrsng.

LUVERA, WILLIAM; Copiague SR HS; Amity Harbor, NY; (Y); Var Crs Cntry; Var Ftbl; Score Keeper; Var Trk; JV Wrstlng; Ind Arts Awd 86; Drftng Awd 86; U Of Syracuse; Arch.

LUYANDO, VERONICA; Maria Regina HS; Yonkers, NY; (Y); 23/127; Civic Clb; Yrbk Stf; Hon Roll; Cert Of Achvt 83; Cert Appreciatn 85.

LY, HUE T; Theodore Roosevelt HS; Bronx, NY; (Y); 1/595; Math Tm; Office Aide; Teachers Aide; Nwsp Ed-Chief; Nwsp Rptr; High Hon Roll; Pres NHS; Val; Untd Fed Tchrs Schlrshp 85; NY ST Rgnts Schlrshp 85; Sophie Davis Schl; Med.

LY, LONG V; Newtown HS; Elmhurst, NY; (Y); 10/603; Pres Chess Clb; Math Clb; Nwsp Stf; Yrbk Stf; Hon Roll; JETS Awd; NHS; Prfct Atten Awd; Untd Fed Tchrs, Regnts Schlrshps 85; Cooper Union Schlrshp 85; Cooper Union; Mech Engr.

LYDFORD, PATRICIA M; Mt Markham HS; W Winfield, NY; (Y); GAA; Math Clb; Band; Chorus; Yrbk Stf; JV Bsktbl; JV Crs Cntry; Stat Score Keeper; L Trk; High Hon Roll; Regents Schlrshp 85; Clark Fndtn Schlrshp 85; Ralph Whipple Schlrshp 85; SUNY Tech Coll; Stndrdbred Mng.

LYDON, REGINA; St Frances Prep; Flushing, NY; (S); 15/693; Church Yth Grp; Math Clb; Office Aide; Ski Clb; School Musical; Tennis; High Hon Roll; NHS; Essay Awd 83-84; Engrng.

LYKE, CARRIE; Saranac Central HS; Morrisonville, NY; (S); 6/104; French Clb; Pres FBLA; Sec Library Aide; Hon Roll; NHS; Girl Scts; Chorus; Yrbk Stf; Cheerleading; Girl Sct Silvr Awd 82; Comp Sci.

LYLE, CORI; Honeoye Central Schl; Honeoye, NY; (S); 5/65; Am Leg Aux Girls St; Nwsp Stf; Trs Jr Cls; Pres Sr Cls; Var L Cheerleading; Capt L Socr; High Hon Roll; NHS; Varsity Clb; Jazz Band; Williams Coll Bk Awd 84; Wrtng Awd 83; Hlth.

LYN, JOHN W; Fordham Prep Schl; New Rochelle, NY; (Y); Aud/Vis; Computer Clb; Var Trk; Var Wrstlng.

LYNAM, JOHN LUKE; Cicero North Syracuse HS; N Syracuse, NY; (S); 37/700; Cmnty Wkr; Exploring; Coach Actv; Var L Gym; CC Awd; High Hon Roll; NHS; Boy Scts; Teachers Aide; Prfct Atten Awd; USGF NY ST Chmp 81; Legue Awd Cnty Gym Tm 84; Athletc Achvt Awd N Syr 83; US Naval Acad; Aviation.

LYNCH, AIMEE; Weedsport Central HS; Weedsport, NY; (Y); DECA; FBLA; Yrbk Stf; JV Bsktbl; Var Cheerleading; JV Var Fld Hcky; Var Trk; Hon Roll; Bus.

LYNCH, BARBARA; St John The Baptist HS; Amityville, NY; (Y); Hosp Aide; MMM; Var Crs Cntry; Swmmng; Var Trk; French Hon Soc; High Hon Roll; NHS; Service Clb; Coach Actv; Music Hnr Soc 83-84; Sci Olympiad Awd Chem 84; Chem.

LYNCH, BRENDAN; Iona Prep; Yonkers, NY; (Y); 111/200; Boy Scts; Computer Clb; Stage Crew; Im Bowling; Im Ftbl; Im Wt Lftg; Manhattan Coll; Mech Engr.

LYNCH, CARRIE ANN; E Islip SR HS; East Islip, NY; (Y); FTA; Mathletes; Lit Mag; Var L Gym; JV Sftbl; Var Trk; French Hon Soc; High Hon Roll; Jr NHS; NHS; Outstndg Soc Stds Stu Awd; Outstndng Bus Dyn Stu Awd; Pres Physcl Ftns Awd; Elem Ed.

LYNCH, CHRIS; Vernon-Verona-Sherrill HS; Vernon, NY; (Y); Radio Clb; High Hon Roll; Hon Roll; Mech Engrng.

LYNCH, CHRISTINE K; Ilion HS; Ilion, NY; (Y); 18/117; Church Yth Grp; Drama Clb; Varsity Clb; Concert Band; Mrchg Band; Orch; Yrbk Stf; JV Vllybl; High Hon Roll; NHS; Regents Schlrshp 85; Mohawk Vly CC; Engr.

LYNCH, CLAIRE; Academy Of St Joseph; Commack, NY; (Y); Dance Clb; FHA; Red Cross Aide; Teachers Aide; Band; Orch; Trs Sr Cls; Exlnce Spnsh 82-83; Marist Clg; Acctg.

LYNCH, COLLEEN; Susquehanna Valley HS; Conklin, NY; (Y); Dance Clb; Pep Clb; Spanish Clb; Variety Show; Yrbk Stf; Sec Soph Cls; Jr Cls; Sec Stu Cncl; Var Capt Cheerleading; Vllybl; 1st Pl In Spnsh Exam 85; Pre-Dnstry.

LYNCH, ELIZABET E; St Marys Girls HS; Flushing, NY; (Y); Ski Clb; Crs Cntry; NYS Regents Schlrshp 85; NHS 84-85; Baruch Coll; Bus.

LYNCH, JAMES; All Hallows HS; Bronx, NY; (Y); 19/100; Var L Ice Hcky; Touro Coll; Phys Thrpst.

LYNCH, JEAN M; Our Lady Of Victory HS; Bronx, NY; (S); 12/159; Church Yth Grp; Hosp Aide; Variety Show; Rep Stu Cncl.

LYNCH, LAURA; Odessa-Montour Central HS; Montour Falls, NY; (Y); Trs Art Clb; Ski Clb; Teachers Aide; Concert Band; Mrchg Band; Yrbk Stf; Lit Mag; JV Bsktbl; JV Sftbl; Hon Roll; Schlstc Art Awd Cert Of Merit 84 & 85; NY ST Smr Schl Of The Arts 85; Schoyler Cnty Art Awd 85; Art.

LYNCH, MARY; St Johns Prep; Jackson Hts, NY; (Y); Church Yth Grp; Girl Scts; Varsity Clb; Church Choir; School Musical; School Play; Stage Crew; Yrbk Stf; Var Socr; Var Sftbl; St Johns U; Accntng.

LYNCH, MICHAEL; St Francis Prep; Flushing, NY; (S); 111/650; Boys Clb Am; Var Bsktbl; Ftbl; JV Trk; Im Vllybl; Wt Lftg; NHS; Schlr/Athlt Awd 83; Acdmc All-Amer 85.

LYNCH JR, ROBERT H; Clarkstown South SR HS; W Nyack, NY; (Y); Exploring; Band; Concert Band; Mrchg Band; Symp Band; Mu Alp Tht; NHS; Ntl Merit Ltr; Bus.

LYNCH, SHEILA; Manhasset HS; Manhasset, NY; (Y); 71/205; Art Clb; Chorus; Concert Band; Mrchg Band; Orch; School Play; Lit Mag; Pep Band; School Musical; Stage Crew; Ctr Creative Yth Wesleyan U 84-85; Svc Assn Manhasset Correspndng Sec 84-85; Hnrs Band Awd 84-85; Catholic U Amer; Music.

LYNCH, TANYA A; Averill Park HS; Troy, NY; (Y); 10/223; Varsity Clb; Off Jr Cls; Bsktbl; Powder Puff Ftbl; Socr; Trk; Vllybl; High Hon Roll; Hon Roll; NHS; Regents Scholarship 85; Geneseo ST; Med Lab Tech.

LYNCH, THOMAS L; Red Jacket HS; Shortsville, NY; (Y); 7/89; Am Leg Boys St; Boy Scts; Chess Clb; Spanish Clb; Varsity Clb; School Play; Stage Crew; VP Sr Cls; Var Ftbl; Var Trk; U S Miltry Acad.

LYNCH, TIM; Wheatly HS; Old Westbury, NY; (Y); Ski Clb; Sftbl; Wrstlng; Hon Roll; Equestrian Awds; Pre-Med.

LYNCH, TIMOTHY; Binghamton HS; Binghamton, NY; (Y); Am Leg Boys St; Political Wkr; Jazz Band; Orch; School Musical; Symp Band; Nwsp Ed-Chief; Rep Stu Cncl; Var Socr.

LYNK, JOHN; J C Birdlebough HS; Phoenix, NY; (Y); Boy Scts; German Clb; Band; Concert Band; Mrchg Band; Pep Band; Stage Crew; Yrbk Stf; JV Var Ftbl; Wt Lftg; Syracuse U; Art.

LYNK, MICHAEL; J C Bridglebough HS; Phoenix, NY; (Y); 20/204; Boy Scts; Church Yth Grp; Drama Clb; Latin Clb; Office Aide; Teachers Aide; Chorus; Church Choir; School Musical; School Play; Eagle Scout 84; U Of Rochester; Pol Sci.

LYNN III, ROBERT; Cold Spring Harbor HS; Huntington, NY; (Y); Intnl Clb; Mathletes; Nwsp Rptr; Var JV Lcrss; Var JV Socr; Hon Roll; CSH Schl Brd Awd 85.

LYNN, SHAWN T; Uniondale HS; Hempstead, NY; (Y); 10/450; Boy Scts; Debate Tm; NFL; Speech Tm; Orch; School Musical; Var Crs Cntry; Var Lcrss; High Hon Roll; Hon Roll; Brown U Bk Awd Impromtu Wrtng 84; NYS Regents Schlrshp 85; Dartmouth U; Pre-Med.

LYNNE, KORI; Spackenkill HS; Poughkeepsie, NY; (Y); 26/168; Temple Yth Grp; Thesps; School Musical; Yrbk Stf; Tennis; High Hon Roll; Hon Roll; NHS; Psych.

LYON, KIMBERLY S; Greene Central HS; Greene, NY; (Y); 4-H; VICA; Sftbl; Tennis; Capt Vllybl; High Hon Roll; Hon Roll; Ntl Merit Ltr; Data Proc.

LYON, TIMOTHY B; Curchville-Chili HS; North Chili, NY; (Y); Pres Church Yth Grp; Jazz Band; School Play; Symp Band; Var Capt Bsktbl; Var Capt Tennis; Hon Roll; NHS; VFW Awd; Pres Acad Ftns Awd 85; Roberts Wesleyan Coll; Bus Admn.

LYONS, ALITA J; Rudolf Steiner HS; New York, NY; (Y); Ed Lit Mag; Rep Frsh Cls; Rep Soph Cls; Rep Jr Cls; Rep Sr Cls; Stu Cncl; Var Capt Bsktbl; Sftbl; Regents Schlrshp 85; 4 Year Scholarship 85; Marine Biology.

LYONS, GILLIAN N; Bronx High School Of Science; New York, NY; (Y); Drama Clb; Latin Clb; Office Aide.

LYONS, LENNIE; Walton HS; Bronx, NY; (Y); 96/679; Debate Tm; Office Aide; Variety Show; Rep Stu Cncl; Hon Roll; Hghst Clss Avg 81-82; Awd For Coop Govt 84-85; Acad Olympic Tm, Nutrtn Cmmtt & Ldrshp Cmmtt 84-85; U Of FL; Hstry.

LYONS, MAUREEN A; Catholic Central HS; Troy, NY; (Y); #88 In Class; Camera Clb; Hosp Aide; Math Clb; Spanish Clb; Chorus; Variety Show; Yrbk Stf; Rep Stu Cncl; Stu Cncl Svc Awd 84-85; Volntr Svc Cert Awd 84-85; Hudson Vly CC; Vet Med.

LYONS, MICHELE; Mayfield Central Schl; Gloversville, NY; (Y); VP Frsh Cls; VP Soph Cls; VP Jr Cls; Sec Rep Stu Cncl; JV Var Cheerleading; JV Var Socr; High Hon Roll; Hon Roll; JCL; Math Tm; MVP Sftbl & All Str Tm 84-85; Mst Outstndng Chrldr 83-84; Coachs Awd Sftbl 84-85; FMCC; Nrsg.

LYONS, ROSALIE; Walton HS; Bronx, NY; (Y); Drama Clb; FBLA; School Play; Nwsp Bus Mgr; Capt Vllybl; Math Awd 84; Hunter Clg; Bus Mgmt.

LYONS, SIOBHAIN C; Cardinal Spellman HS; Bronx, NY; (Y); 4/520; Lit Mag; High Hon Roll; Hon Roll; Numerous Schlrshps; Georgetown U; Finance.

LYONS, TYONA; Cardinal Spellman HS; Bronx, NY; (Y); Girl Scts; Latin Clb; Im Bowling; JV Trk; JV Vllybl; High Hon Roll; Hon Roll; Iona Coll; Comp Pgm.

LYSOGORSKI, REGINA; Mihisink Valley HS; Unionville, NY; (Y); Cmnty Wkr; Computer Clb; Chorus; High Hon Roll; Hon Roll; Girl Scts; Library Aide; Tennis; Paralegl.

LYSYCZYN, CHRISTINE; Haverling HS; Kanona, NY; (S); 13/147; French Clb; JCL; Latin Clb; Math Clb; Yrbk Stf; Rep Stu Cncl; Var Capt Cheerleading; Score Keeper; Sftbl; High Hon Roll; U Of Buffalo; Phy Thrpy.

LYTLE, PAMELA; Sauquoit Valley Central HS; Sauquoit, NY; (Y); Church Yth Grp; Exploring; Girl Scts; Hosp Aide; Chorus; Color Guard; Cheerleading; Engl,Art Awds 84-85; Csmtlgy.

LYTTLE, JULIET E; Evander Childs HS; Bronx, NY; (Y); 51/503; Cmnty Wkr; English Clb; Hosp Aide; Hon Roll; Prfct Atten Awd; Regents Schlrshp 85; SUNY-BINGHAMTON; Biochem.

MA, IVY; Notre Dame Academy HS; Staten Island, NY; (Y); 15/92; Nwsp Stf; Yrbk Stf; NHS; Ntl Merit Ltr; Regents Schlrshp 85; Bus.

MA, JOYCE; Stuyvesant HS; Little Neck, NY; (Y); Science Clb; Teachers Aide; Ed Lit Mag; Hon Roll; Chrmn NHS; Ntl Merit Ltr; Wstnghse Sci Tlnt Srch Hnrs Grp 85; Mnrty Schlstc Achvt Awd 84; Gov Cmmttee Schlstc Achvt Cititn 85; Sci Rsrch.

MA, K-WEN; Flushing HS; Flushing, NY; (Y); Intnl Clb; Science Clb; Hon Roll; NY City Coll.

MA, SREYMOM; Columbus HS; New York, NY; (Y); FNA; Hosp Aide; Variety Show; Nwsp Rptr; Diving; Wt Lftg; Cit Awd; Gov Hon Prg Awd; Voice Dem Awd; NYC Coll; Med.

MAAS, BRIAN; Torrejon American HS; Apo New York, NY; (Y); Spanish Clb; Concert Band; Rep Frsh Cls; Rep Jr Cls; Stat Bsktbl; Var Ftbl; Var Socr; Var Wrstlng; Hon Roll; Long Beach ST; Phys Ed.

MAAS, MICHELLE A; John F Kennedy HS; Mahopac, NY; (Y); 51/184; Dance Clb; JA; Stat Bsktbl; JV Trk; JV Vllybl; Im Wt Lftg; Hon Roll; NY ST Rgnts Schlrshp 85; SUNY-ALBANY; Bus Mgmt.

MAASS, CHARLES; Manhasset HS; Manhasset, NY; (Y); Band; Concert Band; Jazz Band; Mrchg Band; Pep Band; JV Bsbl; Var Swmmng; High Hon Roll; Trs NHS; Am Comm Svc 84-86; Swim Tm Cptn; Chem Engr.

MAC ALALAG, GEVEVIEVE; Stella Maris HS; Howard Beach, NY; (Y); JV Var Math Tm; Spanish Clb; Nwsp Rptr; Nwsp Stf; NHS; St Johns U.

MAC AVERY, JENNIFER; Stissing Mountain JR SR HS; Pine Plains, NY; (Y); AFS; VP Pres Church Yth Grp; Pres 4-H; Variety Show; Var Cheerleading; 4-H Awd; Hon Roll; NHS; SUNY Cobleskill; Equne.

MAC CHEYNE, DENISE L; South Seneca Central HS; Interlaker, NY; (Y); 3/80; Am Leg Aux Girls St; Math Clb; Var L Socr; Var L Sftbl; Var L Vllybl; Cit Awd; DAR Awd; High Hon Roll; NHS; NYS Rgnts Schlrshp 85; U NY Geneseo; Math.

MAC CONNIE, DEBBIE; Sachem H S North Campus; Holbrook, NY; (Y); 154/1300; Ed Yrbk Stf; Lit Mag; Spanish Clb; Yrbk Rptr; Fash Merchndsng.

MAC DONALD, BONNIE; Mt Upton Central HS; Mt Upton, NY; (Y); 4/24; Ski Clb; Pres Spanish Clb; Rep Stu Cncl; Stat Bsktbl; Socr; Sftbl; High Hon Roll; Hon Roll; NHS; Prfct Atten Awd; Elem Educ.

MAC DONALD, DONNA; Barker Central HS; Barker, NY; (Y); 1/100; AFS; Drama Clb; French Clb; Chorus; School Musical; Yrbk Stf; Score Keeper; Hon Roll; Jr NHS; NHS; Binghampton; Bus Mgr.

MAC DONALD, MATTHEW J; Queensbury HS; Glens Falls, NY; (Y); Art Clb; Key Clb; Varsity Clb; School Play; Yrbk Stf; Var Ftbl; Capt Var Trk; Var Wt Lftg; Larry Thayer Mem Schlrshp 85; Tri Cnty Mltpl Lstng Awd 85; Kent ST U; Archtctr.

MAC DONALD, NEIL R; Wallkill HS; Wallkill, NY; (Y); 5/200; Boy Scts; Dance Clb; Band; Chorus; Mrchg Band; School Play; High Hon Roll; NHS; Clarkson U; Mech Engr.

MAC DONALD, SUSAN; North Tonawanda SR HS; North Tonawanda, NY; (Y); 52/476; Yrbk Stf; Rep Stu Cncl; Hon Roll; Jr NHS; NHS; Ntl Merit Ltr; St Schlr; NY ST Regnts & Dr Ernest J Turecki Memrl Schlrshps 85; Pres Acadmc Fit Awds Prog 85; Utica U Of Syracuse; Occptn Thr.

MAC DOUGALL, KIMBERLY G; Adirondack HS; W Leyden, NY; (Y); 4/122; GAA; Pres Spanish Clb; Band; Chorus; School Musical; Rep Frsh Cls; Rep Soph Cls; Rep Jr Cls; Rep Sr Cls; Sec Stu Cncl; Area All-ST Band & Chorus 81-84; NY ST Regents Schlrshp Awd 85; SUNY-ALBANY; Spnsh.

MAC ELROY, EILEEN; Shoreham Wading River HS; Shoreham, NY; (Y); Church Yth Grp; Science Clb; Spanish Clb; Band; Concert Band; Orch; Yrbk Phtg; Yrbk Stf; Rep Frsh Cls; Rep Soph Cls; Belmont Abbey Coll.

MAC ENTEE, CHRISTINE; John S Burke Catholic HS; Chester, NY; (Y); Drama Clb; Pres 4-H; Band; School Play; Stage Crew; Nwsp Rptr; JV Var Trk; JV Var Vllybl; Hon Roll; Voice Dem Awd; 4-H ST Horse Awd 84; Regents Schlrshp 85; Schl Music Awd 85; SUNY-GENESEO; Bio.

MAC FARLAND, WILLIAM; Olean HS; Olean, NY; (Y); 9/250; Boy Scts; Math Clb; Concert Band; Jazz Band; Mrchg Band; Orch; Var Crs Cntry; Capt Var Swmmng; Var Tennis; NHS; 20 Pt Awd 85; Most Outstndng Swmmr Awd; Elect Engrng.

MAC FARLANE, TRACY L; Mayfield HS; Gloversville, NY; (Y); 2/77; Pres 4-H; Varsity Clb; Nwsp Sprt Ed; Yrbk Stf; Rep Jr Cls; Capt Var Bsktbl; Capt Var Socr; Var Sftbl; Capt Var Vllybl; 4-H Awd; Sierra Coll; Elec Engrng.

MAC GIBBON, BRUCE; Walton Central Schl; Walton, NY; (Y); 4/100; Am Leg Boys St; Varsity Clb; Concert Band; Jazz Band; Pres Frsh Cls; Var Ftbl; Wt Lftg; High Hon Roll; NHS; Voice Dem Awd; Math.

MAC INTYRE, KIMBERLEY; Delaware Academy And Central Schl; Delhi, NY; (Y); German Clb; Color Guard; Yrbk Stf; Off Jr Cls; JV Fld Hcky; JV Sftbl; High Hon Roll; NHS; Prfct Atten Awd; AFS; Chld Psychlgy.

MAC KAY, ERIKA I; Richfield Springs Central Schl; Richfield Springs, NY; (Y); 4-H; NFL; Speech Tm; Band; Chorus; School Musical; Mat Maids; Ntl Merit Ltr; Rotary Awd; Debate Tm; Dbl Ruby Awd Natl Frnsc Leag 83-84; NYS Lvstck Jdgng Tm 83; Carleton Coll; Geology.

MAC KAY, HEATHER; Crownpoint Central School; Crown Pt, NY; (S); 1/28; Pres 4-H; Band; School Play; Nwsp Rptr; Pres Stu Cncl; Var Capt Socr; NHS; Ntl Merit SF; Val; Sec Drama Clb; Cornell U; Commnctns.

MAC LAURY, SUE A; Oxford Acad; Mc Donough, NY; (Y); 5/81; Church Yth Grp; French Clb; Hon Roll; NHS; SUNY Morrisville; Acctg.

MAC LEAN, RODERICK J; Vestal SR HS; Vestal, NY; (Y); 38/450; Boys Clb Am; French Clb; German Clb; Ski Clb; Swmmng; High Hon Roll; Hon Roll; Ntl Merit SF.

MAC LEAN, TIM; Victor Central Schl; Victor, NY; (Y); 47/198; Ski Clb; Spanish Clb; Varsity Clb; School Play; Nwsp Ed-Chief; Trs Sr Cls; Socr; Bradley U; Jrnlsm.

MAC LENNAN, C JAMES; Wilson Magnet HS; Clyde, NY; (Y); Computer Clb; Math Tm; Science Clb; High Hon Roll; Pres NHS; Ntl Merit Ltr; Renssalear Mdl Math & Sci 85; Roboties.

MAC LEOD, CASSANDRA ANNE; Midwood HS; Brooklyn, NY; (Y); 4/605; Model UN; Science Clb; Variety Show; Nwsp Ed-Chief; Yrbk Stf; Var Swmmng; Gov Hon Prg Awd; High Hon Roll; Ntl Merit Ltr; St Schlr; Govnr Committee Schlstic Achvt Awd 82; Art Metal 82; Brown U; Pre-Med.

MAC MILLAN, CHRISTINE; La Salle SR HS; Niagara Falls, NY; (S); 15/288; Am Leg Aux Girls St; Drama Clb; Hon Roll; Pres Stu Cncl; Var L Bsktbl; Var L Crs Cntry; JV Sftbl; JV Swmmng; Var L Trk; JV Capt Vllybl; Geneseo; Bio.

MAC MULLIN, CHRISTOPHER W; Wallkill SR HS; Wallkill, NY; (Y); 10/206; Aud/Vis; Drama Clb; Tennis; Trk; High Hon Roll; Hon Roll; NHS; NY ST Rgnts Schlrshp 85; Dptmnt Awd Math 84; Audio Vsul Awd 82-84; US Air Force; Comp Sci.

MAC NEAL, CARL; Schuylerville Central HS; Schuylerville, NY; (Y); 10/99; Capt Math Tm; Var JV Crs Cntry; Var Tennis; Capt Var Wrstlng; Regnts Schlrshp Awd Wnnr 85; Plattsburgh ST; Cmmnctns.

MAC NEAR, LYNN; Valley Central HS; Walden, NY; (Y); Service Clb; Band; Pep Band; Church Yth Grp; VP Science Clb; Concert Band; Mrchg Band; Symp Band; Rep Frsh Cls; Rep Soph Cls; Fife & Drum Corps 82-85; Cornell U; Arch.

MAC NEIL, MICHAEL; New Rochelle HS; Scarsdale, NY; (Y); Church Yth Grp; Pres Model UN; Ski Clb; Symp Band; Rep Jr Cls; Rep Stu Cncl; Im Ice Hcky; JV Lcrss; Hon Roll; NHS; Symphnc Band Awd 83.

MAC PHERSON, JENNIFER E; Moravia Central Schl; Dryden, NY; (Y); 9/101; Ski Clb; Yrbk Stf; Lit Mag; Var L Bsktbl; Var L Crs Cntry; Var L Fld Hcky; Var L Tennis; Var Vllybl; High Hon Roll; NHS; Bio.

MAC PHERSON, KELLY; Cardinal Mooney HS; Rochester, NY; (Y); 105/317; Library Aide; Spanish Clb; Church Choir; Hon Roll; Spanish NHS; Cert Achvt Math Cours 83; Bus Adm.

MAC RONALD, LORI; Lansing HS; Lansing, NY; (Y); Church Yth Grp; French Clb; Church Choir; School Play; Tennis; Vllybl; Hon Roll; Psych.

MAC VEAN, LISA D; Perth Bible Christian Acad; Johnstown, NY; (Y); 3/12; Drama Clb; Varsity Clb; Chorus; School Play; Yrbk Bus Mgr; Var L Cheerleading; Var L Vllybl; High Hon Roll; Teachers Aide; NY ST Regents Schlrshp 84-85; Phonathon Schlrshp 85; Houghton Coll; Teacher.

MACALIK, MICHELLE; Rome Free Acad; Rome, NY; (Y); Intnl Clb; Ski Clb; School Musical; School Play; Powder Puff Ftbl; Var Trk; Hon Roll; Prfct Atten Awd; Bus.

MACARI, DAN; Farmingdale HS; Farmingdale, NY; (Y); JV Var Fld Hcky; JV Lcrss; Var Wrstlng; Sprts Med.

MACCARRONE, TERRY L; Hampton Bays HS; Hampton Bays, NY; (Y); Am Leg Boys St; Computer Clb; Mathletes; Hon Roll; Jr NHS; NHS; Ntl Merit Ltr; Aero Sp Engr.

MACCHIA, LARRY; Mount St Michael HS; Bronx, NY; (Y); 39/308; Im Bsktbl; Im Ftbl; NHS.

MACCHIA, MICHELE L; Maria Regina HS; Scarsdale, NY; (Y); 1/144; Teachers Aide; School Musical; Nwsp Ed-Chief; Nwsp Rptr; Ed Nwsp Stf; Trk; High Hon Roll; NHS; St Schlr; Val; 1st Pl Ntl Chem Olympiad Cntst 83; 1st Hnrs Iona Coll Lang Cntst Spnsh II & III 84-85; Music Awd 85; U Of VA; Lbrl Arts.

MACCONE, JANET; Sachem High School North Campus; Holtsville, NY; (Y); 125/1509; Spanish Clb; Band; Hon Roll; NHS; St Johns U; Pre-Law.

MACDONALD, BRIAN; Tonawanda HS; Tonawanda, NY; (Y); Church Yth Grp; Cmnty Wkr; French Clb; Letterman Clb; Ski Clb; Varsity Clb; Yrbk Stf; VP Sr Cls; Bsbl; Ftbl; Dntl.

MACDONALD, CHRSTINE; Mynderse Acad; Seneca Falls, NY; (Y); Ski Clb; Socr; Cazenovia Coll; Fshn Merch.

MACE, DONNA; North Babylon HS; North Babylon, NY; (Y); Intnl Clb; Chorus; Yrbk Stf; Pom Pon; Var Vllybl; High Hon Roll; Jr NHS; NHS; Spec Educ.

MACEJKA, SHARI; Colonie Central HS; Albany, NY; (Y); Church Yth Grp; Dance Clb; Hosp Aide; Hon Roll; Phys Thrpy.

MACGIBBON, PATRICIA; Walton Central HS; Walton, NY; (Y); Varsity Clb; Bsktbl; Fld Hcky; Trk; Cobleskill; Bio.

MACHABEE, CHARLES; Franklin Acad; Malone, NY; (S); 12/254; French Clb; Ski Clb; Varsity Clb; L Crs Cntry; Hon Roll; NHS; Prfct Atten Awd; Epsilon Hnr Soc 82-85; 85 Schlrs For Dollars Alternate 85; King Of Epsilon 85; Dentistry.

MACHADO, ONIEL; Cardinal Hayes HS; New York, NY; (Y); Cmnty Wkr; JV Var Bsbl; JV Ftbl; JV Wt Lftg; Dentstry.

MACHATA, CHRIS; Rye Neck HS; Rye, NY; (Y); 17/97; Chess Clb; Key Clb; Teachers Aide; Band; School Play; Stage Crew; Bsbl; Bsktbl; Ftbl; Wrstlng; Syracuse U; Cmmnctns.

MACHLIN, DANIEL; Bronx HS Of Science; New York, NY; (Y); Pres NY Metrpltn Chap Yng Jupea 84-85; Resrch Prjct Musm Ntrl Hstery NYC 83-84; Wesleyan U CT; Poli Sci.

MACHONKIN, RICHARD A; Webster HS; Webster, NY; (Y); 1/560; Chess Clb; German Clb; Math Tm; Bausch & Lomb Sci Awd; High Hon Roll; Jr NHS; NHS; Ntl Merit SF; Ntl German Hnr Soc 84; Physics.

MACHUGA, FRANK; Bradford Central HS; Bradford, NY; (S); 3/25; FBLA; Nwsp Ed-Chief; Stu Cncl; Cit Awd; High Hon Roll; Hon Roll; VP NHS; Trs Jr Cls.

MACHUGA, MELISSA; Bradford Central HS; Savona, NY; (S); Church Yth Grp; FBLA; Girl Scts; Chorus; Nwsp Stf; High Hon Roll; Hon Roll; NHS; Prfct Atten Awd; Steuben Cnty Frm Bureau 85; FBLA Treas 85.

MACHYNSKI, CHRISTINE; Villa Maria Acad; Cheektowaga, NY; (S); Computer Clb; FBLA; Spanish Clb; Nwsp Rptr; Bowling; Swmmng; Hon Roll; NHS; Schlrshps 85; Canisius Coll; Accntg.

MACIAG, ROBERT; Notre Dame/Bishop Gibbons HS; Schenectady, NY; (S); 2/121; Computer Clb; Bsktbl; Crs Cntry; Golf; Trk; High Hon Roll; NHS; Engl Awd; Hstry Awd; Union Coll; Engrng.

MACIAS, RUTH E; Our Lady Of Perpetual Help HS; Brooklyn, NY; (Y); Hon Roll; Baruch; Acctng.

MACIEJEWSKI, DANIEL; Alden HS; Alden, NY; (Y); French Clb; JV Bsktbl; Var Tennis; Var Trk; Hon Roll; GMI; Engr.

MACINEIRA, LISSETTE; Aquinas HS; New York, NY; (Y); 78/178; Cmnty Wkr; Computer Clb; Dance Clb; Exploring; Color Guard; Mrchg Band; Katharine Gibbs Schl; Bus Mgt.

MACINTYRE, KELLY; Patchoque-Medford HS; Medford, NY; (S); Dance Clb; Band; Color Guard; Concert Band; Drm & Bgl; Drm Mjr(t); Mrchg Band; School Musical; Hon Roll; Spcl Ed.

MACK III, ARTHUR R; Emmanuel Baptist Acad; Penn Yan, NY; (Y); 3/10; School Play; Yrbk Bus Mgr; Stat Bsktbl; Var L Socr; Var Trk; High Hon Roll; Hon Roll; Pres Chess Clb; Scholastic Bowl; Speech Tm; 1st Pl Chess, 2nd Pl Essay, 2nd Pl Famour Spch ACE Stu Convntn ST 85; Keoka Coll; Math Tchr.

MACK, CATHERINE R; Mary Louis Acad; Flushing, NY; (Y); 2/283; Church Yth Grp; Nwsp Stf; Trk; St Schlr; Cert Natl Frnch Cntst 82; Cert 1st Hnrs Geom; Cert 2nd Hnrs Trig; Fordham U; Acctng.

MACK, MARY-MICHAEL; Notre Dame Bishop Gibbons HS; Schenectady, NY; (S); 3/140; Pres Exploring; Ski Clb; School Musical; Nwsp Stf; Lit Mag; Rep Jr Cls; Trk; High Hon Roll; NHS; French Awd 82-83; English Awd 83-84; Killanova U; Pre-Med.

MACK, PAULINE; Whitesboro SR HS; Whitesboro, NY; (Y); 8/320; Intnl Clb; Lit Mag; JV Fld Hcky; Powder Puff Ftbl; JV Capt Vllybl; High Hon Roll; Hon Roll; Jr NHS; NHS; Math.

MACK, STEVEN; Bronx HS Of Science; New York, NY; (Y); Boy Scts; Church Yth Grp; Orch; Ntl Merit Ltr; Microbio Evolutn Genl Bio Grad Awds 85; Music Awd; Columbia Coll; Biochem.

MACK, WENDY; Cicero North Syracuse HS; Clay, NY; (S); 35/711; Pep Clb; Color Guard; Mrchg Band; Sec Soph Cls; Sec Jr Cls; Pres Sr Cls; Rep Stu Cncl; JV Sftbl; Twrlr; Stat Wrstlng; Alfred ST; Crt Steno.

MACKAY, JAMES; Mount Upton HS; Mt Upton, NY; (Y); Variety Show; Bsbl; Hon Roll; Prfct Atten Awd; Bowling.

MACKENBURG, JENNIFER; Frontier HS; Lakeview, NY; (Y); Aud/Vis; Drama Clb; Red Cross Aide; Ski Clb; Thesps; School Musical; Stage Crew; Nwsp Rptr; Trs Pres Stu Cncl; Hon Roll; Hamburg Yth Buru Outstndng SR Awd 85; Frontr Stu Govt Schlrshp 85; Geneseo ST; Brdcst Jrnlsm.

MACKENZIE, CINDY; Fultonville HS; Fonda, NY; (Y); Hosp Aide; Yrbk Stf; JV Bsktbl; JV Trk; Var Vllybl; Hon Roll; Vet.

MACKEY, ANA-MARIA; Sacred Heart Acad; Valley Stream, NY; (S); 12/186; Church Yth Grp; Debate Tm; Hosp Aide; Library Aide; Spanish Clb; School Musical; School Play; Stage Crew; Nwsp Rptr; Socr; Intl Lawyer.

MACKEY, JAMES; Lansingburgh HS; Troy, NY; (Y); 17/178; Drama Clb; German Clb; Pres Key Clb; Chorus; School Musical; School Play; Nwsp Stf; High Hon Roll; NHS; Pres Schlr; Regnts Schlrshp 85; Art Supv Prz 85; Dramtcs Clb Awd 85; Syracuse U; Arch.

MACKEY, KEITH; Bishop Timon HS; W Seneca, NY; (Y); Boy Scts; Church Yth Grp; Cmnty Wkr; Computer Clb; JA; Ski Clb; Spanish Clb; Varsity Clb; Chorus; Stage Crew; Math Awd-Outstndg Achvt.

MACKEY, MARY ELLEN; St Johns Prep; Middle Vlg, NY; (Y); JV Socr; JV Var Sftbl; Phys Ed Tchr.

MACKIE, ANDREW J; Carmel HS; Stormville, NY; (Y); Trs Computer Clb; Pres VP 4-H; Stage Crew; Ed Lit Mag; 4-H Awd; High Hon Roll; Hon Roll; Princpls Awd 85; Comp Clb Schlrshp 85; SUNY; Bio.

MACKIE, JANE; Sacred Heart Acad; East Meadow, NY; (S); Dance Clb; Chorus; School Musical; Hlth Admin.

MACKIN, ANNMARIE; Hicksville SR HS; Hicksvl, NY; (Y); Church Yth Grp; Sec Frnch Clb; Hosp Aide; VP Key Clb; Latin Clb; Yrbk Stf; Var Trk; Var Vllybl; Hon Roll; Voice Dem Awd; Creatv Wrtng Awd 85; Phys Thrpy.

MACKIN, ARLENE; Cardinal Spellman HS; Bronx, NY; (Y); Church Yth Grp; Cmnty Wkr; Computer Clb; Hosp Aide; Ski Clb; Hon Roll; Fordham U; Bus Mgmt.

MACKIN, JOHN; North Salem HS; Purdys, NY; (Y); 2/82; School Musical; School Play; Variety Show; Trs Frsh Cls; Trs Soph Cls; Trs Jr Cls; Trs Stu Cncl; Var JV Socr; Var Capt Tennis; Ntl Merit Ltr; Phtogrphy Excllnc 84; Advncd Plcmnt Engl Excllnc 85; Frnch Excllnc 82-85; Middlebury Coll.

MACKIN, JULIETTE; Fox Lane HS; Fairfield, CT; (Y); Drama Clb; Chorus; Concert Band; Mrchg Band; School Play; Var Capt Cheerleading; High Hon Roll; NHS; Gymnstcs Tchr 84-85.

MACKINTOSH, ELIZABETH; Murry Bergtraum HS; Staten Island, NY; (Y); 86/576; Church Yth Grp; JA; Church Choir; Var Sftbl; Bkkpg Awd 84; Coop Edctnl Exprnc 84-85; John Jay CUNY; Lwyr.

MACKLE, ANNE; Dominican Acad; Long Island, NY; (Y); Dance Clb; Ski Clb; Rep Soph Cls; Hon Roll; Accntnt.

MACKLIN, ERIC; Ithaca HS; Ithaca, NY; (Y); Boy Scts; Var Capt Crs Cntry; Var L Trk; Jr NHS; NHS; Ntl Merit Schol; Hans Bethe Awd 85; Typng Schlrshp 85; Stanford U; Ecology.

MACKO, ANGELA; Chenango Valley HS; Binghamton, NY; (Y); Drama Clb; Chorus; School Musical; Swing Chorus; Rep Stu Cncl; Var L Cheerleading; JV Sftbl; Achv Phy Ftnss Awd 84-85; Chem Engrng.

MACKOWSKI, FRANK; Fairport HS; Fairport, NY; (Y); Stat Ice Hcky; Hon Roll; Bus Adm.

MACKRELL, CHRISTOP J; Lewiston Porter HS; Lewiston, NY; (Y); 19/273; Key Clb; Ski Clb; Band; Concert Band; Mrchg Band; Rep Soph Cls; Rep Sr Cls; Rep Stu Cncl; JV Var Ice Hcky; High Hon Roll; Cornell U; Bio.

MACLI, LISA; Cardinal Spellman HS; Bronx, NY; (Y); Church Yth Grp; Cmnty Wkr; Girl Scts; Hosp Aide; Math Tm; Teachers Aide; Hon Roll; Fordham U; Fin.

MACOMBER, EDWARD H; Honeoye Falls-Lima SR HS; Honeoye Falls, NY; (Y); Math Tm; Pres Science Clb; Concert Band; Yrbk Phtg; Ed Yrbk Stf; Var Trk; Ntl Merit Ltr; VP Chess Clb; Camera Clb; Pres Computer Clb; Schl Rep NYS Acad Decthln 85; Rep Mobl Sci Olympcs 84; NYS Rgnts Schlrshp 85; Rensselaer Poly; Aerospace Engr.

MACRI, CHRISTINE; Cornwall Central HS; New Windsor, NY; (Y); Drama Clb; Chorus; Concert Band; Jazz Band; Mrchg Band; School Play; Hon Roll; TCHR.

MACRI, JOANN; South Shore HS; Brooklyn, NY; (Y); Dance Clb; Debate Tm; Drama Clb; Girl Scts; Library Aide; Math Clb; Spanish Clb; Teachers Aide; Concert Band; Stage Crew.

MACRONE, TRACY; Smithtown H S West; Smithtown, NY; (Y); GAA; Varsity Clb; Band; Concert Band; Jazz Band; Mrchg Band; Pep Band; Symp Band; Var Sftbl; Ltr & Plaque In Music 85; Ltr In Sftbl 84; Suffolk CC; Music.

MADDEN, ANTHONY; Iona Prep HS; Yonkers, NY; (Y); Rep Jr Cls; Rep Sr Cls; Stu Cncl; JV Bsbl; JV Capt Bsktbl; Var Capt Ftbl; Hon Roll.

MADDEN, MAUREEN; Spackenkill HS; Poughkeepsie, NY; (Y); 20/167; VP German Clb; Yrbk Stf; JV Var Fld Hcky; Var Socr; Ntl Merit Ltr; Intl Bus.

MADDEN, MAUREEN A; Northport HS; E Northport, NY; (Y); 33/656; Church Yth Grp; Keywanettes; Band; Chorus; Mrchg Band; Symp Band; Var Fld Hcky; Var Trk; Var Wt Lftg; Hon Roll; Gifted & Talented 83-84; Coll Of Holy Cross; Pre-Med.

MADDISON, LISA ANN; Hudson HS; Hudson, NY; (Y); 12/161; Pres Band; Jazz Band; School Musical; Yrbk Stf; Sec Frsh Cls; VP Sr Cls; High Hon Roll; NHS; Presdntl Acadmc Ftns Awd 85; HTA Comm Svc Awd 85; SUNY Geneseo; Bus Mgmt.

MADDOCK, THOMAS MORE; Bishop Ludden HS; Camillus, NY; (Y); Cmnty Wkr; Letterman Clb; Spanish Clb; Stage Crew; Yrbk Stf; Golf; Ice Hcky; JV Lcrss; Hon Roll; 1t Pl Rchster Yth Hcky Intl Trnmnt 85; Phy Ed.

MADEIRA, LESLIE; Mount Vernon HS; Mount Vernon, NY; (Y); French Clb; Library Aide; High Hon Roll; Hon Roll; Jr NHS; Fshn Dsgn.

MADERER, CARRIE J; West Seneca West SR HS; West Seneca, NY; (Y); 14/543; Chorus; School Musical; Cheerleading; NHS; Mathletes; Spanish Clb; Sec Jr Cls; Stu Cncl; Hon Roll; JR Miss 85; St Bonaventure U; Jrnlsm.

MADEWELL, JULIE R; Ballston Spa HS; Ballston Spa, NY; (Y); 86/220; Church Yth Grp; French Clb; Service Clb; Church Choir; Color Guard; Nwsp Rptr; Hon Roll; Cazenova Coll; Ed.

MADEWELL, MATT; Clarkstown H S North; New City, NY; (Y); Band; Concert Band; JV Socr; Italian Clb 84-85.

MADGE, JOSEPH; Paul V Moore HS; Cleveland, NY; (Y); 1/297; VP German Clb; Math Tm; Capt L Ftbl; Capt L Trk; High Hon Roll; NHS; Ntl Merit Ltr; Val; Ann Welch Schlsp Awd 85; Regents Schlsp 85; Pres Acad Fitness Awd 85; U PA; Engr.

MADIGAN, GLENN; Center Moriches HS; Ctr Moriches, NY; (Y); Pres Church Yth Grp; Pres Cmnty Wkr; Teachers Aide; Ntl Merit Ltr; Jr Fire Dept Leut & Drill Tm 81; Jr Fire Dept Capt & Drill Tm 82; Ch Attnd & YPF 81-83; Suffolk CC; Elec Tech.

MADIGAN, SALLY; Haverling HS; Bath, NY; (S); VP French Clb; JCL; Latin Clb; Math Clb; Sec Band; Concert Band; Mrchg Band; Orch; School Musical; Symp Band; Legn & Cnty Oratorical Cont 1st Pl 85; Dist Legn Oratorical Cont 2nd Pl; Law.

MADISON, ANDREA; Corinth Central HS; Corinth, NY; (S); Band; Bsktbl; Fld Hcky; Sftbl; Vllybl; High Hon Roll; Hon Roll; NHS; Spanish NHS; Siena; Law.

MADISON, ARTHUR E; Cicero N Syracuse HS; Clay, NY; (Y); Exploring; Ski Clb; Nwsp Rptr; Nwsp Stf; Im Bsktbl; Lion Awd; NY ST Rgnts Schlrshp 85; U Of Northeastern; Comm.

MADISSOO, ANDRES; Jamesville-De Witt HS; Fayetteville, NY; (Y); Boy Scts; Exploring; German Clb; Var Crs Cntry; Var Swmmng; Hon Roll.

MADOFF, STACEY; Onteora HS; Woodstock, NY; (S); Math Tm; Chorus; Swing Chorus; Variety Show; High Hon Roll; NHS; JV Fld Hcky; Roswell Pk Mem Inst Smmr Prog 85.

MADRAY, CHANDRA D; Eastern District HS; Brooklyn, NY; (Y); Cmnty Wkr; English Clb; Spanish Clb; Gym; High Hon Roll; Hon Roll; Typing, Spanish, Bookeeping, Slim Dance, Math & Health Career II 84-85; Hunter Coll; Pediatric Nursing.

MADRIGAL, ELMA CHERYL SARREAL; Albertus Magnus HS; Orangeburg, NY; (Y); 20/196; Civic Clb; Cmnty Wkr; Dance Clb; Drama Clb; Hosp Aide; Math Clb; Math Tm; Office Aide; Science Clb; Spanish Clb; Piano 79-85; Dncg Choreogrphr & Dncr 78-85; 1st Pl Pblshd Mag Covr 81; Ped.

MADSEN, KRISTEN; Liverpool HS; Liverpool, NY; (S); 72/791; AFS; Hosp Aide; School Musical; Symp Band; Ed Lit Mag; Sec Stu Cncl; Hon Roll; Jr NHS; NHS; Ntl Merit Ltr; 2nd Pl Natl Latin Exam Cont 84; Engl.

MADURSKI, MARY JO; Forestville Central HS; Silver Creek, NY; (Y); Mrchg Band; Yrbk Stf; Trs Frsh Cls; VP Soph Cls; Var Bsktbl; JV Cheerleading; Var Sftbl; Var Trk; JV Capt Vllybl; Hon Roll; Air Force; Data Proc.

MAETTA, VINCENT ANTHONY; Bishop Ford C C HS; Brooklyn, NY; (Y); 60/441; Church Yth Grp; Pres Stu Cncl; Var JV Bsbl; Bsktbl; Hon Roll; NHS; Hnr Stu; JV & Var Bsbll & Bsktbll; Pres Advsr; Natl Hnr Soc; Baruch; Bus.

MAFFEI, DANIEL; Nottingham HS; Syracuse, NY; (Y); VP Computer Clb; Math Tm; Nwsp Rptr; High Hon Roll; NHS; Rennsselaer Math & Sci Awd 85; Occupatnl Eductn Advsry Board 84; Med.

MAFFEI, LAURA; Moore Catholic HS; Staten Island, NY; (Y); 5/175; Drama Clb; NFL; Chorus; School Musical; School Play; Stage Crew; Nwsp Stf; Bowling; NHS; Ntl Merit Ltr; Regents Schlrshp 85; Chem Awd 83; Poetry Prz 1st Pl 83-84; SUNY.

MAFFETORE, DONALD A; Holy Trinity Diocesan HS; Bethpage, NY; (S); Math Tm; Political Wkr; Science Clb; High Hon Roll; Gifted Stu Chem Pgm 84.

MAGAHIS, PACIFICO A; Regis HS; Staten Island, NY; (Y); Cmnty Wkr; Computer Clb; Var Bowling; Im Gym; JV Trk; Im Wrstlng; High Hon Roll; Ntl Merit Ltr; Pres Schlr; St Schlr; Schlrshp To Long Islnd U 85; Schlrshp To Fordham 85; Cornell U; Micro Bio.

MAGANIA, JANET M; Bayside HS; Whitestone, NY; (Y); 96/677; Credit Roll Awd 85; Typing Awd 85; Outstndng Acdmc Achvt & Pres Acdmc Ftns Awd 85; Hunter Coll; Prfsnl Phtgrphr.

MAGARA, KENNETH A; Salamanca Central HS; Salamanca, NY; (Y); Am Leg Boys St; Spanish Clb; Color Guard; Concert Band; Mrchg Band; Yrbk Stf; High Hon Roll; NHS; Spanish NHS; Intl Rltns.

MAGARDINO, TOMMY; Edgemont HS; Scarsdale, NY; (S); Hosp Aide; JA; Latin Clb; Mathletes; Model UN; Ski Clb; Pres Jr Cls; Var JV Socr; Var Trk; Med.

MAGARI, SEAN; C W Baker SR HS; Baldwinsville, NY; (Y); Ski Clb; Bsbl; Var Ftbl; Wt Lftg; Hon Roll; Syracuse U; Engrng.

MAGDA, THOMAS; Archbishop Molloy HS; Astoria, NY; (Y); 17/410; Math Tm; Yrbk Stf; NHS; Engrng.

MAGEE, DONALD; St Joseph By The Sea; Staten Island, NY; (Y); Am Leg Boys St; Church Yth Grp; Computer Clb; Nwsp Ed-Chief; Nwsp Rptr; Bausch & Lomb Sci Awd; High Hon Roll; NHS; NEDT Awd; Genevoswo Pope Mem Awd 85; Comp Sci Medal 85; St Johns Ufcomp Sci.

MAGENDANZ, CHAD L; Holland Patent Central HS; Barneveld, NY; (Y); 2/200; Am Leg Boys St; Computer Clb; Mathletes; ROTC; Band; Jazz Band; Orch; Pep Band; School Musical; School Play; Cornell Natl Schlr 85; Rensselaer Polytech Inst Math & Sci Awd 84; Appointd Naval Acad Annapolis 85; Cornell U; Elect Engrng.

MAGGERT, WENDI; Little Falls SR HS; Little Falls, NY; (S); 12/109; Church Yth Grp; Drama Clb; French Clb; FBLA; VP Jr Cls; Bsktbl; Fld Hcky; High Hon Roll; Bus Admn.

MAGGIO, ELIZABETH; Clarkstown High School South; Nanuet, NY; (Y); 75/541; JA; Hon Roll; Jr NHS; Pres Schlr; Dominican Coll Acad Scholar 85; Pres Acad Fit Awd 85; Dominicon Coll Blauvlt; Bus Mgm.

MAGGIO, ROBERT J; Union Springs Central Schl; Auburn, NY; (Y); #13 In Class; Am Leg Boys St; JV Ftbl.

MAGGIO, TIMOTHY M; Wayne Central HS; Sodus, NY; (Y); 5/201; Mathletes; Math Clb; Math Tm; Ski Clb; Capt Bsktbl; Capt Bowling; Capt Crs Cntry; Capt Golf; High Hon Roll; NHS; Regents Schlrshp; Monroe CC; Engrng.

MAGGIORE, JOANN; East Islip HS; Walton, NY; (Y); Office Aide; Teachers Aide; Hon Roll.

MAGGIORE, ROSA; Bishop Kearney HS; Brooklyn, NY; (Y); Church Yth Grp; Math Tm; Hon Roll; Prfct Atten Awd; Sal; 1st,2nd Hnrs; St Johns U; Soclgy.

MAGGS, LORI ANNE; Islip HS; Islip, NY; (Y); 50/260; Im Cheerleading; Var Score Keeper; Pres Schlr; Dowling Acadmc Hnrs Schlrshp 85-86; Dowling Coll; Bus.

MAGGY, TONYA; Saranac Central HS; Morrisonville, NY; (Y); Am Leg Aux Girls St; Cmnty Wkr; Girl Scts; Red Cross Aide; Chorus; Color Guard; Yrbk Stf; Hon Roll; Crary Ed Fund Awd 85; Clinton CC; Hum Sci.

MAGLIATO, KIM; Newburgh Free Acad; Newburgh, NY; (Y); Key Clb; Ski Clb; Yrbk Stf; Rep Jr Cls; Stat Ftbl; High Hon Roll; Hon Roll; Jr NHS; Library Aide; Bus Mgmt.

MAGLIONE, LAURA; Herbert H Lehman HS; Bronx, NY; (Y); #1 In Class; Math Tm; Office Aide; Science Clb; Lit Mag; JC Awd; NHS; Prfct Atten Awd; Val; Hnrbl Mntn City Coll Poetry Cntst 84; Regnts Schlrshp 85; Acadmc Olympcs 85.

MAGNAN, SCOTT; Chonango Valley HS; Binghamton, NY; (Y); French Clb; Bsbl; Bsktbl; Var Socr; Jr NHS; Elec Engrng.

MAGNOLI, PETER VINCENT; Sachem North HS; Ronkonkoma, NY; (Y); Church Yth Grp; Drama Clb; Ski Clb; Spanish Clb; Band; Concert Band; Jazz Band; Mrchg Band; School Musical; School Play; Oswego U; Metrlgy.

MAGRICH, PAUL B; Lasalle SR HS; Niagara Falls, NY; (Y); 96/285; Pres AFS; Boys Clb Am; Drama Clb; JA; Red Cross Aide; VP Chorus; Orch; School Musical; Yrbk Stf; Stu Cncl; Natl Vocl Music Awd 85; ST Of NY Cert Of Merit 85; Niagara U; Thetr.

MAGRINO, JOHN; Albertus Magnus HS; New City, NY; (Y); 35/190; Church Yth Grp; Cmnty Wkr; Math Tm; Service Clb; JV Bsbl; Var Trk; Wt Lftg; Hon Roll; Mu Alp Tht; NHS; Bus.

MAGRYTA, URSZULA; Spackenhill HS; Poughkeepsie, NY; (Y); 17/172; Band; Pep Band; Stage Crew; Rep Soph Cls; Rep Jr Cls; JV Fld Hcky; Var Socr; Hon Roll; NHS; Bus.

MAGSINO, TERESITA; Academy Of St Joseph HS; Coram, NY; (Y); Art Clb; Hosp Aide; Science Clb; Service Clb; Chorus; VP Jr Cls; NHS; NEDT Awd; Frnch Achvt Awd 82-85; Stu Of Trimester 83-84; Intl Stu Ldrshp Inst 84; Brown U; Pre Med.

MAGUIRE, LISA; Pittsford Mendon HS; Pittsford, NY; (Y); Model UN; Hon Roll; NHS; Dely Ambass Hague Intl Model U N 85; Rochester Rotary Scholar Study U N 85.

MAGUIRE JR, ROBERT E; Canajoharie HS; Canajoharie, NY; (Y); 5/100; Acpl Chr; Chorus; School Musical; Yrbk Phtg; L JV Crs Cntry; L Var Ftbl; L Var Trk; L Var Wrstlng; NHS; Ntl Merit Ltr; Regents Schlrshp 85; Mc Donalds Athlete Of Mnth 85; Rochester Inst Tech; Bio Comp.

MAGUIRE, SIOBAN; New Rochelle HS; New Rochelle, NY; (Y); Cmnty Wkr; Debate Tm; JA; Political Wkr; Orch; Yrbk Stf; Tennis; Hon Roll; NHS; Prfct Atten Awd; Orchstra Awd; Hstry Awd; Amer Hstry Hnrs Clss; Hstry.

MAGYAR, BEVERLY LOUISE; Taconic Hills HS; Hillsdale, NY; (Y); 14/125; Intnl Clb; School Musical; Nwsp Bus Mgr; Nwsp Rptr; Yrbk Stf; Rep Stu Cncl; High Hon Roll; Hon Roll; NEDT Awd; Regents Schlrshp 85; Marist; Comm Arts.

MAH, DENNIS; Freeport HS; Freeport, NY; (Y); 30/450; Computer Clb; Pres Science Clb; Pres Spanish Clb; Band; Chorus; Concert Band; Jazz Band; Mrchg Band; Orch; Variety Show; SUNY New Paltz; Bus Mgt.

MAHAFFY, PATRICIA L; Honeoye Falls-Lima HS; Dallas, TX; (Y); 30/175; Cmnty Wkr; Political Wkr; Chorus; Yrbk Bus Mgr; Var Swmmng; French Hon Soc; High Hon Roll; NHS; Val; Dist Delegate Pres Clsrm Yng Am 85; Wnnr NYS Regents Schlrshp Nrsng 85; Oral Roberts U Tulsa; Med.

MAHAGAN, LISA; Skaneateles HS; Skaneateles, NY; (S); Drama Clb; Jazz Band; Orch; School Musical; Symp Band; High Hon Roll; NHS; SND Engrng.

MAHAL, JACQUELINE J; Vestal SR HS; Vestal, NY; (Y); 26/450; Varsity Clb; VP Soph Cls; Rep Sr Cls; Rep Stu Cncl; Var Cheerleading; High Hon Roll; St Schlr; Boston U; Bio Medical Engnrng.

MAHAN, GERARD; Bishop Grimes HS; Syracuse, NY; (Y); Aud/Vis; Var Bsbl; Var Ftbl; Accntng.

MAHANNA, ELLEN; Holland Patent Central Schl; Barneveld, NY; (Y); 81/162; Chorus; Symp Band; Variety Show; Nwsp Sprt Ed; Var Cheerleading; JV Fld Hcky; Capt Powder Puff Ftbl; JV Sftbl; Hon Roll.

MAHAR, DEBORAH A; Solvay HS; Syracuse, NY; (Y); 35/167; Church Yth Grp; Dance Clb; Key Clb; Spanish Clb; Chorus; Concert Band; Trk; Hon Roll; School Musical; Variety Show; NYS Regents Nrs Schlrshp 85; Yth Ldrshp Awd 85; Crouse-Irving Mem Nrs Schl; Nrs.

MAHAR, KATHLEEN; Spackenkill HS; Poughkeepsie, NY; (Y); Varsity Clb; Nwsp Stf; Off Frsh Cls; Trs Soph Cls; Var Bsktbl; JV Cheerleading; Score Keeper; Var Socr; Hugh O Brien Yth Ldrshp Awd 84; All Leag 2nd Team Hnrbl Ment 85; All Cnty Schlstc Soccer.

MAHAR, MICHAEL; Schenectady Christian Schl; Schenectady, NY; (S); 2/16; Church Yth Grp; Yrbk Stf; Pres Trs Stu Cncl; JV Bsktbl; Var Socr; High Hon Roll; Prfct Atten Awd.

MAHER, ANITA; Springfield Gardens HS; Rosedale, NY; (S); 5/508; Mgr Bsktbl; Mgr Capt Sftbl; Mgr Capt Vllybl; Hon Roll; NHS; Ntl Merit Ltr; Queens Coll Pres Awd Achvt 82.

MAHER, BROCK; Pine Bush HS; Pine Bush, NY; (Y); Church Yth Grp; 4-H; Ski Clb; School Play; Var L Crs Cntry; 4-H Awd; Hon Roll; NHS; Prfct Atten Awd; Town Of Crawford Repblcn Clb Schlrshp 85; Orange Cnty CC; Comp Sci.

MAHER, COLLEEN MARIE; Byron Bergen Central HS; Bergen, NY; (Y); 4-H; Band; Concert Band; Jazz Band; Mrchg Band; Rep Stu Cncl; Dance Clb; Harold Milward Schlrshp 85; Music.

MAHER, EDWARD; Longwood HS; Coram, NY; (Y); 115/487; High Hon Roll; Hon Roll; Pol Sci.

MAHER, JOELLE; S Glens Falls Central HS; Wilton, NY; (Y); 7/227; Pres VP 4-H; Chorus; Nwsp Phtg; Nwsp Stf; Yrbk Phtg; 4-H Awd; Jr NHS; NHS; Ntl Merit SF; Paul Howe Memrl Awd Schlrshp 85; Saratoga Cnty Zonta Clb Schlrshp 85; Sectnl 4-H Vet Sci Wnnr 83; Cornell U; Anml Sci.

MAHER, KELLY; Mt Vernon HS; Mount Vernon, NY; (Y); Sec Trs Keywanettes; Spanish Clb; Nwsp Rptr; Nwsp Stf; High Hon Roll; Hon Roll; NHS; Pre-Law.

MAHER, KIMBERLY; St Marys HS; Elma, NY; (S); 27/180; Ski Clb; Varsity Clb; Var Cheerleading; Mgr(s); Var Trk; Hon Roll; Phys Thrpy.

MAHFOUZ, ANNMARIE; Fontbonne Hall Acad; Brooklyn, NY; (Y); 4/138; Church Yth Grp; Drama Clb; Teachers Aide; Chorus; School Musical; Variety Show; Cheerleading; High Hon Roll; NHS; NY ST Regents Schlrshp 85; Pace U; Bus.

MAHON, CHRISTINE M; Lyme Central HS; Chaumont, NY; (Y); FNA; GAA; Band; Chorus; Flag Corp; Mrchg Band; Var Capt Bsktbl; Var Gym; Var JV Score Keeper; Var Socr; Red Crss 1st Aid Cours 82-83; Mst Imprvmt PE 81-82; Mst Improvmt Sci 83-84; Nrsg.

MAHONEY, DONNA; Bethpage HS; Plainview, NY; (Y); VP Frsh Cls; VP Soph Cls; VP Sr Cls; Church Yth Grp; Cmnty Wkr; French Clb; FBLA; Nwsp Sprt Ed; Nwsp Stf; Yrbk Stf; Bsbl Assn SR Ponytail Sftbl Champs MVP 85; St Leos FL; Elem Ed.

MAHONEY, KAREN; Deer Park HS; Deer Park, NY; (Y); 144/422; FBLA; Hosp Aide; Rep Stu Cncl; Hon Roll; Im Crs Cntry; Var Vllybl; Home Ec Awd Fshn & Psych 82-83; Coburn; Fshn Mrchdsng.

MAHONEY, KEVIN; St Josephs Coll Ins HS; Buffalo, NY; (Y); 90/200; FCA; Chorus; Church Choir; Im Bsktbl; Im Bowling; Var Ftbl; Var Trk; Wt Lftg; CYO Treas; Buff ST; Bus.

MAHONEY, SHAFER; Guilderland Central HS; Albany, NY; (Y); 4/375; Math Tm; Quiz Bowl; Chorus; Concert Band; Orch; School Musical; Nwsp Stf; Cit Awd; NHS; Ntl Merit SF; Hghst Hnr Rl 84-85; Harvard Bk Awd, Allamont Alumn Assn Awd Engl 85; Bio Sci.

MAHONEY, THERESA; Sacred Heart Acad; Pt Lookout, NY; (S); Church Yth Grp; Cmnty Wkr; NFL; Speech Tm; Chorus; School Play; JV Swmmng; Var Trk; High Hon Roll; NHS; Nassau Suffolk Catholic League Essay Cont 1st Pl; Nassau Suffolk Catholic HS Swim Chmpns.

MAHONEY III, WILLIAM F; Msgr Farrell HS; Staten Island, NY; (Y); 5/295; Boy Scts; Pres Computer Clb; Math Tm; Var Swmmng; NHS; Ntl Merit Ltr; Rensealeer Poly Inst Sci,Math Medal 84; Sylvester Awd 85; MA Inst Tech; Chem Engr.

MAHONY, DEIRDRE; St Michaels Acad; Astoria, NY; (Y); 7/130; Debate Tm; Red Cross Aide; Teachers Aide; Mrchg Band; Nwsp Rptr; Nwsp Stf; Gym; High Hon Roll; Hon Roll; NHS; Manhattan Coll Pres Schlrshp 85-86; Astoria Cvc Assn Achvt Awd 85-86; Manhattan Coll; Accntng.

MAIDA, JANET; Mt Saint Joseph Acad; Buffalo, NY; (S); 1/60; Spanish Clb; Chorus; School Musical; Swing Chorus; Yrbk Ed-Chief; Yrbk Stf; Pres Jr Cls; Sftbl; High Hon Roll; NHS; Pre Med.

MAIDE, LEILI; Averill Park HS; West Sand Lake, NY; (Y); 3/220; Pres VP 4-H; Rep Key Clb; Math Tm; Ski Clb; Varsity Clb; Jazz Band; Yrbk Stf; Var JV Socr; Var Capt Trk; Pres NHS; E G Craig Reynolds Mem Schlrshp 85; Rensselaer Polytech Inst.

MAIELLARO, MARK; Beaver River Central HS; Beaver Falls, NY; (Y); 10/90; French Clb; Varsity Clb; JV Bsktbl; High Hon Roll; Hon Roll; Trs NHS; Pres Schlr; NY ST Regnst Schlrshp 85; US Navy; Nuclr Engr.

MAIELLARO, MICHELLE; Middletown HS; Middletown, NY; (Y); Teachers Aide; Hon Roll; Nominated Girl State 85; Liberal Arts.

MAIER, CHRISTOPHER W; Edmeston Central Schl; Edmeston, NY; (Y); Am Leg Boys St; Math Clb; Math Tm; Varsity Clb; Band; Chorus; Jazz Band; Mrchg Band; Pep Band; School Musical; Hghst HS Mth Avg Awd 83-85; Hghst Avg Bio 84; Hghst Avg Chem 85; RPI; Comp Engr.

MAIGNAN, SABINE; Queen Of The Rosary Acad; Massapequa, NY; (S); 6/44; Art Clb; Girl Scts; Hosp Aide; Math Clb; Band; Nwsp Rptr; Yrbk Stf; Trk; High Hon Roll; Hon Roll; Princeton U; Pre-Med.

MAINE, WESLEY; Albion HS; Albion, NY; (S); 30/187; Boy Scts; Church Yth Grp; Spanish Clb; Mrchg Band; Var Capt Crs Cntry; Var L Swmmng; Var Tennis; Variety Show; Eagle Awd 84; US Nvl Acad 84; U Of Dayton; Elec Engrng.

MAINELLI, BENJI; Bronx H S Of Science; New York, NY; (Y); Cmnty Wkr; JA; Jazz Band; Var Bsbl; Var Ftbl; Var Sftbl; Hon Roll; NHS; Hnrs Math, Calculus 83-84.

MAINOLFI, ANTHONY J; St Anthonys HS; Smithtown, NY; (Y); Art Clb; Church Yth Grp; Math Clb; Science Clb; Spanish Clb; Rep Stu Cncl; JV Crs Cntry; JV Trk; Hon Roll; NHS; St Anthonys; Meteorlgy.

MAINOLFI, JOSEPH; St Anthonys MS; Smithtown, NY; (Y); Church Yth Grp; Y-Teens; Lit Mag; JV Im Fld Hcky; JV Im Ftbl; Hon Roll; Dan Scutous 82-83; Sng Wrtr.

MAIORANO, MIKE; Pittsford Mendon HS; Pittsford, NY; (Y); Cmnty Wkr; Dance Clb; DECA; Model UN; Radio Clb; Red Cross Aide; Service Clb; Band; Concert Band; Stu Cncl; Decny ST Career Conf 85; Red Crs Yth Svcs Ldrshp Conf 85; Recgntn Outstndng Svc Rochestr Sesqcntnl 84; U NC Chapel Hill; Acctng.

MAIORINO, JOHN E; Hicksville HS; Hicksvl, NY; (Y); Computer Clb; Mathletes; Ski Clb; Drm Mjr(t); Var Bowling; Wt Lftg; JV Wrstlng; High Hon Roll; Jr NHS; NHS; Engrng.

MAIRA, KATHY A; Cardinal Mooney HS; Rochester, NY; (Y); 15/321; Office Aide; Service Clb; Bsktbl; Fld Hcky; Mgr(s); Hon Roll; Hon Roll; NHS; St Schlr; Sibleys Schlrshp Art Show-Blue Rbn; Schl Art Awds; Albany Coll Pharmacy; Pharm.

MAISANO, MICHELE; Moore Catholic HS; Staten Island, NY; (Y); Spanish Clb; Yrbk Stf; Bowling; Hon Roll.

MAITA, DENISE; St Joseph By The Sea HS; Staten Island, NY; (Y); Church Yth Grp; Computer Clb; Math Tm; JV Bsktbl; Bowling; NHS; U Miami; Cmmnctns.

MAIZES, TZIPORA; Torah Acadamy For Girls; Far Rockaway, NY; (Y); 6/27; Pres Civic Clb; Computer Clb; Pres Chorus; School Musical; Yrbk Stf; Hon Roll; NHS; Regnts Nrsng Schlrshp 85; Math.

MAJCHRZAK, LOUIS; West Seneca East SR HS; Buffalo, NY; (Y); Computer Clb; Var Ice Hcky; Var Socr; Var Tennis; JV Trk; Hon Roll; NHS; NY ST Hcky Champs 85; Comp Sci.

MAJDANIK, MICHELLE; Royalton-Hartland HS; Gasport, NY; (Y); 35/125; Trs French Clb; Girl Scts; Varsity Clb; Var L Diving; Var L Trk; Stat Vllybl; Jr NHS; Outstndng French Stu 84-85; Economics.

MAJEED, SHAHZAD; Cardinal Hayes HS; New York, NY; (Y); 5/249; Yrbk Ed-Chief; Stu Cncl; High Hon Roll; Hon Roll; Prfct Atten Awd; Pres Schlr; Diamond H Mdl For Excllnc Hist & Gen Excllnc Mdl 83-84; Hayes H Schlrshp To NY Inst Pf Tech 84-85; NY Inst Of Tech; Aeronautcl En.

MAJKOWSKI, ANNE MARIE; Dominican Commercial HS; Glendale, NY; (Y); 69/273; Cmnty Wkr; Math Clb; Teachers Aide; CC Awd; High Hon Roll; Hon Roll; Jr NHS; Physcl Ed Ldrs Cls 82-83; St Johns U; Acctng.

MAJOR, ROSEMARIE; Springfield Gardens HS; Rosedale, NY; (S); 8/508; Girl Scts; Science Clb; Crs Cntry; L Trk; High Hon Roll; NHS; Prfct Atten Awd; Treas Ntl Hnr Soc 84-85; Pres Hnr Soc Prjct Upward Bound 84-85; Mt Holyoke; Med.

MAJORS, SHAWN; Hilton HS; Hilton, NY; (Y); Camera Clb; Spanish Clb; Bowling; Ftbl; Hon Roll; Military.

MAK, NANCY; Norman Thomas HS; New York, NY; (S); 25/671; Cmnty Wkr; Computer Clb; Dance Clb; JA; Spanish Clb; Orch; Hon Roll; NHS; Prfct Atten Awd; Comp Sci.

MAKARAINEN, MICHAEL; Jamesville-De Witt HS; De Witt, NY; (Y); Boy Scts; Chorus; Concert Band; Pep Band; School Musical; Swing Chorus; Mgr(s); JV Wrstlng; Hon Roll; NHS; Engr.

MAKBOULIAN, SCOTT; Hauppauge HS; Smithtown, NY; (Y); Jazz Band; Orch; Symp Band; JV Var Ftbl; Var Trk; Var Wt Lftg; Hon Roll; Engr.

MAKEY, CAROLYN; Kenmore East SR HS; Tonawanda, NY; (Y); Church Yth Grp; Drama Clb; GAA; School Play; Trs Jr Cls; Var Bsktbl; Var JV Crs Cntry; JV Sftbl; Hon Roll; The Wellesley Book Awd 84-85; MIP For Girls Vrsty Bsktbl Tm 84-85; Art.

MAKINAJIAN, MICHAEL; John H Glenn HS; Huntington, NY; (Y); Im Bowling; Hon Roll; Farmingdale.

MAKINEN, MIKA; Smithtown HS West; Smithtown, NY; (Y); German Clb; Thesps; Chorus; School Play; Rep Sr Cls; Hon Roll; Dip.

MAKLAN, DAVID; Roosevelt HS; Yonkers, NY; (S); Ski Clb; Band; Concert Band; Mrchg Band; Variety Show; Yrbk Stf; Rep Jr Cls; Lcrss.

MAKO, LASZLO; Union-Endicott HS; Endicott, NY; (Y); Var Trk; Hon Roll; Prfct Atten Awd; Rochester Inst Tech; Comp Sci.

MAKOSKY, HELEN; Hugh C Williams HS; Canton, NY; (Y); NHS; Exploring; Chorus; Yrbk Stf; Vllybl; High Hon Roll; Acad Ltr Awd 84 & 85; Bus Exec.

MAKOWSKI, CHRISTOPHER; Hutchinson Central Tech HS; Buffalo, NY; (Y); Hon Roll; Comp Elec.

MAKOWSKI, JASON; Commack H S North; Commack, NY; (Y); MMM; Drm Mjr(t); Jazz Band; Mrchg Band; Orch; School Musical; Swing Chorus; Nwsp Phtg; Yrbk Phtg; Lit Mag; Best Photogrphy-Commack Schl Dist Art Fest 85; Julliard Schl Of Music.

MAKOWSKI, JOHN; Holland Central Schl; Holland, NY; (Y); Boys Clb Am; JV Var Socr; Var Trk; MVP JV Socr 83-84; MIP Var Trk 83-84; MVP Var Trk 84-85; Crimnl Justc.

MAKRIDES, DEENA; Midwood High Schl At Brooklyn Coll; Brooklyn, NY; (Y); 3/750; Office Aide; Band; Concert Band; Pep Band; School Musical; Variety Show; Med Sci.

MAKRIS, ATHENA D; Beach Channel HS; New York, NY; (Y); 10/485; JA; Math Clb; Math Tm; Teachers Aide; Variety Show; Yrbk Ed-Chief; Yrbk Stf; Lit Mag; Gov Hon Prg Awd; High Hon Roll; UN Peace Medl 82; Fordham U; Law.

MALAGESE, MICHELE; Whitesboro SR HS; Yorkville, NY; (Y); Church Yth Grp; Drama Clb; VP VICA; Acpl Chr; Chorus; School Musical; Powder Puff Ftbl; Hon Roll; Cosmetologist.

MALANDRINO, GINA; Notredame Acad; Staten Island, NY; (Y); Math Clb; Capt Swmmng; NHS; Coaches Awd Swmmg 83; Sr Cianciola Schlr Swmr Awd 84; Mst Valbl Swmr 85; Med.

MALANDRO, LAURIE; St Peters Girls HS; Staten Isl, NY; (Y); Computer Clb; Dance Clb; Drama Clb; Girl Scts; Chorus; Church Choir; School Musical; School Play; Yrbk Stf; Capt Cheerleading; Wagnes; Srgcl Nrs.

MALANOWSKI, TIFFANY; Cardinal Mooney HS; Rochester, NY; (Y); Ski Clb; Stage Crew; Rep Frsh Cls; Rep Jr Cls; Var L Cheerleading; French Hon Soc; Hon Roll; NHS; Niagara U; Travl.

MALAR, GREGORY F; Midwood HS; Brooklyn, NY; (Y); 40/604; Political Wkr; Scholastic Bowl; Orch; Nwsp Rptr; Stu Cncl; Crs Cntry; Trk; Cit Awd; NHS; Ntl Merit Ltr; Franklin Coll.

MALARK, VALERIE; Saranac Central HS; Dannemora, NY; (Y); 43/105; Drama Clb; French Clb; Library Aide; Concert Band; School Musical; Stage Crew; Yrbk Stf; Hon Roll; Plattsburgh ST; Math.

MALATINO, JOSEPH; Bishop Maginn HS; Albany, NY; (Y); 7/114; Spanish Clb; High Hon Roll; NHS; NY ST Regnts Schlrshp 85-86; Son Opitaly Schlrshp 85-86; Laborers Locl 190 Schlrshp 85-86; ST U; Comp Sci.

MALBON, SCOTT E; Moriah Central Schl; Mineville, NY; (Y); Aud/Vis; Ftbl; Wt Lftg; Hon Roll; Comp Sci.

MALCHAK, WENDY J; Chenango Valley HS; Chenango Bridge, NY; (Y); 13/190; VP Trs French Clb; Yrbk Ed-Chief; Yrbk Stf; NHS; NYS Regents Scholarship 85; SUNY Binghamton; French.

MALCHO, KARYN; Fairport HS; Fairport, NY; (Y); Church Yth Grp; Ski Clb; JV Capt Swmmng; Coaches Awd-Hghst Awd Given To A Swimmer 84; Leaders Clb 84; Phys Thrpst.

MALCHOW, DANA; Tonawanda JR SR HS; Tonawanda, NY; (Y); Cmnty Wkr; Hosp Aide; Ski Clb; Chorus; Jazz Band; School Musical; Swing Chorus; Yrbk Stf; Cheerleading; Hon Roll; Hugh O Brian Yth Fndtn Ldrshp Awd 84; Crmnl Justc.

MALCOLM, LARELL G; Erasmus Hall; Brooklyn, NY; (Y); 11/433; Church Yth Grp; Office Aide; Socr; Jr NHS; NHS; Ntl Merit Ltr; Prfct Atten Awd; UFT Coll Schlrshp NYS Regents Schlrshp 85; Dowling Coll; Aeron.

MALDONADO, CARA A; New Dorp HS; Brooklyn, NY; (Y); 120/760; Dance Clb; Drama Clb; Pres Spanish Clb; Teachers Aide; Chorus; School Musical; School Play; Variety Show; Nwsp Rptr; Off Sr Cls; Wnnr Of Sing Vrty Shw Choreogrphr, Wrtr, Asst Dir 84; New York U; Theatr Arts.

MALDONADO, JENNIFER; Cardinal Spellman HS; Bronx, NY; (Y); Camera Clb; Dance Clb; Spanish Clb; Band; Yrbk Ed-Chief; Yrbk Phtg; Yrbk Stf; PA ST U; Bankg.

MALDONADO, JORGE; Seaford HS; Seaford, NY; (Y); Boys Clb Am; Boy Scts; Computer Clb; Chorus; JV Capt Socr; Trk; Hofstra; Bus Admin.

MALDONADO, NOREEN; A Philip Randolph Campus HS; Bronx, NY; (Y); Church Yth Grp; Office Aide; Service Clb; Chorus; Mrchg Band; Cheerleading; Med.

MALDONADO, VICTOR; De Witt Clinton HS; Bronx, NY; (Y); Church Yth Grp; Cmnty Wkr; Debate Tm; FCA; Hosp Aide; Intnl Clb; Key Clb; Library Aide; Office Aide; Red Cross Aide; Vlntary Svc Awd 83; Attnd Bond.

MALEADY, ANNE; St Peters H S For Girls; Staten Island, NY; (Y); 15/106; Church Yth Grp; Library Aide; Sec Chorus; Church Choir; School Play; Yrbk Stf; Lit Mag; Hon Roll; Prfct Atten Awd; Soc Studs Silver Medal 85; St Johns U; Elem Ed.

MALEADY, JOE; St Marys Acad; Hoosick Falls, NY; (Y); Yrbk Stf; JV Bsktbl; Coach Actv; Hnr Awd 83-84; Albany Bus Clg; Mktg.

MALEBRANCHE, DAVID; Notre Dame-Bishop Gibbons HS; Schenectady, NY; (S); 6/114; Rep Frsh Cls; Rep Stu Cncl; JV Bsktbl; JV Crs Cntry; Var Ftbl; JV Trk; High Hon Roll; NHS; U S Natl Leadership Merit Awd 84-85; Medicine.

MALEBRANCHE, MICHELLE; Notre-Dame Bishop Gibbons HS; Schenectady, NY; (S); 7/110; French Clb; Ski Clb; Rep Stu Cncl; Var Capt Bsktbl; JV Var Crs Cntry; Var Sftbl; High Hon Roll; Jr NHS; U S Natl Ldrshp Merit Awd 84-85; Natl Science Merit Awards 84-85; Biology.

MALECKI, ELISE A; Corning Painted Post West HS; Painted Post, NY; (Y); 1/241; Art Clb; Math Tm; Scholastic Bowl; Science Clb; Orch; School Musical; Nwsp Stf; JA; Band; Concert Band; All ST Band, Orch 83-84; NY ST Smmr Schl Arts 82; Natl Schltc Art Awds Gld Mdl 83; Case Western Reserve U; Biochem.

MALEK, MARK; Nottingham HS; Syracuse, NY; (Y); French Clb; Swmmng; Elect Engrng.

MALEK, RENAE L; Amherst Central HS; Snyder, NY; (Y); 50/300; French Clb; Pres GAA; Hosp Aide; Orch; Yrbk Phtg; Socr; High Hon Roll; NHS; NYS Rgnts Schlrshp 85; U NH; Micrbio.

MALGIERI, CATHY; Saugerties HS; Saugerties, NY; (Y); 27/250; Cit Awd; DAR Awd; High Hon Roll; NHS; Pre Law.

MALHOTRA, RAJ; Oneonta HS; Oneonta, NY; (Y); Drama Clb; Ski Clb; Thesps; Band; Concert Band; Jazz Band; Mrchg Band; School Musical; School Play; Stage Crew; Math.

MALIK, ZILLE H; Hillcrest HS; Richmond Hill, NY; (Y); 10/755; FNA; Hosp Aide; Math Tm; Teachers Aide; High Hon Roll; NHS; Prfct Atten Awd; Queens Coll Pres Awd-Achvt 84; Regents Schlrshp Nrsng 85; Med.

MALINCHOCK, SUZANNE; Lewiston-Porter HS; Lewiston, NY; (Y); 28/273; Cmnty Wkr; Hosp Aide; Teachers Aide; Yrbk Stf; Hon Roll; NHS; Lmp Lrng Awd Math, Sci, Lang 83; Lmp Lrng Awd Sci 84; Regnts Diplm 85; Niagara County CC; Lib Arts.

MALINOWSKI, BRIAN; Cardinal O Hara HS; Tonawanda, NY; (Y); Nwsp Phtg; Yrbk Phtg; Yrbk Rptr; Yrbk Stf; Im Bowling; Im Vllybl; Hon Roll; Niagara U; Coop Lawyer.

MALINOWSKI, LINDA; Seaford HS; Seaford, NY; (Y); Sec Jr Cls; JV Sftbl; Hon Roll; Bus.

MALKOFF, JASON A; Spring Valley SR Rt 59 HS; Spring Valley, NY; (Y); 34/435; Cmnty Wkr; Computer Clb; Math Clb; Math Tm; Band; Mrchg Band; Rep Frsh Cls; High Hon Roll; Hon Roll; Mu Alp Tht; Schlrshp Cert 82; Washington U St Louis:Engrng.

MALLAMACI, MICHAEL; Lewiston Porter SR HS; Lewiston, NY; (Y); 12/273; Scholastic Bowl; High Hon Roll; Hon Roll; NHS; Ntl Merit Ltr; Duke Wellngtn Memrl Schlrshp 85; Alfred U Presdntl Schlrshp 85; Alfred U Hnrs Prgrm 85; Alfred U; Ceramc Engnrng.

MALLANE, RICHARD; Seaford HS; Seaford, NY; (Y); Computer Clb; Hosp Aide; Intnl Clb; Varsity Clb; Bsbl; Ftbl; Ice Hcky; Hon Roll; Bsbl.

MALLEY, CHRISTOPHER; Galway Central HS; Broadalbin, NY; (Y); 10/80; Math Tm; Bsbl; Socr; High Hon Roll; Prfct Atten Awd; Mst Trustwrthy 83-84; JR Instr Martial Arts 84; Bst Technque 84-85; Clarkson U; Mech Engrng.

MALLEY, WENDY; Valley Central HS; Montgomery, NY; (Y); 85/260; Cmnty Wkr; Pres 4-H; Service Clb; Rep Frsh Cls; Var Cheerleading; JV Mat Maids; Stat Wrstlng; 4-H Awd; Prfct Atten Awd; Co-Op Ext Hrs Proj Awd 82-84; Sprtsmnshp Awd-Hrs Shw 82.

MALLORY, MICHAEL L; Paul V Moore HS; Central Sq, NY; (Y); 7/297; Am Leg Boys St; Math Tm; Pres Concert Band; Jazz Band; Mrchg Band; JP Sousa Awd; NHS; Pres Schlr; Drm & Bgl; Pep Band; Instrmntl Music Awd 85; NY ST Fld Bank Conf Awd 85; Youth Merit Awd 84; SUNY Potsdam; Music Ed.

MALLOW JR, RAY; Thomas A Edison HS; Elmira Hts, NY; (Y); Boy Scts; Church Yth Grp; Chorus; Church Choir; Hon Roll; Eagle Sct 85; Cornins Comm Coll; Auto Mech.

MALLOY, BRIAN; Oneonta SR HS; Oneonta, NY; (Y); Boys Clb Am; Church Yth Grp; Bsbl; Bowling; Phys Thrpy.

MALLOY, JERRY; Union-Endicott HS; Endicott, NY; (S); Concert Band; Jazz Band; Mrchg Band; Bsktbl; Suny Farmingdale; Aerospace Te.

MALLOY, SEAN; Morrisville-Easton Central Schl; Morrisville, NY; (Y); 11/60; Pres VP Am Leg Boys St; Band; Jazz Band; Mrchg Band; Variety Show; Nwsp Rptr; Nwsp Stf; Var Bsbl; Hon Roll; Prof Bnd Skylarks 85; Bio.

MALMQUIST, KAREN; Vestal Central SR HS; Vestal, NY; (Y); Pres Church Yth Grp; French Clb; Sec Girl Scts; Spanish Clb; Varsity Clb; Mrchg Band; Yrbk Stf; Rep Stu Cncl; Var L Fld Hcky; Hon Roll; Intrr Desgn.

MALONE, EVA M; Convent Of The Sacred Heart HS; New York, NY; (Y); Church Yth Grp; Girl Scts; Ntl Merit SF; NEDT Awd; Hnrb Mntn Literary Cntst Short Story 82-83; Ntl Achvt Schlrshp Prog Outstndng Negro Stus 84; Bus.

MALONE, MARIE; G Ray Bodley HS; Fulton, NY; (Y); Drama Clb; Orch; School Musical; School Play; Stage Crew; Prfct Atten Awd; Hgst Avg Frnch III 85; High Avg Physcl Sci 83; Ed.

MALONE, PATRICIA; Little Falls JR SR HS; Little Falls, NY; (Y); 18/109; Drama Clb; GAA; Girl Scts; Ski Clb; Spanish Clb; Band; Concert Band; Mrchg Band; School Play; Nwsp Stf; Bus.

MALONE, THOMAS F; Columbia HS; Castleton, NY; (Y); 8/353; Computer Clb; Var Tennis; Var Vllybl; High Hon Roll; NHS; Ntl Merit SF; NY Mathematics League Merit Awd 84; AFROTC Scholar 84; MA Inst Of Tech; Aerospace Eng.

MALONE, YVONNE; Wayland Central HS; Wayland, NY; (Y); 8/90; French Clb; FBLA; Office Aide; Hon Roll; Ntl Merit Ltr; Commrcl Awd-Gunlocke Co Inc 85; Whitehead Schlrshp Awd 85; Bryant & Stratton Bus Schl.

MALONEY, ADELE; Queen Of The Rosary HS; Wantagh, NY; (Y); Art Clb; Dance Clb; Stage Crew; Hon Roll; NHS; Dance Capt 84-85; Props Capt Sports Day 84-85.

MALONEY, DAN; Notre Dame HS; Elmira, NY; (Y); Church Yth Grp; Dance Clb; Pep Clb; Ski Clb; Spanish Clb; Varsity Clb; School Play; Rep Jr Cls; JV Var Bsbl; Im Bsktbl; Pupl Asstnc Lrning Awd 84-85; Alfred U; Bus.

MALONEY, JANE A; Ossining HS; Briarcliff, NY; (Y); Church Yth Grp; Model UN; Mrchg Band; Nwsp Rptr; Yrbk Ed-Chief; Sec Sr Cls; High Hon Roll; NCTE Awd; Rep Stu Cncl; JV Fld Hcky; Forgn Lang Achvt 82-84; Giftd & Talntd Prog 84; Engl.

MALONEY, KATHLEEN; St John The Baptist HS; Babylon, NY; (Y); Socr; High Hon Roll; Hon Roll; Jr NHS; Accntng.

MALONEY, MARY; Nazareth Acad; Rochester, NY; (Y); Dance Clb; Exploring; French Clb; Latin Clb; Pres Concert Band; Jazz Band; School Musical; French Hon Soc; Hon Roll; NHS; Psych.

MALONEY, PATRICK; Fordham Prep; Mamaroneck, NY; (Y); Camera Clb; Chess Clb; Computer Clb; Ski Clb; Camp Fr Inc; Yrbk Rptr; Rep Soph Cls; VP Jr Cls; Var Capt Wrstlng; Hon Roll; MVP Wrstlng Tm 83-85; Cathlc Champs 83-85; Fairfield U; Bus.

MALONEY, WILLIAM J; Archbishop Stepinac HS; Harrison, NY; (Y); 7/206; Lit Mag; Rep Frsh Cls; JV L Socr; JV L Trk; High Hon Roll; NHS; St Schlr; Teachers Aide; Im Bsktbl; Gov Hon Prg Awd; Siena Clg Hnrary Schlrshp 85; PBA Acad Schlrshp 85; Chem Natl Sci Olympiad Awd 85; Siena Clg; Bio.

MALOY, BETHANNE; Notre Dame Acad HS; Staten Island, NY; (Y); Sec Trs Church Yth Grp; Stage Crew; Nwsp Stf; JV Sftbl; Fashion Inst Tech; Fashn Desgn.

MALPHURS, JULIE; Guilderland Central HS; Schenectady, NY; (Y); Drama Clb; Service Clb; JV Socr; High Hon Roll; Hon Roll; NEDT Awd; Prfct Atten Awd; Hgh Achvt Spnsh Awd 85; Acad Exclnc Hnr Awd Mdl 84; GA Tech; Pre-Med.

MALSEGNA, DAVID R; Hilton HS; Hilton, NY; (Y); Exploring; French Clb; Math Clb; Ski Clb; Band; Jazz Band; Mrchg Band; Crs Cntry; JV Ftbl; Socr; Engrng.

MALSKIS, MELINDA; Longwood HS; Ridge, NY; (S); 3/487; Trs Key Clb; Math Tm; Nwsp Stf; Yrbk Sprt Ed; Sec Sr Cls; Capt Var Socr; Capt Var Sftbl; Var L Trk; High Hon Roll; NHS; West Point; Comp Sci.

MALTBY, PATRICIA; West Seneca East SR HS; West Seneca, NY; (Y); Cmnty Wkr; Nwsp Stf; High Hon Roll; Jr NHS; Merit Awds Spnsh; U Of Buffalo; Nrs.

MALTESE, KARLENE; Notre Dame HS; Utica, NY; (Y); 44/176; Am Leg Aux Girls St; Nwsp Rptr; Yrbk Rptr; Pres VP Stu Cncl; Score Keeper; Trk; Vllybl; Hon Roll; Ntl Merit Ltr; Miss Natl Teen Fnlst-NY ST 85; Schl Svc Awd 85; Hartwick Coll Poetry Cont Fnlst 85; Mohawk Valley CC; Psych.

MALTIE, GAYLA; Freeport HS; Freeport, NY; (Y); Computer Clb; Dance Clb; Key Clb; Band; Concert Band; Mrchg Band; Rep Stu Cncl; Mgr(s); Score Keeper; JV Vllybl; Nassau Comm Coll; Comm.

MALUENDA, ANNETTE; Domincan Acad; Elmhurst, NY; (Y); Latin Clb; Science Clb; Church Choir; School Musical; Nwsp Stf; Yrbk Stf; Rep Stu Cncl; Hon Roll; NHS; Awd Silver Medal & Cert Of Maxima Cum Laude In Natl Latin Exam 84; Pre Law.

MAMALAKIS, KATINA; St Edmund HS; Brooklyn, NY; (Y); 30/187; French Clb; Nwsp Rptr; Hon Roll; Ntl Bus Hnr Soc; Baruch Coll; Bus Admn.

MAMMONE, JYLL; Hudson Falls SR HS; Ft Edward, NY; (Y); 6/215; French Hon Soc; Hon Roll; NHS.

MAN, CHIUMING; Brooklyn Technical HS; Brooklyn, NY; (Y); Math Tm; Office Aide; Hon Roll; NHS; Prfct Atten Awd; Cmmrcl Artst.

MANALASTAS, CARMEN; Jamaica HS; Hollis, NY; (Y); Cmnty Wkr; FBLA; JA; Science Clb; Nwsp Bus Mgr; High Hon Roll; Hon Roll; NHS; Pres Schlr; Dance Clb; Stck Mkt Gm Wnnr 85; Pres Acad Ftnss Awd 85; TV Intrvw W/David Attenborough 84; Baruch; Fin.

MANCHESTER, SCOTT; Southside HS; Wellsburg, NY; (Y); Am Leg Boys St; Pres Church Yth Grp; Drama Clb; Latin Clb; Chorus; Church Choir; Madrigals; School Musical; School Play; Hon Roll; Acctng.

MANCINI, CHRISTOPHER; Bishop Scully HS; Amsterdam, NY; (S); 2/60; Latin Clb; Math Clb; Pres Soph Cls; JV Var Ftbl; High Hon Roll; NHS; RPI; Aeron Engr.

MANCINI, DAWN R; Bronx High School Of Science; Bronx, NY; (Y); Hosp Aide; Key Clb; Office Aide; Lit Mag; Hon Roll; NHS; Spnsh Awd 85; United Hosp Fund Vlntr Serv Awd 85; United Fed Of Tchrs Schlrshp 85; Vassar Clg; Lib Arts.

MANCINI, GEMMA; St Vincent Ferrer HS; Astoria, NY; (Y); 31/114; Cmnty Wkr; Hosp Aide; Teachers Aide; Ed Nwsp Stf; Yrbk Phtg; Hon Roll; Educ.

MANCINO, ANTHONY; St Raymonds Boys HS; Bronx, NY; (Y); 20/189; Computer Clb; Math Tm; Yrbk Ed-Chief; Yrbk Stf; High Hon Roll; Manhattan.

MANCUSO, ELLEN; Sacred Heart Acad; Buffalo, NY; (Y); Pres Spanish Clb; Stage Crew; Im Crs Cntry; Im Trk; Crmnl Jstc.

MANCUSO, JANET; Lincoln HS; Yonkers, NY; (S); #17 In Class; Chorus; Nwsp Rptr; Nwsp Stf; Rep Sr Cls; Rep Stu Cncl; Hon Roll; Sci.

MANCUSO, JULIE; Pelham Memorial HS; Pelham, NY; (Y); Model UN; Ski Clb; Nwsp Rptr; Lit Mag; Var L Fld Hcky; Var L Lcrss; Hon Roll; NHS; Political Wkr; Var Twrlr; Bus.

MANCUSO, NOEL; Churchville-Chili HS; Rochester, NY; (Y); VP JCL; Yrbk Bus Mgr; Rep Stu Cncl; Var Swmmng; Var Trk; Var Wrstlng; High Hon Roll; NHS; JV Crs Cntry; Schltc Ath Wrstlng 85; Maxima Cum Lauda Natl Latin Exam 82; U S Naval Acad; Elec Engrng.

MANDARINO, LUCIA; St Catharine Acad; Bronx, NY; (Y); 4/205; NHS; Acdmc All Amer; Frdhm U; Pre-Law.

MANDARO, RICHARD; St John The Baptist DHS; Deer Park, NY; (Y); 50/575; Exploring; MMM; Band; Concert Band; Jazz Band; Mrchg Band; Var Golf; Im Socr; High Hon Roll; Hon Roll; Lng Islnd Physcs Olympcs Tm; Elec Engrng.

MANDAVA, SURESH; Arlington HS; Poughkeepsie, NY; (Y); 8/558; Math Tm; Band; Concert Band; Jazz Band; Mrchg Band; High Hon Roll; Ntl Merit SF; Elec Engr.

MANDEL, ALICIA; Wilson Central HS; Ransomville, NY; (Y); FBLA; Library Aide; Science Clb; Ski Clb; Y-Teens; Chorus; High Hon Roll; Hon Roll; Ntl Merit Ltr; VFW Awd; Gregg Awds Typg 84; Typg Cntst 84-85; Typg Competn 85; Bryan & Stratton; Bus Mgmt.

MANDEL, HARRY B; Mt Vernon HS; Mt Vernon, NY; (Y); 8/590; Library Aide; Trs Frsh Cls; High Hon Roll; Hon Roll; Jr NHS; Prfct Atten Awd; NY ST Regents Schlrshp 85; 1st Local MMA Math Contest 85; Stu Of Month 85; Reusselair; Computer Sci.

MANDEL, PETER J; Francis Lewis HS; Queens Village, NY; (Y); 47/527; Math Tm; Office Aide; Prfct Atten Awd; Rgnts Schlrshp 85; WSUC Schlrshp 85; NY U; Biology.

MANDEL, SUSAN; Bay Shore HS; Brightwaters, NY; (Y); 29/425; Cmnty Wkr; Office Aide; Mrchg Band; Yrbk Stf; Lit Mag; Stu Cncl; Var Socr; Var Sftbl; High Hon Roll; NHS; Mst Imprvd Plyr Sftbl 84; Ldng Scorer JV Sccr 83-84; Engl Achvt Awd 83; Law.

MANDELBAUM, IVY; South Shore HS; Brooklyn, NY; (Y); Drama Clb; Y-Teens; Chorus; School Musical; School Play; Yrbk Rptr; Yrbk Stf; SUNY; Engl.

MANDERA, CINDY; John H Glenn HS; E Northport, NY; (Y); Drama Clb; FHA; Chorus; Nwsp Rptr; Sec Rep Frsh Cls; Rep Soph Cls; Rep Hst Jr Cls; Trk; High Hon Roll; Hon Roll; Gifted Talntd Pgm.

MANDERY, EVAN; East Meadow HS; E Meadow, NY; (S); 1/414; Math Tm; Jazz Band; Symp Band; Nwsp Ed-Chief; Capt Bowling; Golf; NHS; Val; Computer Clb; Rep Stu Cncl; Rensselear Polytechnic Inst Awd For Execll In Math & Pysics 84; US Senate Yth Pro NY St Fin 84.

MANDIA, RALPH P; Batavia SR HS; Batavia, NY; (Y); Am Leg Boys St; VP Exploring; Political Wkr; Ski Clb; Var L Ftbl; JV Socr; Bus.

MANDILE, JOSEPH A; Cardinal Spellman HS; Brooklyn, NY; (Y); Pres Church Yth Grp; Im Bowling; Var Crs Cntry; Var Trk; Hon Roll; Regents Schlrshp NY 85; 2nd Hnrs 85; Army Accntng.

MANDYCK, JOHN M; Owego Free Acad; Endicott, NY; (Y); 19/235; Am Leg Boys St; Key Clb; Political Wkr; Ski Clb; Nwsp Ed-Chief; Stu Cncl; Golf; Cit Awd; High Hon Roll; JC Awd; Soc Studys Dept Hnrs 85; Edward Hubbard Memrl Schlrshp 85; Syracuse U; Pblc Affrs.

MANDZYK, CHRISTINE; Mount Saint Mary Acad; Buffalo, NY; (Y); Civic Clb; Girl Scts; Spanish Clb; Church Choir; Bio.

MANEEN, MARK S; Frankfort Schuyler HS; Frankfort, NY; (Y); Am Leg Boys St; Church Yth Grp; Rep Frsh Cls; Rep Jr Cls; Rep Stu Cncl; Golf; High Hon Roll; Hon Roll; NHS.

MANEL, JAMES E; Longwood HS; Coram, NY; (Y); 120/500; Am Leg Boys St; VP Computer Clb; Key Clb; Political Wkr; Ed Nwsp Stf; Yrbk Stf; Coach Actv; Socr; Hon Roll; Aviatn.

MANERI, ANTHONY; Cathedral Prep Seminary; Glendale, NY; (Y); Spanish Clb; Nwsp Stf; Sec Frsh Cls; JV Bsktbl; Hon Roll; Pace U; Crmnl Lwyr.

MANETTI, CAROLYN; The Masters Schl; Tarrytown, NY; (Y); Drama Clb; Library Aide; Chorus; School Musical; School Play; Stage Crew; Rep Frsh Cls; Im Fld Hcky; Hon Roll; Law.

MANEY, JAMES S; Holy Trinity HS; Hicksville, NY; (S); Cmnty Wkr; Chrmn Math Clb; Math Tm; Ski Clb; Bowling; Ftbl; Cert Of Awd Spnsh 82-83; Math Schlrshp Awd 83-84; St John U; Accntng.

MANFREDI, RALPH; East Islip HS; Islip Terrace, NY; (Y); Band; Im Bsktbl; Im Ftbl; Ice Hcky; Im Sftbl; Swmmng; Im Vllybl; Wt Lftg; Hon Roll; NY Inst Tech; Engrng.

MANG, JACOB; Kenmore West HS; Kenmore, NY; (Y); 12/450; Math Tm; Political Wkr; Quiz Bowl; JV Socr; JV Trk; Im Vllybl; High Hon Roll; Prfct Atten Awd; NY ST Sci Supv Assn Bio Awd 84; Math.

MANGAN, MICHELE; Liverpool HS; Liverpool, NY; (Y); 115/800; Church Yth Grp; 4-H; Varsity Clb; Color Guard; Concert Band; Mrchg Band; Rep Jr Cls; Var Gym; Hon Roll; Jr NHS; Pres Phys Fit Awd 78-79; U Buffalo; Comp Sci.

MANGIARACINA, DENISE A; Fontbonne Hall Acad; Brooklyn, NY; (Y); Church Yth Grp; Cmnty Wkr; Dance Clb; Ski Clb; Teachers Aide; Chorus; Variety Show; Cheerleading; Pom Pon; Math.

MANGIAROTTI, MARIA; Bishop Kearney HS; Brooklyn, NY; (Y); Office Aide; High Hon Roll; Hon Roll; NHS; Frgn Lang Awd Itln 83; Trvl.

MANGINELL, RONALD; Churchville Chili S HS; Churchville, NY; (Y); Boy Scts; Church Yth Grp; Drama Clb; Office Aide; Ski Clb; Chorus; NHS; Ftbl; Gym; Lcrss; David Wagner Memrl Awd Ftbl 83; Hochstein Music Schl 84-85; Cornell; Phy Sci.

MANGINELLI, CHERYL; Newfield HS; Seldne, NY; (Y); Church Yth Grp; GAA; Political Wkr; VICA; Bsktbl; Hon Roll; Nrs.

MANGIONE, HENRY; Saugerties HS; Saugerties, NY; (S); 11/245; Yrbk Stf; VP Sr Cls; Vllybl; DAR Awd; High Hon Roll; Hon Roll; NHS; Ntl Merit Ltr; NROTC Schlrshp 84-85; NYS Reg Schlrshp Recpnt 85; NY U.

MANGIONE, LORI; Churchville Chili SR HS; Rochester, NY; (Y); Mathletes; Chorus; Vllybl; Hon Roll; All ST & All Cnty Chrs.

MANGRA, NARENDRA; Central Islip HS; Central Islip, NY; (Y); 20/450; Math Clb; JV Tennis; High Hon Roll; NHS; Prfct Atten Awd; Stu Orgnztn & Rgnts Schlrshps 85; Syracuse U; Aerospc Engrng.

MANICCIA, DAYNA M; Linton HS; Schenectady, NY; (Y); JCL; Office Aide; Rep Jr Cls; Off Stu Cncl; JV Cheerleading; JV Var Pom Pon; JV Var Tennis; JV Trk; Hon Roll; Phys Ther.

MANIGAT, NANCY; Christ The King Regional HS; Cambria Hts, NY; (Y); 18/385; Church Choir; Yrbk Stf; Gym; Hon Roll; NHS; Prncpls List; Hampton U; Psych.

MANIGAULT, SANDRA; Aquinas HS; Bronx, NY; (Y); 12/178; Drama Clb; Girl Scts; Hosp Aide; Jazz Band; High Hon Roll; Miss Charity Socialteers 84-85; Syracuse U; Comp Sci.

MANINGAS, MARISSA; Franklin Acad HS; Burke, NY; (S); 2/253; Varsity Clb; Trs Soph Cls; Fld Hcky; Trk; High Hon Roll; Hon Roll; NHS; Sal; French Clb; Yrbk Stf; Epsilon Ball Queen 85; Most Impv Athl Outdoor Track 83; Cert Merity NYS Art Tchrs Assoc 83; Ithaca Coll; Phy Thrpy.

MANION, ANDREA; Bishop Scully HS; Amsterdam, NY; (Y); 13/60; Drama Clb; VP JA; Political Wkr; Band; Drill Tm; Yrbk Stf; Rep Stu Cncl; Hon Roll; NHS; Girl Scts; Pol Sci.

MANION, TERESA; Saranac Central HS; Cadyville, NY; (Y); Concert Band; Variety Show; Timer; High Hon Roll; Hon Roll; NHS; Music.

MANLEY, LISA; Fayetteville-Manlius HS; Manlius, NY; (Y); Church Yth Grp; JCL; Variety Show; Im Socr; JV Sftbl; Var L Tennis; L Var Trk; Hon Roll; Natl Latin Exam Cum Laude 83; Busn Mngmnt.

MANLEY, SARAH; Albion SR HS; Albion, NY; (S); 4/176; Latin Clb; Hon Roll; NHS; Hnr Grad 84-85; Regnts Schlrshp 85; U Dayton; Mech Engrng.

MANN, BONNIE; Bradford Central HS; Bradford, NY; (S); 4/30; FBLA; Camp Fr Inc; Yrbk Ed-Chief; Trs Stu Cncl; Var Capt Bsktbl; Var Capt Socr; Var Capt Sftbl; Timer; Var Capt Vllybl; Trs NHS; Lyman Sheilds Capt Awd; Army Reserve Schlr/Athl Awd; US Marine Corps.

MANN, DAVID; Cicero-North Syracuse HS; North Syracuse, NY; (S); 3/711; Am Leg Boys St; Exploring; Mathletes; Math Tm; Quiz Bowl; Var Tennis; Pres NHS; Ntl Merit Ltr; Optmst Clb Awd 84; Chmbr Comm Schlstc Awd 84; Biochem.

MANN, DEBORAH; Onondaga HS; Syracuse, NY; (S); German Clb; Quiz Bowl; Science Clb; Ski Clb; Spanish Clb; Chorus; Pres Jr Cls; High Hon Roll; NHS; Church Yth Grp; Highest Grd NY ST Bio Regents 84; Med.

MANN, LISA; Vestal Central SR HS; Vestal, NY; (Y); Church Yth Grp; French Clb; Ski Clb; Color Guard; Mrchg Band; Rep Frsh Cls; Rep Soph Cls; Rep Stu Cncl; Var Trk; Leg Intern 84-85; Bus Admin.

MANN, PAMELA; St Francis Prep; Jamaica, NY; (S); Intnl Clb; Chorus; Nwsp Rptr; Hon Roll; Acad All-Amer 84-85.

MANN, ROBERT M; Lawrence HS; Woodmere, NY; (Y); 3/379; Debate Tm; Political Wkr; Y-Teens; Yrbk Phtg; Rep Stu Cncl; Hnr Spkr 85; Lv Dodd Schlrshp 85; Outstndng Physcs Stu 84; U Penn; Intl Rel.

MANNE, KARL E; Pineview Christian Acad; Delmar, NY; (Y); 1/9; Yrbk Ed-Chief; Yrbk Phtg; Yrbk Stf; Pres Jr Cls; VP Sr Cls; Pres Stu Cncl; Var Capt Socr; Val; Hartwick Coll Onedonta; Law.

MANNI, CHRISTINA; Seton Catholic Central HS; Binghamton, NY; (Y); Church Yth Grp; GAA; Pep Clb; Ski Clb; Varsity Clb; Yrbk Stf; JV Cheerleading; Hon Roll; Berklee; Mktng.

MANNIELLO, KIMBERLY; Cold Spring Harbor HS; Cold Spng Harbor, NY; (Y); 19/130; Mathletes; Chorus; School Musical; Yrbk Bus Mgr; Rep Frsh Cls; Rep Soph Cls; Rep Jr Cls; Var Fld Hcky; Var Sftbl; High Hon Roll.

MANNING, ANNE M; Nichols HS; Snyder, NY; (Y); 3/111; Service Clb; Yrbk Rptr; Lit Mag; Off Frsh Cls; Bsktbl; Fld Hcky; Mgr(s); Trk; Hon Roll; Ntl Merit Ltr; Smith Coll; Jrnlsm.

MANNING, ERIC A; Henninger HS; Syracuse, NY; (Y); Church Yth Grp; Capt Var Ftbl; Capt Var Lcrss; Im Wt Lftg; JV Wrstlng; Hon Roll.

MANNING, HOPE; Ti Conderoga HS; Ticonderoga, NY; (Y); Key Clb; Latin Clb; Chorus; Yrbk Stf; Stat Bsktbl; Mgr(s); Hon Roll; Fclty Advsr Awd 83; North Cntry CC.

MANNING, KATHARINA; Willsboro Central Schl; Willsboro, NY; (S); 1/38; Girl Scts; Quiz Bowl; Jazz Band; Trs Soph Cls; Trs Jr Cls; Var Golf; Var Socr; Hon Roll; NHS; Ntl Merit Ltr; Girl Sct Slvr Star Awd 83; Marian Med Awd 83; All Cty Band 84-85.

MANNING, SIDNEY; Corning East HS; Corning, NY; (Y); 36/236; JA; Political Wkr; Yrbk Bus Mgr; Yrbk Phtg; High Hon Roll; Hon Roll; Pres Schlr; Corning CC; Comp Sci.

MANNING, SUSAN; Union Endicott HS; Endicott, NY; (Y); Church Yth Grp; Sec Girl Scts; Mathletes; Color Guard; Concert Band; Mrchg Band; Yrbk Stf; High Hon Roll; Hon Roll; NHS; Engr.

MANNINO, ANNA MARIA; Deer Park HS; Deer Park, NY; (Y); 39/375; Orch; JV Vllybl; High Hon Roll; Hon Roll; Excllnce Italn 84; Cert Orch 83; Nassau CC; Bus.

MANNINO, MATTHEW; Archbishop Molloy HS; Whitestone, NY; (Y); Im Bsbl; Im Bsktbl; Crs Cntry; Im Ftbl; Im Sftbl; Im Wt Lftg; Crim Just.

MANNINO, PETER; V S Central HS; Valley Stream, NY; (Y); Mathletes; Ski Clb; Nwsp Rptr; Im Lcrss; Im JV Socr; Jr NHS; Mu Alp Tht; NHS; Italian Hnr Scty 84; MVP Awd In Soccer 83; Hnr Usher Cls Grad 85; Pre Med.

MANNION, JOHN; Bishop Ludden HS; Syracuse, NY; (S); Boys Clb Am; Church Yth Grp; Mgr Bsktbl; Var Socr; Var Tennis; Cit Awd; High Hon Roll; NHS; New England; Med.

MANNIX, DANIEL; Garden City HS; Garden City, NY; (Y); 125/330; Stu Cncl; JV Var Bsktbl; Coach Actv; Var Socr; Var Capt Tennis; High Hon Roll; Sprtsmnshp Awd Bsktbl 85; U Of Richmond.

MANNIX, DANIEL J; St Marys Acad; Glens Falls, NY; (Y); 14/40; AFS; Computer Clb; Drama Clb; French Clb; Math Clb; Pep Clb; ROTC; Varsity Clb; Drill Tm; Stage Crew; NY ST Regents Schlrshp 85; AZ ST U; Aero Space Engrng.

MANNO, JOSEPH; Herkimer HS; Herkimer, NY; (Y); Var L Bsktbl; Var Ftbl; Trk; Air Force CC; Comp Prgrmr.

MANNO, NINA; Bronx High School Of Science; New York, NY; (Y); Manhattan Borough Pres Cert Excel 82; Eva Fialkoff Mem Schlrshp 85; Allegheny Coll; Ed.

MANOLESCU, KIMBERLY; Notre Dame HS; Utica, NY; (Y); 51/207; Art Clb; Pep Clb; Ski Clb; Varsity Clb; Nwsp Rptr; Nwsp Stf; Yrbk Stf; Rep Frsh Cls; Stu Cncl; Cheerleading; Bst Acad Art Awd 85; Ithaca Coll; Acctng.

MANOLI, VICTOR R; Cairo-Durham HS; Acra, NY; (Y); Boy Scts; Camera Clb; Church Yth Grp; Band; Hon Roll; Ntl Merit Ltr; Comp.

MANOOKIAN, KIMBERLY; New Dorp HS; Staten Island, NY; (Y); Cmnty Wkr; Girl Scts; Intnl Clb; Library Aide; Office Aide; Teachers Aide; Band; Chorus; Concert Band; Symp Band; Hon Rl 83-85; SUNY Oswego; Psych.

MANOR, TAMARA L; Northeaster Clinton Central HS; Rouses Point, NY; (Y); 58/146; Model UN; Band; Concert Band; Nwsp Rptr; Yrbk Stf; Sec Stu Cncl; Var Crs Cntry; Hon Roll; Pep Band; Regents Schlrshp 85; Ortrcl Cont 84; NE U-Boston; Jrnlsm.

MANOUVELOS, FOTIS; Middletown HS; Middletown, NY; (Y); VP Soph Cls; VP Jr Cls; Off Stu Cncl; Var L Ftbl; Wt Lftg; 1st Tm Lnbckr-Sunday Recrd Tri-Cnty All Star Ftbl Tm 84; Bus Admin.

MANSELL, SCOTT; Mynderse Acad; Seneca Falls, NY; (Y); 22/150; Var L Bsbl; Var L Ftbl; Var L Wrstlng; Hon Roll; MVP Wrstlg 84; Pride Awd Bsbl 85; Stu Of Mnth 85; Art.

MANSFIELD, DAVE; Alden Central HS; E Aurora, NY; (Y); 40/198; Church Yth Grp; Letterman Clb; Science Clb; Varsity Clb; Stu Cncl; Var Ftbl; Var Trk; Hon Roll; Rchstr Inst Of Tech; Comp Sci.

MANSFIELD, SEAN F; Saratoga Springs SR HS; Saratoga Springs, NY; (Y); 27/435; Key Clb; Ski Clb; Jazz Band; Rep Soph Cls; High Hon Roll; NHS; NYS Regnts Schlrshp 85; Alfred U; Cermc Engr.

MANSLEY, TOM; Connetquot HS; Bohemia, NY; (Y); Chess Clb; Math Tm; School Play; Socr; Hon Roll; Jr NHS; Ntl Merit SF; Bus Adm.

MANSOUR, DAVID; Niagara Falls HS; Niagara Falls, NY; (Y); 2/225; Church Yth Grp; French Clb; Key Clb; Library Aide; Quiz Bowl; Sec Sr Cls; Var Capt Crs Cntry; Var Capt Trk; High Hon Roll; Hon Roll; Cert Of Achvt In Natl Hstry Day 85.

MANSOURI, RICHARD; Horseheads HS; Horseheads, NY; (Y); 7/405; Am Leg Boys St; Drama Clb; JCL; Science Clb; School Musical; Pres Stu Cncl; Im Ice Hcky; Trs NHS; Ntl Merit Ltr; Mrchng Bnd 1st Pl In Novice Clss, 3rd Pl In AA Clss 81-85; Biomed Engrng.

MANTAI, MICHAEL; Fredonia HS; Fredonia, NY; (Y); 3/186; Am Leg Boys St; French Clb; Concert Band; Jazz Band; Orch; School Musical; Yrbk Stf; Var Bsktbl; Var Socr; Var Tennis; Biomed Engrng.

MANTALBANO, ANGELA; Ogdensburg Free Acad; Ogdensburg, NY; (Y); Trs Key Clb; Chorus; School Play; Yrbk Stf; Var L Crs Cntry; Capt Stat Ice Hcky; Im Socr; Var L Trk; Im Vllybl; Brockport U; Biolgcl Sci.

MANTANI, ANNA LYNN; St Peters Girls HS; Staten Island, NY; (Y); 1/110; Capt Var Cheerleading; Cit Awd; High Hon Roll; Pres NHS; Val; Math Clb; Soroptimist; Chorus; Sec Frsh Cls; Pres Soph Cls; Regents Schlrshp Awd 85; Am Chem Soc Awd 84; Outstndng Sr 84-85; Cornell U; Fd Sci.

MANTELL, TANIA; Midwood HS; Brooklyn, NY; (Y); Library Aide; Math Tm; Model UN; Y-Teens; Chorus; Orch; School Play; Var Cheerleading; Var Pom Pon; Var Socr; Swm Tm Athl Awds 84-86; Acadmc Awds 84; Attndnc Awds 83-85; Binghamton.

MANTELLO, JOSEPH; Niskayuna HS; Schenectady, NY; (Y); Key Clb; JV L Bsbl; JV L Bsktbl; Var L Ftbl; Ntl Merit Ltr; Mechncl Engrng.

MANTELLO, LYNNE; Ellenville HS; Ellenville, NY; (Y); 3/119; VP AFS; Science Clb; Acpl Chr; Jazz Band; School Musical; Yrbk Stf; Capt Tennis; High Hon Roll; NHS; Pres Drama Clb; Prncpl Clarinet Area All-ST Band 84-85; Alt All-ST Band 84-85; Siena Coll; Pre-Med.

MANTHEY, JEFFREY; Peekskill HS; Peekskill, NY; (S); 3/180; Boy Scts; Pres Stu Cncl; Var L Ftbl; Var L Golf; Capt L Swmmng; High Hon Roll; NHS; Engrng.

MANTUANO, SILVIO; Holy Cross HS; Flushing, NY; (Y); Chem.

MANUELE, DONNA; East Meadows HS; East Meadow, NY; (S); Orch; Lcrss; Mgr(s); Score Keeper; Hon Roll; NYSSMA Outstndng Awd 82-84; Advertising.

MANYIN, MARK; Washingtonville HS; Blooming Gro Ve, NY; (Y); 1/300; Pres Temple Yth Grp; Band; Jazz Band; Pep Band; Yrbk Stf; Stu Cncl; Tennis; NHS; Voice Dem Awd; Math Clb; Rensselaer Mdl 85; Hnr Campr New Englnd Music Cmp 84.

MANZARI, H JOHN; Mynderse Acad; Seneca Falls, NY; (S); 2/142; Intnl Clb; Model UN; Yrbk Bus Mgr; Pres Soph Cls; Pres Jr Cls; Crs Cntry; Trk; DAR Awd; High Hon Roll; NHS; Hugh O Brien Ldrshp Awd Sem 84; Red Cross Ldrshp Awd Sem 84.

MANZELLA, KATHLEEN A; Bethelhem Central HS; Slingerlands, NY; (Y); 60/338; Pres Key Clb; VP Stu Cncl; DAR Awd; NHS; Ntl Merit SF; Pres Schlr; VFW Awd; Am Assn Rtrd Prsns Ctznshp Awd 85; D U Rose Mem Schlrshp 85-86; Rgnts Schlrshps 85-89; Drew U; Intl Rel.

MANZELLA, LENORA; Mercy HS; Center Moriches, NY; (Y); 1/124; Nwsp Ed-Chief; Yrbk Rptr; High Hon Roll; Sec NHS; Rotary Awd; St Schlr; Val; Drama Clb; French Clb; Girl Scts; Schlrshps-Ntl Hnr Soc, Assctd U Inc Trste & Bryn Mawr Coll-Grnt 85; Bryn Mawr Coll; Pre Law.

MANZIN, ROBERTA; H Frank Carey HS; West Hempstead, NY; (Y); 65/281; FBLA; VP Spanish Clb; Pom Pon; High Hon Roll; Hon Roll; H Frank Careys Outstndg Bus Admin Stu 84-85; Natl Hon Roll 84-85; 1st Pl Bus Law FBLA Dist Cmptn 85; St Johns U; Acctg.

MANZO, ANDREW K; Farmingdale SR HS; Farmingdale, NY; (Y); 43/625; Pres Key Clb; Mrchg Band; Orch; School Musical; Symp Band; Variety Show; Yrbk Ed-Chief; Var Tennis; NHS; St Schlr; Boston Coll; Lwyr.

MANZO, KENNETH; V S Central HS; Valley Stream, NY; (Y); Computer Clb; Socr; Hon Roll; Prfct Atten Awd; St Johns U; Phrmcy.

MANZOLINA, SANDRA; Longwood HS; Coram, NY; (Y); 73/493; Hosp Aide; Pep Clb; Variety Show; Cheerleading; Hon Roll; Pol Sci.

MAPES, KAREN; Riverside HS; Buffalo, NY; (Y); Debate Tm; Library Aide; Rep Stu Cncl; DAR Awd; Hon Roll; VFW Awd; U Of Buffalo; Acctg.

MAPES, LISA; Lansing HS; Groton, NY; (Y); Pres 4-H; Chorus; Madrigals; Orch; School Musical; Nwsp Rptr; Golf; Cit Awd; High Hon Roll; NHS; Intl Bus.

MAPLE, HENRY; Yonkers HS; Yonkers, NY; (Y); Aud/Vis; Scholastic Bowl; Chorus; Stage Crew; Off Sr Cls; Bsktbl; Ftbl; Wt Lftg; High Hon Roll; Hon Roll.

MAPP, LEA; John Dewey HS; Brooklyn, NY; (Y); Teachers Aide; Lit Mag; Rep Jr Cls; Law.

MAPSTONE, BARBARA; Newburgh Free Acad; New Windsor, NY; (Y); 4/720; Church Yth Grp; Chorus; Church Choir; Orch; School Musical; Yrbk Stf; Pres Soph Cls; JV Cheerleading; JV Vllybl; Cit Awd; Acad Schlrshp Houghton Coll 85; Outstndg Music Tlnt Merit 81-82; NY ST Regents Schlrshp 85; Houghton Coll; Bio.

MAPSTONE, ROBERT; Newburgh Free Acad; New Windsor, NY; (Y); Church Yth Grp; Band; Chorus; Church Choir; Concert Band; School Musical; Yrbk Stf; JV Bsktbl; JV Socr; JV Trk; Hougton Coll; Cmrcl Art.

MAR, GARY; Sheepshead Bay HS; Brooklyn, NY; (Y); Library Aide; Math Tm; Teachers Aide; Yrbk Stf; Var Crs Cntry; Var Trk; Hon Roll; VP Of Arista-Archon 83; Rcvd The Govrnrs Awd 83; Tied For 1st Pl In Sci Fair 83; Econ.

MAR, MAUNG; Brooklyn Tech; New York, NY; (Y); 150/1200; Office Aide; Science Clb; Hon Roll; Prfct Atten Awd; Cornell U; Elec Engr.

MAR, MILLIE; Sheepshead Bay HS; Brooklyn, NY; (Y); Teachers Aide; Socr; Vllybl; Hon Roll; Baruch Coll; Court Rprtr.

MAR, PATRICIA; Seward Park HS; Brooklyn, NY; (Y); School Musical; Vllybl; Prfct Atten Awd; Stwrds.

MARABELLO, DONNA; Bishop Kearney HS; Brooklyn, NY; (S); 18/365; Art Clb; Hon Roll; NHS.

MARADAY, THOMAS; Newburgh Free Acad; Newburgh, NY; (Y); Church Yth Grp; Varsity Clb; Var Bsbl; JV Bsktbl; JV Var Ftbl; Var Vllybl; Var Wt Lftg; Physcl Thrpy.

MARAGIOGLIO, KAREN; East Islip HS; Islip Ter, NY; (Y); 4-H; Flag Corp; Mrchg Band; Im Vllybl; 4-H Awd; Hon Roll; Italian Frgn Lang Hnr Scty 84-85; Frgn Exchng Clb Mbr VP 83-85; Wrk As Page In E Islip Pblc Lbry 82; CPA.

MARAN, SUSAN K; Southampton HS; Water Mill, NY; (Y); 3/108; Drama Clb; Sec VP GAA; Yrbk Bus Mgr; Ed Lit Mag; Pres Sr Cls; Var Cheerleading; Var Capt Fld Hcky; Sec NHS; Cmnty Wkr; French Clb; Hugh O Brian Yth Ldrshp Seminar Rep 83; Rotary Summer Exchange To Finland 83; U Of VA; Psychology.

MARANO, ANNA E; St Johns Prep HS; Middle Village, NY; (Y); 3/415; Yrbk Stf; High Hon Roll; NHS; Trustee Schrshp Pace U 85; Trustees Awd Exc Math 85; Eng Novel Awd; Cert Merit 85; Pace U; Acctng.

MARANTZ, DYLAN; Westhampton Beach HS; East Moriches, NY; (Y); 18/232; French Clb; Latin Clb; VP Temple Yth Grp; Band; Mrchg Band; JV Bsktbl; Var Ftbl; JV Golf; Hon Roll; Mc Gill U; Med.

MARASCA, JO ANNE; Holy Trinity HS; Westbury, NY; (S); Math Clb; Hon Roll; Cert Of Achvmnt Seq I Hnrs 83; Cert Of Achvmnt Seq II Hnrs 84; Adelphi; Bus.

MARBIT, STEPHEN T; Wellington C Mepham HS; Wantagh, NY; (Y); Computer Clb; Debate Tm; Mathletes; Math Clb; Math Tm; Science Clb; Temple Yth Grp; Chorus; Hon Roll; NHS.

MARBLE, DANIEL; Lansingburgh HS; Troy, NY; (Y); Church Yth Grp; VICA; High Hon Roll; Hon Roll; Hudson Valley CC; Carpntr.

MARC, STILE; St John The Baptist HS; Massapegua, NY; (Y); JV Ftbl; High Hon Roll; Hon Roll; Adephi-Acdmc Schlrshp 85; Hofstra-Acdmc Schlrshp 85; Hofstra; Bus.

MARCANO, JOSE C; Walton HS; Bronx, NY; (Y); Crs Cntry; Cardinal Spellman Yth Awd 84; NRA 1st Cls Mrksmnshp Awd 83; Lehman Coll; Bus Mgmt.

MARCANO, MARCUS; All Hallows Inst; New York, NY; (Y); 6/32; Bsbl; Bowling; High Hon Roll; Hon Roll; Med.

MARCANO, MYRNA; Harry S Truman HS; Bronx, NY; (Y); Church Yth Grp; Cmnty Wkr; Office Aide; Yrbk Stf; Rep Jr Cls; Bowling; Capt Sftbl; Capt Tennis; Vllybl; Hon Roll; Law.

MARCANTONIO, RAFFAELLA; Grand Island HS; Grand Is, NY; (Y); Church Yth Grp; Hosp Aide; Chorus; Trs Concert Band; Jazz Band; Pres Madrigals; Mrchg Band; School Musical; Variety Show; Regnts Schlrshp 85; Pres Acadmc Fit Awd 85; John Philip Sousa Awd 85; Stony Brook U; Pre-Med.

MARCARIO, DANIELLE MARIE; Clarkstown North; New City, NY; (Y); 70/440; Band; VP Frsh Cls; Var Gym; Var Socr; Var Trk; Hon Roll; Jr NHS; Mu Alp Tht; MVP Gymnstc Team 85; Coaches Awd Gymnstcs Team 83; Med.

MARCAZZOLO, JAYNE; East Meadow HS; East Meadow, NY; (S); 12/414; FBLA; Key Clb; Temple Yth Grp; Band; Concert Band; Mrchg Band; Bsktbl; High Hon Roll; Jr NHS; NHS; Regents Schlrshp Awd 85; Brandis U; Bio Sci.

MARCEDA, ROSANNE; Valley Stream Central HS; Valley Stream, NY; (Y); Ski Clb; High Hon Roll; Hon Roll; Law.

MARCELLO, SUEANNE; Moore Catholic HS; Staten Island, NY; (Y); Art Clb; Math Tm; NFL; Stage Crew; Yrbk Stf; Diving; Socr; Swmmng; Trk; High Hon Roll; Hghst Scr Girls Vrsty Math Team 85; 1st Pl Sci Fair 85.

MARCHAL, CAMILLA A; Notre Dame HS; New York, NY; (Y); Hosp Aide; Science Clb; Trk; Regents Nrsng Schlrshp 85; Marymnt Mnhttn Coll; Bus Mgmt.

MARCHENA, IRIS; Christopher Columbus HS; New York City, NY; (S); Chorus; School Musical; Nwsp Rptr; Hon Roll; Cmmnctns.

MARCHENA, IVIS; Christopher Columbus HS; Bronx, NY; (Y); 74/792; Drama Clb; Chorus; School Musical; Nwsp Rptr; Arista Hnr Soc 83-85; Pace U; Newscstr.

MARCHIONDA, MARISA; West Seneca East SR HS; Buffalo, NY; (Y); 25/365; Cmnty Wkr; DECA; JA; Spanish Clb; Teachers Aide; Cit Awd; High Hon Roll; JC Awd; NHS; Ntl Merit Ltr; Ntl Hnr Scty Schlrshp 85; Grad Cum Laude 85; Canisus Coll; Bus.

MARCHIONI, MARIA; Niagara Falls HS; Niagara Falls, NY; (Y); 25/246; Hosp Aide; JA; Key Clb; Red Cross Aide; Hon Roll; Jr NHS; VP Pres NHS; Regnts Schlrshp 85; Stheastrn Acad; Trvl.

MARCHONA, PAUL; New Rochelle HS; New Rochelle, NY; (Y); Boys Clb Am; Socr; Swmmng; NHS; Spanish NHS; Spirt Awd Swmng 84; Mst Imprvd Swmr Awd 85; Bus.

MARCILLE, MICHELLE; Amsterdam HS; Amsterdam, NY; (Y); 25/320; Band; Concert Band; Mrchg Band; Yrbk Stf; Hon Roll; Intl Bus.

MARCILLO, MARILU; Manhattan Center For Science & Mathemat; New York, NY; (Y); Computer Clb; Debate Tm; JA; Cit Awd; Hon Roll; Lion Awd; Amer Assoc Adv Sci 84; Acad All-Amer 85; Pan American Scty 85; Arch.

MARCIN, MICHELLE; West Seneca East SR HS; West Seneca, NY; (S); 65/365; Art Clb; VP DECA; Key Clb; Radio Clb; Pres Band; Jazz Band; Mrchg Band; School Musical; JV Bowling; JV Golf; Music Schlrshp 83-84; Commnctns.

MARCKRES, GERALD L; Scmylerville Central HS; Greenwich, NY; (Y); 13/100; French Clb; Math Clb; Ski Clb; Varsity Clb; Stu Cncl; Bsbl; Capt Ftbl; Hon Roll; Regents Schlrshp 84-85; Adiron Dack CC; Bus.

MARCO, CHRISTINE; Pine Bush HS; Pine Bush, NY; (Y); 19/281; Aud/Vis; Math Tm; Ski Clb; Band; Yrbk Stf; Hon Roll; Jr NHS; Kiwanis Awd; NHS; Prfct Atten Awd; Tchrs Assn Schlrshp 85; Orange Cty CC; Bilngl Bus Adm.

MARCOUX, DAVID; Northern Adirondack Central HS; Lyon Mt, NY; (Y); 1/80; Key Clb; Quiz Bowl; School Play; Variety Show; High Hon Roll; Jr NHS; NHS; SAR Awd; Val; Voice Dem Awd; Schlrs For Dollars 84-85; SUNY Plattsburgh; Comp Sci.

MARCUCCI, TIMOTHY; Mckinley HS; Buffalo, NY; (Y); Machinist.

MARCUS, ANDREW; West Hempstead HS; Island Pk, NY; (Y); Am Leg Boys St; Boy Scts; Temple Yth Grp; Nwsp Rptr; Nwsp Sprt Ed; Nwsp Stf; Var Tennis; High Hon Roll; NHS; Italian 3 Awd; Vrsty Tennis Team MVP 2 Yrs; Cornell; Bus.

MARCUS, JESSICA; Curtis HS; Staten Island, NY; (Y); 7/325; Hosp Aide; VP Math Clb; Capt Math Tm; Mrchg Band; Yrbk Stf; Ed Lit Mag; Tennis; High Hon Roll; NHS; St Schlr; NYS Regents Scholar 85; NYS Comptrllrs Awd 85; Delta Kappa Gamma Intl Soc Wmn Edctrs Awd 85; MIT.

MARCUS, JILLIAN M; New Rochelle HS; New Rochelle, NY; (Y); 2/600; Sec Soph Cls; Sec Jr Cls; VP Sr Cls; Stu Cncl; Var Capt Socr; Var L Tennis; NHS; Ntl Merit Ltr; Sal; Spanish NHS; CIBA-GEIGY H S Sci Awd; Princeton U.

MARCYS, NOEL; John Dewey HS; Brooklyn, NY; (Y); 5/750; Bowling; Diving; Gym; Swmmng; Wt Lftg; Engrng.

MARDEN, JEFFREY; Tottenville HS; Staten Island, NY; (Y); Am Leg Boys St; Boy Scts; Computer Clb; Ski Clb; Band; Mrchg Band; Nwsp Phtg; Yrbk Phtg; Rep Soph Cls; Camera Clb; NYC Vocatl Comp Hon Men 85; Sci.

MARDENFELD, SANDRA; Farmingdale HS; Massapequa Lk, NY; (Y); Girl Scts; Temple Yth Grp; Band; Concert Band; Mrchg Band; Orch; Pep Band; School Musical; Symp Band; Yrbk Rptr; Jrnlsm.

MARE, SUSAN; The Ursuline Schl; Scarsdale, NY; (Y); Dance Clb; Drama Clb; School Musical; School Play; Coach Actv; Hon Roll; Excllnc Adv Placemnt Art Portfolio 85; U Hartford; Fine Arts.

MARESCA, PATRICIA M; Holy Trinity HS; Hicksville, NY; (S); 20/404; Math Clb; Drm & Bgl; Nwsp Stf; Stu Cncl; High Hon Roll; NHS; NEDT Awd.

MARESSA, SUSAN E; Hamburg SR HS; Hamburg, NY; (Y); Sec French Clb; FTA; Nwsp Stf; Im Socr; Hon Roll; NHS; Canisius; Acctg.

MARGADONNA, NANCY; St John Villa Acad; Staten Is, NY; (Y); Math Clb; Yrbk Stf.

MARGELLO, GERALDINE; Westlake HS; Thornwood, NY; (Y); 32/146; Debate Tm; Drama Clb; Girl Scts; Hosp Aide; PAVAS; Thesps; Chorus; School Musical; School Play; Stage Crew; Regents Schlrshp 85; Westchester Cnty Music Awd 84; Suny; Nrsng.

MARGESON, ROXANNE M; Churchville-Chili Central Schl; Churchville, NY; (Y); 1/325; Acpl Chr; Chorus; Yrbk Bus Mgr; Var Gym; Var Trk; Cit Awd; Dnfth Awd; NHS; Ntl Merit Ltr; Val; All Cnty Gymnstcs Tm 83-85; Fnlst Pres Schlr 85; Hofstra U Schlrshp 85; SUNY Binghamton NY; Med.

MARGIOTTA, CHARLIE; Hendrick Hudson HS; Verplanck, NY; (Y); Var Capt Ftbl; Trk; High Hon Roll; Hon Roll; NHS; Bus.

MARGOLIES, SHARON; Woodmere Acad; Baldwin Harbor, NY; (S); Ed Nwsp Ed-Chief; Ed Lit Mag; Cmnty Wkr; French Clb; Mathletes; Model UN; Service Clb; Band; French Hon Soc; NCTE Awd.

MARGOLIS, ILONA; The Storm King Schl; Dallas, TX; (S); 2/25; School Play; Nwsp Stf; Yrbk Phtg; Hst Frsh Cls; Off Soph Cls; VP Sr Cls; Stu Cncl; Capt Var Cheerleading; High Hon Roll; U Southern Ca; Arts.

MARGRAF, DIANE; Smithtown High School East; Nesconset, NY; (Y); Band; Concert Band; Mrchg Band; Stu Cncl; Var L Crs Cntry; L Var Socr; L Var Trk; Hon Roll; Bus.

MARHAMATI, DARIUS; Valley Central HS; Maybrook, NY; (Y); 13/350; Natl Beta Clb; Spanish Clb; JV Socr; Tennis; NHS; Spanish NHS; Med.

MARHSALL, KIMBERLY; Union Endicott HS; Endicott, NY; (Y); Key Clb; Variety Show; Ed Nwsp Stf; Var Cheerleading; Hon Roll; Broome CC; Bus.

MARIA, BETTY; Hempstead HS; Hempstead, NY; (S); Cmnty Wkr; FBLA; High Hon Roll; Hon Roll; NY Inst Techlgy; Bus.

MARIA, PAULA; Sacred Heart HS; Yonkers, NY; (S); 52/238; Intnl Clb; Hon Roll; NHS; Manhattan Coll; Bus.

MARIANI, PATRICIA M; City Honors Schl; Buffalo, NY; (Y); 15/97; Band; Concert Band; Mrchg Band; Var L Sftbl; NY ST Regents Schlrshp 85; SUNY-BUFFALO.

MARIANO, JOEL; Newark SR HS; Newark, NY; (Y); 3/200; Church Yth Grp; Concert Band; Jazz Band; Mrchg Band; Var Socr; Var Swmmng; Var Tennis; French Hon Soc; High Hon Roll; NHS; Med.

MARICLE, KATIE; Union Endicott HS; Endicott, NY; (Y); French Clb; Key Clb; Yrbk Stf; Ed Lit Mag; Rep Soph Cls; Sci.

MARICONDA, DOMINICK; Iona Prep Schl; New Rochelle, NY; (Y); 35/200; Boys Clb Am; NFL; Speech Tm; Socr; High Hon Roll; Hon Roll; NHS; Computer Clb; Debate Tm; 6th Pl Declmtn Frnscs Natl 83; 5th Pl ST Frnscs Declmtn 84; 5th Pl ST Frnscs Declmtn 83; Med.

MARIE, ANN; Marlboro Central HS; Milton, NY; (Y); French Clb; Ski Clb; Chorus; Church Choir; Score Keeper; Trk; Vllybl; Hon Roll; Outstndng Art Achvt Awd 84; Pres SADD 85; Dutchess CC; Comp Sci.

MARIE, F DONNA; Smithtown HS West; Smithtown, NY; (Y); Church Yth Grp; Dance Clb; Office Aide; Off Frsh Cls; Off Soph Cls; Mgr(s); Mat Maids; Score Keeper; Hon Roll; Italian Hnr Soc; Bus.

MARIN, CARMELINA D; A Philip Randolph HS; Bronx, NY; (Y); Church Yth Grp; Pres Debate Tm; Church Choir; Variety Show; Hon Roll; Scholar Xavier U SOAR Pgm 85; Pre-Med.

MARIN, GILBERT; Cardinal Hayes HS; New York, NY; (Y); 10/264; Var High Hon Roll; Psych.

MARIN, MINELI; Lindenhurst SR HS; Lindenhurst, NY; (Y); 124/625; Library Aide; Spanish Clb; Varsity Clb; Band; Mrchg Band; Var L Badmtn; Var L Tennis; Hon Roll; Jr NHS; Ntl Hnr Roll 84; Am Leg Auxlry-Past Pres & NY ST Gld Key Awds 85; Adelphi U; Nrsng.

MARINARO, PATRICIA; Mount Saint Mary Acad; Buffalo, NY; (Y); Cmnty Wkr; Chorus; Hon Roll; NYS Regnts Schlrshp 85; Ntl Sci Achvt Awd 83; Alfred U; Math.

MARINCIC, KATHLEEN; Hudson Falls Central HS; Glens Falls, NY; (Y); 14/240; Church Yth Grp; French Clb; Science Clb; Acpl Chr; Chorus; School Musical; High Hon Roll; NHS; H S Ltr Invlvmt Choir, Musicls & Choaliers 85; All ST Chrs 85; Hamilton Coll; Comp Sci.

MARINE, ANNA; Aquinas HS; Bronx, NY; (Y); Camera Clb; Cmnty Wkr; Computer Clb; Latin Clb; Spanish Clb; Hon Roll; Spanish NHS.

MARINELLI, LAURA S; North Babylon SR HS; North Babylon, NY; (Y); 114/556; Church Yth Grp; Drama Clb; French Clb; Pep Clb; Nwsp Stf; Trs Jr Cls; VP Sr Cls; Var Capt Cheerleading; Hon Roll; Art Clb; Regents Schlrshp 85-86; U Delaware; Pol Sci.

MARINELLI, LINDA; Buffalo Traditional HS; Buffalo, NY; (S); Church Yth Grp; French Clb; Var Score Keeper; Mgr Swmmng; French Hon Soc; Hon Roll; Jr NHS; Chld Psych.

MARINELLO, MARK J; Beach Channel HS; Belle Harbor, NY; (Y); 6/500; Math Tm; Scholastic Bowl; Concert Band; Jazz Band; Yrbk Phtg; Pres Sr Cls; Cit Awd; High Hon Roll; NHS; Queens Coll Pres Awd Achvt 85; Biomed Engrng.

MARINESE, VICKI; Harry S Truman HS; Bronx, NY; (Y); Library Aide; Service Clb; Teachers Aide; Band; Orch; Tennis; Hunter Coll; Accntnt.

MARINO, BARBARA; Sachem HS; Lake Ronkonkoma, NY; (Y); 29/1432; FBLA; Library Aide; Pres VP Science Clb; Sec Ski Clb; Spanish Clb; Color Guard; Stage Crew; Yrbk Stf; Jr NHS; NHS; Acctng Achvt Awd; Math Sci Awd; Most Outstndng Bus Stu Awd; C W Post; Bus.

MARINO, BARBARA; West Hempstead HS; W Hempstead, NY; (Y); JV Badmtn; JV Vllybl; Hon Roll; Sec.

MARINO, BRADLEY S; George W Hewlett HS; Hewlett, NY; (Y); 8/350; Debate Tm; Hosp Aide; Chorus; School Musical; School Play; Nwsp Sprt Ed; JV Bsktbl; Var Swmmng; NHS; Ntl Merit Ltr; NYS Regnts Schlrshp; U Of VA; Med.

MARINO, CHRIS; Hicksville HS; Hicksvl, NY; (Y); Cmnty Wkr; Lit Mag; Rep Frsh Cls; Rep Soph Cls; Rep Jr Cls; Rep Stu Cncl; JV Bsbl; Var Capt Bsktbl; Coach Actv; High Hon Roll; MVP Bsktbl 82-85; Gftd Progrm 83-84; Phy-Ed Tchr.

MARINO, FRANK; John F Kennedy HS; Utica, NY; (Y); Am Leg Boys St; Boys Clb Am; Church Yth Grp; Letterman Clb; Science Clb; Varsity Clb; Yrbk Stf; Rep Jr Cls; Bsbl; Bsktbl; Bsbl Achvt Awd 83; Tampa U; Chem.

MARINO, GINA; East Meadow HS; East Meadow, NY; (S); 29/414; Chorus; Color Guard; Drm & Bgl; Yrbk Ed-Chief; Sftbl; Tennis; Cit Awd; Hon Roll; NHS; Nassau Comm Coll; Chiroprct.

MARINO, LAURA; Fayetteville Manlivs HS; Manlius, NY; (Y); GAA; Pep Clb; Stu Cncl; Im Coach Actv; JV Var Socr; Hon Roll; NHS; Church Yth Grp; Cmnty Wkr; Service Clb.

MARINO, MARLEEN; Saint Francis Prep; Glendale, NY; (Y); 143/693; Dance Clb; Optimate Sco 82-83; Law.

MARINO, RIKKI; E J Wilson HS; Rochester, NY; (Y); Chorus; Yrbk Stf; Stu Cncl; High Hon Roll; Hon Roll; NHS; Bus Admin.

MARINO, ROSETTA; Monsignor Scanlan HS; Whitestone, NY; (Y); 64/265; Prncpls Cert Of Merit 84; Schltc Achvt 2nd Hnrs 83.

MARINUCCI, MICHELLE; Nazareth Acad; Rochester, NY; (Y); Church Yth Grp; Dance Clb; Drama Clb; FBLA; Pep Clb; Ski Clb; Spanish Clb; Pep Band; Off Sr Cls; Hon Roll; Alfred U; Pre-Med.

MARION, ANDREA; Our Lady Of Mercy HS; Webster, NY; (Y); 128/212; Spanish Clb; Hon Roll; SUNY; Nrsng.

MARION, KIMBERLY M; Notre Dame Acad; Staten Island, NY; (Y); Pres Church Yth Grp; Girl Scts; Hosp Aide; Intnl Clb; Teachers Aide; Acpl Chr; Chorus; Pres Church Choir; School Musical; Ntl Merit Ltr; Bus Adm.

MARISCO, MICHELE; Briarcliff HS; Briarcliff Manor, NY; (Y); Hosp Aide; Orch; Nwsp Ed-Chief; Fld Hcky; Lcrss; Hon Roll; Q&S; Chorus; Nwsp Rptr; Nwsp Stf; Proj For Schl Imprvmnt 84; Jrnlsm Lectures Columbia U 84-85; Fairfield U; Nrsng.

MARK, LAURA S; Paul V Moore HS; Constantia, NY; (Y); 40/297; AFS; Drama Clb; Radio Clb; Varsity Clb; School Play; Stage Crew; Nwsp Phtg; Nwsp Rptr; Nwsp Stf; JV Var Crs Cntry; Regents Schlrshp 85; Syracuse U; Archtr.

MARK, LILLIAN M; Oakwood Schl; Brooklyn, NY; (Y); Church Yth Grp; Cmnty Wkr; Nwsp Ed-Chief; Nwsp Rptr; Rep Jr Cls; Stu Cncl; Var Crs Cntry; Hon Roll; Ntl Merit Schol.

MARK, NATALIE; Glens Falls HS; Glens Falls, NY; (Y); 21/235; Am Leg Boys St; Teachers Aide; Band; Jazz Band; Orch; Pep Band; School Musical; JV Vllybl; High Hon Roll; NHS; Boston U; Tchng.

MARK, RENE; Wayland Central HS; Perkinsville, NY; (Y); Girl Scts; Pep Clb; Yrbk Stf; Off Jr Cls; Bus.

MARK, RONALD J; Caledonia-Mumford HS; Caledonia, NY; (Y); Boy Scts; Church Yth Grp; French Clb; Band; Chorus; Concert Band; Jazz Band; Mrchg Band; Pep Band; Var VP Socr; Daemen Coll; CPA.

MARKEL, TIFFANY ANN; Lyons Central HS; Lyons, NY; (Y); 14/95; Pres Latin Clb; Pres Model UN; Debate Tm; Voice Dem Awd; AFS; Sec Chess Clb; Ski Clb; School Musical; Stu Cncl; High Hon Roll; D Youville U Hnrs Pgm 85-89; Stu Cong Awd 85; Hnrbl Mntn MUN 84; D Youville U; Lwyr.

MARKELL, ANNETTE; Mexico HS; Fulton, NY; (Y); Spanish Clb; Color Guard; Mrchg Band; Lit Mag; Var Trk; Hon Roll; NHS; Spanish NHS; Presdntl Acadmc Ftns Awd 85; Class Schlrshp 85; Mst Improvd Rifle 82; Oswego ST; Poltcl Sci.

MARKER, SCOTT; Churchille-Chili SR HS; Churchville, NY; (Y); Var Bowling; Capt Crs Cntry; Capt Trk; JV Wrstlng; Hon Roll; Arch.

MARKEWICH, NOAH; Nyack HS; South Nyack, NY; (Y); 12/277; Spanish Clb; Stage Crew; High Hon Roll; NHS; Spanish NHS; NY ST Rgnts Schlrshp 85; Cornell U; Engrng.

MARKHAM, DANIEL; Hendrick Hudson HS; Buchanan, NY; (Y); 25/191; Debate Tm; Nwsp Rptr; Var Bsbl; Var Bsktbl; JV Ftbl; NHS; Ntl Merit Ltr; Pres Schlr; NYS Regents Scholar 85; Ben Franklin Scholar Franklin Coll 85; Natl Pulliam Jrnlsm Scholar 85; Franklin Coll IN; Jrnlsm.

MARKHAM, DANIELLE; Fr Harry S Truman HS; New York, NY; (Y); Band; Chorus; Church Choir; Concert Band; Hon Roll; NHS; Law.

MARKHAM, GERALD G; Washington Acad Salem Central; Salem, NY; (Y); Am Leg Boys St; Church Yth Grp; JV Var Bsbl; JV Bsktbl; Capt Bowling; Hon Roll; Acctng.

MARKHAM, STEVE J; Ellicottville Central HS; Great Vly, NY; (Y); Church Yth Grp; Computer Clb; Var L Bowling; Hon Roll; Comp Sci.

MARKIEWICZ, JAMES; Sherburne-Earlville HS; Earlville, NY; (S); 7/138; Ski Clb; Lit Mag; Hon Roll; NHS; Business.

MARKIEWICZ, KATHRYN; Shenendehowa HS; Clifton Pk, NY; (Y); 107/647; Varsity Clb; Chorus; JV Bowling; JV Crs Cntry; JV Var Mgr(s); JV Trk; High Hon Roll; Hon Roll; NHS; Prfct Atten Awd; Phys Ed Excllnt Prep 82; Vrsty Clb Svc Hrs Pin & Patch 83; Siena Coll; Comp Sci.

MARKLAND, PATRICK; Seaford HS; Wantagh, NY; (Y); Aud/Vis; Church Yth Grp; VP Cmnty Wkr; Drama Clb; Ftbl; JV Lcrss; Clinical Psych.

MARKOPOULOS, CONSTANTINE; Albany HS; Albany, NY; (Y); 5/600; Am Leg Boys St; French Clb; Nwsp Stf; Yrbk Stf; Lit Mag; Hon Roll; NHS; Natl Merit Cmmnded Stdnt 84; Cornell U; Arch.

MARKOPOULOS, MARIANTHI; Albany HS; Albany, NY; (Y); 26/600; VP French Clb; Church Choir; Yrbk Stf; Hon Roll; NHS; NY ST Regents Schlrshp; Rensselaer Polytech Inst.

MARKOV, SAMANTHA; Sheepshead Bay HS; Brooklyn, NY; (Y); Co-Capt Aud/Vis; Debate Tm; Chorus; School Musical; Stage Crew; Crs Cntry; Socr; Trk; Vllybl; Prfct Atten Awd; Law.

MARKOVICH, GAIL L; Kensington HS; Buffalo, NY; (Y); 2/179; Pres Computer Clb; Math Tm; Hon Roll; Pres NHS; Sal; Regents Schlrshp 85; Prncpls Hnrs List 83-84; NY ST U-Buffalo; Comp Sci.

MARKOWICZ, THERESA; Madison Central Schl; Bouckville, NY; (S); 8/40.

MARKS, JILL M; De Sales HS; Waterloo, NY; (Y); Scholastic Bowl; VP Chorus; School Musical; Yrbk Stf; High Hon Roll; NHS; NEDT Awd; Girls St Altrnt; Syracuse U; Eng.

MARKS, MICHELLE; Fashion Industries HS; Brooklyn, NY; (Y); FHA; Office Aide; Eng Hnrs 84; Grad Merit 85; Pratt Inst; Fash Merch.

MARKUS, KIM; Pittsford Sutherland HS; Pittsford, NY; (Y); NHS; Ntl Merit Ltr; High Hon Roll; French Hon Soc; Cit Awd; Yrbk Ed-Chief; JV Tennis; French Clb; Political Wkr; Ski Clb; Natl Frnch,Latn Awd 83-85.

MARKUS, REBECCA; Whitesboro SR HS; Utica, NY; (Y); 26/350; GAA; Intnl Clb; Trs Orch; Lit Mag; Tennis; High Hon Roll; Jr NHS; Trs NHS; Geolgy.

MARKUSEN, JULIA F; Kendall JR & SR HS; Kendall, NY; (Y); 1/90; Trs Drama Clb; Model UN; Pres Spanish Clb; Var L Socr; Var L Vllybl; High Hon Roll; Pres NHS; Val; NY ST Regnts Schlrshp 85; Cornell Natl Schlrshp 85; Cornell U; Engrng.

MARLAR, ANDREA MARIE; Rome Free Acad; Rome, NY; (Y); 57/533; Hosp Aide; Intnl Clb; Pep Clb; Band; Concert Band; Mrchg Band; Hon Roll; NHS; Prsdntl Acad Ftnss Awd 85; SUNY Oswego.

MARLOWE, BRENT; Franklin Acad; Malone, NY; (S); 4/253; Varsity Clb; VP L Crs Cntry; VP L Trk; High Hon Roll; Hon Roll; NHS; Prfct Atten Awd; Halda Palmer Mem Schlrshp 83; Franklin Acad Schlrshp 82; Tim Murphy Awd Engl 79; Bio Med Engrng.

MARLOWE, SHELLY; Franklin Acad; Malone, NY; (Y); 4-H; Church Choir; Rep Stu Cncl; Mohawk Vly CC; Crmnl Jstc.

MARNELLI, JOSEPH; West Seneca West HS; Orchard Pk, NY; (Y); 25/542; Spanish Clb; Chorus; Bsktbl; Tennis; High Hon Roll; Hon Roll; JC Awd; NHS; Prfct Atten Awd; Regents Schlrshp 85; Navy; Elect Engr.

MAROCCO, MATTHEW; Oneida SR HS; Oneida, NY; (Y); Art Clb; Boy Scts; Church Yth Grp; Spanish Clb; Chorus; Golf; Hon Roll; Marine Bio.

MAROLEWSKI, ARIANE; Clarkstown High Schl South; New City, NY; (Y); 4/515; Church Yth Grp; Math Clb; Science Clb; Band; Church Choir; Concert Band; NHS; Ntl Merit Schol; Hope Coll Pres Schlrshp 85; New Cty Rotary Schlrshp 85; Clarkstown Band Schlrshp 85; Hope Coll; Chem.

MARONEY, KATHLEEN; Potsdam SR HS; Potsdam, NY; (Y); Spanish Clb; Church Choir; Gold Key Wnnr Syracuse Mony Art Cntst 84; Hnrbl Mtn 85; Blue Rbbn Wnnr & Hllmrk Nominee 85; ST U Potsdam; Art.

MARONEY, WILLIAM; Allegany Central HS; Allegany, NY; (Y); Band; Concert Band; Jazz Band; Mrchg Band; High Hon Roll; NHS; Prfct Atten Awd; Spec Awd Schlrshp In Bnd 84; Elec Engrng.

MAROTTA, JOSEPH; Aviation HS; Corona, NY; (Y); 117/474; CAP; Computer Clb; Yrbk Stf; Rep Stu Cncl; Var Capt Bsbl; High Hon Roll; Silver Wings Awd 84-85; Daily News, NY Yankees Super Yth 83-84; Peagus Soc 85; St Francis Coll; Aviatn Tech.

MAROTTA, JOSEPH A; Tottenville HS; Staten Island, NY; (Y); Am Leg Boys St; Key Clb; Model UN; Concert Band; Symp Band; Crs Cntry; Trk; Hon Roll; NHS; Coaches Awd Trk 85; NYS Adjudctn Grade Excllnt 83.

MAROTTA, MARK; Riverhead HS; Hampton Bays, NY; (Y); 1/200; JCL; Latin Clb; Mathletes; Chorus; Swing Chorus; Yrbk Stf; High Hon Roll; NHS; Princeton Alumni Assoc Long Isl Awd 84-85; Rensselaer Medal 85-86; Bio-Chem.

MAROTTE, JOSEPH; Susan Wagner HS; Staten Isld, NY; (Y); Bsbl; Bsktbl; Sftbl; Hon Roll; Prfct Atten Awd; Coll Of Staten Island; Engrng.

MAROTTI, AMEDEO; Holy Cross HS; Flushing, NY; (Y); Service Clb; Wt Lftg; Hon Roll; NCTE Awd; Spanish NHS.

MARQUARDT, WILLIAM; Skaneateles HS; Skaneateles, NY; (S); 23/165; Pres Soph Cls; Pres Jr Cls; Pres Stu Cncl; Var L Ftbl; Var L Golf; Var L Ice Hcky; High Hon Roll; VP NHS; Suprntdnt Comm 84-85; Chrmn Stu Agnst Drnk Drvng 84-85; Fin Anlys.

MARQUEZ, JOCELYN; St Johns Prep; Elmhurst, NY; (Y); Im Badmtn; Var Mgr(s); Var Socr; JV Socr; Im Vllybl; Hon Roll; NHS; St Johns U; Comp Sci.

MARRA, PAMELA L; Maria Regina HS; White Plains, NY; (Y); 12/144; Nwsp Rptr; Lit Mag; Rep Frsh Cls; Rep Soph Cls; Capt JV Cheerleading; Hon Roll; VP NHS; 1st Pl Essay Cntst; Regnts Schlrshp; Manhattan Coll; Elec Engr.

MARRAPESE, AMY; Mynderse Acad; Seneca Falls, NY; (S); 6/140; Drama Clb; Sec Trs Intnl Clb; Concert Band; Mrchg Band; School Musical; Yrbk Stf; Sec Soph Cls; Sec Jr Cls; Rep Stu Cncl; Cit Awd; Natl Honor Roll Scty 84; Elem Educ.

MARRERO, ANTONIA; John S Burke HS; Blooming Grove, NY; (Y); Drama Clb; Quiz Bowl; School Play; Sec Stage Crew; Variety Show; Nwsp Rptr; Tennis; High Hon Roll; NHS; Ntl Merit SF; Outstndng Theology Stu 82-83; Law.

MARRERO, GINA; Acad Of St Joseph HS; E Northport, NY; (Y); Hosp Aide; Library Aide; Science Clb; Pres Service Clb; Yrbk Stf; Sec Jr Cls; VP Sr Cls; NHS; Pres Schlr; Gen Exc Awd; Christian Crtsy Med; Magnan Cum Laude Hnrs; Cornell U; Microbio.

MARRERO, ISMAEL; Adlai E Stevenson HS; Bronx, NY; (Y); 26/445; Church Yth Grp; Drama Clb; JA; Yrbk Stf; Rep Stu Cncl; NHS; Rgnts Schlrshp 85; Schl Play 85; Acad Olympc Tm-Brnz, Gld Mdls 85; Brandeis U; Pre Med.

MARRERO, KAREN LOUISE; John Dewey HS; Brooklyn, NY; (Y); Law.

MARRERO, LISA A; Polytechnic Prep Country Day Schl; Brooklyn, NY; (Y); Am Leg Aux Girls St; Chess Clb; Science Clb; Acpl Chr; Chorus; Yrbk Bus Mgr; Ntl Merit Ltr; Pitkow Meml Mdl Spnsh Awd 85; Cathlc Tchrs Assoc Schlrshp 85; Sons Of Itly Amer Schlrshp 85; U Of FL; Pre Med.

MARRIELLO, ROBERT; Archbishop Molloy HS; Woodhaven, NY; (Y); Church Yth Grp; Computer Clb; Intnl Clb; Math Clb; Church Choir; Hon Roll; Accntng.

MARRINER, VANCE; G Ray Bodley HS; Fulton, NY; (Y); Exploring; German Clb; High Hon Roll; Hon Roll; NHS; Military.

MARRIOTT, JOHN; Walt Whitman HS; Huntington Sta, NY; (Y); 102/540; Chorus; Trk; High Hon Roll; Hon Roll; NHS; Prfct Atten Awd; Spanish NHS; C W Post; Bus.

MARRIS, TIM; Cazenovia HS; Erieville, NY; (Y); 11/150; Church Yth Grp; Mathletes; Pres Stu Cncl; Var L Wrstlng; Hon Roll; RIT; Elec Engrng.

MARRO, LAURA; St Joseph By The Sea; Staten Island, NY; (Y); Art Clb; Dance Clb; Drama Clb; School Musical; School Play; Stage Crew; Yrbk Stf; Off Stu Cncl; Hon Roll; Prfct Atten Awd; 2nd Art 85; Art Work Exhibit 85; Fash Inst Tech; Illstrtn.

MARRO, MICHAEL; Victor Central HS; Victor, NY; (Y); Am Leg Boys St; Trs Varsity Clb; VP Frsh Cls; Stu Cncl; Bsbl; Bsktbl; Var Capt Ftbl; Hon Roll; Boys Ldr Awd 85; V Ltr 84; Two Gold Bars 85.

MARRON, JO ANN L; Sidney HS; Masonville, NY; (Y); 3/114; Pres Drama Clb; Sec 4-H; Math Clb; Spanish Clb; Band; Sec Chorus; Capt Color Guard; Concert Band; Drm Mjr(t); Mrchg Band; Olympics Mind Wrld Champ 84; Rotary Intl Frgn Exch Stu 85-86; Brown U; Archlgy.

MARRONE, LISA; Sachem High School North; Farmingville, NY; (Y); Drama Clb; Radio Clb; Chorus; Drm & Bgl; Drm Mjr(t); Flag Corp; Madrigals; School Musical; 1st Pl Rbbn-Long Island Sci Congrss 84; NYSSMA Solo Comptn-A Rtng 85.

MARROON, DEBBIE; Valley Central HS; Walden, NY; (Y); 39/300; Hosp Aide; Color Guard; Frsh Cls; Soph Cls; Jr Cls; Sr Cls; Tennis; Hon Roll; NHS; Spanish NHS; Bio.

MARS, TRACY; Granville Central HS; Pawlet, VT; (Y); 4-H; Rep Frsh Cls; Rep Soph Cls; Rep Jr Cls; Stat Bsktbl; Var Cheerleading; Var Fld Hcky; Var Pom Pon; Var Score Keeper; Var Sftbl; Adirondack Comm Coll; Bus.

MARSAHLL, LORI; George Washington HS; New York, NY; (Y); 141/315; Cheerleading; Sftbl; Vllybl; Wt Lftg; John Jay Coll; Crimnl Lawyer.

MARSALA, GINA; Smithtown High School East; Nesconset, NY; (Y); PAVAS; Political Wkr; Sec VP Thesps; Variety Show; Hon Roll; Pres Jr NHS; NHS; Aud/Vis; Drama Clb; Chorus; Hnr Thespian 85; Best Actress Awds 84-85; Italian Hnr Scty 84-85; Jrnlsm.

MARSANICO, VINCENT; Holy Cross HS; Flushing, NY; (Y); Hosp Aide; Var Bowling; Paramedic.

MARSCH, PETER M; Liverpool HS; Liverpool, NY; (Y); 175/874; Am Leg Boys St; Debate Tm; Exploring; Hosp Aide; Off ROTC; Drill Tm; School Musical; Stage Crew; Rep Stu Cncl; Church Yth Grp; ROTC Supr Prfrmnc Awd 83; Crosue-Irving Memrl Hosp Vlntr Svc Recgntn 83-85; ROTC Acadmc Excllnc Awd; Aerospc Engr.

MARSCHMAN, KRISTIN; Clarkstown South HS; Bardonia, NY; (Y); 17/500; Church Yth Grp; 4-H; German Clb; Nwsp Stf; Yrbk Stf; Lit Mag; Jr NHS; NHS; NY Acad Of Sci Intrnshp Prog 84-85; Sci Lge Bio 84-85; Vet Med.

MARSDEN, ALEXANDRA; St John The Baptist D HS; Deer Pk, NY; (Y); 2/603; Hosp Aide; Sec Math Tm; Sec MMM; Band; Nwsp Stf; French Hon Soc; High Hon Roll; Mu Alp Tht; NHS; Ntl Merit Ltr; Hugh O Brien Ledrshp Seminar Ambassador 84; Trivia Editor 85-86; Soc Of Dist Amer HS Stu 85; Med.

MARSH, DONNA J; Cazenovia HS; Manlius, NY; (Y); 13/150; Pres 4-H; School Musical; School Play; Nwsp Rptr; Yrbk Stf; High Hon Roll; NHS; Ntl Merit Ltr; AFS; Church Yth Grp; NY ST Winner 4-H Public Speaking 84; Schlrshp Forn NYNEX Inc 85; Smith; Intl Communications.

MARSH, JACK; Letchworth Central Schl; Bliss, NY; (Y); AFS; Church Yth Grp; Drama Clb; Pres 4-H; Math Tm; Pres Spanish Clb; Yrbk Ed-Chief; Yrbk Stf; High Hon Roll; Hon Roll; Pres Acadmc Fit Awd 85; Herkimer Co CC; Mortry Sci.

MARSH, JOHN; Union Endicott HS; Endicott, NY; (Y); Boys Clb Am; Boy Scts; Computer Clb; Exploring; Key Clb; Cit Awd; Hon Roll; Opt Clb Awd; Elctrcl Engrng.

MARSH, JULIE A; Corning East HS; Corning, NY; (Y); Dance Clb; Teachers Aide; Drill Tm; Yrbk Stf; Rep Frsh Cls; Rep Soph Cls; Rep Jr Cls; Var Pom Pon; High Hon Roll; Hon Roll; Erly Educ.

MARSH, ROXANNE; Gilboa Conesville HS; Prattsville, NY; (S); GAA; Yrbk Stf; JV Bsktbl; Var Sftbl; High Hon Roll; NHS; Pres Jr Cls.

MARSH, STEVE; Massena Central HS; Massena, NY; (Y); Key Clb; Ed Lit Mag; JV Var Bsktbl; Hon Roll; NHS; Engr.

MARSH, SUZANNE C; Rlington HS; Poughkeepsie, NY; (Y); 89/560; JV Var Sftbl; Regents Schlrshp 85; Clarkson U; Chem Engr.

MARSH, TODD A; Hamurg SR HS; Hamburg, NY; (Y); 4/390; Church Yth Grp; Band; Concert Band; Jazz Band; Mrchg Band; Symp Band; Hon Roll; NHS; Top Ten 82-85; Archtctr.

MARSH, TOM W; Stamford Central HS; Stamford, NY; (Y); French Clb; FBLA; Band; Chorus; Concert Band; Mrchg Band; Yrbk Bus Mgr; Arch.

MARSHALL, CHRIS; Thousand Islands HS; Clayton, NY; (Y); Hon Roll; Lion Awd; Arch.

MARSHALL, DARLEEN; Hempstead HS; Hempstead, NY; (S); 89/333; Drama Clb; Chorus; Church Choir; School Play; Variety Show; JV Mgr(s); Score Keeper; Comp Sci.

MARSHALL, DORENE L; Candor Central Schl; Candor, NY; (Y); 10/88; Drama Clb; Concert Band; School Play; Yrbk Stf; Rep Sr Cls; Stat Bsktbl; Score Keeper; High Hon Roll; Hon Roll; NHS; NYS Regents Schlrshp 85; Colgate U.

MARSHALL, JULIE; De Ruyter Central HS; Sheds, NY; (S); Yrbk Stf; Sec Sr Cls; Hon Roll; Bryant & Straton; Sec.

MARSHALL, KEVIN; Starpoint Central HS; Lockport, NY; (S); 3/200; Church Yth Grp; Varsity Clb; Im Bsktbl; Var Crs Cntry; Im JV Ftbl; Im Sftbl; Var Tennis; Hon Roll; NHS; 1st Pl Educ Essay Cntst 84; Hghst Avg Soc Studies 84; Med.

MARSHALL, KRISTA; Lansing HS; Lansing, NY; (Y); 28/90; Cmnty Wkr; French Clb; Red Cross Aide; Sec Jr Cls; JV Var Cheerleading; Powder Puff Ftbl; Wrstlng; Hon Roll; Bus.

MARSHALL, LAURIE; Pelham Memorial HS; Pelham, NY; (Y); Church Yth Grp; French Clb; Radio Clb; Ski Clb; Spanish Clb; Church Choir; Nwsp Stf; Yrbk Stf; Lit Mag; Rep Frsh Cls; Diplmtc Reltns.

MARSHALL, MICHELLE; Cardinal O Hara HS; Buffalo, NY; (Y); Hosp Aide; School Play; High Hon Roll; Hon Roll; Comp Sci.

MARSHALL, MICHELLE L; Abraham Lincoln HS; Brooklyn, NY; (Y); 42/489; Cmnty Wkr; Sec Office Aide; Sec Spanish Clb; School Musical; Ed Yrbk Stf; Ed Lit Mag; Rep Frsh Cls; Rep Stu Cncl; Prfct Atten Awd; ARISTA Mbr 82-84; Psych.

MARSHALL, RANDY; Mayfield Central HS; Mayfield, NY; (Y); Sec Varsity Clb; Rep Frsh Cls; Rep Soph Cls; Var Bsbl; Var Capt Bsktbl; Var JV Socr; MIP Bsktbl 82-83; MVP Bsbl 83-84; MVP Bsbl, Bsktbl, Coachs Awd Soccer & Donald Gibson Soccer Awd; Comp Sci.

MARSHALL, SHEILA; South Shore HS; Brooklyn, NY; (Y); French Clb; Girl Scts; Church Choir; Variety Show; Readg 83; Howard U; Psych.

MARSHEK, JOHN J; Batavia HS; Batavia, NY; (Y); 14/250; Var Socr; JV Trk; Var Capt Wrstlng; Hon Roll; VP NHS; Merit Tuition Awd Prgm Full Tuition Genesee CC 85; Geneses CC; Elec Engrng.

MARSILLO, ANTHONY; Washingtonville SR HS; Campbell Hall, NY; (S); Chess Clb; Math Tm; Science Clb; Bowling; NHS; Orange Cnty Enrchmnt Grp 84-85; Elec Engrng.

MARSZALEK, BARBARA; Emerson Vocational HS; Buffalo, NY; (Y); Nwsp Rptr; Hon Roll; Prfct Atten Awd; Sgn Lang.

MARTADARMA, PRAMITA; Newtown HS; Rego Park, NY; (Y); 24/603; Hon Roll; Prfct Atten Awd; Cert Of Merit 83-85; Cert Of Ad 83; NY U; Med.

MARTE, EVELYN; Eastern District HS; Brooklyn, NY; (Y); Science Clb; Hon Roll; Cert Awd Achvt Fine Arts 84; Cert Awd Schlstc Achvt Frnch 85; Cert Awd Schlstc Achvt Engl 85; Pharm.

MARTE, STEVEN; Bishop Grimes HS; E Syracuse, NY; (Y); 44/208; CAP; Exploring; Var JV Socr; JV Trk; Hon Roll; NHS; NY ST Regents Schlrshp; Civil Air Ptrl Cert Of Acmplshmnt & Billy Mitchell Awd; Omondaga CC; Law Enfrcmnt.

MARTEK, MICHELE; St Dominic HS; Syosset, NY; (Y); 10/120; Stage Crew; Yrbk Stf; High Hon Roll; NHS; Spns Relgn Awd 84; Hofstra.

MARTELLI, SHARI; La Salle SR HS; Niagara Falls, NY; (Y); AFS; VP Drama Clb; JA; Chorus; Drm Mjr(t); School Musical; School Play; Stage Crew; Lit Mag; Capt Twrlr; Twirlng Camp Scholr 84; Brdcst Jrnlst.

MARTELLO, CHRISTOPHER; Bishop Timon HS; W Seneca, NY; (Y); Church Yth Grp; Computer Clb; French Clb; Latin Clb; Math Clb; Pep Clb; Quiz Bowl; Ski Clb; Chorus; Ftbl; MI ST; Pre-Law.

MARTELLO, DOMINIC A; Holy Trinity D HS; Hicksville, NY; (S); 24/404; Mathletes; Ski Clb; Variety Show; Rep Stu Cncl; JV Var Bsbl; JV Var Ftbl; Wt Lftg; High Hon Roll; NHS; NEDT Awd; St Johns; Acctng.

MARTELLO, JOHN T; T R Proctor HS; Utica, NY; (Y); Pep Clb; Yrbk Phtg; Yrbk Sprt Ed; Stu Cncl; Var Bsbl; Hon Roll; Prfct Atten Awd; Empir ST Games Bsbl Tm 85; Phy Ed.

MARTELLO, MICHAEL J; Holy Trinty HS; Hicksville, NY; (S); 9/300; Math Clb; Math Tm; Ski Clb; Rep Stu Cncl; Var Ftbl; Var Ice Hcky; Wt Lftg; High Hon Roll; Ntl Merit Schol; Acctng.

MARTEN, PATRICIA; Connetquot HS; Ronkonkoma, NY; (S); 2/650; Band; Mrchg Band; Pres Symp Band; VP Frsh Cls; Hst Sr Cls; Var Vllybl; Jr NHS; NHS; Outstndg Bnd 82; Psych.

MARTIN, ANDREW; Sheepshead HS; Brooklyn, NY; (Y); Computer Clb; Office Aide; Bowling; Sci Schlrshp Cert 83; Kingsborough; Comp Prgmr.

MARTIN, ARTHUR; Lindenhurst HS; Lindenhurst, NY; (Y); Boy Scts; Exploring; Rep Frsh Cls; Stu Cncl; Trk; Hon Roll; Eagl Sct 83; Hnr Grd Lng Islnd Ntl Cemtry Memrl Orgnztn 80-83; Constrctn Electrcty.

MARTIN, BETSY; Franklin Acad; Malone, NY; (Y); 21/253; Church Yth Grp; Drama Clb; Spanish Clb; School Play; Acad All Am 84-85; Regnts Schrlshp 85; Womens Rep Clb Schlrshp 85; Geneseo ST; Pub Rel.

MARTIN, BILL; Massena Central HS; Massena, NY; (Y); Computer Clb; Teachers Aide; Stat Ftbl; JV Trk; Im Vllybl; High Hon Roll; NHS; Prfct Atten Awd; Comp Engrng.

MARTIN, BRENDA; South Park HS; Buffalo, NY; (Y); FNA; Hosp Aide; Office Aide; Red Cross Aide; Hon Roll.

MARTIN, CARL D; Bay Shore HS; Bay Shore, NY; (Y); Computer Clb; FFA; Varsity Clb; JV Bsktbl; JV Ftbl; JV Mgr(s); Wt Lftg; Hon Roll; Prfct Atten Awd; Val; Temple U; Comp Sci.

MARTIN, CAROL A; Newfane SR HS; Newfane, NY; (S); #9 In Class; Church Yth Grp; Varsity Clb; Band; Church Choir; School Musical; Jr Cls; Sftbl; Vllybl; High Hon Roll; NHS; Phil Coll Of Bible; Bible.

MARTIN, CATHERINE; Cooperstown SR HS; New Lisbon, NY; (Y); 1/95; Quiz Bowl; Drm Mjr(t); Yrbk Stf; Stu Cncl; Cheerleading; Hon Roll; NHS; Ntl Merit Ltr; Averell Schlrshp Hgst Yr Avg 84; Am Leg Oratrcl Cont 85.

MARTIN, CHRIS; Cardinal Mooney HS; N Chili, NY; (Y); 89/320; Church Choir; School Musical; Score Keeper; Wrstlng; French Hon Soc; Hon Roll; NYS Regnts Scholar 85; St John Fisher Coll; Psych.

MARTIN, CHRIS; Niskayuna HS; Schdy, NY; (Y); Chrmn French Clb; Var Capt Ice Hcky; High Hon Roll; Key Clb; Ftbl; Cornell; Pre-Med.

MARTIN, CHRISTINE; Clayton A Bouton HS; Voorheesville, NY; (Y); 3/103; Band; Stage Crew; Nwsp Rptr; Var L Cheerleading; High Hon Roll; Trs NHS; Ntl Merit Ltr; Cmnty Wkr; Drama Clb; Intnl Clb; 3rd Hghst Overall Avg 3 Yrs; Hgh Avg Spn III 84-85; Med Tech.

MARTIN, CLEVETTE R; Webster HS; Webster, NY; (Y); 53/654; Church Yth Grp; Drama Clb; Girl Scts; Hosp Aide; Speech Tm; Church Choir; School Play; Nwsp Rptr; Jr NHS; NHS; Ntl Achvt Semi Fin 85; Best Actress 85; Psych.

MARTIN, CONNIE J; Worcester Central HS; Worcester, NY; (Y); 4/40; French Clb; Hosp Aide; Chorus; Sec Jr Cls; Sec Sr Cls; Cheerleading; Hon Roll; NHS; Clark Schlrhsp 85; Hartwick Coll Schlrshp 85; Hartwick Coll; Bus Mgt.

MARTIN, DALE; Webster HS; Webster, NY; (Y); 175/550; Church Yth Grp; Concert Band; Var Golf; JV Tennis; High Hon Roll; Socty Distngshd Amer H S Stdnts 85; Acctg.

MARTIN, DANA; James E Sperry HS; Rochester, NY; (Y); Trs Pres Church Yth Grp; JV Var Bsbl; French Hon Soc; Hon Roll; NHS; Jr NHS; Schltc Ltr 85; Engrng.

MARTIN, DEANNA; Northstar Christian Acad; Rochester, NY; (S); 7/25; Church Yth Grp; Drama Clb; JA; Teachers Aide; Chorus; School Play; Stage Crew; Nwsp Stf; Trs Sr Cls; Capt Bsktbl; Soc Distgushd Am HS Stu 83-84; Roberts Weslyan Coll; Ed.

MARTIN, DOLORES; St Francis Prep; Ozone Pk, NY; (Y); Church Yth Grp; Cmnty Wkr; Hosp Aide; Office Aide; Spanish Clb; Teachers Aide.

MARTIN, HEATHER; Gowanda Central Schl; Perrysburg, NY; (Y); 4/132; Dance Clb; Concert Band; Jazz Band; School Musical; Sec Jr Cls; Var Bsktbl; Var Trk; Var Vllybl; High Hon Roll; NHS; NYSSMA All-Cnty Solo Fstvl 83-84; Amer Lgn Hgh Hnr Roll Awd 84-85.

MARTIN, HOLLEY; Williamsville East HS; East Amherst, NY; (Y); 95/302; Church Yth Grp; Latin Clb; Pep Clb; Ski Clb; Yrbk Stf; Rep Stu Cncl; Capt Var Bsktbl; Var L Fld Hcky; JV Mgr(s); Var L Socr; MIP JV Bsktbl 82; Vrsty Bsktbl Best All Arnd, Best Dfnsv, Hnrbl Mntn 83-84; Erie Cnty All Star Tm; Syracuse U; Nutritnst.

MARTIN, JEFF; Saugerties HS; Saugerties, NY; (S); 17/247; Cmnty Wkr; Math Clb; Math Tm; Varsity Clb; Variety Show; JV Var Bsbl; JV Bsktbl; Im Vllybl; High Hon Roll; Pres NHS; L M Cahill Awd 82-83; Ntl Hnr Soc Schlrsph Fnlst 84-85; Marist Coll; Actrl Sci.

MARTIN, JEFF; Smithtown High School East; Smithtown, NY; (Y); Ski Clb; Spanish Clb; Lcrss; Wt Lftg; Wrstlng; High Hon Roll; NHS; Var Wrestlng 4 Yrs; Breandise; Pre-Med.

MARTIN, JO-ANN; Dominican Commercial HS; Middle Vlge, NY; (Y); Dance Clb; Girl Scts; Church Choir; Twrlr; Princpls List 84; Nazareth Coll-Rochester; Psych.

MARTIN, JOHN; Deer Park HS; Deer Pk, NY; (Y); 6/440; Pres Varsity Clb; Var Capt Socr; Var Capt Tennis; High Hon Roll; Jr NHS; Trs NHS; Pres Schlr; Church Yth Grp; Intnl Clb; Band; All Lge,Cnty,ST Socr 84; Top Athlt Schlr Awd 85; Gnl Exclnce Socl Stud & Acctg 85; Wharton Schl; Acctg.

MARTIN, JONATHAN; Garden City HS; Garden City, NY; (Y); VP Church Yth Grp; Cmnty Wkr; VP Drama Clb; Math Tm; School Musical; School Play; Ed Yrbk Stf; JV Ftbl; L I Presbytrn Delg Worldwide Yth Triennium Purdue U 83; Traveler Soviet Union 85; Bus.

MARTIN, JOSEPH C; Newfield HS; Selden, NY; (Y); VICA; Bsktbl; Var Capt Crs Cntry; Var Capt Trk; Hon Roll; MVP V Trck 85; All Cnty Selctn V Trck 84; All League V Crs Cntry 84; Electrncs.

MARTIN, JOYCE; New Hyde Park Memorial HS; New Hyde Park, NY; (S); Church Yth Grp; Dance Clb; Drama Clb; Band; Church Choir; School Musical; School Play; Variety Show; Yrbk Stf; Bsktbl; Bowling Tourn 1st Pl 83; DECA 1st Pl Trphy Awd Mrktng 85; Adelphi; Bus.

MARTIN, JULIE; Clymer Central Schl; Clymer, NY; (Y); Chorus; Church Choir; Pres Frsh Cls; VP Soph Cls; VP Jr Cls; Sec Sr Cls; Var Cheerleading; Var Trk; Var Vllybl; High Hon Roll; Amer Chmcl Scty Chmstry Awd 85; Schlrshp, Ldrshp & Srv Awd 85.

MARTIN, KAREN; Williamsville North HS; E Amherst, NY; (Y); 87/350; VP Pres Church Yth Grp; French Clb; Hosp Aide; Latin Clb; Church Choir; Off Sr Cls; Stu Cncl; Hon Roll; NHS; St Schlr; NYS Regents Schlrshp 85; ST U NY Buffalo; Psych.

MARTIN, KATHLEEN E; Paul V Moore HS; Bernhards Bay, NY; (Y); 12/298; Computer Clb; Drama Clb; Math Tm; School Play; Var JV Sftbl; Var Tennis; Var JV Vllybl; High Hon Roll; NHS; AFS; Ctznshp Awd Home Ec 81-82; SUNY-OSWEGO; Scndry Educ.

MARTIN, KEITH; Msgr Scanlan HS; Bronx, NY; (Y); 50/270; Church Yth Grp; Civic Clb; Cmnty Wkr; JV Var Bsbl; JV Var Bsktbl; JV Bowling; Hon Roll; Bus Adm.

MARTIN, KIMBERLY A; Hunter College HS; Whitestone, NY; (Y); AFS; Yrbk Stf; Pres Frsh Cls; Sec Soph Cls; Var Capt Tennis; Mu Alp Tht; Ntl Merit Ltr; VP Schl Athl Assn 84-85; Schlrshps 83; Hunter Coll; Lbrl Arts.

MARTIN, LEE; Grand Island HS; Grand Island, NY; (Y); Hon Roll; Cert Acadmc Excllnc 83&85; Acadmc Lttr 85; Bus.

MARTIN, MAUREEN; Liverpool HS; Liverpool, NY; (S); 34/800; Church Yth Grp; Chorus; Orch; Symp Band; Yrbk Stf; Rep Stu Cncl; High Hon Roll; Jr NHS; NHS; Ntl Merit Ltr; Prncpl Flautist Syracuse Symphny Yth Orchstr 84-85; Wnnr 82 Cvc Morning Musicals Concerto Comptn 82; Law.

MARTIN, MONIQUE; Walton HS; Bronx, NY; (Y); Art Clb; Computer Clb; 4-H; FHA; Math Tm; Office Aide; Pep Clb; Spanish Clb; Teachers Aide; Stage Crew; Comm Art Inst Pgm Hnrs 85; Fshn Illstrtn Parsons Dsgn Schl Awd 85; Fshn Dsgn Art Outstndng Stu 83; Fshn Inst/Tech; Fshn Dsgn.

MARTIN, NANCY J; Hunter College HS; New York City, NY; (Y); Cmnty Wkr; Pres Drama Clb; Math Clb; Chorus; Stage Crew; Swing Chorus; Nwsp Stf; Yrbk Stf; Mu Alp Tht; Ntl Merit SF.

MARTIN, NINA K; Holland Patent HS; Prospect, NY; (Y); 11/211; Art Clb; French Clb; School Play; Yrbk Ed-Chief; Yrbk Stf; Cheerleading; Fld Hcky; Trk; High Hon Roll; NHS; Regents Schlrshp 85; Ithaca Coll; Radio Comm.

MARTIN, PATRICIA; Academy Fo The Holy Names; Latham, NY; (Y); Sftbl; Chorus; Frnch.

MARTIN, PETER S; Beekmantown Central HS; West Chazy, NY; (Y); 18/134; Model UN; School Play; Nwsp Stf; Yrbk Stf; Var Stu Cncl; Capt Crs Cntry; Capt Trk; Hon Roll; NHS; St Schlr; 1st Pl Archtchr Cmptn 85; Clinton Cty Art Smmr Schlrshp 84; Cornell U; Libri Arts.

MARTIN, RANDY; Greene Central Schl; Chenanago Forks, NY; (Y); Varsity Clb; JV Capt Ftbl; Lineman Of Yr 84; 2nd Tm All Chenango Cnty Defense 84; 2nd Tm All Susquenango W Def Middle Guard 84.

MARTIN, ROSALIND; Flushing HS; Flushing, NY; (Y).

MARTIN, SAMANTHA; Elizabethtown-Lewis C S HS; Lewis, NY; (Y); 1/28; GAA; Scholastic Bowl; School Play; Nwsp Ed-Chief; Yrbk Ed-Chief; Pres Frsh Cls; Pres Sr Cls; Pres Stu Cncl; Var L Bsktbl; Var L Socr; Stu Advsry Cncl Schlrshp 85; Outstndg SR Girl Athl 85; Pres Acad Ftns Awd 85; Vassar Coll; Bus Admin.

MARTIN, SHAWN; Alder Central SR HS; Alden, NY; (Y); Aud/Vis; Boy Scts; French Clb; Band; Concert Band; School Musical; Capt Crs Cntry; Vrsty Rifl Tm; Comp Sci.

MARTIN, SHAWN; West Seneca W SR HS; W Seneca, NY; (Y); Aud/Vis; Ski Clb; Rep Stu Cncl; Vllybl; JC Awd; St Johns U; Crmnl Jstc.

MARTIN, STEPHANIE; Whitesboro SR HS; Utica, NY; (Y); 40/365; Chorus; Sec Jr Cls; Im Powder Puff Ftbl; Hon Roll; Jr NHS; Mohawk Valley CC; Comp Sci.

MARTIN, STEPHANIE ANNE; Saratoga Central Catholic HS; Ballston Spa, NY; (Y); 3/50; Drama Clb; JA; Quiz Bowl; Teachers Aide; School Play; Yrbk Ed-Chief; DAR Awd; High Hon Roll; Rotary Awd; Excell In Unique Plcmnt Prog; Nancy Celeste Awd For Schl Spirit & Svc; John T Eddy Awd For Yrbk; Utica Coll; Occup Thrpy.

MARTIN, SUSAN; Mohawk Central HS; Ilion, NY; (Y); 22/105; Church Yth Grp; Exploring; 4-H; Hosp Aide; Letterman Clb; Band; Chorus; Concert Band; Mrchg Band; Orch; NY Acadmy Of Sci 85; Geneseo; Pre-Med.

MARTIN, THOMAS; Cortland HS; Cortland, NY; (Y); 63/267; VICA; JV Var Bsbl; JV Var Ftbl; Hon Roll; Jr NHS; Morris Noss Schlrshp 85; Merit Awd-Ntl Lvl-AAA Pstr Cntst 85; Stu Of 1/4-Oct, June 84-85; Rchstr Inst Of Tech; Grphcdsgn.

MARTIN, THOMAS; Rome Free Acad; Rome, NY; (Y); Boy Scts; Ski Clb; Band; Concert Band; Mrchg Band; Var Crs Cntry; Var Swmmng; Trk; Hon Roll; Jr NHS; Accntng.

MARTIN, THOMAS; Sachem North Campus HS; Lake Ronkonkoma, NY; (Y); 80/1376; Cmnty Wkr; Ski Clb; Varsity Clb; Band; Concert Band; Jazz Band; Mrchg Band; Orch; School Musical; School Play; US Naval Acad; Aero Engr.

MARTIN, TRAVIS L; South New Berlin Central Schl; New Berlin, NY; (Y); Am Leg Boys St; Boy Scts; Band; Concert Band; Mrchg Band; Hon Roll; Farm Bureau Champ 85.

MARTIN, VERNON; St Joseph By The Sea HS; Staten Island, NY; (Y); Aud/Vis; Computer Clb; Drama Clb; Teachers Aide; Chorus; School Musical; School Play; Nwsp Stf; Yrbk Stf; Hon Roll; Psych.

MARTIN, VICTORIA; Hugh C Williams HS; Canton, NY; (Y); AFS; Varsity Clb; Sec Stu Cncl; Var L Bsktbl; Coach Actv; Lcrss; JV Var Socr; JV Sftbl; High Hon Roll; NHS; Hugh O Brien Yth Fllwshp Awd 84; Bus Adm.

MARTIN, WILLIAM; Windham-Ashland-Jewett-Central HS; Hensonville, NY; (S); Church Yth Grp; French Clb; Var Bsbl; Var Bsktbl; Var Bowling; Var Crs Cntry; Var Capt Socr; Prfct Atten Awd; Hofstra U.

MARTINCICH, MICHAEL; Canarsie HS; Brooklyn, NY; (Y); 75/561; Im Tennis; JV Trk; NY ST Regents Scholarship 85; SUNY Buffalo; Electrical Engrg.

MARTINEZ, ADRIANA; Fashion Industries HS; Corona, NY; (Y); 105/363; Library Aide; Office Aide; Stage Crew; Variety Show; Soph Cls; Vllybl; Prfct Atten Awd; FIT; Fshn Desgnr.

MARTINEZ, BELINDA; Royalton-Hartland Central HS; Gasport, NY; (Y); 13/140; Church Yth Grp; Drama Clb; Girl Scts; Spanish Clb; School Play; Nwsp Bus Mgr; Nwsp Stf; Yrbk Stf; Cheerleading; Trk; Nrs.

MARTINEZ, BETH; A E Stevenson HS; Bronx, NY; (Y); Church Yth Grp; Chorus; Church Choir; St Johns U; Lwyr.

MARTINEZ, BETYS; St Catherine Acad; Bronx, NY; (Y); 60/205; Office Aide; Pep Clb; Teachers Aide; School Musical; Score Keeper; Socr; Trk; Prfct Atten Awd; Achvt Music 85; U Of MD; Bus Adm.

MARTINEZ, CRISTINA; Christ The King Regional HS; Brooklyn, NY; (Y); 199/385; Sec Intnl Clb; Chorus; School Play; Stage Crew; JV Var DECA; High Hon Roll; Hon Roll; NHS; Syracuse U.

MARTINEZ, DEBORAH; St Catherine Acad; Bronx, NY; (Y); 35/205; Hosp Aide; Cert Awd Excel Chem 85.

MARTINEZ, GLADYS; Christopher Columbus HS; Bronx, NY; (Y); 9/792; Key Clb; Teachers Aide; Band; Cit Awd; High Hon Roll; Hon Roll; NHS; Excel Chrctr Cert 82-85; Comp Math, Sci Rsrch Cert 85; Pre Med.

MARTINEZ, JINETTE; Commack High School South; Dix Hills, NY; (S); 56/375; Sec MMM; Off Chorus; Mrchg Band; Orch; Nwsp Stf; Var Crs Cntry; Var Trk; High Hon Roll; Donald P Sties Memrl Awd 84; Full Chrl Schlrshp To USDAN Prfrmng Arts Ctr 83; NYSSMA Solo Rtng 84; Music Educ.

MARTINEZ, JOSE M; Copiague HS; Lindenhurst, NY; (Y); #9 In Class; Church Yth Grp; DECA; FBLA; Spanish Clb; JV Var Socr; High Hon Roll; Hon Roll; NHS; Pres Schlr; Rochester Inst Of Tech; Bio Sci.

MARTINEZ, JUAN; Lasalle Acad; New York, NY; (Y); Art Clb; Church Yth Grp; English Clb; Spanish Clb; Lit Mag; Wt Lftg; Wrstlng; St Johns U; Art.

MARTINEZ, LYNDA N; Bishop Loughlin M HS; Brooklyn, NY; (Y); #5 In Class; Band; Jazz Band; School Musical; High Hon Roll; Med.

MARTINEZ, MARIBEL; Clara Barton HS; Brooklyn, NY; (Y); 26/469; Computer Clb; Spanish Clb; Chorus; Yrbk Phtg; Yrbk Rptr; Yrbk Stf; Cit Awd; Hon Roll; NHS; Bus Advsry Cmmssn Medl 85; Fordham U; Corp Lwyr.

MARTINEZ, MARLEN; Monsignor Scanlan HS; Bronx, NY; (Y); 3/266; Hon Roll; Jr NHS; NHS; Prfct Atten Awd; Span Rgnts 100 Pct Awd; Top 10 Pct Cls Awd; 1st Hnr All Thru HS; NY U; Pre-Med.

MARTINEZ, MARLENE; Cathedral HS; Bronx, NY; (Y); 88/306; Girl Scts; Library Aide; Hon Roll; Pre-Law.

MARTINEZ, MAUREEN; Christopher Columbus HS; Bronx, NY; (Y); 99/492; Computer Clb; Dance Clb; Spanish Clb; Chorus; School Play; Gym; Sftbl; Hon Roll; Prfct Atten Awd; Spanish NHS; Comp.

MARTINEZ, MAURICIO; Archbishop Molloy HS; Woodside, NY; (Y); 79/409; Chorus; Yrbk Phtg; High Hon Roll; Hon Roll; NHS; Ntl Merit Ltr; IONA Coll Lang Cntst Spnsh II 1st Hnrs 84; Pre-Med.

MARTINEZ, MELISSA; Roger B Chaffee HS; FPO New York, NY; (Y); 1/25; Trs FBLA; Nwsp Stf; Ed Lit Mag; Var Cheerleading; Sftbl; JV Trk; NHS; Pres Schlr; Med.

MARTINEZ, MICHELLE; Bronx High School Of Science; Bronx, NY; (Y); Dance Clb; Hosp Aide; Intnl Clb; Red Cross Aide; Rep Spanish Clb; Teachers Aide; Chorus; Rep Jr Cls; Prfct Atten Awd; Medal Hnr Vol Wrk 83; Sophie Davis Schl Biomed; Pedtr.

MARTINEZ, ROLANDO; Hempstead HS; Hempstead, NY; (S); FBLA; Math Clb; School Play; Stage Crew; Yrbk Phtg; Yrbk Stf; High Hon Roll; Hon Roll; NHS; Hoftra Upwrd Bound 84; NY Inst Tech; Comp Grphs.

MARTINEZ, SERGIO; Albertus Magnus HS; Garnerville, NY; (Y); 7/190; Math Tm; Rep Jr Cls; VP Stu Cncl; Var Bsbl; JV Bsktbl; Hon Roll; Mu Alp Tht; NHS; Spanish NHS; Elec Engrng.

MARTINEZ, SYLVIA; St Pius V HS; Bronx, NY; (Y); French Clb; Nwsp Stf; Pres Jr Cls; Rep Stu Cncl; NHS; Prfct Atten Awd; Mary Mount Mahattan; Psych.

MARTINI, DAVID; Solvay HS; Solvay, NY; (Y); 22/160; Key Clb; Math Clb; Rep Sr Cls; High Hon Roll; Rochester Inst Tech; Mech Engr.

MARTINI, JUDE T; Newburgh Free Acad; Newburgh, NY; (Y); 5/750; Cmnty Wkr; Pres Service Clb; Church Choir; Jazz Band; Orch; Trs Soph Cls; High Hon Roll; Opt Clb Awd; Church Yth Grp; Math Tm; Louis Augst Jones Found Schlrshp Wnr 83-84; BASIC Comp Prgm Awd 84; Mem Prz Amer Studies 85; Pre Law.

MARTINI, JULIE M; Canandaigua SR Acad; Canandaigua, NY; (Y); 54/277; Church Yth Grp; Pres Spanish Clb; Church Choir; Var L Socr; Trk; High Hon Roll; Hon Roll; Girl Scts; ST U NY Geneseo; Elem Educ.

MARTINI, LISA; Fox Lane Bedford HS; Pound Ridge, NY; (Y); Ski Clb; Var Cheerleading; JV Powder Puff Ftbl; Sat Live Prog At FIT 84-85; Fox Lane Lay Dsgn For Schl 84-85; Dir Fash Show 84-85; Dsgn & Illstrtn.

MARTINI, MARY-ANTOINETTE; Norman Thomas HS; Astoria, NY; (S); Cmnty Wkr; Pres DECA; Girl Scts; Hosp Aide; VP JA; Office Aide; Red Cross Aide; Teachers Aide; Band; Color Guard; Distrib Educ Clbs NY 84-85; Warner Comm Schlrshp 85; Apprl & Acess 1st NYC Ovrl,2nd ST Ovrl 85; Berkley Schl; Fash Merch.

MARTINI, ROBERT T; Xaverian HS; Brooklyn, NY; (Y); 4/347; Mgr JA; VP Spanish Clb; Nwsp Ed-Chief; Rep Jr Cls; Stu Cncl; Hon Roll; NHS; Pres Schlr; Spanish NHS; Schlrshp To LIU Pharmacy Schl 85; NYU Trustee Schlrshp 85; Letter Of Recomendatn; NYU; Pre Dental.

MARTINIS, FRANK; Lawernce HS; Inwood L I, NY; (Y); Computer Clb; Debate Tm; Mathletes; Math Tm; High Hon Roll; Jr NHS; NHS; Ntl Merit SF; Italian Clb Pres 83-84; Govt Actn Delg Chrmn 85; Med.

MARTINIS, STACEY M; Brentwood Ross HS; Brentwood, NY; (Y); 9/625; FBLA; Hosp Aide; Radio Clb; Nwsp Rptr; Rep Sr Cls; Mgr Wrstlng; Hon Roll; Jr NHS; NHS; Ntl Merit Ltr; SR Class Schlrshp 85; Ntl Assoc Letter Carriers Schlrshp 85; Hofstra U Schlrshp 85; Hofstra U; Intl Bus.

MARTINO, DARNISE A; L A Webber HS; Lyndonville, NY; (S); 5/60; School Play; Sec Frsh Cls; Pres Soph Cls; Pres Sr Cls; VP Stu Cncl; Var Capt Cheerleading; High Hon Roll; Trs NHS; Computer Clb; Math Clb; Student Of The Month; Regents Scholarship Recipient; Suny At Oswego; Industrial Engr.

MARTINO, FRANK; Immaculate Heart Central HS; Watertown, NY; (Y); Cmnty Wkr; Spanish Clb; Variety Show; JV Bsktbl; Var L Ftbl; Prfct Atten Awd; Engnr.

MARTINO, LOUIS; Honeoye Central Schl; Holcomb, NY; (S); 2/61; French Clb; JV Bsktbl; High Hon Roll; Hon Roll; NHS; Sal; Williams; Acctng.

MARTINO, RON; Aquinas Inst; Rochester, NY; (Y); 40/179; Cmnty Wkr; JA; Nwsp Ed-Chief; Nwsp Stf; Rep Soph Cls; Rep Jr Cls; Rep Stu Cncl; Trk; High Hon Roll; Let From Senator Steinfeldt Awd 83; Mech Engnrng.

MARTINO, TERESA; Bloomfield Central HS; W Bloomfield, NY; (Y); Drama Clb; French Clb; Sec Pres Girl Scts; Sec Pres Library Aide; Chorus; Yrbk Phtg; Yrbk Stf; French Hon Soc; Hon Roll; NHS; Middleburg; Lang.

MARTINS, CRISTINE; Sacred Heart Academy; Mineola, NY; (S); Art Clb; Dance Clb; French Clb; Library Aide; Science Clb; Chorus; School Musical; High Hon Roll; NHS; All Cnty Chrs 83-85.

MARTIR, JOYCE; Academy Of Mount St Ursula; New York, NY; (Y); Stage Crew; Yrbk Ed-Chief; Yrbk Stf; Frsh Cls; Pres Soph Cls; Rep Sr Cls; Stu Cncl; Var L Cheerleading; Hon Roll; Natl Lang Arts Olympd Awd 83; Cert Hon Mth 83; Cert Ed Develpmnt Natl 84.

MARTIZEZ, MARLENE; Cathedral HS; New York, NY; (Y); 44/305; Girl Scts; Pace U; Pre-Law.

MARTOCCIA, PAULA A; Carmel HS; Carmel, NY; (Y); 39/370; Cmnty Wkr; PAVAS; Orch; Nwsp Ed-Chief; Lit Mag; Sec Stu Cncl; High Hon Roll; Hon Roll; NHS; Ribbons Artwrk In Local Arts Cncl Exhibits 81-85; Desgnr.

MARTONE, ANDREW; Penn Yan Acad; Penn Yan, NY; (Y); 8/180; Am Leg Boys St; Pres Jr Cls; Pres Sr Cls; JV Bsktbl; Var Ftbl; Var Trk; High Hon Roll; NHS; Vrsty Clb Trk Awd 85.

MARTUCCI, MICHILINA; St Joseph By The Sea HS; Staten Island, NY; (Y); 1/241; Am Leg Aux Girls St; Church Choir; Yrbk Stf; Stu Cncl; High Hon Roll; NHS; Ntl Merit Ltr; NEDT Awd; Drama Clb; George Washington U Engrng Mdl Mth & Sci 85; Sci.

MARTUSCELLO, RENEE; Amsterdam HS; Amsterdam, NY; (Y); 17/294; Varsity Clb; Yrbk Stf; VP Soph Cls; Rep Jr Cls; Var Capt Cheerleading; Hon Roll; NHS; Med Lab Tech.

MARTUSCELLO, SUSAN; Fonda-Fultonville Central HS; Fonda, NY; (Y); 9/119; 4-H; Hosp Aide; Key Clb; Spanish Clb; School Musical; Nwsp Rptr; High Hon Roll; Hon Roll; NHS; Prfct Atten Awd; Regnts Schlrshp 85; Auto Clb Awd 85; St Rose; Biochem.

MARULLI, ROSEANN; St Edmund HS; Brooklyn, NY; (S); 8/190; Hosp Aide; Science Clb; Lit Mag; Bowling; NHS; NEDT Awd; Trs French Clb; Jr Service Awd 84; Ntl Ldrshp Orgnztn 84; Christian Service 82-84; Med.

MARULLO, JO ANNE; Cicero-North Syracuse HS; Clay, NY; (Y); Chorus; Orch; School Musical; Off Stu Cncl; Hon Roll; JP Sousa Awd; Syracuse Symph Yth Orch 84-85; Mus Ed.

MARUSARZ, JENNIFER; Dundee Central Schl; Dundee, NY; (Y); 1/69; Pres Church Yth Grp; Pres Spanish Clb; Teachers Aide; Church Choir; High Hon Roll; NHS; Val; DAR Awd; Prfct Atten Awd; J E Seagram Schlrshp 85; Dundee Rotry Schlrshp 85; Pres Acadmc Ftns Awd 85; Baptist Bible Clg; Elem Educ.

MARUSARZ, KYLE D; Dundee Central Schl; Dundee, NY; (Y); 10/100; Am Leg Boys St; Church Yth Grp; Rep Stu Cncl; Var L Bsktbl; Var L Ftbl; Hon Roll; Offnsve Lineman-Fay Fultz Awd Ftbl 84-85; Alfred Ag & Tech Coll; Ag.

MARVEL, WALTER; Valley Central HS; Walden, NY; (Y); Camera Clb; Church Yth Grp; Science Clb; Spanish Clb; Nwsp Ed-Chief; Rep Soph Cls; Rep Jr Cls; Rep Sr Cls; Spanish NHS; Chrstus Rex Awd 80; Law.

MARVIN, ANNETTE M; Canandaigua Acad; Canandaigua, NY; (Y); Computer Clb; Ski Clb; Spanish Clb; Varsity Clb; Socr; High Hon Roll; NHS; Regents Schlrshp 85; Clarkson U.

MARVIN, DAN; Portville Central HS; Portville, NY; (Y); 6/119; Am Leg Boys St; Debate Tm; Drama Clb; Speech Tm; Teachers Aide; School Play; Off Stu Cncl; High Hon Roll; Lion Awd; NHS; Sthrn Tier Scholar Alfred U 85; Exch Clb Stu Of Mnth 85; Am Leg Const Spch 2nd Dist 84-85; Alfred U; Ceramic Engrng.

MARVIN, DARYL J; Schoharie Central Schl; Schoharie, NY; (Y); 1/90; Am Leg Boys St; Pres Computer Clb; Quiz Bowl; Band; Chorus; Jazz Band; Mrchg Band; Yrbk Stf; Var L Bsbl; Var Capt Socr; Rensselaer Medl 84.

MARZETTE, VANITA; Fayetteville - Manlius HS; Cleveland, OH; (Y); Spanish Clb; Drill Tm; Variety Show; JV L Bsktbl; Var L Cheerleading; Var L Trk; Tp 7 Pr Cnt Minorts PSAT; Cleveland ST U; Mktng.

MARZOCCHI, LOLA; Bishop Grimes HS; Syracuse, NY; (Y); Boy Scts; Dance Clb; Yrbk Ed-Chief; Ed Yrbk Stf; High Hon Roll; Hon Roll; NHS; VP Jr Cls; Golden Galleon Awd Jrnlsm 85; Italian Natl Hnr Scty 84-86.

MARZOCCHI, MARIA; Bishop Grimes HS; Syracuse, NY; (Y); Art Clb; Ed Yrbk Stf; Var Cheerleading; High Hon Roll; NHS; Italian Hnr Scty 82-85; The Holy Crss Bk Prize 85; Natl Socl Stds Olympiad 85; Bio.

MARZOLF, PHILIP; South Shore HS; Brooklyn, NY; (Y); Church Yth Grp; Math Tm; Varsity Clb; Var Crs Cntry; Var Trk; Hon Roll; NHS; Cathedral Coll; Priesthd.

MARZOLF, SHANNON; Alexander Central HS; Darien Center, NY; (S); Drama Clb; Spanish Clb; Chorus; Color Guard; Hon Roll; Jr NHS; NHS; Alfred Tech Inst; Arch.

MARZORCHI, MARIA; Bishop Grimes HS; Syracuse, NY; (Y); Art Clb; Yrbk Stf; Cheerleading; High Hon Roll; Hon Roll; NHS; Itln Hnr Scty 82-85; Holy Crss Bk Prz 85; Natl Soc Stds Olympiad 85; Bio.

MARZULLA JR, NICHOLAS; La Salle Acad; New York, NY; (Y); Rep Soph Cls; Im Bowling; Im Fld Hcky; Im Ftbl; Im Socr; Im Sftbl; Hon Roll; Comp Pgmmr.

MARZZIOTTI, TROY; Mount St Micheal Acad; Yonkers, NY; (Y); 31/308; High Hon Roll; Hon Roll; Jr NHS; NHS; Fresh, Soph Tuitn Schlrshp.

MASCARELL, NESTOR; St Josephs HS; Union City, NJ; (Y); 39/140; Nwsp Stf; Rep Soph Cls; Trs Stu Cncl; JV Bsbl; JV Bsktbl; Capt Var Ftbl; Var Hon Roll; Achvt Acad Ntl Awd 84; NYIT; Arch.

MASCARINI, PATRICK; Bishop Ford HS; Brooklyn, NY; (Y); Cmnty Wkr; Fordham U; Bus.

MASCERA, LAURENCE M; Central HS; Valley Stream, NY; (Y); Boy Scts; Computer Clb; FBLA; Ski Clb; Stu Cncl; JV Bsktbl; Hon Roll; Jr NHS; Ntl Bus Hnr Soc 85; Hofstra U; Bus.

MASCIANA, ANNA; Westlake HS; Thornwood, NY; (Y); Sec Pep Clb; Ski Clb; Mgr Stage Crew; Stu Cncl; Tennis; Mgr Trk.

MASCOLA, SUSANNE; Clarkstown South HS; West Nyack, NY; (Y); 68/550; Cmnty Wkr; Yrbk Stf; Stat Bsktbl; Var Tennis; NHS; Rotary Awd; Ski Clb; Nwsp Stf; Lit Mag; Pres Acad Ftns Awd 85; NY St Regnts Schlrshp 85; Yth Understndng 84; Yth Aganst Cancer 83-85; Lafayette Coll.

MASELLA, DENISE; St Joseph By The Sea HS; Staten Island, NY; (Y); Art Clb; Dance Clb; Yrbk Stf; Pres Soph Cls; Stu Cncl; High Hon Roll; Hon Roll; NEDT Awd; AATSP Ntl Spnsh Exam 84; Math.

MASERCOLA, MARY JO; John F Kennedy HS; Utica, NY; (Y); FBLA; Hosp Aide; Math Clb; Pep Clb; Nwsp Stf; Stu Cncl; JV Cheerleading; Var Vllybl; Spec Ed.

MASERCOLA, TINA; Niskayuna HS; Schdy, NY; (Y); Drama Clb; Acpl Chr; Chorus; Church Choir; School Musical; Swing Chorus; Variety Show; Var Co-Capt Cheerleading; Sec Frsh Cls; Sec Soph Cls; Arts & Craft Head Dir Summr Prog; St Rose; Elem.

MASHANIC, MICHAEL P; St Josephs Collegiate Inst; Kenmore, NY; (Y); 66/201; Church Yth Grp; Cmnty Wkr; Ski Clb; Nwsp Stf; Yrbk Stf; Hon Roll; NHS; Syracuse U & St Bonaventure U & NY ST Regnts Schlrshps 85; St Bonaventure U; Mass Cmmnctns.

MASI, ANGELA; Mary Louis Acad; Floral Park, NY; (Y); Cmnty Wkr; Hosp Aide; Adelphi U; Med.

MASI, SUZANNE; Lindenhurst HS; Lindenhurst, NY; (Y); Hosp Aide; Spanish Clb; Drill Tm; Mrchg Band; Stage Crew; Capt Twrlr; Hon Roll; Jr NHS; NHS; Qn Sons Italy 84; Nrsng.

MASIA, CAROLINE; South Side HS; Pine City, NY; (Y); Key Clb; Latin Clb; Nwsp Stf; SUNY; Phys Asst.

MASIELLO, JOHN; Archbishop Molloy HS; Flushing, NY; (Y); 12/409; Chess Clb; Computer Clb; Science Clb; NHS; Ntl Merit Ltr; 1st Hnrs 83-85; Med.

MASIH-DAS, CARROL; Richmond Hill HS; Queens, NY; (Y); Dance Clb; Drama Clb; FNA; Hosp Aide; Library Aide; Model UN; Red Cross Aide; Service Clb; Sftbl; Nrsg.

MASLEK, MARK; La Salle SR HS; Niagara Falls, NY; (S); 19/350; Varsity Clb; Nwsp Stf; Capt Bsbl; Var Ftbl; JV Swmmng; Var Vllybl; Hon Roll; Jr NHS; Lion Awd; NHS; Engrng.

MASLIJ, NATALIA; St George Acad; New York, NY; (Y); 5/26; Dance Clb; Acpl Chr; Chorus; School Play; Sec Frsh Cls; Score Keeper; Vllybl; Hon Roll; NHS; Pharm.

MASLONA, PETER J; West Seneca East SR HS; West Seneca, NY; (Y); 60/365; Ski Clb; Lit Mag; Vllybl; Hon Roll; Jr NHS; German Merit Awd; Regents Schlrshp; Syracuse U; Elec Engr.

MASON, BYRON; Rome Free Acad; Rome, NY; (Y); Spanish Clb; Chorus; Ftbl; Trk; JV Capt Wrstlng; Hon Roll; NHS; Prfct Atten Awd; MUSIC.

MASON, DAN; Hebkimer HS; Herkimer, NY; (Y); Computer Clb; Band; Concert Band; Jazz Band; Mrchg Band; School Play; Bsbl; L Bsktbl; L Ftbl; L Golf; MST Imprvd Golfr 84; Bus Adm.

MASON, DANIEL J; E J Wilson HS; Spencerport, NY; (Y); Am Leg Boys St; Rep Sr Cls; Var Bsktbl; Var Socr; High Hon Roll; NHS; SAR Awd; Alfred U Presntl Schlr; Alfred U; Accntng.

MASON, DAWN; Hoosick Falls Central Schl; Eagle Bridge, NY; (Y); 3/100; Drama Clb; FBLA; Stage Crew; Yrbk Stf; Stu Cncl; High Hon Roll; NHS; Ntl Math Awd 82-83; Ntl Stu Ldrshp & Svc Awd 83-84; Ldrshp & Svc Awd 84-85.

MASON, DEBORAH J; Sachem HS; Lk Ronkonkoma, NY; (Y); 27/1509; Trs Church Yth Grp; French Clb; GAA; Ski Clb; Yrbk Stf; Lit Mag; Soph Cls; Coach Actv; Var L Gym; NHS; Hgh Hnrs Awd-Long Island Sci Cngrss 83; 1st Pl Resrch Papr-H S Hstry Fair; L I Hstry Fair Hnrb Mntn 84; Sprts Med.

MASON, IRENE; Kingston HS; Rifton, NY; (Y); 15/511; Church Yth Grp; Cmnty Wkr; High Hon Roll; NHS; Drama Clb; Church Choir; Nwsp Stf; Stu Cncl; Jr NHS; Kingston Hosp Nrsng Awd 85; Anne Mae Young Mrsng Awd 85; Kingston Lions Clb Schlrshp 85; Albany Medical Ctr Schl; Nrsng.

MASON, JON; Plattsburgh HS; Plattsburgh, NY; (Y); JV Var Bsktbl; Var Trk; TV.

MASON, MICHELLE; George W Fowler HS; Syracuse, NY; (Y); Dance Clb; Drama Clb; FBLA; Pep Clb; Nwsp Stf; Yrbk Stf; Lit Mag; Awd 2nd Hghst Stdnt Appld Bio 83-84; CCBI; Legl Secy.

MASON, SARAH; Grand Island HS; Grand Island, NY; (Y); 16/325; Off Church Yth Grp; Ski Clb; Varsity Clb; Off Church Choir; Var Socr; Var Sftbl; Hon Roll; NHS; Acdmc Letter 85; Acdmc Achvt Awd 83-85; Outstndng Awd For Chrch Choir 85; Ed.

MASON, STEPHEN V; Heatly HS; Green Island, NY; (Y); 9/26; Am Leg Boys St; Camera Clb; Cmnty Wkr; Key Clb; Varsity Clb; School Play; Variety Show; Yrbk Bus Mgr; Cit Awd; Elks Awd; E R Behrand Schlrshp Awd 85; Rotary Schlrshp 85; Robert Halligan Mem Awd 85; Hudson Vly Comm Coll; Librl Art.

MASON, TAMA A; St Johns Prep HS; St Albans, NY; (Y); 43/450; Church Yth Grp; Civic Clb; Cmnty Wkr; Dance Clb; Variety Show; Yrbk Stf; Rep Frsh Cls; Rep Soph Cls; Rep Sr Cls; Rep Stu Cncl; Englsh Awd; T Johns U; Bus.

MASON, TRACEY; Mercy HS; Pt Jefferson Sta, NY; (Y); Art Clb; Yrbk Stf; VP Frsh Cls; VP Soph Cls; Rep Jr Cls; JV Var Fld Hcky; JV Var Sftbl; Hon Roll; NHS; JV Fldhcky 110 Per Cent 82; Lng Islnd Cath Jrnlsm Awd 85; Mst Imprvd Plyr Awd Var Fldhcky 84; Brdcstng.

MASONE, ANDREW J; Cardinal Spellman HS; Bronx, NY; (Y); Trs Church Yth Grp; Yrbk Stf; Bsktbl; Ftbl; Golf; Sftbl; Wt Lftg; Hon Roll; St Schlr; St Johns U; Phrmcy.

MASRI, ROSE A; Eastchester HS; Eastchester, NY; (Y); 16/163; Ed Yrbk Phtg; Sec Jr Cls; Sec Sr Cls; Sec Stu Cncl; Var Cheerleading; DAR Awd; High Hon Roll; NHS; Spanish NHS; Semi-Fnlst Miss TEEN NY Schlrshp 84; U Of PA.

MASS, NOAH B; Kingston HS; Kingston, NY; (Y); Quiz Bowl; Ski Clb; Yrbk Stf; Rep Stu Cncl; High Hon Roll; Hon Roll; St Schlr; Rensselaer Polytech Inst; Aero.

MASSA, CHRISTINE; Midwood HS; Brooklyn, NY; (Y); Dance Clb; Drama Clb; Girl Scts; Chorus; Nwsp Rptr; Swing Chorus; Sec Frsh Cls; JV Bsktbl; Im Mgr(s); Capt Pom Pon; Fin.

MASSA, DOMINIC; Spackenkill HS; Poughkeepsie, NY; (Y); JV Bsktbl; Var Trk; Hon Roll; Engrng.

MASSA, MARK L; Bishop Kearney HS; Rochester, NY; (Y); Am Leg Boys St; Letterman Clb; Varsity Clb; Rep Frsh Cls; Rep Soph Cls; Im Bsbl; Var L Ftbl; Var L Lcrss; Var Capt Wrstlng; Hon Roll; Outstndng Athlte Awd; Vrsty Clb VP; Alfred ST Coll; Elec Engrng.

MASSAC, ALEXANDER D; Cardinal Spellman HS; Bronx, NY; (Y); Aud/Vis; Off Frsh Cls; Camera Man.

MASSAD, LISA; Massena Central HS; Massena, NY; (Y); French Clb; Pep Clb; Off Jr Cls; Off Stu Cncl; Cheerleading; French Hon Soc; Hon Roll; Acad Achvt Awd 84-85; Mc Gill U; Med.

MASSARELLA, GEORGETTE; Seneca Vocational HS; Buffalo, NY; (Y); 31/180; Church Yth Grp; Red Cross Aide; Varsity Clb; Church Choir; Variety Show; Sec Sr Cls; Bowling; Cheerleading; Trk; Cit Awd; JR Miss Hnr 85; Native Amer Rsrc Pgm Awd 85; Sherman F Feytler Awd 85; Snow Coll; Phy Educ.

MASSARO, MARIA; Niagara Falls HS; Niagara Falls, NY; (Y); VP Pres Drama Clb; French Clb; Model UN; PAVAS; Thesps; School Musical; School Play; Stage Crew; Trs Soph Cls; Pres Stu Cncl; Bst Actrss 84; Bst Thesbian 84 & 85; Bst Actrss 85; Law.

MASSEY, KATHY M; Roy C Ketchem HS; Wappinger Fls, NY; (Y); Church Yth Grp; Cmnty Wkr; Math Clb; Pres Stu Cncl; Crs Cntry; Sftbl; Trk; High Hon Roll; NHS; TEEN Mssnry Mexico Smmr 85; Mssnry Doc.

MASSEY, STEVEN A; Columbia High School HS; Troy, NY; (Y); #69 In Class; Church Yth Grp; Rep Frsh Cls; Rep Jr Cls; JV Var Bsbl; Ntl Merit Ltr; NYS Regents Schlrshp 85; ST U NY Albany; Poli Sci.

MASSINO, ANTHONY; St Francis Prep; Maspeth, NY; (Y); 450/700; Chorus; Im JV Bowling; Ntl Merit Ltr; Im Fld Hcky; Im Score Keeper; Dean Cmmemrtng Dscplnry Excllnc Lttr 85; St Johns U; Finc.

MASTAN, JERRY J; Watervliet HS; Watervliet, NY; (Y); 8/120; Am Leg Boys St; French Clb; Var Capt Crs Cntry; Var Ftbl; Var Capt Wrstlng; High Hon Roll; NHS; Pres Schlr; NY ST Regents Schlrshp 85; Suny AL; Russian & Physics.

MASTEROV, MICHAEL; Bronx H S Of Science; Tenafly, NJ; (Y); Chess Clb; Computer Clb; Library Aide; Math Clb; Office Aide; Political Wkr; Radio Clb; Science Clb; Teachers Aide; School Play; John Hopkins; Genetic Engrng.

MASTERPOLE, NICHOLAS C; Bishop Ludden HS; Syracuse, NY; (Y); Am Leg Boys St; Church Yth Grp; Political Wkr; School Musical; High Hon Roll; Hon Roll; NHS; Var Golf; JV Lcrss; La Mayne Coll.

MASTERS, MIKE; The Wheatley HS; East Williston, NY; (Y); Intnl Clb; Pres Varsity Clb; Var Capt Bsktbl; Var Ftbl; Var Capt Socr; Var Trk; All Conf, All Trnmnt-Bsktbl Chmps 85; All Cnty MVP Nassau Cnty Tm, Chmps-S E Rgnl Chmps Soccer 84; Williams; Econ.

MASTERSON, DONNA; Greenville Central HS; Greenville, NY; (Y); Pep Clb; Spanish Clb; Chorus; JV Bsktbl; Var Trk; Var Vllybl; Cert Rcgntn 85; Jrnlsm.

MASTERSON, KELLY M; St John The Baptist HS; Central Islip, NY; (Y); 36/601; Chorus; Stage Crew; Nwsp Stf; JV Mgr(s); JV Timer; French Hon Soc; High Hon Roll; Hon Roll; NHS; Fairfield U Acad Schlrshp 85; Islandia Civic Assn Acad Schlrshp 85; Hofstra U Acad Schlrshp 85; Fairfield U; Intl Bus.

MASTRANADI, MICHELE; Union-Endicott HS; Endicott, NY; (Y); 60/450; Church Yth Grp; Ski Clb; Band; Mrchg Band; Symp Band; Yrbk Stf; Cheerleading; Hon Roll; NHS; Acctg.

MASTRANDREA, LYNN; Saint Edmund HS; Brooklyn, NY; (S); Art Clb; Drama Clb; English Clb; Science Clb; Spanish Clb; Capt Bowling; Hon Roll; Jr NHS; Stage Crew; Spnsh Awd 84; Cert Awd For Excel In Engl 83-84; Cert Awd For Hstry 83; Cornell U; Engrng.

MASTRANGELO, ERIC; Ravena Coeymans Sellciulz HS; Selkirk, NY; (Y); 9/200; Var Capt Crs Cntry; Var Trk; NHS; HVCC; Engrng Sci.

MASTRANGELO, FRANCES ANN; Bishop Grimes HS; Liverpool, NY; (Y); Var Bowling; JV Var Cheerleading; JV Pom Pon; Hon Roll; Italian NHS Awd 85.

MASTRANGELO, MARIA; Frontier Central HS; Lake View, NY; (S); Cmnty Wkr; Drama Clb; German Clb; Girl Scts; Pep Clb; Teachers Aide; Chorus; Hon Roll; NHS; Prfct Atten Awd; Erly Chldhd Educ.

MASTRO, MARK; East Ridge HS; Rochester, NY; (Y); 28/250; Boy Scts; Pep Clb; Varsity Clb; Band; School Musical; Yrbk Stf; JV Bsbl; JV Var Bsktbl; Var Ftbl; Hon Roll.

MASTROGIACOMO, LINA; Port Chester HS; Port Chester, NY; (Y); Church Yth Grp; Stage Crew; Hon Roll; Prfct Atten Awd; Italn Awd; Bus.

MASTROGIOVANNI, ANNA; Bishop Grimes HS; Syracuse, NY; (Y); Debate Tm; Hosp Aide; Political Wkr; Speech Tm; Yrbk Phtg; Yrbk Stf; Rep Frsh Cls; Bowling; Tennis; High Hon Roll.

MASTROGIOVANNI, ELLEN; John Marshall HS; Rochester, NY; (Y); Church Yth Grp; French Clb; GAA; Girl Scts; Library Aide; Ski Clb; Teachers Aide; Chorus; Church Choir; Stage Crew; Northland Coll; Meterlgy.

MASTROIANNI, ANGELA; Linton HS; Schenectady, NY; (Y); Intnl Clb; Band; Off Jr Cls; NHS; Spansh Awd 83; St Georges Yth Awd 85; Acctnt.

MASTROIANNI, ELEANORA; General D Mac Arthur HS; Levittown, NY; (Y); 1/319; Church Yth Grp; Pres Mathletes; Model UN; Service Clb; Orch; Yrbk Stf; Kiwanis Awd; NHS; Val; Regnts & Kiwanis Clbs & Knights Of Columbus Schlrshps 85; Cornell U.

MASTROPIERRO, MARIO; Sayville HS; Sayville, NY; (Y); 101/350; Computer Clb; Key Clb; Chorus; Capt Var Ftbl; Var Trk; Wt Lftg; Var Wrstlng; Hon Roll; All County Ftbl Tm 85; Comp Analyst.

MASUCCI, AMANDA; Linton HS; Schenectady, NY; (Y); Civic Clb; Drama Clb; Key Clb; Office Aide; Ski Clb; Chorus; School Play; Stat Fld Hcky; Capt Socr; Sftbl; Eng.

MASUICCA, CHRISTOPHER; Pulaski JR & SR HS; Pulaski, NY; (Y); 45/86; Varsity Clb; Band; Concert Band; School Play; Variety Show; Ftbl; Trk; Wt Lftg; School Musical; Coach Actv; Snow Accentive Awd 84; SR Of Mnth 85; Alfred U; Bldg Trades.

MASULLO, GINA M; John Jay HS; Wappingers Fall, NY; (Y); 25/560; Church Yth Grp; Chorus; School Musical; School Play; Yrbk Bus Mgr; Yrbk Rptr; Yrbk Stf; NHS; U Of Steubenville; Cmmnctns.

MATALEVICH, JOHN F; West Hempstead HS; W Hempstead, NY; (Y); Var Crs Cntry; Var Trk; Hon Roll; Civil Engrng.

MATANIC, DENISE P; New Hyde Park Memorial HS; New Hyde Park, NY; (Y); 4/279; Hosp Aide; High Hon Roll; Jr NHS; Twn N Hmpstd Ecol Essay Awd 84; NYS Rgnts Schlrshp 85; Pres Achvt Awd 85; Adelphi U; Nrsg.

MATARASO, VICTOR D; Washingtonville HS; Monroe, NY; (Y); VP Drama Clb; Temple Yth Grp; School Play; Nwsp Stf; Capt Bowling; Rotary Awd; Pres Of Stu Against Driving Drunk 84-8k; Syracuse U; Telecomm Mgmt.

MATARAZZO, DIANA MARIE; Sacred Heart Acad; Floral Park, NY; (S); 4/191; Chess Clb; Sec Girl Scts; Math Tm; Science Clb; Band; High Hon Roll; Hon Roll; NHS; Marion Awd; Manhatan Coll; Eng.

MATASSOV, GEORGE; Richmond Hills HS; Richmond Hill, NY; (Y); Computer Clb; English Clb; Math Clb; Science Clb; Band; Cmpt Engr.

MATEO, FELIX; South Side SR HS; Rockville Ctr, NY; (Y); 29/291; Teachers Aide; Var Socr; Var Trk; Hon Roll; NHS.

MATERAZZO, LISA; Bainbridge Guilford HS; Bainbridge, NY; (Y); 6/72; French Clb; Band; Color Guard; Yrbk Stf; Rep Stu Cncl; Var Bsktbl; Capt Sftbl; High Hon Roll; Rtry Yth Ldrshp Cmp 85; Ms Ten Amer Schlrshp 84; SUCO Stu Ldrshp Wrkshp 85; Engr.

MATHAI, JIJY M; Charles E Gorton HS; Yonkers, NY; (Y); 2/209; Sec Church Yth Grp; Hosp Aide; Office Aide; Teachers Aide; Band; Chorus; Church Choir; Concert Band; Lit Mag; Rep Sr Cls; Govt Svc Awd 84-85; All-Cty Vllybl Tm 81; Yonkes Clb 90 84 & 85; Sophie Davis Schl; Med.

MATHAI, RINY; Maria Regina HS; Mt Vernon, NY; (Y); 16/127; Nwsp Stf; Cit Awd; Hon Roll; NHS; Natl Sci Olympd Awd Chem 84; Columbia U; Physcn.

MATHER, COLETTE M; Lancaster Central HS; Depew, NY; (Y); Church Yth Grp; Dance Clb; Pep Clb; Ski Clb; Teachers Aide; Im Tennis; Im Vllybl; Hon Roll; NY Dnce Olympcs Silvr Awd 85; Summr Dnce Fstvl Chmpshp 85; Mth.

MATHER, COLIN; Pierson HS; Sag Harbor, NY; (Y); Am Leg Boys St; Spanish Clb; JV Bsbl; Var Mgr(s); Hon Roll; Hlth Studies.

MATHER, DAISY; Garden City HS; Garden City, NY; (S); 40/319; German Clb; Library Aide; Pres Science Clb; Chorus; Jazz Band; Orch; NHS; Cornell U.

MATHEW, JINU; Notre Dame Acad; Staten Island, NY; (Y); Church Yth Grp; Computer Clb; Math Clb; Office Aide; Science Clb; Spanish Clb; Church Choir; School Musical; Yrbk Phtg; Yrbk Stf; 500 Dollar Scholar 82-83; Med.

MATHEW, ROY; Sacred Heart HS; Yonkers, NY; (Y); Camera Clb; Chess Clb; Hon Roll; Jr NHS; NHS; Natl Cncl Negro Women 84; Engr.

MATHEWS, BRIAN P; Fairport HS; Fairport, NY; (Y); 25/600; Pres Computer Clb; VP JA; Ski Clb; High Hon Roll; NHS; Ntl Merit Ltr; Sci Olympics Awd 83; Amer Chem Soc Cmptn Awd 84; Regents Schlrshp 85; Cornell U; Elec Engrng.

MATHEWS, MICHAEL; Hamburg SR HS; Hamburg, NY; (Y); 34/358; Nwsp Stf; Hon Roll; NY ST Regents Schlrshp 85; Greg D Hartmen Mem Schlrshp 85; SUNY-STONYBROOK; Math.

MATHIEU, NANCY; Nazareth Regional HS; Brooklyn, NY; (Y); Art Clb; JA; Math Clb; Math Tm; Office Aide; Speech Tm; Chorus; Var Cheerleading; High Hon Roll; Hon Roll; Svc Awd; Phy Ed Awd; Princeton; Premed.

MATHIS, ELLEN A; Le Roy HS; Leroy, NY; (Y); 10/114; Varsity Clb; Yrbk Sprt Ed; VP Jr Cls; VP Sr Cls; Capt Var Bsktbl; Capt Var Socr; Capt Var Vllybl; High Hon Roll; Jr NHS; NHS; Hmcmng Queen 84; Hon Ment All-Grtr Rochester Sccr Team 84; Livingston Cnty Leag All Star Team 84; Ithaca Coll; Phy Thrpy.

MATHIS, ELLEN M; St Francis Prep; Richmond Hill, NY; (Y); Drama Clb; Pep Clb; Color Guard; School Musical; School Play; Stage Crew; Rep Jr Cls; Regents Nrsng Schlrshp 85; Fordham U; Engl.

MATHIS, MAUREEN; Le Roy Central Schl; Leroy, NY; (Y); 10/130; Concert Band; Mrchg Band; Yrbk Sprt Ed; VP Stu Cncl; Var L Bsktbl; Var L Socr; Var L Trk; DAR Awd; High Hon Roll; NHS; Tchng.

MATHIS, SHEILA; Cardinal Spellman HS; Bronx, NY; (Y); Cmnty Wkr; Concert Band; Mrchg Band; Pep Band; Physcl Thrpy.

MATIAS, KURT; Union Endicott HS; Endicott, NY; (Y); Church Yth Grp; Hon Roll; Prfct Atten Awd; Broome Comm Coll; Comp Sci.

MATIAS, MOSES; Manhattan Center HS; New York, NY; (Y); 1/42; Boys Clb Am; Boy Scts; Church Yth Grp; JA; Quiz Bowl; Science Clb; Church Choir; Capt Bsbl; Bsktbl; Capt Ftbl; Achvt Awd 83; Otto P Burgdorf Awd Bio 84; Princpls Lst 85; Bio Engrng.

MATIAS, VIVIAN; Cathedral HS; Newyork, NY; (Y); 93/298; Yrbk Stf; Wood Schl Awd Typg 85; Pace U; Acctnt.

MATIS, SHERI-LYNN B; Little Falls HS; St Johnsville, NY; (Y); Dance Clb; Drama Clb; FBLA; Spanish Clb; Band; Mrchg Band; Nwsp Ed-Chief; JV Var Bsktbl; Var L Sftbl; Hon Roll; Fnlst NYSPHSAA ST Bsktbl Tourn 84-85; Am HS Athl 84-85; Cmnctns.

MATKOVITS, THERESA; Cardinal Ohara HS; Tonawanda, NY; (S); 3/137; Drama Clb; Hosp Aide; VP Spanish Clb; Chorus; School Musical; School Play; High Hon Roll; NHS; JA; U Of Buffalo; Pre-Med.

MATOS, BEATRIZ; John Dewey HS; Brooklyn, NY; (Y); Dance Clb; Science Clb; Chorus; School Play; Nwsp Rptr; Im Bsktbl; Hon Roll; 2nd Pl Swmmng Awd 84; Kingsborough CC.

MATOS, DAISY; Sheepshead Bay HS; Brooklyn, NY; (Y); Hosp Aide; Intnl Clb; Office Aide; Teachers Aide; Variety Show; JV Trk; Cit Awd; Hon Roll; Exec Sec.

MATOS, MARIA; Christ The King Regional HS; Brooklyn, NY; (Y); Art Clb; Library Aide; Chorus; School Play; Jr NHS; NHS; Regnts Schlrshp 84-85; Hgh Hnrs 81-85; NY U.

MATOS, MARISOL; St Johns Prep; Sunnyside, NY; (Y); Debate Tm; Chorus; Church Choir; School Musical; School Play; Variety Show; Rep Jr Cls; Coach Actv; JV Trk; Var Wt Lftg; Coaches Awd-Trck 82-83; St Johns U; Comp.

MATOTT, MARY; Bishop Cunningham HS; Oswego, NY; (S); French Clb; Pep Clb; Ed Lit Mag; Rep Jr Cls; Rep Stu Cncl; JV Var Cheerleading; Var Socr; Var Capt Vllybl; Marn Bio.

MATRAFAILO, JUDY LEE; Washingtonville HS; Rock Tavern, NY; (Y); Ski Clb; VICA; Chorus; Stu Cncl; Capt Var Cheerleading; Stat Score Keeper; Csmtlgy.

MATSON, JONATHAN; Catholic Central HS; Waterford, NY; (S); 20/203; German Clb; VP Jr Cls; Socr; High Hon Roll; Hon Roll; NHS; Big Ten 1st Team Sccr Awd 83-84; Stu Goethe Inst 83; Ag.

MATTACOLA, CARL G; Rome Catholic HS; Rome, NY; (Y); 26/86; Am Leg Boys St; VP Soph Cls; VP Jr Cls; Var L Bsbl; Var L Bsktbl; Var Capt Ftbl; Hon Roll; MVP Ftbl Tm 82; MIP Ftbl 84.

MATTES, WILLIAM; Earl L Vandermeulen HS; Mt Sinai, NY; (Y); 42/286; Boy Scts; Church Yth Grp; Leo Clb; Band; Concert Band; Jazz Band; Mrchg Band; Symp Band; Rep Stu Cncl; JV Gym; Aerospc Engrng.

MATTESON, HOWARD S; Hugh C Williams HS; Canton, NY; (Y); 35/134; Dance Clb; Varsity Clb; School Play; Lit Mag; Sec Stu Cncl; Capt Lcrss; Socr; High Hon Roll; NHS; Church Yth Grp; Academic C For High Honors; Colgate U.

MATTESON, MELANIE; Franklin Acad; Malone, NY; (Y); Intnl Clb; Spanish Clb; Chorus; Drm & Bgl; Drm Mjr(t); Variety Show; JV Cheerleading; Var Swmmng; Prfct Atten Awd; Chrldng Excllnc/Ldrshp Awd 83; Twrlng Ldrshp Awd 84; Elem Tchng.

MATTHEI, JULIE; Manhasset HS; Manhasset, NY; (Y); Cmnty Wkr; GAA; Flag Corp; Nwsp Sprt Ed; Rep Soph Cls; JV Var Socr; Var Sftbl; Mgr Var Swmmng; Tennis; Hon Roll; Commctn Arts.

MATTHEWS, ANGELA; Lansingburg HS; Troy, NY; (Y); French Clb; Varsity Clb; Chorus; Rep Jr Cls; JV Var Bsktbl; Var Capt Socr; Var Sftbl; Var Trk; High Hon Roll; NHS; Clnl Cncl Soccer League All-Str 84; Coll; Bus.

MATTHEWS, DANIEL; Williamsville East HS; Williamsville, NY; (Y); Boy Scts; Chess Clb; VP Church Yth Grp; Yrbk Stf; Rep Stu Cncl; Var Bowling; SUNY Buffalo; Elec Engrng.

MATTHEWS, JEFF; Geneseo Central Schl; Geneseo, NY; (Y); Boy Scts; Concert Band; Mrchg Band; JV Var Bsbl; Im Ftbl; Var L Ice Hcky; Var Capt Socr; Im Wt Lftg; High Hon Roll; VP Jr NHS; Hnrs Engl & Scl Stds Cls 84-85; Comp Pgmmr.

MATTHEWS, KENNETH; Rice HS; Brooklyn, NY; (S); Hosp Aide; Ftbl; Hon Roll; Ctr For Media Arts; TV Dir.

MATTHEWS, LESLIE; Portville Central Schl; Olean, NY; (Y); Pres Trs Church Yth Grp; Pres Drama Clb; VP Chorus; Church Choir; School Musical; School Play; Nwsp Stf; Yrbk Stf; Hon Roll; Houghton Coll; Music.

MATTHEWS, LIZ; Skaneateles HS; Skaneatele, NY; (S); Nwsp Rptr; L Tennis; Hon Roll; NHS; Schl Paper 84.

MATTHEWS, NANCY LEE; Grand Island HS; Grand Island, NY; (Y); Church Yth Grp; Teachers Aide; Church Choir; Variety Show; Yrbk Phtg; Yrbk Stf; Stat Lcrss; Hon Roll; Ntl Merit Ltr; Vllybl; Aerobic Instr Cert 85; Fshn Dsgn.

MATTHEWS, REGINA ELIZABETH; The Brearley Schl; New York, NY; (Y); Political Wkr; School Play; Variety Show; Nwsp Rptr; Rep Frsh Cls; Pres Stu Cncl; Cmnty Wkr; Debate Tm; NFL; Natl Achvt Scholar Commndatn 84; Kurz Art Collectn Awd 82; Writr.

MATTHEWS, SANDRA; Le Roy Central Schl; Leroy, NY; (Y); AFS; 4-H; Spanish Clb; Chorus; School Musical; Cheerleading; Socr; Sftbl; 4-H Awd; High Hon Roll; U Of Buffalo; Physcl Thrpy.

MATTHEWS, SERBRINA; Newburgh Free Acad; Newburgh, NY; (Y); Computer Clb; Chorus; Church Choir; Trk; High Hon Roll; Hon Roll; Prfct Atten Awd; MS ST U; Comp Sci.

MATTHEWS, STEVE; Fonda-Fultonville Central Schl; Fonda, NY; (Y); Band; Concert Band; Jazz Band; Mrchg Band; JV Bsktbl; JV Var Ftbl; Hon Roll; Track Announcer 85; All County Band 83-85; Math Contest Contestent 85; Bus Admin.

MATTHEWS, SUZANNE M; Grand Island HS; Grand Island, NE; (Y); Church Yth Grp; Dance Clb; French Clb; Mathletes; Church Choir; Nwsp Stf; Yrbk Stf; Stu Cncl; Trk; Ntl Merit Ltr; NY ST Rgnts Schlrshp 85; Moore Resrch Schlrshp 85; Alfred U; Cermc Engrng.

MATTHEWS, THOMAS; Seton Catholic Central HS; Endwell, NY; (Y); Boy Scts; Latin Clb; Band; Concert Band; Jazz Band; Pep Band; School Musical; Mech Engr.

MATTHIES, GLENN; Cattaraugus Central HS; Cattaraugus, NY; (Y); Pep Clb; Quiz Bowl; Nwsp Stf; VP Frsh Cls; JV Ftbl; Var Trk; Hon Roll; NHS.

MATTHYS, MICHAEL J; P V Moore HS; Central Sq, NY; (Y); 6/297; AFS; Boy Scts; Radio Clb; School Play; Nwsp Rptr; JV L Bsktbl; Var Capt Socr; Var L Tennis; High Hon Roll; NHS; Lcl Hnr Scty For Frnch 84; Hnrs Schlrshp To Buffalo ST Coll 85; Frgrsn Mem Awd For Cmnctns 85; Buffalo ST Coll; Brdcstng.

MATTICE, MICHELLE; Windham-Ashland-Jewett Central HS; Ashland, NY; (S); French Clb; Yrbk Ed-Chief; Yrbk Stf; Trs Soph Cls; Sec Trs Sr Cls; Cheerleading; High Hon Roll; Pres NHS; Ltr Comndtn Ntl Mrt Schlshp 84; SUNY Oneonta; Chem.

MATTIOLE, RAYMOND; New Utrecht HS; Brooklyn, NY; (Y); Acctng.

MATTIS, JACQUELINE S; Our Savior Lutheran HS; Bronx, NY; (Y); 1/22; Office Aide; Yrbk Ed-Chief; Pres Sr Cls; VP Stu Cncl; Var Bsktbl; Var Trk; High Hon Roll; NHS; Val; Natl Eng Merit Scholar 84-85; Natl Sci Merit Scholar 83-84; Valparaiso U Awd Excllnc 84; Cornell U; Biochem.

MATTIS, MARK; Liverpool HS; Liverpool, NY; (S); 113/791; Nwsp Ed-Chief; Jr NHS; SUNY-OSWEGO; Comp Sci.

MATTISON, EDWARD P; Corning East HS; Corning, NY; (Y); 26/215; Church Yth Grp; Debate Tm; Varsity Clb; Capt Bsbl; Capt Ftbl; Capt Wrstlng; High Hon Roll; NHS; Alfred U Smmr Inst Schlrshp 85; Engr.

MATTISON, JULIANNE; Southside HS; Elmira, NY; (Y); JA; Y-Teens; Band; Concert Band; Mrchg Band; Nrsg.

MATTISON, KEVIN; Fort Ann Central HS; Ft Ann, NY; (Y); Yrbk Sprt Ed; Yrbk Stf; Bsbl; Bsktbl; Socr; MVP Sccr, Bsktbl 84.

MATTIX, CARLA; Bad Kreuznach HS; Apo, NY; (Y); 1/30; Ski Clb; Pres Frsh Cls; Pres Soph Cls; Trs Stu Cncl; Var Bsktbl; Var Tennis; Var Vllybl; Mu Alp Tht; NHS; Val; Boston U; Aerosp Engrng.

MATTU, EUNICE; St Peters HS For Girls; Staten Isl, NY; (Y); Exploring; FNA; Math Clb; Math Tm; Yrbk Stf; Rep Stu Cncl; Tennis; Trk; NHS; Prfct Atten Awd; Untd Cerebral Palsy Grp Ldr 82-85; American U; Comp Sci.

MATUKAS, CHRISTINE; Indian River Central School HS; Theresa, NY; (Y); 25/119; Church Yth Grp; Latin Clb; Chorus; Off Stu Cncl; JV Var Bsktbl; Var Crs Cntry; JV Var Trk; Hon Roll.

MATULEWICZ, RITA; Lowville Academy Central; Lowville, NY; (Y); Hon Roll; Bus.

MATULEWSKI, KENNETH V; Ogdensburg Free Acad; Ogdensburg, NY; (Y); 3/190; Key Clb; Chorus; JV Var Ftbl; High Hon Roll; Hon Roll; NHS; Ntl Merit Ltr; Cornell U; Biology.

MATUSZAK, RUSSELL J; Canisius HS; Buffalo, NY; (Y); 12/148; Computer Clb; Math Clb; Spanish Clb; Var Im Bsktbl; Hon Roll; Mu Alp Tht; Pres Schlr; Spanish NHS; St Schlr; Canisius Coll.

MATZ, NATHALIE; Saint Vincent Ferrer HS; New York, NY; (Y); Computer Clb; French Clb; Library Aide; Service Clb; Ski Clb; Rep Frsh Cls; Rep Soph Cls; Rep Stu Cncl; Swmmng; Tennis; St Johns U; CBA.

MATZAN, CORRY; Massena Central HS; Massena, NY; (Y); French Clb; JV Var Cheerleading; Hon Roll; NHS.

MAU, CHRISTINE; Bishop Ford HS; Brooklyn, NY; (Y); Church Yth Grp; Civic Clb; Cmnty Wkr; Math Clb; Science Clb; Service Clb; Teachers Aide; Rep Frsh Cls; Rep Soph Cls; Rep Jr Cls; St Francis Coll.

MAUL, DEONNA R; Mt St Mary Acad; Grand Island, NY; (Y); 9/96; Church Yth Grp; Debate Tm; Red Cross Aide; Ski Clb; Chorus; School Musical; Yrbk Phtg; Var Badmtn; Hon Roll; NHS; Schlrshps-Rochester Inst Tech, Mt St Mary Acad & NYS Regnts 81-89; Rochester Inst Tech; Phtgrphy.

MAUL, JAY R; Christian Brothers Acad; Albany, NY; (Y); 30/126; Aud/Vis; ROTC; Stu Cncl; Im Bsktbl; JV Var Ftbl; JV Var Trk; JV Var Wt Lftg; JV Var Wrstlng; Hon Roll; NHS; St Miguel Hnr Soc 84-85; Syracuse U; Comm.

MAURER, BRIAN; Manhasset JRSR HS; Manhasset, NY; (Y); Cmnty Wkr; Jazz Band; Mrchg Band; Var Crs Cntry; Var Trk; High Hon Roll; VP NHS; Church Yth Grp; Band; Concert Band; Vrsty Athltc Achvt Awd, Ltr 83-85; LI Math Fair Accmplshmnt Awd 84; Natl Sci Olympd Awd 85; Sci.

MAURER, DAVID; Iona Prep; Pelham, NY; (Y); 98/230; JV Socr; Zoolgy.

MAURER, JEFFREY; Byron-Bergen HS; Bergen, NY; (Y); JV Var Bsktbl; JV Var Socr; Hon Roll; Mech Engr.

MAURER, JOHN; Vestal Central Senior HS; Binghamton, NY; (Y); Boy Scts; Chorus; NHS; Eagle Sct Awd BSA 85; Wrld Conservtn Awd BSA 84; Mth.

MAURER, KATHLEEN; Newark Senior HS; Newark, NY; (Y); 8/198; Church Yth Grp; Chorus; Church Choir; Concert Band; Jazz Band; Mrchg Band; School Musical; Swing Chorus; French Hon Soc; NHS; Music.

MAURER, LARA; Onteora Central Schl; Woodstock, NY; (S); French Clb; Concert Band; Mrchg Band; Yrbk Stf; JV Cheerleading; Mgr(s); Var Tennis; High Hon Roll; NHS.

MAURIZIO, SUSAN; Saint Vincent Ferrer HS; Woodside, NY; (Y); 22/114; Art Clb; Church Yth Grp; Drama Clb; Library Aide; Q&S; Stage Crew; Nwsp Rptr; Hon Roll; Newspaper Rptr Awd 85; Ferrer Ministries Awd 83; Library Awd 85.

MAURO, JAMES; Clarkstown HS North; New City, NY; (Y); Math Tm; Office Aide; Hon Roll; Mu Alp Tht; NHS; Med.

MAURO, MARY E; Hornell SR HS; Hornell, NY; (Y); GAA; Varsity Clb; Var Capt Bsktbl; Var Capt Socr; Var Sftbl; Ithaca Coll; Phy Educ.

MAURO, MELANIE M; Kings Park SR HS; Fort Salonga, NY; (Y); 78/446; Church Yth Grp; Spanish Clb; Chorus; Nwsp Stf; Rep Stu Cncl; Var L Cheerleading; High Hon Roll; Hon Roll; Jr NHS; NHS; Coachs Awd Chrldng 84; MVP Awd Chrldng 84; Regents Nrsng Schlrshp 85; Iona Coll; Bus Admin.

MAURO, MICHAEL; Hauppauge HS; Smithtown, NY; (Y); Exploring; Political Wkr; Jazz Band; Symp Band; Pres Frsh Cls; Pres Soph Cls; Var Capt Crs Cntry; Var Trk; High Hon Roll; VP NHS; Med.

MAURRASSE, DAVID; Mount Vernon HS; Mount Vernon, NY; (Y); VP FBLA; Hon Roll; Jr NHS; Bus Mngmnt.

MAVRIDIS, CHRISTINE; Sachem HS; Holbrook, NY; (Y); Church Yth Grp; Drama Clb; Ski Clb; Spanish Clb; Madrigals; School Play; Nwsp Stf; Lit Mag; Hon Roll; NHS.

MAXEY, TANYA; New Rochelle HS; New Rochelle, NY; (Y); 200/600; Drama Clb; Office Aide; VICA; Chorus; Flag Corp; Orch; Yrbk Stf; Cheerleading; Sftbl; Prfct Atten Awd; Outstndng Volnst 2nd Yr Stu 81; Outstndng Cosmtlgst 85; Berkely Schl; Fashn Merchndsng.

MAXFIELD, DEREK D; Dundee Central HS; Dundee, NY; (Y); 10/110; Pres AFS; Am Leg Boys St; Aud/Vis; Church Yth Grp; Science Clb; Varsity Clb; Nwsp Ed-Chief; Var Mgr(s); Tennis; High Hon Roll; Yates Cnty Teenagr Of Yr 85; Am Leg Oratrcl Cont 2nd Pl 85; Dundee Cntrl Schl Oct Stu Mnth 84; Syracuse U; Comm.

MAXFIELD, JAY; Saranac Lake HS; Saranac Lake, NY; (Y); AFS; Boy Scts; Church Yth Grp; Cmnty Wkr; Computer Clb; 4-H; Library Aide; Variety Show; Antioch Grp 84; Parsh Retrt Team 83-84; Yth Ministry Team 84-85; Comp Pgmr.

MAXNER, AMY; East Islip HS; Islip Terr, NY; (Y); FBLA; Yrbk Stf; Tennis; Hon Roll; Bus Wrld.

MAXWELL, JENNIFER; Clinton HS; Clinton, NY; (Y); 27/140; Cmnty Wkr; 4-H; Red Cross Aide; Ski Clb; Spanish Clb; Varsity Clb; Yrbk Sprt Ed; Yrbk Stf; Var Crs Cntry; Capt L Fld Hcky; Potsdam; Engrng.

MAXWELL, KELLY; Notre Dame HS; Marcy, NY; (Y); 31/177; Im Bsktbl; Var Capt Ftbl; Score Keeper; Var Capt Trk; High Hon Roll; Hon Roll; JC Awd; George Nole Memrl Awd 85; A Grant Alfred U 85; Pres Acadmc Awd 85; Alfred U; Engrng.

MAXWELL, MELISSA DANIELLE; Murry Bergtraum HS; Jamaica, NY; (Y); JA; Library Aide; Office Aide; Bnkng.

MAXWELL, SALLIE; Letchworth Central HS; Silver Springs, NY; (Y); Debate Tm; Drama Clb; 4-H; FFA; Library Aide; Office Aide; Ski Clb; Spanish Clb; Varsity Clb; Chorus; Most Imprvd Math Avg 80-81; Hghst Sci Avg 80-81; Ldrshp Awd 85; Corning CC; Crmnl Jstc.

MAXWELL, SANDRA; Clara Barton HS; Brooklyn, NY; (Y); Hosp Aide; Library Aide; Political Wkr; Teachers Aide; Hon Roll; Prfct Atten Awd; Med Tech.

MAY, ANN; Cardinal Mooney HS; Rochester, NY; (Y); 3/318; Church Yth Grp; Chorus; School Musical; Im Bowling; Var Mgr(s); High Hon Roll; NHS; Spanish NHS; Red Cross Aide; Lit Mag; 1st Pl Mooney ACS Chem Cont 84; Regents Schlrshp 85; Rensselaer Schlrshp 85; Hnrs Engl & Chem Awds 84; Rensselaer Polytech Inst; Chem.

MAY, DENISE; Mamaroneck HS; Mamaroneck, NY; (Y); Girl Scts; Pep Clb; Ski Clb; Varsity Clb; Chorus; School Play; Yrbk Stf; Capt Var Cheerleading; JV Var Lcrss; Pres Schlr; Bus Ed Awd 84; Chrldng Cnty Cmptn Awd; Finance.

MAY JR, DENNIS B; Walt Whitman HS; Huntington Stn, NY; (Y); Boy Scts; JV Lcrss; JV Wrstlng; Eagle Scout 85; Farmingdale ST Coll; Elec Engr.

MAY, HUBERT; A Phillip Randolph Campus HS; New York, NY; (Y); Band; Var Bsbl; Var Bsktbl; Supr Yth Awd 85; Mst Verstl Bsbl Plyr Awd 84; Cornell; Arch.

MAY, JENNIFER; Lansingburgh HS; Troy, NY; (Y); Varsity Clb; Color Guard; Drm & Bgl; Yrbk Stf; JV Capt Cheerleading; High Hon Roll; Hon Roll; Hudson Valley; Med Sec.

MAY, LAWRENCE; Half Hollow Hills HS East; Melville, NY; (Y); Ski Clb; Bsbl; Ftbl; Lcrss; Socr; Wrstlng; Ntl Merit SF.

MAY, PAUL; Lindenhurst HS; Lindenhurst, NY; (Y); Band; Concert Band; Var Socr; Most Imprvd Player-Soccer 85; Outstndng Athltc Achvt Awd-Soccer 85; Comptr Engrng.

MAY, ROBERT; Rye HS; Rye, NY; (Y); 83/181; Key Clb; Var L Bsbl; Var L Ftbl; Trs Wt Lftg; Hon Roll; Mary Friese Lowe Schlrshp 85; Roger Williams Coll; Bus Mgmt.

MAY, ROBIN; Mt Vernon HS; Mount Vernon, NY; (Y); Chorus; Cheerleading; Hon Roll; Bus Adm.

MAY-BEARD, NATHANIEL J; High School Of Fashion Indstrs; Brooklyn, NY; (Y); 23/365; Art Clb; Library Aide; Office Aide; VICA; Chorus; Color Guard; School Play; Stage Crew; High Hon Roll; Hon Roll; Art Schlrshp Parsons Schl Dsgn 83-84; Art Schlrshp Pratt U 82-83; Woodbury U; Fshn Dsgn.

MAYBEE, BOBBIE; Salamanca JR-SR HS; Salamanca, NY; (Y); FBLA; VICA; Yrbk Stf; Stat Bsktbl; Stat Lcrss; Bus Adm.

MAYBEE, STEPHEN; Smithtown High Schl East; Smithtown, NY; (Y); Pres Church Yth Grp; Trs Leo Clb; Ski Clb; School Play; Nwsp Rptr; Nwsp Stf; Im Swmmng; French Hon Soc; NHS; Pres Schlr; Wheaton Coll.

MAYBERRY, CHERYL; Lake Placid Central HS; Lake Placid, NY; (Y); 9/53; AFS; Church Yth Grp; Trs Sec Key Clb; Library Aide; Band; Chorus; Yrbk Sprt Ed; Trs Yrbk Stf; Hon Roll; Lion Awd; AAUW Schlrshp Awd 85; Potsdam ST U Coll.

MAYBLOOM, MICHELE; Canarsie HS; Brooklyn, NY; (Y); 7/561; Office Aide; Service Clb; Teachers Aide; Chorus; School Musical; High Hon Roll; Archon Sec 85; Arista 85; Sci Medal 82; Binghamton U; Dr.

MAYER, BIRGITTA M; Sacred Heart Acad; Garden City, NY; (Y); German Clb; Math Clb; Math Tm; Ed Yrbk Phtg; Pres Jr Cls; Pres Stu Cncl; Tennis; Dnfth Awd; NHS; Acad Amer 84 & 85; Ldrshp Awd 85; Stu Cncl Adv Awd 85.

MAYER, CHRIS; Rhinebeck HS; Rhinebeck, NY; (Y); Computer Clb; Math Clb; Science Clb; Spanish Clb; Band; Jazz Band; High Hon Roll; NHS; Ntl Merit Ltr; AAU Swmmng; Comp Sci.

MAYER, CHRISTOPHER JOHN; West Irondequoit HS; Rochester, NY; (Y); Varsity Clb; Var L Ice Hcky; Var L Lcrss; Var L Socr; JV Socr Ldng Scor 83-84; 3rd Tm All Cnty Hocky 84-85; Bus.

MAYER, HARRY; Msgr Mc Claney HS; Rego Park, NY; (Y); 1/240; Math Clb; Math Tm; Science Clb; Nwsp Rptr; Pres Frsh Cls; Pres Soph Cls; Rep Jr Cls; Sec Stu Cncl; NHS; Pratt Engineering Schl; Engr.

MAYER, LINDA S; Wilson Central HS; Ransomville, NY; (Y); 2/134; Trs Church Yth Grp; Pep Band; School Play; Yrbk Bus Mgr; Var L Fld Hcky; Stat Wrstlng; High Hon Roll; VP NHS; Sal; Aud/Vis; NY ST Regents Schlrshp 85; U Of Buffalo; Ocptnl Therapy.

MAYER, PATRICIA; Cicero North Syracuse HS; Clay, NY; (S); 34/711; Stage Crew; Powder Puff Ftbl; Tennis; Trk; NHS; Albany Coll Of Pharm; Pharm.

MAYER, TERESA; Our Lady Of Mercy HS; Rochester, NY; (Y); 25/200; Church Yth Grp; Sec Exploring; GAA; Varsity Clb; Band; Orch; Var Socr; Capt Var Sftbl; Capt Var Vllybl; High Hon Roll; Sftbl 1st 2nd All Star Tm,Socr All Star Tm 82-84; Math & Physcs Achvt Awd 85; RIT Acadmc Schlrshp 85; Rochester Inst Of Tech; Math.

MAYERFELD, ELI; Shaarei Torah Of Rockland HS; Norma, NJ; (Y); 1/16; Computer Clb; Math Clb; Temple Yth Grp; School Play; Stage Crew; Nwsp Rptr; Yrbk Stf; Lit Mag; NHS; Engrng.

MAYERS, GEORGE; Nazareth Regional HS; Brooklyn, NY; (Y); JA; Science Clb; Trk.

MAYES, CHRIS; Union Endicott HS; Endicott, NY; (S); VP Ftbl; Boys Clb Am; Church Yth Grp; Civic Clb; Ski Clb; Varsity Clb; Hon Roll; Comp Sci.

MAYESS, FRED; Bishop Kearney HS; Rochester, NY; (Y); JV Ftbl; JV Socr; JV Wrstlng; Hon Roll; Engrng.

MAYETTE, RODNEY; Dover JR SR HS; Dover Plains, NY; (S); 22/102; Pep Clb; Ski Clb; Varsity Clb; JV Var Bsbl; JV Var Bsktbl; JV Var Ftbl; Hon Roll; Intl Fest Of Scholars 84; Westchester U; Lib Arts.

MAYEWSKI, CHRISTINE; Warwick Valley HS; Warwick, NY; (Y); 4/200; French Clb; Ski Clb; Yrbk Stf; VP Soph Cls; Sr Cls; Var L Socr; Var Trk; High Hon Roll; NHS; Band; Cert Hnr Ntl Frnch 83; Sci Cngrss Hnrbl Ment 85; Engrng.

MAYFIELD, MICHAEL; Liverpool HS; Liverpool, NY; (S); 111/791; JA; Varsity Clb; Mrchg Band; Pep Band; Rep Stu Cncl; Wrstlng; Jr NHS; NHS; Crew Tm Rowning 81-85; Bio.

MAYHEW, STEPHEN; Royalton-Hartland Central HS; Middleport, NY; (Y); 9/140; Am Leg Boys St; French Clb; Concert Band; Jazz Band; Rep Stu Cncl; JV Var Bsktbl; JV Var Ftbl; Var Trk; High Hon Roll; Pres NHS; US Stu Council Awd 85; Acctng FBI.

MAYNARD, CAROL; Walton HS; Bronx, NY; (Y); Church Yth Grp; Library Aide; Office Aide; Teachers Aide; Chorus; Church Choir; Acctng.

MAYNARD, SUSAN; Mattituck HS; Mattituck, NY; (Y); 79/240; ROTC; Spanish Clb; JV Var Bsktbl; Hon Roll; Outstndng Stu Awd 84; Most Imprvd Plyr Bsktbl 85; Suffolk County CC; Acctng.

MAYNARD II, WILLIAM H; Berlin Central HS; Berlin, NY; (Y); Drama Clb; Red Cross Aide; Chorus; School Musical; School Play; Stage Crew; Swing Chorus; Variety Show; Crs Cntry; Hon Roll; Crmnl Justice.

MAYNE, LENNY SUE; Sherburne-Earlville HS; Sherburne, NY; (S); Trs Drama Clb; French Clb; Girl Scts; VP Chorus; Concert Band; Jazz Band; Rep Stu Cncl; Cheerleading; Capt Swmmng; NHS; Potsdam; Mus Ed.

MAYO, KATHY; Valley Central HS; Montgomery, NY; (Y); 10/300; VP Trs Church Yth Grp; Spanish Clb; Trs Frsh Cls; Stu Cncl; JV Bsktbl; JV Var Sftbl; Elks Awd; NHS; Spanish NHS; Var Bsktbll Mst Val Plyr 84-85; Hlth.

MAYO, MICHELLE M; Whitesboro SR HS; Whitesboro, NY; (Y); 5/380; Sec Church Yth Grp; Cmnty Wkr; Hosp Aide; Orch; Variety Show; Rep Stu Cncl; High Hon Roll; Jr NHS; NHS; Regents Schlrshp 85; All ST Orch 83-84; Oberlin Conservatory; Music.

MAYO, YVETTE; High School Of Fashion Indus; Long Isld Cty, NY; (Y); 33/365; Sec Frsh Cls; Gym; High Hon Roll; Hon Roll; Prfct Atten Awd; Phy Ed Merit Awd 84; Pres Phy Ftnss 83; Bus Mgmnt.

MAYOU, DAVID P; Sodus Central HS; Sodus, NY; (Y); 6/118; Am Leg Boys St; Church Yth Grp; French Clb; VP Model UN; Radio Clb; Band; Concert Band; Mrchg Band; High Hon Roll; NHS.

MAYR, LISA BETH; Holy Trinity Diocesan HS; Freeport, NY; (S); 87/263; Church Yth Grp; Drama Clb; Mathletes; Math Clb; Math Tm; Ski Clb; Spanish Clb; School Musical; School Play; Stage Crew; NEDT Merit Certificate 82; Georgetown; Intl Affrs.

MAYR, SUZANNE M; The Mary Louis Acad; Middle Village, NY; (Y); 28/283; Dance Clb; GAA; Varsity Clb; Church Choir; Sec Soph Cls; Im Bsktbl; Im Coach Actv; Im Mgr(s); Im Score Keeper; Im Sftbl; C C Conway Schlrshp 85; Manhattan Coll Pres Schlrshp 85; Manhattan Coll; Bus.

MAYS, DEBBIE; Glens Falls HS; Glens Falls, NY; (Y); 10/220; AFS; Hosp Aide; Chorus; Powder Puff Ftbl; Var Trk; High Hon Roll; NHS; Prfct Atten Awd; Bio Med Engrng.

MAYS, PAUL; Valley Central HS; Wallkill, NY; (Y); Debate Tm; Mathletes; Spanish Clb; Off Soph Cls; Var Capt Socr; High Hon Roll; Hon Roll; Jr NHS; NHS; Spanish NHS; Arch Theory.

MAYSONET JR, JUAN D; Rice HS; Bronx, NY; (S); High Hon Roll; Hon Roll; Pierre Toussiant Awd 82.

MAYTON, SUE C; Owen D Young Central HS; Mohawk, NY; (Y); 2/23; French Clb; Chorus; School Play; Yrbk Bus Mgr; Yrbk Stf; Pres Stu Cncl; Vllybl; High Hon Roll; Jr NHS; NHS; Mayflower Comp 85; Biol Awd 95 On Regnts 84; Pathlgy.

MAYTUM, CINDY; Chautauqua Central HS; Mayville, NY; (Y); Church Yth Grp; Drama Clb; Ski Clb; Chorus; Concert Band; Var L Bsktbl; Coach Actv; Score Keeper; Capt Var Vllybl; Hon Roll; Rn.

MAZIK, LORI J; Long Lake Central HS; Long Lake, NY; (Y); 3/12; Band; Chorus; Sec Trs Sr Cls; VP Stu Cncl; Badmtn; Bsktbl; Socr; Tennis; Vllybl; High Hon Roll; NYS Schlrshp 85; Hartwick Coll Schlrshp 85; Hartwick Coll.

MAZLISH, STUART; Forest Hills HS; Rego Pk, NY; (Y); 286/881; Debate Tm; Science Clb; Sec Sr Cls; Hon Roll; Forest Hills Hnr Cert Schlrshp; Cert Awd SEER; Sci Mnth.

MAZOUREK, ROBERTA; Newfield Central HS; Newfield, NY; (Y); FHA; Library Aide; Teachers Aide; Chorus; Yrbk Phtg; Yrbk Stf; High Hon Roll; Hon Roll; West Danby Fire Co Awd-Home Ec 82; FHA Certs 81-85; Local FHA-PRES, VP, Sec & Treas; Genessee CC; Biochem.

MAZUR, CYNTHIA; Horseheads SR HS; Horseheads, NY; (S); 39/407; French Clb; Hosp Aide; Ski Clb; Band; Chorus; Church Choir; Color Guard; Concert Band; Mrchg Band; Orch; NY ST Schl Music Assoc 81-82; Penn ST U; Elec Engr.

MAZUR, SUZANNE; Central Islip SR HS; Central Islip, NY; (Y); Boy Scts; Cmnty Wkr; Exploring; Hosp Aide; Color Guard; Flag Corp; Stage Crew; Variety Show; Pom Pon; Hon Roll; Med.

MAZURE, DARRIN J; Ichabod Crane HS; Kinderhook, NY; (Y); #69 In Class; 95 Grd ST Regnts Math Exm; Coll Of St Rose.

MAZZACANO, EDWARD; Saint Francis Prep; Flushing, NY; (Y); 170/750; Math Clb; Math Tm; Crs Cntry; Tennis; Trk.

MAZZAFERRO, CHRISTINE; Greenport HS; Greenport, NY; (Y); 6/48; Mathletes; Quiz Bowl; School Musical; Nwsp Stf; Pres Jr Cls; L Golf; High Hon Roll; NHS; Metro PGA Jr Golf Trnmnt-4th Pl 85; Wmns Clb Chmpnshp Wnnr 84; Voc Muscnshp Awd 85; Plattsburgh ST Coll; Eng.

MAZZARA, MARIE; Our Lady Of Perpetual Help HS; Brooklyn, NY; (Y); JV Bsktbl; High Hon Roll; Secy.

MAZZAROPPI, MATTHEW; Cicero North Syracuse HS; N Syracuse, NY; (S); #10 In Class; Math Tm; Ski Clb; Band; Concert Band; Jazz Band; Mrchg Band; Symp Band; Nwsp Rptr; Trk; JP Sousa Awd; Law.

MAZZELLA, ANGELA M; Saint Barnabas HS; Bronx, NY; (Y); 49/205; Camera Clb; Cmnty Wkr; Math Clb; Office Aide; Pep Clb; Teachers Aide; School Musical; Yrbk Phtg; Pres Soph Cls; Rep Jr Cls; Cert Catechist Frmtn Pgm Reward/Hnr 84-85; Bus.

MAZZELLA, ANNMARIE; Cardinal Spellman HS; Bronx, NY; (Y); Civic Clb; Cmnty Wkr; Stage Crew; Yrbk Phtg; Yrbk Stf; Trk; Ntl Merit Ltr; NY ST Rgnts Schlrshp 85-88; Fordham U; Phys Thrpy.

MAZZELLA, CHRISTINE; Cardinal Spellman HS; Bronx, NY; (Y); 30/600; Computer Clb; Stu Cncl; Var Capt Bsktbl; Var Sftbl; Var Vllybl; High Hon Roll; Hon Roll; NHS; Comps.

MAZZELLA, JOHN; Deer Park HS; Deer Park, NY; (Y); 102/422; Hon Roll; CPR Cert; C W Post; Rl Est.

MAZZENGA, RITA; Hancock Central HS; Lake Como, PA; (Y); Library Aide; Office Aide; Chorus; Yrbk Phtg; Yrbk Stf; VP Soph Cls; VP Jr Cls; Off Stu Cncl; Lion Awd; Bloomsburg U; Elem Ed.

MAZZEO, CARLA; Marlboro HS; Newburgh, NY; (Y); Church Yth Grp; Computer Clb; Dance Clb; Hosp Aide; Var Diving; JV Scrkpr Golf; Var Swmmng; Var Tennis; Var Trk; Bio Sci.

MAZZEO, WILLIAM; Peirson HS; Sag Harbor, NY; (Y).

MAZZI, JOETTE; Kenmore West SR HS; Kenmore, NY; (Y); Dance Clb; Girl Scts; Ski Clb; Variety Show; Yrbk Stf; Off Stu Cncl; Cheerleading; Trk; High Hon Roll; Hon Roll; BUS.

MAZZICA, MARIA; Lincoln HS; Yonkers, NY; (Y); Art Clb; Intnl Clb; Yrbk Stf; Tennis; High Hon Roll; Hon Roll; NHS; Arch.

MAZZIE, MARIA; Jamestown HS; Jamestown, NY; (Y); French Clb; Acpl Chr; Band; Chorus; Concert Band; Madrigals; Mrchg Band; Rep Frsh Cls; Rep Jr Cls; Jr NHS; Band Sec; Treas Apaella Choir; Law.

MAZZO, TERESA; Lindenhurst HS; Lindenhurst, NY; (Y); Cmnty Wkr; Spanish Clb; Band; Concert Band; Mrchg Band; Nwsp Rptr; Nwsp Sprt Ed; Yrbk Stf; Socr; Hon Roll; Law.

MAZZOCCHI, LISA ANNE; Northport HS; E Northport, NY; (Y); 160/652; Church Yth Grp; NY ST Art Tchrs Assoc Awd 85; Pratt Inst Merit Medal 85; Art Hnrs 85; Poster Clbrtn Fnlst 85; New Paltz; Art Educ.

MAZZONE, ANTONETTE; Hudson HS; Hudson, NY; (Y); Red Cross Aide; High Hon Roll; Hon Roll; Jr NHS; NHS; Ntl Merit Ltr; Gen Acad Excllnce ST Marys Hm Schl Assn 82; Krug/Beck Awd Lion Clb Outstndg Comm Ctznshp 82; Rel Awd; Sienna; Bus.

MAZZONI, PAMELA; The Mary Louis Acad; Elmhurst, NY; (Y); 1st Hnrs Eng 85; 2nd Hnrs Hist 85; Psych.

MAZZOTTI III, FRANK A; Cicero-No Syracuse HS; North Syracuse, NY; (Y); 107/764; Aud/Vis; Ski Clb; Band; Chorus; Concert Band; Jazz Band; Mrchg Band; Orch; Pep Band; School Musical; Clay Towne Plyrs Schlrshp 85; Onondaga Comm Coll; Music.

MAZZULLO, TANYA; Oneida HS; Oneida, NY; (S); 13/215; Church Yth Grp; Exploring; Ski Clb; Spanish Clb; Varsity Clb; Tennis; High Hon Roll; NHS; U Of Buffalo; Engrng.

MC ADOO, KEITH ANTHONY; Half Hollow Hills East HS; Wheatley Heights, NY; (Y); Library Aide; Political Wkr; Teachers Aide; Chorus; Rep Stu Cncl; Stat Bsktbl; Mgr(s); DAR Awd; NHS; Prfct Atten Awd; TRI-M Music Hnr Soc 83-85; Law.

MC AFEE, ROBERT; Avon Central HS; Avon, NY; (Y); Church Yth Grp; Dance Clb; French Clb; Ski Clb; Varsity Clb; Band; Golf; Score Keeper; Swmmng; Timer; Aero Sci.

MC ALEE, MARYKATE; Williamsville North HS; Williamsville, NY; (Y); 5/315; Pres AFS; Latin Clb; Concert Band; Jazz Band; Pep Band; School Musical; Trk; Hon Roll; Trs NHS; OH Test Scholastic Achvr French I 82; Classical Assoc Of WNY,Latin III Second Place 84; Baldwin Wallace; Music.

MC ALEER, DIANE; St Francis Prep HS; Whitestone, NY; (S); 69/694; JV Math Tm; Office Aide; Wt Lftg; Hon Roll; NHS; Opt Clb Awd; Acad All-Amer 85; Judo Team 84-85; Aerobics Club 85; Columbia; Sci Fld.

MC ALLISTER, B BUCKLEY; Trinity Schl; New York, NY; (Y); Debate Tm; Chorus; Nwsp Rptr; Crs Cntry; Trk; Wrstlng; Hamilton Coll; Liberal Arts.

MC ALPINE, AMY; James E Sperry HS; Rochester, NY; (Y); 2/311; Pres French Clb; Thesps; Concert Band; Jazz Band; Orch; School Play; NHS; Ntl Merit Ltr; Sal; Eng Dept Awd 85; Awd For Outstndng Interest In Frgn Language 85; Awd For Outstndng Schltc Achvt 82; Syracuse U; Comprtv Lit.

MC ANDREWS, PATRICIA; St Francis Prep; Flushing, NY; (S); 76/693; Drama Clb; School Musical; School Play; Stage Crew; Yrbk Phtg; Yrbk Stf; Rep Soph Cls; Rep Jr Cls; Hon Roll; NHS; Psych.

MC ANIFF, ANTHONY J; The Bronx High Schl Of Science; Bronx, NY; (Y); Am Leg Boys St; Boy Scts; Church Yth Grp; Civic Clb; Computer Clb; Math Clb; Orch; Swmmng; Prfct Atten Awd; Engrng.

MC ANUFF, ANN; Bishop Kearney HS; Brooklyn, NY; (Y); Art Clb; Church Yth Grp; Cmnty Wkr; Girl Scts; Ski Clb; Spanish Clb; Church Choir; Nwsp Rptr; Yrbk Rptr; Lit Mag; MVP Sftbl 83; All Star Tm 83-85; Pre-Law.

MC ARDLE, JOHN R; Regis HS; Yonkers, NY; (Y); 3/125; Am Leg Boys St; Church Yth Grp; Latin Clb; Letterman Clb; Varsity Clb; Nwsp Ed-Chief; Yrbk Stf; Crs Cntry; Trk; Ntl Merit SF; Regis Full Schrlshp 82.

MC ARTHUR, SCOTT; Beacon HS; Beacon, NY; (Y); 52/162; Pres Church Yth Grp; Drama Clb; Varsity Clb; Band; School Play; Nwsp Sprt Ed; Capt Crs Cntry; Ftbl; Trk; NH Coll; Hotel Mgmt.

MC ATEER, LYNN; Tuxedo HS; Sterling Forest, NY; (Y); Office Aide; Rep Jr Cls; Rep Stu Cncl; Cheerleading; Hon Roll; Coop IBM 84-85; Berkeley Waldwick NJ; Lgl Sec.

MC ATEER, TIMOTHY L; South Side HS; Rockville Ctr, NY; (Y); Pres Art Clb; Boy Scts; Pres Church Yth Grp; Drama Clb; Model UN; Chorus; Madrigals; Nwsp Ed-Chief; Lion Awd; Church Choir; LI Fed Of Wmns Clbs Ed Awd 85; U Of Hartford; Grphc Dsgn.

MC AULEY, CHRISTINE; Walter Panas HS; Peekskill, NY; (Y); FBLA; Spanish Clb; Orch; Socr; Credit Roll; SUNY Oreonta; Eng.

MC AULEY, CHRISTINE S; Franklinville Central HS; Franklinville, NY; (Y); Spanish Clb; Varsity Clb; Yrbk Ed-Chief; Yrbk Sprt Ed; Yrbk Stf; Bsktbl; Crs Cntry; Mgr(s); Trk; Engl.

MC AULEY, SEAN; Walt Whitman HS; Huntington Sta, NY; (Y); 30/625; French Clb; Off Key Clb; Var Bsbl; JV Bsktbl; Var Ftbl; Elks Awd; French Hon Soc; High Hon Roll; Var Jr NHS; Sec NHS; NYS Regents Schlrshp 85; Cornell U; Econ.

MC AULIFFE, KATHLEEN; St Edmund HS; Brooklyn, NY; (Y); 25/187; Variety Show; Nwsp Stf; Yrbk Phtg; Yrbk Stf; Hon Roll; NHS; JV Bsktbl; Achvt Spn 83-84; Brdcstng.

MC AVOY, DAVID; Freeport HS; Freeport, NY; (Y); Drama Clb; Ski Clb; Orch; School Musical; School Play; Nwsp Phtg; Nwsp Rptr; Var Swmmng; Hon Roll; Comp Engr.

MC AVOY, JENNIFER; Cicero-North Syracuse HS; Liverpool, NY; (S); 38/622; DECA; VP Sec JA; JV Cheerleading; Hon Roll.

MC AVOY, SANDRA J; Newfane SR HS; Olcott, NY; (S); 1/177; AFS; Exploring; 4-H; Band; Church Choir; Pep Band; Stage Crew; Ed Yrbk Stf; Hon Roll; NHS; Cornell; Vet Med.

MC BATH, EILEEN; Lisbon Central Schl; Lisbon, NY; (S); 2/37; French Clb; GAA; Band; Concert Band; Mrchg Band; Vllybl; High Hon Roll; Hon Roll; NHS; Dnstry.

MC BRIDE, EDWARD; Mechanicville HS; Mechanicville, NY; (S); 1/104; Pres Frsh Cls; Pres Jr Cls; VP Stu Cncl; JV Var Bsbl; Var Capt Bskbl; Var Capt Ftbl; Bausch & Lomb Sci Awd; NHS; Ntl Merit Ltr; French Clb; Renselaer Mdl Math, Sci 84; All Stars Ftbl 84; McAN Schlr Athle Yr 84; Sci.

MC BRIDE, MARIELLEN; Academy Of The Resurrec; Tuckahoe, NY; (Y); Hosp Aide; Library Aide; Band; Stage Crew; Yrbk Stf; Pres Frsh Cls; Sec Soph Cls; Stu Cncl; NHS; Sr Cls Brdg & Fshn Show Chrwmn 85; Fresh-Jr Hallwn Scl Chrwmn 84; Spnsh.

MC BRIDE, THOMAS; St Marys Boys HS; Bellmore, NY; (S); 17/140; Pres Frsh Cls; Pres Soph Cls; Pres Jr Cls; Rep Stu Cncl; Var Bsktbl; Var Capt Socr; Var Trk; High Hon Roll; NHS; US Naval Acad; Engrng.

MC BROOM JR, EDWARD; Hempstead HS; Hempstead, NY; (S); 53/311; Cmnty Wkr; VP Spanish Clb; Im Swmmng; Nassau CC; Law.

MC BURNEY, RICHARD; Smithtown High School West; Smithtown, NY; (Y); Ski Clb; L JV Ftbl; Lcrss; Hon Roll; Comp Sci.

MC CABE, ALICIA; Hoosic Valley Central HS; Schaghticoke, NY; (Y); French Clb; Hosp Aide; Band; School Musical; Cheerleading; JV Var Sftbl; Prfct Atten Awd; Actress.

MC CABE, DARRYN R; Potsdam Central HS; Potsdam, NY; (Y); 26/174; ROTC; JV Bsbl; Var Golf; Var Ice Hcky; Hon Roll; NHS; Boys ST; Talntd Jrs; Clarkson U; Indstrl Engrng.

MC CABE, GILBERT; Sayville HS; Sayville, NY; (Y); 15/370; Pres Key Clb; Capt Crs Cntry; Capt Trk; High Hon Roll; NHS; Prncpls Hnr Awd & Capt Merrill Masin Memrl 85; Congrssnl Cert Merit & Schlr Athl Awd 85; Williams Coll; Psych.

MC CABE, GLIBET J; Sayville HS; Sayville, NY; (Y); 15/363; Pres Key Clb; Var Capt Trk; High Hon Roll; NHS; Var Capt Crs Cntry; Liblit-Freedman Brotherhood Awd 85; Islip Town Ldrshp Awd 85; Regents Schlrshp; Williams Coll; Psych.

MC CABE, KATHRYN M; Garden City SR HS; Gordon City, NY; (Y); 119/319; French Clb; German Clb; Nwsp Phtg; Yrbk Phtg; Lit Mag; JV Lcrss; High Hon Roll; St Schlr; Syracuse U; Engl.

MC CABE, KELLY; Williamson HS; Williamson, NY; (Y); AFS; Drill Tm; Bsktbl; Bowling; Mgr(s); Socr; Trk; High Hon Roll; Hon Roll; Elec Tech.

MC CABE, LAUREN; Cardinal Mooney HS; Rochester, NY; (Y); 40/350; Stage Crew; Cheerleading; Coach Actv; High Hon Roll; Hon Roll; Spanish NHS; RIT; Engrng.

MC CABE, MICHAEL G; Clarkstown H S North; New City, NY; (Y); Math Tm; Scholastic Bowl; Mrchg Band; Orch; Stage Crew; Symp Band; Yrbk Stf; Mu Alp Tht; NHS; Columbia U Sci Hnrs Prog 84-86.

MC CABE, WILLIAM E; Arlington HS; Lagrangeville, NY; (Y); 69/572; Band; Church Choir; Concert Band; Jazz Band; Mrchg Band; Orch; Hon Roll; Ntl Merit Ltr; School Musical; Variety Show; Pres Slavic Lang Hnr Soc; VP Russian Club; Most Musical SR Cls; George Washington U; Pol Sci.

MC CAFFERY, MARC; Westhampton Beach HS; Westhampton, NY; (Y); 17/232; Latin Clb; Yrbk Phtg; Yrbk Stf; L Bsktbl; Var Golf; Hon Roll; NHS; Hghst Avg Latin II & III 84-85; MIP Vrsty Golf 85; Sptsmnshp Awd JV Bsktbl 83-84; Pre-Med.

MC CAFFERY, STEVEN J; Monsignor Farrell HS; Staten Island, NY; (Y); 49/297; Dance Clb; Drama Clb; Thesps; Chorus; School Musical; School Play; High Hon Roll; Im Bsktbl; Im Bowling; Dance Co 84-85; SUNY Binghamton.

MC CAFFREY, KEVIN; Connetquot HS; Oakdale, NY; (Y); 87/750; JV Var Bsbl; Bsktbl; JV Var Ftbl; Pre-Med.

MC CALL, KEVIN; Mount Vernon HS; Mount Vernon, NY; (Y); French Clb; Key Clb; Office Aide; Science Clb; Spanish Clb; Orch; Trs Sr Cls; L Tennis; High Hon Roll; Sec NHS; Stu Of Mnth Mth 84.

MC CALLION, GERALD; East Hampton HS; E Hampton, NY; (Y); 4/116; Im Bowling; Var Ftbl; Im Ice Hcky; Var Socr; Im Wt Lftg; High Hon Roll; Hon Roll; Jr NHS; Lion Awd; NHS; Gld Physics Mdl 85; Gld Spn Mdl 84; Chem, Mth Acad Excllnce 83; Bio Achvt Awd 82; John Drew Tlnt Srch 82; GA Tech; Engrng.

MC CALLUM, WENDY; John H Glenn HS; E Northport, NY; (Y); Debate Tm; Drama Clb; MMM; Acpl Chr; Chorus; Madrigals; School Musical; School Play; Swing Chorus; Math.

MC CANN, DELORES; Cardinal Spellman HS; New York, NY; (S); 27/560; Dance Clb; Service Clb; Stage Crew; Off Jr Cls; Off Sr Cls; Im Bsktbl; Im Vllybl; High Hon Roll; Hon Roll; NHS; Biomed Engrng.

MC CANN, MICHELLE; Palmyra-Macedon Central HS; Palmyra, NY; (Y); Band; Chorus; Mrchg Band; Symp Band; JV Tennis; Hon Roll; Daemen Coll; Physical Thrpy.

MC CARGER, ROBERT; Potsdam SR HS; W Stockholm, NY; (Y); 31/164; French Clb; Varsity Clb; Im Bsktbl; JV L Crs Cntry; JV Var Mgr(s); Var Score Keeper; Timer; Var Trk; Im Vllybl; Hon Roll; Talented Jr Pgm St Lawrence U 84; Potsdam Coll; Chem.

MC CARROLL, RITA; Notre Dame-Bishop Gibbons HS; Schenectady, NY; (S); Var Bsktbl; Crs Cntry; Var Trk; High Hon Roll; NHS; Alg Awd 83.

MC CARRON, KERRY; Lakeland SR HS; Mahopac, NY; (Y); Pres Sec FBLA; Yrbk Stf; Jr NHS; Westchester Bus Inst Bus Ed Awd 85; FBLA Outstndng Awd 85.

MC CARTHY, BRIAN; Saranal Lake Central HS; Saranac Lk, NY; (Y); Church Yth Grp; Quiz Bowl; VP Soph Cls; Var L Bsbl; Var Capt Ftbl; Var Capt Ice Hcky; High Hon Roll; Hon Roll; VP NHS; Prfct Atten Awd; Redletter Awd Hockey 85.

MC CARTHY, COLLEEN; Villa Maria Acad; Cheektowaga, NY; (S); 15/120; Church Yth Grp; Rep Frsh Cls; JV Bowling; Var Capt Cheerleading; Var Gym; Sftbl; JV Capt Vllybl; Hon Roll; Prfct Atten Awd.

MC CARTHY, DANIEL; Thomas Edison R SR HS; Elmira Hts, NY; (Y); Am Leg Boys St; Scholastic Bowl; Nwsp Stf; Rep Stu Cncl; Ftbl; Trk; High Hon Roll; Prfct Atten Awd; Schlstc Art Shw 85; VA Tech; Arch.

MC CARTHY, DANNY; Beacon HS; Beacon, NY; (Y); 5/210; Am Leg Boys St; Pres Key Clb; Varsity Clb; VP Stu Cncl; Var Bsbl; Var Ftbl; High Hon Roll; Jr NHS; NHS; All Cnty Ftbl 84.

MC CARTHY, EDWARD; Solvay HS; Solvay, NY; (Y); Sec Key Clb; Rep Jr Cls; Var Ice Hcky; High Hon Roll; Stat NHS; Ntl Merit Ltr; French Clb; Math Tm; Spanish Clb; Hghst Avg Engl, Socl, Math & Sci 83-85; Membr NY ST Stdnt Forum 85; ESAHA Yth Jdg Tm 84; Cornell; Med.

MC CARTHY, ELIZABETH; Niagara Catholic HS; Niagara Falls, NY; (Y); Dance Clb; Spanish Clb; Stat Bsktbl; Var JV Cheerleading; Stat Vllybl; Hon Roll; NHS; Legal Studies.

MC CARTHY, ELLEN; Fontbonne Hall Acad; Brooklyn, NY; (Y); 79/139; Aud/Vis; Dance Clb; School Musical; Variety Show; Pom Pon; Socr; Sftbl; Vllybl; Hnr Awd Spanish I & II; St Johns U; Bus.

MC CARTHY, KAREN; Notre Dame HS; Horseheads, NY; (Y); Key Clb; Nwsp Ed-Chief; Nwsp Rptr; Var L Bsktbl; Var L Vllybl; Hon Roll; NHS; Chemung Cnty Yuth Cncl 85; Law.

MC CARTHY, KATHERINE; School Of The Holy Child; Pelham Manor, NY; (S); Hosp Aide; Service Clb; Stage Crew; Rep Frsh Cls; Pres Soph Cls; Pres Jr Cls; Var Capt Fld Hcky; Swmmng; Hnrs Awd Mod Eurp Hstry 83-84.

MC CARTHY, KATHLEEN; Villa Maria Acad; Cheektowaga, NY; (S); 5/112; Pres Church Yth Grp; Computer Clb; Pres Sr Cls; Stu Cncl; Var Capt Bsktbl; Capt JV Bowling; Var Sftbl; Var Vllybl; NHS; Ntl Merit Ltr; Niagara U; Bus.

MC CARTHY, KEVIN D; St Francis HS; Orchard Park, NY; (Y); 15/150; Stu Cncl; Var Socr; Capt Var Swmmng; Var Tennis; Hon Roll; NHS; 4 Yr Schlrshp To St Francis College; Student Of The Month; Waterpolo; St Francis College; Chemistry.

MC CARTHY, MARILYN; Auburn HS; Auburn, NY; (Y); 98/413; Varsity Clb; JV Cheerleading; Coach Actv; Gym; Sftbl; Capt Tennis; Hon Roll; Rgnts Schlrshp Nrsng 85; Hgh Hnr Roll 84; Broward CC; Radiolgc Tech.

MC CARTHY, MAURA; Saint Vincent Ferrer HS; Roosevelt Isl, NY; (Y); 2/115; Library Aide; Math Clb; Math Tm; ROTC; Science Clb; Band; Chorus; Yrbk Rptr; Yrbk Sprt Ed; Yrbk Stf; Cornell; Pre Med.

MC CARTHY, MAUREEN; School Of The Holy Child HS; Larchmont, NY; (S); GAA; Teachers Aide; Yrbk Stf; Rep Frsh Cls; Pres Soph Cls; Rep Jr Cls; Pres Stu Cncl; Var Tennis; JC Awd; Hugh Obrien Ldrshp Awd 82; Elem Educ.

MC CARTHY, MEGHAN; Notre Dame Bishop Gibbons HS; Clifton Park, NY; (S); 5/120; Rep Frsh Cls; Rep Soph Cls; Rep Jr Cls; Rep Stu Cncl; Var Bsktbl; Var Sftbl; Var Trk; Var Vllybl; High Hon Roll; NHS; Math Awd 83; Law.

MC CARTHY, MICHAEL E; Elmira Free Acad; Elmira, NY; (Y); Boy Scts; VP Church Yth Grp; Exploring; Latin Clb; Concert Band; Mrchg Band; Orch; Symp Band; High Hon Roll; JA; Acadmc Schlrshp Salem Coll 85; Salem Coll; Yth Agcy Admin.

MC CARTHY, MOLLY; Nardin Acad; Buffalo, NY; (Y); 1/88; Debate Tm; Service Clb; Speech Tm; Pres Frsh Cls; Rep Jr Cls; Rep Sr Cls; Bausch & Lomb Sci Awd; High Hon Roll; NHS; Val; Canisius Coll.

MC CARTHY, PATRICIA; Pearl River HS; Pearl River, NY; (Y); Church Yth Grp; PAVAS; Chorus; School Musical; School Play; Stage Crew; Swing Chorus; Capt Pom Pon; High Hon Roll; NHS; Elem Ed.

MC CARTHY, PAULETTE; Walton HS; Bronx, NY; (S); Church Yth Grp; Office Aide; ROTC; Church Choir; Nwsp Rptr; NHS; Awd For Outstndng Achvt/Acadmc & Extra-Crcclr Actvts 84; Accntng.

MC CARTHY, TAMMY; Mount Mercy Acad; Buffalo, NY; (Y); Girl Scts; JA; Off Jr Cls; Prfct Atten Awd; Cert Jr Cls Del Prom Deco Comm 85; Bryant & Stratton; Fshn Merch.

MC CARTIN, KATHLEEN; Riverhead HS; Calverton, NY; (Y); 4/194; Rep Latin Clb; Trs Band; Chorus; Drm Mjr(t); Orch; Trs Frsh Cls; Crs Cntry; Trk; High Hon Roll; NHS; Cum Laude Natl Latin Exam 85; Pres Phys Ftns Awd 84; Suffolk Clscl Soc Latin III 2nd 84.

MC CARTNEY, WENDY L; Long Island City HS; Long Island City, NY; (Y); 1/579; Exploring; FHA; Math Clb; Service Clb; High Hon Roll; NHS; Acadmc Olympcs 84-85; Acadmc All-Am 84-85; Arista 84-85; Northeast LA U; Spch Path.

MC CARTY, KAREN; Waterloo SR HS; Waterloo, NY; (Y); FTA; Chorus; Swing Chorus; Nwsp Rptr; Nwsp Stf; High Hon Roll; Cayuga Cnty CC; Acctg.

MC CARTY, MATTHEW; Rocky Point JR SR HS; Rocky Point, NY; (S); 3/185; Chess Clb; Pres Computer Clb; Debate Tm; Drama Clb; Thesps; School Play; Nwsp Stf; DAR Awd; Trs NHS; Ntl Merit SF; Litarary Awd 82-84; Rsrch Physics.

MC CARTY, SHEILA; Aquinas Inst; Rochester, NY; (Y); Cheerleading; Pom Pon; Socr; Sftbl; High Hon Roll; Hon Roll.

MC CARTY, SKIP; Odessa-Montour Central Schl; Montour Falls, NY; (Y); Am Leg Boys St; Aud/Vis; Lit Mag; Rep Stu Cncl; Var L Bsbl; Var L Bsktbl; Var L Ftbl; Hon Roll; Prfct Atten Awd; Elmira Coll Key Awd 84-85; Radio.

MC CARVILLE, COLLEEN; Clarkstown HS North; New City, NY; (Y); Girl Scts; JV Bsktbl; Mu Alp Tht; 1st Cls Awd GS Cadts 82-83; Stewrds.

MC CAULEY, BRIAN; Hicksville HS; Hicksvl, NY; (Y); JV Crs Cntry.

MC CAUSLAND, KATHLEEN; Stella Maris HS; Rockaway Park, NY; (Y); Cmnty Wkr; Drama Clb; Girl Scts; Nwsp Rptr; Nwsp Stf; 2nd Pol Athl Leag Essay 84; St Johns U; Jrnlsm.

MC CHARGUE, DENNIS; Rome Free Acad; Rome, NY; (Y); Y-Teens; Var JV Ftbl; Var Stat Trk; Im Wt Lftg; Hon Roll; NHS; Accnt.

MC CLAFFERTY, RITA; Central Islip HS; Central Islip, NY; (Y); 15/450; Varsity Clb; L Stat Mgr(s); Var Capt Sftbl; Var Capt Tennis; Hon Roll; MVP Awd Girls Vrsty Ten 84-85; MIP Awd Vrsty Sftbl 84-85; All Lg Cntrfldr Sftbl 85; Mech Engr.

MC CLAIN, KENDRA; Niagara Catholic HS; Niagara Falls, NY; (Y); Boys Clb Am; Cmnty Wkr; Spanish Clb; Church Choir; Nwsp Stf; Yrbk Stf; Rep Jr Cls; JV Var Cheerleading; Hon Roll; Buffalo ST Coll; Accntg.

MC CLAIN, MARC; Bishop Laughlin HS; Brooklyn, NY; (Y); VP Church Yth Grp; Dance Clb; Chorus; Pres Church Choir; School Play; Library Aide; Gym; Long Islnd U; Music.

MC CLAIRE, TRACY - RENEE; Cardinal Spellman HS; Bronx, NY; (Y); Latin Clb; Pep Clb; Chorus; Mrchg Band; Syracuse U; Comm.

MC CLAVE, MARK P; East Syracuse-Minoa HS; E Syracuse, NY; (Y); Boy Scts; DECA; Mgr(s); Im Wt Lftg; JV Var Wrstlng; Hon Roll; Prfct Atten Awd; NY ST Regents Schlrshp 85; Eagle Scout Awd 85; Oswego ST; Chld Psych.

MC CLEAN, BARBARA; Beach Channel HS; Broad Channel, NY; (Y); 35/482; Band; Concert Band; Hon Roll; Jr NHS; NHS; Princpls List Excel Schlrshp 84-85; Marywood Coll; Comm.

MC CLEAN, DEBRA L; F D Roosevelt HS; Hyde Park, NY; (Y); 53/325; Art Clb; Church Yth Grp; Trk; Hon Roll; St Schlr; ST U Of NY; Bus.

MC CLELLAN, BRIAN; Williamsville South HS; Williamsville, NY; (Y); Art Clb; Church Yth Grp; DECA; Spanish Clb; Chorus; School Play; Stage Crew; Yrbk Stf; JV Var Bsbl; Im JV Ftbl; DECA 84-86; Chrs 84-86; Bsbl 82-86; Williamsville S; Bus.

MC CLELLAN, HERBERT; Charles C D Amico Schl; Albion, NY; (S); Boy Scts; Var Bsbl; Var Ftbl; Hon Roll; NHS; Prfct Atten Awd; Drating.

MC CLELLAND, MICHAEL; Rome Catholic HS; Lee Center, NY; (Y); #4 In Class; French Clb; School Musical; Var Trk; High Hon Roll; NHS; Pres Schlr; NROTC, AFROTC Schlrshps 85; Rensselaer Poly Tech Inst; Engr.

MC CLERNAN, RITA-LOUISE; Saugerties Central HS; Saugerties, NY; (Y); 23/243; Band; VP Mrchg Band; Yrbk Bus Mgr; Yrbk Stf; Stat Trk; High Hon Roll; Hon Roll; NHS; St Schlr; Suny Albany; Econ.

MC CLERNAN, SHARON; Saugerties HS; Saugerties, NY; (S); 1/250; German Clb; Ski Clb; Varsity Clb; Var L Trk; Var L Vllybl; High Hon Roll; NHS; Bio Achvt Awd 84; Amer Legn Auxlry Girls ST 85; Math.

MC CLOSKEY, KEVIN; Monsignor Mc Clancy HS; Woodside, NY; (Y); Church Yth Grp; Cmnty Wkr; Im Bsktbl; High Hon Roll; Hon Roll; Physics Awd 85; Comp Analyst.

MC CLOSKEY, TERRY; Westhampton Beach HS; Speonk, NY; (Y); USAF.

MC CLURKIN, CARI; The Buffalo Acad Of The Sacred Heart; Buffalo, NY; (Y); Pres Church Yth Grp; Pres Exploring; JA; Sec Office Aide; Spanish Clb; Chorus; Pres Church Choir; School Musical; Rotary Awd; Miss Yng, Gftd & Blck Awd 83; RIT; Engrng Physcs.

MC CLUSKEY, JAMES M; Monsignor Farrell HS; Staten Island, NY; (Y); Computer Clb; Drama Clb; Spanish Clb; Bowling; NYS Regents Schlrshp 85; Coll Of Staten Island; Comp.

MC CLUSKY, ANNETTE M; Whitesboro SR HS; Whitesboro, NY; (Y); 20/325; GAA; Intnl Clb; Concert Band; Jazz Band; Mrchg Band; Sftbl; Tennis; Vllybl; Hon Roll; NHS; NYS Rgnts Schlrshp 85; Roch Inst Tech Schlrshp 85; Rochester Inst Tech; Comp Sci.

MC COLLUMN, PATRICIA E; Maine Endwell SR HS; Johnson City, NY; (Y); 11/246; Sec 4-H; Girl Scts; Teachers Aide; Chorus; School Musical; High Hon Roll; Hon Roll; NHS; Ntl Merit Ltr; Rgnts Schlrshp 85; Geneseo Alumni Fllwshp Schlrshp 84; SUNY Geneseo; Tchr.

MC COMB, SUSAN; Richmond Hill HS; Richmond Hill, NY; (Y); English Clb; JA; Math Clb; Office Aide; Spanish Clb; Teachers Aide; High Hon Roll; NHS; Prfct Atten Awd; Spanish NHS; Queens Coll Pres Awd 83; Doc.

MC CONNELL, DONALD W; Arkport Central Schl; Arkport, NY; (Y); 3/46; Ski Clb; Band; Mrchg Band; Coach Actv; Socr; Trk; Wrstlng; High Hon Roll; Hon Roll; NY ST Regents Schlrshp 85; Buffalo U; Aero-Engrng.

MC CONNELL, FIONA; North Shore HS; Glen Head, NY; (Y); 1/215; AFS; Church Yth Grp; Pres VP Exploring; French Clb; Trs Key Clb; Trs Latin Clb; Mathletes; Math Clb; Q&S; Nwsp Rptr; All ST NYSSMA 84-83; Rmngtn Furlong Fclty Awd 85; Columbia U Sci Hnrs Pgm 83-85; Williams Coll MA; Sci.

MC CONNELL, GARY; Mexico Adad & Central Schl; Mexico, NY; (Y); 4-H; Pres Trs FFA; Var Ftbl; Eber Sally Mem Awd 85; Cobleskill; Agri Engr Tech.

MC CONNELL, KATHERINE; East Islip HS; East Islip, NY; (Y); VP FBLA; Nwsp Bus Mgr; Var Tennis; Var Vllybl; Hon Roll; NHS; NEDT Awd; VP Church Yth Grp; Math Tm; Nwsp Stf; Schlrshp Wall St Semnr 85; Al-Leag MVP Grls Vrsty Vllybl Tm 85; Blu Rbn Exclnc Lng Isl Sci Fair 84; Intntl Reltns.

MC CONNELL, ROBERT; North Warren Central Schl; Chestertown, NY; (S); 12/50; Math Clb; Nwsp Ed-Chief; Nwsp Stf; Trs Frsh Cls; Rep Stu Cncl; JV Socr; Tennis; Math.

MC CONNON, SHEILA; Staten Island Acad; Staten Island, NY; (Y); Art Clb; Dance Clb; Drama Clb; Spanish Clb; Mrchg Band; Yrbk Stf; Trk; Hon Roll.

MC COON, STEVEN B; Sidney HS; Sidney, NY; (Y); Am Leg Boys St; Computer Clb; FBLA; Math Clb; Varsity Clb; Yrbk Phtg; High Hon Roll; NHS; Aud/Vis; Boy Scts; Ctzns Schlrshp Fndtn Sidney Schlrshp 85; Natl Scl Stds Olympiad 1st Pl 83; Vrsty Lttrs Rifle 82-85; Broome CC; Ind Engr.

MC CORMACK, KAREN; Bishop Kearney HS; Brooklyn, NY; (Y); 141/346; FTA; Math Tm; Rgnts Schlrshp 85; Ntl Hnr Roll 84-85; St Josephs Coll; Child Stdy.

MC CORMACK, MATTHEW; Hoosie Valley HS; Valley Falls, NY; (Y); Boy Scts; Drama Clb; Band; School Musical; Var JV Bsbl; Im Bowling; Var JV Socr; Order Of Arrow 83; Doctor.

MC CORMACK, PATTIE; Bishop Maginn HS; Albany, NY; (Y); Library Aide; Spanish Clb; Var Capt Cheerleading; Var Pom Pon; Hon Roll; SUNY Oneonta; Tchr.

MC CORMACK, SUSAN; Croton Harmon HS; Croton On Hudson, NY; (Y); 1/111; Varsity Clb; Band; Yrbk Ed-Chief; Var L Bsktbl; Var Capt Fld Hcky; Var Capt Socr; Cit Awd; NHS; Val; Regnts Schrlshp 85; Am Leg Schrlshp Awd 85; Hist Math Awds 85; Dartmouth.

MC CORMICK, CANDY; Spring Valley HS; Spring Valley, NY; (Y); Key Clb; Math Clb; Spanish Clb; JV Cheerleading; JV Sftbl; Hon Roll; Spanish NHS.

MC CORMICK, MICHELLE; C W Baker HS; Baldwinsville, NY; (Y); Yrbk Bus Mgr; Yrbk Ed-Chief; Rep Stu Cncl; Stat Sftbl; High Hon Roll; Jr NHS; NHS; Ntl Merit Ltr; Advrtsng.

MC CORMICK, ROSE; Oneida SR HS; Oneida, NY; (Y); FBLA; Library Aide; Office Aide; Spanish Clb; Hon Roll; Cls Of 45 Awd 83; Sec Clb 83; Occptnl Educ Pgm Cert Wrd Proc 85; Sec.

MC COURTY, PAMELA; H S Of Fashion Indust; Bronx, NY; (Y); 36/365; Dance Clb; JA; Office Aide; Service Clb; Teachers Aide; School Play; Vllybl; Cit Awd; Hon Roll; Prfct Atten Awd; Textl Dsgn.

MC COWAN, DAVID; Corning East HS; Corning, NY; (Y); 14/250; Boy Scts; Drama Clb; Exploring; Math Tm; Model UN; School Play; Yrbk Bus Mgr; Stu Cncl; Trk; NHS; Elec Engrng.

MC COY, MEEGAN; Holland Patent Central Schl; Rome, NY; (Y); 16/196; FTA; VP Girl Scts; Spanish Clb; Band; Chorus; Stage Crew; JV L Tennis; High Hon Roll; NHS; Girl Scout Silvr Awd 84, Gold Awd 85; Vcl Enmbl 85; Coll Of Geneseo; Comp Sci.

MC COY, MOLLY A; Saratoga SR HS; Saratoga Springs, NY; (S); 245/465; Church Yth Grp; DECA; Girl Scts; Office Aide; Science Clb; Orch; Nwsp Stf; Bsktbl; Sftbl; High Hon Roll; Joseph C Arpey Awd Grad 85; Acadmc Awd Bus 85; Pin Awd Orch 85; Dean JC; Visl Arts.

MC COY, SHANTA; St Gabriel HS; Mt Vernon, NY; (Y); 18/61; Yrbk Phtg; Gym; Vllybl; Hon Roll; NY U; Vet.

MC CREA, KATHERINE; Cooperstown Central HS; Cooperstown, NY; (Y); 6/92; 4-H; GAA; Band; Concert Band; Mrchg Band; Pep Band; Var L Crs Cntry; Var L Socr; Var L Trk; High Hon Roll.

MC CREADIE, KEN; Williamsville East HS; East Amherst, NY; (Y); Ski Clb; Im Ice Hcky; JV Trk; High Hon Roll; Engrng.

MC CREAR, KIMBERLY; Forest Hills HS; Jamaica, NY; (Y); 238/881; Hon Roll; U NC Chapel Hill; Psych.

MC CREESH, JENNIFER A; North Babylon SR HS; North Babylon, NY; (Y); 18/556; Cmnty Wkr; French Clb; FTA; Intnl Clb; Pep Clb; Band; Nwsp Ed-Chief; Yrbk Stf; Pom Pon; French Hon Soc; Bio.

MC CROSSAN, DEBBIE A; Maria Regina HS; Bronx, NY; (Y); 75/130; Church Yth Grp; Office Aide; Chorus; School Musical; School Play; Hon Roll; Softbl Outside Sch 83; Psych.

MC CUE, CHARLES; Washingtonville SR HS; Washingtonville, NY; (Y); Pres Church Yth Grp; 4-H; Ski Clb; School Musical; Stage Crew; Yrbk Stf; Bowling; Trk; Hon Roll; Voice Dem Awd; Physics.

MC CUE, GREGORY S; Newburgh Free Acad; New Windsor, NY; (Y); Church Yth Grp; Sec Pres 4-H; Acpl Chr; 4-H Awd; High Hon Roll; NHS; Spanish NHS; Chorus; Variety Show; Jr NHS; Englsh II Awd 85; Brnz Mdl Ntl Sci Olympiad 83; Harvard; Lbrl Arts.

MC CUE, JOHN C; Cardinal Spellman HS; Yonkers, NY; (Y); 6/587; Church Yth Grp; Rep Key Clb; Science Clb; Nwsp Rptr; High Hon Roll; NHS; NEDT Awd; Slvr Mdl CAC 85; Prsh Recog 83-85; Achvt Awds Rel, 83-84, Lat 84; Pre Med.

MC CULLAGH, MARGO ANNE; Farmingdale HS; N Massapequa, NY; (Y); 6/600; Drm Mjr(t); Jazz Band; Flag Corp; Hon Roll; Jr NHS; NHS; Ntl Merit Ltr; Hofstra U.

MC CULLEN, HELEN; Bishop Maginn HS; Albany, NY; (Y); 30/119; Drama Clb; Hosp Aide; Latin Clb; School Musical; Yrbk Stf; Cheerleading; Pom Pon; Score Keeper; Hon Roll; Empire ST Archry 81-84; Maria Coll; Nrsg.

MC CULLEN, JULIANNE; Argyle Central HS; Argyle, NY; (Y); Trs Art Clb; FHA; GAA; Teachers Aide; Chorus; Sftbl; Hon Roll; Prfct Atten Awd; Bus.

MC CULLOUGH, VERNESSA; Benjamin Franklin HS; Rochester, NY; (Y); Church Yth Grp; JA; Spanish Clb; Temple Yth Grp; Church Choir; Cit Awd; Hon Roll; Prfct Atten Awd; Bus.

MC CUMBER, STEPHANIE L; Bainbridge-Guilford JR-SR HS; Bainbridge, NY; (S); 32/70; Hosp Aide; Red Cross Aide; Color Guard; Ed Yrbk Bus Mgr; Sec Stu Cncl; Stat Bsbl; JV Bsktbl; Cit Awd; Cmnty Wkr; Chrprsn JR Clss Prom Sls Comm; Herkimer Cnty CC; Bus Admn.

MC CURRY, AMY; Vestal SR HS; Vestal, NY; (Y); Sec Church Yth Grp; Var Am Leg Aux Girls St; Color Guard; Mrchg Band; Rep Stu Cncl; JV Trk; High Hon Roll; Hon Roll; NHS; Hosp Vlntr 83.

MC CURRY, LISA J; Vestal Central Senior HS; Vestal, NY; (Y); 5/450; Trs Church Yth Grp; VP Drama Clb; Mathletes; Mrchg Band; VP Soph Cls; Rep Jr Cls; Rep Sr Cls; Rep Stu Cncl; Trs NHS; Ntl Merit Ltr; Watson Schlr 85; Cornell; Bio.

MC CUSKER, IAN F; Pelham Memorral HS; Pelham, NY; (Y); 5/177; Am Leg Boys St; Lit Mag; JV Var Tennis; Hon Roll; NHS; Ntl Merit SF; Intl Affairs.

MC DANIEL, WILMA; A Philp Randolph Campus; New York, NY; (Y); 32/284; Church Yth Grp; English Clb; Red Cross Aide; Teachers Aide; Band; Church Choir; Concert Band; School Musical; Gym; Score Keeper; Comp Sci.

MC DERMOTT, CHARMINE; Mt Vernon HS; Mt Vernon, NY; (Y); Office Aide; Varsity Clb; School Play; Bsktbl; Comp Sci.

MC DERMOTT, COLM; Clarkstown High School South; Bardonia, NY; (Y); Church Yth Grp; Computer Clb; Red Cross Aide; Ski Clb; Yrbk Stf; Var Diving; JV Socr; Var Trk; Felix Festa Tutrng Schlrshp 85; Barclonia Ladies Aux 85; Siena Coll 85; Siena Coll; Comp Sci.

MC DERMOTT, DIANE; Mattituck HS; Cutchoque, NY; (Y); Art Clb; German Clb; Chorus; Stage Crew; Variety Show; Yrbk Rptr; Yrbk Stf; Fld Hcky; JV Score Keeper; Hon Roll; Bus Mngmnt.

MC DERMOTT, DONNA MARIE; John H Glenn HS; Huntington, NY; (Y); 57/260; Art Clb; French Clb; Science Clb; Hon Roll; NHS; Rgnts Schlrshp 85; SUNY Binghamton; Lib Arts.

MC DERMOTT, JANE; Valley Central HS; Newburgh, NY; (Y); 40/300; Pres Church Yth Grp; Off Frsh Cls; Off Soph Cls; Off Jr Cls; Capt Cheerleading; Score Keeper; JV Var Sftbl; High Hon Roll; NHS; Spanish NHS; Cntsnt Miss NY Ntl Teen Ager Pagnt 85; Lifeguard 84-85; Little Leag Umpire 84-85.

MC DERMOTT, KAREN; Geneva HS; Geneva, NY; (S); 8/170; Pres Varsity Clb; VP Sr Cls; Var Capt Bsktbl; Var Capt Socr; Var Capt Sftbl; Capt Var Vllybl; DAR Awd; NHS; Ntl Merit Ltr; Math.

MC DERMOTT, MARC S; Yorktown HS; Yorktown Hts, NY; (Y); 6/360; Boy Scts; Key Clb; Radio Clb; Yrbk Stf; Stu Cncl; Bsbl; Crs Cntry; Var Capt Wrstlng; High Hon Roll; NHS; Athl Wk Awd, Con Ed Irwin Klein Schlrshp Awd 85; Fnlst Outstndg Yung New Yrkr 84; Williams Coll.

MC DIARMID, CORINNE; Sayville HS; W Sayville, NY; (Y); Band; Chorus; Mrchg Band; School Play; Yrbk Stf; Fld Hcky; Ice Hcky; Sftbl; Hon Roll; Flute Plyng Awds 83; Sped & Accrcy Trpng Awd 84; Northwood Inst; Bus.

MC DONAGH, PATRICIA; Sacred Heart Acad; Vlg Of Bellerose, NY; (S); 3/200; Science Clb; Nwsp Rptr; Rep Stu Cncl; JV Bsktbl; High Hon Roll; NHS.

MC DONALD, CHRIS; Holy Trinity Diocesan HS; Wantagh, NY; (Y); Church Yth Grp; Cmnty Wkr; Math Clb; Ski Clb; Hon Roll; NEDT Awd; Engr.

MC DONALD, CHRISTOP M; William Floyd HS; Mastic Beach, NY; (Y); 9/428; Intnl Clb; Latin Clb; Science Clb; Var L Bsktbl; Var Capt Golf; Var L Socr; Hon Roll; NHS; St Schlr; Essay Cntst Wnnr 85; Cornell U; Mech Engrng.

MC DONALD, COLIN; William Howard Taft HS; Bronx, NY; (Y); Cmnty Wkr; Debate Tm; Library Aide; Office Aide; Band; Stage Crew; Lit Mag; Cit Awd; Prfct Atten Awd; Socl Stds Awd 83; Consmr Advct Intern Pgm Awd 84; C Wrtng Trphy 83; Bus.

MC DONALD, MARK J; Carthage Central HS; Felts Mill, NY; (Y); 24/177; Am Leg Boys St; Ski Clb; Varsity Clb; Yrbk Stf; Im JV Bsktbl; Coach Actv; Capt Socr; High Hon Roll; Hon Roll; NHS; All Star Vrsty Soccer 1st Tm 83; Sprtsmnshp Team 83-84; Arch Engr.

MC DONALD, MAUREEN; Mt St Mary Acad; Buffalo, NY; (Y); 20/113; Church Yth Grp; Cmnty Wkr; Church Choir; Yrbk Stf; Var Badmtn; Im Gym; Mgr(s); Var Socr; High Hon Roll; Hon Roll; Math Educ.

MC DONALD, SCOTT A; Lancaster Central SR HS; Lancaster, NY; (Y); 110/535; Aud/Vis; Boy Scts; Cmnty Wkr; Crs Cntry; Swmmng; Hon Roll; Erie Cmnty Coll; Fireman.

MC DONALD, SEAN; Chenango Forks HS; Harpursville, NY; (Y); Boy Scts; Ski Clb; JV Var Ftbl; Var Trk; JV Vllybl; High Hon Roll; Hon Roll; Most Imprvd Ftbll 85; Airline Pilot.

MC DONALD, STEVEN A; Xavier HS; Cambria Hts, NY; (Y); 32/222; Chess Clb; Math Clb; ROTC; Teachers Aide; Nwsp Bus Mgr; Lit Mag; VP Stu Cncl; VP Trk; NHS; NEDT Awd; Bus Admin.

MC DONALD, SUSAN; Walton HS; Bronx, NY; (Y); Nwsp Phtg; Vllybl; Hon Roll; Acctng.

MC DONALD, THOMAS; Linton HS; Schenectady, NY; (Y); Boy Scts; Drama Clb; JCL; Office Aide; Teachers Aide; Chorus; Rep Frsh Cls; Var L Bsktbl; Var L Golf; Hon Roll; Gifted & Tlntd Awd 79; Engr.

MC DONELL, HEATHER; Bishop Grimes HS; Syracuse, NY; (Y); Church Yth Grp; Band; Capt Socr; Var Sftbl; Var Trk; JV Vllybl; Bio.

MC DONNELL, CATHERINE; Our Lady Of Victory Acad; New York, NY; (S); 10/156; French Clb; Varsity Clb; Variety Show; Lit Mag; Var Bsktbl; Var Sftbl; JV Vllybl; French Hon Soc; High Hon Roll; NHS; Soph Yr Relg Awd 84; NEDT Awd 84.

MC DONNELL, JENNIFER; Immaculata Acad; Boston, NY; (Y); 2/41; Church Yth Grp; French Clb; Quiz Bowl; Nwsp Rptr; Yrbk Bus Mgr; Yrbk Ed-Chief; Rep Stu Cncl; Hon Roll; Bus Admin.

MC DONNELL, LAURA; Frontier Central HS; Blasdell, NY; (Y); French Clb; Pep Clb; Band; Concert Band; Mrchg Band; School Play; Stu Cncl; Var JV Socr; Stat Swmmng; Hon Roll.

MC DONOUGH, BRIDGET; De Sales Catholic HS; Lockport, NY; (Y); Cmnty Wkr; Hosp Aide; Yrbk Stf; Hon Roll; Kenyon Memrl Schlrshp 85; Schimsheiner Memrl Schlrshp 85; U Of Buffalo; Nrsng.

MC DONOUGH, DENISE; Warwick Valley Central HS; Warwick, NY; (Y); Teachers Aide; Cheerleading; Trk; Hon Roll; Sci Awd 84-85; Fashion.

MC DONOUGH, MATTHEW KIRK; Plainedge HS; N Massapequa, NY; (Y); 103/313; Computer Clb; Quiz Bowl; Yrbk Bus Mgr; Lit Mag; Hon Roll; NYS Regnts Schlrshp 85; NYS Histrcl Assn; NAR; SUNY At Buffalo; Aero Engr.

MC DONOUGH, MICHELE; Corning Painted Post West HS; Corning, NY; (Y); Trs JA; Varsity Clb; Var L Bsktbl; Var Mgr(s); Var Capt Trk; JV Vllybl; High Hon Roll; NHS; PSAT Mrt Awd 85; Bio.

MC DONOUGH, SANDY; Catholic Central HS; Troy, NY; (Y); 50/203; Church Yth Grp; Math Clb; Spanish Clb; Variety Show; Albany Bus Coll; Secrtlr Stds.

MC DONOUGH, STEPHEN; Keveny Memorial Acad; Clifton Park, NY; (Y); Hon Roll; Natl Hnr Roll 85; Natl Ldrshp Orgnztn Natl Hnr Roll 85; St Johns U; Polt Sci.

MC DONOUGH, SUZANNE; St Catherine Acad; Bronx, NY; (Y); Stage Crew; Bsktbl; Coach Actv; Sftbl; Swmmng; Timer; Vllybl; Hon Roll; Ntl Merit Schol; NY ST Professional Schlrshp Nursing 85; MT Saint Vincent; Nursing.

MC DOUGAL, MICHAEL; Copiague SR HS; Copiague, NY; (Y); Boy Scts; Capt L Bsktbl; Ftbl; JV Socr; High Hon Roll; NHS; Rnnr Up NAACP Tlnt Srch Sci 84; Brookhaven Minrty H S Apprntcshp Prog 84; Natl Soc Stds Olympds 85; Engrng.

MC DOUGALL, KERRI; Argyle Central HS; Argyle, NY; (Y); 4/60; Sec Art Clb; French Clb; Yrbk Ed-Chief; Rep Stu Cncl; JV Crs Cntry; High Hon Roll; Hon Roll; Sny Smmr Schl Arts 84; Art Dsgn.

MC DOUGALL, STEVE; Massena Central HS; Massena, NY; (Y); Political Wkr; Varsity Clb; Var Lcrss; JV Var Socr; Band; Mrchg Band; Pre Law.

MC DOWALL, JOHN; Monticello HS; Harris, NY; (Y); 13/177; Quiz Bowl; Band; Orch; Stage Crew; Stu Cncl; Crs Cntry; Trk; Wrstlng; NHS; Pres Schlr; NY Rgnts Schlrshp 85; US Naval Acad; Aerntcl Engrng.

MC DOWELL, CRAIG L; Rome Free Acad; Rome, NY; (Y); Boy Scts; Church Yth Grp; Cmnty Wkr; Drama Clb; Prfct Atten Awd; Outstndng Svd Awd To RFA Cls 85; Bus.

MC DOWELL, DAWN; Bishop Loughlin HS; Brooklyn, NY; (Y); Political Wkr; Service Clb; Chorus; School Play; Pres Jr Cls; Stu Cncl; Trs Cheerleading; High Hon Roll; Hon Roll; Jr NHS; Attndnce Hnr Cert 82-83; Hgh Achvt Awd Math, Engl & Rdng 82; Pace U; Acctng.

MC DUFFEY, KAREN; Eli Whitney Vocation HS; Brooklyn, NY; (Y); English Clb; Exploring; Library Aide; Math Tm; Office Aide; OEA; Church Choir; Drill Tm; Orch; Stat Trk; Scholar 78; Library Aid Awd 80; Mst Ath Awd 79; Sec.

MC DUFFIE, WANDA; Spring Valley SR HS; Spring Valley, NY; (Y); Cmnty Wkr; Hosp Aide; Church Choir; Nrsng.

MC ELIGOT, MICHELLE; Jamesville De Witt HS; Dewitt, NY; (Y); VP JA; Yrbk Stf; Var Trk; High Hon Roll; NHS; Prfct Atten Awd; JR Achvt Ofcr Yr Rnnr Up, SADD 85; Syracuse U; Vet.

MC ELROY JR, BRUCE; Newburgh Free Acad; Newburgh, NY; (Y); Computer Clb; Var Crs Cntry; High Hon Roll; Hon Roll; Engr.

MC ELROY, GEORGE; Jeffersonville Youngsville C HS; Kenoza Lk, NY; (Y); 13/58; Church Yth Grp; Cmnty Wkr; Varsity Clb; Band; Mrchg Band; Hon Roll; Marit Coll Presdntl Schlrshp 85; K & A Luchstcasper & Sadie Egler Schlrshp 85; Marist Coll; Accntng.

MC ELROY, JENNIFER; North Warren HS; Chestertown, NY; (S); 11/50; Var Tennis; JV Vllybl; Hon Roll; Dance.

MC ELROYE, AMY L; Edison Technical & Occupatnl Center; Rochester, NY; (Y); 21/272; VP Church Yth Grp; Model UN; Pres Varsity Clb; Church Choir; School Musical; Rep Frsh Cls; Rep Sr Cls; Mgr(s); Var Trk; Hon Roll; Mt Olivet Church Schlrshp 85; Notre Dame; Arch Eng.

MC ELWAIN, MEG; Salmon River Central HS; Bombay, NY; (S); 14/120; VP Church Yth Grp; Pres VP 4-H; Sec French Clb; Band; Chorus; Pres VP Church Choir; Concert Band; Mrchg Band; Stage Crew; Rep Frsh Cls.

MC ENEANEY, BARBARA; Central HS; Valley Stream, NY; (Y); Trk; Hon Roll; NHS; Mst Artistic 83; Comm Art.

MC ERLEAN, MICHAEL M; St John The Baptist-Diocesan HS; Selden, NY; (Y); MMM; Chorus; Church Choir; Concert Band; School Musical; School Play; Swing Chorus; Symp Band; Variety Show; Ithaca Schl Of Music; Music Ed.

MC EVOY, IRENE C; Notre Dame-Bishop Gibbens HS; Schenectady, NY; (Y); Hosp Aide; Band; School Musical; Nwsp Stf; Lit Mag; Var Trk; Var Vllybl; Hon Roll; NHS; Regnts Schlrshp 85; Music Awd 83; Vanderbilt U; Nrsng.

MC FADDEN, BETH-ANNE; Vestal SR HS; Vestal, NY; (Y); 246/478; FBLA; Varsity Clb; Variety Show; Sec Frsh Cls; Sec Soph Cls; Cheerleading; Mgr(s); Swmmng; FL ST U; Bus Mngmnt.

MC FADDEN, CHERYL; Mount Mercy Acad; Orchard Park, NY; (Y); Pres 4-H; Hosp Aide; Math Clb; Hon Roll; Sec NHS; Yrnk Edtr Sectnl Editor; CCD Tchr; Offc Aide; Intl Bus.

MC FADDEN, KERRY ANN; Southwestern HS; Lakewood, NY; (Y); Church Yth Grp; Cmnty Wkr; Drama Clb; Hosp Aide; Pep Clb; Political Wkr; Ski Clb; Spanish Clb; Chorus; School Musical; Miss Awana 83; Drama.

MC FADDEN, VIRGINIA; Caledonia Mumsford Central Schl; Caledonia, NY; (Y); Drama Clb; Girl Scts; Library Aide; Ski Clb; Band; Chorus; Church Choir; Color Guard; Concert Band; Mrchg Band; Secry Sci.

MC FALL, JONATHAN; Hornell HS; Hornell, NY; (Y); Am Leg Boys St; Church Yth Grp; Latin Clb; Band; Mrchg Band; Symp Band; Jr Cls; Vllybl; High Hon Roll; NHS; Brown U Bk Awd 84-85.

MC FARLAND, ANDREW L; Marcellus HS; Marcellus, NY; (Y); 12/164; Jazz Band; Mrchg Band; Symp Band; Var Tennis; High Hon Roll; NHS; Regnts Schlrshp NY ST 85; Cornell Bk Awd 84; NROTC Schlrshp 85; U Of Rochester; Biochem.

MC FARLAND, BRIAN; Plainview JFK HS; Old Bethpage, NY; (Y); 73/275; Band; Concert Band; Mrchg Band; Variety Show; JV Bsbl; JV Var Bsktbl; Im Socr; Im Sftbl; Im Vllybl; Im Wt Lftg; Got NY ST Regents Schlrshp 85; Offered Acad Schlrshp To Johnson And Wales College 85; Drexel U; Business.

MC FARLAND, KAREN; Manlius Pebble Hill HS; Syracuse, NY; (S); Church Yth Grp; Exploring; School Musical; L Cheerleading; Var L Socr; Chorus; Yrbk Stf; Trk; Vllybl; Mst Imprv Plyr Sccr 83-84; Engrng.

MC FATE, MELISSA J; Averill Park HS; Averill Pk, NY; (Y); Band; Church Choir; Concert Band; Symp Band; Yrbk Ed-Chief; Jr Cls; Phy.

MC FAUL, FAWN; Franklin Acad; Malone, NY; (Y); Hon Roll; Secy.

MC GARITY, FRANK; South Side HS; S Hempstead, NY; (Y); 22/291; Rep Stu Cncl; Var Capt Socr; High Hon Roll; Hon Roll; NHS; Engrg.

MC GARRITY, EDDIE; Commack HS South; Dix Hills, NY; (Y); Aud/Vis; Office Aide; JV Ftbl; Hon Roll; Farmingdale; Acctg.

MC GARRY, AMY; School Of The Holy Child HS; Larchmont, NY; (Y); Pres Dance Clb; Hosp Aide; Teachers Aide; Yrbk Stf; Rep Jr Cls; Var Capt Socr; Var Swmmng; Hon Roll.

MC GARRY, ERIC; Cohoes HS; Cohoes, NY; (Y); Art Clb; DECA; Drama Clb; JA; Red Cross Aide; Varsity Clb; School Play; Nwsp Rptr; Yrbk Ed-Chief; Yrbk Phtg; Hudson Valley CC; Acctg.

MC GARRY, KATE; Chenango Valley HS; Binghamton, NY; (Y); Church Yth Grp; Drama Clb; French Clb; Hosp Aide; Ski Clb; Varsity Clb; Chorus; Yrbk Phtg; Var JV Cheerleading; Var Trk; Boston Coll; Bus.

MC GARRY, TARA A; Maria Regina HS; Crestwood, NY; (Y); Church Yth Grp; Debate Tm; Key Clb; Yrbk Stf; Rep Jr Cls; Rep Sr Cls; Rep Stu Cncl; Coach Actv; Var L Swmmng; Var Trk; Ecnmcs.

MC GARVEY, MICHAEL; H Frank Carey HS; Franklin Sq, NY; (Y); 10/222; Debate Tm; Mathletes; Thesps; Chorus; Nwsp Ed-Chief; High Hon Roll; Jr NHS; NHS; Voice Dem Awd; Church Yth Grp; Talntd Gifted Pgm 84-85; Columbian Squires Yth Org; Pre-Vet.

MC GAUGHEY, CARRIE; Oakfield Alabama Central HS; Oakfield, NY; (Y); 3/100; French Clb; Chorus; Var Capt Bsktbl; Var Capt Socr; JV Vllybl; High Hon Roll; NHS; Geneseo; Elem Educ.

MC GAY, CAROLINE; St John The Baptist HS; Ronkonkoma, NY; (Y); Drama Clb; School Play; Hon Roll; Tchr.

MC GEADY, JAMES; Onteora Central Schl; Woodstock, NY; (Y); Math Tm; Nwsp Rptr; Nwsp Stf; JV Bsktbl; Var L Golf; Var L Tennis; Hon Roll; Ntl Merit Ltr; NY ST Rgnts Schlrshp 85; Elect Engrng.

MC GEE, CARRIE L; Johnsburg Central HS; Bakers Mills, NY; (Y); 3/46; Band; Chorus; Concert Band; Mrchg Band; Gym; High Hon Roll; Hon Roll; NHS; St Schlr; Ciba-Geigy Sci Awd 85; Outstndg Stu Awd 84; Cornell U; Psychlgy.

MC GEE, JOHN; Smithtown East HS; Nesconset, NY; (Y); JV Ftbl; Trk; NY Inst Tech; Engrng.

MC GEE, MICHELLE; Sheepshead Bay HS; Brooklyn, NY; (Y); Office Aide; Mgr Bowling; JV Capt Sftbl; Law Enforce.

MC GEE, TRACY; Candor HS; Candor, NY; (Y); Chorus; Trs Frsh Cls; Trs Soph Cls; Trs Jr Cls; Trs Sr Cls; Rep Stu Cncl; High Hon Roll; Hon Roll; NHS; Comp Sci.

MC GETRICK, MELISSA; Cato-Meridian HS; Jordan, NY; (Y); Stat Bsktbl; Stat Fld Hcky; Var Sftbl; JV Vllybl; Bus Mgmt.

MC GHEE, SHEILA B; Hempstead HS; Hempstead, NY; (S); 24/333; Office Aide; Teachers Aide; Band; Orch; Yrbk Stf; High Hon Roll; Sec NHS; Concert Band; Mrchg Band; Minrty Engrng Prog 81-83; Long Island Sci Congrss 1st Pl Wnnr 81-82; Hofstra U Semnr Prog 82-85; Berkeleys Secy Schl; Wrd Proc.

MC GHIE, DAVY; Mt St Michael Acad; Bronx, NY; (Y); 152/308; Boy Scts; NFL; JV Church Yth Grp; JV Ftbl; Trk; Hon Roll; Bridgeport U; Comp.

MC GILL, LISA; Arlington North Campus HS; Poughkeepsie, NY; (Y); JV Sftbl; Berkley; Secretary.

MC GINLEY, REBECCA; Warwick Valley HS; Princeton, WV; (Y); 1/217; Dance Clb; Pres Drama Clb; Pres French Clb; VP Band; Chorus; Concert Band; Mrchg Band; Orch; School Musical; School Play; Amer U.

MC GINN, MEGAN M; North Rose-Wolcott HS; Wolcott, NY; (Y); Am Leg Aux Girls St; Drama Clb; French Clb; Pep Clb; Ski Clb; Varsity Clb; School Musical; School Play; Variety Show; Yrbk Phtg; Bus.

MC GINNIS, TIM; Westhampton Beach HS; Remsenburg, NY; (Y); Aud/Vis; French Clb; Ski Clb; Nwsp Stf; Yrbk Stf; Rep Stu Cncl; Bsktbl; Var L Golf; Sftbl; Tennis; Bus.

MC GINNIS, YVONNE; Dominican Commercial HS; Pearl River, NY; (Y); Cmnty Wkr; Hosp Aide; Cheerleading; High Hon Roll; NHS; Nrsng.

MC GLONE, COLLEEN; Sodus Central HS; Williamson, NY; (Y); 3/120; French Clb; Girl Scts; Model UN; Office Aide; Band; Mrchg Band; Trs Stu Cncl; Var Tennis; VP NHS; Paidia Awd 85; NYSSMA Music Awd 79-85; Dip Wrk.

MC GLORY, JEFFREY D; Fairport HS; Fairport, NY; (Y); Ski Clb; Im Bsktbl; Var Ftbl; Capt Var Trk; Im Wt Lftg; Hon Roll; Rotary Awd; NYS Regents Schlrshp 85; Clarkson; Mech Engrng.

MC GLYNN, DANIEL; Honeoye Central Schl; Honeoye, NY; (S); Ski Clb; Varsity Clb; Band; Concert Band; Jazz Band; Mrchg Band; Pep Band; Nwsp Rptr; Sec Jr Cls; VP Capt Socr; Dir Awd For Band 84; Pres Schl Hstry Clb 83-85; Music.

MC GLYNN, KELLY; Liverpool HS; Liverpool, NY; (Y); 127/791; Cmnty Wkr; High Hon Roll; NY St Regents Schlrshp 85; Onondoga Comm Coll; Law.

MC GLYNN, MARY ELIZABETH; Gilboa-Conesville HS; Prattsville, NY; (Y); 4/36; Hosp Aide; Pres Spanish Clb; School Play; Ed Nwsp Ed-Chief; VP Stu Cncl; Cheerleading; Sftbl; DAR Awd; NHS; Teenager Of Yr 85; Miss Prattsville 83; Nrsng Schlrshp 85; Delhi Coll; Nrs.

MC GLYNN, THOMAS; Gilboa-Conesville Central Schl; Prattsville, NY; (S); Yrbk Stf; Var Bsbl; Var Stat Bsktbl; High Hon Roll; Hon Roll.

MC GOEY, CHEVONNE; North Salem HS; Purdys, NY; (Y); 38/85; Letterman Clb; Pep Clb; Varsity Clb; Y-Teens; Yrbk Stf; Crs Cntry; Fld Hcky; Var Socr; Swmmng; Timer; Norrtheastern U; Law.

MC GOLDRICK, STEPHEN; Iona Preporatory Schl; Pelham, NY; (Y); 12/196; Service Clb; JV L Crs Cntry; Var L Trk; High Hon Roll; NHS; Pre-Law.

MC GOOKIN, ED; Christian Brothers Acad; Camillus, NY; (Y); 5/97; Pres Church Yth Grp; Exploring; Hosp Aide; PAVAS; Concert Band; Var Capt Swmmng; High Hon Roll; NHS; Acad Schlrshp Le Moyne Coll 85; Rgnts Schlrshp 85; Pres Acad Ftnss Awd 85; Le Moyne Coll; Pre Med.

MC GORRY, JENNIFER; St Francis Prep; Bayside, NY; (S); Church Yth Grp; Cmnty Wkr; GAA; Political Wkr; JV Capt Bsktbl; Coach Actv; JV Capt Sftbl; Var Tennis; JV Vllybl; NHS; Engl Awd Outstndng Achvt 82; CYO Sprtsmnshp Awd 82-83; MVP JV Bsktbl St Francis Prep 83-84; Finc.

MC GOVERN, BRENDAN; Archbishop Molloy HS; Richmond Hl, NY; (Y); 133/409; Boys Clb Am; Boy Scts; Church Yth Grp; Drama Clb; Intnl Clb; Stage Crew; Bsktbl; Ftbl; Sftbl; Hon Roll; Bus Admin.

MC GOVERN, FRANK J; Mount Saint Michael Acad; Yonkers, NY; (Y); Am Leg Boys St; Boy Scts; Cmnty Wkr; Office Aide; Political Wkr; Color Guard; Stage Crew; Bowling; Fld Hcky; Ice Hcky.

MC GOVERN, MARY ROSE; Stella Maris HS; Woodhaven, NY; (Y); Girl Scts; Science Clb; Spanish Clb; Nrsng.

MC GOVERN, ROBERT J; Canandaigua Acad; Canandaigua, NY; (Y); 11/277; German Clb; Ski Clb; Crs Cntry; Socr; Cit Awd; High Hon Roll; NHS; Ntl Merit Ltr; Am Leg Boys St; Marshall Khan Engrng Schlrshp 85; VA Polytechnic Inst; Mech Eng.

MC GOVERN, THOMAS; Central Islip HS; Central Islip, NY; (Y); 23/425; Boy Scts; Var Socr; Var Tennis; Hon Roll; SR Patrl Lf Sct Pursug Eagl 79-85; Perf Attndnc JR Yr 85; Compltd Newsday Long Isl Marathn 85; Engrng.

MC GOWAN, CHAD M; Oxford Academy HS; Oxford, NY; (Y); 25/75; Chess Clb; Socr; Hon Roll; Acad Challenge, Business Seminar, Regents Schlrshp Wnnr; Nazareth Rochester; Psych.

MC GOWAN, EILEEN; Sewanhaka HS; Elmont, NY; (Y); 29/377; Church Yth Grp; FBLA; Lit Mag; Off Frsh Cls; Off Soph Cls; Off Jr Cls; Stu Cncl; Cheerleading; Hon Roll; Spanish NHS; Flrl Pk Ladies Aux Lit Awd 83; Jrnlsm.

MC GOWAN, KATHLEEN; Sewanhaka HS; Elmont, NY; (Y); 39/377; Church Yth Grp; FBLA; Girl Scts; Chorus; Off Frsh Cls; Off Soph Cls; Off Jr Cls; Stu Cncl; Capt Cheerleading; Hon Roll.

MC GRADE, CHRISTINE L; Bellport HS; E Patchogue, NY; (Y); Church Yth Grp; Church Choir; Rep Frsh Cls; Rep Jr Cls; Pom Pon; Score Keeper; Hon Roll; Jr NHS; Suffolk CC; L A Humnts.

MC GRATH, ADRIENNE; Herbert A Lehman HS; Bronx, NY; (Y); Dance Clb; Office Aide; Teachers Aide; Concert Band; Orch; School Musical; Lit Mag; Rep Frsh Cls; Rep Soph Cls; Rep Jr Cls; Gym Awd 85; Sec.

MC GRATH, DONNA; Christopher Columbus HS; Bronx, NY; (S); Hon Roll; Ntl Merit Schol; York Coll; Scl Wrkr.

MC GRATH, KATHLEEN ANN; Herricks HS; New Hyde Park, NY; (S); Sec DECA; Var Bsktbl; Var Crs Cntry; Var Capt Socr; Var Sftbl; Var Trk; 2nd VFW Voice Democracy Cntst 85; All Nassau Cnty Leag Schl Sccr 84; Long Isl JR Select Soccer Tm 83.

MC GRATH, TRACI D; Smithtown H S East; Nesconset, NY; (Y); GAA; Band; Symp Band; Frsh Cls; Crs Cntry; Socr; Trk; NHS; All Leag Crss Cntry 83; Stmfttng Indstry Promtn Fund Schlrshp; Itln Hnr Soc 83-85; NY Inst Of Tech; Comp Sci.

MC GRAW, KELLY; Bishop Maginn HS; Albany, NY; (S); Chrmn Red Cross Aide; JV Var Bsktbl; High Hon Roll; NHS; Prfct Atten Awd; Var Sftbl; JV Var Vllybl; Frnch Awd 84; Sprtsmnshp Awd Bsktbl 83; 110 Pct Awd Vllybl/Bsktbl 84.

MC GRAW, SHAUN; Liverpool HS; Liverpool, NY; (S); 72/754; Soph Cls; Jr Cls; Stu Cncl; JV Swmmng; Jr NHS; NHS; Engr.

MC GRAW, TIM; Grand Island SR HS; Grand Island, NY; (Y); 57/325; Pres Drama Clb; Pres Chorus; Madrigals; School Musical; School Play; Stage Crew; Im Badmtn; Var Socr; NHS; Aud/Vis; Acadmc Ltr; Sptlghtrs Mst Val JR; Elec Engrng.

MC GREEVY, PETER R; Monsignor Farrell HS; Staten Island, NY; (Y); Boy Scts; Chess Clb; Pres Computer Clb; Pres Debate Tm; Office Aide; Political Wkr; Mrchg Band; Im Bsktbl; Hon Roll; St Schlr; NYS Regents Schlrshp 85; SUNY Stony Brook; Bio.

MC GREGOR, DOUG; Coxsackie - Athens HS; Coxsackie, NY; (Y); 20/114; Ski Clb; JV Var Bsbl; JV Var Bsktbl; Var Bowling; High Hon Roll; Hon Roll; Vrsty MVP Bsktbl,All Leag Team 85; All Leag Team V Bsebl 85; Chem Engr.

MC GUIGAN, MARK; Bishop Ludden HS; Syracuse, NY; (S); 3/200; School Play; Var Bsktbl; Var Tennis; Vllybl; High Hon Roll; NHS; Pre-Med.

MC GUINNESS, BRIDGET; Unatego JR SR HS; Otego, NY; (Y); Pres French Clb; Var Capt Bowling; High Hon Roll; Hon Roll; Prfct Atten Awd; Church Yth Grp; Drama Clb; Sec FHA; Hosp Aide; Varsity Clb; SUS Leag-Hgh Trpl For Bwlng & All Star Bwlr 85; Linda Russ Memrl Trphy-Mst Imprvd Bwlr 85; Fulton-Montgomery CC; Nrs.

MC GUINNESS, SHEILA A; Cardinal Spellman HS; Bronx, NY; (Y); Chess Clb; Church Yth Grp; Cmnty Wkr; Stage Crew; High Hon Roll; Hon Roll; NEDT Awd; Catholic U; Educ.

MC GUIRE, BARBARA R; Gates-Chili HS; Rochester, NY; (Y); 106/463; Drama Clb; Chorus; School Musical; School Play; Yrbk Stf; Rep Frsh Cls; Rep Soph Cls; Rep Jr Cls; Mgr Vllybl; Hon Roll; Acad Merit Awd 84-85; Nazareth Coll Rochstr Schlrshp 85-86; Clss Actrs Awd 85; Nazareth Coll; Psych.

MC GUIRE, CLARE; ST Barnabas HS; Bronx, NY; (Y); 4/148; Office Aide; Spanish Clb; Yrbk Stf; Rep Stu Cncl; JV Var Bsktbl; Hon Roll; VP NHS; Prfct Atten Awd; Spanish NHS; Frst Hnrs Spnsh III Iona Coll Lang Cntst 84; 2nd Hnrs Spnsh II Coll Lang Cntst 83; Manhattan Coll; Bus.

MC GUIRE, HEIDI; Fontbonne Hall Acad; Brooklyn, NY; (Y); French Clb; Math Tm; Office Aide; High Hon Roll; Jr NHS; Psych.

MC GUIRE, KELLY; Hendrick Hudson HS; Verplanck, NY; (Y); Var Stat Bsktbl; Var JV Cheerleading; JV Crs Cntry; Var Ftbl; Var Twrlr; Archtctrl Dsgn.

MC GUIRE, LISA; West Seneca West SR HS; West Seneca, NY; (S); 54/543; Art Clb; GAA; Girl Scts; Chorus; Color Guard; Orch; School Musical; School Play; Stage Crew; Yrbk Sprt Ed; Natl Orch Awd 83; Erie Cnty Orch 83; NY ST Area All ST Chrs 83; Fashn Illustratn.

MC GUIRE, MARCIE; Lowville Academy & Central Schl; Lowville, NY; (Y); 3/120; Am Leg Aux Girls St; Spanish Clb; School Play; Nwsp Ed-Chief; Rep Stu Cncl; Var JV Socr; High Hon Roll; NHS; Latin Clb; Chorus; Elmira Coll Key Awd 85; APSL Ntl Ltn Hnr Soc 83, 84; Engl.

MC GUIRE, PAMELA; Cornwall Central HS; Beacon, NY; (Y); 117/198; Trs Library Aide; Teachers Aide; Chorus; Acctng.

MC GULLAM, KATHLEEN; Monroe-Woodbury HS; Monroe, NY; (Y); Art Clb; Yrbk Stf; Hon Roll; Ntl Hnr Roll 83-84; Ramapo Coll; Cntmprary Arts.

MC GUOIRK, ALICIA; Saranac Lake Central HS; Saranac Lk, NY; (Y); Church Yth Grp; Band; Chorus; Church Choir; Concert Band; Var JV Bsktbl; Var Capt Socr; Var L Sftbl; Var JV Vllybl; JV Elks Awd; N Country CC; Phys Ed.

MC GURK, KEVIN; Washingtonville SR HS; New Windsor, NY; (Y); Boy Scts; Church Yth Grp; Cmnty Wkr; Math Clb; Math Tm; Science Clb; Band; Pep Band; School Musical; Symp Band; NY ST Regnts Schlrshp Awd 85; U S Mltry Acad; Mech Engrng.

MC HUGH, CHRISTINE; Valley Stream Central HS; Valley Stream, NY; (Y); Sec AFS; Church Yth Grp; Cmnty Wkr; GAA; Girl Scts; School Musical; Pom Pon; High Hon Roll; Jr NHS; Ntl Bus Hnr Soc 85.

MC HUGH, ELIZABETH; St Edmund HS; Brooklyn, NY; (Y); 68/218; Spanish Clb; Bsktbl; Coach Actv; Score Keeper; Hon Roll.

MC HUGH, MATTHEW; Rocky Point JR SR HS; Rocky Pt, NY; (Y); Cmnty Wkr; French Clb; Hosp Aide; Spanish Clb; Coach Actv; Var JV Lcrss; French Hon Soc; Boston Coll; Bus Adm.

MC HUGH, MAUREEN; Webster HS; Webster, NY; (Y); 63/523; Math Tm; Trs Model UN; Concert Band; Trs Sr Cls; Var Fld Hcky; Var Trk; High Hon Roll; Jr NHS; NHS; Prfct Atten Awd; Outstndng Frsh Stu Yr 83; Outstndng Svc Soph Cls 84; Outstndng Chem Stu 85; Math.

MC HUGH, THERESA ANN; Whitestone Acad; Jamaica Estates, NY; (Y); Trs Church Yth Grp; Im Bsktbl; Stat Sftbl; Var Trk; High Hon Roll; Hon Roll; NHS; Ntl Merit Ltr; Eng 12 Gld, Mth 85; Slvr Mdl Advcd Biol 85; St Johns U; Humn Svcs.

MC ILWAIN, BERNARD; Bishop Loughlin Memorial HS; Brooklyn, NY; (Y); Cmnty Wkr; Political Wkr; Varsity Clb; Var Stu Cncl; Var Wt Lftg; Hon Roll; Acctnt.

MC INERNEY, WILLIAM G; St Anthonys HS; Setauket, NY; (Y); Chorus; Stage Crew; Nwsp Rptr; Nwsp Stf; Im Bsktbl; Var Wrstlng; Hon Roll; Ntl Merit Ltr; Regnts Schlrshp 85; U Of Scranton.

MC INNIS, MICHELLE; Springfield Gardens HS; Rosedale, NY; (Y); 19/508; Church Yth Grp; Aud/Vis; Sec Yrbk Stf; Rep Jr Cls; Hon Roll; NHS; Prfct Atten Awd; Teachers Aide; Prncpls Hnr Soc 81-84; Daily News Supr Yth 83; Arista 83-84; Hofstra U; Acctg.

MC INTIRE, RICHARD; Rice HS; New York, NY; (Y); Boy Scts; JV Im Bsktbl; JV Crs Cntry; L JV Wt Lftg; Hon Roll; Pace U; Busnss Admin.

MC INTOSH, DONALD; Commack HS South; Commack, NY; (Y); 51/374; Boy Scts; Varsity Clb; JV Bsbl; Var Socr; Im Vllybl; High Hon Roll; Intrmrl Hcky 84-85; Golden Quill Engl Wrtg Comptn Wnnr 85; Regnts Schlrshp 85; St Lawrence U; Ec.

MC INTOSH, EYESHA; Laguardia H S Of The Arts; Long Isl City, NY; (Y); 224/600; Dance Clb; Drama Clb; Hosp Aide; PAVAS; Teachers Aide; School Musical; Variety Show; Yrbk Stf; Rep Sr Cls; Rep Stu Cncl; Dance Awd 85; NY U; Brdcstng Jrnlsm.

MC INTOSH, MONICA LYNN; Notre Dame HS; Corning, NY; (Y); 58/125; Key Clb; Trk; NY ST Rgnts Nrsng Schlrshp 85; Steven Medical Axlry Schlrshp 85; St Josephs; Nrs.

MC INTOSH, MORRIS; Pulaski HS; Pulaski, NY; (S); 13/104; Church Yth Grp; FBLA; Varsity Clb; VP Sr Cls; Var Trk; High Hon Roll; Hon Roll; NHS; Houghton Coll.

MC INTOSH, SANDRA; St Catherine Acad; Bronx, NY; (Y); 27/206; Church Yth Grp; Office Aide; High Hon Roll; Hon Roll; Cmndtn For Bio 84; Englsh II Awd 85; Pre-Med.

MC INTYRE, ANN M; Our Lady Of Mercy HS; Rochester, NY; (Y); 6/200; Cmnty Wkr; Service Clb; Varsity Clb; Nwsp Ed-Chief; JV Var Socr; Var Trk; High Hon Roll; NHS; Church Yth Grp; Ski Clb; Latin Award 84; NY State Regents Schlrshp 85; U Of Notre Dame.

MC INTYRE, HOLLY; Gowanda Central HS; Perrysburg, NY; (Y); Art Clb; Sec Church Yth Grp; English Clb; 4-H; French Clb; Library Aide; Spanish Clb; Speech Tm; Nwsp Phtg; Yrbk Phtg; Jamestown CC; Art.

MC INTYRE, LORIA; Herbert Lehman HS; New York, NY; (Y); 6/444; Library Aide; Math Tm; Office Aide; Teachers Aide; Yrbk Stf; Hon Roll; NHS; Prfct Atten Awd; UFT Schlr 85; Princ Hnr Roll 83-85; Syracuse U; Bus Mgmt.

MC INTYRE, SHARLENE E; Charles H Roth HS; W Henrietta, NY; (Y); FBLA; Color Guard; Concert Band; Yrbk Stf; Jr NHS; NHS; Spanish NHS; St Schlr; Exploring; Hon Roll; Stu Cncl Serv Ltr 84; FBLA-1ST Pl Acctng II 85; NY ST Ldrshp FBLA Conf, 4th Pl-Bus Comm 85; SUNY Geneseo; Acctng.

MC INTYRE, WARREN B; Corning East HS; Beaver Dams, NY; (Y).

MC KAIN, MARI; Miller Place HS; Miller Pl, NY; (Y); 14/201; Church Yth Grp; VP FBLA; Nwsp Stf; Yrbk Stf; High Hon Roll; Hon Roll; NHS; Top 10 NY ST FBLA 85; 1st Pl Typing Dstrct Comptn 84; Pre-Med.

MC KANNA, KIMBERLY; Mount Vernon HS; Mount Vernon, NY; (Y); 1/650; Science Clb; Sec Trs Concert Band; Sec Trs Mrchg Band; Orch; School Musical; NHS; Val; Symp Band; High Hon Roll; Nom For Mc Donalds All-Amer H S Bnd 84-85; Mbr Westcheter Area All-ST Bnd 84-85; Clmbia U Sci Hnrs Pr; Physcs.

MC KAY, SCOTT; Blessed Sacrament HS; New Rochelle, NY; (Y); Stage Crew; Wrstlng; Hon Roll; All Cnty,Leage Wrstlng 85; Manhattan Clg; Elec Engr.

MC KAY, THOMAS; Fayetteville Manlius HS; Fayetteville, NY; (Y); Var L Tennis; Hon Roll; Mst Imprvd In Tennis 83; Rookie Of Yr In Tennis 84; Cert Of Awd In Math 84; Elec Engr.

MC KEE, GREGG P; Williamsville South HS; Williamsville, NY; (Y); 46/245; Church Yth Grp; Computer Clb; Ski Clb; Ntl Merit Schol; Boston U; Elec Engr.

MC KEE, JED; Watkins Glen HS; Reading Center, NY; (S); 8/140; Aud/Vis; Church Yth Grp; Band; Chorus; Church Choir; Yrbk Rptr; Var Crs Cntry; Trk; High Hon Roll; Letterman Clb; Media Arts Smmr Schl-SUNY 84; 1st Pl Exprmntl Video & Bst Of Show-Boces Media Shw 85; Media Arts; Music.

MC KEE, KEVIN; Salamanca Central HS; Salamanca, NY; (S); 20/120; Church Yth Grp; Band; Color Guard; Concert Band; Jazz Band; Mrchg Band; Pep Band; High Hon Roll; Hon Roll; Pres NHS; Fredorick Bus Coll; Acctng.

MC KEE, SCOTT E; Frontier Central SR HS; Blasdell, NY; (Y); 36/495; French Clb; Band; High Hon Roll; Hon Roll; NHS; NEDT Awd; Prfct Atten Awd; NY ST Rgnts Schlrshp 85; Rifle Tm-V Ltr; U Of Buffalo; Aerospace Engr.

MC KEEVER, SHANNON; Dryden Central HS; Etna, NY; (Y); 45/150; 4-H; Spanish Clb; Varsity Clb; Yrbk Rptr; Off Frsh Cls; Off Soph Cls; Off Jr Cls; Stu Cncl; Swmmng; Trk; Psych.

MC KEITHEN, KYOMI YOSHIKO; Bishop Loughlin Memorial HS; Brooklyn, NY; (S); 5/185; Church Yth Grp; Civic Clb; Cmnty Wkr; Computer Clb; Girl Scts; Library Aide; Office Aide; Teachers Aide; Church Choir; Nwsp Rptr; Tablet HS Press Awd 84; Baruch; Bus Admin.

MC KELVEY, ELIZABETH; Grace Dodge HS; New York, NY; (Y); Dance Clb; Hon Roll; Bus Admin.

MC KENNA, BARBARA; Sochem North HS; Holbrook, NY; (Y); 318/1500; Dowling Coll Acad Hnr Scholar 85; Dowling Coll; Acctng.

MC KENNA, CHRISTOPHER; Peekskill HS; Peekskill, NY; (S); Am Leg Boys St; Capt Bsbl; Capt Ftbl; Wt Lftg; High Hon Roll; NHS; Math.

MC KENNA, DAVID; Holy Trinity HS; East Meadow, NY; (Y); Church Yth Grp; Cmnty Wkr; Hosp Aide; Math Clb; Spanish Clb; School Musical; School Play; Bsktbl; Cit Awd; Hon Roll; Pre-Med.

MC KENNA, DAWN M; Plainedge HS; N Massapequa, NY; (Y); 8/311; Aud/Vis; Church Yth Grp; French Clb; MMM; Orch; School Play; French Hon Soc; High Hon Roll; NHS; Tufts U; Occp Thrpy.

MC KENNA, JAMES M; North Babylon SR HS; N Babylon, NY; (Y); 1/556; Intnl Clb; Mathletes; Pres Spanish Clb; Band; Mrchg Band; School Musical; Nwsp Stf; Bausch & Lomb Sci Awd; NHS; Val; U Notre Dame; Intl Bus.

MC KENNA, KEVIN; John Glenn HS; Huntington, NY; (Y); Cmnty Wkr; Varsity Clb; JV Ftbl; Var Capt Socr; Var Capt Trk; Im Vllybl; Im Wt Lftg; Hon Roll; NHS.

MC KENNA, PATRICIA; Preston HS; Bronx, NY; (S); Drama Clb; FNA; School Play; Stage Crew; Yrbk Stf; Sec Jr Cls; High Hon Roll; NHS; Child Psych.

MC KENNA, PETER T; West Babylon SR HS; W Babylon, NY; (Y); 35/405; JV Ftbl; NHS; Frank G Leone Mem Schlrshp 85; Polytechnic Inst NY; Aerospace.

MC KENNA, SHARON M; Voorheesville HS; Voorheesville, NY; (Y); 2/123; Math Tm; Chorus; Concert Band; Jazz Band; Yrbk Ed-Chief; Rep Stu Cncl; Fld Hcky; Cit Awd; NHS; Sal; Air Force ROTC Schlrshp 85-89; Josten Schlrshp Fnlst 85; NY ST Regnts Schlrshp; U Of Notre Dame.

MC KENNA, TIMOTHY; Liverpool HS; Liverpool, NY; (Y); Im Coach Actv; Var Ftbl; Capt Var Lcrss; Powder Puff Ftbl; Im Wt Lftg; JV Wrstlng; Var Hon Roll; Engrng.

MC KENNEY, DAVID R; West Seneca Christian Schl; W Seneca, NY; (Y); 8/20; Church Yth Grp; Quiz Bowl; Ski Clb; Band; Concert Band; Stage Crew; Var Capt Bsbl; Var Capt Socr; NY ST Rgnts Schlrshp 85; Marine Corps Schlrshp Fndtn 85; Cedarville Coll; Engrng.

MC KENNEY, GAIL; Germantown Central HS; Ancram, NY; (Y); 4/44; Drama Clb; Chorus; School Play; Yrbk Phtg; Cit Awd; Hon Roll; Trs NHS; Geneseo; Psych.

MC KENNEY, PAULA; Solvay HS; Syracuse, NY; (Y); Sec Math Clb; Spanish Clb; Sec Concert Band; Jazz Band; Orch; Swing Chorus; Variety Show; High Hon Roll; NHS; Berkeley Coll Music Scholar 85; Syracuse Jazz Fest Scholar Awd 85; Estrn U S Music Camp Scholar 84-85; Music.

MC KENZIE, ALICIA; Saratoga Springs SR HS; Saratoga Springs, NY; (Y); 48/465; Teachers Aide; Sec Frsh Cls; Sec Soph Cls; Rep Stu Cncl; High Hon Roll; Hon Roll; NHS; Schlrshp Bus Prof Womans Org 85; Le Moyne Coll; Pol Sci.

MC KENZIE, DEBORAH; The Franciscan Acad; Syracuse, NY; (Y); 11/23; Rep Sec FBLA; Chorus; Yrbk Stf; Trs Sr Cls; High Hon Roll; Hon Roll; Jr NHS; Pres NHS; Cert Of Achvt & Excllnc Of Prfrmnc In Shorthand II 85; Syracuse U; Bio.

MC KENZIE, MICHAEL P; Tolly JR SR HS; Lafayette, NY; (Y); 9/74; Art Clb; French Clb; Math Tm; Yrbk Stf; Trk; Bausch & Lomb Sci Awd; Elks Awd; High Hon Roll; NHS; Prfct Atten Awd; NY Regents Schlrshp 85; Ithaca Coll; Teacher.

MC KEON, E; Our Lady Of Lourdes HS; Staatsburg, NY; (Y); 33/144; Cmnty Wkr; Yrbk Stf; Rep Soph Cls; Rep Jr Cls; JV Var Bsktbl; Var Diving; JV Score Keeper; Var Swmmng; Hon Roll; NHS; Dutchess CC; Math Tchr.

MC KEON, RITA; Cardinal Spellman HS; Bronx, NY; (Y); French Clb; Pep Clb; Frsh Cls; Soph Cls; Hon Roll; Schlrshp St Catherines Acad 82; Fnlst Spellman Schlrshp Comptn 83; Bus.

MC KEOWN, HEATHER; Freeport HS; Freeport, NY; (Y); 39/450; Aud/Vis; Sec Key Clb; Teachers Aide; Chorus; Stage Crew; Variety Show; Yrbk Stf; Var Trk; Hon Roll; Kiwanis Awd; SUNY-FREDONIA; Comp Sci.

MC KEOWN, KAREN; Notre Dame HS; Whitesboro, NY; (Y); 32/178; Tennis; Pres Acad Fit Awd 85; ST U NY Albany; Acctg.

MC KERROW, DARRELL; West Canada Valley HS; Newport, NY; (S); 1/77; Debate Tm; French Clb; Model UN; Varsity Clb; Band; Concert Band; Jazz Band; Mrchg Band; School Musical; Var Bsktbl; Army ROTC Schlrshp 85; Babe Hammersley Awd 84; Syracuse U; Law.

MC KIERNAN, CAROLINE; Mineola HS; Williston Park, NY; (Y); FBLA; Key Clb; Var Gym; High Hon Roll; Hon Roll; Cmmnctns.

MC KIERNAN, CHARLIE; East Islip HS; Islip Terrace, NY; (Y); DECA; Var Ice Hcky; Var Socr; Distrib Ed Clbs Of Amer Top 10 Pct In Suffolk On Trl/Trsm 85; St Johns U; Econ.

MC KINLEY, JOHN; Unatego JR SR HS; Unadilla, NY; (Y); 20/90; French Clb; Spanish Clb; JV Bsbl; Var Bsktbl; Var Trk; High Hon Roll; Prfct Atten Awd; Jotzen Key Awd Wrld Hstry 83; Hghst Ave Awd Susquehanna Area Bsktbl Tms 85; ST U Coll Oneonta; Hstry.

MC KINNEY, KATHLEEN; Tron Vocational HS; Niagara Falls, NY; (Y); VP Church Yth Grp; English Clb; Hosp Aide; VP JA; Chorus; Swmmng; Niagara County CC; Nrsng.

MC KITTY, GERRY; Holy Cross HS; Bayside, NY; (Y); 38/312; Boy Scts; Church Yth Grp; Cmnty Wkr; Political Wkr; Im Bsktbl; Var JV Ftbl; Hon Roll.

MC KNIGHT, AMY B; Jamesville Dewitt HS; Syracuse, NY; (Y); 50/230; Church Yth Grp; Cmnty Wkr; Key Clb; Sec Pres Spanish Clb; School Musical; Stat Bsktbl; Stat Lcrss; L Var Socr; Cit Awd; Dnfth Awd; Faclty Ldrshp Awd 83-85; Faclty Svc Awd 82-85; Lemoyne Coll Smmr Schlr 84; Albany ST U; Soc Svcs.

MC KOY, SHEILA; Hempstead HS; Hempstead, NY; (S); 116/332; Cmnty Wkr; Computer Clb; Dance Clb; Drama Clb; Math Clb; Office Aide; ROTC; Ski Clb; Spanish Clb; Teachers Aide; Alfred U; Bus Adm.

MC LAIN, LAREESA V; Beach Channell HS; Rock Bch, NY; (Y); Debate Tm; Concert Band; Yrbk Stf; Prfct Atten Awd; Mst Imprvd Instrumntl 83; Arete Excllnce Scholar Char & Svc 83; Hnr Cert Eng 83; Law.

MC LAIN JR, STANLEY EUGENE; Oneida SR HS; Oneida, NY; (Y); 26/232; Am Leg Boys St; Debate Tm; Yrbk Bus Mgr; Pres Jr Cls; JV Var Bsktbl; JV Var Trk; Cit Awd; NHS; Pres Schlr; Boy Scts; Knights Pythias Schltc Achvts Awd 85; Dr Frank W Jennings Mem 85; Oneida Dollars For Schlrs 85; Pt Loma Nazarene Coll; Pre-Med.

MC LAIN, TRUDY; Canastota HS; Canastota, NY; (Y); Pres Church Yth Grp; Capt Quiz Bowl; Band; Drm & Bgl; Mrchg Band; Symp Band; Yrbk Stf; JV Var Crs Cntry; JV Trk; Hon Roll; Med.

MC LAREN, TRACY; Southampton HS; Southampton, NY; (Y); 16/110; Spanish Clb; School Play; Nwsp Rptr; Yrbk Stf; Lit Mag; Rep Jr Cls; Im Badmtn; Im Fld Hcky; Sftbl; Hon Roll; Manhattanville Coll.

MC LAUGHLIN, AMY; Jordan-Elbridge HS; Camillus, NY; (Y); Church Yth Grp; Drama Clb; Exploring; French Clb; Flag Corp; Mrchg Band; Hon Roll; Jr NHS; NHS; 2nd Math Sympsm 81; Bus Admin.

MC LAUGHLIN, BRIAN; Guilderland Central HS; Schenectady, NY; (Y); Cmnty Wkr; Library Aide; Var Crs Cntry; JV Trk; High Hon Roll; Awds Math I, II, II, Soc Stds 9, 10, 11, Engl, Grmn II High Acad Achvt; Acctng.

MC LAUGHLIN, CELINDA M; Onondaga Central HS; Nedrow, NY; (Y); Exploring; FBLA; German Clb; GAA; Hosp Aide; Band; Chorus; Yrbk Stf; JV Bsktbl; JV Socr; Bus.

MC LAUGHLIN, CHRISTINA; Bishop Kearney HS; Brooklyn, NY; (S); 29/307; Math Tm; Church Choir; Hon Roll; NHS; Finance.

MC LAUGHLIN, CONSUELO; Martin Luther King HS; Bx, NY; (Y); 8/258; Drama Clb; Math Clb; Pres Sr Cls; Rep Stu Cncl; Bsbl; Vllybl; Hon Roll; Hon Soc 85; Gov Comm Schltc Achvt Citation 85; Outstndng Schltc Achvt Cert 84-85; Hunter Coll; Psych.

MC LAUGHLIN, EILEEN; Notre Dame HS; Utica, NY; (Y); 52/174; Church Yth Grp; Cmnty Wkr; Church Choir; School Musical; School Play; Powder Puff Ftbl; JV Sftbl; Var Tennis; High Hon Roll; Hon Roll.

MC LAUGHLIN, JOHN; Pittsford Mendon HS; Pittsford, NY; (Y); Chess Clb; Latin Clb; Math Clb; Model UN; Ski Clb; Band; Chorus; Nwsp Rptr; Im Mgr Bsktbl; Var Ice Hcky; Maxima Cum Laude Natl Latn Exm 84; Engrng.

MC LAUGHLIN, MICHAEL; Albertus Magnus HS; New City, NY; (Y); JV Bsbl; Hon Roll; Fordham U; Jnrlst.

MC LAUGHLIN, MICHAEL V; St Francis HS; West Seneca, NY; (Y); 5/150; Nwsp Rptr; Nwsp Sprt Ed; Trs Frsh Cls; Var L Ftbl; Var Capt Trk; High Hon Roll; NHS; Ntl Merit Ltr; Williams Coll; Engr.

MC LAUGHLIN, MICHELLE; Marlboro HS; Marlboro, NY; (Y); Varsity Clb; Var Cheerleading; Dutchss CC; Scrtrl.

MC LAUGHLIN, WINIFRED; Immaculata Acad; Hamburg, NY; (Y); Sec Church Yth Grp; Drama Clb; Pres VP JA; Library Aide; PAVAS; Chorus; School Musical; Yrbk Phtg; Ntl Merit Schol; PAVAS Svc Awd 85; JA Mgmt Awd 83; Top 10 Ldrs CYO 85; St Bonaventure U; Acctg.

MC LAURIN, ANISSA; Mount Vernon HS; Mt Vernon, NY; (Y); Boys Clb Am; Dance Clb; Hosp Aide; Office Aide; Teachers Aide; Church Choir; Color Guard; Drm & Bgl; Stat Bsktbl; Hon Roll; Loyola Coll; Comp Sci.

MC LAURIN, BRIAN; Bishop Loughlin Memorial HS; Brooklyn, NY; (Y); School Musical; Stage Crew; Stu Cncl; Bus.

MC LEAN, JARRED T; New Rochelle HS; New Rochelle, NY; (Y); 296/697; Boy Scts; Library Aide; Teachers Aide; Varsity Clb; Acpl Chr; Chorus; Church Choir; Stage Crew; Var Crs Cntry; Capt Var Trk; Arch.

MC LEAN, LISA; Herbert H Lehman HS; Bronx, NY; (Y); 10/444; Church Yth Grp; Office Aide; Teachers Aide; Chorus; Church Choir; School Musical; High Hon Roll; NHS; Prfct Atten Awd; Hghst Scorg SR MAA Cntst 85; Silvr Medls Physcs & Spnsh 85; Fordham U; Math.

MC LEAN, MICHELLE; Freeport HS; Freeport, NY; (Y); Boys Clb Am; Exploring; Hosp Aide; Key Clb; Yrbk Stf; Hon Roll; Ag & Tech Coll; Data Proc.

MC LEER, RICHARD; St Francis Prep; Flushing, NY; (Y); 288/693; Church Yth Grp; Drama Clb; St Johns; Cmmnctns.

MC LELLAN, LISA M; Camden Central HS; Camden, NY; (Y); AFS; Drama Clb; Pep Clb; Varsity Clb; Yrbk Stf; Var Cheerleading; Var Score Keeper; Hon Roll; Rsprtry Thrpy.

MC LELLAN, SONIA; E J Wilson HS; Spencerport, NY; (Y); Church Yth Grp; Drama Clb; French Clb; Varsity Clb; Yrbk Stf; Coach Actv; Socr; Trk; Hon Roll; S Awd-Vrsty Lttrs 85; MVP Awd-Estrn Rgnl Sccr Cmp 83; Sibley, Lindsay, & Curr Schltc Art Awd 82; Brockport ST; Accntng.

MC LENDON, SANDI M; Holy Trinity D HS; Roosevelt, NY; (S); 26/385; Hosp Aide; Library Aide; Math Clb; Rep Frsh Cls; Rep Jr Cls; Var Cheerleading; Var Trk; Var Twrlr; High Hon Roll; Hon Roll; Nassau Cnty Yuth Bd 84-85; Acctng.

MC LEOD, PAMELA; Edison Tech; Rochester, NY; (Y); Art Clb; Camera Clb; Cmnty Wkr; Girl Scts; Library Aide; Office Aide; Red Cross Aide; Y-Teens; Badmtn; Tennis; Amer Red Cross Summr Volntr Awd 83; Graphic Design.

MC LEOD, WENDY; Williamsville East HS; Williamsville, NY; (Y); Latin Clb; Pep Clb; Concert Band; High Hon Roll; Hon Roll; Prfct Atten Awd; Rep Stu Cncl; Educ.

MC LOONE, LYNNE; Sacred Heart Acad; N Merrick, NY; (S); 9/196; Var Bsktbl; Var Sftbl; Var Vllybl; Hon Roll; NHS; JV Bsktbl MVP 83-84; JV Vlybl MVP 83-84; Accntnt.

MC LOUGHLIN, ANN M; Ichabod Crane HS; Schodack Landing, NY; (Y); French Clb; Hosp Aide; Teachers Aide; High Hon Roll; Hon Roll; NHS; Ntl Merit Ltr; NYS Rgnts Schlrshp; Pre-Med.

MC LOUGHLIN, PATRICK; St John The Baptist HS; Central Islip, NY; (Y); FTA; Keywanettes; Math Tm; Nwsp Rptr; Yrbk Phtg; Lit Mag; Crs Cntry; Trk; High Hon Roll; Hon Roll; Ntl Ltn Hnr Soc 85; Sci Olympd Fnlst 84; Biomdcl Engrng.

MC MAHON, BRIAN; Msgr Mc Clancy HS; Woodside, NY; (Y); 49/250; Boy Scts; Church Yth Grp; Office Aide; Pep Clb; Pres Soph Cls; Im Bsktbl; JV Crs Cntry; Im Ftbl; Im Sftbl; Hon Roll; Crmnl Sci.

MC MAHON, DAWN MARIE; Sachem HS; Lake Ronkonkoma, NY; (Y); 49/1478; Cmnty Wkr; Service Clb; Lit Mag; Lcrss; Hon Roll; Jr NHS; NHS; Drama Clb; French Clb; Girl Scts; Sachem PTA & Tchrs Assn Schlrshps 85; Hugh O Brian Yth Semnr 83; SUNY Albany; Tch.

MC MAHON, ELIZABETH; York Central HS; Caledonia, NY; (Y); Church Yth Grp; 4-H; JV Bsktbl; JV Var Cheerleading; JV Var Socr; JV Var Sftbl; JV Var Vllybl; 4-H Awd; Hon Roll; Adver.

MC MAHON, LORRAINE; St Johns Prep; Astoria, NY; (Y); Hosp Aide; Chorus; Hon Roll; Hnr Rl 85; Hunter Clg; Nrsg.

MC MAHON, PATRICK; Aguinas Inst; Rochester, NY; (S); 18/166; Exploring; High Hon Roll; Hon Roll; Aquinas Cert Achvt Analytic Geomtry & Calculus 85; U Of Rochester; Bio.

MC MAHON, PEGGY; Cambridge Central Schl; Cambridge, NY; (Y); 17/100; French Clb; Chorus; Cheerleading; Hon Roll; JP Sousa Awd; Oneonta.

MC MAHON, SANDRA; Sacred Heart Acad; Buffalo, NY; (Y); Church Yth Grp; French Clb; Chorus; Nwsp Stf; Lit Mag; Rep Jr Cls; JV Bsktbl; JV Capt Sftbl; Hon Roll; ST U NY Buffalo; Eng.

MC MAHON, YVETTE M; Penfield HS; Penfield, NY; (Y); Varsity Clb; Pres Frsh Cls; Pres Soph Cls; Pres Jr Cls; Pres Sr Cls; JV Capt Bsktbl; Var Capt Fld Hcky; Radio Clb; Mgr(s); Var Capt Swmmng; Stdnt Senat 82-85; SADD 85; Rules Comm 82-85; Potsdam Coll; Crmnl Justc.

MC MANUS, AMY; Hornell HS; Hornell, NY; (Y); AFS; Art Clb; Spanish Clb; Chorus; Nwsp Rptr; Recreatnl Thrpst.

MC MANUS, ANN M; Clarkstown South HS; New City, NY; (Y); Church Yth Grp; Orch; School Musical; Stu Cncl; Var Swmmng; Soc Stud Cls Rep Stu Cncl; Chrch Lctrs; Intl Bus.

MC MANUS, JAMES K; Wantagh HS; Wantagh, NY; (Y); 29/291; Boy Scts; Sr Cls; Stu Cncl; Var Capt Socr; Var Trk; Cit Awd; Pres NHS; Eagle Scout; US Coast Guard Acad.

MC MANUS, JOHN; John Jay SR HS; Staatsburg, NY; (Y); 30/560; Pres DECA; Nwsp Rptr; Socr; High Hon Roll; Hon Roll; Jr NHS; Pres Schlr; St Schlr; DECA Awd 84-85; DECA Natl Comptn Awd 84; PA ST U; Acctg.

MC MANUS, KEVIN M; Northport HS; Northport, NY; (Y); 35/585; Am Leg Boys St; Nwsp Ed-Chief; Nwsp Rptr; Yrbk Stf; VP Pres Stu Cncl; Var L Bsktbl; Var L Socr; Cit Awd; Hon Roll; NHS; Finc.

MC MANUS, MARY LOU; Cairo Durham HS; Cairo, NY; (Y); 7/90; Political Wkr; Teachers Aide; Band; School Musical; School Play; Stage Crew; Yrbk Stf; Pres Sr Cls; Rep Stu Cncl; Bsktbl; JR Prom Duchss; Ntl Hnr Soc; Siena Coll; Psych.

MC MANUS, MELODY; Bishop Grimes HS; Syracuse, NY; (Y); Cmnty Wkr; Band; Concert Band; School Musical; High Hon Roll; Hon Roll; NHS; SADD 84-85; Bus.

MC MANUS, ROGER; Bishop Ford HS; Brooklyn, NY; (Y); 6/375; Stage Crew; Lit Mag; VP Stu Cncl; JV Var Bsbl; High Hon Roll; NHS; Rgnts Schlrshp 85; Gvrnrs Citation 85; Brooklyn Coll; Wrtng.

MC MANUS, THOMAS G; Bishop Ford C C HS; Brooklyn, NY; (Y); 2/375; Math Clb; Math Tm; Pres Stu Cncl; JV Var Bsbl; Gov Hon Prg Awd; High Hon Roll; Hon Roll; NHS; Rgnts Schlrshp; Gov Citation; Acad Schlrshp; Seton Hall U; Comm.

MC MASTER, MICHELLE; Wyoming Central HS; Warsaw, NY; (S); 4-H; School Play; Yrbk Stf; Trs Jr Cls; Var Pres Stu Cncl; Var Cheerleading; Score Keeper; Socr; Sftbl; NHS; Accntng Awd 84; Math Awd 83-84.

MC MILLAN, KEVIN; South Shore HS; Brooklyn, NY; (Y); Church Yth Grp; Library Aide; Band; JV Ftbl; Hon Roll.

MC MILLAN, STEPHANIE; George Westinghouse Vo-Tech; Brooklyn, NY; (Y); Office Aide; Band; School Musical; School Play; High Hon Roll; Hon Roll; Kngsborough; Comp Pgmng.

MC MILLIN, KELLI; Newark SR HS; Newark, NY; (Y); Band; Concert Band; Jazz Band; Mrchg Band; High Hon Roll; Hon Roll; Comp Sci.

MC MINDES, LESLIE; Mc Kinley HS; Buffalo, NY; (Y); FFA; Concert Band; Swmmng; Drill Tm; Nwsp Rptr; Jessy Ketchum Acad Awd; Vet Med.

MC MULLEN, SARAH; Henninger HS; Syracuse, NY; (Y); Bsktbl; Socr; Hon Roll; Mentor Mnrty Pgm 83-85; Med.

MC MULLEN, SUSAN N; Baldwin SR HS; Baldwin, NY; (Y); Am Leg Aux Girls St; Cmnty Wkr; Hosp Aide; Key Clb; Political Wkr; High Hon Roll; Hon Roll; NHS; Acadmc Achvt Socl Stud,Engl,Bio 83-85; Clsscs.

MC MURRAY, MELINDA; Frankfort-Schuyler Central HS; Frankfort, NY; (S); French Clb; GAA; Band; Jazz Band; Mrchg Band; School Musical; Rep Frsh Cls; Trs Soph Cls; Trs Jr Cls; JV Var Bsktbl; Ithaca Coll; Phy Thrpy.

MC MURRY, DANG; La Salle Acad; Brooklyn, NY; (S); 69/259; Am Leg Boys St; Ski Clb; Rep Soph Cls; Rep Sr Cls; JV Bsktbl; Var L Crs Cntry; Im Ftbl; Var Co-Capt Trk; Hon Roll; Acad All Am 83; Jr Acad Sci 84; U Notre Dame; Bus.

MC NAIR, SABRINA; Eli Whitney HS; Brooklyn, NY; (Y); 2/19; Church Yth Grp; Church Choir; Exec Sec.

MC NAIRN, NAOMI; North Rose-Wolcott HS; Rose, NY; (Y); Church Yth Grp; Intnl Clb; Band; Chorus; Church Choir; Off Stu Cncl; NHS; Glenn Tagg Awd 85; Regnts Schlrshp Alt 85; Home Ec Awd 81; Roberts Wesleyan Coll; Nrsng.

MC NALLY, ADAM; Fayetteville-Manlias HS; Manlius, NY; (Y); Band; Concert Band; Mrchg Band; Ftbl; Trk; Engl.

MC NALLY, KELLI; Earl L Vandermeulen HS; Pt Jefferson, NY; (Y); 1/300; Latin Clb; Mathletes; Chorus; School Musical; School Play; Stage Crew; High Hon Roll; NHS; Ntl Merit Ltr; Art Clb.

MC NALLY, MARK; South Side HS; Rockville Ctr, NY; (Y); Mathletes; Band; Concert Band; Mrchg Band; Pep Band; School Musical; School Play; Stage Crew; Cit Awd; Aerontcs.

MC NAMARA, KERRY; Saranac Lake HS; Saranac Lk, NY; (Y); 3/125; Quiz Bowl; JV Bsbl; JV Var Ftbl; JV Var Trk; Hon Roll; Jr NHS; NHS; Prfct Atten Awd; Marine Sci.

MC NAMARA, MICHAEL; Franciscan HS; Putnam Vly, NY; (Y); Boy Scts; School Play; Yrbk Stf; JV Bsktbl; Mgr(s); Score Keeper; Var Socr; Engrng.

MC NAMARA, SAMANTHA; Rome Free Acad; Rome, NY; (Y); Concert Band; Orch; Trs Frsh Cls; Var Sftbl; High Hon Roll; Jr NHS; Cntrl Oneida Lg All Star Sftbl Hon Men 84, 1st Tm 85; Mst Imprvd Plyr Sftbl Vrsty Tm 84 & 85; Pre-Dent.

MC NAMARA, SCOTT; Mayfield HS; Gloversville, NY; (Y); 7/76; Varsity Clb; Band; Mrchg Band; Pres Frsh Cls; Pres Soph Cls; Pres Jr Cls; Stu Cncl; JV Var Bsktbl; Var Crs Cntry; Var Trk; MVP V Track 85; Coaches Awd Bsktbl,Cross Cty 84-85; Civil Engrng.

MC NAMEE, KAREN; Webster HS; Webster, NY; (Y); Model UN; Hon Roll; Spanish NHS; U Of Buffalo; Phys Thrpy.

MC NAMEE, RONALD R; Grand Island SR HS; Gr Island, NY; (Y); Varsity Clb; Stage Crew; Variety Show; Var L Wrstlng; Grnd Islnd HS Athl Awd 84-85; Embry-Riddle Aerontcl U; Engrng.

MC NAUGHTON, STEVEN; South Glens Falls SR HS; Gansevoort, NY; (Y); 80/237; Hon Roll; Comp Sci.

MC NEAR, DIANA; Academy Of Mount Saint Ursula; Bronx, NY; (Y); Cmnty Wkr; Sec Dance Clb; Drama Clb; Girl Scts; Nwsp Rptr; Nwsp Stf; Var Trk; Hon Roll; Prfct Atten Awd; Trk Mdls & Awds 84; Pre-Vet Med.

MC NEIL, TRACYANN; Walton HS; Bronx, NY; (Y); Chorus; Church Choir; School Play; Hon Roll; Prfct Atten Awd 84-85; Mech Exec.

MC NEIL, TRICIA; Northern Adirondack Central School; Ellenburg Ctr, NY; (Y); Church Yth Grp; Band; Concert Band; Mrchg Band; Pep Band; Swmmng; High Hon Roll; Hon Roll; ST U Canton; Bus Admin.

MC NEILL, DINA; Valley Stream Central HS; Valley Stream, NY; (Y); Var L Bsktbl; Var L Sftbl; Var L Vllybl; Hon Roll; Jr NHS; NHS; Acctg.

MC NEILL, LAUREL; Newfield HS; Selden, NY; (Y); Camera Clb; Cmnty Wkr; Jr NHS; Acad Engl Awd 82-83; Psych.

MC NEILL, MARTIN; Walt Whitman HS; Huntington Stat, NY; (Y); 37/533; JV Lcrss; JV Socr; Var Trk; High Hon Roll; Hon Roll; Jr NHS; Prfct Atten Awd; Spanish NHS; All League Spring Trck 85; Aviation.

MC NEILL, ROBERT J; Newfield HS; Selden, NY; (Y); 36/543; Pres Chess Clb; VP Computer Clb; Hon Roll; Jr NHS; Cmnty Wkr; Drama Clb; Varsity Clb; School Play; Stage Crew; Fncng Tm 83-85; SUNY Binghamton; Prelaw.

MC NEILLY, ANTHONY W; Mt Upton Central HS; Mt Upton, NY; (Y); 1/23; Var Capt Bsktbl; High Hon Roll; NHS; Ntl Merit Schol; Rochester Inst Tech; Elec Engr.

MC NELIS, PATRICK; Commack H S North; East Northport, NY; (Y); Sec Trs MMM; Teachers Aide; Varsity Clb; Acpl Chr; Chorus; School Musical; School Play; Swing Chorus; Variety Show; Rep Frsh Cls; Engrng.

MC NERNEY, MICHAEL; Cathedral Prep; Rockaway Beach, NY; (Y); 1/30; Speech Tm; Mrchg Band; Yrbk Bus Mgr; Pres Frsh Cls; Off Jr NHS; Pres NHS; Principals List; Queens Coll Pres Awd Achvt 83-85; Law.

MC NERNEY, PATRICIA A; Saratoga Central Catholic HS; Ballston Spa, NY; (S); Drama Clb; Varsity Clb; School Play; Yrbk Stf; Bsktbl; Sftbl; Vllybl; NHS; Rotary Awd.

MC NISH, GLADYS; F D Roosevelt HS; Brooklyn, NY; (Y); Hosp Aide; Office Aide; Teachers Aide; Rep Jr Cls; Gym; Hon Roll; Prfct Atten Awd; 2nd Prz Lvl III Ntl Spnsh Exam 84; Phys Ftns Achvt Awd 83.

MC NULTY, CHRIS; Liverpool HS; Liverpool, NY; (Y); Rep Church Yth Grp; Cmnty Wkr; Hosp Aide; Red Cross Aide; Spanish Clb; School Musical; Trs Stu Cncl; Powder Puff Ftbl; Score Keeper; Vllybl; St Joseph Nrsng Schl; Nrsng.

MC NULTY, ERIN; Glens Falls SR HS; Glen Falls, NY; (Y); 4/237; AFS; Drama Clb; Chorus; Madrigals; Powder Puff Ftbl; High Hon Roll; NHS; Ntl Merit Ltr; School Musical; School Play; Outstndng Drma Clb 84; Outstndng Engl Stu 85; Rensselaer Polytech Inst RPI Mdl Math, Sci 85.

MC NULTY, KATHLEEN; Mercy HS; Albany, NY; (Y); Spanish Clb; Chorus; School Play; Stage Crew; Yrbk Stf; Rep Frsh Cls; High Hon Roll; Hon Roll; NHS; Physcl Sci & Eng Awds; Choir Awd & Honrry Alderman; Liturgy Commtt & Eucharistic Minister; Graphic Desgnr.

MC NULTY, LINDA; St Edmund HS; Brooklyn, NY; (S); 1/187; Pres Jr Cls; Var Cheerleading; Im Vllybl; Hon Roll; NHS; Prfct Atten Awd; NEMA Ntl Engl Merit Awd 85; Ntl Lang Arts Olympiad 83; Law.

MC NULTY, SHARON; The Mary Louis Acad; Forest Hills, NY; (Y); GAA; Library Aide; Red Cross Aide; Varsity Clb; JV Var Bsktbl; JV Var Vllybl; Hon Roll; NHS; NEDT Awd; Sprtssmnshp Awd Var Bsktbl 84-85.

MC PEAK IV, ASHLEY J; Fairport HS; Fairport, NY; (Y); Church Yth Grp; Math Clb; Ski Clb; Hon Roll; Regents Schlrshp 85; GA Inst Of Tech; Engrng.

MC PHERSON, LISA Y; La Guardia HS Of Music & The Arts; Bronx, NY; (Y); Church Yth Grp; Office Aide; Teachers Aide; Church Choir; Nwsp Stf; Yrbk Stf; Trk; Atten 83; Art 84; Archtctr.

MC POLIN, JENNIFER; St Joseph Acad; Lake Ronkonkoma, NY; (Y); Church Yth Grp; French Clb; Library Aide; Pep Clb; Chorus; Variety Show; VP Frsh Cls; Sec Stu Cncl; FHA; Service Clb; Frnch Imprvmnt & Efrt Awd 84; Frnch Excllnc Awd 85; Hugh O Brian Yth Ldrshp Sem 84; ISLI Ldrshp Sem 84; Fordham U; Law.

MC QUADE, PATRICK; Union Endicott HS; Endicott, NY; (Y); Bsbl; Ftbl; Golf; Cit Awd; Hstry Clb 85; SUNY System; Comp.

MC QUAIL, THOMAS; St Francis Prep; Middle Village, NY; (S); 67/693; Im Bsktbl; Im Ftbl; Var Trk; Im Vllybl; Hon Roll; Knights Of Columbus Schlrshp 82; Schlrshp St Francis Prep 82; Med.

MC QUICK, MICHAEL; Mount Saint Michael Acad; Bronx, NY; (Y); 66/310; Socr; Hon Roll; Mech Engrng.

MC QUILLAN, MICHAEL; St Johns Prep; Brooklyn, NY; (Y); 2nd Hnrs.

MC RAE, BRIAN; Walt Whitman HS; Huntington Stat, NY; (Y); Im Capt Bsktbl; Capt Im Lcrss; Im Socr; Hnrb Mntn Leage 85.

MC RAE, DENISE; John Dewey HS; Brooklyn, NY; (Y); Im Bowling; Im Sftbl; Im Vllybl; Im Wt Lftg; Hon Roll; Prfct Atten Awd; Hofstra U; Bus Adm.

MC RAE, ROZELA; Saint Catharine Acad; Bronx, NY; (Y); Church Yth Grp; Cmnty Wkr; Church Choir; Im Bsktbl; Cit Awd; Hon Roll; Vol Cmnty Svc Awd 85; Cornell U; Aeronautical Engrng.

MC ROBBIE, EMILY; Potsdam Central HS; Potsdam, NY; (Y); 9/120; Cmnty Wkr; French Clb; JA; Yrbk Stf; Sec Sr Cls; Stu Cncl; Cheerleading; High Hon Roll; Jr NHS; NHS; Natl Sci Merit Awd 84; Mst Imprvd Vllybl 84; Bio.

MC RUCKER, PATRINIA; Buffalo Traditional Schl; Buffalo, NY; (S); 3/130; Debate Tm; Intnl Clb; Spanish Clb; Band; Drill Tm; Mrchg Band; Yrbk Stf; Stu Cncl; NHS; 3rd SR Cls 84-85; Coll Prep Clb 84-85; GMI; Bus Admn.

MC SHAN, EDDIE; Fowler HS; Syracuse, NY; (Y); 20/350; Am Leg Boys St; Dance Clb; Teachers Aide; Nwsp Rptr; Pres Jr Cls; Pres Sr Cls; Capt Ftbl; Var Trk; Capt Wrstlng; Hon Roll; 1st Tm Rnng Back Lg 84; Hon Men Defnse Backer 83; Excllnt Prfrmnce Eng 85.

MC WHORTER, PAUL D; Argyle Central HS; Argyle, NY; (Y); 2/65; Boy Scts; VP French Clb; Math Tm; Ski Clb; Band; Chorus; Yrbk Ed-Chief; Rep Stu Cncl; Var Socr; Var Tennis; Comp Sci.

MC WILLIAMS, FLOYD W; De Sales Regional HS; Geneva, NY; (Y); 3/44; Church Yth Grp; Cmnty Wkr; Computer Clb; French Clb; Math Tm; Nwsp Ed-Chief; Ftbl; High Hon Roll; NHS; Ntl Merit SF; Soph Cls Hmcmng Princ 82; Comp Sci.

MC WITHEY, MICHAEL; J C Birdlebough HS; Fulton, NY; (Y); Church Yth Grp; Church Choir; Hon Roll; Resprtry Thrpst.

MEACHAM, LANA; George Washington HS; New York, NY; (Y); 56/315; Church Yth Grp; Computer Clb; Teachers Aide; Church Choir; Color Guard; Drill Tm; Variety Show; Hon Roll; Prfct Atten Awd; Manhattan Clg Smmr Schlrshp 84; Hnr Rll Abov 85 Ave 84-85; Comprhnsv Math & Sci Awd Engrng 84; NC Central U; Data Proc.

MEACHEM, MARK; Notre Dame Bishop Gibbons HS; Schenectady, NY; (S); 5/141; Rep Jr Cls; Var Bsktbl; Var Crs Cntry; Var Trk; High Hon Roll; NHS; Public Rltns.

MEAD, CYNTHIA A; The Nichols Schl; Buffalo, NY; (Y); 1/113; Trs AFS; Ski Clb; Var Fld Hcky; Var Lcrss; Hon Roll; Colgate U; Math.

MEAD, KATHY; Weedsport Central Schl; Weedsport, NY; (Y); 3/65; Am Leg Aux Girls St; Sec Church Yth Grp; Concert Band; Mrchg Band; School Play; Yrbk Ed-Chief; Sec Sr Cls; DAR Awd; High Hon Roll; Trs NHS; Alumni Assn & NYS Rgnts Schlrshps 85; SUNY-ALBANY; Crmnl Justice.

MEAD, LAURA L; Rome Free Acad; Rome, NY; (Y); 207/478; Church Yth Grp; Intnl Clb; Letterman Clb; Teachers Aide; Varsity Clb; Var Capt Bsktbl; Im Coach Actv; JV Var Sftbl; Hon Roll; Office Aide; Methdst Coll; Phy Ed.

MEADE, DEBORAH L; Churchville-Chili HS; North Chili, NY; (Y); 9/304; Church Yth Grp; Sec Chorus; School Musical; Swing Chorus; Lit Mag; Stu Cncl; Crs Cntry; NHS; Rochester Philhrmnc Devrn Awd Rnnr Up 85; Rochester Inst Of Tech; Math.

MEAGHER, SEAN; Onteora Central HS; West Hurley, NY; (S); 20/225; Am Leg Boys St; Boy Scts; Math Tm; Ski Clb; JV Var Socr; JV Trk; High Hon Roll; NHS; Cert Excllnce Sci; USAF Acad; Engrng.

MEAGLEY III, NORMAN C; Unatego JR SR HS; Otego, NY; (Y); Church Yth Grp; VICA; Chorus; Church Choir; School Musical; School Play; 4-H Awd; Hon Roll; Prfct Atten Awd; Foods ST Conf Awd 85; Drama Clb Awd 83; Bus.

MEAKENS, KAREN D; Bronx HS Of Sci; New Rochelle, NY; (Y); JA; Church Choir; Lit Mag; Regnts Schlrshp 85; Joseph Curron Ntl Un 85; Howard U; Bus Adm.

MEANEY, JAMES; Tully Central Schl; Apolia Sta, NY; (Y); Church Yth Grp; German Clb; Spanish Clb; Yrbk Stf; JV Score Keeper; Hon Roll; Journlsm.

MEANS, LINDA; Union Endicott HS; Endicott, NY; (Y); 54/450; Church Yth Grp; Rep Jr Cls; Rep Stu Cncl; Var Cheerleading; Var Gym; Hon Roll; NY ST U; Bus Admin.

MEASER, JOE; De Pew HS; Depew, NY; (Y); 16/254; Camera Clb; Cmnty Wkr; Political Wkr; VP Soph Cls; VP Jr Cls; Rep Stu Cncl; Mgr Ftbl; Mgr(s); Mgr Trk; Elks Awd; NYS Elks Awd; Schl Ntl Hnr Soc Schlrshp; Eagles Serv Awd; RIT; Comp Engrng.

MECCA, MICHELE; Bethlehem Central HS; Delmar, NY; (Y); 27/312; GAA; Hosp Aide; Trs Key Clb; Rep Stu Cncl; JV Cheerleading; JV Capt Fld Hcky; High Hon Roll; NHS; Bus Admin.

MECCA, STACY; Bethpage HS; Plainview, NY; (Y); Spanish Clb; Farmingdale ST U; Bus.

MECI, SEAN G; Newfield HS; Selden, NY; (Y); 95/549; Church Yth Grp; Cmnty Wkr; Political Wkr; Band; Chorus; Concert Band; Drm Mjr(t); Jazz Band; Mrchg Band; Orch; All ST Band 83-84; All Cntry Band & Orchst 82-84; Intst Wind Ensmbl 84-85; New England Consvtry; Music.

MECOZZI, CHRISTINE M; Frontier SR HS; Blasdell, NY; (Y); Sec Pres Church Yth Grp; Drama Clb; Spanish Clb; Church Choir; Superior Rating In TNT For Yth Grp At Ne Area Comp 84; Bethany Bible Coll; Engl.

MEDDAUGH, NANCY; Sutherland-Sutherland HS; Pittsford, NY; (Y); French Clb; JA; Crs Cntry; Trk; Exch Stu Teenage Diplomat Abroad Avignon France 85; Rochester Inst Of Tech; Bus.

MEDICH, DAVID; South Side HS; Rockville Ctr, NY; (Y); Art Clb; Boy Scts; VP Computer Clb; Drama Clb; Model UN; Madrigals; Hon Roll; Sci Fair Blue Rbbn 85; Union Coll; Comp Sci.

MEDICI, CHRIS; Monsignor Mc Clancy HS; Woodside, NY; (Y); Cmnty Wkr; Political Wkr; Nwsp Stf; Yrbk Stf; Rep Frsh Cls; Rep Soph Cls; Pres Jr Cls; Rep Stu Cncl; Cit Awd; High Hon Roll; Gld Mdl Music Tchrs Assn 84; Slvr Mdl Sci Fair 85; Hnrbl Ment Trk, Fld Day 82; St Johns U; Intl Rel.

MEDICO, COSMO; Cicero-North-Syracuse HS; Mattydale, NY; (S); 100/622; Church Yth Grp; Exploring; JA; Socr; High Hon Roll; Hon Roll; Alfred; Engrng.

MEDINA, ALFREDO; A E Smith HS; Bronx, NY; (S); 2/226; Cmnty Wkr; Varsity Clb; Off Sr Cls; Stu Cncl; Wt Lftg; High Hon Roll; Hon Roll; NHS; Prfct Atten Awd; Sal; Sci Awd 80; Baurch; Bus Admin.

MEDINA, CARMEN; Beacon HS; Beacon, NY; (Y); 39/206; Drama Clb; Latin Clb; Library Aide; Varsity Clb; Chorus; School Play; Nwsp Phtg; Nwsp Rptr; Cheerleading; Optmtry.

MEDINA, CAROLANN; Minisink Valley HS; Westtown, NY; (Y); Chorus; High Hon Roll; Hon Roll; Music.

MEDINA, GILBERT; Christopher Columbus HS; Bronx, NY; (Y); Aud/Vis; Stage Crew; TV Prodctn Awd 83; Cmmnctns.

MEDINA, MARK; Peru JR-SR HS; Peru, NY; (Y); 6/185; Model UN; Var L Bsbl; JV Bsktbl; High Hon Roll; NHS; Ntl Merit Ltr; St Schlr; Pres Natl Hnr Socy 84-85; NYS Regnts Schlrshp 85; Biophyscs.

MEDINA, MICHELLE; Christopher Columbus HS; Bronx, NY; (Y); Key Clb; Library Aide; High Hon Roll; Hon Roll; Cert Of Merit Bio 84; Cert Of Academic Achvmnt Amer Hstry 1 85; Cert Of Merit Sci Resrch 85; Vet.

MEDINA, RICHARD; Cardinal Spellman HS; Bronx, NY; (Y); 123/550; Bsktbl; JV Var Ftbl; Var Mgr(s); Var Trk; Hon Roll; Aviatn.

MEDINA, ROSEANNE; Saint John The Baptist D HS; Brentwood, NY; (Y); Hosp Aide; JV Bsktbl; Var Capt Vllybl; Spanish NHS; Accntng.

MEDLEY, MICHAEL; Weedsport JR SR HS; Weedsport, NY; (Y); 4-H; French Clb; Intnl Clb; Spanish Clb; Bsktbl; High Hon Roll; NHS; Frnch Cert Mrt 85; Anne Sholes Memrl Awd Prfct Scr Math Regnts 83; Cornell U; Sci.

MEDNICK, RHONDA; Ramapo SR HS; Suffern, NY; (Y); VP Cmnty Wkr; Pres Temple Yth Grp; Band; Off Soph Cls; Off Jr Cls; French Hon Soc; Hon Roll; Jr NHS; Mu Alp Tht; NHS; Yth Of Yr Awd 85; Serv Awd 85; Phy Thrpy.

MEDWID, WILLIAM J; Alden Central HS; Alden, NY; (Y); 31/209; AFS; Church Yth Grp; French Clb; Letterman Clb; Science Clb; Thesps; Band; Chorus; Concert Band; School Musical; Frnch Clb Schlrshp 85; Radiolgst.

MEEHAN, AUSTIN; St Marys HS; Glen Cove, NY; (Y); NYS Rgnts Schlrshp 85; Villanova U.

MEEHAN, JAMES; South Side HS; Rockville Ctr, NY; (Y); Boy Scts; Computer Clb; Mathletes; Yrbk Phtg; Var Crs Cntry; Var Trk.

MEEHAN, MIKE; E L Vandermeulen HS; Mt Sinai, NY; (Y); 29/290; FBLA; Leo Clb; Mathletes; Varsity Clb; Chorus; Yrbk Stf; JV Crs Cntry; JV Var Ftbl; JV Gym; Im Lcrss; 3rd Pl Math; Boston Coll; Pre-Med.

MEEHAN, PAUL H; Smithtown East; Nesconset, NY; (Y); Computer Clb; French Clb; Math Tm; Radio Clb; Ski Clb; French Hon Soc; High Hon Roll; NHS; Cornell U; Elect Engrng.

MEEK, JOE ANN; Odessa-Montour Central Schl; Montour Falls, NY; (Y); FHA; Teachers Aide; Cheerleading; Mgr(s); Score Keeper; Sftbl; Trk; Hon Roll; Pres FHA 83-84; Mst Imprvd Chrldng Awd 83-84; Sec Future Sec Of Amer 84-85; Bus.

MEEKER, CINDY; Lansing HS; King Ferry, NY; (Y); Drama Clb; Spanish Clb; Chorus; School Musical; Nwsp Ed-Chief; Tennis; Cit Awd; Hon Roll; Lion Awd; NHS; Spnsh Acadmc Awd 83-84; SUNY Buffalo; Intl Rltns.

MEEKS JR, REGINALD; Mynderse Acad; Seneca Falls, NY; (S); 20/140; Var JV Bsbl; JV Bsktbl; Var Bowling; High Hon Roll; Var Bsbl 84; High Hnr Roll 82-84; J V Bsktbl 83; Clarkson Coll; Engrng.

MEERS, CARLEEN; Mercy HS; Sag Harbor, NY; (Y); Cmnty Wkr; Drama Clb; VP GAA; Ski Clb; Varsity Clb; School Play; Rep Sr Cls; Bsktbl; Coach Actv; Var Sftbl; March Dimes Dstngshd Stu Hlth Awd 85; SUNY Geneseo; Preschl Sp Ed.

MEESE, CRAIG; Foxlane HS; Bedford, NY; (Y); 65/300; Band; Concert Band; Jazz Band; Mrchg Band; Orch; Pep Band; Pres Frsh Cls; Var Bsktbl; Var Golf; Ice Hcky.

MEESE, DAVID; Charles H Roth HS; Rush, NY; (Y); Church Yth Grp; Varsity Clb; JV Bsbl; JV Bsktbl; High Hon Roll; NHS; Prfct Atten Awd; Boy Scts; L Crs Cntry; Hon Roll; Rank Eagle BSA 85; Henrietta Yth Hall Fame 85; Prin Svc Awd 85; Rochester Inst Tech; Drftng.

MEGHJI, SHABNAM; Hillcrest HS; Elmhurst, NY; (Y); 4/750; Cmnty Wkr; Computer Clb; Debate Tm; French Clb; Hosp Aide; Library Aide; Math Clb; Math Tm; Science Clb; Teachers Aide; 1st Prz Queensboro Sci Fair 84; Johnson Nuclear Med Awd 84; Best Rsrch Prj Of Yr 84; Med.

MEGLIORE, MARK; Geneseo Central HS; Geneseo, NY; (Y); 22/100; Ski Clb; Spanish Clb; Band; Chorus; Yrbk Stf; Bsbl; Bsktbl; SUNY-GENESEO; Elem Ed.

MEGNA, CHRISTINE; Smithtown H S West; Smithtown, NY; (Y); Yrbk Stf; Rep Frsh Cls; Rep Soph Cls; High Hon Roll; Jr NHS; NHS; Italian NHS VP 83-86; Var Ltr Competitive Kickline 83-86.

MEGNA, ROSALIE; Commack High School South; Commack, NY; (Y); Cmnty Wkr; Hosp Aide; Pres Soph Cls; VP Jr Cls; Pres Sr Cls; Stu Cncl; JV Sftbl; High Hon Roll; NHS.

MEHL, RICHARD; W C Mepham HS; N Bellmore, NY; (Y); Am Leg Boys St; Boy Scts; Math Tm; Science Clb; Var Socr; Var L Wrstlng; Cit Awd; God Cntry Awd; Hon Roll; Natl Sci Olympd 4th Pl Chem 85; Pres Phys Fit Awd 85; VP Ci Tm 85; UMI; Comp Engrng.

MEHLENBACHER, RANDY C; Wayland Central HS; Wayland, NY; (Y); Am Leg Boys St; Chess Clb; Trs FFA; Ski Clb; Varsity Clb; Capt Crs Cntry; Var Mgr(s); Var Trk; Engrng.

MEHLMAN, TANYA; Stissing Mountian JR SR HS; Ancramdale, NY; (Y); Church Yth Grp; Church Choir; Variety Show; Yrbk Stf; VP Frsh Cls; VP Soph Cls; Stat Ftbl; NCTE Awd; Natl Engl Merit Awd 84; Nrsg.

MEHR, MICHAEL; Spring Valley S HS; Spring Vly, NY; (Y); Computer Clb; Key Clb; Ski Clb; Trs Temple Yth Grp; Band; Concert Band; Jazz Band; Mrchg Band; Orch; Stu Cncl; Arch.

MEHRDAD, HAMID; Barker Central HS; Gasport, NY; (Y); AFS; 4-H; JV Bsktbl; 4-H Awd; Hon Roll; SUNY; Med.

MEHTA, INDIRA; Forest Hills HS; Forest Hills, NY; (Y); 16/881; Sec Exploring; Sec Intnl Clb; Office Aide; Science Clb; High Hon Roll; Jr NHS; Prfct Atten Awd; Phys Fit Achvt Awd 84; Queens Sci Fair 1st, 3rd Pl 83-84; Queens Coll Pres Achvt Awd 83.

MEHTA, PARASTU S; Jamesville-De Witt HS; De Witt, NY; (Y); 8/228; French Clb; Girl Scts; Co-Capt Math Tm; Model UN; Yrbk Ed-Chief; Var Socr; VP NHS; Ntl Merit Ltr; JA; NY ST Regents Schlrshp 85; Cornell U Book Awd 84; Colgate Alumni Memorial Schlrshp 85; Colgate U.

MEI, FEN; Cararsie HS; Brooklyn, NY; (Y); 43/560; Clthng & Math 82; Rgnts Schlrshp 84; NY U; Engr.

MEIER, ELISE; Frontier Central HS; Hamburg, NY; (S); French Clb; Hosp Aide; Var Frsh Cls; Soph Cls; Jr Cls; Stu Cncl; High Hon Roll; Hon Roll; NHS; Prfct Atten Awd; Buffalo ST Coll; Bus.

MEIER, GERDA I; Kingston HS; Rifton, NY; (Y); 63/511; Church Yth Grp; Cmnty Wkr; Drama Clb; German Clb; Latin Clb; Church Choir; Orch; High Hon Roll; Hon Roll; Jr NHS; Presidential Physical Fitness Awd 85; German Honor Society Awd 82; Achvt Social Studies 82; Albany Medical Center; Rn.

MEIER, STEPHANIE; Holy Trinity Diocesan HS; Hicksville, NY; (S); 35/362; Math Clb; Yrbk Stf; Off Frsh Cls; Rep Soph Cls; Off Jr Cls; Rep Sr Cls; Stu Cncl; Var Cheerleading; Hon Roll; Jr NHS; Treas Of Ntl Hnr Soc 84-85; Employee Of Mnth 84; Co-Chair Bld Dr 84-85; Educ.

MEILAK, FRANK J; La Salle Acad; New York City, NY; (S); 3/21; Im Ice Hcky; Cardinal Hayes Hnr Soc 84; Engr Aero.

MEILIKEN, LISA S; Fox Lane HS; Bedford, NY; (Y); 11/300; Mathletes; Political Wkr; Ski Clb; Yrbk Ed-Chief; Stat Bsbl; High Hon Roll; NHS; Columbia U Sci Hnrs Pgm 84-85; U Of Rochester; Bio.

MEILINGER, CHRISTOP S; Northville Central HS; Northville, NY; (Y); Ski Clb; Band; Concert Band; Mrchg Band; Pep Band; School Play; Trk; NEDT Awd; Natl Educ Dev Test Hgh Achvt Bio 83; Band Awd 83; Ithaca Coll; Brdcstng.

MEINARDUS, MICHAEL C; Copiague SR HS; Copiague, NY; (Y); 21/349; DECA; FBLA; Variety Show; Var Capt Bowling; JV Var Ftbl; High Hon Roll; Pres Schlr; Pres Schlrshp U Of Tampa 85; C W Post 85; U Of Tampa; Mktng.

MEISENHEIMER, RICHARD J; Ward Melville HS; Setauket, NY; (Y); 77/730; Church Yth Grp; Im Fld Hcky; JV Ftbl; Im Socr; Im Sftbl; JV Trk; Im Wt Lftg; High Hon Roll; Hon Roll; NHS; Math.

MEISSNER, ELIZABETH; Buffalo Traditional Schl; Buffalo, NY; (S); 14/250; Church Yth Grp; School Play; Pres Frsh Cls; VP Soph Cls; Score Keeper; Swmmng; Vllybl; Hon Roll; NHS; Brigham Young U; Pre Law.

MEISTER, JEFFREY; Buffalo Traditional Schl; Buffalo, NY; (S); 6/123; French Clb; Pres Band; Chorus; Concert Band; Jazz Band; Mrchg Band; Yrbk Stf; Trs Jr Cls; Trs Sr Cls; Ice Hcky; Comm.

MEJIA, MICHELLE; Bishop Ford C C HS; Brooklyn, NY; (Y); 16/449; Girl Scts; Math Tm; Science Clb; Rep Stu Cncl; Bowling; Tennis; Hon Roll; NHS; Bishop Ford Schlrshp 84-85.

MEJIA, NORMAN; Xavier HS; New York, NY; (Y); 24/250; Intnl Clb; ROTC; Spanish Clb; Varsity Clb; Color Guard; Yrbk Stf; Sec Frsh Cls; Rep Sr Cls; Rep Stu Cncl; JV Var Bsbl; Fordham U; Law.

MEJIA, RAYSA; Mount Vernon HS; Mt Vernon, NY; (Y); 481/648; Art Clb; Dance Clb; Office Aide; Spanish Clb; School Play; High Hon Roll; Hon Roll; Ntl Merit Ltr; Natl Merit Ltr 85; Westchester Bus Schl; ADS.

MEKARSKI, MELISSA L; Cheektowaga Central HS; Cheektowaga, NY; (Y); 11/204; Church Yth Grp; Pres JA; Hst JCL; Hst Latin Clb; Teachers Aide; Band; High Hon Roll; NHS; Ntl Merit Schol; Pres Schlr; U Of Buffalo; Sci Tchr.

MELAHRIS, FAY; Earl L Vandermeulen HS; Pt Jefferson, NY; (Y); 38/295; FBLA; Hon Roll; SUNY Stony Brook; Pre-Law.

MELCHER, MARC L; Horace Greeley HS; Mt Kisco, NY; (Y); 4/272; Debate Tm; Math Tm; Nwsp Bus Mgr; Nwsp Rptr; Var Capt Crs Cntry; Var L Trk; Ntl Merit SF; Cert Merit Sup Achvt Math Leag 84.

MELENDEZ, ANTONIO; De Witt Clinton HS; Bronx, NY; (Y); Math Tm; JV Bsbl; High Hon Roll; Hon Roll; Jr NHS; NHS; Marlane Ellen Nussbaum Mem Awd 83; Fclty Achvt 83; Aviatn.

MELENDEZ, DAMARIS; Immaculata HS; New York, NY; (Y); Church Yth Grp; Chorus; Bsktbl; Bowling; Cheerleading; Sftbl; Vllybl.

MELENDEZ, GINA LYNN; Doughkeepsie HS; Poughkeepsie, NY; (Y); AFS; School Musical; Yrbk Stf; Stat Sftbl; Hon Roll; Prfct Atten Awd; Hmrm Perf Atten Chapms Awd 85; Mgr Sftbl 85; V Athl Awd; Bus.

MELENDEZ, JOSEPHINE; Clara Barton HS For Health Professi; Bronx, NY; (Y); Cmnty Wkr; Office Aide; Var Bsktbl; Med.

MELENDEZ, MAGNO; Sarah J Hale HS; Brooklyn, NY; (Y); 13/268; Computer Clb; Trk; Hon Roll; Prfct Atten Awd; Rgnts Schlrshp 85; Queensborough CC; Comp Tech.

MELENDEZ, MARIA; Monsignor Scanlan HS; Bronx, NY; (Y); #53 In Class; Acpl Chr; School Play; Cheerleading; Gym; Hon Roll; NHS; Serra Clb Of Brnx 82; Top 10% Rnk 82-83; Hofstra Coll; Nrsng.

MELENDEZ, MICHAEL; Bishop Ford C C HS; Brooklyn, NY; (Y); Im Bsktbl; Im Bowling; Im Ftbl; Second Honrs 84 & 85; Math.

MELENDEZ, SAMUEL; Richmond HS; Hollis, NY; (Y); 13/298; Church Yth Grp; Office Aide; Teachers Aide; Band; High Hon Roll; Hon Roll; Jr NHS; NHS; Voice Dem Awd; Regnts Schlrshp 85; Baruch Coll; Accntg.

MELFI, JAMES A; Moore Catholic HS; Staten Island, NY; (Y); Bowling; Engrng.

MELFI, PATRICIA; Jordan-Elbridge HS; Elbridge, NY; (Y); 5/130; Stage Crew; Yrbk Ed-Chief; Yrbk Phtg; VP Jr Cls; Rep Stu Cncl; Var Capt Bsktbl; Var Capt Sftbl; Cit Awd; High Hon Roll; NHS; Ithaca Acad Scholar, Grace Howard Awd, Tchrs Assn Awd 85; MVP & All Regn Awd Bsktbl & Socr 83-85; Ithaca; Comm.

MELFI, PATRICK; Bishop Cunningham HS; Oswego, NY; (Y); Yrbk Sprt Ed; JV Var Bsbl; JV Bsktbl; Var Ftbl; Var Golf; Im Wt Lftg; High Hon Roll; Trs NHS.

MELIDONA, ANNA; Niagara Catholic HS; Niagara Falls, NY; (Y); 2/79; Hosp Aide; JA; Pres VP Key Clb; Yrbk Stf; Sec Frsh Cls; Sec Stu Cncl; Bausch & Lomb Sci Awd; High Hon Roll; NHS; Sal; Kiwns Schlrshp 85; Excllnc-Engl, Scl Stds & Spnsh 85; Wdmn Wrld Awd-Prfcncy Am Hstry 85; Suny Coll Geneseo; Eco.

MELITO, LAURA; Albertus Magnus HS; Garnerville, NY; (Y); Church Yth Grp; Library Aide; Ramapo Coll; Bus Admin.

MELITO, PHYLLIS; North Salem HS; N Salem, NY; (Y); 7/84; Church Yth Grp; Concert Band; Yrbk Stf; Sec Stu Cncl; Var Capt Cheerleading; Var Capt Tennis; Var Trk; High Hon Roll; NHS; PTO Scholar; Natl Hnr Soc Scholar; Kenneth Bailey Music Scholar; Coll Of Mt Vincent; Mth.

MELKONIAN, KARIN; Garden City HS; Garden City, NY; (Y); 43/355; Church Yth Grp; Band; Church Choir; Mrchg Band; Badmtn; Tennis; High Hon Roll; Hon Roll; Jr NHS; NHS; All Confrnce Tens Plyr 84; Most Vlble Badmntn Plyr 85; Natl Hnr Soc 85; Med.

MELKONIAN, PETER S; Garden City HS; Garden City, NY; (Y); 102/355; Boy Scts; Key Clb; Concert Band; Mrchg Band; JV Socr; Var Wrstlng; Hon Roll; Jr NHS; Bus Mgmt.

MELLA, GIUSEPPINA; Eastchester HS; Eastchester, NY; (Y); 13/163; Key Clb; Spanish Clb; Varsity Clb; Chorus; Co-Capt Socr; High Hon Roll; Hon Roll; NHS; Spanish NHS; Manhattan Coll; Engrng.

MELLEN, ANDREW; Thousand Islands HS; Chaumont, NY; (Y); Band; School Play; JV Var Bsbl; Jr NHS; NHS; Elmira Key Awd 85; Comp Sci.

MELLEN, BRIAN; Binghamton HS; Binghamton, NY; (Y); Pres Exploring; Hon Roll; Elec Engrng.

MELLENGER, DAVID; St Josephs Collegiate Inst; Amherst, NY; (Y); 45/200; Cmnty Wkr; Yrbk Stf; Stat Bsktbl; Crs Cntry; Stat Socr; Hon Roll; Business Administration.

MELLI, GINA; Curtis HS; Staten Island, NY; (Y); Variety Show; Cheerleading; Englsh.

MELLIEON, LISA; Bishop Loughlin HS; Brooklyn, NY; (Y); Yrbk Stf; Rep Sr Cls; Cheerleading; Hon Roll; NHS; Law.

MELLON, ANDREA; West Valley HS; W Valley, NY; (Y); 5/45; Trs Drama Clb; VP Band; Chorus; Concert Band; Drm Mjr(t); Capt Socr; Capt Sftbl; Capt Vllybl; Hon Roll; Pres NHS; Alum Schlrhsp 85; Regents Schlrshp 84; Girls Athlt Awd 85; Gannon U; Pre-Med.

MELLON JR, WAYNE H; Cicero-North Syracuse HS; North Syracuse, NY; (S); 57/711; Church Choir; Church Yth Grp; Exploring; Bowling; Score Keeper; Hon Roll; VFW Awd; Voice Dem Awd; Corp Lawyer.

MELLOR, KIRSTEN; Fox Lane HS; Mt Kisco, NY; (Y); 17/300; Trs Sec AFS; Drama Clb; Chorus; Madrigals; Yrbk Phtg; Lit Mag; Rep Stu Cncl; JV Lcrss; High Hon Roll; Ntl Merit SF; Brown U Almn Clb Bk Awd Engrng 85; Solo Schl Music Cncrt 85; Electd Pres Natl Hnr Socty 85-86; Phlsphy.

MELLYNCHUK, MARK; Wantagh HS; Wantagh, NY; (Y); JV Lcrss; JV Socr; High Hon Roll; Hon Roll; NHS; Ntl Merit Ltr; Pub Rel.

MELNIK, CHRISTINE K; Harborfields HS; Huntington, NY; (Y); 25/335; Concert Band; Mrchg Band; High Hon Roll; NHS; Excel Bio Awd; Regnts Schlrshp; Pres Acad Ftns Awd; VA Polytech Inst; Vet.

MELNYK, KRISTEN; Schalmont HS; Schenectady, NY; (Y); 3/190; Hosp Aide; Color Guard; Rep Stu Cncl; Var Capt Trk; Var Vllybl; DECA; Hon Roll; Rep NHS; Prfct Atten Awd; Elmira Coll Key Awd 85; Pre-Med.

MELOMO, ANTHONY; Smithtown HS East; Nesconset, NY; (Y); 120/610; Church Yth Grp; Band; Jazz Band; Mrchg Band; JV Var Lcrss; JV Trk; High Hon Roll; Hon Roll; Egl Sct 83.

MELORE, DANIEL ROBERT; Smithtown East HS; Nesconset, NY; (Y); Var L Bsbl; Itln Hnr Soc 84-85; Engrng.

MELTER, VANESSA; Southampton HS; Southampton, NY; (Y); 15/108; Drama Clb; Band; School Play; Adelphi U; Cmnctns.

MELTZER, BRIAN; Deer Park HS; Deer Park, NY; (Y); 2/457; Band; Orch; School Play; Variety Show; Nwsp Ed-Chief; Bausch & Lomb Sci Awd; NHS; Ntl Merit Ltr; Pres Schlr; Sal; U NY; Physcn.

MELTZER, DOUGLAS L; New Rochelle HS; New Rochelle, NY; (Y); 53/600; Ski Clb; Ed Nwsp Phtg; Ed Yrbk Phtg; Rep Sr Cls; Var Mgr(s); NHS; Ntl Merit SF; Hon Roll; Italian Exch; Model Congress.

MELTZER, MARNA; Jamesville De Witt HS; Dewitt, NY; (Y); Cmnty Wkr; Dance Clb; Model UN; Pep Clb; Political Wkr; Spanish Clb; Temple Yth Grp; Chorus; High Hon Roll; Hon Roll; Hon Grad Rabbi Jacob Epstein Schl 85; 5 Yr Prftc Atten Awd-Gronau Danc Studio 83; Syracuse U; Advt.

MELVILLE, MARGARET; Corinth Central HS; Corinth, NY; (S); 1/93; Trs MMM; Band; Chorus; Jazz Band; Cit Awd; French Hon Soc; High Hon Roll; Pres NHS; Natl Merit Schlrshp Letter Of Commendation 84; Colgate; Science.

MELVIN, LEIGH ANN; Commack High School South; Commack, NY; (Y); Church Yth Grp; Spanish Clb; Var Badmtn; JV Tennis; High Hon Roll; NHS; 6th Pl Natl Sci Olympd 85; For Lang.

MELVIN, ROBERT J; Minisink Valley Central HS; Slate Hill, NY; (Y); Boy Scts; Varsity Clb; Rep Jr Cls; JV Bsbl; Var Capt Ftbl; Var Capt Trk; Var Wrstlng; High Hon Roll; Hon Roll.

MELZER, CLAIRE; Emma Willard Schl; Troy, NY; (Y); Church Yth Grp; Cmnty Wkr; Debate Tm; Math Tm; Yrbk Stf; Ed Lit Mag; Im Sftbl; Gov Hon Prg Awd; Yth Of Mnth Awd 83; Arch.

MEMMOTT, MARY E; Archibishop Walsh HS; Olean, NY; (Y); 1/66; French Clb; Pres Math Clb; Math Tm; Yrbk Ed-Chief; Bausch & Lomb Sci Awd; High Hon Roll; NCTE Awd; NHS; Ntl Merit Schol; Val; Brown U.

MEMON, PETER; Monsignor Farrell HS; Staten Island, NY; (Y); 53/295; Computer Clb; Bsktbl; Ftbl; Hon Roll; NHS; St Schlr; RPI Schlrshp 85; Syracuse U Schlrshp 85; Rgnts Schlrshp 85; Rensselaeu Plly Tech; Chem Engr.

MENA, VERONICA; Sacred Heart HS; Hasting-On-Hudson, NY; (S); 25/241; Drama Clb; Hosp Aide; Intnl Clb; Library Aide; School Musical; Nwsp Rptr; Hon Roll; NHS; Nrsng.

MENAGER, GUSTAVE; Springfield Gardens HS; Cambria Hgts, NY; (Y); Art Clb; Office Aide; Im Bsktbl; Im Vllybl; Comp Sci.

MENCHEN, DENISE MICHELE; Westlake HS; Hawthorne, NY; (Y); Model UN; VP Pres Thesps; Lit Mag; High Hon Roll; Cmnty Wkr; Drama Clb; French Clb; Hosp Aide; Chorus; School Musical; Hofstra U; Bio.

MENDELJOHN, JOSEPH; Nickayuna HS; Schenectady, NY; (Y); Boy Scts; French Clb; L JV Socr; JV Trk; Hnrb Mntn Sect II Socr 84; Bus Comp.

MENDELOW, RANDI; John F Kennedy HS; Merrick, NY; (Y); 9/380; Key Clb; Political Wkr; Yrbk Stf; Hon Roll; Sec NHS; Pres Acad Fitnss Awd 85; Cert Of Hon NYS Bar Assoc 85; Cornell; Law.

MENDEZ, CLAUDIA; Clara Barton HS; Brooklyn, NY; (Y); Church Yth Grp; Cmnty Wkr; Hosp Aide; Teachers Aide; Hon Roll; Prfct Atten Awd; Math & Sci Rsrch Achvt Awds 84; Pre-Med.

MENDEZ, ELIZABETH; Cathedral HS; Queens, NY; (Y); Church Yth Grp; Hosp Aide; Intnl Clb; Band; Chorus; Church Choir; Vllybl; High Hon Roll; 2nd Hnrs; Voluntr Serv/Candy Stripper Awd; Hunter Coll.

MENDEZ, IRMA; John Dewey HS; Brooklyn, NY; (Y); Dance Clb; Chorus; School Musical; Pres Frsh Cls; Bsbl; Sftbl; Vllybl; Wt Lftg; Hon Roll; Crmnl Jstc.

MENDEZ, MARTHA; Cardinal Spellman HS; Bronx, NY; (Y); 1/750; Dance Clb; Science Clb; Spanish Clb; Nwsp Stf; Hon Roll; NHS; NEDT Awd; Cert Apprctn Proj Hnds Handcppd 84 & 85; Psych.

MENDEZ, SANDRA; Fashion Industries HS; Brooklyn, NY; (Y); Church Yth Grp; Cmnty Wkr; Office Aide; Chorus; Hon Roll; Prfct Atten Awd; Kingsborough CC; Trvl.

MENDOLA, STEPHEN L; Mc Quaid Jesuit HS; Pittsford, NY; (Y); 14/184; Debate Tm; JA; Model UN; Red Cross Aide; Yrbk Ed-Chief; Ftbl; Socr; Trk; Var Capt Vllybl; High Hon Roll; Schlrshps-NY ST Rgnts & St John Fshr Coll Pres Schlrshp 85; Gannett Yth Cares Awd 84; Colgate U; Lbrl Arts.

MENDONCA, PATRICK; Franklyn D Roosvelt HS; New York, NY; (Y); 30/357; Library Aide; Math Clb; Math Tm; Office Aide; ROTC; Rep Sr Cls; Ftbl; Tennis; Trk; Vllybl; Brooklyn Coll; Engrng.

MENDOZA, MOISES; La Salle Acad; New York, NY; (S); Boy Scts; Math Clb; Yrbk Stf; Rep Soph Cls; Bsktbl; Hon Roll; NY Inst Of Tech; Comp Sci.

MENDOZA, ORLANDO; Christopher Columbus HS; Bronx, NY; (Y); Aud/Vis; Bsbl; Bsktbl; Ftbl; Elctrnc Engrng.

MENDOZA, ZORAIDA; Eli Whitney Voc HS; Brooklyn, NY; (S); English Clb; Math Clb; Office Aide; Science Clb; Teachers Aide; VP Soph Cls; High Hon Roll; Hon Roll; NHS; Ride Of Yankees Awd 84; Elec Engr.

MENDRYSA, SUSAN M; Lackawanna SR HS; Lackawanna, NY; (Y); 3/283; Ski Clb; Spanish Clb; Var Socr; Var Tennis; Var Vllybl; Ntl Merit Ltr; Lackwnna Tchrs Fed 85; Cornl Tradtl Fres Flwshp 85; Cornell U; Bio.

MENECH, DARCY; Bishop Scully HS; Amsterdam, NY; (Y); 21/60; Political Wkr; Spanish Clb; Var Swmmng; Hon Roll; Yth Govt Day 85; Spec Creatv Wrtg Clss; Albany Business Coll; Bus Adm.

MENGE, JAMES; Mayfield JR SR HS; Mayfield, NY; (Y); Var JV Bowling; Air Force; Pilot.

MENIHAN, DAVID M; Cardinal Spellman HS; Bronx, NY; (Y); 161/568; Computer Clb; High Hon Roll; Hon Roll; Regents Schlrshp 85; Iona Coll; Bus.

MENNELLA, DENNIS; Saugerties HS; Saugerties, NY; (Y); 46/236; JA; Math Tm; Ski Clb; Band; Mrchg Band; Var JV Ftbl; Var Trk; Im Vllybl; High Hon Roll; NHS; Palmer Coll; Chriro.

MENNELLA, STEVEN; West Hampton Beach HS; E Quogue, NY; (Y); 30/201; Var Ftbl; JV Trk; Var Wrstlng; NHS; Psychatry.

MENNINGER, SANDRA; Springville Griffith Inst; Colden, NY; (Y); 58/197; Chorus; Concert Band; Mrchg Band; Nwsp Rptr; Nwsp Sprt Ed; Rep Frsh Cls; Rep Sr Cls; Powder Puff Ftbl; Vllybl; Cmnty Wkr; Pres Acad Fit Awd 85; SUNY Plattsburgh; Comm Art.

MENTEKIDIS, DIMITRIOS JAMES; Dobbs Ferry HS; Irvington, NY; (Y); 5/102; Am Leg Boys St; Sec Trs Church Yth Grp; Trs Computer Clb; Math Tm; Model UN; Nwsp Rptr; Rep Stu Cncl; JV Var Socr; French Hon Soc; NHS; Columbia U; Comp Sci.

MENTO, BARBARA; Little Falls JR SR HS; Little Falls, NY; (Y); Drama Clb; Sec FBLA; FHA; Library Aide; Wrstlng; Hon Roll; Bus.

MENTUCK, MICHELLE M; Holy Trinity HS; N Massapequa, NY; (S); 15/334; Church Yth Grp; Stage Crew; L Var Bsktbl; JV Sftbl; High Hon Roll; Hon Roll; Cert Of Achvmnt Math 84.

MENZIE, KATHERINE; Bethlehem Central HS; Delmar, NY; (Y); Sec GAA; Ski Clb; Band; Chorus; Rep Jr Cls; JV Bsktbl; JV Cheerleading; Var JV Socr; Var JV Sftbl; Hon Roll; Bus Admin.

MEO, ANTHONY; Msgr Mc Clancy Memorial HS; Astoria, NY; (Y); 12/229; Math Tm; Science Clb; Yrbk Stf; JV Socr; High Hon Roll; NHS; Prncpls Lst Awds 81-85; Itln Culture Clb Awd 85; NY ST U-Buffalo; Aerospc Engr.

MEQUIA, RITA; Smithtown High Schl West; Smithtown, NY; (Y); Church Yth Grp; Dance Clb; Leo Clb; Teachers Aide; Church Choir; Gym; Hon Roll; Tchr.

MERA, ALEX; United Nations International Schl; New York, NY; (Y); Dance Clb; Drama Clb; Model UN; Ski Clb; Chorus; Church Choir; School Musical; School Play; Stu Cncl; Socr; USC; Intl Rel.

MERCADO, MARGARITA; John F Kennedy HS; Bronx, NY; (Y); 166/986; Dance Clb; Girl Scts; Office Aide; Chorus; Drm & Bgl; Drm Mjr(t); Mrchg Band; School Play; Twrlr; Regnts Diplm Of NYC 85; PELL & TAP Schlrshp; Katherine Gibbs Bus Schl; Secty.

MERCANTE, STEVEN; East Meadow HS; East Meadow, NY; (S); 55/414; Boy Scts; Teachers Aide; Var Ice Hcky; Wrstlng; Hon Roll; NHS; Penn ST; Bio.

MERCEIN, MARYKAREN; Scarsdale HS; Scarsdale, NY; (Y); Cmnty Wkr; Yrbk Stf; Cheerleading; Var Fld Hcky; Var Lcrss; Capt Swmmng; JV Trk; NHS; Ntl Merit SF.

MERCER, AMY; Cato-Meridian HS; Memphis, NY; (Y); 9/68; Cmnty Wkr; 4-H; Trs Soph Cls; Pres Jr Cls; Sec Stu Cncl; Var L Crs Cntry; Var L Trk; NHS; Drama Clb; Model UN; Leadrshp 4-H 84; Public Speakng 4-H 83; Data Processng.

MERCER, LISA M; Shenedehowa HS; Ballston Lk, NY; (Y); Cmnty Wkr; Orch; Sftbl; High Hon Roll; Hon Roll; Russell Sge; Phys Thrpst.

MERCHANT, ERIK J; Cattaraugus Central HS; Cattaraugus, NY; (Y); 5/55; Debate Tm; Scholastic Bowl; Yrbk Sprt Ed; VP Yrbk Stf; High Hon Roll; NHS; Ntl Merit Ltr; Aud/Vis; Church Yth Grp; Library Aide; NYS Rgnts Schlrshp 85; 3rd Pl Wmns Civic Leag Prose Comptn ST Fnls 85; SUNY-GENESEO; Geo.

MERCHEL, SCOTT; Springville Griffith Inst; Springville, NY; (Y); 25/195; Ski Clb; Socr; Var L Tennis; Var L Vllybl; Hon Roll; JETS Awd; U Buffalo; Aero Sp Engr.

MERCIA JR, STEPHEN; Tioga Central HS; Owego, NY; (S); Var L Bsbl; Var L Ftbl; Var L Wrstlng; NHS; Penn ST; Bio Sci.

MERCOGLIANO, VINCENT; Southside SR HS; Rockville Ctr, NY; (Y); Hon Roll; Yth Parade Art Cntst Wnnr 1st Prz 85.

MERCURIO, MARY; Queen Of The Rosary Acad; Bellmore, NY; (Y); Computer Clb; Girl Scts; Library Aide; Science Clb; Hon Roll; NEDT Awd; Hofstra U; Comp Sci.

MERCURIO, PATRICIA; St John The Baptist HS; Patchogue, NY; (Y); Cmnty Wkr; Library Aide; Office Aide; Hon Roll; Prfct Atten Awd; Catechst Cert 85; St Josephs Clg; Sci.

MEREDITH, JON; Germantown Central HS; Germantown, NY; (Y); 3/60; Computer Clb; School Play; Yrbk Stf; VP Sr Cls; JV Capt Bsktbl; JV Socr; High Hon Roll; NHS; Ntl Merit Ltr; NY Rgnts Schlrshp 85; Soc Stds Awd 84; Englsh Awd 83; Syrcuse U; Elec Engrng.

MERGENDAHL, WILLIAM; Saugerties JR-SR HS; Saugerties, NY; (S); Math Tm; Quiz Bowl; Pres Band; Rep Frsh Cls; Trs Soph Cls; VP Jr Cls; VP Stu Cncl; Var Golf; Var Tennis; High Hon Roll; Math.

MERHAI, BRENDA; Richmond Hill HS; Richmond Hill, NY; (Y); 12/250; English Clb; Math Clb; Spanish Clb; Chorus; High Hon Roll; Jr NHS; Prfct Atten Awd; Bus Hnr Soc 85; Intrntl Bus.

MERISCA, ROLANDE; John Jay HS; Brooklyn, NY; (Y); 1/537; Cmnty Wkr; Drama Clb; Teachers Aide; Church Choir; Stage Crew; Variety Show; Nwsp Rptr; Nwsp Stf; Yrbk Stf; Pres Frsh Cls; Brown U Bk Awd 85; Ctzn Serv Awd 85; Pride Of Ynks Supr Yth Awd 85; Pre Med.

MERITT, CYNTHIA RAE; Marcus Whitman HS; Rushville, NY; (Y); 8/128; Pres JCL; Sec Chorus; School Musical; School Play; Stage Crew; Ed Yrbk Ed-Chief; Rep Stu Cncl; Var L Swmmng; High Hon Roll; NHS; Area Yuth Salute; Rgnts Schlrshp Nrsg; Tutoring; D Youville Coll; Nrsg.

MERKEL, DAVID; Cardinal O Hara HS; Kenmore, NY; (S); 2/140; Pres Spanish Clb; Rep Soph Cls; Trs Jr Cls; Trs Sr Cls; Rep Cmnty Wkr; JV Var Bsktbl; Crs Cntry; High Hon Roll; Pres NHS.

MERKERT, WAYNE; East Islipp HS; East Islip, NY; (Y); Math Clb; Service Clb; Nwsp Stf; Trk; High Hon Roll; Hon Roll; Spanish NHS; Silver Mdl Lng Is Math Fair 84; 1st Pl Rbbn Lng Is Sci Congrs 83; 3rd Pl Trphy E Islip Sci Fair 83; Engnrng.

MERKLEN, TERRY; Schoharie Central HS; Central Bridge, NY; (Y); Concert Band; VP Frsh Cls; VP Soph Cls; VP Sr Cls; Bsktbl; Var L Crs Cntry; Trk; Hon Roll; 4-H; Booster Clb Awd Cross Cty 83.

MERKLING, CLIFF; Christian Brothers Acad; Syracuse, NY; (Y); 20/124; Church Yth Grp; Pep Clb; Chorus; Var Capt Ice Hcky; Wt Lftg; Hon Roll; MVP Hockey Team 83-85; All-Star Team 83-84; Clarkson U; Pol Sci.

MERLETTE, TODD; Frontier Central HS; Hamburg, NY; (Y); 37/350; French Clb; Spanish Clb; Var Bowling; Hon Roll; NHS; Pilot.

MERLI, ROBERT F; Northport HS; Northport, NY; (Y); 90/645; Boy Scts; Camera Clb; Computer Clb; Drama Clb; Radio Clb; Stage Crew; Var L Crs Cntry; Jr NHS; Political Wkr; Variety Show; Regents Schlrshp 85; N ROTC Schlrshp 85fcross Cty Race Medals 84; Physics.

MERLINO, MARIO J; Msgr Farrell HS; Staten Island, NY; (Y); 76/300; Art Clb; Computer Clb; Hosp Aide; Band; Rep Soph Cls; Im Bsktbl; Im Ftbl; Hon Roll; Ntl Merit Schol; Sons Italy Schlrshp 85; NYU; Pre-Med.

MEROLA, DONNA; Christ The King RHS HS; Ridgewood, NY; (Y); Library Aide; Red Cross Aide; Service Clb; Teachers Aide; Band; Yrbk Stf; Var Swmmng; Hon Roll; Physcl Ftns Awd 83; Music Awd 83; Stony Brook U; Accntng.

MERRELL, JANINE; Avon JR-SR HS; Avon, NY; (Y); Church Yth Grp; Band; Stat Bsbl; JV Var Cheerleading; Score Keeper; Var Tennis; Hon Roll; Bus.

MERRIGAN, CRAIG P; Webster HS; Webster, NY; (Y); Church Yth Grp; Exploring; Model UN; Ski Clb; Band; Concert Band; Jazz Band; Yrbk Ed-Chief; Rep Stu Cncl; Im Bsktbl; Svc, Music Awd 83; Area All ST Orch, All Cnty Band 84; Babson Coll; Invstmnt.

MERRITT, FRANCINE; Wilson Magnet HS; Rochester, NY; (S); 2/48; Intnl Clb; Model UN; Nwsp Ed-Chief; Nwsp Rptr; Yrbk Rptr; Yrbk Stf; Rep Frsh Cls; Rep Soph Cls; Rep Stu Cncl; High Hon Roll; Syracuse U; Pre Med.

MERRITT, MARLENE; The Bronx High School Of Science; Flushing, NY; (Y); Concert Band; Yrbk Stf; Mgr Swmmng; CC Awd; Ntl Merit Schol; SUNY Binghamton.

MERRITT, PATRICIA; Cicero-North Syracuse HS; North Syracuse, NY; (S); 64/711; Church Choir; JV Bsktbl; Powder Puff Ftbl; JV Socr; NHS; Accntng.

MERRY, GLENN F; Monroe HS; Rochester, NY; (Y); 11/158; Pres Exploring; Math Tm; Rep Jr Cls; Sec Sr Cls; Var Capt Ftbl; Var Trk; NHS; Ntl Merit Ltr; Computer Clb; French Clb; Elmira Coll Key Awd 84; Niagara Pres Schlrshp 85; NY ST Regnts Schlrsp 85; Accntnt.

MERRYWEATHER, CHRISTINE; Linton HS; Schenectady, NY; (Y); 100/265; Pres Church Yth Grp; JCL; Office Aide; Nwsp Rptr; Rep Frsh Cls; Rep Soph Cls; Rep Jr Cls; Stat Bsbl; Var Cheerleading; Var Score Keeper; JR Cyo Grls Chrldng Coach 85; 2nd Pl Diocesan Champnshp 85; Syracuse; Coaching.

MERTZ, KATHRYN A; Holy Trinity HS; Wantagh, NY; (S); 30/402; Camera Clb; Mathletes; Math Clb; Math Tm; Nwsp Phtg; Nwsp Rptr; Yrbk Phtg; Yrbk Rptr; Rep Soph Cls; Sec Jr Cls; Acad All-Amer 84; Math.

MERTZ, TRACIE L; Arlington HS; Poughkeepsie, NY; (Y); 22/586; Drama Clb; Pres French Clb; Key Clb; Nwsp Rptr; Yrbk Phtg; Var Tennis; High Hon Roll; Ntl Merit Ltr; NY ST Regnts Schlrshp 85; Coll Wm & Mary; Psych.

MERZA, MARIA; Saint Peters H S For Girls; Staten Isl, NY; (Y); Exploring; VP Math Tm; Lit Mag; Rep Stu Cncl; Var Tennis; Var Trk; Hon Roll; NHS; Am Leg Essay Cont 1st Pl 84-85; Med Tech.

MERZKE, CINDY; Nazareth Acad; Rochester, NY; (S); Spanish Clb; School Play; Yrbk Stf; Bryant & Stratton; Bus.

MESARD, RENEE H; Harborfields HS; Huntington Sta, NY; (Y); 8/335; Drama Clb; Ski Clb; Thesps; School Play; Mgr Stage Crew; Mgr Variety Show; Yrbk Bus Mgr; Rptr Lit Mag; NHS; Ntl Merit Schol.

MESCALL, MICHELLE; Commack H S North; Commack, NY; (Y); Teachers Aide; Orch; Yrbk Stf; Stu Cncl; High Hon Roll; Hon Roll; Law.

MESCHINO, JOHN; Lekman HS; Bronx, NY; (Y); Band; Concert Band; Orch; School Musical; Hon Roll; Prfct Atten Awd.

MESICK, KENNETH; Hudson HS; Hudson, NY; (Y); 45/159; Trs Band; Concert Band; Jazz Band; Mrchg Band; Orch; Stage Crew; High Hon Roll; Outstndng Instrmntlst 85.

MESLER JR, RAYMOND G; Frewsburg Central HS; Frewsburg, NY; (Y); 2/92; Drama Clb; Quiz Bowl; Chorus; School Musical; Nwsp Ed-Chief; Yrbk Ed-Chief; Hon Roll; NHS; Sal; Pres AFS; Vac Air Alloys Inc Schlrshp 85; NHS Math Awd 85; Jamestown CC; CPA.

MESMER, DAVID J; Grand Island HS; Grand Island, NY; (Y); VP JA; Bio.

MESNIK, PETER; Yorktown HS; Yorktown Hts, NY; (Y); Pres Computer Clb; Key Clb; Teachers Aide; Chorus; Nwsp Stf; Ed Lit Mag; Tennis; High Hon Roll; NHS; Comp Sci.

MESQUITA, ELIZABETH; Highland HS; Poughkeepsie, NY; (Y); AFS; Office Aide; School Musical; School Play; Stage Crew; Yrbk Ed-Chief; Off Jr Cls; Bsktbl; Score Keeper; Comm Art.

MESSA, JO-ANN; Preston HS; Bronx, NY; (S); Yrbk Stf; High Hon Roll; NHS; Half Scholar To Preston H S 83.

MESSANA, MICHAEL M; Monsignor Farrell HS; Staten Island, NY; (Y); Church Yth Grp; Computer Clb; Hosp Aide; Intnl Clb; Math Tm; Chorus; Socr; Hon Roll; Natl Hnr Roll; Regents Schlrshp; Engl,Math & Sci Hnrs Pgms; Mgr JV & Vrsty Sccr Teams; Comp Club; Fairleigh Dickinson; Dntst.

MESSEMER, DENISE; St Franics Prep; Whitestone, NY; (S); Red Cross Aide; Im Bowling; Stat Coach Actv; Im Mgr(s); Sftbl; Im Vllybl; Hon Roll; Opt Clb Awd; CPA.

MESSER, DAWN M; The Franciscan Acad; Syracuse, NY; (S); 5/25; Drama Clb; Latin Clb; MMM; Chorus; School Musical; Yrbk Stf; High Hon Roll; NHS; Latin Honors; IUP; Sci.

MESSER, ROBIN J; Newburgh Free Acad; New Windsor, NY; (Y); Drama Clb; VP 4-H; Latin Clb; Chorus; Elem Ed.

MESSINA, DAVID; Notre Dame HS; Batavia, NY; (S); Var L Bsbl; Im Coach Actv; Var L Ftbl; Var Capt Wrstlng; Hon Roll; NHS; Prfct Atten Awd; Acctng 2nd Ave 83-84; Bus 2nd Ave 83; Notre Dame Sprts Awd 84; Coachs Awd Ftbl 84; MVP Bsbl 81-82; Bus.

MESSINA, MARGARET; Connetquot HS; Bohemia, NY; (S); 27/723; Suny At Oswego; Zoology.

MESSINA, MARIA; Maryvale SR HS; Chktg, NY; (S); 85/333; Church Yth Grp; VP DECA; Drama Clb; GAA; JV Cheerleading; High Hon Roll; Pres Schlr; Girl Scts; Chorus; Church Choir; Daemen Coll Dept Scholar 85; DECA ST Wnnr Apparel & Accssrs 84; DECA Regnl Wnnr 83-85; Mktng.

MESSINA, MICHAEL H; Pittsford Sutherland HS; Pittsford, NY; (Y); Boys Clb Am; Exploring; Trs FBLA; Ski Clb; Socr; NYS Regnts Schlrshp 85; Syracuse U; Mech Engrng.

MESSINA, SHELLEY; Notre Dame HS; Batavia, NY; (S); 16/82; Pep Clb; Spanish Clb; Yrbk Stf; Var Capt Cheerleading; Hon Roll; NHS; Hghst Avg Bus Dynmcs 83; Hghst Avg Shrthnd I 84; Frgn Trvl 84; Bus.

MESSINEO, ALESSANDRA M; John Jay HS; Hopewell Jct, NY; (Y); JA; Ski Clb; Sec Soph Cls; Sec Jr Cls; Sec Sr Cls; Var Cheerleading; High Hon Roll; NHS; Rotary Awd; Miss Photo 85; 1st Tap 2nd Ballet 3rd Ballet Comp 85; Miss John Jay Rep 85; Psych.

MESSINETTI, JOHN; Rocky Point SR JR HS; Rocky Point, NY; (S); 7/200; Church Yth Grp; Varsity Clb; Chorus; School Musical; Variety Show; JV Bsktbl; Var Golf; JV Var Socr; Hon Roll; Atty.

MESSING, DAVID P; Somer HS; Somers, NY; (Y); 14/213; Temple Yth Grp; Yrbk Stf; Stu Cncl; Var L Ftbl; Bausch & Lomb Sci Awd; High Hon Roll; Hon Roll; NHS; Texaco Philonthropic Fndtn Schlrshp 85-86; Duke U; Bio-Med Engrng.

MESSITT, DONALD G; Saratoga Central Catholic HS; Ballston Lake, NY; (S); High Hon Roll; Engrng.

MESTER, SANDOR; Clarkstown South HS; W Nyack, NY; (Y); Boy Scts; Math Tm; Science Clb; Stage Crew; Nwsp Bus Mgr; JV Bsktbl; JV Trk; Mu Alp Tht; NHS; Ntl Merit Ltr; Treas Mu Alpha Theta 86; Cornell U; Engrg.

MESTROU, ALBA; Marlbobo HS; Marlboro, NY; (Y); 19/140; French Clb; Yrbk Stf; High Hon Roll; Hon Roll; NHS; SUNY New Paltz; Frgn Langs.

METCALF, MICHELE; Bishop Cunningham HS; Oswego, NY; (Y); Pep Clb; Spanish Clb; Variety Show; Trs Frsh Cls; Trs Soph Cls; Sec Jr Cls; JV Cheerleading; Stat Socr; Var Sftbl; Var Vllybl; Cert Pblc Accntnt.

METELLUS, REGINE; St Francis Preparatory Schl; Holliswood, NY; (Y); 360/690; Hosp Aide; Drm & Bgl; Mgmnt.

METERA, WM; Binghamton HS; Binghamton, NY; (Y); Church Yth Grp; FCA; Red Cross Aide; Varsity Clb; Im Bsktbl; JV Var Ftbl; JV Trk; Hon Roll; Air Force Acad; Aviation.

METEYER, BRIAN; Bishop Kearney HS; Rochester, NY; (S); 15/141; Church Yth Grp; CAP; Computer Clb; Varsity Clb; Nwsp Phtg; Nwsp Rptr; Yrbk Phtg; Var Coach Actv; Mgr(s); Score Keeper; Psych.

METEYER, LEEANN; Bishop Kearney HS; Rochester, NY; (Y); Church Yth Grp; Ski Clb; Nwsp Rptr; Hon Roll; Jrnlsm.

METHAL, SHANE; Lynbrook HS; E Rockaway, NY; (Y); JA; Band; Concert Band; Madrigals; Mrchg Band; Symp Band; Var Ice Hcky; Stat Score Keeper; Hon Roll; Jr NHS; NYS Regents 85-86; Med.

METIVIER, MICHAEL; Kenmore East HS; Tonawanda, NY; (Y); Church Yth Grp; Math Clb; JV Socr; Var Swmmng; JV Trk; High Hon Roll; NHS; Comp Sci.

METRAS, CINDY; The Franciscan Acad; N Syracuse, NY; (Y); Hon Roll; Ononadago CC; Bus Admin.

METRO, DAWN; East Aurora HS; East Aurora, NY; (S); 19/182; AFS; Camp Fr Inc; Cmnty Wkr; Hosp Aide; Chorus; Nwsp Sprt Ed; Yrbk Stf; DAR Awd; Hon Roll; NHS; Niagara U; Nrs.

METZ, JEANNE; Union Endicott HS; Endicott, NY; (Y); Varsity Clb; Concert Band; VP Soph Cls; VP Jr Cls; Stu Cncl; Var L Bsktbl; Var L Tennis; Natl Cncl Yth Ldrshp 85.

METZ, MARY; Sacred Heart Academy; Rockville Centre, NY; (S); 2/190; French Clb; NFL; Speech Tm; Orch; Nwsp Rptr; Im Socr; Im Tennis; High Hon Roll; NHS.

METZ, REGINA; Sacred Heart Acad; Rockville Centre, NY; (S); 2/186; Pres Debate Tm; Hosp Aide; Var Math Tm; NFL; Pres Speech Tm; Rep Stu Cncl; Var Im Socr; Var Im Tennis; High Hon Roll; Ntl Merit Ltr; Century Three Ldrs Awd 84; Dfndrs Semi Fnl Cntywide 83-84; Cath Leag 3rd Pl Essay Cntst 82; Intl Law.

METZGER, CHRISTINE; Roy C Ketcham HS; Wappingers Falls, NY; (S); 77/576; Pres Church Yth Grp; Drama Clb; Band; Stage Crew; Stat Bsktbl; Hon Roll; NHS; Calvin Coll MI; Ed.

METZGER, JOCELYN M; Brighton HS; New York, NY; (Y); Exploring; Intnl Clb; Ski Clb; Sec Temple Yth Grp; Varsity Clb; Band; Nwsp Rptr; Rep Stu Cncl; Crs Cntry; Var Fld Hcky; Florence Rothman Fisher Awd; Opera Theatre Rochester; Psych.

METZGER, MELINDA; Beacon HS; Beacon, NY; (S); 5/169; Office Aide; Church Choir; Stat Socr; High Hon Roll; Jr NHS; NHS; Bus Excel Awd; Ntl Bus Hnr Soc; Dutchess CC; Bus Admin.

METZLER, KURT DOUGLAS; Dover JR SR HS; Dover Plains, NY; (S); Trs Jr Cls; VP Stu Cncl; High Hon Roll; Jr NHS; NHS; Presdntl Clsrm 85; Mst Imprvd Soph Mem Awd 83-84; Stud Rep For PTSA 85-86; Law.

METZLOFF, PAUL W; Amherst Central HS; Amherst, NY; (Y); 3/300; Cmnty Wkr; Pres German Clb; Quiz Bowl; Church Choir; Ed Nwsp Stf; Var Capt Crs Cntry; Var L Swmmng; NHS; Ntl Merit SF; Voice Dem Awd; Rensselaer Math/Sci Stu Yr 84; Wnnr Nysjcl Awds 84; US Military Acad; Mltry Hist.

MEURY, JOSEPH; St John The Baptist; Amityville, NY; (Y); 69/564; Cmnty Wkr; Computer Clb; Var Bsbl; JV Bsktbl; Hon Roll; Engrng.

MEURY, WILLIAM; St John Th Baptist HS; Amityville, NY; (Y); 60/564; Cmnty Wkr; Computer Clb; Science Clb; Var Bsbl; JV Bsktbl; NHS; Aero-Sci.

MEVORACH, STACEY; George W Hewlett HS; Hewlett Harbor, NY; (Y); Cmnty Wkr; Nwsp Stf; Yrbk Stf; Rep Stu Cncl; Mgr(s); Trk; Hon Roll; NHS.

MEYBAUM, PETER J; Horseheads HS; Horseheads, NY; (Y); 13/405; Am Leg Boys St; Boy Scts; Pres Chess Clb; Church Yth Grp; German Clb; Band; NHS; Ntl Merit Ltr; Cmnty Wkr; Ski Clb; Eagl Sct Awd 84; Elmira Key Awd 85; Cornell U; Sci.

MEYER, AMY J; Nardin Acad; Lake View, NY; (Y); JA; Teachers Aide; Trs Jr Cls; Rep Sr Cls; Coach Actv; Gym; Hon Roll; Acad Recgn Schlrshp 85; Gymstc Comp Regl, Natl 81-85; U MI; Pre Med.

MEYER, ANDREW; Hillcrest HS; Jamaica, NY; (Y); 81/775; Church Yth Grp; Band; Concert Band; Jazz Band; Var Bsbl; Var Bsktbl; Civic Clb; Arista Soc 81-82; U Of Binghamton.

MEYER, BRAYTON; East Aurora HS; E Aurora, NY; (Y); 29/182; Var Crs Cntry; Var Swmmng; Var Capt Trk; Hon Roll; Ntl Merit Ltr; Hamilton Coll.

MEYER, CHRISTOPHER; Millbrook HS; La Grangeville, NY; (Y); Drama Clb; Band; Concert Band; School Play; Crs Cntry.

MEYER, CHRISTOPHER H; Pine Bush HS; Bloomingburg, NY; (Y); 15/195; Yrbk Rptr; Yrbk Stf; High Hon Roll; Hon Roll; NHS; NY Rgnts Schlrshp 85; U Of Stonybrook; Bus.

MEYER, CYNTHIA; St Barnabas HS; Yonkers, NY; (Y); Office Aide; Teachers Aide; VP Jr Cls; Rep Sr Cls; Stu Cncl; Hon Roll; Simmons Schl; Secy.

MEYER, CYNTHIA L; Nortre Dame Acad; Staten Island, NY; (Y); 19/96; Dance Clb; Girl Scts; Ski Clb; Nwsp Stf; Yrbk Stf; Capt Swmmng; NY ST Regents Schlrshp 85; Dickinson Coll; Bio.

MEYER, DAN; West Genesee HS; Syracuse, NY; (Y); Exploring; Im Lcrss; JV Socr; Hon Roll.

MEYER, DANIEL T; Cardinal Mooney HS; Hilton, NY; (Y); 41/323; Pres Trs 4-H; Ski Clb; Stage Crew; Im Bsktbl; Var L Golf; 4-H Awd; High Hon Roll; Hon Roll; NHS; NY Regents Coll Schlrshp 85; Dairy Fashiions Coll Schlrshp 85; MI ST U; Agri Sci.

MEYER, DAVE; St Francis Prep; Bayside, NY; (Y); 400/700; FCA; Math Clb; Teachers Aide; Stage Crew; JV Var Ftbl; JV Var Trk; Wt Lftg; Litl Leage All Star 83; CYO Bsbl MVP 85; High Scr SAT 85.

MEYER, DEBRA LYNN; N Babylon SR HS; N Babylon, NY; (S); 65/650; Church Yth Grp; 4-H; Quiz Bowl; Chorus; Swing Chorus; Nwsp Rptr; Nwsp Stf; 4-H Awd; High Hon Roll; Jr NHS; Long Isl Appaloosa Club 84 Princess 84; Grand Reserve Champ Yth 83-84; Connors ST Warner; Equestrian.

MEYER, HEIDI; Letchworth Central HS; Bliss, NY; (Y); 2/82; AFS; 4-H; French Clb; Ski Clb; Varsity Clb; Sec Trs Concert Band; Mrchg Band; Yrbk Ed-Chief; Var L Bsktbl; Var L Socr; Presdntl Acadmc Ftnss Awd 85; US Army Rsrv Ntl Schlr/Athlt Awd 85; Alfred U; Art Dsgn.

MEYER, JAY; Saugerties HS; Saugerties, NY; (Y); SUNY-NEW Paltz; Comptrs.

MEYER, JENNIFER; Commack H S North; Palos Verdes Ests, CA; (Y); Rep Art Clb; Nwsp Rptr; Nwsp Stf; Yrbk Stf; Lit Mag; Frsh Cls; Soph Cls; Jr Cls; Tennis; Hon Roll; Natl Art Hon Soc 84-85; Jrnlsm.

MEYER, JENNY; Williamsville East HS; East Amherst, NY; (Y); 100/300; Pep Clb; Var Capt Gym; Var Trk; Bus.

MEYER, JOHN; Webutuck HS; Millerton, NY; (Y); 1/43; Ski Clb; Thesps; School Play; Stage Crew; Yrbk Stf; JV Var Socr; Var Tennis; NHS; Ntl Merit Ltr; Drama Clb; Engrng.

MEYER, KELLY; Fayetteville-Manlius HS; Fayetteville, NY; (Y); JA; Chorus; Var Tennis; Hon Roll; Flag Corp; Cert Excellence Var Lttr 84; Cert Excellence Spanish 83; SUNY; Mathematics.

MEYER, LEONE F; Amherst Central SR HS; Amherst, NY; (Y); 116/308; Library Aide; Red Cross Aide; Spanish Clb; Hon Roll; Rgnst Schrlshp Nrsng 85; MVP Gym Cls 82; Erie Comm Coll; Nrs.

MEYER, MARTHA; Kenmore West HS; Kenmore, NY; (Y); Thesps; Band; Mrchg Band; Orch; Yrbk Rptr; High Hon Roll; Natl Spanish Exam 1st Pl 83; Anthropology.

MEYER, SANDRA B; Southampton HS; Southampton, NY; (Y); 6/106; AFS; Band; Concert Band; Mrchg Band; JV Fld Hcky; High Hon Roll; Jr NHS; NHS; NYS Regents Schlrshp 85; Acad All-Am Schlr; Brandeis U; Biochem.

MEYER, STEVEN ANDREW; West Hempsted HS; West Hempstead, NY; (Y); 22/310; Band; Concert Band; Orch; Var Capt Bsktbl; Cheerleading; Coach Actv; L Crs Cntry; Var Capt Lcrss; Wt Lftg; High Hon Roll; La Crosse Nassau Cnty SR All Star Game 85; Cornell U; Htl Mgmt.

MEYER, SUSAN D; Saratoga Springs HS; Saratoga Springs, NY; (Y); 67/465; Drama Clb; Chorus; Jazz Band; Pep Band; School Musical; School Play; Yrbk Stf; Regents Schlrshp 85; Excell Music Awd 82; Hudson Valley CC; Data Proc.

MEYER, TARA M; Garden City HS; Garden City, NY; (Y); 54/319; Chrmn Key Clb; Church Choir; Nwsp Phtg; Yrbk Phtg; Var Bsktbl; JV Sftbl; Var Vllybl; High Hon Roll; Jr NHS; Valparaiso U Schlrshp; Valparaiso U.

MEYER, VALERIE ANNE; Commack HS; Commack, NY; (Y); 111/440; NYS Rgnts Schlrshp, Pres Ftnss Awd 85; Stony Brook U; Gemlgst.

MEYER, WILLIAM; East Syracuse - Minoa HS; Minoa, NY; (Y); Band; Concert Band; Jazz Band; Variety Show; Hon Roll; Jr NHS; Mech Engr.

MEYERS, BETH; Rye Country Day Schl; Greenwich, CT; (Y); AFS; Cmnty Wkr; Drama Clb; GAA; Model UN; Temple Yth Grp; Acpl Chr; Orch; School Musical; Var Tennis.

MEYERS, BRUCE; Camden Central HS; Taberg, NY; (Y); 11/190; Var L Socr; Var L Tennis; High Hon Roll; NHS; Rgnts Schlrshp; Pres Acad Ftns Awd 85; Rgnts Dplma With Hgh Hnrs 85; Mohawk Vly CC; Engrng Sci.

MEYERS, DANIEL L; Pioneer Central HS; Machias, NY; (Y); 47/168; Boy Scts; Church Yth Grp; Church Choir; Buffalo Nws Hnr Carrier Cert 84; Engrng.

MEYERS, ELISABETH; Connetquot SR HS; Ronkonkoma, NY; (Y); 74/702; Trs Art Clb; Church Yth Grp; Office Aide; Yrbk Stf; Rep Stu Cncl; Stat Vllybl; Hon Roll; Jr NHS; NHS; Prfct Atten Awd; NY St Regents Schlrshp 85; Traphagen Schl Fashn; Fashn Ill.

MEYERS, GREGG; Smithtown High School West; Smithtown, NY; (Y); Var Bsbl; Var L Socr; Spec Soccer Prog 83; Accntnt.

MEYERS, JANET; Williamsville North HS; Amherst, NY; (S); DECA; German Clb; Ski Clb; Rep Stu Cncl; JV Socr; Hon Roll; Mock Trl Assn & Interhgh Cncl 84-85; Steering Comm 82-83; Law.

MEYERS, LAYONA; Adeli E Stevenson HS; Bronx, NY; (Y); Political Wkr; Concert Band; Mrchg Band; Nwsp Rptr; Nwsp Stf; Pre-Med.

MEYERS, TONNETTE; Mont Pleaant HS; Schenectady, NY; (Y); JV Sftbl; JV Var Vllybl; Hon Roll; Jr NHS; Comp Sci.

MEYERS, WILLIAM; Ossining HS; Somers, NY; (Y); JV Bsktbl; Var L Ftbl; Var L Lcrss; High Hon Roll; Aerospc Engrng.

MEYERS, WILLIAM BUDDY J; Saugerties JR-SR HS; Saugerties, NY; (Y); 75/242; CAP; Pres JA; Key Clb; Dale Carnegie Schlrshp Publ Spkg Humn Rel 83; Outstndng Achvr Yr 83; VP Mktg Yr 84; Dutchess CC; Acctng.

MEZZA, MARGARET ANN; T R Proctor HS; Utica, NY; (Y); 15/168; Drm & Bgl; Jr NHS; NHS; Valedictorian 81; Herkimer Cnty CC; Data Prcsng.

MICARA, ANNE; Bishop Ford Central Catholic HS; Brooklyn, NY; (Y); 20/449; GAA; Church Choir; Im Bowling; Im Sftbl; Im Tennis; Acadmc Excllnc; 1st & 2nd Hnrs; Brooklyn Coll; Tourism.

MICCICHE, ANGELINA; James E Sperry HS; Rochester, NY; (Y); Rep Chorus; Madrigals; Stage Crew; Stu Cncl; Hon Roll; Music Perf.

MICEK, JILL; Falconer Central HS; Jamestown, NY; (Y); Church Yth Grp; Drama Clb; VP Band; VP Soph Cls; Pres Jr Cls; Rep Stu Cncl; JV Var Cheerleading; Gym; Hon Roll; NHS; Ntl Hnr Soc 84-85; Amercn Cancer Soc Essay Cntst-1st Sincerty 84; Intl Chrldng Fndtn Comptn-1st Pl 84; Travel.

MICELI, CHRISTOPHER; Kendall JR SR HS; Kendall, NY; (Y); Band; Concert Band; Jazz Band; Mrchg Band; Variety Show; Yrbk Phtg; Yrbk Stf; DAR Awd; High Hon Roll; NHS; SUNY Geneseo; Chem Engrg.

MICHAEL, CINDY; Frontier Central HS; Buffalo, NY; (Y); 63/495; Church Yth Grp; FBLA; Ski Clb; Varsity Clb; Band; Concert Band; Mrchg Band; Symp Band; Rep Frsh Cls; Sec Soph Cls; Mst Dedicates Swmmr Awd 84; Bryant & Stratton Secry Schlrshp 85; Bryant & Stratton Bus Inst.

MICHAEL, FREDERICO; Scotia Glenville HS; Scotia, NY; (Y); Cmnty Wkr; 2nd Pl Stu Proj Captl Dis Indstrl 81; 3rd Pl Arts Ass Colony Exhbt 82-83; 1st Pl Shopsmith Cntst 83; Ind Arts.

MICHAEL, NABILA; Middletown HS; Middletown, NY; (Y); Library Aide; Teachers Aide; School Play; Ed Lit Mag; Hon Roll; NHS; Acadmc/Achvt Awd-Eng & Hstry 83-84.

MICHAELS, ALAN; South Shore HS; Brooklyn, NY; (Y); Concert Band; Jazz Band; Orch; School Musical; Variety Show; Outstdng Muscn 84-85; Music Chrmns Awd 84-85; All City H S Schlrshp Awd Music 84-85; Mannes Coll Of Music; Prcsn Prf.

MICHAELS, MAUREEN; Mt Mercy Acad; Buffalo, NY; (Y); Computer Clb; Stage Crew; Yrbk Sprt Ed; JV Capt Badmtn; Stat Bsktbl; Score Keeper; Capt Vllybl; High Hon Roll; Jr NHS; French Clb; U Rochester; Med.

MICHAELS, STEPHEN; Berlin Central HS; Berlin, NY; (S); Church Yth Grp; French Clb; Spanish Clb; Chorus; Concert Band; School Musical; Stage Crew; Rep Stu Cncl; Hon Roll; Nyack Coll; Clergy.

MICHAELS, VALENTINA; Academy Of St Joseph HS; E Patchogue, NY; (Y); Dance Clb; Drama Clb; Model UN; Sec Science Clb; Thesps; School Musical; School Play; Yrbk Stf; NHS; Acad Achvt Awd 83-84; Stu Trimester 83-84; NEDT Achvt Awd 83; Rutgers U; Theatre Arts.

MICHALAK, KATHLEEN; Clayton A Bouton JR SR HS; Voorheesville, NY; (Y); French Clb; Key Clb; Chorus; Variety Show; Yrbk Stf; JV Var Bsktbl; Var Swmmng; High Hon Roll; Hon Roll; Prfct Atten Awd; Mst Imprvd Plyr JV Bsktbl & Hm Ec 82-84; Acctng.

MICHALEK, ANTHONY A; Chatham Central HS; Canaan, NY; (Y); Drama Clb; Pres 4-H; Math Tm; Concert Band; Mrchg Band; Pep Band; School Musical; Var Tennis; Regents Schlrshp.

MICHALKOW, CHRIS; West Genesee SR HS; Warners, NY; (Y); Cmnty Wkr; Teachers Aide; Hon Roll; Onondaga CC; Mech Engnr.

MICHALSKI, SUSAN; Villa Maria Acad; Cheektowaga, NY; (S); Art Clb; Pep Clb; Sec Jr Cls; Rep Stu Cncl; Im Bowling; Hon Roll; NHS; Erie Community Coll; Math.

MICHAUD, DONNA; Gloversville HS; Gloversville, NY; (Y); 16/220; Church Yth Grp; Cmnty Wkr; Dance Clb; Exploring; 4-H; French Clb; Rep Stu Cncl; 4-H Awd; High Hon Roll; Hon Roll; Evelyn Stmpfl Schlrshp; Nazareth Clg; Lang Tchr.

MICHAUD, THOMAS; Christian Brothers Acad; Liverpool, NY; (Y); 30/101; Exploring; JA; Yrbk Rptr; Stu Cncl; Bsbl; Swmmng; Var Trk; Cit Awd; High Hon Roll; Chrstn Bros Acad Schlrshp; Lemoyne Coll; Indstrl Lbr Rltns.

MICHEL, CYNTHIA; St John The Baptist Dioce; Massapequa, NY; (Y); 13/538; Math Clb; Pom Pon; High Hon Roll; Jr NHS; NHS; Spanish NHS; Med.

MICHEL, ELIZABETH J; Columbia HS; E Greenbush, NY; (Y); 92/353; Radio Clb; Ski Clb; Symp Band; Yrbk Ed-Chief; Rep Soph Cls; JV Var Cheerleading; JV Var Tennis; Hon Roll; NHS; Pres Schlr; NY ST U-Plattsburgh; Bus Admn.

MICHEL, MARIE PETIT; Newfield HS; Coram, NY; (Y); Hst Art Clb; Sec Church Yth Grp; Drama Clb; Acpl Chr; Chorus; Church Choir; School Musical; Nwsp Rptr; Nwsp Stf; Lit Mag; MVP Awd Fencng 84 & 85; Cert For Cnty, ST, Estrn ST Chmpnshps-Mile Relay 85; Cert Dstngshd Achv Lit; Librl Arts.

MICHEL, RONIDE; Clara Barton HS; Brooklyn, NY; (Y); Camera Clb; Church Yth Grp; Cmnty Wkr; Pres French Clb; Spanish Clb; School Musical; Yrbk Stf; French Hon Soc; Hon Roll; NHS; Cert Hnr Soc Stud 85; Phys Ftnss Awd 85; Mrt Awd Achvt Math 85; Chem.

MICHELS, KARIN; St Catherine Acad; New York, NY; (Y); Office Aide; Accmndtn Steno 85; Vlntr Tchr CCD 84-85; Bus.

MICHELSON, SCOTT; Pelham Memorial HS; Pelham, NY; (Y); Aud/Vis; Temple Yth Grp; Y-Teens; Var L Bsktbl; Hon Roll; Betty B Schwab Awd 85.

MICHETTI, ROBERT; Mc Kee Vo-Tech HS; Staten Is, NY; (Y); 30/250; Library Aide; Hon Roll; Prfct Atten Awd; Seagull Hnr Soc 85; Grphcs.

MICHIE, CHINITA; Saint Pius V HS; Bronx, NY; (Y); Hosp Aide; School Musical; Variety Show; Bowling; Cheerleading; Score Keeper; Sftbl; Cit Awd; Hon Roll; Prfct Atten Awd; Georgetown; Comp Sci.

MICILCAVAGE, DEBRA; Union-Endicott HS; Endicott, NY; (Y); Exploring; Hosp Aide; Mrchg Band; Yrbk Rptr; Yrbk Stf; Rep Soph Cls; Rep Jr Cls; JV Cheerleading; JV Vllybl; Hon Roll; Phy Thrpy.

MICILLO, GINA; Hilton Central HS; Hilton, NY; (Y); Model UN; Ski Clb; Concert Band; Mrchg Band; Symp Band; Rep Jr Cls; Rep Stu Cncl; Swmmng; High Hon Roll; Trs NHS; 400 Free & 200 Medley Relay Swmmng Rcrds 84.

MICKLE, ANNE R; The Nightingale-Bamford Schl; New York, NY; (Y); GAA; Ed Nwsp Phtg; Yrbk Phtg; Var Capt Badmtn; Var Capt Bsktbl; Stat Gym; Stat Vllybl; Rgnt Schlrshp 85; CT Coll.

MICKLE, DONNA; John A Coleman HS; Kingston, NY; (Y); Drama Clb; French Clb; Key Clb; School Play; Yrbk Stf; Rep Frsh Cls; Bsktbl; Crs Cntry; Trk; Hon Roll; Spcl Tchr.

MICROS, MATTHEW A; The Allendale Columbia Schl; Pittsford, NY; (Y); 1/46; Math Tm; Varsity Clb; Rep Sr Cls; Stu Cncl; Var Capt Bsbl; Var L Bsktbl; Var Capt Socr; Hon Roll; Birghton Pittsford Post All Star Sccr Tm 84-85; NY St Regents Schlrshp 84-85; U Notre Dame; Bus.

MIDDLEBROOK, KRIS; Greenwich Central HS; Greenwich, NY; (Y); AFS; Boys Clb Am; Chorus; School Play; Nwsp Rptr; Nwsp Stf; Sftbl; Adirondack CC; Crmnl Jstc.

MIDDLETON, CHRISTOPHER L; Garden City HS; Garden City, NY; (Y); 20/319; Mathletes; Nwsp Stf; Yrbk Stf; Var Bowling; Var Socr; Var Trk; Hon Roll; Jr NHS; NHS; Ntl Merit SF; Nassau Cnty Mathletes Awd 81-84; Columbia U Hnrs Sci Pgm 84; Math.

MIDDLETON, DAVID W; Hunter-Tannersville Central HS; East Jewett, NY; (Y); 2/30; Band; Chorus; Concert Band; Jazz Band; School Musical; School Play; Lit Mag; Pres Sr Cls; Bausch & Lomb Sci Awd; NHS; NY ST Regents Schlrshp 85; U Of Denver; Music Performance.

MIDDLETON, GREGORY A; Cardinal Hayes HS; New York, NY; (Y); 27/249; Aud/Vis; Church Yth Grp; Cmnty Wkr; Exploring; Service Clb; Band; Stage Crew; Yrbk Phtg; Yrbk Stf; Pierre Toussaint Schlrshp 85; Regents Nrsng Schlrshp 85; Acad Medal Relgion 82-83; Fordham U; Educ.

MIDDLETON, MICHAEL; Cicero-North Syracuse HS; Clay, NY; (S); 14/662; Church Yth Grp; Mathletes; Math Tm; Spanish Clb; Rep Frsh Cls; Rep Stu Cncl; High Hon Roll; Hon Roll; NHS; Opt Clb Awd; Syracuse; Law.

MIDDLETON, SPENCER; Longwood HS; Medford, NY; (Y); Sec Am Leg Boys St; Boy Scts; VP Key Clb; Math Tm; Teachers Aide; Color Guard; Nwsp Phtg; VP Stu Cncl; High Hon Roll; Jr NHS; All County Chorus 83; Gifted & Talented Summr Pgm 84-85; Minority H S Sci Apprentcshp Pgm 83; Pol Sci.

MIDEA, THERESA; Albion HS; Albion, NY; (Y); Girl Scts; School Musical; Rep Stu Cncl; Capt Cheerleading; Spch Thrpy.

MIDZINSKI, TAMI; Tonawanda SR HS; Tonawanda, NY; (Y); Cmnty Wkr; Hosp Aide; JA; High Hon Roll; Hon Roll; NHS; Bryant Straton; Exec Sec.

MIECZKOWSKI, JOHN; St Francis Prep; Maspeth, NY; (Y); Ski Clb; JV Bsbl; Coach Actv; Diving; Im Ftbl; JV Var Swmmng; Phy Ed Ldr Svc Awd 84-85; Engrng.

MIELE, GREGORY; Salesian JR Acad; Goshen, NY; (S); 1/2; Church Yth Grp; Cmnty Wkr; School Play; Yrbk Stf; Pres Jr Cls; VP Stu Cncl; Im Fld Hcky; Hon Roll; VFW Awd; Voice Dem Awd; Don Bosco Coll; Philosphy.

MIETT, ANNE E; Bishop Grimes HS; E Syracuse, NY; (Y); 54/250; Hon Roll; Var L Tennis; Var L Trk; Var L Vllybl; Band; Exploring; GAA; JA; Letterman Clb; Varsity Clb; Pres Schlrshp Wilson Clg; 85; Fly Rd Loc Schlrshp 85; NY Regents Schlrshp 85; Wilson Clg; Equine Mgmt.

MIETT, CATHERINE; Bishop Grimes HS; E Syracuse, NY; (Y); NFL; Ski Clb; Chorus; School Musical; JV Sftbl; Var L Tennis; JV Trk; Var Stat Vllybl; High Hon Roll; NHS; Lib Art.

MIGDALIA, DEJESUS; John Jay HS; Brooklyn, NY; (Y); 14/537; Vllybl; Hon Roll; Math, Alg & Spnsh Awds 84-85; Trvl.

MIGLIACCIO, RICHARD; Farmingdale HS; N Massapequa, NY; (Y); JV Lcrss; Hon Roll; NHS.

MIGLIAZZO, ANTHONY; Niagara Falls HS; Niagara Falls, NY; (Y); Key Clb; Var Socr; Hon Roll; Jr NHS; NHS; Prfct Atten Awd; Cert Top 25 3 Yr Ave 83; Cert Top 10 83; Cert Achvt Natl Hstry Day 85; Bus Adm.

MIGLIN, ROBERT S; Holland Patent HS; Stittville, NY; (Y); 87/200; Trs FBLA; Var L Wrstlng; Hon Roll; Paul Smiths Coll; Forstry.

MIGLIO, CHRISTINE; John Dewey HS; Brooklyn, NY; (Y); Girl Scts; Yrbk Stf; Exec Secy.

MIGNELLA, GABRIEL; Bayside HS; Bayside, NY; (Y); 16/650; Am Leg Boys St; Cmnty Wkr; Political Wkr; Lit Mag; NHS; Rotary Awd; Church Yth Grp; Drama Clb; German Clb; Intnl Clb; Rotry Intertl Exc Stu Schlrshp 85; Cert Apprctn 85; Am Leg Boys ST Cert Attrny Cnslr 85; Bio.

MIGNONE, EDWARD J; Eastchester HS; Scarsdale, NY; (Y); 7/163; Pres Spanish Clb; Jazz Band; Mrchg Band; School Musical; Symp Band; High Hon Roll; Prfct Atten Awd; Spanish NHS; Ciba-Geigy Sci Awd 85; The Cooper Union; Eng.

MIGNONE, MARIE A; Hornell SR HS; Hornell, NY; (Y); 40/200; Latin Clb; Chorus; JV Cheerleading; Var L Sftbl; Hon Roll; Steuben Cnty Nrs & Tchrs Assoc Schlrshp Awd 85; Alfred ST Coll; Nrs.

MIHALKO, CINDY; Rensselaer JR & SR HS; Rensselaer, NY; (S); Yrbk Bus Mgr; Pres Soph Cls; Pres Jr Cls; Pres Sr Cls; Rep Stu Cncl; JV Cheerleading; Stat Ftbl; JV Var Sftbl; DAR Awd; Hon Roll; JR SR Prom Prncss 84; Ftbl Hmcmng Queen 85; Prom Ct; Hudson Valley CC; Human Svcs.

MIKELS, SUE; Union-Endicott HS; Endicott, NY; (Y); Nwsp Stf; Rep Frsh Cls; Rep Soph Cls; Rep Jr Cls; JV Var Bsktbl; Var Socr; Var Socr; Hon Roll; Pres Physcl Ftns Awd 82; Hist Clb 84-85; Delhi; Vet.

MIKI, REBECCA A; Fairport HS; Nashua, NH; (Y); French Clb; Intnl Clb; Yrbk Stf; Lit Mag; Sec Soph Cls; Sec Jr Cls; Sec Sr Cls; Hon Roll; NHS; St Schlr; NYS Regents Schlrshp 85; U MI; Sci.

MIKLAUCIC, SHAWN A; Pittsford-Merdon HS; Pittsford, NY; (Y); Drama Clb; Chrmn Pres Exploring; Latin Clb; Pres Model UN; School Play; Nwsp Stf; Capt Bsktbl; NHS; Ntl Merit SF; Debate Tm; Law Explrng Slvr E Awd 85; MVP JV Bsktbl Tm 85; Hstry.

MIKOLAJCZAK, BERNADETTE; Immaculate Acad; Hamburg, NY; (Y); Church Yth Grp; Debate Tm; JA; Nwsp Stf; Lit Mag; JV Cheerleading; Hon Roll; Ntl Merit Ltr; NEDT Awd; 4 Yr HS Schlrshp 82-86; Canisius Coll; Lawyer.

MIKOWSKI, KAREN A; Cheektowaga Central HS; Cheektowaga, NY; (Y); 28/204; JCL; Keywanettes; Ski Clb; Band; Concert Band; Mrchg Band; Yrbk Stf; Var Fld Hcky; NHS; Hon Roll; NYS Regnts Schlrshp 85; Nrs.

MIKULKO, LYDIA; Hillcrest HS; Kew Gardens, NY; (Y); Trs Sec Church Yth Grp; Office Aide; Chorus; Church Choir; Trs Frsh Cls; Hon Roll; Dist Wnnr Ntl Piano Aud 82; NY St Regents Schlrshp 84; Fordham U; Bus.

MIKUS, JAY; Cicero-North Syracuse HS; Clay, NY; (S); Church Yth Grp; Math Clb; Ski Clb; JV Socr; Var Trk; Colgate; Spts Med.

MILANES, MAX R; Bronx Science HS; New York, NY; (Y); Math Clb; Science Clb; Lit Mag; Hnr Lst Of Wstnghse Comptn 85; Chanclrs Roll Of Hnr 85; Attrny.

MILANESI, LORI E; Academy Of St Joseph HS; Ronkonkoma, NY; (Y); 2/121; Drama Clb; Hosp Aide; Model UN; Pep Clb; Science Clb; NHS; Regnts Schlrshp 85; Presdntl Acadmc Ftnss Awd 85; Fairfield U; Bio.

MILANO, ROBERT J; North Shore HS; Sea Cliff, NY; (Y); Am Leg Boys St; Key Clb; Ski Clb; Varsity Clb; Yrbk Stf; Rep Stu Cncl; JV L Socr; Var L Trk; SUNY-OSWEGO; Bus Adm.

MILAVEC, DANIELLE; Oneonta SR HS; Oneonta, NY; (Y); 7/184; Q&S; Ski Clb; Varsity Clb; Nwsp Bus Mgr; JV Var Cheerleading; High Hon Roll; Hon Roll; NHS; Rep Soph Cls; Trs Jr Cls; Hghst Stndng Mth, Frnch III; Bio.

MILAZZO, CHRISTINE A; C W Baker HS; Syracuse, NY; (Y); 36/441; VICA; Powder Puff Ftbl; High Hon Roll; Hon Roll; Jr NHS; NHS; Johnson & Wales Coll; Htl Mgmt.

MILAZZO, GINA; T R Proctor HS; Utica, NY; (Y); Dance Clb; Pep Clb; Yrbk Stf; Var Cheerleading; Hon Roll.

MILAZZO, LISA; Grover Cleveland HS; Buffalo, NY; (Y); CAP; Science Clb; Nwsp Rptr; Sec Frsh Cls; Sec Jr Cls; Cheerleading; Swmmng; Hon Roll; Prof Pilt.

MILBANK, DANA TIMOTHY; S H Calhoun HS; Merrick, NY; (Y); 5/330; Jazz Band; Nwsp Ed-Chief; Nwsp Sprt Ed; Var Bsktbl; Var Capt Crs Cntry; Capt Var Trk; NHS; Ntl Merit Ltr; Exploring; Hosp Aide; All ST & Cnty Band 84-85; All Div Crss Cntry & Conf Medlst Spg Trck 84-85; Med.

MILBAUER, DEBORAH; Woodlands HS; Hartsdale, NY; (Y); Rep Stu Cncl; Var Capt Fld Hcky; Var Capt Socr; Trk; NHS.

MILBORROW, MICHELE; Greece Athena HS; Rochester, NY; (Y); 40/275; School Musical; Sec VP Symp Band; Hon Roll; Church Yth Grp; JA.

MILCH, DAVID H; John H Glenn HS; E Northport, NY; (Y); 4/260; Pres MMM; School Musical; School Play; Swing Chorus; Lit Mag; Trs NHS; SAR Awd; Drama Clb; Mathletes; Temple Yth Grp; Josten Fndtn Ntl Schlrshp 85; Elwood Music Spnsrs Outstndng Mscn Awd 85; Wesleyan U; Theatre.

MILCZARSKI, THERESA V; Pulaski JR SR HS; Pulaski, NY; (S); French Clb; Math Clb; Ski Clb; Concert Band; Mrchg Band; Socr; Trk; Hon Roll; SUNY Cortland; Physcl Thrpy.

MILEK, SUSAN; Cardinal O Hara HS; North Tonawanda, NY; (S); 8/130; Sec Frsh Cls; Pres Soph Cls; Pres Sr Cls; VP Stu Cncl; Var Capt Bsktbl; Sec NHS; Office Aide; Pep Clb; Quiz Bowl; Yrbk Sprt Ed; All Cath Vlybl & Sftbl 1st Tm; Female Athl Of Yr; Army Outstndng Schlr/Athl Awd; U Of Dayton; Pre Law.

MILENKOVITCH, ANDREW; St Hildsa And St Hughs HS; New York, NY; (Y); Dance Clb; School Play; Stage Crew; Nwsp Stf; Yrbk Phtg; Cit Awd; Intlgnc.

MILES, ANNETTE; Fayetteville-Manlius HS; East Cleveland, OH; (Y); 89/335; Church Yth Grp; Var Cheerleading; Var Trk; Hon Roll; Jr NHS; Pres Schlr; Computer Clb; FHA; Hosp Aide; JA; Latin Awd 84; U Of Chicago; Pre-Med.

MILES, BARBARA; Hempstead HS; Hempstead, NY; (S); 64/333; Church Yth Grp; Pep Clb; Church Choir; Trs Soph Cls; Stu Cncl; Accntng.

MILES, BERNADETTE; Washington Irving HS; New York, NY; (Y); Church Yth Grp; Chorus; Church Choir; Rep Frsh Cls; Capt Badmtn; Capt Coach Actv; Capt Score Keeper; Var Sftbl; Capt Tennis; Capt Vllybl; Nrsg Awd 90 Avg 83; 2 Awd Gym Sprts & Atten 85; Purchase Coll; Nrsg.

MILES, GINNY; Victor Central SR HS; Victor, NY; (Y); JA; Color Guard; Nwsp Stf; Sftbl; Vllybl; High Hon Roll; Hon Roll; Community Coll; Bus.

MILES, JEFF; Churchville Chili HS; Spencerport, NY; (Y); High Hon Roll; Hon Roll; Prfct Atten Awd; JV Var Socr.

MILES, MICHAEL G; Ballston Spa HS; Ballston Spa, NY; (Y); 12/240; Church Yth Grp; Pres Am Leg Aux Girls St; Service Clb; Stage Crew; 4-H Awd; High Hon Roll; NHS; John Robens Memrl Prz Hghst Ave Algbr 82; Pres Acadmc Fit Awd 85; Recog Partcptn Math Cntst 83; Potsdam Coll Of SUNY; Comp Sci.

MILETI, KIM; West Islip HS; West Islip, NY; (Y); 103/525; Aud/Vis; Dance Clb; Library Aide; Office Aide; Chorus; Var Cheerleading; Stat Wrstlng; Hon Roll; NHS; Prfct Atten Awd; Acadmc Excllnc Sequntl Math III 83-84; Suny-Cortland; Scndry Ed.

MILETICH, JOSEPH M; Monsignor Farrell HS; Staten Island, NY; (Y); 49/300; Cmnty Wkr; French Clb; Im Bsktbl; Im Bowling; Ftbl; Hon Roll; NY ST Rgnts Schlrshp 85; Frnch Awds 82-84; Manhattan Coll; Elec Engrng.

MILIN, GREGORY S; Mt St Michael Acad; Bronx, NY; (Y); 3/286; Yrbk Stf; Var Bsbl; JV Ftbl; Im Wt Lftg; Hon Roll; NHS; MMCC Vrsty Bsktbl Chmps 83-84; Spnsh Awd 83-84; U Of Notre Dame; Aerospace Engr.

MILIOTTO, LYNNE; Mount Saint Mary Acad; Tonawanda, NY; (Y); Church Yth Grp; Cmnty Wkr; Dance Clb; Chorus; Lit Mag; Cit Awd; Hon Roll; YES Outstndng Serv Awd 84.

MILIOTTO, MARK; East Aurora HS; East Aurora, NY; (S); 12/183; Boys Clb Am; Boy Scts; Church Yth Grp; Cmnty Wkr; JV Var Bsbl; JV Ftbl; Capt Ice Hcky; Var L Swmmng; Hon Roll; Jr NHS; Biochem Rsrch.

MILITELLO, MARTIN; Forestville Central Schl; Forestville, NY; (Y); Band; Concert Band; Jazz Band; Mrchg Band; School Musical; Symp Band; Stu Cncl; Ftbl; L Armstrong Jazz Awd 85; JR All Amer Hall Fame 84-85; Amer Mus Fndtn Awd 85; Fredonia ST; Mus.

MILITELLO, THOMAS; Thomas R Proctor HS; Utica, NY; (Y); Am Leg Boys St; CAP; Debate Tm; Math Tm; Model UN; High Hon Roll; NHS; Aerontcl Engr.

MILLAN, ROBERT; De Witt Clinton HS; Bronx, NY; (Y); ROTC; Drill Tm; Cit Awd.

MILLAN, ROBERT; Franklin D Roosevelt HS; Brooklyn, NY; (Y); Drama Clb; Stat Wt Lftg; Stat Wrstlng; Staten Island Coll; Comp Prgmr.

MILLAR, WENDY K; Camden SR HS; Blossvale, NY; (Y); Sec Debate Tm; Drama Clb; Chorus; School Musical; School Play; Ed Nwsp Ed-Chief; Var Trk; High Hon Roll; NHS; Ntl Merit Ltr; Simons Rock.

MILLARD, JILL; Fairport HS; Fairport, NY; (Y); Concert Band; Jazz Band; Mrchg Band; High Hon Roll; Ntl Merit SF; Business.

MILLARD, PAUL; F D Roosevelt HS; Hyde Pk, NY; (Y); JV Var Bsbl; Var L Ftbl; Var Capt Ice Hcky; High Hon Roll; Hon Roll; NHS; Poughkeepsie Jrnl Athl Of Wk & Hcky All Star 85; NJ Leag All Star 84-85; Oswego; Bus Adm.

MILLARD, REBECCA; Prattsburg Baptist Christian HS; Naples, NY; (Y); 2/3; Church Yth Grp; Library Aide; Quiz Bowl; Church Choir; School Musical; VP Jr Cls; VP Sr Cls; Stu Cncl; Cit Awd; Hon Roll; Detentn Awd 83-85; 2nd Hgst Avg 84-85; Liberty U; Music.

MILLBYER, L LYNN; North Rose-Wolcott HS; N Rose, NY; (Y); Church Yth Grp; FBLA; Science Clb; Ski Clb; Varsity Clb; Stat Bsktbl; Var Bowling; Vllybl; High Hon Roll; Hon Roll; Arch.

MILLER, ADRIANNE J; Lake Shore Central HS; Angola, NY; (Y); French Clb; Chorus; Concert Band; School Musical; Pres Frsh Cls; VP Stu Cncl; Var Socr; Var Tennis; High Hon Roll; Jr NHS; Band Achvt Awd 83; Acctng.

MILLER, AMY; Alden Central HS; Lancaster, NY; (Y); 66/200; Church Yth Grp; French Clb; Science Clb; School Play; Im Vllybl; Pres Acad Ftns Awd 85; Amer Legion Aux Schl Awd 85; Erie CC; Fd Svc Mgmt.

MILLER, AMY; Gowanda Central HS; Gowanda, NY; (Y); 18/138; VP AFS; Spanish Clb; School Musical; Stage Crew; Nwsp Bus Mgr; Nwsp Rptr; Yrbk Stf; Hon Roll; NHS; Prfct Atten Awd; Ed.

MILLER, ANNEMARIE; Buffalo Academy Of The Sacred Heart; Williamsville, NY; (Y); Hosp Aide; Ski Clb; Spanish Clb; Yrbk Stf; Rep Frsh Cls; VP Soph Cls; Cheerleading; High Hon Roll; Hon Roll; NHS; Pre Law.

MILLER, BETH; Lawrence HS; Woodmere, NY; (Y); 85/397; Spanish Clb; Capt Bsktbl; High Hon Roll; NHS; Regents Schlrshp Wnnr 85; MVP Bsktbl Awd 83; U MA.

MILLER, CAROL A; Fredonia HS; Fredonia, NY; (Y); Church Yth Grp; French Clb; Hosp Aide; Orch; Nwsp Stf; Yrbk Stf; Var L Tennis; Hon Roll; Pres Schlr; Regnts Schlrshp 85; Hnrd Rotary Clb; ST U Coll Geneseo; Bus.

MILLER, CATHRYN A; Huntington HS; Huntington Sta, NY; (Y); 16/433; Band; VP Chorus; Concert Band; VP Orch; School Musical; NHS; AFS; Drama Clb; Mrchg Band; Pep Band; Amer Legn Music Awd 82; 1st Pl Great Neck Symph Socty Comptn 84; 2nd Pl Suffolk Cnty Math Cntst 84; Music Perf.

MILLER, CHARLENE A; Rome Free Acad; Rome, NY; (Y); 2/512; Key Clb; Tennis; Bausch & Lomb Sci Awd; Kiwanis Awd; NHS; Pres Schlr; Sal; Prncpls Awd 84; J G Jeroko Chem Mem Awd, NYS Rgnts Schlrshps 85; Rensselaer Polytech Inst; Pr Md.

MILLER, CHERYL; Frontier Central HS; Hamburg, NY; (S); Aud/Vis; Sec Pres Church Yth Grp; VP Exploring; Sec German Clb; Sec Pres Girl Scts; Stu Cncl; High Hon Roll; NHS; Cmnty Wkr; 4-H; Rifle Tm Lttr 85; Exch Stu Germany 85; Crmnl Justc.

MILLER, CHRISTINE; Lasalle SR HS; Niagara Falls, NY; (Y); Church Yth Grp; Library Aide; High Hon Roll; Hon Roll; NHS; Arch.

MILLER, CHRISTINE ANN; Garden City SR HS; Garden City, NY; (Y); 70/320; Hosp Aide; Pres Latin Clb; Stage Crew; Mgr(s); Hon Roll; Ntl Merit Ltr; Regents Schlrshp 85; Assoc Retarded Childrn Serv Awd 83-84; Cert Latin Lang 82-83; Colgate U; Naturl Sci.

MILLER, CHRISTOPHER; Scarsdale HS; Scarsdale, NY; (Y); Boy Scts; Concert Band; Mrchg Band; School Play; Symp Band; JV Crs Cntry; Var Swmmng; Var Trk; Var Wrstlng; Ntl Merit Schol; Lehigh U; Chem Engrng.

MILLER, CLINTON; Bishop Loughlin M HS; Booklyn, NY; (Y); 4/180; Cmnty Wkr; Nwsp Stf; JV Bsbl; Var Capt Bsktbl; Hon Roll; Math 2nd Hnrs; Ntl Stu Athl Awd; Most Ded Bsktbl V; Southern Connecticut St U.

MILLER, COREY A; Great Neck North HS; Great Neck, NY; (Y); 3/273; Debate Tm; Spanish Clb; Nwsp Ed-Chief; NCTE Awd; Ntl Merit SF; Frgn Svc.

MILLER, DAN; Union Endicott HS; Endicott, NY; (S); Concert Band; Jazz Band; Mrchg Band; Orch; Pep Band; Nwsp Stf; Hon Roll; Ithaca College; Music Educ.

MILLER, DANIEL; Delaware Academy And Central Schl; Treadwell, NY; (Y); Boy Scts; Science Clb; Variety Show; Nwsp Stf; Hon Roll; Prfct Atten Awd; Aerontcl Engrng.

MILLER, DANIELLE; Jamaica HS; Jamaica, NY; (Y); 6/600; JA; Office Aide; Science Clb; Teachers Aide; Yrbk Stf.

MILLER, DAVID; Farmingdale HS; Farmingdale, NY; (Y); 26/644; French Clb; Hosp Aide; Temple Yth Grp; Band; Mrchg Band; Symp Band; Hon Roll; NHS; Sci.

MILLER, DAWN; Greece Athena HS; Rochester, NY; (Y); Church Yth Grp; FBLA.

MILLER, DEANNA LYNN; James E Sperry HS; Rochester, NY; (Y); 20/300; GAA; Latin Clb; Var Bsktbl; Ftbl; Var Vllybl; High Hon Roll; NHS; Pep Clb; Jr NHS; Latin Hnr Soc 85; Acad Letter 85; Athltc Letter 85; Phys Thrpy.

MILLER, DIANA; Notre Dame HS; Le Roy, NY; (S); 2/67; JV Capt Bsktbl; JV Cheerleading; Hon Roll; NHS; Earth Sci Awd Hgst Avr 83-84; Bus Admn.

MILLER, EDUARDO; Cardinal Spellman HS; Bronx, NY; (Y); Chess Clb; Bsbl; Bsktbl; Var Capt Bowling; Ftbl; Vllybl; Wt Lftg; High Hon Roll; Hon Roll; Prfct Atten Awd; Bowling 82-85; 1st Hnrs 82-84; 2nd Hnrs 84-85; Elec Engrng.

MILLER, ERIC; Paul D Schreiber HS; Port Washington, NY; (Y); 69/413; Computer Clb; Mrchg Band; School Musical; Symp Band; Nwsp Stf; Rep Stu Cncl; NHS; Band Awd 83.

MILLER, GARY; Onteora JR SR HS; Glenford, NY; (S); 18/245; Mgr Aud/Vis; German Clb; Quiz Bowl; Hon Roll; NHS; Bst Acctng Stu 83-84; Acctng.

MILLER, GENE; Warwick Valley HS; Warwick, NY; (Y); 94/200; Rptr FFA; JV Var Ftbl; Var L Trk; Hon Roll; Natl Ci Olympd-Bio 85; Knghts Of Clmbs-John F Kennedy Awd 85; Bus Mgmt.

MILLER, GREG; Bishop Kearney HS; Webster, NY; (Y); JA; Bsbl; JV Var Lcrss; JV Var Socr; JV Trk; High Hon Roll; Hon Roll; JA Co Of Yr Awd 84-85; Engrng.

MILLER, HELENE; The Wheatley HS; Albertson, NY; (Y); 8/137; Temple Yth Grp; Sec School Musical; Sec School Play; Variety Show; Yrbk Ed-Chief; JV Var Cheerleading; Fld Hcky; NHS; Regents Schlrshp Fin 85; Am Vet Schlrshp Fin 85; U PA; Med.

MILLER, JACQUELYN LISA; East Meadow HS; E Meadow, NY; (S); 62/414; Cmnty Wkr; Key Clb; Temple Yth Grp; Orch; Nwsp Rptr; Lit Mag; Bsktbl; Vllybl; Hon Roll; All-Div Vllybl Tm 84; Pediatrician.

MILLER, JAMES; Fayetteville-Manlius HS; Manlius, NY; (Y); 5/44; Computer Clb; Debate Tm; JA; Latin Clb; Model UN; NFL; Political Wkr; Stu Cncl; Hon Roll; NHS; NY ST Regnt Schlrshp 85; Wesleyan U; Ec.

MILLER, JAMES; Sandy Creek Central HS; Sandy Creek, NY; (Y); Computer Clb; Ftbl; Mc Donalds Pulaski Schlrshp 85; Schrshp Achvt & Fincl Consdtns; Jefferson Comm Coll; Comp Sci.

MILLER, JAMES D; Hammondsport Central HS; Hammondsport, NY; (Y); 1/75; VP Church Yth Grp; Computer Clb; Capt Scholastic Bowl; Chorus; Church Choir; Nwsp Rptr; Var Capt Tennis; High Hon Roll; NHS; Val; NY ST Regents Schlrshp 85; NROTC Schlrshp 85; Bst Defensive Driver Awd 84; U S Naval Acad; Comp Sci.

MILLER, JANET; Saramac Central HS; Morrisonville, NY; (S); 28/127; Office Aide; Teachers Aide; Hon Roll; Olva; Off Worker.

MILLER, JEFFREY D; Vestal SR HS; Vestal, NY; (Y); 30/452; VP French Clb; Pres Intnl Clb; Pres Spanish Clb; School Play; JV Var Ftbl; Ice Hcky; Wt Lftg; High Hon Roll; NHS; Jessie Baker Scholar Awd 85-86; Pst 89 Achvt Scholar Awd 85-86; NYS Schl Music Assn Awds/Mdls 80-82; SUNY Binghamton; Frgn Lang.

MILLER, JENNIFER A; Jamesville-De Witt HS; De Witt, NY; (Y); Model UN; Temple Yth Grp; Chorus; School Musical; Stage Crew; Swing Chorus; Variety Show; Hon Roll; Visual Perfrmng Arts.

MILLER, JILL; Charles H Roth HS; W Henrietta, NY; (Y); 15/210; 4-H; High Hon Roll; Hon Roll; Jr NHS; NHS; Outstndng Admin Support Awd Coop Work Experience 84-85; Bus Adm.

MILLER, JILL M; Union-Endicott HS; Simi Valley, CA; (Y); 4-H; French Clb; Ski Clb; Band; Flag Corp; Mrchg Band; Rep Frsh Cls; Rep Soph Cls; Rep Jr Cls; 4-H Awd; Pres Ftns Awd 84-85; CA ST U Northridge; Acctg.

MILLER, JOSEPH; Tappan Zee HS; Blauvelt, NY; (Y); 36/270; Boy Scts; JA; Math Clb; Math Tm; Ski Clb; Chorus; Madrigals; Yrbk Stf; Var Golf; Mu Alp Tht; Finance.

MILLER, KAREN L; New Rochelle HS; New Rochelle, NY; (Y); 85/600; Political Wkr; Ski Clb; Rep Jr Cls; Rep Stu Cncl; JV Capt Cheerleading; Var Capt Tennis; NHS; Soph Cls; Regent Schlrshp Wnnr 85; All Conf Tnns Team A-Div 84; MVP Vrsty Tnns Team 84; U Of MI; Polt Sci.

MILLER, KATHLEEN A; East Syracuse-Minoa Central HS; E Syracuse, NY; (Y); 6/350; Latin Clb; Science Clb; Ski Clb; Variety Show; Yrbk Stf; High Hon Roll; Jr NHS; NHS; Ntl Merit Ltr; St Schlr; NYS Regents Schlrshp 85; Tutorial Pgm Mt Holyoke Coll 85-86; Mt Holyoke Coll; Psychbio Rsrch.

MILLER, KEITH; Churchville-Chili HS; Rochester, NY; (Y); 39/317; Boy Scts; Math Tm; Chorus; Madrigals; School Musical; Lit Mag; Crs Cntry; High Hon Roll; NHS; Ntl Ldrshp Orgnztn 84 & 85; Ntl Schl Choral Awd 84-85; Lee Cup Awd From Faclty 84-85; U Of Buffalo-Law.

MILLER, KIMBERLY; Evander Childs HS; Bronx, NY; (Y); Exploring; Chorus; Yrbk Stf; Pres Soph Cls; Rep Jr Cls; Vllybl; Hon Roll; Howard U; Acctng.

MILLER, KIMBERLY S; Pittsford HS; Pittsford, NY; (Y); Am Leg Aux Girls St; Church Yth Grp; Drama Clb; Pres Pep Clb; Chorus; Yrbk Ed-Chief; Yrbk Stf; Capt Var Cheerleading; NHS; Williams Coll Bk Awd 84.

MILLER, LAUREN; Little Falls JR SR HS; Little Falls, NY; (Y); VP Sec Church Yth Grp; Drama Clb; GAA; Spanish Clb; Band; Concert Band; Jazz Band; Mrchg Band; Yrbk Stf; Var Capt Bsktbl; AHSA 84 & 85; MVP Bsktbl 84; Utica Coll.

MILLER, LAURIE; Chenango Forks HS; Port Crane, NY; (Y); 70/183; Church Yth Grp; Teachers Aide; Chorus; Color Guard; Concert Band; Mrchg Band; Symp Band; Hon Roll; JP Sousa Awd; Sec 4-H; David E Frank Mem Awd 85; Deaf Inrprtr.

MILLER, LAWRENCE JAMES; Starpoint HS; No Tonawanda, NY; (Y); 15/194; Debate Tm; Band; Concert Band; Mrchg Band; Symp Band; Nwsp Stf; Hon Roll; NHS; NYS Rgnts Schlrshp, Essay Wnnr 85; Intern Co Leg & Intern Ldr 83-84; All St & Co Bnds 83-84 Bnd Pres; U WI; Pol Sci.

MILLER, LEE; Amsterdam HS; Amsterdam, NY; (Y); 7/300; Ski Clb; Varsity Clb; Rep Frsh Cls; Rep Soph Cls; Pres Jr Cls; Pres Sr Cls; JV Bsbl; JV Capt Bsktbl; Var Ftbl; Hon Roll; Bus Admin.

MILLER, LISA ANNE; Jamesville-Dewitt HS; Manlius, NY; (Y); Var Crs Cntry; Var Trk; Hon Roll; Acctng.

MILLER, LISA D; East HS; Big Flats, NY; (Y); 21/213; Quiz Bowl; Varsity Clb; Yrbk Stf; Trs Stu Cncl; L Tennis; High Hon Roll; NHS.

MILLER, LORI; Cato-Meridian HS; Cato, NY; (Y); Girl Scts; Library Aide; Teachers Aide; Color Guard; JV Vllybl; Hon Roll; NHS; Bellarmine Coll; Comp Sci.

MILLER, LORRIE; Marion Central HS; Walworth, NY; (Y); French Clb; Sec FHA; Ski Clb; Mgr(s); Socr; Trk; Vllybl; Hon Roll; Sec NHS; O Var Lttrs In Trck; Air Force; Phy Thrpy.

MILLER, MARC; Union-Endicott HS; Endicott, NY; (Y); Art Clb; Debate Tm; Drama Clb; Speech Tm; School Play; Socr; Arch.

MILLER, MARK; Aquinas Inst; Rochester, NY; (Y); High Hon Roll; Hon Roll; MVP Ftbl Leag 82; Chmpnshp Trphy Sftbl Leag 83; AP Europn Course 83-84; Intnl Reltns.

MILLER, MARK W; East Syracuse-Minoa HS; Minoa, NY; (Y); 3/338; Church Yth Grp; Ski Clb; Band; Concert Band; School Musical; Variety Show; High Hon Roll; Jr NHS; NHS; Deans Scholar Awd Cornell U 85; Cornell U; Human Services.

MILLER, MELAINA J; Edmeston Central Schl; Edmeston, NY; (Y); Hosp Aide; Red Cross Aide; Teachers Aide; School Play; Socr; JV Var Vllybl; Hon Roll; Prfct Atten Awd; Pres Frsh Cls; Off Jr Cls; Cndystrpng 100 Hrs Awd 82; Vlybl Lttr 85; Mohawk Valley CC; Chldhd Educ.

MILLER, MICHAEL; Dansville SR HS; Groveland, NY; (Y); 13/134; Am Leg Boys St; Pres Church Yth Grp; Math Clb; Concert Band; Mrchg Band; Yrbk Stf; VP Sr Cls; Var Swmmng; NHS; Clarkson U; Engrng.

MILLER, MICHELLE; Waverly HS; Waverly, NY; (Y); Nwsp Stf; Rep Stu Cncl; Var L Trk; High Hon Roll; NHS; Rotary Awd; NY ST Regnts Schlrshp; Natl Merit Hnr Rl; Pres Acadmc Ftns Awd; Arnot Ogden; Nrsg.

MILLER, NANCY; East Hampton HS; E Hampton, NY; (Y); 9/116; Church Yth Grp; Library Aide; Chorus; Orch; Yrbk Stf; Cheerleading; High Hon Roll; Hon Roll; Jr NHS; NHS; Engr.

MILLER, NEIL E; Clinton Central HS; Clinton, NY; (Y); 9/133; Key Clb; Band; Yrbk Sprt Ed; JV Bsktbl; Var L Crs Cntry; Var Trk; High Hon Roll; Hon Roll; NHS; Prfct Atten Awd; Sci Fair 1st Pl 84; Astrnmy.

MILLER, PAUL; Kenmore East; Tonawanda, NY; (Y); Drama Clb; MMM; PAVAS; Acpl Chr; Chorus; School Musical; School Play; Stage Crew; Swing Chorus; Theatr Arts Hnr Rll 84-85; PTA Cert Achv 84-85; NYSSMA Al-ST Vocl Solo 85; Daemen Coll; Bio.

MILLER, PETER K; Mount St Michael HS; Yonkers, NY; (Y); 36/335; Trs Am Leg Boys St; Church Yth Grp; French Clb; Stage Crew; Stat Ftbl; Im Ice Hcky; Im Sftbl; Hon Roll; Peer Grp Facilitation Pgm 84-85; Med.

MILLER, PHILIP; Mynderse Acad; Seneca Falls, NY; (S); Am Leg Boys St; Boy Scts; Model UN; Political Wkr; Pres Stu Cncl; Capt JV Ftbl; JV Lcrss; Capt JV Wrstlng; DAR Awd; Nazareth Coll-Rochester; Hstry.

MILLER, RAYMOND; Pelham Mem HS; Pelham, NY; (Y); 35/154; Aud/Vis; Boy Scts; Library Aide; JV Var Bsbl; JV Var Bsktbl; JV Ftbl; JV Var Wt Lftg; Iona; Comp Tech.

MILLER II, RICHARD J; Lackawanna Senior HS; Lackawanna, NY; (Y); 6/288; Varsity Clb; Var JV Bsktbl; Var Trk; Var Capt Vllybl; Wt Lftg; High Hon Roll; NHS; Ntl Merit SF; MVP Vllybl 85; Super Player Awd Bsktbl 85; Rochester Inst Of Tech; Engrng.

MILLER, ROGENA; Webster SR HS; Penfield, NY; (Y); 46/572; VP Church Yth Grp; Sec German Clb; JA; Band; Church Choir; Concert Band; Mrchg Band; Nwsp Rptr; Rep Frsh Cls; Sec Jr Cls; Rochstr Ganntt Newspr Yth Cares 84; Boy Scts Of Am Yng Am 84; Ger Hnr Soc 84-85; Exchng Stu Ger 84; Talladega Clg; Med.

MILLER, ROGER; Churchville-Chili HS; Rochester, NY; (Y); Boy Scts; Chorus; Var Crs Cntry; Var Trk; Mansfield U; Polt Sci.

MILLER, SHANE; Sodus Central Schl; Sodus, NY; (Y); 11/100; Latin Clb; Pres Science Clb; Crs Cntry; Hon Roll; Prfct Atten Awd; Monroe CC; Elctrnc Engrng.

MILLER, SHANIECE; Kensington HS; Buffalo, NY; (Y); Computer Clb; FNA; Science Clb.

MILLER, SHERI R; Brighton HS; Rochester, NY; (Y); Aud/Vis; Mgr(s); High Hon Roll; Hon Roll; NHS; Biotech.

MILLER, STEVE; Gowanda Central Schl; Collins, NY; (Y); 15/121; Am Leg Boys St; Computer Clb; French Clb; Rep Soph Cls; Pres Jr Cls; Pres Sr Cls; JV Wrstlng; Hon Roll; Fredonia; Acctg.

MILLER, SUSAN; Bishop Kearney HS; Rochester, NY; (Y); Service Clb; Yrbk Stf; St John Fisher; Accntng.

MILLER, SUSAN; Kings Park SR HS; Northport, NY; (Y); Art Clb; Church Yth Grp; Cmnty Wkr; Computer Clb; Drama Clb; Girl Scts; Service Clb; School Play; Variety Show; Yrbk Stf; Bus Mgmt.

MILLER, SUSAN; Lewiston Porter SR HS; Lewiston, NY; (Y); 23/273; Trs Church Yth Grp; Drama Clb; French Clb; Hosp Aide; Ski Clb; Church Choir; Orch; School Play; Yrbk Phtg; High Hon Roll; Roberts Weslyn; Nrsng.

MILLER, SUSANNE; Mercy HS; Old Chatham, NY; (Y); 5/69; 4-H; Yrbk Phtg; Yrbk Stf; Lit Mag; 4-H Awd; High Hon Roll; Rochstr Inst Of Tech Schlrshp 85; Mercy HS Art Hnr Awd 85; Natl Hnr Soc Awds Spnsh 3,Photgpy,Comp Sci; Rochester Inst Tech; Grphc Dsgn.

MILLER, SUZAN A; Andrew Jackson HS; St Albans, NY; (Y); Lit Mag; Hon Roll; Ntl Merit Ltr; Elten Doherty Awd For Excell In Wrtng 85.

MILLER, SYLVIA; Onondaga Central HS; Nedrow, NY; (S); Church Yth Grp; FBLA; German Clb; Spanish Clb; Church Choir; Var Trk; Im Wt Lftg; Hon Roll; U Buffalo; Mech Engrng.

MILLER, TERESA; Mayville Central Schl; Dewittville, NY; (Y); Church Yth Grp; Pres Sec Spanish Clb; Chorus; Church Choir; Bowling; Vllybl; High Hon Roll; Hon Roll; Jr NHS; NHS; Presdntl Acadmc Ftns Awds Pgm 85; 3-1-3 Partcptn Awd 85; Suny Fredonia; Elem Ed.

MILLER, THEODORE; Oneonta HS; Oneonta, NY; (Y); Church Yth Grp; French Clb; Ski Clb; Varsity Clb; JV Var Bsbl; JV Bsktbl; JV Var Socr; Hon Roll; Excell Engl 85; Sci.

MILLER, THOMAS A; Penn Yan Acad; Penn Yan, NY; (Y); 1/200; Scholastic Bowl; Varsity Clb; Pres Frsh Cls; Pres Soph Cls; Rep Jr Cls; Rep Sr Cls; Rep Stu Cncl; Var Capt Bsktbl; Var Capt Trk; Cit Awd; Elmira Key Awd 85; Accordian Prfncy Awd; Cornell U; Cvl Engrng.

MILLER, TODD; Kenmore West HS; Kenmore, NY; (Y); Boy Scts; Church Yth Grp; Ski Clb; Pres Varsity Clb; High Hon Roll; Hon Roll; Var L Socr; Var L Tennis; Comp Tech.

MILLER, TODD; Onteora Central HS; Boiceville, NY; (S); Co-Capt Math Tm; Quiz Bowl; Jazz Band; L Var Socr; Trk; High Hon Roll; NHS; Ntl Merit Fndtn Hnr Roll 85.

MILLER, TRACY; Pierson HS; Sag Harbor, NY; (Y); 7/41; Office Aide; Spanish Clb; Chorus; Nwsp Stf; Yrbk Stf; Fld Hcky; High Hon Roll; Hon Roll; NHS; Hnrs Awd 83-85; Guidance Offc Asst 85; Distngshd Merit Cert 85; Bus Adm.

MILLER, TRAVIS; Maple Hill HS; Castleton, NY; (S); 12/78; Model UN; Ski Clb; Concert Band; Jazz Band; Rep Stu Cncl; Var L Socr; Ntl Merit Ltr; Outstndng Stu Of Music 83; Spngfld MA Congrs Model 85; High Merit 85; Boston U; Comp.

MILLER, VALERIE M; Lawrence HS; Cedarhurst, NY; (Y); 36/425; Nwsp Phtg; Nwsp Stf; Yrbk Stf; Hon Roll; Hon Roll; NHS; Photographs Displayed 84 & 85; NY U Schlrshp 85; NY U; Accntng.

MILLET, SUSAN M; Beach Channel HS; Belle Harbor, NY; (Y); 14/482; Chorus; Yrbk Ed-Chief; Hon Roll; NHS; Ntl Merit Schol; Hnrs Schlr At Stonybrook 86; Stonybrook.

MILLEVILLE, MARK; Niagara-Wheatfield HS; Sanborn, NY; (Y); Pres Church Yth Grp; Cmnty Wkr; Latin Clb; Teachers Aide; Varsity Clb; Var Capt Bowling; Hon Roll; NHS; Prfct Atten Awd; JV Bsbl; Boys St Fin 85; Bio-Med.

MILLEVILLE, PAMELA J; Niagara Wheatfield HS; Niagara Falls, NY; (Y); 39/314; Church Yth Grp; German Clb; JA; Pep Clb; Chorus; Church Choir; Nwsp Phtg; Socr; High Hon Roll; Hon Roll; Awd 98 Pct Engl 85; Schlrshp SAT NYS Rgnts 85; Fredonia Coll; Engl.

MILLEY, MICHELLE; West Seneca East SR HS; Cheektowaga, NY; (Y); Pres German Clb; Nwsp Stf; Yrbk Stf; Rep Frsh Cls; Rep Soph Cls; Rep Jr Cls; Rep Sr Cls; Var Capt Swmmng; High Hon Roll; NHS; Ntl Grmn Hon Soc 83-85; Grm & Frnch Achvt Awds 82-85; Intl Rltns.

MILLHAM, NANCY E; New Paltz HS; New Paltz, NY; (Y); 14/159; Am Leg Aux Girls St; Var Capt Crs Cntry; JV Socr; Var Trk; High Hon Roll; NHS; Pres Schlr; 3 Athlt/Scholar Awds-U S Army Resrv-Ulster Cnty; Nordic Ski Tm-NY ST 5th & Mid Atlntc Div 2nd; New England Coll; Busnss Admin.

MILLIAN, CRAIG S; Sachem HS; Lk Ronkonkoma, NY; (Y); 38/1380; Radio Clb; Science Clb; Service Clb; Ski Clb; Spanish Clb; Orch; NHS; Ntl Merit Ltr; U Of PA; Bioengineering.

MILLIGAN, MAUDENA W; Hillcrest HS; Springfield Grdns, NY; (Y); 178/793; Cmnty Wkr; Hosp Aide; JA; Math Tm; Office Aide; VICA; Yrbk Stf; Rep Sr Cls; High Hon Roll; NHS; 2nd Pl Med Splng HOSA ST Co Nf 84, 3rd Pl Ntl 84; SUNY Stonybrook; Med.

MILLIGAN, VALERIE L; Taconic Hills HS; Ghent, NY; (Y); 5/140; Church Yth Grp; Nwsp Rptr; Yrbk Ed-Chief; Trs Stu Cncl; JV Fld Hcky; High Hon Roll; Hon Roll; VP NHS; NY ST Regents Schlrshp 85; Frnch Awd 84; Englsh Awd 84; Brigham Young U; Accntnt.

MILLINGTON JR, ROBERT; Stillwater Central HS; Saratoga Spgs, NY; (Y); 6/89; French Clb; Key Clb; Math Clb; Ski Clb; Var JV Bsbl; Var JV Ftbl; Wt Lftg; High Hon Roll; Hon Roll; NHS; Aerspc Engrng.

MILLMAN, JONATHAN T; Dobbs Ferry HS; Dobbs Ferry, NY; (Y); 1/103; AFS; Key Clb; Math Tm; Pres Model UN; Political Wkr; Temple Yth Grp; Stage Crew; Nwsp Ed-Chief; Rep Stu Cncl; Capt Var Socr; Oberlin Bk Awd-Top Engl Stu 84; Top Math & Sci Stu 84; Harvard U; Gvmnt.

MILLS, COLLEEN; Stella Maris HS; Broad Channel, NY; (Y); Teachers Aide; Swmmng; Phy Educ.

MILLS, DANIEL F; West Genesee SR HS; Syracuse, NY; (Y); 87/500; ROTC; Chorus; Concert Band; Drm Mjr(t); Jazz Band; School Musical; Variety Show; Var Capt Trk; High Hon Roll; NHS; Empire ST Games 400 Mtr Dash 84; Indr Trk & Fld States Meet 85; Army ROTC 4 Yr Scholar; Clarkson U; Engrng.

MILLS, DAVID; Niagara Wheatfield SR HS; Niagara Falls, NY; (Y); Math Clb; Hon Roll; NHS; Math Tm; Bowling; US Ntl Ldrshp Awd 85; Comp.

MILLS, DAVID T; North Babylon SR HS; North Babylon, NY; (Y); 62/624; Chess Clb; Mathletes; Orch; French Hon Soc; Jr NHS; NHS; Boy Scts; School Musical; High Hon Roll; Lng Islnd Strng Fstvl 83; SCMEA Music Achvts 83; Bus.

MILLS, GREGORY C; Victor Central HS; Victor, NY; (Y); 4-H; Prfct Atten Awd; 4-H Awd; OH U; Elec Engnrng.

MILLS, JACKI; Walton JR SR HS; Walton, NY; (Y); FHA; Varsity Clb; Nwsp Stf; Var L Cheerleading; Var L Gym; Var Trk; Prfct Atten Awd; Secy Sci.

MILLS, JULIE; Glens Falls SR HS; Glen Falls, NY; (Y); 10/230; Hosp Aide; Stat Bsbl; Cheerleading; Pom Pon; Score Keeper; Timer; Vllybl; High Hon Roll; NHS; Natl Hstry & Govt Awd 85; Elem Ed.

MILLS, KELLY; Mexico Acad & Central Sch; Mexico, NY; (Y); 4-H; FFA; Letterman Clb; Pep Clb; Spanish Clb; Teachers Aide; Varsity Clb; Band; Color Guard; Drill Tm; Hgh Pt Indivdl Judng 84; 2nd Pl Judgng Tm 84; World Horseshw OK 84; Morrisvle Ag/Tech; Equine Stud.

MILLS, MARY; Heuvelton Central HS; Ogdensburg, NY; (S); FHA; Latin Clb; Chorus; Color Guard; School Musical; Var Cheerleading; 4-H Awd; NHS; Ntl Merit Ltr; Prfct Atten Awd; Cert Awd Bus Dynamics 83; Cert Awd Hstary 83; Cornell U; Sci.

MILLS, STACY; Tottneville HS; Staten Island, NY; (Y); 212/897; Dance Clb; Girl Scts; Chorus; School Musical; Stage Crew; Regents Diploma 85; Wrd Proc.

MILLSPAUGH, NANCY; Newburgh Free Acad; Newburgh, NY; (Y); Church Yth Grp; Latin Clb; Library Aide; Exec Scrtry.

MILMORE, LYNN; Walter Panas HS; Peekskill, NY; (Y); Drama Clb; Girl Scts; Pep Clb; Chorus; School Musical; School Play; Cheerleading; Socr; High Hon Roll; Hon Roll.

MILNYCZUK, NANCY; Bishop Scully HS; Amsterdam, NY; (Y); Art Clb; Hosp Aide; Yrbk Stf; Var JV Bsktbl; Var Sftbl; Hon Roll; HOBY Fndtn 83; US Art Achvt Awd 83; Cazenovia Coll; Lbrl Arts.

MILO, LORNA; Kings Park Ssr HS; Kings Pk, NY; (Y); Church Yth Grp; Cmnty Wkr; Spanish Clb; Speech Tm; Band; Concert Band; Mrchg Band; Stage Crew; Yrbk Stf; Hon Roll; MVP Bsktbl 84; RIF Rdng Awd 85; Hnr Cerebl Palsy Fair 85; Bus Mgmt.

MILONAS, SOFIA S; Nightingale-Bamford HS; New York, NY; (Y); 3/37; Model UN; Nwsp Rptr; Lit Mag; Var Socr; Var Trk; Var Vllybl; Hon Roll; Ntl Merit Schol; Yale U; Cmprtv Literature.

MILONE, CATHERINE; South Side HS; Rockville Centre, NY; (Y); 70/295; Church Yth Grp; Cmnty Wkr; Key Clb; Chorus; Rep Stu Cncl; Bsktbl; Trk; Vllybl; Hon Roll; Rep Link Pgm 85-86.

MILORD, FABIOLA; Washington Irving HS; Jackson Hts, NY; (Y); English Clb; French Clb; Band; Church Choir; Rep Jr Cls; Hon Roll; Prfct Atten Awd; Frnch Cntst Awd 84; Brooklyn Coll; Pre-Med.

MILORD, MAUD; Fashion Industries HS; Brooklyn, NY; (Y); #59 In Class; Office Aide; Teachers Aide; Chorus.

MILOS, LYNNE MARIE; Catholic Central HS; Troy, NY; (Y); 20/200; 4-H; Math Clb; Ski Clb; Chorus; Hon Roll; NHS; Prncpls Schlrshp 85; Uncle Sam Yrkrs Dist Awd 82-83; Cert Achvt Natl Hist Day 82-83; Lake Erie Coll; Equine Stds.

MILOSKI, DARLENE; Riverhead HS; Calverton, NY; (S); 15/198; Sec DECA; Drama Clb; French Clb; Key Clb; Ski Clb; School Play; VP Frsh Cls; Var Capt Crs Cntry; Var Trk; DECA Awds 1st Pl Telephone Sls, 2nd Pl F E Proj 85; Schl Bus Awd 85; All Lg Crs Cntry 83-85; Pre-Law.

MILTENBERGER, LISA; Windham-Ashland-Jewett Central Schl; Windham, NY; (S); Drama Clb; Pres FBLA; Pres Jr Cls; VP Sr Cls; Capt Cheerleading; High Hon Roll; Hon Roll; K Gibbs Schl; Bus.

MILTON, ANDREA M; Bay Ridge HS; Brooklyn, NY; (Y); 15/266; Church Yth Grp; Dance Clb; Chorus; Nwsp Stf; High Hon Roll; Prfct Atten Awd; Rgnts Schlrshp; Pace U; Pre-Med.

MILTON, GLENN; Half Hollow Hills East HS; Dix Hills, NY; (Y); Boy Scts; Varsity Clb; Orch; Rep Frsh Cls; Ftbl; Lcrss; Socr; Var JV Trk; High Hon Roll; Hon Roll; Stu Of Mth Awd 82-83; Mst Outstndng Music Stu 82-83; Nassau & Suffolk Music Awd 83-85; Psychtry.

MILTON, MARY ANN; Mercy HS; Hampton Bays, NY; (Y); Library Aide; Hst MMM; Church Choir; Yrbk Stf; JV Var Bsktbl; Var Crs Cntry; Var Trk; Mission Club Secy 85-86; Ldrs Club; Bus.

MIMS, MARONDA LISA; Saint Catharine Acad; Bronx, NY; (Y); 63/205; Im Bsbl; ROTC; Engrng.

MINA, TARA; Washingtonville HS; Washingtonville, NY; (Y); Cmnty Wkr; GAA; Spanish Clb; Band; Crs Cntry; Trk; Hon Roll; NHS; Ntl Fed Music Clbs Supr Rtng 84-85; JR Olympcs Jacksnvl FL 84; NYS Trck Mt 6th Pl Medal 85; Bus Adm.

MINARD, JILL; Highland HS; Clintondale, NY; (Y); 10/140; AFS; Church Yth Grp; 4-H; Teachers Aide; Nwsp Ed-Chief; Nwsp Rptr; Nwsp Stf; Yrbk Stf; 4-H Awd; High Hon Roll; Exclince Advancd Keybrdng Awd 84; Albany Coll Of Phrmcy; Phrmcy.

MINAULT, REGGIE; Sheepshead Bay HS; Brooklyn, NY; (Y); Boy Scts; Spanish Clb; Teachers Aide; Band; Ftbl; Trk; JETS Awd; Hon Roll; Perfect Attndnc; Spnsh Cert Schlrshp; Comp Engr.

MINCAR, KENNETH L; C W Baker HS; Baldwinsville, NY; (Y); 1/441; Am Leg Boys St; Ski Clb; Rep Stu Cncl; Var Capt Socr; High Hon Roll; Pres Jr NHS; NHS; Ntl Merit Ltr; Val; Cornell Bk Awd 84; Clarkson U; Engrng.

MINCKLER, RICK; Vestal Central SR HS; Binghamton, NY; (Y); Ski Clb; Varsity Clb; Var Crs Cntry; Var Trk; High Hon Roll; Mth.

MINDEN, HELENE N; Riverhead HS; Riverhead, NY; (Y); Art Clb; Cmnty Wkr; Drama Clb; Band; Chorus; Drm & Bgl; Drm Mjr(t); Jazz Band; Orch; Yrbk Phtg; Photo.

MINEHARDT, TODD; Niskayuna HS; Alplaus, NY; (Y); Church Yth Grp; Jazz Band; Mrchg Band; Symp Band; JV Wrstlng; Indstrl Arts Shw Merch Drawg 83-84; Arch 84-85; Mech Engrng.

MINEI, ELIZABETH; Mercy HS; Miller Place, NY; (Y); #16 In Class; Drama Clb; Service Clb; Church Choir; School Musical; High Hon Roll; Hon Roll; NHS; JV Fld Hcky; Co-Capt Tennis; Trk; Svc Awd Sign Lang 84-85; Svc Awd Comm Skills 84; Med Schl.

MINEO, JOSEPH; Seaford HS; Seaford, NY; (Y); Computer Clb; Band; Var L Trk; High Hon Roll; Hon Roll; Med.

MINER, CHERIE; Hoosick Falls Central HS; Hoosick Falls, NY; (Y); 12/110; Church Yth Grp; VP 4-H; French Clb; Political Wkr; Trs Jr Cls; Stu Cncl; Capt Var Bsktbl; Var Fld Hcky; Var Sftbl; Im Vllybl.

MINER, EDWARD; Delaware Acad; Meridale, NY; (Y); Church Yth Grp; Pres 4-H; Pres FFA; Cit Awd; 4-H Awd; High Hon Roll; Hon Roll; NHS; Cornell U; Ag.

MINER, EVIE; New Field HS; Newfield, NY; (Y); Rep Frsh Cls; Rep Soph Cls; Var JV Bowling; JV Vllybl; Rep Stu Cncl; Math Awd 85; Bwlg Awds 83; Acctnt.

MINER, MARCIE; Hoosick Falls Central HS; Hoosick Falls, NY; (Y); Pres VP 4-H; French Clb; Ski Clb; Stu Cncl; JV Capt Bsktbl; Var Fld Hcky; Var Score Keeper; Var Trk; Kiwanis Awd; Pol Sci.

MINER, MARK; Rome Catholic HS; Rome, NY; (Y); Rep Sr Cls; Var Capt Bsbl; Var Bsktbl; Ntl Merit Ltr; Bio.

MINER, MICHAEL; Lake Placid HS; Lake Placid, NY; (Y); Boy Scts; Key Clb; Varsity Clb; Var Trk; Hon Roll; NHS; N Cntry CC; Criminal Justice.

MINER, TODD; Horseheads HS; Horseheads, NY; (Y); Spanish Clb; Chorus; Corning CC; Bus Adm.

MINETTI, ORLANDA; Bishop Kearney HS; Brooklyn, NY; (Y); Dance Clb; Library Aide; Variety Show; Nwsp Rptr; Hon Roll; Regnts Schlrshp 85; Frst Hnrs 85; Fordham U; Law.

MING, ARETHETTA; Niagara Catholic HS; Niagara Falls, NY; (Y); Spanish Clb; Church Choir; Nwsp Stf; Im Vllybl; Hon Roll; Data Procsng.

MING, ORAIN; Rice HS; New York, NY; (S); Boy Scts; Church Yth Grp; Church Choir; Ftbl; Hon Roll; Military.

MINGO, ERIC; Bronx H S Of Science; New York, NY; (Y); Math Tm; Band; Concert Band; Orch; Symp Band; Hon Roll; Jr NHS; Ntl Merit Ltr; Columbia Coll; Eng Lit.

MINGO, MICHELLE; Columbia HS; E Greenbush, NY; (Y); Key Clb; Sec Sr Cls; JV Cheerleading; JV Crs Cntry; Im Powder Puff Ftbl; JV Capt Socr; Law.

MINICH, VALERIE; Frontier SR HS; Blasdell, NY; (S); FBLA; Pep Clb; Spanish Clb; Concert Band; Mrchg Band; JV Sftbl; Hon Roll; NHS; Stat Bsktbl; Band; Bnkng.

MINICUCCI JR, ROBERT A; Briarcliff HS; Briarcliff, NY; (Y); Drama Clb; French Clb; Chorus; School Musical; Lit Mag; JV Crs Cntry; JV Tennis; JV Trk; NY ST Smmr Schl Of Arts; Engl.

MINIELLI, GINA; St Francis Prep Schl; Flushing, NY; (Y); Art Clb; Aud/Vis; Camera Clb; Nwsp Phtg; Yrbk Phtg; Yrbk Stf; Rep Jr Cls; Fshn Inst Of Tech; Phtgrphr.

MINIKEL, STEPHEN; Msgr Mc Clancy HS; Woodside, NY; (Y); Bowling; Hon Roll; Marine Phy Ftns Team 82-85; Intra-Mural Sprts Actvts 82-85.

MINK, JACQUELINE M; Frontier Central HS; Hamburg, NY; (S); DECA; Office Aide; Pep Clb; Stage Crew; Yrbk Stf; Sec Soph Cls; JV Socr; Wt Lftg; Hon Roll; NHS; Accounting.

MINNECI, ALBERTA; Bishop Kearney HS; Brooklyn, NY; (Y); 36/339; Dance Clb; GAA; Girl Scts; Teachers Aide; Rep Frsh Cls; Rep Soph Cls; Rep Jr Cls; Rep Sr Cls; High Hon Roll; NHS; NYU; Acctnt.

MINNICK, BILL; Southside HS; Rockville Ctr, NY; (Y); Boy Scts; Varsity Clb; Ftbl; Var Socr; JV Trk; Eagle Scout 85; Bus Admin.

MINNIGH, CYNTHIA; Haverling Central HS; Bath, NY; (S); Church Yth Grp; French Clb; JCL; Math Clb; Color Guard; Stat Bsktbl; Var Capt Twrlr; Var Vllybl; Hon Roll; NHS; Economics.

MINNOLERA, MICHAEL E; Iroquois HS; Lancaster, NY; (Y); 18/275; Boy Scts; Debate Tm; Key Clb; Band; Orch; School Musical; Bowling; High Hon Roll; Hon Roll; NHS; Alumni Schlrshp Rochester Inst Tech 85; Rochester Inst Tech; Comp Sci.

MINO, LISA; Our Lady Of Mercy HS; Walworth, NY; (Y); Cmnty Wkr; Exploring; Band; Sec Frsh Cls; Pres Soph Cls; Var Trk; Hon Roll; Kiwanis Awd; Hugh O Brien Yth Fndtn Ldrshp Awd 84; Ped Nrsng.

MINOR, CHRISTINA; Cardinal Mooney HS; Rochester, NY; (Y); Ski Clb; Band; Concert Band; School Musical; Spanish NHS; Var Cncrt Band 85.

MINOR, DOUGLAS; Moravia Central Schl; Moravia, NY; (Y); Am Leg Boys St; French Clb; FFA; Ski Clb; Trk; Vllybl; High Hon Roll; Hon Roll; Cornell U; Vet Med.

MINOTTI, AMY; Thomas A Edison HS; Elmira Hts, NY; (Y); Concert Band; Badmtn; Cheerleading; Diving; Var Capt Gym; Sftbl; Swmmng; Var L Trk; Var Vllybl; Wt Lftg; Gym MVP & Trophy 84-85; Cosmetlgst.

MINTURN, LUCY; Arlington HS; Pleasant Valley, NY; (Y); 60/620; Debate Tm; German Clb; Political Wkr; Im Golf; Sftbl; Vllybl; Hon Roll; Lion Awd; St Schlr; Honor Key Awd 85; Vassar Coll; Intl Pol.

MINTZ, GREG; Mohonasen HS; Schenectady, NY; (Y); Boys Clb Am; Chess Clb; Cmnty Wkr; Debate Tm; Exploring; French Clb; Key Clb; Rep Frsh Cls; Rep Soph Cls; Rep Jr Cls; Schenectady Jaycees Cnty Govt For A Day 1st Pl 85; Cert Lfgrd 84; Lt Govrnr Mohawk S Div 85-86.

MINTZ, HOWARD J; Farmingdale HS; North Massapequa, NY; (Y); 94/625; Computer Clb; Key Clb; Temple Yth Grp; Varsity Clb; Band; Mrchg Band; JV Var Bsktbl; Tennis; Ntl Merit Schol; Silvr Medl LI Math Fair 85; NYS Regnts Schlrshp 85; Rensselaer Polytechnic; Comp Sc.

MINTZ, LIZ; Fayetteville-Manlius HS; Manlius, NY; (Y); Thesps; Acpl Chr; Chorus; School Play; Swing Chorus; Variety Show; Nwsp Phtg; Lit Mag; Sec Jr Cls; Hon Roll; Spnsh Awd A Afg; All Cty Jazz Ensem; NY St Summr Schl Art; Skidmore; Art.

MINTZER, JAMES S; West Islip HS; W Islip, NY; (Y); Church Yth Grp; School Play; Trs Jr Cls; Trs Stu Cncl; JV Wrstlng; Bus Adm.

MINUTO, ANTHONY; Cardinal Spellman HS; Bronx, NY; (Y); High Hon Roll; Hon Roll; Real Estate Brkr.

MIORIN, YVONNE; Keveny Memorial Acad; Troy, NY; (Y); Var JV Bsktbl; Var Sftbl; Var JV Vllybl; Hudson Valley CC; Nrsng.

MIRAGLIA, MARC; Cardinal Spellman HS; Bronx, NY; (Y); Cmnty Wkr; Teachers Aide; Stage Crew; 2nd Hnrs 82-83; Iona Coll; Bus.

MIRAGLIA, MELISSA; West HS; Corning, NY; (Y); 1/250; Church Yth Grp; FCA; Math Tm; Quiz Bowl; Y-Teens; Church Choir; Variety Show; Pres Frsh Cls; Rep Stu Cncl; High Hon Roll; Liberty U; Yth Evanglsm.

MIRANDA, CHRISTOPHER M; Cardinal Spellman HS; Bronx, NY; (Y); Computer Clb; Hon Roll; Schlrshp Iona Coll 85-86; Iona Coll; Comp Sci.

MIRANDA, DEBORAH; Our Saviour Lutheran HS; Bronx, NY; (S); 3/22; Teachers Aide; School Musical; Pres Frsh Cls; Sec Soph Cls; Pres Stu Cncl; High Hon Roll; Hon Roll; NHS; Cert Of Achievement Awd 84; Regents Scholarship 85; Business Admin.

MIRANDA, ENRIQUE; John Dewey HS; Brooklyn, NY; (Y); Air Force; Test Plt.

MIRANDA, FRANCES; New Dorp HS; Staten Island, NY; (Y); Art Clb; Debate Tm; FBLA; GAA; Pres Intnl Clb; Key Clb; Math Tm; Trs Spanish Clb; Nwsp Stf; JA; Cert Recog Barnes Intrmdt Schl PTA 82; Bus Adm.

MIRANDA, FREDDY; Lindenhurst SR HS; Lindenhurst, NY; (Y); Bsktbl; Cartnst.

MIRANDA, JOELLE; Cleveland Hill HS; Cheektowaga, NY; (Y); 4/105; GAA; JCL; Sec Frsh Cls; Sec Soph Cls; Sec Jr Cls; Sec Sr Cls; Var Capt Crs Cntry; Var Trk; High Hon Roll; NHS; Ithaca; Chem.

MIRANDA, JOSE MARTIN; Cardinal Spellman HS; New York, NY; (Y); Church Yth Grp; Computer Clb; Yrbk Stf; Hon Roll; Chorus; Church Choir; Im Bsktbl; Med.

MIRANDA, KIM; West Hampton Beach HS; Remsenburg, NY; (Y); 46/287; Church Yth Grp; Dance Clb; Drama Clb; French Clb; FBLA; Pep Clb; Varsity Clb; Acpl Chr; Chorus; Church Choir; Pre Law.

MIRANDA, LOURDES; Mt St Ursula Acad; Bronx, NY; (Y); Intnl Clb; VP Pres Spanish Clb; Yrbk Stf; Comp Sci.

MIRANDA, MARGARITA GUADALUPE; Sacred Heart HS; New York, NY; (S); 42/240; Church Yth Grp; Drama Clb; Intnl Clb; Teachers Aide; School Musical; Nwsp Ed-Chief; JV Mgr(s); Hon Roll; NHS; Library Aide; Ntl Hnr Roll Yrbk 83-85; NY U; Archlgy.

MIRANDA, MELINDA; Waterford-Halfmoon HS; Waterford, NY; (Y); 5/83; French Clb; Math Clb; Chorus; Yrbk Stf; High Hon Roll; Hon Roll; NHS; NEDT Awd; Church Yth Grp; Computer Clb; Acadmc Achvt Awd Top 10 Pct 84; Math.

MIRANDA, MICHELLE; Torrejon HS; Apo New York, NY; (Y); Church Yth Grp; ROTC; Chorus; Drill Tm; Frsh Cls; Soph Cls; Jr Cls; Cheerleading; Powder Puff Ftbl; Tennis; San Angelo U; Bus Mngmnt.

MIRET, KENNETH; Msgr Mcclancy HS; East Elmhurst, NY; (S); 26/229; Church Yth Grp; Bsktbl; Im Ftbl; Im Ice Hcky; Hon Roll; NHS; Spanish NHS; St Johns U; Pre-Med.

MIRGUET, MATTHEW R; Greece Athena HS; Rochester, NY; (Y); 34/281; DECA; Math Tm; Ski Clb; Rep Stu Cncl; JV Golf; L Socr; Hon Roll; Prfct Atten Awd; St Schlr; Hmcmng King 84-85; Univ Dayton; Engrng.

MIRIANTHOPOULOS, CHRIS; Bronx High Schl Of Sci; Briarwood, NY; (Y); Church Yth Grp; Intnl Clb; Teachers Aide; Camp Fr Inc; Nwsp Stf; Off Soph Cls; Off Jr Cls; Hotel Mgmt.

MIRSKY, DONNA; Pittsford Mendon HS; Pittsford, NY; (Y); Drama Clb; Acpl Chr; Chorus; School Musical; Variety Show; JV Cheerleading; Hon Roll; NHS; Church Yth Grp; Math Clb; Mst Outstndng Chorus Mbr 83.

MIRSKY, MARK; Ossining HS; Ossining, NY; (Y); 16/275; Model UN; JV L Bsktbl; JV L Lcrss; JV L Socr; High Hon Roll; Hon Roll; NHS; Vrsty Sccr Team MVP 84; Excell Engl Awd 83; Frnch Excell Awd 83-84; Liberal Arts.

MIRUCKI, MOLLY; Fayetteville-Manlius HS; Fayetteville, NY; (Y); Church Yth Grp; GAA; JCL; Service Clb; Chorus; Ed Yrbk Stf; Var JV Socr; Hon Roll; Variety Show; Stat Lcrss; Mony Schlstc Art Awd Bl Rbn 83; Cum Laude Natl Ltn Exam 84; Intr Dsgn.

MISAGE, THOMAS J; Greece Acadia HS; Rochester, NY; (Y); 20/290; JV Capt Bsktbl; Var Capt Ftbl; Var L Trk; Hon Roll; NHS; Acad Pin 84; 2nd Team All-Cnty Ftbl 82; Northeastern U; Mech Engr.

MISANTONIS, DIMITRIOS; Albertus Magnus HS; Garnerville, NY; (Y); 13/190; Church Yth Grp; Math Clb; Var Crs Cntry; JV Socr; Var Trk; Hon Roll; Mu Alp Tht; NHS; Ldr Of Altr Bys In Chrch ,4-85; Math.

MISENCIK, JOHN C; Owen D Young HS; Mohawk, NY; (Y); Ski Clb; Capt Bsktbl; Golf; Capt Socr; Hon Roll; SUNY Morrisville; Dsl Mech.

MISENO, NICHOLAS; Amsterdam HS; Amsterdam, NY; (Y); Drama Clb; School Play; Bowling; Golf; Hon Roll; Athlt Of Yr Bwlng 84-85; Fulton Mont CC; Math.

MISERTINO, MICHAEL; Bishop Cunningham HS; Fulton, NY; (Y); 9/28; Spanish Clb; Yrbk Ed-Chief; Bsbl; Var Ftbl; Hon Roll; NHS; Binghamton U; Comp Sci.

MISIAK, MARISLYN J; Villa Maria Acad; Buffalo, NY; (Y); Church Yth Grp; Cmnty Wkr; Dance Clb; Debate Tm; Hosp Aide; JCL; Latin Clb; Pep Clb; Red Cross Aide; Band; Regents Schlrshp 85; 1st Pl Sci Fair 82; Canisius Coll; Psych.

MISIR, KAMILLA; John Jay HS; Brooklyn, NY; (Y).

MISITA JR, ROBERT M; East Islip HS; East Islip, NY; (Y); Math Tm; Red Cross Aide; Im Ice Hcky; Im Sftbl; Var Tennis; High Hon Roll; NHS; Hon Roll; Jr NHS; Long Islnd Sci Cngrss 83 & 85; 1st & 3rd E Sci Fair 83-85; Top 43 JETS Engrng Apttd Tst 84; :Engrng.

MISKANIN, MICHELLE; Ballston Spa HS; Ballston Spa, NY; (Y); 14/250; Cmnty Wkr; Band; Concert Band; Mrchg Band; Yrbk Stf; Stat Socr; High Hon Roll; Hon Roll; Prfct Atten Awd; Saratogian/Skidmore Coll Awds 84; Secondry Ed.

MISSER, MONIQUE; Holy Trinity HS; Hicksville, NY; (Y); Hosp Aide; Math Clb; Cheerleading; Crs Cntry; Sftbl; Swmmng; St Johns U; Phrmclgy.

MISSOFF, SHARON; Cicero-North Syracuse HS; North Syracuse, NY; (S); 146/621; Church Yth Grp; German Clb; Band; Concert Band; Mrchg Band; Ed Lit Mag; Rep Soph Cls; Rep Jr Cls; Sftbl; Tennis; Tchr Educ.

MISTRETTA, PHILIP; Jamestown HS; Jamestown, NY; (Y); 24/376; Church Yth Grp; Concert Band; Jazz Band; Mrchg Band; School Musical; Stage Crew; NHS; Opt Clb Awd; Band; Chorus; Perf Atten 85; Regnts Schlrshp Awd 85; Marchng Band Schlrshp Awd 84-85; Jamestown CC; Engr.

MISTRY, DIPTI; Martin Van Buren HS; Bellerose, NY; (Y); 6/579; Mathletes; Math Tm; Science Clb; School Play; Stage Crew; High Hon Roll; Jr NHS; NHS; Sal; Queensboro Sci Fair 1st Pl Wnnr 85; St Francis Sci Fair 2nd Pl Wnnr 85; Pre-Med.

MISURELLI, DENBY; Saratoga Springs SR HS; Saratoga Sprgs, NY; (Y); 21/410; Ski Clb; Var Bsktbl; Var Tennis; High Hon Roll; Hon Roll; Sci Awd 82-83; MIP In Tennis 82; Wlm Smth Coll; Bio Chmst.

MITCHELL, ANN; St John The Baptist HS; Oakdale, NY; (Y); Hosp Aide; Teachers Aide; JV Cheerleading; High Hon Roll; NHS.

MITCHELL, ANNE; Smithtown High Schl East; St James, NY; (Y); Church Yth Grp; Girl Scts; Hosp Aide; Key Clb; Yrbk Phtg; Off Frsh Cls; Off Soph Cls; Off Jr Cls; Off Sr Cls; Var Crs Cntry.

MITCHELL, BONNIE; C A Bouton JR SR HS; Voorheesville, NY; (Y); Teachers Aide; Yrbk Stf; VP Frsh Cls; Rep Stu Cncl; Stat Bsktbl; Score Keeper; Socr; Cit Awd; High Hon Roll; NHS; Stu Cncl Rep Of Yr 82-83; Trvl.

MITCHELL, DANA; New Rochelle HS; New Rochelle, NY; (Y); FBLA; JA; Sec Key Clb; Model UN; Office Aide; Spanish Clb; Chorus; Lcrss; Powder Puff Ftbl; Socr; Awd Of Excllnce Engl, Chorus, Math 82-84; Psych.

MITCHELL, DANIEL P; Madison Central HS; Madison, NY; (Y); 12/45; Am Leg Boys St; Boy Scts; French Clb; Varsity Clb; Band; Mrchg Band; Pres Jr Cls; Pres Stu Cncl; JV Var Bsbl; Var Capt Bsktbl; Rgnts Schlrshp 85; Alg 82; Geom 83; Mst Outstndng Athl 82; Scr All Leag 83 & 84; Bsktbl All Leag 83 & 84; Mohawk Vly Comm Coll; Acctng.

MITCHELL, DAVID C; Iroquois Central HS; Elma, NY; (Y); 9/300; Am Leg Boys St; Church Yth Grp; Drama Clb; Model UN; Sec Band; School Musical; Var L Ftbl; Var L Ice Hcky; Var Tennis; Hon Roll; All Cnty Band 83; Amer Legns Boys ST 85; Amherst Coll; Preprfssnl.

MITCHELL, DAWN L; Moriah Central HS; Witherbee, NY; (Y); 6/83; AFS; Church Yth Grp; French Clb; GAA; Stu Cncl; Cheerleading; Socr; High Hon Roll; Hon Roll; NHS; NAACP Chrldng Awds 83-85; Natl Ldrshp Awd 84; Natl Phy Ftns Awds 84-85; JR Miss 85; Delhi ATC; Vet Tech.

MITCHELL, DENISE L; Pulaski JR-SR HS; Pulaski, NY; (S); Church Yth Grp; French Clb; GAA; Ski Clb; Band; Mrchg Band; JV Bsktbl; JV Var Socr; Var Trk; MVP Vrsty Track 85; Cortland St.

MITCHELL, HOLLY; Skaneateles HS; Skaneateles, NY; (S); 4-H; Model UN; 4-H Awd; Jr NHS; Cobleskill Ag & Tech; Anml Hsbd.

MITCHELL, JAMES L; Bainbridge Guilford HS; Bainbridge, NY; (Y); Rep Debate Tm; Varsity Clb; Rep Stu Cncl; L Var Bsktbl; L Var Tennis; CC Awd; High Hon Roll; NHS; VP Church Yth Grp; French Clb; Natl Merit Commended Stu 84; Natl French Cntst 81 & 82; Rotary Yth Ldrshp Awd 83; Hartwick Coll; Pol Sci.

MITCHELL, JOANNE; Tottenville HS; Staten Island, NY; (Y); GAA; Key Clb; Library Aide; Ski Clb; Band; Concert Band; Mrchg Band; Yrbk Stf; Lit Mag; Gym; Comm.

MITCHELL, JULIE L; Sachem HS North Campus; Lake Grove, NY; (Y); 219/1463; GAA; Band; Mrchg Band; Var Trk; NHS; Springfield Coll; Rehab.

MITCHELL, KELLY M; Angelica Central Schl; Almond, NY; (Y); 5/24; Debate Tm; French Clb; Science Clb; Chorus; School Play; Variety Show; Pres Jr Cls; Stu Cncl; Cheerleading; Socr; Am Leg Awd 85; Alfred SUNY Tech; Soc Sci.

MITCHELL, LEO F; A Phillip Randolph Campus HS; Springfield Grdns, NY; (Y); Computer Clb; Stage Crew; Nwsp Rptr; Nwsp Stf; Yrbk Phtg; Rep Frsh Cls; Rep Jr Cls; Var Bsbl; Capt Trk; Comp.

MITCHELL, LORI; Charles A Dickerson HS; Trumansburg, NY; (Y); 4-H; Ski Clb; Spanish Clb; Off Jr Cls; Bsktbl; Socr; Trk; 4-H Awd; High Hon Roll; Hon Roll; Davis; Med.

MITCHELL, RAWN; Albion HS; Albion, NY; (Y); Var Bsbl; Var Ftbl; Var Capt Wrstlng; Electrcn.

MITCHELL, RICHARD C; Bishop Cunningham HS; Oswego, NY; (Y); Spanish Clb; Yrbk Ed-Chief; Pres Frsh Cls; Pres Soph Cls; Pres Jr Cls; Rep Stu Cncl; Var L Socr; NHS; Church Yth Grp; Library Aide; Oswego Cty Cnty Yth Advsry Cncl 83-86; NY ST Smmr Ldrshp Trnng Inst 83; Hugh O Brian Yth Fndtn 84; Poli Sci.

MITCHELL, SANDRA; Newark SR HS; Newark, NY; (Y); 19/240; Ski Clb; Band; Concert Band; Mrchg Band; Yrbk Stf; Swmmng; Tennis; Vllybl; High Hon Roll; Hon Roll; JR Honor Girl 85; Elem Eductn.

MITCHELL, SHERVON; Walton HS; Bronx, NY; (Y); Church Yth Grp; Cmnty Wkr; Political Wkr; Band; Church Choir; Trk; Prfct Atten Awd; Hostos CC; RN.

MITCHELL, STEPHANIE; Holy Trinity Diocesan HS; Westbury, NY; (Y); Dance Clb; French Clb; Library Aide; Math Clb; Math Tm; Stage Crew; Yrbk Stf; Stu Cncl; Hon Roll; Mu Alp Tht; Acctng.

MITCHELL, STEPHEN M; Mt St Michael Acad; Bronx, NY; (S); 22/309; Church Yth Grp; Im Bsktbl; JV Crs Cntry; Var JV Trk; High Hon Roll; Hon Roll; Recip Numerous Karate Comp Awds 76-85; Stu Instructr Summr Karate 83-84; Georgetown; Bus Admin.

MITCHELL, SUZANNE; School Of The Holy Child; Bronxville, NY; (S); Rep Church Yth Grp; French Clb; Chorus; Yrbk Stf; Rep Soph Cls; Rep Jr Cls; Capt Bsktbl; Tennis; High Hon Roll; Highest Cls Avg 83-84; Outstndg Eng Awd 84.

MITCHELL, TODD; Kenmore East HS; Tonawanda, NY; (Y); 13/430; Chorus; Orch; Nwsp Rptr; NHS; Voice Dem Awd; Rotary Intrntn Exchnge Stu 83-84; Descndnts Of Mayflwr Awd 85; SUNY At Buffalo; Oriental Stud.

MITCHELL, TROY; La Salle SR HS; Niagara Falls, NY; (Y); Sec Drama Clb; Varsity Clb; Jazz Band; School Musical; School Play; Stage Crew; Nwsp Bus Mgr; Yrbk Bus Mgr; Yrbk Ed-Chief; Off Sr Cls; Trck Vrsty Ltr 85; Rochester Inst; Htl Mngmnt.

MITCHKO, DEBRA; East Meadow HS; E Meadow, NY; (S); 43/414; Trs Church Yth Grp; FBLA; Trs Key Clb; Office Aide; Varsity Clb; Chorus; Church Choir; Yrbk Rptr; Rep Frsh Cls; Rep Soph Cls; Nassau CC; Hotel Mgt.

MITCHKO, PETE; Mineola HS; Williston Park, NY; (Y); Church Yth Grp; VP Computer Clb; Spanish Clb; Band; Concert Band; Mrchg Band; High Hon Roll; Engnr.

MITOLA, DANIEL; Islip HS; Islip, NY; (Y); Chorus; Concert Band; School Musical; Yrbk Stf; Trs Jr Cls; Capt Crs Cntry; Capt Trk; Cit Awd; High Hon Roll; Pres NHS; Cornell U; Law.

MITRANO, JAMES G; Gates Chili HS; Rochester, NY; (Y); 11/464; Spanish Clb; Band; Orch; Var Ftbl; Capt Var Tennis; High Hon Roll; NHS; Ntl Merit Ltr; NY ST Regents Schlrshp; Colgate U; Plntlgy.

MITRAVICH, MELISSA L; Niagara Wheatfield SR HS; Niagara Falls, NY; (Y); 137/314; Pep Clb; Var Bsktbl; Var Socr; Var Sftbl; Var Vllybl; NY ST Regents Schlrshp For Nrsng 85; Acad Convocation Awd 85; U Of Buffalo; Nrsng.

MITSOPOULOS, GEORGE; Brooklyn Technical HS; Brooklyn, NY; (Y); Boy Scts; Church Yth Grp; Office Aide; Rep Soph Cls; Rep Jr Cls; High Hon Roll.

MITTAG, BIRGIT; Riverdale Country Schl; Ardsley, NY; (Y); Key Clb; Teachers Aide; Chorus; Yrbk Stf; JV Var Fld Hcky; Var Sftbl; Adv Plcmnt Frnch 83-84; Intl Rel.

MITTELMAN, MARLO; Newburgh Free Acad; Newburgh, NY; (Y); Girl Scts; Pep Clb; Ski Clb; Chorus; Orch; Cheerleading; High Hon Roll; Hon Roll; Jr NHS; Bio.

MITTEN, SHERRI; Tully Central HS; Tully, NY; (Y); Cmnty Wkr; Hosp Aide; Spanish Clb; Band; Concert Band; Mrchg Band; Yrbk Phtg; Yrbk Stf; Cit Awd; Volunteer Awd 84-85; Upstate Med Ctr; Nrsng.

MITTERANDO, RICHIE; Port Richmond HS; Staten Isld, NY; (Y); School Musical; Yrbk Stf; Hon Roll; NHS; US Jrnlsm Awd 85; Bus.

MITTMAN, LISA; Benjamin N Cardozo HS; Douglaston, NY; (Y); 18/476; Library Aide; Office Aide; Yrbk Stf; NHS; SUNY Binghamton; Nrsng.

MITZELIOTIS, MARIE; Bishop Kearney HS; Brooklyn, NY; (Y); Church Yth Grp; Drama Clb; Girl Scts; Hosp Aide; Red Cross Aide; School Play; Nwsp Rptr; Hon Roll; NHS; Silver Ldrshp Awd 83; Med.

MIX, KATHRYN; Horseheads HS; Horseheads, NY; (Y); 4-H; Capt Quiz Bowl; Spanish Clb; Band; Concert Band; Mrchg Band; Yrbk Stf; Cheerleading; 4-H Awd; Hon Roll; Many Chmpnshps Shwng Horses; Elem Ed.

MIX, MOLLY; Maryvale HS; Cheektowaga, NY; (Y); Church Yth Grp; French Clb; Pres GAA; Chorus; Church Choir; School Musical; Im Socr; Im Vllybl; Hon Roll; NHS; SUNY Buffalo; Phrmcy.

MIXON, SHELANE; Sacred Heart HS; Yonkers, NY; (S); 50/241; Drama Clb; Intnl Clb; Yrbk Stf; Stu Cncl; Var Capt Trk; Hon Roll; Sec NHS; Coll Of Holy Cross; Pol Sci.

MIXON, STEPHEN; The Knox Schl; Greenville, SC; (S); Computer Clb; FCA; Math Clb; Pep Clb; Varsity Clb; Nwsp Ed-Chief; Nwsp Rptr; Nwsp Stf; Yrbk Rptr; Yrbk Stf; 'ead Masters Awd 84; European History Suprior Achvt Awd 83; Bio Supior Achvt Awd 83; Banker.

MIZELL, ALICIA; Eastern District HS; Brooklyn, NY; (Y); Dance Clb; FHA; Hosp Aide; JA; Library Aide; Math Clb; Model UN; Teachers Aide; Chorus; 4-H Awd; Math Tm Awd; Marymount Coll; Bus Adm.

MLYNAR, JANICE; Lyons HS; Lyons, NY; (Y); 7/92; Trs Latin Clb; Model UN; Concert Band; Mrchg Band; NHS; Prfct Atten Awd; Pres Schlrshp Hartwick Coll 85; Edith Kinney Memrl Engl Prz 85; Regnts Schlrshp 85; Hartwick Coll.

MOAN, PATRICIA R; Academy Of St Joseph; East Islip, NY; (Y); Math Clb; Yrbk Stf; Lit Mag; Var Mgr(s); Var Capt Tennis; Sftbl; Jr NHS; NHS; Schlstc Achvt Awd 84; Natl Art Hnr Socty VP 84-85; Chrstn Courtesy Awd 84; NY Inst Of Tech; Comp Sci.

MOCEJUNAS, MICHELLE; Brighton HS; Rochester, NY; (Y); 99/315; Church Yth Grp; Girl Scts; Pep Clb; Spanish Clb; Chorus; Off Jr Cls; Stu Cncl; Trk; St John Fisher; Nrs.

MOCIOLEK, JUDITH; Villa Maria Acad; Buffalo, NY; (Y); Cmnty Wkr; Computer Clb; Latin Clb; Trs Jr Cls; Rep Stu Cncl; High Hon Roll; Hon Roll; Prfct Atten Awd; Phy Thrpy.

MODAFFERI, MARIA; Albertus Magnus HS; New City, NY; (Y); Drama Clb; Exploring; Girl Scts; Varsity Clb; Church Choir; School Musical; Var Cheerleading; USBEA 85; Pysch.

MODAY, KRISTIN; Pelham HS; Pelham, NY; (Y); AFS; Cmnty Wkr; Model UN; Chorus; Lit Mag; Trs Frsh Cls; Trs Soph Cls; Var L Fld Hcky; Var L Lcrss; Hon Roll; Intl Rltns.

MODELL, DANIEL A; John F Kennedy HS; Bronx, NY; (Y); 48/987; Co-Capt Aud/Vis; Office Aide; Prfct Atten Awd; NY ST Regents Schlrshp 85; WSUC Schlrshp NY U 85; NY U.

MODESTI, PHILLIP B; Jamesville-De Witt HS; Fayetteville, NY; (Y); Pres Church Yth Grp; Pres Exploring; Hosp Aide; Red Cross Aide; Yrbk Phtg; Var Lcrss; Ithaca Coll; Bus.

MODICA, PETER; Christ The King RHS; Ozone Pk, NY; (Y); 4/395; Math Tm; Var Bowling; Im Vllybl; High Hon Roll; Hon Roll; NHS; Prfct Atten Awd; Columbus Citzns Fndtn Grant; Exclince Sci; NY U; Bus Adm.

MODLIN, MARIANNA; Solomon Schechter HS; Brooklyn, NY; (Y); 4/23; Computer Clb; Drama Clb; Science Clb; School Play; Nwsp Stf; Off Jr Cls; Sftbl; NHS; Ntl Merit Ltr; NYU; Intl Bus.

MOELLEKEN, SONJA M C; Shaker HS; Loudonville, NY; (Y); Pres German Clb; Im Socr; Hon Roll; NHS; Ntl Merit SF; Latin Clb; Ski Clb; Germn Bk Prz 84; Germn Awd 82; Pre Med.

MOELLER, CHRISTINA; Franciscan HS; Peekskill, NY; (Y); 26/50; Chorus; School Musical; Nwsp Rptr; Yrbk Phtg; Yrbk Stf; Var Stat Bsbl; SUNY-OSWEGO; Cmmnctns Arts.

MOFFA, CATHERINE; Bethpage HS; Bethpage, NY; (Y); 3/300; Sec Mathletes; Spanish Clb; Off Band; Off Concert Band; Off Mrchg Band; Orch; Nwsp Bus Mgr; Stat Bsbl; JV Bsktbl; High Hon Roll; Geo Wshngtn Mdl Of Exc 84; Pres Awd Frm Adelphi 85; Adelphi U; Vtrnrn.

MOFFATT, LAURA; Alexander Hamilton HS; White Plains, NY; (S); Intnl Clb; Key Clb; Band; Concert Band; Yrbk Stf; Sec Stu Cncl; Capt Bsktbl; Capt Vllybl; Jr NHS; NHS; Pace U; Bus.

MOFFATT, PAMELA; Colonie Central HS; Schenectady, NY; (Y); Hon Roll.

MOFFIT, MICHELLE; Pine Valley Central HS; Cattaraugus, NY; (Y); Var Trk; Voice Dem Awd; Rgnts Schlrshp 85; 3-1-3 Stu SUNY Fredna 85; Ethl W Wllms Schlrshp Fund Awd 85; SUNY Fredonia; Elem Tchr.

MOGLIA, ELIZABETH; Hauppauge HS; Hauppauge, NY; (Y); Girl Scts; Hosp Aide; Pres Speech Tm; Nwsp Rptr; Nwsp Stf; Yrbk Stf; Rep Jr Cls; Rep Sr Cls; High Hon Roll; Hon Roll; TAG Summr Boces Inst Eng 84; Stu Action Pres; Nodel Congress Clb; Interact; Spec Olympics; Phych Clb Sec; Intl Rel.

MOGLIA, ROSE ANGELICA; Christopher Columbus HS; Bronx, NY; (Y); 55/792; Drama Clb; Teachers Aide; Chorus; School Musical; School Play; Cit Awd; Hon Roll; Spanish Awd 83; N Y C Assn Of Asst Prncpls Supr Eng In Eng 83; Psychblgy.

MOGRO, PATTY; Niskayuna HS; Schdy, NY; (Y); Church Yth Grp; FBLA; Girl Scts; Pep Clb; Q&S; Var Gym; JV Trk; 1st Pl Arch Drftng Arts Assoc 84; Intl Bus.

MOHAMMED, MICHELE; St Francis Prep; Bayside, NY; (Y); 237/689; Church Yth Grp; Hosp Aide; Service Clb; Chorus; Color Guard; Wt Lftg; Spanish NHS; Regents Schlrshp 85city Schlr Awd; The City Coll; Pre-Med.

MOHAN, ANDREW; Mamaroneck HS; Larchmont, NY; (Y); Art Clb; Camera Clb; Chess Clb; Cmnty Wkr; V Fncng Team 84-85; Jr Acad NY Acad Sci 85; Photos Town Art Show; Phtgrphr.

MOHAN, ERICA E; Benjamin N Cardozo HS; Douglaston, NY; (Y); 118/475; Drama Clb; PAVAS; Chorus; School Play; Yrbk Stf; Swmmng; SUNY At Buffalo.

MOHL, DAVE; Union Endicott HS; Endicott, NY; (S); Boys Clb Am; Church Yth Grp; Dance Clb; Ski Clb; Varsity Clb; Bsktbl; Bowling; Ftbl; Tennis; Trk.

MOHOROVICIC, MARK; Frontier Central HS; Blasdell, NY; (S); German Clb; Nwsp Rptr; High Hon Roll; Hon Roll; NHS.

MOHR, ANDREAS; Union Endicott HS; Endicott, NY; (Y); Ski Clb; Tennis; Gold Key & Blue Ribbn 85; Archt.

MOHR, CHRIS; Washingtonville SR HS; Washingtonville, NY; (Y); Art Clb; Aud/Vis; Drama Clb; Chorus; School Musical; School Play; Stage Crew; Variety Show; Nwsp Stf; Yrbk Ed-Chief; Schl Rep-Green Mountain Chemcl Awareness Semnr 85; Art Show Awds; FIT; Commrcl Artist.

MOHR, KIMBERLEE I; W Seneca East SR HS; Cheektowaga, NY; (Y); 18/375; Camp Fr Inc; Hosp Aide; High Hon Roll; Hon Roll; JC Awd; Jr NHS; NHS; Ntl German Hnr Society 83; Hnr Roll Encyclopeida 84 & 85; Regents Schlrshp 85; Adelphia U; Child Psychology.

MOHR, KRISTI; Patchogue-Medford HS; Medford, NY; (S); 8/748; Band; Concert Band; Jazz Band; Mrchg Band; JV Sftbl; Hon Roll; Jr NHS; NHS; Music.

MOJICA, JESSE; Xavier HS; New York, NY; (Y); 70/227; Spanish Clb; Band; Chorus; Nwsp Stf; Off Soph Cls; Off Jr Cls; Off Soph Cls; Stu Cncl; Hon Roll; Schlrshp NY U Schl Of Arts & Sci 85; Cert Sr Cncl 85; NY U; Med.

MOJICA, NANCY P; Stella Maris HS; Far Rockaway, NY; (Y); Art Clb; Library Aide; Yrbk Stf; Hon Roll; Val; Comp Sci.

MOK, PATRICIA; Franklin D Roosevelt HS; Brooklyn, NY; (Y); 2/530; Debate Tm; Capt Math Tm; Science Clb; Nwsp Rptr; Nwsp Stf; Lit Mag; Var Gym; Var Tennis; NHS; Sal; Hnr Westinghouse Sci Tlnt Srch Comp 85; Hnrbl Ment Borough Sci Fair 84; AEROSP Engr.

MOKS, PAMELA ANNE; Commack H S North; Commack, NY; (Y); 67/440; Cmnty Wkr; French Clb; MMM; Band; Concert Band; Mrchg Band; Orch; Pep Band; School Musical; Symp Band; NYS Rgnts Schlrhsp 85; SUNY Stony Brook; Pre-Vet.

MOLDENHAUER, CHRISTINA R; Fairport HS; Fairport, NY; (Y); German Clb; Chorus; Hon Roll; Regents Schlrshp 85-86; German Achvt Awd 82-83; Westminster Coll; Bus Adm.

MOLDENHAUER, SHERYL; Fairport HS; Fairport, NY; (Y); Church Yth Grp; German Clb; Intnl Clb; Library Aide; Pep Clb; Chorus; Variety Show; Stu Cncl; Hon Roll; NHS; Hnr Roll Cert 81-83; Natl Hnr Roll 83; Intl Rel.

MOLESWORTH, KEITH; Onondaga Central HS; Syracuse, NY; (S); Exploring; Quiz Bowl; Spanish Clb; Varsity Clb; Yrbk Phtg; JV Var Bsbl; JV Var Bsktbl; High Hon Roll; NHS; Jrnlsm.

MOLIK, GLENN; Maryvale HS; Depew, NY; (Y); Band; Jazz Band; Orch; School Musical; School Play; Symp Band; Var Bowling; Var Golf; Hon Roll; NHS; Music Educ.

MOLINA, NANCY; St Raymond Acad; Bronx, NY; (Y); Band; Chorus; Color Guard; Yrbk Stf; VP Stu Cncl; Hon Roll; Prfct Atten Awd; Hunter Coll; Acctng.

MOLINARI, PAUL; Oneonta HS; Oneonta, NY; (Y); 75/184; Boys Clb Am; Church Yth Grp; FBLA; Key Clb; Spanish Clb; Varsity Clb; Nwsp Stf; Yrbk Stf; Pres Stu Cncl; Var Capt Bsktbl; Boy Yr-Bys Clb 84; Htl-Restrnt Mgmt.

MOLINELLI, ROSEMARIE; Newfield HS; Port Jeff Station, NY; (S); 21/521; Varsity Clb; Yrbk Stf; Var Capt Sftbl; Hon Roll; Jr NHS; NHS; Service Clb; Yrbk Rptr; Yrbk Sprt Ed; Bsktbl; All Leag & All Cnfrnc Sftbl 84; Daily Nws Sftbl All-Star 84; All-Leag Fld Hcky 85; Stony Brook U; Rsprtry Thrpst.

MOLINO, TERRI; Groton Central HS; Groton, NY; (Y); Am Leg Aux Girls St; Band; Chorus; VP Soph Cls; JV Var Cheerleading; Var Socr; Var Trk; Dnfth Awd; High Hon Roll; NHS; Cornell U; Exrcs Sci.

MOLITOR, CHAD; Colonie Central HS; Albany, NY; (Y); Ski Clb; Spanish Clb; Elks Awd; Jrnlsm.

MOLL, KIMBERLY; Christ The King R HS; Middle Village, NY; (Y); 35/385; Yrbk Stf; Cheerleading; Gym; Swmmng; High Hon Roll; Hon Roll; Math.

MOLL, STEVEN A; St Anthonys HS; Kings Pk, NY; (Y); Im Bowling; Hon Roll.

MOLLENHAUER, KRISTINA; St Johns Prep Schl; Long Isld Cty, NY; (Y); German Clb; Spd Rdng Honor 82; Pace U; Bus Mgmt.

MOLLICA, KAREN; St John The Baptist HS; Deer Pk, NY; (Y); Orch; Stage Crew; JV Bsktbl; Var Sftbl; Var Vllybl; High Hon Roll; Hon Roll; Vlybl All-Star 84; Pre-Law.

MOLLOY, ANDREW W; Our Lady Of Lourdes HS; Poughkeepsie, NY; (Y); 6/144; Boy Scts; Drama Clb; Exploring; Math Tm; Nwsp Rptr; Lit Mag; NHS; Aud/Vis; Chess Clb; Computer Clb; Frank Gannett Nwspr Carrier Schlrshp 85; NYS Regnts Schlrshp 85; Outstndng Cmnty Svc Awd 85; FL Atlntc U; Marine Bio.

MOLLOY, CHRISTINE; Earl L Vandermuelen HS; Pt Jefferson Sta, NY; (Y); 15/286; Art Clb; FBLA; Leo Clb; Pep Clb; Band; Yrbk Stf; Stu Cncl; Cheerleading; High Hon Roll; Hon Roll; Corp Fin.

MOLLOY, DEBRA; St Francis Prep; Little Neck, NY; (Y); 209/700; JV Sftbl; Polit Sci.

MOLLOY, KRISTEN L; Westhampton Bch HS; Westhampton Bch, NY; (Y); 16/232; FBLA; Spanish Clb; Chorus; Drill Tm; Stat Bsbl; Hon Roll; NHS; Obstetrcs.

MOLLOY, MEGAN; Onteora HS; West Shokan, NY; (S); 18/245; Swing Chorus; Pres Frsh Cls; Trs Soph Cls; VP Stu Cncl; JV Var Vllybl; Hon Roll; NHS; Rotary Awd; Ind Labr Rel.

MOLLOY, MOIRA; West Seneca East SR HS; W Seneca, NY; (Y); Pres Frsh Cls; Off Soph Cls; Rep Stu Cncl; Var Bsktbl; Var Socr; Var Tennis; Var Vllybl; French Hon Soc; NHS; Commnctns.

MOLNER, NANCY A; Seaford Trinity HS; Seaford, NY; (S); French Clb; Ski Clb; Band; Hon Roll; Gold Medal L I Music Tchrs Assn Annual Fstvl 82-84.

MOLODY, MONA; Great Neck South SR HS; Great Neck, NY; (Y); 4/218; French Clb; GAA; Varsity Clb; Nwsp Stf; Var L Crs Cntry; Capt L Trk; Ntl Merit Ltr; Grt Neck Schlr Athlt 85; Stony Brk Schlr Incntvs Awd 85; NY ST Rgnts Schlrshp 85; SUNY; Engrng Sci.

MOLONEY, JAMES; St Marys Boys HS; Brookville, NY; (Y); 11/130; Cmnty Wkr; Radio Clb; Teachers Aide; Nwsp Stf; Lit Mag; Bowling; NHS; Pres Acad Ftns Awd 85; NYS Regents Schlrshp 85; St Marys Hghst Hnrs Scty 85; Boston U; Bus Admin.

MOLONEY, NOREEN; Albertus Magnus HS; New City, NY; (Y); 20/196; Church Yth Grp; Hosp Aide; Yrbk Stf; JV Trk; Var JV Vllybl; Hon Roll; Mu Alp Tht; NHS; Sci Hnr Rl 82-85; Acctng.

MOLSON, MASHIYYAT; North West B A HS; Buffalo, NY; (Y); Computer Clb; FNA; GAA; Hosp Aide; Library Aide; Office Aide; Teachers Aide; Drill Tm; Nwsp Stf; Yrbk Stf; Trophy For Weight Lifting 83-84; ECC; Liberian.

MONACO, KELLI; Mount Mercy Acad; Buffalo, NY; (Y); Art Clb; Church Yth Grp; Cmnty Wkr; French Clb; Girl Scts; Adv.

MONACO, LISA; Immaculata Acad; Orchard Park, NY; (Y); French Clb; Nwsp Ed-Chief; Capt Cheerleading; French Hon Soc; Acad Schlrshp 82; Art Awd 82-84; MVP Chrldng 84-85; Indstrl Art.

MONACO, MICHAEL A; Ballston Spa HS; Ballston Spa, NY; (Y); 40/250; Am Leg Boys St; Ski Clb; Varsity Clb; JV Var Bsbl; JV Var Bsktbl; Var Capt Ftbl; Tennis; High Hon Roll; Hon Roll; Coast Guard Acad; Engr.

MONACO, MICHELE; Hauppauge HS; Hauppauge, NY; (Y); Cmnty Wkr; DECA; FBLA; Hosp Aide; Chrmn JA; Capt Varsity Clb; Sec Soph Cls; Rep Jr Cls; Sec Stu Cncl; Hon Roll; Major Debate Pub Spkr Rep 85; Schl Rep NLTC 85; June Claire Dnce Studio Jazz Co 85; Bus Adm.

MONAGHAN, AMY; Lindenhurst SR HS; Lindenhurst, NY; (Y); Cmnty Wkr; Drama Clb; French Clb; Political Wkr; Thesps; Chorus; Orch; School Musical; School Play; Variety Show; Tchrs Assoc Lindenhrst Achvt Awd 84; Eng.

MONAGHAN, MAUREEN; Nazareth Acad; Rochester, NY; (Y); 22/162; Church Yth Grp; Cmnty Wkr; Drama Clb; Library Aide; Spanish Clb; School Musical; Hon Roll; NHS; Greece Recrtn Comptv Swim Clb; Elem Ed.

MONAGLE, LISA; Manuus Pebble Hill HS; Fayetteville, NY; (Y); Yrbk Stf; Capt Cheerleading; Trk; Hon Roll; Mst Vlbl Chrldr 84-85; Copywrtng.

MONAHAN, BARBARA; Mt St Mary Acad; Amherst, NY; (Y); 27/96; Pep Clb; Ski Clb; Stage Crew; Yrbk Sprt Ed; Yrbk Stf; Rep Stu Cncl; Var Bsktbl; Coach Actv; Var Sftbl; JV Vllybl; NY ST Regents Schlrshp 85; SUNY-GENESEO; Comp Sci.

MONAHAN, KATHY; Olympia HS; Rochester, NY; (Y); 58/316; Church Yth Grp; Ski Clb; Concert Band; Symp Band; High Hon Roll; Hon Roll; SUNY Potsdam.

MONAHAN, LAURA; Curtis HS; Staten Island, NY; (Y); GAA; Teachers Aide; Capt Var Gym; Var Swmmng; L Vllybl; Hon Roll; Sprtsmnshp Coachs Awd Gymnstcs 83-85; Phy Ed.

MONAHAN, MAUREEN T; Hoosick Falls Central HS; Hoosick Fls, NY; (Y); 22/107; Girl Scts; Hon Roll; VP Jr Cls; VP Sr Cls; Stu Cncl; JV Var Bsktbl; JV Sftbl; Var Trk; Cit Awd; Outstndng Stu Awd 82; Prom Ct 84; Tchrs Assoc Awd 85; Hudson Valley CC; Phrmcy.

MONAHAN III, NICHOLAS JAMES; Port Jervis HS; Sparrowbush, NY; (Y); 11/185; Boy Scts; Church Yth Grp; Varsity Clb; Rep Frsh Cls; Rep Soph Cls; Rep Jr Cls; Rep Sr Cls; Pres Stu Cncl; JV Ftbl; Var L Trk; OH ST; Polit Sci.

MONAHAN, PATRICIA; St Barnabas HS; Yonkers, NY; (Y); 19/136; Drama Clb; French Clb; Office Aide; VP Soph Cls; Rep Jr Cls; Rep Sr Cls; Bowling; High Hon Roll; Prfct Atten Awd; Excessv Schl Srvc Awd 84-85; Mercy Coll; Dental Hygnst.

MONAHAN, PATRICIA A; Fayetteville Manlius HS; Manlius, NY; (Y); Cmnty Wkr; Hosp Aide; Pres Soroptimist; Variety Show; Sec Soph Cls; Sec Jr Cls; Sec Sr Cls; Gym; Cit Awd; Hon Roll; All County Onondoga Champ Gym 83; Central Regn Empire Games 84; Home Ec Awd 82-83; Bus.

MONAHAN, RAYMOND; Valley Stream North HS; Franklin Sq, NY; (Y); 15/125; Chess Clb; Chrmn Debate Tm; Drama Clb; Mathletes; Quiz Bowl; Spanish Clb; Ed Nwsp Sprt Ed; Yrbk Stf; Soph Cls; Jr Cls; Deb Best Spkr; Math High Scorer Silver Medlst; Law.

MONASEBIAN, NAZANIEN; Hebrew Academy Of Nassau County; Port Washington, NY; (S); Denas List 83-85; Pediatrtn.

MONASTERIO, CLAUDIA; Berner HS; Massapequa Park, NY; (Y); 34/412; Dance Clb; Drama Clb; GAA; Spanish Clb; Acpl Chr; Chorus; Stage Crew; Var Fld Hcky; Hon Roll; NHS; AATSP Ntl Cntst 2nd Pl 84; Psych.

MONCAYO, MAGALY; Clara Barton HS; Brooklyn, NY; (Y); Church Yth Grp; Cmnty Wkr; Band; Cit Awd; Hon Roll; Jr NHS; NHS; Psychlgst.

MONCAYO, SANDRA; Christ The King Regional HS; Rego Park, NY; (Y); 98/390; Hosp Aide; Spanish Clb; Teachers Aide; Asst Surgn.

MONDESIR, ELIZENDA; South Side HS; Hempstead, NY; (Y); Chorus; Hon Roll; Chem.

MONE, MICHELLE; Fontbonne Hall Academy; Brooklyn, NY; (Y); Church Yth Grp; Office Aide; Teachers Aide; Band; Church Choir; Hon Roll; Prfct Atten Awd; Natl Energy Fndtn Essay Cont 83; Fordham U Dept Italian Stud Poetry Awd 84; 3rd Prz Italian Essay 84; St Joseph Coll Broklyn; Nrsng.

MONES, THOMAS W; Evander Childs HS; Bronx, NY; (Y); Band; Jazz Band; Orch; Rep Stu Cncl; Bowling; JP Sousa Awd; Regnts Schlrshp Awd 85; Acad Olympcs 85; NY City Tech Coll; Elec Engr.

MONETTA, CARMELINA J; St Raymond Academy; Bronx, NY; (Y); 3/91; Computer Clb; PAVAS; School Play; Rep Stu Cncl; Im Coach Actv; High Hon Roll; NHS; Prfct Atten Awd; Val; Yrbk Stf; Elizabeth Ann Seton Gld Medl Excllnc In Lib Arts 85; Schlrshp To West Chester Bu S Inst 85; West Chester Bus Inst; Mgrl Acc.

MONETTE, AMY S; Franklin Acad; Malone, NY; (Y); Church Yth Grp; Key Clb; Pep Clb; Ski Clb; Spanish Clb; Varsity Clb; Chorus; JV Var Cheerleading; JV Crs Cntry; Trvl & Trsm.

MONETTE, BRENDA; Northeastern Clinton Central HS; Champlain, NY; (Y); Church Yth Grp; Cmnty Wkr; Girl Scts; Office Aide; Teachers Aide; Band; Bsktbl; Coach Actv; Score Keeper; Hon Roll; Fash Dsgn.

MONETTE, BRIAN; Franklin Acad HS; Malone, NY; (Y); Bsktbl; Golf; Engr.

MONEYMAKER, DEBORAH; Beacon HS; Beacon, NY; (S); Camera Clb; JA; Math Clb; Nwsp Phtg; Rep Frsh Cls; Rep Soph Cls; Rep Jr Cls; Stat Crs Cntry; Stat Trk; High Hon Roll.

MONFLEURY, LEGRAND; Prospect Heights HS; Brooklyn, NY; (Y); Band; Sec Frsh Cls; Sec Soph Cls; Sec Jr Cls; Sftbl; Swmmng; Trk; Hon Roll; Hunter Coll; Pre-Med.

MONGE, MINOR; St Marys Boys HS; Great Neck, NY; (S); Bsbl; Crs Cntry; Trk; Hon Roll; Manhattan Coll; Engr.

MONGE, RUTH; Adiai Stevenson HS; Bronx, NY; (Y); Church Yth Grp; Debate Tm; Temple Yth Grp; Chorus; Church Choir; School Musical; Hon Roll; Awd Excllnce Music 83; Outstndg Teen Of Yr Awd Yth Soc 83; 2nd Prncss Awd & Outstndg Missionettes 80; Beth Isreal Schl Nrsg; Nrsg.

MONGELLI, DANIELLE; Fontbonne Hall Acad; Brooklyn, NY; (Y); 22/140; French Clb; Yrbk Phtg; Hon Roll; Arch Engr.

MONGELLI, LAURA; West Islip HS; West Islip, NY; (Y); 32/525; Ski Clb; Yrbk Stf; Bsktbl; Cheerleading; Sftbl; Vllybl; Hon Roll; NHS; Colgate U; Pltcl Sci.

MONGELLUZZO, DONNA; John H Glenn HS; Huntington, NY; (Y); Dance Clb; Chorus; Vllybl; Arturo Toscanini Annl Awds 85; Farmingdale; Comp Prog.

MONIE JR, WILLIS; Cooperstown Central HS; Cooperstown, NY; (Y); Church Yth Grp; Varsity Clb; Var Capt Bsktbl; Im Coach Actv; JV Socr; Im Vllybl; Hon Roll; NHS; Mth Comp 2nd Pl 83; Mth Comp 2nd Pl Rapid Calc 84; Engrng.

MONISERA, ANDREA; Port Jervis HS; Sparrowbush, NY; (Y); 10/196; JV Var Socr; U Of SC; Phrmcy.

MONKMAN, MICHELLE M; Carthage Central HS; Carthage, NY; (Y); 3/203; Sec Key Clb; Chorus; School Musical; School Play; NHS; Ntl Merit Ltr; Pres Schlr; Rotary Awd; Church Yth Grp; Drama Clb; Nort Country Schlr 85; Youth Of The Month 85; Conference All State 85; St John Fisher; Optometry.

MONKO, SANDRA A; Patchogue-Medford HS; New York, NY; (Y); 36/711; Library Aide; Stage Crew; Yrbk Stf; Fld Hcky; Hon Roll; NHS; Regents Schlrshp 85; St Joseph U; Psych.

MONNIELLO, MARIA; Oceanside HS; Oceanside, NY; (Y); Computer Clb; Chorus; Off Frsh Cls; Off Soph Cls; Off Jr Cls; Off Sr Cls; Mgr(s); Nassau Coll; Comp Prgm.

MONROE, DORIE; Schuylerville Central School; Gansevoort, NY; (Y); VP French Clb; Math Tm; Band; JV Var Bsktbl; JV Fld Hcky; JV Tennis; High Hon Roll; Hon Roll; NHS; Highest 2 Yr Average 84; Stu Cncl Major Let For Various Activities 85; Bio Sci.

MONROE, JEFFREY; Cardinal Hayes HS; New York, NY; (Y); Aud/Vis; Church Yth Grp; Dance Clb; Sec Jr Cls; JV Bsktbl; Var Bowling; Var Score Keeper; Im Wt Lftg; Comp.

MONROE, JOHN; Highland HS; Highland, NY; (Y); Stage Crew; Var Ftbl; JV Trk; Hon Roll.

MONROE, KEN; Greenwich Central HS; Salem, NY; (Y); 4-H; French Clb; FFA; Band; Trk; 4-H Awd; High Hon Roll; Hon Roll; Prfct Atten Awd; FFA Ag Plcmnt Awd ST & Lcl 84-85; Cobleskill; Ag.

MONROE, KIMBERLY; Adali E Stevenson HS; Bronx, NY; (Y); Girl Scts; Orch; Hon Roll; Prfct Atten Awd; NY Bar Assn Mck Trl 85; Bus Admn.

MONROE, LYNNE M; Mc Greaw Central HS; E Freetown, NY; (S); 9/65; Band; Chorus; Yrbk Ed-Chief; Yrbk Stf; Sec Soph Cls; Sec Jr Cls; Sec Stu Cncl; Bowling; Hon Roll; Jr NHS; CCBI; Wrd Proc.

MONROE, MICHELLE; Norwood-Norfolk Central HS; Norfolk, NY; (Y); VP 4-H; Latin Clb; Library Aide; Quiz Bowl; Off Stu Cncl; High Hon Roll; Kiwanis Awd; Lion Awd; Ntl Merit Ltr; Rgnts Schlrshp; Bennington Coll; Soc Sci.

MONSEES, PETER R; Greece Athenan SR HS; Hilton, NY; (Y); 18/283; Aud/Vis; Church Yth Grp; Exploring; German Clb; Ski Clb; Ftbl; Golf; Hon Roll; Jr NHS; Pres Schlr; NY ST Regents Schlrshp; Minority Stu Awd Pres St John Fisher Coll 85; CPA.

MONTAGUE, COLLIN J; Kingston HS; Lake Katrine, NY; (Y); 32/520; AFS; Aud/Vis; Trs Exploring; Ski Clb; Stage Crew; Yrbk Stf; High Hon Roll; Spanish NHS; Scholarship For New York State 84-85; RPI; Aero Nautical Engr.

MONTAGUE, NATHAN; Lansing HS; Lansing, NY; (Y); #18 In Class; Boy Scts; Ski Clb; School Musical; Stage Crew; Ed Yrbk Phtg; Yrbk Rptr; Yrbk Stf; Var Golf; Var Socr; Var Trk; Photo.

MONTALTO, TARA ELIZABETH; Newfield HS; Selden, NY; (Y); 77/572; Drama Clb; Q&S; Service Clb; Acpl Chr; Chorus; School Musical; School Play; Stage Crew; Lit Mag; Off Frsh Cls; Stu Citizen Of Mnth 82; SUNY Stony Brook U; Theatre.

MONTALVO, ALEX; Brooklyn Technical HS; New York, NY; (Y); Boys Clb Am; JA; Key Clb; Chorus; Tennis; U Miami; Archit.

MONTANA, DEAN; West Genesee HS; Warners, NY; (Y); Band; Concert Band; Jazz Band; Mrchg Band; Orch; Pep Band; School Musical; Symp Band; Rep Frsh Cls; Ftbl; NYSSMA Awd A Ratg Solo Comptn 82-84; Music Dept Recog Awd Music Achvt Music Fest 84; Music.

MONTANA, MICHAELE M; John F Kennedy HS; Utica, NY; (Y); 6/120; Church Yth Grp; Hosp Aide; Pres Math Clb; Yrbk Phtg; Rep Stu Cncl; Var JV Cheerleading; High Hon Roll; NHS; Aud/Vis; Computer Clb; Prof & Bus Womens Clb Scholar 85; Utica Coll; Biol.

MONTANARO, LUCY; John C Birdlebough HS; Pennellville, NY; (Y); 14/180; Latin Clb; Band; School Musical; Yrbk Stf; Trs Stu Cncl; Var JV Bsktbl; Var Sftbl; High Hon Roll; Hon Roll.

MONTANARO, MARY; John C Birdlebough HS; Pennellvl, NY; (Y); 5/190; Band; Mrchg Band; School Musical; Var JV Bsktbl; Var Sftbl; Capt Twrlr; High Hon Roll; NHS; Prfct Atten Awd.

MONTANEZ III, LAWRENCE; Nazareth Regional HS; Brooklyn, NY; (Y); Stage Crew; Nwsp Stf; Yrbk Stf; JV Var Bsbl; JV Crs Cntry; JV Ftbl; JV Var Trk; Var Wrstlng; Art Mdl & Awds 83-85; Pratt; Arch.

MONTANINO, MATTHEW; Lansingburgh HS; Troy, NY; (Y); Boy Scts; Exploring; JA; Service Clb; JV Bsktbl; High Hon Roll; Hon Roll; NHS; Hudson Valley CC; Accntng.

MONTANINO, MICHAEL; Lansingburgh HS; Troy, NY; (Y); Boys Clb Am; Boy Scts; Church Yth Grp; JA; Key Clb; Library Aide; Office Aide; Teachers Aide; High Hon Roll; Hon Roll; Spelling Awd 83; Spelling Bee Awd 80; Arts & Crafts Awd 83; Ofc Job.

MONTANO, AMALIA; The Bronx High School Of Science; Bronx, NY; (Y); Nwsp Rptr; Nwsp Stf; Yrbk Phtg; Yrbk Rptr; Lit Mag; Yrbk Awd 85; Hnrs Bio 82-83; Hnr Eng 82-85; Amer U; Comm.

MONTAQUE, ROBERT; John Dewey HS; Brooklyn, NY; (Y); Church Yth Grp; Hosp Aide; Math Clb; Science Clb; Church Choir; VP Jr Cls; Trk; Hon Roll; Ntl Merit Ltr; Prfct Atten Awd; Pre-Med.

MONTE, DAVID A; Schalmont HS; Duanesburg, NY; (Y); Socr; Trk; Wrstlng; Hon Roll; Engrng.

MONTEAGUDO, CARLOS M; Bronx High Schl Sci; Bronx, NY; (Y); Cmnty Wkr; Pres Key Clb; Office Aide; Spanish Clb; Teachers Aide; Chorus; Church Choir; Acadmc All Amer Band 84-85; Ed.

MONTEFERRANTE, CATHERINE; Farmingdale HS; Farmingdale, NY; (Y); FBLA; GAA; Hosp Aide; Office Aide; Red Cross Aide; JV Bsktbl; Coach Actv; Mgr(s); JV Sftbl; Im Vllybl; MVP Sftbl 82; Law.

MONTEFUSCO, THOMAS; West Hemstead HS; W Hempstead, NY; (Y); Computer Clb; Var JV Bsbl; Var Trk; Hon Roll; Cert Achvt Mth 84; Polytech Inst NY; Comp Sci.

MONTEMARANO, ELLEN; Nazareth Regional HS; Brooklyn, NY; (Y); Am Leg Aux Girls St; VP JA; Math Tm; NFL; Speech Tm; Chorus; Yrbk Phtg; JV Sftbl; Hon Roll; NHS; Rcgntn Svc Disable Prsns Cath Charities 84; Supr Achvt Soc Stud 83; Supr Achvt Comp Sci 85.

MONTEMARANO, LEONARD; Aviation HS; Long Isl City, NY; (Y); 117/417; Nwsp Stf; Aerospc Engrng.

MONTEMURRO, LINDA; Thomas R Proctor HS; Utica, NY; (Y); 12/160; Dance Clb; Drama Clb; Math Tm; Chorus; School Musical; Rep Stu Cncl; Cit Awd; DAR Awd; High Hon Roll; NHS; Amer Leg, Prsdntl Acad Ftnss, Drma Clb Hnr Awds 85; Mohawk Vally CC; Med.

MONTEN, DONNA; Bethpage HS; Plainview, NY; (Y); 37/277; Girl Scts; Spanish Clb; Concert Band; Mrchg Band; School Musical; Swmmng; High Hon Roll; NHS; Ntl Merit Ltr; Desmond Costello Mem Schrlshp Awd 85; Herman Slavin Schlrshp 85; Boston U; Occuptnl Thrpy.

MONTERASTELLI, LISA J; Rome Free Acad; Rome, NY; (Y); 74/630; Church Yth Grp; Intnl Clb; Key Clb; Fld Hcky; Powder Puff Ftbl; Socr; Sftbl; High Hon Roll; Hon Roll; NHS; Oswego ST; Librl Arts.

MONTERO, ELBA; The Mary Louis Acad; Jackson Heights, NY; (Y); Cmnty Wkr; Hosp Aide; Service Clb; Im Bowling; NY U; Psych.

MONTES, MARA; Cardinal Spellman HS; New York, NY; (Y); Camera Clb; Science Clb; Spanish Clb; Color Guard; School Musical; School Play; Trk; 1st & 2nd Hnrs; Nrsng Schlrshp; SUNY-NEW Paltz; Envrnmtl Sci.

MONTESANO, VINCENT; Iona Prep; Mamaroneck, NY; (Y); 16/198; Boy Scts; Chess Clb; Church Yth Grp; Cmnty Wkr; French Clb; JV Bsbl; Var JV Ftbl; JV Mgr(s); JV Score Keeper; JV Trk; Eagle Scout Awd 84; Bus Mgmt.

MONTESI, RONALD S; Queensbury HS; Glens Falls, NY; (Y); 2/226; Am Leg Boys St; French Clb; Pres Key Clb; Band; Yrbk Phtg; JV Crs Cntry; Var Capt Swmmng; JV Trk; DAR Awd; NHS; NY ST Schlrshp 85; Stu Of Qrtr-Soc Stds & Eng; JR Prom King 84; Colgate U; Bio.

MONTEVAGO, JAMES; Wellington Mepham HS; Clearwater, FL; (Y); Capt Ice Hcky; Capt Socr; Var Wrstlng; Tampa U; Bus.

MONTGOMERY, BRENDA; Rhinebeck Central Schl; Rhinebeck, NY; (Y); Art Clb; Cmnty Wkr; Dance Clb; Drama Clb; French Clb; Teachers Aide; Band; School Musical; Stage Crew; Nwsp Rptr; Hugh O Brian Yth Fndtn Ldrshp Awd 83-84; Awd Genl Excllnc Soph Yr 83-84; Comprhnsv Frnch Awd 84-85; Art.

MONTGOMERY, CHER; Churchville-Chili HS; Rochester, NY; (Y); High Hon Roll; Bus Hnr Soc 85.

MONTGOMERY, JONATHAN; New York Military Acad; West Nyack, NY; (S); Church Yth Grp; 4-H; ROTC; Ski Clb; Stage Crew; VP Stu Cncl; JV Ice Hcky; Var Lcrss; Stat Mgr(s); Im Wt Lftg; Math Awd 83; Best New Cadet Awd 83; Medalsin Leadership Dvlpmnt; Political Sci.

MONTGOMERY, LETASHA; Lafayette HS; Buffalo, NY; (Y); Comp Inf Sci.

MONTGOMERY, MARY E; Bishop Kearney HS; Brooklyn, NY; (Y); Ski Clb; Ntl Merit Schol; Cortland ST U; Tchr.

MONTGOMERY, PAT; Auburn HS; Auburn, NY; (Y); JV Bsktbl; Var Trk; High Hon Roll; Hon Roll; Sci.

MONTHIE, KAREN; Cicero North Syracuse HS; Bridgeport, NY; (S); 132/622; Office Aide; Secy.

MONTIE, WALTER; Copiague HS; Copiague, NY; (Y); French Clb; High Hon Roll; Hon Roll; Ntl Soc Stds Olymp Amer Hist 84; Frnch.

MONTONEY, MICHELLE; Cicero-North Syracuse HS; Clay, NY; (S); 5/622; Mathletes; Ski Clb; Trs Band; Drm Mjr(t); Mrchg Band; Symp Band; JV Sftbl; High Hon Roll; JP Sousa Awd; Syracuse Symph Yth Orch 84-85; All Cnty Band Orch 83-84; SSO CMM Yth Concerto Comp 84; Music.

MONTOUTE, VALERIE; Bishop Loughlin M HS; Brooklyn, NY; (Y); Dance Clb; Library Aide; Jr Cls; Mgr(s); Score Keeper; Timer; Prfct Atten Awd; Howard Pace U; Comp Sci.

MONTPLAISIR, DAVID; Liverpool HS; Liverpool, NY; (S); 61/792; Camera Clb; Exploring; Chorus; Yrbk Phtg; Stu Cncl; High Hon Roll; Jr NHS; NHS; St Lawrence U; Chem.

MONTROSE, CEASAR; Boiys And Girls HS; Brooklyn, NY; (Y); Aud/Vis; JA; Political Wkr; Socr; Tennis; High Hon Roll; St John U; Pre-Med.

MONTROY, KATHRYN; Ogdensburg Free Acad; Ogdensburg, NY; (Y); Hosp Aide; Band; Chorus; Mrchg Band; Mater Dei Coll; Opto.

MONTUORI, DAVID A; Deer Park HS; Deer Park, NY; (Y); Camera Clb; DECA; Pres FBLA; Hosp Aide; Yrbk Phtg; JV Score Keeper; Hon Roll; NY Chiropractic Coll; Chiroprc.

MONZON, RUTH M; Lackawanna SR HS; Lackawanna, NY; (Y); Drama Clb; Hon Roll; Long Island U; Nrsng.

MOODIE, DANIELLE; Newtown HS; Elmhurst, NY; (Y); Lit Mag; Swmmng; Hunter Coll; Vet Sci.

MOODIE, SHAWN; St John The Baptist HS; Wyandanch, NY; (Y); Chess Clb; Off Frsh Cls; Crs Cntry; Trk; Hon Roll; Hofstra; Comp Engr.

MOODY, CATHERINE; Fayetteville-Manlius HS; Fayetteville, NY; (Y); 86/346; Church Yth Grp; Hosp Aide; School Musical; Swing Chorus; Ed Yrbk Stf; Sec Stu Cncl; Var Cheerleading; Capt Var Gym; JV Sftbl; NHS; Schl Bus Awd 84; Empire ST Gym Tm 81-83.

MOOK, JOELLE; North Rose-Wolcott HS; Wolcott, NY; (Y); 1/140; School Play; Stage Crew; Var Trk; Bausch & Lomb Sci Awd; Pres NHS; Val; Yrbk Stf; Cit Awd; Ntl Merit Ltr; Rensselaer Polytech Inst Math & Sci Awd 84; NY ST Regents Schlrshp 85; Principals Hnr Roll 81-85; Warcester Polytech Inst; Math.

MOON, CHARLES; John H Glenn HS; E Northport, NY; (Y); 47/261; High Hon Roll; Hon Roll; NHS; Pres Acad Fit Awd 85; Rensselaer Polytech; Comp Sci.

MOON, JULIE; Northstar Christian Acad; Hamlin, NY; (S); 10/28; Drama Clb; Office Aide; Teachers Aide; Church Choir; School Play; Yrbk Stf; Sec Sr Cls; Var Capt Cheerleading; Socr; High Hon Roll; Robert Wesleyan Coll; Music.

MOON, LISA; Tioga Central HS; Smithboro, NY; (S); 18/96; Computer Clb; Varsity Clb; Rep Frsh Cls; Rep Stu Cncl; Var Bsktbl; Var Fld Hcky; Var Sftbl; Var Trk; Hon Roll; NHS.

MOON, STEVE; Bronx High Schl Of Scieće; Fresh Meadows, NY; (Y); Trs Church Yth Grp; Math Tm; Orch; JV Crs Cntry; Ntl Merit SF; Computer Clb; Aerospace Engrng.

MOONEN, PETER; Vernon-Verona-Sherrill HS; Verona, NY; (Y); Varsity Clb; Var L Socr; Var L Wrstlng; Rbt Todd Mem Awd In Wrstlng 83; Paul Hutch Mem Awd In Wrstlng 85; Bus Adm.

MOONEY, BARBARA; Albertos Magnus HS; Orangeburg, NY; (Y); Church Yth Grp; Drama Clb; Service Clb; School Musical; School Play; Stage Crew; Yrbk Stf; Cheerleading; Hon Roll; Mu Alp Tht.

MOONEY, MOIRA; St Barnabas HS; Bronx, NY; (Y); 42/136; JV Cheerleading; French Hon Soc; Prfct Atten Awd; 1st & 2nd Hnrs 84-85; Wood Schl; Bus.

MOONEY, PHILIP; Philip Mooney HS; Mass Pk, NY; (Y); Camera Clb; Cmnty Wkr; Computer Clb; Ski Clb; Yrbk Phtg; JV Socr; Var Tennis; Var Trk; Spec Ed.

MOONEY, ROBERT; Harborfields HS; Huntington, NY; (Y); Var Bowling; Var Tennis; High Hon Roll; Hon Roll; NHS; Cert Achv Ntl Hstry Day 84; Cert Merit Frnch 84; Cert Awd Mechncl Drwng I 85; Arch.

MOONEY, ROBERT; Niagara Wheatfield SR HS; Niagara Falls, NY; (Y); Trs Latin Clb; PAVAS; Symp Band; L Var Swmmng; High Hon Roll; Hon Roll; NHS; Am Leg Boys St; German Clb; Pep Clb; Marine Bio.

MOONEY, SEAN T; Cairo-Durham Central Schl; S Cairo, NY; (Y); 15/81; VP Band; Jazz Band; Pep Band; School Musical; School Play; High Hon Roll; NHS; Art Schlrshp 85-89; Studio Art.

MOONEY, SHANNON; Cardinal Ohara HS; Williamsville, NY; (S); 6/137; French Clb; JA; Rep Sr Cls; Rep Stu Cncl; JV Badmtn; Var L Bowling; JV Cheerleading; High Hon Roll; NHS.

MOORE, ADRIENNE; Yonkers HS; Yonkers, NY; (Y); 2/350; Church Yth Grp; FBLA; MMM; Band; Chorus; Rep Sr Cls; Var Gym; Var Vllybl; High Hon Roll; Hon Roll; Westchester Bus Schl; Legal Sec.

MOORE, ANDREW D; John Jay SR HS; Cross River, NY; (Y); Chess Clb; Math Tm; Science Clb; High Hon Roll; Regents Schlrshp Awd 85; SUNY Albany; Comp Sci.

MOORE, BERNICE; Mount Mercy HS; W Seneca, NY; (Y); Church Yth Grp; Computer Clb; 4-H; Math Clb; Model UN; Chorus; Im Bowling; Stat Vllybl; 4-H Awd; Hon Roll; 4-H Schlrshp; Alfred ST; Agri Sci.

MOORE, BEVERLEY; Washington Irving HS; Brooklyn, NY; (Y); 1/370; Church Yth Grp; FBLA; JA; Chorus; Hon Roll; NHS; Val; Regents Schlrshp 85; Teachers Schlrshp 85; Pace U Trustee Schlrshp 85; Pace U; Acctng.

MOORE, CHRISTINE; Victor SR HS; Victor, NY; (Y); Church Yth Grp; GAA; Ski Clb; Band; Sec Sr Cls; Stu Cncl; Bsktbl; Crs Cntry; Socr; Trk.

MOORE, CINDY; Wellsville HS; Wellsville, NY; (Y); Church Yth Grp; Hosp Aide; Library Aide; Chorus; Church Choir; Madrigals; School Musical; Nwsp Stf; High Hon Roll; William Briggs Nrsng Schrshp 85; St James Nrsng Schl; Nrsng.

MOORE, CLARA R; New Berlin Central HS; New Berlin, NY; (Y); Church Yth Grp; VICA; Band; Concert Band; Mrchg Band; Pep Band; Prfct Atten Awd; Pol Officer.

MOORE, CURLAN; Bishop Loughlin Memorial HS; Brooklyn, NY; (Y); 27/180; PAVAS; Radio Clb; Concert Band; Jazz Band; School Musical; Sempler Fidelis Awd 85; Queensborough; Audio Engr.

MOORE, DANA; Johnstown HS; St Johnsville, NY; (Y); #7 In Class; VP Pres 4-H; Band; Mrchg Band; Stu Cncl; Ftbl; 4-H Awd; Hon Roll; NHS; Prfct Atten Awd; Regents Schlrshp 85; Beta Chi Schlrshp 85; St Marys Schl Nrsng; Nrsng.

MOORE, DIANE; Huntington Christian Schl; Hauppauge, NY; (S); Church Yth Grp; Drama Clb; Chorus; Orch; Sec Frsh Cls; Rep Soph Cls; Rep Jr Cls; Rep Sr Cls; Sec VP Stu Cncl; High Hon Roll; Word Of Life Bible Inst.

MOORE, EL-MELEK ALLEYNE; John Dewey HS; Brooklyn, NY; (Y); Concert Band; School Play; Variety Show; Yrbk Stf.

MOORE, ELISABETH; Auburn HS; Auburn, NY; (Y); Drama Clb; Intnl Clb; Acpl Chr; Chorus; Madrigals; School Musical; School Play; Stage Crew; Swing Chorus; Nwsp Stf; Sprntndnts Awd 85; Caugar Cnty CC; Bus Adm.

MOORE, GERALD; Bishop Ludden HS; Camillus, NY; (Y); Exploring; Model UN; Ski Clb; Band; Pep Band; Lit Mag; JV Var Socr; High Hon Roll; Hon Roll; Prfct Atten Awd.

MOORE, JACQUELINE; Lancaster Central HS; Depew, NY; (S); DECA; Pep Clb; Teachers Aide; School Play; Bryant; Bus Mgmt.

MOORE, JAMES E; Jamesville De Witt HS; Dewitt, NY; (Y); Church Yth Grp; Cmnty Wkr; Concert Band; Jazz Band; Orch; Symp Band; Ftbl; Im Tennis; High Hon Roll; Hon Roll; Syracuse U; Chem.

MOORE, JEANNA; Royalton Hartland HS; Middleport, NY; (Y); Church Yth Grp; Library Aide; Chorus; Church Choir; Hon Roll; Navy; Cook.

MOORE, JOHN; Sheepshead Bay HS; Brooklyn, NY; (Y); Concert Band; Var L Bsbl; PA ST U; Law.

MOORE, KATHLEEN R; Naples Central HS; Naples, NY; (Y); 6/83; Church Yth Grp; Chorus; Concert Band; Mrchg Band; Sec Frsh Cls; Sec Soph Cls; Sec Jr Cls; Capt Cheerleading; Var JV Socr; Var JV Sftbl; Art Awd Consrvtn Dept 82; Monroe CC; Elem Schl Tchr.

MOORE, KATHRYN; Homer Central HS; Preble, NY; (Y); 53/188; Church Yth Grp; 4-H; Hon Roll; Prfct Atten Awd; Outstndng Stu Data Proc 84-85; Amvets Schlrshp 85; Suyn; Comp.

MOORE, KATHRYN M; Notre Dame Acad; Staten Island, NY; (Y); 25/91; Cmnty Wkr; Stage Crew; Nwsp Stf; Capt Cheerleading; NHS; Staten Isl Cath Fed Parents Schlrshp 84; Syracuse U; Comm.

MOORE, KELLY E; Kenmore West SR HS; Kenmore, NY; (Y); Chorus; Color Guard; School Musical; Swing Chorus; Yrbk Phtg; Yrbk Stf; Mgr(s); Hon Roll; Prtcptn Awd St Joes Swing Chr 85; Rochester Inst Tech; Photogrphr.

MOORE, KRISTEN L; Arlington HS; Pleasant Valley, NY; (Y); 83/572; Girl Scts; Intnl Clb; Trs Spanish Clb; Yrbk Stf; Hnr Key 85; Regents Schlrshp 85; St U Albany; Comp Sci.

MOORE, LAUREEN A; Lansingburgh HS; Troy, NY; (Y); 17/190; 4-H; Spanish Clb; Teachers Aide; School Play; Nwsp Stf; Yrbk Stf; Var Trk; High Hon Roll; NHS; Prfct Atten Awd; NY ST Regnts Schlrshp 85; SUNY Albany; Engl.

MOORE, MARI BETH; York Central HS; Leicester, NY; (Y); Sec Church Yth Grp; GAA; Library Aide; Ski Clb; Varsity Clb; Chorus; Var L Bsktbl; Mgr(s); Im Socr; JV Sftbl; Pres Phys Ftns Achvt Awd 83-85; John Casablanca Awd 83; SUNY Geneseo; Bus Mgmt.

MOORE, MICHAEL; Scotia-Glenville HS; Schenectady, NY; (Y); 2/225; Am Leg Boys St; German Clb; Ski Clb; Var Tennis; NHS.

MOORE, MICHAEL D; Schenectady Christian Schl; Alplaus, NY; (Y); 1/11; Yrbk Stf; Pres Stu Cncl; JV Var Bsktbl; JV Var Socr; High Hon Roll; Prfct Atten Awd; Prncpls Awd 82; Stdnt Cncl Svc Awd 83; Sprtsmnshp Awd Bsktbl 82; Mst Improv Awd Bsktbl 83; Union Coll; Elctrcl Engrng.

MOORE, MICHELLE; Broadalbin Central HS; Gloversville, NY; (Y); French Clb; Library Aide; Pep Clb; Fulton Montgomery CC; Nrsng.

MOORE, PAULINE; Grace Dodge Vocational HS; Bronx, NY; (Y); Office Aide; Teachers Aide; School Play; Yrbk Stf; Sftbl; Awd Medcl Asst 84-85; Med Asst.

MOORE, PAULINE; Walton HS; Bronx, NY; (Y); Cmnty Wkr; Exploring; FBLA; Var Score Keeper; Var Swmmng; Capt Tennis; Var Vllybl; Hon Ltr Mayor Koch 84; Pride Yankees Awd 84; Nursing.

MOORE, PETER; St Josephs Collegiate Inst; Williamsville, NY; (Y); Ski Clb; Trk.

MOORE, ROBERT K; Holy Cross HS; Flushing, NY; (Y); Cmnty Wkr; French Clb; Science Clb; Var Crs Cntry; Var Trk; Hon Roll; Jr NHS; Math.

MOORE, S GORDON; Roy C Ketcham HS; Wappingers Fall, NY; (Y); Church Yth Grp; Math Tm; Stage Crew; Pres Jr Cls; JV Bsbl; JV Bsktbl; High Hon Roll; Hon Roll; NHS; GA Tech Mite Prog 85; Engnr.

MOORE, SUSAN; Haverling Central Schl; Bath, NY; (S); 19/150; AFS; French Clb; Math Clb; Acpl Chr; Color Guard; Concert Band; Symp Band; Yrbk Stf; VP Stu Cncl; Cheerleading; Most Val Swmmr 83-84; Chldhd Educ.

MOORE, TABITHA; Gloversville HS; Gloversville, NY; (Y); 25/240; Trs Church Yth Grp; Intnl Clb; Teachers Aide; Band; Chorus; Church Choir; Concert Band; Mrchg Band; Rep Frsh Cls; Rep Soph Cls; Alfre N Johnson Schlrshp Awd 85; Fulton Co Mrch Dimes Schlrshp 85; St John Fisher Coll; Pre Med.

MOORE, TERESA; North Rose-Wolcott HS; N Rose, NY; (Y); Ski Clb; Stage Crew; Nwsp Phtg; Yrbk Phtg; Lit Mag; Cit Awd; High Hon Roll; Hon Roll; NHS; Phtgrphy.

MOORE, TRACY; Byron-Bergen Central HS; Byron, NY; (Y); 2/90; Spanish Clb; Concert Band; Mrchg Band; Pres Sr Cls; Sec Stu Cncl; Capt Cheerleading; Trs Jr NHS; Pres NHS; Prfct Atten Awd; Pres Schlr; Northwood Inst; Bus Adm.

MOOREHEAD, THERESA; Irondequoit HS; Rochester, NY; (Y); 38/393; Church Yth Grp; Hosp Aide; Ski Clb; Stage Crew; Hon Roll; No Truancy Awd 84-85.

MOORES, KEVIN A; Frontier Central HS; Blasdell, NY; (Y); 44/526; Chess Clb; Varsity Clb; Band; Var Capt Socr; Var Tennis; Var Trk; NHS; Boy Scts; German Clb; Math Clb; Stu Govt Sprtsmnshp Awd 84; Clarkson U; Elec Engr.

MOORMAN, JAYNE; Amherst Central Senior HS; Amherst, NY; (Y); 122/310; Library Aide; Ski Clb; Chorus; Church Choir; Madrigals; Hon Roll; Regents Schlrshp 85; Buffalo ST Coll; Jrnlsm.

MOORS, LAURIE ANN; Northeastern Clinton HS; Rouses Point, NY; (Y); FHA; Stage Crew; Variety Show; Var Crs Cntry; JV Tennis; Var Trk; JV Vllybl; Hon Roll; 1st Pl Cookg 85; Ltrs Wntr & Sprg Trck; N TX ST COLL; Chld Dev.

MOQTADERI, ZARMIK; Hackley Schl; Irvington, NY; (Y); 1/87; Debate Tm; Capt Math Tm; Model UN; Nwsp Ed-Chief; Var Fld Hcky; Lcrss; High Hon Roll; Ntl Merit SF; Hackley Bowl 84; Harvard Bk Prz 84; Rensselae Mdl 84; Bio.

MORAG, BOAZ; Niskayuna HS; Schenectady, NY; (Y); Pres French Clb; Mathletes; Q&S; Scholastic Bowl; Science Clb; School Musical; Nwsp Ed-Chief; High Hon Roll; VP NHS; Ntl Merit Ltr; Harvard Bk Awd 84; Gold Medal St Sci 85; NY U Schlrs Awd 85; NY U.

MORAGNE, TAMU AMANI; John Dewey HS; Silver Spring, MD; (Y); Cmnty Wkr; Chorus; Trk; Im Wt Lftg; Hon Roll; Adv Frnch Awd 85; Stenogrphy 85; PTA Spec Achvt Awd 85; OH U; Comm.

MORAHAN, KAREN; Albertus Magnus HS; Nanuet, NY; (Y); Debate Tm; Drama Clb; Spanish Clb; Speech Tm; Yrbk Stf; Nrsg.

MORAIS, AMANDIO; Aviation HS; Jamaica, NY; (Y); 164/417; Church Yth Grp; Cmnty Wkr; JA; VICA; Socr; Cit Awd; Hon Roll; Prfct Atten Awd; Cert Of Grad From Airframe 85; 100% Attndnc Awd 84-85; Embry Riddle Coll; Airpln Mech.

MORALES, AUDREY; Walton HS; Bronx, NY; (Y); Library Aide; Office Aide; Teachers Aide; School Musical; Rep Frsh Cls; Pres Sr Cls; Rep Stu Cncl; Cit Awd; Hon Roll; Acctg.

MORALES, DIANNE; Stuyvesant HS; Brooklyn, NY; (Y); Dance Clb; Drama Clb; Trs Pep Clb; Ski Clb; Teachers Aide; Varsity Clb; School Musical; School Play; Variety Show; Yrbk Phtg; Ntl Hispanic Schlrs Awd 85; Ntl Achvt 85; Dartmouth Coll; Pre-Med.

MORALES, MAYRA; Eastern Districk HS; Brooklyn, NY; (Y); 7/409; Band; Nwsp Rptr; Rep Frsh Cls; Rep Soph Cls; Rep Jr Cls; Rep Sr Cls; Capt Vllybl; High Hon Roll; Hon Roll; NHS; UFT Schlrshp 85; Army Rsrv Awd Medal 85; Spnsh Medal 85; Band Perf Medal 85; Long Island U; Bus Admin.

MORALES, MILAGROS; Dominican Commercial HS; Brooklyn, NY; (Y); Spanish Clb; Teachers Aide; NHS; Prfct Atten Awd; Sierra Clb 82-85; Costa Rican Flklrc Dance Group 82-85; Bus Adm.

MORALES, MIREYA; Adlai Stevenson HS; Bronx, NY; (Y).

MORALES, NILSA ENID; Dodge Voc HS; New York, NY; (Y); 83/500; Dance Clb; Chorus; Color Guard; School Musical; Bsktbl; Gym; Vllybl; 4-H Awd; Hon Roll; Spanish NHS; Awd Punctualty 83-85; Med.

MORALES, PATRICIA; Brewster HS; Brewster, NY; (Y); Trs Spanish Clb; Yrbk Bus Mgr; Yrbk Ed-Chief; Yrbk Sprt Ed; Rep Stu Cncl; DAR Awd; High Hon Roll; Hon Roll; NHS; Spanish NHS; Schlrshp Awd Stud Art 83; Cert Achvt Asian/Afrcn Stud 83; Schlrshp Awd Engl II Adv 85; Bucknell; Engrng.

MORALES, RAMONA G; Westbury SR HS; Westbury, NY; (Y); 27/250; Art Clb; Drama Clb; FBLA; Stage Crew; Yrbk Stf; Stat Bsktbl; Mgr(s); Score Keeper; Timer; Hon Roll; Regnts Schlrshp 85; Howard U; Hotel Mgmt.

MORALES, SHIRLEY; Cicero North Syracuse HS; Clay, NY; (Y); Pre-Law.

MORALES, THELA; Tonawanda JR SR HS; Tonawanda, NY; (Y); Church Yth Grp; French Clb; Ski Clb; Band; Rep Stu Cncl; Stat Vllybl; Hon Roll; Trs JA; Concert Band; Mrchg Band; Arch.

MORAN, ANNE D; Jamesville-Dewitt HS; Jamesville, NY; (Y); Art Clb; Church Yth Grp; Key Clb; Ski Clb; Var Crs Cntry; Var Trk; High Hon Roll; Art Awd 85; Gld Key Art 83; Stdo Art.

MORAN, BRIAN; Smithtown H S East; St James, NY; (Y); Drama Clb; Pep Clb; Ski Clb; Yrbk Stf; Capt L Golf; MVP Golf 85; All Str Slctns Lg Golf 85.

MORAN, CHARLES P; Xavier HS; Rockaway Beach, NY; (Y); 45/227; Red Cross Aide; Service Clb; Varsity Clb; Var L Bsbl; Var L Bsktbl; Var Capt Ftbl; Jr NHS; NHS; Schlr-Athl Awd Ftbl 84; Moynahan Trphy 85; All- Conf 1st Tm 84; Rensselaer Polytech Inst; Math.

MORAN, CORINNE; Whitesboro SR HS; Whitesboro, NY; (Y); GAA; Intnl Clb; Tennis; High Hon Roll; Hon Roll; Hnr European Studies 83-84; Comp Sci.

MORAN, DON J; Clarkston North HS; New City, NY; (Y); 85/498; Boy Scts; Band; Concert Band; Mrchg Band; Hon Roll; Jr NHS; SUNY Bflo; Elec Engrng.

MORAN, KATHY; Skaneateles Central HS; Skaneateles, NY; (S); 14/165; Yrbk Phtg; Stu Cncl; JV Var Sftbl; Var Capt Tennis; High Hon Roll; NHS; Blue Rbn Schltc Art Cmptn; Hnr Mntn Schltc Art Cmptn; Jurors Cmndtn Art; Photo.

MORAN, LAURA; Stella Maris HS; Woodside, NY; (Y); Dance Clb; Band; Engl Awd 85; Fash Merch.

MORAN, MARY E; Cardinal Spellman HS; Bronx, NY; (Y); Stage Crew; Nwsp Stf; Diving; Capt Swmmng; High Hon Roll; Hon Roll; NHS; Ntl Merit Ltr; NY ST Regents Schlrshp 85; St Raymonds Parish Schlrshp 84; Biomed Engr.

MORAN, MATT; Watertown HS; Watertown, NY; (Y); Church Yth Grp; Rep Frsh Cls; Timer; Law Enfrcmnt.

MORAN, MICHAEL; Victor Central HS; Victor, NY; (Y); Quiz Bowl; Band; Concert Band; Mrchg Band; Ftbl; High Hon Roll; Hon Roll; Archtctrl Engrng.

MORAN, NANCY; Solvay HS; Solvay, NY; (Y); Chorus; Yrbk Sprt Ed; Off Frsh Cls; Off Soph Cls; Off Jr Cls; Var Socr; Var Trk; Vllybl; Stat Wrstlng; Hon Roll; Onondaga Cnty Cntrl Div Hnrbl Ment Sccr 83-84; Engl.

MORAN, PATRICIA; West Seneca West SR HS; Cheektg, NY; (S); 152/563; Pres VP DECA; VP Sec Red Cross Aide; Pres VP Stu Cncl; JC Awd; Key Clb; Pres Soph Cls; CC Awd; Pres Schlr; Yorkers; Canisius Coll; Bus.

MORAN, ROBERT; Haldane HS; Cold Spring, NY; (S); 5/69; Drama Clb; Ski Clb; Spanish Clb; Stage Crew; Nwsp Ed-Chief; Nwsp Stf; Trs Stu Cncl; Var Bsbl; High Hon Roll; Pres NHS; Manhatten Coll; Chem Engrng.

MORAN, TERRY; Bloomfield Central HS; W Bloomfield, NY; (Y); 20/87; Church Yth Grp; Drama Clb; English Clb; 4-H; French Clb; Intnl Clb; Latin Clb; Office Aide; Varsity Clb; School Play; NY ST Sci Conf Wrtng 84; In Your Own Writes 83; Jrnlsm.

MORAN, THOMAS P; Holy Trinity HS; Hicksville, NY; (Y); Church Yth Grp; JA; Math Clb; Ski Clb; Varsity Clb; Bowling; Hon Roll; Jr NHS; Mu Alp Tht; NHS; Ithaca Coll; Phys Thrpy.

MORAN, WILLIAM; Bay Shore HS; Brightwaters, NY; (Y); 74/425; Wrstlng; Merchnt Ofcr.

MORAND, EDWARD; Moore Catholic HS; Staten Isl, NY; (Y); Am Leg Boys St; VP Chorus; School Musical; Nwsp Rptr; Yrbk Rptr; Lit Mag; VP Soph Cls; Var L Crs Cntry; Var L Trk; Music Schlrshp 85; Gibbons Hnr Schlrshp 85; Schlr Athl Awd 85; Catholic U; Music.

MORASCO, GENEVIEVE; The Mary Louis Acad; Jamaica Estates, NY; (Y); 22/283; Aud/Vis; High Hon Roll; Hon Roll; NHS; Yrbk Stf; Lit Mag; Im Socr; Mary Louis Acad Schlrshp 81-85; Presntl Schlrshp 85; NY ST Rgnts Schlrshp 85; Manhattan Coll; Elec Engr.

MORAVANSKY, ALAN; Seton Catholic Central HS; Binghamton, NY; (Y); Var Capt Bowling; Mech Engrng.

MORAVEC, JOSEPH P; Archbishop Molloy HS; Middle Village, NY; (Y); 7/371; Church Yth Grp; Computer Clb; Math Tm; Pep Clb; Ski Clb; VP Jr Cls; VP Sr Cls; Cit Awd; High Hon Roll; Kiwanis Awd; Math Trphy Outstndg Achvmt Lg 84; Chpgnt Awd Srvc,Amer Lgn Awd 85; Best Prsnlty Peers; Cornell U; Engineering.

MORAVEC, SHARON MARIE; Vicenza American HS; Apo New York, NY; (Y); 6/55; Band; Yrbk Stf; Lit Mag; Sr Cls; Sec Stu Cncl; Mgr(s); NHS; Pres Schlr; Church Yth Grp; Teachers Aide; Vicenza Off Wives Clb Schlrshp 85; FL Inst Tech; Pre-Med.

MORDA, SCOTT T; Tottenville HS; Staten Island, NY; (Y); Math Tm; Band; Concert Band; Hon Roll; Rochester Inst; Prof Photgraphc.

MORDENO, MICHELE; Sachem HS; Farmingville, NY; (Y); 24/1463; Civic Clb; Cmnty Wkr; Dance Clb; Service Clb; Ski Clb; Spanish Clb; Nwsp Stf; Cheerleading; Timer; Jr NHS; Union Coll.

MORDSFELD, RENE; Tamarac HS; Troy, NY; (Y); 4-H; Spanish Clb; JV Socr; JV Sftbl; Var Vllybl; Hon Roll; Wrd Prcssng.

MORE, TRACEY; Oneonta HS; Oneonta, NY; (Y); 37/184; Rptr 4-H; French Clb; Spanish Clb; Yrbk Stf; Hon Roll; Hghst Ave Bio 83-84; Elem Ed.

MOREAU, DAVE; Roy C Ketcham HS; Wappingers Falls, NY; (Y); AFS; Church Yth Grp; Pres 4-H; Concert Band; Stage Crew; JV Bsktbl; Var Trk; Hon Roll; NHS; Socl Studies Achvt Awd 85; Engrng.

MOREHOUSE, MICHAEL D; Massena Central HS; Massena, NY; (Y); Am Leg Boys St; Church Yth Grp; Key Clb; Band; Church Choir; Mrchg Band; Stu Cncl; JV Var Bsktbl; JV Var Ftbl; JV Var Golf; Highest Avrge In Clss 83-84; Acad Banquet 82-85; Coaches Awd For JV Bsktbl 83-84; Dntstry.

MORELAND, RONETTA; Julia Richman HS; New York, NY; (Y); Dance Clb; Cit Awd; Citzn Wk 81; Robert Tate Love Awd 85; Awds Merit 81; Comp.

MORELL, ANN MARGARET; Roy C Ketcham HS; Wappingers Fls, NY; (Y); 46/507; Church Yth Grp; Girl Scts; Math Clb; Science Clb; Band; Chorus; Color Guard; Concert Band; Mrchg Band; Stu Cncl; Marist Coll; Med Tech.

MORELL, DEANNA; Palmyra Macedon HS; Palmyra, NY; (Y); 17/204; VP Math Tm; Varsity Clb; Chorus; Yrbk Stf; Trs Frsh Cls; JV Bsktbl; JV Var Socr; Var Sftbl; Var Vllybl; Hon Roll; NY Rgnts Schlrshp 85; Pres Acadmc Ftns Awd; U Of Rochester; Optcl Engrng.

MORELL, JAMES ANTHONY; Roy C Ketcham HS; Wappingers Fls, NY; (Y); 80/520; Boy Scts; Cmnty Wkr; Math Clb; Wrstlng; High Hon Roll; Hon Roll; Jr NHS; NHS; Prfct Atten Awd; Pre Law.

MORELL, KIMBERLY A; Coxsackie-Athens Central HS; Coxsackie, NY; (Y); Drama Clb; Pep Clb; Yrbk Stf; Rep Frsh Cls; Rep Soph Cls; Rep Jr Cls; Rep Stu Cncl; Bsktbl; Sci.

MORELLI, MARIANNE; Franciscan HS; Putnam Vly, NY; (Y); 3/60; Drama Clb; Library Aide; Chorus; School Musical; Variety Show; Nwsp Stf; Yrbk Ed-Chief; Trs Jr Cls; High Hon Roll; Sec NHS.

MORELLI, NICOLE; West Babylon SR HS; W Babylon, NY; (Y); 28/485; Variety Show; Yrbk Phtg; Rep Sr Cls; JV Bsktbl; JV Sftbl; Hon Roll; Jr NHS; Dntstry.

MORENO, ANGELICQUE; Cardinal Spellman HS; Bronx, NY; (Y); Latin Clb; Spanish Clb; Color Guard; Hon Roll; 2nd Hnrs Overall Avg 83-85; Pre-Law.

MORENO, FIORDALEZA; Fashion Industries HS; Brooklyn, NY; (Y); 25/463; Church Yth Grp; Computer Clb; FBLA; JA; Stage Crew; All Amer Schlrs Awd 85; Bus Educ Awd 85; Regents Mrt; Pace U; Acctng.

MORENO, JAMES; Bishopo Loughlin M HS; Brooklyn, NY; (Y); 56/186; Computer Clb; Science Clb; Spanish Clb; Bowling; Vllybl; Baruch Coll; Accntg.

MORENO, ROSA; Brooklyn Technical HS; Bronx, NY; (Y); Cmnty Wkr; Office Aide; Off Jr Cls; Trk; Hon Roll; Church Yth Grp; Drama Clb; Library Aide; Teachers Aide; Off Frsh Cls; Intl Rltns.

MORETTI, MICHAEL; Grand Island SR HS; Gr Island, NY; (Y); Boy Scts; Varsity Clb; Band; Stage Crew; JV Socr; Var Swmmng; JV Trk; Hon Roll; Engrng.

MOREY, DANIEL; Peekskill HS; Peekskill, NY; (S); Drama Clb; Teachers Aide; Yrbk Phtg; Yrbk Stf; Rep Frsh Cls; Pres Sr Cls; Rep Stu Cncl; Cit Awd; NHS; Acadmc All-Am 84; Hgh Hnr Rll 82-85; Comp Sci.

MORF, KIM; Eastridge HS; Rochester, NY; (Y); Exploring; GAA; Ski Clb; JV Bsktbl; JV Sftbl; St John Fisher Coll; Law.

MORGAN, BRENDA; John Dewey HS; Brooklyn, NY; (Y); Dance Clb; Teachers Aide; Chorus; School Musical; Capt Badmtn; Gym; Sftbl; Trk; Vllybl; Wt Lftg; Bus.

MORGAN, CHERYL; Norwood-Norfolk Central HS; Norwood, NY; (Y); Red Cross Aide; Chorus; Concert Band; Jazz Band; Swing Chorus; Sec Jr Cls; Stat Bsktbl; Hon Roll; Sec Jr NHS; Sec NHS; Engl Ltr 85; Music Educ.

MORGAN, COLLEEN; Maple Hill HS; Castleton, NY; (Y); 12/86; Nwsp Ed-Chief; Yrbk Bus Mgr; Pres Soph Cls; Capt L Bsktbl; Capt L Fld Hcky; Var L Sftbl; Var L Trk; NHS; Elks Awd; Hon Roll; Sr Athl Awd; MIP Trck; Houghton Coll; Phy Ed.

MORGAN, DARLEEN; Mercy HS; Castleton, NY; (Y); School Play; Stage Crew; Yrbk Stf; High Hon Roll; NHS; Asst Layout Edtr Yrbk 85; Excell In Regents Chem 85; Excell In Regents Bio 84; Elem Educ.

MORGAN, EILEEN M; Commack South HS; Commack, NY; (Y); 20/378; Band; Mrchg Band; Trs Soph Cls; Trs Jr Cls; Trs Sr Cls; Var Bsktbl; Var Capt Socr; Var Vllybl; NHS; JV Sftbl; 2nd Pl Moot Ct Comp 83-84; Gold Key Athletc Awd 85; Colgate U; Neurosci.

MORGAN, GODSFAVOUR S; Greater New York Acad; Brooklyn, NY; (Y); Church Yth Grp; Hosp Aide; Chorus; Drill Tm; Nwsp Ed-Chief; Yrbk Ed-Chief; VP Soph Cls; Sec Stu Cncl; Vllybl; Hon Roll; Andrews U; Pre-Med.

MORGAN, KELLY; The Mary Louis Acad; Maspeth, NY; (Y); French Clb; Yrbk Stf; Cert Merit Ntl Educ Tsts 83; Cert Recgntn Stu Svc 84; Bus Adm.

MORGAN, MICHAEL; La Salle SR HS; Niagara Falls, NY; (S); 23/280; Drama Clb; Ski Clb; Stage Crew; Hon Roll; Jr NHS; NHS; Comp Sci.

MORGAN, MIKE; Tamaroc HS; Troy, NY; (Y); Computer Clb; Intnl Clb; Band; Chorus; Mrchg Band; Pep Band; School Musical; Swing Chorus; Yrbk Stf; Hon Roll; Comp Sci.

MORGAN, PATRICK; Elmira Free Acad; Gillett, PA; (Y); Pres Aud/Vis; Pres Computer Clb; 4-H; JA; Library Aide; VICA; Nwsp Rptr; Nwsp Stf; Crs Cntry; Trk; Comp.

MORGAN, PAUL C; Holy Trinity HS; W Hempstead, NY; (S); 15/335; Math Clb; Bsbl; Capt Bsktbl; Hon Roll; Ntl Merit Ltr; Med.

MORGAN, SANDRA; Camden Central HS; Toberg, NY; (Y); 13/208; Varsity Clb; Yrbk Ed-Chief; Trs Stu Cncl; Capt Cheerleading; Var Sftbl; Var Capt Vllybl; High Hon Roll; NHS; 4-H; Ski Clb; Regents Schlrshp 84-85; Elect Engrng.

MORGAN, SHELBI L; Vestal HS; Vestal, NY; (Y); 102/450; Hosp Aide; Broone CC; CPA.

MORGAN, STEPHEN; La Fayette Central HS; La Fayette, NY; (Y); Cmnty Wkr; French Clb; Model UN; JV Var Bsbl; JV Var Ftbl; JV Wrstlng; High Hon Roll; Hon Roll; St Schlr; NY ST Regents Schlrshp 85; U Of Buffalo; Bio-Sci.

MORGAN, SUZANNE J; De Sales HS; Waterloo, NY; (Y); 7/45; Library Aide; Ski Clb; Band; Chorus; Church Choir; Mrchg Band; School Musical; Nwsp Stf; Var Socr; DAR Awd; Teacher Spec Educ.

MORGAN, TASHA; Harry S Truman HS; Bronx, NY; (Y); Cmnty Wkr; Computer Clb; Dance Clb; Library Aide; Office Aide; Political Wkr; Spanish Clb; Yrbk Phtg; Yrbk Stf; NC A & T; Acctg.

MORGAN, TRACY; Hilton Central HS; Hilton, NY; (Y); 89/350; Nwsp Stf; Capt Cheerleading; Coach Actv; Trk; Hon Roll; All Cnty Trck Tm 83; Cmmnctns.

MORGANI, JACK; Islip HS; Islip, NY; (Y); JV Bsbl; JV Ftbl; Var Hon Roll; Prfct Atten Awd; Sci.

MORGANTI, MARYSUSAN; Henninger HS; Syracuse, NY; (Y); Hosp Aide; Math Tm; Yrbk Phtg; Trs Jr Cls; Rep Stu Cncl; Capt Swmmng; Trk; High Hon Roll; Hon Roll; NHS; Ntl Merit Ltr.

MORGENSTEIN, SAMUEL; Spring Valley SR HS; Spring Valley, NY; (Y); 44/450; Band; Concert Band; Jazz Band; Mrchg Band; Orch; Pep Band; Symp Band; Lit Mag; Hon Roll; NHS; Citatn Conf All St Wind Ensem 84; Outstndng Band Mbr Hnr 85; Regents Schlrshp 85; SUNY; Music.

MORGENTHALER, KAREN M; Port Byron Central HS; Auburn, NY; (Y); 6/81; Am Leg Aux Girls St; Pres French Clb; Hosp Aide; School Musical; Trs Sr Cls; Var Bsktbl; Var Capt Trk; DAR Awd; NHS; NY St Regents Schlrshp 85; Centry III Awd Wnnr 84; St U Binghamton-NY; Law.

MORGIEWICZ, JACQUELINE; Warwick Valley HS; Goshen, NY; (Y); 16/197; Ski Clb; Chorus; Var Capt Vllybl; High Hon Roll; Hon Roll; VP NHS; NY ST Sci Suprvsrs Assn Physcs Awd 85; U Of CO; Psychlgy.

MORIARTY, MARY; Cicero North Syracuse HS; N Syracuse, NY; (S); 20/622; Church Yth Grp; Trs Stu Cncl; JV Bsktbl; JV Var Socr; Sftbl; Hon Roll; Pharm.

MORIARTY, SEAN; Cardinal Spellman HS; New Windsor, NY; (Y); Chorus; School Musical; Nwsp Ed-Chief; Rep Jr Cls; Mgr Swmmng; NHS; Ldrshp Rep Archeliocesan Wrkshp 85; Journlsm.

MORIEN, JEFF; Cardinal Mooney HS; Rochester, NY; (Y); 81/317; JV Bsbl; Hon Roll; Acadmc Awds Achvt-Phys Ed 84; Music.

MORIMOTO, JULIE; Mexico Acad; Central Square, NY; (Y); Spanish Clb; Varsity Clb; Lit Mag; Var JV Bsktbl; Var Crs Cntry; Var Trk; NHS; Prfct Atten Awd; Spanish NHS; Schlr Athlt Awds 2 Gld & 1 Slvr Mdl 83-85; Cross Cntry MVP 84-85; Spnsh Poem Pblctn 85; Comp Sci.

MORITZ, JILLAINE; Rome Fre Acad; Rome, NY; (Y); Cmnty Wkr; Intnl Clb; Band; Sec Frsh Cls; Sec Sr Cls; Sec Stu Cncl; Var L Cheerleading; Var L Gym; High Hon Roll; Jr NHS; Hst Sistr Rotry Exchng Stu Japn 84-85; Intl Stud.

MORLEY, ELIZABETH; Cold Spring Harbor HS; Huntington, NY; (Y); Drama Clb; Varsity Clb; Chorus; School Play; Nwsp Rptr; Nwsp Stf; Golf; Tennis; High Hon Roll.

MORLEY, KIMBERLY A; Midlakes HS; Clifton Springs, NY; (Y); 2/154; Varsity Clb; Nwsp Rptr; Yrbk Stf; Bsktbl; Sftbl; Tennis; High Hon Roll; Hon Roll; NHS; Sal; Ithack Coll Acad Schlrshp; Ithaca; Bus Admin.

MORMAN, DAWN; St Johns Prep; Jamaica, NY; (Y); Chorus; Swing Chorus; Pres Frsh Cls; Rep Soph Cls; Rep Jr Cls; Rep Sr Cls; Rep Stu Cncl; Bernard M Barveh; Bus Admin.

MORMEL, DAVID; Niagara Wheatfield SR HS; Niagara Falls, NY; (Y); JV L Socr; Prfct Atten Awd; Wheatfield Blades Ice Hockey 82-83; Bus Mgt.

MORNEAULT, MICHAEL D; Johnson City HS; Bible School Park, NY; (Y); Cmnty Wkr; Computer Clb; Debate Tm; French Clb; Political Wkr; Quiz Bowl; Science Clb; Speech Tm; Chorus; Madrigals; Legsltv Intrnshp Prog 84; Judcl Intrnshp Prog 85; Cngrssnl Semnr 85; West Point; Spec Frces.

MORNING, ANN; United Nations International Schl; New Rochelle, NY; (Y); Concert Band; Orch; Ntl Merit Ltr; Intl Rel.

MORONE, DAN; Bishop Maginn HS; Albany, NY; (S); 11/118; Computer Clb; Latin Clb; Ski Clb; Im Bsktbl; JV Crs Cntry; Var Ftbl; Var Golf; Clarkson Coll; Comp Sci.

MORREALE, DAVID JUDE; Niagara Catholic HS; Lewiston, NY; (Y); Aud/Vis; Boy Scts; Camera Clb; Church Yth Grp; Cmnty Wkr; Computer Clb; Hosp Aide; Key Clb; Science Clb; Service Clb; Arts.

MORREALE, ELENA; Niagara Catholic HS; Niagara Falls, NY; (Y); 7/81; Spanish Clb; Rep Frsh Cls; Rep Soph Cls; VP Jr Cls; Rep Stu Cncl; Var L Bsktbl; Var L Bowling; Var L Sftbl; Var L Vllybl; Hon Roll; Athlt Yr 84 & 85; Law.

MORREALE, KRISTEN; Smithtown HS East; St James, NY; (Y); VP Camera Clb; FBLA; Orch; Nwsp Phtg; Nwsp Rptr; Nwsp Stf; Rep Stu Cncl; Bsktbl; Sftbl; Vllybl; FBI Agnt; Law.

MORREALE, MARIA J; John F Kennedy HS; Katonah, NY; (Y); 11/184; Cmnty Wkr; JA; Nwsp Ed-Chief; Crs Cntry; Sftbl; High Hon Roll; NHS; Engl Schlrshp 81-82; Ntl Sci Olympd 83-84; Cert Of Hon NYS Bar Assn 83-84; Holy Cross; Pol Sci.

MORRELL, MIA R; Duanesburg Central HS; Delanson, NY; (Y); 10/70; Church Yth Grp; Drama Clb; French Clb; Office Aide; Red Cross Aide; School Play; Yrbk Stf; Pom Pon; Trk; Hon Roll; NY ST Regents Schlrshp In Nursing 85; Ellis Hosp Schl Nrsng; Rn.

MORRELLA, JANICE; Alexander Hamilton HS; White Plains, NY; (S); 2/35; French Clb; Office Aide; Pres Frsh Cls; Trk; CC Awd; High Hon Roll; Hon Roll; Jr NHS; NHS; Rotary Awd; Natl Sci Merit Awd 84.

MORRILL, MARTHA; Hermon Dokalb Central HS; De Kalb Jct, NY; (S); 1/31; VP Drama Clb; Nwsp Rptr; Trs Frsh Cls; Trs Soph Cls; Trs Jr Cls; Trs Sr Cls; Trs Stu Cncl; JV Var Bsktbl; Var Sftbl; Bausch & Lomb Sci Awd; North Cnty Schlr; St Lawrence U; Nrs.

MORRIN, RENEE; Romulus Central Schl; Waterloo, NY; (S); 5/35; 4-H; Girl Scts; Band; Concert Band; Mrchg Band; School Musical; High Hon Roll; Hon Roll; Prfct Atten Awd; Lib Arts.

MORRIS, AMY; Tonawanda SR HS; Tonawanda, NY; (Y); 11/200; Trs Church Yth Grp; Girl Scts; Band; Church Choir; JV Var Vllybl; Hon Roll; NHS; Top 5 Pct Of Cntry On NEDT Tst 83; Math Tutor 85; U Of Buffalo; Med.

MORRIS, CAMILLE LYNNE; Hillcrest HS; Rosedale, NY; (Y); 153/793; Dance Clb; Girl Scts; Radio Clb; Thesps; School Musical; Nwsp Rptr; Pres Stu Cncl; Capt Cheerleading; Ntl Merit SF; Church Yth Grp; Comm.

MORRIS, CHRISTINE; Roy C Ketcham SR HS; Poughkeepsie, NY; (Y); Church Yth Grp; Band; Church Choir; Yrbk Stf; Hon Roll.

MORRIS, JEFFREY; Rice HS; New York, NY; (S); Nwsp Rptr; Cit Awd; Hon Roll; Prfct Atten Awd; Rice Schlrshp-2nd Hnrs 84-85; Jrnlsm.

MORRIS, KEVIN; Sherendehava Central Schl; Clifton Pk, NY; (Y); Aud/Vis; Cmnty Wkr; Computer Clb; English Clb; VP Leo Clb; Rep Soph Cls; Rep Jr Cls; Trk; High Hon Roll; Hon Roll; Pres Phys Ftns Awd 82-83; Bio.

MORRIS, KIMBERLY L; Glens Falls SR HS; Glens Falls, NY; (Y); 4/235; Chorus; VP Jr Cls; VP Sr Cls; Sec Stu Cncl; Powder Puff Ftbl; Capt Var Tennis; High Hon Roll; Jr NHS; NHS; St Schlr; Colgate U; Attrny.

MORRIS, LAURIE; Martin Van Buren HS; Queens Village, NY; (Y); 57/579; Service Clb; Yrbk Stf; Hon Roll; Eng.

MORRIS, MATTHEW; Hebrew Academy Of Nassau County; Woodbury, NY; (S); Cmnty Wkr; Math Clb; Service Clb; Temple Yth Grp; Nwsp Rptr; Capt Socr; Tennis; High Hon Roll; Hon Roll; NHS; Univ Of PA; Law.

MORRIS, MISTY M; Westbury SR HS; Westbury, NY; (Y); 12/250; Debate Tm; Drama Clb; Key Clb; Office Aide; Science Clb; Speech Tm; Varsity Clb; School Play; Lit Mag; Gym; NY ST Regents Schlrshp 85; Cornell U; Anml Sci.

MORRIS, PAUL R; Taconic Hills HS; Philmont, NY; (Y); 7/130; Ed Yrbk Phtg; Yrbk Stf; Var Bsbl; Var Ftbl; Hon Roll; NHS; NY ST Regents Schlrshp 85; Siena Coll; Comp Sci.

MORRIS, RACHEL; Bishop Loughlin Memorial HS; Brooklyn, NY; (S); Church Yth Grp; FCA; JA; Office Aide; Band; Church Choir; Jazz Band; School Musical; School Play; High Hon Roll.

MORRIS, RICHARD; St Marys Boys HS; Williston Pk, NY; (Y); 7/130; Crs Cntry; Trk; Chess Clb; Cmnty Wkr; Nwsp Rptr; Nwsp Stf; Yrbk Stf; Sftbl; Hon Roll; NHS; Comptitv Schlrshp; St Johns U; Acctng.

MORRIS, SHARON; South Shore HS; Brooklyn, NY; (Y); 200/600; Psychlgy.

MORRIS, SHAUN R; Liverpool HS; Liverpool, NY; (Y); 12/750; Am Leg Boys St; Computer Clb; Off Stu Cncl; JV Capt Bsktbl; JV Socr; High Hon Roll; NHS.

MORRIS, SOPHIA; John Dewey HS; Peekskill, NY; (Y); Dance Clb; Drama Clb; PAVAS; Spanish Clb; Chorus; School Musical; School Play; Stage Crew; Swing Chorus; Variety Show; Merit Scholar Awd Alvin Ailey Amer Dnce Ctr 85; Hnr Roll Stu 82-85; SUNY Purchase; Prfrmg Art.

MORRIS, STEPHANIE; Midwood HS; Brooklyn, NY; (Y); Socr; Hon Roll; Prfct Atten Awd.

MORRIS, WILLIAM J; Hendrick Hudson HS; Montrose, NY; (Y); Varsity Clb; JV Var Ftbl; Trk; Wt Lftg; High Hon Roll; Hon Roll; Eugene W Booth Wrtng Awd 85; Mrktng Hghst Avg 85; Dfsnsv Rookie Yr/All Leag Hnrbl Ment 84; Ithaca Coll; Sclgy.

MORRISON, AMY; Longwood HS; Middle Island, NY; (S); 6/500; Math Tm; Chorus; School Musical; School Play; Variety Show; Nwsp Stf; Trk; NHS; 100 All St NYSSMA Comp 85; Best Show Awd Talent 83; Law.

MORRISON, ANDREA; Sachem High School North Campus; Lk Ronkonkoma, NY; (Y); 77/1383; Drama Clb; Math Tm; Orch; Stage Crew; Stat Diving; Stat Swmmng; High Hon Roll; NHS; Superior Achvt Orch 83; Music Educ.

MORRISON, DEBRA A; Arlington HS; La Grangeville, NY; (Y); 81/572; Intnl Clb; Band; Yrbk Stf; Gym; Hon Roll; Pres Schlrshp 85; Regents Schlrshp Prof Nrsng 85; Hnr Key Arlington HS 84; Mount St Mary Coll; Nrsng.

MORRISON, DOUGLAS; North Warren Central HS; Chestertown, NY; (S); 1/50; Computer Clb; Math Clb; Nwsp Rptr; Var Tennis; High Hon Roll; NHS; Val; Rotary Club Stu Mnth 81; MIP Tnns 81; Math Grad Awd 83; Engr.

MORRISON, ELAINE ANNMARIE; Ossining HS; Ossining, NY; (Y); Church Yth Grp; Computer Clb; Hosp Aide; Church Choir; Mrchg Band; School Play; Rep Stu Cncl; Hon Roll; Twrlr; Music Lssns Awd 83; Bryant Coll; Accntng.

MORRISON, G SCOTT; North Shore HS; Glen Head, NY; (Y); Am Leg Boys St; Boy Scts; Key Clb; Varsity Clb; Jazz Band; Mrchg Band; Yrbk Phtg; Var Lcrss; Cit Awd; Chorus; Eagle Scout Awd 84; Cls Advsr 85; NYSSMA; Engrng.

MORRISON, JAMES; Binghamton HS; Binghamton, NY; (Y); Hon Roll; Prfct Atten Awd.

MORRISON, JENNIFER; Albertus Magnus HS; Thiells, NY; (Y); 1/190; Math Clb; Math Tm; Service Clb; French Hon Soc; Hon Roll; NHS; Teacher.

MORRISON, JOANNA; South Side HS; Rockville Ctr, NY; (Y); 72/291; Band; Orch; Stage Crew; Variety Show; Lit Mag; Hon Roll; LI/ATA HS Art Comp Hnrl Mntn 85; Art.

MORRISON, MEG A; West HS; Painted Post, NY; (Y); JA; Letterman Clb; VICA; Acpl Chr; Chorus; Swing Chorus; Variety Show; Mgr(s); Swmmng; Timer; Pre Med.

MORRISON, MICHAEL R; John F Kennedy HS; Brewster, NY; (Y); 12/186; Cmnty Wkr; Hosp Aide; VP JA; Teachers Aide; Nwsp Rptr; Nwsp Sprt Ed; Rep Stu Cncl; Stat Bsktbl; Var Trk; Var Wt Lftg; Overall Acad Excell Awd 82 & 84; Educ & Cultrl Schlrshp Of The Elect Industry 85; Boston Coll; Comm.

MORRISON, MICHELLE; New Dorp HS; Staten Island, NY; (Y); Art Clb; French Clb; Intnl Clb; Office Aide; Teachers Aide; Wt Lftg; High Hon Roll.

MORRISON, SUSAN L; Paul V Moore HS; Brewerton, NY; (Y); 16/279; AFS; Computer Clb; German Clb; Pres Girl Scts; Pres Science Clb; Var Socr; Var Trk; High Hon Roll; NHS; Regents Schlrshp 85; Acad Schlrshp 85; SUNY-COBLESKILL; Lndscp Arch.

MORRISSEY, MARY; Greene Central HS; Greene, NY; (Y); Spanish Clb; Varsity Clb; Yrbk Phtg; Var L Bsktbl; Var L Fld Hcky; Var L Sftbl; High Hon Roll; Hon Roll; MVP Bsktbl 84-85.

MORRISSEY, PATRICIA J; Rocky Point JR-SR HS; Miller Place, NY; (Y); Spanish Clb; Mrchg Band; Symp Band; NHS; Band; Concert Band; Yrbk Stf; High Hon Roll; Hon Roll; Suffolk Cnty CC; Frgn Lang.

MORRITT, KAREN; Newfield Central Schl; Newfield, NY; (Y); 3/58; Am Leg Aux Girls St; School Play; Variety Show; Nwsp Ed-Chief; Yrbk Stf; Var Fld Hcky; High Hon Roll; NHS; Ntl Merit SF; Smmr Visual Arts Prog 83; Art Cntst Hnrbl Mntn 84; Brown U Providence RI; Lang.

MORRONGIELLO, CHRISTOPHER; Bethpage HS; Old Bethpage, NY; (Y); Hst MMM; Capt Band; Concert Band; Drill Tm; Capt Jazz Band; Mrchg Band; Capt Orch; School Musical; School Play; Symp Band; NY ST Cong PTA Pgm 84; Musical Comptn 83-84; Mannes Coll Music; Music.

MORROW, JILL; Churchville-Chili SR HS; Rochester, NY; (Y); FTA; Teachers Aide; Chorus; Yrbk Ed-Chief; Yrbk Stf; Rep Frsh Cls; Sec Soph Cls; Trs Jr Cls; Stu Cncl; Church Yth Grp; YFU Exch Stu Dnmrk 85; Soc Stds.

MORROW, LYNNETTE; Croughton American HS; APO New York, NY; (Y); 14/72; German Clb; Ski Clb; Teachers Aide; Band; Chorus; Yrbk Stf; Trk; Hon Roll.

MORROW, TOM; Long Island Lutheran HS; Huntington, NY; (S); 2/105; Boy Scts; Hosp Aide; Mathletes; Quiz Bowl; School Musical; Nwsp Rptr; Var Bowling; Var Socr; Var Tennis; Kiwanis Awd; Columbia; Pre-Med.

MORSCHAUSER, DANA; John Glenn HS; Greenlawn, NY; (Y); 11/270; French Clb; Variety Show; Rep Frsh Cls; Rep Soph Cls; Rep Jr Cls; VP Sr Cls; VP Stu Cncl; Var L Cheerleading; Var L Trk; French Hon Soc; Hme Econ Slvr Mdl Awd 83; Med.

MORSCHER JR, JOSEPH J; Archbishop Molloy HS; Glendale, NY; (Y); 8/410; German Clb; Teachers Aide; High Hon Roll; NHS; Ntl Merit Ltr; Archbishop Molloy Acad Excllnce Awd 84-85; Mth.

MORSE, AMY L; Moravia Central HS; Locke, NY; (Y); AFS; Church Yth Grp; GAA; Color Guard; Drill Tm; Yrbk Stf; Trk; NY ST Regents Schlrshp 85; Thompkins Cortland CC.

MORSE, CHRISTOP P; Mohonasen HS; Schenectady, NY; (Y); 7/216; Boy Scts; Pres Church Yth Grp; Pres German Clb; Concert Band; Jazz Band; Mrchg Band; Var JV Ftbl; Var L Trk; NHS; Ntl Merit Ltr; NYS Regents Schlrshp 85; Sururban Schltccncl Cncrt Bnd 84; US Mil Acad W Point; Hmnty.

MORSE, HOWARD; Haldane Central HS; Nelsonville, NY; (S); Ski Clb; Band; Jazz Band; School Musical; Stage Crew; Var JV Bsktbl; High Hon Roll; Hon Roll; Jr NHS; NHS; Amer Legn Awd; Highest Frsh Boys Avg; Ind Arts Awd; Central ME Vo Tech; Elec Engrg.

MORSE, JENNIFER; Groton Central HS; Groton, NY; (Y); Church Yth Grp; Chorus; Church Choir; School Musical.

MORSE, LISA MARIE; Morvania Central Schl; Morvavia, NY; (Y); 3/100; Drama Clb; School Musical; School Play; Swing Chorus; Yrbk Bus Mgr; Sec Stu Cncl; Var Vllybl; High Hon Roll; Voice Dem Awd; Am Leg Aux Girls St; Girls ST 85; NY U; Intl Bus.

MORSE, RICHARD; Schoharie Central HS; Esperance, NY; (S); 3/89; Boy Scts; Varsity Clb; Stage Crew; Im Badmtn; Var L Crs Cntry; Var L Trk; Var L Wrstlng; High Hon Roll; Discus Rcrd Hldr 84; Sci.

MORSE, ROBERT; Utica Christian Acad; Whitesboro, NY; (Y); Church Yth Grp; FCA; Radio Clb; Ski Clb; Chorus; Church Choir; School Play; Variety Show; Yrbk Phtg; Yrbk Rptr; Bus.

MORSELLI, THOMAS; Smithtown HS East; Nesconset, NY; (Y); Rep Frsh Cls; Rep Soph Cls; Rep Jr Cls; Stu Cncl; Var Capt Ftbl; Var L Lcrss; Hon Roll; Phys Ther.

MORTLOCK, DOUG; Lansing HS; Lansing, NY; (Y); 2/75; Spanish Clb; Nwsp Stf; Socr; Trk; High Hon Roll; NHS; 1st Pl Lvl 3 Spnsh Exm Dos Rios Rgn AATSP 85; Cornell U; Bio.

MORTON III, GLENN R; Batavia SR HS; Batavia, NY; (Y); French Clb; Ski Clb; Chorus; Madrigals; School Musical; School Play; Swing Chorus; Variety Show; Hon Roll; Regents Schlrshp 85; Stu Of Mnth 84; U Buffalo; Eng.

MORTON, JOHN; Fairport HS; Fairport, NY; (Y); Math Tm; Varsity Clb; Var L Trk; Hon Roll; Prfct Atten Awd; Church Yth Grp.

MORVAY, DANIEL P; Clymer Central HS; Clymer, NY; (Y); 6/38; Boy Scts; Church Yth Grp; Sec Trs Exploring; Var L Ftbl; Var L Trk; Cit Awd; Hon Roll; NHS; Eric Madison Sprtsmnshp Awd 85; MVP Track 85; Rochester Inst Tech; Microelect.

MOSCA, ANNE MARIE; Farmingdale HS; Farmingdale, NY; (Y); Church Yth Grp; French Clb; Girl Scts; Ski Clb; Flag Corp; Ed Nwsp Rptr; Ed Yrbk Sprt Ed; Lit Mag; Mgr(s); Mgr Swmmng; Ltrary Magzn 1st Pl Poetry Awd 85; Ntl Guild Audtns-Piano-Ntl & Dist Lvl 83, 84; Engl Litratr.

MOSCA, DIANE M; T R Proctor HS; Utica, NY; (Y); GAA; JA; Varsity Clb; Off Jr Cls; Off Stu Cncl; Capt Cheerleading; Var Sftbl; Hon Roll; Prfct Atten Awd; Typist Awrd; Bus.

MOSCARELLI, RICHARD; Clarkstown South HS; Nanuet, NY; (Y); 23/540; Trs Drama Clb; Hosp Aide; Acpl Chr; School Musical; School Play; Nwsp Stf; Yrbk Sprt Ed; Rep Stu Cncl; Capt Socr; Mu Alp Tht; Phy Ftnss Awd Outstndng Score; Med.

MOSCATIELLO, MARIA; Stellamaris HS; Ozone Park, NY; (Y); Church Yth Grp; Science Clb; Teachers Aide; Church Choir; Nwsp Rptr; Nwsp Stf; Yrbk Stf; High Hon Roll; Hon Roll; NHS; Pre Med.

MOSCHAK, LISA; Union-Endicott HS; Endwell, NY; (Y); French Clb; Key Clb; JV Var Cheerleading; Hon Roll; Elec Engrng.

MOSCOVIC, DINA; Kenmore East HS; Kenmore, NY; (Y); Dance Clb; Band; Color Guard; Concert Band; Mrchg Band; Ed Yrbk Stf; Coach Actv; Var Pom Pon; Stat Wrstlng; High Hon Roll; Bus.

MOSEGARD, JENNIFER; Mexico HS; Mexico, NY; (Y); German Clb; Varsity Clb; Sec Frsh Cls; VP Soph Cls; JV Var Bsktbl; Var Capt Socr; Var Capt Trk; U NY Buffalo; Nrsng.

MOSELY, ANGELA; Bishop Loughlin M HS; Brooklyn, NY; (S); 48/140; Var Bsktbl; JV Bowling; Var Sftbl; Vllybl; Intl Bus.

MOSENTHIN, SANDRA R; Oppenheim-Ephratah Central School; Johnston, NY; (S); 2/25; Church Yth Grp; Trs Girl Scts; Hosp Aide; Spanish Clb; Nwsp Rptr; Yrbk Phtg; High Hon Roll; Jr NHS; NHS; Yrbk Stf; Amer Legn Ortrcl Cntst 1st Local 4th Cnty Reg 83; Mssns.

MOSER, KATHERINE; St Johns Prep; Glendale, NY; (S); 26/415; Pres Church Yth Grp; Dance Clb; Chorus; Church Choir; Lit Mag; Score Keeper; JV Vllybl; High Hon Roll; NHS.

MOSES, AMY L; Ticonderoga HS; Ticonderoga, NY; (Y); 4/110; Church Yth Grp; FCA; VP French Clb; Girl Scts; Varsity Clb; Yrbk Stf; Rep Frsh Cls; Capt L Cheerleading; Pom Pon; Var L Socr; Pres SADD Chptr 84-85; Rgnts Schlrshp NY ST 85-86; Trustees Hnr Schlrshp 85-86; Baldwin-Wallace Coll; Pre-Med.

MOSES, CHERYL; Chatham Central HS; Valatie, NY; (Y); 5/120; 4-H; Thesps; Band; Concert Band; Mrchg Band; Pep Band; Yrbk Stf; Vllybl; 4-H Awd; High Hon Roll; Catenovia Coll; Equine Stu.

MOSES, MONIKA; Lindenhurst SR HS; Lindenhurst, NY; (Y); VP German Clb; Girl Scts; Band; Concert Band; Mrchg Band; School Musical; Stage Crew; Hon Roll; NHS.

MOSES, REBECCA C; Vernon Verona Sherrill HS; Verona, NY; (Y); 9/246; Ski Clb; Spanish Clb; Church Choir; Rep Stu Cncl; JV Vllybl; High Hon Roll; Lion Awd; NHS; Rgnts Schlrshp Wnnr 85; Pres Acad Ftns Awd 85; Rotary Schlrshp Wnnr 85; Maria Regina Coll; Librl Arts.

MOSES, SCOTT; Kenmore East HS; Kenmore, NY; (Y); Church Yth Grp; German Clb; Im Bsktbl; Im Socr; Im Vllybl; Hon Roll; Pittsburg Art Inst; Comrcl Art.

MOSES, STEVEN C; Valley Stream Central HS; Valley Stream, NY; (Y); FBLA; Ski Clb; Yrbk Stf; JV Var Ftbl; Var Lcrss; NHS; Pre-Law.

MOSES, SUZANNE; Vernon-Verona-Sherrill Central HS; Verona, NY; (Y); AFS; Debate Tm; French Clb; Ski Clb; Church Choir; Rep Frsh Cls; Rep Soph Cls; Sec Jr Cls; Rep Stu Cncl; Score Keeper; Soc Studies Awd Womn Of The Rotary 84; Cert Of Part Concours De Francais 85; Intrln Bus.

MOSHER, AMY; Cicero-North Syracuse HS; Clay, NY; (S); 95/622; Dance Clb; Rep Frsh Cls; Rep Soph Cls; Var Twrlr.

MOSHER, DEBORAH; Brockport Central HS; Hamlin, NY; (Y); 17/300; Trs Church Yth Grp; Exploring; High Hon Roll; NHS; Ntl Merit Ltr; Spansh II,III Awd 83-84; Regents Schlrshp 85; SUNY Coll-Brockport; Arch.

MOSHER, ELAINE J; Delaware Valley HS; N Branch, NY; (Y); 10/35; Drama Clb; Nwsp Rptr; Nwsp Stf; Yrbk Phtg; Yrbk Stf; High Hon Roll; Hon Roll; Ntl Merit Ltr; Rgnts Schlrshp 85; Genessee Cnty CC; Radio TV.

MOSHER JR, EUGENE; Oppenheim-Ephratah HS; St Johnsville, NY; (S); 1/25; Yrbk Sprt Ed; Pres Sr Cls; Var L Bsbl; Var Capt Bsktbl; Var Capt Socr; Hon Roll; Pres Jr NHS; VP NHS; Fred Fuller Memorial 83-84; Rookie Of The Year 81-82; Bus.

MOSHER, LORI; Little Falls JR & SR HS; Little Falls, NY; (S); 11/109; Trs Computer Clb; Sec Girl Scts; Spanish Clb; Band; Concert Band; Mrchg Band; Orch; Pep Band; Symp Band; Trs NHS; Herkimer Cty Comm; Trvl & Touri.

MOSHER, LOUANN; Watertown HS; Watertown, NY; (Y); 65/321; Exploring; Pres Key Clb; Office Aide; Stage Crew; Yrbk Stf; Capt Bowling; Kiwanis Awd; Regents Scholar 85; Kelly Fund Awd 85; Jefferson CC; Mth.

MOSHER, MICHELE; Kenmore West SR HS; Tonawanda, NY; (Y); Drama Clb; Thesps; Band; Concert Band; Jazz Band; Mrchg Band; Orch; School Musical; School Play; Variety Show; Pre-Med.

MOSHER, SUSAN; Corinth Central HS; Corinth, NY; (Y); Church Yth Grp; French Clb; Key Clb; Spanish Clb; Chorus; JV Bsktbl; Mgr Sftbl; French Hon Soc; Hon Roll; SPAN Trnsltr.

MOSHER, WILLIAM; Lyons Central Schl; Lyons, NY; (Y); 7/100; Art Clb; French Clb; Varsity Clb; Var Ftbl; Cit Awd; High Hon Roll; Hon Roll; NHS; James Comstock Mem Schlrshp From Alfred ST 85; Hotchkiss Esstl Oil Co Awd 85; Alfred ST Coll; Engrng Sci.

MOSHIER, MICHAEL P; Rome Free Acad HS; Rome, NY; (Y); 41/512; Church Yth Grp; Intnl Clb; Key Clb; Varsity Clb; Capt Bsbl; Coach Actv; Capt Ice Hcky; Var Socr; High Hon Roll; Jr NHS; Cntrl Oneida League All-Star Soccer 84-85; Rick Adams Memorial Awd In Hockey 84-85; U Of Notre Dame; Genetic Engrng.

MOSIER, CARMEN; La Salle SR HS; Niagara Falls, NY; (Y); Am Leg Aux Girls St; Debate Tm; Drama Clb; Church Choir; Jazz Band; Bowling; Hon Roll; Pres Jr NHS; AFS; Church Yth Grp; All ST Jazz Band 85; Yrbk Copy Ed 86.

MOSKAL, JULIE; Whitesboro SR HS; Utica, NY; (Y); 16/358; Church Yth Grp; Exploring; Chorus; Yrbk Stf; Var JV Cheerleading; High Hon Roll; Hon Roll; Sec Jr NHS; NHS; Med.

MOSKAL, PAULA; Palmyra-Macedon HS; Palmyra, NY; (Y); 1/180; VP Church Yth Grp; Math Tm; Rep Stu Cncl; High Hon Roll; VP NHS; Rochester Harvard Alumni Assoc Awd 85; Math.

MOSKOWITZ, JEFFREY; Jericho HS; Muttontown, NY; (Y); Hosp Aide; Spanish Clb; Teachers Aide; Im Bsktbl; Var Tennis; Hon Roll; NHS; Spanish NHS; Bus.

MOSKOWITZ, LARISSA NOELLE; Charles E Gorton HS; Yonkers, NY; (Y); Hosp Aide; Nwsp Ed-Chief; Rep Soph Cls; Rep Jr Cls; VP Sr Cls; Var Capt Cheerleading; Var L Tennis; High Hon Roll; NHS; Ntl Merit Ltr; Iona Lang Cont Spn II 2nd Hnrs 83; Yonkers Fest Arts & Sci Awd 82; Supt Awd 90 Clb, Century Clb 82-85; Cornell U; Vet Med.

MOSKOWITZ, LORI S; Flushing HS; Flushing, NY; (Y); 16/400; Concert Band; School Musical; Nwsp Stf; Ed Yrbk Stf; Sec Sr Cls; Tennis; Trk; Vllybl; Gov Hon Prg Awd; High Hon Roll; Regnts Schlrshp & Arista 85; SUNY Albany; Bus.

MOSMEN, JENNIFER; Bethlehem Central HS; Delmar, NY; (Y); Church Yth Grp; Hosp Aide; Office Aide; Ski Clb; Rep Frsh Cls; Rep Soph Cls; Rep Jr Cls; Fld Hcky; High Hon Roll; NHS; Med.

MOSS, BRIAN F; Thomas Alva Edison HS; Elmira, NY; (Y); 4/100; Am Leg Boys St; Ski Clb; Band; Mrchg Band; Nwsp Stf; VP Sr Cls; Ice Hcky; Tennis; Hon Roll; Rotary Awd; Bio Sci.

MOSS, DEBBIE; Sachem High School North; Lk Ronkonkoma, NY; (Y); Drm Mjr(t); Jazz Band; Mrchg Band; Orch; Symp Band; Nwsp Stf; Frsh Cls; NHS; Rotary Awd; Radio Clb; Long Isl Sci Congress Blue Ribbon 84; Law.

MOSS, EMMANUEL; Bronx Science HS; Flushing, NY; (Y); Boy Scts; Office Aide; Teachers Aide; Regents Schlrshp 84-85; Culinary Inst Amer; Culnry Arts.

MOSS, JEFFREY; Sachem H S North Campus; Holbrook, NY; (Y); 9/1428; Cmnty Wkr; Hosp Aide; Varsity Clb; L Lcrss; JV Wrstlng; NHS; Ntl Merit SF; Ntl Sci Olympiad-Bio-Suchem H S Soccer Ntl Team Champ 84; Telluride Assn Outstndng Scorers 84; Econ.

MOSS, PATTY; Far Rockaway HS; Far Rockaway, NY; (Y); Key Clb; Chorus; Hon Roll; Prfct Atten Awd; Manhattan Coll; Bus Adm.

MOSS, WILLIAM; Cardinal Hayes HS; New York, NY; (Y); VP Camera Clb; Chess Clb; Church Yth Grp; Cmnty Wkr; Band; Church Choir; Pres Soph Cls; Score Keeper; Wt Lftg; Aud/Vis; Hnry Mbr In A Chrch Scty 85; Syracures.

MOSSELL, KAREN M; Buffalo Acad Of The Sacred Heart; Williamsville, NY; (Y); 10/125; Math Clb; Red Cross Aide; Science Clb; Hon Roll; U S Natl Mathematics Awd Winner 85; ST U New York; Mathematics.

MOSSLER, KURT; Westmoreland Central HS; Rome, NY; (Y); 3/85; Art Clb; Mathletes; Concert Band; Drm & Bgl; Nwsp Rptr; Var JV Crs Cntry; Var JV Score Keeper; Var Capt Vllybl; NHS; Ski Clb; Area All-ST Concert Band Sect IV 83-84; Illus.

MOSTERT, MICHELE; Delaware Acad; Delhi, NY; (Y); Trs Church Yth Grp; Sec Girl Scts; Spanish Clb; Color Guard; Mrchg Band; Yrbk Stf; Var Cheerleading; Score Keeper; Prfct Atten Awd; Natl Hstry Day Competitn Wnnr 81; Bus.

MOSTICA, DANA; Mahopac HS; Carmel, NY; (Y); Trs Church Yth Grp; Temple Yth Grp; Stat Fld Hcky; Trk; Wrstlng; Hon Roll; Aerontcl Engrng.

MOSURE, TERESA; Oakfield Alabama Central HS; Oakfield, NY; (Y); #3 In Class; Drama Clb; Math Tm; Ski Clb; School Play; Crs Cntry; Tennis; Trk; Vllybl; Hon Roll; NHS; Archit.

MOTH, LORI; Bishop Ludden HS; Camillus, NY; (S); Hosp Aide; JV Bsktbl; High Hon Roll; NHS; Comp Spn Awd 83; Phys Sci Awd 83; Comm Serv Awd Dan Duyne Nrsg Hm 83; Bus Mgmt.

MOTH, LYNN; Bishop Ludden HS; Camillus, NY; (S); Hosp Aide; Var JV Bsktbl; Var JV Sftbl; High Hon Roll; NHS; Comp Spn I Awd 83; Phys Sci & Biol Awd 83-84; Comm Serv Awd Van Duyn Nrsg Home 83; Acctg.

MOTLEY, DERRICK W; Pine Bush HS; Middletown, NY; (Y); Aud/Vis; Im Ftbl; Var L Trk; Hon Roll; NC Central U; Bus Admin.

MOTLEY, ROHANA; The Stonybrook Schl; Bronx, NY; (Y); 17/84; Art Clb; Camera Clb; Cmnty Wkr; Dance Clb; School Play; Yrbk Stf; JV Bsktbl; Im Fld Hcky; Mgr(s); JV Sftbl; Martin Luther King Jr Schlrshp 82; Clark Fndtn Schlrshp 82-86; Pdtrcn.

MOTSKO JR, WILLIAM A; Owego Free Acad; Owego, NY; (Y); AFS; Am Leg Boys St; Church Yth Grp; Key Clb; Spanish Clb; Trs Stu Cncl; Var L Socr; Var L Wrstlng; High Hon Roll; NHS; Bio.

MOTT, ELIZABETH; Jordan-Elbridge Central HS; Elbdidge, NY; (Y); Pres Church Yth Grp; Chorus; Church Choir; Drill Tm; Drm Mjr(t); Mrchg Band; Yrbk Ed-Chief; Yrbk Stf; Rep Soph Cls; Var L Bsktbl; Coaches Awd 85; High Recgnt 85; Chem Engnrng.

MOTT, EVELYN; Longwood HS; Middle Island, NY; (Y); Math Tm; Chorus; Stage Crew; Bowling; Tennis; High Hon Roll; Hon Roll; NHS.

MOTT, LAURA; Longwood HS; Yaphank, NY; (Y); Computer Clb; Exploring; 4-H; Office Aide; Chorus; Orch; Var JV Pom Pon; JV Score Keeper; High Hon Roll; BOCES Cultural Arts Schl 83-84; Early Childhd Ed.

MOTTA, LORI BETH; Our Lady Of Victory Acad; White Plains, NY; (S); 5/137; Drama Clb; NFL; Science Clb; Spanish Clb; School Play; Yrbk Phtg; Yrbk Stf; Rep Frsh Cls; Rep Soph Cls; Rep Jr Cls; Veternary Med.

MOTYKA, MARY; Oxford Academy HS; Oxford, NY; (Y); French Clb; Red Cross Aide; Chorus; Color Guard; Mrchg Band; Yrbk Stf; Rep Frsh Cls; Swmmng; Hon Roll; Prfct Atten Awd; Cert Of Hnr Mock Trl; Omeonta ST; Educ.

MOTZER, TAMMY; Columbia HS; Rensselaer, NY; (Y); Art Clb; Spanish Clb; Yrbk Stf; High Hon Roll; Jr NHS; NHS; CPA.

MOUCK, LISA M; G Ray Bodley HS; Fulton, NY; (Y); 120/246; French Clb; Band; Color Guard; Concert Band; Jazz Band; Mrchg Band; Orch; Pep Band; School Musical; School Play; Music Awd French Horn; Solo Comptn Awd French Horn; Central FL CC; Cosmetology.

MOULDER, LAURA M; John Jay HS; Wapp Fls, NY; (Y); 126/560; Ski Clb; Church Choir; Yrbk Stf; Cheerleading; High Hon Roll; Hon Roll; Geneseo; Psych.

MOULTON, DONNA; Bishop Loughlin HS; Rockaway, NY; (Y); 9/33; Cmnty Wkr; Teachers Aide; Varsity Clb; Crs Cntry; Trk; High Hon Roll; Hon Roll; Effrt & Dedctn 82-83; Elec Engrng.

MOULTON, JEANNE; Oneonta HS; Oneonta, NY; (Y); 1/187; Girl Scts; Q&S; Sec Trs Thesps; Stage Crew; Ed Nwsp Stf; JV Capt Socr; High Hon Roll; NHS; Ntl Merit Ltr; Val.

MOULTON, SHERI; Parishville-Hopkinton Central HS; Potsdam, NY; (Y); Hosp Aide; Sec Jr Cls; High Hon Roll; Hon Roll; NHS; Prfct Atten Awd; French Clb; RN.

MOUNT II, ROBERT; Cardinal Mooney HS; Rochester, NY; (Y); 158/315; Band; Concert Band; Orch; Tennis; Cert Merit Percussion & Mus Theory 85; St John Fischer Coll; Bus.

MOUNT, SUSAN B; Shenendehowa HS; Clifton Park, NY; (Y); 13/650; Intnl Clb; Ski Clb; Varsity Clb; Band; Sftbl; Var Capt Swmmng; High Hon Roll; Trs NHS; Adirondack Empr St Gms Swim Tm 84; Mst Hnrd Plyr Awd-Grls Vrsty Swim Tm 84-85; Schl Rcd-100 Bttrfly; Math.

MOUNTZOUROS, VASILIKY; Newfield HS; Pt Jeff Sta, NY; (Y); Art Clb; Nwsp Rptr; Fld Hcky; Hon Roll; Jr NHS; Prfct Atten Awd; Church Yth Grp; Teachers Aide; Chorus; Sec Ntl Art Hnr Soc 85; Sndy Schl Tchr 83-85; St Mary Coll Of MD; Brdcstng.

MOUSAW, KAREN; Colton Pierrepont Central Schl; Colton, NY; (S); 9/33; Cmnty Wkr; French Clb; Ski Clb; Chorus; School Play; Yrbk Stf; Pres Jr Cls; Pres Sr Cls; Var Cheerleading; Var Socr; SUNY; Constrn Engrng Tech.

MOUSER, CHRISTIA M; Kingston HS; Lake Katrine, NY; (Y); 26/630; Art Clb; Boy Scts; Sec Exploring; Spanish Clb; Chorus; Lit Mag; Im Vllybl; High Hon Roll; Hon Roll; NHS; Regents Schlrshp 85; Principia.

MOUSTOPOULOS, FOTIS C; Flushing HS; Flushing, NY; (Y); 64/320; Orch; Hon Roll; Prfct Atten Awd; Regents Scholar 85; Tutor 84; St Johns U; Bus Admin.

MOUTSIAKIS, DEMETRIUS; Lindenhurst SR HS; Lindenhurst, NY; (Y); 3/600; Pres Debate Tm; Trs German Clb; Trs Thesps; Trs Mrchg Band; Var L Crs Cntry; Var L Trk; High Hon Roll; NHS; Church Yth Grp; Library Aide; Ntl Sci Olympiad Brnz Mdlst 85; Tchrs Assn Of Lndnhrst Awd 83; Debate Clb Ldrshp Awd 84; Doctor.

MOUTSIAKIS, VAIA-FOTEINY L; Lindenhurst HS; Lindenhurst, NY; (Y); 13/600; Church Yth Grp; French Clb; Hosp Aide; Math Tm; Varsity Clb; Mrchg Band; Yrbk Phtg; Capt Var Crs Cntry; Co-Capt Var Trk; NHS; Rgnts Schlrshp 85; Physcl Ftns Awd 84; Amr Lgn Bill Maxwell Athl Awd 85; Dowling Coll; Ed.

MOWERS, AMY; Mount Markham SR HS; W Winfield, NY; (Y); 4/116; Church Yth Grp; GAA; Band; Sec Chorus; Bsktbl; High Hon Roll; NHS; Ntl Merit Ltr; Rotary Awd; Houghton Coll; Bio.

MOWERS, LINETTE; De Ruyter Central HS; Deruyter, NY; (S); AFS; Drama Clb; School Play; Yrbk Stf; VP Soph Cls; VP Stu Cncl; Var Capt Cheerleading; Var Mgr(s); Var Sftbl; Hon Roll.

MOWERY, KRISTEN; Middletown HS; New Hampton, NY; (Y); 16/410; Boy Scts; Mrchg Band; Symp Band; Swmmng; Hon Roll; NHS; Eagle Scout 83; Mech Engr.

MOWINS, ELIZABETH; Cicero-North Syracuse HS; N Syracuse, NY; (S); 52/711; GAA; Capt Bsktbl; Socr; Sftbl; CC Awd; NHS; Empire State Games Bsktbl 83-84; Communications.

MOY, ANNA; Brooklyn Technical HS; Elmhurst, NY; (Y); JA; Math Clb; Office Aide; Science Clb; Yrbk Stf; Hon Roll; NHS; Pre-Med.

MOY, STEVE; Sheepshead Bay HS; Brooklyn, NY; (Y); 5/750; Boy Scts; Library Aide; Math Tm; Science Clb; Band; Yrbk Stf; DAR Awd; Gov Hon Prg Awd; High Hon Roll; Spanish NHS; Engrng.

MOY, TSUI GNEE; Beach Channel HS; Rockaway Park, NY; (Y); Library Aide; Office Aide; Teachers Aide; Chorus; School Musical; Yrbk Stf; Ed Lit Mag; Arista Hnr Soc Awd 84-85; Hnry HS Achvt Awd 85; Syracuse U.

MOYAL, DOUGLAS D; Benjamin Cardozo HS; Little Neck, NY; (Y); 59/500; Boy Scts; Cmnty Wkr; Computer Clb; Nwsp Rptr; Rep Sr Cls; Var Golf; Pres Schlr; St Schlr; Amer U Schlrshp; Pol Sci.

MOYE, MONIQUE; Dominican Commercial HS; St Albans, NY; (Y); 66/296; Art Clb; Drama Clb; Spanish Clb; School Musical; Stage Crew; Im Gym; Siena Clb 82-83; Prncpls List 82-85; Piano Clb 83-85; Intl Bus Admin.

MOYEN, VANICK; Catherdal HS; Corona, NY; (Y); 80/340; Intnl Clb; Mrchg Band; School Play; Sr Cls; Long Island Univ; Pre Med.

MOYER, BRIAN; Archbishop Molloy HS; Woodside, NY; (Y); 152/361; Hosp Aide; Rep Stu Cncl; Queens Coll; Lwyr.

MOYER, DEBORAH; Northstar Christian Acad; Rochester, NY; (S); 1/27; Church Yth Grp; Red Cross Aide; Teachers Aide; Band; Chorus; Pep Band; Sftbl; High Hon Roll; NHS; Roberts Wesleyan Coll; Tchr.

MOYER, KENNETH; Caledonia-Mumford HS; Scottsville, NY; (Y); Drm Mjr(t); Jazz Band; Yrbk Sprt Ed; Pres Soph Cls; Pres Stu Cncl; Var L Ftbl; Var L Tennis; Var L Trk; NHS; Pre-Med.

MOYER, MICHELLE; John C Birdlebough HS; Pheonix, NY; (Y); Church Yth Grp; Drama Clb; VP FBLA; Ski Clb; Church Choir; School Play; Yrbk Stf; Var Co-Capt Cheerleading; Crs Cntry; Sftbl; Outstdng Interest & Actv In Scl Stds 84; Awds In Chrldng, Sftbl & Trck 83-85; Philips Inst; Cosm.

MOYNIHAN, MICHAEL; Nyack HS; Valley Cottage, NY; (Y); 23/276; Debate Tm; French Clb; Math Clb; Math Tm; Spanish Clb; Rep Jr Cls; Golf; Socr; French Hon Soc; High Hon Roll; Stu Wk 84-85; 3rd Al Boys ST Ldrshp Pgm 84-85; Notre Dame; Engrng.

MROZ, STEVE; Eden SR HS; Derby, NY; (Y); German Clb; Varsity Clb; Concert Band; Jazz Band; School Play; Stage Crew; Rep Stu Cncl; Var L Swmmng; Im Var Vllybl; Hon Roll; Jazz Awd 85; Acadmc Ftns Awd Prg 85; Alfred G & Tech; Comp Grphcs.

MRZYGLOD, ROBERT; Bugard Vocational HS; Buffalo, NY; (Y); Hon Roll; Auto Mech.

MU, HARRISON TE-MING; Stuyvesant HS; New York, NY; (Y); Boys Clb Am; Tennis; Ntl Merit Ltr; Sci Tlnt Srch Hnrs Grp 85; Cittn Of Merit Mayor Koch NY Cty 85; Chancellors Hnr Rl NYC Brd Of Ed 85; Bio-Chem.

MUCCIGROSSO, DIAHN; Liverpool HS; Liverpool, NY; (S); 45/792; Church Yth Grp; JA; Ski Clb; Chorus; School Musical; School Play; Rep Stu Cncl; Var Tennis; Jr NHS; NHS; Soc Studies Mertorius Achvt Awd; Natl Latin Exam Hnrbl Mntn 84; Geneseo; Elem Educ.

MUCCINI, LAURA L; St Marys Girls HS; Douglaston, NY; (Y); Var Civic Clb; French Clb; Varsity Clb; Rep Soph Cls; Rep Jr Cls; Var Tennis; Hon Roll; NHS; Var Trk; USTA Schltc Rnkg Dbls Ten 84; Capt & Co-Capt Sprts Day 81-82.

MUCHLER, KAREN; Saranac Central HS; Cadyville, NY; (S); 4/125; GAA; JV Bsktbl; JV Var Socr; JV Sftbl; JV Var Vllybl; High Hon Roll; NHS; Embry-Riddle FL; Aeron Engrng.

MUCKLE, SONIA; Nyack HS; Nyack, NY; (Y); VP JA; Mrchg Band; Symp Band; Rep Soph Cls; Rep Jr Cls; Rep Sr Cls; Rep Stu Cncl; Var Trk; High Hon Roll; Hon Roll; Bus.

MUELLER, DOUGLAS S; Springville Griffith Inst; E Concord, NY; (Y); 63/201; Pres Church Yth Grp; Pres Exploring; Speech Tm; Capt Crs Cntry; Capt Trk; God Cntry Awd; NHS; Prfct Atten Awd; Sports Scholar 85; Regents Scholar 85; Alfred U; Ceramic Engrng.

MUELLER, JASON; Havppauge HS; Hauppauge, NY; (Y); Band; Concert Band; Jazz Band; Orch; Symp Band; Im Bowling; Socr; High Hon Roll; NHS; Ntl Merit Ltr; Accptd To Mid Island Bnd Festvl 83-84; Chem Engrng.

MUELLER, KLAUS; Saratoga Central Catholic HS; Ballston Lake, NY; (S); Ski Clb.

MUELLER, MARK; Garden City SR HS; Garden City, NY; (S); Drama Clb; German Clb; School Musical; School Play; Stage Crew; Nwsp Rptr; Lit Mag; JV L Ftbl; Im L Trk; Hon Roll; Garden City Intl Stu Exch 85; Theater.

MUELLER, MONICA L; New Dorp HS; Staten Island, NY; (Y); 4/780; German Clb; Intnl Clb; Key Clb; Math Tm; Cit Awd; Hon Roll; NHS; Pres Spanish NHS; Arista Secy 84-85; Acad Olymp Cpt; U Rochester; Sci Wrtng.

MUELLER, SHARON; Villa Maria Acad; Cheektowaga, NY; (S); 15/112; Trs Computer Clb; FBLA; JCL; Math Clb; Trs Jr Cls; Bowling; High Hon Roll; Trs NHS; Prfct Atten Awd; U Of Buffalo; Accounting.

MUELLER, TIMOTHY; Alden Central HS; Alden, NY; (Y); Church Yth Grp; Yrbk Bus Mgr; Rep Frsh Cls; Rep Soph Cls; Var JV Ftbl; Var Tennis; Im Vllybl; Im Wt Lftg; High Hon Roll; Hon Roll; BUS Adm.

MUFFOLETTO, KIMBERLY; Amherst Central SR HS; Snyder, NY; (Y); 28/280; Acpl Chr; Chorus; Madrigals; School Musical; Swing Chorus; Lit Mag; Im Bsktbl; Var JV Gym; Hon Roll; NHS; Geneseo ST Coll; Fine Arts.

MUGGLIN, KELLEY S; Paul V Moore HS; Central Square, NY; (Y); GAA; Science Clb; Band; Yrbk Phtg; Cheerleading; Gym; Sftbl; Trk; S Hampton U Of NY; Marn Sci.

MUGLESTON, KENRI; G Ray Bodley HS; Fulton, NY; (Y); Boy Scts; Church Yth Grp; Spanish Clb; Varsity Clb; Church Choir; Var Swmmng; Var Tennis; Hon Roll; BYU; Dentstry.

MUHAMMAD, FATIMA; Longwood HS; Coram, NY; (Y); 98/479; Cmnty Wkr; Dance Clb; Library Aide; Office Aide; Orch; Rep Frsh Cls; Rep Jr Cls; Rep Stu Cncl; Score Keeper; High Hon Roll; Grdn Hgts Cmnty Cltr Awd 83 & 84; Cornell U; Bus.

MUINO, ROBERT P; Mckee Technical HS; Staten Island, NY; (Y); Boy Scts; Computer Clb; Stage Crew; Bsktbl; Bowling; Sftbl; Vllybl; Poly Tech Inst Tech; Comp Engr.

MUIR, STEVE; Horseheads HS; Big Flats, NY; (Y); Im Bsktbl; Var L Lcrss; High Hon Roll; Hon Roll; Finance.

MUIRHEAD, SHENYL; Walton HS; Bronx, NY; (Y); Teachers Aide; JV Socr; Prfct Atten Awd; Bunquck Coll; Accntng.

MULCAHY, MICHAEL; Bethpage HS; Bethpage, NY; (Y); 13/287; Off Stu Cncl; Capt Swmmng; High Hon Roll; Hon Roll; Regenst Schlrshp 85; Bethpage Civic Org Schrshp 85; Army Resrv Schlr Ath 85; Maritime Coll; Elect Engrng.

MULFORD, DEBBIE; Pittsford Mendon HS; Pittsford, NY; (Y); Church Yth Grp; Cmnty Wkr; Dance Clb; Band; Chorus; Church Choir; Concert Band; Variety Show; Crs Cntry; Trk; NYS Music Tchrs Assn SR Hnrs Piano 84; NYSSMA Solo Fstvl High Rtng 83-84; All-St Awd For Piano 83; Engrng.

MULHERN, ANNMARIE T; St Marys Girls HS; Little Neck, NY; (Y); 38/154; Art Clb; Church Yth Grp; Pres Cmnty Wkr; Drama Clb; School Musical; School Play; Coach Actv; Var Crs Cntry; NHS; NYS Regents Schlrshp & Diploma 85; Natl Merit Sci Awd 84; St Anastasia Parish Cncl 84; Queensborough CC; Accntng.

MULHOLLAND, KEVIN; Westhampton Beach HS; E Moriches, NY; (Y); Computer Clb; Latin Clb; Var Crs Cntry; Var Ftbl; Var Trk; Law.

MULHOLLAND, PETER; Nazareth Regional HS; Far Rockaway, NY; (Y); Cmnty Wkr; Political Wkr; Phy Ed Awd; Law.

MULLEN, CHERYL; Gouverneur Central HS; Gouverneur, NY; (Y); Band; Chorus; Jazz Band; Mrchg Band; Orch; JV L Cheerleading; Var L Crs Cntry; Var Capt Trk; High Hon Roll; Jr NHS; Frnch I & Frnch III Awd 83 & 85; Acad Ltr 83-85; Clarkson U; Mth.

MULLEN, CHRISTOPHER P; MSGR Mc Clancy Memorial HS; Astoria, NY; (S); 9/249; Boy Scts; Church Yth Grp; Ski Clb; Nwsp Rptr; Im Ftbl; Cit Awd; High Hon Roll; NHS; Spanish NHS; St Johns U; Pre Law.

MULLEN, JONELLE; Eastport HS; Manorville, NY; (S); 1/56; Cmnty Wkr; Debate Tm; Math Tm; Scholastic Bowl; Ski Clb; Varsity Clb; Band; Variety Show; Nwsp Rptr; Nwsp Stf; Hgst Acad Aver 84-85; Mst Outstndg Spnsh, PE, Math 83-84; All Leag Bsktbll Tm 84-85; Cornell U; Bio.

MULLEN, KATHLEEN; Shoreham-Wading River HS; Wading River, NY; (Y); Science Clb; Teachers Aide; Chorus; School Play; Variety Show; Yrbk Stf; Var Mgr(s); Var Trk; Long Island Sci Congress 85; Phys Ther.

MULLEN, KYLE D; Hilton Central HS; Hilton, NY; (Y); 3/280; CAP; VP Math Clb; Model UN; School Play; Yrbk Ed-Chief; Rep Stu Cncl; Crs Cntry; High Hon Roll; Pres NHS; AFROTC Scholarship 85; Purdue U; Aeronautical Enrng.

MULLEN, MARJORIE; E J Wilson HS; Rochester, NY; (Y); Pres Church Yth Grp; Drama Clb; Band; Chorus; Concert Band; Mrchg Band; School Musical; School Play; Stage Crew; Swing Chorus; NRSG.

MULLEN, PATRICIA; Notre Dame Academy HS; Staten Island, NY; (Y); Am Leg Aux Girls St; Rep Stu Cncl; JV Var Bsktbl; Capt Var Sftbl; Jr NHS; Ntl Merit Ltr; JV Bsktbl Team Spirit Awd & All Tourn Team 83-84; Vrsty Sftbl Team Spirit Awd 84-85; Pre-Med.

MULLEN, SHARLENE; Canisteo Central Schl; Canisteo, NY; (Y); 31/80; Art Clb; Color Guard; Orch; JV Bsktbl; Cit Awd; DAR Awd; High Hon Roll; Hon Roll.

MULLER, DIANE; Commack HS North; East Northport, NY; (Y); Church Yth Grp; Teachers Aide; Chorus; Sec Church Choir; High Hon Roll; Hon Roll; Bus.

MULLER, ELLEN; Batavia HS; Batavia, NY; (Y); 10/234; Band; Chorus; Var Diving; Var Golf; Var L Swmmng; High Hon Roll; JP Sousa Awd; NHS; Ski Clb; Outstdg Band Mbr 84; Ntl Cncl Yth Ldrshp Awd 85; Case Western Res U; Biochem.

MULLER, JOHN F; Saratoga Springs HS; Saratoga Sprgs, NY; (Y); 10/500; Yrbk Stf; Rep Stu Cncl; High Hon Roll; NHS; Digital Equip Scholar Wnr Phillips Acad Andover Summr Sessn 84; Union Coll; Lwyr.

MULLER, PATTY; St Francis Prep; Middle Village, NY; (Y); 1/700; Cmnty Wkr; Math Clb; VP Science Clb; Nwsp Ed-Chief; High Hon Roll; NHS; Prfct Atten Awd; Rensselaer Medl 85; Pres Achvt Awd 83-85; Japan-US Senate Schlrshp Semi Fnlst 85; Chem.

MULLER, SHERILYN M; Smihtown HS East; Nesconset, NY; (Y); Spanish Clb; Hon Roll; NHS; Pres Acad Ftnss Awd Prog 85; Frshmn Hnr Schlrshp 85; Lynchburg Coll; Acctng.

MULLER, STEPHEN E; St Anthonys HS; Smithtown, NY; (Y); 55/201; Chess Clb; Nwsp Rptr; Nwsp Stf; Hon Roll; NHS; Ntl Merit Ltr; NYS U Binghamton; Med.

MULLERY III, STEPHEN P; Achbishop Stepinac HS; Yorktown Hts, NY; (Y); 1/206; Trs Church Yth Grp; Computer Clb; Key Clb; Pep Clb; Nwsp Sprt Ed; Yrbk Stf; Sr Cls; Var Capt Bsktbl; Bausch & Lomb Sci Awd; Ntl Merit Schol; Caddie Schlrshp 85; Rensselaer Medal 85; Gen Excell,Relgn,Sci,Latin,Scl Stds Awds 85; Harvard U; Law.

MULLIGAN, DAVID G; Averill Park HS; Averill Pk, NY; (Y); Math Tm; Ski Clb; Chorus; School Musical; School Play; Powder Puff Ftbl; Var JV Socr; JV Tennis; NHS; Art Clb; Natl Sci Olympiad Mdl For Chem 84; Premed.

MULLIGAN, MICHAEL; Shehendehowa HS; Ballston Lake, NY; (Y); 53/650; Computer Clb; Ski Clb; Ftbl; High Hon Roll; Acad Achvt Awd 84-85; Law.

MULLIN, DANIEL R; South Jefferson Central HS; Adams Center, NY; (Y); 15/128; Am Leg Boys St; Church Yth Grp; Computer Clb; FCA; French Clb; Yrbk Stf; JV Var Bsktbl; Hon Roll; NY ST Rgnts Schlrshp 85; Lcl Amer Lgn Schlrshp 85; Jefferson CC; Engrng.

MULLIN, EILEEN; Hunter College HS; Jackson Heights, NY; (Y); Drama Clb; Math Tm; School Play; Yrbk Stf; Lit Mag; Mu Alp Tht; Ntl Merit SF; Amer Assn Tchrs Frnch 83; Engl.

MULLIN, JANINE M; Pine Bush HS; Bloomingburg, NY; (Y) 7/289; Church Yth Grp; Pres Sec 4-H; Var Stat Bsktbl; Var Stat Ftbl; Stat Sftbl; Hon Roll; Jr NHS; NHS; Pace U Trste & Crclvl Vlntr Fire Co Schlrshps 85; Pace U NYC Campus; Fnanc.

MULLIN, KEVIN; Sachem HS; Holbrook, NY; (Y); Var Crs Cntry; Trk; Hon Roll; Sachem H S Hstry Fair 83; Acctg.

MULLIN, MARGERY; Fayetteville-Manlius HS; Fayetteville, NY; (Y); 76/335; Exploring; Hosp Aide; Model UN; Political Wkr; Ski Clb; Variety Show; Nwsp Rptr; Sec Stu Cncl; Socr; Trk; NYS Rgnts Schlrshp 85; Middlebury Coll; Comm.

MULLIN, MARY E; Monroe Woodbury SR HS; Monroe, NY; (Y); 28/386; Office Aide; Flag Corp; Mrchg Band; VP Symp Band; Nwsp Rptr; Sftbl; Swmmng; Lion Awd; NHS; NY ST Regnts Scholar 85; Roger Williams Awd Gftd & Tlntd 83; Colgate U; Eng.

MULLIN, PATTY; Sachem H S North; Lk Ronkonkoma, NY; (Y); Harvard; Psych.

MULLINGS, CAROLYN; South Park HS; Buffalo, NY; (Y); 35/375; Dance Clb; 4-H; Library Aide; Spanish Clb; Chorus; Church Choir; Drill Tm; School Play; Trk; Hon Roll; Perfect Attndnc 83-84; IFLA Intrntl Frgn Lang Awd 85; U Of Buffalo; Med.

MULLINGS, HOPE; Central Islip HS; Central Islip, NY; (Y); Sec Church Yth Grp; Hosp Aide; Library Aide; Sec Red Cross Aide; Science Clb; Temple Yth Grp; Band; Church Choir; School Play; Variety Show; Awded First Frgn Class 82; Awded Giftd And Talntd Stu 84; Sci.

MULLINS, MARGARET; Brooklyn Technical HS; Roosevelt Isl, NY; (Y); Yrbk Ed-Chief; Pres Jr Cls; Capt Tennis; Vllybl; High Hon Roll; NHS; Selctd NY Daily Nws/Ynkee Supr Yth 85; Doc.

MULLOY, KELLY; Sauquoit Valley Central Schl; Sauquoit, NY; (Y); GAA; VICA; Chorus; Stage Crew; Sec Jr Cls; Bowling; Cheerleading; Trk; Prfct Atten Awd; Voctnl Indstrl Clbs Amer 2nd Pl Off Practice ST Conf; Word Proc.

MULRY, JEANNINE; Bay Shore HS; Bay Shore, NY; (Y); Mrchg Band; Yrbk Bus Mgr; Lit Mag; Rep Soph Cls; Rep Jr Cls; VP Sr Cls; Rep Stu Cncl; Var Fld Hcky; Var Vllybl; NHS; All Lg, Conf Field Hockey 84-85.

MULVEHILL, BRIAN; Xavier HS; Brooklyn, NY; (Y); 73/227; German Clb; Teachers Aide; JV Var Bsbl; Coach Actv; JV Var Ftbl; Im Wt Lftg; Im Bsktbl; German Intl Exch Pgm 84-85; MIP Football 82-83; Fairfield U Schlrshp & NYS Regents Schlrshp 85; SUNY Binghamton.

MULVENNA, MARTY; West Seneca West SR HS; West Seneca, NY; (Y); Boy Scts; VICA; Machnst.

MULVEY, KEVIN S; Shaker HS; Loudonville, NY; (Y); Art Clb; Ntl Merit SF; Regnts Schlrshp NY ST Awd 85; Syracuse U; Lib Arts.

MULVEY, LISA L; Westhampton Beach HS; E Quogue, NY; (Y); 49/200; Hosp Aide; Chorus; Drill Tm; School Musical; Nwsp Stf; Pres Frsh Cls; Trs Sr Cls; Score Keeper; Trk; NY St Rgents Schlrshp 85; C W Post Coll; Child Psych.

MULYCA, MARK D; Schalmont HS; Schenectady, NY; (Y); Church Yth Grp; Computer Clb; Ski Clb; Band; Bio 84; Micro/Interface 85; Engnrng.

MUMA, ROBERT W; St John The Baptist HS; Brentwood, NY; (Y); Hon Roll; Cert Profcncy Acctng 85; Bus.

MUMFORD, TINA M; North Rose-Wolcott HS; Wolcott, NY; (Y); Rep Stu Cncl; Var Bsktbl; Var Vllybl; Hon Roll; Natl Hnr Soc Schlstc Awd 85; Niagara U; Socl Work.

MUMMENDEY, KRISTA; H Frank Carey HS; W Hempstead, NY; (Y); 37/216; Lit Mag; Rep Jr Cls; Trs Sr Cls; High Hon Roll; Hon Roll; Voice Dem Awd; Psych.

MUMPTON, GAIL; Rome Free Acad; Rome, NY; (Y); Yrbk Stf; Bsktbl; Hon Roll; Jr NHS; NHS; Comm Art.

MUNDLE, VERNETA; New Rochelle HS; New Rochelle, NY; (Y); Sec MMM; Chorus; Church Choir; Natalie Gallace Awd For Music 83; Pres Homeroom 84-85; Sec Adventist Yth Society 85; Comp Prog.

MUNDY, KATHLEEN; Holy Trinity HS; Wantagh, NY; (S); #2 In Class; Library Aide; Math Clb; Math Tm; Office Aide; Band; Stu Cncl; Im Gym; JV Sftbl; High Hon Roll; NEDT Awd; JV Sftbl Schl MVP 84; All Amer Hall Of Fame Band Fndtn Awd 84.

MUNDY, KRISTIN S; Brockport HS; Spencerport, NY; (Y); 7/300; Church Yth Grp; Var Capt Cheerleading; Var Crs Cntry; Var Trk; High Hon Roll; NHS; Ntl Merit Ltr; Mathletes; Ntl Soc Profsnl Engrs Schlrshp 85; Ltn III Awd 84; Lafayette Coll; Elec Engrng.

MUNESHWAR, BIBI; Stella Maris HS; Richmond Hill, NY; (Y); Computer Clb; English Clb; FNA; Office Aide; Red Cross Aide; Science Clb; Spanish Clb; School Play; Sftbl; Prfct Atten Awd.

MUNGER, STEVEN; Little Falls JR SR HS; Little Falls, NY; (Y); 18/120; French Clb; Pep Clb; Service Clb; Band; Concert Band; Jazz Band; Mrchg Band; Pep Band; Yrbk Rptr; Yrbk Stf; Med Tech.

MUNGIN, MELVIN; Mount Vernon HS; Mount Vernon, NY; (Y); Boy Scts; Church Yth Grp; Computer Clb; Church Choir; Jr NHS; JV Ftbl; JV Wt Lftg; Ntl Hnr Roll 84-85; Hgh Scr Schl Math Cntsts 84 & 85; Math.

MUNIZ, CINDYLISA; Dominican Acad; New York, NY; (Y); Latin Clb; Science Clb; Nwsp Rptr; Nwsp Stf; Yrbk Stf; Sec Soph Cls; Sec Jr Cls; Hon Roll; NHS; Ntl Merit Ltr; Statue Of Librty Enlghtng The Wrld Wrtng 84; Clscl Lgu Silver Medal Latin 84; Columbia U; Journlsm.

MUNIZ, YOLANDA; Maria Regina HS; Yorktown Hghts, NY; (Y); Hosp Aide; Key Clb; Library Aide; Trk; Bus Mngmnt.

MUNLEY, PAUL; Union-Endicott HS; Endicott, NY; (S); Church Yth Grp; Mathletes; Nwsp Rptr; Bsktbl; Var L Ftbl; Trk; High Hon Roll; Hon Roll; Math.

MUNN, ANGELA; La Salle HS; Niagara Falls, NY; (S); 11/278; Sec Church Yth Grp; Drama Clb; School Musical; Hon Roll; Jr NHS; Buffalo ST Coll; Elem.

MUNN, MICHELE; Fayetteville-Marlius HS; Manlius, NY; (Y); Cmnty Wkr; JCL; Political Wkr; Sec Soph Cls; VP Stu Cncl; JV Capt Bsktbl; Var Socr; Var Sftbl; High Hon Roll; Hon Roll; Wellesley Bk Awd 85; Lat Awd 83-84; Med.

MUNRO, CHRISTINE A; Sachem HS; Holbrook, NY; (Y); 72/1428; Pres VP Girl Scts; Hosp Aide; Math Tm; Orch; JV Socr; Var Trk; Wt Lftg; Jr NHS; NHS; Suffolk Cty Bd Directrs 83-85; Girl Sct Gold Awd 83; NY St Regents Schlrshp 85; Albright Coll; Bio.

MUNRO, JUDITH R; Wayland Central HS; Springwater, NY; (Y); Cmnty Wkr; Drama Clb; French Clb; FBLA; Pep Clb; Thesps; Chorus; Yrbk Rptr; Rep Frsh Cls; Rep Stu Cncl; Paul Smith; Hotel Mgt.

MUNRO, KATHERINE; Holy Names Acad; Albany, NY; (Y); Dance Clb; Drama Clb; Lit Mag; Rep Soph Cls; Rep Stu Cncl; Var Cheerleading.

MUNRO, LORI; Niagara Catholic HS; Niagara Falls, NY; (Y); VP French Clb; Hst Key Clb; Trs Jr Cls; Stat Bsktbl; JV Capt Bowling; Var Sftbl; Var Swmmng; Var Capt Vllybl; Hon Roll; NHS; Niagara U; Accntng.

MUNROE, GISELLE; Clara Barton HS; Brooklyn, NY; (Y); JA; Math Tm; PAVAS; Quiz Bowl; Science Clb; Color Guard; Orch; Cit Awd; Hon Roll; Prfct Atten Awd; Bio.

MUNROE, RUSS A; Newark SR HS; Newark, NY; (Y); 23/200; Am Leg Boys St; Political Wkr; Jazz Band; Mrchg Band; French Hon Soc; High Hon Roll; Hon Roll; French Clb; Ski Clb; Variety Show; Wegmans & Regnts Schlrshps 85; Olympcs Mind 84; Cornell U; Cmmnctn Arts.

MUNSON, JENNETT; Indian River Central HS; Evans Mills, NY; (Y); AFS; Band; Chorus; Mrchg Band; Sec Soph Cls; JV Var Cheerleading; Var Crs Cntry; Var Trk; JV Vllybl; Prfct Atten Awd; Law.

MUNYAK, JOHN; Smithtown High Schl East; Nesconset, NY; (Y); Boy Scts; Church Yth Grp; Orch; Bsktbl; God Cntry Awd; High Hon Roll; Hon Roll; NHS; Italian Hnr Soc 84; Ace Carrier Newsday 85; Pre-Med.

MUNZEL, LAURA; Riverhead HS; Riverhead, NY; (Y); 30/250; French Clb; German Clb; Hon Roll; NHS; Bard Coll.

MUNZER, CHRISTINA; St Hughs HS; New York, NY; (Y); Aud/Vis; Cmnty Wkr; Drama Clb; Pep Clb; Acpl Chr; Chorus; School Play; Stage Crew; Yrbk Stf; Stu Cncl; 2nd & 3rd In Shot Put Unis Relays 84-85; Anthropology.

MURANA, DAVID; Ossining HS; Ossining, NY; (Y); Var Ftbl; Var High Hon Roll; Cmrcl Art.

MURANYI, AMY; Riverside HS; Buffalo, NY; (Y); Office Aide; Pep Clb; Pres Spanish Clb; Stage Crew; Rptr Lit Mag; Swmmng; Hon Roll; Jr NHS; NHS; Hghst GPA Spnsh 83-84.

MURARKA, AMAL; Shenendehowa HS; Clifton Pk, NY; (Y); Intnl Clb; Leo Clb; Model UN; Band; JV Crs Cntry; JV Trk; JV Vllybl; High Hon Roll; NHS; Ntl Merit Ltr; Med.

MURASSO, STEPHANIE; Notre Dame Acad; Staten Island, NY; (Y); Computer Clb; Drama Clb; Hosp Aide; Church Choir; School Musical; School Play; Yrbk Stf; Rep Frsh Cls; Rep Soph Cls; Stu Cncl.

MURATORE, DIANE M; Smithtown West HS; Smithtown, NY; (Y); Exploring; Math Tm; Office Aide; Teachers Aide; Band; Church Choir; Color Guard; Jazz Band; Symp Band; VP Frsh Cls; Italian Hnr Soc 83-85; Siena Coll; Educ.

MURCIA, CONNIE; Mt Vernon HS; Mt Vernon, NY; (Y); Cmnty Wkr; Yrbk Rptr; Yrbk Stf; Cit Awd; High Hon Roll; Hon Roll; Prfct Atten Awd; Library Aide; Office Aide; Teachers Aide; Pedtrcn.

MURDICK, MICHELLE; Skaneateles Central HS; Skaneateles, NY; (Y); Sec Church Yth Grp; Chorus; Church Choir; Symp Band; Caygua Cnty CC; Elem Educ.

MURDOCK, MICHELLE; Victor Central SR HS; Victor, NY; (Y); 12/230; French Clb; Varsity Clb; Yrbk Sprt Ed; Stu Cncl; Swmmng; Trk; High Hon Roll; Hon Roll; NHS; WSI Cert 85; NROTC Scholar Fin 85; Annapolis; Aerontcl Engrng.

MURDOCK, RONDA; Mynderse Acad; Seneca Falls, NY; (S); 6/145; VP Intnl Clb; Band; Chorus; Concert Band; Jazz Band; Mrchg Band; Pep Band; School Musical; Yrbk Stf; Rep Stu Cncl; SUNY; Math Educ.

MURDOCK, SUZANNE; Oneonta HS; Maryland, NY; (Y); Cmnty Wkr; Ski Clb; Spanish Clb; Var JV Score Keeper; Bus Adm.

MURILLO, MEDARDO; Eastern District HS; Brooklyn, NY; (Y); 5/415; Office Aide; Teachers Aide; Band; Socr; Hon Roll; Baruch Coll; Comp Sci.

MURMER, MARK; Auburn HS; Auburn, NY; (Y); Chess Clb; School Musical; Bsktbl; Bowling; High Hon Roll; Hon Roll; NHS; Math.

MURPHY, ANITA M; Our Lady Of Victory Acad; Bronx, NY; (Y); Lit Mag; Pres Frsh Cls; Pres Soph Cls; VP Jr Cls; Rep Sr Cls; Regents Schlrshp 85; Comp Sci.

MURPHY, ANN; Colonie Central HS; Loudonville, NY; (Y); 130/530; Church Yth Grp; Band; Concert Band; Pep Band; Symp Band; Nwsp Stf; Yrbk Stf; Cheerleading; Score Keeper; Timer; Coll Of St Rose; Sec Ed.

MURPHY, BARB; James E Sperry HS; Henrietta, NY; (Y); Pep Clb; Ski Clb; Chorus; Nwsp Rptr; Rep Frsh Cls; Pres Soph Cls; VP Stu Cncl; Cit Awd; French Hon Soc; Hon Roll.

MURPHY, BLOSSOM M; Brockport HS; Brockport, NY; (Y); 37/287; Yrbk Sprt Ed; JV Bsktbl; Var JV Socr; Var Trk; JV Var Vllybl; High Hon Roll; NHS; Amer HS Athl 84; Mst Imprvd Sccr 85; Beaver Coll; Int Dsgn.

MURPHY, CAROLYN; Cardinal Mooney HS; Rochester, NY; (Y); Hon Roll; MCC; Bus.

MURPHY, CELESTE MICHELE; Freeport HS; Freeport, NY; (Y); 50/450; Cmnty Wkr; Computer Clb; Pep Clb; Concert Band; Mrchg Band; Rep Frsh Cls; Rep Soph Cls; Rep Jr Cls; Rep Stu Cncl; Var Vllybl; U Of Dayton Smmr Schlrshp-Wmn In Engrng Smnr 84; Syracuse; Elec Engrng.

MURPHY, CHARLES; Columbia HS; Rensselar, NY; (Y); Boy Scts; Computer Clb; Varsity Clb; Var Tennis; Var Trk; High Hon Roll; Hon Roll; NHS; Comp Sci.

MURPHY, DAVID; Archbishop Molloy HS; Bayside, NY; (Y); 45/450; Art Clb; Computer Clb; Science Clb; Yrbk Rptr; Im Bsktbl; JV Crs Cntry; Im Ftbl; Im Sftbl; JV Swmmng; JV Trk; Med.

MURPHY, DAVID; Westhampton Beach HS; E Moriches, NY; (Y); 45/200; Rep Soph Cls; Stu Cncl; JV Bsbl; Var L Bsktbl; Im Lcrss; JV Socr; Var L Trk; Im Wt Lftg; Hon Roll; Vrsty Bsktbl-Mst Imprvd Plyr 85; MVP & Capt-Bsktbl 83; Elec Engrng.

MURPHY, DENNIS; St John The Baptist; W Islip, NY; (Y); 40/500; Computer Clb; Science Clb; Hon Roll.

MURPHY, DYANE G; Westlake HS; Thornwood, NY; (Y); 20/148; AFS; Church Yth Grp; Hosp Aide; Spanish Clb; Cit Awd; High Hon Roll; Hon Roll; NHS; Spanish NHS; Pres Acad Fitnss Awd 85; Geneseo Coll; Elem Ed.

MURPHY, EDWARD D; Newfane HS; Burt, NY; (S); 3/177; Drama Clb; Math Tm; Quiz Bowl; Ski Clb; Varsity Clb; School Play; Stage Crew; Var Capt Wrstlng; Var Hon Roll; NHS; Highest Acad Awd In Frnch 83-84; BMX Rider Of Yr At Somorset Moto Pk 84; EBA Rider 2 In Age Group 84.

MURPHY, FRANCINE; East Islip HS; Great River, NY; (Y); Chorus; Flag Corp; School Musical; High Hon Roll; Hon Roll; Jr NHS; Spanish NHS; Mth.

MURPHY, JEFF; Maryvale SR HS; Cheektowaga, NY; (Y); DECA; Varsity Clb; Variety Show; JV Bsbl; Var L Bsktbl; Var L Ftbl; Var L Trk; High Hon Roll; Prfct Atten Awd; MIP Ftbl 81; CPA.

MURPHY, JIM; Commack High Schl South; Commack, NY; (Y); Art Clb; Chess Clb; Band; Concert Band; Jazz Band; Mrchg Band; School Play; Stage Crew; Symp Band; Mgr(s); Natl Art Hnr Scty 84-85; RI Schl Dsgn; Comm Art.

MURPHY, JIM R J; Fairport HS; Fairport, NY; (Y); Teachers Aide; VICA; Y-Teens; Band; JV Score Keeper; JV Timer; Var L Trk; JV L Wrstlng; Hon Roll; YMCA Yth Of The Yr Awd 84; Military; Chld Psych.

MURPHY JR, JOHN; Susquehanna Valley HS; Conklin, NY; (Y); Church Yth Grp; CAP; Science Clb; Wt Lftg; JV Var Wrstlng; Comp Sci.

MURPHY, JOHN F; Mt St Michael Acad; Yonkers, NY; (S); 5/309; Ski Clb; Yrbk Rptr; Yrbk Stf; Stu Cncl; NHS; Spanish NHS; Camera Clb; Chess Clb; Computer Clb; Stage Crew; Tuitn Schlrshp 82-85; Math.

MURPHY, JOHN M; Mount St Michael Acad; Bronx, NY; (Y); Rep Soph Cls; Rep Jr Cls; Rep Soph Cls; JV Crs Cntry; JV Trk; Rgnts Schlrshp Awd 85; Mercy Coll.

MURPHY, KAREN ANNE; The Academy Of St Joseph; Seaford, NY; (Y); Cmnty Wkr; Service Clb; Speech Tm; Stage Crew; Yrbk Rptr; Bowdoin; Law.

MURPHY, KARL M; Highland HS; Highland, NY; (Y); 12/125; Am Leg Boys St; French Clb; Varsity Clb; School Play; Yrbk Phtg; Yrbk Stf; Ftbl; Hon Roll; NHS; Letterman Clb; NYS Rgnts Schlrshp, Prsdntl Ftnss Awd, C A Simpson Mem Schlrshp, Am Leg Aux Awd 85; Stu Intrn Cngrss; Georgetown U; Fin.

MURPHY, KATHLEEN; Liverpool HS; Liverpool, NY; (Y); 236/874; Hosp Aide; Rep Stu Cncl; Var Capt Swmmng; MIP-SWIMMING 83; Cert Of Achvt For Volntrng 83.

MURPHY, KATHLEEN; The Mary Louis Acad; Middle Village, NY; (Y); Cmnty Wkr; Trk; Lab Tech.

MURPHY, KATHLEEN M; Maria Regina HS; Crestwood, NY; (Y); 25/128; Debate Tm; Sec Key Clb; Sec Yrbk Stf; Var Fld Hcky; Var Swmmng; Var Trk; Brnghmtn ST U; Cmnctns.

MURPHY, KERRY; Skaneateles Central HS; Skaneateles, NY; (S); Cmnty Wkr; Varsity Clb; Yrbk Phtg; Yrbk Stf; Sec Frsh Cls; Sec Soph Cls; Sec Jr Cls; Bsktbl; Coach Actv; Lcrss; New England Area; Soc Wrk.

MURPHY, KIERAN; Green Meadow Waldorf Schl; Spring Valley, NY; (Y); Cmnty Wkr; Teachers Aide; Chorus; Orch; School Play; Yrbk Stf; Off Stu Cncl; Socr; NHS; NYS Regents Scholar 84-85; CT Coll.

MURPHY, LAURA; Albertus Magnus HS; New City, NY; (Y); 2/196; Math Tm; Varsity Clb; Sec Sr Cls; Rep Stu Cncl; JV Var Cheerleading; Hon Roll; Jr NHS; NHS; Spanish NHS; Mth & Sci Natl Hnr Soc.

MURPHY, MARY; Brewster HS; Patterson, NY; (Y); Comp Awarenss Schlrshp 83; Food & Nutrtn IV Schlrshp 84; Hlth Asstg/Geriatrcs Outstndng Awd 85; Nrsng.

MURPHY, MARY; Saratoga Central Catholic HS; Gansevoort, NY; (Y); Drama Clb; Office Aide; Political Wkr; Varsity Clb; Church Choir; School Play; Stage Crew; Yrbk Stf; Bsktbl; Hon Roll; Bus Adm.

MURPHY, MARY B; Cazenovia HS; Erieville, NY; (Y); VP 4-H; Var L Crs Cntry; Var Trk; High Hon Roll; Hon Roll; Ntl Merit Ltr; St Schlr; Ntl Ski Ptrl Alpine 82-85; Albany Coll Of Pharmcy; Phrmcst.

MURPHY, MARY JEAN; Saint Vincent Ferrer HS; Woodside, NY; (Y); 25/115; Art Clb; Cmnty Wkr; Dance Clb; Drama Clb; Girl Scts; Hosp Aide; Pres Pep Clb; Ed Q&S; Service Clb; Y-Teens; Occup Theropist.

MURPHY, MARY K; Seton Catholic Central HS; Endwell, NY; (S); Art Clb; Dance Clb; French Clb; Hosp Aide; Key Clb; Yrbk Stf; Rep Stu Cncl; Le Moyne; Psych.

MURPHY, MATHEW J; Town Of Webb HS; Big Moose, NY; (Y); 1/28; Am Leg Boys St; Cmnty Wkr; Spanish Clb; Trs Frsh Cls; Rep Stu Cncl; Im Badmtn; Var Bsbl; Var Bsktbl; Im Bowling; Im Ftbl; Math Awd 81; ST U NY Albany; Chem Engr.

MURPHY, MAUREEN; Lawrence HS; Cedarhurst, NY; (Y); Pres Sec AFS; Pres Key Clb; Yrbk Bus Mgr; Yrbk Rptr; Rep Soph Cls; Rep Jr Cls; Var Vllybl; NHS; Ntl Merit Ltr; French Clb; Hnr Scty Awd Most Val Mbr 83; AATSP Natl Cont 3rd Pl 83; Liberal Arts.

MURPHY, MAUREEN; Mount Saint Mary Acad; Kenmore, NY; (Y); Hosp Aide; Red Cross Aide; Ski Clb; Chorus; Stage Crew; Im Badmtn; Im Vllybl; Hon Roll; Phys Thrpy.

MURPHY, MELISSA; Wilson Central HS; Lockport, NY; (Y); Chorus; School Musical; School Play; Yrbk Stf; Stu Cncl; Stat Bsktbl; JV Var Sftbl; JV Var Vllybl; Trs NHS; JV Cheerleading; Niagara All Cty Chorus 83-85; Spch Thrpst.

MURPHY, MICHAEL; Archbishop Molloy HS; Forest Hills, NY; (Y); 43/371; Camera Clb; Cmnty Wkr; Debate Tm; Intnl Clb; Nwsp Phtg; Nwsp Stf; Yrbk Phtg; Yrbk Stf; JV Bsbl; Im Bsktbl; Outstndng Cmnty Srv Awd 85; U Of MI; Bus.

MURPHY, MICHAEL; Newfield HS; Selden, NY; (Y); Boy Scts; Church Yth Grp; Exploring; Boy Scts Eagl Sct 85; Rgnt Schlrshp 85; Stony Brook U; Scntst.

MURPHY, MICHELE A; Kenmore West HS; Kenmore, NY; (Y); Debate Tm; French Clb; Model UN; Ski Clb; JV Var Socr; JV Stat Trk.

MURPHY, NANCY; Salamanca Central HS; Salamanca, NY; (Y); Color Guard; Flag Corp; Mrchg Band; High Hon Roll; Hon Roll; Nrsng.

MURPHY, PATRICE; Saint Edmund HS; Brooklyn, NY; (S); 20/187; Church Yth Grp; English Clb; Sec Spanish Clb; Bowling; Hon Roll; Hnr Mntn Language Fair 82; 2nd Pl Language Fair 83; Ntl Bus Hnr Scty 85.

MURPHY, PATRICIA; Bishop Scully HS; Amsterdam, NY; (S); 7/69; French Clb; Varsity Clb; Nwsp Stf; Yrbk Stf; Pres Frsh Cls; Sftbl; High Hon Roll; NHS; Sportmanship Awd 84; Big Bro/Big Sister 84-85; Bentley Coll; Acct.

MURPHY, PATRICIA A; Garden City HS; Garden City, NY; (Y); 99/319; Rep Church Yth Grp; Drama Clb; Hosp Aide; Intnl Clb; Key Clb; Latin Clb; Off Pep Clb; School Musical; School Play; Crs Cntry; Cthlc U Of Amer.

MURPHY, ROBERTA; North Babylon SR HS; North Babylon, NY; (Y); DECA; Drama Clb; Chorus; School Play; Stage Crew; Masonic Yth Org; U ME Farmington; Elem Ed.

MURPHY, ROSANNE; St Peters H S For Girls; Staten Isl, NY; (Y); Pres Am Leg Aux Girls St; Cmnty Wkr; Exploring; Pres FNA; Red Cross Aide; Chorus; School Musical; Stage Crew; Var Trk; St Peters Coll; Hosp Adm.

MURPHY, SABRINA; Cardinal O Hara HS; Buffalo, NY; (Y); Art Clb; VP Church Yth Grp; Drama Clb; French Clb; Latin Clb; Ski Clb; School Musical; School Play; Stage Crew; Yrbk Stf; 20 Ribbons For Eqestrian Riding 82-83; Most Christian Awd 82; St Bonaventure; Comm.

MURPHY, STACEY M; Bishop Kearney HS; Brooklyn, NY; (Y); 66/341; Intnl Clb; Political Wkr; Yrbk Stf; Rep Sr Cls; Hon Roll; NHS; NY ST Regents Coll Schlrshp 85-86; Syracuse U; Public Comm.

MURPHY, SUSAN; Moore Catholic HS; Staten Island, NY; (Y); 6/180; French Clb; Science Clb; Ski Clb; Nwsp Stf; Yrbk Stf; Stu Cncl; JV Cheerleading; NHS; Pres Schlr; Fairfield U; Acctg.

MURPHY, SUSAN; Mount Assumption HS; Peru, NY; (Y); Math Clb; Rep Soph Cls; Rep Jr Cls; Pres Sr Cls; Pres Stu Cncl; Var Socr; JV Var Sftbl; JV Var Vllybl; High Hon Roll; Hon Roll; Med.

MURPHY, TASHA M; The Mary Louis Acad; Jamaica, NY; (Y); Art Clb; French Clb; Hosp Aide; Trs Intnl Clb; Im Bsktbl; Im Ftbl; Var Trk; Volntr Srv Awd 84; Nrsng.

MURPHY, TOM; Attica HS; Varysburg, NY; (Y); 4/150; Math Tm; VP Jr Cls; Trs Sr Cls; NHS; Ntl Sci Merit Awd 83-84; Acad All Amer Awd, Attica Lions Clb Awd 83-85; ST U Geneseo; Pre Engrng.

MURPHY, VERONICA; St John The Baptist Diocesan HS; Central Islip, NY; (Y); Cmnty Wkr; Library Aide; Office Aide; Red Cross Aide; Symp Band; Yrbk Stf.

MURPHY, WILLIAM; North Western Central HS; Chestertown, NY; (S); Nwsp Stf; Socr; Tennis; Hon Roll.

MURPHY III, WM L; Wilson Central HS; Ransomville, NY; (Y); 30/130; Yrbk Stf; VP Soph Cls; Var L Bsbl; Var L Ftbl; Var L Ice Hcky; Hon Roll; Ntl Merit Ltr; Al-Leag Ftbl 84; Robert Ball Awd MVP Ic Hcky 84; Var MVP Awds Ic Hcky 82-84; Bus.

MURRAY, BARBARA; North Shore HS; Glen Head, NY; (Y); French Clb; Varsity Clb; Var Capt Cheerleading; Athl Recog Awd Chrldg 83-85; Knights Of Columbus Awd Chrldg 85; Fshn Coord.

MURRAY, BERNICE; Morrisville-Eaton HS; Peterboro, NY; (Y); Church Yth Grp; Sec GAA; Color Guard; JV Stat Bsktbl; Crs Cntry; Sftbl; Var Trk; Var Vllybl; Hon Roll; Buffalo ST; Photogrphy.

MURRAY, BRIAN; Waterford-Halfmoon HS; Waterford, NY; (Y); 4/80; Math Clb; Math Tm; JV Var Socr; Hon Roll; Top Jr Cls 85; Vet Med.

MURRAY, CASSANDRA; Freeport HS; Freeport, NY; (Y); Church Yth Grp; PAVAS; Teachers Aide; Band; Variety Show; Yrbk Stf; Gym; Tennis; Hon Roll; NHS; Awd Tutorng Comm 85; Fordham U; Bus Adm.

MURRAY, CHRISTOPHER; Fayetteville-Manlius HS; Manlius, NY; (Y); Hon Roll; Engrng.

MURRAY, COLLEEN; Sweet Home SR HS; Amherst, NY; (Y); 80/450; Orch; Off Soph Cls; Co-Capt Var Cheerleading; Hon Roll; Spanish NHS; Ntl Orch Awd 85; Hnr Roll Awd 85; Social Stds Awd 84; ST U Buffalo.

MURRAY, JEAN MARIE; Moore Catholic HS; Staten Isl, NY; (Y); Varsity Clb; Yrbk Ed-Chief; VP Sr Cls; Var Stat Bsktbl; Var Capt Sftbl; High Hon Roll; NHS; Vrsty Club Schlr Athl 85; MVP Vrsty Sftbl 83-84; Regents Schlrshp 85; NJ Inst Tech; Mech Engr.

MURRAY, KAREN; Sacred Heart Acad; Mineola, NY; (S); 2/200; Girl Scts; Math Tm; Spanish Clb; High Hon Roll; Hon Roll; NHS; Chem Awd 83; Cornell U; Vet Med.

MURRAY, KARYN; Pulaski JR-SR HS; Pulaski, NY; (S); 10/99; VP Drama Clb; GAA; Chorus; School Musical; Yrbk Rptr; Var L Socr; Var L Trk; NHS; Ski Clb; Sr Of Mnth 84; All League Sccr 83 & 84; Sunny Geneseo; Bus Mgmt.

MURRAY, KRISTEN; Vestal SR HS; Apalachin, NY; (Y); Political Wkr; Acpl Chr; Band; Church Choir; Sec Mrchg Band; Pep Band; NYSSMA Music Awds 83-85; Educ.

MURRAY, LISA; Corning-Painted Past East HS; Corning, NY; (Y); 10/256; Exploring; FBLA; Color Guard; Trk; High Hon Roll; Jr NHS; NHS; Pres Pres Schlr; NYS Regents Schlrshp 85-86; Alfred U Sthrn Tier Schlrshp 85-86; Carborundum Schlrshp 85-86; Alfred U; Cermc Engrng.

MURRAY, MAUREEN; Skaneateles Central HS; Skaneateles, NY; (S); Church Yth Grp; GAA; Variety Show; Bsktbl; Socr; Sftbl; High Hon Roll; Hon Roll; Jr NHS; NHS; Ed.

MURRAY, MEREDITH A; Baldwin SR HS; Baldwin, NY; (S); Dance Clb; Drama Clb; Model UN; Thesps; Trs Chorus; Capt School Musical; Rep Soph Cls; Rep Jr Cls; Bsbl; Var Trk; Muiscl Stu Of Mnth Concrt Chrs 83-84; Eastern ST Champ Trk 82-83; All Cnty Music Festvl 83 & 85; Boston U; Psych.

MURRAY, MICHAEL; Archbishop Stepinac HS; Briarcliff, NY; (Y); 47/201; VP JA; Key Clb; Chorus; Yrbk Sprt Ed; Yrbk Stf; JV Bsktbl; Var Ftbl; Var Trk; Hon Roll; Bus.

MURRAY, MICHAEL; Cardinal Spellman HS; Bronx, NY; (Y); 85/600; Trs Church Yth Grp; Drama Clb; Letterman Clb; Varsity Clb; Drill Tm; Drm & Bgl; School Play; Rep Frsh Cls; Rep Soph Cls; Rep Jr Cls; Cardnl Spellman CYO Yuth Awd 84; Amer Leg Awd, Svc, Schlrshp Awd 82; Georgetown U; Sci.

MURRAY, MICHELLE; Springfield Gardens HS; Queens, NY; (Y); 181/443; Church Yth Grp; Computer Clb; Science Clb; Church Choir; Frsh Cls; Jr Cls; Gym; Vllybl; Bus Skll Inst 82-85; Dnc Schl; Top Teens Of Distnctn 84-85; Comp.

MURRAY, PATRICIA; Bradford Central HS; Bradford, NY; (S); 1/27; School Play; Yrbk Ed-Chief; VP Jr Cls; VP Sr Cls; VP Stu Cncl; Capt VP Sftbl; Bausch & Lomb Sci Awd; NHS; Regents Schlrshp 85; Rochester Natl Schlrshp 85; Elmira Coll Key Awd 84; U Of Rochester.

MURRAY, PATTI J; Red Jacket Central HS; Clifton Springs, NY; (Y); 31/95; Pres Trs 4-H; Quiz Bowl; Band; Drill Tm; Nwsp Rptr; Nwsp Stf; 4-H Awd; NY ST 4-H Awd 81-82; NY ST 4 H Rsrve Grnd Champ 84; Finger Lakes CC; Data Proc.

MURRAY, ROBERT; New Covenant Christian Schl; Webster, NY; (Y); 3/12; Church Yth Grp; Trs Computer Clb; Spanish Clb; Yrbk Phtg; Yrbk Stf; Var Socr; Var Sftbl; Hon Roll; Library Aide; Rgnts Schlrshp 85; Monroe CC; Cmmnctns.

MURRAY, ROBERT W; Guilderland Central HS; Guilderland, NY; (Y); 5/340; Hosp Aide; Key Clb; Rep Stu Cncl; JV Bsktbl; Var L Crs Cntry; Var L Trk; High Hon Roll; NHS; Ntl Merit Ltr; Varsity Clb; NYS Bar Assoc Cert Of Hon Mock Trl 85; Pre Med.

MURRAY, TRUDY; Madrid-Waddington HS; Waddington, NY; (Y); 9/48; Drama Clb; French Clb; JA; Spanish Clb; Yrbk Stf; Cheerleading; High Hon Roll; NHS; Art Clb; Chorus; Jeffrey Scott Page Mem 85; Champ Hobkirk Am Leg 85; Potsdam St; Soclgy.

MURRAY, VICKI; Madrid-Waddington HS; Waddington, NY; (Y); Drama Clb; Spanish Clb; Chorus; School Musical; Stage Crew; Yrbk Bus Mgr; Yrbk Stf; Var Capt Cheerleading; Var Mgr(s); JV Var Socr; RIT; Crmnl Jstc.

MURRER, PATRICIA; Greece Arcadia HS; Rochester, NY; (Y); 122/292; Ski Clb; Chorus; School Musical; Rep Stu Cncl; Var Mgr(s); JV Var Socr; JV Vllybl; Church Yth Grp; Drama Clb; Nwsp Stf; R T Frnch Home Ec Awd 85; ST Fnlst Miss Amer Co-Ed Pgnt 85; ST U Coll Buffalo; Diettcs.

MURSZEWSKI, BETH; Cleveland Hill HS; Cheektowaga, NY; (Y); Church Yth Grp; Sec FHA; GAA; Hosp Aide; Ski Clb; Chorus; Stu Cncl; JV Var Cheerleading; Var L Vllybl; Hon Roll; Bus.

MURTHA, RICHARD; Regis HS; New York City, NY; (Y); Chess Clb; Latin Clb; Teachers Aide; Stage Crew; Variety Show; Yrbk Stf; JV Bsktbl; Capt Bowling; JV Crs Cntry; French Hon Soc; Natl Hspnc Schlr Awd Wnr 85; U Of VA; Attorney.

MUSA, JOHN; Archbishop Molloy HS; Brooklyn, NY; (Y); 245/409; Spanish Clb; Rep Frsh Cls; Crs Cntry; Swmmng; Trk; Bus.

MUSCARELLA, ANTHONY MARC; York Central HS; Mount Morris, NY; (Y); Ski Clb; JV Bsbl; Var L Ftbl; Var L Trk; Drftng.

MUSCARELLA, DONNA; Bishop Kearney HS; Brooklyn, NY; (Y); Pres Dance Clb; Drama Clb; Spanish Clb; School Play; Variety Show; Hon Roll; NHS; Comp Sci.

MUSCENTE, JOSEPH; Sacred Heart HS; Yonkers, NY; (S); 15/225; Church Yth Grp; Nwsp Rptr; Nwsp Stf; Hon Roll; NHS; 2nd Pl NY Wrtng Cont 83-84; HS Hnrs Courses 84-85; Manhattan Coll; Bio Sci.

MUSCIANESI, DANA; St Joseph By The Sea HS; Staten Island, NY; (Y); 9/280; Yrbk Stf; Stu Cncl; Hon Roll; NHS; NEDT Awd; Acad All Amer Awd 85; Natl Spn Exam Awd 84; Syracuse U; Bus.

MUSELEVICHUS, KAREN; Bay Shore HS; Brightwaters, NY; (Y); 59/412; Camera Clb; Hosp Aide; Office Aide; Nwsp Phtg; Nwsp Rptr; Nwsp Sprt Ed; Yrbk Phtg; JV Var Trk; Outstndng Achvt Bus; Pres Envrnmntl Yth Awd Outstndng Achvt; Comp Sci.

MUSHO, SUZANNE; Dominican Acad; New York, NY; (Y); Hosp Aide; School Play; Rep Stu Cncl; Var Cheerleading; Hon Roll; NEDT Awd; Magna Cum Laude In The Natl Latin Exam 84; Pedtrcn.

MUSSEHL, TRACY; West Seneca West SR HS; Cheektowaga, NY; (Y); Key Clb; Red Cross Aide; Rep Jr Cls; Hon Roll; Cet Achvt Rgnts Bio 84-85; Cert Rcgntn Rgnts Earth Sci 83-84.

MUSSER, CORINNE; Binghamton HS; Binghamton, NY; (Y); VP French Clb; GAA; Hosp Aide; Key Clb; Rep Stu Cncl; Var Sftbl; High Hon Roll; NHS; Rotary Awd; Natl Cncl Yth Ldrshp Salute To Yth Awd 85; Bloomsburg U; Acctg.

MUSSO, MARIA; Stella Maris HS; Howard Beach, NY; (Y); 15/240; Intnl Clb; Library Aide; Science Clb; Church Choir; School Play; High Hon Roll; Hon Roll; NHS; St Johns U; Med.

MUSSO, TERI; West Hempstead HS; W Hempstead, NY; (Y); 4-H; Key Clb; Political Wkr; Spanish Clb; Rep Jr Cls; High Hon Roll; Hon Roll; Jr NHS; Cert Achvt Engl 84; Law Day Essay Cont 85; Natl Scl Stds Olympiad 85; Vet.

MUSSON, FLOYD; Gilbertsville Central HS; Gilbertsville, NY; (Y); Varsity Clb; Band; Concert Band; Mrchg Band; Stage Crew; Bsbl; Bsktbl; Crs Cntry; High Hon Roll; Hon Roll; Hartwick Coll Bsktbl Camp MVP 85; NHS Plugger Awd 85; Amer H S Ath Hon Rl 85; Bsktbl All Star 85; Phys Ed Tchr.

MUSTAFA, SYED AHMED; Corning Painted Post East HS; Corning, NY; (Y); 52/213; Pres AFS; Am Leg Boys St; Boy Scts; Pres Exploring; Sec Model UN; Ski Clb; Band; School Musical; Rep Stu Cncl; Trk; Med.

MUSTICO, CHRISTEN ANNE; Notre Dame HS; Elmira, NY; (Y); Cmnty Wkr; Hosp Aide; Key Clb; Library Aide; Teachers Aide; Thesps; Varsity Clb; Acpl Chr; Band; Chorus; Elem Ed.

MUSTICO, J STEPHEN; Hannibal Central HS; Sterling, NY; (S); AFS; 4-H; VP Key Clb; Band; Chorus; School Musical; Yrbk Stf; Crs Cntry; Trk; 4-H Awd; Pilot.

MUSTO, CAROL; Christ The King R HS; Brooklyn, NY; (Y); 20/384; Math Clb; Math Tm; Nwsp Rptr; Nwsp Stf; Yrbk Stf; Lit Mag; Hon Roll; NHS.

MUSTY, DANIEL; Holland Central Schl; South Wales, NY; (Y); 17/107; Am Leg Boys St; Church Yth Grp; Stu Cncl; High Hon Roll; Hon Roll; Prfct Atten Awd; Aero-Sp Engrng.

MUTARELLI, THOMAS; La Salle Acad; New York, NY; (S); Camera Clb; Chess Clb; Latin Clb; Bsktbl; Socr; Wt Lftg; Hofstra U; Comp.

MUTH, MICHAEL; Shenendehowa HS; Clifton Pk, NY; (Y); Leo Clb; Outstndng Schlstc Achvt Awd 81-85; Bus.

MUTISYA, ELIZABETH M; Bronx High School Of Science; New York, NY; (Y); Hosp Aide; Office Aide; Service Clb; Teachers Aide; Band; Yrbk Stf; Jr NHS; Ntl Merit SF; Prfct Atten Awd.

MUTO, JOHN; Little Falls JR SR HS; St Johnsville, NY; (Y); 9/80; Am Leg Boys St; Varsity Clb; Concert Band; Mrchg Band; Off Frsh Cls; Off Jr Cls; Bsbl; Bsktbl; Bowling; Crs Cntry; Boston Coll; Psych.

MUTO, MARIA; Stella Maris HS; Ozone Park, NY; (Y); Church Yth Grp; Office Aide; Political Wkr; Science Clb; Teachers Aide; Church Choir; Nwsp Rptr; Nwsp Stf; Yrbk Stf; Sec Jr Cls; Police Athl Leag Essay Cntst Awd 84; Rockaway Judeo-Christian Cncl Essay Cntst Awd 84; Sci.

MUTTON, THOMAS; Tonawanda JR SR HS; N Tonawanda, NY; (Y); 46/290; Aud/Vis; Computer Clb; French Clb; Im Bsktbl; Var Trk; Im Vllybl; Hon Roll; Syracuse U; Comp Sci.

MUZZILLO, CLAUDIA; Niagara Catholic HS; Niagara Falls, NY; (Y); Drama Clb; French Clb; Hosp Aide; JA; Key Clb; JV Var Badmtn; High Hon Roll; NHS; Diocese Buffalo Schlrshp 82; Niagara Cnty CC; Bus.

MYATT, BONNIE; Saranac Lake HS; Saranac Lk, NY; (Y); 4-H; FBLA; Red Cross Aide; Yrbk Rptr; Yrbk Stf; L Var Socr; Trk; Vllybl; Prfct Atten Awd; All Around Good Sport JV Soccer 82-83; N Cntry CC; Bus.

MYERS, BOB; Henninger HS; Syracuse, NY; (Y); Ski Clb; Lcrss; Socr; Hon Roll; 1st Tm All Lg Awd Socr 84-85; Empire ST Socr Tm Cntrl Schltc 85; Hon Men La Crosse 84-85.

MYERS, BRUCE E; Camden HS; Taberg, NY; (Y); 10/208; Varsity Clb; JV Var Socr; Var Tennis; Hon Roll; NHS; Mohawk Vly CC; Mech Engrng.

MYERS, CHARLES; Copiague HS; Copiague, NY; (Y); German Clb; Var Bsbl; Hon Roll; Phy Fit Awd 2nd Pl 84-85; Athl Traing.

MYERS, CRAIG; Portville Central HS; Cuba, NY; (Y); Am Leg Boys St; Church Yth Grp; Trk; High Hon Roll; Hon Roll; Math.

MYERS, DEIRDRE; Aquinas HS; Bronx, NY; (Y); Church Yth Grp; Drama Clb; Girl Scts; Chorus; Church Choir; School Musical; School Play; Hon Roll; Masonic Awd; Val; Glee Clb Awd 82-85; USC; Buyer.

MYERS, FRED; Mohawk Central HS; Mohawk, NY; (S); 6/77; Chorus; School Play; JV Tennis; Elec Engr.

MYERS, HEATHER; Skaneateles Central HS; Skaneateles, NY; (S); Trs Church Yth Grp; Yrbk Phtg; Var Bsktbl; Var Socr; Var Trk; High Hon Roll; NHS; 1st Team All Star Soccer 83-84; 1st Pentathalon Wnnr Trk 83; 2 Gold Key Awds Photo 83; Comp Sci.

MYERS, JOSEPH; Salamanca Central HS; Salamanca, NY; (S); 26/129; Letterman Clb; Model UN; Varsity Clb; L Var Bsbl; L Var Bsktbl; L Var Ftbl; Im Wt Lftg; High Hon Roll; Hon Roll; NHS; 1st Tm All-Star Ftbl, 2nd Tm All Wstrn NY Ftbl, 1st Tm All Conf Ftbl 84.

MYERS, KAREN; Falconer Central Schl; Falconer, NY; (Y); 4/134; French Clb; JA; Pres Band; Drm Mjr(t); School Musical; Yrbk Bus Mgr; Rep Stu Cncl; JV Tennis; Hon Roll; NHS; CPA.

MYERS, KRISTEN; Clarkstown High Schl North; Congers, NY; (Y); Pep Clb; Vllybl; MVP Vlybl 84; All Cnty & Cnfrnc For Vlybl 84; Elem Ed.

MYERS, LAURA CHRISTINE; Mercy HS; Selkirk, NY; (Y); 5/49; Church Yth Grp; School Play; Stage Crew; Nwsp Stf; Lit Mag; Trk; High Hon Roll; Jr NHS; Excllnce Awds All Subj; Chem.

MYERS, MIKE; Coxsackie-Athens HS; Athens, NY; (Y); 18/105; Math Clb; Red Cross Aide; Spanish Clb; Off Jr Cls; Rep Stu Cncl; Var Bsbl; Var Bsktbl; Im Tennis; High Hon Roll; NHS; Natl Hnr Soc Achvt Awd 82-83; Pol Sci.

MYERS, PAUL EDWARD; Addison Central Schl; Addison, NY; (Y); 2/95; Am Leg Boys St; Pres Chess Clb; Pres Latin Clb; Ski Clb; Rep Stu Cncl; Bowling; Golf; Bausch & Lomb Sci Awd; DAR Awd; High Hon Roll; DAR 85; Sal 85; Bausch & Lomb Sci 85; Clarkson U; Engr.

MYERS, SHAWN; Fowler SR HS; Syracuse, NY; (S); 8/150; Hst Rptr DECA; Pep Clb; Rep Frsh Cls; Soph Cls; Jr Cls; High Hon Roll; Hon Roll; Prfct Atten Awd; Outstndng Achvt Awd Speaker Of Gen Assembly 84; Outstndng Svc Fowler Stu Assoc Officer 84; Psychology.

MYERS, THOMAS; Archbishop Molloy HS; Flushing, NY; (Y); 287/409; Boy Scts; Civic Clb; Exploring; Math Tm; Office Aide; Pep Clb; Nwsp Stf; Coach Actv; Mgr(s); Var JV Trk; Jr, Sr Ldrshp Awd By Scts Amer 83 & 84; U Of Boston; Sci.

MYERS, THOMAS G; Xavier HS; Jackson Hts, NY; (Y); 28/227; Nwsp Ed-Chief; NHS; NY ST Regents Schlrshp 85; Loyola Coll Pres Schlrshp 85; Loyola Coll.

MYKULA, TANIA; Roosevelt HS; Yonkers, NY; (S); 2/287; Hosp Aide; VP Key Clb; Orch; Nwsp Rptr; Rptr Nwsp Stf; Rptr Lit Mag; Tennis; High Hon Roll; NHS; Ntl Merit Ltr; Rensselaer Polytech Inst Math, Sci Awds 84; Ciba-Geigy Sci Awd 85; Med.

MYREE, STEPHANIE; Lafayette HS; Brooklyn, NY; (Y); Church Yth Grp; Cmnty Wkr; Debate Tm; French Clb; Intnl Clb; ROTC; Church Choir; Nwsp Ed-Chief; Nwsp Rptr; Nwsp Stf; Optmst Oratrcl Awd 82; Daily Nws & NY Ynkees Supr Yth Awd 85; Columbia U; Jrnlsm.

MYRIE, NICOLA; St Agnes Cathedral HS; Hempstead, NY; (Y); 11/435; Cheerleading; Sftbl; Vllybl; High Hon Roll; NHS; Accntng.

MYRTLE, KATHY; Trott Vocational HS; Niagara Falls, NY; (Y); Boys Clb Am; JA; Yrbk Stf; Sec Frsh Cls; Rep Soph Cls; Sec Jr Cls; Mgr Sr Cls; Rep Stu Cncl; Cit Awd; Hon Roll; Cert Of Apprectn Awd-Boys Club 83; Srvc Awds-Guidance & Outstndng Hlpr 83; Culinary Arts.

MYSHALOV, HELEN; Christopher Columbus HS; Bronx, NY; (Y); 20/800; Hon Roll; Excllnce Math 83, 84 & 85; NYU; Comp Sci.

MYSLIK, WAYNE D; Garden City SR HS; Garden City, NY; (Y); 79/320; Boy Scts; Pres Church Yth Grp; French Clb; German Clb; Key Clb; Pres Latin Clb; Spanish Clb; School Play; Nwsp Stf; Yrbk Ed-Chief; NY ST Regents Schlrshp 85; John Hopkins U; Intl Studies.

MYSLIWIEC, DAVID; Catholic Central HS; Watervliet, NY; (S); 13/203; Drama Clb; Math Clb; School Musical; Variety Show; Yrbk Stf; Var Crs Cntry; JV Var Trk; High Hon Roll; NHS; Exc Bus Math Awd 82-83; United Way Vlntr Awd 83-84; SUNYA; Acctng.

NABAGIEZ, JOHN P; Valley Central HS; Walden, NY; (Y); 13/250; Debate Tm; Yrbk Stf; Lit Mag; Off Jr Cls; Off Sr Cls; Sec French Hon Soc; Hon Roll; NHS; Prfct Atten Awd; NY ST Regnts Schlrshp 85; Boston U; Pre-Med.

NABER, NANCY E; Hamburg SR HS; Hamburg, NY; (Y); 72/406; Sec AFS; JCL; Latin Clb; Nwsp Rptr; Nwsp Stf; JV Var Bsktbl; Mgr Ftbl; High Hon Roll; NHS; Prfct Atten Awd; Spencer W Revel PTA Scholar 85; SUNY Fredonia; Comm.

NACCARATO, RONALD J; Kingston HS; Port Ewen, NY; (Y); Aud/Vis; Pres Church Yth Grp; Exploring; Concert Band; Variety Show; Ftbl; NYS Regnts Schlrshp 85; SUNY New Paltz; Comp Sci.

NACHISON, ANDREW E; Stuyvesant HS; Staten Island, NY; (Y); Orch; School Musical; Symp Band; NCTE Awd; Ntl Merit SF; Tanglewood Smmr 84; Dartmouth Coll.

NACHOD, PETER; Amsterdam HS; Amsterdam, NY; (Y); Rep Frsh Cls; Rep Soph Cls; Rep Jr Cls; Rep Stu Cncl; Im Bsktbl; Im Off Ftbl; Var Socr; Var Trk; Hon Roll; Engrng.

NACKLEY II, JAMES J; New Hartford HS; New Hartford, NY; (Y); 11/260; Am Leg Boys St; French Clb; MMM; Stage Crew; Pres Frsh Cls; Rep Soph Cls; Pres Jr Cls; Rep Stu Cncl; Var Capt Socr; Var Tennis; Prncpls Awd 82-83; Eucharistic Mnstr 84-87; Attnd Stu Intrdctn Engr Prog 85; Med.

NACY, ALICIA A; Hudson Falls Senior HS; Hudson Falls, NY; (Y); 6/220; Varsity Clb; Band; Concert Band; Mrchg Band; Off Frsh Cls; Var Cheerleading; Var Sftbl; Var Capt Swmmng; Sec NHS; Spanish NHS; Fthls Cncl All-Star Tm Sftbl 84; Stu Qrtr-Math 84; 5 Vrsty Girls Swmmng Records; U Of CT-STORRS; Actrl Sci.

NACY, KAROLYN; Hudson Falls HS; Hudson Falls, NY; (Y); Varsity Clb; Band; Var L Crs Cntry; Var L Trk; High Hon Roll; NHS; Spanish NHS; Sports Writers Assoc Third Tm Mbr 83; Athl Trang.

NADAL, MARY BETH; Our Lady Of Victory Acad; Yonkers, NY; (S); 28/150; Hosp Aide; Yrbk Stf; Lit Mag; Jr Cls; Sr Cls; Hon Roll; NHS; Stu Recgntn Awd; Comm.

NADAN, PETER W; Rudolf Steiner HS; New York, NY; (Y); 1/20; Model UN; Science Clb; Orch; Nwsp Ed-Chief; Nwsp Rptr; Pres Soph Cls; Rep Stu Cncl; Var Bsktbl; Var Sftbl; Ntl Merit Ltr; Soph Year Steiner Bonn Germany 83; Stanford U.

NADEAU, DARLA; Avon JR SR HS; Avon, NY; (Y); 13/112; AFS; Church Yth Grp; Spanish Clb; Yrbk Stf; Rep Frsh Cls; Rep Soph Cls; Rep Jr Cls; Tennis; High Hon Roll; Jr NHS; Travl.

NADEAU, ROBIN; Valley Central HS; Maybrook, NY; (Y); 30/300; Church Yth Grp; Band; Church Choir; Mrchg Band; School Musical; Var Capt Cheerleading; VP French Hon Soc; Hon Roll; NHS; Rep Frsh Cls; Instrumntl Music Impv Awd 84; Enrichmnt Clb 84; Engrng.

NADEAU, SARA; Ticonderoga HS; Ticonderoga, NY; (Y); Sec 4-H; French Clb; Key Clb; Yrbk Stf; Rep Jr Cls; JV Var Bsktbl; Var Trk; Hon Roll; NHS; Prfct Atten Awd; Vet Sci.

NADEL, FREDRIC D; New Rochelle HS; New Rochelle, NY; (Y); 167/597; Chrmn Debate Tm; School Musical; School Play; Rep Sr Cls; JV Golf; JV Socr; Var Capt Swmmng; NHS; St Schlr; U Of VT; Bus Admin.

NADEL, LAUREN; Spring Valley SR HS; Spring Valley, NY; (Y); 3/426; Cmnty Wkr; Dance Clb; Science Clb; Sec Spanish Clb; Teachers Aide; Band; Lit Mag; NHS; Mrchg Band; Vllybl; Weather Svc Awd 83; Schl Svc Awd 84; Marjorie Kaspar Scholar Fund 85; Lib Art.

NADELL, MARTHA J; Poly Prep CDS HS; Brooklyn, NY; (Y); Cmnty Wkr; Intnl Clb; Pres VP Math Clb; Math Tm; Service Clb; Band; Pep Band; Mgr Nwsp Bus Mgr; Nwsp Ed-Chief; Nwsp Rptr; Amer Schlstc Prss Assn Awd 84; Telluredgeassn Smmr Pgm Schlrshp Fnlst 84; Oasis Clb Indct 84.

NADJADI, CLIFFORD; Havelring Central Schl; Bath, NY; (Y); French Clb; Band; Concert Band; Jazz Band; Mrchg Band; JV Var Socr; JV Var Wrstlng; Recording Workshop; Recdg Engr.

NADLER, RACHELLE; Commack HS South; Commack, NY; (Y); Cmnty Wkr; GAA; Teachers Aide; Band; Drm Mjr(t); Jazz Band; Mrchg Band; School Musical; Symp Band; Stu Cncl.

NADOLNE, BRIAN; Sachem North HS; Holbrook, NY; (Y); 100/1509; Cmnty Wkr; Pep Clb; Radio Clb; Red Cross Aide; Science Clb; Ski Clb; Spanish Clb; Nwsp Rptr; Hon Roll; Jr NHS; Suffolk VP Bnai Brith Yth Org 84-85,Rngl Pres 85; Pre-Med.

NAEGELE, STEVEN M; Herkimer SR HS; Herkimer, NY; (Y); 4/115; Am Leg Boys St; Bsbl; JV Var Bsktbl; JV Var Ftbl; Var L Trk; High Hon Roll; Hon Roll; NHS; Rgnts Schlrshp 85; Rensselaer Polytech Instit.

NAFZIGER, VALERIE; Louville Central HS; Martinsburg, NY; (Y); 20/135; Trs Pres Spanish Clb; Varsity Clb; Var L Bsktbl; Mgr(s); Var L Socr; Hon Roll; NHS; Church Yth Grp; School Play; Stat Sftbl; Molly Pitcher Lewis Hlth Schlrshp 85; Capt Elizabeth B Bush Schlrshp 85; Regents Schlrshp 85; Albany Med Ctr Schl Nrs.

NAGEL, JOSEPH; Turner/Carroll HS; Buffalo, NY; (Y); Chess Clb; Science Clb; Pres Jr Cls; Hon Roll; Earth Sci Awd Of Hnr 83; Fr Cert Merit 84-85; Recrtmnt Svc Awd 85; Comp Sci.

NAGELDINGER, SUSAN L; Marcus Whitman Central Schl; Penn Yan, NY; (Y); 7/122; Church Yth Grp; School Play; Nwsp Ed-Chief; Nwsp Rptr; Yrbk Stf; High Hon Roll; NHS; St Schlr; Church Choir; Bkstr Treas 84-85; CC Finger Lakes; Exec Secy.

NAGELSCHMIDT, GRETCHEN; Tully HS; Tully, NY; (Y); 11/70; Cmnty Wkr; Mgr Drama Clb; Exploring; Hosp Aide; Office Aide; Spanish Clb; School Musical; Stage Crew; Pres Acad Ftnss Awd 85; Hlth Careers Schlrshp Awd 85; Daemen Coll; Phy Ther.

NAGLIERI, RALPH A; Elmont Memorial HS; Elmont, NY; (Y); Am Leg Boys St; Drama Clb; Pres Key Clb; Pres Model UN; School Play; Variety Show; Trs Frsh Cls; Trs Soph Cls; JV Var Lcrss; Hon Roll; Boys ST Awd 85; Bus Admin.

NAGY, DAVID; City Honors HS; Buffalo, NY; (Y); 31/97; Math Tm; Chorus; Concert Band; Jazz Band; Mrchg Band; School Musical; Yrbk Stf; Stat Var Tennis; NYS Regents Schlrshp 84-85; Canisius Coll; Comp.

NAGY, GINA; Sewanhaka HS; Floral Park, NY; (Y); 84/396; Acpl Chr; VP Pres Chorus; School Musical; School Play; Swing Chorus; Variety Show; Cheerleading; Gym; Hon Roll; Wmns Clb Floral Prk Hnrb Mntn Awd 85; Outstndng Choral Musician 85; Adelpi U; Theatre.

NAGY, STEPHEN; Cooperstown Central Schl; Cooperstown, NY; (Y); 8/100; Var L Ski Clb; Varsity Clb; Concert Band; Jazz Band; Mrchg Band; Stu Cncl; JV Socr; Var L Trk; Hon Roll; NHS; NY Acad Sci Rsrch Traing Prog 85; Empire ST Gms Crss Cntry Ski 85.

NAIDU, BABLU; Roy C Ketcham HS; Wapp Fls, NY; (Y); Trs Drama Clb; Hosp Aide; Thesps; Chorus; School Musical; School Play; Off Stu Cncl; High Hon Roll; NHS; Intl Thspn Soc 84-85; Earth Sci Hnrs 83; Lwyr.

NAIFF, STEPHEN; Smithtown H S East; Hauppauge, NY; (Y); Chess Clb; Rep Frsh Cls; Var Golf; Hon Roll; Physics Engrng.

NAIMI, HALEH; Spackenkill HS; Poughkeepsie, NY; (Y); Office Aide; Red Cross Aide; Yrbk Stf; Rep Frsh Cls; Rep Stu Cncl; Mgr(s); Tennis; Trk; UCLA; Engr.

NAISBY JR, JAMES H G; East Islip HS; Great River, NY; (S); 206/475; Ski Clb; Band; Var Capt Crs Cntry; Var Trk; NY ST Intrsctnls 2nd 84; Cnty Comptn 3rd 82-84; Bus Admin.

NAJJAR, DOHA; Fort Hamilton HS; Brooklyn, NY; (Y); Library Aide; Office Aide; School Play; Hon Roll; Hnr Roll-All Sbjcts 82; Theatre Engl Cls 2 Yrs Cnsctvly 83-84; 90 Accntng 2 Yrs Cn Sctvly 83-84; Staten Island Coll; Bus.

NAJJAR, LAURIE; Clyde-Savannah Central HS; Clyde, NY; (Y); Office Aide; Concert Band; Jazz Band; Nwsp Rptr; Rep Stu Cncl; Var L Sftbl; Var L Tennis; High Hon Roll; Hon Roll; Prfct Atten Awd; Crml Just.

NAKATSUGAWA, JUN-YA; Jamesville Dewitt HS; Syracuse, NY; (Y); 22/250; Model UN; Ski Clb; Acpl Chr; School Musical; Swing Chorus; Yrbk Stf; Pres Sr Cls; High Hon Roll; NHS; Cornell U; Pre Med.

NALBACH, CHERYL; Horseheads SR HS; Horseheads, NY; (Y); French Clb; Latin Clb; Chorus; Concert Band; Mrchg Band; Orch; Var Bsktbl; Hon Roll; Marywood Coll; Intr Dsgn.

NALBONE, BRIAN; Falconer HS; Jamestown, NY; (Y); 1/107; Pres FBLA; Pres Stu Cncl; Cit Awd; Dnfth Awd; Trs NHS; Opt Clb Awd; Pres Schlr; Am Leg Boys St; Pres Computer Clb; Pres French Clb; Arion Awd 85; Natl Merit Fnlst 84; St Bonaventure; Math.

NALLI III, ROCCO; Fort Plain Central Schl; Fort Plain, NY; (S); 3/60; Trs Computer Clb; Sec Trs Drama Clb; Pres French Clb; Pres Latin Clb; Band; School Musical; Yrbk Stf; Wt Lftg; NHS.

NAMDAR, BENJAMIN; Ezra Acad; Forest Hills, NY; (Y); 5/30; Chess Clb; Cmnty Wkr; FBLA; JA; Nwsp Phtg; Yrbk Bus Mgr; Yrbk Phtg; Var Capt Bsktbl; Tennis; Hon Roll; Princpls Awd Math Awd 84-85; SUNY; Med.

NANAVATI, NILESH; Monroe HS; Rochester, NY; (Y); Boy Scts; Cmnty Wkr; Mathletes; Math Tm; Model UN; Jr Cls; Crs Cntry; Tennis; Hon Roll; Prfct Atten Awd; Chem Olympd 85; Wrbbt Wrtng Cntst Wnnr; M Mnogrm Athltcs; Babson Coll; Bus Mngmt.

NANCE, DEMETRIUS ENRICO; New Rochelle HS; New Rochelle, NY; (Y); Boy Scts; Church Yth Grp; French Clb; FBLA; Rep Stu Cncl; Var L Bsbl; Var L Socr; L Wrstlng; Attained Rank Eagle Scout 84; Ntl Achv Schlrshp 85; Pre-Law.

NANCY, NAU; Brooklyn Tech HS; Brooklyn, NY; (Y); Church Yth Grp; Dance Clb; Girl Scts; Band; Concert Band; Orch; Lit Mag; Hon Roll; Arista 83; Cert Excllnce Physics 85; Cert Excllnce Alg 83; Phys Ther.

NAND, SUREKHA; Cardinal Spellman HS; Bronx, NY; (Y); Computer Clb; Dance Clb; Key Clb; Pres Science Clb; High Hon Roll; Hon Roll; Jr NHS; NHS; Cornell U; Med.

NANFRO, LORRAINE; Bishop Kearney HS; Brooklyn, NY; (Y); Teachers Aide; Hon Roll; Pace U; Bus.

NANIN, JOSE E; Cardinal Spellman HS; New York, NY; (Y); High Hon Roll; Hon Roll; Natl Ed Dev Tsts-Superior Prfmnc; City U Of NY; Bus Mgmt.

NANNO, EDWARD; Christian Brothers Acad; Syracuse, NY; (Y); 17/100; Chess Clb; Church Yth Grp; JA; Varsity Clb; Yrbk Stf; Swmmng; High Hon Roll; Nyack Pres Schlrshp; Francis Asbury Palmer Schlrshp; Trexler Mem Fund; Nyack Clg; Christn Educ.

NAPOLI, LARAINE; St Edmunds HS; Brooklyn, NY; (Y); 60/190; Sec Frsh Cls; Sec Jr Cls.

NAPOLI, LISA M; New Utrecht HS; Brooklyn, NY; (Y); 26/525; Key Clb; Chorus; School Play; Nwsp Rptr; Lit Mag; Rep Jr Cls; Trs Sr Cls; Pom Pon; NHS; New York State Regents Schlrshp 85; Suny Binghamton.

NAPOLITANO, JOHN; Connetquot HS; Ronkonkoma, NY; (Y); 144/694; Cmnty Wkr; Drama Clb; Chorus; School Musical; School Play; Stage Crew; Swing Chorus; Trk; Hon Roll; Jr NHS; ANYSSMA Mdls 83-84; Music Ltr 84; Aviatn.

NAPOLITANO, LAURA; Sacred Heart Acad; Westbury, NY; (S); 1/198; Cmnty Wkr; Pres Spanish Clb; Chorus; School Musical; High Hon Roll; NHS; Math Clb; Full Tuition Schlrshp 83-85; Ntl Hnr Rll 84-85; Bus Admin.

NAPOLITANO, PHYLLIS ANNE V; Bishop Kearney HS; Brooklyn, NY; (S); Church Yth Grp; Intnl Clb; Chorus; Nwsp Rptr; Lit Mag; Hon Roll; NHS; Prfct Atten Awd; Fr Cert Of Merit 1st Yr Natl Fr Comp Hon 84; Coll Prgm Sr Yr SAY Prgm 84-85; Brooklyn Coll; Bus Admin.

NAPURSKI, TRACY; Sacred Heart HS; Yonkers, NY; (S); 8/236; Church Yth Grp; Drama Clb; Intnl Clb; Library Aide; School Musical; NEDT Awd; Schlrshp To Sacred Hrt H S 81; Maritime Coll; Comp Sci.

NARAINE, RAYMOND S; La Salle Acad; New York, NY; (S); 40/237; Chess Clb; Science Clb; NHS.

NARBY, DAVID A; Homer Central HS; Cortland, NY; (Y); 26/205; Drama Clb; Thesps; Capt Wrstlng; Ntl Merit SF; School Musical; School Play; Var Ftbl; JV Tennis; Var Trk; Btty Crckr Awd; Rotary Exch Stu 85; 6th Pl Wrstlng Empire ST 84; Regnts Schlrshp 85; Comp Sci.

NARCISSE, ALEX; Christ The King Reg HS; Cambria Heights, NY; (Y); 40/385; Boys Clb Am; Computer Clb; FBLA; JA; Nwsp Rptr; Nwsp Sprt Ed; Bsktbl; Ftbl; Hon Roll; Voice Dem Awd; Engrng.

NARCISSE, PIERRE; Fashion Industries HS; New York, NY; (Y); 172/365; Art Clb; Boys Clb Am; Science Clb; Band; Stage Crew; Hon Roll; Prfct Atten Awd; Sci Achvt Awd 83; Boys Clb Bdy Bldg Chmpnshp 85; Music Fld.

NARDONE, EVA; John A Coleman Catholic HS; Kingston, NY; (S); 2/67; Rep Key Clb; Latin Clb; Math Clb; Ski Clb; High Hon Roll; Jr NHS; Engr.

NARDONE, RENEE; Greece Athena HS; Rochester, NY; (Y); 15/281; Exploring; Girl Scts; VP JA; Ski Clb; Teachers Aide; Rep Stu Cncl; Hon Roll; Jr NHS; NHS; Pres Schlr; Acad Lttr 83; Acad Bar 85; Regents Dipl W/Hnrs 85; Purdue U; Rsrch Chem.

NARDONE, STEPHANIE; Bay Shore HS; Bay Shore, NY; (Y); Church Yth Grp; GAA; JA; Varsity Clb; Band; Concert Band; Mrchg Band; Pres Frsh Cls; Pres Soph Cls; Pres Jr Cls; All Star Sftbl 83-85; Suflk Plyr Of Yr Sftbl 84-85; Conf Teen Suic,Drg Alchl Abse 84-85; Psych.

NARDUCCI, BRIAN; Wantagh HS; Wantagh, NY; (Y); Ski Clb; JV Ftbl; JV Var Lcrss; U Of FL; Bus.

NARIKUZHY, HELENA; Uniondale HS; Baldwin, NY; (Y); Church Yth Grp; Cmnty Wkr; Hosp Aide; Key Clb; Yrbk Stf; VP Frsh Cls; VP Jr Cls; VP Sr Cls; Rep Stu Cncl; Var Pom Pon; Knight Of Colmbus 83; Mjr Awd 85; U Of PA; Bus Mgmt.

NARIZZANO, RAVENNA Y; La Guardia H S Of Music & The Arts; New York City, NY; (Y); Teachers Aide; Y-Teens; Chorus; School Musical; Trk; Mc Burney YMCA Yth Of Yr 85; Soc Wrk.

NARLIS, MARIA E; Port Chester HS; Rye Brook, NY; (Y); Aud/Vis; Camera Clb; Church Yth Grp; Cmnty Wkr; Computer Clb; Dance Clb; Debate Tm; Pres Intnl Clb; Key Clb; Library Aide; GOYA 83-84; Outstndg Stu Awd 84-85; Greek & Span Stu; Comp Sci.

NAROW, STEVEN; Susan E Wagner HS; Staten Island, NY; (Y); Stage Crew; High Hon Roll; NHS.

NARVAEZ, KAYRA; Curtis HS; Staten Island, NY; (Y); GAA; ROTC; Teachers Aide; Chorus; Cheerleading; Gym; Mgr(s); Score Keeper; Swmmng; Timer; Bus Admin.

NARVAEZ, ZENAIDA; H S Fashion Industries HS; New York, NY; (Y); 34/473; Art Clb; FBLA; Hon Roll; Hon Svc Cert 82; Cert Achvt 85; Taylor Bus Inst; Travel.

NASEEM, LYLA; Hauppauge HS; Smithtown, NY; (Y); Art Clb; Cmnty Wkr; Exploring; Hosp Aide; Temple Yth Grp; Chorus; Rep Sr Cls; High Hon Roll; Hon Roll; Regnts Schlrshp 85.

NASELLI, CHRISTINE; Gloversville HS; Gloversville, NY; (Y); 44/248; Office Aide; Yrbk Stf; Rep Soph Cls; Rep Jr Cls; Rep Sr Cls; JV Mgr(s); Hon Roll; Acctg.

NASELLI, JOANNE; Gloversville HS; Gloversville, NY; (Y); 19/220; Rep Am Leg Aux Girls St; Intnl Clb; Yrbk Stf; Rep Jr Cls; Rep Sr Cls; JV Trk; Hon Roll; NHS; Pres Schlr; Alfred Johnson Mem Schlrshp 85; Gail Malagisi Mem Schlrshp 85; Nathan Uttaver Hosp Aux Awd 85; Albany Coll; Phrmcy.

NASH, BARRY; Fayetteville Manlius SR HS; Syracuse, NY; (Y); German Clb; Ski Clb; School Musical; JV Ftbl; JV Lcrss; JV Socr; Hon Roll; Jr NHS.

NASH, CHANTELL; Bethlehem Central HS; Delmar, NY; (Y); 172/323; Church Yth Grp; VP DECA; Ski Clb; Variety Show; Score Keeper; Trk; 1st & 2nd Advtsng Svcs 84-85; Hnrbl Mntn Advtsng Svcs DECA 84; Army; Advtsng.

NASH, HUW M; Webster HS; Webster, NY; (Y); 17/700; Model UN; Concert Band; Jazz Band; Nwsp Rptr; Yrbk Phtg; Swmmng; High Hon Roll; Jr NHS; NHS; Ntl Merit SF; Hghst Hnrs ST Sci Congrss 82-84; NASA Regnl Fnlst 84; Biochem.

NASH, MARC; Oceanside HS; Oceanside, NY; (Y); Aud/Vis; Debate Tm; Mathletes; Pres Math Clb; Math Tm; Model UN; Ski Clb; Chorus; Nwsp Rptr; Bsbl; Silvr Medlst NY ST Mathletes 84-85; Math.

NASH, TIMOTHY; Massena Central HS; Massena, NY; (Y); Church Yth Grp; Cmnty Wkr; Political Wkr; Yrbk Rptr; Yrbk Stf; Rep Frsh Cls; Rep Soph Cls; Crs Cntry; Hon Roll; Bus.

NASH, VALERIE; Washington Irving HS; New York, NY; (Y); Church Yth Grp; Cmnty Wkr; Debate Tm; Office Aide; Radio Clb; Color Guard; Nwsp Rptr; Yrbk Rptr; Rep Stu Cncl; Sftbl; Acad Olympics NY Daily News 85; Lincoln Douglas Debates 85; Comm Arts Dept Awd Scholar 85; Jrnlsm.

NASIR, MICHELLE; Bishop Kearney HS; Brooklyn, NY; (S); 1/340; Hosp Aide; Math Tm; Capt Bowling; Gov Hon Prg Awd; High Hon Roll; NHS; Ntl Merit Ltr; Iona Lang Cont Frnch 1st Hnrs 84; Memrl Hnrs Schlrshp Hofstra U 85; Indvdl Achvmnt Math Tm 84; Comp Sci.

NASO, MARK W; Highland HS; Highland, NY; (Y); 4/128; Am Leg Boys St; Math Tm; Quiz Bowl; Band; Var L Bsbl; Var Vllybl; VP Pres NHS; Spanish NHS; Varsity Clb; Chorus; Ambassadr NYS HOBY Sem 84; NYS Cls C ST Chmp Socr Tm 84; Chem Engrng.

NASO, MARY; St John Villa Acad; Staten Island, NY; (Y); Girl Scts; Latin Clb; Ski Clb; Stage Crew; Gym; Swmmng; Vllybl; High Hon Roll; Hon Roll; Wagner Coll; Sci.

NASO, VINCENZA; St Peters High Schl For Girls; Staten Isl, NY; (Y); Math Tm; Yrbk Stf; Hon Roll; Prfct Atten Awd; Excel In Math 82; Hon Mntn Amer Inst Of Sci & Tech 82; St Johns U; Lwyr.

NASS, GREGG E; South Seneca HS; Lodi, NY; (Y); 10/100; Am Leg Boys St; Ski Clb; Spanish Clb; Rep Frsh Cls; Rep Soph Cls; Rep Stu Cncl; JV Bsbl; Var Golf; High Hon Roll; Hon Roll; Hghst Eng Regnts Schl 85.

NASS, RACHAEL; Lafayette HS; Brooklyn, NY; (Y); JA; Teachers Aide; Chorus; Lit Mag; Sftbl; High Hon Roll; NHS; Mck Trl Tm Awd 85; Acad Olympc Tm Awd 85; PTA Schlrshp Awd 83.

NASSAR, MICHAEL; Bay Shore HS; Bay Shore, NY; (Y); 40/412; Political Wkr; Thesps; School Musical; School Play; Nwsp Ed-Chief; Lit Mag; Rep Stu Cncl; Drama Clb; Intnl Clb; PAVAS; Wrkd Mondale/Ferraro Cmpgn & Lcl Hse Of Rep; SADD; Cmnty Theatr Grp-James St Plyrs; Polit Sci.

NASSAU, MICHELLE E; G W Hewlett HS; N Woodmere, NY; (Y); 86/273; Cmnty Wkr; Pep Clb; Political Wkr; Variety Show; Nwsp Stf; Yrbk Stf; Stu Cncl; Hon Roll; St Schlr; Stdnt Coor Annl Dnc Marathn 84; Co Chrprsn SR Prom Cmmttee 85; U Of MI; Psych.

NASSR, JEANMARIE; Notre Dame Acad; Brooklyn, NY; (Y); Church Yth Grp; Cmnty Wkr; Drama Clb; School Play; Var Bsktbl; JV Var Sftbl; Nrsng.

NASTASI, ANTHONY T; G Ray Badley HS; Fulton, NY; (Y); Computer Clb; JA; Latin Clb; Science Clb; Hon Roll; Regents Schlrshp 85; Oswego ST; Lawyer.

NASTI, JOHN; Lafayette HS; Brooklyn, NY; (Y); 76/410; FBLA; JV Bsbl; Cit Awd; JETS Awd; Awds-Engl, Scl Stds, Engrng & Comp Inst 83-85; Pace U; Fnanc.

NASTRI, ERIC; Southampton HS; Southamptn, NY; (Y); Boy Scts; Spanish Clb; Band; Concert Band; Jazz Band; School Play; JV Socr; Var Swmmng; Var Wrstlng; Coachs Awd Swim Tm 83; Cushing Acad; Physician.

NASTRO, CARLA; John Dewey HS; Brooklyn, NY; (Y); Nwsp Rptr; Stock Mrkt Gm 84; Cncl Unity; Stu Mntr; Tns Clb; Acad Fince; Cls Rep; Acctng.

NATALE, ANNA MARIA; Wellington C Mepham HS; Bellmore, NY; (Y); 57/385; Key Clb; Yrbk Stf; Hon Roll; Jr NHS; NHS; Bellmore Merrick Schlrshp 85; Motloys Domincn Schlrshp 85; Pres Acadmc Ftns Awd 85; Molloy Clg; Elem Schl Tchr.

NATALE, JOE; Washingtonville HS; Rock Tavern, NY; (Y); Math Clb; Math Tm; Ski Clb; Crs Cntry; Socr; Trk; Wrstlng; Hon Roll; Rochester Inst Of Tech; Archit.

NATALE, JOHN; Xavier HS; Brooklyn, NY; (Y); #81 In Class; Aud/Vis; Math Clb; Stage Crew; Var Ftbl; Hon Roll; NHS; Ntl Merit Ltr; Bus Accntng.

NATALE, PHILIP C; Newark SR HS; Newark, NY; (Y); 11/201; Am Leg Boys St; Latin Clb; Service Clb; Varsity Clb; Sec Trs Soph Cls; Pres Stu Cncl; Var L Lcrss; Var L Socr; High Hon Roll; NHS; Socr MIP Awd 84; U PA; Pre-Med.

NATALE, TARA; New Utrecht HS; Brooklyn, NY; (Y); 61/605; Band; Mrchg Band; Yrbk Stf; Hon Roll; Arista 84-85; Pace U; Bus.

NATALI, MICHELE; Paul V Moore HS; Brewerton, NY; (Y); 33/297; 4-H; Yrbk Ed-Chief; Pres Jr Cls; Pres Sr Cls; Var Capt Cheerleading; Cit Awd; Hon Roll; NHS; GAA; Ski Clb; Rgnts Schlrshp; Hnr Socty; Fashion Inst Of Tech; Fash Buyg.

NATALIE, LAWRENCE J; Bay Shore HS; Bay Shore, NY; (Y); 30/376; Church Yth Grp; Cmnty Wkr; Yrbk Stf; Off Frsh Cls; Off Soph Cls; Off Jr Cls; Off Sr Cls; Stu Cncl; Socr; Regents Schlrshp 85; Suffolk CC; Liberal Arts.

NATANZON, MIKE; Williamsville East HS; Williamsville, NY; (Y); 95/300; Chess Clb; Im Socr; U B; Math.

NATION, ANISSA; Palmyra-Maredon HS; Palmyra, NY; (Y); Church Yth Grp; Ski Clb; Band; Color Guard; Concert Band; Mrchg Band; Pep Band; Symp Band; Var Capt Cheerleading; Mgr Trk; Med.

NATKIN, MICHAEL; Gates-Chili SR HS; Rochester, NY; (S); 11/463; JA; Math Tm; JV Socr; High Hon Roll; NHS; SUNY Buffalo; Elec Engrng.

NATOLI, NOELLE; Onondaga HS; Syracuse, NY; (S); 18/73; Drama Clb; GAA; Hosp Aide; VP Spanish Clb; Chorus; School Play; Yrbk Stf; Trs Soph Cls; Trs Jr Cls; Trs Sr Cls; Fitness Achv Awd; Oswego ST.

NATOLI, ROSE G; Fontbonne Hall Acad; Brooklyn, NY; (Y); Cmnty Wkr; Math Tm; Service Clb; Teachers Aide; Nwsp Stf; Yrbk Stf; Rep Sr Cls; High Hon Roll; NHS; Golden Achvt Awd 81; NY ST Regents Schlrshp 85; Golden Achvt Awd 85; St Johns U; Law.

NAUGHTON, JEANNE M; Scarsdale HS; Scarsdale, NY; (Y); Letterman Clb; PAVAS; School Musical; School Play; Var Cheerleading; Chorus; Variety Show; JV Trk; Lafayette Coll; Law.

NAUMANN, LORI; John H Glenn HS; Greenlawn, NY; (Y); 27/260; JV Vllybl; Hon Roll; Jr NHS; NHS; Pres Schlr; Church Yth Grp; GAA; ROTC; Color Guard; Drill Tm; Italian Hnr Scty 83-85; Natl Hnr Roll 85; Monmouth Coll; Elec Engr.

NAUMOVSKI, ELIZABETH C; Frontier Central SR HS; Blasdell, NY; (Y); 15/495; Church Yth Grp; DECA; Pres Sec French Clb; Band; Color Guard; High Hon Roll; Hon Roll; NHS; Regents Schlrshp 85; U Of Buffalo; Bus Admin.

NAVARRA, JOAN; Albion HS; Albion, NY; (Y); Church Yth Grp; Pres 4-H; Pres FFA; JV Sftbl; 4-H Awd; Rotry Ag Prz 84-85; Dekalb Ag Accmplshmnt Awd 84-85; Alfred Ag/Tech Schl; Hortcltr.

NAVARRO, RICHARD; Clara Barton HS; Brooklyn, NY; (Y); Nwsp Rptr.

NAVAS, TANYA C; Manhasset HS; Manhasset, NY; (Y); Church Yth Grp; Chorus; Orch; School Musical; School Play; Stage Crew; Symp Band; Hon Roll; Kiwanis Awd; SYMS U Of NH Prtl Schlrshp 83; SCASMMR Stdy Awd Europa Coll 84; German.

NAVITSKY, RICHARD; Valley Central HS; Maybrook, NY; (Y); 25/300; Pres Cmnty Wkr; Pres Science Clb; VP Frsh Cls; Pres Soph Cls; VP Jr Cls; Var Capt Socr; French Hon Soc; Hon Roll; NHS; Rotary Awd; Columbia U Sci Hnrs Pgm 85-86; SUNY New Paltz Summr Sci Sessn 84; Mc Gill U; Bio Sci.

NAWROCKI, JOHN K; New Hyde Park Memorial HS; New Hyde Park, NY; (Y); Am Leg Boys St; Cmnty Wkr; Pres Band; Jazz Band; Orch; School Musical; Nwsp Ed-Chief; High Hon Roll; Jr NHS; NHS; Amer Diabts Assn Estrn Rgnl Chrprson & Yth Actn Cmmtte 85-86; Princeton Bk Awds Fnlst 85; Intl Bus.

NEAL, JULIE E; Frontier Central HS; Lakeview, NY; (Y); 69/500; Church Yth Grp; Drama Clb; Latin Clb; Pep Clb; Red Cross Aide; Ski Clb; School Play; Yrbk Stf; Trs Soph Cls; Rep Stu Cncl; Regents Schlrshp; U Of NY-ALBANY; Scl Welfr.

NEAL, LINDA; Maryvale HS; Cheektowaga, NY; (Y); Church Yth Grp; Chorus; Hon Roll; Bus Mgmt.

NEAL, VICTORIA; J C Birdlebough HS; Phoenix, NY; (Y); Cmnty Wkr; Latin Clb; Sec Temple Yth Grp; Stage Crew; Yrbk Stf; Stu Cncl; Var Cheerleading; Hon Roll; Librl Arts.

NEAMAN, KELLI; Tonawanda SR HS; Tonawanda, NY; (Y); 15/212; Ski Clb; Chorus; Cheerleading; Hon Roll; NY ST Regents Schlrshp 85; Pres Acad Ftns Awd 84-85; Siena Coll; Comp Sci.

NEARY, ANGELA; Shenendehowa HS; Clifton Pk, NY; (Y); Church Yth Grp; GAA; Varsity Clb; Sftbl; Vllybl; High Hon Roll; Hon Roll.

NEARY, COLEEN; Nazareth Acad; Rochester, NY; (Y); 24/110; Dance Clb; Intnl Clb; Chorus; School Musical; School Play; Stage Crew; Yrbk Stf; Off Sr Cls; Rep Stu Cncl; Hon Roll; St Elzbth Schl Nrsng; Nrs.

NEARY, ERIN; Union Endicott HS; Endicott, NY; (Y); Exploring; Key Clb; Ski Clb; Spanish Clb; Band; Concert Band; Mrchg Band; Stat Sftbl; Syracuse U; Pre-Med.

NEARY, MICHAEL; Holy Cross HS; Flushing, NY; (Y); 6/365; Art Clb; Nwsp Stf; Var Capt Bsbl; Var Capt Bsktbl; High Hon Roll; NHS; Peer Cnslr; Bus Admn.

NEBAB, CECILIA; Bishop Kearney HS; Brooklyn, NY; (Y); Church Choir; Var Sftbl; Hon Roll; Law.

NEBORG, PATRICK; Dover JR SR HS; Dover Plains, NY; (S); 5/94; Am Leg Boys St; Computer Clb; Drama Clb; Math Tm; Trs Stu Cncl; JV Var Socr; JV Var Trk; High Hon Roll; Jr NHS; NHS; NY ST Rgnts Schlrshp Rcpnt 85; Dutchess CC; Comp Sci.

NEDOSTUP, REBECCA A; Baldwin SR HS; Baldwin, NY; (Y); 4/502; VP Debate Tm; Orch; School Musical; School Play; Pres Lit Mag; Political Wkr; NHS; Ntl Merit Schol; Red Cross Aide; High Hon Roll; Brown U Bk Awd 84; Telluride Assn Smmr Prog Schlrshp 84; Harvard Coll; Pol Sci.

NEE, SAMANTHA; St Vincent Ferrer HS; Jackson Heights, NY; (S); 12/118; Library Aide; Math Tm; Q&S; Church Choir; Nwsp Rptr; Nwsp Stf; Sftbl; Twrlr; Hon Roll; Jr NHS; Supr Perf Cert NEDT 84.

NEEFE, LAURA K; Gates-Chili SR HS; Rochester, NY; (Y); 18/464; French Clb; Hosp Aide; Service Clb; Ski Clb; JV Var Score Keeper; Timer; Twrlr; Wt Lftg; NHS; Ithaca Col Schlrshp 85; Ithaca Coll; Phy Thrpy.

NEEFUS, BRAD J; Mattituck HS; Mattituck, NY; (Y); 29/118; German Clb; JA; Tennis; Hon Roll; NHS; Frnch I Achvt Awd 85; Tenns Lttrs 83-85; Engr.

NEELEY, BRENT; Warsaw Central Schl; Warsaw, NY; (S); 7/93; Cmnty Wkr; Pres Drama Clb; Mathletes; Band; Chorus; Church Choir; Drm Mjr(t); School Play; Hon Roll; NHS; SUNY Geneseo; Math Tchr.

NEENAN, LINDA; Bishop Maginn HS; Albany, NY; (Y); 26/114; Cmnty Wkr; School Play; Cheerleading; Pom Pon; Hon Roll; JCA Schlrshp 85; JC Albany; Secy.

NEET, MICHELE; Guilderland HS; Altamont, NY; (Y); Church Yth Grp; Girl Scts; Band; School Musical; Rep Stu Cncl; JV Var Crs Cntry; Var Capt Trk; Cit Awd; Art Desgn.

NEGBAUR, GARY L; Trinity Schl; New York, NY; (Y); Dance Clb; Pres Debate Tm; Jazz Band; School Musical; School Play; Swing Chorus; Lit Mag; Pres Sr Cls; Cit Awd; Ntl Merit Ltr; Birch Wathan Debate Trnmnt Best Indvl Speaker 82; Harvard U; Hist Of Sci.

NEGINSKY, CLARA; Pearl River HS; Pearl River, NY; (Y); Computer Clb; French Clb; Swmmng; Vllybl; Prfct Atten Awd; Ldrs In Gym 83-85; NYU; Comp Sci.

NEGLEY, JOHN A; Mount Assumption Inst; Syracuse, NY; (Y); Drama Clb; Math Tm; Band; Jazz Band; School Play; Yrbk Bus Mgr; High Hon Roll; NHS; Regents Schlrshp 85; Plattsburgh ST U; Psych.

NEGRI, JIM; Thomas A Edison HS; Horseheads, NY; (Y); French Clb; Ski Clb; Band; Chorus; Concert Band; Jazz Band; Mrchg Band; School Musical; Variety Show; Var Trk; Math.

NEGRIN, BARRY; Roosevelt HS; Yonkers, NY; (S); 1/287; Political Wkr; Band; Bausch & Lomb Sci Awd; High Hon Roll; NHS; Ntl Merit Ltr; Val; Aud/Vis; Office Aide; Mensa Mbr 84-85; Sci Fctn Fntsy Club Pres & Fndr 84-85; The Cooper Union; Engr.

NEGRIN, BRUCE K; New Rochelle HS; New Rochelle, NY; (Y); Church Yth Grp; Varsity Clb; Band; Concert Band; Ed Nwsp Sprt Ed; Yrbk Rptr; Capt JV Bsbl; Capt Ice Hcky; Sftbl; High Hon Roll; All Cnty Awd In Hockey 85; Bus Law.

NEGRON, LISSETTE; John Dewey HS; Brooklyn, NY; (Y); Dance Clb; Drama Clb; FHA; Library Aide; PAVAS; Teachers Aide; Color Guard; School Musical; School Play; Stage Crew; Color Guard Awd 83; Chatter Boy/Nswpr 83; Attndnc Monior Awd 83.

NEGRON, MICHELLE I; Aquinas HS; Bronx, NY; (Y); 15/178; Camera Clb; Debate Tm; Exploring; Hosp Aide; High Hon Roll; Prfct Atten Awd; Gymnstcs Awd; Voluntr Svc; Prfct Atten; European Cultrl Stud Awd; Genl Chem; Coll Of Mount St Vincent; Nrsng.

NEGRON, NADINE; Norman Thomas C HS; New York, NY; (S); VP DECA; Nwsp Rptr; Hon Roll; Dr Leon Levy Mem Schlrshp Awd 85; NY Tech Coll; Htl-Rest Mgt.

NEHRBASS, SHEILA; Dundee HS; Uncasiville, CT; (Y); 15/69; Church Yth Grp; Exploring; Girl Scts; Church Choir; Color Guard; Hon Roll; Gregg Typg Awd 85; Vet.

NEHRING, LAWRENCE; Eden Central HS; Eden, NY; (Y); 40/190; Pres Trs AFS; Boy Scts; Church Yth Grp; Chorus; Concert Band; Jazz Band; Orch; School Musical; JV Var Trk; NHS; AFS Sumr Excng 84; Regnts Schlrshp 85; VMP Trk 85; U Of Rochester.

NEHRKE, KEITH; Haverling HS; Bath, NY; (S); 4/150; AFS; Boy Scts; French Clb; Math Clb; Band; Jazz Band; Stu Cncl; Crs Cntry; High Hon Roll; Pres Schlr; SUNY-BNGHMPTN; Envrnmtl Engr.

NEICE, JEFFREY D; Walton Central HS; Walton, NY; (Y); Var Bsbl; Var Bowling; JV Crs Cntry; High Hon Roll; Hon Roll; NYS Rgnts Schlrshp; Archery; Ldrs Clb; SUNY Delhi NY; Accntng.

NEIDHARDT, JEFFRY; Morrisville-Eaton Central HS; Morrisville, NY; (Y); 1/60; Am Leg Boys St; Pres Varsity Clb; Bsktbl; Capt Ftbl; Tennis; Wt Lftg; Bausch & Lomb Sci Awd; High Hon Roll; NHS; Val; L O Barnes Schlrshp 85; NYS Regnts Schlrshp 85; Hamilton Coll.

NEIDRAUER, KAREN; Chruchville-Chili SR HS; Churchville, NY; (Y); Exploring; Girl Scts; Band; Concert Band; Mrchg Band; Pep Band; Symp Band; Var Tennis; Im Vllybl; Hon Roll; Girl Scout Silver Gold Awd 82-85; NY St Schl Music Assoc 83; Ed.

NEIL, KARIE; Salem Central HS; Salem, NY; (Y); 7/56; Church Yth Grp; French Clb; GAA; Math Tm; Band; Jazz Band; Yrbk Stf; Var Fld Hcky; High Hon Roll; Sec NHS; All County Band; Alfred ST Ag & Tech; Med Lab.

NEILL, ALFRED M; Fairport HS; Fairport, NY; (Y); Boy Scts; Computer Clb; French Clb; Drm & Bgl; Jazz Band; Mrchg Band; Symp Band; Rep Stu Cncl; Hon Roll; Pol Sci.

NEILL, ROBERT; Masscena Central HS; Massena, NY; (Y); Boy Scts; Church Yth Grp; Leo Clb; Nwsp Phtg; Welda; Sci.

NEILS, COLLETTE; Bronx H S Of Science; New York, NY; (Y); Girl Scts; Key Clb; Library Aide; Math Tm; Chorus; Orch; Hon Roll; Prfct Atten Awd; Smmr Actrl Schlrshp Howard U 85; Sr Orch 83; US Coast Grd Acad Proj Mite 85; Accntnt.

NEINER, STEPHEN; Liverpool HS; Liverpool, NY; (S); 196/792; Var L Bsktbl; JV Ftbl; Var L Lcrss; Jr NHS; Natl Latn Exm Awd Wnnr 84; Clarkson; Mgmt.

NEIRO, MARK; New Rochelle HS; New Rochelle, NY; (Y); Church Yth Grp; Model UN; Ski Clb; Rep Jr Cls; JV Capt Lcrss; High Hon Roll; Hon Roll; NHS; Spanish NHS.

NEISE, DON; Spackenkill HS; Poughkeepsie, NY; (Y); 77/172; Var Bsbl; Var Ftbl; Engrng.

NEISON, LINDA; Burnt Hills Ballston Lake HS; Ballston Lake, NY; (Y); 116/316; Church Yth Grp; Girl Scts; Key Clb; Chorus; Sr Cls; Var Bsktbl; Var Sftbl; Var Swmmng; Hon Roll; Russell Sage Coll.

NEISS, THERESA; Union Endicott HS; Binghamton, NY; (Y); French Clb; Key Clb; Lit Mag; Trk; Hon Roll; Bus.

NEJMAN, RACHEL; Clarkstown HS; New City, NY; (Y); Cmnty Wkr; Temple Yth Grp; JV Var Cheerleading; Powder Puff Ftbl; Spcl Olympcs 82-85; Gridiron Clb Awd 82-84.

NEKRITZ, TIMAN; Weedsport JR SR HS; Weedsport, NY; (Y); 9/90; Am Leg Boys St; French Clb; Intnl Clb; Math Tm; Trs Jr Cls; Stat Bsktbl; Var Trk; High Hon Roll; Jr NHS; NHS; Elmire Coll Key Awd 85; Soc Sci.

NELL, JOHN; Mineola HS; Mineola, NY; (Y); Mathletes; Band; Concert Band; Mrchg Band; JV Bsbl; Im Tennis; High Hon Roll; NHS; Prfct Atten Awd; Engrng.

NELL, LISA; Vernon - Verona - Sherrill HS; Venon, NY; (Y); Rep Frsh Cls; Rep Soph Cls; Rep Stu Cncl; Var L Sftbl; Var L Vllybl; NEDT Awd; Phy Thrpy.

NELLER, DAVID; Middletown HS; Middletown, NY; (Y); Computer Clb; FBLA; Yrbk Phtg; Yrbk Stf; Rep Stu Cncl; Hon Roll; Voctnl Ed Achvt Awd 85; Assmbly Of NY Merit Cert 85; Outstndng Voctnl Stu Awd 85; Orange Cnty Comm Coll; Bus.

NELLIS, KIMBERLY; Fort Plain HS; Ft Plain, NY; (Y); Drama Clb; Office Aide; Varsity Clb; Chorus; Stage Crew; Ed Yrbk Rptr; Yrbk Stf; JV Var Bsktbl; JV Var Socr; Var Sftbl; Engl Awd 85; Bus Awd 85; Bryant Stratton; Trvl.

NELLIS, NICOLE; Gloversville HS; Gloversville, NY; (Y); Intnl Clb; Fld Hcky; Mgr(s); Powder Puff Ftbl; Score Keeper; High Hon Roll; Hon Roll; Psychlgy.

NELS, BETH; Liverpool HS; N Syracuse, NY; (Y); 280/874; Church Yth Grp; Hosp Aide; Hon Roll; Nrsg.

NELSEN, DAVID A; Northport HS; East Northport, NY; (Y); 30/646; Am Leg Boys St; Boy Scts; Computer Clb; Science Clb; Var JV Crs Cntry; Var Capt Trk; Cit Awd; NHS; Ntl Merit Ltr; Grumman Schlrshp Comp 85; Eagle Scout 85; Polytech Inst NY; Elec Engr.

NELSON, CARMEN; Pine Valley Central HS; Cherry Creek, NY; (S); 2/60; Chorus; Madrigals; School Musical; Pres Frsh Cls; Trs Soph Cls; Var Capt Cheerleading; Coach Actv; Hon Roll; Jr NHS; NHS; NY ST Rgnts Schlrshp 85; Hgst Ave Math & JR Girl 84; Suny Jamestn Comm Coll; Nrsng.

NELSON, CHARISSE; Martin Luther King JR HS; Bklyn, NY; (Y); Yrbk Stf; Hon Roll; Am Can Intership Awd 84; Young Playwrite Festvl 84; Sec.

NELSON, CHRISTINA L; Lafayette HS; Buffalo, NY; (Y); 2/236; Drama Clb; Mathletes; Thesps; School Play; Stage Crew; Variety Show; Nwsp Ed-Chief; Nwsp Rptr; Nwsp Stf; Lit Mag; Rensselaer Math & Sci Awd; Syracuse U; Jrnlsm.

NELSON, DANIEL; Jamestown HS; Jamestown, NY; (Y); Quiz Bowl; Ski Clb; Spanish Clb; High Hon Roll; Hon Roll; Jr NHS; NHS; Norman B Tinkham Awd Excllnc Amer Hstry 85; Lwyr.

NELSON, DIANE; Windham-Ashland-Jewett Central Schl; Hensonville, NY; (S); 1/42; Church Yth Grp; French Clb; Band; Chorus; Jazz Band; JV Var Cheerleading; Var Trk; JV Var High Hon Roll; Var NHS; Music Comp Awds 82-84; Greene Cty Music Fest Awds 82-84; Trphy Most Imp Rnnr Trck 84; Music.

NELSON, DONNA L; Comsewogue SR HS; Port Jeff Sta, NY; (Y); 80/346; Color Guard; High Hon Roll; Hon Roll; Outstndng Achvt Adv Drwng & Paintg 83-84; SUNY Farmingdale; Art Dir.

NELSON, JEANNE M; Lakeland HS; Yorktown Hts, NY; (Y); 5/370; VP Sec Drama Clb; Hosp Aide; Chorus; Sec Church Choir; Sec Frsh Cls; Trs Jr Cls; Rep Sr Cls; DAR Awd; Sec NHS; Ntl Merit SF; Soc Dstngshd Amer HS Stu 82; Jaycees Awd 84; Hnr Rll 84; Phy Thrpst.

NELSON, JENNIFER; Smithtown HS East; Saint James, NY; (Y); Cmnty Wkr; Dance Clb; GAA; Girl Scts; Chorus; Cheerleading; Hon Roll; Jr NHS; Natl Jr Hnr Scty; Bus Mgmt.

NELSON, JILL; Parishville Hopkinton Central Schl; Parishville, NY; (S); Band; Concert Band; Jazz Band; Mrchg Band; Orch; Pep Band; School Musical; Symp Band; Variety Show; Hon Roll; Amer Mscl Fndtn Band Hnrs 84; Outstndng Music Awds 83-85; Suny Canton; Nrs.

NELSON, KARIN; Fairport HS; Fairport, NY; (Y); Drama Clb; Hosp Aide; Intnl Clb; Boy Scts; School Musical; Rep Stu Cncl; JV Var Tennis; Hon Roll; NHS.

NELSON, KIRK; Jamestown HS; Jamestown, NY; (Y); Jamestown CC; Engrng.

NELSON, MARIA; New Dorp HS; Staten Island, NY; (Y); Camp Fr Inc; Key Clb; Yrbk Phtg; Off Jr Cls; Pom Pon; U Of Bridgeport; Mass Media.

NELSON, MARK; Kenmore West HS; Kenmore, NY; (Y); 6/450; Am Leg Boys St; French Clb; Math Tm; Model UN; School Musical; Variety Show; Yrbk Sprt Ed; Rep Stu Cncl; JV Capt Socr; Voice Dem Awd; Ntl Merit Spcl Schlrshp 85-89; Cornell U; Law.

NELSON, MARK; Lake George HS; Kattskill Bay, NY; (Y); Am Leg Boys St; German Clb; Varsity Clb; Band; Chorus; Jazz Band; School Musical; Rep Stu Cncl; Var Bsbl; Var Socr; Norwich U; Engr.

NELSON, SARAH; Pittsford Sutherland HS; Pittsford, NY; (Y); Church Yth Grp; Church Choir; Yrbk Ed-Chief; High Hon Roll; Hon Roll; Ldrshp Awd PTSA 85; Frgn Exch Stu Swdn 84; Gettysburg Coll; Bus Mgmnt.

NELSON, SHAUNTE; Mt Vernon HS; Mt Veron, NY; (Y); Church Yth Grp; Drama Clb; FBLA; Office Aide; Teachers Aide; Hon Roll; Comp.

NELSON, STEPHANIE A; Cardinal Mooney HS; Rochester, NY; (Y); 16/317; Drama Clb; Latin Clb; Ski Clb; Chorus; Sec Church Choir; School Musical; School Play; Variety Show; Nwsp Bus Mgr; Yrbk Stf; Drama, A P Amer Hist Awds 84; Nat Latin Awd 84; ST Senate Forum 84; Trustees Schlrshp 85; Geneseo ST Coll; Industrl Engr.

NELSON, THEODORE; De Sales HS; Lockport, NY; (Y); Cmnty Wkr; Pres Computer Clb; FCA; Office Aide; Var Bowling; JV Wrstlng.

NELSON, WILLIAM M; Newfane SR HS; Newfane, NY; (S); 2/190; Math Tm; Concert Band; Jazz Band; Pres Mu Alp Tht; NHS; Wnnr Mansfield Univ Mathematics Contest 84; MA Inst Tech; Mathmtcl Physics.

NEMEC, CHRISTINA; Royalton-Hartland Central HS; Gasport, NY; (Y); Church Yth Grp; Dance Clb; Drama Clb; Chorus; School Musical; School Play; Nwsp Stf; Hon Roll; Bryant & Stratton; Bus.

NEMEC, RICHARD S; Miller Place HS; Miller Place, NY; (Y); 19/199; Varsity Clb; Var L Bsbl; Var L Bsktbl; Var L Socr; Hon Roll; NHS; NY ST Regnts Schlrshp 85; Albright Coll; Acctng.

NENNER, MARK A; Shaare Torah HS; Monsey, NY; (Y); Cmnty Wkr; Computer Clb; Political Wkr; Temple Yth Grp; Varsity Clb; School Play; Variety Show; Nwsp Rptr; Nwsp Stf; Yrbk Stf; NY Rgnts Schlrshp 85.

NENTWICH, KEVIN; Sachem HS; Holbrook, NY; (Y); 150/1500; Var Ftbl; JV Lcrss; Pre-Law.

NERROW JR, DAVID J; Colonie Central HS; Schenectady, NY; (Y); 6/475; Boy Scts; Political Wkr; ROTC; Orch; Nwsp Rptr; Pres Stu Cncl; Bsktbl; JV Var Socr; High Hon Roll; NHS; Natl Eagle Scout Schlrshp 85; Navy, Army ROTC Schlrshps 85; Dartmouth Coll; Law.

NERSES, ANNITA; Huntington HS; Huntington, NY; (Y); 5/433; Capt Mathletes; Chorus; Orch; School Musical; Var Cheerleading; High Hon Roll; Jr NHS; NHS; Brd Of Trustees Schlrshp From Polytech Inst Of NY 85; Polytech Inst Of NY; Mech Engr.

NESBETH, NATALIE; Christopher Columbus HS; Bronx, NY; (Y); 4-H; FNA; Church Choir; Vllybl; 4-H Awd; Hon Roll; Prfct Atten Awd; Avista Soc NHS 85; Fundamntls Of Mth 84-85; Hon Spn I & II 84-85; Mth.

NESBITT, JULIE; Cato-Meridian Central HS; Cato, NY; (Y); 12/74; Sec Church Yth Grp; Drama Clb; French Clb; GAA; Library Aide; Office Aide; School Play; JV Fld Hcky; High Hon Roll; Prfct Atten Awd; Robert & Clara Hardy Scholar 85; Houghton; Elem Ed.

NESCI, LISA; Bishop Grimes HS; Liverpool, NY; (Y); Pep Clb; Cheerleading; High Hon Roll; Hon Roll; NCTE Awd; NHS; Acdmc All Am 84-85; US Bus Educ Awd 84-85; CCBI; Bus.

NESTER, GEORGIA; Sauquoit Valley Central HS; Sauquoit, NY; (S); Sec Drama Clb; Pres Chorus; School Musical; School Play; High Hon Roll; Hon Roll; Rotary Awd; JR B Sharp Musical Club 84; Area All St Zone 4 Music Fest 84; Oneida Cnty JR High Music Fest 83; Vocal Performance.

NESTICO, CHRIS; Alden HS; Alden, NY; (Y); Boys Clb Am; French Clb; Ed Yrbk Rptr; Yrbk Stf; Rep Frsh Cls; Bsktbl; Hon Roll; Cvl Engr.

NETHERCOTT, ELAINE; Auburn HS; Auburn, NY; (Y); 17/444; Cmnty Wkr; Model UN; Ski Clb; Varsity Clb; Rep Jr Cls; Var L Socr; Var L Trk; High Hon Roll; NHS; Red Cross Aide; Pres Acad Fit Awd 85; Binghamton ST U; Acctg.

NETO, MARILENE; Dominican Commercial HS; Richmond Hill, NY; (Y); Church Yth Grp; Pep Clb; Church Choir; Off Soph Cls; Off Jr Cls; Off Sr Cls; Off Stu Cncl; Hon Roll; Prfct Atten Awd; Vlnteer Wrk Mntly Retrded 83-85; Med.

NEU, DEBORAH; Nazareth Acad; Rochester, NY; (Y); Red Cross Aide; Spanish Clb; Stage Crew; Yrbk Stf; High Hon Roll; Hon Roll; NHS; Hgh Spn Avg Awd 82-84; Hghst Math Clss Avg Awd 82-83; Comp Sci.

NEU, MICHAEL D; Lancaster Central HS; Lancaster, NY; (Y); Boys Clb Am; Church Yth Grp; FCA; Varsity Clb; Off Stu Cncl; L Var Bsktbl; L Var Ftbl; Var Wt Lftg; Merit Rl 84-85; Bus Admin.

NEUBAUER, JOANN; Villa Maria Acad; Buffalo, NY; (S); 15/112; Trs Church Yth Grp; Hosp Aide; JCL; Yrbk Stf; Rep Stu Cncl; DAR Awd; Hon Roll; VP NHS; Prfct Atten Awd; Pre Med.

NEUBAUER, MARYANN; Villa Maria Acad; Buffalo, NY; (Y); Computer Clb; Math Clb; Spanish Clb; Rep Stu Cncl; High Hon Roll; NHS; Nrsng.

NEUBERGER, Z M; Hunter College HS; Brooklyn, NY; (Y); Dance Clb; Mathletes; Math Clb; Math Tm; Political Wkr; Service Clb; Yrbk Stf; Var Trk; Ntl Merit SF.

NEUFELD, JOSHUA M; Laguardia Hs Of Music & The Arts; Brooklyn, NY; (Y); 95/588; Art Clb; Office Aide; Service Clb; Teachers Aide; Sec Sr Cls; Hon Roll; Art Exhbtd Schl Semi Annl 81-85; Oberlin; Psych.

NEUGEBAUER, JULIE; Ballston Spa HS; Ballston Spa, NY; (Y); 1/217; Am Leg Aux Girls St; Math Tm; Service Clb; Nwsp Rptr; Stat Crs Cntry; Stat Socr; L Tennis; Stat Trk; NHS; Ntl Merit Schol; Leo Plnt Awd 84; Olympics Of Mind Rgnl Chmp 85.

NEULAND, TYRONE; Norwich HS; Norwich, NY; (Y); 41/174; Spanish Clb; Band; Concert Band; Mrchg Band; Symp Band; VP Jr Cls; Rep Stu Cncl; Var JV Bsbl; JV Bsktbl; Var JV Wrstlng; Stu Rotarn 85; Syracuse U; Advtsg Dsgn.

NEUMAIER, KIRSTEN; East Aurora HS; East Aurora, NY; (S); 18/181; AFS; Letterman Clb; Varsity Clb; Orch; School Musical; Var Fld Hcky; JV Var Socr; Tennis; Jr NHS; NHS; Colgate U; Econ.

NEUMAN, CINDY; Royalton Hartland HS; Middleport, NY; (Y); Computer Clb; Yrbk Stf; Bsktbl; Sftbl; Vllybl; MI Bsktbl Plyr 84-85; Perf Attndnc Schl 84-85.

NEUMAN, JEFFREY A; West Islip HS; Bayshore, NY; (Y); Computer Clb; Mathletes; Ski Clb; Hon Roll; Jr NHS; NHS; Acad Decthln Mdls 85; Cmmnctns.

NEUMANN, JOHN; Springville-Griffith Inst; West Falls, NY; (Y); Chorus; Orch; High Hon Roll; NHS; Red Cross Aide; Ntl Math Exmntn Awd Brnz Medl; CRC Pres Chem Awd; NY HS Al-ST Orchstra Violn; Music.

NEUMANN, MICHELE; St Dominic HS; Bethpage, NY; (Y); 16/119; Im Vllybl; High Hon Roll; NHS; K Of C Schlrshp 85; Hnrbl Ment Awd Theolgy 85; SUNY; Bio.

NEUMANN, ROBERT; Irondequoit HS; Rochester, NY; (Y); 22/387; Pres Model UN; Political Wkr; Jazz Band; Pep Band; School Musical; Symp Band; Hon Roll; NHS; Acad All Amer 85; Tech Mgmt.

NEUROTH, SHAWNE; Andover Central HS; Andover, NY; (S); 4/30; GAA; Band; Chorus; School Play; Swing Chorus; Yrbk Ed-Chief; VP Jr Cls; Pres Stu Cncl; Var Capt Cheerleading; Score Keeper; Alfred ST Coll; Exec Secry.

NEUWIRTH, LINDA I; Herbert H Lehman HS; Bronx, NY; (Y); 2/444; Hosp Aide; Yrbk Stf; NHS; Prfct Atten Awd; Sal; Acad Olympics; Stu Of Mnth; Peer Tutoring.

NEVELOFF, DANIEL I; Tottenville HS; Staten Island, NY; (Y); 96/875; Science Clb; Ski Clb; Stage Crew; Sec Sr Cls; JV Ftbl; Hon Roll; NHS; NY ST Regents Schlrshp 85-89; ST U Of NY Albany; Bus.

NEVERETT, MEREDITH A; Chazy Central Rural Schl; Chazy, NY; (Y); 9/49; Hosp Aide; Model UN; Pep Clb; Ski Clb; Sec Yrbk Stf; Rep Stu Cncl; JV Bsktbl; Var Socr; Stat Sftbl; High Hon Roll; Regnts Schlrshp 85; Siera; Acctg.

NEVILLE, LEIGH; Emma Willard Schl; Vienna, VA; (Y); Band; Concert Band; Mrchg Band; Trs Sr Cls; Var Sftbl; Law.

NEVILLE, SHAMUS; Archbishop Molloy HS; Elmhurst, NY; (Y); #36 In Class; JA; Varsity Clb; Jr Cls; Crs Cntry; Trk; Hon Roll; NHS; Rep Frsh Cls; Engrng.

NEVIN, STEPHANIE; Smithtown H S East; St James, NY; (Y); Art Clb; Camera Clb; FBLA; Yrbk Stf; Hon Roll.

NEVINS, DAVID; Haverling HS; Bath, NY; (Y); Ski Clb; Band; Concert Band; Jazz Band; Mrchg Band; Yrbk Stf; JV Var Swmmng; CC Awd; God Cntry Awd; Hon Roll; Eagle Sct 85; Pre Law.

NEVINS, GRACE; Onteora Central HS; Boiceville, NY; (S); Yrbk Stf; Chrmn Stu Cncl; Var Capt Bsktbl; Var Fld Hcky; Var Trk; High Hon Roll; Sec NHS; 1st Team All Leag Fld Hcky & Bsktbl 84-85; MVP Vrsty Bsktbll 85; Gld Mdl ST Fld Hcky 84-85; Engrng.

NEVINS, SEAN; Desales Catholic HS; Wilson, NY; (S); 5/47; Cmnty Wkr; ROTC; Ed Lit Mag; Var L Socr; NHS; NEDT Awd; Spnsh I Awd, Afro-Asian Hist Awd 82; Hlth Awd 83; Cornell U; Vet Med.

NEVOLA, GREGG; West Babylon SR HS; W Babylon, NY; (Y); 8/420; Hosp Aide; Leo Clb; Cit Awd; High Hon Roll; Jr NHS; NHS.

NEWBERGER, KATHY; Longwood HS; Coram, NY; (Y); Key Clb; Quiz Bowl; Speech Tm; Chorus; Orch; School Musical; School Play; Yrbk Bus Mgr; Lit Mag; NHS.

NEWBORN, JOANNE; Bishop Kearney HS; Brooklyn, NY; (S); 50/366; Church Yth Grp; Office Aide; Nwsp Rptr; Rep Sr Cls; Var Bowling; Hon Roll; NHS; N Y ST Rgnts Schlrshp 85; Pace U; Adv.

NEWBURY, PAMELA; Susquehanna Valley HS; Kirkwood, NY; (Y); Church Yth Grp; Drama Clb; GAA; Pep Clb; Varsity Clb; School Musical; Cheerleading; Crs Cntry; Fld Hcky; Trk; NY ST Inst Tech; Archit.

NEWCOMB, JUDY; Niskyuna HS; Schdy, NY; (Y); AFS; French Clb; Cheerleading; Coach Actv; Elem Tchr.

NEWELL, HOPE; Greenville JR SR HS; Greenville, NY; (Y); 17/96; Pep Clb; Trs Spanish Clb; Sec Concert Band; Sec Jazz Band; Pep Band; School Musical; Sec Symp Band; Stat Bsbl; Stat Bsktbl; Trs NHS; Ltr Awd 83; Spartan Excel Awds 84-85; Music Excel Awd 85; SUNY; Vet Sci.

NEWELL, PAULINE; Harry S Truman HS; Bronx, NY; (Y); Girl Scts; JA; Math Clb; Office Aide; Pep Clb; Teachers Aide; Church Choir; School Musical; School Play; Hon Roll; Bus.

NEWKIRK, BETH; Mayfield Central Schl; Mayfield, NY; (Y); VP Church Yth Grp; Drama Clb; Hosp Aide; Teachers Aide; Band; Chorus; Church Choir; Concert Band; Jazz Band; Mrchg Band; Soclgy.

NEWKIRK, DENISE; Mayfield Central HS; Gloversville, NY; (Y); 7/80; Nwsp Rptr; High Hon Roll; Hon Roll; Ntl Merit Ltr; Girl Scts; Library Aide; Nwsp Stf; Soph Cls; Var Socr; Comp Tech.

NEWMAN, ANDREA; Riverdale Country Schl; New York, NY; (Y); Key Clb; Pres Political Wkr; Capt Bsktbl; Capt Sftbl; Capt Vllybl; Ntl Merit SF.

NEWMAN, BETINA ROSE; George W Fawler HS; Syracuse, NY; (Y); Pep Clb; Variety Show; Nwsp Rptr; Nwsp Stf; Rep Frsh Cls; Sec Jr Cls; Rep Stu Cncl; Var Trk; JV Var Vllybl; Outstdng Minorty Stu 85; Spec Recgntn Var Vllybl 85; Spec Recgntn Var Vllybl 84; Embry-Riddle Aeron U; Comp Sci.

NEWMAN, DAWN V; Benjamin N Cardozo HS; Little Neck, NY; (Y); 67/476; Teachers Aide; Pres Temple Yth Grp; School Musical; Regnts Schlrshp 85; Ldrs VP Govrng Brd 84; Brandeis U.

NEWMAN, GREGORY; Athena HS; Rochester, NY; (Y); Pres German Clb; Pres Science Clb; Ski Clb; Varsity Clb; Var Crs Cntry; Var Capt Trk; Hon Roll; NHS; Stu Pilot 84-86; Outstndng German Stu Yr 84-85; MVP Vrsty Trck 85; Aerontcl Engr.

NEWMAN, LORI; Oneida SR HS; Durhamville, NY; (Y); French Clb; Intnl Clb; Latin Clb; Yrbk Stf; Rep Frsh Cls; High Hon Roll.

NEWMAN, RANDY; Valley Stream Central HS; Valley Stream, NY; (Y); Var Capt Ftbl; Lcrss; NHS; Ski Clb; Yrbk Stf; High Hon Roll; Spanish NHS; Pre-Med.

NEWMAN, ROBIN; Notre Dame Schl; New York, NY; (Y); Chess Clb; Drama Clb; Hosp Aide; Stage Crew; Ed Yrbk Ed-Chief; Pres Sr Cls; Var Cheerleading; Tennis; Trk; NHS; NY ST Volunteer Service Awd 84; NY ST Regents Schlrshp Nursing 85; Bryn Mawr; Biology.

NEWTON, CHRIS; Middletown HS; Middletown, NY; (Y); Key Clb; Ski Clb; Mrchg Band; Symp Band; High Hon Roll; NHS; Ntl Merit Ltr; Vrsty Ski Tm 84-85; Mth Awd 82-83; Pre-Med.

NEWTON, CHRISTOPHER A; Corning-Painted Post East HS; Corning, NY; (Y); Math Tm; Quiz Bowl; Thesps; Ed Yrbk Ed-Chief; High Hon Roll; NHS; Prfct Atten Awd; Cmnty Wkr; Drama Clb; Exploring; 5th Pl Mth Cont Alfred U; Natl H S Inst Northwestern U; Ltr Mayor Orgnztn XMAS Parade; Biol Sci.

NEWTON, ERIC C; Akron Central Schl; Akron, NY; (Y); 6/157; Sec Church Yth Grp; Drama Clb; School Play; Var Wrstlng; Bausch & Lomb Sci Awd; NHS; NY ST Regnts Schlrshp 85; Comp Sci.

NEWTON, JOHN; Andrew Jackson HS; Cambria Heights, NY; (Y); 14/488; Computer Clb; Ed Yrbk Stf; Hon Roll; NHS; Ntl Merit Ltr; Chncllrs Roll Hon 85; Natl Hon Soc Secndry Schls 84-85; Phi Beta Sigma Estrn Rgn Schlrshp Awd 85; Queens Coll; Comp Sci.

NEWTON, KEELAN; Akron Central HS; Akron, NY; (Y); 18/135; Church Yth Grp; Drama Clb; French Clb; Chorus; Church Choir; School Musical; Var Fld Hcky; JV Score Keeper; Var Trk; Hon Roll; Bus Adm.

NEWTON, KEITH; Saugerties HS; Saugerties, NY; (Y); Boy Scts; Church Yth Grp; Varsity Clb; Band; Concert Band; Mrchg Band; Symp Band; Socr; High Hon Roll; Hon Roll; Comp Engrng.

NEWTON, MICHAEL; Kensington HS; Buffalo, NY; (Y); Church Yth Grp; Cmnty Wkr; Computer Clb; Mathletes; Yrbk Stf; Var Bsbl; Var Bowling; Sftbl; Hon Roll; Jr NHS; Mgmt.

NEY, DAWN; Watkins Glen HS; Burdett, NY; (S); 17/141; Church Yth Grp; Math Clb; School Play; Stage Crew; Nwsp Ed-Chief; Sec Jr Cls; Sec Sr Cls; JV Vllybl; Cit Awd; NHS; Air Force; Voice Proc.

NG, DIANA; Brooklyn Technical HS; New York, NY; (Y); 24/1139; Hosp Aide; Library Aide; Red Cross Aide; Science Clb; Orch; Yrbk Stf; Lit Mag; Hon Roll; NHS; Biolgcl Sci Awd 85; Manhattan Borough Pres Cert Exc 82; Un Hosp Fund Vol Svc Awd 83; NY U; Lit Wrtr.

NG, EDA; Cathedral HS; New York, NY; (Y); 96/304; FNA; Hosp Aide; NY U; Srgcl Nrs.

NG, FRANK; Aviation HS; Woodside, NY; (Y); 1/509; Mgr Ed Nwsp Stf; NHS; Opt Clb Awd; Columbia U.

NG, KATHALEEN; Forest Hills HS; Middle Village, NY; (Y); 91/881; Church Yth Grp; Cmnty Wkr; Office Aide; Science Clb; Service Clb; Teachers Aide; Chorus; Hon Roll; Kiwanis Awd; Prfct Atten Awd; Sci Fair 2nd Pl 84; Hon Mtn Sci Fair 85.

NG, KENNEY; Stuyvesant HS; New York, NY; (Y); Computer Clb; Debate Tm; Library Aide; Math Clb; Spanish Clb; High Hon Roll; NHS; Ntl Merit Ltr; Pres Schlr; Spanish NHS; Wstnghse Semifnlst 85; Piano Hnrs 82-85; Semifnlst NYC Math Fair 84; MIT; Engrng.

NG, LINDA; Brooklyn Technical HS; New York, NY; (Y); Drama Clb; Office Aide; Chorus; Yrbk Stf; Hon Roll; NHS; Prfct Atten Awd.

NG, ROBERT; Bronx High School Of Science; New York, NY; (Y); Chess Clb; Computer Clb; Math Tm; Teachers Aide; Prfct Atten Awd; Ind Arts Tech Cert Excllnc 85; SUNY Binghamton; Comp Sci.

NG, RUTH; Sheepshead Bay HS; Brooklyn, NY; (Y); Library Aide; Math Tm; Office Aide; Vllybl; Prfct Atten Awd; Baruch-Cuny; Bus Mgmt.

NG, VELMA; New Utrecht HS; Brooklyn, NY; (Y); 1/605; Hosp Aide; Math Tm; School Musical; Nwsp Rptr; Yrbk Rptr; Im Tennis; High Hon Roll; Ntl Merit Ltr; Val; Ntl Ldrshp Serv Awd 85; Ntl Enrgy Found Essay Cont Wnnr 83; Acad All Am Schlr Awd 84.

NGO, ANH; New Burgh Free Acad; Newburgh, NY; (Y); French Clb; Yrbk Stf; High Hon Roll; Hon Roll; Jr NHS; NHS; Opt Clb Awd; Physics.

NGO, BINH; New Utrecht HS; Brooklyn, NY; (Y); Hon Roll; Arista Awd 85.

NGO, HAI; Mount St Joseph Acad; Buffalo, NY; (Y); 3/100; Aud/Vis; Church Yth Grp; Computer Clb; French Clb; Hosp Aide; Math Tm; Radio Clb; Chorus; Church Choir; Stage Crew; Full Tution Nativity Schl 76-81; Tuition Calasanctn Prep Schl 82-84; Resrch Sem Awd 83; ST U NY; Electrncs.

NGUYEN, DAT TAT; Onteora Central HS; West Hurley, NY; (S); 27/243; Exploring; Hon Roll; NHS; Cornell U; Elec Engrng.

NGUYEN, HA T; L C Obourn HS; E Rochester, NY; (Y); 39/109; JV Var Tennis; Cit Awd; Hon Roll; Monroe CC; Accntng.

NGUYEN, HIEN; G Ray Bodley HS; Fulton, NY; (Y); Math Clb; Off Sr Cls; Bsktbl; Vllybl; Am Ed Asstnce Cncl 86-87; Syracuse U; Elec Engrng.

NGUYEN, HOANG; Ci Cero & North Syracuse HS; N Syracuse, NY; (Y); 205/771; JV Var Socr; JV L Wrstlng; Cicero N Syracus HS Merit Awd 83-85; Le Mayne Coll Upward Bnd Prog 84-85; Elec Engr.

NGUYEN, HUONG T; Curtis HS; Staten Island, NY; (Y); 20/328; Math Tm; Badmtn; Hme Eco, Dctrs Hosp & Engl Scnd Lang Awds 85; SUNY At Stony Brook; Bio.

NGUYEN, JEANNE; Roy C Ketcham HS; Wappingers Fls, NY; (Y); Hon Roll; FIT; Fshn Dsgn.

NGUYEN, JOHN HANH; Peekskill HS; Peekskill, NY; (Y); 12/168; Boy Scts; Chess Clb; Cit Awd; High Hon Roll; Hon Roll; Ntl Merit Ltr; St Schlr; Custodial Maintenance Mem Awd 85; Billy Lowey Mem Awd 85; Wmns Clb Peeksill Voc Scholar 85; SUNY Delhi; Draftng.

NGUYEN, JUDY PHUONG-MINHLE; Gates-Chili HS; Rochester, NY; (S); 4/463; VP JA; Mathletes; Trs Jr Cls; Trs Sr Cls; Im Vllybl; High Hon Roll; NHS; Prfct Atten Awd; Acad Excel Awd Trigonometry & Precalculius 83-84; Acad Excel Awd Eng & Bio 83; Excel Awd Organ 82; Cornell; Medicine.

NGUYEN, MAI; Cicero North Syracuse HS; N Syracuse, NY; (Y); French Clb; French Hon Soc; Prfct Atten Awd; Merit Achvt Awds 81-83; Syracuse U; Bus.

NGUYEN, MARY; Seton Catholic Central HS; Johnson City, NY; (S); French Clb; Ski Clb; Outstndng Stu 83.

NGUYEN, QUOC; Tottenville HS; Staten Island, NY; (Y); Church Yth Grp; Socr; Vllybl; Hon Roll; Karate Awd 82-83; Mayor Koch Cert Merit 84; MVP Sccr Awd; Engr.

NGUYEN, TOAN D; East HS; Rochester, NY; (Y); Am Leg Boys St; Hon Roll; Prfct Atten Awd; Schlrshp Fund Chldrn Memrl 84-85; RIT; Engrng.

NIBLOCK, LORETTA; North Babylon SR HS; N Babylon, NY; (Y); DECA; Mgr Office Aide; Teachers Aide; J J Newberry Awd 85; Farmingdale; Secy.

NICASTRO, JOANNE; Waterloo SR HS; Waterloo, NY; (Y); 39/169; FTA; Library Aide; Ski Clb; Flag Corp; Nwsp Ed-Chief; Yrbk Stf; Var Stat Socr; High Hon Roll; Hon Roll; Prfct Atten Awd; Advnc Plcmnt Histry 83-84; Air Force; Nrs.

NICHOL, JUDENE; Liverpool HS; Liverpool, NY; (S); Aud/Vis; Cmnty Wkr; Hosp Aide; JA; Nwsp Rptr; Stu Cncl; Sftbl; High Hon Roll; Hon Roll; Jr NHS; NY ST Regents 84; Educ.

NICHOLAS, MARIA; Ward Melville HS; S Setauket, NY; (Y); 239/760; Church Yth Grp; Dance Clb; French Clb; Band; Chorus; Concert Band; Mrchg Band; Symp Band; Yrbk Phtg; High Hon Roll; Acad Perf Schlrshp 85; Long Island U; Acctng.

NICHOLAS, VICTORIA; Lansingburgh HS; Troy, NY; (S); Trs French Clb; Varsity Clb; Chorus; Yrbk Stf; Trs Frsh Cls; JV Cheerleading; Var Socr; Var Trk; Cit Awd; High Hon Roll; Typng Awd 84; Phy Ed Awd 83; Math.

NICHOLLS, RENEE; St Joseph HS; Brooklyn, NY; (Y); 16/115; Church Yth Grp; Speech Tm; Band; Variety Show; Yrbk Stf; VP Stu Cncl; Var Cheerleading; Hon Roll; Library Aide; Math Tm; The Golden Rcrd Of Achv Awd 85; Long Island U; Law.

NICHOLS, ADRIANNE L; Livonia Central HS; Geneseo, NY; (Y); Ski Clb; Yrbk Stf; Socr; Sftbl; Trk; Alfred ST Clg; Nrsg.

NICHOLS, ANNETTE; Avon Central Schl; Avon, NY; (Y); 25/104; Church Yth Grp; 4-H; Chorus; School Play; Nwsp Ed-Chief; Socr; Swmmng; Hon Roll; NHS; Roberts Weslyan Coll; Acctng.

NICHOLS, CHRIS; Royalton Hartland HS; Gasport, NY; (Y); 4-H; Sec Frsh Cls; Capt Cheerleading; Capt Sftbl; 4-H Awd; Hon Roll; Prfct Atten Awd; Sec.

NICHOLS, DEBRA; Ringhamton HS; Johnson City, NY; (Y); Church Yth Grp; Computer Clb; French Clb; Girl Scts; Key Clb; Chorus; High Hon Roll; Hon Roll; Prfct Atten Awd; Spllg Awd Easter Seal Troph 82; Nrs.

NICHOLS, KEVIN; Archbishop Molloy HS; Brooklyn, NY; (Y); 23/409; Var Crs Cntry; Var Trk; Hon Roll; NHS.

NICHOLS, KRISTINE; Moore Catholic HS; Staten Island, NY; (Y); Intnl Clb; Yrbk Stf; Tennis; High Hon Roll; Hon Roll; Pharm.

NICHOLS, PAUL; C A Bouton HS; Voorheesville, NY; (Y); Church Yth Grp; Key Clb; Ski Clb; Concert Band; Jazz Band; Nwsp Ed-Chief; Trs Soph Cls; Pres Jr Cls; Pres Stu Cncl; JV Var Ftbl; Bus Admin.

NICHOLS, PAUL; Stockbridge Valley HS; Munnsville, NY; (S); 2/48; Boy Scts; Math Clb; Math Tm; Science Clb; Varsity Clb; Yrbk Sprt Ed; VP Frsh Cls; Pres Sr Cls; Bsbl; Bsktbl; Regents Schlrshp; Syracuse U; Engrng.

NICHOLS, SUSAN; Cazenovia HS; Cazenovia, NY; (Y); 35/155; Jazz Band; Symp Band; Var L Fld Hcky; Var L Sftbl; Hon Roll; Am Leg Aux Girls St; Exploring; Girl Scts; Orch; School Musical; Girl Sct Wider Opprtnty 83; All Star Fld Hcky Tm 84; Biol.

NICHOLSEN, GEORGANN; Holy Trinity Diocesan HS; Westbury, NY; (Y); Math Clb; Math Tm; Stage Crew; Mu Alp Tht; Comm L Kreyer Mem Hist Awd 81; Albany ST U.

NICHOLSON, STEVE E; Paul V Moore HS; Constantia, NY; (Y); 100/300; Exploring; Var L Ftbl; JV Var Golf; Hon Roll; Canton ATC; Comp Engr.

NICHOLSON, SUSAN M; Fayetteville Manlius HS; Fayetteville, NY; (Y); 62/336; Sec Church Yth Grp; Concert Band; Orch; School Musical; Var L Bsktbl; Var Capt Socr; Var L Trk; NHS; Rotary Awd; St Schlr; Clarence E Gaffey Memrl Awd 85; Vrsty Grls Sccr 85; Mst Imprvd Athlt 85; St Bonaventure U; Elem Eductn.

NICHOLSON, THOMAS; Bishop Cunningham HS; Oswego, NY; (S); Computer Clb; French Clb; Yrbk Phtg; Yrbk Sprt Ed; Rep Frsh Cls; VP Soph Cls; VP Jr Cls; Rep Stu Cncl; JV Var Bsbl; VP Ftbl; US Army Schlrshp Wnnr 85; Var Ice Hockey MVP 85; Le Moyne Syracuse; Psych.

NICHOLSON, WYNSTELLE SIMONE; Longwood HS; Coram, NY; (Y); Dance Clb; Girl Scts; Chorus; School Musical; Variety Show; Co-Capt Cheerleading; JV Pom Pon; Hon Roll; Intl Bus.

NICIU, CHRISTIN M; Ward Melville HS; E Setauket, NY; (Y); 37/760; Jazz Band; Mrchg Band; Symp Band; Lit Mag; High Hon Roll; Jr NHS; NHS; Ntl Merit Ltr; Band; Concert Band; NYS Regents Schlrshp 85; Walton Acad Schlrshp Albright Coll 85; Albright Coll; Math.

NICKDOW, JAMES B; Valley Stream Central HS; Valley Stream, NY; (Y); Aud/Vis; Boy Scts; Church Yth Grp; Bowling; SUNY Farmingdale; Elec Eng Tec.

NICKEL, CONNIE; Spackenkill HS; Poughkeepsie, NY; (Y); Church Yth Grp; Drama Clb; Temple Yth Grp; Orch; School Musical; School Play; Var Trk; JV Var Vllybl; NHS; NYSSMA Music Awd 83; Hnrbl Ment All Star Vlybl Team 85; Kings Coll; Phy Educ.

NICKEL, JEFFREY; Bethlehem Central HS; Delmar, NY; (Y); Church Yth Grp; Model UN; Band; Church Choir; Concert Band; Jazz Band; School Musical; Symp Band; High Hon Roll; Hon Roll; Area All St Band 84; NYSSMA Comp 80-84; All St Band 85; Mech.

NICKENS, ROSE; Riverhead HS; Riverhead, NY; (Y); Fld Hcky; Sftbl; JV Var Vllybl; Hon Roll; Prfct Atten Awd; Berkeley.

NICKLA, NANCY G; Smithtown HS West; Smithtown, NY; (Y); Trs Church Yth Grp; Lit Mag; Stu Cncl; Capt Tennis; NHS; Ntl Merit Ltr; Spanish NHS; Prsdntl Acad Fitnss Awd 85; Rgnts Schlrshp 85; Lafayette Coll; Engrng.

NICKLAS, PATRICIA; The Academy Of St Joseph; Islip, NY; (Y); Library Aide; Science Clb; Service Clb; Teachers Aide; Stage Crew; Variety Show; Pres Soph Cls; VP Stu Cncl; Var Badmtn; Var Vllybl; 1st Pl Spnsh Postr Cntst; Ldrshp Conf ISLI At Norr Dame U; Funnst Act Vrty Shw; Eco.

NICKOLA, CHRISTINE; Salamanca Central HS; Salamanca, NY; (S); 13/130; DECA; Girl Scts; Spanish Clb; Yrbk Stf; Off Sr Cls; Var L Sftbl; Var L Vllybl; High Hon Roll; NHS; Spanish NHS; Mrktng.

NICKOLA, KATHLEEN; Salamanca HS; Salamanca, NY; (S); 32/130; DECA; Girl Scts; Spanish Clb; Chorus; Mrchg Band; Yrbk Stf; Hon Roll; NHS; Spanish NHS; Nrsg Hm 83-84; Bus Mgmnt.

NICLAS, KIMBERLY; Mohonasen SR HS; Schenectady, NY; (Y); 32/225; Cmnty Wkr; Key Clb; Color Guard; Drill Tm; Mrchg Band; Twrlr; High Hon Roll; Hon Roll; Pres Schlr; Mst Outstndng Bus Stu 85; SUNY Albany; Acctng.

NICLAS, TANIA; Mohonasen SR HS; Schenectady, NY; (Y); Church Yth Grp; Cmnty Wkr; High Hon Roll; Hon Roll; Yth Awd 85.

NICOLAISEN, KRISTA; Oneida HS; Oneida, NY; (Y); Cmnty Wkr; Debate Tm; Exploring; Band; Mrchg Band; Pep Band; Stage Crew; Yrbk Stf; Rep Stu Cncl; High Hon Roll; Rotary Critical Issues Conf 86; Psych.

NICOLAS, WOODY; Christ The King HS; Queens Village, NY; (Y); 135/377; Rep Frsh Cls; JV Gym; Engr.

NICOLELLIS, DEBORAH L; Longwood HS; Yaphank, NY; (Y); 20/545; VP Pres Exploring; Girl Scts; Pres Intnl Clb; Key Clb; School Musical; High Hon Roll; NHS; Rotary Awd; St Schlr; Chorus; Rotary Yuth Exc Stu Mexico 83-84; Exc Grade NY St Schl Music 82-83; Boston U; Intl Bus.

NICOLELLIS, KEVIN; Longwood HS; Yaphank, NY; (Y); Boy Scts; Computer Clb; Pres Exploring; Band; Concert Band; Mrchg Band; Hon Roll; Comp Sci.

NICOLETTA, GINA; Newark SR HS; Newark, NY; (Y); Aud/Vis; Cmnty Wkr; Dance Clb; French Clb; Chorus; Swing Chorus; Nwsp Stf; Lit Mag; Im Vllybl; French Hon Soc; Sec Natl Hnr Soc 85-86; Prsntatn Concord Resort Hotel For ACTION Chapter 84-85; Intl Bus.

NICOLETTI, PAM; Niagara Falls HS; Niagara Falls, NY; (Y); Church Yth Grp; Girl Scts; Political Wkr; Yrbk Stf; Cheerleading; Coach Actv; Hon Roll; Jr NHS; First Class Citn 82; Silvr Awd Girl Scts 82; Marian Medl 84.

NICOLICH, LINDA; St Francis Prep; Bayside, NY; (S); 20/693; Church Yth Grp; NFL; Speech Tm; Chorus; Vllybl; High Hon Roll; Jr NHS; NHS; Bus.

NICOLL, HOWARD; W C Mepham HS; N Bellmore, NY; (Y); VP Pres Drama Clb; Acpl Chr; Chorus; School Musical; School Play; Nwsp Stf; VP Frsh Cls; Im Bsktbl; Im Socr; NHS; U Of MI; Bus.

NICOSIA, GRACE; Bishop Kearney HS; Brooklyn, NY; (Y); Dance Clb; Yrbk Stf; Cheerleading; Hon Roll; NHS; St Josephs Coll Grnt 85; NY U; Corp Lwyr.

NICOSIA, LORI; Our Lady Of Perpetual Help HS; Brooklyn, NY; (Y); Aud/Vis; FBLA; Office Aide.

NIEDERBERGER, KEN; Farmingdale HS; Farmingdale, NY; (Y); 28/645; Church Yth Grp; Computer Clb; German Clb; Varsity Clb; Mrchg Band; Var L Lcrss; JV L Socr; Wrstlng; High Hon Roll; Jr NHS; La Crosse All Cnty, All Leag, Long Islnd Team, Empire ST Comp 85; Engr.

NIELI, MARY JANE; Lindenhurst HS; Lindenhurst, NY; (Y); Chess Clb; Sec Debate Tm; Key Clb; Speech Tm; Yrbk Stf; NHS.

NIELSEN, MAUREEN; Webster SR HS; Webster, NY; (Y); 45/562; Sec Church Yth Grp; Cmnty Wkr; Y-Teens; Band; Chorus; Church Choir; Nwsp Rptr; Yrbk Ed-Chief; NHS; Drama Clb; YMCA Yth Of Yr; German Hnr Soc; Elaine Kent Schlrshp; Springfield Colge; YMCA Prof.

NIELSEN, TINA; Wheatland-Chili/Penfield HS; Penfield, NY; (Y); Exploring; Library Aide; Hon Roll; Pol Sci.

NIELSON, CHRISTINE; Whitesboro SR HS; Marcy, NY; (Y); Orch; Hon Roll; Jr NHS; NHS; Rochester Inst; Engrg.

NIEMANN, ANDREW J; Mineola HS; Mineola, NY; (Y); Aud/Vis; CAP; Exploring; Hosp Aide; Stage Crew; Trk; High Hon Roll; Aerospc Engrng.

NIEMEYER, GINA; Waterloo SR HS; Waterloo, NY; (Y); Intnl Clb; Letterman Clb; VP Spanish Clb; Varsity Clb; Chorus; JV Var Cheerleading; L Trk; Hon Roll; Ntl Hnr Rl 85; All ST Chours 82; Ensem 83-85; Math.

NIERER, CYNTHIA; Dominican Commercial HS; Bellerose, NY; (Y); 12/200; Hosp Aide; Spanish Clb; Jr NHS; Washington Wrkshp Congrsm Schlrshp 84-85; Prncpls List GPA Awd 82-85; St Johns U; Law.

NIESE, KELLY A; Fayetteville-Manlius HS; Manlius, NY; (Y); 62/332; JCL; Var L Socr; Var Trk; JV Cmnty Wkr; Hon Roll; Regents Schlrshp 85; Natl Latin Exam Awd Cum Laude 82-83; Alfred U; Engr.

NIEVES, ALEX; Brooklyn Technical HS; New York, NY; (Y); Hon Roll; Chem.

NIEVES, ANNA; Brentwood H S Ross; Brentwood, NY; (Y); 34/625; Cmnty Wkr; Computer Clb; Girl Scts; Hosp Aide; Teachers Aide; Nwsp Rptr; Nwsp Stf; High Hon Roll; Hon Roll; Jr NHS; Scottish Rite Schlrshp; Adelante Sfflk Cnty Schlrshp 85; SUNY-STONY Brook; Engl Tchr.

NIEVES, CORINNE; Murry Bergtraum HS; Brooklyn, NY; (Y); Cheerleading; Swmmng; Tennis; Twrlr; Achvt Awd Comp Sci 85; Pace U; Comp Pgmmng.

NIEVES, ELIZABETH; Mabel Dean Bacon V HS; Bronx, NY; (S); 10/299; Chorus; Church Choir; Color Guard; Nwsp Ed-Chief; Prfct Atten Awd; Hnr Soc Co-Pres 84-85; Super Youth Awd 83 & 84; Pace U; Bus Admin.

NIEVES, FIRGIA; Sarah J Hale HS; Brooklyn, NY; (Y); Red Cross Aide; Spanish Clb; School Play; Nwsp Rptr; Lit Mag; Sec Frsh Cls; Pres Soph Cls; Hon Roll; Spanish NHS; Regents Schlrshp 85; Engr.

NIEVES, LILIAN; John F Kennedy HS; New York, NY; (Y); Prfct Atten Awd; Conselor Yr Awd 85; NY City Tech Coll; Nrs.

NIEVES, MARIA; Walton HS; Bronx, NY; (S); 4/679; Yrbk Stf; NHS; Cert Merit Geom, Hist & Engl 83-84; Pre-Med.

NIEVES, NANCY M; John Jay SR HS; Fishkill, NY; (Y); Dance Clb; Debate Tm; Hon Roll; Chorus; Rep Frsh Cls; Rep Soph Cls; Cheerleading; Erly Coll Attndnc Prog 85; Berkeley Schl; Legl Secy.

NIEVES, TARA; Warwick Valley HS; Warwick, NY; (Y); 17/201; Church Yth Grp; Drama Clb; Girl Scts; Math Tm; Stage Crew; Yrbk Stf; Sr Cls; JV Var Socr; Stat Swmmng; High Hon Roll; Elem Schl Vlntr 82-85; Psychlgy.

NIKAS, ARTHUR; Bethpage HS; Bethpage, NY; (Y); 104/350; Boys Clb Am; German Clb; Political Wkr; Ski Clb; Variety Show; Pres Stu Cncl; JV Bsktbl; JV Ftbl; Var Capt Lcrss; Var Wt Lftg; Pres Stu Cncl 85-86; MVP Defnsemn 84; Grmn Clb & Itln Soc; Elec Engrng.

NIKOLAIDIS, THOMAS; St Francis Prep; Jackson Hts, NY; (S); Science Clb; High Hon Roll; Rgnts Schlrshp 85; Manhattan Coll Schlrshp 85; Manhattan Coll; Comp Inf Sys.

NIKOLATOS, ANDREW; Poughkeepsie HS; Poughkeepsie, NY; (Y); 22/195; Church Yth Grp; Computer Clb; High Hon Roll; Hon Roll; Ntl Merit Ltr; Prfct Atten Awd; Fl Inst Of Tech; Comp Engr.

NIKOLITS, STEPHEN A; Hackley Schl; Pleasantville, NY; (Y); 7/87; Debate Tm; Hosp Aide; Key Clb; Model UN; Political Wkr; Jazz Band; Im Ice Hcky; Var Tennis; High Hon Roll; Ntl Merit Ltr; Williams Coll; Polt Sci.

NIKSTENAS, JOSEPH E; Amsterdam HS; Amsterdam, NY; (Y); 12/312; Boy Scts; Pres Church Yth Grp; JA; Band; Church Choir; Concert Band; Mrchg Band; Rep Frsh Cls; High Hon Roll; Hon Roll; Carrier Of Yr Awd 83; Hghst Fund Raiser MDA Dance A Thon 84; Elec Engrng.

NILES, BROOKE; Hoosick Falls Central Schl; Eagle Bridge, NY; (Y); 23/101; 4-H; French Clb; Ski Clb; Sec Frsh Cls; VP Soph Cls; VP Jr Cls; Stu Cncl; Var Capt Bsktbl; JV Var Fld Hcky; Var Capt Sftbl; Outstndng Stu Awd 84; Wmns Sprts Fndtn HS All Star Awd 85; Bus Adm.

NILES, DAVID A; La Salle Inst; Averill Park, NY; (Y); 4/80; Drama Clb; ROTC; Chorus; Concert Band; Drill Tm; Jazz Band; Rep Soph Cls; High Hon Roll; NHS; Ntl Merit Ltr; Williams Coll; Pol Sci.

NILES, ELIZABETH; Newark Valley HS; Neward Valley, NY; (Y); 7/120; Church Yth Grp; German Clb; Red Cross Aide; Varsity Clb; Sec Stu Cncl; Var Capt Bsktbl; Var Capt Crs Cntry; Var Trk; High Hon Roll; JETS Awd; TC3 HS Comptn 84-85; Ntl Yth Ldrshp Cncl 85; U Of Rochester; Optcl Engrng.

NILES, MARK; Greece Athena HS; Rochester, NY; (Y); Boy Scts; Church Yth Grp; Ski Clb; Band; Ftbl; God Cntry Awd; Hon Roll; MCC; Electrical Engrng.

NILES, SHARLEEN; Mc Graw Central Schl; Mc Graw, NY; (Y); 2/59; Sec 4-H; Pres French Clb; Pres Band; Trs Chorus; Yrbk Rptr; Pres Stu Cncl; Capt Sftbl; High Hon Roll; NHS; Sal; Delta Kappa Gamma Soc Schlrhshp 85; Rgnts Schlrshp 85; NY Telephone Schlrshp 85; SUNY Cortland NY; Elem Ed.

NILES, TAMI; Perry Central HS; Perry, NY; (Y); Library Aide; Pep Clb; Chorus; Stage Crew; Nwsp Rptr; Nwsp Stf; Vllybl; Hon Roll; Arlngtn U TX; Jrnlsm.

NILL, JOLAIN; Westhampton Beach HS; E Quoque, NY; (Y); 11/242; French Clb; Band; Chorus; Concert Band; School Musical; Stu Cncl; Cheerleading; Trk; NHS; SADD.

NILSEN, STEPHEN; St John The Baptist HS; Ronkonkoma, NY; (Y); Chess Clb; MMM; Band; Concert Band; Jazz Band; Mrchg Band; High Hon Roll; Hon Roll; Jr NHS; Bio Med Engrng.

NING, CHAO HUI; Seward Park HS; New York, NY; (Y); 1/35; Cit Awd.

NINOMIYA, KENNETH; Aviation HS; New York, NY; (Y); Boy Scts; Debate Tm; Drama Clb; Library Aide; Chorus; School Musical; School Play; Stage Crew; Variety Show; Lincoln Douglass Debt Schlrshp 84; Perfrmg Arts.

NINOS, NIKOLAS J; Alfred Almond Central Schl; Alfred, NY; (Y); Am Leg Boys St; Church Yth Grp; Computer Clb; Latin Clb; Letterman Clb; Yrbk Stf; VP Sr Cls; Rep Stu Cncl; L Crs Cntry; Capt L Socr; Engrng.

NIQUETTE, CINDY SUE; Cambridge Csentral HS; Buskirk, NY; (Y); Yrbk Stf; JV Cheerleading; JV Fld Hcky; JV Vllybl; Regents Schlrshp 85; Elmira Coll.

NIR, DROR N; Ramaz Upper Schl; Flushing, NY; (Y); Cmnty Wkr; Office Aide; Political Wkr; Teachers Aide; Temple Yth Grp; Band; Capt Ftbl; Mgr Var Sftbl; Rgnts Schlrshp 84; Queens Coll; Law.

NISANIAN, ANAHID JAQUELLINE; Forest Hills HS; Sunnyside, NY; (Y); 85/881; Exploring; Library Aide; Teachers Aide; Orch; High Hon Roll; Prfct Atten Awd; Cert Awd Sci Fair & Exhibtn 84; Amer Inst Sci & Tech NYC; Cert Partcptn Sci Proj Schl Sci Fair 85; Med.

NISHIDA, MIHO; Woodlands HS; White Plains, NY; (Y); Debate Tm; Math Tm; School Musical; Var Tennis; Hon Roll; NHS; Stu Mnth Awd 84; Spec Comm Awd Debate 84-85; Vol Election Hlpr 84; Elect Engrng.

NISSAN, EDNA; Herricks SR HS; New Hyde Park, NY; (S); 43/306; Sec DECA; Girl Scts; Key Clb; Library Aide; School Musical; Hon Roll; Voice Dem Awd; Gnrl & Apprl Mrchndng DECA 1st Pl 84-85; 2nd Pl Mrchndng Math DECA 84; Bus Admin.

NISSMAN, LARRY; Blind Brook HS; Rye Brook, NY; (Y); Jazz Band; Orch; Music.

NISTICO, CARMELLA N; Whitesboro SR HS; Whitesboro, NY; (Y); Art Clb; Dance Clb; Spanish Clb; Yrbk Stf; Lit Mag; Capt JV Bsktbl; Powder Puff Ftbl; Hon Roll; Mohawk Valley CC; Psych.

NIVER, TIM; Victor Central HS; Victor, NY; (Y); Band; Concert Band; Drm & Bgl; Mrchg Band; Orch.

NIVER, TIMOTHY; Victor Central HS; Victor, NY; (Y); Band; Concert Band; Drm & Bgl; Mrchg Band; Orch.

NIWLAYSEN, ANDREW; Mineola HS; Mineola, NY; (Y); Hst Church Yth Grp; FBLA; Sec Trs Key Clb; Service Clb; Spanish Clb; Rep Jr Cls; Rep Sr Cls; JV Bowling; Variety Show; Rep Frsh Cls; Hugh O Brian Smnr 84; Mst Outstndg JR Awd 85; Math Sympsm 83-84; Hofstra; Acctng.

NIXON, CHARLES; Iona Prep Schl; Yonkers, NY; (Y); Art Clb; Dance Clb; Library Aide; Varsity Clb; Bsktbl; Crs Cntry; Trk; Wt Lftg; High Hon Roll; Hon Roll; Bio.

NIXON, PAUL; Mohonasen HS; Schenectady, NY; (Y); VP Key Clb; Yrbk Stf; Var Bowling; JV Var Ftbl; Var Trk; High Hon Roll; Hon Roll; NHS.

NIXON, SHEILA; North Babylon SR HS; N Babylon, NY; (Y); 350/560; Girl Scts; Varsity Clb; VICA; Var Gym; Var Trk; Gym Commnty Schl 81-83; Sullivan Comm Coll; Cosmo.

NJAPA, MARY; St Gabriel HS; Bronx, NY; (Y); 14/61; Hosp Aide; Drama Clb; Lehman Coll; Pedtrcn.

NOBBS, TOBI; Southwestern Central Schl; Jamestown, NY; (Y); Church Yth Grp; FCA; Pres JA; Letterman Clb; Office Aide; Quiz Bowl; Varsity Clb; Band; Concert Band; School Musical; US Marine Corps Distgshd Athlte Awd 85; Sftbl, Bsktbl Div 1 All Star 85; Syracuse U; Sports Psych.

NOBLE, CHERYL; Acad Of St Joseph; Bay Shore, NY; (Y); Art Clb; Church Yth Grp; Hosp Aide; Church Choir; Variety Show; Yrbk Stf; Pres Sr Cls; NHS; Nwsp Rptr; Eng Achvt Awd 83; Chrstn Courtesy Awd 84; Art Achvt Awd 84 & 85; Spec Ed.

NOBLE, DIANA E; Waterford-Halfmoon HS; Waterford, NY; (Y); 4/90; 4-H; Math Clb; Yrbk Phtg; Yrbk Stf; 4-H Awd; Hon Roll; Sec NHS; Ntl Merit SF; NEDT Awd; Anthrplgy.

NOBLE, JENNIFER; Mineola HS; Mineola, NY; (Y); Key Clb; Mrchg Band; Nwsp Rptr; Yrbk Stf; Rep Stu Cncl; High Hon Roll; NHS; Band; Concert Band; Var Capt Bowling; Vllybl All Cnty Vrsty Capt 84-85; Bwlg All Cnty Membr Champ ST Tm 83-85; Sftbl All Leag Vrsty Capt 85; Pre-Med.

NOBLE, JOHN E; Watertown HS; Watertown, NY; (Y); Exploring; Capt Golf; High Hon Roll; NHS; Williams Coll Bk Awd 85; Athl Awd 84-85; Math Awd 83-84; U Of Rochester; Chem.

NOBLE, KRISTAN; Houghton Acad; Belmont, NY; (Y); 5/28; VP Church Yth Grp; Teachers Aide; Chorus; Yrbk Stf; Sec Frsh Cls; Im Badmtn; JV Vllybl; High Hon Roll; Jr NHS; NHS; Houghton Coll; Gen Sci.

NOBLE, MARK; Bishop Grimes HS; Syracuse, NY; (Y); FBLA; Ski Clb; Var Crs Cntry; Im Ftbl; Var Trk; High Hon Roll; Hon Roll; Math.

NOBLE, MISHELLE R; Somers HS; Mahopac, NY; (Y); 3/213; AFS; Church Yth Grp; Drama Clb; Intnl Clb; Band; Chorus; Madrigals; Orch; School Musical; School Play; SS Stu Of Mnth 82; Rgnts Schlrshp 85; Holy Cross Coll; Bio.

NOBLES, SHEILA; Caledonia-Mumford Central Schl; Scottsville, NY; (Y); Art Clb; Trs French Clb; Math Tm; Science Clb; High Hon Roll; Hon Roll; NHS; Rotary Awd; St Martins Schl Lond VK; Art.

NOCELLA, STEVE L; Sewanhaka HS; Franklin Square, NY; (Y); 27/300; Am Leg Boys St; Exploring; Hosp Aide; Variety Show; VP Stu Cncl; Bsbl; Bsktbl; Ftbl; Hon Roll; NHS; Engrng.

NOCERA, MELISSA; Frontier Central HS; Blasdell, NY; (Y); 89/500; FBLA; Office Aide; High Hon Roll; Hon Roll; NHS; H H Clifton Am Leg 85; Erie CC; Data Proc.

NOCERA, MICHAEL; Kenmore East HS; Tonawanda, NY; (Y); Debate Tm; Math Tm; Quiz Bowl; Radio Clb; Ski Clb; Speech Tm; School Musical; JV Ftbl; Cmnctns.

NOCHLIN, KAYLEE; Shulamith HS; New York, NY; (Y); Yrbk Stf; Pres Stu Cncl; Bausch & Lomb Sci Awd; Hon Roll; Nrsng Schlrshp Awd 84; Hunter Coll; Phy Thrpy.

NOCILLA, CHARLES; Martin Van Buren HS; Bayside, NY; (Y); 130/621; Chorus; Nwsp Rptr; Nwsp Stf; JV Bsktbl; Bowling; Regents Schlrshp 85; Queens Coll; Accntnt.

NOCITO, KENNETH; Rome Free Acad; Rome, NY; (Y); Am Leg Boys St; Concert Band; Jazz Band; Var Socr; Hon Roll; Italn Amer Essy Cntst Awd 82; Pres All Cnty Ldrshp Clb 83; NYSSMA Solo & Qrtet Awds 83 & 85; Clarkson U; Elctrcl Engrng.

NOEL, BRIGITTE; Catholic Central HS; Troy, NY; (Y); French Clb; Hosp Aide; Office Aide; Teachers Aide; Church Choir; School Play; Variety Show; Var Pom Pon; High Hon Roll; Hon Roll; Mth 10 Regents Awd; Phrmcy.

NOEL, TERRENCE; Brooklyn Tech HS; Bronx, NY; (Y); Boys Clb Am; Computer Clb; Comp Sci.

NOEL, TINA; G Ray Bodley HS; Fulton, NY; (Y); Office Aide; Band; Color Guard; Concert Band; Mrchg Band; JV Bsktbl; Var Trk; Hon Roll; Crafton Hills CA; Bus.

NOELLER, THOMAS; Frontier Central HS; Hamburg, NY; (S); Math Tm; Concert Band; Jazz Band; Yrbk Stf; High Hon Roll; NHS; Ntl Hist,Gov Awd 85; Rensselaer Math,Sci Awd 85; Med.

NOFER, JOHN S; Paul D Schreiber HS; Port Washington, NY; (Y); 51/442; Nwsp Stf; NCTE Awd; NHS; NY ST Schlrshp 84-85; St Johns U Schlrshp Awd 85; Engl.

NOFTSIER, JUDY; Beaver River Central HS; Croghan, NY; (Y); Church Yth Grp; Drama Clb; GAA; Office Aide; Yrbk Stf; Var Trk; High Hon Roll; NHS; Thelma Nortz Awd 85; Sectrl Wrk.

NOGLE, JULIE A; Waterloo SR HS; Waterloo, NY; (Y); 11/179; Pres Spanish Clb; Trk; High Hon Roll; Hon Roll; NHS; Regents Engl Awd; Dickinson Coll; Lang.

NOLAN, COURTNEY; Notre Dame HS; New York, NY; (S); Dance Clb; Drama Clb; School Play; Variety Show; Yrbk Stf; Soph Cls; Jr Cls; Cheerleading; Second Honors.

NOLAN, KENNETH A; St John The Baptist HS; Babylon, NY; (Y); 5/601; Office Aide; Political Wkr; Science Clb; NHS; Spanish NHS; Social Studies Hghst Avg 84-85; Acadmc All-Am 84-85; Intl Frgn Language Awds Wnnr 84-85; American U; Poltcl Sci.

NOLAN, KERRY; Northstar Christian Acad; Spencerport, NY; (S); 5/27; Cmnty Wkr; Drama Clb; JA; Church Choir; School Play; Sec Stu Cncl; JV Var Cheerleading; Capt Var Socr; High Hon Roll; NHS; 1st Rochester Essay Cntst 84; Seton Hill Coll; Fshn Dsgn.

NOLAN, KEVIN; Spencerport Cen Schl; Spencerport, NY; (Y); JCL; Latin Clb; Varsity Clb; L Var Golf; Var Ice Hcky; JV Socr; JV Var Swmmng; Jr NHS; Natl Hnr Soc Awd In Phy Ed 85; Rochester Inst Tech.

NOLAN, MARIEAD; Mercy HS; Southold, NY; (Y); GAA; Sec MMM; Service Clb; Chorus; Stage Crew; Trk; High Hon Roll; Hon Roll; NHS; NEDT Awd; MIP Trk 85; Pre Med.

NOLAN, MAUREEN; Commack HS North; Smithtown, NY; (Y); 44/450; Church Yth Grp; French Clb; Stage Crew; Nwsp Rptr; Badmtn; French Hon Soc; High Hon Roll; NHS; Ntl Merit Ltr; Pres Schlr; Pres Grnt Sienna Coll 85; Pres Acad Ftnss Awd 85; Regents Schlrshp 85; Sienna Coll; Pre Med.

NOLAN, NILS; Garden City HS; Garden City, NY; (Y); Boy Scts; German Clb; Im Bsktbl; Im Ftbl; JV Lcrss; Var Wrstlng; High Hon Roll; Hon Roll; Bus Adm.

NOLAN, NOEL; St Saviour HS; Brooklyn, NY; (Y); 19/80; Hosp Aide; Yrbk Stf; Rep Soph Cls; Im Cheerleading; Var Capt Swmmng; High Hon Roll; NHS; U Northeastern Grant 85; Northeastern U; Engrng.

NOLAN, PATRICIA; Sacred Heart Acad; Rockville Centre, NY; (S); 2/187; Library Aide; Office Aide; Pres Science Clb; Chorus; School Musical; Rep Frsh Cls; High Hon Roll; NHS; Marquette U; Med Res.

NOLAN, ROBERT B; John F Kennedy HS; Plainview, NY; (Y); 25/275; Chess Clb; Church Yth Grp; Cmnty Wkr; Pres 4-H; Mathletes; Im Sftbl; 4-H Awd; Hon Roll; NHS; St Johns U; Comp Sci.

NOLAN, STACEY; Commack High School North; Smithtown, NY; (Y); Church Yth Grp; Cmnty Wkr; French Clb; Teachers Aide; Chorus; Stage Crew; Nwsp Rptr; Yrbk Stf; Rep Frsh Cls; Rep Soph Cls.

NOLAN, TERESA; The Mary Louis Acad; Bellerose, NY; (Y); Church Yth Grp; 4-H; Church Choir; Variety Show; Bowling; 4-H Awd; NEDT Awd; Italian Poetry Awd Spch 82-83; VP Ambulance Corps JR Corps 85-86; Bus Adm.

NOLAN, THOMAS J; La Salle Acad; New York, NY; (S); Cmnty Wkr; Im Bowling; Hon Roll; Church Mrt Awd 83; Pace; Law.

NOLAND, SHAWN M; August Martin HS; Springfield Gd, NY; (Y); Church Yth Grp; CAP; Bsktbl; Ice Hcky; Vllybl; Wt Lftg; Regents Diploma 85; Art Awd 85; Merit Hnr Roll 85; Queens Coll; Comp Sci.

NOLANDER, ERIC E; Holland Patent HS; Rome, NY; (Y); 11/198; Ftbl; Trk; High Hon Roll; NHS; Ntl Merit Ltr; Outstndng Trk Athlete Trophy 84; Track Leag All Star 85; JETS Outstndng Engrng Aptitude Awd 83; Civil Engr.

NOLEN, SCOTT E; Charles H Roth HS; Rush, NY; (Y); 43/210; Am Leg Boys St; Boy Scts; Exploring; Latin Clb; Ski Clb; Varsity Clb; Var Trk; Hon Roll; Jr NHS; NHS; U Of VT.

NOLETTE, DENISE; Sharon Springs Central HS; Sharon Springs, NY; (S); 1/42; Chorus; Pres Frsh Cls; VP Soph Cls; Pres Jr Cls; Pres Sr Cls; Sec Stu Cncl; Score Keeper; DAR Awd; Hon Roll; NHS; Stdnt Cncl Ldrshp Awd 84; Rotarian Brosis Awd 84; Cntrl Natl Bk Soc Stud Awd 84; SUNY Cobleskill; Bus Admin.

NOLL, NANCY; Jamesville-Dewitt HS; Fayetteville, NY; (Y); Church Yth Grp; Church Choir; Jazz Band; Mrchg Band; Swing Chorus; Symp Band; Lit Mag; Hon Roll; NHS; Faculty Service Awd 85; Jrnlsm.

NOLL, RICHARD E; Port Richmond HS; Staten Island, NY; (Y); 73/612; Am Leg Boys St; Boy Scts; Jazz Band; School Musical; Pres Jr Cls; Var Ftbl; Trk; Acad All Amer 85; Daily Nws Supr Yth 84; Ordr Of Arrow 84; Pre-Law.

NOLL, STEPHEN; South HS; Valley Stream, NY; (Y); 7/178; AFS; Chess Clb; Computer Clb; Mathletes; Nwsp Rptr; High Hon Roll; NY ST Rgnts Schlrshp; Hofstra U; TV Prgmmng.

NOON, JOANNE T; Our Lady Of Lourdes; Wappingers Falls, NY; (Y); 17/144; Church Yth Grp; Chorus; Yrbk Stf; High Hon Roll; NHS; Duquesne U; Finc.

NOONAN, JAMES; Mt St Joseph Acad; Buffalo, NY; (Y); Boys Clb Am; Boy Scts; Camera Clb; Computer Clb; Drama Clb; Stage Crew; Ntl Merit Ltr.

NOONAN, KATHLEEN; New Rochelle HS; New Rochelle, NY; (Y); Church Yth Grp; JA; Sec Latin Clb; Model UN; Political Wkr; Nwsp Rptr; Nwsp Stf; Sec Frsh Cls; NHS; Psych.

NOONAN, LINDA; Holy Angels Acad; Cheektowaga, NY; (Y); 13/40; Drama Clb; French Clb; Chorus; School Musical; Nwsp Rptr; Rep Frsh Cls; VP Soph Cls; Pres Jr Cls; Pres Stu Cncl; Hon Roll; Englsh Awd 84; Buffalo ST Coll; Spcl Ed.

NOONAN, MATTHEW J; Monroe Woodbury HS; Monroe, NY; (Y); Am Leg Boys St; FBLA; Hosp Aide; Nwsp Stf; Yrbk Bus Mgr; JV Golf; Hon Roll; Amer Mgt Assoc Oper Entrprs 83; Bus.

NOONAN, RACHEL E; Brockport HS; Brockport, NY; (Y); Exploring; Model UN; Band; Symp Band; High Hon Roll; Hon Roll; Church Yth Grp; Latin Clb; Mathletes; Radio Clb; Regent Schlrshp 85; Frshmn Schlrshp-Houghton 85; Houghton; Librl Arts.

NOONE, SARAH E; Saint Saviour HS; Brooklyn, NY; (Y); School Play; Stage Crew; Yrbk Stf; Trs Jr Cls; JV Cheerleading; French Hon Soc; Hon Roll; NHS; NEDT Awd; Steamfttg Industry Lcl 638 Schlrshp 85; NY U Ttee Schlrshp 85; St Johns U Schlstc Exclnc Schlrshp 85; SUNY At Stonybrook; Meteorolog.

NORBERG, KAREN; Moore Catholic HS; Staten Isl, NY; (Y); Cmnty Wkr; St Johns U; Bus.

NORBERG, MICHAEL; Mc Kee Tech HS; Staten Island, NY; (Y); 27/268.

NORBERTO, CAROL; Maria Regina HS; Yonkers, NY; (Y); 11/130; Church Yth Grp; Hosp Aide; Key Clb; Library Aide; Nwsp Rptr; High Hon Roll; NHS; Nwsp Stf; Hon Roll; Prfct Atten Awd; Hnrs Convoctn 83-85; Pblc Reltns 84-85; Yonkers Rotary Clb Awd 82; Iona Coll; Math.

NORBERTO, MICHAEL; West Babylon SR HS; W Babylon, NY; (Y); Pres Computer Clb; Band; Concert Band; Mrchg Band; Orch; Hon Roll; NHS; NYS Regents Schlrshp 85; Hofstra U; Intl Bus.

NORCROSS, JENNIFER L; Clymer Central Schl; Findley Lake, NY; (Y); Chorus; School Play; VP Frsh Cls; VP Soph Cls; VP Jr Cls; Cheerleading; High Hon Roll; Hon Roll; NHS; AFS; NY ST Regentc Schlrshp 85; Geneseo ST U; Accntnt.

NORDEN, KELLI ANN; Mercy HS; Centereach, NY; (Y); Hosp Aide; VP Service Clb; Ski Clb; Chorus; Sftbl; Vllybl; High Hon Roll; Hon Roll; Sec NHS.

NORDIN JR, RICHARD G; Saratoga Central Catholis HS; Wilton, NY; (S); 4-H; Pep Clb; Varsity Clb; Yrbk Stf; VP Jr Cls; Var Capt Golf; High Hon Roll; Hon Roll; NHS; Pep Clb; Outstndng Chrctr, Prncpls 82; Bus Admn.

NORDMAN, MEGAN E; Moore Catholic HS; Staten Island, NY; (Y); 2/180; French Clb; Capt NFL; Rptr Nwsp Stf; Gym; NHS; Ntl Merit Ltr; Rgnts Schlshp 85; Acad All Amer 85; Bucknell; Math.

NORDSTROM, LISA; Smithtown High School East; Saint James, NY; (Y); Band; Concert Band; Mrchg Band; Var Bsktbl; Var Fld Hcky; JV Vllybl; Hon Roll; Jr NHS; Socl Wrk.

NORDSTROM, LORI J; Shoreham Wading River HS; Shoreham, NY; (Y); Church Yth Grp; Math Tm; Orch; Variety Show; Ed Lit Mag; JV Capt Sftbl; NHS; Ntl Merit SF; Cmnty Wkr; Mathletes; Math Fair Bronze Medal Wnnr 83; Sci Congress White Ribbon 83; 1st County Math Contest 84.

NOREAULT, SHANN; Northeaster Adirondack Central HS; Merrill, NY; (Y); Key Clb; Nwsp Stf; Sec Frsh Cls; Rep Stu Cncl; JV Var Score Keeper; Hon Roll; Wrestling Booster Clb 82-85; Tompkins Cortland Comm; Travel.

NOREN, DEBBIE; Clarence HS; Akron, NY; (Y); 4/289; Varsity Clb; Orch; School Musical; Nwsp Stf; Rep Sr Cls; Var Crs Cntry; Var Trk; Im Wt Lftg; High Hon Roll; NHS; PTO Hghst Acad Excell 81-83; Most Imprvd Rnrr Crss Cntry 83,Trck 85; Cornell.

NOREN, TAMMY; Clarence Central SR HS; Akron, NY; (Y); 22/289; French Clb; Band; Concert Band; Mrchg Band; Pep Band; Symp Band; JV Crs Cntry; Var Trk; Im Vllybl; Hon Roll.

NORMAN, BARBARA; The Stony Brook Schl; Stony Brook, NY; (Y); 31/84; Church Yth Grp; Chorus; Nwsp Rptr; Bsktbl; Crs Cntry; Fld Hcky; JV Sftbl; Trk; Hon Roll; Schl Wrk Prog; Bus.

NORMAN, CHRISTY; Massena Central HS; Massena, NY; (Y); French Clb; Band; Concert Band; Mrchg Band; Var JV Cheerleading; Hon Roll; Psych.

NORMAN, CLAUDIA; Mount Vernon HS; Mount Vernon, NY; (Y); Church Yth Grp; Science Clb; Spanish Clb; Chorus; Church Choir; Orch; Symp Band; Nwsp Stf; High Hon Roll; Hon Roll; Stdnt Mnth Spnsh 85; Media Cmmnctns.

NORMAN, DONNA; Mc Graw Central HS; Mc Graw, NY; (Y); 6/40; Am Leg Aux Girls St; French Clb; Pres Jr Cls; Var L Cheerleading; Cit Awd; High Hon Roll; Hon Roll; Jr NHS; NHS; Drama Clb; NY St Farm Bureau Citznshp Awd 85; Stu Mnth 85; Cortland ST; Math.

NORMAN, GAIL; Ripley Central Schl; Ripley, NY; (Y); 4/27; School Play; NHS; NEMA 84; USA Schlrshp 85; Jamestown CC; Crmnl Jstc.

NORMAN, JOANNE; Sacred Heart Acad; Elmont, NY; (S); Varsity Clb; Stage Crew; Var Bsktbl; Var Vllybl; NHS; J V Hgh Scorer 82; 2nd Hnrs H S Spnsh Test Iona Coll 84; Comp Sci.

NORMAN, MARK; Mayfield Central Schl; Gloversville, NY; (Y); Church Yth Grp; Math Tm; Varsity Clb; Var L Bsbl; Var L Bsktbl; Var L Bowling; Stat Socr; High Hon Roll; NHS; Mgr(s); Mst Imprvd JV Bsktbl 84.

NORMAN, MELANIE; Tuxedo HS; Tuxedo, NY; (Y); Nwsp Rptr; High Hon Roll; Hon Roll; Nwsp Stf; Yrbk Stf; Lit Mag; Awd For 92 Amer Hstry Regnts 84; SUNY Cortland; Psych.

NORMAND, JOHN E; Monsignor Farrell HS; Staten Island, NY; (Y); 85/296; Computer Clb; Debate Tm; Drill Tm; Yrbk Stf; Capt Bowling; Hon Roll; NY ST Regents Schlrshp 85; Bus.

NORMANDIN, JOELLE; Glens Falls SR HS; Glens Falls, NY; (Y); 52/273; AFS; Key Clb; Nwsp Rptr; Var Crs Cntry; Powder Puff Ftbl; Var Capt Trk; Hon Roll; NY ST Trk & Field Champnshps 84 & 85; Empire ST Games 84; Soc Stud Stu Of Quarter 84; U Of CT; Jrnlsm.

NORMANDIN, SHANNON; Cohoes HS; Cohoes, NY; (Y); Hon Roll; Hudson Valley Comm; Exec Sec.

NORMANN, PARKER; Fox Lane HS; Bedford, NY; (Y); Intnl Clb; Service Clb; Varsity Clb; Yrbk Phtg; Ice Hcky; Var Socr; Swmmng; Var Tennis; Var Capt Wrstlng.

NORMILE, CHRISTIAN A; Brasher Falls Central HS; Brasher Falls, NY; (Y); Am Leg Boys St; Trs French Clb; Letterman Clb; Chorus; JV Var Bsbl; Capt Var Bsktbl; Hon Roll; Prfct Atten Awd; Pre-Law.

NORMILE, KATHRYN; Spackenkill HS; Poughkeepsie, NY; (Y); Sec Church Yth Grp; Hosp Aide; Band; Church Choir; Flag Corp; Pep Band; School Musical; Nrsg.

NORMILE, MARIA; Corinth Centgral HS; Corinth, NY; (S); 2/98; MMM; Jazz Band; Pres Sr Cls; NHS; Band; Rep Jr Cls; French Hon Soc; High Hon Roll; Academic Achvmnt Awd 84; Top Hnrs; Suny Albany; Math.

NORMOYLE, MICHAEL; Sacred Heart HS; Hastings, NY; (S); Boy Scts; JV Bsbl; JV Capt Bsktbl; Var Trk; Hon Roll; NHS; Bus Admin.

NOROIAN, LISA B; Minisink Valley HS; Middletown, NY; (Y); 11/232; Band; Mrchg Band; Nwsp Stf; Yrbk Stf; JV Socr; High Hon Roll; NHS; Engl.

NOROTSKY, RANDI M; Tappan Zee HS; Tappan, NY; (Y); 59/300; VP Temple Yth Grp; Rptr Nwsp Stf; Rptr Yrbk Stf; Trs Frsh Cls; Trs Soph Cls; Rep Stu Cncl; JV Capt Bsktbl; Var Twrlr; Ntl Merit Hnr Rl 85; Knights Pythias Schlstic Awd 85; Binghamton U.

NORRIS, KELLY; Mont Pleasant HS; Schenectady, NY; (Y); 58/201; Key Clb; Office Aide; Pep Clb; Ski Clb; Chorus; Bsktbl; Sftbl; Vllybl; Hon Roll; Cert Achv Recgntn Vlntry Svc Cmnty 85; Air Frc; Eltroencphtgrph Tech.

NORRIS, MARIE; Kenmore West SR HS; Kenmore, NY; (Y); Church Yth Grp; French Clb; Yrbk Ed-Chief; Yrbk Sprt Ed; Yrbk Stf; Lit Mag; Mgr(s); Score Keeper; Timer; High Hon Roll; U Buffalo; Phys Ther.

NORRIS, SKEETER; Far Rockaway HS; Far Rockaway, NY; (Y); Key Clb; Chorus; Nwsp Stf; Hon Roll.

NORTH, RANDALL W; Hartford Central Schl; Argyle, NY; (Y); Drama Clb; Trs French Clb; Band; Chorus; Orch; Yrbk Stf; Pres Sr Cls; Score Keeper; Bausch & Lomb Sci Awd; NHS; Daemen Coll.

NORTHROP, AMANDA; Guilderland Central HS; Guilderland, NY; (Y); Cmnty Wkr; Dance Clb; Key Clb; Library Aide; Office Aide; Teachers Aide; Variety Show; Yrbk Stf; Fld Hcky; Cit Awd; Wnnr Cobleskll Dance Cont 82-83; Bus Mgmt.

NORTHROP, ANDREW D; Hugh C Williams HS; Canton, NY; (Y); 1/135; School Play; Yrbk Stf; VP Stu Cncl; High Hon Roll; NHS; Ntl Merit Ltr; Art Clb; Church Yth Grp; Cmnty Wkr; Math Clb; Dartmouth Coll Alumni Awd 84; Ntl Soc Stud Olymp Awd 84; St Lawrence Cnty Bar Assoc Schlrshp 85; Stanford U.

NORTHROP, MICHAEL; Corning-Painted Port West HS; Painted Post, NY; (Y); Sec Key Clb; Letterman Clb; Varsity Clb; Rep Frsh Cls; Rep Jr Cls; Im Bsktbl; Var L Crs Cntry; Var Capt Trk; High Hon Roll; NHS; All-League Crss Cntry Sectnl Trck Champ 84-85; Athlt Of The Mnth; Engrng Schl; Engrng.

NORTHRUP, NICOLE; John F Kennedy HS; Utica, NY; (Y); 1/130; Sec Pres Key Clb; Band; Yrbk Ed-Chief; Rep Sec Stu Cncl; JV Cheerleading; NHS; Ntl Merit SF; Church Yth Grp; Cmnty Wkr; Computer Clb; Smmr Fllwshp-Masonic Medcl Resrch Lab 85; RPI Medal-Sci/Math 84-85; Smmr Intrnshp-NY Acad Of Sci 84; Vetrnrn.

NORTHRUP, PAUL; Eastport HS; Eastport, NY; (S); 1/56; Scholastic Bowl; Nwsp Rptr; VP Stu Cncl; Bausch & Lomb Sci Awd; Cit Awd; NHS; Ntl Merit Ltr; NEDT Awd; Computer Clb; Drama Clb; Phi Beta Kappa Awd 85; Vrsty Handball Team MVP 83-84; Schl Musical Tech Dsgn 85; Dowling Coll; Sci.

NORTHRUP JR, RONNIE; Penn Yan Acad; Penn Yan, NY; (Y); Im Bsktbl; High Hon Roll; Hon Roll; NHS; SUNY Oswego; Math.

NORTHRUP, SCOTT R; Massena Central HS; Massena, NY; (Y); 10/300; Cmnty Wkr; Rep Stu Cncl; JV Var Bsbl; JV Var Ice Hcky; JV Var Socr; Cit Awd; High Hon Roll; Hon Roll; NHS; Prfct Atten Awd; MVP & Most Outstndnd Mdgt Awd In Hockey 85; Pre-Med.

NORTON, CAROLYN; Chester HS; Chester, NY; (Y); 1/70; Band; Jazz Band; VP Soph Cls; Var Capt Bsktbl; Var Socr; Var Capt Vllybl; High Hon Roll; NHS; Mrchg Band; Rep Jr Cls; Harriet H Fowler Awd Math 85; Sportsmanshp Awd Bsktbl,Vlybl 85; Sienna Coll; Sports Med.

NORTON, ELIZABETH A; De Ruyter Central HS; De Ruyter, NY; (Y); Yrbk Stf; VP Soph Cls; Pres Rep Jr Cls; Rep Stu Cncl; Socr; High Hon Roll; NHS; Drama Clb; Band; Concert Band; Scholar Cup 82-84; Clarkson Schl 84-85; Clarkson; Electrcl.

NORTON, JULIE; Alexander Central HS; Batavia, NY; (S); Church Yth Grp; Band; Chorus; Var Socr; Var Capt Trk; Jr NHS; NHS; AFS; 4-H; Concert Band; All-County Band 83-85; All-County Chorus 83-84; Genesee Reg Leag All-Star Team Track 82-84; Phy Thrpy.

NORTON, KELLIE; Cicero North Syracuse HS; N Syracuse, NY; (S); Band; Concert Band; Mrchg Band; Symp Band; SR High All Cnty Band 84.

NORTON, KIMBERLY; Cleveland Hill HS; Cheektowaga, NY; (Y); 5/100; GAA; JCL; VP Stu Cncl; Var Trk; High Hon Roll; Hon Roll; Prfct Atten Awd.

NORTON, TERRY; Gouverneur Central Schl; Gouverneur, NY; (Y); PAVAS; Band; Color Guard; Concert Band; Jazz Band; Mrchg Band; Orch; School Musical; DAR Awd; Prfct Atten Awd; Bsktbl Awds 82-83; Art Awd, Artist Yr 84-85; Mar Engrng.

NORTON, WENDY; Binahamton HS; Binghamton, NY; (Y); Am Leg Aux Girls St; Art Clb; Sec Church Yth Grp; Girl Scts; Hosp Aide; Spanish Clb; Nwsp Stf; Yrbk Stf; Im Badmtn; JV Var Score Keeper; Outstndng Achvt Frgn Lang, Art Stu Mnth 84; Phtgrphy.

NORTZ, JULIE; Beaver River Central HS; Beaver Falls, NY; (Y); French Clb; GAA; Chorus; Church Choir; Drm Mjr(t); School Musical; JV Var Cheerleading; Computer Clb; NHS; Voice Dem Awd; NY ST Knights Of Columbus Fmly Yr 84; Gftd & Tlntd 82-83; Acctng.

NORWOOD, MARCY; Bronx High Schl Of Science; Bronx, NY; (Y); Ed Camera Clb; Hosp Aide; Math Tm; Teachers Aide; School Play; Nwsp Stf; Lit Mag; Stu Cncl; Vllybl; MAA Hnr Rl 82-83; Natl Frnch Competitn 83-84 & 84-85; Schl Hnr Rl 82-85; Med.

NOSTRANT, KELLY; Bishop Ludden HS; Syracuse, NY; (S); Church Yth Grp; Variety Show; Var Cheerleading; High Hon Roll; NHS; 3rd Pl Chrldng Awd 83; Hm Ec Awd 84; Bio.

NOSTROM, KRISTAN; Franklin Acad; Malone, NY; (Y); Pep Clb; Spanish Clb; Chorus; JV Var Cheerleading; Var Swmmng; Var Trk; Hon Roll; Spirit Awd Chrldng 83-84; Child Psych.

NOTARNICOLA, SONIA; Coxsackie-Athens Central HS; Athens, NY; (Y); Spanish Clb; Yrbk Stf; Off Frsh Cls; Off Soph Cls; Off Jr Cls; High Hon Roll; Hon Roll; Baypath JR Coll; Trvl & Trsm.

NOTAROBERTO, LISA; Sacred Heart Acad; E Meadow, NY; (S); 2/196; Cmnty Wkr; Library Aide; Pres Math Clb; Math Tm; Office Aide; High Hon Roll; NHS; Iona Coll 2nd Hnrs Frnch Awd 84; Ntl Ldrshp Orgzn 83-85; Cert Hnr NY ST Bar Assn 83; Math.

NOTIDES, THOMAS; Brighton HS; Rochester, NY; (Y); Boy Scts; Varsity Clb; Var Crs Cntry; JV Trk; Engrng.

NOUR, MAGDA; Hunter College HS; New York, NY; (Y); Computer Clb; Math Tm; Acpl Chr; Chorus; Swing Chorus; Var L Bsktbl; Im Bowling; Var L Sftbl; Mu Alp Tht; Ntl Hspnc Schlr Awd Schlrshp 85-86; Bell Bal Ntl Schlrshp 85-89; NYS Math Leag Cert Merit 84; MA Inst Tech; Comp Sci.

NOVAK, ANDREW P; Washingtonville HS; Campbellhall, NY; (Y); Bsktbl; Socr; Tennis; La Crosse U; Bus Mgmt.

NOVAK, CINDY LYNN; Roxbury Central Schl; Roxbury, NY; (Y); 4/30; Office Aide; Yrbk Stf; Sec Soph Cls; Rep Jr Cls; JV Var Cheerleading; JV Var Socr; High Hon Roll; Hon Roll; NHS; Bst Apprnc-Grmng 81-82; Mary Baldwin Coll; Bus.

NOVAK, JASON; New Berlin HS; New Berlin, NY; (Y); French Clb; JA; Math Tm; Science Clb; Var Bsbl; Var Bsktbl; Var Ftbl; High Hon Roll; Pres Jr NHS; Pres NHS; Rotry Yth Ldrshp Awd 85; NY Acad Scis 84-85; Mock Trial Tm 83; Frgn Exchng Stu.

NOVAKOVIC, DIANA; Greater New York Acad; Woodside, NY; (S); Cmnty Wkr; Teachers Aide; Nwsp Rptr; VP Frsh Cls; Rep Jr Cls; Rep Sr Cls; High Hon Roll; NHS; Pre Med.

NOVICK, BETH; Commack HS North; Commack, NY; (Y); Pres Temple Yth Grp; Chorus; Stage Crew; High Hon Roll; NHS; Merit Srv Ntl Cnfrnc Of Syng Yth 83.

NOVOGRODSKY, LISA; Wellington C Mepham HS; N Bellmore, NY; (Y); 65/385; Art Clb; Cmnty Wkr; Debate Tm; Trs Drama Clb; French Clb; School Musical; School Play; Rep Stu Cncl; Var Badmtn; Hon Roll; Peter Shea Math Awd 82; Regents Schlrshp NY ST 85; U Of VT; Math.

NOVOTNY, JANET; Beacon HS; Beacon, NY; (S); 12/169; Am Leg Aux Girls St; Church Yth Grp; Latin Clb; Office Aide; VP Jr Cls; Sec Stu Cncl; Hon Roll; Jr NHS; NHS; JR Prom Queen 84; Hmcmng Ct 84-85; Cortland Coll; Chld Educ.

NOVOTNY, SUSAN; Williamsville East HS; Williamsville, NY; (Y); Drama Clb; Latin Clb; Pep Clb; VP Chorus; School Musical; School Play; Swing Chorus; Rep Stu Cncl; JV Var Cheerleading; U Buffalo-New York; Acctng.

NOWAK, JULIE; Albion HS; Albion, NY; (Y); 38/179; Pres VP Church Yth Grp; Trs Rptr VICA; School Musical; Trs Jr Cls; Rep Sr Cls; Hon Roll; Orleans Niagara Skls Comp 85; Word Precssng.

NOWAK, KATHLEEN; Frontier Central HS; Blasdell, NY; (Y); French Clb; FBLA; Pep Clb; School Play; Yrbk Stf; Rep Jr Cls; Vllybl; Hon Roll; Prfct Atten Awd; Daemen Coll; Pre-Law.

NOWAK, KRISTIN; Walton Central HS; Walton, NY; (Y); 6/100; AFS; Key Clb; Model UN; Varsity Clb; Band; Chorus; Nwsp Ed-Chief; Stu Cncl; Fld Hcky; NHS; Cngrssmns Mdl Merit 85; Intl Rel.

NOWAK, SUSAN; Niagara Wheatfield SR HS; N Tonawanda, NY; (Y); Am Leg Aux Girls St; Church Yth Grp; Latin Clb; Pep Clb; Political Wkr; Chorus; Church Choir; VP Frsh Cls; Var Capt Cheerleading; Var JV Sftbl; Engrng.

NOWAKOWSKI, GREGORY L; Greece Athena SR HS; Rochester, NY; (Y); 2/281; Church Yth Grp; Trs German Clb; Math Tm; Im Ftbl; Var Capt Golf; High Hon Roll; Hon Roll; Prfct Atten Awd; Sal; German Stu Of Yr 83-84; Excllnc In Chem 83; Var Golf MVP Awd 84; Law.

NOWAKOWSKI, LUBA S; St George Acad; New York, NY; (Y); 2/35; Church Yth Grp; Ski Clb; Spanish Clb; Yrbk Bus Mgr; Yrbk Stf; Sec Soph Cls; Sec Jr Cls; Sec Sr Cls; Var Capt Vllybl; High Hon Roll; Athl Awd 85; Pace U & Ukranian Orgnztn Schlrshps 85; Pace U; Fincl Mgmt.

NOWAKOWSKI, SUSAN; Grand Island HS; Grand Is, NY; (Y); Church Yth Grp; French Clb; Teachers Aide; Chorus; Stage Crew; Variety Show; Yrbk Stf; Rgnts Schlrshp 85; Niagara U; Nrsg.

NOWALK, TAMMIE L; Oxford Acad; Greene, NY; (Y); 2/81; French Clb; Ski Clb; Concert Band; Nwsp Stf; Yrbk Ed-Chief; Trs Stu Cncl; High Hon Roll; Hon Roll; NHS; Prfct Atten Awd; NYS Regnts Schlrshp 85; SUNY Binghamton; Acctg.

NOWICKI, GREGORY; Lackawanna SR HS; Lackawanna, NY; (Y); Boy Scts; Rep Stu Cncl; Var Bowling; Var Tennis; High Hon Roll; Hon Roll; NHS; Eagle Bdge,Brnze Palm,Gld Palm 82-84; U Of Buffalo; Comp Sci.

NOWICKI, KERRY ANN; Maryvale HS; Lancaster, NY; (Y); French Clb; Band; Symp Band; Trk; Hon Roll; Chorus; Concert Band; Mrchg Band; School Play; Yrbk Stf; Media Cmmnctns.

NOWORYTA, LINDA; Niagara Catholic HS; Niagara Falls, NY; (Y); Church Yth Grp; French Clb; Hosp Aide; VP Soph Cls; Var Badmtn; Var Bsktbl; JV Vllybl; High Hon Roll; Hon Roll; NHS; Hnrb Mntn Wrld Of Poetry 84; Jrnalsm.

NOWOTARSKI, LUANN; John F Kennedy HS; Cheektowaga, NY; (Y); 21/141; Chorus; School Musical; Nwsp Stf; Yrbk Stf; Hst Stu Cncl; Ocngrphy.

NOXON, BRUCE; E J Wilson HS; Spencerport, NY; (Y); Exploring; Hosp Aide; Latin Clb; Jazz Band; Symp Band; Rep Soph Cls; Var Golf; JV Socr; Hon Roll; Pre-Med.

NOZELL, LORI J; L C Obourn HS; E Rochester, NY; (Y); 38/111; Drama Clb; Exploring; French Clb; Model UN; Chorus; School Musical; School Play; Yrbk Stf; Stu Cncl; Hon Roll; Tchrs Assoc Awd 85; Wrtng Cntst 1st Pl 84; 3rd Pl Art Cntst 84; NY ST U Fredonia; Chldhd Ed.

NOZYCE, SUSAN; New Rochelle HS; New Rochelle, NY; (Y); Drama Clb; Temple Yth Grp; Band; School Play; Yrbk Stf; Lit Mag; Rep Sr Cls; High Hon Roll; Hon Roll; NHS; Span & Drama Awd, Outstndng Band Mbr Awd 83.

NUCCI, MICHELE; Gates-Chili HS; Rochester, NY; (Y); 101/463; Church Yth Grp; NY ST Regents Schlrshp 85; U Of OR; Pub Relations.

NUCHESI, MADELYN; Auburn HS; Auburn, NY; (Y); Chess Clb; Hosp Aide; Latin Clb; Chorus; Church Choir; High Hon Roll; Hon Roll; Vrsty Lttr-Choir 85; Cayuga CC; Comp Sci.

NUDD, MELODY; Lyons HS; Lyons, NY; (Y); 3/90; Trs AFS; Rep Frsh Cls; Pres Soph Cls; Pres Jr Cls; Pres Stu Cncl; Stat Bsbl; Im Bowling; JV Socr; Hon Roll; NHS; Rensselaer Poly Inst; Arch.

NUDELMAN, SHARI; Bethpage HS; Plainview, NY; (Y); 12/280; Pres Service Clb; Spanish Clb; VP Temple Yth Grp; Varsity Clb; Var Gym; Var Swmmng; Var Tennis; High Hon Roll; Hon Roll; NHS; Phrmcy.

NUESSLE, CARL W; Williamsville South HS; Williamsville, NY; (Y); 22/245; Chess Clb; Science Clb; DAR Awd; NHS; Ntl Merit Ltr; St Schlr; Grove City Coll; Pre-Law.

NUGENT, KIMBERLY; Rocky Point JR SR HS; Rocky Point, NY; (S); 16/188; GAA; Varsity Clb; Band; Mrchg Band; Capt Var Cheerleading; Capt L Crs Cntry; Im Socr; Capt L Trk; Hon Roll; NHS.

NUGENT, PATRICK; Tonawanda HS; Tonawanda, NY; (Y); 100/240; Art Clb; Boys Clb Am; Boy Scts; Church Yth Grp; Var Capt Ice Hcky; Socr; Kiwanis Awd; Rotary Awd; Rochester Inst Tech 85; IM Flr Hockey 85; Yng Life 84 & 85; Rocheser Inst Tech; Prntng Tech.

NUMSSEN, VALERIE; Sayville HS; Sayville, NY; (Y); 16/363; Cmnty Wkr; Key Clb; Mrchg Band; Symp Band; Var Gym; Var Tennis; Var Vllybl; High Hon Roll; Jr NHS; NHS; Stony Brook U; Me.

NUNES, DAVID; St Agnes HS; New York, NY; (Y); Boys Clb Am; Computer Clb; Dance Clb; Band; Im Bsktbl; Im Ftbl; Hon Roll; FAU; Lwyr.

NUNEZ, ALEX; Iona Preparatory HS; Larchmont, NY; (Y); 64/196; Computer Clb; Trk; Hon Roll.

NUNEZ, INGRID; Fashion Industries HS; New York City, NY; (Y); 3/473; Rep Sr Cls; Sftbl; Vllybl; CC Awd; Cit Awd; Gov Hon Prg Awd; Hon Roll; NHS; Ntl Merit Ltr; Prfct Atten Awd; Regnts, UFT Schlrshps 84-85; Baruch Coll; Econ.

NUNEZ, NOEMI; James Monroe HS; Bronx, NY; (Y); 1/250; Latin Clb; Political Wkr; Spanish Clb; Off Sr Cls; Bsktbl; Hon Roll; Prfct Atten Awd; MFT Schlrshp 85; 3 Gld Medl Spnsh & Bilngl Prog 85; Hnr Stdnt 85; Lehman Coll; Law.

NUNGE, MARK; Potsdam Senior HS; Potsdam, NY; (Y); 4/160; Chess Clb; Computer Clb; French Clb; JA; Latin Clb; Math Tm; Varsity Clb; Var JV Bsbl; Var Capt Bsktbl; JV Socr; Law.

NUNN III, JOHN A; Alden Central HS; Alden, NY; (Y); Boy Scts; Church Yth Grp; FFA; School Musical; Ethnlgy.

NUNNING, KIMBERLY J; Liverpool HS; Liverpool, NY; (Y); Church Yth Grp; Exploring; Office Aide; Concert Band; Merit Roll; NYSSMA Music Awd; Vtrnrn Tech.

NURENA, KATHLEEN R; Acad Of The Resrectn; Harrison, NY; (Y); Math Clb; Var Swmmng; Hon Roll; Merit Awd Acad Achvt NY ST Senator 84; Athltc Awd Extracurr Actvties 83 & 85; Lib Art.

NURSE, ALTHEA; Edward R Murrow HS; Queens, NY; (Y); 119/725; Spanish Clb; Teachers Aide; Chorus; Rep Jr Cls; Rep Sr Cls; Rep Stu Cncl; Hon Roll; $1500 Schlrshp Johnson & Wales Coll 85; $400 Schlrsp Franklin Pierce Coll 85; Pace U; Accntng.

NUSBICKEL, ERIC; Calaedonia-Momford Central Schl; Caledonia, NY; (Y); Church Yth Grp; Science Clb; Band; Chorus; Jazz Band; Swing Chorus; Im Bsktbl; Var L Socr; Im Vllybl; Hon Roll; Rochester Inst Of Tch; Comp Sci.

NUSSER, KRYSTLE; Berne Knox Westerlo HS; Altamont, NY; (Y); FBLA; Capt Drm Mjr(t); Mrchg Band; Rep Stu Cncl; Var Co-Capt Cheerleading; Twrlr; Hon Roll; Med Secy.

NUTTER, HEIDI; Bainbridge-Guilford HS; Bainbridge, NY; (S); 4/76; Band; Chorus; Drm Mjr(t); Orch; Rep Stu Cncl; JV Capt Bsktbl; Sftbl; High Hon Roll; Jr NHS; NHS; Chemistry.

NYAHAY, DENISE A; John F Kennedy HS; Carmel, NY; (Y); 13/194; JA; Varsity Clb; Stat Bsktbl; Var Capt Socr; Stat Trk; Var Vllybl; High Hon Roll; Hon Roll; St Schlr; Acadmc Achvt Awd 84; NY ST Regnts Schlrshp 85; Villanova U; Acctng.

NYE, MIKE; Wellsville HS; Wellsville, NY; (Y); 71/133; DECA; Exploring; JV Var Ftbl; Wellsville Police Benevolent Assn Schlrshp 85; Finger Lakes CC; Consrv.

NYLAND, LORIANN; Stella Maris HS; Middle Village, NY; (Y); Girl Scts; Science Clb; Color Guard; Hon Roll; Hgh Hnr Roll 81; Nrsng.

O BANNON, CHRISTOPHER; Brentwood HS; Bay Shore, NY; (Y); 9/625; Computer Clb; Hst DECA; Math Tm; High Hon Roll; Jr NHS; NHS; Adelphi U; Bus Mgt.

O BANNON, JACQUELYN; Cardinal O Hara HS; Tonawanda, NY; (Y); Drama Clb; French Clb; Varsity Clb; JV Var Cheerleading; Var Score Keeper; Trk; Chrldng Chmpnshp Comptn 3rd Pl 85; Niagra U; Nrse.

O BEIRNE, FAITH; Our Lady Of Mercy HS; Rohcester, NY; (Y); Exploring; Acpl Chr; Chorus; Church Choir; School Musical; School Play; Lit Mag; Pres Jr Cls; Pres Stu Cncl; Trk; Theology Awd; Music Awd; Voice Training Awd; Engl.

O BRIEN, ALICE; Bishop Cunningham HS; Oswego, NY; (Y); 1/55; Church Yth Grp; Latin Clb; Library Aide; Ski Clb; Spanish Clb; School Play; Variety Show; Rep Frsh Cls; Rep Soph Cls; VP Jr Cls; Pre Med.

O BRIEN, BRIDGET; Albertus Magnus HS; West Nyack, NY; (Y); 27/190; Church Yth Grp; Mathletes; Varsity Clb; Church Choir; Var Socr; Var JV Vllybl; Hon Roll; Mu Alp Tht; Leukemia Type Ahton; MI V Vlybl,Soccer Plyr; Math.

O BRIEN, BRIDGET; Glen Falls HS; Glens Falls, NY; (Y); 16/235; AFS; Varsity Clb; Yrbk Stf; Swmmng; High Hon Roll; Jr NHS; NHS; Ntl Merit Ltr; Regents Schlrshp 85; Niagara U; Nrs.

O BRIEN, CATHERINE A; Mount Mercy Acad; E Aurora, NY; (Y); Art Clb; Boys Clb Am; JCL; Latin Clb; Model UN; Ski Clb; Yrbk Stf; Stu Cncl; Var Badmtn; Var Tennis; NY ST Regent Schlrshp 85; U Of Toronto; Engl.

O BRIEN, CORMAC; Webster HS; Webster, NY; (Y); Church Yth Grp; Ski Clb; Band; Concert Band; Jazz Band; School Musical; L Bsbl; JV Wrstlng; High Hon Roll; Hon Roll; Hist.

O BRIEN, DEBORAH; Frankfort Schuyler HS; Frankfort, NY; (S); 19/99; FBLA; GAA; Key Clb; Math Tm; Yrbk Stf; Rep Soph Cls; Var Capt Badmtn; Var Fld Hcky; High Hon Roll; Hon Roll; Herkimer County Comm Coll; Ed.

O BRIEN, JACLYN; St John Villa Acad; Staten Island, NY; (Y); 11/150; Hosp Aide; Pep Clb; Im Bsktbl; Im Bowling; Hon Roll; Manhattan Coll; Engr.

O BRIEN, JAMES PATRICK MICHAEL; Seton Catholic Central HS; Binghamton, NY; (S); 12/140; Church Yth Grp; Science Clb; Varsity Clb; Rep Stu Cncl; JV Bsbl; JV Bsktbl; JV Var Ftbl; High Hon Roll; NHS; Prfct Atten Awd; Clarkson; Elec Engrng.

O BRIEN, JOSEPH; Geneseo Central HS; Geneseo, NY; (Y); Mathletes; Bsbl; Bsktbl; French Hon Soc; High Hon Roll; Jr NHS; NHS; NEDT Awd.

O BRIEN, KAREN; St Agnes HS; Beechhurst, NY; (Y); Church Yth Grp; GAA; Lit Mag; Ny ST Regents Schlrshp 85; Manhattan College Pres Schlrshp 85; Manhattan College Schlrshp 85; Manhattan College; Engineering.

O BRIEN, LISA; Cardinal Mooney HS; Rochester, NY; (Y); Library Aide; Service Clb; Teachers Aide; Stage Crew; Rep Soph Cls; Rep Jr Cls; Rep Stu Cncl; High Hon Roll; Hon Roll; Bus Admin.

O BRIEN, MARK; Cardinal Mooney HS; Rochester, NY; (Y); School Musical; School Play; JV Socr; Var Hon Roll; Monroe CC; Biochem.

O BRIEN, MATTHEW; Tamarac HS; Troy, NY; (Y); Intnl Clb; Math Tm; Science Clb; Yrbk Stf; Rep Frsh Cls; Hon Roll; NHS.

O BRIEN, MAUREEN E; Academy Of The Holy Names; Albany, NY; (Y); 4-H; French Clb; Pres GAA; Hosp Aide; Nwsp Sprt Ed; Lit Mag; Frsh Cls; Stu Cncl; Bsktbl; Socr; Schl Dstngshd Serv, Athlte & Stu Cncl Serv Awds 84-85; U Of Notre Dame; Arts.

O BRIEN, MEGHAN E; Bishop Cunningham HS; Oswego, NY; (Y); 1/28; Pres Sr Cls; JV Cheerleading; Var Swmmng; Var Tennis; Elks Awd; High Hon Roll; NHS; Pres Schlr; St Schlr; Val; Coll Of William Smith.

O BRIEN, MICHAEL; Cardinal Spellman HS; Bronx, NY; (Y); Church Yth Grp; Im Bsktbl; Im Ftbl; High Hon Roll; NEDT Awd; Med.

O BRIEN, PAT; Somers HS; Amawalk, NY; (Y); Cmnty Wkr; Nwsp Rptr; Yrbk Stf; Bsbl; JV Capt Socr; Comm.

O BRIEN, PATRICK; Mynderse Acad; Seneca Falls, NY; (Y); Church Yth Grp; Cmnty Wkr; Band; Chorus; Church Choir; Concert Band; Mrchg Band; Swing Chorus; Rep Frsh Cls; Rep Stu Cncl; All Cnty Choir Outstndng Tenr 85.

O BRIEN, PAUL; Hicksville HS; Hicksville, NY; (Y); Var Bsbl; Im Bsktbl; Var Crs Cntry; Var Trk.

O BRIEN, TIMOTHY; Allegany Central HS; Olean, NY; (Y); 5/90; Art Clb; Church Choir; Stu Cncl; Var L Crs Cntry; Var L Trk; High Hon Roll; NHS; AROTC Schlrshp 84; NYS Rgnts, Clarkson Coll Acad Schlrshp; Clarkson U; Chem Engrng.

O BRIEN, TIMOTHY; Pittsford Mendon HS; Pittsford, NY; (Y); Church Yth Grp; Ski Clb; Yrbk Phtg; Yrbk Stf; JV Socr; Hon Roll; Rochester Bassmasters Cnsrvtn & Envrnmnt Awd 85; 1st & 2nd Pl Fishing Tournmnt 85.

O BRIEN, TIMOTHY P; St Anthonys HS; Bayshore, NY; (Y); Nwsp Stf; Yrbk Phtg; Yrbk Stf; Lcrss; Socr; Dons Scotus; Fin.

O BRYAN, KAREN S; Williamsville HS; E Amherst, NY; (Y); 52/315; Church Yth Grp; Ski Clb; Var Diving; Var Capt Socr; Var Swmmng; JV Vllybl; High Hon Roll; Hon Roll; Jr NHS; NHS; Mst Valb Sccr Plyr Awd 84; SUNY Brockport; Nrsg.

O BRYAN, TIMOTHY; Notre Dame HS; Elmira, NY; (Y); Church Yth Grp; Computer Clb; Math Tm; Stage Crew; Var Crs Cntry; Var Trk; Hon Roll; Elec Engr.

O BYRNE, TIMOTHY K; Monsignor Farrell HS; Staten Island, NY; (Y); 10/300; Am Leg Boys St; Capt Exploring; Hosp Aide; VP JA; Var Capt Wrstlng; High Hon Roll; NHS; Boy Scts; Church Yth Grp; Cmnty Wkr; Navy ROTC Schlrshp 85; U Schlr NY U 85; Pres Schlr Brooklyn Coll 85; Brooklyn Coll; Med.

O CONNELL, J MICHAEL; Saratoga Spgs HS; Saratoga Spgs, NY; (Y); 1/465; Am Leg Boys St; Debate Tm; Cit Awd; High Hon Roll; NHS; Ntl Merit Ltr; Val; Rensselaer Polytech Inst; Bio.

O CONNELL, JOHN; Union-Endicott HS; Endicott, NY; (Y); Varsity Clb; L Socr; Var Trk.

O CONNELL, KIM MARIE; Nazareth Acad; Rochester, NY; (Y); 13/110; Drama Clb; French Clb; Latin Clb; Quiz Bowl; School Musical; Lit Mag; Rep Sr Cls; Hon Roll; NHS; NEDT Awd; Aviation Sci.

O CONNELL, MARK A; Garden City SR HS; Garden City, NY; (Y); 8/319; Pres Chess Clb; Computer Clb; French Clb; Pres Mathletes; High Hon Roll; Jr NHS; NHS; Ntl Merit SF; Geo Washington Engrng Awd 84; Amer HS Math Awd 84; Nassau Cty Math Awd 84; Engineering.

O CONNELL, SEAN; Seaford HS; Seaford, NY; (Y); English Clb; Lit Mag; Jr Cls; Ftbl; Lcrss; 2nd Pl Sci Awd 83; Lawyer.

O CONNELL, SHARON E; Greece Arcadia HS; Rochester, NY; (Y); 15/291; Varsity Clb; Trs Soph Cls; Trs Jr Cls; VP Sr Cls; Var JV Socr; JV Capt Sftbl; High Hon Roll; Hon Roll; NHS; Pres Schlr; NYS Regents Schlrshp 85; Colleen Of Shamrocks Fnlst Schlrshp 85; Niagra U; Engl.

O CONNELL, TARA; Saranac Central HS; Cadyville, NY; (S); 28/128; Church Yth Grp; Drama Clb; Band; Church Choir; Concert Band; School Musical; School Play; Rep Frsh Cls; Rep Soph Cls; Rep Jr Cls; Bio.

O CONNOR, AMY E; G Ray Bodley HS; Fulton, NY; (Y); 27/240; VP Sr Cls; JV Var Cheerleading; Var Capt Crs Cntry; Var Capt Trk; Cit Awd; High Hon Roll; Hon Roll; NHS; French Clb; VP Frsh Cls; Jr Prom Queen 84; Elks Teen Yr 85; Fulton Tchr Assoc Schlrshp 85; SUNY Cortland; Elem Educ.

O CONNOR, ANN; Preston HS; Bronx, NY; (S); Pres FNA; Yrbk Stf; Im Vllybl; Hon Roll; NHS.

O CONNOR, CHRISTOPHER; Bishop Kearney HS; Rochester, NY; (S); Church Yth Grp; Debate Tm; NFL; Red Cross Aide; Speech Tm; School Play; Nwsp Stf; Bowling; Crs Cntry; Trk; Hugh O Brian Ldrshp Awd 2nd Pl 83-84; Oratrcl Cntst 2nd Pl 82; U Of Dayton; Law.

O CONNOR, DANIEL F; Mohonasen HS; Schenectady, NY; (Y); 6/216; Church Yth Grp; German Clb; Key Clb; Nwsp Ed-Chief; Rep Stu Cncl; Var Socr; Capt Var Trk; NHS; Ntl Merit SF; Voice Dem Awd; Capt Answers Please Team 83-84; Physics.

O CONNOR, EDWIN T; St Marys Acad; Glens Falls, NY; (S); 8/43; Varsity Clb; Yrbk Ed-Chief; Pres Jr Cls; Var Bsbl; JV Var Bsktbl; Var Capt Ftbl; Hon Roll; NHS; St Schlr; Siena Coll; Mgt.

O CONNOR, JACQUELINE G; Ursuline HS; Bronxville, NY; (Y); 25/130; Church Yth Grp; Cmnty Wkr; Computer Clb; French Clb; Ski Clb; Spanish Clb; Rep Frsh Cls; Rep Sr Cls; Stu Cncl; Trk; Boston Coll; Ed.

O CONNOR, JASON; Kenmore West SR HS; Kenmore, NY; (Y); Concert Band; Jazz Band; Band; Mrchg Band; Orch; Symp Band; Variety Show; Var Capt Swmmng; High Hon Roll; Hon Roll; Sci.

O CONNOR, JENNIFER; Stamford Central Schl; Stamford, NY; (S); 4/25; Band; Chorus; Color Guard; Concert Band; Yrbk Stf; Sec Frsh Cls; Pres Soph Cls; Cheerleading; Hon Roll; Stamfords Crtv Wrtng Awd 82; Engl Educ.

O CONNOR, JOHN; Newfield HS; Selden, NY; (S); 9/565; VP Q&S; Varsity Clb; Nwsp Ed-Chief; Nwsp Rptr; Nwsp Stf; Var Tennis; High Hon Roll; Jr NHS; NHS; Engl & Chem Awds 81-83; Ntl Ldrshp & Ntl Jrnlsm Awds 83-84; Georgetown U; Med.

O CONNOR, KEVIN; Iona Prep; Scarsdale, NY; (Y); 32/200; JV Var Bsbl; JV Var Bsktbl; JV Trk; High Hon Roll; Hon Roll; NHS.

O CONNOR, LYNNE M; Mohonasen Senior HS; Rotterdam, NY; (Y); 18/190; Church Yth Grp; Drama Clb; French Clb; Nwsp Stf; Var Socr; High Hon Roll; NHS; Var L Sftbl; French.

O CONNOR, MARK; Liverpool SR HS; Liverpool, NY; (S); 62/756; Cmnty Wkr; JA; Latin Clb; Spanish Clb; School Musical; Yrbk Stf; Rep Stu Cncl; Hon Roll; Sec Jr NHS; Trs NHS; Cornell U; Pre Vet.

O CONNOR, MAUREEN; Ft Hamilton HS; Brooklyn, NY; (Y); Teachers Aide; Band; Chorus; Variety Show; Danc Stdnt Joffrey Ballet Schl NYC 80-85; Hnrs Frnch 83; Engl Hnrs 84; Hnrs Slmnstcs 84; Hnrs Htlh 85; Brooklyn Coll CUNY; Danc.

O CONNOR, MAUREEN; Holy Trinity HS; Levittown, NY; (Y); 26/373; Church Yth Grp; Cmnty Wkr; English Clb; Library Aide; Mathletes; Math Clb; Math Tm; Office Aide; Science Clb; Ski Clb; Pre-Med.

O CONNOR, MEGAN; Lansingburgh HS; Troy, NY; (Y); 12/180; Drama Clb; VP German Clb; Band; Concert Band; Mrchg Band; Pep Band; School Play; Off Sr Cls; VP Stu Cncl; High Hon Roll; Phi Delta Kappa Schlrshp Grant 85; Siena Coll; Math Tchr.

O CONNOR, NANCY L; East HS; Rochester, NY; (Y); 2/267; Cmnty Wkr; French Clb; Model UN; Red Cross Aide; Yrbk Stf; Trs Stu Cncl; NHS; Ntl Merit SF; Sal; Church Yth Grp; Harvard Book Awd 84; Phi Beta Kappa Awd 84; Intl Relations.

O CONNOR, NUALA; Herricks HS; Williston Park, NY; (Y); 33/306; Dance Clb; Q&S; Scholastic Bowl; VP Chorus; Drm Mjr(t); Nwsp Ed-Chief; NHS; Ntl Merit Ltr; Church Yth Grp; Outstndng Achvt Frnch 85; Amer Legion Svc Awd 85; Outstndg Svc HS Nwspr 85; Princeton U; Econ.

O CONNOR, PATRICIA; Bethpage HS; Bethpage, NY; (Y); 1/287; Rep GAA; Spanish Clb; Bsktbl; Fld Hcky; Capt Lcrss; Sftbl; High Hon Roll; VP NHS; Rotary Awd; Val; Excllnc Awd Histy 84-85; US Army Rsv Ntl Schlr Athlt Awd 85; Hugh Coyle Annl Schlrshp 85; Fairfield U; Bus.

O CONNOR, PETER J; John A Coleman HS; Saugerties, NY; (Y); 7/68; VP Church Yth Grp; Key Clb; School Play; Stage Crew; L Bsbl; High Hon Roll; JC Awd; NHS; US Naval Acad; Engr.

O CONNOR, SCOTT; Tupper Lake HS; Tupper Lake, NY; (Y); Church Yth Grp; Drama Clb; Trs Sec 4-H; Spanish Clb; Stu Cncl; Var L Bsbl; Var L Socr; High Hon Roll; Boy Scts; Computer Clb; Chem Awd 85; Columbian Squires Trea 83; Ski Tm Downhl & X-Cntry Ltrd 83-85.

O CONNOR, TERESA; James E Sperry HS; Henrietta, NY; (Y); GAA; Hosp Aide; JA; Pep Clb; Chorus; Sec Frsh Cls; Sec Soph Cls; Stu Cncl; Var Capt Cheerleading; Hon Roll; Psych.

O COUGHLIN, LOREN; Union-Endicott HS; Endicott, NY; (Y); Chorus; Church Choir; Broome CC; Nrsng.

O DEA, EUGENE V; Valley Central HS; Walden, NY; (Y); 60/300; Chess Clb; CAP; Sec 4-H; Science Clb; Var Swmmng; Coast Guard Acad.

O DEE, CORINNE E; Frontier Central HS; Hamburg, NY; (Y); Drama Clb; Spanish Clb; Chorus; School Musical; School Play; Stage Crew; Yrbk Stf; U Of Miami; Marine Bio.

O DELL, DENISE; Avoca Central Schl; Avoca, NY; (Y); VP FBLA; Chorus; Stage Crew; Yrbk Stf; Score Keeper; JV Socr; JV Sftbl; Var Trk; JV Vllybl; High Hon Roll; Bus.

O DELL, SCOTT; Walton Central HS; Walton, NY; (Y); 8/102; Varsity Clb; Pres Soph Cls; Trs Jr Cls; Rep Stu Cncl; Var Ftbl; Var Trk; Var Wrstlng; High Hon Roll; Hon Roll; Brd Ed Awd Hghst Avg Complt Crs Spnsh 85; 2nd Tm Leag Offnsv Ctr Ftbl 84; Hotel-Restrnt Mgt.

O DONNELL, BRIAN; Saugerties HS; Rochester Hills, MI; (Y); 11/236; Boy Scts; JA; Library Aide; Ski Clb; Band; Chorus; School Musical; Symp Band; L Socr; Trk; Sci.

O DONNELL, CATHERINE; Lindenhurst HS; Lindenhurst, NY; (Y); Church Yth Grp; German Clb; Varsity Clb; VP Sr Cls; Var Badmtn; JV Var Fld Hcky; Var Trk; Most Imprvd Athlete 85; Nrsng.

O DONNELL, CHRISTOPHER; Rome Free Acad; Rome, NY; (Y); Hon Roll; NHS; Ind Arts 85; Ag & Tech Coll Delhi; Cvl Engnr.

O DONNELL, COLLEEN; Mont Pleasant HS; Schenectady, NY; (Y); 11/300; Church Yth Grp; Chorus; Var L Crs Cntry; Var L Trk; Hon Roll; NHS; Spnsh Awd 84-85; Siena; Bus.

O DONNELL, DANIEL M; St Anthonys HS; E Northport, NY; (Y); 67/500; Nwsp Rptr; Yrbk Rptr; JV Ice Hcky; High Hon Roll; Hon Roll; NHS; Spanish NHS; Im Bowling; Capt Of Northport Yth Ctr Soccer 83; Engrng.

O DONNELL, EILEEN M; Cardinal Spellman HS; Bronx, NY; (S); 2/540; Cmnty Wkr; Var Bsktbl; Var Sftbl; High Hon Roll; NHS; US Army Rsrv Ntl Schlr/Athl Awd 84; Cncl Of Ldrs Nghbrhd Yth Awd 82-84; Math.

O DONNELL, ELIZABETH; Liverpool HS; Liverpool, NY; (Y); Church Yth Grp; JA; Band; Concert Band; Bus.

O DONNELL, GLORIA JEAN; St Vincent Ferrer HS; New York, NY; (Y); Library Aide; Math Clb; School Play; High Hon Roll; Hon Roll; NHS; NEDT Awd; Nwsp Rptr; Yrbk Bus Mgr; Yrbk Stf; Achvt Awd Phy Ed 85; Achvt Aswd Am Lit 83-84.

O DONNELL, JOHN; Ossing HS; Ossining, NY; (Y); Church Yth Grp; JA; Var JV Bsbl; Var Im Ftbl; High Hon Roll; Italian Cert Of Praise 83-85; Brnz, Slvr & Gld Schlrshp Pins 83-85; Ltrs & Pin For Vrsy Bsbl & Ftbl 84; Bus Adm.

O DONNELL, KATHLEEN; Saint Catharine Acad; Bronx, NY; (Y); 64/205; 1st & 2nd Hnrs 84-85; Baruch; Acctng.

O DONNELL, KATIE; Niagara Catholic HS; Niagara Falls, NY; (Y); JV Badmtn; Var Cheerleading; Niagara Cnty CC; Bus.

O DONNELL, KELLY A; C W Baker HS; Baldwinsville, NY; (Y); 8/441; Key Clb; Ski Clb; Lit Mag; Var Socr; High Hon Roll; JC Awd; Jr NHS; NHS; NYS Rgnts Schlrshp 85; Clarkson U; Mech Engrng.

O DONNELL, MARY E; Sachem North HS; Holtsville, NY; (Y); Chorus; Bus.

O DONNELL, NOREEN M; Sheepshead Bay HS; Brooklyn, NY; (Y); Cmnty Wkr; JA; Yrbk Ed-Chief; Regents Schlrshp 85; Hnr Awds Acctng 82-85; Hnr Awd Econ 85; Brooklyn Coll; Law.

O DONNELL, PHYLLIS M; Saint Joseph By-The-Sea HS; Staten Island, NY; (Y); 2/250; Band; Drm Mjr(t); Mrchg Band; Twrlr; High Hon Roll; NHS; NEDT Awd; Acad All Amer 84; Tutor 84-85.

O DRISCOLL, CATHERINE; Bronx H S Of Science; Bronx, NY; (Y); Church Yth Grp; JA; Office Aide; Teachers Aide; Tennis; Trk; Hon Roll; CUNY; Nrsng.

O DWYER, MAUREEN; Washingtonville HS; Washingtonville, NY; (S); Hosp Aide; Trs JA; Ski Clb; Spanish Clb; Symp Band; Rep Sr Cls; JV Capt Bsktbl; Var Capt Vllybl; VP NHS; NE U; Comp Sci.

O DWYER, THOMAS; Holy Cross HS; Bayside, NY; (Y); 48/312; Chess Clb; Church Yth Grp; Computer Clb; Var Crs Cntry; Var Trk; NHS; Sci.

O FARRELL, JAMES F; Cardinal Spellman HS; Bronx, NY; (Y); Church Yth Grp; Intnl Clb; JV Var Bsbl; Var Capt Socr; Var Trk; Hon Roll; Bsbl, Socr, Trk Var Ltrs 84 & 85; 1st Hnrs 82-85; Engrng.

O FARRILL, FROILAN; De Witt Clinton HS; Bronx, NY; (Y); Aud/Vis; Cmnty Wkr; Drama Clb; JV Bsbl; Phy Ftnss Awd 82; John Jay; Sec Serv.

O GARRO, SHARON; Walton HS; Bronx, NY; (Y); 60/679; Church Yth Grp; Hosp Aide; Chorus; Church Choir; Yrbk Stf; Tennis; Syracuse U; Nrsg.

O GORMAN, CONNIE; J C Birdlebough HS; Phoenix, NY; (Y); 9/164; Hosp Aide; Concert Band; Drm Mjr(t); Mrchg Band; Pep Band; School Musical; Yrbk Stf; High Hon Roll; Secy.

O GORMAN, DINA M; Mc Graw Central HS; Cortland, NY; (Y); 4/66; Trs Drama Clb; Rep French Clb; Hosp Aide; Band; Chorus; Nwsp Bus Mgr; Trs Nwsp Stf; Rep Jr Cls; Rep Sr Cls; Rep Stu Cncl; Regnts Schlrshp 85; Le Moyne; Pedtrcn.

O GRADY, CHRIS; St Mrys HS; Long Beach, NY; (Y); 15/130; Ice Hcky; Lcrss; St Regnts Schlrshp 85-86; Siena Coll Grnt 85-86; Siena Coll; Comp Sci.

O GRADY, SEAN O; St Josephs Collegiate Inst; Kenmore, NY; (Y); 32/192; Chorus; Socr; Swmmng; High Hon Roll; NHS; Boy Scts; Ski Clb; Swing Chorus; Church Choir; Yrbk Phtg; Dentstry.

O GRADY, TRACY; Auburn HS; Moravia, NY; (Y); Exploring; JA; Chorus; Church Choir; Stage Crew; Hon Roll; Cauga CC; Dental Assntnt.

O HAGAN, MAURA; Walt Whitman HS; Huntington, NY; (Y); 63/500; Debate Tm; Band; Stage Crew; Mgr Bsktbl; French Hon Soc; High Hon Roll; Hon Roll; Drama Clb; French Clb; Concert Band; Wrld Hist Olympd 84; Am Hist Olympd 85; Psych.

O HAGEN, KAREN; Centereach HS; Centereach, NY; (Y); 14/475; Hosp Aide; Band; Chorus; School Musical; Ed Yrbk Stf; Hon Roll; NHS; St Schlr; MIP Fencer 84; Co-Cptn Vrsty Fencng Tm 84; Ntl Camprs & Hikrs Assoc Schlrshp 84; Rochester U; Chem.

O HALLORAN, KEVIN; Camden HS; Taberg, NY; (Y); 5/204; Am Leg Boys St; Drama Clb; Ski Clb; Madrigals; School Musical; School Play; Nwsp Ed-Chief; Pres Stu Cncl; High Hon Roll; DAR 84; Sed Of Selflessness Awd 84-85; Harvard U.

O HALLORAN, MAUREEN; St John Villa Acad; Bklyn, NY; (Y); Math Tm; Teachers Aide; Church Choir; Mgr Stage Crew; Ed Nwsp Stf; Yrbk Stf; Rep Soph Cls; Swmmng; Hon Roll; NHS; Gen Excllnc & Hnr Roll 82-85; Englsh Awds 84-85; Hotel Rest Mgmt.

O HALORAN, KEVIN; Camden Central HS; Taberg, NY; (S); 5/250; Pres Drama Clb; Ski Clb; Chorus; Madrigals; School Musical; School Play; Nwsp Ed-Chief; Pres Stu Cncl; Cit Awd; High Hon Roll; Harvard U.

O HANLON, DENISE; New Dorp HS; Staten Island, NY; (Y); 2/804; Am Leg Aux Girls St; Pres Key Clb; Variety Show; Nwsp Ed-Chief; Capt Pom Pon; Var Socr; NHS; Hosp Aide; Intnl Clb; Math Tm; 1st Pl Mdl & Cert Scl Stds Fair 85; Cert For Hours Wrkd At Hosp 84; SUNY Albny; Cpa.

O HANLON, MICHAEL; St John The Baptist HS; Copiague, NY; (Y); 212/546; Bsbl.

O HARA, JENNIE R; Mamaroneck HS; Larchmont, NY; (Y); Latin Clb; Political Wkr; Service Clb; Ski Clb; Variety Show; Pres Soph Cls; Bsktbl; Coach Actv; Var Fld Hcky; JV Capt Socr; Law.

O HARA, JENNIFER; Port Jervis HS; Port Jervis, NY; (Y); 11/200; Spanish Clb; Varsity Clb; Sec Frsh Cls; Sec Soph Cls; Sec Jr Cls; Rep Stu Cncl; JV Var Cheerleading; Var Vllybl; High Hon Roll; Hon Roll; Mst Imprvd Bsktbl Chrldr 83-84.

O HARA, KATE; Albertus Magnus HS; Pearl River, NY; (Y); Church Yth Grp; Cmnty Wkr; Math Tm; Varsity Clb; Stage Crew; Nwsp Stf; Var Socr; Hon Roll; NHS.

O HARA, KELLY A; Kenmore East HS; Tonawanda, NY; (Y); Computer Clb; German Clb; GAA; Pep Clb; Yrbk Stf; Bowling; Socr; Swmmng; Comp Sci.

O HARA, LAURA; Camden HS; Camden, NY; (Y); Office Aide; Fld Hcky; Golf; High Hon Roll; Bu.

O HARA, PATRICK J; Williamsville East HS; Williamsville, NY; (Y); 75/276; Var L Bsbl; Var L Bsktbl; Var L Socr; Var L Trk; High Hon Roll; Prfct Atten Awd; St Schlr; NY ST Regents Schlrshp 85; Var Sccr Tm Awd 83-84; Var Bsbll Schl Record For Stolen Bases In 1 Season; SUNY At Buffalo; Engrng.

O HARA, RICHARD J; Camden HS; Camden, NY; (Y); 3/200; AFS; Varsity Clb; Yrbk Stf; Var L Bsbl; Var L Bsktbl; Var L Ftbl; Im Wt Lftg; High Hon Roll; NHS; Tri-Vly Lg Def Bck 1st Tm All Str Ftbl 84-85; Engrng.

O HARE, KELLY L; West Seneca E HS; West Seneca, NY; (Y); 21/365; Sec Church Yth Grp; Pres Trs GAA; Mgr Bsktbl; Var Fld Hcky; Capt Var Socr; High Hon Roll; NHS; Regents Schlrshp 85; St Lawrence U Schlrshp 85; Schlst Achvt Awd 84; St Lawrence U; Math.

O HARE, VIRGINIA; John F Kennedy HS; Plainview, NY; (Y); 5/275; Dance Clb; Girl Scts; Intnl Clb; Math Tm; Model UN; School Play; Variety Show; Nwsp Rptr; Nwsp Stf; Yrbk Stf; B Nai Brith Schlrshp 85; Awd For Outstndng Schl Srv 85; Swarth More Coll; Psychlgy.

O HERRON, ELIZABETH H; Elmira Southside HS; Elmira, NY; (Y); 28/333; Drama Clb; Latin Clb; Thesps; Chorus; Madrigals; Mrchg Band; School Play; Stage Crew; Symp Band; Ntl Merit Ltr; Regents Schlrshp 85; St Bonaventure U; Pre-Med.

O KANE, JOHN; St Ohn The Baptist HS; Islip, NY; (Y); 88/602; Var Capt Ftbl; Var Capt Lcrss; JV Wrstlng; Hon Roll; NY Regents Schlrshp 85-86; Marist Pres Schlrshp 85-86; Marist Coll; Comp Sci.

O KEEFE, DARLENE; Malverne HS; Lynbrook, NY; (Y); Camera Clb; Yrbk Phtg; Hon Roll; Soc Studies Awd 85; Nrs.

O KEEFE, DAVID; Bishop Ludden HS; Camillus, NY; (S); Boys Clb Am; Church Yth Grp; Var Bsktbl; High Hon Roll; Bus Admn.

O KEEFE, JODI; E J Wilson HS; Spencerport, NY; (Y); Drama Clb; Ski Clb; Spanish Clb; Chorus; School Musical; Swing Chorus; JV Var Cheerleading; Wrkng Hndcpd Chldrn 81-82; Monroe CC; Med Sec.

O KEEFE, JOHN M; Bishop Timon HS; Buffalo, NY; (S); #5 In Class; Yrbk Stf; Lit Mag; Socr; High Hon Roll; Hon Roll; Sci Awd 83.

O KEEFE, KATHLEEN; Penn Yan Acad; Penn Yan, NY; (Y); 1/168; Off Church Yth Grp; Pep Clb; Ski Clb; Variety Show; Var Cheerleading; Elks Awd; High Hon Roll; NHS; Ntl Merit Ltr; Val; Brown U; Lbrl Arts.

O KEEFE, KIMBERLY; Glens Falls SR HS; Glens Falls, NY; (Y); AFS; Hosp Aide; Political Wkr; Chorus; Var Crs Cntry; Powder Puff Ftbl; Var Trk; High Hon Roll; NHS; Sci.

O KEEFE, LEANNE; Walter Panas HS; Peekskill, NY; (Y); Pres Drama Clb; Teachers Aide; Chorus; Church Choir; School Musical; School Play; Stage Crew; High Hon Roll; Pres Schlr; Area All ST Chrs 83-85; Panas Pyrs Schlrshp 85; Albany ST U.

O KEEFE, MARLENE; Malverne HS; Lynbrook, NY; (Y); Rep Jr Cls; High Hon Roll.

O LEARY, ELIZABETH M; Williamsville East HS; Williamsville, NY; (Y); Latin Clb; Ski Clb; Rep Frsh Cls; Rep Soph Cls; Rep Jr Cls; Rep Sr Cls; Stu Cncl; JV Powder Puff Ftbl; Var L Socr; Var L Tennis; Regnts Schlrshp 85; Potsdam Coll; Microbio.

O LEARY, HELENBETH; Notre Dame Acad; Staten Island, NY; (Y); 28/94; Drama Clb; Hosp Aide; Teachers Aide; School Musical; School Play; Stage Crew; Yrbk Stf; Var Cheerleading; Phillips Beth Israel Schl Of Nrsng Schlrshp 85-86; Regents Schlrshp 85; Phillips Beth Israel Schl; Nrs.

O LEARY, JEAN MARIE; White Plains HS; White Plains, NY; (Y); 26/490; Am Leg Aux Girls St; French Clb; Orch; Pres Frsh Cls; Pres Soph Cls; Sec Stu Cncl; Var L Crs Cntry; Var L Trk; Cit Awd; NHS; NHS Awd 85; G O Stu Svc Aw 85; Polc Benevolnt Assn White Plains Scholar 85; Rutgers U; Intl Bus.

O LEARY, JOE MICHAEL; Wellington L Mepham HS; N Bellmore, NY; (Y); Math Tm; Jazz Band; Mrchg Band; Trs Symp Band; Crs Cntry; Ftbl; Var Trk; Var High Hon Roll; Jr NHS; NHS; Top 10 In Sci Olympiad In Bio & Chem84-85; Cllctd $ For Schl Schlrshp Day & For Cerbral Palsey 84; U Of Rochester; Patnt Law.

O LEARY, JUDY; Bishop Kearney HS; Rochester, NY; (S); 20/321; Hosp Aide; Model UN; Speech Tm; School Musical; Nwsp Stf; Rep Stu Cncl; Var L Crs Cntry; Var Vllybl; NHS; Ntl Merit Ltr; NY Regents Schlrshp 85; Natl Comm Acad 85; Natl Frnsc Leag Mbr 85.

O LEARY, KELLY; Whitesboro SR HS; Whitesboro, NY; (Y); 105/365; Church Yth Grp; Hosp Aide; Library Aide; Variety Show; Rep Stu Cncl; Var Cheerleading; Powder Puff Ftbl; Hon Roll; Cmmrcl Art.

O LEARY, MICHAEL; Beacon HS; Beacon, NY; (Y); #7 In Class; Math Clb; Varsity Clb; Var Bsbl; Var Ftbl; High Hon Roll; Hon Roll; NHS; Engrng.

O LEARY, MICHAEL; John A Coleman HS; Ulster Park, NY; (Y); Chess Clb; Bsktbl; Crs Cntry; Trk; Hon Roll; Engl Lit.

O LOUGHLIN, HEATHER; Woodlands HS; Hartsdale, NY; (Y); Cmnty Wkr; Hosp Aide; Varsity Clb; Cheerleading; Cmnctns.

O LOUGHLIN, SUSAN; Waterloo Central Schl; Waterloo, NY; (Y); 20/173; Pres FTA; Spanish Clb; Teachers Aide; Chorus; Hon Roll; Prfct Atten Awd; Elmira Coll Key 84; Waterloo Educ Assn Schlrshp 85; UNY Geneseo; Elem Educ.

O MALLEY, KERRI-ANN; Connetgout HS; Bohemia, NY; (S); 13/743; Church Yth Grp; Hst Drama Clb; Pres Intnl Clb; School Musical; Swing Chorus; Symp Band; Ed Lit Mag; Jr NHS; NHS; 1st Cls Girl Scout Awd 82; Georgine Krepela Svc Awd 82; Music.

O MALLEY, KIRSTEN; John Dewey HS; Brooklyn, NY; (Y); Cmnty Wkr; Drama Clb; Political Wkr; School Play; Nwsp Stf; Pres Frsh Cls; Cit Awd; Hon Roll; Jr NHS; Sal; Cmnty Action Chrprsn 84-85; Socl Sci.

O MARA, ERIN; Oneonta HS; Oneonta, NY; (Y); Drama Clb; Q&S; Thesps; Varsity Clb; Stage Crew; Yrbk Ed-Chief; Yrbk Sprt Ed; Var Bsktbl; Var Socr; NY ST West Select Soccr Tm U-16, U-17 84-85; Jrnlsm.

O NEAL, THURSTON D; Wyandanch JR SR HS; Baldwin, NY; (Y); 15/120; Am Leg Boys St; Boys Clb Am; Church Yth Grp; Drama Clb; Band; Chorus; Church Choir; Concert Band; Drm & Bgl; School Play; SUNY; Comp Engrng.

O NEIL, CHRISTINA S; Sachem HS; Lake Ronkonkoma, NY; (Y); 75/1430; French Clb; Hosp Aide; Hon Roll; Jr NHS; Ntl Merit SF; NY U CBPA Schlrshp 85; Regnts Schlrshp 85; NY U; Acctng.

O NEIL, KEVIN P; Binghamton HS; Binghamton, NY; (Y); 44/464; Varsity Clb; Concert Band; Mrchg Band; Symp Band; Var Capt Bsktbl; Ftbl; Hon Roll; St Schlr; Hobart Coll Geneva NY; Pre-Med.

O NEIL, KIM; Copiague HS; Copiague, NY; (Y); Spanish Clb; Yrbk Stf; Rep Soph Cls; Rep Jr Cls; Rep Sr Cls; Trs Stu Cncl; Var JV Bsktbl; Var Trk; JV Var Vllybl; NHS; Brookhaven Ntl Lab Smmr Prog 84; Howard U; Bus.

O NEIL, LEIGH E; Greene HS; Greene, NY; (Y); Var Ftbl; JV Wrstlng; NYS Regnts Schlrshp 85; Ithaca; Physcs.

O NEIL, MARY KAY; Solvay HS; Syracuse, NY; (Y); Church Yth Grp; Intnl Clb; Spanish Clb; Chorus; School Musical; Off Soph Cls; Off Jr Cls; Off Sr Cls; Rep Stu Cncl; Phy Thrpy.

O NEIL, PATRICIA; Linton HS; Schenectady, NY; (Y); Pres AFS; Hst Mgr Drama Clb; Pres JCL; Thesps; Mrchg Band; School Musical; School Play; Stage Crew; Hon Roll; Service Clb; JCL Awd 85; US Navy; Advncd Tech Fld.

O NEIL, PATRICK M; Chatham HS; Chatham, NY; (Y); 11/130; Stage Crew; High Hon Roll; NHS; Hudson Vly CC; Elect Engrng.

O NEILL, BOB; Clarkstown South SR HS; New City, NY; (Y); JV L Bsbl; JV Ftbl.

O NEILL, JACQUELINE; Holy Trinity HS; Uniondale, NY; (Y); 36/356; Church Yth Grp; GAA; High Hon Roll; Hon Roll; Jr NHS.

O NEILL, KELLIE; The Mary Louis Acad; Bronxville, NY; (Y); Church Yth Grp; GAA; Hosp Aide; Yrbk Stf; Ftbl; Powder Puff Ftbl; Swmmng; Trk; NEDT Awd; Sci Hnrs; NEDT Achvt Awd; Sprts Med.

O NEILL, KELLY; St Edmund HS; Brooklyn, NY; (S); 9/190; Spanish Clb; High Hon Roll; NHS; JV Bsktbl; NY Police Dept Holy Name Soc Scholar 82-83.

O NEILL, LORI; Saint Catharine Acad; New York, NY; (Y); Church Yth Grp; Svc Awd Guidnc Dept; Awd Relgs Instrctns; Geometry Accom; Lib Arts.

O NEILL, LUCIEN; Nazareth Regional HS; Brooklyn, NY; (Y); Drama Clb; Im Bsktbl; Im Ftbl; Var Socr; Im Sftbl; Im Vllybl; High Hon Roll; Chem Awd 85; NY U; Gyn.

O NEILL, PEGGY ANN; Riverhead HS; Riverhead, NY; (Y); 43/247; Acpl Chr; Chorus; Var Sftbl; Hon Roll; SCCC; Pre-Med.

O NEILL, TERRI; Port Jervis HS; Westbrookville, NY; (Y); 18/180; 4-H; Capt Math Tm; Capt Bowling; L Mat Maids; Hon Roll; NHS; Med.

O NEILL, THOMAS B; Stissing Mountain JR SR HS; Red Hook, NY; (Y); Church Yth Grp; Cmnty Wkr; Varsity Clb; Yrbk Stf; Var Bsktbl; Var Ftbl; Mgr(s); High Hon Roll; Hon Roll; NHS; Natl Englsh Mrt Awd 84.

O REILLY, KEVIN P; Sachem HS; Lake Ronkonkoma, NY; (Y); 33/1463; Church Yth Grp; Computer Clb; Math Tm; Ski Clb; Mrchg Band; Symp Band; Rep Jr Cls; Rep Sr Cls; Jr NHS; NHS; LIU.

O ROURKE, CHERYL A; West HS; Painted Post, NY; (Y); Mrchg Band; Trk; Capt L Twrlr; Hon Roll; Bus.

O ROURKE, MICHAEL J; South Lewis Central HS; Constableville, NY; (Y); 5/103; Quiz Bowl; Ski Clb; Varsity Clb; Drm & Bgl; Jazz Band; Nwsp Rptr; Trs Stu Cncl; Capt Ftbl; Trk; NHS; Boston Coll; Ec.

O SHEA, DANNY; Mount Saint Michaels Acad; New York, NY; (S); Church Yth Grp; Im Bsbl; Im Bsktbl; Im Fld Hcky; Im Ftbl; Im Trk; Im Hon Roll; Hnrs 3 Yrs; Fordham U; Law.

O SHEA, JAMES J; Bronx High School Of Science; New York, NY; (Y); Computer Clb; JA; Math Clb; Math Tm; Science Clb; Yrbk Ed-Chief; Yrbk Rptr; Yrbk Stf; Im Bsbl; Im Bsktbl; 44th Westinghouse Sci Tlnt Srch 85; NY Cty Hsng Auth Schlrshp 85; St Johns U Sci & Humnts Sympsm 85; U Of PA; Engrng.

O SHEA, JANET M; Yorktown HS; Yorktown Hts, NY; (Y); Dance Clb; Sec German Clb; Key Clb; School Musical; School Play; Stu Cncl; High Hon Roll; NHS; Church Yth Grp; Chorus; Partl Dance Schlrshp For Westchester Ballet Ctr 84-85; AATG Smmr Prog In Grmny 85; 1 Stu Senate Lttr; Lang.

O SHEA, LORRAINE A; Riverdale Country Schl; Bronx, NY; (Y); CAP; Science Clb; Lit Mag; Coach Actv; Score Keeper; Ntl Merit SF; Wrtng.

O SHEA, M NICOLE; Garden City SR HS; Garden City, NY; (Y); 9/320; Church Yth Grp; Key Clb; Pep Clb; Chrmn Spanish Clb; Rep Frsh Cls; Rep Jr Cls; Rep Sr Cls; JV Fld Hcky; Hon Roll; NHS; NYS Regnts Schlrshp 85; H K Stanford Schlrshp 85; Pol Sci.

O SHEA, WILLIAM; St Johns Prep; Astoria, NY; (Y); Drama Clb; Hosp Aide; School Play; Bsbl; Bsktbl; Prfct Atten Awd; John Jay Coll; FBI Agnt.

O SULLIVAN, GRACE; St John The Baptist HS; Massapequa Pk, NY; (Y); Debate Tm; Math Tm; Speech Tm; Mrchg Band; Nwsp Stf; Twrlr; Law.

O SULLIVAN, MARY BETH; Academy Of The Resrrctn; Crestwood, NY; (Y); Hosp Aide; Chorus; School Play; Trs Soph Cls; Var Swmmng; 2nd Hnrs 85; Iona; Bus Admin.

O SULLIVAN, SEAN G; St Josephs Coll Inst; Snyder, NY; (Y); 17/202; School Musical; Hon Roll; NHS; St Schlr; Church Yth Grp; Drama Clb; French Clb; Model UN; Chorus; Nwsp Stf; CYO 1 Act Ply Comp Bst Supprtg Actr 84; U Buffalo.

O TOOLE, STACY ANN; The Ursuline Schl; New Rochelle, NY; (Y); 8/129; Lit Mag; Hon Roll; NHS; NYS Rgnts Schrlshp Wnnr 85; Awd Exc Lang Study 85; Schls Cert Exc Math Spnsh 85; NY U; Bilingual.

OAKES, CHRISTINA A; Northeastern Clinton Central Schl; Altona, NY; (Y); 24/146; Model UN; Acpl Chr; Concert Band; Jazz Band; Madrigals; Mrchg Band; Orch; Pep Band; School Musical; NHS; NY All-ST Music Fest 84; All-Eastern Music Fest 85; Regents Schlrshp 85; Potsdam U; Math.

OAKES, JULIE A; Massena Central HS; Massena, NY; (Y); French Clb; Stat JV Bsktbl; Powder Puff Ftbl; Stat Var Socr; Sftbl; Vllybl; High Hon Roll; Hon Roll; NHS; Acad Banquet Aten 83-85; U R; Engrng.

OAKES, OLIVER DAVID; Corning-Painted Post West HS; Corning, NY; (Y); 10/254; Boy Scts; Key Clb; Ski Clb; Thesps; VP Band; School Musical; Var Crs Cntry; Var Trk; High Hon Roll; NHS; Hopwood Smr Schlrshp 84; MA Inst Of Tech; Ench Engr.

OAKLEY, ROBERT; North Tonawanda HS; N Tonawanda, NY; (Y); Am Leg Boys St; Boy Scts; Varsity Clb; Nwsp Rptr; Yrbk Bus Mgr; Stu Cncl; Swmmng; Trk; Hon Roll; NHS; Rchstr Inst Of Tech; Comp Engrn.

OBAS, REMY; The Kew-Forest Schl; Holliswood, NY; (Y); 9/32; French Clb; Science Clb; Ed Nwsp Phtg; Ed Yrbk Phtg; Socr; Sftbl; Ntl Merit Ltr; Med.

OBER, JOSEPH; Commack High School South; Commack, NY; (Y); Computer Clb; Mathletes; Math Tm; Office Aide; Nwsp Stf; Im Bsktbl; JV Ice Hcky; NHS; Ntl Merit Ltr; Teachers Aide; Natl Sci Olympiad 84-85; Air Force Acad; Pre Med.

OBER, LISA; E J Wilson HS; Spencerport, NY; (Y); Varsity Clb; Band; Concert Band; Mrchg Band; Yrbk Ed-Chief; Yrbk Phtg; JV Socr; Var L Vllybl; Hon Roll; Rutgers U; Phrmcy.

OBERER, JAMIE; Byron-Bergen Central Schl; Byron, NY; (Y); Prfct Atten Awd; Art.

OBERYSZYN, ANDRIJ; St George Acad; Jamaica, NY; (Y); Cmnty Wkr; Dance Clb; Ski Clb; VP Soph Cls; Var Socr; Var Vllybl; NHS; NEDT Awd.

OBREGON, JANET; St Vincent Ferrer HS; New York, NY; (Y); 4/114; Drama Clb; Library Aide; Math Tm; Pep Clb; Science Clb; Service Clb; Yrbk Stf; Hon Roll; NEDT Awd; High Hon Roll; 1st Hnr Iona Lang Cntst Spnsh Natv 84; Engl 84; Hstry 83.

OBRIEN, KELLY; Rome Catholic HS; Rome, NY; (Y); Cmnty Wkr; Drama Clb; Chorus; School Musical; Nwsp Bus Mgr; Trs Stu Cncl; Socr; High Hon Roll; Masonic Awd; Prfct Atten Awd; Heisey Fndtn Awd For Schlrshp & Ctznshp 83; Intrprtg.

OBRIEN, KEVIN; Catholic Central HS; Troy, NY; (Y); Boy Scts; Church Yth Grp; Cmnty Wkr; JA; Math Clb; Math Tm; Band; L Rep Soph Cls; Rep Jr Cls; Im Bsktbl; Siena Coll; Acctng.

OBRIEN, MARK; Newark SR HS; Newark, NY; (Y); 30/199; Am Leg Boys St; Church Yth Grp; Drama Clb; Pep Clb; Spanish Clb; Thesps; Acpl Chr; Band; Chorus; Church Choir; Calvin Coll; Teacher.

OBRIEN, RICHARD; Northern Adirondack HS; West Chazy, NY; (Y); Concert Band; Bsktbl; JV Socr; Timer; High Hon Roll; Hon Roll; NHS.

OBRIEN, THOMAS; Valley Stream Central HS; Malverne, NY; (Y); Art Clb; FBLA; Variety Show; Yrbk Stf; Jr Cls; Ftbl; Lcrss; Wt Lftg; Wrstlng; Hon Roll; BUS Admn.

OBRIEN, WILLIAM; Cazenovia HS; Cazenovia, NY; (Y); Cmnty Wkr; FFA; Bsktbl; Ftbl; Wt Lftg; Hon Roll; Engrng.

OBRIST III, JOHN; Cicero N Syracuse HS; N Syracuse, NY; (S); 28/711; Mathletes; NHS; Art.

OBSTARCZYK, CHERYL; Mt St Joseph Acad; Buffalo, NY; (Y); Drama Clb; School Musical; School Play; Yrbk Bus Mgr; Yrbk Stf; Badmtn; Sftbl; Vllybl; Hon Roll; NHS; Canisus Coll; Bus Adm.

OCAMPO, MARIA; Cathederal HS; Woodisde, NY; (Y); 9/298; Library Aide; Hon Roll; Dona Lang Contest Spnsh 85; Red Crss Vol Svc Awd 84; Corp Law.

OCASIO, DOLORES; St Catharine Acad; New York, NY; (Y); Stu Cncl; Swmmng; Nrsng.

OCASIO, MARY L; Mabel Dean Bacon HS; Brooklyn, NY; (S); 25/225; Hosp Aide; Hon Roll; 9th Grd Engl Awd 82; Hnr Soc Pin 84; Nrsng.

OCASIO, YOLANDA; Cathedral HS; New York City, NY; (Y); 123/298; Hosp Aide; Intnl Clb; Sec Jr Cls; Bus Admin.

OCCHIPINTI, FRANK; Lakeland SR HS; Peekskill, NY; (Y); Var Bsbl; Coach Actv; Var Ftbl; Var Socr; Wt Lftg; Var Wrstlng; Highest Achvt In Phy Ed 82-83; Bst Athlete 82-83; Coaches Awd 82-83; Karl J Kinzler Mem Awd 84; Bus.

OCCHIPINTI, SALVATOR A; Xavier HS; Brooklyn, NY; (Y); Church Yth Grp; ROTC; Drill Tm; Off Frsh Cls; Off Soph Cls; Tennis; JROTC Gold Ldrshp 84, Silver Ldrshp 85; Natl Champ Drill Team 84; Med.

OCCHIUZZO, KELLY A; Lawrence HS; Cedarhurst, NY; (Y); Art Clb; Drama Clb; French Clb; Orch; School Musical; School Play; Ed Lit Mag; Hon Roll; Purchase Awd 82; Archon Svc Hnr Soc 84-85; Fine Arts.

OCCHIUZZO, TARA; Lawrence HS; Cedarhurst, NY; (Y); Dance Clb; Drama Clb; French Clb; Sec Orch; School Musical; Cheerleading; Gym; High Hon Roll; Hon Roll; Jr NHS; Fr Awd Excllnce 83; Archon Natl Hnr Soc 85.

OCKE, DARRIN T; Wayne Central SR HS; Ontario, NY; (Y); 12/205; Political Wkr; Chorus; School Musical; Swing Chorus; Yrbk Ed-Chief; Cit Awd; DAR Awd; Ntl Merit Ltr; Church Yth Grp; Math Tm; Outstndg Perf Vocal Music 84; Acad Excell Adv Plcmnt Amer Hist 84; NYSSMA GA Rtng 84; SUNY-OSWEGO; Polt Sci.

OCONNELL, KATHRYN; Rome Catholic HS; Rome, NY; (Y); 21/80; School Musical; Yrbk Stf; Mgr(s); High Hon Roll; Hon Roll; Hist,Bus,Physcl Ed Awd 83-85; Bus Adm.

OCONNELL, KEVIN D; Olean Public Schools; Olean, NY; (Y); 13/187; Political Wkr; Red Cross Aide; Varsity Clb; JV Var Bsbl; JV Var Ftbl; Im Sftbl; Im Vllybl; Im Wt Lftg; High Hon Roll; Co-Capt Dfnsv Ftbl Team 84; Co-Capt Ftbl Team 85; Bus.

OCONNELL, MARJORIE; East Hampton HS; E Hampton, NY; (Y); 2/120; Library Aide; Band; Yrbk Stf; Sec Jr Cls; Var Pres Sr Cls; Rep Stu Cncl; Cheerleading; High Hon Roll; Lion Awd; NHS.

OCONNELL, MONICA; Academy Of Mount St Ursula; Bronx, NY; (Y); Debate Tm; Science Clb; Stage Crew; Cheerleading.

OCONNELL, ROBERT; Tappan Zee HS; Blauvelt, NY; (Y); Aud/Vis; Boy Scts; Church Yth Grp; Math Tm; Stage Crew; Yrbk Stf; Stat Score Keeper; JV Socr; Math Hnr Soc 84-85; Engrng.

OCONNOR, CHRISTINE; Far Rockaway HS; Far Rockaway, NY; (Y); Computer Clb; Key Clb; Office Aide; Nwsp Rptr; High Hon Roll; NHS; Prfct Atten Awd; Band; Nwsp Stf; Yrbk Stf; Alpha Prep Awd Asst Stu 85; Intrnshp Awd 85; Arista 85; St Johns U; Bus Adm.

OCONNOR, DAVID; Weedsport Central HS; Weedsport, NY; (Y); AFS; Pres Church Yth Grp; Math Clb; Trs Frsh Cls; Trs Soph Cls; Trs Jr Cls; Var L Bsbl; Var L Ftbl; Var L Swmmng; Hon Roll; Finished 4th NY ST Swmmng Champnshp 84.

OCONNOR, JAMES; Bishop Ford HS; Brooklyn, NY; (Y); Boy Scts; Math Tm; Bsktbl; Hon Roll; Mc Quaid Jesuit Otstndg Achvt Awd Rgnts Schlrshp 86; Boston Coll; Statistics.

OCONNOR, MICHAEL; St John The Baptist DHS; Brightwaters, NY; (Y); Varsity Clb; Nwsp Rptr; Nwsp Sprt Ed; Var Capt Crs Cntry; Var Capt Trk; Hon Roll; Eastern ST Trk Chmp 3200 Mtr 85; CHSAA Lg Chmp 3200 Mtrs 85; Lg All Star 83-85; All Star Crs Cntry 85.

OCONNOR, ROBIN; Allegany Central HS; Allegany, NY; (Y); Art Clb; Ski Clb; Varsity Clb; Band; Concert Band; Mrchg Band; Pep Band; Yrbk Stf; Var Cheerleading; Hon Roll; Mst Imrpvd Artst 83; Elem Ed.

OCONNOR, SUSAN; Albertus Magnus HS; Pearl River, NY; (Y); 65/196; Boys Clb Am; Camp Fr Inc; Church Yth Grp; FHA; Letterman Clb; VICA; Stage Crew; Swing Chorus; Mat Maids; Pom Pon; Grtst Am Lvr Awd 83 Exotic Dncng Awd 84; 1st Pl Ntl Spttng Cntst 82; Rockland CC; NYC Plcwmn.

ODDO, ANDREA; St Edmund HS; Brooklyn, NY; (Y); 12/187; School Musical; Nwsp Rptr; Yrbk Stf; Var JV Cheerleading; Cit Awd; High Hon Roll; NHS; Ntl Merit Schol; Prfct Atten Awd; Hgh Schltc Achvt Awd 3 Yrs 85; St Johns U; CPA.

ODDO, RICHARD; Cardinal Mooney HS; Rochester, NY; (Y); 23/333; Intnl Clb; Var L Bowling; Score Keeper; JV Var Socr; Hon Roll; U Of R; Math.

ODDO, SAMANTHA; Lake George Central HS; Lake George, NY; (Y); Cmnty Wkr; Yrbk Ed-Chief; Yrbk Rptr; High Hon Roll; Hon Roll; Jr NHS; NHS; Rotary Awd; Acadmc All-American Awd 83-84; Exchange Student 85-86; FL ST U; French.

ODDY, CAROL JANET; Nottingham HS; Syracuse, NY; (Y); 40/220; Drama Clb; French Clb; Latin Clb; Orch; School Musical; Lit Mag; Hon Roll; NHS; Ntl Merit SF; Pres Schlr; Natl Lat Exam Gold Medl 83-85; Syracuse; Music.

ODE, DAWN; Mount Mercy Acad; Buffalo, NY; (Y); FHA; Red Cross Aide; Chorus; Church Choir; JV Badmtn; Var Cheerleading; Paralegal.

ODEA, MARGARET; Our Lady Of Mercy HS; Rochester, NY; (Y); Hon Roll; Alt Schlrshp St Boniface Schl 82.

ODEBRALSKI, JOHN J; Dunkirk SR HS; Dunkirk, NY; (Y); 16/220; Computer Clb; School Musical; Stage Crew; Ftbl; High Hon Roll; Hon Roll; NHS; Regents Schrlshp 85; Henry King Stanford Schlrshp 85; U Of Miami; Comp Prgmr.

ODELL, KIMBERLY; Mt Upton Central HS; Mt Upton, NY; (Y); Ski Clb; Variety Show; Trs Frsh Cls; Trs Soph Cls; Trs Jr Cls; JV Bsktbl; JV Var Socr; Var Sftbl; Hon Roll; Chngo Cnty Dairy Prncs 85; Mrsvl Agri & Tech; Agri Bus.

ODESSA, JOANNE; St Joseph By The Sea; Staten Island, NY; (Y); Art Clb; Yrbk Stf; Hon Roll; Law.

ODLE, SARAH; James E Sperry HS; Henrietta, NY; (Y); Office Aide; Hon Roll; Educ Tchr.

ODONNELL, KATHLEEN; Franciscan HS; Peekskill, NY; (Y); 14/58; Church Yth Grp; Girl Scts; Library Aide; Spanish Clb; Nwsp Bus Mgr; Nwsp Rptr; Nwsp Stf; Yrbk Rptr; Yrbk Stf; Hon Roll; Hopwood Schlrshp 85; Lynchburg Clg; Intl Stud.

ODONNELL, TOM; Arlington HS; Poughkeepsie, NY; (Y); Church Yth Grp; Hon Roll; Bus Mgmt.

ODWYER, JEFFREY S; Pittsford Mendon HS; Pittsford, NY; (Y); 50/265; Varsity Clb; Band; Rep Frsh Cls; Trs Soph Cls; VP Jr Cls; Rep Sr Cls; Var Capt Tennis; Hon Roll; Ntl Merit Ltr; Sect V Singls Tnns Champ 82-84; Princeton U; Attorney.

ODZA, KENNETH M; Amherst Central HS; Williamsville, NY; (Y); Math Clb; Math Tm; Quiz Bowl; Pres Temple Yth Grp; Nwsp Bus Mgr; Nwsp Stf; VP Swmmng; High Hon Roll; VP NHS; St Schlr; NELFTY Winterkallah Coordntr 85; U Of Rochester.

OECHSLE, SUZANNE; Churchville Chili HS; Spencerport, NY; (Y); 11/308; Church Yth Grp; FTA; Math Tm; Chorus; Nwsp Stf; Lit Mag; Stu Cncl; JV Var Swmmng; High Hon Roll; Lion Awd; Roberts Wesleyan Coll; Tchr.

OEHLER, VIVIAN G; Huntington HS; Huntington, NY; (Y); 1/433; Capt Mathletes; Orch; JV Fld Hcky; High Hon Roll; NHS; Ntl Merit Ltr; Val; Chorus; Capt Flag Corp; School Play; Outstndng Soph 83; Harvard Bk Clb Awd 84; Regents Schlrshp 85; Harvard U; Bus.

OEI, CHRISTOPHER K; Garden City HS; Garden City, NY; (Y); Chess Clb; Computer Clb; Mathletes; Teachers Aide; Trk; High Hon Roll; Long Island Math Fair Comp Prog Awd 83; Nassau Cnty Interschlstc Math Lgu Awd 83-85; Sci.

OEY, DAVID; Ithaca HS; Ithaca, NY; (Y); Boy Scts; Intnl Clb; Model UN; Band; School Musical; School Play; Variety Show; Jr NHS; NHS; Ntl Merit Ltr; Cornell U; Bio Sci.

OEY, REBECCA; Franklin Acad; Malone, NY; (S); 7/253; AFS; Church Yth Grp; VP Sec 4-H; Sec Intnl Clb; Model UN; VP Spanish Clb; Swing Chorus; Ntl Merit Ltr; Acpl Chr; NYSSMA Solo Medals 83-84; Music Lttr All ST Conf; Frgn Exchng Schlrshp; Lang.

OFFEN, KELLY L; Churchville-Chili HS; Rochester, NY; (Y); 10/317; Church Yth Grp; Chorus; School Play; Ed Lit Mag; VP Rep Frsh Cls; Stat Bsktbl; NHS; Drama Clb; Math Tm; Model UN; Menc All Eastrn Chrs 84-85; Yth Cares 84-85; Roberts Wesleyan Clg; Musc Ed.

OFORI-MANKATA, JULIET; Unite Nations International Schl; Teaneck, NJ; (Y); Church Yth Grp; Debate Tm; Hosp Aide; Office Aide; Nwsp Rptr; Lit Mag; Rep Stu Cncl; Var Capt Bsktbl; Var Capt Trk; Var Vllybl; U Thant Schlr Of Yr 85-86; Mst Spirited Trk Ath 83; Georgetown U; Intl Reltns.

OGATA, STELLA M; C W Baker HS; Baldwinsville, NY; (Y); 5/441; Ski Clb; Spanish Clb; Trs Sr Cls; Powder Puff Ftbl; High Hon Roll; Hon Roll; Jr NHS; Var Capt Vllybl; James L Sears Memrl Fund 85; Colgate; Bio.

OGBURN, ANGELA; Murry Bergtraum HS; Brooklyn, NY; (Y); 82/576; Church Yth Grp; JA; Chorus; VP Church Choir; Hon Roll; FL A&M U; Accntnt.

OGDEN, LINDA; Rocky Point JR SR HS; Rocky Point, NY; (S); 2/200; Sec Cmnty Wkr; VP German Clb; Thesps; Chorus; Madrigals; Orch; School Musical; School Play; Symp Band; Hon Roll; Congress-Bundestag Schlrshp Prog 84-85; Grmn.

OGEKA, CHUCK; Mercy HS; Moriches, NY; (Y); 2/105; Ski Clb; Varsity Clb; Nwsp Rptr; VP Jr Cls; Pres Stu Cncl; Var Bsbl; Capt Var Ftbl; Capt Var Wt Lftg; High Hon Roll; NHS; MVP Offns Ftbl 83; Vrsty Ftbl 84; Georgetown; Dentist.

OGI, AMY; Fairport HS; Fairport, NY; (Y); Drama Clb; Exploring; French Clb; Sec Trs Model UN; School Musical; School Play; Yrbk Stf; Rep Jr Cls; Rep Stu Cncl; Hon Roll; Bio.

OGNIBENE, VINCENT; Christ The King R HS; Brooklyn, NY; (Y); 11/385; Church Yth Grp; Computer Clb; JV Ftbl; Wt Lftg; Hon Roll; St Johns U; Lwyr.

OGONOWSKI, MATTHEW P; Utica Free Acad; Utica, NY; (Y); 3/300; Mathletes; Political Wkr; Ice Hcky; Lion Awd; Ntl Merit Ltr; Opt Clb Awd; NYS Regents Schlrshp; Son Of Italy ST Schlrshp; Polt Sci.

OGRADY, KATHLEEN; Mercy HS; Ctr Moriches, NY; (Y); Drama Clb; Math Tm; PAVAS; Service Clb; Church Choir; Jazz Band; School Musical; School Play; High Hon Roll; NHS; NEDT Hgh Perf Cert 83-84; BOCES Smmr Inst Gifted & Tlntd 82-84; Theatre.

OH, DIANA; Seaford HS; Seaford, NY; (Y); Dance Clb; Band; Concert Band; Flag Corp; Mrchg Band; Nwsp Ed-Chief; Nwsp Rptr; Nwsp Stf; Capt Pom Pon; Hon Roll.

OH, JANE; Brighton HS; Rochester, NY; (Y); 6/320; Math Tm; Band; Concert Band; Jazz Band; Orch; Nwsp Bus Mgr; Yrbk Stf; JV Trk; Ntl Merit Schol; Spcl Schlrshp Awd Ntl Merit Corp 85; Bard Coll Outstndng Vrtng Awd 85; Monroe Soc Engrs Schlrshp 85; Stanford U; Engrng.

OH, SUNAH; New Utrecht HS; Brooklyn, NY; (Y); 1/557; Math Tm; Chorus; Rep Sr Cls; Var Badmtn; Gov Hon Prg Awd; Val; US Achvt Acad Natl Awd 84; Arista 84-85; NY U; Bio.

OHMANN, KYLE; Saranoc Lake HS; Saranac Lk, NY; (Y); Boy Scts; Church Yth Grp; CAP; Computer Clb; Exploring; Var Ftbl; Hon Roll; Comp Progrmmr.

OHST, AMANDA; Mexico Acad-Central HS; Oswego, NY; (Y); Church Yth Grp; Hon Roll; Dilagence & Achvt Schlrshp 85; Outstndng Eng Achvt Awd 85; SUNY-OSWEGO.

OHSTROM, KELLY; Hornell HS; Hornell, NY; (Y); AFS; Art Clb; Camp Fr Inc; Church Yth Grp; Latin Clb; Ski Clb; Band; Chorus; Swmmng; Tennis; Yrbk Editr 85-86; Chrldg 83-85; Hnr & Hgh Hnr Rolls; Fredonia; Int Dsgn.

OJAKLI, ZIAD; Xaverian HS; Brooklyn, NY; (S); 9/350; Drama Clb; Sec Trs French Clb; Speech Tm; School Musical; School Play; Rep Sr Cls; Trk; High Hon Roll; Jr NHS; Pres NHS; Acad Excel Awd; Law.

OKEEFE, LYNN; Holy Child HS; Mount Vernon, NY; (Y); Church Yth Grp; Cmnty Wkr; Drama Clb; Stage Crew; Yrbk Phtg; Yrbk Stf; Bus.

OKEKE, IFEACHOR B; Midwood HS; Brooklyn, NY; (Y); 31/605; Church Yth Grp; Chorus; Church Choir; Concert Band; Jazz Band; Lit Mag; Var Trk; NHS; Ntl Merit SF; Pre-Med.

OKERLUND, KENDA; Mayville Central Schl; Mayville, NY; (S); 6/55; Church Yth Grp; Cmnty Wkr; VP Spanish Clb; Chorus; School Musical; School Play; Nwsp Rptr; Yrbk Stf; Pres Frsh Cls; VP Soph Cls; Nrthestrn U; Phy Thrpy.

OKOLOWICZ, CHERRIE; E J Wilson HS; Spencerport, NY; (Y); Exploring; French Clb; Trs Math Clb; Ski Clb; Mrchg Band; Symp Band; Yrbk Stf; Hon Roll; Red Ribn Music Solo Fest 83; SUNY Geneseo; Fince.

OKONIEWSKI, MELANIE; Holy Angels Acad; Buffalo, NY; (Y); Art Clb; Church Yth Grp; Dance Clb; 4-H; Political Wkr; Varsity Clb; Chorus; School Musical; Socr; Swmmng; Hnr Work Drawing & Painting 84-85; 2nd Pl Groom Pony Clb 85; Graphic Arts.

OKRENT, DEBORAH A; Beacon HS; Beacon, NY; (S); Sec French Clb; Chorus; Concert Band; Mrchg Band; School Musical; Hon Roll; Jr NHS; Ntl Merit Ltr; Frnch Exc Awd 84; NY St Schl Music Awds 78-84; Bus Adm.

OLAFSON, STEVEN; East Islip HS; East Islip, NY; (Y); Aud/Vis; Computer Clb; Capt Math Tm; Nwsp Rptr; High Hon Roll; Pres Jr NHS; NHS; Ntl Merit Ltr; Frgn Lang Hnr Soc 84-85; SADD-VP 84-85; Engrng.

OLBERDING, DEBORAH A; Cardinal Spellman HS; Bronx, NY; (Y); 186/568; Pres German Clb; VP Intnl Clb; Key Clb; Math Tm; Co-Capt Pep Clb; Science Clb; Ski Clb; Lit Mag; JV Crs Cntry; Church Yth Grp; NY Regents Schlrshp 85-86; SUNY-ONEONTA; Scndry Educ.

OLBIE, JENNIFER; Amsterdam HS; Amsterdam, NY; (Y); Girl Scts; Yrbk Stf; Var Cheerleading; Hon Roll; NHS; Rep Stu Cncl; Dsgnd Amsterdam Yrbk Covr 85; Rochstr Inst Of Tech; Med Illus.

OLDEN, STACEY; Clara Barton HS; Brooklyn, NY; (Y); Church Yth Grp; Cmnty Wkr; JA; Library Aide; Math Tm; Teachers Aide; Band; Chorus; Church Choir; Color Guard; Ldrshp Awd 83; Ctzn Mnth Hnr Cert 82; Math Awd 82; Comp Sci.

OLEARY, JENNIFER; Maria Regina HS; Yonkers, NY; (Y); 40/127; Co-Capt Trk; High Hon Roll; Hon Roll; Bio.

OLEARY, MICHAEL; Iona Prep; Purchase, NY; (Y); Capt Swmmng; High Hon Roll; Hon Roll; Bus Admin.

OLEARY, MICHELE; Corning-Paited Post West HS; Painted Post, NY; (Y); JA; Letterman Clb; Varsity Clb; School Musical; School Play; Rep Frsh Cls; Stu Cncl; Var L Swmmng; Var L Trk; Hon Roll.

OLEARY, SUE; Albany HS; Albany, NY; (Y); 4-H; French Clb; Ski Clb; Rep Stu Cncl; Var JV Cheerleading; Hon Roll; Cert Merit Fr 83-84; Med Tech.

OLENDER, PATRICIA; Cardinal O Hara HS; Tonawanda, NY; (Y); Church Yth Grp; Cmnty Wkr; Drama Clb; Quiz Bowl; School Musical; Variety Show; Lit Mag; High Hon Roll; Hon Roll; NHS; Ntnwd On Stndrdzd Tstng 83; Outstndng Cmnty Svc 84; Mt St Mary Acad Schlrshp 82; Loyola Coll; Psych.

OLENIUS, LARS C; John F Kennedy HS; Brewster, NY; (Y); 90/185; Church Yth Grp; Teachers Aide; NY ST Regents Schlrshp 85; Detrmntn Bus Awd 85; Bus.

OLIN, CRAIG H; South Side HS; Rockville Ctr, NY; (Y); 10/284; Boy Scts; Exploring; Hosp Aide; Pres Spanish Clb; Band; Ed Nwsp Stf; JV Var Tennis; Cit Awd; High Hon Roll; Pres NHS; LI Sci Congrs Hgh Hnrs 84; Tufts U; Pre-Med.

OLINTO, LUIGI T; Mount St Michael HS; Bronx, NY; (S); 15/300; Var Capt Ice Hcky; High Hon Roll; Hon Roll.

OLIPHANT, MELISSA; Jamesville Dewitt HS; Fayetteville, NY; (Y); 3/250; Exploring; French Clb; Pres Latin Clb; Variety Show; Var Gym; Var Capt Trk; High Hon Roll; NHS; Mth Awd 84.

OLIVA, LISA M; The Mary Louis Acad; Bayside, NY; (Y); Intnl Clb; Yrbk Ed-Chief; Yrbk Phtg; Sec Soph Cls; Var Tennis; Vet Admin Yth Voluntr 84; St Johns U Jamaica NY; Pre-Med.

OLIVER, AMENA; Northwest Acad; Jamaica, NY; (Y); Drama Clb; Nwsp Ed-Chief; VP Sr Cls; Hon Roll; Editr Schls Nwspr Nrthestrn Acad 84-85; Jrnlst Awd Wrtrs Wrkshp Yth Actn 84; Acadmc Achv Awd Jrnlsm 85; Jrnlsm.

OLIVER, DENISE; Saugerties HS; Saugerties, NY; (Y); Pres French Clb; Math Tm; Varsity Clb; Mrchg Band; Symp Band; Yrbk Stf; Rep Stu Cncl; JV Bsktbl; Hon Roll; NHS; Lang.

OLIVER, MICHAEL H; Beach Channel HS; Howard Bch, NY; (Y); 98/482; Debate Tm; FFA; Library Aide; Science Clb; Yrbk Stf; Lit Mag; Bausch & Lomb Sci Awd; Hon Roll; Co Pres Beach Channel Weather Stn 83-85; Schl Rep Amer Acad Of Sci Confn 84; Schl Rep Marine Bio Confn; Huner Coll; Metrlgy.

OLIVER JR, STEPHEN W; Ravena Coeymans Selkirk SR HS; Selkirk, NY; (Y); 4/200; Am Leg Boys St; Debate Tm; Key Clb; Concert Band; Jazz Band; Yrbk Stf; Var Tennis; High Hon Roll; NHS; Stu Cncl; USAF ROTC Schlrshp 84-85; Petrolane Inc Schlrshp 84-85; Clarkson U; Elect Engrng.

OLIVER, STORMIE; Medina SR HS; Medina, NY; (Y); Church Yth Grp; 4-H; Girl Scts; Pep Clb; Chorus; Im Badmtn; Im Bowling; Im Vllybl; 4-H Awd; High Hon Roll; Syracuse U; Bio.

OLIVER, SUSAN L; Littls Falls JR SR HS; Little Falls, NY; (Y); 4/9; Drama Clb; FBLA; GAA; Spanish Clb; Orch; School Play; Stu Cncl; Cheerleading; Fld Hcky; Trk; NY ST Rgnts Schlrshp 85; Siena; Fin Pgm.

OLIVER, TAD; Turner/Carroll HS; Buffalo, NY; (Y); Cmnty Wkr; FBLA; OEA; Band; Yrbk Bus Mgr; Bowling; Socr; Hon Roll; NHS; Prfct Atten Awd; Hghst Hnrs 82-83; Canisius Coll; Bus Admn.

OLIVER, WILLIAM E; Lawrence HS; Inwood, NY; (Y); 33/382; Var Ftbl; Var Trk; High Hon Roll; NHS; Ntl Merit Schlrshp Outstdng Negr Stu 84; All Conf Sfty Ftbl 84; All Div Hrdlr-Trk 84; Acctng.

OLIVERA, AUDREY; Cardinal Spellman HS; Bronx, NY; (S); 10/526; Cmnty Wkr; Hosp Aide; Varsity Clb; Rep Frsh Cls; Gym; Capt Vllybl; NHS; Computer Clb; Dance Clb; Latin Clb; JR Schlrshp Awd Gen Excllnc 83-84; Svc Awd Vol Nrsng Hm; Cornell U; Bio Sci.

OLIVERI, SHERYL ANN; Dundee Central HS; Rock Stream, NY; (Y); 4/100; AFS; Am Leg Aux Girls St; Trs Spanish Clb; Concert Band; Drm & Bgl; Drm Mjr(t); Jazz Band; Mrchg Band; NHS; VFW Awd.

OLIVETT, PAUL; Coxsackie-Athens Central HS; Athens, NY; (Y); 25/104; Spanish Clb; Pres Jr Cls; Stu Cncl; Var L Bsbl; Var Capt Bsktbl; Var Capt Ftbl; Hon Roll; NHS; MVP Bsebl Awd 85; Phy Educ.

OLIVIERI, JOSEPH A; Liverpool HS; Liverpool, NY; (S); 95/792; Exploring; JA; Var Bowling; Var L Tennis; Hon Roll; Jr NHS; NHS; Rochester Inst Tech; Comp Sci.

OLMSTEAD, BOB; Oneonta HS; Oneonta, NY; (Y); Boy Scts; Church Yth Grp; Ski Clb; Band; Concert Band; Mrchg Band; Cit Awd; Mohawk Vly Comm Coll; Data Prcs.

OLNEY, MELISSA; Rome Free Acad; Westernville, NY; (Y); Church Yth Grp; Intnl Clb; Band; Concert Band; Mrchg Band; Im Bsktbl; Prfct Atten Awd; Math.

OLNEY, SARAH; Rome Free Acad; Rome, NY; (Y); Church Yth Grp; Key Clb; Ski Clb; Varsity Clb; Chorus; Var Fld Hcky; JV Vllybl; Hon Roll; Jr NHS; NHS; Drug Awrnss Essay Cntst 1st Pl 83; Math.

OLSCHEWSKI, KAREN; Northstar Christian Acad; Spencerport, NY; (S); 6/26; Church Yth Grp; Exploring; Teachers Aide; Church Choir; Var Bsktbl; Hon Roll; NHS; Amer-Chrstn Hnr Soc 84; 3rd Sci Fair 83; 2nd Bio, Sci Proj 84; Travel.

OLSEN, ANN M; Averill Park HS; Troy, NY; (Y); 30/210; JV Capt Cheerleading; Var Powder Puff Ftbl; High Hon Roll; JV Chrldng Awd 84; Gregg Typng Awd 83 & 85; Hudson Vly CC; Radiolgc Tech.

OLSEN, DANA; Union-Endicott HS; Endicott, NY; (Y); Dance Clb; Hosp Aide; Key Clb; Flag Corp; Hon Roll; Child Psych.

OLSEN, ELIZABETH S; Elba Central Schl; Elba, NY; (Y); 1/41; Pres Sec Concert Band; Stu Cncl; Bausch & Lomb Sci Awd; DAR Awd; NHS; Pres Schlr; St Schlr; Val; French Clb; Math Tm; Schlstc Awd & 4th Pl Genesee Cnty JR Miss Pgm 84; All-ST Flute Choir 83; Lttr Cmmndtn PSAT Scrs 84; Rochester Inst Tech; Htl Mgmt.

OLSEN, GAIL; Walton Central HS; Sidney Center, NY; (Y); Drama Clb; Model UN; Varsity Clb; Chorus; Pres Sr Cls; Var Bsktbl; Var Tennis; Var Trk; Trs NHS; Prfct Atten Awd; Ldrshp Conf Go For It 84-85; Eng.

OLSEN, KAREN; Copiague SR HS; Copiague, NY; (Y); Church Yth Grp; Computer Clb; Library Aide; Spanish Clb; Church Choir; Stage Crew; Yrbk Stf; Hon Roll.

OLSEN, KEITH G; St Anthonys HS; Pt Jeff Stat, NY; (Y); Chorus; Nwsp Stf; Yrbk Rptr; Socr; Hon Roll; NHS; Syracuse; Bus.

OLSEN, PAUL M; Clarkstown North HS; New City, NY; (Y); 13/480; Church Yth Grp; Math Tm; Nwsp Rptr; Bsbl; Var L Trk; Mu Alp Tht; NHS; Rensselaer Mdl For Math & Sci 83-84; U S Military Acad; Engr.

OLSEN, WALTER; Riverhead HS; Riverhead, NY; (Y); 39/195; French Clb; Ski Clb; Yrbk Phtg; Capt Crs Cntry; Trk; Hon Roll; Photography.

OLSMSTED, ANNA; Ravena-Coeymans-Selkirk HS; Coeymans, NY; (Y); Off Frsh Cls; Off Soph Cls; Off Sr Cls; Cert Hnr Engl 85; Secy.

OLSON, ANN M; The Brearley Schl; New York, NY; (Y); Church Yth Grp; Model UN; Political Wkr; Acpl Chr; Mgr Chorus; Mgr(s); Aacadmc Distnctn Spansh 83; Jrnlst.

OLSON, AUDREY; Valley Stream Central HS; Malverne, NY; (Y); 50/350; AFS; Church Yth Grp; 4-H; FBLA; Hosp Aide; Cheerleading; Gym; NYS Regnts Schlrshp Nrsg 85; Albany ST U; Bus.

OLSON, GREGORY G; Scotia-Glenville HS; Schenectady, NY; (Y); 13/225; Cmnty Wkr; Key Clb; Acpl Chr; L Mgr(s); Var Score Keeper; Var Capt Socr; Var L Tennis; Var High Hon Roll; NHS; German Clb; Engrng.

OLSON, STEPHANIE; Niagara Falls HS; Niagara Falls, NY; (Y); Debate Tm; Drama Clb; French Clb; Hosp Aide; Office Aide; Rep Stu Cncl; Hon Roll; NHS; Aerosp Engrng.

OLSON, TRACY; Earl L Vandermuelen HS; Mt Sinai, NY; (Y); Concert Band; Mrchg Band; Yrbk Stf; Rep Stu Cncl; Hon Roll; Polit Sci.

OLSOVSKY, DONNA; Chenango Forks HS; Binghamton, NY; (Y); Church Yth Grp; Teachers Aide; Band; Chorus; Color Guard; Concert Band; Drm Mjr(t); Mrchg Band; Wintergrd 84 Mid-York Chmpns 84; Bus.

OLSZOWY, CHERYL R; Shenendehowa HS; Clifton Park, NY; (Y); Church Yth Grp; Trs Intnl Clb; Jr Cls; High Hon Roll; Hon Roll; NHS; Sup Hnr Rl; Engrng.

OLTMAN, ELAINE; Batavia HS; Batavia, NY; (Y); Band; Color Guard; Concert Band; Mrchg Band; Orch; School Musical; Intl Bus.

OLTORIK, DAVID; West Irondequoit HS; Rochester, NY; (Y); Church Yth Grp; Cmnty Wkr; French Clb; Math Clb; Political Wkr; Radio Clb; Scholastic Bowl; Ski Clb; Teachers Aide; Stu Cncl; USAF Acad Appt, ROTC, US Navy Schlrshps 85; USAF Acad; Astrn Engrng.

OMANOFF, RODNEY; Riverdale County HS; Riverdale, NY; (Y); Aud/Vis; Cmnty Wkr; Key Clb; Library Aide; Math Tm; Pres Science Clb; Service Clb; Spanish Clb; Teachers Aide; Nwsp Bus Mgr; Amer Legns Awd 80; Fencng Tm Vrsty Ltrs 83-86; Engrng.

OMANS, GEORGE M; Keshequa HS; Portageville, NY; (Y); 23/100; Cmnty Wkr; Computer Clb; Office Aide; Spanish Clb; Band; Concert Band; Mrchg Band; Orch; Hon Roll; Regents Schlrshp Awd 85; ANYSSMA Solo Ensemble Awd 83; Lvngstn Cnty Grmnt Intern Awd 84; U S Marines; Avionics Elect.

ONDUS, SCOTT; Gowanda Central Schl; Gowanda, NY; (Y); Am Leg Boys St; Band; Concert Band; Jazz Band; Mrchg Band; Pep Band; Hon Roll; Prfct Atten Awd; Comp Engr.

ONEILL, MAUREEN; Sanford H Calhoun HS; Merrick, NY; (Y); Drama Clb; Spanish Clb; Chorus; Nwsp Stf; Var Badmtn; Var Bsktbl; Var Capt Vllybl; Hon Roll; VP NHS; Church Yth Grp; All-Cnty Bdmntn 3rd Sngls & 2nd Sngls Champ 83-85; Sprts Bstrs Wnr Nicholas Sabetto Awd 85; Mrktg.

ONEILL, NANCY; Vestal SR HS; Apalachin, NY; (Y); Drama Clb; High Hon Roll; Hon Roll; Cmnctns.

ONEILL, TIM; John F Kennedy HS; Utica, NY; (Y); Aud/Vis; Pres Drama Clb; Math Clb; School Play; Nwsp Rptr; JV Var Bsktbl; Var Golf; Socr; Actng.

ONGJOCO, ROXANNE C S; Perry Central Schl; Perry, NY; (Y); 2/100; French Clb; Math Tm; Band; Concert Band; Jazz Band; Mrchg Band; Orch; Pres Soph Cls; Cheerleading; High Hon Roll; U Of Rochester Paideia Awd 85; Cert Merit Frnch 84-85.

ONISZCZAK, JANE; Depew HS; Depew, NY; (Y); 21/254; JCL; Latin Clb; Band; Concert Band; Mrchg Band; Orch; Yrbk Stf; Hon Roll; Jr NHS; NY ST Regents Schlrshp 85; U Of NY Buffalo; Acctng.

ONSI, DOUGLAS E; Jamesville-De Witt HS; De Witt, NY; (Y); Pep Band; School Musical; Swing Chorus; Yrbk Bus Mgr; Trs Jr Cls; Var L Bsbl; Var L Socr; NHS; Church Yth Grp; Hosp Aide; Franklin & Marshall Coll Bk Prz 85.

ONTKUSH, MARK; Niskayuna HS; Schdy, NY; (Y); Chess Clb; German Clb; Key Clb; Ski Clb; JV Crs Cntry; Var Wrstlng; German Hnr Soc; Ed.

ONYEIJE, UZOMA C; Liverpool HS; Liverpool, NY; (Y); 231/791; Pres Church Yth Grp; Trs Exploring; ROTC; Rep Stu Cncl; Var L Trk; Im Wt Lftg; DAR Awd; Hon Roll; Voice Dem Awd; Outstndng Achvmnt Awd At V A Hosp 83-84; Elec Engr.

OPIEL, ELIZABETH; West Seneca West SR HS; W Seneca, NY; (Y); DECA; JV Crs Cntry; Prfct Atten Awd; Wildlf Technlgy.

OPIO, ELIZABETH; Hunter College HS; New York, NY; (Y); Trs Chorus; Swing Chorus; Yrbk Stf; Soph Cls; Jr Cls; Mu Alp Tht; Ntl Hispanic Merit 84-85; NY Regnts Schlrshp 85-86; Hunter Coll; Nrsng.

OPLANICH, DAVID J; Aviation HS; Long Isl City, NY; (Y); 8/417; JA; High Hon Roll; Hon Roll; NHS; Prfct Atten Awd; Silvr Wngs 85; Pegasus Hnr Soc 85; Pace U; Acctg.

OPP, KAREN; Union-Endicott HS; Endicott, NY; (Y); Nwsp Rptr; Nwsp Stf; Yrbk Ed-Chief; Yrbk Phtg; Yrbk Rptr; Yrbk Sprt Ed; Yrbk Stf; French Clb; Girl Scts; Ski Clb; Syracuse U; Jrnlsm.

OPPENHEIMER, DEANNA; Jericho HS; Jericho, NY; (Y); Art Clb; Trs Service Clb; Stage Crew; Nwsp Stf; Yrbk Stf; Bowling; Trk; Hon Roll; NHS; Spanish NHS; Ntl Art Hnr Soc 83-85; Adv.

OPPONG, MAURICE K; Collegiate School; Bronx, NY; (Y); Chess Clb; Cmnty Wkr; Math Tm; NFL; Speech Tm; Chorus; School Musical; Swing Chorus; Nwsp Rptr; Stat Bsktbl; Chem.

OPRE, STEPHANIE; Williamsville South HS; Williamsville, NY; (Y); Ski Clb; Rep Frsh Cls; Bsbl; Cheerleading; Gym; Sftbl; Swmmng; Vllybl; Bus Adm.

OQUENDO, VIVIAN LEE; Cathedral HS; Woodside, NY; (Y); 72/298; Hon Roll; Trvl.

ORAM, DAWN; Liverpool HS; N Syracuse, NY; (S); 128/791; Var Crs Cntry; JV Var Trk; Jr NHS; NHS; U Buffalo; Phy Thrpy.

ORANGE, DARRYL; Saint Agnes HS; Far Rockaway, NY; (Y); Dance Clb; Yrbk Stf; Var Crs Cntry; Capt Trk; Hon Roll; Temple U; Bus Mgmt.

ORANGES, JOANN; Roy C Ketcham HS; Wappinger Fls, NY; (Y); Drama Clb; Girl Scts; Political Wkr; Band; Chorus; Concert Band; Mrchg Band; School Musical; Stage Crew; Yrbk Stf; Girl Scout Silver Awd 84, Gold Awd 85; Child Psych.

ORANTES, FIDEL; Eastern District HS; Bronx, NY; (Y); 1/415; Math Tm; Hon Roll; Val; Cty Coll Schlrs Merit Awd 85; NYS Regents Schlrshp 85; City Coll NY; Elect Engrng.

ORBAND, MICHELLE C; Seton Catholic Central HS; Binghamton, NY; (Y); 42/152; Key Clb; Ski Clb; Chorus; Yrbk Stf; Rep Stu Cncl; JV Cheerleading; Hon Roll; NHS; Phy Thrpy.

ORBE, LYDIA; Islip HS; Islip, NY; (Y); Band; Concert Band; Mrchg Band; School Musical; Stat Tennis; JV Trk; Hon Roll; Bio.

ORDON, DARLENE; Schalmont HS; Schenectady, NY; (Y); Church Yth Grp; Drama Clb; French Clb; Office Aide; School Play; Yrbk Phtg; Yrbk Rptr; Yrbk Stf; Rep Soph Cls; Stu Cncl; Orignl Art Wrk 85; Soc.

OREN, PHILLIP; Spackenkill HS; Poughkeepsie, NY; (Y); 5/160; Aud/Vis; Teachers Aide; Temple Yth Grp; Orch; School Musical; Socr; High Hon Roll; NHS; Ntl Merit SF; Med.

ORENSTEIN, MATTHEW; Washingtonville HS; Monroe, NY; (Y); 10/290; Symp Band; JV Bsbl; Var Bsktbl; Var Socr; Var Tennis; High Hon Roll; NHS; Times Herald Rcrd Schlr Athlt Awd 85; VFW Ctznshp & Patrtsm Schlrsh Awd 85; Army ROTC Schlrshp Awd; Syracuse U; Civil Engr.

ORFANIDES, KEITH; Haverling Central HS; Kanona, NY; (Y); French Clb; Math Clb; Band; Concert Band; Mrchg Band; School Musical; Nwsp Stf; Yrbk Stf; High Hon Roll; Ntl Social Stds Olympd 82-83.

ORFF, EDWARD J; Garden City HS; Garden City, NY; (Y); Pres Latin Clb; Concert Band; Jazz Band; Mrchg Band; Sftbl; Hon Roll; NY ST Rgnts Schlrshp 85; Pres Acad Ftns Awd 85; U Of Rochester; Bio.

ORGANISCIAK, MARK; Frankfort-Schuyler Central HS; Frankfort, NY; (S); VP Computer Clb; French Clb; Key Clb; Concert Band; Jazz Band; Mrchg Band; Bsktbl; Var L Trk; High Hon Roll; NHS; RPI; Engrng.

ORIN, LORI K; Cairo-Durham HS; Acra, NY; (Y); Dance Clb; Pep Clb; Band; Chorus; Concert Band; Jazz Band; Mrchg Band; Pep Band; School Play; Rep Jr Cls.

ORIOLI, MARIE; Henninger HS; Syracuse, NY; (Y); Intnl Clb; Ski Clb; Variety Show; Rep Soph Cls; Rep Jr Cls; Rep Sr Cls; Stu Cncl; JV Sftbl; Hon Roll; NHS; Bristol Myers Schlrshp 85; Regents Diploma 85; Onondoga CC; Math.

ORLANDO, ANGELA; Lake Placid Central HS; Waltham, MA; (Y); VP Drama Clb; Key Clb; Varsity Clb; Chorus; School Musical; JV Bsktbl; Var Socr; Hon Roll; NHS; Outstndng Chorl 84; Athltc Cert Vrsty Ltr 84; Boston Coll; Engl.

ORLANDO, DAVID; Holy Cross HS; New York, NY; (Y); 51/300; PAVAS; Im Trk; Schlrshp 82; Bus.

ORLANDO, GIOVANNA; Bishop Kearney HS; Brooklyn, NY; (S); 56/356; Drama Clb; Math Tm; Speech Tm; Band; Chorus; Hon Roll; NHS; Regnts Schlrshp 85; Brooklyn Coll Frshmn Schlr Schlrshp 85; Fordham U Lincoln Ctr; Math.

ORLANDO, KAREN A; Plainview Old Bethpage HS; Plainview, NY; (Y); 81/194; Church Yth Grp; Drama Clb; FCA; Thesps; Acpl Chr; Chorus; Church Choir; Madrigals; School Musical; School Play; Outstndg Soph Music Awd 83; Greg Typng Awd 70 WPM 84; Opera.

ORLANDO JR, STEPHEN P; Solvay HS; Syracuse, NY; (Y); Trs Art Clb; VP Church Yth Grp; Jazz Band; School Musical; Swing Chorus; Ed Yrbk Stf; Pres Jr Cls; Capt Trk; Hon Roll; NAJE Spec Citatn Outstndg Musicnshp Prcssn 84; All Cnty Chrs 83-85; Cert Ind Cmmndatn Drama Fstvl 85; Grphc Art.

ORLANDO, TAMMY; York Central HS; Retsof, NY; (Y); 9/67; 4-H; Key Clb; Chorus; School Musical; Swing Chorus; Nwsp Rptr; NHS; Sr Play 85; Asst Editor Schl Yrbk 85; St John Fisher; Bus Mgmt.

ORLOFF, STACEY; Clarkstown North HS; New City, NY; (Y); Pep Clb; Stage Crew; Yrbk Stf; Mgr(s); Elem Educ.

ORLOWSKI, DIANE; Frontier Central HS; Blasdell, NY; (S); Aud/Vis; VP French Clb; FBLA; Pep Clb; Spanish Clb; Sec Color Guard; Hon Roll; NHS; NEDT Awd; Speech Pathology.

ORME, SAM; Tioga Central HS; Nichols, NY; (Y); 3/96; Boy Scts; Pres Church Yth Grp; Variety Show; Trs Jr Cls; Var JV Bsktbl; High Hon Roll; JETS Awd; NHS; Ntl Merit Ltr; Prfct Atten Awd; Brigham Young U; Chem.

ORMISTON, MATT; Maple Hill HS; Castleton, NY; (S); 8/80; Church Yth Grp; Spanish Clb; JV Bsktbl; Var L Socr; Var L Tennis; Elks Awd; Hon Roll; NHS; Pol Sci.

ORMSBEE, JUDY; Northeastern Clintion Central Schl; Moeers, NY; (Y); Girl Scts; Yrbk Stf; JV Bsktbl; JV Cheerleading; Var Crs Cntry; Var Socr; Hon Roll; Clinton CC; Sec.

ORNT, TINA; Churchville-Chili HS; Rochester, NY; (Y); 25/313; Church Yth Grp; Cmnty Wkr; Hosp Aide; JCL; Latin Clb; Model UN; Office Aide; Yrbk Stf; Lit Mag; Hon Roll; Engr.

OROPALLO, MARY BROOKE; Auburn HS; Auburn, NY; (Y); 12/444; Church Yth Grp; German Clb; Hosp Aide; Tennis; High Hon Roll; NHS; Ntl Merit Ltr; Pres Schlr; Exclinc In Grmn 85; U Of NH; Culnry Arts.

OROSZLANY, NORA E; Dominican Acad; New York, NY; (Y); Girl Scts; PAVAS; School Musical; Stage Crew; Rep Jr Cls; Sftbl; Tennis; Hon Roll; Prfct Atten Awd; NYS Regents Schlrshp 85; Manhattanville.

ORR, CHRISTINE F; Alexander JR SR HS; Alexander, NY; (Y); 14/88; Sec Church Yth Grp; Trs Drama Clb; Girl Scts; Spanish Clb; Teachers Aide; Chorus; Church Choir; Hon Roll; NHS; Houghton Frshman Schlrshp 85; Regents Csoll Schlrshp 85; Houghton Coll; Elem Ed.

ORR, DAVID H; Pulaski JR SR HS; Pulaski, NY; (S); Boy Scts; French Clb; Ski Clb; Varsity Clb; Band; Yrbk Stf; Var Bsbl; Var Bsktbl; Var Tennis; Hon Roll; James Madison U; Cmmnctns.

ORR, DEBORAH A; Utica Free Acad; Utica, NY; (Y); Drama Clb; English Clb; Nwsp Stf; High Hon Roll; NHS; Vol Mnth Awd 83; SUNY-OSWEGO; Zoology.

ORR, DONNA; Cardinal Spellman HS; Bronx, NY; (Y); Church Yth Grp; Chorus; Church Choir; Hon Roll; FIT; Bus.

ORR, JAMES; Alexander Central HS; Alexander, NY; (S); High Hon Roll; Jr NHS; NHS; Cnmtgrphy.

ORR, MICHAEL; Archbishop Stepinac HS; Elmsford, NY; (Y); Church Yth Grp; Exploring; Hosp Aide; JA; Orch; Yrbk Stf; Trk; High Hon Roll; NHS.

ORR, TRACY; Lansing HS; Ithaca, NY; (Y); French Clb; Chorus; School Musical; Nwsp Stf; Yrbk Ed-Chief; Lit Mag; JV Crs Cntry; JV Var Tennis; JV Var Trk; Hon Roll; Creatv Wrtng Awd 85; Frnch Awd 85; Cornell; Englsh.

ORRANTIA, ANTONIO D; Bronx High School Of Science HS; Brooklyn, NY; (Y); Boy Scts; Var Crs Cntry; Var Trk; Ntl Merit SF; Spanish NHS; Dartmouth Coll; Comp Sci.

ORRINGER, RHONDA M; Union-Endicott HS; Endwell, NY; (Y); 9/431; Sec French Clb; Pres Temple Yth Grp; Concert Band; School Play; Nwsp Stf; Yrbk Stf; Sec Jr Cls; Rep Stu Cncl; Hon Roll; Sec NHS; NYS Regents Schlrshp 85-86; St U NY Albany; Psych.

ORSI, CYNTHIA; Lasalle SR HS; Niagara Falls, NY; (S); 14/278; Cmnty Wkr; Yrbk Stf; Rep Sr Cls; High Hon Roll; Hon Roll; NHS; Niagara U; Accntng.

ORSINI, JEFFREY L; Franklinville Central HS; Franklinville, NY; (Y); 11/64; Nwsp Stf; Trs Stu Cncl; Crs Cntry; Ntl Merit Schol; NY ST Regents Schlrshp 85; NY Inst Of Tech Hnr & Challng Grnt 85; NY Inst Of Tech; Archtctr.

ORSO, LISA; Academy Of Saint Joseph HS; Copiague, NY; (Y); Dance Clb; Nwsp Rptr; Nwsp Stf; Cmndtn In Sci 84-85; Cmndtn In Hmnts II 83-84; Cmndtn In Amer Studies 84-85; Adelphi; Law.

ORSZULAK, DENISE; Attica SR HS; Cowlesville, NY; (S); Sec Band; Mrchg Band; Trs Frsh Cls; Var Capt Bsktbl; JV Sftbl; Var Vllybl; All Cnty Band 83-85.

ORTEGA JR, JOSE; Bishop Ford C C HS; Brooklyn, NY; (Y); Ski Clb; Teachers Aide; Rep Jr Cls; Pres Sr Cls; Bsbl; Bsktbl; Bowling; Ftbl; Var Swmmng; Cit Awd; Cert WA Wrkshps 85; NYU; Pol Sci.

ORTEGA, LOURDES; Norman Thomas HS; Brooklyn, NY; (S); 14/671; Pres Cmnty Wkr; Dance Clb; Pres Spanish Clb; Variety Show; Cit Awd; Gov Hon Prg Awd; Hon Roll; NHS; Val; Regents Coll Schlrshp 85; Playwriting Cert 85; NY U; Sociology.

ORTEGA, MICHELLE; Christopher Columbus HS; Bronx, NY; (Y); Badmtn; Bsktbl; Gym; Vllybl; Cit Awd; Hon Roll; Prfct Atten Awd; Spnsh Awd 83; Hunter Coll; Ed.

ORTEGA, WLADIMIR; St Johns Prep; Woodside, NY; (Y); Aud/Vis; Computer Clb; Exploring; Spanish Clb; Chorus; Crs Cntry; Trk; Hon Roll; St Johns U; Phrmclgy.

ORTH, SUSAN; John F Kennedy HS; Bronx, NY; (Y); 282/982; Cmnty Wkr; Chorus; Pace U Pleasantville; CPA.

ORTIZ, CARLOS; East Islip HS; E Islip, NY; (Y); Pep Clb; Spanish Clb; Lit Mag; VP Frsh Cls; Rep Jr Cls; Rep Stu Cncl; JV Var Ftbl; Im Sftbl; Im Wt Lftg; US Merchant Marine Acad; Comp.

ORTIZ, DAMARIS; Mabel Dean Bacon V HS; New York City, NY; (S); 26/299; Chorus; Church Choir; Yrbk Stf; Mktg.

ORTIZ, ELIZABETH; Norman Thomas HS; New York, NY; (S); 16/671; Cit Awd; High Hon Roll; Hon Roll; Prfct Atten Awd; Comp Engr.

ORTIZ, GLORIA; Cardinal Spellman HS; Bronx, NY; (Y); Computer Clb; Science Clb; Hon Roll; Pre-Med.

ORTIZ, GRISEL; St Raymond Acad; Bronx, NY; (Y); 13/86; Hosp Aide; Band; Church Yth Grp; Cmnty Wkr; Hon Roll; 1st Pl Awd Essy Wrttn 84; U Of Humacao Puerto Rico.

ORTIZ, JEANNETTE F; HS Of Art & Design; Bronx, NY; (Y); Yrbk Stf; Var Bowling; Hon Roll; Prfct Atten Awd; Natl Art Hnr Socty 85; JR Arista 82; Hnbl Mntn Postr Cntst 84; Fash Inst Tech; Advtsg Desgn.

ORTIZ, LILLIAN; Bushwick HS; Brooklyn, NY; (Y); 5/208; Chorus; School Play; Nwsp Phtg; Yrbk Stf; Rep Frsh Cls; Rep Soph Cls; Rep Jr Cls; Pres Sr Cls; Stu Cncl; Bausch & Lomb Sci Awd; Rootbert Fund Schlrshp 85-86; Regents Schrlshp 85-89; Mt Holyoke Coll; Pub Rel.

ORTIZ, LISA D; Cuba Central Schl; Black Creek, NY; (Y); 5/62; Pres Spanish Clb; Chorus; Nwsp Rptr; Sec Frsh Cls; VP Jr Cls; Var Capt DECA; Var Capt Trk; Var Capt Vllybl; High Hon Roll; Sec NHS; NY ST Regents Schlrshp 85; Hghst Avg Hist 83-84; NY ST All-Star Plyr Vlybl 84-85; U Of Buffalo; Bio.

ORTIZ, MARIBEL; Hillcrest HS; Jamaica, NY; (Y); Color Guard; School Play; Hon Roll; Spanish NHS; Comp.

ORTIZ, MARILYN; Adlai E Stevenson HS; Bronx, NY; (Y); Church Yth Grp; Band; Chorus; Church Choir; Concert Band; Orch; School Musical; School Play; Hon Roll; Prfct Atten Awd; John Jay Coll Crmnl Justc; Crim.

ORTIZ, MICHAEL; South Shore HS; Brooklyn, NY; (Y); CAP; Exploring; NHS.

ORTIZ, MOLLY SOL AMALIA; Desales HS; Geneva, NY; (Y); 16/44; Varsity Clb; Chorus; School Musical; Hon Roll; NHS; NEDT Awd; NYS Regents Schlrshp 85; Ftbl Chrldng Capt; Bsktbl Chrlndg; St John Fisher.

ORTIZ, RAMONA; Mt St Joseph Acad; Buffalo, NY; (Y); 6/56; Political Wkr; Church Choir; Pres Sr Cls; VP Stu Cncl; Var Cheerleading; Pres NHS; JA; Bowling; Hon Roll; Outstndng Stu Clss, Alpha Kappa Boule, NYS Rgnt Schlrshps 85; Georgetown U; Intl Law.

ORTIZ, SANTIAGO; All Hallows HS; New York, NY; (Y); Rep Frsh Cls; Rep Church Yth Grp; Rep Jr Cls; Rep Stu Cncl; Bowling; Mgr(s); JV Score Keeper; High Hon Roll; Hon Roll; Pre-Med.

ORTIZ, VIRGINIA; Norman Thomas HS; New York, NY; (S); 67/651; Church Yth Grp; Hosp Aide; Rep Sr Cls; Stu Cncl; Bowling; Cit Awd; High Hon Roll; Hon Roll; Sal; Comp Sci.

ORTIZ, YOMAYRA; St Johns Prep; Kew Gardens, NY; (Y); Dance Clb; Latin Clb; MMM; PAVAS; Spanish Clb; Band; Variety Show; Yrbk Stf; Jr Cls; Vllybl; Hunter; Phys Thrpst.

ORTMANN, ERIK; Islip HS; Bayshore, NY; (Y); School Musical; Nwsp Stf; Rep Jr Cls; Rep Sr Cls; JV Socr; Hon Roll; Camera Clb; Drama Clb; Scholastic Bowl; Chorus; Adelphi U Sci Hnrs Pgm 84; Spec Schlstc Bwl 85; Law.

ORTON, DAVID W; South Glens Falls Central Schl; Wilton, NY; (Y); 26/263; Computer Clb; High Hon Roll; Union Coll; Chem.

ORZESZEK, LYNN; John F Kennedy HS; Sloan, NY; (Y); 8/149; Pres Church Yth Grp; Cmnty Wkr; Office Aide; School Play; Nwsp Rptr; Yrbk Stf; Stu Cncl; Hon Roll; NHS; Yth Engagd In Svc Comm Awd 84; Canisius Coll; Accntnt.

ORZOL, CATHERINE B; Cleveland Hill HS; Cheektowaga, NY; (Y); 6/101; Sec Trs Church Yth Grp; GAA; Band; Chorus; Church Choir; Swmmng; Hon Roll; NHS; Regnts Schlrshp 85; U Of Buffalo; Wldlf Consrvtn.

OSBORN, KIMBERLY; Oneonta HS; Oneonta, NY; (Y); Church Yth Grp; Pres FBLA; Key Clb; Hon Roll; Acctng.

OSBORN, KYLE; Fayetteville-Manlius HS; Manlius, NY; (Y); Church Yth Grp; Model UN; Political Wkr; VP Frsh Cls; VP Soph Cls; Trs Pres Stu Cncl; JV Bsbl; Var Socr; NHS.

OSBORN, LISA; Watkins Glen HS; Rock Stream, NY; (Y); 14/128; Band; Stage Crew; Swing Chorus; Trs Frsh Cls; Trs Soph Cls; Trs Jr Cls; Var Mgr(s); French Hon Soc; Hon Roll; Art Clb; Acadmc All Amer 85; Vet Med.

OSBORNE, ANNE; Hamburg Central HS; Hamburg, NY; (Y); 19/396; Church Yth Grp; Chorus; Church Choir; Concert Band; Mrchg Band; Orch; Symp Band; Rep Soph Cls; Tennis; NHS; Elmira Coll Key Awd & Scholar 84; Most Improved Tennis Player 83; SUNY Genesseo; Med Tech.

OSBORNE, CATHERINE; Liverpool HS; Liverpool, NY; (Y); 383/874; Rep Church Yth Grp; FBLA; Girl Scts; JA; Yrbk Bus Mgr; Yrbk Stf; Merit Role 82-85; Acctng.

OSBORNE III, GEORGE B; New Covenant Christian Schl; Walworth, NY; (S); 1/14; Church Yth Grp; VP Computer Clb; Spanish Clb; Yrbk Stf; Capt Socr; High Hon Roll; Acpl Chr; Chorus; Church Choir; Concert Band; Mens Quartet 83-85; Adv Plcmnt Math 84-85; Regnl Concert Band 83-84; U Of Rochester; Phy Sci Rsrch.

OSBORNE, JASON W; Horseheads HS; Horseheads, NY; (Y); Am Leg Boys St; Boy Scts; Varsity Clb; Concert Band; Mrchg Band; Ed Nwsp Stf; Crs Cntry; Trk; NHS; Ntl Merit Ltr; Amer HS Athltc 84-85; Ivy Leag; Engrng.

OSBORNE, JOHN; Granville Central HS; Granville, NY; (S); 11/122; Church Yth Grp; Church Choir; Comp Pgrmr.

OSBORNE, MARIBETH L; Greece Athena HS; Rochester, NY; (Y); 45/280; Mathletes; Science Clb; Spanish Clb; Teachers Aide; Off Sr Cls; Stu Cncl; High Hon Roll; Hon Roll; NY ST Regnts Schlrshp 85; U Buffalo; Elect Engr.

OSCAR, CORLISS; Clara Barton HS; Brooklyn, NY; (Y); Computer Clb; Nwsp Rptr; Yrbk Stf; Bus Adm.

OSEKOSKI, CHRISTINE; Corning Painted Post West HS; Corning, NY; (Y); Church Yth Grp; Drama Clb; Pres Girl Scts; Ski Clb; Thesps; Varsity Clb; Band; Concert Band; Jazz Band; Madrigals.

OSGOOD III, RICHARD M; Horace Greeley HS; Chappaqua, NY; (Y); 24/276; Capt Debate Tm; French Clb; Intnl Clb; Math Tm; Service Clb; Ed Nwsp Stf; Crs Cntry; Trk; Ntl Merit SF.

OSHATZ, DANIEL T; Scarsdale HS; Scarsdale, NY; (Y); Ski Clb; Band; Im Ftbl; Var Golf; Im Sftbl; Ntl Merit SF; Business.

OSHEA, ANNE M; Old Westbury Schl Of The Holy Child; Point Lookout, NY; (Y); Church Yth Grp; School Musical; School Play; Nwsp Ed-Chief; Nwsp Stf; Yrbk Ed-Chief; Yrbk Stf; Off Frsh Cls; Off Soph Cls; Off Jr Cls.

OSHER, MARIEANN; Lansingburgh HS; Troy, NY; (Y); Girl Scts; Band; Sftbl; High Hon Roll; Hon Roll; Typng Awd 83.

OSIAS, MITCHELL; James Madison HS; Brooklyn, NY; (Y); 21/800; Cmnty Wkr; Debate Tm; Math Clb; Orch; School Musical; School Play; Nwsp Rptr; Regnts Schlrshp & NY Yankee Awd 84-85; UCLA; Bus.

OSIKA, MARK; F D Roosevelt HS; Staatsburg, NY; (Y); Cmnty Wkr; Math Clb; Hon Roll; NHS; Prfct Atten Awd; Bus.

OSINSKI, SUSAN M; Mount St Mary Acad; Grand Island, NY; (Y); 23/96; Hosp Aide; Intnl Clb; Stage Crew; Nwsp Rptr; Yrbk Stf; Lit Mag; Hon Roll; NY ST Regent Schlrshp 85; U Of Dayton; Comm Arts.

OSLAND, KIMBERLEE; Lockport SR HS; Lockport, NY; (Y); 127/411; French Clb; Intnl Clb; Rep Frsh Cls; Rep Soph Cls; Rep Jr Cls; Rep Stu Cncl; Im Bowling; Im Sftbl; Im Vllybl; High Hon Roll; Spch Pathlgy.

OSLANSKY, AUDRA L; Sachem SR HS; Holtsville, NY; (Y); 231/1462; Drama Clb; Radio Clb; Orch; Nwsp Rptr; Yrbk Stf; Ed Lit Mag; French Clb; Quiz Bowl; Temple Yth Grp; Chorus; NY ST Regents Schlrshp 85; High Hnrs & $50 At Long Isl Sci Cngrs 83; Ithaca Coll; English.

OSLUND, LISA; La Salle SR HS; Niagara Falls, NY; (Y); Drama Clb; Girl Scts; Lib Band; Concert Band; Jazz Band; School Musical; School Play; Stage Crew; High Hon Roll; NHS; NU; Physics.

OSSENBERG, MICHELE; Nottingham HS; Syracuse, NY; (Y); Sec Church Yth Grp; FBLA; Spanish Clb; Chorus; Rep Frsh Cls; Rep Soph Cls; JV Var Sftbl; JV Var Vllybl; Hon Roll; NHS.

OSSONT, KRISTINA; Remsen Central HS; Remsen, NY; (Y); 4-H; Girl Scts; Color Guard; Drill Tm; Mrchg Band; Socr; Sftbl; Vllybl; Cit Awd; Hon Roll; Comp.

OST, GEORGE; Aviation HS; Long Isl City, NY; (Y); 100/463; High Hon Roll; High Hon Roll; Hon Roll; Certfd FAA Aircrft Mech 85; U S Coast Grd Cert Grad Boatg Skls & Seamnshp 85; Cert Excllnc Engl 83-84; Acad Of Aeronautics; Hlcptr Pil.

OST, LORETTA; Attica HS; Alden, NY; (Y); Band; Color Guard; Concert Band; Mrchg Band; Stat Bsktbl; Oral Rbts U; Nrs.

OSTER, DAVID G; Notre Dame HS; Utica, NY; (Y); Am Leg Boys St; Service Clb; Rep Frsh Cls; JV Var Bsbl; Socr; High Hon Roll; Hon Roll; NHS.

OSTERHOUDT, ALEXANDRA; Our Lady Of Lourdes HS; Poughkeepsie, NY; (Y); 34/144; Bsktbl; Trk; High Hon Roll; NHS; Bentley Coll; Bus.

OSTERHOUDT, KYLE; Sharon Springs Central HS; Sharon Springs, NY; (S); Spanish Clb; Band; Concert Band; Jazz Band; Mrchg Band; Pep Band; Bsbl.

OSTERHOUDT, ROBERT W; Marlboro HS; Newburgh, NY; (Y); 16/164; High Hon Roll; Hon Roll; Jr NHS; Arch.

OSTERHOUT, KATHY; Shenendehawa HS; Ballston Lk, NY; (Y); Church Yth Grp; CAP; 4-H; FBLA; Girl Scts; Leo Clb; Office Aide; High Hon Roll; NHS; Prfct Atten Awd; Bus.

OSTERMEIER, EARL; Grand Island HS; Gr Island, NY; (Y); Sec Band; Concert Band; Pep Band; School Musical; Hon Roll; Outstndng Section Ldr Awd 85; Accntng.

OSTRANDER, ANTHONY R; Catholic Central HS; Troy, NY; (Y); 100/203; Cmnty Wkr; JA; MMM; Band; Chorus; Jazz Band; School Musical; Stage Crew; Variety Show; Hon Roll; Hudson Valley CC; Mrktng.

OSTRANDER, REBECCA S; Hancock Central HS; Fishs Eddy, NY; (Y); Am Leg Aux Girls St; Church Yth Grp; GAA; Office Aide; Spanish Clb; Pres Band; Trs Chorus; Church Choir; Pres Concert Band; Pres Jazz Band; Coll; Dietetics.

OSTROMECKI, KAREN; Greece Arcadia HS; Rochester, NY; (S); DECA; Yrbk Stf; Var Tennis; JV Vllybl; Hon Roll; Local Rcgntn DECA 83-84 & 84-85; Hnrl Mntn Art Work Cmmnty Art Exhibit 83-84; Envrnmntl Dsgn.

OSTROVSKY, MAX; Midwood HS; Brooklyn, NY; (Y); 72/605; Chess Clb; Math Clb; Math Tm; Science Clb; Lit Mag; Hon Roll; Jr NHS; Arista Hnr Socty 84; Med.

OSTWALD, PETER B; Saratoga Springs SR HS; Saratoga Springs, NY; (Y); 21/465; Rep Stu Cncl; Var Capt Tennis; High Hon Roll; Pres NHS; St Lawrence U; Govt.

OSUCH, BARBARA; Sweet Home HS; Amherst, NY; (Y); 129/425; Trs Church Yth Grp; Library Aide; Yrbk Bus Mgr; Yrbk Stf; Soph Cls; Amherst YES Outstndng Vlntr 82-84; NCCJ Sistrhd Yth 84; Erie Comm Coll; Legal Asst.

OSVATH, STEVE; Niagara Wheatfield SR HS; North Tonawanda, NY; (Y); Varsity Clb; JV Var Ftbl; JV Var Lcrss; High Hon Roll; NHS; Prfct Atten Awd; U Of Buffalo; Engrng.

OSWALD, ALLISON; Berlin Central HS; Cherry Plain, NY; (S); Camp Fr Inc; Chorus; Mgr(s); Score Keeper; Socr; Hon Roll; United Way Vlntr Awd 84; Pupuls Perf Attend Cert 83.

OSWALD, ANNETTE; Roy C Ketcham HS; Wappingers Falls, NY; (S); 66/507; Nwsp Stf; Stu Cncl; Cheerleading; High Hon Roll; Hon Roll; Jr NHS; Acdmc All Amer 84; Marist Coll; Comp Sci.

OSWALD, STEPHANIE; Saugerties HS; Saugerties, NY; (S); 3/242; French Clb; School Play; Nwsp Ed-Chief; Yrbk Bus Mgr; JV Var Cheerleading; High Hon Roll; JC Awd; NHS; VFW Awd; Sec Church Yth Grp; Ntl JR Achv Conf Rep 82; NYS Rgnts Schlrshp Wnr 85; IBM Watson Schlrshp Wnr 85; Boston U; Brdcst Journlsm.

OSWALT, EDWARD F; Royalton Hartland Central HS; Lockport, NY; (Y); 8/129; 4-H; Im Ftbl; Cit Awd; High Hon Roll; Hon Roll; Regents Schlrshp 85; RIT Almuni Schlrshp 85; Bio Awd 82; Rochester Inst Tech; Elec Engr.

OSWALT, MARSHA; Royalton-Hartland HS; Lockport, NY; (Y); 23/141; French Clb; Spanish Clb; Yrbk Stf; Sec Soph Cls; Stu Cncl; Trk; Hon Roll; NHS; Intr Dsgn.

OTANO, JOHNNY F; Richmond Hill HS; Richmond Hl, NY; (Y); Boy Scts; Cmnty Wkr; English Clb; Library Aide; Spanish Clb; Teachers Aide; Band; Church Choir; School Musical; Variety Show; Media Engr.

OTERO, KENT; Ralph Mc Kee HS; Staten Is, NY; (Y); 74/238; Hnr Scty 85.

OTHMAN, SAMI; Hillcrest HS; Woodhaven, NY; (Y); 72/793; JA; Library Aide; Teachers Aide; Rep Frsh Cls; Hon Roll; Rgnts Schlrshp 85; Cornell U; Med.

OTORO, MARIA; Lowville Academy Central Schl; Lowville, NY; (Y); Spanish Clb; Mohawk Vly CC; Reprtry Thrpy.

OTT, GRETCHEN; Niagara Wheatfield HS; Niagara Falls, NY; (Y); 4-H; JA; Latin Clb; Chorus; 4-H Awd; High Hon Roll; Hon Roll; NHS; Niagara Cty Legstltv Intrn 85; Niagara Cty Intrn Ldr 85; Niagara Cty 4-H Polo Tm 85-87; SUNY Buffalo; Poli Sci.

OTT, JENNIFER; Saranac Central HS; Cadyville, NY; (S); #13 In Class; Cmnty Wkr; French Clb; Var L Socr; Var L Sftbl; Var L Vllybl; High Hon Roll; Hon Roll; Champlain Vly Athl Conf All Star Shrtstp Offnsv Sftbl Plyr Of Yr & All Star Socr Forwd 84; Psych.

OTT, MARK; Frontier Central HS; Buffalo, NY; (Y); Varsity Clb; Capt Swmmng; Ind Arts Awd 82-83; Comp Aid Dsgn.

OTT, MELINDA; Copiague HS; Copiague, NY; (Y); FBLA; Teachers Aide; Var Capt Sftbl; High Hon Roll; Hon Roll; Hnrbl Ment All Leag Sftbl 85; Phy Thrpy.

OTTE, JOHN; Mohonasen SR HS; Schenectady, NY; (Y); 7/186; Boy Scts; Sec Church Yth Grp; Spanish Clb; Drm Mjr(t); Mrchg Band; Pres Stu Cncl; Var Bsktbl; Var Socr; High Hon Roll; NHS; Bio Chem.

OTTEN, BRIAN; Hicksville SR HS; Hicksville, NY; (Y); French Clb; MMM; Sec Science Clb; Orch; School Musical; Symp Band; Rep Stu Cncl; Var Crs Cntry; High Hon Roll; NHS; Frnch Hnr Soc; Pre-Med.

OTTENWAELDER, JAMIE S; Kings Park SR HS; Kings Park, NY; (Y); 5/444; Am Leg Aux Girls St; Church Yth Grp; Hst Debate Tm; Math Clb; Sec Trs NFL; ROTC; Science Clb; Sec Trs Spanish Clb; Band; Church Choir; AIM Pgm US Coast Guard Acad; Yng Schlrs Pgm SUNY Stonybrook; Brookhvaen Natl Lab Physcs Pgm; Cornell; Mech Engrng.

OTTER, JULIE C; Harrison HS; Harrison, NY; (Y); 7/200; Band; Yrbk Stf; Rep Frsh Cls; Rep Soph Cls; Rep Jr Cls; Sftbl; Trk; NHS; CIBA GEIBY HS Sci Awd 85; Regents Schlrshp 85; Med.

OTTO, DAVID H; Scarsdale HS; Scarsdale, NY; (Y); Boy Scts; Church Yth Grp; Cmnty Wkr; Varsity Clb; School Musical; Stage Crew; Ftbl; Trk; High Hon Roll; NHS; Schlr Athlt Awd; Westchester Chptr; Natl Ftbl Fndtn; Hall Of Fame; Tom Dean & Buchanan Mem Schlrshp Ftbl; Bowdoin Coll; Librl Arts.

OTTO, PAULA J; Newburgh Free Acad; Newburgh, NY; (Y); 52/720; Pres Sec Church Yth Grp; Key Clb; VP Y-Teens; Acpl Chr; Orch; Stage Crew; Yrbk Stf; High Hon Roll; Jr NHS; NHS; Cardinal Spellman Yth Awd 84; Regents Shclrshp 85; CUNY At Cobleskill; Frsty.

OTTOMANELLI, ANGELA; Christopher Columbus HS; Bronx, NY; (S); English Clb; Chorus; Nwsp Rptr; Nwsp Stf; Cit Awd; Hon Roll; Prfct Atten Awd; Acad All Amer Awd 85; Arista 83-85; Govnr Comm Schlstc Achvt Cit 83; Bus Admn.

OUDT, RICHARD; Shenendehowa SR HS; Ballston Lake, NY; (Y); Boy Scts; Church Yth Grp; Computer Clb; JA; Chorus; JV Socr; Hon Roll; Boston Arch Ctr; Arch.

OUELLETTE, PENNY; Morrisville-Eaton HS; Morrisville, NY; (Y); Exploring; Band; Church Choir; Concert Band; Mrchg Band; Orch; Var Trk; High Hon Roll; Hon Roll; NHS; Music Hall Of Fame.

OUGHTON, TERESA; Greater Johnstown HS; St Johnsville, NY; (Y); Ski Clb; VP Frsh Cls; Var L Bsktbl; Var Capt Crs Cntry; Var L Socr; Var L Sftbl; Var Trk; High Hon Roll; Hon Roll; NHS; MVP Crs Cntry Rnnr 84; Mst Outstndng Trk Evnts Athl; Mst Imprvd Crs Cnty Runnr & Skier 84; Engrng.

OURIEL, JEFFREY; Irondequoit HS; Rochester, NY; (Y); Latin Clb; Radio Clb; Bsbl; Bowling; Soc Stud.

OUTERBRIDGE, CRYSTAL; George Washington HS; New York, NY; (Y); Columbia U; Comm.

OUTLAW, FELICIA; Monsignor Scanlan HS; New York City, NY; (Y); 44/265; Color Guard; Drm & Bgl; Var Cheerleading; Hon Roll; 1st Hnrs 82-83; Acad Awds Hist, Engl, Spnsh 83-84; 2nd Hnrs 84-85; Hamilton; Psych.

OUTLAW, TERESA; Cardinal Spellman HS; Bronx, NY; (Y); NFL; Office Aide; Speech Tm; Stage Crew; Hon Roll; Hon Roll; Psych.

OUTMAN, TINA M; Angelica Central Schl; Angelica, NY; (Y); 11/23; Church Yth Grp; Teachers Aide; Chorus; Nwsp Stf; Yrbk Stf; High Hon Roll; Hon Roll; Church Choir; Stat Bsktbl; Coach Actv; Raftng Clb 83; All Cty Choir 82-84; Olean Bus Inst; Mgmt.

OVERBAUGH, JOHN; Charles O Dickerson HS; Trumansburg, NY; (Y); Am Leg Boys St; Boy Scts; Drama Clb; Spanish Clb; Thesps; Jazz Band; School Play; Yrbk Phtg; Mgr Bsktbl; Var Socr; Comm.

OVERHOLSER, OCTAVIA A; Spence Schl; New York, NY; (Y); 3/37; Cmnty Wkr; Dance Clb; French Clb; Chorus; Nwsp Rptr; Lit Mag; High Hon Roll; Hon Roll; Ntl Merit Schol; Columbia U; Fashn Mktg.

OVERMOHLE, MICHELLE; Bishop Ludden HS; Liverpool, NY; (S); Cmnty Wkr; Band; JV Socr; Im Sftbl; Im Vllybl; High Hon Roll; NHS; Rochester Inst Tech; Comp Sci.

OVERSLAUGH, MARGARET; Charles O Dickerson HS; Trumansburg, NY; (Y); 15/85; Girl Scts; Pep Clb; Spanish Clb; Yrbk Stf; Trs Jr Cls; JV Var Bowling; Var Capt Cheerleading; Var Capt Pom Pon; Im Sftbl; Var L Tennis; Med Tech.

OVERSLAUGH, SUE; Pittsford Mendon HS; Pittsford, NY; (Y); Orch; School Musical; Yrbk Stf; JV Fld Hcky; Hon Roll; Church Yth Grp; Cmnty Wkr; Yrbk Rptr; Rep Frsh Cls; Stat Ice Hcky; Econ.

OVERWEG, ELIZABETH; Bronx Science HS; Riverdale, NY; (Y); MMM; Office Aide; PAVAS; Chorus; Orch; School Play; Nwsp Rptr; Nwsp Stf; Off Soph Cls; Off Sr Cls; Grad Juilliard Schl Pre-Coll Hnr Stu 85; Rgnts Schlrshp 84-85; J Bingham Music Wnnr 85; Barnard; Pre-Med.

OWENS, AUDREY; Holy Trinity HS; Roosevelt, NY; (Y); Hosp Aide; Mathletes; Band; Concert Band; Yrbk Stf; Mu Alp Tht; Prfct Atten Awd; Comp Sci.

OWENS, BETH ANN; E J Wilson HS; Spencerport, NY; (Y); 3/294; Am Leg Aux Girls St; Trs French Clb; Hosp Aide; Symp Band; Capt Var Bsktbl; Var Socr; Var Swmmng; Var Trk; High Hon Roll; NHS; Ntl Schlr Athl 85; Orayon Schlrsh Phartwick Coll 85; Regents Schlrshp 85; Hartwick Coll; Nrsng.

OWENS, BRIAN; Fairport HS; Fairpot, NY; (Y); DECA; Exploring; Wrstlng; Astrophysics.

OWENS, CAROLYN; Haverling Central HS; Bath, NY; (S); 28/140; Rep Soph Cls; JV Trk; High Hon Roll; Hon Roll; NHS; Trenton ST Coll; Elem Ed.

OWENS, JOHN; St Marys Boys HS; E Williston, NY; (Y); 39/130; Bowling; Hon Roll; Racquetbl Awd 83-85; Catholic U Of Amer; Busnss Admn.

OWENS, MARGARET M; Curtis HS; Staten Island, NY; (Y); 11/389; Computer Clb; Math Tm; Office Aide; Political Wkr; Teachers Aide; Chorus; Nwsp Rptr; Lit Mag; High Hon Roll; NHS; NYS Regents Schlrshp 85; U PA; Bio.

OWENS, MARK D; Southern Cayuga HS; Aurora, NY; (Y); 16/89; Boy Scts; FFA; Band; Jazz Band; Hon Roll; NYS Regents Schlrshp 85; Alfred U; Ind Engr.

OWENS, SHARON; Valley Stream North HS; N Valley Stream, NY; (Y); 25/125; Stage Crew; Variety Show; Yrbk Stf; Off Jr Cls; Bowling; Sftbl; Vllybl; High Hon Roll; Hon Roll; All Conf, All Cnty Bwlng 85; Comm.

OWENS, TIMOTHY; Lansingburgh HS; Troy, NY; (S); 3/220; Church Yth Grp; Math Tm; Bsktbl; Golf; High Hon Roll; Jr NHS; NHS; Prfct Atten Awd; Bus Admin.

OWENS, VANESSA M; Holy Trinity Diocesan HS; Roosevelt, NY; (Y); Dance Clb; Band; Concert Band; Variety Show; Hon Roll; U Of SC-COLUMBIA; Bus Admin.

OWLETT, SUE; Charles O Dickerson HS; Trumansburg, NY; (Y); 11/85; Am Leg Aux Girls St; Pres Spanish Clb; Varsity Clb; Trs Sr Cls; Var Capt Cheerleading; Var Capt Socr; Var Capt Sftbl; Hon Roll; NHS; A Bennet Mem Schlrshp, Am Hist Awd, Rookie Yr Awd Art 85; Rochester Inst Tech; Rtl Mgmnt.

OWUSU, MONICA; John Dewey HS; Brooklyn, NY; (Y); Drama Clb; Library Aide; Spanish Clb; School Play; Stage Crew; Variety Show; Ed Nwsp Rptr; Yrbk Phtg; Yrbk Rptr; Rep Soph Cls; Natl Self-Govt Grant 84; NY ST Bar Assn Cert Hnr 85; Pre-Law.

OZA, ANIS; Aviation HS; Corona, NY; (Y); Hon Roll; Prfct Atten Awd; Aviation Maint.

OZIMKOWSKI, EDWARD; Bethpage HS; Bethpage, NY; (Y); Spanish Clb; Band; Concert Band; Mrchg Band; Orch; Socr; Hon Roll; Culinary Inst; Culinary Arts.

PAAR, CHRISTINA M; Immaculata Acad; Hamburg, NY; (Y); French Clb; Girl Scts; Library Aide; Im Vllybl; Hon Roll; Sci Cngrss Awd 83; Outstndng Achvt Acctng I 85; Canisius Coll Buffalo; Psych.

PABEY, HAYDEE; Norman Thomas HS; New York, NY; (S); 85/670; Church Yth Grp; VP JA; Band; Chorus; Church Choir; Cit Awd; Hon Roll; Prfct Atten Awd; Sal; Acad All Amer 85; Manhattan Borough Pres Cert Excllnce 82; Amer Leg Citznshp Medl 82; City Coll; Comp Prmg.

PABIS, JAMES; Bishop Scully HS; Hagaman, NY; (S); 6/56; JA; Latin Clb; Math Clb; Varsity Clb; VP Soph Cls; Var Bsbl; High Hon Roll; NHS.

PABIS, LISA; Thomas A Edison HS; Elmira, NY; (Y); Am Leg Aux Girls St; Red Cross Aide; Varsity Clb; Chorus; Nwsp Stf; Rep Stu Cncl; Capt Var Cheerleading; JV Trk; Hon Roll; Trvl Trsm.

PABLO, LOURDES; St Francis Preparatory HS; Queens Village, NY; (S); 3/693; Cmnty Wkr; Band; Concert Band; Mrchg Band; Hon Roll; NHS.

PACANOWSKI, KATHRYN; Westfield Acad; Westfield, NY; (S); Key Clb; Quiz Bowl; Teachers Aide; Rep Frsh Cls; Rep Jr Cls; Cheerleading; High Hon Roll; NHS; Prfct Atten Awd; Voice Dem Awd; PSYCHLGY.

PACCIO, CLAUDINE; Union Ardicott HS; Endwell, NY; (Y); 110/440; Pres Church Yth Grp; German Clb; GAA; Spanish Clb; Drill Tm; Flag Corp; Stu Cncl; Capt Bsktbl; Pom Pon; Swmmng; Miss JR ACRY 83-84; Broome CC; Engrng Sci.

PACCIONE, LUCILLE; St Johns Prep; Astoria, NY; (Y); Sec Science Clb; Wrstlng; 2nd Pl Sci Fair 84; Hunter Coll; Indus Psych.

PACCIONE, MARIA; Dominican Commercial HS; Ozone Park, NY; (Y); 39/273; Mathletes; Office Aide; Rep Soph Cls; Rep Jr Cls; Rep Sr Cls; Hon Roll; Jr NHS; NHS; Ntl Bus Hnr Soc Treas 84-85; Comp, Math, & Accntng Tchrs Aide 84-85; St Johns U; Bus Admin.

PACE, GREG M; Waterloo SR HS; Waterloo, NY; (Y); Am Leg Boys St; Church Yth Grp; Cmnty Wkr; Letterman Clb; Yrbk Phtg; Var L Tennis; Hon Roll; Most Contrbtng Sr Class 85; MIP Tennis 84-85; Vrsty Club 85; Alfred ST; Bus Admin.

PACE, MELINDA D; West Seneca East SR HS; W Seneca, NY; (Y); 29/365; Trs Church Yth Grp; German Clb; GAA; Ski Clb; Var Fld Hcky; Hon Roll; JC Awd; NHS; Pres Camp Fr Inc; Chorus; NY ST Regents Schlrshp Wnnr 84-85; Natl German Hnr Scty 83-85; SUNY-GENESEO; Bio.

PACE, MICHAEL; West Seneca West HS; West Seneca, NY; (Y); DECA; Trs Key Clb; Spanish Clb; Concert Band; Jazz Band; Mrchg Band; Orch; Capt Ice Hcky; Var Capt Vllybl; Hon Roll; 2nd All-Star Vllybl Tm Of Western NY 84; Natl Hnr Rll 85; Bus Mgmt.

PACHECO, CELIA; Norman Thomas HS; Bronx, NY; (S); 13/671; Math Tm; Chorus; Hon Roll; Prfct Atten Awd; Math Clb; Regents Scholar Awd; Natl Hon Soc; Arista; Baruch Coll; Acctg.

PACHECO, NELSIE; St Catharine HS; Bronx, NY; (Y); 59/205; Cmnty Wkr; Office Aide; Teachers Aide; Rep Jr Cls; Rep Stu Cncl; Hon Roll; NHS; Prfct Atten Awd.

PACHEO, ROBERT; Clarkstown H S North; New City, NY; (Y); Boy Scts; Spanish Clb; Rep Jr Cls; JV Golf; Var Socr; JV Trk; Aerontcl Engrg.

PACHETTI, JOSEPHINE; Buffalo Alternative HS; Buffalo, NY; (Y); Cmnty Wkr; JA; Office Aide; Teachers Aide; Atty.

PACHNOS, HELENE; St Edmund HS; Brooklyn, NY; (S); 2/190; English Clb; Spanish Clb; Nwsp Rptr; Lit Mag; High Hon Roll; Jr NHS; NEDT Awd; 200.00 Schlrshp 83-84; Principals List All Yrs; Corporate Law.

PACHONKA, TIMOTHY S; Hackley Schl; Yonkers, NY; (Y); Key Clb; Varsity Clb; Acpl Chr; Stu Cncl; Stat Bsktbl; Var L Ftbl; Var L Lcrss; High Hon Roll; Hon Roll; Ntl Merit SF; Academic All-American 84.

PACHUCINSKI, MICHAEL; Caharaugus Central HS; Gowanda, NY; (Y); Band; Mrchg Band; Trs Jr Cls; Var Bsbl; JV Bsktbl; Var Ftbl; Var Trk; NHS; Bio.

PACHUCKI, DOROTHY; Guilderland Central HS; Altamont, NY; (Y); Pres Rep 4-H; JV Bsktbl; High Hon Roll; Cobeskill; Comp Sci.

PACI, LEONARD-ROBERT; Flushing HS; Flushing, NY; (Y); 66/367; Debate Tm; Orch; Nwsp Stf; High Hon Roll; Arista 85; Fordham U; Psych.

PACIFIC, ALEX D; Immaculate Heart Central HS; Watertown, NY; (Y); 3/81; Cmnty Wkr; Drama Clb; Intnl Clb; Teachers Aide; Band; Variety Show; Nwsp Bus Mgr; Yrbk Bus Mgr; High Hon Roll; NHS; Diocesan Awd Outstndng Cath Schl Grad 85; Pres Acad Ftns Awd 85; Merit Schlrshp, NYS Rgnts Schlrshp; SUNY Potsdam; Math Educ.

PACITTI, JODY; Falconer HS; Falconer, NY; (Y); 12/105; Hst FBLA; Girl Scts; Trs Spanish Clb; Band; Mrchg Band; Hon Roll; NHS; Ntl Merit Ltr; Pres Acad Ftns Awd 85; NY ST Regents Schlrshp 85; Unified Stu Asstnc Schlrshp 85; Jamestown CC; Polt Sci.

PACK, DAN; Solvay HS; Syracuse, NY; (Y); Ski Clb; Stage Crew; Nwsp Phtg; Nwsp Stf; Yrbk Phtg; Yrbk Stf; VP Jr Cls; Ftbl; Hon Roll; NYS Rgnts Schlrshp 84-85; NY ST U-Buffalo; Wrtr.

PACKER, WILLIAM; East Meadow HS; East Meadow, NY; (S); Debate Tm; Mathletes; VP Temple Yth Grp; Nwsp Stf; Var Crs Cntry; Var Trk; Hon Roll; Pres Jr NHS; Sec NHS; Pres Rotary Awd; Intl Rltns.

PACZKOWSKI, LINDA; Martin Van Buren HS; Jamaica, NY; (Y); 9/579; JA; Math Clb; Science Clb; Teachers Aide; Varsity Clb; School Musical; School Play; Variety Show; Bsktbl; Tennis; Queens Coll Pres Awd For Achiev 84.

PADDEN, AMY; Wellsville HS; Wellsville, NY; (Y); 15/130; Nwsp Stf; Ed Yrbk Stf; Sftbl; High Hon Roll; Hon Roll; Beta Sigma Phi Schlrshp; SUNY-ALFRED; Crt Rprtng.

PADDOCK, RALPH; Dundee Central Schl; Dundee, NY; (Y); 13/66; Am Leg Boys St; Ski Clb; Varsity Clb; Chorus; School Musical; JV Bsbl; Var L Trk; Chmcl Tech.

PADERNACHT, SHERI; North Rockland HS; West Haverstraw, NY; (Y); 15/561; Pres JA; Ed Nwsp Ed-Chief; Ed Yrbk Stf; Capt Bowling; Elks Awd; High Hon Roll; NHS; Pres Schlr; Drama Clb; Sec Latin Clb; Stu Of Yr 84; HOBY Ldrshp Wnr 83; Democrtc Comm Scholar 85; Brandeis U; Pre-Law.

PADGETT, JEFFREY J; Oneonta HS; Oneonta, NY; (Y); Boys Clb Am; German Clb; Ski Clb; Varsity Clb; Nwsp Phtg; Var Capt Bsktbl; Var Capt Ftbl; Hon Roll; Athltc Scholar 85-86; Wagner Coll; Biol.

PADILLA, CRISTINA A; Bishop Kearney HS; Jackson Heights, NY; (Y); Art Clb; Intnl Clb; Library Aide; Science Clb; Chorus; Yrbk Stf; Hon Roll; Rgnts Schlrshp 85; NY U SEHNAP Schlrshp 85; NY U; Bus Mgmt.

PADILLA, GRACE; Bishop Loughlin Memorial HS; Brooklyn, NY; (Y); Computer Clb; Nwsp Stf; Rep Soph Cls; Rep Jr Cls; Hon Roll; NHS; Child Psych.

PADILLA, JONATHAN; Fordhma Prep; New York, NY; (Y); Art Clb; Camera Clb; Yrbk Stf; Fthr Francis Friffin Schlrshp 85; Carleton Coll; Arch.

PADIN, ANA; John Jay HS; Brooklyn, NY; (Y); Dance Clb; Cheerleading; Trk; Vllybl; Commndtn For Outstdng Spnsh 85; Comp.

PADMORE, LA VOUGHN; George W Wingate HS; Brooklyn, NY; (Y); Math Tm; Band; Concert Band; Trk; Hon Roll; Arista 82-83; Law.

PADMORE, MIATTA; Christopher Columbus HS; Bronx, NY; (Y); GAA; Office Aide; Variety Show; JV Var Bsktbl; Trk; Hon Roll; Ntl Merit Ltr; Prfct Atten Awd; Cert Merit, Excllnce Fine Arts 84-85; Cert Mert, Excllnce Acctg 84-85; MVP JV Bsktbl 81-82; Syracuse U; Acctg.

PADOVA, BARBARA M; Williamsville South HS; Williamsville, NY; (Y); 6/245; Sec VP AFS; Drama Clb; French Clb; JA; Math Clb; School Play; Yrbk Stf; High Hon Roll; Rep Sec NHS; NY ST Regents Schlrshp 85; Cornell U; Intnl Affairs.

PADOVANO, LINDA; St John The Baptist HS; Bay Shore, NY; (Y); 32/627; JCL; Rep Frsh Cls; Rep Soph Cls; Mgr Lcrss; Stat Score Keeper; JV Sftbl; High Hon Roll; Hon Roll; NHS; Latin Hon Soc 85; Bio-Med Engrng.

PADUA, HORACIO; Franklin Academy HS; Malone, NY; (S); 8/253; French Clb; Concert Band; Jazz Band; Var L Crs Cntry; Var L Trk; NHS; Ski Clb; Epsilon Hnr Scty 82-85; U Of Rochester; Med.

PADULA, ROBERT; Rome Catholic HS; Utica, NY; (Y); Ski Clb; JV Ftbl; Var Ftbl; Var Socr; Wt Lftg; Hon Roll; Pharm.

PADWORSKI, THOMAS; Beacon HS; Wappingers Falls, NY; (Y); Chorus; Ftbl; Dutchess CC; Bus Adm.

PAEK, SUNHYE; Christopher Columbus HS; Bronx, NY; (S); High Hon Roll; Hon Roll; Prfct Atten Awd; Acadmc All Amer 84-85; ST U NY Stony Brook; Comp Sci.

PAETZOLD, STEPHAN; West Genesee SR HS; Syracuse, NY; (Y); Orch; Im Socr; High Hon Roll; NHS; Prfct Atten Awd; Engrng.

PAGAN, JULIO; De Witt Clinton HS; Bronx, NY; (Y); Cmnty Wkr; Key Clb; Teachers Aide; Yrbk Stf; Var Golf; Hon Roll; JETS Awd; NHS; Prfct Atten Awd; Hgst Grade Pt Avg Ntl Hnr Soc 84; Civil Engr.

PAGAN, MICHAEL; Cardinal Spellman HS; Bronx, NY; (Y); Boy Scts; NFL; Pres Science Clb; Pres Speech Tm; Stage Crew; Off Sr Cls; JV Ftbl; Hon Roll; Ad Altare Dei Awd 82; Pope Pius XII Awd 83.

PAGANO, DANIEL L; Kings Park SR HS; Kings Park, NY; (Y); 87/450; Capt Debate Tm; NFL; Political Wkr; ROTC; Speech Tm; Varsity Clb; Stu Cncl; Var Capt Golf; Var Socr; High Hon Roll; ROTC Schlrshp; 2nd Pl NY ST Stu Congress Eliminators; 1st Pl Lincoln-Douglas Debate; Dickinson Coll; Political Sci.

PAGANO, MARISA; Susan E Wagner HS; Staten Island, NY; (Y); Science Clb; Yrbk Stf; High Hon Roll; Jr NHS; NHS; Acd Olympics 85; Asian-Amercn Clb 84-85; NCTE Achvt Awd Cont 85; Pre-Law.

PAGANO, MICHAEL; Westbury HS; Westbury, NY; (Y); 1/225; Mathletes; Varsity Clb; VP Stu Cncl; Var L Bsbl; Var Capt Bsktbl; Socr; High Hon Roll; Sec NHS; Ntl Merit Ltr; Val; G Wash U Engrng Mdl Excel Math, Sci, NYS Bsktbll Chmps 85.

PAGANO, PATRICK; Shenendehowa HS; Clifton Pk, NY; (Y); Leo Clb; Jazz Band; Variety Show; JV Bsbl; JV Golf; Pres Phys Ftns & Schltc Achvt Awds 82-84; Bus.

PAGANO, SALVATORE A; Mount St Michael HS; Bronx, NY; (S); 10/308; Rep Stu Cncl; High Hon Roll; Hon Roll; Jr NHS; NHS; Holly Rosary Effort Awd 81; Manhattan; Pre-Med.

PAGANO, STEVEN; Cicero North Syracuse HS; North Syracuse, NY; (Y); 22/711; Math Tm; Jazz Band; Mrchg Band; Symp Band; NHS; Ntl Merit Ltr; Mathletes; Math Clb; Band; Concert Band; 2nd Pl ST Amer H S Math Exm 85; 1st Pl County Onondaga Cnty Math Cntst 85; Drew U; Med.

PAGANUCCI, JOHN A; Valley Stream Central HS; Valley Stream, NY; (Y); 2/365; Band; Orch; VP Stu Cncl; JV Var Bsbl; JV Ftbl; Jr NHS; Mu Alp Tht; NHS; Ntl Merit Ltr; Pres Schlr; Cooper Union; Engrng.

PAGANUZZI, BARBARA M; Pelham Memorial HS; Pelham, NY; (Y); 42/177; AFS; Church Yth Grp; Drama Clb; Pres Math Tm; Teachers Aide; Chorus; Rep Jr Cls; Hon Roll; NY ST Regents Schlrshp 85; Delta Kappa Gamma Schlrshp Awd 85; Peer Counselor 84-85; New Rochelle Coll; Ed.

PAGANUZZI, ENEZ; Academy Of The Resurrection HS; Eastchester, NY; (Y); Dance Clb; Debate Tm; GAA; Girl Scts; NFL; Stage Crew; Rep Jr Cls; Pres Stu Cncl; Hon Roll; NHS; CYO Art Awd 85; Grl Scout Patch Dsgn Wnnr 84.

PAGE, JAMES H; Greece Athena HS; Rochester, NY; (Y); 5/295; Pres Varsity Clb; Trs Sr Cls; Rep Stu Cncl; Var L Bsbl; Var L Bsktbl; Im Vllybl; High Hon Roll; High Hon Roll; NHS; DECA; NY ST Rgnts Schlrshp 85; VA Polytechnical Inst; Finance.

PAGE, JANINE; Harpursville Central HS; Binghamton, NY; (S); 6/70; French Clb; Spanish Clb; VP Chorus; VP Sr Cls; High Hon Roll; Hon Roll; Trs NHS; Voice Dem Awd; Youth Salute 84; Achvt Awd For Highest Average In Hstry & Frnch 83-84; Breome CC; Health.

PAGE, JULIA; Morris Central HS; Mt Vision, NY; (Y); Am Leg Aux Girls St; 4-H; Quiz Bowl; Chorus; Color Guard; School Play; Bsktbl; Socr; 4-H Awd; High Hon Roll; Intl Frgn Lang Awd; Nat Sci Merit Awd; Acadmc All Am; Psych.

PAGE, JUNE M; Northport HS; E Northport, NY; (Y); 87/645; Band; Concert Band; Mrchg Band; JV Stat Bsktbl; Var Capt Fld Hcky; Var Capt Sftbl; Im Vllybl; Hon Roll; Gold Key Awd 85; All Lge Fld Hcky & Rcvd Fld Hcky MVP 85; All Lge Sftbll & All Conf Awd 83 & 84; SUNY Stony Brook; Math.

PAGE, KATHRYN; Catholic Central HS; Troy, NY; (S); 14/203; Teachers Aide; High Hon Roll; NHS; Lois C Smith Chemistry Schlrshp 84; Engrng.

PAGE, KEVIN L; Croton-Harmon HS; Croton-On-Hudson, NY; (Y); 14/107; Pres AFS; Drama Clb; French Clb; Thesps; School Play; Nwsp Stf; Rep Stu Cncl; Socr; Capt Tennis; Hon Roll; Intl Bus.

PAGE, KIM; Albion HS; Albion, NY; (Y); 32/162; Ski Clb; Mat Maids; High Hon Roll; Hon Roll; Regents Schlrshp Awd 85; Hnr Roll 84; Hnr Pass Ctznshp 84-85; Monroe CC; Bus Mgmt.

PAGE, MORLENE L; The Harvey Schl; Bedford, NY; (Y); 1/39; Girl Scts; Model UN; Yrbk Stf; Var Capt Bsktbl; Var Capt Socr; Var Capt Sftbl; Val; Church Yth Grp; GAA; Hosp Aide; Founders Cup 85; Schlr/Athl Awd 85; Math Awd 85; Sci Awd 85; Hamilton Coll; Math.

PAGE, ROBERT; Gates Chili SR HS; Rochester, NY; (S); 61/463; Rep Frsh Cls; Pres Jr Cls; Pres Sr Cls; Var L Bsbl; Ftbl; Wt Lftg; High Hon Roll; Hon Roll; Ldrshp Awd 84; 2nd Team All Cnty Ftbl 84-85; Hnrbl Mntn All Grtr Rochester & Super 22 85; Acctng.

PAGE, THOMAS; Frontier Central HS; Blasdell, NY; (Y); Varsity Clb; JV L Ftbl; Var Capt Wrstlng; Mst Imvrpd Wrstlr Awd 82-83; Outstndng Wrstlr & Prtcptn & Ldrshp Awd 84-85; Ntl Athl Plcmnt Srv 84-85; Tchr.

PAGLIA, JOANNE; Mercy HS; Moriches, NY; (Y); 8/100; Service Clb; High Hon Roll; Hon Roll; NHS; NEDT Awd; Annual Chem Tst Schl Rep 85; Hnr Hstry Clss 83-84; Hnrs Math Clss 84-85; Accntng.

PAGLIA, PAUL; Carmel HS; Carmel, NY; (Y); Boy Scts; CAP; Trs Computer Clb; Exploring; Band; JV Trk; High Hon Roll; Hon Roll; Embry-Riddle; Aeron Engrng.

PAHL, LISA; Naples Central Schl; Naples, NY; (Y); 10/70; Chorus; School Play; Stage Crew; Yrbk Ed-Chief; Yrbk Stf; Trs Sr Cls; Cheerleading; Vllybl; High Hon Roll; Hon Roll; Ethel Foster Grey Schlrshp 85; Pell Grant 85; Spplmntl Grant 85; U Of New Orleans; Gen Bus.

PAHMER, ALLYSON; Sanford H Calhoun HS; Merrick, NY; (Y); VP DECA; Nwsp Sprt Ed; Yrbk Sprt Ed; Rep Soph Cls; Pres Jr Cls; Var Cheerleading; Mgr(s); Cit Awd; High Hon Roll; NHS; Outstndng All Around Stu 85; Outstndng DECA Stu 85; Pre-Law.

PAHWA, SUZANNE; John H Glenn HS; E Northport, NY; (Y); Mathletes; Trs Science Clb; Nwsp Stf; Hon Roll; NHS; Adelphia U; Bus Mngmnt.

PAICE, KARRI; G Ray Bodley HS; Fulton, NY; (Y); French Clb; Yrbk Stf; Crs Cntry; Trk; John & Wales Coll; Culnry Arts.

PAIGE, KATHERINE B; Roy C Ketcham HS; Wappinger Fls, NY; (Y); DECA; FBLA; Concert Band; Nwsp Rptr; Cheerleading; High Hon Roll; Church Yth Grp; Drama Clb; 4-H; Girl Scts; U Of MD; Dntl Hygn.

PAIKIN, SUSAN L; Bishop Grimes HS; Liverpool, NY; (Y); 22/207; Church Yth Grp; Rep Soph Cls; Rep Jr Cls; VP Stu Cncl; JV Bsktbl; Var Socr; JV Sftbl; Var Vllybl; Hon Roll; NHS; Le Moyne Coll; Accntnt.

PAINTER, DOROTHA; Addison Central Schl; Elkland, PA; (Y); 6/97; Sec 4-H; JCL; Latin Clb; Letterman Clb; Sec Science Clb; Ski Clb; Varsity Clb; Color Guard; High Hon Roll; NHS; Ntl Engl Merit Awd 84; Mansfield U; Nutrtn.

PAIS, SALVATORE; Brooklyn Technical HS; Jackson Heights, NY; (Y); 45/750; Computer Clb; Math Clb; Math Tm; Lit Mag; High Hon Roll; Hon Roll; NHS; Cert Merit Math 83-85; Cert Merit Physics 85; Citation NYS Math Leag Nwsltr Problem 2.6; Renseaaler Polytech Inst; Math.

PAISLEY, JOAN; Clara Barton HS; Bronx, NY; (Y); Hosp Aide; Bsktbl; Hon Roll; Phy Ftnss Awd 83; Attndnc Awd Cert 83-84; Chem.

PAJAK, ARTHUR; Xavier HS; Brooklyn, NY; (Y); 3/227; Math Tm; Stage Crew; Bsktbl; Ftbl; High Hon Roll; Jr NHS; NHS; NY ST Regents Schlrshp; 1st & 3rd Pl Iona Coll Lang Cont-Spnsh; Bucknell U; Comp Sci.

PAJONK, STEPH; Valley Central HS; Montgomery, NY; (Y); 37/350; Debate Tm; JV Capt Bsktbl; JV Capt Cheerleading; Var Tennis; Var DAR Awd; NHS; Spanish NHS; Band; Concert Band; Jazz Band; Most Impvd-Tennis, Vlybl 85; Psych.

PAK, LYNDA; Bronx H S Of Science; Flushing, NY; (Y); VP Church Yth Grp; JA; Office Aide; Teachers Aide; Sec Band; Church Choir.

PAK, NANCY; St Francis Prep; Bayside, NY; (S); 4/704; Computer Clb; Chorus; Stage Crew; Im Sftbl; Hon Roll; Prncpls List 83-84; Phy Thrpy.

PAKATAR, KRISTIN; Waterford-Halfmoon HS; Waterford, NY; (Y); Cmnty Wkr; Chorus; Hon Roll; NHS; Bsktbl; Ctznshp Awd Hilltop Bowl 85; Jrnlsm.

PALACIOS, PATRICK; Mount Saint Michael Acad; Bronx, NY; (Y); 7/308; Ski Clb; Rep Jr Cls; Rep Stu Cncl; Im Bsktbl; Im Fld Hcky; Im Ftbl; Im Sftbl; High Hon Roll; Jr NHS; NHS; Mechncl Engrng.

PALADINO, ANN MARIE; East Islip HS; East Islip, NY; (Y); Cmnty Wkr; FBLA; Hosp Aide; Flag Corp; Mrchg Band; Stage Crew; Rep Jr Cls; High Hon Roll; Hon Roll; NHS; Candy Stripng 82-85; Clarkson U; Bus Adm.

PALAGIANO, ANN MARIE; St Joseph By The Sea HS; Staten Island, NY; (Y); 14/284; Church Yth Grp; Dance Clb; Drama Clb; Hosp Aide; School Musical; Off Jr Cls; Hon Roll; NHS; Bio.

PALANCA, ANTOINETTE; Yonkers HS; Yonkers, NY; (Y); 10/378; Yrbk Stf; Rep Soph Cls; Mgr Ftbl; Var Mgr(s); CC Awd; High Hon Roll; NHS; Socl Stds Awds; Supt Awd; Achv Awd; Mercy Coll; Comp.

PALASCIANO, STEVE; Lincoln HS; Yonkers, NY; (S); Key Clb; Stage Crew; Nwsp Phtg; Nwsp Rptr; Yrbk Phtg; Crs Cntry; Trk; Crss Cntry Cty Chmpns 84; Comp Sci.

PALASKI, TAMARA; Notre Dame HS; Whitesboro, NY; (Y); 48/174; Off ROTC; Chorus; Drill Tm; Yrbk Stf; High Hon Roll; Hon Roll; Regents Diploma 85; Utica Coll; Med Tech.

PALAZZO, ROSEMARIE F; Niagara Wheatfield HS; Niagara Falls, NY; (Y); 312/625; Pep Clb; Band; Concert Band; Mrchg Band; School Play; Sftbl; Hon Roll; Prfct Atten Awd; NCCC; Bus.

PALDINO, LAURIE JANE; Mamaroneck HS; Mamaroneck, NY; (Y); VP JA; Key Clb; Spanish Clb; Chorus; Swing Chorus; DAR Awd; Daug Am Revltn Good Citznshp Awd; Pace Outstndng Achvt Awd 82-83; Schrrshp JR Achvt Dale Carnegie Pub; Coll New Rochelle; Adv.

PALEOLOGOPOULOS, BILLY; Lindenhurst HS; Lindenhurst, NY; (Y); German Clb; Teachers Aide; Concert Band; Nwsp Stf; Bsbl; Ftbl; Score Keeper; Wt Lftg; High Hon Roll; Hon Roll; NYSME 83; BOCES Giftd Talntd 84-85; Pre-Med.

PALERMO, AMY; Frontier Central HS; Buffalo, NY; (Y); Church Yth Grp; Spanish Clb; Yrbk Stf; Hon Roll; Buffalo ST Coll; Social Wrk.

PALERMO, CATHERINE; Webster HS; Webster, NY; (Y); French Clb; Chorus; School Musical; Yrbk Stf; Off Soph Cls; Apprctn Cert Ctznshp, Ldrshp & Schlrshp 84-85; Psychlgy.

PALERMO, CHARLES; Jamestown HS; Jamestown, NY; (Y); Boys Clb Am; Boy Scts; Golf; Hon Roll; Math.

PALERMO, TINA MARIE; Avon Central JR SR HS; Avon, NY; (Y); Art Clb; Girl Scts; Stu Cncl; JV Im Bsktbl; JV Socr; Var Swmmng; High Hon Roll; Hon Roll; Ntl Merit Ltr; Accntnt.

PALETTA, LAURA A; Fox Lane HS; Bedford, NY; (Y); 6/295; Cmnty Wkr; Pres Sr Cls; JV Var Vllybl; NHS; Girl Scts; Intnl Clb; Political Wkr; Ski Clb; Yrbk Stf; Rep Frsh Cls; NYS Regnts Schlrshp 85; All Leag Vllybl 84-85; Frnch Awd 81-85; Holy Cross Coll; Pol Sci.

PALEY, JEFFREY E; Yesmiva University HS; Teaneck, NJ; (Y); Co-Capt Chess Clb; Debate Tm; Sec Math Clb; Math Tm; Science Clb; Ed Nwsp Stf; Yrbk Stf; NHS; Ntl Merit SF; Westnghse Sci Tlnt Srch Semi Fnlst 85; Med.

PALEY, PAMELA H; Shaker HS; Latham, NY; (Y); French Clb; GAA; Yrbk Rptr; Yrbk Stf; Capt Fld Hcky; Gym; Capt Trk; DAR Awd; High Hon Roll; NHS; Am HS Stu Athl 85; Princeton U; Sprts Psych.

PALGON, JACKIE; Bronx H S Of Science; Hollis, NY; (Y); French Clb; JA; Library Aide; Teachers Aide; Lit Mag; Prfct Atten Awd.

PALIJARO, JOSEPHINE; Spring Valley SR HS; Spring Valley, NY; (Y); French Clb; Prfct Atten Awd; Corp Lwyr.

PALIOURAS, ELENI J; L C Obourn HS; Pittsford, NY; (Y); 21/121; Latin Clb; Model UN; Varsity Clb; Chorus; Church Choir; Yrbk Phtg; Stu Cncl; Regents Schlrshp Awd 85; Rochester Inst Of Tech; PR.

PALITSCH, MAURA; Catholic Central HS; Troy, NY; (S); 3/203; Drama Clb; German Clb; Math Clb; School Musical; School Play; Yrbk Stf; High Hon Roll; Jr NHS; NHS; Lois Smith Chem Scholar 84; Natl Math Assn Awd Excllnc 82-83; Rensselaer Plytech; Mtl Engr.

PALIWODA, RICHARD; Archbishop Molloy HS; Ridgewood, NY; (Y); 33/409; French Clb; Yrbk Stf; VP Stu Cncl; Im Bsktbl; L Trk; Jr NHS; VP NHS; Intl Rel.

PALKA, JOSEPH; Union-Endicott HS; Endicott, NY; (Y); Var L Bsbl; Var L Bsktbl; High Hon Roll; Engrng.

PALLACK, SCOTT W; Northport HS; Northport, NY; (Y); Pres Church Yth Grp; Lit Mag; JV Var Bsktbl; Fnlst S V A Schlrsp Test 84-85; Illustration.

PALLADINO, DIANNE K; Westhill HS; Syracuse, NY; (Y); 5/168; AFS; Sec French Clb; FBLA; Key Clb; Math Tm; Ski Clb; Band; Nwsp Stf; Yrbk Ed-Chief; Yrbk Stf; Onondaga Cmnty Scshlr; All-Cnty Bnd; Clarkson U; Comp Engrng.

PALLENTINO, LYNN; Fontbonne Hall Acad; Brooklyn, NY; (Y); Church Yth Grp; Cmnty Wkr; Office Aide; Teachers Aide; Church Choir; School Musical; School Play; Variety Show; Tennis; High Hon Roll; 5 Yr Svc Awd 83; Merit Awd Outstndg Accmplshmnt Relig Ed 84 & 85; Albany ST U; Pre-Med.

PALLESCHI, CHRISTINA; Weedsport JR SR HS; Pt Byron, NY; (Y); Church Yth Grp; Office Aide; Band; Yrbk Phtg; Yrbk Stf; Bsktbl; Fld Hcky; Trk; Busn.

PALLOGUDIS, PENNY; Mineola HS; Mineola, NY; (Y); Girl Scts; Key Clb; Spanish Clb; Lit Mag; Psych.

PALLOTTA, SCOTT; Amsterdam HS; Amsterdam, NY; (Y); 13/319; Varsity Clb; Concert Band; Jazz Band; Mrchg Band; Var Socr; Var Trk; Hon Roll; NHS; Engrng.

PALMA, PAOLA; Bishop Kearney HS; Brooklyn, NY; (S); 2/364; Cmnty Wkr; Math Tm; Political Wkr; Chorus; Nwsp Ed-Chief; Ed Nwsp Rptr; Lit Mag; High Hon Roll; 1st In Cls Schlrshp; Hon Mentn Italian Cont; 3rd Pl Italian Poetry Cont; Med.

PALMATEER, DAWN; Highland HS; Highland, NY; (Y); 15/127; AFS; Chorus; School Play; Hon Roll; Jr NHS; NHS; Bus Awd 84; Psych.

PALMATIER, CYNTHIA; Wellsville HS; Alma, NY; (Y); 42/130; Pres Church Yth Grp; Drama Clb; Chorus; Madrigals; Mrchg Band; JV Capt Cheerleading; All County Choir Medal 85; Alfred ST Coll; Lib Arts.

PALMATIER, THOMAS; Bishop Scully HS; Amsterdam, NY; (Y); Boy Scts; Pres Frsh Cls; Pres Jr Cls; Pres Sr Cls; JV Var Bsbl; JV Var Ftbl; JV Stat Score Keeper; Fulton-Montgomery CC; Bus Adm.

PALMER, CARRIE; Horseheads HS; Horseheads, NY; (S); 4/407; French Clb; Chorus; Concert Band; Jazz Band; Mrchg Band; School Musical; Variety Show; Stu Cncl; High Hon Roll; NHS; Albany Coll Of Pharm; Pharm.

PALMER, DAWN; Groton Central Schl; Groton, NY; (Y); Church Yth Grp; Pres Girl Scts; Sec Band; Chorus; Sec Concert Band; Jazz Band; Mrchg Band; Yrbk Stf; Hon Roll; Bus.

PALMER, DOUGLAS D; Hartford Central Schl; Granville, NY; (Y); Drama Clb; French Clb; Mathletes; Science Clb; School Play; Trs Jr Cls; JV Bsbl; High Hon Roll; Ntl Merit Ltr; Ski Clb; NYS Rgnts Schlrshp 85; Clarkson Schl; Engrng.

PALMER, GAYLAN; Mount Morkham SR HS; W Winfield, NY; (Y); 4/135; Church Yth Grp; Debate Tm; Drama Clb; French Clb; Girl Scts; Intnl Clb; Speech Tm; Acpl Chr; Band; Chorus; Cls Music Awds Top Musician Cls 83-85; Stage Band All Star Band Awd 85; Eastman Schl; Music.

PALMER, JOSEPH P; Canajoharie HS; Canajoharie, NY; (Y); 8/86; Am Leg Boys St; Trs FCA; Varsity Clb; Stage Crew; Yrbk Sprt Ed; Sec Jr Cls; Var L Bsktbl; Var L Ftbl; Var L Trk; Im Vllybl; Bio Regnts NYS Tst Awd Hghst Grd Schl 84; Prfct Scor Area HS Dys Comp Tst SUNY 85; Rochester Inst Tec; Biomed Comp.

PALMER, LAURA; Rome Free Acad; Rome, NY; (Y); Church Yth Grp; Drama Clb; Girl Scts; Intnl Clb; Varsity Clb; Nwsp Rptr; Yrbk Stf; JV Bsktbl; Yrbk Phtg; NHS; Hgh Hnr Roll 83-85; Hghst Avg Engl Awd 83; Hghst Avg Hist Awd 83; Engl.

PALMER JR, LYNN; Canton HS; Rens Falls, NY; (Y); 52/115; Bsbl; Bsktbl; Socr; Hon Roll; NYS Rgnts Schlrshp 85; Crmnl Justc.

PALMER, MARYKAY; Garden City HS; Garden City, NY; (Y); 54/319; Church Yth Grp; Drama Clb; French Clb; Key Clb; Concert Band; Mrchg Band; School Musical.

PALMER, MICHELLE; Vestal SR HS; Binghamton, NY; (Y); Hstry.

PALMER, NICOLA; Prospect Heights HS; Brooklyn, NY; (Y); Dance Clb; FBLA; Pep Clb; Off Stu Cncl; Gym; Recrd Kepng Awd 85; Fash Merch.

PALMER, ROCCO J; T R Proctor HS; Utica, NY; (Y); 14/202; Boys Clb Am; Church Yth Grp; Bsbl; Coach Actv; Crs Cntry; Score Keeper; Wrstlng; Hon Roll; Jr NHS; NY ST Regents Schlrsp 85; TR Proctor Certfct Of Excellnc 85; US Air Force; Crim Justc.

PALMER, SCOTT M; Homer HS; Cortland, NY; (Y); 30/200; Concert Band; Drm Mjr(t); Mrchg Band; School Musical; JV Trk; Shakespearian Society 84-85; NY ST Regents Schlrshp 85; BPOE Elks Stu Of Month 85; MA Maritime Acad; Coast Guard.

PALMER, SIMONE; Springfield Gardens HS; Laurelton, NY; (S); Drama Clb; Church Choir; Cheerleading; Hon Roll; Jr NHS; NHS; Schltc Achvt Awd 84; Math Aw, Sci Awd, Spnsh Awd 81-82; Bio Awd 84; Med.

PALMER, TINA M; Hilton Central HS; Hilton, NY; (Y); Church Yth Grp; Office Aide; Nwsp Rptr; Nwsp Stf; Yrbk Stf; Rep Jr Cls; High Hon Roll; NHS; NY ST Regents Schlrshp 85; Suburban News Recgntn Awd For Jrnlsm 85; Daemen Coll; Hstry.

PALMER, VICKY; Waverly HS; Waverly, NY; (Y); 5/135; Church Yth Grp; Cmnty Wkr; Rep Stu Cncl; Var L Crs Cntry; Var L Trk; High Hon Roll; Hon Roll; Trs NHS; Rotary Awd; New York ST Regents Schlsp 85; Houghton Coll Trustees Schlsp 85; West Schlsp 85; Houghton Coll.

PALMERI, JENNIFER; Kenmore West SR HS; Tona, NY; (Y); Church Yth Grp; Stage Crew; Variety Show; Rep Stu Cncl; JV Var Cheerleading; JV Trk; Im Vllybl; Hon Roll; Prfct Atten Awd; Bus.

PALMIERI, LAURA; Birnghamton HS; Binghamton, NY; (Y); Church Yth Grp; Band; Mrchg Band; High Hon Roll; Broome CC; Bus.

PALMIERI, PATRICIA M; Thomas R Proctor HS; Utica, NY; (Y); GAA; JV Var Bsktbl; Var Crs Cntry; Var Capt Fld Hcky; Var Sftbl; NHS; US Army Resrv-Ntl Schlr/Athlt Awd 85; Grls Athltcs-Sprtsmnshp Awd 84 & 85; Eng.

PALMIERI, PETER; Stillwater Central HS; Stillwater, NY; (Y); 10/97; Pres Church Yth Grp; Key Clb; Var Wrstlng; Bausch & Lomb Sci Awd; High Hon Roll; Hon Roll; NHS; Mr & Mrs Malcolm Borst Awd For Hghst Avg In Sci Regents 85; Earl J Manning Post Awd Hghst Avg Physcs; Clarkson U; Cvl/Envir Engrng.

PALMIOTTI, ANDREW; Highland HS; W Park, NY; (Y); Concert Band; Jazz Band; Mrchg Band; JV Socr; NHS; Engrng.

PALMITER, MICHELLE S; Cortland JR SR HS; Cortland, NY; (Y); 10/235; Trs Thesps; Pres Chorus; School Musical; Sec Jr Cls; Var L Tennis; High Hon Roll; NHS; School Play; Rep Stu Cncl; Outstndng Ldrshp Cert Of Awd 84; Ntl Thsp Awd 83; Rgnts Schlrshp 85; Thtr.

PALOMBELLA, MIKE; Auburn HS; Auburn, NY; (Y); Church Yth Grp; Var JV Ftbl; Hon Roll; Crim Just.

PALOWICH, REBECCA; Notre-Dame Bishop Gibbons HS; Schenectady, NY; (S); 17/108; Red Cross Aide; Nwsp Sprt Ed; Stu Cncl; Var Capt Bsktbl; Sftbl; Swmmng; High Hon Roll; JC Awd; NHS; Religion Awd; Law.

PALOZZI, CHRISTOPHER M; Greece Olympia HS; Rochester, NY; (Y); 24/316; Cmnty Wkr; JA; Math Clb; Math Tm; Science Clb; Yrbk Stf; Var Socr; High Hon Roll; NHS; Pres Schlr; Ntl Schlrshp, Trustee Schlrshp & Boston U Grant 85; Boston U; Bio.

PALUMBO, ANNA; Christopher Columbus HS; Bronx, NY; (S); 15/676; Dance Clb; Drama Clb; Math Clb; Math Tm; Band; Chorus; School Musical; School Play; Off Frsh Cls; Off Soph Cls; Netwk Organztn Bronx Womn Laureate Awd 85; Daily Nws Prd Yankees Supr Yth Outstndng Achvt 83; Boston Conservatory; Actg.

PALUMBO, DANIELA; Dover JR SR HS; Dover Plains, NY; (S); 3/100; Varsity Clb; Yrbk Ed-Chief; Pres Frsh Cls; Trs Soph Cls; Trs Jr Cls; Trs Sr Cls; Var Bsktbl; Capt Fld Hcky; High Hon Roll; Sec Trs NHS; Stevens Inst Of Tech Women In Engrng Pgm 84; Finance.

PALUMBO, DAVID; East Meadow HS; East Meadow, NY; (S); Computer Clb; Debate Tm; FBLA; Mathletes; Math Tm; Science Clb; Ski Clb; Nwsp Rptr; Nwsp Stf; Rptr Lit Mag; Pre-Med.

PALUMBO, LISA; Hilton Central HS; North Greece, NY; (Y); Trs French Clb; Mrchg Band; Variety Show; Ed Yrbk Stf; Var Capt Cheerleading; NHS; Best All-Arnd Chrldr 85; Best Sr Chrldr 85; Deans Schlrshp 85; Ladies Aux Schlrshp 85; Daemen Coll; Phys Thrpy.

PALUMBO, MARY; Ballston Spa SR HS; Ballston Spa, NY; (Y); 16/238; Chorus; Yrbk Stf; Stat Fld Hcky; High Hon Roll; Hon Roll; NHS; Pres Fit Awd; Hnrd Skidmore Coll For Top 10 Pct Of Clss; Vrsty Ltr Fld Hcky Stats; ST U NY Albany; Psych.

PALUMBO, MARY; Dover JR SR HS; Dover Plains, NY; (S); 2/100; VP Varsity Clb; Sec Band; Pres Soph Cls; Pres Jr Cls; Var Bsktbl; Var Fld Hcky; Var Sftbl; High Hon Roll; Jr NHS; Pres NHS; Fld Hcky All-Star Team 84; NYSSMA Solo-Grade VI-OUTSTNDNG; Engrng.

PALUMBO, THERESA; Frankfort Schuyler Central HS; Frankfort, NY; (S); FBLA; Key Clb; Yrbk Stf; Rep Soph Cls; Trs Jr Cls; Trs Stu Cncl; Hon Roll; NHS.

PALYS, MICHELLE; Villa Maria Acad; Buffalo, NY; (Y); Red Cross Aide; Church Choir; Bowling; Score Keeper; Vllybl; Hon Roll; NYS Rgnts Awd Perf Sw Handbell Chr 84; Cert Basic Eng 85; Prfct Attndnce Awd 85; Erie CC; Emer Med Tech.

PAM, AARON; Sleepy Hollow HS; North Tarrytown, NY; (Y); Church Yth Grp; French Clb; JA; Ftbl; Am Leg Aux Girls St; Hon Roll; Natl Achvt Schlrshp Pgm Outstndng Negro Stu 84; U MD; Crim Justice.

PAMUKCOGLU, MICHAEL C; Wellsville HS; Wellsville, NY; (Y); Stage Crew; Stu Cncl; Bsbl; Bsktbl; Socr; Hon Roll; NY ST Regnts Schlrshp 85; U Of Buffalo.

PAN, BRIAN C; Spring Valley SR HS; Monsey, NY; (Y); 1/435; Church Yth Grp; Computer Clb; Debate Tm; German Clb; Key Clb; Math Clb; Math Tm; ROTC; Science Clb; Chorus; German Essay Wnner 84, Ntl Hnr Soc 83; MA Inst Tech; Elec Engr.

PAN, LI-WEN; St Johns Preparatory Schl; Elmhurst, NY; (S); Band; Orch; High Hon Roll; Hon Roll; NHS; Ntl Merit Ltr; Stony Brook ST U.

PANAGAKIS, ANDREA; Cicero-North Syracuse HS; Clay, NY; (S); 9/662; Dance Clb; Girl Scts; Pep Clb; Drill Tm; Mrchg Band; Orch; Hon Roll; Bio.

PANAGAKOS, PETER; Archbishop Iakovos HS; Jamaica, NY; (S); 1/15; Boy Scts; Church Yth Grp; Cmnty Wkr; Computer Clb; Math Clb; Church Choir; VP Jr Cls; Stu Cncl; Var Bsktbl; JV Coach Actv.

PANAHBARHAGH, DENNY; Solomon Secheter HS; Brooklyn, NY; (Y); English Clb; Ski Clb; Jazz Band; Nwsp Stf; Off Jr Cls; Bsbl; Bsktbl; Bowling; Fld Hcky; Socr; Brooklyn Coll; Comp.

PANAK, LISA; St Peters HS For Girls; Staten Isl, NY; (Y); Chorus; School Musical; School Play; Jr NHS; NHS; Prfct Atten Awd; Orientatn Comm 84; Emergency Care Tm 84; St Johns U.

PANARELLI, JANET; Valley Stream Central HS; Valley Stream, NY; (Y); AFS; Art Clb; Ski Clb; Mgr(s); Sftbl; Vllybl; Jr NHS; Nassau; Psych.

PANARIELLO, JO ANN; Bishop Kearney HS; Brooklyn, NY; (Y); Off Teachers Aide; Chorus; Kingsborough CC; Physcl Thrpy.

PANARISI, PROVVIDENZA; St Johns Prep HS; Astoria, NY; (Y); 13/415; Cmnty Wkr; Dance Clb; Ski Clb; Nwsp Ed-Chief; Nwsp Rptr; Yrbk Rptr; Yrbk Stf; Badmtn; Hon Roll; NHS; Girls Ping Pong Chmp 82-83; Boston U; Bus Mngmnt.

PANASCI, THOMAS; Rome Catholic HS; Rome, NY; (Y); Church Yth Grp; Science Clb; Var L Bsbl; JV Bsktbl; Hon Roll; Effort Awd Bio 84; MIP Bsbl 83; Bio.

PANAYIOTOU, ANDREW; W C Bryant HS; Jackson Heights, NY; (Y); 36/579; Church Yth Grp; Cmnty Wkr; Debate Tm; FBLA; FTA; Political Wkr; Band; Jazz Band; Nwsp Phtg; Tennis; Math & Engl Ltr 84; Bus Law & Dist Atty Awds 84; Boston Coll; Bus Law.

PANCHERI, BRUNA T; Stissing Mt JR SR HS; Red Hook, NY; (Y); Dance Clb; Jr Cls; Trk; Hon Roll; Hnr Keys; Suprstr Awd Trck; Marist Coll; Art.

PANCOAST, DARRIN; Victor Central HS; Macedon, NY; (Y); Art Clb; Boy Scts; Exploring; JA; Band; Mrchg Band; Hon Roll; Prfct Atten Awd; Boy Scts Eagle Awd 85; Ad & Altare & Del 84; Art.

PANCZNER, GREGORY; Mont Pleasant HS; Pattersonville, NY; (Y); Pres Chess Clb; JA; Key Clb; Spanish Clb; Chorus; Yrbk Phtg; Stu Cncl; Hon Roll; NHS; Technel Serv Clb Pres; SR VA; Comptr Clb; FIT; Comptr Sci.

PANCZYK, RICHARD; Cheektowaga Central HS; Tucson, AZ; (Y); 1/204; Computer Clb; Hon Roll; Jr NHS; NHS; Ntl Merit Schol; Val; Voice Dem Awd; Karr Parker Engrng Schlrshp 85; U Buffalo Hnrs Schlrshp 85; U AZ; Elec Engr.

PANDYA, ANAND; East Meadow HS; East Meadow, NY; (S); Co-Capt Math Tm; Orch; Ed Nwsp Stf; Ed Lit Mag; George Washington U Engrng Mdl 85; Hugh O Brian Rep St Sem 84.

PANEK, LEA ANN; Lockport SR HS; Lockport, NY; (Y); 40/450; Trs AFS; Church Yth Grp; Girl Scts; Concert Band; Mrchg Band; Symp Band; Rep Stu Cncl; JV Var Swmmng; God Cntry Awd; Hon Roll; Sci Congrss 83; Syracus U; Mechncl Engrng.

PANEK, REGINA; Fowler HS; Syracuse, NY; (S); 4/250; Church Yth Grp; GAA; Quiz Bowl; Science Clb; Lit Mag; Bsktbl; High Hon Roll; Awds Hnrs Engl 83; Rgnts Bio 84; Syracuse U; Math.

PANELLA, TONY; Greece Athena SR HS; Rochester, NY; (Y); Var Ftbl; Hon Roll; Jrnymn Tool & Die.

PANEPENTO, SAMUEL; St Josephs Collegiate Inst; Kenmore, NY; (Y); 85/200; Band; Church Choir; Concert Band; Jazz Band; Orch; Pep Band; School Musical; Yrbk Stf; Hon Roll; Natl Arion Instrmntl Trmpt 85; Schl Inst Awd; Buffalo ST U; Law.

PANESSA, MARY B; Arlington HS; Poughkeepsie, NY; (Y); 256/558; Drama Clb; Intnl Clb; Office Aide; Red Cross Aide; Spanish Clb; Chorus; School Musical; School Play; Variety Show; Rep Frsh Cls; Miss Loyalty Day Queen 84; Arts.

PANETTA, JOSEPH R; Notre Dame HS; Oriskany, NY; (Y); Am Leg Boys St; Cmnty Wkr; School Musical; Nwsp Rptr; Yrbk Stf; High Hon Roll; NHS; Rep NYS Commssnr Ed Stu Advsry Comm 84-86; Acad All Amer 85; Int Affrs.

PANG, JOSEPH; Sachem HS; Lake Ronkonkoma, NY; (Y); 140/1463; Computer Clb; Math Tm; Science Clb; Jr NHS; NHS; Purdue U; Engrng.

PANGARO, ALLEN; Bainbridge-Gilford Central HS; Bainbridge, NY; (Y); 12/75; Band; Orch; Pres Jr Cls; Rep Stu Cncl; JV Bsktbl; Var Ftbl; Var Trk; Hon Roll; Pres Jr NHS; Prom King 85; Interact 84-85; Engrng.

PANICCIA, SUSAN M; Mont Pleasant HS; Schenectady, NY; (Y); 15/250; Band; Concert Band; Mrchg Band; JV Sftbl; French Hon Soc; NHS.

PANKONIN, CHRIS; Fayeteville-Manlius HS; Manlius, NY; (Y); Chrmn Church Yth Grp; Hosp Aide; Ski Clb; Chorus; Diving; Powder Puff Ftbl; Elem Eductn.

PANNETTA, KERRY; St Peters H S For Girls; Staten Isl, NY; (Y); Boy Scts; Exploring; VP FNA; Church Choir; Lit Mag; Sec Jr Cls; Prfct Atten Awd; Untd Cerebrl Plsy Volntr 82-85; Pace U; Math.

PANNONE, ANTHONY; St Joseph By The Sea; Staten Island, NY; (Y); Am Leg Boys St; Computer Clb; Pres Stu Cncl; Var Bsbl; Wt Lftg; Hon Roll; Hghst Rnk In Math & Bio 85; Dntl.

PANOS, SPYROS N; Midwood HS; Brooklyn, NY; (Y); 11/620; Boy Scts; Chess Clb; Church Yth Grp; French Clb; Math Tm; Varsity Clb; Lit Mag; Bsktbl; Socr; Jr NHS; Regents Schlrshp 85; Sophie Davis CC NY; Pre-Med.

PANTANO, LYNNE M; Nardin Acad; Buffalo, NY; (Y); 2/100; Cmnty Wkr; Hosp Aide; Yrbk Stf; Ed Lit Mag; Rep Jr Cls; Sec Sr Cls; NHS; Ntl Merit Ltr; Pres Schlr; Sal; Regnts Schlrshp; Excllnc Chem, Engl Hnrs III, Albgr II & Trig, Geom; Its Academic Tm Capt; St Bonaventure U.

PANTAZI, GINA; St Johns Preparatory Schl; L I C, NY; (S); 39/415; Yrbk Stf; Hon Roll; NHS; Fordham U; Comp Sci.

PANTAZOPOULOS, STEPHANIE; Cathedral HS; Bronx, NY; (Y); FNA; Girl Scts; Hosp Aide; Library Aide; Band; Yrbk Phtg; NHS; Ntl Merit Ltr; St Johns U; Mrktng.

PANTINA, ROSEMARY; St John Villa Academy HS; Staten Is, NY; (Y); Church Yth Grp; Cheerleading; Crs Cntry; Trk; Hon Roll; Achvt Awd Italian II 83-84; Acctng.

PANTOJA, MARIA; Dodge Vocational HS; Bronx, NY; (Y); 70/439; Dance Clb; Math Clb; School Play; Vllybl; Hon Roll; Mth 82-84; Bookkpng 84; Bookkeeping.

PANTOJA, MICHAEL; Cardinal Hayes HS; New York, NY; (Y); 85/264; Varsity Clb; Bsktbl; Var Trk; Prfct Atten Awd; NY Inst Of Tech; Law Enfrcmnt.

PANULA, NANCY; St Francis Prep; Queens Village, NY; (S); 18/690; Cmnty Wkr; Teachers Aide; Sftbl; NHS; Principals List 85; Molloy Coll; Nrsg.

PANYARD, DAVID; Henninger HS; Syracuse, NY; (Y); Band; Concert Band; Jazz Band; Mrchg Band; Pep Band; School Play; Socr; High Hon Roll; Hon Roll; Jr NHS; Hofstra; Stck Brkr.

PANZARELLA, JANICE; Mt St Joseph Acad; Buffalo, NY; (S); 4/60; Church Yth Grp; Yrbk Stf; High Hon Roll; Hon Roll; NHS; Sister Sylvia Schlrshp Awd 81-82; SUNYAB; Pharmacy.

PANZARELLA, ROSA; Niagara Falls HS; Niagara Falls, NY; (Y); 19/250; Church Yth Grp; Cmnty Wkr; JA; Yrbk Stf; Hon Roll; NHS; Ntl Merit Ltr; Prfct Atten Awd; NYS Rgnts Schlrshp 85; Alumni Schlrshp 85; Rochester Inst Of Tech; Ele Eng.

PANZICA, ROSE; Jamestown HS; Jamestown, NY; (Y); Band; Chorus; Color Guard; Concert Band; Mrchg Band; Symp Band; Bryant & Stratton; Bus.

PAOLANTONIO, JO ANN; Sewanhaka HS; Stewart Manor, NY; (Y); 110/360; Drama Clb; Girl Scts; Thesps; Chorus; School Musical; School Play; Swing Chorus; Variety Show; JV Cheerleading; Hon Roll; Miss American Coed Pgnt-St Fnlst 85; Perfrmng Arts.

PAOLILLO, MATTHEW; Tottenville HS; Staten Island, NY; (Y); Boy Scts; Hosp Aide; Teachers Aide; NHS; NY St Regent Schlrshp Wnnr 85; Ntl French Cont 83-84; Black Belt Karate 81-85; Suny-Binghamton; Med.

PAOLILLO, MICHELE; Bellport HS; Bellport, NY; (Y); Ski Clb; JV Var Cheerleading; JV Score Keeper; JV Socr; SUNY Farmingdale; Elec Engrng.

PAOLONI, CHRISTINA; Long Island City HS; Astoria, NY; (Y); 82/579; Church Yth Grp; Cmnty Wkr; Office Aide; Lit Mag; Im Sftbl; Im Vllybl; Cit Awd; Hon Roll; Dr N Elliot Awd Sec Studies 85; Hunter Coll.

PAOLUCCI, JANINE; Bishop Kearney HS; Brooklyn, NY; (Y); Exploring; Teachers Aide; Chorus; Church Choir; School Musical; Variety Show; Gym; Im Swmmng; Tennis; NYU.

PAOLUCCI, MICHELE; Mount Mercy Acad; Buffalo, NY; (Y); Trs VP French Clb; Crs Cntry; Gym; Ntl JR Hnr Soc 82; Gymnstcs Cls I ST Chmpnshp 81-85; Phy Thrpy.

PAONESSA, MAUREEN; Our Lady Of Mercy HS; Rochester, NY; (Y); 21/200; School Musical; Nwsp Rptr; Rep Soph Cls; Rep Jr Cls; Rep Sr Cls; Bsktbl; Trk; Hon Roll; Rgnts/Deans Schlrshp Fordham 85; MVP Trk 83-85; Cptn Trk Tm 83-85; Fordham U.

PAPA, DEBORAH; Fonda Fultonville Central Schl; Fonda, NY; (Y); Band; Trs Frsh Cls; Trs Soph Cls; Trs Jr Cls; Trs Sr Cls; Stu Cncl; Var Cheerleading; Var Socr; Var Trk; JV Capt Vllybl.

PAPA, LIZ; Pelham Memorial HS; Pelham, NY; (Y); AFS; Church Yth Grp; GAA; Girl Scts; Chorus; Rep Jr Cls; JV Var Bsktbl.

PAPAEMANUEL, JIMMY; Sheepshead Bay HS; Brooklyn, NY; (Y); Wt Lftg; Hon Roll; Exec Intrnshp Pgm 84; John Jay Coll; Crim Just.

PAPAGEORGE, ANNA; F D Roosevelt HS; Brooklyn, NY; (Y); 55/716; Library Aide; Office Aide; Teachers Aide; Band; Hon Roll; Arista 83; Lioness Club 83; Brooklyn Coll; Educ.

PAPAGEORGE, GEORGE; Liverpool HS; Liverpool, NY; (Y); Off Church Yth Grp; DECA; Exploring; Chorus; Nwsp Sprt Ed; Stu Cncl; Im Mgr Bsktbl; Trk; Hon Roll; Prfct Atten Awd; 4th Pl NY St Fnls DECA Comptn 85; Awd Gold Merit Achvt DECA 85; Lawyer.

PAPAIAKOVOU, STACEY; John Dewey HS; Brooklyn, NY; (Y); Teachers Aide; School Play; High Hon Roll; Prfct Atten Awd; Comp Sci.

PAPARELLA, DONALD; Little Falls HS; Little Falls, NY; (S); 6/95; Am Leg Boys St; Church Yth Grp; Cmnty Wkr; Drama Clb; Exploring; FBLA; Varsity Clb; School Play; Nwsp Phtg; Yrbk Phtg; MDS Comp Class 84; Herkimer Cty Yth Bureau Adv 84-86; Comp Engr.

PAPARELLA, SUSAN; Notre Dame Acad; Staten Island, NY; (Y); Drama Clb; Exploring; Hosp Aide; Pres Science Clb; Rep Frsh Cls; Rep Soph Cls; Rep Stu Cncl; Cit Awd; NHS; Intnl Clb; Rep Natl Ldrshp Traing Ctr 83; ST U NY Binghamton; Med.

PAPARUCRI, SCOTT; Holy Trinity HS; Hicksville, NY; (S); Math Clb; Ski Clb; Yrbk Stf; Pres Soph Cls; Stat Ftbl; Var Golf; JV Lcrss.

PAPE, BELINDA; Freeport HS; Freeport, NY; (Y); 4-H; Girl Scts; Library Aide; Chorus; School Play; Variety Show; Off Sr Cls; Sftbl; Vllybl; 4-H Awd; Schl Performing Arts; Actress.

PAPE, LISA; Onteora JR SR HS; Boiceville, NY; (S); Hosp Aide; Math Tm; Chorus; Yrbk Stf; Capt Cheerleading; Stat Ftbl; Stat Trk; High Hon Roll; NHS; Roswell Pk Mem Inst Smmr Rsrch Pgm 85; Top Math Stu 85; 11th Yr Math Awd 85; Biomed Engr.

PAPE, PEGGY L; Webster HS; Webster, NY; (Y); 107/525; Church Yth Grp; Drama Clb; German Clb; Sec JA; Office Aide; Band; Stage Crew; Lit Mag; JV Var Fld Hcky; Hon Roll; Law.

PAPIERZ, HEATHER M; Lackawanna SR HS; Lackawanna, NY; (Y); 65/288; VP GAA; Office Aide; Spanish Clb; Rep Stu Cncl; Capt Var Cheerleading; Score Keeper; Capt Var Socr; Capt Var Vllybl; Hon Roll; Buffalo ST Coll; Poli Sci.

PAPP, MARY; West Genesee SR HS; Camillus, NY; (Y); Ski Clb; High Hon Roll; Hon Roll; Comp Pgmmr.

PAPPADIO, MARISA; Floral Park Memorial HS; Floral Park, NY; (Y); 1/200; Church Yth Grp; Cmnty Wkr; VP Mathletes; Office Aide; PAVAS; Science Clb; Church Choir; Orch; School Musical; School Play; Hugh O Brien Ldrshp Ambssdr 83; Sons Of Itly Awd 85; Fidelity Svngs Bnk Floral Pk Yth Awd 85; Columbia Coll; Math.

PAPPAGALLO, MIA; Mount Saint Joseph Acad; Cheektowaga, NY; (S); Church Yth Grp; Girl Scts; Hosp Aide; Yrbk Ed-Chief; Lit Mag; Bausch & Lomb Sci Awd; Hon Roll; NHS; Ntl Merit Ltr; Nwsp Rptr; Girl Scout 1st Class Awd 80; Marian Medal 81-82; Sr Sylvia Schlrshp Excell Engl 80-84; Phy.

PAPPALARDO, FAUNA; Bishop Kearney HS; Penfield, NY; (Y); 4-H; Band; Concert Band; Mrchg Band; School Play; Yrbk Stf; Trk; JC Awd; Bio.

PAPPAS, CHRISTIN P; Midwood HS; Brooklyn, NY; (Y); 261/605; School Musical; Nwsp Stf; Cheerleading; Regents Schlrshp 85; Brooklyn Coll.

PAPPAS, DEMITRA; St Francis Prep; Bayside, NY; (S); 10/700; Debate Tm; Library Aide; Math Clb; Model UN; Nwsp Rptr; Nwsp Stf; Rep Frsh Cls; High Hon Roll; NHS; Acad All Am 85; Eng.

PAPPAS, JOSEPH; Monsign Mcclancy HS; Woodside, NY; (S); 1/229; Math Tm; Var L Trk; High Hon Roll; VP NHS; Queens Coll Pres Awd For Achvt 83; Aerospace Engr.

PAPPAS, PATRICIA; Susquehanna Valley HS; Conklin, NY; (Y); 5/177; Church Yth Grp; Spanish Clb; Yrbk Ed-Chief; Yrbk Stf; Sec Jr Cls; Rep Stu Cncl; Stat Bowling; Capt Fld Hcky; High Hon Roll; Hon Roll; SUNY-BINGHAMTON; Econ.

PAPPAS, SOTERIOS; Croton Harmon HS; Croton, NY; (Y); #6 In Class; AFS; JV Bsktbl; Var Capt Socr; Var Capt Trk; High Hon Roll; Hon Roll; Jr NHS; NHS; 85 Wntr Trck All Lge Team 85; Hnrble Mntn Sccr & Sprng Trck 84-85; Grk Schl High Hnr Roll 82.

PAPUCCI, NELSON; Seton Catholic Central HS; Endwell, NY; (S); Cmnty Wkr; Nwsp Rptr; Nwsp Stf; Var Wrstlng; High Hon Roll; Ltn Clss Trip; Marine Bio Study; U Of CA-RIVERSIDE; Med.

PAPULA, AGNES; Beacon HS; Beacon, NY; (Y); 25/216; Key Clb; Varsity Clb; Cheerleading; Sftbl; NHS; Rep Beacon HS Mis Teen Dutchess Cty Fair Pagnt; Sports Mgmt.

PAQUETTE, JANINE; Whitesboro Central HS; Utica, NY; (Y); 28/313; Intnl Clb; Acpl Chr; Mrchg Band; Nwsp Ed-Chief; Lit Mag; High Hon Roll; Jr NHS; Pres Schlr; Model UN; Concert Band; 600 Hrs Comm Svc Hosp Aide 84; Exch Stu Philippines Rotary Intl 83-84; U S Navy; Surg Nrsg.

PAQUETTE, KIM M; Immaculate Heart Central HS; Watertown, NY; (Y); Cmnty Wkr; Var L Sftbl; Hon Roll; NHS; Natl Latin Awd Slvr Mdl 84; Jefferson CC; Accnt.

PAQUETTE, KRISTINE E; Immaculate Heart Central HS; Watertown, NY; (Y); Cmnty Wkr; Girl Scts; Spanish Clb; Nwsp Stf; Yrbk Stf; Bsktbl; JV Vllybl; High Hon Roll; NHS; Pres Acad Ftnss Awd Prgm 85; Jefferson CC; Bus Admin.

PAQUETTE, MICHELLE; Westport Central Schl; Westport, NY; (S); 3/21; Band; School Play; Nwsp Ed-Chief; Yrbk Stf; Sec Frsh Cls; Pres Jr Cls; Sec Sr Cls; Trs Stu Cncl; Var Sftbl; Hon Roll; Amer Assn French Tchrs Natl Cntst Awd 83; Natl Sci Olympd Awd 82; Mount Holyoke Coll; Asian.

PARADA, DARRIN A; Medina HS; Medina, NY; (Y); 24/156; Am Leg Boys St; Ski Clb; Bsbl; Ftbl; NHS; Reese Mem Hist Awd; Bio.

PARADA, MICHAEL W; Arkport Central Schl; Arkport, NY; (Y); 3/60; Am Leg Boys St; Boy Scts; Ski Clb; Concert Band; Mrchg Band; School Play; Trs Yrbk Bus Mgr; Elks Awd; High Hon Roll; Arkport Acadmc Soc 85; Accntng.

PARADIS JR, VINICIO; All Hallows Inst; New York, NY; (Y); Church Yth Grp; Temple Yth Grp; Bsbl; JV Bsktbl; Capt Trk; Capt Wt Lftg; High Hon Roll; Hon Roll; NHS; Ntl Merit Ltr; No Tuitn Schlrshp 82-83; Constc Engrng.

PARADISE, STEVEN; Mynderse Acad; Seneca Falls, NY; (Y); Art Clb; Aud/Vis; Chess Clb; Library Aide; Var Bsbl; Var Golf; High Hon Roll; Hon Roll; Sparton.

PARADISO, KENNETH; Clarkstown North HS; New City, NY; (Y); Church Yth Grp; Exploring; Spanish Clb; Band; Church Choir; Concert Band; Im Wrstlng; High Hon Roll; Hon Roll; Pre Med.

PARAISO, EDELYN B; Notre Dame Acad HS; Staten Island, NY; (Y); 7/93; Art Clb; Computer Clb; Key Clb; Math Tm; Chorus; Nwsp Rptr; Yrbk Stf; Cit Awd; NHS; Regnts Schlrshp 85; U S Math Exam Awd 84; Rensselaer Polytechnic; Elctrcl.

PARALEMOS, PARASKEVI; St Francis Preparatory HS; Bayside, NY; (S); 7/693; Church Yth Grp; Cmnty Wkr; Model UN; High Hon Roll; Hon Roll; NHS; Bus.

PARASKEVA, HELEN; Center Moriches HS; Ctr Moriches, NY; (Y); Art Clb; Church Yth Grp; Computer Clb; Library Aide; Spanish Clb; Drill Tm; Hon Roll; Awd For Drug Abuse Pstr Cont 3rd L 83; Cert Of Mrt To Become A Peer Ldrshp Cnsl 84; Comp.

PARASMAR, MEETA; Spackenkill HS; Poughkeepsie, NY; (Y); 21/153; Hosp Aide; Nwsp Stf; Yrbk Stf; Trk; Hon Roll; Bio.

PARATORE, CLAUDIA; Sanford H Calhoun HS; Merrick, NY; (Y); Computer Clb; Key Clb; Yrbk Stf; Soph Cls; Jr Cls; Stat Wrstlng; High Hon Roll; Hon Roll; Bus Mktng.

PARDI, KAREN; Christ The King Reginal HS; Rego Park, NY; (Y); 1/385; Computer Clb; Math Clb; Office Aide; Hon Roll; NHS; Ntl Merit Ltr; Queens Coll Pres Awd Achvt 83 & 85; Princpls Hnrs.

PARDI, WILLIAM; Thomas R Proctor HS; Utica, NY; (Y); Church Yth Grp; Computer Clb; Church Choir; Crs Cntry; Socr; Trk; Hon Roll; Comp Prgmng.

PARDO, GISSELLA; Bishop Ford C C HS; Brooklyn, NY; (Y); French Clb; Stage Crew; Hon Roll; Pre-Med.

PARDO, ROSA M; The Mary Louis Acad; South Ozone Park, NY; (Y); Church Yth Grp; Debate Tm; Spanish Clb; Variety Show; Lit Mag; Im Trk; High Hon Roll; Hon Roll; NEDT Awd; Prfct Atten Awd; Music Awd Gold Medal Piano 83; John Jay Coll; Criminal Justc.

PAREENE, TAMMY L; Averill Park HS; W Sand Lk, NY; (Y); JV Var Trk; Hon Roll; 85 Clb-Avgs Of 85 & Hghr.

PARES, NAYDA; John Dewey HS; Brooklyn, NY; (Y); Aud/Vis; Church Yth Grp; Dance Clb; Spanish Clb; Variety Show; Yrbk Stf; Rep Soph Cls; Rep Jr Cls; Jr NHS; Foreign Lang Mdl Spnsh Lvl 2 83; Dnce Tlnt Hon Awd 83; Cmnctns.

PARHAM, ARISSA; Bishop Laughlin Memorial HS; Brooklyn, NY; (Y); VP Church Yth Grp; Office Aide; VP Church Choir; Yrbk Stf; Sec Sr Cls; Off Stu Cncl; Hon Roll; Hon Roll; Slvr L Awd 83-84; Comm Arts.

PARIANOS, MARIA; St Johns Prep HS; Astoria, NY; (Y); Camera Clb; Church Yth Grp; Library Aide; Stu Cncl; Hon Roll; Jr NHS; NHS; Prfct Atten Awd.

PARILLO, CHRISTOPHER; Amsterdam HS; Amsterdam, NY; (Y); 15/250; Boy Scts; Rep Soph Cls; Rep Jr Cls; Rep Stu Cncl; Hon Roll; NHS; Pres Schlr; St Schlr; SAT Schlrshp 85; Syracuse U; Aero Engr.

PARIS, JACK; Troy HS; Troy, NY; (Y); VP French Clb; German Clb; Sec Ski Clb; Varsity Clb; Nwsp Rptr; Rep Jr Cls; Var Socr; Capt Var Tennis; High Hon Roll; Jr NHS; Hobart Coll; Ortho.

PARIS, JESSICA; Medina SR HS; Medina, NY; (Y); #3 In Class; Church Yth Grp; Drama Clb; Scholastic Bowl; Band; Off Frsh Cls; VP Stu Cncl; JV Bsktbl; JV Cheerleading; Var Crs Cntry; JV Fld Hcky; Mock Trl Team 2nd ST; Lib Arts.

PARIS, JOHN; Walt Whitman HS; Huntington Stat, NY; (Y); 31/540; Church Yth Grp; Key Clb; Spanish Clb; Band; Mrchg Band; Trk; High Hon Roll; Jr NHS; Spanish NHS; Engl Achvt Awd 83; Engrng.

PARIS, KIMBERLY; Corning Painted Post West HS; Corning, NY; (Y); Varsity Clb; Chorus; Yrbk Phtg; Var Crs Cntry; Var Trk; High Hon Roll; Hon Roll; Rdlgy.

PARISH, KAREN; Mynderse Acad; Seneca Falls, NY; (S); JA; Bsktbl; Vllybl; High Hon Roll; Hon Roll; Acctng.

PARISI, ANTHONY; Arch Bishop Steinac HS; Mamaroneck, NY; (Y); 41/201; Boy Scts; Science Clb; Bsktbl; Hon Roll; Eng.

PARISI, JENNIFER; Notre Dame Acad; Staten Island, NY; (Y); Cmnty Wkr; Computer Clb; Science Clb; Chorus; Var JV Crs Cntry; Var JV Trk; NHS; Ntl Merit SF; Mst Imprvd Plyr Trk & Field 85; Comp Sci.

PARISI, LAURA; Seaford HS; Seaford, NY; (Y); Socr; Hon Roll; Spec Educ.

PARISI, MELINDA; Franciscan HS; Peekskill, NY; (Y); 1/58; Church Choir; School Musical; Variety Show; Nwsp Stf; Yrbk Phtg; Stat Vllybl; High Hon Roll; NHS; NEDT Awd; Spanish NHS; Psychlgy.

PARISI, MICHELLE; The Mary Louis Acad; Flushing, NY; (Y); Art Clb; Church Yth Grp; JV Bowling; JV Sftbl; JV Trk; St Johns U.

PARK, CHONG H; Fordham Preparatory Schl; Yonkers, NY; (Y); Key Clb; Rep Frsh Cls; Rep Soph Cls; Im Fld Hcky; Var JV Trk; High Hon Roll; Gen Excel Schlrshp; Magna Cum Laude Ntl Latin Ex; Headmstr Hnr Rl; Med.

PARK, EUGENE; Wheatley HS; Old Westbury, NY; (Y); 12/133; VP Chess Clb; Computer Clb; Hosp Aide; Mathletes; Band; NHS; Prfct Atten Awd; Outstndng Chem,Musician Stu 84; 2nd Prz Frnch Cntst; Silver Pin Math; 8th Pl Chess Clb 85; Med.

PARK, EUNHAE; Bronx H S Of Science; Bronx, NY; (Y); Church Yth Grp; Hosp Aide; Intnl Clb; Library Aide; Teachers Aide; Church Choir; Med.

PARK, HENRY; Bronx High School Of Science; Woodside, NY; (Y); Church Yth Grp; Office Aide; Teachers Aide; Off Jr Cls; Bsbl; Bsktbl; Prfct Atten Awd; Med.

PARK, JI HOON; Williamsville South HS; Williamsville, NY; (Y); 16/256; Church Yth Grp; Hosp Aide; Math Clb; Science Clb; Ski Clb; Church Choir; Socr; Tennis; Hon Roll; NHS; NY ST Regents Schlrshp 85; Schls Table Tenns Tourn 84-85; Schls Vlybl Tourn 84; Carnegie-Mellon U; Engr.

PARK, JIHOON; Williamsville South HS; Williamsville, NY; (Y); 16/260; Church Yth Grp; Math Clb; Science Clb; Ski Clb; Church Choir; Var Socr; Var Tennis; Hon Roll; NHS; NY ST Regnts Schlrshp 85; Won Schl Tabl Tnns Tourn Dbl & Sngl 85; Carnegie Mellon U; Engrng.

PARK, JOHNNY; Lawrence HS; Inwood, NY; (Y); Chess Clb; Church Yth Grp; Computer Clb; French Clb; Mathletes; Math Tm; Science Clb; Y-Teens; Church Choir; Orch; Med.

PARK, JONATHAN; Mount Saint Michael Acad; Bronx, NY; (Y); 16/286; PAVAS; Yrbk Ed-Chief; Stu Cncl; High Hon Roll; NHS; NYS Regents Schlrshp 85; Cornell U; Bus Mgt.

PARK, JULIE; Villa Maria Acad; Cheektowaga, NY; (Y); GAA; JCL; Latin Clb; Sec Frsh Cls; JV Var Bsktbl; Im Bowling; Stat Score Keeper; Var Sftbl; Im Vllybl; Hon Roll; Acctnt.

PARK, JUNG EUN G; Cathedral HS; Woodside, NY; (Y); Hosp Aide; Intnl Clb; Library Aide; Chorus; Yrbk Stf; Hon Roll; Columbia; Law.

PARK, KRISTINA; Haverling Central Schl; Bath, NY; (S); French Clb; Girl Scts; JCL; Latin Clb; Math Clb; Band; Church Choir; Color Guard; Concert Band; Flag Corp.

PARK, RODGER; Union-Endicott HS; Endicott, NY; (Y); Boy Scts; Church Yth Grp; Key Clb; Ski Clb; Church Choir; Concert Band; Mrchg Band; Stage Crew; Swmmng; Hon Roll; Polit Sci.

PARK, ROSANNE E; Arlington HS; Hopewell Jct, NY; (Y); 5/555; Debate Tm; Drama Clb; Math Tm; Ski Clb; Orch; School Play; JV Trk; Ntl Merit SF; Concert Mstr Arlington H S Strng Ensmbl 84-85; Econ.

PARK, SUZANNE; Villa Maria Acad; Cheektowaga, NY; (S); 10/112; Computer Clb; Latin Clb; Math Clb; Pres Jr Cls; Bowling; Cheerleading; Sftbl; Hon Roll; NHS; H S Academic Schlrshp 81; Niagara U; Math Teacher.

PARK, WAYNE; Groton Central Schl; Groton, NY; (Y); 30/66; Church Yth Grp; VP 4-H; Hon Roll; Var Ftbl; Var L Trk; Fin.

PARK, WILLIAM; Irvington HS; Irvington, NY; (Y); 9/125; Hosp Aide; Key Clb; Ski Clb; Yrbk Ed-Chief; Yrbk Stf; Lit Mag; JV Var Ftbl; Var Capt Golf; Im Sftbl; Im Vllybl; Westinghouse Fmly Schlrshp 85; All-Leag Hnrb Mntn-Golf 84; U Of PA.

PARK, YOSOP; Sheepshead Bay HS; New York, NY; (Y); 100/500; Church Yth Grp; Computer Clb; Math Clb; Teachers Aide; Church Choir; Orch; Yrbk Stf; Var Trk; Hon Roll; JETS Awd; Bus Mgmt.

PARKER, ANITA; Albion HS; Albion, NY; (S); 6/176; Pres 4-H; Latin Clb; Sec Chorus; Color Guard; Yrbk Stf; 4-H Awd; High Hon Roll; NHS; NY Rgnts Schlrshp 85; SUNY Geneseo.

PARKER, BRAD; Pioneer Central HS; Machias, NY; (Y); 40/230; Am Leg Boys St; Church Yth Grp; VP JA; Lit Mag; Stu Cncl; Roger Williams Coll; Hist.

PARKER, DEAN M; Westmoreland Central HS; Rome, NY; (Y); 1/87; Pres VP Math Clb; Jazz Band; Ed Yrbk Ed-Chief; Trs Stu Cncl; Co-Capt Bsktbl; Var Co-Capt Tennis; Pres NHS; Ntl Merit SF; Val; Regnts Schlrshp 85; Sctnl Champ Tnns 84; HS Hnr Amer Athl 85; Clarkson U; Elec Engr.

PARKER, DONOVAN; William Howard Taft HS; Bronx, NY; (Y); Computer Clb; Teachers Aide; Comp Sci.

PARKER, ELIZABETH; Cicero North Syracuse HS; Clay, NY; (Y); Ski Clb; Band; Chorus; Concert Band; Jazz Band; Mrchg Band; Orch; School Musical; School Play; Symp Band; All Cnty Chorus 85; All Cnty Band 85; All ST Hgh Scores Clarinet 85; Fredonia; Music.

PARKER, JEFFERY A; Weedsport Central JR SR HS; Weedsport, NY; (Y); 13/64; Im Bsktbl; Var L Trk; Im Vllybl; Hon Roll; Prfct Atten Awd; All League Tm-Trck 84; Anne Sholes Awd 82; SUNY; Elec Const.

PARKER, JILL P; Port Jervis HS; Port Jervis, NY; (Y); 41/200; Church Yth Grp; 4-H; Spanish Clb; Varsity Clb; Off Frsh Cls; VP Soph Cls; VP Jr Cls; Rep Stu Cncl; Cheerleading; Hon Roll; Pop Warner Chrldng Scholar 85; Jayne Polanis-Kathy Laizure Outstndng Chrldr Awd 85; Orange County CC; Acctng.

PARKER, JULIE; Akronc Entral HS; Akron, NY; (Y); 7/140; Girl Scts; Chorus; Sec Stu Cncl; Var Swmmng; Var Trk; Hon Roll; NHS; Ntl Merit Schol; Church Yth Grp; Math Tchr.

PARKER, KATHY; Bayside HS; Bayside, NY; (Y); 281/686; Dance Clb; Office Aide; School Musical; School Play; Variety Show; Nwsp Phtg; Sec Jr Cls; Rep Stu Cncl; Pride Of Yankees Supr Yth 84 & 85; SUNY; Theatr Art.

PARKER, KEITH; Akron Central HS; Basom, NY; (Y); JV Var Bsbl; Merit Awd 84-85; Law Enf.

PARKER, LAURA J; Smithtown E HS; St James, NY; (Y); French Clb; Ski Clb; Stage Crew; Yrbk Phtg; L Trk; French Hon Soc; High Hon Roll; Hon Roll; NHS; Ntl Merit Schol; Vet Sci.

PARKER, MANDY A; DODS Alconbury HS; Apo, NY; (Y); 18/49; Church Yth Grp; Dance Clb; Exploring; Girl Scts; Math Clb; DAR Awd; Prfct Atten Awd; U T San Antonio Pre Frshmn Engrng Prep Prog 84; Physcs Hgh Achvt Acadmc Awd 85; Grl Sct Gld Awd 84; TX A&M; Elctrcl Engrng.

PARKER, MARK; Caledonia-Mumford Central Schl; Scottsville, NY; (Y); Computer Clb; Pep Clb; Varsity Clb; Bsbl; Ftbl; Hon Roll; Ntl Merit Schol; Prfct Atten Awd; Comp Prog.

PARKER, MARY ANNE; Fillmore Central Schl; Houghton, NY; (S); 8/50; Chorus; Stage Crew; High Hon Roll; Hon Roll; NHS; Stndrd Bearer/JR Mrshll 84-85; Cnty Govrnmnt Intern 84; Roberts Wesleyan Coll; Comm.

PARKER, MELODY; Lyndonville Central HS; Lyndonville, NY; (Y); Girl Scts; Varsity Clb; VICA; Chorus; Color Guard; School Play; Var JV Cheerleading; Sftbl; Trk; Prfct Atten Awd; Orleans Cnty Yth Recgntn Awd 85; Perfct Attndnc Awd 82-85; Perfct Attndnc Awd 83-85; Doemen; Pre-Med.

PARKER, PAM; Lansing HS; Freeville, NY; (Y); Spanish Clb; Chorus; Stage Crew; Im Gym; JV Var Vllybl; Hon Roll; Stat Bsbl; Var Powder Puff Ftbl; JV Score Keeper; Amer Assoc Tchrs Spnsh & Portgs Cert Merit 85; Intr Dsgnr.

PARKER, ROBERT A; New Hartford SR HS; New Hartford, NY; (Y); Art Clb; CAP; Drama Clb; School Play; Nwsp Stf; Yrbk Stf; Powder Puff Ftbl; Brockport; Mech Engrng.

PARKER, SCOTT G; Ganadna Central HS; Walworth, NY; (Y); Am Leg Boys St; JV Bsktbl; Var Capt Socr; Wt Lftg; CC Finger Lks Sci Olympcs 84; Am Leg Boys ST Siena Coll Albany 85; Biol Sci.

PARKER, STACY OMAR; Long Island Lutheran HS; Westbury, NY; (S); 10/55; Aud/Vis; Boy Scts; Church Yth Grp; French Clb; Ski Clb; Varsity Clb; Band; Chorus; Concert Band; Jazz Band; Wake Forest U; Poltical Sci.

PARKER, THOMAS; Valley Central HS; Newburgh, NY; (Y); 7/300; Spanish Clb; Bsbl; Bsktbl; JV Socr; Hon Roll; Lion Awd; NHS; Spanish NHS; Merit Reward-Math Regnts Exam; CPA.

PARKER, WILLIAM; Brighton HS; Rochester, NY; (Y); 115/315; Radio Clb; Varsity Clb; Yrbk Stf; Lit Mag; Im JV Ftbl; JV Capt Trk; JV Capt Wrstlng; Outstndng Camper Awd U S Space Camp 84; Aerospc Engrng.

PARKHURST, LORETTA; Hannibal HS; Fulton, NY; (S); Sec Pres 4-H; French Clb; 4-H Awd; High Hon Roll; Psych.

PARKINSON, ZOY; Evander Childs HS; Bronx, NY; (Y); Prfct Atten Awd; Subjct Awds 84-85; Law.

PARKMAN, KIM; Chautauqua Central HS; Ashville, NY; (Y); Sec Church Yth Grp; Band; Sec Yrbk Stf; High Hon Roll; Hon Roll; Sec 4-H; Library Aide; 4-H Awd; Pst Jrnl A Pge 85; WJTN 85; Comp Grphcs.

PARKS, AMY; Palmyra-Macedon Central HS; Macedon, NY; (Y); 5/189; Hosp Aide; Color Guard; Trk; High Hon Roll; NHS; NY ST Rgnts Schlrshp 85; Commnd Stu-Ntl Merit Schlrshp 83; Cert Merit-PA Soc Prof Engrs 84; SUNY Coll Fredonia; Psychlgy.

PARKS, ELAINE M; Shenendehowa HS; Clifton Park, NY; (Y); 48/650; 4-H; Sec Key Clb; Rep Sr Cls; JV Crs Cntry; NCTE Awd; NHS; Rotary Awd; Rep Frsh Cls; Rep Soph Cls; Rep Jr Cls; Amer Nuclr Soc Essay Cont 1st Pl 84; Key Clb Mem Awd For Svc 84; Skidmore Coll Awd Acad Excel 84; FBI.

PARKS, KEITH D; Hempstead HS; Hempstead, NY; (S); 41/333; Dance Clb; Drama Clb; Band; Chorus; Mrchg Band; School Musical; School Play; Tennis; Trk; Hon Roll; Johnson & Wales Coll; Travl.

PARKS, KRISTY; Nazareth Acad; Rochester, NY; (Y); Church Yth Grp; Spanish Clb; Hon Roll; Urban Lg Blck Scholar Erly Recog Pgm 84-85; Comp Pgmmg.

PARKS, NANCY J; Our Lady Of Mercy HS; Rochester, NY; (Y); Sec Church Yth Grp; Pep Clb; VP Service Clb; Ski Clb; Mrchg Band; Rep Frsh Cls; Cit Awd; Hon Roll; NYS Regnts, Clarkson U Schlrshps 85; Clarkson U; Accntng.

PARLIMAN, BRIAN G; Stissing Mt JR SR HS; Pine Plns, NY; (Y); AFS; Aud/Vis; Church Yth Grp; Library Aide; PAVAS; Radio Clb; Teachers Aide; Boy Scts; Stage Crew; JV Ftbl; 1st Arch,Dftg & Dsgn Cntnt 83; Pres Of BF Enterp 83; 2nd Arch,Drftg & Dsgn Cntst 84-85; Air Force; Aircft Maint.

PARLITSIS, MARIA; Roosevelt HS; Yonkers, NY; (S); Drama Clb; Hosp Aide; Service Clb; Band; Lit Mag; Stu Cncl; JV Var Cheerleading; High Hon Roll; Hon Roll.

PARLO, KIMBERLY A; Northport HS; E Northport, NY; (Y); 62/661; Hosp Aide; Band; Concert Band; Mrchg Band; Var Socr; JV Trk; Var Vllybl; Hon Roll; NHS; NY ST Rgnts Schlrshp 85; Villanova U; Nrsng.

PARMER, MICHELLE; Penn Yan Acad; Penn Yan, NY; (Y); Pres Intnl Clb; Varsity Clb; Capt Color Guard; Nwsp Ed-Chief; Yrbk Sprt Ed; Im Badmtn; Im Bsktbl; Var Trk; Im Vllybl; Elks Awd; Intl Clb Schlrshp Awd For Spnsh 85; Rgnts Schlrshp 85fyates Cnty Nrsng Schlrshp 85; SUNY Buffalo; Nrs.

PAROLINE, KRISTINE; Minisink Valley HS; New Hampton, NY; (Y); Sec Church Yth Grp; Library Aide; Chorus; Rep L Frsh Cls; Rep Soph Cls; Socr; High Hon Roll; Hon Roll.

PARR, RONALD; Smithtown High Schl East; Saint James, NY; (Y); Teachers Aide; High Hon Roll; Jr NHS; NHS; 1st Pl Gld Mdl Suffok Cnty Math Fair 83; Itln Hnr Soc 84; 3rd Pl Bus Law Lng Islnd Bus Cmpttn 85.

PARR, SCOTT KENNETH; Kenmore East SR HS; Tonawanda, NY; (Y); Church Yth Grp; Varsity Clb; Nwsp Rptr; Var Capt Bsbl; Var Capt Bsktbl; High Hon Roll; Hon Roll; NHS; Kenmore Town Tonawanda Poetry Anthlgy 83; Comp Sci.

PARRA, FLAMINIA; Immaculata HS; New York, NY; (Y); Church Yth Grp; Church Choir; Hon Roll; Hnrbl Mntn For Average 82-85; Baruch Coll; Bus Admin.

PARRA, SONIA C; Murry Bergtraum HS; Brooklyn, NY; (Y); 17/576; Church Yth Grp; VP JA; Teachers Aide; Rep Jr Cls; Gov Hon Prg Awd; Hon Roll; NCTE Awd; NHS; Excllnce Frgn Lang 85; Acad Olympcs Cert 85; Cornell Scholar 85; Cornell U; Bus Mngmnt.

PARRADO, HANS; John Dewey HS; Brooklyn, NY; (Y); FCA; FBLA; Bsktbl; Mgr(s); Trk; NYC Tech Coll.

PARRAGA, AUDREY; The Mary Louis Acad; Kew Gardens, NY; (Y); Hosp Aide; Library Aide; Trs Spanish Clb; Regnts Schlrshp 85-86; USUC Schlrshp 85-86; Queens Coll.

PARRELLA, NICOLE; Middletown HS; Middletown, NY; (Y); Library Aide; Teachers Aide; Chorus; School Play; Yrbk Phtg; Pace U; Acctnt.

PARRILLO, SARA; Cooperstown Central HS; Cooperstown, NY; (Y); Red Cross Aide; Chorus; Yrbk Stf; Swmmng; Schlstc Art Awd Hnbl Mntn 83; Advrtsg Dsgn.

PARRINELLI, NICHOLAS; Floral Park Memorial HS; Floral Park, NY; (Y); 9/180; Mathletes; Band; School Play; Ed Nwsp Stf; Yrbk Stf; Lit Mag; Stu Cncl; Socr; NHS; Ntl Merit Schol; Rutgers U; Poli Sci.

PARRINELLO, MICHAEL C; Copiague HS; Copiague, NY; (Y); Boy Scts; English Clb; OEA; ROTC; Hon Roll; St Johns U; Engrng.

PARRISH, DEIRDRE JEANNE; Babylon HS; Babylon, NY; (Y); Am Leg Aux Girls St; Yrbk Stf; Pres Soph Cls; VP Jr Cls; Sec Stu Cncl; Var Fld Hcky; Var Vllybl; High Hon Roll; Hon Roll; Schlstc Awd Math 80-81; Schlstc Awd Music 81-82; Hnrb Mntn Vllybl Leag 85.

PARRISH, LAURA MICHELLE; Cicero North Syracuse HS; Clay, NY; (S); 71/622; Girl Scts; Thesps; Chorus; School Musical; School Play; Swing Chorus; JV L Vllybl; Hon Roll; NHS; Rochester Inst Of Tech; Engr.

PARRISH, TAWNYA; Mc Graw Central HS; Mcgraw, NY; (Y); Varsity Clb; Var Capt Cheerleading; Var Score Keeper; Sftbl; Stu Mnth 83-85.

PARROTT, JANICE L; Hudson Falls HS; Hudson Falls, NY; (Y); 14/215; French Clb; Varsity Clb; Band; Chorus; Yrbk Phtg; Yrbk Sprt Ed; JV Var Fld Hcky; French Hon Soc; Hon Roll; NHS; Actrl Sci.

PARROTT, REBECCA; Fort Ann Central HS; Ft Ann, NY; (Y); French Clb; High Hon Roll; Hon Roll; NHS; Nrsng.

PARROTTE, CRAIG; Mount Assumption Inst; Plattsburgh, NY; (Y); Math Tm; Ed Nwsp Stf; Yrbk Stf; NEDT Awd; Band; High Hon Roll; Comp Prg.

PARROTTE-WOOD, NANCY; Corning-Painted Post East HS; Beaver Dams, NY; (Y); Art Clb; Church Yth Grp; Color Guard; Stage Crew; Bsktbl; High Hon Roll; Hon Roll; Outstndng Effrt Awd; Soc Stds Awd; Law.

PARRY, MARIANNE; Stissing Mt JR SR HS; Red Hook, NY; (Y); #10 In Class; French Clb; Concert Band; Yrbk Stf; Sec Soph Cls; Stu Cncl; Fld Hcky; Trk; High Hon Roll; NHS; Ntl Merit Schol; Regnts Schlrshp Nrsg 85; Indep Ordr Odd Fellws Awd 85; Rowl Methdst Chch Awd 85; Manst Coll; Med Lab Techncn.

PARRY, TAMMY L; Waterville Central HS; Oriskany Falls, NY; (Y); 2/87; English Clb; Mathletes; Ski Clb; Nwsp Stf; Yrbk Stf; Stu Cncl; High Hon Roll; NHS; Sal; Chess Clb; NYS Rgnts Schlrshp 85; Ithaca Coll Ithaca; Photo.

PARSELL, RICHARD; Gowanda Central HS; Collinc, NY; (Y); Am Leg Boys St; JV Bsktbl; Var Stat Ftbl; High Hon Roll; Aero Engrng.

PARSON, THOMAS R; Uniondale HS; Hempstead, NY; (Y); Am Leg Boys St; Spanish Clb; JV Bsbl; JV Socr; High Hon Roll; Hon Roll; Jr NHS; NEDT Awd; Sports Med.

PARSONS, DANIEL J; Fairport HS; Fairport, NY; (Y); Church Yth Grp; Var L Ftbl; St Schlr; CYO Bsktbl All Star Tm 84 & 85; NYS Rgnts Schlrshp; Hon Mntn Super 22 Ftbl 84; Siena Coll; Bus Admin.

PARSONS, DAVID; Sharon Springs Central HS; Sharon Springs, NY; (S); 4-H; Trs Band; Chorus; Concert Band; Jazz Band; Mrchg Band; School Musical; Stu Cncl; Socr; Var Bausch & Lomb Sci Awd; Lappeus Sci Awd 83; Brosis Awd 82-83; Comp Engr.

PARSONS, GWENDOLYN M; Troy HS; Wynantskill, NY; (Y); 18/449; Sec French Clb; Pep Clb; High Hon Roll; Jr NHS; NHS; Exc French IV Awd 85; Ins Women Albanys Anul Schlrshp 85; Hudson Valley Comm Coll; Bus Ad.

PARSONS, JOHNNY; Naples Central Schl; Naples, NY; (Y); 3/70; Rep Soph Cls; Pres Jr Cls; Trs Stu Cncl; JV Bsbl; JV Socr; Bausch & Lomb Sci Awd; High Hon Roll; NHS; Ntl Merit SF; Pres Schlr.

PARSONS, MIKE; Webster HS; Webster, NY; (Y); 47/530; Boy Scts; Pres Church Yth Grp; Ski Clb; JV Var Lcrss; NHS; Spanish NHS; Spanish Clb; Lit Mag; JV Coach Actv; Im Ftbl; Math, Spnsh Schlrshp Cert Hnr 84; Phys Sci.

PARSONS, PAUL R; City Honors Schl; Buffalo, NY; (Y); 64/97; Debate Tm; French Clb; Red Cross Aide; Teachers Aide; Nwsp Phtg; Nwsp Rptr; Yrbk Phtg; Stu Cncl; Var L Bsbl; Var Capt Socr; Natl Ski Patrol 85; Career Ofcr.

PARSONS, SARAH E; Port Jervis HS; Port Jervis, NY; (Y); 13/196; Aud/Vis; Church Yth Grp; Scholastic Bowl; Acpl Chr; Band; Jazz Band; Orch; School Musical; Stage Crew; Drama Clb; NYS Rgnts Schlrshp 85; Buffalo U; Comm.

PARSONS, STEVEN; Nazareth Regional HS; Brooklyn, NY; (Y); Boy Scts; Computer Clb; Dance Clb; Office Aide; PAVAS; Service Clb; Stage Crew; Rep Stu Cncl; Comp Sci.

PARTEE, MONIQUE; South Shore HS; Brooklyn, NY; (Y); Church Yth Grp; Girl Scts; Church Choir; Bowling; Gym; Swmmng.

PARTENIO, SUZANNE; E Islip HS; Islip Terrace, NY; (Y); Art Clb; FBLA; Nwsp Stf; Lit Mag; JV Var Bsktbl; Fld Hcky; Mgr(s); Var Sftbl; High Hon Roll; Hon Roll; Bus Admin.

PARTHE, SONYA; St Francis Prep; Whitestone, NY; (Y); Dance Clb; Chorus; Yrbk Phtg; Im Sftbl; Photo.

PARTON, BRENDA; Le Roy Central HS; Le Roy, NY; (Y); Varsity Clb; Band; JV Bsktbl; JV Sftbl; Var L Vllybl; High Hon Roll; Jr NHS; NHS; Church Yth Grp; Spanish Clb; Sectn V All Tourn Team Sftbl 85; Schl Lab Asst 85-86.

PARTON, SHARON L; Leroy Central HS; Le Roy, NY; (Y); 23/118; Pres Sec Church Yth Grp; French Clb; L Chorus; Church Choir; Swing Chorus; Yrbk Stf; Var L Tennis; High Hon Roll; Trs Jr NHS; Genesee Reg Wmns Ins Assn Schlrshp 85; Amer Bptst Wmn NY St Schlrshp 85; Genesee Cnty Bptst Assn Schl; Alfred St Coll; Exec Secy.

PARTRIDGE, JANINE; Frontier Central HS; Hamburg, NY; (Y); 15/495; Drama Clb; Band; School Play; Stage Crew; Nwsp Ed-Chief; Trs NHS; Ntl Merit Ltr; Pres Schlr; Mock Trial Assn; Utica Coll; Ocptnl Thrpy.

PARZUCHOWSKI, MICHAEL J; The Fox Lane HS; Pound Ridge, NY; (Y); 28/300; Concert Band; Jazz Band; VP Capt Crs Cntry; High Hon Roll; NHS; Area All-ST Orch 85; NY ST Regents Schlrshp 85; Westchester Arts Pgm Brass Quintet 85; MA Inst Tech; Engr.

PASCAL, TAMMY; Cornwall Central HS; Newburgh, NY; (Y); Chrmn Civic Clb; Hosp Aide; Co-Capt Math Tm; Chorus; Nwsp Stf; Var L Trk; JV Vllybl; High Hon Roll; Jr NHS; NHS; HOBY-OUTSTNDNG Soph 84; Blackburn Coll; Bio.

PASCALE, CATHY; Lindenhurst HS; Lindenhurst, NY; (Y); Girl Scts; Key Clb; School Play; 2nd Pl Long Island Lang Fair 83; Acct.

PASCALE, MARGARET; Bishop Kearney HS; Brooklyn, NY; (Y); 30/357; Rep Frsh Cls; Rep Soph Cls; Rep Jr Cls; Stu Cncl; Im Bowling; Hon Roll; Psych.

PASCARELLA, KHRIS; Salamanca Central HS; Salamanca, NY; (S); 10/130; Am Leg Boys St; JV Bsktbl; JV VP Ftbl; VP Trk; Cit Awd; French Hon Soc; High Hon Roll; NHS; Natl Hnr Roll 84; U Of FL; Bus Admin.

PASCARELLA, MARIBETH; Liverpool HS; Liverpool, NY; (S); 162/950; Camera Clb; Rep Soph Cls; Rep Jr Cls; Rep Sr Cls; Rep Stu Cncl; Hon Roll; Jr NHS; NHS; Stu Cncl Cabnt; Oswego ST; Poltcl Sci.

PASCERI, KRISTA M; Lockport SR HS; Lockport, NY; (Y); 47/455; Latin Clb; Off Frsh Cls; Off Sr Cls; Cheerleading; Var Capt Socr; JV Var Sftbl; JV Var Vllybl; Hon Roll; Jr NHS; Pres Acdmc Ftns Awd 85; Geneseo ST; Spcl Educ.

PASCIAK, DOLORES; Kenmore East HS; Buffalo, NY; (Y); 3/330; Cmnty Wkr; Pep Clb; Yrbk Stf; Var Trk; High Hon Roll; Jr NHS; NHS; Ntl Merit Ltr; Rgnts & Oswego Almni Assn Schlrshps 85; Erie & Niagara Schltc Achvt Recgntn 85; Suny Coll Oswego; Metrlgy.

PASCIAK, PAMELA; North Tonawanda SR HS; No Tonawanda, NY; (Y); 7/450; Teachers Aide; Concert Band; Mrchg Band; Symp Band; Hon Roll; Jr NHS; Sec NHS; Chmstry Awd 84; Rookie Of Yr Cncrt Bnd Awd 84; NY ST Rgnts Schlrshp 85; Rchstr Inst Of Tech; Bio-Tech.

PASCOCELLO, CHRISTOPHER; Central HS; Valley Stream, NY; (Y); Art Clb; Camera Clb; Cmnty Wkr; FBLA; Letterman Clb; Nwsp Ed-Chief; Nwsp Phtg; Nwsp Rptr; Nwsp Stf; NHS; CW Post Jrnlsm Scholar, Acad Achvt Awd 85; Crier Cert Of Merit 85; C W Post U; Jrnlsm.

PASCOCELLO, STEPHANIE; Sachem HS; Farmingville, NY; (Y); 43/1463; Computer Clb; Math Tm; Pres Science Clb; Jr NHS; NHS; NYS Regnts Schlrshp 85; Suffolk Co Hlth Cntr 84-85; 2nd Pl Spnsh Essay 83; Ithaca Coll; Math.

PASCOE, TRACEY; Baupa HS; Buffalo, NY; (Y); #9 In Class; Aud/Vis; Library Aide; Radio Clb; Stage Crew; Yrbk Stf; Hon Roll; NHS; Prfct Atten Awd; Mayor Yth Achvt Awd 85; Buffalo ST Coll; Brdcstng.

PASCUAL, MARIA; Notre Dame Acad; Staten Island, NY; (Y); Intnl Clb; Yrbk Stf; Bowling; Cheerleading; Trk; Partcptd Natl Frnch Cntst 83; Hlth Prof.

PASCUCCI, FRANK; Farmingdale HS; Farmingdale, NY; (Y); Hon Roll; Prfct Atten Awd; City U NY; Acctng.

PASEK, ANDY; Whitesboro Central HS; Utica, NY; (Y); 42/325; Boy Scts; Hosp Aide; Ski Clb; Lit Mag; Var Crs Cntry; Var Ice Hcky; Var L Tennis; Hon Roll; Rotary Awd; Regents Schlrshp 85; Adv Plcmnt Engl 84-85; Acclrtd Sci & Math 80-85; St Lawrence U; Law.

PASEK, MATT; Whitesboro HS; Utica, NY; (Y); 145/360; Church Yth Grp; Cmnty Wkr; Science Clb; Ski Clb; Varsity Clb; Band; Concert Band; Drm & Bgl; Jazz Band; Mrchg Band; Accntnt.

PASH, TIM; Chenango Valley HS; Binghamton, NY; (Y); Boy Scts; French Clb; Ski Clb; Band; Concert Band; Mrchg Band; School Musical; School Play; Symp Band; Syracuse U; Mech Engrng.

PASHTOON, FARID; E L Vandermeulen HS; Pt Jefferson, NY; (Y); 1/280; Computer Clb; French Clb; Mathletes; Nwsp Stf; Lit Mag; High Hon Roll; NHS; Prfct Atten Awd; Rensselaer Poly-Tech Math & Sci Awd 85; 1st Pl Ntl Sci Olympd Physcs 85; Comp Sci.

PASI, SUNIL; Herkimer SR HS; Herkimer, NY; (Y); 11/150; Aud/Vis; Computer Clb; Yrbk Stf; Trs Soph Cls; Rep Jr Cls; Rep Stu Cncl; Var L Trk; Hon Roll; VP NHS; Ntl Merit Ltr; Med.

PASK, SHELLY; Albion HS; Albion, NY; (Y); Church Yth Grp; 4-H; Color Guard; Flag Corp; Yrbk Stf; JV Badmtn; JV Fld Hcky; 4-H Awd; Hon Roll; Prfct Atten Awd; Stu Of The Mnth 85; Mrt Rll Awds 84-85; Brockport ST; Acctng.

PASLAWSKY, NATALIE; Villa Maria Acad; Buffalo, NY; (Y); Church Yth Grp; Girl Scts; JV Bowling; Var Vllybl; Hnrs Math 82-85; Accntng.

PASNIK, KEVIN A; Saint Francis HS; Lake View, NY; (Y); 5/143; Church Yth Grp; Var Capt Bsktbl; High Hon Roll; NHS; St Schlr; Comp Sci.

PASQUALE, TOM; Union Endicott HS; Endicott, NY; (S); JV Bsbl; JV Var Ftbl; Hon Roll.

PASQUALE, VICTORIA; New Rochelle HS; New Rochelle, NY; (Y); Cmnty Wkr; Dance Clb; Library Aide; School Musical; High Hon Roll; Betty Schwab Awd 84; Am Ballet Theater Schlrshp 84; Schl Of Am Ballet Schlrshp 84; Ballet Dancr.

PASQUARELLA, MICHAEL V; Schalmont HS; Schenectady, NY; (Y); Ski Clb; JV Var Bsbl; Bsktbl; Socr; Im Wrstlng; Hon Roll; U Of MN Mpls; Arspc Engrng.

PASQUARIELLO, VINCENT J; Monsignor Farrell HS; Staten Island, NY; (Y); 7/297; Am Leg Boys St; Computer Clb; Pres JA; Nwsp Ed-Chief; Nwsp Rptr; Im Bsktbl; Im Bowling; Ftbl; Trs NHS; Ntl Merit SF.

PASSALACQUA, MICHAEL; Nazareth Regional HS; Brooklyn, NY; (Y); Boy Scts; Hon Roll; NY U; Acctnt.

PASSERO, JULIE; Greece Olympia HS; Rochester, NY; (Y); 5/316; JA; Ski Clb; High Hon Roll; Hon Roll; NHS; Ntl Merit Schol.

PASSINEAU, HELEN; Tamarac HS; Johnsonville, NY; (Y); Intnl Clb; Political Wkr; Varsity Clb; Chorus; School Musical; Yrbk Stf; Stu Cncl; Bsktbl; Socr; Trk; Sci Fair 3rd Pl 83; Sectnls Trk 2nd Pl 84; Sectnls Bsktbl 1st Pl 85; Comm Artist.

PASSMORE, KATHLEEN; Ellenville Central HS; Ellenville, NY; (Y); Sec Pres AFS; German Clb; Pep Clb; Chorus; School Play; Yrbk Ed-Chief; Yrbk Stf; Rep Frsh Cls; Rep Soph Cls; Rep Jr Cls; Sectn 9 All Around Gym Champ 85; Physcl Thrpst.

PASSMORE, PATRICK; Pioneer Central HS; Arcade, NY; (Y); Church Yth Grp; JA; Latin Clb; Capt JV Socr; Capt Var Swmmng; Math.

PASTAKIA, NEPA; Richmond Hill HS; Woodhaven, NY; (Y); 8/300; English Clb; Math Clb; Spanish Clb; Rep Soph Cls; High Hon Roll; NIKE Hnr Soc 82-83; Med.

PASTALAN, ELAINA; Newark Valley HS; Newark Vly, NY; (Y); 1/120; Art Clb; Drama Clb; Pres Ski Clb; Sec Frsh Cls; Sec Soph Cls; Sec Jr Cls; Sec Sr Cls; Rep Stu Cncl; Var JV Bsktbl; NHS; Art Awd Wnr Locl Shows 85; JETS Tm 84 & 85; Lib Art.

PASTERNACK, MICHAEL; Freeport HS; Freeport, NY; (Y); 6/455; Quiz Bowl; Science Clb; Teachers Aide; Nwsp Ed-Chief; Nwsp Rptr; Yrbk Ed-Chief; Yrbk Rptr; NHS; Pres Schlr; St Schlr; Brondeis U Scholar 85; John W Hughtine Mem Scholar 85; March Dimes Hlth Career Dstngshd Stu Awd 85; Brandeis; Med.

PASTORE, MARIA; Cathedral HS; Astoria, NY; (Y); 10/298; Hon Roll; Prfct Atten Awd; Spanish Awd 83; Pace U; Acctg.

PASTORINO, STACEY; Onteora HS; Woodstock, NY; (S); 2/210; Drama Clb; Scholastic Bowl; School Musical; Nwsp Ed-Chief; Chess Clb; High Hon Roll; Pres NHS; C W Post Schlrshp 84; Cert Of Excel In Englsh & Soc Studies 85.

PASTULA, JOSEPH H; Chatham Central HS; Chatham, NY; (Y); 45/135; Church Yth Grp; 4-H; Chorus; Church Choir; Madrigals; School Musical; Stage Crew; 4-H Awd; High Hon Roll; Hon Roll; Hofstra U; Mech Engrng.

PASZTOR, FRANK; Solvay HS; Syracuse, NY; (Y); Off French Clb; Band; Concert Band; Jazz Band; School Musical; Swing Chorus; High Hon Roll; Hon Roll; All Cnty Sax Jazz; Vrsty Ltr Bnd 84-85; Med.

PATA, CYNTHIA M; Hilton HS; Hilton, NY; (Y); Church Yth Grp; Church Choir; Concert Band; Symp Band; Var L Swmmng; High Hon Roll; JR SR Homecmng Float Wnrs 81-84; Pres Physcl Ftns Awd 84-85; Top Of Cls; Monroe CC; Bus Admin.

PATALINO, PATRICK; Solvay HS; Solvay, NY; (Y); Church Yth Grp; Library Aide; Variety Show; Off Frsh Cls; Off Soph Cls; Off Jr Cls; JV Var Bsbl; Capt Var Bsktbl; Capt Var Ftbl; Hon Roll; Buffalo ST; Law.

PATANE, CHRISTINA; St Edmund HS; Brooklyn, NY; (S); Cmnty Wkr; Drama Clb; Hosp Aide; School Play; Nwsp Rptr; JV Cheerleading; Coach Actv; High Hon Roll; Ntl Merit Ltr; Math Awd 84; SUNY.

PATANE, PATRICIA M; Northport HS; E Northport, NY; (Y); 52/648; Cmnty Wkr; Mrchg Band; Symp Band; Nwsp Stf; Im Socr; Stat Trk; Hon Roll; NHS; Regnts Schlrshp 85; James Madison U.

PATANE, SEBASTIAN; George W Fowler HS; Syracuse, NY; (Y); #12 In Class; Computer Clb; JV Bsktbl; JV Socr; Hon Roll; NHS; Cert Of Awd For Rgnts Chem 85; Le Moyne Coll; Comp Sci.

PATANZO, LISA; Newark HS; Newark, NY; (Y); Dance Clb; French Clb; GAA; Service Clb; Ski Clb; Yrbk Stf; Rep Jr Cls; Var Socr; JV Var Swmmng; Physical Therapy.

PATCHEN, JASON; Bethlehem Central HS; Delmar, NY; (Y); Boy Scts; Yrbk Ed-Chief; Rep Soph Cls; Rep Jr Cls; JV Var Bsbl; JV Var Socr; Hon Roll; Sccr Schlrshp 85; Rensselaer Polytech; Astro Engr.

PATE, SCOTT; Freeport HS; Freeport, NY; (Y); 25/900; Computer Clb; Math Tm; Yrbk Sprt Ed; Bsktbl; Crs Cntry; Trk; Hon Roll; NHS; Mltry Law.

PATEL, JITEN; Union Endicott HS; Ft Lauderdale, FL; (Y); Exploring; Ski Clb; Var Socr; Hon Roll; U Of Miami; Med.

PATEL, JYOTI C; Forest Hills HS; Forest Hills, NY; (Y); 33/881; Science Clb; Band; School Play; Variety Show; Nwsp Sprt Ed; Rep Soph Cls; High Hon Roll; NHS; Aud/Vis; English Clb; Englsh Awd; Grl Ldr Of Arista; NYU; Law.

PATEL, KRUPABEN; East Meadow HS; East Meadow, NY; (S); 34/414; Hosp Aide; Band; Lit Mag; Stu Cncl; Hon Roll; NHS; Spkr Of Grad JR Hgh 82; Awd Volntr Wrk Nassau Cnty Med Ctr 84; Cert Excllnc Frnch 80; Pre-Med.

PATEL, KUSHAL A; Roosevelt HS; Bayside, NY; (Y); Debate Tm; Drama Clb; Quiz Bowl; Service Clb; Speech Tm; School Play; Stage Crew; Yrbk Stf; Sec Soph Cls; Pres Jr Cls; Columbia U; Elec Engrng.

PATEL, MOHIT K; Forest Hills HS; New York, NY; (Y); 39/881; Intnl Clb; Teachers Aide; Hon Roll; Prfct Atten Awd; Arista 83 & 85; Math Awd 83; Typng Awd 83; Pilot.

PATERAS, KATHERINE; Archbishop Iakovos HS; Jamaica, NY; (S); 1/15; Church Yth Grp; Cmnty Wkr; Computer Clb; Library Aide; Math Clb; Office Aide; Teachers Aide; Chorus; Church Choir; Yrbk Ed-Chief; Qns Coll Pres Awd 83-85; NY U; Law.

PATERNO, PETER; Xavier HS; Jersey City, NJ; (Y); 10/250; Chess Clb; Church Yth Grp; Math Clb; ROTC; Sona Coll Lang Awd Hnrs 85; NY U; Sci.

PATERSON, ANDREW S; Baldwin SR HS; Baldwin, NY; (Y); 59/502; Varsity Clb; Band; Stat Bsktbl; Var Lcrss; NHS; St Schlr; Lacrosse All Stars 84-85; Cornell U; Law.

PATHAMMAVONG, SOMPHANE; Batavia HS; Batavia, NY; (Y); Church Yth Grp; Letterman Clb; Var Bsktbl; Coach Actv; Var Socr; Var Trk; Hon Roll; Stu Mnth Awd 84; Fredonia St; Tech.

PATLA, JOY M; The Mary Louis Acad; Jackson Hts, NY; (Y); 32/282; GAA; Pres Jr Cls; Pres Sr Cls; Im Bsktbl; Im Bowling; Im Ftbl; Capt Var Sftbl; NHS; Most Sprtd Plyr Sftbl 84; AAA Drivers Educ Awd 84; C W Post Ctr; Bus.

PATMOS, AMY; Grand Island HS; Grand Island, NY; (Y); 15/285; Office Aide; Off Church Choir; Concert Band; Yrbk Sprt Ed; Var L Bsktbl; Var L Swmmng; Var L Tk; Var L Vllybl; CC Awd; Hon Roll; Princpls Schlrshp Awd 85; Army Reserv Acadmc Athltc Schlrshp 85; Alfred U; Cermc Engrng.

PATNAUDE JR, FRANK W; Chazy Central Rural Schl; Chazy, NY; (Y); Boy Scts; Chess Clb; Church Yth Grp; Model UN; Pep Clb; Yrbk Phtg; Yrbk Stf; Stat Bsktbl; Score Keeper; L Socr; NY ST Regents Schlrshp 85; Cert Of Achvt U S Army 84; Cert Of Merit Congressman Martin 81; Embry-Riddle Aero U; Aero Engrg.

PATRAW, MICHELLE M; Hugh C Williams HS; Canton, NY; (Y); 5/130; Exploring; Thesps; School Musical; Stage Crew; Nwsp Ed-Chief; High Hon Roll; NHS; Pres Schlr; French Clb; Chorus; Carl E Ladd Fndtn 85; Zonta Clb Schlrshp 85; Cornell U; Anml Sci.

PATRIC, LA QUITA; Nazareth Acad; Rochester, NY; (Y); Chorus; Trk; Hon Roll; Clark Clg; Bus Admin.

PATRICCA, THOMAS L; Linton HS; Schenectady, NY; (Y); 17/251; Church Yth Grp; Pres Exploring; JCL; Chorus; Jr Cls; Sr Cls; High Hon Roll; NHS; Outstndng Achvt Acctng 85; Pres Acad Fitnss Awd 85; Siena Coll; Finance.

PATRICIA, ADAMS; Victor SR HS; Victor, NY; (Y); Ski Clb; Varsity Clb; Stu Cncl; Socr; Trk; Hon Roll; Prfct Atten Awd.

PATRICK, SARAH M; Corcoran HS; Syracuse, NY; (Y); 1/200; Math Tm; Ski Clb; Concert Band; Sec Stu Cncl; Capt Var Crs Cntry; Var Trk; High Hon Roll; NHS; Pres Schlr; St Schlr; Engr.

PATRICK, SHAWN; Linton HS; Schenectady, NY; (Y); 13/287; Church Yth Grp; Rep Stu Cncl; Im JV Bsktbl; JV Socr; Var Tennis; Kiwanis Awd; NHS; Lintonians Schl Svc Org Pres 84-85; Schenectady Suprvsry Assn Schlr 84-85; U Of Notre Dame; Bus Adm.

PATRIGNANI, ANTHONY; Waterford Halfmoon HS; Waterford, NY; (Y); Boy Scts; Red Cross Aide; Band; Chorus; Nwsp Ed-Chief; Lit Mag; Wrstlng; Cmnty Wkr; French Clb; Letterman Clb; Booster Clb Sports Camp Schrlshp 83-85; Ntl Soc Studies Awd 1st Pl 83; Stu SADD Org 85; Albany St; Jrnlsm.

PATSARICAS, MARIKA; Bishop Kearney HS; Brooklyn, NY; (Y); Nwsp Phtg; Trk; U Of PA; Bio.

PATTENGILL, VIKKI; South New Berlin Central Schl; S New Berlin, NY; (Y); 6/34; Math Tm; Yrbk Phtg; JV Var Score Keeper; Socr; High Hon Roll; Lion Awd; NHS; Hghst Rgnts Mrks-Bio & Math 83-85.

PATTERSON, DAVID K; New Hartford HS; New Hartford, NY; (Y); MMM; Pep Clb; Ski Clb; Concert Band; Jazz Band; Mrchg Band; Pep Band; Var Tennis; JETS Awd; NHS; Clarkson U; Engrng.

PATTERSON, ELEZABET J; Herkimer HS; Herkimer, NY; (Y); 24/115; Dance Clb; French Clb; Political Wkr; Var Gym; Utica Dance Works 83-84; Mohawk Vly Perf Arts Dance Co 84; Skidmore Coll; Dance.

PATTERSON, JANET A; Lake Shore SR HS; Derby, NY; (Y); Church Yth Grp; Band; Chorus; Jazz Band; Orch; Yrbk Stf; Var Tennis; Hon Roll; NHS; Prfct Atten Awd; Phy Thrpst.

PATTERSON, JASON; New Berlin Central Schl; New Berlin, NY; (Y); 1/54; French Clb; ROTC; Yrbk Stf; Off Frsh Cls; Off Jr Cls; Bsbl; Bsktbl; Bowling; Crs Cntry; Ftbl; ROTC Coll; Pilot.

PATTERSON, JENNIFER; John A Coleman HS; New Paltz, NY; (Y); French Clb; Hosp Aide; Key Clb; Yrbk Stf; Capt Cheerleading; Capt Crs Cntry; Trk; Hon Roll; MVP Cross Cty 84-85; Trinity Dublin; Jrnlsm.

PATTERSON, KERRY; Port Jervis HS; Sparrowbush, NY; (Y); Yrbk Stf; Trs Frsh Cls; Trs Soph Cls; Rep Stu Cncl; JV Bsktbl; JV Fld Hcky; High Hon Roll; Hon Roll; NHS; SUNY Albany; Jrnlsm.

PATTERSON, LANI; Seward Park HS; Los Angeles, CA; (Y); Art Clb; Aud/Vis; Drama Clb; Stage Crew; Variety Show; NY ST Regents Schlrshp 84-85; Santa Monica CC; Grphc Art.

PATTERSON, MARGARET; Cardinal O Hara HS; Kenmore, NY; (S); 6/130; Chrmn Church Yth Grp; Cmnty Wkr; Drama Clb; Exploring; Church Choir; School Musical; School Play; Im Bowling; NHS; Kenmore Exch Clb Yth Mth Awd 84; Outstndng Svc Awd 84; Diecese Buffalo Respct Life Yth Awd 84; Vet Med.

PATTERSON, MELISSA; Dunkirk HS; Dunkirk, NY; (Y); 1/250; Church Yth Grp; Pres French Clb; Key Clb; Chorus; School Musical; Sec Frsh Cls; Stu Cncl; High Hon Roll; NHS; Cmnty Wkr; Rensselaier Mdl Math & Sci 85; NYSSMA Voice Solo 84 & 85; Cert Achvt All Clss 82-85; Bio Med Rsrch.

PATTERSON, MELISSA; Ravena-Coeymans-Selkirk SR HS; Coeymans Hlw, NY; (Y); Art Clb; Church Yth Grp; Pres VP 4-H; Trs Spanish Clb; Church Choir; JV Capt Bsktbl; Var L Tennis; Rep Soph Cls; Rep Jr Cls; Rep Sr Cls; 4-H Schlrshp 85; Hnrbl Mntn All Stars Bsktbl 83-84; Art & Bsktbl Schlrshp Cazenovia 85; Cazenovia; Intr/Arch Dsgn.

PATTERSON, PATRICIA; Saugerties HS; Saugerties, NY; (Y); Drama Clb; German Clb; JA; Ski Clb; Score Keeper; Trk; High Hon Roll; Hon Roll; Ntl Merit Ltr; Cmpt Sci.

PATTERSON, SCOTT; South Lewis Central HS; Greig, NY; (Y); Band; Pres Stu Cncl; Im JV Bsbl; Im JV Bsktbl; Var Trk; Var Wt Lftg; High Hon Roll; Hon Roll; NHS; Prfct Atten Awd; Stu Sci Recgntn 85; SUNY At Delhi; Arch.

PATTERSON, TANYA YVETTE; Andrew Jackson HS; Queens, NY; (Y); Church Yth Grp; Key Clb; Keywanettes; Office Aide; Service Clb; Teachers Aide; Church Choir; Gov Hon Prg Awd; Cert Hnr Tutorng 84-85; Mayors Vlntry Actn Ctr 85; Nrsg.

PATTI, DENISE R; Kenmore West SR HS; Kenmore, NY; (Y); Band; Concert Band; Mrchg Band; School Musical; Ed Yrbk Stf; JV Trk; Hon Roll; U Of Buffalo.

PATTI, MICHELE L; Averill Park HS; Troy, NY; (Y); Varsity Clb; VP Soph Cls; JV Bsktbl; JV Socr; JV Sftbl; High Hon Roll; NHS; Gifted & Talented Clb; Biol Sci.

PATTIE, KATHRYN; Fredonia HS; Fredonia, NY; (Y); GAA; Key Clb; Science Clb; Spanish Clb; Chorus; Var Capt Bsktbl; Coach Actv; Var Capt Sftbl; CCIAC Div I All Str 85; Natl Athl Recrtg Guid 85; Crmnl Justc.

PATTISON, TRACY LYNN; Pioneer Central HS; Chaffee, NY; (Y); Dance Clb; French Clb; GAA; Library Aide; School Musical; School Play; Swing Chorus; Variety Show; Lit Mag; Gym; Dance.

PAUL, ALISSA; Allendale/Columbia HS; Rochester, NY; (Y); Math Clb; Chrmn Model UN; Jazz Band; School Play; Var Capt Socr; Swmmng; Trk; Magna Cum Laude Ntl Ltn Exam 82; All Cnty Band 84; Correll; Arch.

PAUL, AMY; Troupsburg Central HS; Woodhull, NY; (S); 3/14; VP Computer Clb; Band; Chorus; Concert Band; Mrchg Band; Sec Soph Cls; Sec Jr Cls; Var Bsktbl; Score Keeper; Var Socr; Mst Imprvd Plyr Bsktbl Awd 83-84.

PAUL, ANDREW; Kenmore West SR HS; Kenmore, NY; (Y); 10/445; Orch; School Musical; Im Socr; High Hon Roll; Hon Roll; NHS; Ntl Merit Ltr; Pres Schlr; Hamilton Clg.

PAUL, BETH ANN; Gates-Chili HS; Rochester, NY; (S); 37/464; Trs Frsh Cls; Trs Soph Cls; Stu Cncl; JV Var Socr; DAR Awd; High Hon Roll; Trs NHS; Outstndg Accmplsmnt Excell Scl Stds 83; Dist Achvt Ldrshp 83; Cert Merit Svc 84.

PAUL, CAMILLE; Springfield Gardens HS; Rosedale, NY; (Y); Church Yth Grp; Debate Tm; School Play; VP Soph Cls; Capt Fld Hcky; Cit Awd; Prfct Atten Awd; Med.

PAUL II, FREDERICK E; Mayfield JR SR HS; Gloversville, NY; (Y); Var L Bowling; Var Trk.

PAUL, JOHN H; Paul V Moore HS; Hastings, NY; (Y); 30/324; Am Leg Boys St; Trs Church Yth Grp; Exploring; Socr; Hon Roll; Capt CQ Rifle Team 85-86; All Star Leag Shooter 83-85; Librl Arts.

PAUL, LEONARD; Northeastern Acad; Brooklyn, NY; (Y); 7/65; Art Clb; Varsity Clb; Capt Bsbl; Capt Trk; Var Vllybl; Cit Awd; Otto T Burfgdoff Awd 84; Neurlgy.

PAUL, LOUIS C; Baldwin SR HS; Baldwin, NY; (Y); 1/502; Mathletes; Science Clb; Chorus; Jazz Band; Mrchg Band; Orch; Nwsp Ed-Chief; JV Tennis; French Hon Soc; High Hon Roll; 44th Annual Westinhse Sci Tlnt Srch Wnnr 85; Phi Beta Kappa Alumni Assn Awd 85; Lng Islnd Sci Cngrs 84; Princeton U; Law.

PAUL, NEIL; Jamesville-Dewitt HS; Jamesville, NY; (Y); Varsity Clb; Var L Ftbl; Var L Lcrss; Stat Vllybl; Im Wt Lftg; Wrstlng; Law.

PAUL, NIRVA; Acad Of Mt St Ursula; Bronx, NY; (Y); Debate Tm; Drama Clb; Yrbk Ed-Chief; French Hon Soc; St Johns U; Pre-Law.

PAULEY, AMY I; Lockport SR HS; Lockport, NY; (Y); 4/388; Pres Church Yth Grp; Scholastic Bowl; Yrbk Stf; Rep Frsh Cls; Rep Soph Cls; Rep Jr Cls; Rep Sr Cls; Rep Stu Cncl; Var L Swmmng; NHS; Smith Coll; Pre Med.

PAULEY, BRIAN; Royalton Hartland HS; Gasport, NY; (Y); 26/140; Church Yth Grp; French Clb; Sec Band; Church Choir; Jazz Band; Stu Cncl; Var Capt Socr; Var Swmmng; Var Tennis; Hon Roll; Jr All Am Band Hnrs 84; All Cty Chorus 82-83; All Cty Band 82; Suny; Law.

PAULIN, MARY; Lockport SR HS; Lockport, NY; (Y); 36/411; Sec Church Yth Grp; Latin Clb; Nwsp Rptr; Yrbk Ed-Chief; Rep Jr Cls; Rep Stu Cncl; Var Tennis; Jr NHS; NHS; Prim Ed.

PAULIN, STEPHANIE; Northville Central HS; Northville, NY; (Y); Trs Jazz Band; Symp Band; Yrbk Ed-Chief; Pres Stu Cncl; NHS; Church Yth Grp; Cmnty Wkr; Library Aide; Political Wkr; Acpl Chr; Eng,Psnsh Earth Sci Prz 83-85; Georgetown; Pol Sci.

PAULIN, TRACEY; Lockport SR HS; Lockport, NY; (Y); 22/455; Latin Clb; Yrbk Ed-Chief; Frsh Cls; Soph Cls; Jr Cls; Sr Cls; Stu Cncl; Var Capt Tennis; Hon Roll; NHS; SUNY Geneseo; Spch Pathlgy.

PAULINSKI, CHRISTINE; Wells Central Schl; Piseco, NY; (S); 4/33; Band; Chorus; Jazz Band; Yrbk Bus Mgr; Trs Frsh Cls; Sec Soph Cls; Sec Stu Cncl; Var Cheerleading; NHS; Mc Donalds All Am Mrchng Band Fnlst 84; Embry-Riddle Aero U; Aerntc Sci.

PAULIS, MARK W; Regis HS; Sea Cliff, NY; (Y).

PAULK, KIM; Cathedral HS; Bronx, NY; (Y); 102/298; Cmnty Wkr; Intnl Clb; Varsity Clb; Church Choir; Stage Crew; Bsktbl; Sftbl; Pre-Law.

PAULUS, ELIZABET A; Lafayette HS; Buffalo, NY; (Y); 3/243; French Clb; Girl Scts; Math Tm; Red Cross Aide; Variety Show; Nwsp Stf; Cheerleading; High Hon Roll; Hon Roll; Prfct Atten Awd; Regnts Schlrshp 85-89; SUNY Buffalo; Biochem.

PAULY, GREG; St Josephs Collegiate Insti; Snyder, NY; (Y); 45/230; Cmnty Wkr; Ski Clb; Varsity Clb; Band; Var Im Ice Hcky; Var L Socr; CC Awd; Cit Awd; High Hon Roll; Ice Hockey Coachs Awd 84-85.

PAULY, SCOTT; Olean HS; Olean, NY; (Y); Ski Clb; Im JV Bsktbl; JV Trk; Hon Roll; St Bonaventure; Law.

PAUQUETTE, LISA J; Shaker HS; Loudonville, NY; (Y); GAA; Chrmn Key Clb; Variety Show; Var L Socr; Var Sftbl; Ntl Merit SF; Natl Merit Schlrshp Semi-Fnlst 85; Engl.

PAUQUETTE, PAUL; Coxsackie-Athens Central HS; Earlton, NY; (Y); 4/120; Computer Clb; Quiz Bowl; Science Clb; Band; Jazz Band; High Hon Roll; NHS; Physics.

PAUSE, MICHELLE S; Delaware Acad - Central Schl; Hamden, NY; (Y); Church Yth Grp; Debate Tm; Pres 4-H; Band; Concert Band; Mrchg Band; Orch; 4-H Awd; Prfct Atten Awd; Delhi AG & Tech Coll; Secy Sci.

PAVLENYI, JACQUES; Mahopac SR HS; Mahopac, NY; (Y); 13/397; AFS; Aud/Vis; Drama Clb; Math Tm; Thesps; Band; Chorus; Concert Band; Mrchg Band; Orch; Mc Gill U; Chem Engr.

PAVLENYI, PIERRE; Mahopac HS; Mahopac, NY; (Y); 24/397; AFS; Aud/Vis; Chess Clb; Computer Clb; Trs Drama Clb; Math Clb; Math Tm; Thesps; Band; Chorus; Mc Gill U Montreal; Elec Engr.

PAVLIK, TONY J; Corning East HS; Corning, NY; (Y); Cmnty Wkr; Letterman Clb; Varsity Clb; Yrbk Stf; Var Bsbl; JV Bsktbl; JV L Ftbl; JV L Lcrss; All ST, Twn Tiers, Bck Yr Ftbl 84; Emp ST Gms Lacrsse 85; Bus.

PAVLIN, JORDAN; The Wheatley Schl; Albertson, NY; (Y); Cmnty Wkr; Drama Clb; PAVAS; School Play; Stage Crew; Nwsp Stf; Rep Stu Cncl; Score Keeper; NCTE Awd; Chrprsn-Wheatleys Altrntv Schl 85; Engl.

PAVLOVIC, THOMAS; Beacon HS; Beacon, NY; (S); 9/160; Var Am Leg Boys St; Math Tm; Varsity Clb; VP Jr Cls; Capt Ftbl; High Hon Roll; Jr NHS; NHS; Best Lineman 81; Boston U; Biomed Engr.

PAWELA, MARK; Frontier Central HS; Hamburg, NY; (S); Var Ice Hcky; Hon Roll; NHS; NEDT Awd; Aero Engr.

PAWELCZAK, BARBARA; West Seneca East SR HS; Cheektowaga, NY; (Y); Cmnty Wkr; DECA; Rep Frsh Cls; Trs Soph Cls; Rep Jr Cls; VP Sr Cls; Var Cheerleading; Im Trk; Hon Roll; NHS; Lat Awd Summa Cum Laude 82-85; Bstkbl Champ Southline 84-85; Food Svc Mgr.

PAWLACZUK, MICHELE; Albion Central HS; Albion, NY; (Y); 4-H; Chorus; JV Gym; Geneesee CC; Psych.

PAWLAK, JAMES; Holland Central Schl; Holland, NY; (Y); 27/108; AFS; Boys Clb Am; Church Yth Grp; Varsity Clb; Band; Mrchg Band; Coach Actv; Im Var Socr; Capt Var Wrstlng; Hon Roll; Spcl Svc Awd Holland Kiwanis 85; Syracuse U; Envrnmntl Engrng.

PAWLIKOWSKI, CINDY; Vernon-Verona-Sherrill HS; Verona, NY; (Y); Girl Scts; Band; Chorus; Church Choir; Concert Band; Drm & Bgl; Jazz Band; Mrchg Band; Orch; Pep Band; Rookie Of The Yr Awd 83; Musicianship Awd 85; Music Educ.

PAWLIKOWSKI, DENNIS; Mexico HS; Parish, NY; (Y); 1/350; Math Clb; Red Cross Aide; Var Bowling; Var Capt Ftbl; Im Ice Hcky; Var L Trk; Im Vllybl; Im Wt Lftg; High Hon Roll; Drama Clb; Acad All Amer 85; Schlr/Ath Gold & Silver Mdls 84 & 85; Physcs.

PAWLOWSKI, ANNEMARIE; West Seneca East SR HS; Cheektowaga, NY; (Y); Score Keeper; JV Sftbl; Hon Roll; Jr NHS; Spnsh Merit Awd 83; AAA Poster Cont 1st Plz Lcl,3rd Prz Natl 85; Psych.

PAWLOWSKI, CHRISTINE; Cardinal O Hara HS; Buffalo, NY; (S); 5/150; Church Yth Grp; Yrbk Stf; JV L Badmtn; Var L Bsktbl; Var L Sftbl; Var L Vllybl; High Hon Roll; All Catholic Hnrb Mntn Vllybl 84; All Catholic 2nd Tm Sftbl 83-84; Coed Intramurals 1st Badminton 84; Canisius Coll; Med Tech.

PAWLOWSKI, LYNETTE; John F Kennedy JR SR HS; Buffalo, NY; (Y); Stu Cncl; Im Bowling; Hon Roll; Jr NHS; NHS; VFW Awd; Voice Dem Awd; NY ST Art Tchrs Assn Excllnce Vis Arts 85; Michael S Siemankowski Mem Scholar Art 85; MD Inst Of Art; Grphc Dsgn.

PAWLOWSKI, MARY; Christ The King R HS; Maspeth, NY; (Y); Art Clb; Cmnty Wkr; Dance Clb; Drama Clb; Chorus; Church Choir; School Musical; School Play; Yrbk Rptr; Vllybl; ST Fnlst-Miss NY Amer Co-Ed Pagnt 85; Natl Hnr Roll 85; St Johns U; Teachng.

PAWSON, TIMOTHY; Westhampton Beach HS; Manorville, NY; (Y); 37/217; Science Clb; Chorus; JV Bsktbl; Hon Roll; Law.

PAWUL, ANNA B; Northport HS; E Northport, NY; (Y); 28/648; Church Yth Grp; Hosp Aide; Science Clb; Jazz Band; Mrchg Band; Pres Orch; JV Fld Hcky; NHS; Debate Tm; Band; Pre-Coll Div Julliard Schl Of Music 84-85; All Eastern Orch 85.

PAYMENT, SIMONE; Honcoye Falls-Lima HS; Honeoye Falls, NY; (Y); 1/160; JA; Chorus; Variety Show; VP Frsh Cls; VP Jr Cls; Sec Sr Cls; Cit Awd; High Hon Roll; NHS; Val; Cornell U; Arts & Sci.

PAYNE, ANDRE; John F Kennedy HS; Bronx, NY; (Y); JA; Science Clb; Service Clb; Jazz Band; Orch; Yrbk Stf; Pres Frsh Cls; Stu Cncl; Crs Cntry; Ftbl; Cert Of Compltn Comp Mth & Sci Pgm 84-85; Cert Of Compltn Cornell U MIT Pgm 85; Elec Engrng.

PAYNE, BERTRAM; Friends Acad; Roosevelt, NY; (Y); Trs Church Yth Grp; Varsity Clb; Acpl Chr; Church Choir; Nwsp Rptr; JV Bsktbl; Var Crs Cntry; Var Trk; Empire ST Games 84; E Regn Treas Jack & Jill Of Amer Inc 84.

PAYNE, DEBRA J; Paul V Moore HS; Hastings, NY; (Y); 28/297; Var Varsity Clb; JV Var Vllybl; High Hon Roll; Hon Roll; NHS; Regnts Nrsng Schlrshp 85-86; Crouse Irving Memrl Schl Nrsng Schlrshp 85-86; Crouse Irving Memorial; Nrsng.

PAYNE, ELIZABETH ASHLEY; Fairport HS; Fairport, NY; (Y); Church Yth Grp; French Clb; Intnl Clb; Ski Clb; Flag Corp; Jazz Band; Mrchg Band; Symp Band; JV Var Fld Hcky; Hon Roll; Music Educ.

PAYNE, KATHERINE; Binghamton HS; Binghamton, NY; (Y); Sec Key Clb; Ski Clb; Sec Jr Cls; Rep Stu Cncl; Score Keeper; Capt Swmmng; High Hon Roll; Hon Roll; NHS; STAC All Star Swmmng 84; Salute Yth Ldrshp Awd 85; Arch.

PAYNE, LA TONYA; St Francis Prep; Jamaica, NY; (S); 113/693; Church Yth Grp; Dance Clb; Hosp Aide; Yrbk Phtg; Cheerleading; Hon Roll; NHS; Acad All-Amer Ntl Scndry Ed Cncl 85; Pre-Med.

PAYNE, MARY; St Catherine Acad; Bronx, NY; (Y); Girl Scts; Hosp Aide; Office Aide; Chorus; Rep Stu Cncl; Fld Hcky; Capt Ice Hcky; Cmmndtn Reprt Socl Stdy & Ofc Aide 83 & 84-85; John Jay Law Schl; Corp Law.

PAYNE, MICHAEL; West Seneca West SR HS; Buffalo, NY; (Y); Ftbl; JV Socr; U Buffalo; Law.

PAYNE, PETER E; Midlakes SR HS; Clifton Springs, NY; (Y); French Clb; JV L Ftbl; Im Wt Lftg; High Hon Roll; Hon Roll; NHS; Member Of Olympics Of The Mind Competition 81-83; English Teacher.

PAYNE, ROBERT L; Margaretville Central HS; Margaretville, NY; (Y); Am Leg Boys St; Rep Frsh Cls; Rep Soph Cls; Rep Jr Cls; Rep Sr Cls; Var Bsbl; Var Wrstlng; Hon Roll; Chess Clb; Spanish Clb; Air Force.

PAYNE, RODNEY; Altmar-Parish-Williamstown HS; Altmar, NY; (Y); Dance Clb; Ski Clb; Varsity Clb; Bowling; Trk; Hon Roll; Acctg.

PAYNE, SUSAN; Linton HS; Schenectady, NY; (Y); 17/300; Pres Key Clb; Service Clb; Ski Clb; Orch; Off Frsh Cls; Off Soph Cls; Off Jr Cls; Stat Bsbl; Hon Roll; NHS; Engrng.

PAYNE, TRACY M; Bad Kreuznach American HS; APO New York, NY; (Y); Church Yth Grp; Pres Exploring; Hosp Aide; Library Aide; ROTC; Teachers Aide; Band; Church Choir; Mrchg Band; Symp Band.

PAYNE, TYRONE; Hempstead HS; Hempstead, NY; (S); 63/333; Var L Ftbl; Var Capt Lcrss; Var Capt Wrstlng; All Leag Lacrosse 84; Mech Engr.

PAYSON, RONALD; Germantown Central HS; Germantown, NY; (Y); Ski Clb; Band; Chorus; Concert Band; Jazz Band; School Musical; Pres Stu Cncl; Lawyer.

PAYTON, LISA MICHELLE; Bishop Ford Central Catholic HS; Brooklyn, NY; (Y); Yrbk Stf; Bowling; Cheerleading; Pom Pon; Hon Roll; Syracuse U; Comm.

PAZ, MICHAEL; Long Beach HS; Lido Beach, NY; (S); 11/295; Key Clb; Math Tm; Science Clb; Band; Chorus; Concert Band; Mrchg Band; School Musical; Yrbk Phtg; Yrbk Rptr; Long Isl Sci Cong High Hnrs 82-83; U S Naval Awd Marine Bio 83; Med.

PAZ, SANDRA; Hillcrest HS; New York, NY; (Y); 123/730; Church Yth Grp; Hosp Aide; Ski Clb; Orch; Super Yth 83; Regnts Schlrshp 85; Natl Hispnc Schlr Awds Prog Semi Fnlst 85; Queens Coll.

PAZDA, KIMBERLY J; Lancaster Central HS; Depew, NY; (Y); Church Yth Grp; Pep Clb; Ski Clb; Chorus; Church Choir; Color Guard; School Musical; High Hon Roll; Jr NHS; NHS; Elem Educ.

PAZO, MARISOL; Saint Vincent Ferrer HS; Elmhurst, NY; (Y); 1/116; Dance Clb; Library Aide; Spanish Clb; Hon Roll; NHS; Biol Awd 84; Eng & Hstry Awds 85; Archit.

PEABODY, JULIE; Monticello HS; Monticello, NY; (Y); Church Yth Grp; 4-H; Math Tm; Office Aide; Trs Sr Cls; Rep Stu Cncl; Var Vllybl; 4-H Awd; Hon Roll; Jr NHS; Bus.

PEABODY, SHANNON; Pulaski HS; Pulaski, NY; (Y); Drama Clb; GAA; Chorus; Color Guard; School Musical; School Play; Yrbk Phtg; Yrbk Stf; Jr Cls; Score Keeper; Comm.

PEACE, SONDRA; Portville Central Schl; Portville, NY; (Y); Office Aide; Chorus; Sec Soph Cls; Var Golf; Var Sftbl; Capt Vllybl; Hon Roll; All Star On Sftbl Tms 84-85; Vllybl All-Star 84; Vrsty Lttr Sftbl & Vllybl & Golf 82-85; Ed.

PEACH, CORRI; Franklin Acad; Malone, NY; (Y); Camp Fr Inc; Spanish Clb; Spnsh Merit Awd; Potsdam ST-PLATTSBURG; Tchng.

PEACOCK, BRITTANY; Francis Lewis HS; Bayside, NY; (Y); 49/527; Hosp Aide; Office Aide; Nwsp Ed-Chief; Nwsp Rptr; Yrbk Stf; Rep Soph Cls; Pres Jr Cls; Pres Stu Cncl; Hon Roll; NHS; NYC Chancellors Awd Jrnlsm 85; UFT Awd Exclnce Soc Stud 85; Williams Coll Williamstown; Eng.

PEACOCK, CHRISTINE; St John Villa Acad; Staten Island, NY; (Y); Hosp Aide; Bowling; Accntng I 84; A P Engl 85; Accntng I 85; St Johns U; Accntng.

PEACOCK, SUZANNE; Irondequoit HS; Rochester, NY; (Y); 17/373; Church Yth Grp; Cmnty Wkr; Sec Radio Clb; Teachers Aide; Yrbk Phtg; High Hon Roll; Hon Roll; Nrs.

PEAN, JEANET; St Johns Prep; Laurelton, NY; (Y); Church Yth Grp; Intnl Clb; OEA; Science Clb; Yrbk Stf; Lit Mag; Stu Cncl; Im Socr; Var Trk; Im Wt Lftg; Engrng.

PEARCE, CHRISTOPHER J; Beach Channel HS; Ozone Pk, NY; (Y); Computer Clb; Science Clb; Yrbk Stf; Bowling; Hon Roll; Polytechnic; Comp Sci.

PEARCE, JENNIFER; Hilton Central HS; Hilton, NY; (Y); Drama Clb; Exploring; Model UN; Pres Chorus; School Musical; Variety Show; High Hon Roll; Lawyer.

PEARCE, LORNA; Delaware Acad & Central; Delhi, NY; (Y); 4-H; Pres FHA; Intnl Clb; Spanish Clb; Band; Concert Band; Mrchg Band; 4-H Awd; SUNY Oneonta; Ed.

PEARLMAN, BRIAN L; Clarkstown H S North; New City, NY; (Y); 9/480; Library Aide; Cit Awd; High Hon Roll; Jr NHS; Mu Alp Tht; NHS; St Schlr; U Of Miami; Physician.

PEARSALL, MARLA; Watkins Glen HS; Watkins Glen, NY; (S); 5/145; Math Clb; Stage Crew; Nwsp Stf; Yrbk Bus Mgr; Yrbk Ed-Chief; Hon Roll; NHS; Johnson & Wales Coll; Hotel Mgt.

PEARSE, WILLIAM; Archbishop Molloy HS; Elmont, NY; (Y); 215/410; Church Yth Grp; Var L CAP; Im Sftbl; Hon Roll; Jrnlsm.

PEARSON, EILEEN; Amsterdam HS; Amsterdam, NY; (Y); Yrbk Stf; Hon Roll; Acctg.

PEARSON, ERIKA; South Kortright Central Schl; Delhi, NY; (Y); 5/32; Varsity Clb; Pres Frsh Cls; Rep Soph Cls; Rep Sr Cls; VP Stu Cncl; Var Capt Bsktbl; Var Capt Socr; High Hon Roll; NHS; Ntl Arm Rsrv Athlt/Schlr Awd 83-84; Babe Ruth Sprtsmnshp Awd 83-85; SUNY At Geneseo; Elem Ed.

PEARSON, JOHN; Bayport-Blue Point HS; Massapequa, NY; (Y); 82/250; Church Yth Grp; Varsity Clb; Chorus; Var L Ftbl; JV Trk; Var Wt Lftg; Var Wrstlng; Hon Roll; Ntl Merit SF; All Leag Vrsty Ftbl Hon Mntn 83-84; All Star Ftbl 85; Wrstlng Tm Went To West Point For NYS Cup 85; Central CT ST U; Psych.

PEARSON, MICHELE M; Fontbonne Hall Acad; Brooklyn, NY; (Y); 40/138; Drama Clb; Hosp Aide; Stage Crew; Variety Show; Nwsp Phtg; Yrbk Rptr; Lit Mag; Var Capt Tennis; Hon Roll; NEDT Awd; Creighton U; Med.

PEARSON, PHILLIP; Vestal HS; Aumsville, OR; (Y); CAP; Drama Clb; Exploring; Science Clb; School Play; Yrbk Stf; Soph Cls; Jr Cls; Stu Cncl; Trk; St Olaf; Marin Bio.

PEARSON, RENEE L; Ogdensburg Free Acad; Ogdensburg, NY; (Y); 13/189; Pep Clb; Band; Concert Band; Mrchg Band; Pep Band; Yrbk Stf; Var L Bsktbl; Var L Socr; Pres NHS; NY ST Regents Schlrshp; Academic Excellence Awds; SUNY Potsdam; Education.

PEART, DESIREE N; Holy Trinity HS; Freeport, NY; (Y); 169/369; Mathletes; Rep Stu Cncl; Var Bsktbl; Var Trk; Winter & Spring Trk All Star Tm NSCHAA Lg 84-85; Winter/Spring Trk NYC Catholic All Star Tm 84-85; Bus Admin.

PEART, PATRICIA A; Freeport HS; Freeport, NY; (Y); 130/450; Art Clb; Church Yth Grp; French Clb; Hosp Aide; Office Aide; Church Choir; Molloy Coll; Nrs.

PEART, RENEE; Holy Trinity HS; Freeport, NY; (Y); Var Trk; Howard U; Nrse.

PEARTE, LISA; Elmira Southside HS; Elmira, NY; (Y); Cmnty Wkr; Girl Scts; Hosp Aide; Latin Clb; Model UN; Band; Mrchg Band; High Hon Roll; NHS; Ntl Amer Life Hby Essay Wnr 84; Miss Teen Of Amer Ntl Schlrshp 84; SADD 84-85; Elmira Bus Inst; Lgl Sctry.

PEASE, DEAN; Greene Central HS; Greene, NY; (Y); Am Leg Boys St; French Clb; Sec Trs Chorus; Concert Band; Mrchg Band; Ed Yrbk Stf; Bowling; Socr; Vllybl; Hon Roll.

PEASE, JAMES; Batavia HS; Batavia, NY; (Y); Church Yth Grp; French Clb; Math Tm; Y-Teens; Var L Ftbl; Var Wt Lftg; Hon Roll; Prfct Atten Awd; Arch.

PEATON, GLENDA; Our Lady Of Lourdes HS; Poughkeepsie, NY; (Y); 30/145; Variety Show; Hon Roll; NHS; Dutchess CC; Elec Engrng.

PEBWORTH, RUSSELL W; Hendrick Hudson HS; Croton-On-Hudson, NY; (Y); Boy Scts; Math Tm; Pres Science Clb; NHS; Ntl Merit Ltr; Pres Schlr; NY ST Brd Rgnts Schlrshp 85; Sci Dptmntlab Asst 85; Bstn U Smmer Schl Schlrshp 84; Egl Sct; Worcester Poly Inst; Engr.

PECCHIE, PAUL; St Francis Prep; Fresh Meadows, NY; (Y); Science Clb; Service Clb; Teachers Aide; Church Choir; Comp Sci.

PECHMAN, SHLOMO; Yeshiva Of Far Rockaway HS; Belle Harbor, NY; (Y); 1/9; Debate Tm; Office Aide; Yrbk Ed-Chief; Pres Sr Cls; Pres Stu Cncl; Capt Bsbl; Capt Fld Hcky; Capt Trk; Hon Roll; NY ST Regnts Schlrshp 84-85.

PECK, ALAN H; Gloversville HS; Gloversville, NY; (Y); Am Leg Boys St; JA; Nwsp Rptr; Var Ftbl; Var Trk; Im Wt Lftg; Athl Training.

PECK, BARBARA E; Mineola HS; Williston Park, NY; (Y); 8/257; Spanish Clb; Thesps; Chorus; Color Guard; Orch; School Musical; Var Badmtn; High Hon Roll; VP NHS; JV Bowling; NY ST Regents Schlrshp 85; Pit Orchstra Awd 83 & 84; SUNY At Stonybrook; Bio Rsrch.

PECK, BENJAMIN W; Fayetteville-Manlius HS; Fayetteville, NY; (Y); 81/332; Trs Church Yth Grp; Pres DECA; Exploring; Model UN; Bsktbl; JV Lcrss; Hon Roll; NHS; Ntl Merit Ltr; Fresh Acad Schlrshp 85-86; Bentley Coll; Accntnt.

PECK, CRAIG; Smithtown HS East; Saint James, NY; (Y); Am Leg Boys St; Spanish Clb; Symp Band; Var L Bsktbl; Var L Ftbl; Var L Lcrss; Hon Roll; Jr NHS; NHS; Ntl Merit Ltr.

PECK, DAPHNE A; Brushton Moira Central HS; North Bangor, NY; (Y); 6/58; French Clb; Ski Clb; School Play; Yrbk Stf; Rep Stu Cncl; JV Score Keeper; Hon Roll; NHS; Potsdam ST U; Comp Sci.

PECK, DARRIN; Wilson Central HS; Lockport, NY; (Y); Church Yth Grp; Pres 4-H; Band; Church Choir; Concert Band; Pep Band; Trk; 4-H Awd; Hon Roll; Niagara Co CC; Dsgnr.

PECK, DEBORAH; Schuylerville Central HS; Saratoga Springs, NY; (Y); 6/98; Trs Drama Clb; VP 4-H; French Clb; Math Clb; Math Tm; Chorus; Church Choir; Mrchg Band; School Play; Stage Crew; Natl 4-H Hm Envrnmt Wnnr 84; Ltr & Swtr 84; Le Moyne Coll; Ec.

PECK, DERRON; Eastport HS; Manorvlle, NY; (S); 4/56; Am Leg Boys St; Scholastic Bowl; Varsity Clb; Trs Sr Cls; Var Capt Bsbl; Var L Bsktbl; High Hon Roll; Jr NHS; NHS; Computer Clb; NY ST Regnts Schlrshp 84-85; Aevntcal Engr.

PECK, JOSEPH; Half Hollow Hills High School East; Dix Hills, NY; (Y); JV Crs Cntry; Var Trk; High Hon Roll.

PECK, KERYN; Union Springs Acad; Oswego, NY; (Y); Church Yth Grp; Ski Clb; Church Choir; Yrbk Stf; Pres Frsh Cls; Im Ftbl; Score Keeper; Im Sftbl; Im Vllybl; USBEA Typing II 84-85; Gregg Typing Prod Awd 84-85; Deans List 84-85; SUNY Oswego; Psych.

PECK, LORI A; Hoosick Falls Central HS; Hoosick, NY; (Y); 2/106; Drama Clb; School Play; Stage Crew; Rep Stu Cncl; JV Var Cheerleading; Cit Awd; Hon Roll; NHS; Sal; Outstdng Stu Awd 83; Schlrshp Awd 82; Dickinson Coll.

PECK, RICHARD F; Taconic Hills HS; Copake Falls, NY; (Y); 9/130; Am Leg Boys St; Art Clb; Sec French Clb; Church Choir; Yrbk Stf; Sec Sr Cls; Hon Roll; NHS; Prfct Atten Awd; Outstndng Achvt Frnch 83-84; Siena Coll; Trnsltng.

PECK, SHERRY L; Northville Central HS; Northville, NY; (Y); 1/61; Pres Church Yth Grp; Pres Band; Jazz Band; Co-Capt Yrbk Ed-Chief; Var Socr; Bausch & Lomb Sci Awd; Pres NHS; Val; Cornell U.

PECK, VIRGINIA; Midlakes HS; Phelps, NY; (Y); 1/154; Drama Clb; Hosp Aide; Band; School Musical; Yrbk Stf; Sec NHS; Ntl Merit SF; Val; Model UN; Service Clb; Tdu Drctr Fall Play; Dns Schlr At Cornell U; Area All-ST Orchstra; Cornell U; Gvrnmnt.

PECKALLY, MICHELE; Elmira Free Acad; Elmira, NY; (Y); Sec Church Yth Grp; Library Aide; Chorus; Church Choir; Nwsp Rptr; Yrbk Stf; Rep Stu Cncl; Hon Roll; Socl Wrk.

PECKINGHAM, JILL; Clinton HS; Clinton, NY; (Y); 4/134; Exploring; Model UN; Pres Sec Service Clb; Varsity Clb; Nwsp Stf; Yrbk Stf; Var L Golf; Var L Tennis; Capt L Vllybl; High Hon Roll; MIT; Engrng.

PECKMAN, LINDA; Roy C Ketcham S HS; Poughkeepsie, NY; (Y); French Clb; High Hon Roll; Hon Roll; Prncpls Awd 82-83; Live Oak HS Adcmc Cert 84; FIT; Phtgrphy.

PECOR, DONNA; Whitesboro HS; Whitesboro, NY; (Y); Dance Clb; Trs Band; Concert Band; Mrchg Band; Orch; School Play; Variety Show; Ed Yrbk Stf; Powder Puff Ftbl; Hon Roll; Flute Duet & Rated Excllnt NYSMA 83; Mohawk Vly CC; Psych.

PECORA, TRACY F; Palmyra-Macedon Central HS; Macedon, NY; (Y); 42/205; VP 4-H; Band; Symp Band; Mat Maids; Hon Roll; Regents Schlrshp 85; BUNY Brockport; Bio Sci.

PECORARO, ANTHONY; Timon HS; Buffalo, NY; (Y); 12/163; Church Yth Grp; Cmnty Wkr; Library Aide; Hon Roll; Htl Mngmnt.

PEDALINO, MARIA; Bishop Kearney HS; Brooklyn, NY; (Y); Drama Clb; FNA; Science Clb; Teachers Aide; Orch; Yrbk Stf; Hon Roll; NHS; Abraham Sonefeld Memrl Awd Humtrnsm 83; Comptrllr Awd Outstndng Achvt Sci, Math, Comptr Tech, Ec 83; Pre-Med.

PEDDY, CHRISTOPHER; Bronxville HS; Bronxville, NY; (Y); 23/78; Political Wkr; Band; School Musical; School Play; VP Jr Cls; Im Bowling; JV Lcrss; Hon Roll; Political Wkr; Variety Show; Pres Clsrm WA DC 85; Citibnk Essay Cnst 83; NY Regents Schlrshp Wnnr 85; Tufts U Medford; Economics.

PEDERSEN, JEFFREY L; Oriskany Falls Union Free HS; Oriskany Falls, NY; (Y); Am Leg Boys St; Ski Clb; Spanish Clb; Varsity Clb; Band; Mrchg Band; JV Var Bsktbl; Var Ftbl; JV Socr; Hon Roll; MI JV Bsktbl 83.

PEDERSEN, JENNIFER; Notre Dame Acad HS; Staten Island, NY; (Y); Church Yth Grp; Drama Clb; Hosp Aide; Variety Show; NHS; Ntl Merit Ltr; Engrng.

PEDERSON, NEIL; G Ray Bodley HS; Fulton, NY; (Y); Frsh Cls; Rep Stu Cncl; Im Ftbl; Var Capt Lcrss; JV Var Socr; Capt JV Wrstlng; Hon Roll; Rcvd 4 Am Hist Adv Plcmnt Pgm Tst 85; Math.

PEDI, THERESA; St Agnes HS; Fraklin Sq, NY; (Y); 21/350; Computer Clb; Dance Clb; English Clb; Pep Clb; Variety Show; Sec Soph Cls; Cheerleading; High Hon Roll; NHS; C W Post Schlrshp 85; C W Post; Comp Sci.

PEDRETTI, FRANK A; Cardinal Spellman HS; Bronx, NY; (Y); Computer Clb; Crs Cntry; Regnts Schlrshp; Fordham U.

PEDRICO, ELENA SHAUN; Ripley Central Schl; Ripley, NY; (S); 7/28; Church Yth Grp; French Clb; Office Aide; Chorus; School Musical; Yrbk Stf; Sec Jr Cls; Rep Stu Cncl; Var L Cheerleading; L Tennis; NYSSSA-VA 84; Cngrsnl Art Cmptn 84; Cert Rcgntn 84; Art.

PEDRO, THERESA; Granville Central HS; Granville, NY; (Y); 13/121; AFS; Drama Clb; Chorus; Trs Jr Cls; Var Capt Cheerleading; Interact Clb Awd 85; Maria Coll; Occup Thrpy.

PEDROSA, DIANE; Yonkers HS; Yonkers, NY; (Y); Key Clb; Nwsp Ed-Chief; Lit Mag; Rep Frsh Cls; Rep Soph Cls; Sec Jr Cls; Hon Roll; Achvt Awd 84 & 85; Psych.

PEDUZZI, AUDREY; Monsignor Scanlan HS; Queens Vlg, NY; (Y); 19/265; Cmnty Wkr; Red Cross Aide; Var Sftbl; Var Vllybl; Ntl Ldrshp & Serv Awd 85; Soc Wrk.

PEEBLES, STEVE; Vestal SR HS; Apalachin, NY; (Y); French Clb; Sec Varsity Clb; Pres Chorus; Pres Jr Cls; Rep Stu Cncl; L Crs Cntry; L Trk; Var Wrstlng; High Hon Roll; NHS; Med.

PEEK, JOHN J; Mont Pleasant HS; Schenectady, NY; (Y); 15/198; Drama Clb; French Clb; Sec German Clb; Spanish Clb; French Hon Soc; High Hon Roll; NHS; Spanish NHS; Chorus; Drill Tm; Theatr.

PEELEN, JUDY; Newark SR HS; Newark, NY; (Y); 7/250; Pres Church Yth Grp; Cmnty Wkr; GAA; Varsity Clb; Crs Cntry; Trk; French Hon Soc; High Hon Roll; NHS; Prfct Atten Awd; 5th Pl Inrsectnl Trk Meet 83; JR Hnr Girl 85; Scholar Achvts Recog 85; Calvin Coll; Phys Ther.

PEELER, SCOTT; Whitney Point SR HS; Conklin, NY; (S); Cmnty Wkr; JCL; Latin Clb; Science Clb; Hon Roll; Crime Prvntn Compstn Cntst 79; Bio.

PEENE, JOHN; Don Bosco Prep; Nanuet, NY; (Y); 24/206; Chess Clb; Bsbl; Bsktbl; High Hon Roll; Hon Roll; Jr NHS; NHS; All Suburb, All-Leag Bsktbll 85; Sci Awd 83; Geom Awd 85; Bus Mgmt.

PEETERS, TINA; Ticonderoga HS; Ticonderoga, NY; (Y); 5/125; Key Clb; JV Var Bsktbl; Var Socr; Var Sftbl; High Hon Roll; NHS; Prfct Atten Awd; Engrng.

PEIMER, ELISA H; Ossining HS; Ossining, NY; (Y); 27/267; Off Radio Clb; Acpl Chr; Chorus; School Musical; Swing Chorus; Nwsp Rptr; Yrbk Rptr; Sec Jr Cls; High Hon Roll; Sec NHS; NY U; Music Tech.

PEINKOFER, MARTIN; Salamanca Central HS; Salamanca, NY; (S); Am Leg Boys St; Letterman Clb; Ski Clb; Spanish Clb; Varsity Clb; Yrbk Phtg; Yrbk Stf; Var L Ftbl; Var L Trk; High Hon Roll; Annapolis; Engnr.

PEIRICK, MARY; Holland Central HS; Holland, NY; (Y); Dance Clb; Varsity Clb; Variety Show; Capt Cheerleading; Coach Actv; JV Var Socr; High Hon Roll; Hon Roll; Jr NHS; Pres Schlr; Rgents Schlrshp 85; Pres Acad Ftns Awd 85; SUNY; Acctng.

PEITA, DOUG; Kenmore East SR HS; Bufflo, NY; (Y); German Clb; Intnl Clb; Temple Yth Grp; School Play; Stu Cncl; Coach Actv; Score Keeper; High Hon Roll; Jr NHS; NHS; Sci.

PEKARIK, EDWARD; Monsignor Mc Clancy HS; Glendale, NY; (S); 30/229; Var Capt Bsbl; Im Bowling; Im Ftbl; Trk; ROTC; Jr NHS; NHS; Cert 1st Hnrs, Prncpls Lst 83-84; Mst Vlbl Plyr-Bsebl 83; 4 Yrs Of Intrmrls 81-84; Engrng.

PEKOLA, TODD; Holland Patent Central Schl; Holland Patent, NY; (Y); 26/151; Boy Scts; Band; Jazz Band; Symp Band; Wrstlng; Hon Roll.

PELAEZ, CARMELA; Dominican Commercial HS; Queens Village, NY; (Y); 60/273; Church Yth Grp; Spanish Clb; Ntl Merit Ltr; Pres Schlr; Pres Acdmc Ftns Awd 85; 2nd Hnrs In Spnsh In Iona Coll Lng Cntst 85; St Johns U.

PELAK, ROBERT A; Washington SR HS; Monroe, NY; (Y); 1/300; Boy Scts; Capt Math Tm; Ski Clb; Trs Stu Cncl; Im Stat Bowling; NHS; Ntl Merit SF; Chess Clb; Science Clb; Pep Band; H S Smmr Prog Rennslaer Polytech Inst 83; Sci Hnrs Prog Columbia U 83-84; All Cnty Band 84-85; Physics.

PELCZYNSKI, DARLEEN; Villa Maria Acad; Buffalo, NY; (Y); Church Yth Grp; Computer Clb; VP FBLA; Pep Clb; Teachers Aide; Stu Cncl; Vllybl; Hon Roll; Canisius Coll; Med Fld.

PELHAM, KIM; Sheepshead Bay HS; Brooklyn, NY; (Y); Teachers Aide; Brooklyn Coll; Sys Anlyst.

PELICANO, THOMAS C; Vernon-Verona Sherrill Central HS; Verona, NY; (Y); 22/249; Church Yth Grp; Church Choir; Concert Band; Jazz Band; School Musical; High Hon Roll; NHS; Ntl Merit Ltr; Pres Schlr; Rep Stu Cncl; NYS Rgnts Schlrshp 85; SUNY Potsdam; Phycs.

PELISSIER, CASSANDRA; Dominican Commercial HS; Queens Vlge, NY; (Y); Science Clb; Church Choir; Variety Show; Yrbk Stf; Pres Frsh Cls; Capt Vllybl; NHS; Med.

PELLEGRINI, CHRISTINE; Half Hollow Hills High School East; Dix Hills, NY; (Y); Cmnty Wkr; Service Clb; Band; Mrchg Band; Symp Band; Yrbk Rptr; Yrbk Stf; High Hon Roll; Jr NHS; NHS; Bio.

PELLEGRINO, BETH M; Adirondack Central HS; Boonville, NY; (Y); Am Leg Aux Girls St; Church Yth Grp; Ski Clb; Spanish Clb; Chorus; Church Choir; School Musical; Yrbk Stf; Sec Frsh Cls; Sec Jr Cls; U S Senate Yth Pgm 85; HOBY Pgm 84; Elem Ed.

PELLEGRINO, CRYSTI; Gloversville HS; Gloversville, NY; (Y); VP Rep Intnl Clb; Teachers Aide; Yrbk Stf; JV Fld Hcky; High Hon Roll; Hon Roll; Bus.

PELLEGRINO, MICHELLE; Lindenhurst HS; Lindenhurst, NY; (Y); 89/500; Church Yth Grp; Spanish Clb; Vllybl; Hon Roll; NHS; Hofstra; Bio.

PELLEGRINO, MONICA; La Salle SR HS; Niagara Falls, NY; (S); 16/270; Pres Church Yth Grp; Girl Scts; Yrbk Sprt Ed; Yrbk Stf; Swmmng; Hon Roll; Jr NHS; NHS; Med.

PELLEGRINO, RAYMOND; North Babylon SR HS; North Babylon, NY; (Y); Intnl Clb; Mathletes; Spanish Clb; Jr NHS; NHS.

PELLER, JOEL P; Shenendehowa SR HS; Ballston Lake, NY; (Y); High Hon Roll; Hon Roll; Pres Frsh Cls; Pres Soph Cls; Pres Jr Cls; Pres Sr Cls; VP Stu Cncl; JV Crs Cntry; Var Trk; NY ST Yth Cncl 84-86; Boy ST 85; Pre-Law.

PELLERIN, ARTHUR; Northeastern Clinton Central Schl; Alburg, VT; (Y); 4/146; Pres Church Yth Grp; JCL; Math Tm; Var Bsbl; Var Ftbl; NHS; Ntl Merit Ltr; Pres Schlr; Dance Clb; Debate Tm; Vermont Schlr 85; Potsdam U; Math.

PELLET, JENNIFER A; Caridnal Spellman HS; New York, NY; (Y); 17/560; Church Yth Grp; Dance Clb; Yrbk Stf; Twrlr; Hon Roll; Manhattan Coll; Math.

PELLETIER, CHRISTINE; Delaware Acad And Central Schl; Bovina Ctr, NY; (Y); Church Yth Grp; German Clb; Variety Show; Yrbk Stf; Var Cheerleading; JV Score Keeper; SUNY.

PELLETIER, M SUZANNE; Catholic Central HS; Troy, NY; (Y); 21/200; Cmnty Wkr; Math Clb; Red Cross Aide; Ski Clb; Chorus; School Musical; School Play; Variety Show; Yrbk Stf; Cheerleading; Excel Afro-Asian Studys & Ofc Prctce; New Rochelle Coll; Cmmnctn Arts.

PELLETIER, STEPHEN D; Troy HS; Troy, NY; (Y); 10/450; Boy Scts; Band; Concert Band; Mrchg Band; School Musical; School Play; Hon Roll; NHS; NYS Regnts Schlrshp 85; Hudson Valley CC; Math.

PELLETTERI, GERRIE MARIE; St Edmund HS; Brooklyn, NY; (Y); Science Clb; Law.

PELLICANE JR, ANTHONY; Oceanside HS; Baldwin, NY; (Y); Bsbl; Ftbl; Sftbl; Hon Roll; Nassau Tech; Aviation.

PELLICANO, CARMELA; Lockport SR HS; Lockport, NY; (Y); Church Yth Grp; Dance Clb; Intnl Clb; Spanish Clb; Band; Church Choir; Yrbk Stf; Var Stu Cncl; Sftbl; Hon Roll; Cortland; Pre Law.

PELLICANO, LAURIE K; East HS; Corning, NY; (Y); Dance Clb; VP Pres JA; Ski Clb; Band; Color Guard; Concert Band; Drill Tm; Mrchg Band; Pom Pon; Trk; St John Fisher; Bus Admin.

PELLINI, LYNN ANN; John Jay SR HS; Katonah, NY; (Y); Chorus; Jazz Band; Yrbk Ed-Chief; VP Soph Cls; VP Jr Cls; Pres Stu Cncl; JV Capt Cheerleading; High Hon Roll; Sec Trs Jr NHS; NHS; Ntl Bank Awd 85; Biology.

PELLIZZARI, PATRICIA; Solvay HS; Solvay, NY; (Y); Math Clb; Chorus; Variety Show; Frsh Cls; Soph Cls; Jr Cls; Var Socr; Var Vllybl; High Hon Roll; Mu Alp Tht; Gregg Awd 85; Shrthnd 83; All Str Vlybl 85; All St Baldwinsville & Grimes Torney 84; All Cntry Chorus 82; Bus.

PELLOW, PATRICK; Kenmore East SR HS; Buffalo, NY; (Y); Varsity Clb; Var Capt Socr; Var Swmmng; CC Awd; High Hon Roll; NHS; Awds Excllnc Math 83-85; Engrng.

PELOW, MICHELLE; Altmar-Parish-Williamstown HS; Parish, NY; (Y); 3/95; Yrbk Phtg; Yrbk Stf; High Hon Roll; Hon Roll; NHS; NY ST Regents Scholar 85; Hon Grad 85; Pres Acad Fitnss Awd 85; Rochester Inst Tech; Photogrphy.

PELUSO, MIA ANN; St Gabriel HS; Mt Vernon, NY; (Y); 41/61; Hosp Aide; Berkley; Sec.

PELUSO, STEPHANIE; John Dewey HS; Brooklyn, NY; (Y); Val; Library Aide; Band; Wt Lftg; High Hon Roll; Prfct Atten Awd; Comptrollers Awd 83; Goldn Recrd Of Achvt 83; Mth Achvt Awd 83; Baruch Coll; Comp Pgmmr.

PEMBERTON, JANICE R; Saint Francis Prep; S Ozone Park, NY; (Y); Am Leg Aux Girls St; Cmnty Wkr; JA; Library Aide; Math Clb; Acpl Chr; Chorus; School Musical; Var JV Bowling; Hon Roll; Choral Stu Dir Awd 84-85; Libr Apprctn Awd 84-85; Intermrl High Ser Bwlng Awd 84-85; Long Island U; Brdcstng Comm.

PEMBERTON, STEPHEN; Saratoga Central Catholic HS; Saratoga Springs, NY; (Y); 4/50; Cmnty Wkr; Yrbk Stf; High Hon Roll; NHS; VFW Awd; NY ST Rgnts Schlrshp 85; 2nd Pl Outstndng Yng New Yrker Cmptn 85; Golub Fndtn Schlrshp 85; Adirondach CC; Elec Tech.

PEMBROKE, MATTHEW; E J Wilson HS; Spencerport, NY; (Y); Boy Scts; JCL; Off Latin Clb; Varsity Clb; Yrbk Stf; Off Soph Cls; Off Jr Cls; Off Sr Cls; Var L Bsbl; Var L Trk; Buffalo ST; Law.

PENA, ALTAGRACIA; Mabel Dean Bacon V HS; New York, NY; (S); 23/299; Church Yth Grp; French Clb; Girl Scts; Math Tm; Church Choir; Orch; Cheerleading; Trk; Vllybl; High Hon Roll; Svc Awd 82; Attndnc Awd 82.

PENA, ANGELA; John Dewey HS; Brooklyn, NY; (Y); Color Guard; Concert Band; Orch; Badmtn; Gym; Trk; Wt Lftg; Hon Roll; Benjamin S Chancy Citatn Hnr 83; Principls Awd 83; ARISTA 83; USAF; Comp Bus.

PENA, FRANCES; Bishop Kearney HS; Brooklyn, NY; (Y); Church Yth Grp; Cmnty Wkr; JA; Church Choir; Rep Frsh Cls; Hon Roll; Prfct Atten Awd; Psych.

PENALVA, LUIZ; Solvay HS; Solvay, NY; (Y); Church Yth Grp; Hosp Aide; Spanish Clb; Band; Concert Band; Yrbk Bus Mgr; JV Var Trk; High Hon Roll; Hon Roll; NHS; Phy Thrpy.

PENBERTHY, PAMELA K; Tonawanda JR SR HS; Tonawanda, NY; (Y); 6/250; Drama Clb; Teachers Aide; Chorus; School Musical; School Play; Swing Chorus; Yrbk Stf; Cheerleading; Cit Awd; High Hon Roll; Regents Nrsng Schlrshp 85; Qlty Stu Awd-Tonawanda Indstrl Expansion Corp 85; Buffalo ST U; Pub Rel.

PENCE, HEATHER E; Oneonta SR HS; W Oneonta, NY; (Y); 4/161; Drama Clb; French Clb; Key Clb; Thesps; Concert Band; Mrchg Band; Stage Crew; Swmmng; High Hon Roll; NHS; Area All State Bnd 84; All County Bnd 84 & 85; Genesseo; Comp Sci.

PENCEK, KRISTEN; Union Endicott HS; Endwell, NY; (Y); Sec Church Yth Grp; Drama Clb; Hosp Aide; Color Guard; Mrchg Band; Orch; School Play; Yrbk Phtg; Stu Cncl; Frgn Lang Tchr.

PENDELL, MARY LOU; Crown Point Central Schl; Crown Pt, NY; (S); 5/34; Sec Varsity Clb; Sec Frsh Cls; Sec Soph Cls; Sec Jr Cls; Var Socr; Hon Roll; Sec NHS.

PENDER, EDWARD; Somers HS; Shenorock, NY; (Y); Boys Clb Am; Boy Scts; Intnl Clb; JA; ROTC; Golf; Cit Awd; High Hon Roll; Hon Roll; FL Inst Tech; Law.

PENDER, WALTER; Sheep Shed Bay HS; Brooklyn, NY; (Y); Aud/Vis; Computer Clb; Drama Clb; FCA; FNA; ROTC; Nwsp Sprt Ed; Yrbk Sprt Ed; Bsbl; Sftbl; Sports 82-84; Sports.

PENDERGAST, MICHELLE; Cicero-North Syracuse HS; N Syracuse, NY; (S); 46/622; Math Clb; Teachers Aide; Chorus; Color Guard; Hon Roll; Kiwanis Sftbl 1st Pl 83; YABA Bwlng 1st Pl & Hgh Ave Awd 84; Math.

PENDLETON, EDWIN; North Rose Wolcott HS; Wolcott, NY; (Y); Ski Clb; Socr; Swmmng; Hon Roll.

PENDLETON, TED; North Rose-Wolcott HS; Wolcott, NY; (Y); Socr; Swmmng.

PENET, CRAIG F; Sauquoit Valley HS; Sauquoit, NY; (Y); 5/120; Am Leg Boys St; Pres Varsity Clb; Yrbk Ed-Chief; VP Capt Bskbtl; Capt Bowling; Var L Trk; High Hon Roll; NHS; Opt Clb Awd; Republican Clb Awd 85; Mohawk Valley CC; Law.

PENG, TIMOTHY R; Smithtown H S East; St James, NY; (Y); Aud/Vis; Office Aide; School Musical; Nwsp Rptr; Mgr(s); Var L Trk; Hon Roll; Jr NHS; NHS; Ntl Merit Ltr.

PENIZOTTO, LORRAINE C; Liverpool HS; Liverpool, NY; (S); 38/790; Ski Clb; Chorus; School Musical; Rep Stu Cncl; JV Cheerleading; Var L Tennis; Jr NHS; NHS.

PENN, PHILLIP J; Regis HS; Yonkers, NY; (Y); Chess Clb; Hosp Aide; Nwsp Rptr; Rep Jr Cls; Rep Sr Cls; Var L Trk; St Schlr; Regis Schlrshp 81; Cornell U; Pre-Vet Med.

PENNA, TOM; Niagara Wheatfield SR HS; Niagara Falls, NY; (Y); German Clb; Model UN; Varsity Clb; Band; Var Lcrss; High Hon Roll; NHS; Prfct Atten Awd; Physics.

PENNACHIO, ROBERT; St Marys Boys HS; Douglaston, NY; (S); Yrbk Ed-Chief.

PENNER, JUDY; Sherburne-Earlville HS; Sherburne, NY; (S); 15/142; Am Leg Aux Girls St; Trs Band; Concert Band; Mrchg Band; Capt Var Cheerleading; Var Diving; Capt Var Swmmng; Cit Awd; High Hon Roll; NHS; Cobelskill Vo Tech; Flortclture.

PENNEY, KEITH; Smithtown H S East; Saint James, NY; (Y); German Clb; Stu Cncl; Var L Ftbl; Var L Lcrss; Var L Wrstlng; High Hon Roll; Hon Roll; Jr NHS; NHS; Ger Hnr Soc 83-85; Pre-Med.

PENNING, CHRISTOPHER; South Glens Falls SR HS; S Glens Falls, NY; (Y); 28/237; Hon Roll; Achv In Math 83; Mrt Awd Top 5% On PSAT 85; Karate Clb 84-85; Arch.

PENNINGTON, DEMETRIA; Clara Barton HS; Brooklyn, NY; (Y); 7/469; Band; Gym; Sftbl; Hon Roll; NHS; Prfct Atten Awd; Arista 81-82; Cornell U; Bio.

PENNINGTON, RUSS; Vestal HS; Vestal, NY; (Y); Ski Clb; Varsity Clb; Rep Jr Cls; Im Bsktbl; JV Lcrss; JV Var Socr; Var Trk; High Hon Roll; Hon Roll; NHS; Cornell; Elec Engrng.

PENNISI, FRANCESCA; Mt Vernon HS; Mt Vernon, NY; (Y); 6/600; FTA; Key Clb; Nwsp Ed-Chief; Lit Mag; Crs Cntry; High Hon Roll; NHS; Regents Schlrshp 85; Columbia Coll; Teacher.

PENNISI, JOSEPH M; Troy High; Troy, NY; (Y); 2/450; Boy Scts; JV Var Socr; JV Var Trk; Bausch & Lomb Sci Awd; High Hon Roll; Trs NHS; Ntl Merit Ltr; Sal; Rensselaer Medal 84; Rensselaer Polytech; Elec Engr.

PENNON, BETTINA VITA; Center Moriches HS; Ctr Moriches, NY; (Y); Church Yth Grp; Band; Chorus; Church Choir; Sec Frsh Cls; Sec Soph Cls; Sec Jr Cls; Pres Sr Cls; Sec Stu Cncl; Var Capt Cheerleading; Hofstra U; Psych.

PENNY, BRETT A; Hampton Bays HS; Hampton Bays, NY; (Y); 19/122; Aud/Vis; Yrbk Rptr; Yrbk Stf; Var Bsbl; JV Wrstlng; High Hon Roll; Hon Roll; NY St Regents Schlrshp 85; NY Inst Technology; Arch.

PENROSE, DINA A; Acad Of St Joseph; Coram, NY; (Y); VP Trs Church Yth Grp; Hosp Aide; Service Clb; Ski Clb; Teachers Aide; Chorus; Church Choir; Hon Roll; Mth.

PENSABENE, DONNA; South Shore HS; Brooklyn, NY; (Y); 26/668; Math Tm; Concert Band; Orch; Nwsp Ed-Chief; Yrbk Stf; Co-Capt Cheerleading; Co-Capt Sftbl; NHS; Ntl Merit Schol; Rgnts & NYU Trste Schlrshps 85; NY U; Pol Sci.

PEPE, KATHERINE; Academy Of The Holy Names; Ballston Lake, NY; (Y); Cmnty Wkr; Teachers Aide; Varsity Clb; Var JV Socr; Var Trk; Hotel Mgmt.

PEPER, ANN; Preston HS; Bronx, NY; (Y); Yrbk Stf; VP Frsh Cls; Pres Soph Cls; Trs Jr Cls; Bowling; IA Coll; Finc.

PEPLIN, JENNIFER D; Springville G I HS; West Falls, NY; (Y); 34/201; Pres AFS; VP French Clb; Acpl Chr; Chorus; Nwsp Rptr; Yrbk Bus Mgr; Rep Stu Cncl; Stat Trk; NHS; NYS Rgnts Schlrshp 85; Pres Schlrshp 85; Kent ST U; Telecomm.

PEPPER, COLLEEN; Port Jervis HS; Port Jervis, NY; (Y); 26/160; Varsity Clb; Band; JV Var Bsktbl; High Hon Roll; Hon Roll; Rotary Awd; SUNY Geneseo; Acctg.

PEPPER, MARGARET A; Arlington HS; Poughkeepsie, NY; (Y); 33/572; Church Yth Grp; Girl Scts; Ski Clb; Orch; Hon Roll; Intl Yth & Music Fest 2nd Pl 84; Dutchess CC; Engr.

PEPPER, MELISSA; Addison Central Schl; Woodhull, NY; (S); GAA; Ski Clb; Band; Concert Band; Mrchg Band; Sec Jr Cls; Var Capt Cheerleading; JV Var Sftbl; High Hon Roll; NHS; Houghton.

PEQUEEN, CANDICE; Kenmore West HS; Kenmore, NY; (Y); French Clb; Band; Concert Band; Mrchg Band; School Musical; Fld Hcky; JV Var Swmmng; Var Trk; Hon Roll; Trck-NFL All Star Awd 85; Excllnt Attndnc 83-85.

PERALTA, XIOMARA; George Washington HS; New York, NY; (Y); Band; Orch; Off Sr Cls; Prfct Atten Awd.

PERALVO, SYLVIA; Bishop Ford C C HS; Brooklyn, NY; (Y); 1st & 2nd Hnrs 84-85; John Jay Coll; Law.

PERAZA, GISELLE; Notre Dame Acad; Staten Island, NY; (Y); Drama Clb; Hosp Aide; PAVAS; Chorus; School Musical; School Play; Swmmng; Ansthslgst.

PERBOO, HEMDAT; Walotnm HS; New York City, NY; (S); Capt Tennis; Cit Awd; NHS; Sci Awd 82; Polytech Inst; Engr.

PERCENTI, THERESA A; Saratoga Central Catholic HS; Mechanicville, NY; (S); French Clb; Hosp Aide; Ski Clb; Yrbk Stf; French Hon Soc; High Hon Roll.

PERCIAVALLE, PETER; Thomas Edison HS; Richmond Hill, NY; (Y); 1/419; Office Aide; Nwsp Bus Mgr; Nwsp Rptr; Cit Awd; Gov Hon Prg Awd; Sec NHS; Val; Phi Beta Kappa Schlrshp Hofstra U 85; Catholic Teachers Assn Schlrshp 85; Acad Olympic Tm Capt 83-85; Hofstra U.

PERDOMO, ROBERT; Biship Ford Central C HS; Brooklyn, NY; (Y); Im Bowling; Im Fld Hcky; Scl Sci.

PEREIRA, ARIEL; St Francis Prep; Corona, NY; (Y); 191/690; Model UN; Opt Clb Awd; Rgnts Schlrshp 84; Corp Law.

PEREIRA, EDDIE; Saint Francis Prep; Corona, NY; (Y); CAP; Lit Mag; Socr; Regents Spn; Lwyr.

PEREIRA, MARIA; Sacred Heart HS; Yonkers, NY; (S); 2/250; Hosp Aide; Intnl Clb; Pres JA; Trs Stu Cncl; High Hon Roll; NHS; NEDT Awd; Half Yr Schlrsp 82; Schlrshp Mahanttan Coll 85; Ntl Hnr Roll; Lawyer.

PERERA, HYACINTH; Central Islip HS; Central Islip, NY; (Y); Computer Clb; Math Clb; Math Tm; JV Socr; Hon Roll; FTA; Library Aide; Teachers Aide; Band; Concert Band; Achv Awd Technel Comp 85; Grumman Data Inst; Comps.

PERESS, HARRY; Rye Country Day Schl; Harrison, NY; (Y); 10/82; AFS; Art Clb; Cmnty Wkr; Hosp Aide; Science Clb; Nwsp Stf; Yrbk Stf; Lit Mag; Natl Frnch Cntst 4th 83; Cmnty Svc Awd 85.

PERETO, JEANNE; Rome Free Academy; Rome, NY; (Y); 63/480; Cmnty Wkr; Intnl Clb; Key Clb; Pep Clb; Yrbk Stf; Rep Stu Cncl; Im Powder Puff Ftbl; Var L Vllybl; Hon Roll; Jr NHS; Regents Schlrshp Wnnr; SUNY Binghamton; Comp.

PERETZ, SAMUEL R; New Rochelle HS; New Rochelle, NY; (Y); 7/597; Intnl Clb; Var Crs Cntry; Var Trk; NHS; Ntl Merit SF; Rennselaer Olytechnic Inst Awd 85; :Bio.

PEREZ, AIMEE; Sacred Heart HS; Yonkers, NY; (Y); Intnl Clb; Yrbk Stf; Hon Roll; Columbia U; Math.

PEREZ, ANGEL; Cardinal Spellman HS; New York, NY; (Y); JV Capt Bsbl; JV Bsktbl; JV Var Ftbl; Fordam U; Jrnlsm.

PEREZ, ANGELICA; Norman Thomas HS; New York, NY; (S); 20/671; Dance Clb; DECA; FBLA; Math Tm; Hon Roll; NHS; Prfct Atten Awd; Art Medal 81; Hnrs Medal 78; Sci Medal 81; Med.

PEREZ, BLANCA; John Dewey HS; Brooklyn, NY; (Y); Sec Church Yth Grp; Pres JA; Math Tm; Color Guard; School Musical; High Hon Roll; Prfct Atten Awd; Awd Of Apprctn Urban Yth Alliance Inc 84; Spansh Awd 83; Sci Awd 83.

PEREZ, CARLOS; Port Chester HS; Port Chester, NY; (Y); 2/250; Rep Am Leg Boys St; Boy Scts; VP Key Clb; Yrbk Ed-Chief; Rep Stu Cncl; Var Capt Crs Cntry; Var Capt Trk; Mu Alp Tht; Pres NHS; Spanish NHS; Rensselaer Polytechnic Inst Medal 84; West Point.

PEREZ, CARMEN R; Mabel Dean Bacon HS; Astoria, NY; (S); 20/299; Concert Band; Drm Mjr(t); Yrbk Phtg; Yrbk Stf; Teachers Aide; Chorus; Variety Show; Bsktbl; Fld Hcky; Vllybl; Air Stewd.

PEREZ, CAROLYN; Ossining HS; Ossining, NY; (Y); French Clb; Model UN; Radio Clb; Stage Crew; Nwsp Rptr; Ed Yrbk Rptr; High Hon Roll; Hon Roll; NHS; Frnch Awd; Bus.

PEREZ, DANIEL; Xavier HS; New York, NY; (Y); Cmnty Wkr; Hosp Aide; VP Soph Cls; Stu Cncl; Im Bsktbl; 2nd 3rd Hnrs 83-85; Sport Awds Bsktbl,Bsbl 84-85; Pace U; Med.

PEREZ, DAVID A; Archbishop Molloy HS; Corona, NY; (Y); Church Yth Grp; Spanish Clb; School Play; Variety Show; Lit Mag; Im Sftbl; JV Trk; Spanish NHS; NYS Regnts, LI U & ROTC Schlrshps 85; St Johns U; Law.

PEREZ, EILEEN; Far Rockaway HS; Far Rockaway, NY; (Y); Church Yth Grp; Drama Clb; Teachers Aide; Chorus; Church Choir; Nwsp Stf; Mgr.

PEREZ, ELSA; Aquinas HS; New York, NY; (Y); 49/178; Art Clb; Cmnty Wkr; Computer Clb; Dance Clb; French Clb; Red Cross Aide; Variety Show; Hon Roll; Pres Envirmntl Yth Awds 83; Ltr Refrnce Merit Achvt Awd 85; Psych.

PEREZ, JASMIN; High School Of Music & Art; Brooklyn, NY; (Y); 114/588; Art Clb; Cmnty Wkr; Office Aide; PAVAS; Teachers Aide; Yrbk Bus Mgr; Yrbk Stf; Lit Mag; Hon Roll; NHS; Lawyer.

PEREZ, MARIA; John Dewey HS; Brooklyn, NY; (Y); Church Yth Grp; Office Aide; Spanish Clb; Teachers Aide; Hon Roll; Amer Assn Tchrs Spnsh & Portguese Cert 84; Acctg.

PEREZ, MARTHA; Cardinal Spellman HS; New York, NY; (Y); Cmnty Wkr; Church Choir; Flag Corp; School Musical; School Play; 1st Hnrs 84-85; Comp.

PEREZ, MARTHA; St Pius V HS; Bronx, NY; (Y); Intnl Clb; Service Clb; Chorus; Yrbk Stf; Pres Soph Cls; Sec Jr Cls; Bsktbl; Hon Roll; NHS; Relgn, Alg & Hon Ment Phy Ed; Morrisville Coll; Engl.

PEREZ, NANCY; St Johns Prep; Astoria, NY; (Y); Chorus; Church Choir; School Musical; Variety Show; Rep Jr Cls; Sec Sr Cls; Sec Stu Cncl; Law.

PEREZ, PAULINA; St Johns Preparatory HS; Jackson Hts, NY; (Y); Jr Schl Dnc Awd 85; Tchng.

PEREZ, RICHARD; St Agnes HS; Queens, NY; (Y); 1/100; Chess Clb; Church Yth Grp; Model UN; Spanish Clb; Nwsp Stf; High Hon Roll; NHS; Comm.

PEREZ, SOFIA; Hunter College HS; Astoria, NY; (Y); Cmnty Wkr; Hosp Aide; Political Wkr; Chorus; Church Choir; Im Bsktbl; Mgr(s); Mu Alp Tht; Ntl Merit Ltr; 3 Hnr Rll Cert Piano 82-84; 1st Spnsh Cntst 83; Semi Fnlst Ntl Hspnc Schlr Awd Pgm 84; Chem.

PEREZ JR, THOMAS; Xaverian HS; Brooklyn, NY; (Y); 3/345; Chess Clb; JA; JV Math Tm; VP Spanish Clb; Im Bsktbl; Im Ftbl; Im Sftbl; Hon Roll; Ntl Merit SF; Prfct Atten Awd; NY Regents Schlrshp.

PEREZ, WANDA; H S Of Fashion Industri; New York, NY; (Y).

PERFETTO, LOUIS; Nazareth Regional HS; Brooklyn, NY; (Y); Boy Scts; Church Yth Grp; JV Var Bsbl; High Hon Roll; Hon Roll; Pre-Med.

PERFITT, KIM; Oakfield-Alabma Central Schl; Oakfield, NY; (Y); #65 In Class; Church Yth Grp; Dance Clb; GAA; Ski Clb; Varsity Clb; Band; Chorus; Church Choir; Var Socr; Var Sftbl; Rtl Buying.

PERGEA, LESLIE; Cicero North Syracuse HS; Bridgeport, NY; (Y); 110/800; Aud/Vis; Boy Scts; Auto Mech.

PERGOLA, PATRICIA; Canarsie HS; Brooklyn, NY; (Y); Vllybl; NCTE Awd; Pres Schlr; NYS Schlrshp 85; Accntng.

PERGOLIZZI, JANINE; Sacred Heart Acad; Rosedale, NY; (S); 12/186; French Clb; Math Clb; School Musical; Nwsp Rptr; Yrbk Stf; Lit Mag; High Hon Roll; Hon Roll; NHS; Umbrlla For Undrstndg Awd Schl Svc 84; Prncpls List 82; Comms.

PERHAM, MARIA; Gloversville HS; Gloversville, NY; (Y); 15/250; Church Yth Grp; French Clb; Intnl Clb; Sec Key Clb; Color Guard; Mrchg Band; Yrbk Stf; High Hon Roll; Cvl Engrng.

PERI, CHRISTINE; Seaford HS; Seaford, NY; (Y); Band; Cheerleading; Hon Roll; Corp Law.

PERI, DOMINICK; Lynbrook HS; Lynbrook, NY; (Y); Spanish Clb; Pep Band; Bowling; Hon Roll; NY Polytech Inst; Elec Engrng.

PERIANO, KARIN; Miller Place HS; Miller Pl, NY; (Y); JV Socr; Photgrphy Awd 85; Stony Brook U.

PERILLO, BARBARA; St Francis Prep; Richmond Hill, NY; (S); 77/690; Girl Scts; Math Clb; Teachers Aide; Opt Clb Awd; Regents Schlrshp 85; Natl Hnr Roll 85; Queens Coll.

PERILLO, CONCETTA; Our Lady Of Perpetual Help HS; Brookly, NY; (Y); Nwsp Stf; High Hon Roll; Hon Roll; Jr NHS; NHS; Prfct Atten Awd; Perfect Atten Awd 81-85; Pace U; Psych.

PERINE, JESSICA; Sandord H Calhoun HS; Merrick, NY; (Y); Key Clb; Band; School Play; Yrbk Stf; Var Badmtn; Var L Tennis; Var L Trk; Hon Roll; NHS; Psych.

PERITZ, CRAIG; Seaford HS; Seaford, NY; (Y); VP Rep Frsh Cls; Rep Soph Cls; Rep Jr Cls; Stu Cncl; Var Crs Cntry; Var Trk; Hon Roll; Im Vllybl; Sinai Hnr Soc 85; All-Cnty Chorus Select 82; Stu Against Drunk Drvng 83-85; Eng.

PERITZ, LANI; Smithtown High Schl East; Saint James, NY; (Y); Temple Yth Grp; Sec Frsh Cls; Sec Jr Cls; Var L Badmtn; Score Keeper; Var L Tennis; High Hon Roll; NHS; Ntl Merit Ltr; Spanish NHS; Ldrshp Trnng Prog Schlrshp 85; VP Yth Grp Suffolk Cnty 85; Art.

PERKINS, ALBERT; John F Kennedy HS; New York, NY; (Y); Chorus; Variety Show; Off Sr Cls; Im Bsktbl; Im Ftbl; Sci Awd 82; Kingsborough; Cmmnctns.

PERKINS, AVA; St Johns Prep; Queens, NY; (S); 141/415; Church Yth Grp; Drama Clb; Chorus; Church Choir; Jazz Band; School Musical; Var L Bsktbl; JV Trk; Physcl Thrpy.

PERKINS, BARBARA; Wells Central Schl; Speculator, NY; (S); 1/30; Drama Clb; French Clb; Trs Yrbk Stf; VP Frsh Cls; Var Socr; Var Sftbl; Var JV Vllybl; Bausch & Lomb Sci Awd; NHS; NYS Regnts Schlrshp 85; Math.

PERKINS, DAVID C; Union Endicott HS; Endicott, NY; (Y); 20/430; Chess Clb; Church Yth Grp; Computer Clb; Ski Clb; Varsity Clb; Trk; High Hon Roll; Hon Roll; NHS; Ntl Phy Educ Awd 85; Ltr Trck 84-85; VA Pooltech Inst; Elec Engrng.

PERKINS, EUNICE; Aquinas HS; Bronx, NY; (Y); 3/178; Science Clb; Yrbk Stf; VP Jr Cls; Sec Stu Cncl; High Hon Roll; NHS; Spanish NHS; Pres Envrnmntl Yth Awd 84; Aquinas HS Awd Acad Exclnc 85; Sci Fair Cert Hon 2nd Prz 85; Bio.

PERKINS, JULIE M; Camden Central HS; N Bay, NY; (Y); AFS; Ski Clb; High Hon Roll; Mth.

PERKINS, MATTHEW; Columbia HS; E Greenbush, NY; (Y); Jazz Band; Mrchg Band; JV Bsktbl; Var Bowling; JV Ftbl; JV Socr; Var Tennis; JV Vllybl; Im Wt Lftg; JV Var Wrstlng; Drake U; Comp.

PERKINS, PAMELA; South Shore HS; Brooklyn, NY; (Y); Church Yth Grp; Dance Clb; FCA; Church Choir; Proficncy Cert Typng 85; Atten Awd 85; NY Tech Coll; Lab Tech.

PERKINS, TAMMY; Skaneateles Central HS; Auburn, NY; (S); Sec Church Yth Grp; Band; Chorus; Orch; JV Bsktbl; Hon Roll; NHS; Gregg Typng Awd 85; Med Secy.

PERKINS, TROY; Haverling HS; Bath, NY; (Y); 50/139; French Clb; Var Ftbl; Corning CC; Engrng Sci.

PERKOWSKI, BETH E; Ichabod Crane HS; Valatie, NY; (Y); 3/172; VP French Clb; Ski Clb; Yrbk Stf; Rep Stu Cncl; Elks Awd; High Hon Roll; Sec NHS; Ntl Merit Ltr; Pres Schlr; Treas SADD 85; Regents Schlrshp 85; Siena Coll; Chem.

PERKOWSKI, MAUREEN; Susan E Wagner HS; Staten Island, NY; (Y); Office Aide; Yrbk Sprt Ed; Lit Mag; Rep Frsh Cls; Rep Soph Cls; Rep Jr Cls; Rep Stu Cncl; High Hon Roll; NHS.

PERKOWSKY, ADAM; New Field HS; Coram, NY; (Y); Computer Clb; Intnl Clb; Spanish Clb; Nwsp Stf; High Hon Roll; Hon Roll; Spanish NHS; SUNY Albany; Cmnctns.

PERKUS, BENJAMIN; Guilderland Central HS; Altamont, NY; (Y); 17/385; Computer Clb; School Musical; Lit Mag; Socr; Trk; High Hon Roll; NCTE Awd; NHS; Ntl Merit Schol; St Schlr.

PERLMUTTER, TODD D; Half Hollow Hills H S East; Melville, NY; (Y); Boy Scts; Computer Clb; Temple Yth Grp; Hon Roll; Ner Tamid-Religious Awd Boy Scouts Of Amer 83; Comp Engr.

PERLOWSKI, HENRY M; New Dorp HS; Staten Island, NY; (Y); 1/780; Am Leg Boys St; French Clb; Hosp Aide; Key Clb; Math Tm; Quiz Bowl; Bausch & Lomb Sci Awd; Cit Awd; High Hon Roll; Val; Brown U Bk Awd Scholar & Exclnce Eng 84; Gov Committee Awd 85; Pres Hnr Awd 85; Duke U; Bio.

PERNA, DIANE; Greece Arcadia HS; Rochester, NY; (Y); 14/296; Cmnty Wkr; FBLA; GAA; Hosp Aide; JA; Math Clb; Math Tm; Varsity Clb; Yrbk Stf; Sec Frsh Cls; Prncpls Awd, Outstndng Ath Awd Booster Clb, Army Ntl Schlr Ath Awd 84-85; U Rochester; Econ.

PERNICK JR, JAMES A; St Josephs Collegiate Inst; Kenmore, NY; (Y); Letterman Clb; Library Aide; Varsity Clb; Church Choir; Yrbk Sprt Ed; Var Capt Bsbl; JV Im Bsktbl; Im JV Ftbl; Im Wt Lftg; Hon Roll; MVP W Seneca Bsbl Trnmnt 85; Capt JV Bsbl Tm 84-85; To 10 Athltes Of Kenmore 85; Niagara; Bus.

PERO, ANNE; Nazareth Acad; Rochester, NY; (S); Pres Church Yth Grp; Exploring; Latin Clb; Library Aide; Chorus; School Musical; Stage Crew; Rep Frsh Cls; Rep Soph Cls; Off Jr Cls; Magna Cum Laude Ntl Lat Exm 84; Pschlgy.

PEROHA, LISA; Notre Dame Bishop Gibbons HS; Schenectady, NY; (S); 15/108; VP Frsh Cls; Rep Stu Cncl; Stat Crs Cntry; Stat Trk; High Hon Roll; NHS; Ntl Ldrshp Merit Awd 84; All-Amer Acad Awd 84; Northeastern U; Acctng.

PEROTTI, JEFF; Solvay HS; Syracuse, NY; (Y); Trs Spanish Clb; Yrbk Bus Mgr; Yrbk Stf; Soph Cls; Jr Cls; Sr Cls.

PERPETUA, MICHELLE; Beacon HS; Beacon, NY; (Y); High Hon Roll; Hon Roll; Jr NHS; NHS; Bus.

PERRAUD, CAROLYN; Preston HS; Bronx, NY; (Y); 18/76; Cmnty Wkr; Stage Crew; Var Capt Twrlr; Hon Roll; NY ST Regents Schlrshp 85; Regents Diploma 85; Fordham U; Bus Admin.

PERRAULT, JEANNINE; Cicero-North Syracuse HS; Clay, NY; (Y); 42/711; Band; Chorus; Concert Band; Mrchg Band; Orch; Pep Band; School Musical; Symp Band; Crs Cntry; Powder Puff Ftbl; Goucher Coll Centennial Schlrshp Fin 85; Goucher Coll.

PERRAULT, TINA; Southside HS; Elmira, NY; (Y); Art Clb; Dance Clb; French Clb; Key Clb; Math Clb; Chorus; JV Bsktbl; JV Sftbl; JV Vllybl; Hon Roll; PAL, FSA 84-85; Bus.

PERREAULT, THOMAS; Salamanca Central HS; Salamanca, NY; (S); 5/130; Am Leg Boys St; Cmnty Wkr; French Clb; Model UN; Co-Capt Var Crs Cntry; Var Trk; French Hon Soc; High Hon Roll; NHS; Entomology.

PERRECA, LOUISE M; Sachem HS; Farmingville, NY; (Y); 38/1482; Ski Clb; Nwsp Ed-Chief; Nwsp Phtg; Yrbk Phtg; Twrlr; Jr NHS; NHS; Boy Scts; Office Aide; Spanish Clb; NY ST Regents Schlrshp 85; NE US Solo Champ 83-84; LI Sci Congrss 1st Pll 83; E Carolina U; Psych.

PERRIELLO, MARYBETH; Greece Athena HS; Rochester, NY; (Y); 79/285; DECA; JA; Ski Clb; JV Sftbl; St Osewego U.

PERRIELLO, SANDRA; White Plains HS; White Plains, NY; (Y); Capt Var Gym; Meritorious Awd & Vrsty Monogrm Gym 83; YWCA East Regn Chmpnshps Gym 82; 2nd Pl Cls II Gym 83; Iona Coll; Bus.

PERRIGO, MARTIN; Tupper Lake HS; Tupper Lk, NY; (Y); 6/115; Art Clb; Drama Clb; 4-H; School Musical; School Play; Stage Crew; JV Bsktbl; Cit Awd; Hon Roll; RPI Medal Math,Sci 85; Electrncs.

PERRIN, BLAINE; Franklin Acad; Malone, NY; (Y); Varsity Clb; Var L Bsbl; Var L Ftbl; Var L Ice Hcky; NHS; Acad All Amer 84-85; MVP & Mst Defnsve Bsebl 85.

PERRIN, JACQUELINE J; Notre Dame Acad; Staten Island, NY; (Y); Drama Clb; Chorus; School Musical; Nwsp Phtg; Nwsp Stf; Yrbk Phtg; Ed Yrbk Stf; Ed Lit Mag; NHS; Ntl Merit SF; Photo Jrnlsm.

PERRIN, MICHELLE; Alexander Central HS; Alexander, NY; (Y); 60/87; Drama Clb; 4-H; Ski Clb; Color Guard; Mrchg Band; Yrbk Ed-Chief; Yrbk Stf; JV Var Socr; JV Vllybl; Hon Roll; Bryant & Stratton; Acctng.

PERRINO, MARY; Preston HS; Bronx, NY; (S); 2/104; Yrbk Stf; High Hon Roll; NHS; NEDT Awd; Sal; Govrnrs Citatn Awd; Half Scholar; St Johns U; Acctg.

PERRINO, PETER; Whitestone Acad; Whitestone, NY; (S); Boys Clb Am; Boy Scts; Bus Dynmcs 84; Chem 84; Geom 83; Aerontcl Engrng.

PERROT, TINA; Lockport SR HS; Lockport, NY; (Y); Spanish Clb; Niagara CC; Bus.

PERROTTA, JOSEPH; Henninger HS; Syracuse, NY; (Y); 5/400; Computer Clb; Exploring; French Clb; Intnl Clb; JA; Key Clb; Sec Mathletes; Math Clb; NHS; Prfct Atten Awd; Cornell U Bk Awd 84; NYS Regents Scholar 85; Kiwanis Scholar 85; Am Leg Scholar 85; Rochester Inst Tech; Bio.

PERROTTA, PASQUALE; Archbishop Stepinac HS; Mt Vernon, NY; (Y); 100/210; Political Wkr; Pres Jr Cls; Pres Sr Cls; Pres Stu Cncl; JV Capt Socr; Fordam U; Lawyer.

PERROTTI, DAVID; Liverpool HS; Liverpool, NY; (Y); Rep Stu Cncl; Var L Bsbl; Var L Bsktbl; Im Wt Lftg; Hon Roll; Ntl Merit Ltr; Comp.

PERRY, BRIAN; Ravena Coeymans Selkirk HS; S Bethlenem, NY; (Y); Yrbk Stf; Pres Church Yth Grp; Var Capt Crs Cntry; JV Socr; Var Trk; Var Capt Wrstlng.

PERRY, CHRISTINE; Ithaca HS; Ithaca, NY; (Y); JA; Orch; Jr NHS; Ntl Merit Ltr; Ithaca Coll; Bio.

PERRY, DENISE; Uniondale HS; Uniondale, NY; (Y); Hosp Aide; Red Cross Aide; Yrbk Stf; Pom Pon; High Hon Roll; Hon Roll; Jr NHS; VP NHS; Outstndg Achvt Fr 82-83; Cert Apprec Red Crs Volnteer 84; Corp Law.

PERRY, DONALD C; Erasmus Hall HS; Brooklyn, NY; (Y); 7/433; Math Tm; VP Science Clb; Yrbk Stf; Mgr(s); NHS; The Cooper Union; Elec Engrng.

PERRY, DONNA A; Valley Stream Central HS; Valley Stream, NY; (Y); Hosp Aide; Red Cross Aide; Chorus; Madrigals; Crs Cntry; Trk; High Hon Roll; Jr NHS; NHS; Spanish NHS; Biol.

PERRY, EDWIN; Cardinal Hayes HS; New York, NY; (Y); 70/284; Boy Scts; Chorus; Color Guard; School Musical; Rep Sr Cls; Rep Stu Cncl; Bsbl; Ftbl; Wt Lftg; Hon Roll; Eagle Scout 85; Engrng.

PERRY, JILL; Geneva HS; Geneva, NY; (Y); Church Yth Grp; Cmnty Wkr; Girl Scts; Hosp Aide; Latin Clb; Model UN; Ski Clb; Varsity Clb; Band; Church Choir; Sci.

PERRY, JULIE E; Red Creek JR SR HS; Red Creek, NY; (Y); 1/68; VP Pres French Clb; Yrbk Sprt Ed; Var Capt Bsktbl; Var Capt Socr; Var L Sftbl; DAR Awd; Trs Pres NHS; Val; Cmnty Wkr; NY ST Regents Schlrshp Recpnt 85; Outstndng H S Athlts In Amer 82-83; NYSPHSAA Clss C All-ST Tm; Hobart; Bio.

PERRY, KARLA M; Franklin Acad; Malone, NY; (Y); Spanish Clb; Teachers Aide; Rep Stu Cncl; US Marin Corps; Spnsh.

PERRY, KRISTEN; Parishville-Hopkinton Central HS; Potsdam, NY; (Y); 4/44; Church Choir; Color Guard; Stage Crew; Hon Roll; NHS; Prfct Atten Awd; Sec Trs Church Yth Grp; Var Capt Cheerleading; Exclinc Keybrdng & Cmmnctns 84; Exclinc Course II Math 84; Spnsh Trnsltr.

PERRY, MEENA; Bishop Kearney HS; Brooklyn, NY; (Y); Art Clb; Camera Clb; Church Yth Grp; FNA; Hosp Aide; Service Clb; Ski Clb; Hon Roll; Mdcl.

PERRY, MICHAEL L; Hillcrest HS; Jamaica, NY; (Y); 96/793; JA; Library Aide; Office Aide; Science Clb; Yrbk Stf; Lit Mag; Stu Cncl; Swmmng; Vllybl; Wt Lftg; Hillcrest HS Pre-Med Prog 81-85; Vol Mt Sinai Hosp 83; Vol X-Mas Party Mntly & Phys Hndcpd 81-84; Fmly Prctnr.

PERRY, RICH; Massena Central HS; Massena, NY; (Y); 10/280; Pres Frsh Cls; Pres Soph Cls; Pres Jr Cls; JV L Bsbl; Var L Ftbl; Var L Trk; Var L Wrstlng; High Hon Roll; NHS; Cmnty Wkr; Acad Banq; Exec Brd Massena Yth Cncl; Syracuse U; Advrtsng.

PERRY JR, RICHARD C; Fort Plain Central Schl; Fort Plain, NY; (S); 6/82; Rep Am Leg Boys St; Aud/Vis; Boy Scts; Computer Clb; Drama Clb; Math Clb; School Musical; Yrbk Phtg; DAR Awd; NHS.

PERRY, SHEILA; Franklin Acad; Malone, NY; (Y); Church Yth Grp; Prfct Atten Awd; Malone Off Prod Bus Awd 84-85; Women Moose Schlrshp 84-85; Epsilon Schl Hnr Scty 83-85; Canton Coll; Data Proc.

PERRY, THOMAS M; West Seneca East HS; West Seneca, NY; (Y); 8/365; Boy Scts; Pres Exploring; Quiz Bowl; Jazz Band; Ftbl; NHS; Ntl Merit Ltr; Chess Clb; Church Yth Grp; Computer Clb; Eagle Scout; German Natl Hnr Soc; Grad Magna Cum Laude; Comp Elec Engrnrng.

PERRY, TODD; Pittsford Sutherland HS; Pittsford, NY; (Y); FCA; Nwsp Rptr; Var Wt Lftg; High Hon Roll; Bsbl; Bsktbl; Var Ftbl; Engr.

PERSAUD, CHANDRA; Norman Thomas HS; Brooklyn, NY; (S); 64/669; Dance Clb; FCA; Prfct Atten Awd; Baruch Coll; Accntng.

PERSAUD, CHANDRADAI ANNIE; John Jay HS; Brooklyn, NY; (Y); 271/537; Cmnty Wkr; Cit Awd; Brnrd M Baruch; Bus.

PERSCHBACH, PENNY; Newfield HS; Selden, NY; (Y); Hosp Aide; Teachers Aide; Var Chorus; Spanish NHS; Natl Spnsh Hnr Soc 85; C W Post; Accntng.

PERSCHE, MICHAEL; Farmingdale HS; Farmingdale, NY; (Y); 10/650; Ski Clb; Varsity Clb; Var L Lcrss; Var L Socr; Hon Roll; Jr NHS; NHS.

PERSICO, JERILYN; St Francis Prep; Bellerose, NY; (Y); 190/704; Church Yth Grp; GAA; Varsity Clb; JV Var Bsktbl; Var Fld Hcky; Var Tennis; Var Trk; Wt Lftg; Rankd 10th USTA/ETA Dbls Ten; Med Tech.

PERSICO, LISA; Amsterdam HS; Amsterdam, NY; (Y); Hosp Aide; Political Wkr; Yrbk Stf; High Hon Roll; Stu Govt Grad Ushr; Oneonta ST; Elem Educ.

PERSON, AMANDA; Broadalbin Central HS; Gloversville, NY; (Y); 18/54; Cmnty Wkr; French Clb; Library Aide; Variety Show; Yrbk Stf; Score Keeper; Stat Socr; High Hon Roll; Hon Roll; Auto Clb Merit Awd 85; 1st PTO Wrtng Cntst 85; Hudson Valley CC; Soc Wrk.

PERSON, JENNIFER; H Frank Carey HS; Garden City So, NY; (Y); 39/228; Hosp Aide; Varsity Clb; Orch; Yrbk Stf; Var L Crs Cntry; Var L Trk; Moorehead U; Secdry Ed.

PERSONTE, TRACY L; Naples Central Schl; Naples, NY; (Y); 27/83; Church Yth Grp; Chorus; Church Choir; Color Guard; Var JV Cheerleading; High Hon Roll; Hon Roll; Sec Sci.

PERVAAZ, JAVEED; Bronx High School Of Science; New York, NY; (Y); Art Clb; Boy Scts; Computer Clb; Math Tm; Science Clb; Yrbk Phtg; High Hon Roll; Hon Roll; NHS; Prfct Atten Awd; 44th Annl Westinghse Sci Tlnt Srch Hnrs Grp 75; NYC Sch Sci Fair 85; NY ST Enrgy Rsch Compt Fnlst.

PESA, NEVEN; Bethpage HS; Bethpage, NY; (Y); 40/290; JV Bowling; Var Ftbl; Var Capt Socr; Var Trk; Hon Roll; Jr NHS; CW Post; Acctng.

PESCE, FRANK; Garden City HS; Garden City, NY; (Y); Camera Clb; Drama Clb; Band; School Play; Socr; Wrstlng.

PESCE, JANINE; St Barnabas HS; Bronx, NY; (Y); 10/150; Church Yth Grp; Cmnty Wkr; GAA; Office Aide; Pres Sr Cls; Var Capt Bsktbl; Sftbl; Vllybl; NHS; NYS Regents Schlrshp, Math Awd 85; Full Acadmc Schlrshp Mercy Coll 85; Mercy Coll; Accntng.

PESCE, LAURA F; St John Villa Acad; Staten Island, NY; (Y); 7/130; Church Yth Grp; Debate Tm; Girl Scts; Intnl Clb; Library Aide; Church Choir; Stage Crew; Variety Show; Cheerleading; Mgr(s); Italian Awd 85; La Morte Lodge Schlrshp 85; Pace U; Cmnctns.

PESCE, ROBERT; Lynbr3ok HS; Lynbrook, NY; (Y); Hon Roll; Mech Engr.

PESNER, JONAH; Bronx High School Of Science; New York, NY; (Y); Cmnty Wkr; Debate Tm; NFL; Political Wkr; Speech Tm; Pres Temple Yth Grp; Rep Frsh Cls; Soph Cls; Rep Stu Cncl; Hon Roll; Ntl Forensic Lgu 83-85; Deg Of Mert, Excllnc, Distntn & Spcl Distntn 83-85; Pride Of NY 83-85; Govrnmt.

PETA JR, JOSEPH; Liverpool HS; Liverpool, NY; (S); 69/850; Drama Clb; Chorus; Jazz Band; Orch; School Musical; School Play; Symp Band; Hon Roll; Jr NHS; NHS; Acdmc All-Amer 85; U Of Miami; Music.

PETER, ANILA; Blessed Sacrement St Gabriel HS; Pelham, NY; (Y); 1/180; Spanish Clb; Teachers Aide; Nwsp Phtg; Yrbk Rptr; Pres Sr Cls; Pres Stu Cncl; Hon Roll; Jr NHS; NHS; Ntl Merit Ltr; Hugh O Brian Ldrshp Ambssdr Awd 83-84; Natl Merit Ltr 84-85; Pre-Med.

PETER, LAURA; St Marys HS; Depew, NY; (S); Camera Clb; Yrbk Stf; Hon Roll; NHS; Bus Mgmnt.

PETERMAN, RENEE; Valley Stream Central HS; Valley Stream, NY; (Y); VP Service Clb; Band; Concert Band; Mrchg Band; Orch; Var Cheerleading; Mgr(s); Var Socr; NHS; Tempo Mus Hnr Soc 83-86; Racquetball 82-86.

PETERMANN, ANNE E; East Aurora HS; E Aurora, NY; (Y); 60/186; Camp Fr Inc; Drama Clb; Chorus; School Musical; Trk; Hon Roll; Jr NHS; Regnts Schlrshp; Geneseo; Bio.

PETERS, BONNIE; St Dominic HS; Syosset, NY; (Y); 40/119; Computer Clb; Drama Clb; Quiz Bowl; Ski Clb; Spanish Clb; Band; School Musical; School Play; Stage Crew; Nwsp Rptr; Wst Palm Awd; Comp Schlrshp; Long Island U; Crmnl Law.

PETERS, DEBBIE; Wellsville HS; Wellsville, NY; (Y); 10/130; Church Yth Grp; Key Clb; School Musical; Nwsp Bus Mgr; Nwsp Rptr; Nwsp Stf; Hon Roll; NHS; Ithaca Coll; Comm.

PETERS, JAMES; St Josephs Collegiate Inst; Cheektowaga, NY; (Y); 31/200; Boy Scts; Stage Crew; Im Bowling; JV Trk; Hon Roll; NHS; Eagl Sct 83; Elctrcl Engrng.

PETERS, JEFF; Beacon HS; Beacon, NY; (S); 21/210; Nwsp Rptr; Bsbl; Ftbl; Hon Roll; Jr NHS; U S Army Mrt Achvt Atltcs 83-84; Dutchess Cc.

PETERS, KEITH; Remsen Central Schl; Remsen, NY; (Y); FFA; Band; Concert Band; Mrchg Band; JV Bsktbl; JV Var Socr; Var Trk; Hon Roll; Awd Ctznshp Eng 85; Air Force Acad; Elctrncs.

PETERS, LEE G; Cortland HS; Cortland, NY; (Y); 26/245; Am Leg Boys St; Varsity Clb; Lit Mag; JV Bsbl; Var Capt Bsktbl; Ftbl; Socr; Wt Lftg; High Hon Roll; NHS; Regents Scholar 85; 1st Tm All Lg Place Kickr 85; Hobart Coll.

PETERS, MICHELLE; Bishop Ford C C HS; Brooklyn, NY; (Y); Bowling; Cheerleading; Swmmng; Trk; Howard U; Psychlgy.

PETERS, SCOTT; Aquinas Inst; Rochester, NY; (Y); 28/163; Spanish Clb; Varsity Clb; Stage Crew; Bsbl; Ice Hcky; Trk; Hon Roll; IPS Achvt Awd 82-83; Rochester Inst Tech; Elec Engr.

PETERS, SHARON; Smithtown H S East; Smithtown, NY; (Y); Cmnty Wkr; Yrbk Rptr; Yrbk Stf; Rep Jr Cls; Rep Stu Cncl; Capt Cheerleading; Trk; Hon Roll; Barbizon Schl Modeling; Fash De.

PETERS JR, THOMAS ANTHONY; Greece Athena HS; Rochester, NY; (Y); 23/258; Boy Scts; DECA; Exploring; JA; Var Capt Socr; High Hon Roll; Hon Roll; NHS; Prfct Atten Awd; Buffalo U; Engr.

PETERSEN, DENISE; Holy Trinity HS; Hicksville, NY; (Y); #25 In Class; French Clb; Pep Clb; Cheerleading; Score Keeper; Hon Roll; NY ST Regents Nrsg Schlrshp 85; Adelphi U; Bus Mngmnt.

PETERSEN, JEFF; Mckee Vo-Tech; Staten Is, NY; (Y); 56/238; Hon Roll; Indus Maint.

PETERSEN, ROCHELLE; Grace Dodge V HS; Bronx, NY; (Y); Church Yth Grp; Cmnty Wkr; Girl Scts; Science Clb; Church Choir; Concert Band; Regstrd Nrs.

PETERSEN, TINA; North Babylon HS; Bronx, NY; (Y); 100/500; Cmnty Wkr; Drama Clb; Intnl Clb; Spanish Clb; Chorus; School Musical; School Play; Variety Show; Var Crs Cntry; Var Gym; Acad Ftnss Awd 85; Spnsh Awd 83; Drama Awd 82; NY U; Bio.

PETERSON, AMY; Linton HS; Schenectady, NY; (Y); Church Yth Grp; Office Aide; Mnstry Tchr.

PETERSON, BARBARA; Central Islip HS; Central Islip, NY; (Y); Dance Clb; Girl Scts; Red Cross Aide; VICA; Band; Concert Band; Mrchg Band; JV Mgr(s); JV Timer; Church Yth Grp; GSA Gld Awd 85; Suffolk Co Edduc Assoc 82; NYS Mus Assoc Mdl 84; Air Force Pilot.

PETERSON, BARBARA; Washingtonville HS; Campbell Hall, NY; (Y); Church Yth Grp; Cmnty Wkr; Drama Clb; Hosp Aide; Band; Color Guard; Flag Corp; Mrchg Band; Cit Awd; High Hon Roll; Young Womens Medallion 85; Camp Crafters 85; BYS.

PETERSON, ELIZABETH; Delaware Valley Central HS; Hankins, NY; (S); 3/38; Church Yth Grp; Drama Clb; Acpl Chr; Chorus; School Musical; School Play; Yrbk Stf; Var L Cheerleading; High Hon Roll; NHS; All-St Mixed Chorus 84; Natl Chrldng Assn Natl Comp 83; Sullivan Cnty Fire Prev Wk Poster 84.

PETERSON, GINGER; Southampton HS; Southampton, NY; (Y); 9/105; Drama Clb; Ski Clb; Spanish Clb; Nwsp Rptr; Lit Mag; Var Sftbl; Hon Roll; Jr NHS; NHS; Rotary Awd; Phy Thrpy.

PETERSON, KEITH E; Harborfields HS; Centerport, NY; (Y); Boy Scts; Church Yth Grp; Computer Clb; Mathletes; Concert Band; Mrchg Band; Nwsp Stf; Yrbk Stf; JV Wrstlng; NHS; Outstndng Achvt Chem Awd 85; Pres Acadmc Fit Awd 85; Regnts Clg Schlrshp 85; Cornell U; Biochem.

PETERSON, KIM; Hornell SR HS; Hornell, NY; (Y); Church Yth Grp; Ski Clb; Band; Concert Band; Yrbk Phtg; Yrbk Sprt Ed; Yrbk Stf; JV Var Cheerleading; High Hon Roll; Hon Roll.

PETERSON, QUANDELIN; Cathedral HS; Ny, NY; (Y); Library Aide; Teachers Aide; Chorus; Church Choir; Hon Roll; Prfct Atten Awd; Hofstra U; Med.

PETERSON, ROBERT; East Meadow HS; East Meadow, NY; (S); 40/414; Hosp Aide; Concert Band; Mrchg Band; Orch; Symp Band; JV Bsktbl; Hon Roll; NHS; NY ST Regents Schlrshp 85; Nassau Cnty Med Ctr Volntr Awd 84; Vrsty Lttr Mrchng Band 84; Engrng.

PETERSON, SHARON; Vestal Central HS; Endicott, NY; (Y); Church Yth Grp; Dance Clb; French Clb; High Hon Roll.

PETERSON, TAMMY; Westmoreland Central HS; Westmoreland, NY; (Y); Church Yth Grp; FHA; GAA; Band; Church Choir; Mrchg Band; Pep Band; Trk; Vllybl; High Hon Roll; MUCC; Comp Mgmt.

PETERSON-SMALL, KELLY; Bishop Loughlin Memorial HS; Brooklyn, NY; (Y); Dance Clb; Drama Clb; Teachers Aide; Chorus; School Play; Yrbk Rptr; Yrbk Stf; Cit Awd; High Hon Roll; Sal; Acadmc Achvt Of Mth 83; Hghst Achvr Soc Studies Medal 82; Pace U; Nrsng.

PETHICK, TRACEY; Schoharie Central HS; Schoharie, NY; (S); 15/94; Sec Key Clb; Trs Varsity Clb; Yrbk Stf; Capt Socr; L Trk; High Hon Roll; Geneseo ST; Med Tech.

PETILLI, STEPHEN G; Roy C Ketcham HS; Poughkeepsie, NY; (Y); Boy Scts; Church Yth Grp; Computer Clb; Band; Concert Band; Stu Cncl; JV Ftbl; High Hon Roll; Hon Roll; NHS; IBM Bsbl All Str 84; Elctrcl Engrng.

PETISI, PAULA; E J Wilson HS; Rochester, NY; (Y); Dance Clb; Sec Varsity Clb; Chorus; School Musical; Rep Frsh Cls; Rep Soph Cls; Rep Jr Cls; Stu Cncl; JV Var Cheerleading; NHS; 1st Pl Dane Comp Invitational Jazz 85; Top Ten Beauty Pageant 83; Hm-Cmng Queen 84-85.

PETIT, MARIE; Northeastern Acad; Brooklyn, NY; (S); #3 In Class; Church Yth Grp; Hosp Aide; Acpl Chr; Band; Church Choir; School Play; Frsh Cls; Soph Cls; Sftbl; NHS; Ntl Sci Merit Awd; Ntl Engl Merit Awd; Oakwood Coll; Psych.

PETIX, MICHAEL; Grand Island HS; Grand Island, NY; (Y); 80/330; Computer Clb; Mathletes; Ski Clb; Varsity Clb; Stu Cncl; Var Capt Ice Hcky; Var L Lcrss; Var L Socr; Chess Clb; Church Yth Grp; Podiatrist.

PETKOVSEK, WILLIAM; Little Falls Central Schl; Little Falls, NY; (Y); Spanish Clb; JV Var Bsbl; JV Var Bsktbl; JV Var Crs Cntry; HCCC; Bus.

PETKUS, ANNMARIE A; Division Avenue HS; Levittown, NY; (Y); 11/352; Cmnty Wkr; Concert Band; Jazz Band; Sec Trs Frsh Cls; Trs Soph Cls; Trs Jr Cls; Trs Sr Cls; Var L Tennis; High Hon Roll; Aud/Vis; Oustndng Band 83-84; Tricia Kanaby Memrl Sprtsmnshp Awd 84-85; George Fodor Memrl Humntrn Awd 84-85; SUNY Oneonta; Secy Ed.

PETLEY, THEODORE D; Norwich HS; Norwich, NY; (Y); Am Leg Boys St; Math Tm; High Hon Roll; Hon Roll; Ntl Merit Ltr; Capt Var Rifle Tm 84-85; Supa-English, Sclty & Calculus 85-86; Engr.

PETOSA, THERESA; Solvay HS; Solvay, NY; (Y); 17/170; Church Yth Grp; Math Clb; Chorus; School Musical; Variety Show; Off Frsh Cls; Pres Soph Cls; Off Jr Cls; Off Sr Cls; Var Capt Bsktbl; Bio Awd 83; Engl Awd 82; Le Moyne Coll; Envirnmntl Sci.

PETRAGLIA, LAURA; Lincoln HS; Yonkers, NY; (S); 7/425; Art Clb; Drama Clb; School Play; Nwsp Rptr; High Hon Roll; NHS; Natl Art Hnr Scty 85.

PETRAGNANI, DARREN; Bishop Grimes HS; Syracuse, NY; (Y); 30/150; Hosp Aide; Chorus; School Musical; Variety Show; Rep Frsh Cls; Rep Soph Cls; Rep Jr Cls; JV Bsbl; Bsktbl; JV Socr; Radio.

PETRAITIS, GLENN; John H Glenn HS; E Northport, NY; (Y); Church Yth Grp; Varsity Clb; JV Bsktbl; JV Lcrss; Var Socr; Hon Roll; Chorus; Nwsp Stf; Law Clb 83-85; SADD 84; Pre-Law.

PETRANCHUK, AMY; Indian River Central HS; Evans Mills, NY; (Y); Chorus; School Play; Sec Frsh Cls; VP Soph Cls; Var JV Cheerleading; Var JV Sftbl; Var Tennis; Var Trk; Chrldng Awds 84 & 85; Bus Mgt.

PETRAS, JENNIFER; Auburn HS; Auburn, NY; (Y); Church Yth Grp; VP Drama Clb; Ski Clb; Chorus; School Musical; School Play; Stage Crew; JV Tennis; High Hon Roll; NHS; Int Arch.

PETRAUSKAS, BARBARA ANN; Corcoran HS; Syracuse, NY; (Y); Am Leg Aux Girls St; School Musical; Crs Cntry; NHS; GAA; Pres Spanish Clb; Band; Hon Roll; Cmnty Schlr 85; Herald Jrnl Paper Crrier 83.

PETRI, ELIZABETH M; Sachem HS; Holbrook, NY; (Y); 6/1430; Math Tm; Science Clb; Service Clb; Orch; Ed Lit Mag; Stu Cncl; Jr NHS; NHS.

PETRICCIONE, PETER; St Anthonys HS; E Northport, NY; (Y); 8/490; JV Bsbl; JV Bsktbl; Im Bowling; NHS; Spanish NHS; Regnts Schlrshp 85; Untd Italn Amer Progress Schlrshp 85; Italn Natl Hnr Socty; Polytechnic Inst NY; Chem Engr.

PETRIE, JENNIE; Rome Free Acad; Rome, NY; (Y); Varsity Clb; Trs Soph Cls; Trs Jr Cls; JV Var Fld Hcky; JV Var Sftbl; JV Var Vllybl; DAR Awd; Hon Roll; Trs Jr NHS; NHS; Hghst Acad Avg Indstrl Arts 82-83; Teugega Cntry Clb Girls JR Golf Chmpn 82; Psych.

PETRIE, RUSSELL C; Waterville Central HS; Oriskany Falls, NY; (Y); Am Leg Boys St; Varsity Clb; Concert Band; Yrbk Stf; VP Soph Cls; Rep Stu Cncl; Capt Socr; Cit Awd; NHS; Ski Clb; Local Rotary Awd 85; SUNY.

PETRILLO, RICHARD; Mt Vernon HS; Scarsdale, NY; (Y); Am Leg Boys St; Hosp Aide; Key Clb; Ski Clb; VP Jr Cls; Var Capt Bsbl; High Hon Roll; Bsbl Sports Awd All Leag Hnrbl Mntn 85.

PETRILLO, SUE; Whitesboro SR HS; Whitesboro, NY; (Y); Church Yth Grp; Science Clb; Variety Show; JV Score Keeper; High Hon Roll; Vet.

PETRILLO, VINCENT; Lindenhurst HS; Lindenhurst, NY; (Y); Boy Scts; Science Clb; Hon Roll; NHS; Cert Of Cmmndtn Itln 84; Itln Clb 83-85; Stu For Scl Rspnsblty 84-85; Cornell U; Astrphyscs.

PETRIZZO, CATHY; West Hempstead HS; W Hempstead, NY; (Y); Drama Clb; Ski Clb; School Play; Rep Frsh Cls; Var Badmtn; Var Swmmng; Hon Roll; Sci, Bus Math, & Accntng Outstndng Achvt 83-85; SUNY Schls; Accntng.

PETRO, KIMBERLEY; Binghamton HS; Binghamton, NY; (Y); Art Clb; Girl Scts; Ski Clb; Band; Chorus; Concert Band; Jazz Band; Mrchg Band; Orch; Pep Band; SUNY Potsdam; Mus Educ.

PETROCELLI, GREGG; Holy Cross HS; Bayside, NY; (Y); 34/350; Church Yth Grp; Letterman Clb; Nwsp Rptr; Var Bsbl; JV Socr; Hon Roll; NHS; Prfct Atten Awd; St Johns; Comp Sci.

PETROCONE, ROBERT; Mineola HS; Mineola, NY; (Y); Boy Scts; Computer Clb; English Clb; Key Clb; Lit Mag; High Hon Roll; Hon Roll; Aero Engrng.

PETRONE, MARIE; Academy Of Mount Saint Ursula; Bronx, NY; (Y); Trs Camera Clb; Church Yth Grp; Yrbk Bus Mgr; Yrbk Phtg; Cheerleading; Med.

PETRONI, GINO; Archbishop Molloy HS; Flushing, NY; (Y); 92/361; Church Yth Grp; Cmnty Wkr; Computer Clb; Nwsp Stf; Ed Yrbk Stf; Im Bowling; Hon Roll; NHS; Itln Clb Treas 84-85; Tutrng Clb 83, 85; Iona Lang Cntst Itln 1st & 2nd Hnrs 83 & 84; Fordham U; Bus Adm.

PETRONIS, SHELLY; Lansingburgh HS; Troy, NY; (Y); Computer Clb; Spanish Clb; Teachers Aide; Nwsp Ed-Chief; Yrbk Phtg; Rep Stu Cncl; Capt Cheerleading; 4-H Awd; High Hon Roll; Jr NHS; Louis C Smith Schlrshp 84-85; Troy Wmns Clb Schlrshp 85; Rensselaer Polytech Inst Schlrshp 85; Rensselaer Polytech Inst; Bio.

PETROV, ANDREW; Clarkstown North HS; New City, NY; (Y); Boy Scts; Church Yth Grp; Exploring; Ski Clb; Ice Hcky; Socr; Swmmng; Trk; Wt Lftg; High Hon Roll.

PETROZAK, BRENDA; Middletown HS; Middletown, NY; (Y); Key Clb; Acpl Chr; Chorus; School Musical; School Play; Swing Chorus; Var Cheerleading; Hon Roll; NHS; Acad Achvt Awd Outstndng Achvt In Soc Studies 85; Mst Imprvd Chrldr Awd 85; Miss Ulster Area Tnagr 85; Syracuse U; Comm.

PETRUCCO, ARLEEN E; St Francis Prep; Bayside, NY; (Y); 3/690; Band; Concert Band; School Musical; School Play; Stage Crew; Nwsp Rptr; Gov Hon Prg Awd; High Hon Roll; NHS; Ntl Merit Ltr; City Comptrllr Awd 85; St Johns Excell & Comptv Schlrshp 85; SUNY-BUFFALO Pres Schlrshp 85; St Johns U; Pharm.

PETRULLI, DONNA; Bethpage HS; Bethpage, NY; (Y); #10 In Class; Art Clb; VP Trs French Clb; Mathletes; Sec Chorus; Nwsp Stf; High Hon Roll; Hon Roll; NHS; Acctng,Chorus,Frnch Awd; Acctng.

PETRULLO, MICHAEL; Mount St Michael Acad; Bronx, NY; (Y); 10/308; JV Bsbl; JV Bsktbl; JV Var Ftbl; JV Var Socr; JV Var Wt Lftg; Hon Roll; NHS; Spanish NHS; Albany ST; Pol Sci.

PETRY, JEFF; Jamestown HS; Jamestown, NY; (Y); 5/405; Ski Clb; Band; Concert Band; Drm & Bgl; Jazz Band; Mrchg Band; Stat Bsktbl; Var Socr; Capt L Tennis; Wt Lftg; Amer Lgn Awd 82; Legsltv Intern 84; James Prentergast Schlrshp & Hon Soc Schlr 85; Jamestown CC; Econ.

PETRY, NANCY; Jamestown HS; Jamestwon, NY; (Y); Church Yth Grp; Trs Debate Tm; Sec Trs Latin Clb; Political Wkr; Spanish Clb; Chorus; Rep Stu Cncl; High Hon Roll; Jr NHS; Sec NHS; Oral Voctns Ltn 84-85; Norman H Tinkham Awd 85; Pre Med.

PETSCHKE, CHRISTINE; Kenmore East HS; Kenmore, NY; (Y); Church Yth Grp; Dance Clb; Math Clb; Band; Color Guard; Concert Band; Pom Pon; High Hon Roll; NHS; Engnr.

PETTAWAY, DONALD; Hempstead HS; Hempstead, NY; (Y); Art Clb; Computer Clb; FCA; Var Bsktbl; Hon Roll; Ceta Prog Job Opprtnts 82-83; Johnson C Smith U; Auto Engrng.

PETTERSEN, DONNA; St Peters H S For Girls; Staten Island, NY; (Y); Cmnty Wkr; FNA; Office Aide; Chorus; Church Choir; Swing Chorus; Yrbk Stf; SI Coll; Prmry Educ.

PETTFIELD, STEVEN A; Westlake HS; Hawthorne, NY; (Y); Am Leg Boys St; Church Yth Grp; Yrbk Stf; Rep Jr Cls; JV Var Bsktbl; JV Var Ftbl; Var Trk; Hon Roll; Rec Stu Outstndng Amer Stud; Pace U; Bus.

PETTI, ANGELA J; St Barnabas HS; Yonkers, NY; (Y); 36/157; Cmnty Wkr; Office Aide; Teachers Aide; Hon Roll; 2nd Hnrs 85; Iona Coll; Lib Arts.

PETTI, DAVID A; Mount Saint Michael Acad; Bronx, NY; (S); 2/308; Chess Clb; Lit Mag; Stu Cncl; Crs Cntry; Trk; Hon Roll; NHS; Spanish NHS; Lit Magzn Shrt Stry Cntst Wnnr 84; Lit Magzn Poetry Cntst Wnnr 85.

PETTIT, ALLYSON; Greenville Central HS; Earlton, NY; (Y); 16/92; Am Leg Aux Girls St; Drama Clb; Key Clb; Teachers Aide; Trs Sr Cls; Capt Bsktbl; Hon Roll; Chorus; Yrbk Stf; Score Keeper; Greenville Repblcn Clb Awd 85; Greenville Demcrtc Clb Awd 85; Millie Simpson Mem Awd 85; Hudson Valley CC; Mrktng.

PETTIT, JOEL D; La Fargeville Central School HS; Clayton, NY; (Y); Am Leg Boys St; Chorus; School Play; Pres Stu Cncl; JV Var Bsktbl; Var Socr; High Hon Roll; Hon Roll; Annual Stu Cnty Gvmnt Day 84; Jfrsn CC; Comp Sci.

PETTIT, KENNETH F; Minisink Valley Central HS; Middletown, NY; (Y); #17 In Class; Pres Key Clb; Ski Clb; Band; Concert Band; Jazz Band; Mrchg Band; Stage Crew; Yrbk Stf; Rep Frsh Cls; Var Socr; NY ST Regents Schlrshp 85; U Of MD; Aerospace Engrng.

PETTIT, MARK; Johnstown HS; Johnstown, NY; (Y); 50/250; Boy Scts; ROTC; Ftbl; Trk; Wrstlng; Hon Roll; Navy; Nuclr Sci.

PETTUS JR, RICHARD S; New Dorp HS; New York, NY; (Y); Am Leg Boys St; Mathletes; Capt Math Tm; Office Aide; Teachers Aide; Nwsp Rptr; Hon Roll; Jr NHS; NHS; Prfct Atten Awd; Sci Fair Ctywde Wnr U S Army Navy & Savitt Sci Awd 84; Metro NY Mth Gold Mdlst 84; NYC Acad Olymp 85; Sci.

PETZEN, LISA; Wellsville HS; Shinglehouse, PA; (Y); Band; Jazz Band; Mrchg Band; School Musical; Nwsp Rptr; Nwsp Sprt Ed; Nwsp Stf; Score Keeper; Trk; High Hon Roll; Pre-Law.

PETZOLD, JOHN; Wantagh HS; Seaford, NY; (Y); 81/291; Computer Clb; Ski Clb; Im Capt Bsktbl; Capt L Ftbl; Capt L Lcrss; Var L Wrstlng; Hon Roll; Science Clb; Im Capt Vllybl; Im Wt Lftg; Am Leg Cert Schl Awd 84; Mark Hnatt Mem Schlrshp 85; Queens Coll; Acctng.

PEYMAN, ZANDIEH; St Francis Prep; Whitestone, NY; (S); 26/693; Drama Clb; Science Clb; Concert Band; Jazz Band; Mrchg Band; School Musical; Vllybl; High Hon Roll; NHS; Academic All American Schlr Awd; Medicine.

PEYTON, DONNA M; Far Rockaway HS; Far Rockaway, NY; (Y); 20/500; Church Yth Grp; Cmnty Wkr; English Clb; Key Clb; Keywanettes; Natl Beta Clb; Office Aide; Service Clb; Teachers Aide; Band; Arista Awd 85; Peer Alpha Systm 85; Intership Awd 83-85; Hofstra; Bus Adm.

PEZONE, BETH; Notre Dame Acad; Staten Island, NY; (Y); Hosp Aide; Pep Clb; Science Clb; Acpl Chr; Yrbk Stf; Cheerleading; Hon Roll; Jr NHS; NHS.

PEZZINO, LISA; Kenmore East SR HS; Kenmore, NY; (Y); Art Clb; Computer Clb; Girl Scts; School Musical; Trs Sr Cls; Var Capt Vllybl; Nursing.

PFAFF, KRISTEN; Clarkstown H S North; New City, NY; (Y); 29/450; Church Yth Grp; Exploring; French Clb; Ski Clb; Band; Rep Jr Cls; JV Var Twrlr; High Hon Roll; Hon Roll; Jr NHS; Notre Dame; Law.

PFEIFER, AUDREY; Westhampton Beach HS; Remsenburg, NY; (Y); Church Yth Grp; Teachers Aide; Drill Tm; Var Gym; Spec Ed Tchr.

PFEIFER, LORI; Fontbonne Hall Acad; Brooklyn, NY; (Y); 6/130; Math Tm; Pom Pon; Tennis; High Hon Roll; Law.

PFEIFFER, MARCIA; Alden Central HS; Lancaster, NY; (Y); Art Clb; Camera Clb; Church Yth Grp; Science Clb; Yrbk Stf; Im Vllybl; Acadmc Awd Acadmc & Extrcrrclr Achvt 85.

PFEUFFER, WENDY MARIE; Rome Free Acad; Rome, NY; (Y); 7/536; Church Yth Grp; Drama Clb; Girl Scts; Nwsp Stf; Yrbk Stf; Var L Swmmng; Jr NHS; NHS; Griffiss Offcrs Wvs Clb Schlrshp 85; Slngrlnd Prz, Spkng Cntst, 1st 84; Oyaron Schlrshp 85; Hartwck Coll; Hstry.

PFIESTER, CHRISTINE; Tully Central HS; Tully, NY; (Y); Drama Clb; Hosp Aide; Spanish Clb; Varsity Clb; School Musical; Yrbk Phtg; Sec Sr Cls; Cheerleading; Socr; Sftbl; Psych.

PFROMMER, LISA K; Wayne Central HS; Ontario, NY; (Y); 9/201; Am Leg Aux Girls St; Girl Scts; Math Tm; Chorus; Concert Band; Stage Crew; Bsktbl; Score Keeper; Socr; High Hon Roll; Purdue U; Engrng.

PFUNDSTEIN, THOMAS; Nazareth Regional HS; Brooklyn, NY; (Y); 19/260; Var Bsbl; JV L Crs Cntry; JV L Trk; High Hon Roll; Hon Roll; NHS; Coachs Awd Track 83; Polytechnic Inst-NY; Elec Engr.

PFUNTNER, KIMBERLEY PFUNTNER; Geneseo Central HS; Geneseo, NY; (Y); #13 In Class; Pres 4-H; Ski Clb; Varsity Clb; Stu Cncl; Bsktbl; Socr; Vllybl; Hon Roll; Jr NHS; NHS; Miss Schl Spirit 83-84; Geneseo Vrsty Girls Sccr MIP 84-85; Syracuse U; Sprts Med.

PHAM, NGOC; Liverpool HS; Liverpool, NY; (S); 41/792; Chess Clb; Church Yth Grp; Computer Clb; Exploring; French Clb; Trs JA; Library Aide; Hon Roll; Jr NHS; NHS; Data Processing I & II 83; UCLA; Electrical Engineering.

PHAM, PHUONG U; Curtis Ny; Staten Island, NY; (Y); Math Clb; Math Tm; Hon Roll; Awd At French Contest 84; Honor Key 85; Regents Schlrshp 85; Engrng.

PHARMER, ANDREW; Lake George HS; Lk George, NY; (Y); Art Clb; School Play; Stage Crew; Variety Show; Lit Mag; Hon Roll; Stu Mnth In Art; Art.

PHARR, BRIDGETTE ROLANDA; Westlake HS; Pleasantville, NY; (Y); 36/152; Church Yth Grp; Debate Tm; French Clb; Pres Church Choir; Concert Band; Mrchg Band; Hon Roll; Rotary Awd; DE ST Coll; Acctg.

PHELIX, RANDAL; Norwood-Norfolk HS; Chase Mills, NY; (Y); Latin Clb; Jazz Band; Mrchg Band; Stage Crew; JV Socr; Hon Roll; High Hnr Rl Cert 83; SUNY; Sci.

PHELPS, DAVID; Camden Central HS; Camden, NY; (Y); Pres Church Yth Grp; Cmnty Wkr; Varsity Clb; Jazz Band; Var JV Bsbl; Var L Crs Cntry; Var L Ftbl; Var L Vllybl; Hon Roll; Rotary Awd; Am Leg Bsbl 84-85; Rotary Club Acad Ath Awds 84-85; Cortland St; Crimnl Just.

PHELPS, DENISE; Alexander Central Schl; Darien Center, NY; (S); Trs Spanish Clb; Varsity Clb; Band; Chorus; Jazz Band; Swing Chorus; Var Capt Bsktbl; Var Sftbl; Var Vllybl; NHS; All Amer Hall Fame Band Hnrs 84.

PHELPS, KITTY L; John C Birdlebough HS; Fulton, NY; (Y); 13/190; Cmnty Wkr; Stat Timer; Var L Trk; Wt Lftg; High Hon Roll; Hon Roll; Prfct Atten Awd.

PHELPS, MICHELLE; Alexander Central Schl; Darien Center, NY; (S); 9/89; Spanish Clb; Teachers Aide; Band; Off Jr Cls; Rep Stu Cncl; Var Cheerleading; Var Sftbl; Var Swmmng; Jr NHS; NHS; Merit Tuition Awd 85; Genessee CC; Bus Mgmnt.

PHELPS, RICHARD B; Remsen Central HS; Remsen, NY; (Y); Pres Church Yth Grp; Pres Band; Pres Concert Band; Pres Jazz Band; Pres Mrchg Band; Yrbk Stf; Sec Frsh Cls; JV Capt Bsktbl; JV Capt Socr; Mohawk Valley; Nrsng.

PHIFER, LISA; Ossining HS; Ossining, NY; (Y); Church Yth Grp; Acpl Chr; Band; Church Choir; Concert Band; Mrchg Band; Orch; Symp Band; High Hon Roll; Hon Roll; Ossing Schrlshp Pin 85; Howard U; Bus.

PHILBIN, MICHAEL; Fairport HS; Fairport, NY; (Y); Drama Clb; Spanish Clb; School Play; Stage Crew; Yrbk Bus Mgr; VP Sr Cls; Hon Roll; NHS; Ntl Merit Ltr; Spanish NHS; Law.

PHILIE, DANIELLE; East Islip HS; East Islip, NY; (Y); Hon Roll.

PHILIPPS, PEGGY; Williamsville North HS; Amherst, NY; (S); DECA; Girl Scts; Ski Clb; Phy Thrpy.

PHILIPS, ALLISON; Central Islip HS; Islip Terrace, NY; (Y); 14/431; Office Aide; Band; Drm Mjr(t); Mrchg Band; School Musical; Stage Crew; Nwsp Stf; JV Mgr(s); JV Sftbl; Hon Roll; Spec Ed.

PHILIPS, WARD A; Hadley-Luzerne Central Schl; Hadley, NY; (Y); 2/70; Church Yth Grp; Band; School Play; Yrbk Stf; Lit Mag; Var L JA; Var Tennis; NHS; Sal; Aud/Vis; Army & Marine Schlrshps 85; US Mltry Acad; Mech Engrng.

PHILLIP, DI-ANN; Nazareth Regional HS; Brooklyn, NY; (Y); Acpl Chr; Chorus; School Musical; JV Mgr(s); JV Score Keeper; Sftbl; High Hon Roll; Hon Roll; NHS; Engl Awd 85; Singing Awd 84 & 85; NYU; Med.

PHILLIPS, ANN MARIE; Highland HS; Highland, NY; (Y); 22/130; Camera Clb; Church Yth Grp; GAA; School Play; Yrbk Phtg; Sec Jr Cls; Sec Stu Cncl; Stat Socr; Sftbl; Hon Roll; Ntl Cncl Tchrs Eng Awd 85.

PHILLIPS, BILL; Mont Pleasant HS; Schenectady, NY; (Y); 3/250; Am Leg Boys St; Boy Scts; Church Yth Grp; Concert Band; Jazz Band; Mrchg Band; NHS; Spanish NHS; Aud/Vis; Spanish Clb; RPI Math/Sci Awd 85; Elec Engrng.

PHILLIPS, CHRISTINE; Cleveland Hill HS; Cheektowaga, NY; (Y); VP Church Yth Grp; Cmnty Wkr; VP FHA; GAA; Hosp Aide; Teachers Aide; Band; L Sftbl; Capt L Swmmng; CC Awd; Prnt Tchrs Assn Schlrshp 85; Buffalo ST Coll; Spcl Educ.

PHILLIPS, DEBORAH; New Berlin Central HS; New Berlin, NY; (Y); Church Yth Grp; VP French Clb; Band; Concert Band; Jazz Band; Mrchg Band; Yrbk Ed-Chief; Pres Jr Cls; Pres Sr Cls; Rep Stu Cncl; Cert Hnr 84; Natl Sci Merit Awd Bio 84, Chem 85; Bus.

PHILLIPS, DONNA; St Edmund HS; Brooklyn, NY; (S); 17/187; Cmnty Wkr; French Clb; Hosp Aide; Varsity Clb; Im Bsktbl; Var L Sftbl; Var L Vllybl; Hon Roll; Ldrshp, Chem Awd 84; SUNY Stonybrook; Phys Therapy.

PHILLIPS, GRAHAM V; John Jay HS; Katonah, NY; (Y); 5/290; Church Yth Grp; JV Var Bsbl; JV Bsktbl; Hon Roll; St Schlr; NY St Regents Schlrshp 85-89; Syracuse U; Eng.

PHILLIPS, JAMES; Rochester Christian HS; Rochester, NY; (S); 1/14; Chorus; Church Choir; Orch; Yrbk Stf; Trs Stu Cncl; Capt Bsktbl; Capt Socr; Trk; Hon Roll; Prfct Atten Awd; Rochester Christn H S Sprtsmnshp Awd 84; Ed.

PHILLIPS, JOANN; Cardinal Spellman HS; Bronx, NY; (Y); Science Clb; Service Clb; Ski Clb; High Hon Roll; Thrpst.

PHILLIPS, KRISTINE; Amsterdam HS; Amsterdam, NY; (Y); Sec Trs 4-H; Band; Concert Band; Mrchg Band; 4-H Awd; Radio/TV Brdcstng.

PHILLIPS, LAUREEN; Sacred Heart Acad; Buffalo, NY; (Y); 12/145; Church Yth Grp; Science Clb; Spanish Clb; Stage Crew; Nwsp Stf; Yrbk Stf; High Hon Roll; Hon Roll; Engrng.

PHILLIPS, LAURIE; Frontier Central HS; Lakeview, NY; (Y); 13/250; Church Yth Grp; Girl Scts; Latin Clb; Pep Clb; Band; Concert Band; Mrchg Band; JV Cheerleading; Im Tennis; Hon Roll; Bus Adm.

PHILLIPS, OCTOBER M; Salamanca Central HS; Warrington, FL; (Y); Pres Church Yth Grp; Drama Clb; Spanish Clb; Chorus; Concert Band; Mrchg Band; Pep Band; Hon Roll; Potsdam Coll; Engl.

PHILLIPS, RENEE; Frontier HS; Hamburg, NY; (Y); Pep Clb; Pres Jr Cls; Co-Capt Cheerleading; JR Cls Hmcmng Attndnt 84; Natl Chrldrs Assn All Amer Finlst 84.

PHILLIPS, ROBERT; Bishop Scully HS; Amsterdam, NY; (Y); 16/56; Church Yth Grp; Computer Clb; Varsity Clb; Nwsp Sprt Ed; Rep Stu Cncl; Var Bsbl; Var Capt Bsktbl; High Hon Roll; Hon Roll; NHS; Hghst Avg Awd Bus Cours 84; Bus Mgt.

PHILLIPS, ROBERT; Springville-Griffith Inst & C S; Colden, NY; (Y); 16/201; Am Leg Boys St; Boy Scts; Church Yth Grp; Church Choir; Ftbl; Trk; Wrstlng; High Hon Roll; NHS; MVP Wrstlng 84-85.

PHILLIPS, ROGER; Mahopac HS; Mahopac, NY; (Y); 143/400; Wrstlng; Stu Mnth Art Dept; Var Ltr; Channel B Stu Art Fest Awd; SUNY Purchase; Fine Art.

PHILLIPS, SCOTT; Stillwater Central HS; Stillwater, NY; (Y); 10/100; Math Tm; Capt Ftbl; Var Wrstlng; High Hon Roll; Hon Roll; NHS; Union Coll; Elec Engrng.

PHILLIPS, THERESA; Mc Kee Technical HS; Staten Island, NY; (Y); 72/271; Hon Roll; ICS; Intr Decrtng.

PHILLIPS, VERNYL; Mout Saint Michael Acad; Bronx, NY; (S); 41/308; Chess Clb; Computer Clb; Im Bsktbl; Im Ftbl; Im Sftbl; Trk; Hon Roll; JV Ice Hcky; Mns Clb Schlrshp 84; Bus.

PHILMON, CAROL; Nazareth Acad; Rochester, NY; (Y); Church Yth Grp; Dance Clb; FBLA; Girl Scts; Math Tm; Red Cross Aide; Science Clb; Chorus; Color Guard; Yrbk Stf; Bus Wmn Quarter 84-85; John Steinbeck Awd 84-85; MCC; Accntnt.

PHILPOTTS, YOLANDA O; William H Maxwell Vocational HS; Brooklyn, NY; (Y); 8/255; Teachers Aide; Nwsp Rptr; Pres Jr Cls; Capt Sftbl; High Hon Roll; NHS; Comptrollers Awd For Econ 85; Columbia Pitctures & NY Post Sylvester Awd 85; NYC Tech Coll; Med Tech.

PHIPPEN, MARY JANE; Paul V Moore HS; Central Square, NY; (Y); 21/302; Church Yth Grp; Ski Clb; Trs Soph Cls; Sec Jr Cls; Stat Bsktbl; Var Trk; High Hon Roll; NHS; Gld Key Art Awd 85; Jr Prom Qn 84; Central City Bus Inst.

PHOENIX, RHONDA; Walton JR SR HS; Walton, NY; (Y); FHA; Cheerleading; Wt Lftg; Bus.

PHUNG, THUY; Walton HS; Brooklyn, NY; (S); Math Tm; Band; Variety Show; Sec NHS; Prfct Atten Awd; 1st Prz Natl Career Wk Postr 83; Cert NY City Brd Ed Acad Olym Squad 84; U Of Rochester; Math.

PIACENTINO, DAVID D; Notre Dame HS; Utica, NY; (Y); 82/175; Church Yth Grp; FBLA; Yrbk Stf; Capt L Bsbl; Im Bsktbl; High Hon Roll; COL All Star Shortstop 84 & 85; MVP Catholic Yth Orgnztn Bsktbl 84 & 85; Utica Coll; Bus Admin.

PIACITELLI, FRANK; Cazenovia HS; Cazenovia, NY; (Y); Drama Clb; Chorus; School Musical; School Play; JV Tennis; High Hon Roll; Hon Roll; Prfct Atten Awd.

PIAGENTINI, DEBORAH; Deer Park HS; Deer Park, NY; (Y); 65/422; Art Clb; Camera Clb; Computer Clb; English Clb; Orch; Yrbk Stf; Lit Mag; Rep Stu Cncl; Var Socr; Var Sftbl; Finea Rt Awd Fetsvl Best Show 83; Most Artistc Cls 83; Deer Pk Booster Clb Spirit Awd Sftbl 85; Physcl Thrpy.

PIAGNERI, PAUL A; St Johns Prep HS; Astoria, NY; (Y); 89/415; Boys Clb Am; Ski Clb; Varsity Clb; Rep Sr Cls; Rep Stu Cncl; Bsbl; Bowling; Coach Actv; Ftbl; Mgr(s); St Johns U; Bus Admin.

PIANELLA, MARIA L; Driskany Central HS; Rome, NY; (Y); 62/99; Varsity Clb; VICA; Variety Show; Capt Bsktbl; L Socr; Var Capt Trk; Vllybl; Exploring; Spanish Clb; Chorus; Intr-Vly Leag All-Star Track; Mark R Montgomery Mem/Athl Awd MVP; Empire ST Games Trck 84; Mohawk Valley CC; Nrs.

PIANO, JOHN; Greece Olympia HS; Rochester, NY; (Y); 50/300; Letterman Clb; Ski Clb; Varsity Clb; Yrbk Stf; Capt Ftbl; Trk; Wt Lftg; Hon Roll; Regents Schlrshp 85; Syracuse U Schlrshp 85; Syracuse U; Lib Arts.

PIANTO, DEIRDRE MARIE; Commack High School North; Commack, NY; (Y); Aud/Vis; Office Aide; Teachers Aide; Im Mgr(s); Im Score Keeper; JV Trk; Hon Roll; Busnss.

PIARULLI, FRED; Greece Athena HS; Rochester, NY; (Y); 30/260; Church Yth Grp; Latin Clb; Science Clb; Var Bsktbl; JV Ftbl; Var Golf; Im Socr; Hon Roll; MVP-VRSTY Golf Team 83-84; Shootng Awd-Bsktbl 83-84; Coaches Sportsmnshp Awd-Ftbl 82-83; Engrng.

PIAZZA, JOANNE M; Rome Free Acad; Rome, NY; (Y); 150/512; Intnl Clb; Chorus; School Play; Im Crs Cntry; Hon Roll; NHS; Mr Capparelli Mem Schlrshp 85; Good Attndnc Awd At BOCES 85; Agri & Tech Coll; Comp Info Sys.

PIAZZA, LISA; Nazareth Regional HS; Brooklyn, NY; (Y).

PICARD, NANCY; Dominican Commercial HS; Queens Vlge, NY; (Y); Intnl Clb; Chorus; Church Choir; School Musical; Yrbk Stf; High Hon Roll; Hon Roll; Biochem.

PICARDI, CHRISTINA; Paul D Schreiber HS; Port Washington, NY; (Y); 141/413; Cmnty Wkr; Trs PAVAS; Ski Clb; Trs Band; Concert Band; Mrchg Band; Symp Band; Trs Variety Show; Yrbk Stf; Trs Soph Cls; Chld Psych.

PICARIELLO, JIMMY; St Raymond High Schl For Boys; Bronx, NY; (Y); 4/184; Math Tm; JV Bsbl; Im Bsktbl; JV Crs Cntry; Im Ftbl; JV Trk; Hon Roll; Mech Engr.

PICCIANO, JODIE ANN; The Mary Louis Acad; Fresh Meadows, NY; (Y); Church Yth Grp; Drama Clb; Girl Scts; VP Pres Chorus; School Musical; School Play; Nwsp Rptr; NEDT Awd; Spec Ed.

PICCIONE, KRISTEN; Nyack SR HS; Valley Cottage, NY; (Y); Yrbk Stf; Cheerleading; Fld Hcky; Hon Roll; NHS; NY Rgnts Schlrshp, Prsdntl Acad Ftnss Awd 85; Oswego SUNY; Acctng.

PICHARDO, AIMEE; St Francis Prep; Flushing, NY; (Y); Cmnty Wkr; Chorus; Church Choir.

PICKELS, CINDY; Vernon-Verona-Sherrill Central Schl; Sherrill, NY; (Y); AFS; Pres Church Yth Grp; Varsity Clb; Rep Soph Cls; Rep Jr Cls; Stu Cncl; Var Capt Tennis; JV Vllybl; High Hon Roll; NHS; Spec Olympcs Bddy 82-84; Mst Outstndng St Helenas Yth Grp 83; Boston U; Phy Thrpy.

PICKERING, GINA; Tupper Lake HS; Tupper Lk, NY; (Y); 2/126; JA; Nwsp Stf; Yrbk Ed-Chief; High Hon Roll; NHS; Trs Frsh Cls; Pres Soph Cls; Rep Jr Cls; Rep Stu Cncl; Augsbury N Cntry Schlr 85; Girls All ST Awd Lrdshp 85; St Lawrence U; Elem Tchr.

PICKERING, ROY; Cardinal Spellman HS; Bronx, NY; (Y); Church Yth Grp; Band; Mrchg Band; Im Bsktbl; Im Ftbl; High Hon Roll.

PICKERT, REBECCA; Mc Graw Central Schl; Mcgraw, NY; (Y); Am Leg Aux Girls St; Varsity Clb; Capt Color Guard; VP Soph Cls; Var Bsktbl; JV Capt Cheerleading; Socr; Sftbl; High Hon Roll; Jr NHS; MVP All-Star Sccr & Sftbl 84-85; MVP Chrldng 83-84; Gym Tchr.

PICKETT, DANIEL; Mechanicville HS; Mechanicville, NY; (S); Computer Clb; French Clb; Letterman Clb; Ski Clb; Varsity Clb; Rep Frsh Cls; Rep Soph Cls; Rep Jr Cls; Rep Stu Cncl; High Hon Roll; Philomatheon Clb Math Awd 83; Skidmore Coll Awds Dnnr 84.

PICKETT, KIMBERLY A; Lake George Central HS; Glens Falls, NY; (Y); 24/78; VP Girl Scts; Library Aide; Band; Flag Corp; Mrchg Band; School Play; NY St Regents Schlrshp 85; Suny Plattsburgh; Nrsng.

PICKETT, NANCY; Hamburg SR HS; Hamburg, NY; (Y); Church Yth Grp; VP JA; Library Aide; Teachers Aide; Chorus; Church Choir; Orch; L Crs Cntry; Hon Roll; NHS; Bus Admin.

PICKREIGN, LUANN; Saranac Lake HS; Saranac Lk, NY; (Y); FBLA; Cheerleading; Hon Roll; Persnl Mgr.

PICOLLA, JOHN A; Oneonta SR HS; Oneonta, NY; (Y); 21/187; Am Leg Boys St; Boy Scts; Concert Band; Drm Mjr(t); Jazz Band; Mrchg Band; Orch; Pep Band; School Musical; Rep Stu Cncl; NY ST Sci Awd 83; Syracuse U; Engrng.

PICONE, MONICA; Lynbrook SR HS; Lynbrook, NY; (Y); FBLA; Hosp Aide; Leo Clb; Spanish Clb; Varsity Clb; Yrbk Stf; Var Socr; Hon Roll; Vol Hosp Wrk Awd 84; Phrmcy.

PICOZZI, JANETTE; Walt Whitman HS; Huntington Sta, NY; (Y); 68/540; Yrbk Stf; Var Capt Cheerleading; High Hon Roll; Hon Roll; Jr NHS; Church Yth Grp; Band; Yrbk Phtg; Stat Lcrss; Trk; Awd Of Mrt Spanish 83; Psych.

PIDGEON, MICHAEL J; Ballston Spa HS; Ballston Spa, NY; (Y); Church Yth Grp; High Hon Roll; Hon Roll; Acad Achvt Awd 84; Comp Sci.

PIECH, KARI; Whitney Point Central HS; Richford, NY; (Y); Trs French Clb; Ski Clb; Cheerleading; Hon Roll; NHS; Broome CC; Acctnt.

PIECH, KRISTEN; Lockport SR HS; Lockport, NY; (Y); 10/411; AFS; Drama Clb; Intnl Clb; Drm Mjr(t); Flag Corp; Mrchg Band; School Musical; Symp Band; Im Cheerleading; Hon Roll; Engrng.

PIECZONKA, LISA; Mount Mercy Acad; Blasdell, NY; (Y); Science Clb; Spanish Clb; School Musical; Trs Swing Chorus; High Hon Roll; Hon Roll; NHS; 2nd Pl Miss Diamond Jubilee Pgnt 84; Mt Mercy Melodears Silver Mdl 85; Intl Music Fest; Med.

PIEJKO, ARTHUR R; Whitesboro Central HS; Marcy, NY; (Y); 19/327; Orch; Hon Roll; JC Awd; Kiwanis Awd; NHS; Clarkson U Trstees Scholar 85; Clarkson U; Elec Engrng.

PIEL, SCOTT; Williamsville South HS; Williamsville, NY; (Y); Cmnty Wkr; Ski Clb; Spanish Clb; Rep Jr Cls; Var Bsktbl; Var Ftbl; MVP Bsktbl,Ftbl 83; Capt Bsktbl Tm 85-86; Bus.

PIEN, GRACE; Southside HS; Pine City, NY; (Y); Sec Key Clb; Latin Clb; Varsity Clb; Orch; School Musical; Yrbk Ed-Chief; Var Trk; High Hon Roll; Sec NHS; Chorus; Mansfield U Math Cont Medlln Wnnr 84 & 85; Physcn.

PIENTA, AMY; Frontier Central HS; Blasdell, NY; (Y); Art Clb; JA; Pep Clb; Ski Clb; Orch; Var Crs Cntry; Var Trk; High Hon Roll; Hon Roll; NHS; Pre Med.

PIERAKOS, ILIA; Buffalo Acad For Visual Prfmng Arts; Buffalo, NY; (Y); 1/98; Dance Clb; French Clb; Math Tm; School Musical; Yrbk Stf; Stu Cncl; Cheerleading; High Hon Roll; NHS; Val; NYS Regnts Schlrshp 85; Regnts Cert Merit 84; SUNY Coll Buffalo; Secdry Ed.

PIERCE, CARLA; Newfield HS; Newfield, NY; (Y); Camera Clb; Drama Clb; FHA; Library Aide; Teachers Aide; Varsity Clb; VICA; School Play; Yrbk Stf; Score Keeper; Pres Phy Ftnss Awd 79-85; Beautician.

PIERCE, CHUCK; Pittsford Mendon HS; Pittsford, NY; (Y); Tennis; Hon Roll; Orthodontist.

PIERCE, CRYSTAL A; G Ray Bodley HS; Fulton, NY; (Y); 10/258; Science Clb; School Musical; School Play; Capt Var Cheerleading; High Hon Roll; VP NHS; NY ST Regents Schlrshp 85; Geneseo Coll; Psychology.

PIERCE, DANIEL J; Cardinal Mooney HS; Rochester, NY; (Y); 9/319; Mgr School Play; Pres Sr Cls; Im Bsktbl; Var Socr; Var Trk; Cit Awd; High Hon Roll; NHS; NY ST Boys Chmpnshp Soccer Team 83; Faith Through Sprts Awd 85; Syracuse U; Arch.

PIERCE, DAVID; Solvay HS; Syracuse, NY; (Y); Boy Scts; Church Yth Grp; Pres Key Clb; Church Choir; Concert Band; JV Var Trk; High Hon Roll; NHS; Jazz Band; Talnts Christ Comptn Scholar 85; Pastor.

PIERCE, DAVID A; Lewiston-Porter HS; Lewiston, NY; (Y); 34/273; Sec Key Clb; Rep Soph Cls; Rep Stu Cncl; Hon Roll; NHS; Intrnshp Prog Niagara Cnty Dist Attrny 85; Semnr Schlrshp Wnnr Attnd WA Wrkshps 84; SUNY-BINGHAMTON; Pol Sci.

PIERCE, GEOFFREY; Watkins Glen HS; Watkins Glen, NY; (Y); 21/132; Am Leg Boys St; Church Yth Grp; Dance Clb; Letterman Clb; Math Clb; Nwsp Rptr; Nwsp Stf; Rep Frsh Cls; Rep Soph Cls; JV Bsktbl; Mnsfld T Coll; Crmnl Jstc.

PIERCE, JACQUELINE; Pulaski JR SR HS; Pulaski, NY; (S); 1/120; Trs AFS; Drama Clb; French Clb; Math Clb; Spanish Clb; High Hon Roll; Sec NHS; Intl Frng Lang Awd 84; Ntl Ldrshp Awd 85; Geology.

PIERCE, JEFFREY; Onondage Central HS; Syracuse, NY; (S); Jazz Band; VP Frsh Cls; Rep Soph Cls; Off Stu Cncl; Var Capt Bsbl; Var Capt Bsktbl; Var Capt Ftbl; High Hon Roll; Hon Roll; NHS; Hugh O Brien Yth Awd Wnnr 83; Math.

PIERCE, JOHN; Stony Brook Schl; Orange, NJ; (Y); 44/80; Boy Scts; Church Yth Grp; Band; Chorus; Concert Band; Mrchg Band; Orch; Stage Crew; Yrbk Phtg; Rep Frsh Cls; Wright ST Coll; Bus Admin.

PIERCE, MACHELLE; Dundee Central Schl; Dundee, NY; (Y); #7 In Class; Am Leg Aux Girls St; Band; Concert Band; Mrchg Band; Bsktbl; High Hon Roll; Hon Roll; NHS; Pres Schlr; St Schlr; Cazenovia Coll; Mngmnt.

PIERCE, NICHOLAS; Hempstead HS; Hemstead, NY; (Y); ROTC; Color Guard; Concert Band; High Hon Roll; Hon Roll; Outstdng Cmnty Awds 83-85; JR Marine Corp ROTC 83-85; Alpha Kappa Alpha Awd-Amer Mgmt Awd 84; Naval Acad; Marine Corp Offcr.

PIERCE, PAULA; Minisink Valley Central HS; New Hampton, NY; (Y); Dance Clb; Yrbk Stf; Hon Roll; Dentl Asst.

PIERCE, RONALD; Saranac HS; Dannemora, NY; (S); 8/106; Church Yth Grp; Band; Church Choir; Mrchg Band; Math.

PIERCE, SEAN D; Uniondale HS; Hempstead, NY; (Y); 1/498; Cmnty Wkr; Pres Debate Tm; Math Tm; NFL; Orch; School Musical; VP Stu Cncl; High Hon Roll; NHS; Ntl Merit Ltr; Hgst Medl Merit 82; Mirty Schlstc Achvt Awd 84; Fnlst Mr Uniondale Cntst 84; Elec Engr.

PIERCE, STEPHANIE; Sandy Creek Central Schll; Lacona, NY; (Y); 1/90; Pres Drama Clb; Band; Chorus; Drm Mjr(t); School Musical; Var L Socr; Sec NHS; Voice Dem Awd; VP Church Yth Grp; Sec Intnl Clb; St Fnlst Amer Lgn Ortrcl Cntst 85; Are-All St Orch & Bnd 83 & 84; All Cty Jzz Bnd 84 & 85; Law.

PIERCE, TIMOTHY; Onondaga Central HS; Syracuse, NY; (S); VP Frsh Cls; VP Soph Cls; VP Jr Cls; Rep Stu Cncl; Var L Bsbl; JV Bsktbl; Var L Ftbl; High Hon Roll; Hon Roll; NHS; Math.

PIERCE, WILLIAM; Gouverneur Central HS; Gouverneur, NY; (Y); Chess Clb; Computer Clb; Rep Library Aide; VP Art Clb; Rep Boy Scts; Prfct Atten; Potsdam ST; Comp Sci.

PIERCE WEBSTER, BRIAN LOWELL; Akron Central HS; Akron, NY; (Y); 11/157; Cmnty Wkr; Ski Clb; Capt Crs Cntry; Capt Trk; Hon Roll; NHS; NY ST Regents Schlrshp 85; NY ST Smmr Schl Vsl Arts 84; OH ST U; Art.

PIERIDES, EVANGELIA; Bronx High School Of Science; Flushing, NY; (Y); 95/714; Church Yth Grp; Dance Clb; Office Aide; Teachers Aide; Vllybl; NHS; Ntl Merit SF; Regnts, St Johns Schlrshps 85; St Johns U; Bus.

PIERLEONI, MARIA VIRGINIA; Greece Arcadia HS; Rochester, NY; (Y); 1/319; Hosp Aide; Math Tm; Chorus; School Musical; Cheerleading; NHS; Pres Schlr; Val; High Hon Roll; Hon Roll; Phi Beta Kappa Schlr Awd 85; Womens Educ & Ind Union Schlrshp 85; Rochester Phi Delta Kappa Teachng 85; ST U Of NY-BINGHAMTON; Math.

PIERRE, MARTIN; Bishop Loughlin MAS HS; Brooklyn, NY; (S); Cmnty Wkr; Computer Clb; Dance Clb; Debate Tm; Speech Tm; Varsity Clb; Nwsp Stf; Crs Cntry; Trk; Wt Lftg; Purpl L Awd 84; Cathlc H S Athl Assn Awd 84; Boston Coll; Bio.

PIERRE, ROLAND SAINT; Saint-Francis Preparatory Schl; Hollis, NY; (Y); 147/693; Sec Debate Tm; Math Clb; Model UN; Im Bsbl; Im Fld Hcky; Ftbl; Im Socr; Im Sftbl; Im Tennis; Im Vllybl; Awd & Cert Pol Sci Clb 85; Schl Ltr Invlvmnt Intrmrls 85; Columbia U; Chmcl Engr.

PIERRE, SANDRA; Manhattan Center For Science & Math; Brooklyn, NY; (Y); #1 In Class; Cmnty Wkr; School Play; Vllybl; High Hon Roll; NHS; Val; Teachers Aide; Nwsp Stf; Yrbk Stf; Bowling; Selct Pgm In Sci & Engrng Awd 82; Manhattan Math/Sci Smmr Inst Math Awd 83; Regnts Schlrshp 85; Cornell U; Cvl Engrng.

PIERRE, YUAN CLAUDE; Spacken Kill HS; Poughkeepsie, NY; (Y); Church Yth Grp; Thesps; School Musical; School Play; Rep Frsh Cls; Rep Soph Cls; Rep Jr Cls; Bsktbl; Ftbl; Boy Scts; Bus Law.

PIERRE-LOUIS, EDNA; Nazareth Regional HS; Brooklyn, NY; (Y); 57/260; Science Clb; Speech Tm; Chorus; Nwsp Rptr; Hon Roll; NHS; Elem Calculus Mdl 85; Engl Wrtng Awd 85; Rgnts Diploma 85; Fordham U; Pre-Med.

PIERRE-LOUIS, LINDA; Saint Joseph HS; Brooklyn, NY; (Y); 1/114; Dance Clb; Drama Clb; Hosp Aide; Red Cross Aide; Camp Fr Inc; Yrbk Stf; Rep Stu Cncl; Bsktbl; High Hon Roll; Sal; Brooklyn Catholic Interracl Cncl Scholar 81-85; Tablet All Schltc Tm Awd 85; Gov Comm Schltc Achvt 85; Long Island U; Phrmcy.

PIERRELOUIS, JEAN; St Francis Preparatory Schl; Flushing, NY; (Y); 133/690; Church Yth Grp; VP JA; Teachers Aide; VP Ftbl; Trk; Wt Lftg.

PIERRI, FRANCIS; Mount Saint Michael Acad; Bronx, NY; (Y); 30/308; Ski Clb; Lit Mag; Im Ice Hcky; Var Socr; Im Wrstlng; Hon Roll; Jr NHS; NHS; Bus.

PIERRO, JACQUELINE; General Douglas Mac Arhthur HS; Seaford, NY; (Y); 111/319; Sec Office Aide; Sec Teachers Aide; Var Trk; Sec Wrstlng; Hon Roll; Jr NHS; Mst Interstng Of SR Clss 84-85; Bst Drssd 84-85; Frndlst Of SR Clss 84-85; Excell In Culnry Art 84-85; Fashin Inst Of Tech; Fshn Merch.

PIERSON, KRISTEN S; Pine Bush HS; Pine Bush, NY; (Y); 31/287; VP Church Yth Grp; Concert Band; Mrchg Band; School Musical; Rep Jr Cls; JV Var Socr; Hon Roll; Jr NHS; NHS; Band; NY ST Regents Schlrshp 85; Crusade Citation Cancer Soc 83; Boces Enrchmnt Prgm 84-85; Marist Coll; Psychology.

PIERSON, MICHAEL; Newfield HS; Coram, NY; (S); 13/563; Chess Clb; Cmnty Wkr; Q&S; Varsity Clb; Nwsp Ed-Chief; Stu Cncl; NHS; Prfct Atten Awd; Jr NHS; Fencing Tm Capt 83-84 & 84-85; Stu Ldrs Org 84-85; NY T Regents Schlrshp; Cvl Engrng.

PIERSON, PAUL; Newfield HS; Coram, NY; (Y); Cmnty Wkr; Concert Band; Mrchg Band; VP Frsh Cls; JV L Ftbl; High Hon Roll; Jr NHS; NHS; Prfct Atten Awd; Chess Clb; JV V Let Fencing; Math.

PIERSON, RONALD C; Vestal SR HS; Vestal, NY; (Y); 19/450; Mathletes; Chorus; JV Capt Bowling; High Hon Roll; Ntl Merit SF; Prfct Atten Awd; Intntl Frgn Lang Awd 83; Ntl Yth Ldrshp Awd 84; Sprtsmnshp Awd 84; NY U Binghamton; Comp Sci.

PIERZCHANOWSKI, PAUL; Riverhead HS; Riverhead, NY; (Y); 34/230; Aud/Vis; ROTC; Color Guard; Drill Tm; Yrbk Phtg; Lion Awd; VFW Awd; NJROTC Outstndng Cdt 83-84; U Of AZ; Phtgrphy.

PIETRASZAK, JULIE; Amherst SR HS; Amherst, NY; (Y); 146/310; Church Yth Grp; Cmnty Wkr; Pep Clb; Chorus; School Musical; Hon Roll; Volunteer Of The Year 81-83; Buffalo ST Coll; Chldhd Ed.

PIETRIS, CHRISTINE; Lakeland HS; Shrub Oak, NY; (Y); 37/380; German Clb; Hosp Aide; Yrbk Stf; Var Socr; NHS; NY ST Rgnts Schlrshp 85; U NY Albany.

PIETROCARLO, LISA; Mynderse Acad; Seneca Falls, NY; (Y); 5/132; Am Leg Aux Girls St; GAA; Intnl Clb; JV Var Bsktbl; Var Capt Socr; Var Capt Sftbl; High Hon Roll; NHS; Model UN; All Tourn Tm Sftbl 85; Regnts Schlrshp 85; SUNY Cortland; Sprts Med.

PIETROCARLO, ROBERT; Frontier Central HS; Lakeview, NY; (Y); Drama Clb; Stage Crew; Buffalo ST; Crmnl Justice.

PIETROMONACO, MICHAEL; MSGR Mc Clancy Memorial HS; Astoria, NY; (Y); Church Yth Grp; German Clb; Accntng.

PIETROWICZ, MICHELE; Fowler HS; Syracuse, NY; (S); Exploring; Pep Clb; Science Clb; Yrbk Ed-Chief; Rep Stu Cncl; Hnrs Astronomy 83; Stu Gov 83; Yr Bk 84; Onodoga Comm Coll.

PIETROWICZ, THERESA; Cicero-North Syracuse HS; Clay, NY; (S); 52/622; Pres Exploring; Mathletes; Math Tm; Red Cross Aide; JV Var Vllybl; Hon Roll; Acctg.

PIETRZAK, THOMAS J; Warwick Valley Central HS; Pine Island, NY; (Y); 76/204; Boy Scts; FFA; SR Indstrl Arts Awd 85; Plnt Sci Awd 84; Sam Paffen Roth Awd For Ag 85; SUNY-OSWEGO; Indstrl Arts Tchr.

PIETRZYK, HEIDI; Turner/Carroll HS; Buffalo, NY; (Y); Service Clb; Nwsp Stf; Yrbk Stf; Awd Hnr Excllnt Wrk Subj Hlth 83; Svc Awd Yrbk 85; D Joyville; Nrsg.

PIETRZYKOWSKI, LORI; Byron-Bergen Central HS; Bergen, NY; (Y); 4-H; Var L Bsktbl; Var L Socr; Var L Sftbl; 4-H Awd; Hon Roll; Jr NHS; Prfct Atten Awd; 4-H; Genesee Rgn All Stars Bsktbl 85; Allg Rtr Rchstr Hnrbl Ment Scr 84; All Trnmnt Tm 84-85; Bus Admn.

PIETZ, CHERYL LYNN; West Seneca East SR HS; W Seneca, NY; (Y); Pres Church Yth Grp; Dance Clb; DECA; Variety Show; Rep Frsh Cls; Capt Cheerleading; Capt Pom Pon; Sec Jr NHS; Fstvl Lghts Chrldg Chmpnshp-Top Chrldr Awd 85; DECA Rgnls-1st Pl Rgn, 3rd NY ST Fnls 85; Bus Admin.

PIGA, MONICA; Sachem High School North; Holbrook, NY; (Y); 250/1600; Pres Sec Church Yth Grp; Cmnty Wkr; FNA; Girl Scts; Spanish Clb; Church Choir; Color Guard; Trk; Twrlr; Creative Wrtng Awd 83; Psych.

PIGNATARO, ROSE MARIE; The Mary Louis Acad; Maspeth, NY; (Y); Am Leg Aux Girls St; Girl Scts; Library Aide; Service Clb; Chorus; Variety Show; Lit Mag; Hon Roll; Hunter U Of NY; Phy Thrpy.

PIGNATARO, ROSE-MARIE; The Mary Louis Acad; Maspeth, NY; (Y); Am Leg Aux Girls St; Girl Scts; Library Aide; Chorus; Variety Show; Lit Mag; Hon Roll; Physcl Thrpy.

PIGNATELLI, ROBERT; Nyack HS; Valley Cottage, NY; (Y); 14/277; Debate Tm; French Clb; Mathletes; Math Clb; Math Tm; Spanish Clb; Bowling; Var Crs Cntry; Im Ftbl; JV Var Lcrss; SUNY; Bio Engr.

PIGOTT, MELISSA; Churchville-Chili HS; Churchville, NY; (Y); Church Yth Grp; VP GAA; JA; VP Sr Cls; Capt Cheerleading; Var L Socr; Var L Trk; High Hon Roll; Hon Roll; NHS; Air Force Acad.

PIKE, CHRISTINE; School Fo The Holy Child; New Rochelle, NY; (S); JV Var Bsbl; JV Var Bsktbl; JV Var Fld Hcky; Hon Roll; Ldrs JR Cls 85; Dartmouth; Tchr.

PIKE, CHRISTOPHER; Onteora HS; Woodstock, NY; (S); German Clb; Math Tm; Band; Concert Band; Jazz Band; Nwsp Rptr; Socr; Trk; Hon Roll; NHS; Sci.

PIKE, DAVID; Hartford Central HS; Hartford, NY; (S); 3/44; Boy Scts; Computer Clb; Drama Clb; Math Tm; Chrmn Science Clb; School Play; Variety Show; Yrbk Phtg; High Hon Roll; NHS; Ciba-Geigy Sci Awd 85; Regents Schlrshp 85; Sandy Hill Grant 85; Clarkson U; Engrng.

PIKE, LAWRENCE; Lansingburgh HS; Troy, NY; (Y); Var VP Bsbl; Var Bsktbl; Var Ftbl; Trk; Hon Roll; Air Force; Comp.

PIKE, LISA; Irondequoit HS; Rochester, NY; (Y); Computer Clb; Socr; Hon Roll; NHS; Regents Scholar 85; SUNY Binghamton; Bio Sci.

PIKE, WENDY; Frontier Central HS; Hamburg, NY; (Y); Church Yth Grp; Drama Clb; Spanish Clb; Chorus; School Musical; School Play; Stage Crew; High Hon Roll; Hon Roll; Fnlst Miss Hemisphere Pgnt 83; U Of Buffalo; Chmstry.

PILARINOS, GEORGIA; St Johns Prep; Astoria, NY; (Y); Chorus; Wt Lftg; Hon Roll; Prfct Atten Awd; 1st Hnrs Acad Awd 85; Awd Rec Tutoring 83; Baruch Collfbus.

PILKINGTON, LAURA; Rocky Point HS; Rocky Pt, NY; (Y); Church Yth Grp; Drama Clb; Band; Concert Band; Mrchg Band; Fld Hcky; Trk; Hon Roll; Bst Imprvd Awd Fld Hcky 83-84; Nutrtn.

PILLA, MARIA; Preston HS; Bronx, NY; (S); 1/28; Yrbk Stf; NHS.

PILLITTERI, JOSEPHINE; Sacred Heart Acad; West Hempstead, NY; (S); FTA; Library Aide; Hon Roll; NHS; Tchr.

PILLITTIERI, TINA M; Jamestown HS; Jamestown, NY; (Y); Band; Color Guard; Mrchg Band; Tennis; High Hon Roll; Hon Roll; Jr NHS; NHS; Sec Frsh Cls; Sec Soph Cls; Edctn.

PILLO, DEIDRE ANN; Notre Dame HS; Batavia, NY; (S); Pep Clb; Ski Clb; Yrbk Stf; Sec Frsh Cls; Var JV Socr; Var JV Tennis; Var JV Vllybl; High Hon Roll; Hon Roll; NHS; Sec Sci.

PILNY, LUCILLE R; Sewanhaka HS; Elmont, NY; (Y); 48/350; Mgr Variety Show; Off Frsh Cls; Off Soph Cls; Off Jr Cls; Off Sr Cls; Stu Cncl; Capt Cheerleading; Hon Roll; NHS; Church Yth Grp; Stu Exch Merit Awd; Most Schl Spirited, Does Most For Sr Cls.

PILUSO, TRACY J; Mechanicville HS; Mechanicville, NY; (Y); 16/104; Church Yth Grp; Ski Clb; Spanish Clb; CC Awd; High Hon Roll; Hon Roll; Jr NHS; NHS; Regents Schlrshp 85; RIT Schlrshp 85; Rochester Inst Of Tech; Bio.

PIMENTEL, JOAN; Cathedral HS; Ny, NY; (Y); 80/299; Church Yth Grp; French Clb; Library Aide; Band; Mrchg Band; Lbrary Aid Awd 83; Comp Sci.

PIMM, MICHELLE R; Byron Bergen Central HS; Bergen, NY; (Y); VP Pres 4-H; VP Jr Cls; Rep Stu Cncl; Var Capt Cheerleading; JV Var Socr; Jr NHS; NYS Regents Schlrshp Nrsng 85; Genesee CC; Travel.

PINCHOOK, STEPHANIE; Glens Falls HS; Glens Falls, NY; (Y); 21/240; AFS; Hosp Aide; Ski Clb; High Hon Roll; Hon Roll; Ntl Merit SF; Sec Jr Cls; Sec Sr Cls; Var L Crs Cntry; Powder Puff Ftbl; Pre-Med.

PINCKERT, ERIC; Nyack HS; Upr Nyack, NY; (Y); 3/277; Pres French Clb; School Musical; School Play; Yrbk Phtg; Var Golf; Var Capt Tennis; VP NHS; Church Yth Grp; Math Clb; Quiz Bowl; Chief Justice Gen Org Crt 85; Rnssnce Stu Awd 85; DAR NY ST Schlrshp 85; Stanford U; Chem.

PINCKNEY, CYNTHIA; Bay Ridge HS; Brooklyn, NY; (Y); 34/266; Church Yth Grp; Sec Cmnty Wkr; Computer Clb; Dance Clb; Math Tm; Chorus; Church Choir; Yrbk Stf; Sr Cls; Hon Roll; Barauch Coll; Comp Op.

PINCKNEY, LESLIE J; Murry Bergtraum HS; Bronx, NY; (S); 93/576; JA; VP Sr Cls; Stu Cncl; Chorus; Church Choir; Stage Crew; Bowling; Top Seller Awd 82; Acctng.

PINCUS, MIRIAM B; Francis Lewis HS; Fresh Meadows, NY; (Y); 2/527; Hosp Aide; Office Aide; High Hon Roll; NHS; Ntl Merit Ltr; Sal; Regnts Schlrshp 85; Acadmc Olympc 85; Barnard Coll.

PINDER, MICHELLE M; Newburgh Free Acad; New Windsor, NY; (Y); French Clb; Ski Clb; Yrbk Stf; Jr Cls; Off Sr Cls; Hon Roll; Secy.

PINE, CRAIG; Hoosick Falls Central HS; Buskirk, NY; (Y); 4/95; Band; Hon Roll; NHS.

PINEDA, IRIS; St Pius V HS; Bronx, NY; (Y); 2/40; Chess Clb; Intnl Clb; Latin Clb; Sec Jr Cls; Hon Roll; Jr NHS; NHS; Hghst Avg Engl & Hnrbl Ments 84; Hghst Avg Frnch & Hnrbl Ments 85; Polt Sci.

PINEL, PATRICIA; Lakeland HS; Putnam Vly, NY; (Y); French Clb; Yrbk Stf; French Hon Soc; Hon Roll; Frnch GPA Awd 83; Spn GPA Awd 82-83; Math 9-Algbr GPA Awd 83; Langs.

PINES, TODD; Jericho HS; Old Westbury, NY; (Y); Varsity Clb; Tennis; NHS; Spanish NHS.

PINGARO, DON; Haldane HS; Cold Spring, NY; (S); 2/70; Ski Clb; Rep Frsh Cls; Rep Stu Cncl; JV Var Bsktbl; Capt L Crs Cntry; Var L Wrstlng; High Hon Roll; Jr NHS; NHS; Sal; RPI Math, Sci Awds 84; U Of FL Miami; Pre-Med.

PINGELSKI, LORI; Mechanicville HS; Mechanicville, NY; (Y); Hosp Aide; Nwsp Rptr; Rep Frsh Cls; Rep Soph Cls; Rep Jr Cls; JV Bsktbl; High Hon Roll; Hon Roll; Samaritan Hosp Schl Nrs; Nrs.

PINGRYN, MICHAEL; Auburn HS; Auburn, NY; (Y); JV Var Bsbl; Var Bowling; High Hon Roll; Hon Roll; Psych.

PINHEIRO, NATASHA; Brooklyn Technical HS; Brooklyn, NY; (Y); Camera Clb; Church Yth Grp; Cmnty Wkr; Drama Clb; JV Stat Swmmng; Hon Roll; Exclnce Am Govt 84-85; Exclence Eng IV 84; Alaw.

PINKHAM, THAD; Cornwall Central HS; Cornwall, NY; (Y); Rep Frsh Cls; Var JV Bsktbl; Var JV Ftbl; Im Trk; JV Var Wt Lftg; Hon Roll; Comm Art.

PINKLEY, LAURA; North Rose Wolcott HS; North Rose, NY; (Y); FBLA; Girl Scts; School Musical; School Play; Sec Jr Cls; Var Crs Cntry; JV Trk; Hon Roll; Mdcl.

PINKNEY, KIRSTEN M; Allendale Columbia Schl; Palmyra, NY; (Y); 4/47; Church Yth Grp; Pres 4-H; French Clb; Math Tm; Model UN; Ski Clb; Varsity Clb; Chorus; School Musical; Yrbk Bus Mgr; Cornell U; Bio.

PINKNEY, WILFORD; Cardinal Spellman HS; Bronx, NY; (Y); 230/568; Chess Clb; Sec Science Clb; Var L Bsktbl; L Ftbl; Var L Trk; Hon Roll; Ntl Merit Schol; Regnts & Rochester Ntl Schlrshps 85; U Of Rochester; Opt Engr.

PINNER, MIRIAM; Whitney Point HS; Whitney Point, NY; (S); Trs Church Yth Grp; JCL; Latin Clb; Chorus; Church Choir; High Hon Roll; Hon Roll; Chldhd Ed.

PINNEY, CARLA; Chenango Forles HS; Binghamton, NY; (Y); Church Yth Grp; Drama Clb; Chorus; School Play; Stage Crew; JV Bsktbl; Mgr(s); Swmmng; Hon Roll; Girl Scts; Achvt Awd Engl; Bio Chem.

PINNOCK, ANDREA W; John F Kennedy HS; Brooklyn, NY; (Y); 24/982; Office Aide; Teachers Aide; Hon Roll; NHS; Regents Schlrshp 85; Trig Regents Awd 84; Geom Regents Awd 83; ST U Stony Brook; Accntng.

PINNOCK, NORDIA; Wonder Childs HS; Bronx, NY; (Y); Pres Jr Cls; VP Stu Cncl; Capt Bowling; Brach Coll; Bus Lwyr.

PINNOLA, JOHN; Monsignor Farrell HS; Staten Island, NY; (Y); 3/296; Pres JA; Math Tm; Nwsp Rptr; Im Bsktbl; Im Bowling; Im Ftbl; Var Wrstlng; Hon Roll; Pres NHS; Ntl Merit Ltr; Schlrshp Natl Secdry Ed Cncl 85; Schlrshp Columbian Socty Police Dept NY 85; Iona Coll Langue Cntst; Cornell U; Elctrcl Engrng.

PINSON, JANEEN; Bishop Loughlin HS; Brooklyn, NY; (Y); High Hon Roll; Hon Roll; CPA.

PINTO, JOHN; Seton Catholic Central HS; Johnson City, NY; (Y); Church Yth Grp; Sec Trs Science Clb; Varsity Clb; Stu Cncl; Bsbl; Bsktbl; Hon Roll.

PINTO, LISA M; Immaculata Acad; Hamburg, NY; (Y); 3/71; Girl Scts; Quiz Bowl; Spanish Clb; Y-Teens; Nwsp Sprt Ed; Var L Bsktbl; JV Vllybl; High Hon Roll; NHS; Cert Recog-Voluntr-Recrtn Nght For Handicapped 84; SUNY Buffalo; Phrmcy.

PINTO, MANUEL; Archbishop Stepinac HS; White Plains, NY; (Y); Exploring; VP JA; Key Clb; School Musical; School Play; Yrbk Stf; Stat Ftbl; JV Socr; Var Capt Swmmng; All Cnty Swim Team; All Star Swim; MVP In Swim; Lawyer.

PINTO, STEVEN; Monticello HS; Rock Hill, NY; (Y); Yrbk Bus Mgr; VP Sr Cls; Stu Cncl; Capt Var Bsbl.

PINTRO, HARRY; Harry S Truman HS; Bronx, NY; (Y); Var Crs Cntry; Capt Socr; JV Trk; Prfct Atten Awd; St John U; Bus.

PINZAS, JESSICA; Windsor Central HS; Conklin, NY; (Y); Art Clb; Chorus; Color Guard; JV Crs Cntry; JV Trk; Hon Roll; Natl Frnch Cont Top 10 Broome Cnty 82-83; Schlstc Achvt Awds 82-84; SUNY Binghamton; Poltcl Sci.

PINZON, GABRIELLE; The Mary Louis Acad; Jamaica, NY; (Y); Church Yth Grp; Orch; Yrbk Phtg; Yrbk Stf; Hon Roll; NHS; Med.

PIOCH, KRISTI; Eastridge HS; Rochester, NY; (Y); 29/215; French Clb; JA; Band; Color Guard; Concert Band; Mrchg Band; Pep Band; School Musical; Im Var Sftbl; Hon Roll; NYSMA Mdl For Flute Quintet 8; Zoolgy.

PIORUN, TOM; Moravia Central HS; Moravia, NY; (Y); JV Bsktbl; Var Mgr(s).

PIOTROWSKI, LEAH; Rome Free Acad; Rome, NY; (Y); Church Yth Grp; Church Choir; Variety Show; Hon Roll; Jr NHS; NHS; Hghst Acad Avg Girls 83; Hghst Acad Avg Alg 83; Hghst Acad Avg JR Eng 85.

PIOTROWSKI, PAULA; Mont Pleasant HS; Schenectady, NY; (Y); 20/206; Hosp Aide; Pep Clb; Chorus; Symp Band; Rep Frsh Cls; French Hon Soc; Jr NHS; Key Clb; Ski Clb; Frnch Embssy Cert Of Excel 85; Ntl Frnch Cntst Cert Of Hnr 83-85; Lucienne Bechard Memrl Awd 85; Lwyr.

PIOVANETTI, DAVID; Sheepshead Bay HS; Brooklyn, NY; (Y); Drama Clb; Office Aide; Service Clb; School Musical; School Play; Nwsp Rptr; Yrbk Stf; Stu Cncl; Pride Of Ynkees Awd 84-85; Schlrshp Attnd Boston U 85; Conting Educ Units 85; Theatre.

PIPER, DERRICK; Cicero North Syracuse HS; Clay, NY; (Y); 70/715; Im Bsbl; Im Bsktbl; Im Ftbl; JV Socr; NHS; Math.

PIPER, JAY; Elmira Southsede HS; Elmira, NY; (Y); Am Leg Boys St; Art Clb; Church Yth Grp; Drama Clb; French Clb; Trs JA; Key Clb; Latin Clb; OEA; Pep Clb; Intl Music Fest Vienna 83; Schltc Awd Achvt Art 83; Lang.

PIPER, SCOTT; Mohawk Central HS; Franfort, NY; (Y); Art Clb; Church Yth Grp; JA; Office Aide; Chorus; Tennis; Hon Roll; ST U At Buffalo; Elect Engr.

PIPHER, TAMMY; Candor HS; Candor, NY; (Y); Varsity Clb; Chorus; Mrchg Band; Sec Frsh Cls; Sec Soph Cls; Rep Sr Cls; Pres Stu Cncl; Capt Cheerleading; Powder Puff Ftbl; JV Sftbl; Miss Southerntier Pageant 84-85; Strwbry Fstvl Queen 84; Miss Teen NY Pageant 84-85; TC 3; Modeling.

PIRAINO, SUSAN; Moore Catholic HS; Staten Island, NY; (Y); Bowling; Hon Roll; Cmnctns.

PIRAINO, TINA M; Jamesville De Witt HS; Syracuse, NY; (Y); 66/225; Church Yth Grp; Exploring; French Clb; Key Clb; Band; Coach Actv; Pom Pon; U Of Rochester; Med.

PIRONE, CHRISTINE; Mineola HS; Mineola, NY; (Y); 10/257; Church Yth Grp; Key Clb; Spanish Clb; Orch; Trs Frsh Cls; Trs Soph Cls; Trs Jr Cls; Trs Sr Cls; High Hon Roll; NHS.

PIROTTA, STEVEN; Frontier HS; Hamburg, NY; (S); Science Clb; Crs Cntry; Trk; High Hon Roll; Hon Roll; NHS; Prfct Atten Awd; Mech Engrng.

PIROZZI, FRANCIS; Mount Saint Michael Acad; Bronx, NY; (Y); 29/289; Ski Clb; Lit Mag; Im Ice Hcky; Var Socr; Hon Roll; NHS.

PIROZZI, STEPHEN; Geneva HS; Geneva, NY; (S); 11/170; Am Leg Boys St; Cmnty Wkr; French Clb; School Musical; School Play; Stage Crew; Nwsp Stf; VP NHS; Cornell U; Fac Plng Mgmt.

PIROZZOLO, SUSAN; Horseheads HS; Horseheads, NY; (S); 20/410; Church Yth Grp; Pres Drama Clb; Intnl Clb; School Musical; School Play; Rep Sr Cls; High Hon Roll; NHS; Gateways Gifted & Talntd Prog; Chairprsn Magazine Dr #1 In Natn.

PIRTHIPAL, INDRA; Andrew Jackson HS; Queens, NY; (Y); Off Frsh Cls; Off Sr Cls; Bsktbl; Gym; Tennis; Rep Vllybl; Cit Awd; Bus Mgmt.

PISANI, JANINE; Pelham Memorial HS; Pelham, NY; (Y); 17/177; AFS; Yrbk Stf; Sec Jr Cls; Sec Sr Cls; Cheerleading; Fld Hcky; Bausch & Lomb Sci Awd; High Hon Roll; NHS; Pres Schlr; U Of Rochester; Psych.

PISANI, KRISTIN; Pelham Memorial HS; Pelham, NY; (Y); AFS; GAA; Pep Clb; Ski Clb; Varsity Clb; Rep Stu Cncl; JV Var Cheerleading; JV Var Fld Hcky; Im Gym; JV Var Lcrss.

PISANO, PAUL; Mount Vernon HS; Mt Vernon, NY; (Y); Yrbk Stf; High Hon Roll; Hon Roll; Itln Clb 82; Hnr Roll-Geomtry 83; CPA Clb 85; Iona Coll; Bus.

PISAPIA, DENISE A; Holy Trinity HS; Levittown, NY; (S); 13/302; Math Tm; Office Aide; JV Cheerleading; Capt JV Gym; Stat Score Keeper; Stat Timer; Cit Awd; Hon Roll; Ntl Merit Ltr; NEDT Awd; Accntnt.

PISCIARINO, DENISE; Liverpool HS; Liverpool, NY; (S); 29/792; Ski Clb; Spanish Clb; Yrbk Stf; Stu Cncl; Hon Roll; Jr NHS; NHS; Bus.

PISELLO, IRENE; Kenmore East HS; Tonawanda, NY; (Y); JV Socr; Hon Roll; Im Vllybl; ST U NY Buffalo; Archt.

PISINO, LYNN; Newfield HS; Centreach, NY; (Y); Aud/Vis; Lit Mag; Hon Roll; Prfct Atten Awd; Wrtng.

PISKORZ, JEFF A; Cheektowaga Central HS; Cheektowaga, NY; (Y); 7/204; JCL; Latin Clb; Trs Band; Concert Band; Mrchg Band; Hon Roll; Jr NHS; NHS; NYS Regents Schlrshp 85; Canisius Coll Deans Schlrshp 85; Canisius Coll; Comp Sci.

PISTON, EDWARD J; Liverpool HS; Liverpool, NY; (Y); 71/792; Church Yth Grp; Exploring; Spanish Clb; Teachers Aide; Im Bsbl; Im Ftbl; High Hon Roll; Jr NHS; NHS; St Schlr; Syracuse U; Math.

PISTONE, LISA; Dominican Commercial HS; Brooklyn, NY; (Y); Siena Clb Princpls List 82-85; Schl Tchr.

PITA, AGUSTIN J; St Johns Prep; Queens, NY; (S); Hon Roll; Spanish NHS; Columbia U; Pre-Med.

PITAWALA, ASANKA; St Raymonds HS For Boys; Bronx, NY; (Y); 3/182; Computer Clb; Hosp Aide; Math Tm; NFL; Pres Science Clb; Nwsp Rptr; Nwsp Stf; Var Stu Cncl; Tennis; High Hon Roll; JR Vsty Math Awd 84-85; Prncpls Hnr Roll 84-85; NY ST Snt Stu Polcy Forum 84-85; Bio Me.

PITCHER, STEPHANIE; Maple Hill HS; Castleton, NY; (S); 4/80; Spanish Clb; Band; Concert Band; Variety Show; Sec Frsh Cls; Cheerleading; Tennis; High Hon Roll; Hon Roll; NHS; Performed In ESIPA 82-84; Exch Stu To Spain 84; Coll; Foreign Lng.

PITKANEN, DARLENE; Smithtown High Schl West; Hauppauge, NY; (Y); Color Guard; Yrbk Stf; Stat Bsbl; French Hon Soc; Hon Roll; Coll; Bus Adm.

PITKIN, DARRIN; General Brown HS; Dexter, NY; (Y); 8/197; Am Leg Boys St; Boy Scts; JCL; School Play; JV Var Bsbl; JV Var Bsktbl; JV Var Ftbl; High Hon Roll; NHS; Prfct Atten Awd; All Str Bsktbl Frontr A Div 83-85; All Str Bsbl Sprtsmn Leag 84; U S Army Resrv Natl Schlr-Athl Awd 85; Potsdam Coll; Engrng.

PITMAN, JULIE; Half Hollow Hills East HS; Melville, NY; (Y); Cmnty Wkr; FBLA; Leo Clb; Service Clb; Teachers Aide; Temple Yth Grp; Yrbk Stf; Mgr(s); Socr; High Hon Roll; Outstndg Svc Awd 85; Mth.

PITMAN, KEITH D; Marathon Central HS; Marathon, NY; (Y); 1/65; Band; L Bsbl; L Bsktbl; Bausch & Lomb Sci Awd; NHS; Ntl Merit Ltr; Val; Scholastic Bowl; Mrchg Band; Variety Show; RPI Medl 84; MVP Bsktbl 84; 2nd Hghst Scr Bsktbl 85; Hobart Coll; Law.

PITSIOS, KATHLEEN; H Frank Carey HS; Garden City S, NY; (Y); 7/222; Cmnty Wkr; Nwsp Rptr; Nwsp Stf; Lit Mag; Rep Jr Cls; High Hon Roll; Hon Roll; NHS; Spanish NHS; Voice Dem Awd; Ltry Magzne Edtr 83-84 & 85-86; Lbrl Arts.

PITTARI, LISA; St John Villa Acad; Staten Is, NY; (Y); Dance Clb; Drama Clb; Variety Show; Yrbk Stf; Bsktbl; Gym; Sftbl; Poly Tech Of NY; Metalurgy.

PITTARI, PAUL; Archbishop Molloy HS; Middle Village, NY; (Y); 2/409; Math Clb; Math Tm; JV Crs Cntry; Var Trk; High Hon Roll; NHS; Ntl Merit Ltr; Queens Coll Pres Awd Achvt 83-84; Rensselaer Medl Excllnc Math & Sci 85; Pre-Med.

PITTELLI, DEBRA; Academy Of St Joseph; Holtsville, NY; (Y); Cmnty Wkr; Dance Clb; Library Aide; Math Tm; Service Clb; Spanish Clb; Orch; JV Bsktbl; Coach Actv; Supr Acad Achv In Italian 85; Part In Suffolk Cnty SR Hgh Math League 85; Pace U; Acctng.

PITTMAN, CARLANE; Harry S Truman HS; Bronx, NY; (Y); Church Yth Grp; Science Clb; Service Clb; Teachers Aide; Orch; Cit Awd; Prfct Atten Awd; Cmnty Wkr; Dance Clb; Library Aide; Ms Jr Debtnt Qun 83; Ms Congenlty 85; Ms Dbtnt Qun 85; Psychtry.

PITTMAN, PAUL; Eli Whitney HS; Brooklyn, NY; (Y); Trk; Wt Lftg; Hon Roll; NHS; SYRACUSE U; Elec Engnr.

PITTMAN, ROSEANDA; Joseph L Wilson Magnet HS; Rochester, NY; (Y); Church Yth Grp; Latin Clb; Chorus; Rep Jr Cls; JV Bsktbl; JV Mgr(s); Var Sftbl; JV Var Vllybl; High Hon Roll; Hon Roll; Hghst Achvt Itln, Lat II & Sci 83; Comp Sci.

PITTMAN, ZOE L; Williamsville East HS; Buffalo, NY; (Y); 4-H; Band; Concert Band; Jazz Band; Mrchg Band; Pep Band; School Musical; Yrbk Phtg; Trs Frsh Cls; Socr; Louis Armstrong Jazz Awd 84; All Cnty Jazz Ensmbl 85; SUNY Fredonia; Music.

PITTNER, JULIE; Bishop Grimes HS; Syracuse, NY; (Y); Church Yth Grp; Bsktbl; Socr; Sftbl; Hon Roll; NHS; Acad All-Amer; 2nd Team All Cnty Bsktbl & Sftbl.

PITTS, CLAUDE; Hartford Central HS; Fort Ann, NY; (Y); French Clb; Pep Clb; Science Clb; Yrbk Sprt Ed; Yrbk Stf; High Hon Roll; Hon Roll; Air Force.

PITTS, JERROD; N Babylon SR HS; N Babylon, NY; (S); Pres DECA; Drama Clb; Spanish Clb; Chorus; School Musical; School Play; Stage Crew; Variety Show; Nwsp Rptr; Nwsp Stf; Norfolk ST U; Jrnlsm.

PITTS, SHERIA; St Edmunds HS; Brooklyn, NY; (Y); 186/190; Church Yth Grp; Office Aide; Teachers Aide; Church Choir; School Play; Variety Show; Im Badmtn; Im Bsktbl; Im Gym; Im Trk; John Jay Coll; Law.

PITTS, YOLANDA; Clara Barton HS; Brooklyn, NY; (Y); Art Clb; Mathletes; Office Aide; Spanish Clb; Teachers Aide; Hon Roll; Hunter Coll; Human Svcs.

PITZ, SHEILA E; Yorktown HS; Yorktown, NY; (Y); Var Swmmng; Busnss Mgmt.

PIUREK, TERRI; Amsterdam HS; Amsterdam, NY; (Y); Drm Mjr(t).

PIXLEY, MARY; Oneonta SR HS; Oneonta, NY; (Y); 13/186; VP Pres Church Yth Grp; Drama Clb; Key Clb; Thesps; Chorus; Madrigals; School Musical; Nwsp Stf; High Hon Roll; Hon Roll; Bst Actrss 83; Lib Arts.

PIZARRO, ANTHONY P; La Salle Acad; New York, NY; (S); 37/237; Boys Clb Am; Teachers Aide; Bsktbl; Bowling; Crs Cntry; Ftbl; Score Keeper; Sftbl; Trk; NHS; La Guardia Coll; Bus.

PIZARRO, SOMARI; Seward Park HS; New York, NY; (Y); Hon Roll; Cert Awd Band 85; Comm Excel Engl 83.

PIZER, ADAM; Onteora Central Schl; Woodstock, NY; (S); Math Tm; Quiz Bowl; Ski Clb; Var Crs Cntry; Var L Trk; Hon Roll; NHS.

PIZZARELLI, JOE; Mercy HS; Peconic, NY; (Y); Red Cross Aide; Trs Rep Frsh Cls; Stu Cncl; Var L Bsbl; Var L Ftbl; Hon Roll; NHS; Computer Clb; Ski Clb; Spanish Clb; Bsbl-All Leag 83-84; Ftbl-All Leag, All Conf, All Cnty & All NY ST Tm MVP 84-85; Ftbl-MVP 82-83; Engrng.

PIZZINGRILLO, JUDITH; Lindenhurst SR HS; Lindenhurst, NY; (Y); GAA; Yrbk Stf; Bsktbl; Fld Hcky; Sftbl; Vllybl; Hon Roll; Elem Ed.

PIZZO, JOSEPH; St Peters Boys HS; Staten Isld, NY; (Y); 104/160; Im Ftbl; JV Ice Hcky; St Johns U; Law.

PIZZOLA, NICHOLAS A; Homer Central HS; Cortland, NY; (Y); Boy Scts; Camera Clb; Chess Clb; Computer Clb; Exploring; Latin Clb; Ski Clb; Thesps; School Musical; School Play; Alfred Ag & Tech; Comp Sci.

PIZZURRO, JOHN; St Francis Prep; Flushing, NY; (Y); Am Leg Boys St; Church Yth Grp; Civic Clb; Cmnty Wkr; Service Clb; Bsbl; Var Capt Socr; Ntl Merit Ltr; Ntl Merit Ltr; Prfct Atten Awd; Engrng.

PLACE, KAREN; Oxford Acad; Oxford, NY; (S); Sec Rep FFA; Varsity Clb; Bsktbl; Fld Hcky; Sftbl; Hon Roll; SUNY Morrisville; Env Sci.

PLACE, SUZANNE; Vestral SR HS; Vestal, NY; (Y); Church Yth Grp; Pres German Clb; Girl Scts; Band; Mrchg Band; Pep Band; Symp Band; Hon Roll; SUNY Potsdam; Math Tchr.

PLACKIS, BRIAN; Saint Dominic HS; Levittown, NY; (Y); 2/114; Quiz Bowl; Nwsp Rptr; JV Bsbl; Im JV Bsktbl; Var Ftbl; NHS; NEDT Awd; Sal; Math Awd 85; Rgnts Schlrshp 85; Rensselaer Poltech Inst; Engrng.

PLANAS, KIMBERLY M; Lakeland HS; Lake Peekskill, NY; (Y); Dance Clb; Drama Clb; Hosp Aide; School Musical; Variety Show; Nwsp Stf; Yrbk Stf; VP Frsh Cls; Hon Roll; Ntl Merit SF; Diploma Of Merit Excellence In Spanish 82-83; Marymount Manhattan; Creatv Wrt.

PLANTE, DONNAMARY; Holy Trinity HS; W Hempstead, NY; (S); Drama Clb; Math Clb; Math Tm; Ski Clb; Chorus; Stage Crew; Ed Yrbk Stf; Stu Cncl; Hon Roll; Math.

PLANTE, ROBERT; Lansingburgh HS; Troy, NY; (Y); Boys Clb Am; High Hon Roll; Hon Roll; Art Schl; Commercial Artist.

PLANTEMOLI, LEONARD JOHN; Xaverian HS; Brooklyn, NY; (S); 9/347; Spanish Clb; Stage Crew; Stu Cncl; Crs Cntry; Trk; NHS; Spanish NHS; Princpls List Medl 82-84; Natl Ldrshp Traing 84; Pre-Law.

PLANTENBERG, KIM S; Wayne Central HS; Ontario, NY; (Y); 12/195; Rep Church Yth Grp; Sec Trs 4-H; Chorus; Church Choir; Lit Mag; Var Trk; 4-H Awd; Hon Roll; NHS; Bible Quiz Sect Hi Point Quizzer; Regents Schlrshp Wnnr; NYS Asmbly God Schlrshp Rnnr Up; Evangel; Psych.

PLASS, JEFF; Ticonderoga HS; Silver Bay, NY; (Y); French Clb; Rep Soph Cls; JV Bsbl; Im Bsktbl; Var Capt Socr; Im Vllybl; Im Wrstlng; High Hon Roll; Hon Roll.

PLATA, LISSEL; Bronx H S Of Science; New York, NY; (Y); Office Aide; Varsity Clb; Capt Socr; St Johns U; Phrmcst.

PLATE, MICHAEL; St Francis Prep; Flushing, NY; (Y); Drm & Bgl; Im Capt Bsktbl; Im Capt Ftbl; Im Sftbl; Tennis.

PLATE, PATRICIA; Commack High School North; Commack, NY; (Y); GAA; Teachers Aide; Off Frsh Cls; Off Soph Cls; Off Jr Cls; Scrkpr Lcrss; Var Tennis; High Hon Roll; Hon Roll; NHS; Math Fld.

PLATH, HARWOOD J; Columbia HS; Averill Park, NY; (Y); 55/353; Key Clb; NHS; Ntl Merit SF; NY ST Math Cont Awd 84; U Of Rochester Schlrshp 85; ROTC-NAVAL Alternate 85; U Of Rochester; Engrng.

PLATT, MICHAEL WILLIAM; Guilderland Central HS; Guilderland, NY; (Y); 120/169; CAP; ROTC; Drill Tm; Rep Stu Cncl; Hon Roll; Squadron Cadet Commandr; Rochester Inst; Engrng.

PLATT, REBECCA; South Lewis Central HS; Constableville, NY; (Y); Spanish Clb; Chorus; School Musical; Crs Cntry; Trk; Hon Roll; Psych.

PLATT, SABRINA; Susan E Wagner HS; Staten Island, NY; (Y); Office Aide; Temple Yth Grp; Variety Show; Yrbk Stf; Lit Mag; Var L Swmmng; High Hon Roll; NHS; Awd Acadmc Achvt Ec & Spnsh 8 85; Swmg Troph & Ltr 83-85.

PLATT, TIMOTHY; Unatego JR SR HS; Otego, NY; (Y); 8/88; Trs Band; Trs Sr Cls; Var Capt Crs Cntry; Var Capt Trk; Trs NHS; NY St Sprts Wrtrs Assc All-St X-C 1st Tm 83, 3rd Tm 84; Siena Coll; Psych.

PLATZ, MARCIE; Troupsburg Central HS; Knoxville, PA; (Y); 4/13; Aud/Vis; Computer Clb; Yrbk Stf; Trs Frsh Cls; Trs Soph Cls; Trs Jr Cls; Score Keeper; High Hon Roll; Hon Roll; 4-H; Unsung Hero Awd 85; Bus Mgmt.

PLESCIA, AUDREY; Sachem HS; Lake Grove, NY; (Y); 61/1428; Chorus; Orch; School Musical; School Play; Yrbk Stf; Stat Bsbl; Capt Var Cheerleading; Sftbl; Swmmng; Jr NHS; Bucknell U; Pre-Law.

PLESHETTE, ELIZABETH R; Blinel Brook HS; Rye Brook, NY; (Y); Cmnty Wkr; Drama Clb; French Clb; MMM; Political Wkr; Temple Yth Grp; Chorus; School Play; Tennis; Art Clb; Presdntl SR Prtcpnt 84; Local 1262 Schlrshp 85; Mock Elctn Reprtr 84; Columbia U.

PLESS, WANDA; Brooklyn Vo Tech; Brooklyn, NY; (Y); FTA; Teachers Aide; Band; Swmmng; Spellman U; Dsgnr.

PLESSAS, JUDE; Bishop Grimes HS; Syracuse, NY; (Y); 1/200; Church Yth Grp; English Clb; Band; Pres Stu Cncl; Bsktbl; Ftbl; Capt Tennis; High Hon Roll; Hon Roll; NHS; RPI Math & Sci Awd 85; Math Tchrs Awd 85; Bio Tchrs Awd 84; Archlgy.

PLETER, MELISSA; Binghampton HS; Binghamton, NY; (Y); Hosp Aide; Pres Temple Yth Grp; Nwsp Ed-Chief; Rep Stu Cncl, Hon Roll; NHS; NCYS Yth Of Yr 85; Phys Ther.

PLETINCKS, JAN; Nyack HS; Nyack, NY; (Y); 18/277; Church Yth Grp; Church Choir; NHS; Pres Schlr; Spanish NHS; Nyack Coll.

PLEVA, DAVID; East Meadow HS; East Meadow, NY; (S); Computer Clb; FBLA; Stu Cncl; JV Bsbl; JV Var Ftbl; Hon Roll; NHS; Bus Mgmt.

PLEVNIAK, SALLY A; Williamsville HS North; East Amherst, NY; (Y); 23/315; Mathletes; Ski Clb; Varsity Clb; Yrbk Stf; Mgr(s); Var Capt Swmmng; High Hon Roll; NHS; St Schlr; Rochester Inst Of Tech; Microel.

PLEWAK, GRETCHEN; North Tonawanda SR HS; N Tonawanda, NY; (Y); 49/470; Am Leg Aux Girls St; VP Band; Concert Band; Sec Jazz Band; Mrchg Band; Pres Sr Cls; Stu Cncl; Hon Roll; NHS; Hugh O Brian Awd 83; Lieutnant Edward Belbas SR Mem Schlrshp 85; Ithaca Coll; Bus.

PLOEGER, BETH; Pierson HS; Sag Harbor, NY; (Y); 9/48; Mgr Drama Clb; PAVAS; Mgr School Musical; Mgr School Play; Mgr Stage Crew; Yrbk Ed-Chief; Pres Frsh Cls; Pres Soph Cls; Pres Jr Cls; Pres Sr Cls; Forrest Glen Thayer JR Mem Schlrshp 85; Knights Of Columbus Schlrshp 85; John Martin JR Mem Awd 85; Rochester Inst Of Tech; Design.

PLOPPER, STEVE; Hilton Central HS; Hilton, NY; (Y); Concert Band; Mrchg Band; Pep Band; Symp Band; High Hon Roll; Hon Roll; Comp Sci.

PLUAS, ROXANA; Washingtin Irving HS; New York, NY; (Y); Teachers Aide; Dnfth Awd; High Hon Roll; Hon Roll; Prfct Atten Awd; Acad Olympcs Awd 85; Bus Hnr Soc Awd 85; Sec.

PLUFF, MICHAEL; Altmar-Parish Williamstown HS; Parish, NY; (Y); French Clb; Mathletes; Varsity Clb; JV Var Bsbl; JV Var Bsktbl; JV Var Ftbl; Hon Roll; Prfct Atten Awd; Law.

PLUMADORE, DANIELLE; Tamarac HS; Troy, NY; (Y); 6/106; Intnl Clb; Yrbk Stf; Var L Socr; Hon Roll; NHS; Edtih Grace Reynolds Schlrshp 85; Brunswick Bus & Prfssnl Assn Awd 85; Hgh Hnrs Grad 85; HYCC; Accntng.

PLUMB, JENNIFER; Oriskany Central HS; Oriskany, NY; (Y); 11/90; Cmnty Wkr; Key Clb; Spanish Clb; Varsity Clb; Yrbk Stf; Socr; Trk; DAR Awd; High Hon Roll; Hon Roll; 1st Lieutnt Govrnr NYS 84-85; Temple U; Acturl Sci.

PLUMMER, CAMILLA; Andrew Jackson HS; St Albans, NY; (Y); Office Aide; Chorus; Church Choir; Hunter Coll; Nrsng.

PLUMMER, CHARLES L; Charles W Baker HS; Baldwinsville, NY; (Y); 70/441; Rep Frsh Cls; Bsktbl; JV Socr; NY ST Empire ST Games-Archery 82, 83, 85; James Madison U; Engrng.

PLUNKETT, PRUDENCE; East Islip HS; Great River, NY; (Y); 11/475; Cmnty Wkr; Political Wkr; Orch; School Musical; High Hon Roll; Hon Roll; Jr NHS; Masonic Awd; NHS; Ntl Merit Ltr; Music Ltr, Pin 84-85; Outstndng Achvt Socl Studies, Frnch 84-85; Bryn Mawr Coll; Poltcl Sci.

PLURETTI, SUSANNE; Mynderse Acad; Seneca Falls, NY; (Y); Girl Scts; JV Bsktbl; Var L Sftbl; Var L Vllybl; Hon Roll.

PLYTER, LISA; Newark SR HS; Newark, NY; (Y); 6/200; Am Leg Aux Girls St; Cmnty Wkr; Spanish Clb; Sec Ed Yrbk Stf; Mgr(s); Var Capt Swmmng; High Hon Roll; NHS; Spanish NHS; Mst Vlbl Swmr 83 & 85; Mst Prmsng Swmng 83; Bus Mngmnt.

POCHATKO, GARY; La Salle SR HS; Niagara Falls, NY; (Y); VP Stu Cncl; JV Var Ftbl; Trs NHS; Pltcl Sci.

POCHUNOW, ANN MARIE; Bishop Kearney HS; Rochester, NY; (Y); Cmnty Wkr; GAA; JA; Office Aide; Band; Yrbk Stf; Bowling; Coach Actv; Score Keeper; Sftbl; Jrnlsm.

PODADERA, JOSE LUIS; Set Agnes HS; Jackson Hts, NY; (Y); 9/100; Boy Scts; JV Bsktbl; Capt Vllybl; Hon Roll; NHS; Elec Engr.

PODSIADLO, JENNIFER M; Lancaster Central HS; Depew, NY; (Y); 54/550; Key Clb; Pep Clb; Varsity Clb; JV Cheerleading; Var L Fld Hcky; Var Trk; Hon Roll; Jr NHS; NHS; Ntl Merit Ltr; Labor Rel Mngr.

POELLER, ROBERT; Alden HS; Alden, NY; (Y); Aud/Vis; Band; Mrchg Band; Var Crs Cntry; JV Trk; U Buffalo; Comp Pgrmng.

POERSCHKE, SUSAN; Niagara Wheatfield HS; N Tonawanda, NY; (Y); Am Leg Aux Girls St; Trs Church Yth Grp; Office Aide; Hon Roll; NHS; Accntng.

POGACT, TRACY A; Charles W Baker HS; Baldwinsville, NY; (Y); 59/441; Art Clb; JV Socr; MONY Schlstc Awd 81-82; Athl Mnth 81-82; Fredonia-Suny.

POHL, CENA A; Lakeland HS; Yorktown Heights, NY; (Y); 24/360; Drama Clb; German Clb; Q&S; Radio Clb; School Musical; Yrbk Stf; Rep Soph Cls; Rep Sr Cls; Stu Cncl; Crs Cntry; Washington U St Louis.

POINTER, RACHEL; Fairport HS; Fairport, NY; (Y); Dance Clb; Service Clb; Chorus; Stage Crew; Rep Stu Cncl; Hon Roll; NHS; Prfct Atten Awd.

POIRIER JR, JAMES; Linton HS; Schenectady, NY; (Y); Var Bsbl; JV Var Ftbl; High Hon Roll; Physics.

POISSANT, JULIE; Franklin Acad; Malone, NY; (Y); Church Yth Grp; Drama Clb; French Clb; Hosp Aide; Ski Clb; School Play; Stage Crew.

POKLADOWSKI, VIOLET; The Mary Louis Acad; Glendale, NY; (Y); Debate Tm; Trk; Hon Roll.

POKOWICZ, STEPHEN; Walt Whitman HS; Huntington, NY; (Y); 39/540; Boy Scts; Cmnty Wkr; Band; Concert Band; Mrchg Band; School Play; Im JV Ftbl; Var JV Lcrss; Im Trk; High Hon Roll; Chrprctr.

POKOWITZ, CAROLYN; Connetquot HS; Bohemia, NY; (Y); Church Yth Grp; GAA; Yrbk Stf; VP Stu Cncl; Capt Cheerleading; Capt Gym; Trk; High Hon Roll; Hon Roll; Jr NHS; MVP & Coachs Awd Trck & Fld 84-85; 2nd Suffolk Cnty Trck & Fld 13th NY St 85; Psychlgy.

POKOWITZ, JOSEPH BRIAN; John A Coleman HS; Rosendale, NY; (S); 5/70; Church Yth Grp; French Clb; Key Clb; Stage Crew; Yrbk Bus Mgr; Yrbk Phtg; Trs Jr Cls; High Hon Roll; NHS; Scty Dist Amer HS Stus 84; Intl Rel.

POLASHENSKI, WALTER; Liverpool HS; Liverpool, NY; (S); 50/850; Exploring; Lit Mag; JV Bsbl; Hon Roll; Jr NHS; NHS; Ntl Merit Ltr; Bio.

POLCYN, JAMES; Notre Dame HS; Elmira, NY; (Y); Nwsp Stf; Var Bsbl; Var Bsktbl; Var Capt Ftbl; Hon Roll; Bus.

POLESHUCK, ELLEN; Brighton HS; Rochester, NY; (Y); 45/315; Cmnty Wkr; Latin Clb; Ski Clb; Spanish Clb; Sec Temple Yth Grp; School Play; Stage Crew; Nwsp Rptr; Yrbk Stf; Ntl Merit Ltr; Comm Serv Awd 84-85.

POLETTO, VALENTINA KATHRYN; Saugerties HS; Saugerties, NY; (Y); 2/248; Am Leg Aux Girls St; French Clb; Ski Clb; Mrchg Band; Symp Band; JV Var Cheerleading; High Hon Roll; NHS.

POLICANO, ALBERT; East Meadow HS; E Meadow, NY; (S); Varsity Clb; Band; Var L Bsbl; Var Crs Cntry; Trk; Hon Roll; Prfct Atten Awd; Schltc Achvt Awd 83; Cortland; Engrng Tech.

POLISENO, DOMINIC; Floral Park Memorial HS; Floral Park, NY; (Y); 18/184; VP Computer Clb; Mathletes; Variety Show; Nwsp Rptr; Yrbk Stf; Var L Trk; High Hon Roll; Hon Roll; Trs NHS; NY ST Rgnts Schlrshp 85; Polytechnic Inst Of Tech; Engrg.

POLITO, DEBORAH; Port Jervis HS; Port Jervis, NY; (Y); Aud/Vis; Boy Scts; Chorus; Concert Band; Jazz Band; Mrchg Band; Orch; School Musical; Stage Crew; Prfct Atten Awd; ST U Potsdam; Music.

POLITO, DEBRA; Connetquot HS; Oakdale, NY; (S); 25/723; Var Sftbl; Hon Roll; Math & Sci Awd 81-82; Intl Frgn Lang Awd 83-84; Biomed Engrng.

POLITO, LAURA; Buffalo Academy Of The Sacred Heart; Williamsville, NY; (Y); Cmnty Wkr; Orch; School Musical; Nwsp Phtg; Nwsp Stf; Yrbk Stf; Rep Frsh Cls; Rep Jr Cls; Var Capt Cheerleading; Var Capt Socr; NY ST U Buffalo; Banking.

POLIZZI, CAROL; The Mary Louis Acad; Flushing, NY; (Y); 2/230; Hosp Aide; Teachers Aide; High Hon Roll; NHS; Ntl Merit SF; Queens Coll Pres Awd Achvt 84; Schlrshp Soph Yr 83; Trustee Schlrshp NYU 85; NY U; Musician.

POLK, DONNA M; Copiague HS; Amityville, NY; (Y); 2/349; Math Clb; Church Choir; School Play; Var Fld Hcky; Bausch & Lomb Sci Awd; NHS; Prfct Atten Awd; Sal; Church Yth Grp; Cmnty Wkr; Ntl Merit Comm Stu 84; Rochester Engr Schlrshp U,COPTA Schlrshp 85; Rochester U; Engr.

POLLACK, DARREN; Hudson HS; Hudson, NY; (Y); Cmnty Wkr; Band; Concert Band; Jazz Band; Mrchg Band; Orch; Var L Bsbl; Var Capt Ftbl; Church Yth Grp; Cmnty Wkr; Rookie Instrmntlst Of Yr; St Rose Wittenberg; Mgmt.

POLLACK, DAVID; South Side HS; Rockville Ctr, NY; (Y); 101/315; Computer Clb; Mathletes; Pres VP Temple Yth Grp; Band; Concert Band; Mrchg Band; Pep Band; School Musical; Hon Roll; U Of Rochester; Bio-Chem.

POLLACK, JAMES; Port Richmond HS; Staten Isld, NY; (Y); 30/750; Drama Clb; Library Aide; Math Clb; Math Tm; School Play; Stage Crew; Yrbk Stf; Physcs.

POLLACK, JENNY; School Of Performing Arts; New York, NY; (Y); 16/588; Drama Clb; Stage Crew; Yrbk Stf; High Hon Roll; Jr NHS; NCTE Awd; NHS; Merit Awd Exc Actng 85; Merit Awd Exc Theatre 85; Northwestern U.

POLLICINO, DEBRA A; Bishop Kearney HS; Brooklyn, NY; (Y); 156/341; Camera Clb; Cmnty Wkr; Hosp Aide; Science Clb; St Schlr; Regent Schlrshp; Brooklyn Coll; Bio.

POLLINA, KELLY A; Kensington HS; Buffalo, NY; (Y); FBLA; GAA; Chorus; School Musical; Gym; Sftbl; Trk; ECC Coll; Child Care.

POLLINA, STACY L; Sacchem HS North Campus; Holbrook, NY; (Y); 1/1420; Math Tm; Science Clb; Spanish Clb; Concert Band; Orch; Ed Lit Mag; NHS; Val; Acadmc Grnt U Of PA 85; Schlstc Achvtm 85; U Of PA; Med.

POLLISH, HOWARD; South Shore HS; Brooklyn, NY; (Y); 11/668; Service Clb; School Musical; Yrbk Sprt Ed; Rep Sr Cls; Rep Stu Cncl; Var L Crs Cntry; High Hon Roll; NHS; Math Tm; Office Aide; Grtr Mtrpltn Math Fair Brnz Medal 82-83; Acdmc Olympics 83-85; Outwrd Bnd Alumnus 84; U Of VA; Aero-Engrng.

POLLITT, MAUREEN; Albertus Magnus HS; Stony Pt, NY; (Y); 18/190; Church Yth Grp; Math Tm; Varsity Clb; School Musical; Var Bsktbl; Var Tennis; Twrlr; High Hon Roll; NHS; Var Tnns MVP 84; Var Bsktbl Mst Imprvd Plyr 84-85; Engrng.

POLLOCK, CHRISTOPHER; Walt Whitman HS; Huntington, NY; (Y); 40/540; Church Yth Grp; Drama Clb; Key Clb; Band; L Concert Band; Mrchg Band; Orch; School Musical; Symp Band; Lit Mag; Hon Mntn Engl & Music 83; NYS Schl Music Assoc Mdl 83-84; Bus Admin.

POLLOCK, STEPHEN; Tamarac HS; Troy, NY; (Y); Boy Scts; Math Tm; Band; Chorus; Var Ftbl; Var Tennis; Var Wrstlng; Hon Roll; Pep Band; School Musical; Amer HS Athltc Assoc 85; Instrmntl Music.

POLLONI, ERIC; Msgr Mc Clancy Memorial HS; Jackson Hts, NY; (S); 4/229; Science Clb; Nwsp Rptr; High Hon Roll; NHS; Outstndng Svc Italian Cultre Clb Awd 81-82; VP Italian Cultre Clb 83-84; Accntg.

POLLY, MELISSA; Henninger HS; Syracuse, NY; (Y); Color Guard; Rep Frsh Cls; Hon Roll; Prfct Atten Awd; Math.

POLO, JAY; Horseheads HS; Big Flats, NY; (S); 53/407; Am Leg Boys St; Boy Scts; Church Yth Grp; Science Clb; Varsity Clb; Concert Band; Mrchg Band; Rep Stu Cncl; JV Var Diving; JV Var Trk; Engrng.

POLONCARZ, PAULETTE K; West Seneca East SR HS; West Seneca, NY; (Y); 32/365; DECA; Rep Frsh Cls; Rep Soph Cls; Trs Jr Cls; Trs Sr Cls; Rep Stu Cncl; Trk; Vllybl; High Hon Roll; NHS; St Bonaventure U; Comm.

POLONSKI, TODD; Longwood HS; Shirley, NY; (Y); Varsity Clb; VICA; Trk; Hon Roll; Air Cond.

POLOVICK, DENISE; Thomas A Edison HS; Elmira Hts, NY; (Y); French Clb; Varsity Clb; Color Guard; Mrchg Band; Stage Crew; Cheerleading; Hon Roll; Fshn Dsgn.

POLSINELLI, VITO; Mont Pleasant HS; Schenectady, NY; (Y); 8/260; Ski Clb; Spanish Clb; JV Ftbl; Wt Lftg; JV Var Wrstlng; Hon Roll; NHS; Spanish NHS; Mechncl Engr.

POLSTRA, MONICA A; Solvay HS; Solvay, NY; (Y); 7/167; Art Clb; French Clb; JA; Office Aide; School Musical; School Play; Stage Crew; Variety Show; Nwsp Rptr; Nwsp Stf; AAA Sfty Pstr Comp 1st Lcl, 3rd Ntl 84; NY ST Rgnts Schlrshp 85; 2nd Ntl Leag Amer Wmn Ptry/Art 85.

POLVERINO, IMMA; Bishop Kearney HS; Brooklyn, NY; (Y); Art Clb; Cmnty Wkr; Intnl Clb; Library Aide; Teachers Aide; Hon Roll; Brooklyn Coll; Frgn Lang.

POLZINETTI, JOHN; De Sales HS; Seneca Falls, NY; (Y); 14/45; Scholastic Bowl; School Musical; Vllybl; High Hon Roll; Hon Roll; NHS; NEDT Awd; Pres Schlr; Computer Clb; Ski Clb; Regents Schlrshp 85; Amer Studies Awd 84; Physics Awd 85; Le Moyne Coll; Physics.

POMANA, JOANNE; Attica HS; Cowlesville, NY; (Y); Drama Clb; GAA; Library Aide; Chorus; Color Guard; Score Keeper; Vllybl; Prfct Atten Awd; Cazenovia Coll; Bus.

POMERANTZ, MICHAEL; Connetquot HS; Bohemia, NY; (Y); Nwsp Stf; Var Crs Cntry; Var Golf; JV Socr; JV Tennis; Var Trk; Hon Roll; 4th Prz Ntl Sci Cngrs Fair 82; Mechncl Engr.

POMERANZ, LARRY; Niskayuna HS; Niskayuna, NY; (Y); VP Pres Temple Yth Grp; Var JV Golf; Hon Roll; NHS; Natrl Sci.

POMEROY II, DONALD G; Newfane SR HS; Newfane, NY; (S); 8/166; Trs AFS, Boy Scts; Varsity Clb; Trs Frsh Cls; Var Crs Cntry; God Cntry Awd; High Hon Roll; VP NHS; Ntl Merit Ltr; Band; Eagle Scout BSA 82; Hghst Av Regents Chem Cls 84; Lawyer.

POMPONIO, ELANA; Springfille Griffith Inst; Springville, NY; (Y); 120/201; Church Yth Grp; FBLA; Library Aide; Teachers Aide; Band; Chorus; Color Guard; Mrchg Band; School Musical; Tennis; Erie CC; Wrd Prcsng.

PON, DARRAN; St Agnes HS; Woodside, NY; (Y); 15/100; JA; Service Clb; Teachers Aide; Hon Roll; NHS; 2nd Hrs 83-85; Engrng.

PONG, CAROL; Oyster Bay HS; E Norwich, NY; (Y); French Clb; Chorus; Yrbk Phtg; High Hon Roll; NHS; Med.

PONTICELLI, JOSEPHINE; Christ The King HS; Ozone Park, NY; (Y); 97/385; Yrbk Stf; Second Hnrs 82-83; St Francis Coll; Phys Therapy.

PONZI, SUSAN L; Niabara Wheatfield SR HS; N Tonawanda, NY; (Y); 29/305; VP Pep Clb; Hst PAVAS; Sec Band; Capt Color Guard; School Musical; School Play; Rep Stu Cncl; Hon Roll; Sec NHS; Ntl Merit Ltr; Niagara-Wheatfield H S Bst Actrss 83; Niagara-Wheatfield H S Bst Supptg Actrss 84; Canisius Coll; Cmmnctns.

POOLE, BETH ANN; Ithaca HS; Ithaca, NY; (Y); Sec Pres Church Yth Grp; GAA; Capt Quiz Bowl; Varsity Clb; School Play; Yrbk Sprt Ed; Var Capt Cheerleading; High Hon Roll; Cmnty Wkr; Dance Clb; Jansen Awd 84-85; Arthur Parsons Schlrshp 84-85; Southeastern Coll; Schl Tchr.

POOLE, JULIUS; Medina SR HS; Medina, NY; (Y); Art Clb; Computer Clb; Chorus; Church Choir; Yrbk Phtg; Yrbk Rptr; Yrbk Stf; VP Frsh Cls; Rep Stu Cncl; JV Var Socr; Stu Assn Awd 85; Cazenovia Coll; Bus Admin.

POOLE, PATRICIA; The Mary Louis Acad; Flushing, NY; (Y); Office Aide; Ftbl; Powder Puff Ftbl.

POOLE, STACIE PRECIA; Nightingale-Banford HS; New York, NY; (Y); Dance Clb; Drama Clb; Chorus; School Musical; Swing Chorus; Variety Show; Bsktbl; Sftbl; Trk; Co-Capt Vllybl; Regents Schlrshp 85; Outstndng Musicianshp Awd 82; Yale U; Music.

POON, PETER; W C Bryant HS; Long Island, NY; (Y); 48/600; Chess Clb; Math Tm; Quiz Bowl; Color Guard; Stage Crew; Lit Mag; Cit Awd; Hon Roll; NHS; Pres Schlr; Math Tm Cty Rnnr Up SR Tm 84-85; Polytech Schlrshp; Polytechnic Inst; Mech Engr.

POONAI, KAMALA; Christopher Columbus HS; Bronx, NY; (Y); Yrbk Stf; Cit Awd; Hon Roll; Prfct Atten Awd; Arista 84; Psych.

POPE, PATRICIA; Attica HS; Attica, NY; (S); Drama Clb; Band; Concert Band; Mrchg Band; School Play; Rep Soph Cls; Score Keeper; Tennis; Law Enforce.

POPOLI, TERRI; St Catharine Acad; Bronx, NY; (Y); 42/205; Teachers Aide; Hon Roll; Jr NHS; NHS; Excllnce Sci 83; Excllnce Eng 10 84; Excllnce Eng 11 85.

POPOLI, TINA; Mount Vernon HS; Mount Vernon, NY; (Y); 47/590; FBLA; Office Aide; Teachers Aide; Tennis; Cit Awd; High Hon Roll; Hon Roll; Mt Vernon Yth Brd 85; Iona Coll; Bus Adm.

POPOVIC, MARTIN; Christopher Columbus HS; Bronx, NY; (Y); 5/792; Key Clb; Yrbk Stf; Hon Roll; Sec NHS; Cvl Engr.

POPOVICH, PHILLIP; Corning Painted Post West HS; Painted Post, NY; (Y); JA; Varsity Clb; Var Bsbl; JV Bsktbl; JV Golf; High Hon Roll; Hon Roll; NHS; Pre-Med.

POPP, AILEEN Y; Letchworth Central Schl; Castile, NY; (Y); 5/83; Church Yth Grp; Computer Clb; 4-H; Math Tm; VP Spanish Clb; Band; Mrchg Band; Yrbk Stf; Var Sftbl; Pres NHS; NY ST Regents Schlrshp 85-89; Cornell U; Animal Sci.

POPPITO, NORA; Saint Anthonys HS; Wantagh, NY; (Y); Drama Clb; Concert Band; School Musical; Nwsp Rptr; Rep Stu Cncl; JV Crs Cntry; Var Sftbl; JV Swmmng; Var Trk; NHS; U Of Dallas Scholar 85; Var Kickline 83-84; U Of Dallas; Med.

POPPOON, JENNIFER J; Marcus Whitman CHS; Canandaigua, NY; (Y); 1/122; Am Leg Aux Girls St; Jazz Band; Orch; DAR Awd; JP Sousa Awd; NHS; Val; JCL; Pep Clb; Teachers Aide; NY ST Regnts Schlrshp 85; All Estrn Conf Band 85; All ST Band Wind Ens 83-84; Music.

PORADA, DOLORES; Bishop Kearney HS; Brooklyn, NY; (Y); Rep Soph Cls; Rep Sr Cls; Tennis; NHS; Fr Cont Iona Coll 85; Scholar Bishop Kearney 82; MVP Ten Tm 85; Mth.

PORCARI, LISA M; Saunders Trades & Technical HS; Yonkers, NY; (Y); 1/198; VICA; Yrbk Stf; Lit Mag; Var Vllybl; High Hon Roll; NHS; Val; D Balmori Schlrshp 85; Tufts U.

PORCELLI, JEFFREY; Cardinal Mooney HS; Rochester, NY; (Y); 18/330; Exploring; Ski Clb; JV Ftbl; High Hon Roll; Ntl Merit SF; Math, Chem, Lat Awds; Comp.

PORCO, MARIA M; Cardnial Spellman HS; New York, NY; (S); Key Clb; Math Tm; Pep Clb; Rep Frsh Cls; Rep Soph Cls; Rep Jr Cls; Rep Sr Cls; High Hon Roll; Hon Roll; NHS; Bus Finc.

POREMBA, SHARON; Cardinal O Hara HS; Buffalo, NY; (Y); Spanish Clb; Nwsp Rptr; Yrbk Stf; Im Bowling; Daemen Coll; Pre-Med.

POROSKY, CHRIS; Notre Dame HS; Elmira, NY; (Y); Computer Clb; Quiz Bowl; Science Clb; School Play; Crs Cntry; Trk; French Hon Soc; Hon Roll; Engr.

PORPA, LESLIE; Hudson HS; Hudson, NY; (Y); Girl Scts; Ski Clb; Pres Temple Yth Grp; Band; Nwsp Stf; Off Sr Cls; Var Bowling; JV Var Sftbl; Var Tennis; Hon Roll; Mst Imprvd Plyr Vrsty Grls Tnns 84-85; Dentl Hygn.

PORRELLO, FRANCES; Sacred Heart Acad; Bellerose Village, NY; (Y); Yrbk Stf; Hon Roll; NHS; NASSAU CC; Nrsg.

PORTA, KAREN; Bihsop Kearney HS; Brooklyn, NY; (Y); Church Yth Grp; Cmnty Wkr; Varsity Clb; Var Cheerleading; High Hon Roll; Natl Latin Awd-Slvr Medal 84; Math.

PORTEOUS, LEIGH; Albion HS; Albion, NY; (S); 26/188; Trs Spanish Clb; Band; Pep Band; Pres Frsh Cls; Rep Jr Cls; Trs Cheerleading; Var Pom Pon; Var Sftbl; Hon Roll; Cornell U; Pol Sci.

PORTER, DONALD P; Smithtown East; Hauppauge, NY; (Y); 93/540; Frsh Cls; Soph Cls; Jr Cls; Sr Cls; Stu Cncl; Var Capt Bsbl; Hon Roll; NHS; Spanish NHS; Villanova U; Pre Med.

PORTER, JAMES; Gilbertsville Central HS; Gilbertsville, NY; (Y); 1/27; Am Leg Boys St; Varsity Clb; School Play; Pres Frsh Cls; Trs Soph Cls; Rep Pres Stu Cncl; Var Bsbl; JV Bsktbl; Var Capt Socr; High Hon Roll; FHD Mecklenburg Consv Fllwshp 84; Elmira Coll Key Awd 85; Albany Coll Phrmcy; Phrmcy.

PORTER, JEANNETTE HILL; Hunter College HS; Bronx, NY; (Y); Model UN; Office Aide; Chorus; Swing Chorus; Rep Stu Cncl; Mu Alp Tht; Ntl Merit SF; NY Clscl Soc Latin Excllnc Awd 82; Swarthmore Coll; Economics.

PORTER, JENNIFER; Grand Island HS; Grand Is, NY; (Y); 3/280; Church Yth Grp; Hosp Aide; Teachers Aide; Variety Show; Ed Yrbk Stf; VP Stu Cncl; Var Tennis; Hon Roll; NHS; Pres Schlr; Rgnts Schlrshp; Niagara Frntr Athlt Assn Schlrshp; PTSA Awd For Acdmc Achvt; Alfred U; Ceramic Engr.

PORTER, JENNIFER T; Albany Academy For Girls; Ghent, NY; (Y); 1/25; Pres 4-H; Quiz Bowl; Chorus; Sec Jr Cls; Rep Stu Cncl; Var Capt Fld Hcky; Sftbl; Var JV Vllybl; Cit Awd; 4-H Awd; 4-H Awd; Cum Laude; Cornell; Bio.

PORTER, JOHN; Trott Vocational HS; Niagara Falls, NY; (Y).

PORTER, KRISTA; New Berlin Central HS; New Berlin, NY; (Y); 4/48; Varsity Clb; Concert Band; Jazz Band; Yrbk Phtg; Var Bsktbl; Var Sftbl; High Hon Roll; Jr NHS; NHS; Church Yth Grp; Tri-Vly All Star Bsktbl & Sftbl 85; ST U Of OneontaSECONDRY Educ.

PORTER, LAURA; Oakfield Alabama Central HS; Oakfield, NY; (Y); 60/100; Var Socr; Var Sftbl; V Ltr 85; Genesee CC; Trvl.

PORTER, LINDA; Churchville Chili HS; Rochester, NY; (Y); Chorus; Church Choir; Hon Roll; Rochester Inst Tech; Comp Pgmng.

PORTER, SEAN; St John The Baptist HS; Lindenhurst, NY; (Y); Stu Cncl; JV Capt Bsbl; Bus.

PORTER, THERESA; Ellenville Central HS; Napanoch, NY; (Y); Trs FHA; Im JV Trk; Hon Roll; Elem Tchr.

PORTER, TOM; Fox Lane HS; Pound Ridge, NY; (Y); 7/258; Am Leg Boys St; Drama Clb; Science Clb; Chorus; Madrigals; Orch; School Musical; NHS; Ntl Merit Schol; Church Yth Grp; All ST Chorus-Prfct Scr; Columbia Bk Awd.

PORTHUN, CHRISTINE; St Francis Prep; Woodhaven, NY; (S); 39/694; Church Yth Grp; Math Tm; Teachers Aide; Chorus; School Play; Stage Crew; Sftbl; Hon Roll; NHS; St Johns U.

PORTIS, KERI; Roosevelt JR SR HS; Roosevelt, NY; (Y); 4-H; Teachers Aide; Church Choir; Concert Band; Mrchg Band; Yrbk Stf; Sec Frsh Cls; Rep Jr Cls; Hon Roll; Prfct Atten Awd; NAACP Awd For Blck Poetry 83; Miss Blck Teen Wrld NY ST Schlrshp 84; U Of MD/Schlrshp VA Union; VA Union; Pblc Rltns.

PORTNER, TRACY A; Corning East HS; Corning, NY; (Y); Ski Clb; Spanish Clb; Chorus; Rep Soph Cls; Rep Jr Cls; JV Var Cheerleading; High Hon Roll; Hon Roll; Corning CC; Hotel Mgmt.

PORTNOY, JILL; Commack HS; Commack, NY; (Y); Spanish Clb; Temple Yth Grp; Mrchg Band; Symp Band; Yrbk Stf; Off Frsh Cls; Soph Cls; Jr Cls; High Hon Roll; Trs NHS; Math.

PORTO, MARYANNE; Holland Central Schl; South Wales, NY; (Y); 4/107; AFS; Varsity Clb; Yrbk Stf; Fld Hcky; High Hon Roll; Hon Roll; Jr NHS; NHS; Prfct Atten Awd; SUNY-BUFFALO; Pharm.

PORUPSKI, JAMES; Newark Valley HS; Owego, NY; (Y); 52/120; 4-H; 4-H Awd; High Hon Roll; Hon Roll; Comp Sci.

PORZIO, ELIZABETH; St Edmunds HS; Brooklyn, NY; (Y); 41/187; 1st Hnrs Cert 84; St Francis Coll; Elem Tchr.

POSLUSZNY, DAVE; Depew HS; Lancaster, NY; (Y); 32/254; French Clb; Band; Chorus; Drm Mjr(t); Jazz Band; Pres Mrchg Band; School Musical; Swing Chorus; Rep Stu Cncl; NHS; ST Of NY Regents Schlrshp 84-85; SR All-Amer Hall Of Fame Bnd Hnrs 84-85; Amer Musical Fndtn Bnd Hn; U Of NY Buffalo; Psych.

POSLUSZNY, DAVID J; Depew HS; Lancaster, NY; (Y); 32/254; Pres Band; Chorus; Concert Band; Drm Mjr(t); Jazz Band; Mrchg Band; School Musical; Variety Show; Rep Stu Cncl; Hon Roll; American Musical Foundation Band Hnrs 84; NY ST Regenst Schlrshp 85; Natl Honor Roll 85; U Of NY Buffalo; Psychology.

POSNER, DAVID B; Horace Mann Schl; Riverdale, NY; (Y); Debate Tm; Intnl Clb; Nwsp Rptr; Nwsp Stf; Lit Mag; Ntl Merit SF; Hstry.

POSSER, JOCELYN; Academy Of St Joseph; Nesconset, NY; (Y); Hosp Aide; Library Aide; Orch; Nwsp Ed-Chief; Nwsp Rptr; Sup Perf Natl Edduc Dvlpmnt Test 83; Sup Acad Achvt Bus 85; Vol Svc Awd 83-85; Law.

POST, ALEXANDER A; New Hyde Park Memorial HS; New Hyde Park, NY; (Y); 7/269; Spanish Clb; Varsity Clb; Var L Ftbl; Var L Trk; Trs Jr NHS; NHS; Publ Natl Hnr Rll 84; NY ST Regnts Coll Schlrshp 84; Trstee Schlr NY U 85; NY U; Bio.

POST, DONNA; Nazareth Acad; Pittsford, NY; (Y); Camera Clb; Math Clb; Vllybl; Nwsp Rptr; Nwsp Stf; Yrbk Phtg; Yrbk Stf; Ice Hcky; Socr; Tennis; Comp Sci.

POST, FRAYDI R; Torah Academy For Girls; Farrock Away, NY; (Y); 7/27; Temple Yth Grp; Chorus; School Musical; Stage Crew; Yrbk Phtg; Capt Jr Cls; Hon Roll; Brooklyn Coll; Wrtng.

POSTA, SARA DELLA; Gowanda Central Schl; Gowanda, NY; (Y); 8/140; Drama Clb; Ski Clb; Thesps; Band; Chorus; Mrchg Band; School Musical; Stu Cncl; Hon Roll; NHS; Sempre Fedalis Awd 85; All-ST Band 84; Music.

POSTELL, ELIZABETH; Cicero-North Syracuse HS; Brewerton, NY; (S); 4/711; GAA; JV L Bsktbl; Powder Puff Ftbl; Var Capt Socr; JV Sftbl; Hon Roll; Cornell Bk Club Awd 83; Literary Awd 83; Optimist Club Yth Apprctn Awd 84; Cornell; Bio Sci.

POSTULLO, DONNA; Jericho SR HS; Jericho, NY; (Y); Dance Clb; GAA; Mgr(s); Capt Socr; Sftbl; Vllybl; MVP Soccer 83-85; SADD Stu.

POTCHINSKY, STUART; Binghamton HS; Binghamton, NY; (Y); Am Leg Boys St; Cmnty Wkr; Band; Jazz Band; Nwsp Rptr; Im JV Bsbl; High Hon Roll; NHS; Spanish Clb; Temple Yth Grp; Ntl Cncl Yth Ldrshp 84-85; Stu JCY 82-86.

POTH, JEFFREY D; West Seneca West SR HS; W Seneca, NY; (Y); Sec French Clb; Ski Clb; Crs Cntry; Hon Roll; Cert Achvt Chem 85; Paul Smiths Coll Art; Htl Mgmnt.

POTORTI, ROSANNA; Our Lady Of Victory HS; Eastchester, NY; (S); 4/150; French Clb; VP Frsh Cls; Trs Soph Cls; Sec Jr Cls; Sftbl; Vllybl; Cit Awd; French Hon Soc; High Hon Roll; NHS; OLV Schlrshp 83.

POTRATZ, JENNIFER; Mt Mercy Acad; Buffalo, NY; (Y); 14/150; Computer Clb; Science Clb; Buffalo Zoo Vol Pgm 83-84; Niagara Swim Leag 3rd Pl 2nd Pl Relays 85; Canisuis Coll; Phrmcy.

POTTER, ANN MARIE; St Marys Acad; Glens Falls, NY; (S); 6/42; Church Yth Grp; Pres French Clb; Girl Scts; Key Clb; Nwsp Rptr; Yrbk Ed-Chief; Pres Frsh Cls; Pres Sr Cls; Powder Puff Ftbl; Hon Roll; St John Fisher Coll; Comm.

POTTER, BOB; Hilton HS; North Greece, NY; (Y); Concert Band; Mrchg Band; Symp Band; High Hon Roll; Hon Roll; Ntl Merit SF; OPTCL Engr.

POTTER, CARL W; Liverpool HS; Liverpool, NY; (Y); 142/792; Trs VP Computer Clb; Pres JA; Church Choir; Mrchg Band; School Musical; Variety Show; Rep Stu Cncl; JV Socr; High Hon Roll; Jr NHS; NY ST Regents Schlrshp 85; Syracuse U; Mngmnt.

POTTER, DOROTHY; Waterford Halfmoon HS; Waterford, NY; (Y); 10/87; Church Yth Grp; Math Clb; Ski Clb; Teachers Aide; Band; Chorus; Madrigals; Nwsp Rptr; Yrbk Stf; Fld Hcky; 1 Of 8 Schlrshps Spain YFU; SUNY; Vet.

POTTER, ELIZABETH KATE; Gloversville HS; Mayfield, NY; (Y); Hosp Aide; Varsity Clb; Rep Jr Cls; Off Sr Cls; JV Var Bsktbl; JV Cheerleading; Var Crs Cntry; Powder Puff Ftbl; Var Trk; High Hon Roll; Govt.

POTTER, JON; Skaneateles HS; Skaneateles, NY; (S); Church Yth Grp; High Hon Roll; Hon Roll; NHS; U Of Tampa; Fine Arts.

POTTER, LAURIE; Allegany Central HS; Allegany, NY; (Y); 20/90; Church Yth Grp; Chorus; Church Choir; School Musical; School Play; Stu Cncl; JV Var Cheerleading; Var L Sftbl; High Hon Roll; NHS; IAABO Outstndng Chrldr Awd 84; Cedarville Coll; Comm.

POTTER, MARY ANNE; Sperry HS; Rochester, NY; (Y); GAA; Teachers Aide; Var Coach Actv; Var Sftbl; French Hon Soc; Hon Roll; Jr NHS; NHS; Ntl Merit Ltr; Art Clb; Nazereth Coll; Erly Chldhd Educ.

POTTER, REBECCA A; Naples HS; Naples, NY; (Y); 4-H; Chorus; Bsktbl; Sftbl; Graphic Art & Bus.

POTTER, TAMMY; Odessa-Montour Central Schl; Montour Falls, NY; (Y); VICA; VP Chorus; School Musical; Stage Crew; Swing Chorus; Mgr Trk; High Hon Roll; Hon Roll; Prfct Atten Awd; Corning CC; Data Processing.

POTTS, EDWARD; Cardinal Ohara HS; N Tonawanda, NY; (Y); Boy Scts; Pres Spanish Clb; Rep Frsh Cls; Rep Stu Cncl; JV Var Bsktbl; JV Var Crs Cntry; JV Var Trk; God Cntry Awd; Hon Roll; NHS; Engrng.

POUND, LAURA; Frontier Central HS; Hamburg, NY; (S); French Clb; Hosp Aide; Ski Clb; Spanish Clb; Band; Rep Soph Cls; Var Socr; Hon Roll; NHS; National French Contest Awd 84-85.

POURAKIS, ANNE; New Hyde Park Memorial HS; New Hyde Park, NY; (S); 38/269; Church Yth Grp; DECA; Hst FBLA; Varsity Clb; Yrbk Stf; Var Bsktbl; Var Sftbl; High Hon Roll; NHS; Mrktng.

POVERELLI, VICKI; St Francis Prep Schl; Whitestone, NY; (Y); Camera Clb; Computer Clb; Dance Clb; Hosp Aide; Band; Concert Band; Im Fld Hcky; Im Ftbl; Im Socr; Im Sftbl; Bus.

POVEROMO, ANDREA; North Babylon SR HS; North Babylon, NY; (Y); DECA; FBLA; Office Aide; Yrbk Stf; Sec Sr Cls; Trs Stu Cncl; Sftbl; High Hon Roll; Hon Roll; Jr NHS; Suffolk Cnty CC; Travl.

POVLOCK, SUE; Unatego Central HS; Unadilla, NY; (Y); Exploring; 4-H; Girl Scts; Chorus; Rep Stu Cncl; JV Var Fld Hcky; Var Capt Vllybl; High Hon Roll; NHS; Prfct Atten Awd; Hnr Soc 83-85; Geneseo; Bio.

POWCH, OKSANA; Eldred Central Schl; Glen Spey, NY; (Y); Church Yth Grp; Ski Clb; Varsity Clb; Yrbk Ed-Chief; Pres Frsh Cls; Pres Soph Cls; Pres Sr Cls; Var L Bsktbl; Var L Trk; VP NHS; Stu Senate 84; Art Awds 81-85; Union Coll.

POWELL, ANNE K; Minisink Valley HS; Middletown, NY; (Y); 4/230; Pres Church Yth Grp; Band; Sec Sr Cls; Sec Trs Stu Cncl; JV Var Bsktbl; Var Capt Crs Cntry; Var Trk; VP NHS; Ntl Merit SF; Voice Dem Awd; Outstndng Engl Stu 83-84; Gnrl Exclnc Awd 83-85; Bucknell U; Pre Med.

POWELL, DARIUS; Saint Francis Prep; Maspeth, NY; (S); 120/693; Boy Scts; Service Clb; Fld Hcky; Opt Clb Awd.

POWELL, DAVID; Springville Griffith Inst HS; Springville, NY; (Y); Boy Scts; Capt Debate Tm; Exploring; Band; Nwsp Rptr; Rep Soph Cls; Rep Stu Cncl; Im Golf; DAR Awd; Hon Roll; Hnr NY ST Bar Assn 85; Med.

POWELL, ELIZABETH; Utica Free Acad; Utica, NY; (Y); Computer Clb; Debate Tm; Latin Clb; Library Aide; Mathletes; NFL; Q&S; Service Clb; Speech Tm; Nwsp Ed-Chief; 2nd Pl Scottsh Rite Essy Cntst 84; Lions Clb Schlstc Awd 84; Elmira Coll Key Awd 85; Biomed Engrng.

POWELL, JAMES; Lake George HS; Lk George, NY; (Y); 2/83; Am Leg Boys St; Pres German Clb; Varsity Clb; School Play; Pres Jr Cls; Stu Cncl; Var Bsktbl; Var Tennis; High Hon Roll; Jr NHS; Wlms Coll Alumni Bk Awd 85; Physcl Sci.

POWELL, JENNIFER; Hapursville Central HS; Binghamton, NY; (Y); 2/80; VP Band; Sec VP Chorus; Rep Trs Stu Cncl; JV Var Bsktbl; JV Var Fld Hcky; JV Var Sftbl; High Hon Roll; NHS; 1st Pl Actvty Awd 85; All ST Band 84; Marine Biolgst.

POWELL, KECIA; Martin L King JR HS; New York, NY; (Y); Office Aide; Quiz Bowl; Yrbk Stf; Rep Frsh Cls; Tennis; Hon Roll; Natl Sci Merit Awds 85; Engrng.

POWELL, LEVON; Monore JR SR HS; Rochester, NY; (Y); Computer Clb; Exploring; German Clb; Office Aide; Tennis; High Hon Roll; Hon Roll; Barbizon; Make-Up Artstry.

POWELL, LISA; Midwood HS; Brooklyn, NY; (Y); 186/625; Service Clb; Chorus; Variety Show; Ntl Merit SF; Prfct Atten Awd; Stony Brook; Nrs.

POWELL, MARY; Bishop Kearney HS; Rochester, NY; (Y); Church Yth Grp; Hosp Aide; Ski Clb; School Musical; Bowling; JV Var Socr; ST U Buffalo; Nrsg.

POWELL, RICK; Vestal HS; Apalachin, NY; (Y); 40/450; Off Frsh Cls; L Ftbl; L Lcrss; Cert Merit Assmbly NYS 85; Awd Excllnce Tri Cities Art Exhibit 82; Vestal Cert Merit Achvt Art 82; Broom Tech CC; Mech Drawng.

POWELL, STEPHANIE; Greenville Central HS; Earlton, NY; (Y); Camera Clb; French Clb; Sec Latin Clb; Chorus; School Play; Pres Frsh Cls; Sec Stu Cncl; Bsktbl; Socr; Law.

POWELL, SUZANNE M; Scotia-Glenville HS; Scotia, NY; (Y); 30/270; Pres Exploring; Pres 4-H; Key Clb; Band; Concert Band; Mrchg Band; Hon Roll; NHS; NYS Regnts Schlrshp 85; St John Fisher Coll Admssns Schlrshp & Regnts Schlrshp Mtchng Grnt 85; St John Fisher Coll; Pre-Vet.

POWER, ANNE; St Vincent Ferrer HS; Astoria, NY; (Y); 30/130; Rep Frsh Cls; Sec Soph Cls; Rep Jr Cls; Off Sr Cls; Stu Cncl; High Hon Roll; Hon Roll; Church Yth Grp; Service Clb; Yrbk Bus Mgr; Israel Med Ctr; Nrsg.

POWER, KERRY; St Vincent Ferrer HS; Sunnyside, NY; (Y); 45/114; Church Yth Grp; Dance Clb; Girl Scts; Church Choir.

POWERS, AMY E; Shenendehowa HS; Clifton Park, NY; (Y); Drama Clb; Key Clb; Yrbk Phtg; JV Cheerleading; JV Var Mgr(s); High Hon Roll; NHS; Powder Puff Ftbl; Supr Hnr Rll 83-85; Acad Achv Awds Dnnr Top 10% Clss 84; Schlstc Achv Awd 83-85; Cornell; Bus.

POWERS, CHRISTOPHER; Potsdam Central HS; Potsdam, NY; (Y); Var Socr.

POWERS, DAWN; Hudson Falls HS; Hudson Falls, NY; (Y); 1/223; Drama Clb; Exploring; Science Clb; Spanish Clb; Thesps; Yrbk Stf; NHS; Ntl Merit SF; Spanish NHS; School Musical; John Hopkins U SMPY 82; Ntl Sci Olympd 82; Phys.

POWERS, EDWARD DAVID; Stuyvesant HS; Brooklyn, NY; (Y); Cmnty Wkr; Debate Tm; Hosp Aide; Science Clb; Lit Mag; Elks Awd; Hon Roll; NHS; Ntl Merit Ltr; Pres Shryvesant Philatelic Soc 82-85; Brown U Providence; Art Hist.

POWERS, KELLY; Emma Willard Schl; Latham, NY; (Y); Cmnty Wkr; Dance Clb; Hosp Aide; Ski Clb; Nwsp Rptr; Yrbk Stf; Bus.

POWIS, DINA; Brewster HS; Brewster, NY; (Y); Church Yth Grp; French Clb; Varsity Clb; School Musical; School Play; Variety Show; Var Sftbl; Var Capt Vllybl; Psychlgy.

POWLESS, DAWN M; Lockport SR HS; Lockport, NY; (Y); Latin Clb; Varsity Clb; Pres Frsh Cls; Rep Soph Cls; Rep Jr Cls; Rep Stu Cncl; Capt Var Cheerleading; Hon Roll; Jr NHS; Chorus; Psych.

POWLIN, MIKE; Lowville Central Schl; Lowville, NY; (Y); Am Leg Boys St; School Play; Rep Stu Cncl; JV Var Bsktbl; JV Var Ftbl; Var Golf; Hon Roll; NHS; Civil Engr.

POWLIS III, VOLNEY A; North Babylon SR HS; North Babylon, NY; (Y); Church Yth Grp; Intnl Clb; Varsity Clb; Chorus; Church Choir; Bsktbl; Ftbl; High Hon Roll; Hon Roll; Jr NHS; U Of MD.

POYNEER, RACHAEL; Elmira Free Acad; Elmira, NY; (Y); Church Yth Grp; Acpl Chr; Chorus; Hon Roll; Prfct Atten Awd; Bus.

POZNICK, JILL; Half Hollow East HS; Melville, NY; (Y); 64/586; Service Clb; Mrchg Band; Var Badmtn; Var Mgr(s); French Hon Soc; High Hon Roll; Jr NHS; NHS; Long Isl Cncl Scl Stds Achvt Awd 82; Hofstra Frnch Poetry Cont 83; Pres Acad Ftns Awd 85; U Of MI; Comm.

POZZA, KARI; Arlington HS; Pleasant Vly, NY; (Y); Prfct Atten Awd; Aminal Breedr.

PRADA, STEFAN; Spackenkill HS; Poughkeepsie, NY; (Y); 7/135; Hosp Aide; Varsity Clb; Coach Actv; Var Capt Socr; Wt Lftg; High Hon Roll; RPI/Albany Med Coll; Bio-Med.

PRAGER, ALAN B; Stuyvesant HS; Brooklyn, NY; (Y); Math Tm; Science Clb; Teachers Aide; Orch; Hon Roll; Jr NHS; NHS; Ntl Merit Ltr; Wstnghse Sci Tlnt Srch Semifnlst 85; Chem.

PRAGMAN, CHRISTOPHER; Franklin Delano Roosevelt HS; Hyde Park, NY; (Y); Concert Band; Jazz Band; Mrchg Band; School Musical; Stage Crew; Symp Band; Variety Show; Hon Roll; Ntl Merit SF; Cornell U; Engrng.

PRAINITO, ANN M; Ossining HS; Ossining, NY; (Y); Pres Exploring; FNA; Hosp Aide; Chorus; Color Guard; JV Gym; Var Mgr(s); Hon Roll; Westchester CC; Nrsg.

PRAKASH JR, OM; Hunter College HS; Holliswood, NY; (Y); Boy Scts; Math Tm; Model UN; Chorus; Lit Mag; Var Trk; Mu Alp Tht; Natl Socl Stud Olympiad Awd 84; USAF Acad; Fighter Pilot.

PRASHAW, BETTINA; Tupper Lake HS; Tupper Lk, NY; (Y); Sec Frsh Cls; VP Soph Cls; Rep Jr Cls; Rep Sr Cls; Pres VP Stu Cncl; Var JV Crs Cntry; Var Socr; Var Trk; Var JV Vllybl; Bio Chem.

PRASSEL, RONNA; Roy C Ketcham HS; Wappingers Fls, NY; (Y); Cmnty Wkr; FBLA; Yrbk Stf; Im Bowling; JV Vllybl; Hon Roll; Tompkins-Cortland CC; Lib Arts.

PRATT, CARL; Whitney Point HS; Whitney Pt, NY; (Y); 26/120; Boy Scts; High Hon Roll; Hon Roll; Var Bsbl; L Ftbl; Var Wt Lftg; Var Wrstlng; Coach/Gym Tchr.

PRATT, DAVID; Kenmore West SR HS; Kenmore, NY; (Y); Church Yth Grp; JV Socr; Var Trk; High Hon Roll; NYS Sci Supvsrs Assn Bio Awd 84; Niagara Frntr Leag Al-Star Awd 84; Outstndng Achv/Hgh Jmp Ad 85; Chem Engrng.

PRATT, KAREN; Harpursville Central HS; Harpursville, NY; (S); #4 In Class; Varsity Clb; Vllybl; Hon Roll; NHS; Prfct Atten Awd; Voice Dem Awd; All State Choir 82-84; Marn Bio Fld Stu 82-83; Ntl Yth Salut 84; Broome CC; Elec Eng.

PRATT, MELODY; Berlin Central HS; Stephentown, NY; (Y); 18/60; Band; Chorus; Concert Band; Mrchg Band; School Musical; School Play; Hon Roll; Music & Mrt Awd 85.

PRATT, RONALD; Granville Central JR SR HS; Wells, VT; (Y); 2/135; French Clb; Math Tm; Yrbk Ed-Chief; Rep Jr Cls; Bausch & Lomb Sci Awd; High Hon Roll; NHS; Rotary Awd; MWA Schlrshp 85; Bausch & Lomb Sci Schlrshp Full Tuitn 85; VT Schlrshp 85; U Of Rochester; Mech Engrng.

PRATT, STEVEN B; Holland Patent Central HS; Holland Patent, NY; (Y); 4/153; Am Leg Boys St; Boy Scts; Chorus; School Play; Variety Show; VP Stu Cncl; JV Var Bsbl; JV Var Socr; Var Swmmng; NHS; Area All-St Chrs Bass 83 & 84; Amateur Radio Oper 81; Barbershop Qrtet 84 & 85.

PRATT, TAMMY; Pineview Christian Acad; Nassau, NY; (Y); Sec Church Yth Grp; Pep Clb; Chorus; School Musical; Yrbk Stf; VP Jr Cls; Capt Cheerleading; Vllybl; Central City Bus Inst; Bus Mgmt.

PRAUS, JENNIFER; Schoharie Central Schl; Schoharie, NY; (S); 1/83; Church Yth Grp; 4-H; Band; Chorus; Church Choir; School Musical; Rep Stu Cncl; High Hon Roll; Law.

PREISSLER, MICHAEL F; Tuxedo HS; Tuxedo Park, NY; (Y); 12/92; Am Leg Boys St; Boy Scts; Math Tm; Stat Ski Clb; Sec Spanish Clb; Var Bsbl; Var Socr; High Hon Roll; NHS; Yrbk Stf; Eagle Scout 85; Engrng.

PRENDERGAST, DANIEL; Arch Bishop Molloy HS; Woodside, NY; (Y); Crs Cntry; Trk; Kiwanis Awd; Lion Awd; Crs Cntry All Star Tm 82; Acctng.

PRENTICE, TODD; Highland HS; Highland, NY; (Y); Church Yth Grp; French Clb; Diving; JV Socr; Hon Roll; Highest Acadmc Achvt-Comptr Sci 84-85; Comptrs.

PRESCOTT, DEBORAH; Mercy HS; Albany, NY; (Y); Cmnty Wkr; Dance Clb; Stage Crew; High Hon Roll; Hon Roll; Awd Excllnc Phy Sci 83; Awd Excllnc Socl Stud 83; Psychlgy.

PRESCOTT, RANDY; Berlin Central Schl; Berlin, NY; (Y); Yrbk Stf; JV Var Bsktbl; Var Socr; Hon Roll; Prfct Atten Awd; Engrng.

PRESENDOR, MARIE; John Dewey HS; Brooklyn, NY; (Y); Church Yth Grp; Dance Clb; Girl Scts; Church Choir; Variety Show; Rep Frsh Cls; NY U; Lib Arts.

PRESSIMONE, DARIO A; Mount Saint Michael Acad; Bronx, NY; (S); 12/305; Cmnty Wkr; Hon Roll; NHS.

PRESTEL, BETH ANN; St Peters Girls HS; Staten Isl, NY; (Y); FNA; JV Var Sftbl; Hon Roll; Prfct Atten Awd; Chld Psych.

PRESTI, LENORE N; Valley Stream Central HS; Valley Stream, NY; (Y); 86/365; Chess Clb; Drama Clb; Chorus; School Play; Nwsp Stf; Stu Cncl; Var Socr; Tennis; Hon Roll; Engl Awd 82; Adelphia U; Stckbrkr.

PRESTIA, JOHN; East Seneca SR HS; Cheektowaga, NY; (Y); VICA; Music.

PRESTIFILIPPO, THERESA; St Francis Prep; Flushing, NY; (S); 180/690; NYS Schlrshp 85; Stonybrook; Nrs.

PRESTON, JAMES; Archbishop Molloy HS; Bayside, NY; (Y); 45/363; Sec Band; Stage Crew; Yrbk Stf; Im Bsktbl; Im Bowling; Im Ftbl; High Hon Roll; NHS; Ntl Merit Schol; Art Clb; 8th Rank Report Card 82; Schlr Incntve Schlrshp SUNY Stony Brook 85; VA Polytechnic Inst; Elec Engr.

PRESTON, LAHNEY; Richfield Springs Central HS; Richfield Spg, NY; (Y); 3/60; JCL; Latin Clb; Model UN; Varsity Clb; Band; Chorus; Concert Band; Jazz Band; Mrchg Band; School Musical; Clark Schlrshp 85; Natl Merit Schlrshp Corp Suburban Propane 85; Cornell U; Anml Sci.

PRESTON, SANDRA; Acad Of The Holy Name; Albany, NY; (Y); Cmnty Wkr; Drama Clb; Hosp Aide; Latin Clb; Service Clb; School Play; Nwsp Bus Mgr; Nwsp Rptr; Nwsp Stf; Lit Mag; Natl Olym Chem Awd 85; Vol Awd Mem Hosp 100 Hr Pin 83.

PRESTON, SUSAN; Williamsville South HS; Williamsville, NY; (Y); 120/245; Drama Clb; Hosp Aide; Pep Clb; Ski Clb; Acpl Chr; Yrbk Stf; Capt Fld Hcky; Sftbl; Trk; Vllybl; OH Wesleyan U; Surgcl Nrsng.

PRESTON, WILLIAM ANDRE; Kensington HS; Buffalo, NY; (Y); Hosp Aide; Band; Chorus; School Musical; Rep Jr Cls; JV L Bsktbl; Var Capt Bowling; Var L Ftbl; Var L Trk; St Schlr; Schlrshps St Josephs Collgt Inst 82 & 83; Radlgy.

PRESTOPNIK, GRACE; Little Falls JR SR HS; Little Falls, NY; (S); 17/109; Boy Scts; Drama Clb; GAA; Spanish Clb; Band; Mrchg Band; School Musical; School Play; Variety Show; Var L Badmtn; Math.

PRETORIUS, PETER; The Knox Schl; E Northport, NY; (S); 2/28; Library Aide; Spanish Clb; Chorus; Lit Mag; Bowling; Sftbl; Tennis; Wrstlng; High Hon Roll; Hon Roll.

PRETTITORE, GINA; St Francis Prep Schl; Flushing, NY; (S); 126/693; Church Yth Grp; FCA; Sftbl; Wt Lftg; Hon Roll; Opt Clb Awd; Acad All Am Awd 85.

PREVOST, PATRICK; St Agnes HS; Rosedale, NY; (Y); Bsktbl; Ftbl; Sftbl; Tennis; Hon Roll; 2nd Hnrs 82-83; NYU; Med.

PREVOST, SUSAN; Shenendehowa HS; Clifton Pk, NY; (Y); GAA; Girl Scts; Hosp Aide; Pep Clb; Red Cross Aide; Ski Clb; Varsity Clb; Band; Concert Band; Jazz Band; Silvr Awd GS 83-84; Empir ST Gams Fgr Sktng-Fld Hcky 85-86; NYSSM Music Festvl Clrnt-Sax Ratng A; Boston U; Phy Thrpy.

PRIAL, ELIZABETH M; Sacred Heart Acad; Uniondale, NY; (Y); 42/186; Pep Clb; School Play; Hon Roll; NHS; Ntl Merit Schol; St Francis College Schlrshp 85; St Francis.

PRIAMO, CHRISTINA; Amsterdam HS; Amsterdam, NY; (Y); Rep Soph Cls; Rep Jr Cls; Trs Sr Cls; Art.

PRIBIS, DOUGLAS; Ichabod Crane HS; Valatie, NY; (Y); 9/183; Computer Clb; German Clb; High Hon Roll; NHS.

PRICE, AMY; Walton Central HS; Walton, NY; (Y); Church Yth Grp; Key Clb; Varsity Clb; Chorus; Church Choir; JV Var Fld Hcky; Im Socr; JV Sftbl; Cit Awd; High Hon Roll; Bus.

PRICE, ANDREW; Webster HS; Webster, NY; (Y); 136/562; Boy Scts; JA; Ski Clb; Band; Concert Band; JV Swmmng; Var Tennis; Hon Roll; Prfct Atten Awd; Egl Sct Awd 82; MI ST U; Comp Engrng.

PRICE, CECELIA; Clara Barton HS; Brooklyn, NY; (Y); Dance Clb; Hosp Aide; Library Aide; Math Clb; Teachers Aide; Variety Show; Vllybl; Cit Awd; Prfct Atten Awd.

PRICE, CHRISTINE; Garden City HS; Garden City, NY; (Y); 68/370; German Clb; Pres Key Clb; Church Choir; Capt Bsktbl; Tennis; Mst Imprvd Tnns Plyr 85; Bus.

PRICE, CLAIRE; St Francis Prep; College Point, NY; (S); 17/690; Dance Clb; Library Aide; VP Band; Concert Band; Drm & Bgl; Jazz Band; Mrchg Band; High Hon Roll; NHS; Ntl Merit Ltr; Regents Schlrshp 85; Bus Adm.

PRICE, CRAIG; Port Jervis HS; Sparrowbush, NY; (Y); VP Aud/Vis; Boy Scts; Concert Band; Jazz Band; Mrchg Band; Orch; Pep Band; Stage Crew; High Hon Roll; NHS; 6 NYSMA Awds Mus 84 & 85; Pre-Med.

PRICE, ELAINE; Smithtown H S East; St James, NY; (Y); Yrbk Phtg; Yrbk Stf; Off Frsh Cls; Sec Soph Cls; Sec Jr Cls; Mgr(s); Hon Roll; Spanish NHS; Presdntl Acad Ftns Awd 85; FL U Gainesville; Bus.

PRICE, JENNIFER; Middletown HS; Middletown, NY; (Y); Key Clb; Teachers Aide; Symp Band; Yrbk Stf; Var Cheerleading; JV Vllybl; Hon Roll; SUNY Binghampton; Accntng.

PRICE, LAURA J; Dunkirk HS; Dunkirk, NY; (Y); 13/220; Sec Computer Clb; Letterman Clb; Nwsp Sprt Ed; Yrbk Sprt Ed; Capt Diving; High Hon Roll; NHS; German Clb; GAA; Q&S; Michelle Fisk Swmng Awd 84; Rgnts Schlrshp 85; Rgnts Exam Awd 85; Math.

PRICE, MICHELLE; Schoharie Central HS; Schoharie, NY; (Y); Hosp Aide; Latin Clb; JV Bsktbl; Var Socr; Var Sftbl; Var Swmmng; Hon Roll; RN.

PRICE, NATALIE; Villa Maria Acad; Buffalo, NY; (Y); Church Yth Grp; JA; JCL; Latin Clb; Pep Clb; Political Wkr; Quiz Bowl; Bsktbl; Mgr(s); Score Keeper; JA Merit Awd 84; NCL Magna Cum Laude 84 & 85; St Lawrence U; Intl Law.

PRICE, RICHARD L; La Salle Acad; Manhattan, NY; (S); Boys Clb Am; Boy Scts; Mathletes; Drill Tm; Sftbl; Vllybl; High Hon Roll; Hon Roll.

PRICE, ROBERT P; Pioneer Central HS; Java Center, NY; (Y); Am Leg Boys St; 4-H; French Clb; Ski Clb; Concert Band; JV Socr; Elmira; Syst Anal.

PRICE, TERRI; Falconer Central Schl; Kennedy, NY; (Y); Church Yth Grp; Drama Clb; Hosp Aide; Band; Church Choir; Concert Band; Mrchg Band; Pep Band; Bsktbl; Sftbl; Radiolgy.

PRICE, TRACY M; Mscr Scanlan HS; Bronx, NY; (Y); Church Yth Grp; Church Choir; Variety Show; Rep Stu Cncl; L Var Trk; Acad Commendtn Bio, Chem, Physlgy; Top 10 Pcntl; Bio Med Resrch.

PRIETO, ANTHONY M; Salesian JR Seminary; Goshen, NY; (S); 1/5; Church Yth Grp; School Play; Yrbk Stf; Pres Stu Cncl; Var Capt Bsktbl; High Hon Roll; Val; Camera Clb; Cmnty Wkr; Best Stu Of Yr Awd 81-84; Hugh O Brien Yth Fndtn Ldrshp Sem 82-83; NEDT Awd 81-82; Don Bosco Coll; Psych.

PRIETO, CESAR; Immaculata HS; New York, NY; (Y); Pres Jr Cls; Capt Bowling; Swmmng; Hon Roll; Reg Dip Frgn Lang 85; Dip Math 85; Fin.

PRIME, AMY; Ft Plain HS; Ft Plain, NY; (Y); Math Clb; Varsity Clb; Mrchg Band; Yrbk Stf; Rep Soph Cls; Rep Jr Cls; JV Var Cheerleading; Score Keeper; Stat Socr; Var Sftbl; Mrktng/Rtlng.

PRIME, GREGORY W; Garden City HS; Garden City, NY; (Y); 70/319; Pres Key Clb; Spanish Clb; Nwsp Phtg; Yrbk Bus Mgr; JV Socr; JV Trk; Im Wt Lftg; Capt Var Wrstlng; High Hon Roll; Jr NHS; Decker Awd 83-84; Hamilton Coll; Bus.

PRIMERANO, GINA; Cicero N Syracuse HS; N Syracuse, NY; (S); 13/662; Hon Roll; Bus Mgmt.

PRINCE, JOELLE L; Brockport HS; Brockport, NY; (Y); 1/300; Mathletes; Science Clb; Band; Jazz Band; School Musical; Bausch & Lomb Sci Awd; NHS; St Schlr; Val; Church Yth Grp; Phi Beta Kappa Outstdg Acad 85; Cornell U; Chem Engr.

PRINCE, LISA M; White Plains HS; White Plains, NY; (Y); Band; Mrchg Band; School Musical; VP Soph Cls; Cheerleading; Fld Hcky; Mgr(s); Tennis; Twrlr; Hon Roll; Ntl Achvt Schlrshp Pgm Outstndng Negro Stu 84-85; Sprtsmnshp Awd Rye Tnns Acad; Econ.

PRINCE, SHARON; Cardinal Spellman HS; Bronx, NY; (Y); Dance Clb; Drama Clb; Library Aide; Office Aide; Teachers Aide; Chorus; School Musical; Yrbk Phtg; Rep Stu Cncl; JV Mgr(s); Cert Awd Sci Proj 83; Ntl Hnr Soc 83; NY U Cornell U; Psychlgy.

PRINCIPAL, SAUVETA; Samuel J Tilden HS; Brooklyn, NY; (Y); 16/502; Hosp Aide; Library Aide; Office Aide; Teachers Aide; Yrbk Stf; Lit Mag; Hon Roll; NHS; Chancellors Rll Of Hnr Samuel J Tilden HIP Achv Awd 85; Frnch Slvr Mdl 82; Caravan Awd 85; Adelphi U; Nrsng.

PRINGLE, CHARLENE L; Hillcrest HS; Jamaica, NY; (Y); 147/793; Church Yth Grp; Hosp Aide; Office Aide; Science Clb; Church Choir; Rep Stu Cncl; Elks Awd; Hon Roll; NHS; Prfct Atten Awd; St Johns U; Phrmcy.

PRINTY, DALE; Hornell HS; Hornell, NY; (Y); 10/185; Am Leg Boys St; Pres Art Clb; Church Yth Grp; Ski Clb; Rep Stu Cncl; JV Var Ftbl; Var L Trk; High Hon Roll; NHS.

PRINZI, MARK; Avon Central HS; Avon, NY; (Y); 10/111; Am Leg Boys St; French Clb; Science Clb; Varsity Clb; Acpl Chr; Drill Tm; Nwsp Rptr; Off Jr Cls; High Hon Roll; NHS; Vet Sci.

PRINZO, SUZANNE; Fayetteville Manlius HS; Fayetteville, NY; (Y); Church Yth Grp; Cmnty Wkr; Chorus; Stat Score Keeper; Var Swmmng; Stat Timer; Le Moyne Coll; Cmnctns.

PRINZO, THERESA; St Edmund HS; Brooklyn, NY; (Y); Church Yth Grp; Dance Clb; GAA; JV Cheerleading; Exclnce Spnsh I & Music 82-83; 2nd & 3rd Hnrs 82-85; Exclnce Steno I 84-85.

PRIOLA, KARIN; Seaford HS; Seaford, NY; (Y); Cmnty Wkr; Concert Band; Drm Mjr(t); School Play; Var Bsktbl; High Hon Roll; NHS; Var Fld Hcky; Var Sftbl; Im Vllybl; Maria Levy Awd 83; Outstndng Athlt 83; Engl Awd Schlrshp Awd 83.

PRITCHARD, COLIN J; Greenwood Central HS; Rexville, NY; (Y); 6/20; Varsity Clb; Band; Concert Band; Mrchg Band; Yrbk Stf; VP Jr Cls; Pres Sr Cls; Rep Stu Cncl; Bsbl; Bsktbl; Alfred A&t Coll; Liberal Arts.

PRITCHARD, DENISE M; Frankfort Schuyler HS; Frankfort, NY; (Y); Pres GAA; Math Clb; Yrbk Stf; Rep Stu Cncl; Capt Var Bsktbl; Capt Var Fld Hcky; Capt Var Trk; High Hon Roll; NHS; Bsktbl All-Stars Awd 84; Fld Hcky All-Star Awd 84; Trck Sctn III Awd 84; Comp Sci.

PRITCHARD, JAMES; Schenectady Christian Schl; Ballston Spa, NY; (S); 3/16; Pres Church Yth Grp; Ed Yrbk Stf; Rep Jr Cls; Co-Capt Socr; Var Trk; Hon Roll; Mst Imprv Socr 83-84; Mst Imagntv 84-85; Engrng.

PRITCHARD, LEEANNE; Fowler HS; Syracuse, NY; (Y); Key Clb; Sftbl; High Hon Roll; Hon Roll; NHS; Bus Hnr Soc 84-85; Bio, Gen Sci Awd 84-85; CCBI; Bus.

PRIVITAR, DONNA M; St Barnabas HS; Bronx, NY; (Y); 11/137; Cmnty Wkr; Pres Drama Clb; School Play; Nwsp Rptr; NHS; St Schlr; Fld Hcky; French Hon Soc; Hon Roll; Drew U; Jrnlsm.

PRIVITERA, MARY JO; Cardinal Ohara HS; N Tonawanda, NY; (Y); Church Yth Grp; Cmnty Wkr; Office Aide; Pep Clb; Teachers Aide; Church Choir; Hon Roll; Good Ctznshp Awd 80 & 82; Bus.

PROBERT, KIMBERLY; Plattsburgh HS; Plattsburgh, NY; (Y); 30/180; AFS; Cmnty Wkr; Sec French Clb; PAVAS; Chorus; Jazz Band; School Musical; Variety Show; Hon Roll; NHS; Schlrshp Awds; Plattsburgh ST U; Engl.

PROBST, MICHAEL D; Frontier Central HS; Blasdell, NY; (Y); 65/500; Church Yth Grp; Cmnty Wkr; Trs Varsity Clb; Stat Bsktbl; Var Coach Actv; Var Score Keeper; Capt Tennis; Var Vllybl; Hon Roll; NHS; Frontier Cntrl Teacher Assc 85; Robert Tenabruso Awd 85; Sprtsmnshp Awds 84-85; Canisius Coll; Bus.

PROCARIO, JESSICA; West Lake HS; Valhalla, NY; (Y); Nwsp Stf; Yrbk Ed-Chief; VP Soph Cls; VP Jr Cls; VP Sr Cls; Var Trk; High Hon Roll; Hon Roll; NHS; Stu Recgntn Awds 84 & 85; Engl.

PROCEL, ROBERT; La Salle Acad; New York, NY; (Y); Boy Scts; Math Tm; Rep Frsh Cls; Hon Roll.

PROCK, CHRISTINA; Catholic Central HS; Wynantskill, NY; (S); 24/203; Math Clb; Ski Clb; Chorus; Var Capt Cheerleading; High Hon Roll; NHS; Phys Thrpy.

PROCOPIO, CHRISTINE; Henninger HS; Syracuse, NY; (Y); Church Yth Grp; Cmnty Wkr; Yrbk Stf; Hon Roll; Prfct Atten Awd; Mth.

PROCOPIO, LINDA; Nottingham HS; Cazenovia, NY; (Y); 3/220; Latin Clb; Chorus; High Hon Roll; NHS; Outstndng Achvt Math 82; Regents Achvt Engl 82; Outstnding Achvt Regents Bio 83; Le Moyne Coll; Elem Ed.

PROCOPIO, MARY J; Sauquoist SR HS; Chadwicks, NY; (S); GAA; Concert Band; Mrchg Band; Rep Stu Cncl; Var Socr; Drct Accep Sch Vsl Arts 85; MONY Reg Schlstc Art Awd 82-84; Syracuse U; Art.

PROEFROCK, KRISTEN; Niagara Wheatfield HS; North Tonawanda, NY; (Y); Church Yth Grp; Pep Clb; Spanish Clb; Hon Roll; Prfct Atten Awd; Comm Art.

PROFACI, DOMINICK; Newburgh Free Acad; Newburgh, NY; (Y); 15/655; Key Clb; High Hon Roll; Jr NHS; NHS; Pres Schlr; Italian Clb Pres 84-85; Italian Clb Treas 83-84; Italian Natl Hnr Soc 83-85; Manhattan Coll; Engrng.

PROFETA, ADRIANNE; Maria Regina HS; Yonkers, NY; (Y); Cmnty Wkr; Political Wkr; Lit Mag; High Hon Roll; Hon Roll; NHS; Schlstc Achvt Awd 82-85; Vet Med.

PROFETA, LISA M; St Johns Prep; Astoria, NY; (Y); 8/415; Ski Clb; Church Choir; Nwsp Rptr; Yrbk Stf; Vllybl; High Hon Roll; NHS; Rgnts Coll Schlrshp 85; Natl Sci Olympaid Chem 83; Attestato Di Lode Italian 82; Cert St Johns U 85; St Johns U; Pharm.

PROIOS, JOHN; Hicksville SR HS; Hicksville, NY; (Y); Church Yth Grp; ROTC; Library Aide; Hon Roll; 3rd Pl Phy Ed Trck 84-85; Avtn.

PRONESTI, SCOTT; Henninger HS; Syracuse, NY; (Y); 15/500; Concert Band; Jazz Band; Mrchg Band; Pep Band; Symp Band; Yrbk Phtg; Yrbk Sprt Ed; Var Swmmng; High Hon Roll; NHS; Med.

PROPIS, MICHAEL; George W Hewlett HS; Hewlett Harbor, NY; (Y); Ski Clb; Temple Yth Grp; JV Var Socr; Var Tennis; High Hon Roll; Hon Roll; Hebrew Schl Awds 77-80; Ldrshp Awds In Camp 83; Bus Mgt.

PROSCHEL, CHRISTY; Holy Trinity HS; E Meadow, NY; (S); 30/400; Dance Clb; Drama Clb; Math Clb; Ski Clb; School Musical; School Play; Stage Crew; Stu Cncl; High Hon Roll; Hon Roll; Thtre.

PROSCHER, LINDA; Ossining HS; Ossining, NY; (Y); 4-H; 4-H Awd; High Hon Roll; Hon Roll; Sec.

PROSCIA, JENNIFER L; St Marys Girls HS; Manhasset, NY; (Y); 16/180; Ski Clb; Stage Crew; Nwsp Phtg; JV Crs Cntry; Im Tennis; High Hon Roll; Hon Roll; NHS; Bus.

PROSCIA, REGINA M; Northport HS; Northport, NY; (Y); 131/585; Civic Clb; GAA; Band; Concert Band; Mrchg Band; Variety Show; Yrbk Stf; JV Socr; Var Trk; Hon Roll.

PROSKIN, LISA A; Shalcer HS; Menands, NY; (Y); VP JA; Political Wkr; Spanish Clb; Pres Temple Yth Grp; Yrbk Sprt Ed; Off Soph Cls; Trs Jr Cls; Trs Sr Cls; Hon Roll; NHS; Elmira Coll Key 84; Rep At Pres Clssrm For Yng Amer 85; Yth Grp Awd For Meritorious Svc 83; John Hopkins U; Pre-Law.

PROSSER, KIM; Clyde Savannah Central HS; Clyde, NY; (Y); Drama Clb; Concert Band; Jazz Band; Mrchg Band; Rep Stu Cncl; Var L Bsktbl; Var L Sftbl; Var L Tennis; Stat Vllybl; Hon Roll.

PROTASS, JOSH M; Rye Country Day Schl; New Rochelle, NY; (Y); Model UN; Concert Band; Nwsp Ed-Chief; Rep Soph Cls; Rep Jr Cls; Rep Sr Cls; VP Stu Cncl; Capt Tennis.

PROUD, KRISTIN M; Homer SR HS; Homer, NY; (Y); 3/215; Am Leg Aux Girls St; Pres French Clb; Political Wkr; Nwsp Bus Mgr; Nwsp Ed-Chief; High Hon Roll; NHS; Church Yth Grp; Nwsp Rptr; Nwsp Stf; Elmira Coll Key Awd & Scholar 85; WA Wrkshp Cngrsnl Sem 85; Frnch I & Ii Awds; Brdcstng.

PROUTY, CHARLES D; Wells Central HS; Northville, NY; (Y); 5/31; Am Leg Boys St; Ski Clb; Trs Frsh Cls; VP Stu Cncl; VP Bsbl; VP Bsktbl; VP Socr; High Hon Roll; NYS Regnts & Rochester Inst Tech Schlrshps 85; Rochester Inst Tech; Comp Sci.

PROVEN, SUSAN; Patchogue-Medford HS; Medford, NY; (Y); 33/748; Drama Clb; Band; Mrchg Band; Orch; Nwsp Rptr; Ed Nwsp Sprt Ed; Vllybl; Jr NHS; NHS; Pres Schlr; Commndtns Math Regnts II 81; C W Post Schlrshp 85; Hofstra Schlrshp 85; Fordham U; Jrnlsm.

PROVONCHA, CAROL; Ticonderoga HS; Ticonderoga, NY; (Y); #18 In Class; Drama Clb; 4-H; French Clb; Key Clb; Latin Clb; Acpl Chr; Chorus; Madrigals; School Play; Swing Chorus; All Cnty Chrs 85; Jrnlst.

PROVOST, MICHELE D; Scotia-Glenville HS; Scotia, NY; (Y); 3/255; VP Church Yth Grp; Hosp Aide; JA; Orch; Yrbk Phtg; Lit Mag; JV Socr; High Hon Roll; NHS; Pres Schlr; Oyaron Schlr 85; Regnts Schlrshp 85; Outscndng Sci Stu 85; Hartwick Coll; Bio.

PROWELLER, AARON; Dunkirk Senior HS; Dunkirk, NY; (Y); 2/225; Camera Clb; Pres Computer Clb; German Clb; VP Science Clb; Stage Crew; Lit Mag; Socr; High Hon Roll; NHS; Sal; NYS Regents Schlrshp 85; Oberlin Coll; Bio.

PROWSE, DARLENE; Maryvale SR HS; Cheektowaga, NY; (Y); Spanish Clb; Chorus; Orch; Off Stu Cncl; Socr; Vllybl; High Hon Roll; NHS; Ed.

PROZNY, PENELOPE L; Williamsville South HS; Williamsville, NY; (Y); 41/245; AFS; Stage Crew; Nwsp Rptr; Yrbk Phtg; Trs Yrbk Stf; Var L Fld Hcky; Hon Roll; Vrsty Rifle Team 3 Ltrs 82-85; NYS Rgnts Schlrshp; Joy Mfg Co Schlrshp; USMA; Engrng.

PROZOR, DAWN; Lindenhurst SR HS; Lindenhurst, NY; (Y); Cmnty Wkr; French Clb; Key Clb; Mathletes; Chorus; Badmtn; French Hon Soc; High Hon Roll; Frnch Poetry Cntst 84; Crew Mem Of Mnth 85; Socl Wrk.

PRUCHNOWSKI, DONNA; Cardinal O Hara HS; Tonawanda, NY; (Y); Trs Spanish Clb; Capt Var Cheerleading; Trk; Hon Roll.

PRUMMELL, DONNA; Newfield HS; Selden, NY; (Y); Mgr(s); Hon Roll; Rep Awd Soc Studies 83; Soc Wrk.

PRUNCHAK, LISA; Niagara Wheatfield Central Schl; N Tonawanda, NY; (Y); Drama Clb; FBLA; Pep Clb; PAVAS; Ski Clb; Spanish Clb; School Play; Stu Cncl; Hon Roll; Adv.

PRUNOSKE, PAM; Hornell SR HS; Hornell, NY; (Y); Art Clb; Latin Clb; Ski Clb; Stat Trk; Hon Roll; Daughtrs Amer Revltn 81; Alfred U; Engl.

PRUSKO, CONSTANCE; Scotia-Glenville HS; Schenectady, NY; (Y); Sec Trs Exploring; JA; Vet.

PRUSKO, PATRICE A; Linton HS; Schenectady, NY; (Y); 21/300; Church Yth Grp; Hosp Aide; Key Clb; Chorus; Yrbk Stf; Rep Frsh Cls; Rep Soph Cls; Rep Jr Cls; Rep Sr Cls; Rep Stu Cncl; Frnch Mrt Awd 84; Comm Svc Awd 83; Med.

PRUYN, PETER W; Collegiate Schl; New York, NY; (Y); Computer Clb; Debate Tm; Math Tm; Speech Tm; NY ST Cath Frsncs Leag 5th Pl 84; Cornell U; Sci.

PRYOR, KENNETH A; Holy Trinity HS; Levittown, NY; (S); 50/369; Nwsp Stf; Rep Frsh Cls; Rep Soph Cls; JV Bsktbl; Capt Var Crs Cntry; Var Trk; Hon Roll; Jr NHS; All Long Isl Cross Cntry 4th Leag Chmps 84; Soph Champshp, 1st Mile Intrsctns 84.

PRYOR, MICHELE; Churchville-Chili SR HS; Rochester, NY; (Y); Church Yth Grp; Office Aide; Yrbk Ed-Chief; Rep Stu Cncl; JV Sftbl; High Hon Roll; Model UN; Yrbk Rptr; Yrbk Stf; 1st Pl Frgn Lng Cmptn 85.

PRYVES, MICHAEL DAVID; Hicksville SR HS; Hicksville, NY; (Y); German Clb; ROTC; VP Science Clb; Ski Clb; Spanish Clb; Rep Stu Cncl; JV Socr; Var L Tennis; Hon Roll; Ger Hnr Soc; Bus.

PRYZGODA, DENNIS; Sacred Heart HS; Yonkers, NY; (Y); Nwsp Sprt Ed; JV Var Bsbl; JV Var Bowling; Var Trk; Hon Roll; Task Orntd Ldrshp Training Pgm 85; Bsbl Leag Ldr 85; All City Bowler 83-84; LIU; Marine Sci.

PRYZYBYLO, MARIA A; Lackawanna SR HS; Lackawanna, NY; (Y); Hosp Aide; Library Aide; Office Aide; Red Cross Aide; Drm Mjr(t); Rep Frsh Cls; Rep Soph Cls; Stu Cncl; Hon Roll; BOCES 84-85; Hlth Asstng Cls; Hnr Rl; Air Force; Nrsg.

PRZEDWIECKI, STEPHANIE; Sachem North HS; Farmingville, NY; (Y); Church Yth Grp; GAA; Spanish Clb; JV Bsktbl; Var Socr; Var Vllybl; Bus.

PRZETAK, COLLEEN; St Marys HS; Depew, NY; (S); 5/220; Church Yth Grp; Cmnty Wkr; Girl Scts; Nwsp Stf; Yrbk Stf; Badmtn; Hon Roll; NHS; Bryant & Shatton Inst; Comp Prg.

PRZYBYLA, ANDREA; Notre Dame Acad; Staten Island, NY; (Y); Camera Clb; Church Yth Grp; Science Clb; Nwsp Stf; Var Swmmng; Ntl Merit Ltr; Journ Photo.

PRZYBYLO, KIM MARIE; Amsterdam HS; Amsterdam, NY; (Y); 10/230; Church Yth Grp; High Hon Roll; Hon Roll; NHS; Prfct Atten Awd; William Anninger Awd 85; Russell Sagg Coll; Medcl Tech.

PRZYBYSZ, SUZANNE M; Buffalo Acad Of The Sacred Heart; Buffalo, NY; (Y); 3/114; Pres Camp Fr Inc; VP Science Clb; Lit Mag; High Hon Roll; Hon Roll; Pres NHS; Ntl Merit Ltr; Regents Schlrshp 84-85; Eclgy Club; Suny Coll; Biochemstry.

PSARRAS, DEBORAH; Sheepshead Bay HS; Brooklyn, NY; (Y); JA; Teachers Aide; Band; School Play; Trs Sr Cls; Capt Cheerleading; Schl Visual Arts; Video.

PTACHEWICH, NAOMI; Scarsdale HS; Scarsdale, NY; (Y); Service Clb; Ed Yrbk Stf; VP Trk; Dance Clb; Drama Clb; Exploring; Spanish Clb; Temple Yth Grp; Varsity Clb; Band; Pre Med.

PTACHICK, ERIN; Bishop Scully HS; Amsterdam, NY; (S); 11/69; VP Hst Art Clb; Camp Fr Inc; Math Clb; Spanish Clb; Varsity Clb; Var Co-Capt Bsktbl; Var Capt Sftbl; High Hon Roll; Hon Roll; NHS; Natl Hnr Scty VP 82; Colgate; Pre-Med.

PTAK, CYNTHIA; Villa Maria Acad; Depew, NY; (S); Girl Scts; Chorus; Yrbk Ed-Chief; Im Bowling; Hon Roll; Pres NHS; NEDT Awd; Prfct Atten Awd; Canisius Coll; Accntnt.

PTAK, THOMAS R; North Collins Central Schl; North Collins, NY; (Y); FFA; VICA; Prfct Atten Awd; Merit Rl Cert 85.

PUCELLO, MARGARETHA; Solvay HS; Solvay, NY; (Y); Church Yth Grp; Ski Clb; Hon Roll; U S FL.

PUCKETT, SCOTT AUSTIN; Greece Arcadia HS; Rochester, NY; (Y); Boy Scts; Church Yth Grp; Var L Trk; High Hon Roll; NHS; Teachers Aide; Band; Symp Band; JV Im Bsktbl; JV Ftbl; Outstndng Achvt German 84-85; BSA Eagle Wrld Consrvtn Awd 83; Community Svc Awd 83; U IL; Med.

PUERNER, SUSAN; Maryvale HS; Cheektowaga, NY; (Y); Church Yth Grp; GAA; Varsity Clb; Rep Frsh Cls; Rep Soph Cls; Rep Jr Cls; Rep Sr Cls; Stu Cncl; JV Var Cheerleading; Hon Roll; Tchr.

PUFPAFF, SUSAN; St Marys HS; Sloan, NY; (S); Am Leg Aux Girls St; High Hon Roll; Med.

PUGH, KELLY; Lindenhurst HS; Lindenhurst, NY; (Y); Church Yth Grp; French Clb; Key Clb; Varsity Clb; Yrbk Stf; JV Var Bsktbl; Var Fld Hcky; Im JV Sftbl; JV Vllybl; Hon Roll; Flagler Coll Of FL; Eng.

PUGH, RICHARD J; Homer Central HS; Homer, NY; (Y); 28/198; Chorus; Jazz Band; Pep Band; School Play; Symp Band; Nwsp Stf; High Hon Roll; NHS; Pres Schlr; Area All-ST Symph Band 83-84; Nutual NY Gold Key Art Awd 81; St Bonaventure U.

PUGH, TIMOTHY; Onondaga HS; Nedrow, NY; (S); Drama Clb; Spanish Clb; Band; Chorus; Jazz Band; School Musical; School Play; Yrbk Stf; VP Soph Cls; Rep Stu Cncl; Cmmnctns.

PUGLIESE, CYNTHIA; Marlboro HS; Marlboro, NY; (Y); Stat Bsbl; High Hon Roll; NHS; Bus Mgmt.

PUGLIO, BRENDA; Cornwall Central HS; Cornwall, NY; (Y); Yrbk Phtg; Yrbk Stf; Band; Color Guard; Concert Band; Mrchg Band; Var JV Trk; Phtgrphy.

PUGLISI, LORI; Linton HS; Schenectady, NY; (Y); French Clb; Intnl Clb; Off Jr Cls; Acctg.

PULASKI, STEPHANIE ELIZABETH; Medina HS; Medina, NY; (Y); 12/160; Am Leg Aux Girls St; Model UN; Acpl Chr; Chorus; Cit Awd; Hon Roll; Pres NHS; Ntl Merit Ltr; Phy Sci.

PULEO, PAUL; Frankfort-Schuyler Central HS; Frankfort, NY; (Y); 26/100; Math Clb; Sec Jr Cls; Rep Stu Cncl; Var Bsbl; Var Capt Ftbl; Hon Roll; NHS; Dorothy Leland HS Awd 85; All Acdmc 84-85; Natl Ldrshp & Svc Awd 85; Alfred U; Gramic Engrng.

PULIKOWSKI, DEBORAH; Maple Hill HS; Castleton, NY; (Y); 3/94; Stu Cncl; Fld Hcky; Hon Roll; NHS; Yrbk Stf; Trk; Vllybl; High Hon Roll; Schodack Tchrs Schlrshp 85; Ambrose Donovan Awd 85; SUNY-ALBANY; Sci.

PULLANO, GIA; The Franciscan Acad; Syracuse, NY; (S); 9/25; FBLA; JA; Ski Clb; Nwsp Sprt Ed; Stu Cncl; High Hon Roll; Hon Roll; Jr NHS; NHS; Ntl Merit Ltr; Prom Prncess 84; Art Awd 83.

PULLEN, STEVEN; Fairport HS; Fairport, NY; (Y); Computer Clb; Science Clb; Rep Stu Cncl; Var Wrstlng; High Hon Roll; Hon Roll; NHS; Joe Cummings Awd 82; Biochem.

PULLIAM, SAMANTHA; The Stonybrook HS; Beckley, WV; (Y); 3/84; Church Yth Grp; Orch; Stage Crew; Rep Soph Cls; Var L Bsktbl; Var L Fld Hcky; High Hon Roll; Hnrd-Cum Laude Soc; Math.

PULLINS, PAIGE; Fayetteville-Manius HS; Fayetteville, NY; (Y); Church Yth Grp; Exploring; Trs German Clb; Chorus; Orch; Coach Actv; Im Socr; Hon Roll; Exch Stu Germany ASSE 84; Syracuse Mag Art Awd 84; MONY Schltc Art Awd 84; Syracuse U; Archit.

PULLO, DOMINIC; Niagara Falls HS; Niagara Falls, NY; (Y); Computer Clb; Trs Drama Clb; Model UN; Ski Clb; Thesps; Trs Band; Jazz Band; Mrchg Band; Orch; Yrbk Stf; US Spch & Drama Awd 84-85; Acad All Amer 84-85; Med.

PULLO, SCOTT; St Josephs Collegiate Inst; N Tonawanda, NY; (Y); 15/200; Ski Clb; L Var Ice Hcky; L Var Socr; NHS; Law.

PULTORAK, ANNE E; East Syracuse-Monoa HS; E Syracuse, NY; (Y); Capt Mrchg Band; Variety Show; Score Keeper; Capt Twrlr; High Hon Roll; Hon Roll; Jr NHS; NHS; Regnts Nrsng Schlrshp 85; Onondaga CC; Nrsng.

PULVER, JOSEPH W; Ichabod Crane HS; Kinderhook, NY; (Y); 24/180; Exploring; French Clb; Quiz Bowl; Ski Clb; Varsity Clb; Var Socr; Hon Roll; NHS; ST U Of NY-ALBANY; Bus Admin.

PULVIRENTI, PATRICIA; St Joseph-By-The-Sea HS; Staten Island, NY; (Y); 4/240; Red Cross Aide; JV Var Socr; JV Trk; High Hon Roll; NHS; Alisi Concours Ntl Frnch Cntst.

PUMA, NICK; Byron Bergen HS; Bergen, NY; (Y); French Clb; Math Tm; Teachers Aide; Yrbk Phtg; Ed Yrbk Stf; Trk; Hon Roll; NHS; Cert Of Awd For Achvt 83-85; Cert Of Achvt 83-84.

PUMFORD, BRIAN; Falconer Central HS; Jamestown, NY; (Y); Am Leg Boys St; Church Yth Grp; Cmnty Wkr; Teachers Aide; Band; Mrchg Band; VP Stu Cncl; JV Bsktbl; Var Crs Cntry; Var Trk; Jamestown CC.

PUMFORD, KEN; Falconer Central HS; Jamestown, NY; (Y); 8/107; Letterman Clb; Quiz Bowl; Scholastic Bowl; School Play; Var Trk; Var Vllybl; NHS; Ntl Merit Schol; NY ST Rgnts Schlrshp 85; Full Tuition Schlrshp Jamestown CC 85; Jamestown CC; Engr.

PUMILIA, VICKI; Marlboro HS; Milton, NY; (Y); 10/168; Camera Clb; Trs 4-H; Nwsp Stf; Yrbk Stf; Var Vllybl; High Hon Roll; Jr NHS; NHS; Niagara U; Transprttn.

PUNK, LISA; West Babylon HS; W Babylon, NY; (S); Capt Dance Clb; Pres DECA; Tennis; Lab Inst Of Merch; Fshn Merch.

PUOPOLO, KATHLEEN; Liverpool HS; Liverpool, NY; (S); 103/791; Hosp Aide; Ed Yrbk Stf; High Hon Roll; Bus Admin.

PUPPIO, JOSEPHINE; West Hempstead HS; W Hempstead, NY; (Y); Art Clb; English Clb; Pres French Clb; Pres Radio Clb; Var Badmtn; Capt Bowling; Var Pom Pon; High Hon Roll; Art Hnr Soc 83-85; Doctor.

PUPPO, MARC A; Massapequa HS; Massapequa Park, NY; (Y); 50/500; Am Leg Boys St; JV Bsbl; JV Var Ice Hcky; Cit Awd; Hon Roll; NHS; Prfct Atten Awd; West Point Military Acad; Frgn.

PURCELL, VERONICA; Herbert H Lehman HS; Bronx, NY; (Y); Debate Tm; Office Aide; Science Clb; Varsity Clb; Chorus; Rep Frsh Cls; Rep Soph Cls; Trk; Hon Roll; NHS; UCLA; Pol Sci.

PURCHIA, PATSY N; Marlboro Central HS; Marlboro, NY; (Y); Church Yth Grp; Band; Concert Band; Mrchg Band; Wt Lftg; Outstndg Effort Awd Remedial Readng 79.

PURDY III, GORDON L; Wells Central Schl; Speculator, NY; (Y); 6/34; Band; Pres Frsh Cls; Pres Soph Cls; Var L Bsbl; Var L Bsktbl; Var L Socr; Cit Awd; NY ST Regents Schlrshp 85; Babe Ruth Sports Awd 82; Houghton Coll; Sports Med.

PURDY, KEITH; Midwood HS; Brooklyn, NY; (Y); Model UN; School Musical; School Play; Stage Crew; Var Bsbl; Var Bowling; Wrstlng; Hon Roll; Arista 85-86; Med.

PURDY, MYRON H; Franklin Acad; Malone, NY; (Y); Aud/Vis; Cmnty Wkr; Thesps; Chorus; Stage Crew; Swing Chorus; Variety Show; Im Golf; Im Vllybl; Prfct Atten Awd; Bus Mgmt.

PURDY JR, WILLIAM; Cicero North Syracuse HS; Clay, NY; (S); 100/711; Church Yth Grp; Im Bowling; Accntng.

PURETAS, CYNTHIA; St Pius V HS; Bronx, NY; (Y); Intnl Clb; Teachers Aide; Trs Jr Cls; Rep Stu Cncl; High Hon Roll; Jr NHS; NHS; Cornell U; Pedtrcn.

PURGAR, MARY; Smithtown H S East; Nesconset, NY; (Y); Camera Clb; Cmnty Wkr; Exploring; VP Pres 4-H; Office Aide; Red Cross Aide; Chorus; Stage Crew; 4-H Awd; Hon Roll; Pre-Med.

PURNER, MATTHEW; Queensbury HS; Glens Falls, NY; (Y); Intnl Clb; Band; Chorus; Concert Band; Pep Band; School Play; Var Diving; Var Swmmng; JV Trk; Hon Roll; Bio.

PURTELL, COLLEEN; Jamestown HS; Jamestown, NY; (Y); Latin Clb; Spanish Clb; Chorus; Orch; Stu Cncl; High Hon Roll; Jr NHS; NHS; U Of Buffalo; Sci.

PURTELL, JULIE; Horseheads HS; Horseheads, NY; (S); 33/407; Spanish Clb; Sec Varsity Clb; Stu Cncl; Cheerleading; Capt Vllybl; Hon Roll; NHS; Empire ST Gms Cntrl Regn Vllybl Team 84; SFC All Star Vllybl Team 84; U Of DE; Psych.

PURTELL, KAREN A; Sleepy Hollow HS; Tarrytown, NY; (Y); 8/160; Church Yth Grp; Sec German Clb; Hosp Aide; VP Model UN; Band; Var Crs Cntry; Var Trk; High Hon Roll; Pres NHS; NY ST Regnts Coll Schlrshp 85; Henry H Reichhold Schlrshp 85; Vassar Coll.

PURVEE, DAVID; Kendall Central HS; Kendall, NY; (Y); Church Yth Grp; FFA; Ski Clb; Hon Roll; Prfct Atten Awd; Crmnl Jstc.

PUSATERE, KIMBERLY; Ballston Spa HS; Ballston Spa, NY; (Y); 10/250; Cmnty Wkr; Hosp Aide; Nwsp Rptr; Yrbk Sprt Ed; Rep Soph Cls; Rep Jr Cls; High Hon Roll; NHS; Achvt Awd 84.

PUSATERI, KIMBERLY; Kings Park SR HS; Ft Salonga, NY; (Y); 94/393; Art Clb; Cmnty Wkr; Computer Clb; Drama Clb; Service Clb; Chorus; Variety Show; Yrbk Stf; Hon Roll; Natl Sci Olympiad Awd 83; Bus Adm.

PUSHKARSH, VANESSA; Saint Patricks Ctl Catholic HS; Durham, NY; (Y); Drama Clb; Office Aide; Teachers Aide; School Play; Stage Crew; Rptr Nwsp Stf; Yrbk Stf; Sec Jr Cls; Hon Roll; Amer Cncr Soc Dffdl Prncss 84-85; Psych.

PUSKARZ, JACQUELINE CAROL; Gloversville HS; Gloversville, NY; (Y); 3/234; Am Leg Aux Girls St; Nwsp Ed-Chief; Yrbk Ed-Chief; Trs Frsh Cls; Trs Soph Cls; Trs Jr Cls; Trs Sr Cls; Rep Stu Cncl; High Hon Roll; NHS; 1st Pl Art Cont 84; PAL; Fine Arts.

PUSKULDJIAN, JAMES; Archbishop Molloy HS; Rockaway Bch, NY; (Y); 199/412; Science Clb; Yrbk Stf; Im Bsktbl; Im Ftbl; Im Sftbl; Full Hnrs Courses; St Johns U; Bus Adm.

PUSTELNIK, CHARLES; Bishop Timon HS; Buffalo, NY; (Y); Nwsp Rptr; Nwsp Stf; Yrbk Rptr; Yrbk Stf; Im Vllybl; Hon Roll; Pre-Law.

PUSZ, JOSEPH; Mohonasen SR HS; Schenectady, NY; (Y); Teachers Aide; Var Capt Bsbl; Var Bsktbl; Var Golf; High Hon Roll; MVP Vrsty Bsbl 84; Accntng.

PUTKOWSKI, KAREN; Amsterdam HS; Amsterdam, NY; (Y); 70/294; Spanish Clb; Varsity Clb; Yrbk Stf; Rep Stu Cncl; Vllybl; Hon Roll; Maria Coll; RN.

PUTMAN, ANN; Heuvelton Central HS; Heuvelton, NY; (S); Latin Clb; Band; Church Choir; Concert Band; Mrchg Band; Trs Jr Cls; NHS; Prfct Atten Awd; Cert Of Merit Latin II & Engl; Josten Hnr Awd; Tchng.

PUTMAN, JAMES; Hannibal Central HS; Sterling, NY; (S); Var Ftbl; Var Capt Trk; High Hon Roll; Hon Roll; NHS; Ntl Merit Ltr; Prfct Atten Awd; Mech Drwng.

PUTMAN, TRICIA; Johnstown HS; Johnstown, NY; (Y); AFS; Dance Clb; Intnl Clb; Yrbk Stf; VP Frsh Cls; Coach Actv; Var L Fld Hcky; Var L Sftbl; JV Vllybl; Hon Roll; NYS Fld Hcky Chmpns 84-85; Acctnt.

PUTNAM, BETH Z; Cassadaga Valley HS; Stockton, NY; (Y); Ski Clb; Thesps; Band; Mrchg Band; School Musical; Yrbk Stf; Trs Sr Cls; Var Capt Vllybl; NHS; Wilma Boyd Trvl Sch; Trvl Mgmnt.

PUTNAM, JAMES; Hannibal Central HS; Sterling, NY; (Y); 7/108; School Play; Var L Ftbl; Var L Trk; Cit Awd; High Hon Roll; Hon Roll; NHS; Prfct Atten Awd; Engr.

PUTNEY, ANGELA; Mamaroneck HS; Larchmont, NY; (Y); Computer Clb; Math Tm; Chorus; NHS; Spanish NHS; 2nd Pl Computr Slvg Cont 84; Amer Chem Soc Exam Chem 84; Vrsty Ltr Fencng 84-85, Capt Fencg 85-86; Sci.

PUTTEN, RICHARD VANDER; St John The Baptist HS; Bohemia, NY; (Y); Church Yth Grp; Church Choir; Orch; Hotel Mgmt.

PUZEY, MATTHEW; Cazenovia Central HS; Cazenovia, NY; (Y); 1/150; Boy Scts; Church Yth Grp; Exploring; Quiz Bowl; Chorus; High Hon Roll; Prfct Atten Awd; Elec Engr.

PYLAND, KELLY; Lowville Acad; Lowville, NY; (Y); Church Yth Grp; Hosp Aide; Church Choir; Im Badmtn; Im Bsbl; Im Bsktbl; Im Crs Cntry; Im Golf; Im Gym; JV Var Socr; JCC; Nrsng.

PYLE, ALYSON; Depew HS; Depew, NY; (Y); 54/258; Drama Clb; School Musical; School Play; Variety Show; Yrbk Stf; Cheerleading; Crs Cntry; Gym; Trk; Hon Roll; Prncpls Ldrshp Awd 85; FL Sthrn Coll; Bio Sci.

PYLE, HEIDI J; Horseheads HS; Big Flats, NY; (S); 1/407; Church Yth Grp; Cmnty Wkr; VP Trs 4-H; Band; Yrbk Stf; High Hon Roll; NHS; Ntl Merit Ltr; Drama Clb; Exploring; Elmira Coll Key Awd; Rensselaer Plytchnc Inst Math Sci Awd; Awds Dstnctn Math, Engl, Frnch; Med.

PYM, MARY; Dundee Central HS; Dundee, NY; (Y); AFS; Church Yth Grp; Spanish Clb; Chorus; Color Guard; Yrbk Stf; JV Var Bsktbl; High Hon Roll; Hon Roll; NHS; Dundee Tchrs Assn Highest Achvt Span 83-84; Boces Finger Lks Occu Schl; RN.

PYSHER, PAUL A; Catskill HS; Cementon, NY; (Y); 2/132; French Clb; Ski Clb; Yrbk Stf; High Hon Roll; NHS; Sal; NY ST Regents Schlrshp 85; Elec Engr.

PYSKADLO, MICHELE; Kereny Memorial Acad; Cohoes, NY; (S); Spanish Clb; Band; Concert Band; High Hon Roll; Hon Roll; Sec Soph Cls; Var Cheerleading; Var Sftbl; Nrsng.

PYSKATY, JEFFREY; Barker Central HS; Barker, NY; (Y); 3/90; AFS; 4-H; French Clb; VP Jr Cls; Rep Stu Cncl; JV Bsktbl; JV Ftbl; JV Var Tennis; Variety Show; Hon Roll; SUNY Potsdam; Math.

PYSTADLO, MICHELE; Keveny Memorial Acad; Cohoes, NY; (Y); Spanish Clb; Band; Sec Soph Cls; Var Cheerleading; Sftbl; High Hon Roll; Hon Roll; NHS; Ntl Merit Ltr; Nrsng.

PYSZCZEK, LISA; John F Kennedy HS; Cheektowaga, NY; (Y); 45/140; Political Wkr; Varsity Clb; Yrbk Stf; Im Bowling; Var Socr; Poli Sci.

QUACKENBUSH, CRAIG M; Waterloo SR HS; Waterloo, NY; (Y); Am Leg Boys St; Boy Scts; Dance Clb; JV Var Lcrss; Cit Awd; Prfct Atten Awd; Egl Sct 84; Hmcmng Flt Cmmttee 82-85; Jrnlsm.

QUACKENBUSH JR, EDWARD; Westport Central HS; Westport, NY; (S); 2/22; Am Leg Boys St; Jazz Band; Nwsp Sprt Ed; Var Frsh Cls; Pres Soph Cls; Rep Stu Cncl; Var Bsktbl; Var Golf; Var Socr; Hon Roll; DAR Hist Awd 82; Whitford Mtrs Awd Acad/Athl 83; Harvard Bk Clb Awd 85; Military.

QUACKENBUSH, JAMES; Rhinebeck Central HS; Rhinebeck, NY; (Y); 20/99; Boy Scts; Drama Clb; Spanish Clb; Varsity Clb; Band; School Musical; School Play; Stage Crew; Stu Cncl; Bsbl; Pre Law.

QUACKENBUSH, JANICE; Watervliet HS; Watervliet, NY; (Y); 10/130; Drama Clb; Ski Clb; Spanish Clb; Varsity Clb; School Play; Yrbk Rptr; Yrbk Stf; Rep Stu Cncl; Var Capt Bsktbl; Im Bowling; NYS Regnts Schlrshp Nrsng Awd 85; SUNY Albany.

QUACKENBUSH, MELISSA; Liverpool HS; Liverpool, NY; (S); 14/792; Am Leg Aux Girls St; Exploring; VP Pres JA; Math Tm; Yrbk Sprt Ed; Rep Stu Cncl; Var Cheerleading; Var Trk; Hon Roll; NHS; 1st Pl In Span Intrprtn 82; Dartmouth Bk Awd 84; Chnnl 13 Star Stu 85; U Of Rochester; Med.

QUACKENBUSH, STEVE L; Waterloo HS; Waterloo, NY; (Y); Am Leg Boys St; Drama Clb; Varsity Clb; Band; Chorus; School Musical; Var Bsktbl; Var Trk; Hon Roll; Letterman Clb; Al-Cnty Chorus; Engrng.

QUADAGNO, MICHAEL; Archbishop Stepinac HS; Harrison, NY; (Y); 32/215; Church Yth Grp; Key Clb; Rep Frsh Cls; Rep Soph Cls; Rep Jr Cls; Var Capt Lcrss; High Hon Roll; NHS; JV Ftbl; JV Trk; Ldrshp Peer Cnclng; Engrng.

QUADRINI, MICHAEL A; St Anthonys HS; Northport, NY; (Y); Church Yth Grp; Computer Clb; Stage Crew; JV Ftbl; Var Swmmng; Hon Roll; Drexel U; Comp Sci.

QUAGLIANA, DOUGLAS; St Josephs Collegiate Inst; Williamsville, NY; (Y); Boy Scts; Church Yth Grp; JA; Library Aide; Concert Band; Im Bowling; JV Trk.

QUAGLIANA, PAUL M; Amherst Central SR HS; Snyder, NY; (Y); 4/292; Boy Scts; VP German Clb; Math Tm; Quiz Bowl; Jazz Band; Yrbk Ed-Chief; High Hon Roll; NCTE Awd; NHS; Ntl Merit SF; Cornell U; Engrng.

QUAGLIARA, SUSANNE; Maria Regina HS; Bronx, NY; (Y); School Musical; Rep Jr Cls; Rep Sr Cls; Stu Cncl; Hon Roll; Hnr Apprctn Awd 83-85; Scl Wrk.

QUAIN, HELEN; Bishop Kearney HS; Brooklyn, NY; (Y); 37/370; Library Aide; Band; Rep Sr Cls; Swmmng; ROTC.

QUAIN, KATHLEEN M; Johnson City HS; Johnson City, NY; (Y); 40/212; Drama Clb; French Clb; Band; Concert Band; Mrchg Band; School Play; Yrbk Stf; St Schlr; Schlstc Excell Awd 82; SUNY-BINGHAMTON; Math.

QUALEY, RICHARD; West Seneca East HS; W Seneca, NY; (Y); JV Var Bsktbl; JV Var Ftbl; JV Var Trk; Hon Roll; JC Awd; NHS; Spnsh Hnrs Awd 83-85; Govt Srv.

QUARANTA, LISA; East Meadow HS; E Meadow, NY; (S); 28/414; FBLA; Nassau CC; Acctng.

QUARM, JEANNE; Honeoye HS; Holcomb, NY; (S); French Clb; Pres Concert Band; Mrchg Band; Pep Band; Var Socr; JV Capt Sftbl; Var Vllybl; Hon Roll; Law.

QUARRIE, EUGEN A; Byram Hills HS; Armonk, NY; (Y); Am Leg Boys St; Church Yth Grp; Intnl Clb; Math Clb; Math Tm; Nwsp Stf; Rep Sr Cls; Stu Cncl; Bsktbl; Crs Cntry; Ntl Conf Chrstns & Jews 84; Co-Chrm Humanties Fest 85; Poltcl Sci.

QUEARLES, TINA; Hempstead HS; Hempstead, NY; (S); 59/355; Dance Clb; FBLA; Nwsp Stf; Yrbk Stf; Sr Cls; Stu Cncl; Gym; High Hon Roll; NHS; Ntl Merit Schol; Nassau Comm Coll; Acctng.

QUELLHORST, ERIC; Arlington HS; Poughkeepsie, NY; (Y); Boy Scts; Exploring; Red Cross Aide; Med.

QUENNEVILLE, MICHAEL; Massena Central HS; Massena, NY; (Y); 154/294; VP Church Yth Grp; Cmnty Wkr; VP French Clb; Varsity Clb; Var Capt Bsbl; Var L Ftbl; Var L Ice Hcky; Var L Socr; Knights Of Columbus & Robt T Moses Schlrshps 85; Canton ATC; Indvl Stds.

QUEREN, ELIZABETH; St Francis Prep; New York, NY; (S); 160/693; Band; Mrchg Band; Orch; Trk.

QUEVEDO, JOSEPH; Albertus Magnus HS; Tappan, NY; (Y); 20/185; Math Clb; Math Tm; Service Clb; School Play; Yrbk Sprt Ed; Sec Soph Cls; VP Jr Cls; VP Sr Cls; Var Socr; Muhlenberg Coll Schlrshp 85-86; Muhlenberg Coll; Bio.

QUEZADA, EDWIN; James Monroe HS; Bronx, NY; (Y); 4/250; Debate Tm; Latin Clb; Office Aide; Chorus; Vllybl; Gov Hon Prg Awd; Hon Roll; NHS; Pres Schlr; Spanish NHS; Lehman Coll; Sci.

QUEZADA, ISABEL; Washington Irving HS; New York, NY; (Y); Dance Clb; Drama Clb; Math Clb; Math Tm; Chorus; School Play; Doctor.

QUICK, CLIFTON J; Kingston HS; Port Ewen, NY; (Y); Am Leg Boys St; Cmnty Wkr; Math Tm; Ski Clb; Spanish Clb; Teachers Aide; Var L Crs Cntry; Var Trk; High Hon Roll; Hon Roll; Engnrng.

QUICK, STEVEN; Riverhead HS; Riverhead, NY; (Y); 35/215; Church Yth Grp; Cmnty Wkr; Computer Clb; JCL; Mathletes; Ski Clb; Teachers Aide; Socr; Rgnts Schlrshp 85; ST U Of NY; Stny Brk; Comp Sci.

QUICKENTON, TAMAR; Schoharie Central Schl; Schoharie, NY; (S); 3/94; Church Yth Grp; GAA; Sec Varsity Clb; Band; Chorus; Trs Frsh Cls; Trs Soph Cls; Var Socr; Var Sftbl; NHS; Houghton Coll; Elem Ed.

QUIDORT, CHRIS; Union-Endicott HS; Endicott, NY; (Y); Boys Clb Am; Cmnty Wkr; German Clb; Key Clb; Letterman Clb; Mathletes; Varsity Clb; L Crs Cntry; L Trk; Ntl Merit Ltr; MI Ann Arbor; Anthroplgy.

QUIETT, D ERIC; Barker Central Schl; Barker, NY; (Y); AFS; Boy Scts; Church Yth Grp; Computer Clb; Varsity Clb; Var Crs Cntry; Var Trk; God Cntry Awd; Hon Roll; Aero-Ntcl Engrng.

QUIGLEY, MAUREEN; Ithaca HS; Ithaca, NY; (Y); French Clb; Ski Clb; Color Guard; Variety Show; Yrbk Ed-Chief; Yrbk Phtg; Yrbk Stf; Rep Sr Cls; Stu Cncl; Var JV Cheerleading; Natl Frnch Awd Semi-Fnlst 82; U Of MA.

QUIGLEY, MICHELLE; Geneva HS; Geneva, NY; (S); 26/174; French Clb; Hosp Aide; Ski Clb; Varsity Clb; Band; Jazz Band; School Musical; Stu Cncl; Socr; NHS; All ST Wind Ensmbl 84; Syracuse U.

QUIJANO, SONIA; Mabel Dean Bacon V HS; Bronx, NY; (S); 19/299; Church Yth Grp; Red Cross Aide; Sec Sr Cls; Hon Roll; Prfct Atten Awd; Office Aide; Teachers Aide; Yrbk Stf; Rep Soph Cls; Rep Jr Cls; Att Awd 82; Hnr Soc Mdl 84; Deer Tutrng Cert 84; Baruch; Bus Admin.

QUILES, ARLENE; John Dewey HS; Brooklyn, NY; (Y); Art Clb; Camera Clb; Cmnty Wkr; FBLA; Chorus; Yrbk Stf; Im Tennis; Im Trk; Im Wt Lftg; Coll Of Staten Island; Real Est.

QUIMBY, ELIZABETH; Le Roy Central HS; Leroy, NY; (Y); 2/110; AFS; French Clb; Math Tm; Band; Chorus; School Musical; VP Sr Cls; L Tennis; Jr NHS; NHS.

QUIMBY, SHARON; Le Roy Central HS; Leroy, NY; (Y); 1/110; AFS; Latin Clb; Spanish Clb; Chorus; School Musical; JV Sftbl; High Hon Roll; Jr NHS; NHS; Summa Cm Laud Ntl Latn Exm 84; Hghst Grad Schl Amer Chemcl Soc Exm 85; Classcs.

QUINLAN, CYNTHIA; John H Glenn HS; Greenlawn, NY; (Y); Church Yth Grp; Library Aide; Office Aide; ROTC; Varsity Clb; Church Choir; Variety Show; Yrbk Stf; Var Capt Bsktbl; Var Vllybl; All Leag Suffolk Cnty 83-85; Bsktbl MVP 83-85; Speech Thrpy.

QUINLAN, JENNIFER; Candor Central HS; Candor, NY; (Y); 4-H; Church Choir; Mrchg Band; Yrbk Stf; Sec Sr Cls; JV Var Bsktbl; JV Var Sftbl; JV Trk; JV Vllybl; High Hon Roll; Girls St 85; Comp Sci.

QUINLAN, KIM; Nazareth Regional HS; Brooklyn, NY; (Y); Hon Roll; Nwsp Bus Mgr; Variety Show; Rep Stu Cncl; Var Cheerleading; Law.

QUINN, BILL; John S Burke Catholic HS; Middletown, NY; (Y); Pres Church Yth Grp; Church Choir; Nwsp Phtg; Yrbk Phtg; Var Crs Cntry; Var Trk; High Hon Roll; NHS; Pres Scholar American U 85; John Dolan Mem Awd 85; American U; Intl Rel.

QUINN, CHRISTINE; Academy Of St Joseph; Smithtown, NY; (Y); Cmnty Wkr; Hosp Aide; Church Choir; Sftbl; Vlntr Svc Awd 80-83; Bus.

QUINN, CHRISTINE M; Manhasset HS; Manhasset, NY; (Y); 14/209; Service Clb; Sec Band; Nwsp Bus Mgr; Rep Stu Cncl; Capt Var Crs Cntry; High Hon Roll; Sec NHS; NY ST Crss Cntry Champ Meet 83; U Of VA; Engr.

QUINN, ERIC; Weedsport JR SR HS; Sennett, NY; (Y); 11/83; Pres Church Yth Grp; Band; Yrbk Sprt Ed; Yrbk Stf; Var L Bsktbl; Pres L Trk; Hon Roll; Jr NHS; NHS; Cayuga Cnty CC; Archit.

QUINN, FAITH; Grand Island HS; Gr Island, NY; (Y).

QUINN, JENNIFER; Camden Central HS; Camden, NY; (Y); 11/208; Drama Clb; Varsity Clb; Chorus; School Musical; School Play; Swing Chorus; Yrbk Stf; Pres Frsh Cls; Rep Soph Cls; Sec Trs Jr Cls; U Rochester; Mech Engrng.

QUINN, KELLY; Villa Maria Acad; Buffalo, NY; (S); 3/114; Church Yth Grp; Computer Clb; French Clb; Math Clb; Pep Clb; Rep Jr Cls; High Hon Roll; NHS; Prtl Schlrshp 82-85; Niagara U; Bio.

QUINN, LEO; Saratoga Central Catholic HS; Ballston Spa, NY; (S); Aud/Vis; Boy Scts; Var L Bsktbl; High Hon Roll; Hon Roll; Bus.

QUINN, MARYANNE; Mount Mercy Acad; Buffalo, NY; (Y); Cmnty Wkr; VP JA; Latin Clb; Science Clb; Spanish Clb; Chorus; Yrbk Bus Mgr; Yrbk Stf; Trk; Grace Spadone Ctznshp Awd 79-80; Chorus Awd 79-80; Hilbert Coll; Law.

QUINN, MATTHEW; Cicero-North Syracuse HS; N Syracuse, NY; (S); 21/711; Math Clb; Ski Clb; Trs Frsh Cls; Trs Soph Cls; Trs Jr Cls; Trs Sr Cls; Rep Stu Cncl; JV Golf; JV Lcrss; Var L Wrstlng; West Point Acad; Micro Elect.

QUINN, SABU; Bronx H S Of Science; New York, NY; (Y); JA; Math Tm; Teachers Aide; Band; Concert Band; Arista Soc Stud Achvt Awd, Mth Achvt Awd & Band Achvt Awd 83; Comm Art.

QUINN, TIMOTHY J; Vestal SR HS; Vestal, NY; (Y); Am Leg Boys St; Model UN; Political Wkr; Nwsp Rptr; Rep Frsh Cls; Pres Soph Cls; Hon Roll; Cert Of Merit HS Prfrmnce 85; Outstndng Delg Awd; Croome Cnty Justice Prog Cert Of Merit 84; Le Moyne Coll; Pol Sci.

QUINONES, ARLENE; Christopher Columbus HS; New York, NY; (Y); 164/792; Cmnty Wkr; Office Aide; Teachers Aide; Band; Art Awd 83; Span Awd Lvl 6 84; John Jay Coll; Crim Just.

QUINONES, JEANETTE; St Michaels Acad; New York, NY; (Y); Church Yth Grp; Cmnty Wkr; Computer Clb; FHA; Hon Roll; NY U; Lbrl Arts.

QUINONES, JOSE; Seward Park HS; New York, NY; (Y); Band; Prfct Atten Awd; Comp Pgmmr.

QUINTANA, CARMEN; Chelsea V HS; Brooklyn, NY; (Y); 4/208; Church Yth Grp; Yrbk Stf; Rep Soph Cls; Rep Jr Cls; Rep Sr Cls; Cit Awd; High Hon Roll; Hon Roll; NHS; Sal; UFT Schlrshp 85; Cath Tchrs Assn J C Driscoll Schlrshp 85; Eng J K Hackett Mdl Ortory; Atty Gen Awd; Pratt Inst; Elec Engr.

QUINTANA, ROSITA; Aquinas HS; Bronx, NY; (Y); 86/178; Church Yth Grp; Chorus; School Play; Nwsp Rptr; Pres Frsh Cls; Var Bsktbl; Sftbl; Hon Roll; Political Wkr; Score Keeper; Occup Ther.

QUINTO, PAUL; West Hempstead HS; Island Pk, NY; (Y); Stu Cncl; Var Ftbl; Var Lcrss; Var Trk; Hon Roll; NHS; Physical Sci & Bus Comp Awds; MIP JV Ftbl MIP V La Crosse; Bus.

QUINZI, JOHN D; L C Obourn HS; E Rochester, NY; (Y); 2/122; Am Leg Boys St; FBLA; Varsity Clb; Boy Scts; Var JV Bsbl; Var JV Bsktbl; Im Vllybl; Cit Awd; High Hon Roll; NHS; MVP Bsbl 84-85; All Cnty 2nd Tm Bsbl 85; Engrng.

QUIRK, BRENDA A; Scotia-Glenville HS; Scotia, NY; (Y); 29/245; Band; Concert Band; Jazz Band; Mrchg Band; Orch; Yrbk Stf; Var L Bsktbl; NHS; French Clb; School Musical; Glenville Grnge Awd 85; Pres Acad Phys Ftnss Awd 85; Russell Sage Coll Troy; Ntrtn.

QUIRKE, DEIRDRE; Cardinal Spellman HS; Bronx, NY; (Y); Art Clb; Church Yth Grp; Cmnty Wkr; Vllybl; Hon Roll; Prfct Atten Awd; 2nd Hnrs Awd 84; NY U; Med.

QUIST, NICOLA A; Midwood HS; Brooklyn, NY; (Y); 172/605; Socr; Brown Blt Awd Karate 84; Cvl Engr.

QURAISHI, HUMA; Bronx High School Of Science; Tenafly, NJ; (Y); French Clb; Library Aide; Teachers Aide; Lit Mag; Ntl Merit SF; Arista 84-85; Intersp Cloisters 84; Natl Science Tlnt Srch Comp Smfnlst 84; Art History.

QURESHI, AMER; Curtis HS; Staten Island, NY; (Y); Computer Clb; Lit Mag; Crs Cntry; Golf; Trk; Haney Medal Fine Art 83; Comp Sci.

RA, LUCILLE; West Hempstead HS; W Hempstead, NY; (Y); Key Clb; Science Clb; Nwsp Rptr; Frsh Cls; Soph Cls; Jr Cls; Badmtn; Swmmng; Tennis; Vllybl; Bio Awd Cert 83-84; Boston U; Psych.

RAAB, HOLLY M; Newburgh Free Acad; Newburgh, NY; (Y); 72/780; Church Yth Grp; Chorus; High Hon Roll; Hon Roll; Regents Schlrshp 85; Cert Wrkng Consrvtn Day 83; Cert Chorus 82; NY ST U-Albany.

RABASCO, SAVERIO; Nazareth Regional HS; Brooklyn, NY; (Y); Var Ftbl; Var Capt Socr; Hon Roll.

RABB, LATIFAH A; F H La Guardia H S Of Music & Arts; New York City, NY; (Y); 65/588; Cmnty Wkr; Library Aide; Office Aide; Political Wkr; Teachers Aide; Y-Teens; Yrbk Stf; Lit Mag; Rep Stu Cncl; Hon Roll; Grphcs Awd 82-83; Photo Awd 84; Howard U; Photo.

RABBACH, CHARLES; Whitestone Acad; Flushing, NY; (S); Hon Roll; Hofstra; Psychlgy.

RABE, SCOTT; Rome Free Acad; Rome, NY; (Y); Ski Clb; Spanish Clb; Yrbk Stf; JV Socr; Tennis; Hon Roll; NHS; Clarkson; Electrcl Engrng.

RABE, THOMAS E; Marathon Central HS; Marathon, NY; (Y); Am Leg Boys St; Drama Clb; Band; School Play; Rep Stu Cncl; Trk; Hon Roll; Math Clb; Quiz Bowl; Ski Clb; Wnnr Lcl Am Leg Ortrcl Cntst 84; Bst Prfrmnc Drmtc Pairs Cntst SUNY Crtlnd 85; Dntstry.

RABECK, MARCY; Harry S Truman HS; Bronx, NY; (Y); 56/544; Service Clb; Chorus; Church Choir; Hon Roll; NHS; Law Team Co-Capt 84-85; Asst Tchr 84-85; Syracuse U; Mktg.

RABEL, NANCY; Canarsie HS; Brooklyn, NY; (Y); 18/567; Camera Clb; Computer Clb; Office Aide; Service Clb; Teachers Aide; Hon Roll; NHS; Prfct Atten Awd; FL Inst Of Tech; Comp Engr.

RABIN, JEFF; Bronx Science; New York, NY; (S); JA; Varsity Clb; Var Socr; Var Tennis; BA; Buisiness Administration.

RABIN, MELISSA; Bronx High School Of Science; New York, NY; (Y); Debate Tm; NFL; Speech Tm; JA; Yrbk Stf; JV Gym; JV Vllybl; Ntl Merit Ltr; NY ST Chmpn Debat Tm 82-83; NY ST Sem-Finlst Spch Tm 85-86; NY ST Qurtr-Fnlst Debat Tm 84-85; Georgetwn U; Intl Reltns.

RABINOVITZ, ALISON; George W Hewlett HS; N Woodmere, NY; (Y); French Clb; Pep Clb; Temple Yth Grp; School Play; Stonybrook U NY; Physcl Trpy.

RACANIELLO, MICHAEL; Holy Cross HS; Whitestone, NY; (Y); JV Var Ftbl.

RACANO, ANTHONY; Cardinal Spellman HS; Bronx, NY; (Y); Aud/Vis; Camera Clb; Church Yth Grp; Computer Clb; Stage Crew; Nwsp Phtg; Yrbk Phtg; Lit Mag; Stu Cncl; Media Arts.

RACCHUMI, EVELYN; Cathedral HS; New York, NY; (Y); 71/298; Church Yth Grp; Intnl Clb; Library Aide; Office Aide; Teachers Aide; Color Guard; Mrchg Band; Hon Roll; Spanish NHS; Marchng Band Awd 82-83; Pre-Med.

RACE, JOLENE; Hudson HS; Hudson, NY; (Y); Church Yth Grp; Cmnty Wkr; Dance Clb; Band; Church Choir; Concert Band; Mrchg Band; Variety Show; Var JV Mgr(s); Var Pom Pon; Herkimer; Occuptn Thrpst.

RACHOW, KIMBERLY; Hilton Central HS; Hilton, NY; (Y); 70/350; Nwsp Rptr; Lit Mag; Rep Soph Cls; Rep Jr Cls; Var Cheerleading; High Hon Roll; Hon Roll; Jrnlsm.

RACHUM, DORTHEA; Coxsackie Athens Central Schl; West Coxsackie, NY; (Y); 36/104; Spanish Clb; Chorus; Nwsp Rptr; High Hon Roll; Hon Roll; Outstndng Accmplshmnts NHS 83; Engl Lit.

RACINE, BRIAN; Farmingdale HS; N Mass, NY; (Y); Church Yth Grp; JV Var Socr; Comp Sci.

RACINE, NICOLE; Northeastern Clinton Central Schl; Rouses Pt, NY; (Y); Jazz Band; Mrchg Band; School Musical; High Hon Roll; NHS; Augsbury-N Cntry Schlr 84-85; Outstndng Chem Stu 84-85; Outstndg Spnsh Stu 84-85; Pre-Med.

RACITANO, ROXANNE; Jamestown HS; Jamestown, NY; (Y); Church Yth Grp; 4-H; Ski Clb; VP Spanish Clb; Band; Chorus; Color Guard; Stage Crew; Chautaugua Cnty Legsltve Intrn Pgm 85; Arts Fstvl 83-85; Art.

RACKMYRE, CHRISTINA; Gloversville HS; Gloversville, NY; (Y); Var Capt Bsktbl; Var Sftbl; Var Trk; Var Capt Vllybl; Hon Roll; Girls Bsktbl MVP 83-84; Girls Bsktbl Most Imprvd 84; Vllybl Coaches Awd 83-84; Best All Arnd 84-85.

RACLAWSKI, AL; Hutchinson Central Tech HS; Buffalo, NY; (Y); Hon Roll; Fin.

RACQUET, JOHN C; Columbia HS; Castleton, NY; (Y); 2/354; Computer Clb; Math Tm; Ed Lit Mag; High Hon Roll; JP Sousa Awd; NHS; Ntl Merit SF; Pres Schlr; Sal; NYS Sci Bio Awd 82; Columbia HS Bio Awd 82; NYS Sci Chem Awd 83; Siena Coll; Comp Sci.

RADECKI, MICHAEL; Commack High Schl North; E Northport, NY; (Y); Aud/Vis; Capt Varsity Clb; Var Crs Cntry; Var Capt Trk; All Leag Crss Cntry 84; All Conf Wntr Trck 85; All Leag Sprng Trck 85; Villanova U; Bus.

RADESI JR, FELIX JOHN; York Central HS; Leicester, NY; (Y); 1/90; VP Frsh Cls; VP Soph Cls; VP Jr Cls; Var L Bsbl; Var Capt Bsktbl; Var Capt Ftbl; Jr NHS; NHS; Am Leg Boys St; Math Tm; Clsrm Hnrs Soc Stud 83; Clsrm Hnrs Mth 84-85; Engrng.

RADICE, ELIZABETH; Saint John The Baptist HS; Massapequa, NY; (Y); Art Clb; Dance Clb; Math Clb; Math Tm; Teachers Aide; Rep Jr Cls; Rep Stu Cncl; High Hon Roll; Hon Roll; Channel 13 7th Annl Stu Art Fest Awd, Reliqious Stu Pgm Catechist Cert 85; Schl Of Visual Arts; Comm Art.

RADIN, JEFFREY; The Nichols Schl; Kenmore, NY; (Y); ROTC; Nwsp Phtg; Yrbk Phtg; JV Bsbl; Im Crs Cntry; JV Ice Hcky; Im Tennis; Var Trk; Rdrs Dgst Schlrshp 83-85; Regents Schlrshp 85; Kenyon Coll; Med.

RADIN, JENNIFER M; The Chapin Schl; New York, NY; (Y); Cmnty Wkr; Dance Clb; Latin Clb; Office Aide; Political Wkr; Service Clb; Teachers Aide; Temple Yth Grp; Varsity Clb; Var Bsktbl; Ntl Latin Exam Magna Cum Laude 83; NY Rgnts Schlrshp 85; NYS Stdnt Senate 84; Amherst Coll; Classics.

RADLIFF, BRYAN; Shenendehowa HS; Clifton Park, NY; (Y); FFA; Ski Clb; Band; Symp Band; Var L Ftbl; Var L Lcrss; JV Socr; Var L Wrstlng; Wrstlng Class A Champ 84-85; NYS PHSAA La Crosse & Wrstlng Sect 2 84-85; Law.

RADMAND, ROSHANAK; Lynbrook HS; Lynbrook, NY; (Y); French Clb; Spanish Clb; Var Trk; Hon Roll; Bio.

RADMORE, DAVID M; Cortland JR SR HS; Cortland, NY; (Y); Thesps; VP Chorus; Hon Roll; NHS; Am Leg Boys St; Church Yth Grp; Latin Clb; VP MMM; School Musical; School Play; Outstndng Ldrshp Awd Chorus 84-85; Onstage Ntl Thespian Awd 83-84; Choral Studies 84; Music.

RADOMSKI, THOMAS; Niagara Catholic HS; Niagara Falls, NY; (Y); Church Yth Grp; French Clb; Varsity Clb; Capt Var Bsbl; JV Var Bsktbl; Im Ftbl; Hon Roll; Prfct Atten Awd; Cornell U; Elec Engr.

RADUNS, STEVE; Akron Central HS; Akron, NY; (Y); Boy Scts; Bsbl; Niagara CC; Comp Aid Drftng.

RAEMORE, MICHAEL C; Corning East HS; Corning, NY; (Y); Varsity Clb; Yrbk Bus Mgr; Var L Bsbl; JV Ftbl; Ice Hcky; High Hon Roll; NHS; All Sthrn Trls Conf Bsebl Tm 85; All Twin Tiers Bsebl Tm 85; All Sthrn Trls Conf Altrnt Bsebl Tm 84; Bus Mgmt.

RAFALSKI, DAWN; Fillmore Central HS; Houghton, NY; (Y); Church Yth Grp; Letterman Clb; Service Clb; Varsity Clb; Chorus; School Play; Nwsp Rptr; Yrbk Rptr; Capt Var Bsktbl; Hon Roll; Athl Awds-Girls Vrsty Tm Bsktbl 85; Stu Cncl Tlnt Show-1st Pl Grp Skit 85; Athl Cert/Awds Bsbl,Sftbl; Hilbert Coll; Crmnl Justc.

RAFEL, SHARI L; Sheepshead Bay HS; Brooklyn, NY; (Y); 47/465; School Musical; Nwsp Stf; Yrbk Bus Mgr; Yrbk Stf; Stu Cncl; Mgr Bsbl; Mgr Socr; Tennis; Regents Schlrshp 85; Arista 84-85; Archon 84-85; SUNY-ALBANY; Law.

RAFFAELE, ALICE; Brooklyn Acad; Brooklyn, NY; (Y); Art Clb; Camp Fr Inc; Church Yth Grp; FNA; Hosp Aide; Teachers Aide; Sftbl; Prfct Atten Awd; Office Aide; Church Choir; St Johns; Early Child Care.

RAFFERTY, BONNIE L; Waverly JR-SR HS; Lowman, NY; (Y); DECA; Pep Clb; Band; Concert Band; Mrchg Band; Im Vllybl; Hon Roll; Cert Recogntn Peer Tchng 85; Herkimer County CC; Psych.

RAFFERTY, DENISE; The Academy Of St Joseph; Commack, NY; (Y); Cmnty Wkr; FHA; Hosp Aide; Library Aide; NEDT Awd; Regina Teens Candystriping Svc Recgntn Cert-60 Hrs 83-84; Regina Teens Candystriping Svc Recgntn Cert.

RAFFERTY, MATTHEW; Northstar Christain Acad; Rochester, NY; (S); Church Yth Grp; Drama Clb; FCA; Varsity Clb; Chorus; VP Frsh Cls; Pres Jr Cls; Var Capt Bsktbl; Var JV Socr; Hon Roll; Math.

RAFFERTY, SARAH; Mineola HS; Mineola, NY; (Y); Art Clb; Key Clb; Nwsp Phtg; Yrbk Phtg; Rep Soph Cls; Hon Roll; Outstndng Stu Extra-Currclr Actvts 84-85; Photgrphy.

RAFIQ, AMERHA; Hillcrest HS; Flushing, NY; (Y); #6 In Class; Cmnty Wkr; Hosp Aide; Math Tm; Chorus; Nwsp Ed-Chief; Hon Roll; Jr NHS; VP NHS; Prfct Atten Awd; Amer Frgn Polcy Esy Cont Wnr 83; Schl Sci Congress-Bst In Subj Area 83; Artcl In NY Times; Union Coll; Pre Med.

RAFLA, NATASHA; Notre Dame Acad; Staten Island, NY; (Y); Camera Clb; Computer Clb; Math Clb; Science Clb; Nwsp Rptr; Lit Mag; Sec Stu Cncl; JV Var Bsktbl; Var Socr; NY Fash Inst Tech; Fash Buyer.

RAFT, ADRIENNE; Warwick Valley HS; Warwick, NY; (Y); 36/205; Cmnty Wkr; Teachers Aide; Frsh Cls; Swmmng; Trk; Hon Roll; NHS; Prfct Atten Awd; Drama Clb; French Clb; Berkley Bus Schl Schlrshp 85; Hnr Roll Schlrshp Lttr 82-85; Ctznshp Awd; Hunter Coll.

RAGHUNATHAN, PRATIMA L; Fairport HS; Fairport, NY; (Y); Political Wkr; Chorus; Yrbk Stf; Rep Stu Cncl; High Hon Roll; NCTE Awd; Pres NHS; Ntl Merit SF; Yearbook Layout Editor 84-85; Biology Chem.

RAGO, PETER; Archbishop Molloy HS; Greenpoint, NY; (Y); Computer Clb; Chrmn Science Clb; Church Choir; Im Socr; NYC Schl Sci Fair 83; Intrschlstc Sci Fair 1st Prz 85; Cty Creative Wrtng Awd 83; U Sydny Astrla; Phrmclgst.

RAGONA, JOANIE; South Side HS; Rockville Centr, NY; (Y); 15/287; VP Frsh Cls; VP Soph Cls; VP Jr Cls; Off Sr Cls; VP Stu Cncl; Capt L Cheerleading; Var L Trk; Cit Awd; NHS; St Schlr; Nassau Cnty Exec Awd 85; Fndr & Pres SADD Hotline 84-85; DAR Amer Hist Awd 85; Vassar Coll; Polt Sci.

RAGONE, JOHN; Msgr Mc Clancy HS; Mddle Village, NY; (Y); Church Yth Grp; Cmnty Wkr; JA; Fld Hcky; Ftbl; Ice Hcky; Sftbl; Wt Lftg; Hon Roll; Engr.

RAGONESE, MARK; Cicero North Syracuse HS; North Syracuse, NY; (S); 81/711; Church Yth Grp; Pres Frsh Cls; JV Bsktbl; Var Score Keeper; JV Socr; Hon Roll; Jr NHS; Engrng.

RAGOSTA, CAROL; East Islip HS; Islip Terr, NY; (Y); FBLA; Forgn Lang Hnr Socty 84-85; 2nd Pl FBLA Shrthd Comptn Suffolk 84-85; UCLA; Bus.

RAGUSO, LAURA; Aquinas HS; Bronx, NY; (Y); 4/178; School Play; Yrbk Stf; VP Soph Cls; Pres Jr Cls; Rep Stu Cncl; High Hon Roll; Hon Roll; NHS; NEDT Awd; Itln Hon Soc 85; Acad Art Hnrs 83-85; Fine Arts.

RAHALEWICZ, STEPHANIE L; Fairport HS; Fairport, NY; (Y); Intnl Clb; Varsity Clb; Chorus; Yrbk Stf; Stu Cncl; Var L Trk; Hon Roll; Regents Schlrsph 85; Gerber Chldrns Ed Schlrshp 85; VA Commonwlth U; Occuptnl Thrp.

RAHILLY, CHRISTINE; Cardinal Spellman HS; Bronx, NY; (Y); Ski Clb; Nwsp Stf; Var L Swmmng; Hon Roll; NHS; NEDT Awd.

RAHMAN, WAHEEDA; Richmond Hill HS; Queens, NY; (Y); Teachers Aide; Chorus; Hon Roll; Prfct Atten Awd; Cartooning Art Awd 85; Hnr Roll 85; Perfct Attndnc 83 & 85; Med.

RAHNER, ANDREA M; Maine-Endwell SDR HS; Endwell, NY; (Y); 35/280; GAA; Var Crs Cntry; Var Trk; Hon Roll; NHS; NYS Regents Schlrshp 85; Var Ltr Track & Indoor Track, LOCA Art Awd 84; Syracuse U; Comp Graph.

RAI, RABINDRA S; Newtown HS; Elmhurst, NY; (Y); Chess Clb; Math Tm; Science Clb; Bsktbl; Swmmng; Tennis; High Hon Roll; Westinghouse Sci Awd 85; St Johns U Rsrch Cmptn 85; NY Acad Of Sci Rsrch Cmptn 85; Pre-Med.

RAIBLE, LISA; Rhinebeck HS; Rhinebeck, NY; (Y); AFS; Church Yth Grp; Cmnty Wkr; Stage Crew; Trs Jr Cls; Rep Stu Cncl; Bsktbl; Sftbl; Hon Roll; Wnr Natl Frnch Cntst 84; Advncd Plcmnt Spnsh 85; Spnsh Achvt Test 85; Intl Rel.

RAIMOND, JOSIE; Bishop Kearney HS; Rochester, NY; (Y); Church Yth Grp; Ski Clb; Var Bsktbl; Var Socr; Var L Sftbl; Var Vllybl; High Hon Roll; Hon Roll; Ntl Merit Ltr; Lwyr.

RAINBOW, JODI; Liverpool HS; Liverpool, NY; (Y); Dance Clb; Ski Clb; Stu Cncl; JV Var Cheerleading; Powder Puff Ftbl; Score Keeper; High Hon Roll; Jr NHS; NHS; Hnrbl Merit Awd Ntl Latin Ex 84; Comp Sci.

RAIOLA, JENNIFER; Bishop Kearney HS; Brooklyn, NY; (Y); Aud/Vis; Cmnty Wkr; JA; Speech Tm; Nwsp Rptr; Rep Frsh Cls; Rep Soph Cls; Pres Jr NHS; Intl Stds Assoc Partl Schlrshp 85; BQC Frnsc Leag 5 Awds 82-85; Tablet News Stry Awd Hnrbl Ment 85; Law.

RAITI, ADAM; Liverpool HS; Liverpool, NY; (S); 78/798; Art Clb; Church Yth Grp; Wrstlng; High Hon Roll; Hon Roll; Jr NHS; NHS; 3 Schltc Achv Awds For Art 82-84; 3 Hnrb Mntns & 2 Blue Rbbns In The Mony Regnl Schltc Art Awds 84-85; RI Schl Of Design; Art.

RAKITIN, BRIAN; Smithtown H S East; Smithtown, NY; (Y); Radio Clb; Scholastic Bowl; High Hon Roll; NHS; Ntl Merit SF; Frgn Svc Offcr.

RAKOCZY, SUZANNE; Copiague HS; Copiague, NY; (Y); Cmnty Wkr; FTA; Stage Crew; Nwsp Ed-Chief; Ed Yrbk Stf; Lit Mag; Stat Bsktbl; Var L Fld Hcky; Cit Awd; Pres NHS; Ftns Awd 84; VFW Essay Wnnr 80-82; Hmntrn Awd 83; Columbia Schl Vis Arts; Com Art.

RAKOWSKI, SANDRA; Trumansburg HS; Ithaca, NY; (Y); 12/89; Model UN; Spanish Clb; School Play; Yrbk Stf; Stu Cncl; Var Bsktbl; JV Sftbl; High Hon Roll; Hon Roll; NHS; Bus Mgt.

RALLIS, SALOME M; St Francis Prep; Astoria, NY; (Y); 144/673; Church Yth Grp; Math Clb; Band; Drm & Bgl; Im Sftbl; Im Vllybl; Im Wt Lftg; Hon Roll; Opt Clb Awd; Awd Excllnc Drum Corp 83-85; Hnr-Outstndng Achv Spnsh 83-84; St Johns U; Bus Law.

RALSTON, ELIZABET S; Buffalo Seminary; Buffalo, NY; (Y); 14/34; French Clb; Science Clb; Ski Clb; School Play; Var Tennis; Hon Roll; NHS; Cert From Roswell Park Mem Inst Smr Cmp 84; Hrsbck Riding Ribbons; Wlcmng Committee Pin; Kenyon; Bio-Chem.

RALSTON, LARRAINE; Massena Central HS; Massena, NY; (Y); Church Yth Grp; Sec Key Clb; Radio Clb; Band; Concert Band; Jazz Band; Mrchg Band; Pep Band; Yrbk Bus Mgr; Stu Cncl; Band Mst Imprvd Awd 84; Canton ATC; Rtl Bus Mgmnt.

RAM, ROSITA; John Jay HS; Brooklyn, NY; (Y); 10/537; Cmnty Wkr; Dance Clb; Office Aide; Science Clb; Nwsp Stf; VP Jr Cls; Wt Lftg; Prfct Atten Awd; Cert For Arista 85; Yale; Pre-Med.

RAMA, CHRIS; Mamaroneck HS; Mamaroneck, NY; (Y); FBLA; Ftbl; Wt Lftg; Wrstlng; Pharmcy.

RAMBADT, MICHAEL P; Carmel HS; Patterson, NY; (Y); 121/390; Art Clb; Drama Clb; Intnl Clb; Chorus; School Musical; School Play; Yrbk Ed-Chief; Lit Mag; Hon Roll; Art Awds 84; Fordham; Engl.

RAMBAROSE, CANDICE; Middletown HS; Middletown, NY; (Y); Drama Clb; Girl Scts; Teachers Aide; Chorus; School Musical; School Play; Hon Roll; Buffalo ST U; Pre-Med.

RAMBAUD, VERONICA; New Lebanon HS; Williamstown, MA; (Y); Sec French Clb; Ski Clb; Yrbk Stf; Sec Frsh Cls; Hon Roll; Prfct Atten Awd; Drvr Ed Awd; Schlrshp Awd; Becker JC; Trvl & Trsm.

RAMBERT, DARNELL; Long Island Lutheran JR/SR HS; Hempstead, NY; (S); Drama Clb; Speech Tm; Chorus; Jazz Band; School Musical; School Play; Yrbk Phtg; Trs Stu Cncl; Hon Roll; NHS; Music.

RAMBERT, LINDA; Senior HS; Brooklyn, NY; (Y); 15/250; Cmnty Wkr; JA; Crs Cntry; Trk; Cit Awd; High Hon Roll; Hon Roll; NHS; Sal; Louglin Gold Ltr 82-85; Trk Fld 84; Comm Serv Awd 85; Math.

RAMIA, ANDALIB; Binghamton HS; Binghamton, NY; (Y); Boys Clb Am; Debate Tm; PAVAS; Speech Tm; Nwsp Ed-Chief; Nwsp Rptr; Nwsp Stf; Lit Mag; Vllybl; French Hon Soc; Essy Cntst Awd 82-83; Photgrphy & Ntl Hnrng Crtvty Awds 84-85.

RAMIEZ, EMPERATRIZ; Cathedral HS; Brooklyn, NY; (Y); 29/298; Chorus; Hon Roll; Psych.

RAMIN, JANET R; Sewanhaka HS; Floral Park, NY; (Y); 3/367; FBLA; Mathletes; Spanish Clb; Drill Tm; Nwsp Rptr; Yrbk Rptr; Lit Mag; Rep Stu Cncl; High Hon Roll; Hon Roll; FBLA 1st Pl ST, Dist Bus 83-84; Hnr Socs 84-85NYS Regnts Schlrshp 85; Manhattan Coll; Bus Adm.

RAMIREZ, CATHY; St Johns Prep; S Ozone Pk, NY; (Y); JV Vllybl; Hon Roll; Assist St Johns U For Regents Diploma 85; St Johns U; Engrng.

RAMIREZ, DAVID; St Fransis Preporatory Schl; Elmhurst, NY; (Y); 380/700; Chorus; Ftbl; Syracuse U; Bus Orgnztn.

RAMIREZ, EMPERATRIZ; Cathedral HS; Brooklyn, NY; (Y); 29/298; Chorus; Hon Roll; Psych.

RAMIREZ, EVELYN; Immaculata HS; New York, NY; (Y); Church Yth Grp; Chorus; Pres Frsh Cls; Pres Soph Cls; Sec Stu Cncl; Hon Roll; St Johns U; Psych.

RAMIREZ, JOSE; Lindenhurst SR HS; Lindenhurst, NY; (Y); Church Yth Grp; Debate Tm; German Clb; Spanish Clb; Band; Concert Band; Mrchg Band; School Play; Stage Crew; VP NHS; VFW Awd Voice Demcrcy 85.

RAMIREZ, LORENA; Hillcrest HS; Elmhurst, NY; (Y); Hosp Aide; Math Tm; Chorus; Color Guard; School Musical; Rep Soph Cls; Rep Jr Cls; Rep Stu Cncl; Hon Roll; Prfct Atten Awd; Lab Tech.

RAMIREZ, MICHELE; La Guardia High School Music & Arts; New York, NY; (Y); 68/590; Yrbk Stf; Jr NHS; NHS; Vassar; Anthropology.

RAMIREZ, PRISCILLA; St Johns Prep; Corona, NY; (Y); Dance Clb; Rep Stu Cncl; Girl Scts; Rep Jr Cls; Hon Roll; St Johns U; Law.

RAMIREZ, YAEL; Mabel Dean Bacon V HS; New York, NY; (S); 11/299; Drama Clb; Hosp Aide; Teachers Aide; Chorus; Yrbk Stf; Rep Jr Cls; Cit Awd; High Hon Roll; Hon Roll; NHS; Hon Soc Gold Pin Awd 84; Honrd City Stu By Mayor 84; Gold Mdl Excllnc Lang Arts 81; Baruch Coll; Lib Arts.

RAMLOGAN, KUSHMAWATTIE; Flushing HS; Flushing, NY; (Y); Camp Fr Inc; Dance Clb; Drama Clb; Exploring; Hosp Aide; Math Clb; Model UN; Yrbk Rptr; Socr; Vllybl; Hunter Coll; Chld Psych.

RAMON, MARIA DE JESUS; Murry Bergtraum HS; Queens, NY; (Y); 2/576; Orch; Hon Roll; NHS; Accntng 82-83; Bus Law 83-84; Chem 83-84; Bernard M Baruch Coll; CPA.

RAMOS, ALEJANDRA; Norman Thomas HS; Jamaica, NY; (S); 1/671; Computer Clb; FBLA; Pres Spanish Clb; Chorus; Rep Sr Cls; VP NHS; Val; Regents Scholar 85; NYC FBLA Comp Pace U 3rd Pl Stenogrphy 85; Norman Thomas Essay Cont 1st Pl 84; Bus Admin.

RAMOS, ANNETTE; Norman Thomas C HS; Bronx, NY; (S); 80/671; Debate Tm; Library Aide; Chorus; Color Guard; Rep Frsh Cls; Wt Lftg; Cit Awd; Hon Roll; JP Sousa Awd; Jr NHS.

RAMOS, CARMEN; John Jay HS; Brooklyn, NY; (Y); 45/533; Pres Church Yth Grp; Band; Church Choir; Nwsp Rptr; Nwsp Stf; The Kings Coll; Psychlgy.

RAMOS, CLARA; Cathedral HS; Ny, NY; (Y); 7/289; Chorus; Mrchg Band; Nwsp Rptr; Nwsp Stf; Yrbk Phtg; Yrbk Rptr; Yrbk Stf; VP Frsh Cls; Rep Soph Cls; Im Gym; MIT; Mech Engrng.

RAMOS, CRISTINA J; High School Of Art And Design; Bronx, NY; (Y); Art Clb; Teachers Aide; Lit Mag; Hon Roll; Patricia Slayton Mem Art Awd 83; Artst.

RAMOS, EDDY; All Hallows HS; Bronx, NY; (Y); Boys Clb Am; Camera Clb; Drama Clb; MMM; Band; Drm Mjr(t); Mrchg Band; School Musical; School Play; JV Bsbl; JR & Stu Achvt Awds 85; Law.

RAMOS, HENRY; Newtown HS; Elmhurst, NY; (Y); 262/603; Concert Band; Teachers Aide; Orch; Awd Svc Video 84; Ntl Hspnc Schlr Awds; Radio & TV.

RAMOS, JACQUELINE; Theodore Roosevelt HS; New York, NY; (Y); Drama Clb; Math Clb; Office Aide; Service Clb; School Musical; School Play; Variety Show; Pres Stu Cncl; Gym; Vllybl; Mth Tutor; Stoney Brook U; Dentist.

RAMOS, KARLA; Adlai Stevenson HS; Bronx, NY; (Y); 78/445.

RAMOS, NANCY; Yonkers HS; Yonkers, NY; (Y); Yrbk Stf; Hon Roll; Soc Studys Awd 83; Wilfred Acad; Artst.

RAMOS, SONIA M; St Johns Prep; Jackson Hts, NY; (Y); Camera Clb; Dance Clb; Latin Clb; Yrbk Stf; Rep Stu Cncl; Wt Lftg; St Johns U; Pre-Med.

RAMOS, VICTOR; Archbishop Molloy HS; Elmhurst, NY; (Y); 90/410; Latin Clb; Im Bsktbl; Im Coach Actv; Im Ftbl; Im Sftbl; Engr.

RAMOS, WILMA; Our Lady Of Perpetual Help HS; Brooklyn, NY; (Y); 24/162; Drama Clb; Chorus; School Musical; Pres Stage Crew; Bowling; Twrlr; Jr NHS; NHS; Prfct Atten Awd; St Johns U; Psych.

RAMP, DENISE; New Rochelle HS; New Rochelle, NY; (Y); Cmnty Wkr; French Clb; Pep Clb; Red Cross Aide; School Play; Trs Stu Cncl; Cheerleading; French Hon Soc; Jr NHS; Sec NHS; Sci, Engl, Hstry Achvt 82-83; Intl Undrstndng Awd 83-84; Schl Spirit 83-84; Outdoor Ed Awd 83-84; Socl Wrk.

RAMPERSAUD, SATTIE; William Homard Taft HS; Bronx, NY; (Y); 3/32; Jazz Band; School Musical; Variety Show; Off Sr Cls; High Hon Roll; Hon Roll; NEDT Awd; Key Clb; Math,Key Bdg; Prfct Atten 85; Word Proccsng.

RAMSAY, JIM; L T Lutheran HS; Huntington, NY; (S); Varsity Clb; Nwsp Sprt Ed; Yrbk Ed-Chief; JV Bsktbl; JV Coach Actv; JV Ftbl; Var Golf; Tennis; Hon Roll; NHS; Sprts Commntr.

RAMSEY, CAITLYN; Warwick Valley HS; Pine Island, NY; (Y); 1/200; Math Tm; Science Clb; Nwsp Ed-Chief; Nwsp Stf; High Hon Roll; Lion Awd; 1st Pl Spanish Awd 83-85; Charles Hawkens Prz Chem 84; 1st Pl Math Assoc Amer Cntst 85; Sci Journlst.

RAMSEY, D LISA; Longwood HS; Coram, NY; (Y); 47/450; Q&S; Nwsp Rptr; Lit Mag; Rep Jr Cls; Rep Sr Cls; Rep Stu Cncl; JV Var Cheerleading; JV Var Vllybl; High Hon Roll; Hon Roll; U Center Binghamton; Law.

RAMSEY, JANIS; Fort Edward HS; Ft Edward, NY; (Y); 2/43; Church Yth Grp; Drama Clb; Hosp Aide; Spanish Clb; Drm & Bgl; Trs Frsh Cls; High Hon Roll; NHS; Ntl Merit Ltr; Political Wkr; Plattsburgh ST Coll; Med Tech.

RAMSEY, MAUREEN E; Nardin Acad; Buffalo, NY; (Y); 4/90; Political Wkr; Service Clb; Ski Clb; Spanish Clb; Gym; Swmmng; Hon Roll; Library Aide; Teachers Aide; Chorus; 2nd Pl Essay Cntst 85; NYS Regnts, Boston Coll Schlrshps 85; Math II, Chem & Spnsh Awds 83-84; Boston Coll; Bus Adm.

RAMSEY, ROBERTB; Gates-Chili SR HS; Rochester, NY; (Y); 62/463; JA; Math Tm; Pres Ski Clb; Ftbl; Var Golf; High Hon Roll; Hon Roll; NY ST Regents Schlrshp 85; Wegmans Schlrshp 85; Ithaca College; Finance.

RAMSEY, STEPHEN M; St Anthonys HS; Smithtown, NY; (Y); 43/201; Church Yth Grp; Cmnty Wkr; Variety Show; Stu Cncl; Golf; French Hon Soc; NHS; NY ST Rgnts Schlrshp 85; Duns Scotus Acad Awd 82-85; Frnch Achvmnt Awd 82 & 84; Stena Coll; Lib Arts.

RANADO, MARI LOUISE A; Corinth Central HS; Corinth, NY; (S); Drama Clb; French Clb; Key Clb; MMM; Varsity Clb; Sec Yrbk Stf; Cheerleading; High Hon Roll; NHS; Skidmore Acad Achvmnt Awd 83; Ntl Hnr Roll 84; Law.

RANCIER, DANIEL; Living Word Acad; Clay, NY; (Y); 1/12; Camera Clb; Nwsp Phtg; Nwsp Stf; Yrbk Phtg; VP Sr Cls; Capt Socr; High Hon Roll; Prfct Atten Awd; Val; All Star Awd Soccer 84-85; Schlrshp Syracuse U 85; Syracuse U; Med.

RANDAISI, ROBERT; Valley Central HS; Montgomery, NY; (Y); Band; Concert Band; Jazz Band; Mrchg Band; Pep Band; Symp Band; Rep Stu Cncl; Crs Cntry; Ftbl; Trk; SUNY Cortland; Sprts Med.

RANDALL, BARBARA; North Rose-Wolcott HS; N Rose, NY; (Y); Trs Spanish Clb; Sec Band; Chorus; Rep Frsh Cls; Pres Soph Cls; Rep Jr Cls; Sec Stu Cncl; Var L Sftbl; Mgr Swmmng; Cit Awd; U Of Rochester Paideia Awd 85; NYSSMA Music Awds & Hugh O Brien Yth Ldrshp Sem 84; Sports Med.

RANDALL, ERIC J; Arlington HS; Pleasant Valley, NY; (Y); 79/586; Aud/Vis; Drama Clb; Library Aide; Ski Clb; Stage Crew; Yrbk Phtg; Yrbk Stf; Ntl Merit Ltr; NY ST Regents Schlrshp 85; Hnr Key Awd 85; NC ST U; Mech Engr.

RANDALL, HOLLY; Corinth Central HS; Corinth, NY; (S); 4/95; French Clb; Band; Chorus; Yrbk Stf; Var L Vllybl; French Hon Soc; High Hon Roll; Jr NHS; NHS; Saratogan & Gannet News Acadmc Achvmt Awd; Phys Thrpy.

RANDALL, JAMES C; Whitesboro SR HS; Whitesboro, NY; (Y); 31/349; Chess Clb; Cmnty Wkr; Exploring; Lib Acpl Chr; Band; Lib Church Choir; Nwsp Stf; Lit Mag; Hon Roll; Hopwd Schlrshp Lynchburg Coll 84-86; Trustees Schlrshp; NY St Regents Schlrshp; Houghton Coll; Eng.

RANDALL, JEAN; Auburn HS; Auburn, NY; (Y); Church Yth Grp; ROTC; Acpl Chr; Band; Chorus; Church Choir; Mrchg Band; School Musical; High Hon Roll; Hon Roll; Vrsty Lttr-Music 85.

RANDALL, KIM MARIE; Tonawanda JR SR HS; Tonawanda, NY; (Y); Church Yth Grp; Dance Clb; FNA; Ski Clb; Sftbl; Vllybl; Hon Roll; Buffalo ST Coll; Phy Thrpy.

RANDALL, KWAFI; Art & Design HS; Bronx, NY; (Y); 128/411; FTA; Girl Scts; Service Clb; Hon Roll; FIT; Fash Merch.

RANDALL, MARCEA; Schoharie Central HS; Schoharie, NY; (S); Church Yth Grp; French Clb; Key Clb; Band; Chorus; Church Choir; Concert Band; Jazz Band; Symp Band; Instr Mag Merit Awd 84; FIT; Fshn Mrchdsng.

RANDALL, STEPHANIE; Barker Central HS; Barker, NY; (Y); 9/92; AFS; French Clb; Teachers Aide; Varsity Clb; Variety Show; Var Swmmng; Hon Roll; NHS; Legsltv Intern Pgm 85; Most Dedctd Swmmr 83; Bronze Pin 83; Silver Pin 85; Phy Thrpy.

RANDALL, THERESA; Groton Central HS; Groton, NY; (Y); Pres VP 4-H; FNA; Sec Sr Cls; JV Var Cheerleading; Var Sftbl; JV Var Vllybl; 4-H Awd; High Hon Roll; Natl Beta Clb; Pep Clb; MVP Vlybl 85; Mst Outstndng Chrldr Bsktbl 85; Beta Chi Eta Nrsng Schlrshp 84-85; Tompkins-Cortland CC; Nrsng.

RANDALL, TOM; Newburg Free Acad; Newburgh, NY; (Y); 18/650; High Hon Roll; Jr NHS; NHS; Prfct Atten Awd; Mount St Marys Coll; Cmnctns.

RANDAZZO, JOSEPH; St Raymonds HS; Bronx, NY; (Y); 36/203; Var Bsbl; JV Bsktbl; JV Socr; St Johns; Sprts Med.

RANDAZZO, THOMAS A; Archbishop Molloy HS; Bellerose, NY; (Y); 207/409; Cmnty Wkr; Hon Roll; Phrmcy.

RANDOLPH, DAVINA; Monroe School Of The Arts; Rochester, NY; (Y); Church Yth Grp; Acpl Chr; Chorus; Church Choir; School Musical; School Play; Bowling; Cheerleading; Trk; Hon Roll; Music.

RANDOLPH, KEVIN S; Watkins Glen HS; Watkins Glen, NY; (Y); 14/145; Am Leg Boys St; Pres Math Clb; Ski Clb; Chorus; Jazz Band; Swing Chorus; Trs Jr Cls; JV Golf; Timer; Pres Schlr; Regnst Schlrshp 85; SUNY Geneseo; Bio.

RANDOLPH, MARVIN T; West Seneca West SR HS; Cheektowaga, NY; (Y); 189/541; Var Bsktbl; Var Trk; DAR Awd; NY ST Regents Schlrshp 85; U Of Buffalo; Engr.

RANDOLPH, TOM; Royalton Hartland Cent; Gasport, NY; (Y); 57/130; Church Yth Grp; French Clb; Varsity Clb; Chorus; JV Ftbl; Var Capt Socr; Var Swmmng; Var Trk.

RANDS, KENLEY; Union-Endicott HS; Endicott, NY; (Y); Boy Scts; Exploring; JV Ftbl; Brigham Young U; Elect Engrng.

RANDY, SPRINGER; A Phillip Randolph HS; New York, NY; (Y); Yrbk Stf; Bsbl; Bsktbl; NY Daily Nws Supr Yths Outstndg Achvt Awd 85; Morehouse U; Comms.

RANER, RANDOLPH E; Alfred-Almont Central HS; Almond, NY; (Y); Church Yth Grp; Varsity Clb; Yrbk Stf; JV Bsbl; JV Var Bsktbl; JV Var Socr; High Hon Roll; Hon Roll; NY ST Regents Schlrshp 85-88; Alfred ST; Electronic Engnrng.

RANGER, NADINE; Bay Ridge HS; Brooklyn, NY; (Y); 11/366; Church Yth Grp; 4-H; Library Aide; Math Tm; Political Wkr; Chorus; Church Choir; Drill Tm; School Play; Pres Soph Cls; Effrt & Prgss Cert 80; Acad Excllnc Cert 82; NY Physcs Clb Awd 85; Brooklyn Coll; Bio.

RANGHELLI, STEFANIE; Connetquot HS; Bohemia, NY; (Y); 72/685; Chorus; Concert Band; School Musical; Swing Chorus; Variety Show; Rep Frsh Cls; Rep Stu Cncl; JV Cheerleading; JV Vllybl; High Hon Roll; Merit Fllwshp 85; Hnrs Schlrshp 85; LIU CW POST; Frgn Lang.

RANKA, JAYSHREE; Roy C Ketcham SR HS; Poughkeepsie, NY; (Y); 58/507; Concert Band; Symp Band; Yrbk Stf; JV Socr; High Hon Roll; NHS; Prfct Atten Awd; Girl Scts; Band; Orch; Amer Chem Socty Awd Outstndng Achvt 84; U S Army Awd Sci & Engnrg Fairs 84; Sierra Clb Awd 83; Dutchess CC; Elctrcl Engrng.

RANKEL, ALEXANDRA; Valley Central HS; Walden, NY; (Y); 18/300; Church Yth Grp; Church Choir; Rep Frsh Cls; Stu Cncl; Tennis; Hon Roll; NHS; Spanish NHS.

RANKIN, DONNA; Tioga Central HS; Nichols, NY; (Y); 5/92; Trs Soph Cls; Rep Jr Cls; Rep Stu Cncl; Var L Bsktbl; Capt Bowling; Var L Vllybl; High Hon Roll; NHS; Engrng.

RANKIN, KAUNITA; Niagara Falls HS; Niagara Falls, NY; (Y); Pres Church Yth Grp; JA; Office Aide; Acpl Chr; Church Choir; School Musical; Rep Jr Cls; Rep Stu Cncl; Commendbl Achvt 84-85; Industrl Engrng.

RANSOM, RENEE; Mohonasen HS; Schenectady, NY; (Y); Sec Dance Clb; 4-H; French Clb; Band; Church Choir; Concert Band; Drill Tm; Mrchg Band; Rep Stu Cncl; NHS; Hnr & High Hnr Roll 83-85; All State Sub Cncl 83-85; Bio.

RANSOM, THERESA; Salmon River Central HS; Hogansburg, NY; (S); 10/87; Ski Clb; Concert Band; Mrchg Band; Pep Band; Rep Frsh Cls; Rep Jr Cls; JV Bsktbl; Mgr(s); Var Capt Socr; Trk; Potsdam ST; Ed.

RANT, PETER J; New York Military Acad; Marlboro, NY; (Y); 5/77; Am Leg Boys St; Boy Scts; ROTC; Ski Clb; Band; Concert Band; Jazz Band; Nwsp Stf; Yrbk Stf; Var Ftbl; Legn Of Valor Bronze Cross 85; Cadet 1st Capt 84-85; Clarkson U; Electrcl Engrng.

RANTA, CHARLES; Walt Whitman HS; Huntington Stn, NY; (Y); 115/625; Boy Scts; Computer Clb; Debate Tm; Library Aide; Mathletes; Hon Roll; NHS; Ntl Merit Ltr.

RAO, ANJALI; Jericho HS; Syosset, NY; (Y); Cmnty Wkr; Drama Clb; Girl Scts; Key Clb; Model UN; Teachers Aide; Varsity Clb; Chorus; Church Choir; School Play.

RAO, SANJAI; Bishop Scully HS; Amsterdam, NY; (S); 8/64; Computer Clb; JA; Latin Clb; Math Clb; Trs Soph Cls; Var Capt Tennis; High Hon Roll; NHS.

RAPA, PAUL; La Salle Acad; New York, NY; (Y); 7/260; Church Yth Grp; Ftbl; Im Sftbl; High Hon Roll; Hon Roll; NHS; Baruch Coll; Accntnt.

RAPAGLIA, ERIC D; Tottenville HS; Staten Island, NY; (Y); Political Wkr; Rep Frsh Cls; Rep Soph Cls; Var Socr; Gov Hon Prg Awd; High Hon Roll; Jr NHS; NHS; St Schlr; NY Daily Nws Supr Yth Achvt 84; NY Inst Martial Arts Dedctn Awd 84; St Johns U Acadmc Schlrshp 85; St Johns U; Law.

RAPKIN, MITZI; Brighton HS; Rochester, NY; (Y); 87/315; Varsity Clb; Yrbk Stf; Rep Frsh Cls; JV Cheerleading; JV Diving; Var Gym; Var Trk; Athltc Adventure Day 84.

RAPP, MARK; Richmond Hill HS; Ozone Park, NY; (Y); English Clb; FBLA; Spanish Clb; Teachers Aide; Hon Roll; Spanish NHS; Acctg Hnrs 83-85; Span Hnrs 83-85; Svc Hnr 85; St Johns U; Bus.

RAPP, WENDY; Fairport HS; Fairport, NY; (Y); Drama Clb; Ski Clb; School Play; Yrbk Stf; Rep Stu Cncl; JV Swmmng; High Hon Roll; Hon Roll; Spanish NHS; English.

RAPPA, LISA; South Shore HS; Brooklyn, NY; (Y); Drama Clb; Girl Scts; Library Aide; Office Aide; Science Clb; Chorus; Church Choir; School Musical; School Play; Nwsp Stf; Sci Fair Awd 83; Math Awd & Food & Nutrition Awd 82; Music Awd & Jrnlsm Awd 82; Buffalo U; Forsenic Sci.

RAPPAZZO, ROSANNA; Albany HS; Albany, NY; (Y); Hon Roll; NHS; ST U NY Albany; Mth.

RAPPL, MARY; Sacred Heart Acad; Williamsville, NY; (Y); Pres German Clb; Teachers Aide; School Musical; Swing Chorus; Pres Soph Cls; Rep Jr Cls; Pres Stu Cncl; Hon Roll; Jr Vocal Awd 85; Chem.

RAPTIS, THOMAS; New Rochelle HS; New Rochelle, NY; (Y); Aud/Vis; Church Yth Grp; Radio Clb; Chorus; Stage Crew; JV Var Coach Actv; Var L Trk; JV Var Elks Awd; Hon Roll; Cmnty Wkr; Jog-A-Thon For Leukemia Awd 85; Greek Orthdx Olympics-NY St 81-85; Mdls In Trck & Sftbl; John Jay Coll Of Crmnl Just.

RAQUEL, CABALLES; Clarkstown South HS; W Nyack, NY; (Y); Drama Clb; Hosp Aide; Trk; NHS; Engl.

RASCHDORF, ADRIANN A; St Anthonys HS; Commack, NY; (Y); 28/228; Hosp Aide; Yrbk Ed-Chief; Yrbk Phtg; Yrbk Stf; Badmtn; Bsbl; Swmmng; Tennis; NHS; NEDT Awd; Natl Hnr Rll; Fordham U; Law.

RASCO, MARTA; Keene Central HS; Keene, NY; (S); 2/13; Varsity Clb; Yrbk Stf; Sec Jr Cls; Sec Sr Cls; Cheerleading; Score Keeper; Socr; Sftbl; High Hon Roll; Hon Roll; Excellence In Business 84; Plattsburgh ST; Bus.

RASINSKI, JENNIFER; Immaculata Acad; Collins, NY; (Y); Cmnty Wkr; French Clb; Hosp Aide; Library Aide; Science Clb; Orch; Im Badmtn; Stat Vllybl; Sci Congress 84; Jr Freeman Awd; Franciscan Marion Awd 85; Harvard Naval Acad; Renaissnce.

RASMUSSEN, JILL; Bethlehem Central HS; Delmar, NY; (Y); 9/338; Dance Clb; Teachers Aide; Band; Yrbk Stf; Var Cheerleading; JV Mgr(s); High Hon Roll; NHS; Ntl Merit Ltr; Pres Schlr; AAA Drivers Educ Awd 85; U Of VA; Arch.

RASMUSSEN, MELISSA; Narrowsburg Central Schl; Narrowsburg, NY; (Y); Sec Church Yth Grp; Ski Clb; Sec Band; Chorus; School Play; Yrbk Stf; Rep Soph Cls; Rep Jr Cls; Trs Stu Cncl; Hon Roll; Boome CC; Med Rcds Tech.

RASMUSSEN, SCOTT; Jamestown HS; Jamestown, NY; (Y); Art Clb; French Clb; Chorus; Stu Cncl; Trk; Cit Awd; Hon Roll; Jr NHS; Prfct Atten Awd; Jamestown CC; Engrng.

RASMUSSEN, TINA; Clayton A Bouton JR SR HS; Slidell, LA; (Y); 21/114; Drama Clb; 4-H; Band; Chorus; School Play; Stage Crew; Yrbk Stf; Tennis; Pres Acadmc Achvt Awd 85; Selctd NYSMA Area All ST Chrs 83-85; Emerson Coll; Advtsg.

RASO, MICHAEL; Clarkstown South HS; W Nyack, NY; (Y); Teachers Aide; Trs Lit Mag; Im Bsktbl; Bus.

RASPANTI, SUZANNE; Southside HS; Rockville Ctr, NY; (Y); Key Clb; Model UN; Yrbk Stf; Mgr(s); Htl Mgmt.

RASZEJA, BARBARA A; Villa Maria Acad; Cheektowaga, NY; (Y); 15/112; Trs Church Yth Grp; JCL; Latin Clb; Yrbk Stf; Cheerleading; Hon Roll; Ntl Merit Ltr; Prfct Atten Awd; Cum Laude 81-83; Regents Schlrshp 85; SUNY-BUFFALO; Phy Thrpy.

RATAJACK, BILL; Brewster HS; Brewster, NY; (S); 57/173; Aud/Vis; Church Yth Grp; Cmnty Wkr; Yrbk Stf; Var Socr; Var Capt Wrstlng; Hon Roll; Pres NHS; PACE Consrvtn Awd 84; Sci Achvt Awd 80; Frgn Lang, Scl Stds Recgntn Awds 81; NY Inst Tech; Arch.

RATAJCZAK, CINDY; St Marys HS; Cheektowaga, NY; (S); 21/185; Cmnty Wkr; Ski Clb; Spanish Clb; School Musical; Nwsp Rptr; Hghst Acad Achvt European Cultres Hnrs 84; Educ.

RATAJCZAK, GARY; Amsterdam HS; Amsterdam, NY; (Y); Hon Roll; Fulton Montgmery CC; Elec Tech.

RATER, MARTY; Clymer Central Schl; Clymer, NY; (Y); VP Pres FFA; Pres Jr Cls; Pres Stu Cncl; JV Var Bsktbl; JV Var Ftbl; Var Trk; Cit Awd; High Hon Roll; Band; School Play; Chautauqua Cnty FFA Star Frmr; NY ST FFA Empir Dgre; Ag.

RATHBUN, JEANNE L; Cherry Valley Central Schl; Schenevus, NY; (Y); 4/40; Trs Drama Clb; Varsity Clb; Chorus; Var L Cheerleading; Var L JA; Elks Awd; High Hon Roll; NHS; Church Yth Grp; 4-H; Clarks Fndtn Schlrshp 85-86; NY ST Regents Schlrshp 85-86; SUNY At Geneseo.

RATTOBALLI, RICHARD; St Marys Boy HS; West Hempstead, NY; (S); 5/158; JV Var Lcrss; St Marys Boys Hghst Hnrs 83-84; MVP La Crosse Plyr JV 83.

RAUCH, HEIDI E; G Ray Bodley HS; Fulton, NY; (Y); 29/250; Cmnty Wkr; Drama Clb; Pres German Clb; Science Clb; Nwsp Rptr; Nwsp Stf; JV Sftbl; Var Vllybl; Cit Awd; High Hon Roll; Wmns Clb Schlrshp 85; NY ST Rgnts Schlrshp 85; Schlrshp Awd 83; SUNY A&T Morrisvl; Jrnlsm.

RAUCH, LEE; Spring Valley HS; Monsey, NY; (Y); Cmnty Wkr; French Clb; Hosp Aide; Key Clb; Chorus; Hon Roll; Ntl Merit Ltr; Outstdng Achv In Soc Stds; Cmnty Svc Awd; Cert Of Part In Schl Medtn Proj.

RAUER, SCOTT J; Rocky Point JR SR HS; Rocky Point, NY; (Y); 24/185; Math Tm; Mrchg Band; Yrbk Ed-Chief; Sec Soph Cls; Pres Jr Cls; L Crs Cntry; L Lcrss; Hon Roll; Boy Scts; Church Yth Grp; Eagle Sct 84; Regents Schlrshp Wnnr 85; St U NY; Naval Arch.

RAUSCH, ERIK; Long Island Lutheran HS; Hicksville, NY; (S); Church Yth Grp; Jazz Band; Var Bsbl; Var Bsktbl; Var Ftbl; Cit Awd; High Hon Roll; NHS; Engr.

RAUSCHENBACH, KENNETH; W C Medham HS; Bellmore, NY; (Y); Nwsp Stf; Rep Stu Cncl; Var JV Bsbl; Var JV Bsktbl; JV Capt Socr; High Hon Roll; Jr NHS; Pres NHS; Computer Clb; Yrbk Rptr; John F Kennedy Awd 83; Hnrbl Mntn Conf Bsbl 85; Doctr.

RAUSCHENBACH, RONALD; Arlington HS; Poughquag, NY; (Y); Ski Clb; Band; Jazz Band; JV Socr; Var Trk; Hon Roll; Lit Soc Fndtn Inc Slvr Cert 84; Cert Merit Outstndng Perf AATG Grmn Tst, Outstndng Achvt Stu Grmn; Law.

RAUSHI, DEBORAH; Scotia-Glenville HS; Scotia, NY; (Y); Sec VP Church Yth Grp; Key Clb; Service Clb; Band; Orch; High Hon Roll; NHS; Prfct Atten Awd; Concert Band; Mrchg Band; GE Hll Hstry Fndtns Essay Cont Wnnr 85; Jr Coll Albany Smmr Inst Russn Studs 85.

RAUTINE, TANYA S; Spencer-Van Etten JR SR HS; Spencer, NY; (Y); 6/100; Hosp Aide; Band; School Play; Yrbk Phtg; Sec Stu Cncl; JV Var Cheerleading; Score Keeper; High Hon Roll; NHS; Rgnts Schlrshp 85; Cornell U; Comm Arts.

RAVEN, MARK; Perth Central Schl; Amsterdam, NY; (Y); 3/53; Varsity Clb; Yrbk Sprt Ed; Stu Cncl; Stat Bsbl; JV Bsktbl; Var Golf; Var Score Keeper; High Hon Roll; NHS; NYS Regents Schlrshp 85; Early Admin Stu Pulton-Montgomery CC 85; Pres Schlrshp Wnnr FMCC 85; Syracuse U; Brdcst Jrnlsm.

RAVIN, KAREN A; The Nichols Schl; Hamburg, NY; (Y); VP AFS; Capt Red Cross Aide; Chorus; Ed Lit Mag; JV Mgr(s); Sftbl; Swmmng; Vllybl; Hon Roll; Ntl Merit Ltr; Hon Mntn Schl Sci Fair 83; Franklin; Pre Med.

RAVINDRAN, PRAMOD; Greece Athena HS; Rochester, NY; (Y); 13/300; Boys Clb Am; JA; Math Tm; Ski Clb; Varsity Clb; Tennis; Vllybl; Hon Roll; NHS; Prfct Atten Awd; Regents Schlrshp & Diploma W/Hnrs 85; Pres Acad Ftns Awd 85; Vrsty MVP Athena Tennis Tm 85; PA ST U; Engnrng.

RAWSON, KAREN; Mexico HS; Mexico, NY; (Y); JA; Rep Stu Cncl; JV Capt Socr; Var Vllybl; Ntl Merit Ltr; Art Clb; Cmnty Wkr; DECA; Spanish Clb; Varsity Clb; Gld Mdl Girls Acad Athltc Achvt 85; Acad/Athltc Achvt Hon Men 83; Abve 85 Avg 85; Alfred Ag & Tech Coll; Retl Bus.

RAY, AMIT; Jamesville-De Witt HS; Dewitt, NY; (Y); Chorus; Nwsp Ed-Chief; JV Bsbl; Biochem Rsrch Surgry Dept Upstate Med Ctr 85; Cornell; Med.

RAY, GORDON K; Utica Free Acad; Utica, NY; (Y); Am Leg Boys St; Key Clb; Keywanettes; Ski Clb; Orch; Rep Stu Cncl; Var L Bsbl; Var L Bsktbl; Var L Socr; JETS Awd; US Nvl Acad; Aerospc Engrng.

RAY, LINDA; Fort Ann Central HS; Comstock, NY; (Y); GAA; Letterman Clb; Red Cross Aide; Varsity Clb; Band; Yrbk Phtg; Yrbk Sprt Ed; Yrbk Stf; Bsktbl; Sftbl; MVP Bsktbl 82; MVP Sftbl 82; Bst Dfnse Plyr Bsktbl 83; N Country CC; Secrtrl.

RAY, PETER; Fayetteville-Manlius HS; Fayetteville, NY; (Y); Model UN; Pres Lib Concert Band; Orch; School Musical; School Play; Variety Show; High Hon Roll; NHS; Chess Clb; Exploring; Cornell Clb Bk Awd 85; Awd For Englsh Litrtr 84; Awd For Frnch 85; Intl Rel.

RAYDER, SCOTT; Fayetteville-Manlius HS; Fayetteville, NY; (Y); Political Wkr; Socr; Trk; Hon Roll; Hamilton Coll; Pre-Law.

RAYESKI, ELIZABETH A; Corning-Painted Post West HS; Corning, NY; (Y); Cmnty Wkr; Chorus; Church Choir; School Musical; Rep Jr Cls; Stu Cncl; Var L Cheerleading; High Hon Roll; NHS; Rep Frsh Cls; Phys Ther.

RAYFIELD, DONNA; Rocky Point JR SR HS; Rocky Pt, NY; (Y); German Clb; VICA; Band; Orch; Wt Lftg; Hon Roll; Csmtlgy.

RAYL, MARCITA; Wilson Central Schl; Ransomville, NY; (Y); 13/146; Science Clb; Stage Crew; Variety Show; Nwsp Ed-Chief; Yrbk Stf; Stu Cncl; Powder Puff Ftbl; Hon Roll; NHS; Pres Acad Ftns Awd 85; Lynn Freatman Mem Schlrshp 85; Bryant & Stratton; Comp Pgrmr.

RAYMON, RODHERICK; Indian River Central HS; Theresa, NY; (Y); Am Leg Boys St; Boy Scts; Cmnty Wkr; Ski Clb; School Play; L Tennis; Prfct Atten Awd; NY ST Regents Schlrshp 85.

RAYMOND, LAURA; Franklin Acad; Malone, NY; (Y); French Clb; JA; Spanish Clb; Church Choir; Mrchg Band; Rep Soph Cls; JV Cheerleading; Twrlr; French Hon Soc; Hon Roll; Pfct Attend 83 & 84; Highest Av Span Cls 84; Sr Twirler Mst Dedicated 84; Lang.

RAYMOND, STACEY; Moriah Central HS; Mineville, NY; (Y); 1/86; AFS; 4-H; French Clb; GAA; Hosp Aide; Stu Cncl; JV Var Score Keeper; Stat Sftbl; 4-H Awd; High Hon Roll; Sci.

RAYMOND, TONA R; Izmir American HS; Ft Leonard Wood, MO; (Y); Girl Scts; Chorus; School Musical; Stage Crew; Sec Frsh Cls; Rep Jr Cls; Coach Actv; Var L Socr; Var L Sftbl; Var L Vllybl; Soccer Coach & Refre Yth Actvs; WA ST U; Arch.

RAYNOR, JUDY; Fredonia HS; Fredonia, NY; (Y); Science Clb; Chorus; Church Choir; Hon Roll; NYSSMA Blue Ribbn 83 & 84; Geneseo; Wildlife Consrvtn.

RAZEY, CHRISTINE; Portville Central HS; Olean, NY; (Y); Pres Church Yth Grp; Church Choir; Concert Band; Mrchg Band; Hon Roll; All Cnty Music Awd 83-85; Bible Coll; Cnslng.

REA, SALLY; Msgr Scanlan HS; Flushing, NY; (Y); 32/265; Hosp Aide; Intnl Clb; Spanish Clb; Mrchg Band; Prfct Atten Awd; Drm & Bgl; Top 10% Cls 82 & 83; 2nd Hnrs 84; 1st Hnrs 85; Med.

READ, ALICE; Miller Place HS; Miller Pl, NY; (Y); FBLA; Varsity Clb; Nwsp Sprt Ed; Bsktbl; Fld Hcky; Vllybl; Hon Roll; VP Frsh Cls; VP Soph Cls; VP Jr Cls; Socl Stds Outstndng Awd 84-85.

READE, ROBIN; Sachem HS North; Lk Ronkonkoma, NY; (Y); 24/1386; Church Yth Grp; Spanish Clb; Concert Band; Jr NHS; NHS; Drama Clb; Orch; Stage Crew; Acctng.

READER, ANDREW; East Meadow HS; E Meadow, NY; (S); 36/414; Nwsp Sprt Ed; Nwsp Stf; Bowling; NHS; Biolgy.

REAGAN, CHRISTINE M; Campbell Central Schl; Campbell, NY; (Y); 3/46; Pres French Clb; GAA; Color Guard; Yrbk Stf; Capt Var Bsktbl; Capt Var Socr; Capt Var Trk; Capt Var Vllybl; High Hon Roll; NHS; Amer HS Athl Hnr 85; Schlstc Achvt Awd 85; Alfred Ag & Tech; Med Lab Tech.

REAGAN, RONALD; Potsdam Central HS; Norwood, NY; (Y); 10/128; French Clb; Varsity Clb; Rep Frsh Cls; Rep Soph Cls; Stu Cncl; JV Var Bsbl; JV Ftbl; Var Ice Hcky; Hon Roll; NHS; Tlntd JRS 85; Clarkson; Elec Engrng.

REAL, EDUARDO; La Salle Acad; New York City, NY; (S); Cmnty Wkr; Hon Roll; Fordham U; Comp Tech.

REALBUTO, JAMES A; Somers HS; Amawalk, NY; (Y); 8/213; AFS; Computer Clb; Intnl Clb; Nwsp Bus Mgr; Nwsp Ed-Chief; Nwsp Rptr; JV Crs Cntry; JV Socr; Var Trk; High Hon Roll; St La Salle Hnr Soc 85; Manhattan Coll; Comp.

REALE, PASQUALE; Cardinal Mooney HS; Rochester, NY; (Y); Var Capt Socr; Hon Roll; Prfct Atten Awd; Rochester Inst Of Tech; Engrng.

REALI, DEAN A; Brockport HS; Spencerport, NY; (Y); French Clb; Mathletes; Math Clb; Math Tm; Model UN; Radio Clb; Science Clb; Varsity Clb; Nwsp Ed-Chief; Nwsp Stf; Siena Coll; Bio.

REALS, SARA M; Guilderland Central HS; Altamont, NY; (Y); Pres Church Yth Grp; GAA; Red Cross Aide; Church Choir; Orch; Var Bsktbl; Var Vllybl; High Hon Roll; NHS; PTSA Schlrshp 85; Sceptre Serv Schlrshp 85; RPI Schlrshp 85; Rensselear Polytech; Aerosp Eng.

REARDON, JENNIFER; East Aurora HS; East Aurora, NY; (S); 22/186; Trs AFS; JA; Key Clb; Ski Clb; Varsity Clb; Yrbk Ed-Chief; Rep Sr Cls; Rep Stu Cncl; Var Capt Swmmng; VP NHS; Cmmty Resrc Cncl 82-83; Accntnt.

REARDON, MATT; Spacken HS; Poughkeepsie, NY; (Y); 10/169; Thesps; School Musical; Yrbk Ed-Chief; Ftbl; Var L Trk; L Var Wrstlng; NHS; Ntl Merit SF; Yrbk Stf; Rep Frsh Cls; Team MVP-WRSTLNG 85; ETS Excllnce In Educ Cont Winner 85; West Point; Comp Sci.

REARDON, RITA E; Glens Falls SR HS; Glens Falls, NY; (Y); 41/233; AFS; Pres Key Clb; Yrbk Stf; Sec Stu Cncl; JV Bsktbl; JV Fld Hcky; Powder Puff Ftbl; Trk; Hon Roll; Rgnts Schlrshp 85; Clarkson; Engrng.

REARDON, SHARON; Salmon River Central HS; Bombay, NY; (S); 11/112; Church Yth Grp; French Clb; Band; Hon Roll; NHS; Prfct Atten Awd; Potsdam ST; Elem Ed.

REARER, KERRYANN; Fontboone Hall Acad; Brooklyn, NY; (Y); Civic Clb; Drama Clb; French Clb; Girl Scts; Hosp Aide; Political Wkr; School Play; Stage Crew; Hon Roll; Peer Grp Ldrshp, Slvr Mdl Ntl Latin Exm 85; Biogcl Sci.

REARSON, DARRYL M; Fairport HS; Fairport, NY; (Y); Church Yth Grp; Ski Clb; Nwsp Stf; Socr; Hon Roll; NY ST U Buffalo; Architect.

REAUME, JEFFREY S; Chittanango HS; Chittenango, NY; (Y); 8/188; Am Leg Boys St; Church Yth Grp; Ski Clb; Church Choir; Bausch & Lomb Sci Awd; NHS; Pres Schlr; French Clb; Science Clb; High Hon Roll; AMA Opertn Entprs 84; MONY Schltc Art Awds Hnrb Mntn 85; Regents Schlrshp 85; Clarkson; Engrng.

REAVES, ANGELA; Nottingham SR HS; Syracuse, NY; (Y); Church Yth Grp; Spanish Clb; Chorus; Nwsp Stf; 9 Acadmc Awds Comptn Urban Leag 84-85; Sevrl Outstndng Acadmc Achvt Awds Chch 84-85; Comp Sci.

REAVES, NANCY M; Ellsworth J Wilson HS; Rochester, NY; (Y); Jazz Band; Pres Symp Band; Rep Sr Cls; Var Cheerleading; Hon Roll; NHS; Church Yth Grp; Drama Clb; Math Clb; Y-Teens; Urban Leag Rochstr Blck Schlr 84; Natl Achvt Schlrshp Pgm 84; Area All-ST Band & All Cty Band 82-84; Engr.

REBELO, PAUL; Minisink Valley HS; Middletown, NY; (Y); 15/250; Church Yth Grp; JV Var Socr; High Hon Roll; Hon Roll; Prfct Atten Awd; Engr.

REBEOR, DANIEL; G Ray Bodley HS; Fulton, NY; (Y); Aud/Vis; German Clb; Library Aide; Nwsp Sprt Ed; Nwsp Stf; Sec Bsktbl; Sec Ftbl; JV Var Lcrss; Score Keeper; Var Swmmng; Coast Guard Acad; Mltry.

REBERHOLT, MICHELLE D; Marlboro HS; Marlboro, NY; (Y); Varsity Clb; Var Gym; Var Trk; High Hon Roll; Hon Roll; Marist Coll; Comp Sci.

REBRES, ROBERT; Fairport HS; Fairport, NY; (Y); Church Yth Grp; Computer Clb; Math Tm; Crs Cntry; Trk; Hon Roll; Chem Exam Amer Chem Socty Fnlst 85; Bio.

RECHEN, EILEEN; New Paltz HS; Highland, NY; (Y); 24/130; Church Yth Grp; Variety Show; Var Fld Hcky; JV Var Sftbl; High Hon Roll; Hon Roll; NHS; Physcl Thrpst.

RECHIN, DONNA; Immaculata Acad; Derby, NY; (Y); Dance Clb; Girl Scts; Hosp Aide; Ski Clb; Nwsp Stf; Sec Jr Cls; Sftbl; Im Vllybl; Hon Roll; Cls Offcr Awd 85; Cert Of Schlstc Merit 85; Hnr Roll Cert 84; Physcl Thrpy.

RECLA, ADRIENNE; Nyack HS; Valley Cottage, NY; (Y); 28/264; Rep Frsh Cls; Rep Soph Cls; Sec Jr Cls; Sec Sr Cls; Var Bsktbl; Var Cheerleading; Var Lcrss; High Hon Roll; NHS; Spanish NHS; U MA; Acctng.

RECORD, JENNIFER; Irondequoit HS; Rochester, NY; (Y); 2/393; Church Yth Grp; Math Clb; Ski Clb; Varsity Clb; Chorus; School Musical; JV Socr; Var Swmmng; High Hon Roll; NHS; Dartmouth Club Of Rochester Book Awd 85; Electrcl Engr.

RECTOR, CARI; Charles O Dickerson HS; Trumansburg, NY; (Y); 5/85; Pres Drama Clb; French Clb; Trs Model UN; Pres Thesps; Chorus; School Play; Stage Crew; Yrbk Ed-Chief; High Hon Roll; NHS; Griswald Telephn Schlrshp 85; Boston U; Intl Rel.

RECTRA, PHILIP; Lowville Acad; Lowville, NY; (Y); 13/130; Am Leg Boys St; VP French Clb; Chorus; School Musical; Rep Frsh Cls; Rep Soph Cls; Rep Jr Cls; Rep Stu Cncl; Capt Var Socr; Var Capt Tennis; Yth Of Amer Eurpn Tour 85; Comm.

REDA, GARY; St Raymonds Boys HS; Bronx, NY; (Y); 9/182; Computer Clb; Yrbk Stf; High Hon Roll; Hon Roll; Comp Sci.

REDA, VIVIAN F; Fontbonne HS; Brooklyn, NY; (Y); 11/138; Dance Clb; Math Tm; Teachers Aide; Nwsp Rptr; High Hon Roll; NHS; Ntl Merit Schol; NY ST Regents Schlrshp 85-89; Acad Grant From St Johns U 85-89; St Johns U; Bus.

REDDEN, LYNN; Attica HS; Strykersville, NY; (Y); Sec Church Yth Grp; Drama Clb; 4-H; Church Choir; Concert Band; Mrchg Band; 4-H Awd; Hon Roll; NHS; Bernice Blom Incentive Awd 84; Acctng.

REDDING, SUSAN M; Jamesville-Dewitt HS; Dewitt, NY; (Y); 64/240; CAP; Chorus; School Musical; School Play; Stage Crew; High Hon Roll; Hon Roll; Amerlia Earheart Awd Civil Air Patrol 85; Acad Awd Soc Studs 85; AFROTC Scholar Alt 85; Boston U; Aerospc Engr.

REDDOCK, EARLYN; Sheepshead Bay HS; Brooklyn, NY; (Y); Psych.

REDDY, BRIAN; St Francis Prep; Ozone Park, NY; (S); 68/698; Science Clb; Service Clb; Band; Concert Band; Jazz Band; Mrchg Band; Orch; Im Bsktbl; Im Vllybl; NHS; Knights Of Columbus Schlrshp 82; St Francis Prep Schlrshp 82; Phy.

REDHEAD, SCOTT R; John C Birdlebough HS; Phoenix, NY; (Y); 2/200; Latin Clb; Library Aide; Political Wkr; Band; Color Guard; Concert Band; Flag Corp; Jazz Band; Mrchg Band; Nwsp Bus Mgr; Hist Key 85; Ldrshp Colr Grd 85; Outstndng Perfrmnc Stu Cncl Awd 85; Hofstra U; Intl Financr.

REDICK, TINA L; Averill Park HS; Troy, NY; (Y); 13/220; Art Clb; Drama Clb; Varsity Clb; School Musical; School Play; Yrbk Stf; Var L Cheerleading; CAP; Var L Trk; High Hon Roll; Perfect Attendance 75-84; Regents Schlrshp 85; Ntl Hnr Society 84; Arthitect.

REDLER, KENNETH SEAN; Suffern HS; Suffern, NY; (Y); 8/400; Ed Nwsp Stf; Rep Stu Cncl; VP Tennis; VP Trk; Math Tm; Quiz Bowl; Orch; High Hon Roll; NHS; Ntl Merit SF.

REDMAN, DAWN N; Caledonia-Mumford Central HS; Leroy, NY; (Y); 21/91; Aud/Vis; Pres Drama Clb; French Clb; Library Aide; Nwsp Ed-Chief; Yrbk Stf; Var L Bsbl; Score Keeper; Var L Sftbl; High Hon Roll; Urban Lg Blck/Schlr Awd 85; Monroe CC; Human Svc.

REDMOND, MARK; Solvay HS; Solvay, NY; (Y); Exploring; Trs Key Clb; Rep Jr Cls; Var Bsktbl; Recgntn Cerebral Palsy Ctr 84; Achvr Key Clb 85; Engrng.

REDMOND, RANDY J; Oriskany HS; Oriskany, NY; (Y); 6/88; Boy Scts; Chess Clb; Church Yth Grp; Drama Clb; Exploring; Key Clb; Mathletes; Varsity Clb; School Play; Stage Crew; Regents Scholar 85; Le Moyne Coll; Acctng.

REDMOND, RICHARD; North Warren Central HS; Chestertown, NY; (S); 8/50; Boy Scts; Pres Computer Clb; School Play; Nwsp Stf; Var Bsktbl; Var Golf; Hon Roll; VFW Awd; Bus Mngmt.

REDMOND, TIFFANY; Bishop Scully HS; Amsterdam, NY; (S); 3/56; Math Clb; Political Wkr; JV Cheerleading; High Hon Roll; NHS; Med.

REEB, JILL M; Oakfield-Alabama Central Schl; Basom, NY; (Y); 5/74; Church Yth Grp; French Clb; Hosp Aide; Library Aide; Lit Mag; JV Cheerleading; Hon Roll; NHS; Regents Scholarship 85; Valley Forge Christian; Nurse.

REECE, SOPHIA ALLISON; Mt Vernon HS; Mt Vernon, NY; (Y); 17/600; Cit Awd; Frnch Awd 82-83; Awd In Geo 83-84; Awd In Trig 84-85; Lehman Coll; Nrsng.

REED, ANDY; James O Neil HS; West Point, NY; (Y); 10/250; Church Yth Grp; Cmnty Wkr; Ski Clb; Jazz Band; Stage Crew; Rep Jr Cls; JV Bsktbl; Golf; L Swmmng; NHS; Bst JR Hist Stu 84-85; Bio Med Engrng.

REED, CHERYL; Greece Olympia HS; Rochester, NY; (Y); 27/316; Am Leg Aux Girls St; JA; Color Guard; Rep Soph Cls; Trs Jr Cls; Trs Sr Cls; JV Vllybl; Hon Roll; NHS; Pres Schlr; Amer Assn Of U Wmn; Park Ridge Schl Awd; SUNY Albany; Econ.

REED, DONALD; Lynbrook HS; Lynbrook, NY; (Y); JV Bsbl; Hon Roll.

REED, JEFF; Haverling HS; Bath, NY; (Y); JV Ftbl; JV Wrstlng; Hon Roll.

REED, KIRSTIN; Valley Central HS; Montgomery, NY; (Y); Church Yth Grp; Debate Tm; French Clb; Math Clb; Math Tm; Mrchg Band; Symp Band; French Hon Soc; 4-H Awd; NHS; Pres 4-H Grp 84-85; Tres Chrch Yth Grp 84-85; Most Val Mbr Chrch Yth Grp 84-85; Bus Mgmt.

REED, KRISTI A; New Berlin Central HS; New Berlin, NY; (Y); FHA; Trs VICA; Color Guard.

REED, LONNITA; Riverside HS; Buffalo, NY; (S); Church Yth Grp; Cmnty Wkr; Debate Tm; GAA; Girl Scts; Library Aide; Pep Clb; Spanish Clb; Speech Tm; Chorus; Top 12 Stus SR Class 85; Central ST U; Comp Sci.

REED, MARK T; Gouverneur JR SR HS; Gouverneur, NY; (Y); NFL; Gov Hon Prg Awd; High Hon Roll; NHS; Ntl Merit SF; Aud/Vis; Camera Clb; Church Yth Grp; Computer Clb; Debate Tm; Yng Sci Trphy 84; Outstndg Physics Stu 84; St Lawrence U Augsbury Schlr Awd 84; Spch ST Tourn 83; Biochem.

REED, NOEL; Archbishop Molloy HS; Woodhaven, NY; (Y); 20/409; French Clb; Sec Sr Cls; JV Crs Cntry; JV Trk; Sec NHS.

REED, ROBERT; Walton Central Schl; Hollywood, FL; (Y); Boy Scts; Computer Clb; Drama Clb; Model UN; High Hon Roll; Hon Roll; Ntl Merit Rocognition 83-84; Boyd Airline/Trvl Schl; Rsrvtns.

REED, SCOTT; Gouverneur JR-SR HS; Gouverneur, NY; (Y); Computer Clb; German Clb; NFL; Swing Chorus; Gov Hon Prg Awd; High Hon Roll; NHS; Camera Clb; Church Yth Grp; Library Aide; Clrkson U Outstndg Yng Sci Awd 84; Amer Assoc HS Phycs Tchrs Awd 85; NY Regnl Amer Comp Sci Leag 85; Astrophy.

REED, SEAN; Bishop Loughlin Memorial HS; Brooklyn, NY; (S); Chess Clb; Computer Clb; Science Clb; Trs Jr Cls; High Hon Roll; NHS; Cornell U; Comp Sci.

REED, STEVEN BRIAN; West Genesee HS; Camillus, NY; (Y); Church Yth Grp; Key Clb; Bsbl; Bsktbl; JV Golf; Hon Roll; Hustlr Trphy Smmr Bsktbl; WGAC Smmr Bsbl; Foul Shtng Trphy Bsktbl; Jrnlsm.

REEDY, KAREN; Colonie Central HS; Albany, NY; (Y).

REEP, DEBORAH R; Corning East HS; Corning, NY; (Y); Dance Clb; Chorus; Off Frsh Cls; Off Soph Cls; Off Jr Cls; Rep Stu Cncl; JV Cheerleading; High Hon Roll; Hon Roll; NHS; Plqe Hlpng Crng Fry Chrldg 85.

REESE, DENISE; Wantagh HS; Wantagh, NY; (Y); Computer Clb; Ski Clb; Chorus; Nwsp Stf; Pom Pon; Hon Roll; Fashion Inst Of Tech; Fshn Buyr.

REESE, EDWARD; Medina Central HS; Medina, NY; (Y); 10/156; Boy Scts; Co-Capt Model UN; Science Clb; Chorus; Var L Ftbl; Var L Lcrss; Var L Trk; Var L Wrstlng; High Hon Roll; Hon Roll; Schlrshp; Honorati; Sprtsmnshp; Engrng.

REESE, GREGORY J; Cardinal Mooney HS; Rochester, NY; (Y); 1/318; Yrbk Sprt Ed; Var Capt Crs Cntry; Trk; High Hon Roll; NHS; Ntl Merit Ltr; Val; Smmr Sci Sem USAF Acad 84; ACS HS Exam Hnr Sect 83; Outstndng Phys Stu Of Yr-Cardinal Mooney NPTA; Renselaer Polytech Inst; Engrng.

REESE, JAMES F; Reed Creek JR SR HS; Red Creek, NY; (Y); 7/70; Boy Scts; Chorus; School Play; Yrbk Sprt Ed; Yrbk Stf; Pres Stu Cncl; Var Bsktbl; Var Capt Crs Cntry; Elks Awd; High Hon Roll; Paul Smith Coll; Envrnmntl Sci.

REESE, JONATHAN P; West Babylm HS; W Babylon, NY; (Y); Am Leg Boys St; VP Stu Cncl; Var L Bsktbl; Var L Ftbl; Var Capt Lcrss; High Hon Roll; NHS; All Co Ftbl 83 & 84; All St Ftbl 84; All Co La Crosse 83 & 84; LI Rgn Empire St Tm La Crosse 84 & 85; Lib Arts.

REETH, JANICE; Smithtown H S East; Nissequoque, NY; (Y); Cmnty Wkr; English Clb; Trs Service Clb; Teachers Aide; Yrbk Stf; Stu Cncl; MD.

REEVE, FRED; L C Obourn HS; East Rochester, NY; (Y); 6/112; Pres Model UN; Acpl Chr; Stu Cncl; Capt Var Swmmng; Capt Im Vllybl; Pres Hon Roll; NHS; Rotary Awd; Math Tm; Frank Gannett Schlrshp 85; La Faye Sci Awd 85; American Chem Soc Awd 84; OH ST U; Chem.

REGAN, CHRISTOPHER; New Paltz Central HS; Walden, NY; (Y); 28/160; Pres Band; Chorus; School Musical; Variety Show; High Hon Roll; JP Sousa Awd; NHS; VP Frsh Cls; Pres Soph Cls; Off Jr Cls; PTSO Instrmntl Music Awd; Rotary Club Ldrshp Smnr; All-Cnty Band; Ithaca Coll; Jrnlsm.

REGAN, JENNIFER; Delaware Academy And Central HS; Delhi, NY; (Y); Spanish Clb; Teachers Aide; Chorus; Color Guard; Variety Show; Bsktbl; Crs Cntry; Trk; Hon Roll; NHS; All Cnty Chr 84-85.

REGAN, KATHLEEN M; John Jay HS; Katonah, NY; (Y); VP French Clb; VP Jr Cls; Pres Sr Cls; JV Var Bsktbl; JV Var Socr; Var Vllybl; High Hon Roll; Hon Roll; NHS; St Schlr; West Point Military Acad.

REGER, MICHELE; Union Endicott HS; Endicott, NY; (Y); Band; Var Trk; Empire ST Games & Cls I Regnl Champ Gym Qualfr 83; NY Cls I ST Champ Gym Qualfr 83-85; Engrng.

REGINA, JOYCE; Dominican Commercial HS; Flushing, NY; (Y); 26/293; Hosp Aide; Office Aide; Yrbk Stf; Jr NHS; Sienna Club 83-85; Elem Eductn.

REGINA, MARIO J; Mt St Michael Acad; Bronx, NY; (Y); 75/286; Exploring; Fld Hcky; Var JV Ftbl; Im Sftbl; Hon Roll; First Second Hnrs 81-85; Varsity Letters 81-85; Regents Schlrshp 85; IN Inst Of Tech; Engineering.

REGISFORD JR, HENLEY; St Johns Prep HS; New York, NY; (Y); Boys Clb Am; Band; Concert Band; Jazz Band; Mrchg Band; Bsbl; Crs Cntry; Trk; Wt Lftg; Hon Roll; La Salle U; Acctnt.

REGOLINO, ANTHONY; Archbishop Molloy HS; Richmond Hl, NY; (Y); Aud/Vis; Ed Lit Mag; JV Bowling; Hon Roll; Queens Coll; Film Edtng.

REHAC, LORI; West Seneca West SR HS; Buffalo, NY; (Y); Teachers Aide; Chorus; Color Guard; School Play; Stage Crew; Cert Merit Peer Cnslng 85; Fredonia; Spch Pathlgy.

REHBERG, KIMBERLY S; Honeoye Falls-Lima HS; Honeoye Falls, NY; (Y); 30/173; Am Leg Aux Girls St; Girl Scts; Intnl Clb; Political Wkr; Red Cross Aide; Scholastic Bowl; Acpl Chr; Chorus; NHS; Ntl Merit Ltr; Natl Teen-Age Repblcn Conf Delg; Intl Rel.

REHOR, MARIA T; Dominican Commercial HS; Brooklyn, NY; (Y); 120/274; Church Yth Grp; Girl Scts; Teachers Aide; Varsity Clb; Score Keeper; High Hon Roll; Hon Roll; Prfct Atten Awd; NYS Regnts Nrs Schlrshp 85; Siena Clb Awd 83-84; Hunter Coll; Nrs.

REHREY, SHAWN; Newburgh Free Acad; Newburgh, NY; (Y); Boy Scts; Trs Exploring; Chorus; Hon Roll; Auto Mech.

REICH, CHRISTOPHER; Minisink Valley HS; Westtown, NY; (Y); Letterman Clb; Varsity Clb; Band; Concert Band; Jazz Band; Mrchg Band; Pep Band; Pres VP Jr Cls; Var L Bsbl; JV Var Ftbl.

REICHERT, PAUL; Hamburg SR HS; Hamburg, NY; (Y); 20/390; Am Leg Boys St; Boy Scts; Church Yth Grp; Model UN; Band; Chorus; Madrigals; School Musical; NHS; Ntl Merit SF; Top 10 Awd 83; Pol Sci.

REICHERT, THOMAS; Brockport HS; Spencerport, NY; (Y); Church Yth Grp; Exploring; Pres German Clb; Chorus; Var Mgr(s); Mgr JV Socr; High Hon Roll; NHS.

REICHMAN, LORIANN; Tioga Centeral HS; Tioga Center, NY; (Y); 4-H; Library Aide; Radio Clb; Band; Chorus; Church Choir; JV Var Score Keeper; 4-H Awd; Valley Forge Chrstn Coll; RN.

REICKERT, MATTHEW C; Columbia HS; Castleton, NY; (Y); Computer Clb; JV Var Socr; High Hon Roll; Hon Roll; NHS; U Of Rochester; Comp Engr.

REID, CHRISTINA; Mount Saint Mary Acad; Kenmore, NY; (Y); Ski Clb; Socr; Sftbl; NY U; Bus Mgmt.

REID, DAVID A; New Rochelle HS; New Rochelle, NY; (Y); 54/597; Debate Tm; Ski Clb; Band; Jazz Band; Symp Band; Var Lcrss; NHS; Ntl Merit Ltr; Spanish NHS; Semifnlst Natl Achvmnt Schlrshp Pgm 84; Med.

REID, DONNA; Albion Central HS; Eagle Harbor, NY; (Y); Church Yth Grp; VP Sec 4-H; Teachers Aide; Ed Lit Mag; French Hon Soc; Day Care.

REID, FAYETTE LOLITA; Freeport HS; Freeport, NY; (Y); Science Clb; Band; Concert Band; Jazz Band; Mrchg Band; Pep Band; Sec Frsh Cls; JV Bsktbl; JV Var Vllybl; Hon Roll; Sci Fair Awd; Tutoring Awd; Hmpton Inst; Lawyer.

REID III, JACK; Mc Kinley HS; Buffalo, NY; (Y); Rep Frsh Cls; Rep Soph Cls; Pres Jr Cls; Stu Cncl; Bsktbl; Crs Cntry; Trk; Cit Awd.

REID, KEVIN L; Charles E Gorton HS; Yonkers, NY; (Y); 43/209; Pres Church Yth Grp; Cmnty Wkr; Computer Clb; FBLA; Church Choir; VP Sr Cls; Stu Cncl; Trk; Hon Roll; NHS; Tuskegee U; Comp Sci.

REID, NIGEL; Birch Wathen HS; New York, NY; (Y); Computer Clb; Library Aide; Stage Crew; Im Bsktbl; Im Bowling; Im Ftbl; Im Socr; Im Sftbl; Im Vllybl; Im Wt Lftg; Arista Hnr Soc 82; ABC Prog Schlrshp 82; Lawyer.

REID, PHILLIP D; Midwood HS; Brooklyn, NY; (Y); 38/605; Math Tm; Lit Mag; Ftbl; Hon Roll; Ntl Merit SF; Pre-Med.

REID, TAMI; Saint Peters H S For Girls; Staten Isl, NY; (Y); Red Cross Aide; Chorus; School Musical; School Play; Stage Crew; Rep Stu Cncl; Im Coach Actv; Im Mgr(s); JV Sftbl; Im Tennis; Phrmcst.

REID, TYRA; Hempstead HS; Hempstead, NY; (Y); Hon Roll; Bus Mgr.

REID, URSULA; Cathedral HS; New York, NY; (Y); 40/325; Cmnty Wkr; Nwsp Stf; Hon Roll; Hunter Coll; Sys Anlyst.

REID JR, WILLIAM; A Philip Randolph HS; Bronx, NY; (Y); Aud/Vis; Band; Trk; Elec Engr.

REIDLICH, PATRICIA; Sachem HS; Lk Ronkonkoma, NY; (Y); 100/1385; Ski Clb; Spanish Clb; Band; Concert Band; JV Var Cheerleading; Stat Lcrss; Hon Roll; Sci Fair-Hnrbl Mntn 83; Soc Stud Fair-Hnrbl Mntn 83 & 84.

REIDLINGER, LINDA J; Hillcrest HS; Richmond Hill, NY; (Y); 24/793; Church Yth Grp; Cmnty Wkr; French Clb; Hosp Aide; Teachers Aide; Hon Roll; Jr NHS; Ntl Merit Ltr; Daily News Super Youth 83; NY U; Comp Sci.

REIFF, NEIL; South Shore HS; Brooklyn, NY; (Y); 20/668; Math Tm; Scholastic Bowl; Band; Jazz Band; Orch; Rep Sr Cls; NHS; Regnts Schlrshp 85; Outstndng Progress-Music 85; SUNY-BINGHAMTON.

REIHING, PATRICIA; Mineola HS; Mineola, NY; (Y); #7 In Class; Art Clb; Drama Clb; Stage Crew; High Hon Roll; Hon Roll; NHS; Certfd Pblc Accntnt.

REILING, PETER B; Canisius HS; E Aurora, NY; (S); Boy Scts; Drama Clb; PAVAS; Chorus; School Musical; Nwsp Ed-Chief; JV Wrstlng; Jr NHS; Ntl Merit Ltr; Engl.

REILLEY, MARIA E; Rome Catholic HS; Rome, NY; (Y); 8/81; School Musical; Nwsp Stf; Pres Sr Cls; Stu Cncl; Cheerleading; Powder Puff Ftbl; Tennis; High Hon Roll; NHS; NYS Regents Schlrshp 85; SR Mnth 84; Trinity Coll; Bio.

REILLEY, MARK; Auburn HS; Auburn, NY; (Y); Ski Clb; Hon Roll; U CA LA; Surgeon.

REILLY, ANDREA J; Academy Of The Ressrctn; Scarsdale, NY; (Y); 4/63; Dance Clb; Drama Clb; Hosp Aide; Math Clb; NFL; Ski Clb; Chorus; School Musical; Var Trk; High Hon Roll; U Notre Dame Schlr 85; NYS Regents Schlrshp 85; U Notre Dame.

REILLY, DENIS; Lasalle Acad; Middle Village, NY; (S); 70/254; Drama Clb; School Musical; School Play; Nwsp Rptr; Var Crs Cntry; Trk; Hon Roll; Albany ST; Acctnt.

REILLY, ELLEN; St Francis Prep; Middle Village, NY; (S); 28/693; Cmnty Wkr; Service Clb; Gym; High Hon Roll.

REILLY, GAVIN; St Marys Boys HS; N Merric, NY; (Y); 6/158; Bowling; High Hon Roll.

REILLY, IRENE; Queen Of The Rosary Acad; Ptlookout, NY; (Y); Church Yth Grp; Cmnty Wkr; Drama Clb; Co-Capt Pep Clb; Varsity Clb; School Musical; School Play; Co-Capt Sftbl; Var Vllybl; Hon Roll; Molloy Coll; Nrsng.

REILLY, JAMES; St Marcis Acad; Glens Falls, NY; (S); 4/45; Church Yth Grp; French Clb; Ski Clb; Varsity Clb; Sec Jr Cls; Var Bsbl; Var Bsktbl; Var Crs Cntry; Var Ftbl; Hon Roll; Mech Engrng.

REILLY, JUDITH; Hunter College HS; Long Island City, NY; (Y); Hosp Aide; Library Aide; Model UN; Chorus; Stage Crew; Mu Alp Tht; Ntl Merit SF; Engrng.

REILLY, KATHLEEN; Maria Regina HS; Yonkers, NY; (Y); 35/130; Church Yth Grp; Dance Clb; Hosp Aide; Library Aide; Teachers Aide; Chorus; CC Awd; High Hon Roll; Hon Roll; Librn Cert Awd 83-85; Friendly Visitrs Awd 83 & 85; Hmrm Hlpr 84; Missn Outrch Clb Awds 84-85; Mt St Vincents; Nrsng.

REILLY, KEVIN; South Side HS; Rockville Ctr, NY; (Y); Boy Scts.

REILLY, KIM; Warwick Valley HS; Warwick, NY; (Y); Capt Crs Cntry; Capt Trk; Hon Roll; MVP Outdr Trk 83 & 85; 2 Mi Relay NY ST Chmps 85; 5 Schl Trk Rcds 82-85; Ed.

REILLY, MATTHEW E; West Seneca West SR HS; West Seneca, NY; (Y); 49/543; Spanish Clb; Rep Stu Cncl; Tennis; Hon Roll; NHS; Regnts Schlrshp 85; Chem Hnr Rll 84; Lehigh U; Bus Adm.

REILLY, MAUREEN; Holy Trinity HS; Levittown, NY; (Y); Church Yth Grp; Math Clb; Math Tm; Stage Crew; Yrbk Stf; Stu Cncl; Mu Alp Tht; Nassau CC; Acctng.

REILLY, MICHAEL; Stuyvesant HS; New York, NY; (Y); JV Debate Tm; Nwsp Rptr; Nwsp Stf; Semi Finlst Natl Hispanc Schlr Awd 85; NY ST Regnts Scholar Wnr 85; Intl Relatns.

REILLY, MICHAEL C; Fordham Prep; New York, NY; (Y); School Play; Rep Frsh Cls; Rep Soph Cls; Im Ftbl; Im Sftbl; Jesuit Pres Scholar Fordham Prep 82; Eng Prof.

REILLY, PAMELA; Sachem HS; Holbrook, NY; (Y); 221/1383; Spanish Clb; Chorus; Trs Sr Cls; St Josephs Coll; Pre-Law.

REILLY, PATRICK T; Regis HS; Staten Island, NY; (Y); German Clb; Hosp Aide; Ski Clb; Case Western Reserve U; Bio.

REILLY, RENEE; Rome Free Acad; Rome, NY; (Y); Intnl Clb; Key Clb; Chorus; Yrbk Bus Mgr; Yrbk Phtg; Trs Stu Cncl; Var Bowling; Score Keeper; Hon Roll; Jr NHS; Selctd Hd Phtgrphr Yrbk Stff 82-83; Bnkg.

REILLY, THERESA P; Clarkstown North HS; Congers, NY; (Y); Church Yth Grp; Spanish Clb; Mrchg Band; Nwsp Rptr; Yrbk Phtg; Yrbk Sprt Ed; Off Stu Cncl; Var Bsktbl; Score Keeper; Physcs.

REILLY, TIMOTHY; St Agnes HS; E Meadow, NY; (Y); 70/400; Church Yth Grp; 4-H; Hosp Aide; Letterman Clb; Service Clb; Varsity Clb; Yrbk Stf; Sec Jr Cls; High Hon Roll; Ntl Hnr Soc 84-85; Stu Cncl Pres 84-85; Vrsty Capt Lacrosse; Pace U; Pblc Accntng.

REIMANN, LORI-ANN; Port Chester HS; Port Chester, NY; (Y); 4/240; FTA; Spanish Clb; Capt Color Guard; Mrchg Band; Ed Yrbk Stf; Var Capt Bowling; Mu Alp Tht; VP NHS; Spanish NHS; Iona Coll; Ed.

REIMELS, AMANDA; Watkins Glen HS; Watkins Glen, NY; (S); 6/145; Chess Clb; Math Clb; Off Sr Cls; Var L Swmmng; Hon Roll; Bio.

REIMER, JOANNA; Mc Mahon HS; Buffalo, NY; (Y).

REIMER, ROSS; South Western Central HS; Bemus Point, NY; (Y); Church Yth Grp; Dance Clb; Ski Clb; Spanish Clb; Chorus; Church Choir; Var Bsktbl; Im Ftbl; Var Golf; Var Capt Socr; Bus.

REINA, JEFFREY; Tonawanda JR SR HS; Tonawanda, NY; (Y); French Clb; Red Cross Aide; Varsity Clb; Var Ftbl; Var Capt Swmmng; Pres NHS; Pol Sci.

REINA, LEONARD; Bishop Ford Central Catholic HS; Brooklyn, NY; (Y); 50/445; Computer Clb; Math Clb; Math Tm; Fld Hcky; Wt Lftg; Hon Roll; Arch.

REINER, DEBRA A; Hunter College HS; Bayside, NY; (Y); Hosp Aide; Math Clb; Political Wkr; Teachers Aide; VP Chorus; Sec School Musical; VP Swing Chorus; Lit Mag; Ntl Merit Ltr; Psychology.

REINER, MICHAEL; Croton-Harmon HS; Croton-On-Hudson, NY; (Y); 12/104; Varsity Clb; Stu Cncl; Var Ftbl; Var Trk; Hon Roll; Ntl Merit Ltr; Pres Schlr; Brandeis U; Econ.

REINGOLD, JAY R; Hunter College HS; Brooklyn, NY; (Y); Pres Model UN; VP Jr Cls; Pres Sr Cls; Ntl Merit SF; Nwsp Stf; Yrbk Stf; JV Vllybl; Political Sci.

REINHARDT, CHRISTOPHER S; Connetquot SR HS; Oakdale, NY; (Y); 121/781; Church Yth Grp; Var L Lcrss; Var L Socr; Trk; Hon Roll; Prfct Atten Awd; NY St Regents Schlrshp 85; Stony Brook U; Engrng Sci.

REINHARDT, ELLEN; Westlake HS; Thornwood, NY; (Y); 7/156; Pres AFS; Church Yth Grp; Sec French Clb; Chorus; Trs Sr Cls; Var L Socr; DAR Awd; High Hon Roll; NHS; Pres Schlr; Thornwood Women Clb, PTA Schlrshps, Excel Frnch Awd 85; Lafayette Coll; Econ.

REINHARDT, LAURA; Jamestown HS; Jamestown, NY; (Y); Church Yth Grp; Spanish Clb; Teachers Aide; Band; Church Choir; Nwsp Stf; U Buffalo; Jrnlsm.

REINMUTH, JARED D; Saugerties HS; Saugerties, NY; (Y); 10/250; Math Tm; Varsity Clb; Pres Frsh Cls; Pres Soph Cls; Var Capt Crs Cntry; Var Capt Trk; Im Vllybl; Var Capt Wrstlng; High Hon Roll; Hon Roll; Pre Law.

REINMUTH, KRIS; Saugerties HS; Saugerties, NY; (Y); FFA; NFL; Spanish Clb; Varsity Clb; Jazz Band; Var L Socr; Var L Trk; Var L Wrstlng; Var High Hon Roll; NHS; Columbia U; Pre-Med.

REINO, CHRISTOPHER V; Sachem HS; Holtsville, NY; (Y); 311/1463; Trk; C W Post APA 85; Suffolk Cnty Hmn Rghts Commssn-Essay Awd 83; Pres Acadmc Ftnss Awd 85; Ace Nwsdy Carr; C W Post; Bus.

REINWALD, ANDREA; Scarsdale HS; Scarsdale, NY; (Y); Varsity Clb; AFS; Debate Tm; Hosp Aide; Spanish Clb; Yrbk Stf; Rep Frsh Cls; Rep Soph Cls; Rep Jr Cls; Sr Cls; Cornell U; Law.

REISER, JESSICA; Fairport HS; Fairport, NY; (Y); 4-H; Church Choir; Mrchg Band; Symp Band; Mgr Var Fld Hcky; Var Mgr(s); Cit Awd; 4-H Awd; Hon Roll; NHS; YMCA Yth Of Hr Awd 83; Nomnt Rochstr Yng Amer Awd 84; Red Raider Sprk Plg Awd 85; Bio.

REISERT, JOSEPH R; Garden City SR HS; Garden City, NY; (Y); 3/320; VP French Clb; Pres Mathletes; Pres Science Clb; Ed Nwsp Stf; Jr NHS; NHS; Ntl Merit SF; Chess Clb; Computer Clb; Frnch, Chem Dpt Awd; Rensselaer Mdl Math , Sci 84; Intl Rel.

REISKIND, ANDREW S; Bronx H S Of Science; Bronx, NY; (Y); Math Tm; Office Aide; Trs NHS; Ntl Merit SF; ACS Exam 83; 2nd Hnrs Iona Coll Physics Comp 84; NYC Math Team 84; Chem Engr.

REISS, IRA; Walter Panas HS; Peekskill, NY; (Y); FBLA; Teachers Aide; Y-Teens; Orch; Nwsp Stf; Off Stu Cncl; JV Ftbl; Var Lcrss; NHS; Columbia; Bus Fin.

REISS, JULIANA B; La Guardia HS Of Music And The Arts; Brooklyn, NY; (Y); 25/600; Jr NHS; NHS; NY ST Regents Schlrshp 85; Mayor Kochs Outstndg Yth Awd 84; Alvin Ailey Merit Schlrshp 83; U Of MI; Engl.

REISTER, JOSEPH; Utica Free Acad; Utica, NY; (Y); Debate Tm; Drama Clb; Model UN; Spanish Clb; Thesps; School Play; Stage Crew; Variety Show; High Hon Roll; NHS; Intl Rel.

REITER, LARRY; Oceanside HS; Oceanside, NY; (Y); Capt Sftbl; Hon Roll; Jr NHS; NHS; Albany; Dentist.

REITER, SCOTT W; Clinton Central HS; Clinton, NY; (Y); 15/146; Am Leg Boys St; Boy Scts; Model UN; Drill Tm; Nwsp Ed-Chief; Trs Jr Cls; JV Socr; L Tennis; NHS; Trs Drama Clb; Bronze Palm Eagle Scout 84; Natl Sco Studs Olympd Wnnr 84; Mst Imprvd Chorus 85; Top Mag Slsmn; Pol Sci.

REKERS, WENDI; Irondequoit HS; Rochester, NY; (Y); 5/393; Latin Clb; Ski Clb; Varsity Clb; Coach Actv; Var Diving; Var Gym; Var Swmmng; Im Wt Lftg; High Hon Roll; Jr NHS; Maxima Cum Laude Natl Lat Exm 85; 5th Pl Sect V Divng & ST 85; Cornell U; Vet.

RELLA, DEANNA; Pelham Memorial HS; Pelham, NY; (Y); Cmnty Wkr; PAVAS; School Musical; Nwsp Rptr; Nwsp Sprt Ed; Nwsp Stf; Var Bsktbl; JV Lcrss; Var Tennis; High Hon Roll.

RELYEA, FLOYD; Canastota HS; Verona, NY; (Y); 23/135; Church Yth Grp; Cmnty Wkr; High Hon Roll; Hon Roll; NHS; Drama Clb; FTA; Teachers Aide; Chorus; School Musical; 1st Pl In Essay Cont For The Amer Lgn 85; Schlrshp For Acad Grds Cmnty Wrk 85; Schlrsp Dilly Farfaglia; SUNY Morrisville Ag & Tech.

RELYEA, MARY E; Canastota HS; Canastota, NY; (Y); 24/131; French Clb; Intnl Clb; Science Clb; Yrbk Stf; Swmmng; Vllybl; Hon Roll; NHS; St Schlr; Outstndng Achvt Eng 85; Dollars Schlrs Schlrshp 85; Albany Coll; Phrmcy.

RELYEA, SCOTT; Colonie Central HS; Albany, NY; (Y); JV Lcrss; Var Capt Socr; Hon Roll; Engrng.

RELYEA, TIMOTHY; Whitesboro HS; Whitesboro, NY; (Y); 11/384; Pres Church Yth Grp; Intnl Clb; Science Clb; Church Choir; Jazz Band; Pres Orch; Rep Stu Cncl; L Crs Cntry; Var Tennis; NHS; NY St Schoolstc Music Assoc 84; Prncpl Bassist-Area All-St Fstvl 84; Med.

REMENTER, MIKE; Center Moriches HS; Ctr Moriches, NY; (Y); Ski Clb; JV Var Bsbl; JV Var Socr; Var Trk; Ltr All Sprts, JV, V 82-85; Arch.

REMEY, BRENDA; Minisink Valley HS; Middletown, NY; (Y); 25/225; High Hon Roll; Hon Roll; Presdntl Acadmc Ftnss Awd 85; Liberty Baptist U.

REMEY, SANDRA; Minisink Valley HS; Middletown, NY; (Y); 24/225; High Hon Roll; Hon Roll; Pleasure Horse Crse Highst Avg 83; Liberty U; Acct.

REMINGTON, DANIELLE; Newark SR HS; Newark, NY; (Y); 16/200; Ski Clb; Band; Concert Band; Mrchg Band; Pep Band; Variety Show; Yrbk Ed-Chief; Yrbk Stf; Pres French Hon Soc; High Hon Roll; JR Hon Grl 85; Hartwick; Psych.

REMINGTON, RYAN; Marion Central Schl; Marion, NY; (Y); Boy Scts; German Clb; Model UN; Office Aide; Quiz Bowl; Ski Clb; Temple Yth Grp; JV Var Bsbl; JV Var Bsktbl; Swmmng; Exclince Soc Stud 83; 1st Pl Knwldge Qz Bwl 85; Exclince ACT & SAT Tsts 83-85; U UT; Surgcl Tech.

REMO, ROSANNA; Aquinas HS; Bronx, NY; (Y); 8/178; Chorus; School Musical; High Hon Roll; Bus, Italn Awds; Bus.

REMSKAR, ANDREW; Saugerties HS; Saugerties, NY; (Y); Chess Clb; German Clb; Math Tm; Ski Clb; Im Bsktbl; Im Fld Hcky; JV Socr; Im Sftbl; JV Swmmng; Im Vllybl; Cvl Engrng.

RENCHER, KATHRYN; North Babylon SR HS; North Babylon, NY; (Y); DECA; GAA; Office Aide; Yrbk Stf; Rep Stu Cncl; Var Fld Hcky; Var Vllybl; High Hon Roll; Pres NHS; Mktng.

RENDA, BRIAN A; St Pauls Schl; Forest Hills, NY; (Y); Pres Church Yth Grp; Sec Varsity Clb; Nwsp Stf; Lit Mag; Sec Jr Cls; Rep Sr Cls; Sec Rep Stu Cncl; Var Bsbl; Var Socr; High Hon Roll; Cum Laude Soc; CT Coll; Pol Sci.

RENDEIRO, DANIELLE M; St Joseph By The Sea HS; Staten Island, NY; (Y); Dance Clb; Drama Clb; French Clb; School Play; Yrbk Stf; Eng.

RENDINARO, PETER; MSGR Farrell HS; Staten Island, NY; (Y); Church Yth Grp; Civic Clb; Hosp Aide; Ski Clb; Rep Sr Cls; Im Bsktbl; Var L Ftbl; Wt Lftg; JV Wrstlng; Hon Roll; Schl Hnr Rl 81-85; Natl Hnr Rl 85; Iona Clg; Bus.

RENDINO, CHRISTINE; Bishop Ludden HS; Baldwinsville, NY; (S); Political Wkr; Speech Tm; Var Trk; NHS; Schlrshp Syracuse U Pre Coll Prog 84.

RENICK, MICHELLE; Copiaque SR HS; Amity Harbor, NY; (Y); DECA; FBLA; GAA; Yrbk Phtg; Yrbk Stf; Fld Hcky; Hon Roll.

RENKEN, JOHN; Rocky Point HS; Rocky Pt, NY; (Y); Varsity Clb; Nwsp Rptr; Nwsp Sprt Ed; Sec Frsh Cls; Sec Soph Cls; VP Jr Cls; Var Capt Bsktbl; Var Capt Lcrss; Var Capt Socr; Al-Leag Sccr Goalie 83-84; Al-Leag La Crosse Midfldr 85.

RENNER, STACEY; Stillwater Central HS; Stillwater, NY; (Y); 1/100; Key Clb; Math Tm; Varsity Clb; JV Var Ftbl; Wt Lftg; High Hon Roll; NHS; Ntl Merit SF; Val; Drama Clb; Phys Sci.

RENNIE, ANNE; Holy Angels Acad; Kenmore, NY; (S); 5/38; Chorus; School Musical; Nwsp Stf; Yrbk Stf; VP Frsh Cls; VP Sr Cls; Stu Cncl; High Hon Roll; Pres NHS; Rep Soph Cls; Gymnstc Clss I ST Comp NY Empire ST Games 84-85; Eucharistic Minister; Psych.

RENSKY, FILIP; Bronx HS Of Science; New York, NY; (Y); Computer Clb; JA; Office Aide; Ski Clb; Teachers Aide; Hon Roll; Ntl Merit Ltr; Prfct Atten Awd; Bus.

RENTA, KENNETH; Wallkill SR HS; Plattekill, NY; (Y); 25/200; Drama Clb; Jazz Band; School Play; Swing Chorus; Rep Frsh Cls; Rep Soph Cls; Rep Jr Cls; Rep Sr Cls; Rep Stu Cncl; Trk; NY All St Choir 83; Bus.

RENTAS, MYRA; Cathedral HS; Neyork, NY; (Y); 187/349; Hosp Aide; Color Guard; Rep Frsh Cls; Rep Stu Cncl; Intnl Clb; Band; Mrchg Band; Yrbk Stf; Sftbl; Aviatn.

RENTZ, STEPHEN; Columbia HS; Castleton, NY; (Y); Computer Clb; Ski Clb; Jazz Band; Mrchg Band; Orch; Pep Band; Symp Band; Var Capt Golf; Hon Roll; Comp Sci.

RENWICK IV, JOHN P; John Jay HS; Katonah, NY; (Y); 1/290; Variety Show; Trs Jr Cls; Rep Sr Cls; Rep Stu Cncl; Golf; Socr; Wrstlng; High Hon Roll; NHS; Spanish NHS; Regnts Schlrshp 85; Sprtsmshp Awds-Wrstlng, Soccr 83-85; Middlebury Coll; Ecnmcs.

RENZ, LISA D; Mohonasen HS; Schenectady, NY; (Y); 2/216; Church Yth Grp; German Clb; Key Clb; Concert Band; Mrchg Band; Rep Stu Cncl; High Hon Roll; Trs NHS; Ntl Merit Ltr; Sal; Regnts Schlrshp 85; Cncrt Band Solo NYS Music Comptn 83; NYSMTA Piano Comptn 81-83; Tufts U; Med.

REO, PAUL; Mohonasen HS; Schenectady, NY; (Y); Band; Concert Band; Drill Tm; Jazz Band; Mrchg Band; Pep Band; Golf; Law.

REPASS, DAVID; Dansville SR HS; Dansville, NY; (Y); Am Leg Boys St; Cmnty Wkr; Drama Clb; Varsity Clb; Band; Chorus; Rep Stu Cncl; JV Capt Ftbl; Var Trk; Church Yth Grp; Child Psychlgy.

REPICCI, CARMEN; Gowanda Central HS; Gowanda, NY; (Y); JV Var Bsktbl; Var Sftbl; Hon Roll; Elect Engr.

REPOLLE, DAMIAN; Walter Panas HS; Peekskill, NY; (Y); Ski Clb; Yrbk Phtg; Trs Frsh Cls; Trs Soph Cls; Trs Jr Cls; Var Bsbl; Var Socr; High Hon Roll; Hon Roll; NHS; Engrng.

RERES, ANTHONY; Monsignor Mc Clancy Memorial HS; Maspeth, NY; (Y); 2/250; Math Tm; Science Clb; Spanish Clb; Nwsp Stf; Rep Jr Cls; Rep Stu Cncl; High Hon Roll; NHS; Spanish NHS; Queens Coll Pres Awd Achvt 84; Columbia U; Med.

RESNICK, ALEXANDER; Northport SR HS; E Northport, NY; (Y); DECA; Im Bowling; Business Hnr Soc 84-85; Albany U; Accntng.

RESNICK, JENNIFER; Tottenville HS; Staten Island, NY; (Y); 124/897; Key Clb; Yrbk Stf; Rep Frsh Cls; Rep Soph Cls; Rep Jr Cls; Rep Sr Cls; Mgr(s); Score Keeper; Var JV Vllybl; High Hon Roll; Qulty Ltnnt Gov Key Clb 85; Daily News Super Yth 84; Outstndng Key Clb Pres 84; Suny Buffalo; Accntng.

RESNICK, MOIRA S; Williamsville N HS; Williamsville, NY; (Y); 13/315; Latin Clb; Spanish Clb; Frsh Cls; Var L Fld Hcky; Var Socr; Hon Roll; NHS; NYS Rgnts Schlrshp 85; Wstrn ; Ny Clsscl Assns Latin Hnrbl Ment 82, 84; Cornell U; Vet.

RESNICK, STEPHEN S; Pittsford Sutherland HS; Pittsburg, NY; (Y); Cornell U; Agriculture.

RESNICK, THEODORE A; Tottenville HS; Staten Island, NY; (Y); 65/897; Pres Debate Tm; Key Clb; School Musical; School Play; Stage Crew; Nwsp Rptr; Yrbk Phtg; Yrbk Rptr; Hon Roll; NHS; Natl Hnr Roll 84-85; Fencing Clb 85; ST U Of NY Binghamton.

RESNIKOFF, JOHANNA; Amherst Central HS; Snyder, NY; (Y); Art Clb; Cmnty Wkr; Dance Clb; Debate Tm; Drama Clb; GAA; Pep Clb; Radio Clb; Rep Frsh Cls; Im Badmtn; NY ST Rgnts Schlrshp 85; U Of Albany; Pub Rel.

RESTIERI, LAWRENCE; Cold Spring Harbor HS; Cold Spring Har, NY; (Y); 2/144; Mathletes; Jazz Band; School Musical; Nwsp Stf; Capt JV Ftbl; JV Lcrss; High Hon Roll; Jr NHS; Rotary Awd; Sal; Vrsty Lttr Ftbl 84; Bus.

RESTINO, STEPHEN J; Fayetteville-Manlius HS; Manlius, NY; (Y); 70/350; JCL; Band; Chorus; Mrchg Band; Stu Cncl; Socr; High Hon Roll; Hon Roll; Engl & Ltn Awd 82 & 83; SUNY-POTSDAM; Comp Sci.

RESTIVO, JOHN T; Connetquot HS; Bohemia, NY; (Y); 42/693; Chorus; High Hon Roll; Hon Roll; Outstndng Acad Achvt Awd 82; Soc Studies Achvt Awd 82; NYS Rgnts Schlrshp 85; Stonybrook; Lbrl Arts.

RESTIVO, VINNY; Lincoln HS; Yonkers, NY; (Y); Hon Roll; Elec.

RESTUCCIO, STEPHANIE; Bishop Cunningham HS; Oswego, NY; (Y); Church Yth Grp; Pep Clb; Teachers Aide; Varsity Clb; Yrbk Stf; Rep Stu Cncl; Bsktbl; Socr; Swmmng; High Hon Roll; St John Fisher Coll; Engl.

RESTUCCIO, THOMAS; Bishop Cunningham HS; Oswego, NY; (S); 9/28; Computer Clb; French Clb; Yrbk Ed-Chief; Yrbk Phtg; Yrbk Stf; JV Bsktbl; Var L Socr; Var L Tennis; SUNY Oswego; Engr.

RESZITNYK, SONYA; St George Acad; Jersey City, NJ; (Y); Cmnty Wkr; Dance Clb; Drama Clb; Church Choir; School Musical; School Play; Stage Crew; Pres Frsh Cls; Vllybl; High Hon Roll; St Johns U; Psych.

RETZ, SUSAN; Union Springs Acad; Chittenango, NY; (S); 7/54; Hosp Aide; Math Tm; Bsktbl; Ftbl; Score Keeper; Sftbl; Vllybl; High Hon Roll; Sec Trs NHS; Andrews U; Phy Thrpst.

RETZER, JOSEPH A; Keshequa Central Schl; Mt Morris, NY; (Y); Key Clb; Math Tm; Varsity Clb; Var JV Bsbl; Var JV Bsktbl; Hon Roll; NHS; Prfct Atten Awd; U Buffalo; Comp Sci.

REUBEN, WINSOME; Hempstead HS; Hempstead, NY; (S); NHS; Adelphi U; Accntng.

REUTER, BENJAMIN H; Jefferson Central Schl; E Worcester, NY; (Y); 2/17; Am Leg Boys St; Band; Concert Band; Jazz Band; Mrchg Band; School Musical; Stage Crew; Trs Sr Cls; Var L Bsbl; Var L Bsktbl; MVP JCS Vrsty Bsbl Tm 84-85; 1st Trmpt DE All Cnty Band 83-85.

REUTER, CHRISTOPHER; Roxbury Central HS; Grand Gorge, NY; (S); 5/35; Computer Clb; Library Aide; VP Jr Cls; Bsktbl; Golf; High Hon Roll; Highst Ave Typng 83-84; Outstndng Ctznshp 82-83; Ag.

REUTER, PAMELA; Manhasset HS; Manhasset, NY; (Y); Varsity Clb; Chorus; Flag Corp; Variety Show; Nwsp Rptr; Lit Mag; Stu Cncl; Var Swmmng; Var Tennis; Bus.

REUTHER, DEBORAH A; Cardinal Spellman HS; Bronx, NY; (Y); 75/530; Girl Scts; Teachers Aide; Stage Crew; Im Bsktbl; NYS Regnts Schlrshp 85; Parsons Schl Design; Bus Adm.

REUTLINGER, LEAH E; East Syracuse-Minoa C HS; E Syracuse, NY; (Y); 23/340; Latin Clb; Science Clb; Variety Show; Bsktbl; Socr; Var L Trk; High Hon Roll; Jr NHS; NHS; JA; MVP Indoor Trck; Cornell U; Ag Engrng.

REVENSON, KAREN; Tottenville HS; Staten Island, NY; (Y); 13/897; Camera Clb; Math Tm; Band; School Play; Nwsp Phtg; Yrbk Phtg; Tennis; High Hon Roll; NHS; Prfct Atten Awd; Ansel Adams Phtgrphy Awd 85; Pfrct Atndnc Awd 85; Ntl Hnr Scty 85; SUNY Binghmtn; Bio.

REVETTE, RENEE T; Paul V Moore HS; Central Square, NY; (Y); 54/300; Church Yth Grp; GAA; VP Jr Cls; VP Sr Cls; JV Cheerleading; Var Capt Gym; Mst Val Gymnast 84; Mst Imprvd Chrldr 83; ST U Potsdam NY; Comp Sci.

REXFORD, LORI; Alexandria Central HS; Redwood, NY; (Y); 2/55; Sec French Clb; Band; Trs Concert Band; Trs Mrchg Band; Sec Trs Jr Cls; Var Bowling; Var Score Keeper; Var Tennis; Hon Roll; NHS; Schlrhsp Pin 83-85; Jeff Lewis Bi Cnty Band Awd 85.

REY, CESAR; Power Memorial Acad St Agnes HS; New York, NY; (Y); 15/100; JA; Band; Bsktbl; Trk; Hon Roll; 1st & 2nd Hnrs 81-85; Princpls Lst Awd 82; NHS Awd 85; Manhattan Coll; Engrng.

REYES, ANDRIANNA; Bronx HS Of Sci; New York, NY; (Y); SYRACUSE U; Chld Psych.

REYES, ANN MARIE; Academy Of St Joseph; Central Islip, NY; (Y); Church Yth Grp; Cmnty Wkr; Office Aide; Service Clb; Temple Yth Grp; Band; Chorus; Church Choir; School Musical; School Play; Achvt Awd Effrt 82; Med Secy.

REYES, BERNADETTE; St John The Baptist HS; Amity Hbr, NY; (Y); Chess Clb; Debate Tm; Hosp Aide; Nwsp Rptr; Ntl Merit SF; Pre Med.

REYES, EDITH; Norman Thomas HS; Jackson Heights, NY; (S); 85/677; Church Yth Grp; Church Choir; Rep Frsh Cls; Rep Soph Cls; Rep Jr Cls; Off Stu Cncl; Eastern NM U; Soc.

REYES, JAIME; La Salle Acad; New York, NY; (S); 10/250; Math Clb; Rep Sr Cls; JV Crs Cntry; Var Socr; JV Trk; Hon Roll; Jr NHS; NHS; Columiba Schl Of Sci; Comp Sci.

REYES, JOE; New Rochelle HS; New Rochelle, NY; (Y); Art Clb; Spanish Clb; Lit Mag.

REYES, MAGALI; Bronx HS Of Science; New York City, NY; (Y); JA; Latin Clb; Concert Band; Capt Swmmng; High Hon Roll; NHS; MVP Grls Swm Tm 85; VFT Awd Acadmc Achv 85; PSAL Awd Athltcsm Ldrshp & Acadmcs 85; U Of PA; Bioengrng.

REYES, MARIA V; Seward Park HS; New York, NY; (Y); FNA; Yrbk Phtg; Bsbl; Cheerleading; Gym; Swmmng; Vllybl; Wt Lftg; High Hon Roll; Hon Roll; Econ 82.

REYES, MATTHEW M; Archbishop Molloy HS; S Ozone Pk, NY; (Y); 66/361; Yrbk Stf; JV Var Bsbl; Var L Trk; NHS; NYS Rgnts Schlrshp 85; USMA West Point; Engrng.

REYES, MYRNA; Aquinas HS; Bronx, NY; (Y); 24/178; Service Clb; Spanish Clb; Chorus; Drm Mjr(t); School Play; Rep Soph Cls; Rep Stu Cncl; Twrlr; Hon Roll; Ldrshp Wrkshp; Soph Acad Hnrs; Ushrtte Sprng Mscl; Fordham U; Elem Ed.

REYMERS, KURT; Sherburne-Earlville Central Schl; Earlville, NY; (S); 3/150; Drama Clb; Math Tm; VP Ski Clb; Trs Concert Band; Jazz Band; Mrchg Band; School Play; NHS; Ntl Merit Ltr; Potsdam; Mus Perf.

REYNARDUS, MARIA; The Mary Louis Acad; Jamaica, NY; (Y); Church Yth Grp; Cmnty Wkr; Computer Clb; Dance Clb; Office Aide; Spanish Clb; Stage Crew; Variety Show; Yrbk Stf; Rep Frsh Cls; Hofstra U; Comp Sci.

REYNIAK, ANDREW; Collegiate Schl; New York, NY; (Y); Pres French Clb; Ed Nwsp Stf; Ed Yrbk Stf; Ed Lit Mag; Socr; Trk; Cum Laude 84; Yale U.

REYNOLDS, CHRISTINA; West Babylon HS; W Babylon, NY; (Y); 30/450; Service Clb; High Hon Roll; Hon Roll; Pre Law.

REYNOLDS, DANIEL H; North Shore HS; Glenwood Landing, NY; (Y); Church Yth Grp; CAP; 4-H; ROTC; Band; Chorus; Color Guard; Concert Band; Mrchg Band; Orch; TX A&M; Engrng.

REYNOLDS, DAVID; Hilton Central HS; Hilton, NY; (Y); Hon Roll; Art Achv Awd 82; Brockport; Bio.

REYNOLDS, GENE P; Bishop Ford Central Catholic HS; Brooklyn, NY; (Y); Computer Clb; Drama Clb; JA; Science Clb; School Play; Stage Crew; Sr Cls; Im Bowling; Stu Cncl; Ntl Sci Olympiad 83-84; Coll Of Staten Island; Teach.

REYNOLDS, JANE; Onteora JR-SR HS; Bearsville, NY; (S); Math Tm; Quiz Bowl; Band; Chorus; Var L Bsktbl; Var L Tennis; Var L Trk; Dnfth Awd; High Hon Roll; NHS.

REYNOLDS, JILL; Gouverneur JR & SR HS; Richville, NY; (Y); 2/135; Quiz Bowl; Concert Band; Mrchg Band; Orch; Sec Soph Cls; Socr; High Hon Roll; NHS; VP Jr NHS; VP Timer; Yorker Hist Bowl Team 83-85; Med.

REYNOLDS, JODY; Hornell HS; N Hornell, NY; (Y); Pres Sec Church Yth Grp; Math Clb; High Hon Roll; Hon Roll; Acctg.

REYNOLDS, LAURA; Salamanca City Central HS; Salamanca, NY; (S); 1/129; Drama Clb; French Clb; Band; Chorus; Jazz Band; School Play; French Hon Soc; High Hon Roll; NHS; Church Yth Grp; Schlrshp Outstndg Muscn NYS 84; Appld Mus.

REYNOLDS, MARIANNE; Sachem HS; Holtsville, NY; (Y); 330/1309; Cmnty Wkr; Teachers Aide; Orch; Yrbk Stf; Hon Roll; Stoney Brook U; Law.

REYNOLDS, MICHAEL; Pelham Memorial HS; Pelham, NY; (Y); Ed Am Leg Boys St; Church Yth Grp; Trs Drama Clb; Ed Nwsp Stf; Ed Lit Mag; NHS; French Clb; School Play; High Hon Roll; Ntl Merit Ltr; Rensselaer Polytechnic Inst Mdl For The Mst Outstdng JR In Math & Sci 85; Latin Natl Exam 83.

REYNOLDS, RACHAEL; Bainbridge-Guilford HS; Bainbridge, NY; (Y); 11/80; Pres Church Yth Grp; French Clb; Band; Concert Band; Jazz Band; Orch; Yrbk Stf; Jr NHS; Prfct Atten Awd; Syracuse U; Ed.

REYNOLDS, RENAE; Pulaski JR SR HS; Richland, NY; (S); French Clb; Acpl Chr; Chorus; Yrbk Stf; Sec Soph Cls; Cheerleading; Hon Roll; Geneseo; Psych.

REYNOLDS, SAMUEL F; Kensington HS; Buffalo, NY; (Y); 5/197; Computer Clb; Debate Tm; Library Aide; Science Clb; Speech Tm; Pres Soph Cls; Pres Sr Cls; Rep VP Stu Cncl; Hon Roll; NHS; Black Achvrs Awd 84; Syracuse U; Communications.

REYNOLDS, SCOTT D; Wayne Central HS; Walworth, NY; (Y); 12/205; Math Tm; Concert Band; Jazz Band; School Musical; Yrbk Stf; Var L Tennis; Cit Awd; Hon Roll; NHS; Prfct Atten Awd; Plymouth ST Coll Pres Schlrshp 85-86; Plymouth ST Coll; Meteorology.

REYNOLDS, TINA; North Hoosick HS; North Hoosick, NY; (Y); Computer Clb; FBLA; Pep Clb; Chorus; Hon Roll; Fash Merch.

RHATIGAN, REGINA; Bishop Maginn HS; Albany, NY; (Y); 31/115; 4-H; Red Cross Aide; Service Clb; Spanish Clb; School Play; Yrbk Stf; Pres Sr Cls; Off Stu Cncl; JV Var Cheerleading; Var Crs Cntry; Natl Athltc & Gym Abilities Awd 85; ST U Oneonta; Spec Ed.

RHEE, DAE-SUNG; Manhasset HS; Melville, NY; (Y); Capt Chess Clb; Church Yth Grp; Computer Clb; JV Var Bsbl; JV Var Socr; Hon Roll; Natl Sci Olympd Bio 84; Sci.

RHEE, JONG; Flushing HS; Flushing, NY; (Y); Art Clb; Aud/Vis; Boy Scts; Camera Clb; Math Clb; Science Clb; Drm Mjr(t); Symp Band; Nwsp Stf; Yrbk Phtg; Polytech U; Comp Graph Engr.

RHEE, PHILLIP; Uniondale HS; Uniondale, NY; (Y); Hon Roll; St Johns Art Schlrhsp Prog 84-85; Sci Fair Hnrb Mntn 83; Automtv Engr.

RHEOME, JUDITH; Charles W Baker HS; Baldwinsville, NY; (Y); 65/441; French Clb; Rep JA; Radio Clb; Teachers Aide; Color Guard; School Musical; Nwsp Ed-Chief; Nwsp Rptr; Jr NHS; Wsen-WBXL Comm Schlrshp 85; Suny Oswego; Comm.

RHIND, KIRSTEN; Chatham HS; Chatham, NY; (Y); 26/136; Church Yth Grp; Chorus; Orch; School Musical; Hon Roll; Phy Thrpy.

RHO, ALOYSIUS; Regis HS; Searingtown, NY; (Y); Church Yth Grp; Teachers Aide; Varsity Clb; Orch; Ed Lit Mag; Crs Cntry; Trk; Wesleyan U; Chem.

RHOADS, GERALD; Aguinas Inst; Rochester, NY; (Y); 80/160; Varsity Clb; Var Crs Cntry; Mgr(s); Var L Trk; Hon Roll; Achv Awd Germn II 83-84; Mste Imprvd Crs Cntry Indr Trk, Sprng Trk 84-85; Oswego ST U; Acctng.

RHODEHAMEL, MARI; Nework SR HS; Newark, NY; (Y); Church Yth Grp; Service Clb; Band; Chorus; School Musical; Swing Chorus; Lit Mag; High Hon Roll; Hon Roll; NHS; Bio.

RHODEN, KURT; Freeport HS; Freeport, NY; (Y); Band; Chorus; Church Choir; Var Bsbl; Acctng.

RHODES JR, ALAN; Oakfield-Alabama Central Schl; Oakfield, NY; (Y); Art Clb; Prfct Atten Awd; Art.

RHODES, LIESL C; Lewiston Porter SR HS; Lewiston, NY; (Y); French Clb; GAA; Ski Clb; Concert Band; Orch; Var Trk; Var Capt Vllybl; Hon Roll; NHS; Aud/Vis; Marine Bio.

RHODES, MICHAEL E; Glen Falls HS; Glens Falls, NY; (Y); 9/253; Drama Clb; Key Clb; Math Tm; Varsity Clb; Band; Chorus; Jazz Band; Orch; Pep Band; Frsh Cls; Colgate U; Polt Sci.

RHODY, STEPHEN; Fairport HS; Fairport, NY; (Y); Mathletes; Jazz Band; Orch; School Musical; Rep Stu Cncl; NHS; Ntl Merit SF; Intract Clb/Brd Dirctrs 83-86.

RIBA, PEDRO; Msgr Mc Clancy Memorial HS; Jackson Hts, NY; (S); 24/229; Math Tm; Pres Spanish Clb; Nwsp Rptr; Yrbk Rptr; Trs Stu Cncl; NHS; Spanish NHS; Library Aide; Math Clb; Stu Cncl Ldrshp Awd 84; US Stu Cncl Awd 84; Prncpls List 81-83; Syracuse U; Cvl Engrng.

RIBADENEYRA, ROBERTO; St Johns Prep; Long Isld Cty, NY; (Y); JV Spanish Clb; JV Bsbl; Im JV Bsktbl; Im Sftbl; Im Cit Awd; Im Socr; CPA.

RIBANDO, JOHN; Mnsgr Mc Clancy Memorial HS; Bellerose, NY; (Y); 80/225; Variety Show; VP Frsh Cls; VP Soph Cls; VP Jr Cls; Bsbl; Bsktbl; Ftbl; Spanish NHS; Drivers Ed Awd 85; Catholic Charoties-Hlpng Handicapped Kid Cert 84 & 85; Pace U; Accntng.

RIBAUDO, CHRISTINA; Christopher Columbus HS; Bronx, NY; (Y); 22/750; Key Clb; Math Clb; Math Tm; Teachers Aide; Yrbk Stf; Bsktbl; Cit Awd; High Hon Roll; Hon Roll; Hunter Coll; Accntnt.

RIBBY, NATALIE; Churchville - Chili SR HS; Churchville, NY; (Y); Exploring; Ski Clb; Band; Mrchg Band; JV Sftbl; Var Swmmng; High Hon Roll; NHS; Lwyr.

RIBEIRO, MARGARITA; Newburgh Free Acad; New Windsor, NY; (Y); Church Yth Grp; Acpl Chr; Orch; Nwsp Stf; Yrbk Stf; JV Sftbl; NHS; Opt Clb Awd; Latin Clb; Math Tm; Amer Lgn Schl Awd 83; Rnslr Math & Sci Awd 85.

RICARDO, HENRY; Regis HS; Tappan, NY; (Y); 1/115; Debate Tm; Hosp Aide; NFL; Science Clb; Speech Tm; Teachers Aide; Off Soph Cls; Off Jr Cls; Off Sr Cls; Stu Cncl; T J Watson Meml, Natl Hispanc, John Jay, NY ST Regnts & Bellarmine Schlrshps 85; Princeton U; Medicine.

RICCA, JEANINE M; Carmel HS; Carmel, NY; (Y); 17/371; Trs Spanish Clb; Yrbk Stf; JV Cheerleading; Score Keeper; JV Socr; Vllybl; High Hon Roll; NHS; Pres Schlr; MIP 82-83; St Mary Coll; Pre-Med.

RICCARDELLI, SILVESTRO; St John The Baptist HS; Oakdale, NY; (Y); 13/546; Church Yth Grp; Red Cross Aide; Var Socr; Swmmng; Trk; Hon Roll; NHS; Spanish NHS; Cornell; Engrng.

RICCARDI, TIZIANA; St Peters High School For Girls; Staten Isl, NY; (Y); Yrbk Stf; Ed.

RICCELLI, MARIANNE T; Maria Regina HS; Yonkers, NY; (Y); 51/150; Chorus; Church Choir; Rep Soph Cls; Rep Jr Cls; Rep Stu Cncl; Hon Roll; Rnnr Up Natl Chem Cont 85; Serv Awd 84&85; Sprtsmnshp Awd; Manhatan Coll; Cmpt Sci.

RICCELLI, SHARI; West Genesee HS; Camillus, NY; (Y); Camp Fr Inc; Church Yth Grp; Cmnty Wkr; Dance Clb; Office Aide; Variety Show; High Hon Roll; Prfct Atten Awd; Amatr Horsemnshp Open Hunter Euittn Champ 85 & Novice Champ 83; Daemen Coll; Physcl Thrpy.

RICCHIUTI, MICHAEL; W Islip HS; W Islip, NY; (Y); Band; Jazz Band; School Musical; Swing Chorus; Bsbl; Hon Roll; NHS; Prfct Atten Awd; Ski Clb; Frederick Chopin Piano Awd 85; Jazz Rock Chorus Awd 83; Music.

RICCI, DANA; Pelham Memorial HS; Pelham, NY; (Y); AFS; Church Yth Grp; Drama Clb; Nwsp Stf; Lit Mag; Sec Sr Cls; Capt Twrlr; Hon Roll; NHS; Frgn Lang.

RICCI, DORIS MARIE; New Rochelle HS; New Rochelle, NY; (Y); Boys Clb Am; Church Yth Grp; Cmnty Wkr; Chorus; Stat Bsbl; Stat Bsktbl; Var Capt Cheerleading; Stat Socr; Stat Bowling; Mst Outstndng Chrldr Awd Salesian H S 85; Christian Actn Awd 85.

RICCI, TRACY; Waterford-Halfmoon HS; Waterford, NY; (Y); 2/86; Math Tm; VP Pep Clb; Teachers Aide; Stu Cncl; JV Fld Hcky; Score Keeper; Sftbl; Hon Roll; Sec NHS.

RICCIO, GRACE; Bishop Kearney HS; Brooklyn, NY; (Y); Service Clb; Teachers Aide; Band; Chorus; School Musical; School Play; Stage Crew; Yrbk Stf; Hon Roll; Italn Hnr Awd 83; Brooklyn Coll; Comp Bus.

RICCOBONO, THERESA; H Frank Carey HS; Franklin Sq, NY; (Y); 23/222; Church Yth Grp; Letterman Clb; School Musical; Sftbl; Vllybl; High Hon Roll; Hon Roll; Jr NHS; NHS; Spanish NHS; All Div Vllybl,Sftbl 84-85; Art.

RICE, BRENDA; G Ray Bodley HS; Fulton, NY; (Y); Church Yth Grp; Dance Clb; Latin Clb; Chorus; Madrigals; School Musical; School Play; Var Capt Socr; Trk; Vllybl; Nrsng.

RICE, DANIEL; Hunter College HS; Flushing, NY; (Y); VP Computer Clb; Math Clb; Temple Yth Grp; Concert Band; School Play; Mu Alp Tht; Ntl Merit SF; Comp Sys.

RICE, DAVID; St Josephs Collegiate Inst; Buffalo, NY; (Y); 47/198; Yrbk Rptr; Var Trk; Hon Roll; Church Yth Grp; Model UN; Nwsp Stf; Yrbk Stf; Im Bsktbl; Dnstry.

RICE JR, DAVID; Rice HS; New York, NY; (S); #2 In Class; Crs Cntry; Trk; High Hon Roll; Hon Roll; Schlrshp Rice H S 82-84; 2nd Merit Awd 84.

RICE, JENIFER C; Hutchinson Central Tech HS; Buffalo, NY; (Y); Pres Church Yth Grp; Color Guard; Yrbk Stf; Sec Pres Stu Cncl; Ftbl; Var Tennis; Var Vllybl; Hon Roll; NHS; Prfct Atten Awd; Acctg.

RICE, JENNIFER; Charles O Dickerson HS; Trumansburg, NY; (Y); 34/85; Church Yth Grp; VP Spanish Clb; Sec Trs Varsity Clb; VP Sr Cls; Rep Stu Cncl; Var Socr; Var L Trk; Var L Vllybl; Chorus; Yrbk Stf; Hmncng Queen 85; TSTB Schlrshp 85; Mst I Mprvd Vlybl Plyr; Suny Geneseo; Human Svcs.

RICE, JOANNE; Draper HS; Schenectady, NY; (Y); Girl Scts; Pres Service Clb; Pres Spanish Clb; Band; Chorus; Yrbk Bus Mgr; Crs Cntry; Trk; High Hon Roll; Trs NHS; Le Moyne Coll; Acctng.

RICE, KEVIN; Patchogue-Medford HS; Patchogue, NY; (Y); 65/650; School Musical; Gateway Playhouse Smmr Stock-Actor 81; Troma Prod Actor 82; Pratt U; Film.

RICE, KIMBERLY S; Skanoateles HS; Auburn, NY; (S); VP Church Yth Grp; Dance Clb; Girl Scts; JV Var Cheerleading; Trk; High Hon Roll; Jr NHS; Acctg.

RICE, KYLE; Byron-Bergen Central Schl; Byron, NY; (Y); Aud/Vis; Computer Clb; Band; Chorus; Concert Band; Mrchg Band; Stage Crew; Variety Show; Bsktbl; Var Golf; Aerontcs.

RICE, MARY; Mynderse Acad; Seneca Falls, NY; (S); 35/132; Band; Chorus; Color Guard; Concert Band; Mrchg Band; Stage Crew; High Hon Roll; Hon Roll; NHS; Natl Hnr Soc 84; Geneseo; Nursery.

RICE, ROBERT; Albion HS; Albion, NY; (S); 25/180; Var L Bsbl; Var L Ftbl; Var L Wrstlng; Acctg.

RICE, SHARLET; Sachen North HS; Holbrook, NY; (Y); 281/1383; Dance Clb; Spanish Clb; Acpl Chr; Chorus; Madrigals; Nwsp Stf; NYSSMA Lcl Solo Comp 3e 83; Vcl Grp Comp A- 84.

RICE, STEPHEN A; St Anthonys HS; Smithtown, NY; (Y); 10/450; CAP; French Clb; Latin Clb; Drill Tm; Jazz Band; Pep Band; Symp Band; Nwsp Stf; Yrbk Phtg; NHS.

RICE, TERRI; St Hildas & St Hughs Episcopal HS; New York, NY; (Y); 4/22; Church Yth Grp; Cmnty Wkr; Drama Clb; Hosp Aide; Chorus; Hon Roll; NHS; Johns Hopkins; Doc.

RICE, THERESA; Smithtown High Schl West; Smithtown, NY; (Y); School Musical; Stage Crew; Nwsp Stf; Var Trk; High Hon Roll; NHS; Ntl Merit Ltr; Spanish NHS; ST Fnlst Miss Coed Pagnt 84; Natl Wnr Spn Trvl Scholar 85; Med Explrs 84-85; Biol.

RICE, TODD; Sherburne-Earlville Central HS; Sherburne, NY; (S); 2/138; Cmnty Wkr; Ski Clb; High Hon Roll; NHS; Engrng.

RICE, TRISHA B; Scotia-Glenville HS; Scotia, NY; (Y); 29/255; Computer Clb; French Clb; Acpl Chr; Yrbk Ed-Chief; Rep Stu Cncl; Var Tennis; Var Trk; Stat Vllybl; Hon Roll; NHS; U NH; Math Educ.

RICH, JO ANN; Chittenango HS; Chittenango, NY; (Y); 97/197; French Clb; Pres Girl Scts; Band; Mrchg Band; Central City Bus Inst; Ofc Svcs.

RICH, KAREN M; Walt Whitman HS; Huntington, NY; (Y); 12/625; Church Yth Grp; Key Clb; Concert Band; Mrchg Band; Yrbk Stf; JV Gym; French Hon Soc; High Hon Roll; NHS; Sports Nite Chrldr; Messiah Coll; Pre-Vet Med.

RICH, KERRY; Frontier Central HS; Hamburg, NY; (S); 10/500; Spanish Clb; Mrchg Band; Trs Soph Cls; Off Stu Cncl; Var Bsktbl; Var Capt Socr; Var Swmmng; Var Vllybl; High Hon Roll; NHS; Dirctrs Awd Band; Cortland SUNY; Phy Ed.

RICH, KIAWANA; St Peters Girls HS; Staten Isl, NY; (Y); Chorus; Lit Mag; NHS; Bio.

RICH, KRISTINA; Alexander Central HS; E Bethany, NY; (S); 10/88; Sec Frsh Cls; Rep Soph Cls; Coach Actv; Var Capt Socr; Var Trk; Hon Roll; Jr NHS; NHS; All-Star Track; MIP Winter Track.

RICH, LISA; Sperry HS; Henrietta, NY; (Y); 15/307; GAA; Chorus; Rep Frsh Cls; Rep Soph Cls; Rep Jr Cls; Rep Sr Cls; Rep Stu Cncl; JV Bsktbl; Var Socr; Var Sftbl; U S Army Res Schlr/Ath Awd 85; Ldrshp Awd 83; All County, 1st Tm Socr 83-85; MCC; Engrng Sci.

RICHAEL, CRAIG; Parishville Hopkinton Central HS; Hopkinton, NY; (Y); 1/40; Church Yth Grp; 4-H; Quiz Bowl; JV Var Bsbl; 4-H Awd; High Hon Roll; NHS; Val; VP Frsh Cls; Tchrs Assoc Schlrshp 85; Outstndng Stu 82-85; Cornell U; Plnt Sci.

RICHARD, DANY; Rice HS; New York, NY; (S); 2/96; NHS.

RICHARD, JODI A; Holland Patent C S; Remsen, NY; (Y); 49/299; Art Clb; Church Yth Grp; Cmnty Wkr; FCA; Orch; Stage Crew; Nwsp Ed-Chief; Yrbk Stf; Var Vllybl; Hon Roll; NY ST Rgnts Schlrshp 85; Edward Christiana Art Schlrshp 85; Amer Lgn God Ctzn Awd 85; Mowhawk Vly CC; Advtsng Dsgn.

RICHARDS, CHERYL; Sachem HS; Holtsville, NY; (Y); 82/1428; Civic Clb; Service Clb; Yrbk Stf; Outstndng Negro Studnt 84.

RICHARDS JR, JAMES F A; Archbishop Molloy HS; E Elmhurst, NY; (Y); 77/409; Art Clb; Dance Clb; NHS; NY ST Regnts Schlrshp; Comm Art.

RICHARDS, KARIN; Watkins Glen HS; Reading Center, NY; (S); 6/146; Letterman Clb; Math Clb; Drm & Bgl; Yrbk Stf; Rep Stu Cncl; Capt L Swmmng; L Var Trk; French Hon Soc; Hon Roll; Girl Scts; Rotary Intl Exchg Stu Finland 83-84; Med.

RICHARDS, KIRA; Hilton Central HS; Hilton, NY; (Y); 82/310; Boy Scts; Camp Fr Inc; Drama Clb; JA; Model UN; Chorus; Color Guard; School Musical; School Play; Stage Crew; Acctng.

RICHARDS, MARK; Jamaica HS; Jamaica, NY; (Y); Chorus; School Musical; Nwsp Stf; Hon Roll; Roll Of Merit 83; Music.

RICHARDS, MARTU J; St Raymond Acad; Bronx, NY; (Y); 20/68; Church Yth Grp; Computer Clb; GAA; Spanish Clb; Church Choir; Pres Frsh Cls; Pres Soph Cls; Var Bsktbl; Var Vllybl; Prfct Atten Awd; Comp Engrng.

RICHARDS, TODD; Salmon River Central HS; Ft Covington, NY; (Y); Church Yth Grp; French Clb; Clarkson; Acctg.

RICHARDS, WILLIAM M; New Hartford SR HS; New Hartford, NY; (Y); 46/264; Jr NHS; Mohawk Valley CC; Math.

RICHARDSON, AMY J; The Mary Louis Acad; Forest Hills, NY; (Y); 7/283; GAA; Girl Scts; Teachers Aide; Sec Soph Cls; Sec Jr Cls; JV Var Bsktbl; Var Sftbl; Cit Awd; High Hon Roll; Hon Roll; Rgnts Schlrshp 85; Sftbll Awd 82; Schlstc Excel Schlrshp 85; St Johns U; Bus.

RICHARDSON, CARLA; Springfields Gardens HS; Queens, NY; (Y); Dance Clb; GAA; Office Aide; Teachers Aide; School Play; Bsktbl; Gym; Sftbl; Capt Vllybl; Cit Awd; Readng Awd 84; Yale U; Pre.

RICHARDSON, CLINTON; Central Islip HS; Central Islip, NY; (Y); 35/450; Chess Clb; Variety Show; Hon Roll; Chem.

RICHARDSON, DEBBIE A; Curtis HS; Staten Island, NY; (Y); 18/328; Drama Clb; Key Clb; ROTC; Teachers Aide; Y-Teens; NHS; Rgnts & ROTC Schlrshp 84; Psych.

RICHARDSON, DELLA P; Brentwood-Ross HS; Brentwood, NY; (Y); 67/625; French Clb; Orch; School Musical; Rep Jr Cls; Rep Sr Cls; Rep Stu Cncl; NHS; FBLA; School Play; Score Keeper; Natl Schl Orch Awd 85; Outstndg Stu Orch 83; Mst Outstndg Orch 82-85; Syracuse U; Acctg.

RICHARDSON, LORENE; Adlai Ewing Stevenson HS; Bronx, NY; (Y); Office Aide; Teachers Aide; Nwsp Ed-Chief; Nwsp Rptr; Nwsp Stf; Hon Roll; Mst Outstdng Typst 85; Syracuse U; Comm.

RICHARDSON, LORI; Canton HS; Canton, NY; (Y); 13/115; Church Yth Grp; Chorus; Trs Jr Cls; Trs Sr Cls; Socr; Sftbl; Trk; High Hon Roll; Hon Roll; NHS.

RICHARDSON, MIKE; Williamson SR HS; Williamson, NY; (Y); Varsity Clb; Band; Concert Band; Mrchg Band; JV Var Bsbl; JV Var Bsktbl; Im Ftbl; Cortland ST; Phy Ed.

RICHARDSON, MONICA; Portville Central HS; Westons Mills, NY; (Y); 19/120; Intnl Clb; Chorus; Yrbk Stf; High Hon Roll; Hon Roll; Prfct Atten Awd; Unifd Stu Assistnc Schlrshp 85; NY ST Scientfc Regnts Diplma 85; Jamestwn CC; Crimnlgy.

RICHARDSON, RANDALL; Hempstead HS; Hempstead, NY; (S); Art Clb; Model UN; Band; Concert Band; Jazz Band; Mrchg Band; Orch; Nwsp Rptr; Trk; Regence Schlrshp 85; Psychlgy.

RICHARDSON, REGINA; Albany HS; Albany, NY; (Y); Boys Clb Am; Pres Church Yth Grp; Pres Church Choir; Rep Frsh Cls; Rep Soph Cls; Var Bsktbl; JV Sftbl; Var Trk; Hon Roll; Prfct Atten Awd; Comp Sci.

RICHARDSON, RINA; St Johns Prep; Richmond Hl, NY; (Y); Girl Scts; Chorus; Variety Show; JV Sftbl; JV Vllybl; High Hon Roll; NHS; Phy Thrpst.

RICHARDSON, ROBERT; Gouverneur Central HS; Gouverneur, NY; (Y); Varsity Clb; Rep Stu Cncl; Var JV Bsktbl; Var Golf; Var JV Socr; NHS; Cornell U; Chmcl Engrng.

RICHARDSON, THOMAS; Aquinas Inst; Rochester, NY; (Y); 43/167; Trk; Hon Roll; Rnr-Up NY ST HS Pwrlftng Chmpnshps 84; Bio Awd 83; Crmnl Justc.

RICHARDSON, YVETTE; Eli Whitney Voc HS; Brooklyn, NY; (S); Church Yth Grp; Office Aide; Pres Soph Cls; Hon Roll; NHS; Electrncs Engr.

RICHER, DENNIS; Liverpool HS; Liverpool, NY; (S); 53/792; Boy Scts; Church Yth Grp; Red Cross Aide; ROTC; Hon Roll; Jr NHS; NHS; Ntl Merit Ltr; AF ROTC Schlrshp 84; Magna Cum Laude Ntl Ltn Exam 84; MI ST U; Elec Engrng.

RICHER, HAROLD J; Elmira Free Acad; Elmira, NY; (Y); 2/249; Bsbl; Hon Roll; St Schlr; NY ST Regents Schlrshp 85; Muskingum Coll Almni Schlrshp; Muskingum Coll; Accntnt.

RICHEY, GORDON; Irondequoit HS; Rochester, NY; (Y); Boy Scts; Church Yth Grp; Drama Clb; Radio Clb; Chorus; Orch; School Musical; School Play; Stage Crew; Tennis.

RICHMAN, ANDREW D; Riverdale Country Schl; New York, NY; (Y); Chess Clb; French Clb; Math Tm; Political Wkr; Acpl Chr; Nwsp Ed-Chief; Nwsp Phtg; Yrbk Phtg; Socr; High Hon Roll.

RICHMAN, LEE; Smithtown High School East; Saint James, NY; (Y); Pres Camera Clb; Chess Clb; Ski Clb; Teachers Aide; Nwsp Phtg; Yrbk Phtg; Lit Mag; Stu Cncl; Im Sftbl; Exprmnt Intl Livng Exc Stu Japan 85.

RICHMAN, SCOTT A; Jericho JR SR HS; Jericho, NY; (Y); 8/230; FBLA; Pres Model UN; Science Clb; Trs Temple Yth Grp; Ed Nwsp Stf; High Hon Roll; Trs NHS; Ntl Merit SF; Spanish NHS; Brown U Bk Awd In Engl 84; Bus.

RICHMOND, EMILY; Brighton HS; Rochester, NY; (Y); 1/315; Pres Trs Church Yth Grp; Trs French Clb; Varsity Clb; Trs Soph Cls; Var Crs Cntry; JV Var Trk; Bio.

RICHMOND, MARIETTA; Notre Dame Acad; Staten Island, NY; (Y); Sec Church Yth Grp; Drama Clb; French Clb; Library Aide; Science Clb; Teachers Aide; School Musical; School Play; Stage Crew; Bsktbl; Med.

RICHMOND, MEAGHAN; Jamestown HS; Jamestown, NY; (Y); Acpl Chr; Band; Mrchg Band; Rep Frsh Cls; Rep Soph Cls; Rep Jr Cls; Rep Stu Cncl; Hon Roll; Jr NHS; NHS; Culinary.

RICHTER, BRENDA; Tioga Central HS; Owego, NY; (S); 12/96; Church Yth Grp; Cmnty Wkr; Variety Show; Sec Frsh Cls; Sec Soph Cls; Rep Jr Cls; Bsktbl; Vllybl; High Hon Roll; NHS; Bus.

RICHTER, PAMELA K; Benjamin N Cardoza HS; Bayside, NY; (Y); 96/476; VP JA; Pres Temple Yth Grp; Nwsp Rptr; Yrbk Phtg; Yrbk Rptr; Hon Roll; St Schlr; NYS Regnts Schlrshp 85; Hofstra U Acad Schlrshp 85; UN Intl Yth Cmmtt 83-84; Hofstra U; Accntng.

RICHTHAMMER, AMY; Hamburg SR HS; Hamburg, NY; (Y); German Clb; Chorus; NHS; German Clb Schlrshp 85; SUNY; Mech Engrng.

RICIGLIANO, TOM; Gr Island SR HS; Gr Island, NY; (Y); Band; Concert Band; Jazz Band; Mrchg Band; Pep Band; School Musical; Variety Show; Hon Roll; JP Sousa Awd; Outstndg Jazz Musician 85; Fredonia ST; Prof Musician.

RICKARD, DEBRA M; Horseheads HS; Horseheads, NY; (Y); French Clb; FNA; Red Cross Aide; Teachers Aide; Chorus; Mgr Socr; Swmmng; Wrk Wth Hndcppd.

RICKARD, PATRICIA M; North Salem HS; Brewster, NY; (Y); 11/82; Church Yth Grp; Variety Show; VP Stu Cncl; JV Capt Cheerleading; Var Fld Hcky; Var Capt Socr; Var Trk; NHS; NY ST Regents Schlrshp 85; Holy Cross; Economics.

RICKEN, JILL; Onteora HS; Woodstock, NY; (S); Ski Clb; Chorus; Thesps; JV Var Cheerleading; Var Tennis; Hon Roll; NHS; Mid-Hudson Athltc Leag Tennis Chmpn 84; Ulster Cnty JR Tennis Chmpn 83; Pre-Law.

RICKENBACH, NANCY; Greene Central HS; Chenango Forks, NY; (Y); 2/95; Church Yth Grp; Spanish Clb; Chorus; Concert Band; Mrchg Band; School Musical; Yrbk Ed-Chief; NHS; Earth Sci Fclty Key Awd; Med Lab Tech.

RICKETTS, TODD H; Fillmore Central Schl; Hume, NY; (Y); 12/46; Varsity Clb; Var Bsbl; Var Bsktbl; Var Socr; High Hon Roll; Hon Roll; NY ST Regents Schlrshp 85; Geneseo; Engineering.

RICKS, FELISA YVETTE; South Side HS; Rockville Ctr, NY; (Y); Drama Clb; Teachers Aide; Chorus; Variety Show; Trk; Hon Roll; Church Yth Grp; Girl Scts; JA; Molloy Coll; Ed.

RICO, DANIEL; Central Islip HS; Central Islip, NY; (Y); Crs Cntry; Socr; Wt Lftg; Spanish NHS; Spn Awd 82; NY U; Corp Banking Exec.

RICO, RUDOLPH; St Joseph Collegiate Inst; Williamsville, NY; (Y); 2/190; Church Yth Grp; Im Bowling; JV Ftbl; Capt Sftbl; High Hon Roll; Engrng.

RICO, SERGIO A; Bronx Science HS; Forest Hills, NY; (Y); Computer Clb; Math Tm; Rep Soph Cls; Rep Jr Cls; Sci Fair Awd 82; Hofstra U; Comp Sci.

RICOTTA, PATRICK; Salamanca Central HS; Salamanca, NY; (S); 29/125; DECA; FBLA; Math Clb; Science Clb; Spanish Clb; Varsity Clb; Var Golf; Hon Roll; 2nd Pl Dist Educ Rgnl Sales Demnstrtn 84; Rifle Clb 82; Pre-Med.

RIDDELL, TAMMI; Charlotte Valley HS; Davenport Center, NY; (S); 9/35; Band; Chorus; Concert Band; Jazz Band; Sec Jr Cls; JV Var Cheerleading; High Hon Roll; NHS; Exc In Music 85; Austin Perry; Music.

RIDDLE, CARRIE E; Salamanca Central HS; Little Valley, NY; (Y); Debate Tm; Spanish Clb; Varsity Clb; JV Var Bsktbl; Var Crs Cntry; Var Sftbl; JV Var Vllybl; Cit Awd; Spanish NHS; Chorus; Cnty Dairy Prncss 85; Mst Imprv Plyr Sftbl, Vlybl 83; Sci.

RIDER, ANN; Kenmore East SR HS; Kenmore, NY; (Y); German Clb; GAA; Intnl Clb; Im Bsktbl; JV Socr; Hon Roll; Bus Admin.

RIDER, SAMANTHA; Highland HS; Highland, NY; (Y); Chrmn Church Yth Grp; Sec French Clb; Girl Scts; Ed Yrbk Phtg; Yrbk Stf; JV Sftbl; French Hon Soc; High Hon Roll; Hon Roll; NHS; Hghst Acad Achvt Fr III 85; Intrprtr.

RIDER, SANDY; Fairport HS; Fairport, NY; (Y); Model UN; Science Clb; Ski Clb; Varsity Clb; JV Var Fld Hcky; Trk; Biochem.

RIDGE, MELANIE E; Manlius Pebble Hill HS; Liverpool, NY; (Y); Model UN; Stage Crew; Vllybl; Hon Roll; NHS; Hnr Roll 83-85; Pre-Law.

RIDLEY, KIRSTEN; Haverling Central Schl; Bath, NY; (S); Pres French Clb; Drm Mjr(t); Yrbk Stf; Stu Cncl; Capt Cheerleading; Twrlr; High Hon Roll; NHS; Fshn Merch.

RIDLEY, LAURA; La Salle SR HS; Niagara Falls, NY; (Y); Church Yth Grp; Chorus; Hon Roll; Exec Secy.

RIEBEL, SCOTT T; Shenendehowa HS; Ballston Lake, NY; (Y); Boy Scts; Church Choir; Jazz Band; School Play; Im JV Ftbl; NHS; Prfct Atten Awd; Band; Concert Band; Orch; Prz Wnr Amer Assn Tchrs Of German 84-85; Eagle Scout 79-85; Good Ctznshp Ctn From Amer Lgn 83; Pre-Law.

RIEDEL, MICHAEL F; Geneseo Central HS; Geneseo, NY; (Y); 1/73; Drama Clb; Political Wkr; School Play; Nwsp Bus Mgr; VP Stu Cncl; Tennis; DAR Awd; French Hon Soc; Pres NHS; Val; John Marshall Schlrshp 85; Johns Hopkins U; Pre-Law.

RIEDERER, MICHELE; Hamburg SR HS; Hamburg, NY; (Y); Spanish Clb; Orch; Rep Stu Cncl; Var Bsktbl; Var Fld Hcky; Var Capt Sftbl; Var Vllybl; Hon Roll; Amos J Leigh Hunt Minkel Stu Awd 85; Freida W Waugh Mem Schlrshp 85; Cortland Coll; Elem Educ.

RIEGL, EDWARD; South Side HS; S Hempstead, NY; (Y); 38/284; Boy Scts; Exploring; Key Clb; Model UN; Concert Band; Jazz Band; Cit Awd; High Hon Roll; NHS; VFW Awd; Eagle Sct Awd 82; Vigil Hnr Order Of Arrow 84; Louis Armstrong Jazz Awd 85; Franklin Marshall; Bus Mgmt.

RIEHL, DIANE SUSAN; Central Islip HS; Central Islip, NY; (Y); Civic Clb; Ski Clb; Concert Band; Mrchg Band; Var Coach Actv; Var Diving; Var Mgr(s); Pom Pon; Var Swmmng; Comp Sci.

RIEHL, JOHN D; Wantagh SR HS; Wantagh, NY; (Y); Computer Clb; Mathletes; Nwsp Sprt Ed; JV Bsbl; JV Bsktbl; JV Socr; JV Wrstlng; Hon Roll; Engrng.

RIESE, CARYN; John Adams HS; Howard Bch, NY; (Y); Service Clb; Yrbk Stf; Acctng.

RIFENBURGH, CHRISTINE; Lindenhurst HS; Lindenhurst, NY; (Y); 23/600; Church Yth Grp; Chorus; Variety Show; Nwsp Rptr; Nwsp Stf; Hon Roll; Jr NHS; NHS; Pres Schlr; Adelphi Trustee Scholar 85; Knights Pythias Awd 85; Lindy Trib Awd 85; Adelphi U; Elem Ed.

RIFENBURGH, CONNIE; Beacon HS; Beacon, NY; (S); #16 In Class; Varsity Clb; Variety Show; Nwsp Rptr; Var Crs Cntry; Var L Trk; Jr NHS; Most Artstc Soph 84; Art.

RIFFKIN, JODI B; New Rochelle HS; Scarsdale, NY; (Y); 49/650; Model UN; Var Diving; Var Gym; French Hon Soc; High Hon Roll; NHS; St Schlr; Gym Achvt Awd 84; Regnts Schlrshp 85; Cornell U; Nutrtnl Sci.

RIFFLARD, TAMMY; Washingtonville HS; Washingtonville, NY; (Y); Church Yth Grp; Girl Scts; Rep Stu Cncl; Var Cheerleading; Var Vllybl; Stat Wrstlng; Hon Roll; Mst Improved Fall Chrldr 84; Elem Educ.

RIGANOTTI, DOMINIC R; Batavia SR HS; Batavia, NY; (Y); 38/243; Stu Cncl; Ski Clb; Nwsp Stf; Yrbk Stf; Golf; Hon Roll; NYS Regnts Schlrshp 85; Ntl Ldrshp, Svc Awds 85; Achvt Awd 84; Rochester Inst Tech; Biotech.

RIGAUD, SUKAINA; Bishop Kearney HS; Brooklyn, NY; (Y); Pres Camera Clb; Hosp Aide; Key Clb; Ski Clb; Pres Band; Ed Nwsp Phtg; Yrbk Phtg; Off Frsh Cls; Off Soph Cls; Gold Seal Awd 85; NY U; Med.

RIGGERT, KIMBERLY A; Scotia-Glenville HS; Scotia, NY; (Y); 12/244; Church Yth Grp; Red Cross Aide; Chorus; Jazz Band; Yrbk Stf; Var L Bsktbl; L Sftbl; NHS; Pres Schlr; Science Clb; Denise Lyn Simmons Awd 85; Regents Scholar 85; Sci Dept Awd 85; Schenectady Gazette Awd 85; U WI; Cmmnctns.

RIGGI, JOSEPH A; Byron Bergen Central Schl; Byron, NY; (Y); Sec Trs AFS; Art Clb; Boy Scts; 4-H; Yrbk Phtg; Swmmng; Exch Stu Denmark 84; Genesee CC; Model Making.

RIGGS, ADRIENNE; Mount Vernon HS; Mount Vernon, NY; (Y); 71/586; FHA; Yrbk Stf; Var Crs Cntry; Var Trk; Hon Roll; Jr NHS; Prfct Atten Awd; Fordham U; Vet.

RIGGS, GORDON; Spackenkill HS; Poughkeepsie, NY; (Y); School Play; Variety Show; Var Crs Cntry; Var Trk; Mst Imprvd Athlt Trk 85; Comp Sci.

RIGNEY, MARY K; Clarkstown North HS; New City, NY; (Y); Church Yth Grp; Math Tm; Scholastic Bowl; Band; Mrchg Band; Symp Band; Gym; Jr NHS; NHS.

RIKER, BECKY A; Westhampton Beach HS; Westhampton, NY; (Y); Drill Tm; Nrsng.

RILES, DARYL; Riverside HS; Buffalo, NY; (S); Bsktbl; Trk; Aud/Vis; FCA; JA; Library Aide; Stage Crew; Prfct Atten Awd; Radio Brdcstng.

RILEY, AMY; Churchville-Chili HS; Churchville, NY; (Y); Church Yth Grp; Ski Clb; Spanish Clb; JV Var Cheerleading; Engrng.

RILEY, CATHLEEN; Cicero-North Syracuse HS; N Syracuse, NY; (S); 105/622; Spanish Clb; Band; Concert Band; Mrchg Band; Powder Puff Ftbl; Nrsg.

RILEY, DORA; Charlotte JR-SR HS; Rochester, NY; (S); 5/93; Drama Clb; French Clb; Variety Show; Yrbk Sprt Ed; Ed Yrbk Stf; Rep Frsh Cls; Pres Stu Cncl; Var L Cheerleading; Sftbl; High Hon Roll; Most Enthusiastic Chrldr 82-83; Outstndng Preformance Art,Drama Engl & Soc Stud 83-84; Outstndg Freshm; NC ST U; Business Management.

RILEY, ELIZABETH; Bishop Ludden HS; Syracuse, NY; (Y); Art Clb; Rep Jr Cls; Socr; Sftbl; Art.

RILEY, HEATHER; Auburn HS; Auburn, NY; (Y); Math Clb; Acpl Chr; Band; Chorus; Concert Band; Jazz Band; Mrchg Band; Orch; School Musical; Symp Band; Music.

RILEY, JANET; Ward Melville HS; Stony Brook, NY; (Y); Trs Boy Scts; French Clb; Service Clb; Yrbk Rptr; Yrbk Stf; Stu Cncl; High Hon Roll; Jr NHS; NHS; Indctn Spkr For Schlrshp JR Natl Hnr Soc 83; Chem Engrng.

RILEY, KATHLEEN A; Livonia HS; Lakeville, NY; (Y); 1/130; Chorus; School Musical; Yrbk Ed-Chief; Pres Sr Cls; Capt Socr; Capt Trk; Cit Awd; DAR Awd; NHS; Val; Soccer Perfmnc Schlrshp 85; Acad Trustees Schlrshp 85; US Army MVP Soccer Awd 85; Houghton Coll; Elem Ed.

RILEY, PATRICIA; Hicksville HS; Hicksvl, NY; (Y); Hosp Aide; Color Guard; Mrchg Band; Var L Pom Pon; Var L Sftbl; JV Vllybl; High Hon Roll; Hon Roll; Jr NHS; NHS; Spnsh Awd 85; HHS Mrchng Comets Coquts Awd 85; Molly Coll; Nrs.

RILEY, SUNDAE; Corning-Painted Post West HS; Pine City, NY; (Y); Drm Mjr(t); Mrchg Band; Im Bowling; Im Twrlr; High Hon Roll; Hon Roll; Teachers Aide; Band; Concert Band; Schl Ltr Band & Badg & Cert 83-85; Corning CC; Cmnl Justc.

RINALDI, JOHN; Molloy HS; Bellerose, NY; (Y); 112/409; Computer Clb; Stu Cncl; Ftbl; Schltc Hnrs 83-84 & 84-85; Civil Engrng.

RINALDI, JOHN; Saint John The Baptist HS; Deer Park, NY; (Y); Band; Concert Band; Mrchg Band; Var Bowling; Var Socr; Law.

RINALDO, FRANK C; Oneida SR HS; Oneida, NY; (Y); 25/220; Am Leg Boys St; Letterman Clb; Varsity Clb; Symp Band; Yrbk Stf; Pres Soph Cls; Ftbl; Trk; Hon Roll; Church Yth Grp; Myrs Yth Advsry Cncl; Pre-Med.

RING, JAMES; Sayville HS; Sayville, NY; (Y); 68/358; Service Clb; Varsity Clb; Concert Band; Jazz Band; Orch; Yrbk Sprt Ed; Trs Stu Cncl; Bsbl; Mgr(s); Score Keeper; Swmng 7th In Nation 400 Free Rly 83-84; Suffolk Cty Brststrk Chmpn 83-85; LI Chmpn 84-85 Bsbl All-Str; Bus.

RINGGARD, PETER; Fairport Central HS; Fairport, NY; (Y); Ski Clb; Var L Ftbl; JV Lcrss; Wt Lftg; High Hon Roll; Hon Roll; NHS; NYS Regnts Schlrshp 85; Pres Acadmc Fit Awd 85; Engl.

RINGO, TIMOTHY; Hugh C Williams HS; Canton, NY; (Y); JA; Lit Mag; Var Golf; High Hon Roll; Hon Roll; Acadmc Ltr Awd 83-85; Cornell U; Chem.

RINK, CHERYL; Homell SR HS; Hornell, NY; (S); 1/198; JCL; Band; Rep Stu Cncl; Var L Socr; High Hon Roll; Pres NHS; Val; Latin Clb; Math Clb; Pep Clb; Harvard Bk Awd 84; Magna Cum Laude Ntl Ltn Exm 84.

RINK, RUSSELL; Kenmore West SR HS; Buffalo, NY; (Y); 137/445; JA; Spanish Clb; Varsity Clb; Rep Sr Cls; Crs Cntry; Socr; Trk; Hon Roll; Schl Rcrd 800 M Run 85; 5th Empire ST Games 85; Fredonia ST U; Bio-Med Rsrch.

RINKER, RONALD W; Friendship Central HS; Friendship, NY; (Y); 6/28; Am Leg Boys St; Exploring; School Play; Trs Jr Cls; Pres Stu Cncl; Bsktbl; Socr; High Hon Roll; Hon Roll; NHS; USAF; Mechnc.

RINONOS, MARLO; Clarkstown South HS; W Nyack, NY; (Y); Dance Clb; Hosp Aide; Trs Intnl Clb; Chorus; Church Choir; Variety Show; Nwsp Stf; Yrbk Stf; Powder Puff Ftbl; Nrsng.

RIOBO, CARLOS; Saint Francis Prep; Fresh Meadows, NY; (S); 28/700; Trs Science Clb; Band; Concert Band; Mrchg Band; Pep Band; JV Crs Cntry; Var Trk; Vllybl; High Hon Roll; NHS; Prncpls Lst Awd 84-85; Acad All-Amer Awd 85; MA Inst Of Tech; Gntc Engrng.

RIORDAN, DANIELLE H; Amherst Central HS; Amherst, NY; (Y); 52/310; Spanish Clb; Teachers Aide; Yrbk Ed-Chief; Yrbk Phtg; Yrbk Stf; Var Sftbl; High Hon Roll; Hon Roll; Sec Jr NHS; NHS; Rgnts Schlrshp 85; Photogphy Hon Mntn 85; U Of Dayton.

RIORDAN, DIANA; Mcgraw Central HS; Marathon, NY; (Y); 3/40; French Clb; Varsity Clb; Band; Chorus; Color Guard; Jazz Band; Mrchg Band; Swing Chorus; L Socr; NHS; NYSMA Solo Comp 6-A In Vocals 84; Jazz 1st Trumpet All-Star Awd 85; JR Clss Prom Ct 85.

RIORDAN, JEWEL; Mount Mercy Acad; Buffalo, NY; (Y); Am Leg Aux Girls St; French Clb; Stage Crew; Pres Jr Cls; VP Stu Cncl; Var Socr; High Hon Roll; NHS; Quiz Bowl; Im Badmtn; Stu Relts Bd Stu Forum; Peer Mnstry; Cornell; Stocks.

RIORDAN, MICHAEL; Archbishop Molloy HS; Maspeth, NY; (Y); 79/414; Church Yth Grp; Computer Clb; Intnl Clb; JV Crs Cntry; JV Trk; Accntng.

RIOS, EVETTE; John Jay HS; Brooklyn, NY; (Y); Dance Clb; FBLA; Office Aide; Teachers Aide; Prfct Atten Awd; Perfct Attndnc Awd 83; Pace U; Law.

RIOS, GLORIA; St Francis Prep; Astoria, NY; (S); 71/750; Debate Tm; Church Choir; Color Guard; Hon Roll; Optimate Scty 83-84; Law.

RIOS, GREGORY; Lyons HS; Lyons, NY; (Y); 17/96; AFS; French Clb; Chorus; School Musical; Nwsp Stf; Hon Roll; NHS; Regnst Schlrshp 85; Rotry Clb Prz 85; Hnr Pass Awd 82-85; Geneseo SUNY; Bus Mgt Scis.

RIOS, JOSE; John Dewey HS; Brooklyn, NY; (Y); Chess Clb; Teachers Aide; Orch; Nwsp Rptr; Nwsp Stf; Lit Mag; Rep Frsh Cls; Rep Soph Cls; Rep Jr Cls; Hnr 2 Time Acdmc Olympc Team 83-84; Fordham U; Busn Lawyer.

RIOS, WANDA; Eastern District HS; Brooklyn, NY; (Y); 13/408; Church Yth Grp; Chorus; Church Choir; Yrbk Bus Mgr; Ed Yrbk Stf; High Hon Roll; Hon Roll; Prfct Atten Awd; Chancellors Rl Hnr 85; Soc Women Engrs Cert Merit 85; Yrbk Awd; Princpls Awd 85; Baruch Coll; Off Adm.

RIOUX, SHEILA; Cicero-North Syracuse HS; Mattydale, NY; (S); 2/622; German Clb; Math Tm; Ski Clb; Drill Tm; Mrchg Band; Sec Stu Cncl; Stat Score Keeper; High Hon Roll; Hon Roll; NHS; Bio.

RIOZZI, JEFFREY; Saugerties HS; Saugerties, NY; (Y); Varsity Clb; Rep Frsh Cls; Rep Soph Cls; Rep Jr Cls; Rep Sr Cls; Var Bowling; Var Crs Cntry; Hon Roll; Old Babe Ruth Bsbl MVP Awd 84; Siena; Bus.

RIPIC, MELISSA M; Cortland SR HS; Cortland, NY; (Y); 35/239; Drama Clb; GAA; Letterman Clb; Ski Clb; Varsity Clb; School Musical; Yrbk Stf; Trs Soph Cls; Off Jr Cls; Rep Stu Cncl; Regnts Schlrshp; Oneonta; Pre-Law.

RIPLEY, DAVID; Horseheads HS; Horseheads, NY; (Y); Boy Scts; VP JA; Model UN; Cit Awd; God Cntry Awd; Hon Roll; Ntl Merit Ltr; Achvt Exec Awd 85; Corning CC; Law.

RIPLEY, MICHAEL; Walton JR SR HS; Walton, NY; (Y); Church Yth Grp; Rep Stu Cncl; Var Bsbl; Var Bsktbl; Var Ftbl; Hon Roll; SUNY Cortland; Elec.

RIPPERGER, KIM; Coxsackie-Athens Central HS; Athens, NY; (Y); Camera Clb; Red Cross Aide; VP Spanish Clb; Band; Yrbk Phtg; Yrbk Stf; Rep Jr Cls; Rep Stu Cncl; Co-Capt Cheerleading; Var Sftbl; Bus.

RISEBROW, JOHN; Harborfields HS, Huntington, NY; (Y); Intnl Clb; Office Aide; Ski Clb; High Hon Roll; Rep Soph Cls; Rep Stu Cncl; Im Badmtn; Im Bsktbl; JV Lcrss; Var Socr.

RISINIT, MICHAEL; Archbishop Stepinac HS; Rye, NY; (Y); 53/201; Boy Scts; Cmnty Wkr; Bio.

RISOLO, JOHN; Bishop Kearney HS; Rochester, NY; (Y); JA; Var Capt Ftbl; Im Sftbl; Var L Wrstlng; High Hon Roll; Ntl Merit Ltr; Schl Scholar 83; Med.

RISPOLI, FRANK; Niskayuna HS; Scotia, NY; (Y); French Clb; Key Clb; Stage Crew; JV Capt Bsbl; JV Var Ftbl; Var Mgr(s); Holy Cross JR; Bus.

RITCHIE, HEATHER; Plattsburgh HS; Plattsburgh, NY; (Y); Varsity Clb; VP Frsh Cls; VP Soph Cls; VP Jr Cls; VP Sr Cls; Crs Cntry; Vllybl; NHS; Church Yth Grp; Cmnty Wkr; Natl Piano Plyg Auditns USA Regnl Comp 83 & 84; JR Cls Prom Qn 85; Fstvl Lfe Gld Mdlst Chrl Comp 83; Int Des.

RITCHIE, JIM; F D Roosevelt HS; Pleasant Valley, NY; (Y); Boy Scts; Ski Clb; Band; Mrchg Band; Symp Band; Var Capt Socr; Prfct Atten Awd; Stotesbry Cup Regatta 84; Natls Boy Jr Crw 85; Comp Sci.

RITTER, DANAH; Spackenkill HS; Poughkeepsie, NY; (Y); #31 In Class; Drama Clb; Leo Clb; Temple Yth Grp; Thesps; Band; Concert Band; Pep Band; School Musical; School Play; Stage Crew.

RITTER, JENNIFER; Albertus Magnus HS; Tuxedo Park, NY; (Y); Drama Clb; Library Aide; Math Tm; Spanish Clb; Stage Crew; Yrbk Stf; Vllybl; Hon Roll; Mu Alp Tht; NHS; Math.

RITTER, JENNIFER L; Jericho HS; Jericho, NY; (Y); 16/230; Drama Clb; Political Wkr; Thesps; Band; Chorus; School Musical; School Play; NHS; All Cnty Chrs 85; Cmmndtn Actng One Act Play Cntst 83.

RITTER, KRISTINE; Mynderse Acad; Seneca Falls, NY; (Y); Bsktbl; Sftbl; Trk; Bus.

RITTO, PATRICK M; L C Obourn HS; East Rochester, NY; (Y); 3/108; Computer Clb; Drama Clb; French Clb; Math Tm; Chorus; School Play; Variety Show; High Hon Roll; NHS; Ntl Merit Ltr; Pres Acdmc Ftns Awd 85; NY ST Rgnts Schlrshp 85; MA Inst Of Tech; Comp Sci.

RITZMANN, CHERI A; Franklin Acad; N Bangor, NY; (Y); 17/250; French Clb; Pep Clb; Varsity Clb; Chorus; School Play; Swing Chorus; Rep Stu Cncl; Cheerleading; Elks Awd; NHS; Presntl Schlrshp At Tampa U 85-89; Tampa U FL; Marine Sci.

RIVALDO, CHRISTINA; Bishop Kearney HS; Rochester, NY; (S); 1/169; Church Yth Grp; Debate Tm; Model UN; NFL; Varsity Clb; Rep Jr Cls; Crs Cntry; Score Keeper; Trk; High Hon Roll; Harvard Prize Bk Awd 84; Yr Bk Layout Edtr 84; Natl Merit Schlr 84; Med.

RIVELLINI, TOM P; Gouverneur Central HS; Gouverneur, NY; (Y); Pres French Clb; Stage Crew; JV Var Socr; JV Var Trk; French Hon Soc; Hon Roll; NHS; Regents Schlrshp 85; Syracuse U; Mech.

RIVENBURGH, DOUGLAS; Greenwich Central HS; Schaghticoke, NY; (Y); 6/80; Computer Clb; Var L Golf; NHS; Prsdntl, Rgnts Schlrshps 85; Hartwick; Math.

RIVERA, AILEEN; Norman Thoams HS; New York, NY; (S); 41/671; Band; Bsktbl; Capt Sftbl; Capt Vllybl; Hon Roll; NHS; NYC Psal Sel All City Sftbl 83; Outstandng Athlete 83; Cardinal Spellman Yth Awd 82; Pace U; Comp Sci.

RIVERA, ANA L; Clara Barton HS; Brooklyn, NY; (Y); 49/469; Pres Church Yth Grp; Debate Tm; Sec Office Aide; Teachers Aide; Church Choir; Hon Roll; Prfct Atten Awd; OR Nrs.

RIVERA, ANNLYSETTE; Midwood HS; Brooklyn, NY; (Y); Rep Stu Cncl; Var Swmmng; Phys Educ.

RIVERA, CARLOS; Uniondale HS; Uniondale, NY; (Y); 27/450; Church Yth Grp; Mathletes; Math Clb; Orch; School Musical; Yrbk Ed-Chief; Trs Stu Cncl; High Hon Roll; Jr NHS; NHS; Cmnty Svc & Acadmc Excllnc Citatn 84-85; Amer Legn Aux Amercnsm Awd 81-82; City U NY Brklyn Coll; Bio.

RIVERA, CHERIE; Domincian Commerical HS; Richmond Hill, NY; (Y); 19/273; Cmnty Wkr; School Musical; Stu Cncl; Gym; Prncpls Lst 85; Siena Clb 85; Congrssnl Medl Merit 85; St Johns U; Acctg.

RIVERA, DEBBIE; Christopher Columbus HS; New York, NY; (S); Aud/Vis; Computer Clb; Dance Clb; Drama Clb; Library Aide; Office Aide; PAVAS; Spanish Clb; Teachers Aide; Chorus; Schl Of Media Arts; Thrtr.

RIVERA, DONNA M; Naples American HS; FPO, NY; (Y); Pres Church Yth Grp; Chorus; School Musical; School Play; Lit Mag; High Hon Roll; NHS; Ntl Merit SF; Spanish NHS; Val; Optimist Speech Cont 82; Cameron U Scholastic Competition 84; Top 10% Engl 84; Grinell U; Engrng.

RIVERA, EMMA; Bronx High School Of Science; Bronx, NY; (Y); Spanish Clb; Teachers Aide; Chorus; Orch; Yrbk Stf; High Hon Roll; Val; Regents Schlrshp Winner; Semi Finalist In Natl Hispanic Schlr Awds Prog; Barnard; Psychology.

RIVERA, GINA; La Guardia HS Of Music & The Arts; New York, NY; (Y); 117/590; Alvin Ailey Am Dance Ctr Schlrshp 82-84; Opera Hse NY; Hotel Adm.

RIVERA, IDIA; St Catharine Acad; Bronx, NY; (Y); Dance Clb; Stu Cncl; Lang.

RIVERA, ISABEL E; Cathedral HS; Ny, NY; (Y); 13/315; Art Clb; Church Yth Grp; Intnl Clb; Mrchg Band; Nwsp Rptr; Nwsp Stf; Pres Frsh Cls; Pres Soph Cls; Pres Jr Cls; Columbia U; Comm.

RIVERA, JANET; High School Of Fashion Ind; Bronx, NY; (Y); 92/365; Debate Tm; Cit Awd; Hon Roll; NHS; Ntl Merit Schol; Pres Schlr; Spanish NHS; Val; Hunter Coll; Comp Sci.

RIVERA, JESUS; Alfred E Smith HS; New York, NY; (S); 3/226; Library Aide; School Play; Stage Crew; Nwsp Stf; Yrbk Stf; Hon Roll; NHS; Engr.

RIVERA, JOANNA; De Witt Clinton HS; Bronx, NY; (Y); Cmnty Wkr; Hosp Aide; JA; Office Aide; Concert Band; Nwsp Ed-Chief; Nwsp Rptr; Rep Stu Cncl; Pres NHS; Bronx Week Cert For Ctznshp 84; Pre Med.

RIVERA, JOHN; Frontier Central HS; Hamburg, NY; (Y); Drama Clb; Varsity Clb; Band; Concert Band; Jazz Band; School Musical; School Play; Var Ftbl; Mgr(s); Hon Roll.

RIVERA, JOSE A; Alfred E Smith HS; Bronx, NY; (Y); 21/226; Teachers Aide; Yrbk Stf; Rep Stu Cncl; Hon Roll; NHS; Prfct Atten Awd; St Schlr; Bio Regnts 83; Technol Draftng 84; ST Wd Regnts Schlrshp 85; Rensselaer Plytech Inst; Arspc.

RIVERA, KIM; Christopher Columbus HS; Bronx, NY; (Y); 45/792; Dance Clb; Drama Clb; Key Clb; Office Aide; Orch; Nwsp Rptr; Yrbk Rptr; Vllybl; Cit Awd; Hon Roll; RN.

RIVERA, LIZZETTE; Norman Thomas HS; Bronx, NY; (S); 35/671; Hon Roll; Baruch Coll; Mrktng Mgmt.

RIVERA, LUIS; William Howard Taft HS; Bronx, NY; (Y); Camera Clb; CAP; Spanish Clb; Teachers Aide; Cit Awd; High Hon Roll; Hon Roll; Psych.

RIVERA, MANUEL G; Hillcrest HS; Corona, NY; (Y); 14/793; Hosp Aide; Hon Roll; NHS; St Schlr; Math Tm; Teachers Aide; Yrbk Stf; Natl Hispnc Schlr Awds 85; Queens Coll Pres Awd Achvt 82; NY Daily News Super Youth 83; Yale Coll; Law.

RIVERA, MARISAL; Central Islip HS; Central Islip, NY; (Y); Church Yth Grp; Cmnty Wkr; Spanish Clb; Chorus; Flag Corp; Stage Crew; Nwsp Stf; Yrbk Stf; Lit Mag; Sec Frsh Cls; 3rd Acad Awd 3rd Hghst Acad Avg 83; Intl Rel.

RIVERA, MARISEL; Peekskil HS; Peekskill, NY; (S); Church Yth Grp; Yrbk Stf; VP Jr Cls; High Hon Roll; Hon Roll; NHS; Comp.

RIVERA, MARY ANN; Bishop Ford HS; Brooklyn, NY; (Y); Girl Scts; Hon Roll; Pre-Law.

RIVERA, MICHELE; Newburgh Free Acad; Newburgh, NY; (Y); Science Clb; Band; Concert Band; Jazz Band; Mrchg Band; Orch; Symp Band; JV L Vllybl; Hon Roll; Comp.

RIVERA, MICHELLE; Aquinas HS; Bronx, NY; (Y); 17/178; Cmnty Wkr; Science Clb; Yrbk Stf; High Hon Roll; NHS; Spanish NHS; 2nd Sci Fair 85; Psych.

RIVERA, MICHELLE; St Vincent Ferrer HS; New York, NY; (Y); 34/114; Dance Clb; Math Clb; Pep Clb; Swmmng; Math Leag Awd 85.

RIVERA, MIGUEL A; La Salle Acad; Brooklyn, NY; (Y); Boy Scts; Drama Clb; School Play; Nwsp Rptr; Yrbk Stf; VP Church Yth Grp; Capt Bowling; Hon Roll; NHS; Pres Acad Fitnss Awd 85; Manhattan Coll; Engrng.

RIVERA, NOEMI; Murry Bergtraum For Business Careers; Brooklyn, NY; (Y); 40/765; Computer Clb; Church Choir; Pres Frsh Cls; Rep Soph Cls; Rep Jr Cls; Bsbl; High Hon Roll; NHS; Prfct Atten Awd; 100 Pcnt Atten Awd 82-84; Excllnce Comp 85; Comp Pgmmr.

RIVERA, PATRICIA; A Philip Randolph Campus HS; Bx, NY; (Y); 13/165; Office Aide; Political Wkr; Service Clb; Stu Cncl; L Sftbl; Hon Roll; NHS; Prfct Atten Awd; Daily News Prncpls Awd 85; NY Mntrng Prog Awd 84-85; Law.

RIVERA, RAMON; Seward Park HS; New York, NY; (Y); Church Yth Grp; Crs Cntry; Swmmng; Trk; Wt Lftg; Val; Hnr Roll 84; Trck Team & X-Cntry Awd 85; Stoney Brook; Pedtrcn.

RIVERA, THERESA M; Aquinas HS; Bronx, NY; (Y); 7/169; Church Yth Grp; Drama Clb; Chorus; School Musical; School Play; Nwsp Stf; Sec Jr Cls; VP Sr Cls; Sec Stu Cncl; Gov Hon Prg Awd; SR Acadmc Ellclnc 82-85; Sci Awd 82-84; Ldrshp Wrkshp Iona 82-84; Ione Coll; Med Tech.

RIVERA, YOLANDA; Ichabod Crane HS; Stuyvesant, NY; (Y); 36/175; Drama Clb; Chorus; Color Guard; Nwsp Stf; Lit Mag; High Hon Roll; Hon Roll; NY ST Music Assn Chorus 82-83; NY ST Solo Eval 82-83; NY ST Solo Eval 83-84; Astrnmy.

RIVERA, YVETTE; Mabel Dean Bacon VHS; New York, NY; (S); 13/299; Office Aide; Teachers Aide; Chorus; High Hon Roll; Hon Roll; NHS; Comp Pgmmng.

RIVIECCIO, LUCIA; Commack High School North; Commack, NY; (Y); 36/440; School Musical; School Play; Lit Mag; Rep Frsh Cls; Chrmn Stu Cncl; French Hon Soc; High Hon Roll; VP NHS; Pres Schlr; Rgnts Schlrshp 85; Itln Awd 85; CHSN Ldrshp Awd 85; Smith Clg; Thtre.

RIVIERE, TAMARA; Kendall HS; Kent, NY; (Y); 19/90; Church Yth Grp; Ski Clb; Band; Concert Band; Jazz Band; Mrchg Band; Pep Band; Sec Jr Cls; Trs Sr Cls; Rep Stu Cncl; MVP Vlybl 84; Jr Prom Ct 85; Sr All Cty Band 84; Math.

RIZOS, JIMMY; Park West HS; New York, NY; (Y); 9/559; Debate Tm; Office Aide; Socr; Hon Roll; Prfct Atten Awd; U S Naval Acad; Econ.

RIZZA, CAROL; Mercy HS; Shirley, NY; (Y); Hon Roll; NHS; Prin List Awd 84-85; Hnrs Math Awd 84-85.

RIZZI, ANGELA; Walt Whitman HS; Huntington Sta, NY; (Y); 50/540; Office Aide; Yrbk Phtg; Yrbk Stf; JV Var Cheerleading; JV Gym; JV Trk; Btty Crckr Awd; High Hon Roll; Hon Roll; Jr NHS; Awd Of Merit In Spanish,Science 83.

RIZZI, REMO R; H Frank Carey HS; Franklin Sq, NY; (Y); Boys Clb Am; JA; Varsity Clb; Pres Frsh Cls; Pres Soph Cls; VP Jr Cls; Capt Ftbl; Im Mgr Trk; Im Mgr Wt Lftg; Med.

RIZZI, TOM; St Francis Prep; Maspeth, NY; (Y); Var JV Bsbl; Var JV Bsktbl; Var JV Ftbl; JV Bsebl MVP 83-84; JV Bsktbl MVP Stu Athl 83-84; Boston Coll; Math.

RIZZO, CLAUDIA; Oneida HS; Oneida, NY; (Y); Camera Clb; Church Yth Grp; Pep Clb; Ski Clb; Varsity Clb; Yrbk Sprt Ed; Yrbk Stf; Off Jr Cls; Off Stu Cncl; Cheerleading.

RIZZO, DAVID; Iona Preparatory HS; Eastchester, NY; (Y); 3/196; Church Yth Grp; Cmnty Wkr; French Clb; NFL; Red Cross Aide; Service Clb; Speech Tm; Lit Mag; JV Crs Cntry; Var Trk; Achvt Awds Globl Concrns Socty, Fornscs, Yng Chrstn Stdnts 86; Achvt Awds Yng Chrstn Stdnts 84-85; Psych.

RIZZO, JAMES; Frontier SR HS; Hamburg, NY; (S); 33/500; Chess Clb; Bsktbl; Mgr(s); Score Keeper; Vllybl; Hon Roll; NHS; Prfct Atten Awd; Psychlgy.

RIZZO, JO ANNE M; Maria Regina HS; Hillsdale, NY; (Y); Church Yth Grp; Key Clb; Library Aide; Band; Chorus; Concert Band; Mrchg Band; School Musical; Sr Cls; Socr; NYS Regnts Nrs Schlrshp 85; Siena Coll; Biol.

RIZZO, JOHN C; Bishop Cunningham HS; Oswego, NY; (Y); Variety Show; Stu Cncl; Ftbl; Ice Hcky; FL Inst Tech; Underwater Tech.

RIZZO, KAREN MARIE; Falconer Central HS; Jamestown, NY; (Y); 23/135; GAA; Hosp Aide; Spanish Clb; Varsity Clb; Var L Bsktbl; Var L Tennis; Var L Trk; Var L Vllybl; Hon Roll; NHS; U Of Buffalo; Med Sci.

RIZZO, LAURA; Cardinal O Hara HS; Tonawanda, NY; (S); Pres Frsh Cls; Sec Soph Cls; Sec Sr Cls; Rep Stu Cncl; Var L Bsktbl; Im Bowling; Mgr(s); Var L Sftbl; High Hon Roll; Prncpls Schlrshp 81; Wilson Schlrshp 81.

RIZZO, NICHOLAS; Frontier Central HS; Hamburg, NY; (S); 15/300; Varsity Clb; Bsktbl; Vllybl; Hon Roll; NHS; Prfct Atten Awd; Ntl Hist, Govt Awd 85; Bus Admn.

ROACH, KEITH J; Ilion SR HS; Ilion, NY; (Y); 35/118; Pres Trs French Clb; Pep Clb; Concert Band; Jazz Band; Mrchg Band; Orch; Pep Band; Yrbk Stf; JV Vllybl; High Hon Roll; Mohawk Vlly CC; Elctrcl Engrng.

ROACH, MICHELLE; Auburn HS; Auburn, NY; (Y); Dance Clb; Hon Roll; Bryant Stratton; Legl Secy.

ROACH, RONALD DALE; Walton Central HS; Binghamton, NY; (Y); Aud/Vis; Boys Clb Am; Chess Clb; Exploring; 4-H; Library Aide; VICA; Y-Teens; Band; Chorus; Army Natl Guard Cert; Crimnl Justc.

ROAP, MUCHAMAD; Seward Park HS; Brooklyn, NY; (Y); 18/760; NHS; Prfct Atten Awd; City Coll CUNY Schlrshp 85; City Coll CUNY; Elec Engrng.

ROARK, LISA; Plattsburgh HS; Plattsburgh, NY; (Y); Model UN; Service Clb; Ski Clb; Varsity Clb; Sec Jr Cls; Sec Stu Cncl; Sftbl; Trk; Vllybl; Hon Roll.

ROARK, SHERI; Whitesboro SR HS; Utica, NY; (Y); Band; Concert Band; Yrbk Stf; Crs Cntry; Hon Roll; Herkmer County CC; Accntng.

ROBARE, DAVID J; Au Sable Valley Central Schl; Keeseville, NY; (Y); 1/128; Key Clb; Model UN; ROTC; Chorus; School Play; Stage Crew; Stu Cncl; Socr; Trk; High Hon Roll; Rochester Tech Inst; Ele Engrng.

ROBARGE, MARY; Franklin Acad; Malone, NY; (Y); French Clb; Chorus; Swing Chorus; Rep Frsh Cls; NYS Solo Music Assoc A Rtng 83-84; Music Lttr 85epsilon Hnr Scty; Allegro Club; Phi Sigma Srty; Accntnt.

ROBBINS, DARRELL W; Hartford Central Schl; Hartford, NY; (Y); 2/47; Camera Clb; Computer Clb; Drama Clb; Math Tm; Pep Clb; Ski Clb; Yrbk Stf; Var L Bsbl; High Hon Roll; NHS; Regents Schlrshp Awd 85; SUNY-POTSDAM; Engr.

ROBBINS, DENISE M; Islip HS; Islip, NY; (Y); 50/280; Hosp Aide; Office Aide; Nwsp Phtg; Nwsp Rptr; Nwsp Sprt Ed; Yrbk Rptr; Stu Cncl; Stat Bsktbl; Var L Tennis; Var Trk; Cmmnctns.

ROBBINS, ERIN E; Sandy Creek Central Schl; Lacona, NY; (Y); Band; Chorus; School Musical; Stage Crew; Yrbk Ed-Chief; Sec Sr Cls; Stu Cncl; Capt Cheerleading; Hon Roll; NHS; Rgnts Schlrshp 85; SUNY Oswego; Elem Ed.

ROBBINS, MARY THERESE; Suffern HS; Monsey, NY; (Y); 65/430; Mrchg Band; Orch; School Musical; Stu Cncl; JV Lcrss; Powder Puff Ftbl; Church Yth Grp; Cmnty Wkr; Pep Clb; Radio Clb; St Bonaventure U; Comm.

ROBBINS, SARAH B; Palmyra Macedon Central HS; Palmyra, NY; (S); 2/205; Civic Clb; Sec Trs Church Yth Grp; Math Tm; Chorus; Stage Crew; Stu Cncl; JV Capt Tennis; Hon Roll; VP NHS; Sal; Natl Hnr Roll 84; JV Girls Tennis Awd 82; Varsity Girls Tennis Awd 83; Coll; Pre-Law.

ROBBINS, STEVEN; Central Islip HS; Central Islip, NY; (Y); #3 In Class; Am Leg Boys St; Chess Clb; Nwsp Ed-Chief; Lit Mag; Tennis; Hon Roll; NHS; Ntl Merit Ltr; NEDT Awd; Empire ST Stu Prss Assc 2nd Pl 84; Civil Rghts Essy Cont 3rd Pl 84; LI U Outstndg Accmpl Bowl 85; Med.

ROBBINS, TERRY; Victor Central HS; Victor, NY; (Y); Science Clb; JV Trk; High Hon Roll; Hon Roll; Prfct Atten Awd; 90 Or Above Avg Awd 83-85.

ROBE III, ROBERT G; Gowanda Central HS; Gowanda, NY; (Y); Band; Concert Band; Jazz Band; Mrchg Band; School Musical; Stage Crew; Symp Band; Var JV Bsbl; Var JV Ftbl; JV Wrstlng; Arch.

ROBERSON, KIMBERLY; Pine Bush HS; Bullville, NY; (Y); 32/298; GAA; Concert Band; Drm Mjr(t); Mrchg Band; VP Sr Cls; Rep Stu Cncl; Var Capt Cheerleading; JV Sftbl; NHS; Educ.

ROBERSON, LISA; Wilson Magnet HS; Rochester, NY; (S); Chorus; Church Choir; Variety Show; Mgr(s); Score Keeper; Sftbl; Vllybl; Cit Awd; Hon Roll; Prfct Atten Awd; Klepper Awd Athl Achvt 85; Cmmnctns Proj Indep Stdy.

ROBERT, LEE; Seward Park HS; New York, NY; (Y); Aud/Vis; Church Yth Grp; Computer Clb; Library Aide; Office Aide; Teachers Aide; Orch; Stage Crew; Wt Lftg; Hon Roll.

ROBERT, WADE; Skaneateles SR HS; Skaneateles, NY; (S); Band; Jazz Band; Orch; Hon Roll; NHS; Church Yth Grp; Church Choir; Concert Band; Mrchg Band; Pep Band.

ROBERTI, SUSAN; Cardinal Spellman HS; Bronx, NY; (Y); Art Clb; Cmnty Wkr; Hosp Aide; Library Aide; Office Aide; Teachers Aide; Rep Frsh Cls; Rep Soph Cls; Rep Jr Cls; Hon Roll; Cmmncng.

ROBERTO, CHRISTIAN; Minisink Valley Central HS; Middletown, NY; (Y); Band; Concert Band; Jazz Band; Mrchg Band; Pep Band; Rep Stu Cncl; Ftbl; Mgr(s); Avatn.

ROBERTO, DONNA; Union Endicott HS; Endicott, NY; (Y); Cmnty Wkr; Key Clb; Band; Mrchg Band; Stu Cncl; Hon Roll; Cert Cmnty Svc Yth Indpndnce Pgm 85; Schl Tchr.

ROBERTS, ALAN C; Elmira Free Acad; Elmira, NY; (Y); 4/256; Pres Key Clb; Stage Crew; Nwsp Ed-Chief; Yrbk Bus Mgr; Pres Jr Cls; Pres Sr Cls; JV Capt Bsbl; JV VP Ftbl; NHS; Ntl Merit SF.

ROBERTS, ALVIN LEE; Fairport HS; Fairport, NY; (Y); Boy Scts; Church Yth Grp; Sec Exploring; Red Cross Aide; Orch; Cit Awd; Hon Roll; NHS; Prfct Atten Awd; Library Aide; Outstndg Yng Amer Awd Explr Sct Prog 85; Med.

ROBERTS, AMY; North Warren Central HS; Chestertown, NY; (S); 9/50; 4-H; Band; Chorus; Concert Band; Mrchg Band; 4-H Awd; High Hon Roll; Hon Roll.

ROBERTS, ANDREA; Charles G Gorton HS; Yonkers, NY; (Y); Church Yth Grp; Hon Roll; Cert Outstndng Partcptn Chrstn Ed & Art Achvt & Cert Of Compltn Christ Theolgy Semnary 83-84; Pre-Law.

ROBERTS, ANNE MICHELE; Mount St Mary Acad; Williamsville, NY; (Y); #1 In Class; Computer Clb; Library Aide; NFL; Scholastic Bowl; Speech Tm; High Hon Roll; NHS; Ntl Merit SF; Val; 1st Pl Oral Interp Daemen Coll 81; Williams Coll Alumni Bk Awd 84; Frgn Lang.

ROBERTS, ARLENE; St Pius V HS; Bronx, NY; (Y); Pres Frsh Cls; VP Soph Cls; VP Jr Cls; Rep Stu Cncl; Hon Roll; NHS; Prfct Atten Awd; IA; Law.

ROBERTS, CINDY; Sweethome SR HS; Williamsville, NY; (Y); 99/425; Exploring; Hosp Aide; Color Guard; Concert Band; Swmmng; Vllybl; Ldrshp Awd 83; Outstndg Volntr 84; Buffalo ST Coll; Spec Ed Tchr.

ROBERTS, DARYL; Chruchville-Chili HS; Rochester, NY; (Y); Boy Scts; Church Yth Grp; Church Choir; Rep Frsh Cls; Rep Soph Cls; Rep Jr Cls; Im Capt Bsktbl; Im Capt Socr; Hon Roll; Urban Leag Early Schlr Recgntn 85; MVP Sccr; Chem Engr.

ROBERTS, DAVE; Cohoes HS; Cohoes, NY; (Y); Varsity Clb; JV Bsbl; Score Keeper; Trk; Wrstlng; Hon Roll; Aviatn.

ROBERTS, DAVID P; Baldwin SR HS; Baldwin, NY; (Y); Am Leg Boys St; High Hon Roll; Hon Roll; Merit Awd Spn 84; Cert Achvt Soc Stud 83-85; Cert Achvt Drftg Tech 83; SUNY; Pre-Law.

ROBERTS, DIANA; Shoreham Wading River HS; Shoreham, NY; (Y); Mathletes; Yrbk Ed-Chief; Yrbk Stf; JV Gym; NCTE Awd; NHS; Brnz Medal Long Islnd Math Fair 83; Poetry Wnnr Schl Cont 84-85; Boces Gifted & Tlntd Pgm 85; Scl Sci.

ROBERTS JR, FRANK WILLIAM; Coxsackie-Athens JR SR HS; Athens, NY; (Y); Boy Scts; Cmnty Wkr; 4-H; Chorus; Rep Frsh Cls; Rep Soph Cls; Rep Jr Cls; Rep Stu Cncl; High Hon Roll; Hon Roll; Prfssnl Firefghtr.

ROBERTS, FRED D; Irondequoit HS; Rochester, NY; (Y); 5/337; Church Yth Grp; Latin Clb; Chorus; Rep Jr Cls; Rep Sr Cls; Rep Stu Cncl; High Hon Roll; NHS; Cmnty Wkr; Am Clscl Leag Ntl Latin Ex 83-85; Humanitian Awd 83-84; U Dayton; Engrng.

ROBERTS, GORDON; Remsen Central Schl; Remsen, NY; (Y); Concert Band; Jazz Band; Mrchg Band; High Hon Roll; NHS; Elec Engrng.

ROBERTS, HARRISON; Earl L Vandermeulen HS; Pt Jefferson, NY; (Y); 15/325; Latin Clb; Leo Clb; School Play; Nwsp Rptr; Nwsp Stf; Yrbk Ed-Chief; Lit Mag; Trk; High Hon Roll; NHS; Centennial Prz Schlrshp 84; Stu Orgnztn Achvt Awd 84; U Of Rochester; Engrng.

ROBERTS, HEATHER; Westmoreland Central HS; Westmoreland, NY; (Y); GAA; JV Var Bsktbl; JV Var Score Keeper; JV Var Socr; Var Capt Trk; JV Stat Vllybl; High Hon Roll; Hon Roll; Band; Chorus; Inter Vlly Lge All Star Trck 83-84; MVP Awd Trck 83-84; Comp.

ROBERTS, JENNIFER; Walton Central HS; Walton, NY; (Y); 12/105; AFS; Model UN; Varsity Clb; Nwsp Ed-Chief; Var Crs Cntry; Var Trk; NHS; Potsdam; Bhvrl Sci.

ROBERTS, JOYCE ANN; Pulaski JR SR HS; Pulaski, NY; (S); 10/95; Pres Trs Church Yth Grp; Drama Clb; Chorus; Var Vllybl; Cit Awd; JC Awd; NHS; Acadmc All-Amer 84-85; Snow Fndtn Advncd Studies Schlrshp At Hartwick Coll 83-84; Bethany Bible Coll; Relgn.

ROBERTS, JULIE; Mount St Mary Acad; Williamsville, NY; (Y); Computer Clb; Intnl Clb; Library Aide; Scholastic Bowl; Teachers Aide; Chorus; Variety Show; Lit Mag; High Hon Roll; Hon Roll; Research Asst Bio Lab 85; Co-Author Sci Artcle Publictn; ST U NY Buffalo; Bio Rsrch.

ROBERTS, KENNETH; Yonkers HS; Yonkers, NY; (Y); Church Yth Grp; Church Choir; Pres Stu Cncl; Var Capt Bowling; High Hon Roll; Rep Frsh Cls; Rep Soph Cls; Rep Jr Cls; Rep Sr Cls; Ntl Soc Studies Olympd 83; Achvt Awd 85; Atten Ntl Ldrshp Trang Ctr 85; Acctng.

ROBERTS, KEVIN; Bishop Loughlin Memorial HS; Brooklyn, NY; (S); 2/182; Nwsp Rptr; Yrbk Stf; Rep Stu Cncl; Trk; High Hon Roll; ABC Schlrshp 81-84; Rgnts Schlrshp; Spring Garden Coll; Elec Engr.

ROBERTS, KRISTA L; St Joseph Hill Aca; Staten Island, NY; (Y); 16/103; Spanish Clb; Variety Show; Trk; Vllybl; Hon Roll; Staten Island; Nursing.

ROBERTS, KRISTINE; Byron-Bergen Central HS; Byron, NY; (Y); FTA; Spanish Clb; Teachers Aide; Drill Tm; Var Cheerleading; Capt Pom Pon; Stat Socr; Jr NHS; Prfct Atten Awd; Danc Awd Modrn Jazz 85; Genesee CC; Comp Prgrmr.

ROBERTS, MARK N; The Nichols Schl; Clarence, NY; (Y); 53/100; JA; Chorus; Concert Band; Jazz Band; Orch; School Musical; Var Socr; Var Trk.

ROBERTS, MARK T; Oneida SR HS; Oneida, NY; (Y); 29/240; Am Leg Boys St; Church Yth Grp; Cmnty Wkr; Letterman Clb; Ski Clb; Spanish Clb; Varsity Clb; Yrbk Sprt Ed; Yrbk Stf; VP Jr Cls; Ntl JR Ldrshp Awd 85; Mohawk Valley CC; Acctng.

ROBERTS, MELISSA; Chenango Forks Central HS; Chenango Forks, NY; (Y); 2/200; Exploring; VP Trs Band; VP Frsh Cls; Rep Soph Cls; Rep Stu Cncl; Capt Var Socr; NHS; Sal; Cmnty Wkr; Ski Clb; All Cnty Band 83; Intnshp Bio Med 84-85; Salute To Yth 85; Cornell; Bio.

ROBERTS, MICHELE DENISE; Remsen Central HS; Remsen, NY; (Y); Drama Clb; Yrbk Stf; High Hon Roll; Hon Roll; JV Socr; Crtv Wrtng Excllnc Awd 85; Hnrb Mntn NYS Assoc Hmnts Ed 83; Mohawk Vlly Comm Coll.

ROBERTS, MICHELLE; Springfield Gardens HS; Rochdale Village, NY; (S); 10/528; Cmnty Wkr; Dance Clb; Drama Clb; FBLA; Office Aide; School Play; Cit Awd; High Hon Roll; Hon Roll; NHS; Acad All Amer Schlr 84; Iwin Tobin Phy Ed Awd 82; Hunter Coll; Comp Sci.

ROBERTS, PAUL; Stony Brook Prep Schl; Wenham, MA; (Y); 24/87; Cmnty Wkr; Intnl Clb; Scholastic Bowl; Chorus; Madrigals; Orch; School Play; Crs Cntry; Trk; Hon Roll; Mrvn Gldbrg Crss Cntry Awd, Excllnc Cntrbtn 85; Kresge Chrstn Ldrshp & Ldly Perrn Schlrshps 83-85; Law.

ROBERTS, PAULA L; Angelica Central Schl; Angelica, NY; (Y); 3/24; Yrbk Stf; Sec Frsh Cls; Sec Sr Cls; Sec Stu Cncl; High Hon Roll; Hon Roll; NHS; French Clb; Pep Clb; Science Clb; Ntl Sci Olym Awd Chem 84, Physcs 85; Ntl Hnr Soc Schlrshp 85; Houghton Coll; Bus Admn.

ROBERTS, RENEE; Horseheads HS; Big Flats, NY; (Y); Church Yth Grp; Varsity Clb; Sec Y-Teens; Chorus; Church Choir; Powder Puff Ftbl; L Socr; Var L Trk; Stat Vllybl; Hon Roll; Adlscnt Psych.

ROBERTS, RICHARD; Granville Central HS; Granville, NY; (Y); 5/121; Math Tm; Spanish Clb; Rep Stu Cncl; Var Bsbl; Var Bsktbl; Var Ftbl; Var Golf; High Hon Roll; NHS; Prfct Atten Awd; Knghts Pyths Awd 85; Msnc Ldge Awd 85; Lcl Union Schlrshp 85; Union Coll; Comm.

ROBERTS, ROBYN; St Hildas And St Hughs HS; Bronx, NY; (Y); 8/23; Pres Church Yth Grp; Chorus; Pres Stu Cncl; Var Mgr(s); Hon Roll; NHS; 1st Pl Wnnr Black Oratrcl Cont. 84 & 85; Algeb II/Trig Awd 85; Northwestern U; Brdcstg.

ROBERTS, SHARON; Colonie Central HS; Loudonville, NY; (Y); Art Clb; Church Yth Grp; Cmnty Wkr; FBLA; Intnl Clb; Pres Church Choir; Mrchg Band; Stage Crew; Variety Show; Rep Stu Cncl; Chem Engnrng.

ROBERTS, TANYA; Alden Central Schl; Alden, NY; (Y); 72/203; Church Yth Grp; VP Library Aide; Stu Librarian 82-85; Psych.

ROBERTS, THERESA; Horseheads SR HS; Horseheads, NY; (Y); Girl Scts; Spanish Clb; Chorus; Church Choir; Rep Stu Cncl; Hon Roll; D Youville; Nrsng.

ROBERTS, TOBE; The Bronx HS Of Science; New York, NY; (Y); Aud/Vis; Computer Clb; JA; Wash Sq U Schlrshp, Awd TV Prod 85; NYU; Telecomm.

ROBERTSON, ALEXANDRA N; Packer Collegiate Inst; Brooklyn, NY; (Y); Drama Clb; Thesps; School Musical; School Play; Stage Crew; Variety Show; Ed Yrbk Rptr; Lit Mag; Vllybl; Marjorie O Munson Schlrshp Art 84; Theatre Dept Book Prize 84; Theatre Mgmnt.

ROBERTSON, JEFFREY; Caledonia-Mumford Central Schl; Caledonia, NY; (Y); 5/96; Math Tm; Hst Spanish Clb; Band; Chorus; Yrbk Ed-Chief; Var Golf; High Hon Roll; NHS; NY St Yorker Map Cont Wnnr 84; NY St Yorker Clb Pres 84; Acctng.

ROBERTSON, MICHAEL; Bishop Timon HS; W Seneca, NY; (Y); Chorus; JV Var Bsbl; JV Bsktbl; JV Var Ftbl; Var Ice Hcky; 1st Tm All Cathlc Qtrbck & 2nd Tm Ptchr 84-85; Chsen No 2 Chnnl 7 Supr 7 Athlts Wk 84.

ROBERTSON, STEPHEN; United Nations International HS; Jamaica, NY; (Y); Band; Variety Show; Lit Mag; Var Bsktbl; Var Sftbl.

ROBERTSON, WILLIAM; Eastridge HS; Rochester, NY; (Y); Exploring; JV Tennis; High Hon Roll; Hon Roll; Acad All Amer 85; Aero Tech.

ROBERTSON, ZHAKOOR; Boys & Girls HS; Brooklyn, NY; (Y); 1/30; Computer Clb; Debate Tm; Ftbl; Engrng.

ROBICHAUD, TIMOTHY; Stillwater Centran HS; Stillwater, NY; (Y); Am Leg Boys St; Pres Key Clb; Math Tm; Varsity Clb; VP Frsh Cls; Pres Soph Cls; Capt Ftbl; High Hon Roll; NHS; Ntl Merit SF; Physcl Sci.

ROBILLARD, CHRISTOPHER; Bishop Timon HS; Buffalo, NY; (Y); Computer Clb; Spanish Clb; Chorus; Jr Cls; Sr Cls; Stu Cncl; JV Var Bsbl; JV Var Ftbl; JV Ice Hcky; Hon Roll; St Bonaventure; Marktng.

ROBINS, IRENE; Niagara Falls HS; Niagara Falls, NY; (Y); Girl Scts; Library Aide; Yrbk Stf; Rep Stu Cncl; Cheerleading; Crs Cntry; Sftbl; Trk; High Hon Roll; Hon Roll; Brnz Schl Awd; Nrsg.

ROBINSON, ANDREA; St Catherine Acad; Bronx, NY; (Y); Church Yth Grp; GAA; Office Aide; Teachers Aide; Church Choir; Rep Soph Cls; Rep Stu Cncl; NHS; Engl Commndtn 83; Smmr HS Mnrty Pgm 84; PA U; Bio Sci.

ROBINSON, CHRIS P; Glen Falls HS; Glens Falls, NY; (Y); 2/239; Am Leg Boys St; Nwsp Rptr; Rep Trs Stu Cncl; Stat Var Bsktbl; Coach Actv; Stat Var Fld Hcky; Var Mgr(s); Powder Puff Ftbl; Var Score Keeper; JV Var Timer; Phillip C Brown Awd; Cls Of 24 Engl Awd; Le Moyne Coll; Math.

ROBINSON, FRANK; Andrew Jackson HS; New York, NY; (Y); Boy Scts; Church Yth Grp; Varsity Clb; Church Choir; Color Guard; Var Bsbl; Var Bsktbl; JV Ftbl; Cit Awd; Hon Roll; St Johns; Comp Pgmr.

ROBINSON, FRANK; Oyster Bay HS; Oyster Bay, NY; (Y); Var Capt Socr; Var Trk; High Hon Roll; NHS; All League Fncng & Sccr 85; MIP Fncng 84 & 85; MIP Sccr 84.

ROBINSON, HORACE; Andrew Jackson HS; St Albans, NY; (Y); 60/521; Church Yth Grp; English Clb; Varsity Clb; Band; Chorus; Church Choir; School Musical; VP Stu Cncl; Crs Cntry; Socr; St Johns U; Bus Adm.

ROBINSON, JOHN; Grand Island SR HS; Grand Island, NY; (Y); 65/325; Civic Clb; Variety Show; Var JV Ftbl; Var JV Lcrss; Var Swmmng; Im Vllybl; Im Wt Lftg; Prfct Atten Awd; Engrng.

ROBINSON, JOSEPH A; St Anthonys HS; Huntington Sta, NY; (Y); Ski Clb; Band; Concert Band; Stage Crew; Symp Band; Var JV Lcrss; Var JV Socr; Hon Roll; Im Bsbl; Regents Schlrshp 85; West Point Prep; Lwyr.

ROBINSON, KENT S; Lakeland HS; Putnam Valley, NY; (Y); Church Yth Grp; JV Socr; Var Trk; Hon Roll; NY ST Regents Schlrshp 85; NC ST U; Elec Engrng.

ROBINSON, KEVIN M; South Park HS; Buffalo, NY; (Y); Am Leg Boys St; Band; Concert Band; Jazz Band; Mrchg Band; Orch; Pep Band; Crs Cntry; Trk; Hon Roll; Sherman F Feyler Awd 85; NHS Stu Cntrbtn Awd 85; U Buffalo; Mus Educ.

ROBINSON, LAWRENCE K; Alfred Almond Central HS; Alfred, NY; (Y); 14/70; JCL; Yrbk Stf; VP Soph Cls; Pres Jr Cls; Var Bsbl; Var Socr; Hon Roll; NHS; Boy Scts; JA; Regnts Schlrshp 85; Allegany Cnty Natl Hnr Socty Schlrshp 85; U Of MA Amherst; Mgmt.

ROBINSON, LEONIE; Adlai E Stevenson HS; Bronx, NY; (Y); Library Aide; Quiz Bowl; Vllybl; Hon Roll; NHS; Prfct Atten Awd; Engrng.

ROBINSON, MICHELLE LEE; Kensington HS; Buffalo, NY; (Y); 8/197; Church Yth Grp; JA; Chorus; Church Choir; Sec Stu Cncl; Var Cheerleading; Hon Roll; NHS; Spanish Clb; Rep Frsh Cls; Buffalo Yth Awd 85; Proc Common Cncl Buffalo 85; Houghton Coll; Psych.

ROBINSON, NADINE; Cardinal Spellman HS; New York, NY; (Y); Church Yth Grp; Church Choir; Variety Show; Lit Mag; Im Trk; Sal; Cardinal Spellman Studio Art Awd 84; 1st Hnrs Hgh Avg 82-85; Fshn Inst Of Tech; Fshn Ilstrtr.

ROBINSON, NICHOLE; Evander Childs HS; Bronx, NY; (Y); Art Clb; Camera Clb; Computer Clb; Dance Clb; Drama Clb; English Clb; GAA; Model UN; MMM; Science Clb; City Coll NY; Comp Sci.

ROBINSON, PAULA; Eastridge HS; Rochester, NY; (Y); 11/255; Pres Church Yth Grp; GAA; Spanish Clb; Varsity Clb; Band; Concert Band; Yrbk Stf; VP Frsh Cls; JV VP Fld Hcky; JV VP Sftbl; Lbrl Arts.

ROBINSON, REGINALD D; Hillcrest HS; Corona, NY; (Y); 28/793; Math Tm; Band; Gym; Sftbl; Trk; Hon Roll; Kiwanis Awd; NHS; West Point; Comp Engr.

ROBINSON, ROBIN A; Fayetteville Manlius HS; Manlius, NY; (Y); Bus Awd 85; Med.

ROBINSON, ROSLYN; Purson HS; Sag Harbor, NY; (Y); 15/30; Dance Clb; Band; Chorus; School Musical; School Play; Yrbk Stf; Pres Frsh Cls; Trs Soph Cls; Trs Jr Cls; Capt Var Cheerleading; Howard U; Dnc.

ROBINSON, SANDRA; Wilson Magnet HS; Rochester, NY; (S); 4/49; Church Yth Grp; Office Aide; Chorus; Church Choir; Yrbk Stf; Pres Stu Cncl; Cit Awd; High Hon Roll; NHS; Prfct Atten Awd; Stu Advsry Brd 84; Yth Treas 84-85; Blck Shlr Awd 84-85; Rochester Inst Of Tech; Lwyr.

ROBINSON, SCOTT; North Tonawanda SR HS; N Tonawanda, NY; (Y); Chorus; JV Bsbl; Bsktbl; Im Bowling; Ftbl; Sftbl; Wt Lftg; Prfct Atten Awd; Cmptrs.

ROBINSON, SHARON; West Genesee SR HS; Camillus, NY; (Y); Church Yth Grp; Library Aide; Speech Tm; Chorus; Concert Band; Mrchg Band; High Hon Roll; Hon Roll; Jr NHS; Prfct Atten Awd; Secy SADD 84-85; Nice Kid Awd 82-83; Law.

ROBINSON, SHARON J; Williamsville East HS; Williamsville, NY; (Y); 32/300; Sec AFS; Church Yth Grp; Latin Clb; School Musical; Yrbk Stf; Bowling; High Hon Roll; NCTE Awd; Ntl Merit SF; French Clb; Newfane Math Contest Team Placed 2nd 82-83; Vet Med.

ROBINSON, SUZANNE; Lindenhurst SR HS; Lindenhurst, NY; (Y); 4/600; Dance Clb; Ski Clb; Color Guard; Variety Show; Yrbk Stf; High Hon Roll; Pres NHS; Camera Clb; Church Yth Grp; Cmnty Wkr; Pres Acadmc Fit Awd 84-85; Robert J Little Memrl Brothrhd Awd 84-85; Mrch Dimes 84-85; U Of CA San Diego; Biochem.

ROBINSON, THOMAS; Northeastern Clinton Central Schl; Mooers Forks, NY; (Y); JV Bsbl; Var Bsktbl; Var Ftbl; Var Socr.

ROBINSON, TIMOTHY; Pioneer Central HS; Arcade, NY; (Y); Boys Clb Am; Ftbl; Hon Roll; Elec Engr.

ROBINSON, TRACI ELLEN; New Rochelle HS; New Rochelle, NY; (Y); Cmnty Wkr; Drama Clb; Trs FBLA; JA; NFL; School Play; Lit Mag; Pres Sr Cls; Vllybl; Jr NHS; 1st Pl Westchester County Publc Spkng FBLA 85; Pres F Willia Dans Lg Grls 85-86; Brdcst Jrnlsm.

ROBINSON, WENDY J; Bay Shore HS; Bay Shore, NY; (Y); Cmnty Wkr; Intnl Clb; Library Aide; Im Badmtn; JV Trk; Im Vllybl; Hon Roll; Cert Merit Outstndng Bus Stu 85; Outstndng Achvt Soc Stud/Amer Stud 84-85; Cert Awd Libr Cncl 84; Med Tech.

ROBINSON, YOLANDA; Harry S Truman HS; Bronx, NY; (Y); Debate Tm; Teachers Aide; Lit Mag; Hugh O Brian Yth Found Outstndng Stu 84; Cert Awd Tabernacle Bible Inst 84; Cert Awd It Mag Prod 85; City Coll-New York; Jrnlsm.

ROBISCH, EDWIN; Liberty Central HS; Liberty, NY; (Y); 4-H; Crs Cntry; Trk; 4-H Awd; Hon Roll; Ulster Cnty CC; Dsgn.

ROBISON, MATTHEW; T R Proctor HS; Utica, NY; (Y); Pres Church Yth Grp; Rep Drama Clb; Exploring; Rep Pep Clb; Acpl Chr; Chorus; Church Choir; Madrigals; School Musical; School Play; Curran Music Schlrshp 85; Outstndng Achvts In Vcl Music 85; Bsharp & Etude Music Schlrshp 85; Crane Schl Of Music; Music.

ROBISTOW, JODI; Franklin Academy SR HS; Malone, NY; (Y); Miltry.

ROBLYER, WENDY; Odessa-Montour Central Schl; Montour Falls, NY; (Y); 1/86; Trs Band; Lit Mag; Trs Frsh Cls; Trs Soph Cls; Rep Stu Cncl; JV Var Bsktbl; Var Trk; JV Var Vllybl; High Hon Roll; NHS; Miss Mountour Falls 83-84; Outstndng Plyr Awd 84; Physcl Thrpy.

ROBSON, DENA; Westfield Academy And Central Schl; Westfield, NY; (Y); 20/78; Sec 4-H; Ski Clb; Y-Teens; Yrbk Stf; Rep Stu Cncl; L Bsktbl; L Sftbl; L Vllybl; High Hon Roll; Hon Roll; Westminster Coll; Corp Lwyr.

ROBY, MARY; Warwick Valley HS; Warwick, NY; (Y); 42/205; Cmnty Wkr; Teachers Aide; Varsity Clb; Var Capt Bsktbl; Stat Ftbl; Var Capt Sftbl; Hon Roll; NHS; MVP Bsktbll, Sftbll Vrsty Team 85; All-Star Bsbll 85; NAMES Bsbll 85; Educ.

ROCA, JOSEPH W; Regis HS; Bronx, NY; (Y); Chess Clb; Exploring; School Musical; School Play; Cheerleading; Im Gym; Var L Trk; Im Wt Lftg; Im Wrstlng; Ntl Merit Ltr; Mgr Of Cheerldrs 84; Trustee Schlr St Lawrence U 85; USAA Natl Awd 85.

ROCCA, STEVE; Palmyra-Macedon HS; Palmyra, NY; (Y); 32/189; Am Leg Boys St; Boy Scts; Church Choir; School Musical; Nwsp Rptr; Yrbk Stf; Var JV Tennis; Cit Awd; Prfct Atten Awd; Sec Frsh Cls; Eagl Sct 84; Amer Lgn Schlstc Achv Awd 82; Bus Mgt.

ROCCI, CHUCK A; T R Proctor HS; Utica, NY; (Y); Church Yth Grp; Bsktbl; Ftbl; Golf; Wt Lftg; High Hon Roll; NHS; Colgate Smnr 84-85; Lrbl Arts.

ROCCO, JON; Frankfort-Schuyler HS; Frankfort, NY; (S); 14/97; FBLA; Spanish Clb; Varsity Clb; Nwsp Sprt Ed; Yrbk Sprt Ed; VP Sr Cls; Var Capt Crs Cntry; Var Golf; Var Wrstlng; NHS; 2nd Pl Cntntl Math Leag 81-82; Crs Cntry All Leag & All Star 83 & 84; Pblc Spkr Future Bus Ldrs 85; SUNY Geneseo; Bus Admin.

ROCCO, TOM; Half Hollow Hills East HS; Dix Hills, NY; (S); 113/566; Cmnty Wkr; Hosp Aide; Teachers Aide; Varsity Clb; Nwsp Rptr; Var Capt Bsbl; Var Capt Ftbl; High Hon Roll; Jr NHS; NHS; All-Cnty Ftbl 84; Vlntr Achvmnt Awd 84; Sci.

ROCCOS, ALEXIS; Mount Vernon HS; Mount Vernon, NY; (Y); Boy Scts; Math Tm; Office Aide; Var L Crs Cntry; Var L Wrstlng; High Hon Roll; Hon Roll; NHS; Engrng.

ROCHE, EDWARD; Iona Prep; Scarsdale, NY; (Y); Cmnty Wkr; Hosp Aide; Red Cross Aide; Nwsp Rptr; Off Sr Cls; JV Bsktbl; Hon Roll; Church Yth Grp; Stage Crew; Middlebury Coll; Hstry.

ROCHE, MICHAEL; Christian Brothers Acad; Syracuse, NY; (Y); 6/97; Trs Boys Clb Am; Trs Boy Scts; Trs Exploring; Hosp Aide; Var Capt Crs Cntry; Var Capt Trk; High Hon Roll; NHS; Pres Schlr; Im Bsktbl; USAF ROTC Schlrshp 85; U Dayton Pres Schlrshp 85; Navy Marine ROTC Schlrshp Army ROTC Schlrshp 85; Dayton U; Crmnl Justice.

ROCHE, MICHAEL; W Seneca East SR HS; W Seneca, NY; (Y); FCA; Im Bsktbl; Var L Ftbl; JV Trk; Im Vllybl; Hon Roll; Prfct Atten Awd; Sapan Awd 85; AZ ST U; Bus Admin.

ROCHE, PEGGY; Rocky Point JR SR HS; Rocky Pt, NY; (Y); Church Yth Grp; Spanish Clb; Teachers Aide; Flag Corp; Mrchg Band; Var L Crs Cntry; Var L Trk; Crss Cntry All Leag, All Conf Hnrs 83-84; MVP Crss Cntry 83; Elem Ed.

ROCHE, SHAWN; Delaware Valley Central HS; Callicoon, NY; (S); Drama Clb; Chorus; Concert Band; Jazz Band; Yrbk Sprt Ed; Yrbk Stf; Var Trk; High Hon Roll; NHS; All ST Chr 83-84; Hartwick MENC Chrl Fest 83-84; All Cnty Chrs 82-85; Elect Engr.

ROCHE, YVETTE; Cardinal Spellman HS; Bronx, NY; (Y); 75/526; Church Yth Grp; Dance Clb; Pep Clb; Capt JV Cheerleading; Hon Roll; Prfct Atten Awd; NYU; Psych.

ROCHFORD, SUZANNE; Central Islip HS; Central Islip, NY; (Y); 5/350; Stage Crew; Nwsp Sprt Ed; Tennis; Hon Roll; NHS; NEDT Awd; Acad All Amer 84.

ROCHROCK, TIMOTHY; Avon Central HS; Avon, NY; (Y); 37/105; Church Yth Grp; Drama Clb; Ski Clb; Spanish Clb; Varsity Clb; Chorus; School Musical; Yrbk Stf; VP Sr Cls; JV Bsbl; JV Bsbl Capt 83 & 84; JV & Var Ftbl Capt 83 & 85; JV County Wrstlng Champ 84; Phys Ther.

ROCK, ANGIE; Saranac Central HS; Morrisonville, NY; (S); 20/125; Office Aide; Band; Concert Band; Yrbk Stf; L Capt Cheerleading; Hon Roll; Prfct Atten Awd; Siena Coll; Math.

ROCK, KAREN; Ticonderoga HS; Putnam Station, NY; (Y); Church Yth Grp; Acpl Chr; Chorus; Church Choir; Madrigals; Swing Chorus; Yrbk Ed-Chief; Yrbk Phtg; Yrbk Stf; Prfct Atten Awd; Summr Bibleschl Compltn Cert 84; Word Of Life Bible Inst; Soclgy.

ROCK, MICHELLE; Liverpool HS; Liverpool, NY; (S); Trs Art Clb; Drama Clb; Ski Clb; School Musical; School Play; Nwsp Stf; Yrbk Stf; Rep Stu Cncl; Hon Roll; Outstndng Stu Sculpture 83-84.

ROCKE, JOLIE A; La Guardia High Sch Of Music & Art; Springfield Grdns, NY; (Y); 135/588; Office Aide; Service Clb; Chorus; Church Choir; School Musical; Rep Frsh Cls; Rep Soph Cls; Rep Jr Cls; Rep Sr Cls; NHS; Music Honor League 83-85; Music Educ.

ROCKER, MATTHEW G; Madrid-Waddington HS; Madrid, NY; (Y); 2/55; Drama Clb; French Clb; JA; Stage Crew; VP Frsh Cls; Bsbl; Bsktbl; Crs Cntry; Golf; Trk; Elec Engr.

ROCKHILL, CAROLYN A; Brushton Moira Central HS; Moira, NY; (Y); 5/60; VP French Clb; Band; Jazz Band; School Play; Yrbk Sprt Ed; Rep Stu Cncl; Var Sftbl; Var Vllybl; Pres NHS; Regents Schlrshp 85; Proj Challenge 84; Area All St Bnd Zone 6 84; Albany Coll Pharmacy; Pharm.

ROCKMORE, ALLISON; Lawrence HS; N Woodmere, NY; (Y); AFS; Spanish Clb; Temple Yth Grp; Band; Concert Band; Mrchg Band; Stu Cncl; High Hon Roll; Hon Roll; NHS; Mst Outstndng Perfrmr Awd Wind Ensmbl 82-83; Law.

ROCKNEY, TRACY; Brentwood Sonderling HS; Brentwood, NY; (Y); 11/625; Church Yth Grp; DECA; French Clb; Band; Drm Mjr(t); Mrchg Band; Nwsp Stf; Hon Roll; Jr NHS; NHS; SUNY Albany; Intl Law.

ROCKOW, MICHAEL; Bronx H S Of Science; Bronx, NY; (Y); Math Clb; Math Tm; Office Aide; Concert Band; Orch; Yrbk Stf; Hon Roll; NHS; Teachers Aide; Band; Esther Dichter Mem Awd Outstndg Char 85; Scholar & Svc Mth Dept 85; Cert Schl Mth Bulltn Lyout Edtr 84; U MI; Geolgy.

ROCKWELL, BECKY; Fayetteville-Manilus HS; Manlius, NY; (Y); Church Yth Grp; 4-H; Ski Clb; Yrbk Stf; Crs Cntry; Vllybl; High Hon Roll; Bus Admin.

ROCKWELL, EDWARD; Schoharie Central HS; Esperance, NY; (Y); Church Yth Grp; Cmnty Wkr; FFA; Band; Church Choir; Concert Band; Mrchg Band; Pep Band; Stage Crew; Var Im Socr; FFA Chap Frmrs Awd 84; FFA Green Hand Awd 84.

ROCKWELL, LISA; Dolgeville Central HS; Stratford, NY; (Y); Varsity Clb; Chorus; Var Stu Cncl; Var Cheerleading; Var Socr; Var Sftbl; JV Vllybl; Cit Awd; High Hon Roll; Hon Roll; Laura F Helterline Awd 84; Herkimer CC; Elem Educ.

ROCKWELL, ROBERT; Salamanca Central HS; Killbuck, NY; (Y); 20/120; French Clb; Ski Clb; Hon Roll; Flagler Coll; Accntng.

ROCKWOOD, RONALD; Lowville Central HS; Lowville, NY; (Y); French Clb; Quiz Bowl; Trs Spanish Clb; School Play; Nwsp Sprt Ed; Yrbk Stf; Pres Stu Cncl; JV L Bsbl; Var Golf; JV L Socr; Engrng.

RODA, DOMINICK; Oneonta HS; Oneonta, NY; (Y); German Clb; Ski Clb; JV Ftbl; Var Trk; High Hon Roll; Ger Awd 82-83; Arch.

RODA, PEGGY; Minisink Valley HS; Slate Hill, NY; (Y); Varsity Clb; Var Capt Bsktbl; Var Socr; Var Capt Vllybl; Hon Roll; Vtrnrn.

RODAK, NICHOLAS; Atica HS; Warsaw, NY; (S); 9/160; AFS; Debate Tm; JA; Math Tm; Band; Concert Band; Jazz Band; Crs Cntry; Trk; Intl Frgn Lang Awd Frnch 85; Soc Dstngshd HS Stdnt Awd 84; SUNY Fredonia; Pol Sci.

RODDEN, CHRISTINE; St Vincent Ferrer HS; New York, NY; (Y); Drama Clb; Q&S; Chorus; Madrigals; School Musical; School Play; Stage Crew; Nwsp Rptr; Yrbk Stf; Voluntr Svc Awd 83; Psych.

RODDY, JOSEPH; Bishop Ford C C HS; Brooklyn, NY; (Y); Exploring; Ski Clb; Stage Crew; Elec Engrng.

RODDY, ROBERT; Waterford-Halfmoon HS; Waterford, NY; (Y); French Clb; Chorus; Church Choir; Concert Band; Madrigals; VP Sr Cls; Stat Bsktbl; Hon Roll; Saratoga Co/Skidmore Coll Acad Achvt Awd 84; Waterford Yth Cncl Sprtsmnshp Awd 85; Mus.

RODENAS, ALMA; Springfield Gardens HS; Laurelton, NY; (S); 8/500; Im Trk; NHS; Med.

RODER, M THERESA; North Rose Wolcott HS; Northrose, NY; (Y); 10/129; FBLA; Teachers Aide; Varsity Clb; Yrbk Stf; Pres Soph Cls; Var Capt Swmmng; High Hon Roll; NHS; Regnts Schlrshp 85; Psych.

RODERICK, DENISE; North Salem HS; N Salem, NY; (Y); Bsktbl; Mgr(s); Score Keeper; Socr; Sftbl; High Hon Roll; NHS; Med.

RODGER, BETH; Northstar Christian Acad; Rochester, NY; (S); 8/26; Church Yth Grp; Debate Tm; Spanish Clb; Speech Tm; Teachers Aide; Rep Stu Cncl; Var Capt Bsktbl; Var Capt Socr; Sftbl; Soccer MVP 84; Army Schlr/Athl Awd 84; Emmaus Bible Coll; Bsns.

RODGERS, ARTHUR; City Honors HS; Buffalo, NY; (Y); 40/97; Boy Scts; Computer Clb; JA; Math Clb; Math Tm; Spanish Clb; School Play; Im Bowling; Var Mgr(s); Stat Swmmng; Architecture.

RODGERS, JOHN; Jeaford HS; Seaford, NY; (Y); Math Tm; Quiz Bowl; Nwsp Ed-Chief; Yrbk Stf; Lit Mag; Im Vllybl; High Hon Roll; Trs NHS; Perf Scr Math PSAT 84; Intl Lang Awd 84-85; Math Schlrshp Awd 83-85.

RODGERS, WM; Long Island Lutheran HS; Hicksville, NY; (Y); Church Yth Grp; French Clb; Key Clb; Library Aide; Office Aide; Ski Clb; Nwsp Stf; Yrbk Rptr; Yrbk Stf; Crs Cntry; Pres SADD; Nrs Aide Awd; Fashion Inst Of Tech; Bus.

RODRIGO, RACHAEL; Saugerties HS; Glasco, NY; (Y); French Clb; Math Tm; Varsity Clb; Band; Mrchg Band; Symp Band; Yrbk Stf; High Hon Roll; NHS; Scholar Woodstock Schl Art 85; Art.

RODRIGUE, BRENDA; Churchville-Chili SR HS; Rochester, NY; (Y); 33/307; Hosp Aide; High Hon Roll; NHS; Presdntl Acadmc Ftnss Awd 85; Rgnts Prof Ed Nrsng Schlrshp 85; Monroe CC; Psychlgy.

RODRIGUEZ, ANGEL; Mount St Michael Acad; Bronx, NY; (Y); 4/286; Rep Stu Cncl; Im Bsktbl; Im Ftbl; Hon Roll; NHS; Spanish NHS; Fordham U; Bio.

RODRIGUEZ, ANGEL; Trinity Schl; New York, NY; (Y); Lcrss; Wt Lftg; Wrstlng; Ntl Merit SF; Spanish NHS; Haverford Coll; Engl.

RODRIGUEZ, ANGELO; Christ The King Reg HS; Hollis, NY; (Y); Gym; NY City Tech Coll; Med Lab Tec.

RODRIGUEZ, ANNE MARIE; Hauppauge HS; Smithtown, NY; (Y); Chorus; Concert Band; Mrchg Band; School Musical; Variety Show; Rep Frsh Cls; Rep Soph Cls; VP Pres Stu Cncl; Dnfth Awd; Emerging Ldr Awd 85; Music Ads 83-85; Theater Awds 83 & 84; Middlebury Coll; Cmmnctns.

RODRIGUEZ, ANNMARIE; Aviation HS; Jackson Hts, NY; (Y); Library Aide; VICA; Stage Crew; Rep Frsh Cls; Rep Soph Cls; Hon Roll; Prfct Atten Awd; Air Force Acad; Airforce Pilot.

RODRIGUEZ, ANTONIO; Murray Bergtraum HS; Bronx, NY; (Y); 87/576; Computer Clb; JA; Varsity Clb; Rep Stu Cncl; Coach Actv; JV Capt Ftbl; Mgr(s); Cit Awd; Hon Roll; UFT Acadmc Exclln & Schl Svc 85; SUNY-STONY Brook; Comp Sci.

RODRIGUEZ, AWILDA; Park West HS; Bronx, NY; (Y); Dance Clb; JA; Band; Chorus; Concert Band; Twrlr; Wt Lftg; Wrstlng; Bus Adm.

RODRIGUEZ, CYNTHIA; Nyack HS; Valley Cottage, NY; (Y); 13/257; Concert Band; Yrbk Stf; Sec Jr Cls; Stu Cncl; Var Capt Lcrss; Var Capt Socr; French Hon Soc; High Hon Roll; NHS; Spanish NHS; Socr MVP Awd 84; Lcrss All Conf, All Assn, All Sectn Hnrs 85; Med.

RODRIGUEZ, DENISE MARIE; St Catharines Acad; Bronx, NY; (Y); 31/205; Dance Clb; Teachers Aide; Yrbk Stf; Hon Roll; Jr NHS; NHS; Fordham U.

RODRIGUEZ, ERICA; Eastchester HS; Scarsdale, NY; (Y); Church Yth Grp; Key Clb; Latin Clb; Chorus; Off Jr Cls; Cheerleading; Sftbl; Wt Lftg; Hon Roll; Jr NHS; Ms Westchester Cnty Teen-Ager Pag Fnlst 84; Bio.

RODRIGUEZ, ERICA HELENE; Hunter College HS; New York, NY; (Y); Church Yth Grp; Yrbk Stf; Lit Mag; Ntl Merit Schol; Chorus; School Play; Schl Of Visual Arts Schlrshp Awd 85; Natl Spanish Exam Hnrb Mntn 83; Natl Hispanic Schlr Awd Pgm 85; Illustration.

RODRIGUEZ, FREDDY; Hicksville HS; Hicksville, NY; (Y); Drama Clb; Model UN; Science Clb; Orch; Variety Show; Nwsp Phtg; Nwsp Rptr; JV Crs Cntry; JV Trk; Hon Roll.

RODRIGUEZ, GEORGE; The Bronx H S Of Science; Ft Totten, NY; (Y); Office Aide; West Point Military Acad; Law.

RODRIGUEZ, GEORGE THOMAS; The Bronx H S Of Science; Queens, NY; (Y); Drama Clb; Math Tm; Science Clb; Variety Show; Rep Jr Cls; Rep Sr Cls; Rep Trk; Hon Roll; NHS; Ntl Merit SF; Schl Rep Bronx Physcl Ftns Comptn 83-85; Columbia; Pre Med.

RODRIGUEZ, GINETTE; Grace Dodge Voc HS; Bronx, NY; (Y); Score Keeper; Vllybl; Bronx CC; Art.

RODRIGUEZ, GRACE; Longwood HS; Coram, NY; (S); 4/487; Am Leg Aux Girls St; Hosp Aide; Math Tm; Nwsp Bus Mgr; High Hon Roll; Pres Jr NHS; NHS; Key Clb; Gftd & Tlntd Smmr Inst 81-83; Wash Workshp Congrsnl Smnr 84; Engrng.

RODRIGUEZ, IRENE; Mt Vernon HS; Mount Vernon, NY; (Y); 33/650; Keywanettes; Office Aide; Political Wkr; Spanish Clb; Capt Pom Pon; High Hon Roll; Hon Roll; Jr NHS; NHS; Comptr Sci.

RODRIGUEZ, ISAURA; Herbert H Lehman HS; Bronx, NY; (Y); 113/473; Service Clb; Hon Roll; Prfct Atten Awd; Mst Serious Pgmmr Comp Tech 84; Engl Awds 83-85; Excllnce Basic Psych 84; RN.

RODRIGUEZ, IVETTE; Lehman HS; Bronx, NY; (Y); 62/444; Church Yth Grp; Yrbk Stf; Rep Sr Cls; Pres Stu Cncl; Bsktbl; Cit Awd; Hon Roll; NHS; Prfct Atten Awd; Laureate Awd Bronx Network Women 85; Triple C Awd 85; Hunter Coll; Pol Law.

RODRIGUEZ, JOANNE; Aquinas HS; New York, NY; (Y); 48/178; Camera Clb; Computer Clb; Girl Scts; Hosp Aide; Red Cross Aide; Chorus; School Musical; School Play; Hon Roll; Nrsg.

RODRIGUEZ, JOSE; John Jay HS; Brooklyn, NY; (Y); Var Bsbl; Clg Bnd Prog Hnr Achvt 85; Cmmndtn Outstndng Schlrshp Typwrtg 85; Engrng.

RODRIGUEZ, JULIA; Croton-Harmon HS; Croton On Hudson, NY; (Y); 20/120; JA; Model UN; Band; Nwsp Rptr; JV Socr; Var Tennis; NHS; Brandeis U; Socialogy.

RODRIGUEZ, LISA; Bishop Loughlin Memorial HS; Brooklyn, NY; (S); 10/181; Q&S; Teachers Aide; School Play; Nwsp Ed-Chief; Yrbk Stf; Trs Jr Cls; Pres Sr Cls; Stu Cncl; Hon Roll; Trs NHS; Slvr Awd Bishop Loughlin 84; 3rd Prz HS Press Awd Gen Excel 84, Bst Feature 83; Pre Law.

RODRIGUEZ, LIZETTE; John Dewey HS; Richmond Hill, NY; (Y); Orch; Yrbk Stf; Vllybl; Prfct Atten Awd; NY U.

RODRIGUEZ, MARCIA; Murry Bergtraum HS; New York, NY; (Y); Church Yth Grp; Computer Clb; Dance Clb; Math Clb; Math Tm; Science Clb; Teachers Aide; Chorus; Church Choir; Prfct Atten Awd; Arch.

RODRIGUEZ, MARIA E; Norman Thomas HS; Bronx, NY; (S); 11/671; Computer Clb; FBLA; Office Aide; Cit Awd; Hon Roll; NHS; Prfct Atten Awd; All Am Awd 85; Gold Cert 85; Bus.

RODRIGUEZ, MARINA C; George Washington HS; New York, NY; (Y); 5/315; Dance Clb; Band; Concert Band; Orch; Rep Frsh Cls; Rep Jr Cls; Rep Sr Cls; Rep Stu Cncl; High Hon Roll; Hon Roll; Achvt Awd Engl 85; Verne Canter Awd 85; Dnc, Spnsh & Typng Awd 85; Asc Tchrs Scl Stds Awd Merit 85; Baruch Coll; Bus Admin.

RODRIGUEZ, MARITZA; Aquinas HS; New York, NY; (Y); 26/178; Cmnty Wkr; Chorus; Hon Roll; Prfct Atten Awd; Acad Of Aeronautics.

RODRIGUEZ, MIGUEL; Oyster Bay HS; E Norwich, NY; (Y); Exploring; Library Aide; Hon Roll; Oral Roberts U; Med.

RODRIGUEZ, MONICA; Albertus Magnus HS; Stony Point, NY; (Y); 18/185; Church Yth Grp; Drama Clb; Girl Scts; Spanish Clb; Stage Crew; Ed Yrbk Stf; NHS; Math Honor Society 84; Science Honor Society 84; Regents Scholarship 85.

RODRIGUEZ, NANCY; Queen Of The Rosary Acad; Roosevelt, NY; (Y); Church Yth Grp; Girl Scts; Bus.

RODRIGUEZ, NELLY; John Jay HS; Brooklyn, NY; (Y); Chorus; Church Choir; School Play; Variety Show; Bsktbl; Vllybl; High Hon Roll; Hon Roll; Prfct Atten Awd; Sci Schlrshp Cert 84; Algbr & Econmcs Schlrshp Cert 85; Lawyer.

RODRIGUEZ, OLIVIA F; Stella Maris HS; Rockaway Beach, NY; (Y); 14/185; Church Yth Grp; Cmnty Wkr; Trs Science Clb; Trs Band; Chorus; Church Choir; Drm & Bgl; High Hon Roll; Natl Sci Olympd 81; Med.

RODRIGUEZ, OSCAR; Peekskill HS; White Plains, NY; (S); Chess Clb; Var Socr; High Hon Roll; Hon Roll; NHS; Law.

RODRIGUEZ, RAFAEL; Chelsea Vocational HS; New York, NY; (Y); 7/202; Church Yth Grp; Office Aide; Church Choir; Trs Frsh Cls; High Hon Roll; Hon Roll; NHS; Prfct Atten Awd; Untd Methdst Schlrshp 85; Binghamton.

RODRIGUEZ, ROBIN; St Raymond Acad; Bronx, NY; (Y); Cmnty Wkr; Pep Clb; Nwsp Rptr; Nwsp Stf; VP Jr Cls; Stu Cncl; Sftbl; Vllybl; U Of Sthrn CA; Chld Psychlgy.

RODRIGUEZ, ROSA; Eastern District HS; Brooklyn, NY; (Y); Exec Sec.

RODRIGUEZ, SUSAN; Newark SR HS; Newark, NY; (Y); Chorus; Nwsp Stf; Brooklyn Campus; Frgn Intrptr.

RODRIGUEZ, VANESSA ANN; St Barnabas HS; Bronx, NY; (Y); Church Yth Grp; Cmnty Wkr; Key Clb; Pep Clb; Spanish Clb; School Play; Stage Crew; Stu Cncl; Sftbl; Swmmng; CCD Tchr Cert 86; Adelphi U; Bus Admin.

RODRIGUEZ, VICTOR N; Seward Park HS; New York, NY; (Y); 47/270; Hosp Aide; Red Cross Aide; Science Clb; Hon Roll; NHS; Brooklyn Coll; Pre Med.

RODRIQUEZ, BARBARA D; St Nicholas Of Tolentine HS; Bronx, NY; (Y); 42/145; Cmnty Wkr; Drama Clb; School Musical; Rep Jr Cls; Pres Sr Cls; JV Var Swmmng; High Hon Roll; Hon Roll; NHS; Debate Tm; Consistnt Effrt Intro To Comp 83-84; Lehman Clg; Lwyr.

RODRIQUEZ, JOSEFINA; Cathedral HS; Ny, NY; (Y); Intnl Clb; Med.

RODRIQUEZ, MARISOL; Middletown HS; Middletown, NY; (Y); Pres Church Yth Grp; Sec Latin Clb; Spanish Clb; Teachers Aide; Acpl Chr; Church Choir; Madrigals; Variety Show; Off Frsh Cls; Off Soph Cls; Stone New Haven; Exec Sec.

ROE, ALEXANDRA; Riverdale Country Schl; Bronxville, NY; (Y); Chorus; Sec Soph Cls; Var Diving; Var Fld Hcky; Var Ice Hcky; Var Lcrss; Ntl Merit Ltr; Hon Roll; Cert Hnr Cncrs Natl De Francs 83; Hd Actvties Frshm Clss 82-83; Med.

ROE, JULIE; Rome Catholic HS; Rome, NY; (Y); 18/84; Cmnty Wkr; Hosp Aide; Library Aide; Color Guard; Drm & Bgl; Twrlr; High Hon Roll; Pre-Law.

ROE, LAURA; Rome Catholic HS; Rome, NY; (Y); 20/86; High Hon Roll; Hon Roll; NY ST Regents Scholar 85; Southeastern Acad; Travel.

ROEBUCK, MALIK; Park West HS; New York, NY; (Y); Math Clb; Off Drm & Bgl; VA Union U; Comp Pgmng.

ROEDER, BRIAN; Delaware Valley Central Schl; Hortonville, NY; (S); 2/36; Chorus; School Musical; Yrbk Stf; Var Bsbl; Var Bsktbl; Co-Capt Ftbl; Sftbl; Co-Capt Trk; Wt Lftg; Hon Roll; Area All-State Chr 84; Chem Awd; WSL Ftbl 1st Team 84; West Point; Elec Engrng.

ROEDER, VICTORIA JOY; Washingtonville HS; Campbell Hall, NY; (Y); 10/291; 4-H; French Clb; Intnl Clb; Teachers Aide; Nwsp Stf; Var Crs Cntry; Var Trk; God Cntry Awd; Hon Roll; NHS; Athlt Schlr Awd 84-85; Rotary & Regents Schlrshps 85; Rochester U; Bio.

ROEHRE, EDWARD J; Niagara Falls HS; Niagara Falls, NY; (Y); 32/241; Boy Scts; Drama Clb; Hosp Aide; Thesps; Pres Band; Jazz Band; School Musical; School Play; Var Tennis; NHS; Perfct Attndnc 84-85; SUNY Buffalo; Comp Sci.

ROEHRIG, LINDA; C Pp West HS; Corning, NY; (Y); Untd Wslyn Coll; Bus.

ROESCH, CRAIG; Kenmore East SR HS; Tonawanda, NY; (Y); Varsity Clb; Stat Bsktbl; Capt Crs Cntry; Var Trk; Canisius Coll; Comp Prog.

ROESCH, ERIC; Hilton HS; Hilton, NY; (Y); 36/325; Boy Scts; Church Yth Grp; German Clb; JA; Model UN; Teachers Aide; Swmmng; Tennis; Timer; High Hon Roll; Bio Sci.

ROESSNER, KRISTIN; Long Island Lutheran HS; Hempstead, NY; (S); 18/94; Ski Clb; Band; Chorus; Drm & Bgl; Orch; Lit Mag; Pres Frsh Cls; JV Cheerleading; Hon Roll; NHS; Lit Awd 83; Natl Merit Semi-Fin 85; All Cnty Bnd 85; Wrtr.

ROETTGERS, AUDREY H; Nanuet SR HS; Pearl River, NY; (Y); 5/175; Exploring; Math Tm; Quiz Bowl; Orch; Nwsp Rptr; Sec Stu Cncl; Tennis; Mu Alp Tht; NHS; Ntl Merit SF; Princeton; Ped.

ROG, DOUGLAS L; St Josephs Collegiate Inst; N Tonawanda, NY; (Y); 26/202; Var Capt Ice Hcky; Wt Lftg; High Hon Roll; NHS; Prfct Atten Awd; NY St Regents Schlrshp 85; Trustees Awd Clarkson U 85; Clarkson U; Mech Engrng.

ROGALA, ERIC; Hilton Central HS; Hilton, NY; (Y); 1/322; Computer Clb; Exploring; Math Clb; Model UN; Var Tennis; High Hon Roll; NHS; Rochester U Paideia Awd Cert 85; Med.

ROGALIN, MICHELE; Odessa-Montour Central HS; Odessa, NY; (Y); Computer Clb; Letterman Clb; Varsity Clb; Yrbk Stf; Lit Mag; VP Soph Cls; Rep Stu Cncl; Stat Bsbl; Mgr(s); Score Keeper; Marine Bio.

ROGERS, CHARLES; Harpursville JR SR HS; Harpursville, NY; (S); Cmnty Wkr; Sec Trs Band; Pres Chorus; Trs Concert Band; Jazz Band; Mrchg Band; Pep Band; School Play; Stage Crew; Yrbk Phtg; Selection To Area All ST Band; Outstndng Stu Photgrphy & Graphics Class; Broome CC; Elec Engr.

ROGERS, CLAUDETTE H; Macs HS; Mexico, NY; (Y); Church Yth Grp; Sec 4-H; Chorus; Church Choir; Concert Band; Mrchg Band; Vllybl; 4-H Awd; Hon Roll; NHS.

ROGERS, COLLEEN; East Islip HS; East Islip, NY; (Y); Am Leg Aux Girls St; Art Clb; Math Tm; Ed Lit Mag; Im Vllybl; NHS; Ntl Merit Ltr; Service Clb; Stage Crew; Nwsp Stf; Long Island Cncl Soc Stds Achv 84; 1st Pl Trphy-Schl Sci Fair 84; Outstdng Englsh Stu 83; Med.

ROGERS, DARCY; Keveny Memorial Acad; Waterviet, NY; (Y); French Clb; GAA; Band; Var L Bsktbl; Tennis; Vllybl; Hon Roll; Bsktbl Hnrbl Mntn All-City 85; Bsktbl Patroon Conf 3rd Team 85; Bus Admin.

ROGERS, ERIN; The Stony Brook Schl; Setauket, NY; (Y); 21/84; Church Yth Grp; Cmnty Wkr; Ski Clb; Chorus; Nwsp Rptr; Nwsp Stf; Yrbk Stf; Var Cheerleading; Var Tennis; Var Trk; Slvr Mdl Trk 84; Gld Mdl 85; Bio.

ROGERS, JOHN P; St John The Baptist HS; Great River, NY; (Y); 30/601; Quiz Bowl; Nwsp Stf; Lit Mag; VP Sr Cls; Rep Stu Cncl; High Hon Roll; Hon Roll; NCTE Awd; NHS; Ntl Merit Ltr; Boston Coll; Law.

ROGERS, JULIE; Gowanda Central HS; Gowanda, NY; (Y); Church Yth Grp; Band; Concert Band; School Play; Nwsp Stf; Yrbk Stf; Stat Bsktbl; Score Keeper; JV Trk; Hon Roll; Liberty U; Resprtry Thrpst.

ROGERS, KAREN; Salem Central Schl; Salem, NY; (Y); Church Yth Grp; VP Pep Clb; Concert Band; Trs Jr Cls; L Fld Hcky; High Hon Roll; NHS; French Clb; GAA; Math Tm; Peer Cnslng 85 Hnr Lttr; Educ.

ROGERS, KELLY; Bradford Central HS; Bradford, NY; (S); 2/30; FBLA; Yrbk Ed-Chief; Pres Soph Cls; Pres Jr Cls; Cheerleading; Socr; Sftbl; High Hon Roll; NHS; Prfct Atten Awd.

ROGERS, KIM; Riverhead HS; Riverhead, NY; (Y); 25/180; Sec FBLA; Rep VICA; Sec Nwsp Rptr; Sec Nwsp Stf; Berkeley; Sec.

ROGERS, LAURA; Sheepshead Bay HS; Brooklyn, NY; (Y); Hnrs Inst Pgm; Psych.

ROGERS, LAURA L; Mt Markham SR HS; W Winfield, NY; (Y); Drama Clb; Sec FHA; Red Cross Aide; Speech Tm; Chorus; Church Choir; School Play; Stage Crew; Yrbk Stf; Hon Roll; Slvr Dllr Perf Effrt 85; Awd Play 84; Utica Schl Comm; Secy.

ROGERS, NANCY; Amsterdam HS; Amsterdam, NY; (Y); 5/320; VP Church Yth Grp; VP Trs Hosp Aide; Band; Church Choir; Yrbk Stf; High Hon Roll; NHS; Pres Schlr; Latin Awd 85; PTA Jenkins Schlrshp 85; NY St Regents Schlrshp 85; Potsdam Coll; Math.

ROGERS, PAUL; Depew HS; Depew, NY; (Y); 41/265; Boys Clb Am; Hon Roll; Dept Awd Hghst Avg Drftg 85; ST U NY Buffalo; Arch.

ROGERS, TRISHA; Gloversville HS; Gloversville, NY; (Y); 12/245; Church Yth Grp; Band; Chorus; Church Choir; Stage Crew; Yrbk Stf; High Hon Roll; Prfct Atten Awd; Math.

ROGERS, WILLIAM; Brewster HS; Brewster, NY; (Y); ROTC; Band; Concert Band; Jazz Band; School Musical; Crs Cntry; Ftbl; Lcrss; Art Clb; Drill Tm; 1st, 2nd, 3rd Pl Battle Of The Barrds 83-85; SR Merit Awd Phys Fit 84; Music.

ROGGIE, KELLY; Lowville Academy Central Schl; Lowville, NY; (Y); Sec VP Art Clb; Nrthrn NY Art Shws Cert Merit 84-85; Mohawk Vly CC; Advtsng/Prod.

ROGGIE, WAYNE; Lowville Acad; Lowville, NY; (Y); 11/135; Am Leg Boys St; 4-H; FFA; JV Var Bsktbl; JV Var Socr; Cit Awd; NHS; Rep Frsh Cls; Rep Soph Cls; Hon Roll; Menno Simons Schlrshp 85; Michael Paddock Memrl Schlrshp 85; K K Kilpatrick Memrl Schlrshp 85; Estrn Mennonite Coll; Bus.

ROGGOW, DAN; Lockport SR HS; Lockport, NY; (Y); Aud/Vis; Latin Clb; Varsity Clb; Capt Swmmng; Hon Roll; Jr NHS; NHS; Niagera Co All St Tm Swiming 83, 84 & 85; YMCA Natl Swim Tm 85; Inter-Sctnl Swim Tm 85.

ROGLIERI, MICHAEL J; Kingston HS; Kingston, NY; (Y); Key Clb; Pep Clb; Ski Clb; School Musical; Stage Crew; Yrbk Phtg; Yrbk Stf; Jr NHS; St Schlr; Hon Roll; Germn Hnr Socty 84-85; Boston U; Pre-Med.

ROGOVE, TAMI; Herricks SR HS; Roslyn, NY; (Y); Cmnty Wkr; Dance Clb; Intnl Clb; Temple Yth Grp; Socr; SADD; Schlrshp Israel Plgrmg; Phy Thrpy.

ROGOZINSKI, DEBORAH; Mattituck HS; Mattituck, NY; (Y); 5/118; Church Yth Grp; German Clb; Mathletes; Church Choir; JV Sftbl; Hon Roll; NHS; Ski Clb; German Hnr Soc 85; Intl Bus.

ROHAN, BRIAN; Msgr Mc Clancy HS; Forest Hills, NY; (S); School Musical; School Play; Stage Crew; Nwsp Stf; Yrbk Stf; Hon Roll; Drama.

ROHAN, PATRICK; East Meadow HS; East Meadow, NY; (S); 10/390; Band; Jazz Band; Mrchg Band; Symp Band; Pres Soph Cls; Pres Jr Cls; Ftbl; Lcrss; Hon Roll; Hst NHS; US Srv Acad.

ROHE, LINDA; St Johns Prep; Astoria, NY; (Y); Computer Clb; High Hon Roll; Jr NHS; NHS; Ntl Merit Ltr; Prfct Atten Awd; Natl Sci Olympiad 84; 1st Hnrs Acad Awd 85; Queens Coll; Comp.

ROHER, MICHAEL A; Madison Central HS; Bouckville, NY; (Y); 11/50; Am Leg Boys St; French Clb; FFA; High Hon Roll; Prfct Atten Awd; Morrisville; Digital Logic Dsgn.

ROHL, JEFF; Amherst Central HS; Eggertsville, NY; (Y); Rep Stu Cncl; Var Socr; Hon Roll; Lutheran Yth Cnsltng Comm 83-84; Church Yth Group Pres 84-85; 1st Tm All Star Goalie 84-85; Canisius Coll; Accntng.

ROHROSEN, JANET C; John H Glenn HS; E Northport, NY; (Y); Art Clb; Chorus; School Musical; Stage Crew.

ROIG, MILAGROS; Cathedral HS; Brooklyn, NY; (Y); Church Yth Grp; Dance Clb; Band; Yrbk Stf; Badmtn; Vllybl.

ROITBERG, DAPHNE; Jericho HS; Jericho, NY; (Y); 12/230; Dance Clb; Drama Clb; Key Clb; Library Aide; Temple Yth Grp; Im Bsktbl; Hon Roll; NHS; 4 Yr Schlrshp Awd To Queens Coll 85; Regents Schlrshp 85; SUNY Binghamton; Psyclgst.

ROJANO, MADELEINE; Dominican Commercial HS; Briarwood, NY; (Y); 51/275; Hosp Aide; Hon Roll; Prfct Atten Awd; Hunter Coll; Nrsg.

ROJAS, ARTHUR F; St Francis Preparatory Schl; Queens Village, NY; (Y); 87/693; Am Leg Boys St; Sec Chess Clb; Pres Debate Tm; Pres Intnl Clb; Pres JA; Sec Model UN; Jr NHS; Political Wkr; Stu Actvty Awd Poli Sci Clb 85; Poli Sci.

ROJAS, CLARA INES; Academy Of St Joseph; Brentwood, NY; (Y); Art Clb; Drama Clb; Hosp Aide; Library Aide; Math Tm; Chorus; School Musical; Var Socr; NHS; Ntl Merit Ltr; Ntl Art Hnr Soc 85; Acadmc Schlrshp 84-85; Ntl Latn Exm-Maxim Cm Laud; Pre-Med.

ROJAS, ERNESTO; High Schl; Elmont, NY; (Y); Boy Scts; Church Yth Grp; CAP; Band; Color Guard; Concert Band; Jazz Band; Stage Crew; Wrstlng; CC Awd; Awd Merit Eagl Sct 84; Citatn Meritrous Svc Cereb Plsy 84; Citatn Twn Of Hepstd George Madison 84; New York Tech; Arch.

ROJAS, EUGENIA; John Jay HS; Brooklyn, NY; (Y); 18/525; Cmnty Wkr; Girl Scts; Spanish Clb; Chorus; Lit Mag; Gym; Vllybl; Prfct Atten Awd; Voice Dem Awd; NYC Frgn Lang Chrmns Assn Cert Excell In Spnsh 85; Pace U; Human Rel.

ROJAS, GINA M; Notre Dame Schl; Rosedale, NY; (Y); 1/55; Var Cheerleading; Var Sftbl; Swmmng; Bausch & Lomb Sci Awd; Hon Roll; NHS; Val; ST Of NY Regnts Schlrshp Awd 85; NY U Schlrshp Awd 85; U Of S CA Schlrshp Awd 85.

ROJAS, JULIO; Stevenson HS; Bronx, NY; (Y); 17/524; Prfct Atten Awd; Lehman Coll; Acctng.

ROLDAN, KAMALA DEVI; St Raymond Acad; Bronx, NY; (Y); 7/68; Science Clb; Jr Cls; Trs Stu Cncl; Hon Roll; Math & Hlth Awds 83-84; Pre Med.

ROLF, LISA; Springville Griffith Inst; Springville, NY; (Y); 77/210; French Clb; GAA; JV Bsktbl; JV Cheerleading; Var JV Sftbl; Var JV Vllybl; Hon Roll; Conisius; Bus Mgmt.

ROLF, MIRIAM; Springville G I HS; Springville, NY; (Y); 3/150; Sec French Clb; Chorus; Orch; School Musical; Trs Sr Cls; Tennis; Vllybl; High Hon Roll; Hon Roll; NHS; Hghst Frnch Avr 2nd & 3rd Yr 84-85; CRS Pres Cmstry Achvt Awd 85; Med.

ROLL, KRISTA L; Galwag Central HS; Galway, NY; (Y); 1/80; Pres Church Yth Grp; Pres Drama Clb; Pres Chorus; School Play; Hst Sr Cls; JV Capt Cheerleading; DAR Awd; High Hon Roll; NHS; Val; Ntl Sci Olympd; Engl, Hist Awds; NYS Regnts Schlrshp; SUNY Pittsburgh; Comms.

ROLL, VANESSA; Pioneer Central HS; Sandusky, NY; (Y); French Clb; Chorus; Church Choir; School Musical; School Play; Swing Chorus; Cheerleading; Hon Roll; Music Hnr Awd; Pres Acad Ftnss Awd; Syracuse U; Bio.

ROLLER, KAREN G; Valley Stream South HS; Valley Stream, NY; (Y); 2/178; Pres AFS; FTA; Mathletes; Science Clb; Temple Yth Grp; High Hon Roll; NHS; Prfct Atten Awd; Sal; Math.

ROLLER, MICHELE; Garden City SR HS; Garden City, NY; (Y); 80/360; Exploring; Hosp Aide; Mrchg Band; Rep Soph Cls; Rep Jr Cls; JV Bsktbl; JV Fld Hcky; Var Trk; Hon Roll; Jr NHS; Finance.

ROLLING, ANGELA E; Sheepshead Bay HS; Brooklyn, NY; (Y); 28/465; Computer Clb; Math Tm; Off Sr Cls; Bowling; Math, Sci Achvt Awd 82-84; Chem, Math, Typng Awds 82-83; Cert Excll 82; Med.

ROLLINS, DIANA; St Francis Prep; Bayside, NY; (Y); Art Clb; Dance Clb; Office Aide; Varsity Clb; Var Sftbl; 1st Pl Miss Long Isl Beauty Pagnt 85; 4th Rnnr-Up Miss NY Finals; St Johns U; Bus.

ROLLINS, LESLYE J; Newburgh Free Acad; Newburgh, NY; (Y); Church Yth Grp; Cmnty Wkr; Drama Clb; Library Aide; PAVAS; Rep Frsh Cls; Rep Soph Cls; Rep Jr Cls; Rep Sr Cls; Rep Stu Cncl; JR Debutante 85; Debutante To-Be 86; Howard U; Pre-Med.

ROLLS, BARBARA; St Marys HS; W Seneca, NY; (S); 4/197; VP Chess Clb; CAP; Computer Clb; VP Science Clb; JV Badmtn; Sftbl; JV Var Vllybl; Hon Roll; Trs NHS; Cadet Of Yr Civil Air Patrol 84; Air Force Acad; Space.

ROLON, JOSE A; New Utrecht HS; Brooklyn, NY; (Y); 65/557; Rgnts Schlrshp; St Johns U; Athletic Admin.

ROLOSON, LORRAINE K; Waterloo HS; Waterloo, NY; (Y); 14/178; Drama Clb; 4-H; JA; Pep Clb; Ski Clb; Chorus; Color Guard; Rep Soph Cls; Hon Roll; Regents Schlrshp 85; Schl Key Awd 82; Geneseo ST U; Librl Arts.

ROM, ROBERT; Archbishop Molloy HS; Ridgewood, NY; (Y); 37/409; Camera Clb; Computer Clb; Dance Clb; German Clb; Science Clb; Yrbk Phtg; Yrbk Stf; Im Bsbl; Im Sftbl; 1st Hnrs 84-85; Photogrphy.

ROMA, MARIA; Union-Endicott HS; Endicott, NY; (Y); Church Yth Grp; Cmnty Wkr; Key Clb; Off Soph Cls; Hon Roll; SUNY.

ROMACK, JAMES; Marion Central HS; Marion, NY; (Y); 2/113; Am Leg Boys St; Library Aide; Concert Band; Jazz Band; Mrchg Band; Trk; High Hon Roll; JP Sousa Awd; NHS; Sal; Cornell U; Ag Econ.

ROMAINE, JAMES R; Valley Central HS; Walden, NY; (Y); Boy Scts; Math Clb; Math Tm; Band; Concert Band; Mrchg Band; NHS; Prfct Atten Awd; Spanish NHS; Enrichment Prgrm 84-85; Comp Sci.

ROMAINE, JOAN; Valley Central HS; Walden, NY; (Y); 44/310; Service Clb; Varsity Clb; Color Guard; Var Lit Mag; Sec Jr Cls; Stu Cncl; JV Sftbl; Var Capt Tennis; NHS; Spanish NHS; Ida A Ruscitti Awd 84; Psych.

ROMAN, BARBARA; Academy Of St Joseph; Ronkonkoma, NY; (Y); Dance Clb; Girl Scts; Hosp Aide; Pres Model UN; Teachers Aide; Capt Var Cheerleading; Hon Roll; NEDT Awd; Orch; Acctg.

ROMAN, CRAIG L; East Hampton HS; E Hampton, NY; (Y); 4/148; Boy Scts; Debate Tm; Band; Mrchg Band; Nwsp Rptr; Nwsp Stf; Yrbk Stf; Lit Mag; Bsbl; Var Capt Socr; All-League Bsbll 85; Gold Medal & Outstndg Fren Stu 85; Schlr Athlete Awd 85; Hamilton Coll; Intl Law.

ROMAN, FRANCIS M; The Loyola Schl; Woodside, NY; (Y); Drama Clb; Leo Clb; Ski Clb; Speech Tm; School Play; Stage Crew; Variety Show; Nwsp Rptr; Nwsp Stf; Yrbk Phtg; Fordham U; Engl.

ROMAN, GRISEL; Eastern District HS; Brooklyn, NY; (Y); FNA; Teachers Aide; Variety Show; Yrbk Stf; Var Bowling; Var Cheerleading; JV Gym; Hon Roll; Mount Holyoke; Pre-Med.

ROMAN, JACQUELINE; Aquinas HS; Bronx, NY; (Y); 23/178; Cmnty Wkr; Hosp Aide; Spanish Clb; Chorus; School Musical; School Play; High Hon Roll.

ROMAN, JAIME; John Dewey HS; Brooklyn, NY; (Y); Art Clb; Office Aide; Science Clb; Spanish Clb; Spanish NHS; 1st Pl Illustrated Poetry Awd PAC 85; Accident Prevntn Awd 85; Graphic Arts.

ROMAN, JIMMY; De Witt Clinton HS; Bronx, NY; (Y); Yrbk Stf; Rep Jr Cls; Hon Roll; Arch.

ROMAN, JOHN; Rocky Point Jr Sr HS; Rocky Point, NY; (S); 17/238; Var L Golf; Stat Bsktbl; Stat Socr; Church Yth Grp; Chorus; Church Choir; Madrigals; Mrchg Band; School Musical; French Clb.

ROMAN, LILLIAN; Newburgh Free Acad; Newburgh, NY; (Y); Church Yth Grp; VICA; Sftbl; High Hon Roll; Hon Roll; Ntl Merit Ltr; Ottaway Fndtn Schlrshp; Zelda K Herbst Mem Schlrshp; Westchester CC; Rsprtry Thrpy.

ROMAN, MARI PAT; Oriskany Central Schl; Rome, NY; (Y); 8/80; Sec Political Wkr; Spanish Clb; Band; School Play; Lit Mag; VP Stu Cncl; Socr; High Hon Roll; Hon Roll; Drama Clb; Natl Cncl Tchrs Frnch Awd 84; Concours Natl De Francais Merit Awd 84; Vassar Coll; Amer Stds.

ROMAN, REGINA; West Hempstead HS; W Hempstead, NY; (Y); Drama Clb; Band; Chorus; Church Choir; Concert Band; Jazz Band; Mrchg Band; School Musical; School Play; Hon Roll; English Achvt Awd; Spnsh Dplma Of Merit; Theater Actng Awd; Wagner Coll; Muscl Thrtr.

ROMAN, STEVE; Kings Park HS; Kings Park, NY; (Y); 44/393; DECA; Science Clb; Trs Jr Cls; Stu Cncl; JV Ftbl; JV Wt Lftg; Var Wrstlng; High Hon Roll; Hon Roll; VP NHS; 2nd Pl Wrstlng Leag Trnmnt 83; 1st Pl-NY OEC 85; Stroudsburg Wrestlng Chmpn 84.

ROMAN, YVONNE; Eastern District HS; Brooklyn, NY; (Y); 12/379; FHA; Math Tm; Teachers Aide; Chorus; Yrbk Stf; Off Stu Cncl; Bowling; Attndnce Awd 85; St Johns U; Law.

ROMANCHIK, LORI; Brewster HS; Brewster, NY; (Y); 34/186; Church Yth Grp; Pep Clb; Radio Clb; Color Guard; Swmmng; Trk; NHS; Robert A Cook Schlrshp Kings Coll 85; Brewster Starr Schlrshp 85; Kings Coll; Bio.

ROMANELLI, MICHELE; Farmingdale HS; Farmingdlae, NY; (Y); Trs Frsh Cls; Trs Soph Cls; Pres Jr Cls; Pres Sr Cls; Rep Stu Cncl; Capt JV Cheerleading; Office Aide; Political Wkr; Service Clb; Mgr(s).

ROMANEO, JEFFREY; East Aurora HS; East Aurora, NY; (S); 22/186; AFS; Ski Clb; Hon Roll; NHS; Karate Brown Belt 81-85; Brkfst Clb 83-85; Skiing 79-85; RIT; Engrng.

ROMANI, WILLIAM A; Ithaca HS; Ithaca, NY; (Y); Am Leg Boys St; Service Clb; VP Rep Stu Cncl; Var JV Bsbl; JV Ftbl; Var L Golf; Var L Ice Hcky; Jr NHS; NHS; Ntl Merit Ltr; Atty Gen Boys Natn Alt NYS Boys 85; Hlth Prof.

ROMANKI, MATTHEW; Odessa-Montour Centeral Schl; Horseheads, NY; (Y); Chess Clb; Band; Concert Band; Jazz Band; Mrchg Band; Orch; Pep Band; Symp Band; Lit Mag; JV Bsbl; St John Fisher; Psych.

ROMANO, CHRISTOPHER; Port Jervis HS; Port Jervis, NY; (Y); 28/200; Boy Scts; Dance Clb; Hosp Aide; Varsity Clb; Yrbk Phtg; Rep Frsh Cls; Off Soph Cls; Pres Jr Cls; Pres Sr Cls; Rep Stu Cncl; Physcl Thrpy.

ROMANO, DANIEL; Fort Hamilton HS; Brooklyn, NY; (Y); 69/553; Church Yth Grp; Band; Concert Band; Jazz Band; Variety Show; Hon Roll; NHS; Chem, Amer Govt, Engl, Acctng, Comp Lit Hnrs 85; Bus Ed Assn Cert Achvt Acctng, Bio Hnr 84-85; LI U Brooklyn; Pharm.

ROMANO, JOSEPH; Maryvale HS; Cheektowaga, NY; (Y); Cmnty Wkr; Spanish Clb; Chorus; School Musical; Im Vllybl; Hon Roll; Accntnt.

ROMANO, PATRICIA; East Islip HS; East Islip, NY; (Y); 4/475; Drama Clb; Spanish Clb; Chorus; Madrigals; School Musical; School Play; Swing Chorus; Lit Mag; Sftbl; Bausch & Lomb Sci Awd; Lafayette Coll; Bio.

ROMANO, PAUL; Aquinas Insti; Rochester, NY; (Y); Boy Scts; Exploring; Marine Corps.

ROMANO, ROSEANN; Bishop Maginn HS; Albany, NY; (Y); Latin Clb; Yrbk Stf; Hon Roll; NHS; Suny At Albany; Econ Mgmt.

ROMANO, TERRI; Spackenkill HS; Poughkeepsie, NY; (Y); 17/167; Church Yth Grp; Hosp Aide; Thesps; Band; Concert Band; Pep Band; School Musical; Stage Crew; Stu Cncl; Var Capt Vllybl.

ROMANO, VIRGINIA SUSAN; Valley Stream Central HS; Valley Stream, NY; (Y); 4/385; Science Clb; Band; Chorus; Orch; Yrbk Ed-Chief; High Hon Roll; NHS; Ntl Merit Ltr; Prfct Atten Awd; Spanish NHS; Music Hnr Soc 84-85; Cornell U; Pre-Vet.

ROMANO, WAYNE; Aquinas Inst; Spencerport, NY; (S); 4/162; Science Clb; Ski Clb; School Play; Yrbk Sprt Ed; Ftbl; Trk; Wt Lftg; Wrstlng; High Hon Roll; Silvr Medlst 84 Empire ST Games 84; All-Star Awd Ftbl 84 Trk 83-85; Natl Chem Merit Awd 84; Cornell; Elec Engrng.

ROMANOS, CHRISTINE J; Cornwall Central HS; Cornwall, NY; (Y); 6/198; VP Pres Library Aide; Hon Roll; NHS; Ntl Merit Ltr; Pres Schlr; SUNY New Paltz; Engrng.

ROMANOW, JEFFREY E; John F Kennedy HS; Plainview, NY; (Y); 44/275; Political Wkr; Yrbk Stf; Trs Jr Cls; Pres Sr Cls; Var Ice Hcky; Hon Roll; NHS; St Schlr; Im Bsktbl; Im Socr; Schl Svc Awd 84; Bus Hnr Soc 85; Boston U; Bus Adm.

ROMANOWSKI, CRAIG; Royalton-Hartland HS; Gasport, NY; (Y); 44/119; Bsbl; Bsktbl; JV Capt Ftbl; Mst Imprvd Lineman 83; MIP Bsktbl 83-84; 2nd Tm All Lgu Cntr Ftbl 84; Bucknell; Elec Engr.

ROMANOWSKI, REBECCA; Union Endicott HS; Endicott, NY; (Y); Church Yth Grp; Latin Clb; Color Guard; Drill Tm; Yrbk Stf; JV Swmmng.

ROME, KERRI; St Francis Prep; Ozone Park, NY; (S); 40/650; Capt Dance Clb; Hosp Aide; Math Clb; Service Clb; Ski Clb; Spanish Clb; Cheerleading; Pom Pon; High Hon Roll; NHS; Suny At Stony Brook; Med.

ROMEO, BARBARA; Msgr Scanlan HS; Bronx, NY; (Y); 30/265; Intnl Clb; Nwsp Rptr; NHS; Prfct Atten Awd; Clss Top 10 Pct 82-83.

ROMEO, MARIANNE L; West Hempstead HS; W Hempstead, NY; (Y); 9/310; Key Clb; Spanish Clb; Yrbk Stf; Stu Cncl; NHS; Scty Womens Engrs Hgh Hnr Cert 85; Ladies Aux Amercnsm Awd 85; Marion Sirota Mem Awd 85; Tufts U; Biomed Engr.

ROMER, DAVID; St Peters HS; Staten Isld, NY; (Y); Church Yth Grp; Bsbl; Bsktbl; JV Crs Cntry; Var Socr; Swmmng; Tennis; JV Trk; St Peters Vrsty Chmps Soccer 84-85; St Patricks Bsktbl CYO JV, Vrsty MVP 84 & 85.

ROMER, MARGARET E; Columbia HS; East Greenbush, NY; (Y); 37/353; Key Clb; Yrbk Stf; Elks Awd; Hon Roll; JC Awd; Pres Schlr; Dorothy King Memrl Awd Schlrshp 85; SUNY Coll-Geneseo.

ROMERO, JUDITH B; Hillcrest HS; Jackson Hts, NY; (Y); 13/960; Church Yth Grp; Cmnty Wkr; Math Tm; Office Aide; Science Clb; Varsity Clb; High Hon Roll; Trs NHS; Ntl Merit Schol; Untd Fdrtn Of Tchrs Schlrshp 85; Pres Awd For Achvt 82; Columbia U; Med.

ROMERO, SANDRA; Mineola HS; Mineola, NY; (Y); French Clb; Rep Stu Cncl; Var Capt Cheerleading; Var Gym; Hon Roll; Comp Pgmr.

ROMERO, SORAYA; Copiague HS; Copiague, NY; (Y); Camera Clb; Dance Clb; French Clb; Hosp Aide; Office Aide; Chorus; Stage Crew; Variety Show; Yrbk Stf; Rep Soph Cls; Svc Stdnt Cncl 85; Schlrshp Russn 83; St Johns; Lang.

ROMERO, VICTORIA; Oneonta HS; Oneonta, NY; (Y); Church Yth Grp; JA; Model UN; Chorus; Church Choir; Hon Roll.

RONAN, JUDITH; Notre Dame HS; Batavia, NY; (S); 20/85; Drama Clb; Pep Clb; School Musical; School Play; Nwsp Rptr; Sec VP Stu Cncl; Capt Cheerleading; Trk; High Hon Roll; NHS; Comm.

RONBERG, ELON; Susan E Wagner HS; Staten Island, NY; (Y); Socr; Hon Roll.

RONCSKA, ANDREA; Springville Griffith Inst; Springville, NY; (Y); 30/200; French Clb; GAA; Key Clb; Chorus; School Musical; Var Diving; JV Var Gym; High Hon Roll; Hon Roll; NHS.

RONDA, MICHELLE; St Francis Prep; Astoria, NY; (Y); 73/690; Pep Clb; Chorus; Rep Jr Cls; Rep Sr Cls; Hon Roll; NHS; Spanish NHS; Ntl Hspanic Schlrshp Comp 84-85; SUNY.

RONDINARO, MARGARET; Watkins Glen HS; Watkins Glen, NY; (S); 4/125; Am Leg Aux Girls St; 4-H; Jazz Band; School Play; Nwsp Bus Mgr; Rep Stu Cncl; Bsktbl; Hon Roll; NHS; Ntl Merit Ltr; Coll; Teacher.

RONEY, JOHN; Greenwich Central HS; Greenwich, NY; (Y); Art Clb; Cmnty Wkr; Pep Clb; Varsity Clb; School Play; Yrbk Stf; Var Ftbl; Var Trk; Wt Lftg; Hon Roll; Art.

RONZONI, RICHARD; Manhasset HS; Manhasset, NY; (Y); Boys Clb Am; Science Clb; Pres Service Clb; Chorus; Rep Stu Cncl; High Hon Roll; Pres NHS; Chess Clb; Stage Crew; Nwsp Rptr; Attitd & Perfmnc Awd For Archry 83; Attitd & Perfmnc Awd For Riflry 85; Archry & Riflt Tm Cptn 83-85; Sci.

ROODMAN, ADAM D; New Rochelle HS; New Rochelle, NY; (Y); Camera Clb; Church Yth Grp; Computer Clb; Church Choir; Yrbk Phtg; Var Wrstlng; Im Bsktbl; Var Trk; Hon Roll; NY ST Regents Schlrshp Awd 84-85; NY ST Assmbly Cert Merit 84-85; Accidental Coll; Econ.

ROODMAN, DAVID; Binghamton HS; Binghamton, NY; (Y); 1/500; Computer Clb; Capt Mathletes; Variety Show; High Hon Roll; NHS; Ntl Merit Ltr; Prfct Atten Awd; Val; Rensselaer Mdl 85; Amer HS Math Exam Awd 85; Lbrl Arts.

ROOK, MICHAEL P; Buffalo Acad/Visual & Perfrmng Arts; Buffalo, NY; (Y); 5/98; Pres Computer Clb; Math Tm; Yrbk Ed-Chief; Yrbk Phtg; Trs Jr Cls; Rep Sr Cls; Rep Stu Cncl; Capt Tennis; Hon Roll; NHS; NY ST Summer Schl Arts 83; Buffalos Our Best Art Show & Book 80-84; Rochester Inst Of Tech; Graphic.

ROONEY JR, JOHN F; Lackawanna SR HS; Lackawanna, NY; (Y); 7/285; Am Leg Boys St; Red Cross Aide; Spanish Clb; Band; High Hon Roll; Hon Roll; NHS; Prfct Atten Awd.

ROONEY, PAUL; Smithtown HS West; Smithtown, NY; (Y); JV Var Bsktbl; Hon Roll.

ROONEY, TOM; St Francis Preparatory Schl; Whitestone, NY; (Y); Church Yth Grp; Cmnty Wkr; Coach Actv; Var Diving; Var Capt Swmmng; Exc In Discipline 82-85; Bus.

ROOS, CHRISTINE; Curtis HS; Staten Island, NY; (Y); #25 In Class; Office Aide; Science Clb; Concert Band; Mrchg Band; Nwsp Stf; Yrbk Stf; JV Cheerleading; NHS; Regents Schlrshp 85; NY U.

ROOSA, LEIGH; Marlboro Central HS; Newburgh, NY; (Y); 6/160; Am Leg Boys St; Church Yth Grp; Band; High Hon Roll; Jr NHS; NHS; Ntl Sci Olympd-Hghst In Chem Cls 85; Mechncl Drwng Awd-Triple R Indstrs 85; Elec Engr.

ROOT, CAREY; Tupper Lake HS; Tupper Lake, NY; (Y); 7/104; Yrbk Bus Mgr; Yrbk Ed-Chief; Yrbk Rptr; Yrbk Sprt Ed; Yrbk Stf; Sec Soph Cls; Sec Jr Cls; Sec Sr Cls; Stu Cncl; JV Bsktbl; Goff-Chevette Scholar 85; Potsdam ST Coll; Eng.

ROOT, GEORGE N; Lockport HS; Lockport, NY; (Y); #25 In Class; Letterman Clb; Varsity Clb; School Play; Golf; Hon Roll; Jr NHS; NHS; Opt Clb Awd; Prfct Atten Awd; Pres Schlr; U NY Buffalo; Aerosp Engr.

ROOT, JULIE; Caledonia-Mumford Central Schl; Caledonia, NY; (Y); 4/95; Church Yth Grp; French Clb; Science Clb; Ski Clb; Chorus; School Musical; Swing Chorus; Yrbk Bus Mgr; Var L Trk; NHS; Varty Shw Music Schlrshp 85; Regnts Schlrshp 85; Grove City Coll.

ROOT, MAUREEN; Mechanicville HS; Mechanicville, NY; (Y); 16/105; French Clb; Spanish Clb; Nwsp Ed-Chief; Nwsp Rptr; Yrbk Phtg; Yrbk Stf; Hon Roll; NHS; Hofstra U; Comm.

ROPERS, CHRISTINA; Beach Channel HS; Glendale, NY; (Y); GAA; Intnl Clb; Rep Frsh Cls; Hon Roll; Jr NHS; Girl Scts Slvr Awd 84; Comm Art.

ROQUE, DONNA; John Adams HS; S Ozone Pk, NY; (Y); Teachers Aide; Variety Show; Vllybl; Ntl Merit Schol; Prfct Atten Awd; Cert 2nd Hnrs Schlrshp 84-85; Vlybl Trphy Awd 84; Hunter Coll; Med Sci.

RORER, KATHRYN E; Earl L Vandermeuen HS; Pt Jefferson, NY; (Y); 1/275; Model UN; Acpl Chr; Capt Color Guard; School Musical; School Play; Nwsp Ed-Chief; Var Cheerleading; Cmnty Wkr; French Clb; Speech Tm; Brown U Bk Awd 84; Rensselaer Poly Tech Inst Math & Sci Awd 84; AUI Trustee Schlrshp 85; Harvard; Med Physics.

ROSADO, ALBERT; Cardinal Hayes HS; New York, NY; (Y); Yrbk Stf; Hon Roll; Acctg.

ROSADO, BERNICE; Herbert H Lehman HS; Bronx, NY; (Y); 65/555; Drama Clb; English Clb; Math Tm; Science Clb; Orch; School Play; Variety Show; Nwsp Rptr; Sr Cls; Stu Cncl; Tripl C Awd 85; Phillips Beth Israel Schlrshp 85; Excllnc Hnrs Engl 85; Phillips Beth Israel Schl Nrsg.

ROSADO, JEANETTE; Clara Barton HS; Brooklyn, NY; (Y); 23/469; Spanish Clb; Hon Roll; NHS; NY U; Psych.

ROSADO, JOSE; Richmond Hill HS; Richmond Hill, NY; (Y); Office Aide; Hon Roll; Spanish NHS; Bus Hnr Soc 84-85; Math Hnr Soc 85; Accntng.

ROSADO, MARILYN; Mabel Dean Bacon HS; New York, NY; (S); 4/299; Trs Church Yth Grp; Office Aide; Vllybl; Hon Roll; Prfct Atten Awd; Cert Of Awd Sci 82; Hnr Soc 83; Acctng.

ROSALIA JR, ANTHONY; Sheepshead Bay HS; Brooklyn, NY; (Y); Cmnty Wkr; Office Aide; Science Clb; Teachers Aide; Nwsp Phtg; High Hon Roll; Prfct Atten Awd; Comptrlrs & Comp Awds 83; Brd Of Educ Dist Compt Litrcy Cntst 83; Brooklyn Coll; Mdcl.

ROSALIA, FRANKLIN M; Earl L Vandermeulen HS; Pt Jefferson, NY; (Y); Computer Clb; Nwsp Stf; Lit Mag; JV Trk; High Hon Roll; Ntl Merit SF; Regents Scholar 86; SUNY Stony Brook; Mech Engrng.

ROSARIO, ALICIA; The Mary Louis Acad; Richmond Hill, NY; (Y); Sec Cmnty Wkr; Hosp Aide; Office Aide; Chorus; Nwsp Phtg; Iona Coll Lang Comptn 1st Hnrs Spanish Native 85; Med.

ROSARIO, LIZETTE; Adlai E Stevenson HS; Bronx, NY; (Y); Church Yth Grp; School Musical; School Play; Nwsp Rptr; Nwsp Stf; Rep Jr Cls; Hon Roll; Cmnty Wkr; Drama Clb; MVP Hndbl Trphy 85; Jrnlsmn Awd 85; Spch Pthlgst.

ROSARIO, REY F; Walton Hihg Schl; Bronx, NY; (Y); Church Yth Grp; English Clb; Bsbl; Trk; St Johns U; Pre Med.

ROSASCO, LORI; Duanesburg Central HS; Delanson, NY; (Y); 1/48; Drama Clb; 4-H; Chorus; Mrchg Band; Swing Chorus; Nwsp Ed-Chief; Cheerleading; Socr; Pres NHS; Lions Clb Del -Haly-Smmr 85; Biochem.

ROSASCO, MICHELLE; Duanesburg Central HS; Delanson, NY; (Y); 3/48; Drama Clb; 4-H; Chorus; Mrchg Band; Swing Chorus; Rep Stu Cncl; Var Cheerleading; Var Socr; NHS; Lions Clb Delg France 85; Hmn Eclgy.

ROSBROOK, CHRISTOPHER S; New Hartford Central Schl; New Hartford, NY; (Y); Exploring; Var Ice Hcky; High Hon Roll; Jr NHS; Physics.

ROSBROOK, WAYNE; Indian River Central HS; Philadelphia, NY; (Y); Rep Stu Cncl; Var L Ftbl; Var L Wrstlng; NEDT Awd; All Nrth All Star Ftbl 84; Frntr Leag Hnrb Mntn Ftbl 84.

ROSCELLO, WALTER; Dryden HS; Dryden, NY; (Y); 3/125; Trs VP French Clb; Ski Clb; Chorus; Ed Yrbk Stf; JETS Awd; Boy Scts; Church Yth Grp; High Hon Roll; NHS; Ntl Merit SF; Congours De Francais-Frnch Lang Fndtn 85; Am Chemcl Soc Chemcl Olympd 85.

ROSCINI, ROBYN; Fayetteville Manlius HS; Fayetteville, NY; (Y); Church Yth Grp; Civic Clb; Cmnty Wkr; Sec JA; Swmmng; Syracuse Symphny JR Gld; Amer Lng Assoc,Cntrl NY Ronald Mc Donald Hse,Grtr Syracuse SR Golf Vlntr; Savannah Coll Art & Dsgn; Arch.

ROSE, CHARLES; Hempstead HS; Hempstead, NY; (S); 54/332; Church Yth Grp; Off FBLA; Hon Roll; Acctng.

ROSE, CHRISTOPHER M; Rushford Central Schl; Caneadea, NY; (Y); 1/33; Band; Chorus; Concert Band; Jazz Band; Pep Band; School Play; Yrbk Ed-Chief; Pres Jr Cls; Rep Stu Cncl; Bausch & Lomb Sci Awd; 3rd Pl William Varick Nevins II HS Comp 84; Elec Engrng.

ROSE, CRAIG; James E Sperry HS; Pittsford, NY; (Y); Church Yth Grp; Radio Clb; Thesps; School Play; Nwsp Rptr; Lit Mag; JV Var Crs Cntry; JV Trk; Hon Roll; NHS; Andrsn Coll; Jrnlsm.

ROSE, DAVID; Cicero-North Syracuse HS; North Syracuse, NY; (S); 86/711; Drama Clb; French Clb; Trs Key Clb; Political Wkr; School Play; VP Bsbl; NHS; Prfct Atten Awd; Im Badmtn; Bsktbl; Babe Ruth All-Star Bsbl Team 81; Merit Roll 81-82; St Lawrence; Bus Admin.

ROSE, DENISE L; Indian River Central HS; Antwerp, NY; (Y); 6/103; Church Yth Grp; French Clb; Band; Chorus; Church Choir; Concert Band; Mrchg Band; Orch; School Play; Stage Crew; Regents Scholarship Of New York State 85; Canton ATC; Accounting.

ROSE, DONA A; Oneida Senior HS; Oneida, NY; (Y); 29/229; Dance Clb; 4-H; Band; Chorus; Mrchg Band; Pep Band; High Hon Roll; Hon Roll; NYS Regents Schlrshp Nrsng 85; Pres Acad Fitness Awd 85; Morrisville Ag & Tech; Nrsng.

ROSE, DONYA; Mercy HS; Middle Island, NY; (Y); 6/123; Church Yth Grp; Civic Clb; Dance Clb; Hosp Aide; Key Clb; Spanish Clb; High Hon Roll; Hon Roll; NHS; Miss Blck Suffolk Cnty 83; Miss Mtrpltn 83; Miss Teen Ultmt 83; Georgetown; Pre-Med.

ROSE, JEFFREY; Hebrew Academy Of Nassau County; W Hempstead, NY; (S); Math Tm; Quiz Bowl; Hon Roll; NHS; NEDT Awd.

ROSE, JOANNE; Joanne M Rose HS; Laurens, NY; (Y); 6/40; Drama Clb; Key Clb; Ski Clb; Sec Spanish Clb; Varsity Clb; Var Cheerleading; Var Sftbl; Var Vllybl; High Hon Roll; NHS; Acctng.

ROSE, JUDITH; James I Oneill HS; Highland Falls, NY; (Y); 7/119; School Play; Rep Stu Cncl; Stat Bsktbl; Sftbl; Swmmng; High Hon Roll; NHS; St Schlr; Schlrshp Yth Understanding Exch Stu Venezuela 83 & Japan 84; St U Ctr Binghamton.

ROSE, KERRY D; Albertus Magnus HS; Monsey, NY; (Y); 20/190; Sec 4-H; VP Latin Clb; Ed Yrbk Ed-Chief; Yrbk Stf; 4-H Awd; High Hon Roll; Hon Roll; NHS; Prfct Atten Awd; 4-H County Medal Wnnr 84; Rcklnd Cnty ST Fair Rep Hrse Demo 85; Awd Natl Latin Hnr Scty 84.

ROSE, KRISTIN; Hilton Central HS; Hilton, NY; (Y); 43/343; Chorus; Concert Band; Mrchg Band; High Hon Roll; Hon Roll; Prncpls Lst 83-84; Amer Chem Socty Awd 84-85; SUNY Brockport; CPA.

ROSE, KRISTINE; Sachem HS; Holbrook, NY; (Y); 218/1500; Science Clb; Yrbk Stf; Var Bowling; Vllybl; Jr NHS; Sci.

ROSE, MICHELLE; Springfield HS; New York, NY; (Y); Church Yth Grp; English Clb; Science Clb; Teachers Aide; Chorus; Yrbk Stf; Sr Cls; Gym; Vllybl; Hon Roll; Air Force; Comp.

ROSE, PATTI A; North Babylon HS; North Babylon, NY; (Y); DECA; Intnl Clb; VICA; Stage Crew; Yrbk Stf; Mgr(s); Sftbl; Dntl Hgyne.

ROSE, RAYMOND; George Wingate HS; Brooklyn, NY; (S); 5/360; Socr; Hon Roll; Val; Pilot.

ROSE, WENDY; Mechanicville HS; Mechanicville, NY; (Y); Church Yth Grp; Teachers Aide; Hon Roll; Lttr From Senate Being On Hnr Roll 84; Softbl Awd 80; NY ST Physical Fitness Awd 82; Hudson Valley CC; Erly Childhd.

ROSEBERRY, ELWOOD L; Lafayette HS; Lafayette, NY; (Y); 13/101; Am Leg Boys St; Cmnty Wkr; 4-H; Spanish Clb; Rep Soph Cls; Rep Jr Cls; Rep Stu Cncl; Var Wrstlng; 4-H Awd; Hon Roll; Amer Lgn Schlstc Awd 85; Amer Lgn Schlrshp 86; Syracuse U; Bus Adm.

ROSEBOOM, VALERIE; Mont Pleasant HS; Schenectady, NY; (Y); 157/257; Church Yth Grp; Cmnty Wkr; DECA; Exploring; Key Clb; Pep Clb; Red Cross Aide; Chorus; Church Choir; Symp Band; Bus.

ROSEEN, KAREN; Frankfort Schuyler HS; Frankfort, NY; (S); 4/100; French Clb; VP GAA; Pres Concert Band; Var L Bsktbl; Var L Sftbl; Var L Tennis; Hon Roll; VP NHS; Frnch Clb Membrshp Awd 84; NY ST Rgnt Schlrshp 85; Medcl Tech.

ROSELL, DAVID; Shenendohowa Central HS; Ballston Lake, NY; (Y); Camera Clb; Cmnty Wkr; Ski Clb; Temple Yth Grp; Off Jr Cls; JV Socr; Capt Trk; High Hon Roll; Outstndng Schltc Achvt Awd 83, 84-85; Empire Winter ST Games NYS 84-85; U Of VT; Lib Arts.

ROSELL, LYN; Rhinebeck Central Schl; Rhinebeck, NY; (Y); AFS; Church Yth Grp; Hosp Aide; Sec Soph Cls; Rep Stu Cncl; Var Bsktbl; Var Fld Hcky; Var Sftbl; Var Vllybl; Hon Roll; Pres Phys Ftns Awd 84-85; MVP Var Vllybl 85; All Leage All Star Tm Sftbl 85; Dutchess CC.

ROSELLI, LISA; New Hyde Park Memorial HS; New Hyde Park, NY; (S); 65/269; Sec DECA; FBLA; High Hon Roll; Hon Roll; Brnz Mdl Honor Soc 84; St John; Bus.

ROSEMAN, TERRY; Eden SR HS; Eden, NY; (Y); Prfct Atten Awd.

ROSEN, CRAIG L; Kingston HS; Kingston, NY; (Y); Debate Tm; NFL; Ski Clb; Concert Band; Pres Frsh Cls; Rep Stu Cncl; Var L Bsbl; Var L Ftbl; Regents Schlrshp; SUNY Albany.

ROSEN, DAVID L; Benjamin N Cardozo HS; Douglaston, NY; (Y); 129/476; Cmnty Wkr; Computer Clb; Temple Yth Grp; Y-Teens; Band; Concert Band; School Play; Hon Roll; Prfct Atten Awd; Rgnts Schlrshp 85; ST U Of Binghamton; Math.

ROSEN, EILEEN; WC Mepham HS; N Bellmore, NY; (Y); 19/385; Drama Clb; Mathletes; Model UN; Hst Orch; Yrbk Stf; Rep Soph Cls; Rep Jr Cls; Rep Sr Cls; Var L Twrlr; Hon Roll; Natl Hispanic Schlrs Awd Fnlst 84; Cornell U; Hotel Admin.

ROSEN, ERIK M; Montecelo Central Schl; Rock Hill, NY; (Y); Debate Tm; Key Clb; Math Clb; Math Tm; Ski Clb; Speech Tm; Yrbk Bus Mgr; Yrbk Rptr; Yrbk Stf; Pres Soph Cls; Econmcs.

ROSEN, JODI S; G W Hewlett HS; Hewlett, NY; (Y); 37/278; AFS; Chess Clb; French Clb; MMM; Science Clb; Concert Band; Lit Mag; Ntl Merit Ltr; Varsity Fencing; Doc.

ROSEN, LISA; Oceanside HS; Oceanside, NY; (Y); 55/550; Cmnty Wkr; Hosp Aide; Office Aide; Temple Yth Grp; Nwsp Ed-Chief; Yrbk Phtg; Rep Frsh Cls; Rep Soph Cls; Rep Jr Cls; Hon Roll; Abraham Joshua Heschel USY Hnr Soc 84-85; Hebrew Awd 85; Natl Fdrtn Mns Clbs Awd 83.

ROSEN, REBECCA; Onteora Central Schl; Boiceville, NY; (S); 18/245; Teachers Aide; Stat Ftbl; Mgr Trk; High Hon Roll; Hon Roll; NHS; Rochester Inst Tech; Comp Mth.

ROSEN, ROBIN; Sachem High School North; Lk Ronkonkoma, NY; (Y); Drama Clb; French Clb; Ski Clb; Chorus; Madrigals; School Musical; Nwsp Stf; Yrbk Stf; Stu Cncl; Tennis; NYSSMA Vocal Comptn-6a 85; Schl Sci Fair-Meritorious Awd 83; Hstry.

ROSEN, VICKI; Massapequa HS; Massapequa, NY; (Y); 52/450; Cmnty Wkr; Pep Clb; Rep Jr Cls; Pres Stu Cncl; Stat Bsktbl; Stat Ftbl; High Hon Roll; NHS; French Clb; Spanish Clb; Regnts Schlrshp 85; Comm Ldrshp Awd; Northwestern U; Polit Sci.

ROSENBAUM, MORRIS; Forest Hills HS; Forest Hills, NY; (Y); 238/881; Office Aide; Band; Concert Band; Jazz Band; Var Bowling; Prfct Atten Awd; Daily News Pride Of Yankees Awd 85.

ROSENBERG, ANDREW; Lawrence HS; Woodmere, NY; (Y); 28/379; Cmnty Wkr; Key Clb; VP Science Clb; Spanish Clb; JV Var Bsbl; High Hon Roll; NHS; Long Islnd Sci Cngrs Merit Awd 83; U Binghamton; Med.

ROSENBERG, BETH; Lawrence HS; Atlantic Beach, NY; (Y); DECA; JA; Pep Clb; Spanish Clb; Temple Yth Grp; Chorus; Capt Cheerleading; Gym; Hon Roll; Chrldng Awd Vrsty Chrldr 84-85; Psych.

ROSENBERG, DEBRA; Midwood HS; Brooklyn, NY; (Y); Science Clb; Service Clb; Temple Yth Grp; Chorus; Variety Show; Lit Mag.

ROSENBERG, MARC; Midwood HS; Brooklyn, NY; (Y); 196/600; Cmnty Wkr; Political Wkr; Teachers Aide; Chorus; Color Guard; Ftbl; Score Keeper; Coll Entrnc Pgm; Amer Hist Advnc Plcmnt; NY U; Phys Ther.

ROSENBERG, MICHELE; John Glenn HS; E Northport, NY; (Y); Cmnty Wkr; Red Cross Aide; Temple Yth Grp; Y-Teens; Chorus; Orch; Hon Roll; Cert Advncd Life Svng 83; Burger King Food Prod Ldr 85; Law.

ROSENBERG, MICHELLE; Northport HS; Northport, NY; (Y); 26/650; Pres French Clb; Acpl Chr; Concert Band; Mrchg Band; School Musical; Symp Band; Variety Show; High Hon Roll; NHS; NYS Rgnts Schlrshp 85; Awd For Excel Frnch 85; SUNY-BINGHAMTON; Intl Lwyr.

ROSENBERG, SHERYL; Valley Central HS; Walden, NY; (Y); 10/294; Mgr Church Yth Grp; Capt Math Tm; Spanish Clb; Hon Roll; NHS; Prfct Atten Awd; Spanish NHS; Enrchmnt Pgm 85-86.

ROSENBERG, STEVEN; Spring Valley HS; Spring Valley, NY; (Y); 3/420; Trs Computer Clb; Mathletes; Math Clb; Math Tm; Quiz Bowl; Science Clb; Sec Temple Yth Grp; Lit Mag; Pres Sr Cls; Trk; Cornell Clb Outstndng JR Of Rcklnd Cnty 85; Rensselaer Medal Achvt In Sci & Math 85.

ROSENBERGER, LAURA; Rocky Point JR SR HS; Rocky Point, NY; (S); 2/200; Var Crs Cntry; Var Trk; Hon Roll; NHS; Cross Ctry All Conf 82-84; Track All Conf 82-84; Crossctry 82; Stony Brook U; Genetic Res.

ROSENBLATT, JILL; Sachem North HS; Holtsville, NY; (Y); 467/1383; Intrprtr Frgn Lang.

ROSENBLATT, PAULETTE D; Art & Design HS; New York, NY; (Y); 13/411; High Hon Roll; Hon Roll; NHS; Ntl Art Hnr Soc 85; Awd Recgntn Svc Art & Design 84.

ROSENBLUM, JONATHAN; Albany HS; Albany, NY; (Y); 31/600; Sec Temple Yth Grp; Ed Nwsp Phtg; Yrbk Bus Mgr; Ed Yrbk Phtg; Hon Roll; NHS; Abraham Joshua Heschel Hnr Soc 83-85; Tufts U; Mech Engr.

ROSENECKER, JULIE A; Mount St Mary Acad; Tonawanda, NY; (Y); 13/96; French Clb; Stage Crew; Nwsp Ed-Chief; Yrbk Bus Mgr; Stu Cncl; Im Badmtn; Coach Actv; Hon Roll; NHS; Schlrshp U Of Caen France 85; Syracuse U; Broadcast Jrnlsm.

ROSENFELD, JOHN J; Horseheads HS; Horseheads, NY; (Y); 76/407; Chess Clb; Ski Clb; Var L Golf; Var L Tennis; Hon Roll; St Schlr; U Of Buffalo; Math.

ROSENFELD, JOSEPH W; Bay Shore HS; Bay Shore, NY; (Y); 2/376; Math Tm; Capt Gym; Lcrss; Pres NHS; Pres Schlr; Sal; Outstndng Eng Stu 85; Steuben Awd 85; Boston U Schlrshp 85; Boston U; Bus.

ROSENFELD, LINDA; Lynbrook HS; E Rockaway, NY; (Y); Pres FBLA; Mathletes; Spanish Clb; Temple Yth Grp; Varsity Clb; Yrbk Ed-Chief; Yrbk Stf; Cheerleading; Hon Roll; NHS.

ROSENFIELD, PAUL A; Rye Country Day Schl; Hartsdale, NY; (Y); AFS; Model UN; Scholastic Bowl; Ski Clb; Chorus; Jazz Band; Var Crs Cntry; Var Lcrss; Ntl Merit SF; Harvard U Bk Awd-Acadmc Excllnc 85; George Washington U Medal-Math & Sci 85; Med.

ROSENSTEIN, ELLEN; Edward R Murrow HS; Brooklyn, NY; (Y); 125/725; Hosp Aide; Library Aide; Brooklyn Coll; Spec Ed Tchr.

ROSENSTEIN, SHARI L; Washingtonville HS; Blooming Grove, NY; (Y); French Clb; Pres JA; Spanish Clb; Rep Frsh Cls; Rep Soph Cls; Rep Jr Cls; Rep Sr Cls; Rep Stu Cncl; Var Mgr(s); Rgnts Schlrshp 85; Boston U; Mrktng.

ROSENTHAL, BRENDA; Brighton HS; Rochester, NY; (Y); 1/320; Pres Spanish Clb; Yrbk Stf; VP Jr Cls; Sec Stu Cncl; Margaret Wosnawski Scholar Spn Achvt 85; Georgetown U.

ROSENTHAL, CHERYL; Kings Park HS; Kings Pk, NY; (Y); 42/393; Political Wkr; Pres Temple Yth Grp; Lit Mag; JV Capt Socr; Var JV Vllybl; High Hon Roll; NHS; Var Ltr Soccr,Vllybl 83-85; Polticl Sci.

ROSENTHAL, DIANE; Syosset HS; Woodbury, NY; (Y); 23/524; Cmnty Wkr; Political Wkr; Lit Mag; Rep Stu Cncl; Capt Var Tennis; NHS; NYS Yth Cncl 84-85; Yth Particptn Proj 83-85; HOBY Fndtn Ldrshp Sem 83; U PA.

ROSENTHAL, MATTHEW H; Coxsackie/Athens HS; Athens, NY; (Y); 7/108; Math Clb; Spanish Clb; Band; Chorus; Stu Cncl; Bsktbl; Ftbl; High Hon Roll; NHS; Engrng.

ROSENTHAL, RICHARD H; Fayetteville-Manlius HS; Manlius, NY; (Y); Drama Clb; JCL; Sec Temple Yth Grp; Chorus; School Musical; Variety Show; Nwsp Phtg; Nwsp Stf; High Hon Roll; Hon Roll; Sci Olympiad Bio & Chem; Mdlst Natl Latin Exam; Pre-Law.

ROSENTHAL, ROBYN; The Bronx HS Of Science; Bronx, NY; (Y); Cmnty Wkr; Office Aide; Teachers Aide; Sr Cls; NHS; Cornell U; Nutrition.

ROSENZWEIG, DENISE; White Plains HS; White Plains, NY; (Y); 48/500; Art Clb; Dance Clb; English Clb; Ski Clb; Spanish Clb; Temple Yth Grp; Y-Teens; Nwsp Phtg; Nwsp Stf; Yrbk Stf; Rich Awd 85; Cornell Ap Summr Prog 85; Bus.

ROSER, CATHY; Altmar-Parish-Williamstown HS; Altmar, NY; (Y); 13/98; Mrchg Band; Bsktbl; Socr; Hon Roll; Camera Clb; Varsity Clb; Band; Concert Band; Orch; Sftbl; Faculty Awd 85; Potsdam ST; Engl.

ROSERO, ALEX; St Johns Prep; Corona, NY; (Y); Ski Clb; JV Socr; Swmmng; High Hon Roll; Hon Roll; Prfct Atten Awd; St Johns U; Real Estate.

ROSHAY, KATHY; Christopher Columbus HS; New York, NY; (Y); Band; Hon Roll; Teachers Aide; Concert Band; Orch; Yrbk Stf; Swmmng; High Hon Roll; Bus Mgmt.

ROSKE, MICHAEL F; Vestal SR HS; Vestal, NY; (Y); 17/450; Boy Scts; Church Yth Grp; Mathletes; Band; Church Choir; Trs Mrchg Band; Socr; High Hon Roll; Ntl Merit SF; Cmnty Wkr; Clarkson U; Comp Sci.

ROSKOS, ROBERT; Sachem High School North; Holbrook, NY; (Y); 42/1509; Boy Scts; Science Clb; Spanish Clb; Sachem HS Achvt Awd Resrch 83; Engrng.

ROSNER, BETH A; George W Hewlett HS; Valley Stream, NY; (Y); 51/270; French Clb; Ed Yrbk Stf; Rep Frsh Cls; Off Soph Cls; Rep Jr Cls; VP Sr Cls; Stu Cncl; Var L Cheerleading; Var L Trk; Hon Roll; Brandeis U; Psychlgy.

ROSNER, CHERAY; Yeshiva University High Schl Girls; Passaic, NJ; (Y); 1/99; Cmnty Wkr; Scholastic Bowl; Temple Yth Grp; Ed Nwsp Stf; Ed Yrbk Stf; High Hon Roll; NHS; Val; Rabbi Dr Samuel Blekin Meml Awd Excell Hrns, Jewish & Gen Stds 85; Fclty Awds Adv Plcmt & AP Math 85.

ROSPARS, WILLIAM G; Saint Dominic HS; New London, CT; (Y); Scholastic Bowl; Stage Crew; Var Bsbl; Var Capt Ftbl; Im Vllybl; Im Wt Lftg; High Hon Roll; Hon Roll; NHS; Ntl Merit Ltr; Outstndng SR Boy In Schlrshps, Athl & Achvt 85; Apptd U S Coast Grd Acad 85; U S Coast Guard Acad; Civl Engr.

ROSS, ANDREW M; Yorktown HS; Peeksill, NY; (Y); 37/368; Chorus; School Play; Variety Show; Nwsp Stf; Rep Stu Cncl; High Hon Roll; Ntl Merit Ltr; Trs Radio Clb; Thesps; School Musical; Dir Schl Play 84; Wllmstwn Thtre Fest 84; Lwyr Stu Bar Assoc 82-85; Natl Arts Rec & Tlnt Srch 84-85; Actor.

ROSS, BEATRICE; Haverling Central HS; Bath, NY; (Y); Exploring; Latin Clb; Capt JV Bsktbl; Var Trk; Stat Wrstlng; Mst Imprv Trk & Field 85; SUNY Brockport; Ath Training.

ROSS, BRIAN K; Hudson Falls HS; Hudson Falls, NY; (Y); 5/210; French Clb; Key Clb; Acpl Chr; Orch; Symp Band; Yrbk Ed-Chief; Crs Cntry; Swmmng; French Hon Soc; Trs Pres NHS; Schl Mscl 84; U Of CT; Actrl Sci.

ROSS, CAROLINE M; St Marys Girls HS; Manhasset, NY; (Y); 2/154; Pres Trs Service Clb; Yrbk Stf; Var Capt Swmmng; Im Tennis; High Hon Roll; Kiwanis Awd; NHS; Sal; Ski Clb; Cert Of Supr Achvt NY Math League 84; Georgetown U; Bus.

ROSS, DANIEL; Nev Rochelle HS; New Rochelle, NY; (Y); Co-Capt Math Tm; Model UN; Band; Jazz Band; Symp Band; Rptr Lit Mag; Ntl Merit SF; Sec Spanish NHS; Temple Yth Grp; Mrchg Band; U Of PA Aluni Assn Awd For Acdmc Exc 85; Iona Lng Cntst 2nd Hnrs 85; Pre-Law.

ROSS, DEANNE M; Greece Athena HS; Rochester, NY; (Y); 67/282; Hon Roll; Ntl Merit Ltr; NY ST Regents Schlrshp 84-85; SUNY Oswego; Computer Science.

ROSS, DIANNE; Christopher Columbus HS; Bronx, NY; (Y); 100/760; Church Yth Grp; Dance Clb; Drama Clb; Library Aide; Chorus; Church Choir; School Play; Hon Roll; Prfct Atten Awd; Hygiene Excell Awd 84; Psych Excell Awd 85; Law.

ROSS, JAMES; Nottingham HS; Syracuse, NY; (Y); Church Yth Grp; Im JV Ftbl; Im Mgr(s); Im Score Keeper; Im Timer.

ROSS, JENNIFER; Cicero-North Syracuse HS; Clay, NY; (S); 1/711; Math Tm; Church Choir; Orch; School Musical; Hon Roll; NHS; Ntl Merit SF; Val; German Clb; Mathletes; Rensselaer Math & Sci Awd 84; Wellesley Book Awd 84; Archaeslogy.

ROSS, KATHRYNE; Ichabod Crane HS; Valatie, NY; (Y); 3/183; Drama Clb; German Clb; GAA; Flag Corp; Var L Crs Cntry; Var L Trk; High Hon Roll; NHS; Rotary Awd; Outstdng Soph For Part In The Hugh O Brian Yth Fndtn Ldrshp Semnr 84; Intl Stds.

ROSS, KRISTEN; La Salle SR HS; Niagara Falls, NY; (Y); Girl Scts; Hon Roll; Jr NHS; NHS; Prfct Atten Awd; SOC Wrk.

ROSS, LANA; Ticonderoga HS; Hague, NY; (Y); Varsity Clb; Rep Frsh Cls; Rep Soph Cls; Rep Jr Cls; VP Stu Cncl; Capt Cheerleading; Var Gym; High Hon Roll; Hon Roll; NHS; Elem Educ.

ROSS, LISA; Trott Voc & Tech HS; Niagara Falls, NY; (Y); Hosp Aide; Nwsp Stf; Ed Yrbk Stf; NHS; Psych.

ROSS, LORRIE; Corning-Painted Post West; Corning, NY; (Y); 32/264; Thesps; Band; Concert Band; Mrchg Band; School Musical; Rep Frsh Cls; Rep Jr Cls; High Hon Roll; Natl Hnr Soc 85; Corning CC; Comp Sci.

ROSS, MICHELLE; Edison Tech; Rochester, NY; (Y); Exploring; Office Aide; Teachers Aide; Varsity Clb; Rep Frsh Cls; Var Capt Bsktbl; Var Trk; Var Capt Vllybl; Hon Roll; Rchstr Lge All-Star Team Bsktbl 83-85; Sctn V Sprtsmnshp Awd 85; Awd Trk & Vlybl 83-85; Elec Engr.

ROSS, NINA L; Briarcliff HS; Briarcliff, NY; (Y); Cmnty Wkr; French Clb; Red Cross Aide; Teachers Aide; Yrbk Ed-Chief; Trs Soph Cls; Pres Sr Cls; Rep Stu Cncl; Mgr Var Fld Hcky; High Hon Roll; Sci Hnrs Program At Columbia U; Civil Engrng.

ROSS, PATRICIA; Tottenville HS; Staten Island, NY; (Y); French Clb; GAA; MMM; Ski Clb; Yrbk Rptr; Yrbk Stf; Cheerleading; Score Keeper; Tennis; Hon Roll; St Johns U; Bus.

ROSS, ROBERT; Bearer River Central HS; Lowville, NY; (Y); Trs Church Yth Grp; French Clb; Teachers Aide; Church Choir; Nwsp Stf; Ed Yrbk Phtg; Yrbk Stf; Trs Stu Cncl; Mgr(s); Outstndng Svc To Faculty & Stu 84-85; Stu Govt Schlrshp 85; Canton ATC; Accntng.

ROSS, ROBERT; Franklin Acad; Malone, NY; (Y); 35/252; Chorus; Swing Chorus; JV Crs Cntry; JV Var Trk; Prfct Atten Awd; Profsnl Chef.

ROSS, SCOTT M; West Babylon HS; W Babylon, NY; (Y); 3/400; Nwsp Rptr; Nwsp Stf; Var Capt Socr; Var Capt Tennis; High Hon Roll; Jr NHS; NHS; Newsdays Ldng Schlstc Achvr 85; NYS Rgnts Schlrshp 85; All Cnty Soccr Tm 85; Rensselaer Polytech Inst; Bus.

ROSS, VICTORIA L; Voorheesville JR SR HS; Voorheesville, NY; (Y); 3/123; Key Clb; Concert Band; Trs Jr Cls; Trs Sr Cls; Var L Cheerleading; Capt L Crs Cntry; Var Trk; Dnfth Awd; High Hon Roll; VP NHS; Hartwick Coll; Med.

ROSSELLI, PAULA; Lockport SR HS; Lockport, NY; (Y); Latin Clb; Cheerleading; Explorers Group Law 84; U Buffalo; Law.

ROSSETTI, TIMOTHY S; Greece Athena HS; Rochester, NY; (Y); 26/281; DECA; Math Tm; Varsity Clb; Yrbk Stf; Var Bsbl; Var Bsktbl; Var Socr; Hon Roll; NHS; NYS Regents Schlrshp 85; Pres Acad Fitness Awd 85; VA Tech; Elect Engrng.

ROSSETTIE, JOHN C; Corning Painted Post East HS; Corning, NY; (Y); Church Yth Grp; Varsity Clb; L Bsktbl; L Ftbl; L Lcrss; Hon Roll; Letterman Clb; Rep Frsh Cls; Rep Soph Cls; Rep Jr Cls; All Lg Lacrosse 85.

ROSSI, DANNY A; Sachem HS North; Holbrook, NY; (Y); 116/1442; Computer Clb; German Clb; Carnegie Mellon U; Computer Eng.

ROSSI, ELIZABETH A; Rome Free Acad; Rome, NY; (Y); 26/536; Cmnty Wkr; Chorus; Nwsp Ed-Chief; Hon Roll; Jr NHS; NHS; Area All ST Choir; Acad All Amer; U S Jrnlsm Awd; Colgate U.

ROSSI, ERIC S; Commack H S North; Commack, NY; (Y); Am Leg Boys St; MMM; Chorus; Madrigals; School Musical; Swing Chorus; Nwsp Rptr; High Hon Roll; Ntl Merit Ltr; All Cnty Chrs 83 & 84; Polit Stud.

ROSSI, JANET; Lynbrook HS; Lynbrook, NY; (Y); 15/265; Hon Roll; NY ST Regnts Schlrshp 85; Suburban Tech Schl Schlrshp 85; Suburban Tech Schl; Elec Tech.

ROSSI, LAURA; St John Villa Acad; Staten Island, NY; (Y); Hon Roll; Natl Sci Olympiad 84; Comm.

ROSSI, MARK; Skaneateles HS; Skaneateles, NY; (S); 16/165; Church Yth Grp; Cmnty Wkr; Drama Clb; Exploring; Math Clb; Nwsp Stf; Pres Soph Cls; Var L Tennis; High Hon Roll; NHS; Natl Merit Sci Awd 83; Bsns Admin.

ROSSI, PETER; Union-Endicott HS; Endicott, NY; (Y); Hon Roll; Opt Clb Awd; Yth Apprctn Week Citatn 84; RPI Medal Outstndng Math & Sci 84; Earl Brink Schlrshp 85; DE Vly Coll; Landscp Des.

ROSSI, VINCENT; Nazareth Regional HS; Brooklyn, NY; (Y); Math Tm; Im Bsbl; Im Fld Hcky; Im Ftbl; NHS; Geometry Anlys Hnrs & Calculus 83-84 & 85; Bio-Chem, & Earth Sci 83-84 & 85; European Cltrl Studies 84; Math.

ROSSILLO, MARIA; Bishop Ford Central Catholic HS; Brooklyn, NY; (Y); St Francis Coll; Accntng.

ROSSINI, ANTHONY; St Francis Prep; Beechhurst, NY; (Y); 220/700; Hon Roll; Optimat Soc; Med.

ROTELLA, JANINE; Saint Barnabas HS; Bronx, NY; (Y); Library Aide; Twrlr; Initl Cert Catechist Frmatn Pgm 84; Westchester CC; Lib Art.

ROTERS, STEPHANIE; Cathedral HS; Astoria, NY; (Y); 37/298; Art Clb; Church Yth Grp; Variety Show; Hon Roll; Medal In Art 85; Mtl Mngmnt.

ROTH, CHARLES; Tha Albany Acad; Voorheesville, NY; (Y); 2/62; Nwsp Rptr; Yrbk Stf; Var L Crs Cntry; Var L Trk; Var Capt Wrstlng; Ntl Merit SF; Sal; Math Tm; Varsity Clb; Socr; Colonial Cncl 98 Lb Wrstlng Chmpn 84; Williams Coll Bk Awd 84; 1st Pl Colonial Cncl Math Contst 83; U Of PA; Chem Engrng.

ROTH, CHEDVA; Shulamith HS; Brooklyn, NY; (S); Art Clb; High Hon Roll.

ROTH, JOHN; Whitesboro SR HS; Utica, NY; (Y); Boy Scts; Church Yth Grp; Science Clb; Chorus; Rep Stu Cncl; Wrstlng; Hon Roll; 2nd Pl SR Div-Utica Coll Sci Fair 84; Pre Law.

ROTH, KATHY; Holland Central HS; Holland, NY; (Y); Varsity Clb; Band; Concert Band; Mrchg Band; Var Bsktbl; Var Vllybl; Hon Roll.

ROTH, KIMBERLY; Ichabod Crane HS; Valatie, NY; (Y); 15/185; Drama Clb; Library Aide; Math Clb; Color Guard; School Play; Yrbk Stf; Lit Mag; JV Fld Hcky; Var Mgr(s); High Hon Roll; Sci Puzzle Wnnr 82-83; Mst Imprvd Soc Studs 83-84 & 84-85; Effort & Achvt Mth 83-84 & 84-85; SUNY; Nrsng.

ROTH, KRISTEN; G Ray Bodley HS; Fulton, NY; (S); Science Clb; Chorus; Church Choir; Concert Band; Jazz Band; Mrchg Band; Orch; Var L Crs Cntry; High Hon Roll; Trs Sec Church Yth Grp; Best Marching Woodwind 84; Mst Val Woodwind Member Marching Bnd 83.

ROTH, ROBERT; The Bronx HS Of Science; Bayside, NY; (Y); Art Clb; JA; Nwsp Stf; Yrbk Stf; Cooper Un Sat Pgm 82-84; NY Hrt Assoc Ftns Awd 83; Bx HS Sci Athl Awd 83; Comm.

ROTH JR, RONALD M; Greenville Central HS; Greenville, NY; (Y); Am Leg Boys St; Boy Scts; Sec Spanish Clb; School Musical; Nwsp Rptr; Ed Nwsp Stf; VP Stu Cncl; Var Crs Cntry; JV Var Socr; Var Trk; Jrnlsm.

ROTH, TIMOTHY; Farmingdale HS; Farmingdale, NY; (Y); Drama Clb; Chorus; Madrigals; School Musical; Hon Roll; NHS; Nassau Cnty Music Fstvl 85; A On NYSSMA Vocl Solo 85.

ROTHAUG, TINA; Middleburgh Central HS; Middleburgh, NY; (S); 3/90; Am Leg Aux Girls St; Trs Sec Church Yth Grp; Chorus; Trs Concert Band; Jazz Band; Mrchg Band; Var L Bsktbl; Hon Roll; Sec Jr NHS; Pres NHS; Elmira Coll Key Awd 84; Clscl Leag Cum Laude Cert 84; Engrng.

ROTHENBERG, ERIC M; Woodlands HS; Hartsdale, NY; (Y); 21/188; Drama Clb; Key Clb; Yrbk Stf; Rep Stu Cncl; JV Bsbl; Var L Ice Hcky; Im Lcrss; Var Capt Socr; NHS; Lehigh U; Med.

ROTHERMEL, CAITLIN; St Vincent Ferrer HS; New York, NY; (Y); Drama Clb; Science Clb; Acpl Chr; Chorus; Church Choir; Madrigals; School Musical; School Play; Hon Roll; NEDT Awd; Sci Natl Olympd Hgh Scoring Medl Soph & SR Yrs; NYU.

ROTHFARB, LILLY A; Walt Whitman HS; Huntington, NY; (Y); 7/625; Pres German Clb; Key Clb; Mathletes; Stage Crew; Lit Mag; High Hon Roll; Jr NHS; NHS; Ntl Merit Ltr; St Schlr; Stu Of Yr 82; Cornell U; Psychlgy.

ROTHMAN, ILYSSA; James Madison HS; Brooklyn, NY; (S); Debate Tm; Math Tm; Quiz Bowl; School Musical; Variety Show; Yrbk Ed-Chief; Ed Lit Mag; High Hon Roll; Sal; Chorus; Arista-Archon Pres 83; Model City Congress 84-85; Fidelitas 84-85; Law.

ROTHMAN, JONATHAN H; New Rochelle HS; New Rochelle, NY; (Y); 62/597; Library Aide; Spanish Clb; Temple Yth Grp; Jazz Band; Orch; Lit Mag; NHS; Pres Spanish NHS; Prncpls Awd Beth El Hebrew H S 83; ST U NY Binghamton; Intl Rel.

ROTHMAN, ROBERT; Commack North HS; Commack, NY; (Y); Exploring; Service Clb; Temple Yth Grp; Mrchg Band; Stu Cncl; Var Tennis; High Hon Roll; NHS; Med.

ROTHROCK, TIMOTHY; Avon Central HS; Avon, NY; (Y); 38/107; Church Yth Grp; Drama Clb; Ski Clb; Spanish Clb; Varsity Clb; Chorus; School Musical; Yrbk Stf; VP Sr Cls; JV Capt Bsbl; Physcl Thrpy.

ROTHRUM, KIMBERLY; Cicero-North Syracuse HS; Clay, NY; (S); 45/711; Exploring; JA; Stu Cncl; Powder Puff Ftbl; Hon Roll; NHS; Stu Tutrng Awd 83; Engr.

ROTHSTEIN, MIRIAM; Nyack SR HS; S Nyack, NY; (Y); Drama Clb; School Musical; School Play; Yrbk Ed-Chief; Pres Frsh Cls; High Hon Roll; NHS; Pres Schlr; Band; Mrchg Band; Century III Ldrshp Schlrshp 85; Congrssnl Mdl Of Mrt 85; NY U.

ROTHWELL, MICHAEL J; Nurnburg American HS; APO, NY; (Y); Band; Concert Band; Jazz Band; Mrchg Band; Trs Stu Cncl; Var L Bsktbl; Var L Tennis; High Hon Roll; Jr NHS; NHS; Engrng.

ROTT, DEBORAH; Kenmore West SR HS; Tonawanda, NY; (Y); 53/445; Trs Math Tm; Concert Band; Mrchg Band; Rep Stu Cncl; Var Bsktbl; Var Socr; Hon Roll; Ntl Merit Ltr; NYS Rgnts Schlrshp, Prsdntl Acad Ftnss Awd 85; Renssalawer Polytech Inst:Comp.

ROTTENBERG, JUDITH L; Hendrick Hudson HS; Peekskill, NY; (Y); 11/194; Cmnty Wkr; Yrbk Stf; Pres Frsh Cls; Var Capt Cheerleading; High Hon Roll; NHS; Ntl Merit Schol; Pres Schlr; Office Aide; Rotry Exchng N Ireland 83; Tufts U; Jrnlsm.

ROTTER, SHARON; Shulamith HS; Brooklyn, NY; (S); 1/28; Chorus; School Musical; Nwsp Ed-Chief; Yrbk Ed-Chief; Pres Jr Cls; NHS; NEDT Awd; Brooklyn Coll.

ROTUNNO, ANDREA; Earl L Vandermeulen HS; Mt Sinai, NY; (Y); 52/286; Leo Clb; Hon Roll; Fash Desgnr.

ROTUNNO, BARBARA; Commack HS South; Commack, NY; (S); 108/400; Cmnty Wkr; Drama Clb; MMM; Chorus; School Musical; Stage Crew; Variety Show; Nwsp Stf; Stu Cncl; Hon Roll.

ROULHAC, ARLETTE; Walt Whitman HS; Huntington, NY; (Y); Library Aide; Teachers Aide; Chorus; Yrbk Stf; Lit Mag; Stu Cncl; Mgr(s); 3rd Pl Spch Cntst 83; Acctg.

ROUNDS, DEAN; Newfane Central HS; Newfane, NY; (Y); Latin Clb; Archit Engrng.

ROUNDS, MARK; General Brown HS; Watertown, NY; (Y); Church Yth Grp; Key Clb; Church Choir; Rep Jr Cls; Var L Bsktbl; Cit Awd; Hon Roll; NHS; Prfct Atten Awd; Varsity Clb; Yorker Clb 84-85; Clarkson U; Engrng.

ROUNDTREE, DEBRA; La Salle SR HS; Niagara Falls, NY; (S); 9/258; Hon Roll; Hnr Roll 81-84; Top Ten Awd 84-85; NCCC; Engr.

ROUNDY, RICHARD; Msgr Mc Clancy HS; Woodside, NY; (Y); Sci Fair-Merit Awd 83; Hnr Cert-1st & 2nd Hnrs 83-85; Muscn.

ROUNSAVILLE, BETTY; De Ruyter Central Schl; De Ruyter, NY; (S); #4 In Class; 4-H; Girl Scts; Yrbk Stf; VP Frsh Cls; Pres Soph Cls; Rep Stu Cncl; Var Vllybl; 4-H Awd; Hon Roll; NHS; Delhi Ag & Tech; Ag.

ROURA, DAVID; Deer Park HS; Deer Park, NY; (Y); 7/450; Math Tm; Spanish Clb; Hon Roll; St Schlr; NY ST Rgnts Schlrshp 85; Boston U; Engrng.

ROURKE, BRIDGET; Academy Of The Holy Names; Albany, NY; (Y); Debate Tm; Drama Clb; NFL; Thesps; School Play; Nwsp Stf; Rep Jr Cls; Swmmng; Tennis; Hon Roll; NYS Mrt Awd Bio 85; Acad Holy Names Awd Alg II 85; Rec Stu Cncl 86; Northeastern Ithaca; Phy Thrpy.

ROURKE, ELIZABETH A; Clayton A Bouton JR SR HS; Voorheesville, NY; (Y); Am Leg Aux Girls St; Sec Trs 4-H; Sec French Clb; Band; Chorus; JV Cheerleading; Var L Trk; Cit Awd; High Hon Roll; NHS; Frnch Hghst Avg 85; Nrsng.

ROUSE, AUDREY ROSE; Queen Of The Rosary Academy; Wantagh, NY; (S); 3/44; Pres Drama Clb; Math Clb; School Musical; School Play; Stage Crew; Variety Show; Yrbk Stf; Pres Soph Cls; Pres Jr Cls; Pres Sr Cls; Molloy Coll; Nrs.

ROUSE, JENNIFER; Waterloo SR HS; Waterloo, NY; (Y); 20/168; Varsity Clb; Jazz Band; Mrchg Band; Yrbk Stf; Stu Cncl; Cheerleading; Twrlr; High Hon Roll; Deservng SR 85; Outstndng Color Guard/Twirlr 84 & 85; ST U Of Geneseo; Specl Eductn.

ROUSE, YOLANDD; La Guardia H S Of Music & The Arts; New York, NY; (Y); 40/580; Church Yth Grp; Cmnty Wkr; Library Aide; Office Aide; Chorus; Church Choir; Variety Show; Hon Roll; Jr NHS; NHS; Outstndg Schl Svc Awd 85; Music & Art Hnr Leag 85; Natl Cncl Tchrs Engl Wrtng Awd 84; Psych.

ROUX, ALEX; Westmoreland Central Schl; Westmoreland, NY; (Y); Ski Clb; Concert Band; Jazz Band; Mrchg Band; Var L Bsbl; Var L Ftbl; Hon Roll; Bus Adm.

ROUX, GERALD; St Francis Preparatory Schl; Bethpage, NY; (Y); 20/690; Church Yth Grp; Church Choir; Im Bsktbl; Coach Actv; Im Ftbl; Im Vllybl; High Hon Roll; Ntl Merit Ltr; Natl Hispnc Schlrshp Awd Semi-Fnlst 83-84; St Johns Schlrshp Awd 84-85; Hofstra U Schlrshp 84-85; U Of PA; Bus.

ROWE, BRIAN; Mattituck HS; Mattituck, NY; (Y); French Clb; Chorus; Variety Show; Hon Roll; Psych.

ROWE, COURTNEY M; Northeastern Clinton Central HS; Champlain, NY; (Y); 15/146; Model UN; Band; Pres Sr Cls; Var JV Cheerleading; Stat Ice Hcky; Score Keeper; High Hon Roll; Hon Roll; NHS; Ntl Merit Ltr; NE Clinton Cntrl Tchrs Assn Scholar 85; Chmpln Lit Awd 85; 1st Atten JR Prom 84; Bowdoin Coll.

ROWE, DONNA; Mt Upton Central HS; Gilbertsville, NY; (Y); 1/25; Trs 4-H; Capt Quiz Bowl; Trs Frsh Cls; Var Capt Bsktbl; Var L Socr; Var Trk; 4-H Awd; High Hon Roll; NHS; Rochester Inst Tech; Sci.

ROWE, ERICA; Andrew Jackson HS; Jamaica, NY; (Y); VP Church Yth Grp; Debate Tm; Band; Church Choir; Concert Band; Mrchg Band; Nwsp Sprt Ed; Var Trk; Hon Roll; Prfct Atten Awd; Arista Pgm 85; Law.

ROWE, FRANCIS; Boys And Girls HS; Brooklyn, NY; (Y); Boy Scts; CAP; Nwsp Phtg; Bsbl; Diving; Ftbl; Sftbl; Trk; High Hon Roll; JETS Awd; Acad Of Aernautics; Flght Engrg.

ROWE, JEFF; Elmira Free Acad; Elmira, NY; (Y); Boy Scts; Church Yth Grp; Cmnty Wkr; French Clb; Latin Clb; VP Ski Clb; Concert Band; Tennis; High Hon Roll; Trs NHS; Ntl Frnch 7th Reg 85; Engrng.

ROWE, JENNY; Gilbertsville Central HS; Gilbertsville, NY; (Y); 4-H; GAA; Varsity Clb; VP VICA; Pres Frsh Cls; VP Jr Cls; Var L Bsktbl; Var Score Keeper; Var L Socr; High Hon Roll; Outstndg Stu Awd BOCES 84-85; Comp Sci.

ROWE, KAREN; Lindenhurst SR HS; Lindenhurst, NY; (Y); Church Yth Grp; Color Guard; Flag Corp; Mrchg Band; School Musical; Sftbl; Pre Elem Educ.

ROWE, LISA; Harpursville Central HS; Harpursville, NY; (S); 3/67; Pres Concert Band; Mrchg Band; School Play; Rep Stu Cncl; Var L Bsktbl; Var L Cheerleading; JV Fld Hcky; Var Sftbl; High Hon Roll; Sec NHS; Yth Ldrshp Awd 84; 2nd Tm All League All-Star Ptchr 84; All-State Cncrt Band 83-84; SUNY; Lib Arts.

ROWE, PAUL; Edmeston Central HS; Edmeston, NY; (Y); 3/36; Am Leg Boys St; 4-H; French Clb; Math Tm; Quiz Bowl; Band; Mrchg Band; School Play; Yrbk Stf; Pres Jr Cls; Whipple, Clark Schlrshps, R Bowen Mem 85; Morrisville Coll; Acctng.

ROWE, PENNIE; Union-Endicott HS; Endicott, NY; (Y); 104/430; Band; Flag Corp; Mrchg Band; Symp Band; Hon Roll; Broome CC; Acctg.

ROWELL, DAVID W; Onondaga Central HS; Marietta, NY; (S); Trs Computer Clb; Spanish Clb; JV Crs Cntry; Var Trk; High Hon Roll; NHS; Comp Prg.

ROWELL, MONICA; Saranac Lake HS; Raybrook, NY; (Y); AFS; Band; Concert Band; Jazz Band; Yrbk Stf; JV Socr; Trk; Hon Roll; Spnsh.

ROWEN, MARK L; B N Cardozo HS; Bayside, NY; (Y); Computer Clb; Concert Band; School Play; Nwsp Rptr; Yrbk Stf; Lit Mag; Rep Sr Cls; Jr NHS; NHS; Comm Svc Holocust Rsrch Ctr 84; SUNY Stony Brook; Phys.

ROWLAND, KRISTINE J; East Islip HS; Islip Terrace, NY; (Y); 26/475; Teachers Aide; Band; Concert Band; Mrchg Band; JV Bsktbl; NY ST Regents Schlrshp 85; Sci Fair Awd 82; Acad Prfmnc Awd LIU 85; LIU; Marine Bio.

ROWLAND, PATRICK; Roy C Ketcham HS; Wappingers Fall, NY; (Y); High Hon Roll; Hon Roll; Elec Engrng.

ROWLAND, THERESA; Kensington HS; Buffalo, NY; (Y); ST U Of NY Buffalo; Comp Sci.

ROWLEY, CHARLENE; St Joseph HS; Brooklyn, NY; (Y); School Musical; Rep Frsh Cls; Rep Soph Cls; Rep Jr Cls; Yrbk Stf; Trk; Btty Crckr Awd; Rgnt Nrsng Schlrshp; Niagara; Nrsng.

ROY, DANIEL; Newcomb Central Schl; Newcomb, NY; (Y); 2/15; Band; Pres Frsh Cls; Trs Soph Cls; Trs Jr Cls; Rep Stu Cncl; Socr; Cit Awd; High Hon Roll; NHS; Canton; Bldg Constrctn.

ROY, JOHN; Jamesville-De Witt HS; Dewitt, NY; (Y); French Clb; JV Golf; Var Capt Swmmng; High Hon Roll; Hon Roll; H S All Amer 50 Yd Frstyle & 100 Yd Frstyle 85; Ath Rep Exec Comm Niagara Dist U S Swmmng 85-86.

ROY, MELISSA L; Nyack SR HS; Vly Cottage, NY; (Y); 47/254; Nwsp Stf; Yrbk Stf; VP Jr Cls; Rep Stu Cncl; Stat Bsktbl; Hon Roll; NHS; Ntl Merit Ltr; Pres Schlr; Spanish NHS; NY ST Secndry Schl Stu Orgnztn 85; NAACP Yth Delg Natl Convntn Dallas 85; Stu Of Mnth 84; Tufts U; Intl Reltns.

ROY, PATRICIA; Perth Central HS; Fort Johnson, NY; (Y); Church Yth Grp; DECA; Drama Clb; French Clb; Church Choir; Stage Crew; Yrbk Stf; Trk; Vllybl; High Hon Roll; Cvl Engrng.

ROY, TRACEY; Cardinal Mooney HS; Rochester, NY; (Y); 176/325; Office Aide; Band; Concert Band; Orch; School Musical; Crs Cntry; Music Apprctn Awd 82-85; Natl Piano Plyng Audtns 81-85; NYSMTA Stu Of Achvt Awd 84 & 85; U Of Southern FL; Psych.

ROYCE, JOLENE; Mt Markham HS; W Winfield, NY; (Y); GAA; Girl Scts; Acpl Chr; School Musical; Swing Chorus; Rep Stu Cncl; JV Capt Fld Hcky; Var Sftbl; High Hon Roll; NHS; Top Stu SR Chorus 83-84; Rochester Tech; Ultrsnd Technlg.

ROYCROFT, JEANETTE; Monticello HS; Kauneonga Lake, NY; (Y); 4/163; Key Clb; Math Tm; Concert Band; Orch; School Musical; Yrbk Ed-Chief; Var L Vllybl; High Hon Roll; NHS; Prfct Atten Awd; NYS Regnts Schlrshp 85; Cornell U; Vet.

ROYSTER, INDIE; Villa Maria Acad; Buffalo, NY; (Y); Art Clb; Church Yth Grp; Cmnty Wkr; Hosp Aide; JA; JCL; Latin Clb; Bsktbl; Bowling; Canisius Coll; Pre Med.

ROZANSKI, ANDREA; Perry Central HS; Perry, NY; (Y); 46/80; Church Yth Grp; FFA; Chorus; Church Choir; Nwsp Rptr; Nwsp Stf; Yrbk Rptr; Cit Awd; Hon Roll; Hugh O Brien Yth Fndtn Awd 84; Psych.

ROZANSKI, SCOTT; Perry Central HS; Perry, NY; (Y); 14/92; Varsity Clb; JV Stat Bsbl; Im Bowling; Var Im Coach Actv; Im Ice Hcky; Var Socr; Im Stat Sftbl; Im Wt Lftg; Howard Hunt Mem 85; St Bonaventure U; Bus.

ROZELL, AMY L; Hudson Falls SR HS; Hudson Falls, NY; (Y); Cmnty Wkr; Drama Clb; Pres Trs Thesps; School Musical; School Play; Yrbk Ed-Chief; Pres Trs Stu Cncl; CC Awd; DAR Awd; High Hon Roll; Regents Schlrshp 85; Hugh O Brien Ldrshp Sem 83; Geneseo; Brdcstng.

ROZWOD, ROBERT A; Liverpool HS; Liverpool, NY; (Y); 159/792; Church Yth Grp; Variety Show; JV Bsbl; Im Ftbl; Im Wt Lftg; Hon Roll; Jr NHS; NYS Regnts Schlrshp 85; Potsdam Coll; Math.

ROZYCKI, JENNIFER; Gloversville HS; Gloversville, NY; (Y); 23/266; French Clb; Chorus; Stat Bsktbl; Capt Cheerleading; High Hon Roll; Hon Roll; NHS; Alfred Johnson Schlrshp 85; Sports Booster Clb Awd 85; Laurel G Awd 85; Potsdam Coll; Bus.

RUAIS, KRISTEN; Sachem HS; Centereach, NY; (Y); 134/1380; Chorus; Mrchg Band; School Musical; Lit Mag; Cheerleading; Stat Lcrss; Pom Pon; Drama Clb; Madrigals; Hopwood Schlrshp Lynchburg Coll 85; NY ST Regnts Schlrshp 85; Allstate Chorus 83; Clemson U; Eng.

RUBBO, DEBBIE M; Mepham HS; N Bellmore, NY; (Y); Church Yth Grp; Library Aide; Church Choir; Nwsp Rptr; Yrbk Stf; Off Jr Cls; Stu Cncl; Gym; Twrlr; High Hon Roll; 4th 220 Yd Dsh 83; Soc Stu Fr Awd 83; Sci Clb Cert Treas 84; Acctng.

RUBECK, JACQUELYN K; Pioneer Central Schl; Java Center, NY; (Y); 20/142; CAP; 4-H; Latin Clb; Library Aide; Sec Jr Cls; JV Capt Cheerleading; 4-H Awd; Phy Thpry.

RUBEL, SCOTT E; Pittsford Sutherland HS; Rochester, NY; (Y); 1/220; Boy Scts; Model UN; Ski Clb; Ed Yrbk Stf; Swmmng; Hon Roll; Trs NHS; Ntl Merit SF; Local & Regnl Plcmnt Natl Fr Cont 82-85; Natl Chem Soc Hon Men 83; Yale Coll; Physics.

RUBENCHIK, IRINA; Solomon Schechter HS; Brooklyn, NY; (Y); 1/42; Math Clb; Nwsp Ed-Chief; Nwsp Stf; Rep Stu Cncl; Vllybl; Gov Hon Prg Awd; NHS; Ntl Merit Ltr; Val; Govrnrs Commtt On Schltc Achvt Schlrshp 85; Polytech Inst Of NY; Elec Engr.

RUBENS, CINDY; Brighton HS; Rochester, NY; (Y); Ski Clb; Spanish Clb; Chorus; Socr.

RUBILLO, PAUL A; Gorton HS; Yonkers, NY; (Y); Nwsp Rptr; Lit Mag; Bsbl; Hon Roll.

RUBIN, ADAM; Hicksville HS; Hicksville, NY; (Y); JV Ftbl; JV Lcrss; Phys Ed.

RUBIN, ALEXANDE S; Horace Greeley HS; Chappaqua, NY; (Y); 89/279; JV Im Bsktbl; Var JV Lcrss; Ntl Merit Ltr; St Schlr; Regents Schlrshp 85.

RUBIN, CRAIG; Hicksville HS; Hicksvl, NY; (Y); Bus.

RUBIN, DOUGLAS; Lynbrook HS; Hewlett, NY; (Y).

RUBIN, JASON; Lynbrook HS; Hewlett, NY; (Y).

RUBIN, JASON; Mepham HS; N Bellmore, NY; (Y); Computer Clb; Mathletes; VP Math Clb; Math Tm; Scholastic Bowl; Temple Yth Grp; Chorus; Socr; NHS; Ntl Merit SF; Math Awds 83-85; Natl Sci Olmpd Tst Chem Medl 1st Pl 85; Olympcs Of Mind Tm 3rd Nassau Cnty 83; Math.

RUBIN, LARA R; The Nightingale-Bumford Schl; New York, NY; (Y); Nwsp Stf; Pres Stu Cncl; Var Bsktbl; Capt Var Vllybl; Ntl Merit Ltr; Political Wkr; Chorus; Nwsp Rptr; Lit Mag; Var Sftbl; NB Awd 82-85; Yale U.

RUBIN, MARK; Commack H S South; Commack, NY; (Y); 150/400; Ski Clb; Teachers Aide; Temple Yth Grp; Y-Teens; JV Var Bsbl; JV Ftbl; Hon Roll; Smithtown Recreation Bsebl Cmp Schlrshp 83; Bst Offnsve Bsebl Plyr Awds 82-84; All Star Bsebl 84; Bus.

RUBIN, MICHAEL; West Hempstead HS; Island Park, NY; (Y); Aud/Vis; Key Clb; VP Temple Yth Grp; School Play; Var Golf; Im Wt Lftg; Hon Roll; Kiwanis Awd; UNC Chapel Hill.

RUBIN, SYDELLE; Commack H S North; Smithtown, NY; (Y); Am Leg Aux Girls St; Exploring; Hosp Aide; MMM; Orch; Nwsp Rptr; Rep Stu Cncl; NHS; Simons Fellow SUNY Stony Brook 84; Intrdscplnry Sci Rsrch Prog SUNY Binghamton 85.

RUBINO, MICHAEL J; St Francis HS; West Seneca, NY; (Y); 80/160; Spanish Clb; Varsity Clb; Nwsp Rptr; Im Bsktbl; Var Ftbl; Var Ice Hcky; Im Wt Lftg; Hon Roll; Rgnts Schlrshp Awd 85; Geneseo ST U; Engrng.

RUBINSTEIN, PAMELA; Freeport HS; Freeport, NY; (Y); Var Gym; Im Lcrss; Var Tennis; Cmmnctns.

RUBIO, SHARIH; Hornell HS; Hornell, NY; (S); 8/198; Pres AFS; Am Leg Aux Girls St; Library Aide; Chorus; School Play; Nwsp Stf; Rep Sr Cls; Var Vllybl; NHS; Prfct Atten Awd; Bus Mgmt.

RUBY, MELINDA J; Rome Free Acad; Rome, NY; (Y); 6/536; Cmnty Wkr; Girl Scts; Hosp Aide; Intnl Clb; Red Cross Aide; Speech Tm; Yrbk Ed-Chief; Cit Awd; High Hon Roll; Jr NHS; Wells Coll Hghst Engl Ave Awd 83; Colg U Hgh Ablty Semnr 84-85; Holy Cross Coll; Acctg.

RUBY, SHANNON MARIE; Mexico Acad; Mexico, NY; (Y); German Clb; Varsity Clb; Color Guard; Variety Show; Sec Frsh Cls; Sec Soph Cls; Off Stu Cncl; JV Var Cheerleading; Hon Roll; Schlr Ath Silver Mdl 85; Outstndng Achvt Ger 85; Schlr Ath Hnrb Mntn 83; SUNY Oswego; Bus Admin.

RUCHANDANI, NANDITA; Union-Endicott HS; Endicott, NY; (Y); Boy Scts; Key Clb; Mathletes; Chorus; School Play; Ed Yrbk Stf; Rep Jr Cls; High Hon Roll; Hon Roll; Jr NHS; NYSSMA Blue Ribbon Solo Sing Perf 85; Yth Trng Schlrshp 83; John Hopkins U; Srgn.

RUCKER, VANESSA; Willaim Howard Taft HS; Bronx, NY; (Y); Cmnty Wkr; Office Aide; High Hon Roll; Hon Roll; NHS; Ntl Merit Ltr; Prfct Atten Awd; Stanley Simon 85; Super Yth 84-85; Ctznshp From Taft 85; Pedtrcn.

RUDD, ALEXIS H; Columbia Grammar & Prep; New York, NY; (Y); Var L Bsbl; Var Co-Capt Bsktbl; Ntl Merit Ltr; Acadmc Awd Lit & Wrtng 83; Russian Clb; Cornell U.

RUDD, DEBBIE; Sweet Home SR HS; North Tonawanda, NY; (Y); 73/425; Chess Clb; Trs Church Yth Grp; Trs FHA; GAA; Girl Scts; Science Clb; JV Swmmng; High Hon Roll; Hon Roll; Outsndng Volntr Awd YES Amhrst 84; Girl Scouts 1s Cls Awd; Buffalo ST U; Chem.

RUDD, MELISA; Oakfield Alabama HS; Basom, NY; (Y); 15/93; Debate Tm; Office Aide; Teachers Aide; Band; Mrchg Band; School Musical; Symp Band; Var Mgr(s); Var Score Keeper; Sftbl; Cert Awd 80-81; Achvt Awd Art 82; Utica Coll; Acturl Sci.

RUDDOCK, NICHOLA; Hillcrest HS; Queens Village, NY; (Y); Pres Church Yth Grp; Service Clb; Teachers Aide; Band; Church Choir; Concert Band; Orch; Variety Show; Yrbk Stf; Nrsng.

RUDDY, MARIANNE; Bronx H S Of Science; Bronx, NY; (Y); Drama Clb; Math Clb; Office Aide; Red Cross Aide; School Play; Yrbk Stf; Lit Mag; Im Ftbl; Sftbl; Northeastern U; Sci.

RUDICK, JOHN; Irvington HS; Irvington, NY; (Y); Computer Clb; JV Var Bsbl; JV Var Bsktbl; Im Sftbl; Im Vllybl; High Hon Roll; Hon Roll; Med.

RUDINSKI, JULIE; Warwick Valley HS; Pine Isld, NY; (Y); VP FFA; Hon Roll; Cert Awd Hnr Rll 83; Star Grnhnd/Star Chap Frmr FFA Awds 83-84; NY FFA Ind Accmplshmnt Awd 84; New Paltz; Math.

RUDOLPH, DENISE; Minisink Valley HS; Middletown, NY; (Y); Band; Drill Tm; Capt Flag Corp; Mrchg Band; High Hon Roll; Hon Roll; Orange Co CC; Tchng.

RUDOLPH, EDNA A; Freeport HS; Freeport, NY; (Y); 30/450; Church Yth Grp; Chorus; VP Mrchg Band; Orch; School Musical; Variety Show; Nwsp Rptr; Sec Stu Cncl; High Hon Roll; NHS; Hofstra U; Brdcst.

RUDOLPH, MAUREEN; Stella Maris HS; Breezy Point, NY; (Y); 19/185; Church Yth Grp; Spanish Clb; Nwsp Stf; Yrbk Stf; VP Stu Cncl; Hon Roll; NY ST Regnts Schlrshp 85; Fordham U Rose Hill; Bus.

RUEB, ERIKA; St Francis Prep; Whitestone, NY; (S); 99/693; Dance Clb; Hosp Aide; Math Clb; L Crs Cntry; NHS; Opt Clb Awd; Bus.

RUEBEN, STEVEN L; John Dewey HS; Brooklyn, NY; (Y); Aud/Vis; Cmnty Wkr; Mathletes; Math Clb; Math Tm; Office Aide; Science Clb; Service Clb; Ski Clb; Temple Yth Grp; Resturant Mgr.

RUECKHER, NIAMH; Christ The King Regional HS; Ridgwood, NY; (Y); 15/386; Aud/Vis; German Clb; Intnl Clb; Office Aide; Service Clb; Chorus; Stat Swmmng; Hon Roll; NHS; Voice Dem Awd; Pace U; Accntnt.

RUF, RACHEL; Mexico Acad; Oswego, NY; (Y); German Clb; Ski Clb; Spanish Clb; Varsity Clb; Color Guard; Var Cheerleading; Hon Roll; Prfct Atten Awd; Pres 4-H; Band; Delta Epsilon Phi; Bronze Medal Schlr Athl Awd; SUNY-CORTLAND; Educ.

RUF, TONI; Gloversville HS; Glvoersville, NY; (Y); 59/248; Trs DECA; Rep Frsh Cls; Rep Soph Cls; Var Bsktbl; Fld Hcky; Hon Roll; Stu Of Mnth 84; Mgr Of Schl Store 83-84; Law.

RUFF, SHERRY; Holy Angels Acad; Buffalo, NY; (Y); Church Yth Grp; JA; Spanish Clb; Stage Crew; Nwsp Rptr; Nwsp Stf; Rep Soph Cls; Rep Jr Cls; Rep Sr Cls; JV Bsktbl; ST U Of NY; Spcl Educ.

RUFFINO, GINA; Gatavia SR HS; Batavia, NY; (Y); Dance Clb; Lockport Savings Bank Bus Admin Awd 85; Nicoletta M Valle Mem Awd 85; Genesee CC; Exec Sec.

RUGALA, DOUGLAS; Alexander Central HS; Alexander, NY; (S); 13/86; Am Leg Boys St; Band; Pres Chorus; Drm Mjr(t); Jazz Band; Swing Chorus; Pres Jr Cls; Stu Cncl; Capt Trk; Cit Awd; NYS Fair Champ Drum Major Tm 83; All Cnty Chrs & Band 82-85; Homecmng Prince 83; FL ST U; Hotel Mgmt.

RUGAR, ROBYN; Sherburne-Earlville JR/SR HS; Hamilton, NY; (Y); Band; Chorus; Concert Band; Mrchg Band; Almada Literary Society 83-84; Regents Scholarship 84-85; Alfred U; Computer Sci.

RUGGERI, GRACE; Saratoga Central Catholic HS; Saratoga Springs, NY; (S); 9/52; Church Yth Grp; Drama Clb; School Play; Stage Crew; Crs Cntry; Score Keeper; High Hon Roll; Trs NHS; St Schlr; Pres Schlrshp Mt St Mary Coll 85; NY ST Regnts Schlrshp Nrsng 85; Mt St Mary Coll; Nrsng.

RUGGERI, KATHLEEN; Smithtown HS East; Smithtown, NY; (Y); Hosp Aide; Ski Clb; Spanish Clb; Band; Mrchg Band; JV Bsktbl; High Hon Roll; NHS; Spanish NHS; Selctd All Cnty Band Clarnt 83; Comp Engr.

RUGGERI, KRISTINA M; Smithtown HS East; Smithtown, NY; (Y); Hosp Aide; Ski Clb; VP Spanish Clb; Var L Fld Hcky; Var Trk; High Hon Roll; NHS; Spanish NHS; Girls Ldrs Clb 84-85; Yth In Govt 81; Bucknell U; Accntng.

RUGGIERO, LINDA; East Meadow HS; E Meadow, NY; (S); Teachers Aide; Band; JV Bsktbl; Capt Cheerleading; Capt Coach Actv; JV Lcrss; JV Socr; JV Vllybl; Hon Roll; Math.

RUGGIERO, PAUL; John F Kennedy HS; Utica, NY; (Y); Bsbl; Bsktbl; Ftbl.

RUGGIERO, RAFFAELLA; Linton HS; Schenectady, NY; (Y); Key Clb; Teachers Aide; Cit Awd; Hon Roll; Accntng.

RUHL, KIM D; Berner HS; Massapequa, NY; (Y); 7/426; Drama Clb; Band; Drm & Bgl; Drm Mjr(t); Flag Corp; Mrchg Band; Orch; Nwsp Rptr; Hon Roll; NHS; Regnts Schlrshp; U Of NC Chapel Hill; Jrnlsm.

RUHMEL II, JOSEPH F; Notre Dame HS; Horseheads, NY; (Y); 44/127; German Clb; Key Clb; Math Clb; Pep Clb; Science Clb; Yrbk Stf; Rep Frsh Cls; Hon Roll; Arnot-Ogden Mem Hosp Cmnty Svc Fnd Schlrshp Awd 85; Vol Svc Hnr Awd-Elmira Psych Ctr 85; SUNY Oswego; Metrlgy.

RUHMEL, RHONDA; Southside HS; Elmira, NY; (Y); 88/333; French Clb; Chorus; Var L Crs Cntry; Var L Gym; Var L Socr; Var L Trk; Feml Athlt Yr 85; Sctn IV Chmpn 100 M Dsh 85; Sctn IV Chmpn 50 M Dsh 85; Elmira Coll; Spch.

RUIGROK, GERALD C; Cincinnatus Central HS; Pitcher, NY; (Y); 1/40; Band; Chorus; School Play; Trs Sr Cls; Var L Bsbl; Var Capt Socr; High Hon Roll; VP NHS; Pres Schlr; St Schlr; Natl Sci Mrt Awd; Utica Coll; Comp Sci.

RUIZ, ALFREDO; Msgr Mcclancy HS; Flushing, NY; (S); 10/225; Math Clb; Math Tm; Nwsp Rptr; NHS; Principals List; First Hnrs List; NY U; Film & T V.

RUIZ, CAROL; Eli Whitney Vocational HS; Brooklyn, NY; (Y); Computer Clb; Office Aide; Lgl Sec.

RUIZ, EVELYN; John Dewey HS; Brooklyn, NY; (Y); Cmnty Wkr; Teachers Aide; Law.

RUIZ, JOSE; Cardinal Spellman HS; Bronx, NY; (Y); Dance Clb; Spanish Clb; Teachers Aide; Im Bsktbl; Im Ftbl; Hon Roll; Ntl Merit SF; Cardinals Ldrshp Proj 85-86; Columbia; Bus Engr.

RUIZ, LILLIAN; Susan E Wagner HS; Staten Island, NY; (Y); 26/470; Sec Key Clb; School Musical; Nwsp Rptr; Yrbk Stf; Rep Stu Cncl; Hon Roll; Sec NHS; Ed Yrbk Stf; Rep Frsh Cls; Rep Soph Cls; UF Tchrs Schlrshp 85; Govnrs Comm Schlstc Achvt 85; Pres Acdmc Ftns Awd Prog 85; Rochester U; English.

RUIZ, RALPH; Central Islip HS; Central Islip, NY; (Y); Art Clb; Aud/Vis; Cmnty Wkr; Band; School Play; Stage Crew; Im Bsbl; Im Ftbl; Im Score Keeper; Im Wrstlng; Phys Fit Awd Top 10 81; AV Awd 82; Cert Inst Gifted & Tlntd Yth 84; Five Towns Coll; Music Inst Rep.

RUIZ, SHARON; Academy Of Mount Saint Ursula HS; Bronx, NY; (Y); Camera Clb; Computer Clb; Library Aide; Teachers Aide; Chorus; Yrbk Stf; Stu Cncl; High Hon Roll; Jr NHS; Spanish NHS; NY U; Med.

RUIZ, YVETTE; St Barnabas HS; Bronx, NY; (Y); 38/136; Spanish Clb; Hon Roll; Berkeley Bus Schl; Mktg.

RULE, CYNDEE; William Floyd HS; Mastic, NY; (Y); 38/429; MMM; Orch; School Play; Yrbk Stf; French Hon Soc; NHS; Chess Clb; English Clb; French Clb; Tri-M Scholar Awd 85; Music Faclty Scholar 85; WVU Awd Schl Auditn 85; WV U; Mus.

RULISON, REBECCA; Broadalbin Central HS; Broadalbin, NY; (Y); 8/73; French Clb; Girl Scts; Math Tm; Chorus; Church Choir; Concert Band; Mrchg Band; Socr; Sftbl; High Hon Roll; Fltn Cnty Music Fstvl 83 & 85; Psychlgy.

RULLAN, NOEMI; Mount Mercy Acad; Buffalo, NY; (Y); Church Yth Grp; FHA; JA; Red Cross Aide; Spanish Clb; Church Choir; Nwsp Stf; Hon Roll; Secy Sci.

RUMPF, SCOTT; Gouverneur Central HS; Gouverneur, NY; (Y); 9/145; JV Var Crs Cntry; Var Trk; Hon Roll; SUNY-BINGHAMPTON; Bio.

RUMSEY, DAVID; Horseheads SR HS; Millport, NY; (S); 25/407; High Hon Roll; NHS; Achvt Awd Latin 82; Corning CC; Comp Sci.

RUMSEY, JOSEPH; Haverling Central HS; Bath, NY; (S); 30/147; French Clb; Math Clb; Ski Clb; School Musical; Yrbk Phtg; Yrbk Sprt Ed; Var L Bsbl; Var L Socr; High Hon Roll; NHS; Coll; Engrng.

RUNFOLA, ANNE; Warsaw Central HS; Warsaw, NY; (S); 4/93; VP French Clb; Mathletes; Chorus; Pres Frsh Cls; Rep Sec Stu Cncl; Socr; Trk; High Hon Roll; NHS.

RUNIONS, KEVIN; Mexico HS; Fulton, NY; (Y); Spanish Clb; Band; Concert Band; Jazz Band; Mrchg Band; Im Bsbl; Var L Socr; Var L Trk; Var L Wrstlng; NHS; Grand Prize Awd Local Comptn ST Sci Congrss 85; Schltc Ath Awd Gold Medal 84-85, Silver Medal 83-84; Offcr.

RUNNE, JENNIFER; Clarkstown SHS South; New City, NY; (Y); Band; Mrchg Band; NJ Sci Leag Bio; Corp Law.

RUNYON, EILEEN; Northstar Christian Acad; Rochester, NY; (S); 2/27; Church Yth Grp; Band; Chorus; Pep Band; Yrbk Stf; Trs Frsh Cls; Cit Awd; High Hon Roll; NHS; Music Awd 82; Messiah Coll; Rsrch Bio.

RUPPE, KENNETH; Hudson HS; Claverack, NY; (Y); Church Yth Grp; Yrbk Stf; Var Bsbl; L Golf; Var Socr; High Hon Roll; Hon Roll; NHS; Engrng.

RUPPERT, PAULA A; Lancaster HS; Lancaster, NY; (Y); Chrmn Church Yth Grp; Pep Clb; JV Bsktbl; JV Var Tennis; JV Var Vllybl; Sprtsmnshp Awd Tnns 84; Mst Imprvd Plyr Tnns 84; Phy Thrpy.

RUPRACHT, LESLIE; Sachem High School North; Holbrook, NY; (Y); 147/1383; Cmnty Wkr; Radio Clb; Science Clb; Band; Concert Band; Orch; Pep Band; Yrbk Phtg; Yrbk Stf; Lit Mag; Long Isl Sci Congrs Hgh Hnrs Awd 83; Schl Sci Fair Supr Awd 83; NYSSMA Music Mdls Piano & Orch; Suny At Geneseo; Jrnlsm.

RUREY, BRYAN; Pulaski JR SR HS; Pulaski, NY; (Y); Drama Clb; French Clb; Band; Chorus; Church Choir; Concert Band; Drm Mjr(t); Mrchg Band; School Musical; Stage Crew; Snow Enrchmnt Awd Appld Piano 84, Fld Drctng 85; SUNY-FREDONIA; Scndry Music.

RUSCH, BARBARA A; Dunkirk HS; Dunkirk, NY; (Y); 49/222; Church Yth Grp; French Clb; Pres Key Clb; Rep Stu Cncl; Hon Roll; NY ST Regnts Schlrshp; Merit Awds Comp Sci, Bkkpng, Acctng; ST U Of NY Geneseo; Spec Ed.

RUSCITTI, KELLY; Newburg Free Acad HS; New Windsor, NY; (Y); 4/720; Drama Clb; Pres Intnl Clb; Ski Clb; Acpl Chr; Madrigals; School Musical; Rep Sr Cls; Cheerleading; Gym; NHS; Edw Skyer Mem Schlrshp Rtry Awd 85; Outstndng & Unique Drma Awd 85; Top Ten Math & Sci Awd; Cornell; Bio-Med.

RUSH, KRISTIN M; Pittsford Mendon HS; Pittsford, NY; (Y); 2/270; French Clb; Latin Clb; Math Tm; Pep Clb; Service Clb; Yrbk Stf; Var Capt Fld Hcky; Hon Roll; NHS; Latn Awd-Magna Cum Laude 83; Med.

RUSH, PATRICIA A; Amsterdam HS; Amsterdam, NY; (Y); 30/334; Hosp Aide; Orch; Hon Roll; NHS; NY ST Regents Schlrshp 85; SUNY; Rad Tech.

RUSH, STEVEN; New Amsterdam HS; Amsterdam, NY; (Y); 24/294; High Hon Roll; Hon Roll; Comp Prog.

RUSHIE, MARITZA; Yonkers HS; Yonkers, NY; (Y); Girl Scts; Chorus; Hon Roll; Howard U; Comp Sci.

RUSHOK, STEVEN; Alden Central HS; Alden, NY; (Y); Aud/Vis; Letterman Clb; Stage Crew; Rep Sr Cls; Im Bsktbl; JV Var Ftbl; Erie CC; Comptr Sci.

RUSNAK, CATHY; Binghamton HS; Binghamton, NY; (Y); Mathletes; High Hon Roll; Hon Roll; Opt Clb Awd; Sys Engr.

RUSNICA, DIANA TINA; Linton HS; Schenectady, NY; (Y); Boys Clb Am; Computer Clb; Exploring; Casinovia Coll; Wrd Proc.

RUSS, GLENN A; Unatego JR SR HS; Otego, NY; (Y); 24/90; Am Leg Boys St; Varsity Clb; Chorus; Concert Band; Var Bsktbl; JV Ftbl; Var Trk; High Hon Roll; Prfct Atten Awd; Bus Admin.

RUSSELL, AMY; Whitesboro SR HS; Whitesboro, NY; (Y); 28/358; Church Yth Grp; Exploring; Intnl Clb; Mathletes; High Hon Roll; Hon Roll; Jr NHS; NHS; Engrng.

RUSSELL, BERNADITH A; Midwood HS; Brooklyn, NY; (Y); 77/605; Exploring; Math Tm; Orch; Lit Mag; Sec Cmnty Wkr; Capt Cheerleading; Mgr(s); Hon Roll; Biology.

RUSSELL, CHARLES W; L C Obourn HS; E Rochester, NY; (Y); 36/113; Am Leg Boys St; Drama Clb; Model UN; Varsity Clb; Band; Chorus; Yrbk Stf; Capt Swmmng; Tennis; Eagle Scout; U Rochester; Jrnlsm.

RUSSELL, CRYSTAL; Nazareth Acad; Rochester, NY; (S); Art Clb; French Clb; Yrbk Stf; Sec Soph Cls; Sec Jr Cls; Hon Roll; Monroe CC; Bus.

RUSSELL, D TODD; Frontier Central HS; Lakeview, NY; (S); Boy Scts; German Clb; Varsity Clb; Mgr(s); Var Socr; Var Tennis; U Of IN; Dnstry.

RUSSELL, DAVID A; Pioneer Central HS; Java Center, NY; (Y); 25/268; Boys Clb Am; Boy Scts; Church Yth Grp; Spanish Clb; Var Crs Cntry; Var Ftbl; Capt Trk; Hon Roll; Olympcs Of Mnd 83; Houghton Coll; Mssnry.

RUSSELL, DAVID L; Walton Central School; Walton, NY; (Y); 3/103; Pres Trs 4-H; Rep Stat FFA; Jazz Band; High Hon Roll; NHS; Am Leg Boys St; Pres Church Yth Grp; Band; Chorus; Concert Band; Ben Marvin Soc Studies Awd 85; Ag.

RUSSELL, DONNA; Parishville-Hopkinston Central HS; Parishville, NY; (Y); Chorus; Variety Show; Hon Roll; NHS.

RUSSELL, HENRY J; St Anthonys HS; Pt Jeff Stat, NY; (Y); Nwsp Rptr; JV Crs Cntry; Var Trk; French Hon Soc; NHS; Henry Russell Awd Crss Cntry 83; Duns Scotus Awd 84; Cmmnctns.

RUSSELL, JESSICA; Salmon River Central HS; Ft Covington, NY; (S); 4/95; Church Yth Grp; 4-H; French Clb; GAA; Band; Concert Band; Mrchg Band; Pres Soph Cls; Rep Jr Cls; Socr; European Bnd Tour 84; 1st Tm All-Northern Racewalk-Track, 2nd Tm All-Northern-Racewalk-Indoor Trck 84; Phys Ther.

RUSSELL, JOHN; Shenendehowa HS; Clifton Park, NY; (Y); JV Bsktbl; Im Ftbl; High Hon Roll; Hon Roll; Bsktbl Hnr; Psychlgy.

RUSSELL, JULIA; Clifton-Fine Central HS; Newton Falls, NY; (S); 10/50; French Clb; Hosp Aide; Band; Chorus; Mgr School Play; Yrbk Ed-Chief; Yrbk Phtg; Sec Sr Cls; Hon Roll; NHS; Phys Ther.

RUSSELL, KARYN; Maryvale HS; Cheektowaga, NY; (Y); Church Yth Grp; Spanish Clb; Yrbk Stf; Stu Cncl; Hon Roll.

RUSSELL, KELLEY SUZANNE; Eden SR HS; Eden, NY; (Y); AFS; Am Leg Aux Girls St; Pres Sec Band; Chorus; Mrchg Band; School Musical; Nwsp Stf; Sec Jr Cls; Sec Stu Cncl; Var Capt Cheerleading; Engl.

RUSSELL, MARY; West Genesee SR HS; Syracuse, NY; (Y); Mathletes; Rep Math Clb; Math Tm; Off Jr Cls; Stu Cncl; Var Debate Tm; High Hon Roll; Jr NHS; NHS; NYS Fnlst In Swmng 83-85; Ntl Sci Olympiad Cert Of Dstnctn In Chmstry 85; Bio.

RUSSELL, MAURA; South Side SR HS; Rockville Ctr, NY; (Y); Hon Roll; Jr NHS; Law.

RUSSELL, MEGAN; The Stony Brook Schl; Setauket, NY; (Y); Church Yth Grp; Latin Clb; Teachers Aide; Chorus; Church Choir; School Musical; School Play; Nwsp Rptr; Yrbk Rptr; Var L Cheerleading.

RUSSELL, MICHELLE; Monsignor Scanlon AP Randolph HS; New York, NY; (Y); Church Yth Grp; Math Clb; Spanish Clb; Teachers Aide; Church Choir; Color Guard; Drm & Bgl; Stu Cncl; Trk; Cit Awd; VA ST U; Med.

RUSSELL, RENEE; Horseheads SR HS; Horseheads, NY; (Y); Church Yth Grp; Dance Clb; Debate Tm; Drama Clb; JA; School Musical; School Play; Im Cheerleading; Var Swmmng; High Hon Roll; Fshn Rtlng.

RUSSELL, ROXANNE; Clara Barton HS; New York, NY; (Y); 89/469; Cmnty Wkr; Band; Chorus; Nwsp Ed-Chief; Rep Stu Cncl; Hon Roll; Syracuse U; Nws Brdcstr.

RUSSELL, STEVEN; Falconer Central HS; Falconer, NY; (Y); French Clb; JA; Varsity Clb; Im Bsbl; Var Ftbl; Var Vllybl; Hon Roll; Jamestown CC; Nuclr Engrng.

RUSSELL, TODD; Fronter Central HS; Lakeview, NY; (Y); Boy Scts; German Clb; Varsity Clb; JV Var Socr; Var Tennis; High Hon Roll; Hon Roll; Prfct Atten Awd; NEDT Tstng Awd; Medcl Sci.

RUSSELL, WILLIAM J; Salesian HS; New York, NY; (Y); 8/78; JV Bsbl; Var JV Diving; Var JV Swmmng; Hon Roll; Regeants Schlrshp 85; Manhattan Coll; Mech Engrng.

RUSSI, KIM; Penfield HS; Rochester, NY; (Y); Church Yth Grp; Cmnty Wkr; Stage Crew; Stu Cncl; Hon Roll; JA; Red Cross Aide; Service Clb; Yrbk Stf; Rochester Inst Tech; Comm Art.

RUSSIN, TIMOTHY G; Seton Catholic Central HS; Binghamton, NY; (Y); 13/150; Boys Clb Am; Var L Bsbl; Var JV Bsktbl; High Hon Roll; NHS; Prfct Atten Awd; Church Yth Grp; Cmnty Wkr; JV Socr; Harold C & C Claire Burns Schlrshp 85; Bus Awd 85; All Star Bsbl Awd 84-85; ST U Of NY; Comp Sci.

RUSSO, AMY; Johnstown HS; Johnstown, NY; (Y); Band; Chorus; Drm Mjr(t); Jazz Band; Nwsp Rptr; Rep Sr Cls; Hon Roll; NHS; Grtst Degree Of Ldrshp-Band 84-85; SUNY At Buffalo; Occptnl Thrpy.

RUSSO, ANTHONY; Smithtown West HS; Smithtown, NY; (Y); 85/500; Math Clb; Math Tm; Ski Clb; Yrbk Stf; Ftbl; High Hon Roll; Hon Roll; Ntl Merit Schol; Regents Scholar ST NY; Hofstra U; Law.

RUSSO, CHARLES W; Smithtown H S East; Smithtown, NY; (Y); Spanish Clb; Jr NHS; NHS; NYS Regnts Schlrshp; U Of Central FL; Bus Mtkg.

RUSSO, CHRIS; Hendrick Hudson HS; Verplanck, NY; (Y); Dance Clb; Office Aide; Teachers Aide; Yrbk Phtg; Yrbk Stf; Score Keeper; Sftbl; High Hon Roll; Hon Roll; NHS; Gregg Awd Shrthnd 84-85; Exec Sec.

RUSSO, DONNA; St Edmund HS; Brooklyn, NY; (Y); 39/187; Art Clb; Hosp Aide; Service Clb; Stage Crew; Trs Frsh Cls; JV Bsktbl; Im Bowling; JV Sftbl; Im Vllybl; Hon Roll; Italn Awd 83-84; Relgn Awd 85; Pre-Med.

RUSSO, GRACE; Frontier SR HS; Blasdell, NY; (Y); Latin Clb; Pep Clb; JV Crs Cntry; JV Trk; Erie CC; Bus.

RUSSO, JENNIFER; Valley Stream North HS; Elmont, NY; (Y); FTA; Hosp Aide; JV Sftbl; Swmmng; Tennis; Cit Awd; Hon Roll; Ntl Merit Schol; Home Ec Hnr Scty 85; Tchng.

RUSSO, JOANN; Christ The King Regional HS; Ridgewood, NY; (Y); 13/385; Yrbk Stf; Rep Soph Cls; Rep Jr Cls; Pres Sr Cls; Pres Stu Cncl; JV Var Sftbl; High Hon Roll; Hon Roll; NHS; St Johns U; Bus.

RUSSO, JOHN; Seaford HS; Seaford, NY; (Y); 8/246; Church Yth Grp; Drama Clb; Spanish Clb; Nwsp Stf; Yrbk Ed-Chief; Rep Frsh Cls; Tennis; High Hon Roll; NHS; St Schlr; U Of VA; Engrng.

RUSSO, JOSEPH; Archibishop Molloy HS; Flushing, NY; (Y); 84/409; Var Capt Bsbl; JV Bsktbl; Coach Actv; Elks Awd; Hon Roll; NHS; CHSAA 1st Tm All City Bsbl 84; Bus.

RUSSO, KAREN; St Francis Prep; Rosedale, NY; (Y); Rep Soph Cls; Rep Jr Cls; JV Twrlr; Im Vllybl; Jr NHS; Acctng.

RUSSO, KIMBERLY M; Immaculata Acad; Lake Vw, NY; (Y); Church Yth Grp; Dance Clb; Drama Clb; FNA; JA; PAVAS; Nwsp Stf; Cheerleading; Golf; Med Sci.

RUSSO, LAUREN; St Peters For Girls; Staten Isl, NY; (Y); Drama Clb; Chorus; School Musical; School Play; Variety Show; Sec Jr Cls; JV Var Cheerleading; Voice.

RUSSO, LORIANN; West Hempstead HS; W Hempstead, NY; (Y); Yrbk Phtg; Hon Roll; Bocees; Cosmtlgst.

RUSSO, NANCY; Academy Of The Resurctn; Pt Chester, NY; (Y); Dance Clb; Math Clb; Chorus; School Musical; Yrbk Stf; High Hon Roll; Ntl Merit Ltr; Knights Columbus Schlrshp 82-86; Acad Resurrection Schlrshp 82-86; Corpus Christi Schl Mem Schlrshp 86; Frgn Lang.

RUSSO, PETER E; Ross Brentwood HS; Brentwood, NY; (Y); 27/560; Boy Scts; Band; Nwsp Stf; Capt Ftbl; Hon Roll; Jr NHS; NHS; Regnts Schlrshp 85; Silver Medals Lit & Soc Studies 84; Pace U; Pre-Med.

RUSSO, SANTA; Bishop Kearney HS; Brooklyn, NY; (Y); Art Clb; Library Aide; Teachers Aide; Chorus; School Musical; Yrbk Ed-Chief; Yrbk Stf; Hon Roll; Svc Awd 83; Prncpls Lst 83.

RUSSO, TERESA; Richmond Hill HS; Richmond Hill, NY; (Y); Cmnty Wkr; Spanish Clb; Yrbk Stf; High Hon Roll; Engl Hnr Soc 85; St Johns U; Wrtng.

RUST, LORRAINE J; Chateaugay Central HS; Burke, NY; (Y); 1/42, Church Yth Grp; Pres 4-H; Sec FFA; Gym; Socr; Bausch & Lomb Sci Awd; NHS; Val; NY ST Achvt In Volunteerism 83; Cornell U; Agri Ed.

RUST, TAMMIE K; Saratoga Springs SR HS; Gansevoort, NY; (Y); 14/450; Sec Trs Camera Clb; GAA; Hosp Aide; Intnl Clb; Key Clb; High Hon Roll; NHS; Pres Schlr; Kraft Plan & Party Scholar Wnnr 85; Saratoga Springs JR Miss 85; Mst Outstndng Jobs Daughters 82; Trinity Coll; Bio Chem.

RUST, WILLIAM; Lyme Central HS; Limerick, NY; (Y); Varsity Clb; Pres Frsh Cls; Rep Stu Cncl; Var Bsbl; Var Bsktbl; Capt Coach Actv; Stat Score Keeper; Var Socr; Hon Roll; Prfct Atten Awd; Hotel Mgmt.

RUSTIA, ROSALIE PAYAWAL; Stella Maris HS; Howard Beach, NY; (Y); Drama Clb; NFL; Science Clb; Chorus; School Play; Pres Jr Cls; Hon Roll; Outstng Svc & Contrbtns To Hmrm As Pres 84-85; Music Awd 83-84; St Johns U.

RUSTON, JOSEPH; Harpursville Central HS; Harpursville, NY; (S); School Play; Stage Crew; VP Stu Cncl; Var L Bsbl; Var L Bsktbl; Prfct Atten Awd; Lib Arts.

RUSTRIAN, INGRID; Richmond Hill HS; Richmond Hl, NY; (Y); Teachers Aide; JV Var Socr; French Hon Soc; Hon Roll; NHS; Prfct Atten Awd; Acctg.

RUSYNIAK, KIMBERLY A; Rome Free Acad; Rome, NY; (Y); 47/512; Pres Drama Clb; Red Cross Aide; VP Speech Tm; Band; Mrchg Band; School Play; Var L Swmmng; Hon Roll; Jr NHS; NHS; Colgate Semnr 84-85; Amer Red Crss Chptr Volntr Of Yr 83; St Francis Xavier U; Psych.

RUTAN, ADRIANE; Canastota HS; Canastota, NY; (Y); Office Aide; High Hon Roll; Hon Roll; Bryant & Stratton; Bus.

RUTANARUGSA, TRIPET; Mount St Michael Acad; Bronx, NY; (Y); 155/308; Boy Scts; Chess Clb; Church Yth Grp; English Clb; Intnl Clb; Badmtn; Socr; Swmmng; Vllybl; Hon Roll; Penn ST U; Elec Engrng.

RUTIGLIANO, PAULA; New Dorp HS; Staten Island, NY; (Y); School Musical; Rep Stu Cncl; Socr; Hon Roll; Acctng.

RUTIGLIANO, TOM; Smithtown HS West; St James, NY; (Y); Computer Clb; Math Tm; Quiz Bowl; Ntl Merit SF; Hgh Scorer-Math Tm 85.

RUTKOSKE, MICHAEL; Mattituck HS; Laurel, NY; (Y); 9/110; Computer Clb; French Clb; Mathletes; Math Clb; Math Tm; ROTC; Stage Crew; Rep Frsh Cls; Rep Soph Cls; JV Var Socr; Worcester Polytechnic Inst.

RUTKOWSKI, CATHY; Palmyra-Macedon Central HS; Palmyra, NY; (Y); Church Yth Grp; 4-H; Band; Symp Band; 4-H Awd; Hon Roll; Geneseo; Bus.

RUTKOWSKI, CHERYL; Mattituck HS; Mattituck, NY; (Y); 39/118; Art Clb; Computer Clb; French Clb; Variety Show; Fld Hcky; Sftbl; French Hon Soc; Hon Roll; Salve Regina; Psych.

RUTKOWSKI, RICHARD; Springville Griffith Inst; West Falls, NY; (Y); Pres VP 4-H; Band; Jazz Band; Mrchg Band; Orch; JV Var Trk; Hon Roll; NHS; Chorus; Symp Band; Amer Lgn Schl Awd 83; Schl Rep Hugh O Brian Yth Ldrshp Smnr 84.

RUTLEDGE, CHRISTINA; Mahopac HS; Mahopac, NY; (Y); 12/423; Math Clb; Nwsp Rptr; Nwsp Stf; Off Frsh Cls; Capt Bsktbl; Fld Hcky; Socr; Hon Roll; Boston Coll; Math.

RUTSCHMANN, KAREN M; Chatham Central Schl; Ghent, NY; (Y); 5/140; Band; Chorus; Concert Band; Jazz Band; Mrchg Band; Orch; Pep Band; School Musical; Yrbk Stf; Pres Frsh Cls; Capitol Nthwy Zone Phys Ed Schlrshp 85; Cornell Natl Schlr 85; U Of MA; Exercise Physlgy.

RUTTER, LORI; Martin Van Buren HS; Bayside, NY; (Y); 1/621; Math Tm; Scholastic Bowl; Jazz Band; School Play; Nwsp Rptr; Yrbk Stf; French Hon Soc; High Hon Roll; NHS; Val; Gov Cmm Schlstc Achvt, UFT, Queensbro Fed Prnts Schlrshps; Minerav Awd; ST Chmps Mck Trl Law Tm; Harvard; Govt.

RUTTER, MARIE; Bishop Ford C C HS; Brooklyn, NY; (Y); 50/450; Art Clb; Aud/Vis; Camera Clb; Stage Crew; Bowling; Trk.

RUTTNER, ORA C; BAS Torah Acad; Monsey, NY; (Y); 1/20; Computer Clb; Math Tm; Capt Quiz Bowl; Capt Scholastic Bowl; Yrbk Ed-Chief; VP Jr Cls; Pres Sr Cls; Im Sftbl; High Hon Roll; Val; NY ST Regents Schlrshp 85; Columbia U; Comp Engrng.

RUVA, JENNIE; Auburn HS; Auburn, NY; (Y); Drama Clb; Ski Clb; School Musical; School Play; Stage Crew; Fld Hcky; Score Keeper; High Hon Roll; Hon Roll; Sec NHS; Natl Guild Competitn Pianist 83 & 84; Fashn Desgn.

RUVOLO, JOANNE; St Catherine Acad; Bronx, NY; (Y); Bus.

RUVOLO, KRISTINA MARIE; Our Lady Of Perpetual Help; Brooklyn, NY; (Y); Drama Clb; Pres Intnl Clb; Chorus; School Musical; School Play; Yrbk Phtg; Yrbk Stf; Rep Soph Cls; High Hon Roll; Hon Roll; Perf Atten 82-85; Brooklyn Coll; Theater.

RYAN, ANDREW; Saratoga Central Catholic HS; Ballston Spa, NY; (S); Trs Soph Cls; Var Ftbl.

RYAN, CHERYL; Cohoes HS; Cohoes, NY; (Y); 7/192; Exploring; Key Clb; JV Cheerleading; Var L Trk; High Hon Roll; NHS; Albny Coll; Phrmcy.

RYAN, CHERYL; Delaware Acad; E Meredith, NY; (Y); Drama Clb; English Clb; German Clb; Varsity Clb; Color Guard; Yrbk Stf; Var Cheerleading; Var Twrlr; Girl Scts; Library Aide; Brdcstng Jrnlst.

RYAN, CHRISTOPHER DANIEL; New York Military Acad; Houston, TX; (S); Drama Clb; Nwsp Rptr; Yrbk Rptr; Var Swmmng; Var Capt Tennis; NEDT Awd; Wnnr Mid Hudson Athl Leag Champ 84; Cadet Capt Athl Coord 84; Founder Debate Clb 84; Bus.

RYAN, EILEEN MARIE; Saugerties HS; Saugerties, NY; (Y); 24/240; Aud/Vis; Cmnty Wkr; Math Clb; Teachers Aide; Trs Varsity Clb; Stage Crew; Variety Show; Stat Bsktbl; High Hon Roll; NHS; Siena Coll; Accntng.

RYAN, FRANCES; Mount Assumption Inst; Plattsburgh, NY; (Y); Nwsp Rptr; Nwsp Stf; Rep Soph Cls; Rep Jr Cls; Rep Stu Cncl; JV Var Bsktbl; Capt Powder Puff Ftbl; JV Var Socr; JV Vllybl; Le Moyne; Englsh.

RYAN, GINA; St Lawrence Central HS; Brasher Falls, NY; (Y); Church Yth Grp; Teachers Aide; Church Choir; Rep Frsh Cls; Cheerleading; Var Mgr(s); Var Score Keeper; Hon Roll; Prfct Atten Awd; Pres Schlr; Sci.

RYAN, GRETCHEN; Catholic Central HS; Grafton, NY; (S); 18/203; Church Yth Grp; Cmnty Wkr; Hosp Aide; Math Tm; Red Cross Aide; Stage Crew; Yrbk Stf; Hon Roll; Dstngshed Yorker Awd 82-83; Math Cntst 81-82; Phonathon Wrkr 81-85; Rensselaer Polytec; Math.

RYAN, JOHN; Nyack SR HS; S Nyack, NY; (Y); 25/256; Debate Tm; Math Clb; Model UN; ROTC; School Play; Stage Crew; Nwsp Phtg; Nwsp Rptr; Nwsp Stf; Yrbk Ed-Chief; Boys ST 1st Alt 85; Rotary Yth Ldrshp Conf 84; Outstndg Achvt Sci 85; Bio Stds.

RYAN, JULIE; Onondaga Central HS; Nedrow, NY; (S); #5 In Class; GAA; Spanish Clb; Band; Chorus; Variety Show; Jr Cls; Trk; High Hon Roll; NHS; Mst Outstndg 2nd Yr Spn Stu 84.

RYAN, KAREN M; Mac Arthur HS; Wantagh, NY; (Y); 6/319; Church Yth Grp; Cmnty Wkr; 4-H; Badmtn; Socr; Tennis; Trk; Cit Awd; 4-H Awd; Jr NHS; Gen Excllnc Awd Nat Hnr Socty 85; Cornell U; Engrng.

RYAN, KATHLEEN; Notre Dame Bishop Gibbons HS; Schenectady, NY; (S); 4/108; Hosp Aide; Rep Stu Cncl; Var Capt Bsktbl; JV Crs Cntry; Var Tennis; Var Trk; Var Capt Vllybl; High Hon Roll; NHS; French Awd 83; Boston Coll; Math.

RYAN, KELLEY; G Ray Bodley HS; Oswego, NY; (Y); Trs German Clb; Band; Concert Band; Mrchg Band; Orch; Pep Band; School Musical; Cit Awd; Germ.

RYAN, KERRY ANNE; Pearl River HS; Pearl River, NY; (Y); 45/220; Am Leg Aux Girls St; Church Yth Grp; French Clb; Nwsp Rptr; Rep Stu Cncl; Var Capt Cheerleading; Hon Roll; NHS; Mst Imprvd Chrldr 83; Blue Ribbon Rockland Cty Music Teachers Guild Ratngs 83; Engl.

RYAN, KRISTEN; Plattsburgh HS; Plattsburgh, NY; (Y); 17/180; GAA; Teachers Aide; Var L Socr; Var L Sftbl; Var L Swmmng; Var L Vllybl; High Hon Roll; Hon Roll; NHS; Nicholas B Ottaway Fndtn Schlrshp 85; Pres Acad Ftnss Awd 85; Syracuse U; Hmn Dev.

RYAN, LAURA; The Mary Louis Acad; Flushing, NY; (Y); GAA; Band; Orch; Nwsp Stf; Lit Mag; JV Vllybl; High Hon Roll; Jr NHS; NHS; NEDT Awd; 1st Pl Engl Schl Essay Cont; Engl Mdlst Exam Gold Medal; Cornell U; Bio.

RYAN, LEISYL; Fayetteville-Manluis HS; Fayetteville, NY; (Y); Church Yth Grp; Political Wkr; Rep Stu Cncl; JV Fld Hcky; Var Mgr(s); Var JV Score Keeper; Hon Roll; Bus Awd Typng 83; Yth Advsry Del Synod NE 84; Rcrdng Secy Delta Kappa Beta 84 & 85; Bus.

RYAN, LISA LYNN; Cortland JR SR HS; Cortland, NY; (Y); 5/239; Nwsp Rptr; Yrbk Stf; Lit Mag; High Hon Roll; NHS; Fnlst Hartwick Poet Cont 84; Philip S Nason Mem Scholar 85; Mary E Gerealds Scholar 85; Sarah Lawrence Coll; Creat Wrtg.

RYAN, MARGARET; Bishop Kearney HS; Brooklyn, NY; (S); Church Yth Grp; Ski Clb; Chorus; Church Choir; Rep Frsh Cls; Pres Stu Cncl; Bsktbl; Tennis; Hon Roll; Ntl Merit Ltr; Natl Merit Awd Bio 82-83.

RYAN, MARGARET MARY; St Johns Acad; Plattsburgh, NY; (Y); Am Leg Aux Girls St; Drama Clb; Latin Clb; Model UN; Political Wkr; Scholastic Bowl; Chorus; Socr; NHS; Rotary Awd; Political Sci.

RYAN, MARTIN A; St Johns Acad; Plattsburgh, NY; (Y); 4/50; Boy Scts; French Clb; Latin Clb; Model UN; Scholastic Bowl; VP Jr Cls; Var Crs Cntry; Var Trk; Pres NHS; Variety Show; US Mil Acad.

RYAN, MARY; Bronx High School Of Science; Bayside, NY; (Y); Church Yth Grp; Cmnty Wkr; Girl Scts; Office Aide; Service Clb; Band; Church Choir; Mrchg Band; Yrbk Stf; Trk; AF RTOC Schlrshp 85; Civic Awrns Awd 85; U Notre Dame; Elect Engr.

RYAN, MATTHEW C; Cazenovia Central HS; Cazenovia, NY; (Y); 35/155; Computer Clb; Exploring; Letterman Clb; Bsbl; Ice Hcky; High Hon Roll; Hon Roll; St Schlr; Clarkson U; Comp Engrng.

RYAN, MAUREEN; Victor Central Schl; Victor, NY; (Y); 30/201; Ski Clb; Sec JV Varsity Clb; Chorus; School Musical; School Play; VP Frsh Cls; Rep Stu Cncl; Var Capt Cheerleading; Socr; High Hon Roll; Pres Awd Physcl Ftnss 84; SNUY; Comm.

RYAN, MELANIE A; Academy Of St Joseph; St James, NY; (Y); Cmnty Wkr; Dance Clb; Hosp Aide; Rep Math Tm; Church Choir; School Play; Ed Yrbk Ed-Chief; High Hon Roll; NHS; Pres Schlr; Simons Fellowship Prog,Research Prog 84; Newsday High Hnrs Schlrshp Comp 85; Regents Schlrshp 85; MA Inst; Biology.

RYAN, MICHAEL; Moore Catholic HS; Staten Island, NY; (Y); Varsity Clb; Nwsp Ed-Chief; Lit Mag; Pres Sr Cls; Rep Stu Cncl; Var Capt Bsbl; Var Capt Bsktbl; High Hon Roll; Jr NHS; NHS; Columbia U Acad Schlrshp 85; NY ST Regents Schlrshp 85; Columbia U; Hist.

RYAN, MICHAEL W; Cicero North Syracuse HS; Clay, NY; (Y); 114/711; Ski Clb; Nwsp Stf; Ftbl; Lcrss; Cit Awd; St Schlr; Natl Ldrshp & Svc Awd 84-85; SUNY Geneseo; Wrtr.

RYAN, MICHELE; Horseheads SR HS; Horseheads, NY; (Y); Church Yth Grp; German Clb; Girl Scts; Band; Chorus; Church Choir; Concert Band; Mrchg Band; Orch; School Musical; Upstate Med Syracuse; Phys Thrp.

RYAN, MONICA J; The Mary Louis Acad; Jackson Heights, NY; (Y); Cmnty Wkr; French Clb; Hosp Aide; Library Aide; Service Clb; Var Bowling; Fld Hcky; Ftbl; Prfct Atten Awd.

RYAN, PATRICIA; Nazareth Acad; Rochester, NY; (Y); 1/110; Church Yth Grp; French Clb; Latin Clb; Math Tm; Ski Clb; Chorus; Lit Mag; Rep Frsh Cls; Rep Stu Cncl; JV Cheerleading; NY ST Regnts Schlrshp 85; U Of Dallas Natl Comptv Exm Schlrshp 84-85; U Of Rochester; Pre-Med.

RYAN, SHEILA M; Academy Of St Joseph; Hauppauge, NY; (Y); Model UN; Nwsp Stf; Yrbk Stf; Var Bsktbl; NHS; NEDT Awd; Yuth In Govt 85; Mock Trial Comp 84-85; NYS Rgnts Schlrshp 85; St Johns U; Intl Rel.

RYAN, STEVEN; Dryden Central HS; Freeville, NY; (Y); High Hon Roll; NHS; Engrng.

RYAN, THOMAS F; New Hartford HS; New Hartford, NY; (Y); JV Bowling; Var JV Socr; Var JV Tennis; Var JV Wrstlng; Hon Roll; Jr NHS; NHS; Comp Sci.

RYAN, TIM; Cardinal Mooney HS; Rochester, NY; (Y); Art Clb; Trk; Hon Roll; Spanish NHS; Schlstc Art Show Awd 85; Art.

RYAN JR, WILLIAM; Oneonta HS; Oneonta, NY; (Y); French Clb; Key Clb; Band; Concert Band; Jazz Band; Mrchg Band; Pep Band; Nwsp Sprt Ed; L Bsbl.

RYAN, WINTER BROOK; Northport HS; E Northport, NY; (Y); 40/646; Debate Tm; Mathletes; Jazz Band; Mrchg Band; Pep Band; Yrbk Stf; High Hon Roll; NHS; Hnrs Schlrshp 85; Regents Schlrshp 85; Boston Coll; Law.

RYBARCZYK, RENEE M; Williamsville North HS; N Tonawanda, NY; (Y); 45/311; Church Yth Grp; Hosp Aide; Concert Band; School Musical; Lib Symp Band; Bowling; Mgr(s); JV Socr; Hon Roll; NHS; Rgnts Schrlshp 85; Rookie Yr Pit Band 81; NY Coll Geneseo; Med Tech.

RYBARCZYK, TAMMY; Auburn HS; Auburn, NY; (Y); French Clb; Pep Clb; Ski Clb; Chorus; Stage Crew; Jr Cls; JV Sftbl; Tennis; Boston Coll; Law.

RYDER, MAUREEN ELIZABETH; Newfield HS; Selden, NY; (Y); Cmnty Wkr; Service Clb; Stu Cncl; Mgr Bsbl; Coach Actv; Fld Hcky; Swmmng; Thomas M Loudoaina Mem Awd 83; Hlth Sci.

RYDER, ROGER; Corinth HS; Corinth, NY; (S); Am Leg Boys St; Key Clb; MMM; Spanish Clb; Band; Jazz Band; Trk; VP Jr NHS; NHS; Prfct Atten Awd; USNLMA, USAA 83; Geology.

RYDER, SCOTT; Twin Tiers Baptist HS; Elmira, NY; (S); 2/23; Church Yth Grp; Chorus; School Play; VP Jr Cls; VP Sr Cls; Var Bsktbl; Var Socr; Cit Awd; High Hon Roll; Rep Stu Cncl; Coaches Awd Basketball 83-84; Select Choir 83-85; Co-Editor Yrbk 84-85.

RYDER, SHAWN; Guilderland Centrall HS; Schenectady, NY; (Y); Dance Clb; 4-H; 4-H Awd; Hon Roll; Buffalo U; Engrng.

RYDER, TOM; Hamburg Central HS; Hamburg, NY; (Y); 61/412; Church Yth Grp; German Clb; Band; Concert Band; Jazz Band; Mrchg Band; Symp Band; JV Socr; High Hon Roll; NHS; MI ST; Bio.

RYDZEWSKI, DOUGLAS; North Babylon SR HS; North Babylon, NY; (Y); Gym; Hon Roll; Accntng.

RYERSON, CARYN; Port Jervis HS; Pt Jervis, NY; (Y); VP Pep Clb; Yrbk Stf; Hon Roll; Educ.

RYNGWALSKI, ANDREA; Villa Maria Acad; Buffalo, NY; (S); 5/118; Church Yth Grp; Computer Clb; Rep Stu Cncl; Bowling; Gym; Mat Maids; High Hon Roll; Prfct Atten Awd; Natl Hnr Soc 84-85; U S Natl Ldrshp Awd Wnnr 84-85; Stu Cncl Schl Spirit Comm 84-85; Math.

RYNKIEWICZ, MICHAEL; Jordan Elbridge JR SR HS; Elbridge, NY; (Y); 1/130; Concert Band; Jazz Band; Mrchg Band; JV Bsktbl; Var Golf; NHS; Ntl Merit Ltr; French Clb; School Musical; Hon Roll; Cornell Clb Bk Awd 85; Lions Clb ST Yth Band 85; County Yth Govt Day 84; Sci Rsrch.

RYSZKA, LISA; Mount Mercy Acad; W Seneca, NY; (Y); Spanish Clb; Nwsp Rptr; Nwsp Stf; Lit Mag; Hon Roll; SUNYAB.

RZEMEK, LYNN; Villa Maria Acad; Cheektowaga, NY; (S); 6/116; Computer Clb; Quiz Bowl; Var Bsktbl; Var Bowling; Var Sftbl; Var Vllybl; Sec NHS; NEDT Awd; Math.

RZESZOT, DAWN; Villa Maria Acad; Buffalo, NY; (Y); Art Clb; Dance Clb; Girl Scts; Latin Clb; Chorus; Church Choir; School Musical; School Play; Gym; Utica Coll; Occptnl Thrpy.

SAARMAA, ERIK; Freeport HS; Freeport, NY; (Y); Mathletes; Quiz Bowl; Ski Clb; Teachers Aide; Ed Nwsp Stf; High Hon Roll; Pres NHS; Ntl Merit SF; Math Clb; Math Tm; Trnddrlsrt Mdl 85; Gld Mdl LI Math Fair 83; Slvr, Gld Mdla Math Leag 84-85; Sci Engrng.

SABA, GEORGE; Cardinal Hayes HS; New York, NY; (Y); 23/287; Art Clb; Aud/Vis; Church Yth Grp; Computer Clb; PAVAS; Spanish Clb; Bowling; Score Keeper; High Hon Roll; Hon Roll; Cener Of Media Arts; Camermn.

SABA, LAURA; St Peters For Girls; Staten Island, NY; (Y); Church Yth Grp; Key Clb; Office Aide; Teachers Aide; Chorus; Nwsp Rptr; Nwsp Stf; JV Cheerleading; JV Swmmng; Var Tennis; Natl Stu Exchg Pgm 83-84; Schlrshp Pgm In Curtis HS 82-84; Wagner Coll.

SABATER, LUCIA A; Scarsdale HS; Scarsdale, NY; (Y); Cmnty Wkr; Hosp Aide; Office Aide; Spanish Clb; School Play; Pres Stu Cncl; NHS; Ntl Merit SF; Drama Clb; French Clb; Wellesley Clg Awd 84.

SABATINI, DAVID; Riverdale Country Schl; New Rochelle, NY; (Y); Math Tm; Science Clb; Nwsp Rptr; Swmmng; Tennis; High Hon Roll; Hon Roll; Ntl Merit SF.

SABATINI, LINDA A; Mary Louis Acad; Flushing, NY; (Y); 26/286; Art Clb; Church Yth Grp; NHS; Iona Coll Lang Cntst 1st Hnrs 83-85; Iona Coll Lang Cntst 2nd Hnrs 85; St Johns U.

SABATINO, JEROME E; Regis HS; Corona, NY; (Y); Church Yth Grp; Cmnty Wkr; Yrbk Stf; Im Bowling; Hon Roll; Ntl Merit Ltr; Jesuit Comm Schlrshp 85; Presdntl Schlrshp 85; NYS Regnts Schlrshp 85; Fordham Coll; Pre-Med.

SABELLA, SALLY; Solvay HS; Syracuse, NY; (Y); Mgr Church Yth Grp; VP Sec Band; Trs Chorus; School Musical; Nwsp Rptr; Yrbk Bus Mgr; Trs Jr Cls; Var Bowling; Var Trk; Spec Svc Awd 85; Adver.

SABIA, CHRISTOPHER; Commack High School South; Commack, NY; (S); 217/374; Cmnty Wkr; Drama Clb; Thesps; Chorus; School Musical; School Play; Stage Crew; Variety Show; High Hon Roll; Hon Roll; Shclrshp BOCES Inst For Gifted And Talented 84; Theatre.

SABIN, LAURAL A; Southside HS; Elmira, NY; (Y); 13/333; Trs Church Yth Grp; VP Key Clb; Latin Clb; Pep Clb; Varsity Clb; Band; Church Choir; Concert Band; Mrchg Band; Symp Band; Rgnts Schlrshp; Deans Lst; Alpha Sigma Lambda Hnr Soc; Elem Educ.

SABIN, TODD A; Southside HS; Elmira, NY; (Y); 2/325; Boy Scts; Chess Clb; Church Yth Grp; Latin Clb; Ski Clb; Band; High Hon Roll; Rgnts Schlrshp; Deans Lst; Alpha Sigma Lambda Hnr Soc; Comp Sci.

SABINO, CHRISTINE; Jamestown HS; Jamestown, NY; (Y); Church Yth Grp; Spanish Clb; Band; Concert Band; Mrchg Band; Symp Band; Nwsp Stf; Jamestown CC; Psych.

SABINO, JOHN R; Jamestown HS; Jamestown, NY; (Y); 27/375; Church Yth Grp; Spanish Clb; Rep Soph Cls; Hon Roll; NHS; Prfct Atten Awd; Jamestown Comm Coll; Psychlgy.

SABLICH, CARMELA; St Johns Prep; Astoria, NY; (Y); Hon Roll; NHS; Bus.

SABO, CHRISTIE; Mount Mercy Acad; W Seneca, NY; (Y); 13/166; French Clb; Science Clb; Nwsp Rptr; Nwsp Stf; Lit Mag; Hon Roll; VP NHS; Sci Fair Awd Hnrbl Ment; Math.

SABO, PATTY; Dover JR SR HS; Dover Plains, NY; (S); 4/115; Concert Band; Jazz Band; JV Cheerleading; JV Fld Hcky; Var Tennis; High Hon Roll; Jr NHS; NHS; Acad All-Amer 84; Marist Coll; Acctng.

SABOGAL, ANDREW; Middletown HS; Middletown, NY; (Y); 30/396; Band; Concert Band; Symp Band; JV Ftbl; Var Capt Swmmng; Var L Tennis; Hon Roll; ST U-Albany; Bio.

SABOGAL, MAURICE; Middleton HS; Middletown, NY; (Y); Teachers Aide; Concert Band; Symp Band; JV Bsbl; Var Swmmng; Hon Roll; Accntng.

SABOL, ANDREW; Waterville Central Schl; Waterville, NY; (Y); 3/101; Boy Scts; Mathletes; Ski Clb; Temple Yth Grp; School Musical; Stage Crew; Nwsp Stf; JV Socr; High Hon Roll; NHS; Colgate Seminar 85; Med.

SACCO, THERESA; Waverly JR SR HS; Waverly, NY; (Y); Drama Clb; Red Cross Aide; School Play; Lit Mag; Trs Jr Cls; Trs Sr Cls; NHS; Ntl Merit Ltr; Rotary Awd; Church Yth Grp; Am Leg Oratrcl Cntst 2nd Pl; Herkimer County CC; Comm Adv.

SACCONE, LORRAINE; New Hyde Park Memorial HS; Garden City Park, NY; (Y); JV Var Cheerleading; JV Var Gym; JV Stat Vllybl; U Central FL; Bus.

SACHS, MARIA L; Bronxville HS; Bronxville, NY; (Y); 1/80; Capt Math Tm; Rep Soph Cls; Var L Crs Cntry; Var L Trk; High Hon Roll; Ntl Merit SF; Rensalaer Math & Sci Awd 84; Mt Holyoke Book Awd 84; George Washington U Math & Sci Awd 84; Chem.

SACHS, MICHAEL; Williamsville North HS; Williamsville, NY; (Y); 72/314; Latin Clb; Quiz Bowl; Hon Roll; NHS; Hnr Cert NY Bar Assn 84-85; U Of MD; Pre-Law.

SACKS, ERIK J; The Bronx High Schl Of Science; Flusing, NY; (Y); Debate Tm; NFL; Lit Mag; Bio.

SACKS, LYNNE D; Albany HS; Albany, NY; (Y); 41/600; Latin Clb; Pres Temple Yth Grp; Nwsp Ed-Chief; Rptr Nwsp Stf; Lit Mag; Pres NHS; Ntl Merit SF; Tellvride Assoc Smmr Prog Schlrshp 84; Lit.

SACKS, STEVEN; Spring Valley SR HS; Spring Vly, NY; (Y); Key Clb; Ski Clb; Sec Temple Yth Grp; Chorus; JV Tennis; Hon Roll.

SADA, TONY; Liverpool HS; Liverpool, NY; (Y); Church Yth Grp; Cmnty Wkr; FBLA; Ski Clb; Rep Stu Cncl; Im Bsktbl; Im Tennis; Im Vllybl; JETS Awd; Ntl Merit Ltr; Natl Merit Lttr 85; Bus Ldr Amer 84-86; Chrch Yth Grp/Cmnty Wrkr 82-83; Ithaca/Siena Coll; Bus Admin.

SADDLEMIRE, RAY; Maine Endwell HS; Endwell, NY; (Y); Spanish Clb; High Hon Roll; Hon Roll; Rochester Inst Tech; Elec Engrg.

SADDLUR, PAIGE; Cardinal Spellman HS; Bronx, NY; (Y); French Clb; Office Aide; Pep Clb; Diving; Swmmng; Tennis; Trk; Vllybl; Hon Roll; Kiwanis Awd; Frsh 1st Hnrs; Jr & Sr 2nd Hnrs; Pre-Med.

SADEGHIAN, SCOTT; East Aurora HS; East Aurora, NY; (S); 3/182; School Musical; Yrbk Sprt Ed; Trs Jr Cls; Trs Sr Cls; Trs Stu Cncl; Capt Tennis; Pres NHS; Ntl Merit Ltr; Key Clb; Capt Quiz Bowl; Gifted & Talented Prog; Mst Likly To Succeed; Rev Hetherington Sptsmshp Awd Tennis; Princeton.

SADINOFF, JONATHAN A; The Ramaz Upper Schl; Great Neck, NY; (Y); Chess Clb; Computer Clb; Chorus; Nwsp Rptr; Im Ftbl; Sftbl; Ntl Merit SF.

SADLER, TRACY; Monsignro Scanlan HS; New York, NY; (Y); Intnl Clb; Political Wkr; Spanish Clb; Hon Roll; NHS; Prfct Atten Awd; Psych.

SADLON, BARBARA; Little Falls JR SR HS; Little Falls, NY; (S); 15/109; Pres Church Yth Grp; Exploring; GAA; Hosp Aide; Spanish Clb; Band; Concert Band; Mrchg Band; Orch; High Hon Roll; Russell Sage Coll; Phys Ther.

SADOWITZ, MARCH; Onteola Central HS; Woodstock, NY; (Y); 61/243; Chess Clb; Drama Clb; French Clb; Math Tm; Hon Roll; Boston U; Engr.

SADOWSKI, MIKE; Albertus Magnus HS; Suffern, NY; (Y); 16/185; Spanish Clb; Varsity Clb; Stu Cncl; Bsbl; Socr; High Hon Roll; Mu Alp Tht; NHS; Spanish NHS; Sci Hnr Scty; Hnrb Mntn All-Cnfrnc Soccer; Ntl Schlr Athlt Awd; Villanova U; Cvl Engrng.

SADRIEH, TAHIRIH; Manlius Pebble Hill HS; Syracuse, NY; (Y); Cmnty Wkr; Model UN; Band; Chorus; Madrigals; School Musical; Ed Lit Mag; Hon Roll; NHS; Ntl Merit SF; Vassar; Engl.

SAENZ-DE-VITERI, MONICA; St Pius V HS; Bronx, NY; (Y); #1 In Class; Chess Clb; Pres Soph Cls; High Hon Roll; NHS; Prfct Atten Awd; Schlrshp 83-84.

SAEZ, MICHELLE; Dolgeville Central HS; Stratford, NY; (Y); Art Clb; Drama Clb; GAA; Library Aide; Chorus; Color Guard; School Musical; School Play; Variety Show; Pres Soph Cls; Creatvty In Art Awd 84-85; Photogrphy Awd 84-85; Poem Pblshd-Apprentice Wrtr Pblctn 85; Wright ST U; Theatre Arts.

SAEZ, MIRIAN; Walton HS; Bronx, NY; (S); Church Yth Grp; Office Aide; Teachers Aide; Chorus; NHS; Cert Recgntn Korsczak Essy Cont 83; Math Cert 84; Acctng.

SAFEER, RICHARD SCOTT; Williamsville East HS; Williamsville, NY; (Y); 7/283; Latin Clb; Math Tm; Pres Temple Yth Grp; School Musical; Im Socr; Var L Tennis; Var L Vllybl; High Hon Roll; VP NHS; Voice Dem Awd; Rgnts Schlrshp NY ST; PTA Wmsvl East Awd; Jolly Boys Of Wmsvl; SUNY; Med.

SAFIS, KENNETH N; La Salle SR HS; Niagara Falls, NY; (Y); JA; Math Clb; Math Tm; Scholastic Bowl; Band; Concert Band; Jazz Band; Mrchg Band; Orch; Stage Crew; Chem Engr.

SAGE, DANIEL S; William Nottingham HS; Syracuse, NY; (Y); 1/220; Math Tm; Quiz Bowl; Concert Band; Var Tennis; High Hon Roll; NHS; Ntl Merit SF; 5th NYS Stdnt Enrgy Rsrch Comp 84; Gold Mdl Ntl Latin Exam 81-84; Top Ten Cnty Math Leag 84; Phy Sci.

SAGE, KIMBERLY; James E Sperry HS; Henrietta, NY; (Y); 1/309; French Clb; Teachers Aide; L Swmmng; French Hon Soc; VP NHS; Ntl Merit Ltr; Val; Church Yth Grp; Cmnty Wkr; Library Aide; Geneseo Alumni Fllws Schlrshp 85; Phi Delta Kappa Fred Bennett Schlrshp 85; SUNY-GENESEO; Spcl Eductn.

SAGER, CHIRSTOP R; Cicero-North Syracuse HS; Clay, NY; (Y); 230/859; Boy Scts; JV Pres Chess Clb; VP Church Yth Grp; Stage Crew; Im Bowling; JV Golf; NY ST Regents Schlrshp 85; Canton ATC; Cvl Engr.

SAGER, PATRICIA; Gowanda Centra School; Perrysburg, NY; (Y); 15/150; Church Yth Grp; Ski Clb; Band; Concert Band; Mrchg Band; Capt L Bsktbl; Capt L Sftbl; JV L Vllybl; Hon Roll; NHS; Sci.

SAGER, SCOTT; Liverpool HS; Liverpool, NY; (S); 92/898; Exploring; Trs JA; Mathletes; Math Tm; Im Bsbl; Var L Bowling; Hon Roll; Jr NHS; NHS; Ntl Merit Schol; 1st Pl Math Awd 83; Mech Drwng Awd 81; Bowling Awd 85; SUNY-GEOSEO; Accntnt.

SAHA, JOLLY; Clarkstown North HS; Congers, NY; (Y); Cmnty Wkr; Hon Roll; Pre-Law.

SAHANSRA, CHARANJIT; Forest Hills HS; Corona, NY; (Y); 119/881; Intnl Clb; Library Aide; Office Aide; Teachers Aide; Hon Roll; Chem.

SAHM, JIM; Cicero-N Syracuse HS; Clay, NY; (Y); 120/700; Band; Concert Band; Madrigals; Mrchg Band; Orch; Pep Band; School Musical; Symp Band; NHS; Forstry.

SAHM, PETER; Onodaga HS; Syracuse, NY; (Y); Computer Clb; German Clb; Ski Clb; Band; Jazz Band; Variety Show; Var Crs Cntry; Var Trk; NHS; Physcs.

SAHMEL, HEIDI; Cardinal Mooney HS; Rochester, NY; (Y); Church Yth Grp; Teachers Aide; Band; Church Choir; Concert Band; School Musical; JV Socr; Hon Roll; SUNY; Paralgl.

SAHNER, KELLY PAIGE; Half Hollow Hills H S East; Dix Hills, NY; (Y); Art Clb; Camera Clb; Cmnty Wkr; FBLA; German Clb; GAA; Leo Clb; Variety Show; Nwsp Phtg; Yrbk Phtg; Photo.

SAILER, JAMES; Warwick Valley Central HS; Warwick, NY; (Y); Am Leg Boys St; School Musical; Nwsp Bus Mgr; Yrbk Ed-Chief; Pres Stu Cncl; JV Var Bsktbl; Tennis; High Hon Roll; NHS; Ntl Merit SF; Otstndg Chem Stu 85; Top Geom Stu 84.

SAISON, TANIA; Friends Acad; Westbury, NY; (Y); Orch; Full Merit Schlrshp-Alvin Ailey Schl Of Dance 86; H S Acadmc Schlrshp; Pre-Med.

SAITZYK, ARLENE; Flushing HS; Flushing, NY; (Y); 3/400; Math Tm; Band; School Musical; School Play; Ed Nwsp Stf; Ed Yrbk Stf; Var Cheerleading; Var Tennis; High Hon Roll; NHS; Cornell U; Liberol Arts.

SAK, ADAM R; Columbia Prep; New York, NY; (Y); Drama Clb; School Play; Stage Crew; Yrbk Stf; Rep Soph Cls; Var Socr; St Schlr; Andrew Carnegie Awd-Carnegie Mellon U 85; Carnegie Mellon U; Engl.

SAKAI, SHUJI; Valley Stream Central HS; Valley Stream, NY; (Y); Computer Clb; Mathletes; Math Clb; Math Tm; Ski Clb; Teachers Aide; Chorus; School Play; Nwsp Ed-Chief; Nwsp Phtg; Long Is Schl Press Assoc Bst Edtrl Awd 85; NY Japanese Amer Soc Outstndng Stu Awd 85; Bio Med Engnrng.

SAKIS, GEORGE; St Francis Prep; Whitestone, NY; (Y); 158/698; Im Fld Hcky; Im Ftbl; Im Sftbl; Prfct Atten Awd; Amer Lgn Ctznshp Awd 82; Deans Good Bhvr Cmndtn 85; Hofstra U; Bus.

SALADINO, MARY ANN; St Anthonys HS; Commack, NY; (Y); Computer Clb; Drama Clb; Chorus; School Musical; School Play; Stage Crew; Nwsp Rptr; Yrbk Stf; High Hon Roll; NHS; Awds-Hnrs Bio & Math II 83-84; Prncpls Lst 81-85; Coll Of New Rochelle; Educ.

SALAMIDO, PAT; Union-Endicott HS; Endicott, NY; (S); 143/435; VP Band; Concert Band; Jazz Band; Mrchg Band; Orch; JV Socr; JV Var Wrstlng; Hon Roll; Arch.

SALAMON, ANDREW; Rhinebeck Central HS; Clinton Corners, NY; (Y); 4/112; Am Leg Boys St; Ski Clb; Im Badmtn; Var Trk; High Hon Roll; NHS; Ntl Merit SF; Rnnr Up Natl Frnch Cont 85; Cornell U; Bio.

SALAMY, JOSEPH; Long Beach HS; Long Beach, NY; (S); 36/316; Camera Clb; Computer Clb; Exploring; French Clb; ROTC; Ski Clb; Spanish Clb; Varsity Clb; Band; Yrbk Sprt Ed.

SALANGER, JEFFREY M; Charles W Baker HS; Baldwinsville, NY; (Y); 41/440; Bsktbl; Var Capt Ice Hcky; JV Var Lcrss; JV Var Socr; High Hon Roll; Hon Roll; Jr NHS; NHS; Athltc Schlr Awd 85; Empire ST Gms La Crosse 84; MVP Awd Lacrosse 85; U Of MA Amherst; Bus Mngmnt.

SALAS, JANINE; Clara Barton HS; Richmond Hill, NY; (Y); Hosp Aide; Spanish Clb; Stage Crew; Vllybl; Cit Awd; Med.

SALASNY, JODIE; Mount Mercy Acad; Orchard Park, NY; (S); 22/200; French Clb; Q&S; Spanish Clb; Nwsp Phtg; JV Im Vllybl; Hon Roll; NHS; Long Island U; Math.

SALAT, MICHAEL; John H Glenn HS; E Northport, NY; (Y); Boy Scts; Drama Clb; Key Clb; MMM; PAVAS; ROTC; Spanish Clb; Chorus; Color Guard; Drill Tm; Exec Ofcr-ROTC 84-85; ROTC Awds 82-85; Cornell; Polit Sci.

SALATTE, THOMAS; Cicero-N Syracuse HS; N Syracuse, NY; (S); 5/711; Boy Scts; Debate Tm; Exploring; JV Crs Cntry; JV Trk; Trs NHS; Opt Clb Awd; Natl Hstry & Govt Awd 84; SR Starlght 84; Hamilton Coll; Pre-Law.

SALATTI, CHRIS; Sachem HS; Holtsville, NY; (Y); 27/1500; Science Clb; Varsity Clb; NHS; Var Capt Crs Cntry; Var Capt Trk; Natl Sci Olympiads Bio 84; Natl Sci Olympiad ST Comp 85; Cornell U; Wildlife Bio.

SALAV, MICHAEL; Smithtown H S East; Nesconset, NY; (Y); Drama Clb; Temple Yth Grp; Rep Thesps; Chorus; School Musical; School Play; High Hon Roll; Hon Roll; Jr NHS; NHS; Bst Spprtng Actr 84-85; Med.

SALAZAR, JOSE; Msgr Mc Clancy Memorial HS; Long Island City, NY; (S); 14/230; Pres Chess Clb; Cmnty Wkr; Hosp Aide; Science Clb; Yrbk Ed-Chief; Yrbk Phtg; Bowling; High Hon Roll; Hon Roll; Jr NHS; Acad All Amer 84; Distngshd HS Stu 84; Queens Coll; Med.

SALAZAR, REBECCA; Hunter College HS; New York, NY; (Y); Church Yth Grp; Cmnty Wkr; Chorus; Var Sftbl; VFW Awd; Hispanic Natl Merit SF 85; Williams Coll; Intl Rel.

SALCE, STACEY; East Syracuse-Minoa HS; Kirkvl, NY; (Y); JA; Nwsp Ed-Chief; Ed Yrbk Stf; Hon Roll; Jr NHS; NHS.

SALDERFER, WILLIAM; Phoenix Central HS; Phoenix, NY; (Y); JA; ROTC; Ski Clb; Var L Swmmng; Var L Trk; High Hon Roll; NHS; Rgnst Schlrhsp 84; Rotary Schlrhsp 85; Phenix Fest 83; Army; Auto Engr.

SALEM, MOLLY; Bishop Grimes HS; E Syracuse, NY; (Y); 14/207; Ski Clb; Off Sr Cls; High Hon Roll; Hon Roll; NHS; RIT Schlrshp; Regents Schlrshp; Fly Road Schlrshp; Rochester Inst Of Tech; Engrng.

SALERNO, DAVID; Minisink Valley HS; Port Jervis, NY; (Y); Band; Concert Band; Jazz Band; Mrchg Band; JV Socr; Var Trk; High Hon Roll; NHS; Bio.

SALERNO, LAURENE; Albertus Magnus HS; Valley Cottage, NY; (Y); Yrbk Stf; Hon Roll; Psych.

SALERNO, STEPHEN M; Rome Free Acad; Rome, NY; (Y); 9/530; Political Wkr; Jazz Band; Symp Band; Trs Sr Cls; NHS; Ntl Merit Ltr; Pres Schlr; Computer Clb; Key Clb; Army Navy Air Frce ROTC Scholar 85; Natl Lat Exam Slvr Medl Recip; Rensselar Polytech; Biomed Comp.

SALERNO, TRACEY L; North Rose-Wolcott HS; N Rose, NY; (Y); Church Yth Grp; FBLA; Ski Clb; Swmmng; Tennis; Trk; High Hon Roll; Hon Roll; NHS.

SALES, CRISTINA; Academy Of St Joseph; Hauppauge, NY; (Y); Drama Clb; Hosp Aide; Chorus; Variety Show; Yrbk Phtg; Pres Jr Cls; NHS; Aud/Vis; Service Clb; Chrstn Courtsey Medal; Spnsh Awd; Law.

SALES, RICHARD; Port Chester HS; Port Chester, NY; (Y); CAP; Computer Clb; Exploring; JCL; MMM; Spanish Clb; Chorus; Nwsp Rptr.

SALGADO, ANGELI DAYANAN; Albertus Magnus HS; Vly Cottage, NY; (Y); 1/185; Drama Clb; Math Tm; School Play; Yrbk Stf; Im Badmtn; JV Vllybl; French Hon Soc; Mu Alp Tht; NHS; Hon Roll; Sci Hnr Scty 85; Frnch Awd 85; Bio Awd 85; MA Inst Tech; Math.

SALINOVICH, STACEY; Marlboro HS; Newburgh, NY; (Y); #42 In Class; FBLA; Chorus; Color Guard; Nwsp Rptr; Nwsp Stf; High Hon Roll; Hon Roll; Bus.

SALISBURY, ANITA; Marion HS; Marion, NY; (Y); 3/118; Band; Concert Band; Mrchg Band; School Musical; School Play; Yrbk Bus Mgr; Var Cheerleading; Socr; NHS; Ntl Merit Ltr; Monroe CC Schlr Awd 85; Rgnts Schlrshp 85; St Ofcr Cnstlltn Jr Strs 85-86; Monroe CC; Comp Sci.

SALISBURY, CAROL; Cicero-North Syracuse HS; Clay, NY; (Y); 273/713; JA; High Hon Roll; Prfct Atten Awd; Math Awd 82; Acctnt.

SALISBURY, KAREN; Baker HS; Baldwinsville, NY; (Y); 84/440; Church Yth Grp; GAA; Ski Clb; Teachers Aide; Sec Frsh Cls; Sec Soph Cls; Var Rep Stu Cncl; Powder Puff Ftbl; JV Socr; Hon Roll; Schlrshps-Cmnty & Niagara U Pres 85; Miagara U; Nrsng.

SALISBURY, MARGARET W; Nardin Acad; Eden, NY; (Y); Model UN; Political Wkr; Ski Clb; Nwsp Bus Mgr; Nwsp Stf; Yrbk Ed-Chief; Yrbk Stf; Stu Cncl; Im Lcrss; Var Socr; Rgnts Schlrshp 85; Denison U; Govt.

SALISBURY, MIKE; Newark SR HS; Newark, NY; (Y); Twrlr; Band; Sec Frsh Cls; Sec Soph Cls; Var Bsbl; JV Bsktbl; JV Var Ftbl; Cit Awd; High Hon Roll; Spanish NHS; Harvard Bk Prz 85; All Cnty Band 85; MI Stu Ldrshp Forum Rep 83; Polit Sci.

SALISBURY, ROD; Newburgh Free Acad; Newburgh, NY; (Y); Science Clb; Teachers Aide; High Hon Roll; Equestrian.

SALKEY, ANDREW A; Spingfield Gasden HS; Cambria Heights, NY; (Y); Sftbl; Tennis; Vllybl; Prfct Atten Awd; Mech Engr.

SALLADE, JENNIFER; Horseheads HS; Horseheads, NY; (Y); Spanish Clb; Varsity Clb; Diving; Gym; Swmmng; Trk; Lewis L Kelley Awd 85; Fredonia; Elem Educ.

SALLEMI, LORRAINE; Lindenhurst HS; Lindenhurst, NY; (Y); 71/500; Sftbl; Tennis; Vllybl; Hon Roll; NHS; Church Yth Grp; Cmnty Wkr; Spanish Clb; Bowling; Vetrns Of Frgn Wars Awd 80; NY U; Bnkng.

SALMON, BRADLEY; Tonawanda SR HS; Tonawanda, NY; (Y); Pres Letterman Clb; Ski Clb; Pres Varsity Clb; Trs Soph Cls; Trs Stu Cncl; Var Socr; Var Tennis; Var Wrstlng; Hon Roll; NEDT Awd; Hnr Mst Valubl & 2nd Tm All Str Wrstlg 84; Mst Valubl Wrstlg 85; Bus.

SALMON, GERALD J; Vestal SR HS; Vestal, NY; (Y); French Clb; Ski Clb; Varsity Clb; VP Jr Cls; Co-Capt Socr; Trk; High Hon Roll; Hon Roll; All Conf Div I Sccr 84; Votd MI Plyr Sccr 84; Georgetown; Law.

SALMON, NADINE; Northeastern Acad; Bronx, NY; (S); 4/49; Church Choir; Sec Frsh Cls; Sec Civic Clb; Bsktbl; Vllybl; Hon Roll; Oakwood SDA; Med.

SALMON, REBECCA; Camden HS; Taberg, NY; (Y); Cmnty Wkr; Debate Tm; Exploring; 4-H; Chorus; JV Var Fld Hcky; Im Lcrss; Mgr(s); JV Vllybl; Mgr Stat Wrstlng; Pol Sci.

SALONY, ROBERT A; Middle College HS; Woodside, NY; (Y); Chess Clb; Debate Tm; Exploring; Chorus; School Play; Var Sftbl; Prfct Atten Awd; FL ST U; Acctng.

SALPHINE, KENNETH G; Gates Chili HS; Rochester, NY; (Y); 33/476; Am Leg Boys St; Boy Scts; Computer Clb; Service Clb; Trs Lit Mag; Rep Soph Cls; High Hon Roll; NHS.

SALSBERG, DAVID H; Ramaz HS; New York, NY; (Y); Art Clb; Aud/Vis; Cmnty Wkr; School Play; Stage Crew; Pres Sr Cls; Stu Cncl; Var Fld Hcky; Var Trk; St Schlr; SUNY Albany; Psychtrst.

SALUATO, LINDA; H Frank Carey HS; Franklin Square, NY; (Y); Leo Clb; Hon Roll; Intrior Dsgn.

SALUZZO, TOM; West Seneca East HS; Cheektonaga, NY; (Y); Pres VICA; Var Socr; Var Trk; High Hon Roll; Hon Roll; VICA Schlrshp 85; Spanish Awd 81-84; Erie Cmnty Coll; Elec Engr.

SALVA, LAURA; Franciscan HS; Mohegan Lake, NY; (Y); Library Aide; Stage Crew; Variety Show; Nwsp Rptr; Stat Bsktbl; High Hon Roll; NHS; Spanish NHS; Natl Essay Cont 2nd Pl 85; Nrsng.

SALVATI, AMY; Auburn HS; Auburn, NY; (Y); Library Aide; Lit Mag; High Hon Roll; VP NHS.

SALVATI, JOHN; Notre Dame HS; Pine City, NY; (Y); 48/125; Pres Chess Clb; Trs JA; Trs Band; Jazz Band; Nwsp Phtg; Yrbk Phtg; Mgr Socr; Hon Roll; Treas Of The Yr-Jr Achvt 84; Delegate To Natl Jr Achvt Conv 83-84; Mst Imprvd Plyr-Band 83; Corning Cmnty Coll; Accntng.

SALVATORE, DAVID; Eastridge HS; Rochester, NY; (Y); Aud/Vis; Exploring; JA; JV Crs Cntry; Var Tennis; High Hon Roll; Hon Roll; Travel Mgmt.

SALVATORE, GARY; Niagara Wheatfield HS; Sanborn, NY; (Y); Church Yth Grp; Latin Clb; PAVAS; Varsity Clb; JV Ftbl; Var Socr; Var Tennis; Hon Roll; NHS; Boys ST Fnlst 85; Dentstry.

SALVATORE, MARSHA; Avon JR-SR HS; Avon, NY; (Y); Church Yth Grp; GAA; Girl Scts; Spanish Clb; Band; Mrchg Band; Yrbk Stf; Sftbl; Vllybl; Hon Roll; Band All Cnty Awd 85; St John Fischer; Sci.

SALVATORE, PEGGY; Commack H S North; E Northport, NY; (Y); 116/440; Chorus; Rep Jr Cls; Var L Trk; High Hon Roll; Hon Roll; Pres Schlr; Pace U; Bus.

SALVATORE, PRAINITO; New Utrecht HS; Brooklyn, NY; (Y); 5/605; VP Key Clb; Math Tm; Science Clb; Chorus; Rep Jr Cls; Hon Roll; NHS; Arista Boy Ldr 85-86; Natl Ldrshp Awd 85; Natl Sci Merit Awds 84-85; Med.

SALVERSON, MARGARET; Wilson Magnet HS; Rochester, NY; (Y); Church Yth Grp; Comptr Sci.

SALVI, FRANK; Archbishop Stepinac HS; Dobbs Ferry, NY; (Y); 13/201; Church Yth Grp; Cmnty Wkr; Yrbk Bus Mgr; Yrbk Stf; VP Stu Cncl; JV Socr; Hon Roll; NHS; Career Day Rep 85; Med.

SALZER, STACEY; Berne Knox Westerlo HS; Berne, NY; (Y); Trs Church Yth Grp; Band; Mrchg Band; JV Capt Bsktbl; Var Socr; Var Sftbl; Hon Roll; Concert Band; Jazz Band; Pep Band; Musician Yr Awd Bnd 84; All Star Soccer 84; Music Tchr.

SALZMANN, JEFFREY K; Depew HS; Depew, NY; (Y); 38/254; CAP; Computer Clb; Quiz Bowl; Wrstlng; Jr NHS; NHS; Hon Roll; Amelia Earhart Awd 84; Billy Mitchell Awd 81; IACE 85; Rochester Inst Of Tech; Engrng.

SAM, SANDRA; Bishop Kearney HS; Brooklyn, NY; (S); 40/344; Cmnty Wkr; Dance Clb; Hosp Aide; Math Tm; Ski Clb; Trk; Hon Roll; NHS; Prfct Atten Awd; Dean Schlrshp 85; Educ Opprtnty Schlrshp 85; Ithaca Coll; Phy Thrpy.

SAMAAN, ANDREW W; Garden City SR HS; Garden City, NY; (Y); 56/319; Office Aide; Ski Clb; Nwsp Stf; Pres Jr Cls; Stu Cncl; Var Lcrss; Var Co-Capt Socr; High Hon Roll; NHS; Ntl Merit Ltr; Chrmn SADD 84-85; U Miami; Pre-Med.

SAMAD, SHEUL; Clara Barton HS; New York, NY; (Y); Teachers Aide; Chorus; Vllybl; High Hon Roll; Hon Roll; NHS; Ntl Merit Schol; Prfct Atten Awd; Tennis Awd & Medal,Volunteer Svc Awd 84; Med.

SAMALA, GEORGE; Nyack HS; Nyack, NY; (Y); 17/285; JA; Math Tm; Sec Spanish Clb; School Play; Stage Crew; Rep Jr Cls; Var Capt FBLA; Var Trk; Im Wt Lftg; Var Wrstlng; MVP JV Ftbl 84; Exch Stu Japan 85; 3rd Pl Mth Competitn Martin County, Coral Spngs FL 83; Elec Engr.

SAMANICH, KAREN; Mary Louis Acad; Jackson Heights, NY; (Y); Girl Scts; Hosp Aide; Service Clb; Im Bowling; Im Ftbl; Natl JR Clsscl Lg Cum Laude Lat Awd Exam 83; 13 Yr Ballet Awd 85; Med.

SAMAROO, KARAMCHAND; Bronx High School Of Science; New York, NY; (Y); Cmnty Wkr; JA; Science Clb; Service Clb; Teachers Aide; High Hon Roll; Hon Roll; NHS; Prfct Atten Awd; Pres Schlr; Elec Engrng.

SAME, JENNIFER; Mynderse Acad; Seneca Falls, NY; (Y); Church Yth Grp; Cmnty Wkr; Dance Clb; Yrbk Stf; Var L Cheerleading; Score Keeper; Psychlgy.

SAMES, MATTHEW; Plattsburgh HS; Plattsburgh, NY; (Y); Boy Scts; Model UN; Radio Clb; School Play; Pres Soph Cls; Pres Jr Cls; Pres Sr Cls; Rep Stu Cncl; JV Var Bsbl; Var Capt Bsktbl; Bus Mgt.

SAMET, SCOTT; Commack High Schl South; Dix Hills, NY; (Y); Computer Clb; Mathletes; Math Clb; Spanish Clb; Temple Yth Grp; Ed Nwsp Rptr; Yrbk Stf; Var Tennis; High Hon Roll; NHS; Silvr Mdl Math Fair 82; NSMA 84; Natl Sci Olympiad 85.

SAMIS, STEVEN; Le Roy HS; Leroy, NY; (Y); Varsity Clb; Im Bowling; Capt L Ftbl; Var L Trk; Im Wt Lftg; High Hon Roll; Hon Roll; Livingston Cnty All Str Tm Def Bck 84; MVP Le Roy Trck 84; Drftg.

SAMLAND, SUSAN; Grand Island HS; Grand Island, NY; (Y); 4/325; Church Yth Grp; GAA; Varsity Clb; Band; Concert Band; Mrchg Band; Var Swmmng; High Hon Roll; Hon Roll; NHS; Swmmng Awds 81-83; Engrng.

SAMMONS, STEPHANIE; York Central HS; Leicester, NY; (Y); Church Yth Grp; Key Clb; Service Clb; Band; Chorus; School Musical; Yrbk Stf; Stat Ftbl; Hon Roll; NHS; Med Tech.

SAMOLIS, ELENA; Amsterdam HS; Amsterdam, NY; (Y); Sec 4-H; Capt Socr; Varsity Clb; 4-H Awd; JV Bsktbl; JV Var Mgr(s); JV Var Score Keeper; Col Of St Rose; Specl Ed.

SAMPINO, FRANCES; St Francis Prep; Howard Beach, NY; (Y); JA; Im Powder Puff Ftbl; Im Sftbl; Im Vllybl; Hon Roll; Opt Clb Awd; St Johns U.

SAMPLINSKI, RICHARD; Grand Island HS; Gr Island, NY; (Y); 106/326; Am Leg Boys St; Boys Clb Am; Varsity Clb; Bsbl; Bsktbl; Ftbl; Hon Roll; Bsbl All Niagara Frontier Leag 83-86; All Buffalo,Western Bsbl 85; SC; Bus.

SAMPSON, ANNE; Greene Central HS; Greene, NY; (Y); Library Aide; Spanish Clb; Band; Chorus; Church Choir; Concert Band; Mrchg Band; School Musical; Symp Band; Yrbk Stf; Law.

SAMPSON, DONNA; Martin Van Buren HS; Queens Village, NY; (Y); 39/570; Dance Clb; Teachers Aide; Chorus; School Musical; Variety Show; Hon Roll; Jr NHS; Svc Awd Svc Hnr Soc 85; Schlrshp Awds Engl Spnsh, Bio; Ind & Labr Reltns.

SAMPSON, ELIZABETH; Roy C Ketcham SR HS; Wappingers Fls, NY; (Y); Church Yth Grp; Cmnty Wkr; Drama Clb; Hosp Aide; JCL; Concert Band; School Musical; School Play; Stage Crew; Symp Band; Project Adventure 83; Music.

SAMPSON, HOLLY; Pioneer HS; Bliss, NY; (Y); 35/168; Church Yth Grp; Cmnty Wkr; French Clb; FNA; Hosp Aide; Chorus; Church Choir; School Musical; School Play; Nwsp Stf; Music Ltr Awd 83; Music Pin Awd 84; Nrsg.

SAMPSON, ROBERT; Altmar Parish Williamstown Cnt HS; Parish, NY; (Y); Hon Roll; Prfct Atten Awd; NY Coll Of Optmtry; Optmtrst.

SAMROENGRAJA, RUNGSON; Pelham Memorial HS; Pelham, NY; (Y); Computer Clb; School Play; Rptr Lit Mag; Trs Jr Cls; Trs Sr Cls; Hon Roll; VP NHS; Ntl Merit Ltr; Spanish NHS; Sci Hnrs Pgm 84-86; Bst Spkr Comm New Rochelle Mdl Cngrss 85; Pgr Gftd 83; Columbia U; Comp Sci.

SAMS, LAUREL; Hicksville HS; Hicksville, NY; (Y); Band; Concert Band; Mrchg Band; School Musical; Yrbk Rptr; Trk; Var Hon Roll; SUNY-STONYBROOK; Accntng.

SAMSON, ROSANNE; Emma Willard Schl; Loudonville, NY; (Y); 20/96; Computer Clb; Stage Crew; Nwsp Stf; Trs Jr Cls; Rep Stu Cncl; Cheerleading; Im Sftbl; Ntl Merit Ltr; School Play; Yrbk Stf; Prctr 85-86; Emma Willard Schl Bstr Awd 85.

SAMSON, TROY; Horseheads HS; Horseheads, NY; (S); 50/407; Var Wrstlng; Hon Roll; Mark Palladino Memorial Awd 84; SUNY; Jr Cvl Engr.

SAMSON, WILNER; Clara Barton HS; Brooklyn, NY; (Y); 1/400; Church Yth Grp; Yrbk Stf; Rep Stu Cncl; Bowling; Tennis; Hon Roll; Prfct Atten Awd; Englsh Awd 83; Mdcl Sci Inst Hnrs Prgm 83-86; NYU Clmba; Med.

SAMUDA, BELINDA; Dominican Acad; New York, NY; (Y); 34/53; Church Yth Grp; Hosp Aide; Church Choir; School Musical; Hon Roll; Ntl Merit Ltr; Schlrhsp Spelman Coll 85; Spelman Coll; Pol Sci.

SAMUEL, ALICE; Valley Central HS; Montgomery, NY; (Y); Church Yth Grp; Dance Clb; Band; Chorus; Concert Band; Mrchg Band; Lit Mag; Rep Jr Cls; Trk; Hon Roll; Jrnlsm.

SAMUEL, ALLYSON; Cathedral HS; Bx, NY; (Y); 136/298; Intnl Clb; Chorus; Mrchg Band; Syracuse U; Cmmnctns.

SAMUEL, ROSLYN; Saugerties HS; Saugerties, NY; (Y); 13/241; Am Leg Aux Girls St; Band; Mrchg Band; Symp Band; JV Var Cheerleading; High Hon Roll; Hon Roll; NHS; Am Leg Aux Grls ST Alt 85; Htl Mngmnt.

SAMUEL, SALIM; Bronx H S Of Science; Flushing, NY; (Y); JA; Orch; Ntl Merit Ltr; Prfct Atten Awd; Am H S Mth Exam Awd 84; Natl Merit Fndtn Natl Hnr Roll 85.

SAMUEL, THOMAS; Cardinal Hayes HS; Bronx, NY; (Y); 112/249; Boys Clb Am; Church Yth Grp; Var Crs Cntry; Var Trk; Prfct Atten Awd; St Johns & Fordham Schlrshp 85; St Johns U; Bus Admin.

SAMUEL, TONYA; Cardinal Spellman HS; Bronx, NY; (Y); Computer Clb; Science Clb; Chorus; Hon Roll; Armed Forces Orientatn Engrng Careers Pgm 83; U PA; Bio.

SAMUELS, CHRISTIAN; MSGR Mc Clany Memorial HS; Queens Village, NY; (Y); Church Yth Grp; Cmnty Wkr; Service Clb; Varsity Clb; Im Bsktbl; Im Ftbl; JV Var Tennis; JV Trk; High Hon Roll; Hon Roll.

SAMUELS, DAVID J; Ramaz Schl; West Orange, NJ; (Y); Debate Tm; Political Wkr; Nwsp Ed-Chief; Trs Stu Cncl; Ntl Merit SF; Exec Comm Amer Dem Act 84-85; Pres NY H S Chptr 84-85; Pol Sci.

SAMUELS, DIONNE; Gorton HS; Yonkers, NY; (Y); Med.

SAMUELSON, ERIC; Faith Heritage HS; Fayetteville, NY; (Y); 4/25; Church Yth Grp; Ski Clb; Band; Nwsp Rptr; Trs Jr Cls; Pres Stu Cncl; Var Socr; JV Var Trk; Hon Roll; Stu Cncl Rep 83-85; Air Force; Pilot.

SAMULKA, CARY M; Seton Catholic Central HS; Endwell, NY; (Y); 5/160; Church Yth Grp; VP Key Clb; Capt Mathletes; Pres VP Ski Clb; Chorus; School Musical; Rep Stu Cncl; Var L Socr; Var L Trk; High Hon Roll; T J Watson Memrl Schlrshp 85; Rgnts Schlrshp NY ST; College Of The Holy Cross.

SAN ANGELO, AUDRA; Newark SR HS; Newark, NY; (Y); Church Yth Grp; Chorus; Church Choir; Color Guard; School Musical; Stage Crew; Bowling; Genessee Cmnty Coll; Socl Wrkr.

SANABRIA, KENNETH; Cardinal Hayes HS; New York, NY; (Y); 129/264; Teachers Aide; Elem Eductn.

SANBORN, SHELLEY; Canastota HS; Canastota, NY; (Y); GAA; Yrbk Stf; Bowling; Hon Roll; Bryant & Stranton; Acctng.

SANCHEZ, ALEX; The Bronx HS Of Science; Flushing, NY; (Y); Computer Clb; Latin Clb; Mathletes; Teachers Aide; Band; Concert Band; Yrbk Stf; Trk; NHS; Semi Fnlst Ntl Hispnc Schlr Awds Pgm 85; Rgnts Schlrshp 85; Elec Engr.

SANCHEZ, GLENN; Smithtown High School West; Smithtown, NY; (Y); Science Clb; Ski Clb; Bsktbl; Coach Actv; Var Crs Cntry; Var Capt Lcrss; Var JV Socr; JV Wrstlng; NHS; Brookhaven Ntl Lab Model Bridge Cntst 85; U VA; Chem Engr.

SANCHEZ, JAY; William Floyd HS; Shirley, NY; (Y); 8/425; Aud/Vis; Off Jr Cls; Pres Stu Cncl; Var L Wrstlng; Pres NHS; DAR Awd; Rotary Awd; Century III Ldrs ST Finlst 84-85; Homecoming King 84-85; Assocd U Inc Trustees Scholar Wnr 85; U S Military Acad; Intl Affairs.

SANCHEZ, JOHN; Mount St Michael HS; Bronx, NY; (Y); 3/286; Var L Ftbl; Hon Roll; NHS; Ntl Merit SF; Pres Schlr; Spanish NHS; Manhattan Coll; Engrng.

SANCHEZ, MARIA; Earl L Vandermeulen HS; Mt Sinai, NY; (Y); 30/270; Var Cheerleading; Trk; Vllybl; High Hon Roll; Math Cntst 82-83; Most Imprvd Plyr Trck 82-83; Hofstra; Bus.

SANCHEZ, MARILU; Clara Barton HS; Brooklyn, NY; (Y); 6/469; Dance Clb; Hosp Aide; VP Spanish Clb; VP Jr Cls; Cit Awd; Hon Roll; NHS; Untd Fed Tchrs Schlrshp; St Regents Schlrshp; Shakespeare Recitation Comp 1st; Brown U; Med.

SANCHEZ, MATTHEW; Archbishop Molloy HS; Rosedale, NY; (Y); 143/409; Dance Clb; Spanish Clb; Trk; Hon Roll; Cert Acad Achvt 82-83; Tutrng Clb 83-84; Engnr.

SANCHEZ, MIGUEL; St Agnes HS; Ny, NY; (Y); Computer Clb; Chorus; Bsbl; Aerontcl Engr.

SANCHEZ, PATRICIA; St John The Baptist; Brentwood, NY; (Y); 13/588; Hosp Aide; Im Twrlr; High Hon Roll; NHS; Spanish NHS; Wnnr Ntl Sci Olympd 84; Ntl Sci Olympd Hnr Mntn 85; Engrng.

SANCHEZ, SOPHIA; Cairo Durham HS; Round Top, NY; (Y); Dance Clb; Drama Clb; Ski Clb; Spanish Clb; Elks Awd; Home Ec Awd-2nd Pl Bakng 83-84; Russel Saye; Pediatrc Nursng.

SANCHEZ, TINA M; Vernon-Verona-Sherrill HS; Rome, NY; (Y); Church Yth Grp; Girl Scts; Hosp Aide; Sec Spanish Clb; Chorus; Color Guard; Drm & Bgl; Drm Mjr(t); Im Badmtn; Var Cheerleading; Counsil 82-Secrty & Law Enfrcmnt Schlrshp 85; Travel/Tourism.

SANCHEZ, YVETTE; The Mary Louis Acad; Floral Park, NY; (Y); Variety Show; JV Stat Bsktbl; Spanish Clb; St Johns U; Phrmclgy.

SANCHEZ-MARTINEZ, EMMANUEL; Bishop Loughlin HS; Brooklyn, NY; (Y); Chess Clb; Church Yth Grp; Computer Clb; Dance Clb; Science Clb; Speech Tm; School Play; Rep Frsh Cls; Rep Jr Cls; Rep Stu Cncl.

SANCHIRICO, JOHN; Shenen De Howa HS; Ballston Lk, NY; (Y); Varsity Clb; JV Var Ftbl; Var Trk; Hon Roll; Med.

SANCHIRICO, KAREN; John Bowne HS; Flushing, NY; (Y); Science Clb; Band; Concert Band; Madrigals; Yrbk Phtg; Ed Yrbk Stf; Ntl Merit SF; Geophyscs.

SANDAHL, WENDY; Jamesville-De Witt HS; Manhattan, KS; (Y); Church Yth Grp; Library Aide; Pep Clb; Teachers Aide; Im Bsktbl; Var Crs Cntry; Var Trk; Im Vllybl; Hon Roll; Camera Clb; KS ST U; Bus Admin.

SANDBRAND, FLORENTINA; Sacred Heart HS; Yonkers, NY; (S); 32/278; Hosp Aide; High Hon Roll; Hon Roll; NHS; Columbia U; Med.

SANDER, HENRY; Delaware Academy & Central HS; Delhi, NY; (Y); Var L Ftbl; Var L Trk; Im Wt Lftg; Delhi Ag & Tech Coll; Arch.

SANDERS, BEATRICE; Park West HS; Brooklyn, NY; (Y); VICA; Sftbl; Pride Of Yankees 85; Newburg Coll; Htl Mgmt.

SANDERS, CRAIG; Wheatley Schl; Old Westbury, NY; (Y); 8/105; Computer Clb; Hosp Aide; Intnl Clb; Mathletes; Math Clb; Math Tm; Chorus; Concert Band; Jazz Band; Mrchg Band; 3rd Pl Pratt Comp Cntst Schlrshp 85; Slvr Mdl Hofstra Math Fair 85; Bio-Engrng.

SANDERS, DANIELLE S; East Hampton HS; Montauk, NY; (Y); 6/148; French Clb; Girl Scts; Chorus; Var Capt Fld Hcky; Var L Gym; High Hon Roll; Jr NHS; NHS; Pres Schlr; St Schlr; Gold Medal Chem 84; Rambler Bk Awd 82; Schlrshp Awds French II,III,Eng,Soc Studies 82-83; West Chester U; Nrsng.

SANDERS, LEO S; Yeshiva Univhigh Schl For Boys; Flushing, NY; (Y); Computer Clb; Math Tm; Ski Clb; Temple Yth Grp; Yrbk Stf; VP Stu Cncl; Var Trk; High Hon Roll; NY ST Rgnts Schlrshp 85; Arista Hnr Roll 85; Yeshiva U; Comp Sci.

SANDERS, ROBIN; Weedsport HS; Weedsport, NY; (Y); French Clb; JV Cheerleading; JV Sftbl; Hon Roll; Prfct Atten Awd; Commnctns.

SANDERSON, BRYAN; Oceanside HS; Oceanside, NY; (Y); Var Bsbl; High Hon Roll; Hon Roll.

SANDFORD, PATRICIA; Fonda Fultonville Central HS; Fonda, NY; (Y); 7/119; Band; Chorus; Mrchg Band; Var Capt Crs Cntry; Var Capt Trk; High Hon Roll; Hon Roll; NHS; Balfour Loylty Achvt Awd 85; Natl Schlr Athlt Awd; OH ST U.

SANDHU, FAZEELAH; Pittsford Mendon HS; Pittsford, NY; (Y); 4/250; Yrbk Stf; French Clb; Girl Scts; Nwsp Phtg; Nwsp Stf; Socr; Tennis; Trk; Hon Roll; Nazareth Coll Rochester; Biol.

SANDHU, PAPU; Eastport HS; Speonk, NY; (S); Mathletes; Quiz Bowl; Scholastic Bowl; JV Bsbl; Bsktbl; Cit Awd; High Hon Roll; Hon Roll; NHS; Prfct Atten Awd; Pre Law.

SANDIN, LAURA L; South Kortright HS; Bloomville, NY; (Y); 1/35; Band; Trs Nwsp Stf; VP Frsh Cls; Pres Soph Cls; VP Jr Cls; VP Sr Cls; Trs Stu Cncl; Var L Socr; Bausch & Lomb Sci Awd; NHS; Sccr MPV 84; Century III Ldrs Awd 85; Regents Schlrshp 85; Cornell U; Pre-Med.

SANDLEITNER, DARCY; School Of The Holy Child; Scarsdale, NY; (Y); Capt Sftbl; Vllybl; Hosp Aide; Key Clb; Swmmng; Pre Med.

SANDLER, MINDY; Shulamith HS; Flushing, NY; (S); 5/32; Red Cross Aide; Chorus; School Musical; Yrbk Stf; High Hon Roll; NHS.

SANDOR, MELISSA A; Buff Acad Of The Sacred Heart; Kenmore, NY; (Y); 25/124; Church Yth Grp; Cmnty Wkr; English Clb; French Clb; Nwsp Sprt Ed; Yrbk Stf; Lit Mag; Sftbl; Hon Roll; NHS; All Cath 2nd Tm Sftbl 84; Northeastern U; Mktng.

SANDOVAL, ALIEDA; East Islip HS; East Islip, NY; (Y); 32/475; Aud/Vis; Intnl Clb; Mathletes; Math Clb; Math Tm; Variety Show; Im Fld Hcky; Var Trk; Im Vllybl; Hon Roll; Regents Schlrshp 85-86; Tufts Schlrshp 85-86; Tufts U; Intrl Rltns.

SANDOVAL, DIANA; Hillcrest HS; Hollis, NY; (Y); Church Choir; Orch; Nrsng.

SANDOVAL, MARY; Croton-Harmon HS; Croton Harmon, NY; (Y); 2/104; AFS; Yrbk Stf; Hon Roll; Capt NHS; Natl Hspnc Schlrshp Semi-Fin 85; Ciba-Geigy Sci Awd 85; JR Key 84; Yale U; Sci.

SANDRA, VALENTIN; Walton HS; Bronx, NY; (Y); Bronx CC; Bus.

SANDS, JOSEPH P; Jericho SR HS; Jericho, NY; (Y); 90/250; FBLA; Science Clb; Varsity Clb; Nwsp Rptr; Nwsp Stf; Var Stu Cncl; JV Var Ftbl; Trk; High Hon Roll; Hon Roll; NYS Regnts Schlrshp 85; George Washington U; Bus.

SANDS, STEPHANIE B; Mary Louis Acad; Little Neck, NY; (Y); 15/310; French Clb; Hosp Aide; Service Clb; Chorus; Orch; School Musical; Lit Mag; High Hon Roll; NHS; Ntl Merit Ltr; NYS Regents Schlrshp 85; Queens Coll; Mus.

SANDS, WENDY; Byron-Bergen Central HS; Bergen, NY; (Y); 27/88; Church Yth Grp; FTA; Office Aide; Teachers Aide; Band; Concert Band; Mrchg Band; Yrbk Stf; Trs Pres Stu Cncl; Bsktbl; Female Athlte Of The Yr 85; Good Ctznshp Awd 85; Byron-Bergen Sprt Boosters Trnmnt All-Star 85; Genesee Cmnty Coll; Sprts Mgt.

SANELLI, CHRISTIAN; Gates-Chili SR HS; Rochester, NY; (S); 1/463; Church Yth Grp; Computer Clb; VP JA; School Musical; High Hon Roll; NHS; Val; Top Mathlt Monroe Cnty 83-84; Chem & Physcs Stu Of Mnth 83; Stu Of Yr 83-84; NYS Mth Lg Am & Regnl Lg; Comp Engrng.

SANELLI, JOSEPH; St Francis Prep; Maspeth, NY; (S); 100/700; Im Bsbl; Im Bsktbl; Im Ftbl; Im Sftbl; Im Vllybl; Hon Roll; Opt Clb Awd; Prfct Atten Awd; NY U; Pre-Med.

SANFILIPPO, LISA S; Seton Catholic Central HS; Binghamton, NY; (Y); 31/152; Key Clb; Ski Clb; Band; Jazz Band; School Musical; VP Pres Stu Cncl; VP Tennis; VP Trk; NHS; Rotary Awd; Regents Schlrshp 85.

SANFORD, DANIEL; Charlotte Valley Central HS; Davenport, NY; (S); 5/33; Spanish Clb; Sec Varsity Clb; Sec Frsh Cls; VP Var Bsbl; JV Var Bsktbl; Var Mgr(s); Var Socr; High Hon Roll; NHS.

SANFORD, LORI; Eastridge HS; Rochester, NY; (Y); 7/249; Exploring; Speech Tm; Varsity Clb; Var Fld Hcky; High Hon Roll; Hon Roll; NHS; Rochester Yng Amer Awd 85; Fld Hcky All Leag Awd 84; Nrsng.

SANFORD, REBECCA; Oakfield-Alabama HS; Oakfield, NY; (Y); 25/80; Art Clb; Camera Clb; Church Yth Grp; French Clb; Office Aide; Teachers Aide; Yrbk Phtg; Yrbk Stf; Var Capt Cheerleading; Hon Roll; SUNY Brockport; Elem Educ.

SANFORD, SALLY; Charlotte Valley Central HS; Davenport, NY; (S); GAA; Pres Frsh Cls; Pres Soph Cls; Bsktbl; Socr; Stat Sftbl; Trk; Hon Roll; NHS; Bus.

SANFT, ANDREW J; Northport HS; East Northport, NY; (Y); 2/661; Computer Clb; Pres DECA; Co-Capt Mathletes; Var L Bowling; NHS; Rotary Awd; Sal; Cmnty Wkr; Trs Intnl Clb; Model UN; Schl Store Mngr 83-85; 3rd NYS DECA Stu Of Yr Comp 85; SUNY Binghamton; Accntng.

SANGEN, MONICA A; Floral Park Memorial HS; Floral Pk, NY; (Y); 15/184; Pres Mathletes; Chorus; Mrchg Band; Orch; School Musical; Variety Show; Nwsp Stf; High Hon Roll; NHS; Ntl Merit Ltr; NY ST Regnts Schlrshp 85; Floral Pk Memrl Music Stu Of Mnth 84; Physcs Olympiad Cert Of Merit 84.

SANGIORGIO, ANN; Smithtown H S East; St James, NY; (Y); Hon Roll; Pres Schlr; Regents Schrlshp 84-85; Suffolk Comm Coll; Bus.

SANGIULIANO, NICOLA; Union-Endicott HS; Endicott, NY; (Y); 41/436; Trs Sr Cls; Rep Stu Cncl; Capt Sftbl; Capt Tennis; Capt Vllybl; High Hon Roll; NHS; Exploring; Key Clb; Rotary Yth Ldrshp Awd 84; Robert Wurtenburg Mem Scholar 85; Regnts Scholar 85; Penn ST; Ind Engrng.

SANGUEDOLCE, JOANNE; Nazareth Acad; Spencerport, NY; (Y); GAA; Hosp Aide; JA; Pep Clb; Red Cross Aide; Chorus; Yrbk Stf; Rep Frsh Cls; Sftbl; Itln Awd; Engl Awd; PSYCHLGY.

SANGVIC, HARRIET; Lindenhurst HS; Lindenhurst, NY; (Y); 22/594; Art Clb; Math Tm; Ski Clb; Spanish Clb; Thesps; Varsity Clb; Chorus; School Musical; School Play; Nwsp Sprt Ed; MVP Tnns 84; 2nd Pl Voice Demcrcy Essy Cntst 84; Drama Awd 83; Cmmcntns.

SANICOLA, PETER; MSGR Mc Clancy HS; Woodside, NY; (Y); 170/250; Boy Scts; Church Yth Grp; Varsity Clb; Nwsp Rptr; Socr; Trk; St John U; Bus.

SANKAR, DOUGLAS D; Locust Valley HS; Glen Head, NY; (Y); 6/186; Hosp Aide; Capt Mathletes; Math Tm; Var Crs Cntry; Var Trk; High Hon Roll; NHS; Ntl Merit SF; Rsrch Prtcpnt Chmthrptc Agnt 84; Mdl Math & Sci 84; Rsrch Asstnt Cold Spring Hrbr Labs 84-85; Med.

SANKAR, SHOBHA; Herricks SR HS; Manhasset Hls, NY; (Y); Computer Clb; Dance Clb; French Clb; Hosp Aide; Key Clb; FCA; Trk; Library Aide; Service Clb; Variety Show; Business.

SANON, EDISON; Nazareth Regional HS; Brooklyn, NY; (Y); Sec Cmnty Wkr; JA; Latin Clb; Math Tm; NFL; Trs Speech Tm; U Of CA-BERKELEY; Acctng.

SANSARICQ, PATRICIA; Mary Louis Acad; Flushing, NY; (Y); Hosp Aide; Sec Soph Cls; Rep Stu Cncl; Var Trk; Art Clb; Church Yth Grp; Im Ftbl; Concours Ntl De Francais Awd 83-85; Ntl Ed Dvlpmnt Awd 83; Math Cert Of Hnr 83; Bus.

SANTA-CRUZ, OSWALDO J; Msgr Mc Clancy Memorial HS; Jackson Heights, NY; (S); 42/229; Camera Clb; Science Clb; Spanish Clb; Yrbk Phtg; Hon Roll; NHS; Spanish NHS; Profsnl Plt.

SANTAGADA, VICTOR; Christofer Columbus HS; Bronx, NY; (Y); Capt Ftbl; Cit Awd; Hon Roll; Perfect Attndnc Awd; Excell Awd Global Stds,Ath & Italian.

SANTANGELO, FINA; Cicero-N Syracuse HS; N Syracuse, NY; (S); 104/711; GAA; Rep Stu Cncl; JV Var Bsktbl; Capt Powder Puff Ftbl; JV Var Socr; JV Var Sftbl; JV Vllybl; NHS; Cortland; Phys Educ.

SANTANGELO, MARIA; St Johns Prep; Brooklyn, NY; (Y); Fashion Desgnr.

SANTANGELO, PASQUALE V; Bishop Ford C C HS; Brooklyn, NY; (Y); Computer Clb; Intnl Clb; JA; Math Tm; Science Clb; Nwsp Rptr; Trs Stu Cncl; Capt Bowling; Hon Roll; Partcptn Publcty 84; Iona Lang Cntst 2nd Hnrs 84; Natl Sci Olympd Chem Team 84; St Johns U; Pre Optmtry.

SANTANIELLO, NINA; Our Lady Of Victory Acad; Mount Vernon, NY; (S); Art Clb; Natl Beta Clb; PAVAS; Political Wkr; Teachers Aide; Lit Mag; High Hon Roll; NHS; Spanish NHS; Spnsh Mdl 83-84.

SANTARPIA, TERESA A; St Catharine Acad; Bronx, NY; (Y); Hosp Aide; Rep Stu Cncl; Sftbl; NYS Regnts Schlrshp 85; SUNY Oswego; Bio.

SANTARSIERE, FREDERICK J; Mc Kee Vocational & Technical HS; Staten Island, NY; (Y); 13/238; Boy Scts; VP Church Yth Grp; School Musical; Pres Soph Cls; Pres Jr Cls; Var Ftbl; Prfct Atten Awd; NY Hrt Asoc Bd Ed 83-84; NYC Outstndng Stu 84; Engrng.

SANTARSIERO, ANGELA; Dominican Commercial HS; Elmhurst, NY; (Y); 98/273; Drama Clb; Intnl Clb; Acpl Chr; Chorus; School Musical; School Play; Stage Crew; Yrbk Stf; Rep Stu Cncl; Siena Awd; Baruch Clg; Arts Admin.

SANTEE, LORRIE; Solvay HS; Syracuse, NY; (Y); JA; Ski Clb; Rep Frsh Cls; Rep Soph Cls; Rep Jr Cls; Rep Stu Cncl; JV Rep Sftbl; JV Rep Trk; Prfct Atten Awd; Italian Clb Secy 83; Art Awd 83; Air Force.

SANTELLI, CHRISTINE; Shenendehowa HS; Ballston Lake, NY; (Y); Church Yth Grp; Drama Clb; JA; Band; Chorus; Church Choir; Swing Chorus; Yrbk Stf; Stu Cncl; Socr.

SANTER, FRANTZ; Bishop Loughlin HS; Brooklyn, NY; (Y); Art Clb; French Clb; JA; Math Clb; PAVAS; Varsity Clb; Band; Drill Tm; Nwsp Stf; Yrbk Stf; Frnch Hon Soc 84; JR Engrng Tech Soc Awd 85; Constr Engrng.

SANTHA, JOSEPH; Lindenhurst HS; Lindenhurst, NY; (Y); CAP; Hon Roll; NHS; Elctrnc Engr.

SANTIAGO, CARLOS; Dewitt Clinton HS; Bronx, NY; (Y); Key Clb; Yrbk Stf; John Jay Coll; Police Officer.

SANTIAGO, CYNTHIA; Curtis HS; Staten Island, NY; (Y); Dance Clb; Swmmng; High Hon Roll; Hon Roll; Hnrs Awd 82-83; Merit Awd 83-84; Pace U; Comp Sci.

SANTIAGO, EDWARD; Park West HS; Brooklyn, NY; (Y); 68/558; Boy Scts; Rep Frsh Cls; Rep Soph Cls; VP Jr Cls; Pres Sr Cls; Var Crs Cntry; Police & Crime 82; Trignmtry 84; Wood Eng Metal Shop 82-84; Phrmcst.

SANTIAGO, ELIZABETH; Clara Barton HS; Brooklyn, NY; (Y); Office Aide; Spanish Clb; Speech Tm; Teachers Aide; Stage Crew; Off Jr Cls; Bsktbl; Gym; Mgr(s); Mat Maids; Soc Stud Awd 82; Spnsh Awd 82; RN.

SANTIAGO, FELIX; St Nicholas Of Tolenhne HS; Bronx, NY; (Y); Chorus; Comp Prog.

SANTIAGO, LIGIA; John Jay HS; Brooklyn, NY; (Y); 65/500; Camera Clb; Dance Clb; Math Tm; Teachers Aide; Chorus; Color Guard; Tennis; Hon Roll; Math Awd 83; Ctzn Svc Awd 85; NYU; Flght Attndnt.

SANTIAGO, MARIA; Cathedral HS; Ny, NY; (Y); 65/298; Girl Scts; Library Aide; Nrsng.

SANTIAGO, MARIA; Central Islip HS; Central Islip, NY; (Y); #32 In Class; English Clb; Library Aide; Sec Chorus; School Musical; Nwsp Stf; Lit Mag; Bowling; Hon Roll; Ntl Merit Ltr; Tempo Awd Music Natl Hnr Socty 85; NYSMMA All ST Awd Grd A On Solo 85; Geneseo; Engl.

SANTIAGO, MILDRED; John Jay HS; Brooklyn, NY; (Y); Cmmendtn Outstndng Schlrshp/Secrtrl Stds 85; NY City Tech Coll; Exec Sec.

SANTIAGO, WILLIE; Longwood HS; Coram, NY; (Y); Art Clb; JV Jr Cls; Var Socr; JV Trk; Stonebrook U; Envrnmntl Bio.

SANTIANO, JOANNA; Kenmore East HS; Tonawanda, NY; (Y); Hosp Aide; Intnl Clb; Nwsp Ed-Chief; Nwsp Rptr; Nwsp Stf; JV Score Keeper; JV Socr; High Hon Roll; NHS; Kenmore E Aluni Assn Awd 85; Syracuse U; Brdcst Jrnlsm.

SANTINI, BETSY MARIE; John F Kennedy HS; Bronx, NY; (Y); 117/982; Office Aide; Political Wkr; Rep Sr Cls; Hon Roll; NHS; Daily News Supr Yth Awd 83; Bronx Pres Cert Of Achvt 84; NYS Regnts Schlrshp 85; U Center Binghamton; Pol Sci.

SANTINI, PATRICIA; Sacred Heart HS; Yonkers, NY; (S); 1/216; Yrbk Rptr; High Hon Roll; Hon Roll; Trs NHS; Schlr Sacrd Heart H S 83-84; Italn Lang Cntst 1st Hnrs 84; Comp.

SANTINO, RENEE; Newar SR HS; Newark, NY; (Y); Service Clb; Varsity Clb; Variety Show; Var L Socr; Var L Swmmng; Var L Trk; Hon Roll; Prfct Atten Awd; Wayne Cnty Arts, Actn 83-85; Art.

SANTINO, SHANNON; Newark SR HS; Newark, NY; (Y); Art Clb; Church Yth Grp; Latin Clb; Yrbk Stf; Sec Trs Sr Cls; Stu Cncl; Mgr(s); Var Swmmng; Advrtsg.

SANTISARIO, SUSAN; New Rochelle HS; New Rochelle, NY; (Y); Church Yth Grp; French Clb; Yrbk Stf; Hon Roll; NHS; Bus.

SANTON, DOUGLAS; Bishop Scully HS; Amsterdam, NY; (S); 7/56; Math Clb; High Hon Roll; NHS.

SANTONASTASO, DONNA; Lindenhurst HS; Lindenhurst, NY; (Y); Varsity Clb; VP Soph Cls; VP Jr Cls; Var Cheerleading; Var Trk; Catherin Gibbs; Ex Sec.

SANTORELLI, DINA M; Forest Hills HS; Middle Village, NY; (Y); 3/881; Math Clb; Concert Band; Stage Crew; Nwsp Rptr; NHS; Val; Cmmnctns.

SANTORIELLO, JENNIFER; Miller Place HS; Sound Bch, NY; (Y); FBLA; Hosp Aide; Sec Soph Cls; Sec Jr Cls; Badmtn; Capt Cheerleading; Vllybl; NY ST Rgnts Nrsng Schlrshps ALT 85; Spnsh Awd 83; Beth Israel Schl Nrsng; Nrsng.

SANTORO, DENISE; Bay Shore HS; Brightwaters, NY; (Y); 120/420; Var Fld Hcky; JV Var Sftbl; Bus.

SANTORO, FRANCINE C; Tottenville HS; Staten Island, NY; (Y); Teachers Aide; Band; Mrchg Band; Yrbk Phtg; Rep Frsh Cls; Trk; Twrlr; Hon Roll; NY Tech Coll; Dental Asst.

SANTORO, JOSEPH; Rocky Point JR SR HS; Rocky Point, NY; (S); French Clb; Mathletes; Band; Chorus; Church Choir; Concert Band; Jazz Band; Madrigals; Mrchg Band; Orch; All-Cnty Orch Frnch Horn; All-ST Band Alt Frnch Horn; Physics.

SANTORO, LINDA; Wantagh HS; Wantagh, NY; (Y); Key Clb; Nwsp Stf; JV Mgr(s); Capt Pom Pon; Hon Roll; NHS; Bus.

SANTOS, ARMANDO J; Louis D Brandeis HS; New York, NY; (Y); Prfct Atten Awd; Hunter Coll.

SANTOS, GRACELYN FERNANDEZ; St Peters High School For Girls; Staten Island, NY; (S); Hosp Aide; Math Tm; Ed Lit Mag; VP Frsh Cls; Trs Soph Cls; Sec Jr Cls; VP Stu Cncl; Hon Roll; NHS; Miss Metro NY Ntl Tngr 85; Ntl Hnr Rll 85; Gold Mdl Excel Rcqutbll 83-85; Cty Coll NY; Pre Med.

SANTOS, JOSE ALEXANDRE; St Joseph By The Sea HS; Staten Island, NY; (Y); 40/205; Art Clb; Scholastic Bowl; Yrbk Phtg; Bowling; High Hon Roll; Hon Roll; Mission Rep 81-83; Intramural Bowling 84-85; NJ Inst Of Tech; Architecture.

SANTOS, KELLY; Walt Whitman HS; Huntington Stat, NY; (Y); Art Clb; Cmnty Wkr; Hosp Aide; Nwsp Rptr; Nwsp Stf; Yrbk Stf; Rep Frsh Cls; Trs Soph Cls; Stu Cncl; Hon Roll; Stu Cncl Awd; Art Awd & Schlrshp; Stu Ldrshp Awd; Cmmnctns.

SANTOS, KIMBERLY; Lincoln HS; Yonkers, NY; (Y); Church Yth Grp; Cmnty Wkr; Computer Clb; Dance Clb; MMM; PAVAS; Church Choir; Jazz Band; School Musical; Variety Show; Westchester Cnsrvtry Mus Schlrshp 84-85; Cmmnty Svc & Cmmnty Wrk 84-85; Cmmnty Awd Mus 84-85; Jrnlsm.

SANTOS, KRISTEN; Bishop Scully HS; Amsterdam, NY; (S); 1/73; Cmnty Wkr; French Clb; Nwsp Stf; Yrbk Stf; Capt Cheerleading; High Hon Roll; Pres NHS; Val; Pre-Med.

SANTOS, MARK; Solvay HS; Solvay, NY; (Y); Church Yth Grp; Band; Concert Band; Stage Crew; Rep Frsh Cls; Rep Jr Cls; JV Bsktbl; JV Ftbl; High Hon Roll; Hon Roll; NYSSMA Solo Awd 82; Le Moyne; Acctng.

SANTOSA, AGNES; Bronx High Schl Of Sci; Flushing, NY; (Y); Hosp Aide; Teachers Aide; Concert Band; Lit Mag; Vllybl; Prfct Atten Awd; Cunningham Tennis Most Outstndg Plyr Tp Rphy 84; Med Doctr.

SANTOSUS, PATTI; Mineola HS; Mineola, NY; (Y); Key Clb; Band; Concert Band; Mrchg Band; Pep Band; School Musical; JV Var Cheerleading; Var Socr; JV Var Sftbl; Hon Roll; St Johns; Accntng.

SANTOWSKI, BECKY; St Marys HS; Depew, NY; (S); Science Clb; Lit Mag; Stat Bsktbl; Var Crs Cntry; Score Keeper; Timer; High Hon Roll; Hon Roll; NHS; Psych.

SANTUCCI, BEVERLY; Yorktown HS; Mt Kisco, NY; (Y); Church Yth Grp; German Clb; Hosp Aide; Nwsp Rptr; Nwsp Stf; Lit Mag; Trs Frsh Cls; Candystrpr Awd Wrkng 50,100 Hrs 83-84; Jrnlsm News Reptng Awd 85; Jrnlsm.

SAPONE, NICOLE; Keveny Memorial Acad; Clifton Park, NY; (S); Computer Clb; Girl Scts; Office Aide; Political Wkr; Band; Chorus; Concert Band; Jazz Band; Mrchg Band; Sftbl; Cornell U; Bio.

SAPORITO, ANNA MARIA; Saint Joseph-By-The-Sea HS; Staten Island, NY; (Y); Drama Clb; School Musical; School Play; Swing Chorus.

SAPOSHNIK, THALIA T; Jericho HS; Jericho, NY; (Y); 50/240; Orch; School Musical; VP Frsh Cls; Soph Cls; Hon Roll; NHS; Schlrshp Aspen Music Fstvl 82-83; Schlrshp Juilliard Schl 84; Jrnlsm.

SAPPELSA, LAURA; H Frank Carey HS; Franklin Sq, NY; (Y); 9/222; Band; High Hon Roll; Trs Jr NHS; NHS; VP French Clb; Yrbk Stf; Var Tennis; Hon Roll; Frgn Lang Hon Soc 84-85; Outstndng Achvt Frnch Awd 84 & 85; Exch Stu France 85; Med.

SAPPINGTON, JOHN; Cicero-North Syracuse HS; Mattydale, NY; (Y); 100/660; Var JV Bsbl; JV Bsktbl; NHS; Prfct Atten Awd; Le Moyne Coll; Accntng Comp.

SAPUTO, YVONNE; Riverhead HS; Wading River, NY; (Y); 15/237; Church Yth Grp; Latin Clb; Band; Yrbk Stf; NHS; U Of FL Gainsville; Pharmacy.

SAR, BUNNA; Nottingham HS; Syracuse, NY; (Y).

SARACENI, CYNTHIA A; Batavia HS; Batavia, NY; (Y); 3/234; Hosp Aide; Chorus; Lit Mag; Cheerleading; High Hon Roll; NHS; NYS Rgnts Schlrshp; E Cramer Awd Bio; Acad All Amer; Rochester Inst Tech; Biotech.

SARACINO, PHILIP; Valley Stream Central HS; Valley Stream, NY; (Y); Computer Clb; Hon Roll; Jr NHS; Mu Alp Tht; Italian Hnr Soc 84; Hofstra; Bus.

SARAZEN, JANELLE; Hudson Falls SR HS; Hudson Falls, NY; (Y); Drama Clb; French Clb; Key Clb; Orch; School Musical; Stage Crew; NYS; Bus Adm.

SARDARO, DANIELLE; Stissing Mountain HS; Red Hook, NY; (Y); AFS; Sec VP Church Yth Grp; Varsity Clb; Yrbk Stf; JV Var Fld Hcky; Var Trk; Hon Roll; Chorus; Milan Fire Dept Membr 84-85; Arson Invstgtn.

SARDELLI, MARIA; Walt Whitman HS; Huntington, NY; (Y); 120/520; Chorus; Mktg.

SARDINA, DONNA; Maryvale HS; Cheektowaga, NY; (Y); Yrbk Stf; Hon Roll; Bryant; Med Asst.

SARDINA, HEATHER; Fillmore JR SR HS; Freedom, NY; (S); 12/70; Church Yth Grp; Band; Chorus; Church Choir; Concert Band; Mrchg Band; JV Bsktbl; Var Score Keeper; Hon Roll; NHS; Hougton; Music.

SARFATI, CARYN R; Benjamin N Cardoz HS; Flushing, NY; (Y); 1/476; Math Tm; Scholastic Bowl; Ed Lit Mag; Trk; NHS; Rotary Awd; Val; Hnr Westnghs Sci Tlnt Srch 85; Grtr Metro NY Math Fair 82-83; Queens Coll Pres Awd Achvt 83-84; Princeton U.

SARGEANT, STEVEN J; Honeoye Falls-Lima HS; Honeoye Falls, NY; (Y); 17/169; Camera Clb; Frsh Cls; Stu Cncl; High Hon Roll; Hon Roll; St Schlr.

SARGEANT, WILLIAM; Horseheads HS; Erin, NY; (Y); Church Yth Grp; Chorus; School Musical; High Hon Roll; Hon Roll; NHS; Ntl Merit Ltr; Comp Sci.

SARGENT, CASSANDRA; Altmar Parish Williamtown Ctrl HS; Parish, NY; (Y); 7/90; French Clb; Girl Scts; Mrchg Band; Pep Band; Bsktbl; Socr; Cit Awd; DAR Awd; NHS; Dlrs For Schlrs Awd 85; Potsdam Suny; Elem Ed.

SARGENT, COLLEEN B; Rome Free Acad; Rome, NY; (Y); Hosp Aide; Pep Clb; Ski Clb; Nwsp Rptr; Im Bsktbl; Im Socr; Im Vllybl; Jr NHS.

SARIKEY, LEAH; West Valley Central HS; W Valley, NY; (Y); 1/45; Pres Soph Cls; Pres Jr Cls; Sec Sr Cls; Rep VP Stu Cncl; NHS; Pres Schlr; Val; Stat Bsktbl; Cit Awd; Hon Roll; Empire St Math Sci Tchr Schlrshp 85-86; Sci Awd 85; Math Awd 85; Rochester Inst Tech; Math.

SARITA, JOSE; Eli Whitney Vocational HS; Brooklyn, NY; (Y); Wt Lftg; Hon Roll; John Jay Coll; Lawyr.

SARNOWSKI, PATRICIA; Notre Dame Bishop Gibbons HS; Scotia, NY; (S); Nwsp Rptr; Rep Jr Cls; Hon Roll; NHS; English.

SAROSY III, ANDREW; E Rockaway HS; E Rockaway, NY; (Y); 7/125; School Play; High Hon Roll; Hon Roll; Pres Schlr; Bard Schlrshp 85-86; NY ST Regnts Schlrshp 85; E Rockaway H S Math Awd Hghst Ave 85-86; Bard Coll.

SARRETT, JEFFREY; Oceanside HS; Oceanside, NY; (Y); Computer Clb; Key Clb; Mathletes; Math Clb; Science Clb; Ski Clb; Spanish Clb; Nwsp Stf; Hon Roll; Jr NHS; NHS; Gld Mdl Long Island Math Fair 83; Excell Recgntn Long Island Sci Fair 83; Finc.

SARROUF, THOMAS; New York Military Acad; Belmont, MA; (S); 9/80; Boy Scts; ROTC; Mrchg Band; Crs Cntry; Trk; Wrstlng; High Hon Roll; ROTC Achvt Awd 83-84; Army.

SARTORI, MICHAEL A; Hudson HS; Hudson, NY; (Y); AFS; Boy Scts; Chess Clb; Church Yth Grp; Chorus; God Cntry Awd; High Hon Roll; Hon Roll; NHS; Eagle Scout 81; World Conservation Awd Boy Scout 80; Amer Legion Good Ctzn Citation 81; Bio Chem.

SARTWELL, ELAINE; Albion HS; Albion, NY; (S); 1/170; VP Drama Clb; Hst Latin Clb; Capt Color Guard; School Musical; School Play; Variety Show; Var Cheerleading; Dnfth Awd; Pres NHS; Val; Isaac S Signor Prize Acting Awd 84; Communications.

SARUBBI, ANNA; Bishop Kearney HS; Brooklyn, NY; (S); 4/339; Cmnty Wkr; Math Tm; Political Wkr; Service Clb; Chorus; Nwsp Bus Mgr; Nwsp Rptr; Lit Mag; High Hon Roll; Amer Assn Tchrs Italn Excllnc Hnbl Mntn Levl II 84; Physcn.

SARULLO, CHARLIE; New Utrecht HS; Brooklyn, NY; (Y); 30/605; Camera Clb; Key Clb; Band; Mrchg Band; School Play; Nwsp Phtg; Yrbk Phtg; Cit Awd; JP Sousa Awd; NHS; Bio.

SARULLO, VINCENT M; Monsignor Farrell HS; Staten Island, NY; (Y); 96/297; Yrbk Sprt Ed; Pres Frsh Cls; VP Soph Cls; Rep Jr Cls; Stat Mgr Ftbl; Hon Roll; Centenial Scholarship To U Of Rochester 85; U Of Rochester; Biology.

SARVIS, RODRICK; Cardinal Hayes HS; Bronx, NY; (Y); 60/290; Boy Scts; Computer Clb; Church Choir; Hon Roll; 2nd Hnrs 84-85; Comp Sci.

SASSENHAUSEN, AMY; Webster HS; Webster, NY; (Y); 28/564; Church Yth Grp; JA; Trs Model UN; Trs Spanish Clb; Lit Mag; Hon Roll; Jr NHS; NHS; Ntl Merit Ltr; Spanish NHS; U Rochester; Eng.

SASSO, MARY BETH; Amsterdam HS; Amsterdam, NY; (Y); Hudson Vlly CC; Accntng.

SASSO, SISTO; Amsterdam HS; Amsterdam, NY; (Y).

SATCHELL, CARRIE; Martin L King JR HS; Ny, NY; (Y); Debate Tm; Office Aide; Color Guard; Yrbk Stf; Trs Sr Cls; Tennis; Cit Awd; Hon Roll; Jr NHS; NHS; Cazenoria; Bus Mgmt.

SATCHELL, SANDRA; St Francis Prep; S Ozone Pk, NY; (Y); Debate Tm; Hosp Aide; Intnl Clb; Library Aide; Political Wkr; Service Clb; Speech Tm; Band; Church Choir; Nwsp Rptr; Cert Of Prtcptn-NY ST Sntr Stu Policy Forum 85; Vlntr Svc Awd-Mary Immaculate Hosp 85; Law.

SATELMAJER, HEIDI; Union Springs Acad; Union Springs, NY; (S); Leo Clb; Ski Clb; Band; Hon Roll.

SATTERLEE, REBECCA; Broadalbin Central HS; Broadalbin, NY; (Y); Library Aide; Spanish Clb; Yrbk Stf; Stat Bsktbl; Mgr(s); Score Keeper; Timer; Trk; Var Vllybl; High Hon Roll; Angela Cassano Math Awd Hgh Avg.

SATTERLEE, THOMAS D; Batavia SR HS; Batavia, NY; (Y); Church Yth Grp; Drama Clb; Variety Show; Nwsp Ed-Chief; Ed Lit Mag; Var Socr; L Trk; Prfct Atten Awd; Auspices Am Scandinavian Stu Exch Jr Yr Stdyng In Kolding Denmark 83-84; Marlboro; Wrtng.

SATTERLIEE, STACEY; Johnstown HS; Johnstown, NY; (Y); Intnl Clb; Varsity Clb; Nwsp Sprt Ed; Yrbk Stf; Pres Stu Cncl; L Bsktbl; Fld Hcky; Trk; Vllybl; Hon Roll; Typg Awd 82; SR Ltr Wnr Bst Recd H S Art 85; Robert Mc Feeley Mem Scholar 85; SUNY Cortland.

SATTLER, PAUL; Copiague HS; Copiague, NY; (Y); Computer Clb; Dance Clb; German Clb; Math Tm; Nwsp Bus Mgr; Nwsp Rptr; Socr; Cit Awd; Hon Roll; NHS; Ger Natl Hnr Soc 84-85; Gftd & Tlntd; Bus.

SAULLE, MARIA; The Mary Louis Acad; Jamaica, NY; (Y); Church Yth Grp; Hosp Aide; Office Aide; Yrbk Stf; Hon Roll; Italian Lvl II & III Iona Coll Cont; Gold Mdl Music Awd Piano; Pedtrcn.

SAULYS, TOMAS A; Shoreham-Wading River HS; Shorehaum, NY; (Y); Chess Clb; Church Yth Grp; Computer Clb; Mathletes; Var L Trk; NHS; Ntl Merit Ltr; Hnrs Grp Westnghse Sci Tlnt Srch 85; 2 Slvr/1 Brnz Mdls Math Fair 82-84; Math.

SAUMIER, TIMOTHY; George W Fowler HS; Syracuse, NY; (Y); 29/188; Boys Clb Am; Church Yth Grp; Computer Clb; FBLA; Science Clb; Variety Show; Var Socr; Hon Roll; NHS; Prfct Atten Awd; RITF Schlrshp 85; Rochester Inst; Comp Sci.

SAUNDERS, BRIAN; Mechanicville HS; Mechanicville, NY; (Y); 4-H; Math Tm; Band; Var Bsktbl; JV Socr; NHS; SUNY Potsdam; Sec Sci Ed.

SAUNDERS, MICHAEL; La Salle Military Acad; Queens, NY; (Y); 1/91; Red Cross Aide; School Musical; School Play; Mgr Stage Crew; Nwsp Ed-Chief; Var Crs Cntry; Var Capt Trk; Hon Roll; NHS; Schlr/Ath 85; NYS Regents Scholar 85; Natl Achvt Scholar 85; Cornell U; Bio.

SAUNDERS, PRISCILLA; Copiague SR HS; N Amityville, NY; (Y); Spanish Clb; Drill Tm; JV Bsktbl; Pharmacy.

SAUNDERS, RAY; Guilderland Central HS; Schenectady, NY; (Y); Ski Clb; Stage Crew; Im Bsbl; Im Bsktbl; Im Ftbl; Im Ice Hcky; Im Swmmng; Im Vllybl; Excllnc Amer Stds 85; Outstndng Achvt Bus Law 85; Math Cours III 85; Math.

SAUNDERS, RENEE; Westfied Academy And Central; Westfield, NY; (S); Scholastic Bowl; Ski Clb; Band; Concert Band; Nwsp Rptr; VP Frsh Cls; VP Jr Cls; Rep Stu Cncl; Var L Cheerleading; High Hon Roll.

SAUNDERS, SUSAN; Romulus Central HS; Geneva, NY; (S); Pres Church Yth Grp; Girl Scts; Library Aide; Office Aide; Band; Church Choir; Concert Band; Jazz Band; Mrchg Band; Hon Roll; Bus.

SAUNDERS, VERETTA; Niagara Falls HS; Niagara Falls, NY; (Y); 18/256; Sec Church Yth Grp; JA; Chorus; Pres Church Choir; Variety Show; Nwsp Rptr; Hon Roll; J M Bradley Scholar Awd 85; Bufalo ST Coll; Bus Mgmt.

SAUR, DREW; Farmingdale HS; Farmingdale, NY; (Y); German Clb; Mrchg Band; Symp Band; Yrbk Rptr; Lit Mag; Hon Roll; NHS; Comm.

SAUTER, ANDREA; The Franciscan Acad; N Syracuse, NY; (Y); Art Clb; Church Yth Grp; Cmnty Wkr; FBLA; Girl Scts; JA; MMM; Chorus; Church Choir; School Musical; Psych.

SAUTER, JUDITH; Nazareth Acad; Rochester, NY; (Y); 5/110; Hosp Aide; Spanish Clb; Chorus; Jr Cls; Var Cheerleading; High Hon Roll; Hon Roll; NHS; Altrnt Rgnts Nrsng Schlrshp 85; Hghst Avr In Spnsh 85; Pres Acdmc Ftns Awd 85; U Of Dayton; Biology.

SAUTTER, TODD; West Babylon HS; W Babylon, NY; (Y); 17/490; Varsity Clb; Sec Stu Cncl; Var Bsbl; Var Bsktbl; Var Ftbl; Hon Roll; NHS; Offnsv Rookie Of Yr Ftbl 84.

SAUVE, JOCIANA; Cathedral HS; Ny, NY; (Y); 40/298; Art Clb; Cmnty Wkr; Band; Mrchg Band; Pres Frsh Cls; Hon Roll; Comm.

SAVACCHIO, LISA; Connetquot HS; Oakdale, NY; (S); 14/675; Concert Band; Mrchg Band; Symp Band; High Hon Roll; Jr NHS; Ntl Merit Ltr; Flen Bliss Awd For Excel In Sci 82; Aero Engr.

SAVAGE, ANNE; Yorktown HS; Yorktown Hts, NY; (Y); Cmnty Wkr; Chorus; Jazz Band; School Musical; Symp Band; VP Stu Cncl; High Hon Roll; NHS; Band; Concert Band; Smith Coll Bk Awd 85.

SAVAGE, CHERYL; G Ray Bodley HS; Fulton, NY; (S); Exploring; Hosp Aide; Latin Clb; Color Guard; Mrchg Band; Orch; School Musical; Cheerleading; Crs Cntry; NYSSMA Solo Awd 80; Oswego ST Coll.

SAVAGE, SUZANNE V; Glens Falls SR HS; Hudson Falls, NY; (Y); 20/250; AFS; Drama Clb; Key Clb; Math Clb; Bsktbl; Diving; Swmmng; Cit Awd; High Hon Roll; NHS; Regents Schlrshp; U Rochester; Physics.

SAVARESE, MARK; Fairport HS; Fairport, NY; (Y); Rep Jr Cls; Var Wrstlng; High Hon Roll; Hon Roll; Engr.

SAVARI, SERAP A; Benjamin N Cardozo HS; Bayside, NY; (Y); 2/500; Mathletes; Math Clb; Math Tm; Capt Quiz Bowl; Ed Lit Mag; NHS; Qns Clg Pres Awd Achvt 83-85; Sumr Stud Math 84-85; Sci Hnrs Prog 85.

SAVICH, DIANE M; Johnson City SR HS; Johnson City, NY; (Y); 24/212; Church Yth Grp; French Clb; Color Guard; Mrchg Band; Yrbk Rptr; Yrbk Stf; Stu Cncl; Hon Roll; St Schlr; Schlstc Exc Awd 81-84; SUNY Potsdam; Comp Sci.

SAVIDGE, PETE; Archbishop Molloy HS; Whitestone, NY; (Y); 139/409; Art Clb; Church Yth Grp; Computer Clb; Ski Clb; Spanish Clb; Stu Cncl; Bsktbl; Crs Cntry; Var JV Trk; Im Ftbl; Engrng.

SAVILLE, RUSSELL; Hudson Falls SR HS; Hudson Falls, NY; (Y); 35/230; 4-H; Acpl Chr; Chorus; School Musical; Cit Awd; Dnfth Awd; DAR Awd; 4-H Awd; Agr.

SAVINO, MICHELE; Tappan Zee HS; Tappan, NY; (S); 13/293; Pres DECA; Color Guard; Capt Flag Corp; Mrchg Band; Rep Stu Cncl; JV Bsktbl; Swmmng; Capt Twrlr; NHS; Italian Am Schlrshp 85; Manhatten Coll Pres Schlrshp 85; Regnts Schlrshp 85; Manhattan Coll; Engrng.

SAVINO, TRACEY ANNE; East Islip SR HS; Islip Terrace, NY; (Y); Church Yth Grp; Concert Band; Mrchg Band; Orch; High Hon Roll; Jr NHS; NHS; Band; Var Mgr(s); JV Score Keeper; NY ST Schltc Music Assn-Clarinet 83 & 85; Frgn Language Hnr Soc 85; Vrsty Letter-Bsktbll Mgr 83-84; Eductn.

SAVIO III, JOHN A; Alexander Central HS; Alexander, NY; (S); 5/89; Math Tm; Spanish Clb; Rep Frsh Cls; Rep Soph Cls; JV Ftbl; JV Var Wrstlng; High Hon Roll; NHS; St Schlr; NY Inst Tech; Mech Engrng.

SAVKAR, SUNIL; Niskayuna HS; Schdy, NY; (Y); Computer Clb; Library Aide; Mathletes; Jazz Band; Mrchg Band; Orch; Symp Band; Nwsp Stf; Chess Clb; German Clb; NMSQT Letter Of Comm 83; NY St Rgnts Schlrshp 85; Cornell U; Elec Engrng.

SAVOIE, MICHELE; Cohoes HS; Cohoes, NY; (Y); 22/160; Cmnty Wkr; French Clb; Ski Clb; Chorus; Yrbk Stf; High Hon Roll; Hon Roll; Hudson Valley CC; Exec Sec.

SAVONE, DINO; Lincoln HS; Yonkers, NY; (Y); Camera Clb; Computer Clb; FBLA; Stage Crew; Hon Roll.

SAVORY, KEVIN; Grand Island HS; Grand Island, NY; (Y); 46/325; Boy Scts; Trs Church Yth Grp; Ski Clb; VP Concert Band; Jazz Band; Variety Show; Var Swmmng; High Hon Roll; NHS; Eagle Scout 83; Mst Imprvd Muscn 85; Engrng.

SAVOY, JAMES N; Seward Park HS; Brooklyn, NY; (Y); Dance Clb; Drama Clb; Concert Band; Drm Mjr(t); Variety Show; Off Jr Cls; Crs Cntry; Gym; Cit Awd; Crss Cntry Awd 85; Hnr Fr Solo Prt On Drms 83; Attndnc Awd 83; Actr.

SAWH, DOLLY; Hillcrest HS; Jamaica, NY; (Y); Badmtn; Bsktbl; Gym; Tennis; Trk; Vllybl; Wt Lftg; Hon Roll; Accntng.

SAWHNY, NEAL; Richmond Hill HS; New York, NY; (Y); 31/300; Chess Clb; English Clb; Math Clb; School Musical; Im Bsktbl; Var Tennis; Im Vllybl; French Hon Soc; Hon Roll; NHS; Regnts Schlrshp 85; Plytechnc Schlrshp; Polytechnic Inst NY; Aerosp.

SAWICKI, FRANCIS MICHAEL; Lackawanna SR HS; Lackawanna, NY; (Y); Spanish Clb; Concert Band; Jazz Band.

SAWICKI, THOMAS; Greene Central HS; Greene, NY; (Y); Letterman Clb; Ski Clb; Var Ftbl; Trk; Wt Lftg; High Hon Roll; Penn ST; Engr.

SAWKIW, MICHAEL; Cohoes HS; Cohoes, NY; (Y); 5/250; Spanish Clb; Rep Frsh Cls; Rep Soph Cls; Rep Jr Cls; Rep Stu Cncl; High Hon Roll; NHS; Ntl Merit Schol; Rensselaer Inst; Comp Engrg.

SAWTELL, SEAN E; Roy C Ketcham HS; Wappinger Fls, NY; (Y); Chess Clb; 4-H; High Hon Roll; Jr NHS; NHS; Elec Engr.

SAWTELLE, SCOTT; Millbrook HS; Millbrook, NY; (Y); Nwsp Sprt Ed; Var Capt Bsbl; JV Var Bsktbl; JV Var Ftbl; High Hon Roll; Hon Roll; Math 11 Awd 84; Accntng.

SAWYER, ELIZABET M; Maria Regina HS; Yonkers, NY; (Y); Computer Clb; Debate Tm; Drama Clb; NFL; Speech Tm; Chorus; Church Choir; School Musical; School Play; Variety Show; Mercy Coll Schlrshp 85; NY ST Regents Schlrshp 85; Sona Coll Pres Awd 85; Manhattan Coll Schlrshp 85; Mercy Coll; Comp Sci.

SAWYER, RUSSELL; G Ray Bodley HS; Fulton, NY; (Y); 90/257; Computer Clb; Drama Clb; Band; Chorus; School Musical; School Play; Crs Cntry; ST U NY Oswego; Comp Sci.

SAWYER, SUZANNE; Wellsville HS; Wellsville, NY; (Y); 24/130; Key Clb; Color Guard; Stu Cncl; Mst Imprvd Colorguard 82; Lioness Clb Scholar 85; Alfred Ag & Tech; Lib Arts.

SAWYKO III, LEON T; Aquinas Inst; Rochester, NY; (S); 1/163; Boy Scts; JV Capt Socr; High Hon Roll; William Stolze Schlrshp 82-85.

SAXE, FRANK; Wheatland-Chili Central Schl; Scottsville, NY; (Y); Aud/Vis; Boy Scts; Model UN; Nwsp Ed-Chief; Nwsp Rptr; Yrbk Stf; Stu Cncl; Cit Awd; Hon Roll; Drama Clb; Eagle Sct Boy Scts Of Amer 85; Brdcst.

SAXENA, MANU; Beach Channel HS; Rockaway, NY; (Y); Computer Clb; Math Tm; Science Clb; Nwsp Stf; High Hon Roll; NHS; Math & Sci Mdls 85; Astrnmy.

SAXENIAN, LINDA; West Genessee HS; Syracuse, NY; (Y); Church Yth Grp; GAA; Yrbk Stf; Off Sr Cls; Bsktbl; Socr; Sftbl; Vllybl; High Hon Roll; Yrbk Phtg; Bsktbl Trphys & Vsty Ltr 82-85; 6 Mdls JR Grk Orthdx Olympcs 81-84; Bus.

SAYA, RUTH; The Franciscan Acad; Syracuse, NY; (S); 4/25; GAA; NFL; Ski Clb; Yrbk Stf; Tennis; Hon Roll; NHS; Judith Giannino Schlrshp Awd 82; Latin I & Ii Hnrs 83-84; MONY Regnl Scholastic Art Awd 83; Biological Sci.

SAYEGH, MICHAEL; Sacred Heart HS; Yonkers, NY; (Y); Church Yth Grp; JA; Chorus; School Play; JV Var Ftbl; High Hon Roll; Hon Roll; Fordham U; Pre Med.

SAYER, SYLVIA; St Vincent Ferrer HS; Jackson Hts, NY; (Y); 17/123; Hon Roll; Chld Psychlgst.

SAYERS, FAWN; Connectquot HS; Oakdale, NY; (Y); Art Clb; Church Yth Grp; Varsity Clb; Chorus; Stage Crew; Var Cheerleading; Var Gym; Hon Roll; Awd Gymnstcs MV 83-84; Coachs Awd Gymnstcs 85; Ldrs Clb 85; Hnr Hldg Ofc Grnd Rep ME Intl Rainbw 85; Palmer Coll Of Chiropractic.

SAYERS, GREGG; St Johns Acad; Plattsburgh, NY; (Y); 9/45; Pres Jr Cls; Pres Sr Cls; Trs Stu Cncl; Var L Bsbl; L Capt Ftbl; Hon Roll; Mst Deserving Awd Ftbl 83; Ftbl All Strs 83-84; Hobart Coll; Pol Sci.

SAYRE, ELIZABETH; Cicero-North Syracuse HS; Clay, NY; (S); 101/711; Church Yth Grp; German Clb; Ski Clb; Church Choir; Rep Jr Cls; Stu Cncl; Powder Puff Ftbl; NHS; Delhi Agri; Exec Sec.

SBARRA, JOANN; Fairport HS; Fairport, NY; (Y); 55/610; Trs Cmnty Wkr; Intnl Clb; JA; Key Clb; Math Tm; Model UN; Rep Stu Cncl; Hon Roll; NHS; Wnr Regents Schlrshp 85; Fnlst U Of Rochester Alumni Schlrshp 85; U Of Rochester; Comp Sci.

SCAFIDE, LISA; Smithtown H S West; Hauppauge, NY; (Y); Church Yth Grp; Dance Clb; Drama Clb; Teachers Aide; Cheerleading; Hon Roll; Itln Hnr Soc 84-85; FIT; Fshn Merch.

SCAGNELLI, MARIA; Christopher Columbus HS; Bronx, NY; (S); 7/792; Service Clb; Hon Roll; Hnr Rll 84-85; Bus.

SCAIFE, JENNIFER; Linton HS; Schenectady, NY; (Y); 7/270; Service Clb; Acpl Chr; Band; Church Choir; Orch; School Play; Var L Socr; Var L Trk; Pres NHS; Church Yth Grp; Peer Leaders/Co Ldr 85; Mth.

SCAIFE, REBECCA J; Linton HS; Schenectady, NY; (Y); 1/301; Sec AFS; Sec Trs JCL; Band; Chorus; Church Choir; Mgr(s); Bausch & Lomb Sci Awd; DAR Awd; NHS; Ntl Merit SF; The Rensselaer Medal 84; Phys Thrpy.

SCALA, ANDREA; South Side HS; Rockville Ctr, NY; (Y); 111/300; Church Yth Grp; Cmnty Wkr; VP Drama Clb; Latin Clb; Thesps; School Musical; School Play; Stage Crew; Variety Show; Hon Roll; Tech Thrtr.

SCALA, NANCY; John A Coleman HS; Saugerties, NY; (Y); 19/70; French Clb; Key Clb; Yrbk Ed-Chief; Yrbk Stf; Var Cheerleading; Var Trk; Var Vllybl; Engl.

SCALCIONE, KERRY; St John The Baptist HS; Massapequa, NY; (Y); 76/550; Cmnty Wkr; Math Clb; Yrbk Stf; Hon Roll; Art Awd-WNET/13 84; CCD Cert 85; Bus.

SCALERA, FRANK; Valley Stream North HS; Malverne, NY; (Y); 13/165; Chess Clb; Drama Clb; Quiz Bowl; School Play; Socr; High Hon Roll; Mu Alp Tht; NHS; Pres Schlr; Hofstra U; Comp Sci.

SCALI, LISA; Sacred Heart Acad; N Merrick, NY; (S); 6/186; Church Yth Grp; FTA; Math Clb; Math Tm; Bowling; NHS; Comp Sci.

SCALI, MARGO; Longwood HS; Coram, NY; (S); 43/487; Hosp Aide; Key Clb; Nwsp Bus Mgr; Nwsp Rptr; Yrbk Bus Mgr; Yrbk Stf; Tennis; Hon Roll; Jr NHS; Hnr Rl 82-85; Comm.

SCALISE, ANDREA; Jamestown HS; Jamestown, NY; (Y); Ski Clb; Spanish Clb; Concert Band; Mrchg Band; Orch; Var L Trk; Hon Roll; Jr NHS; NHS; Music.

SCALISE, ARTHUR M; Babylon HS; Babylon, NY; (Y); 12/143; Mathletes; Capt Math Tm; Yrbk Stf; Lit Mag; Im Bowling; Var L Ftbl; Var L Lcrss; High Hon Roll; Mu Alp Tht; NHS; NYS Regnts Schlrshp 85; Math, Sci Awds 81-84; Stonybrook U; Mech Engr.

SCALISI, SALVATORE; St Raymonds HS For Boys; Bronx, NY; (Y); 7/182; Computer Clb; Math Clb; Science Clb; Hon Roll; Doctor.

SCALLEY, VICKI; Copiague SR HS; Copiague, NY; (Y); Church Yth Grp; Hosp Aide; Red Cross Aide; Spanish Clb; Yrbk Phtg; Fld Hcky; Score Keeper; Hon Roll; NHS; Bio.

SCALZO, CHERYL A; Ravena Cocymans Celkirk HS; Coeymans, NY; (Y); 6/200; Key Clb; Yrbk Stf; Rep Frsh Cls; Rep Soph Cls; JV Cheerleading; Socr; Var Trk; JV Capt Vllybl; High Hon Roll; NHS; Regents Schlrshp 85; Clarkson U; Elect Engrng.

SCALZO, CHRISTINE; Lindehurst HS; Lindenhurst, NY; (Y); Key Clb; Spanish Clb; Varsity Clb; Sftbl; Hon Roll; Bio.

SCALZO, DAVID; Jamesville-De Witt HS; Dewitt, NY; (Y); Church Yth Grp; Cmnty Wkr; Hosp Aide; Pres Model UN; Variety Show; Ed Nwsp Stf; Var L Crs Cntry; Var L Trk; NHS; Ntl Merit SF; Best Delg Awd 85; Hnry Ment Awd Hilton Model Un Conf 84; Best Delg Awd Cnymun Conf 84; Med.

SCANDALIATO, JO ANN; Commack HS; Commack, NY; (Y); Cmnty Wkr; Teachers Aide; Stage Crew; Bus.

SCANLAN, GERARD A; Clarkstown High Schl South; New City, NY; (Y); Am Leg Boys St; Boy Scts; Church Yth Grp; Cmnty Wkr; Stage Crew; JV Var Lcrss; Cit Awd; Eagle Scout 85; Vigil Hnr Mbr Order Arrow 84; Lodge Chief Munsi Lodge Arrow 84-85; Sci.

SCANLON, JENNIFER A; Garden City SR HS; Garden City, NY; (Y); 2/319; French Clb; Nwsp Phtg; Yrbk Ed-Chief; Ed Lit Mag; Var Trk; Mgr Wrstlng; Var High Hon Roll; Pres NHS; Var Ntl Merit SF; Var Sal; Brown U Book Awd 84; Am Assn Of Teachers French 83; Otstndg French Stu Awd 83-84.

SCANLON, KATHLEEN; The Mary Louis Acad; Glendale, NY; (Y); Art Clb; Girl Scts; Intnl Clb; Bowling; Hon Roll; NEDT Awd; Horse Shws 82; CENTENERY; Equine Stds.

SCANLON, MARY BETH; Immaculata Acad; Hamburg, NY; (Y); 17/77; Pep Clb; Science Clb; Spanish Clb; Nwsp Rptr; Capt Cheerleading; Gym; Hon Roll; Ntl Merit Ltr; Chrldng Mst Valbl 84-85; Schlrshp Univ Sth FL 85; U Sth FL; Marine Bio.

SCANNOPIECO, THOMAS; Hicksville HS; Hicksville, NY; (Y); Boy Scts; Science Clb; Ski Clb; Rep Frsh Cls; Var Bowling; JV Golf; Im Ice Hcky; High Hon Roll; Jr NHS; NHS; Engrng.

SCAPATICI, ALISA; Saranac Lake HS; Saranac Lk, NY; (Y); 1/124; Ski Clb; Band; Mrchg Band; Nwsp Rptr; Nwsp Sprt Ed; Pres Frsh Cls; Stu Cncl; Pom Pon; Trk; Wt Lftg; Mrs Hugh M Kinghorn Engl Awd 83-84; Hghst Engl Regnts 85; Engl.

SCARANGELLA, KAREN; St Francis Prep; Elmhurst, NY; (S); Library Aide; Concert Band; Mrchg Band; Hon Roll; NHS; St Johns U Cmptv Schlrshp 85; U Scranton, NYS Regnts Schlrshps 85; U Of Scranton; Engl.

SCARANO, ANTHONY; Little Falls JR SR HS; Little Falls, NY; (Y); Varsity Clb; Var Ftbl; Var Trk; Var Trk; Hon Roll.

SCARBOROUGH, SHANNAN; Springfield Gardens HS; Rosedale, NY; (Y); Comp Processor.

SCARCELLA, SANTINO ROBERT; St Peters For Boys; Staten Island, NY; (Y); 12/192; Cmnty Wkr; Library Aide; Teachers Aide; Rep Jr Cls; Rep Stu Cncl; Im Ftbl; Im Sftbl; High Hon Roll; Hon Roll; NHS; Acad All Amer Awd 85; Wagner Scholar Awd 85; Merit Awds Bus & Italian 85; Wagner Coll; Bus.

SCARDETTA, MICHELE A; Our Lady Of Mercy HS; Rochester, NY; (Y); 29/200; Church Yth Grp; French Clb; Hosp Aide; JA; Chorus; Yrbk Stf; Rep Frsh Cls; High Hon Roll; Hon Roll; Frnch 2, 3 Awds 82-83; NYS Nrs Schlrshp 85; Niagara U; Nrs.

SCARDIGNO, FRANCINE T; Dominican Commercial HS; Elmhurst, NY; (Y); 38/273; Teachers Aide; Stage Crew; Yrbk Stf; Rep Stu Cncl; Hon Roll; Siena Awd 83-85; Pres Acad Ftnss Awd 85; St Johns Schl; Phrmclgy.

SCARDINO, RICHARD; St Francis Prep; Ozone Park, NY; (S); 13/698; Math Tm; High Hon Roll; NHS; Med.

SCARFINO, ANTHONY; Hherringer HS; Syracuse, NY; (Y); Church Yth Grp; Rep Stu Cncl; Var Ftbl; Var Lcrss; Var Capt Wrstlng; Cit Awd; Hon Roll; NHS; SUNY Cortland; Radio.

SCARINGE, DELYNN; Colonie Central HS; Albany, NY; (Y); Drama Clb; Hosp Aide; Pres Sec Key Clb; VP Pep Clb; Ski Clb; Spanish Clb; Orch; School Play; Variety Show; Nwsp Stf; ST U Albany; Lang.

SCARINGELLA, MICHELE; Sacred Heart Acad; New Hyde Park, NY; (S); Intnl Clb; Math Clb; Math Tm; School Play; Nwsp Rptr; Socr; NHS; Cathlc Dtrs Of Amer Essay Cntst 2nd Pl 83; Bus.

SCARLOTTA, FRANK; Granville HS; Granville, NY; (Y); Church Yth Grp; Ski Clb; Variety Show; Pres Frsh Cls; Pres Soph Cls; Rep Jr Cls; VP Sr Cls; Pres Stu Cncl; JV Var Bsbl; JV Ftbl; Law.

SCAROZZA, CONCETTA; H C Technical HS; Buffalo, NY; (Y); Church Yth Grp; Band; Church Choir; Concert Band; Jazz Band; Mrchg Band; Jr Cls; Stu Cncl; Swmmng; Phy Thrpy.

SCARPATI, LISA; Sheepshead Bay HS; Brooklyn, NY; (Y); Dance Clb; Girl Scts; Teachers Aide; Y-Teens; Chorus; School Musical; School Play; Sftbl; Swmmng; Tennis; Dnce, Steno Awds.

SCARPELLI, ANDREA; Holy Trinity HS; West Hempstead, NY; (Y); 36/364; Aud/Vis; Math Tm; Stage Crew; Sr Cls; Stu Cncl; Mu Alp Tht; NEDT Awd; SUNY; Pol Sci.

SCARPULLA, ZINA; St Francis Prep; Bayside, NY; (S); 49/690; Art Clb; Cmnty Wkr; Office Aide; Chorus; School Musical; School Play; Im Vllybl; NHS; Prncpls List 83-84; Optimates Scty 81-83; Italian Ntl Hnr Scty 84-85; Commerical Design.

SCARRY, THOMAS; Stepinac HS; Harrison, NY; (Y); Boy Scts; Church Yth Grp; Computer Clb; JA; Key Clb; Ski Clb; Rep Frsh Cls; Rep Soph Cls; Bsbl; High Hon Roll; Pharm.

SCATTAGLIA, CHRISTINA; Saint John Villa Acad; Staten Island, NY; (Y); Art Clb; Dance Clb; Math Tm; Stage Crew; Yrbk Stf; Rep Jr Cls; VP Sr Cls; Stu Cncl; Ntl Sci Olympd-Physcl Sci 83; Ntl Sci Olympd-Bio 84; FIT; Fshn Merch.

SCAVONE, MARIE; Deer Park HS; Deer Park, NY; (Y); 32/469; Church Yth Grp; Cmnty Wkr; GAA; Intnl Clb; Spanish Clb; Varsity Clb; Band; Mrchg Band; Capt Socr; Hon Roll; Won All-Leag Slctn Sccr 85; Oswego; Pre-Med.

SCAVULLO, DENISE; Mercy HS; Loudonville, NY; (Y); 1/60; Hosp Aide; Ski Clb; Church Choir; School Play; Sec Stu Cncl; High Hon Roll; NHS; Ntl Merit Ltr; Schenectady County CC Cert Rec 84; Cert St Rose Wrkshp 85; Natl Hnr Rl 84 & 85; Engrng.

SCELZO, WILLIAM A; Baldwin SR HS; Baldwin, NY; (Y); 52/502; VP Concert Band; Mrchg Band; Orch; JV Tennis; JV Wrstlng; Hon Roll; NHS; Ntl Merit Ltr; Vrsty Capt Archry Cnty 2nd Pl 84-85; Vrsty Capt Riflery All Leag All Div 84-85; Hofstra U; Bio Engrng.

SCERBO, ED; G Ray Bodley HS; Fulton, NY; (Y); Exploring; Letterman Clb; Ski Clb; JV Lcrss; Var Socr; Var Wrstlng; Hon Roll; Aircrft Sys Mgmt.

SCHABEL, JOY E; Walt Whitman HS; Melville, NY; (Y); 2/625; Sec German Clb; Hosp Aide; Key Clb; Sec Mathletes; Symp Band; Nwsp Stf; Tennis; Bausch & Lomb Sci Awd; CC Awd; VP NHS; Geo Wshngtn U Schl Engrng & Applied Sci Medal 84; Jostens Fndtn Schlrshp 85; AAL Schlrshp 85; U Of Miami; Med.

SCHABER, KURT; Alden Central HS; Lancaster, NY; (Y); Pres Art Clb; Drama Clb; Ski Clb; Varsity Clb; Chorus; School Play; Yrbk Stf; Rep Jr Cls; Im Socr; Hon Roll; Grphc Dsgn.

SCHABER, REBA; Mount Assumption Inst; Plattsburgh, NY; (Y); 4/66; 4-H; Ed Nwsp Ed-Chief; Im Powder Puff Ftbl; High Hon Roll.

SCHACHT, CHRISTA MARIA; St Francis Prep; Forest Hills, NY; (Y); 185/700; Am Leg Aux Girls St; Dance Clb; NFL; Speech Tm; Pres Sr Cls; Mrymnt Schlrshp 82; SUNY Binghamton; Law.

SCHACKLINSCKY, JANET; Hendrick Hudson HS; Montrose, NY; (Y); 28/196; Office Aide; VP Sr Cls; Var L Fld Hcky; Var L Trk; High Hon Roll; Hon Roll; NHS; W Burke Awd, Mst Physclly Ftnss SR Grl 85; FL ST U; Hosp Admn.

SCHACKMAN, LAURA; Vestal HS; Vestal, NY; (Y); 55/455; Drama Clb; French Clb; Ski Clb; Varsity Clb; Yrbk Rptr; Yrbk Stf; Var Tennis; Hon Roll; Tufts U; Comp Sci.

SCHADE, PETER A; Palmyra-Macedon HS; Palmyra, NY; (S); 12/205; Church Yth Grp; Ski Clb; Band; Concert Band; Mrchg Band; Symp Band; Golf; Hon Roll; NHS; Ntl Merit SF; Engr.

SCHAEDLER, JERRY; Lindenhurst HS; Lindenhurst, NY; (Y); 27/625; Pres Computer Clb; German Clb; Var L Crs Cntry; JV Socr; JV Trk; Hon Roll; Jr NHS; NHS; Ntl Merit Ltr; RIT Alumni Scholar 85; NYS Regnts Scholar 85; Rochester Inst Tech; Info Sys.

SCHAEFER, CATHERINE M; Villa Maria Acad; Sloan, NY; (Y); Pres VP Church Yth Grp; French Clb; Girl Scts; Variety Show; Bowling; Var Cheerleading; Gym; Canisius Coll; Rsprtry Thrpst.

SCHAEFER, CHRISTOPHER; Chaminade HS; Oceanside, NY; (Y); 9/425; Stage Crew; Nwsp Stf; Jr NHS; NHS; Ntl Merit Ltr; Pres Schlr; Cath Leag Relgs & Cvl Rghts 82-85; Georgetown U; Bus.

SCHAEFER, JOHN; Carmel HS; Patterson, NY; (Y); 1/370; Am Leg Boys St; Chess Clb; Math Tm; Band; Mrchg Band; Pres Stu Cncl; DAR Awd; NHS; Ntl Merit SF; Val; IBM Watson 85; Haverford; Astrophyscs.

SCHAEFER, KATIE; Richmond Hill HS; Richmond Hl, NY; (Y); Church Yth Grp; Hst Key Clb; JV Var Bsktbl; Var Crs Cntry; Var Trk; Hon Roll; Advrtsng.

SCHAEFER, LYNN; St John Villa Acad; Staten Island, NY; (Y); 9/124; JV Var Sftbl; Hon Roll; Stevens Schlrshp 85-86; Pres Acad Ftns Awd 85; Calculus I Awdd 85; Stevens Inst Tech; Engr.

SCHAEFER, MARK; Tamarac HS; Troy, NY; (Y); Intnl Clb; Math Tm; Pres Band; Mrchg Band; School Musical; Swing Chorus; Yrbk Ed-Chief; Pres Stu Cncl; High Hon Roll; NHS; Intntl Clb Lang Awd 85; Mae Assn Tchrs Germn Cert Merit 85; Frgn Lang.

SCHAEFER, MICHELLE B; St Francis Prep; Glendale, NY; (Y); 15/690; Rep Soph Cls; Coach Actv; JV Sftbl; Var Capt Vllybl; Hon Roll; NHS; Ntl Merit Ltr; Acadmc Schlrshp 85; C W Post Hnrs Schlrshp 85; Regnts Schlrshp 85; C W Post; Fnce.

SCHAEFFER, STEPHEN C; Scotia Glenville HS; Scotia, NY; (Y); 49/255; Drama Clb; Orch; School Musical; Yrbk Phtg; Yrbk Rptr; Var JV Bsktbl; Var Ftbl; High Hon Roll; Elmira Coll Key Awd Schlrshp 84; Ithaca Coll; Brdcstng.

SCHAFER, KIMBERLY; Walt Whitman HS; Huntington, NY; (Y); 133/535; Girl Scts; Teachers Aide; Chorus; High Hon Roll; Animal Sci.

SCHAFFEL, DEBRA L; Suffern HS; Suffern, NY; (Y); 1/390; Quiz Bowl; Nwsp Ed-Chief; Nwsp Rptr; Yrbk Bus Mgr; Yrbk Phtg; Yrbk Stf; Bausch & Lomb Sci Awd; High Hon Roll; NHS; Ntl Merit SF; Biometry.

SCHAFFEL, JONATHAN; Elmont Memorial HS; Elmont, NY; (Y); 10/249; Key Clb; Model UN; Chorus; Church Choir; School Musical; Var JV Socr; NHS; Ntl Merit Ltr; Voice Dem Awd; Aud/Vis; NY ST Regents Schlrshp 85; Best Div Rprtr NY Dist Key Club 85.

SCHAFFER, CAROL R; Joel Braverman HS; Brooklyn, NY; (Y); Hosp Aide; Library Aide; Office Aide; Chorus; Yrbk Stf; High Hon Roll; JETS Awd; NHS; Ntl Merit SF; Meritonous Svc Awd Cony Islnd Hosp 85; Harvard U; Biol.

SCHAFFER, MICHAEL; Clarkstown HS North; New City, NY; (Y); Boy Scts; Computer Clb; Spanish Clb; Nwsp Rptr; Nwsp Stf; Cmnty Ambulance Corps 85; Tutoring Squad Comp Sci 85; Feed The Wrld Clb 85; Bus.

SCHAFFSTALL, MICHAEL; St Marys HS; West Seneca, NY; (S); JV Var Bsbl; JV Var Ftbl; Var Ltr Ftbl; Var Ltr Bsbl; Phys Ther.

SCHAIBLE, DAVE; R C Ketcham HS; Poughkeepsie, NY; (Y); 99/500; Boy Scts; Church Yth Grp; Hon Roll; NHS; Pres Schlr; NY ST Rgnts Schlrshp 85; Natl Sci Olym-Bio 85; SUNY Geneseo; Bio-Chem.

SCHALCK, DENISE; Narrowsburg Central HS; Narrowsburg, NY; (Y); Church Yth Grp; Chorus; Yrbk Stf; Sec Frsh Cls; Sec Soph Cls; Sec Jr Cls; Sec Sr Cls; JV Var Cheerleading; JV Var Socr; Elks Awd; Houghton; Comp Sci.

SCHALGE, SUSAN L; Akron Central HS; Akron, NY; (Y); #15 In Class; Office Aide; Political Wkr; Var Capt Cheerleading; Congrssnl Page Postn 84; Regents Schlrshp Wnnr 85; MI ST U; Polt Sci.

SCHALK, NADINE; Royalton-Hartland Central HS; Middleport, NY; (Y); 31/128; Art Clb; Camera Clb; Sec Church Yth Grp; Spanish Clb; Chorus; Pres Orch; School Musical; Lit Mag; Prfct Atten Awd; Music Clb Schlrshp Awd 85; NYSSMA 83-85; Concordia; Music.

SCHALK, RICHARD; Cardinal O Hara HS; Tonawanda, NY; (S); #16 In Class; French Clb; Stat Bsktbl; Var Capt Ftbl; High Hon Roll; Hon Roll.

SCHALL, KIRK; Grand Island HS; Grand Island, NY; (Y); 31/325; Church Yth Grp; Mathletes; Ski Clb; Varsity Clb; Church Choir; JV Golf; Var L Swmmng; Im Vllybl; Hon Roll; Engrng.

SCHALL, LORRAINE J; Brentwood HS; Brentwood, NY; (Y); 9/625; Computer Clb; Mrchg Band; Rep Sr Cls; Pom Pon; Socr; High Hon Roll; Jr NHS; NHS; Pres Schlr; Challng & Hnrs Schlrshp NYIT 85; NY Regents Schlrshp 85; Regents Hnr Diplma 85; NY Inst Of Tech; Comp Sci.

SCHALLER, KATHLEEN; Spring Valley SR HS; Monsey, NY; (Y); Church Yth Grp; Spanish Clb; Church Choir; Nwsp Stf; High Hon Roll; Sec Jr NHS; Mu Alp Tht; NHS; Ntl Merit Ltr; Spanish NHS; Bus.

SCHANTZ JR, ROBERT E; Fairport HS; Fairport, NY; (Y); Prfct Atten Awd; St Schlr; Im Bsbl; Im Bsktbl; Var JV Ftbl; Var L Tennis; Ftbl 1st Tm All-Cnty Awd 84-85; Ftbl 2nd Tm All-Greater Rochester 84-85; Fairport H S Ldrshp Awd 84-85; NC ST U; Engrng.

SCHAPDICK, CHRIS; White Plains HS; White Plains, NY; (Y); 123/396; Chess Clb; Pres German Clb; Iona Lang Cont,2nd Hghst Hnrs Germn 84; AP Germn 85-86; Jacksonville U; Aviatn Mgmt.

SCHAPER, CHRISTINA R; East Islip HS; East Islip, NY; (Y); 2/475; Am Leg Aux Girls St; Church Yth Grp; Trs Band; Trs Chorus; Mrchg Band; Ed Lit Mag; Rep Stu Cncl; JV Fld Hcky; Cit Awd; High Hon Roll; YFU Semi-Fnlst Schlrshp 84; Pol Sci.

SCHAPERJAHN, DEREK; Golway Central Schl; Galway, NY; (Y); Pres Varsity Clb; Chorus; Variety Show; Trs Soph Cls; Capt L Socr; Capt L Wrstlng; Prfct Atten Awd.

SCHARF, SARA L; Salamanca Central HS; Salamanca, NY; (Y); 2/120; DECA; Trs Soph Cls; Trs Jr Cls; Trs Sr Cls; Var Capt Bowling; Var Sftbl; French Hon Soc; High Hon Roll; NHS; Coll Of Acctg; Acctg.

SCHARNING, KAMILA; East Islip HS; E Islip, NY; (Y); Aud/Vis; Cmnty Wkr; JV Bsktbl; JV Sftbl; JV Vllybl; Hon Roll; AMVETS Aux Hosp Yth Vol Awd 84-85; Phy Thrpy.

SCHASSBERGER, STEVEN; Bethpage HS; Bethpage, NY; (Y); 45/290; Chess Clb; Church Yth Grp; German Clb; Library Aide; Ftbl; Lcrss; Hon Roll; US Army; Comp Sci.

SCHATTINGAR, RICHARD; Auburn HS; Auburn, NY; (Y); Varsity Clb; Lcrss; Hon Roll.

SCHATZLE, PEGGY; Haldane Central HS; Cold Spring, NY; (S); 7/70; Spanish Clb; Teachers Aide; Yrbk Stf; Cheerleading; Score Keeper; Tennis; Trk; High Hon Roll; Hon Roll; Jr NHS; Ed.

SCHAUER, CINDY; East Islip SR HS; Islip Terrace, NY; (Y); 49/500; Sec GAA; Pres Trs Intnl Clb; Key Clb; JV Var Socr; JV Var Vllybl; Cit Awd; High Hon Roll; Pres NHS; Spanish NHS; Sci Fair 3rd Pl Trphy Bio 84; Sci Fair 1st Pl Trphy Bio 85; March Of Dimes PTSA Schlrshp 85; Springfield Clg; Phys Thrpy.

SCHAUFFELE, SUSAN; Joseph C Wilson Magnet HS; Rochester, NY; (S); Church Yth Grp; Ed Yrbk Stf; Sec Soph Cls; Sec Jr Cls; Stat Bsktbl; Mgr(s); Score Keeper; Socr; High Hon Roll; NHS; Eng.

SCHAUS, LESLEY; Cardinal OHARA HS; Kenmore, NY; (S); 15/140; Ski Clb; Sec Pres Stu Cncl; Capt Badmtn; Bsktbl; Mgr(s); Socr; Sftbl; Tennis; Hon Roll; NHS; Canisius Coll; Law.

SCHAUS, MARYBETH; Cardinal O Hara HS; Kenmore, NY; (Y); Church Yth Grp; Hosp Aide; Quiz Bowl; Ski Clb; Spanish Clb; Yrbk Stf; VP Rep Stu Cncl; JV Badmtn; Var L Bsktbl; JV Cheerleading; Daeman; Phy Thrpy.

SCHECHTER, ADAM; Christopher Colombus HS; Bronx, NY; (Y); 36/792; Nwsp Rptr; Yrbk Stf; Lit Mag; Hon Roll; Comm Art.

SCHECTER, MATTHEW; Hendrick Hudson HS; Croton On Hudson, NY; (S); 94/194; Pres Debate Tm; French Clb; NFL; Speech Tm; Nwsp Stf; Yrbk Stf; L Capt Trk; Hon Roll; NFL, CFL Ntls Debate 84; All County High Jump Track 84; Liberal Arts.

SCHEFFLER, RONALD; Frontier Central HS; Blasdell, NY; (S); Im Bsktbl; High Hon Roll; Hon Roll; NHS; NEDT Awd; Engrng.

SCHEFTER, STEPHEN; Fayetteville-Manlius HS; Syracuse, NY; (Y); Camera Clb; JA; JCL; Latin Clb; Teachers Aide; Variety Show; Yrbk Phtg; Rep Soph Cls; Rep Jr Cls; Im Wt Lftg; Natl Sci Olympd Top 10 Chem 85; Cornell U; Bus Mgmt.

SCHEID, DAVID; Canastota HS; Canastota, NY; (Y); Var Bsbl; Var Ftbl; Hon Roll; Mst Outstndg Soph Athlete 83-84; Mst Dedctd Bsebll 84-85; Phy Ed.

SCHEIDELER, KATHY; Hauppauge HS; Smithtown, NY; (Y); Church Yth Grp; Stage Crew; Yrbk Stf; JV Var Cheerleading; Mgr(s); JV Tennis; Var Trk; High Hon Roll; Hon Roll; NHS; Psych.

SCHEIDT, LESLIE A; United Nations International Schl; New York, NY; (Y); Cmnty Wkr; Political Wkr; Orch; Yrbk Phtg; Yrbk Rptr; Yrbk Stf; Ed Lit Mag; Rep Stu Cncl; Var Sftbl; Var Trk; NY ST Regnts Schlrshp 84; Cornell U; Engl.

SCHEIFLA JR, ALBERT; Hutch Tech; Buffalo, NY; (Y); JA; Spanish Clb; Im Socr; Daemen Coll; Surgcl Tech.

SCHEINA, MARTHA; Sachem HS; Farmingville, NY; (Y); Church Yth Grp; GAA; Varsity Clb; Var JV Trk; Hon Roll; Prfct Atten Awd; J V Gradutng Numbers Trk 83; V Ltr 84.

SCHEINER, BETH L; Smithtown High Schl East; St James, NY; (Y); Pres Aud/Vis; Cmnty Wkr; Pres Dance Clb; Drama Clb; Hosp Aide; Office Aide; Temple Yth Grp; Thesps; Acpl Chr; Chorus; Hnr Roll 81-85; Best Thespian 85; Dir Of Trnmnt Of Plays 84; MA U; Hotel Mgmt.

SCHELERO, DAWN; Lynbrook SR HS; Lynbrook, NY; (Y); Church Yth Grp; 4-H; Latin Clb; Varsity Clb; Variety Show; Nwsp Rptr; Nwsp Stf; Var Im Cheerleading; Im Mgr(s); Var Pom Pon; Acctng.

SCHELL, TIM; Indian River JR SR HS; Evans Mills, NY; (Y); 1/125; AFS; Pres VP 4-H; Latin Clb; Band; Chorus; Pres Rep Stu Cncl; Var L Crs Cntry; NHS; Key Clb; Office Aide; Pres Clssrm Yng Amer 85; Amer Exch Stdnt Forum Yng Canadns 85; Locl Govt Intrn 85; Pol Sci.

SCHELLBERG, CHRISTINE; Sachem HS; Holbrook, NY; (Y); 67/1500; Radio Clb; Service Clb; Ski Clb; Varsity Clb; Orch; Yrbk Stf; Var Tennis; Var Trk; Hon Roll; NHS; Hstry Fair Awd 2nd Pl; Sci Fair Awd 1st Pl; Intl Bus.

SCHELLING, ANNA; Corning-Painted Post West HS; Corning, NY; (Y); Art Clb; Exploring; JA; High Hon Roll; NHS; Coring YMCA Yth Ldr/Yr 84; Schltc Art Awds 83; USGF Cls II ST Tm Gymnstc Chmpn 83; Indstrl Dsgnr.

SCHELLING, STEVEN; Pine Bush HS; Pine Bush, NY; (Y); 34/290; Im Bsbl; Var L Crs Cntry; JV Score Keeper; Var L Trk; Hon Roll; NHS; NY ST Rgnts Schlrshp Wnnr 85; AP Math 81-85; Embry-Riddle Aerntcl U; Engnrng.

SCHELTZ, LISA; Mynderse Acad; Seneca Falls, NY; (S); 32/131; Intnl Clb; JA; Band; Color Guard; Concert Band; Mrchg Band; Stage Crew; Im Vllybl; High Hon Roll; Monroe Commn Colg; Dentistry.

SCHEMBRI, LISA; Washingtonville HS; Washingtonville, NY; (Y); Church Yth Grp; French Clb; Pep Clb; Ski Clb; Spanish Clb; Varsity Clb; Cheerleading; Gym; Pom Pon; Hon Roll; Law.

SCHEMBRI, PAMELA J; Marlboro Central HS; Newburgh, NY; (Y); 3/200; Drama Clb; Thesps; Band; School Musical; Nwsp Rptr; Var L Crs Cntry; Var L Sftbl; Var L Swmmng; Dnfth Awd; NHS; 1st Pl NYS Engry & Resrch Dvlpmnt 83 & 4th Pl 84; High Hnr Roll; Richmond.

SCHEMITSCH, RICHARD; MSGR Mc Clancy HS; Glendale, NY; (Y); Hosp Aide; Church Choir; Im Trk; Hon Roll; 2nd & 3rd Pl Sci Fair 84-85; Poltechnic Inst NY; Elec Engr.

SCHENCK, WILLIAM; Aquinas Inst; Rochester, NY; (S); 25/156; Drama Clb; Political Wkr; School Musical; School Play; Stage Crew; Nwsp Rptr; JV Ftbl; Army Intelligence; Army.

SCHENKMAN, MARK; E L Vander Meulen HS; Mt Sinai, NY; (Y); Temple Yth Grp; Band; Concert Band; Jazz Band; Mrchg Band; Symp Band; Crs Cntry; JV Im Socr; Trk; Hon Roll; Regents Schlrshp 86; Extrdnry Serv Awd Jazz Band 85; NYSS Ma 84; Bio.

SCHERHAUFER, SCOTT; Chenango Forks HS; Castle Creek, NY; (Y); FCA; Pres Frsh Cls; Var L Bsbl; Var Capt Wrstlng; Hon Roll; Var Crs Cntry; JV Socr; NY ST Wrstlng Fnlst 85; Envrnmntl Sci.

SCHERMERHORN, CARRIE; Whitney Point HS; Whitney Pt, NY; (Y); Church Yth Grp; French Clb; Ski Clb; Band; Concert Band; Jazz Band; Mrchg Band; Hon Roll; Fshn Merch.

SCHERRER, ANDREW M; Skaneateles Central Schl; Skaneateles, NY; (Y); Church Yth Grp; JV Var Bsbl; Var Ftbl; Communications.

SCHESCHAREG, ROB A; Northport HS; Northport, NY; (Y); 49/595; DECA; FBLA; Service Clb; Ski Clb; School Musical; School Play; Stage Crew; Variety Show; Nwsp Rptr; Nwsp Stf; Outstndng Mech Drwg 83-84; Regnts Schlrshp; Finc.

SCHEUERMANN, KRISTAL; Warwick Valley HS; Warwick, NY; (Y); 58/210; Church Yth Grp; FNA; Girl Scts; Varsity Clb; Church Choir; Var Bsktbl; High Hon Roll; Hon Roll; Drake County CC; RN.

SCHIANO, STEPHEN M; Gates Chili HS; Rochester, NY; (Y); 40/463; Math Tm; Rep Frsh Cls; Tennis; High Hon Roll; Hon Roll; NHS; Regnts Schlrshp; U Of Rochester; Pre-Med.

SCHIATTARELLA, CARLO; Xavier HS; New York, NY; (Y); 5/245; Var JV Bsktbl; Wt Lftg; High Hon Roll; Hon Roll; Polit Sci.

SCHIAVONE, JOSEPH; Bethpage HS; Bethpage, NY; (Y); 91/290; Camera Clb; Bowling; Golf; Tennis; Hon Roll; Prfct Atten Awd; Acctg.

SCHIAVONE, PAUL M; Moore Catholic HS; Staten Island, NY; (Y); Am Leg Boys St; Drama Clb; Math Clb; NFL; Speech Tm; Chorus; School Musical; Bsbl; Bowling; Crs Cntry; Rutgers U; Law.

SCHIAVONI, CHARLES; Cold Spring Harbor HS; Cold Spring Har, NY; (Y); 9/140; Intnl Clb; Mathletes; Math Clb; Math Tm; JV Lcrss; Var Swmmng; High Hon Roll; Hon Roll; NHS; Bus.

SCHICKEL, HUBERT; Franklin Acad; Malone, NY; (Y); AFS; Am Leg Boys St; Boy Scts; Church Yth Grp; Drama Clb; English Clb; French Clb; Intnl Clb; Letterman Clb; Model UN; Sci, Math & Lang Merits; Pre-Med.

SCHIFF, CORINNE L; Hunter College HS; New York, NY; (Y); Pres French Clb; Yrbk Phtg; Yrbk Stf; Var Capt Tennis; Mu Alp Tht; Arts Recgntn & Tlnt Srch 85.

SCHIFF, JEFFREY C; Binghamton HS; Binghamton, NY; (Y); 13/475; Pres Drama Clb; Pres Chorus; School Musical; Yrbk Stf; Lit Mag; Trs Sr Cls; Sec Stu Cncl; NHS; Ski Clb; High Hon Roll; Co-Anchor News For Kids 83-84; All ST Chorus Solo 84; European Cncrt Tour 85; Northwestern U; Music.

SCHIFFERT, MONICA; De Sales Catholic HS; Lockport, NY; (S); 1/35; High Hon Roll; NHS; NEDT Awd; Math.

SCHIFFHAUER, DAVE; Grand Island HS; Grand Island, NY; (Y); Ski Clb; Concert Band; Jazz Band; Pep Band; School Musical; JV Ice Hcky; JV Tennis; Hon Roll; NHS; Mathletes; Engrng.

SCHIFFHAUER, LEE; West Seneca West SR HS; Orchard Park, NY; (Y); JV Var Ice Hcky; Hon Roll; JC Awd; Engr.

SCHIFFMACHER, BILL; Huntington Christian Schl; Levittown, NY; (S); Spanish Clb; Varsity Clb; Chorus; Rep Soph Cls; VP Jr Cls; Var Bsbl; Var Bsktbl; Var Crs Cntry; Var Socr; High Hon Roll; Messiah Coll; Engr.

SCHIFFMAN, DAVID J; Sachem HS; Holbrook, NY; (Y); 2/1463; Sec Drama Clb; Acpl Chr; Chorus; Madrigals; Orch; Swing Chorus; Ntl Merit Ltr; Sal; All-Eastern Choir, All State Orch, All St Mixed Chorus; Harvard U; Med.

SCHIFLA, KELLY L; Lancaster HS; Lancaster, NY; (Y); Church Yth Grp; JA; Pep Clb; Color Guard; Mrchg Band; Var L Socr; Var Swmmng; Research Sci.

SCHILDKRAUT, RICHARD; Sheapshead Bay HS; Brooklyn, NY; (Y); Cmnty Wkr; Office Aide; Teachers Aide; School Play; Trk; Vllybl; Wt Lftg; Bio II 84; Perfect Attndnc Awd 85; Kingsboro CC.

SCHILLAWSKI, DAVID; Holland Patent HS; Holland Patent, NY; (Y); Pres 4-H; French Clb; FFA; Varsity Clb; Var Wrstlng; 4-H Awd; Hon Roll; Pres JR Holstein Assn Cauyga Cnty 84; Anml Hsbndry.

SCHILLING, AMY; Warwick Valley HS; Sugar Loaf, NY; (Y); 45/207; Drama Clb; Chorus; School Play; Var Capt Swmmng; Var Trk; JV Vllybl; Hon Roll; NHS; MVP Swmmng 84-85; Marist Coll; Fashn Merchnsng.

SCHILLING, LAURA; Schreiber HS; Sands Point, NY; (Y); #56 In Class; Latin Clb; VP Temple Yth Grp; Nwsp Ed-Chief; Off Soph Cls; Off Jr Cls; JV Var Bsktbl; JV Var Sftbl; Var Tennis; Hon Roll; NHS; Vol Helen Keller Inst Deaf & Blind 83-84; Pblshd Poetry 84-85.

SCHILLING, MARGARET E; John Jay HS; Katonah, NY; (Y); Cmnty Wkr; Girl Scts; Teachers Aide; Variety Show; Rep Sr Cls; Rep Stu Cncl; Var Capt Fld Hcky; Var Capt Socr; High Hon Roll; NHS; NY ST Regents Schlrshp 85; Field Hcky All-Cnty 84; Sccr All-Cnty 82-84; NY ST Empire Tm 82-84; Bio Engrng.

SCHILLINGER, DIANE; Victor Central Schl; Victor, NY; (Y); 21/201; Pres Stu Cncl; Church Yth Grp; PAVAS; Ski Clb; Spanish Clb; Varsity Clb; Acpl Chr; Band; Chorus; Church Choir; All ST Chrs 85; U Of DE; Food Svc.

SCHILLINGER, JAMES; Horseheads HS; Elmira, NY; (Y); 24/405; Am Leg Boys St; Boy Scts; Latin Clb; Science Clb; Concert Band; Rep Stu Cncl; Var Crs Cntry; Capt L Swmmng; Var L Trk; NHS; MVP Crss Cnty 82-84; Pres Acadmc Fitnss 85; Gannett Schlrshp 85; VA Polytech Inst & ST U; Engr.

SCHILLINGER, JOSEPH A; Horseheads HS; Elmira, NY; (Y); 80/407; Boy Scts; Chess Clb; Ski Clb; Band; Concert Band; Mrchg Band; JV Socr; Hon Roll; Youth County 84; Engineering Day 84; Regents Scholarship 85; Drexel U; Mechanical Engineerng.

SCHILTZ, GREGG; Holland Central HS; Holland, NY; (Y); Boys Clb Am; Stu Cncl; JV Var Bsbl; JV Bsktbl; JV Var Socr; Prfct Atten Awd; ECIC Div III Soccr All Star 84-85; Alfred Ag & Tech; Bldng Tech.

SCHIMANSKI, LORI A; Bethlehem Central HS; Delmar, NY; (Y); 9/338; Cmnty Wkr; Sec Hst PAVAS; Band; Orch; School Musical; School Play; Sec Swing Chorus; Variety Show; Fld Hcky; Vllybl; Elmira Coll Key Awd 84; Chem Engrng.

SCHIMENTI, MICHELLE; Williamsville North HS; Getzville, NY; (Y); Cmnty Wkr; DECA; Ski Clb; Spanish Clb; JV Var Bowling; JV Socr; Var JV Sftbl; Hon Roll; NHS; NY ST Regents Schlrshp 85; Rchstr Inst Tech; Bus.

SCHIMMOLLER, BRIAN; Shenendehowa Central HS; Bow, NH; (Y); Church Yth Grp; Cmnty Wkr; Im Bsktbl; Im Ftbl; Im Sftbl; Im Trk; High Hon Roll; NHS; Prfct Atten Awd; Pres Schlr; Acad Awd 84-85; Career Semnrs 84-85; Arch.

SCHINAMAN, SUSAN; Tonawanda JR SR HS; Tonawanda, NY; (Y); JV Var Bsktbl; Coach Actv; JV Socr; Hon Roll; NHS; Psych.

SCHINDELMAN, GARY; Sheepshead Bay HS; Brooklyn, NY; (Y); Math Tm; Science Clb; Teachers Aide; Chorus; Yrbk Stf; Cit Awd; High Hon Roll; Lion Awd; Humn Reltns Clb Pres 83; Attrny Gnrls Trpl C Awd 83; Pre-Med.

SCHINDLER, BARBARA; Oyster Bay HS; E Norwich, NY; (Y); Spanish Clb; Chorus; Yrbk Stf; Rep Frsh Cls; Rep Soph Cls; Rep Jr Cls; VP Sr Cls; Capt L Cheerleading; JV Capt Vllybl; High Hon Roll; Retl.

SCHINDLER, JULIE; Irondequoit HS; Rochester, NY; (Y); 30/323; Aud/Vis; Church Yth Grp; Mgr Radio Clb; Chorus; Church Choir; School Musical; School Play; Stage Crew; Hon Roll; Ntl Merit SF; Soc Dstngshd Amer H S Stu 85; Rochester Vo Tech; Comp Sci.

SCHINTZIUS, LORI; West Seneca West SR HS; W Seneca, NY; (Y); Key Clb; Mathletes; Pep Clb; Spanish Clb; Church Choir; Stat Ftbl; Hon Roll; NHS.

SCHIRALLI, JOSEPH J; St Frances Prep; Ozone Park, NY; (Y); 53/693; Ski Clb; Var Bsbl; Var Swmmng; NHS; NY ST Rgnts Schlrshp 85; St Johns & Hofstra Univ Schlrshps 85; Hofstra U; Bus Mgmt.

SCHIRANO, JO ANN; Churchville-Chili HS; Churchville, NY; (Y); Exploring; GAA; JCL; VP Jr Cls; VP Sr Cls; Rep Stu Cncl; Swmmng; Vllybl; NHS; Latin Clb; Forgn Exch Stdnt 84; Monroe CC; Comp Sci.

SCHIRMER, KYLE E; Dansville SR HS; Dansville, NY; (Y); Boy Scts; Drama Clb; Math Clb; Chorus; Drm & Bgl; Mrchg Band; Stage Crew; Yrbk Stf; Stat Bsktbl; Prfct Atten Awd; Regents Schlrshp 85; RIT; Computer Science.

SCHIRTZER, ROSANNE M; Woodlands HS; Hartsdale, NY; (Y); 20/180; FBLA; Key Clb; Service Clb; Spanish Clb; Teachers Aide; Band; Concert Band; Nwsp Rptr; High Hon Roll; NHS; Regents Schlrshp 85; ST U Of NY Buffalo; Chem Engr.

SCHLAEG, ERIC; North Warren HS; Brant Lake, NY; (Y); 12/50; Var Bsbl; JV Bsktbl; Var Golf; Hon Roll; Math.

SCHLAGENHAUF, JOHN; Oakfield Alabama C S HS; Basom, NY; (Y); Am Leg Boys St; Church Yth Grp; Dance Clb; French Clb; Varsity Clb; Var Bsbl; Var Bsktbl; JV Ftbl; U Of SC; Pol Sci.

SCHLAGENHAUF, JOHN; Oakfield-Alabama HS; Alabama, NY; (Y); Am Leg Boys St; Church Yth Grp; French Clb; Political Wkr; Varsity Clb; Rep Stu Cncl; Var Bsbl; Var Capt Bsktbl; JV Ftbl; U Of SC; Polt Sci.

SCHLANGER, MARGO JANE; Horace Greeley HS; Chappaqua, NY; (Y); 8/271; Acpl Chr; Chorus; Madrigals; Orch; Nwsp Phtg; Nwsp Stf; Ed Lit Mag; NHS; Ntl Merit SF.

SCHLEE, KRISTINE; Connetquot HS; Ronkonkoma, NY; (S); 19/723; Band; Drm Mjr(t); Mrchg Band; School Musical; Pres Frsh Cls; Trs Stu Cncl; Var Capt Fld Hcky; JV Vllybl; NHS; Nwsp Stf; Stu Rep Brd Of Educ; Hugh O Brian NYS Ldrshp Smnr Rep; Loyola Coll; Bus Admin.

SCHLEGEL, KARRI; Scotia-Glenville HS; Scotia, NY; (Y); 19/255; Ski Clb; Concert Band; Mrchg Band; JV Bsktbl; Var L Sftbl; Var L Swmmng; High Hon Roll; Hon Roll; Travel Team Highland Soccer Clb 83-84; Pres Acad Fitness Awd 85; Sr Athltc Awd 85; Worcester Poly Inst; Aeron Engr.

SCHLEICH, LAURA A; Colonie Central HS; Loudonville, NY; (Y); 334/425; Hosp Aide; Yrbk Stf; High Hon Roll; Hon Roll; Awd Tchng Relgn Clss 81-82; Awd Hlpng Tchng Vactn Bible Schl 82; St Michaels Coll; Jrnlsm.

SCHLEIN, ROBERT M; Blind Brook HS; Rye Brook, NY; (Y); Chorus; School Musical; Nwsp Stf; Pres Soph Cls; Pres Sr Cls; Var JV Bsktbl; Var JV Socr; Var JV Tennis; Ntl Merit SF; All Leag Hnrbl Mntn Tnns 84.

SCHLEITH, HELMUT; Hicksville HS; Hicksville, NY; (Y); Science Clb; JV Bsbl; Var Capt Bowling; Var L Tennis; High Hon Roll; Jr NHS; NHS; Natl Lang Arts Olympiad Awd 83; Soc Stds Achv Awd 84-85; Hofstra U.

SCHLEMMER, BRANDON; Springville Griffith Inst; Glenwood, NY; (Y); Ski Clb; Varsity Clb; Nwsp Rptr; Stu Cncl; L Ftbl; L Trk; L Wt Lftg; Hon Roll; NHS; U Of Boston; Pre-Med.

SCHLETTER, DONNA L; Grover Cleveland HS; Middle Village, NY; (Y); 28/659; Camera Clb; Key Clb; Math Tm; Science Clb; Teachers Aide; Yrbk Stf; Hon Roll; Regents Schlrshp 85; Arista Secy 84-85; Pace Trustee Schlrshp 85; John Jay Coll; Crmnl Just.

SCHLEY, JAISHREE; Bronx High Schl Of Science; Bronx, NY; (Y); Debate Tm; NFL; Political Wkr; Rep Soph Cls; Rep Stu Cncl; Var Cheerleading; Prfct Atten Awd; Dstnctn Natl Frnsc Leag 85; Bio.

SCHLICK, CRAIG; Hoosick Falls Central HS; N Hoosick, NY; (Y); Ski Clb; Hon Roll; St Leo Coll; Htl Mgmt.

SCHLIENTZ, KATHRYN; Southampton HS; Southampton, NY; (Y); GAA; Girl Scts; Hosp Aide; Band; Sec Jr Cls; Rep Stu Cncl; Var Fld Hcky; Hon Roll; Prfct Atten Awd; French Clb; Fld Hcky Al-Leag 84.

SCHLINGER, STEPHEN; Chester HS; Chester, NY; (Y); Chess Clb; Computer Clb; Bsbl; Hon Roll; NHS.

SCHLOSSBERG, KAREN R; Horace Greeley HS; Chappaqua, NY; (Y); 8/272; Debate Tm; French Clb; Temple Yth Grp; Acpl Chr; Chorus; Madrigals; Nwsp Bus Mgr; NHS; Ntl Merit SF; Amer Assn Tchrs Frnch Cont-Cert Of Merit 83-84; NY ST Assemby Cert Of Honor Frnch 84; Medvl Studies.

SCHLUNTZ, KAREN; Sachem North HS; Holbrook, NY; (Y); Comp Repair.

SCHMACKENBERG, HEIDI L; Hudson HS; Claverack, NY; (Y); 6/180; VP Church Yth Grp; VP 4-H; VP Band; VP Chorus; VP Concert Band; Jazz Band; VP Mrchg Band; School Musical; Yrbk Bus Mgr; Rep Stu Cncl; Hopwood Smmr Schlrshp 84; Columbia Co 4-H Awd 84; Sccr Awd 82-83; Potsdam Coll; Mus.

SCHMALE, LINDA; Valley Stream Central HS; Valley Stream, NY; (Y); Church Yth Grp; Ski Clb; Badmtn; Crs Cntry; Socr; French Hon Soc; NHS; Accntnt.

SCHMIDL, DEBORAH J; Niagara Wheatfield HS; Niagara Falls, NY; (Y); 13/313; Chess Clb; German Clb; High Hon Roll; Hon Roll; NHS; Prfct Atten Awd; NY ST Regnts Schlrshp 85; Grad Hnrs 85; Acadmc Hnrs Awd 82; Rochester Inst Of Tech; Math.

SCHMIDLIN, ROBERT; Longwood HS; Shirley, NY; (S); 15/467; Debate Tm; Speech Tm; Ed Nwsp Stf; Pres Sr Cls; Rep Stu Cncl; High Hon Roll; Jr NHS; NHS; Yrbk Stf; Ed Lit Mag; Washington Wrkshp Prog 84; Pol Sci.

SCHMIDT, CAROLYN; Cicero North Syracuse HS; Liverpool, NY; (Y); 33/711; German Clb; Color Guard; Mrchg Band; Socr; Hon Roll; NHS; Oswego; Accntng.

SCHMIDT, CHRISTINE; Gouverneur JR SR HS; Gouverneur, NY; (Y); Office Aide; Teachers Aide; High Hon Roll; Hon Roll.

SCHMIDT, DAVID; Bronx High School Of Science; Hollis Hills, NY; (Y); Computer Clb; Office Aide; Teachers Aide; VICA; Prfct Atten Awd; Indpndnt Stdy Expermntl Robotics Prog 84-85; Inpdndnt Stdy Comp Aided Dsgn 83-85; Vol To Rehab Nrt Trl; Engrng.

SCHMIDT, DAVID; St Marys HS; Cheektowaga, NY; (S); 10/185; Church Yth Grp; Varsity Clb; JV Bsktbl; Var Crs Cntry; Var Trk; NHS; Canisius Coll; Econmcs.

SCHMIDT, DONNA; Maryvale SR HS; Cheektowaga, NY; (Y); Cmnty Wkr; GAA; Pres Girl Scts; Chorus; Stu Cncl; JV Var Bowling; Var Diving; Var Trk; High Hon Roll; NHS; GS Silver Awd 85.

SCHMIDT, DOUGLAS; Tonawanda SR HS; Tonawanda, NY; (Y); 8/223; Teachers Aide; JV Bsbl; High Hon Roll; NHS; THS Fac Hnr Awd 85; Canisius Coll; Math.

SCHMIDT, FRANK; Mahopac HS; Mahopac, NY; (Y); 5/423; VP Computer Clb; Var L Socr; High Hon Roll; NHS; Mst Imprvd Plyr Soccer 84; Comp Sci.

SCHMIDT, JANET; Clarkstown South HS; New City, NY; (Y); Church Yth Grp; Church Choir; Bsktbl; Ice Hcky; Sftbl; Psych.

SCHMIDT, JULIANNE; Stella Maris HS; Woodhaven, NY; (Y); 1/185; Art Clb; Pres Intnl Clb; Math Clb; Math Tm; Science Clb; Yrbk Stf; High Hon Roll; Jr NHS; Pres NHS; Val; Queens Coll Pres Awd For Achvt 81; NY ST Regents Schlrshp 85; Fordham Deans Schlrshp 85; Fordham U; Math.

SCHMIDT, JUSTINE; Cleveland Hill HS; Cheektowaga, NY; (Y); AFS; Cmnty Wkr; Drama Clb; FHA; GAA; JCL; Office Aide; Church Choir; Concert Band; School Musical; Spllng 82; 600 M Trk Rcd 83; Svc Awd Schl Ofc 84; Cornell U; Bus Adm.

SCHMIDT, KATHLEEN; Belmont Central HS; Belmont, NY; (Y); Sec FNA; Hosp Aide; Spanish Clb; Yrbk Stf; Sec Sr Cls; Stat Bsktbl; Var L Socr; Var L Sftbl; Hon Roll; Prfct Atten Awd; Alfred SUNY.

SCHMIDT, KELLEY; Whitesboro SR HS; Whitesboro, NY; (Y); Art Clb; Church Yth Grp; Intnl Clb; VP Science Clb; Chorus; Var Trk; Hon Roll; Psych.

SCHMIDT, KRISTIE; Northport HS; E Northport, NY; (Y); 60/652; Science Clb; Band; Jazz Band; Mrchg Band; Orch; School Musical; Variety Show; Hon Roll; NHS; Outstndg Ldrshp 82; Mrchng Symph Band Awd 85; Smith Coll; Psych.

SCHMIDT, KRISTINA M; Keveny Memorial Acad; Cohoes, NY; (S); 6/37; Church Yth Grp; Drama Clb; 4-H; Library Aide; Band; Chorus; Concert Band; Jazz Band; Mrchg Band; School Play; Amer Athltc Soc; Natl Hnr Roll; Siena Coll; Pre Law.

SCHMIDT, KRISTINE J; Northport HS; E Northport, NY; (Y); 60/646; PAVAS; Science Clb; Acpl Chr; Band; Concert Band; Jazz Band; Mrchg Band; Orch; School Musical; School Play; Outstndg Ldrshp 82; Smith Coll; Psychology.

SCHMIDT, PAMELA; Oneonta SR HS; W Oneonta, NY; (Y); FBLA; Key Clb; Bowling; Albany Schl Cosmtlgy; Beautcn.

SCHMIDT, PAUL; Huntington Christian HS; Farmingdale, NY; (S); Boy Scts; Church Yth Grp; Varsity Clb; Chorus; Yrbk Sprt Ed; Var L Bsbl; Var Score Keeper; Var L Socr; High Hon Roll; Hon Roll; Presdntl Physical Fitness 82; Art Awds 82-83; Bsbl Outstndng Future Athltc 83.

SCHMIDT, SHEILA A; Poughkeepsie HS; Poughkeepsie, NY; (Y); 2/195; Church Yth Grp; Chorus; Church Choir; Lit Mag; Trk; High Hon Roll; NHS; Sal; Natl Ldrshp & Svc Awd; Rgnts Schlrshp; Marist Coll.

SCHMIDT, SUSAN L; Haf Hollow Hills High School East; Dix Hills, NY; (Y); Cmnty Wkr; Intnl Clb; Teachers Aide; Co-Capt Color Guard; Mrchg Band; JV Bsktbl; High Hon Roll; Hon Roll; Jr NHS; NHS; Physcl Thrpy.

SCHMIDTGALL, LORIE; Clyde Savannah HS; Savannah, NY; (Y); Art Clb; Camera Clb; French Clb; Yrbk Phtg; Yrbk Rptr; Yrbk Stf; JV Cheerleading; High Hon Roll; Hon Roll; Prfct Atten Awd; Animation.

SCHMIED, ALISON; Geneseo Central HS; Geneseo, NY; (Y); 5/90; Am Leg Aux Girls St; Pres Church Yth Grp; Girl Scts; Pres NHS; Ntl Merit SF; NEDT Awd; Drama Clb; VP 4-H; French Clb; Mathletes; Hugh O Brien Yth Fndtn Ldrshp Smnr 84; VP Western NY Conf 85; Untd Mthdst Conf Cncl Yth Mnstrs; Cornell U; Chlf Psyclgy.

SCHMIEDER, LAURA; Fairport HS; Fairport, NY; (Y); Drama Clb; English Clb; Pep Clb; Teachers Aide; School Play; Yrbk Stf; Rep Stu Cncl; JV Var Fld Hcky; High Hon Roll; Hon Roll; Math.

SCHMIT, ELIZABETH; North Collins Central HS; Lawtons, NY; (Y); Teachers Aide; Yrbk Stf; Hon Roll; Prfct Atten Awd; Hghst Schlstc Avg 84-85; Merit Roll; Delphi; Vet Sci Tech.

SCHMITT, AMY; Fayetteville-Manlius HS; Fayetteville, NY; (Y); English Clb; Latin Clb; Math Clb; Varsity Clb; Var JA; Var Vllybl; High Hon Roll; NHS; Girl Scts; Ski Clb; 1st Team All-Cnty Sccr Tm Mbr 84; NY ST Slct Tm Mbr U17 85; Cumlaude Latin 83; VA U; Pre-Med Htl Admin.

SCHMITT, BRIAN; Cleveland Hill HS; Cheektowaga, NY; (Y); Varsity Clb; Band; Concert Band; Var Bsbl; JV Crs Cntry; Var Ftbl; Var Capt Swmmng; JV Trk; U Of Buffalo; Med Tech.

SCHMITT, DAYNA; Clarence SR HS; Akron, NY; (Y); 123/260; Church Yth Grp; Cmnty Wkr; Chorus; Mrchg Band; Stage Crew; Var Bowling; Capt Twrlr; Hon Roll; Bryant & Stratton; Bus.

SCHMITT, JENNIFER; Mahopac HS; Mahopac, NY; (Y); 36/423; Dance Clb; Chorus; Hon Roll; NHS; Stu Mnth Frnch Lang 84; SUNY Albany; Frgn Lang.

SCHMITT, KAREN; Maryvale SR HS; Cheektowaga, NY; (Y); German Clb; JV Var Socr; JV Var Swmmng; Bio.

SCHMUKLER, LINDA K; Lawrence HS; Lawrence, NY; (Y); 30/379; Key Clb; School Play; Nwsp Stf; Yrbk Stf; Ed Lit Mag; High Hon Roll; Ntl Merit Ltr; Art Hnr Society 84-85; Regents Schlrshp 84; Bowdoin Coll; Sci Designer.

SCHNABEL, HILDA; New Utrecht HS; Brooklyn, NY; (Y); 45/557; Church Yth Grp; Office Aide; Teachers Aide; Hon Roll; Wrd Proc Awd 85; Bus Ed Hnr Soc Awd 85; Baruch Coll; Bus Admin.

SCHNABEL, PETER A; Francis Lewis HS; Bayside, NY; (Y); 23/512; Church Yth Grp; JA; Math Tm; Orch; Tennis; Hon Roll; NHS; Polytechnic Instit Of Tech.

SCHNACKENBERG, HEIDI; Hudson HS; Claverack, NY; (Y); 6/180; VP Church Yth Grp; VP 4-H; VP Band; VP Chorus; Jazz Band; School Musical; Yrbk Bus Mgr; VP Jr Cls; Capt Socr; NHS; Hopwood Summr Scholar 84; 4-Her Of Yr 85; Dorothy E Simon Scholar 85; SUNY Potsdam; Musc Ed.

SCHNAUBER, DEBBIE; Churchville Chili SR HS; Rochester, NY; (Y); Ski Clb; Yrbk Stf; Socr; Sftbl; Hon Roll; Advncd Plcmnt Amer Hstry 84-85; Endicott Coll; Travel.

SCHNAUBER, GLENN; Churchvulle-Chili SR HS; Rochester, NY; (Y); 10/350; Latin Clb; Math Tm; Model UN; Ski Clb; Nwsp Ed-Chief; Off Stu Cncl; Capt Golf; Swmmng; High Hon Roll; Church Yth Grp; Air Force; Aerontcl Engr.

SCHNECKENBURGER, JILL K; Springfield Griffith Inst; Glenwood, NY; (Y); Church Yth Grp; Cmnty Wkr; Chorus; Church Choir; Swmmng; Hon Roll; NHS; Pres Schlr; SUC Geneseo; Spcl Ed.

SCHNECKER, MARIAN E; Ossining HS; Ossining, NY; (Y); Cmnty Wkr; Hosp Aide; Pres Band; Sec Orch; Rep Stu Cncl; Var L Socr; High Hon Roll; Hon Roll; VP NHS; Ruth M Knight Theater Awd 82; Hugh O Brien Outstndg Stu 83; All Leag Hnrbl Mntn Soccer Awd-Girls 84.

SCHNEIDER, BRADLEY M; Beach Channel HS; Belle Harb, NY; (Y); Debate Tm; Library Aide; Varsity Clb; Chorus; Yrbk Stf; Rep Soph Cls; Tennis; Hon Roll; Law.

SCHNEIDER II, JAMES; Bishop Kearney HS; Rochester, NY; (Y); Boy Scts; JA; Stage Crew; Nwsp Phtg; Nwsp Rptr; Yrbk Phtg; Yrbk Rptr; Rep Frsh Cls; Rep Soph Cls; Rep Jr Cls; Bio.

SCHNEIDER, JENNIE L; Flushing HS; Flushing, NY; (Y); 2/366; Math Tm; Office Aide; Chorus; School Musical; Yrbk Stf; Var Capt Cheerleading; Var L Tennis; High Hon Roll; Hon Roll; Sal; Univ Schlr Storybrook 85; Storybrook U; Elect Engrng.

SCHNEIDER, KIRSTIN; Lafayette HS; Jamesville, NY; (Y); Church Yth Grp; GAA; Spanish Clb; Band; Color Guard; School Musical; Yrbk Stf; Cheerleading; Hon Roll.

SCHNEIDER, ROBERT J; Francis Lewis HS; Flushing, NY; (Y); 82/527; Chess Clb; JA; Office Aide; Science Clb; Yrbk Stf; Cit Awd; Hon Roll; NY ST Regents Schlrshp 85; SUNY At Albany; Comp Sci.

SCHNEIDER, SUSAN; Plattsburgh HS; Plattsburgh, NY; (Y); Cmnty Wkr; Office Aide; JV Cheerleading; Hon Roll; Notre Dame NH; Poli Sci.

SCHNEIDERMAN, ELAYNE D; Valley Central HS; Wallkill, NY; (Y); 4/250; Camera Clb; Natl Beta Clb; Yrbk Phtg; Yrbk Stf; Lit Mag; Stu Cncl; French Hon Soc; Hon Roll; NHS; VFW Awd; Regents Schlrshp 85; SUNY Buffalo; Comm.

SCHNELL, BRIAN; Grand Island SR HS; Grand Island, NY; (Y); High Hon Roll; Hon Roll; Mst Outstndng Regents Bio Stu 83; Mst Outstdng Regents Chem Stu 84; PTSA Hnrs Acad Achvmnt Awd 83-84; Med.

SCHNELL, HANS C; Hornell HS; Hornell, NY; (Y); 27/200; Am Leg Boys St; Band; Ftbl; Wt Lftg; Hon Roll; Alfred U; Ind Engrng.

SCHNELLER, EDDIE; Walter Panas HS; Peekskill, NY; (Y); Drama Clb; Band; Chorus; Concert Band; Drm Mjr(t); Mrchg Band; School Musical; School Play; Sec Jr Cls; Stu Cncl; Ntl Hnr Soc, Outstndng Band Awd 85-86; Actng.

SCHNITZER, DAWN MARIE; Niagara Catholic HS; Niagara Falls, NY; (Y); Church Yth Grp; Drama Clb; Girl Scts; Hosp Aide; Spanish Clb; School Play; Var Mgr Bsktbl; Score Keeper; Stat Vllybl; Hgh Achvt Awds 83-85; Villia Maria Coll; Gerontlgy.

SCHNOES, CYNTHIA D; Walter Panas HS; Peekskill, NY; (Y); #17 In Class; Ski Clb; Yrbk Ed-Chief; Yrbk Phtg; Stu Cncl; Diving; Capt Var Gym; Im Vllybl; Yrbk Stf; JV Socr; Var Swmmng; Rgnts Schlrshp 85; Peekskill Comm Hosp Aux Shlrshp 85; SUNY Binghamton; Med.

SCHNURBUSCH, TAMIE; James E Sperry HS; Rochester, NY; (Y); 69/271; GAA; Girl Scts; JA; Spanish Clb; School Play; Crs Cntry; Var Gym; Var Mgr(s); Hon Roll; Jr NHS; Chem.

SCHOBER, ANDREW; Mount St Michael HS; Bronx, NY; (Y); 48/310; Chess Clb; Ski Clb; JV Var Ftbl; JV Var Golf; JV Trk; JV Var Wt Lftg; NHS; U VA; Mech Engrng.

SCHOCK, EVA; Port Jervis HS; Pt Jervis, NY; (Y); 31/210; VP Pres 4-H; Varsity Clb; Stat Bsktbl; Var Score Keeper; Var Trk; Prfct Atten Awd; Equine Studs.

SCHOEMAKER, LISA; G W Fowler HS; Syracuse, NY; (S); 2/321; French Clb; Band; Nwsp Stf; Pres Frsh Cls; Rep Soph Cls; Bsktbl; Bowling; Socr; Sftbl; High Hon Roll; Syracuse Synchronized 80; Swim Team & Duet Championship 81; Syracuse U; Communications.

SCHOENBORN, WILLIAM C; Hamburg Central HS; Hamburg, NY; (Y); 19/387; Im Var Bsbl; Im JV Ftbl; NHS; Cornell; Bio.

SCHOENING, INGRID A; Smithtown HS West; Smithtown, NY; (Y); Rep Church Yth Grp; Hosp Aide; Church Choir; High Hon Roll; NHS; Ntl Merit Ltr; Spanish NHS; U Schlr SUNY 85; Regents Schlrshp 85; NY ST U-Stony Brook; Pre-Med.

SCHOENTHAL, JULIE; West HS; Painted Post, NY; (Y); Church Yth Grp; Concert Band; Jazz Band; Mrchg Band; School Musical; Nwsp Rptr; Jr Cls; High Hon Roll; NHS; Ntl Merit Ltr; Chld Educ.

SCHOEPFLIN, MONTY L; Springville-Griffith Inst; Springville, NY; (Y); 5/200; Am Leg Boys St; Band; Concert Band; Jazz Band; Mrchg Band; Orch; Var Crs Cntry; Var Trk; High Hon Roll; NHS; NY Regnts Schlrshp Wnnr 85; U S Coast Grd Appt Acad 85; Natl Schlr Athl Awd U S Army Resrv 85; U S Coast Guard Acad; Cvl Engrg.

SCHOFIELD, JOHN; Fairport HS; Fairport, NY; (Y); Exploring; Ski Clb; Chorus; School Musical; Rep Stu Cncl; Socr; Optmtry.

SCHOLL, HEATHER; Westfield Acad And Central HS; Westfield, NY; (S); Church Yth Grp; Ski Clb; Band; Chorus; Mrchg Band; School Musical; School Play; Swing Chorus; Sec Soph Cls; Rep Sec Stu Cncl; St Lawrence U; Bio.

SCHOLTEN, HEIDI; Cold Spring Harbor HS; Huntington, NY; (Y); 37/130; Cmnty Wkr; Drama Clb; Intnl Clb; School Play; Rep Frsh Cls; Rep Soph Cls; Rep Jr Cls; Rep Sr Cls; JV Var Cheerleading; Hon Roll; Bus.

SCHOLTEN, LISA; Newark SR HS; Newark, NY; (Y); Pres Church Yth Grp; Trk; High Hon Roll; Prfct Atten Awd; O Briens Schl; Cosmotology.

SCHOLZ, ERIKA; Victor Central HS; Victor, NY; (Y); 43/229; Acpl Chr; Mgr Chorus; Color Guard; School Musical; Stage Crew; Variety Show; Yrbk Phtg; Yrbk Stf; High Hon Roll; Sybleys Stu Art Shw 84; Advtsng.

SCHOLZ, LAURA; Sachem North Campus HS; Holtsville, NY; (Y); 105/1309; Art Clb; Church Yth Grp; Girl Scts; Lit Mag; Badmtn; Hon Roll; Jr NHS; NHS; Grl Scout Silver Awd 83; Art Thrpy.

SCHOMAKER, JOHN; Ichabod Crane HS; Kindershook, NY; (Y); #83 In Class; Pres Church Yth Grp; Cmnty Wkr; Library Aide; Ed Lit Mag; JV Socr; Church Choir; High Hon Roll; Hon Roll; NHS; NY Inst Tech; Elec Engr.

SCHOMBER, ERIC; Williamsville South HS; Williamsville, NY; (Y); 143/210; Aud/Vis; Drama Clb; Thesps; School Musical; School Play; Mgr Stage Crew; Socr; Stage Crw Awd 82-83, Mst Vlbl 83-84, Outstndng Svc 84-85; Elec.

SCHON, LAURIE J; Alfred-Almond Central Schl; Alfred Station, NY; (Y); 2/70; French Clb; Chorus; Yrbk Stf; Sec Jr Cls; Trs Sr Cls; JV Socr; Var L Trk; High Hon Roll; NHS; Sal; NYS Accompanist Schlrshp, Smmr Schl Arts-Choral Stud 84; Nazareth Coll Schlrshp 85; NHS 85; Nazareth Coll Rochester; Bus Ed.

SCHONER, THERESA; Groton Central Schl; Groton, NY; (Y); 12/70; GAA; Library Aide; Office Aide; Chorus; Lit Mag; Stat Crs Cntry; Swmmng; High Hon Roll; NHS; Acctng Shorthand Awd 83-85; Sec.

SCHOOLEY, TAMMIE; Mynderse Acad; Seneca Falls, NY; (S); 8/142; Church Yth Grp; Band; Jazz Band; School Musical; Swing Chorus; Sec Jr Cls; Rep Stu Cncl; High Hon Roll; NHS; Intnl Clb.

SCHOON, PHYLLIS; St John The Babtist HS; N Babylon, NY; (Y); Church Yth Grp; Cmnty Wkr; Dance Clb; Chorus; Psych.

SCHOONERMAN, LISA; Marion JR-SR HS; Marion, NY; (Y); 8/113; Am Leg Aux Girls St; Band; Yrbk Ed-Chief; Pres Stu Cncl; Var Sftbl; Var Tennis; Var Vllybl; Cit Awd; DAR Awd; Pres NHS; Rgnts, J A Shoales Mem, Marion Rotary Clb Dr A Besemer Schlrshps 85; St Bonaventure U; Mass Comm.

SCHOONMAKER, DUANA; Eastern District HS; Brooklyn, NY; (Y); Bsktbl; Hon Roll; Acctg.

SCHOONOVER, CHARLES J; York Central HS; Piffard, NY; (Y); Aud/Vis; Cmnty Wkr; Key Clb; Band; Chorus; Concert Band; Jazz Band; Mrchg Band; School Musical; Swing Chorus; Clsrm Hnrs Soc Stud 85; Monroe Comm Coll; Crimnl Justc.

SCHOSGER, LAURALYNN; Corning-Painted Post HS; Painted Post, NY; (Y); AFS; Pres Exploring; Hosp Aide; Varsity Clb; Var L Cheerleading; High Hon Roll; Letterman Clb; Church Choir; Mrchg Band; Orch; Chldrn Amer Rev Pres & VP; SR Prfmng Elmira-Corning Ballet Co; Colonl Days Queen 82; Frgn Exch St 83; Hope Coll Holland; Pre-Med.

SCHOTSKY, LAURA E; Half Hollow Hills HS East; Melville, NY; (Y); 34/568; Political Wkr; Service Clb; Temple Yth Grp; Var Badmtn; Mgr(s); High Hon Roll; Jr NHS; NHS; Spanish NHS; NY Rgnts Schlrshp 85; Tufts U.

SCHOTT, LARA; Brockport HS; Brockport, NY; (Y); 55/300; Band; Concert Band; Mrchg Band; Symp Band; Capt Sftbl; High Hon Roll; Hon Roll; NHS; Regents Schlrshp 85; MVP Vrsty Sftbl 84; SUNY-ALBANY; Psych.

SCHOTZ, SHARON; Wilson Central HS; Wilson, NY; (Y); 4-H; Office Aide; Quiz Bowl; Yrbk Bus Mgr; Yrbk Stf; Cit Awd; 4-H Awd; High Hon Roll; Hon Roll; Cnty Altnt Dairy Princess 85-86; Farm Bur Citznshp Altnt 85; Comp Sci.

SCHOUTEN, STEPHEN J; Watkins Glen HS; Reading Center, NY; (Y); 27/135; Am Leg Boys St; Letterman Clb; Math Clb; Spanish Clb; Varsity Clb; Nwsp Sprt Ed; Rep Frsh Cls; Rep Soph Cls; Rep Jr Cls; JV Bsbl; Engrng.

SCHOVE, JOHN R; Williamson SR HS; Williamson, NY; (Y); 6/112; Pres Exploring; Science Clb; Var L Tennis; Hon Roll; NY ST Regents Schlrshp 85; Fredonia U; Bio.

SCHRADER, JILL; Wayland Central HS; Wayland, NY; (Y); Church Yth Grp; Pres FBLA; Math Tm; Ski Clb; Varsity Clb; Yrbk Stf; JV Var Cheerleading; JV Var Socr; Var Trk; High Hon Roll; Paralegal.

SCHRADER, SCOTT; Attica Central Senior HS; Strykersville, NY; (Y); 4-H; Band; Concert Band; Mrchg Band; Socr; Hon Roll; Olymp Mind Tm; Marine Bio.

SCHRAGE, KAREN; Bethpage HS; Plainview, NY; (Y); 7/272; Church Yth Grp; Spanish Clb; Church Choir; JV Var Fld Hcky; Gym; Hon Roll; Jr NHS; NHS; Ntl Merit Schol; U Notre Dame.

SCHRAGE, RICHARD; Bethpage HS; Plainview, NY; (Y); 4/290; JV Ftbl; JV Lcrss; Hon Roll; NHS.

SCHRAGER, NORMAN; Roosevelt HS; Yonkers, NY; (S); Band; Concert Band; Mrchg Band; Variety Show; Yrbk Stf; Rep Jr Cls; JV Var Bsbl; High Hon Roll; Hon Roll; NHS; JR All-Amer Hall Fame Band Hnrs 84-85.

SCHRAMEL, JANET; Sachene North HS; Lk Ronkonkoma, NY; (Y); Orch; Outstndg Musicnshp 82-83; Tchg.

SCHRANK, ADAM L; Tottenville HS; Staten Island, NY; (Y); 28/897; JV Var Ftbl; Wt Lftg; Hon Roll; NHS; Regents Schlrshp 84-85; Coaches All Star 84-85; Fugazzi All Star 84-85; Penn ST; Engrng.

SCHRANKEL JR, PETER J; Union Springs Acad; Cohocton, NY; (Y); Drama Clb; Chorus; Church Choir; VP Stu Cncl; Var Bsktbl; Im Sftbl; Hon Roll; NHS; Monitr Yr 83-84; Rochester Inst Of Tech; Comp.

SCHRANTZ, MARIE; Dunkirk HS; Dunkirk, NY; (Y); 18/211; Rep Stu Cncl; High Hon Roll; Trs NHS; Exc Eng Medal 85; Daniel F Aanson Schrlsh P85; 1st Hnrs 85; Fredonia St U; Psych.

SCHRAVEN, KRISTIN; Albion HS; Albion, NY; (S); 1/200; Ski Clb; Spanish Clb; Rep Stu Cncl; JV Cheerleading; JV Socr; Var L Trk; Hon Roll; Jr NHS; NHS; Val; Acdmc Decathalon Team 85; Mock Trial 85; Coll; Law.

SCHRECK, DARLEEN A; Sauquoit Valley Central HS; Sauquoit, NY; (Y); Trs GAA; Varsity Clb; Band; School Play; Variety Show; VP Soph Cls; Var Capt Bsktbl; Var Capt Socr; Var Capt Sftbl; Jr NHS; Herkimer County CC; Occ Thrpy.

SCHREFFLER, SUSAN; Maria Regina HS; White Plains, NY; (Y); 57/130; GAA; Key Clb; Math Clb; Science Clb; Yrbk Ed-Chief; Yrbk Stf; Rep Jr Cls; Rep Stu Cncl; Var Bsktbl; Var Capt Tennis; Cert Of Apprctn Stu Cncl 85; Psychlgy.

SCHREIBER, ALLISON; New Rochelle HS; Scarsdale, NY; (Y); Cmnty Wkr; FBLA; Temple Yth Grp; Y-Teens; Stage Crew; Yrbk Stf; Rep Soph Cls; Rep Jr Cls; Var L Diving; Var Swmmng; YM YWHA Mid-Westchester Svc Awd 83; Coach Awd 85; Bus.

SCHREIBER, MARKUS; Sheepshead Bay HS; Brooklyn, NY; (Y); 6/465; Library Aide; Office Aide; High Hon Roll; Regents Schlrshp 85; Brooklyn Coll Acadmc Mrt Schlrshp 85; Brooklyn Coll; Cmptr Sci.

SCHREINER, CURTIS; Hadley-Luzerne Central HS; Day, NY; (Y); 1/70; Band; Socr; Bausch & Lomb Sci Awd; High Hon Roll; NHS; Val; Mbr Jr Wrld Canoeing & Bathion Chmpnshp M 83 & 85; Skidmore; Engnrng.

SCHREINER, SUSAN E; Fox Lane HS; Mt Kisco, NY; (Y); 27/300; Exploring; French Clb; Girl Scts; Mathletes; Powder Puff Ftbl; High Hon Roll; NHS; Church Yth Grp; Orch; French Achvmnt Awd 82-84; Varsity Letter 84; Girl Scout Gold Awd 85; Rochester Inst; Computer Sci.

SCHREIVOGL, STACY; Berne-Knox-Westerlo Central HS; East Berne, NY; (Y); 16/80; Color Guard; Nwsp Rptr; Yrbk Stf; Rep Frsh Cls; Rep Soph Cls; Sec Jr Cls; Pres Sr Cls; JV Trk; Var Socr; Var Vllybl; Math.

SCHREMMER, TOBY; Manhasset HS; Manhasset, NY; (Y); JV Bsbl; JV Bsktbl; JV Socr; Bus Comp.

SCHRETZMAN, ROBERT E; St Francis Perparatory Schl; Rosedale, NY; (Y); 125/720; Camera Clb; JA; Letterman Clb; Boston U; Phys.

SCHRIER, DEBBIE; Haverling Central HS; Bath, NY; (Y); French Clb; Girl Scts; Latin Clb; Math Clb; Ski Clb; Chorus; Yrbk Stf; JV Swmmng; Hon Roll; NHS; Acctg.

SCHRIER, THOMAS; Haverling Central HS; Bath, NY; (S); 7/146; JCL; Math Clb; Ski Clb; School Musical; Nwsp Sprt Ed; Yrbk Phtg; Rep Stu Cncl; Var Capt Swmmng; High Hon Roll; NHS; Pre-Med.

SCHRILLA, SCOTT; Cicero North Syracuse HS; Clay, NY; (S); 76/622; JV Golf; Math Engrng.

SCHRODER, KATHLEEN A; Sanford H Calhoun HS; Merrick, NY; (Y); 5/336; Church Yth Grp; DECA; Varsity Clb; Band; Concert Band; Mrchg Band; Orch; Nwsp Stf; Yrbk Stf; Off Soph Cls; DECA 1st Pl Nassau Cnty Apparel Accs; Presdntl Athltc Awd; Engr.

SCHRODER, RENEE; Riverhead HS; Jamesport, NY; (Y); JCL; Latin Clb; Science Clb; Ski Clb; Varsity Clb; Band; Capt Drm Mjr(t); Rep Stu Cncl; Var Capt Twrlr; Hon Roll; Cvl Law Qual 84; Stu Bar Assn 85; Ntl JR Clsscl Leag 1st Pl 83; Pol Sci.

SCHRODER, SUSIE; Jamesville-De Witt HS; De Witt, NY; (Y); 36/224; Church Yth Grp; Varsity Clb; Var L Swmmng; High Hon Roll; NHS; Capt Sftbl; Swmng Awd Rotary Clb 83; Swmng Aawd Chmbr Comm 84; Dist Swmng Assoc Awd 83, 84 & 85; Nalt Jr Olym 83-85; Villanova U; Chem.

SCHROEDER, DOTTI; H Frank Carey HS; W Hempstead, NY; (Y); 32/225; Trs Dance Clb; FBLA; German Clb; Hon Roll; 5th Cnty Fut Bus Ldrs 85; Acctng.

SCHROEDER, EILEEN; St Joseph By The Sea HS; Staten Island, NY; (Y); Girl Scts; Nwsp Stf; Var Capt Crs Cntry; Var Capt Trk; Hon Roll; Coachs Awd X-Cntry 82-83; Coachs Awd Indoor-Outdoor 83-85; Phys Ther.

SCHROEDER, MARK; Rensselaer JR SR HS; Rensselaer, NY; (S); 5/35; Boys Clb Am; Computer Clb; Math Tm; Capt Bsktbl; JV Var Ftbl; Swmmng; Trk; High Hon Roll; NHS; St Schlr; Boys State Awd 85; RPI; Engineering.

SCHROEDER, TRACEY; Smithtown H S East; St James, NY; (Y); Cmnty Wkr; Sec German Clb; JV Bsktbl; JV Vllybl; Hon Roll; NHS; German Hnr Soc 83-86; Outstndng Achvt Awd-Fld Srvy Of Hlth Careers 83-84; Hmn Dev.

SCHROH, WILLIAM; Sssining HS; Ossining, NY; (Y); Church Yth Grp; JA; Model UN; Yrbk Stf; JV Var Crs Cntry; JV Var Trk; All Cnty Crss Cntry 84.

SCHROLL, SUSAN; Auburn HS; Auburn, NY; (Y); Model UN; Chorus; High Hon Roll; NHS; Helen Synott Schlrshp 85; Outstndng Bus Stdnt Awd 85; Nozzolio Intrnshp Awd 85; Cayuga County CC.

SCHROT, LISA; Walter Panas HS; Peekskill, NY; (Y); Drama Clb; Sec FBLA; Chorus; School Musical; School Play; Rep Jr Cls; Rep Sr Cls; Rep Stu Cncl; Hon Roll; Jr NHS.

SCHROT, RUDY; Olean SR HS; Olean, NY; (Y); 2/215; Pres Drama Clb; Political Wkr; Pres Thesps; Trs Chorus; Pres Orch; School Musical; School Play; NHS; Sal; Twnty Point Awd 85; NYSSMA All ST Chorus 84; Amer Lgn Bys ST 85.

SCHRUEFER, KIM; West Seneca West SR HS; West Seneca, NY; (S); DECA; Chorus; JV Bsktbl; JV Bowling; Prfct Atten Awd; Outstndng Chapter Awd State Level 83-84; Buffalo ST Coll; Spec Ed.

SCHRYVER, JILL; Tupper Lake HS; Tupper Lk, NY; (Y); 5/117; Church Yth Grp; Rep Frsh Cls; Rep Soph Cls; Rep Jr Cls; Rep Stu Cncl; Var JV Cheerleading; High Hon Roll; Hon Roll; NHS; Pre Med.

SCHUBAUER, MARY BETH; Sweet Home SR HS; Eggertsville, NY; (Y); 40/425; Pres Trs Church Yth Grp; GAA; Girl Scts; Yrbk Ed-Chief; Lit Mag; Var L Sftbl; High Hon Roll; NHS; Red Cross Aide; Teachers Aide; Amherst YES Outstndng Volntr 83-84; Girl Sct 1st Cls Awd 82; Phys Thrpy.

SCHUBERT, ROBIN; Caledonia-Mumford HS; Churchville, NY; (Y); 33/83; Science Clb; Ski Clb; Pres Spanish Clb; Band; Chorus; Swing Chorus; Trs Jr Cls; Stat Bsbl; Capt Cheerleading; MVP Chrldng 84 & 85; Geneseo ST; Psych.

SCHUBERT, STACEY S; E J Wilson HS; Spencerport, NY; (Y); 1/291; Drama Clb; Pres Model UN; Ski Clb; Chorus; Yrbk Bus Mgr; Sec Stu Cncl; Var Swmmng; NHS; Ntl Merit Ltr; Pres Schlr; MI Annual Givng Awd 85; Spencer Fclty Asoc Schlrshp 85; MI U; Chem Engr.

SCHUBERT, YISROEL; Mirrer Yeshiva HS; Brooklyn, NY; (Y); 1/23; Co-Capt Temple Yth Grp; Capt Bsbl; Im Bsktbl; Im Ftbl; St Schlr; Mirrer Yeshiva Centrl Inst.

SCHUCK, CHRISTINE P; Bennett HS; Buffalo, NY; (Y); 2/219; High Hon Roll; NHS; Regnts Schlrshp 85; NY ST U Buffalo; Pre-Law.

SCHUDER, KIRSTEN G; Hackley HS; Eastchester, NY; (Y); 33/99; Art Clb; Church Yth Grp; Debate Tm; Drama Clb; Key Clb; Model UN; Band; Chorus; Church Choir; Concert Band; Dartmouth; Lang.

SCHUEBLER, PETER; Archbishop Molloy HS; Ridgewood, NY; (Y); 55/409; Boy Scts; Im Bsktbl; Im Ftbl; Im Sftbl; Hon Roll; NHS.

SCHUERMANN, DIANE; Walton Central Schl; Walton, NY; (Y); 18/100; AFS; Cmnty Wkr; Key Clb; Chorus; Color Guard; Mrchg Band; Cheerleading; High Hon Roll; Hon Roll; NHS; 8 Tm Ltr Wnnr 83-85; Adv Plcmt 85; NY ST Regnts Diplm 85; SUNY Oneonta; Math.

SCHUH, DAVID W; Bishop Grimes HS; Syracuse, NY; (Y); 8/200; Cmnty Wkr; Math Clb; Ski Clb; Chorus; School Musical; Rep Frsh Cls; High Hon Roll; 1st Pl Cnty Math Sypmsm 81-82; NY ST Rgnts Schlrshp 84-85; U Of Rochester; Sci Engr.

SCHUKAL, KRISTEN J; John Jay SR HS; Hopewell Jct, NY; (Y); 168/560; AFS; School Play; Var Capt Fld Hcky; Hon Roll; Prfct Atten Awd; St Schlr; Athltc Awd Fld Hcky 83-84; Cert Of Merit 84-85; Pres Acadmc Ftns Awd 84-85; Dutchess CC; Libl Arts.

SCHULER, GRETA A; Ticonderoga HS; Ticonderoga, NY; (Y); 2/108; Trs FCA; Trs French Clb; Key Clb; Varsity Clb; Band; Chorus; Jazz Band; Ed Yrbk Stf; Stu Cncl; Var L Bowling; 2nd Pl Amer Legion Oratorical Cntst 84; 2nd Rnr Up JR Miss 84; Mt Holyoke Coll; Economics.

SCHULER, TODD; Cardinal O Hara HS; Kenmore, NY; (Y); Chess Clb; Computer Clb; Stage Crew; JV Var Socr; JV Trk; Hon Roll; Prfct Atten Awd; Comp Prgrmr.

SCHULITZ, CHRISTIAN; Churchville-Chill SR HS; Rochester, NY; (Y); 5/308; Am Leg Boys St; Boy Scts; Math Tm; Model UN; Band; Jazz Band; Pep Band; Tennis; High Hon Roll; Ntl Merit SF; NY St Regnts Schlrshp 85; U Rochester.

SCHULITZ, MIKE; Churchville-Chili SR HS; Rochester, NY; (Y); Am Leg Boys St; Boy Scts; JCL; Capt Math Tm; Model UN; Ski Clb; Chorus; Mrchg Band; School Play; Symp Band; 2nd Best Delg Syracuse Model UN 85; All-ST Math Team 85.

SCHULMAN, GAIL; Commack HS North; E Northport, NY; (Y); French Clb; Library Aide; Temple Yth Grp; Off Soph Cls; Off Jr Cls; Rep Stu Cncl; High Hon Roll; Hon Roll.

SCHULMAN, JASON; Geroger W Hewlett HS; Woodmere, NY; (Y); MMM; Pres Temple Yth Grp; Band; Orch; High Hon Roll; NHS; Chorus; Concert Band; Jazz Band; Mrchg Band; Pauline Winick Memrl Schlrshp 82-85; Edward T Sandrow Awd-Hghst Acadmc Achvt 85; Cardiac Srgn.

SCHULMAN, STEVEN F; Smithtown East HS; Smithtown, NY; (Y); Bsbl; L Capt Bsktbl; Coach Actv; Var L Ftbl; Hon Roll; St Schlr; All Leag Bsktbl 84-85; Syracuse.

SCHULT, HEIDI; Clarkstown North HS; New City, NY; (Y); Church Yth Grp; Exploring; Spanish Clb; Yrbk Stf; Rep Jr Cls; Rep Stu Cncl; Fld Hcky; Trk; Bus Ed Awd Outstndg Achvt H S Bus 85; Coaches Awd Fld Hcky 83.

SCHULTEISS, JULIE L; Charles H Roth HS; W Henrietta, NY; (Y); 19/210; Drama Clb; Thesps; School Musical; School Play; Stage Crew; Hon Roll; Jr NHS; NHS; Spanish NHS; Schltc Letter 83-84; Regents Schlrshp 85; MCC; Bus.

SCHULTHEISS, SUSAN; Cohocton Central HS; Cohocton, NY; (Y); 7/26; Church Yth Grp; 4-H; French Clb; Band; Chorus; Mrchg Band; Yrbk Stf; Sec Sr Cls; Rep Stu Cncl; Stat Var Score Keeper; Don Mehlenbach Mem Chrl Awd 85; Typg Awd 85; Cohoctn Supprt Grp Schlrshp 85; U Of Buffalo; Phys Thrpy.

SCHULTZ, CINDY; Coxsackie-Athens HS; W Coxsackie, NY; (Y); 6/110; German Clb; Ski Clb; Chorus; High Hon Roll; Hon Roll; NHS; Accntnt.

SCHULTZ, DANIEL; Skaneateles Central HS; Skaneateles, NY; (S); Exploring; Model UN; Ski Clb; Var Socr; Var Trk; High Hon Roll; Hon Roll; NHS; Mock Trl 85; Tlntd Gftd Prog 84-85; Intl Rel.

SCHULTZ, DORIANNE L; Wilson Central HS; Ransomville, NY; (Y); Church Yth Grp; Hosp Aide; Chorus; School Musical; Swing Chorus; Yrbk Stf; Sec Soph Cls; Sec Jr Cls; Rep Stu Cncl; Phy Thrpy.

SCHULTZ, ELIZABETH; St Johns Prep; Astoria, NY; (Y); Church Yth Grp; Cmnty Wkr; High Hon Roll; Prfct Atten Awd; NY U; Wrtng.

SCHULTZ, KAREN; Commack North HS; Commack, NY; (Y); Spanish Clb; Nwsp Stf; Lit Mag; Cheerleading; Ftbl; Score Keeper; Socr; Trk; Hon Roll; Albany ST; Law.

SCHULTZ, TINA; Wilson Central Schl; Ransomville, NY; (Y); Camera Clb; Dance Clb; Ski Clb; Band; Pep Band; Yrbk Stf; JV Var Cheerleading; Powder Puff Ftbl; Var Trk; Hon Roll; ST U NY; Danc.

SCHULZ, CHRISTINA; Smithtown East HS; St James, NY; (Y); Cmnty Wkr; VP FBLA; Political Wkr; Radio Clb; Yrbk Stf; Vllybl; Jr NHS; NHS; Spanish NHS; Fordham U; Fin.

SCHULZ, JOHN; Lake George Central HS; Glens Fls, NY; (Y); Varsity Clb; Band; Jazz Band; Mrchg Band; Var Bsbl; JV Bsktbl; Var Ftbl; Var Socr; Hon Roll.

SCHULZE, KATHLEEN; Roy C Ketcham HS; Wappinger Falls, NY; (Y); FBLA; JV Var Cheerleading; High Hon Roll; NHS; JV Var Cheerleading; Stu Cncl.

SCHUM, JANE; Chenango Valley HS; Binghampton, NY; (Y); French Clb; Rep Sr Cls; Var L Bsktbl; JV Socr; Var L Sftbl; Var L Tennis; Hon Roll; Acctng.

SCHUMACHER, ELISA ANN; Uniondale HS; Hempstead, NY; (Y); Church Yth Grp; Sec Drama Clb; Acpl Chr; Chorus; Jazz Band; School Play; Stage Crew; Nwsp Phtg; Nwsp Rptr; JV Cheerleading; Messiah Coll; Polit Sci.

SCHUMACHER, JANET L; West Valley Central Schl; West Valley, NY; (Y); 4/44; Band; Chorus; Drm Mjr(t); Jazz Band; School Musical; Yrbk Ed-Chief; Yrbk Stf; NHS; Prfct Atten Awd; Regents Schlrshp 85; SUNY Fredonia; Chem Ed.

SCHUMACHER, MARY; Niagara Wheatfield SR HS; N Tonawanda, NY; (Y); 66/319; VP German Clb; JA; Latin Clb; Pep Clb; PAVAS; Chorus; School Play; Nwsp Rptr; Nwsp Stf; Stat Bsktbl; Acad Awd; Whte Paper Rdr; Acad Hnrs; Niagara Cnty CC; Comm.

SCHUMAKER, SHERRY; Hannibal HS; Hannibal, NY; (S); 14/107; Band; Color Guard; Mrchg Band; Off Jr Cls; Stu Cncl; Var Socr; Var Vllybl; Hon Roll; Comm Art.

SCHUMAN, MICHAEL; Niagara Wheatfield HS; Niagara Falls, NY; (Y); Jazz Band; Stage Crew; Variety Show; High Hon Roll; Hon Roll; NHS; Fredonia ST; Music.

SCHUMAN, STACY; Bethpage HS; Plainview, NY; (Y); 7/298; Spanish Clb; Temple Yth Grp; Yrbk Ed-Chief; High Hon Roll; Hon Roll; Jr NHS; NHS; Springfield Coll Humanic Awd 85; Bethpage H S Humanic Awd 85.

SCHUMANN, KARI R; East HS; Rochester, NY; (Y); 1/270; Nwsp Stf; Yrbk Bus Mgr; Yrbk Sprt Ed; Pres Jr Cls; Rep Stu Cncl; NHS; Ntl Merit Ltr; Val; VFW Awd; Cmnty Wkr; Dartmouth Bk Awd; Outstndng Frnch Awd; Carleton Coll; Chem Engr.

SCHUMANN, SVEN; Pierson HS; Sag Harbor, NY; (Y); 6/49; Math Tm; Spanish Clb; Yrbk Stf; Sec Soph Cls; Hon Roll; Masonic Awd; NHS; Hgh Scorer Math Tm; Dist Newslttr-Co-Edtr; ST U Of NY Stonybrook; Dentst.

SCHUMM, MARIANNE; North Babylon SR HS; North Babylon, NY; (Y); Art Clb; French Clb; Intnl Clb; Lit Mag; JV Capt Gym; French Hon Soc; Jr NHS; NHS; Boston U; Adv Dsgn.

SCHUNER, JACQUI; L A Webber Schl; Lyndonville, NY; (S); Varsity Clb; Concert Band; Mrchg Band; School Musical; JV Bsktbl; JV Var Socr; JV Var Sftbl; JV Var Vllybl; Hon Roll; NHS; SUNY At Buffalo; Nrs.

SCHUNK, CARYN; Eden SR HS; Eden, NY; (Y); 20/192; 4-H; FFA; Ski Clb; Orch; Yrbk Phtg; Yrbk Stf; Off Sr Cls; High Hon Roll; Hon Roll; NHS; Pres Acad Ftns Awd 85; Embers Cert Mbrshp 85; SUNY Fredonia; Chem Engrng.

SCHUNK, DARRYL; Westhampton Beach HS; Westhamptn Bch, NY; (Y); 92/250; Aud/Vis; Boy Scts; Church Yth Grp; Pres Computer Clb; Elect Engr.

SCHUNK, JUDY; Springville Griffith Institute HS; Springville, NY; (Y); 24/200; AFS; Band; Chorus; Mrchg Band; Orch; JV Var Bsktbl; Var Capt Sftbl; Var L Tennis; JV Capt Vllybl; High Hon Roll; AFS Exchng Stu Brzl 84; Outstndng SR Feml Athlt 85; L J & J Reed Mem Schlrshp,Sprngvl Athltc Schlrsp; U Of Buffalo; Sprts Med.

SCHUR, DAVID; Cardinal Mooney HS; N Chili, NY; (Y); 25/317; Boy Scts; Ski Clb; Nwsp Rptr; Nwsp Stf; Crs Cntry; Ntl Merit Ltr; Lat Ntl Hnr Soc 82-84; Purdue U; Elec Engrng.

SCHURKUS, LISA M; Williamsville North HS; E Amherst, NY; (Y); 40/315; Church Yth Grp; Cmnty Wkr; Girl Scts; Latin Clb; Spanish Clb; Church Choir; School Musical; Hon Roll; NHS; Pres Schlr; Svc Aide Bar-Wrkng W/Handicapped 83; ST U NY Genesco; Ind Psych.

SCHUSTER, ANNETTE L; Ellicottville Central HS; Ellicottvle, NY; (Y); 12/63; AFS; Science Clb; Concert Band; Mrchg Band; Yrbk Stf; Rep Stu Cncl; Dnfth Awd; High Hon Roll; Hon Roll; NHS.

SCHUSTER, GRETCHEN E; Irondequoit HS; Rochester, NY; (Y); 7/377; Church Yth Grp; Ski Clb; Chorus; School Musical; Trs Stu Cncl; Var Socr; Bausch & Lomb Sci Awd; NHS; Varsity Clb; Swing Chorus; Rennselaer Mdl Sci & Math 84.

SCHUSTER, LINDA M; Williamsville North HS; West Amherst, NY; (Y); Sec Exploring; Off Chorus; School Musical; Stage Crew; Swing Chorus; Stu Cncl; Hon Roll; NHS; ST Rgnts Nrsng Schlrshp 85; U Of Buffalo; Nrsng.

SCHUTZER, ERIC P; Scarsdale HS; Scarsdale, NY; (Y); Hosp Aide; Letterman Clb; Math Tm; Quiz Bowl; Science Clb; Varsity Clb; Var Capt Swmmng; Jr NHS; NHS; Ntl Merit Ltr; Russain Great Achvt 83; MAA Awd 84; Regents Schlrshp 85; Most Valuable Player 85; Columbia; Medicine.

SCHWAB, ALEXANDRA; Pelham Memorial HS; Pelham Manor, NY; (Y); Am Leg Aux Girls St; Civic Clb; Cmnty Wkr; English Clb; Girl Scts; Model UN; Spanish Clb; Nwsp Stf; Yrbk Stf; Jr Cls; Stu Assn Svc Awd 85; Smith Coll Lit Awd 85; Amer Lung Assn 83-84; Lang.

SCHWABL, JILL; Mount Mercy Acad; Buffalo, NY; (Y); 8/165; Dance Clb; Model UN; Ski Clb; Rep Jr Cls; Var Cheerleading; Im Tennis; Im Vllybl; High Hon Roll; Hon Roll; Highest Math Av 84; 1st 2nd Pl Awds Dance Comp 83-85; Math.

SCHWAGER, ELISA H; Yorktown HS; Yorktown Hts, NY; (Y); Key Clb; Temple Yth Grp; Nwsp Stf; Fld Hcky; High Hon Roll; NHS; Psych.

SCHWAGER, STUART A; Cortland JR SR HS; Cortland, NY; (Y); 12/237; Am Leg Boys St; Capt Quiz Bowl; Nwsp Sprt Ed; L Crs Cntry; Capt Tennis; L Trk; Kiwanis Awd; NHS; Ntl Merit Ltr; St Schlr; Soc Of Mayflower Descndnts Awd Exclinc In Amer Hist 84; Colgate U; Hist.

SCHWALLER, JOHN; Cucning-Painted Post West HS; Painted Post, NY; (Y); Cmnty Wkr; Key Clb; Varsity Clb; Band; JV Bsktbl; Var JV Ftbl; Var Trk; Wt Lftg; High Hon Roll; NHS; JV Ftbl Awd 83; Var Ftbl Awd 84; Syracuse; Mech Engrng.

SCHWALLER, PETER J; Somers HS; Somers, NY; (Y); 6/213; Church Yth Grp; Chorus; School Musical; School Play; Symp Band; Socr; Trk; High Hon Roll; VP NHS; Ntl Merit SF.

SCHWARTZ, BRIAN D; Jericho SR HS; Jericho, NY; (Y); 1/230; Computer Clb; Science Clb; Trs Service Clb; Teachers Aide; Rptr Nwsp Stf; NHS; Val; FBLA; Model UN; Nwsp Rptr; Hewsday High Hnrs Fnlst 85; Geo Washington U Excl Awd Sci, Math 84; Harvard U; Med.

SCHWARTZ, BRIAN P; Camden HS; Blossvale, NY; (Y); AFS; Am Leg Boys St; Cmnty Wkr; Ski Clb; Chorus; Church Choir; Yrbk Bus Mgr; High Hon Roll; NHS; Colgate; Chmst.

SCHWARTZ, DAVID; Massapequa HS; Massapequa, NY; (Y); 7/447; Hosp Aide; Key Clb; Nwsp Bus Mgr; Yrbk Bus Mgr; Yrbk Phtg; JV Crs Cntry; Var L Tennis; Hon Roll; NHS; Pres Schlr; NY St Regents Schlrshp 85; Duke U.

SCHWARTZ, DAVID; Newfield HS; Selden, NY; (S); 1/563; Computer Clb; Math Tm; Spanish Clb; Varsity Clb; Band; Tennis; High Hon Roll; NHS; Spanish NHS; Val; Stu Ctzn Of Mnth; Pensselaer Bolytechnic; Comp.

SCHWARTZ, DAVID D; Ramapo SR HS; Suffern, NY; (Y); 94/519; Band; Stage Crew; Yrbk Stf; Ed Lit Mag; Sr Cls; JV Tennis; Ntl Merit Ltr; Arts Recng & Tlnt Spch 85; 1st Pl Creatn Art Cnst & Fnlst Cnty Postr 85; Adv.

SCHWARTZ, DEBORAH; New Rochelle HS; Scarsdale, NY; (Y); Mrchg Band; Symp Band; Nwsp Rptr; Nwsp Stf; High Hon Roll; NHS; Spanish NHS; Spnsh Dept Awd Excell 83; 1st Pl Hnrs Iona Coll Lang Cont Spnsh IV 85; Valedictorian 85.

SCHWARTZ, ELIZABETH; Washingtonville SR HS; Washingtonville, NY; (Y); Dance Clb; Girl Scts; PAVAS; JV Cheerleading; JV Pom Pon; High Hon Roll; Hon Roll; Engl.

SCHWARTZ, GARRY H; Jamesville-Dewitt HS; Dewitt, NY; (Y); 14/240; French Clb; Bsbl; Bowling; Score Keeper; High Hon Roll; NHS; Regnts Schlrshp NY ST 85; Clss 64 Memrl Schlrshp Awd 85; Cornell U; Bio.

SCHWARTZ, JEFFREY J; Baldwin SR HS; Baldwin Harbor, NY; (Y); 24/503; Exploring; Key Clb; Mathletes; VP Temple Yth Grp; Var L Tennis; High Hon Roll; Hon Roll; Spanish NHS; Math Fair Medalist 81; Ribbon Winner 85; Binghamton.

SCHWARTZ, JOAN; Commack High School South; Commack, NY; (Y); Pres Chorus; Nwsp Bus Mgr; Pres Frsh Cls; JV Bsktbl; Var Cheerleading; JV Sftbl; Hon Roll; NCTE Awd; Ntl SS Olympd 3rd Pl NY Schls; Jrnlsm.

SCHWARTZ, JODI; South Shore HS; Brooklyn, NY; (Y); Math Tm; Service Clb; Teachers Aide; Varsity Clb; Chorus; School Musical; Variety Show; Cheerleading; High Hon Roll; Ntl Merit Ltr; NYU; Lawyer.

SCHWARTZ, LISSA; West Seneca East SR HS; W Seneca, NY; (Y); Sec Church Yth Grp; Key Clb; Ski Clb; Nwsp Stf; Yrbk Stf; VP Lit Mag; VP Frsh Cls; Stu Cncl; High Hon Roll; NHS; Houghton Coll; Scl Wrk.

SCHWARTZ, MARK; Churchville-Chili HS; Churchville, NY; (Y); Model UN; Pep Clb; Ski Clb; Im Bowling; L Trk; High Hon Roll; Hon Roll; Arch.

SCHWARTZ, MICHAEL; Lawrence HS; Woodmere, NY; (Y); Chess Clb; Cmnty Wkr; Math Tm; Service Clb; Spanish Clb; Var Socr; Im Capt Sftbl; Var Wrstlng; High Hon Roll; NHS; Lttr Commndtn Attndnc 84-85; Schl Hnr Socty; Sci Fair Cert 83-84; Med.

SCHWARTZ, PETER W; Lakeland Senior HS; Mohegan Lake, NY; (Y); 7/350; Off Jr Cls; Off Sr Cls; Stu Cncl; Trk; Rensselaer Poly Tech; Mngmnt.

SCHWARTZ, SUSAN; Binghamtopn HS; Binghamton, NY; (Y); Cmnty Wkr; Key Clb; Ski Clb; Stu Cncl; Mgr(s); Score Keeper; High Hon Roll; Jr NHS; Outstndng Ptrt Cmnty Serv Awd 85; Bus.

SCHWARTZ, WAYNE F; Camden HS; Blossvale, NY; (Y); 4/207; AFS; Cmnty Wkr; Ski Clb; Chorus; Nwsp Rptr; Nwsp Stf; High Hon Roll; NHS; NY ST Regents Schlrshp 84-85; Le Moyne Coll; Pre-Med.

SCHWARZ, CHRISTIAN K; Gloversville HS; Gloversville, NY; (Y); 21/226; Sec Computer Clb; Math Tm; Science Clb; Teachers Aide; Mrchg Band; Stage Crew; Var Tennis; Capt Trk; High Hon Roll; Hon Roll; Rgnts Schlrshp; Rochester Inst Of Tech; Comp.

SCHWARZ, CHRISTY; School Of The Holy Child; Rye, NY; (Y); Drama Clb; Chorus; School Musical; Nwsp Stf; Yrbk Ed-Chief; Yrbk Stf; Fld Hcky; Tennis; All 3 Yrs Won Vari Schlstc Awds Schl Subj; Ec.

SCHWARZ, ERIC A; Blind Brook HS; Rye Brook, NY; (Y); Computer Clb; Model UN; Spanish Clb; Teachers Aide; Ntl Merit SF; Bio Sci.

SCHWARZ, KARIN; Riverdale Country Schl; Riverdale, NY; (Y); Temple Yth Grp; Nwsp Rptr; JV Trk; Hon Roll; Prfct Atten Awd; Regents Schlrshp 85; Columbia U; Psych.

SCHWARZ, KRISTEN; School Of The Hly Chld; Rye, NY; (S); Cmnty Wkr; Drama Clb; Thesps; School Play; Nwsp Stf; Yrbk Stf; Fld Hcky; Tennis; High Hon Roll.

SCHWARZ, VERA; Hicksville SR HS; Hicksvl, NY; (Y); German Clb; Spanish Clb; JV Sftbl; High Hon Roll; Jr NHS; NHS; Prfct Atten Awd; Steuben Awd Germn III 85; Delta Epsiln Phi Germn Natl Hnr Socty 85; Soc Stds Achvt Awd 84-85; Penn ST U; Vet.

SCHWARZENBERG, ANN; H Frank Carey HS; Franklin Sq, NY; (Y); 54/281; Cmnty Wkr; 4-H; Orch; Yrbk Stf.

SCHWEDE, KELLY; Mt Mercy Acad; Buffalo, NY; (Y); Camp Fr Inc; French Clb; Service Clb; Rep Soph Cls; Geneseo; Bus Mgmt.

SCHWEIGER, ROBERT F; N Tonawanda SR HS; N Tonawanda, NY; (Y); 5/470; Am Leg Boys St; Hosp Aide; Library Aide; Mrchg Band; Bowling; L Tennis; Hon Roll; NHS; Ntl Merit Ltr; Egl Sct 82; MI ST U; Engrng.

SCHWEITZER, SANDY L; Hilton HS; Hamlin, NY; (Y); 7/280; Model UN; Ski Clb; Nwsp Rptr; Swmmng; Trk; NHS; Pres Schlr; Teachers Aide; Ruth Roy Mem Scholar 85; CAP Awd 85; Mst Spirited Swm Tm 85; Geneseo ST; Elem Ed.

SCHWEIZER, DONALD; Holland Central HS; Holland, NY; (Y); Am Leg Boys St; FFA; Var Bsbl; High Hon Roll.

SCHWEIZER, LISA; Moore Catholic HS; Staten Island, NY; (Y); French Clb; Hosp Aide; Ski Clb; School Musical; Stage Crew; JV Sftbl; Hon Roll; NHS; 1st Pl Schl Sci Fair 84; Frgn Lang.

SCHWENDY, KENT M; Beaver River Central Schl; Carthage, NY; (Y); Am Leg Boys St; School Musical; Nwsp Rptr; Yrbk Ed-Chief; Lit Mag; Var Capt Swmmng; Var Trk; High Hon Roll; Hon Roll; NHS; Aeronutcl Engr.

SCHWENKLER, MARY; Notre Dame HS; Elmira, NY; (Y); Ski Clb; Band; Church Choir; Rep Frsh Cls; Var Sftbl; Hon Roll; NHS; All Cnty Band 83-85; Schlrshp Notre Dame HS 83; Educ.

SCHWERDT, PAULA; Frankfort-Schuyler HS; Ilion, NY; (S); 25/99; Key Clb; Math Tm; Spanish Clb; High Hon Roll; Hon Roll; NHS; Herkimer County CC; Comp Sci.

SCHWINGEL, GARY S; Wayland Central Schl; Wayland, NY; (Y); 1/91; Pres Varsity Clb; Yrbk Stf; Pres Jr Cls; JV Var Bsbl; Var L Cheerleading; Var L Socr; High Hon Roll; NHS; Val; Sthrn Tier, NYS Rgnts Schlrshps; Alfred U; Bnkng.

SCHWINN, ADAM; Archbishop Molloy HS; Glendale, NY; (Y); 184/409; Computer Clb; Varsity Clb; Pres Soph Cls; Pres Jr Cls; Pres Sr Cls; Socr; USAFA; Engrng.

SCIABARRA, DENISE NOEL; Earl L Vandermuelen HS; Mt Sinai, NY; (Y); 19/276; FBLA; Leo Clb; Pres Frsh Cls; VP Sr Cls; Capt Var Cheerleading; High Hon Roll; NHS; St Schlr; Art Clb; Cmnty Wkr; All-Amer Chrldr 83-84; Stu Cncl Serv Awd 82-83; Stu Cncl Ldrshp Awd 82-83; Hofstra U; Comm.

SCIABARRA, GERALDINE; Bishop Karney HS; Brooklyn, NY; (Y); Church Yth Grp; GAA; Italian Awds; Sci Awd; NY U; Dnstry.

SCIABARRASI, KELLY; Mc Mahon HS; Buffalo, NY; (Y); Rep Frsh Cls; Rep Soph Cls; Trs Stu Cncl; Im Bowling; Var Im Sftbl; NHS; Achiev Awd Math 84-85; Achiev Awd Chem 84-85.

SCIACCHITANO, ANNE MARIE; Ctr Moriches HS; Ctr Moriches, NY; (Y); 2/74; Pres Trs Girl Scts; Nwsp Ed-Chief; Yrbk Stf; High Hon Roll; Trs NHS; Ntl Merit Ltr; Drama Clb; French Clb; Trs Latin Clb; Ski Clb; 1st Clss Girl Scout; Psych.

SCIALDONE, ANTHONY; Mynderse Academy; Seneca Falls, NY; (Y); JV Bsktbl; Old Dominion; Math.

SCIALDONE, BARBARA; Whitesboro Central Schl; Whitesboro, NY; (Y); 47/358; Church Yth Grp; Cmnty Wkr; Hosp Aide; Chorus; Variety Show; VP Frsh Cls; VP Soph Cls; JV Var Cheerleading; Powder Puff Ftbl; Hon Roll.

SCIALDONE, RICHARD; Kings Park SR HS; Kings Pk, NY; (Y); 116/394; Cmnty Wkr; Concert Band; Yrbk Stf; Stu Cncl; Htl/Rstrnt Mgt.

SCIALDONE, VINCENT; Utica Free Acad; Utica, NY; (Y); 4-H; Key Clb; Spanish Clb; Stu Cncl; Var Bsbl; High Hon Roll; Jr NHS; NHS; Vet Med.

SCIANDRA, ANGELO; Seneca Voc HS; Buffalo, NY; (Y); Office Aide; VP Sr Cls; Bus.

SCIARABBA, CHARLES; Commack High School South; Commack, NY; (Y); Variety Show; Var Capt Socr; Var Wrstlng; High Hon Roll; Hon Roll; All League Soccer 84-85; All League Wrstlng 83-85; PA ST; Phys Thrpy.

SCIARRA, APRIL; Herkimer SR HS; E Herkimer, NY; (Y); 10/129; Cmnty Wkr; Rep Stu Cncl; JV Var Cheerleading; Var Trk; High Hon Roll; NHS; Psych.

SCIARRINO JR, MATTHEW; Tottenville HS; Staten Island, NY; (Y); High Hon Roll; Hon Roll; NHS; Schltc Achvt Awd; Law.

SCICCHITANO, FRANK; Olean SR HS; Olean, NY; (Y); CAP; FBLA; School Play; Bsbl; Bsktbl; Wt Lftg; Cert Achvt Bkkpng II 85; Oswego ST U; CPA.

SCICUTELLA, ANGELA; John Adams HS; Richmond Hl, NY; (Y); Church Yth Grp; Teachers Aide; High Hon Roll; Jr NHS; NHS; Prfct Atten Awd; Senator Weinstein Awd 82; Cert Merit & 1st Hnrs 84; 1st Hnrs 85; Comp Pgmmr.

SCIME, DON; Mount Saint Joseph Acad; Buffalo, NY; (S); Pres Drama Clb; School Musical; School Play; Stage Crew; Yrbk Stf; Lit Mag; Hon Roll; NHS; Sister Sylvia Schlrshp Wnnr 82-84; Sprtsmn Assoc Awd Schlstc Achvt 82-83; Art Educ.

SCIMECA, MARK D; Kenmore East SR HS; Buffalo, NY; (Y); 1/340; Math Clb; Math Tm; Political Wkr; Ed Nwsp Ed-Chief; High Hon Roll; Jr NHS; NCTE Awd; NHS; Ntl Merit SF; Val; Myflwr Dscndnts Hist Awd 84-85; Rensselaer Polytech Inst Math, Sci Mdl 84; Dist Anthlgy Poetry 82; Pre Med.

SCINTA, GINA; Alden Central HS; Alden, NY; (Y); Spanish Clb; Rep Stu Cncl; Rep NHS; Ntl Sci Plym 83-85; V Mbr Schl Rifle Tm 83-85; St Johns U; Pre-Law.

SCINTO, LAWRENCE J; Monsignor Farrell HS; Staten Island, NY; (Y); 50/300; Aud/Vis; Boy Scts; Cmnty Wkr; Debate Tm; Exploring; JA; Red Cross Aide; Science Clb; Service Clb; Yrbk Rptr; Eagl Sct; Ad Altare Del Relg Awd; Cooper Union; Engrng.

SCINTO, LORRAINE; Lawrence HS; Atlantic Beach, NY; (Y); 47/400; AFS; French Clb; Sec Key Clb; Nwsp Sprt Ed; Lit Mag; Rep Stu Cncl; Var Tennis; French Hon Soc; High Hon Roll; NHS; Art Purchase Awd 82; Boston Coll; Bio.

SCIOLI, GINA M; West Seneca West HS; West Seneca, NY; (Y); 6/543; German Clb; VP Key Clb; Teachers Aide; Nwsp Ed-Chief; High Hon Roll; Hon Roll; JC Awd; Jr NHS; NHS; Voice Dem Awd; Rgnts Schlrshp; D Youville Coll; Nrsg.

SCIROCCO, MICHELE; Scotia-Glenville HS; Scotia, NY; (Y); Sec Key Clb; Chorus; Sec Frsh Cls; Sec Soph Cls; Sec Stu Cncl; Socr; Tennis; Hon Roll; NHS; Peer Ldr Awd 85; Potsdam; Elem Eductn.

SCISM III, JAMES H; Rondout Valley HS; Kingston, NY; (Y); Am Leg Boys St; JA; Chorus; Concert Band; Jazz Band; School Musical; Stage Crew; JV Var Ftbl; JV Var Wrstlng; NHS; Biomedcl Engrng.

SCIULLA, VINCENT; New Utrecht HS; Brooklyn, NY; (Y); Key Clb; JR Avg 91 82-86; NY U; Govrnmnt.

SCIULLI, ALISA J; Irvington HS; Irvington, NY; (Y); 4/122; Art Clb; Church Yth Grp; Chorus; School Musical; School Play; Stage Crew; Swing Chorus; Vllybl; High Hon Roll; Ntl Merit Ltr; Barnard Coll; Theater.

SCLAFANI, ANTHONY; St Raymonds - Boys HS; New York, NY; (Y); 9/191; Art Clb; Church Yth Grp; Cmnty Wkr; Rep Stu Cncl; Bsktbl; Fld Hcky; Ftbl; Sftbl; Wt Lftg; Jr NHS; NHS; NY St Regnts Schlrshp 85-86; Local 174 Schlrshp 85-86; Fordham U; Eng.

SCLAFANI, FRANK; Archbishop Stepinac HS; Port Chester, NY; (Y); Im JV Ftbl.

SCLAMO, LOUISA M; Jefferson HS; Rochester, NY; (Y); 4/100; High Hon Roll; Hon Roll; Sec NHS; Prfct Atten Awd; Regents Schlrshp 85; Awd Italian 83; Nazareth Coll-Rochester; Eng.

SCOCCHERA, RICHARD; Frontier SR HS; Hamburg, NY; (S); Spanish Clb; Nwsp Ed-Chief; High Hon Roll; Hon Roll; NHS; Ntl Merit Ltr; Cert Ed Dev Ntl 83; Cert Hnr Mock Trl Part NY St Bar Assoc 85; Law.

SCOGNAMIGLIO, JOHN; Moore Catholic HS; Staten Island, NY; (Y); Boys Clb Am; Boy Scts; Ski Clb; Yrbk Stf; VP Soph Cls; VP Jr Cls; Rep Stu Cncl; JV Bsktbl; Var Capt Bowling; Hon Roll.

SCOGNAMIGLIO, MARIA; St Edmund HS; Brooklyn, NY; (S); 15/188; Cmnty Wkr; Office Aide; Political Wkr; Varsity Clb; Nwsp Rptr; Yrbk Rptr; Cheerleading; Hon Roll; Acad All-Amer Schlr Prgm 85; Fordham U; Psychology.

SCOLLAN, DAVID F; Union-Endicott HS; Endicott, NY; (Y); 3/429; Boys Clb Am; Key Clb; Varsity Clb; Nwsp Ed-Chief; Var L Crs Cntry; Var L Trk; High Hon Roll; Ntl Merit SF; Intrnshp Kopernik Obsrvtry 83-84; Aerospc Engr.

SCOLNIK, MERYL; Earl L Vandermeulen HS; Port Jefferson, NY; (Y); Sec Art Clb; French Clb; Pep Clb; Spanish Clb; Chorus; School Musical; Capt Cheerleading; Hon Roll; NYSSMA 84; SADD Smnr SUNY-STONY Brook 85; Natl Spnsh Exm 85; Chld Psych.

SCORDARAS, MARIA; St Edmund HS; Brooklyn, NY; (Y); 27/187; Romance Lang.

SCORDO, CHERYL A; Bishop Grimes HS; E Syracuse, NY, (Y); 27/207; Church Yth Grp; Exploring; Hon Roll; Sec NHS; Relgs Hnrs; Italn Natl Hnr Soc; Lemoyne Coll; Acctng.

SCOTT, ANDREA; Rome Catholic HS; Rome, NY; (Y); School Musical; Yrbk Ed-Chief; Rep Frsh Cls; Sec Soph Cls; Sec Jr Cls; Sec Stu Cncl; JV Var Cheerleading; Stat Ice Hcky; High Hon Roll; Hon Roll; Latin Achvt Awd 85; Comp Sci.

SCOTT, ANDREA L; Gates-Chili SR HS; Rochester, NY; (Y); 43/463; Sec Church Yth Grp; JA; Church Choir; Variety Show; Var Capt Bsktbl; JV Cheerleading; Var Trk; High Hon Roll; Hon Roll; NHS; GMI; Elec Engrng.

SCOTT JR, BERNARD; Bishop Loughlin Memorial HS; Brooklyn, NY; (Y); Boy Scts; Church Yth Grp; Cmnty Wkr; Computer Clb; Band; Church Choir; Concert Band; School Musical; Bsktbl; Cit Awd; Comp Sci.

SCOTT, BRADLEY C; Haverling JR SR HS; Savona, NY; (Y); 81/168; Aud/Vis; JCL; Latin Clb; Math Clb; Ski Clb; Yrbk Phtg; Yrbk Stf; Golf; Socr; Hon Roll; NY St Regnts Schlrshp; Clemson; Law.

SCOTT, CATHERINE; Oneonta SR HS; Oneonta, NY; (Y); 14/144; Drama Clb; Thesps; Chorus; Madrigals; School Musical; Stage Crew; Off Stu Cncl; Swmmng; Hon Roll; NHS; WA Wrkshps Sem 85; Lindenwood Scholar 85; Jacqueline Bary Awd 85; Lindenwood Coll; Theater Arts.

SCOTT, DANESSIA MARIE; Mount Saint Joseph Acad; Buffalo, NY; (S); Church Yth Grp; Cmnty Wkr; Hosp Aide; Library Aide; Church Choir; Pres Jr Cls; Rep Stu Cncl; High Hon Roll; Canisius Coll; Law.

SCOTT, DANIEL; Franklin Acad; Constable, NY; (Y); 15/253; Spanish Clb; Varsity Clb; Off Jr Cls; Bowling; Trk; Vllybl; Hon Roll; NHS; Prfct Atten Awd; Sci Olympd 83 & 84; Frstry.

SCOTT, DARNIECE; Villa Maria Acad; Buffalo, NY; (Y); Computer Clb; Girl Scts; Hosp Aide; Pep Clb; Chorus; Drill Tm.

SCOTT, GARY; Pelham Memorial HS; Pelham, NY; (Y); Church Yth Grp; Var L Bsbl; Var L Bsktbl; Var L Ftbl; Wt Lftg; Hon Roll; NHS; All Cnty Bsktbl, MVP.

SCOTT, GREGORY; Frontier Central HS; Hamburg, NY; (S); 12/550; French Clb; JV Bsbl; JV Ftbl; Hon Roll; NHS; NEDT Awd; SUNY Albany; Comp Sci.

SCOTT, HUGH J; New Rochelle HS; New Rochelle, NY; (Y); 262/700; Aud/Vis; Political Wkr; Ftbl; Var Trk; Wt Lftg; Elks Awd; Busi Admin.

SCOTT, JAMES; Vestal SR HS; Binghamton, NY; (Y); Church Yth Grp; German Clb; Spanish Clb; Rep Frsh Cls; JV Bsktbl; JV Crs Cntry; Im Lcrss; Sftbl; High Hon Roll; Hon Roll; Chem.

SCOTT JR, JAMES JOSEPH; St Johns Preparatory Schl; Astoria, NY; (S); 20/415; Pres Camera Clb; VP 4-H; Pres Science Clb; Concert Band; Stage Crew; L Trk; 4-H Awd; High Hon Roll; NHS; Mrchg Band; Elmira Coll Key Awd 84; Alfred U; Engrng.

SCOTT, JEREMY L; Nottingham HS; Syracuse, NY; (Y); 58/220; Drama Clb; Chorus; Lit Mag; NHS; Grinnell Coll; Anthro.

SCOTT, JULIE; Trott Vocational HS; Alden, NY; (Y); Church Yth Grp; Cmnty Wkr; FNA; Hosp Aide; JA; Chorus; Church Choir; Drm Mjr(t); Yrbk Rptr; Yrbk Stf; Niagara U; Rn.

SCOTT, KAMMIE M; Churchville-Chili S H HS; Churchville, NY; (Y); 43/324; Church Yth Grp; GAA; Ski Clb; Lit Mag; JV Var Socr; Var L Trk; Im Vllybl; High Hon Roll; Hon Roll; NHS; Army ROTC Schlrshp 85; Bwlng Green ST U OH; Nrs.

SCOTT, LINDA; Caledonia Mumford Central Schl; Caledonia, NY; (Y); Sec French Clb; Math Tm; Hon Roll; NHS.

SCOTT, LISA R; Amsterdam HS; Fort Johnson, NY; (Y); 40/332; Political Wkr; Chorus; Church Choir; Capt Drm Mjr(t); Yrbk Bus Mgr; Yrbk Stf; Rep Stu Cncl; Hon Roll; Church Yth Grp; Cmnty Wkr; Amsterdam Evening Rcrdr Carrier Yr 83; Regents Schlrshp Wnnr 85; Russell Sage Coll; Biochem.

SCOTT, MARION; Northeastern Acad; Bronx, NY; (Y); Church Yth Grp; Cmnty Wkr; Drama Clb; Girl Scts; Church Choir; Var Bsktbl; Hon Roll; Howard U; Law.

SCOTT, MARY; Preston HS; Bronx, NY; (S); 2/28; Pep Clb; Varsity Clb; Nwsp Stf; Yrbk Stf; Sec Jr Cls; Bsktbl; Coach Actv; Vllybl; High Hon Roll; Hon Roll; Pace Bus Schl Schlrshp 84; Engl Awd 80; Baruch Coll; Bus.

SCOTT, MICHELE; Coxsackie-Athens HS; Coxsackie, NY; (Y); 9/140; Cmnty Wkr; Drama Clb; 4-H; Red Cross Aide; Spanish Clb; Yrbk Stf; Var L Cheerleading; Var L Score Keeper; Var L Timer; High Hon Roll; Fshn Merchndsng.

SCOTT, MICHELLE; Newark Valley Central HS; Newark Vly, NY; (Y); 34/120; Art Clb; Cmnty Wkr; Chorus; High Hon Roll; Hon Roll; CPA.

SCOTT, MIKE; Scotia Glenville HS; Scotia, NY; (Y); 25/250; Var Bsktbl; Var Tennis; Engr.

SCOTT, MONICA; St Catharine Acad; Bronx, NY; (Y); 71/205; Church Yth Grp; Drama Clb; Chorus; Church Choir; Off Jr Cls; Off Stu Cncl; Trk; Hon Roll; Svc Awd; Trck Awd; Englsh Awd; Soc Stds Awd; Mt Holyoke; Comm.

SCOTT, PATRICIA; Academy Of St Joseph; Hauppauge, NY; (Y); Hosp Aide; Library Aide; Math Tm; Teachers Aide; Yrbk Ed-Chief; NHS; Ntl Merit Ltr; Prtl Schlrshp Acad St Joseph 83; Chem Exclnce Awd 85; Math Exclnce Awd 83; Accntng.

SCOTT, PATRICIA; Roosevelt HS; Roosevelt, NY; (Y); Church Yth Grp; Exploring; Office Aide; Bowling; Sftbl; Martin Luther King Awd Of Acdmc 84; Nrs.

SCOTT, SHAUN T; John F Kennedy HS; West Seneca, NY; (Y); 25/149; Computer Clb; Drama Clb; Quiz Bowl; School Play; Stu Cncl; Var L Crs Cntry; Boy Scts; Library Aide; Stage Crew; Nwsp Stf; NYS Regents Schlrshp 84-85; Joy Mfg Schlrshp 84-85; Buffalo ST Coll; Theatre.

SCOTT, SHEILA D; Uniondale HS; Uniondale, NY; (Y); Church Yth Grp; Cmnty Wkr; Hosp Aide; Office Aide; Church Choir; Yrbk Phtg; Yrbk Stf; VP Frsh Cls; Pres Soph Cls; Cheerleading.

SCOTT III, THOMAS P; Oneill HS; Ft Montgomery, NY; (Y); 55/119; Drama Clb; School Play; JV Bsktbl; Capt Crs Cntry; JV Ftbl; Capt Trk; Hon Roll; All ST Trck Crss Cntry NY ST 84; Empire ST Games Champ 3000 M Steepl Chs 84; Cnty & Sec Champ 85; Niagara U; Bus.

SCOTT, TIMOTHY; Franklin Acad; Constable, NY; (S); 6/256; AFS; Drama Clb; 4-H; French Clb; Intnl Clb; Model UN; Ski Clb; Chorus; School Play; Swing Chorus; Pre Law.

SCOTT, TINA; Cornwall Central HS; Mountainville, NY; (Y); 26/198; Pres VP Church Yth Grp; Sec VP Library Aide; Capt Var Vllybl; Hon Roll; Lion Awd; NHS; Mntnvl Engin Co No 3 Awd 85; Cochs Awd 85; Stu Librn Yr Awd 84 & 85; Orange Cntry CC; Math.

SCOTT, WAYNE; North Babylon SR HS; N Babylon, NY; (Y); DECA; Badmtn; Bsbl; Bsktbl; Ftbl; Socr; Sftbl; Vllybl; Cit Awd; Superior Physcl Ftns Awd 84; Acad Aeronautics; Pilot.

SCOTT, WENDY A; Whitesboro SR HS; Whitesboro, NY; (Y); 6/325; Cmnty Wkr; Intnl Clb; Color Guard; Ed Yrbk Stf; Powder Puff Ftbl; Hon Roll; Jr NHS; NHS; Yrbk Sprt Ed; Rgnts Schlrshp 85; NY ST Senate Stu Polcy Forum 84; Vassar Coll; Pre-Law.

SCOTTI, ANTHONY; St Francis Preparatory Schl; Elmhurst, NY; (Y); Var Crs Cntry; Accntng.

SCOTTO, MARIA; St Francis Prep; Douglaston, NY; (S); 23/690; Drama Clb; JA; Service Clb; Yrbk Phtg; Yrbk Rptr; Im Gym; Im Powder Puff Ftbl; Im Vllybl; Hon Roll; NHS; Acad All-Amer; Acctng.

SCOTTO, MICHELE; St Joseph By The Sea HS; Staten Island, NY; (Y); Computer Clb; Color Guard; Mrchg Band; Nwsp Ed-Chief; Yrbk Stf; VP Jr Cls; Hon Roll.

SCOTTO DI MASO, MICHAEL; North Babylon SR HS; North Babylon, NY; (Y); Intnl Clb; Capt Trk; Hon Roll; NHS; Ftbl; Tennis; Jr NHS; Superior Phys Fit Awd 85; Sports Med.

SCOVILLE, JENNIFER; Geneseo Central Schl; Geneseo, NY; (Y); 10/86; Ski Clb; Spanish Clb; Rep Stu Cncl; JV Var Socr; JV Var Sftbl; High Hon Roll; Hon Roll; NHS; Spanish NHS; Travel Clb 82-85; Jrnlsm.

SCOVILLE, KELLI; Camden HS; Camden, NY; (Y); Red Cross Aide; Teachers Aide; Yrbk Phtg; Yrbk Stf; Pres Frsh Cls; Sec Soph Cls; Stu Cncl; Cheerleading; High Hon Roll; Hon Roll; Dntst.

SCRACE, JENNIFER; Alden Central HS; Alden, NY; (Y); Spanish Clb; Yrbk Stf; VP Frsh Cls; Sec Soph Cls; VP Sec Stu Cncl; JV Var Socr; Im Vllybl; Hon Roll; NHS; Acad Ltr; ST U NY Buffalo; Phrmcy.

SCRIMALE, RICHARD; Solvay HS; Solvay, NY; (Y); Church Yth Grp; Math Clb; Var Capt Bsktbl; Stat Ftbl; Var Ftbl; High Hon Roll; NHS; JA; Off Frsh Cls; Off Jr Cls; Chem 85; Bio 84; Soc Stds 84-85; Lemoyne; Acctng.

SCRIVANI, PETER VINCENT; Niagara Wheatfield SR HS; Niagara Falls, NY; (Y); 11/313; Pres Church Yth Grp; Pres Latin Clb; Math Clb; Pep Clb; Sec PAVAS; Nwsp Rptr; Var Swmmng; Trk; Hon Roll; NHS; Regents Scholarship 85; Cornell U; Veterinary Med.

SCUDERI, ANTHONY; New Dorp HS; Staten Island, NY; (Y); Drama Clb; Teachers Aide; School Play; Lit Mag; Wt Lftg; Prfct Atten Awd; Brown U Bk Awd 85.

SCUDERI, CARYN; Bishop Grimes HS; Fayetteville, NY; (Y); Ski Clb; Sec Frsh Cls; JV Socr; Hon Roll; NHS; Bus Mgmt.

SCUDERI, THOMAS; Sheepshead Bay HS; Brooklyn, NY; (Y); Office Aide; Science Clb; Teachers Aide; Varsity Clb; Capt Bowling; Capt Golf; Hon Roll; Arista 84-85; Lwyr.

SCUDIERE, ROBERT; Carmel HS; Carmel, NY; (Y); 46/370; Trs Frsh Cls; Bsbl; JV Ftbl; Wrstlng; High Hon Roll; Hon Roll; Schlrshp Bentley 84-85; Bentley; Bus.

SCULLION, KATHRYN; Jeffersonville-Youngsville Cen Schl; North Branch, NY; (S); 2/60; Pres Church Yth Grp; Chorus; Pres Frsh Cls; Rep Soph Cls; Pres Jr Cls; Var Trk; High Hon Roll; NHS; Sal; Drama Clb; CYO Cardinal Spellman Yth Awd 85; Catskill Art Soc 3rd Pl Awd-Sclptr 84; Bio.

SCULLY, CHRISTINE; Stella Maris HS; Rockaway Beach, NY; (Y); 36/208; Drama Clb; Library Aide; NFL; School Play; Stu Cncl; Bsktbl; Sftbl; Vllybl; Nrsng.

SCUTARI, CHARMAINE; Long Beach HS; Long Beach, NY; (S); 1/290; Gym; Hon Roll; NHS; Val; Bronze Mdls Abacus 81-83; Tufts U; Bio.

SCUTT, CHRISTOPHER; Troupsburg Central HS; Troupsburg, NY; (S); 2/12; Computer Clb; Trk; High Hon Roll; Prfct Atten Awd; Church Yth Grp; Trs Band; Concert Band; Mrchg Band; Score Keeper; Timer; Comp Presentation Awd Appple Comp Shw 84; Tribune Games Medalst Discus 83-84; Mst Imprvd Trk Tm Awd 83; Elec Engrng.

SCUTT, EILEEN; Bishop Ludden HS; Syracuse, NY; (S); NFL; High Hon Roll; NHS.

SEABURY, GORDON P; Sayville HS; Sayville, NY; (Y); 29/360; Boy Scts; VP Church Yth Grp; Key Clb; Mathletes; Capt Var Bsktbl; Var JV Ftbl; JV Trk; Cit Awd; High Hon Roll; NHS; Rgnts Schlrshp 85; Vrsty Awd Bsktbl & Ftbll 83 & 84; Hamilton Coll; Bio.

SEACOTT, JAMES ANTHONY; Mc Kee Vo Tech HS; Staten Island, NY; (Y); 20/238; Aud/Vis; Church Yth Grp; Office Aide; Teachers Aide; Lit Mag; JV Trk; Hon Roll; Prfct Atten Awd; Elctrncs.

SEAGER, PHILIP H; Wheatland Chili Central HS; Scottsville, NY; (Y); 5/70; Ski Clb; Chorus; School Play; Nwsp Stf; Yrbk Ed-Chief; Var Tennis; High Hon Roll; NHS; Messiah Coll; Journ.

SEALES JR, RICHARD; Waterford-Halfmoon HS; Waterford, NY; (Y); 2/86; Am Leg Boys St; Math Clb; Math Tm; Yrbk Stf; Var Trk; Hon Roll; NHS; NEDT Awd; VP SADD 84-85; Engrng.

SEALY, HENNESSEY A; Cathedral Preparatory Seminary HS; Brooklyn, NY; (Y); 2/16; Church Yth Grp; Cmnty Wkr; Library Aide; NFL; Speech Tm; Chorus; Nwsp Rptr; Nwsp Stf; Var L Bsktbl; Hon Roll; Minstry.

SEAMAN, JULIE; Garden City HS; Garden City, NY; (Y); 103/355; Cmnty Wkr; Drama Clb; Hon Roll; Engrng.

SEAMAN, KEVIN; Susan E Wagner HS; Staten Isld, NY; (Y); Band; Concert Band; Jazz Band; Orch; School Musical; Bsbl; Bsktbl; Gym; Hon Roll; Church Yth Grp; 3rd Hnrs; Acad Achv Awd For Hstry; Music.

SEAMAN, KEVIN; Thousand Islands HS; Clauton, NY; (Y); 13/78; Church Yth Grp; Ski Clb; Varsity Clb; Church Choir; JV Bsbl; Var L Socr; High Hon Roll; Hon Roll; Ntl Merit Ltr; NEDT Awd; Linda Rode Mem Schlrshp 85; NYS Regnts Schlrshp 85; Roberts Wesleyan Coll Acad Schlrshp 85; Roberts Wesleyan Coll; Comp Sci.

SEAMAN, MAUREEN E; Elmira Free Acad; Elmira, NY; (Y); 45/266; Cmnty Wkr; Pres Trs Key Clb; Ski Clb; Stu Cncl; Bsktbl; Crs Cntry; Sftbl; Hon Roll; NY ST Regents Schlrshp 85; St Bonaventure U; Busnss.

SEAMAN, MYRA J; Williamsville North HS; E Amherst, NY; (Y); 28/311; Church Yth Grp; Drm Mjr(t); Jazz Band; Mrchg Band; Lib Symp Band; JV Socr; Twrlr; Hon Roll; Hst Jr NHS; NHS; Rgnts Schlrshp 85; NY Coll Geneseo; Bio.

SEAMAN, STACEY; Beacon HS; Beacon, NY; (S); 12/213; Varsity Clb; Capt L Crs Cntry; L Var Trk; Hon Roll; Cross Cntry Awd 83; West Point; Arch.

SEAMAN, WILL; Mexico Acad; Oswego, NY; (Y); Girl Scts; Var Trk; Hon Roll.

SEAMANS, LAURIE; Pulaski JR SR HS; Pulaski, NY; (Y); Girl Scts; Band; Color Guard; Mrchg Band; Yrbk Stf; Var JV Cheerleading; Mohawk Valley CC; Graphc Arts.

SEARCHWELL, NADJA; The Mary Louis Acad; Cambria Heights, NY; (Y); Church Yth Grp; Girl Scts; Hosp Aide; Spanish Clb; Band; Orch; Law.

SEARLE, KANDI; Onondaga Central HS; Marietta, NY; (S); Church Yth Grp; Drama Clb; Spanish Clb; Chorus; School Play; Rep Stu Cncl; JV Var Bsktbl; JV Trk; High Hon Roll; Hon Roll; SU Nwhse Schl Comm; Brdct Jrnl.

SEARLE, KENNETH J; Tuxedo HS; Greenwood Lake, NY; (Y); Am Leg Boys St; Math Tm; Var Bsbl; Var Bsktbl; Var Capt Socr; Cit Awd; High Hon Roll; Jr NHS; NHS; RPI Medl 85.

SEARLES, BARBARA; Ballston Spa HS; Ballston Spa, NY; (Y); 62/253; Church Yth Grp; 4-H; Service Clb; Chorus; Church Choir; High Hon Roll; Hon Roll; Russell Sage Coll; Physcl Thrpy.

SEARLES, BRIDGETTE L; Odessa-Montour HS; Alpine, NY; (Y); 8/82; Trs Varsity Clb; Concert Band; Mrchg Band; JV Var Bsktbl; JV Var Vllybl; High Hon Roll; NHS; VFW Awd; Cntry III Ldrshp Awd 84-85; NY ST Regents Schlrshp 85; Odessa-Montour Tchrs Assoc Educ Schlrshp 85; St Bonaventure U; Pre-Law.

SEARLES, TINA; Adessa Montour Central Schl; Alpine, NY; (Y); 4-H; Chorus; Lit Mag; Prfct Atten Awd; 1st Pl NY ST Cnfrnc In Extmprns Spkng 85; Nrs.

SEARS, APRIL; New Lebanon HS; E Chatham, NY; (Y); Var Socr; Var Sftbl; Hon Roll; Stu Cncl Scholar 85; Lebanon Vly Wmns Clb Stu Fund 85; Norstar Bank Awd 85; SUNY; Htl Tech.

SEARS, LISA; Desales HS; Phelps, NY; (Y); FTA; Intnl Clb; Trs Spanish Clb; Band; Concert Band; Yrbk Phtg; Yrbk Stf; Hon Roll; 1st Frgn Lang Affair Cultural Exhibit 83; 1st Schl Art Show 83-84.

SEARS, SEAN M; Shenendehowa HS; Clifton Park, NY; (Y); Cmnty Wkr; Library Aide; High Hon Roll; ROTC; Bnkg.

SEARS, TOBI; Lake Placid Central Schl; Lake Placid, NY; (Y); Sec AFS; VP Sec Band; VP Sec Concert Band; VP Sec Jazz Band; Mrchg Band; School Musical; Var Cheerleading; Var Trk; Wrkd W/Tech Crews On Sets Etc In Smmr Stck Music Thtr 85; Math.

SEAY, DONAVAN; Walt Whitman HS; Huntington, NY; (Y); 131/540; Computer Clb; Spanish Clb; High Hon Roll; Hon Roll; Jr NHS; Spanish NHS; Aud/Vis; Hon Men Awd Eng 82-83; Numerous Spn Awds 84-85; Law.

SEBASTIANO, ANNA M; Half Hollow Hills East HS; Titusville, FL; (S); Art Clb; Church Yth Grp; Dance Clb; Drama Clb; Chorus; Church Choir; Nwsp Rptr; Nwsp Stf; Cheerleading; High Hon Roll; Med.

SEBESTA, JOHN R; St Anthonys HS; Smithtown, NY; (Y); Boy Scts; Drama Clb; Chorus; School Musical; School Play; Stage Crew; Nwsp Rptr; Crs Cntry; French Hon Soc; NHS.

SEBOLD, DWAYNE; Huntington HS; Huntington, NY; (Y); 191/433; Varsity Clb; Band; Concert Band; Jazz Band; Mrchg Band; Pep Band; Rep Frsh Cls; Var Bsbl; Im Bsktbl; Var Ftbl; NY ST Rgnts Schlrshp 85; All Sfflk Cnty Ftbl Team 85; Ithaca Coll; Bus Mngmnt.

SECCIA, PETER A; Xavier HS; Brooklyn, NY; (Y); Model UN; Political Wkr; Nwsp Sprt Ed; VP Frsh Cls; Sec Soph Cls; Rep Sr Cls; JV Bsbl; JV Bsktbl; Var L Ftbl; Rep Jr Cls; All Leag 1st Tm Ftbl 84; NY ST Regents Schlrshp 85; Polt Sci.

SEDA, YOLANDA; Adlai E Stevenson HS; Bronx, NY; (Y); Church Yth Grp; Teachers Aide; Band; Church Choir; Concert Band; Capt Vllybl; Prfct Atten Awd; Exec Secy.

SEDGELEY, KATHLEEN; Mt Markham HS; W Winfield, NY; (Y); 3/113; GAA; Ski Clb; Band; Yrbk Stf; VP Frsh Cls; VP Soph Cls; Rep Stu Cncl; Var Fld Hcky; NHS; MVP-JV Fld Hcky 82; All-Star Vrsty Fld Hcky 84; Intl Bus.

SEDNER, LAURIE J; John C Birdlebough HS; Pennellville, NY; (Y); 21/200; AFS; French Clb; Yrbk Stf; High Hon Roll; Regents Schlrshp 85; SUNY-OSWEGO; Bus Admin.

SEE, DONNA; Commack High School North; Hauppauge, NY; (Y); 20/440; French Clb; Teachers Aide; Band; Ed Yrbk Stf; Lit Mag; JV Sftbl; High Hon Roll; Jr NHS; NHS; Pres Schlr; Johns Hopkins U.

SEECHARRAN, ANNETTA; A E Stevenson HS; Bronx, NY; (Y); Hosp Aide; Library Aide; Office Aide; Teachers Aide; Stage Crew; Tennis; Hon Roll; Prfct Atten Awd; Cmnty Wkr; Dance Clb; Libry Svc Awd 85; Socl Stud Awd 83; Stg, Art Dsgn Aid 83; Psychlgst.

SEEGER, KATHRYN; Washingtonville HS; Newburgh, NY; (Y); Church Yth Grp; 4-H; Chorus.

SEEKINGS, CARRIE; Cassadaga Valley HS; Cassadaga, NY; (Y); Am Leg Aux Girls St; Math Clb; Spanish Clb; Varsity Clb; Chorus; Concert Band; Var Cheerleading; JV Sftbl; JV Var Vllybl; Law.

SEELEY, JODI L; East Aurora HS; E Aurora, NY; (Y); 19/187; AFS; Camp Fr Inc; Varsity Clb; Stage Crew; Socr; Hon Roll; NHS; Ntl Merit Ltr; NY ST Regents Schlrshp 85; PA ST U; Law.

SEELEY, JOY; Corning East HS; Corning, NY; (Y); Dance Clb; Gym; Hon Roll; Crmnl Justice.

SEELEY, MICHAEL; Edison Tech HS; Rochester, NY; (Y); Aud/Vis; Boy Scts; Stage Crew; Nwsp Stf; JV Wrstlng; High Hon Roll; Hon Roll; Graphic Arts.

SEEMAN, DON; Beach Channel HS; Howard Beach, NY; (Y); 2/484; Camera Clb; Pres Debate Tm; Model UN; Scholastic Bowl; Yrbk Ed-Chief; Ed Lit Mag; Stu Cncl; 4-H Awd; Sal; Voice Dem Awd; Ntl Camping & Hiking Assn Envrnmntl Schlrshp 85; Intl Schlrshp Camp Rising Sun 84; Harvard; Zoology.

SEEMAN, PAUL D; Commack H S South; Dix Hills, NY; (Y); 4/374; Hosp Aide; JV Tennis; High Hon Roll; NHS; Natl Sci Olympiad Physcs 84-85; Duke U; Surgn.

SEEPAUL, MANESHWAR; William Howard Taft HS; New York City, NY; (Y); Off Sr Cls; Bsbl; Bsktbl; Fld Hcky; Trk; Vllybl; Wt Lftg; Prfct Atten Awd; Cert Merit Frnch 84-85; Cert Outstndng Achvt Engl 83-84; Hunter Coll; Elec Engrng.

SEEPERSAD, DOOKRAN; Norman Thomas HS; Queens, NY; (S); 73/671; Var Bsbl; Var Hon Roll.

SEERY, JOHN; Holy Trinity HS; West Hempstead, NY; (Y); JV Crs Cntry; Var Trk; Wt Lftg; JV Wrstlng; Mrktng.

SEGAL, ALAN Z; Vestal HS; Vestal, NY; (Y); 2/450; Dance Clb; Debate Tm; Hosp Aide; Capt Mathletes; Political Wkr; VP Temple Yth Grp; Jazz Band; School Play; L Tennis; Bausch & Lomb Sci Awd; Telluride Assn Smmr Pgm 84; NY ST Hnr Rll, MAA Math Exm 82; Med.

SEGAL, DAVID; Blind Brook HS; Rye Brook, NY; (Y); Political Wkr; Band; Jazz Band; School Play; Stage Crew; Yrbk Phtg; Socr; Concert Band; CIBA-GEIGY HS Sci Awd 85; NY St Regents Schlrshp 85; NY Acad Sci Cert Merit 84-85; Cornell U; Bio.

SEGAR, KAREN; James E Sperry HS; Henrietta, NY; (Y); Thesps; Chorus; Jazz Band; Madrigals; School Musical; School Play; Stage Crew; French Hon Soc; NHS; French Clb; Rochester Hrvrd Clb Bk Awd 85.

SEGAR, TODD; Jordan-Elbridge HS; Jordan, NY; (Y); Church Yth Grp; Hon Roll; Data Proc.

SEGARRA, ROSEMARIE; St Michaels HS; Brooklyn, NY; (Y); 17/124; FTA; Girl Scts; Yrbk Phtg; Yrbk Stf; Sftbl; Cit Awd; Hon Roll; NHS; Sylvester Awd 85; Ntl Hspnsh Schlrshp 85; Regnts Schlrshp 85; Coll New Rochelle; Educ.

SEGUIN, KEVIN B; Ogdensburg Free Acad; Ogdensburg, NY; (Y); 26/190; Math Clb; Hon Roll; NY ST Regents Schlrshp 85; Clarkson Trustees Schlrshp 85; Clarkson U; Cvl Engrng.

SEGUIN, RICHARD; Northeastern Clinton Central Schl; Rouser Point, NY; (Y); Ski Clb; Hon Roll; Prfct Atten Awd; Meteorology.

SEHGAL, MONA K; Acad Of Mount St Ursula; Yonkers, NY; (Y); 21/168; Camera Clb; JA; Library Aide; Teachers Aide; Stu Cncl; High Hon Roll; NY ST Regents Diploma 85; NY U; Pre-Med.

SEID, MARC; Tottenville HS; Staten Island, NY; (Y); 64/897; Key Clb; JV Crs Cntry; JV Var Trk; High Hon Roll; Hon Roll; Jr NHS; VP NHS; St Schlr; SUNY Binghamton; Lwyr.

SEID, WAYNE; H Frank Carey HS; Franklin Sq, NY; (Y); 53/301; Band; Concert Band; Jazz Band; Stage Crew; Stage Band Cert Of Achvt 83-85; Med.

SEIDBERG, NEAL A; Fayetteville-Manlius HS; Jamesville, NY; (Y); Camera Clb; Computer Clb; Debate Tm; Concert Band; Jazz Band; Mrchg Band; Pep Band; Nwsp Phtg; Hon Roll; Band; NYS Regents Schlrshp; Bio, Chem & Earth Sci Olympiad Awds; Natl Schltc Art Awds In Photography; Bio.

SEIDE, DAVID; Lewiston-Porter HS; Lewiston, NY; (Y); 41/273; Key Clb; Sec Trs Temple Yth Grp; Golf; Socr; VP Capt Swmmng; High Hon Roll; NHS; Lamp Of Lrnng Awd 84 & 85; Jr King Of Hill-Bowlng Awd 85; Actn Lrnng Intrnshp Pgm 84-85; U Of IL-CHAMPAIGN; Arch.

SEIDEL, SUZANNE; Salmon River Central HS; Ft Covington, NY; (S); 5/115; Church Yth Grp; French Clb; Band; Chorus; Mrchg Band; Pep Band; Var Trk; NHS; Hon Roll; Lang.

SEIDER, DAVID F; Hudson HS; Hudson, NY; (Y); 19/156; AFS; Drama Clb; Model UN; Ski Clb; Chorus; School Musical; Var Capt Socr; Var Tennis; Hon Roll; Amer Fld Svc Amer Abrd Prog Gotland Sweden Smmr 84; Harvard Modl UN Delg 84; NY ST Regnts 85; Amer U; Forgn Crrspndnt.

SEIDMAN, CYNTHIA; Half Hollow Hills East HS; Dix Hills, NY; (S); FBLA; Service Clb; Trs Temple Yth Grp; Sec Varsity Clb; Nwsp Ed-Chief; Nwsp Stf; Yrbk Stf; Var Socr; Var Trk; Var Vllybl; Outstndg Achvt Ind Arts 83; All Lg Socr Selctn 83; All Cnty All Lg Socr Selctn 84.

SEIFERT, CHRISTINA L; Berne-Knox-Westerlo HS; East Berne, NY; (Y); 2/88; Nwsp Stf; Yrbk Stf; Lit Mag; High Hon Roll; Kiwanis Awd; NHS; Ntl Merit Ltr; NEDT Awd; Sal; NY ST Regnts Schlrshp 85; SUNY Albany; Acctg.

SEIFERTH, APRIL HOLLY; Mamaroneck HS; Larchmont, NY; (Y); FBLA; Pres Key Clb; Margaret Reich Mem Schlrshp 85; Amer Legion Larchmont Aux Schlrshp 85; Westchstr Cmnty Coll; Clnry Art.

SEIFFERT, REBECCA A; Our Lady Of Mercy HS; Penfield, NY; (Y); 9/200; Church Yth Grp; Sec VP Exploring; Church Choir; Yrbk Stf; Rep Stu Cncl; Hon Roll; NHS; NYS Rgnts Schlrshp; Great Books Clb; U Of MI.

SEILER, STEPHANIE H; John L Miller Great Neck N SR HS; Great Neck, NY; (Y); 15/271; Pep Clb; Temple Yth Grp; Band; Nwsp Rptr; Yrbk Phtg; JV Cheerleading; Mgr(s); Ntl Merit Schlrshp Semi Fnlst 84; Bio Resrch.

SEISCHAB, LISA; Cardinal Mooney HS; Hilton, NY; (Y); 57/325; Band; Orch; School Musical; Symp Band; Hon Roll; Dr Louis Sepctor Schlrshp 84-85; Schlrshp Bostonu 84; Musicl Encntrs Awd 84; Musical Perf.

SEITZ, DEBRA; Webster HS; Webster, NY; (Y); 9/562; Ski Clb; Yrbk Ed-Chief; Yrbk Stf; JETS Awd; NHS; Ntl Merit Ltr; Pres Spanish NHS; Rochester Engr Scty Schlrshp 85; Gleason Mem Schlrshp 85; U Of Rochester Cntnl Prz 85; U Of Rochester; Optcl Engr.

SEITZ, ERIKA; Indian River Central HS; Evans Mills, NY; (Y); AFS; French Clb; Chorus; Mrchg Band; School Musical; School Play; Score Keeper; Socr; Vllybl; Prfct Atten Awd; SUNY Oneonta; Math.

SEIWELL, LISA; Niagara Wheatfield SR HS; Niagara Falls, NY; (Y); Model UN; Pep Clb; PAVAS; Band; Chorus; School Musical; Var Cheerleading; Var L Tennis; Var L Trk; Prfct Atten Awd; Buffalo ST Coll; Elem Ed.

SEKELSKY, TERRI; West Seneca East SR HS; Buffalo, NY; (Y); Church Yth Grp; DECA; Ski Clb; Im Tennis; Hon Roll; Jr NHS; Acctg.

SELAND, ALICE; Eastchester HS; Scarsdale, NY; (Y); Trs Church Yth Grp; Key Clb; Latin Clb; Hon Roll; Bus Mgmt.

SELBST, MICHAEL E; Harrison HS; Purchase, NY; (Y); 17/200; AFS; Trs French Clb; Ed Lit Mag; Trk; French Hon Soc; NHS; Ntl Merit Ltr; Rotary Awd; Sec Stu Cncl; Cert Dhonneur Alliance Francasi 83-84; Cert Of Merit; Regents Scholarship 85; Cornell U; Business.

SELBY, ALEXANDER J; Hunter College HS; Brooklyn, NY; (Y); Drama Clb; French Clb; Math Tm; Thesps; Chorus; Orch; School Musical; School Play; Swing Chorus; Mu Alp Tht; Dartmouth Coll; Math.

SELCA, GEORGE; Christopher Columbus HS; Bronx, NY; (Y); 1/792; Math Tm; Orch; Hon Roll; Jr NHS; NHS; Arista Ldrs 83; Comptrollers Awd Sci, Mth & Comp 83; Merit Awds All Acad Subjects 83-85.

SELDIN, AMY; Croton-Harmon HS; Croton-On-Hudson, NY; (Y); 12/111; AFS; Sec Drama Clb; Key Clb; Varsity Clb; Band; Nwsp Rptr; Yrbk Sprt Ed; Yrbk Stf; Off Jr Cls; Sec Sr Cls; Mt Holyoke Coll; Psych.

SELDITCH, APRIL Y; Centereach HS; Centereach, NY; (Y); 41/475; Dance Clb; Pres FTA; Hosp Aide; Pres Intnl Clb; Office Aide; Teachers Aide; VP Temple Yth Grp; Variety Show; Sftbl; Hon Roll; Earth Sci Acadmc Awd & Danc Comptn Awd 82; Regnts Nrsng Schlrshp Awd 85; 1st Pl Smmr Sftbl Awd 84; Yeshiva U; Lib Arts.

SELEE, BRYAN; Camden SR HS; Camden, NY; (Y); 9/235; Church Yth Grp; Debate Tm; Jazz Band; VP Jr Cls; Rep Stu Cncl; JV Bsbl; JV Ftbl; High Hon Roll; NHS; Rotary Awd; Coast Guard Acad; Engr.

SELIGER, WILLAM M; Kings Park HS; Fort Sabonga, NY; (Y); 38/460; Civic Clb; Drama Clb; Leo Clb; Math Clb; Math Tm; PAVAS; Radio Clb; Science Clb; Service Clb; Ski Clb; Northwestern U; Mus.

SELIGMAN, JASON; United Nations International Schl; New York, NY; (Y); Debate Tm; Ski Clb; School Musical; Off Jr Cls; Crs Cntry; Mgr(s); Timer; Trk; Intl Balcaleariate Courses 84-86; Studies Pol Sci Columbia U 85; Oper Party Premtn Co 85; Bus.

SELKOW, MICHAEL; La Salle Acad; New York, NY; (S); Im Bsktbl; Hon Roll.

SELLARS, LA TANYA; Haupauge HS; Hauppauge, NY; (Y); Camera Clb; FBLA; Office Aide; Nwsp Phtg; Fld Hcky; Var Trk; Hon Roll; Prfct Atten Awd; Church Yth Grp; Cmnty Wkr; Suffolk CC; Bus.

SELLER, STUART; Williamsville North SR HS; Williamsville, NY; (Y); 25/315; VP Temple Yth Grp; Band; Socr; High Hon Roll; NHS; Regents Schlrshp 85; Prof Ski Inst 83; Clark U; Gov.

SELLERS, STACEY; Miller Place HS; Miller Place, NY; (Y); 15/200; Pres Sec Drama Clb; Thesps; Yrbk Stf; Var Badmtn; High Hon Roll; Hon Roll; NHS; Spnsh, Math & Bus Math Awds 84 & 85; C W Post; Spnsh.

SELMENSBERGER, JAMES; St Josephs HS; Cheektowaga, NY; (Y); 35/210; Varsity Clb; Bsktbl; Ftbl; High Hon Roll; Engrng.

SELTZER, GLENN; Monticello HS; Forestburgh, NY; (Y); Ski Clb; Comp Sci.

SELWOOD, DEBORAH; Herkimer HS; Herkimer, NY; (Y); Drama Clb; Girl Scts; School Musical; Yrbk Stf; Sec Sr Cls; Var Cheerleading; Var Tennis; High Hon Roll; Hon Roll; Voice Dem Awd; Biochem.

SEMAAN, INGRID E; Vestal Central SR HS; Binghamton, NY; (Y); 9/450; French Clb; Hosp Aide; Intnl Clb; Service Clb; Ski Clb; High Hon Roll; NHS; Mc Gill U; Econ.

SEMAR, CINDY; Oakfield-Alabama HS; Oakfield, NY; (Y); Genesee CC; Bus.

SEMC KEN, ADAM; Farmingdale HS; Farmingdale, NY; (Y); 87/650; Boy Scts; Lit Mag; NYSSMA Blue Ribbon Piano 83.

SEMEL, MICHAEL A; Hanppauge HS; Smithtown, NY; (Y); 4/513; Ski Clb; Yrbk Ed-Chief; Yrbk Stf; Ed Lit Mag; Var Tennis; Chrmn NHS; Ntl Merit Ltr; Voice Dem Awd; Worker With Emotnly Dist Chldrn 84-85; Jostens Golden Galeon Yrbk Awd 84-85; Amherst Coll; Psych.

SEMENTINO, MARY JEAN; Nazareth Acad; Rochester, NY; (Y); Red Cross Aide; Ski Clb; Sec Sr Cls; Var Capt Cheerleading; High Hon Roll; Hon Roll; NHS; Pre-Med.

SEMET, DENNIS J; Aviation HS; New York, NY; (Y); 11/508; Pep Clb; Service Clb; Ski Clb; VICA; Nwsp Stf; Lit Mag; New York State Regents Schlrshp 85; Challenge Schlrshp Awd 85; NY Inst Of Tech; Aerospace.

SEMIDEY, JUANITA; Manhatten General For Science & Math; New York, NY; (Y); Camera Clb; Hosp Aide; Teachers Aide; Color Guard; School Play; Yrbk Stf; Cheerleading; Sftbl; Vllybl; Hon Roll; Marshall Squad 82; Tutorial Pgm 83-85; Obstet.

SEMIDEY, PASCUAL; De Witt Clinton HS; Bronx, NY; (Y); Nwsp Rptr; Nwsp Stf; Hon Roll; NHS; Prfct Atten Awd; Achvmnt Awds In Englsh & Math 85; Bronze, Silver & Gold Mdls In The Schls Acad Olympics 83; Genetcs.

SEMINARIO, MARGARITA; Ossining HS; Ossining, NY; (Y); French Clb; Model UN; Radio Clb; Spanish Clb; School Play; Yrbk Phtg; Yrbk Rptr; JV Socr; Hon Roll; Hgh Hnrs Iona Coll Lang Cntst 85; Lawrence U; Jrnlsm.

SEMITECOLOS, DANIELLE; Northshore HS; Lattingtown, NY; (Y); FHA; Office Aide; VP Jr Cls; Swmmng; Wt Lftg; Top Ten Nation Swimmng 3 Events 81-84; ST Outstndng Awd 83; CW Post; Child Psychlgy.

SEMO, TODD; Shenendehowa HS; Ballston Lake, NY; (Y); 198/630; Camera Clb; Ski Clb; Varsity Clb; Band; Concert Band; Jazz Band; Yrbk Phtg; JV Var Lcrss; JV Socr; Hon Roll; Hnr Roll Awd 83; Photo.

SEMPLE, ELIZABETH; E J Wilson HS; Rochester, NY; (Y); Math Clb; Ski Clb; Spanish Clb; Stage Crew; Yrbk Stf; High Hon Roll; Hon Roll; NHS; Cont Sibleys Art Show 84-85.

SENALL, FRANCINE; Valley Stream Central HS; Valley Stream, NY; (Y); Drama Clb; Teachers Aide; Chorus; Orch; Yrbk Stf; Var L Crs Cntry; Var L Trk; Hon Roll; Mu Alp Tht; NHS; All Div Cross Cty 82-83; Ed.

SENECAL, MICHELLE; Spring Valley SR HS; Spring Valley, NY; (Y); Library Aide; Office Aide; Teachers Aide; Chorus; School Play; Bsktbl; Vllybl; Katherine Gibbs Schl; Secy.

SENFT, ANNE; Auburn HS; Auburn, NY; (Y); Drama Clb; FBLA; Chorus; School Musical; School Play; Nwsp Ed-Chief; Nwsp Rptr; Nwsp Stf; Lit Mag; High Hon Roll; Le Moyne; Bus.

SENG, JEFFREY M; Center Moriches HS; Center Moriches, NY; (Y); 4/87; Var Bsbl; Im Sftbl; Var Trk; Im Vllybl; Hon Roll; Sec NHS; Comp Sci.

SENGES, LARA R; Fairport HS; Fairport, NY; (Y); Ski Clb; School Play; Yrbk Stf; Rep Soph Cls; Rep Sr Cls; Stu Cncl; Var Fld Hcky; Hon Roll; VFW Awd; Rochester Panhellenic Schlrshp 85; NYS Regents Schlrshp 85; Allegheny Coll; Intl Bus.

SENGLE, GARY; Irondequoit HS; Rochester, NY; (Y); 68/393; Church Yth Grp; Exploring; Model UN; Var Ice Hcky; Var Lcrss; Hon Roll; 3rd Pl Ntl Latin Exam 85; Sctn V Hcky Chmp 85; Bus.

SENHOUSE, MICHAEL; E Meadow HS; E Meadow, NY; (S); 18/414; Aud/Vis; Computer Clb; Drama Clb; Key Clb; Math Tm; School Musical; Stage Crew; Nwsp Sprt Ed; Lit Mag; Var L Trk; Natl Hon Roll 84-85; Premed.

SENIOR, KELLY; Newfield HS; Selden, NY; (Y); Church Yth Grp; Hosp Aide; Chorus; Var Bsktbl; Var Tennis; Trk; Vllybl; All Lge Bsktbl.

SENKOWSKY, SONYA K; Spencer Van Eten HS; Van Etten, NY; (Y); 4/94; Am Leg Aux Girls St; Sec Aud/Vis; Pres Science Clb; Band; Concert Band; School Play; Nwsp Ed-Chief; High Hon Roll; Jr NHS; NHS; Eng,Bio,Soc Studies,Jrnlsm Awds; All Cty Band; MVP Band; Eng.

SENN, HEATHER; Frontier Central HS; Hamburg, NY; (Y); German Clb; Girl Scts; JA; Key Clb; Spanish Clb; School Musical; Stage Crew; Nwsp Rptr; Yrbk Stf; Swmmng; NY ST Regents Schlrshp 85; Academic All American Scholar; Buffalo ST; Journalism.

SENSENEY, MICHAEL B; Hamburg SR HS; Hamburg, NY; (Y); 1/400; CAP; Model UN; Capt Quiz Bowl; Nwsp Rptr; Lit Mag; Var Ftbl; Var Vllybl; NHS; Ntl Merit SF; German Clb; Harvard Alumni Awd Outstnding JR 84; Gen Carl A Spaatz Awd 84; Aero.

SENTER, GINA; Huntington HS; Huntington, NY; (Y); 141/400; DECA; FBLA; Band; Concert Band; Mrchg Band; Cheerleading; Fld Hcky; Gym; Hon Roll; Typing Awd 81-82; Farmingdle; Bus Adm.

SEO, SUSAN; Garden City SR HS; Garden City, NY; (Y); Church Yth Grp; Computer Clb; French Clb; Mathletes; Teachers Aide; Chorus; Jazz Band; Mrchg Band; Nwsp Ed-Chief; Yrbk Stf; Columbia U; Chem.

SEPE, DEBORAH ANNE; East Meadow HS; East Meadow, NY; (S); 39/414; Orch; School Musical; Jack Ostrofsky Instrum Awd 82; Mst Mscl 85; Prof Cellist.

SEPE, PETER; Romulus Central Schl; Romulus, NY; (S); 2/43; VP JA; Ski Clb; Yrbk Stf; Var L Ftbl; Var L Wrstlng; VP NHS; Ntl Merit Ltr; Sal; Im Bsktbl; NY Math Leag Awd 84; Top Linemn Awd 82; N Seneca Amblnc Awd 84; Ntl Sci.

SEPHTON, AMY; Westhampton Beach HS; Mastic, NY; (Y); 72/232; Computer Clb; Dance Clb; FBLA; Band; Concert Band; Mrchg Band; Pep Band; Yrbk Stf; Hon Roll; Acctg.

SERAYDARIAN, ROSINE; Cathedral HS; Jackson Hgt, NY; (Y); French Clb; Yrbk Stf; Hon Roll; Gold Medal Mth Outstndng Achvt 85; Cert Prfct Atten 83-85; Hnrb Mntn Bus 84; Manhattan Coll; Elec Engrng.

SERBALIK, JOYCE; Mechanicville HS; Mechanicville, NY; (S); 2/110; Computer Clb; French Clb; JV Cheerleading; High Hon Roll; NHS; Ntl Merit Ltr; Hghst Avg Engl 10; Saratogian/Skidmore Coll Hnr Dnnr; Law.

SERCHUK, BRUCE; John Jay HS; Katonah, NY; (Y); French Clb; Math Tm; Bsbl; Im Bsktbl; JV Trk; Prfct Atten Awd; Regnts Schlrshp NYS 85; Mech Drwg Awd 83; Lehigh U; Cvl Engrng.

SEREMET, JENNIFER; Bishop Ludden HS; Camillus, NY; (Y); 3/179; Exploring; Intnl Clb; JV Sftbl; Var JV Vllybl; Bausch & Lomb Sci Awd; High Hon Roll; NHS; U Of Rochester; Frgn Lang.

SERENO, JOSEPH; Bishop Cunningham HS; Oswego, NY; (Y); 2/27; Yrbk Stf; Sec Soph Cls; JV Bsbl; JV Var Bsktbl; JV Var Socr; Elks Awd; Hon Roll; NHS; Sal; Yvone Arnold Schlrshp 85; Elks Teenager Mnth 85; Math & Sci Schlrshp; Le Moyne; Bio.

SERGEANT, KRISTI; Our Lady Of Mercy HS; Sodus, NY; (Y); 58/200; Church Yth Grp; Exploring; Girl Scts; Chorus; Church Choir; Im Ftbl; Hon Roll; Genl Chem Awd 84; Mayfield C Dwyer Hlth Career Awd 85; Girl Scts Of Am Silv Awd; 1str Cls Girl Sct Awd; Utica Clg; Occptnl Thrpy.

SERGEL, JULIE A; Ellicottville Central HS; Ellicottville, NY; (Y); 2/50; Ski Clb; Varsity Clb; Rep Stu Cncl; JV Var Cheerleading; Mgr(s); High Hon Roll; Hon Roll; NHS; Fashion Inst Of Tech; Fshn Mrch.

SERINO, NANCY; Beacon HS; Beacon, NY; (S); 14/160; Rep Jr Cls; Rep Sr Cls; Hon Roll; Jr NHS; Sci Awd 84; Bio.

SEROWIK, MARGE; Union Endicott HS; Endicott, NY; (Y); 141/435; VP Church Yth Grp; Mrchg Band; Symp Band; Nwsp Stf; St Bonaventure U; Jrnlsm.

SERPE, THOMAS; Bellport HS; Bellport, NY; (Y); 4/306; Am Leg Boys St; Chess Clb; Quiz Bowl; Nwsp Rptr; JV Ftbl; JV Var Socr; Capt Var Tennis; High Hon Roll; NHS; Prfct Atten Awd; NY Regents Schlrshp 85; Bellport Mddl Schl PTO Schlrshp 85; Bellport H S Schlr Athlt Awd 85; Coll Of Agri & Life Sci; Genetc.

SERPI, JAMES W; Monsignor Farrell HS; Staten Island, NY; (Y); 63/293; Crs Cntry; Trk; High Hon Roll; Regents Schlrshp 85; Schlrshp To Manhattan Coll; Manhattan; Mech Engrng.

SERRA, LOUIS; Central Islip SR HS; Central Islip, NY; (Y); NY Inst Tech; Bus Adm.

SERRA, ROBERT F; Canisius HS; Elma, NY; (Y); Am Leg Boys St; Camera Clb; Ski Clb; Yrbk Phtg; Var Bsbl; Var Ftbl; Var Trk; Var Wrstlng; Engrng.

SERRANO, JUAN CARLOS; Archbishop Holloy HS; S Ozone Pk, NY; (Y); Art Clb; Spanish Clb; Yrbk Phtg; Im Bowling; 1st & 2nd Hnrs; Jrnlsm.

SERRANO, NEYDA; Cathedral HS; Ny, NY; (Y); 59/298; Church Yth Grp; Law.

SERRANO, RICHARD; Regis HS; Bronx, NY; (Y); Cmnty Wkr; Nwsp Ed-Chief; Nwsp Rptr; Capt Bowling; Teachers Aide; Church Choir; School Play; Stage Crew; Im Bsktbl; Im Fld Hcky; Four Yr Schlrshp To Regis HS 81-85; Ntl Hispnc Schlr Awds Pgm Semi Fnlst 85; Engrng.

SERRANO, ROBERT; A F Stevenson HS; Bronx, NY; (Y); Computer Clb; Debate Tm; Service Clb; Varsity Clb; Stage Crew; Nwsp Stf; Bsbl; Golf; Tennis; Wt Lftg; Acad Achvt 82-85; Attendnc Awds 84-85; Vrsty Awd 83-84; St Johns; Acctg.

SERRATORE, ELIZABETH; Nyack SR HS; Vly Cottage, NY; (Y); Sec Frsh Cls; Sec Soph Cls; Sec Pres Stu Cncl; Var Capt Fld Hcky; JV Sftbl; Cit Awd; Spanish NHS; Spanish Clb; Natl Cncl Jewsh Womn Comm Serv Awd 85; A W Rittershausen Schlrshp 85; SUNY Oneonta; Publ Rel.

SERRI, ELENA; Sachem North HS; Lake Ronkonkoma, NY; (Y); 574/1383; French Clb; 4-H; Office Aide; OEA; Teachers Aide; Hon Roll; NY Inst Of Tech; Crmnl Jstc.

SERRITELLA, MIA; Fiarport HS; Fairport, NY; (Y); Sec Pep Clb; Lit Mag; Rep Stu Cncl; High Hon Roll; Sec NHS; Ntl Latin Ex Magna Cum Laude 85; Rep Cncl Arts 84; Law.

SERRO, JAMES; H F Carey HS; Franklin Sq, NY; (Y); 4/225; Church Yth Grp; Pres Soph Cls; High Hon Roll; Jr NHS; NHS; Spanish NHS; Voice Dem Awd; Tlntd & Gftd Prog 85; Hugh O Brien Ldrshp Awd 84; Bus.

SERVEY, MELISSA; Wellsville HS; Wellsville, NY; (Y); 4/119; Church Yth Grp; Intnl Clb; Key Clb; Concert Band; Mrchg Band; Orch; Bsktbl; High Hon Roll; NHS; Ntl Merit Ltr; Pre-Med.

SERVISS, TRACY; Webster HS; Penfield, NY; (Y); 93/567; French Clb; Ski Clb; Teachers Aide; Jazz Band; Var Capt Swmmng; French Hon Soc; High Hon Roll; Hon Roll; Jr NHS; NHS; Distngshd Schl Citzn Awd Stag Bnd Fr II,Fr III 82-84; MI ST U; Zoolgy.

SESHADRI, SVETHA; Hicksville HS; Hicksville, NY; (Y); French Clb; Hosp Aide; Crs Cntry; Tennis; Trk; French Hon Soc; High Hon Roll; Jr NHS; NHS; All Div X-Cntry Rnnr 84.

SESSA, STACEY; St Peters H S For Girls; Staten Isl, NY; (Y); Church Yth Grp; Trs Soph Cls; Pres Jr Cls; JV Bsktbl; JV Sftbl; St Johns U; Crmnl Justc.

SESSIONS, RAMONA; School Without Walls HS; Rochester, NY; (Y); Art Clb; Cmnty Wkr; Exploring; Model UN; Political Wkr; Chorus; Yrbk Stf; Stu Cncl; Badmtn; Tennis; Travl.

SETARO, ANGELO; Bishop CC HS; Brooklyn, NY; (Y); Intnl Clb; Hon Roll; Cert Excllnce Italian Studs 82-83; Brooklyn Coll; Anthroplgy.

SETHI, GAIL; The Mary Louis Acad; Flushing, NY; (Y); Computer Clb; Drama Clb; Office Aide; Spanish Clb; Teachers Aide; Temple Yth Grp; Nwsp Stf; Off Frsh Cls; Prfct Atten Awd; Merit Awd 83; Guidance Awd 85; Awd Wrkng Sec Law Clb 85; Harvard; Law.

SETIK, JULIE; Williamsville East HS; E Amhurst, NY; (Y); Church Yth Grp; Pep Clb; Orch; Hlth.

SEUL, MICHAEL; St Anthonys HS; Centereach, NY; (Y); Computer Clb; Library Aide; Service Clb; Teachers Aide; Nwsp Sprt Ed; Nwsp Stf; Hon Roll; NHS; Yth Rep Parish Cncl 85-86; Usher Assumptn Chrch 82; Phrmcy.

SEVERN, JODIE; Liverpool HS; Liverpool, NY; (S); 88/792; Exploring; JA; Office Aide; Rep Jr Cls; Rep Sr Cls; Rep Stu Cncl; JV Sftbl; Var Tennis; JV Var Vllybl; Hon Roll; Syracuse U; Acctng.

SEWARD, AMY ELIZABETH; Corning Painted Post West HS; Corning, NY; (Y); 9/254; Church Yth Grp; Ski Clb; School Musical; Yrbk Stf; Off Frsh Cls; Off Soph Cls; Off Jr Cls; Off Sr Cls; Off Stu Cncl; Var Socr; Bnfcl Hodson Schlrshp 85; Hood Coll; Psychlgy.

SEWARD, SANDRA J; Byron-Bergen Central HS; Byron, NY; (Y); Church Yth Grp; Cmnty Wkr; Chorus; Swing Chorus; Hon Roll; Jr NHS; Prfct Atten Awd; Mrt Tuition Awd-Genesee CC 85; Regents Schlrshp Awd 85; Genesee CC.

SEWELL, ANTOINETTE; Catherine Mc Auley HS; Brooklyn, NY; (Y); 9/68; Church Yth Grp; Chorus; Stage Crew; Nwsp Stf; JV Sftbl; Hon Roll; NHS; Ldrshp Clb.

SEWKUMAR, AMANDA; St Catharine Acad; Bronx, NY; (Y); 40/205; Dance Clb; JA; Library Aide; Office Aide; School Musical; School Play; Rep Jr Cls; Stu Cncl; Hon Roll; Math Commdtn Reprt; Lehman Coll; Accntnt.

SEXTON, PATRICIA; Bishop Ludden HS; Syracuse, NY; (S); Cmnty Wkr; JV Cheerleading; High Hon Roll; NHS; Geo Awd Hghst Aver 83; Albany ST; Acctng.

SEXTON, VIRGINIA; Hempstead HS; Hempstead, NY; (S); 36/333; Band; Chorus; Church Choir; Concert Band; Mrchg Band; Orch; Rep Stu Cncl; High Hon Roll; Hon Roll; Psychology.

SEYCHEW, KRISTIN K; Holy Angels Acad; Kenmore, NY; (S); 4/36; Math Tm; Quiz Bowl; Chorus; Nwsp Stf; Yrbk Stf; Rep Soph Cls; Stu Cncl; JV Bsktbl; High Hon Roll; NHS; Hugh O Brien Ldrshp Fndtn Awd 84; Georgetown U; Med.

SEYFERT, JULIE; Williamsville North HS; Williamsvl, NY; (S); 127/315; AFS; Sec DECA; Drama Clb; Ski Clb; Chorus; School Musical; Stu Cncl; Var Cheerleading; JV Socr; Sec Church Yth Grp; 1st Pl Wnr DECA Regnls Appar1 & Access 84 & 85; Outstndg Cmpr Awd DECNY Ldrshp Trnng Camp 84; NYU; Brdcstg.

SEYFRIED, ELIZABETH; West Seneca East SR HS; Cheektowaga, NY; (Y); 106/365; Hon Roll; Ntl Merit Ltr; Prfct Atten Awd; Church Yth Grp; French Clb; Peer Cnslng Awd 85; Actn Learng Intershp Pgm Awd 85; Alfred ST; Animal Sci.

SEYMOUR, KAREN M; James I O Neil HS; Garrison, NY; (Y); 3/119; French Clb; Nwsp Ed-Chief; Nwsp Rptr; Yrbk Stf; Ed Lit Mag; VP Jr Cls; High Hon Roll; VP NHS; Englsh Acad Awd; Earth Sci Acad Awd; Bio Acad Awd; Geo Acad Awd; SUNY At Binghamton; Biolgcl Sc.

SFILIGOI, DANIEL; St John The Baptist D HS; Lindenhurst, NY; (Y); 3/546; Chess Clb; Church Yth Grp; Exploring; Math Clb; Math Tm; Stage Crew; Nwsp Phtg; High Hon Roll; Mu Alp Tht; NHS.

SGAMBATI, CAROLYN; Mechanicville HS; Mechanicville, NY; (S); 18/160; Computer Clb; GAA; Spanish Clb; Varsity Clb; VP Soph Cls; Bsktbl; Socr; Sftbl; Hon Roll; Advrtsng.

SGARLATA, DANIELLE; Clarkstown High School South; W Nyack, NY; (Y); Church Yth Grp; Cmnty Wkr; GAA; Service Clb; Rep Stu Cncl; Var Capt Bsktbl; Var Fld Hcky; JV Var Sftbl; Hon Roll; NHS; All Cnty Field Hockey 84; Pediat.

SGOBBO, ANGELO; Harrison HS; E White Plains, NY; (Y); 8/201; Math Tm; JV Bsbl; NHS; Italian Nat Hnr Soc 84-85; Italian Club VP 84-85; Cooper Union; Civil Engrng.

SGRECCI, JILL; Watkins Glen HS; Watkins Glen, NY; (S); 16/146; 4-H; Nwsp Stf; Sftbl; High Hon Roll; Hon Roll; NHS; Corning CC; Lib Arts.

SGRO, MARIA; Churchville-Chili SR HS; Rochester, NY; (Y); Ed Yrbk Stf; Trs Sr Cls; Bowling; Hon Roll; U Of Buffalo.

SGROI, PATRICK; East SR HS; West Seneca, NY; (S); VP DECA; VP Varsity Clb; VP Jr Cls; Var Capt Bsktbl; Var Capt Ftbl; Var Trk; Hon Roll; Jr NHS; Bus Mgmt.

SGUERA, MARIA; Earl L Vandermeulen HS; Mt Sinai, NY; (Y); 33/260; Art Clb; Camera Clb; Exploring; Girl Scts; Spanish Clb; Yrbk Stf; Rep Frsh Cls; Rep Soph Cls; Mgr(s); Btty Crckr Awd; Johnson & Wales; Fashn Mdse.

SHABUNIA, CAROLYN; New Hyde Park Memorial HS; New Hyde Park, NY; (S); 90/269; DECA; Varsity Clb; Band; Capt Bsktbl; Capt Fld Hcky; Sftbl; Nassau Cnty DECA Fnlst Rstrnt Mrktng 85; Field Hockey All-Cnty 84; Bsktbl All Div 83-84; Accntnt.

SHACKELFORD, MATT; Hilton Central HS; Hilton, NY; (Y); JV Ftbl; Wrstlng; Rado Cmmnctn.

SHACKELTON, GEOFFREY S; Walton Central Schl; Walton, NY; (Y); Am Leg Boys St; VP Key Clb; Varsity Clb; Band; Jazz Band; VP Pres Stu Cncl; JV Var Bsbl; JV Var Bsktbl; JV Var Ftbl; Computer Clb; All-Lg Rnng Back 84-85; Cortland; Phys Ed.

SHAENER, MARC; Nanuet HS; Nanuet, NY; (Y); DECA; FBLA; Political Wkr; Nwsp Rptr; Yrbk Sprt Ed; Var Bsktbl; JV Ftbl; Im Wt Lftg; High Hon Roll; NHS; Ntl Hnr Soc 85; Ntl Merit Schlrshp 85; Regents Schlrshp 86; Med.

SHAFER, JODY; Royalton-Hartland Central HS; Middleport, NY; (Y); Art Clb; FFA; Hosp Aide; Teachers Aide; Chorus; Sftbl; Vllybl; Hon Roll; Prfct Atten Awd; Art Stu Mnth; Fash Dsgnr.

SHAFER, MICHAEL; Schoharie Ctr; West Berne, NY; (S); 6/84; Computer Clb; Ski Clb; Band; Concert Band; Hon Roll; Nysma Tuba Solo 84; Math Awd 3rd Pl 83; Brass Choir 80-82; Comp Sci.

SHAFER, NANCY; West Irondequoit HS; Rochester, NY; (Y); 6/393; Orch; Rep Frsh Cls; Rep Soph Cls; Rep Sr Cls; Rep Stu Cncl; Var Swmmng; High Hon Roll; Hon Roll; NHS; Hrvrd Bk Awd 85; Pre Med.

SHAFFER, CHRISTINE; Charles H Roth HS; W Henrietta, NY; (Y); 151/210; Girl Scts; Hon Roll; Prfct Atten Awd; Outstdng Voctnl Stu In Nrsng 85; RSLPN; Nrsng.

SHAFFER, MARLA; Southside HS; South Hempstead, NY; (Y); 91/291; Girl Scts; Hosp Aide; Key Clb; Temple Yth Grp; Band; Concert Band; Jazz Band; Pep Band; School Musical; Hon Roll; Music.

SHAFFER, SCOTT; Union-Endicott HS; Endicott, NY; (Y); Boys Clb Am; Church Yth Grp; Varsity Clb; Bsbl; Ftbl; Engr.

SHAGOURY, JANINE; Spring Valley SR HS; Spring Valley, NY; (Y); Church Yth Grp; Var Socr; French Hon Soc; Hon Roll; Frnch & Social Stds Awd 83.

SHAH, DIPTI; Hillcrest HS; Corona, NY; (Y); 22/793; Hosp Aide; Office Aide; Ski Clb; Teachers Aide; Hon Roll; NHS; Regnts Schlrshp 85; Sophie Davis Schl; Med.

SHAH, FALGUNI; Dover JR SR HS; Dover Plains, NY; (S); Drama Clb; Girl Scts; Y-Teens; School Play; Variety Show; Pres Frsh Cls; Pres Soph Cls; Pres Jr Cls; High Hon Roll; RPI New York; Elctrcl Engrng.

SHAH, MARK; Mynderse Acad; Seneca Falls, NY; (S); Boy Scts; Band; Boy Scts; Jazz Band; Mrchg Band; School Musical; Var L Crs Cntry; Var L Trk; High Hon Roll; Aviation.

SHAH, MONICA RAVINDRA; Oswego HS; Oswego, NY; (Y); 2/371; Am Leg Aux Girls St; Cmnty Wkr; Latin Clb; Mrchg Band; Variety Show; Nwsp Rptr; Trs Frsh Cls; VP Soph Cls; Rep Stu Cncl; Cheerleading; Maxime Cm Laud Slvr Mdls Nat Latn Exm 82-85; Brown U; Med.

SHAH, NEELESH R; Oswego HS; Oswego, NY; (Y); Am Leg Boys St; Trs Latin Clb; Mrchg Band; Symp Band; Stu Cncl; Var L Crs Cntry; Var Capt Swmmng; Var L Tennis; Pres NHS; NEDT Awd; :Bio Engr.

SHAH, VAISHALI; St Johns Prep; Woodside, NY; (Y); Camera Clb; Intnl Clb; Science Clb; Temple Yth Grp; VP Frsh Cls; Rep Stu Cncl; Wt Lftg; Religious & Cultural Dances Of India Awd 83; Bio.

SHALLO, SCOTT; Hudson HS; Hudson, NY; (Y); Church Yth Grp; Intnl Clb; Model UN; Band; Mrchg Band; Yrbk Stf; Var Tennis; High Hon Roll; Hon Roll; Accntng.

SHAMLIAN, HARRY R; Shaker HS; Latham, NY; (Y); Church Yth Grp; Key Clb; Leo Clb; Jr Cls; Sr Cls; JV Socr; Regnts Coll Schlrshp 85; Rochester Inst Of Tech; Accntng.

SHAMPANIER, JUDY; Commack H S North; Commack, NY; (Y); Office Aide; Temple Yth Grp; Yrbk Ed-Chief; Off Jr Cls; Var Badmtn; French Hon Soc; NHS; Intnl Clb; Chorus; Yrbk Stf; Rsrch Stonybrook U 85; Hnr Outstndng Frnch Stu 83; Boces Gifted Summr Pgm Scholar 84-85.

SHAMPINE, KIMBERLY; George W Fowler HS; Syracuse, NY; (Y); Exploring; Library Aide; Pep Clb; Band; Rep Sec Stu Cncl; JV Var Tennis; High Hon Roll; NHS; Le Moyne Coll HEPP Pgm Bio 82; Rotary Intl Exch Stu 84-85; Bus Admin.

SHAMPNOIS, KATIE; Alexander Hamilton HS; Elmsford, NY; (S); 5/52; French Clb; Key Clb; Office Aide; Sr Cls; Capt Cheerleading; Capt Sftbl; Stat Vllybl; High Hon Roll; Jr NHS; NHS; Schlr Athl Awd Sftbl 84; Schlr Athl Awd Sftbl 83; Cchs Awd Chrldng 84; Accntng.

SHAMROTH, JANET; New Field HS; Selden, NY; (S); 11/570; Drama Clb; Math Tm; Service Clb; Chorus; Nwsp Rptr; Yrbk Ed-Chief; Rep Stu Cncl; Sec NHS; FBLA; School Musical; NY St Regts Schlrshp Wnnr 85; Temple Choir 83-85; Acctng.

SHANAHAN, MAUREEN J; Bronx HS Of Science; Bronx, NY; (Y); Church Yth Grp; Hosp Aide; Pres Key Clb; Library Aide; Chorus; JV Trk; Soc Sci.

SHANAHAN, PATRICK; Sachem HS; Lake Grove, NY; (Y); 350/1550; Computer Clb; Drama Clb; Ski Clb; Varsity Clb; Chorus; Madrigals; School Musical; School Play; VP Frsh Cls; JV Var Trk; NYSMA Gr O Medl Solo Comp 84; Notre Dame; Engrng.

SHANAHAN, TIMOTHY; East Meadow HS; E Meadow, NY; (Y); 22/414; Pres Key Clb; Band; Rep Sr Cls; Var Lcrss; Capt Wrstlng; VP NHS; Boy Scts; Mrchg Band; School Play; US Marine Corp ROTC Schlrshp 85; Michael J Kostynick & John Barbou Mem Schlrshp 85; U Of Notre Dame; Acctng.

SHAND, JAMES; G Ray Bodley HS; Fulton, NY; (Y); Exploring; German Clb; Yrbk Stf; Canton Ag & Tech Coll; Envr Sci.

SHAND, NATALIE A; Curtis HS; Staten Island, NY; (Y); 44/328; Key Clb; Chorus; Jazz Band; Mrchg Band; School Musical; School Play; Stage Crew; Variety Show; Cheerleading; Jr NHS; Brooklyn Coll; Music.

SHANE, LISA M; South Side HS; Rockville Ctr, NY; (Y); 2/284; Pres Computer Clb; Pres Mathletes; Trs Science Clb; School Musical; Yrbk Stf; NHS; Sal; Debate Tm; French Clb; Pres Math Tm; Soc-Women In Engr 1st Pl 85; Assoc-Phys Teachers Awd 85; NY ST Supervisors Awd-Bio 83; MIT; Chem.

SHANLEY, MARY; Lockport SR HS; Lockport, NY; (Y); 23/474; Aud/Vis; Latin Clb; Varsity Clb; Yrbk Stf; Rep Stu Cncl; L Var Cheerleading; L Var Swmmng; L Var Trk; Hon Roll; Jr NHS.

SHANNON, SUSAN A; Whitesboro SR HS; Whitesboro, NY; (Y); 10/325; Exploring; VP GAA; VP Acpl Chr; Band; School Musical; Yrbk Rptr; Var Capt Powder Puff Ftbl; Var Capt Tennis; Var Trk; NHS; NY Regents Schlrshp 85; Political Sci.

SHANTIE, KERRY; Franklin Acad; Malone, NY; (S); 11/255; AFS; Sec Church Yth Grp; Pres VP 4-H; Model UN; School Play; 4-H Awd; Hon Roll; Sec NHS; Mdl NYSSMA Solo Voice 83; Mdl NYSSMA Madrgl 84; Houghton Coll; Psych.

SHAPIRO, ANDREW J; Spring Valley SR HS; Spring Valley, NY; (Y); 14/435; Scholastic Bowl; Jazz Band; Orch; Nwsp Stf; Yrbk Rptr; High Hon Roll; Mu Alp Tht; NHS; Ntl Merit Ltr; Schl Century III Ldrshp Awd 84-85; U Of PA; Intl Rel.

SHAPIRO, BARRY; Valley Stream North HS; Franklin Sq, NY; (Y); Debate Tm; Ski Clb; Band; Mrchg Band; Symp Band; Bsbl; Bsktbl; Golf; Hon Roll; NHS; SUNY Buffalo; Comp Sci.

SHAPIRO, KAREN; Lawrence HS; Cedarhurst, NY; (S); 29/381; AFS; Cmnty Wkr; Concert Band; Mrchg Band; Orch; School Musical; Stage Crew; High Hon Roll; Jr NHS; NHS; Co Advsr Mentor Pgm Hnr Scty 84-85; Pre Med.

SHAPIRO, MARCUS; Hauppauge HS; Hauppauge, NY; (Y); Temple Yth Grp; Sec Sr Cls; Off Stu Cncl; Mgr Bsktbl; Var Socr; Hon Roll; Hnr Rl Cert; Med.

SHAPIRO, MICHAEL; Monticello HS; Kauneonga Lake, NY; (Y); Boy Scts; Math Tm; Temple Yth Grp; School Musical; Stage Crew; Var L Bsbl; JV L Wrstlng; High Hon Roll; Jr NHS; NHS; Regent Schlrshp; Clarkson; Engrng.

SHAPIRO, SIDRA LEE; Pittsford Mendon HS; Pittsford, NY; (Y); French Clb; Pep Clb; Ski Clb; Temple Yth Grp; Lit Mag; Var Fld Hcky; High Hon Roll; NHS; Ntl Merit Ltr; Randolph-Macon Wmns Coll Dist Schlr Awd 85; Regents Schlrshp 85; Randolph-Macon Wmns Coll; Bio.

SHAPLEY, GENIA; Oneonta HS; Oneonta, NY; (Y); 26/150; Key Clb.

SHARICK, LORI A; Pembroke HS; Corfu, NY; (Y); 3/125; Trs Ski Clb; Varsity Clb; Rep Frsh Cls; Rep Stu Cncl; Stat Bsktbl; VP Socr; VP Capt Trk; Hon Roll; NHS; NY Regnts Schlrshp 85; Geneseo ST Coll.

SHARIF, KHADIJAH; John Adams HS; S Ozone Pk, NY; (Y); Library Aide; Office Aide; Service Clb; Chorus; Capt Crs Cntry; Capt Trk; High Hon Roll; Hon Roll; Prfct Atten Awd; Cornell U; Neurosci.

SHARMA, RAVI; Freeport HS; Freeport, NY; (Y); Science Clb; Var Trk; Var Wrstlng; Hofstra; Bus.

SHARP, CAROLYN; West Genesee HS; Syracuse, NY; (Y); 51/450; Hosp Aide; Library Aide; Office Aide; Orch; School Musical; High Hon Roll; Hon Roll; Jr NHS; NHS; Outstndg Undrclssmn String Awd 84-85; All-ST Conf Strng Orch Awd 84; Syrcs Symph Orch Cert 84-85.

SHARP, KAREN; Immaculata Acad; W Seneca, NY; (Y); French Clb; Nwsp Rptr; Yrbk Phtg; Rep Soph Cls; VP Jr Cls; VP Sr Cls; Rep Stu Cncl; Hon Roll; Comp Sci.

SHARP, WILLIAM; Saranac Central HS; Morrisonville, NY; (S); 17/106; Cmnty Wkr; Model UN; Band; Concert Band; Jazz Band; Pep Band; Var Bsbl; Bsktbl; High Hon Roll; Hon Roll; CA ST U; Comp Engr.

SHARPE, TERRILYN; Liverpool HS; Liverpool, NY; (S); 52/792; Cmnty Wkr; Exploring; Hosp Aide; Ski Clb; Off Soph Cls; Off Sr Cls; Stu Cncl; High Hon Roll; Hon Roll; Jr NHS; Biomed Engrng.

SHARROTT, JULIE; Sackets Harbor Central Schl; Sackets Harbor, NY; (Y); 1/25; Pres Church Yth Grp; JA; Variety Show; Yrbk Stf; VP Jr Cls; Rep Stu Cncl; Hon Roll; PTSF Awd Hghst Ave 85; 3 Schlrshp Awds 82-85; Mssns Mexico; Trvl.

SHARROW, MARGARET; Holy Angels Acad; Buffalo, NY; (S); 1/38; Art Clb; School Musical; Ed Nwsp Phtg; Rptr Yrbk Phtg; Ed Yrbk Stf; High Hon Roll; VP NHS; Prfct Atten Awd; Capt Its Academic Tm 84-85; 12 Yrs Classicl Ballet Study; Euchosistic Ministr Holy Angels Acad 84-86; Librl Arts.

SHATRAU, TRACY; G Ray Bodley HS; Oswego, NY; (S); Drama Clb; Chorus; Church Choir; Madrigals; Orch; School Musical; School Play; High Hon Roll; Hon Roll; Music.

SHATTUCK, KENNETH; Granville Central HS; Hampton, NY; (Y); 28/123; Pres AFS; French Clb; Mathletes; Red Cross Aide; Science Clb; Nwsp Stf; Rotary Awd; Grastorfs Pres Grphcs Awd 85; Jrnlsm Pin 84; Cazenovia Coll; Arch.

SHATZ, STEPHANIE M; St John The Baptist HS; Bayshore, NY; (Y); 23/610; Exploring; Girl Scts; MMM; Chorus; Nwsp Rptr; Sec Jr Cls; Cheerleading; High Hon Roll; NHS; Spanish NHS.

SHAUGHNESSY, DANNY; Caledonia-Mumford HS; Caledonia, NY; (Y); Church Yth Grp; Ski Clb; Nwsp Phtg; Yrbk Stf; Off Soph Cls; Bsbl; Bowling; Ftbl; Socr; Ltrs Ftbl Bsbl 80-82; Most Imprvd Plyr Awd Bsbl 82; Elec.

SHAUGHNESSY, JAMES; St Francis Prep; Holliswood, NY; (Y); 338/690; Im Ftbl; Im Socr; Im Sftbl; Im Vllybl; Hon Roll; Rgnts Schlrshp 85; Hnr Schlrshp NYIT 85; NY Instit Of Tech; Arch.

SHAUGHNESSY, JOHN C; Pine Bush Central HS; Pine Bush, NY; (Y); 20/300; Church Yth Grp; DECA; 4-H; Rep Frsh Cls; Rep Soph Cls; VP Jr Cls; Var Bsbl; Var Bsktbl; Capt Var Ftbl; Jr NHS; AFROTC 4 Yr Schlrshp 85; Var Ftbl Ldrshp Awd 85; Var Bsktbl Coaches Awd 85; Accntng.

SHAUGHNESSY, JOHN L; Milton Central HS; Hilton, NY; (Y); 98/276; Wrstlng; High Hon Roll; Hon Roll; Hilbert Clg; Libl Arts.

SHAUGHNESSY, YVONNE; Cicero-N Syracuse HS; N Syracuse, NY; (S); 95/711; Exploring; Office Aide; Band; Concert Band; Mrchg Band; Hon Roll; NHS; Prfct Atten Awd; Bryant & Stratton; Comp Pgmg.

SHAVER, CHRISTOPHER; St Marys Acad; Fort Edward, NY; (S); 3/41; ROTC; Yrbk Stf; JV Capt Bsbl; Im Bsktbl; Bausch & Lomb Sci Awd; High Hon Roll; French Clb; Key Clb; Color Guard; ROTC Awds 82-85; Clarkson U; Engr.

SHAVER, RENEE; Delaware Acad; Delhi, NY; (Y); Church Yth Grp; Spanish Clb; Band; Chorus; Church Choir; Concert Band; Jazz Band; Mrchg Band; Stage Crew; Hartwick Coll; Nrs.

SHAVER, TIMOTHY P; Schuylerville Central HS; Schuylerville, NY; (Y); 9/106; Am Leg Boys St; Math Tm; Pres Sr Cls; Rep Stu Cncl; Capt Bsbl; Capt Ftbl; DAR Awd; High Hon Roll; Jr NHS; NHS; Glens Falls Fndtn Awd SR Sgnifnct Schl Svc 85; Marist Coll; Bus Adm.

SHAW, CHRISTOPHER J; Churchville-Chili HS; Rochester, NY; (Y); Boy Scts; Math Tm; Spanish Clb; Im Bowling; High Hon Roll; Hon Roll; NHS; St Schlr; NY ST Rgnts Schlrshp 85; Pres Acad Fi Tns Awd 85; Monroe CC.

SHAW, DEBRA; Valley Stream Central HS; Valley Stream, NY; (Y); AFS; Church Yth Grp; Computer Clb; Mathletes; Band; Chorus; Orch; Jr NHS; Mu Alp Tht; NHS; Comp Sci.

SHAW, FREEDA C; New Dorp HS; New York, NY; (Y); Intnl Clb; Key Clb; Chorus; Church Choir; Color Guard; Pres Sr Cls; Rep Stu Cncl; Bsktbl; Cheerleading; Capt Trk; Myr Kochs Spr Yths 82-85.

SHAW, IDA; St Raymond Academy For Girls; New York, NY; (Y); 12/68; Cmnty Wkr; Library Aide; Office Aide; Band; Off Jr Cls; Pom Pon; Hon Roll; Mrchg Band; Yrbk Stf; Ntl Merit SF; Smmr Vol Little Sis Assmptn 82; Barnard Princeton; Jrnlst.

SHAW, JAMES S; Clarkstown High School North; New City, NY; (Y); Math Tm; Scholastic Bowl; Trs Spanish Clb; Yrbk Bus Mgr; JV Var Bsbl; Gov Hon Prg Awd; Mu Alp Tht; NHS; JV Ftbl; JV Trk; Rennsalear Mdlln Math & Sci 85; Cornell Club 85; Med.

SHAW, KATHLEEN M; The Mary Louis Acad; Rockaway Park, NY; (Y); 27/283; Sec Intnl Clb; Pres Latin Clb; Var Cheerleading; Var Trk; Hon Roll; NHS; NY Rgnts Schlrshp 85; Ntl Latin Exam 82-84; Phys Thrpy.

SHAW, KRISTIN; Yorktown HS; Yorktown Hts, NY; (Y); 30/340; Church Yth Grp; Cmnty Wkr; Dance Clb; Teachers Aide; JV Var Vllybl; High Hon Roll; NHS; St Schlr; Helvetian Acres Wmns Clb Schlrshp 85; Rensselaer Polytech Inst; Engr.

SHAW, LESLIE; West Seneca East SR HS; W Seneca, NY; (Y); Church Yth Grp; French Clb; Ski Clb; Nwsp Rptr; Lit Mag; Hon Roll; Jr NHS; NHS; Key Clb; Library Aide; Fr Stu Of Yr 82-83; Chld Psych.

SHAW, LYNDA ANNE; Gates-Chili HS; Rochester, NY; (Y); Exploring; Service Clb; Ski Clb; Band; Mrchg Band; School Musical; Rep Stu Cncl; High Hon Roll; NHS; MVP-GATES-CHILI Mrchng Band 84; Arch Engrng.

SHAW, MARK A; Thomas A Edison HS; Elmira, NY; (Y); 3/90; Off Am Leg Boys St; Drama Clb; French Clb; Acpl Chr; Concert Band; School Musical; Stu Cncl; Bsbl; Bsktbl; Ftbl; Hobart Coll; Math.

SHAW, NADINE M; La Guardia HS Of Music & The Arts; Brooklyn, NY; (Y); 179/588; Church Yth Grp; Cmnty Wkr; Dance Clb; Drama Clb; Girl Scts; Math Clb; Office Aide; Teachers Aide; Chorus; Church Choir; Achvt & Accmplshmt Citation 83; Hal Jacksons Tlntd Teen Miss NY ST; Music.

SHAW, PAMELA; Lakeland SR HS; Mahopac, NY; (Y); Var Capt Bsktbl; JV Var Sftbl; Var Capt Vllybl; Hon Roll; Bus Adm.

SHAW, R DOUGLAS; Sayville HS; Sayville, NY; (Y); 25/380; Church Yth Grp; Drama Clb; Intnl Clb; PAVAS; Political Wkr; Orch; School Musical; School Play; Stage Crew; Nwsp Stf; Rotary Intl Yth Exch 83-84; All ST Orch 81-84; Long Island Strng Fstvl 81-85; Hamilton Coll; Pol Sci.

SHAW, REBECCA M; Gowanda Central HS; Collins, NY; (Y); 13/159; AFS; Aud/Vis; Church Yth Grp; Drama Clb; Pres VP French Clb; VP Thesps; Band; School Musical; School Play; Stu Cncl; SPICE Pgm Fndr 84-85; Jamestown CC; Ins.

SHAW, SCOTT; Northern Adirondack HS; Altona, NY; (Y); Color Guard; Hon Roll; Hnr Rll Awd 82-84; Machnst.

SHAWLEY, PATRICIA J; Arlington HS; Poughkeepsie, NY; (Y); 36/560; Hosp Aide; Band; Jazz Band; Mrchg Band; Symp Band; Hon Roll; Regents Nrsng Schlrshp 85; Honor Key 85; Dutchess CC; Nrsng.

SHAY, SUSAN; F D Roosevelt HS; Poughkeepsie, NY; (Y); Eugene Lang Coll; Jrnlst.

SHEA, DEBBIE; Liverpool HS; Liverpool, NY; (S); JA; Office Aide; Stu Cncl; Capt Tennis; Vllybl; Jr NHS; Var Titles/Awds Tennis; 2 Vrsty Ltrs; Bus Admin.

SHEA, DIANE; Liverpool HS; Liverpool, NY; (S); 101/792; JA; Office Aide; Rep Stu Cncl; Var Tennis; Hon Roll; Jr NHS; NHS; MIP Vrsty Tennis 84; 1st Cnty Leag 84, 2nd 81; Siena Coll; Bus.

SHEA, DOROTHY; Villa Maria Acad; Cheektowaga, NY; (S); 8/112; Math Clb; Nwsp Stf; Yrbk Stf; Var Badmtn; JV Bowling; Im Swmmng; JV Vllybl; High Hon Roll; NHS; Athl Assn Schlrshp 84-85; SUNY Buffalo; Occ Thrpy.

SHEA, DOROTHY H; Kenmore West SR HS; Kenmore, NY; (Y); French Clb; Band; Concert Band; Mrchg Band; Rep Jr Cls; Rep Stu Cncl; JV Capt Swmmng; Hon Roll; Prfct Atten Awd; GAA; Bus Mgmt.

SHEA, JEFFREY A; Byron-Bergen Central Schl; Bergen, NY; (Y); 11/88; Cmnty Wkr; Computer Clb; Math Tm; Swing Chorus; Nwsp Rptr; L Capt Bsbl; L Bsktbl; JV Var Trk; Hon Roll; Chess Clb; Regents Schlrshp 85; Postdam ST U; Teacher.

SHEA, JOHN; Hamilton Central Schl; Hudson, OH; (Y); 5/55; Nwsp Ed-Chief; Yrbk Ed-Chief; Lit Mag; VP Sr Cls; Stu Cncl; Var Crs Cntry; Var Golf; Debate Tm; Drama Clb; School Play; Boston Coll; Jrnlsm.

SHEA, MARY E; Villa Maria Acad; Cheektowaga, NY; (S); 1/112; Nwsp Rptr; Yrbk Ed-Chief; Swmmng; JV Capt Vllybl; Bausch & Lomb Sci Awd; CC Awd; High Hon Roll; NHS; NEDT Awd; Its Acad Cert Of Achvt 84; Prfct Attdnce Awd 82-83; Biochmstry.

SHEA, MICHAEL F; St Francis HS; Hamburg, NY; (Y); Rep Stu Cncl; JV Bsktbl; Var Capt Crs Cntry; Var Capt Trk; Hon Roll; NYS Regents Schlrshp 84-85; Canisius Coll Buffalo; Bus Ad.

SHEA, SALLY; Mt Mercy Acad; Buffalo, NY; (Y); JA; Trs Spanish Clb; Chorus; Stage Crew; Rep Frsh Cls; Im Badmtn; Im Vllybl; Hon Roll; Miagra U; Nrsng.

SHEARER, LAURA; Clayton A Bouton HS; Voorheesville, NY; (Y); Drama Clb; Girl Scts; Intnl Clb; Ski Clb; Varsity Clb; Chorus; Stage Crew; Fld Hcky; Trk; Hon Roll; Silver Awd Grl Scts 85; Mst Imprvd Chorus 83; Elem Educ.

SHEARING, CYNTHIA; Perry Central HS; Perry, NY; (Y); 4/80; 4-H; Rptr FFA; Band; Concert Band; Mrchg Band; School Musical; 4-H Awd; Natl FFA Bnd 85; Cornell U; Prevet Med.

SHEARING, MICHAEL; Perry Central HS; Perry, NY; (Y); 3/90; Pres 4-H; Pres FFA; JV Var Ftbl; Bausch & Lomb Sci Awd; Hon Roll; NHS; Cornell U; Ecnmcs.

SHEBROE, DAVID; Connetquot HS; Lk Ronkonkoma, NY; (Y); 120/670; Boy Scts; Capt Chess Clb; Pres Exploring; Rep Frsh Cls; Rep Soph Cls; Rep Jr Cls; Off Sr Cls; Var Trk; DAR Awd; Jr NHS; Coe Coll; Phy Thrpst.

SHEDLIN, ROBIN D; Scarsdale HS; Scarsdale, NY; (Y); Cmnty Wkr; Hosp Aide; Political Wkr; Sec Spanish Clb; Ed Yrbk Stf; Lit Mag; Rep Stu Cncl; Var Tennis; NHS; Ldrshp Essay Cntst 84; NYS Regnts Schlrshp 85; Dartmouth Coll.

SHEEHAN, ANDREW; Turner/Carroll HS; Buffalo, NY; (Y); 30/115; Boy Scts; Computer Clb; VICA; Im Bowling; Im Ice Hcky; JV Trk; Var Wrstlng; Regents Diploma 84-85; SUNY-BUFFALO; Industrl Engrng.

SHEEHAN, ANNE; Albertus Magnus HS; Stony Pt, NY; (Y); Camera Clb; Stage Crew; Im Bsktbl; JV Socr; Hon Roll; Chrstn Svc Awd 82; Ed.

SHEEHAN, ANNEMARIE; Valley Central HS; Walden, NY; (Y); Acpl Chr; Var Trk; Rep Natl Yth Bus Smnr 85; Educ.

SHEEHAN, CAROLYN; Northport HS; Northport, NY; (Y); 47/650; Hosp Aide; Band; Mrchg Band; Orch; Symp Band; Capt Fld Hcky; Trk; Vllybl; Elks Awd; NHS; Mary Washington Anonymous Scholar 85; Outstndng Schlr Long Islnd Tchr Assoc 85; Mary Washington Coll; Econ.

SHEEHAN, ERIN; Oneonta HS; Oneonta, NY; (Y); 19/184; Church Yth Grp; Drama Clb; French Clb; Red Cross Aide; Spanish Clb; Thesps; Color Guard; Hon Roll; Natl Yth Svc Brd Vlntr Yr 83.

SHEEHAN, JOSEPH R; Wheatland Chili HS; Scottsville, NY; (Y); Band; Chorus; Concert Band; Jazz Band; Mrchg Band; Pep Band; School Musical; Var Crs Cntry; Hon Roll; Astophysics.

SHEEHAN, JULIE; Mount Mercy Acad; Orchard Park, NY; (Y); Model UN; Ski Clb; Spanish Clb; Chorus; Yrbk Stf; Rep Stu Cncl; Tennis; Hon Roll; NHS; Siena; Sci.

SHEEHAN, KEVIN; Mount Saint Michael HS; Yonkers, NY; (Y); 35/305; Art Clb; Drama Clb; Stage Crew; Hon Roll; NHS; Spanish NHS; Englsh.

SHEEHAN, MAURA D; Rocky Point HS; Rocky Point, NY; (S); Computer Clb; Debate Tm; Sec Radio Clb; Science Clb; Spanish Clb; School Play; Stage Crew; JV Crs Cntry; Var Trk; Stony Brook U Schlr Incen Pgm 84; Smmr Inst Gifted & Talntd Yth Creative Wrtng & Game Theory 82-83; ST U NY Stony Brook; Psych.

SHEEHAN, ROBIN J; Scotia-Glenville HS; Scotia, NY; (Y); Cmnty Wkr; French Clb; Hosp Aide; Key Clb; Teachers Aide; Concert Band; Mrchg Band; Hon Roll; Prfct Atten Awd; Elem Tchr.

SHEEHAN, SEAN; Bethlehem Central HS; Slingerlands, NY; (Y); Am Leg Boys St; Sec Church Yth Grp; Ski Clb; Concert Band; Jazz Band; Var Frsh Cls; Rep Soph Cls; Pres Jr Cls; Pres Sr Cls; Rep Stu Cncl; NYSSMA Exclnt Solo Ratng 83.

SHEEHY, DOUGLAS T; Harrison HS; Harrison, NY; (Y); 11/200; Pres Ski Clb; Nwsp Bus Mgr; Trs Frsh Cls; Trs Soph Cls; Pres Jr Cls; Pres Sr Cls; Tennis; NHS; Ntl Merit Ltr; Century III Ldr 85; Dartmouth.

SHEEHY, SHARLENE; Fairport HS; Fairport, NY; (Y); Church Yth Grp; Sec Girl Scts; Hosp Aide; Trs Math Clb; Ski Clb; Yrbk Stf; Stu Cncl; Cheerleading; Hon Roll; Regents Schlrshp 85; MI St U; Physcl Sci.

SHEELEY, SUSETTE; Ellenville Central HS; Phillipsport, NY; (Y); 3/120; High Hon Roll; NCTE Awd; NHS; Drama Clb; Band; Concert Band; Jazz Band; School Musical; School Play; JV Cheerleading; Ellenville Hghs Hgh Hnr Awd 83-85; SUNY Binghamton.

SHEEN, MARY K; Notre Dame HS; Elmira, NY; (Y); 82/123; Key Clb; Ski Clb; Cheerleading; Sftbl; Amer Exchnge Stu 84; PAL Vltr Of The Yr Awd 85; St Bonauenture U; Psychmtry.

SHEENAN, ANNE; Albertus Magnus HS; Stony Point, NY; (Y); Camera Clb; Spanish Clb; Im Bsktbl; JV Socr; Hon Roll; Chrstn Svc Awd 82; Elem Ed.

SHEERAN, LEIGH KRISTIN; Schuyierville HS; Saratoga Springs, NY; (Y); Aud/Vis; Drama Clb; Trs FBLA; Library Aide; Office Aide; Ski Clb; Chorus; Nwsp Rptr; Var Cheerleading; Var Trk; Trvl & Trsm.

SHEETO, SARAH A; Pittsford Mendon HS; Pittsford, NY; (Y); Church Yth Grp; Chorus; Rptr Yrbk Stf; Hon Roll; NHS; Ntl Merit Ltr; NYS Regnts Schlrshp 85; Ntl Frnch Cntst 82-85; PTSA Frnch Awd 84; U Of Rochester; Bio.

SHEFF, DANIEL; Frontier Central SR HS; Hamburg, NY; (S); 1/500; Am Leg Boys St; Boy Scts; Pres Exploring; Var JV Socr; High Hon Roll; Hon Roll; NHS; NEDT Awd; Eagle Scout 83; NHGA 85; NLSA 85; CPA.

SHEFFIELD, AMY; Brockport Central HS; Brockport, NY; (Y); 4-H; High Hon Roll; Hon Roll; UCLA; Sci.

SHEFFIELD JR, FREDERICK M; Oswego HS; Oswego, NY; (Y); Am Leg Boys St; Rep Soph Cls; Var Bsktbl; Capt Var Ftbl; Powder Puff Ftbl; Var Trk; Im Vllybl; Cortland ST; Phy Ed.

SHEFFIELD, JOE H; Williamsville S HS; Williamsville, NY; (Y); 51/245; Exploring; Ski Clb; JV Var Bsbl; JV Var Ftbl; Wt Lftg; Regnts Schlrshp 85; Engr.

SHEFFIELD, MATTHEW J; Ilion HS; Ilion, NY; (Y); 4/118; Band; Jazz Band; Mrchg Band; Orch; Trk; High Hon Roll; NHS; Ntl Merit Ltr.

SHEFFIELD, PATRICIA; Mexico Acad; Oswego, NY; (Y); German Clb; Concert Band; Jazz Band; Mrchg Band; Variety Show; Pres Frsh Cls; Sec Jr Cls; Var Cheerleading; Pom Pon; Trk; Bryant Stratton; Med Asst.

SHEFFIELD, SCOTT; Randolph Central HS; Randolph, NY; (Y); 26/83; Pres French Clb; Ski Clb; Acpl Chr; Chorus; School Musical; Pres Stu Cncl; Var Bowling; Var Ftbl; Var Golf; Amer Lgn Ortrcl Cntst 1st Lcl, 2nd County 85; Wstrn NY French Spkng Cntst 1st 84; Bus Adm.

SHEIDLOWER, JESSE T; Woodmere Acad; Woodmere, NY; (Y); Pres Chess Clb; Computer Clb; Chrmn Exploring; Pres Math Tm; Ski Clb; Band; Concert Band; Jazz Band; Nwsp Phtg; Yrbk Phtg; Columbia U Sci Hnrs Pgm 84-85; Rensselaer Polytech; Astrophys.

SHEIL, CRAIG T; La Salle Acad; Brooklyn, NY; (S); Hosp Aide; St Johns U; Phrmcy.

SHEILS, DANIEL; Saugerties HS; Saugerties, NY; (S); 19/238; Pres Frsh Cls; Pres Soph Cls; Pres Jr Cls; Pres Sr Cls; Pres Stu Cncl; JV Var Ftbl; Var L Wrstlng; High Hon Roll; NHS; Key Clb; Math.

SHEINWOLD, SHARON; Islip HS; Islip, NY; (Y); 11/350; Pres Art Clb; Quiz Bowl; Jazz Band; Ed Nwsp Stf; VP Jr Cls; Stat Bsktbl; NHS; Rep Frsh Cls; Rep Soph Cls; Fnlst Bk Awd 85; Schl Rep Hugh O Brien Ntl Ldrshp Conf 84; Yrbk Wrkshp 85.

SHELANSKEY, TAMI; Corning-Painted Post West HS; Painted Post, NY; (Y); Church Yth Grp; Cmnty Wkr; FBLA; Hosp Aide; Spanish Clb; Y-Teens; Drm & Bgl; Stage Crew; Var Trk; High Hon Roll; Hgh Spnsh Avg Awd 81-82; Elem Tchr.

SHELDON, BILL; Clarkstown South HS; New City, NY; (Y); Church Yth Grp; Cmnty Wkr; 4-H; Socr; Wrstlng.

SHELDON, CAROLINE; St Joseph By The Sea HS; Staten Island, NY; (Y); Drama Clb; FTA; Lawyr.

SHELDON, JENNIFER; Hoosick Falls Central HS; Petersburg, NY; (Y); French Clb; Band; Yrbk Ed-Chief; Yrbk Stf; Rep Stu Cncl; Var Capt Fld Hcky; Var L Trk; Cit Awd; High Hon Roll; Sec NHS; JR Prom Ct 85; Chrprsn JR Prom 85; All Cnty Band 85-86; Hotel Admin.

SHELL, JULIE; Victor Central SR HS; Victor, NY; (Y); Ski Clb; Teachers Aide; Varsity Clb; Var Coach Actv; Var Socr; Var Capt Trk; Hon Roll; Nrs.

SHELLARD, JERRY T; Shenendehowa HS; Waterford, NY; (Y); Ski Clb; Off Jr Cls; JV Socr; Hon Roll.

SHELLEY, ALICIA; Dominican Commercial HS; Cypress Hills, NY; (Y); Art Clb; Church Yth Grp; Cmnty Wkr; Girl Scts; Teachers Aide; Church Choir; School Play; Stage Crew; Rep Soph Cls; Rep Jr Cls; Howard Golden Record Achvt Awd 82; Girl Sct Silver Awd 83; Girl Sct Gold Awd 85; Psychlgy.

SHELMIDINE, NANCI; Hugh C Williams HS; Canton, NY; (Y); Var Sftbl; Stat Trk; St Lawrence U; Frgn Lang.

SHELTON, COLLEEN; Lindenhurst SR HS; Lindenhurst, NY; (Y); Drama Clb; Girl Scts; Thesps; Varsity Clb; Yrbk Stf; Var Stat Diving; JV Var Ftbl; JV Var Lcrss; Var L Swmmng; Letterman Clb; Vrsty Clb Svc Awd 84-85; U CA San Diego; Mrn Bio.

SHELTON, GEORGIANA; Paul D Schreiber HS; Port Washington, NY; (Y); 24/414; Drama Clb; Spanish Clb; Chorus; Nwsp Stf; Yrbk Stf; Lit Mag; High Hon Roll; NHS; Psych.

SHELTON, LISA; Mount Vernon HS; Mt Vernon, NY; (Y); Church Yth Grp; FBLA; Church Choir; Hon Roll; Morgan ST U; Comp Sci.

SHELTON, ROBERT; West Irondequoit HS; Rochester, NY; (Y); 13/380; Boy Scts; Orch; School Musical; Var JV Ftbl; Var Capt Wrstlng; Dartmouth Bk Clb Awd 85; NYSSMA Comp Solo Cello Red Ribn 83; Carleton Coll; Engl.

SHENBAUM, STEVEN; Niskayuna HS; Schdy, NY; (Y); Cmnty Wkr; French Clb; Hosp Aide; Spanish Clb; VP Temple Yth Grp; Concert Band; Mrchg Band; Orch; School Musical; Symp Band; Cert Of Achvt Volntry Serv To Cmmnty 85.

SHENE, HEATHER M; Riverhead HS; Riverhead, NY; (Y); 29/200; Acpl Chr; Chorus; Concert Band; Jazz Band; Orch; Swing Chorus; Yrbk Stf; Sec Soph Cls; Sec Jr Cls; JV Stat Crs Cntry; All Cnty Bnd 83 & 84; Jrnlsm.

SHENE, MARTHA; Clifton-Fine Central HS; Harrisville, NY; (S); 1/56; Pres French Clb; Rep Soph Cls; Pres Sr Cls; Var L Bsktbl; Var Capt Socr; Capt Var Trk; High Hon Roll; NHS; N Cntry Augsbury Schlr 84; Tlntd JR 83; St Lawrence U; Soc Psych.

SHEPARD, DAVID; Hornell HS; Canistro, NY; (Y); Ski Clb; School Musical; School Play; Var L Ftbl; Var Trk; Var L Wt Lftg.

SHEPARD, JIM; Aguinas Inst; Rochester, NY; (Y); Boy Scts; French Clb; Ftbl; Hon Roll; Alfred; Auto Mech.

SHEPARD, LORI; Earl Vandermeulen HS; Mt Sinai, NY; (Y); 23/286; Hosp Aide; Latin Clb; Jr Cls; Bsbl; Bsktbl; Bowling; Score Keeper; Sftbl; Vllybl; Hon Roll; Modern Miss NY ST Fnlst 85; Pre-Med.

SHEPARD, LYNDA; Mohawk Central HS; Mohawk, NY; (S); 3/99; French Clb; VP JA; Im Powder Puff Ftbl; VP Tennis; High Hon Roll; Jr NHS; NHS; JR Achvmnt Cert Accomplishment, Perfect Attndnce 84; 1st Prize Bus Engl Contest 84; Bio.

SHEPARD, PETER; Kenmore East HS; Tonawanda, NY; (Y); German Clb; Band; VP Concert Band; Jazz Band; VP Mrchg Band; Orch; School Musical; Outstdn Soc Stds Stu 85; Bnd Rookie Of The Yr 82; ST U Coll At Buffalo; Math.

SHEPARD, RHONDA; Schoharie Central HS; W Berne, NY; (Y); Chorus; School Play; Stage Crew; CPA.

SHEPARDSON, J A; Chatham HS; Chatham, NY; (Y); 18/130; Ski Clb; Band; Chorus; Church Choir; Mrchg Band; Pep Band; School Musical; Yrbk Stf; Var Crs Cntry; Bio.

SHEPARDSON, NANCY ELIZABETH; Auburn HS; Auburn, NY; (Y); FBLA; JA; Hon Roll; Typwrtng Prfcncy Cert 84-85; Bryant & Stratton; Exec Sec.

SHEPARDSON, STEVE D; West Genesee HS; Camillus, NY; (Y); 59/470; Rep Jr Cls; Rep Sr Cls; Im Bsktbl; Var L Golf; Var L Socr; Hon Roll; NHS; Outstndg Stdnt Soc Studies 85; Springfield Coll Acadmc/Wrkstdy Schlrshp 85; Springfield Coll; Hlth Ftnss.

SHEPHARD, SHANNON; Akron Central HS; Akron, NY; (Y); 1/143; Church Yth Grp; Drama Clb; French Clb; School Musical; School Play; Yrbk Phtg; Var Cheerleading; High Hon Roll; NHS; Semi-Fin Miss NY Co-Ed Pagnt 85; Pre-Law.

SHEPHERD, JULIA; Niagara Falls HS; Niagara Falls, NY; (Y); Church Yth Grp; Computer Clb; Lib Band; Chorus; Mrchg Band; Nwsp Stf; Yrbk Stf; Rep Soph Cls; Rep Stu Cncl; Hon Roll; Commendable Achvt 85-86; Audio Technlgy.

SHEPHERD, KELLY; High School Of Fashion Indust; Brooklyn, NY; (Y); 146/473; Civic Clb; Cmnty Wkr; Dance Clb; Intnl Clb; Office Aide; Pep Clb; Service Clb; Band; Stage Crew; Variety Show; Fshn Shw Modl 82-85; Spkr HS Nght JR HS Orntatn 82-85; Fshn Shw Ushr; NY City Tech Coll; Art.

SHEPKER, ELIZABETH; Eden SR HS; Angola, NY; (Y); 38/193; Band; Pep Band; School Musical; Symp Band; Nwsp Phtg; Yrbk Phtg; Yrbk Stf; Rep Frsh Cls; Rep Soph Cls; Rep Jr Cls; Hme Buerau Schlrshp 85; Ithaca Coll; Spch Pathlgy.

SHER, MICHAEL L; New Dorp HS; Staten Island, NY; (Y); Am Leg Boys St; Boy Scts; Trs Computer Clb; Math Tm; Red Cross Aide; Science Clb; Tennis; High Hon Roll; NHS; 3rd Awd Borough Wide Sci Fair Winner 84; Pre-Med.

SHERADIN, TIMOTHY L; Dundee Central HS; Dundee, NY; (Y); 7/75; Am Leg Boys St; Band; Chorus; Jazz Band; NHS; Pres Schlr; AFS; Mrchg Band; School Musical; Simper Fidelis Awd Outstndng Instrmntl Stu 85; Arion Music Awd Outstndng Chrl & Band Performnce 85; NY ST U; Music.

SHERIDAN, REGINA; Washingtonville HS; Monroe, NY; (Y); Teachers Aide; Law.

SHERIDAN, ROBERT A; A G Berner HS; Massapequa Park, NY; (Y); 67/250; Mgr Drama Clb; Chrmn Acpl Chr; Jazz Band; Madrigals; Orch; School Play; Variety Show; Lit Mag; NY ST Rgnts Schlrshp 85; NY Inst Of Tech; Ostpthc Med.

SHERIDAN, SCOTT P; Westhill SR HS; Syracuse, NY; (Y); 40/168; Drama Clb; FBLA; Stage Crew; Var JV Ftbl; Var Trk; Hon Roll; NYS Regnts Schlrshp 85; Syracuse U; Comp Engr.

SHERJANE, NAVEEDA; Midwood HS; Brooklyn, NY; (Y); Girl Scts; Hosp Aide; Intnl Clb; JA; Math Clb; Math Tm; Chorus; Nwsp Phtg; Yrbk Phtg; Lit Mag; Med Sci.

SHERMAN, BARBARA L; Albany HS; Albany, NY; (Y); 21/600; Latin Clb; Ski Clb; Temple Yth Grp; Nwsp Stf; Lit Mag; Pres Sr Cls; Var Cheerleading; Hon Roll; NHS; Ntl Merit Ltr; NYS Regnts, U Of MI, Schlrshps 85; 1st Pl Crtv Wrtng 82-83; U Of CA Berkeley; Pre Med.

SHERMAN, DOUG; Newburgh Free Acad; Newburgh, NY; (Y); Key Clb; Ski Clb; Var Capt Crs Cntry; Var Capt Trk; Var Wrstlng; Hon Roll; Mst Dedctd Crss Cntry Rnnr 84; Jumbo Jim Elliot Mem Awd Trck 85; NY U; Sec Educ.

SHERMAN, JOHN; Newburgh Free Acad; Newburgh, NY; (Y); Boy Scts; Cmnty Wkr; DECA; Drama Clb; Office Aide; Political Wkr; Service Clb; Acpl Chr; Chorus; Church Choir; Awd For Hlpng The Hndcppd 80; VP Of Interact Clb 85; Selected For Yth & Govt 85; Real Ests Mgmt.

SHERMAN, JONATHAN C; Tonawanda JR-SR HS; Tonawanda, NY; (Y); #5 In Class; Varsity Clb; Band; Jazz Band; Mrchg Band; Pep Band; VP Sr Cls; Stu Cncl; Var L Bsbl; Var L Bsktbl; Crs Cntry; Outstndg Sci Stu 83; TNT Alumni Awd 84; Quality Stu 85; Bio Tchr.

SHERMAN, MATTHEW; Scotia Glenville HS; Scotia, NY; (Y); Im Bsktbl; JV Var Ftbl; Im Score Keeper; Im Timer; Ntl Merit Ltr; Math Cntst Wnr 81; Engrng.

SHERMAN, MICHAEL; New Dorp HS; Staten Island, NY; (Y); Math Tm; Quiz Bowl; Science Clb; Orch; Nwsp Rptr; Cit Awd; Hon Roll; NHS; Comptrlrs Math & Sci Awd; Baruch Coll; Stck Anlys.

SHERMAN, SANDRA; Corinth Central Schl; Corinth, NY; (S); 4/94; Drama Clb; French Clb; Girl Scts; Key Clb; Pres MMM; Pres Pep Clb; Varsity Clb; Band; Chorus; Concert Band; Academic All-American Awd 84; West Point; Bio-Chem.

SHERONY, MELANIE; Bishop Kearney HS; Fairport, NY; (Y); Mrchg Band; Yrbk Stf; Lit Mag; Twrlr; High Hon Roll; NHS; NY ST Regents Scholar 85.

SHERRILL, MARTIN; North Rose-Wolcott HS; Savannah, NY; (Y); Am Leg Boys St; Ski Clb; Pres Frsh Cls; Socr; High Hon Roll; Hon Roll; NHS; Engrng.

SHERRITON, KIMBERLY; Longwood HS; Coram, NY; (Y); 72/550; Girl Scts; Temple Yth Grp; Yrbk Phtg; Yrbk Stf; Rep Sr Cls; High Hon Roll; Hon Roll; Jr NHS.

SHERROCK, ERIC; Islip HS; Islip, NY; (Y); Math.

SHERRY, ANN; Pierson HS; Sag Harbor, NY; (Y); Church Yth Grp; French Clb; Hosp Aide; Office Aide; Teachers Aide; Yrbk Stf; Stu Cncl; Bsktbl; Btty Crckr Awd; Hon Roll; Katharine Gibbs Sec Schl; Sec.

SHERRY, JENNIFER; Monsignor Scanlan HS; Whitestone, NY; (Y); Art Clb; School Play; Coach Actv; Gym; Swmmng; Trk; 2nd Hnrs 83-84; Attndnc Awds 82-86; Fashn Inst Tech; Fashn Byg.

SHERRY, KATHLEEN; Sweet Home SR HS; Town Of Tonawanda, NY; (Y); 10/425; Cmnty Wkr; GAA; Model UN; Spanish Clb; Yrbk Stf; Capt Fld Hcky; Hon Roll; VP NHS; VP Spanish NHS; Sci Ntl Hnr Sco 83-85; Stu Action Comm 83-85; Med.

SHERRY, LISA; The New Lincoln Schl; Riverdale, NY; (Y); Cmnty Wkr; Drama Clb; Pres Temple Yth Grp; Y-Teens; Chorus; School Musical; Yrbk Bus Mgr; Var Bsktbl; Var Sftbl; JV Var Vllybl; Natl Hebrew Culture Cont 82; Hebrew Ayin Awd 82; Declamation Cont Engl 82; Goucher Coll; Bus.

SHERWIN, CAROL; Manhasset HS; Floral Pk, NY; (Y); French Clb; Nwsp Rptr; Yrbk Ed-Chief; Lit Mag; High Hon Roll; NHS; Colby Coll Bk Awd Hgh Acad Achvt 84-85; Soc Schl Serv 82-84; Swarthmore Coll; Gentc Rsrch.

SHERWIN, THOMAS; Cicero-North Syracuse HS; North Syracuse, NY; (S); 51/650; German Clb; Hon Roll; Comp Pgm.

SHERWINTER, TOVA; Yeshiva University H S For Girls; Monsey, NY; (Y); Cmnty Wkr; English Clb; Hosp Aide; Quiz Bowl; Scholastic Bowl; Service Clb; Rep Jr Cls; Stu Cncl; High Hon Roll; Ntl Merit Ltr; Max Stern Schlrshp 85-89; Piano Pract Study 76-85; Blue Gold Medls Music Comp 82-85; Yeshiva U; Pre-Med.

SHERWOOD, DAVID; Southampton HS; Southampton, NY; (Y); 10/110; Boy Scts; French Clb; Band; Jazz Band; Sec Soph Cls; Socr; Tennis; High Hon Roll; NHS; Arch.

SHERWOOD, JASON TATE; Oneonta HS; Otego, NY; (Y); 18/180; Pres French Clb; Varsity Clb; Rep Stu Cncl; Bsbl; Bsktbl; Hon Roll; Drama Clb; Key Clb; Nwsp Rptr; Nwsp Stf; Sprts Rprtr.

SHERWOOD, KIMBERLY S; Victor Central HS; Victor, NY; (Y); 9/201; Am Leg Aux Girls St; Pres Church Yth Grp; Ski Clb; School Play; Ed Yrbk Stf; Stu Cncl; Swmmng; Cit Awd; High Hon Roll; NHS; UT ST U; Acctg.

SHERWOOD, KRIS; Victor HS; Victor, NY; (Y); 41/258; Pres Church Yth Grp; French Clb; Varsity Clb; Band; Church Choir; Orch; Variety Show; Yrbk Ed-Chief; Rep Stu Cncl; Im Bsktbl; Diving Chmpn 85; AZ ST; Chem Engrng.

SHERWOOD, NANCY; Faytteville Manlius SR HS; Manlius, NY; (Y); Church Yth Grp; Hosp Aide; JCL; Model UN; Stu Cncl; NHS; Chch Yth Grp; Hosp Aide Cndy Strpr; JR Clsscl Leag Co Pres; Model UN; Vrty Shw & Stdnt Cncl.

SHETH, URESH R; Scarsdale HS; Scarsdale, NY; (Y); JA; JV Ftbl; Hosp Aide; Stage Crew; Yrbk Phtg; Im Wt Lftg; NYS Regents Schlrshp 85; Safe Rides Of Scarsdale 84-85; Carnegie Mellon U; Mech Engrng.

SHEW, KATRINA; Remsen Central HS; Remsen, NY; (Y); 4-H; Mathletes; VP Band; VP Jr Cls; Pres Sr Cls; Rep Stu Cncl; Cheerleading; High Hon Roll; Hon Roll; NHS; Bio-Sci.

SHEWELI, WILLIAM; Aquinas Inst; Rochester, NY; (Y); 70/180; Church Yth Grp; Civic Clb; Teachers Aide; Lit Mag; Hon Roll; Spanish NHS; Grad T Shevchenko Schl Of Ukranian Stds 85; Sub Deacon Aftr Ordnd Metro N Amer Diocese Hgh Hnr 83; U Of Rochester; Acctg.

SHIEH, KWANG-TZE; Central Islip HS; Ronkonkoma, NY; (Y); 1/450; Aud/Vis; Library Aide; Math Tm; Quiz Bowl; Chorus; Trs Sr Cls; Hon Roll; Trs NHS; Ntl Merit Ltr; NEDT Awd; Med.

SHIEH, YUHUI; South Shore HS; Brooklyn, NY; (Y); Chorus; Prfct Atten Awd; Rgnts Endrsmnt 85; Phy Sci Excllnc Medal 85; Comp Math Excllnc Cert 85; Baruch Coll; Accntng.

SHIELDS, ERIKA; Unatego JR SR HS; Morris, NY; (Y); French Clb; Band; Chorus; Concert Band; Mrchg Band; Pres Frsh Cls; Pres Soph Cls; Rep Jr Cls; Rep Stu Cncl; Var Bsktbl; Rotry Exchng Stu-Netherlnds 85-86.

SHIELDS, JAMES C; Pawling HS; Holmes, NY; (Y); 2/70; Math Clb; Math Tm; VP Sr Cls; Rep Stu Cncl; High Hon Roll; NHS; Sal; St Schlr; Continental Math Leage Awd And Medal 81; SUNY Manitone; Marine Engrng.

SHIELDS, KEVIN M; La Salle Military Acad; Manhasset, NY; (Y); ROTC; Service Clb; School Play; Stage Crew; Variety Show; Off Soph Cls; Off Jr Cls; Off Sr Cls; JV Crs Cntry; Hon Roll; Outstndng Underclsmn Theatre Awd; Outstndng Contribtn Theatre; NY ST Ag & Tech; Vet.

SHIELDS, THOMAS; Vernon Verona Sherrill HS; Vernon, NY; (Y); 1/225; Rep Stu Cncl; Var Bsbl; JV Bsktbl; Var Socr; High Hon Roll; Pres NHS; Rensselaer Mdl 85; Engrng.

SHIESLEY, RICHARD; Kenmore West SR HS; Kenmore, NY; (Y); JV Bsbl; Var JV Bsktbl; Var Tennis; Hon Roll; Prfct Atten Awd; JV Bsbl Niagara Rvr Champs 84; JV Bsktr Champs 85; JV Bsktbl High Socrer, Ldng Rbncr 85; Buffalo U.

SHIFFER, JAMES E; Scarsdale HS; Scarsdale, NY; (Y); Political Wkr; Rep Stu Cncl; Ntl Merit SF; Writer.

SHILLING, ERWIN W; Hollard Patent HS; Stittville, NY; (Y); 9/198; Band; Concert Band; Drm & Bgl; Orch; School Play; Rep Frsh Cls; Sec Soph Cls; Var Swmmng; JP Sousa Awd; VP NHS; Jr B Musical Schlrshp Awd 84; Ithaca Coll; Accntng.

SHILLINGFORD, HAZEL; George Wingate HS; Brooklyn, NY; (Y); Hon Roll; Princpls List 84; Arista 84; Accntnt.

SHILT, ANDREA; Brighton HS; Rochester, NY; (Y); 99/315; Pres German Clb; Cmnty Wkr; Intnl Clb; Pep Clb; Ski Clb; School Musical; Pres Of Welcomng Committee 84-86; Awd For Perfrmnc In German 84; United Way Rep 85; Engl.

SHIMKIN, CHRISTOPHER; Mamaroneck HS; Larchmont, NY; (Y); L Crs Cntry; L Trk; MVP 85; Coachs Awd 84; Clark Instrs & Sprtsmnshp Trophys 80-83; U Of RI.

SHIMMEL, JENNIFER; Brushton-Moira Central HS; Moira, NY; (Y); French Clb; Ski Clb; Sec Jr Cls; Cheerleading; Crs Cntry; Hon Roll; Ntl Hist Gov Awd 85.

SHIMMEL, MARIA; Akron Central HS; Akron, NY; (Y); French Clb; Hosp Aide; Ski Clb; Chorus; Hon Roll; Stu Achvt Awd 84-85; Natl Schl Chrl Awd 85; Music Awd 84-85; Geneseo SUNY; Psych.

SHINDELMAN, ANDREA L; Tottenville HS; Staten Island, NY; (Y); 109/850; Pres Trs Key Clb; Mrchg Band; Nwsp Rptr; Yrbk Bus Mgr; Var Swmmng; Kiwanis Awd; NHS; NYS Rgnts Schlrshp 85; Emory U; Intrntl Pol.

SHINDELMAN, ELLEN; Warwick Valley HS; Warwick, NY; (Y); 36/206; Pres Temple Yth Grp; Chorus; Nwsp Stf; Sec VP Stu Cncl; Cit Awd; Hon Roll; NHS; VP Drama Clb; Ski Clb; Nwsp Bus Mgr; Pres Cntrl NY Fed Temple Yuth 84-85; C S Lazear Mem Citatn, Spkr Grdtn 85; Alfred U; Atty.

SHINE, JOE F; Corning East HS; Beaver Dams, NY; (Y); Church Yth Grp; Varsity Clb; Band; Concert Band; Mrchg Band; Rep Frsh Cls; Rep Soph Cls; Rep Jr Cls; VP Sr Cls; JV Bsktbl; MVP JV Lcrss; Var Ftbl Ltr; Alfred Engrng Summr Wrkshp Scholar; Bio Chem.

SHINE, ROBERT; Bishop Timon HS; Buffalo, NY; (Y); Chess Clb; Computer Clb; JA; Ski Clb; Teachers Aide; Chorus; Variety Show; Yrbk Stf; Bowling; Im JV Ftbl; Dentstry.

SHIOMOS, CHRIS; Jamesville-Dewitt HS; Dewitt, NY; (Y); 24/250; Church Yth Grp; Dance Clb; French Clb; Yrbk Sprt Ed; Yrbk Stf; Im Bsbl; Im JV Bsktbl; Var L Socr; High Hon Roll; NHS.

SHIPLEY, LOREN; Glens Falls HS; Glen Falls, NY; (Y); 55/277; Boy Scts; Church Yth Grp; Drama Clb; Exploring; 4-H; Ski Clb; Spanish Clb; Varsity Clb; Chorus; Crs Cntry; Med.

SHIPWAY, PATRICIA; Pulski JR SR HS; Pulaski, NY; (S); 8/95; Church Yth Grp; GAA; Math Tm; Ski Clb; Band; Cheerleading; Var L Socr; Var Sftbl; Var L Vllybl; Hon Roll; Snow Incnetive Awd 84; Mgmnt.

SHIRAZI, SHERIN; Grand Island HS; Grand Island, NY; (Y); Am Leg Aux Girls St; French Clb; Chorus; Rep Jr Cls; Stu Cncl; Var L Bsktbl; Var L Cheerleading; Var L Trk; Hon Roll; NHS; Emory U; Med.

SHIRES, BRENT; Fairport HS; Fairport, NY; (Y); Church Yth Grp; Concert Band; Jazz Band; Mrchg Band; Orch; Pep Band; Yrbk Phtg; Yrbk Stf; Hon Roll; Prfct Atten Awd; Gannett Newspaper Carrier Serv Awd 83; Music Ed.

SHIRLEY, CHAN; Lafayette HS; Brooklyn, NY; (Y); 12/400; Brklyn Coll.

SHIRLEY, SHARON; Hermon-Dekalb Central HS; De Kalb Jct, NY; (S); 2/45; Drama Clb; French Clb; Mgr Stage Crew; Yrbk Stf; Wrstlng; High Hon Roll; NHS; Pep Clb; Chorus; Nwsp Rptr; 1st Pl TDS Essay Cntst; Talented Jnrs; Cmmnctns.

SHISHIK, SERENE; Keveny Acad; Waterford, NY; (Y); 8/40; Drama Clb; Ski Clb; Color Guard; Orch; School Play; Yrbk Stf; Var Cheerleading; JV Sftbl; Var Capt Tennis; High Hon Roll; Natl Bus Hnr Soc 85; Georgetown; Dentistry.

SHIU, CHEUKPING; Adlai E Stevenson HS; Bronx, NY; (Y); 11/445; JA; Math Clb; Chorus; Stage Crew; Rep Sr Cls; Rep Stu Cncl; Gov Hon Prg Awd; High Hon Roll; Hon Roll; Pres NHS; Untd Fed Of Tchrs & Local 23-25 Txtbk Schlrshps 84-85; Mayor Super Yth Mdl Hnr Awd 84-85; Fordham U; Comp Sci.

SHIVER, KESHIA; Norman Thomas HS; Brooklyn, NY; (S); 76/671; Church Yth Grp; Computer Clb; Debate Tm; FBLA; School Play; Rep Jr Cls; Rep Sr Cls; Hon Roll; NHS; Prfct Atten Awd; 4th Pl Wnnr Nwspr Essay 84; NC ST Raleigh; Spch.

SHIVERS, SHEREE; Dominican Commercial HS; Jamaica, NY; (Y); Art Clb; Church Yth Grp; Computer Clb; Dance Clb; Girl Scts; Hosp Aide; Spanish Clb; Diving; Swmmng; Hon Roll; Dcrtng Cmmtte 81; Nrsng.

SHKRELI, FANDA; Fanda M Shkreli HS; Bronx, NY; (Y); Yrbk Stf; Bus Mgmnt.

SHOEMAKER, CHERYL; Charlotte Valley Central HS; Davenport, NY; (S); 2/40; Drama Clb; Chorus; Color Guard; Drill Tm; School Play; Yrbk Stf; Trk; NHS; Prfct Atten Awd; Engl, Art, Soc Stds Excllnc; Mohawk Valley Coll; Art.

SHOEMAKER, JOEL; Greater New York Acad; Babylon, NY; (Y); 1/40; Pres Soph Cls; Pres Jr Cls; Pres Stu Cncl; Hon Roll; Ntl Merit Schol; Val; Brooklyn Clg.

SHOEMAKER, KELLY SUE; Cazenovia HS; Chittenango, NY; (Y); Band; Mrchg Band; Symp Band; High Hon Roll; Hon Roll; Hghst Achvt Bus Math 84-85; Hgst Achvt Math 83-85; Morrisville; Accntnt.

SHOEMAKER, STEFFANI; Richfield Springs Central HS; Richfield Spgs, NY; (Y); Church Yth Grp; French Clb; GAA; Teachers Aide; Band; Church Choir; Concert Band; Mrchg Band; Var Capt Cheerleading; Tennis; Secry.

SHOLDMON, ANDREI; Sheepshead Bay HS; Brooklyn, NY; (Y); Math Clb; Math Tm; Socr; Law.

SHONDELLE, HILL; Adlai Stevenson HS; Bronx, NY; (Y); Church Yth Grp; Dance Clb; Drama Clb; English Clb; Office Aide; Teachers Aide; Orch; School Musical; Mathletes; Chorus; Econ Awd Mtl 83; Attndnc Awd 84; John Jay Coll; Lwyr.

SHONGO, ALEXIS; Salamanca Central HS; Salamanca, NY; (Y); Drama Clb; French Clb; Letterman Clb; Model UN; Ski Clb; Spanish Clb; Varsity Clb; Band; Concert Band; Var Bsktbl; Seneca Ntn Athlt Yr; Excllnc & Imprvmnt Engl & Am Studs; Jr Attndnt Sr Ball; Nrsg.

SHONGO, MICHELLE; Southwestern Central HS; Celoron, NY; (Y); German Clb; St Bonaventure; German.

SHOOK, TIM; Washingtonville HS; Sterling, VA; (Y); Civic Clb; Cmnty Wkr; Letterman Clb; Service Clb; Yrbk Stf; Score Keeper; Var Tennis; JV L Trk; JV Wrstlng; Hon Roll; U VA; Engrng.

SHOOP, CHRISTINE; Wilson Central HS; Lockport, NY; (Y); 1/143; Cmnty Wkr; Trs Pres FBLA; Rep Band; Pep Band; Variety Show; Nwsp Stf; Ed Yrbk Stf; Sec Soph Cls; Sec Jr Cls; Sec Sr Cls; Niagra Cnty Peach Qun 84-85; US Army Resrv Ntl Schlr/Athlt Awd 85; Exctv Wmns Intntl Schlorshp 85; Niagara U; Bus Adm.

SHORE, ANDREW; Washingtonville HS; Monroe, NY; (Y); Spanish Clb; Temple Yth Grp; JV Var Bsktbl; JV Ftbl; Hon Roll; NHS; Law.

SHORE, RICHARD; Horseheads HS; Elmira, NY; (S); 10/407; Am Leg Boys St; Church Yth Grp; German Clb; JCL; Sec Latin Clb; Math Tm; Quiz Bowl; Pres Science Clb; Band; Chorus; Hugh O Brian Yth Ldrshp Rnnr-Up 82; All-State Band, Orch 81-84; Horseheads Ldrshp Awd 81; U Of VA; Chem.

SHOTTER, JANET; Seaford HS; Seaford, NY; (Y); VP Soph Cls; Cheerleading; Score Keeper; Sftbl; High Hon Roll; Hon Roll; Erth Sci Hghst Avg 84; Lbrl Arts.

SHOTTER, KATHLEEN A; Baldwin SR HS; Balwin, NY; (Y); 81/502; Sec Chess Clb; Church Yth Grp; Exploring; Sec VP FNA; Church Choir; Hon Roll; Moll Coll; Nrsng.

SHOWA, MARY BETH; Frankfort Scheyler HS; Utica, NY; (S); Office Aide; Spanish Clb; Chorus; School Play; Stu Cncl; Bowling; Trk; High Hon Roll; Hon Roll; NHS; Utica Coll; Occup Thrpy.

SHRADER, GREGORY W; Vestal Central HS; Apalachin, NY; (Y); 71/451; Boy Scts; Church Yth Grp; French Clb; Ski Clb; Varsity Clb; Coach Actv; Var Capt Swmmng; NHS; Rep Jr Cls; Socr; Empire St Games Swimming 8 2; Vestal Booster Clb Sprtsmnshp Awd 85; Villanova U; Engrng.

SHRAUGER, ERIKA; Clarence Central HS; Clarence, NY; (Y); 10/275; Concert Band; Mrchg Band; Orch; Pep Band; Var Socr; Var Swmmng; High Hon Roll; NHS; Arts Recgtn & Talent Srch Natl Comp Semi-Fnlst 85; NY All-ST Orch 84; Buffalo Philhrmnc Orch 85; Music.

SHREFLER, WAYNE; Vestal HS; Vestal, NY; (Y); Band; JV Wrstlng; Hon Roll; Ntl Merit Schol.

SHRIMPTON, MICHELLE; Town Of Webb HS; Old Forge, NY; (S); Drama Clb; Girl Scts; Varsity Clb; Chorus; Concert Band; Jazz Band; School Musical; School Play; Variety Show; Yrbk Stf; Niagara U; Theatr Arts.

SHUBA, TERESA; Cato-Meridian HS; Cato, NY; (Y); Trs FFA; JA; Leo Clb; High Hon Roll; Hon Roll; Outstndng Achvt Awd Occptnl Ed 84-85; Alfred ST; Horticulture.

SHUBERT, TRACI L; Grand Island SR HS; Grand Island, NY; (Y); Church Yth Grp; Drama Clb; Ski Clb; Teachers Aide; Chorus; Concert Band; JV Socr; JV Vllybl; High Hon Roll; NHS; Rotary Intl Yth Exch Stu To Japan 84-85; Purdue; Bio Gynclgy.

SHUHART, BETH ANNE; Rensselaer JR SR HS; Rensselaer, NY; (Y); Yrbk Stf; 4-H Awd; Hon Roll; Stu Cncl; ABC In Albany; Bus.

SHULLA, MICHELE; Neward SR HS; Newark, NY; (Y); Church Yth Grp; French Clb; Girl Scts; Hosp Aide; French Hon Soc; High Hon Roll; Hon Roll; Prfct Atten Awd; Cortland; Elem Ed.

SHULMAN, ALISSA M; Williamsville North HS; North Tonawanda, NY; (Y); 3/315; Library Aide; Concert Band; Yrbk Ed-Chief; Trs Stu Cncl; DAR Awd; NHS; Ntl Merit Schol; French Clb; German Clb; Latin Clb; Wellesly Book Awd 84; Pres Schlrshp 85; Roswell Park Mem Inst Summer Prgm 84; U Of Buffalo; Med.

SHULMAN, JASON R; Collegiate HS; New York, NY; (Y); Cmnty Wkr; Varsity Clb; School Play; Stage Crew; Nwsp Stf; Bsbl; Bsktbl; Ftbl; Socr; St Schlr.

SHULMAN, MONA; Lawrence SR HS; Lawrence, NY; (Y); Cmnty Wkr; Pres Debate Tm; Pres FTA; Hosp Aide; Key Clb; Political Wkr; Spanish Clb; Ed Lit Mag; Rep Soph Cls; Rep Jr Cls; Crimnl Law.

SHULTIS, JENNIFER; Ithaca HS; Ithaca, NY; (Y); 4-H; Quiz Bowl; Ski Clb; Rep Stu Cncl; Var Crs Cntry; Var Trk; 4-H Awd; Bus Adm.

SHULTS, DALE; Carnajoharie Central HS; Canajoharie, NY; (Y); 39/86; 4-H; Ski Clb; Varsity Clb; Wt Lftg; Wrstlng; Office Aide; Chorus; Cit Awd; 4-H Awd; Pres 4-H Teen Cncl 84-85; Arch.

SHULTS, MARCIE; Kenmoore East HS; Tonawanda, NY; (Y); Ski Clb; Var Gym; Var Trk; U Of Buffalo; Nrsg.

SHULTZ, ALEXANDRA; Mamaroneck HS; Larchmont, NY; (Y); 5/381; Math Tm; School Play; Stage Crew; Swmmng; Jr NHS; Trk; Ntl Merit Schol; Joseph E Hughes Schlrshp 85; Oberlin Coll; Chem.

SHULTZ, JAMES; Lowville Central HS; Lowville, NY; (Y); Trs VP 4-H; Pres FFA; Latin Clb; Math Tm; Quiz Bowl; Spanish Clb; Im Bsktbl; Cit Awd; Dnfth Awd; 4-H Awd; Clarkson U; Engr Sci.

SHULTZ, TANYA; Smithtown H S West; Smithtown, NY; (Y); Cmnty Wkr; French Clb; Chorus; Church Choir; Drill Tm; Mrchg Band; Yrbk Stf; Stu Cncl; Gym; French Hon Soc; Chld Psych.

SHULTZ, TRACY; Smithtown High Schl West; Smithtown, NY; (Y); Church Yth Grp; Cmnty Wkr; Office Aide; Drill Tm; Yrbk Stf; Off Jr Cls; Pom Pon; Hon Roll; Bus Admin.

SHUMA, STEPHEN; Ontedra HS; Shokan, NY; (S); 1/245; Math Tm; Quiz Bowl; Rep Soph Cls; Rep Jr Cls; Var Crs Cntry; Var Trk; High Hon Roll; Trs NHS; Val; Oceonography Trip; Comp Sci.

SHUMAN, AVIVA; Calasanctius Preparatory Schl; Buffalo, NY; (Y); Chorus; Yrbk Phtg; Mgr(s); Var L Sftbl; NY ST Regnts Schlrshp 85; Calasanctius Awd Excllnc Semnr Prog 84; Natl Ed Devlpmt Tst Awd 82; Oberlin Coll; Engl.

SHUMWAY, ESTHER L; Saranac Lake Central HS; Bloomingdale, NY; (Y); 21/136; Church Yth Grp; GAA; Hosp Aide; Ski Clb; Church Choir; Nwsp Rptr; Nwsp Stf; Lit Mag; Crs Cntry; NHS; Lillian B Johnson Awd 85; NYS Regents Nrsng Scholar 85; Ononondaga CC; Dentstry.

SHUSTACK, STEPHANIE; Clarkstown HS North; Congers, NY; (Y); 169/480; Girl Scts; Jr NHS; 1st Clss Grl Sctng Awd 81; Fshn Byng.

SHUSTER, TINA; St Johnsville Central HS; St Johnsville, NY; (Y); 4/25; Church Yth Grp; Sec Trs 4-H; Sec French Clb; Band; VP Chorus; Mrchg Band; 4-H Awd; Hugh OBRIEN Yth Fdntn Awd 84.

SHUSTERMAN, EUGENE; Brighton HS; Rochester, NY; (Y); 27/320; Chess Clb; Hosp Aide; Socr; Ntl Merit SF; Med.

SHUTE, KAREN; Gates-Chili Senior HS; Rochester, NY; (S); 8/463; Band; School Musical; Rep Jr Cls; Rep Sr Cls; Capt Var Crs Cntry; Var Trk; High Hon Roll; Pres NHS; Ntl Merit Ltr; Prfct Atten Awd; Cornell; Psych.

SHUTE, MICHELLE; Springvcille-Griffith Insti; Springville, NY; (Y); 33/197; AFS; Camera Clb; Pep Clb; Nwsp Ed-Chief; Nwsp Phtg; Yrbk Phtg; Yrbk Stf; Var Tennis; High Hon Roll; Kiwanis Awd; Daemen Coll; Phy Thrpy.

SHUTT, BRIAN M; Thomas A Edison HS; Elmira Heights, NY; (Y); Am Leg Boys St; Art Clb; Varsity Clb; L Var Ftbl; Capt Var Trk; Hon Roll; Soc Svc.

SHUTTS, STEVEN; Unatego JR SR HS; Unadilla, NY; (Y); Band; Concert Band; Jazz Band; Mrchg Band; Pep Band; School Musical; Swing Chorus; Var L Bsktbl; Var L Ftbl; High Hon Roll.

SIAGRIS, SOPHIA; Flushing HS; Whitestone, NY; (Y); 24/364; Church Yth Grp; Cmnty Wkr; Office Aide; Nwsp Stf; Socr; High Hon Roll; Hon Roll; NHS; NY U; Pre-Law.

SIBEN, SHARON; East Islip HS; East Islip, NY; (Y); Math Tm; Nwsp Rptr; Yrbk Stf; Sec Lit Mag; Mgr Sftbl; Var Tennis; High Hon Roll; Jr NHS; NHS; Pres Spanish NHS; 2nd Pl Trophy Sci Fair 85; Long Island Sci Congrss 2nd Pl 83; 2nd Pl Suffolk Cnty Rotary Essay Cont 85; Lib Art.

SICA, NANCY A; Maria Regina HS; Mt Vernon, NY; (Y); Teachers Aide; VICA; School Musical; High Hon Roll; Hon Roll; NHS; Lbry Ade Awd 83-84; Mth Awd 83-84; Mth.

SICH, ANDREW J; Alfred Almond Central HS; Alfred Station, NY; (Y); French Clb; Band; Jazz Band; Nwsp Stf; Soph Cls; Crs Cntry; Diving; Socr; Swmmng; Trk; Regents Schlrshp Recpnt 85; Bst Male Brststrk S Tier Swm Leag 85; Ithaca Coll; Cinema.

SICHERMAN, JESSICA; Morrisville-Eaton HS; Nelson, NY; (Y); 4/60; Drama Clb; VP Varsity Clb; Band; Mrchg Band; VP Jr Cls; Trs Stu Cncl; Var Crs Cntry; Var Trk; Var Vllybl; High Hon Roll; Center ST Conf All Star Cross Cnty 83-85; Psych.

SICIGNANO III, HENRY; Williamsville East HS; Williamsville, NY; (Y); 4/320; Am Leg Boys St; Pres Soph Cls; Pres Stu Cncl; Var Capt Crs Cntry; Var Capt Trk; Cit Awd; High Hon Roll; NHS; Cmnty Wkr; Computer Clb; Spk NY ST Schl Admnstrs Assoc Conf 84; Outstndng Indiv Perfrmr Crss Cntry & Wntr & Spg Trck 84; Corp Finc.

SICIGNANO, VALERIE J; Bishop Kearney HS; Brooklyn, NY; (Y); Library Aide; Political Wkr; Nwsp Rptr; Vllybl; Rep Jr Cls; NY ST Rgnts Schlrshp 85; C W Post; Commnctns.

SICILIANO, CARL; Lindehurst HS; Lindenhurst, NY; (Y); Cmnty Wkr; Library Aide; Q&S; ROTC; Spanish Clb; Chorus; Orch; Nwsp Bus Mgr; Yrbk Stf; Hon Roll; USMC, JROTC, NCO Ldrshp Awd 84; Orch Ltr 85; Med.

SICILIANO, VINCENZA; Acad Of Mt St Ursula; Bronx, NY; (Y); Socr; Hon Roll; Iona Lang Cntst Itln III 2nd Hnr & Native Itln 1st Hnr 84-85; Bus Admin.

SICK, BRANDON R; Wayland Central Schl; N Cohocton, NY; (Y); 5/91; Drama Clb; Intnl Clb; Math Clb; Chorus; School Play; Yrbk Stf; Var L Socr; Var L Swmmng; Var L Tennis; Bausch & Lomb Sci Awd; Pre Medicine.

SICK, JEFFREY; Cohocton Central HS; Cohocton, NY; (Y); 1/26; Pres Soph Cls; Pres Jr Cls; Pres Sr Cls; Var JV Socr; Bausch & Lomb Sci Awd; JP Sousa Awd; NHS; Val; Am Leg Boys St; Pres Church Yth Grp; Jostens Fndtn Schlrshp 85; AAL Schlrshp 85; U Of Rochester; Bio-Chem.

SICKO, HEATHER; Berlin Central HS; Petersburg, NY; (Y); Camp Fr Inc; Girl Scts; Yrbk Phtg; Sec Soph Cls; VP Jr Cls; Sec Stu Cncl; Var Cheerleading; JV Score Keeper; Ntl Merit Ltr; Chorus; Prom Princess 84-85; Hotel/Motel Mgmt.

SICOLO, JAMES; Newburgh Free Acad; Newburgh, NY; (Y); Debate Tm; French Clb; Capt Math Tm; High Hon Roll; NHS; Regents Schlrshp 84-85; First In Schl American Standrd Hig Schl Math 84-85; Varsity Letter 84-85; Buffalo U; Computer Engnrg.

SIDBERRY, JANET L; Andrew Jackson HS; St Albans, NY; (Y); 36/466; Band; Pres Church Choir; Jazz Band; Mrchg Band; School Musical; School Play; High Hon Roll; Masonic Awd; NHS; Protstnt Tchrs Awd 85; Nealite Schlrshp 85; Mt Olivet Baptist Chrch Schlrshp 85; St Augustine Coll; Spec Educ.

SIDDHARTH, MEERA; Commack High School South; Dix Hills, NY; (Y); Cmnty Wkr; Hosp Aide; Math Tm; Nwsp Sprt Ed; Stu Cncl; Capt Var Badmtn; Var Tennis; NCTE Awd; NHS; Ntl Merit SF.

SIDDIQI, IRAM; Brooklyn Tech; Flushing, NY; (Y); 3/1000; Cmnty Wkr; Office Aide; Service Clb; Varsity Clb; Yrbk Stf; Capt Tennis; NHS; Baruch Schlrshp 85; 600 Svc Crdt Awd 85; Svc Squad Mdl 85; Baruch Coll; Bus.

SIDDIQUI, SAMEER; Nanuet SR HS; Nanuet, NY; (Y); 12/173; Boy Scts; Math Clb; Math Tm; Scholastic Bowl; JV Trk; High Hon Roll; Hon Roll; Mu Alp Tht; NHS; NY ST Sci Suprvsr Assn Physcs Awd 85; Math Leag Rgnl Chmp/1st Rocklnd Co 85; NY ST Rgnts Schlrshp; John Hopkins U; Biomed Engrng.

SIDNAM, KIM; St John Villa Acad; Staten Island, NY; (Y).

SIDNEY, BETH; Lynbrook HS; Lynbrook, NY; (Y); Temple Yth Grp; Stat Bsktbl; Stat Ftbl; Chld Psych.

SIDONI, LAURA; Niagara Falls HS; Niagara Falls, NY; (Y); Office Aide; Yrbk Stf; Hon Roll; Jr NHS; NHS; Top 10 Schlr 83; Cert Of Achvmnt Natl Hstry Day 85; Buffalo ST Coll; Dietcs.

SIDONI, PAMELA; Buffalo Acad Of The Sacred Heart; Snyder, NY; (Y); French Clb; Model UN; Science Clb; Stage Crew; Nwsp Stf; Yrbk Stf; VP Frsh Cls; Socr; Hon Roll; Bus.

SIDOTI, ANGELA; Moore Catholic HS; Staten Island, NY; (Y); 16/185; Cmnty Wkr; Intnl Clb; Ski Clb; Chorus; Bowling; High Hon Roll; NHS; Itln Comptn 83-85; Pharm.

SIEBERT, JEANNINE; Tottenville HS; Staten Island, NY; (Y); 129/867; French Clb; Variety Show; Lit Mag; Var Cheerleading; Var Sftbl; Var Trk; French Hon Soc; SUNY-ONEONTA.

SIEBOR, ADAM; Bishop Ford C C HS; Brooklyn, NY; (Y); Computer Clb; JA; Nwsp Rptr; Var Swmmng; Hon Roll; Ntl Merit Ltr; Karat Clb 83-84; Kngs Bay YM-YWHA Swm Tm 84-85; Rgnts Diplom-Schlrshp 84-85; Navy; Acctng.

SIECZKA, MICHAEL; Mattituck HS; Mattituck, NY; (Y); 18/125; Drama Clb; ROTC; Spanish Clb; Color Guard; Drill Tm; School Musical; Mgr Stage Crew; Variety Show; Hon Roll.

SIEE, SCOTT; Smithtown West HS; Stony Brook, NY; (Y); 20/477; Boy Scts; Church Yth Grp; Cmnty Wkr; Spanish Clb; Chorus; Rep Jr Cls; Bsktbl; Hon Roll; NHS; Spanish NHS; Schlrshp Dowling Coll 85; Regents Schlrshp 86; Norwich U; NROTC.

SIEGA, STEVEN; Bronx H S Of Science; Middle Vl, NY; (Y); Computer Clb; Debate Tm; Library Aide; Science Clb; Varsity Clb; JV Crs Cntry; JV Trk; Ntl Merit SF; Prfct Atten Awd; Italian Litry Awd 2nd Pl 83; Queensborough CC; Rl Est Devpr.

SIEGEL, AUDRA; Commack High School South; Commack, NY; (S); Drama Clb; MMM; Office Aide; PAVAS; Teachers Aide; Acpl Chr; Chorus; School Musical; School Play; Stage Crew; BOCES Inst Schlrshp 84; NYSSMA Medalsd 83-84; All-Cnty Choir 82-84; Music Thrpy.

SIEGEL, JEFFREY D; Ramaz HS; New York City, NY; (Y); Church Yth Grp; Computer Clb; English Clb; Math Tm; Mgr(s); Score Keeper; Ntl Merit SF; St Schlr; Brandeis U; Med.

SIEGEL, JEFFREY I; Theodore Roosevelt HS; Yonkers, NY; (Y); 5/287; High Hon Roll; Hon Roll; NHS; NYS Regents Schlrshp 85; Yonkes Super Awd Acad Exclnce 84; 90 Club 84-85; Cooper Union; Engrng.

SIEGEL, JILL; Commack HS North; E Northport, NY; (Y); Cmnty Wkr; French Clb; Latin Clb; Temple Yth Grp; Off Frsh Cls; Var Badmtn; French Hon Soc; High Hon Roll; NHS; Achvt Engl; Med.

SIEGEL, JILL; James Sperry HS; Henrietta, NY; (Y); Drama Clb; French Clb; Thesps; Chorus; Madrigals; School Musical; School Play; French Hon Soc; Hon Roll; NHS; Music Thrpy.

SIEGEL, LEE S; Half Hollow Hills HS East; Dix Hills, NY; (Y); 86/566; Political Wkr; Q&S; Pres Radio Clb; Service Clb; Temple Yth Grp; Nwsp Ed-Chief; Yrbk Rptr; High Hon Roll; NHS; Pres Schlr; Congrsnl Merit Awd 85; NY ST YMCA Best Press Awd 83-85; Cert Of Merit 84-85; IN U Bloomington; Jrnlsm.

SIEGEL, MICHAEL; George W Hewlett HS; Hewlett Harbor, NY; (Y); 51/200; Pres Boy Scts; VP 4-H; Spanish Clb; Var Capt Tennis; Hon Roll; Spanish NHS; Babson Coll; Bus.

SIEGEL, MIKE; Middletown HS; Middletown, NY; (Y); Band; Concert Band; Drm Mjr(t); Jazz Band; Mrchg Band; School Musical; Symp Band; Frshmn Yr Mrch Bnd 83; All Co Jazz Band 84 & 85; Mus.

SIEGEL, PAUL; Half Hollow Hills East HS; Dix Hills, NY; (S); Mathletes; Temple Yth Grp; Nwsp Sprt Ed; Var Socr; High Hon Roll; NHS; Im Bsktbl; Long Ilnd Lang Fair 2nd Pl Spnsh Poetry 82-83; Athlt Achvt 82-83; Med.

SIEGEL, STACY; Williamsville East HS; E Maherst, NY; (Y); Latin Clb; Ski Clb; Drill Tm; Capt Var Cheerleading; Hotel Mngmnt.

SIEGEL, STUART A; General Douglas Mac Arthur HS; Levittown, NY; (Y); 31/280; Cmnty Wkr; Science Clb; NHS; NY ST Regents Schlrshp 85; Drexel U; Engrng.

SIEGEL, TRACY; Oceanside HS; Rockville Ctr, NY; (Y); French Clb; Key Clb; Orch; Nwsp Stf; Yrbk Stf; French Hon Soc; Hon Roll; Trs Jr NHS; U Of CO Boulder; Bus.

SIEGLE, ELIZABETH; Union Endicott HS; Endicott, NY; (Y); Ski Clb; Band; Yrbk Rptr; Yrbk Stf; Hon Roll; Math.

SIELING, LAURIE; Kings Park S HS; Kings Park, NY; (Y); 73/393; Hosp Aide; Spanish Clb; Color Guard; Concert Band; Mrchg Band; School Play; High Hon Roll; Hon Roll; Ntl Sci Olympd 82-83; Ntl Lang Arts Olymp 82-83; Pre-Med.

SIEVERS, MARIA; Commack H S North; E Northport, NY; (Y); Church Yth Grp; Cmnty Wkr; French Clb; Office Aide; Nwsp Stf; Lit Mag; Off Frsh Cls; Off Soph Cls; Off Jr Cls; High Hon Roll.

SIFERT, ROBIN MICHAEL; Saratoga Central Catholic HS; Schuylerville, NY; (S); 14/51; Yrbk Ed-Chief; JV Ftbl; Wt Lftg; Hon Roll; NHS; Mech Engrng.

SIGMONE, HARRY; Holy Cross HS; Flushing, NY; (Y); Art Clb; Spanish Clb; Teachers Aide; Trs Frsh Cls; Sec Sr Cls; JV Bsbl; Var Ftbl; JV Trk; Hon Roll.

SIGNOR, PATRICK; Immaculate Heart Central HS; Watertown, NY; (Y); School Play; Variety Show; Var Bsbl; JV Bsktbl; Hon Roll; Ntl Merit Ltr; Allegheny Clg; Bus.

SIGNORELLI, LINDA A; Shenendehowa HS; Ballston Lake, NY; (Y); 88/650; Church Yth Grp; Sec Key Clb; Varsity Clb; Var Crs Cntry; Var Trk; NHS; Off Frsh Cls; Off Soph Cls; Off Jr Cls; Mgr Bsktbl; Pres Phys Ftns Awd 82-83; Prncpls Outstndng Schltc Achvt Awd 82-85; Sprts Hnr Ltr 84-85; Engrng.

SIGNORILE, JANEEN; St John The Baptist HS; Massapequa Pk, NY; (Y); 72/660; Hosp Aide; Rep Soph Cls; Rep Jr Cls; Var Socr; Hon Roll; Phy Thrpy.

SIKORA JR, ROBERT A; Mercy HS; Aquebogue, NY; (Y); Boy Scts; Chess Clb; Capt Cmnty Wkr; Mathletes; Red Cross Aide; Bowling; High Hon Roll; NHS; NEDT Awd; Mem Of OA 83; Mem Of Ldrshp Corps BSA 82; Premed.

SIKORSKI, ANNE N; Manhasset HS; Manhasset, NY; (Y); 29/210; Church Yth Grp; Service Clb; Chorus; Lit Mag; Rep Stu Cncl; Capt Crs Cntry; Capt Trk; NHS; Rotary Awd; Cmnty Wkr; NY ST Regents Schlrshp 85; All-Cnty Cross-Cntry 82; Villanova U; Bus.

SIKORSKI, RAYMOND; Manhasset HS; Manhasset, NY; (Y); Debate Tm; Mathletes; Nwsp Ed-Chief; Rep Stu Cncl; Band; Concert Band; Mrchg Band; Stage Crew; Nwsp Rptr; Nwsp Stf; Long Islnd Mth Fair Cert; 1st Pl Silvr Mdl Long Islnd Mth Fair Cert; Nassau Mth Tourn; Soclgy.

SILACO, ANNMARIE; Lindenhurst SR HS; Lindenhurst, NY; (Y); Church Yth Grp; FFA; Girl Scts; Hosp Aide; Key Clb; Leo Clb; Band; Chorus; Color Guard; Drill Tm; 1st Pl Orch Prctc Chart 83; Nassau; Paralegal.

SILAIKA, SCOTT; Niskyuna HS; Schdy, NY; (Y); French Clb; Mathletes; Tech Advnmnt.

SILBER, ERIC A; Brewster HS; Brewster, NY; (Y); Band; Concert Band; Jazz Band; Mrchg Band; School Musical; Crs Cntry; Trk; High Hon Roll; NHS; Music.

SILBERBUSCH, JULIE M; Patchogue-Medford HS; Patchogue, NY; (Y); 42/711; DECA; Math Tm; Sec Jr Cls; Pres Sr Cls; Var L Fld Hcky; Var L Vllybl; NHS; Drama Clb; Leo Clb; School Musical; DECA Anti Shplftng Camp 85; Vlybl MVP 84; Jr Prom Queen 85; Albany; Bus Adm.

SILBERSTEIN, ANDREW; North Rockland HS; Haverstraw, NY; (Y); 32/567; Math Tm; JV Bsbl; Var Trk; Hon Roll; NHS; Jrnl News Athlete Of Wk 84; Nanuet Ntl Bk Schlrshp 85; Princeton; Comp Sci.

SILCOX, MINDY; Westhampton Beach HS; E Quogue, NY; (Y); 86/200; Cmnty Wkr; Office Aide; Drill Tm; Pom Pon; Cit Awd; AL U Auburn; Jrnlsm.

SILENO, CHRISTINA; Roy C Ketcham HS; Wappingers Falls, NY; (Y); 13/507; Drama Clb; Math Clb; Math Tm; Color Guard; Stu Cncl; Cheerleading; High Hon Roll; Jr NHS; NHS; Pres Schlr; 2nd Pl Natl Latin Exam; Cortland Frshmn Schlrshp; Wappingers Tchrs Schlrshp; SUNY Cortland; Elem Ed.

SILEO, MARIA LAINA; Ressurrection Acad; Port Chester, NY; (Y); 17/62; Church Yth Grp; Girl Scts; Math Tm; Stage Crew; Ed Yrbk Phtg; Yrbk Stf; Hon Roll; NHS; Port Chstr Rye Brk Plc Benevolent Assn Schlshp 85; Tri Cnty Fdrtn Of Plc Schlrshp 85; Syracuse U; Comp Sci.

SILFEN, MIRIAM; Sheepshead Bay HS; Brooklyn, NY; (Y); 1/465; Cmnty Wkr; Var Hosp Aide; School Musical; Trs Stu Cncl; Val; Art Clb; English Clb; Teachers Aide; Prfct Atten Awd; Math, Sci Awds 84; UFT Schlrshp 85; Pres Acad Ftnss Awd; Cornell U; Bio.

SILFER, KYLE R; Fort Plain Central Schl; Fort Plain, NY; (Y); 4/85; Church Yth Grp; Pres Computer Clb; Pres Drama Clb; Math Clb; School Musical; Variety Show; High Hon Roll; Pres NHS; Ntl Merit SF; Comp Sci.

SILICH, ROBERT C; Regis HS; Staten Island, NY; (Y); Hosp Aide; VP Ski Clb; School Play; Lit Mag; Rep Frsh Cls; Rep Soph Cls; Rep Jr Cls; Bsktbl; Swmmng; High Hon Roll; Acad Schlrshp Regis H S 81-85; Genrl Acad Excel; Georgetown U; Pre Med.

SILKO, CHERYL; Sachem North HS; Holbrook, NY; (Y); 202/1509; Dance Clb; Pres French Clb; Science Clb; Band; Chorus; Drm & Bgl; Sec Jazz Band; Mrchg Band; Trk; Hon Roll; Outstndg Musicn Awd; Vrsty Ltr; Ithaca Coll; Music.

SILLS, ERIC H; Guilderland Central HS; Guilderland, NY; (Y); 18/369; Pres Key Clb; Ski Clb; Varsity Clb; Var Capt Tennis; High Hon Roll; Jr NHS; NHS; Rgnts Schlrshp 85; 2 1st Pl Awds-Cptl Dist Indstrl Arts Assn Colnie Exhbt 84; U Of Rochester; Psych.

SILLS, KIMBERLY; Medina SR HS; Knowlesville, NY; (Y); 37/139; AFS; Pres Church Yth Grp; Library Aide; Office Aide; Band; Concert Band; Im Badmtn; Sec Bowling; Im Vllybl; Hon Roll; Svc To JR Clss 85; Bowlng Intrmrls Awd 85; Bryant & Stratton Bus Coll.

SILVA, RICHARD C; East Islip HS; Islip Ter, NY; (Y); Boy Scts; JV Var Ftbl; 1st Pl Sci Fair 84; 2nd Pl Long Island Mth Fair 84; 3rd Pl Long Island Sci Congrss 84; GA Tech; Chem Engrng.

SILVAGGIO, ELIZABETH; Bishop Ludden HS; Syracuse, NY; (S); Intnl Clb; Math Tm; Yrbk Stf; High Hon Roll; NHS; JV Var Vllybl; Le Moyne Schlr 84; St John Fisher Coll; Intl Bus.

SILVANIC, GARY; Susquehanna Valey HS; Binghamton, NY; (Y); Chess Clb; Spanish Clb; Nwsp Stf; Yrbk Stf; Pres Jr Cls; Rep Stu Cncl; Hon Roll; Jr NHS; Spanish NHS; Salute Yth Awd 85; Bus Mgmt.

SILVER II, GEORGE; Union Springs Acad; Henrietta, NY; (Y); 8/53; FCA; German Clb; Ski Clb; Stu Cncl; Im Ftbl; Var Gym; Im Sftbl; Var Vllybl; High Hon Roll; Germ Hnr Soc; RIT; Bio.

SILVER, LISA; Northern Adirondack Central HS; Ellenburg Ctr, NY; (Y); Pres 4-H; VP FFA; Church Choir; Nwsp Stf; Yrbk Stf; Trs Soph Cls; JV Var Bsktbl; Var Socr; JV Sftbl; Hon Roll; Animal Husb.

SILVER, RINA; Newfield HS; Selden, NY; (Y); Quiz Bowl; Nwsp Rptr; Yrbk Stf; High Hon Roll; Jr NHS; Corp Lwyr.

SILVER, ROBERT J; Grand Island HS; Grand Island, NY; (Y); Am Leg Boys St; Church Yth Grp; Varsity Clb; Off Church Choir; Variety Show; Var L Ftbl; Capt Ice Hcky; Swmmng; Var L Tennis; Capt Vllybl; Moore Bus Forms Scholar 85; NYS Regents Scholar 85; Acad Achvt Awd 82; Clarkson U; Mech Engrng.

SILVERBERG, CAROL E; Hillcrest HS; Jamaica, NY; (Y); 64/793; English Clb; Office Aide; Political Wkr; Teachers Aide; Variety Show; Yrbk Stf; Lit Mag; Hon Roll; Prfct Atten Awd; Regents Schlrshp 85; Trustee Schlrshp 85; Pace U; Theatre Arts.

SILVERIO, ARLENE B; Franklin Delano Roosevelt HS; Poughkeepsie, NY; (Y); 1/325; Hosp Aide; Math Tm; Yrbk Stf; Var Cheerleading; Hon Roll; NHS; Val; NY ST Regents Schlrshp 85; NY ST Mnrty Schlstc Achvt Awd 84; Hyde Pk Jaycees Outstndg Yng Tngr 84; Union Coll; Med.

SILVERMAN, CINDY; Seaford HS; Seaford, NY; (Y); Band; Concert Band; Mrchg Band; Rep Frsh Cls; Capt Pom Pon; Vllybl; Hon Roll; Earth Sci Olym Dstnctn 85; Elem Spec Educ.

SILVERMAN, DAVID S; Kingston HS; Kingston, NY; (Y); 12/520; Pres Chess Clb; VP Exploring; Quiz Bowl; Band; Nwsp Stf; Yrbk Stf; Lit Mag; High Hon Roll; NHS; Ntl Merit SF; German Hnr Soc Sec; Comp Sci.

SILVERMAN, JESSE V; Far Rockaway HS; Far Rockaway, NY; (Y); 3/295; Capt Math Tm; High Hon Roll; Ntl Merit SF; Rensselaer Mdl Achvt Math & Sci 83-84; Elec Engrng.

SILVERMAN, JOSEPH; Yeshiva Univ HS; Brooklyn, NY; (Y); Drama Clb; Math Tm; Office Aide; Ski Clb; Temple Yth Grp; School Play; Rep Stu Cncl; St Schlr; NY Math Leag Cert Merit 85; NY U; Bus.

SILVERMAN, JUDITH A; New Rochelle HS; New Rochelle, NY; (Y); Temple Yth Grp; Nwsp Rptr; Lit Mag; Pres Stu Cncl; Hon Roll; NHS; Magna Cum Laud 85; Acadmc Profcncy/Motvtn Awd Trp Isrl 85; Pres HS Stu Bdy 85-86; Scrtry 84-85; Englsh.

SILVERMAN, MARCI; John F Kennedy HS; Bronx, NY; (Y); 9/982; Capt Debate Tm; Nwsp Ed-Chief; Yrbk Rptr; VP Sr Cls; Rep Stu Cncl; Tennis; Cit Awd; High Hon Roll; NHS; Voice Dem Awd; Natl Orgnztn Of Bronx Womn Laurerte Awd 85; NY DA Meroca-Outstndng Citznshp Awd 85; Law Inst Gld Mdl; SUNY-BINGHAMTON; Law.

SILVERMAN, MINDY J; Namuet SR HS; Nanuet, NY; (Y); 2/173; Math Tm; Rep Soph Cls; Rep Jr Cls; Rep Stu Cncl; Var Capt Tennis; Var Capt Vllybl; Hon Roll; Mu Alp Tht; NHS; Ntl Merit Ltr; Rensselaer Polytech Inst Mdl Math & Sci 84; U PA.

SILVERMINTZ, DANIEL; Lynbrook HS; E Rockaway, NY; (Y); Computer Clb; Drama Clb; Mathletes; NFL; Pres Temple Yth Grp; Nwsp Bus Mgr; Nwsp Ed-Chief; NHS; Physcns Social Response Essay Cont Fin 85; Cmnty Svc Awd 85; Pol Sci.

SILVERSTEIN, KAREN; E L Yandermeulen HS; Pt Jefferson Sta, NY; (Y); Art Clb; Civic Clb; French Clb; Pep Clb; Yrbk Stf; Bsktbl; Gym; Tennis; Hon Roll; SADD; Desgnd Clss Wnng Float Hmcmg 84; Advrtsg.

SILVERY, RENEE; New Utrecht HS; Brooklyn, NY; (Y); 35/605; Key Clb; Off Sr Cls; Tennis; Vllybl; High Hon Roll; Psychlgy.

SILVESTRI, DAWN; Glen Cove HS; Glen Cove, NY; (S); Dance Clb; VP DECA; French Clb; Girl Scts; Hosp Aide; Variety Show; Trk; Hon Roll; NHS; Score Keeper; Nassau DECA Apparel & Accessrs 1st Pl Supv Level Awd 85; PSAT Merit Awd 84; Law.

SILVESTRO, DENISE A; St Johns Prep; Astoria, NY; (Y); 5/415; Am Leg Aux Girls St; Ed Nwsp Ed-Chief; Yrbk Ed-Chief; Lit Mag; Stu Cncl; Var Sftbl; NHS; Office Aide; Band; U Schlr NY U 85; NYS Regnts Schlrshp 85; Pres Achvt Awd 84; NY U; Pre-Law.

SIMANDLE, ROBERT P; New Hartford Central HS; Whitesboro, NY; (Y); 36/264; Boy Scts; FTA; JCL; Yrbk Phtg; Socr; Hon Roll; Jr NHS; Rep Frsh Cls; Var Bowling; Regents Schlrshp 85; Cum Laude Cert Natl Latin Exam 84; Clarkson U; Engr.

SIMBARI, LISA; Frankfort Schuyler HS; Frankfort, NY; (Y); 8/95; Yrbk Stf; Trs Frsh Cls; Off Soph Cls; Off Jr Cls; Off Sr Cls; Stu Cncl; Bsbl; Tennis; Trk; High Hon Roll; Natl Hnr Soc 83-85; Top 10 Grad 85; Prsdntl Schlr Alfred Univ 85; Alfred U; Pre Med.

SIMCHIK, CHRISTINE; V V S Central Schl; Vernon, NY; (Y); Church Yth Grp; Dance Clb; Chorus; JV Fld Hcky; Herkimer CC; Trvl.

SIMIELE, MARY BETH; Solvay HS; Solvay, NY; (Y); Yrbk Ed-Chief; Mgr Frsh Cls; Soph Cls; Jr Cls; JV Socr; JV Sftbl; JV Var Vllybl; High Hon Roll; Hon Roll; NHS; Soc Studys, Sci, Bio & Amer Hstry Awds 82-85; SUNY-BUFFALO; Phrmcy.

SIMIONE, CHRISTINA; Notre Dame Acad; Staten Island, NY; (Y); Cmnty Wkr; Hosp Aide; Library Aide; Yrbk Stf; Jr NHS.

SIMITIAN, RICHARD; Long Island City HS; Astoria, NY; (S); 24/560; Civic Clb; JA; Math Clb; Office Aide; Radio Clb; Teachers Aide; Band; Orch; Nwsp Ed-Chief; Yrbk Stf; Pace U; Acctng.

SIMM, KEDRA; Liverpool HS; Liverpool, NY; (S); 13/792; Pres Church Yth Grp; Trs Girl Scts; Math Tm; Mrchg Band; Var Trk; DAR Awd; High Hon Roll; NHS; Ntl Merit Ltr; Century III Schlr; Elec Engrng.

SIMMERMACHER, TODD; Vestal HS; Apalachin, NY; (Y); Boy Scts; Natl Beta Clb; Band; Jazz Band; Pep Band; School Musical; Symp Band; Crs Cntry; God Cntry Awd; Perfect Attndnc Awd; Aerontcl Engr.

SIMMONDS, JAMES A; Scotia-Glenville HS; Scotia, NY; (Y); 3/255; Pres Drama Clb; French Clb; Thesps; Chorus; School Musical; Variety Show; Yrbk Stf; Capt Crs Cntry; Capt Trk; High Hon Roll; NY Sci Assn Chmstry Awd 83; Gnrl Elec Steinmetz Awd 85; Williams Coll; Chmstry.

SIMMONS, ALEX C; Pine Plains Central Schl; Ancram, NY; (Y); 30/79; Aud/Vis; Ski Clb; Bsbl; Bsktbl; High Hon Roll; Hon Roll; Ntl Merit Ltr; Regents Schlrshp 84-85; Columbia Greene; Engr.

SIMMONS, AMANDA; G Ray Bodley HS; Fulton, NY; (Y); Acpl Chr; Chorus; Color Guard; Mrchg Band; School Musical; Hon Roll; Prfct Atten Awd; Culinary Arts.

SIMMONS, BOBBI L; Canandagua Acad; Canandaigua, NY; (Y); 6/277; Computer Clb; German Clb; Color Guard; Yrbk Stf; Socr; High Hon Roll; NHS; Represted Schl In Schlstc Art Awds 84-85; U Of Rochester; Pre-Med.

SIMMONS, CHRISTOPHER; Northstar Christian Acad; Cannandaigua, NY; (S); Church Yth Grp; Band; VP Frsh Cls; Pres Soph Cls; Jr Cls; JV Bsbl; Var Capt Bsktbl; Var Capt Socr; Hon Roll; NHS; Bus.

SIMMONS, JULIE; Guilderland Central HS; Altamont, NY; (Y); JV Var Trk; Imprvmnt & Incrsd Rspnsblty Scl Stds 82; Fshn Inst NY; Csmtlgy.

SIMMONS, KATHLEEN; Saint Francis Prep; Queens Village, NY; (S); Library Aide; Rep Sr Cls; Hon Roll; NHS; Molloy Coll Dominican Schlrshp 84-85; Rgnnts Schlrshp 84-85; Molloy Coll; Nrsng.

SIMMONS, KEVIN; Williamsville East HS; East Amherst, NY; (Y); Boy Scts; Pres Church Yth Grp; Math Tm; Ski Clb; School Play; Var L Crs Cntry; Var L Trk; PA SST Athl Yrbk 83-84; Brigham Young U; Bus Mgmt.

SIMMONS, LORENZO; Herbert H Lehman HS; Bronx, NY; (Y); Church Yth Grp; Computer Clb; Hosp Aide; Hon Roll; Hnr Awd In Astrnmy 84; Hnr Awd In Electrncs & Econ 85; Howard U; Astrnmy.

SIMMONS, MARTHA; Sacred Heart Acad; Seaford, NY; (S); Math Clb; Math Tm; Service Clb; Band; Chorus; Church Choir; Color Guard; Concert Band; Madrigals; School Musical; Natl Hnr Roll 83-85; Adopt-A-Grandparent Hmrm Rep 83-85; Economics.

SIMMONS, RALPH; Cardinac Hayes HS; New York, NY; (Y); 50/267; Aud/Vis; Boy Scts; Computer Clb; Math Tm; Political Wkr; JV Bsktbl; Var Ftbl; Accntng.

SIMMONS, SIMMONE; Saugerties HS; Saugerties, NY; (Y); Pep Clb; Chorus; School Play; Variety Show; Yrbk Rptr; Off Jr Cls; Var Cheerleading; Gym; JV Pom Pon; Swmmng; Physclly Ft Grl Ulstr Cnty 80; Vrsty Ltr Vrsty Sprts 83-85; U Of S FL; Data Proc.

SIMMONS, STEPHANIE D; Cuba Central HS; Black Creek, NY; (Y); 6/60; Am Leg Aux Girls St; Model UN; Spanish Clb; Pres Frsh Cls; Var Bsktbl; Var Socr; Var Sftbl; Var Capt Vllybl; NHS; Voice Dem Awd; Hgst Avg Math,Chem; Altn Acad; SUNY; Math.

SIMMS, DARRYL; Evander Childs HS; Queens, NY; (Y); Bsbl; Bsktbl; Gym; Swmmng; Engrng.

SIMMS, STEVEN; Long Beach SR HS; Long Beach, NY; (S); 15/316; Key Clb; Ski Clb; Temple Yth Grp; JV Tennis; High Hon Roll; NHS; Hnrbl Ment Sci Fair 82.

SIMNER, JANNI LEE; Oceanside HS; Oceanside, NY; (Y); 6/600; Trs Girl Scts; Pres Mathletes; Ed Lit Mag; Rep Soph Cls; High Hon Roll; NHS; Ntl Merit SF; ST Wnnr PTA Reflections Cont Lit 83; Girl Scout Recgntn 81; Chem.

SIMOLO, HENRY; Mynderse Acad; Seneca Falls, NY; (Y); 33/140; Drama Clb; Hon Roll; Syracuse U; Radio.

SIMON, ERNEST W; Williamsville South HS; Williamsville, NY; (Y); 55/245; Art Clb; Letterman Clb; Spanish Clb; Lit Mag; Off Stu Cncl; Coach Actv; Capt Swmmng; Timer; High Hon Roll; Annl Eugene Ormosdicke Awd 85; Erie Cnty All Str Swm Tm 82-85; Wnnr Trip Swornvl Frm Spnsh Clb 85; Nashville Auto-Diesel; Toll Bth.

SIMON, HOWARD; Sheepshead Bay HS; Brooklyn, NY; (Y); Aud/Vis; Library Aide; Office Aide; Spanish Clb; Temple Yth Grp; School Musical; Nwsp Rptr; Var L Tennis; Hon Roll; NHS; NYU; Film.

SIMON, MARY; Alden Central HS; Alden, NY; (Y); 4/198; Yrbk Stf; Stat Bsktbl; Stat Trk; Hon Roll; Rgnts, Trocaire Merit Schlrshps , Prsdntl Acad Ftnss Awd 85; Trocaire Coll; Radlgc Tech.

SIMON, RICHARD; Roy C Ketcham HS; Poughkeepsie, NY; (Y); Temple Yth Grp; Band; Hon Roll; Prfct Atten Awd; Amer Stds II Excllnc & Reg 84-85; Psychlgy.

SIMON, ROBERT; Lackawanna SR HS; Lackawanna, NY; (Y); Im Wt Lftg; Hon Roll.

SIMON, SUSAN H; Lawrence HS; Atlantic Beach, NY; (Y); 23/383; Chrmn Debate Tm; Chorus; Trs Concert Band; Jazz Band; Mrchg Band; Orch; Nwsp Ed-Chief; Cheerleading; High Hon Roll; NHS; All Nassau Cty Orchestra 85; Assoc Ed Awd 84; Archon Ntl Serv Hon Soc 85; Music.

SIMON, TAMMY; Susquehanna Valley HS; Binghamton, NY; (Y); Key Clb; Yrbk Stf; Rep Stu Cncl; JV Trk; Hon Roll; Mktng.

SIMON, THOMAS; Frontier Central HS; Hamburg, NY; (S); Boy Scts; Civic Clb; Hon Roll; NHS.

SIMONCIC, MICHAEL F; Sayville HS; Sayville, NY; (Y); 85/360; Key Clb; Var Crs Cntry; JV Tennis; Var Trk; High Hon Roll; Hon Roll; Ntl Merit SF; NYS Rgnts Schlrshp 85; SUNY-GENESEO.

SIMONDS, BRIAN; Victor SR HS; Victor, NY; (Y); Ski Clb; Stage Crew; Stu Cncl; Im Badmtn; Var L Crs Cntry; Var Trk; Alfred A&t; Agri-Bus.

SIMONDS, TIMMIE; Binghamton HS; Binghamton, NY; (Y); Boy Scts; Church Yth Grp; Cmnty Wkr; Debate Tm; Drama Clb; Hosp Aide; Key Clb; Varsity Clb; Band; Chorus; Med.

SIMONE, ANNA; Franklin Delano Roosevelt HS; Brooklyn, NY; (Y); English Clb; Intnl Clb; Office Aide; Science Clb; Teachers Aide; Lit Mag; Gov Hon Prg Awd; High Hon Roll; Hon Roll; NCTE Awd; Itln Ptry Awd 85; NYU Coll; Pre-Law.

SIMONE, LISA; Auburn HS; Auburn, NY; (Y); Spanish Clb; Hon Roll; Bus.

SIMONE, STEPHANIE; Fontbonne Hall Acad; Brooklyn, NY; (Y); 1/140; Political Wkr; School Play; Nwsp Sprt Ed; Sftbl; Hon Roll; NHS; Ntl Merit Ltr; Drama Clb; Library Aide; Outstndng Achvt Awd HS Math Leag 85; HS Schlrshp For Acad Achvt 83-85.

SIMONS, ANN; Waverly JR SR HS; Waverly, NY; (Y); 6/135; Math Tm; Scholastic Bowl; Sec Trs Concert Band; Jazz Band; Mrchg Band; L Crs Cntry; Trk; High Hon Roll; Sec NHS; Pres Schlr; Guthrie Clnc Hlth Prof Scholar 85; Polyhymnia Scholar 84; Samper Fidelis Awd 85; Rensselaer Polytech Inst; Med.

SIMONS, DALE; Norwood-Norfolk Central Schl; Norfolk, NY; (Y); Yrbk Stf; Rep Jr Cls; Rep Sr Cls; Rep Stu Cncl; JV Bsbl; JV Bsktbl; Hon Roll; NHS; Rep Frsh Cls; Rep Soph Cls; Rep Soc Stud Awd; SUNY; Comp Sci.

SIMONS, IVETTE; Cardinal Spellman HS; Bronx, NY; (Y); 116/700; Computer Clb; JV Trk; Hon Roll; Cert Ed Dev Natl 83; 1st Hnrs 82-85; Acctg.

SIMONS, NATHAN; Tully Cental HS; Muscoda, WI; (Y); 1/70; Church Yth Grp; Latin Clb; Office Aide; Quiz Bowl; Church Choir; Mrchg Band; High Hon Roll; NHS; Med & Cert For GPA A 83; 9th & 10th Pl Latin Clb; WI U; Med.

SIMONS, SONYA L; Uniondale HS; Uniondale, NY; (Y); #6 In Class; Drama Clb; Mathletes; Office Aide; Chorus; Church Choir; Orch; School Musical; Tennis; Trk; High Hon Roll; Ldrs Clb Pres & Treas 82-85; Boosters Clb 83-85; Black Studies Clb 83-85; Psych.

SIMONSEN, MARYKAY; Franklin Acad; Constable, NY; (Y); Pep Clb; Trk; Cmnty Wkr; Trvl/Toursm.

SIMONTON, KIMBERLY; Resurrection Acad; Rye, NY; (Y); Camera Clb; Math Clb; Swmmng; Trk; Hon Roll; NHS; ITV Tm Awd 84-85; Engrng.

SIMPKINS, ALICIA; George W Wingate HS; Bklyn, NY; (Y); Dance Clb; Drama Clb; Office Aide; Science Clb; Variety Show; Yrbk Stf; Sftbl; Hon Roll; Prfct Atten Awd; Cert Of Merit Hematolgy 85; Physcl Ftns Achvt Awd 83-84; Englsh Hnr Cert 84; NY U; Med Sci.

SIMPSON, BRANDON M; Avon Central Schl; Avon, NY; (Y); Spanish Clb; Chorus; Soph Cls; Bsktbl; Ftbl; Trk; Hon Roll; Cnslr.

SIMPSON, CARLA; Mount Vernon HS; Mount Vernon, NY; (Y); Dance Clb; FBLA; School Play; Gym; Socr; Trk; High Hon Roll; Stu Of Mnth 84-85; Bus.

SIMPSON, GAELLYN; Newark SR HS; Newark, NY; (Y); VP GAA; Letterman Clb; Spanish Clb; Varsity Clb; Variety Show; Var Socr; Var Trk; Hon Roll; Spanish NHS; Sectn V Chmpn 800m Run & 1600m Relay 84; Sectn V Chmpn 1600 Relay, 3200m Relay & 400m Relay 83; Cazenovia; Fashion Merch.

SIMPSON, GEORGE E; Moriah Central Schl; Mineville, NY; (Y); Aud/Vis; French Clb; Ski Clb; Yrbk Stf; Rep Jr Cls; Hon Roll; Prfct Atten Awd; SUNY Plattsburgh; Comp Prog.

SIMPSON, JANE-MARIE; Dominican Acad; Flushing, NY; (Y); Hosp Aide; Latin Clb; Science Clb; School Play; Nwsp Stf; Yrbk Stf; Hon Roll; NHS; NEDT Awd; Columbia U Sci Hnrs Pgm 85; Maxima Cum Laude Awd Natl Lat Exam 84; Med.

SIMPSON, JENNIFER L; Scotia-Glenville HS; Duluth, GA; (Y); 63/255; Sec French Clb; Key Clb; Band; Chorus; Concert Band; Drm Mjr(t); Mrchg Band; Orch; School Musical; Var Capt Swmmng; Dept Music Awd 85; Darlene Hill Mem Schlrshp 85; Frnds Of Music Awd 85; Berry Coll; Bus.

SIMPSON, KELLY; Romulus HS; Geneva, NY; (S); 5/44; Office Aide; Sec Soph Cls; Sec Jr Cls; Sec Sr Cls; Var Bsktbl; Var Socr; Var Sftbl; Tennis; Sec NHS; Natl Engl Merit Awd 84-85.

SIMPSON, LISA; Cicero N Syracuse HS; Clay, NY; (S); 40/771; Hosp Aide; Color Guard; Mrchg Band; Powder Puff Ftbl; Worked School Bookstore 84-85; Ceratificate Syracuse VA 50 Hrs Of Service 84; Bus Mgmnt.

SIMPSON, MARK; Hugh C Williams HS; Dekalb, NY; (Y); 7/145; Church Yth Grp; Varsity Clb; Yrbk Stf; Pres Stu Cncl; Var JV Bsktbl; Capt Golf; Var JV Socr; High Hon Roll; Pres NHS; School Play; St Lawrence Cnty Yth Brd Stdnt Rep 85; Canton Yth Ctr Brd Membr 84-85.

SIMPSON, THERESA; Smithtown HS East; Smithtown, NY; (Y); Exploring; Hosp Aide; Math Clb; Stu Cncl; Var Capt Cheerleading; High Hon Roll; Hon Roll; Jr NHS; NHS; Spanish NHS; Rgnts Schlrshp NY St 85; 1st Accntng I Lng Isl LIBEC 84; Pres Acdmc Ftns Awd 85; SUNY Oswego; Math Tchr.

SIMS, SANDRA; Longwood HS; Middle Island, NY; (S); 10/523; Math Tm; Band; Concert Band; Mrchg Band; Orch; School Musical; High Hon Roll; NHS; JR All Amer Hl Fm Band Hnrs 82; NYSSMA Solo Grd A 83; Nclr Engrng.

SINAGUGLIA, STEPHEN; Bishop Kearney HS; Rochester, NY; (Y); Church Yth Grp; High Hon Roll.

SINCLAIR, CASWIN; Evander Childs HS; Bronx, NY; (Y); Art Clb; Cmnty Wkr; Hosp Aide; Library Aide; Chorus; School Musical; Swmmng; Prfct Atten Awd; Behvrl Sci 85; Hlthc Career 85; Anatmy & Physlgy 85; Med.

SINCLAIR, JANE; Notre Dame HS; E Pembroke, NY; (S); 6/66; Drama Clb; School Musical; School Play; Yrbk Rptr; Yrbk Stf; Hon Roll; NHS; Music Appr Awd 83; Health Awd 84; Psych.

SINCLAIR, JENNIFER; Rome Free Acad; Rome, NY; (Y); Church Yth Grp; Dance Clb; Trs Exploring; Trs Intnl Clb; Pep Clb; Yrbk Stf; Hon Roll; Jr NHS; Outstndng Perf Mech Drwng 83; Elect Engrng.

SINCLAIR, JUDITH; Prospect Heights HS; Brooklyn, NY; (Y); FBLA; Acad All Amer 85; Bus Mngmnt.

SINCLAIR, ROBIN; Cornwall Central HS; New Windsor, NY; (Y); Trs Church Yth Grp; Ski Clb; Band; Church Choir; Trs Frsh Cls; Trs Soph Cls; Trs Jr Cls; Trs Sr Cls; Stu Cncl; Var Capt Cheerleading; Cmmnctns.

SINDA, ED; Amsterdam HS; Amsterdam, NY; (Y); Band; Concert Band; Mrchg Band; Symp Band; Rep Frsh Cls; Hon Roll; NHS.

SINDACO, SANDRA; Kings Park HS; Northport, NY; (Y); 106/393; Cmnty Wkr; Girl Scts; Intnl Clb; Office Aide; Chorus; Sec Frsh Cls; Sec Soph Cls; Var Capt Crs Cntry; Var Capt Trk; Hon Roll; Cross Cntry MVP 82-84; Winter Track MVP 84-85; Spring Track MVP 83; Physcl Thrpy.

SINDONE, JENNIFER; Cicero N Syracuse HS; N Syracuse, NY; (S); 48/622; Key Clb; Ski Clb; Teachers Aide; Var Fld Hcky; JV Sftbl.

SINDONI, KATHY; Waverly HS; Waverly, NY; (Y); 42/140; Pres Frsh Cls; Pres Soph Cls; Pres Jr Cls; Bsktbl; Sftbl; Vllybl; High Hon Roll; Drama Clb; Spanish Clb; Variety Show; Rotary Svc Awd 85; Outstndng Sr Fm Athlt 85; Outstndng Sr Athlt Sftbl 85; Bio.

SINFIELD, JOY; Warwick Valley HS; Warwick, NY; (Y); 78/201; Computer Clb; Drama Clb; 4-H; Library Aide; Band; Chorus; Concert Band; Mrchg Band; Stage Crew; Symp Band; Marine Bio.

SINGER, ALAN; Sheepshead Bay HS; Brooklyn, NY; (Y); 17/465; Computer Clb; Office Aide; Spanish Clb; Chorus; Nwsp Bus Mgr; Nwsp Rptr; Swmmng; Im Capt Vllybl; Cit Awd; High Hon Roll; Regnts Schlrshp 85; Most Imprvd Swmr 85; Citznshp & Serv Awd 85; Comp Sci 85; Brooklyn Clg; Comp Sci.

SINGER, LISA A; West Seneca West SR HS; West Seneca, NY; (Y); 13/543; Mathletes; Math Tm; Office Aide; Red Cross Aide; Spanish Clb; Score Keeper; JV Tennis; High Hon Roll; Hon Roll; NHS; NYS Regnts Schlrshp 85; Schlstc Lttr 82; ST U NY Buffalo; Med Tech.

SINGER, MARK D; Nanuet SR HS; Nanuet, NY; (Y); 5/180; Boy Scts; Math Clb; Math Tm; Temple Yth Grp; Nwsp Rptr; Nwsp Stf; Var JV Tennis; High Hon Roll; Hon Roll; Mu Alp Tht; NY ST Sci Supv Assn Earth Sci Awd 83; U Of PA; Archit Engrng.

SINGER, RENA L; Tottenville HS; Staten Island, NY; (Y); 46/900; Pres Temple Yth Grp; Rep Soph Cls; Rep Jr Cls; Rep Sr Cls; Pres NHS; Debate Tm; Drama Clb; Hosp Aide; Ski Clb; School Musical; Regents Schlrshp 85; Hnrb Mntn Borough-Wide Sci Fair 82; WA U St Louis; Med.

SINGER, STACEY; Far Rockaway HS; Far Rockaway, NY; (Y); 14/295; Drama Clb; Hosp Aide; Teachers Aide; Temple Yth Grp; Concert Band; Drm & Bgl; School Musical; Swmmng; High Hon Roll; NHS; Tachna Mem Awd 85; Dept Cert Of Merit In Scl Stds 85; Hlth Careers Awd 85; ST U NY; Stny Brk; Pre-Med.

SINGH, GURPREET; Hillcrest HS; Jamaica, NY; (Y); Pres Computer Clb; Pres Math Clb; Trs Office Aide; Science Clb; Band; Trs Yrbk Bus Mgr; Trs Sr Cls; Chess Clb; Intnl Clb; Mathletes; Hnr Roll 84; Arista Hnr Soc 83; RPI; Pre-Med.

SINGH, HOMDAT; Herbert H Lehman HS; Bronx, NY; (Y); Teachers Aide; Nwsp Ed-Chief; Nwsp Stf; Yrbk Stf; Cit Awd; Prfct Atten Awd; Constnt Effrt Engl & Soc Stds 84; Aerosp Engr.

SINGH, SUBASH; Mt Vernon HS; Mount Vernon, NY; (Y); Computer Clb; FBLA; Key Clb; Office Aide; Yrbk Stf; Cit Awd; High Hon Roll; Hon Roll; Jr NHS; NHS; CPA Awd 84; Hgh Hnr Roll Awd 85; Sci Stu Mnth 84; Math Awd 83-85; Hmnts Pgm 83; Engr.

SINGLETON, DEBORAH; Newtown HS; Long Island Cit, NY; (Y); 563/772; FBLA; Teachers Aide; Band; Prfct Atten Awd; Bus Admin.

SINICROPI, JOE; Amsterdam HS; Amsterdam, NY; (Y); Wt Lftg; Hon Roll; Fulton-Montgomery; Accntng.

SINICROPI, MICHAEL; Amsterdam HS; Amsterdam, NY; (S); 1/332; Varsity Clb; VP Jr Cls; Rep Stu Cncl; Var L Bsbl; Var L Bsktbl; Var L Ftbl; High Hon Roll; NHS; Pre Med.

SINIGAGLIA, JOANNE M; St Agnes Academic HS; Flushing, NY; (Y); 4/302; Hosp Aide; VP JA; Nwsp Ed-Chief; Nwsp Stf; Coach Actv; Sftbl; High Hon Roll; NHS; Rgnts Schlrshp NY ST; St Johns U; Acctnt.

SINK, JENNIFER; Royalton Hartland HS; Gasport, NY; (Y); 59/128; Church Yth Grp; Cmnty Wkr; Drama Clb; Girl Scts; Hosp Aide; Office Aide; Teachers Aide; Gregg Typg Awd 85; Bryant & Stratton; Legl Sec.

SINKLER, MICHELE; Nazareth Academy HS; Rochester, NY; (Y); Church Yth Grp; Varsity Clb; Crs Cntry; Vllybl; High Hon Roll; Hon Roll; William Shakespear Awd 85; Excell Rcrdkpng 85; Expert Typst 85; U Of Rochester; Accntnt.

SINNOTT, ADRIENNE; Brentwood Ross HS; Brentwood, NY; (Y); 39/623; Cmnty Wkr; Office Aide; Trs Spanish Clb; Chorus; Mgr Variety Show; Nwsp Rptr; Yrbk Stf; Off Sr Cls; Trs Stu Cncl; High Hon Roll; Spec Olympcs Awd 83 & 85; Caesar Trunzo Awd 84; Pres Acad Fit Awd 85; SUNY Farmingdale; Bus Admin.

SINNREICH, REBECCA; Edgemont HS; Scarsdale, NY; (Y); French Clb; Model UN; School Musical; School Play; Stage Crew; Var Trk; Ntl Merit Ltr; St Schlr; Tufts U; Intl Rel.

SINROD, MARLO; Hicksville HS; Westbury, NY; (Y); English Clb; Math Clb; Spanish Clb; Color Guard; Yrbk Ed-Chief; Stat Bsktbl; Mgr Cheerleading; Hon Roll; Spec Olympics; Prncpls List.

SIPL, LINDA; Cardinal Spellman HS; Bronx, NY; (Y); German Clb; Church Choir; Stage Crew; Ed Lit Mag; Hon Roll; Actvts Awds 84-85; Cmmrcl Art.

SIPPLE, AUDRA; Delaware Valley Central Schl; Mileses, NY; (Y); 5/42; VP Spanish Clb; Teachers Aide; Chorus; Nwsp Rptr; Pres Frsh Cls; Rep Soph Cls; Pres Jr Cls; Rep Stu Cncl; Cit Awd; Hon Roll; Eductn.

SIRABELLA, LISA; Bishop Kearney HS; Brooklyn, NY; (S); Library Aide; Ski Clb; Nwsp Ed-Chief; Ed Nwsp Phtg; Yrbk Phtg; Yrbk Stf; High Hon Roll; NHS; NY ST Rgnts Schlrshp 85.

SIRAGUSA, JOSEPH; General Brown HS; Dexter, NY; (Y); 15/121; VP JCL; Key Clb; School Play; VP Sr Cls; Var Capt Tennis; Hon Roll; NHS; CSEA Schlrshp 85; NY ST Regents Schlrshp 85; SUNY Plattsburgh; Bus.

SIRAGUSA, PAUL R; Baldwin HS; Baldwin, NY; (Y); 31/502; Aud/Vis; Model UN; Concert Band; Jazz Band; Mrchg Band; Orch; High Hon Roll; NHS; Ntl Merit Ltr; Ntl Merit Spcl Schlrshp 85; Cert Of Achvt 84; Indstrl Arts Awd Of Excel 82; Lehigh U; Bus Admin.

SIRANO, MICHELE; Solvay HS; Solvay, NY; (Y); 8/171; Boy Scts; Exploring; Math Clb; Spanish Clb; Concert Band; Off Frsh Cls; Off Soph Cls; Off Jr Cls; Bsktbl; JV Var Socr; Solvay Tigers Awd & Scholar 85fNY ST Rgnts Scholar 85; Bryant & Stratton Scholar 85; Le Moyne Coll; Acctg.

SIRGANT, DANIELLE; Cathedral HS; Jackson Hgt, NY; (Y); 14/298; French Clb; Intnl Clb; Hon Roll; Assoc Amer Des Pfofesseurs De Francais Concours Natl De Francais 2nd Pl 85; Frgn Lang.

SIRICO, LORRAINE; St John Villa Acad; Staten Island, NY; (Y); Yrbk Phtg; Yrbk Stf; Tennis; Wt Lftg; Relgn Hnrs 82; Iona Coll; Mrktng.

SIRIGNANO, JACQUELINE; The Mary Louis Acad; Richmond Hill, NY; (Y); Church Yth Grp; Cmnty Wkr; Drama Clb; Exploring; GAA; Political Wkr; Spanish Clb; JV Vllybl; Hon Roll; St Johns U; Econ.

SIRLIN, CLIFF; Rye Neck HS; Mamaroneck, NY; (Y); Key Clb; Radio Clb; VP Ski Clb; Nwsp Ed-Chief; Nwsp Rptr; Nwsp Sprt Ed; Yrbk Stf; Rep Stu Cncl; Var Golf; Var Capt Socr; Colgate; Bus.

SIRUGO, CAROL L; Performing Arts Schl; New York, NY; (Y); 77/588; School Play; 2-Person Drama Proj Slctd For Spcl Schl Assembly 84; Actress.

SISKAVICH, THERESA; Northern Adirondack Central Schl; Lyon Mt, NY; (Y); French Clb; Library Aide; Yrbk Stf; Var Socr; Var Sftbl; Var Vllybl; High Hon Roll; NHS; Physcl Thrpy.

SISTO, JOHN; Bishop Grimes HS; Syracuse, NY; (Y); Church Yth Grp; Band; Jazz Band; JV Bsbl; Im Bowling; Golf; Im Wt Lftg; Hon Roll; Comp Sci.

SITAREK, KATHLEEN E; Frontier Central HS; Blasdell, NY; (Y); French Clb; GAA; JA; Library Aide; Pep Clb; School Play; Im Sftbl; JV Vllybl; Hon Roll; Hilbert; Acctg.

SIUDA, BOB; Bishop Timon HS; Buffalo, NY; (Y); 65/195; Church Yth Grp; Cmnty Wkr; French Clb; Stage Crew; Lit Mag; Im Bsktbl; Im Ftbl; Hon Roll; Comm Svc Awd 83-84; Comm.

SIVADASAN, REKHA; Our Lady Of Victory Acad; Yonkers, NY; (S); 1/139; Hosp Aide; Variety Show; Nwsp Rptr; Yrbk Stf; Rep Stu Cncl; VP French Hon Soc; NHS; NEDT Awd; Schlrshp Our Lady Of Victry Acad 82; Genl Excllnc Medl; Med.

SIVAPALASINGAM, SUMATHI; Bronx High School Sci; Bronx, NY; (S); Hosp Aide; Lit Mag; Capt Tennis; High Schl Internshp Einstein Med Coll 84; Med.

SIXT, CHERYL; Horseheads HS; Horseheads, NY; (Y); Church Yth Grp; Spanish Clb; High Hon Roll; NHS; Achvt Awd 83; Schlrshp Alfred U Smmr Inst 85; Math.

SIXT, PAUL; Sauquoit Valley HS; Sauquoit, NY; (Y); Am Leg Boys St; Varsity Clb; Yrbk Stf; Capt Var Ftbl; Mst Imprvd Ftbl 84.

SJOBERG, JACQUELINE; St Vincent Ferrer HS; New York, NY; (Y); 17/102; Science Clb; Church Choir; Hon Roll; Guitar Clb Awd 81-85; Kateri Plesidence Awd 85; WA Sq U Coll Schlrshp NY U 85; NYU Arts; Bio.

SKAARUP, MATTHEW E; La Salle Inst; Troy, NY; (Y); 11/77; ROTC; Nwsp Sprt Ed; Yrbk Ed-Chief; Yrbk Phtg; Rep Frsh Cls; High Hon Roll; Jr NHS; NHS; Service Clb; JV Bsbl; NYS Rgnts Schlrshp 85-86; Manhattan Coll Pres Schlrshp 85-86; Manhattan Coll; Engrng Sci.

SKADBERG, INGRID; Smithtown H S East; St James, NY; (Y); Hosp Aide; Pres Ski Clb; Teachers Aide; Church Choir; School Musical; Off Sr Cls; Stu Cncl; French Hon Soc; High Hon Roll; NHS; NYSMA 81-83; Gettysburg Coll.

SKAIR, RICHARD; Bishop Loughlin HS; Brooklyn, NY; (Y); 11/32; Varsity Clb; Variety Show; Gym; Sftbl; Trk; Hon Roll; 2nd Hnrs Awd 83-84; Prfct Attndnc 84-85; Hunter; Accntng.

SKALA, TODD; Smithtown High School East; Nesconset, NY; (Y); Stu Cncl; Bsbl; Socr; Wrstlng; Hon Roll; Phy Educ.

SKALYO, TERESA J; Westhampton Beach HS; E Moriches, NY; (Y); 20/199; Church Yth Grp; Sec Exploring; Hosp Aide; Spanish Clb; Chorus; Church Choir; School Musical; Ed Yrbk Stf; Ed Lit Mag; Fld Hcky; Hnrbl Mntn Drwg Shw Parsh Art Musm 85; 1st Pl Paintg Dist Art Olympcs Long Isld 85; Colgate U; Bio.

SKANGOS, STACY; Fontbonne Hall Acad; Brooklyn, NY; (Y); Hosp Aide; Yrbk Stf; Sftbl; Hon Roll; Jr NHS; NHS; Ntl Merit Schol; Prfct Atten Awd; Regnts Schlrshp 85; NY U.

SKARDINSKI, KATIE A; Jordan-Elbridge HS; Jordan, NY; (Y); 8/144; Church Yth Grp; Cmnty Wkr; Girl Scts; Spanish Clb; Teachers Aide; Chorus; High Hon Roll; Hon Roll; Jr NHS; NHS; Spnsh Lang.

SKELLY, COLLEEN; Farmingdale HS; Farmingdale, NY; (Y); Ski Clb; Rep Stu Cncl; Coach Actv; JV Sftbl; Var Swmmng; ST U NY; Modeling.

SKELTON, JEFFREY A; Westhill HS; Syracuse, NY; (Y); 27/167; Debate Tm; Spanish Clb; Nwsp Stf; JV Bsbl; JV Ftbl; Hon Roll; NHS; NYS Bar Assn Trl 82-85; St Lawrnece U; Govt.

SKELTON, KEITH; Shenendehowa HS; Dayton, OH; (Y); Computer Clb; Ski Clb; Tennis; High Hon Roll; Rensselaer Poly Inst; Comp Sci.

SKELTON, PAUL; Oakfield-Alabama Central Schl; Batavia, NY; (Y); 14/95; VP French Clb; Var Ftbl; Var Swmmng; Var Trk; Hon Roll; NHS; Bio.

SKILLACI, BECKY JUDE; Kenmore West SR HS; Kenmore, NY; (Y); Dance Clb; Drama Clb; Office Aide; Thesps; Chorus; Stage Crew; Variety Show; Yrbk Phtg; High Hon Roll; Hon Roll; 9th Pl In A Natl Spnsh Exam 83; Dnc.

SKILLO, KAREN; East Rochester HS; E Rochester, NY; (Y); 21/107; Exploring; Nwsp Stf; Cit Awd; Latin Clb; Model UN; Pep Clb; Red Cross Aide; Spanish Clb; Chorus; La Fay Sci Awd 85; E Rochester Vlntr Amblnc Corps Schlrshp 85; Amer Red Cross Schlrshp 85; Suny; Bio.

SKINNER, ANN MARIE; St Francis Prep; Douglaston, NY; (Y); 350/700; Cmnty Wkr; Drama Clb; Office Aide; Teachers Aide; Thesps; Varsity Clb; Chorus; Var Cheerleading; Var Fld Hcky; Powder Puff Ftbl; NYS Fld Hcky Tm 83-84; PA ST U; Intl Svc.

SKINNER, CHERYL; Buffalo Traditional HS; Buffalo, NY; (S); 14/116; Exploring; Intnl Clb; Spanish Clb; Var Swmmng; Hon Roll; Tutorial Prog 84-85; Buffalo ST Coll; Criminal Just.

SKINNER, DAN; Vestal Central SR HS; Binghamton, NY; (Y); Church Yth Grp; VP Varsity Clb; Rep Frsh Cls; Rep Soph Cls; Rep Jr Cls; Sec Sr Cls; JV Bsktbl; Var Capt Socr; Var Trk; Hon Roll.

SKINNER, SHEILA; Belmont Central HS; Belmont, NY; (Y); 1/31; Political Wkr; Spanish Clb; Chorus; Yrbk Bus Mgr; Trs Stu Cncl; JV Var Score Keeper; Var Tennis; JV Var Timer; High Hon Roll; NHS; Polit Sci.

SKINNER, SUZANNE F; Albany HS; Albany, NY; (Y); 18/600; French Clb; Latin Clb; Capt Var Crs Cntry; Var Capt Trk; Im Vllybl; Hon Roll; NHS; Regnts Schlrshp; Brown U; Bio.

SKLAR, WENDY; Roosevelt HS; Yonkers, NY; (S); Band; Mrchg Band; Yrbk Stf; JV Cheerleading; High Hon Roll; Hon Roll; Coll; Med.

SKLAVER, IAN; Ramapo SR HS; Monsey, NY; (Y); 8/519; School Musical; Ed Yrbk Stf; VP Jr Cls; Off Sr Cls; JV Socr; Var Swmmng; High Hon Roll; Mu Alp Tht; NHS; Spanish NHS; March Dimes Hlth Career Awd 85; E Ramapo Ctrl Schl Dist Schlrshp 85; NYS Regnts Schlrshp 84; Cornell U; Bio.

SKLENAR, JOHN A; North Rose Wolcott HS; N Rose, NY; (Y); Am Leg Boys St; Ski Clb; Var L Socr; Var L Tennis; Hon Roll; Engrng.

SKODNEK, JULIANNE; Half Hollow Hills H S East; Dix Hills, NY; (Y); Temple Yth Grp; Chorus; Stage Crew; Yrbk Stf; Trk; Vllybl; Hon Roll; Cmnctn.

SKOGSTRAND, INGRID; Broadalloin Central HS; Broadalbin, NY; (Y); 7/60; French Clb; Band; Concert Band; Mrchg Band; Yrbk Bus Mgr; VP Soph Cls; Pres Jr Cls; Rep Stu Cncl; JV Bsktbl; JV Socr; Tchrs Assc Prize For Engl 85; Schltc Awd 85; Presntl Acad Ftnss Awd 85; Schenectady Cnty Cmnty Coll.

SKOK, SUSANNE V; Lakeland SR HS; Yorktown Hts, NY; (Y); Church Yth Grp; Cmnty Wkr; German Clb; Office Aide; Rep Frsh Cls; Rep Soph Cls; Sec Jr Cls; VP Sr Cls; Rep Stu Cncl; Hon Roll; Lakelnd Prnts Clb Schlrshp 85; Engl Dept Awd 85; Manhattan Coll Pres Schlrshp 85; NY ST U-Binghamton; Math.

SKOLNIK, BRETT; Spring Valley SR HS; Spring Vly, NY; (Y); Key Clb; Ski Clb; Temple Yth Grp; Yrbk Phtg; JV Tennis; Engrng.

SKORDY, ANN-MARIE; Mynderse Acad; Seneca Falls, NY; (S); GAA; JV Var Socr; Var L Trk; JV Vllybl; Hon Roll.

SKORUPA, THOMAS A; Pelham Memorial HS; Pelham, NY; (Y); 8/177; Pres AFS; Concert Band; Jazz Band; Mrchg Band; Ed Lit Mag; L Crs Cntry; Hon Roll; NHS; AFS Exch Stu To Sweden 83-84; NY U; Languages.

SKORUPSKI, EDMUND; Hoosick Falls Central HS; Hoosick Falls, NY; (Y); #1 In Class; Ski Clb; Bsbl; Ftbl; Hon Roll; NHS; Ntl Merit SF; RPI Sci & Math Mdl; Open Door Exchnge Prog.

SKRELJA, ANA; Aquinas HS; Bronx, NY; (Y); 10/178; Cmnty Wkr; Intnl Clb; Library Aide; Teachers Aide; Nwsp Rptr; Yrbk Stf; VP Frsh Cls; VP Pres Jr Cls; High Hon Roll; Hon Roll; Cmmssnr Day Cntst Wnnr 85; Cmmnty Wrk Awd 83; Boston Coll; Jrnlst.

SKRETNY, AMY; Nardin Acad; S Cheektowaga, NY; (S); Chorus; Orch; School Musical; Lit Mag; Var Tennis; NHS; Church Yth Grp; Ski Clb; Bea Massman Leag 1st & 2nd Pl Dbls 84 & 85.

SKRETNY, DEBORAH; West Seneca West SR HS; Buffalo, NY; (Y); English Clb; Key Clb; Red Cross Aide; Spanish Clb; Teachers Aide; School Play; Rep Frsh Cls; Rep Soph Cls; Trk; Hon Roll; Niagra U; Nrsg.

SKROBOLA, CYNTHIA; Peekskill HS; Peekskill, NY; (S); 9/156; Am Leg Aux Girls St; Hosp Aide; Yrbk Stf; JV Var Cheerleading; Capt Sftbl; Var Tennis; High Hon Roll; NHS; Pugsley Awd Chem 84; SUNY Binghamton; Chem.

SKROCKI, ROBIN; Onondaga Central HS; Syracuse, NY; (S); FBLA; GAA; Spanish Clb; Rep Stu Cncl; Cheerleading; JV Tennis; High Hon Roll; NHS; Attorney Of Law.

SKRUPA, SUSAN; West Genesee HS; Camillus, NY; (Y); Camera Clb; Dance Clb; French Clb; Ski Clb; Off Sr Cls; Cheerleading; Gym; High Hon Roll; Pep Clb; Pres Awd Physical Fitness 82-83.

SKURCENSKI, KRISTEN; Pine Valley Central Schl; Cherry Creek, NY; (S); 1/65; Sec AFS; Sec Pres 4-H; Ski Clb; Chorus; Trs Frsh Cls; Stat Bsktbl; Var Trk; JV Var Vllybl; Hon Roll; Jr NHS; PTA Awd Hghst Avg 84; Hghst Avg Awds Geom, Trig & Engl 83-84.

SKYER, NICOLE A; Midwood HS; Belle Harbor, NY; (Y); 86/605; Cmnty Wkr; Office Aide; Hon Roll; Regents Schlrshp 85; Brooklyn Coll; Ntrtnl Sci.

SLABY, RONALD; Barker Central HS; Barker, NY; (Y); AFS; Church Yth Grp; French Clb; FFA; Letterman Clb; Yrbk Phtg; JV Bsbl; JV Var Bsktbl; JV Ftbl; Geneseo; Bus Admn.

SLACHMUYLDER, LENA; John Jay SR HS; Katonah, NY; (Y); 3/300; Debate Tm; Variety Show; Ed Nwsp Stf; Rep Stu Cncl; Var Fld Hcky; Var Socr; NHS; Drama Clb; French Clb; Intnl Clb; NHS Schlrshp Awd 85; Fndr Katonah-Lewisboro Safe Rides 84-85; Bedford Yth Court 84-85; Stanford U; Pol Sci.

SLADE, TRINA; Cardinal Spellman HS; Bronx, NY; (Y); Yrbk Stf; Lit Mag; Fashn Dsgn.

SLAGER, LISA KIM; Naples Central Schl; Naples, NY; (Y); Church Yth Grp; Pres VP 4-H; Chorus; Nwsp Rptr; JV Var Bsktbl; JV Var Socr; JV Var Sftbl; JV Var Vllybl; 4-H Awd; Hon Roll; All Awd JR Engl Equitn Ridr 83; Schlrshp Goals Sccr Cmp NJ 83; 1st Pl Hrse Judg Awd Ontario Cnty 84; Jrnlsm.

SLAMOWITZ, STEPHEN; Yeshiva University HS; New York, NY; (Y); Chess Clb; Computer Clb; Math Tm; Band; Yrbk Stf; JV Im Ftbl; NY ST Regents Schlrshp Wnr 85; Brooklyn Coll; Elec Engrng.

SLANETZ, CAROLYN ABIGAIL; Portledge HS; Locust Valley, NY; (S); 1/23; Cmnty Wkr; Sec Math Clb; Political Wkr; Teachers Aide; School Play; Stage Crew; Nwsp Rptr; Nwsp Sprt Ed; Nwsp Stf; Yrbk Phtg; Sky Day Bnnr Cont 1st Pl 84; Frnch Achvt Awds 82-84; Engl Achvt Awds 82-83; Bio & Hist Achvt Awds 82; Smith Coll; Bio Sci.

SLASKI, JEFFREY; Auburn HS; Auburn, NY; (Y); JV Ftbl; Cayuga CC; Math.

SLATER, IAN H; Herricks SR HS; Searingtown, NY; (Y); 142/306; Aud/Vis; School Musical; Stage Crew; Yrbk Phtg; 1st Pl Yth Consmr Nassau Cty 84; Suny Brockport; Comms.

SLATER, JENNIFER LYNN; Our Lady Of Victory Acad; New York, NY; (Y); 36/137; Nwsp Stf; Hon Roll; NHS; Spanish NHS; Regnts Schlrshp 85; Volntr Schl Ofc Wrk 84-85; Volntr Infirmary For Nuns; Comptv Smmg & Divg 82-83; Coll Mt St Vincent NY; Ed.

SLATER, JOSEPH; Liverpool HS; Liverpool, NY; (S); 64/792; Math Tm; Jazz Band; Mrchg Band; Orch; Symp Band; Stu Cncl; Hon Roll; NHS; Ntl Merit Ltr; Computer Clb; Schltc Achvt Awd For Excllnc In Geometry82; SUNY Buffalo; Aerospace Engrng.

SLATER, LAURA J; North Tonawanda SR HS; N Tonawanda, NY; (Y); 10/470; Church Yth Grp; Cmnty Wkr; Band; Concert Band; Jazz Band; Mrchg Band; Symp Band; Rep Frsh Cls; JV Sftbl; JV Swmmng; Gen Motors Co Op Prog 84-85; Engrng.

SLATER, TAMMY; Sandy Creek Central HS; Sandy Creek, NY; (Y); 5/105; Sec Drama Clb; JCL; Band; Chorus; Mrchg Band; School Musical; Var Socr; JV Var Vllybl; Hon Roll; Trs NHS; Sci.

SLATTERY, CAROL A; Sanford H Calhoun HS; Merrick, NY; (Y); Hst Key Clb; Mathletes; Band; Sec Soph Cls; Hon Roll; NHS; Vlntr Mnth 83; Outstndg Key Clb Plaque 85; Med.

SLATTERY, MARYELLEN; Msgr Scanlan HS; Whitestone, NY; (Y); 75/361; Math Tm; St Johns U; Bus Mngmnt.

SLAUGHTER, JANET; Walt Whitman HS; Huntington Stat, NY; (Y); 128/500; Church Yth Grp; Chorus; Trk; High Hon Roll; Hon Roll; Accntng.

SLAVEN, SHAWN; Le Roy Central HS; Leroy, NY; (Y); Spanish Clb; School Musical; School Play; Var Bsbl; Var Ftbl; Hon Roll; Comp Sci.

SLAVENAS, PAUL; St Joseph Collegiate Inst; Kenmore, NY; (Y); Boy Scts; Library Aide; Office Aide; Ski Clb; Nwsp Rptr; Yrbk Rptr; Lit Mag; High Hon Roll; NHS; Acad H S Scholar 82; Bst Scouting Spirit Of Yr 83; SUNYAB; Med.

SLAVER, ART; Keveny Memorial Acad; Cohoes, NY; (Y); Chess Clb; Computer Clb; Debate Tm; Drama Clb; Drill Tm; School Play; Var L Bsbl; Var L Bsktbl; Var L Socr; Im Vllybl; Hudson Vly; Acctg.

SLAVICKAS, KERRI; Emma Willard HS; Troy, NY; (Y); Pre-Vet.

SLAVIK, JACQUELINE M; Kingston HS; Lake Katrine, NY; (Y); 9/511; Chorus; School Play; Yrbk Phtg; Yrbk Stf; Lit Mag; Hon Roll; NHS; Ntl Merit Ltr; Spanish NHS; Spanish Clb; NYS Regents Schlrshp 85; SUNY Albany; Bio.

SLAVIK, MARK; Whitney Point SR HS; Whitney Point, NY; (Y); 30/119; Boy Scts; 4-H; JCL; Latin Clb; Chorus; Stu Cncl; Crs Cntry; Socr; Tennis; Trk; SUNY; Naval Arch.

SLAWSON, TODD M; St Josephs Collegiate Inst HS; Depew, NY; (Y); 55/199; JV Var Ftbl; JV Var Ice Hcky; Engr.

SLAYTON, KAREN; St John The Baptist D HS; W Babylon, NY; (Y); 36/601; Church Yth Grp; Computer Clb; VP Girl Scts; Spanish Clb; Speech Tm; Nwsp Stf; Yrbk Stf; Hon Roll; Spanish NHS; SUNY-STONY Brook; Psych.

SLAYTON, MELISSA; Avaca Central Schl; Avoca, NY; (Y); 9/45; Church Yth Grp; French Clb; Chorus; Mrchg Band; School Play; Rep Stu Cncl; Cheerleading; Pom Pon; French Hon Soc; Hon Roll; Outstndng Vocl Solo AU Cnty Choir 83; Recrd Album 82; Briant & Strantan; Comp.

SLEDGE, DYVONNE; Allegany HS; Allegany, NY; (Y); Art Clb; Chorus; Church Choir; Color Guard; Drill Tm; John Powers; Modelng.

SLEPECKI, EVA M; Pittsford-Mendon HS; Pittsford, NY; (Y); Latin Clb; French Hon Soc; High Hon Roll; NHS; Ntl Merit Ltr; Schlrshp Grnt Eastman Schl Music 83-85; Forgn Exch Japan Smmr 84; Johns Hopkins U; Bio.

SLIFKIN, DAVID; Herricus SR HS; Albertson, NY; (Y); Mathletes; Rep Frsh Cls; Var Ftbl; Hon Roll; Ntl Merit Ltr; U PA; Bus.

SLIKER, BRENDA; Madison Central HS; Bouckville, NY; (Y); 7/40; Varsity Clb; Jazz Band; Yrbk Bus Mgr; Trs Frsh Cls; JV Var Bsktbl; JV Var Socr; Var Capt Sftbl; JV Vllybl; High Hon Roll; NHS; Am Leg Post Schlrshp 85; Herkimer County CC; Sports Med.

SLIKER, LAURA; York Central Schl; Leicester, NY; (Y); Art Clb; 4-H; Sec Key Clb; Sec Band; Mrchg Band; Yrbk Stf; Im Var Bsktbl; Im Var Socr; Im Vllybl; US Pony Clb 83-85; Equine.

SLILATY, ANN-MARIE; Binghamton HS; Binghamton, NY; (Y); 60/510; Hon Roll; Prfct Atndnc 82-85; SUNY Bnghmtn; Trvl Agnt.

SLINGERLAND, AMY; Minisink Valley HS; Westown, NY; (Y); 5/225; Church Yth Grp; Drama Clb; PAVAS; Scholastic Bowl; Chorus; School Play; French Hon Soc; High Hon Roll; Hosp Aide; Math Tm; Mst Imprvd SR Voice 85; RWC Acad Schlrshp 85; RWC Dept Schlrshp 85; Roberts Wesleyan Coll; Bio.

SLIPPY, MATT; Grand Island HS; Gr Island, NY; (Y); VP Church Yth Grp; Varsity Clb; Church Choir; JV Bsbl; JV Bsktbl; JV Socr; Vllybl; Hon Roll; Grace Coll.

SLIVA, KAREN ANN; Fairport HS; Victor, NY; (Y); Ed Nwsp Rptr; JV Capt Fld Hcky; Jrnlsm.

SLIWA, KIMBERLEY; Horseheads SR HS; Big Flats, NY; (S); 29/407; Drama Clb; French Clb; Acpl Chr; Band; Chorus; Color Guard; Concert Band; Mrchg Band; School Musical; School Play; Ryant Coll; Accntnt.

SLIWINSKI, GORDON J; Whitesboro SR HS; Whitesboro, NY; (Y); Varsity Clb; Var Bowling; JV Ftbl; JV Golf; JV Var Lcrss; Im Wt Lftg; Hon Roll; Mech Engrng.

SLOAN, ANDREA L; La Guardia H S Of Music And Art; New York, NY; (Y); 75/588; Teachers Aide; Yrbk Stf; Hon Roll; NHS; Ntl Achvt Semi-Fnlst 84-85.

SLOAN, KEYNA M; Palmyra-Macedon Central HS; Palmyra, NY; (Y); 13/189; Am Leg Aux Girls St; Church Yth Grp; Girl Scts; Math Tm; Church Choir; High Hon Roll; NHS; Hosp Aide; Library Aide; Math Clb; Wooster Schlrshp 85; Summr Sci Wrkshp 84; Hon Mntn Sci Cngrss Lecture Dmnstrtn 81; Wooster; Chmstry.

SLOAN, KRISTIN; Liverpool HS; Liverpool, NY; (S); 123/780; Ski Clb; Nwsp Phtg; Nwsp Rptr; Nwsp Stf; Yrbk Phtg; Yrbk Stf; Var Capt Gym; NHS; Vrsty Rowing Team 83-85; Syracuse U; Comm.

SLOAN, MARYMARGARET; Greenwich Central Schl; Greenwich, NY; (Y); Ski Clb; Band; Swing Chorus; Yrbk Stf; Pres Frsh Cls; Pres Soph Cls; Pres Jr Cls; Pres Bsktbl; Var Cheerleading; JV Fld Hcky; Elctd Membr Queens Ct 85; Mktg.

SLOANE, CAROLANN; Bishop Kearney HS; Brooklyn, NY; (Y); High Hon Roll; Hon Roll; Princpls List 83; Princpls Awd 82; Art Awd 82; Ed.

SLOCUM, CATHERINE; Unatego JR SR HS; Unadilla, NY; (Y); 10/86; Girl Scts; Hosp Aide; Yrbk Stf; JV Var Vllybl; Cit Awd; DAR Awd; NHS; Church Yth Grp; Varsity Clb; Band; Vlybl-Susquenango Assn All Star Awd 85; Fire Qn-Unadilla Fire Dept 85; 1st Pl Girl Sct 16 Mi Endrnc Rc; Cortland ST Coll; Spch Path.

SLOCUM, JEFF; Cazenovia HS; New Woodstock, NY; (Y); Trs Church Yth Grp; Cmnty Wkr; FCA; Var Bsbl; Hon Roll; Prfct Atten Awd; Engrng.

SLOCUM, KATHRYN ANN; Cazenovia HS; New Woodstock, NY; (Y); Am Leg Aux Girls St; Church Yth Grp; Yrbk Stf; Var Capt Sftbl; Vllybl; DAR Awd; Hon Roll; Tri Vly Lg All Star Hnrb Mntn Sftbl 85; Ithaca Coll; Phys Thrpy.

SLOCUM, KATHY; Cazenovia JR & SR HS; New Woodstock, NY; (Y); Am Leg Aux Girls St; Church Yth Grp; Yrbk Stf; Coach Actv; Var Capt Sftbl; JV Vllybl; Hon Roll; Hnrb Mntn-Sftbl Tri-Vly Lge 85; Mst Imprvd-Chem 85; Ithaca Coll; Phy Thrpy.

SLOCUM, RANDY; Bishop Scully HS; Amsterdam, NY; (Y); JV Bsktbl; JV Var Ftbl; Hon Roll; Bus Mgmt.

SLOCUM, TOM; Alleguny Central HS; Allegany, NY; (Y); L Bsbl; Cheerleading; Coach Actv; Capt L Ftbl; Wt Lftg; Hon Roll; Appntd Stu Rep Behavrval Comm 85; MV Def Lineman Ftbl 84; Comm.

SLOMOVITZ, JORDANA LEE; Bethpage HS; Plainview, NY; (Y); 4/277; Off Drama Clb; VP Mathletes; Spanish Clb; Temple Yth Grp; School Musical; School Play; JV Cheerleading; High Hon Roll; Jr NHS; NHS; NY ST Rgnts Schlsrhp 85; Archie Mc Cord Awd Of Amer 85; SUNY Bnghmtn; Comp Sci.

SLOSBERG, BARBARA L; La Guardia HS Of Music & The Arts; Riverdale, NY; (Y); 115/590; Cmnty Wkr; Hosp Aide; Office Aide; Service Clb; Lib Temple Yth Grp; Y-Teens; Orch; Hon Roll; NHS; Usic Hnr League 84-85; NY St Regents Schlrshp Awd 84-85; St U NY-BUFFALO; Bus.

SLOTTJE, JOSH; Vestal SR HS; Vestal, NY; (Y); 90/600; Boys Clb Am; Ski Clb; Hon Roll; Ntl Merit Ltr; Engrng.

SLOVIC, THOMAS M; Schalmont HS; Schenectady, NY; (Y); Var Socr; JV Tennis; Var Wrstlng; Hon Roll; Stdnt Spectrm Awd 82-83; Altrnt Amer Legn Boys ST 84-85; Schlrshp Elmira Coll; Lwyr.

SLUCE, SALLY; Alden HS; Alden, NY; (Y); Art Clb; French Clb; Yrbk Stf; Var Bsktbl; JV Sftbl; Var Trk; Var Vllybl; Comp.

SLY, CHRISTINE; Cicero-North Syracuse HS; Clay, NY; (S); 12/622; Ski Clb; Band; Concert Band; Mrchg Band; Orch; Pep Band; Symp Band; High Hon Roll; Hon Roll; Biology.

SLY, MICHELLE J; Marcellus SR HS; Mc Graw, NY; (Y); 2/164; Church Yth Grp; Ski Clb; Chorus; Church Choir; Sec Sr Cls; JV Im Vllybl; High Hon Roll; NHS; Ntl Merit Ltr; Sal; Pres Marcellus Chptr Natl Hnr Soc 84-85; Schltc Achvt Awd 81-82; Regents Schlrshp 85; Nazareth Coll; Psych.

SLY, SEAN; Mc Graw JR SR HS; Mcgraw, NY; (Y); Boy Scts; Church Yth Grp; French Clb; Quiz Bowl; Ski Clb; Varsity Clb; Var Bsbl; Var Socr; High Hon Roll; Hon Roll; Engrng.

SLYMAN, DE ANNE; Oceanside HS; Oceanside, NY; (Y); Dance Clb; German Clb; JA; School Play; Stage Crew; Cheerleading; Coach Actv; Vllybl; Hon Roll; Outstndng Perfrmnce Ger Awd 85; Bst Poem Channel 13 TV 83; St Johns U; Bus.

SLYWKA, MARK; St Marys Acad; Diamond Point, NY; (S); 5/48; Drama Clb; French Clb; ROTC; Ski Clb; Chorus; Color Guard; Drill Tm; Nwsp Sprt Ed; Var L Bsbl; Var Capt Wrstlng; Regents Schlrshp; Binghamton; Phy.

SMAIL, MICHAEL; West Seneca West HS; West Seneca, NY; (Y); 118/543; Spanish Clb; Varsity Clb; Rep Sr Cls; Rep Stu Cncl; Var Socr; Var Swmmng; Var Vllybl; Bsktbl; Rgnts Schlrshp; Alfred ST Coll; Comp Grphcs.

SMALL, ANDREW; Midwood HS; Brooklyn, NY; (Y); 50/670; Drama Clb; Intnl Clb; Math Tm; Jazz Band; School Play; Symp Band; Variety Show; Rep Stu Cncl; Hon Roll; 1st Pl Pratt Inst Comp Cntst 85.

SMALL, CONSTANCE; Alden Central HS; Alden, NY; (Y); Trs 4-H; FTA; Sec Chorus; Rep Jr Cls; Rep Stu Cncl; JV Sftbl; Hon Roll; Sec NHS; French Clb; Science Clb; 1st Pl Awd 84; Hnrbl Ment Reg Lang Fair 85; Bio.

SMALL, MICHAEL R; St Anthonys HS; Smithtown, NY; (Y); Boy Scts; Camera Clb; Chess Clb; Hon Roll; Duns Sct Awd 83 & 85; Law.

SMALLEN, GAIL; Williamsville East HS; Williamsville, NY; (Y); 2/278; Pres AFS; Drama Clb; Math Clb; Orch; School Musical; School Play; Symp Band; High Hon Roll; NCTE Awd; NHS; Wellesley Bk Awd 84; Mst Outstndng Frshmn & Soph 82-83; Biophysics.

SMALLS, ANTHONY; Cardinal Hayes HS; New York, NY; (Y); 77/264; Yrbk Stf; Hnrs Awd 84; Pre-Law.

SMALLS, SHARRON; Lehman HS; Bronx, NY; (Y); 40/473; JA; Orch; Lit Mag; High Hon Roll; Hon Roll; NHS; Ntl Merit Ltr; Girl Scts; Ed Yrbk Stf; Arista Hnr Socty 83-85; Bst Blck Achvr Awd 83; Harvard-Radcliff; Law.

SMALLS, TAMARA L; Adlai E Stevenson HS; Bronx, NY; (Y); Drama Clb; Chorus; School Musical; Nwsp Ed-Chief; Rep Jr Cls; Aud/Vis; Dance Clb; PAVAS; Teachers Aide; Church Choir; Hnry Awd From Bar Assn For Being In Mock Trial 85; Awd For Litry Piece 83; Rep In A Yth Rally 85; USC; Pre-Law.

SMALLWOOD, CHARLES; H S Of Fashion Industrs; Brooklyn, NY; (Y); Art Clb; Church Yth Grp; JA; Library Aide; Office Aide; Service Clb; School Play; Rep Stu Cncl; Hon Roll; Prfct Atten Awd; Exec Internshp Awd 84; Jr Achv Cert 81; Brooklyn Coll; Accntnt.

SMALLWOOD, RICARDO A; South Shore HS; Brooklyn, NY; (Y); 4-H; Socr; ST U Of NY Buffalo; Areosp En.

SMART, KIMBERLY; Bloomfield Ctr; Ionia, NY; (Y); Latin Clb; Ski Clb; Band; Mrchg Band; School Musical; VP Jr Cls; Var Cheerleading; High Hon Roll; NHS; Church Yth Grp; Fortnightly Awd 85; 1st Rnnr Up Girls St 85; Sci Olymp 84.

SMART, LINDA G; Sherburne Earlville Central Schl; Norwich, NY; (Y); 2/150; Pres Drama Clb; Sec Stu Cncl; Girl Scts; Math Tm; Ski Clb; Band; Chorus; Concert Band; Jazz Band; Mrchg Band; Carleton Cll; Engl Tchr.

SMART, LORALIE; Earl L Vandermeulen HS; Pt Jefferson, NY; (Y); Church Yth Grp; Latin Clb; Acpl Chr; Chorus; Stage Crew; Nwsp Rptr; Nwsp Stf; Lit Mag; NHS; Church Choir; ST U NY; Math.

SMATLAK, ANNE-MARIE; St John The Baptist P HS; Brightwaters, NY; (Y); Cmnty Wkr; Hosp Aide; Sftbl; Vllybl; High Hon Roll; Hon Roll; U Of VT; Bus Admin.

SMAWLEY, KRISTINE; Lindenhurst HS; N Lindenhurst, NY; (Y); Church Yth Grp; French Clb; Girl Scts; Key Clb; Spanish Clb; Chorus; Church Choir; Yrbk Phtg; Yrbk Stf; Swmmng; Sci.

SMEAD, JULIE M; Averill Park HS; Sand Lk, NY; (Y); 1/200; Varsity Clb; Concert Band; Jazz Band; Yrbk Stf; Socr; Vllybl; High Hon Roll; NHS; Band; Pep Band; Ntl Sci Olympd Awd 85; Rensselear Medal-Math & Sci 85; Prncpls Medal 83-85.

SMEAL, TROY A; Lewiston-Porter Central HS; Lewiston, NY; (Y); 1/250; Am Leg Boys St; Cmnty Wkr; French Clb; JA; Political Wkr; Pres Sr Cls; High Hon Roll; NHS; Ntl Merit Ltr; Polit Sci.

SMEDLEY, PAMELA; Bainbridge-Guilford HS; Bainbridge, NY; (Y); Pres VP 4-H; Hosp Aide; Spanish Clb; Mrchg Band; Var Cheerleading; JV Sftbl; Capt JV Vllybl; Cit Awd; Hon Roll; Prfct Atten Awd; Army; Radlgy.

SMELSKI, KAREN; Cato-Meridian HS; Weedsport, NY; (Y); French Clb; Yrbk Stf; Score Keeper; Trk; Vllybl; Hon Roll; Jr NHS; Prfct Atten Awd; Bus.

SMELSKI, MARK A; Cato-Meridian HS; Weedsport, NY; (Y); 23/80; Am Leg Boys St; French Clb; Varsity Clb; Trs Sr Cls; Trs Stu Cncl; Var Capt Bsbl; Var Crs Cntry; Var Ftbl; Var Capt Wrstlng; Hon Roll; Wrstlng Century Clb 100 Wins 85; Sprtsmnshp Awd 85; Alum Schlrshp; Cntrl CT ST U; Bus.

SMERAGLIA, VINCENT; Bishop Ford HS; Brooklyn, NY; (Y); Bowling; Bus Mgmt.

SMERAGLIUOLO, MICHELLE; Jamestown SR HS; Jamestown, NY; (Y); 102/405; Church Yth Grp; Church Choir; Concert Band; Mrchg Band; Orch; Yrbk Bus Mgr; Trs Soph Cls; Hon Roll; Jr NHS; Spanish Clb; Selctd Sister Cty Comm Exc Stu 84; Jamestown Comm Coll; Forgn Lang.

SMIGEL, BETH; Greenville Central HS; Medusa, NY; (Y); Aud/Vis; 4-H; French Clb; Latin Clb; Spanish Clb; Chorus; School Musical; Stage Crew; Stat Trk; 4-H Awd; Elem Ed.

SMITH, ALISA M; Salamanca JR SR HS; Salamanca, NY; (Y); French Clb; Ski Clb; VICA; Yrbk Stf; Sec Sr Cls; Var Swmmng; Hon Roll; Hotel Mgmt.

SMITH, AMY; Avon Central HS; Avon, NY; (Y); French Clb; GAA; Chorus; Sec Frsh Cls; Sec Soph Cls; VP Jr Cls; Var Swmmng; Var Capt Trk; High Hon Roll; Ski Clb; Most Imprvd Awd-Track 84; Geneseo-SUNY; French.

SMITH, AMY; Warwick Valley HS; Warwick, NY; (Y); 20/204; Library Aide; Office Aide; High Hon Roll; Hon Roll.

SMITH, AMY K; Lancaster Central HS; Lancaster, NY; (Y); 103/420; JA; Library Aide; Office Aide; Pep Clb; Chorus; Mrchg Band; Cheerleading; Stat Ftbl; Score Keeper; Mgr Swmmng; Genesee CC; Exec Sec.

SMITH, ANGELA; Edison Tech & Occupational Educ Cnt; Rochester, NY; (Y); Church Yth Grp; Girl Scts; Office Aide; Church Choir; Variety Show; Sec Frsh Cls; VP Jr Cls; VP Sec Sr Cls; Var Cheerleading; JV Sftbl; Delaware ST Coll; Comp.

SMITH, ANNETTE; Horseheads HS; Horseheads, NY; (Y); 90/378; Pres Church Yth Grp; Girl Scts; Band; Mrchg Band; Nwsp Rptr; Nwsp Stf; Yrbk Ed-Chief; Yrbk Stf; Trs Jr Cls; Stu Cncl; Rsprty Thrpy.

SMITH, APRIL E; Homer SR HS; Homer, NY; (Y); 17/200; Church Yth Grp; Sec Spanish Clb; Nwsp Ed-Chief; Yrbk Bus Mgr; High Hon Roll; NHS; NYS Rgnts Schlrshp 85; St John Fisher Coll; Acctng.

SMITH, BARB; Hilton Central HS; Hilton, NY; (Y); VP Sec Church Yth Grp; Band; Church Choir; Concert Band; Jazz Band; Mrchg Band; Pep Band; School Musical; Symp Band; High Hon Roll; Roberts Weslyan Coll; Music.

SMITH, BILL; Franklin Acad; N Bangor, NY; (Y); Speech Tm; Chorus; Church Choir; School Play; Score Keeper; Hon Roll; Epsilon Hnr Scty 84-86; Schlrs For Dollars 84-85; Pblc Rltns.

SMITH, BRANDON JOHN; Hadley-Luzerne Central Schl; Lake Luzerne, NY; (Y); Am Leg Boys St; Varsity Clb; Var Bowling; Prfct Atten Awd; Fnlst NROTC Scholar Cont 85-86; Rensselaer Polytech; Archit.

SMITH, BRENDA; Guilderland HS; Guilderland Ctr, NY; (Y); Church Yth Grp; Letterman Clb; Teachers Aide; Varsity Clb; JV Bsktbl; Score Keeper; Var L Sftbl; Bio.

SMITH, BRIAN; Valley Stream North HS; Franklin Square, NY; (Y); Chess Clb; Cmnty Wkr; Computer Clb; Debate Tm; Drama Clb; 4-H; Model UN; Political Wkr; Chorus; Church Choir; NY Regnts Schlrshp 85; Hofstra Coll Spch Awd 85; Model Cong Bst Spkr Awd 85; Nassau CC; Cmmnctns.

SMITH, BRUCE; Tioga HS; Barton, NY; (S); 11/78; Pres Chess Clb; Pres Computer Clb; Trs Sr Cls; Var L Bsbl; Var L Bsktbl; Var L Ftbl; High Hon Roll; Hon Roll; Hnr Soc; Baseball 2nd Team All-League; Ftbl 1st Team All-League; FL Inst Of Tech; Computer Sci.

SMITH, CAROLE; Lisbon Central HS; Lisbon, NY; (S); 3/47; Trs Church Yth Grp; Trs French Clb; Trs Library Aide; Chorus; Yrbk Stf; High Hon Roll; Pres NHS; Ntl Merit SF; Prfct Atten Awd.

SMITH, CAROLYN; Green Central/Seton Catholic HS; Binghamton, NY; (Y); 29/150; Drama Clb; Key Clb; Ski Clb; Band; Chorus; Mrchg Band; Yrbk Stf; Fld Hcky; Hon Roll; NHS; SUNY-BINGHAMTON; Math.

SMITH, CAROLYN; Roy C Ketcham SR HS; Poughkeepsie, NY; (Y); Hon Roll; Graphic Desgn.

SMITH, CATHERINE; Harry S Truman HS; Bronx, NY; (Y); 82/544; Hosp Aide; Service Clb; Concert Band; Orch; School Musical; Symp Band; Crs Cntry; Trk; Hon Roll; Syracuse U; Elem Schl Tchr.

SMITH, CATHERINE S; Academy Of St Joseph; Brightwaters, NY; (Y); Pres Orch; Yrbk Rptr; VP Frsh Cls; VP Soph Cls; Tennis; Elks Awd; VP NHS; Ntl Merit Ltr; Sal; Model UN; Yth Yr 84-85; Chncllr Schlrshp TX Chrstn U 85; Sthrn Meth U Schlrshp 85; TX Chrstn U; Pre-Med.

SMITH, CHERIE; Greece Athena HS; Rochester, NY; (Y); 2/270; VP Pres DECA; Math Tm; Ski Clb; Symp Band; Sec Frsh Cls; VP Soph Cls; VP Pres Stu Cncl; JV Var Socr; JV Capt Vllybl; NHS; Lilac Teen Semi-Fnlst 85; Acad All-Amer 83-84; Engr.

SMITH, CHRISTIN M; Newtown HS; Jackson Heights, NY; (Y); 193/603; Drama Clb; Rep Frsh Cls; SUNY Coll New Paltz.

SMITH, CHRISTOPHER J; Johnson City SR HS; Johnson City, NY; (Y); 38/212; Mathletes; Math Tm; Var L Mgr(s); St Schlr; Church Yth Grp; Exploring; Broome Comm Coll; Comp Pgm.

SMITH, CHRISTOPHER S; Stissing Mtn JR SR HS; Ancram, NY; (Y); Hon Roll; Vet Med.

SMITH, CONSTANCE; Manhattan Center For Science & Math; Brooklyn, NY; (Y); Library Aide; Math Clb; Quiz Bowl; High Hon Roll; Hon Roll; Prfct Atten Awd; Econmcs, Math 85; Howard U; Elec Engrng.

SMITH, CYNDI; Dryden Central HS; Dryden, NY; (Y); Church Yth Grp; Dance Clb; Drama Clb; FHA; Library Aide; Chorus; School Play; Lit Mag; Rep Jr Cls; Hon Roll; NY City U; Music Thrpst.

SMITH, CYNTHIA; Jamestown HS; Jamestown, NY; (Y); Trs Church Yth Grp; Spanish Clb; Rep Frsh Cls; Rep Jr Cls; Rep Stu Cncl; Var Capt Bsktbl; Var Crs Cntry; Var Capt Trk; Hon Roll; Jr NHS; Rookie Yr V Girls Track 83; MVP Girls Bsktbl 83-84; Girls V Tourn Tm 85; Acctng.

SMITH, DANIEL; Columbia HS; E Greenbush, NY; (Y); 180/375; Nwsp Rptr; Im JV Bsktbl; Powder Puff Ftbl; Suburban Councl All Star Bsktbl Team; Allll Capitalland Bsktbl Team; Accntng.

SMITH, DANIEL; Greece Arcadia HS; Rochester, NY; (Y); 23/292; Church Yth Grp; JV Socr; Var L Trk; Im Library Aide; High Hon Roll; Hon Roll; NHS; Pres Schlr; St Schlr; 1st Level Acad Achvt 84; NYS Regents Schlrshp 85; U Of Buffalo; Arch.

SMITH, DANIEL; Oakfield-Alabama Central HS; Batavia, NY; (Y); Drama Clb; Trs French Clb; Thesps; Varsity Clb; Concert Band; Mrchg Band; School Musical; School Play; Var L Bsbl; Var L Ftbl; Bdcstng.

SMITH, DANIEL C; Williamsville North HS; East Amherst, NY; (Y); 80/316; Band; Chorus; Madrigals; School Musical; Swing Chorus; Nwsp Stf; Yrbk Stf; Hon Roll; NYS Regnts Schlrshp 85; ST U NY Fredonia; Mus.

SMITH, DARCY; Berlin Central HS; Berlin, NY; (Y); 18/80; GAA; Chorus; School Play; Yrbk Rptr; Rep Stu Cncl; JV Bsktbl; Var Socr; Var Sftbl; Hon Roll; Hnbl Mntn Vrsty Sccr 85.

SMITH, DAVID; Wellsville HS; Wellsville, NY; (Y); 31/130; School Play; Stage Crew; Nwsp Rptr; Nwsp Sprt Ed; Nwsp Stf; Rep Sr Cls; Rep Stu Cncl; Var JV Bsbl; Var JV Bsktbl; Var JV Socr; Wellsville Alumni Assn Schlrshp 85; Charles Engeldar Memrl Schlrshp 85; US Marine Corp Athlte Awd 85; Finger Lakes CC; Mrktng.

SMITH, DAVID M; Carmel HS; Patterson, NY; (Y); 6/370; Pres Soph Cls; JV Bsbl; Var L Bsktbl; Var Capt Ftbl; High Hon Roll; NHS; Golden Dozen Stu Athl Awd; Ftbl Found Hall Fame 85; All Cty Hnrbl Ment Ftbl 83-84; Boston Coll.

SMITH, DAVID M; Whitesboro SR HS; Marcy, NY; (Y); 35/358; Pres Church Yth Grp; Model UN; Orch; Ed Lit Mag; Var Golf; Hon Roll; Opt Clb Awd; ST U-Albany; Russn Lang.

SMITH, DAWN; Mayfield JR SR HS; Gloversville, NY; (Y); Girl Scts; Varsity Clb; Sr Cls; Cheerleading; Crs Cntry; Socr; Trk; Hon Roll; Fultn Mntgmry CC; Bus Cnsltnt.

SMITH, DAWN; Mt Vernon HS; Mt Vernon, NY; (Y); FHA; Teachers Aide; Badmtn; Bsktbl; Vllybl; Hon Roll; Recog Cert 83; Cmmndtn Sci Hnr Roll Cert 83; Hampton U; Soc Wrk.

SMITH, DAWN; Tottenville HS; Staten Island, NY; (Y); 21/862; Dance Clb; School Musical; School Play; Variety Show; Nwsp Ed-Chief; Nwsp Rptr; Yrbk Ed-Chief; Lit Mag; High Hon Roll; Jr NHS; Paul Driscoll Awd Ecnmcs & Scl Stds 85; NYC Brd Of Ed Chncllrs Roll Hnr Ctns 85; SI AANP Assoc Awd; NY U; Jrnlsm.

SMITH, DEBBI; Germantown Central HS; Germantown, NY; (Y); 12/50; Pep Clb; Band; Chorus; Concert Band; Mrchg Band; Yrbk Stf; JV Fld Hcky; JV Gym; High Hon Roll; Hon Roll; Spnsh Awd 83; Fld Hcky Athl Awd 84; Nrsng.

SMITH, DECEMBER LOUANN; Sigonella American HS; FPO, NY; (Y); 3/18; Drama Clb; ROTC; Var L Chorus; Rptr Nwsp Rptr; Yrbk Phtg; Var L Tennis; High Hon Roll; Pres NHS; Acadmc Excllnc Ltr Maury HS 82; NJ ROTC Acadmc Team 83; Word Prcsng.

SMITH, DEREK S; Roslyn HS; Roslyn, NY; (Y); 2/250; Pres Chess Clb; Pres Computer Clb; Capt Debate Tm; Science Clb; Nwsp Stf; JV Socr; Var Trk; NHS; Ntl Merit SF; 2nd Pl NY ST Energy Res Comp 84; 1st & 3rd Cnty Chess Tourn 82; Chem Resrch Schlrshp U Of TX 84; Med.

SMITH, DERRICK B; Rome Free Acad; Rome, NY; (Y); 81/512; German Clb; Latin Clb; Letterman Clb; Varsity Clb; JV Badmtn; Var Capt Ftbl; Capt Trk; Hon Roll; Jr NHS; NHS; Empire ST Games Trck & Fld 84; Regents Schlrshp 85; SUNY Cortland; Phy Thrpy.

SMITH, DIANNA; Lowville Acad And Central Schl; Lowville, NY; (Y); Pres FBLA; Color Guard; Rep Frsh Cls; Rep Soph Cls; Var Capt Cheerleading; JV Var Socr; JV Var Sftbl; JV Swmmng; JV Vllybl; Gregg Shorthand Awd 85; Exec Sec.

SMITH, DINA; Stissing Mountain HS; Red Nook, NY; (Y); Hon Roll; Marit Coll; Chld Cre.

SMITH, DONALD; St Josephs Collegiate Inst; N Tonawanda, NY; (Y); 10/200; Boys Clb Am; Yrbk Phtg; High Hon Roll; NHS; Engrng.

SMITH, DONALD E; Vestal HS; Vestal, NY; (Y); 100/475; Church Yth Grp; Var Capt Lcrss; Var L Socr; NYS Rgnts Schlrshp 85; Stu Of Qtr 85; Clarkson U; Chem Engr.

SMITH, DONNA; Sacred Heart Acad; Lynbrook, NY; (S); 33/186; Sec Debate Tm; Math Tm; NFL; Chorus; School Musical; Rep Stu Cncl; Hon Roll; NHS; Accntnt.

SMITH, DOUGLAS; Bishop Kearney HS; Webster, NY; (Y); JV Ftbl; High Hon Roll; NHS; Prfct Atten Awd; Natl Sci Merit Awd 84; Engr.

SMITH, DUSTIN; West Irondequoit HS; Rochester, NY; (Y); 75/378; Aud/Vis; Model UN; Ski Clb; School Musical; School Play; JV Var Trk; Im Vllybl; Boy Scts; Camera Clb; Chess Clb; Semi Fnlst Acadmc Decthln Tm Selctn 85; Intl Rel.

SMITH, DWAYNE V; Midwood HS; Brooklyn, NY; (Y); 166/605; Boy Scts; Chess Clb; Lib Chorus; Madrigals; School Musical; Ed Lit Mag; Im Bsktbl; Im Vllybl; Hon Roll; Prfct Atten Awd; Dist Attys Ldrshp Awd 81; Engrng.

SMITH, EDNA; Susquehanna Valley HS; Conklin, NY; (Y); Church Yth Grp; GAA; Girl Scts; JA; FCA; 4-H; Office Aide; Varsity Clb; Im Badmtn; Im Bsbl; Stac All-Star Ctchr 84; Mst Vlbl Plyr In Sccr 83; Bus.

SMITH, EDWARD; Newfield HS; Centereach, NY; (S); 5/560; Varsity Clb; Band; Co-Capt Bsktbl; NHS; All Leag Team Bsktbl 84-85; NYS Assn Of Hlth Phys Ed & Rec Awd 84-85; Engrng.

SMITH, ELIZABETH; Sacred Heart Acad; Garden City, NY; (S); Church Yth Grp; Dance Clb; VP Drama Clb; Pres Q&S; Chorus; Madrigals; School Musical; Pres Frsh Cls; Sec Trs Stu Cncl; JC Awd; Hugh O Bryan Ldrshp Found Ambsdr 84; U S Stu Counc Awd 84; U S Ntl Ldrshp Mer Awd 84; Drama.

SMITH, ELIZABETH A; Marcellus SR HS; Marcellus, NY; (Y); 26/173; Drama Clb; Chorus; Church Choir; School Musical; Stage Crew; Variety Show; Yrbk Stf; Socr; Trk; Vllybl; Hobart & William Smith; Psych.

SMITH, FRANK A; Pittsford-Mendon HS; Pittsford, NY; (Y); Model UN; Concert Band; Jazz Band; Pep Band; Ed Yrbk Phtg; JV Socr; JV Trk; Hon Roll; Pres NHS; Ntl Merit SF; All ST & County Bands 81-84; Rochester Philhrmnc Yth Orch 84-85; PTA Music 84; PTA Chem Awd 83; Chem.

SMITH, GREGORY M; Queensburg HS; Glen Falls, NY; (Y); 12/222; Math Clb; Var L Trk; High Hon Roll; NHS; Ntl Merit Ltr; NYS Regents Schlrshp 85; Albany Intl Schlrshp 85; Rensselaer Polytech Inst; Elect.

SMITH, HEIDI J; Bloomfield Central HS; Holcomb, NY; (Y); Pres AFS; Am Leg Aux Girls St; Church Yth Grp; Color Guard; Concert Band; Yrbk Stf; VP Stu Cncl; High Hon Roll; NHS; Trs Frsh Cls; Htl Rest Mngmnt.

SMITH, HEIDI J; Gouverneur Central HS; Gouverneur, NY; (Y); Acpl Chr; Church Choir; School Musical; School Play; Stage Crew; Socr; Sftbl; Hon Roll; Jr NHS; NHS; Rensselaer Polytech Inst; Engr.

SMITH, HOLLY L; Cazenovia Central HS; Manlius, NY; (Y); 4/155; 4-H; Band; Chorus; Jazz Band; Mrchg Band; Var Tennis; 4-H Awd; High Hon Roll; NHS; NY ST Regents Schlrshp Awd 85; NY ST Diary Princess 85; Pred Acad Fitness Awds 85; SUNY Potsdam; Comp Sci.

SMITH, HORACE; Mc Kee Vocational & Tech; Staten Is, NY; (Y); 18/238; Varsity Clb; Var Ftbl; Hon Roll; NHS.

SMITH, HURDIS; St Johns Prep; South Ozone, NY; (Y); Hon Roll; John Jay Schl Law; Lwyr.

SMITH, JACKLYN; Washington Irving HS; Brooklyn, NY; (Y); Dance Clb; Hosp Aide; PAVAS; Off Jr Cls; Badmtn; Bsbl; Bowling; Coach Actv; Gym; Sftbl.

SMITH JR, JAMES R; Owen D Young HS; Van Hornesville, NY; (Y); Ski Clb; Band; Chorus; Drm & Bgl; Mrchg Band; Stage Crew; JV Var Bsktbl; Mgr(s); Var Socr; DAR Awd; Bus.

SMITH, JANET; St Pius V HS; Bronx, NY; (Y); English Clb; Library Aide; Church Choir; Fordham U; Pre-Med.

SMITH, JARED S; Pelham Memorial HS; Pelham, NY; (Y); 7/177; Band; Mrchg Band; Lit Mag; Var Ftbl; Var Trk; Hon Roll; NHS; Ntl Merit SF.

SMITH, JEFFREY; Webster HS; Easton, CT; (Y); 22/560; Church Yth Grp; Computer Clb; Drama Clb; German Clb; Thesps; Band; Chorus; Church Choir; Concert Band; Jazz Band; Ntl Schl Chrl Awd, Rgnts Schlrshp 85; Grmn Ntl Hnr Soc 84-85; Clarkson U; Elec Engrng.

SMITH, JEFFREY K; Arkport Central Schl; Arkport, NY; (Y); 8/48; Chorus; Var Mgr(s); Var Trk; Im Wt Lftg; Stat Wrstlng; High Hon Roll; Hon Roll; ST Rgnts Schlrshp 85; Alfred Ag & Tech; Elec Mechncl.

SMITH, JEFFREY W; Johnstown HS; Johnstown, NY; (Y); Church Yth Grp; Cmnty Wkr; Math Clb; JV Bsktbl; Im Ftbl; Capt Socr; Hon Roll; NHS; NY ST Rgnts Schlrshp Wnr 85-89; Union Coll; Medicine.

SMITH, JENNIFER; Camden Central HS; Camden, NY; (Y); Debate Tm; Drama Clb; Nwsp Stf; Yrbk Stf; High Hon Roll; NHS; Intl Affrs.

SMITH, JENNIFER A; Salamanca HS; Killbuck, NY; (Y); #3 In Class; Am Leg Aux Girls St; Model UN; Ski Clb; Varsity Clb; Band; Pres Stu Cncl; Capt Swmmng; French Hon Soc; High Hon Roll; NHS; Med.

SMITH, JENNIFER B; Bishop Loughlin M HS; Jamaica, NY; (S); 31/185; Church Yth Grp; Dance Clb; Speech Tm; Chorus; Church Choir; School Play; Yrbk Stf; Im Trk; Im Vllybl; Hon Roll; Catholic U America; Chldhd Educ.

SMITH, JENNIFER J; Au Sable Valley Central Schl; Keeseville, NY; (Y); 7/128; Model UN; Band; Rep Frsh Cls; Rep Stu Cncl; Var Capt Bsktbl; Var Stat Score Keeper; Var Capt Swmmng; Var L Trk; Hon Roll; VP NHS; Regents Schlrshp; Swimming States; Track & Swimming Records; Siena Coll; Pre-Law.

SMITH, JENNIFER L; East Aurora HS; East Aurora, NY; (Y); 23/182; Camp Fr Inc; Church Yth Grp; School Musical; AFS; Var Socr; Hon Roll; Jr NHS; NHS; Amer Wmns Bus Assoc Schlrshp 85; Le Moyne Acad Schlrshp 85; Le Moyne; Engl.

SMITH, JILL; Mynderse Acad; Seneca Falls, NY; (S); 21/132; Stage Crew; Yrbk Stf; Var Trk; High Hon Roll; Hon Roll; Bsns Mgmt.

SMITH, JIM; Edmeston Central HS; Edmeston, NY; (Y); Am Leg Boys St; 4-H; Chorus; Yrbk Ed-Chief; Pres Frsh Cls; Pres Soph Cls; Trs Jr Cls; Pres Sr Cls; Var Bsbl; Chess Clb; Amer Lgn Aux Essay Cntst; Sat Smnr Prog; Amer Lgn Aux Schlrshp; Plattsburgh ST; Sec Ed.

SMITH, JOANNE; Whitney Point SR HS; Whitney Point, NY; (Y); 4/114; Sec Band; Concert Band; Mrchg Band; Yrbk Bus Mgr; Sec Soph Cls; VP Jr Cls; Sec Stu Cncl; JV Var Cheerleading; JV Vllybl; High Hon Roll; Regnts Schlrshp 85; Pres Acadmc Fit Awd 85; Broome CC; Chem Engrng Tech.

SMITH, JOHANNA M; St Barnabas HS; Bronx, NY; (Y); French Clb; Office Aide; Teachers Aide; Twrlr; Hon Roll; Nrsg Rgnts Schlrshp 85; Coll Mt St Vincent; Nrsg.

SMITH, JOSIE A M; Ogdensburg Free Acad; Ogdensburg, NY; (Y); Cmnty Wkr; Hosp Aide; Chorus; Color Guard; Mrchg Band; Nwsp Stf; JV Cheerleading; Var Trk.

SMITH, JULIE; Chautauqua Central HS; Mayville, NY; (Y); Ski Clb; Band; Chorus; Rep Frsh Cls; Rep Soph Cls; JV Var Bsktbl; Var Sftbl; Var Swmmng; High Hon Roll; NHS; Awd Outstndng Photo 84; Math.

SMITH, JULIE A; Midlakes HS; Geneva, NY; (Y); 23/154; Red Cross Aide; Service Clb; Yrbk Sprt Ed; VP Frsh Cls; Pres Sr Cls; Rep Stu Cncl; Var L Cheerleading; Var L Socr; High Hon Roll; NHS; Outstndng Teen Of Finger Lakes 84; Crannett Yth Cares Awd 84; NY ST Regents Schlrshp Winner 85; ST U Geneseo; Business Admin.

SMITH, KAREN; Onteora HS; Pine Hill, NY; (S); 7/245; Math Tm; Orch; Var Capt Crs Cntry; Var L Trk; Wt Lftg; High Hon Roll; NHS; Ntl Merit Ltr.

SMITH, KAREN; Rome Free Acad; Rome, NY; (Y); 1/512; Girl Scts; Varsity Clb; Rep Stu Cncl; Var L Cheerleading; JV Fld Hcky; Var L Trk; Var L Twrlr; DAR Awd; NHS; Ntl Merit SF; Preprofessional.

SMITH, KATHI; Elmira Free Acad; Elmira, NY; (Y); Trs Church Yth Grp; JA; VICA; High Hon Roll; Corning CC; Comp Prgrmr.

SMITH, KATHLEEN; Onteora Central HS; Bearsville, NY; (S); Math Tm; Chorus; Orch; School Musical; Ed Nwsp Stf; Rep Jr Cls; Var Capt Bsbl; Fld Hcky; Var Trk; High Hon Roll; Nwspr Edtr 85-86; Orchstr Crct Mistrs 85-86; Pres 85-86.

SMITH, KATHRYN; Harry S Truman HS; Bronx, NY; (Y); Church Yth Grp; Trs Church Choir; Orch; Sftbl; Hon Roll; NHS; Arista 82; Psych.

SMITH, KELLI; Conastota HS; Canastota, NY; (Y); High Hon Roll; Hon Roll; Lion Awd; Ntl Merit Ltr.

SMITH, KELLY; Broadalbin Central HS; Broadalbin, NY; (Y); Drama Clb; Girl Scts; Hosp Aide; Pep Clb; Varsity Clb; Band; School Play; JV Var Socr; Var Capt Trk; JV Var Vllybl; Girl Scouts Gold Awd; Psych.

SMITH, KELLY; Marion Central HS; Marion, NY; (Y); French Clb; VP FBLA; Band; Color Guard; Concert Band; Yrbk Stf; Tennis; Bus Mgmt.

SMITH, KENT; Mercy HS; Shoreham, NY; (Y); Boy Scts; Chess Clb; Ski Clb; JV Ftbl; Var Golf; JV Var Wt Lftg; Ntl Merit Ltr; NEDT Tst Awd Lttr; U Of South FL; Bus Admin.

SMITH, KERRI; Harborfields HS; Centerport, NY; (Y); Drama Clb; Hosp Aide; Teachers Aide; Yrbk Stf; Lit Mag; NHS; Huntington Twp Chmbr Of Cmmrce Essay Cntst 84; Huntington Hosp JR Axlry Serv Awd 84; Pre-Med.

SMITH, KEVIN; Little Falls JR & SR HS; Little Falls, NY; (S); 3/100; Am Leg Boys St; Church Yth Grp; FBLA; JA; Natl Beta Clb; Spanish Clb; Varsity Clb; JV Bsbl; Var Bsktbl; JV Var Ftbl; DAR Good Ctznshp Awd; Boston Coll; Bus Adm.

SMITH, KEVIN; Maryvale HS; Cheektowaga, NY; (Y); Varsity Clb; JV Var Bsbl; JV Var Ftbl; Trk; Hon Roll; VP NHS; ST U Of New York; Engnrng.

SMITH, KEVIN; Shenendehowa HS; Clifton Park, NY; (Y); Leo Clb; Ski Clb; Soph Cls; JV Bsbl; High Hon Roll; NHS; Saratogian Acad Achvt Awd Wnnr 84; Engrng.

SMITH, KEVIN; Whitesboro HS; Whitesboro, NY; (Y); Church Yth Grp; FCA; Ski Clb; Band; Church Choir; Bsktbl; Clarkson Coll; Engrng.

SMITH, KIM; Seaford HS; Seaford, NY; (Y); Yrbk Stf; Cheerleading; Htl Mngmnt.

SMITH, KIMBERLEIGH; Horseheads HS; Horseheads, NY; (S); 59/407; Drama Clb; German Clb; Ski Clb; Band; Concert Band; Mrchg Band; Orch; Ed Nwsp Stf; Yrbk Stf; Hon Roll; Area All ST Band; Jrnlst.

SMITH, KWAW D; Mt Vernon HS; Mt Vernon, NY; (Y); 81/700; DECA; Hon Roll; Regnts Schlrshp 85; U Of MD College Park; Bus Adm.

SMITH, LAURIE; Batavia SR HS; Batavia, NY; (Y); 23/217; Cmnty Wkr; Natl Beta Clb; Office Aide; Political Wkr; Service Clb; Ski Clb; Color Guard; School Musical; Yrbk Stf; Hon Roll; Hghst Engl Avg Awd 84-85; Pre Law.

SMITH, LAURIE A; Commack High Schl South; Commack, NY; (Y); 6/374; Math Tm; Variety Show; Yrbk Stf; Socr; Var Capt Trk; High Hon Roll; NHS; Admsn Schlrshp St John Fisher 85; Excptnl Sr Game 84; NASA Sp Shuttle Stu Invlvmnt Awd 83, 84 & 85; St John Fisher; Pre-Vet.

SMITH, LAWRENCE M; Newfield HS; Selden, NY; (Y); Boy Scts; Church Yth Grp; Spanish Clb; JV Ftbl; Hon Roll; Prfct Atten Awd; Outstndng Sci Stud Awd 83; Mvp Baseball 84; All Star Baseball 84; Aeronautcl Engr.

SMITH, LESLIE A; Dominican Commercial HS; Flushing, NY; (Y); 52/277; Dance Clb; Drama Clb; Hosp Aide; Chorus; School Play; Yrbk Phtg; Yrbk Stf; Siena Clb Acadmc Achvt 82-85; Natl Hnr Rl Natl Merit Schlrshp 84-85; Pres Acadmc Ftns Awd 85; Hunter Clg; Med.

SMITH, LILLIAN; Academy Of St Joseph HS; Brightwaters, NY; (Y); Drama Clb; Library Aide; Speech Tm; Chorus; School Play; Variety Show; Yrbk Stf; Trs Soph Cls; Pres Stu Cncl; NHS; H S Schrlshp For $300 84-85; Chosen For Ldrshp Prog At U Of Nortre Dame 84-85; Cum Laude Awd 83-84; Pre-Law.

SMITH, LINDA A; Shaker HS; Latham, NY; (Y); Church Yth Grp; Key Clb; Latin Clb; Lit Mag; VP Frsh Cls; VP Soph Cls; JV Fld Hcky; High Hon Roll; Hon Roll; Ntl Merit Ltr; Regnts Schlrshp 85; U Of Rochester.

SMITH, LISA; Forestville Central Schl; Forestville, NY; (Y); Ski Clb; Varsity Clb; Flag Corp; Yrbk Stf; Var Capt Cheerleading; Art Schlrshp 85; Fredonia ST U; Des.

SMITH, LISA; Hicksville SR HS; Hicksville, NY; (Y); Hosp Aide; Ski Clb; Band; Hon Roll; Bus Adm.

SMITH, LISA; Smithtown H S West; Smithtown, NY; (Y); Var Trk; Hon Roll; Ltr In Track 83; Mass Cmnctns.

SMITH, LORI; Niagara Catholic HS; Niagara Falls, NY; (Y); 8/77; Pres Church Yth Grp; French Clb; Ski Clb; Church Choir; Yrbk Stf; Off Frsh Cls; Var Capt Badmtn; Tennis; Hon Roll; NHS; Diocesan Rep 84; Hope Coll Holland; Nrsg.

SMITH, LORRAINE D; Lake Placid Central Schl; Lake Placid, NY; (Y); 2/53; AFS; Sec Computer Clb; Rep Stu Cncl; NHS; Sal; Regents Schlrshp 85; SUNY Potsdam; Biology.

SMITH, LYNN B; Pulaski JR SR HS; Pulaski, NY; (S); Boy Scts; Exploring; Trk; High Hon Roll; NHS; Teacher.

SMITH, LYNNETTE; Grover Cleveland HS; Hollis, NY; (Y); 169/659; Hon Roll; Prfct Atten Awd; Comp Prgmr.

SMITH, MARCIA; Geneva HS; Geneva, NY; (S); 5/170; French Clb; Hosp Aide; Ski Clb; School Musical; JV L Socr; Var Trk; Ntl Merit Ltr; Model UN; Frnch Awd; Yth Ldrshp Salute; Engrng.

SMITH, MARK W; Honeoye Falls-Lima HS; Lima, NY; (Y); 10/160; Am Leg Boys St; Pres Church Yth Grp; French Clb; Model UN; Chorus; School Musical; NHS; Cert Merit Eastmn Schl Of Music 84; Cmmnty Ed Div Schlrshp Eastmn 82-86.

SMITH, MARY; Notre Dame HS; Elmira, NY; (Y); Cmnty Wkr; Key Clb; Rep Soph Cls; Rep Stu Cncl; JV Var Cheerleading; Hon Roll.

SMITH, MARY ANNE; Mount Markham Central; W Winfield, NY; (Y); #33 In Class; Pres Church Yth Grp; Model UN; Chorus; Concert Band; Pres Frsh Cls; Pres Soph Cls; Capt Var Cheerleading; Hon Roll; Drama Clb; French Clb; Louis T Groat Awd For Outstndng Ctznshp 84; Thtr.

SMITH, MARY BETH; Clayton A Bouton HS; Voorheesville, NY; (Y); Sec Pres Key Clb; Nwsp Phtg; Nwsp Stf; Yrbk Phtg; Capt Powder Puff Ftbl; Sftbl; Trk; Kiwanis Awd; Mst Vlbl Mbr In Key Clb 84-85; Mst Imprvd In Hm Ec 83; Nrsng.

SMITH, MATT; Ossining HS; Ossining, NY; (Y); 34/260; Exploring; Temple Yth Grp; DAR Awd; Hon Roll; Engrng.

SMITH, MATTHEW; Camden Central HS; Camden, NY; (S); Am Leg Boys St; Hosp Aide; Chorus; Yrbk Ed-Chief; Pres Soph Cls; Pres Stu Cncl; Var JV Bsbl; Var JV Bsktbl; Var JV Ftbl; High Hon Roll; Harvard; Dentist.

SMITH, MATTHEW G; Lake Shore Central HS; Derby, NY; (Y); 1/259; School Musical; Yrbk Stf; Pres CAP; JV Var Bsbl; JV Var Ftbl; NHS; Val; 4-H; Chorus; Cit Awd; Colgate Mem Alumni Schrshp 85; MI St Cert 85; Athl Cncl Stu Athl Awd 85; Colgate U; Lib Arts.

SMITH, MAUREEN; Notre Dame Bishop Gibbons HS; Ballston Lk, NY; (Y); Rep Frsh Cls; Rep Soph Cls; Rep Jr Cls; Rep Stu Cncl; Var L Trk; Church Yth Grp; GAA; JA; Letterman Clb; Red Cross Aide; MVP-SPRING & Indoor 84-85; American H S Athlete 85; Phy Ed Teacher.

SMITH, MAUREEN P; Eastchester HS; Eastchester, NY; (Y); 8/163; Key Clb; Ed Yrbk Stf; Co-Capt Trk; Hon Roll; Pres NHS; Ntl Merit Ltr; Sec Soph Cls; NYS Regnts Schlrshp 85; Duke U.

SMITH, MELISSA; Morrisville-Eaton Hs; Morrisville, NY; (Y); 6/60; Cmnty Wkr; 4-H; GAA; VP Soph Cls; Rep Stu Cncl; Bsktbl; Cheerleading; Fld Hcky; Trk; High Hon Roll; Elem Ed.

SMITH, MICHAEL; Amsterdam HS; Amsterdam, NY; (Y); Boy Scts; Letterman Clb; Varsity Clb; Y-Teens; Im Ftbl; Var L Socr; Var L Trk; Northeastern U; CPA.

SMITH, MICHELE; Waterfoed-Halfmoon HS; Waterford, NY; (Y); Soroptimist; Chorus; Yrbk Stf; Coach Actv; JV Var Sftbl; JV Capt Vllybl; Hon Roll; JV Bsktbl; Vllybl Hghst Pnt Screr 83-84.

SMITH, MICHELLE; Brooklyn Tech HS; Brooklyn, NY; (Y); Dance Clb; Office Aide; Yrbk Stf; Capt Cheerleading; Vllybl; Hon Roll; Jr NHS; Teachers Aide; Comm.

SMITH, MICHELLE; Brooklyn Tech HS; Brooklyn, NY; (Y); Hosp Aide; Variety Show; Hon Roll; Exclnc Global Hstry 84; Bio.

SMITH, MICHELLE; Roy C Ketcham SR HS; Poughkeepsie, NY; (Y); 36/507; AFS; Drama Clb; Radio Clb; Thesps; School Play; Stage Crew; Yrbk Phtg; Var JV Swmmng; High Hon Roll; NHS; Bst Supprtng Actrss 85; Mst Individualistic Cls 85; U Albany.

SMITH, NANCY; Cicero N Syracuse HS; N Syracuse, NY; (S); 43/711; Church Yth Grp; Stage Crew; Powder Puff Ftbl; MONY Schlstc Art Awd 83; Natl Schlstc Art Awd 83; Studio Art.

SMITH, NICK; Alden Central HS; Alden, NY; (Y); Church Yth Grp; Letterman Clb; Yrbk Phtg; Im Var Bsktbl; Var Crs Cntry; Var Trk; Geology.

SMITH, NORINE L; Nanuet SR HS; Nanuet, NY; (Y); 23/180; Church Yth Grp; Math Clb; School Play; Yrbk Ed-Chief; Lit Mag; Var Trk; Capt Vllybl; Hon Roll; NHS; Rotary Awd; PTA & Rotry Schlrshps; U Of DE.

SMITH, PATRICIA; Ichabod Crane HS; Valatie, NY; (Y); 42/150; JV Var Bsktbl; Var Mgr(s); JV Sftbl; JV Vllybl; Hon Roll; NHS; Mst Imprvd Plyr Awd-Vrsty Bsktbl 83-84; 2 Cert Achvt Bus 84 & 85; Vrsty Pin Sftbl & Bsktbl 83-84; Army; Bus Mngmt.

SMITH, PATRICIA; Owen D Young Central Schl; Richfield Springs, NY; (S); 2/13; Q&S; Nwsp Bus Mgr; Nwsp Stf; Yrbk Ed-Chief; Yrbk Stf; Pres Sr Cls; VP Stu Cncl; Cit Awd; Hon Roll; Sal; Herkimer County CC; Acctng.

SMITH, PATRICK; Martin Luther King Jr HS; Ny, NY; (Y); 23/280; Band; Bsbl; Hon Roll.

SMITH, PATTY; Boliver Central HS; Little Genesee, NY; (Y); Spanish Clb; Varsity Clb; Band; Concert Band; Mrchg Band; Pep Band; JV Bowling; Var Cheerleading; Mgr(s); Mgr Sftbl; Costmlgst.

SMITH, PATTY; Hamburg HS; Hamburg, NY; (Y); 268/390; Band; Concert Band; Jazz Band; Mrchg Band; Orch; School Musical; Symp Band; Im Swmmng; Band Secr & Librarian 84-85; Natl Band Awd 85; Buffalo U; Music.

SMITH, PAULA MARIE; Faith Heritage HS; Pulaski, NY; (Y); 9/22; Chorus; Yrbk Rptr; Ed Yrbk Stf; VP Sr Cls; Var Socr; Var Trk; Hon Roll; NHS; Homng Ct 84; Meet The Teens/Herald-Journl 85; Bus Adm.

SMITH, PEGGY; Molland Central HS; Holland, NY; (Y); Church Yth Grp; Score Keeper; Timer; Hon Roll; Scl Wrk.

SMITH, PENNY; Tri-Valley Central HS; Claryville, NY; (Y); Drama Clb; Chorus; Concert Band; School Musical; Yrbk Stf; High Hon Roll; NHS; Girl Scts; Pep Clb; Political Wkr; Am Musical Found Band Hnrs 83; US Senate Page 84; Appt Intrnshp Sen John East NC 86; Comm.

SMITH, PHILIP; Valley Stream North HS; Valley Stream, NY; (Y); 15/120; Debate Tm; Math Tm; Model UN; Quiz Bowl; Nwsp Bus Mgr; High Hon Roll; Hon Roll; Acad All Amer 85.

SMITH, RACHEL; Forestville Central HS; Forestville, NY; (Y); Spanish Clb; Yrbk Stf; VP Rep Frsh Cls; Rep Soph Cls; Off Jr Cls; Trs Sr Cls; Sec Stu Cncl; Var Capt Bsktbl; Var L Sftbl; Var L Vllybl; Brockport ST; Sociology.

SMITH, RACHEL A; Midlakes HS; Geneva, NY; (Y); 12/174; Cmnty Wkr; Model UN; Service Clb; Yrbk Stf; French Clb; Hosp Aide; Thesps; High Hon Roll; Hon Roll; NHS; Regents Schlrshp 85; Beneficial Hodson Merit Schlrshp 85; Washington Coll; Pre Law.

SMITH, REBECCA; Mohonasen HS; Schenectady, NY; (Y); Trs Key Clb; Spanish Clb; Var Bsktbl; JV Vllybl; High Hon Roll; Hon Roll; NHS.

SMITH, REBECCA; Tonawanda SR HS; Tonawanda, NY; (Y); Service Clb; Stu Cncl; Capt Var Cheerleading; Spec Educ.

SMITH, REBECCA A; Fox Lane HS; Pound Ridge, NY; (Y); 12/300; Yrbk Stf; High Hon Roll; NHS; Pony Club Awds 78-85; Current Events Awd 84; Sci Hnrs Pgm 84-85; Wesleyan U; Geolgy.

SMITH, REBEKAH L; Wilson Central HS; Newfane, NY; (Y); 25/134; Church Yth Grp; Hosp Aide; Thesps; Chorus; School Musical; School Play; Rep Stu Cncl; Var Trk; Hon Roll; Regnts Schlrshp 85; Extr Chrstn HS Stu Awd 84; Eastern Nazerene; Nrs.

SMITH, RICHARD; Bronx High School Of Science; New York, NY; (Y); Yrbk Stf; Lit Mag; LIU Scholar Acad Excllnce 85; Awd Exmplry Libr Svc 85; Musc Dept Achvt 85; Long Island U Brooklyn; Phrmcy.

SMITH III, ROBERT T; Alexander Central HS; Alexander, NY; (Y); 15/85; AFS; Boy Scts; 4-H; Varsity Clb; Band; Stu Cncl; Var L Bsbl; Var Capt Crs Cntry; Im Trk; Var L Wrstlng; Comp Sci.

SMITH, RODGER; Niagara Falls HS; Niagara Falls, NY; (Y); 1/200; Am Leg Boys St; VP French Clb; Key Clb; Pres Jr Cls; Pres Sr Cls; Rep Stu Cncl; Var Bsbl; Var Capt Ftbl; Trs NHS; Val; Dan Mitulinsky Awd Ftbl 84; Golden Glove Bsbl 85; Unsung Hero Bsbl 85.

SMITH, ROGER K; Hunter College HS; Brooklyn, NY; (Y); Drama Clb; Math Tm; Pres Chorus; School Play; VP Swing Chorus; Mu Alp Tht; Ntl Merit SF.

SMITH, SARA H; Nardin Acad; Williamsville, NY; (Y); Church Yth Grp; Model UN; Ski Clb; School Play; Hon Roll; NYS Rgnts Schlrshp; 2nd Hnrs; St Bonaventiere; Bus.

SMITH, SHANE R; Baldwin SR HS; Baldwin, NY; (Y); 65/500; Am Leg Boys St; Key Clb; Drm Mjr(t); Lcrss; High Hon Roll; Hon Roll; NHS; Battalion Chief Naval Resv Ldrshp Awds 84-85; V Riflery 83-85; W Point Military Acad; Chem Eng.

SMITH, SHARON A; Harborfield HS; Huntington, NY; (Y); 6/335; Intnl Clb; Y-Teens; Band; Concert Band; Mrchg Band; Pep Band; Symp Band; JV Var Badmtn; High Hon Roll; Lion Awd; Joseph Codella Eng Awd 82; Span Awd 82; Lions Clb Schlrshp 85; SUNY Albany; Comp Sci.

SMITH, SHAWN; Newfield HS; Selden, NY; (Y); JV Bsktbl; Var Bowling; Hon Roll; PA ST; Engr.

SMITH JR, SHEDRICK; Hutch Tech HS; Buffalo, NY; (Y); Church Yth Grp; JA; Var L Bsbl; Var Bowling; Var L Ice Hcky; NC A&T ST U; Comp Sci.

SMITH, SHELLEY G; Notre Dame-Bishop Gibbons HS; Schenechacy, NY; (Y); 33/112; Red Cross Aide; Var Capt Cheerleading; High Hon Roll; NHS; Regents Schlrshp 85; Comm Serv Awd 83; Marist Coll; Comm.

SMITH, SHERI; Pulaski Scad Central Schl; Pulasky, NY; (Y); Drama Clb; French Clb; GAA; Math Clb; Yrbk Phtg; Yrbk Stf; Bsktbl; Socr; Trk; Cit Awd; Criminolgy.

SMITH, STACY L; Odessa-Montour Central Schl; Odessa, NY; (Y); 1/80; Ski Clb; Band; Rep Stu Cncl; High Hon Roll; NHS; Prfct Atten Awd; Pres Schlr; NY ST Rgnts Schlrshp 85; Fut Sech Amer; Pres SADD; William Smith Coll.

SMITH, STEPHANIE; Uniondale HS; Hempstead, NY; (Y); 19/480; Aud/Vis; Drama Clb; Speech Tm; Acpl Chr; Chorus; Orch; Yrbk Phtg; High Hon Roll; Hon Roll; NHS; Film Making.

SMITH, STEPHEN; Smithtown East HS; Saint James, NY; (Y); VP Spanish Clb; Im Bsktbl; Crs Cntry; Var Tennis; Hon Roll; NHS; Sec Spanish NHS; John Hopkins Talent Srch 81; Bus.

SMITH, STEVE; Warwick Valley Central HS; Warwick, NY; (Y); 50/210; FFA; Letterman Clb; Quiz Bowl; Ski Clb; Varsity Clb; JV L Bsbl; Var L Ftbl; Hon Roll; Sprts Mgt.

SMITH, SUSAN M; Potsdam Central HS; Potsdam, NY; (Y); 10/160; Church Yth Grp; French Clb; Concert Band; Mrchg Band; Orch; Pep Band; Timer; Hon Roll; NHS; Ntl Merit Ltr; Regents Schlrshp 85; Natl Sci Merit Awd 85; Albany Coll; Pharm.

SMITH, SUSANNE; Cold Spring Harbor HS; Huntington, NY; (Y); 27/147; Intnl Clb; Yrbk Phtg; Var Socr; Var Capt Sftbl; High Hon Roll; Hon Roll; NHS; MVP Sftbl 84-85; All Conf Sccr & Sftbl 84-85; Lang.

SMITH, SUZANNE; Bishop Kearney HS; Brooklyn, NY; (Y); 14/350; Hosp Aide; Key Clb; Math Tm; Office Aide; Ski Clb; Rep Stu Cncl; High Hon Roll; NHS; MVP Ski Team 85; Natl Achvt Awd Bio 83; Engrng.

SMITH, TAMELA; Buffalo Acad Of The Sacred Heart; Buffalo, NY; (Y); Church Yth Grp; Spanish Clb; Church Choir; Prfct Atten Awd; Acctng I 97 Avg 85; Gulf Coast Bible Coll; Accntnt.

SMITH, TAMMY; Lake Placid Central Schl; Lake Placid, NY; (Y); Trk; High Hon Roll; Hon Roll; Renee Bloch Awd 85; Bus Educ.

SMITH, TARA ANN; Herricks SR HS; New Hyde Park, NY; (S); 67/306; Key Clb; Chorus; JV Sftbl; VP DECA; Var Cheerleading; Brdcst Jrnlst.

SMITH, TERRI; Amsterdam HS; Amsterdam, NY; (Y); 1/250; Hon Roll; Fash Merch.

SMITH II, THEODORE; North Collins Central Schl; N Collins, NY; (Y); 5/74; Mrchg Band; Nwsp Sprt Ed; VP Jr Cls; VP Sr Cls; Rep Stu Cncl; Bsktbl; Socr; Hon Roll; NHS; Ntl Merit Ltr; MVP JV Bsktbl 83-84.

SMITH, THERESA; Clarence SR HS; Clarence Ctr, NY; (Y); Church Yth Grp; DECA; VP FBLA; Church Choir; 4th Pl DECNY Hotl-Motl Mgmt Comp 84-85; Bus Mgmt.

SMITH, TIMOTHY; Bishop Maginn HS; Albany, NY; (S); 5/119; Exploring; Latin Clb; Red Cross Aide; Var Capt Bsktbl; Var Golf; Tennis; High Hon Roll; Pres NHS; Frgn Lang Awd; Sci.

SMITH, TINA; Romulus Central HS; Romulus, NY; (S); 4/45; GAA; Sec Varsity Clb; Drm Mjr(t); Trs Soph Cls; Trs Jr Cls; Trs Stu Cncl; Var Bsktbl; Var Socr; Var Sftbl; Capt Vllybl; Crmnl Jstce.

SMITH, TRACEY; Corning Painted Post West HS; Corning, NY; (Y); Exploring; Thesps; Chorus; Drm & Bgl; School Musical; Hon Roll; Preincipls Awd Peer Ldrshp 83; Humn Svcs.

SMITH, TRACIE; Wellsville Central Schl; Wellsville, NY; (Y); 62/130; Church Yth Grp; FBLA; Key Clb; Color Guard; Mrchg Band; Orch; Bus Adm.

SMITH, TRACY; Perry Central HS; Perry Central, NY; (Y); 5/91; Band; Color Guard; Concert Band; Yrbk Stf; Hon Roll; NHS; Rgnts Schlrshp 85; SUNY Fredonia; Spcl Educ.

SMITH, VALGEEN; Newark SR HS; Newark, NY; (Y); Red Cross Aide; Teachers Aide; VICA; Nwsp Stf; Lit Mag; Hon Roll; Cert Of Apprec 85; Chldcre.

SMITH, VICTORIA L; Our Lady Of Lourdes HS; Verbank, NY; (Y); 12/147; Band; Drm Mjr(t); Mrchg Band; Var Capt Socr; Var Capt Vllybl; High Hon Roll; Hon Roll; Jr NHS; Coachs Awd All Conf Div B Tm 83-85; Coachs Awd 84-85; 2nd Pl Awd Spnsh 84-85; Pace U Pleasantvl; Comp Sci.

SMITH, WANDA; H S Of Fashion Indus; Brooklyn, NY; (Y); 37/473; Hon Roll; NHS; Bus Ed Assn Awd 85; Exec Intrnshps Prgm Cert Of Rcgntn Awd 84; Morgan ST U; Bus Adm.

SMITH, WENDY; Potsdam Central HS; Potsdam, NY; (S); Varsity Clb; JV Var Cheerleading; Potsdam Booster Clb Sprtsmnshp Awd 84; US Chrldr Achvt Awds 83-85; Potsdam ST U; Tchr.

SMITH, WENDY ANNE; Minerva Central Schl; Minerva, NY; (Y); 6/13; School Musical; Yrbk Bus Mgr; VP Sr Cls; Var Sftbl; Var Vllybl; Cit Awd; NHS; Aud/Vis; Drama Clb; French Clb; Vllybl MVP 85; Smith-Howe Memrl & C T Barnes Awds 85; SUNY Plattsburgh; Jrnlsm.

SMITH, YOLANDA M; Cathedral HS; Bronx, NY; (Y); Intnl Clb; Band; Awd Band 83; Awd Frnch Comptn 85; Mary Mount; Fashn Merch.

SMITS, RAYMOND; Gloversville HS; Gloversville, NY; (Y); Spanish Clb; Thesps; Band; Chorus; Concert Band; Jazz Band; Mrchg Band; School Musical; School Play; Swing Chorus; Med.

SMOKOWSKI, JAMES; Bishop Timon HS; Lackawanna, NY; (S); Drama Clb; Hon Roll.

SMOLEN, CHRIS M; Voorheesville Central HS; Voorheesville, NY; (Y); 18/128; Church Yth Grp; Computer Clb; Drama Clb; Spanish Clb; Band; Chorus; Jazz Band; School Play; Stage Crew; Symp Band; Verbatims Natl Comp Prgrmng Cont Wnr 84; U Of Buffalo; Comp Eng.

SMOLEN, LAURA J; Catholic Central HS; Melrose, NY; (Y); 50/200; Dance Clb; JA; Math Clb; Service Clb; Spanish Clb; Variety Show; Rep Jr Cls; Rep Sr Cls; Pom Pon; High Hon Roll; Russell Sage Schlrshp 85-86; Grad Hnr 85; Russell; Spcl Ed.

SMOLEN, MICHELLE; The Franciscan Acad; Syracuse, NY; (S); 2/27; Church Yth Grp; GAA; Political Wkr; Speech Tm; Var L Tennis; High Hon Roll; NHS; Cmnty Wkr; Acad All-Amer 84; Ntl Hnr Roll 84; Ntl Hist Govt Awd 83; Pol Sci.

SMOTHERS, LORI; Camden HS; Taberg, NY; (Y); Band; Chorus; Concert Band; Orch; Hon Roll; Envrnmntl Sci.

SMUGLIN, ILYA M; Forest Hills HS; New York, NY; (Y); Ski Clb; Spanish Clb; Crs Cntry; Socr; Swmmng; Tennis; Brown Belt Karate 85; Med.

SMUKALL, CARL; Ahica Central HS; Darien Ctr, NY; (S); 2/150; Church Yth Grp; Fld Hcky; Socr; Lion Awd; NHS; Prfct Atten Awd; Geneseo; Accntng.

SMULLEN, ROBERT; Gloversville HS; Gloversville, NY; (Y); 24/260; Computer Clb; French Clb; Speech Tm; Nwsp Ed-Chief; Nwsp Stf; JV Socr; High Hon Roll; Hon Roll; Amer Leg Oratorical 85; Air Force Acad.

SMYK, ANDREW; Clinton SR HS; Clinton, NY; (Y); Art Clb; Model UN; Ski Clb; JV Var Socr; Cit Awd; High Hon Roll; Hon Roll; Outstdng Achv In Acctng 84; Clarkson; Acctng.

SMYLIE, TU LYNN M; Alfred G Berner HS; Massapequa, NY; (Y); 12/426; Acpl Chr; Variety Show; Nwsp Rptr; VP Frsh Cls; VP Soph Cls; VP Jr Cls; VP Sr Cls; Socr; Tennis; Hon Roll; NYS Rgnts Schlrshp 85; Stu Advsry Cncl 83-85; Columbia U; Intl Stds.

SMYTH, BARBARA; Southside HS; Rockville Centre, NY; (Y); Art Clb; Cmnty Wkr; Hosp Aide; Intnl Clb; Key Clb; Mathletes; Pres Science Clb; VP Spanish Clb; Trs VICA; Chorus; Dr Braverman Mem Schlrshp 85; Cross Cnty MVP 85; Mount ST Vincent; Interntl Std.

SMYTH, KELLY ANN; Hicksville HS; Hicksville, NY; (Y); Math Tm; Chorus; Var L Socr; Var L Trk; High Hon Roll; NHS; MVP Wntr Trck All Cnty 84-85; Mech Engr.

SMYTH, MARY T; Our Lady Of Perpetual Help HS; Brooklyn, NY; (Y); Camera Clb; Chorus; Stage Crew; Yrbk Stf; Hon Roll; Bus Secry.

SMYTH, PATRICK; Cardinal Spellman HS; Yonkers, NY; (Y); Church Yth Grp; Off Sr Cls; Iona Coll; Comp Sci.

SMYTH, PATTI; Fowler HS; Syracuse, NY; (S); Church Yth Grp; Yrbk Stf; Rep Frsh Cls; Hon Roll; Engl Awd 82; 2nd Pl Awd Black Hist Paper 84; Hnr Scty Awd 83-84; Onondaga CC; Bus Mgmt.

SNARE, DAVID; Mont Pleasant HS; Schenectady, NY; (Y); 20/250; Church Yth Grp; German Clb; Acpl Chr; Band; Chorus; Concert Band; Jazz Band; Mrchg Band; Hon Roll; Germn Natl Hnr Socty 84-86; Elctrnc Engrng.

SNEDEKER, MICHAEL; Charles O Dickerson HS; Trumansburg, NY; (Y); VP Frsh Cls; Rep Frsh Cls; L Stu Cncl; L Ftbl; High Hon Roll; NHS; Engrng.

SNELL, KATHLEEN; Potsdam Central HS; Potsdam, NY; (Y); Church Yth Grp; JA; Spanish Clb; Varsity Clb; Nwsp Stf; JV Cheerleading; Im Powder Puff Ftbl; JV Socr; Var Trk; Hon Roll; Bishops Awd 82; Knghts Of Columbus Essay Wnnr 82; Bio.

SNELL, KATHRYN; Mount Assumption Inst; Plattsburgh, NY; (Y); Dance Clb; Math Tm; Nwsp Ed-Chief; Nwsp Rptr; Yrbk Rptr; Cheerleading; Gym; Dnfth Awd; NHS; Natl Hon Soc Sec 84-85 VP 85-86; Capt Gymnastics Team 85-86; Psych.

SNELL, MARTHA; Victor Central HS; Victor, NY; (S); Church Yth Grp; Model UN; Chorus; Mrchg Band; Pep Band; School Musical; School Play; Bsktbl; Mgr Crs Cntry; Hon Roll; Proficiency Awd Canada 83; Monroe CC.

SNELL, STACY A; Norwich HS; Norwich, NY; (Y); 15/174; French Clb; Math Tm; Chorus; School Musical; Stage Crew; JV Vllybl; High Hon Roll; NHS; Regnts Schlrshp 85; Bus Adm.

SNELLINGER, LUCY; Port Jervis HS; Port Jervis, NY; (Y); 1/180; Scholastic Bowl; Varsity Clb; Acpl Chr; Yrbk Ed-Chief; Trs Stu Cncl; Socr; Trk; High Hon Roll; NHS; Ntl Merit Ltr; RPI Sci & Math Awd 85; All-Cnty, All ST Chorus 84; All Cnty Chorus 85; Rotary Clb Awd-Trk 83 & 84; Med.

SNIDER, TAMMY; Clifton-Fine HS; Star Lake, NY; (S); French Clb; Band; Chorus; Church Choir; Pres Frsh Cls; Sec Jr Cls; Cheerleading; Socr; Trk; High Hon Roll; Talented JR 83; Potsdam ST; Music Ed.

SNIZEK, PAUL; Vernon Verona Sherrill HS; Vernon, NY; (Y); Computer Clb; Spanish Clb; Var Golf; JV Socr; Engrng.

SNODGRASS, HILDI; Amsterdam HS; Amsterdam, NY; (S); 7/332; Band; Concert Band; Mrchg Band; Yrbk Stf; Rep Frsh Cls; Sec Soph Cls; Rep Jr Cls; VP Stu Cncl; High Hon Roll; Hon Roll; Amstrdam HSS No 1 Clb 84; NY ST Rgnts Schlrshp 85; Engrng.

SNOGLES, JEFFREY; Cicero-North Syracuse HS; N Syracuse, NY; (Y); 114/622; Pres Exploring; Ski Clb; Hon Roll; NHS; Mrtl Arts Comptns Numrs Awds 79-85; Achvd Blck Blt 84; Syracuse U; Crmnl Justice.

SNOW, CINDY; Union-Endicott HS; Endicott, NY; (Y); Church Yth Grp; Key Clb; Concert Band; Cit Awd; High Hon Roll.

SNOWBERGER, DEBRA; Union Endicott HS; Endicott, NY; (Y); Ski Clb; Mrchg Band; Symp Band; Rep Soph Cls; Rep Jr Cls; Rep Stu Cncl; Hon Roll; NHS; Engrng.

SNOWDEN, CHRIS; Sacred Heart HS; Bronx, NY; (Y); Cmnty Wkr; Drama Clb; School Musical; School Play; Yng Dirctns Co-Host On Cable TV; Drama.

SNURKOWSKI, LORRAINE; Spencer Ven Elten JR SR HS; Newfield, NY; (Y); 10/100; 4-H; French Clb; Quiz Bowl; Yrbk Bus Mgr; Yrbk Stf; High Hon Roll; Jr NHS; NHS; Seneca Cnty JR Shepard Awd 84; NY ST Livestock Jdgng 4th Pl 83-84; Typing & Trig Awd 83-84; Math.

SNYDER, BRAD; Byron-Bergen Central Schl; Byron, NY; (Y); Art Clb; Camera Clb; French Clb; Model UN; Band; Chorus; Color Guard; Mrchg Band; Swmmng; Trk; Chef.

SNYDER, BRAD; Whitney Point Central HS; Whitney Pt, NY; (Y); 6/135; French Clb; Science Clb; Chorus; School Musical; Crs Cntry; Trk; Wrstlng; Hon Roll; NHS; Mech Engr.

SNYDER, BRIAN W; Schalmont HS; Pattersonville, NY; (Y); 11/188; Math Tm; JV Var Bsktbl; Socr; High Hon Roll; Hon Roll; Rochester Inst Tech; Mech Engr.

SNYDER, CHERI; Cicero North Syracuse HS; Clay, NY; (Y); Art Clb; Computer Clb; Office Aide; Stage Crew; Rep Stu Cncl; Im Vllybl; Hon Roll; MONY Rgnl Schlstc Art Awds 83; Art Achv Awd 83; Humn Svcs.

SNYDER, CHRISTINA; Rensselaer JR SR HS; Rensselaer, NY; (S); Trs DECA; Red Cross Aide; Nwsp Stf; Yrbk Bus Mgr; Rep Stu Cncl; JV Sftbl; Hon Roll; NHS; Distributive Ed Clbs Of Am Mst Outstndng Member 84; Nrsng.

SNYDER, CHRISTINE; Albion HS; Albion, NY; (S); 33/180; 4-H; VP L Bsktbl; VP L Crs Cntry; VP L Sftbl; VP L Vllybl; All-Leag Hnrb Mntn-Sftbl 84; Merit Rll; Rotry Clb SR All-Star Bsktbl 85; Army; Crmnl Justc.

SNYDER JR, CLAIR; Hornell SR HS; Hornell, NY; (Y); Var L Wrstlng; Hon Roll; Prfct Atten Awd; Diesel Engr.

SNYDER, DANIEL R; Johnson City SR HS; Johnson City, NY; (Y); 7/212; Pres Church Yth Grp; Mathletes; Im Bsktbl; Var Capt Crs Cntry; Var Capt Trk; High Hon Roll; Hon Roll; Regnts Schlrshp 85; Schlstc Excllnc 82-85; Clarkson U; Mech Engrng.

SNYDER, DAVID; New Rochelle HS; New Rochelle, NY; (Y); Debate Tm; Band; Yrbk Stf; Bands Battle Wnnr 85; Advrtsng.

SNYDER, ERIC; Lindenhurst HS; Lindenhurst, NY; (Y); Church Yth Grp; Drama Clb; French Clb; Thesps; School Musical; School Play; Nwsp Phtg; Nwsp Stf; Yrbk Stf; VP Soph Cls; Hugh O Brian Ldrshp Semnr Columbia U 84; V Chrprsn Stus Soc Respnsblty 85; Columbia U; Law.

SNYDER, JANE; Nardin Acad; Kenmore, NY; (Y); 4/85; Service Clb; Church Choir; School Musical; School Play; Rep Frsh Cls; High Hon Roll; NHS; Wellesley Coll.

SNYDER, JEFFREY; St Johnsville Central HS; St Johnsville, NY; (S); 1/25; Ski Clb; Pres Band; Jazz Band; Mrchg Band; Stu Cncl; Bsktbl; Socr; Jr NHS; NHS; Hghst Avg-Frshmn & Soph; Boys ST; Buffalo U; Dentstry.

SNYDER, LINDA J; Batavia HS; Batavia, NY; (Y); 17/234; Church Yth Grp; Teachers Aide; Color Guard; High Hon Roll; NHS; Yth Salute Awd 85; Regents Schlrshp 85; U Buffalo; Accntng.

SNYDER, MICHELE; Notre Dame HS; Batavia, NY; (S); 7/82; Pep Clb; Bsktbl; Cheerleading; Tennis; Trk; High Hon Roll; Hon Roll; NHS; Genesee CC; Data Proc.

SNYDER, RANDI; Susan E Wagner HS; East Stroudsburg, PA; (Y); 19/597; JA; Math Clb; Math Tm; Science Clb; Service Clb; Teachers Aide; Band; Concert Band; School Play; Mgr Nwsp Bus Mgr; Pres Acad Fit Awd 85; Top Sci & Sci Resrch Awd 85; NHS 83-85; Law.

SNYDER, ROBERT; Riverside HS; Buffalo, NY; (Y); JA; Yrbk Stf; High Hon Roll; NHS; Art Awd 85; Musicn.

SNYDER, SHARON; Henninger HS; Syracuse, NY; (Y); Art Clb; Camera Clb; Dance Clb; Drama Clb; Hosp Aide; JA; Office Aide; PAVAS; Ski Clb; Teachers Aide; Csmtlgy.

SNYDER, WENDY; Brighton HS; Rochester, NY; (Y); 1/315; Temple Yth Grp; Sec Thesps; Chorus; School Musical; School Play; Stage Crew; Variety Show; Ntl Merit Ltr; Outstndng Spnsh Stdnt Awd 85; Med.

SNYDER, WILLIAM A; Saratoga Springs HS; Saratoga, NY; (Y); Am Leg Boys St; JA; JV Bsbl; Var Bowling; JV Var Golf; High Hon Roll; Hon Roll; Jr NHS; NHS; Skidmore Coll Acad Achvt Awd 85; Cert Achvt Spn, Bus, Mth 84 & 85; Bus.

SNYDER, WILLIAM J; Holy Trinity HS; Hicksville, NY; (S); 29/362; Math Clb; Stage Crew; Nwsp Rptr; Nwsp Sprt Ed; VP Soph Cls; VP Jr Cls; VP Sr Cls; Var Bsktbl; Var Capt Lcrss; Hon Roll; Lawyer.

SOBCZAK, CHRISTINE A; Frontier Central HS; Blasdell, NY; (Y); French Clb; GAA; Office Aide; Pep Clb; Science Clb; Ski Clb; Chorus; Powder Puff Ftbl; Sftbl; Hon Roll; Cornell; Law.

SOBCZYK, MICHAEL; Niagara Catholic HS; Niagara Falls, NY; (Y); 6/100; Am Leg Boys St; Church Yth Grp; Spanish Clb; Bsbl; Bsktbl; Ftbl; Golf; Tennis; High Hon Roll; NHS.

SOBE, SHONIA; Curtis HS; Staten Island, NY; (Y); Drama Clb; Band; Var Trk; Var Vllybl; Hon Roll; Ntl Merit Ltr; Howard U; Law.

SOBEK, RONDA; Smithtown H S West; Smithtown, NY; (Y); Cmnty Wkr; VP Temple Yth Grp; Thesps; Stage Crew; Trk; Hon Roll; SUNY; Bus Mngmnt.

SOBER, MELISSA; Lansingburgh HS; Troy, NY; (Y); Hon Roll; Accntng.

SOBIERAJ, BILL; Palmyra-Macedon Central HS; Macedon, NY; (Y); 30/205; Church Yth Grp; Math Tm; Ski Clb; Varsity Clb; Band; Concert Band; Jazz Band; Mrchg Band; School Play; Symp Band; Sctn V Champs Tennis 84; All Cnty Band 85; Clarkson U; Elec & Comp Engrng.

SOBIERAJ, LORRAINE; Oreida SR HS; Verona Bch, NY; (Y); High Hon Roll; Hon Roll; Bryant & Straton; Exec Sec.

SOBIERAJ, SANDRA; Churchville-Chili HS; Churchville, NY; (Y); 2/324; Yrbk Ed-Chief; Pres Stu Cncl; High Hon Roll; NHS; Pres Schlr; Sal; Math Tm; Model UN; Ski Clb; Y-Teens; Princeton U; Intl Rltns.

SOBKOWICH, SUSAN; Amsterdam HS; Amsterdam, NY; (S); 40/332; Band; Concert Band; Drm Mjr(t); Mrchg Band; Yrbk Phtg; Yrbk Stf; Rep Soph Cls; Rep Jr Cls; Sec Stu Cncl; Hon Roll; U S Stu Council Awd 85; Northeastern U; Physical Ther.

SOBKOWICZ, SANDY; Bishop Scully HS; Amsterdam, NY; (Y); 12/59; Drama Clb; French Clb; Trs Frsh Cls; Hon Roll; NHS; SUNY Cobleskill; Wildlife Bio.

SOBOCINSKI, MIKE; Frewsburg Central HS; Jamestown, NY; (Y); Outstndng Achvt Awd Autobody 84-85; Autobody Repairmn.

SOBOLEWSKI, DAVID; Cns HS; N Syracuse, NY; (S); 89/622; Boys Clb Am; Chess Clb; German Clb; Nwsp Rptr; Coach Actv; Im Trk; Var Wrstlng.

SOCCODATO, VIRGINIA A; Cardinal Spellman HS; Bronx, NY; (Y); VP French Clb; Pep Clb; Yrbk Stf; Stu Cncl; Cheerleading; High Hon Roll; NHS; Drill Tm; Rep Frsh Cls; Rep Soph Cls; Manhattan Coll Schlrshp & Grnt; NYS Regnts Schlrshp; Manhattan Coll; Elctrcl Engrng.

SOCIA, STEPHAN S; Christian Brothers Acad; Skaneateles, NY; (Y); Am Leg Boys St; Church Yth Grp; Cmnty Wkr; German Clb; Letterman Clb; Varsity Clb; Var Lcrss; Hon Roll; St Schlr; Law.

SOCIE, DAVID; Niagara Wheatfield SR HS; Niagara Fls, NY; (Y); Var Capt Socr; Hon Roll; NHS; Prfct Atten Awd; VP German Clb; Varsity Clb; Boys Vrsty Sccr Team MVP 84; 2nd Team All-Frontier Div Sccr Team 84; Boys St 85.

SODER, ADRIENNE; Connetquot HS; Ronkonkoma, NY; (S); 20/723; Band; Mrchg Band; School Musical; Mgr Fld Hcky; Vllybl; Hon Roll; Jr NHS.

SODIKOFF, KARIN; Oceanside SR HS; Oceanside, NY; (Y); Debate Tm; Hosp Aide; Nwsp Stf; Yrbk Stf; Hon Roll; Jr NHS; Bst Spkr In Commtt-Model Cngrss 85; Chrmn Awd-Oceanside Model Cngrss 85; Accntng.

SOEDARMASTO, HARRY; Park West HS; Jackson Hts, NY; (Y); 40/558; Church Yth Grp; Band; Badmtn; Socr; Hon Roll; Dowling Coll; Flght Tech.

SOFIA, KIMBERLY; Edison Vo Tech; Rochester, NY; (Y); Library Aide; Hon Roll; Comp.

SOFIA, THERESA; Corning-Painted Post West HS; Corning, NY; (Y); 50/240; Letterman Clb; Varsity Clb; Yrbk Sprt Ed; Rep Frsh Cls; Rep Soph Cls; Rep Jr Cls; Rep Stu Cncl; Var L Trk; High Hon Roll; NHS; Manatee JC; Psych.

SOFIELD, GREGORY; Long Beach HS; Long Beach, NY; (S); 21/291; Church Yth Grp; Key Clb; Rep Stu Cncl; Var Capt Ftbl; Var Capt Ice Hcky; Var Capt Lcrss; Wrstlng; NHS.

SOHRAB, SHAHRAM; West Genesee SR HS; Camillus, NY; (Y); Camera Clb; Exploring; Math Clb; Math Tm; Yrbk Phtg; Rep Jr Cls; Sr Cls; Socr; High Hon Roll; NHS; OCML Top Scorer Awd 84-85; Clarkson; Engrng.

SOKOL, MICHAEL; East Meadow HS; East Meadow, NY; (S); 63/414; Boy Scts; Drama Clb; Exploring; Thesps; Stage Crew; Nwsp Rptr; NHS; Ntl Merit Ltr; U Of FL Gainesville; Vet.

SOKOLOFF, ELLIOT J; Riverdale Country HS; Bronx, NY; (Y); Hosp Aide; Office Aide; Pres Science Clb; Spanish Clb; Sec Temple Yth Grp; L Varsity Clb; Y-Teens; Chorus; Nwsp Rptr; Lit Mag; Sci Awd 84; Med.

SOKOLOWSKI, THERESA; The Mary Louis Acad; Woodside, NY; (Y); Cmnty Wkr; French Clb; NFL; Speech Tm; Fld Hcky.

SOKOLOWSKI, THERESA L; Holy Trinity Dioceson HS; N Bellmore, NY; (S); 5/365; Math Clb; Teachers Aide; Stu Cncl; Cheerleading; High Hon Roll; Mu Alp Tht; NHS; Bus Mgmt.

SOKOLOWSKI, WILLIAM; Liverpool HS; North Syracuse, NY; (S); Computer Clb; Jazz Band; Mrchg Band; Orch; School Musical; Symp Band; Variety Show; Var Capt Gym; Hon Roll; Conf All ST Wind Ensemble 84; Crane Schl Music; Music Educ.

SOLA, SAMUEL; Mt St Michael Acad; Yonkers, NY; (Y); Am Leg Boys St; CAP; Cmnty Wkr; Drill Tm; Capt Bsbl; Capt Bsktbl; Capt Ftbl; Mgr(s); High Hon Roll; Hon Roll; Mt ST Michael Acad Scholar 82-83; Bro Jude Acad Scholar 83-84; Cmnty Svc Awd 83; Aero Engrng.

SOLANKI, SUNITA; John Jay HS; Brooklyn, NY; (Y); 30/197; Church Yth Grp; Cmnty Wkr; Computer Clb; Hosp Aide; Church Choir; Jr Cls; Cit Awd; Brooklyn; Nrs.

SOLDO, KIM; Lehman HS; Bronx, NY; (Y); 36/450; Chorus; Concert Band; Jazz Band; Orch; School Musical; School Play; Nwsp Ed-Chief; Nwsp Rptr; Vllybl; Hon Roll; Audio Engr.

SOLERO, SYLVIA; Clara Barton HS; Bronx, NY; (Y); Computer Clb; Girl Scts; Hosp Aide; Spanish Clb; Yrbk Stf; Pres Soph Cls; Pres Jr Cls; Sftbl; Pres Spanish NHS; Columbia; Med.

SOLES, LIESA; Haverling Central HS; Bath, NY; (S); 15/154; French Clb; FTA; Math Clb; Chorus; Church Choir; VP Sr Cls; High Hon Roll; NHS; Asst Mgr And Mgr Of Haverling School Store 82-85; Delhi; Restaurant Mgmnt.

SOLEY, JOHN L; Scarsdale HS; Scarsdale, NY; (Y); Am Leg Boys St; Aud/Vis; Boy Scts; Sec Computer Clb; Stage Crew; Comp Sci.

SOLIN, ALLISON; New Rochelle HS; New Rochelle, NY; (Y); Art Clb; Cmnty Wkr; Model UN; Teachers Aide; Temple Yth Grp; Chorus; Stage Crew; Lit Mag; Painting Dedicatn 83.

SOLIZ, SYDNEY; Blind Brook HS; Rye Brook, NY; (Y); Cmnty Wkr; Drama Clb; Model UN; Spanish Clb; School Play; JV Socr; JV Tennis; Engl Lit.

SOLLITTO, DONNA; Valley Stream Central HS; Valley Stream, NY; (Y); Church Yth Grp; Ski Clb; Var Badmtn; Var Cheerleading; Var Capt Socr; Var Capt Vllybl; Jr NHS; Bus.

SOLOMON, BARBRA; Forest Hills HS; Rego Park, NY; (Y); 1/881; Drama Clb; English Clb; Math Clb; Math Tm; Model UN; Red Cross Aide; Teachers Aide; Temple Yth Grp; Varsity Clb; Nwsp Phtg; JHS Salutrn Of Halsey JHS 83; Daily News Super Yth 84; Sing Commssnr 85-86.

SOLOMON, GABRIELLE; Hunter College HS; City Island, NY; (Y); Cmnty Wkr; Debate Tm; Lit Mag; Mu Alp Tht; Ntl Merit Ltr; Cty Coll NY Ptry Cntst Hnrbl Mntn 84.

SOLOMON, IRENE; Stuyvesant HS; New York, NY; (Y); Political Wkr; Science Clb; Temple Yth Grp; Acpl Chr; School Musical; Yrbk Phtg; Yrbk Stf; NHS; Ntl Merit Schol; St Schlr; N Bergodano Mem Awd 85; Edison Mc Graw Sci Comp SF 84; Ed-Chf Stuyvesant Westinghouse Rsch Anth 84; U MI; Phys Sci.

SOLOMON, JAY K; Sachem High School North; Lake Grove, NY; (Y); 92/1350; Band; Jazz Band; Mrchg Band; Orch; VP Frsh Cls; VP Soph Cls; VP Jr Cls; Stu Cncl; NHS; Soc Stu Awd 2nd County 84; Hnbl Mntn Sci Awd 84; Stu Govt Awd 85; Elect Engrng.

SOLOMON, KEREN; Great Neck South HS; Great Neck, NY; (Y); 22/218; Cmnty Wkr; French Clb; GAA; Varsity Clb; Nwsp Ed-Chief; Ice Hcky; Lcrss; Ntl Merit SF; Var Capt Bowling; Score Keeper; Jos E Seagram & Sons Inc Bronfman Schlr 85; Prnt Tchr Stu Assn Outstndng Frnch Stu 85; Hlth Car Awd 85; U PA; Phys Ther.

SOLOMON, RONALDO; Whitney Point HS; Castle Creek, NY; (Y); 1/130; Boy Scts; French Clb; Science Clb; Yrbk Stf; Trs Jr Cls; JV Socr; Var Trk; High Hon Roll; NHS; Ntl Merit SF; Intl Stud Assoc Schlrshp 85; U S Naval Acad; Elec Engrng.

SOLOMON, STEPHEN B; Roslyn HS; Roslyn Harbor, NY; (Y); 1/240; Computer Clb; Capt Math Tm; Ed Nwsp Stf; Im Bsktbl; Im Tennis; Bausch & Lomb Sci Awd; Ntl Merit Schol; Val; Westinghouse Sci Talent Srch SF 85; Rensselaer Mdl Exclnce Math & Sci 84; 3rd NY JA Sci Rsrch 85; Harvard Coll; Molecular Bio.

SOLOMON, TIMOTHY E; Clara Barton HS; Brooklyn, NY; (Y); French Clb; Scholastic Bowl; High Hon Roll; Acdmc All-Amer 85; Milton Forrest Awd 83; Gld Mdl Fr Ovrachvt In Soc Stds 83; Pre-Med.

SOLOMOS, CONSTANTINE; Clayton A Bouton HS; Voorheesville, NY; (Y); Church Yth Grp; Cmnty Wkr; Intnl Clb; Ski Clb; Spanish Clb; Concert Band; Sec Soph Cls; Rep Stu Cncl; Var L Socr; Var L Tennis; Pol Sci.

SOLORZANO, SANDY; Walton HS; Bronx, NY; (Y); 25/550; Band; Orch; Rep Soph Cls; NHS; Prfct Atten Awd; Peer Tutor 82-85; Acacmc Olympcs 84-85; Pre Tchg Acad 85; John Jay Coll; Pol Ofcr.

SOLOTOFF, ERIC; Newfield HS; Coram, NY; (Y); 14/542; Quiz Bowl; Scholastic Bowl; Pres VP Temple Yth Grp; JV Var Bsktbl; Im Wt Lftg; Hon Roll; Jr NHS; Prfct Atten Awd; NY St Regents Schlrshp 85; St U NY; Bus.

SOLTYS, CHRISTOPHER JOHN; Msgr Mc Clancy Memorial HS; Astoria, NY; (Y); Church Yth Grp; Rep Sr Cls; Rep Stu Cncl; High Hon Roll; NHS.

SOLUSKE, LAURA E; East Syracuse-Minoa HS; Kirkville, NY; (Y); Science Clb; Nwsp Ed-Chief; Nwsp Rptr; JV Fld Hcky; Hon Roll; NHS; Schlstc Awd Achvt Engl 83; SUNY-OSWEGO; Anthrplgy.

SOMERS, JEFFREY M; Scotia-Glenville SR HS; Amsterdam, NY; (Y); 1/244; Cmnty Wkr; Drama Clb; Math Tm; Thesps; Acpl Chr; Church Choir; School Musical; Variety Show; Yrbk Bus Mgr; Yrbk Phtg; Schl Dept Awd Math, Sci & Eng 85; OM/Chevron Schlrshp 85; GE STAR Awd 85; Williams Coll; Math.

SOMERS, LAUREL; Smithtown HS East; St James, NY; (Y); Band; Hon Roll; School Musical; Symp Band; Variety Show; JV Crs Cntry; NYSSMA 83; NYSSMA All St Level 85; Psych.

SOMMA, GREGG; M Oore Catholic HS; Staten Island, NY; (Y); 50/215; Var Bsbl; Var Bowling; 2nd Hnrs 83-85; Acctg.

SOMMER, CLIFFORD G; St Anthonys HS; Smithtown, NY; (Y); Ski Clb; Im Fld Hcky; St Schlr; Marist Coll; Comp Sci.

SOMMER, MAURA; Frdoma HS; Fredonia, NY; (Y); Art Clb; Church Yth Grp; Science Clb; Spanish Clb; Var Capt Bsktbl; JV Var Vllybl; Kiwanis Awd; Embry Riddle; Aerontcs.

SOMMER, SHEILA; Fredonia HS; Fredonia, NY; (Y); 3/190; Church Yth Grp; 4-H; GAA; Hosp Aide; Key Clb; Science Clb; Ski Clb; Spanish Clb; Orch; School Musical; Western NY Lang Fair 2nd Pl Spn Essay 85; Mth.

SOMMERS, SHERYL; Hudson HS; Hudson, NY; (Y); Camera Clb; 4-H; Ski Clb; Band; Chorus; Rep Stu Cncl; JV Cheerleading; VP Diving; Var Swmmng; Timer; Rochester Inst Tech; Photo.

SONKIN, MICHAEL; East Islip HS; East Islip, NY; (Y); Teachers Aide; Off Stu Cncl; Bsktbl; Ftbl; High Hon Roll; Hon Roll; Jr NHS; NHS; Prfct Atten Awd; Spanish NHS; Pre Law.

SONNAK, SAMANTHA; Beacon HS; Beacon, NY; (S); 5/200; Drama Clb; Math Clb; Science Clb; School Musical; School Play; Stage Crew; Nwsp Ed-Chief; High Hon Roll; Jr NHS; NHS; SYEP Employee Of The Year 83; Pre-Med.

SONNEBORN, KRISTA; Allegany Central Schl; Allegany, NY; (Y); 9/91; Am Leg Aux Girls St; Church Yth Grp; Varsity Clb; School Play; Yrbk Sprt Ed; VP Sr Cls; Capt Crs Cntry; High Hon Roll; NHS; Pres Schlr; Hmcmng Queen; Best Overall Spkr; Gavin Schlrshp; Ithaca Coll; Phys Thrpy.

SONNENBERG, KELLIE; Oneonta HS; Oneonta, NY; (Y); 40/180; Church Yth Grp; Cmnty Wkr; Drama Clb; Spanish Clb; Psych.

SONNENBLICK, AMY; Hebrew Academy Of Nassau County; Manhasset Hills, NY; (S); Hosp Aide; Pep Clb; Capt Scholastic Bowl; School Play; Nwsp Stf; High Hon Roll; NHS; Ntl Merit SF; Debate Tm; Math Tm; Poetry-1st Prz 83; Northwestern U; Physcn.

SONNENSTEIN, MICHAEL; E Meadow HS; E Meadow, NY; (S); FBLA; Pres Key Clb; Sec Temple Yth Grp; Symp Band; Nwsp Ed-Chief; Var Crs Cntry; Var Capt Trk; VP NHS; Columbia Sci Hnrs Prgrm Columbia U 84-85; Bus.

SONNER, MICHELLE; Holland Central HS; S Wales, NY; (Y); Church Yth Grp; 4-H; Var JV Cheerleading; High Hon Roll; Hon Roll; Jr NHS; Pres Ftns Awd 82-84; Holland Alumni Schlrshp Awd 85; Genesee Comm Coll; Aviatn.

SOOD, VANDANA; Southwestern HS; Jamestown, NY; (Y); German Clb; Hosp Aide; Pep Clb; Ski Clb; Spanish Clb; Yrbk Stf; Hon Roll; NHS; Prfct Atten Awd; Math Awd 84-85; Dntl.

SOOKDEO, DIANE; Richmond Hill HS; Richmond Hl, NY; (Y); Church Yth Grp; Office Aide; PAVAS; ROTC; Teachers Aide; Church Choir; Drill Tm; Orch; Nwsp Stf; Prfct Atten Awd; Phy Thrpst.

SOONG, SO BING; Brooklyn Technical HS; New York, NY; (Y); Library Aide; Orch; Prfct Atten Awd; Pres Schlr; NY U; Graphic Arts.

SOPCHAK, CYNTHIA; Cicero-North Syracuse HS; Mattydale, NY; (S); 89/754; German Clb; Ski Clb; Hon Roll; NHS; Ntl Hnr Soc 83; Syracuse U; Comp Sci.

SOPICKI, LAURA; Immaculata Acad; Lackawanna, NY; (Y); 9/48; French Clb; Orch; School Musical; School Play; Yrbk Stf; Rep Stu Cncl; L Trk; Prfct Atten Awd; Nwsp Stf; Hon Roll; MI Trck; Excllnc Frnch I, II & III; Intl Rel.

SOPKO, DAWN M; South Park HS; Buffalo, NY; (Y); 11/375; Cmnty Wkr; Hosp Aide; Math Tm; Office Aide; Service Clb; Nwsp Rptr; Lit Mag; Cit Awd; Hon Roll; NHS; Ithaca Coll Schlrshp; NYS Regents Schlrshp; Ithaca Coll; Psychlgy.

SORAR, JENNIFER; East JR SR HS; Rochester, NY; (Y); Exploring; Office Aide; Stage Crew; Hon Roll; Bus Adm.

SORBELLO, ELIZABETH; Rome Catholic HS; Rome, NY; (Y); Chorus; School Musical; Nwsp Rptr; Yrbk Stf; Stu Cncl; Trk; High Hon Roll; NHS; Prfct Atten Awd; Prsdntl Physcl Ftnss Awd 83-85; Spch Thrpy.

SORBERO, RICHARD J; Amsterdam HS; Amsterdam, NY; (Y); 1/330; Wt Lftg; Bausch & Lomb Sci Awd; High Hon Roll; NHS; Ntl Merit SF; Pres Schlr; Val; Chem Awd; Union Coll; Elect Engr.

SORCE, MARIA; Niagara Wheatfield HS; Niagara Fls, NY; (Y); Dance Clb; FBLA; VP Pep Clb; Hon Roll; NHS; Outstndng Achvt Awd-Acadmc Excllnc 85; Bus.

SORENSEN, CAROL; Ossining HS; Ossining, NY; (Y); Var Capt Gym; JV Socr; Amer H S Ath Gym 85; Frnch Awd Outstndng Achvt 83 & 85; Pre-Med.

SORENSEN, JEANINE A; Northport HS; Northport, NY; (Y); 18/650; Church Yth Grp; Drama Clb; Acpl Chr; Jazz Band; Mrchg Band; Orch; School Musical; Swmmng; Trk; NHS; Henrietta F Ackerly Schlrhp 85; NY ST Regnts Schlrshp 85; Bd Of Educ Cert Of Achvt 85; U Of MD; Engrng.

SORENSEN, KRISTINA; South Seneca HS; Ovid, NY; (Y); Church Yth Grp; FHA; Letterman Clb; Spanish Clb; Varsity Clb; Church Choir; Stat Bsktbl; JV Cheerleading; Var Capt Crs Cntry; Var Sftbl; Tchrs Aid 83-84; Jr Prom Ct 85; Nrsg.

SORENSEN, STEVEN A; Waverly JR SR HS; Waverly, NY; (Y); Aud/Vis; Boys Clb Am; Church Yth Grp; Pres Computer Clb; NHS; St Schlr; Var Trk; High Hon Roll.

SORENSEN, THOMAS; Candor HS; Candor, NY; (Y); 1/85; Am Leg Boys St; School Play; Stage Crew; Yrbk Phtg; Ftbl; Bausch & Lomb Sci Awd; Val; U Of Rochester Engrng Scholar 85-86; U Of Rochester; Engrng.

SORENSON, CATHERINE; Bishop Kearney HS; Brooklyn, NY; (Y); Church Yth Grp; Exploring; Library Aide; Spanish Clb; Teachers Aide; Church Choir; School Musical; Yrbk Stf; Swmmng; Hon Roll.

SORGIE, JOSEPH; Wm Floyd HS; Mastic Beach, NY; (Y); Var Trk; Comp.

SORHAINDO, KATHRYN R; New Rochelle HS; New Rochelle, NY; (Y); 13/600; Trs Chess Clb; Var Capt Crs Cntry; Var Trk; French Hon Soc; NHS; Cmmnded Stdnt Natl Merit Schlrshp 84; MVP Crss Cntry 83; Russian Clb; Stanford U; Intl Stds.

SORIANO, DINA; St John The Baptist HS; Ronkonkoma, NY; (Y); Church Yth Grp; MMM; Chorus; Drm & Bgl.

SORIANO, ELIZABETH; St Francis Prep; Flushing, NY; (S); 16/693; Cmnty Wkr; Drm & Bgl; High Hon Roll; NHS; Mst Dedctd Plyr Judo 84; Prncpls Lst 83-84; Med Tech.

SORIANO, MARIA JULITA; St Johns Prep; Elmhurst, NY; (Y); Intnl Clb; Var Bowling; Im Vllybl; High Hon Roll; Hon Roll; NHS; Rotary Awd; John Hopkinsu; Ped.

SORIANO, SALVATORE A; Archbishop Molloy HS; Rosedale, NY; (Y); 47/361; Computer Clb; Math Tm; Im Bsktbl; Im Ftbl; Im Sftbl; NHS; NYS Regents Schlrshp 85; Prtl Schlrshp Polytechnic Inst NY 85; Polytechnic Inst NY; Comp Engr.

SORICE, GINA; La Salle SR HS; Niagara Falls, NY; (S); 26/278; Drama Clb; Thesps; School Musical; School Play; Rep Jr Cls; Rep Stu Cncl; Hon Roll; Jr NHS; Alfred ST Drama Festival 84; Best Thespian-Female 82; Boston U; Pre-Law.

SORRENTINO, CHARLES S; Lakeland HS; Yorktown Heights, NY; (Y); 3/350; High Hon Roll; NHS; Pace U; CPA.

SORRENTINO, NANCY L; Hamburg SR HS; Hamburg, NY; (Y); DECA; Rep Frsh Cls; Rep Soph Cls; Swmmng; Hon Roll; NHS; Acad Fitness Awd 85; Ithaco Coll; Bus.

SORRENTO, SHERRI; Kenmore East HS; Tonawanda, NY; (Y); JV Socr; High Hon Roll; Hon Roll; Buffalo ST; Elem Ed.

SORTINO, ADRIENNE; Seaford HS; Massapequa Pk, NY; (Y); Teachers Aide; Bus Awd Typng 84; Hofstra; Bus.

SOSA, JULIANA; Manhasset HS; Manhasset, NY; (Y); Cmnty Wkr; GAA; Orch; JV Bsktbl; Var Cheerleading; Var JV Lcrss; Var Swmmng; Var Tennis; High Hon Roll; Hon Roll; Languages.

SOSSI, MATTHEW E; John S Burke Catholic HS; New Windsor, NY; (Y); 15/144; Boy Scts; Band; Yrbk Ed-Chief; Crs Cntry; Trk; High Hon Roll; Hon Roll; NHS; NY ST Regents Schlrshp 85; VA Military Inst; Chem.

SOTIRIOU, MARGARET; St Francis Prep; Hollis, NY; (S); 211/690; Drama Clb; Library Aide; Chorus; School Musical; Rep Jr Cls; Rep Sr Cls; Rgnts Schlrshp 85; Acad All-Amer 85; St Johns U; Phrmcy.

SOTO, BILLY; Cathedral Prep HS; Brooklyn, NY; (Y); 6/15; French Clb; Color Guard; Drill Tm; Var Bsbl; Perfect Attndnc Awd 83-85; Yth Ftns Achvt Awd 83-85; NROTC; Naval Flght Offcr.

SOTO, CHRISTOPHER; Mount Saint Micheal Acad; Mt Vernon, NY; (Y); 33/320; Am Leg Boys St; Dance Clb; Rep Jr Cls; Rep Stu Cncl; Crs Cntry; Ftbl; Trk; High Hon Roll; Hon Roll; Spanish NHS; Cardinals Ledrshp Proj; Air Force Acad; Engnr.

SOTO, NOREEN; Sheepshead Bay HS; Brooklyn, NY; (Y); Intnl Clb; Office Aide; Band; Hon Roll; Bus Admin.

SOTO, RAFAEL; St Agnes HS; New York, NY; (Y); Chess Clb; Bowling; Ftbl; Wt Lftg; NHS; Columbia U; Comp Engrng.

SOTOLONGO, FRANK; John Dewey HS; Brooklyn, NY; (Y); JA; Science Clb; Nwsp Rptr; Nwsp Stf; High Hon Roll; Jr NHS; NHS; Cert Merit 82-83; Pride Yankees Awd 83-84; Med.

SOTOMAYOR, ERIC; La Salle Academy HS; New York, NY; (S); Rep Frsh Cls; Crs Cntry; Trk; Hon Roll.

SOUCHECK, BLANCHE E; Smithtown HS West; Kings Park, NY; (Y); VP Thesps; Mrchg Band; Pep Band; School Musical; Symp Band; JV Socr; Var L Trk; Hon Roll; Spanish NHS; NYSSMA Awd 84; Wntr Trck Lttrs 82-84; Spg Trck Lttr 84; SUNY Albany; Med.

SOUSIE, STACY; Franklin Acad; Bombay, NY; (Y); Hosp Aide; Varsity Clb; School Play; Swmmng; U Dayton; Spanish Interpret.

SOUTHALL, ELIZABETH; Mt Vernon HS; Mt Vernon, NY; (Y); 15/595; Girl Scts; Latin Clb; High Hon Roll; Acadmc All-Amer Awd 84-85; Alpha Kappa Alpha Sor Schlrshp 85; Sarah Rudolph Willng Prz 85; Fordham U; Bio.

SOUTHARD II, JOHN L; Thomas A Edison HS; Elmira, NY; (Y); Am Leg Boys St; VP Frsh Cls; Pres Soph Cls; Pres Jr Cls; Pres Stu Cncl; Swmmng; Trk; High Hon Roll; Chess Clb; French Clb; Elmira Coll Key Awd 85; Rensselaer Polytech Inst Math & Sci 85; Physcs.

SOUTHARD, TERRI; Southside HS; Elmira, NY; (Y); Pep Clb; Ski Clb; Spanish Clb; Varsity Clb; Chorus; Nwsp Stf; Tennis; Hon Roll; Yth Cnty 85; Sthside Mrchr Ftbl Seasn 83-84; Bus.

SOUTHWORTH, DARLEEN; Stockbridge Valley Central HS; Munnsville, NY; (S); 1/46; Am Leg Aux Girls St; Church Yth Grp; Drama Clb; Girl Scts; Office Aide; Science Clb; Yrbk Stf; High Hon Roll; Sec NHS; Val; Med Astnt Schlrshp 85; Bryant & Stratton Powleson; Med.

SOUTHWORTH, JOANN; Chateaugay Central HS; Burke, NY; (Y); 13/40; Chorus; School Musical; School Play; Yrbk Phtg; L Var Bsktbl; L Var Socr; L Var Sftbl; Prfct Atten Awd; Vocal Music Awd 85; Plattsburgh ST U.

SOUZA, MARK; Oppenhiem Ephrath Central Schl; St Johnsville, NY; (S); 7/24; Pres Band; Mrchg Band; Nwsp Rptr; Yrbk Phtg; Rep Sr Cls; VP Stu Cncl; Var Capt Bsktbl; Hon Roll; Herkimer Coll; Police Ofcr.

SOVIERO JR, RONALD; E L Vandermeulen HS; Port Jefferson, NY; (Y); 12/286; Boy Scts; Church Yth Grp; Spanish Clb; Var Golf; JV Socr; High Hon Roll; Hon Roll.

SOVIK, CHARLES; Christian Brothers Acad; Syracuse, NY; (Y); 11/103; Hosp Aide; Ski Clb; Nwsp Stf; Yrbk Stf; St Lawrence U; Bus Econ.

SOWA, RICHARD; Archbishop Molloy HS; Flushing, NY; (Y); 100/394; Church Yth Grp; Cmnty Wkr; Math Clb; Math Tm; Im Ftbl; Im Sftbl; High Hon Roll; Hon Roll; Natl Honor Roll 85; Manhattan Coll; Pre-Med.

SPADA, JOE; John A Coleman HS; Stone Ridge, NY; (Y); 2/100; Art Clb; Math Tm; Quiz Bowl; Varsity Clb; Band; VP Frsh Cls; Sec Soph Cls; Rep Jr Cls; Rep Stu Cncl; Var Capt Bsktbl.

SPADA III, LAWRENCE N; Rome Free Acad; Rome, NY; (Y); 26/80; Cmnty Wkr; Drama Clb; Library Aide; Nwsp Stf; Yrbk Stf; Hon Roll; NEDT Awd; Teachers Aide; Chorus; School Play; Latin I Awd 82-83; Relgn 9 Awd 82-83; Relgn 10 Awd 83-84; USAF; Med.

SPADARO, ROSEMARY; Bishop Maginn HS; Albany, NY; (S); 15/116; French Clb; Hosp Aide; Yrbk Stf; Trs Jr Cls; VP Sr Cls; Pres Stu Cncl; High Hon Roll; Hon Roll; NHS; Bio.

SPADOLA, ANGELA; Christopher Columbus HS; Bronx, NY; (S); 142/747; Dance Clb; Office Aide; Service Clb; Cit Awd; Hon Roll; NHS; Prfct Atten Awd; Art Awd; Cert Of Merit; Baruch Coll.

SPADONE, JOHN; Lackwanna SR HS; Lackawanna, NY; (Y); Sec Varsity Clb; Band; JV Var Bsbl; Var Capt Ftbl; JV Var Ice Hcky; Mrn Blgy.

SPAGNOLO, ANTHONY; Spring Valley SR HS; Spring Vly, NY; (Y); 6/470; Church Yth Grp; Key Clb; Math Clb; Science Clb; Band; Yrbk Stf; Hon Roll; Jr NHS; NHS; Spanish NHS; Elec Engrng.

SPAGNUDO, FELICIA; Dominican Commercial HS; Middle Vlge, NY; (Y); Rep Stu Cncl; Var Vllybl; Prncpls Lst 84-86; 2 Cls St Johns U-Recvd A Bth Cls 85; Acctng.

SPAHN, CHERYL; Wantagh HS; Wantagh, NY; (Y); 30/295; Church Yth Grp; FBLA; Key Clb; Varsity Clb; Band; Concert Band; Flag Corp; Mrchg Band; Orch; Yrbk Stf; Fordham U; Finc.

SPAHN, MICHAEL; Bishop Timon HS; Lackawanna, NY; (S); Chess Clb; Computer Clb; High Hon Roll.

SPAKER, PAMELA; Bishop Kearney HS; Rochester, NY; (Y); JV Var Cheerleading; Drama Clb; 1st Pl Chrldng Trnmnts 82-84; Sctn 5 4th Pl Wnr Chrldng 85; Hmcmng King 84-85; Embry Riddle Aero U; Piloting.

SPAKOSKI, JUSTINE; Amsterdam HS; Amsterdam, NY; (Y); 33/394; Spanish Clb; Yrbk Stf; JV Sftbl; Hon Roll; NHS; Utica Coll; Actuarial Sci.

SPALDING, BETHANY; James I O Neill HS; Garrison, NY; (Y); 2/121; Church Yth Grp; Pres French Clb; German Clb; Pep Clb; Nwsp Rptr; Yrbk Sprt Ed; Sec Jr Cls; Var Tennis; Var Vllybl; High Hon Roll; Williams College.

SPALLER, DAVID M; Palmyra-Macedon Central HS; Macedon, NY; (Y); 36/200; Church Yth Grp; Ski Clb; Varsity Clb; Trs Soph Cls; Trs Jr Cls; Trs Sr Cls; Var Capt Ftbl; Var Trk; Cit Awd; NYS Regents Schlrshp 85; Hmcmng King 84-85; Embry Riddle Aero U; Piloting.

SPANAKOS, HELEN; Garden City SR HS; Garden City, NY; (Y); VP Church Yth Grp; GAA; Varsity Clb; Band; Yrbk Stf; JV Fld Hcky; Var Sftbl; Ntl Hnr Soc 83; Bus Mgmt.

SPANGENBURG, CHRIS; Kendall JR SR HS; Kendall, NY; (Y); 29/87; FHA; FTA; Teachers Aide; VP Chorus; Color Guard; School Musical; Capt Var Cheerleading; Score Keeper; JV Var Socr; Hon Roll; Outstndng Chrldr 84-85; Elem Ed.

SPANGLER, ANN E; Houghton Acad; Andover, NY; (Y); 9/28; Sec Church Yth Grp; Concert Band; Yrbk Bus Mgr; Trs Soph Cls; Var Vllybl; DAR Awd; High Hon Roll; NHS; Regents Schlrshp NY ST 85; Pioneer Grls 83-84; Messiah Coll.

SPANO, ALBERT; Mamaroneck HS; Mamaroneck, NY; (Y); Boy Scts; Ski Clb; JV Var Bsktbl; JV Var Ftbl; Im Golf; JV Var Wt Lftg; Midgt Ftbl Awd 6 Yrs 81.

SPANO, CARMEL; Lowville Central HS; Lowville, NY; (Y); 50/137; Church Yth Grp; Concert Band; Mrchg Band; Rep Frsh Cls; Rep Jr Cls; Rep Sr Cls; Cheerleading; Band; School Musical; James L Leonard Schlrshp 85; MVP Chrldr 83; Onondaga Cmnty Coll; Dntl Hygne.

SPARACIA, DONNA; St Joseph By-The-Sea HS; Staten Island, NY; (Y); 13/275; High Hon Roll; NHS.

SPARGO, LAURI; Guilderland Central HS; Guilderland, NY; (Y); Camp Fr Inc; Sec Pres Key Clb; Varsity Clb; Church Choir; School Musical; Rep Stu Cncl; Im Var Socr; High Hon Roll; Hon Roll; NHS; Pre-Med.

SPARLING, JANICE; Ripley Central HS; Ripley, NY; (Y); #6 In Class; Pep Clb; Trs Frsh Cls; Pres Jr Cls; Pres Sr Cls; Rep Stu Cncl; Var Bsktbl; Var Sftbl; Var Vllybl; NHS; Otstndng Sprtsmnshp Lylty Spirit 84; Mercyhurst Coll; Sprts Med.

SPARLING, MARGARET; Southside HS; Elmira, NY; (Y); Aud/Vis; JA; Radio Clb; Spanish Clb; Chorus; School Play; Stage Crew; Nwsp Rptr; Hon Roll; Prfct Atten Awd; Jr Achvt-Achvr Awd, Jr Exec Awd & Exec Awd 84; Elmira Business Inst; Exec Sec.

SPATH, CATHERINE M; New Hartford HS; New Hartford, NY; (Y); 33/264; Latin Clb; Pep Clb; Varsity Clb; Nwsp Rptr; Nwsp Stf; Rep Frsh Cls; Off Jr Cls; Rep Stu Cncl; Var Capt Bsktbl; Var Capt Fld Hcky; MVP Fld Hcky, Bsktbl, Leag All Star Fld Hcky, Bsktbl 84-85; Brown U; Pre Med.

SPATH, RACHEL; Hudson HS; Hudson, NY; (Y); Dance Clb; Acpl Chr; Band; Chorus; Concert Band; Mrchg Band; School Musical; Var Pom Pon; Hon Roll; Rookie Vocalst Awd 83; RN.

SPATOLA, ROBERT; Mount Vernon HS; Mount Vernon, NY; (Y); Trs FBLA; High Hon Roll; Hon Roll; NHS; U IA; Accntng.

SPATZ, ROBBY; Forest Hills HS; Forest Hills, NY; (Y); 20/881; Computer Clb; Mathletes; Math Clb; Math Tm; Science Clb; Var Tennis; High Hon Roll; NHS; Quiz Bowl; Teachers Aide; 1st Pl NY City Sci Fair & Queens Fin 83; 2nd Pl Queens Borough Sci Fair 84; 2nd Pl Queens Borough Sci; Princeton; Appld Math.

SPAULDING, KIMBERLY; North Tonawanda SR HS; N Tonawanda, NY; (Y); Chorus; Color Guard; Mrchg Band; Hon Roll; Jr NHS.

SPEAKER, KIM; Lackawanna SR HS; Lackawanna, NY; (Y); 35/288; Spanish Clb; Var Bowling; Hon Roll; Daemens Dean Schlrhsp 85; Daemens Psychlgy Schlrshp 85; Daemen Coll; Psychlgy.

SPEAR JR, JOHN E; Skaneateles HS; Skaneateles, NY; (S); Boy Scts; Jazz Band; Orch; Symp Band; Yrbk Ed-Chief; Var Trk; High Hon Roll; Jr NHS; Syracuse Yth Symph Orch 84; Schl Talented & Gifted Pgm 84.

SPEAR, LAURANCE; Clarkstown North HS; New City, NY; (Y); Math Tm; Crs Cntry; Socr; Var Trk; VP Mu Alp Tht; NHS; Ntl Merit Ltr; Band; Rep Stu Cncl; Outstndng Profcncy Awd,Amer Math Exam 83; Amer Invitatnl Math Exam 85; Capt Varsty Ski Team 84; Cornell U; Engr.

SPEAR, SYDNEY B; Bayshore HS; Bayshore, NY; (Y); Art Clb; Drama Clb; Math Clb; School Musical; School Play; Stu Cncl; Im Bowling; JV Var Tennis; Im Vllybl; Hon Roll; Art Awd 83; Hofstra U; Psych.

SPECHT, ADAM; Hebrew Academy Of Nassau County; Bethpage, NY; (S); 4/72; Drama Clb; Math Tm; Temple Yth Grp; Nwsp Stf; JV Socr; Cit Awd; High Hon Roll; NHS; NEDT Awd; Computer Clb; Hist Awd 83; Pre-Med.

SPECIALE, MICHELE; Cardnal Mooney HS; Rochester, NY; (Y); Cmnty Wkr; Lit Mag; Rep Frsh Cls; Rep Soph Cls; Rep Jr Cls; VP Stu Cncl; JV Var Socr; Hon Roll; Schltc Art Awds Shw, Key Awd-Blue Rbbn Wnnr 85; Art.

SPECTOR, JEFFREY A; Martin Van Buren HS; Floral Park, NY; (Y); 4/621; Library Aide; Scholastic Bowl; Chorus; School Musical; Symp Band; Gov Hon Prg Awd; High Hon Roll; NHS; Debate Tm; English Clb; Exclnce Writing Awd 82; Westinghouse Sci Tlnt Srch Hnrs Grp Wnnr 85; Cornell U; Indstrl Rel.

SPECTOR, TAMI; Christopher Columbus HS; New York City, NY; (Y); 51/792; Office Aide; Spanish Clb; Band; Chorus; Hon Roll; NHS; Arista 83; NYU; Med.

SPEED, GINNY; Stissing Mountain SR HS; Stanfordville, NY; (Y); 22/85; VP Pres AFS; Church Yth Grp; Girl Scts; Yrbk Stf; Pres Jr Cls; Var Fld Hcky; Hon Roll; NCTE Awd; NHS; Frgn Exchng Stu W Ger 84; PTO Schlrshp 85; AFS Schlrshp 85; SUNY Coldeskill; Htl/Rest Mgmt.

SPEEZ, CYNTHIA; Oceanside HS; Oceanside, NY; (Y); 4/650; 4-H; Girl Scts; Chorus; Im Swmmng; JC Coll; Legal Sec.

SPEIDEL, PAULA; S Park HS; Buffalo, NY; (Y); Church Yth Grp; Girl Scts; Office Aide; Teachers Aide; Band; Concert Band; Flag Corp; Mrchg Band; Stu Cncl; Hon Roll; Band Awd; Tchr.

SPEIGHTS, SHELDON; Bishop Ford CCHS HS; Brooklyn, NY; (Y); 10/450; Math Tm; JV Trk; Hon Roll; Bus.

SPELINA, JILL; Freeport HS; Freeport, NY; (Y); 125/450; Band; Concert Band; Mrchg Band; Stage Crew; Variety Show; Nwsp Stf; Lit Mag; Var JV Mgr(s); Score Keeper; Var Capt Swmmng; Volntr Schlrshp 85; SUNY-OSWEGO; Elem Educ.

SPENCER, BRETT M; Gananda Central HS; Walworth, NY; (Y); 4/33; Cmnty Wkr; Science Clb; Variety Show; Rep Soph Cls; Stu Cncl; Var L Bsbl; Var Capt Bsktbl; L Socr; High Hon Roll; Hon Roll; Natl Sci Olympiad 84; Hnrb Mntn Chem 84; Appt To US Air Force Acad 85; NY ST Regents Schlrshp 85; SUNY.

SPENCER, CAROL; Dominican Commerical HS; Jamaica Est, NY; (Y); 20/250; Church Yth Grp; Girl Scts; Hosp Aide; Pres Frsh Cls; Pres Soph Cls; Pres Jr Cls; Rep Stu Cncl; JV Bsktbl; Sftbl; NHS; Hunter Coll; Nrsng.

SPENCER, CAROLYN KLESH; Groton Central HS; Cortland, NY; (Y); Church Yth Grp; Stat Score Keeper; Var Trk; Hon Roll; Bus.

SPENCER, CHRISTOPHER A; Hamburg SR HS; Hamburg, NY; (Y); 86/406; 4-H; Intnl Clb; JCL; Latin Clb; Im Vllybl; 4-H Awd; Regents Schlrshp 85; U Buffalo; Engrng.

SPENCER, CYNTHIA; East Aurora HS; East Aurora, NY; (S); 24/182; Sec Church Yth Grp; Drama Clb; NFL; School Musical; Trs Yrbk Stf; Sr Cls; Sr Cls; Hon Roll; NHS; Vrsty Ltr 84; 5th Pl Forensics ST Mt 81; Spch Path.

SPENCER, DEBORAH; Forest Hills HS; Long Is, NY; (Y); Dance Clb; Girl Scts; Hon Roll; Psych.

SPENCER, ELIZABETH; Fayetteville Manlius HS; Manlius, NY; (Y); Cmnty Wkr; Pres VP Temple Yth Grp; Chorus; Off Stu Cncl; Hon Roll; Cum Honore 84.

SPENCER, JACQUELINE MARIE; Academy Of St Joseph; N Babylon, NY; (Y); Hosp Aide; Teachers Aide; Orch; High Hon Roll; Am Stds Awd 84-85; Bio.

SPENCER, JAMES; John Jay HS; Wappingers Fall, NY; (Y); Math Tm; Pres Orch; Trs Jr Cls; Trs Sr Cls; Ntl Merit Ltr; Debate Tm; Stu Cncl; High Hon Roll; 3rd Pl Intl Sci & Engrng Fair 85; Gld Mdl NY Mth Fair 85; Columbia U Sci Hnrs Pgm 85; Mth.

SPENCER, JEFFREY; Dover Plains JR SR HS; Dover Plains, NY; (Y); Boy Scts; Church Yth Grp; Math Tm; Band; Concert Band; Drm & Bgl; Jazz Band; Pep Band; School Play; Tennis; Rochester Inst Tech; Elec Engr.

SPENCER, REBECCA; Warsaw Central Schl; Warsaw, NY; (S); 15/93; Drama Clb; French Clb; Rep Frsh Cls; VP Sr Cls; Rep Stu Cncl; JV Cheerleading; JV L Socr; Hon Roll; Jr NHS; Prncpls Acad Awd Achvt 83; Soc Dist Amer HS Stu Awd 84; Retail Mgmt.

SPENGLER, STEPHANIE W; Connetquot HS; Bohemia, NY; (S); 16/671; Intnl Clb; Math Tm; Thesps; Mrchg Band; School Play; Nwsp Sprt Ed; Rep Frsh Cls; Var Bsktbl; NHS; Army ROTC Schlrshp Wnnr 84; Political Sci.

SPERA, MICHAEL; Valley Stream Central HS; Valley Stream, NY; (Y); Computer Clb; Mathletes; Var Socr; Jr NHS; Mu Alp Tht; NCTE Awd; NHS; Spanish NHS; Rensselaer Poly Inst Medal 85; George Washington U Medal 85; Cooper Union; Chem Engr.

SPERES, CONSTANTINE A; Garden City HS; Garden City, NY; (Y); 61/319; Pres Church Yth Grp; Office Aide; Yrbk Stf; Im Bsktbl; Var Ftbl; High Hon Roll; NY ST Regents Schlrshp 85; Lafayette; Govt & Law.

SPERICO, LORI A; Eastport SR HS; Eastport, NY; (S); 3/55; Scholastic Bowl; Ski Clb; Varsity Clb; Yrbk Ed-Chief; Var Capt Bsktbl; Var Capt Socr; Var Capt Sftbl; Hon Roll; Pres Jr NHS; NHS; Soccer All-Suffolk Cnty 84; Bsktbl All-League 84-85; Sftbl All-Suffolk Cnty 84; Engrng.

SPERLING, ANDREA L; Laguardia H S Of Music & The Arts; Woodside, NY; (Y); 170/675; Chorus; School Musical; Yrbk Stf; Lit Mag; Gym; Trk; Hon Roll; Eng.

SPERLING, LINNAE R; Binghamton HS; Binghamton, NY; (Y); 33/487; Cmnty Wkr; Hosp Aide; Rep Stu Cncl; High Hon Roll; Hon Roll; Rgnts Schlrsph 85; Rotry Clb Outstndng SR Awd 85; Hlmrk Pho Cntst Hnrb Mntn 84; Boston U; Lib Arts.

SPERO JR, RICHARD B; East Hampton HS; Amagansett, NY; (Y); 19/157; School Play; Variety Show; VP Sr Cls; Var Capt Bsbl; Var Capt Ftbl; Im Wt Lftg; Var Wrstlng; Cit Awd; High Hon Roll; VFW Awd; All Leag Bsbl,Ftbl 84-85; Stu Ldrs 83-85; PA ST; Wildlf Sci.

SPERONI, JOHN V; Division Avenue HS; Levittown, NY; (Y); 5/358; Computer Clb; Ski Clb; Band; Jazz Band; Orch; High Hon Roll; NCTE Awd; NHS; Ntl Merit Ltr; PA ST Schlrs Prog 84; Polytechnic Inst Of NY; Elec E.

SPEROS, ELEFTHERIA; Cardinal Spellman HS; Bronx, NY; (Y); Cmnty Wkr; Dance Clb; Pep Clb; Ski Clb; Jr Cls; Sr Cls; Hon Roll; NHS; Cty Islnd Vlntr Ambulnce Corp Co Sec 83-85; Comm.

SPEROS, GEORGE E; Cardinal Spellman HS; Bronx, NY; (Y); Cmnty Wkr; Dance Clb; Ski Clb; Yrbk Stf; Off Jr Cls; Off Sr Cls; Trs Stu Cncl; CC Awd; Regnts Schlrshp 85; Iona Coll; Comm.

SPETTER, VICTORIA C; Gen D Mac Arthur HS; Wantagh, NY; (Y); 7/319; Hosp Aide; Science Clb; Nwsp Bus Mgr; Nwsp Stf; Yrbk Bus Mgr; Var Tennis; Var Trk; High Hon Roll; Jr NHS; NHS; Rgnts Schlrshp 85; Colgate Schlrshp 85; 3 Yr Hnr Soc Awd 85; Colgate U; Lib Arts.

SPEVAK, JARET A; Newburgh Free Acad; Newburgh, NY; (Y); 13/800; French Clb; Math Tm; Y-Teens; Band; High Hon Roll; Jr NHS; Hgh Scr On Math Tm 85; Lwyr.

SPICCI, ANTHONY A; Greece Olympia HS; Rochester, NY; (Y); Am Leg Boys St; Boy Scts; Pres Drama Clb; Math Clb; Ski Clb; Chorus; School Musical; Ed Yrbk Stf; Var Trk; NHS; Acad Decthln 85; Bst Chorus Schl Musical 85; St Thomas Moore Clb 83; Bio.

SPICER, ALISA; James Madison HS; Brooklyn, NY; (S); Church Yth Grp; Girl Scts; Hosp Aide; VP JA; Teachers Aide; Hon Roll; Mandel; Dental Tech.

SPICER, DARRON; St Peters Boys HS; Staten Island, NY; (Y); 113/194; Im Bsktbl; Im Ftbl; Im Wt Lftg; Hon Roll; 3rd Hnrs 81-83; NY Tech Clg; Elec Technlgy.

SPICER, DEIDRE K; Walt Whitman HS; Huntington, NY; (Y); 19/630; Capt Color Guard; Concert Band; Orch; Nwsp Rptr; Capt Pom Pon; JV Vllybl; Jr NHS; Trs NHS; Ntl Merit Ltr; Spanish NHS; 2nd Bassnst NY All ST Band 83; Atlntc Wind Symphnys Outstndg Band Stu Awd 84; PSYCHTRY.

SPICER, VELVET; Oakfield-Alabama HS; Oakfield, NY; (Y); Art Clb; Drama Clb; Color Guard; School Musical; School Play; Soph Cls; Jr Cls; 1st Pl JR Bwlng TV 84; Fshn Mrchndsng.

SPICIARICH, LINDA; Red Hook Central HS; Tivoli, NY; (Y); Trs 4-H; Var Trk; Lang.

SPICKER, BRENDA; Webster HS; Webster, NY; (Y); 5/560; Church Yth Grp; Varsity Clb; Rep Sr Cls; Var Capt Cheerleading; High Hon Roll; NHS; Sal; Spanish NHS; Spanish Clb; Gold & Blue Awd 85; Wellesley Coll Bk Awd 84; Engl Awd 82-85; Wake Forest U; Liberal Arts.

SPIEGLER, MARC; Hawthorne Valley HS; Philmont, NY; (Y); 1/15; Cmnty Wkr; School Play; Rep Frsh Cls; Rep Soph Cls; Rep Jr Cls; Rep Stu Cncl; JV Var Bsktbl; JV Var Vllybl; School Musical; Yrbk Rptr.

SPIELMAN, MICHELLE; Union Springs Acad; Pine City, NY; (S); Ski Clb; Spanish Clb; Varsity Clb; Chorus; Church Choir; School Musical; Stage Crew; Nwsp Stf; Cheerleading; Hon Roll; Gold Key Awd Art 83; Andrews U.

SPIESS, DAWN; Buffalo Acad Of The Sacred Heart; Cheektowaga, NY; (Y); Spanish Clb; JV Badmtn; Hon Roll; JV Sftbl; JV Trk; Prfct Atten Awd; Chem.

SPIESS, KELLI; Liverpool HS; Liverpool, NY; (S); 5/792; Quiz Bowl; Concert Band; Jazz Band; Mrchg Band; Orch; Pep Band; Symp Band; High Hon Roll; Jr NHS; NHS; Am Leg Cert Of Schl Awd 81; NYSSMA Conf All ST Concrt & Band 84; Outstndng Achvt Math Awd 82; Comp Sci.

SPIEZIO, MARGARET; Mercy HS; Albany, NY; (Y); 16/65; Dance Clb; Chorus; Stage Crew; Lit Mag; Bowling; High Hon Roll; Awd In Paintn & Drwng 84-85; Awd In Englsh 12 84-85; Mst Attrctv 84-85; Coll Of St Rose; Comm Art.

SPILKO, HOWARD T; Smithtown HS West; Smithtown, NY; (Y); Cmnty Wkr; French Clb; Varsity Clb; Im Bowling; Im Golf; Var L Socr; French Hon Soc; High Hon Roll; Hon Roll; NHS; Regents Schlrshp Awd; SUNY Binghampton; Bus Mgt.

SPILLE, KIRSTEN; Corning-Painted Post West HS; Painted Post, NY; (Y); Pres Art Clb; Intnl Clb; School Musical; Nwsp Rptr; Nwsp Stf; Yrbk Stf; Rep Jr Cls; Trk; Hon Roll; Yrbk Copy Edtr, Asstnt Edtr 84-85; Publc.

SPILLMAN, CHRISTOPHER E; Livonia Central HS; Conesus, NY; (Y); 18/142; Am Leg Boys St; Varsity Clb; Band; Concert Band; Mrchg Band; Pep Band; Im Bsktbl; Var L Socr; High Hon Roll; Hon Roll; Bst Dfnsv Plyr Awd Sccr 84.

SPINELLA, VICKI; Rocky Point JR SR HS; Sound Bch, NY; (Y); Church Yth Grp; Office Aide; Spanish Clb; Variety Show; Yrbk Stf; Crs Cntry; Trk; Dietcn.

SPINELLI, CHRIS; Xaverian HS; Brooklyn, NY; (S); 5/400; Drama Clb; PAVAS; Spanish Clb; Stage Crew; Lit Mag; Trs Stu Cncl; Lcrss; NHS; Trs Spanish NHS; Presdtl Acadmc Ftnss Awd 85; Marine Corps Phycl Ftnss Awd 85; Intl Brthrhd Teamstrs Schlrshp Fnlst 85; Cooper Union; Art.

SPINELLI, GENA MARIE; Maine-Endwell SR HS; Endwell, NY; (Y); Cmnty Wkr; VP FHA; Spanish Clb; Yrbk Bus Mgr; Yrbk Stf; Hon Roll; NHS; Recgnz Ntl Cncl Yth Ldrshp 85; Engrng.

SPINELLI, KAREN; Smithtown High School West; Smithtown, NY; (Y); Hosp Aide; Trs Yrbk Stf; VP Frsh Cls; VP Soph Cls; Pres Jr Cls; Stu Cncl; High Hon Roll; NHS; Itln Natl Hnr Scty 84-86; Law.

SPINELLO, ANTHONY; Eastridge HS; Rochester, NY; (Y); 30/235; Varsity Clb; Var Bsbl; Var Socr; Hon Roll; Hnrbl Mntn All-Cnty Bsbl 85; Bus Admin.

SPINK, CHRISTOPHER M; Batavia HS; Batavia, NY; (Y); Pres VP Church Yth Grp; Capt Math Tm; Church Choir; Co-Capt JV Bsktbl; Coach Actv; Var JV Socr; Hon Roll; Pres NHS; Acad All Am 84 & 85; Natl Ldrshp & Svc Awd 84 & 85; Roberts Wesleyan Coll; Comp Sci.

SPINK, TAMMY; Sackets Harbor Central HS; Sackets Harbor, NY; (Y); 10/46; Chorus; Sec Mrchg Band; Yrbk Stf; Pres Sr Cls; Pres Stu Cncl; Capt Var Cheerleading; Capt Socr; Cit Awd; DAR Awd; NHS; NY Telephone Schlrshp 85; NY Cnfrnc All State Chorus 84; Stu Cncl Srv Awd 85; Jfrsn CC; Bus Adm.

SPINOSO, LISA M; St John The Baptist HS; East Islip, NY; (Y); 18/601; Hosp Aide; Stu Cncl; Var Tennis; French Hon Soc; High Hon Roll; NHS; PA ST U; Med.

SPIRA, PETER D; Lewiston Porter HS; Youngstown, NY; (Y); 1/273; Pres Church Yth Grp; Key Clb; Capt Ice Hcky; Var Socr; Hon Roll; Pres NHS; Sal; NROTC 85; Altrnt Cmnty Ambssdrs Pgm 84; U Of Rochester; Chemcl Engnrng.

SPITHOGIANIS, DESPINA; Whitestone Acad; Whitestone, NY; (S); 1/38; Awds Engl, Civic, Earth Sci, Alg, Spnsh I Greek 83; Awds Engl, Wrld Hstray Geom Biol Spnsh II 84; Bus.

SPITZ, DONNA; Bishop Maginn HS; Ravena, NY; (Y); Art Clb; Dance Clb; Office Aide; Pep Clb; Red Cross Aide; Ski Clb; Spanish Clb; Teachers Aide; Yrbk Stf; Tennis; Educ.

SPITZER, JOHN C; Williamsville North HS; Williamsville, NY; (Y); 31/310; Church Yth Grp; JV Crs Cntry; JV Trk; JV Vllybl; Hon Roll; ST U Of NY Buffalo; Accntng.

SPITZERS, DOMINIQUE A; Webster HS; Webster, NY; (Y); German Clb; Score Keeper; Hon Roll; Prfct Atten Awd; German Natl Hnr Soc 84; German Awd 84; Office Awd 83; Johnson & Wales Coll; Travel.

SPIVEY, SCOTT; Sacred Heart HS; Yonkers, NY; (S); 7/216; VP Soph Cls; JV Capt Bsktbl; Im Trk; Hon Roll; NHS; Ntl Cncl Negro Womn Acad Achvt Awd 83-84; ASU; Engr.

SPIWAK, SCOT K; Half Hollow Hills East HS; Dix Hills, NY; (Y); 144/547; Aud/Vis; Computer Clb; Spanish Clb; Hon Roll; Pres Schlr; LA U Srv Awds 83 & 84; FL Atnltc U; Accntng.

SPODARYK, KRISTEN; Bishop Scully HS; Broadalbin, NY; (Y); Drama Clb; French Clb; Varsity Clb; School Play; Bsktbl; Cheerleading; Pom Pon; Math.

SPOHR, BARBARA; Albion HS; Albion, NY; (Y); Chorus; Hon Roll; Chamberlayne JC; Int Dsgn.

SPOLARICH, MICHAEL J; New Hyde Park Memorial HS; New Hyde Park, NY; (Y); Am Leg Boys St; Boy Scts; Trs Band; Trs Jazz Band; Yrbk Sprt Ed; Var Ftbl; Var Lcrss; High Hon Roll; VP Jr NHS; Trs Concert Band; Hgh Hnrs Grd 7-11.

SPORN, ROBERT A; Dalton Schl; New York, NY; (Y); Civic Clb; Library Aide; Math Tm; Model UN; Temple Yth Grp; Nwsp Stf; Ntl Merit SF; Pblc Affairs Jrnl Editor.

SPOSILI, MICHAEL; Oneonta HS; Oneonta, NY; (Y); German Clb; Ski Clb; Bowling; Golf; Marion Gail Wilson Awd 79-80; Law.

SPOTILA, JENNIFER; Cardinal O Hara HS; Tonawanda, NY; (S); 2/145; Pres Debate Tm; French Clb; Quiz Bowl; School Musical; Nwsp Ed-Chief; Nwsp Rptr; Ed Lit Mag; High Hon Roll; NHS; Schl Voice Democracy Competition 84; Bronze Sci Awd 82; Law.

SPOTO, MARK D; Southwestern Central HS; Jamestown, NY; (Y); Am Leg Boys St; Concert Band; Jazz Band; Mrchg Band; Var Vllybl; Dnfth Awd; NHS; Ntl Merit SF; Ski Clb; High Hon Roll; Mst Outstndng Band Stu 82 & 85; Englsh, Chem, Math & Social Stds Awd 83-85; Mid E Symphnc All Star Bnd; Engr.

SPRADLIN, TINA; Waterloo HS; Waterloo, NY; (Y); Church Yth Grp; 4-H; Girl Scts; Science Clb; Temple Yth Grp; Chorus; Church Choir; 4-H Awd; Hon Roll; Girls Camp Awd 83; Brigham Young U; Nrsng.

SPRAGUE, DEAN; Falconer Central HS; Falconer, NY; (Y); 19/134; Church Yth Grp; 4-H; FFA; Spanish Clb; Teachers Aide; Stage Crew; JV Vllybl; 4-H Awd; NYS Grang Pub Spkg Cont 2nd Pl 84; FFA Chptr Star Green Hnd 84; Ag Tchr.

SPRAGUE, JO; Horseheads HS; Horseheads, NY; (Y); 26/405; Cmnty Wkr; Girl Scts; Spanish Clb; Band; Church Choir; Color Guard; Mrchg Band; Var Tennis; High Hon Roll; NHS.

SPRANGER, KELLY; The Hewitt HS; New York, NY; (Y); Yrbk Phtg; Ed Lit Mag; Sec Frsh Cls; Pres Soph Cls; Pres Jr Cls; VP Sr Cls; Sec VP Stu Cncl; Var Badmtn; Hon Roll; St Schlr.

SPRIK, GRACE; Aquinas Inst; Penfield, NY; (S); 8/182; Drama Clb; Hosp Aide; Ski Clb; Nwsp Rptr; Yrbk Phtg; Rep Frsh Cls; Swmmng; Timer; High Hon Roll; Rep Stu Cncl; MI ST; Bio.

SPRINGER, BERNICE; George W Wingate HS; Brooklyn, NY; (Y); Teachers Aide; Band; Chorus; Concert Band; Prfct Atten Awd; Psych.

SPRINGER, KATHY; James I O Neill HS; West Point, NY; (Y); French Clb; German Clb; Hosp Aide; Red Cross Aide; School Musical; School Play; Variety Show; Yrbk Stf; Var L Swmmng; Var L Trk; YFU Smr Frnc 85; East Stroudsburg U.

SPRINGER, SEAN; Hudson HS; Hudson, NY; (Y); 11/200; AFS; Chess Clb.

SPRINGER, SHARON L; Hudson HS; Hudson, NY; (Y); 3/160; VP AFS; Sec Concert Band; Jazz Band; Mrchg Band; Orch; School Musical; Yrbk Stf; High Hon Roll; NHS; Ntl Merit Ltr; Middlebury College; Italian.

SPRINGER, STACEY; SHEEPSHEAD Bay HS; Brooklyn, NY; (Y); Dance Clb; Girl Scts; MMM; Office Aide; PAVAS; Band; Chorus; Concert Band; School Musical; School Play; Citznshp 79; Band 82; Brooklyn Coll; Acctg.

SPRINGER, SUSAN; Cardinal Cooney HS; Rochester, NY; (Y); 29/333; Church Yth Grp; High Hon Roll; Hon Roll; Spanish NHS; Bio.

SPROAT, DEBBIE; Shenendehowa HS; Rexford, NY; (Y); Church Yth Grp; Chorus; Church Choir; High Hon Roll; Hon Roll; Prfct Atten Awd; Accntnt.

SPROUT, WENDY E; Royalton-Hartland Central Schl; Middleport, NY; (Y); 15/135; Varsity Clb; Sftbl; Natl Hnr Socty 85; Regnts Schlrshp 85; Hnbl Mntn All Leag Sftbl 84; Genesee CC.

SPROW, LAURA; Potsdam HS; Hannawa Falls, NY; (Y); 24/124; AFS; French Clb; Math Clb; Varsity Clb; Nwsp Stf; Yrbk Stf; JV Var Sftbl; JV Var Vllybl; Math.

SPRUNG, KRISTA; Byron-Bergen JR SR HS; Bergen, NY; (Y); Church Yth Grp; Drama Clb; Band; Chorus; Church Choir; Color Guard; Concert Band; Flag Corp; Mrchg Band; Yrbk Stf; Genessee Comm Cazenovia; Tchng.

SPRY, LISA; Chenango Forks HS; Port Crane, NY; (Y); Key Clb; Sec.

SQUEO, MARYANN; St Joseph By The Sea HS; Staten Island, NY; (Y); Hon Roll; Hghst Avg Yr European Hist, Gen Chem, Intl Alg; Trnsltr.

SQUICCIARINI, PAUL; Saint John The Baptist HS; W Islip, NY; (Y); 5/625; Chess Clb; Computer Clb; Math Clb; Math Tm; Science Clb; Nwsp Ed-Chief; Nwsp Phtg; Hon Roll; Jr NHS; NHS; Med Tecnlgy.

SQUIER, DENISE; Lakeland SR HS; Mahopac, NY; (Y); Church Yth Grp; 4-H; Band; Chorus; Mrchg Band; Stu Cncl; High Hon Roll; NHS; Debate Tm; Drama Clb; Area All ST Band 85; ST Fnlst Modrn Miss Schlrshp Pagnt NY ST 85; Intl Rel.

SQUIER, RANDALL W; Owego Free Acad; Apalachin, NY; (Y); Am Leg Boys St; Key Clb; Yrbk Sprt Ed; Pres Frsh Cls; Pres Sr Cls; Rep Stu Cncl; Var L Bsktbl; Var L Ftbl; Var L Trk; Hon Roll; Physcs Engr.

SQUILLACE, LINDA; Linton HS; Schenectady, NY; (Y); 1/243; Trs AFS; Sec Intnl Clb; Concert Band; Lit Mag; Rep Frsh Cls; Rep Soph Cls; Rep Jr Cls; Hon Roll; VP NHS; Smith Coll Bk Awd 85.

SQUILLANTE, ANGELINA; St Johns Prep; Long Isld Cty, NY; (Y); Church Yth Grp; Cmnty Wkr; FTA; Hosp Aide; Office Aide; Teachers Aide; Chorus; Church Choir; Hon Roll; Amer Hstry.

SQUIRES, BARBARA; Elmira Southside HS; Elmira, NY; (Y); 43/350; Cmnty Wkr; Sec Library Aide; Political Wkr; Radio Clb; Y-Teens; Concert Band; Mrchg Band; Trs Nwsp Rptr; Hon Roll; Computer Clb; Rgnts Schlrshp Wnnr NYS; Corning CC; Acctnt.

SQUIRES, DAVID; Grand Island SR HS; Gr Island, NY; (Y); French Clb; Varsity Clb; Socr.

SRINIVASAN, RAVI; Gloversville HS; Gloversville, NY; (Y); 1/220; Math Clb; Nwsp Rptr; Stu Cncl; JV Socr; Bausch & Lomb Sci Awd; High Hon Roll; NHS; Ntl Merit Ltr; Val; Most Outstndng Sr 85; Phi Delta Signa Eng Prz 85; Elizabeth Stewearts Math Prz 85; Brown U; Med.

SRIUBAS, ANDY R; Carmel HS; Carmel, NY; (Y); Am Leg Boys St; Boy Scts; VP 4-H; Varsity Clb; Yrbk Rptr; Trs Jr Cls; Pres Stu Cncl; Var Capt Trk; Cit Awd; NHS; United Nations Stu Rep 85; Pres Classrm 85; Stu Senate Econ Rep-Albany 85; Econ.

SRIVASTAVA, MONISHA; Longwood HS; Port Jeff, NY; (Y); 30/570; Variety Show; Var Tennis; High Hon Roll; Hon Roll; Bus.

ST CLAIR, ANGELA; Saranac Central HS; Plattsburgh, NY; (S); 2/106; Chrmn French Clb; Girl Scts; Rep Stu Cncl; JV Cheerleading; Hon Roll; NHS; G S Silver Awd 82; JV Chrldng Ldrshp Trophy 84; Bio.

ST DENIS, REJEANNE; Franklin Academy SR HS; Malone, NY; (Y); 4-H; Acctnt.

ST FLEUR, DOMINIQUE; Fort Hamilton HS; Brooklyn, NY; (Y); 70/535; FNA; Office Aide; Rep Sr Cls; Hon Roll; NHS; Hlth Career Hnr Rll 84 & 85; Spn Hnr Rll 82-84; Comp Math Hnr Rll 85; Hunter Coll; Nrsng.

ST GEORGE, JENNIFER; Schoharie HS; Schoharie, NY; (S); 12/78; Drama Clb; French Clb; Hosp Aide; Key Clb; Rep Stu Cncl; Hon Roll; Hartwick Coll; Psych.

ST GEORGE, PATRICIA; Middleburgh Central HS; Middleburgh, NY; (S); Am Leg Aux Girls St; Church Yth Grp; CAP; Cmnty Wkr; GAA; Spanish Clb; Varsity Clb; Band; Chorus; Church Choir; Alfred U; Ceramic Engnrng.

ST GERMAIN, LEO; Heuvelton Central HS; Heuvelton, NY; (S); 4/51; Chess Clb; Sec FFA; NHS; Canton ATC; Data Proc.

ST JOHN, AMY; Glens Falls SR HS; Glen Falls, NY; (Y); Nwsp Stf; Crs Cntry; Trk; High Hon Roll; Boston U; Mech Engrng.

ST JOHN, IRENE; Fort Edward Union Free Schl Dist 1; Ft Edward, NY; (Y); Spanish Clb; Band; Yrbk Sprt Ed; Pres Jr Cls; Var Capt Bsktbl; Var JV Vllybl; Hon Roll; NHS; Hnr Schlrshp & Bio Schlrshp Frm New Rochelle Coll 85; US Army Rsrv Athlt/Schlr Awd 85; New Rochelle Coll; Bio.

ST JOHN, JENNIFER; Brewster HS; Patterson, NY; (S); 22/176; Drama Clb; Nwsp Phtg; Yrbk Phtg; Stu Cncl; Crs Cntry; Trk; NHS; Spanish NHS; VFW Awd; Voice Dem Awd; 1st Pl, Bst Show Phtgrphy Putnam Cty Art Show 84; Comms.

ST JOHN, KATHLEEN; Remsen Central Schl; Forestport, NY; (Y); Sec Trs Church Yth Grp; Church Choir; Yrbk Stf; High Hon Roll; Hst NHS; 4-H Local Govt Intrn Pgm 85; Alumni Awd 83; Mrktg Rsrch.

ST JOHN, MONIQUE; Catholic Central HS; Troy, NY; (S); 19/203; German Clb; Hosp Aide; Math Clb; Band; Yrbk Stf; Hon Roll; NHS; Arch.

ST JOHN, SCOTT; Cooperstown Central Schl; Cooperstown, NY; (Y); Am Leg Boys St; Varsity Clb; Concert Band; Mrchg Band; Trs Stu Cncl; Var L Bsktbl; Var L Golf; Var Capt Socr; Hon Roll; NHS; Band Cncl 82-84; Soccer All Star 82-84.

ST JOHN, THOMAS; Richmond Hill HS; Richmond Hl, NY; (Y); Computer Clb; School Play; Rep Soph Cls; Stat Mgr(s); High Hon Roll; Hon Roll; NHS; Ordr Of The Owl; Med.

ST LAURENT, MICHELLE; Pittsford Mendon HS; Pittsford, NY; (Y); Pep Clb; Stage Crew; Yrbk Stf; Cheerleading; Powder Puff Ftbl; JV Vllybl; Hon Roll; Engr.

ST ONGE, DAVID; Wilson Central HS; Lockport, NY; (Y); Ski Clb; Yrbk Stf; Hon Roll; Recrdng Engr.

ST ONGE, SCOTT; Hoosic Valley HS; Schagticoke, NY; (Y); Var Bsbl; Army.

ST PETER, SCOTT; Peekskill HS; Peekskill, NY; (S); 1/187; Chess Clb; Bausch & Lomb Sci Awd; NHS; NY ST Regents Schlrshp 85; Pre-Med.

ST PHILLIPS, GINA S; Auburn HS; Auburn, NY; (Y); 16/444; Chorus; Jazz Band; Mrchg Band; School Musical; Symp Band; NHS; Ntl Merit Ltr; Art Clb; Dance Clb; Girl Scts; Schlstc Art Awds 83-85; NYSSMA Conf All-ST Band 83; NYSSSA Visual Arts 84; SUNY-BUFFALO; Graphic Arts.

ST THOMAS, MICHAEL; Gloversville HS; Gloversville, NY; (Y); Math Tm; Teachers Aide; Nwsp Bus Mgr; Var L Golf; Var Tennis; High Hon Roll; Law.

STAAB, MICHELLE L; Centereach HS; Centereach, NY; (Y); 3/475; Q&S; Concert Band; Mrchg Band; Orch; School Musical; Nwsp Rptr; Yrbk Stf; Jr NHS; Trs NHS; Adelphi U; Math.

STABILE, RICHARD P; Saint Anthonys HS; Huntington, NY; (Y); Nwsp Stf; Yrbk Stf; Im Bowling; Var Capt Swmmng; Tennis; High Hon Roll; Hon Roll; NHS; Spanish NHS; Med.

STABILE, THERESA J; Garden City HS; Garden City, NY; (Y); 49/319; Cmnty Wkr; Rep Jr Cls; Cheerleading; Coach Actv; Gym; Mgr(s); High Hon Roll; NHS; Orch; 3rd Pl Uneven Bars Chmpn 84; NYS Rgnts Schlrshp 85; U Of Richmond; Bus.

STABY, SCOTT; Eden Central SR HS; Eden, NY; (Y); 16/200; JV Ftbl; Var Ice Hcky; Var Capt Swmmng; Var Tennis; AFS; Cmnty Wkr; Computer Clb; Letterman Clb; Varsity Clb; Band; Clarkson U; Ind Mngmnt.

STACHOWIAK, MICHELLE; Villa Maria Academy; Buffalo, NY; (S); 1/106; Art Clb; Cmnty Wkr; Computer Clb; JCL; Pres Service Clb; High Hon Roll; NHS; NEDT Awd; Scholar Villa Maria Acad 83-84; Cert Of Merit Afro-Asian Soc Essay Cont 84; Pediatrcn.

STACHOWICZ, TIMOTHY; North Rose-Wolcott HS; Red Crk, NY; (Y); Boy Scts; French Clb; Band; Var Bsbl; JV Bsktbl; JV Socr; Im Vllybl; High Hon Roll; Hon Roll; NY ST Regnts Schlrshp Wnnr 85; Army; Helicptr Chew Chf.

STACHURA, JOELLE; Williamsville South HS; Williamsville, NY; (Y); AFS; French Clb; Hon Roll; Psych.

STACHURA, RACHELLE A; Niagara Wheatfield HS; N Tonawanda, NY; (Y); 3/315; Church Yth Grp; Pres French Clb; Latin Clb; VP Math Clb; Pep Clb; PAVAS; High Hon Roll; NHS; Prfct Atten Awd; JA; Regents Schlrshp Wnnr NY 85; Geneseo; Bio-Chem.

STACKEL, GREGORY; Jericho SR HS; Brookville, NY; (Y); 43/230; Computer Clb; VP JA; JCL; Trs Latin Clb; Math Clb; Nwsp Rptr; Var Tennis; Hon Roll; NHS; Arts Recgnititon/Tlnt Srch Cntsnt 84; Literature.

STACKELHOUSE, STACEY J; Bitburg American HS; Apple Valley, CA; (Y); 16/129; Model UN; Chorus; VP Stu Cncl; Var L Tennis; Hon Roll; Jr NHS; Pres Schlr; Church Yth Grp; Office Aide; Spanish Clb; Hmcmn Qun 84; FAA Plt Flght Schl Solo 85; Wrttn Lit Awd 84; U ND; Mrktg.

STACKMAN, GARRETT L; South Side HS; Rockville Centre, NY; (Y); 20/285; Key Clb; Spanish Clb; Acpl Chr; Chorus; NHS; Ntl Latin Hnr Soc 83-84; JETS Clb Pres 84-85; JETS Clb Vp 83-84; NY ST Rgnts Schlrshp; Cornell U; Medicine.

STADELMAN, KAREN; De Sales HS; Lockport, NY; (S); 2/45; Hosp Aide; High Hon Roll; NHS; Ntl Merit Ltr; Pro-Life Awd Wnnr 84; Boston U; Med.

STADLER, DAWN M; Lake Shore HS; Angola, NY; (Y); Ski Clb; Band; Chorus; Concert Band; Jazz Band; Mrchg Band; Orch; Stage Crew; High Hon Roll; Hon Roll; NYS Regents Schlrshp 84-85; U Rochester.

STADTLANDER, SHARON; Lansingburgh HS; Troy, NY; (Y); Cmnty Wkr; Key Clb; Varsity Clb; Yrbk Stf; Capt JV Bowling; Var Crs Cntry; Var Trk; High Hon Roll; NHS; Spec Educ.

STADTMILLER, DAVID; Oneida SR HS; Oneida, NY; (Y); 36/225; Am Leg Boys St; Computer Clb; Varsity Clb; Rep Soph Cls; JV Bsbl; JV Bsktbl; Var JV Ftbl; High Hon Roll; Hon Roll; Rotary Awd; Mohawk Vly CC; Engrng.

STADTMILLER, KEITH F; Edison Tech & Ocptnl Ed Cntr; Rochester, NY; (Y); 5/271; Boy Scts; Exploring; Varsity Clb; Var Vllybl; High Hon Roll; VP NHS; NY ST Regnt Schlrshp 85; Alfred ST Coll; Elctr Mech.

STAEUBLE, CHRISTA JAYNE; Seton Catholic Central HS; Endicott, NY; (Y); 6/152; Cmnty Wkr; Mathletes; Service Clb; High Hon Roll; NHS; NYS Rght To Lf & Regnts Schlrshps; Natl Yth Ldrshp Awd; Cornell U; Vet.

STAFFEN, TODD; Tonawanda JR SR HS; Tonawanda, NY; (Y); 2/235; Concert Band; Jazz Band; School Musical; Stu Cncl; Var L Bsbl; Var L Socr; Hon Roll; NHS; Pres Schlr; Sal; Ron Traver Mem Scholar 85; T-NT Frnds & Alumni Awd 84; Case Western Reserve U; Engrng.

STAFFORD, GREGORY; Geneseo Central HS; Conesus, NY; (Y); 20/87; Sec Frsh Cls; Sec Soph Cls; Sec Jr Cls; Sec Sr Cls; Hon Roll; Jr NHS.

STAFFORD, KELLY; Scotia-Glenville HS; Scotia, NY; (Y); Church Yth Grp; Girl Scts; Hosp Aide; Key Clb; Pres Frsh Cls; Stu Cncl; Mgr(s); JV Vllybl; Masonic Awd; Schl Dist Pyrmd Prog 85; Prfct Attndnce 81; Grphc Dsgnr.

STAFFORD, LAURIE J; Marcellus SR HS; Marcellus, NY; (Y); 26/163; Band; Orondaga CC; Data Proc.

STAFFORD, MICHELE; Villa Maria Acad; Buffalo, NY; (S); 15/118; JCL; Latin Clb; Red Cross Aide; Chorus; Swmmng; Hon Roll; NEDT Awd; Oceanogrphy.

STAFFORD, SIOBHAN; St Vincent Ferrer HS; New York, NY; (Y); Drama Clb; Political Wkr; Stage Crew; Bus Mgmt.

STAGNER, MARY B; Camden Central HS; Blossvale, NY; (Y); AFS; 4-H; Ski Clb; Varsity Clb; Golf; High Hon Roll; Hon Roll; Acctnt.

STAHEL, LAURA; Garden City HS; Garden City, NY; (Y); 61/355; Pep Clb; JV Var Cheerleading; Var L Gym; JV Var Socr; Var L Trk; High Hon Roll; Hon Roll; Jr NHS; L Bsktbl; Fld Hcky.

STAHL, CLAIRE; Buffalo Acad Of The Sacred Heart; Williamsville, NY; (Y); 18/124; Red Cross Aide; Spanish Clb; Trs Sr Cls; JV Badmtn; Cheerleading; High Hon Roll; Hon Roll; SUNY Buffalo; Engrng.

STAHL, JACQUELINE A; Little Falls JR SR HS; Little Falls, NY; (Y); Girl Scts; Band; Concert Band; Mrchg Band; Bus.

STAHL, THOMAS G; Rome Free Acad; Rome, NY; (Y); 245/553; Camera Clb; Nwsp Phtg; Nwsp Rptr; Nwsp Stf; Off Sr Cls; Vllybl; Hon Roll; Hussen Coll; CPA.

STAHLMAN, JASON; Jamestown HS; Jamestown, NY; (Y); Am Leg Boys St; Capt Quiz Bowl; Orch; Rep Jr Cls; Hon Roll; Pres Jr NHS; NHS; Ski Clb; Spanish Clb; Rep Frsh Cls; Richard J Sciascia Awd Top Sci Stu 83; James Prendergast Awd Top Chem Stu 84; Norman M Tinkham Awd 85; Aerospace Engnr.

STAHURA, MARY; Frontier SR HS; Blasdell, NY; (S); Church Yth Grp; Hosp Aide; Library Aide; Pep Clb; Chorus; Church Choir; Color Guard; Mgr(s); Hon Roll; NHS; Med Tech.

STAIB, PAUL; Vestal SR HS; Apalachin, NY; (Y); Pres Church Yth Grp; Varsity Clb; JV Var Bsktbl; Coach Actv; JV Capt Ftbl; JV Var Lcrss; Hon Roll; Prfct Atten Awd; Comp Sci.

STAIGAR, LESLIE; Saratoga Springs HS; Saratoga Springs, NY; (Y); Drama Clb; Y-Teens; School Play; JV Var Cheerleading; JV Sftbl; Stat Wrstlng; High Hon Roll; Hon Roll; Cobleskill Coll; Bsns Mgmt.

STAINBROOK, CARRIE; Horseheads HS; Elmira, NY; (Y); Church Yth Grp; Drama Clb; Orch; Yrbk Stf; Sftbl; Hon Roll; Big Flats Cmnty Days Queen 85; Big Flats Cinderella All Star 81-84.

STAKEY, ELIZABETH A; Riverhead HS; Aquebogue, NY; (Y); Pres Church Yth Grp; German Clb; Ski Clb; Band; Church Choir; Mrchg Band; Ed Yrbk Phtg; Yrbk Stf; Jr NHS; NHS; Grmny Exch Stdnt; Sundy Schl Tchr; Syracuse U; Psych.

STALEY, BRIAN M; Whitesboro SR HS; Whitesboro, NY; (Y); 39/320; Boy Scts; Drama Clb; Intnl Clb; Chorus; Nwsp Stf; Hon Roll; Regents Schlrshp 85; Mohawk Vly CC; Bus Admin.

STALEY, CONNIE; Bishop Scully HS; Amsterdam, NY; (Y); Cmnty Wkr; 4-H; JA; Sec Frsh Cls; Sec Soph Cls; Pres Jr Cls; VP Sr Cls; Hon Roll; JV Capt Bsktbl; Var Sftbl; Med Sec.

STALEY, LYNN; Saranac Central HS; Saranac, NY; (S); 19/106; Drama Clb; French Clb; Girl Scts; Chorus; Yrbk Stf; Hon Roll; Nrsng.

STALEY, PATRICIA; Dominican Commercial HS; St Albans, NY; (Y); Dance Clb; Drama Clb; School Play; Yrbk Stf; Gym; Trk; Current Events & Law Awd 84; Schltc Achvt Dnce 84; Pre-Law.

STALKER, JULIE; Lyndonville HS; Lyndonville, NY; (Y); Band; Drm Mjr(t); School Musical; Sec Jr Cls; Sec Stu Cncl; Var Capt Cheerleading; Var Socr; Hon Roll; Jr NHS; Prfct Atten Awd; Bus.

STALKER, MARK D; Chatham HS; East Chatham, NY; (Y); Ski Clb; L Chorus; School Play; Swing Chorus; Variety Show; L Trk; Wt Lftg; Hon Roll; Hudson Vly Coll; Criminal Justc.

STALLINGS, DANYAN; Roosevelt HS; Yonkers, NY; (Y); 15/390; Political Wkr; Var Capt Bsbl; Var Capt Socr; High Hon Roll; NHS; Schlr/Athlte Awd 85; Regnl Art Awd 85; Suprntndnts Acad Achvt 84 & 85; Tuskegee Inst; Pre Med.

STALLSWORTH, DARRELL; Aviation HS; E Elmhurst, NY; (Y); CAP; Service Clb; Ski Clb; Nwsp Rptr; Bsktbl; Cit Awd; JETS Awd; Prfct Atten Awd; Pegasus Soc Awd 85; Cert Of Apprctn Cabl TV 85; Cert Of Gradtn 85; Embry Riddle U; Comml Pilt.

STALMACK, TAMMY; Central Islip HS; Central Islip, NY; (Y); Band; Concert Band; Jazz Band; Mrchg Band; Orch; Pep Band; School Musical; Mgr Yrbk Bus Mgr; Yrbk Stf; NYSSMA Music Awd 83; Top Ten Phy Ftns Awd 85; Boces Dept Fire Sfty & Cert Part Awd 85-86; Farmingdale; Lab Tech.

STALOFF, DAVID B; Mineola HS; Albertson, NY; (Y); 55/257; Boy Scts; Pres Computer Clb; Ntl Merit Ltr; Regnts, Rensselaer Schlrshp 85; Rensselaer Plytech; Comp Sci.

STALZER, HERBERT; Bethpage HS; Plainview, NY; (Y); 75/270; German Clb; Var Capt Bsbl; Var Capt Ftbl.

STAMAS, ELLEEN; Lansingburgh HS; Troy, NY; (Y); 57/180; Varsity Clb; Chorus; Yrbk Stf; Off Stu Cncl; Cheerleading; Hon Roll; Fresh Jr Vrsty & Vrsty Chrldng 82-85; Concert Choir 82-85; Stu Cncl; Hudson Vly CC; Bus Admin.

STAMM, ANNA; Vestal SR HS; Vestal, NY; (Y); German Clb; Lib Acpl Chr; Lib Chorus; Lib Orch; School Musical; Yrbk Bus Mgr; Yrbk Ed-Chief; Yrbk Sprt Ed; High Hon Roll; NHS; Cornell; Engrng.

STAMOS, NICHOLAS D; Westhill HS; Syracuse, NY; (Y); 2/168; Art Clb; Camera Clb; Church Yth Grp; Cmnty Wkr; Drama Clb; Exploring; French Clb; FBLA; JA; Math Clb; Scv Clbs Math Ldrshp Awd 85; Ntl Bsktbl Assn Schlrshp 85; MA Inst Of Tech; Engrng.

STAMP, TERESA; Wathkins Glen HS; Rock Stream, NY; (Y); 14/130; Pres Rep 4-H; Letterman Clb; Math Clb; Band; Chorus; School Play; Var Swmmng; Cit Awd; DAR Awd; 4-H Awd; Make Yourself Wool 2nd St 83; Farm Bureau Citizshp Awd 85; Elem Ed.

STANAVICH, DAVID J; Bishop Scully HS; Amsterdam, NY; (Y); Art Clb; PAVAS; Nwsp Stf; Yrbk Ed-Chief; Pres Soph Cls; Pres Sr Cls; JV Bsktbl; Var Capt Crs Cntry; Hon Roll; Prmnt Collctn Awd 82; Senate Stdnt Plcy Frum 84; Imgntn Clbrtn Fnlst 84; Pratt Inst; Fine Arts.

STANCHFIELD, HELEN; Rome Free Acad; Taberg, NY; (Y); 39/533; Am Leg Aux Girls St; Spanish Clb; Chorus; Drill Tm; School Play; Var L Mgr(s); Var L Sftbl; Hon Roll; Jr NHS; Civitan Smnr 84; N Cntry CC; Psychlgy.

STANCZYK, LISA; Villa Maria Acad; Buffalo, NY; (Y); Art Clb; Sec Church Yth Grp; Hst Pres FBLA; Sec Soph Cls; Sec Stu Cncl; Futr Bus Ldrs Amer 1st Pl Clrk Typst NY ST & 2nd Pl Publc Spkng 84 & 85; Court Rptng.

STANDERA, BRIAN F; Wayne Central HS; Ontario, NY; (Y); 24/201; Mathletes; Math Clb; Math Tm; Ski Clb; Rep Stu Cncl; Golf; Hon Roll; NHS; Monroe CC; Engrng.

STANDERWICK, CHRISTIAN; Oyster Bay HS; Oyster Bay, NY; (Y); Boy Scts; Church Yth Grp; German Clb; Chorus; Trs Stu Cncl; Bsbl; Bsktbl; Ftbl; Golf; Hon Roll.

STANDHART, MICHAEL; Gilboa-Conesville Central HS; Gilboa, NY; (Y); 7/34; Am Leg Boys St; Boy Scts; Cmnty Wkr; Spanish Clb; Teachers Aide; Varsity Clb; Variety Show; Pres Frsh Cls; Pres Stu Cncl; Var Bsbl; Jewelry & Mach Trades Awd 84-85; Susquehanna Trl Post Am Lg Awd 84-85; Memorial Awd 84-85; Alfrd ST; Bldg Constr.

STANEK, MICHAEL; Alden Central HS; Alden, NY; (Y); Computer Clb; Ski Clb; Band; Concert Band; Jazz Band; Mrchg Band; School Musical; Ftbl; 4th Pl Western New York Comp Prog Contest 85; Webbs Inst; Naval Archt.

STANFIELD, DEAN; Williamsville East HS; East Amherst, NY; (Y); JA; Pep Clb; Ski Clb; Ice Hcky; Socr; Var Trk; Woodwrkg Achvt Awd 82; St Bonaventure; Mktg.

STANISH, TAMMY; Niagara Wheatfield SR HS; Niagara Falls, NY; (Y); 28/319; Church Yth Grp; Trs French Clb; FBLA; JA; Nwsp Rptr; Stu Cncl; High Hon Roll; Hon Roll; NHS; Distngushd Stu Merit Schlrshp Awd 85; Schlrshp Christn Ed Comm 85; Local Elect Un Schlrshp 85; Niagara County Comm Coll; Bus A.

STANISZ, DIANNE; Niagara Falls HS; Niagara Falls, NY; (Y); Pep Clb; Yrbk Stf; Var Cheerleading; Ntl Hstry Day Hnr Excllnt Achvt Cert 85; Hair Dsgn.

STANISZEWSKI, AUDREY; Villa Maria Acad; Lancaster, NY; (S); 4/102; Chrmn Computer Clb; Var JCL; Natl Beta Clb; Pres Service Clb; Concert Band; Trs Stu Cncl; High Hon Roll; NHS; NY Bd Rgnts Cert Rcgntn 84; Euprean Cult Hghst Aver Awd 84; U Buffalo; Optmtrst.

STANISZEWSKI, DIANE; N Babylon HS; North Babylon, NY; (Y); VICA; JV Socr; Albany Med Ctr; Nrsng.

STANKO, STACEY; Longwood HS; Coram, NY; (Y); 73/487; Variety Show; Rep Stu Cncl; Var Cheerleading; JV Co-Capt Pom Pon; Hon Roll; Crmnl Justc.

STANKOVICH, STANLEY A; St Patricks C C HS; Catskill, NY; (Y); 20/45; Boy Scts; Computer Clb; Ski Clb; Yrbk Sprt Ed; Yrbk Stf; Var L Bsbl; Var JV Bsktbl; L Socr; Hon Roll; Prfct Atten Awd; NY ST Regnts Schlrshp; 1110 SAT Score; Mst Imprv Plyr Sccr; Springfield Coll; Hlth.

STANLEY, CONSTANCE; Fort Edward SR HS; Ft Edward, NY; (Y); 10/37; Art Clb; Camera Clb; Computer Clb; Drama Clb; PAVAS; Color Guard; Drm & Bgl; School Play; Yrbk Ed-Chief; Yrbk Phtg; NYS Art Tchrs Assn 85; Comm Arts.

STANLEY, GEORGE; Nottingham HS; Syracuse, NY; (Y); Am Leg Boys St; Boy Scts; Church Yth Grp; French Clb; Quiz Bowl; Red Cross Aide; Band; Concert Band; Jazz Band; School Play; Comm Svc Awd 85; Cornell; Med.

STANLEY, JENNIFER; Shaker HS; Latham, NY; (Y); Dance Clb; Trs French Clb; Latin Clb; Chorus; School Musical; Var Co-Capt Cheerleading; High Hon Roll; Hon Roll; NHS; Lbrl Arts.

STANLEY, SUZANNE; Sacred Heart Acad; Levittown, NY; (S); 6/189; Math Clb; Math Tm; Spanish Clb; Chorus; Stage Crew; Variety Show; Bowling; NHS; Accntnt.

STANNARD, ELIZABETH L; Shenandehowa HS; Ballston Lake, NY; (Y); Church Yth Grp; Drama Clb; FCA; Band; Church Choir; Concert Band; Symp Band; High Hon Roll; Hon Roll; NHS; St Rose-Albany NY; Muscl Tech.

STANTON, DAVID; Fairport HS; Fairport, NY; (Y); Hon Roll; Berklee Schl Music; Prof Guitar.

STANTON, ELIZABETH A; St Marys Girls HS; Port Washington, NY; (Y); 19/159; Hosp Aide; Key Clb; Math Clb; Office Aide; Ski Clb; Teachers Aide; Chorus; Nwsp Ed-Chief; Im Lcrss; JV Swmmng; Deans Schlrshp Fordham U 85; Regnts Schlrshp 85; Coll Of The Holy Cross.

STANTON, JOHN; Fonda-Fultonville Central HS; Fonda, NY; (Y); Trs Church Yth Grp; Key Clb; Chorus; Crs Cntry; Trk; Hon Roll; Comp Sci.

STANTON, KIM M; Byron-Bergen HS; Byron, NY; (Y); AFS; Church Yth Grp; FTA; Library Aide; Office Aide; Teachers Aide; Chorus; Hon Roll; Accntng.

STANTON, MARY; Resurrection Acad; White Plains, NY; (Y); Church Yth Grp; Service Clb; School Musical; Pres Frsh Cls; JV Cheerleading; JV Swmmng; JV Trk; Hon Roll; NHS; Chorus; Schlrshp To Resurrection Acad 82-86; 3rd Pl & 1st Pl In CYO Art Cont 84; 2nd Pl Awd In CYO Art Cont; Bus Mgmt.

STANTON, PATRICK; Bishop Timon HS; W Seneca, NY; (S); Spanish Clb; Chorus; Var Ftbl; Ice Hcky; Trk; Wt Lftg; Hon Roll.

STANTON, WILLIAM; Bronx High School Of Science; New York, NY; (S); School Play; Var Bsktbl; Var Golf; JV Trk.

STANWICK, SUSAN; Cocócton Central HS; Cohocton, NY; (Y); 12/26; Church Yth Grp; French Clb; GAA; Varsity Clb; Band; Mrchg Band; School Musical; School Play; Yrbk Stf; JV Var Cheerleading; Chrldg Champs 85; Sftbl All Tourn Tm 85; Central City Bus Inst; Ct Rprt.

STAP, JOYCE; Valley Central HS; Montgomery, NY; (Y); 33/289; Band; Concert Band; Mrchg Band; Yrbk Stf; Vllybl; High Hon Roll; NHS; Spanish NHS; NY ST Schlstc Music Assoc Comptn Flute,Piccolo 84-85; Vet Tech.

STAPLES, TIMOTHY; Fonda Fultonville Central Schl; Fonda, NY; (Y); Church Yth Grp; Nwsp Rptr; Trk; High Hon Roll; NHS; Ntl Merit Ltr; Highest Av Frshmn Boy 83; Highest Av Soph Boy 84.

STAPLETON, SHANNON; Auburn HS; Auburn, NY; (S); 10/405; Mrchg Band; Orch; School Musical; Symp Band; High Hon Roll; Pres NHS; Ntl Fdrtn Of Music Clbs Comptn NY ST & Liberty Dist Wnnr 85; Amer Lgn Empire Grls ST Alt 85; Music.

STARK, ANDREW; Maple Hill HS; Castleton, NY; (S); 1/72; Pres Key Clb; Stage Crew; Yrbk Bus Mgr; Rep Stu Cncl; JV Var Bsktbl; JV Var Socr; NHS; USAFA Smmr Sci Semnr 85; Elctrcl Engrng.

STARK, FRED; Ellenville HS; Ellenville, NY; (Y); 12/114; Am Leg Boys St; Chess Clb; Drama Clb; Teachers Aide; Stage Crew; JV L Ftbl; Var L Socr; Var Trk; Capt JV Wrstlng; Hon Roll; Ntl Sci Olympd Mdlst 83-85; Ulster Cnty CC; Bio.

STARK, JAMIE C; Gowanda Central HS; Gowanda, NY; (Y); 7/154; AFS; Spanish Clb; Band; Chorus; Nwsp Phtg; Stu Cncl; Var Mgr Trk; High Hon Roll; NHS; 3-1-3 Stu SUNY Fredonia 84-85; SUNY Fredonia; Chem.

STARK, JENNIFER; Fort Ann Central HS; Ft Ann, NY; (Y); Cheerleading; High Hon Roll; Hon Roll; NHS; Nrs.

STARK, JENNIFER L; Our Lady Of Mercy HS; Rochester, NY; (Y); Exploring; VP Sec 4-H; Ski Clb; Drill Tm; Nwsp Rptr; Trk; 4-H Exch Stu Orange Cnty VA 85; Mendon Pony Clb C-2 Ratg 83; 3rd Pl Mendon Hrse Trial 85; Econ.

STARK, JOANNA; Mercy HS; Riverhead, NY; (Y); Church Yth Grp; GAA; Intnl Clb; JCL; Key Clb; Latin Clb; Ski Clb; Var Tennis; Im Vllybl; Hon Roll; 110 Per Cent Tenns Awd 84; Bus.

STARK, JOANNE; Potsdam Central HS; Potsdam, NY; (Y); Camera Clb; JV Bsktbl; Bowling; Var Sftbl; Var Trk; Utica Schl Of Commerce; Accntng.

STARK JR, JOSEPH; East Syracuse Minoa HS; E Syracuse, NY; (Y); Trs 4-H; JA; Science Clb; Badmtn; Bsktbl; Tennis; Vllybl; Hon Roll; Jr NHS; Prfct Atten Awd; Rochstr Inst Tech Schlrshp Awd 85-86; NY ST Rgnts Schlrshp 85-89; Navy ROTC Alt; Rochestr Inst Of Tech; Comp Sci.

STARK, LISA; Mt Upton Central HS; S New Berlin, NY; (Y); Band; Chorus; Concert Band; Sec Frsh Cls; High Hon Roll; NHS; Prfct Atten Awd; Hnr Soc Vp, Sec & Treas 84-85; Bus.

STARK, LORNA L; Catskill HS; Catskill, NY; (Y); 4/134; Church Yth Grp; Office Aide; Yrbk Phtg; Yrbk Stf; Stu Cncl; Score Keeper; High Hon Roll; Hon Roll; NHS; NYS Regnts Schlrshp 85; ST U NY Albany; Math.

STARK, S PETER; Susan Wagner HS; Staten Island, NY; (Y); 26/480; Nwsp Ed-Chief; High Hon Roll; NHS; USMA Wst Pnt 85; Ldrshp Awd 85; Intl Rotary Hlth Care Awd 85; USMA West Point.

STARK, VALERIE H; Albany HS; Albany, NY; (Y); 7/600; Church Yth Grp; Latin Clb; Lit Mag; Var L Trk; Hon Roll; NHS; Ntl Merit SF; Comp Engrng.

STARKEY, SHEILA T; Amherst Central HS; Snyder, NY; (Y); GAA; Capt L Bsktbl; Capt L Fld Hcky; Var Score Keeper; Var L Socr; Var L Vllybl; Hon Roll; NHS; Outstndng Part Awd Intercollegiate Athl 84; Regents Schlrshp 85; Chmbr Comm Athl Of Yr 85; SUNY Geneseo.

STARKS, DANA; Massena Central HS; Massena, NY; (Y); Church Yth Grp; Band; Concert Band; Mrchg Band; Pep Band; Var Cheerleading; JV Gym; Ice Hcky; Hon Roll; Prfct Atten Awd; Massena Schl Bus; Scrtrl.

STARKWEATHER, MICHELLE; Oakfield Alabama Central HS; Basom, NY; (Y); 8/90; AFS; Sec Church Yth Grp; Church Choir; Mgr(s); Hon Roll; NHS; SUNY Geneseo; Elem Educ.

STARLING, REBECCA; East Aurora HS; East Aurora, NY; (S); 9/182; Church Yth Grp; Chorus; Church Choir; School Musical; NHS; Hon Roll; Jr NHS; Attnd U S Nvl Acad Sci & Engrng Semnr 84; Attnd Inst Fenix Cuern Mex 84; Yth Actvty Brd Baptst 84-85; Drew U NJ; Spnsh.

STAROPOLI, LYNNE; Nazareth Acad; Rochester, NY; (Y); Church Yth Grp; Dance Clb; Latin Clb; Varsity Clb; VP Frsh Cls; JV Var Bsktbl; JV Var Socr; JV Var Sftbl; High Hon Roll; NHS; Schl Rep-Notre Dame Jr Of The Yr 85; Socl Wrk.

STAROWITZ JR, LEO; Byron Bergen Central Schl; Elba, NY; (Y); Camera Clb; 4-H; Science Clb; Band; Concert Band; Mrchg Band; Stage Crew; Stu Cncl; Var Golf; 4-H Awd; 4-H Ag Bus Awd Trip 84; Genesse CC; CPA.

STARR, LYNN MARIE; Lafayette HS; Buffalo, NY; (Y); Library Aide; Office Aide; Nwsp Rptr; Nwsp Stf; Prfct Atten Awd; Italian Club 82-85; Long Island; Jrnlsm.

START, TRACY ANN; Fort Hamilton HS; Brooklyn, NY; (Y); 159/553; Office Aide; Teachers Aide; Im Bowling; Hon Roll; John Jay Coll Of Crmnl; Attrny.

STASINSKI, ALICIA; John Dewey HS; Brooklyn, NY; (Y); Spanish Clb; Prfct Atten Awd; Lang Arts Engl Awd 82; Cmmnty Serv Awd 82; Ec.

STASIO, LISA; Mount Mercy Acad; Buffalo, NY; (S); 42/161; JA; Math Clb; Spanish Clb; Nwsp Rptr; Nwsp Stf; Hon Roll; Math.

STASZAK, LYNN A; Depew HS; Depew, NY; (Y); 3/254; GAA; Tennis; High Hon Roll; Trs NHS; Pres Schlr; St Schlr; SUNY Buffalo; Biophyscs.

STATEN, MICHELE; Hendrick Hudson HS; Verplanck, NY; (Y); Church Yth Grp; Church Choir; Sec Soph Cls; VP Jr Cls; VP Sr Cls; Stu Cncl; Var Capt Bsktbl; Var L Sftbl; High Hon Roll; NHS; Smith Bk Awd 85; JR Cls Awd 85; All-Sect Sftbl 85; Physcn.

STATHOPOULOS, JIM; Churchville-Chili SR HS; Rochester, NY; (Y); 16/324; Varsity Clb; Var Capt Bsktbl; Var L Socr; High Hon Roll; Hon Roll; NHS; SAR Awd; MVP Vrsty Sccr & Bsktbl 84-85; Pres Acad Ftnss Awd 84-85; Ntl Hnr Roll 84-85; Clarkson U; Engrng.

STATLER, DIANNE; West Hempstead HS; Island Pk, NY; (Y); Art Clb; Yrbk Stf; Ntl Art Hnr Scty 85; Hofstra U.

STATON, JOANN; Clara Barton HS; Brooklyn, NY; (Y); 35/469; Dance Clb; Band; School Musical; Nwsp Ed-Chief; High Hon Roll; Hon Roll; NHS; Ntl Merit Ltr; NY ST Sen Achvt Awd 84; Binghamton U; Biogcl Rsrch.

STATT, LISA; E J Wilson HS; Rochester, NY; (Y); Drama Clb; VP Exploring; French Clb; Girl Scts; Math Tm; Stage Crew; Symp Band; Yrbk Stf; Hon Roll; Phrmcy.

STATTLER, RICHARD; Longwood HS; Shirley, NY; (S); 1/492; Intnl Clb; Math Tm; Quiz Bowl; Nwsp Rptr; High Hon Roll; NHS; Ntl Merit Ltr; VFW Awd; Selctd Peer Ldrshp Tm Forc Prog 85; Arch.

STATTLER, RICK; Longwood HS; Shirley, NY; (Y); 1/492; Intnl Clb; Math Tm; Quiz Bowl; Nwsp Rptr; High Hon Roll; NHS; Ntl Merit Ltr; VFW Awd.

STAUB, SCOTT; Susquehanna Valley HS; Conklin, NY; (Y); Chess Clb; Church Yth Grp; English Clb; Exploring; French Clb; Math Clb; Ski Clb; Nwsp Rptr; Nwsp Stf; Lit Mag.

STAUROWSKY, CHERYL; Geneva HS; Geneva, NY; (Y); Varsity Clb; Stu Cncl; Cheerleading; Socr; Trk; Hon Roll; Rotary Awd; Blck G Awd 3 Vrsty Sports 84; Cosmtlgy Awd Outstndng Perf; Cosm Fash Dsgn.

STAUSS, CAROLYN L; Academy Of Saint Joseph HS; E Northport, NY; (Y); 3/120; Hosp Aide; Library Aide; Math Clb; Science Clb; Chorus; Yrbk Stf; Pres Schlrshp From Coll Of New Rochelle 85; Alumni Schlrshp From Coll Of Mt St Vincent 85; Mt St Vincent Coll; Nursing.

STAVISKI, WILLIAM R; Thomas Edison JR SR HS; Elmira, NY; (Y); 13/89; Am Leg Boys St; Quiz Bowl; Science Clb; Varsity Clb; Yrbk Stf; Rep Sr Cls; Var L Bsbl; Var L Bsktbl; High Hon Roll; Rgnts Schlrshp 85; Corning Comm Coll; Crmnl Just.

STEADY, CANDACE; Wilson Central HS; Ransomville, NY; (Y); 30/140; 4-H; Science Clb; Band; Pep Band; School Play; Stu Cncl; Capt Trk; Vllybl; High Hon Roll; Pres Schlr; Police Athlt League Schlrshp 85; Rnsmvl Fire Co Axlry Awd 85; Wlsn Tcrh Assn Schlrshp 85; SUNY Aswego; Bio Chmstry.

STEARNS, REBECCA; Midlakes HS; Clifton Spgs, NY; (Y); 5/145; Church Yth Grp; School Musical; Tennis; Vllybl; Sec NHS; French Clb; Thesps; Church Choir; Color Guard; Deans Schlrshp 85-86; Gypsm Kngs Dghtrs & Sons Inc Awd 85; Pres Acad Ftns Awd 85; Brigham Young U; Accntnt.

STEARNS, SARAH DICKEY; South Glens Falls SR HS; Gansevoort, NY; (Y); 1/237; Am Leg Aux Girls St; Quiz Bowl; Ski Clb; Varsity Clb; Band; Chorus; Nwsp Stf; Rep Jr Cls; Rep Stu Cncl; Var Fld Hcky; Outstndng Frshmn Awd 82-83; Hghst Acad Avg 83-84; Stu Cncl Schl Serv Awd 83-85; Lbrl Arts.

STEBBINS, GARY; Lansingburgh HS; Troy, NY; (Y); Boys Clb Am; Varsity Clb; JV Var Bsbl; JV Var Bsktbl; Var Crs Cntry; Im Score Keeper; Hon Roll; Hudson Vly CC; Bus.

STEBBINS, MARK; West Genesee SR HS; Camillus, NY; (Y); Trs Church Yth Grp; Exploring; French Clb; Ski Clb; Church Choir; High Hon Roll; Hon Roll; Mech Engrng.

STEBBINS, TAMMY; Waterloo SR HS; Waterloo, NY; (Y); 43/168; Church Yth Grp; Hosp Aide; Ski Clb; Varsity Clb; Band; Chorus; Concert Band; Sftbl; Upstate Medical; Phy Thrpy.

STEDMAN, GEOFFREY; Greenville Central HS; Norton Hill, NY; (Y); 8/89; Am Leg Boys St; Church Yth Grp; Band; School Musical; JV Var Bsktbl; JP Sousa Awd; NHS; Drama Clb; Key Clb; Spanish Clb; SCIAA 1st Tm All Star 85; Rgnt Schlrshp 85; Ltr G Awd 83; Houghton Coll; Sprts Med.

STEDMAN, STEVE; Attica Central HS; Attica, NY; (Y); Band; Concert Band; Jazz Band; Mrchg Band; JV Bsktbl; Hon Roll; NHS; Rochester Inst Of Tech; Math.

STEDMAN, TERRANCE; Westmoreland Central HS; Rome, NY; (Y); Mathletes; Math Clb; Spanish Clb; Band; Concert Band; Drm & Bgl; Jazz Band; Mrchg Band; Pep Band; Trs Frsh Cls.

STEEB, KRISTINE; Greece Athena HS; Rochester, NY; (Y); 81/241; Dance Clb; Pep Clb; Varsity Clb; Acpl Chr; Sec Chorus; Swing Chorus; JV Capt Cheerleading; Var Pom Pon; Hon Roll; Mst Outstndng Vrsty Chrldr 83; Best All Arnd Vrsty Chrldr 85; Solo Comptn NYSSMA A Rtng 85; Elem Ed.

STEED, SALLY; Trott Vocational HS; Niagara Falls, NY; (Y); Pres Hosp Aide; Pres JA; Chorus; Church Choir; Variety Show; Sec Frsh Cls; JV Trk; Lion Awd; Nrs.

STEEL, CHRIS; Springville Griffith Inst; Springville, NY; (Y); French Clb; Spanish Clb; Rep Frsh Cls; Var Capt Ftbl; Var Trk; Var Capt Wrstlng; JR Vrsty Ftbl MI Rnng Bck 83-84; Trck All Str Tm Wstrn NY 84-85; Frshmn Ftbl Tm Capt 82-83; ST U NY Buffalo; Physcs.

STEELE, ERIC JAMES; Wheatland Chili HS; Scottsville, NY; (Y); 9/69; Cmnty Wkr; Pres Frsh Cls; Rep Soph Cls; Rep Stu Cncl; Var Bsbl; Var Socr; Var Capt Swmmng; DAR Awd; Hon Roll; NHS; NYS Rgnts Schlrshp; U Of Notre Dame; Engl.

STEELE, JULIE; Washingtonville HS; Washingtonville, NY; (Y); FCA; Natl Beta Clb; Speech Tm; Chorus; Yrbk Stf; JV Var Fld Hcky; Hon Roll; NCTE Awd; NHS; Voice Dem Awd; Appalachian ST U; Pol Sci.

STEELE, SARAH MICHELLE; Torrejon American HS; San Bernadino, CA; (Y); 7/87; Cmnty Wkr; Political Wkr; Yrbk Ed-Chief; Pres Frsh Cls; VP Trs Stu Cncl; High Hon Roll; Hon Roll; Jr NHS; Pres NHS; Pres Schlr; Tacso Schlrshp 85; Top 10 Pct Schlr Cert 85; Career Day Coor 85; U CA-RIVERSIDE; Comp Anly.

STEEN, EUNICE; Salmon River Central HS; Bombay, NY; (S); 8/97; Drama Clb; Band; VP Soph Cls; Sec Jr Cls; VP Sr Cls; Pres Stu Cncl; Var Swmmng; High Hon Roll; Hon Roll; Hosp Aide; Russn Achvt Awd 85; Canton ATC; Secy Sci.

STEEN, LYNNE; Ammaculata Acad; Buffalo, NY; (Y); Debate Tm; Hosp Aide; Latin Clb; Trs Red Cross Aide; Nwsp Rptr; Hon Roll; Latn Natl Hnr Socty 85; U Of Buffalo; Pre-Med.

STEEN, TERESA; Lockport SR HS; Lockport, NY; (Y); 10/500; Latin Clb; Yrbk Stf; Trs Soph Cls; Cheerleading; Hon Roll; Jr NHS; NHS; Ntl Merit SF; Pre Law.

STEENBURGH, THOMAS; Auburn HS; Auburn, NY; (Y); Letterman Clb; Model UN; Ski Clb; Varsity Clb; School Play; Symp Band; Ftbl; Tennis; High Hon Roll; NHS; Vrsty Ltr Ftbl Tnns 84-85; Engrng.

STEENCKEN II, JOE; Little Falls JR SR HS; Little Falls, NY; (Y); Computer Clb; English Clb; Pres FBLA; Pres JA; Mathletes; Math Clb; Math Tm; Im Bsktbl; JV Ice Hcky; JV L Lcrss; Exc Top Slsprsn 84; Onondaga Cty Math Tchrs Awd 83; 2nd Pl Entrep Bus Math 85; Bkng.

STEFANELLI, MICHAEL; W C Mepham HS; North Bellmore, NY; (Y); 29/385; Band; Yrbk Stf; Trs Stu Cncl; JV Bsbl; Var Capt Bsktbl; Var Socr; Im Sftbl; High Hon Roll; Pres NHS; Hofstra U; Pre Med.

STEFFAN, JAMES; Salamanca Central HS; Salamanca, NY; (Y); Church Yth Grp; DECA; Band; Concert Band; Drm & Bgl; Mrchg Band; Pep Band; School Musical; JV Bsktbl; Hon Roll; Htl/Rstrnt Mgmt.

STEFFEN, ALEX; Green Meadow Waldorf HS; Monsey, NY; (Y); Acpl Chr; Chorus; School Play; Symp Band; Var L Bsktbl; Var L Lcrss; Var L Socr; Ntl Merit SF; Drama Clb; Madrigals; Hist.

STEFL, KIM; Union Springs Acad; Salamanca, NY; (Y); Ski Clb; Band; Church Choir; Concert Band; School Musical; Stage Crew; Yrbk Stf; Sec Trs Stu Cncl; Gym; Hon Roll; Andrews U; Bus Educ.

STEFURA, PATRICIA; Coxsackie-Athens Central HS; Coxsackie, NY; (Y); 2/94; Math Clb; Band; Rep Stu Cncl; Var Bsktbl; Var Capt Socr; Vllybl; Bausch & Lomb Sci Awd; High Hon Roll; Pres NHS; Sal; Mayflower Schlrshp 85; Rotary Club Schlrshp 85; Ithaca Coll; Physics.

STEGMEIER, ROBERT; St Marys HS; Alden, NY; (S); JV Var Wrstlng; Vet.

STEHLE, JANNINE; Nanuet HS; Stony Point, NY; (Y); 73/177; Trs DECA; Intnl Clb; JA; Spanish Clb; JV Socr; JV Sftbl; Plattsburgh; Bus.

STEHN, KERRY; James E Sperry HS; Henrietta, NY; (Y); 52/302; German Clb; GAA; Hosp Aide; Pep Clb; Pres VP Stu Cncl; Cheerleading; Stat Lcrss; Socr; Monroe CC; Med Lab Tech.

STEICHEN, MARK; Valley Central SR HS; Walden, NY; (Y); French Hon Soc; Arch.

STEICHEN, MARY; Valley Central HS; Walden, NY; (Y); 41/250; Band; Off Stu Cncl; Crs Cntry; Trk; NHS; Spanish NHS; Commnctns.

STEIDLE, KATHLEEN; East Meadow HS; East Meadow, NY; (S); FBLA; Political Wkr; Science Clb; Yrbk Phtg; Var Tennis; Hon Roll; Jr NHS; Girl Scts; Var JV Fld Hcky; NHS; Skidmore Coll; Bus.

STEIGER, VERONICA; Lindenhurst HS; Lindenhurst, NY; (Y); French Clb; Nwsp Rptr; Nwsp Stf; Stu Cncl; Crs Cntry; Fld Hcky; Trk; Hon Roll; NHS; Voice Dem Awd; Geneseo; Ed.

STEIGLEHNER, LAURA T; Hendrick Hudson HS; Peekskill, NY; (Y); 7/200; Mathletes; Office Aide; Yrbk Stf; Lit Mag; Rep Frsh Cls; Rep Stu Cncl; Var Tennis; High Hon Roll; NHS; JR Prom Comm Mem 85; Miss Amer Co-Ed Pgnt Cont 84; Tutor 84-85; SADD Rep 84-85.

STEIN, ANDREW; Lynbrook HS; Lynbrook, NY; (Y); AFS; Mathletes; Spanish Clb; Nwsp Ed-Chief; Nwsp Rptr; Nwsp Sprt Ed; Nwsp Stf; JV Bsktbl; Mgr(s); JV Capt Socr; Pre-Law.

STEIN, CARYN; Oceanside HS; Oceanside, NY; (Y); Cmnty Wkr; Hosp Aide; Library Aide; Band; Concert Band; Var Badmtn; Trk; Elem Schl Tchr.

STEIN, DAVI; High Of Art & Design; New York, NY; (Y); 14/439; Sec Intnl Clb; School Musical; Stage Crew; Variety Show; Nwsp Phtg; Stu Cncl; Hon Roll; NHS; Camera Clb; Math Tm; Daily News Spr Yth Outstndng Achvt 83; Ntl Art Hnr Soc 83-85; Kodak Intl Nwspaper Snpsht Awd 84; Sci.

STEIN, MIA; Christopher Columbus HS; Bronx, NY; (Y); Key Clb; Teachers Aide; Temple Yth Grp; Chorus; School Musical; Nwsp Stf; Hon Roll; Prfct Atten Awd; Chorus 85; Global Hist Awd 83; Eng 84.

STEIN, SHARON; Rye Neck HS; Mamaroneck, NY; (Y); AFS; Aud/Vis; Hosp Aide; School Musical; Stage Crew; Variety Show; Yrbk Sprt Ed; Var L Bsktbl; Var L Fld Hcky; Var Capt Sftbl; All Lge Sftbll 83; MVP All Lge All Co Sftbll 85; Russell Sage Coll.

STEIN, STACEY; Greece Athena SR HS; Rochester, NY; (Y); 52/290; Cmnty Wkr; DECA; Symp Band; Yrbk Sprt Ed; Sec Jr Cls; Sec Stu Cncl; Var Cheerleading; Var Trk; Hon Roll; Hosp Aide; Student Council Serv Awd 83; Hugh O Brien Fnlst 84; Communictns.

STEINAS, STEPHANIE; Nozareth Acad; Rochester, NY; (S); Church Yth Grp; Ski Clb; Spanish Clb; Teachers Aide; Sec Rep Stu Cncl; Gym; High Hon Roll; Hon Roll; NHS; Buswmn 1st Qtr 84-85; Bkkpg Awd 84-85; Spnsh Awd 83-84; ST U NY Geneseo; Tchng.

STEINBERG JR, JOSEPH F; Henninger HS; Syracuse, NY; (Y); Var Ftbl; Var Lcrss; Hon Roll; Natl Hon Rl Bk 83-84.

STEINBERG, JUDI; Christopher Columbus HS; Bronx, NY; (S); #17 In Class; Dance Clb; Chorus; School Musical; School Play; Cit Awd; High Hon Roll; Prfct Atten Awd; St Schlr; Regnts Schlrshp 85; SUNY Purchase.

STEINBERG, MARCY A; Mac Arthur HS; Seaford, NY; (Y); 40/319; AFS; VP Debate Tm; Pres French Clb; Orch; School Musical; Yrbk Rptr; Var Tennis; Jr NHS; NHS; Cmnty Wkr; NY St Regents Schlrshp 85; Betty Tettleson Mem Schlrshp 85; Suny Albany; Bus.

STEINBERG, ROBBIE; Comsewogue HS; Terryville, NY; (Y); 5/400; French Clb; Band; Jazz Band; Orch; French Hon Soc; High Hon Roll; St Schlr; PTA Awd Wnnr 85; Outstndng Achvt Awds Eng, S S, Fr 84 & 85; Music Achvt Awd 83; Stonybrook U; Bio Sci.

STEINBERG, SCOTT; Roy C Ketchan HS; Poughkeepsie, NY; (Y); 30/500; Im Bsbl; Im Coach Actv; JV Mgr(s); High Hon Roll; Jr NHS; NHS; Clarkson U; Mechncl Ind Engrng.

STEINBERGER, BETH A; Washingtonville SR HS; Blooming Grove, NY; (Y); VP Trs Church Yth Grp; Computer Clb; French Clb; Teachers Aide; Yrbk Stf; Pres Stu Cncl; JV Var Bsktbl; JV Vllybl; Hon Roll; NHS; SCI.

STEINBERGER, CRAIG; Hebrew Academy Of Nassan County; W Hempstead, NY; (S); 8/70; Math Tm; Stage Crew; Yrbk Bus Mgr; Pres Stu Cncl; Capt L Ice Hcky; Var Swmmng; L Trk; NHS; Ntl Merit SF; NY Rgnts Schlrshp 84-85; Deans List; Cooper Union; Mech.

STEINDL, MICHAEL P; Greenwich Central HS; Greenwich, NY; (Y); 12/85; AFS; Am Leg Boys St; CAP; Band; Chorus; Jazz Band; School Musical; Swing Chorus; Yrbk Stf; L Crs Cntry; Norwich U; Mech Engrng.

STEINER, LORI; Wagner HS; Staten Is, NY; (Y); JA; Pep Clb; School Play; Nwsp Rptr; Nwsp Stf; Rep Frsh Cls; Rep Soph Cls; Rep Jr Cls; Rep Stu Cncl; Cheerleading; Hghst Hnrs Spn Level 4; Awd Achvt Achvt Chem I & II, Trig I & II; NYU; Brdcst Jrnlsm.

STEINER, MATTHEW; Alden Central HS; Alden, NY; (Y); Church Yth Grp; FTA; Teachers Aide; Nwsp Rptr; JV Crs Cntry; JV Ftbl; Var Wrstlng; Eductn.

STEINER, PATRICK; MSGR Mc Clancy HS; Astoria, NY; (Y); VP Chess Clb; High Hon Roll; NHS; Italian Clb; JR Acad Of Sci; CCD Tchr; Aeronaut Enrgnr.

STEINER, SUSAN CAROL; Alden Central HS; Alden, NY; (Y); School Musical; School Play; Yrbk Ed-Chief; Rep Stu Cncl; Stat Bsktbl; Im Vllybl; NHS; GAA; Yrbk Bus Mgr; Yrbk Phtg; Ntl Sci Olymp Awds 83-85; Miss Teenager Am Grand Fnlst 85; Acad Awds 83-85.

STEINESS, SUSAN; Northport HS; Northport, NY; (Y); 38/623; Pep Clb; Var Cheerleading; High Hon Roll; Hon Roll; NHS; Bus Hnr Soc 85; Boston U; Bus Mgmt.

STEINHART, DARCY A; Albany Academy For Girls; Delmar, NY; (Y); Dance Clb; Model UN; Ski Clb; Chorus; School Musical; Nwsp Stf; Ed Lit Mag; Pres Jr Cls; Stu Cncl; 3rd Pl In Hudson Vlly Regn In Natl Frnch Con 82; Regents Schlrshp 85; U Of WI; Intl Rel.

STEINHUEBEL, HANS; Iona Prep; Pt Chester, NY; (Y); 75/195; German Clb; Law.

STEINKE, CHRISTOPHER; Roy C Ketcham HS; Poughkeepsie, NY; (Y); Chess Clb; Library Aide; High Hon Roll; Comp Sci.

STEINKE, STEVEN; Seaford HS; Seaford, NY; (Y); Church Yth Grp; Exploring; Hon Roll; Natl Soc Stds Olympiad 8k; Albany ST; Law.

STEINSCHADEN, HEIDI VIENNA; Sachem HS; Holbrook, NY; (Y); 47/1463; Pres German Clb; Hosp Aide; Pres Ski Clb; Concert Band; Sec Sr Cls; Cit Awd; Jr NHS; Sec NHS; Miss NY St Ntl Teenager 84; No 1 Natv Spkr Ger On Long Is 82; NYMSSA Medal-Flute 82-84; Elkerd Coll; Mdrn Lang.

STEITLER, JASON; Newark Central HS; Newark, NY; (Y); 80/201; Trs Boy Scts; Cmnty Wkr; Drama Clb; Office Aide; Acpl Chr; Chorus; School Musical; School Play; Stage Crew; Lit Mag; Solo Fest Baritone Awd Excell 83-84; Pre-Law.

STEITZ, NANCY; Saugerties HS; Saugerties, NY; (Y); 52/250; French Clb; JV Var Cheerleading; Powder Puff Ftbl; High Hon Roll; Hon Roll; NHS; Vrsty Awd Chrldng 84-85; Vrsty Awd JV Chrldng 83-84; Comm.

STELLA, KATRHYN E; The Academy Of Mt St Ursula; Bronx, NY; (Y); 30/170; Spanish Clb; High Hon Roll; Hon Roll; Spanish NHS; Spnsh 2nd Hnr Cont Awd; Spnsh Soc Hnry Awd; NYU; Nrsg.

STELLA, MICHELLE; Beacon HS; Beacon, NY; (S); Drama Clb; Trk; High Hon Roll; Jr NHS; Prfct Atten Awd; Fash Merc.

STELLING, BETH ANN; Port Richmond HS; Staten Island, NY; (Y); 36/586; Sec Church Yth Grp; Band; Church Choir; School Musical; Capt L Swmmng; Hon Roll; NHS; Eastern Dist FCYF Mus Comp Supr 85; Natl FCYF Mus Fest Excllnt 85; Eastern Dist FCYF Mus Comp Excll; Nyack Coll; Mus.

STELLMANN, DAWN; Richmond Hill HS; New York, NY; (Y); Drama Clb; English Clb; Office Aide; School Musical; School Play; Nwsp Stf; VP Stu Cncl; Hon Roll; Jr NHS; NHS; Pride Yankees Awd 84-85; Italian Natl Hnr Scty 85; Hlth & Phy Educ Vlybl 84; NY U; Dance Tchr.

STEMLEY, TINA; Roosevelt JR SR HS; Roosevelt, NY; (Y); Hosp Aide; Spanish Clb; Sec Church Choir; Color Guard; Mrchg Band; Hon Roll; Prfct Atten Awd; Spanish NHS; Awds-Ntl Ldrshp & Ntl Frgn Lang 84-85; Johnson & Wales; Comp Sci.

STEMMER, CYNTHIA; Cicero-North Syracuse HS; Clay, NY; (S); 8/622; Church Yth Grp; VP JA; Teachers Aide; Band; Drill Tm; Tennis; 4-H Awd; Hon Roll; Engrng.

STEMPERT, SHERRY A; Port Jervis HS; Port Jervis, NY; (Y); 11/196; VP Church Yth Grp; Sec Drama Clb; Sec Trs Chorus; Ed Yrbk Stf; Sec Rep Stu Cncl; DAR Awd; Elks Awd; High Hon Roll; NHS; Pres Schlr; Prncpls Prestgs Excell Diploma 85; Hartwick Coll; Mgmt.

STEMPLES, PATTI JO; Ogdensburg Free Acad; Ogdensburg, NY; (Y); 2/200; Church Yth Grp; Quiz Bowl; Nwsp Rptr; Yrbk Stf; Rep Stu Cncl; CC Awd; High Hon Roll; NHS; Ntl Merit Ltr; 4-H; VA Tech; Comp Sci.

STEMPOWSKI, JENNIFER; St Marys HS; West Seneca, NY; (S); 26/204; Girl Scts; Model UN; Yrbk Ed-Chief; Rep Stu Cncl; Hon Roll; NHS; Cmnty Wkr; Intnl Clb; Red Cross Aide; 1st Class Girl Scout; Intl Exchnge Pgm England; Pres Ntl Hnr Soc; Caniss Coll; Acctng.

STEMPSEY, SUSAN; Bishop Maginn HS; Albany, NY; (Y); Am Leg Aux Girls St; Latin Clb; JV Var Bsktbl; Var Tennis; Var Capt Vllybl; Hon Roll; NHS; Prsdntl Acad Ftnss Awd 84-85; Engrng.

STENSTROM, ANDREA; Falconer Central HS; Falconer, NY; (Y); Church Yth Grp; Varsity Clb; VP Band; Pres Frsh Cls; Pres Soph Cls; Rep Stu Cncl; Var Capt Bsktbl; Var Sftbl; Var JV Vllybl; Fredonia; Acctng.

STENTA, MARYANN; Binghamton HS; Binghamton, NY; (Y); Key Clb; Pep Clb; Sec Frsh Cls; VP Jr Cls; Bsktbl; Cheerleading; Socr.

STENTO, DANIELLE; Seton Catholic Central HS; Binghamton, NY; (Y); Church Yth Grp; Dance Clb; Varsity Clb; Yrbk Stf; Rep Stu Cncl; Var Capt Cheerleading; High Hon Roll; Hon Roll; Cortland ST; Sprts Med.

STENZEL, SHARON V; Fairport HS; Fairport, NY; (Y); Rep Stu Cncl; Hon Roll; NY ST Regents Schlrshp 85; Skidmore Coll; Libeal Arts.

STEPHAN, CATHY; St Marys Miocesan HS; Lancaster, NY; (S); 44/180; Varsity Clb; Rep Frsh Cls; Rep Soph Cls; Rep Jr Cls; JV Badmtn; JV Tennis; Var Trk; Hon Roll; NHS; Intl Stu Ldrshp Inst At Notre Dame U; Sci.

STEPHAN, DINA; Mynderse Acad; Seneca Falls, NY; (S); 14/141; High Hon Roll; NHS.

STEPHANI, ANDREW; Valley Central HS; Montgomery, NY; (Y); 3/326; AFS; French Clb; Math Tm; Natl Beta Clb; Band; Concert Band; Mrchg Band; School Musical; Trs French Hon Soc; NHS; NYSSMA 85; Pre-Law.

STEPHANY, NOLAN; Williamson Central HS; Williamson, NY; (Y); 3/100; Boy Scts; French Clb; Pres Radio Clb; Science Clb; Band; Concert Band; Mrchg Band; High Hon Roll; NHS; Prfct Atten Awd; Soph Of Yr 84; Order Of Arrow Hnrs 84-85; Olym Of Minds 85; Syracuse U; Radio.

STEPHEN, WAYNE; West Seneca SR HS; Buffalo, NY; (Y); Aud/Vis; Drama Clb; JA; Teachers Aide; Color Guard; Flag Corp; Mrchg Band; School Musical; School Play; Stage Crew.

STEPHENS, KERRI ANN; Middleburgh Central Schl; Fultonham, NY; (S); 5/85; Art Clb; Chess Clb; 4-H; Spanish Clb; Stage Crew; Yrbk Stf; Var JV Bsktbl; Var Bowling; High Hon Roll; Hon Roll; Lawrence Drinon Mem Math Awd 83; Lynn S Cleary Mem Spanish Awd 83; Middleburgh Centrl Schl Merit Awd; Syracuse U; Architecture.

STEPHENS, LAURA; Depew HS; Depew, NY; (Y); Chorus; School Musical; Rep Frsh Cls; Rep Soph Cls; Var Cheerleading; Stat Swmmng; Hon Roll; Jr NHS; Bus Admin.

STEPHENS, LORRAINE; Martin Van Buren HS; Jamaica, NY; (Y); 54/579; Trs Church Yth Grp; Trs Cmnty Wkr; Var JA; Math Clb; Science Clb; Service Clb; Band; Church Choir; Hon Roll; Jr NHS; Svc Hnr Soc Cert Merit 85; Cert Scholar 85; 2nd Pl Schl Sci Fair 84; Syracuse U; Acctg.

STEPHENS, MARK P; Notre Dame HS; Elmira, NY; (Y); 18/125; Hon Roll; Ntl Merit Ltr; 1st Pl Saunders Scholar Competitn Chem 85; 1st Pl JETS Tm Competitn Chem 85; U Dayton; Chem Engrng.

STEPHENS, SEAN E; John H Glenn HS; Huntington, NY; (Y); Boy Scts; Chess Clb; Drama Clb; Letterman Clb; Spanish Clb; Band; Jazz Band; Var Bsktbl; Var Socr; Var Tennis; Rsrch Apprntce Awd 83; NYU-STONYBROOK; Bus Admin.

STEPHENS, SUSAN; Jasper Central Schl; Jasper, NY; (Y); 4-H; Sec French Clb; Teachers Aide; Chorus; Church Choir; Pres Soph Cls; Bsktbl; Score Keeper; Socr; Hon Roll; Cert Awd 83-85; Liberty U; Music.

STEPHENSON, APRIL; Sayville HS; Sayville, NY; (Y); 13/355; Church Yth Grp; French Clb; Key Clb; JV Vllybl; High Hon Roll; NHS; SYMBA SR Art Scholar 85; GA Inst Tech; Engrng.

STEPHENSON, COLEEN; Massena Central HS; Massena, NY; (Y); French Clb; Yrbk Stf; Crs Cntry; Trk; Eng.

STEPHENSON, KELLIE; Lockport SR HS; Lockport, NY; (Y); Drama Clb; English Clb; Girl Scts; Intnl Clb; Spanish Clb; Im Bowling; Im Score Keeper; Hon Roll; Millard Fillmore Buffalo; Nrsng.

STEPHENSON, TAIWO; Chenango Forks HS; Chenango Forks, NY; (Y); Church Yth Grp; Exploring; Rep Frsh Cls; Rep Soph Cls; Rep Jr Cls; Rep Sr Cls; Pres Stu Cncl; Hon Roll; NHS; Debate Tm; NY ST Mock Trial Tourn 82-85; Cornell; Bio.

STEPINA, EDWARD D; Garden City HS; Garden City, NY; (Y); Cmnty Wkr; Nwsp Phtg; Ed Yrbk Phtg; Lit Mag; Hon Roll; Prfct Atten Awd; Bus Mngmnt.

STEPNIAK, DARCY; Seton Catholic Central HS; Binghamton, NY; (Y); 18/170; Art Clb; Drama Clb; Nwsp Stf; Cheerleading; Oneonta ST U Coll; Bus Ecnmcs.

STEPNOWSKI, DAWN; East Meadow HS; East Meadow, NY; (S); FBLA; Key Clb; NHS; :Psych.

STEPNOWSKY, CYNTHIA; Mattituck HS; Cutchogue, NY; (Y); 37/115; Mathletes; Band; School Play; Variety Show; Yrbk Ed-Chief; Rep Jr Cls; Rep Stu Cncl; Hon Roll; Sec Trs 4-H; German Clb; Grmn Hnr Soc 84; Hgh Hnr Rl Grmn 83; Bus Admn.

STERLING, MATTHEW T; Heatly HS; Greenisland, NY; (Y); Am Leg Boys St; Boy Scts; French Clb; Key Clb; Yrbk Stf; Sec Frsh Cls; Var Stat Bsbl; Stat Bsktbl; Hon Roll; NHS; Accntng.

STERN, JOSH B; Bronx H S Of Science; Glendale, NY; (Y); Library Aide; Teachers Aide; Rep Jr Cls; Im Bsktbl; Im Sftbl; Jr NHS; Ntl Merit Ltr.

STERN, JUDITH L; HAFTR HS; Woodmere, NY; (Y); 19/62; Cmnty Wkr; Drama Clb; Temple Yth Grp; Yrbk Stf; NHS; NY ST Rgnt Schlrshp 83-85.

STERN, KEELAN J; Ardsley HS; Ardsley, NY; (Y); Hosp Aide; Key Clb; Band; School Musical; Diving; Sftbl; Co-Capt Swmmng; Intrnshp NY Acad Sci 83-84; Stu Achvt Awd 85; Bnai Brith Yth Grp VP 83-84,Pres 84-85; ISF Chrprsn 84; Brown U; Engr.

STERN, KIMBERLY; Sheepshead Bay HS; Brooklyn, NY; (Y); Computer Clb; School Musical; Trk; Comp Sci.

STERN, RACHEL; The Wheatley Schl; Old Westbury, NY; (Y); Office Aide; Teachers Aide; Temple Yth Grp; Chorus; School Musical; School Play; Nwsp Bus Mgr; Nwsp Stf; Yrbk Stf; Lit Mag; Bus.

STERNBERG, WENDY; Port Richard HS; Staten Isld, NY; (Y); School Musical; Yrbk Stf; Co-Capt Swmmng; High Hon Roll; NHS; Physcl Thrpy.

STERNER, EMILY; John Dewey HS; Brooklyn, NY; (Y); Drama Clb; Math Tm; Science Clb; School Musical; Hon Roll; Jr NHS; :Astronomy.

STERRITT, JENNIFER; Coxsackie Athens Central HS; West Coxsackie, NY; (Y); 13/84; German Clb; Nwsp Phtg; Yrbk Phtg; Yrbk Stf; Off Sr Cls; High Hon Roll; Hon Roll; Cmnty Wkr; Pres Sec 4-H; Off Frsh Cls; Albany Coll Pharm; Pharm.

STEUERWALD, BEVERLY; Center Moriches HS; Manorville, NY; (Y); 3/95; Computer Clb; Spanish Clb; Yrbk Stf; Trs Jr Cls; Hon Roll; Trs Jr NHS; NHS; FBLA; Science Clb; Ski Clb; Valedictorian, Bus Dynamics, Outstnd Achv In Eng & Comp Sci Awds; Penn St; Comp Sci.

STEVENS, BRENDA; Bishop Loughlin HS; Brooklyn, NY; (Y); Church Yth Grp; Cmnty Wkr; Dance Clb; Girl Scts; Hosp Aide; Church Choir; School Play; Hon Roll; NHS; Pre-Med.

STEVENS, CAREY; Westhmapton Beach HS; Westhamptn Bch, NY; (Y); 126/232; Office Aide; Drill Tm; Hghst Avg Engl II Contmpry 85; U Of San Diego; Engl.

STEVENS, DENISE; Trott Vocational HS; Niagara Falls, NY; (Y); Am Leg Aux Girls St; Hosp Aide; Engrng.

STEVENS, HENRY; All Hallows Inst; New York, NY; (Y); JA; Socr; Swmmng; Wt Lftg; Cit Awd; Hon Roll; Jr NHS; NHS; Mercy Coll; Bio.

STEVENS, JENNIFER A; Shenendehowa HS; Clifton Park, NY; (Y); Ski Clb; Orch; JV Cheerleading; JV Sftbl; High Hon Roll; Hon Roll; Prfct Atten Awd; Schnctdy Symphny Orch 84-85; Empire ST JR Orch 82-84; Miss Shenendehowa Sftbl Leag 2-84; All-Stars 83.

STEVENS, JOHN; Avon JR SR HS; Avon, NY; (Y); 20/100; Boy Scts; Chess Clb; Var Crs Cntry; Var Trk; High Hon Roll; Hon Roll; Jerry Shaw Memrl 85; Comp Sci.

STEVENS, KIMBERLEY; Niskayuna HS; Schdy, NY; (Y); Spanish Clb; School Play; VP Soph Cls; VP Jr Cls; VP Sr Cls; Capt Gym; Var JV Socr; Var Trk; Dnfth Awd; High Hon Roll; Elmira Key Awd; Law.

STEVENS, LESLIE; Andover Central HS; Andover, NY; (Y); 2/20; Model UN; Ski Clb; Yrbk Ed-Chief; Capt Rptr Jr Cls; Stu Cncl; Var Cheerleading; Var Tennis; DAR Awd; High Hon Roll; NHS; Socl Stud John Karkanes Awd; Amer Hstry Awd; Amercnsm Plaq-Frank Mckibben Awd; Exec Scty.

STEVENS, OWEN; Allegany Central HS; Allegany, NY; (Y); 8/126; Church Yth Grp; Band; Jazz Band; School Musical; School Play; Yrbk Bus Mgr; Crs Cntry; Tennis; High Hon Roll; NHS; Robert P Phearsdorf Mem Scholar 84; Chapin Engl Scholar 84; Band Scholar 83; Engrng.

STEVENS, PHILIP; Berne-Knox-Westerlo HS; Berne, NY; (Y); 15/85; Aud/Vis; Church Yth Grp; Cmnty Wkr; Radio Clb; Ski Clb; Varsity Clb; Yrbk Stf; Var Bsbl; Var Bsktbl; Var Socr; Engrng.

STEVENS, ROBERT; La Salle SR HS; Niagara Falls, NY; (Y); Boy Scts; Sec Church Yth Grp; Exploring; Ski Clb; Var Ftbl; Var Swmmng; Var Tennis; Syracuse; Arch.

STEVENS, SHERI L; Wilson Central HS; Lockport, NY; (Y); Nwsp Stf; Yrbk Stf; JV Sftbl; Hon Roll; Secy.

STEVENS, SUSAN E; Bishop Grimes HS; Bridgeport, NY; (Y); Pres Trs Church Yth Grp; Cmnty Wkr; Teachers Aide; Band; Concert Band; JV Var Tennis; JV Var Vllybl; NY ST Rgnts Schlrshp 85; Bishop Grimes Mystery Plyrs 85; Geneseo; Env Sci.

STEVENS, TERESA; Southwestern Central HS; Lakewood, NY; (Y); Church Yth Grp; FCA; Trs Frsh Cls; VP Soph Cls; VP Jr Cls; JV Bsktbl; Bowling; Var Crs Cntry; JV Gym; Sftbl; Hghst Avg Art & Scl Stds 83; Pres Awd 80-82; I Believe In America Essay Cont 82; Houghton; Law.

STEVENS, VICTORIA; Rome Free Acad; Rome, NY; (Y); 15/460; Church Yth Grp; Intnl Clb; Key Clb; Ski Clb; Pres Frsh Cls; Pres Soph Cls; Pres Sr Cls; Rep Stu Cncl; Var Capt Tennis; Jr NHS; Lbrl Arts.

STEVENSON, DAVID A; Huntington HS; Huntington Bay, NY; (Y); 25/440; Boy Scts; Ski Clb; Nwsp Stf; Yrbk Stf; Lit Mag; Var Trk; Hon Roll; Jr NHS; NHS; St Schlr; Fncng Tm Capt & 4 Yrs Vrsty; Eagl Sct Awd 84; U Of MI Ann Arbor; Anml Behvr.

STEVENSON, VALERIA; Dominican Commercial HS; Jamaica, NY; (Y); Church Yth Grp; Acpl Chr; Chorus; Church Choir; Silna Clb 83-85; Principals List 82-85; York Coll; Med Tech.

STEWARD, DANIEL; Randolph Central Schl; Kennedy, NY; (Y); Am Leg Boys St; Drama Clb; VP Soph Cls; Var Bsbl; Var Bsktbl; Var Ftbl; Hon Roll; NHS.

STEWART, CATHERINE M; Liverpool HS; Liverpool, NY; (S); 9/792; Church Yth Grp; Exploring; Trs FBLA; VP Trs Girl Scts; Stu Cncl; L Var Bowling; Hon Roll; NHS; JA; L Swmmng; Grl Sct 1st Clss Awd 82; 1st Pl ST FBLA Acctng I Comp 84; Acctng.

STEWART, COLLEEN M; North Rose-Wolcott HS; S Butler, NY; (Y); Church Yth Grp; FBLA; Spanish Clb; Varsity Clb; Chorus; Madrigals; School Musical; Yrbk Ed-Chief; Var Vllybl; NHS; Phys Ther.

STEWART, DAVE; James Madison HS; Brooklyn, NY; (Y); Boy Scts; Church Yth Grp; Computer Clb; Exploring; JA; Office Aide; Spanish Clb; School Play; Socr; Swmmng; Law.

STEWART, DAVID M; Thomas Alva Edison HS; Elmira Heights, NY; (Y); 1/92; Pres Aud/Vis; Band; Trs Chorus; Mgr Stage Crew; Nwsp Stf; Bausch & Lomb Sci Awd; Ntl Merit Ltr; Val; Quiz Bowl; Color Guard; Rensselaer Polytchnc Inst Math Sci Awd 84; Chem Bwl 84; Outstndng Muscn Awd 82; Carnegie-Mellon U; Comp Engrng.

STEWART, JAY; Delaware Acad; Delhi, NY; (Y); Spanish Clb; Orch; Yrbk Stf; Var Golf; Oswego ST; Genetics.

STEWART, JEFF; South Glens Falls Central Schl; S Glens Falls, NY; (Y); 24/225; Pres Varsity Clb; Pres Chorus; Nwsp Sprt Ed; Rep Stu Cncl; Capt Ftbl; Capt Trk; Capt Wrstlng; Mrchg Band; School Musical; MVP In Ftbl & Track 85; Schlrshps For Spec Cntrbtn To Schl & Schl Sprt 85; Sprtsmnshp Awd 85; Alfred U; Mech Engrng.

STEWART, KERRI; Bklyn Technical HS; Brooklyn, NY; (Y); Girl Scts; Hon Roll; VFW Awd; Journlsm.

STEWART, LATONYA; Bayshore HS; Bayshore, NY; (Y); Band; Chorus; Church Choir; Concert Band; Drill Tm; Mrchg Band; Nwsp Sprt Ed; Yrbk Stf; Sec Frsh Cls; Stu Cncl; Cortz Peters Awd 84-85; Bridgeport U.

STEWART, LINDA A; Holy Trinity HS; East Meadow, NY; (S); 11/430; Var Cheerleading; High Hon Roll; NHS; Berkeley-Claremont; Fash Byng.

STEWART, MELISSA; Long Island Lutheran HS; Westbury, NY; (S); Var Bsktbl; Var Socr; Var Trk; High Hon Roll; NHS; Girls Scr MVP 83.

STEWART, OWEN; Springfield Gardens HS; New York, NY; (Y); 5/42; Art Clb; Camera Clb; Debate Tm; FBLA; Library Aide; Math Tm; Yrbk Stf; Rep Stu Cncl; Bsktbl; Ftbl; Howard U; Elec Engrng.

STEWART, PATRICIA A; Ichabod Crane Central HS; Kinderhook, NY; (Y); 18/190; Trs French Clb; Nwsp Rptr; Yrbk Rptr; Rep Frsh Cls; Rep Soph Cls; Rep Jr Cls; Rep Sr Cls; Rep Stu Cncl; Stat Fld Hcky; Stat L Sftbl; St Marys Coll; Tech Wrtg.

STEWART, PETER W; Minerva Central HS; Olmstedville, NY; (Y); 1/12; Boy Scts; Exploring; Chorus; School Play; Capt Tennis; NHS; Prfct Atten Awd; Ciba Geigy Sci Awd 85; Am Hist Awd 84; NY St Regnts Awd 85; Adirondack Comm Coll; Lib Art.

STEWART, SARA; Schenectady-Christian HS; Scotia, NY; (S); Church Yth Grp; Cmnty Wkr; Drama Clb; Hosp Aide; Concert Band; School Play; Rep Frsh Cls; Var L Bsktbl; Var Cheerleading; High Hon Roll; Top 2 Pct Math Part Of SATS 85; Bus.

STEWART, SCOTT J; Wallkill HS; Newburgh, NY; (Y); Am Leg Boys St; Boy Scts; Drama Clb; School Play; Var Socr; Archlgy.

STEWART JR, WILLIAM L; Brasher Falls Central HS; Brasher Falls, NY; (Y); Score Keeper; Prfct Atten Awd; Outstndng Achvt Soc Stud 84; Hnrb Mntn Soc Stud 11 85.

STEWART, YVONNE; Bronx HS; E Elmhurst, NY; (Y); Hosp Aide; Library Aide; Teachers Aide; Math.

STGERMAINE, CYNTHIA; Mynderse Acad; Seneca Falls, NY; (Y); Intnl Clb; Band; Color Guard; Concert Band; Jazz Band; Mrchg Band; Pep Band; School Musical; Twrlr; Hon Roll.

STIBINGER, CINDY; Mohonasen HS; Schenectady, NY; (Y); 48/216; Sec Church Yth Grp; Pres Key Clb; Band; Concert Band; Mrchg Band; Pep Band; Nwsp Rptr; Nwsp Stf; Sec Yrbk Stf; Rep Stu Cncl; Mohanaser Key Clb Awd 84; Rotterdam Kiwanis Schlrshp 85; Maria Coll; Lgl Offc Asst.

STICCA, DENISE; Lakeland HS; Mahopac, NY; (Y); FBLA; Girl Scts; Hon Roll; NHS; Outstndng Bus Achvmnt Awd Westchester Bus Ins 83-84; Krissler Bus Inst; Sec.

STICCA, PATRICIA; W Seneca East SR HS; W Seneca, NY; (Y); 11/365; Am Leg Aux Girls St; JA; Yrbk Stf; Off Sr Cls; Stu Cncl; Socr; High Hon Roll; Trs Jr NHS; NHS; Pep Clb; Rgnt Schlrshp 85; Awds Math, Sci, Lang & Hm Ec 84; U Of Rochester; Pre Med.

STICH, ELAINE; Gates-Chili HS; Rochester, NY; (S); 5/463; Church Yth Grp; Exploring; Math Tm; Pres Science Clb; Spanish Clb; School Play; Gym; Socr; Hon Roll; NHS; Bus.

STIEF, ILANA; South Shore HS; Brooklyn, NY; (Y); 32/600; Teachers Aide; Band; Orch; School Musical; Cheerleading; Cit Awd; Hon Roll; NHS; Music Svc Awd 85; Rgnts Schlrshp 85; Brooklyn Coll; Pre-Med.

STIEHM, HOLLY; Spackenkill HS; Poughkeepsie, NY; (Y); Var Tennis; Var Trk; U Of WI; Psychlgy.

STILES, KAREN; Bishop Maginn HS; Rensselaer, NY; (Y); Ski Clb; Spanish Clb; School Musical; School Play; Yrbk Stf; Cheerleading; Pom Pon; 4-H Awd; Hon Roll; Comp Med.

STILES, LORRI; Union-Endicott HS; Endicott, NY; (Y); School Musical; Rep Jr Cls; Var Crs Cntry; Var L Trk; Hon Roll; Comp Prg.

STILLIONS, DUANE; Charles O Dickerson HS; Trumansburg, NY; (Y); 4/90; Am Leg Boys St; French Clb; Model UN; Band; Jazz Band; VP Soph Cls; Pres Stu Cncl; JV Tennis; Hon Roll; NHS; Chem Awd 85; Doc; Med.

STILLWELL, JUDY; Union Springs Acad; Ithaca, NY; (Y); Church Yth Grp; Chorus; Church Choir; Cheerleading; Vllybl; Typng Awd, Gold Music Awd 85; Atlantic Union Coll; Erlychd Ed.

STILLWELL, LAURIE; Shenendehowa Central HS; Clifton Park, NY; (Y); Cmnty Wkr; English Clb; Symp Band; Im JV Sftbl; Im JV Trk; High Hon Roll; JP Sousa Awd; Girl Scts; Band; Yrbk Stf; Cert Of Achvt Essy Cntst 85; Schltc Awd Super Grade Avrg 84-85; Microbio.

STILSON, LORI L; Corning East HS; Corning, NY; (Y); Church Yth Grp; Dance Clb; Drama Clb; JA; Drill Tm; Stage Crew; Var Cheerleading; Var Pom Pon; JV Trk; High Hon Roll; Ath Awd Bsktbl Chrldg 84-85; Awd Dance Tm 84-85; Old Dominion U; Bus.

STILWELL, JAMES; F D Roosevelt HS; Staatsburg, NY; (Y); Acpl Chr; Band; Chorus; Church Choir; Concert Band; Mrchg Band; School Musical; School Play; Stage Crew; Symp Band; Air Force Acad; Aerontcl Engr.

STIMERS, SANDRA; Liverpool HS; Liverpool, NY; (Y); Church Yth Grp; Cmnty Wkr; Hosp Aide; Chorus; Orch; Stage Crew; Hon Roll; Jr NHS; Cert Achv Cmnty Svc 84; Cert Hnr-Onandoga Al-Cnty Music Fstvl 83; Cmnctns.

STINSON, DEXTER; Cardinal Hayes HS; Bronx, NY; (Y); 15/284; Camera Clb; Church Yth Grp; Computer Clb; Debate Tm; Speech Tm; Teachers Aide; Church Choir; Yrbk Phtg; Yrbk Stf; Hon Roll; Comp Sci.

STINSON, STACIE; Arlington HS; La Grangeville, NY; (Y); Church Yth Grp; Debate Tm; French Clb; Intnl Clb; Math Tm; Church Choir; Yrbk Stf; VFW Awd; Voice Dem Awd; U Of ME; E Engr.

STIO, ANGELA; Commack H S South; Dix Hills, NY; (Y); 92/374; Church Yth Grp; Drama Clb; School Musical; Yrbk Ed-Chief; VP Jr Cls; VP Sr Cls; NHS; School Play; Stage Crew; Variety Show; Theodore R Spedelle Awd Svc Schl; St Bonaventure U Friars Schlrshp; V Plaques; St Bonaventure U; Comm.

STITH, ADRIENNE; James I O Neill HS; West Point, NY; (Y); Cmnty Wkr; Computer Clb; Exploring; French Clb; Girl Scts; Band; Var L Swmmng; High Hon Roll; NHS; Pre Med.

STITH, QUENTIN; Cardinal Hayes HS; New York, NY; (Y); Church Yth Grp; Church Choir; Var L Ftbl; Wt Lftg; Prfct Atten Awd; 2nd Pl Oratrcl Cont Wnnr 84; Pres JR Hmrm 84-85; Hon Cls 84-85; Syracuse; Cmmnctn.

STITH, TANYA; Queen Of The Rosary Acad; Roosevelt, NY; (Y); Church Yth Grp; Drama Clb; Girl Scts; Church Choir; School Play; Variety Show; Yrbk Stf; 4-H Awd; Hon Roll; Nassau Comm Coll; Bus Adm.

STITT, DOUGLAS F; Ogdensburg Free Acad; Odgensburg, NY; (Y); 27/186; Am Leg Boys St; Church Yth Grp; Key Clb; Quiz Bowl; Ice Hcky; Capt Socr; Trk; Hon Roll; St Schlr; Natl Socl Studies Olympd Hnr 85; West Point; Intl Rel.

STIVERSON, SHELLI; Fairport HS; Fairport, NY; (Y); Church Yth Grp; German Clb; Girl Scts; L Orch; Rep Stu Cncl; Var L Swmmng; Hon Roll; SUNY Geneseo; Elem Ed.

STIVES, BILL J; Belmont Central HS; Belmont, NY; (Y); Am Leg Boys St; Spanish Clb; Yrbk Stf; Sec Frsh Cls; Trs Jr Cls; JV Var Bsktbl; JV Ftbl; Var L Tennis; Var L Trk; High Hon Roll; Alfred U; Advncd Math.

STIVES, BOB; Portville Central HS; Portville, NY; (Y); Ski Clb; Band; Trs Concert Band; Jazz Band; Mrchg Band; Pep Band; High Hon Roll; Hon Roll; Prfct Atten Awd; Corp Lawyer.

STOBER, ROBERT C; Islip HS; Bay Shore, NY; (Y); Cmnty Wkr; Stu Cncl; Hon Roll; St Schlr; NY Regent Schlrshp 85; Hartwick Coll Schlrshp 85; Hartwick Coll; Mgmt.

STOBNICKI, LISA; Villa Maria Acad; Buffalo, NY; (S); Computer Clb; Im Bowling; High Hon Roll.

STOCK, PAMELA; Cleveland Hill HS; Cheektowaga, NY; (Y); Teachers Aide; Band; Yrbk Stf; Bsktbl; Svc Awd 85; Cert Prfcncy Cntry 21 Accntng 85 & Credit 84; Accntng.

STOCKMAN, KEVIN; Queensbury HS; Glens Falls, NY; (Y); 31/226; Church Yth Grp; Spanish Clb; Var JV Diving; Im Gym; Var Im Socr; Var JV Swmmng; Pres Schlr; Houghton Coll; Spnsh.

STOCKMAN, LISA; Maple Hill HS; Schodack Landing, NY; (S); Spanish Clb; Chorus; Church Choir; Nwsp Stf; Yrbk Stf; Var Capt Cheerleading; Var Capt Sftbl; Var Capt Vllybl; Hon Roll; Bus.

STOCKMAYER, KRISTIN L; Chatham Central HS; Chatham, NY; (Y); 12/120; Intnl Clb; Orch; School Musical; Nwsp Stf; Yrbk Ed-Chief; JV Vllybl; Prfct Atten Awd; Psych.

STOCUM, EMILY; Whitney Point HS; Castle Creek, NY; (Y); 5/150; Chorus; Frsh Cls; Soph Cls; Jr Cls; Bsktbl; Fld Hcky; Sftbl; Hon Roll; NHS; Rotary Awd; Excllnc Engl 84; Excllnc Phy Ed 82-85; Chch Yth Grp 84-85; Cmmnctn.

STOCUM, SUE; Watkins Glen HS; Watkins Glen, NY; (S); 7/150; French Clb; Letterman Clb; Var Capt Bsktbl; Stat Ftbl; Var Capt Trk; Var Capt Vllybl; French Hon Soc; Hon Roll; NHS; Bus Admin.

STODDARD, THEODORE; Onondaga Central HS; Medrow, NY; (Y); Boy Scts; Exploring; German Clb; Spanish Clb; Stage Crew; Rep Jr Cls; Rep Sr Cls; Rep Stu Cncl; Ftbl; Golf; Law.

STODDART, DOUGLAS; East Aurora HS; East Aurora, NY; (S); 25/182; Science Clb; Hon Roll; NHS; Tech Drwng Awd 84; Tri-State U; Aerospace Engrng.

STOEHR, ROBERT M; St Anthonys HS; Smithtown, NY; (Y); Art Clb; French Clb; Nwsp Rptr; Yrbk Rptr; Crs Cntry; JV Trk; French Hon Soc; High Hon Roll; NHS; Prncpls List; Bus.

STOFF, MATTHEW; Oceanside HS; Oceanside, NY; (Y); Boy Scts; Concert Band; Jazz Band; Trs Mrchg Band; Orch; School Musical; JV Trk; Wrstlng; Cit Awd; Rifle-Capt, Vrsty, MVP & All-Cnty 84-85 & 85-86.

STOFFEL, ANNE; Alden Central HS; Lancaster, NY; (Y); GAA; School Musical; Yrbk Stf; Stat Bsktbl; Im Fld Hcky; Im JV Vllybl; Hon Roll; NHS; Prfct Atten Awd; Physcl Ftns Awd 85; Acad Ltr Awd 85; U Buffalo; Bus.

STOFFERS, CAROL; St Peters H S For Girls; Staten Isl, NY; (Y); Boy Scts; VP Exploring; Library Aide; Red Cross Aide; Spanish Clb; Chorus; School Play; Hon Roll; NHS; School Musical; Med.

STOFKO, LISA; Cardinal Spellman HS; Yonkers, NY; (Y); 5/590; Debate Tm; Key Clb; Science Clb; High Hon Roll; NHS; Ntl Merit Ltr; NEDT Awd; Church Yth Grp; Pep Clb; Rensselaer Polytech Inst Awd Outstndg JR Mth & Sci 85; Brown U; Corp Law.

STOGRAN, CYNTHIA M; Maine-Endwell SR HS; Endwell, NY; (Y); VP JA; Political Wkr; VP Service Clb; Ski Clb; Var L Tennis; NHS; Pres Schlr; St Schlr; Aud/Vis; Church Yth Grp; JR Achvt Rep NE Conf 83; Broome Cnty Leg Intrn Rep ME 83; Manhattan Coll; Elec Engr.

STOIO, ANGELA; Whitesboro SR HS; Whitesboro, NY; (Y); Exploring; GAA; Hosp Aide; Concert Band; Mrchg Band; Cheerleading; Crs Cntry; Capt JV Fld Hcky; Powder Puff Ftbl; Sftbl; Pre-Med.

STOJANOVSKI, KOSTA; Lackawanna SR HS; Lackawanna, NY; (Y); French Clb; Varsity Clb; Rep Stu Cncl; Var Bowling; Var Capt Socr; Hon Roll; Ntl Merit Ltr; Prfct Atten Awd; 2nd Tm All Star Plyr Soccer 84; Chem Engr.

STOKER, KENNETH; Stockbridge Valley Central Schl; Munnsville, NY; (S); 4/47; Church Yth Grp; Mathletes; Math Clb; VP Science Clb; Nwsp Ed-Chief; Trs Frsh Cls; Trs Soph Cls; VP Stu Cncl; JV Bsktbl; JV Socr; Vet.

STOKER, MARY; Stockbridge Valley Central HS; Munnsville, NY; (S); 1/44; GAA; Spanish Clb; Varsity Clb; Band; JV Bsktbl; JV Socr; Var Socr; JV Var Vllybl; High Hon Roll; NHS; Sprts Med.

STOKES, REBECCA; Nyack HS; Upper Nyack, NY; (Y); 14/274; School Musical; School Play; Stage Crew; Tennis; High Hon Roll; NHS; Rotary Awd; Drama Clb; French Clb; Math Tm; Iona Coll Lang Cont 85; Outstndg Accmplshmnt Awd Scl Stds 85; Natl Piano Plyng Auditions Wnnr 83-85.

STOKOE, GAIL E; Wheatland Chili HS; Scottsville, NY; (Y); 11/77; Model UN; Pres Ski Clb; Band; Concert Band; Jazz Band; Yrbk Stf; Var Cheerleading; Var Vllybl; Hon Roll; Prfct Atten Awd; Farm Bur Ctznshp Awd; St Bonaventure U; Pre Med.

STOLAR, BRIAN; Alfred G Berner HS; Massapequa Park, NY; (Y); 3/413; Computer Clb; Nwsp Rptr; Lit Mag; Rep Soph Cls; Var L Bsbl; Var Socr; NHS; Ntl Merit Ltr; George Washington U Awd Excllnc Math & Sci; Robtcs Electrncs Clb; Pre-Med.

STOLDT, ANDREA; Alden Central HS; Alden, NY; (Y); 22/198; Science Clb; Band; Chorus; Mrchg Band; Orch; School Musical; School Play; Swing Chorus; Rep Stu Cncl; Hon Roll; Acad Ltr; Pres Ftns Awd; Regents Schlrshp; U NY-BUFFALO; Med.

STOLL, MARY ELLEN; St Marys HS; Cheektowaga, NY; (S); 14/200; Church Yth Grp; Nwsp Rptr; Rep Stu Cncl; Mgr(s); Hon Roll; NHS; Regents Schlrshp 85; Buffalo ST Coll; Comm.

STOLLER, AMY; Canarsie HS; Brooklyn, NY; (S); 3/561; School Musical; Nwsp Stf; Yrbk Stf; L Twrlr; High Hon Roll; Hon Roll; NHS; Acadmc Olympcs; Natl Serv Soc; Contntl Math Leag-2nd Pl; Cornell; Engrng.

STOLLER, FRAN; Wellington C Mepham HS; N Bellmore, NY; (Y); Lib Band; Yrbk Stf; Jr Cls; Stu Cncl; Hon Roll; Jr NHS; NHS; Temple Yth Grp; School Play; Nwsp Stf; Awd Excell Math 83; Acht Awds 82-85; Co-Chrmn Prom Commtt 83 & 86.

STOLLER, STACY R; Roy C Ketcham HS; Wappingers Fls, NY; (Y); Drama Clb; Political Wkr; Temple Yth Grp; Nwsp Rptr; Stu Cncl; JV Capt Socr; JV Swmmng; Var Trk; High Hon Roll; NHS.

STOLLERY, MICHAEL A; Wheatland-Chili Central HS; Scottsville, NY; (Y); Boy Scts; Church Yth Grp; Computer Clb; Drama Clb; Exploring; Model UN; Chorus; Church Choir; Jazz Band; School Musical; Natl Hnr Rll 84-85; Comp Sci.

STOLLMAN, DAWN; Fallsburg Central HS; S Fallsburg, NY; (Y); Leo Clb; Varsity Clb; Band; Yrbk Stf; VP Pres Stu Cncl; JV Var Bsktbl; JV Sftbl; Var Tennis; Hon Roll.

STOLZENBURG, MARIBETH; Schoharic Central HS; West Berne, NY; (S); 2/90; Pres Trs FFA; Concert Band; School Musical; Yrbk Bus Mgr; Cit Awd; NHS; Sal; Trs Ski Clb; Acpl Chr; Band; Schltc Cnty Dairy Princess 84-85; Century Iii Leader 84-85; Amer Legion Americanism Awd 84; AL ST U; Meteorology.

STONE, AMY; E J Wilson HS; Spencerport, NY; (Y); 139/294; Drama Clb; Pres 4-H; Math Tm; Ski Clb; Teachers Aide; Varsity Clb; Chorus; Crs Cntry; Var L Swmmng; Timer; Alfred ST Ag & Tech; Ag Sci.

STONE, CARMELLA; Mohawk Central HS; Frankfort, NY; (S); Sec French Clb; Band; Concert Band; Jazz Band; Mrchg Band; Sec Jr Cls; VP Stu Cncl; Bsktbl; Powder Puff Ftbl; Capt Vllybl; Psych.

STONE, DONNA; Richmond Hill HS; Richmond Hl, NY; (Y); Computer Clb; Girl Scts; Key Clb; Math Tm; Socr; Vllybl; French Hon Soc; High Hon Roll; Jr NHS; NHS.

STONE, JANET; Fayetteville Manlius HS; Manlius, NY; (Y); German Clb; JCL; Model UN; Chorus; High Hon Roll; NHS; Ntl Merit Ltr; Pres Of JR Pro Art 85-86.

STONE, KERRI A; Kenmore West SR HS; Buffalo, NY; (Y); 72/495; Debate Tm; FBLA; Model UN; Pep Clb; Ski Clb; Spanish Clb; Stage Crew; Variety Show; Rep Frsh Cls; Rep Soph Cls; Regents Schlrshp 84-85; MI ST U; Bus Mngmt.

STONE, KERRIE; Queen Of The Rosary Acad; Wantagh, NY; (Y); Drama Clb; Library Aide; Math Clb; School Play; Nwsp Rptr; Socr; Hon Roll; Rep Jr Cls; Lab Aid; Recrtmnt Clb; Schl Debate; Med.

STONE, LESLEY; Hoosic Valley Central HS; Valley Falls, NY; (Y); Band; School Musical; School Play; Sec Frsh Cls; Sec Soph Cls; Rep Stu Cncl; Mgr(s); Hon Roll; NHS; Drama Clb; NY ST Summer Schl Of The Arts 85; Grphc Dsgn.

STONE, MATTHEW; Brighton HS; Rochester, NY; (Y); 1/315; JV Var Golf; Ntl Merit Ltr; Amer Chem Soc Exam 84; Bus Adm.

STONE, NANCY; East Hampton HS; E Hampton, NY; (Y); 22/170; AFS; Church Yth Grp; Dance Clb; Drama Clb; Intnl Clb; Political Wkr; Varsity Clb; Band; Chorus; Church Choir; LVIS; Best Dir Schl; U DE; Intl Rel.

STONE, PATTI; Valhalla HS; Valhalla, NY; (Y); 26/120; French Clb; Library Aide; Chorus; Variety Show; Cheerleading; Hon Roll; Stotly Schlrshp 85; Walter Stenn Bus Schlrshp 85; Home Ec, Frnch Awds 85; York Coll; Fash Merch.

STONE, STEPHEN S; Holy Trinity HS; Syosset, NY; (S); 18/404; Ski Clb; Stage Crew; Lit Mag; Var Lcrss; JV Trk; High Hon Roll; NHS; Voice Dem Awd; Euchastic Mnstr; Manhattan Coll; Engrng.

STONE, STEVEN E; Hammondsport Central Schl; Bath, NY; (Y); 25/72; Boy Scts; Civic Clb; Varsity Clb; Band; Concert Band; Jazz Band; Mrchg Band; Yrbk Stf; Trk; Wt Lftg; Regnts Schlrshp 85; SUNY Oswego.

STONECIPHER, ALLAN; Skaneateles Central Schl; Skaneateles, NY; (Y); Computer Clb; Office Aide; Ski Clb; Hon Roll; Cayuga Cty CC; Comp Tech.

STONEFOOT, CYNTHIA; Silver Creek Central HS; Silver Creek, NY; (Y); 1/75; Church Yth Grp; Bausch & Lomb Sci Awd; DAR Awd; High Hon Roll; NHS; Ntl Merit Ltr; Val; Voice Dem Awd; PA York Sectn Amer Chem Soc Cert 85; Grove City Coll; Cmmnctns.

STONER, KIMBERLY D; Fayetteville-Manlius HS; Manlius, NY; (Y); Church Yth Grp; Exploring; Band; Chorus; Concert Band; Variety Show; Hon Roll; STPA Spansh Awd 82; Cert Of Excllnc-Spansh 82; Penn ST U; Electrcl Engrng.

STOPHER, MARK A; Jamesville Dewitt HS; Syracuse, NY; (Y); 50/225; Boy Scts; Church Yth Grp; JV Var Ftbl; JV Var Lcrss; Wt Lftg; High Hon Roll; Hon Roll; NHS; St Schlr; All Cnty Tms Ftbl; Syracus U; Elec Engr.

STOPPACHER, ROBERT; Westlake HS; Valhalla, NY; (Y); Dance Clb; Spanish Clb; JV Bsbl; JV Var Socr; High Hon Roll; Hon Roll; Var Spanish NHS; Georgetown U; Pre-Med.

STORA, JANINE; St Francis Prep; Glendale, NY; (Y); 69/693; Cmnty Wkr; Office Aide; Im Sftbl; Hon Roll; Retreat Ldr Ltr 85; Law.

STORDY, MATHEW; Ramstein HS; Apo New York, NY; (Y); Boy Scts; Chess Clb; Exploring; Ski Clb; JV Crs Cntry; JV Trk; Hon Roll; Engrng.

STORELLA, JOSEPH A; St Anthonys HS; Ft Salonga, NY; (Y); Church Yth Grp; Ski Clb; Var Crs Cntry; Var Ice Hcky; Trk; NY ST Ice Hcky Chmps 83-84; Aero Space Engrng.

STORM, GRETCHEN; Voorheesville HS; Slingerlands, NY; (Y); Drama Clb; Key Clb; Ski Clb; Trs Spanish Clb; Yrbk Stf; VP Jr Cls; Rep Stu Cncl; Cheerleading; High Hon Roll; NHS; Outstndng Achvt Math 83-84; SUNY Binghamton; Accntng.

STORY, ROBIN; Tioga Central HS; Owego, NY; (Y); Trs Church Yth Grp; Varsity Clb; Church Choir; Variety Show; Rep Frsh Cls; Var Stat Score Keeper; Sftbl; Capt Vllybl; Chroprctr.

STOTT, DELLA; New Rockelle HS; New Rochelle, NY; (Y); VP Church Yth Grp; Cmnty Wkr; Intnl Clb; Church Choir; Rep Stu Cncl; Var Bsktbl; NAACP-NEW Rchll Yth Chptr 82-84; Blk Cltr Clb-Prlmntrn 84-86.

STOUT, JAMIE; Washingtonville HS; Rock Tavern, NY; (Y); Trs Red Cross Aide; Im Ftbl; Im Wt Lftg; Miami U; Math Engr.

STOVALL III, DAVID; Cardinal Spellman HS; Bronx, NY; (Y); Church Yth Grp; Debate Tm; Drill Tm; Jazz Band; Variety Show; Yrbk Stf; Lit Mag; Ntl Merit Ltr; C W Post; Comm.

STOVELL, THERESA M; Cardinal Spellman HS; Bronx, NY; (Y); 78/568; Church Yth Grp; Computer Clb; Debate Tm; NFL; Im Vllybl; Hon Roll; Natl Frnscs Leag Degrees Merit, Dist, Excell 83-84; NYC Natl Frnscl Leag 3rd Pl Dist, 5th Pl Chmp 84; ST U Of NY; Spec Educ.

STOVER JR, RICHARD; Amherst Central HS; Amherst, NY; (Y); 56/310; Cmnty Wkr; Chorus; Church Choir; School Musical; Yrbk Stf; Lit Mag; Socr; Hon Roll; NHS; Im Vllybl; Outstndng Indust Art Stu 81-82; Awd U S Navy Recruit Wrk 85; U S Navy; Aviation.

STOWELL, SHEILA G; Washington Irving HS; Brooklyn, NY; (Y); 2/370; Math Tm; Concert Band; Lit Mag; Pres Sr Cls; Gov Hon Prg Awd; NCTE Awd; NHS; Pres Schlr; Sal; Brown U; Bio-Med.

STPEHENSON, LISA O; Beach Channel HS; Arverne, NY; (Y); Debate Tm; Concert Band; Hon Roll; NHS; Prfct Atten Awd; Cent Fed Svgs Schlrshp Awd 83.

STRACHAN, TRACY; Far Rockaway HS; Jamaica, NY; (Y); Key Clb; Library Aide; Band; Concert Band; School Play; Hon Roll; NHS; Stonybrook St Johns; Pre Med.

STRACHER, DAVID; Long Beach HS; Lido Beach, NY; (S); 4/297; Trs Concert Band; Jazz Band; Mrchg Band; School Musical; Mgr Stage Crew; Bausch & Lomb Sci Awd; NHS; Ntl Merit Ltr; Math Tm; Crew-Capt Vrsty 83-85; Future Doctors Of Amer VP & Secy 81-85; MA Inst Tech; Bio-Med.

STRADAR, ANN D; Newburgh Free Acad; Newburgh, NY; (Y); 8/750; French Clb; Ski Clb; Chorus; Nwsp Stf; Yrbk Stf; High Hon Roll; Sec Jr NHS; Rep Soph Cls; VP Jr Cls; Var Sftbl; Overall Acdmc, Shclrshp, Sprtsmnshp & Englsh Awd 83; Frnch Awdh 84.

STRAEHLE, AMY; St Gabriels HS; New Rochelle, NY; (Y); 17/61; Sec Church Yth Grp; Trs Drama Clb; Library Aide; School Play; Rep Soph Cls; Rep Jr Cls; Rep Stu Cncl; Sftbl; Hon Roll; NHS; Natl Soc Stds Olympd Awd 84; Iona Coll; Ed.

STRAHS, RACHEL S; Bronx High School Of Science HS; Flushing, NY; (Y); Girl Scts; Library Aide; Office Aide; Science Clb; NHS; Ntl Merit SF; Westnghse Semi Fnlst 85; Regnts Schlrshp 85; Comp Awd Mt Holyoke 83; U Of Chicago; Psych.

STRAIGHT, DARRYL; Troy HS; Troy, NY; (Y); German Clb; JA; Ski Clb; JV Socr; Var Tennis; Hon Roll; NHS; Regnts Schlrshp 85; German Exchng Stu 84; Rochester Inst Of Tech; Comp.

STRAIL, BARBARA J; Camden Central HS; Camden, NY; (Y); 4-H; Girl Scts; Library Aide; Pep Clb; Var L Cheerleading; Cit Awd; High Hon Roll; Hon Roll; Canton; Lab Tech.

STRAND, LOREN C; Hamilton Central HS; Hamilton, NY; (Y); Art Clb; JCL; Chorus; School Musical; Nwsp Ed-Chief; Rep Stu Cncl; Bsktbl; Crs Cntry; Trk; Hon Roll; NT Boys ST 85; Lions Clb Yth Exhng/Nethlnds 85; Comp Sci.

STRANDBERG, MICHELE; Seaford HS; Seaford, NY; (Y); Church Yth Grp; Girl Scts; Band; Church Choir; Concert Band; Mrchg Band; Nwsp Stf; Pom Pon; Hon Roll; Educ.

STRANG JR, CHARLES F; Owego Free Acad; Owego, NY; (Y); 44/249; Am Leg Boys St; Boy Scts; Camera Clb; Exploring; Varsity Clb; JV Var Socr; God Cntry Awd; Library Aide; Nwsp Rptr; Hon Roll; Eagle Scout W/ Bronze Palm 82; Amer Lgn Aux Awd For Amer 85; Appntd USMMA 85; USMMA; Ofcr.

STRANGE, DEBORAH; Harrison HS; White Plains, NY; (Y); 35/206; AFS; Church Yth Grp; Nwsp Stf; Rep Sr Cls; Var Bsktbl; Var Bowling; Var Crs Cntry; Var Fld Hcky; JV Var Sftbl; NHS; Coaches Awd Bowling, Softball 85; SUNY Albany; Bus.

STRANGE, RODNEY J; Southside HS; Elmira, NY; (Y); French Clb; Hosp Aide; Pep Clb; Political Wkr; Nwsp Stf; Sec Soph Cls; Sec Jr Cls; Pres Sr Cls; Rep Stu Cncl; Hon Roll; Yth Cnty Rep Mock Gvt 85; Hosp Vol Awd 84; Pol Sci.

STRANGIS, FRANCO; La Salle SR HS; Niagara Falls, NY; (Y); Drama Clb; Library Aide; Stage Crew; Socr; Var Trk; High Hon Roll; Hon Roll; NHS; Itln.

STRASENBURGH, MIKE; E J Wilson HS; Spencerport, NY; (Y); Exploring; French Clb; Band; Concert Band; Jazz Band; Mrchg Band; Orch; JV Bsktbl; JV Socr; JV Vllybl.

STRASSBERG, IRA; The Bronx High Schl Of Science; Briarwood, NY; (Y); Serv Awd Holocaust Ctr Bronx 84-85; Assoc Tchrs Soc Studies 84-85; Georgetown U; Bus Adm.

STRASSBURG II, WILLIAM L; Tonawanda JR SR HS; Tonawanda, NY; (Y); 37/235; Pres Varsity Clb; Stu Cncl; L Bsbl; L Bsktbl; Var Capt Ftbl; Cit Awd; Hon Roll; NHS; Hon Mntn Bsktbl 84-85; 1st Tm All Star Ftbl 84; Qlty Stu Of The Tonas 85; Canisius Coll; Pol Sci.

STRASSELL, LISA; Our Lady Of Mercy; Pittsford, NY; (Y); Church Yth Grp; Intnl Clb; Chorus; Cheerleading; Tennis; Hon Roll.

STRASSER, ALISON; Suffern HS; Suffern, NY; (Y); 2/440; Mrchg Band; Orch; School Musical; Symp Band; Nwsp Rptr; Yrbk Bus Mgr; Rep Stu Cncl; High Hon Roll; NHS; Ntl Merit Ltr; Regnl AATF Frnch Comptn-2nd Pl 83 & 84; Area All St-Music Flute Comptn 84 & 85.

STRASSER, BETH; Frontier Central HS; Hamburg, NY; (Y); 93/500; GAA; Red Cross Aide; Varsity Clb; Yrbk Ed-Chief; Yrbk Stf; Stu Cncl; JV Var Sftbl; JV Var Vllybl; Hon Roll; NHS; Canisius Coll; Athletic Trng.

STRATH, ERIC MATTHEW; Ellenville JR SR HS; Ellenville, NY; (Y); Boy Scts; Chess Clb; Computer Clb; Office Aide; Pres Science Clb; Spanish Clb; Teachers Aide; Lit Mag; Mgr(s); CC Awd; Wnnr On The Plus Sice Ctznshp Awd 85; Cathedral Coll; Canon Law.

STRATMANN, JENNIFER; Avon JR SR HS; Avon, NY; (Y); 51/105; Girl Scts; Library Aide; Teachers Aide; Band; Chorus; Concert Band; Mrchg Band; Pep Band; Sftbl; Hon Roll; Hnr NYSSMA 84-85; Bwlng Trphy 83-84; Awd Vrsty Athltc Awd Sftbl 83-85; Accntng.

STRATTON, DIANE; Westfield Central HS; Westfield, NY; (Y); Yrbk Stf; Var Capt Bsktbl; Var Capt Sftbl; High Hon Roll; Hon Roll; NHS; Natl Hnr Rll 83-85; Gunnard Carlson Chem Awd 85; William E Vorce Schlrshp 85; Jamestown CC; Crmnl Just.

STRATTON, TAMARA L; Homer Central HS; Homer, NY; (Y); 26/209; Church Yth Grp; French Clb; Ski Clb; Varsity Clb; Yrbk Sprt Ed; Rep Stu Cncl; Fld Hcky; Sftbl; Hon Roll; NHS; Regents Schlrsph 85; Syracuse U; Lbrl Arts.

STRATTON, THOMAS; Susquehanna Valley HS; Binghamton, NY; (Y); Boy Scts; Camera Clb; Computer Clb; French Clb; Ski Clb; Chorus; Bsbl; Ftbl; Golf; Trk; Broome CC; Comp Tech.

STRAUB, SHERI; John F Kennedy HS; Utica, NY; (Y); 16/120; Nwsp Stf; Hon Roll; Jr NHS; Prfct Atten Awd; Mohawk Valley CC; Bus.

STRAUB, TAMMY; Tupper Lake HS; Tupper Lk, NY; (Y); 45/102; Letterman Clb; Ski Clb; Varsity Clb; Crs Cntry; Trk; Hon Roll; SONY Coll Cortland; Phy Ed.

STRAUCHON, KIMBERLY ANN; Shenendehowa HS; Clifton Park, NY; (Y); 53/650; Pep Clb; Orch; Off Soph Cls; Off Jr Cls; Rep Stu Cncl; High Hon Roll; NHS; Outstndgn Acadmc Achvt 84-86; Presndtl Awd Stu Fclty Adm Senate 85; Bio.

STRAUGHAN, PHILLIP; Mt Vernon HS; Mount Vernon, NY; (Y); 36/590; Church Yth Grp; Pres French Clb; Trs JA; Key Clb; Ski Clb; Chorus; Orch; School Musical; Yrbk Stf; Stu Cncl; Cornell U; Arch.

STRAUS, SHERRY; Jamaica HS; Jamaica, NY; (Y); 10/600; Chess Clb; Math Clb; Nwsp Stf; Var Trk; High Hon Roll; Hon Roll; Jr NHS; NHS; Prfct Atten Awd; Prncpls Pride Yankees Awd Oustndng Achvt Acadmc & Extracurr Actvts 85; Acadmc All Amer 85.

STRAUSS, NICHOLAS; Oneida SR HS; Oneida, NY; (Y); Church Yth Grp; Letterman Clb; Spanish Clb; Varsity Clb; Rep Frsh Cls; Trs Soph Cls; Rep Jr Cls; JV Var Bsbl; JV Bsktbl; JV Var Socr; Physcs.

STRAUSS, RICHARD; Oyster Bay HS; E Norwich, NY; (Y); Nwsp Phtg; Ed Yrbk Phtg; Ed Yrbk Sprt Ed; Lit Mag; JV Bsktbl; Var Bowling; Var Socr; Var Tennis; High Hon Roll; NHS; MIP Tnns Awd Vrsty 85; Svc SR Ctzn Ctr 85; Comp Engrng.

STRAUSS, ROBIN; Oyster Bay HS; Oyster Bay, NY; (Y); 5/130; VP French Clb; Capt Mathletes; Sec Chorus; Mgr School Musical; Nwsp Ed-Chief; Ed Yrbk Stf; Rep Stu Cncl; High Hon Roll; NHS; PSTA Scholar 85; Pres Acad Fit Awd 85; Cornell U; Bus Mgmt.

STRAZZERI, MICHELE; Hornell HS; Harnell, NY; (S); 6/199; Chorus; Yrbk Phtg; Yrbk Rptr; Yrbk Stf; Coach Actv; Var L Swmmng; High Hon Roll; Hon Roll; Ntl Hist, Gov Awd 83; Cert Merit Excel Wrttn Exprssn 84; Graphic Dsgn.

STRCICH, FRANK; Commack North HS; Commack, NY; (Y); Cmnty Wkr; FCA; Varsity Clb; Rep Stu Cncl; JV Var Bsbl; JV Var Ftbl; Var Capt Wrstlng; High Hon Roll; Hon Roll; Ntl Merit Schol; Leigh U; Engrng.

STREB, THOMAS; Avon JR-SR HS; Avon, NY; (Y); Band; Jazz Band; Mrchg Band; Yrbk Stf; Wrstlng; High Hon Roll; Jr NHS; Prfct Atten Awd; Schlstc Art Show Schlrshp 85; Rochester Inst Tech; Comm Illst.

STREET, NANCY; Honeoye Central Schl; Honeoye, NY; (S); 4/70; French Clb; Concert Band; Jazz Band; Pres Jr Cls; Var Capt Bsktbl; Var Capt JA; High Hon Roll; NHS; Mrchg Band; Pep Band; Amer H S Athl 84; Smith Coll; Math.

STREETER, JENNIFER A; Greenwood Central Schl; Canisteo, NY; (Y); 3/19; Varsity Clb; Concert Band; Mrchg Band; Yrbk Ed-Chief; Pres Stu Cncl; Capt Cheerleading; Capt Socr; Bausch & Lomb Sci Awd; Hon Roll; VP NHS; Acad All-Amer 84-85; Wmns Scty Of Prof Engrs 85; U S Army Awd 85; Alfred Ag Tech; Med Rcrds Tech.

STREICHER, FRANCINE L; Sachem High Schl North Campus; Holtsville, NY; (Y); 300/1500; Art Clb; Cmnty Wkr; Drama Clb; PAVAS; Band; Concert Band; Drm & Bgl; School Musical; Variety Show; Lit Mag; Fredona; Elem Ed.

STREIT, PETER N; Pittsford Mendon HS; Rochester, NY; (Y); Var Lcrss; Im Wt Lftg; Hon Roll; Im Bsktbl; Var Ftbl; Hnrbl Mntn All-Cnty La Crosse 85; Engrng.

STREPPEL, CHRISTINE; Monsignor Sconlan HS; Flushing, NY; (Y); #12 In Class; Math Tm; Pres Frsh Cls; Pres Jr Cls; Rep Stu Cncl; Hon Roll.

STRETCH, ALYSON; Bay Shore HS; Bayshore, NY; (Y); 54/469; Debate Tm; Drama Clb; Nwsp Ed-Chief; Stu Cncl; Fld Hcky; CC Awd; Cit Awd; Elks Awd; Hon Roll; Ntl Merit Ltr; 2nd Pl NY ST Mock Trl 85; Bst Ltrary Mgzne NY ST 85; Trinity Coll; Ecolgy.

STRICKLAND, CARTER; Fayetteville-Manlius SR HS; Fayetteville, NY; (Y); Model UN; L Var Ftbl; Var L Lcrss; Hon Roll; NHS; Ntl Merit Ltr; Engrng.

STRIEGLER, SUSAN; Frankfort Schuyler Central HS; Frankfort, NY; (S); Spanish Clb; Band; Concert Band; Mrchg Band; Pep Band; Var Bowling; Var Fld Hcky; High Hon Roll; NHS; Bio Sci.

STRINGFELLOW, JENNIFER; Fayetteville Manlius HS; Manlius, NY; (Y); Art Clb; Church Yth Grp; Girl Scts; JA; Latin Clb; Chorus; Stage Crew; Nwsp Rptr; Nwsp Stf; Trk; Mony Schltc Art Awd 85; Cmmrcl Art.

STROBER, BENNA; Lawrence HS; Woodmere, NY; (Y); Drama Clb; Pres Key Clb; Model UN; School Play; Var Cheerleading; High Hon Roll; NHS; AFS; Temple Yth Grp; Orch; Hgh Achvt Chem & Peer Grp Rcgntns; Frnds Pgm; Bus.

STROKA, ERIC; Alden Central HS; Corfu, NY; (Y); 7/211; French Clb; Science Clb; Acad Tm 85; Elec Engrng.

STROMAN, MATTHEW; Elmira Free Acad; Elmira, NY; (Y); Church Yth Grp; Drama Clb; Chorus; Church Choir; Off Soph Cls; Off Jr Cls; Off Sr Cls; Stu Cncl; Hon Roll; Voc Indus Clbs Am 82-83; Princpl Assist Lrng Pgm 85-86; Fd Svc Mgmt.

STROMBERG, KIRK; Smithtown HS West; Smithtown, NY; (Y); Boy Scts; Science Clb; Ski Clb; Rep Jr Cls; JV Bsktbl; Var Crs Cntry; JV Var Lcrss; Im Socr; High Hon Roll; Hon Roll; Awd Blue Belt Jiu Jitsu 85; Brkhvn Ntl Briddge Bldg Cntst 24th Pl 85; Astrnutcl.

STROMSKI, JOHN; Riverhead HS; Riverhead, NY; (Y); Var L Bsbl; Var JV Bsktbl; Var L Ftbl.

STRONG, JANICE; Tioga Central Schl; Barton, NY; (S); 4/71; Pres GAA; Yrbk Stf; Rep Jr Cls; Pres Sr Cls; Var Capt Bsktbl; Var Capt Fld Hcky; Var Sftbl; High Hon Roll; Prfct Atten Awd; Defensive Awd Field Hockey & Bsktbl 81-84; Elmira Coll Key Awd 84; IAC All Star Field Hockey 82-84; Mansfield; Elem Educ.

STRONG, JEFF; Falconer Central HS; Jamestown, NY; (Y); 29/106; Boy Scts; Chess Clb; Church Yth Grp; Letterman Clb; Chorus; Bsktbl; Trk; Vllybl; God Cntry Awd; Hon Roll; Eagle Scout 83; Roberts Wesleyan Coll; Art.

STRONG, LISA; Union Springs Acad; Kansas City, MO; (Y); Art Clb; Library Aide; Ski Clb; Teachers Aide; Varsity Clb; Church Choir; Var Cheerleading; Bus Mgmt.

STRONG, PAM LEA; Odessa-Montour Central Schl; Montour Fls, NY; (Y); 15/80; Art Clb; Church Yth Grp; Drama Clb; FBLA; Library Aide; Teachers Aide; VP Varsity Clb; Chorus; Concert Band; Jazz Band; St Bonaventure U; Pre-Law.

STRONG, STEVEN P; Mc Quaid Jesuit HS; Rochester, NY; (Y); 2/150; Latin Clb; VP Swmmng; High Hon Roll; Jr NHS; Ntl Merit SF; NEDT Awd; Rickover Sci Inst 84; Cal-Tech; Physcs.

STRONG, SUSAN; Rocky Point JR-SR HS; Rocky Pt, NY; (Y); 23/208; Church Yth Grp; Spanish Clb; Hst Capt Bsktbl; Var Sftbl; Hon Roll; MIP Bsktbl Tm 83-84; MIP Sftbl Tm 82-84; Physcl Thpy.

STRONG JR, WILLIAM H; Madison Central HS; Oriskany Falls, NY; (Y); Church Yth Grp; Band; Jazz Band; Mrchg Band; School Musical; Yrbk Stf; High Hon Roll; NHS; Cert Achvt Math; Regents Schlrshp Wnnr 85; Whipple Schlrshp Wnnr; Morrisville; Comp Sci.

STRONY, KRISTEN J; Clarkstown HS; Bardonia, NY; (Y); 56/541; Aud/Vis; Church Yth Grp; Cmnty Wkr; Drama Clb; Stu Cncl; Diving; Swmmng; NHS; Ntl Merit Schol; Home Ec Schlrshp 85; Baldwin-Wallace Coll Schlrshp 85; James Madison U; Pre-Med.

STROTHMAN, ELIZABETH; Richmond Hill HS; Richmond Hill, NY; (Y); English Clb; High Hon Roll; NHS; VFW Awd; Voice Dem Awd; Womn Mke Nws Essy Cntst 3rd Pl 85; Bus Hon Soc 84-85; St Johns U; Sec.

STROWBRIDGE, LAURA; Bethpage HS; Plainview, NY; (Y); 15/295; Church Yth Grp; Library Aide; Spanish Clb; Yrbk Stf; High Hon Roll; Hon Roll; NHS; Cert Distinctn Natl Soc Studs Olympd 84-85; Civil Engrng.

STROZEWSKI, KRISTEN M; Nardin Acad; Alden, NY; (Y); 10/89; Cmnty Wkr; Debate Tm; Ski Clb; Chorus; School Musical; School Play; Sec Jr Cls; VP Sr Cls; Hon Roll; NHS; Grove City Coll; Med.

STRUBLE, BONNIE; Albion HS; Albion, NY; (S); #2 In Class; Girl Scts; Spanish Clb; Color Guard; High Hon Roll; Jr NHS; NHS; Prfct Atten Awd; Acad Decathalon 84; Engnrng.

STRUCIC, LIZETTE MARIE; Cathedral HS; Long Is Cy, NY; (Y); 48/325; Library Aide; Chorus; Church Choir; Hon Roll.

STRUWING, SCOTT T; Paul V Moore HS; Central Square, NY; (Y); 52/297; AFS; Ski Clb; Concert Band; Jazz Band; Mrchg Band; Symp Band; Im Vllybl; NY ST Regents Schlrshp; Utica Coll Of Syracuse U; Accnt.

STUART, BRIAN D; Fayetteville-Manlius HS; Manlius, NY; (Y); 63/332; Boy Scts; German Clb; Pres Radio Clb; Teachers Aide; Socr; Var Capt Trk; Im Wt Lftg; Hon Roll; Jr NHS; NHS; U Of Rochester; Optcl Engr.

STUART, JULIE; Sacred Heart Acad; Williamsville, NY; (Y); Spanish Clb; Varsity Clb; Mgr Stage Crew; Yrbk Phtg; Yrbk Stf; Lit Mag; Rep Frsh Cls; Rep Soph Cls; Badmtn; Vllybl; Dietc.

STUART, RALPH; Frontier SR HS; Lakeview, NY; (S); Pres Band; Concert Band; Mrchg Band; School Musical; Yrbk Stf; Bsbl; High Hon Roll; Jr NHS; NHS; Naval Acad; Engineering.

STUBA, BETH; Canton-Hugh C Williams HS; Canton, NY; (Y); 1/125; Church Yth Grp; Stat Bsktbl; Var Cheerleading; JV Var Socr; Var Trk; High Hon Roll; NHS; Tlaentd Jr Awd 85; Clarkson Sci Day 84; VP Chrch Yth Grp 85; Cornell.

STUBITS, RICHARD W; Monsignor McCLANCY HS; Jackson Heights, NY; (Y); 38/220; Church Yth Grp; High Hon Roll; Hon Roll; NYS Regnts Schlrshp 85-89; Fordham U; Fin.

STUCZYNSKI, DAVID; St Marys HS; Depew, NY; (S); 30/197; Computer Clb; Science Clb; Nwsp Rptr; NHS; Canisius; Bus Mgmt.

STUDDIFORD, JOHN P; Jamesville-De Witt HS; Jamesville, NY; (Y); 45/220; Concert Band; Var JV Bsbl; Bsktbl; Var Bowling; High Hon Roll; Hon Roll; NHS; Regents Schlrshp 85; Franklin & Marshall Coll; Bio.

STUDENIC, LESLIE; Gloversville HS; Gloversville, NY; (Y); Ski Clb; Band; Concert Band; Mrchg Band; Rep Soph Cls; Rep Jr Cls; Cheerleading; Trk; Crmnlgy.

STUDT, BRIAN; Onteora Central HS; Boiceville, NY; (S); Aud/Vis; Chorus; Stage Crew; Socr; Hon Roll; NHS; Engrng.

STUFANO, ANNA; Mount Vernon HS; Mount Vernon, NY; (Y); 23/585; Hosp Aide; Pres Keywanettes; Latin Clb; Nwsp Stf; NHS; Engl & Tchrs Awds 85; Fordham U; Tchng.

STUHR, KEITH; Eden Central HS; Eden, NY; (Y); 9/202; Varsity Clb; Yrbk Stf; JV Bsbl; Var Capt Golf; High Hon Roll; NHS; Prfct Atten Awd; NY ST Regents Scholar 85; Jerry Knoll Scholar 85; Svc Awd 85; Syracuse U; Cmmnctns.

STULL, ELIZABETH; Saugerties HS; Saugerties, NY; (Y); 22/230; Church Yth Grp; Cmnty Wkr; Drama Clb; French Clb; Thesps; Varsity Clb; Orch; School Play; Stage Crew; Yrbk Phtg.

STUMACHER, RICHARD; Susan E Wagner HS; Staten Island, NY; (Y); Science Clb; School Musical; Ed Nwsp Phtg; Yrbk Phtg; Pres Frsh Cls; Rep Soph Cls; Rep Jr Cls; Rep Stu Cncl; High Hon Roll; Pres NHS; Cornell U; Bio-Med.

STUMP, CARL A; Rushford Central Schl; Rushford, NY; (Y); 10/27; Am Leg Boys St; Boy Scts; Library Aide; Varsity Clb; VP Frsh Cls; Bsbl; Socr; Civil Engr.

STUMPF, LISA; Haverling Central HS; Bath, NY; (S); 27/150; Sec AFS; French Clb; JCL; Trs Latin Clb; Math Clb; Color Guard; Yrbk Stf; JV Swmmng; High Hon Roll; NHS; SUNY; Engrng.

STUNDTNER, ELIZABETH A; East HS; Corning, NY; (Y); 10/212; Drama Clb; Spanish Clb; Stage Crew; Rep Soph Cls; Rep Jr Cls; JV Tennis; High Hon Roll; NHS; WA Wrkshp Congrssnl Sem 85; Yth Crt Side Jdge 85; Law.

STURA, DIANE; Rocky Point HS; Long Island, NY; (Y); Mrchg Band; Cheerleading; Trk; Wt Lftg.

STURGESS, KATHLEEN; Cicero-N Syracuse HS; N Syracuse, NY; (S); 24/699; Band; Concert Band; Mrchg Band; Orch; Pep Band; School Musical; Symp Band; Nwsp Stf; Hon Roll; Jrnlsm.

STURGESS, KELLEY; Unatego Central HS; Unadilla, NY; (Y); 3/88; Am Leg Aux Girls St; 4-H; Spanish Clb; Concert Band; Jazz Band; School Play; Vllybl; NHS; Aeronautical Engrng.

STURM, MICHELLE; Union Springs Acad; Union Springs, NY; (S); Leo Clb; Library Aide; Ski Clb; Teachers Aide; Concert Band; Trs Frsh Cls; Im Bsktbl; Im Socr; Im Sftbl; Im Swmmng; Bus.

STURM, NANCY; York Central HS; Le Roy, NY; (Y); Am Leg Aux Girls St; Church Yth Grp; 4-H; Band; Pres Jr Cls; Sec Stu Cncl; Var Capt Cheerleading; Var Socr; Var Trk; High Hon Roll; Liv Co Alternate Dairy Princess 85; Cmmrcl Art.

STUTO, TERESA; Bishop Ford C C HS; Brooklyn, NY; (Y); Dance Clb; Ski Clb; Vllybl; Nrsng.

STUZIN, MICHELLE NANCY; Bethpage HS; Plainview, NY; (Y); VP French Clb; Rep Frsh Cls; Rep Soph Cls; Rep Jr Cls; Var Bsktbl; Var Fld Hcky; Var Gym; Capt Lcrss; High Hon Roll; Rep FBLA; Frnch Awds 85; Mst Schl Sprtd 85; Intl Bus.

STYC, DAMIAN; New Hartford HS; New Hartford, NY; (Y); Chess Clb; Computer Clb; Rep Stu Cncl; Wt Lftg; Wrstlng; Hon Roll; Comp Prgrmr.

STYLES, AURIA O; Shenendehowa HS; Clifton Park, NY; (Y); AFS; Church Yth Grp; Girl Scts; Intnl Clb; Church Choir; Symp Band; Sec Soph Cls; Sec Jr Cls; Rep Stu Cncl; JV Var Fld Hcky; Niel Hesson Awd Outstndg Char Ctznshp Scholar 85; Lib Art.

SU, LISA; Bronx HS Of Science; Bayside, NY; (Y); VP Intnl Clb; Math Tm; Service Clb; Teachers Aide; Orch; Yrbk Stf; JV Crs Cntry; Hon Roll; Jr NHS; NHS.

SU, VICKI; Forest Hills HS; New York, NY; (Y); 32/881; Church Yth Grp; Library Aide; Math Clb; Math Tm; Science Clb; Teachers Aide; Church Choir; School Musical; School Play; Nwsp Stf; 1st Pl Queensboro Fair Awd 84; Hnrs Schl Sci Fair Cert 84; Mssnry Wrkr.

SUAREZ, BARBARA; St Catharine Acad; Bronx, NY; (Y); 29/205; Teachers Aide; Nwsp Stf; Fld Hcky; NHS.

SUAREZ, DANIELLE; Mercy HS; Albany, NY; (Y); Drama Clb; Hosp Aide; Office Aide; Spanish Clb; Teachers Aide; Band; Chorus; School Play; Stage Crew; Rep Frsh Cls; Achvt Hnr Awd For Spanish I 82-83; Saint Rose Coll; Music.

SUAREZ, JACQUELINE; Cathedral HS; Woodside, NY; (Y); 6/325; Intnl Clb; Nwsp Stf; Yrbk Phtg; Yrbk Stf; High Hon Roll; Hon Roll; Prfct Atten Awd; 1st Hnrs Iona Coll Spnsh Cntst 85; Pres Ftns Acdmc Achvt Awd 85; Pres Schlrshp To Mnhtn Coll 85; Mnhtn Coll; Elec Engrng.

SUAREZ, KRISTINE; H Frank Carey HS; Garden City, NY; (Y); 52/213; Art Clb; Chorus; Fashion Inst; Intr Desgn.

SUAREZ, LISA; Tottenville HS; Staten Island, NY; (Y); Teachers Aide; Chorus; SUNY Albany; Psych.

SUAREZ, NOREEN; St Catherine Acad; Bronx, NY; (Y); 33/205; Cmnty Wkr; Hosp Aide; Library Aide; Hon Roll; NHS; Cmnty Svc Awd 85; Vlnteer Svc Awd 85; Mth.

SUAREZ, PEDRO J; Nazareth Regional HS; Brooklyn, NY; (Y); Am Leg Boys St; Hosp Aide; Speech Tm; Nwsp Rptr; Rep Sr Cls; Stu Cncl; JV Crs Cntry; JV Trk; Var Wrstlng; 1st Alt Boys Natn 85; USAF Acad; Aerospc Engrng.

SUAREZ, VINCENT RAYMOND; Aviation HS; Woodside, NY; (Y); 2/509; VP Debate Tm; JA; Ski Clb; Bowling; Chrmn NHS; Prfct Atten Awd; SF Natl Hispanic Schlr Awds Pgm 85; NY Regents Schlrshp 84-85; Wings Awd 84-85; Pagasus Soc 84-85; Queens Coll; Pol Scsi.

SUAZO, KAREN; Cardinal Spellman HS; Bronx, NY; (Y); Dance Clb; Spanish Clb; Im Vllybl; Nrsg.

SUBIK, ELIZABETH; Johnstown HS; Johnstown, NY; (Y); Intnl Clb; Concert Band; School Play; Sec Soph Cls; Capt Tennis; High Hon Roll; NHS; Spnsh Awd 84-85; Regents Schrlshp Awd 85; St Lawrence U.

SUBIK, KAREN; Johnstown HS; Johnstown, NY; (Y); 33/177; Ski Clb; School Play; Yrbk Stf; Trs Frsh Cls; Trs Soph Cls; Trs Jr Cls; Trs Sr Cls; Capt Crs Cntry; Powder Puff Ftbl; Capt Trk; Keene ST; Dietcs.

SUCATO, GINA S; Arlington HS; La Grangeville, NY; (Y); 19/595; Dance Clb; Yrbk Stf; Rep Sr Cls; JV Var Cheerleading; Ntl Merit SF; Child Psych.

SUCATO, JAMES JOSEPH; Our Lady Of Lourdes HS; Poughkeepsie, NY; (Y); 43/144; Aud/Vis; Drama Clb; School Musical; School Play; Variety Show; High Hon Roll; Hon Roll; Jr NHS; NHS; U Of Detroit MI; Pol Sci.

SUCHSLAND, DAVID N; Lakeland HS; Yorktown Hts, NY; (Y); 11/360; German Clb; Rep Soph Cls; L Crs Cntry; L Trk; Capt L Wrstlng; Hon Roll; NHS; Ntl Merit Ltr; All-Cnty Wrstlng Team 84 & 85; Temple U; Actuarial Sci.

SUDAC, IVAN; Cardinal O Hara HS; Buffalo, NY; (S); Trs Stu Cncl; Bsktbl; Var Golf; Var Tennis; Schlrshp & Hnr Roll; Electrncs.

SUDHALTER, ADRIAN V; Laguardia HS Of Music And The Arts; Manhattan, NY; (Y); 53/588; Art Clb; Yrbk Stf; Lit Mag; NHS; Hnr Mntn Fine Arts; Hnr Mntn Poetry 83-84; Mt Holyoke.

SUDLIK, MARY; Kenmore East S HS; Tonawanda, NY; (Y); 25/350; Capt Dance Clb; Drill Tm; Mrchg Band; Nwsp Rptr; Ed Yrbk Rptr; Yrbk Stf; Pom Pon; High Hon Roll; Hon Roll; NHS; NY ST Rgnts Schlsrhp 85; Pres Acdmc Ftns Awd 85; Syrcus U; Tlcmnctns.

SUFNARSKI, MICHAEL; Granville Central HS; Wells, VT; (S); 3/130; Rep Frsh Cls; Rep Soph Cls; Rep Jr Cls; Var Capt Bsbl; Var L Bsktbl; Capt Var Ftbl; High Hon Roll; NHS; NEDT Awd; Most Outstndng Seq II,Span II 84; Ntl Athletc Merit Serv 85.

SUGAR, MARNI; Beach Channel HS; Rockaway, NY; (Y); Yrbk Phtg; Yrbk Rptr; Socr; Vllybl.

SUGARMAN, DEBBIE; Clarkstown South HS; New City, NY; (Y); Sftbl; Hon Roll; Mu Alp Tht; Math Awd For Achiev 82-83; Tutor 83-84.

SUGIN, AMY J; Baldwin SR HS; Baldwin, NY; (Y); 46/502; Cmnty Wkr; Drama Clb; Hosp Aide; Key Clb; Temple Yth Grp; Thesps; School Musical; School Play; High Hon Roll; Hon Roll.

SUGRIMSINGH, MAHINDRA; Walton HS; Bronx, NY; (Y); Rep Stu Cncl; Cit Awd; Excll Svc, Pnctlty, & Atten 82-83; Schlstc Achvt 84 & 85; Comp.

SUH, ANDY; The Bronx H S Of Science; Flushing, NY; (Y); Computer Clb; Library Aide; Science Clb; Bausch & Lomb Sci Awd; NHS; Ntl Merit Ltr; Prfct Atten Awd; Amer Chemical Societys Awd 84; Cornell U; Mech Engrng.

SUKALAC, THOMAS R; Mayville Central Schl; Mayville, NY; (Y); 8/50; Boy Scts; Q&S; Band; Chorus; Stage Crew; Yrbk Bus Mgr; VP Jr Cls; VP Stu Cncl; NHS; Ntl Merit Ltr; NYS Rgnts Schlrshp 85; GA Tech; Elec Engrng.

SUKER, DAVID; Uniondale HS; Uniondale, NY; (Y); Ftbl; Hon Roll; Law.

SUKIENIK, LISA E; Yeshiva Of Flatbush HS; Jamaica Estates, NY; (Y); Drama Clb; Chorus; School Musical; School Play; Variety Show; Lit Mag; Var Bsktbl; Ntl Merit Ltr; Queens Teen Tlnt Comptn Fnlst 82; Hnry Lttr Prfrmnc NY City Hall 83; Thrtr.

SULLIVAN, BERNADETTE; Newfield HS; Selden, NY; (S); 61/568; Hosp Aide; Chorus; Yrbk Stf; Rep Stu Cncl; Var Capt Fld Hcky; Var Capt Vllybl; Hon Roll; Jr NHS; Trs NHS; Swing Chorus; Stu Of The Mnth Jan 82; Preview Magzns Stu/Athlt Of Mnth Jan 85; Schlstc Athlt Awd 82; Fairleigh Dickinson; Phy Ther.

SULLIVAN, CAROL; Thousand Islands HS; Cape Vincent, NY; (Y); AFS; Variety Show; Trs Frsh Cls; Trs Soph Cls; Trs Jr Cls; JV Socr; Hon Roll; NHS; Church Yth Grp; JV Bsktbl; Lions Schlr 85; AFS Stdnt Abroad Smmr Pgrm 85; Cmpt Sci.

SULLIVAN, CHARLES; Franklin Acad; Malone, NY; (S); 12/253; Am Leg Boys St; Pres Trs 4-H; Pres Model UN; Chorus; Swing Chorus; Cit Awd; 4-H Awd; Hon Roll; NHS; ST Hist Day Cont 81; PAFC Ldrshp Awd 84; Math, Sci, Hist Cont Wnnr 82-85; St Lawrence U; Pre-Law.

SULLIVAN, COLLEEN; Liverpool HS; Liverpool, NY; (Y); DECA; Rep Stu Cncl; Powder Puff Ftbl; Sftbl; Psych.

SULLIVAN, DARIN; Portledge Schl; Locust Valley, NY; (S); 2/15; School Play; Yrbk Stf; Pres Frsh Cls; VP Jr Cls; Stu Cncl; Ice Hcky; Lcrss; Socr; High Hon Roll; Bus.

SULLIVAN, DIANE E; Corning East HS; Corning, NY; (Y); JA; Ski Clb; Drill Tm; Yrbk Stf; Trs Sr Cls; Stu Cncl; Lcrss; High Hon Roll; Hon Roll; Jr NHS; Prom Comm; Htl Mngmnt.

SULLIVAN, ELIZABETH; Aquinas Inst; Rochester, NY; (S); 31/161; Drama Clb; Exploring; French Clb; Band; Drm & Bgl; School Musical; Nwsp Rptr; Bsktbl; High Hon Roll; Hon Roll; Spnsh Achvt Awd 83; Frnch Achvt Awd 84; Howard U; Lang.

SULLIVAN, ELLEN A; Our Lady Of Mercy Acad; Hicksville, NY; (Y); Dance Clb; Spanish Clb; St Johns U; Elem Ed.

SULLIVAN, JAMES D; Regis HS; Brooklyn, NY; (Y); Church Yth Grp; VP Stu Cncl; Var Capt Bsktbl; Ntl Merit Ltr; NY Telphn Schlrshp 85; J A Beirne Mem Schlrshp 85; Regnts Schlrshp 85; NY ST U Albany; Engl.

SULLIVAN, JEFFERY P; Dansville HS; Dansville, NY; (Y); 21/160; Am Leg Boys St; Ski Clb; Varsity Clb; Yrbk Phtg; Trs Frsh Cls; Trs Soph Cls; Trs Jr Cls; Trs Sr Cls; Var Capt Bsbl; JV Bsktbl; St John Fischer Coll; Acctg.

SULLIVAN, JEFFREY; Webster SR HS; Webster, NY; (Y); Boy Scts; School Play; Stage Crew; JV Trk; High Hon Roll; Outstndng Achvt Awd Mc Quaid Jesuit 83; 1st Hnbl Mntn Phtgrphy Cntst 85; Acadmc Ltr Mc Quaid Jesuit 84.

SULLIVAN, KAREN; Cardinal Spellman HS; New York, NY; (Y); Church Yth Grp; GAA; Nwsp Rptr; Bsktbl; Crs Cntry; Trk; High Hon Roll; NHS; Ntl Merit Ltr.

SULLIVAN, KAREN; St Marys Girls HS; Port Washington, NY; (Y); 6/154; Cmnty Wkr; Hosp Aide; Service Clb; Off Ski Clb; Chorus; Nwsp Ed-Chief; Lit Mag; Pres Frsh Cls; Off Soph Cls; Stu Cncl; Nassau Cty Chors 82; Sci Awd 82; Schlrshp Fordham U 85; Boston Coll; Pul Rltns.

SULLIVAN, KAROLYN; Clymer Central Schl; Clymer, NY; (Y); AFS; Church Yth Grp; Band; Chorus; VP Sr Cls; Var L Bsktbl; Var L Sftbl; Var L Vllybl; High Hon Roll; NHS; Schlrshp Svcshp Ldrshp Awds Brz & Slvr, Bst Def Plyr Awd Bsktbl 84-85; Phy Ed.

SULLIVAN, KELLY; Bayport-Bluepoint HS; Bayport, NY; (Y); VP Art Clb; PAVAS; Nwsp Ed-Chief; Nwsp Phtg; Yrbk Phtg; Dance Clb; Band; Mrchg Band; Nwsp Rptr; Nwsp Stf; See-Bees Schlrshp Phtgrphy 85; Ann-Marie Merenda Schlrshp 85; Hnrbl Mntn Phtgrphy-Coll Notre Dame 84; Fashion Inst Of Tech; Phtgrphy.

SULLIVAN, KIMBERLY; St John The Baptist HS; Nesconset, NY; (Y); GAA; Girl Scts; Office Aide; Varsity Clb; Var Capt Bsktbl; Coach Actv; Var Score Keeper; Hon Roll; Sprts Med.

SULLIVAN, LARA M; Corning Painted Post West HS; Painted Post, NY; (Y); Hosp Aide; JA; Varsity Clb; Nwsp Stf; Var L Tennis; Var L Trk; JV Vllybl.

SULLIVAN, MARK; Liverpool HS; Liverpool, NY; (Y); French Clb; Ski Clb; Chorus; JV Socr; Var Swmmng; Im Wt Lftg; Ocean Engr.

SULLIVAN, MARYELLEN; Cardinal Spellman HS; Yonkers, NY; (S); 5/528; Trs Church Yth Grp; Dance Clb; Off Sr Cls; Stu Cncl; Bsktbl; Crs Cntry; Im Mgr Vllybl; Gov Hon Prg Awd; Pres NHS; Ntl Merit Ltr; Bio.

SULLIVAN, MICHAEL; Bishop Kearney HS; Rochester, NY; (S); Aud/Vis; Boy Scts; Church Yth Grp; Varsity Clb; Nwsp Phtg; Nwsp Rptr; Capt Crs Cntry; Socr; Trk; Hon Roll; Niagara U; Travel.

SULLIVAN, MICHAEL P; Newburgh Free Acad; Newburgh, NY; (Y); 33/720; Boy Scts; Chess Clb; French Clb; Math Tm; Socr; High Hon Roll; NHS; Manhattan Coll; Elec Engrng.

SULLIVAN, MICHELE; Acad Of The Holy Names; Delmar, NY; (Y); Church Yth Grp; Nwsp Rptr; Sec Jr Cls; VP Sr Cls; Socr; Trk; Mst Imprvd Trck 84; MVP Sccr, Trck 85; Lbrl Arts.

SULLIVAN, MICHELE D; Seaford SR HS; Seaford, NY; (Y); 17/246; Band; Concert Band; Mrchg Band; High Hon Roll; Hon Roll; NHS; U Of Richmond; Pol Sci.

SULLIVAN, NANCY; New Dorp HS; Staten Island, NY; (Y); Church Yth Grp; Cmnty Wkr; Hosp Aide; Chorus; Hon Roll; Prfct Atten Awd; Concordia Coll; Elem Educ.

SULLIVAN, NICOLE; St Marys Acad; Glens Falls, NY; (S); 13/42; Drama Clb; Sec French Clb; FFA; Pres Key Clb; Pep Clb; ROTC; Varsity Clb; Band; Chorus; Church Choir; Parish Schlrshp St Rose Coll 85; Coll Of St Rose; Engl.

SULLIVAN, SHANNON; Stissing Mt JR SR HS; Red Hook, NY; (Y); AFS; JV Bsktbl; Capt Var Fld Hcky; Var Trk; Hon Roll; Ithaca Coll; Poltcl Journlsm.

SULLIVAN, SHARI; Kenmore West SR HS; Kenmore, NY; (Y); 125/453; Var L Swmmng; Hon Roll; Buffalo ST Coll.

SULLIVAN, SHEILA; Waterloo SR HS; Waterloo, NY; (Y); 1/161; Drama Clb; Band; Lit Mag; Stu Cncl; Bausch & Lomb Sci Awd; Jr NHS; Sec NHS; Rotary Awd; Val; Gannett Nswp Yth Care Awd 84; NAP Philips Schlrshp 85; Ntl Hnr Rll 85; Music Theatr.

SULLIVAN III, THOMAS F; Nazareth Regional HS; Belle Hrbr, NY; (Y); Chess Clb; Cmnty Wkr; Stu Cncl; Ice Hcky; Mgr(s); Fr Edward Troike Ldrshp Pgm Achvt, Speed Reading Awds 82; Top 10 Scorer Hockey Clb 85.

SULLIVAN, TIMOTHY; Rhinebeck HS; Rhinebeck, NY; (Y); 13/97; Church Yth Grp; Ski Clb; JV Bsktbl; JV Var Socr; Hon Roll; Amer Lgn Awd 85; Alfred U; Ceramc Engrng.

SULLIVAN, WAYNE C; Saint Anthonys HS; Deer Park, NY; (Y); FBLA; Model UN; Chrmn Ski Clb; Capt Trk; High Hon Roll; Mu Alp Tht; Pres Schlr; SAR Awd; Voice Dem Awd; Caffe Achvrs Schlrshp 85; Daily Trib Outstndng Sr Awd 85; Engrng.

SULTANA, VINCENT M; La Salle Acad; New York, NY; (S); School Play; Stage Crew; Nwsp Phtg; Nwsp Stf; Yrbk Phtg; Rep Frsh Cls; Pres Soph Cls; Sec Jr Cls; Rep Stu Cncl; Hon Roll; Bus Admin.

SUMMERFIELD, SONYA; Dover JR & SR HS; Wingdale, NY; (S); Church Yth Grp; Drama Clb; VP Spanish Clb; Chorus; Stat Bsktbl; Mgr Cheerleading; High Hon Roll; Hon Roll; Century III Ldrshp 84; Fashn Merch.

SUMMERFORD, CANDACE; Vestal SR HS; Vestal, NY; (Y); Church Yth Grp; Cmnty Wkr; Band; Church Choir; Yrbk Stf; Rep Stu Cncl; Swmmng; High Hon Roll; NHS; Spanish NHS; Med.

SUMMERS, JOHN; Oakfield Alabama Central Schl; Basom, NY; (Y); Aud/Vis; Camera Clb; Chess Clb; Church Yth Grp; English Clb; 4-H; Library Aide; Stage Crew; Nwsp Rptr; Nwsp Sprt Ed; Northeastern U; Law Enfrcmt.

SUMMERS, THEODORE V; Sutherland HS; Pittsford, NY; (Y); 92/232; Boy Scts; Trs Model UN; Var L Crs Cntry; DAR Awd; All-Cnty Crss-Cntry Ski Team 85; Empire ST Wntr Games Crss-Cntry Skng 84-85; NY ST Regents Schlrshp; Purdue U.

SUMMERS, TODD; The Norman Howard HS; Rochester, NY; (Y); Yrbk Stf; Rep Jr Cls; Art Clb; Schlstc Art Awd 82-83 & 84-85.

SUMMERS, VICTORIA S; The Nichols Schl; Cheektowaga, NY; (Y); 2/111; AFS; Church Yth Grp; Red Cross Aide; Chorus; Church Choir; School Musical; School Play; Vllybl; Ntl Merit Ltr; Flag Corp; Ntl Achvmnt Schlrshp Semi-Fnlst 85; Nuclr Engrng.

SUMMERSON, SCOTT; Wheatland-Chili Central Schl; Scottsville, NY; (Y); Church Yth Grp; Var Bsbl; Var Bsktbl; Var Socr; Hon Roll; Dayton; Elec Tech.

SUMMERVILLE, DARCIE; Gray Bodley HS; Fulton, NY; (S); Sec Church Yth Grp; Sec 4-H; Spanish Clb; Orch; School Musical; Rep Stu Cncl; JV Socr; Var Trk; 4-H Awd; Hon Roll; Syracuse Symphny Yth Orch 84; Crane Schl Of Music Summer Pgm 81-84; Music Awds; Music.

SUMMERVILLE, KIMBERLY X; Emerson Vocational HS; Buffalo, NY; (Y); 1/88; JA; Pep Clb; Nwsp Stf; Yrbk Stf; Sec Sr Cls; Stat Bsktbl; Mgr(s); Stat Sftbl; Timer; High Hon Roll; NYS Regnts Schlrshp 85; Acad Excl Awd 83; Edinboro U Of PA; Comp Engr.

SUMMIT, JOSHUA; Southampton HS; Water Mill, NY; (Y); Drama Clb; Spanish Clb; School Play; Lit Mag; Rep Stu Cncl; Socr; Trk; Hon Roll; NHS; Duke U; Eng.

SUMNER, LEE; Amsterdam HS; Amsterdam, NY; (Y); Church Yth Grp; Civic Clb; Wt Lftg; Wrstlng; Hon Roll; Prfct Atten Awd; Optmtrst.

SUMTER, WENIFRED; Freeport HS; Freeport, NY; (Y); Pep Clb; Varsity Clb; Church Choir; Nwsp Sprt Ed; Rep Jr Cls; Pres Stu Cncl; L Var Badmtn; Stat Trk; Hon Roll; Mgmt Awd Mgmt Explrtn 85 & Oprtn Entrprs 84; Purchsng.

SUNDARAMURTHY, MALLI; West Genesee HS; Camillus, NY; (Y); Exploring; Office Aide; Chorus; High Hon Roll; Med.

SUNDAY, SCOTT; Westfield Acad & Central; Portland, NY; (Y); L Var Ftbl; L Var Wrstlng; High Hon Roll; Hon Roll; NHS; Bret Smith Mem Ldrshp Awd 85; Mst Outstdng SR Wrstlr 85; Eng Outstndg Achvt Awd 85.

SUNDBERG, MICHAEL; Centereach HS; Centereach, NY; (Y); Rptr Cmnty Wkr; Crs Cntry; Hon Roll; Bowling Trophies 83; USN; Electronics.

SUNDELL, VIRGINIA; Hamburg SR HS; Hamburg, NY; (Y); AFS; Trs Church Yth Grp; Drama Clb; NFL; Speech Tm; School Play; Yrbk Stf; Tennis; NHS; Pres Schlr; Regents Schlrshp 85; SUNY At Stony Brook; Psych.

SUNG, SUE; Bronx High School Of Science; New York, NY; (Y); VP Church Yth Grp; Library Aide; Office Aide; Teachers Aide; Church Choir; Yrbk Stf; JV Trk; Assembly Teen Talnt 2nd Pl 83.

SUNNINGHAM, JAMES; W Genesee HS; Syracuse, NY; (Y); 253/503; Camp Fr Inc; NFL; Political Wkr; God Cntry Awd; Voice Dem Awd; Dance Clb; FHA; Drill Tm; Drm & Bgl; Mat Maids.

SUNSHINE, GARY M; Gen D Mac Arthur HS; Seaford, NY; (Y); 5/319; Cmnty Wkr; VP Pres Model UN; Band; School Musical; School Play; Nwsp Ed-Chief; Ed Yrbk Rptr; Hst Stu Cncl; High Hon Roll; Trs NHS; Optimist Intl NY ST Oratorical Chmpn 81; All-Nassau Cnty HS Band 84famer Schlstc Press Assn 85; Princeton U.

SUPLEY, JENNIFER; Northern Adirondack Central Schl; Merrill, NY; (Y); French Clb; Hon Roll Awd; Clinton CC; Reg Nrse.

SUPON JR, DONALD; La Salle SR HS; Niagara Falls, NY; (Y); CAP; JV Var Ftbl; JV Trk; Hon Roll; NHS; Prfct Atten Awd; New Cadet Awd 84; Mst Imprvd Plyr Vrsty Ftbl 84; Syracuse U; Engnrg.

SUPPA, BERNARDI M; Eldred Central HS; Glen Spey, NY; (Y); 1/42; Trs Church Yth Grp; Varsity Clb; Band; Chorus; Nwsp Stf; Yrbk Stf; Stu Cncl; Bsktbl; Bausch & Lomb Sci Awd; High Hon Roll; NY ST Rgnts Schlrshp 85; Muhlenberg; Pre Med.

SUPPA, BERNARDINE; Eldred Central Schl; Glen Spey, NY; (Y); 1/42; Trs Church Yth Grp; Band; Chorus; Nwsp Rptr; Yrbk Stf; Sec Stu Cncl; Var Bsktbl; Bausch & Lomb Sci Awd; Pres NHS; Val; Pres Acadmc Fit Awd 85; Dist Cncl Carpntrs Schlrshp 85; Lioness Clb Schlrshp 85; Muhlenberg Coll; Pre-Med.

SURDICH, ANTHONY; St Francis Prep; College Point, NY; (S); 153/693; Im Ftbl; Acad All Amer 84-85; CUNY; Bus Mgmt.

SURDYKOWSKI, LESTER; Christ The King R HS; Brooklyn, NY; (Y); 33/385; Boy Scts; Camera Clb; Film Study.

SURLESS, PAMELA; E Meadow HS; E Meadow, NY; (S); 14/414; FBLA; Girl Scts; Band; Concert Band; Mrchg Band; Symp Band; Var Pom Pon; Hon Roll; NHS; Frnch Awd 82; Acadmc Excllnc Awd 82; Outstndng Muscn Awd 82; St Johns U; Eductn.

SURRA, CHRIS; St Josephs Collegiate Inst; Buffalo, NY; (Y); 30/200; Church Yth Grp; Acpl Chr; Band; Trs Chorus; Church Choir; School Musical; Pres Swing Chorus; Lit Mag; JV Bsbl; Capt JV Bsktbl; Bsktbl MIP 83.

SUSAMMA, JOHN; Dominican Commercial HS; Jamaica, NY; (Y); Hosp Aide; Teachers Aide; WA Wrskhp Scholar 85.

SUSICE, CHRISTINE; St Regis Falls Central Schl; St Regis Falls, NY; (S); 2/21; Girl Scts; Office Aide; Band; Chorus; Sec Frsh Cls; Var JV Cheerleading; High Hon Roll; Hon Roll; NHS; Rochester Busin Inst; Accountnt.

SUSICE, TONI; St Regis Falls Central HS; St Regis Falls, NY; (S); Chorus; Concert Band; Mrchg Band; Trs Frsh Cls; JV Var Bsktbl; JV Var Socr; Var Sftbl; JV Var Vllybl; Hon Roll; NHS; Paul Smiths Coll; Hotel Mgt.

SUSMAN, AMY R; Wellington C Mepham HS; Merrick, NY; (Y); 18/385; Debate Tm; Sec Pres Orch; Capt Cheerleading; Cit Awd; Kiwanis Awd; NHS; Cmnty Wkr; Key Clb; Science Clb; Nwsp Rptr; Schl Spirit Awd 85; Cntry III Schl Wnnr 85; Adele Kangur Mem Awd 85; Bellmore-Merrick Schlrshp Awd 85; Cornell U; Human Devlpmnt.

SUSMAN, CHRISTINE; Liverpool HS; Liverpool, NY; (S); 257/729; Art Clb; Girl Scts; JA; Pep Clb; Cheerleading; Certf Of Mrt 80; Hnr Mntn 80; Coll Of St Rose Art Awd 85; St Rose; Advtsng.

SUSMAN, ELIZABETH; W C Mepham HS; Merrick, NY; (Y); 49/385; Model UN; VP Orch; Nwsp Ed-Chief; Yrbk Rptr; VP Soph Cls; VP Jr Cls; Off Sr Cls; Hon Roll; NHS; Pres Schlr; NY St Regnts Scholar 85; Pres Acad Fit Awd 85; W C Mepham PTA Scholar Awd 85; Boston U; Comm.

SUSS, DEBBIE; Commack High Schl North; Commack, NY; (Y); Cmnty Wkr; Dance Clb; Girl Scts; Teachers Aide; Chorus; Mrchg Band; Yrbk Stf; Rep Stu Cncl; Var Vllybl; Stat Wrstlng; Svc Cert Awd Outstndng Aide 85; Bus Adm.

SUSZCZYNSKI, JEAN E; Commack High School South; Commack, NY; (Y); Pres Church Yth Grp; Cmnty Wkr; Hosp Aide; Y-Teens; Chorus; Var JV Bsktbl; JV Socr; Var L Trk; Var JV Vllybl; Hon Roll; Stu Recgntn Day 83-85; Most Imprv Soccer Plyr 84.

SUSZEK, GINA; Smithtown H S East; Nesconset, NY; (Y); Cmnty Wkr; Spanish Clb; Teachers Aide; Off Soph Cls; Var Badmtn; Mgr(s); High Hon Roll; Hon Roll; NHS; FBLA; Pres Acad Fit Awd Pgm 85; SUNY Farmingdale; Bio Tech.

SUSZKA, LYNN; St Marys HS; Alden, NY; (S); 17/217; 4-H; Hosp Aide; Science Clb; Im Bowling; 4-H Awd; Hon Roll; Art Awd 83-84; Med.

SUTCH, BRIAN; Scotia Glenville HS; Scotia, NY; (Y); Ebmry Riddle Aerontcl; Air Crft.

SUTEL, RACHEL; Emma Willard Schl; Lawrence, NY; (Y); School Play; Yrbk Ed-Chief; Yrbk Phtg; Yrbk Stf; Lit Mag; JV Var Bsktbl; Var JV Fld Hcky; Var Lcrss; Declamation Cntst Wnnr; Culinary Schl.

SUTFIN, MIKE; East Syracuse-Minoa HS; Kirkville, NY; (Y); Church Yth Grp; Latin Clb; Red Cross Aide; Science Clb; Ski Clb; Variety Show; Im Bsktbl; Var L Ftbl; Var L Lcrss; Var Cmnty Wkr; Envrnmntl Engr.

SUTHERLAND, PAULA A; Catherine Mc Auley HS; Brooklyn, NY; (Y); #2 In Class; Church Yth Grp; Nwsp Rptr; Nwsp Stf; Yrbk Stf; Rep Sr Cls; Rep Stu Cncl; Hon Roll; NHS; Prfct Atten Awd; Brooklyn Coll; Bio.

SUTHERLAND, SHARON A; Ossining HS; Ossining, NY; (Y); JV Var Socr; High Hon Roll; Hon Roll; Psych.

SUTLIFF, EVORA; Schl Of The Arts At Monroe; Rochester, NY; (Y); Girl Scts; Acpl Chr; Chorus; Drill Tm; School Musical; School Play; Stage Crew; Swing Chorus; Variety Show; Yrbk Stf; Geomtry Awd Outstndng Stu 85; Med.

SUTLIFF, MARILYN J; Hadley Luzerne Central Schl; Hadley, NY; (Y); 3/70; Office Aide; Trs Soph Cls; Trs Jr Cls; Bsbl; Bsktbl; Stat Ftbl; Stat Socr; Hon Roll; NHS; Hugh O Brien Ldrshp Fdtn Smnr 83; NYS Rgnts Schlrshp 85; SUNY Plattsburgh; Psychlgy.

SUTTON, BEVERLY; Sauquoit Valley Central HS; Sauquoit, NY; (Y); High Hon Roll; Hon Roll; NHS; NEDT Awd; Prfct Atten Awd; Wrthy Advsr Rnbw Mohwk Vly-Msnc Yth Grp 85; Comp Sci.

SUTTON, CRAIG; Hutchinson Central Vo Tech; Buffalo, NY; (Y); Boy Scts; Exploring; JA; Nwsp Rptr; Nwsp Stf; Elec Tech.

SUTTON, JUDY E; Canarsie HS; Brooklyn, NY; (Y); 40/565; Office Aide; Service Clb; Teachers Aide; School Musical; Nwsp Rptr; Yrbk Stf; Vllybl; Courier Life Publications Essay Awd 84; American Pen Women Society 84-85; Syracuse U; Journalism.

SUTTON, LEON; West High Corning Painted Post; Beaver Dams, NY; (Y); Computer Clb; Key Clb; Letterman Clb; Varsity Clb; Rep Soph Cls; Var L Ftbl; L Trk; Hon Roll; Stu Media Fstvl 84; Comp Tech.

SUTTON, MARY; Saint John The Baptist HS; W Islip, NY; (Y); Office Aide; Varsity Clb; Trk; Hon Roll; V Trk Awd 85; Vet.

SUTTON, RICHARD; W Seneca West SR HS; W Seneca, NY; (Y); Aud/Vis; Boy Scts; Chess Clb; Church Yth Grp; Im Bsktbl; JV L Ftbl; Var L Wrstlng; Hon Roll; Recgntn Outstndng Reg Bio 83-84; Elect Tech.

SUTTON, SHERRI; Skaneateles SR HS; Skaneateles, NY; (S); Variety Show; Tennis; High Hon Roll; NHS; Mth.

SUTTON, STANLEY R; Jasper Central Schl; Jasper, NY; (Y); 3/29; 4-H; Pres FFA; Pres Varsity Clb; Yrbk Stf; Var Bsbl; Var Bsktbl; Capt Var Socr; Var Trk; Pres NHS; Sal; De Kalb Ag Accomplshmnt Awd 85; Steuber Cnty Dairy Prince 85; Empire Farmer Degree 84; Alfred Ag Tech; Data Processing.

SUTTON, SUSAN; Broadalbin HS; Broadalbin, NY; (Y); Pres Church Yth Grp; Girl Scts; Letterman Clb; Library Aide; Spanish Clb; Sec Varsity Clb; Chorus; Mgr Yrbk Bus Mgr; Yrbk Stf; Trs Stu Cncl; MVP Trk & Fld 84; Pres Phys Fit Awd 82-85; Bus.

SUTTON, TERESA; Alexander Central HS; Alexander, NY; (Y); Cmnty Wkr; Dance Clb; Drama Clb; GAA; Teachers Aide; Chorus; Mrchg Band; School Musical; JV Var Bsktbl; JV Var Socr; Elem Educ.

SVAHN, SATU; Rome Free Acad; Lantana, FL; (Y); Key Clb; Ski Clb; Chorus; Hon Roll.

SVARPLAITIS, TERRI; Dover JR SR HS; Wingdale, NY; (Y); Varsity Clb; Band; Drm & Bgl; Mrchg Band; JV Var Bsktbl; JV Var Sftbl; Var Capt Vllybl; Hon Roll; Voice Dem Awd; NYSSMA Solo Mdls 81-84; Cls C Hon Men Sftbl 84-85; Scholar Awd Mth III 84'-85; Comp Sci.

SVARZKOPF, AMY; St Marys HS; East Aurora, NY; (S); JV Bsktbl; Hon Roll; Engr.

SVENDSEN, LISA; Immaculate Heart Central HS; Watertown, NY; (Y); FBLA; Yrbk Stf; Hon Roll.

SVENSSON, KRISTIN; Pine Bush HS; Pine Bush, NY; (Y); 10/289; Dance Clb; Concert Band; School Musical; School Play; Swing Chorus; Var L Fld Hcky; NHS; 4-H; GAA; Math Tm; All-Cnty Band 85; Area-All State Band 84; All-Cnty Chorus 84; Rensselear Poly Inst; Bio-Engrn.

SVERDLOVE, JILL; Mamoroneck HS; Mamaroneck, NY; (Y); Pres Temple Yth Grp; Concert Band; Mrchg Band; School Musical; JV Var Vllybl; High Hon Roll; NHS; Spanish NHS; Office Aide; Ski Clb; Creat Wrtg Awd 83-84; Excllnce Spn Awd 83-84; All Cnty Prcssn 81-82, All ST 84 & 85.

SVETVILAS, CHULEENAN; Notre Dame HS; Elmira, NY; (Y); 5/127; Ski Clb; Concert Band; Yrbk Ed-Chief; Tennis; Trk; High Hon Roll; JP Sousa Awd; NHS; NY ST Regents Schlrshp 85; Gold Key Awd Schlstc Art Cont 85; NYSSSA Permnt Coll Art Wrk 83; Brown U.

SVOBODA, MATTHEW; Commack North HS; Smithtown, NY; (Y); Boy Scts; Church Yth Grp; Math Tm; Band; Concert Band; Mrchg Band; Symp Band; Im Bowling; Var JV Trk; High Hon Roll; Eagle Sct 85; Bus Adm.

SWAIN, ANTOINE; North Babylon SR HS; North Babylon, NY; (Y); 200/601; Art Clb; Church Yth Grp; Computer Clb; Spanish Clb; Teachers Aide; Chorus; Orch; Bsktbl; Trk; Prfct Atten Awd; Winston Salem ST U; Economics.

SWAIN, LOIS; Clara Barton HS; Brooklyn, NY; (Y); Church Yth Grp; Math Tm; Chorus; Church Choir; Hon Roll; NHS; Prfct Atten Awd; Hon Roll & Soc 84 & 85; Supr Yth 84-85; Harvard U; Ped.

SWAN, DEAN; Fairport HS; Fairport, NY; (Y); Sec Computer Clb; Math Tm; Var Crs Cntry; Var Ice Hcky; Var Trk; Am Comp Sci Lege 84-85; NY ST Regnts Schlrshp 85; Clarkson U; Comp.

SWAN, KIMBERLY; Kenmore West SR HS; Kenmore, NY; (Y); Church Yth Grp; Cmnty Wkr; Hon Roll; Ntl Sports Festvl Swmmng 85; Gold,Bronze Medal Empire ST Games 85; Poems Pub; PA ST; Comp Sci.

SWAN, TOM; Warrensburg Central HS; Warrensburg, NY; (S); Exploring; 4-H; Band; School Play; Yrbk Ed-Chief; Yrbk Stf; Rep Stu Cncl; 4-H Awd; Hon Roll; NHS; ST Wnnr Natl 4-H Frstry Pgm 84; Hghst Grade Regents Test Alg & Earth Sci 82-83; Sci.

SWANCOTT JR, BRIAN; Rome Free Academy; Rome, NY; (Y); Im Bsbl; Var Capt Crs Cntry; Im Socr; Var Trk; COL All Star X-Cntry 85; COL All Star Track 86; Alfred Ag & Tech; Intl Marktng.

SWANSON, ERIC S; St Francis HS; Collins, NY; (Y); PAVAS; Chorus; School Musical; JV Bsbl; Im Bsktbl; Var JV Ftbl; Hon Roll; Svc Awd Fine Arts 85; Paul Smiths Coll; Frstry.

SWANSON, MARK; Thomas Edison HS; Horseheads, NY; (Y); Am Leg Aux Girls St; Trs Church Yth Grp; Varsity Clb; Chorus; Church Choir; School Musical; Rep Stu Cncl; Var L Bsbl; Var L Bsktbl; Var L Ftbl; Wendy Rdo Stn Awd Bsbl 85; MD U Coll Park; Crmnl Jstc.

SWANZ, MATTHEW C; Ten Broeck Adad; Franklinville, NY; (Y); 3/50; Am Leg Boys St; Boy Scts; Spanish Clb; School Musical; VP Jr Cls; Rep Pres Stu Cncl; Capt Crs Cntry; Capt Swmmng; Capt Trk; Hon Roll; Elmira Key Awd 84-85.

SWAPCEINSKI, JOHN; Bryon-Bergen HS; Bergen, NY; (Y); Math Tm; Model UN; Stu Cncl; Bsktbl; Golf; Socr; Hon Roll; NHS; Ntl Merit Ltr; Elec Engr.

SWARNS, CHRISTINA; Notre Dame Acad; Staten Island, NY; (Y); Computer Clb; Band; Concert Band; Mrchg Band; Symp Band; Trk; Howard U; Crimnl Law.

SWARTHOUT, JILL; Wellsville HS; Wellsville, NY; (Y); Sec Trs Key Clb; Ed Nwsp Stf; Yrbk Stf; Pres Jr Cls; Pres Sr Cls; Stat Bsktbl; JV Capt Socr; Var Trk; High Hon Roll; NHS; Ed.

SWARTZ, LLOYD J; Moriah Central HS; Moriah, NY; (Y); Ski Clb; Band; Concert Band; Orch; Variety Show; Bsktbl; Golf; Hon Roll; JP Sousa Awd; Regnt Schlrshp 85; SUNY; Crmnl Justc.

SWAUGER, TINA; Cattaraugus Central HS; Cattaraugus, NY; (Y); 10/50; Pres Church Yth Grp; VP Frsh Cls; Trs Sr Cls; Var JV Bsktbl; Var JV Socr; Var Sftbl; DAR Awd; Hon Roll; NHS; Chorus; NYS Regnts Schlrshp 85; Houghton Coll; Pre-Vet.

SWAVELY, WILLIAM G; Rome Free Acad; Rome, NY; (Y); Church Yth Grp; Hon Roll; JETS Awd; Jr NHS; Chem Engr.

SWEATMAN, CARRIE; Gilboa-Conesville Central HS; Gilboa, NY; (S); Spanish Clb; Band; Chorus; School Musical; Nwsp Stf; Yrbk Stf; Cheerleading; Vllybl; High Hon Roll; Accntnt.

SWEEDLER, EMILY; Ossining HS; Ossining, NY; (Y); Radio Clb; Ski Clb; Pres Orch; School Musical; School Play; Nwsp Stf; Yrbk Sprt Ed; Rptr Lit Mag; Rep Stu Cncl; JV Capt Fld Hcky; Area All ST Orch & Yth Symph 83-85; Fine Art.

SWEENEY, JASON; Bishop Scully HS; Mayfield, NY; (Y); 35/70; 4-H; Varsity Clb; JV Var Ftbl; Art Awd; Fulton Montgomery Cnty Coll.

SWEENEY, JOSEPH C; Monsignor Farrell HS; Staten Island, NY; (Y); 162/298; Chess Clb; Church Yth Grp; Computer Clb; Stage Crew; Soph Cls; Im Bsktbl; Im Bowling; Swmmng; Hon Roll; Schlstc Athletic Incntv Awd In Swmng 81-82; Loyola Coll Mrylnd; Bus Admin.

SWEENEY, KATHLEEN; Holy Angels Acad; Grand Island, NY; (Y); Church Yth Grp; French Clb; Hosp Aide; Math Clb; Quiz Bowl; Pres Ski Clb; Varsity Clb; School Musical; School Play; Stage Crew.

SWEENEY, KIM; Thousand Islands HS; Clayton, NY; (Y); JV Socr; JV Vllybl; High Hon Roll; Hon Roll; Jr NHS; Lion Awd; NHS; Bus Mgmt.

SWEENEY, MARGARET B; Briarcliff HS; Briarcliff, NY; (Y); AFS; Drama Clb; Trs French Clb; Hosp Aide; Chorus; School Play; Tennis; Trk; High Hon Roll; Hon Roll; NY ST Regnts Schlrshp 85.

SWEENEY, MARIE; St Francis Prep; Whitestone, NY; (Y); 190/700; Chorus; JV Crs Cntry; Im Sftbl; Var Timer; JV Trk; Im Vllybl; Opt Clb Awd.

SWEENEY, MAUREEN; Liverpool HS; Liverpool, NY; (S); 143/790; Church Yth Grp; Ski Clb; Sec Stu Cncl; Elem Ed.

SWEENEY, MICHAEL; Canisius HS; Grand Island, NY; (S); 8/140; JCL; Latin Clb; Nwsp Ed-Chief; Nwsp Phtg; Nwsp Stf; High Hon Roll; Mu Alp Tht; Math Clb; Ftbl; Pre-Med.

SWEENEY, TAMMY; Parishville-Hopkinton Central HS; Potsdam, NY; (Y); Drill Tm; Off Jr Cls; Mgr(s); Score Keeper; Socr; Sftbl; Vllybl; Hon Roll; NHS; Sec.

SWEENEY, WILLIAM; Amsterdam HS; Hagaman, NY; (Y); 40/330; Band; Concert Band; Jazz Band; Mrchg Band; Ftbl; Hon Roll; NHS; Bio.

SWEET, ANGLEA; Franklin Acad; Malone, NY; (Y); Church Yth Grp; Church Choir; Jr NHS; Prfct Atten Awd; Nursng.

SWEET, JENNIFER; Sodus Central HS; Sodus Point, NY; (Y); 7/108; Church Yth Grp; Model UN; Science Clb; Varsity Clb; Concert Band; Mrchg Band; JV L Crs Cntry; Var L Trk; High Hon Roll; NHS; Arch.

SWEETSER, TORREY; Fayetteville-Manlius HS; Fayetteville, NY; (Y); Church Yth Grp; Exploring; Var Mgr Bsktbl; Var Socr; Prfct Atten Awd; Manlius Pebble Hill Acad Grnt 83-84; Bus Admin.

SWENSON, CONSTANCE; Longwood HS; Coram, NY; (Y); Church Yth Grp; Library Aide; Office Aide; Chorus; Crs Cntry; Score Keeper; Trk; High Hon Roll; Hon Roll; Spllng Awd North Coleman Rd 77; Hnr Rll 81; Stony Brook U; Grd Schl Tchr.

SWENSON, DAVID R; Brewster HS; Brewster, NY; (Y); Var Bsbl; Var Ftbl; Var Trk; High Hon Roll; Hon Roll; Cert Hnr Engl 84; U Of Miami; Comp Prgrmr.

SWENSON, ERICA; Charles O Dickerson HS; Trumansburg, NY; (Y); 2/84; Church Yth Grp; French Clb; Model UN; Science Clb; Varsity Clb; Pres Band; Chorus; Pres Concert Band; Jazz Band; Mrchg Band; Bio Awd 84; Mus Schlrshp 85; Model UN Awd 85; Cornell.

SWENSON, LINDA; Folconer Central Schl; Falconer, NY; (Y); 23/132; Trs Ski Clb; Spanish Clb; Varsity Clb; Band; Color Guard; Var L Crs Cntry; Sftbl; Var L Trk; Vllybl; Letterman Clb; Sports Med.

SWETLAND, KIMBERLY; Allegany Central HS; Allegany, NY; (Y); Cmnty Wkr; Hosp Aide; Political Wkr; Concert Band; School Musical; Nwsp Rptr; Yrbk Stf; JV Tennis; High Hon Roll; Hon Roll; NYSSMA Area All ST Music Fest 82; Miss Teen NY Pgnt 84; Law.

SWETZ, THOMAS; Sacred Heart HS; Yonkers, NY; (S); 54/238; Boy Scts; Drama Clb; School Musical; School Play; Stage Crew; Yrbk Stf; Crs Cntry; Trk; Hon Roll; NHS; 2nd Hnrs 84; Iona Coll; Comp Sci.

SWETZ, TRACY; Aquinas Inst; Rochester, NY; (S); 2/166; Church Yth Grp; German Clb; JA; Math Tm; Ski Clb; Stu Cncl; Socr; Sftbl; High Hon Roll; Jr NHS; St Thomas Club 82-85; Med.

SWIATEK, CHRISTOPHER; Bishop Timon HS; W Seneca, NY; (Y); Pep Clb; Chorus; Sec Stu Cncl; JV Bsbl; Var Golf; Var Capt Ice Hcky; Lion Awd; Ldrshp & Svc Cath Action 85; Canisius Coll; Bus Mgt.

SWIDERSKI, EMILIA; Oneonta HS; Oneonta, NY; (S); Key Clb; Q&S; Spanish Clb; Sec Varsity Clb; Nwsp Ed-Chief; Yrbk Stf; Off Stu Cncl; Var Trk; Hon Roll; NHS; Journalism Awd 84; High Achievement 82; Skidmore Coll; Law.

SWIERAT, MICHELE; Lancaster SR HS; Lancaster, NY; (S); DECA; Girl Scts; Office Aide; Pep Clb; Teachers Aide; Stu Cncl; Hon Roll.

SWIERSKI, CHARLES; West Seneca East SR HS; W Seneca, NY; (Y); Boys Clb Am; Varsity Clb; Nwsp Rptr; Sec Sr Cls; Var L Bsbl; Var Capt Bsktbl; Var Capt Vllybl; Hon Roll; JC Awd; Prfct Atten Awd; 95 Avg Or Bttr Spnsh I-II 84-85; Cum Laude Latn II 83; Erie Cnty Intrschlstc Conf Bsktb Hnbl Mntn 85.

SWIETONIOWSKI, DENISE; Auburn HS; Auburn, NY; (Y); 37/444; Model UN; Chorus; Yrbk Stf; High Hon Roll; NHS; SK Schlrshp 85; Le Moyne Coll; Acctng.

SWIFT, CYNTHIA; Liverpool HS; Liverpool, NY; (Y); Exploring; Band; Chorus; Concert Band; Mrchg Band; School Play; Data Prcssg.

SWIFT, KATHLEEN; Bishop Maginn HS; Albany, NY; (S); 1/118; Spanish Clb; Nwsp Rptr; Sec Sr Cls; JV Bsktbl; High Hon Roll; NHS; Val; Rnsslr Plytchnc Awd Math & Sci; Sch Eng Awd; Sch Chem Awd; Engr.

SWIFT, LINDA; Our Lady Of Mercy; Henrietta, NY; (Y); 33/200; JA; Latin Clb; NFL; School Play; Hon Roll; SUNY Oswego; Bio.

SWINDELL, THERESA A; Footbonne Hall Acad; Brooklyn, NY; (Y); 70/138; Dance Clb; Hon Roll; St Schlr; Hunter Coll; Nrs.

SWINDELLS, CATHERINE A; Notre Dame HS; Corning, NY; (Y); 29/134; Key Clb; Library Aide; Ski Clb; Varsity Clb; Stage Crew; Nwsp Stf; Lit Mag; Tennis; Hon Roll; Frnch Schlstc Awd 82; Ithaca Coll; Comm.

SWINEHART, SUSAN C; Homer Central HS; Cortland, NY; (Y); VP Trs French Clb; Hosp Aide; Capt Quiz Bowl; Var L Tennis; High Hon Roll; NHS; Ntl Merit SF; Val; Olympic Mind Tm Rnsslr Plytchnc Inst Mdlst 84; Mst Outstndng Stu Advncd Plcmnt Engl 84; Hghst Avg Hist Spnsh 83-84; Princeton; Elec Engr.

SWING, PATTI A; West Genesee SR HS; Camillus, NY; (Y); Art Clb; Church Yth Grp; Key Clb; Library Aide; Band; Color Guard; Flag Corp; Mrchg Band; Rep Jr Cls; High Hon Roll; Miss Govt Awd 83; CYO Sec 84; Bus Admin.

SWINGLE, CHRISTINE M; East HS; Rochester, NY; (Y); 10/280; Church Yth Grp; Math Tm; Red Cross Aide; Stage Crew; Yrbk Ed-Chief; Var Capt Crs Cntry; Var Trk; Hon Roll; NHS; Ithaca Coll, Rgnts Schlrshp 85-86; Ithaca Coll; Comm.

SWINTON, BONNIE; Ticonderoga HS; Hague, NY; (Y); FTA; Key Clb; Office Aide; Hon Roll; Cosmtlgy.

SWIRE, MARK R; Westmoreland HS; Rome, NY; (Y); 19/87; Boy Scts; English Clb; French Clb; FTA; Model UN; Political Wkr; Teachers Aide; Nwsp Ed-Chief; Nwsp Stf; Yrbk Ed-Chief; Rome Polish Home Schlrshp 85; Teachers Schlrshp 85; Questers Awd-Histrcl Soc 81; SUNY-BROCKPORT; Eductn.

SWIRE, ROSANNE; Chatham HS; Chatham, NY; (Y); 2/135; Quiz Bowl; Band; Chorus; Jazz Band; Mrchg Band; Orch; Pep Band; School Musical; Yrbk Ed-Chief; High Hon Roll; Outstndng Musician Schlrshp NY ST Music Camp 84; Music Educ.

SWIRIDUK, DANIEL; West Seneca East SR HS; Buffalo, NY; (Y); French Clb; Im JV Ftbl; Hon Roll; Jr NHS; NHS; Natl Germn Hnr Socty; Med.

SWISS, CARISSA; Huntington HS; Huntington, NY; (Y); DECA; Key Clb; Drill Tm; Orch; Lit Mag; Rep Frsh Cls; Rep Soph Cls; High Hon Roll; Trs Jr NHS; Trs NHS; Arch.

SWITALSKI, KEVIN C; Cleveland Hill HS; Cheektawaga, NY; (Y); 19/116; Jazz Band; Orch; School Musical; JCL; Latin Clb; Concert Band; Hon Roll; Buffalo Yth Orch Concerto Comptn Wnnr 85; Ithaca Coll Strng Comptn Wnnr 84.

SWITUSZAK, IRENE; St Johns Preparatory HS; Astoria, NY; (Y); Church Yth Grp; Rep Jr Cls; Rep Stu Cncl; Var Vllybl; High Hon Roll; Hon Roll; Prfct Atten Awd; Lit Mag; JV Score Keeper; Mercy Coll; Psych.

SWITZER, LINDA; West Seneca East SR HS; W Seneca, NY; (Y); DECA; GAA; Rep Frsh Cls; Rep Soph Cls; Trs Jr Cls; Sec Sr Cls; JV Bsktbl; JV Sftbl; Var Capt Tennis; Var Capt Vllybl; DECA 2nd Pl ST Comp Job Intrvw 85; Jayncee Awd Vlybl 84,Tennis 85; Spec Educ.

SWITZER, MARY; Bethlehem Central HS; Glenmont, NY; (Y); Church Yth Grp; GAA; Girl Scts; Hosp Aide; School Musical; Symp Band; Rep Stu Cncl; JV Capt Fld Hcky; Score Keeper; NHS; Mth.

SWITZER, MICHELE; Rome Free Acad; Rome, NY; (Y); Chorus; School Play; Yrbk Stf; JV Bowling; Hon Roll; Jr NHS; ST U Of NY Potsdam; Elem Ed.

SWOBODA, KERN; Plattsburgh SR HS; Plattsburgh, NY; (Y); 21/164; Am Leg Boys St; Model UN; Radio Clb; Concert Band; Mrchg Band; Var L Ice Hcky; Var L Socr; Hon Roll; Church Yth Grp; Cmnty Wkr; Yng Vol Actn Vol Mnth 84; Clarkson U; Chem Engnrng.

SYBERT, CHRISTOPHER; Victor Central HS; Victor, NY; (Y); 43/248; Model UN; Church Choir; School Musical; Var Crs Cntry; Var Trk; High Hon Roll; Hon Roll; Private Liberal Arts Schl; Bus.

SYDNEY, RICHARD; Victor Central HS; Victor, NY; (Y); Ski Clb; JV Bsktbl; Var Golf; High Hon Roll; Hon Roll; Busnss.

SYDOROWYCH, MARK; Jamesville-Dewitt HS; Dewitt, NY; (Y); Boy Scts; Exploring; School Play; Stage Crew; Yrbk Stf; Hon Roll; Ntl Merit Ltr; Sci Awd 83; Comp Awd 85; PAC Clb 83; Engrng.

SYKEN, BETHEL; Port Richmond HS; Staten Isld, NY; (Y); Art Clb; Ski Clb; Teachers Aide; Orch; Yrbk Stf; Pres Pres Frsh Cls; Pres Jr Cls; Hon Roll; Cert De Merite 84-85.

SYKES, ANGELA; Buffalo Traditional Schl; Buffalo, NY; (S); 14/115; Debate Tm; Pres Intnl Clb; Drill Tm; Yrbk Stf; VP Jr Cls; VP Sr Cls; Mgr Stat Bsktbl; Mgr Trk; Hon Roll; NHS; Accntnt.

SYKES, GLENN; Grand Island HS; Gr Island, NY; (Y); Boy Scts; JA; L Bsbl; JV Bsktbl; L Ftbl; Var Golf; Var Score Keeper; Im Vllybl; Vet Med.

SYKES, JANET Y; Arlington HS; Hopewell Junction, NY; (Y); 31/600; Cmnty Wkr; Debate Tm; Hosp Aide; Intnl Clb; Teachers Aide; Hon Roll; Clarkson U; Mgmt Eng.

SYKORA, KAREN; Earl L Vandermeulen HS; Miller Place, NY; (Y); 14/228; French Clb; Leo Clb; Spanish Clb; Concert Band; Cheerleading; High Hon Roll; NHS; Pep Clb; Band; SCMEA 83; 2nd Pl Suffolk County Wrtng Comptn 83; NYSSMA 83; Bus.

SYLKA, WENDY; Villa Maria Academy; Buffalo, NY; (S); 5/118; JCL; Rep Jr Cls; Gym; Swmmng; Hon Roll; NEDT Awd; Rochester Inst Of Tech; Aero En.

SYLOR, COLLEEN; Akron HS; Akron, NY; (Y); 4/159; French Clb; Nwsp Rptr; Nwsp Stf; Yrbk Stf; Fld Hcky; DAR Awd; High Hon Roll; Hon Roll; VP NHS; Wililams Coll Bk Awd 84; Fclty Assn Schlrshp 85; IBEW Schlrshp 85; SUNY Geneseo; Bio.

SYLVESTER, PATRICIA; Beacon HS; Beacon, NY; (Y); 11/206; Key Clb; Varsity Clb; Yrbk Stf; Sec Jr Cls; Var Sftbl; Var Vllybl; High Hon Roll; Hon Roll; Jr NHS; NHS; Engnr.

SYLVESTER, RAYE ANN; Cicero-North Syracuse HS; N Syracuse, NY; (Y); German Clb; Office Aide; Color Guard; Mrchg Band; Stat Bsktbl; Cert Outstndg Prfrmnce & Ded Bnd 83 & 84; Cert Merit Assmbly Of ST NY Colorgrd 85.

SYMONDS, MICHELLE; Troupsburg Central HS; Troupsburg, NY; (S); 1/14; Chorus; Yrbk Stf; Pres Soph Cls; Pres Jr Cls; Sec Stu Cncl; Var Cheerleading; Score Keeper; Var L Socr; Var L Trk; High Hon Roll; Giftd & Talntd Clb.

SYMONDS, TOBY; Spackenkill HS; Poughkeepsie, NY; (Y); 72/175; Am Leg Boys St; School Musical; VP Frsh Cls; VP Soph Cls; VP Jr Cls; VP Sr Cls; Trs Stu Cncl; Var Capt Socr; JV Trk; All Leag, Selct Tm Sccr 84-85; Trvl Tm Sccr 82-85; Duke; Bus.

SYMONDS, VIRGINIA; Sherburne-Earlville JR-SR HS; Sherburne, NY; (S); 8/130; Hosp Aide; Varsity Clb; Chorus; School Musical; Yrbk Bus Mgr; Yrbk Ed-Chief; Pres Frsh Cls; Pres Soph Cls; VP Jr Cls; VP Sr Cls; SUNY Geneseo; Spch Cmmnctns.

SYMULA, DEREK; Palmyrs-Macedon HS; Macedon, NY; (Y); 2/200; Tennis; Hon Roll; Trs NHS; Ntl Merit Ltr; Sal; Mc Louth Chev Awd Lang 85; Vet Med Awd 85; E R Parker Awd Alt 85; Cornell U; Bio.

SYP, THOMAS; Manlius-Pebble Hill HS; Syracuse, NY; (Y); Computer Clb; Var Capt Bsktbl; Var L Socr; Var L Tennis; NHS.

SYPOSS, RACHEL; Mount Saint Mary Acad; Sanborn, NY; (Y); 4-H; Chorus; High Hon Roll; Hon Roll; Jr NHS; Cobleskill; Anml Hsbndry.

SYSAK, IRENE; St George Acad; New York, NY; (Y); Art Clb; Drama Clb; School Musical; Nwsp Stf; Rep Frsh Cls; Hon Roll; NHS; Chorus; School Play; NYU; Nrs.

SZABLEWICZ, JENNIFER; Smithtown High School West; Smithtown, NY; (Y); Rep Frsh Cls; Rep Soph Cls; Rep Stu Cncl; Var Bsktbl; Var Tennis; Germ Hnr Soc 85-86; Bus.

SZABLEWSKI, BARBARA; St Marys HS; Depew, NY; (S); Letterman Clb; Science Clb; Varsity Clb; Stage Crew; Nwsp Rptr; Yrbk Stf; Var Bsktbl; Var Crs Cntry; Score Keeper; Var Trk; Mohawk Vly CC; Art.

SZABLEWSKI, JACQUELINE; St Marys HS; Depew, NY; (S); 1/196; Cmnty Wkr; Girl Scts; Pres Varsity Clb; Nwsp Ed-Chief; Ed Lit Mag; Trs Sr Cls; Capt Crs Cntry; Capt Trk; High Hon Roll; Hmcmng Qn 84-85; Niagara Frontier Police Athltc Assn Schlrshp 84-85; Ithaca Coll; Psych.

SZABO, CAROLINE J; St Francis Prep; Flushing, NY; (Y); 1/690; Hosp Aide; Nwsp Ed-Chief; Bausch & Lomb Sci Awd; Gov Hon Prg Awd; NHS; Ntl Merit Ltr; Val; Cmnty Wkr; Math Tm; Political Wkr; Amer Acad Of Achvt 85; Qns Coll Pres Awd Achvt 83-85; Schlrshp-U Of Miami 85; U Of Miami; Med.

SZABO, CHRISTIE L; South Side HS; S Hempstead, NY; (Y); 22/284; Church Yth Grp; VP Computer Clb; Exploring; Pres Science Clb; Pres Band; Jazz Band; School Musical; Nwsp Stf; Badmtn; JP Sousa Awd; Mst Vlble Plyr Bdmntn 85; Fortnghtly Clb Schlrshp 85; Coaches Awd Bdmntn 85; VA Tech; Comp Sci.

SZABO, GREGG; Columbus HS; New York, NY; (Y); 135/792; Office Aide; Teachers Aide; Cit Awd; Hon Roll; Prfct Atten Awd; Econ 85.

SZABO, SHELLEY; Duanesburg Central HS; Esperance, NY; (Y); Pres VP 4-H; Red Cross Aide; VICA; Band; Chorus; Yrbk Stf; JV Var Cheerleading; JV Socr; 4-H Awd; Prfct Atten Awd; Outstndng Stu Scholar Vo-Tech 84-85; Acctg.

SZAKALY, SANDRA; Mt St Joseph Acad; Amherst, NY; (S); Drama Clb; Ski Clb; Chorus; Lit Mag; Rep Frsh Cls; Var L Badmtn; Var L Bowling; Var L Sftbl; Hon Roll; NHS; Acadmc All Am 85; Bwlng Tm High Scr 84; SUNY Buffalo; Engrng.

SZALACH, SARAH L; Immaculate Heart Centra HS; Watertown, NY; (Y); Pres French Clb; Pres Intnl Clb; Ski Clb; Mrchg Band; Trs Frsh Cls; Trs Sr Cls; Rep Stu Cncl; Mgr(s); Tennis; Hon Roll; Hamilton Coll.

SZANTOR, KIRSTEN; Wilson Central HS; Wilson, NY; (Y); Church Yth Grp; Computer Clb; Model UN; Band; Church Choir; School Musical; Yrbk Stf; Stu Cncl; Hon Roll; Perf Attndnc Awd 82-83; All Cnty Band 83; Proj ADEPT For Tlntd Awd 84; Elem Ed.

SZARKA, MELISSA; Massena Central HS; Massena, NY; (Y); Church Yth Grp; Office Aide; Political Wkr; Stu Cncl; Hon Roll; Psych.

SZATANEK, JEFFERY; Liverpool HS; Liverpool, NY; (S); 20/800; Art Clb; Exploring; Trs Stu Cncl; Bsbl; Var Capt Golf; High Hon Roll; Jr NHS; Trs NHS; Ntl Merit Ltr; Drama Clb; 2nd Pl Frnch Upper Lvl Interprtv Reading 83; Air Force Rotc Schlrshp Fnlst 85; Navy ROTC Schlrshp 85; Cornell; Arch.

SZATANEK, MICHELLE; Liverpool HS; Liverpool, NY; (S); 139/797; FBLA; JA; Office Aide; Spanish Clb; School Musical; Nwsp Rptr; Rep Stu Cncl; Jr NHS; NHS; Rutgers Coll; Comm.

SZCZECH, LYNDA ANNE MARIE; Vestial SR HS; Binghamton, NY; (Y); 12/450; Hosp Aide; Mathletes; Science Clb; Band; Church Choir; Mrchg Band; Pep Band; High Hon Roll; NHS; Ntl Merit Ltr; Natl Yth Ldrshp Cncl Awd 84; Penn ST; Surgn.

SZCZESNIAK, KATHY; Sweet Home SR HS; Amherst, NY; (Y); GAA; Var Trk; French Hon Soc; High Hon Roll; Bus Mgmt.

SZCZUR, DARIA; Charles E Gorton HS; Yonkers, NY; (Y); Church Yth Grp; Cmnty Wkr; Dance Clb; Spanish Clb; High Hon Roll; Hon Roll; Pre-Law.

SZCZYGIELSKI, ANNE; Villa Maria Acad; Buffalo, NY; (Y); Computer Clb; Gym; Data Proc.

SZEFLINSKI, STACEY; Richfield Spring Central HS; Richfield Spgs, NY; (Y); GAA; Band; Rep Stu Cncl; Var Capt Bsktbl; Var Capt Sftbl; High Hon Roll; Jr NHS; NHS; Center ST Conf 1st Tm All Str Bsktbl & 2nd Tm All Str Sftbl; Sprts Med.

SZEMATOWICZ, CAMILLE; Hamburg SR HS; Hamburg, NY; (Y); 3/397; AFS; Trs NFL; Madrigals; Symp Band; Yrbk Stf; Rep Jr Cls; Mgr(s); High Hon Roll; Jr NHS; Ntl Merit Ltr; Crmnl Jstc.

SZEPATOWSKI, DAVID; Linton HS; Schenectady, NY; (Y); 6/254; Pres Drama Clb; Speech Tm; Thesps; Acpl Chr; Chorus; Madrigals; Mrchg Band; School Musical; School Play; Sr Cls; Hispanic Soc Awd 84; Chr Awd 85; Cert Merit Frnch 88; Hofstra U; Theatre.

SZETO, MICKEY; Brooklyn Technical HS; Brooklyn, NY; (Y); Hon Roll; Polytech Inst Of NY; Engrng.

SZUCH, JON; Clerkstown North HS; W Nyack, NY; (Y); Boy Scts; Spanish Clb; Band; Jazz Band; Mrchg Band; Orch; Symp Band; JV Trk; Hon Roll; Hnr Roll 82-84; Band Cert Awd 83-84; Phys Fit Awd 83-84; Boston U; Pol Sci.

SZUCS, MONIKA; St Johns Prep; Astoria, NY; (Y); Hosp Aide; Office Aide; Chorus; Yrbk Stf; Stu Cncl; VP Tennis; High Hon Roll; Hon Roll; NHS; Prfct Atten Awd; Stonybrook U; Nrsng.

SZUKALA, SHARON; Fredonia HS; Fredonia, NY; (Y); Church Yth Grp; French Clb; Key Clb; Science Clb; Var Tennis; Med.

SZUL, OREST; St George Acad; New York, NY; (Y); 2/36; Boy Scts; Camera Clb; Church Yth Grp; Cmnty Wkr; Ski Clb; Church Choir; Yrbk Stf; Var Capt Bsktbl; Var Socr; Var Capt Vllybl; Comptrllrs Awd-Athltc Awd 85; NY St Regents Schlrshp 84-85; Ntl H S Awd For Excllnc 85; Polytechnic Inst Of NY; Engrng.

SZULGIT, DAVID; Pittsford Mendon HS; Pittsford, NY; (Y); Exploring; Nwsp Stf; Yrbk Stf; French Hon Soc; High Hon Roll; Pre-Med.

SZUMILOSKI, JOHN; Webster HS; Webster, NY; (Y); 4/530; Rep Soph Cls; Rep Jr Cls; Stu Cncl; Var L Bsktbl; Var L Socr; High Hon Roll; NHS; Ntl Merit SF; Chess Clb; Church Yth Grp; Amer Invntnl Math Exam 84 & 85; Nat Sci.

SZUSTAK, SCOTT L; Wilson Central HS; Ransomville, NY; (Y); 47/134; Ski Clb; Pres Soph Cls; Im Bsktbl; Var Capt Trk; Stat Vllybl; High Hon Roll; Hon Roll; NY ST Regents Schlrshp 85; U Of OH Dayton; Mech Engrng.

SZWED, TAMMY A; Villa Maria Acad; W Seneca, NY; (Y); Computer Clb; French Clb; Math Clb; Red Cross Aide; Yrbk Stf; Hon Roll; NHS; NEDT Merit Awd 81-82; Niagara U Pres & Acad Schlrshps 84-85; Niagara U; Intl Bus.

SZYCH, CHRISTINE M; Our Lady Of Mercy HS; Penfield, NY; (Y); 3/200; NFL; Spanish Clb; Variety Show; Yrbk Stf; JV Socr; High Hon Roll; NHS; Howard Hanson Piano Awd 85; NY ST Forensics League 82; Chem Hnrs Awd 84; Cornell U; Pre-Med.

SZYMANSKI, BRIAN P; St Anthonys HS; Nesconset, NY; (Y); Church Yth Grp; Church Choir; Rep Soph Cls; Im Bsktbl; Var L Golf; Im Sftbl; Hon Roll; Jr NHS; NHS; Spanish NHS; NY ST Rgnts Schlrshp 85; Coll Of Wm & Mary; Acctng.

SZYMANSKI, SHERYL A; Kenmore West SR HS; Kenmore, NY; (Y); 44/445; Math Tm; Orch; Var Swmmng; High Hon Roll; Hon Roll; NHS; Hnr Clb 84-85; Allegheny Coll; Bio.

SZYMKO, SHELLEY; Whitesboro Central SR HS; Marcy, NY; (Y); Pres VP 4-H; GAA; Chorus; Orch; Yrbk Stf; Var Cheerleading; JV Score Keeper; Var Socr; High Hon Roll; NHS; NY Acad Of Sci Sci Rsrch Trng Pgm Intrn 85; Schl Ltr W Athltc 85; Socr Pin 85; Biol.

TA LAMO, PHILIP; Fordham Preparatory Schl; Yonkers, NY; (Y); Nwsp Sprt Ed; JV Bsbl; JV Var Ftbl; Im Sftbl; Im Wt Lftg; Hon Roll; Awds Excllnc In Math I, Ltn I, Bio & Rlgn I 82-83; Awd For Gen Excllnc & Schlrshp 83-84.

TA VAREZ, JOSE; Bronx High School Of Science; New York, NY; (S); Church Yth Grp; Cmnty Wkr; Spanish Clb; Varsity Clb; Band; Capt Bsktbl; U Of PA; Pre-Law.

TABACCO, ANNE; Commack H S North; E Northport, NY; (Y); Art Clb; Cmnty Wkr; 4-H; Office Aide; Stage Crew; Nwsp Stf; Yrbk Stf; Lit Mag; High Hon Roll; NHS; Disply Wrk In Dist Art Festvl 85; Chld Psych.

TABAK, PAUL; Emerson Voc HS; Buffalo, NY; (Y); Church Yth Grp; Yrbk Stf; Var Bsbl; Var Socr; High Hon Roll.

TABB, JACOB; Edward R Murrow HS; Brooklyn, NY; (Y); 76/725; Spanish Clb; Band; School Play; Rep Jr Cls; Im Trk; Hon Roll; Val; Rep Soph Cls; Irvng Flaumenbaummem Schlrshp 85; Regents Schlrshp 85; St U NY; Engrng.

TABER, CATHY A; Argyle Central Schl; Argyle, NY; (Y); Art Clb; 4-H; French Clb; GAA; Yrbk Stf; Var Bsktbl; Var Fld Hcky; Var Sftbl; Var Vllybl; Hon Roll; Art.

TABER, GINNY; Guilderland HS; Altamont, NY; (Y); Cmnty Wkr; Cit Awd; High Hon Roll; Hon Roll; Awd Achvt Soc Studies,Math Eng 83-85; Tchr.

TABERSKI, ANN; Tha Mary Louis Acad; Flushing, NY; (Y); Drama Clb; Teachers Aide; Orch; School Musical; Variety Show; Nwsp Rptr; Nwsp Stf; Hon Roll; Bio.

TABOR, RACHEL S; Greenport HS; Orient, NY; (Y); 7/56; 4-H; Spanish Clb; School Musical; Nwsp Rptr; VP Jr Cls; Var Capt Cheerleading; JV Var Fld Hcky; NHS; Robin Clark Mem Awd 4-H 82; Grt Greenport Lit Cntst 1st 83; SUNY Albany; Law.

TABORA, KATHY; Colonie Central HS; Albany, NY; (Y); Church Yth Grp; Drama Clb; FBLA; Intnl Clb; School Musical; Score Keeper; Socr; High Hon Roll; Hon Roll; NHS; Sienna Coll; Frgn Lang.

TACKABURY, ROBERT L; Sherburne-Earlville HS; Poolville, NY; (Y); 36/141; Am Leg Boys St; FBLA; Ski Clb; Spanish Clb; Sec Sr Cls; Capt Bowling; Cit Awd; Prfct Atten Awd; Utica Coll; Bus Admin.

TACKE, SONJA; Commack High School South; Commack, NY; (Y); Teachers Aide; School Musical; Yrbk Stf; JV Tennis; High Hon Roll; Hon Roll; Noble Awd Spnsh 84.

TACKENTIEN, LORI ANN; Cattaraugus Central HS; Cattaraugus, NY; (Y); 10/55; Cmnty Wkr; Pep Clb; Chorus; Pres Frsh Cls; Pres Sr Cls; VP Stu Cncl; Var Capt Bsktbl; Coach Actv; Var Socr; Var Sftbl; Scer MVP Cnty, Tm, All Star 85; Bsktbl All Star 85; Vllybl & Sftbl MVP Tm & All Star 85; SR Athlt 85; SUNY At Cortland; Phy Ed.

TACY, DALE; Franklin Acad; Borke, NY; (S); 5/253; Pres 4-H; French Clb; Intnl Clb; Model UN; Ski Clb; Concert Band; Dnfth Awd; 4-H Awd; Hon Roll; Clarkson U; Elctrcl Engrng.

TADDEO, ANNALISA; Sachem North HS; Farmingville, NY; (Y); Church Yth Grp; Drama Clb; French Clb; Hosp Aide; Orch; School Play; Yrbk Stf; Hon Roll; Blue Ribbn Metab NYSSMA 84; Molloy; Nrsng.

TADDONI, VINCENT S; Monsignor Farrell HS; Staten Island, NY; (Y); Computer Clb; French Clb; JA; Science Clb; Nwsp Rptr; VP Jr Cls; Wt Lftg; High Hon Roll; Prfct Atten Awd; Pres Schlr; Am U Pres Schlrshp 85; Fordham U Deans Schlrshp 85fNY St Regents Schlrshp 85; NY U; Pre Law.

TADROS, MONA; St Peters For Girls; Staten Island, NY; (Y); Church Yth Grp; FNA; Regents Dip 85; Med.

TADT, NANCY L; Fredonia HS; Fredonia, NY; (Y); 39/186; Church Yth Grp; FTA; Key Clb; ROTC; Pres Science Clb; Band; Chorus; School Musical; Symp Band; Lit Mag; Beaver Clb Schlrshp 85; PTSA Stu Rep 84-85; GPA Excllnc Pres Awd 85; Fredonia ST; Elem Ed.

TAFFURI, CHRISTINE N; West Islip HS; W Islip, NY; (Y); Chorus; Yrbk Stf; Mgr(s); Stat Swmmng; High Hon Roll; Hon Roll; Jr NHS; Bio Achvt 83; Bus Dynmcs Excllnc 83; Bus Mgmt.

TAFT, JEFFREY; J C Birdlebough HS; Fulton, NY; (Y); 7/191; VP Band; Concert Band; Mrchg Band; Yrbk Stf; VP Stu Cncl; Var L Bsbl; Var JV Bsktbl; High Hon Roll; NHS; Prfct Atten Awd; Clarkson; Chem Engr.

TAFT, SHERRY; Churchville-Chili HS; Churchville, NY; (Y); Church Yth Grp; Cmnty Wkr; FTA; Library Aide; Chorus; Church Choir; Trk; Hon Roll; Cert Walk A Thon 84; Natl Piano Plyng Evaltns Cert 84; Socl Wrk.

TAFURI, LENA; Oceanside HS; Oceanside, NY; (S); VP DECA; Chorus; Cheerleading; Sftbl; Trk; Citation Of Mrt 84; On Jerry Lewis Telephon For Raising Mst Money For MDA 85; Nassua; Fshn Merch.

TAGGARD, MATTHEW A; Highland HS; Highland, NY; (Y); Band; Church Choir; High Hon Roll; Hon Roll; NHS; Spn Hnr Soc 85; JHS 80-82; Engrng.

TAGGART, KEVIN J; St Anthonys HS; E Northport, NY; (Y); Church Yth Grp; Varsity Clb; Chorus; Nwsp Sprt Ed; JV Crs Cntry; Var Trk; NHS; Spanish NHS; Bus & Fin.

TAGLIAFERRI, ELIZABETH; Longwood HS; Coram, NY; (Y); Girl Scts; Pep Clb; Drill Tm; Yrbk Stf; JV Cheerleading; Var Pom Pon; Hon Roll; Stony Brook U; Bus.

TAGLIARINI, FELIX; F D R HS; Brooklyn, NY; (Y); Ski Clb; Hon Roll; Prfct Atten Awd; Culinary Arts.

TAGLIONE, MARTINA T; Roy C Ketcham HS; Poughkeepsie, NY; (Y); Stu Cncl; Var Crs Cntry; Var Swmmng; Var Trk; JV Vllybl; High Hon Roll; Jr NHS; NHS.

TAGLIONE, MICHAEL A; Stillwater Central HS; Stillwater, NY; (Y); 3/86; Drama Clb; French Clb; Key Clb; Math Clb; Ski Clb; School Play; Stage Crew; Trs Jr Cls; Pres Sr Cls; High Hon Roll.

TAGLIONI, SYLVIA; MonroeWOODBURY Senior HS; Monroe, NY; (Y); 10/385; Cmnty Wkr; Computer Clb; Drama Clb; Intnl Clb; Political Wkr; Sec Orch; School Musical; Variety Show; High Hon Roll; NHS; Awd Ntl Schl Chestra Assoc 85; Soc Studs Hnrs 83-84; Schlrshp Monroe Woodbury Teachrs Assoc 85; Wentwoth Inst Tech; Mfg Engrng.

TAI, ATHENA; Yestal SR HS; Binghamton, NY; (Y); French Clb; Hosp Aide; Sec Orch; School Play; Rep Frsh Cls; Trs Soph Cls; Trs Stu Cncl; High Hon Roll; NHS; Drama Clb; Intl Frgn Lang Awds 84; Acad All Amer Awd 84; Yth Ldrshp Salute 85; Pre-Med.

TAI, SIU LAN; James Madison HS; Brooklyn, NY; (Y); 19/812; Var Diving; Co-Capt Gym; Capt Swmmng; Var Vllybl; Hon Roll; UFT Schlrshp Fund 85; Athlt Yr 85; Schlr Athlt Gymnstcs 84 & 85; MVP Swmmng 85; NY U.

TAIT, HEATHER; Walton HS; Bronx, NY; (Y); Office Aide; Teachers Aide; Nwsp Rptr; Socr; Prfct Atten Awd; Bus Mgmt.

TAKAC, KRISTEN; Orchard Park HS; Buffalo, NY; (S); 79/400; DECA; French Clb; Hon Roll; St Schlr; Restrnt Marktng & Mgmt Wnnr-Local & ST Lvl 84-85; Restrnt Marktng & Mgmt-Natl 2nd Pl 84-85; U Of Buffalo; Busnss Admin.

TAKACH, MONICA; Maryvale SR HS; Chktg, NY; (S); DECA; French Clb; JA; Spanish Clb; Varsity Clb; Rep Frsh Cls; Rep Soph Cls; Rep Jr Cls; Off Sr Cls; Var L Cheerleading; Buffalo ST Coll; Pol Sci.

TAKATS, PAUL; Centereach HS; Centereach, NY; (Y); 7/480; Cmnty Wkr; JV Socr; Hon Roll; Jr NHS; Prfct Atten Awd; Regents Schlrshp Awd 85-89; SUNY-STONY Brook; Bio Sci.

TALAMO, PHILIP; Fordham Prep; Yonkers, NY; (Y); Nwsp Sprt Ed; JV Bsbl; Var Ftbl; Im Sftbl; Im Wt Lftg; High Hon Roll.

TALAMO, TERESA; Lafayette HS; Brooklyn, NY; (Y); Church Yth Grp; Office Aide; Teachers Aide; Stage Crew; Nwsp Rptr; Nwsp Stf; Yrbk Stf; Rep Jr Cls; Bowling; NHS; Bus Adm.

TALARICO, LISA; Middletown HS; Middletown, NY; (Y); Church Yth Grp; Key Clb; High Hon Roll; Hon Roll; Comm.

TALARICO, RE GINA; Bishop Scully HS; Broadalbin, NY; (Y); 17/69; Drama Clb; Library Aide; Spanish Clb; Color Guard; Bsktbl; Mgr(s); Score Keeper; Socr; High Hon Roll; Hon Roll; St John Fisher; Bio.

TALDONE, LYNDA; Cardinal Spellman HS; New York, NY; (Y); 1st Hnrs NEDT Awd 82-85; Bus.

TALHAM, DARREN; Fayetteville Manlius HS; Fayetteville, NY; (Y); VP Debate Tm; Speech Tm; L Var Socr; Hon Roll; Debate Comptn Trophy 84; Artificl Intelligence.

TALLARINI, THOMAS; New Rochelle HS; New Rochelle, NY; (Y); Capt Math Tm; Model UN; Band; Jazz Band; Mrchg Band; Pep Band; Symp Band; Hon Roll; NHS; George Washington U Schl Engnrng & Appld Sci 85; Columbia U Bk Awd 85.

TALLCHIEF, PATRICIA A; Salamanca Central HS; Salamanca, NY; (Y); DECA; Yrbk Phtg; Yrbk Rptr; Yrbk Stf; Hon Roll; Dstngshd Achvt Awd, Outstndng Attitude, Efrt, Achvt Awd, Seneca Yuth Dncrs 85; Seneca Yuth Cncl 84-85; Alfred ST Coll; Data Proc.

TALLIE, PATRINA C; Newburgh Free Acad; Newburgh, NY; (Y); Pres Church Yth Grp; Civic Clb; Cmnty Wkr; Debate Tm; Political Wkr; Teachers Aide; Band; Church Choir; Mrchg Band; School Play; Ntl Achvt Schlrshp Prog 84; Bio.

TALLMAN, MICHAEL L; Ithaca HS; Ithaca, NY; (Y); Rep Stu Cncl; Var Capt Bsbl; Var Ftbl; Var Ice Hcky; Hon Roll; 1st Tm All STAC Conf Bsebl 85; 1st Tm All STAC Conf Glf 84; 1st Tm All CNYSHSL Hcky 85; Bus Mgmt.

TALTY, MEG; Mt Mercy Acad; Buffalo, NY; (Y); 3/200; Church Yth Grp; Cmnty Wkr; Computer Clb; 4-H; French Clb; Math Clb; Office Aide; Quiz Bowl; Teachers Aide; Rep Soph Cls; Western NY Sci Lang Fair Bronze Awd 82-85; Concours Ntl De Francais Awd 83; CPA.

TALVI, NANCY; Thomas A Edison HS; Elmira, NY; (Y); Church Yth Grp; Drama Clb; Pep Clb; Spanish Clb; Chorus; Church Choir; School Musical; School Play; High Hon Roll; Hon Roll; All ST Chrs NY Soloist 84; Area All ST 82 & 83; Eng.

TAM, TUNG LOK; Bay Shore HS; Bay Shore, NY; (Y); Computer Clb; Intnl Clb; Varsity Clb; Bowling; Trk; Pres Schlr; Pres Acad Ftnss Awd 85; Pace U; Bus.

TAMASI, KATHERINE A; Linton HS; Schenectady, NY; (Y); 11/300; Drama Clb; Hosp Aide; Pres Key Clb; Stage Crew; Ed Yrbk Stf; Hon Roll; NHS; Regents Schlrshp 85; Siena Coll; Pre-Med.

TAMBACAS, ELAINE; Williamsville East HS; Williamsville, NY; (Y); Cmnty Wkr; Drama Clb; French Clb; GAA; Latin Clb; Pep Clb; Ski Clb; Yrbk Stf; Fld Hcky; Powder Puff Ftbl; Regents Schlrshp 85; Magna Cum Laude 84; Outstndg Svc Awds Latin Club 83-85; Med.

TAMBE, KATHY; Oakfield-Alabama Central HS; Oakfield, NY; (Y); Trs Band; Chorus; Concert Band; Drm Mjr(t); School Musical; Swing Chorus; JV Cheerleading; JV Socr; Stat Trk; Hon Roll; Music Therapy.

TAMBINAYAGAM, JACQUELINE; Nottingham HS; Syracuse, NY; (Y); 89/220; Drama Clb; Exploring; French Clb; JA; Latin Clb; Spanish Clb; Band; Concert Band; Pep Band; Stage Crew; Merit Roll; SUNY Oswego.

TAMBURELLO, ROSALIE; East Meadow HS; East Meadow, NY; (Y); Office Aide; Teachers Aide; Chorus; Church Choir; School Play; Stage Crew; Variety Show; Yrbk Stf; JV Var Crs Cntry; Var JV Trk; Pride Yankees Awd; Intl Bus.

TAMBURO, JOSEPH M; Elmont Memorial HS; Elmont, NY; (Y); 7/247; Mrchg Band; School Musical; Variety Show; Yrbk Sprt Ed; Im JV Socr; NHS; Ntl Merit Ltr; Regents Schlrshp 85; Brown U Bk Awd 84; All League NCSCA Soccer Tm 83 & 84; Hofstra U; Bus.

TAMBURRI JR, ROBERT; Lynbrook HS; Lynbrook, NY; (Y); Exploring; FBLA; Spanish Clb; Lit Mag; NHS; Finance.

TAMBURRINO, FRANK; Msgr Mc Clancy HS; Astoria, NY; (Y); Church Yth Grp; High Hon Roll; Hon Roll; 3rd Sci Fair; Catechist Cert; Accntng.

TAMER, THOMAS; Saranac Central HS; Cadyville, NY; (Y); Model UN; Rep Frsh Cls; Rep Stu Cncl; JV Bsktbl; Capt Var Ftbl; Pltsbrgh ST U; State Trpr.

TAMILIA, LISA; Liverpool HS; Liverpool, NY; (S); Cmnty Wkr; Hosp Aide; School Musical; School Play; Hon Roll; Lemoyne U.

TAMUCCI, GAYLE DYANN; Resurrection Acad; Rye Brook, NY; (Y); Church Yth Grp; Dance Clb; Drama Clb; Hosp Aide; Acpl Chr; Chorus; School Musical; JV Bsktbl; JV Vllybl; Hon Roll; Hannon Memrl Schlrshp Awd 82-84; Bus.

TAN, REMI Y; The Fox Lane HS; Bedford Hills, NY; (Y); 7/300; Am Leg Boys St; Trs Science Clb; Concert Band; Jazz Band; Mrchg Band; Stu Cncl; JV Crs Cntry; High Hon Roll; NHS; Ntl Merit Ltr; NY All ST Band 83-84; Westchester Cty Band 84-85; U Of CA Berkeley; Arch.

TAN, SELENA P; John Adams HS; Jamaica, NY; (Y); 21/591; Latin Clb; CAP; Swmmng; Vllybl; Hon Roll; NHS; Prfct Atten Awd; NYS Regnts Schlrshp 85; All Amer Schlrs Awd 85; Wiliams Coll; Frgn Lang.

TANCINCO, MARY J; Richmond Hill HS; Richmond Hl, NY; (Y); 7/350; English Clb; Math Clb; Office Aide; Spanish Clb; Chorus; Hon Roll; NHS; Prfct Atten Awd; Schlstc Achvt 83-84; Aeronautics.

TANG, CHIN C; The Bronx High Schl Of Science; Jamaica Ests, NY; (Y); Boy Scts; Office Aide; Orch; Ntl Merit Ltr; Asian Cultrl Soc VP, Bd Dir; Med.

TANG, JENNIFER; New Utrecht HS; Brooklyn, NY; (Y); Chorus; Nwsp Rptr; Lit Mag; Hon Roll; Engl.

TANG, WINGSUN; Newtown HS; New York, NY; (Y); 96/686; Church Yth Grp; Computer Clb; Orch; Hon Roll; Regnts & Polytech Inst Schlrshps 85; Polytech Inst NY; Elec Engr.

TANGEN, MICHELLE; Sperry HS; Henrietta, NY; (Y); Pres French Clb; Ski Clb; Soph Cls; Rep Stu Cncl; Socr; French Hon Soc; Hon Roll; Sec NHS; Rochester Inst Tech; Bio.

TANGER, MELISA A; Lockport SR HS; Lockport, NY; (Y); 1/455; Pres AFS; Var L Bowling; Swmmng; High Hon Roll; NHS; Val; Drama Clb; Intnl Clb; Latin Clb; Spanish Clb; Robert C Pringle Engrng Schlrshp 85; NY ST Regents Schlrshp 85; Rochester Inst Techngly; Comp.

TANGORRA, JENNIFER; Frankfort-Schuyler HS; Frankfort, NY; (S); GAA; Spanish Clb; Teachers Aide; Frsh Cls; Stu Cncl; Cheerleading; Vllybl; High Hon Roll; Hon Roll; NHS; Babysitting 82; Playgrnd Atten 84; Mohawk Valley CC; Bus.

TANINSKI, DIANE; Eastern District HS; Brooklyn, NY; (Y); FHA; Girl Scts; Hon Roll; Elizabeth K Levy Awd Hmmkng 83.

TANKSLEY, BETH; Shenendehowa HS; Ballston Lk, NY; (Y); Church Yth Grp; Girl Scts; High Hon Roll; Jr NHS; Prfct Atten Awd.

TANNAR, AUDREY; Glen Ridge HS; Warwick, NY; (Y); 63/200; Aud/Vis; Church Yth Grp; JA; Chorus; Church Choir; Swing Chorus; Var Cheerleading; Var Trk; Hlth/Sci Awd 85; North Park; Comm.

TANNEHILL, CAROL; St John The Baptist HS; Deer Pk, NY; (Y); 89/630; Church Yth Grp; Cmnty Wkr; Debate Tm; Hosp Aide; Model UN; Ed Nwsp Stf; Yrbk Stf; JV Vllybl; Oneata; Chld Psych.

TANNENBAUM, BILL; Sacred Heart HS; Yonkers, NY; (S); 12/220; School Musical; Co-Capt Bowling; Var Trk; High Hon Roll; Hon Roll; NHS; Engr.

TANNENBAUM, JAY; Ossining HS; Ossining, NY; (Y); Am Leg Boys St; Model UN; Ski Clb; Concert Band; Jazz Band; Mrchg Band; School Musical; School Play; Nwsp Ed-Chief; Trs Jr Cls; Northwestern U; Film Dir.

TANNER, AMY; Hudson HS; Hudson, NY; (Y); 24/165; Ski Clb; Chorus; Yrbk Stf; Trs Soph Cls; Rep Jr Cls; Stu Cncl; Var JV Cheerleading; Swmmng; Pres Sr Cls; Jrnlsm.

TANNER, DIANE; Madison Central HS; Madison, NY; (S); 6/38; Church Yth Grp; French Clb; Teachers Aide; Varsity Clb; VP Band; Chorus; Church Choir; Mrchg Band; School Musical; Swing Chorus; Regents Schlrshp 85; ST U-Geneseo; Elem Educ.

TANNER, JEANNIE; West Hempstead HS; Island Pk, NY; (Y); Var Badmtn; Astrnmy Awd 85.

TANNER, JULIE; Berlin Central HS; Petesburg, NY; (S); 8/106; GAA; Ski Clb; Chorus; School Musical; Var Cheerleading; Var Socr; Hon Roll; U S Chrldr Achvt Awd 85.

TANNER, KATHLEEN; St Francis Prep; Bayside, NY; (Y); 6/723; Church Yth Grp; Hosp Aide; Variety Show; Var Capt Cheerleading; Var Sftbl; Gov Hon Prg Awd; High Hon Roll; NHS; Ntl Merit Schol; Pres Schlr; St Johns U Compt Schlrshp 85; NY U Trustee Schlrshp 85; Notre Dame Schlr 85; Manhattan Coll; Engr.

TANNIN, BETTY Y; Horace Greeley HS; Chappaqua, NY; (Y); 24/272; French Clb; Hosp Aide; Pres Temple Yth Grp; Drm Mjr(t); Mrchg Band; Orch; Pep Band; Rep Stu Cncl; Dance Clb; NHS; Benjamin Rabinovitch Schlrshp Israel Study 84; NY ST Regents Schlrshp 85; U Of PA; Health Sci.

TANON, ROBERT; St Francis Preparatory HS; Flushing, NY; (Y); 316/693; Church Yth Grp; Hosp Aide; JA; Political Wkr; Nwsp Ed-Chief; VFW Awd; NY U; Cmmnctns.

TANSEY, DEBBIE; Central Islip HS; Central Islip, NY; (Y); Mrchg Band; L Pom Pon; JV Capt Sftbl; Chorus; School Musical; Hon Roll; Katherine Gibbs; Exec Sec.

TANZ, STEVEN M; Ramaz Schl; New York City, NY; (Y); School Musical; Yrbk Stf; Lit Mag; Stat Bsktbl; Var Ftbl; JV Mgr(s); Var JV Score Keeper; Var Sftbl; Spanish NHS; St Schlr; NY U.

TANZA, GINA MARIE; Smithtown HS West; Smithtown, NY; (Y); Church Yth Grp; Office Aide; Spanish Clb; Band; Concert Band; Jazz Band; Mrchg Band; Symp Band; Yrbk Stf; Capt Pom Pon; SUNY Stonybrook.

TANZI, JOHN A; Kings Park HS; Kings Park, NY; (Y); 55/400; Am Leg Boys St; Science Clb; Service Clb; L Var Lcrss; High Hon Roll; NHS; Church Yth Grp; Computer Clb; Var Socr; Hon Roll; 2 Schl Svc & Chrctr Awds 85; All Leag La Crss Plyr 85; Rensselaer Poly Inst; Arch.

TAORMINA, SCOTT; Walter Panas HS; Peekskill, NY; (Y); Boys Clb Am; Computer Clb; Band; JV Bsbl; Var Ftbl; Comp Sci.

TAP, SUSAN; St Francis Prep; Douglaston, NY; (S); 133/690; Hosp Aide; Chorus; Tennis; Hon Roll; NHS; U Of Albany; Bus Mgmt.

TAPIA, JOHN A; Cardinal Spellman HS; Bronx, NY; (Y); Pres Church Yth Grp; Computer Clb; Dance Clb; Latin Clb; Church Choir; Lit Mag; Im Bsktbl; Hon Roll; NYS Regnts Schlrshp 85; S Methodist U; Minstry.

TAPLEY, MARGARET E; St Edmund HS; Brooklyn, NY; (Y); Hosp Aide; Kingsborough Coll; Nrsng.

TAPLIN JR, WAYNE; Pulaski JR SR HS; Richland, NY; (Y); Varsity Clb; VP Frsh Cls; VP Soph Cls; Pres Jr Cls; Stu Cncl; Var Bsbl; Bsktbl; Capt Var Ftbl; Wt Lftg; Cit Awd; Snow Incntv Awds-2 82-84; Bsbl-1st Tm All Lge 84; Ftbl-Hnrb Mntn 85; Phy Ed.

TARAGIN, BRUCE K; Yeshiva Univ High Schl For Boys; Monsey, NY; (Y); 35/106; Tennis; Hon Roll; St Schlr.

TARALLO, BETHANY A; Schalmont HS; Schenectady, NY; (Y); 12/130; French Clb; Concert Band; Mrchg Band; Yrbk Stf; Rep Soph Cls; Score Keeper; Hon Roll; NHS.

TARANTINO, LISA; St Marys Acad; S Glens Falls, NY; (S); 5/45; Drama Clb; School Musical; Var Cheerleading; L Sftbl; Hon Roll; Art Clb; Cmnty Wkr; French Clb; Pep Clb; Psychology.

TARANTINO, LYNDA; Canisteo Central HS; Canisteo, NY; (Y); 4/65; Am Leg Aux Girls St; Ski Clb; Band; Yrbk Ed-Chief; VP Jr Cls; Pres Stu Cncl; JV Golf; Var JV Socr; High Hon Roll; NHS; DAR Hstry Essay 80; Mgmt.

TARANTO, JOSEPH; South New Berlin Central HS; S New Berlin, NY; (Y); 3/30; Pres Church Yth Grp; Pres Frsh Cls; High Hon Roll; Jr NHS; Lion Awd; NHS; Rotary Yth Ldrshp Awd 85; West Point; Pilot.

TARASCO, SUSAN; Clarkstown North HS; New City, NY; (Y); Church Yth Grp; Band; JV Var Twrlr; Clarkstown Smmr Theatr Fstvl 83-85; Dntstry.

TARASOFF, SANDRA; Clarkstown H S North; Congers, NY; (Y); Pep Clb; Rep Frsh Cls; JV Vllybl; High Hon Roll; Hon Roll; Jr NHS; Mu Alp Tht; West Point; Law.

TARASOFF, SUSAN; Clarkstown H S North; Congers, NY; (Y); 52/480; Church Yth Grp; Drama Clb; Math Tm; Spanish Clb; Nwsp Bus Mgr; DAR Awd; High Hon Roll; Mu Alp Tht; TX Tech U; Brdcst Commctns.

TARASZEWSKI JR, STANLEY; Union-Endicott HS; Endicott, NY; (Y); 22/500; Key Clb; VP Stu Cncl; JV Bsbl; JV Bsktbl; High Hon Roll; Jr NHS; Prfct Atten Awd; Hon Roll; NHS; Ntl Cncl Yth Ldrshp 85; Marine Bio Pgm 85; 1st,2nd,3rd Pl Awds Karate 83-85; USMA; Bio.

TARBY, JANNI; Auburn HS; Auburn, NY; (Y); 7/444; Sec Soph Cls; High Hon Roll; NHS; Ntl Merit Ltr; Pres Schlr; Regents Schlrshp 85; Outstndng Comp Sci Awd 85; Cayuga CC; Fnncl Plnng.

TARBY, JENNIFER A; Notre Dame HS; Elmira, NY; (Y); 16/135; Key Clb; Pep Clb; Ski Clb; Stage Crew; Yrbk Phtg; Rep Frsh Cls; JV Bsktbl; Var Trk; JV Vllybl; Hon Roll; St Bonaventure U; Lbrl Arts.

TARCHA, NICHOLAS A; Johnson City HS; Binghamton, NY; (Y); VP Church Yth Grp; Key Clb; JV Bsktbl; L Ftbl; NYS Boys ST 85; Natl Ukrainian Orthodx Of Yr Awd 84; Engrng.

TARDUGNO, DARRYL C; Rome Free Acad; Rome, NY; (Y); Var Capt Golf; Hon Roll; Jr NHS; NHS; Ntl Merit Ltr; Fairleigh Dickinson U; Bus.

TARDY, CASSANDRA L; Byron-Bergen Central Schl; Bergen, NY; (Y); 4/93; AFS; Am Leg Aux Girls St; Pres Spanish Clb; Chorus; Concert Band; Trs Frsh Cls; Sec Stu Cncl; L Capt Socr; Hon Roll; VP Jr NHS; Regents Schlrshp 84-85; Top Ten Awd 85; Geneseo Coll Geneseo; Am Hist.

TARKOWSKI, KIM; Frankfort Schuyler Central HS; Frankfort, NY; (S); Cmnty Wkr; GAA; Spanish Clb; Trk; High Hon Roll; Hon Roll; NHS; Pre-Vet.

TARNAGORSKI, CHRISTINE; St John The Baptist HS; N Massapequa, NY; (Y); Girl Scts; Library Aide; Varsity Clb; Yrbk Bus Mgr; Trk; UCLA; Hist.

TARNOFF, MELANIE; Harpursville Central Schl; Harpursville, NY; (S); 7/68; Church Yth Grp; Pres French Clb; Ski Clb; Pres Spanish Clb; School Play; Yrbk Stf; Sec Trs Soph Cls; Pres Jr Cls; Pres Sr Cls; L Var Bsktbl; Natl Cncl Yth Ldrshp Regnl Wnnr, Yth Salute Southern Tier Wnnr 84; Am Leg Oratorical Contest 82; Intl Rel.

TARQUINO, CHERYL; Auburn HS; Auburn, NY; (S); Color Guard; Mrchg Band; High Hon Roll; NHS; Cayuga County CC.

TARRANT, KATHLEEN; Stella Maris HS; Woodhaven, NY; (Y); Church Yth Grp; Cmnty Wkr; Teachers Aide; Nwsp Rptr; Yrbk Stf; Hon Roll; Science Clb; Nwsp Stf; Yrbk Rptr; Police Athletic Leag-Storytelling Contest 84; Queens Coll; Nutrtn.

TARRE, SHARI J; Horace Greeley HS; Chappaqua, NY; (Y); 17/272; Debate Tm; Drama Clb; Temple Yth Grp; School Musical; School Play; Stage Crew; Chrmn Stu Cncl; Var Tennis; Ntl Merit SF; Drama Asst Dir, Bus Prod, Stg Mgr & Costms Head; Berkshire Theat Fstvl; Bio Sci.

TARSIA, LILIANA; Central HS; Valley Stream, NY; (Y); French Clb; School Play; French Hon Soc; NCTE Awd; Hofstra; Bus.

TARTAGLIA, BETH; Bishop Ludden HS; Liverpool, NY; (Y); Church Yth Grp; Nwsp Phtg; Nwsp Rptr; Yrbk Phtg; Var Capt Bsktbl; Mgr(s); Score Keeper; Var L Socr; High Hon Roll; Art Hnrb Mntn; Money Schltc Art Cont Hnrb Mntn; Socr All Stars; Cortland ST Coll.

TARTAGLIA, DOMINICK; Lafayette HS; Brooklyn, NY; (Y); Arch.

TARTER, MELISSA; John H Glenn HS; E Northport, NY; (Y); Art Clb; Drama Clb; MMM; Temple Yth Grp; Chorus; School Musical; School Play; Stage Crew; Yrbk Phtg; Lit Mag; Triam Modern Music Masters 83-86.

TARULLO, CHRISTY; Voorheesville HS; Voorheesville, NY; (Y); French Clb; Band; Chorus; Yrbk Stf; Var Bsktbl; Var Fld Hcky; Var Vllybl; High Hon Roll; Hon Roll; Church Yth Grp; Colonial Cncl All-Star 2nd Tm Bsktbl 85; NYSSMA Ffest Awd 83; Bus Admin.

TARZIA, MICHELE; Liverpool HS; Clay, NY; (Y); Concert Band; Pep Band; School Musical; Drama.

TASCILLO, MARK; Mayfield Central HS; Gloversville, NY; (Y); Church Yth Grp; Hon Roll; Prfct Atten Awd; Elctrncs Engrng.

TASH, APRIL E; Bronxville HS; Bronxville, NY; (Y); 4/80; Chess Clb; Cmnty Wkr; Yrbk Stf; Ed Lit Mag; High Hon Roll; Ntl Merit Ltr; Pres Schlr; Co-Capt Mathletes; Nwsp Rptr; Rep Jr Cls; Japan-US Senate Smmr Schlrshp 84; Sci Hnrs Pgm 83-85; Wellesley Bk Prz 84; Harvard; Intl Law.

TASHKOVICH, MARK A; Fox Lane HS; Pound Ridge, NY; (Y); 4/300; Am Leg Boys St; VP Mathletes; Chorus; Jazz Band; Var Socr; Var Swmmng; Var Trk; High Hon Roll; NHS; Cornell U; Eastern Phil.

TASMIN, VINETTE; Washington Irving HS; Brooklyn, NY; (Y); Library Aide; Chorus; Hon Roll; Attrny Gen Trpl C Awd 83; Achvt Cert Histry, Sci & Rdng 83; Soc Stds Cert Of Merit 83.

TASSIOPULOS, IRENE; Kenmore East SR HS; Tonawanda, NY; (Y); Sec Church Yth Grp; Drama Clb; Pep Clb; PAVAS; Radio Clb; Teachers Aide; Thesps; Chorus; Church Choir; School Musical; Outstndng Cntry Butiaz To Theatre 85; NY ST Saratoga Theatre Fin 85; Performing Arts.

TAUB, HEATHER ANN; William Nottingham HS; Syracuse, NY; (Y); 49/220; French Clb; Latin Clb; Ski Clb; Stage Crew; Stu Cncl; Hon Roll; NHS; 4th Pl Ntl Ltn Exam 85; NYS Rgnts Schlrshp 85; Pres Acad Ftnss Awd 85; Mitchell Coll; Marine Bio.

TAUBE, ERIC H; Brentwood Ross HS; Brentwood, NY; (Y); 32/625; Church Yth Grp; Computer Clb; German Clb; Rep Jr Cls; Rep Sr Cls; Im Socr; Var Tennis; High Hon Roll; NHS; Prfct Atten Awd; SUNY Stony Brook; Engrng.

TAUBES, JEFF; Smithtown HS; Smithtown, NY; (Y); Hon Roll; SUNY; Bus.

TAVANO, KATHLEEN; Niagara Catholic HS; Niagara Falls, NY; (Y); 6/81; Drama Clb; French Clb; JA; Trs Key Clb; School Play; Nwsp Stf; Yrbk Stf; Hon Roll; NHS; Nwsp Rptr; Hnbl Mntn Fr Kroupa Awd 85; Vet.

TAVAREZ, NORALIN; A E Stevenson HS; Bronx, NY; (Y); Dance Clb; Library Aide; Service Clb; Varsity Clb; Sec Soph Cls; Sec Jr Cls; Var Gym; Capt Sftbl; Capt Vllybl; Hon Roll; Columbia U; Bus Adm.

TAVELLA, MICHAEL; Connetquot Public HS; Bohemia, NY; (Y); AFS; Aud/Vis; Teachers Aide; Chorus; Stage Crew; Yrbk Stf; Hon Roll; Prfct Atten Awd; Elctrncs.

TAVERAS, IRMA; John Adams HS; S Ozone Park, NY; (Y); Cmnty Wkr; JA; Teachers Aide; Chorus; Rep Stu Cncl; High Hon Roll; NHS; Prfct Atten Awd; Hunter Coll; Hlth Career.

TAVERAS, IVETTE; Cathedral HS; Ny, NY; (Y); 127/298; Library Aide; Yrbk Stf; John Jay Crmnl Just; Pre Law.

TAVERAS, JUAN; Bishop Loughlin Memorial HS; Brooklyn, NY; (S); 39/189; Church Yth Grp; Spanish Clb; Teachers Aide; Band; Capt Bsbl; Mgr(s); Score Keeper; Hon Roll; Prfct Atten Awd; Spanish NHS; Kingsborough; Bus Admin.

TAVERAS, RICHARD; John Jay HS; Brooklyn, NY; (Y); CAP; Computer Clb; Exploring; ROTC; Science Clb; Prfct Atten Awd; Wrd Prcssng Awd 85; Air Force Acad; Pilot.

TAVERNIA, TAMMY; Franklin Acad; Malone, NY; (Y); Sec 4-H; Chorus; Swing Chorus; Lit Mag; Hon Roll; NCTE Awd; Prfct Atten Awd; Madrigals; Nwsp Rptr; 4-H Awd; Epsilon 85; Schl Music Letter Awd 85; Voice & Guitar Solo Awds 84-85; Crane Schl Of Music; Voice.

TAVERNIER, MAUREEN; Fillmore Central HS; Fillmore, NY; (S); 9/52; Pep Clb; Varsity Clb; Chorus; Church Choir; Orch; Variety Show; Rep Stu Cncl; Cheerleading; Tennis; Area All-ST Chorus 83; Nazareth Coll Rochstr; Spec Ed.

TAVERNIER, RONALD; Franklin Acad; Malone, NY; (Y); Church Yth Grp; 4-H; French Clb; Ski Clb; Band; Concert Band; Yrbk Stf; Pres Frsh Cls; JV Crs Cntry; JV Trk; Lawyer.

TAVLARIDES, MNOSTULA A; Fayetteville-Manlius HS; Fayetteville, NY; (Y); 33/335; JV Co-Capt Vllybl; Hon Roll; NHS; Church Yth Grp; Political Wkr; Chorus; Church Choir; Rep Soph Cls; JV Fld Hcky; NY Msc Tchrs Assoc-4th Prz Wnr Piano 83; Schlstc Art Comp 84-85; NY ST Rgnts Schlrshp 84-85; Columbia U; E Asian Stud.

TAVOLILLA, CARMELA; Academy Of The Resurrec; Tuckahoe, NY; (Y); Dance Clb; Hosp Aide; Library Aide; Chorus; School Play; Ed Yrbk Stf; Cheerleading; Coach Actv; Hon Roll; Cath Daugh Am Poetry Cont 1st Pl 83-84.

TAVORMINA, PAULA; Amityville Memorial HS; Massapequa, NY; (Y); 23/238; Drama Clb; Chorus; School Musical; School Play; Swing Chorus; Nwsp Rptr; Lit Mag; Ntl Merit Schol; Drama Clb Awd 85; Farmingdale.

TAWNEY, MICHELE; Northstar Christian Acad; Rochester, NY; (S); 4/27; Church Yth Grp; Debate Tm; Drama Clb; Office Aide; Speech Tm; Church Choir; School Play; Sec Yrbk Stf; Sec NHS; VP Sr Cls; Bnkng.

TAYABA, ROEL G; La Salle Acad; New York, NY; (S); 21/237; Cmnty Wkr; Hosp Aide; Office Aide; Mrchg Band; NYU; Acctg.

TAYLOR, AMY; Chenango Valley HS; Binghamton, NY; (Y); 38/187; French Clb; Varsity Clb; Hon Roll; NHS; Broome Cty NAACP Acad Achvt Awd 85; Slumni Schlrshp 85; Broome Cty Urban Leag Schlrshp 85; ST U; Bus Adm.

TAYLOR, APRIL; Hudson HS; Hudson, NY; (Y); #2 In Class; AFS; Pres Church Yth Grp; Chorus; Church Choir; School Musical; Nwsp Ed-Chief; Var Crs Cntry; JV Sftbl; High Hon Roll; NHS; Archit.

TAYLOR, ARMINDA; James Madison HS; Brooklyn, NY; (Y); 214/754; Sec Church Yth Grp; Sec Office Aide; Sec Teachers Aide; Chorus; Sec Church Choir; Variety Show; Baruch; Bus Adm.

TAYLOR, DARYL ANN; Colonie Central HS; Albany, NY; (Y); 48/471; Pres FBLA; Hst Jr Cls; Sr Cls; Stu Cncl; JV Vllybl; Elks Awd; High Hon Roll; NHS; Pres Schlr; Colonie Centrl Actv Awd 85; Lamame Coll Grnt Awd 85; Le Moyne Coll; Comp Sci.

TAYLOR, DEBORAH; Indian River Central HS; Evans Mills, NY; (Y); 12/106; Church Yth Grp; School Play; Stage Crew; Hon Roll; Ty Bradley Schlrshp 85; Jefferson CC; Comp.

TAYLOR, ELLEN; Mt Mercy Acad; Buffalo, NY; (Y); JV Bsktbl; Hon Roll; Peer Ministry; Acctng.

TAYLOR, JIM; Fayetteville-Manlius HS; Fayetteville, NY; (Y); Var Lcrss; Hon Roll; Onondaga Cnty Math Awd 83; Comp Sci.

TAYLOR, JODI; Oneonta HS; Oneonta, NY; (Y); Mathletes; Math Clb; Math Tm; Chorus; Diving; Swmmng; Vllybl; Math.

TAYLOR, KARA; Arlington HS; Hopewell Jct, NY; (Y); French Clb; Ski Clb; Band; Rep Sr Cls; Var Bsktbl; Score Keeper; Socr; JV Vllybl; Hon Roll; All Cnty Sccr Tm 83-85.

TAYLOR, KIM; Norman Thomas HS; New York, NY; (S); 22/671; Cmnty Wkr; JA; Hon Roll; NHS; Rochester Inst Of Tech; Bus Adm.

TAYLOR, LONA G; Fillmore Central HS; Houghton, NY; (Y); 9/47; Varsity Clb; Concert Band; School Play; VP Stu Cncl; Capt Socr; Capt Sftbl; Capt Vllybl; High Hon Roll; NHS; Regnts Schlrshp 85; Keuka Coll; Nrs.

TAYLOR, LYNORE; N Babylon SR HS; N Babylon, NY; (Y); 2/514; Am Leg Aux Girls St; Trs Intnl Clb; Mathletes; VP Spanish Clb; VP Frsh Cls; High Hon Roll; Jr NHS; Lion Awd; NHS; Office Aide; George Washington U Schl Engrng & Appld Sci Engrng Medl Excllnc Stdy Math & Sci 85; Elctrcl Engrng.

TAYLOR, MALIK E; Rice HS; New York, NY; (S); Cmnty Wkr; Computer Clb; Debate Tm; Lit Mag; Rep Stu Cncl; Hon Roll; Library Aide; Im Bsktbl; Swmmng; Cath Schlrshps Negroes Inc 84; Comp Instctr NY Pub Lib 83-85; CCNY NE Resource Ctr Sci/Engrng 84; Fordham U; Comp Sci.

TAYLOR, MARCI JAN; Salem Central HS; Pawlet, VT; (Y); GAA; Fld Hcky; Trk; High Hon Roll; Hon Roll; Green Mountain Coll; Bus Mgmt.

TAYLOR, MICHELLE; Vestal SR HS; Binghamton, NY; (Y); Church Yth Grp; Drama Clb; Chorus; Church Choir; School Musical; Sec Jr Cls; Rep Stu Cncl; Hon Roll; NHS; Comp Sci.

TAYLOR, OLIVIA; August Martin HS; Jamica, NY; (Y); 50/528; Cmnty Wkr; Debate Tm; Office Aide; Teachers Aide; School Play; Lit Mag; Hon Roll; Queens DA Cert Of Prtcptn 85; NY ST Bar Assn-Prtcptn As Law Tm Mbr 84-85; Eng.

TAYLOR, OPAL; Bishop Loughlin Memorial HS; Brooklyn, NY; (Y); Library Aide; Trk; Vllybl; High Hon Roll; Hon Roll; Nrsng.

TAYLOR, PATRICIA A; C W Baker HS; Baldwinsville, NY; (Y); 161/441; Art Clb; Hosp Aide; Chorus; School Musical; Co-Capt Sftbl; Var L Vllybl; Hon Roll; Rec Vol Wrk 83-84; Dean JC; Phy Ed.

TAYLOR, PATRICIA E; South Shore HS; Brooklyn, NY; (Y); 90/668; Debate Tm; Drama Clb; Office Aide; Teachers Aide; School Play; Im Gym; Prfct Atten Awd; Ntl Negro Schlrshp; Baruch Coll; Acctng.

TAYLOR, PATRICK C; Skaneateles HS; Skaneateles, NY; (Y); Church Yth Grp; Cmnty Wkr; Latin Clb; Variety Show; Var Capt Bsbl; Var Bsktbl; Var Capt Ftbl; JV Golf; High Hon Roll; Hon Roll; Yth Minstry Hlpr Awd 85.

TAYLOR, QUINTELLA; Our Lady Of Mercy HS; Rochester, NY; (Y); 73/200; Church Yth Grp; Cmnty Wkr; Hosp Aide; Spanish Clb; School Play; Rep Soph Cls; Rep Jr Cls; Trk; Hon Roll; Urkan Lgu Black Schlr Awd; Sisters For Btr Black Comm Schlrshp; Spelman Coll; Pre-Law.

TAYLOR, REGINA; Woodlands HS; White Plains, NY; (Y); Pres FBLA; Band; Yrbk Ed-Chief; Rep Frsh Cls; Rep Soph Cls; Rep Jr Cls; Var Cheerleading; Var Trk; Hon Roll; Law.

TAYLOR, ROBERT; Pincrest Christain HS; Salisbury Ctr, NY; (Y); Church Yth Grp; Band; Bsktbl; Ftbl; Wt Lftg; Le Moyne Coll; Accntng.

TAYLOR, RONNIE; Park West HS; Bronx, NY; (Y); Drama Clb; Office Aide; Teachers Aide; Var Cheerleading; Score Keeper; Hon Roll; Johnson & Wales; Accntng.

TAYLOR, SANDRA L; Horace Greeley HS; Chappaqua, NY; (Y); 8/300; Var Capt Sftbl; Var Capt Vllybl; NHS; Colgate U; Bio.

TAYLOR, SHUNDA M; St Anthonys HS; Deer Park, NY; (Y); 54/273; Church Yth Grp; Computer Clb; Math Clb; Chorus; Stu Cncl; Bsktbl; Mgr(s); Trk; Hon Roll; Prfct Atten Awd; Brown U; Comp Sci.

TAYLOR, TOM; Bishop Grimes HS; Syracuse, NY; (Y); 48/210; Concert Band; Jazz Band; School Musical; Im Bsktbl; JV Crs Cntry; NHS; Crane Schl Music Schlrshp 84-85; SUNY; Music Educ.

TAYLOR, TRACY A; Newfane SR HS; Appleton, NY; (S); 2/166; Church Yth Grp; Varsity Clb; Trs Band; School Musical; Capt Vllybl; Hon Roll; Trs Mu Alp Tht; Pres NHS; Sal; Gold Music Awd 83-84; Niagara County CC.

TAYLOR, WENDY; Sodus Central HS; Williamson, NY; (Y); 23/120; French Clb; Varsity Clb; Concert Band; Sec Frsh Cls; Var JV Cheerleading; Var Sftbl; Var Tennis; High Hon Roll; Hon Roll; Hghst Grd Annl H S Math Exm 85.

TAYLOR, ZAN; Fort Ann Central HS; Ft Ann, NY; (Y); Computer Clb; Exploring; French Clb; Math Clb; Stage Crew; Golf; Score Keeper; High Hon Roll; Hon Roll; NHS; Record Setting Answrs Please Tm 84-85; Dungeons & Dragns Clb Pres 83-85; RPI Coll; Systems Anlst.

TAYYABKHAN, REHBAR; Long Island City HS; Astoria, NY; (S); 4/569; Debate Tm; JA; Math Clb; Math Tm; Quiz Bowl; Scholastic Bowl; Band; Nwsp Bus Mgr; Nwsp Stf; Yrbk Stf; Arista; NYU; Pre-Med.

TCHOU, BETTY; Midwood HS; Brooklyn, NY; (Y); 159/638; Teachers Aide; Cheerleading; Prfct Atten Awd; Accntnt.

TE SELLE, JOCELYN; Nottingham HS; Davis, CA; (Y); Church Yth Grp; 4-H; Ski Clb; Chorus; Church Choir; Crs Cntry; Trk; Ntl Merit Ltr; Stu Senate 82-85; Indoor Track 81-83 & 84-85; Spnsh I Hnr Roll 84-85.

TEALE, MICHELE; Gloversville HS; Gloversville, NY; (Y); Color Guard; Mrchg Band; Capt Bsktbl; Capt Cheerleading; Sftbl; Hon Roll; Navy; Physcl Thrpy.

TEALL, JENNIFER; Nazareth Acad; Rochester, NY; (Y); Drama Clb; Chorus; Madrigals; School Musical; School Play; Stage Crew; Swing Chorus; Variety Show; French Clb; Nwsp Sprt Ed; Outstdng Chorus Mbr 83; Outstdng Voice Stu 85; Voice & Drama.

TEATOR, HOLLY; Rensselaer HS; Rensselaer, NY; (Y); DECA; Nwsp Rptr; Nwsp Stf; Yrbk Rptr; Yrbk Stf; Cheerleading; Pom Pon; Trk; Hon Roll; Bus Admn.

TEATOR, SHARON A; Cairo Durham Central HS; Durham, NY; (Y); 1/90; Pres 4-H; Concert Band; Ed School Musical; Ed School Play; Ed Yrbk Stf; Rep Stu Cncl; Capt Cheerleading; Socr; Tennis; Bausch & Lomb Sci Awd; Elks ST Scholar 85; Regents Scholar 85; Hartwick Coll.

TEBCHERANY, FADIA; Anthony A Hennwger HS; Raleigh, NC; (Y); 3/500; Intnl Clb; Red Cross Aide; Ski Clb; Hon Roll; NC ST U; Mgmt.

TEDD II, MICHAEL T; Goshen Central HS; Goshen, NY; (Y); 7/250; Drama Clb; Ski Clb; Spanish Clb; School Musical; School Play; JV Socr; High Hon Roll; NHS; Pre-Law.

TEDESCO, DONNA MARIE; Connetquot HS; Ronkonkoma, NY; (Y); GAA; Aud/Vis; Chorus; Rep Frsh Cls; Rep Stu Cncl; Capt JV Cheerleading; Capt Socr; High Hon Roll; Hon Roll; Jr NHS; MVP Socr 83; Coachs Awd Socr Vrsty 84; MVP Chrldng 83; Ldrs Clb 83; Stonybrook U; Comp Sci.

TEDESCO, JULIE; Depew HS; Depew, NY; (Y); Art Clb; Cmnty Wkr; Hon Roll; NHS; Prfct Atten Awd; Art Inst Pittsburgh; Comm Art.

TEDESCO, KATLEEN; St Marys Acad; Glens Falls, NY; (S); 6/47; Art Clb; Cmnty Wkr; VP Drama Clb; French Clb; Key Clb; Pep Clb; Ski Clb; Chorus; School Musical; Nwsp Rptr; Jrnlst.

TEDESCO, LORI; Mont Pleasant HS; Schenectady, NY; (Y); Office Aide; Spanish Clb; Yrbk Bus Mgr; Var Socr; High Hon Roll; Hon Roll; NHS; Spanish NHS; Harvard Bk Awd 85; Bus Adm.

TEECE, DOUG; Clarktown High School North; New City, NY; (Y); Graphc.

TEEHAN, FRANCIS; St Raymonds HS For Boys; Bronx, NY; (Y); 11/200; Math Tm; Science Clb; Bsbl; Bsktbl; Sftbl; High Hon Roll; Hon Roll; Geortetown.

TEELING, KATHERINE; Academy Of St Joseph; Sayville, NY; (Y); Hosp Aide; Library Aide; Nwsp Rptr; Liberal Arts.

TEEPS, DAVID; Vernon-Verona-Sherrill HS; Vernon, NY; (Y); Church Yth Grp; Computer Clb; Band; Concert Band; Mrchg Band; High Hon Roll; Hon Roll; NHS; Clarkson U; Elec.

TEETER, MARCIA; Newark HS; Newark, NY; (Y); Teachers Aide; Concert Band; Nwsp Stf; Yrbk Stf; Var Swmmng; French Hon Soc; High Hon Roll; Hon Roll; NHS; French Clb; Honorng Excllnc Awd 85; Girls Var Swmmng Most Imprvd Swmmr 83; Nrsng.

TEFFT, JULIE; Fayetteville-Manlius HS; Fayetteville, NY; (Y); Cmnty Wkr; Hosp Aide; Pep Clb; Var Capt Cheerleading; Var Capt Pom Pon; Hon Roll; Bakg Awd 79; Gymnstc Awd 80; Occptnl Thrpy.

TEGTMEIER, SUSAN; F D Roosevelt HS; Hyde Park, NY; (Y); Church Yth Grp; Band; Concert Band; Score Keeper; JV Vllybl; Hon Roll; NHS; Math.

TEHAN, PATRICIA; Frankfort-Schuyler HS; Frankfort, NY; (S); Drama Clb; French Clb; Chorus; Color Guard; Mrchg Band; School Musical; JV Bsktbl; Var Tennis; Hon Roll; NHS; Nrsng.

TEIBEL, MELISSA; Williamsville East HS; Williamsville, NY; (Y); 26/288; Cmnty Wkr; FBLA; Nwsp Ed-Chief; Trs Soph Cls; High Hon Roll; NHS; Trs Latin Clb; Ski Clb; School Musical; Powder Puff Ftbl; Sr Mnth 85; Northwestrn U.

TEICH, JAMES; Bishop Ludden HS; Syracuse, NY; (S); Cmnty Wkr; Exploring; Nwsp Stf; High Hon Roll; VP Jr NHS; Natl Hnr Rll 84; Bus Clb Pres 84-85; Holy Family CYO Bsktbl 82-85.

TEICH, MICHAEL L; Beach Channel HS; Rock Bch, NY; (Y); Chess Clb; Computer Clb; Math Tm; Temple Yth Grp; Drm Mjr(t); Var L Swmmng; Hon Roll; Trk; Ntl Merit Schol; NYC Comptllrs Awd 83; Top Mth Stu, Sci Stu 83; Vet Med.

TEICH, TRACY; Bishop Ludden HS; Syracuse, NY; (S); 14/179; Exploring; MMM; Band; Stage Crew; Variety Show; Var Capt Bsktbl; Var Sftbl; High Hon Roll; NHS; Hamilton Coll Oprtn Entrprse Schlrshp 84; Onondaga CC Schlr 84; OCC; Sprts Med.

TEICHMAN, AMY; Poughkeepsie HS; Poughkeepsie, NY; (Y); Yrbk Stf; Stat Bsktbl; Mgr(s); Mgr Socr; Hon Roll; NHS; 2 Gold Mdls At Empire ST Games For Rowing 84; Bronze Mdl At Natl Schlstc Regatta For Rowing 85; Psych.

TEILLON, MICHELLE; Liverpool HS; Liverpool, NY; (S); 8/792; Math Tm; Chorus; School Musical; Yrbk Stf; Stu Cncl; Cheerleading; High Hon Roll; Trs Jr NHS; VP NHS; Ski Clb; Rock Ensmbl; Wellesley Bk Awd; All Cnty Chorus; Chem Engr.

TEITELBAUM, JENNIFER; Island Trees HS; Levittown, NY; (Y); Cmnty Wkr; Debate Tm; Drama Clb; Nwsp Ed-Chief; Nwsp Rptr; Yrbk Stf; Stu Cncl; Bsktbl; Vllybl; Indstrl Arts Awd 81-82; Schlrshp Prfrmng Arts 85; Cmnctns.

TEITTER, JOHN E; Saugerties JR SR HS; Saugerties, NY; (Y); 30/243; Math Tm; Science Clb; Teachers Aide; Band; Concert Band; Mrchg Band; Symp Band; High Hon Roll; Hon Roll; NHS; NY St Regents Schlrshp 85; Boston U; Doctor.

TEJANI, SHARYN; Garden City HS; Garden City, NY; (Y); 3/355; German Clb; Band; Nwsp Rptr; Yrbk Sprt Ed; Jr NHS; NHS; Ntl Merit Ltr; Nwsp Nws Edtr 85-86; Amer Lgn Axlry Awd 85.

TEKVERK, STEPHEN; Commack High School North; Commack, NY; (Y); Aud/Vis; Boy Scts; Church Yth Grp; Computer Clb; FBLA; Stage Crew; KC; Elec.

TELA, ANN C; Chatham HS; Canaan, NY; (Y); Library Aide; Band; Concert Band; Mrchg Band; Orch; Pep Band; Yrbk Stf; Sec Jr Cls; Cheerleading; Trk; Elem Ed.

TELESCA, PAMELA; Acad Ressurrection HS; Rye Brook, NY; (Y); Art Clb; Cmnty Wkr; Math Tm; Teachers Aide; Chorus; Stage Crew; Ed Yrbk Stf; Rep Stu Cncl; Hon Roll; NHS; Tchr.

TELESCO, WILLIAM J; John Jay SR HS; Katonah, NY; (Y); 3/300; Boys Clb Am; Math Tm; Ski Clb; Im Bsktbl; JV Var Ftbl; Var Swmmng; Hon Roll; Regents Schlrshp 85; Rensselaer Polytech Ins; Arch.

TELFORD, DANNY; West Hempstead HS; Island Pk, NY; (Y); Key Clb; Var Ftbl; Golf; Var L Trk; Top 1/4 Cls AHSME Test 85; Comp Sci Mgmt.

TELGHEDER, DAVID; Minisink Valley HS; Slate Hill, NY; (Y); 79/232; Band; Concert Band; Var Capt Bsbl; Var Capt Ftbl; JV Wrstlng; Bsbl Schlrshp To U Of MA 85; U Of MA; Ag.

TELGHEDER, NANCY; Minisink Valley HS; Slate Hill, NY; (Y); Key Clb; Capt Color Guard; Mrchg Band; Capt Mat Maids; Sftbl; Scl Wrk.

TELL, HEIDI; Shenendehowa HS; Clifton Park, NY; (Y); Leo Clb; Temple Yth Grp; Orch; Jr Cls; Im Sftbl; Im Vllybl; High Hon Roll; Hnr Rll Awd 83-85.

TEMPLE, DONNA; Murray Bergtraum HS; Bronx, NY; (Y); Teachers Aide; Hon Roll; NHS; Chapel Hills; Accntnt.

TEMPLE JR, RICHARD E; Waverly JR SR HS; Waverly, NY; (Y); Am Leg Boys St; Art Clb; Aud/Vis; Boy Scts; Computer Clb; Exploring; Hosp Aide; Radio Clb; Spanish Clb; Chorus; Bio.

TEMPLER, THERESA; Niskayuna HS; Schdy, NY; (Y); Key Clb; Pep Clb; Varsity Clb; Yrbk Stf; Var Capt Cheerleading; Sftbl; Bus.

TEN, AIDA E; Tottenville HS; Staten Island, NY; (Y); 130/897; Church Yth Grp; Cmnty Wkr; Key Clb; Office Aide; Teachers Aide; Chorus; School Musical; Variety Show; NYS Regents Schlrshp 85; Boston U; Intl Rltn.

TEN HAGEN, PETER G; Pittsford Mendon HS; Pittsford, NY; (Y); 1/280; Band; Concert Band; Im Bsbl; JV Var Bsktbl; Im Golf; JV Var Socr; Hon Roll; NHS; Air Force ROTC 4 Yr Schlrshp 85; Navy ROTC 4 Yr Schlrshp 85; Cornell U; Elec Engrng.

TENACE, MELISSA; Mont Pleasant HS; Schenectady, NY; (Y); 19/210; Trs German Clb; JA; Office Aide; Pep Clb; Off Soph Cls; Off Jr Cls; Stat Sftbl; Hon Roll; Grmn Awd Exc In Cls 83-85; Coll; Accntng.

TENAGLIA, ELIZABETH; Oxford Academy HS; Mc Donough, NY; (Y); Am Leg Aux Girls St; Drama Clb; French Clb; Concert Band; Jazz Band; Nwsp Stf; High Hon Roll; Hon Roll; NHS; Prfct Atten Awd; Oper Entrprs Schrshp Wnnr 85; Elmira Coll Key Awd 85; Jr Hgst Avg 85; Bio.

TENEBRUSO, MICHAEL A; Batavia HS; Batavia, NY; (Y); Pres Chess Clb; Ski Clb; Rep Jr Cls; Im Badmtn; Im Bsbl; Im Bsktbl; Im Bowling; Var L Ftbl; Var L Golf; Im Sftbl.

TENEDORIO, MICHAEL; Mineola HS; Mineola, NY; (Y); JV Bsktbl; Var Ftbl; High Hon Roll; Hon Roll; Jr NHS; Embry Riddle; Aeron Plt.

TENEYCK, SAMANTHA; Saugerties HS; Saugerties, NY; (Y); 52/245; French Clb; Symp Band; Suny New Paltz; French.

TENG, ERIC; Herricks SR HS; New Hyde Park, NY; (S); Boy Scts; Hst DECA; Math Clb; Nwsp Stf; Yrbk Ed-Chief; Hon Roll; Jr NHS; VFW Awd; Voice Dem Awd; Albany Cnctn Yth Bd 84-85; Hrnbl Mntn Awd Cnsmr Affrs Prj 83-84; Rcvd Achvt Awd Grphic Desgn 83-84; Cmmrcl Art.

TENISON, RUTH E; Amsterdam HS; Amsterdam, NY; (Y); 7/332; Yrbk Stf; High Hon Roll; Hon Roll; NHS; Prfct Atten Awd; Regents Schlrshp 84-85; Pblsh Poem In Creative Collection II 85; Accntnt.

TENNENT, KEILA; Dewitt Clinton HS; Bronx, NY; (Y); Church Yth Grp; Cmnty Wkr; Nwsp Rptr; Nwsp Stf; VP Stu Cncl; Hon Roll; NHS; Pride Of Yankees Awd 85; Cornell U; Med.

TENNEY, JOHN; Rocky Poitn JR SR HS; Rocky Point, NY; (S); 4/200; French Clb; Madrigals; Mrchg Band; Symp Band; Trs Jr Cls; Off Stu Cncl; Var Capt Socr; Var L Trk; JV Wrstlng; Hon Roll; All-Cnty Band 82; All-Cnty Chorus 82; Intrprtr.

TENNYSON, GREG; North Warren HS; Pottersville, NY; (Y); Var Golf; High Hon Roll; Engrng.

TENNYSON, STEVE; North Warren Central HS; Pottersville, NY; (Y); 4/50; Computer Clb; Math Tm; NHS; Exclinc Comp Sci Awd 85; Hghst Ovrll Math Ave Awd 85; Hghst Ave Clss Attnd ACC Awd 85; Adirondack CC; Engrng.

TENSHAW, LINDA; Liverpool HS; Liverpool, NY; (S); 130/792; AFS; Church Yth Grp; Ski Clb; Stu Cncl; Trk; Hon Roll; Jr NHS; NHS; Syracuse U; Comp Sci.

TEPEDINO, FRANK; Farmingdale HS; N Massapequa, NY; (Y); 1/560; Varsity Clb; Jazz Band; Mrchg Band; Orch; Symp Band; Ed Yrbk Phtg; L Var Trk; Trs NHS; Ntl Merit Ltr; All Cnty Music Fest Parcpnt 85; Trck Coachs Awd Wnnr 85; MVP Frshmn Trck 83; Bio.

TEPPER, BONNIE E; Sachem North HS; Holbrook, NY; (Y); 76/1506; Ski Clb; Spanish Clb; Yrbk Phtg; Yrbk Stf; Jr Cls.

TEPPER, JONATHAN D; New Rochelle HS; New Rochelle, NY; (Y); Camera Clb; Ski Clb; Nwsp Stf; Rep Jr Cls; JV Bsbl; JV Lcrss; NHS; Ntl Merit Ltr; Temple Yth Grp; Bus Admin.

TERAN, BETTY; John Jay HS; Queens, NY; (Y); Spanish Clb; Vllybl.

TERASKIEWICZ, TINAMARIE; Bishop Kearney HS; Brooklyn, NY; (Y); Cmnty Wkr; Pres Dance Clb; Pres FTA; Teachers Aide; VP Chorus; Church Choir; School Musical; Variety Show; Off Frsh Cls; Rep Jr Cls; Oper FUN Cert-Cmp For Hndcpd 82-85; Chorus Cert 83-85; Merit Cert-NY ST Assn Fo Frgn Tchrs 84; St Francis Coll; Spec Ed.

TERCHOWITZ, CELIA; John F Kennedy HS; Utica, NY; (Y); 4/135; Band; Concert Band; Bowling; High Hon Roll; Hon Roll; Jr NHS; Utica Coll; Bus Admin.

TERIC, ELYSA; James Madison HS; Brooklyn, NY; (S); 5/803; Math Tm; Office Aide; Ski Clb; Color Guard; School Musical; Rep Soph Cls; Rep Stu Cncl; Var Tennis; Gov Hon Prg Awd; Hon Roll; Prncpls Pride Of The Ynks Awd 84-85; Gov Comm Schlstc Achvmnt 84-85; Comm.

TERILLI, MARC J; Pelham Memorial HS; Pelham, NY; (Y); Boys Clb Am; Y-Teens; Im Ftbl; Hon Roll; NY Inst Of Techlgy; Elec Tech.

TERILLI, MATTHEW; Archbishop Stepinac HS; Ossining, NY; (Y); 11/206; Art Clb; Church Yth Grp; Computer Clb; JV Tennis; Hon Roll; NHS; Natl Hnr Rl Natl Ldrshp Org 84-85; Manhattan Coll; Engrng.

TERLIZZI, STEPHEN; Fox Lane HS; Mount Kisco, NY; (Y); 60/275; Current Events Awd 83; Arch.

TERPIN, CHRISTOPHER; St Josephs Collegiate Inst; Buffalo, NY; (Y); 10/189; Boy Scts; Church Yth Grp; Quiz Bowl; Science Clb; Nwsp Rptr; Lit Mag; Im Bsktbl; Im Bowling; High Hon Roll; Poetry Cont 1st Pl 85; Exc Ratng Ntl Fed Jr Fest Piano Solo 85; Comp Sci.

TERRACINO, LISA; Academy Of St Josep; Ronkonkoma, NY; (Y); Teachers Aide; Var Bsktbl; Var Mgr(s); Var Socr; Var Sftbl; Ithica; Comp Engr.

TERRANO, MARK C; Newburgh Free Acad; Newburgh, NY; (Y); 13/730; Debate Tm; Math Tm; Ski Clb; High Hon Roll; Jr NHS; Trs NHS; St Schlr; Itln Hnr Soc 83-85; Mst Outstndng Math Stu 83-84; Rnslr Plytech Inst; Elec Engr.

TERRELL, DANIEL A; The Stony Brook Schl; Smithtown, NY; (Y); Ski Clb; Spanish Clb; Jazz Band; Sr Cls; JV Bsbl; Capt L Socr; High Hon Roll; Var Wrstlng; Hon Roll; Ntl Merit SF; Rgnts Schlrshp Awd 85; Gold Mdl Geom & Math 83; All Leag Tm I Scr & Bst Ovrall Perf 84-85; Lehigh U; Elec Engr.

TERRIGNO, DONNA; Maria Regina HS; Yonkers, NY; (Y); 29/127; NFL; Cheerleading; Hon Roll; Iona Coll; Comps.

TERRITO, WILLIAM; Frewsburg Central Schl; Frewsburg, NY; (Y); 10/80; Chess Clb; Church Yth Grp; Computer Clb; FCA; Bsbl; Ftbl; Golf; Hon Roll; Prfct Atten Awd; Stdnt Yr Mech Drwg 83; Jamestown CC; Bus.

TERRY, AMY; Westhampton Beach HS; Westhampton, NY; (Y); 104/253; Church Yth Grp; Spanish Clb; Yrbk Phtg; Yrbk Stf; Off Stu Cncl; Stat Ftbl; JV Sftbl; Prfct Atten Awd; Fashn Merch.

TERRY, BERNARD; Cardinal Hayes HS; New York, NY; (Y); Yrbk Stf; Cit Awd; Prfct Atten Awd; St Johns; Law.

TERRY, MATTHEW; Irondequoit HS; Rochester, NY; (Y); Art Clb; Church Yth Grp; Model UN; Varsity Clb; JV Var Bsbl; JV Var Bsktbl; Hon Roll; Blue Rbbn Fnlst-Schltc Art Awds Regnl Exhbtn 84; Sectn V Cls AAA Champnshp Bsbll Team 85.

TERSIP, LORI; Remsen Central HS; Remsen, NY; (Y); 4-H; FFA; Color Guard; Mrchg Band; Yrbk Stf; VP Sr Cls; Sftbl; Hon Roll; Accntng Awd Highest Avg 85; The Amer Lgn Scl Awd 83; Accntng.

TERTINEK, ERIC; Cattaraugus Central HS; Cattaraugus, NY; (Y); 13/65; Pep Clb; Ski Clb; Spanish Clb; Band; Jazz Band; Trs Stu Cncl; Var Crs Cntry; Var Trk; Hon Roll; Concert Band; Acad Clb; Cls Msct; Engrng.

TERWILLIGER, DIANE; Center Moriches HS; Ctr Moriches, NY; (Y); 9/71; French Clb; Ski Clb; Sec Soph Cls; Var L Fld Hcky; Var L Socr; Var L Sftbl; Hon Roll; NHS; Eng Awd; Leaders Club; U Of DE; Busnss Admin.

TERZIAN, DONNA; Mount Vernon HS; Mt Vernon, NY; (Y); 13/580; Aud/Vis; FBLA; Key Clb; Science Clb; Spanish Clb; Var L Crs Cntry; Var Gym; Pom Pon; High Hon Roll; NHS; ST U NY Albany; Psych.

TERZIAN, PETER E; Shaker HS; Latham, NY; (Y); Church Yth Grp; Drama Clb; Political Wkr; Stage Crew; Ed Nwsp Stf; NY ST Regnts Schlrshp 85; Boston U.

TERZULLI, FRANCINE; Midwood HS; Brooklyn, NY; (Y); Intnl Clb; Office Aide; Teachers Aide; School Musical; Variety Show; Med Sci.

TESAURO, JONI; St John The Baptist DHS; Bayshore, NY; (Y); Art Clb; PAVAS; Rep Soph Cls; JV Cheerleading; FIT; Fshn.

TESIERO, KELLY; Columbia HS; Rensselaer, NY; (Y); Key Clb; Orch; Yrbk Stf; Rep Soph Cls; Rep Sr Cls; Im JV Sftbl; Im JV Vllybl; High Hon Roll; NHS; Variety Show; SADD Treas 84-85; All Cnty Music Fstvl 82-84; All Star Sprtsmnshp Sftbl 83-84; Rusell Sage; Phy Thrpy.

TESMER, DAWN; Riverside HS; Buffalo, NY; (Y); Library Aide; Hon Roll; NHS; Cosmtlgst.

TESORO, MARY KAY; Auburn HS; Auburn, NY; (Y); 53/440; Model UN; JV L Sftbl; High Hon Roll; Hon Roll; VFW Awd; Voice Dem Awd; Christopher Columbus Schlrshp Awd 85; Clarkson U; Comp Sci.

TESSIER, D WARREN; Fayetteville Manlius HS; Manlius, NY; (Y); Boy Scts; Chorus; Mgr Concert Band; Mrchg Band; VP Orch; School Musical; Swing Chorus; Hon Roll; NHS; 300 Clb NY ST Math Rgnts 85; Awd Outstndng Achvt Bnd 84 & 85; Awd Outstndng Achvt Choir 83; Engnrng.

TESSIER, TROY A; Brasher Falls Central HS; Nicholville, NY; (Y); 1/100; Band; Concert Band; Mrchg Band; Pres Frsh Cls; Pres Soph Cls; JV Var Bsktbl; Var Socr; High Hon Roll; Hon Roll; Outstndng Sci Stu Awd Clarkson Coll Sci Stu Rec Day 82-83.

TESSITORE, RICHARD; Oneonta HS; Oneonta, NY; (Y); Art Clb; Hon Roll; Ntl Soc Studys Olympd Awd 85; Soc Studys & Art Awds 84 & 85; Army.

TESTA, ELIZABETH; William Nottingham HS; Syracuse, NY; (Y); 60/220; Drama Clb; French Clb; Sec Chorus; School Musical; School Play; Stage Crew; Swing Chorus; Lit Mag; Frnch, Drama Dept Awds 85; Cvc Ctr Theater Fest Cmmndtn 85; Syracuse U; Drama.

TESTA, MARGARET; Corinth Central Schl; Corinth, NY; (S); Sec 4-H; French Clb; Hosp Aide; MMM; Band; Chorus; Pep Band; Sec Stu Cncl; JV Fld Hcky; 4-H Awd; James D Smith Mem Schlrshp 84; NYSMA Solo Awd 84.

TESTA, STEPHEN H; Garden City SR HS; Garden City, NY; (Y); 40/320; Spanish Clb; Nwsp Stf; Pres Stu Cncl; Var Ftbl; JV Socr; Var Tennis; Jr NHS; Kiwanis Awd; Colgate U.

TESTANI, ANDREA; Hornell HS; Hornell, NY; (Y); AFS; Ski Clb; Band; Chorus; Mrchg Band; School Musical; School Play; Swing Chorus; JV Var Socr; Elmira Coll.

TESTMAN, SAMANTHA; Walton HS; Bronx, NY; (Y); Cmnty Wkr; FNA; FTA; Hosp Aide; OEA; Red Cross Aide; Band; Mrchg Band; Yrbk Phtg; Val; Home Ec Spec Recogntn 85; Vlntrs Annual Recogntn Day Awd 85; Coll Mt St Vincent; Nrsng.

TESTONE, JOSEPH; Liverpool HS; Liverpool, NY; (S); 109/792; Cmnty Wkr; DECA; JA; Ski Clb; Sr Cls; High Hon Roll; Hon Roll; NHS; 3rd DECA Regl Comp 84; 3rd DECA ST Comp 84; NY ST U Albany; Accntng.

TETTA, ANNALINA; Yonkers HS; Yonkers, NY; (Y); Intnl Clb; Cit Awd; Ntl Merit Ltr; Soc Stud Awd 82-83; Soc Stud Merit & Achvt Awd 84-85; Sci.

TETTERIS, BILLY; Mineola HS; Albertson, NY; (Y); Key Clb; Yrbk Stf; High Hon Roll; Acctng.

TEUDNOWSKI, JANET; Forestville HS; Forestville, NY; (Y); Ski Clb; Varsity Clb; Bsktbl; Var Sftbl; JV Var Vllybl; NHS; Church Yth Grp; 4-H; GAA; Girl Scts; Fredonia ST; Bio.

TEWANI, ALKA; Fox Lane HS; Katonah, NY; (Y); 70/300; Camera Clb; FBLA; VP JA; Yrbk Phtg; Yrbk Sprt Ed; Yrbk Stf; Powder Puff Ftbl; JV Socr; Var Capt Sftbl; Outstndng Commitment Photography 84-85; Outstndng Shrthnd & Keybrdng 82-83 & 83-84; Outstndng Span 83; Fshn Inst Tech; Fshn Merch.

TEWES, ERIC M; Pelham Memorial HS; Pelham, NY; (Y); Office Aide; Radio Clb; Ski Clb; Hon Roll; Prfct Atten Awd; Hnrs Physics 85-86; Pre-Med.

TEWEY, MARGARET; Roy C Ketcham HS; Fishkill, NY; (S); AFS; Chorus; School Play; Symp Band; Lit Mag; Pres Stu Cncl; DAR Awd; High Hon Roll; NHS; Rotary Awd; PA ST U; Pre Law.

TEXIDOR, JOSE; Walton HS; Bronx, NY; (Y); Capt Swmmng; Tennis; Prfct Atten Awd; Pediatrician.

TEZAK, CHRISTINE; Johns Burke Catholic HS; West Point, NY; (Y); 7/140; Church Yth Grp; School Play; Stage Crew; Nwsp Rptr; Vllybl; High Hon Roll; NHS; Outstndng Achvt Eng 84; Boston Coll; Pol Sci.

THAI, SENH; New Utrecht HS; Brooklyn, NY; (Y); Nwsp Rptr; Apieta Arista 85; Awd Geo, Vlbll, Englsh 5 & Lab Tech 84 & 85; NY U; Med.

THAKUR, SANJIV K; Dansville SR HS; Dansville, NY; (Y); 12/146; Computer Clb; FBLA; Math Tm; Ski Clb; Varsity Clb; Stage Crew; JV Var Bowling; JV Var Socr; High Hon Roll; NYS Rgnts Schlrshp Wnr 85; Elec Comp Engr.

THALER, LEONARD; East Meadow HS; East Meadow, NY; (S); Var Capt Tennis; Pres NHS; Computer Clb; FBLA; Math Tm; Nwsp Rptr; Socr; Hon Roll; Ntl Merit Ltr; Acadmc All-Am 85.

THALMANN, F CHRISTOPHER; Cicero-North Syracuse HS; Liverpool, NY; (S); 70/622; Boy Scts; Exploring; JV Trk; Hon Roll; Phys Sci.

THAM, KHAI; Far Rockaway HS; Far Rockaway, NY; (Y); 3/300; Key Clb; Office Aide; Scholastic Bowl; Teachers Aide; Capt Tennis; Wrstlng; Hon Roll; Queens Coll Awd 84; Daily News Super Yth 85; Med.

THATCHER, MATT; Kings Park HS; Kings Pk, NY; (Y); Var Bsktbl; Var Capt Ftbl; Var Lcrss; Wt Lftg; Hnrbl Ment Ftbl; All Lge; Acctng.

THAYER, JOHN A; Panama Central Schl; Ashville, NY; (Y); 5/75; Pep Clb; Pres Frsh Cls; VP Soph Cls; VP Jr Cls; VP Sr Cls; Pres Stu Cncl; Var Bsktbl; Var Ftbl; Hon Roll; NHS; Jamestown CC; Art.

THAYER, JOHN P; Ilion JR-SR HS; Ilion, NY; (Y); 11/118; Church Yth Grp; Band; Chorus; Church Choir; Jazz Band; Mrchg Band; Orch; Swing Chorus; Yrbk Stf; NHS; Regents Schlrshp 85; NY ST Senate Stu Policy Forum 85; NY ST U Potsdam; Music Ed.

THEBAUD, SANDRA; The Mary Louis Acad; Richmond Hill, NY; (Y); Hosp Aide; Library Aide; Outstndng Achvt Awd 83; Psych.

THEIRSE, DARRYL; St Agnes Cathedral HS; Hempstead, NY; (Y); 12/425; Pres Drama Clb; Pres Spanish Clb; School Play; Variety Show; Stu Cncl; High Hon Roll; Hon Roll; Jr NHS; NHS; Ntl Merit Ltr; Admn Awd, Excel Thtre Arts, Cuj Laude Awd 85; Brown U; Lib Arts.

THEISE, MICHAEL; Binghamton Central HS; Binghamton, NY; (Y); 35/560; Lcrss; Tennis.

THEOBALD, CAROL L; H C Williams-Canton Central HS; Canton, NY; (Y); 19/140; 4-H; Ed Chrmn Lit Mag; Var Co-Capt Bsktbl; Var Co-Capt Sftbl; High Hon Roll; VP NHS; Varsity Clb; Cit Awd; 4-H Awd; Elmira Coll Schlrshp 84; Regnts Schlrshp 85; Stu Of Mnth 85; Cornell U; Lndscp Arch.

THEODORAKAKOS, JENNY; Long Island City HS; Astoria, NY; (Y); 3/579; Math Clb; Cit Awd; French Hon Soc; High Hon Roll; Mu Alp Tht; NHS; Bus Hnr Soc 85; Govt Svngs Bnd On Merit 82; Hist Medal On Merit 82; St Johns U; Pharm.

THEODORE, LUCY; Canarste HS; Brooklyn, NY; (Y); 19/561; Church Yth Grp; Cmnty Wkr; French Clb; Hosp Aide; Science Clb; Teachers Aide; Church Choir; Yrbk Stf; Swmmng; Tennis; Sylvester Awd, Uft Schlrshp 85; Pres Volntr Awd 84; Blck Stdnt Yr 85; Resrch Awd; St Lawrence U; Pre-Med.

THEODORE, SOPHIA; Potsdam Central HS; Potsdam, NY; (Y); 15/120; AFS; Girl Scts; Math Clb; Math Tm; Orch; Nwsp Stf; High Hon Roll; NHS; Dance Clb; Commndtn Exclnce Biol 84; Awd Of Merit Summr Poetry Cont 84; Awd Of Merit Octoberfest Poetry Cont 83; Psych.

THERENCY, MARIE MAGDALA; Cathedral HS; Brklyn, NY; (Y); 100/290; Church Yth Grp; FNA; Hosp Aide; Church Choir; Mrchg Band; Capt Gym; Phys Ftns Awd 83; Gymnstcs Awd & Mdls 82-85; Prfct Atten Awd 82; Med Tech.

THERIAULT, BRIAN; Gouverneur HS; Gouverneur, NY; (Y); Church Yth Grp; Trs 4-H; Socr; Hon Roll.

THERO, DANIEL P; La Salle Inst; Latham, NY; (Y); 1/88; Am Leg Boys St; Service Clb; Drill Tm; Nwsp Rptr; Crs Cntry; Trk; High Hon Roll; Trs NHS; ROTC; Off Frsh Cls; Rensselaer Mdl Excel In Sci & Math 85; Medcl.

THIBAUT, MICHELE B; Hilton Central HS; Hilton, NY; (Y); 48/299; Sec Church Yth Grp; Ski Clb; Church Choir; Var Fld Hcky; JV Sftbl; High Hon Roll; Hon Roll; Prfct Atten Awd; Princpls Lst 84; Oswego ST Coll; Mth.

THIEBLEMONT, MICHAEL A; Sayville HS; Sayville, NY; (Y); Exploring; Stage Crew; Im Swmmng; Hon Roll; Ntl Merit Schol; U NY Stony Brook; Pre Med.

THIEL, ALAN RIED; Freeport HS; Freeport, NY; (Y); Ski Clb; Var Socr; US Marine Corp Dstngshd Athl 85.

THIEL, DARCI; Royalton-Hartland HS; Lockport, NY; (Y); 6/125; Church Yth Grp; Drama Clb; Pres Sec Chorus; Swing Chorus; Var Bsktbl; Capt Cheerleading; Pres NHS; Pep Clb; School Musical; School Play; Regnts Schlrshp 85; All ST Womns Choir 84; Grand Rapids Baptist; Mssnry.

THIELE, ROBERT; Kings Park SR HS; Kings Pk, NY; (Y); 37/420; Church Yth Grp; Hosp Aide; Service Clb; Var JV Bsktbl; High Hon Roll; Jr NHS; NHS; Spanish NHS; JV Lcrss; Spnsh Nat Hnr Scty 83; Med.

THIER, KRISTA D; Hahn HS; Apo New York, NY; (Y); Drama Clb; Pep Clb; School Play; Rep Stu Cncl; Var Capt Cheerleading; JV Gym; High Hon Roll; Hon Roll; SFB Arts & Crafts Art Shw 2nd Pl Rbn 84; Comm Art.

THIERMAN, DONALD; Olean HS; Olean, NY; (Y); 66/250; Church Yth Grp; Var Trk; Im Vllybl; Var Wrstlng.

THIIM, CHRISTIAN; Onteora Central HS; Chichester, NY; (Y); Am Leg Boys St; Math Tm; Band; Concert Band; Mrchg Band; Yrbk Phtg; Crs Cntry; Socr; Trk; High Hon Roll; Raised Funds For Amer Cancer Soc 82; Ski Tm; Binghamton; Mech Engrng.

THISTLE, MEGAN; Painted Post West HS; Painted Post, NY; (Y); Chorus; School Musical; JV Trk; NHS; Phys Therapy.

THOM, JEAN K; High School Of Art And Design; Brooklyn, NY; (Y); 12/439; Teachers Aide; Nwsp Stf; Hon Roll; NHS; Prfct Atten Awd; Ntl Art Hnr Soc; Fashion Inst Of Tech; Fshn Dsgn.

THOM, TERRIE L; Newfane Senior HS; Burt, NY; (Y); 27/166; Drama Clb; Library Aide; Math Clb; Varsity Clb; Y-Teens; Chorus; School Musical; Stage Crew; Var Trk; Hon Roll; Regnts Schlrshp 85; U Of Buffalo; Pre-Law.

THOMANN, DAVID J; Webster HS; Webster, NY; (Y); Exploring; German Clb; Ski Clb; Band; JV Var Bsbl; JV Socr; High Hon Roll; Outstndng Math Stu 83; Cert Schlrshp German 85; Cert Hnr Keybrdng 85; Engrng.

THOMAS, ANASTASIA; The Righ Schl Of Fashion Industri; Bayside, NY; (Y); FCA; GAA; Girl Scts; JA; Service Clb; Stage Crew; Yrbk Stf; Bsktbl; Cheerleading; Coach Actv.

THOMAS, ANDREW S; Professional Childrens Schl; Schenectady, NY; (Y); Camera Clb; Schlrshp Schl Amer Ballet 81-85; David Kahane Schlrshp Prof Childrn Schl 81-85; NY ST Schl Art 82-83; Danc.

THOMAS, ANGELICA L; Richmond Hill HS; Richmond Hill, NY; (Y); Debate Tm; Drama Clb; English Clb; Nwsp Ed-Chief; Rep Frsh Cls; Rep Soph Cls; Sec Jr Cls; Trs Stu Cncl; JV Var Crs Cntry; NHS; Super Yth Awd 83-85; Hnr Rl Achvt 82-85; Frgn Lang Hnr Soc Span & Frnch 82-85; Intl Reltns.

THOMAS, ANGIE; Liverpool HS; Liverpool, NY; (Y); Camera Clb; Dance Clb; DECA; Drama Clb; French Clb; FBLA; JA; Library Aide; Varsity Clb; Band; Assoc Schl Inc; Stewardess.

THOMAS, ANN; Oneida HS; Oneida, NY; (S); 2/225; Sec VP Computer Clb; Key Clb; Spanish Clb; Nwsp Stf; Ed Yrbk Stf; High Hon Roll; Jr NHS; Sec NHS; Sal; Proj-Site Math Sci Pgm; Pres Phy Fitness Awd; Colgate U Semnr Pgm; Engr.

THOMAS, ANTHONY; William Howard Taft HS; Bronx, NY; (Y); Hunter Coll; Comp Sci.

THOMAS, AUDRIS; A Philip Randolph Campus; Jamaica, NY; (Y); 85/250; Debate Tm; Girl Scts; Chorus; Church Choir; Concert Band; School Play; Var Bowling; Sftbl; Hon Roll; Awds For Sfbl Tm 84-85; Awd For Bwlng Tm; Cornell U; Com Prog.

THOMAS, BILL; Sherendahowa HS; Rexford, NY; (Y); 53/650; Var Bsbl; Var Bsktbl; Var Ftbl; High Hon Roll; NHS; Principals Awd 83; Aerontcl Engrng.

THOMAS, CALVAN L; Parishville Hopkinton CS HS; Parishville, NY; (Y); Aud/Vis; Teachers Aide; Varsity Clb; Band; Concert Band; Jazz Band; Mrchg Band; Symp Band; Variety Show; JV Var Bsbl; Tchrs Aid Awd 84-85; Technel Careers Inst; Welding.

THOMAS, COLLEEN A; Massena Central HS; Hogansburg, NY; (Y); Cmnty Wkr; JV Sftbl; JV Var Vllybl; Bus Admin.

THOMAS, DARLENE; Franklin Acad; N Bangor, NY; (Y); Church Yth Grp; Hst FBLA; Hosp Aide; 1st Pl Awd Filng 85; Legal Sec.

THOMAS, DAVID; Kenmore East SR HS; Buffalo, NY; (Y); 8/330; Mathletes; Math Clb; Varsity Clb; JV Bsbl; Var Bsktbl; Diving; Ftbl; Golf; High Hon Roll; NHS; NYS Rgnts Schlrshp 85; Frank C Densberger & Luke Welgoss Memrl Awds 85; NY ST U-Buffalo; Pre Med.

THOMAS, DEANA; South Park HS; Buffalo, NY; (Y); Nrsng.

THOMAS, DINAH; Trott Vocational HS; Niagara Falls, NY; (Y); 55/140; Church Yth Grp; Church Choir; Yrbk Stf; NHS; Contenental Beauty Schl; Csmtlg.

THOMAS, FELICIA; Elmira Free Acad; Elmira, NY; (Y); Computer Clb; JA; Y-Teens; Bsktbl; Sftbl; Trk; High Hon Roll; Hon Roll; Data Entry Clerk.

THOMAS, GARY; Murry Bergtraum HS; Brooklyn, NY; (Y); 150/475; JA; Teachers Aide; Prfct Atten Awd; Math Algbr; Queens Coll; Comp Sci.

THOMAS, GEORGETTE; Tamarac HS; Troy, NY; (Y); Boy Scts; Varsity Clb; Yrbk Stf; Rep Jr Cls; Rep Sr Cls; JV Var Bsktbl; JV Var Socr; Var Sftbl; Hon Roll.

THOMAS, IMOGEN; Curtis HS; Staten Island, NY; (Y); Church Yth Grp; Teachers Aide; Church Choir; Drill Tm; Prfct Atten Awd; Merit Rl 82-85; Bus Mgmt.

THOMAS, JENNIFER; Eastridge HS; Rochester, NY; (Y); 26/150; Church Yth Grp; Spanish Clb; Sec Varsity Clb; Band; Church Choir; Drm Mjr(t); Jazz Band; Mrchg Band; School Musical; Trs Soph Cls; Fredonia; Bio.

THOMAS, JOHN; Yonkers HS; Yonkers, NY; (Y); 98/398; Aud/Vis; Computer Clb; Library Aide; Varsity Clb; Stage Crew; Bsbl; Wt Lftg; High Hon Roll; Soc Stds Hnrs Awd; Cert Of Exc; Pace Bus Schl; Comp Prgmr.

THOMAS, JOHN T; Caledonia-Mumford Central Schl; Caledonia, NY; (Y); 36/94; Am Leg Boys St; Pres Science Clb; Pres Soph Cls; VP Stu Cncl; Stat Bsktbl; Var Crs Cntry; Stat Sftbl; Var Tennis; Stat Vllybl; Hon Roll; Nazareth Coll; Accntnt.

THOMAS, KATHLEEN; John C Birdlebough HS; Phoenix, NY; (Y); Hosp Aide; Latin Clb; Band; Mrchg Band; VP Soph Cls; Sec Jr Cls; Sec Sr Cls; Stu Cncl; JV Cheerleading; High Hon Roll; U Buffalo; Nuclr Med Tech.

THOMAS, KELLI; Rome Free Acad; Rome, NY; (Y); Intnl Clb; Key Clb; Concert Band; Mrchg Band; Trs Sr Cls; JV Var Fld Hcky; JV Vllybl; Hon Roll; NHS; Ski Clb; MIP Fld Hcky 84; Natl JHA 85; Engrng.

THOMAS, KELLY M; Whitesboro SR HS; Utica, NY; (Y); 10/325; Acpl Chr; Madrigals; Swing Chorus; Sec Lit Mag; Hon Roll; Jr NHS; NHS; Intnl Clb; Spanish Clb; Carmencita De Pickett Spnsh Awd 84; Sound Of Amer Hnr Band & Chorus 84; Phrmcy.

THOMAS, KRISTINE M; Honeoye Central Schl; Hemlock, NY; (Y); 9/61; VP Sr Cls; Var JV Bsktbl; Var JV Socr; High Hon Roll; NHS; NY ST Bsktbl Chs Assc Acad Tm 85; NY ST Regents Nrsng Schlrshp 85; Army Schlr/Athl Awd 85; Brigham Young U; Nrs.

THOMAS, LENA; Newburgh Free Acad; Newburgh, NY; (Y); 133/629; French Clb; Sci Awd; Upward Bound 84; Ntl Hnr Soc Awd 84; Newburgh Free Acad Lassies Clb Awd 85; Fash Merch.

THOMAS, LEONTYNE A; Hunter College HS; Laurelton, NY; (Y); Model UN; Band; JV Bsktbl; Ntl Merit SF; Pre Med.

THOMAS, LYDIA T; George W Wingate HS; Brooklyn, NY; (Y); JA; Teachers Aide; Prfct Atten Awd; Cert Prtcptn Arista 84; Prin Lst 85; Doc.

THOMAS, MARY; Hannibal Central Schl; Hannibal, NY; (Y); Church Yth Grp; Cmnty Wkr; French Clb; Quiz Bowl; Swmmng; High Hon Roll; Hon Roll; Pre-Med.

THOMAS, MICHAEL B; Hackley Schl; Yonkers, NY; (Y); 23/95; Dance Clb; VP Key Clb; ROTC; VP Service Clb; Var Ftbl; Var Swmmng; Var Trk; Hon Roll; Intl Rel.

THOMAS, NADIA; Midwood HS; Brooklyn, NY; (Y); Drama Clb; Girl Scts; Hosp Aide; Chorus; Badmtn; Cheerleading; Crs Cntry; Trk; NYU; Pre-Med.

THOMAS, PATRICK; South Shore HS; Brooklyn, NY; (Y); PAVAS; Varsity Clb; Nwsp Stf; Lit Mag; Gym; Socr; Art Edtr Schl Nespapr 85; 2nd Pl Indust Art Slkscrn Mirror 84; 1st Pl Indust Arts Mech Drwngs 85; Cornell U; Aero Engrng.

THOMAS, PATTI; Lyndonville Central HS; Waterport, NY; (S); 4/60; Varsity Clb; Band; Capt Color Guard; Concert Band; VP Frsh Cls; Cheerleading; Hon Roll; NHS; Pre Med.

THOMAS, PENNY; Hendrick Hudson HS; Montrose, NY; (Y); 11/200; Drama Clb; Sec Exploring; Drill Tm; School Play; Yrbk Stf; Jr Cls; Capt Cheerleading; Sftbl; High Hon Roll; NHS; Rgnts Schlrshp 85; Presntl Acad Ftnss Awd 85; Dr Vincent Haight Awd 84; PA ST; Math.

THOMAS, RENU; Wellsville HS; Wellsville, NY; (Y); Pres Debate Tm; Intnl Clb; NFL; Capt Quiz Bowl; Pres Speech Tm; Nwsp Ed-Chief; Rep Soph Cls; Cit Awd; High Hon Roll; Pres NHS; Qual Natl Cathlc Fornsc Leag Champ 83-85; Spkr Awds Var Debt Tourn 84-85; Law.

THOMAS, SARAH; Geneva HS; Geneva, NY; (Y); Church Yth Grp; Sec Cmnty Wkr; Ski Clb; Trs Jr Cls; JV Var Cheerleading; Hon Roll; Latin Achvt Awd 82-83; Fndraiser Bsktbl Chrldng 84-85.

THOMAS, SARAH; Hastings HS; Hastings-On-Hudsn, NY; (S); 2/117; AFS; Band; Chorus; Orch; Rep Jr Cls; Bsktbl; Fld Hcky; Sftbl; NHS; Ntl Merit Ltr; George Washington U Awd 84; Westchester Area All ST Band 83-85; All Am Band Hall Fame 83-85.

THOMAS, SHARON; John F Kennedy HS; Utica, NY; (Y); Church Yth Grp; 4-H; Key Clb; Church Choir; Rep Stu Cncl; Vllybl; Hon Roll; Syracuse U; Accntnt.

THOMAS, SIMEON; Cardinal Hayes HS; New York, NY; (Y); 33/264; Church Yth Grp; Yrbk Stf; Prfct Atten Awd.

THOMAS, SUSAN; Beacon HS; Beacon, NY; (Y); 1/216; Key Clb; Varsity Clb; Trs Soph Cls; Trs Jr Cls; Cheerleading; Sftbl; High Hon Roll; Jr NHS; NHS; Val; Comp Sci.

THOMAS, TANIA; Saint Catharines Acad; Bronx, NY; (Y); Merit Awd 78; Outstndng Math Wrk 79; Elem Ed.

THOMAS, TRACEY; Kensington HS; Buffalo, NY; (Y); JA; Teachers Aide; Chorus; Drill Tm; Morgan U; Accntnt.

THOMAS, TREVOR; Medina HS; Medina, NY; (Y); 30/170; L Bsbl; L Bsktbl; L Ftbl; Hon Roll; Honorati 84-85; Houser Men Awd 82-83; Sprtmnshp Awd 83-84.

THOMAS, YANIC; Northeastern Acad; New York, NY; (S); Church Yth Grp; Drama Clb; Hosp Aide; Drill Tm; Flag Corp; School Play; Variety Show; Nwsp Ed-Chief; Nwsp Rptr; Nwsp Stf; Geo Awd; Pathfinder Yr Awd; Alg Awd; Med.

THOMASES, ANDREW N; Clarkstown High Schl North; New City, NY; (Y); 5/450; Math Clb; Math Tm; Band; Trk; High Hon Roll; Outstndng Jr Sci 85; Acad Sci Merit 85; Am Chem Soc Test 84; Sci.

THOMASSON, DEBRA; East Islip HS; Islip Terrace, NY; (Y); 8/475; Cmnty Wkr; Political Wkr; Stu Cncl; Var L Tennis; High Hon Roll; NHS; Pres Schlr; Hon Roll; Jr NHS; Hnr Soc & Rgnts Schlrshps 85; Soc Dstngshd Am HS Stu 84; SUNY Stony Brook; Pol Sci.

THOMPSON, ALBERT; Ticonderoga HS; Ticonderoga, NY; (Y); Church Yth Grp; JV Bsbl; JV Var Bsktbl; Hon Roll; Actg.

THOMPSON, AMY C; Hilton Central HS; Hilton, NY; (Y); Concert Band; Jazz Band; Mrchg Band; School Musical; Symp Band; High Hon Roll; Hon Roll; Symphc Band Cncrt Mstr NW Arts Cncl Awd 84-85; Symphc Band Outstndng Feml Musicn & Marchg Band 84-85; Monroe CC; Lib Arts.

THOMPSON, ANNE; Notre Dame Acad; Staten Island, NY; (Y); 2/93; Concert Band; Capt Crs Cntry; Var Trk; NHS; Ntl Merit SF; Med.

THOMPSON, ANTHONY M; Mt Saint Michael Acad; Bronx, NY; (Y); 88/308; JV Crs Cntry; Im Ftbl; JV Var Trk; Hon Roll; 2nd Hnrs 84; NY U; Jrnlst.

THOMPSON, BRENDA; Far Rockaway HS; Far Rockaway, NY; (Y); Chorus; Church Choir; Gym; Swmmng; Trk; Vllybl; High Hon Roll; God Cntry Awd; Prfct Atten Awd; Law.

THOMPSON, BRIAN; Oakfield-Alabama Central HS; Basom, NY; (Y); Chess Clb; 4-H; Letterman Clb; Varsity Clb; Ftbl; Trk; Wt Lftg; Wrstlng; Hon Roll; NHS; Bus Math Awd-Hghst Avg 83-84; Bus.

THOMPSON, BRYAN D; Dansville SR HS; Dansville, NY; (Y); 32/150; Am Leg Boys St; Spanish Clb; Varsity Clb; Chorus; Jazz Band; Var L Ftbl; Suny Geneseo; Bio-Chem.

THOMPSON, CARLA; Wheatland Chili HS; Scottsville, NY; (Y); Sec Exploring; Band; Chorus; Concert Band; Jazz Band; Mrchg Band; School Musical; Nwsp Rptr; Nwsp Stf; Yrbk Stf; Hghst Avg Awd Readg 81; Theocratic Mnstry Schl; Publ Sv.

THOMPSON, CARMEN N; Kensington HS; Buffalo, NY; (Y); 24/197; Church Yth Grp; JA; Pep Clb; Church Choir; Hon Roll; Canisius Clg; Comm.

THOMPSON, CAROLE; Gowanda Central Schl; Irving, NY; (Y); Key Clb; Spanish Clb; Band; Chorus; Concert Band; Mrchg Band; Rep Frsh Cls; Rep Stu Cncl; Var JV Bsktbl; Stat Lcrss; Cornell; Law.

THOMPSON, CHRISTOPHER HARLOW; St Josephs By The Sea HS; Staten Island, NY; (Y); Church Yth Grp; Cmnty Wkr; Yrbk Ed-Chief; JV L Bsktbl; JV L Bsktbl; Im Bowling; Coach Cmnty Bsktbl Tm 84-85; Loyola; Finc.

THOMPSON, DAVID; Bishop Kearney HS; Rochester, NY; (Y); Service Clb; Bowling; High Hon Roll; Hon Roll; JETS Awd; NHS; Ntl Merit Ltr; Rochester Inst Of Tech; Engr.

THOMPSON, DEBBIE; Hornell SR HS; Hornell, NY; (Y); AFS; Latin Clb; Band; Concert Band; Mrchg Band; Sec Frsh Cls; Stu Cncl; JV Var Cheerleading; Bio.

THOMPSON, DELIA D; Grace H Dodge Vocational HS; Bronx, NY; (Y); Church Yth Grp; Church Choir; RCT Schlrshp 85; SUNY New Paltz.

THOMPSON, DENISE; Bishop Loughlin Memorial HS; Brooklyn, NY; (S); Church Yth Grp; Office Aide; Hon Roll; NHS; Jazz Band; High Hnrs 84; Nrs.

THOMPSON, DONNA; Windham Ashland Jewett Central HS; Jewett, NY; (S); 5/42; Drama Clb; French Clb; Chorus; Church Choir; School Play; Yrbk Stf; Pres Frsh Cls; Sec Pres Stu Cncl; Var Capt Cheerleading; Hon Roll; Sociology.

THOMPSON, ELIZABETH; Cicero Nroth Syracuse HS; Clay, NY; (S); 103/622; Church Yth Grp; Girl Scts; Teachers Aide; Stage Crew; Rep Jr Cls; Hon Roll.

THOMPSON, HOLLY; Ticonderoga HS; Ticonderoga, NY; (Y); 4-H; Key Clb; Varsity Clb; Rep Frsh Cls; JV Capt Bsktbl; Var L Socr; Var L Sftbl; High Hon Roll; NHS; Prfct Atten Awd; Phy Thrpy.

THOMPSON, JERRY; Potsdam SR HS; Potsdam, NY; (Y); Aud/Vis; School Musical; Stage Crew; SUNY Canton; Engnr Tech.

THOMPSON, JILL E; Oswego HS; Oswego, NY; (Y); Church Yth Grp; Ski Clb; Variety Show; Var L Bsktbl; Var L Cheerleading; Powder Puff Ftbl; Var Vllybl; Abilene Christian U; Secdry Ed.

THOMPSON, JIM; Grand Island HS; Grand Island, NY; (Y); Church Yth Grp; Varsity Clb; Church Choir; Var L Ftbl; Var Capt Swmmng; JV Trk; Niagara Frontier Athltc Yth Cncl 84-85; Specl Olympcs Chrmn 85; Valpariaso U; Bus Adm.

THOMPSON, JULIE; Madrid-Waddington HS; Chase Mills, NY; (Y); Church Yth Grp; Girl Scts; Chorus; Church Choir; School Musical; School Play; Ice Hcky; Socr; Swmmng; Vllybl; Elem Tchr.

THOMPSON, KAREN; Kings Park SR HS; Kings Pk, NY; (Y); Art Clb; Church Yth Grp; Drama Clb; Girl Scts; Office Aide; VICA; Chorus; Church Choir; Stage Crew; Off Frsh Cls; Natl Lang Arts Olympiad 83; VICA Geers 85; VICA Hands 85.

THOMPSON, KAREN H Y; Midwood HS; Brooklyn, NY; (Y); 198/600; Church Yth Grp; Drama Clb; Service Clb; Concert Band; Yrbk Stf; Cheerleading; Prfct Atten Awd; Regents Schlrshp 85; Corp Law.

THOMPSON, KATHLEEN; Olean HS; Olean, NY; (Y); Aud/Vis; 4-H; FHA; Library Aide; Office Aide; Science Clb; Teachers Aide; Chorus; Color Guard; School Musical.

THOMPSON, KATHLEEN; Queensbury HS; Glens Falls, NY; (Y); Key Clb; Spanish Clb; VFW Post 6196 Annisdean Mem Awd 85; Mohawk Valley CC; Med.

THOMPSON, KATRINA; Oakfield-Alabama Central HS; Oakfield, NY; (Y); French Clb; Varsity Clb; Band; Chorus; Jazz Band; Mrchg Band; Pres Frsh Cls; Rep Stu Cncl; Crs Cntry; JV Socr; MIP Trck 84-85; Hnr Roll 82-84; Geneseo; Biochem.

THOMPSON, KELLY L; Bloomfield Central Schl; Canandaigua, NY; (Y); 4/89; Chess Clb; Pres VP 4-H; Var Bsktbl; Var Socr; Var Sftbl; Var Trk; Cit Awd; High Hon Roll; NHS; Ntl Merit SF; Dairylea Yng Coop Fred H Sexaver Awd 84; Frtnghty Awd 84; West Point.

THOMPSON, KEVIN; Silver Creek Central HS; Silver Creek, NY; (Y); Key Clb; Ski Clb; Spanish Clb; Varsity Clb; Var Bsbl; Var L Crs Cntry; Var L Ftbl; Church Yth Grp; Band; Concert Band.

THOMPSON, KIRSTEN; Port Richard HS; Staten Isld, NY; (Y); 40/550; Church Yth Grp; Drama Clb; Office Aide; Church Choir; School Musical; Hon Roll; Prfct Atten Awd; 2nd Pl Ntl Frnch Concours 85; Prfct Sndy Schl Atndnc 85; Temple U; Elem Tchr.

THOMPSON, LORI; Kenmore East SR HS; Kenmore, NY; (Y); Pep Clb; Var Cheerleading; JV Swmmng; Hon Roll; Schl Svc Awd 85; Math.

THOMPSON, MARIA; Attica Central HS; Attica, NY; (Y); AFS; Chorus; Yrbk Rptr; Yrbk Stf; Var Stat Crs Cntry; Mgr(s); Var Trk; E MI U; Psych.

THOMPSON, MARY BETH; Mt Mercy Acad; Buffalo, NY; (Y); 4/204; Pres Spanish Clb; School Play; Stage Crew; High Hon Roll; NHS; Regents Scholar 85; Pres Acad Fit Awd 85; Buffalo Alumnae Panhellenic Assn Awd 85; U Of Buffalo; Law.

THOMPSON, MICHANN; Lafayette HS; Brooklyn, NY; (Y); Library Aide; Office Aide; Political Wkr; Teachers Aide; Nwsp Stf; Yrbk Stf; Cheerleading; Soc Stds Hnr Rll 83; Comm.

THOMPSON, MICHELE; Northport HS; East Northport, NY; (Y); Church Yth Grp; Cmnty Wkr; Girl Scts; Intnl Clb; PAVAS; Spanish Clb; Chorus; School Musical; School Play; Rep Stu Cncl; C W Post; Bus Admin.

THOMPSON, PAUL; Midwood HS; Glendale, NY; (Y); Chess Clb; Band; Concert Band; Jazz Band; Mrchg Band; Stage Crew; Serv Awd 83; St Johns; Army.

THOMPSON, PENNY; York Central Schl; Leicester, NY; (Y); Sec Soph Cls; Sec Jr Cls; Var Cheerleading; Var Socr; Var Sftbl; Var Vllybl; Hon Roll; MVP JV Vllybl; MVP V Cheerldng; Sci.

THOMPSON, ROBIN C; Scotia Glenville HS; Scotia, NY; (Y); Variety Show; Var Capt Socr; Empire ST Tm Soccer 84-85; CDYSL Select Tm 83-84; MVP Awd Girls Soccer 84-85; Bus.

THOMPSON, SHAWN C; Auburn HS; Auburn, NY; (Y); 115/444; Am Leg Boys St; Cmnty Wkr; Pres FBLA; JA; Chorus; High Hon Roll; Soc Stds Hnr; Accntng II Hnr; Future Bus Ldr Of Amer Awd; Coyuga Comm Coll; Bus.

THOMPSON, SHAWNTEL; Frankfurt American HS; Apo New York, NY; (Y); 7/320; Church Yth Grp; FBLA; Pres Keywanettes; Ed Nwsp Rptr; Rep Soph Cls; Rep Stu Cncl; High Hon Roll; NHS; Pres Schlr; Cmnty Wkr; Eagle Acdmc Awd 85; Hnr Grad 85; Talon Ltry Mgzn Poetry Edtr 85; U Of TX Sn Antonio; Bus.

THOMPSON, SUNDAE J; Charlotte JR SR HS; Rochester, NY; (Y); 2/100; Var Capt Bsktbl; Var Capt Sftbl; Var Capt Tennis; Var Capt Vllybl; Bausch & Lomb Sci Awd; Jr NHS; Sal; Model UN; Ski Clb; Band; NY ST Regents Awd; Cornell Natl Schlrshp; US Army Rsrv Natl Schlr Athl Awd; Cornell U; Ntrtnl Sci.

THOMPSON, TERESA; Albion Central HS; Albion, NY; (Y); 32/174; Church Yth Grp; Cmnty Wkr; Band; Concert Band; Drm & Bgl; Flag Corp; Jazz Band; Mrchg Band; Symp Band; Hon Roll; Cert Merit 85; Cmmndtn Report Math II & Comp II 85; Rochester Inst Tech; Comp Engr.

THOMSEN, BILL; Seaford HS; Seaford, NY; (Y); Ice Hcky; High Hon Roll; Hon Roll; 1st Pl Champ Rqtbll Clb 84-85; Archt.

THOMSEN, EVA; South New Berlin Central HS; S New Berlin, NY; (Y); #1 In Class; Pres Jr Cls; Pres Sr Cls; Var Capt Socr; Bausch & Lomb Sci Awd; Cit Awd; DAR Awd; Elks Awd; High Hon Roll; NHS; Val; Ithaca Coll; Phys Thrpy.

THOMSON, JAMES; Clinton SR HS; Clinton, NY; (Y); Boy Scts; French Clb; Anthrplgy.

THOMSON, JAMES; Niagara Wheatfield SR HS; Lake City, FL; (Y); 4-H; VP German Clb; Model UN; Band; Jazz Band; 4-H Awd; High Hon Roll; Hon Roll; NHS; Prfct Atten Awd; Acadmc Hnr Awds 82-85; Mny Hnrs Music 82-85; Law.

THOMSON, REBECCA H; Kingston HS; Rifton, NY; (Y); 10/520; Church Yth Grp; Cmnty Wkr; Acpl Chr; Chorus; Church Choir; Orch; Yrbk Stf; Stu Cncl; High Hon Roll; Jr NHS; SUNY Albany; Pre Med.

THORN, MARY; South Park HS; Buffalo, NY; (Y); French Clb; Office Aide; Varsity Clb; Rep Frsh Cls; Rep Soph Cls; Stu Cncl; Cheerleading; Swmmng; High Hon Roll; Hon Roll.

THORNDIKE JR, EDWARD H; Pittsford Mendon HS; Pittsford, NY; (Y); Drama Clb; Ski Clb; School Play; Pres Stu Cncl; Var Ftbl; Var Lcrss; Wt Lftg; Regenst Schlrshp 85; Wesleyan U; Drama.

THORNDIKE, PATRICIA; Emma Willard Schl; Pownal, VT; (Y); Thesps; School Play; Stage Crew; Yrbk Phtg; Lit Mag; Pres Frsh Cls; JV Capt Fld Hcky; Gym; Lcrss; Score Keeper; JV Fld Hcky MVP 84; Pine Cobble Dramtc Awd 83; Fnlst ESU Shakespeare Recitatn 85; Dram Art.

THORNE, DYON; Christopher Columbus HS; Bronx, NY; (Y); Debate Tm; JA; Office Aide; Chorus; VP Frsh Cls; Wt Lftg; Cit Awd; Hon Roll; Prfct Atten Awd.

THORNER, TERI; Smithtown HS West; Hauppauge, NY; (Y); Natl Beta Clb; Pep Clb; Spanish Clb; Y-Teens; Yrbk Stf; Rep Frsh Cls; Rep Soph Cls; Rep Jr Cls; Rep Sr Cls; Rep Stu Cncl.

THORNHILL, SELENA M; Loguardia H S Of Music & The Arts; Jackson Heights, NY; (Y); 139/588; Drama Clb; Office Aide; Chorus; Church Choir; Drill Tm; Rep Sr Cls; Old Dominion U; Engrng.

THORNTON, JEAN M; Lakeland SR HS; Putnam Valley, NY; (Y); 21/350; Church Yth Grp; Girl Scts; Service Clb; Chorus; Nwsp Ed-Chief; Yrbk Stf; Rep Frsh Cls; Rep Jr Cls; Rep Sr Cls; Rep Stu Cncl; NY ST Rgnts Schlrshp Awd 85; NY ST Schl Music Assn Festvl Lvl V-Excllnt 84; SUNY Binghamton; Math.

THORNTON, JOCELYN; Chenango Forks HS; Binghamton, NY; (Y); FBLA; Ski Clb; School Play; Yrbk Bus Mgr; Trs Jr Cls; Rep Stu Cncl; High Hon Roll; NHS; Rotary Awd; Stu Of Yr For Bus Math 84; Salute Yth Recgntn By Cmnty 85; Gld Hnr Cert 3 Yrs Hnr Roll 85; Syracuse U; Bus Mngmt.

THORNTON, SALLEY A; Marcus Whitman HS; Rushville, NY; (Y); 12/128; Spanish Clb; Varsity Clb; Band; Chorus; School Play; Yrbk Stf; Pres Stu Cncl; JV Var Cheerleading; High Hon Roll; Pres NHS; Regents Schlrshp 85; Cmnctns Profiency Awd 85; Honor Acad Schlrshp 85; Mount Union Coll; Pub Rltns.

THORNTON, TERESA A; Hermon Dekalb Central Schl; Dekalb Jct, NY; (Y); 5/32; Cmnty Wkr; French Clb; Concert Band; School Play; Nwsp Rptr; Yrbk Ed-Chief; Rep Stu Cncl; Hon Roll; NHS; Edwards Telephone Co Annl Essay Cont 84; NYS Regents Nrsng Schlrshp 85; Whiz Quiz Team Cont 82-85; SUNY; Nrsng.

THORP, DEBBIE; Andover Central Schl; Andover, NY; (S); 5/30; Chorus; School Play; Pres Soph Cls; VP Sr Cls; Rep Stu Cncl; Capt Cheerleading; Capt Vllybl; High Hon Roll; GAA; Band; Frshmn Athl Awd 82; Hall Of Fame 85; Afred ST Coll; Bnkng.

THORPE, ANN MARIE; August Martin HS; Brooklyn, NY; (Y); 124/375; Pres FBLA; Office Aide; Var Pep Clb; Teachers Aide; Chorus; Yrbk Stf; Rep Jr Cls; Rep Sr Cls; Var Crs Cntry; Var Trk; Dst Partcptn Cert FLBA 85; Wagner Coll; Bus Admn.

THORPE, DOREEN A; Cornwall Central HS; New Windsor, NY; (Y); 32/198; Church Yth Grp; 4-H; Girl Scts; Ski Clb; Spanish Clb; Teachers Aide; Stat Bsbl; Mgr(s); Powder Puff Ftbl; Score Keeper; C M Velten Tchrs Awd; Prsdntl Ftnss Awd; Fredonia ST; Prof Ed.

THORSEN, ANGELA; Rome Free Acad; Rome, NY; (Y); French Clb; Intnl Clb; Bowling; NHS; Syracuse U; Comp Prgmr.

THORSTEN, YANG NAE; St Barnabas HS; Bronx, NY; (Y); Camera Clb; Camp Fr Inc; Cmnty Wkr; Exploring; GAA; Girl Scts; VP Intnl Clb; Office Aide; Teachers Aide; Varsity Clb; Bus.

THRALL, WILLIAM; Riverhead HS; Riverhead, NY; (Y); Church Yth Grp; JCL; Latin Clb; Mathletes; Acpl Chr; Band; Chorus; Mrchg Band; Orch; Stage Crew; Music Tech.

THRASYBULE, LINDA; Dominican Commercial HS; Queens Vlge, NY; (Y); Drama Clb; Chorus; Gym; Hon Roll; Siena Clb 83-85; Jrnlsm.

THUMAN, JAMES; Islip HS; Islip, NY; (Y); 27/300; Camera Clb; Church Yth Grp; Jazz Band; Nwsp Phtg; Yrbk Phtg; Hon Roll; Clarkson; Military.

THURAU, CARRIE; Alexander Central HS; Alexander, NY; (S); 11/100; Yrbk Stf; Rep Soph Cls; Stu Cncl; Var Cheerleading; Var JV Sftbl; Var JV Vllybl; Hon Roll; Jr NHS; Trs NHS; ST U Of NY Coll Potsdam; Comp.

THURBER, SANDRA; Oakfield-Alabama Central Schl; Basom, NY; (Y); 12/93; Church Yth Grp; Teachers Aide; Band; Church Choir; Mrchg Band; Hon Roll.

THURNHERR, MICHAEL; West Sensca East SR HS; Cheektowaga, NY; (S); 19/365; Trs DECA; VP Pres Varsity Clb; Nwsp Sprt Ed; Yrbk Bus Mgr; Pres Soph Cls; Capt Var Crs Cntry; Capt Var Trk; JC Awd; NHS; Off Frsh Cls; Mst Vlbl Perfmr Cross Cntry 83-84; Ldng Scorer Trk 84; Hghst Acad Achvt Cross Cntry 83-84; Georgetown; Intl Mngmnt.

THURSTON, TAMARA; Marion JR SR HS; Marion, NY; (Y); 8/113; Ski Clb; Varsity Clb; Pres Band; Jazz Band; Mrchg Band; School Play; Var JV Tennis; High Hon Roll; Pres NHS; Key Awd Sibleys Art Shw Dirct Accptnc NY Smmr Schl Arts 83; Area All ST Band Hnr 85; Brigham Young U; Grphc Dsgn.

THWEATT, THOMAS E; Uniondale HS; Uniondale, NY; (Y); 91/480; Aud/Vis; JV Bowling; Crs Cntry; Ntl Merit SF; High Hnr Roll 84; Comp Graph.

THYRET, JUSTINE; Akron HS; Akron, NY; (Y); 21/154; Debate Tm; Ski Clb; Chorus; VP Concert Band; VP Mrchg Band; Bsktbl; Swmmng; Miss Congnlty Snow Queen Pgnt 84; Pastors Schlrshp 85; Liberty Baptist Coll.

TIAMSIC, MARY GRACE; Saint George Acad; Hollis, NY; (Y); Art Clb; Computer Clb; Dance Clb; Ski Clb; Nwsp Phtg; Nwsp Rptr; Nwsp Sprt Ed; Nwsp Stf; Vllybl; Hon Roll; MIT; Robot Tech.

TIBAS, MARIA; Murry Bergtraum HS; Long Is Cy, NY; (Y); 14/576; Yrbk Stf; Hon Roll; Jr NHS; NHS; NY U; Lawyer.

TIBERIA, FRANK; Notre Dame HS; Elmira, NY; (Y); Pep Clb; Ski Clb; Stage Crew; JV Bsbl; JV Var Ftbl; Score Keeper.

TICE, EDWARD; West Hempstead HS; Island Pk, NY; (Y); Band; Concert Band; Drm & Bgl; Jazz Band; Mrchg Band; Orch; Nassau CC; Optician.

TICHENSKY, DOUGLAS A; Red Creek JR SR HS; Red Creek, NY; (Y); Office Aide; Rep Varsity Clb; Stage Crew; Yrbk Stf; Rep Sr Cls; Rep Stu Cncl; Var L Bsbl; JV Socr; Im Wt Lftg; Prfct Atten Awd; U Of NY-DELHI; Crpntr.

TICHY, ANDREW; All Hallows HS; Bronx, NY; (Y); 26/117; Church Yth Grp; Computer Clb; ROTC; Church Choir; Drill Tm; Diving; Swmmng; Wt Lftg; Comp Tech.

TICKNOR, AMANDA; Whitney Point Central HS; Whitney Point, NY; (Y); 3/120; Sec French Clb; Varsity Clb; Chorus; Var Tennis; High Hon Roll; NHS; Pres Schlr; Church Yth Grp; Regnts & Clute Memrl & Raola Hibbard Memrl Schlrshps 85; Broome CC; Med Recrd Tech.

TICKNOR, JEFFREY L; John Marshall JR SR HS; Rochester, NY; (Y); 9/184; Church Yth Grp; French Clb; Red Cross Aide; Spanish Clb; Teachers Aide; Mrchg Band; Variety Show; Rep Stu Cncl; Mgr Ftbl; Prfct Atten Awd; US Achvt Acad Awd 84; US Achvt Acad Ntl Ldrshp & Serv Awd 85; Canisius Coll; Accntng.

TICKNOR, JENNIFER M; Laurens Central Schl; Otego, NY; (Y); Cmnty Wkr; Key Clb; Political Wkr; Red Cross Aide; Service Clb; Yrbk Stf; High Hon Roll; Ntl Merit Ltr; St Schlr; Clark Foundation Scholarship 85; SUNY Geneseo; Engl Journalism.

TIEDE, LYNN; Vilseck American HS; Apo, NY; (Y); 1/35; Hosp Aide; JCL; Latin Clb; Letterman Clb; Math Clb; Math Tm; Pep Clb; Scholastic Bowl; Science Clb; Band; Top Biol Stu Awd 83-84; JR Sci & Humnities Symp London 84-85; Intl Stu Ldrshp Inst 84-85; Bus.

TIEDEMANN, ELIZABETH; Skaneateles HS; Skaneateles, NY; (Y); 33/165; Church Yth Grp; Drama Clb; Band; School Musical; Symp Band; Yrbk Phtg; High Hon Roll; NHS; Hon Roll; Regents Schlrshp 85; Acad Schlrshp From Westminster Coll 85; Westminster Coll.

TIEDEMANN, KATHLEEN; Freeport HS; Freeport, NY; (Y); 58/450; Sec Key Clb; Chorus; Nwsp Rptr; Sec Jr Cls; JV Bsktbl; Var Sftbl; Var Tennis; Hon Roll; Stonybrook U; Psychlgy.

TIEDEMANN, ROBERT; H Frank Carey HS; Franklin Square, NY; (Y); Pres Jr Cls; Pres Sr Cls; High Hon Roll; Hon Roll; Hofstra Distngshd Acad Achvt Scholar 85; St Johns Annual Competitv Scholar 85; Chrmn Blood Drive 85; Hofstra U; Acctng.

TIERNAN, CHRISTIN M; Notre Dame Acad; Brooklyn, NY; (Y); 4/91; Church Yth Grp; Cmnty Wkr; Nwsp Stf; Yrbk Stf; NHS; NY ST Regents Schlrshp 85; Fairfield U; English.

TIERNAN, JULIE; Norwood-Norfolk Central HS; Chase Mills, NY; (Y); Hon Roll.

TIERNEY, JEAN M; Bay Shore HS; Brightwaters, NY; (Y); 21/400; Drama Clb; Band; Chorus; Church Choir; Concert Band; Mrchg Band; School Musical; Yrbk Stf; Lit Mag; Socr; Regents Schlrshp Awd 85; Villanova; Arch.

TIERNEY, JENNIFER; Franklin Acad; Malone, NY; (Y); Pres 4-H; French Clb; Varsity Clb; Var L Cheerleading; Cit Awd; 4-H Awd; Hon Roll; Trs NHS; Ntl Merit Ltr; Chrldng Sprt Awd 85; Top Dairy Judge Frm Awd 85; Anml Sci.

TIERNEY, KATHLEEN; Dominican Acad; Flushing, NY; (Y); Latin Clb; School Play; Yrbk Bus Mgr; Rep Soph Cls; Stu Cncl; High Hon Roll; NHS; Rep Frsh Cls; Educ Dev Ntl Cert 83; Hnrbl Merit-Maxima Cum Laude Cert 84; Spanish/Latin Achiev 85.

TIERNEY, PATRICK; Vernon-Verona-Sherrill Ctr Schl; Verona, NY; (Y); 41/249; AFS; Boy Scts; Debate Tm; Latin Clb; Spanish Clb; Thesps; Band; Church Choir; Drm & Bgl; Jazz Band; Congrssnl Medl Merit 85; U Of Rochester; Biomed.

TIERNEY, THOMAS F X; Newfield HS; Coram, NY; (Y); 65/472; Nwsp Rptr; Nwsp Stf; Hon Roll; Gifted & Tlntd Engl & Scl Stds Awd 83; MI ST U; Media Jrnlst.

TIETJEN, MICHAEL; Moore Catholic HS; Staten Isl, NY; (Y); Bsbl; Bsktbl; Prfct Atten Awd; St John Fisher Coll; Mgmt.

TIFFANY, TERESA; Victor Central Schl; Victor, NY; (Y); 8/248; Model UN; Science Clb; Concert Band; Mrchg Band; Var Crs Cntry; JV L Socr; JV L Vllybl; High Hon Roll; Bio.

TIFFT, KIMBERLY; Canastota HS; Canastota, NY; (Y); 27/132; FTA; Science Clb; Teachers Aide; Varsity Clb; Band; Chorus; Yrbk Stf; Tennis; High Hon Roll; Lion Awd; Canastota Tchrs Assn 85; Canastota Liontts 85; Mohawk Valley CC; Humn Svcs.

TIGER, CARYN; East Meadow HS; East Meadow, NY; (S); 86/414; Rep FBLA; Math Clb; Spanish Clb; Temple Yth Grp; Orch; Var Bowling; Var Capt Tennis; U Of Buffalo; Business Admin.

TIGHE, MICHAEL S; Cobleskill Central HS; Howes Cave, NY; (Y); 7/132; Pres Varsity Clb; Band; Mrchg Band; Orch; Var Capt Crs Cntry; Var L Trk; NHS; Ski Clb; DAR Awd; Acadmc Achvt Schrlshp Clarkson U 85-89; NY ST Regnts Schlrshp 85-89; Clarkson U; Indstrl Dist.

TILIGADAS, MARGARITA; Bronx High School Of Science; Flushing, NY; (Y); French Clb; Chorus; Hon Roll; Ntl Merit Ltr; Pres Camera Clb; Science Clb; Teachers Aide; Prfct Atten Awd; Grtr Mtrpltn NY Math Fair Cert Of Merit 85; Srv Awd Cert Phy Sci 83; Coll.

TILISON, DAWN; Scotia-Glenville HS; Scotia, NY; (Y); Var Powder Puff Ftbl; JV Var Sftbl; High Hon Roll; German Awd High Av; Softbl Athltc Awd; Sec.

TILL, JACQUELINE B; Mercy HS; Ridge, NY; (Y); 8/124; Dance Clb; Key Clb; Yrbk Stf; Cheerleading; Trk; High Hon Roll; Hon Roll; Jr NHS; Sec NHS; NEDT Awd; Syracuse U; Food Svc Mgmt.

TILLOTSON, CAROLYN A; St John The Baptist D HS; Brightwaters, NY; (Y); 10/600; Nwsp Rptr; Yrbk Ed-Chief; Ed Lit Mag; Hon Roll; NCTE Awd; NHS; Ntl Merit SF; NEDT Awd; Spanish NHS; Isaac Bashevis Sngr, Schlrshp 85; Magna Cum Laude Natl Latin Ex 82; English.

TILLOTSON, JULIE; Whitney Point HS; Richford, NY; (Y); 9/114; Church Yth Grp; 4-H; French Clb; Chorus; Church Choir; Tennis; High Hon Roll; NHS; Pres Schlr; SUNY; Ed.

TILLOTSON, LAURIE; Whitney Point Central Schl; Richford, NY; (Y); 11/120; VP 4-H; Teachers Aide; Church Choir; Var Tennis; High Hon Roll; Hon Roll; NHS; TAP Awd; ST U NY; Elem Educ.

TIMMEL, CAROLANN; St Joseph By The Sea HS; Staten Island, NY; (Y); Art Clb; Computer Clb; Drama Clb; Acpl Chr; Chorus; School Musical; School Play; Swing Chorus; Yrbk Phtg; Yrbk Stf.

TIMMERMAN, WENDY; Little Falls JR SR HS; Little Falls, NY; (S); 5/100; Church Yth Grp; GAA; Spanish Clb; Concert Band; Mrchg Band; Var Badmtn; Var JV Fld Hcky; High Hon Roll; Hon Roll; NHS; Ntl Hnr Roll Mbr 85; Cnty Dairy Princs Alt 85; Chld Psychlgst.

TIMMERMANS, ROBERT J; Monsignor Farrell HS; Staten Island, NY; (Y); 1/296; Cmnty Wkr; Nwsp Rptr; Rep Soph Cls; High Hon Roll; NHS; Ntl Merit Ltr; Pres Schlr; Val; Ntl Engl, Ldrshp Awds 84-85; Knights Pythias Schlstc Achvt Awd 83-84; Med.

TIMMONS, ANN; Franklin Acad; Malone, NY; (Y); Pep Clb; Spanish Clb; Nwsp Ed-Chief; Nwsp Sprt Ed; Yrbk Sprt Ed; Yrbk Stf; Rep Stu Cncl; JV Var Bsktbl; Prfct Atten Awd; All Nrthrn Vrsty Bsktbl Hon Men, MIP 85; Spn Excllcne Awd 83; Ed.

TIMPSON, CRAIG; Onteora HS; Oliverbridge, NY; (Y); 49/245; Ski Clb; Var Capt Ftbl; Wt Lftg; Hon Roll; St Schlr; Hamilton Coll; Law.

TIN HAN, ERIK; Houghton Acad; Rushford, NY; (Y); 10/28; Hon Roll; Ntl Merit Ltr; Regnts Schlrshp 85; NY ST U Buffalo; Premed.

TINDALE, THOMAS; Bishop Kearney HS; Rochester, NY; (Y); Variety Show; JV Ftbl; Im Sftbl; JV Wrstlng; Sci.

TINGER, ALFRED; Nanuet SR HS; Nanuet, NY; (Y); Exploring; Math Tm; Varsity Clb; JV Ftbl; Var Trk; Wt Lftg; High Hon Roll; Mu Alp Tht; NHS; Pres Schlr; JR Ntl Bllrds Champs 84; Sci Awd 85; SUNY Binghamton; Physc.

TINGUE, AMY; Gowanda Central HS; Gawanda, NY; (Y); 16/125; Pres AFS; VP French Clb; Thesps; Nwsp Rptr; Rep Soph Cls; VP Stu Cncl; Trk; High Hon Roll; Hon Roll; NHS; Dremen Coll; Law.

TINKER, LEON; Brooklyn Tech; Brooklyn, NY; (Y); Church Yth Grp; Band; Swmmng; Advrtsg.

TINNEY, JOSEPH; Le Roy HS; Leroy, NY; (Y); AFS; Am Leg Boys St; Math Tm; Socr; NHS; Latin Clb; Chorus; High Hon Roll; Jr NHS; Sci.

TINNEY, SUSAN; Tioga Central HS; Owego, NY; (S); Dance Clb; Ski Clb; Varsity Clb; Rep Frsh Cls; Rep Soph Cls; Rep Jr Cls; Stu Cncl; Var JV Fld Hcky; JV Sftbl; Physcl Therpy.

TIRADO, ELISSA; Villa Maria Acad; Buffalo, NY; (Y); Church Yth Grp; Computer Clb; Math Clb; High Hon Roll; Hon Roll; Spanish NHS; Cornell U; Vet.

TIRADO, ELIZABETH; Mount Vernon HS; Mt Vernon, NY; (Y); Library Aide; Office Aide; NHS; PTA Griffith Valentino Awd 81; Adm Sec.

TIRADO, GISELA; Mabel Dean Bacon HS; Bronx, NY; (S); 29/299; Yrbk Stf; Rep Soph Cls; Rep Jr Cls; Rep Stu Cncl; Pres Hon Roll; Comm Arts Awd 82; Math & Sci Awd 83; UFT Schlrshp; NYU; Pediatrician.

TIRADO, PAUL; St Agnes HS; New York, NY; (Y); 3/100; VP JA; Yrbk Stf; Sec Stu Cncl; Wt Lftg; VP NHS; Harvard; Bus.

TIRENDI, RICHARD; Valhalla HS; N White Plains, NY; (Y); 25/120; High Hon Roll; Hon Roll; Pres Acad Fitnss Awd 85; Outstndng Stu 83; James Hoffman Memrl Schlrshp 85; Northeastern; Comp Engrng.

TIRONE, LISA; Cardinal O Hara HS; Tonawanda, NY; (S); 14/142; Church Yth Grp; FBLA; Yrbk Stf; Rep Frsh Cls; Rep Soph Cls; Rep Jr Cls; Stu Cncl; JV Capt Cheerleading; High Hon Roll; Business.

TIRRITO, LOUISE; Farmingdale HS; Farmindale, NY; (Y); Trs 4-H; Girl Scts; Merit Roll 80-85; Mth Awd 76-77; Katherine Gibbs Schl; Acctg.

TISCHLER, INGRID; Potsdam HS; Potsdam, NY; (Y); 16/160; French Clb; JA; Varsity Clb; Mgr Yrbk Stf; Rep Stu Cncl; JV Var Bsktbl; JV Var Vllybl; Hon Roll; Jr NHS; NHS; Potsdam Coll; Comp Sci.

TISDALL, STACEY; Cicero-N Syracuse HS; Clay, NY; (S); 83/771; Church Yth Grp; Hosp Aide; Spanish Clb; Stu Cncl; Ftbl; Phy Fitness Awd 82-83; Law.

TISEO, DAVE; Valley Stream Central HS; Valley Stream, NY; (Y); JV Bsbl; JV Wrstlng; Hon Roll; Cvl Lawyr.

TISO, MARCELLO; Clarkstown South HS; Nanuet, NY; (Y); Boy Scts; Church Yth Grp; Computer Clb; Im Ice Hcky; Var L Socr; NY Acad Sci Intern 84-85; Spec Olympcs 82-85; Elec Engr.

TITCOMBE, MATT; Southwestern Central HS; Lakewood, NY; (Y); Church Yth Grp; Letterman Clb; Spanish Clb; Ftbl; Vllybl; Hon Roll; Boston U; Aerospc Engrng.

TITE, CYNTHIA L; Tully Central HS; Tully, NY; (Y); 6/72; French Clb; Band; VP Soph Cls; Trs Jr Cls; Pres Sr Cls; Var Socr; Var Sftbl; Elks Awd; Hon Roll; NHS; Colgate U.

TITOLO, MATT; Curtis HS; Staten Island, NY; (Y); Jolin Jay Coll; Law.

TITONE, ELIZABETH; Curtis HS; Staten Island, NY; (Y); Drama Clb; PAVAS; Stage Crew; Nwsp Phtg; Lit Mag; NY Tech Coll; Grphc Arts.

TITONE, JILL J; Roy C Ketcham HS; Wapp Fls, NY; (Y); Drama Clb; Thesps; Concert Band; School Musical; School Play; Stat Var Bsktbl; JV Capt Socr; High Hon Roll; Jr NHS; NHS; Med.

TITUS, ALBERT H; Sauquoit Valley Central Schl; Sauquoit, NY; (Y); 1/118; Band; Jazz Band; Nwsp Stf; Im Bsktbl; Bowling; Trk; Bausch & Lomb Sci Awd; High Hon Roll; Pres NHS; NEDT Awd; Bausch & Lomb Sci Scholar U Rochester 85; Pres Scholar SUNY Buffalo 85; Hnrs Pgm SUNY Buffalo 85; SUNY Buffalo; Elec Engrng.

TITUS, DAN; Horseheads HS; Horseheads, NY; (Y); 121/407; NFL; Variety Show; JV Var Socr; JV Wrstlng; NY ST Rgnts Schlrshp 85; Crnl Emply Tuition Grnt 85; FL ST U; Htl Adm.

TO, EDWARD HA; Brooklyn Technical HS; Elmhurst, NY; (Y); 40/1200; Math Clb; Math Tm; Pres Science Clb; Ed Lit Mag; Hon Roll; NHS; Comptrllrs Awd 83; Elect Engrng.

TO, QUY; Herbert Holehman HS; Bronx, NY; (Y); Science Clb; Schl Mth & Soc Stud Awds 84 & 85; Columbia U; Med.

TOBACK, KAREN ELLEN; Deer Park HS; Deer Park, NY; (Y); 135/468; Art Clb; Cmnty Wkr; FBLA; Girl Scts; Science Clb; Chorus; School Musical; Lit Mag; Art Awd Mnth 82; Gftd & Tlntd Prog In Suny Farmingdale 83; Farmingdale; TV.

TOBAR, DAVID; Naples American HS; F P O New York, NY; (Y); Am Leg Boys St; Quiz Bowl; Scholastic Bowl; Var Capt Bsktbl; Var L Ftbl; Var L Socr; Bausch & Lomb Sci Awd; Hon Roll; ROTC Air Force Schlrshp 85; Carnegie-Mellon U; Offcr.

TOBAR, SILVIA; Freeport HS; Freeport, NY; (Y); Art Clb; French Clb; Spanish Clb; Chorus; High Hon Roll; NHS; Lang.

TOBBINS, TERRY; Victor Central Schl; Victor, NY; (Y); Science Clb; Trk; High Hon Roll; Hon Roll; Prfct Atten 84-85; Maintaing 90 Or Abv Avg For Yr 83-85; Air Force Acad; Navigatr.

TOBEY, BRIAN; Lansing Central Schl; Lansing, NY; (Y); 5/80; Computer Clb; Spanish Clb; Stage Crew; Socr; Trk; High Hon Roll; Sci, Soc Stds & Spnsh Acad Awds 83-85; Engr.

TOBEY, STACEY; Saugerties HS; Saugerties, NY; (Y); Chorus; Hon Roll; NHS.

TOBIAS, GREG V; Frontier SR HS; Blasdell, NY; (Y); Latin Clb; Gym; Hon Roll; Canisius; Pre-Med.

TOBIN, ELLEN R; Our Lady Of Mercy HS; Rochester, NY; (Y); 8/200; Cmnty Wkr; Pres Latin Clb; NFL; Science Clb; Chorus; Lit Mag; Sec Trs NHS; Math Acclrtd Prog 81-82; Latin Awds 82-84; NY ST Rgnts Schlrshp 85; U Of Richmond; Pre Law.

TOBIN, ERICA; Midwood Hs-Medical Science Inst; Brooklyn, NY; (Y); 50/638; French Clb; Hosp Aide; Math Tm; Concert Band; Rep Frsh Cls; VP Soph Cls; Rep Jr Cls; Church Yth Grp; Cmnty Wkr; Office Aide; Arista, Archon Svc Leag Cert Membrshp Excllnc Svc Chrctr Schlrshp 85; Cert Mert Amer Assn Tchrs Frnch; Bryn Mawr Coll; Biochem.

TOBIN, KELLY; Eldred Central HS; Pond Eddy, NY; (S); Ski Clb; Varsity Clb; Band; Chorus; Madrigals; Yrbk Stf; Trs Soph Cls; Pres Jr Cls; Var L Bsktbl; Var L Socr; Wstrn Sullivan Leag All Leag All-Star Soccer 83-84; Reg All-Star Soccer 83; Orthdntst.

TOBIN, REGINA; Cicero-North Syracuse HS; North Syracuse, NY; (S); 6/622; Church Yth Grp; Exploring; JA; Color Guard; High Hon Roll.

TOBON, LYNN; Moore Catholic HS; Staten Island, NY; (Y); Pres Church Yth Grp; Math Tm; Speech Tm; Chorus; Lit Mag; NHS; Ntl Merit Ltr; Hgh Sccr Math Leag 85.

TOCKARSHEWSKY, ROBERT; St Francis Prep; Flushing, NY; (Y); Am Leg Boys St; Pres Stu Cncl; Bsktbl; Im Ftbl; Im Sftbl; Var Trk; Im Vllybl; Stu Athl Awd 83; Bus.

TODARO, LAURA; Frontier SR HS; Blasdell, NY; (Y); 71/514; French Clb; Science Clb; Chorus; Nwsp Stf; Var Mgr(s); Hon Roll; NHS; Prfct Atten Awd; Girl Scts; Color Guard; Outstndng Wrkr Awd 85; Natl Frnch Tst Merits 83-84; Silver Ldrshp Awd 84; ST U Buffalo; Bus Mngmnt.

TODARO, PAUL; Eden SR HS; Eden, NY; (Y); 27/193; Aud/Vis; Var Socr; JV Tennis; NHS; Alfred U; Ceramic Engrng.

TODARO, PHYLLIS; Letchworth Central HS; Silver Spgs, NY; (Y); Spanish Clb; Varsity Clb; Chorus; Socr; Sftbl; High Hon Roll; Hon Roll; Livingston Cnty Div II All Star Soccer Tm; Ron Smith Sportsmnshp Awd; Regents Nursng Schlrshp Rnnr Up; Marions Whelan Schl Of Nursing.

TODD, BRENT; Norwood-Norfolk Central Schl; Norfolk, NY; (Y); Latin Clb; Band; Mrchg Band; Rep Frsh Cls; Rep Soph Cls; Var Ice Hcky; Hon Roll; Jr NHS; Engrng.

TODD, MICHAEL; Saranac Lake HS; Saranac Lk, NY; (Y); Church Yth Grp; JV Var Ftbl; JV Var Ice Hcky; JV Var Trk; Var Wt Lftg; JV Var Hon Roll; Bus Mgmt.

TODER, NORA; Susan E Wagner HS; Staten Island, NY; (Y); Girl Scts; Band; Concert Band; Mrchg Band; Pep Band; Stage Crew; Swing Chorus; Variety Show; Rep Soph Cls; Rep Jr Cls; Socl Wrk.

TODRANK, GREGORY A; Rome Free Acad; Rome, NY; (Y); Boy Scts; Intnl Clb; Spanish Clb; Band; Mrchg Band; JV Ftbl; High Hon Roll; Hon Roll; Prfct Atten Awd; Eagle Scout 85; Ord Of Arrow 83.

TOELLER, SUSAN; East Hampton HS; E Hampton, NY; (Y); FBLA; Off Jr Cls; Score Keeper; Trk; S Hmpton Coll; Psychtry.

TOENNIESSEN, AMY; De Sales Catholic HS; Lockport, NY; (Y); 4/35; Am Leg Aux Girls St; Cmnty Wkr; Ski Clb; Stat Bsktbl; Cheerleading; Sftbl; Vllybl; Hon Roll; Accntng.

TOFANI, AMY; Liverpool HS; Liverpool, NY; (S); 196/792; Hosp Aide; Off Varsity Clb; VP Stu Cncl; Var L Socr; Var L Trk; Bus Mgmt.

TOFTE, TAMMY; Mechanicsville HS; North Troy, NY; (S); Computer Clb; French Clb; Ski Clb; Pres Jr Cls; Sftbl; High Hon Roll; NHS; Ntl Merit Ltr; Highest Average; Alebra Awd; Saratogian Skidmore Coll Hnr Dinner; Comp Tech.

TOGUVILLE, JOHN G; La Salle Acad; Elmhurst, NY; (S); 37/237; NHS.

TOIA, LISA; N Babylon SR HS; N Babylon, NY; (S); 140/550; DECA; Chorus; Mgr(s); Hon Roll; NHS; 2 Brnze Merit Awds Mrktng 84-85; Macys Mrktg Awd 84; Hon Men DECA Suffolk Cnty Testing 85; Nassau CC; Marketng.

TOJEIRA, MARIA; New Utrecht HS; Brooklyn, NY; (Y); 2/605; Key Clb; Office Aide; Band; Mrchg Band; Nwsp Rptr; Nwsp Stf; Lit Mag; Hon Roll; JP Sousa Awd; Ntl Merit Ltr; Arista 85; Jrnlsm.

TOKARSKA, BARBARA; St Johns Preparatory HS; Brooklyn, NY; (S); 1/548; Am Leg Aux Girls St; Rep Soph Cls; Rep Jr Cls; Rep Stu Cncl; High Hon Roll; Hon Roll; NHS; Natl Sci Olymp 83; Comp Anlys.

TOKASZ, KRISTIE; Mount Saint Joseph Acad; Cheektowaga, NY; (S); Hosp Aide; Library Aide; Pep Clb; Political Wkr; Yrbk Stf; Lit Mag; Trs Jr Cls; Var JV Badmtn; Hon Roll; NHS; Pre-Law.

TOLEDO, ANGEL D; St Johns Prep; Brooklyn, NY; (Y); NY Inst Tech; Comm Arts.

TOLENTINO, ANDREW M; La Salle Acad; New York, NY; (S); Church Yth Grp; Church Choir; Nwsp Rptr; VP Frsh Cls; VP Soph Cls; Im Bsktbl; Im Ftbl; Var Socr; Im Sftbl; Var Tennis; Elec Engrng.

TOLENTINO, EUGENIA; Academy Of Saint Joseph; Great River, NY; (Y); Hosp Aide; Yrbk Stf; Sec Frsh Cls; JV Bsktbl; Tennis; Ntl Merit Ltr; NEDT Awd; Creighton U; Physcn.

TOLESON, MITCHELL C; Paul V Moore HS; Constantia, NY; (Y); Am Leg Boys St; ROTC; JV Bsbl; Daedalian JR ROTC Achvt Awd 85; AFJROTC Acad Awd 84 & 85; Sci.

TOLLERS, ELIZABETH MARIE; Brockport HS; Brockport, NY; (Y); Political Wkr; Ski Clb; VP Frsh Cls; VP Soph Cls; VP Stu Cncl; NHS; VFW Awd; Church Choir; High Hon Roll; Outstndng Stu Awd; Privt Pian Lssns; Yrbk Clbs & Actvts Sect Edtr; U Of Rochester; Poli Sci.

TOLLIVER, FELICIA; James D O Neil HS; West Point, NY; (Y); Church Yth Grp; Cmnty Wkr; FHA; Pep Clb; Red Cross Aide; Acpl Chr; Church Choir; Nwsp Stf; Plaq 2nd Pl Spch Cntst 83; Howard U; Cmmnctns.

TOLLIVER, SHERYL; Lindenhurst HS; Lindenhurst, NY; (Y); Sec Church Yth Grp; Chorus; Church Choir; Nwsp Rptr; Yrbk Rptr; Yrbk Sprt Ed; Yrbk Stf; Pres Frsh Cls; Var Cheerleading; Im Gym; Outstndng Fres Chrldr; Gregg Typg Awd; Yrbk Awd; Oral Roberts U; Elem Educ.

TOM, ANDREW; Brooklyn Technical HS; New York, NY; (Y); 91/1139; Office Aide; Teachers Aide; Ftbl; Hon Roll; NHS; Stevens Inst Of Tech; Elec Engr.

TOM, CONNIE; Bayside HS; Bayside, NY; (Y); 9/677; Teachers Aide; Concert Band; Rep Jr Cls; Rep Sr Cls; High Hon Roll; Jr NHS; NHS; Office Aide; Cit Awd; Prfct Atten Awd; NY Regents Schlrshp 85; NY U; Comp Sci.

TOM, JOHN; La Salle Acad; New York, NY; (S); 11/237; Chess Clb; Math Clb; Math Tm; Nwsp Rptr; Rep Soph Cls; Im Bowling; High Hon Roll; NHS; NY U; Comp Sci.

TOM, VICKI P; Bronx H S Of Science; Elmhurst, NY; (Y); Intnl Clb; Office Aide; Teachers Aide; VICA; Band; Yrbk Stf; Lit Mag; Hon Roll; NY U; Comp Sci.

TOMAINE, CATHLEEN; Union Endicott HS; Endicott, NY; (Y); 54/430; French Clb; Key Clb; Flag Corp; Rep Stu Cncl; Hon Roll; Regnts Schlrshp 85; SUNY Oswego; Chemistry.

TOMANEK, MARGARET R; Johnson City HS; Binghamton, NY; (Y); 39/212; Church Yth Grp; French Clb; Pep Clb; Color Guard; Rep Frsh Cls; Rep Soph Cls; Rep Jr Cls; Rep Sr Cls; Rep Stu Cncl; Cheerleading; NYS Rgnts Nrsng Schlrshp 85; Schlstc Excel Awd 82 & 83; SUNY Delhi; Nrs.

TOMARAS, BILL; Aviation HS; Astoria, NY; (Y); 105/417; Debate Tm; Aerontcl Engrng.

TOMASELLO, ANGELO; Cardinal O Hara HS; Buffalo, NY; (Y); Ftbl; Hon Roll; ST U New York; Engrg.

TOMASESKI, KAREN; Saugerties SR HS; Saugerties, NY; (Y); 47/250; French Clb; Office Aide; Band; NHS; Hon Roll; SUNY Oneonta; Ed.

TOMASI, CHRISTOPHER; Clevaland Hill HS; Cheektowaga, NY; (Y); Church Yth Grp; Varsity Clb; Variety Show; Crs Cntry; Socr; Swmmng; Trk.

TOMASINI, HEATHER; East Islip HS; E Islip, NY; (Y); Church Yth Grp; Pep Clb; Teachers Aide; Varsity Clb; JV Capt Cheerleading; Var JV Tennis; JV Trk; Var Stat Vllybl; Hon Roll; Hst Jr NHS; Intl Bus.

TOMASINI, JENNY; Gorton HS; Yonkers, NY; (Y); Spanish Clb; Stage Crew; Nwsp Stf; Lit Mag; Hon Roll; 3rd Annl Sklls Olympcs Awd Pace Bus Schl 84; Sklls Olympcs Awd Pace Bus Schl 85; Bus Mgmt.

TOMASULO, AIME; Kenmore East HS; Tonawanda, NY; (Y); Dance Clb; School Musical; Pom Pon; Inter Design.

TOMASZEWSKY, MICHAEL A; St George Acad; New York, NY; (Y); Church Yth Grp; Dance Clb; Stage Crew; Nwsp Sprt Ed; VP Frsh Cls; Trs Soph Cls; VP Jr Cls; Im Bsktbl; Im Lcrss; Var Mgr(s); Natl Athl Plcmnt Svcs 85; Engrng.

TOMBACK, DAVID B; Midwood HS; Brooklyn, NY; (Y); 5/605; Math Tm; Science Clb; Soroptimist; Nwsp Ed-Chief; Pres Jr Cls; Cit Awd; NHS; Ntl Merit Ltr; Val; Math Fair Wnnr; Princeton; Bio.

TOMBARI, MICHELE; Lyndonville Central Schl; Lyndonville, NY; (Y); 14/60; Chorus; Sftbl; Hon Roll; Sibleys Art Show Awd Hnrbl Ment 84; Accntnt.

TOMBLINE, BERNADETTE; Brewster HS; Brewster, NY; (S); 10/176; Ski Clb; Spanish Clb; Chorus; School Musical; Rep Soph Cls; Rep Jr Cls; Rep Stu Cncl; Hon Roll; VP NHS; Spanish NHS; Area All ST Chorus 83; Trphs, Mdls Prz Wnnr Irish Stp Dncr 81-82.

TOMCZAK, JENNIFER C; North Collins Central HS; Springville, NY; (Y); 1/79; Drama Clb; Chorus; Color Guard; School Musical; School Play; Nwsp Stf; Lit Mag; Trk; Bausch & Lomb Sci Awd; High Hon Roll; Marines; Lang.

TOMCZAK, KIM; Nazareth Acad; Rochester, NY; (S); JA; Library Aide; Speech Tm; Yrbk Stf; Lit Mag; Rep Frsh Cls; Rep Soph Cls; Hon Roll; NHS; Jrnlsm.

TOMIC, JERRY; Longwood HS; Shirley, NY; (Y); Math Clb; Math Tm; Yrbk Stf; High Hon Roll; Hon Roll; Acadmc Decthln Suffolk Cnty 85.

TOMKOS, JOHN; Onondaga Central HS; Nedrow, NY; (Y); German Clb; Letterman Clb; Yrbk Sprt Ed; Yrbk Stf; Var VP Bsktbl; Coach Actv; Var Ftbl; Score Keeper; Var Trk; Prfct Atten Awd; Onondaga CC; Accntng.

TOMLINSON, GREGG; Broadalbin HS; Broadalbin, NY; (Y); Drama Clb; Letterman Clb; Varsity Clb; Chorus; Church Choir; Variety Show; Var L Socr; Capt L Trk; High Hon Roll; Jr NHS; Coachs Sccr Awdd Most Dedictn 85; Fulton-Montgmry CC; Law.

TOMLINSON, LISA; Bethlehem Central HS; Delmar, NY; (Y); Church Yth Grp; Key Clb; Model UN; Band; Church Choir; Var L Sftbl; Var L Tennis; Vllybl; High Hon Roll; NHS; NY ST Schl Of Music Assn Awd 83.

TOMPKINS, AMY; G Ray Bodley HS; Fulton, NY; (Y); French Clb; Color Guard; Mrchg Band; Yrbk Phtg; Yrbk Stf; Trs Frsh Cls; Trs Soph Cls; Trs Jr Cls; Trs Stu Cncl; Var Score Keeper; Cls Ldrshp 85; Prom Qn 85.

TOMPKINS, CHRISTINE L; Cherry Valley Central Schl; Cherry Valley, NY; (Y); 1/40; Drama Clb; Jazz Band; Pres Stu Cncl; Var L Bsktbl; Var L Socr; Bausch & Lomb Sci Awd; Pres NHS; Val; Clark Fndtn Schlrshp 85-86; Yale U.

TOMPKINS, ERIC; Medina SR HS; Medina, NY; (Y); Computer Clb; ROTC; Band; Concert Band; Mrchg Band; JV Ftbl; JV Score Keeper; JV Wrstlng; Hon Roll; Comp Sci.

TOMPKINS, JODI A; Whitney Point Central HS; Richford, NY; (Y); 2/122; French Clb; Bsktbl; Co-Capt Fld Hcky; Sftbl; High Hon Roll; Trs NHS; Ntl Merit Ltr; Regents Schlrshp; St John Fisher; Accntng.

TOMPKINS, JOHN; Newfield HS; Newfield, NY; (Y); Drama Clb; Math Clb; PAVAS; School Musical; School Play; Stage Crew; JV Var Bsktbl; JV Ftbl; Hon Roll; Natl Spch & Drama Awdd 85; Tech Thtr Arts.

TONETTI, LARRY J; Bronx H S Of Science; Bronx, NY; (Y); English Clb; Nwsp Rptr; Nwsp Stf; Soph Cls; Jrnlsm.

TONGUE, SHALON; Arstell Maris HS; Jamaica, NY; (Y); Intnl Clb; Spanish Clb; Hon Roll; Amer Stds Hnr Clss 84-85; St Johns U; Comp.

TOOHEY, JOHN P; Walt Whitman HS; Huntington Sta, NY; (Y); 4/540; Am Leg Boys St; Mathletes; Nwsp Sprt Ed; Capt L Tennis; Pres French Hon Soc; High Hon Roll; Computer Clb; George Washington U Engr & Appld Sci Mdl; Brown U Bk Awd; Cnty Mth Cntst 2nd Pl; Math.

TOOLEY, KATHLEEN; Williamsville South HS; Williamsville, NY; (Y); 110/250; Drama Clb; Acpl Chr; Chorus; Madrigals; School Musical; Swing Chorus; Area All State Chorus 84; Wlmsvl S Fncng Clb 84-85; SUNY Fredonia; Music Thrpy.

TOOLEY, KRISTIN; Indian River HS; Evans Mills, NY; (Y); Church Yth Grp; Band; Chorus; Church Choir; Jazz Band; Mrchg Band; Swing Chorus; Cheerleading; Area, Conf All ST Mixed Chorus 84; Bus.

TOOMBS, REBECCA; Geneva HS; Geneva, NY; (S); 15/170; Church Yth Grp; Hosp Aide; Ski Clb; Varsity Clb; Band; Concert Band; Mrchg Band; Orch; Yrbk Stf; Rep Stu Cncl; Girls ST Cand 83; Outsndng Spanish 84; Burknell U; Spanish.

TOOMER, MARK; Bronx H S Of Science; Brooklyn, NY; (Y); Boy Scts; Church Yth Grp; Cmnty Wkr; Church Choir; Rgnts Schlrshp 85; Rchestr Inst Tech; Bus Info Sys.

TOOMEY, ANNE; Cardinal Mooney HS; Rochester, NY; (Y); Art Clb; Church Yth Grp; Drama Clb; Church Choir; School Musical; Nwsp Phtg; Yrbk Stf; Rep Frsh Cls; Rep Jr Cls; Hon Roll; VP For Campus Ministry Outrch Prog 85-86; 1 Of 50 Stu To Part In Peer Ministry Crs 85-86; Niagra; Cnslng.

TOOMIN, AMY; Clarkstown H S South; New City, NY; (Y); Drama Clb; Pres 4-H; Orch; School Musical; School Play; 4-H Awd; Jr NHS; Stu Mannes Coll Music Prep Div 84-85; ST Ctznshp Awd 4-H 83; Comm.

TOPENCIK, ANTHONY; Union Endioh HS; Endwell, NY; (Y); Boy Scts; Var Ice Hcky; Hon Roll; Eagl Awd 85; Broome Cnty All Str 85; Embry-Riddle Aerontcl; Engnrg.

TOPINI, ANGELA; Bishop Maginn HS; Albany, NY; (Y); Church Yth Grp; JA; Yrbk Stf; High Hon Roll; Hon Roll.

TOPOR, LISA; Villa Maria Acad; Cheektowaga, NY; (Y); Computer Clb; Church Choir; Swmmng; Hon Roll; Swim Club Awd 83; Medallion Church Choir 83; Spec Educ.

TOPPIN, STEPHANIE; Liverpool HS; Liverpool, NY; (S); Off Varsity Clb; Rep Frsh Cls; Rep Soph Cls; Rep Jr Cls; Rep Sr Cls; Rep Stu Cncl; Powder Puff Ftbl; Socr; Var Sftbl; Hon Roll; Most Valuable Player Awd Soccer 84; Sports Psychology.

TOPPIN, SUSAN; Osterholz American HS; APO New York, NY; (Y); Church Yth Grp; Band; Church Choir; Concert Band; Mrchg Band; Symp Band; Nwsp Rptr; Nwsp Stf; Hon Roll; NHS; Exclnce Advncd Band Awd 85; Exclnce French II Awd 85.

TOPPING, DAVE; Thomas A Edison HS; Elmira Hts, NY; (Y); Am Leg Boys St; Drama Clb; Varsity Clb; Y-Teens; Nwsp Sprt Ed; Nwsp Stf; Stu Cncl; Bsbl; Bsktbl; Coach Actv; Kiawanis Athlte Of Mnth Awd 85; MVP Ftbl; All Leag Awd Bst Offnsve Ftbl 85; MVP Bsebl; Cmmnctns.

TORCELLO, TINA MARIE; Batavia HS; Batavia, NY; (Y); 20/250; Red Cross Aide; Teachers Aide; Variety Show; Yrbk Bus Mgr; Yrbk Phtg; Lit Mag; Coach Actv; Hon Roll; Kiwanis Awd; NHS; D Youville Coll Hnrs Schlrshp 85; Rgnts Schlrshp 85; Kiwanas Svc Awd 85; D Youville Coll; Elem Educ.

TORCH, MICHAEL; Newburgh Free Acad; Newburgh, NY; (Y); Camera Clb; Pres Computer Clb; Swmmng; Comp Tech.

TORCHIA, NANETTE; Hudson HS; Hudson, NY; (Y); Girl Scts; Ski Clb; Yrbk Ed-Chief; Pres Frsh Cls; Pres Soph Cls; Pres Jr Cls; Cheerleading; Off Jr Cls; Prfct Atten Awd; Rotary Awd; AZ ST; Cnslng.

TORINO, DONALD; Uniondale HS; Uniondale, NY; (Y); 9/480; Aud/Vis; Nwsp Sprt Ed; Var L Golf; Var L Lcrss; Var L Socr; High Hon Roll; Jr NHS; NHS; Ntl Merit SF; Outstndng Chem Stu Awd 85; PA ST U; Pre-Med.

TORIZO, JUDY ANN; St Edmund HS; Brooklyn, NY; (S); 14/187; Dance Clb; Math Clb; Science Clb; Cheerleading; Comp Sci.

TORMEY, LEANNE; New Rochelle HS; New Rochelle, NY; (Y); Pres Dance Clb; Drama Clb; School Musical; Variety Show; Ed Nwsp Ed-Chief; Ed Yrbk Ed-Chief; Pres Frsh Cls; Pres Soph Cls; Pres Jr Cls; Rep Stu Cncl; Semi-Fin US-JAPAN Sen Exch 85; Pinebrk Awd Of Ldrshp 83; Bonnie Crest Awd Stu Awareness 83; Lib Art.

TORNATORE, BETH; John C Birdlebough HS; Pennellvl, NY; (Y); 14/186; AFS; Church Yth Grp; Drama Clb; Latin Clb; Ski Clb; Color Guard; School Musical; School Play; Hon Roll; NHS; Outstndng Achvt Ltn II 83-84; Engl.

TORNATORE, MARIA; John A Coleman HS; Kingston, NY; (Y); Key Clb; Hon Roll; Prfct Atten Awd; CVA; Chldrns Theater; Elem Ed.

TORRE, DONNA M; Bishop Kearney HS; Brooklyn, NY; (S); 70/354; Church Yth Grp; Dance Clb; FNA; Girl Scts; School Musical; Hon Roll; NHS; Rep Frsh Cls; Rep Soph Cls; VP Jr Cls; Brooklyn Coll; Pre-Med.

TORRES, ALISSA FRIEDMAN; The Mary Louis Acad; Flushing, NY; (Y); AFS; Church Yth Grp; Dance Clb; French Clb; NFL; Orch; Hon Roll; NHS; NEDT Awd; Prfct Atten Awd; Intl/Intrcltrl Pgms 84-85; Alvin Ailey Amer Dnc Cntr 84-85; Math, Hist, Frnch, Chem, Bio & Rlgn Hnrs; Cornell U; Ag Sci.

TORRES, ANGELA; Cardinal Spellman HS; Bronx, NY; (Y); 48/500; Computer Clb; Dance Clb; Political Wkr; Color Guard; Flag Corp; Yrbk Stf; Lit Mag; Hon Roll; NEDT Awd; NY U; Corp Lawyer.

TORRES, BLANCA ADRIANA; John Bowne HS; Queens, NY; (Y); 280/657; Church Yth Grp; Dance Clb; Service Clb; Spanish Clb; Gym; Prfct Atten Awd; Spanish NHS; Queens Coll; Sci.

TORRES, CYNTHIA; Mother Cabrini HS; Englewood, NJ; (Y); 4-H; Science Clb; Sec Teachers Aide; Color Guard; Yrbk Phtg; Rep Sr Cls; Hon Roll; Stu Svc Awd 85; Fairleigh Dickinson U; Pre-Med.

TORRES, GLADYS; Monres HS; Rochester, NY; (Y); AFS; Latin Clb; Office Aide; Spanish Clb; Teachers Aide; Hon Roll; Monroe CC; Bus Mgmt.

TORRES, JANET; Bishop Loughlin HS; Brooklyn, NY; (Y); Teachers Aide; Hon Roll; Prfct Atten Awd; Capt Coach Actv; Stat Score Keeper; Pedtrc.

TORRES, JANET; Hillcrest HS; Jamaica, NY; (Y); Office Aide; Teachers Aide; Band; Nwsp Rptr; Rep Soph Cls; Rep Jr Cls; Pres Sr Cls; Rep Stu Cncl; Prncpls-Pride Of Yankees-Supr Yth Awd 84; Cert Hon-NY Bar Assn 85; Spcl Congrsnl Recog Cert 85; Georgetown; Bus.

TORRES, KENNETH; Newfield HS; Selden, NY; (Y); FBLA; Crs Cntry; Trk; HI U Of Psych; Psych.

TORRES, LUCESITA; Francis Lewis HS; Flushing, NY; (S); Sec Church Yth Grp; Drama Clb; Spanish Clb; Band; Hon Roll; NHS; Prfct Atten Awd; Med.

TORRES, VICTOR; Cardinal Hayes HS; New York, NY; (Y); 25/284; Dance Clb; Latin Clb; Stage Crew; Nwsp Stf; Yrbk Sprt Ed; Rep Sr Cls; Bowling; Var Ftbl; Trk; Wt Lftg; Hispanic Ldrshp 85-86; Pre-Med.

TORREY, JENNIE; Pavilion Central HS; Stafford, NY; (Y); Art Clb; Political Wkr; Ski Clb; Yrbk Stf; Rep Soph Cls; Rep Jr Cls; Rep Sr Cls; VP Stu Cncl; Cit Awd; High Hon Roll; Outstndng Stu Cncl Awd 84; Bryant & Stratton; Sec Sci.

TORSELL, KIRSTEN P; Buffalo Acad Of The Sacred Heart; Amherst, NY; (Y); 5/124; Latin Clb; Model UN; Hon Roll; NYS Rgnts Schlrshp 85; Ntl Engl Merit Awd 85; ST U Coll Buffalo; Elem Ed.

TORTORA, JAMES; Solvay HS; Syracuse, NY; (Y); Band; Concert Band; Jazz Band; School Musical; Variety Show; High Hon Roll; Hon Roll; Radio.

TORTORELLO, LISA; Fairport HS; Fairport, NY; (Y); VP JA; Office Aide; Pep Clb; Ski Clb; Varsity Clb; Yrbk Stf; Rep Stu Cncl; Stat Mgr(s); L Socr; Capt Sftbl; Lilc Tn Fnlst 84; Cnty Sftbl Tm 84-85; Athlt Of The Wk 85; Union Clg; Bio.

TORTORICE, PAMELA; Albion HS; Albion, NY; (S); 8/170; Trs Drama Clb; JCL; Pres Latin Clb; Color Guard; School Musical; School Play; Variety Show; Hon Roll; Jr NHS; NHS; Spec Educ.

TORTORICI, MARYANN; Smithtown H S West; Smithtown, NY; (Y); Band; Mrchg Band; Symp Band; Yrbk Stf; Hon Roll; Hofstra U; Pre-Law.

TORZEWSKI, MICHELLE; Mount Mercy Acad; W Seneca, NY; (S); 9/161; Cmnty Wkr; Hosp Aide; Nwsp Rptr; Nwsp Stf; Lit Mag; Hon Roll; Peer Ministry 83-84; Hnrb Mntn Ntl Poetry Press Cont 83; Hnrb Mntn Wrld Poetry Cont 84; Nrsng.

TOSCANO, JOSEPH; Aquinas Instit; Rochester, NY; (S); 14/167; Ski Clb; Varsity Clb; Bsbl; Var Capt Ftbl; Wrstlng; Hon Roll; Acadmc Schlrshp Aquinas.

TOSCANO, MARIA; Narrowsburg Central HS; Lk Huntington, NY; (Y); Camera Clb; Ski Clb; Chorus; School Musical; School Play; Yrbk Phtg; VP Jr Cls; Sullivan CC; Trvl.

TOSCANO, PATRICIA; St Francis Prep HS; Douglaston, NY; (S); 13/690; Hosp Aide; Math Clb; School Musical; School Play; Stage Crew; Hon Roll; NHS; Spanish NHS; Knights Columbus Schlrshp; St Johns Comp Schlrshp; Principals List; Bus.

TOSCANO, TRACY; Smithtown H S West; Smithtown, NY; (Y); Radio Clb; Im Fld Hcky; Im Sftbl; Carpentry.

TOSH, CHRISTOPHER; Saratoga Central Catholic HS; Saratoga Spg, NY; (Y); Drama Clb; Varsity Clb; Stage Crew; Var Ftbl; Var Golf; Var Wt Lftg; Cert Of Merit-Senator Bruno Scholastic Achvt 85; Highest Avg In Art-3 Yrs 85; Busnss.

TOSH, GAIL; Jamesville-Dewitt HS; Fayetteville, NY; (Y); Cmnty Wkr; Drama Clb; Girl Scts; Concert Band; School Musical; School Play; Nwsp Stf; Bsktbl; Pep Clb; Sftbl; Susquehanna Vly Band 82-84; Dist Band 83; Educ.

TOSI, JEANMARIE; Bronx H S Of Science; Bronx, NY; (Y); Teachers Aide; Var Capt Sftbl; High Hon Roll; Daily News HS Grls All Star Sftbl Tm 82-85; Prtcpntnt Voter Regstrtn Dr 82; Brockport Suny; Accntng.

TOSTANOSKI, TINA M; Corning-Painted Post West HS; Corning, NY; (Y); Girl Scts; Varsity Clb; Band; Chorus; Var Sftbl; Var Vllybl; Hon Roll; Corning CC; Nrsng.

TOSTO, STEVE; Eastridge HS; Rochester, NY; (Y); 35/250; Varsity Clb; Band; JV Bsbl; Var JV Ftbl; Wt Lftg; NHS; Bus Mgmnt.

TOTA, DANIEL; Jamestown HS; Jamestown, NY; (Y); Church Yth Grp; French Clb; Chorus; Var Bowling; L Trk; Hon Roll; Jr NHS; Dnstry.

TOTA, PAULETTE; Mount Saint Mary Acad; Williamsville, NY; (Y); Church Yth Grp; Debate Tm; VP Pres NFL; Speech Tm; Chorus; Stage Crew; Hon Roll; Prfct Atten Awd; Voice Dem Awd; Mt St Mary Acad Alumnae Schlrshp 83; U Of Buffalo; Cmmrcl Artist.

TOTH, LESLIE; Riverside HS; Buffalo, NY; (Y); JA; Library Aide; Rep Soph Cls; Rep Jr Cls; Hon Roll; U Buffalo; Acctg.

TOTORO, ANNMARIE; Roy C Ketcham HS; Poughkeepsie, NY; (Y); Church Yth Grp; Office Aide; Ski Clb; Rep Jr Cls; Rep Stu Cncl; Cheerleading; Gym; Socr; Hon Roll; Elem Ed.

TOUART, TINA; Queensbury HS; Glens Falls, NY; (Y); Chorus; Madrigals; School Musical; Hon Roll.

TOUHY, DEBORAH M; New Hartford Central HS; New Hartford, NY; (Y); Spanish Clb; Varsity Clb; JV Bsktbl; Var Socr; Hon Roll; Jr NHS; NY ST Schl; Psych.

TOUKATLY, DEAN; Oriskany Central Schl; Whitesboro, NY; (Y); 18/101; Pres Varsity Clb; VP L Bsbl; JV Bsktbl; Capt Bowling; Var L Ftbl; Capt L Trk; Wt Lftg; High Hon Roll; Hon Roll; Tchrs Scholar 85; Alfred A&T; Elec Engrng.

TOUSSAINT, MARY; Brooklyn Technical HS; Brooklyn, NY; (Y); Church Yth Grp; Girl Scts; Teachers Aide; Church Choir; Rep Soph Cls; Rep Jr Cls; French Hon Soc; Hon Roll; NHS; Prfct Atten Awd; ARISTA Ntl Hnr Soc 84-85; Hrn Roll 83-85; Church Yth Sec 84-85; Med.

TOW, MICHAEL H; Great Neck South HS; Great Neck, NY; (Y); Model UN; Temple Yth Grp; Chorus; Jazz Band; School Musical; Ed Nwsp Stf; Ed Lit Mag; Cmnty Wkr; Acpl Chr; Madrigals; Natl Bibl Cntst Fnlst 83; Music Tchrs Lge 85; Natl Cncl Tchrs Engl Schl Rep 85; Law.

TOWERS, MARY; F D Roosevelt HS; Poughkeepsie, KY; (Y); Cmnty Wkr; Color Guard; Mrchg Band; Stage Crew; Var Trk; Hon Roll; NHS; V Ltrmn Band 84; Lang.

TOWERS, SANDRA; Corinth Central HS; Corinth, NY; (S); Drama Clb; French Clb; MMM; VP Band; Chorus; Yrbk Stf; French Hon Soc; Jr NHS; NHS; Capt Cheerleading; Realtrs Strngth Natn Essay Cont 84; Natl Acad Achvt Dnnr 84; Hnr Ment Natl Frnch Cont 82; Spec Ed.

TOWLE, JENNIFER ANNE; Franklin Acad; Malone, NY; (Y); French Clb; Pep Clb; Ed Nwsp Stf; Yrbk Ed-Chief; Ed Yrbk Stf; Pres Soph Cls; Pres Jr Cls; Pres Sr Cls; Rep Stu Cncl; Capt L Cheerleading; Ldrshp Awd Excllnc Cheerg Capt 84; Jrnlsm.

TOWNE, GEORGE; Port Jervis HS; Port Jervis, NY; (Y); 34/181; Church Yth Grp; Ski Clb; Varsity Clb; Rptr Yrbk Stf; Stu Cncl; Var Trk; Hon Roll; VP NHS; Smr Schl Visual Arts 85; Yth Gov 83-85; Art.

TOWNE, KERI; Middleburgh Central HS; Middleburgh, NY; (S); 6/77; Trs Jr Cls; Sec Stu Cncl; High Hon Roll; Hon Roll; Pres Jr NHS; Sec Trs NHS; Ntl Merit SF; Chess Clb; Church Yth Grp; NY ST Schl Mus Assn Chorus 83, & Womns Chorus 84; Appld Mus.

TOWNE, LISA; Port Jervis HS; Port Jervis, NY; (Y); 4/190; Dance Clb; Drama Clb; Acpl Chr; VP Chorus; School Musical; School Play; Yrbk Ed-Chief; Rep Stu Cncl; L Mat Maids; Pres NHS; Rotary Clb Schlrshp 85; Nancy Mc Cracken Dance Awd 85; E B Morgan Schlrshp 85; Wells Coll; Bio.

TOWNE, SHAWN; Ticondeioga HS; Ticonderoga, NY; (Y); Pres Church Yth Grp; Cmnty Wkr; Drama Clb; French Clb; Chorus; Church Choir; Madrigals; School Play; Stage Crew; Rep Jr Cls; Music Awds 83-85; Bus Adm.

TOWNE, SHERRY; Edwards Central HS; Edwards, NY; (Y); 1/25; VP French Clb; GAA; Concert Band; Pres Frsh Cls; Pres Soph Cls; Pres Jr Cls; Pres Sr Cls; Capt Bsktbl; L Cheerleading; Capt Socr; Frshmn Hnrs Schlrshp SUNY 85; Cortland ST U.

TOWNSEND, BECKY; Town Of Webb HS; Inlet, NY; (S); Varsity Clb; Chorus; School Play; Var Capt Bsktbl; Var L Socr; Var L Sftbl; Var L Trk; JV L Vllybl; Hon Roll; NY ST Publ H S Athl Assn 82; Acctnt.

TOWNSEND, BUDDIE; Weedsport HS; Weedsport, NY; (Y); Boy Scts; French Clb; Var JV Bsbl; Var JV Bsktbl; Var JV Ftbl; Var Trk; JV Wrstlng; Hon Roll; Prom Ct 85; Spllng Bee 2nd Pl 82; Real Est.

TOWNSEND, GREGORY W; Batavia SR HS; Batavia, NY; (Y); Debate Tm; Drama Clb; Exploring; Varsity Clb; School Play; Nwsp Rptr; Nwsp Stf; Im Ftbl; Var Wrstlng; Regents Scshlrshp Wnnr 84-85; Alfred; Surveying.

TOWNSEND, MARY JO; Harpursville JR SR HS; Harpursville, NY; (Y); 14/100; School Play; Stage Crew; VP Soph Cls; VP Jr Cls; Var Fld Hcky; Var Sftbl; JV Vllybl; Hon Roll; Spirit Awd Var Vllybl 84; MVP Var Vllybl 85; All Star Awd Field Hockey 85; Joseph Bulova Schl; Gemology.

TOWNSEND, STACEY; Olean HS; Olean, NY; (Y); Library Aide; Orch; Hon Roll; Olean Bus Inst; Legl Sec.

TRABAL, MILTON; A Philip Randolph Campus; Bronx, NY; (Y); Church Yth Grp; Computer Clb; Lit Mag; Law.

TRABERT, KRISTEN A; Royalton Hartland HS; Gasport, NY; (Y); 21/125; FTA; Girl Scts; Var L Crs Cntry; Var Swmmng; Var L Trk; High Hon Roll; Hon Roll; NHS; Natl Frgn Lang Awd 84; Acad All Amer 84; Natl Ldrshp Awd 85; SUNY Fredonia; Hosp Admin.

TRACEY, SHEILA; Arlington HS; Poughkeepsie, NY; (Y); FNA; Bsktbl; Sftbl; Swmmng; Capt Vllybl; Dance Clb; Hosp Aide; Band; Flag Corp; Mgr(s); Travl.

TRACHTA, SUSAN VERONICA; St Joseph Hill Acad; Staten Island, NY; (Y); 2/150; Art Clb; NFL; Chorus; School Musical; Nwsp Ed-Chief; NHS; Ntl Merit Schol; Am Leg Aux Girls St; Computer Clb; Debate Tm; USA Presdtl Schlr 85; 4-Yr NROTC Schlrshp Winner 85; Amer Acad Of Achvt 85; Harvard U; Intl Law.

TRACHTER, DAVID M; Midwood HS; Brooklyn, NY; (Y); 19/605; Color Guard; Yrbk Stf; Lit Mag; Im Bsktbl; Im Vllybl; Jr NHS; NHS; Writer Law Jrnl 85; Epilog Yrbk 85; Law.

TRACKEY, DAVID; Hudson Falls Central HS; Hudson Falls, NY; (Y); 30/206; Rochest Inst Of Tech.

TRACY, DAVID GREGORY; Jamesville De Witt HS; Fayetteville, NY; (Y); 60/260; Im JV Lcrss; JV Socr; Bio.

TRACY, DAWN; Schem HS; Lk Ronkonkoma, NY; (Y); GAA; Ski Clb; Nwsp Rptr; Socr; Sftbl; Vllybl; Jr NHS; NHS; MVP Frshmn Sccr 83; Smmr Intern Suffolk Cnty Med Exmnrs Ofc 85; Pre-Med.

TRACY, JENNIFER L; Rome Free Acad; Rome, NY; (Y); 164/530; Intnl Clb; Key Clb; Band; Concert Band; Rep Stu Cncl; JV Var Tennis; NHS; Mrchg Band; Orch; Rep Sr Cls; B Sharp Etude Clb-Utica Symphny Awd 85; A Gertrude Nourse Music Awd 85; Potsdam Coll.

TRACY, JOANNE; Greenwich Central HS; Greenwich, NY; (Y); AFS; 4-H; Band; JV Fld Hcky; Var Trk; High Hon Roll; Hon Roll; Skidmore Coll 85; Arch.

TRACY, KEVIN P; Lockport SR HS; Lockport, NY; (Y); 12/411; Am Leg Boys St; Boy Scts; CAP; Varsity Clb; Var Capt Crs Cntry; JV Trk; Hon Roll; Jr NHS; NHS.

TRACY, MARGUERITE; Holy Child HS; Scarborough, NY; (Y); Drama Clb; Service Clb; Thesps; Chorus; School Musical; School Play; Nwsp Stf; Yrbk Stf; Off Frsh Cls; Off Soph Cls; Bst Drctr 2nd Hnrs 83.

TRACY, ROBIN; Waverly JR-SR HS; Waverly, NY; (Y); Art Clb; Nwsp Ed-Chief; Yrbk Stf; Bsktbl; High Hon Roll; Hon Roll; Jr NHS; NHS; Schlstc Gold Key Awd 85; Pomona Grange Art Awd 84; J Wm Merril Mem Prize Art 85; Corning CC; Art.

TRACY, SANDI; Millbrook HS; Millbrook, NY; (Y); Church Yth Grp; Cmnty Wkr; FBLA; Political Wkr; Ski Clb; Chorus; School Play; Variety Show; Yrbk Bus Mgr; Yrbk Stf; Bus Math Awd 85; Dutches CC; Bus Admin.

TRAD, MICHAEL; Bishop Ford Central Catholic HS; Brooklyn, NY; (Y); Camp Fr Inc; Church Yth Grp; Ftbl; Trk; Nassau CC; Chiro.

TRAINA, MARIA T; Sacred Heart Acad; Oceanside, NY; (Y); 25/186; Math Tm; Acpl Chr; Chorus; Church Choir; School Musical; Hon Roll; NHS; Ntl Merit SF; Carnegie-Mellon U; Engrng.

TRAINOR, TRICIA; St John The Baptist HS; S Hauppauge, NY; (Y); Church Yth Grp; Dance Clb; Hosp Aide; Library Aide; Office Aide; Rep Frsh Cls; Rep Soph Cls; Rep Jr Cls; JV Swmmng; Hon Roll; Hgh Awds In Irsh Stp Dncng 82-85; Manhattan Coll; Accntng.

TRAINOR JR, WILLIAM T; Cornwall Central HS; Cornwall Hudson, NY; (Y); 22/197; High Hon Roll; Pres Acad Ftns Awd 84-85; Regents Schlrshp Awd 84-85; ST U-Albany; Acctng.

TRAMMEL, KEVIN; Chenango Forks HS; Binghamton, NY; (Y); Am Leg Boys St; Pres Frsh Cls; VP Stu Cncl; Golf; Hon Roll; Jr NHS; NHS; Prfct Atten Awd; Socr; Yth Salute; Broone Comm Coll; Mech Engrng.

TRAMONTO, GIA; Irandequoit HS; Rochester, NY; (Y); Sec DECA; High Hon Roll; Hon Roll; Monroe CC; Fash Merch.

TRAMPOSCH, LISA; The Mary Louis Acad; Middle Village, NY; (Y); Art Clb; Cmnty Wkr; Exploring; Teachers Aide; Nwsp Rptr; Hon Roll; St Johns U; Math.

TRAN, HA; Walton HS; Bronx, NY; (Y); Church Choir; Merit Achvt Awd 83-84; Engr.

TRAN, THIEN L; Kensington HS; Buffalo, NY; (Y); 4/197; Chess Clb; Computer Clb; Mathletes; Math Clb; High Hon Roll; Hon Roll; NHS; Prfct Atten Awd; Rep Stu Cncl; NYS Rgnts Schlrshp 85; Math Leag Top Scorer 83-84; Police Athl Assn Schlrshp 84-85; U Buffalo; Comp Sci.

TRAN, THUAN; Roy C Ketcham HS; Wappingers Fls, NY; (Y); High Hon Roll; Hon Roll; Dutchess CC; Elec Engrng.

TRANQUILLI, GAIL; Bishop Kearney HS; Brooklyn, NY; (S); High Hon Roll; NHS; Schltc Achvt Awd 83-84; St Johns Acad Excllnce Scholar 84-85; Regents Scholar 84-85; St Johns U; Mgmt.

TRANQUILLI, MICHELE; Alden Central HS; Lancaster, NY; (Y); FFA; Ski Clb; Color Guard; Rep Frsh Cls; Rep Jr Cls; Rep Stu Cncl; JV Sftbl; Im Twrlr; AG Bus Awd FFA 83-84; Alfred; Ag Bus.

TRANUAAG, SABRINA; Bainbridge-Guilford HS; Bainbridge, NY; (Y); 7/80; French Clb; Rep Jr Cls; Rep Stu Cncl; Var JV Bsktbl; High Hon Roll; Hon Roll; Bus Mgmt.

TRAPASO, JOHN; Canastota HS; Canastota, NY; (Y); Aud/Vis; Boy Scts; Computer Clb; Band; Tennis; Hon Roll; Morrisville Coll NY; Comp.

TRAPLETTI, LUCY; Mt Vernon HS; Mount Vernon, NY; (Y); Key Clb; Band; Mrchg Band; Gym; Hon Roll; Poem Pub Our Worlds Mst Beloved Poems 85.

TRASHER, DIANE M; York Central HS; Leicester, NY; (Y); 1/67; Trs Sec 4-H; Math Tm; Band; Trs Jr Cls; Var Capt Socr; Var Capt Trk; Bausch & Lomb Sci Awd; NHS; St Schlr; Val; Houghton College; Mathematics.

TRASHER, STEVE; York Central Schl; Leicester, NY; (Y); 20/100; Church Yth Grp; Ski Clb; Varsity Clb; Band; Rep Jr Cls; Var L Bsbl; Var L Bsktbl; Var L Ftbl; Im Vllybl; Hon Roll; Math.

TRAUB, JOANNE; West Genesee SR HS; Syracuse, NY; (Y); Church Yth Grp; Hosp Aide; Ski Clb; Color Guard; Mrchg Band; Tennis; High Hon Roll; Hon Roll; Jr NHS; NHS; U Of Pittsburgh; Bus.

TRAUBEL, BARBARA; Carthage Central HS; Philadelphia, PA; (Y); Varsity Clb; Yrbk Stf; Socr; High Hon Roll; Hon Roll; Math.

TRAUBEL, WILLIAM V; Carthage HS; Ft Monmouth, NJ; (Y); 7/200; Am Leg Boys St; School Play; Nwsp Rptr; Var Golf; Var Socr; Elks Awd; NHS; Pres Schlr; Arnold Schlrshp U Of CO 85; Vrsty Ski Tm; U S Military Acad.

TRAUFFER, ELIZABETH A; New Paltz Central HS; New Paltz, NY; (Y); 10/150; Pres Church Yth Grp; Library Aide; Chorus; Church Choir; Concert Band; Madrigals; Mrchg Band; High Hon Roll; NHS; PTSO Frgn Lang Awd-Spnsh 85; Eastern Nazarene Coll; Mssn Wrk.

TRAUTMANN, E STEPHANIE; Green Meadow Waldorf HS; Mahwah, NJ; (Y); Band; Chorus; Church Choir; Concert Band; Orch; School Musical; Yrbk Stf; Sec Jr Cls; Lcrss; Church Yth Grp; Music Perf.

TRAVAGLINO, ROSANGELA; Preston HS; Bronx, NY; (S); 6/104; Yrbk Stf; Pres Soph Cls; VP Jr Cls; Trs Sr Cls; Im Vllybl; High Hon Roll; Hon Roll; NHS; Berkley; Legal Sec.

TRAVER, TODD W; Chatham HS; Chatham, NY; (Y); Boy Scts; Exploring; Band; Concert Band; Mrchg Band; Orch; Ftbl; Hon Roll; SCI.

TRAVERS, DAN; Ithaca HS; Ithaca, NY; (Y); Im Bsktbl; Stat Diving; Var L Lcrss; Stat Swmmng; Hon Roll; NHS; Ntl Merit Ltr; Terbush Awd 85; Cornell; Comp Sci.

TRAVERS, MICHELLE; Mount St Mary Acad; Buffalo, NY; (Y); Church Yth Grp; French Clb; Hosp Aide; Chorus; High Hon Roll; Hon Roll; Euchrstc Mnstr 85; Crmnl Justice.

TRAVIESO, HECTOR; Truman HS; Bronx, NY; (Y); Service Clb; Teachers Aide; NHS; Comp Sci.

TRAVIS, CHIP; Rome Catholic HS; Rome, NY; (Y); Var Letterman Clb; Trs Sr Cls; Var L Bsbl; Var L Ftbl; Var L Ice Hcky; Arch.

TRAVIS, DANIEL; Bronx H S Of Science; Forest Hills, NY; (Y); Key Clb; Science Clb; Temple Yth Grp; Nwsp Ed-Chief; Lit Mag; Crs Cntry; Trk; Hon Roll; NHS; NCSY Schlr 85; Belkin Schlrshp 85-86; Westinghouse Sci Proj 84-85; Yeshiva U; Med.

TRAVIS, JENNIFER; Woodmere Acad HS; Lawrence, NY; (Y); Yrbk Stf; Cheerleading; Var Capt Tennis; Vllybl; Outstndg Engl Achvt 84; Vassar; Engl.

TRAVIS, KRIS; Chenango Forks HS; Binghamton, NY; (Y); Drama Clb; French Clb; Ski Clb; School Play; Yrbk Stf; Coach Actv; Stat Ftbl; Stat Lcrss; Mgr(s); Score Keeper; Cortland U; Math.

TRAVIS, MARK A; Liverpool HS; Liverpool, NY; (Y); Boy Scts; Chorus; Hon Roll; Order Of Arrow; NY Regents Schlrshp; SADD VP; St Lawrence U; Bus Mngmnt.

TRAVIS, MICHAEL; Penn Yan Acad; Penn Yan, NY; (Y); Am Leg Boys St; Pres Model UN; Rep Soph Cls; Stu Cncl; Capt Golf; High Hon Roll; Voice Dem Awd; Ski Clb; Chorus; Stage Crew; 3rd Pl Lcl Amer Lgn Ortrl Cntst 83-84; Hndbk Cmmtte 84-85; Intl Finc.

TRAVIS, SHIRLEY; Savona Central HS; Savona, NY; (Y); Band; Concert Band; Mrchg Band; School Play; Symp Band; Yrbk Bus Mgr; Yrbk Stf; Masonic Awd; NHS; Hmmkng Awd, Imprvd Bus Stu, Bkkpng Awd, Hghst Avr Commrcl Subjcts 85; Central City Bus Inst; Lgl Admn.

TRAVIS, TODD; Potsdam HS; Potsdam, NY; (Y); Band; Mrchg Band; Orch; School Musical; Hon Roll; Music.

TRAVISS, NORA M; Maria Rfegina HS; White Plains, NY; (Y); 3/144; JA; Nwsp Rptr; Nwsp Stf; Capt Trk; NHS; Maria Regina 4 Yr Schlrshp 81-85; Manhatan 4 Yr Compl Pres Schlrshp 85-89; Iona Coll Lang Cntst 1st 84; PA ST U; Engrng.

TREACY, CHRISTINE E; O L P H HS; Brooklyn, NY; (Y); 94/160; Church Yth Grp; Drama Clb; Girl Scts; Church Choir; School Musical; JV Capt Bsktbl; Bowling; Score Keeper; Socr; Timer; Mst Dedctd Plyr, Citation Hnr DA, NYS Rgnts Diplma 85; Grace Inst; Lgl Secr.

TREACY, PETER; Iona Prep; Rye, NY; (Y); 78/198; Dance Clb; Pep Clb; Ski Clb; Ftbl; Var Golf; Var Capt Lcrss; Bus.

TREANOR, THERESA; St Peters H S For Girls; Staten Island, NY; (Y); Yrbk Stf; St Johns U.

TREANOR, WILLIAM P; Cardinal Spellman HS; Bronx, NY; (Y); 117/568; Civic Clb; Dance Clb; Rep Sr Cls; Stu Cncl; Var L Ftbl; NY ST Regents Schlrshp 85; Second Hnrs 81-85; Manhattan Coll; Civil Engrng.

TREASURE, RONALD; Mount Saint Michael Acad; Bronx, NY; (Y); 76/308; Chess Clb; Church Yth Grp; Computer Clb; Dance Clb; Im Bsktbl; Mgr(s); Powder Puff Ftbl; Im Sftbl; Hon Roll.

TREFZER, SHARON A; St Agnes Academic HS; Whitestone, NY; (Y); 28/302; Church Yth Grp; Cmnty Wkr; Yrbk Stf; High Hon Roll; Hon Roll; St Schlr; St Johns U; Phrmcy.

TREIS, TERRI; Our Lady Of Mercy HS; Fairport, NY; (Y); 17/200; Church Yth Grp; Service Clb; Ski Clb; Spanish Clb; Band; Stage Crew; Gym; Trk; Vllybl; High Hon Roll; Natl Merit Sci Awd-Bio; Accntng I & II Awd; U Of Albany; Accntng.

TREMBLAY, J PAUL; Seton Catholic Central HS; Apalachin, NY; (S); Church Yth Grp; Syracuse U; Engr.

TREMBLAY, MICHELE T; Avoca Central HS; Prattsburg, NY; (Y); JCL; Latin Clb; Band; Twrlr; High Hon Roll; Hon Roll; NHS.

TREMKO, MICHELLE; Our Lady Of Victory Acad; Bronx, NY; (S); 10/152; French Clb; Yrbk Stf; French Hon Soc; High Hon Roll; NHS; Vet.

TRENNERT, JASON; Hauppauge HS; Smithtown, NY; (Y); 10/500; Political Wkr; Jazz Band; Orch; Symp Band; Var JV Bsbl; High Hon Roll; Ntl Merit Ltr; Ski Clb; Band; Concert Band; All Cnty, ST Orch 83-84; NYSMA Lev 6 85; Harvard Sec Smnr Schl 85; Intl Rel.

TRENT, MATTHEW; Xavier HS; New York, NY; (Y); Computer Clb; JV Bsbl; Im JV Bsktbl; Im Fld Hcky; Im Ftbl; NHS; Ntl Merit Ltr; MI ST U; Vet Med.

TRETOLA, MICHAEL JAMES; Bethpage HS; Hicksville, NY; (Y); 15/300; JV Var Bsbl; JV Var Bsktbl; High Hon Roll; Hon Roll; Ntl Merit Ltr; Natl Math Test-Top Score 85; West Point; Engrng.

TRETSCH, ROBERT; Chenango Forks HS; Binghamton, NY; (Y); German Clb; Ski Clb; JV Ftbl; Var Socr; Var Trk; Im Vllybl; Clemson; Arch.

TREUBERT, ELIZABETH; Acad Of Saint Joseph HS; Centereach, NY; (Y); Aud/Vis; Drama Clb; Hosp Aide; Library Aide; Church Choir; School Play; Mgr Stage Crew; NEDT Awd; Nrsng.

TREVETT, LYNN; Gloversville HS; Gloversville, NY; (Y); Drama Clb; Trs Intnl Clb; Chorus; School Musical; Stage Crew; Swing Chorus; Variety Show; Nwsp Stf; Yrbk Stf; NHS; Music.

TREVVETT, DAVID P; Poland Central HS; Cold Brook, NY; (Y); Am Leg Boys St; French Clb; Varsity Clb; Band; Socr; Tennis; Badmtn; Vllybl; Pre-Law.

TREZENSKI, NANCY; Immaculata Acad; Dunkirk, NY; (Y); Debate Tm; Political Wkr; Nwsp Rptr; Nwsp Stf; Lit Mag; Rep Frsh Cls; Rep Stu Cncl; Mgr(s); L Capt Vllybl; Hon Roll; U Of Rochester; Astrphyscs.

TREZZA, LORRAINE M; Oyster Bay HS; East Norwich, NY; (Y); 7/130; AFS; Art Clb; Chorus; Yrbk Stf; Lit Mag; Stu Cncl; Fld Hcky; Gym; Sftbl; Bus.

TREZZA, MARIE JANIS; Lindenhurst HS; Lindenhurst, NY; (Y); Spanish Clb; Orch; School Musical; Stage Crew; Yrbk Stf; High Hon Roll; Hon Roll; Jr NHS; NHS; CPA.

TRIANO, PAULINE; Yorktown HS; Yorktown Hts, NY; (Y); Hosp Aide; Key Clb; Band; Concert Band; Pep Band; Nwsp Bus Mgr; Crs Cntry; Trk; High Hon Roll; Hon Roll; All-Cnty, All-Sctn & All-Divsn Crss Cntry 83-84; Recgntn Awd All-Cnty Crss Cntry 85; Syracuse; Phys Ther.

TRIASSI, SUSAN; Aquinas Inst; Pittsford, NY; (S); Girl Scts; Hosp Aide; Socr; High Hon Roll; Acad Schlrshp 84; Med.

TRIBUNELLA, TODD; Fairport HS; Fairport, NY; (Y); 137/600; Varsity Clb; JV Bsbl; Ftbl; JV Var Ftbl; JV Wrstlng; Hon Roll; NHS; Roger Coke Mem Schlrhshp Ftbl 85; Morrisville Coll; Engr.

TRICE, MARY; Hamberg SR HS; Hamburg, NY; (Y); JA; Hon Roll; Bus Mgmt.

TRICHILO, ANGELO; Christian Brothers Acad; Albany, NY; (Y); 4/98; FCA; ROTC; Stu Cncl; Im Bsktbl; JV Var Trk; Im Vllybl; High Hon Roll; Jr NHS; NHS; Manhattan Coll Pres Scholar 85; Manhattan Coll; Engrng.

TRIEB, PENNY; Irvington HS; Irvington, NY; (Y); Pres Cmnty Wkr; Computer Clb; Exploring; Sec Library Aide; Spanish Clb; Band; Mrchg Band; Pep Band; School Musical; Symp Band; Dist Wnnr-Natl Piano Guild Adtns 85; Fnlst Poetry-Spnsrd By Gannett Pprs 85; Psych.

TRIES, COURTNEY A; Nardin Acad; Buffalo, NY; (Y); Church Yth Grp; Library Aide; Im Badmtn; Im Swmmng; Hon Roll; Pres Schlr; Exclnce Latin 84; Exclnce Chem 84; Lake Erie Coll; Bio.

TRIFARO, MARY L; Farmingdale SR HS; Massapequa Park, NY; (Y); 35/625; Cmnty Wkr; Key Clb; Cheerleading; Mgr(s); Trk; Hon Roll; NHS; Regents Schlrshp Awd 85; Columbia U Seas; Engrng.

TRIFIRO, JOANNE; Cardinal Mooney HS; Rochester, NY; (Y); Office Aide; Hon Roll; Spanish NHS; St John Fisher; Tchr.

TRIHY, KRISTINE; St John The Baptist HS; Great River, NY; (Y); Sftbl; Tennis; French Hon Soc; Hon Roll; MVP Varsity Sftbll Tm, Tnns Tm 85; Sci.

TRILLY, JONATHAN; S H Calhoun HS; Merrick, NY; (Y); 59/336; Church Yth Grp; Drama Clb; Key Clb; Band; Concert Band; Jazz Band; School Musical; School Play; Symp Band; Rep Stu Cncl; U Of TX Austin; Law.

TRIM, REBECCA; Saranacc Lake HS; Saranac Lake, NY; (Y); 6/134; Chorus; Yrbk Stf; Var L Cheerleading; JV Trk; JV Vllybl; High Hon Roll; Hon Roll; NHS; Regents Scholar 85; Alumni-Cmnty Scholar 85; Pres Fitnss & Achvt Awd 85; N Country CC; Mth.

TRIMARCHI, CATHY; Preston HS; Bronx, NY; (S); 24/76; Church Yth Grp; Pep Clb; VP Sr Cls; Bowling; NHS; Hugh O Brien Yth Fndtn 82; Presl Classrm Alumni 84; Fordham; Mrktng.

TRIMBUR, CYNTHIA; Cicero North Syracuse HS; East Syracuse, NY; (S); 67/711; Church Yth Grp; Drama Clb; Thesps; Stage Crew; Cit Awd; Hon Roll; NHS; Volnteer Of Yr Awd 83; CCBI; Exec Sec.

TRINCO, LISA A; T R Proctor HS; Utica, NY; (Y); VP Art Clb; Church Yth Grp; Drama Clb; Hosp Aide; Pep Clb; Spanish Clb; Stage Crew; Hon Roll; Art 85; Mony Regnl Schlstc Awd Partcptn Art 85; Daemen Coll; Cmrcl Art.

TRINK, ERICA; Midwood High Schl At Brooklyn College; Brooklyn, NY; (Y); 28/587; Church Yth Grp; Math Tm; Lit Mag; High Hon Roll; NHS; Sal; Teachers Aide; Orch; Archon Outstndng Svc 85; Harrison J Golden Comptrollers Awd 83; Iona Coll; Spch Pathlgy.

TRINKLE, RAE E; Cambridge Central HS; Buskirk, NY; (Y); 17/83; Am Leg Aux Girls St; 4-H; FFA; Concert Band; Mrchg Band; Yrbk Stf; Sec Soph Cls; Pres Jr Cls; Pres Sr Cls; Pres Stu Cncl; New York State Regents Schlrshp 85; Cobleskill SUNY; Floriculture.

TRINY, KRISTINE; St John The Baptist HS; Great River, NY; (Y); Sftbl; Tennis; French Hon Soc; Hon Roll; MVP Vrsty Sftbl Tm Awd 85; MVP Vrsty Tinnis Tm Awd 85; Sci.

TRIPI, TERRI; Cardinal Mooney HS; Rochester, NY; (Y); 27/335; Church Yth Grp; Library Aide; Teachers Aide; Rep Soph Cls; Rep Jr Cls; Cheerleading; Hon Roll; NHS; Chrldng Coach 83-85; Clark U; Dntstry.

TRIPOLI, LAURA; James Madison HS; Brooklyn, NY; (Y); 84/812; Art Clb; Library Aide; Office Aide; Chorus; Lit Mag; NHS; NY ST Rgnts Schlrshp 85; Brooklyn Coll; English.

TRIPP, BARBARA A; Johnson City HS; Johnson City, NY; (Y); 2/212; Latin Clb; Sec Pep Clb; Teachers Aide; Varsity Clb; Yrbk Sprt Ed; Yrbk Stf; VP Jr Cls; Pres Stu Cncl; L Cheerleading; L Tennis; NY ST Regents Schlrshp 84-85; Clarkson U Trustee Schlrhp 85; Acad Excel 81-85; Clarkson U; Engrng.

TRIPP, RENEE D; Newfane SR HS; Newfane, NY; (S); 4/166; AFS; Sec Math Clb; Chorus; Yrbk Ed-Chief; Pres Frsh Cls; Stu Cncl; JV Var Fld Hcky; JV Trk; High Hon Roll; Mu Alp Tht; Engrng.

TRIPP, STEPHANIE; Harpursville JR-SR HS; Port Crane, NY; (S); #26 In Class; Chorus; Color Guard; Concert Band; Mrchg Band; School Play; Stage Crew; Sec Jr Cls; Stu Cncl; Capt JV Cheerleading; Twrlr; Area All ST Music 84; Nyssma Solo Comp 82-84; ST U Fredonia; Lang.

TRIPPY, RENEE; Westfield Academy & Central Schl; Westfield, NY; (Y); Ski Clb; Band; Trs Frsh Cls; VP Soph Cls; Sftbl; Vllybl; Hon Roll; Jamestwn Bus Coll; Med Off Asst.

TRIVEDI, KAMINI; Niagara Catholic HS; Grand Island, NY; (Y); 1/81; Drama Clb; Sec Trs French Clb; VP Key Clb; Temple Yth Grp; Nwsp Rptr; Nwsp Stf; Yrbk Stf; Cit Awd; High Hon Roll; NHS; SUNYAB Alumni Ass & Fr Kroupa Awds 85; Med.

TRIVEDI, VAISHALI J; Niagara Catholic HS; Grand Island, NY; (Y); 1/80; Drama Clb; French Clb; Pres JA; Var L Badmtn; DAR Awd; High Hon Roll; Pres NHS; St Schlr; VFW Awd; Church Yth Grp; Washington Workshops Congressional Seminar 84; Vassar College; Pre Medicine.

TRIZINSKY, LORI; Cornwall Central HS; Cornwall, NY; (Y); Dance Clb; Drama Clb; Rep Jr Cls; Rep Sr Cls; Rep Stu Cncl; JV Var Cheerleading; Powder Puff Ftbl; Swmmng; High Hon Roll; Hon Roll; Bus.

TROCCIA, KATHY; Elmira Free Acad; Elmira, NY; (Y); AFS; French Clb; Yrbk Stf; Sec Frsh Cls; Cheerleading; Med.

TROCH, RODNEY; Center Moriches HS; Center Moriches, NY; (Y); Ski Clb; Yrbk Stf; Exclln ce Comp Stu 85; Exclln ce Bus Dynamics 83; Comp Sci.

TROCHE, LISA; La Gardia HS Of Music And Art; New York, NY; (Y); GAA; Spanish Clb; Varsity Clb; Band; Chorus; Madrigals; Stage Crew; Variety Show; Bsbl; Bsktbl; Johy Jay Coll; Crmnl Just.

TROIA, MARK; La Salle SR HS; Niagara Falls, NY; (S); 3/278; Computer Clb; Math Tm; Ski Clb; Yrbk Stf; Var Bsbl; Hon Roll; NHS; Clarkson U; Elec.

TROISI, CHRISTOPHER J; Seaford HS; Wantagh, NY; (Y); 40/246; Am Leg Boys St; Political Wkr; Nwsp Ed-Chief; Nwsp Sprt Ed; Yrbk Stf; Lit Mag; Rep Frsh Cls; Trs Jr Cls; Trs Stu Cncl; Hon Roll; Thomas Gulotta Comm Svc Awd 85; Seaford-Wantagh Exclln c In Jrnlsm Awd 85; Comm Svc Awd 85; Siena Coll; Librl Arts.

TROISI, JEANETTE M; F D Roosevelt HS; Hyde Park, NY; (Y); 29/325; Church Yth Grp; Hosp Aide; Band; Jazz Band; Mrchg Band; Trs Frsh Cls; Var Soph Cls; Var Stu Cncl; High Hon Roll; Ntl Merit Ltr; Brd Trustees Hnr Schlrshp 85-89; George Washington U; Pre-Med.

TROMBINO, ERIN; Lyons JR SR HS; Lyons, NY; (Y); 9/96; 4-H; French Clb; Latin Clb; Ski Clb; Varsity Clb; Concert Band; Mrchg Band; Cheerleading; Hon Roll; NHS; Rgnts Schlrshp 85; Alumni Schlrshp 85; U Of Rochester.

TROMBLEY JR, ARLINGTON J; Franklin Acad; Malone, NY; (Y); Pres Speech Tm; Chorus; Madrigals; Stage Crew; Swing Chorus; Capt Sec Bowling; Hon Roll; Trs Frsh Cls; Trs Soph Cls; Bwlng Trphys-Awds 77-85; Engl, Scl Awds 83; Spch Awds-Trphy Ltr Pin 82-85; Math Tchr.

TROMBLEY, KELLIE JOELLE; Fort Edward HS; Fort Edward, NY; (Y); Am Leg Aux Girls St; Spanish Clb; Drm & Bgl; Yrbk Stf; Sec Frsh Cls; Sec Soph Cls; Sec Jr Cls; Var Cheerleading; Powder Puff Ftbl; Hon Roll; Niagara U; Trvl.

TROMBLEY, MICHAEL; Oneida HS; Durhamville, NY; (S); Pres Computer Clb; French Clb; Mathletes; Varsity Clb; Var L Socr; High Hon Roll; Jr NHS; Trs NHS; Rotary Awd; Comp.

TROMBLY, ROBERT E; St Anthonys HS; Commack, NY; (Y); Var Golf; Capt Ice Hcky.

TROPEA, DAWN M; Division Avenue HS; Levittown, NY; (Y); 6/352; Chorus; School Musical; Variety Show; Yrbk Ed-Chief; Sec Frsh Cls; Rep Stu Cncl; Tennis; High Hon Roll; NHS; NMSQT Letter Of Commendation 84; NY ST Regents Schlrshp 85; Wellesley Coll.

TROPP, JONATHAN B; Herricks HS; New Hyde Park, NY; (Y); 3/306; Mathletes; Trs Stu Cncl; Bausch & Lomb Sci Awd; NHS; Ntl Merit Schol; Aud/Vis; Computer Clb; Math Tm; Quiz Bowl; Rep Frsh Cls; US Sen Yth Prog Del NY ST 85; Lawrence Livermore Natl Labs Super Cmptng Prog NY ST Rep 85; Harvard U; Chem.

TROTSKY, JULIE; Villa Maria Acad; Buffalo, NY; (Y); Computer Clb; FBLA; Gym; Hon Roll; Hilbert Coll; Sec.

TROTTA, ANNAMARIE; Hicksville HS; Hicksvl, NY; (Y); Church Yth Grp; Computer Clb; Drama Clb; Thesps; Band; Chorus; Church Choir; School Musical; School Play; Stage Crew; Adelphi; Spch Pthlgy.

TROTTA, MARK; Port Jervis HS; Port Jervis, NY; (Y); Varsity Clb; JV Bsbl; Coach Actv; Var Ftbl; Var Wrstlng; God Cntry Awd; High Hon Roll; NHS; Treas Wrstlng Clb 84-85; Comp Sci.

TROUPE, TANIKA; Adali E Stevenson HS; Bronx, NY; (Y); Capt GAA; Office Aide; Teachers Aide; Capt Tennis; Prfct Atten Awd; Baruch; Bus.

TROVATO, BONNIE; South Seneca HS; Interlaken, NY; (Y); 9/80; School Musical; High Hon Roll; Hon Roll; NHS; Seneca Cnty Chldrns Comm Schlrshp 85; S Seneca Tchrs Assoc Schlrshp 85; Griswld Tele Schlrshp 85; SUNY Geneseo; Elem Educ.

TROWBRIDGE, KRISTINE G; Pittsford Mendon HS; Pittsford, NY; (Y); AFS; Hosp Aide; Orch; Nwsp Ed-Chief; Pres Soph Cls; VP Stu Cncl; Var Capt Gym; NHS; Ntl Merit SF; Rep Sr Cls; Pres Stu Cncl Monroe Cty; Rochester Wellesley Bk Awd; Biomed Engr.

TROY, MAUREEN; St Johns Prep; Astoria, NY; (Y); Church Yth Grp; Hosp Aide; Chorus; School Play; Cheerleading; Swmmng; Hon Roll.

TROYAN, DAVID; Riverhead HS; Aqueboque, NY; (Y); 3/194; Science Clb; JV Golf; High Hon Roll; NHS; Prfct Atten Awd; Bio & Math Awds 84; Soc Stds Awd 85.

TRUAX, CYNTHIA; Massena Central HS; Massena, NY; (Y); Thesps; Band; Chorus; Madrigals; Mrchg Band; School Play; Gym; Hon Roll; Sci.

TRUAX, JACKIE L; Le Roy Central HS; Le Roy, NY; (Y); 13/114; French Clb; Color Guard; Nwsp Phtg; Nwsp Rptr; Yrbk Phtg; Bsktbl; High Hon Roll; Hon Roll; Jr NHS; NHS; Acad Lttr 85; First Aid.

TRUDEAU, CHERIE; Ticonderoga HS; Ticonderoga, NY; (Y); Drama Clb; Trs Key Clb; Band; Chorus; Concert Band; Jazz Band; School Play; Stage Crew; Yrbk Stf; Rep Soph Cls; Key Clb Dclty Advsrs Awd 85; SUNY Oneonta; Psychlgy.

TRUDEAU, MARK; Ticonderoga HS; Ticonderoga, NY; (Y); Varsity Clb; Pres Jr Cls; Rep Sr Cls; Rep Stu Cncl; Var Capt Bsbl; Var Capt Bsktbl; Vllybl; High Hon Roll; NHS; MVP Bsktbl 84-85; All-Star Team Bsktbl 84-85; Dartmouth; Math.

TRUDEAUX, LYLE; Union Endicott HS; Endicott, NY; (Y); Boys Clb Am; Church Yth Grp; Ftbl; NAACP Cmnty Awd 85; Urbn Leag Achv Awd 85; Broome CC Potsdam; Comp Sci.

TRUESDALE, KIMBERLY; Mc Kinley HS; Buffalo, NY; (Y); Library Aide; School Musical; Nwsp Stf; Var Cheerleading; Ice Hcky; Hon Roll; Prfct Atten Awd; Nrs.

TRUEX, SHELLEY; Susquehanna Valley HS; Binghamton, NY; (Y); Drama Clb; Spanish Clb; Nwsp Rptr; Yrbk Stf; Trs Stu Cncl; Var Vllybl; High Hon Roll; Sec NHS; Opt Clb Awd; SUNY Binghamton; Pre-Law.

TRUEX, VICKI; Susquehanna Valley HS; Binghamton, NY; (Y); Band; Chorus; Concert Band; Mrchg Band; School Musical; School Play; Variety Show; Var Capt Tennis; Var L Vllybl; Drama Clb; Acad All Amer 85; Music.

TRUKAWINSKI, SUSAN E; Bishop Ford Central Catholic HS; Brooklyn, NY; (Y); 1/375; Math Tm; Science Clb; Drm & Bgl; School Musical; Nwsp Rptr; Nwsp Stf; Yrbk Stf; Vllybl; Ntl Merit SF; Boy Scts; Cornell U; Bio.

TRUMBLE, LISA C; Colonie Central HS; Albany, NY; (Y); 4/455; Pres Camera Clb; Computer Clb; Intnl Clb; Trs Spanish Clb; Concert Band; Orch; Symp Band; Yrbk Phtg; High Hon Roll; NHS; Buffalo ST Coll Hnrs Schlrshp 85; St Rose Coll Alumni Awd 85; Rgnts Schlrshp 85; SUNY Albany-Buffalo; Educ.

TRUMBORE, MARGARET; Pavilion Central HS; Pavilion, NY; (Y); AFS; Art Clb; Church Yth Grp; Chorus; School Play; JV Cheerleading; JV Socr; Var Capt Sftbl; JV Vllybl; High Hon Roll; U Dayton; Intr Dsgn.

TRUMP, ANN E; Linton HS; Schenectady, NY; (Y); 8/287; AFS; Art Clb; Drama Clb; Hosp Aide; Stage Crew; Yrbk Phtg; Yrbk Stf; Lit Mag; Hon Roll; NHS; Pace U Schlrshp 85-89; Regnts Schlrshp 85-89; Frnch Allince Awd 85; Pace U; Comp Graphs.

TRUMPOWSKY, ERIC; James E Sperry HS; Rochester, NY; (Y); Acpl Chr; Chorus; Jazz Band; Madrigals; Stat Bsbl; French Hon Soc; High Hon Roll; Hon Roll; Jr NHS; NHS; Sclstc Lttr 85; Law.

TRUOCCHIO, RALPH; Longwood HS; Middle Island, NY; (S); 22/545; Key Clb; High Hon Roll; NHS; Acadmc All-Am Schlr Pgm 85; NY U; Med.

TRUONG, HAROLD; Smithtown High School East; Smithtown, NY; (Y); Computer Clb; Off Frsh Cls; Off Soph Cls; High Hon Roll; Hon Roll; Engnrng.

TRUONG, MYPHUONG; Curtis HS; Staten Island, NY; (Y); Math Clb; Service Clb; Prfct Atten Awd; Hnr Key 85; Super Youth 84; Med Pgm.

TRUONG, NGHIA; West Irondequoit HS; Rochester, NY; (Y); Boys Clb Am; Boy Scts; Model UN; Red Cross Aide; Concert Band; Mrchg Band; Socr; Vllybl; Cit Awd; Cmnty Wkr; Electrnc.

TRYBALSKI, FRANCINE; Rome Catholic HS; Rome, NY; (Y); Church Yth Grp; Girl Scts; Hosp Aide; School Musical; Yrbk Ed-Chief; Yrbk Stf; Sec Frsh Cls; Stu Cncl; Score Keeper; Var Trk; Amer Govt Awd 84-85; RN.

TRYBALSKI, JOHN; Cattaraugus Central Schl; Cattaraugus, NY; (Y); 12/65; Boy Scts; Comp Tech.

TRYFONOS, JAMES; Copiague HS; Copiague, NY; (Y); Computer Clb; French Clb; FBLA; Math Tm; Var Socr; 3rd Pl NY St Bus Math 84; 2nd Pl Acctng FBLA 85.

TRYON, LINETTE; Weedsport HS; Weedsport, NY; (Y); DECA; Hosp Aide; Band; Drill Tm; JV Fld Hcky; High Hon Roll; Hon Roll; Bronze Merit Awd 85; Outstndg Achvmnt Awd 85; Reg Finals Compttn 85; Inter Decor.

TRZASKA, COLLEEN; Villa Maria Acad; Buffalo, NY; (Y); 23/116; Pres Church Yth Grp; Computer Clb; French Clb; Math Clb; Acpl Chr; Chorus; Church Choir; Rep Soph Cls; Gym; Im Swmmng; Baldwin Wallace Coll; Comp Sci.

TRZECIAK, CAROLYN; Cornwall Central HS; Cornwall, NY; (Y); Frsh Cls; Hon Roll; Comm.

TSAI, EN J; Midwood High Schl At Brooklyn Coll; Brooklyn, NY; (Y); 48/605; Church Yth Grp; FCA; Intnl Clb; Math Tm; Office Aide; Chorus; Church Choir; Variety Show; Lit Mag; Ntl Merit Ltr; Rensselaer Polytech Inst.

TSAI, JOE; Mont Pleasant HS; Schenectady, NY; (Y); Boy Scts; Church Yth Grp; Computer Clb; Exploring; Key Clb; French Hon Soc; Hon Roll; Chess Clb; Service Clb; Tennis; Frnch Embssy Cert Of Excell 84-85; Natl Frnch Cont Cert Of Hnr Hudson Vlly Chap 84-85; Brigham Young U; Elec Engrng.

TSAI, JOSEPH; Mont Pleasant HS; Schenectady, NY; (Y); Aud/Vis; Boy Scts; Chess Clb; Church Yth Grp; Computer Clb; Key Clb; Service Clb; Tennis; French Hon Soc; High Hon Roll; Fr Embassy Cert Exclnc 85; Natl Fr Cont Cert Hnr Lvl 2-B 85; Brigham Young U; Elec Engr.

TSANG, ANNA; Midwood HS; Brooklyn, NY; (Y); 65/605; Math Tm; Office Aide; Science Clb; Chorus; School Musical; Yrbk Stf; Lit Mag; Cit Awd; Hon Roll; Untd Fdrtn Of Tchrs Schlrshp Awd; ARISTA Hnr Soc-Grl Ldr; NY U; Chem.

TSANG, LUCY; La Guortia H S Of Music & The Arts; New York, NY; (Y); 2/588; Hosp Aide; Office Aide; Chorus; Lit Mag; Sec Sr Cls; Cit Awd; High Hon Roll; NHS; Sal; Govnrs Cmmttee Schlstc Achvt 85; Untd Fdrtn Tchrs Schlrshp 85; Yale U.

TSANG, OILING; John Dewey HS; Brooklyn, NY; (Y); Library Aide.

TSANG, SHIRLEY; Connetgunt HS; Bohemia, NY; (S); 6/730; Trs FBLA; Trs Intnl Clb; Math Tm; Jr NHS; NHS; 2nd NY St Accntng Ii Contest FBLA 84; 2nd NY St Addirgand Calculating Awd FBLA 84; NY U; Accntng.

TSAO, DAVID K W; Forest Hills HS; Flushing, NY; (Y); 10/762; Boy Scts; Math Clb; Math Tm; Science Clb; Westinghse Sci Tlnt Srch Hnrs Grp 85; Brown U; Med.

TSAO, KUANGWEN; Forest Hills HS; Flushing, NY; (Y); 10/762; Boy Scts; Math Tm; Science Clb; Temple Yth Grp; Brown U; Med Rsrch.

TSCHANG, MING MEI; Irondequoit HS; Rochester, NY; (Y); 31/350; Hosp Aide; Chorus; School Musical; Yrbk Stf; Chrmn Jr Cls; Chrmn Sr Cls; Hon Roll; NHS; U Buffalo; Bus Admn.

TSCHAPP, AIMEE; Gowanda Central HS; Gowanda, NY; (Y); Thesps; Band; School Musical; School Play; Yrbk Ed-Chief; Pres Frsh Cls; Trs Soph Cls; Stat Bsktbl; Var Trk; NHS; Bowling Green ST U; Intl Mgmt.

TSCHIDERER, MARY; Cardinal Mooney HS; Rochester, NY; (Y); 62/315; Cmnty Wkr; Teachers Aide; JV Bsktbl; Var Socr; JV Capt Sftbl; Hon Roll; NHS; Spanish NHS.

TSE, ANN; Newtown HS; Ridgewood, NY; (Y); 200/800; Camera Clb; Cmnty Wkr; English Clb; FNA; Math Tm; Office Aide; Pep Clb; Service Clb; Teachers Aide; Nwsp Stf; Bonough Of Mark CC; Sec.

TSE, BARRY; Brooklyn Tech; Brooklyn, NY; (Y); 3/1200; Math Tm; Teachers Aide; Var Tennis; Hon Roll; Cornell U; Med.

TSE, ELIZABETH; Amsterdam HS; Amsterdam, NY; (Y); 1/332; Quiz Bowl; Concert Band; Mrchg Band; Yrbk Phtg; Yrbk Stf; Stu Cncl; Var Sftbl; Var Capt Tennis; Sal; Red Cross Aide; Hrvrd Almni Book Awd; NY ST Rgnts Schlsrhp; St Angello Schlrshp; Yale U; Pltcl Sci.

TSUI, RAYMOND; Fallsburg Central HS; S Fallsburg, NY; (Y); 1/57; Drama Clb; Leo Clb; Co-Capt Quiz Bowl; Thesps; School Musical; Variety Show; Rep Frsh Cls; Swmmng; High Hon Roll; Hon Roll; Engrng.

TSUNG, PATRICIA; Roosevelt HS; Hyde Park, NY; (Y); Hosp Aide; Library Aide; Lcrss; Tennis; Hon Roll; NHS; Delta Sigma Theta Sorority Hnr 85.

TSUNIS, GEORGE; Commack H S North; Commack, NY; (Y); Sec Am Leg Boys St; Pres Trs Church Yth Grp; Cmnty Wkr; Co-Capt Debate Tm; Office Aide; Political Wkr; Yrbk Phtg; Yrbk Stf; Rep Jr Cls; Rep Sr Cls; Stony Brook U; Pol Sci.

TSZ MEI CHO, SUSAN; Seward Park HS; New York, NY; (Y); 125/760; Church Yth Grp; FCA; Intnl Clb; Soroptimist; Teachers Aide; Y-Teens; Chorus; Rep Sr Cls; Rep Stu Cncl; Cit Awd; Ofcr & Treas Yth Chrch Grp 82-85; YMCA Vol Wrk; Borough Manhattan Pres Awd 85; Pace U; Bus.

TUBBS, JO ANN; Auburn HS; Auburn, NY; (Y); Church Yth Grp; Drama Clb; Hosp Aide; Chorus; Church Choir; Color Guard; Mrchg Band; School Musical; Symp Band; Hon Roll; Music.

TUBLISKY, ILYSE; Smithtown H S West; Kings Pk, NY; (Y); Office Aide; Yrbk Sprt Ed; Yrbk Stf; Stu Cncl; Var Bsbl; JV Var Cheerleading; Mgr(s); High Hon Roll; NHS; Spanish NHS; Bus Mgmt.

TUBRIDY, DIANNE; Hamburg SR HS; Hamburg, NY; (Y); 206/416; AFS; DECA; French Clb; Service Clb; Rep Soph Cls; Rep Jr Cls; Sec Sr Cls; Stu Cncl; Socr; Capt Swmmng; Frnch Merit Awd 82-83; DECA Awd 84; Keene ST Coll; Sprts Med.

TUCCI, JOHN; V S Central HS; Valley Stream, NY; (Y); 4-H; Science Clb; Ski Clb; Chorus; Capt Wrstlng; Hon Roll.

TUCCI, LARRY; Lindenhurst HS; Lindenhurst, NY; (Y); Bsbl; Diving; Swmmng; Advtsng.

TUCCILLO, KELLY; Connetquot HS; Ronkonkoma, NY; (Y); Cmnty Wkr; School Play; Nwsp Stf; Stu Of The Mnth 82-83; Schlstc Achv Awd In Alg 82-83; Englsh, Micro Comp, Soc Stds & Sci 82-83; Psych.

TUCCILLO, NICHOLAS J; Schalmont HS; Schenectady, NY; (Y); French Clb; Chorus; Concert Band; Jazz Band; Mrchg Band; Var Socr; Var Trk; Im Wrstlng; Hon Roll; Ntl Merit Ltr; Union Coll; Elec Engrng.

TUCEK, TIM; Bainbridge-Guilford Central HS; Bainbridge, NY; (Y); Ski Clb; JV L Ftbl; Im Ice Hcky; Trk; Hon Roll; Chmcl Engrng.

TUCKER, DORRIS; Kenmore West HS; Kenmore, NY; (Y); Pres French Clb; Acpl Chr; Chorus; School Musical; Swing Chorus; Variety Show; Rep Stu Cncl; JV Var Cheerleading; Hon Roll; 3rd US Chrldng Assn Ntl Chmp 84; Bio.

TUCKER, JOSEPHINE; Curtis HS; Staten Island, NY; (Y); Church Yth Grp; Cmnty Wkr; GAA; Varsity Clb; Church Choir; Color Guard; Var Bsktbl; Mgr(s); Schl Merit Roll 84-85; Hofstra U; Acctng.

TUCKER, KATHY; Warrensburg Central HS; Warrensburg, NY; (Y); Yrbk Stf; Sec Sr Cls; Prfct Atten Awd; Bus Math Awdd 84; Bkkpng/Accntng Awd 85; Adv Keybrdng Awd 85; Bus.

TUCKER, LESLIE; Perry Central HS; Perry, NY; (Y); 24/91; Off AFS; Sec Off Drama Clb; 4-H; French Clb; Ski Clb; Band; Concert Band; Jazz Band; Mrchg Band; School Musical; Accntng Awd 85; St John Fisher Coll; Accntng.

TUCKER, LISA M; Iroquois Central HS; Elma, NY; (Y); French Clb; Red Cross Aide; Socr; Hon Roll; Kiwanis Awd; St Schlr; Regnt Schlrshp 85; Adv Plcmnt Engl 85; Ithaca Coll; TV.

TUCKER, MICHELE; Amherst Central HS; Amherst, NY; (Y); 75/310; Church Yth Grp; Chorus; Concert Band; School Musical; Symp Band; Hon Roll; NHS; Regents Schrlshp 85; SUNY; Bio.

TUCKER, RICHARD; Vestal HS; Binghamton, NY; (Y); Aud/Vis; Chess Clb; Church Yth Grp; French Clb; Speech Tm; Hon Roll; Prfct Atten Awd; Brdcstg.

TUCKER, SHARON; Benjamin Franklin HS; Rochester, NY; (Y); FBLA; High Hon Roll; Prfct Atten Awd; Clrk Typst Awd 3rd Pl 85; Bus Admin.

TUDMAN, DENNIS M; Vernon-Verona-Sherrill HS; Sherrill, NY; (Y); Chess Clb; Ski Clb; Var Vllybl; High Hon Roll; Hon Roll; Golden Eagle Awd 82-83; Cert Part Pre-Coll Ocngrphy 84-85.

TUFANO, TAMMY; East Meadow HS; E Meadow, NY; (S); FBLA; Key Clb; Yrbk Stf; Var Lcrss; Hon Roll; NHS; Sci.

TUITE, CATHERINE; Sacred Heart Acad; Merrick, NY; (S); 12/186; Debate Tm; Math Clb; School Play; Nwsp Stf; Bowling; JV Crs Cntry; Hon Roll; NHS; Pre Med.

TUJAK, LAURA; Benjamin N Cardozo HS; Little Neck, NY; (Y); 27/476; Cmnty Wkr; Hosp Aide; Pres Science Clb; Service Clb; Band; School Musical; High Hon Roll; Hon Roll; Hnrs Westinghouse Sci Tlnt Srch 85; Pediatrcn.

TULIN, MARK; Sperry HS; Pittsford, NY; (Y); Temple Yth Grp; Thesps; Trs Concert Band; Jazz Band; School Musical; Stage Crew; High Hon Roll; Hon Roll; Jr NHS.

TULIPANO, MARIEL A; Cathedral HS; Brooklyn, NY; (Y); 50/325; Chess Clb; VP French Clb; Intnl Clb; School Musical; Nwsp Ed-Chief; Yrbk Stf; Rep Frsh Cls; Rep Sr Cls; Im Gym; Ntl Merit Ltr; Italn Native Cont 2nd Hnrs Cert; Italn Poetry Cont Cert Achvt; Gymnastics 2nd Pl Vault; LI U; Med Tech.

TULL, DAMON; Cardinal Spellman HS; Bronx, NY; (Y); Computer Clb; Bsktbl; JV Ftbl; Hon Roll; Profssnl Actr SAG Membr; Engrng.

TULL, MICHELLE; Colonie Central HS; Albany, NY; (Y); 71/511; DECA; Hosp Aide; Ski Clb; Flag Corp; School Musical; Variety Show; JV Var Cheerleading; Coach Actv; Var Sftbl; Swmmng; St Bonoventure; Childhd Studies.

TULLAR, TERI; Cicero-North Syracuse HS; Clay, NY; (S); 80/662; Pres Church Yth Grp; English Clb; Ski Clb; Teachers Aide; Band; Church Choir; Concert Band; Mrchg Band; High Hon Roll; Hon Roll; Pre-Med.

TULLY, BRIAN PATRICK; St Marys Boys High Schl; New Hyde Park, NY; (Y); 20/170; Church Yth Grp; Cmnty Wkr; Political Wkr; Teachers Aide; Var L Crs Cntry; Var L Trk; Hon Roll; Acad All Amer 85; MVP Trk 83-84; Peer Grp Ldr 85-86; Bus.

TULLY, TRACEY; Liverpool HS; Liverpool, NY; (S); 33/780; Ski Clb; Chorus; Nwsp Ed-Chief; Yrbk Ed-Chief; VP Stu Cncl; Capt Cheerleading; Trk; Hon Roll; NHS; Ntl Merit Ltr; Outstndng Frshman 81-82; Boston Coll.

TULOWIECKI, ANDREW; Liverpool HS; Liverpool, NY; (S); Wrstlng; NHS; Potsdam ST; Comp Sci.

TULOWIECKI, LINDA; Liverpool HS; Liverpool, NY; (Y); Bryant & Stratton; Exec Sec.

TUMBLIN, SHANNON; Oriskany Central HS; Rome, NY; (Y); 13/92; Key Clb; Spanish Clb; Varsity Clb; Band; Mrchg Band; Nwsp Rptr; Nwsp Stf; Yrbk Stf; Trs Frsh Cls; Sec Jr Cls; Paul J Headd Aptitude Achvt Scholar 85; Central Cty Bus Inst; Acctng.

TUMMINIA, LOUIS G; Half Hollow Hills High School East; Dix Hills, NY; (Y); Spanish Clb; Ice Hcky; Socr; Spanish NHS; SUNY Stony Brook; Med.

TUMMIOLO, ROSA; Bishop Kearney HS; Brooklyn, NY; (Y); 100/360; Debate Tm; Girl Scts; Pep Clb; PAVAS; Ski Clb; Bowling; Hon Roll; Bus Hnr Soc; JR Achvt; St Johns U; Bus.

TUMMONS, MIKE J; Franklin Academy HS; Malone, NY; (Y); 53/253; Varsity Clb; JV Var Bsbl; JV Wrstlng; NY ST Regents Scholarship 85; Canton ATC; Computer Science.

TUMMONS, TAMMY; Franklin Acad; Malone, NY; (Y); N Country CC; Med Sec.

TUNCA, DENIZ; Franklyn D Roosevelt HS; Brooklyn, NY; (Y); Aud/Vis; Cmnty Wkr; Math Tm; Concert Band; Lit Mag; Im Bsktbl; Im Sftbl; Cit Awd; Bus.

TUNG, TSUYOSHI M; Edgemont HS; Scarsdale, NY; (Y); CAP; Mathletes; Var L Crs Cntry; Var L Trk; French Hon Soc; Ntl Merit Ltr; Air Force ROTC Schlrshp 85; Civil Air Patrl Amelia Earhart Awd 85; Trck Coachs Awd 84-85; US Air Force Acad; Aerospace.

TUNNING, DOUGLAS; Savona Central Schl; Big Sandy, TN; (Y); 4/23; Church Yth Grp; Exploring; Chorus; School Play; Stage Crew; Yrbk Phtg; Yrbk Stf; Var Bsktbl; Hon Roll; NHS; Emrgcy Med Tech.

TUNSTALL, MARC; Allegany Central HS; Allegany, NY; (Y); 18/94; Boy Scts; Rep Soph Cls; Trs Jr Cls; Trs Sr Cls; Trs Stu Cncl; Var Crs Cntry; Var Socr; Var Trk; High Hon Roll; Hon Roll; Eagle Scout Awd 85; Organzd Triathlon To Benefit Cystic Fibrosis 85; Military Pilot.

TUOHEY, MELISSA; Maple Hill HS; Castleton, NY; (S); 15/78; Drama Clb; Ski Clb; Spanish Clb; Band; Concert Band; School Play; Sec Soph Cls; Fld Hcky; Sftbl; Hon Roll; Pre Law.

TUOHY, DANIELLE; St Vincent Ferrer HS; Woodside, NY; (Y); 16/114; Art Clb; Hon Roll; Prfct Atten Awd; Adelphi; Nrsng.

TURANICZO, STEPHANIE; Curtis HS; Staten Island, NY; (Y); Office Aide; Teachers Aide; Cert Of Achv In Proj Invst Mrt Rll; Tchng.

TURANO, TERI; Wantagh SR HS; Wantagh, NY; (Y); Chorus; Var Capt Cheerleading; Mgr(s); Socr; Sftbl; Vllybl; Hon Roll.

TURCHIN, DEBORAH N; Newfield HS; Selden, NY; (Y); 84/550; Pres Art Clb; Stage Crew; Hon Roll; Natl Art Hnr Scty 84-85; Red Ink & Rewrts Art Awd 83; Most Artistic 85; Art.

TURCOTTE, ALLEN; Newcomb Central Schl; Newcomb, NY; (Y); Band; Chorus; Jazz Band; Var Bsbl; Capt Var Bsktbl; Capt Var Socr; Lion Awd; Delhi Ag Tech; Bldg Const.

TURCZYN, STEVEN; John F Kennedy HS; Utica, NY; (Y); Exploring; Ski Clb; Band; Jazz Band; Mrchg Band; Nwsp Rptr; Yrbk Phtg; Yrbk Rptr; Bowling; Tennis; Schl A Hnr Rl 84-85; RPI; Engrng.

TUREK, JULIE; Cardinal Mooney HS; Rochester, NY; (Y); 3/320; Ski Clb; Stage Crew; Var Socr; JV Vllybl; French Hon Soc; High Hon Roll; NHS; English 10 Hnrs Awd 84; Regents Bio Awd 84; Frnch 3 Awd 85.

TURENNE, MARC; Beacon HS; Beacon, NY; (Y); Drama Clb; Hosp Aide; Latin Clb; Church Choir; School Play; Stage Crew; Black Belt Tae Kwon Do 85.

TURER, JOLEEN GEORGI; New Rochelle HS; New Rochelle, NY; (Y); Cmnty Wkr; Model UN; Var L Tennis; Hon Roll; NHS; MVP Ten Sngles 83; Ten Mag JR Sprtsmsnshp Awd 84; Svc Awd 83.

TURHAN, FILIZ; Freeport HS; Freeport, NY; (Y); 10/450; Drama Clb; Key Clb; Chorus; School Musical; School Play; Stage Crew; Variety Show; Yrbk Stf; Lit Mag; High Hon Roll; NY U; Engl.

TURHAN, NILAY; Wilson Magnet HS; Rochester, NY; (Y); Library Aide; Nwsp Rptr; Yrbk Ed-Chief; Ed Lit Mag; Rep Jr Cls; Cit Awd; High Hon Roll; Hon Roll; Prfct Atten Awd; Outstndng Svc Schl 85; Outstndng Svc/Ldrshp 85; U Of Rochester.

TURI, LINDA; John F Kennedy HS; Utica, NY; (Y); Chorus; Nwsp Bus Mgr; Nwsp Ed-Chief; Nwsp Phtg; Nwsp Rptr; Yrbk Ed-Chief; Badmtn; Hon Roll; Jr NHS; NHS; Regents Schlrshp 86; ST U Geneseo.

TURIC, MICHELLE; Thomas A Edison HS; Elmira Hts, NY; (Y); GAA; Varsity Clb; Sec Frsh Cls; Sec Soph Cls; Sec Jr Cls; Sec Sr Cls; Stu Cncl; Capt L Bsktbl; Var L Sftbl; Var L Swmmng; ST Grls Vllybl Team 85; Grls Bsktbl Rep WENY Banquet 85; Slvr & Brnze Mdls Trck 83; Corning CC; Acctng.

TURK, DIANA; Masters Schl; Dobbs Ferry, NY; (Y); GAA; Key Clb; Service Clb; Varsity Clb; Acpl Chr; Nwsp Bus Mgr; Nwsp Rptr; Nwsp Stf; Yrbk Rptr; Yrbk Stf; Amer H S Athlete; Eng.

TURKER, BILGIN; High School Of Fashion Ind; Flushing, NY; (Y); 41/413; Library Aide; Office Aide; Teachers Aide; Variety Show; Yrbk Stf; Vllybl; Hon Roll; CATS Cntst 85; Hudson-Shatz Mural Dsgn Cntst 84-85; Stu Art Fstvl 85; Art.

TURKOVICH, MICHAEL R; Archbishop Stepinac HS; Yonkers, NY; (Y); 63/206; Pres Church Yth Grp; Church Choir; Bowling; Hon Roll; Ntl Merit Ltr; St Schlr; Mt St Vincent Alumni Coll Schlrshp 85-86; NYS Rgnts Schlrshp 85-86; Mt St Vincent Coll; Rssn.

TURNBULL, CHRISTINE M; Sayville HS; Sayville, NY; (Y); 53/363; Mathletes; Var Capt Bsktbl; Var Capt Sftbl; Var Capt Tennis; Im Vllybl; High Hon Roll; Regents Schlrshp 85; SUNY At Geneseo; Crmnl Justice.

TURNBULL, NATALIE; Southside HS; South Hempstead, NY; (Y); 17/291; Key Clb; Chorus; Orch; Sec Jr Cls; Sec Stu Cncl; JV Socr; Var Trk; High Hon Roll; Jr NHS; NHS; Spnsh Exchg Stu 85.

TURNER, ALLEN; Albion HS; Albion, NY; (S); 21/171; Band; Concert Band; Jazz Band; Mrchg Band; Pep Band; Symp Band; DAR Awd; NHS; NY ST Regents Scholar Wnr 85; Royson N Whipple Scholar Wnr SUNY Ag & Tech 85; SUNY Ag & Tech Morrisvl; Music.

TURNER, BUFFY; Remsen Central HS; Remsen, NY; (Y); 4-H; Library Aide; Teachers Aide; Concert Band; Capt Swmmng; High Hon Roll; NHS; Ntl Merit Ltr; HMH Schlrshp Smmr Prog 84; 1st Pl Swim-A-Thon Awd 84; Marine Bio.

TURNER, CADENCE; Curtis HS; Staten Island, NY; (Y); 19/328; VP Church Yth Grp; Intnl Clb; Math Tm; Quiz Bowl; Science Clb; Yrbk Ed-Chief; Capt L Swmmng; High Hon Roll; Ntl Merit SF; Girl Scts; Staten Is PTA Schlrshp MVP Swmmg 84 & 85; Ostepthc Ftns Awd 85; Hnr Bnnr 85; Bates Coll; Sprts Med.

TURNER, CAREY; Port Richmond HS; Staten Island, NY; (Y); Cmnty Wkr; Drama Clb; Spanish Clb; Temple Yth Grp; School Play; Stage Crew; Lit Mag; Hon Roll; Law.

TURNER, CAROL A; Livonia HS; Groveland, NY; (Y); 19/132; Var Cheerleading; JV Socr; JV Sftbl; Var Trk; SUNY Oswego; Spnsh.

TURNER, DARLENE R; Wheatland Chili Central Schl; Scottsville, NY; (Y); 10/69; JA; Model UN; Yrbk Ed-Chief; Var Score Keeper; JV Socr; Var Sftbl; Var Swmmng; Hon Roll; Prfct Atten Awd; Rotary Awd; Regents Schlrshp 85; Sftbl All-Star Hnrbl Mntn 83; Alfred Tech; Chem Tech.

TURNER, DEBORAH; Martin Luther King HS; Ny, NY; (Y); 59/258; Art Clb; Science Clb; Chorus; Bsbl; Bsktbl; High Hon Roll; Hon Roll; Prfct Atten Awd; Med.

TURNER, DEBORAH; Sherburne-Earlville HS; Sherburne, NY; (S); 8/150; Band; Concert Band; Mrchg Band; Var L Bsktbl; Cit Awd; Hon Roll; NHS; Prfct Atten Awd; SUNY Albany; Math.

TURNER, JILL; Half Hollow Hills HS East; Dix Hills, NY; (Y); 30/499; Cmnty Wkr; Debate Tm; Leo Clb; Nwsp Stf; Yrbk Stf; Lit Mag; Mgr(s); French Hon Soc; Jr NHS; NHS; Amer Bar Assn Awd 85.

TURNER, JILL E; Madrid Waddington HS; Waddington, NY; (Y); Drama Clb; French Clb; Trs Band; Chorus; Concert Band; Mrchg Band; Pep Band; School Musical; Stage Crew; Yrbk Rptr; Creatve Wrtng Awd For Excel 85; U Of Houston; Crmnl Justice.

TURNER, KELLEE; Urban League HS; Rochester, NY; (Y); English Clb; JA; Office Aide; Quiz Bowl; Teachers Aide; Frsh Cls; Bsktbl; Cheerleading; Gym; Sftbl; Hnrs Engl 82-83; Regents Engl 84-85; Bus Mgmt.

TURNER, MARY; Lansingburgh HS; Troy, NY; (Y); Office Aide; Nwsp Stf; Yrbk Stf; Varsity Clb; Stu Cncl; Cheerleading; Trk; High Hon Roll; NHS; Prfct Atten Awd; Bus Stu Of Yr 85; Outstdng Bus Stu Furthering Educ In Bus/Mrktng 85; Magna Cum Laude; Hudson Valley CC; Bus Adm.

TURNER, NICOLE; Kensington HS; Buffalo, NY; (Y); FBLA; GAA; Office Aide; Science Clb; Teachers Aide; Bsktbl; Sftbl; Vllybl; Bus.

TURNER, RAY; Bishop Ford HS; Brooklyn, NY; (Y); Church Yth Grp; Computer Clb; JV Bowling; Brooklyn Coll; Acctng.

TURNER, RITA; Sherburne Earlville HS; Earlville, NY; (S); 4-H; French Clb; Sec Band; Trs Frsh Cls; Trs Soph Cls; Rep Jr Cls; Trs Stu Cncl; Bsktbl; NHS.

TURNER, SHEEN; Walton HS; Bronx, NY; (Y); Hosp Aide; PAVAS; Band; Orch; Nwsp Phtg; Tennis; Prfct Atten Awd; North Eastern.

TURNER, STEPHANIE; Myndersc Acad; Seneca Falls, NY; (Y); Yrbk Stf; Cheerleading; Sftbl; Vllybl; Bryant & Stratton; Bus.

TURNER, STEPHENIE; Auburn HS; Auburn, NY; (Y); 123/400; Cmnty Wkr; ROTC; Nwsp Stf; Fld Hcky; Hon Roll; Militry Ordr Wrld Wars 83; Natl Sojournrs 84; Retird Ofcrs Assn 85; Crmnl Jstc.

TURNER, TERESA M; John Jay HS; Warrenton, VA; (Y); 33/563; AFS; Church Yth Grp; Girl Scts; Ski Clb; Stage Crew; Lit Mag; Rep Frsh Cls; VP Soph Cls; Stat Bsktbl; Var L Trk; Two/Ten Fndtn Scholar 85; Rochester Natl Scholar 85; NYS Rgnts Scholar 85; U Rochester; Mech Engrng.

TURNEY, MELISSA; Cicero North Syracuse HS; Bridgeport, NY; (S); 70/711; Spanish Clb; Rep Frsh Cls; Rep Soph Cls; Rep Jr Cls; Rep Sr Cls; Var Cheerleading; Hon Roll; NHS; Owsego; Educ.

TURNIPSEED, ALFRED D; Midwood HS; Brooklyn, NY; (Y); 122/605; Office Aide; Science Clb; Service Clb; Orch; School Musical; Stage Crew; Nwsp Stf.

TURNQUIST, SHARON; Lindenhurst SR HS; Lindenhurst, NY; (Y); Church Yth Grp; Yrbk Phtg; Yrbk Stf; Trk; Hon Roll.

TUROCZI, MICHELLE J; Hendrick Hudson HS; Peekskill, NY; (Y); Drama Clb; Orch; Nwsp Stf; Lit Mag; Stat Fld Hcky; Hghst Avg Itln Daily Lvng I; Drama Clb & Orchstra Prfrmnces Recgntn; Trvl.

TURPIN, DONNA; Riverhead HS; Riverhead, NY; (Y); Var Fld Hcky; Var Trk; Sec.

TUSZYNSKI, DEBORA J; Greece Athena HS; Rochester, NY; (Y); 13/280; Nwsp Rptr; High Hon Roll; Hon Roll; Acad Lttr 82-84; Outstndg SS Stu 84-85; NYS Regnts Schlrshp 85; U Of MO Columbia; Engl.

TUTHILL, DAVID; Mattituck HS; Laurel, NY; (Y); 40/120; Band; Chorus; Stage Crew; Rep Stu Cncl; Var L Socr; Var L Wrstlng; Hon Roll; Boostr Clb Hrdst Wrkr Awd Wrstlng 84-85; 4th Pl Leag 7 Wrstlng 84-85; Crmnl Justic.

TUTTLE, BRIAN D; Waterville Central Schl; Waterville, NY; (Y); 6/89; Am Leg Boys St; Church Yth Grp; Varsity Clb; Jazz Band; Stu Cncl; Var L Crs Cntry; Var L Socr; Var L Tennis; High Hon Roll; NHS; Rochester Inst Tech; Comp Sci.

TUTTY, CHRISTOPHER; Aquinas Inst; Rochester, NY; (S); Drama Clb; Spanish Clb; Varsity Clb; School Play; Nwsp Stf; Rep Jr Cls; Pres Stu Cncl; Var Bsbl; Capt Ftbl; High Hon Roll; Sci & Spnsh Achvt Awd 82-83; Lbrl Arts.

TVAROHA, DANIEL; Groton Central Schl; Groton, NY; (Y); 5/67; Am Leg Boys St; Red Cross Aide; Rep Stu Cncl; Capt Crs Cntry; Var Trk; Cit Awd; Dnfth Awd; DAR Awd; High Hon Roll; NHS; Elmira Coll Key Awd 85; Crimnl Jstc.

TWAROG, PAUL; Saint Marys HS; Elma, NY; (S); Varsity Clb; School Musical; School Play; Yrbk Stf; Rep Jr Cls; Chrmn Stu Cncl; Var Crs Cntry; Var Tennis; Hon Roll; NHS; Stu Svc Awd Campus Mnstry 84; Class Accmdtns 82-84; Pre Med.

TWEEDDALE, JACKIE; St John Villa Acad; Staten Is, NY; (Y); Girl Scts; Katherine Gibbs; Sec.

TWIRBUTT, GREGORY; Garden School Inc; Forest Hills, NY; (Y); 2/26; Computer Clb; Debate Tm; French Clb; Nwsp Rptr; Rep Soph Cls; Rep Jr Cls; Hon Roll; Jr NHS; NHS; Prfct Atten Awd; ST Of NY Rgnts Coll Schlrshp & Cert Of Merit 85; Cornell U; Scntst.

TWISS, KIM; Columbia HS; Rensselaer, NY; (Y); 84/353; Variety Show; Rep Stu Cncl; NHS; Hum Rel Co Ldr 84-85; Prsdntl Acad Ftnss Awds 85; Potsdam Coll; Lib Arts.

TWITCHELL, BRIAN; Sauquoit Valley SR HS; Cassville, NY; (S); 4/110; Varsity Clb; Acpl Chr; Band; Jazz Band; Var Capt Bsktbl; Var Capt Ftbl; Trk; NHS; Opt Clb Awd; Bio.

TWOMEY, DONALD; Mercy HS; Jamesport, NY; (Y); 36/110; Letterman Clb; Spanish Clb; Varsity Clb; Nwsp Rptr; Yrbk Stf; Off Jr Cls; Off Sr Cls; Bsbl; Ftbl; Wt Lftg.

TWOMEY, LISA; Liverpool HS; Liverpool, NY; (S); 75/800; Spanish Clb; Chorus; Trs Sr Cls; Rep Stu Cncl; Var Crs Cntry; Var Trk; Hon Roll; NHS; SUC; Lib Arts.

TWYFORD, KATHERINE; Moore Catholic HS; Staten Island, NY; (Y); Math Clb; Co-Capt NFL; Spanish Clb; School Play; Stage Crew; Lit Mag; Rep Jr Cls; Stu Cncl; Socr; Hon Roll; Intl Rltns.

TYLER, EDWARD K; Westhill HS; Syracuse, NY; (Y); 17/169; AFS; Key Clb; Ski Clb; Spanish Clb; Var Tennis; Hon Roll; NHS; NY ST Sci Cngrss Hnrs 3rd Pl 82; NY ST Prodigy Srch Wnnr Sci Div 85; ROTC Schlrshp 85; UCLA; Astrnmy.

TYLER, JENNIFER; Mount Vernon HS; Mount Vernon, NY; (Y); Office Aide; Hon Roll; Math.

TYLER, JOSEPH; Walton Central Schl; Walton, NY; (Y); 4/100; AFS; Church Yth Grp; Pres Computer Clb; Drama Clb; Sec Model UN; Chorus; School Play; Var L Trk; Bausch & Lomb Sci Awd; High Hon Roll; Intl Comp Prblm Slvng Cont Tri-Cnty Wnnr 84; Math Exam Awd Wnnr 85; Daily Star Carrier Of Yr 84; Purdue U; Engrng.

TYLUTKI, THOMAS; Bishopscully HS; Amsterdam, NY; (Y); 9/61; 4-H; Latin Clb; Math Clb; Capt Quiz Bowl; Stu Cncl; Var Crs Cntry; 4-H Awd; High Hon Roll; NHS; Mont Cnty Dairy Cattle Jdgng Trophy 83; Cornell U; Vet.

TYMANN, RUTH F; Bishop Ludden HS; Syracuse, NY; (Y); 3/179; Cmnty Wkr; 4-H; German Clb; GAA; Girl Scts; Hosp Aide; Political Wkr; Red Cross Aide; Nwsp Rptr; Nwsp Stf; Alfred U Pres Schlr 85; GE Fndtn Star Awd Wnnr 85; NYS Rgnts Schlrshp; Alfred U; Bio-Med.

TYNAN, ANN MARIE; The Mary Louis Acad; Flushing, NY; (Y); Teachers Aide; Capt Bowling; NEDT Awd; Manhatten Coll; Engnr.

TYNAN, KEVIN; Jericho HS; Westbury, NY; (Y); Var Co-Capt Bsktbl; Long Isl Empire St Bsktbl Tm 85; All Co Bsktbl 1st Tm 85; All Co Bsktbl 2nd Tm 84; Pre-Law.

TYNAN, MARY; Academy Of Mt St Ursula HS; New York, NY; (Y); 1/137; Rep Computer Clb; Exploring; Hosp Aide; Sec Library Aide; Rep Science Clb; Rep Jr Cls; Rep Stu Cncl; High Hon Roll; Hon Roll; Prfct Atten Awd; Manhattan Coll; Engrng.

TYNDELL, JENNIFER; Corning West HS; Beaver Dams, NY; (Y); Cmnty Wkr; Exploring; JA; Ski Clb; Chorus; High Hon Roll; NHS; SUNY Buffalo; Dentstry.

TYO, SUZANNE; Red Jacket Central HS; Shortsville, NY; (Y); 1/95; Am Leg Aux Girls St; French Clb; Spanish Clb; Chorus; Yrbk Stf; Pres Stu Cncl; Var Capt Cheerleading; NHS; Church Yth Grp; Cmnty Wkr; NY ST Teen Age Rep V Chairmn 85; SADD VP 84-85; BYOB 84-85; Lang.

TYRE, KENDAL H; Fairport HS; Fairport, NY; (Y); Intnl Clb; Model UN; Political Wkr; Pres Band; Mrchg Band; Pres Sr Cls; Rep Stu Cncl; Var Trk; Hon Roll; NHS; Pol Sci.

TYRRELL, KIMBERLY; Gloversville HS; Gloversville, NY; (Y); Rep AFS; Cmnty Wkr; Rep Intnl Clb; Library Aide; Thesps; Var Chorus; Stage Crew; Hon Roll; NHS; Phys Thrpy.

TYSON JR, OSCAR A; Hutch-Tech HS; Buffalo, NY; (Y); 66/262; Aud/Vis; Stage Crew; Rep Stu Cncl; Var Bsktbl; Crs Cntry; Martin Luther King Schlrshp 85-86; Canisius Coll; Pre-Med.

TYSON, ROBERT; St Marys Boys HS; Roslyn Heights, NY; (S); 3/132; JV L Trk; High Hon Roll; Hon Roll; NHS; Micro Elec Engrng.

UBA, MARK R; Canisius HS; Williamsville, NY; (Y); 10/144; Computer Clb; VP JA; Model UN; Pep Clb; Ski Clb; Nwsp Stf; VP NHS; Ntl Ski Ptrl; JR Clssel Leag Latin Awd; U Of Notre Dame; Gvt Svc.

UBIETA, JOHN; Saint Agnes HS; New York, NY; (Y); Cmnty Wkr; Library Aide; Wt Lftg; Law.

UDLE, KELLIE; Connetquot HS; Ronkonkoma, NY; (Y); 207/696; Ski Clb; Varsity Clb; Var Bsktbl; Var Fld Hcky; Var Sftbl; Hon Roll; Church Yth Grp; Cmnty Wkr; DECA; Exploring; All League All Conf 84; NY St Champ Fld Hockey 84; Coach Awd Sftbl 84; UCLA; Athl Traner.

UDY, KAREN; Niagara Falls HS; Niagara Falls, NY; (Y); 1/247; Pres Church Yth Grp; Band; Bausch & Lomb Sci Awd; High Hon Roll; NHS; Ntl Merit Schol; Val; Rochester Natl Scholar 85; U Of Rochester; Elec Engrng.

UH, BENJAMIN S; Newfield HS; Coram, NY; (Y); Math Tm; Concert Band; Jazz Band; Mrchg Band; Trk; French Hon Soc; NHS; Prfct Atten Awd; Spanish NHS; Black Belt Tae Kwon Do 83.

UHROVCIK, WENDY; Lansing HS; Lansing, NY; (Y); Spanish Clb; VP Soph Cls; VP Jr Cls; Pres Sr Cls; JV Var Cheerleading; Powder Puff Ftbl; Cit Awd; High Hon Roll; Hon Roll; Sec NHS; 1st Pl Spnsh Song Awd 85; Vsly Hndcp Tchr.

ULICKI, ANNE; Mount Mercy Acad; West Seneca, NY; (Y); Church Yth Grp; Computer Clb; Latin Clb; Chorus; Yrbk Stf; Cheerleading; Coach Actv; Score Keeper; JV Sftbl; Hon Roll; Silver Ldrshp Awd; Pepperdine U; Pre-Med.

ULLOA, FRANCISCO; Cardinal Hayes HS; New York, NY; (Y); 64/289; Dance Clb; High Hon Roll; Prfct Atten Awd; Bus Mgmt.

ULRICH, ANNE; Desales Catholic HS; Lockport, NY; (S); 6/47; Nwsp Stf; Yrbk Stf; Rep Stu Cncl; Var Cheerleading; Var Capt Tennis; Var Vllybl; Hon Roll; NHS; Intl Frgn Lang Awd; Law.

ULRICH, CHRISTINE; Alden Central HS; Alden, NY; (Y); JA; Science Clb; Chorus; Concert Band; Jazz Band; Mrchg Band; Score Keeper; Sftbl; Vllybl; Chem Engnr.

ULRICH, RICHARD; East Islip HS; Islip Terrace, NY; (Y); Aud/Vis; Pres Band; Pres Mrchg Band; Ed Nwsp Phtg; Electrnc Engr.

UMBERTO, LORI; Warwick Valley HS; Warwick, NY; (Y); Dance Clb; Girl Scts; Teachers Aide; Concert Band; Bowling; High Hon Roll; Hon Roll; Fash Inst Tech; Art.

UMSCHEID, DAVID; Dryden Central HS; Dryden, NY; (Y); 46/150; 4-H; Var Bsktbl; Im Socr; Im Tennis; 4-H Awd; Aud/Vis; Radio Clb; Hon Roll; 4-H Volntr Ldrshp Awd 84; Communctns Awd 84; Tompkins-Cortland CC; Commnctn.

UMSCHEID, MARC; Dryden HS; Dryden, NY; (Y); Church Yth Grp; 4-H; Varsity Clb; Capt Bowling; Var Capt Socr; 4-H Awd; High Hon Roll; NHS; IAC Hnrbl Ment Sccr 84; Chem, Phy Ed Awds 85; Fncnl.

UNDERBERG, KATHRYN H; Pittsford-Mendon HS; Pittsford, NY; (Y); Ed Lit Mag; Pres Frsh Cls; Sec Soph Cls; Stu Cncl; Cheerleading; French Hon Soc; High Hon Roll; Dist Engl Awd 84; Natl Frnch Cntst Cnty Fnlst 85; Cornell Natl Schlr 85; Cornell U; Jrnlst.

UNDERHILL, MARY EMILY; Scotia-Glenville HS; Scotia, NY; (Y); Sec Key Clb; Varsity Clb; Var JV Cheerleading; JV Var Fld Hcky; NHS; Phrmcy.

UNDERWOOD, LYNN M; Franklin Acad; Burke, NY; (Y); Hosp Aide; Epsian Clb; LPN.

UNGARO, DONNA; Tuckahoe HS; Bronxville, NY; (Y); Sec Varsity Clb; Nwsp Bus Mgr; Nwsp Stf; Ed Yrbk Stf; JV Capt Cheerleading; Coach Actv; JV Stat Sftbl; Hon Roll; Engl II Awd 84-85; United Chrldng-Sngles Comp 85.

UNGEHEUER, HARRY; Cambridge Central HS; Buskirk, NY; (Y); 6/84; Band; JV Var Socr; Var Trk; High Hon Roll; Hon Roll; NHS.

UNGER, LORI; John C Birdlebough HS; Pennellville, NY; (Y); Camp Fr Inc; Stage Crew; Socr; Grphc Arts.

UNGER, LYNNE; Mount Mercy Acad; W Seneca, NY; (Y); Chorus; School Musical; School Play; Variety Show; Sec Sr Cls; JV Bsktbl; Timer; Var Hon Roll; Buffalo ST Coll; Ed.

UNGERMANN, CINDY; Cuba Central HS; Cuba, NY; (Y); FFA; JV Bsktbl; High Hon Roll; NHS; Hon Roll; Dairy Frmng.

UNIVERSAL, KEVIN; La Salle SR HS; Niagara Falls, NY; (Y); Am Leg Boys St; Yrbk Ed-Chief; Im Bsbl; Var Ftbl; Capt Var Trk; Hon Roll; Jr NHS; NHS; Ntl Merit Ltr; Prfct Atten Awd; Engrng.

UNRUH, SEAN; Sanford H Calhoun HS; N Merrick, NY; (Y); Library Aide; Mathletes; Var Trk; Hon Roll; NY Inst Tech; Comp Engrng.

UNSELT, STACY; Attica Central HS; Alden, NY; (S); 16/150; Trs AFS; Church Yth Grp; Trs Band; Capt Color Guard; Nwsp Rptr; Rep Stu Cncl; Var Cheerleading; Var Trk; IFLA 85; Inter Dsgn.

UNZUE, MARIA; The Mary Louis Acad; Forest Hills, NY; (Y); Fordham; Intl Crprt Law.

UPDEGROVE, DEBORAH L; Newfane Central HS; Burt, NY; (Y); Varsity Clb; Y-Teens; Band; Nwsp Ed-Chief; Bsktbl; Fld Hcky; Sftbl; Trk; Hon Roll; Mu Alp Tht; Dist Stu Merit Schlrshp Awd NCCC 85; NCCC; Phy Ther.

UPHAM, JENNIFER A; Pawling JR-SR HS; Pawling, NY; (Y); 4/72; Cmnty Wkr; Dance Clb; Drama Clb; Band; Chorus; Church Choir; Var JV Cheerleading; High Hon Roll; Hon Roll; NHS; Outstndng Achvt Span II; NYS Regents Schlrshp; Fr Du Pont Hnr Tuition Schlrshp-St Michaels Coll; St Michaels Coll.

UPRIGHT, JAMES; Highland HS; Highland, NY; (Y); Boy Scts; Church Yth Grp; French Clb; Quiz Bowl; Band; Jazz Band; Var Crs Cntry; High Hon Roll; Jr NHS; NHS; Bst Calc Stu Awd 85; Bst Social Stds Stu Awd 84-85; Physcl Sci.

URAM, MIROSLAWA; Yonkers HS; Yonkers, NY; (Y); Hon Roll; Manhattan Col; Med.

URBACH, WILLIAM R; G Ray Bodley HS; Fulton, NY; (Y); 18/258; Cmnty Wkr; High Hon Roll; Hon Roll; Prfct Atten Awd; Regents Schlrshp 85; Onondaga CC; Math.

URBAN, CHRISTOPHER J; North Babylon HS; N Babylon, NY; (Y); 56/560; Chess Clb; Band; Var Ftbl; Hon Roll; Jr NHS; NHS; Ntl Merit Schol; AZ ST U; Adv.

URBAN, ELIZABETH; Holy Trinity Diosesan HS; Levittown, NY; (Y); Church Yth Grp; Dance Clb; Drama Clb; English Clb; PAVAS; Ski Clb; Spanish Clb; Varsity Clb; Capt Socr; Swmmng.

URBAN, JACQUELINE; Sachem HS; Farmingville, NY; (Y); 77/1509; GAA; Girl Scts; Spanish Clb; Bsktbl; JV Diving; Var JV Socr; Sftbl; JV Swmmng; Var Trk; Vllybl; Med.

URBAN, JUANITA L; Williamson Central HS; Williamson, NY; (Y); 1/112; Pres AFS; Am Leg Aux Girls St; Girl Scts; Sec Science Clb; Pres Service Clb; Trs Varsity Clb; JV Var Socr; NHS; Val; Church Yth Grp; Old English W Awd 82-84; American Legion Oratorical Contest 84-85; Best Of The Class Tv10 85; St John Fisher; Marine Biology.

URBAN, MICHAEL; Longwood HS; Coram, NY; (Y); VICA; Stage Crew; Ftbl; Trk; High Hon Roll; Hon Roll; 1st Pl VICA 85; BOCES II; Crpntry.

URBANCZYK, DAVID; Kenmore East SR HS; Tonawanda, NY; (Y); 30/330; Boy Scts; Varsity Clb; Nwsp Ed-Chief; Nwsp Rptr; Nwsp Sprt Ed; Yrbk Sprt Ed; Yrbk Stf; Im Bsktbl; Capt Socr; Im Vllybl; US Nvl Acad Smmr Semnr 85; Sccr Coachs Awd 83; Publshd Kenmore Schls Anthlgy Orgnl Vers 82 & 84; Aerosp Scis.

URBANK, ANDREW J; Gowanda Central HS; Gowanda, NY; (Y); 19/163; Am Leg Boys St; Ski Clb; Band; School Musical; VP Sr Cls; JV Var Bsbl; JV Var Ftbl; Hon Roll; NHS; All Western NY Rnng Bck 84-85; Walter C Peters Awd Outstndng Ftbl Plyr 85; 1st Tm Rnnng Bck Div I; Alfred U; Elec Engrng.

URBANO, RICARDO; Regis HS; Barnegat, NJ; (Y); Computer Clb; Hosp Aide; Yrbk Stf; Im Bowling; Intl Forgn Lang Awd Spnsh 84; Natl Hspnc Schlrshp Awd Prog Semi-Fin 85; Columbia U; Bio.

URBANSKI, ANDRE; New Paltz HS; New Paltz, NY; (Y); 30/160; Radio Clb; ROTC; Chorus; Yrbk Stf; Stu Cncl; Var Capt Bsktbl; Var Capt Ftbl; High Hon Roll; ROTC Schlrshp 85; Carnegie Mellon U; Bus.

URBANSKI, PAMELA; S S Seward Inst; Florida, NY; (Y); Sec FFA; Spanish Clb; Nwsp Rptr; Yrbk Stf; Rep Stu Cncl; Var Bsktbl; Var Socr; JV Sftbl; Hon Roll; Girl Scts; Most Imprvd Spanish 83-84; Greenhand Awd FFA 82; U NC Chapel Hill; Jrnlsm.

URCIUOLI, JILL; West Genesee SR HS; Warners, NY; (Y); Off Jr Cls; Prfct Atten Awd; Chld Psych.

UREN, GREGORY; Oakfield Alabama Central HS; Oakfield, NY; (Y); 5/80; Math Clb; Math Tm; Ski Clb; Varsity Clb; VP Frsh Cls; VP Jr Cls; Trs Sr Cls; Var Bsktbl; Var Crs Cntry; JV Ftbl; Purdue U; Engrng.

UREN, JIM; Batavia SR HS; Batavia, NY; (Y); Computer Clb; Political Wkr; Ski Clb; Yrbk Phtg; Yrbk Stf; Rep Frsh Cls; JV Coach Actv; Var Trk; Wt Lftg; High Hon Roll; Rochester Inst Tech; Comp Sci.

URENA, BETTY; Dominican Commercial HS; Jamaica, NY; (Y); Intnl Clb; Chorus; Princpls Lst 82-84; Siena Clb 82-83 & 83-84.

URESK, STEPHEN; Commack South HS; Commack, NY; (Y); Teachers Aide; Stage Crew; Nwsp Rptr; Ed Nwsp Stf; Yrbk Stf; Sec Sr Cls; High Hon Roll; Hon Roll; Bio.

URSILLO, MONICA; St Joseph By The Sea HS; Staten Island, NY; (Y); 7/284; Computer Clb; Drama Clb; Mgr Chorus; School Musical; School Play; Nwsp Stf; Yrbk Stf; Sec Frsh Cls; Sec Jr Cls; High Hon Roll; Italian Achvt Awds 83-85; Psych.

URSINO, JOSEPH; Bishop Ford HS; Brooklyn, NY; (Y); Boy Scts; Bsbl; Bsktbl; Wt Lftg; Law.

URTZ, SHERRI; Bolton Central HS; Bolton Ldg, NY; (Y); Varsity Clb; Chorus; Mrchg Band; School Play; Nwsp Stf; Yrbk Stf; Sec Soph Cls; Cheerleading; Gym; Socr; SUNY Potsdam; Secndry Mth Ed.

USHER, BILL; Greene Central HS; Greene, NY; (Y); Church Yth Grp; Band; Chorus; Church Choir; Concert Band; Jazz Band; Mrchg Band; Swing Chorus; Music.

USZACKI JR, RAYMOND J; St Joseph By The Sea HS; Staten Island, NY; (Y); Hosp Aide; Im Bowling; Socr; Accntnt.

UYAR, DEBBIE; Academy Of St Joseph HS; Bay Shore, NY; (Y); 1/128; Art Clb; Hosp Aide; Library Aide; Teachers Aide; Yrbk Stf; Trs Jr Cls; Var Bsktbl; Tennis; NHS; NEDT Awd; Art Hnr Soc 85; Spn Awd 82-83; Cert Of Recgntn For Excllnc-Am Stds 84-85.

VABNICK, FELICE; Tottenville HS; Staten Island, NY; (Y); 43/897; French Clb; Girl Scts; Key Clb; Library Aide; Teachers Aide; Temple Yth Grp; Yrbk Bus Mgr; Yrbk Rptr; Yrbk Stf; JV Crs Cntry; Cert Dmerite Natl Frnch Cont 83-84; Athl Awd Crss Cntry, Sprng & Outdr Trck 83; SUNY-BINGHAMTON; Bio Sci.

VACALOPOULOS, TINA; Saint Johns Prep; Astoria, NY; (Y); Library Aide; Spanish Clb; Chorus; School Musical; Gym; Hon Roll; Prfct Atten Awd; Corp Exec.

VACCARIELLO, JANINE; Mercy HS; Southold, NY; (Y); GAA; Ski Clb; Var Bsktbl; Var Fld Hcky; Var Sftbl; All Conf, All Lgu Sftbl 85; All Lgu Fld Hcky 84; Fld Hcky Awd 110 Per-Cnt 84; Accntng.

VACCARO, GAETANO; Long Island City HS; Long Isld Cty, NY; (Y); 80/353; Aud/Vis; Dance Clb; Drama Clb; Library Aide; Teachers Aide; School Musical; Cit Awd; Hon Roll; NHS; Ntl Merit Schol; Peer Cnslr Awd 83; Bst Dncr 85; Wagner Coll; Thtr.

VACCARO, JOSEPH; South Side HS; S Hempstead, NY; (Y); 7/272; Key Clb; Chorus; JV Var Bsbl; High Hon Roll; Jr NHS; NHS; Ntl Merit Schol.

VACCARO, PAUL; Iona Prep; Scarsdale, NY; (Y); 20/200; Pres Church Yth Grp; Math Tm; Ski Clb; Rep Jr Cls; Rep Sr Cls; Rep Stu Cncl; Var Capt Ftbl; Elks Awd; Hon Roll; NHS; Latin, Math Awds 82-84; Ntl Pop Wnnr Schlr Athl 82; Capt Corp 83-85; Engrng.

VACCARO, STEPHEN; St Francis Prep; Howard Bch, NY; (Y); Ski Clb; JV L Ftbl; Im Socr; Im Sftbl; Im Vllybl; Stony Brook; Engrng.

VACCARO, VICKI; Gates Chile SR HS; Rochester, NY; (Y); 140/463; Cmnty Wkr; Library Aide; Office Aide; Chorus; Rep Frsh Cls; VP Soph Cls; Rep Jr Cls; Rep Sr Cls; JV Capt Bsktbl; JV VP Socr; Athl Achvt 82; Europn Cultrs 83; Monroe CC; Gen Stds.

VACCARO JR, VICTOR W; Rome Free Acad; Rome, NY; (Y); 17/450; Spanish Clb; Varsity Clb; Yrbk Rptr; Var L Bsbl; JV Bsktbl; JV Socr; High Hon Roll; Hon Roll; NHS; Ntl Merit SF; Accntng.

VACHERON, PAMELA; The Wheatley Schl; E Williston, NY; (Y); Varsity Clb; Band; Chorus; Stu Cncl; JV Bsktbl; Var Fld Hcky; Var Lcrss.

VADALA, TONY; Bishop Ludden HS; Liverpool, NY; (Y); Boy Scts; Chess Clb; Nwsp Ed-Chief; Nwsp Phtg; Nwsp Rptr; Yrbk Phtg; Ed Lit Mag; JV Ftbl; JV Var Golf; Var Trk; Onodaga CC; Radio.

VADLAMUDI, LAKSHMI; Ilion JR Sr HS; Ilion, NY; (Y); 6/120; Jazz Band; Orch; Yrbk Stf; Var Tennis; High Hon Roll; Jr NHS; NHS; French Clb; Varsity Clb; School Musical; Arion Awd Orch; Natl Sci Merit Awd; Natl Frgn Lang Awd; Union Coll; Med.

VAETH, J GREGORY; Irondwquoit HS; Rochester, NY; (Y); 19/360; Art Clb; Boy Scts; Latin Clb; Science Clb; Ski Clb; Golf; Hon Roll; NHS; Prfct Atten Awd; Eagle Scout 84; Chem Engr.

VAFEAS, JAMES P; St Francis Prep; Flushing, NY; (Y); 182/690; JV Bsbl; Ftbl; Im Ice Hcky; Im Vllybl; Regnts Schlrshp 85; Hofstra U; Bio.

VAIL, AMY-CHRISTINE; Jamestown HS; Jamestown, NY; (Y); 22/375; Pres Church Yth Grp; Ski Clb; Mrchg Band; School Musical; Hst Sr Cls; Var L Sftbl; Var L Swmmng; NHS; Alfred U; Crmc Engrng.

VAILE, MARA; Sachem HS; Holbrook, NY; (Y); Dance Clb; Pep Clb; Temple Yth Grp; Varsity Clb; Variety Show; Nwsp Stf; JV Var Socr; Var Trk; Cit Awd; Opt Clb Awd; Suny-Stonybrk; Atty.

VAILLANCOURT, GREG; Stockbridge Balley Central HS; Munnsville, NY; (S); 6/50; Mathletes; VP Band; Nwsp Ed-Chief; Yrbk Rptr; Pres Soph Cls; Rep Stu Cncl; JV Var Bsktbl; JV Var Socr; High Hon Roll; Hon Roll; Spcl Olympcs Buddy.

VAINUR, CHARA; James Madison HS; Brooklyn, NY; (Y); Art Clb; Drama Clb; French Clb; Hosp Aide; JA; Drill Tm; Stage Crew; Hon Roll; Merit Roll 85; Fash Desgnr.

VAJDA JR, GREGORY; Iona Prep; New Rochelle, NY; (Y); Boy Scts; Dance Clb; Stage Crew; Hon Roll; Big Bros 85-86; Iona Coll; Comp Sci.

VAKILI, SUSAN; Oneonta HS; Oneonta, NY; (S); 2/184; Art Clb; Church Yth Grp; VP French Clb; Thesps; Chorus; Church Choir; School Musical; School Play; Nwsp Rptr; High Hon Roll; Elem Educ.

VALADE, LARRY; Rome Free Acad; Lee Center, NY; (Y); Hon Roll; Mth.

VALAZQUEZ, MONIQUE T; Hunter College HS; New York, NY; (Y); GAA; Hosp Aide; Y-Teens; Chorus; JV Var Bsktbl; Stat Score Keeper; Var Timer; Natl Hispanic Schlr 84; Arch.

VALCEANU, JOHN G; Baldwin SR HS; Baldwin, NY; (Y); 170/502; Debate Tm; Nwsp Rptr; Nwsp Stf; Lit Mag; NY ST Rgnts Schlrshp 84-85; Sara Lawrence Coll; Lib Arts.

VALDES, DAVID; Union Springs Acad; Norridgewock, ME; (S); 2/53; Drama Clb; Concert Band; Mrchg Band; Yrbk Ed-Chief; High Hon Roll; NHS; Sal; Chorus; Church Choir; Drill Tm; Capman Hall Mens Clb Offcr 83-85; Stu Assoc Soc VP 84-85; Tourng Choir 83-85; Atlantic Union Coll; Comm Art.

VALDMANIS, MARITA; Hastings HS; Hastings-On-Hudsn, NY; (S); 5/117; VP AFS; French Clb; Key Clb; Chrmn Model UN; Chorus; Madrigals; Nwsp Stf; Co-Capt Twrlr; High Hon Roll; NHS; AFS Smmr Pgm Stu Costa Rica 84; Georgetown U; Bus.

VALENCIA, MONICA; Richmond Hill HS; Richmond Hill, NY; (Y); 19/298; English Clb; French Clb; Hosp Aide; Math Clb; Office Aide; School Musical; Hon Roll; Trs NHS; NYS Regnts Schlrshp 85; Hunter Coll; Lib Arts.

VALENCIA, ROBERT E; Benjamin N Cardozo HS; Bayside, NY; (Y); 201/476; Science Clb; VFW Awd; Voice Dem Awd; NY ST Regents Schlrshp 84-85; CUNY; Polt Sci.

VALENSI, PHILIP; Sheepshead Bay HS; Brooklyn, NY; (Y); Computer Clb; English Clb; Chorus; Capt Var Tennis; Syracuse U; Acctg.

VALENTA, CORINNE; Groton Central HS; Groton, NY; (Y); Cmnty Wkr; Ski Clb; Spanish Clb; Yrbk Rptr; High Hon Roll; NHS; Mth.

VALENTA, JOSEPH A; Oneonta SR HS; Oneonta, NY; (Y); Camera Clb; FBLA; Key Clb; Church Choir; School Musical; Variety Show; Ed Nwsp Phtg; Nwsp Stf; Ed Yrbk Phtg; Yrbk Stf; 3 Photo Awds 85; Music.

VALENTE, JOHN; Bishop Maginn HS; Albany, NY; (S); 17/118; Capt Bsbl; Capt Bsktbl; Trk; High Hon Roll; NHS; Bus.

VALENTI, MONICA; Binghamton HS; Binghamton, NY; (Y); 101/597; Church Yth Grp; Band; Concert Band; Mrchg Band; Rep Stu Cncl; JV Var Socr; Hon Roll; Elem Educ.

VALENTI, PAUL; Honroye Falls-Lima HS; Honeoye Falls, NY; (Y); 2/160; Am Leg Boys St; Pres Math Clb; Pres Model UN; Scholastic Bowl; JETS Awd; NHS; Sal; Computer Clb; Coach Actv; Var Capt Crs Cntry; Air Force ROTC Schlrshp; Senate Stu Policy Forum; HFC Bwlng Champ; API; Comp Engnrng.

VALENTIN, MADELINE; Valley Central HS; Maybrook, NY; (Y); Chorus; Yrbk Stf; Rep Jr Cls; High Hon Roll; NHS; Ntl Merit Schol; Prfct Atten Awd; Spanish NHS; Math Merit 83-84; Lehman; Acctng.

VALENTIN, MAYRA; St Catharine Acad; Bronx, NY; (Y); 95/205; Church Yth Grp; Computer Clb; Spanish Clb; Teachers Aide; Rep Vllybl; Spanish NHS; Johnson & Wales; Travel.

VALENTINA, SUSAN; Bishop Kearney HS; Brooklyn, NY; (S); Dance Clb; Girl Scts; Hosp Aide; Key Clb; Math Tm; Im Bowling; High Hon Roll; Hon Roll; Bio.

VALENTINI, CHRISTINA; Holy Trinity HS; Hicksville, NY; (Y); 61/325; Church Yth Grp; Dance Clb; Hosp Aide; Math Clb; Ski Clb; Spanish Clb; School Play; Yrbk Stf; Hon Roll; Mu Alp Tht; Adelphi U; Bio.

VALENTINO, JOHN; Albertus Magnus HS; New City, NY; (Y); Drama Clb; Church Choir; School Play; Ed Yrbk Phtg; Yrbk Stf; Var Crs Cntry; Var Swmmng; Trk; Bus.

VALENZA, MARK; Newburgh Free Acad; Wallkill, NY; (Y); Pride Week Essay Cont 2nd Pl 84; Phys Sci.

VALENZANO, DONNA MARIE; St Francis Prep; Auburndale, NY; (Y); 162/702; Dance Clb; Drama Clb; Library Aide; School Musical; School Play; Stage Crew; Variety Show; Opt Clb Awd; Fshn Inst Tech; Fshn Merch.

VALENZANO, POLLY J; Canandaigua Acad; Canandaigua, NY; (Y); 10/277; Am Leg Aux Girls St; Girl Scts; Library Aide; Ski Clb; Band; Chorus; Concert Band; Jazz Band; Mrchg Band; Orch; Wellsley Bk Awd; Crane Schl Music Potsdam; Mus.

VALENZUELA, CARMEN G; Beach Channel HS; Rock Bch, NY; (Y); Debate Tm; Yrbk Stf; Cit Awd; Hon Roll; Jr NHS; Arete 83; Amer Assoc Trchrs Frnch 85, Spnsh & Portgs 83; Bus.

VALERA, ANTHONY; Bushwick HS; Brooklyn, NY; (Y); 9/208; Cmnty Wkr; JA; Office Aide; OEA; Service Clb; Ski Clb; School Play; Yrbk Stf; Sr Cls; Hon Roll; Regents Schlrshp 85; Baruch-CUNY; Mgt.

VALERIO, MICHELE; Gates Chili HS; Rochester, NY; (Y); 69/463; Science Clb; Ski Clb; Trk; Schlstc Ntl Art Awds Pgm Gld Medl 85; Presdntl Acadmc Ftns Awds Pgm 85; Rochester Inst Tech; Grphc Dsgn.

VALERIO, PETER; Amsterdam HS; Amsterdam, NY; (Y); 10/319; Am Leg Boys St; VP Drama Clb; Concert Band; Jazz Band; Mrchg Band; School Play; Trk; Pres NHS; Ntl Merit Ltr; Hugh O Brian Youth Orgnztn 84; Math.

VALESKY, PAUL J; Oneida SR HS; Oneida, NY; (Y); 10/180; Am Leg Boys St; Band; Jazz Band; Mrchg Band; Yrbk Phtg; Var L Tennis; High Hon Roll; NHS; Ntl Merit Ltr; Jr NHS; US Naval Acad Smn Session 85; Engrng.

VALLA, KATHY; Mineola HS; Albertson, NY; (Y); Spanish Clb; Band; Concert Band; Mrchg Band; Var L Socr; Swmmng; Hon Roll; Bus.

VALLABHONENI, SURENDRA; High School HS; Hauppauge, NY; (Y); AFS; Trs Chess Clb; VP Computer Clb; Debate Tm; VP Math Tm; Political Wkr; Sec Spanish Clb; 4-H Awd; High Hon Roll; Hon Roll; Miami U; Pre-Med.

VALLARIO, MARIA; Bishop Ford Central HS; Brooklyn, NY; (Y); Office Aide; Service Clb; Teachers Aide; Chorus; Cit Awd; Hon Roll; Prfct Atten Awd; Bus Mgmt.

VALLE, DAVID; Roy C Ketcham HS; Poughkeepsie, NY; (Y); Church Yth Grp; Drama Clb; Orch; Nwsp Stf; Var L Trk; Hon Roll; Prfct Atten Awd; Dutchess CC; Med.

VALLEE, JOHN; Stillwater Central Schl; Schuylerville, NY; (Y); 1/100; Varsity Clb; Trs Frsh Cls; Var Bsbl; Var Ftbl; High Hon Roll; NHS; Val; Acad Achvt Awd Skidmore Coll 84; Saratoga Cnty Drama Tm 84; Substance Abuse Tm 84-85; Rensselear Poly Tech Inst; Engr.

VALLELY, SANDI E; Mineola HS; Mineola, NY; (Y); Pres Camera Clb; Key Clb; Service Clb; Spanish Clb; Nwsp Rptr; Nwsp Stf; Yrbk Phtg; Yrbk Stf; Lit Mag; Frsh Cls; Pre-Law.

VALLON, KIMBERLY; East Aurora HS; West Falls, NY; (S); 32/182; Cmnty Wkr; Dance Clb; Intnl Clb; Spanish Clb; Yrbk Phtg; Rep Jr Cls; High Hon Roll; Hon Roll; NHS; Prfct Atten Awd; Legsltv Internshp 84; Typng & Shrthnd Awds 81-85; Gifted & Tlntd 84.

VALLONE, PAUL J; Penfield HS; Penfield, NY; (Y); 40/370; Nwsp Rptr; Var Capt Bsbl; Var Capt Ftbl; Wt Lftg; Var Capt Wrstlng; High Hon Roll; NHS; Pres Schlr; St Schlr; Penfield Schlrshp Assoc 85; Penfield Educ Assoc Schlrshp 85; Franklin & Marshall Coll; Bio.

VALOIS, JOHN D; Schalmont Central HS; Duanesburg, NY; (Y); 6/188; French Clb; Socr; Trk; Wrstlng; Hon Roll; NHS; Ntl Merit SF; Trk MVP 84; Col Cncl 2nd Team Sccr 84; RPI.

VAMBUTAS, PAUL; Friends Acad; Douglaston, NY; (Y); Cmnty Wkr; Teachers Aide; Nwsp Rptr; Nwsp Stf; Bsktbl; Bowling; Ftbl; Swmmng; JV Tennis; Inkwell Edtrshp 84; Regnts Schlrshp 85; Lehigh U; Journlsm.

VAN, WALTER W; La Salle Acad; Brooklyn, NY; (S); Church Yth Grp; Math Clb; NHS; Hnr If La Salle Acad 82-84; John Jay Coll Math Course 84; Ho-Nan Shao-Lin Gldn Dragon Tm 82; Cooper Union; Mechanical Engr.

VAN ALLER, GLENN; Middleburgh Central HS; Middleburgh, NY; (S); Band; Chorus; Concert Band; Mrchg Band; School Musical; JV Bsktbl; Var L Bowling; JV Ftbl; High Hon Roll; Hon Roll; Mohawk Vly CC; Sci Lab Tech.

VAN ALSTINE, ROSE; Springfield Central HS; Ft Plain, NY; (Y); Art Clb; Church Yth Grp; GAA; Red Cross Aide; School Play; Yrbk Stf; Var Capt Socr; Hon Roll; Var Capt Sftbl; Nrsng Rgnts Schlrshp 85; Rgnts Dplma 85; Utica Schl Of Sycracuse; Rn.

VAN ALSTYNE, PETER C; Gloversville HS; Gloversville, NY; (Y); Key Clb; Yrbk Phtg; JV L Ftbl; Var L Trk; Regents Schlrshp 85; Fulton-Montgomery CC; Phy Ed.

VAN ANTWERP, THOMAS S; Liverpool HS; N Syracuse, NY; (Y); 28/768; Am Leg Boys St; Trs Church Yth Grp; Swing Chorus; NHS; Exploring; Church Choir; Stu Cncl; High Hon Roll; Jr NHS; Stud Advsry Cmmttee 84-86.

VAN BENTHUYSEN, WILLIAM; Cicero-N Syracuse HS; Clay, NY; (S); 16/621; Church Yth Grp; Mathletes; Math Tm; Hst Stu Cncl; Bsbl; Trk; High Hon Roll; Hon Roll; Prom Committee.

VAN BRUNT, JAMES; Sherburne-Earlville JR SR HS; Sherburne, NY; (S); Am Leg Boys St; 4-H; Ski Clb; Band; Concert Band; Mrchg Band; JV Lcrss; Hon Roll; NHS; Hon Soc 84-85; NYSSMA; ST U Of Oswego; Crim Justice.

VAN BUREN, JEFFREY; Liverpool HS; Liverpool, NY; (Y); VP JA; Off Varsity Clb; Band; Yrbk Ed-Chief; Yrbk Phtg; Rep Stu Cncl; Var Capt Swmmng; NYS Public H S Ath Assoc ST Champ Swmmng 84-85; MVP Swmmng 83-84.

VAN BURGER, CHERILYN; Union-Endicott HS; Owego, NY; (S); Mgr Color Guard; Concert Band; Mrchg Band; Orch; Symp Band; Yrbk Rptr; Yrbk Stf; Hon Roll; Band; All Amer Hall Of Fame Band Hnrs 84-85; Travel Agnt.

VAN COTT, KAREN; Earl L Vandermeulen HS; Mt Sinai, NY; (Y); Var Cheerleading; JV Crs Cntry; Var Gym; JV Trk; Hon Roll.

VAN DER MEID, GRETCHEN; Webster HS; Webster, NY; (Y); Church Yth Grp; Cmnty Wkr; Nwsp Stf; Lit Mag; JV Bsktbl; JV Fld Hcky; JV Vllybl; Randolf-Macon Wmns Coll; Psych.

VAN DER POEL, RAINA; John A Coleman HS; Saugerties, NY; (S); 7/67; French Clb; Key Clb; School Play; Var Sftbl; Var Capt Vllybl; High Hon Roll; Hon Roll; JA; Math 9 1st Hnrs Awd 82-83; Math 10 1st Hnrs Awd 83-84; Soc Stds 10 2nd Hnr Awd 83-84; Educ.

VAN DERVEER, LISA; Skaneateles Central HS; Skaneateles, NY; (S); Church Yth Grp; Variety Show; Rep Soph Cls; Powder Puff Ftbl; Tennis; High Hon Roll; Hon Roll; NHS.

VAN DERWERKER, LESLIE; Mayfield JR SR HS; Gloversville, NY; (Y); Drama Clb; Stage Crew; Nwsp Stf; Greg Typng Awds 83-85; Bus.

VAN DERWERKER III, WILLIAM R; Ballston Spa HS; Ballston Spa, NY; (Y); 3/220; Am Leg Boys St; Church Yth Grp; Church Choir; Concert Band; Jazz Band; Mrchg Band; Var L Socr; Var L Trk; High Hon Roll; Pres NHS; Rensselaer Poly Tech; Arch.

VAN DEUSEN, LAURA; Le Roy Central HS; Bergen, NY; (Y); Sec 4-H; French Clb; 4-H Awd; Hon Roll; Anml Sci.

VAN DEWERKER, LISA; Fort Plain Central HS; Ft Plain, NY; (S); Math Clb; Varsity Clb; Yrbk Stf; Rep Frsh Cls; Rep Soph Cls; Rep Jr Cls; Rep Stu Cncl; Cheerleading; Socr; Cit Awd; Acad All Amer 84; Hudson Valley; Med Lab Tech.

VAN DEWERKER, TED; Fort Plain Central HS; Fort Plain, NY; (S); Computer Clb; Math Clb; Varsity Clb; Var Capt Bsktbl; Socr; Trk; Hon Roll; NHS; Engrng.

VAN DIER, DIANNE; Minisink Valley HS; New Hampton, NY; (Y); 2/225; Church Yth Grp; Varsity Clb; Var Crs Cntry; JV Socr; Var Trk; High Hon Roll; NHS; Ntl Merit Ltr; Latin II,Eng Awd 84-85; Kings Coll; Bio.

VAN DUSEN, SCOTT; Romulus Central School; Geneva, NY; (S); 6/45; Band; Mrchg Band; School Musical; School Play; Trs Soph Cls; Pres Jr Cls; Var JV Bsbl; Var JV Bsktbl; Var JV Ftbl; NHS; Presof Appl Econ Class 83; Elec Engr.

VAN EPPS, DAVID E; Webster HS; Webster, NY; (Y); 26/560; VP Exploring; Var L Bsbl; JV Im Bsktbl; Var L Ftbl; Var Vllybl; Var Wt Lftg; High Hon Roll; Hon Roll; Jr NHS; NHS; Rit Pres Schlrshp 85; Mock Trial Wstrn NY Champs 84; Rochester Inst Tech; Comp Sci.

VAN EPPS, MARK; Auburn HS; Auburn, NY; (Y); Acpl Chr; Concert Band; Jazz Band; Mrchg Band; School Musical; Swing Chorus; VP Hon Roll; Band; Church Choir; Madrigals; Union Endicott Jazz Fest All Star Band 84; Civic Ctr Jazz Fes Outstndng Muscn 85; NYSSMA Soloist 85; Musc.

VAN GELDER, COLLEEN A; Canandaigua Acad; Canandaigua, NY; (Y); 50/277; AFS; Teachers Aide; JV Socr; Var Capt Swmmng; High Hon Roll; Hon Roll; NYS Regnts Schlrshp 85; ST U NY Albany; Pol Sci.

VAN GORDER, DONNA; Frankfort-Schuyler HS; Frankfort, NY; (S); 25/100; FBLA; Pep Clb; Nwsp Stf; Yrbk Stf; High Hon Roll; NHS; 1st Pl Shrthnd II Notre Dame Dist VII Comp 85; Gregg Shrthnd Speed Cert 60-110 WPM 85; Nazareth Coll; Bus Educ.

VAN HATTEN, KEN; Whitesboro HS; Whitesboro, NY; (Y); Intnl Clb; Letterman Clb; Spanish Clb; Varsity Clb; Var L Socr; Im Wt Lftg; Rochester Inst Tech; Elec Eng.

VAN HISE, BETH; Irondeqvoit HS; Rochester, NY; (Y); 61/393; Church Yth Grp; Drama Clb; Hosp Aide; Model UN; Ski Clb; Chorus; Church Choir; Orch; School Musical; School Play.

VAN HORN, KARYN; Eastridge HS; Rochester, NY; (Y); 18/237; Hosp Aide; Concert Band; Jazz Band; School Musical; Pres Stu Cncl; Swmmng; Hon Roll; NHS; Trs Exploring; Varsity Clb; U Of Rochester; Nrsng.

VAN HOUTE, TERRI; Newark SR HS; Newark, NY; (Y); Art Clb; Cmnty Wkr; Library Aide; Office Aide; Teachers Aide; Mgr Stage Crew; Lit Mag; Pom Pon; Hon Roll; U TX; Comm Artist.

VAN IHSEM, SANDY; Washington Irving HS; Elmhurst, NY; (Y); Concert Band; School Play; Variety Show; High Hon Roll; Hon Roll; Awd Sci 83; Awd Super Achvt Spnsh 84; Mbr Jr Arista Soc 83; Comp Sci.

VAN LIESHOUT, ANNE; Albion HS; Albion, NY; (S); 8/180; 4-H; Latin Clb; Teachers Aide; Color Guard; Stage Crew; Yrbk Ed-Chief; Rep Sr Cls; 4-H Awd; Hon Roll; Variety Show; Dairy Princess 84-85; Cornell U; Consmr Econ.

VAN MAARSEVEEN, BERNARD J; Liverpool HS; Liverpool, NY; (Y); 82/792; Camera Clb; JA; Mrchg Band; Variety Show; Nwsp Stf; Lit Mag; Twrlr; Ntl Merit SF; Oswego; Wrtng.

VAN NESS, JENNIFER; St Francis Prep; Whitestone, NY; (S); 9/700; Cmnty Wkr; Crs Cntry; Im Sftbl; Im Tennis; Trk; Im Vllybl; High Hon Roll; NHS; Acadmc All Amer 85.

VAN NORT, CHRISTINE; Sauquoit Valley Central HS; Sauquoit, NY; (Y); 10/118; Drama Clb; GAA; Band; Chorus; Drm & Bgl; School Play; Yrbk Phtg; High Hon Roll; Hon Roll; NHS; Elem Educ.

VAN OORT, GLENDA; Maple Hill HS; Castleton, NY; (S); 16/80; Church Yth Grp; Pres Rptr 4-H; Ski Clb; Spanish Clb; Band; Concert Band; JV Trk; Hon Roll; Pre-Vet.

VAN ORD, AMY; Chautauqua Central HS; Sherman, NY; (Y); 1/36; Church Yth Grp; Drama Clb; Pres 4-H; Scholastic Bowl; Chorus; School Play; Swmmng; 4-H Awd; High Hon Roll; Jr NHS.

VAN PATTEN, DEBBIE; Mexico Acad & Central Schls; Mexico, NY; (Y); Exploring; Spanish Clb; Band; Concert Band; Mrchg Band; Nwsp Ed-Chief; Nwsp Phtg; Nwsp Rptr; Nwsp Stf; Rep Stu Cncl; US Natl Jrnlsm Awd 84; Oswego Cnty Press Clb Schlrshp 85; Knights Of Pythias Awd 85; Morrisville; Jrnlsm.

VAN PUTTE, ANDREW; Gates Chili Sr HS; Rochester, NY; (S); 2/463; Church Yth Grp; Math Tm; Var L Socr; High Hon Roll; NHS; Ntl Merit SF; Sal; Chem Engr.

VAN RIET, MICHAEL J; Massena Central HS; Massena, NY; (Y); 1/300; Key Clb; Variety Show; JV VP Crs Cntry; VP Trk; High Hon Roll; NHS; Hghst Avrg JR Boys 85; Rosenbaum Awd 85; Aero Engr.

VAN SCHAICK, RACHEL; Ft Plain HS; Ft Plain, NY; (S); Pres VP Church Yth Grp; Computer Clb; Math Clb; Stage Crew; Yrbk Stf; Rep Jr Cls; Rep Stu Cncl; Ed High Hon Roll; Hon Roll; NHS; Suny Plattsburgh; Tchr.

VAN SICKELS, JAMES F; Jericho HS; Hicksville, NY; (Y); 28/250; Teachers Aide; Stage Crew; Hon Roll; NHS; Ntl Merit Schol; Poly Schlrshp 85; Polytech Inst NY; Cvl Engr.

VAN SICKLE, SUSAN; Mynderse Acad; Seneca Falls, NY; (Y); 30/180; Art Clb; Ski Clb; Stu Cncl; Crs Cntry; Trk; Cit Awd; Elks Awd; High Hon Roll; Hon Roll; SUNY Delhi; Vet Asst.

VAN SLYKE, DAVID; Beacon HS; Beacon, NY; (Y); 31/215; Am Leg Boys St; Pres Church Yth Grp; Cmnty Wkr; FCA; German Clb; Latin Clb; Varsity Clb; Var Capt Crs Cntry; Var Capt Trk; Hon Roll; Natl Jr Olympc 1500 M Racewalking Champ 84; Varsty Clb Trphies For CC, Wntr Track, Sprng Track 85; VMI; Mech Engnrng.

VAN STRY, SHARON; Frewsburg Central HS; Frewsburg, NY; (Y); Pep Clb; Frsh Cls; VP Soph Cls; VP Stu Cncl; Var Bsktbl; Var Sftbl; Var Capt Vllybl; Sprts Qn 83-85; JR Hmcmg Qn 84-85; Jamestown CC; Med Lab Tech.

VAN VALEN, THERESE; Lindenhurst SR HS; Lindenhurst, NY; (Y); Church Yth Grp; Drama Clb; Thesps; Chorus; School Musical; School Play; Swing Chorus; Var Badmtn; Psych.

VAN VALKENBURGH, AMY R; Greenville Central HS; Westerlo, NY; (Y); 3/100; Drama Clb; Key Clb; Math Tm; Science Clb; Band; Lit Mag; Cheerleading; 4-H Awd; High Hon Roll; NHS; Regents Schlrshp 85; Cmdtn Natl Merit Schlrshp 84; Cornell U; Vet.

VAN VALKENBURGH, KAREN; Lancaster HS; Lancaster, NY; (Y); Church Yth Grp; Office Aide; Pep Clb; Ski Clb; Teachers Aide; Band; Concert Band; Mrchg Band; Rep Stu Cncl; Capt Var Bowling; Fredonia ST; Elem Ed.

VAN VALKENBURGH, MINDY JO; Scotia Glenville HS; Scotia, NY; (Y); Drama Clb; Ski Clb; Thesps; Chorus; School Musical; Variety Show; Cheerleading; Vllybl; Hon Roll; NHS; Theater.

VAN VALKENBURGH, SHERRY; Greenville Central HS; Westerlo, NY; (Y); Church Yth Grp; Chorus; High Hon Roll; Hon Roll; Gymstc Comp ST Meet 82-84; Math.

VAN VALKENBURGH, STACY; Charlotte Valley Central HS; Charlottville, NY; (S); 7/32; FFA; Hon Roll; Prfct Atten Awd; Acad Mech Drawng 83-84; Ag.

VAN VOLKENBURGH, JOHN; Cicero N Syracuse HS; Brewerton, NY; (S); 85/771; Boy Scts; Math Clb; Teachers Aide; Acctg.

VAN VOOLEN, DONNA J; Jamesville-Dewitt HS; Jamesville, NY; (Y); 6/225; Exploring; Hosp Aide; Spanish Clb; Chorus; School Musical; High Hon Roll; NHS; Cmnty Wkr; Library Aide; Office Aide; Outstndng Achvt Awd Span 84; Natl Hnrs Piano Solo-Natl Fed Fest 84; Cornell U.

VAN WAGENEN, PAUL; Spackenkill HS; Poughkeepsie, NY; (Y); Am Leg Boys St; Variety Show; Church Yth Grp; 4-H; Letterman Clb; Political Wkr; Teachers Aide; Varsity Clb; Bsktbl; Crs Cntry.

VAN WINKLE, DORIS; Altmar-Parish-Williamstown HS; Williamstown, NY; (Y); Church Yth Grp; Library Aide; Yrbk Rptr; Yrbk Stf; JV Cheerleading; High Hon Roll; Hon Roll; Prfct Atten Awd; MED Sec.

VAN WOERT, JAMES SCOTT; Harpursville HS; Harpursville, NY; (Y); Am Leg Boys St; Aud/Vis; Cmnty Wkr; Ski Clb; Stage Crew; Var L Bsbl; Var L Bsktbl; Var Vllybl; High Hon Roll; Bus Adm.

VAN WORMER, MARK; Pulaski JR SR HS; Pulaski, NY; (Y); Boy Scts; Exploring; Math Clb; Yrbk Stf; Tennis; John Ben Snow Awd For Art 85; Canton NY.

VAN ZANDT, ADAM F; Seton Catholic Central HS; Binghamton, NY; (Y); 65/153; Varsity Clb; Var Ftbl; Var Capt Trk; Lcl Gvt Scl Justc Pgm 85; Trk & Ftbl Div All-Str 84-85; SUNY Albany; Lwyr.

VAN ZUTPHEN, ALISSA; Voorheesville HS; Voorheesville, NY; (Y); Hosp Aide; Key Clb; Nwsp Ed-Chief; Rep Stu Cncl; Var Cheerleading; Sec NHS; Ntl Merit SF; Math Tm; Chorus; Concert Band; Elmira Coll Key Awd 85; Alfred U Schlrshp 85; Exceptnl Spnsh Achvt Awd 85; Duke U; Marine Bio.

VANARNUM, KIM; Schuylerville HS; Ft Edward, NY; (Y); French Clb; FBLA; Chorus; Var JV Sftbl; RN.

VANAUKEN, TOM; Eastridge HS; Rochester, NY; (Y); 3/236; Boy Scts; Math Clb; Varsity Clb; Var Bsbl; JV Ftbl; Im Socr; Wt Lftg; High Hon Roll; Clarkson; Comp Engrng.

VANBODEN, KEVIN; Onondaga Central Schl; Syracuse, NY; (Y); Chess Clb; German Clb; Varsity Clb; Crs Cntry; Trk; Hon Roll; Engnrng.

VANBUREN, DEBORA; Unatego Central HS; Wellsbridge, NY; (Y); Camera Clb; Spanish Clb; Chorus; JV Bowling; High Hon Roll; Hon Roll.

VANCANEGHEM, ROBERT; Mc Kee Vo-Tech; Staten Is, NY; (Y); High Hon Roll; Hon Roll; Staten Isl Clg; Elec Engr.

VANCE, KRISTEN; Ellsworth J Wilson HS; Spencerport, NY; (Y); 2/296; Am Leg Aux Girls St; Sec Drama Clb; Pres French Clb; School Play; Stage Crew; Var Tennis; High Hon Roll; NHS; Library Aide; Intrntl Forgn Lang Awd 85; SR Flag Guardian 85; Suny -Geneseo; Eng Ed.

VANCE, RUSSELL; Longwood HS; Coram, NY; (Y); Cmnty Wkr; Ski Clb; Varsity Clb; JV Bsbl; JV Var Bsktbl; JV Var Ftbl; Var Trk; Hon Roll; St Johns; Criminal Justice.

VANCE, TRACEY; John F Kennedy HS; Utica, NY; (Y); FBLA; Nwsp Stf; Trs Frsh Cls; Trs Soph Cls; Rep Jr Cls; Rep Stu Cncl; Capt Cheerleading; High Hon Roll; Hon Roll, Recvd Invtn Natl Hnr Socty Indctn 85; Acctg.

VANCURA, SHARON M; Ramapo HS; Pomona, NY; (Y); 29/475; Church Yth Grp; Service Clb; DAR Awd; High Hon Roll; NHS; Cmnty Wkr; Office Aide; Ldrshp Awd, Frgn Lang Hnr Soc, Itln Awd 85; Mck Trl Awds 84-85; Itln.

VANDE BOGART, JEREMY; Sherburne-Earlville HS; Earlville, NY; (S); 14/134; Church Yth Grp; Bsbl; L Capt Bsktbl; L Capt Lcrss; Hon Roll; NHS; Mst Valubl Defnsman La Crosse 83-84; All Tourn Tm Bsktbl 84; Ag & Tech At Morrisville; Desgn.

VANDEN BERG, TIM; Greece Olympia HS; Rochester, NY; (S); DECA; JV Trk; Hon Roll; Plcd In Top 10 Ntls Deca 85; 2nd Pl NY Deca 85; Mrktng.

VANDER WAL, ANN; De Ruyter Central HS; De Ruyter, NY; (Y); Camera Clb; Church Yth Grp; Cmnty Wkr; Debate Tm; French Clb; Sec Girl Scts; Intnl Clb; Library Aide; Red Cross Aide; Teachers Aide; Slvr Grl Sct Awd 85; SADD Pres 85; Schl Serv Awd 85; Philadelphia Coll; Soc Wrk.

VANDERBORG, SUSAN J; Stuyvesant HS; Flushing, NY; (Y); Cmnty Wkr; FTA; Office Aide; Lit Mag; French Hon Soc; Gov Hon Prg Awd; High Hon Roll; Hon Roll; NCTE Awd; Ntl Merit SF; Grtr Metro NY Math Fair-Slvr Mdl 83; City Coll Poetry Cntst 3rd Pl 84; City Coll Poetry Cntst Hrn Mtn; Yale; Eng.

VANDERGROEF, CHRISTINA; Mount Markham SR HS; W Winfield, NY; (Y); 30/111; Pres Church Yth Grp; Drama Clb; FHA; Library Aide; Acpl Chr; Chorus; Church Choir; JV Fld Hcky; High Hon Roll; Ntl Merit Ltr; Clark Schlrshp 84-85; Calvin Coll; Elem.

VANDERLAAN, BRETT; Fort Plain HS; Fort Plain, NY; (S); 1/60; VP Church Yth Grp; Computer Clb; Intnl Clb; Quiz Bowl; Band; Chorus; Var L Socr; NHS; Voice Dem Awd; Math Clb.

VANDERLINDE, KRISTEN; Clarkstown South HS; West Nyack, NY; (Y); Church Yth Grp; GAA; Pres Frsh Cls; Pres Jr Cls; Pres Sr Cls; Stu Cncl; JV Capt Bsktbl; Capt Var Lcrss; Capt Socr; Cit Awd; Hmcmng Queen For Clrkstown S 85; Gene Bagliere Mem Awd For La Crosse 85; Grls Athltc Assn Awd 85; Fairfield U CT; Lbrl Arts.

VANDERPOT, MARTHA S; Croton-Harmon HS; Croton-On Hudson, NY; (Y); #8 In Class; Hon Roll; NHS; Zoology.

VANDERSTEUR, DEREK; Oakfield Alabama Central HS; Oakfield, NY; (Y); Trs Church Yth Grp; Drama Clb; 4-H; School Play; Stu Cncl; Var Trk; Wt Lftg; 4-H Awd; Hon Roll; NHS; Intrmdt Alg Awd 83; Engrng.

VANDETT, ALLAN D; General Mac Arthur HS; Wantagh, NY; (Y); Church Yth Grp; ROTC; Science Clb; Nwsp Rptr; Nwsp Stf; JV Ftbl; Var Trk; High Hon Roll; Hon Roll; Jr NHS; Mst Vlbl Plyr In Trck 83; Nassau CC; Bus.

VANDUZER, LISA; Warwick Valley HS; Warwick, NY; (Y); #33 In Class; Drama Clb; Office Aide; Varsity Clb; School Play; Var Trk; High Hon Roll; Hon Roll; NHS; Lamp Of Knowldg Awd 83-84; Rado.

VANHORNE, SUZANNE; West Irondequoit HS; Rochester, NY; (Y); 50/375; Church Yth Grp; Hosp Aide; JA; Ski Clb; Chorus; Church Choir; JV Swmmng; JV Tennis; Piano Awd; Messiah Coll; RN.

VANIER, LISA; Franklin Acad; Malone, NY; (Y); AFS; Jazz Band; Symp Band; Trs Jr Cls; High Hon Roll; Hon Roll; NHS; Church Yth Grp; French Clb; Intnl Clb; Frnkln Acad Schlrshp; NYSSMA Solo Comp; Music.

VANKIRK, AMY; Washingtonville SR HS; Washingtonville, NY; (Y); French Clb; Varsity Clb; Band; Concert Band; Symp Band; Sec Stu Cncl; Var Capt Cheerleading; JV Socr; Var Trk; Hon Roll.

VANLEUVEN, ANNE; Minisink Valley Central HS; Middletown, NY; (Y); 46/225; Aud/Vis; FHA; Library Aide; Office Aide; Teachers Aide; Yrbk Stf; Btty Crckr Awd; High Hon Roll; Pres Acadmc Fit Awd 85; Home Ec Outstndng Achvt 85; Outstndng Home Ec Stu 84.

VANMATER, WENDY; Pittsford Sutherland HS; Pittsford, NY; (Y); Church Yth Grp; Yrbk Sprt Ed; Tennis; Hon Roll; Bus.

VANN, LISA; Commack HS South; Commack, NY; (S); 12/400; MMM; Office Aide; Teachers Aide; Temple Yth Grp; Chorus; School Musical; Variety Show; Yrbk Stf; High Hon Roll; NHS; NYSSMA 82-84; All Cnty Chrs Fstvl 82; Ntl Hnr Roll 84; Educ.

VANN, SHARON; Newburgh Free Acad; Newburgh, NY; (Y); 107/720; Chorus; Church Choir; Rep Stu Cncl; Var Trk; Var Vllybl; High Hon Roll; Hon Roll; NHS; Opt Clb Awd; Ctzn Mth 85; Dutchess CC; Bus Adm.

VANNI, ROBERT; L C Obourn HS; East Rochester, NY; (Y); 8/112; Mathletes; Math Tm; Scholastic Bowl; Ski Clb; Bsktbl; JV Ftbl; Var Capt Socr; Var Trk; Hon Roll; Regnts Schlrshp 85; U Of Rochester; Comp Sci.

VANOSKY JR, ROBERT JAMES; Mont Pleasant HS; Schenectady, NY; (Y); 17/239; Chess Clb; Church Yth Grp; Cmnty Wkr; Key Clb; Service Clb; Spanish Clb; High Hon Roll; Hon Roll; Spanish NHS; SUNY; Acctng.

VANSAVAGE, KATHERINE; Susquehanna Valley HS; Binghamton, NY; (Y); Mathletes; Ski Clb; Yrbk Stf; High Hon Roll; Pres Jr NHS; NHS; Trs Frsh Cls; Bsktbl; Fld Hcky; Trk; Treas Spirit Clb 84-85; Salute-Yth Outstndg 85.

VANT, STEPHEN; G Ray Bodley HS; Fulton, NY; (Y); 85/249; 4-H; JA; Political Wkr; Stu Cncl; Cit Awd; 4-H Awd; NY Rgnts Schlrshp 85; Ctznshp Schlrshp 85; Natl Hstrcl Soc Essy Awd 84; SUNY Fredonia; Envrmntl Dsgn.

VANVALKENBURG, LISA; Chenango Forks HS; Binghamton, NY; (Y); Church Yth Grp; French Clb; Ski Clb; Teachers Aide; JV Bsktbl; JV Var Socr; High Hon Roll; Hon Roll; Acctng.

VANWICKLER, BILL; Freeport HS; Freeport, NY; (Y).

VANWIE, REBECCA; Fonda-Fultonville Central HS; Fonda, NY; (Y); Cmnty Wkr; Pres 4-H; Pres Intnl Clb; Pres Key Clb; Chorus; Concert Band; VP Sr Cls; Var L Swmmng; Hon Roll; Band; Hugh Obrien Ldrshp Awd 83-84; Intr Dsgn.

VANWOERT, NANCY; Oneonta HS; Oneonta, NY; (Y); Bowling; Trk; VP 4-H; Typg Awd 84; Chem Awd 85; Cazenovia; Sec.

VARA, RUSSELL; West Seneca East HS; W Seneca, NY; (Y); Cmnty Wkr; DECA; JA; Office Aide; Hon Roll; Jr NHS; NHS; Prfct Atten Awd; 4th Pl DECA Regnl Comptn 85; Spnsh Awd Acadmc Excllnc 84 & 85; BUS Mgt.

VARELA JR, JESUS; Eastern District HS; Brooklyn, NY; (Y); Aud/Vis; English Clb; Library Aide; Spanish Clb; Teachers Aide; Ftbl; John J Coll; Crmnl Law.

VARGA, RACHEL S; Professional Childrns; New York, NY; (Y); Hon Roll; Solist Sr Cncrt Orch Carnegie Hall 83; Julliard; Violinist.

VARGAS, CARMEN; Julia Richman HS; Brooklyn, NY; (Y); DECA; FBLA; JA; Latin Clb; ROTC; Spanish Clb; Sec Stu Cncl; JV Vllybl; Wt Lftg; Prfct Atten Awd; Putstndng Ldrshp Prfrmnc Awd 84; Bilingual Acad Bus Skill Intrnshp Awd 84; Universidad Interamercna; Tchr.

VARGAS, DENISE; St Johns Prep; Elmhurst, NY; (Y); Hon Roll; Psych.

VARGAS, EUNICE; John Jay HS; New York, NY; (Y); Teachers Aide; Yrbk Stf; Gym; Cit Awd; French Hon Soc; High Hon Roll; NHS; Val; Cmmndtn Outstndg Scholar Typg 3 85; Cmmndtn Fr 4 85; Notre Dame; Dctr.

VARGAS, MARTINA; De Witt Clinton HS; Bronx, NY; (Y); Church Yth Grp; Orch; Nwsp Rptr; Nwsp Stf; Hon Roll; Prfct Atten Awd; Training Opportunities Pgm 85.

VARGAS, MYRA; Msgr Scanlan HS; New York, NY; (Y); Dance Clb; Intnl Clb; Cheerleading; Wt Lftg; Intr Desgnr.

VARGAS, VIVIANA; Yonkers HS; Yonkers, NY; (Y); Church Yth Grp; Latin Clb; Spanish Clb; Chorus; Church Choir; Variety Show; Nwsp Rptr; Nwsp Sprt Ed; Nwsp Stf; Yrbk Stf; Mt St Vincent; Nrs.

VARGHESE, ANNE; Our Lady Of Perpetual Help HS; Brooklyn, NY; (Y); Cmnty Wkr; Office Aide; Chorus; High Hon Roll; Hon Roll; Prfct Atten Awd; Pedeatrcn.

VARGHESE, ELIZABETH; Dominican Commercial HS; Richmond Hill, NY; (Y); Church Yth Grp; Service Clb; Spanish Clb; Teachers Aide; Nwsp Rptr; Jr NHS; WA Wrkshps Congrssnl Sem Part 85.

VARISCO, DINA; Christ The King Regional HS; Ridgewood, NY; (Y); 74/385; English Clb; Library Aide; Teachers Aide; Band; Drm & Bgl; Flag Corp; Orch; Yrbk Stf; Hon Roll; NHS; Psych.

VARNER, KIMBERLY; Cardinal Spellman HS; Bronx, NY; (Y); Hosp Aide; Hon Roll; Actvts Awd Pres Afro Amer Clb 84-85; Pre-Med.

VARNEY, SCOTT; Hudson Falls HS; Hudson Falls, NY; (Y); Boy Scts; Computer Clb; Spanish Clb; Off Frsh Cls; Crs Cntry; Tennis; Prfct Atten Awd; Forestry.

VARONE, RUSSELL; Lindenhurst SR HS; Lindenhurst, NY; (Y); ROTC; Ski Clb; Golf; Wrstlng; Physics.

VARRIALE, CHRISTINE; Bethpage HS; Bethpage, NY; (Y); 34/290; JV Bsbl; Var Fld Hcky; Hnr Rll 83-85; Hofstra; Acctng.

VARSHAVCHIK, SEMYON; Bay Shore HS; Bay Shore, NY; (Y); Computer Clb; Math Clb; 2nd Pl Pratt Inst Comp Cont 84; Comp Clb Achvt Awd 85; Comp Wrtr.

VARTANIAN, ROBERT; La Salle Acad; New York, NY; (S); Aud/Vis; Camera Clb; Hosp Aide; ROTC; High Hon Roll; NHS; Rutgers U; Mech Engr.

VARY, DONNA R; Odessa-Montour HS; Montour Fls, NY; (Y); Art Clb; Church Yth Grp; Drama Clb; Teachers Aide; Varsity Clb; Crs Cntry; Tennis; Masonic Awd; Prfct Atten Awd; Houghton Coll; Law.

VASILE, PAMELA; Harrison HS; White Plains, NY; (Y); 8/211; Cmnty Wkr; Hosp Aide; VP Band; VP Concert Band; Jazz Band; Mrchg Band; Stage Crew; Nwsp Stf; Italn Ntl Hnr Sco 84; Band Ded Awd 82; NYSSMA Solo Comp 85; Bio.

VASKA, PAUL; Potsdam Central HS; Norwood, NY; (Y); 1/163; Math Clb; Concert Band; Jazz Band; Orch; School Musical; JV Var Socr; NHS; Ntl Merit Ltr; Val; All Coll Luthrn Scholar 85; Clarkson U; Physcs.

VASKOVIC, CHRISTINE; Seton Catholic Central HS; Binghamton, NY; (Y); 16/167; Church Yth Grp; Hon Roll; NHS; Bus Adm.

VASQUENZ, SABRINA; St Peters HS For Girls; Staten Island, NY; (Y); FNA; Hosp Aide; Chorus; Church Choir; School Musical; School Play; Variety Show; Yrbk Stf; Regnts Diploma 86; Wagner Coll.

VASQUEZ, LISSETTE; Curtis HS; Staten Island, NY; (Y); Key Clb; ROTC; Drill Tm; Variety Show; Capt Var Cheerleading; Gym; Var Swmmng; Hon Roll; Stoneybrook; Comp Engrng.

VASQUEZ, RAYMOND; Cardinal Hayes HS; New York, NY; (Y); 10/293; Computer Clb; Dance Clb; Debate Tm; English Clb; French Clb; Math Clb; JV Bsktbl; High Hon Roll; Hon Roll; Prfct Atten Awd; Comp.

VASQUEZ, VICTOR; Yonkers HS; Yonkers, NY; (Y); Art Clb; FHA; Gym; JETS Awd; Art Awd 80; Math Awd 82; CC NY; Arch.

VASS, STEVEN; Kenmore East HS; Tonawanda, NY; (Y); Orch; School Musical; Hon Roll; Pol Sci.

VASSALLO, FRANK; Jamestown HS; Jamestown, NY; (Y); French Clb; Band; Chorus; Trs Mrchg Band; Stu Cncl; JV Bsktbl; Var L Golf; High Hon Roll; Jr NHS; NHS; Bnkng.

VASSALLO, STEPHANIE; St John The Baptist HS; Seaford, NY; (Y); Teachers Aide; Rep Frsh Cls; Rep Soph Cls; Sec Jr Cls; Sec Sr Cls; Cheerleading; High Hon Roll; Hon Roll; Socr; Cert Of Achvt-Yth In Govt Day; Psych.

VASSE, MARY B; New Paltz HS; New Paltz, NY; (Y); 22/134; Drama Clb; Science Clb; Band; Sec Chorus; Concert Band; Mrchg Band; School Musical; Stat Socr; L Trk; Hon Roll; SADD 85-86; Psychlgy.

VASSILAS, CHRISTINA; Fontbonne Hall Acad; Brooklyn, NY; (Y); 1/138; Cmnty Wkr; Office Aide; Service Clb; Teachers Aide; Hon Roll; NHS; Prfct Atten Awd; Val; Natl Ldrshp Merit Awd 83-84; Acad All-Am Awd 83-84; Manhattanville Coll; Law.

VASSO, JANE; Our Lady Of Victory Acad; Yonkers, NY; (S); 7/159; Spanish Clb; Speech Tm; Teachers Aide; Pres Soph Cls; Trs Jr Cls; Stu Cncl; High Hon Roll; NHS; Spanish NHS; Math Awd.

VASTO, STEVEN; Ravena-Coeymans-Selkirk Centrl HS; Ravena, NY; (Y); 25/194; Pres DECA; Yrbk Bus Mgr; Rep Frsh Cls; Rep Soph Cls; Rep Jr Cls; VP Sr Cls; Rep Stu Cncl; Stat Bsktbl; Var Capt Socr; Var Capt Trk; Bus Law Awd, RCS Class Of 81 Mem Schlrshp, Teenager Of Month 85; Hudson Vlly Comm Coll; Mktg.

VAUGHAN, KERRY M; August Martin HS; Springfield Gdns, NY; (Y); 6/375; Boys Clb Am; Computer Clb; High Hon Roll; Arista Hnr Soc 83-85; Princeton; Elec Engr.

VAUGHN, ARTHUR; Uniondale HS; Uniondale, NY; (Y); Church Yth Grp; FBLA; Spanish Clb; Chorus; Nwsp Stf; Rep Soph Cls; JV Bsktbl; Var L Ftbl; Var L Trk; Hon Roll; Long Island JR Olympcs 1st Pl 85; Comp Sci.

VAUGHN, COLLEEN; Voorheesville HS; Voorheesville, NY; (Y); 2/120; Math Tm; Concert Band; Jazz Band; Nwsp Rptr; Cit Awd; NHS; Ntl Merit Ltr; Prfct Atten Awd; Teachers Aide; Band; Gftd & Tlntd Clb 84; Anthrplgy.

VAUGHN, MICHAEL A; Elmira Free Acad; Elmira, NY; (Y); Church Yth Grp; Pres Spanish Clb; Band; Church Choir; Concert Band; Mrchg Band; Yrbk Stf; Rep Soph Cls; Rep Jr Cls; Rep Sr Cls; Rochester Inst Of Tech; Sci.

VAUGHN, PAMELA; Horseheads HS; Horseheads, NY; (Y); Drama Clb; German Clb; Ski Clb; Band; Chorus; Jazz Band; Mrchg Band; Yrbk Phtg; Hon Roll; SUNY Buffalo; Occp Thrpy.

VAUGHN, WENDY ANN; Vernon-Verona-Sherrill HS; Vernon, NY; (Y), 17/249; VP Church Yth Grp; Drm & Bgl; Yrbk Bus Mgr; JV Bsktbl; JV Var Tennis; NHS; CSFA Schlrshp 85; VVS Tchr Assn Schlrshp 85; St John Fisher Coll; Acctng.

VAUGHT, MICHELE; Baker HS; Baldwinsville, NY; (Y); Church Yth Grp; Dance Clb; Drama Clb; 4-H; French Clb; FBLA; Teachers Aide; Off Sr Cls; JV Trk; Hon Roll; Spec Ed Clss Plaque 85; Culver-Stockton Coll; Pre-Med.

VAUTRIN, LORRAINE; Waterford Halfmoon HS; Waterford, NY; (Y); 23/89; Computer Clb; French Clb; Church Choir; Yrbk Stf; Cheerleading; SUNY; Bus.

VAYNBERG, ALBERT; Susan E Wagner HS; Staten Island, NY; (Y); Art Clb; Computer Clb; Spanish Clb; Band; Hon Roll; Cert Merit-Dsgn-A-Card Cntst Comptn 83; Cert Excllnc Glbl Hstry I 83; Electrncs.

VAZQUEZ, ANGELIQUE; Herbert H Lehman HS; New York, NY; (Y); Art Clb; Girl Scts; Leo Clb; Chorus; School Musical; Swing Chorus; Yrbk Rptr; Jr Cls; Cheerleading; Coach Actv; Creatve Wrtg Awd 82; Mercy Coll; Exec Sec.

VAZQUEZ, ANODEL; Cathedral HS; Bx, NY; (Y); Drama Clb; Library Aide; Office Aide; Var Bsktbl; Var Sftbl; Fordham U; Law.

VAZQUEZ, ESTEBAN; Cardinal Hayes HS; Bronx, NY; (Y); 48/267; Computer Clb; Dance Clb; Office Aide; Var Trk; Hon Roll; Iona; Comp Prgrmr.

VAZQUEZ, GIANNA; Columbus HS; Bronx, NY; (Y); 50/792; Dance Clb; Hosp Aide; Office Aide; Teachers Aide; Chorus; Hon Roll; Lehman Coll; Paralegal.

VAZQUEZ, JAVIER E; John Dewey HS; Brooklyn, NY; (Y); Church Yth Grp; Library Aide; Prfct Atten Awd; NY U; Bus Adm.

VAZQUEZ, NANCY; Norman Thomas HS; Jamaica, NY; (S); 34/671; Church Yth Grp; Computer Clb; Dance Clb; Exploring; FBLA; JA; Office Aide; Church Choir; School Play; Yrbk Stf; Baruch Coll; Accntng.

VEA, MARIE; Notre Dame HS; Horseheads, NY; (Y); Church Yth Grp; FNA; Science Clb; Chorus; Church Choir; Nwsp Rptr; Ed Nwsp Stf; Rep Jr Cls; Rep Sr Cls; Rep Stu Cncl; Mst Outstndng Engl; Chemung County Yth Cncl; Pre-Med.

VEASLEY, TIRONE; Turner-Carroll HS; Buffalo, NY; (Y); Pres Frsh Cls; Capt Var Bsktbl; Capt Var Ftbl; Trk; Hon Roll; Prfct Atten Awd; MVP Bsktbl 83-84; Canisus Coll Hustle Awd 83; Mst Dedctd Ftbl Plyr 83; Acctng.

VECCHIAELLI, CLAUDINE; Spackenkill HS; Poughkeepsie, NY; (Y); Stage Crew; Yrbk Stf; Rptr Frsh Cls; Rep Soph Cls; Rep Jr Cls; Rep Sr Cls; Stat Ftbl; Mgr(s); Hon Roll; Ntl Frnch Exm Hnrbl Mntn; Psychlgy.

VECCHIO, ROSEANN; Our Lady Of Perpetual Helph; Brooklyn, NY; (Y); Rep Soph Cls; Var Bsktbl; Var Bowling; Hon Roll; Prncpls Lst 82-85; Bus.

VECCHIO, SOFIA C; Fiorello La Guardia HS; New York, NY; (Y); 9/590; Art Clb; Church Yth Grp; English Clb; Office Aide; PAVAS; Lit Mag; Hon Roll; NHS; Natl Arts Recgntn Talnt & Srch 85; Hon Ment Natl Schlstc Art Awds 81; Visual Art.

VECCHIONE, CATHERINE; Sanford H Calhoun HS; Merrick, NY; (Y); 15/336; Nwsp Rptr; Rep Soph Cls; Hst Stu Cncl; Hon Roll; Nrthwstrn U.

VECCHIONE, JOSEPH M; Cardinal Spellman HS; Bronx, NY; (Y); 4/568; Debate Tm; Trs NFL; Speech Tm; Rep Stu Cncl; Gov Hon Prg Awd; Hon Roll; Jr NHS; NHS; Ntl Merit Ltr; NY City Dist Champ Boys Extemporaneous Spch 84; Contstnt NFL Natl Champnshp Tournmnt San Antonio Tx; Georgetown U; Intl Law.

VECELLIO, KEVIN; Notre Dame HS; Pine City, NY; (Y); Nwsp Rptr; Yrbk Stf; Off Jr Cls; JV Var Bsktbl; Var Socr; Trk; Hon Roll; NHS; Red Crs Yth Ldrshp 84.

VECIANA, HIRAM; Regis HS; New York, NY; (Y); Computer Clb; Yrbk Stf; Sec Sr Cls; Im Bsktbl; Ntl Merit Ltr; Semi Fnlst Natl Hispnc Schlrs Awds 85; NY ST Regents Schlrshp Wnnr 85; 4 Yr H S Schlrshp 81-85; Engrng.

VEDDER, MICHELLE; Duanesburg Central HS; Delanson, NY; (Y); Cmnty Wkr; Drama Clb; School Play; JV Var Bsktbl; Var Capt Crs Cntry; Var Capt Trk; Hon Roll; Church Yth Grp; 4-H; French Clb; Athl Yr 84-85; Grls Bsktbl 84-85; Peer Ldr Substnce Abuse Prvntn Pgm 84-85; Spec Awd Svc Drama 84-85; NY U; Actng.

VEEDER, ABIGAIL; Pineview Acad; Albany, NY; (Y); 2/13; Church Yth Grp; Drama Clb; Chorus; Rep Frsh Cls; Sec Soph Cls; Off Jr Cls; Var Vllybl; Hon Roll; Camera Clb; Cmnty Wkr; Outstndng Achvt Eng,Soc Studies,Bible; St U-New York; Ed.

VEGA, FERNANDO A; Eastern District HS; Brooklyn, NY; (Y); Math Tm; Science Clb; Band; Rep Sr Cls; Hon Roll; Hunter Coll; Sci.

VEGA, MARIBEL; Newtown HS; Elmhurst, NY; (Y); Cert Merit Spn 85; Bus.

VEGA, ROSEMARIE; Aquinas HS; Bronx, NY; (Y); 30/178; Cmnty Wkr; Computer Clb; Debate Tm; Science Clb; Yrbk Stf; High Hon Roll; Hon Roll; NHS; Spanish NHS; UCLA; Bio.

VEGA, WANDA; Our Lady Of Perpetual Help HS; Brooklyn, NY; (Y); Bowling; High Hon Roll; Hon Roll; Prfct Atten Awd; Comp Sci.

VEGSO, BETSY A; City Honors HS; Buffalo, NY; (Y); Dance Clb; English Clb; JA; Ski Clb; Ed Lit Mag; Stat Bsbl; Var Socr; Ntl Merit Ltr; Mgr(s); Score Keeper; JA VP Of Yr Mrktng Wstrn NY 83-84; Washington U; Bus.

VEIDIS, INGRID; Cold Spring Harbor HS; Huntington, NY; (Y); 36/150; Church Yth Grp; Girl Scts; Church Choir; Orch; L Bowling; JV Fld Hcky; JV Lcrss; High Hon Roll; Hon Roll; Sec-Latvian Yth Grp 85-86; Grad Of Latvian Saturdy Schl 86.

VELA, ENRIQUE; St Francis Prep; Elmhurst, NY; (Y); 163/750; Spanish Clb; Im Bsktbl; Im Ftbl; Im Sftbl; L JV Tennis; Im Wt Lftg; Spanish NHS; Ntl Hispnc Schlrshp; Regents Schlrshp; Fordham U; Acctng.

VELARDO, MARIA; Ossining HS; Ossining, NY; (Y); 84/300; Dance Clb; Girl Scts; Hon Roll; Bus Eductn Awd-Outstndng Detrmntn 84; Catherine Gibbs-New York; Bus.

VELASCO, MARTHA; Ossining HS; Ossining, NY; (Y); French Clb; Hosp Aide; Math Tm; High Hon Roll; Hon Roll; Mu Alp Tht; NHS; Natl Frnch Cont 4th Pl Lcl & 5th Rgnl 85; Iona Coll Lang Cont Frnch II 2nd Hnrs 85; Surgn.

VELASCO, SONIA; Cardinal Spellman HS; Yonkers, NY; (Y); Trs Key Clb; Science Clb; Nwsp Stf; Hon Roll.

VELASQUEZ, DIANA; Adlai E Stevenson HS; Bronx, NY; (Y); Exploring; Band; Jazz Band; Bowling; Cheerleading; Crs Cntry; Prfct Atten Awd; MMM; Awd For Achvng 80 Or Above Avrge 84-85; NY U; Pre-Med.

VELASQUEZ, LILLIAN; Franklin Delano Roosevelt HS; Brooklyn, NY; (Y); 64/600; Hosp Aide; Office Aide; Teachers Aide; Pres Frsh Cls; Hon Roll; Spanish Clb; Band; Pep Band; Variety Show; Schl Svcs Awd 83-84; Bnd Ldr Awd 83-84; Brooklyn Coll; Med.

VELASQUEZ, MATEO; Cardinal Hayes HS; New York, NY; (Y); 22/264; Var Socr; Hon Roll; Prfct Atten Awd; 2nd Plc Outstdng Soccer Plyr 84; 1st Hnr Acad 83; Fairleigh Dickinson U; Comp Sci.

VELAZQUEZ, CARMEN; Walton HS; Bronx, NY; (Y); Fordham U; Comp Sci.

VELAZQUEZ, CECIL; Rice HS; Bronx, NY; (Y); Teachers Aide; Stu Cncl; Var Bsbl; Im Bsktbl; Crs Cntry; Ftbl; JV Var Trk; High Hon Roll; Hon Roll; Prfct Atten Awd; Baruch; Acctg.

VELEZ, EILEEN; Bronx Science HS; New York, NY; (Y); VP JA; Spanish Clb; Orch; Jr NHS; Prfct Atten Awd; Marlane Ellen Nussbaum Mem Awd 83; Ass Americaine Des Professeurs De Francais Cert Merit 85; Columbia U; Bio.

VELEZ, GINO; Warwick Valley HS; Sugar Loaf, NY; (Y); 59/212; Var Ftbl; Var Trk; Stu Linson; Jr Senator; Discipline Comm; Psychlgy.

VELEZ, LILIA; Cardinal Spellman HS; Bronx, NY; (Y); Art Clb; Latin Clb; Teachers Aide; Stage Crew; Hon Roll; Psych.

VELEZ, LUZ; St Pius V HS; Bronx, NY; (Y); Hosp Aide; Stu Cncl; Regents Spn Awd 85; Psych.

VELEZ, MARGARITA; St Pius V HS; Bronx, NY; (Y); Church Yth Grp; Church Choir; Sec Jr Cls; Stu Cncl; Hon Roll; Religion 83-84; Engl/Lang Arts 83-84; Steno 85; Grace; Exec Sec.

VELEZ, RAFAEL; Herbert H Lehman HS; Bronx, NY; (Y); 33/473; Camera Clb; MMM; Science Clb; Jazz Band; Mrchg Band; Orch; Var Bsbl; Vllybl; Hon Roll; Arista Hnr Soc 85; Long Island U; Dntst.

VELEZ, RICHARD; John Jay HS; Palm Beach Grdns, FL; (Y); Church Yth Grp; Ntl Merit Ltr; Outstndng Schlrshps-Spnsh, Math & Hstry 84-85; Engrng.

VELIA, ELIZABETH; Canaserage Central HS; Canaseraga, NY; (Y); 5/19; Science Clb; Sec Frsh Cls; Trs Soph Cls; Rep Jr Cls; Hon Roll; NHS.

VELILLA, ANGEL; Curtis HS; Staten Island, NY; (Y); Math Tm; Band; Drill Tm; JV Var Bsbl; Soc Studs 83; Criminal Law.

VELLA, CAMI; Cardinal Mooney HS; Rochester, NY; (Y); Cmnty Wkr; Dance Clb; Teachers Aide; Niagara U; Lib Arts.

VELLA, STEVEN; Susan E Wayner HS; Staten Island, NY; (Y); 75/600; Am Leg Boys St; Band; Concert Band; Var Ftbl; Var Wt Lftg; Hon Roll; Gen Excellnc 79; St Johns; Accntng.

VELLEY, LILLIAN; Franklin Acad; Burke, NY; (Y); Bus.

VELTRE, GENEVIEVE; Nazareth Acad; Rochester, NY; (Y); Drama Clb; PAVAS; Red Cross Aide; Chorus; School Musical; Sec Frsh Cls; Pres Stu Cncl; Coach Actv; Fshn Inst Tech; Adv.

VELTRI, ALBERT; Fordham Preparatory Schl; Bronx, NY; (Y); Aud/Vis; Chess Clb; Hosp Aide; Science Clb; Concert Band; Jazz Band; Yrbk Rptr; Rep Soph Cls; Im Sftbl; Im Var Swmmng; Excllnc-Bio 83; Excllnc-Physics 85; Engg, Trig & Amer Hstry 85; Bio-Chem.

VELZ, MARY E; Bishop Scully HS; Amsterdam, NY; (Y); 12/70; Art Clb; Cmnty Wkr; French Clb; Yrbk Stf; Var Capt Cheerleading; Pom Pon; High Hon Roll; Sec Natl Hnr Soc; Natl Art Hnr Soc; Fairfield U; Law.

VENABLE, MARY; Eastern District HS; Brooklyn, NY; (Y); Hosp Aide; Sec Office Aide; Church Choir; Hon Roll; Engl, Soc Stds Achvt 85; Hnr Rll 85; Long Island U; Nrs.

VENDITTI, THOMAS H; Kingston HS; Ulster Park, NY; (Y); 10/511; Stage Crew; Rep Stu Cncl; Var Capt Socr; Hon Roll; Kiwanis Awd; Lion Awd; NHS; Spanish NHS; Am Leg Boys St; Amer H S Athlt 84-85; Holy Cross; Bio Chem.

VENETIAN, ANTHONY; St Joseph By The Sea HS; Staten Island, NY; (Y); Art Clb; Computer Clb; Concert Band; Nwsp Stf; Yrbk Stf; Rep Frsh Cls; Im Bsktbl; Im Golf; St Johns U; Engr.

VENETTOZZI, CINDY; Whitesboro SR HS; Whitesboro, NY; (Y); 97/365; JV Var Powder Puff Ftbl; Utica Schl Of Commerce; Med Sec.

VENEY, PHYLLIS; Cathedral HS; New York, NY; (Y); 65/325; Church Yth Grp; French Clb; Intnl Clb; Yrbk Stf; Prfct Atten Awd; Pres Acadmc Ftns Awd 85; Regnts Schlrshp 85; Cardinal Spellman Yth Awd 85; Long Island U; Chld Psych.

VENEY, SHERYLYN; Hauppauge HS; Hauppauge, NY; (Y); Cmnty Wkr; Band; Concert Band; Mrchg Band; Orch; Pep Band; School Musical; Symp Band; Variety Show; Fld Hcky; Vrsty Fld Hcky Awd 84; UYSSMA Music Awd 83 & 84; Penn St; Commnctns.

VENEZIA, JODY; Byron-Bergen Crntral HS; Byron, NY; (Y); Computer Clb; VICA; Chorus; Color Guard; Mrchg Band; Yrbk Stf; Cheerleading; Pom Pon; Score Keeper; Socr; Awd Sprts Achvt 83; Awd Drvrs Ed-Obsrvtn, Manuvr 85; Awd Recog 83; Air Force; Data Prsccng.

VENEZIA, JOSEPH; Richmond Hill HS; Richmond Hill, NY; (Y); English Clb; Math Clb; Spanish Clb; Var Socr; High Hon Roll; NHS; Spanish NHS; Math,Eng Hnr Soc 85; C W Post; Surgeon.

VENEZIA, MIKE; New Dorp HS; Staten Island, NY; (Y); Latin Clb; Mathletes; JV Var Bsbl; JV Var Bsktbl; High Hon Roll.

VENEZIANO, DOREEN; Our Lady Of Perpetual Help HS; Brooklyn, NY; (Y); Pres Frsh Cls; Sec Stu Cncl; Cheerleading; High Hon Roll; Hon Roll; Pre-Law.

VENEZIANO, THOMAS; Bishop Ford Central Catholic HS; Brooklyn, NY; (Y); Church Yth Grp; Cmnty Wkr; Computer Clb; Dance Clb; JA; Office Aide; Political Wkr; Church Choir; Stage Crew; Rep Soph Cls; Awds For Activities Cncl; Frgn Lang Italian; Muscular Dystrophy Dance-A-Thon Cert; St Johns U; Accntnt.

VENGALLI, CHRISTINA; Lakeland SR HS; Mohegan Lake, NY; (Y); Rep Frsh Cls; Var JV Bsktbl; Var Capt Sftbl; Var Capt Tennis; Credit Rl 83-85; All Div Tennis,Sftbl 83-85; Acctng.

VENIA, NICHOLAS JAMES; Pelham Memorial HS; Pelham Manor, NY; (Y); Church Yth Grp; Radio Clb; Rep Stu Cncl; Var JV Bsbl; JV Ftbl; JV Socr; JR Prom King 85; Bus.

VENNE, DAWN; Saranac Central HS; Cadyville, NY; (S); Hosp Aide; Teachers Aide; Chorus; Church Choir; Var Mgr(s); Var Score Keeper; JV Var Socr; JV Var Sftbl; JV Var Vllybl; Hon Roll; Army; Nursing.

VENNE, MARY; Moriah Central HS; Mineville, NY; (Y); AFS; GAA; Ski Clb; Band; Concert Band; Mrchg Band; Rep Stu Cncl; Var Socr; Bnkg.

VENNOCHI, LESLIE; New Rochelle HS; New Rochelle, NY; (Y); Church Yth Grp; Cmnty Wkr; Girl Scts; Hosp Aide; Library Aide; Spanish Clb; Y-Teens; Lit Mag; High Hon Roll; Hon Roll; Hum Svcs.

VENSKYTIS, ERIC; Dendee Central HS; Dundee, NY; (Y); Church Yth Grp; Cmnty Wkr; Bsktbl; Ftbl; Trk; Wt Lftg; High Hon Roll; Hon Roll; Air Force.

VENTARALA, ANTHONY; Mount Saint Michael Acad; Bronx, NY; (Y); 6/308; Chess Clb; Computer Clb; Lit Mag; JV Bsbl; Im Bsktbl; JV Bowling; Im Sftbl; Hon Roll; NHS; Spanish NHS; Engrng.

VENTAROLA, ANTHONY; Mount St Michael Acad; Bronx, NY; (S); 6/308; Chess Clb; Computer Clb; Lit Mag; Rep Jr Cls; Bsbl; Bsktbl; Var Bowling; Sftbl; Hon Roll; NHS; Spanish NHS; Engrng.

VENTIMIGLIA, PAULA M; Uniondale HS; Uniondale, NY; (Y); 12/480; Red Cross Aide; Concert Band; Mrchg Band; Orch; Pep Band; School Musical; Sec Stu Cncl; High Hon Roll; Hon Roll; Jr NHS; Domincn Schlrshp 85; Nrsng Regents Schlrshp 85; Specl Awd Achvt 85; Molloy Coll; Nrsng.

VENTRA, ZENNA; Oxford Academy HS; Oxford, NY; (Y); 5/98; French Clb; Ski Clb; Concert Band; School Play; Yrbk Phtg; Rep Frsh Cls; Rep Soph Cls; Rep Jr Cls; High Hon Roll; Hon Roll; Actng.

VENTRE, DONALD; Oneonta SR HS; Oneonta, NY; (Y); 11/180; French Clb; Ski Clb; JV Bsbl; JV Bsktbl; Hon Roll; Syracuse U; Comm Art.

VENTRE, EDNA R; Franklin K Lane HS; Glendale, NY; (Y); 10/900; Cmnty Wkr; Key Clb; Pep Clb; Band; Concert Band; Jazz Band; School Musical; School Play; Variety Show; Nwsp Stf; Mayors Vol Svc Awd 85; Binghamton; Ind Psych.

VENTURA, CARA DELLA; Notre Dame Acad; Staten Island, NY; (Y); Church Yth Grp; Cmnty Wkr; Hosp Aide; Pres Math Clb; VP Science Clb; School Musical; Nwsp Stf; Cheerleading; NHS; Ntl Merit Ltr; American Chem Soc Annual Outstndng Chem Student Awd 84; ALISI Ntl Spanish Exam Awd 85; Biolgcl Sci.

VENTURA, HEATHER ANNE; Adirondack Central Schl; Boonville, NY; (Y); 14/120; Church Yth Grp; Spanish Clb; Acpl Chr; Chorus; Church Choir; Concert Band; Jazz Band; School Musical; Rep Frsh Cls; NHS; Susquehanna U; Music.

VENTURA, LESLIE; St Pius HS; Bronx, NY; (Y); Art Clb; Church Yth Grp; Cmnty Wkr; Dance Clb; JA; PAVAS; Teachers Aide; Variety Show; Bsbl; Bowling; Tchrs Aid Awd 85; Dance Proj Awd 85; Leman Coll; Dance.

VENTURA, LISA J; Greenville Central HS; Greenville, NY; (Y); Drama Clb; Sec Key Clb; Sec Latin Clb; Sec Spanish Clb; Yrbk Stf; VP Jr Cls; Var Socr; Hon Roll; Timer; Chorus; Ntl Chrl Awd, James Adams Mem Awd 85; Geneseo; Law.

VENTURA, MICHELE; Frankfort-Schuyler HS; Frankfort, NY; (S); FBLA; GAA; Pres Spanish Clb; Band; Rep Frsh Cls; Rep Soph Cls; Rep Jr Cls; Rep Sr Cls; Stu Cncl; NHS; 1st Rnnr Up NYS Miss TEEN Pagnt 84; Miss Cogeniality 84; SR Suprlatv Clss Entrtnr 85; St Elizabeths Schl; RN.

VENTURIN, KATHY; Niagara Wheatfield SR HS; Niagara Falls, NY; (Y); Pep Clb; Pres PAVAS; VP Pres Chorus; Church Choir; School Musical; Swing Chorus; JV Var Socr; Hon Roll; NHS; Tri M Music Hnr Soc 85.

VERA, STEVE; De Witt Clinton HS; Bronx, NY; (Y); Boy Scts; Church Yth Grp; ROTC; Chorus; Drill Tm; Pres Frsh Cls; VP Stu Cncl; Cit Awd; Prfct Atten Awd; Hon Roll; Awd Purpl Hrt Mdl Cadt Corp 84; Stony Brk LI; Pre-Med.

VERAS, RICARDO; Cardinal Hayes HS; New York, NY; (Y); Computer Clb; JV Trk; Hon Roll; Comp Bus.

VERBANIC, NICHOLAS; Lackawanna SR HS; Lackawanna, NY; (Y); 11/288; Am Leg Boys St; Pres Ski Clb; Spanish Clb; Pres Stu Cncl; Var Capt Socr; Var Tennis; NHS; Regents Schlrshp 85; Knights Phythias Awd 85; Robert Bilowus Mem Schlrshp 85; SUNY-BUFFALO; Aerosp Engr.

VERBRIDGE, WENDY; Marion JR SR HS; Marion, NY; (Y); 10/89; Library Aide; Band; Concert Band; Jazz Band; Mrchg Band; School Musical; Var JV Socr; Var Sftbl; Hon Roll; NHS; Cornell; Comp Sci.

VERDE, JOANNE; Crmel HS; Carmel, NY; (Y); Yrbk Stf; High Hon Roll; Hon Roll; Actng.

VERDERBER, SUZANNE M; Tottenville HS; Staten Island, NY; (Y); 1/897; Drama Clb; Quiz Bowl; Sec Ski Clb; Teachers Aide; School Musical; School Play; Stage Crew; Nwsp Ed-Chief; Nwsp Rptr; Yrbk Ed-Chief; ALISI Concours Natl Frnch Cont 83-85; NY Daily News Spryth Awd 83-84; Boroughwide Soc Stud Fair 84; Dartmouth Coll; Engl.

VERDI, KATHLEEN ANNE; Bishop Cunningham HS; Fulton, NY; (Y); Hon Roll; Pblc Comm.

VERDILE, TINA M; Bay Shore HS; Brightwaters, NY; (Y); 25/400; Cmnty Wkr; Hosp Aide; Intnl Clb; Math Clb; Math Tm; Lit Mag; Bowling; NHS; Regents Schlrshp 85; 1st Bay Shore Suffolk Cty Math Cont 82; St Johns U; Ed.

VEREEN, AUDREY LYNN; Norman Thomas HS; New York, NY; (S); 49/671; Pres Church Yth Grp; Cmnty Wkr; FBLA; JA; Rep Sr Cls; Var Bsktbl; High Hon Roll; Trs NHS; Prfct Atten Awd; Prncpl Commdtn 84; Comp Sci Awd 85; NC ST U; Pre Vet.

VERHAEG, LEONARD EDMUND; Saratoga SR HS; Saratoga Springs, NY; (Y); 49/465; Am Leg Boys St; German Clb; Varsity Clb; JV Bsbl; JV Ftbl; Wt Lftg; Cit Awd; High Hon Roll; NHS; NYS Rgnts, D Nolan Outstndng SR Schlrshps 85; Ftbll Boostr Clb Awd 84; SUNY Brockport; Law Enfrcmnt.

VERINI, CHRISTINE; Cardinal Spellman HS; Bronx, NY; (Y); Pep Clb; Service Clb; Ski Clb; Nwsp Stf; Yrbk Phtg; Yrbk Stf; VP Sr Cls; VP Stu Cncl; Cheerleading; Hon Roll; Acadmc All Amer 85; Svc Awd 85; St Johns U; Phar.

VERKLEIR, KELLEY; Amsterdam HS; Amsterdam, NY; (Y); 1/319; Var Tennis; Var Twrlr; High Hon Roll; NHS; SUNY Plattsburgh; Envrnmntl.

VERMEIRE, JIM; Greece Athena HS; Rochester, NY; (Y); 25/258; JV Ftbl; Hon Roll; Rochester Inst Tech; Engrng.

VERMEULEN, KAREN A; Newark SR HS; Newark, NY; (Y); Church Yth Grp; FHA; Band; Chorus; Concert Band; Mrchg Band; Pep Band; Lit Mag; Hon Roll; Cert Comp Achvt 85; SUNY Morrisville; Bus Adm.

VERMEULEN JR, LEE C; Newfane SR HS; Newfane, NY; (Y); 15/167; Boy Scts; Math Clb; Band; Jazz Band; JV Ftbl; Mu Alp Tht; NHS; NYS Regents Schlrshp 85; U Buffalo; Pharm.

VERMILYEA, ANNA; Walton Central HS; Walton, NY; (Y); 2/100; Chorus; Church Choir; Concert Band; Mrchg Band; Orch; Variety Show; Yrbk Stf; High Hon Roll; NHS; Sal; Bst Sngr & All Arnd Muscn 85; Hghst Ave Grds 82-84; Hghst Ave Bio 83; Berklee Coll Music; Music Engr.

VERNA, MICHELE; West Irondequoit HS; Rochester, NY; (Y); 27/388; JA; Chorus; Madrigals; School Musical; School Play; Rptr Nwsp Rptr; Var Crs Cntry; Hon Roll; NHS; Prfct Atten Awd; NY ST; Psych.

VERNI, DENISE; West Babylon SR HS; W Babylon, NY; (Y); 2/420; Leo Clb; Varsity Clb; Concert Band; Mrchg Band; Yrbk Stf; Var Socr; High Hon Roll; Jr NHS; NHS; Engrng.

VERNI, SCOTT A; Mt St Michael Acad; Bronx, NY; (Y); 1/286; Stu Cncl; High Hon Roll; NHS; Spanish NHS; Val; Dr Cerrato Annual Schlrshp 82; Fordham U; Pre-Med.

VEROSTEK, JOHN; Bishop Ludden HS; Syracuse, NY; (Y); Math Tm; Quiz Bowl; Flag Corp; Nwsp Stf; Var Ftbl; Var Vllybl; High Hon Roll; Prfct Atten Awd; Regnts Schlrshp 85; RIT; Chem.

VERRELLI, GINA; Renss JR SR HS; Rensselaer, NY; (Y); Art Clb; 4-H; FBLA; Key Clb; Varsity Clb; Church Choir; School Play; Fld Hcky; Sftbl; Tennis; Hudson Vly; Data Procssng.

VERRENTI, CATHERIN M; Rome Catholic HS; Rome, NY; (Y); 7/81; Key Clb; Drm & Bgl; School Musical; Nwsp Rptr; Nwsp Stf; Yrbk Stf; Var JV Socr; Var L Trk; High Hon Roll; Jr NHS; Regents Schlrshp; Outstndg Achvt Awds Math,Sci & Scl Stds; Hartwick Coll; Engl.

VERRICO, JAMES A; Amherst Central HS; Amherst, NY; (Y); 23/311; German Clb; Latin Clb; Quiz Bowl; Pres Frsh Cls; Pres Sr Cls; Capt Swmmng; JV Vllybl; High Hon Roll; Hon Roll; NHS; Mark Molin Awd 83-84 & 84-85; U MI Alumni Schlr Awd 85; U MI; Law.

VERRIGNI, LORI; Guilderland HS; Schenectady, NY; (Y); Sec Key Clb; Trs Ski Clb; Sec Varsity Clb; Variety Show; Capt Cheerleading; Pom Pon; Psych.

VERSACE, OLGA; H Frank Carey HS; Franklin Sq, NY; (Y); 76/222; Cmnty Wkr; Pres Leo Clb; Cit Awd; Lion Awd; Pres Lions Awd 85; Volntry Wrk SR Ctzns Awd 85; Cert Of Merit 85; Psych.

VERSO, LAURA; Mc Mahon HS; Kenmore, NY; (Y); Latin Clb; Nwsp Phtg; Nwsp Rptr; Yrbk Ed-Chief; Yrbk Phtg; Yrbk Rptr; Yrbk Sprt Ed; Yrbk Stf; Pres Jr Cls; Rep Stu Cncl; Engl Awd Hghst Avg Thru Out Yr 83-85; Eurpn Cultrs Awd & Bio Awd Thru Out Yr 84; Crmnlgy.

VERSTRAETE, SANDY; Williamson Central HS; Williamson, NY; (Y); AFS; Camera Clb; Exploring; Concert Band; Mrchg Band; JV Socr; JV Trk; Var Vllybl; Fest Of Arts 3rd Pl Poetry & Hnrbl Mntn Poetry 83-84; Wide Horizons Prog 83-85; Photography.

VERTETIS, THOMAS; John A Coleman HS; Kingston, NY; (Y); Drama Clb; Key Clb; Letterman Clb; Ski Clb; Varsity Clb; Var L Bsbl; Var L Bsktbl; Var L Socr; High Hon Roll.

VERTINO, ANNETTE; Williamsville East HS; Williamsville, NY; (Y); Cmnty Wkr; Sec Drama Clb; GAA; School Musical; School Play; Sftbl; Vllybl; High Hon Roll; Hon Roll; Acpl Chr; Pedtrcs.

VERVLIED, JULIE; Newburgh Free Acad; Newburgh, NY; (Y); Band; Concert Band; Jazz Band; Mrchg Band; Orch; School Musical; Bsktbl; Stat Swmmng; Stat Trk; Hon Roll; Vis Arts Awd Mech Drwng 84-85; Dstngshd Svc Mus 84-85; Polices Benevolent Assoc Schlrshp Cmnty Svc 85; U Miami; Arch.

VESCIO, PAUL A; Nyack SR HS; Valley Cottage, NY; (Y); 20/281; Capt Math Tm; Mgr Stage Crew; Var L Golf; Im JV Socr; French Hon Soc; High Hon Roll; NHS; Spanish NHS; Drama Clb; Exploring; Pres Envirnmntl Yth Awd Outstndng Achvt Envirnmntl Protctn Svcs 83 & 85; Stu Exch Pgm Japan 84; Bio-Chem.

VESPUCCI, LISA; Archbishop Walsh HS; We Clarksville, NY; (Y); 5/66; Art Clb; GAA; Spanish Clb; Varsity Clb; Var Capt Bsktbl; JV Var Coach Actv; High Hon Roll; Jr NHS; NHS; Spanish NHS; Southern Tier Schlrshp 85; Deans Schlrshp 85; Moulton Schlrshp 85; Daemen Coll; Physcl Thrpy.

VETERE, DONNA; St Vincent Ferrer HS; Elmhurst, NY; (Y); 14/115; Library Aide; Nwsp Rptr; Nwsp Stf; Yrbk Stf; Rep Soph Cls; Hon Roll; NHS; Psych.

VETRANO, KRISTINE; St Joseph By The Sea HS; Staten Island, NY; (Y); Yrbk Stf; Score Keeper; Sftbl; Hon Roll; Rankind 2dn Gen Chem 84-85; Coll Of S I; Nrsng.

VETTER, ELIZABETH; Mahopac HS; Mahopac, NY; (Y); Church Yth Grp.

VETTER, SHARON J; North Rose Wolcott HS; North Rose, NY; (Y); 20/140; Sec Ski Clb; Yrbk Stf; Sec Sr Cls; Rep Stu Cncl; Swmmng; Tennis; High Hon Roll; Hon Roll; NHS; Ntl Merit Ltr; Schlrshp U Dallas 85; Sci Awd 84; Mst Imprvd Tnns Plyr 84; U Dallas; Politics.

VEXLER, DAVID P; Horace Greeley HS; Chappaqua, NY; (Y); 8/272; NFL; Jazz Band; Mrchg Band; Orch; Variety Show; Nwsp Ed-Chief; L Var Bsktbl; NHS; Ntl Merit Schol.

VICARY, MARY M; Leroy Central Schl; Stafford, NY; (Y); AFS; Spanish Clb; JV Sftbl; Stat Wrstlng; Hon Roll; NYS Regents Schlrshp 85; Suny Brockport.

VICECONTE, ROBERT; Central HS; Valley Stream, NY; (Y); 4-H; Mathletes; Lit Mag; Itlan Hnr Soc 84-85; Hofstra; Acctg.

VICENTE, BRIAN; Houppauge HS; Hauppauge, NY; (Y); JA; Service Clb; Band; Concert Band; Jazz Band; Mrchg Band; Pep Band; School Musical; Symp Band; High Hon Roll; Htl Adm.

VICKERS, DEBBIE; Eli Whitney V HS; Brooklyn, NY; (Y); Church Yth Grp; Library Aide; Office Aide; Band; Church Choir; Rep Jr Cls; JV Bowling; JV Cheerleading; Vllybl; NHS; Natl Hnr Soc 84-85; Attndnce Awds 84-85; St Johns U; Obstetrics.

VICTORIA, ELIZABETH A; Laguardia Middle College HS; Woodside, NY; (Y); Computer Clb; Dance Clb; Drama Clb; Hosp Aide; Sftbl; Hon Roll; Pedtrcn.

VIDA, PETER; Pulaski JR SR HS; Pulaski, NY; (Y); Chess Clb; Computer Clb; Yrbk Phtg; Sci.

VIDAL, JEROME; St Agnes HS; Woodside, NY; (Y); 5/110; Hon Roll; NHS; 1st & 2nd Hnrs; Htl Mgr.

VIDUCICH, ROBERT R; Smithtown HS East; Smithtown, NY; (Y); Debate Tm; Hosp Aide; Library Aide; Spanish Clb; Jr Cls; Sr Cls; Var Ftbl; Wt Lftg; High Hon Roll; NHS; Itln Hnr Soc 83; NY ST Ltr Of Awd 83; Notre Dame Schlr 85; U Of Notre Dame; Sci.

VIEIRA, TERESA; Corning Painted Post East HS; Corning, NY; (Y); 25/249; Varsity Clb; Cheerleading; Gym; Pom Pon; Swmmng; High Hon Roll; Hon Roll; NHS; Rep Frsh Cls; Rep Soph Cls; Mst Imprvd Swmmr 82; Mst Vlbl Teammt Gymnstcs 81; Balance Beam Rcrd 81; Brockport; Acctng.

VIEKOS, JOHN; High School Of Art & Design; New York, NY; (S); Computer Clb; Ski Clb; Rep Frsh Cls; Rep Soph Cls; Jr Cls; Stu Cncl; Hon Roll; Ntl Merit Ltr; Supr Yth 84; Arch.

VIENNEAU, JEAN; Sperry HS; Rochester, NY; (Y); Church Yth Grp; French Clb; French Hon Soc; Hon Roll; NHS; Sci.

VIENS, ROBERT J; Averill Park HS; W Sand Lk, NY; (Y); Art Clb; Pres Aud/Vis; Drama Clb; Chorus; School Musical; School Play; Nwsp Ed-Chief; Yrbk Phtg; JV Socr; NHS; Astrnmy.

VIERA, KATHLEEN M; Holy Trinity Diocesan HS; Bethpage, NY; (S); 22/303; Math Clb; Ski Clb; Variety Show; Yrbk Ed-Chief; Stu Cncl; Twrlr; High Hon Roll; NHS; C W Post Academic Awd 85; Molloy; Nrsng.

VIERHILE, JOSEPH; Naples Central Schl; Naples, NY; (Y); 8/83; Boy Scts; Band; Chorus; Nwsp Rptr; VP Soph Cls; Pres Stu Cncl; Var L Socr; Var Capt Swmmng; Var L Tennis; High Hon Roll; VFW Spch Wnnr 85; Gftd & Tlntd Pgm 81-85; U Notre Dame; Acctg.

VIEUX FORT, MICHELE; Northeastern Acad; Bronx, NY; (S); 1/45; Church Yth Grp; Chorus; VP Pres Stu Cncl; High Hon Roll; Hon Roll; Prfct Atten Awd; Val; Bio, Algbr I & Geog Awds 82-83; Chem & Amer Hstry Awds 83-84; Oakwood Coll; Bio.

VIEYRA, ROB; Union-Endicott HS; Endicott, NY; (Y); Spanish Clb; Var Ice Hcky; Engr.

VIGGIANO, CHRISTINE; Sacred Heart Acad; W Hempstead, NY; (S); 16/196; Church Yth Grp; Cmnty Wkr; Math Clb; Math Tm; Pep Clb; Crs Cntry; Hon Roll; NHS; Acctng.

VIGGIANO, PAUL; Auburn HS; Auburn, NY; (Y); 72/444; Debate Tm; Library Aide; Model UN; Ski Clb; School Play; Nwsp Ed-Chief; Rep Sr Cls; Stu Cncl; High Hon Roll; Hon Roll; Cayuga CC; Humanities.

VIGNAPIANO, JO ANN; Fonthonne Hall Acad; Brooklyn, NY; (Y); Dance Clb; Hosp Aide; Office Aide; Teachers Aide; Church Choir; Mrchg Band; Regents Nrs Schlrshp 85; Staten Isl Coll; Nrs.

VIGNOLA, LORI ANN; Walt Whitman HS; Huntington Sta, NY; (Y); 7/540; Spanish Clb; Mrchg Band; School Musical; School Play; Capt Cheerleading; Gym; High Hon Roll; Jr NHS; Spanish NHS; Office Aide; Bst Span Stud 83; Hnbl Mntn Engl Awd 83; Med.

VILARDI, GREGORY; East Meadow HS; East Meadow, NY; (S); Computer Clb; Library Aide; Mathletes; Chorus; Hon Roll; NHS; Ntl Merit Ltr; Math Tm; Egl Sct Awd 85; Rensaeler Polytechnic Awd For Scientfc Excllnc 85; Rensaeler Polytech Inst; Engrng.

VILARDO, KENNETH J; Niagara Wheatfield SR HS; Sanborn, NY; (Y); 128/315; Varsity Clb; L Bsbl; L Socr; Niagara County Comm Coll; Bus A.

VILARDO, TOM; Niagara Wheatfield HS; Sanborn, NY; (Y); Im Bowling; Im Fld Hcky; Hon Roll; Niagara Cnty CC; Accntnt.

VILATO, LISSETTE; Sacred Heart HS; Yonkers, NY; (Y); Hon Roll; Secy.

VILCHEZ, CAROLINE; The Mary Louis Acad; Flushing, NY; (Y); Library Aide; Office Aide; Service Clb; Teachers Aide; Orch; Sec Frsh Cls; Sec Jr Cls; Hon Roll; Iona Lang Cont 2nd Hnrs Spn Natve 85; Cert Achvt Soc Stud 83 & 84; Med.

VILETA, JOCELYN; Tappan Zee HS; Tappan, NY; (Y); Office Aide; Var Capt Cheerleading; Var Trk; ST U NY Stony Brook; Bio.

VILLA, PATRICIA; Clara Barton HS; Brooklyn, NY; (Y); Church Yth Grp; Girl Scts; Spanish Clb; Hon Roll; Med Off Asstng Awd 85; Spec Ed Tchr.

VILLACRES, CELIA M; Saunders Trade & Tech HS; Yonkers, NY; (Y); 46/198; VICA; JV Var Bsktbl; JV Var Sftbl; JV Var Vllybl; High Hon Roll; Hon Roll; Craftsmnshp Awd 85; Manhattan Coll; Elec Engrng.

VILLALBA, CARMEN; Gorton HS; Yonkers, NY; (Y); Spanish Clb; Band; Chorus; Lit Mag; Var Cheerleading; NHS; Vet Med.

VILLALBA, ELISEO; Cardinal Spellman HS; Bronx, NY; (Y); #5 In Class; Computer Clb; Bowling; Var Hon Roll; Engrng.

VILLALOBOS, JACKELINNE; St Edmund HS; Brooklyn, NY; (S); 15/190; French Clb; Hosp Aide; Var Cheerleading; High Hon Roll; Hon Roll; NHS; St Edmund Schlrshp 84-85; Prncpls & 1st Hnrs 83-84; Math Awd 84; Med.

VILLANTE, MICHAEL; Greene Central HS; Greene, NY; (Y); Boy Scts; French Clb; Varsity Clb; Chorus; Var JV Bsktbl; JV Bowling; Var JV Golf; Var Capt Socr; Capt Im Vllybl; Vrsty Glf Awd Mst Sprtsmnshp 85; Temple; Bio Mdcl Engrng.

VILLANUEVA, MARIE-CLAIRE; Kenmore East HS; Kenmore, NY; (Y); Hosp Aide; Intnl Clb; Pep Clb; Orch; Yrbk Stf; Trs Frsh Cls; Pres Stu Cncl; JV Var Tennis; Hon Roll; NHS; U Of Buffalo; Law.

VILLANUEVA, RICHARD J; Tappan Zee HS; Orangeburg, NY; (Y); Am Leg Boys St; Pres German Clb; Math Tm; Madrigals; Nwsp Stf; Stu Cncl; JV Tennis; Pres NHS; Rensselaer Polytech Inst Math & Sci Awd 85; Cornell Clb Mst Outstndng Jr 84-85.

VILLAREAL, JOYCE; Christ The King Reg HS; S Ozone Park, NY; (Y); Camera Clb; Tennis; Hon Roll; NY U.

VILLOTA, DORIS; Longwood HS; Coram, NY; (Y); 22/492; Stage Crew; Nwsp Ed-Chief; Pres Jr Cls; Stu Cncl; Cheerleading; High Hon Roll; NHS; Comms.

VILORIA, HIDA; St Francis Prep; Flushing, NY; (S); 121/693; Hosp Aide; Math Tm; Political Wkr; Speech Tm; Chorus; Var JV Cheerleading; Hon Roll; NHS; Opt Clb Awd; Columbia U; Law.

VINALS, ANTONIO; Garden City SR HS; Garden City, NY; (Y); 5/319; Computer Clb; Trs Math Clb; Lit Mag; Var Tennis; High Hon Roll; Jr NHS; NHS; Mathletes; Nwsp Rptr; Ntl Merit Ltr; Lang Dpt Awd Best Spnsh Stu 83; Black Belt Tae-Kwon-Do-Karate; Natl Hispanic Scholar 85; Columbia Univ; Pre-Med.

VINCENT, ALLEN; St Francis Prep; Whitestone, NY; (S); Computer Clb; Math Clb; Ski Clb.

VINCENT, BRYAN; Byron Bergen Central HS; Byron, NY; (Y); Pres French Clb; Nwsp Ed-Chief; Lit Mag; Sec Jr Cls; VP Sr Cls; Var Diving; Var Swmmng; Jr NHS; Trs NHS; Arch.

VINCENT, GRANT; Sweet Home SR HS; Williamsville, NY; (Y); JA; Model UN; Yrbk Phtg; Yrbk Sprt Ed; Sec Stu Cncl; Var Tennis; JV Trk; French Hon Soc; Hon Roll; NHS.

VINCENT, KELLY; Hornell SR HS; Hornell, NY; (Y); Aud/Vis; Hon Roll; Engl.

VINCENT, LAURA A; Notre Dame HS; Ilion, NY; (Y); 17/174; FBLA; Hosp Aide; ROTC; Chorus; Nwsp Rptr; Var L Vllybl; High Hon Roll; Hon Roll; NHS; NYS Rgnts Schlrshp 85; :Ind Engrng.

VINCENT, NORA; Jordan-Elbridge HS; Jordan, NY; (Y); 11/130; Ski Clb; Color Guard; Drill Tm; Flag Corp; Mrchg Band; Bowling; Tennis; CC Awd; Hon Roll; Jr NHS; CCBI Partial Schlrshp 85; Ccbi; Med Admin.

VINCENT, REBECCA; Albion HS; Albion, NY; (S); 27/161; Sec VP Church Yth Grp; Exploring; 4-H; Teachers Aide; Trs Band; Chorus; Church Choir; Concert Band; Mrchg Band; Swing Chorus; NY ST Rgnts Schlrshp 85-89; Niagara U Pres Schlrshp And Acad Schlrshp 85-89; Nirgara U; Nrsng.

VINCENT, VICKLYN M; Bishop Ford Central C HS; Brooklyn, NY; (Y); JA; Chorus; Yrbk Stf; Var Bsktbl; Var Sftbl; Capt Vllybl; Hon Roll; NHS; Schl Sprt Awd 85; Stony Brook U; Comp Sci.

VINCH, DANA; Cicero-North Syracuse HS; N Syracuse, NY; (S); 28/622; VP Exploring; Var Crs Cntry; Var Trk; Crss Cntry 500 Mile Clb Awd 83-84.

VINCI, BRIAN; Bishop Kearney HS; Rochester, NY; (Y); Varsity Clb; Stat Bsktbl; JV Var Ftbl; JV Var Lcrss; JV Mgr(s); Im Sftbl; High Hon Roll; NHS; Ntl Merit Ltr.

VINCI, ROBERT; Chaenango Valley HS; Binghamton, NY; (Y); Art Clb; Drama Clb; French Clb; School Play; Nwsp Rptr; Yrbk Bus Mgr; Yrbk Phtg; Socr; Jr NHS; Sec NHS; Pre-Med.

VINCZE, JUDITH M; St Francis Prep; Bayside Hills, NY; (Y); Girl Scts; Hosp Aide; Band; Chorus; Church Choir; Color Guard; Concert Band; Drm Mjr(t); Mrchg Band; Prfct Atten Awd; Regents Schlrshp 85; Hofstra U; Math.

VINE, LISA D; Falconer Central HS; Kennedy, NY; (Y); 7/134; Church Yth Grp; FHA; GAA; Teachers Aide; Varsity Clb; Sec Soph Cls; Var Capt Bsktbl; Sftbl; Var Capt Trk; Var Capt Vllybl; Track Recrd, Girls ST Fnlst 84-85; 1st Pl Cnty Long Jump 84-85; Med Recrds.

VINETTE, KERRI; Victor Central HS; Victor, NY; (Y); Science Clb; Ski Clb; Acpl Chr; Chorus; Stage Crew; Crs Cntry; Mgr(s); Timer; Trk; Hon Roll; Biochmstry.

VINSON, MONIQUE; Norman Thomas HS; New York, NY; (S); DECA; Drama Clb; Cit Awd; Ntl Merit Ltr; Mktg.

VINTON, PATTI; Solvay HS; Solvay, NY; (Y); Church Yth Grp; Cmnty Wkr; Exploring; Hosp Aide; Intnl Clb; JA; Key Clb; Library Aide; Political Wkr; Spanish Clb; Music Serv Awd 83-85; Serv Cmnty 83-85; Comp High Avrge 85; Liberty Bapt U; Bible Elem Educ.

VINUEZA, EDUARDO P; La Salle Acad; New York, NY; (Y); Church Yth Grp; Yrbk Stf; Hon Roll; NHS; Rep Sr Cls; Gold Medal Excllnce Engl 85; Ltr & Plaque Prayer Comm 84-85; Ltr Yrbk Artwork 85; St Johns U; Physcns Asst.

VIOLA, FRANK; Roosevelt HS; Yonkers, NY; (Y); Var Socr; Var Trk; Arch.

VIOLA, JEFFREY; La Salle Acad; Ridgewood, NY; (S); 35/237; Church Yth Grp; Math Clb; Im Bsktbl; Im Bowling; Im Ftbl; Vassar Coll; Bus Admin.

VIOLA, MARIA C; Poughkeepsie HS; Poughkeepsie, NY; (Y); Debate Tm; Latin Clb; Cit Awd; Cert Of Awd-Miss JR Contst 84; Patriotic Art Awd 85; FIT.

VIOLANDO, CHERYL; G Ray Bodley HS; Fulton, NY; (Y); 13/232; Latin Clb; Pep Clb; Science Clb; Spanish Clb; Cit Awd; High Hon Roll; NHS; Philip Morris Coll Scholar 85; NYS Regents Scholar 85; Pres Acad Fit Awd 85; ST U Oswego; Cmmnctns.

VIOLANTE, ANN MARIE; Greece Athena HS; Rochester, NY; (Y); DECA; FBLA; JA; Ski Clb; Yrbk Stf; Rep Frsh Cls; Rep Soph Cls; Rep Jr Cls; Sec Sr Cls; Hon Roll; Miss Monroe Cnty Teenagr Pagnt 84; Miss NY ST Teenagr Pagnt 85; Yrbk Wrkshp 85; Niagara U; Trvl Agnt.

VIPULIS, JOHN; Haldan Central HS; Cold Spring, NY; (S); 4/70; Ski Clb; Var Bsktbl; Var Ftbl; Vllybl; High Hon Roll; NHS; Prfct Atten Awd; Hnrbl Mntn Bsktbl 83-84; All League Ftbl 84-85; U Of MD; Engrng.

VIRELLA, ROBERT; Cardinal Hayes HS; Bronx, NY; (Y); 20/40; Church Yth Grp; JV Bsbl; JV Ftbl; High Hon Roll; Prfct Atten Awd; Vlntr Excep Chldrns Pgm; Stage Mgr; Hispanc Ldrshp Proj; Manhattan Col6; Mech Engr.

VIRGA, MATTHEW; Ward Melville HS; Setauket, NY; (Y); 241/760; Cmnty Wkr; Exploring; JV Ftbl; JV Lcrss; JV Wrstlng; 3 Vlg 4 Sprt Awd 82-83; U MA.

VIRGA, MICHAEL; Longwood HS; Coram, NY; (Y); Church Yth Grp; Church Choir; School Musical; CC Awd; Hon Roll; Awds Span, Eng & Soc Stu 82; Houghton Coll; Cmnctns.

VIRGINIA, ELIZABETH; Notre Dame Acad; Staten Island, NY; (Y); Pres Computer Clb; Hosp Aide; Math Clb; Math Tm; Science Clb; Spanish Clb; School Musical; Bsktbl; Swmmng; NHS; RCCC Swmmng Divng Tm Cptn 82; NDA Swim Tm Schlstc Achvtg Awd 83-85; Empire St Games 84-85; Med.

VIRGINIA, WATERS; Garden City HS; Garden City, NY; (Y); 98/355; Church Yth Grp; Band; Mrchg Band; Yrbk Stf; High Hon Roll; Hon Roll.

VIRGO, WANDA V; St Barnabas HS; Bronx, NY; (Y); 56/198; Cmnty Wkr; Hosp Aide; Office Aide; Nwsp Rptr; Nwsp Stf; Pres Stu Cncl; Bsktbl; Swmmng; Vllybl; Hon Roll; Lehman Coll; Nrsg.

VIRKLER, STEVE; Lowville Central Schl; Lowville, NY; (Y); Am Leg Boys St; Pres Pep Clb; VP Frsh Cls; VP Soph Cls; VP Jr Cls; VP Sr Cls; Stu Cncl; Bsbl; Bsktbl; Ftbl; All Star Tm Ftbl 84; Ed.

VIRTUOSO, CLAUDINE M; Niagara Catholic HS; Niagara Falls, NY; (Y); 5/76; French Clb; Key Clb; Red Cross Aide; Im JV Vllybl; High Hon Roll; Hon Roll; NHS; Regnts Schlrshp 85; SUNY Geneseo; Accntng.

VIRUET, SEAN; Cardinal Hayes HS; Bronx, NY; (Y); 20/269; Boys Clb Am; Cmnty Wkr; FCA; Letterman Clb; Band; Concert Band; Jazz Band; Mrchg Band; JV Bsbl; Var Capt Ftbl; Elect Engr.

VISCIANO, CAROLYN; Commack H S North; Commack, NY; (Y); Spanish Clb; Var Cheerleading; Hon Roll; Spnsh Tuter 84-85; Kickline 82; Bus.

VISCONTI, ROBERT; Little Falls JR SR HS; Little Falls, NY; (Y); Letterman Clb; Band; Mrchg Band; JV L Bsbl; Var L Bsktbl; Var L Ftbl; Var L Socr.

VISCONTI, SCOTT D; Archbishop Stepinac HS; Mamaroneck, NY; (Y); 6/206; Cmnty Wkr; Computer Clb; Radio Clb; Lit Mag; Bowling; NHS; Ntl Hnr Roll 84; Ciba-Geigy Sci Awd 85; Rgnts Schlrshp 85; Mnhtn Coll; Elec Engrng.

VISCOSI, JOHN F; Oriskany Central Schl; Oriskany, NY; (Y); Drama Clb; Band; Im Bowling; Im Vllybl; Hon Roll; NHS; Earth Sci Awd 84; NY ST Regents Schlrshp 85; Utica Coll; Geogrphy.

VISVALINGAM, NANDO; Stuyvesant HS; New York, NY; (Y); Chess Clb; Cmnty Wkr; Math Clb; Office Aide; Science Clb; Band; Ed Nwsp Stf; NHS; Slvr Cert Schlrshp 81-84; Med.

VITA, PETER; Lindenhurst SR HS; Lindenhurst, NY; (Y); 3/500; Chess Clb; French Clb; Math Tm; High Hon Roll; Hon Roll; NHS; Ntl Merit Ltr; Rnslr Awd For Math & Sci 85; Awd Forf High Avr In Frnch & Italian 84; Pre-Med.

VITACCO, JOSEPH; Midwood HS; Brooklyn, NY; (Y); Church Choir; Nwsp Phtg; Yrbk Phtg; Yrbk Sprt Ed; Yrbk Stf; Bio.

VITAGLIANO, ANNA; Cardinal Spellman HS; Bronx, NY; (Y); 20/600; Art Clb; Camera Clb; Church Yth Grp; French Clb; Library Aide; Service Clb; Church Choir; High Hon Roll; Hon Roll; Jr NHS; Fordham U; Lang.

VITAGLIANO, SAMANTHA A; Guilderland Central HS; Albany, NY; (Y); 8/385; Girl Scts; Math Tm; Orch; School Play; Var L Crs Cntry; High Hon Roll; NHS; Ntl Merit Ltr; UB Univ Hnrs Schlr, Pres Schlrshp 85; NY ST Regents Schlrshp 85; Cntntl Math League Awd 83; SUNY At Buffalo; Aero Engnrg.

VITALE, ERIC; Mount St Michael HS; Yonkers, NY; (Y); 12/309; Chess Clb; Church Yth Grp; Drama Clb; Sftbl; High Hon Roll; Hon Roll; NHS; Spanish NHS; Elec Engrng.

VITALE, JENNIFER A; St Marys Girls HS; Bellerose Village, NY; (Y); 11/165; Math Clb; Pep Clb; Rep Service Clb; Chorus; Stage Crew; Lit Mag; Coach Actv; High Hon Roll; Sec NHS; Teachers Aide; Natl Merit Sci Awd Biol 83; Chem Engrng.

VITALE, LUIGI; Franciscan HS; Peekskill, NY; (Y); School Play; Stage Crew; Stu Cncl; Pace U; Crmnl Just.

VITALE, WILLIAM; Oyster Bay HS; E Norwich, NY; (Y); Mathletes; Acpl Chr; Chorus; School Musical; Yrbk Stf; Bowling; Trk; High Hon Roll; NHS; Natl Hnr Socty 84-85; Comp Sci.

VITARBO, GREGORY M; North Rockland HS; Thiells, NY; (Y); Chrmn Am Leg Boys St; Pres Church Yth Grp; JV Var Ftbl; Var Wt Lftg; JV Var Wrstlng; High Hon Roll; NHS; Colby Book Prize 85; 2nd Hnrs Iona Coll Lang Cont 85; U VA; Hstry.

VITERE, CYNTHIA LYNN; Pelham Memorial HS; Pelham, NY; (Y); Aud/Vis; Political Wkr; Yrbk Stf; JV L Bsktbl; JV L Sftbl; JV Var Vllybl; Hon Roll; NHS; Hstry Pol Sci.

VITI, JAMES A; T R Proctor HS; Utica, NY; (Y); Boys Clb Am; Church Yth Grp; Elks Awd; Hon Roll; Prfct Atten Awd; Mohawk Vly Comm Coll; Accntng.

VITIELLO, LISA; W C Mepham HS; N Bellmore, NY; (Y); Church Yth Grp; 4-H; Yrbk Rptr; Yrbk Stf; Cheerleading; Sftbl; Tennis; 4-H Awd; Hon Roll; PTA Awd 85; St Johns U; Pre Law.

VITO, JAMES; Cardinal Mooney HS; Rochester, NY; (Y); Hon Roll; Natl Athl Plcmnt 85; All Str Bsbl Tm Organized Bsbl; Engrng.

VITOULIS, GREGORY; Germantown Central Schl; Elizaville, NY; (Y); 6/44; Chorus; Yrbk Rptr; Yrbk Stf; Pres Frsh Cls; High Hon Roll; Hon Roll; Ntl Merit Ltr; Voice Dem Awd; Jrnlsm.

VITRANO, LISA; Maryvale HS; Cheektowaga, NY; (Y); German Clb; Cosmtlgy.

VITRANO, VICTORIA; Sacred Heart Acad; Rockville Centre, NY; (S); 16/191; Hosp Aide; VP Intnl Clb; Math Tm; Nwsp Rptr; Yrbk Stf; Pres Soph Cls; Pres Jr Cls; Ntl Merit Ltr; Ntl Hnr Roll Yrbk 83-85; Schl Rep US Senate Yth Pgm 84; Hnrble Mention Catholic Heritage Essay Con 84; Dartmouth; Law.

VITTORIO, MELODIE; Liverpool HS; Liverpool, NY; (Y); Capt Band; Color Guard; Mrchg Band; Rep Stu Cncl; High Hon Roll; Hon Roll; NBTA Trophies 82-84; Modlng Trophies & Rbns 82-84; Co-Capt Awds 82-85; Le Moyne Coll; Comp Engr.

VITULLO, MARY; La Salle SR HS; Niagara Falls, NY; (S); 5/278; Girl Scts; Capt Quiz Bowl; Nwsp Ed-Chief; Yrbk Ed-Chief; Yrbk Sprt Ed; Pres Frsh Cls; Trs Stu Cncl; Hon Roll; NHS; Hnr Awd; Engr.

VIVENZIO, LAUREN; New Dorp HS; Staten Island, NY; (Y); Sec Key Clb; Service Clb; Teachers Aide; Chorus; School Musical; Ed Nwsp Rptr; Cheerleading; Hon Roll; Dly Nws Prncpls Pride Yankees Supr Yth Awd 84; Hnr Cert Excptnl Achvt Spnsh 83; Partcpt Close Up 83-84; Drama.

VIVIANI, PETER; Rome Free Acad; Rome, NY; (Y); Intnl Clb; Key Clb; Ski Clb; Var JV Lcrss; Hon Roll; Jr NHS; Arch.

VIVONA, ROBERT; Franklin D Roosevelt HS; Hyde Park, NY; (Y); 8/365; Band; Concert Band; Jazz Band; Mrchg Band; School Musical; Symp Band; Tennis; Hon Roll; NHS; NY ST Regents Schlrshp 85; Mech Engrng.

VLADYKA, SHARON A; Whitehall Central Schl; Whitehall, NY; (Y); 1/78; Trs Yrbk Stf; VP Jr Cls; VP Sr Cls; Var L Bsktbl; Var L Fld Hcky; Var L Sftbl; Var L Vllybl; Bausch & Lomb Sci Awd; Pres NHS; Val; JR Miss 1st Rnnr Up 84; RPI Awd 84; Regents Schlrshp 85; Russel Sage; Phy Thrpy.

VLANTIS, NICK; Bronx H S Of Science; New York, NY; (Y); L Boy Scts; Church Yth Grp; Cmnty Wkr; Hosp Aide; Church Choir; School Play; VP Sr Cls; Im Bsktbl; Im Ftbl; Im Socr; Volnteer Wrk Columbia Presb Hosp NCYC 120 Hrs 84; Fordham U; Pre-Med.

VLASTELICA, LISA A; Clarkstown North HS; Congers, NY; (Y); Hosp Aide; Ntl Merit SF; Biol Sci.

VO, NGA; Falconer Central HS; Flaconer, NY; (Y); Church Yth Grp; Drama Clb; Spanish Clb; Chorus; Drill Tm; Rep Stu Cncl; Tennis; Vllybl; GAA; Mrchg Band; Jamestown CC; Accntnt.

VOCE, DANIEL A; Whitesboro SR HS; Whitesboro, NY; (Y); 55/313; Ski Clb; Varsity Clb; Band; Concert Band; Jazz Band; Mrchg Band; Golf; Socr; NY ST Regents Scholar 85; Pres Acad Fitnss Awd 85; Potsdam Coll Arts/Sci; Comp Sci.

VOELKER, DIANE; Eastridge HS; Rochester, NY; (Y); 5/227; Trs FBLA; Math Clb; Band; High Hon Roll; Comp Pgrmnr.

VOELKER, JANINE MARIE; Niagara Wheatfield HS; Niagara Falls, NY; (Y); 47/315; Trs Church Yth Grp; Latin Clb; Band; Chorus; Church Choir; Concert Band; Mrchg Band; Pep Band; School Musical; Bsktbl; Area All ST Band; Susquehanna U; Music.

VOGEL, DEBORAH A; Stissing Mountain HS; Stanfordville, NY; (Y); 14/72; AFS; Varsity Clb; Yrbk Stf; Rep Jr Cls; Capt Fld Hcky; Hon Roll; NHS; Al-Star Fld Hocky Tm 85; SUNY Cortland; Bio.

VOGEL, LYNN; Kenmore East HS; Kenmore, NY; (Y); Pep Clb; Stage Crew; Var Fld Hcky; JV Trk; High Hon Roll; Church Yth Grp; Hgh Hnrs Spnsh Awds; Dietcs.

VOGEL, ROBYN; Spring Valley HS; Spring Valley, NY; (Y); 101/450; Cmnty Wkr; Key Clb; Temple Yth Grp; Thesps; Chorus; School Musical; Variety Show; Nwsp Stf; Yrbk Phtg; Yrbk Stf; Scholar Awd GPA; Bst Actrs Carousel; Chrs Awd; Oswego SUNY; Cmnctns.

VOGEL, RONALD; Clarkstown North HS; Congers, NY; (Y); VP French Clb; Math Tm; Scholastic Bowl; Stage Crew; High Hon Roll; Mu Alp Tht; NHS; 2nd Hnrs-Iona Coll Lang Comptn 84; 3rd Pl-St Thomas Acquinas Coll Chem Comptn 84.

VOGELMAN, CHRISTINE; Kenmore East SR HS; Tonawanda, NY; (Y); Church Yth Grp; Chrmn Pep Clb; Nwsp Rptr; Var Capt Cheerleading; High Hon Roll; Hon Roll; NHS; Human Rel Peer Tm 84-85; Chrch Acolyte 80-85; Psych.

VOGT, COLLEEN; Eastridge HS; Rochester, NY; (S); DECA; Elks Awd; DECA Food Mktng 3rd ST NY 85; DECA Natls 8th Food Mktng; Monroe CC; Crimnl Justc.

VOGT, SANDRA; Cicero-N Syracuse HS; Clay, NY; (S); 24/711; Church Yth Grp; Math Tm; Teachers Aide; Band; Concert Band; Mrchg Band; Hon Roll; NHS; Airlines.

VOHRA, AJAY; Middletown SR HS; Middletown, NY; (Y); Im Bsktbl; Im Fld Hcky; Im Swmmng; Acad Achvt Awd 84; Engrng.

VOLK, JOHN; St John The Baptist D HS; Massapequa, NY; (Y); 10/602; Boy Scts; Nwsp Stf; Lit Mag; Var Diving; Var Trk; Hon Roll; NHS; Spanish NHS; Pre-Med.

VOLKERT, CAROL D; Christian Central Acad; Tonawanda, NY; (S); Church Yth Grp; Drama Clb; Girl Scts; Service Clb; Chorus; Church Choir; School Musical; Nwsp Rptr; Yrbk Ed-Chief; Stu Cncl; Sci Fair 2nd Prz 84; Houghton.

VOLKMAN, PATRICIA L; Clymer Central HS; Findley Lk, NY; (Y); Office Aide; Teachers Aide; Chorus; Yrbk Stf; Trs Stu Cncl; Var Cheerleading; Var L Sftbl; Var Capt Vllybl; High Hon Roll; NHS; Phrmcy.

VOLLER, SANDRA L; Schroon Lake Central HS; Schroon Lake, NY; (S); VP French Clb; Varsity Clb; Chorus; School Musical; School Play; Sec Sr Cls; Capt Bsktbl; Capt Socr; Capt Sftbl; NHS; All-Star Team Trphy 85; Sprtsmshp Trphy 85; Stu Senate 84; St John Fisher; Comp Sci.

VOLLERTHUN, WILLY T; West Hempstead HS; West Hempstead, NY; (Y); 11/310; VP Chess Clb; German Clb; Quiz Bowl; Scholastic Bowl; Band; Mrchg Band; Variety Show; Lit Mag; Hon Roll; NHS; Hofstra U Frnscs Trnmnt-Persasv Spch 85; Stebn Gld Mdl Excllnc 4th Yr Grmn 85; Rgnts Schlrshp 85; NY U; Phlsphy.

VOLLERTSEN, JIM; E J Wilson HS; Rochester, NY; (Y); Rochester Inst Tech; Cinmtgrphy.

VOLLMER, DAVID L; Watkins Glen HS; Tyrone, NY; (Y); Letterman Clb; Pep Clb; Rep Frsh Cls; Var Capt Crs Cntry; Var Trk; Var Wrstlng; High Hon Roll; Hon Roll; American H S Athlete 84-85; Forestry.

VOLOSHEN, CHERYL; Susquehanna Valley HS; Conklin, NY; (Y); Chorus; Var Capt Cheerleading; Spanish NHS; Sci.

VOLPE, DENISE; Lindenhurst HS; Lindenhurst, NY; (Y); German Clb; Science Clb; Color Guard; Drill Tm; Mrchg Band; Yrbk Stf; Im Bowling; NHS; Bio.

VOLPE, JACKIE; Richburg Central HS; Richburg, NY; (S); Nwsp Rptr; Stu Cncl; Cheerleading; Score Keeper; Socr; Sftbl; Hon Roll; Jr NHS; NHS.

VOLZ, THOMAS; Liverpool HS; Liverpool, NY; (S); 201/792; ROTC; Var Bsbl; Ftbl; Hon Roll; Army.

VOMVOLAKIS, JOHN; Mount Vernon HS; Mount Vernon, NY; (Y); 35/650; Latin Clb; Math Tm; Bsbl; Capt Var Ftbl; Wt Lftg; Hon Roll; Jr NHS; Dentstry.

VON AHNEN, WILLIAM H; Delaware Valley Central HS; Callicoon, NY; (Y); Varsity Clb; Band; Pep Band; Capt Bsbl; Capt Bsktbl; NY ST Regents Schlrshp 85; Springfield Coll; Phy Ed.

VON BARGEN, LISA; Long Island Lutheran HS; Oyster Bay, NY; (S); 5/56; Church Yth Grp; Nwsp Sprt Ed; Var Capt Bsktbl; Var Capt Socr; Var Capt Sftbl; High Hon Roll; Hon Roll; NHS; Acad Rnk Grd Hghst 81-82; MVP Sftbl,Bkstbl,Sccr 84-85; Nassua-Sufolk All-Star Secr,Bsktbl 84-85; Valparaiso U.

VON GLAHN, STEFANIE V; Sachem HS; Holbrook, NY; (Y); 121/1300; Church Yth Grp; Cmnty Wkr; German Clb; Ski Clb; Orch; Yrbk Ed-Chief; Yrbk Phtg; Rep Stu Cncl; Hon Roll; NHS; NYSSMA Awd Viola Solo 83-85; Stonybrook; Chirprctr.

VON KESSEL, SUSAN; Bishop Ford Central Catholic HS; Brooklyn, NY; (Y); Computer Clb; Science Clb; Prsdntl Acad Ftnss Awd, Rgnts Schlrshps 85; Stony Brook; Pre Vet.

VON SEGGERN, KRISTEN; Bishop Grimes HS; Syracuse, NY; (Y); Cmnty Wkr; FBLA; Model UN; Political Wkr; Ski Clb; VP Band; Concert Band; School Musical; Yrbk Stf; Var Crs Cntry; Acad All Amer 85; Collegiate Windband Awd 85; All Star X-C Tm 84-85; Skidmore Coll; Bus Mgmt.

VONA, MICHELLE M; Homer SR HS; Cortland, NY; (Y); 3/203; Spanish Clb; Trs Nwsp Stf; Sec Bsktbl; Mgr Ftbl; Mgr(s); High Hon Roll; Kiwanis Awd; NHS; NYS Regnts Schlrshp 85; St Lawrence U; Arts.

VONORTAS, VIVIAN; Long Island City HS; Astoria, NY; (Y); 96/597; Church Yth Grp; Cmnty Wkr; Dance Clb; Political Wkr; Service Clb; Teachers Aide; Nwsp Rptr; Rep Sr Cls; Rep Stu Cncl; Cit Awd; St Johns U; Bus Adm.

VONSCHILLER, ERIKA; Clinton Central HS; Clinton, NY; (Y); Art Clb; Church Yth Grp; Political Wkr; Chorus; School Musical; Socr; Math Tchr.

VONSEE, DIANE I; Freeport HS; Freeport, NY; (Y); Badmtn; Socr; High Hon Roll; Hon Roll; Engr.

VOORHEES, SETH; Cato-Meridian HS; Cato, NY; (Y); Art Clb; Church Yth Grp; French Clb; Varsity Clb; Var Bsbl; JV Var Bsktbl; Im Var Ftbl.

VORCE, CYNTHIA; Whitesboro Central HS; Marcy, NY; (Y); Church Yth Grp; Orch; Powder Puff Ftbl; Vllybl; High Hon Roll; Highest Average In Bus Dept 84-85; SUNY At Oswego; Accntng.

VORCE, LINDA; Indian River Central Schl; Black River, NY; (Y); 15/126; Band; Concert Band; Jazz Band; Mrchg Band; School Play; Stage Crew; JV Var Sftbl; Var Tennis; High Hon Roll; Hon Roll; Hartwick Coll; Bio Chmstry.

VOSBURG III, JOHN F; Galamanca HS; Salamanca, NY; (S); 7/125; Am Leg Boys St; Pres Chess Clb; Thesps; Var Capt Swmmng; Bausch & Lomb Sci Awd; French Hon Soc; High Hon Roll; NHS; Spanish NHS; Drama Clb; Physics.

VOTRA, LISA; Parishville-Hopkinton Central HS; Potsdam, NY; (S); 2/50; Band; School Musical; School Play; Variety Show; High Hon Roll; Hon Roll; Secy.

VOUGIOUKAS, DEBBIE; Fort Hamilton HS; Brooklyn, NY; (Y); 20/553; Church Yth Grp; English Clb; FHA; FNA; Library Aide; Office Aide; Red Cross Aide; Spanish Clb; Teachers Aide; Chorus; Brooklyn Coll; Med.

VOUITSIS, OLYMPIA; Beach Channel HS; Rock Bch, NY; (Y); Office Aide; Vllybl; Hon Roll; Queens Coll Pres Awd For Achvmnt 82-83; Psych.

VOYIAS, LISA; Francis Lewis HS; Flushing, NY; (Y); 5/527; Church Yth Grp; Band; Church Choir; Orch; Yrbk Stf; Vllybl; French Hon Soc; Gov Hon Prg Awd; High Hon Roll; Hnr Awds Comp, Physcs, Math, Hstry, Ec, Frnch, Bio 82-84; Barnard Coll; Psych.

VOZENILEK, STEVEN E; Notre Dame HS; Elmira, NY; (Y); 33/128; Exploring; Math Clb; Science Clb; Concert Band; Var Tennis; High Hon Roll; NHS; Boy Scts; Pres JA; Symp Band; NY Regnts Schlrshp 85; Exec Awd JA 85; Corning CC; Bus Admin.

VRAHATIS, JENNIFER; Valley Stream Central HS; Valley Stream, NY; (Y); AFS; Dance Clb; Pres Service Clb; Drill Tm; School Musical; Variety Show; Trs Soph Cls; Psych.

VREELAND, MATTHEW; Charles H Roth HS; Rush, NY; (Y); 49/210; Cmnty Wkr; Drama Clb; Exploring; Ski Clb; Spanish Clb; Pres Thesps; School Musical; School Play; Stage Crew; Hon Roll; U Of Rochester; Bio.

VREJAN, SANDRA; Bethpage HS; Plainview, NY; (Y); 33/290; Drama Clb; French Clb; German Clb; Science Clb; Spanish Clb; Chorus; School Musical; High Hon Roll; NYSSMA Mdl Piano 84; Fulbright-Hayes Exch Stu Prog 84; Natl Soc St Amer Hist Cntst 85; Law.

VROMAN, JOHN; Gloversville HS; Gloversville, NY; (Y); Am Leg Boys St; Band; Pep Band; Symp Band; Var Im Bsktbl; Var Im Ftbl; High Hon Roll; Hon Roll.

VROMAN, LAURIE; Schoharie Central Schl; Schoharie, NY; (S); Key Clb; Sec Trs VICA; Band; JV Var Cheerleading; Tennis; Hon Roll; Exec Sec.

VROOMAN, MALIA; Amityville Memorial HS; Amityville, NY; (Y); 14/196; Art Clb; Church Yth Grp; Drama Clb; Girl Scts; Band; Concert Band; Mrchg Band; Orch; School Play; High Hon Roll.

VUKSIC, PAULA; St Catharine Acad; Clifton, NJ; (Y); 10/205; Service Clb; Teachers Aide; Rep Frsh Cls; Rep Soph Cls; Rep Jr Cls; Stu Cncl; Jr NHS; NCTE Awd; Acctnt.

VULCANO, MICHAEL; Frankfort-Schuyler Central HS; Frankfort, NY; (S); Drama Clb; Exploring; Spanish Clb; School Musical; Stage Crew; Rep Stu Cncl; Var JV Ftbl; Mgr(s); JV Trk; High Hon Roll; Pre-Med.

VUNK, MICHAEL P; Patchogue-Medford HS; Patchogue, NY; (Y); 53/750; Key Clb; School Musical; School Play; Stage Crew; Yrbk Phtg; Hon Roll; NHS; Prfct Atten Awd; NY ST Regents Schlrshp 85; Boston U; Brdcstng.

VUONG, THIEU; T R Proctor HS; Utica, NY; (Y); Yrbk Stf; High Hon Roll; Hon Roll; Prfct Atten Awd; Sci.

VURAL, MATTHEW; Jamesville-Dewitt HS; Dewitt, NY; (Y); 6/260; Ski Clb; Stage Crew; Nwsp Stf; Var L Crs Cntry; Var L Trk; High Hon Roll; NHS; Ntl Merit SF; Schlstc Awds Chem-Soc Studies & Bio 84; Honble Merit Plcmnt Natl French Comptn 84; Bio Chem.

VYSTUP, KIM; Depew HS; Depew, NY; (S); DECA; French Clb; GAA; School Musical; JV Tennis; JV Vllybl; Hon Roll; Bus.

WAASDORP, EMILY J; East HS; Rochester, NY; (Y); 13/267; Church Yth Grp; Model UN; Chrmn Ski Clb; Yrbk Phtg; Yrbk Stf; Var Socr; Hon Roll; Pres NHS; St Lawrence U; Bio.

WACCARD, CRISTENE; Liverpool HS; Liverpool, NY; (Y); Spanish Clb; Orch; School Musical; Symp Band; Var Crs Cntry; Var Trk; High Hon Roll; NHS; NYSSMA All ST Wind Ensmbl 84; Stu Advsry Comm 84-86; Sci.

WACHEN, MARK E; Great Neck South HS; Great Neck, NY; (Y); 6/218; Capt Math Tm; Nwsp Ed-Chief; Nwsp Rptr; Nwsp Stf; Stu Cncl; Ntl Merit Ltr; Foye Perry Awd Excel Math, H E Newman Awd Acad Excel, LI Cncl Achvt Awd Soc Stds, K Harris Lit Awd; Dartmouth Coll.

WADE, MARY E; F D Roosevelt HS; Hyde Park, NY; (Y); Pres Am Leg Aux Girls St; Church Yth Grp; Band; Concert Band; Sec Frsh Cls; Sec Soph Cls; Sec Jr Cls; Sec Sr Cls; JV Capt Bsktbl; Var L Sftbl; Area All ST Orch 83; Rotry Yth Ldrshp Conf Schlrshp 84; MVP Sftbl Tm 84; Psych.

WADE, MILLICENT; Aquinas HS; Bronx, NY; (Y); 27/131; School Play; Nwsp Stf; Cheerleading; Hon Roll; NEDT Awd; Natl Hnr Roll 83-85; Martin Luther King Jr Schlrshp 85; LIU CW Post; Bio.

WADE, NOEL RONALD; Frontier Central HS; Blasdell, NY; (Y); Varsity Clb; Rep Frsh Cls; Rep Jr Cls; Ftbl; Ice Hcky; Hon Roll; Vrsty Ftbl Co-Capt 85; Vrsty Hockey Capt 84-85; Bus.

WADE, OTIS; Clara Barton HS; New York, NY; (Y); Teachers Aide; Nwsp Rptr; Obstrcs.

WADE, PAUL; Mt St Michael Acad; Bronx, NY; (Y); 25/286; Church Yth Grp; Acpl Chr; Church Choir; JV Bsktbl; Ftbl; NHS; Spanish NHS; Rgnts Schlrshp 84-85; Northwestern U; Elec Engr.

WADE, RICHARD D; Irvington HS; Irvington, NY; (Y); Boy Scts; Church Yth Grp; Computer Clb; Band; Concert Band; Jazz Band; Mrchg Band; Capt Socr; Army; Helicopter Pilot.

WADHAMS, JENNIFER; Red Jacket Central HS; Shortsville, NY; (Y); 10/95; Science Clb; School Play; Yrbk Bus Mgr; Yrbk Stf; NHS; Pres Schlr; St Schlr; Girl Scts; Hosp Aide; Quiz Bowl; R J Cmnty Schlr 85; U Of Rchstr Almni Assoc Schlr 85; Roberts Wesleyan Coll; Bio Chem.

WADHAMS, VONDA; Albion HS; Albion, NY; (S); Church Yth Grp; Quiz Bowl; Spanish Clb; Teachers Aide; Band; Church Choir; Concert Band; Stat Bsktbl; Score Keeper; NHS; Engl.

WADKINS, TRACEY; St1ttgart American HS; Apo New York, NY; (Y); Hosp Aide; Office Aide; Ski Clb; Band; Concert Band; Drill Tm; Mrchg Band; Yrbk Stf; Pom Pon; Trk; European Trk Fnls 84; AAA Ramstein Fnls 85; European Munich Fnls 85; AZ ST UMA; Fash Dsgn.

WADSWORTH, JOAN; Northville Central Schl; Northville, NY; (Y); Am Leg Boys St; Am Leg Aux Girls St; Library Aide; Yrbk Sprt Ed; Yrbk Stf; Socr; High Hon Roll; Hon Roll; Jr NHS; NHS; Hnr Rll 84-85.

WAECHTER, ROB; Lakeland HS; Yorktown Hts, NY; (Y); JV Var Lcrss; Militry Sci.

WAGAMAN, SCOTT; Liverpool HS; Liverpool, NY; (S); 46/791; Exploring; Band; Concert Band; Jazz Band; Mrchg Band; Pep Band; School Musical; Hon Roll; Jr NHS; NHS; Engr.

WAGAR, MURENE; Gloversville HS; Gloversville, NY; (Y); 7/226; Teachers Aide; Band; Concert Band; Mrchg Band; Rep Jr Cls; Rep Sr Cls; High Hon Roll; Hon Roll; Prfct Atten Awd; William H St Thomas Sectrl Awd 85; Fulton Montgomery CC; Accntng.

WAGENER, DONNA; St Marys HS; Marilla, NY; (S); Church Yth Grp; Science Clb; Ski Clb; Varsity Clb; Rep Stu Cncl; Var Cheerleading; NHS; English Clb; Library Aide; Hmcmng Queens Attndnt 84; Most Imprvd Rnnr Trk 82; Geneseo Coll-NY; Spch Comm.

WAGER, SCOTT; Odessa-Montour Central Schl; Burdett, NY; (Y); Concert Band; Drm & Bgl; Jazz Band; Mgr Lit Mag; Ntl Merit Ltr; Band; Mrchg Band; Pep Band; High Hon Roll; Hon Roll; Jrnlsm.

WAGLER, JENNIFER; Spackenkill HS; Poughkeepsie, NY; (Y); Drama Clb; Thesps; Stage Crew; Nwsp Bus Mgr; NHS; Concert Band; Pep Band; Engrng.

WAGMAN, TRACEY; Wantagh HS; Wantagh, NY; (Y); Key Clb; Mathletes; Math Tm; Pres Spanish Clb; Temple Yth Grp; Nwsp Rptr; Yrbk Stf; Rep Frsh Cls; Rep Soph Cls; Rep Stu Cncl; Acctng.

WAGNER, ANNE R; Middletown HS; Middletown, NY; (Y); 30/396; Key Clb; Band; Symp Band; Nwsp Phtg; Nwsp Rptr; Yrbk Phtg; Vllybl; NY ST Regents Schlrshp 85; Acad Achvt Awd 85; U Of Rochester.

WAGNER, CHRISTINE; Auburn HS; Auburn, NY; (Y); Dance Clb; Varsity Clb; Nwsp Stf; Yrbk Ed-Chief; Lit Mag; Sec Soph Cls; Pres Jr Cls; Off Sr Cls; JV Socr; JV Sftbl; Phys Ed.

WAGNER, CHRISTINE; Mexico HS; Mexico, NY; (Y); Spanish Clb; Teachers Aide; Yrbk Ed-Chief; Yrbk Phtg; Yrbk Rptr; Yrbk Stf; Rep Stu Cncl; Cheerleading; High Hon Roll; Kauka Coll; Spch Thrpst.

WAGNER, CHRISTOP E; Edison Technical/Occupational Ctr; Rochester, NY; (Y); 16/271; Library Aide; Math Clb; Rep Soph Cls; NHS; Rotary Awd; Machinst Yr 82-83; U Buffalo; Mech Engrng.

WAGNER, ELIZABETH; Cardinal O Hara HS; Tonawanda, NY; (Y); GAA; Rep Jr Cls; Rep Sr Cls; Rep Stu Cncl; JV Badmtn; Var Capt Bsktbl; Bowling; Var Capt Sftbl; Var Vllybl; Hon Roll; Vllybl & Sftbl 2nd Tm All Catholic 83-84; Bsktbl SR All Star Tm 83-84; Sftbl-1st Tm All Catholc 84-85; Bryant & Strahor; Fashn Merch.

WAGNER, JOHANNA; Southampton HS; Southampton, NY; (Y); Chrmn VICA; Hon Roll; VFW Awd; Culinary Inst Amer; Clnry Arts.

WAGNER, JOHN; Cathedral Prep Seminary; Glendale, NY; (Y); 2/25; French Clb; NFL; School Play; Variety Show; Nwsp Stf; Lit Mag; Im Capt Ftbl; Im Capt Vllybl; High Hon Roll; NHS; Schlrshp 82-85; Frnch, Latn Lang Awds 83-84; NY U; Jrnlsm.

WAGNER, JOYCE; Lockport SR HS; Lockport, NY; (Y); 18/411; Girl Scts; JA; Nwsp Stf; Hon Roll; Jr NHS; NHS; AFS; Intnl Clb; Pep Clb; Undrgrdt Stdy; His.

WAGNER, KATY; Acad Of The Holy Names; Guilderland, NY; (Y); NFL; Church Choir; School Play; Nwsp Rptr; Rep Frsh Cls; VP Soph Cls; Pres Jr Cls; Pres Sr Cls; Holy Cross Bk Prz 85; Pre-Med.

WAGNER, KIM; Sacred Heart Acad; Williamsville, NY; (Y); Dance Clb; Red Cross Aide; Science Clb; Ski Clb; Spanish Clb.

WAGNER, KRISTIN; Glen Cove HS; Glen Cove, NY; (S); DECA; Pep Clb; Rep Stu Cncl; Vllybl; NHS; Computer Clb; Key Clb; Spanish Clb; Trk; Hon Roll; Gold DECA Merit Awd 85; Law.

WAGNER, LYNN; Remsen Central HS; Remsen, NY; (Y); 4-H; Sec Band; Concert Band; Jazz Band; Cheerleading; Socr; Trk; High Hon Roll; Hon Roll; Sec NHS; Mst Congnl Chrldr 84-85; Ctznshp In Englsh 84-85; Pol Sci.

WAGNER, MICHELLE; East Seneca HS; W Seneca, NY; (Y); DECA; Girl Scts; Pres JA; Trs Key Clb; Spanish Clb; Outstndng Serv Awd 85; Merit Awd Spnsh 82-84; RN.

WAGNER, SCOTT; Maryvale SR HS; Depew, NY; (Y); Office Aide; Spanish Clb; Nwsp Rptr; High Hon Roll; Hon Roll; Prfct Atten Awd; Karate Ornge Blt; SUNY-BUFFALO; Sci.

WAGNER, STEPHEN; Bishop Kearney HS; Henrietta, NY; (Y); JA; JV Var Ftbl; JV Var Trk; Hon Roll; Minor & Major Athltc Ltr; Bus.

WAGONER, BARBARA S; Schalmont SR HS; Schenectady, NY; (Y); Church Yth Grp; Sec Dance Clb; Trs 4-H; Concert Band; Flag Corp; Var Trk; High Hon Roll; Masonic Awd; Sec NHS.

WAGSTAFF, DEBRA; Bishop Loughlin Memorial HS; Brooklyn, NY; (S); Computer Clb; Nwsp Stf; Yrbk Stf; Baruch; Acctng.

WAHLSTEDT, DIANE; Huntington Christian HS; Glen Cove, NY; (S); 1/20; Office Aide; Teachers Aide; VP Varsity Clb; Chorus; VP Jr Cls; Var Capt Socr; Var L Sftbl; High Hon Roll; Hon Roll; NHS; Liberty Bapt Coll; Bible.

WAHRHEIT, ZACHARY; Smithtown High Schl East; St James, NY; (Y); Boy Scts; Hon Roll; SUNY Stony Brook; Engrng.

WAI, CYNTHIA; Brooklyn Technical HS; New York, NY; (Y); #5 In Class; Hosp Aide; Library Aide; Math Clb; Office Aide; Teachers Aide; Hon Roll; Chem Sci Span Hist Eng 84; French Matl Sci 83; Eng Amer Govt Physics 85; Albany Coll Pharm; Pharmacist.

WAIBEL, THOMAS; St Francis Prep; Bellerose, NY; (Y); 548/700; Aud/Vis; Computer Clb; Drama Clb; German Clb; Red Cross Aide; Science Clb; Service Clb; Band; School Musical; School Play; Stage Crew; Comp Sci.

WAINIO, LISA; Liverpool HS; Liverpool, NY; (S); 31/792; Cmnty Wkr; Ski Clb; Sec Sr Cls; Rep Stu Cncl; Var Cheerleading; Cit Awd; Hon Roll; Jr NHS; NHS; Opt Clb Awd; Optmst Club Awd Rep Todays Yth 84-85; Boston Coll; Psych.

WAITE, KATHLEEN; Comsewogue HS; Terryville, NY; (Y); 38/380; Dance Clb; Girl Scts; Ski Clb; High Hon Roll; Hon Roll; Ntl Comp Shclrshp Awd 84-85; Outstndng Freshmn Hm Ec 81-82; Outstndng Jr Graphic Arts 83-84; U Dallas; Pre-Law.

WAITE, TODD; Salamanca Central HS; Salamanca, NY; (Y); 10/135; Am Leg Boys St; Drama Clb; French Clb; Model UN; Thesps; Band; Chorus; Concert Band; Jazz Band; Mrchg Band; Cornell U; Pre-Law.

WAKEMAN, DAN; Oakfield-Alabama Central HS; Basom, NY; (Y); 1/77; Boy Scts; Church Yth Grp; Math Tm; Swing Chorus; Var Crs Cntry; Var Capt Trk; Bausch & Lomb Sci Awd; NHS; Val; Ithaca Coll; Comp Sci.

WAKEMAN, ROXANNE; Candor Central HS; Candor, NY; (Y); Powder Puff Ftbl; Var Sftbl; High Hon Roll; Sec NHS; Comp Sci.

WAKEMAN, STEPHEN; Lockport Senior HS; Lockport, NY; (Y); 15/411; Varsity Clb; Pres Band; Pep Band; Pres Frsh Cls; Pres Jr Cls; Pres Sr Cls; VP Stu Cncl; Var Bsbl; Var Capt Golf; Archt Engr.

WAKIE, LISA; Seaford HS; Seaford, NY; (Y); GAA; Varsity Clb; Nwsp Rptr; Nwsp Stf; Yrbk Stf; Sftbl; Tennis; High Hon Roll; Hon Roll; NY Inst Of Tech; Communctns.

WALAG, KATHY E; Brewster HS; Patterson, NY; (Y); Church Yth Grp; Varsity Clb; VP Frsh Cls; Rep Stu Cncl; JV Bsktbl; JV Var Fld Hcky; Var Sftbl; Var JV Trk; Hon Roll; NHS; Schlrshp Hnr Phy Ed 84-85; Schlrshp Achv Sculptr 84-85; Awd Mert Math II 83-84; Art.

WALCZYK, DAVID; Mohonasen SR HS; Schenectady, NY; (Y); Church Yth Grp; Key Clb; Band; Concert Band; Mrchg Band; Yrbk Rptr; Yrbk Stf; Socr; Prgmr 84 Natl Mock Electn 84; Comp Sci.

WALCZYK, MARK; Bishop Ludden HS; Syracuse, NY; (S); Boys Clb Am; Boy Scts; Exploring; Math Tm; Ski Clb; Ftbl; DAR Awd; High Hon Roll; Hon Roll; NHS.

WALD, DINA J; Yeshiva University H S Girls; New York, NY; (Y); Cmnty Wkr; Temple Yth Grp; School Musical; School Play; Nwsp Stf; Stu Cncl; Coach Actv; Capt Vllybl; Navy; Pilot.

WALDBAUM, BRIAN; Ward Melville HS; Centereach, NY; (Y); Chess Clb; French Clb; Mathletes; School Musical; Rep Frsh Cls; Rep Stu Cncl; High Hon Roll; NHS; Val; Bsbl; Frnch Natl Comp Lvl II,IV 82-84; LI Lang Fair Orgnl Essy Cat 83; Trustees,Engl,Sci,Latn,Frnch,Math; SUNY Binghamton; Life Sci.

WALDER, KAREN A; Wilosn Central HS; Newfane, NY; (Y); 4/134; 4-H; Band; Yrbk Stf; Var L Crs Cntry; JV Sftbl; High Hon Roll; NHS; Ntl Merit Ltr; Science Clb; Im Powder Puff Ftbl; Outstndng Niagara Cnty Legstltv Intrn 84; NY ST Regnts Schlrshp 85; Cornell U; Mech Engrng.

WALDMAN, BENJAMIN; Plainview-Old Bethpage HS; Plainview, NY; (Y); 1/194; Capt Math Tm; Pres Model UN; VP Thesps; Acpl Chr; Ed Lit Mag; Trs Sr Cls; Ntl Merit Schol; Val; Computer Clb; Pres Debate Tm; Westinghse Sci Talnt Srch 85; Hnrs Grp; Sci Humanties Symp 85; Tech Awd 85; Harvard U; Physics.

WALDMAN, DAVID; East Islip HS; Islip Terrace, NY; (Y); Teachers Aide; School Musical; Nwsp Rptr; Rep Jr Cls; JV Socr; High Hon Roll; Jr NHS; Prfct Atten Awd; Service Clb; Acpl Chr; 1st Pl Rbbn Bio 85; Bsktbl 84; 3rd Pl Bio Proj 83; Engrng.

WALDMAN, OWEN; Clarkstown North HS; West Nyack, NY; (Y); Spanish Clb; JV Var Bsktbl; Wt Lftg; Bus Adm.

WALDMAN, ROBERT; East Islip SR HS; Islip Terrace, NY; (Y); Math Tm; Concert Band; School Musical; Socr; Hon Roll; Jr NHS; Prfct Atten Awd; Service Clb; Band; Jazz Band; Bst Mer Hstry Stu 84-85; Nrb Mntn-LI Math Fair Fnls 84-85; Presdngl Phy Ftns Awd 85; US Air Force Acad; Pilot.

WALDMAN, RUTH D; La Guardia HS For Music & The Arts; New York, NY; (Y); 36/600; Dance Clb; PAVAS; Y-Teens; Ed Lit Mag; Hon Roll; Hon Roll; St Schlr; Art Hist.

WALDMANN, JOHN; Glens Falls HS; Glens Falls, NY; (Y); Math Tm; Var L Tennis; Hon Roll; NHS; NY St Regent Schlrshp 85; Clarkson U; Math.

WALDMILLER, BRIAN; Aquinas Inst; Rochester, NY; (S); 4/161; Drama Clb; Church Choir; School Musical; School Play; Stage Crew; Nwsp Stf; High Hon Roll; Ntl Merit SF; Biol Achvmnt Awd 83; Natl Sci Merit Awd Chem 85; Rochester Inst Of Tech; Physics.

WALDMILLER, THOMAS; Churchville Chili SR HS; Rochester, NY; (Y); School Musical; Yrbk Stf; Stu Cncl; High Hon Roll; Fthr Gieger Schlrshp Awd 82; Prfct Attndnce Awd 84.

WALDRON, BONNIE; Saranac Central HS; Saranac, NY; (S); 10/129; Library Aide; High Hon Roll; Trs NHS; Ntl Nonor Roll; Plattsburgh ST U; Com Sci.

WALDRON, ROBERT G; Columbia HS; E Greenbush, NY; (Y); 71/353; Cmnty Wkr; High Hon Roll; Hon Roll; NHS; Ntl Hnr Roll 85; Schenectady CC; Clnry Arts.

WALDRON, VALERIE E; Moriah Central HS; Port Henry, NY; (Y); 12/77; GAA; Trs Sr Cls; Capt Cheerleading; Capt Sftbl; High Hon Roll; Regnts Schlrshp 85; Hudson Vlly CC; Radlgy.

WALES, SHERRY; Twin Tiers Baptist HS; Millerton, PA; (S); 5/23; Chorus; School Play; Stage Crew; High Hon Roll; NHS; Trs Frsh Cls; Trs Jr Cls; Trs Sr Cls; Var Capt Bsktbl; Var Socr; Bsktbl Mst Insprtnal 84, Most Imprvd 81-82; Fash Merch.

WALKER, ANGELA MICHELLE; Hutchinson-Central Technical HS; Buffalo, NY; (Y); Church Yth Grp; JA; Library Aide; Natl Beta Clb; Church Choir; Nwsp Rptr; Nwsp Stf; Bowling; DAR Awd; Rochester Inst Of Tech; Comp.

WALKER, ANTHONY; John Adams HS; New York, NY; (Y); Boy Scts; Church Yth Grp; CAP; Band; US Marines.

WALKER, ANTHONY B; Cardinal Hayes HS; New York, NY; (Y); Church Yth Grp; English Clb; Church Choir; Crs Cntry; Trk; NY ST Regents Nrsng Schlrshp 85; Bethany Baptist Mrt Schlrsp 85; Southeastern U; Bus Admin.

WALKER, BLONDELL; Walton HS; Bronx, NY; (Y); Chorus; Nwsp Phtg; Nwsp Rptr; Tennis; Prfct Atten Awd.

WALKER, CASSANDRA; The Franciscan Acad; Syracuse, NY; (S); 15/24; Chorus; Yrbk Stf; Hon Roll; Doctor.

WALKER, CHARLES E; Lewiston - Porter Central Schl; Lewiston, NY; (Y); 1/273; Boy Scts; Co-Capt Var Crs Cntry; Var Trk; NHS; Ntl Merit Ltr; VA Tech; Engrng.

WALKER, DEBORAH; Westport Central HS; Westport, NY; (Y); 3/22; Trs Church Yth Grp; Drama Clb; Ski Clb; Yrbk Ed-Chief; Sec Frsh Cls; VP Jr Cls; JV Var Cheerleading; JV Var Socr; JV Var Sftbl; NHS; Upward Bound Stu SUNY Plattsburgh 83-85; St Lawrence; Math.

WALKER, DEIDRE; The Franciscan Acad; Syracuse, NY; (S); 5/26; FBLA; GAA; Yrbk Stf; Vllybl; Hon Roll; Jr NHS; NHS; Algebra-Math 9 82-83; Spanish III 83-84; Latin II 83-84; Math.

WALKER, DENNIS; Newfield HS; Newfield, NY; (Y); 10/50; Am Leg Boys St; Varsity Clb; Band; Jazz Band; Var Capt Bsktbl; Var Ftbl; Var Trk; Hon Roll; Masonic Awd; MVP Awd Bsktbl 84-85; Trvl.

WALKER, ERRICA; Mc Kinley HS; Buffalo, NY; (Y); Church Yth Grp; FCA; Hosp Aide; Acpl Chr; Church Choir; Variety Show; Trs Jr Cls; Capt Cheerleading; Hon Roll; Pep Clb; Ms Nrthestrn Yth Conf Newark NJ 83-84; Ms Lynwd Chrch Chrst Pgnt Bflo NY 82-83; Pri-Elem Ed.

WALKER, GAYLE; Union-Endicott HS; Endicott, NY; (Y); Cmnty Wkr; Hosp Aide; Key Clb; Rep Stu Cncl; JV Bowling; Var Score Keeper; Stat Sftbl; Hon Roll; Law.

WALKER, JANICE; Ellenville Central Schl; Ellenville, NY; (Y); Church Yth Grp; FHA; Var Cheerleading; JV Score Keeper; Ftbl Chrldng Most Enthustc 83; St Johns U; Bus Admin.

WALKER, JILL; Mexico Acad And Central; Mexico, NY; (Y); German Clb; Chorus; Church Choir; Madrigals; School Musical; Swing Chorus; Hon Roll; NHS; Grmn Ntl Hnr Soc 84-86; Pre Law.

WALKER, JOAN; Smithtown West HS; Smithtown, NY; (Y); Cmnty Wkr; Drama Clb; Hosp Aide; MMM; Thesps; Chorus; School Play; Yrbk Stf; Hon Roll; Ntl Merit SF; Hon Awd Vlntrng Serv Nrsng Hme 85; St Johns U; Bus.

WALKER, KEITH; Archbishop Stepinac HS; Yonkers, NY; (Y); 55/201; Boy Scts; 4-H; Im Bsktbl; JV L Ftbl; JV L Trk; Hon Roll; Bus.

WALKER, KEITH; Pineview Christian Acad; Schenectady, NY; (Y); 2/9; Variety Show; Yrbk Sprt Ed; Jr Cls; VP Stu Cncl; Var Capt Bsktbl; Var Capt Socr; Cit Awd; Sal; Hstry; Engl; Math; Hartwick Coll; Bus Mgt.

WALKER, KIERSTEN; Sodus Central HS; Sodus, NY; (Y); Sec AFS; VP Varsity Clb; Rep Soph Cls; Rep Jr Cls; Var Bsktbl; Var Socr; Var Trk; Var Vllybl; NHS; Yale; Pediatritian.

WALKER, LISA C; Williamsville East HS; East Amherst, NY; (Y); 59/300; Church Yth Grp; Teachers Aide; Chorus; Yrbk Phtg; Rep Church Yth Grp; Rep Jr Cls; Var Capt Swmmng; Var Trk; High Hon Roll; Syraucse U; Law.

WALKER, LLOYD; Bronx High School Of Science; Jamaica, NY; (Y); Boys Clb Am; Office Aide; Chorus; Yrbk Phtg; Rep Frsh Cls; Rep Soph Cls; Rep Jr Cls; Rep Sr Cls; Capt Var Gym; Outstndng Achvt Gymnstcs 85; Manhattan Coll Mdl 85; Julie Beckenstein Hlth Promotn Awd 85; Wesleyan U; Med.

WALKER, MARYBETH; Ossing HS; Ossining, NY; (Y); Dance Clb; Drama Clb; Spanish Clb; Acpl Chr; Chorus; Church Choir; High Hon Roll; Hon Roll; Spanish NHS; Music.

WALKER, MELISSA; Tioga Central HS; Barton, NY; (S); 12/96; Church Yth Grp; Latin Clb; High Hon Roll; Hon Roll; NHS; Comp Sci.

WALKER, NANCY; Smithtown H S East; Smithtown, NY; (Y); Hosp Aide; Spanish Clb; Varsity Clb; Mrchg Band; Bsktbl; Fld Hcky; Capt Vllybl; Hon Roll; Spanish NHS.

WALKER, RENEE A; Malverne HS; West Hempstead, NY; (Y); Church Yth Grp; Varsity Clb; Variety Show; Bsktbl; Trk; Vllybl; God Cntry Awd; Jr NHS; Prfct Atten Awd; All County Vllybl 84-85; Dowling Coll; Bus Admin.

WALKER, ROBERT; Remsen Central HS; Remsen, NY; (Y); FFA; Score Keeper; Socr; Military Schl; Electrncs.

WALKER, SALLY; Franklin Acad; Malone, NY; (Y); Epsilon 83-85.

WALKER, SANDY; Clarkstown North HS; New City, NY; (Y); Computer Clb; FBLA; Spanish Clb; Teachers Aide; Temple Yth Grp; Rep Jr Cls; Pres Stu Cncl; Var L Bsktbl; Coach Actv; Jr NHS; Comp Sci.

WALKER, SHEILA; Victory Central Schl; Victor, NY; (Y); French Clb; GAA; Varsity Clb; Rep Stu Cncl; JV Var Bsktbl; JV Var Socr; Var Swmmng; JV Vllybl; Hon Roll; V Ltr 83; Sectn V Swmmng Champ 82-84; Perdu U; Bus Mgmt.

WALKER, STEPHEN; Mcquaid Jesuit HS; Rochester, NY; (Y); 27/190; Church Yth Grp; Computer Clb; German Clb; JA; School Musical; Yrbk Stf; Hon Roll; Ntl Merit Ltr; Medicine.

WALKER, STEVEN; Cooperstown Central HS; Fly Creek, NY; (Y); 17/100; Concert Band; Mrchg Band; JV L Bsbl; Var L Ftbl; Var Golf; Hon Roll; Pres NHS; Rotary Yth Ldrshp Camp Nom 85; 2nd Prize Schls Sci Fair Cntst 85; Math.

WALKER, TYRONE; The Lenox Schl; New York, NY; (Y); Nwsp Rptr; Yrbk Stf; Var Im Bsktbl; Im Vllybl; 1st Graduating Class Of Prep For Prep Educational Organization 84; Sci.

WALKER, VALERIE; Washington Irving HS; New York, NY; (Y); FHA; Hosp Aide; JA; Science Clb; Chorus; Bio.

WALKER, WILLIAM; Amityville Memorial HS; Amityville, NY; (Y); 25/255; Am Leg Boys St; Pres Church Yth Grp; Varsity Clb; VP Church Choir; Rep Frsh Cls; Pres Soph Cls; Rep Stu Cncl; Capt JV Bsktbl; Capt Var Crs Cntry; NHS; Med.

WALKER, WILLIE; Riverhead HS; Riverhead, NY; (Y); Ftbl; Ice Hcky; Mgr(s); Wt Lftg; Wrstlng; Hon Roll; Prfct Atten Awd; Mst Pts Scored Wrstlng Tm 82-83; Mst Imprvd Wrstlr Mst Pts 83-84; Mst Pts & Mst Pins 84-85.

WALKER, WONATHAN; Mt Vernon HS; Mount Vernon, NY; (Y); Computer Clb; FBLA; Key Clb; Science Clb; Spanish Clb; JV Var Ftbl; Hon Roll; Prfct Atten Awd; High Hnr Roll; Capt IV Ftbl; Tri Capt Vrsty Ftbl Amer Eductl Asst Cncl; Syracuse U; Elec Engnrng.

WALL, DEIRDRE K; St Joseph Acad; Smithtown, NY; (Y); Church Yth Grp; Cmnty Wkr; Hosp Aide; Math Tm; Service Clb; Teachers Aide; Church Choir; Variety Show; Yrbk Ed-Chief; Sec NHS; Holy Cross Bk Awd 83-84; Outstndng Span Stu 81-82; Outstndng Effort Awd Math 83-84; Mount St Marys Coll; Bus.

WALL, KENNETH; Brooklyn Acad Prep; Brooklyn, NY; (Y); Boys Clb Am; Boy Scts; ROTC; Band; Mrchg Band; Var JV Bsktbl; Im Bowling; Im Coach Actv; Im Ftbl; Im Sftbl; Schl Scholar 82; Comp.

WALL, KIMBERLY; Massena Central HS; Massena, NY; (Y); Church Yth Grp; French Clb; Intnl Clb; Varsity Clb; Band; Church Choir; Stu Cncl; JV Cheerleading; JV Mgr(s); JV Score Keeper; Law.

WALL, MARY GRACE; Fox Lane HS; Bedford, NY; (Y); 36/280; Intnl Clb; Pres Pep Clb; Ski Clb; Rep Jr Cls; JV Var Bsktbl; Var Capt Fld Hcky; Var Capt Lcrss; Capt Powder Puff Ftbl; Hon Roll; Church Yth Grp; Reilly Awd Outstndng Ath; Bus.

WALL, STEPHANIE; Bishop Kearney HS; Brooklyn, NY; (S); 70/360; Church Yth Grp; FCA; Var L Bsktbl; High Hon Roll; NHS; St Schlr; Univ Schlrshp To NYU 85; Athlt Schlrshp To NYU 85; Regents Dilpoma With Hnrs 85; NY U; Nrsng.

WALLACE, ANDREW; West Irondequoit HS; Rochester, NY; (Y); #22 In Class; Latin Clb; Band; Jazz Band; Orch; School Musical; Variety Show; Bsbl; Hon Roll; NHS; Law.

WALLACE, BRENDA A; Lake Shore Central SR HS; Angola, NY; (Y); Drama Clb; Pres Rptr 4-H; JA; Stage Crew; 4-H Awd; Hon Roll; Nrsng.

WALLACE, CAROL; Whitesboro SR HS; Yorkville, NY; (Y); Hosp Aide; Acpl Chr; Pres Chorus; Orch; Yrbk Stf; Rep Stu Cncl; High Hon Roll; Pres Jr NHS; NHS; Drama Clb; Frgn Exch Stu To Frnc 85-86; All-State Orchestra; Coll.

WALLACE, DONALD; Indian River C S HS; Calcium, NY; (Y); 17/126; Boy Scts; Church Yth Grp; Latin Clb; Stu Cncl; JV Wrstlng; Elmira Key Awd 85; Natl Educ Dvlpmnt Test Cert 83; Mbr Order Arrow; Bus.

WALLACE, HELEN; John A Coleman HS; Hurley, NY; (Y); 4-H; Girl Scts; Ski Clb; JV Fld Hcky; Var Sftbl; 1st Hnrs Alg, 2nd Engl 83; 1st Hrns Lat, Kybrdng , Bus Comm, Alg II, Rlgn 84.

WALLACE, JAMES; Saint Marys Boys HS; Westbury, NY; (Y); 49/130; Church Yth Grp; Varsity Clb; Church Choir; School Musical; School Play; JV Diving; JV Lcrss; JV Swmmng; Var Trk; Hon Roll; Vrsty Handball Capt 84-85; SUNY-OLD Westbury; Corp Law.

WALLACE, JULIE; Spackenkill HS; Poughkeepsie, NY; (Y); School Musical; Variety Show; Yrbk Stf; Sec Soph Cls; Sec Jr Cls; Var Bsktbl; JV Var Cheerleading; Stat Socr; Var Sftbl; All Cnty Hnrb Mntn Sftbl 85; Scl Sci.

WALLACE, KIMBERLY; Cicero-North Syracuse HS; Bridgeport, NY; (S); 43/711; Capt Bowling; Hon Roll; NHS; Distgwshd Amer Hgh Schl Stu 82-84; U Of Buffalo; Engrng.

WALLACE, LISA; Clara Barton HS; Brooklyn, NY; (Y); Hosp Aide; Teachers Aide; Chorus; Swing Chorus; Vllybl; Hon Roll; Pre-Med.

WALLACE, LORIE; Camden Central HS; N Bay, NY; (Y); Church Yth Grp; Hosp Aide; High Hon Roll; Hon Roll; Hlth.

WALLACE, ROBERT; Dewitt Clinton HS, Bronx, NY; (Y); Debate Tm; Teachers Aide; Trk; Prfct Atten Awd; Acctng.

WALLACE, SANDRA; Westbury HS; Westbury, NY; (Y); Art Clb; FHA; GAA; Varsity Clb; Bsktbl; Mgr(s); Sftbl; Trk; Vllybl; Hon Roll; Hlgh Phys Educ.

WALLACE, SANDY; G Ray Bodley HS; Fulton, NY; (Y); 15/257; Variety Show; Pres Frsh Cls; Pres Soph Cls; Pres Jr Cls; Pres Sr Cls; Var Capt Bsktbl; Var Capt Socr; Var Capt Sftbl; Cit Awd; High Hon Roll; Womans Club & Polish Home Schlrshp 85; Most Outstndg Sr Athl 85; MVP Sccr 82-84; Achvt Bsktbl & Sftbl; Herkimer CC; Trvl.

WALLER, BRIAN; Lakeland HS; Yorktown Hts, NY; (Y); Cmnty Wkr; Debate Tm; NFL; Temple Yth Grp; Rep Jr Cls; VP Sr Cls; High Hon Roll; NHS; Debt Chmpnshp 84-85; Natl Debt Trnmnt 85; SUNY Binghamton.

WALLESHANSER, KENNETH; Maryvale SR HS; Cheektowaga, NY; (Y); JV Var Socr; Hon Roll; Damean Coll; Pre-Law.

WALLS, EILEEN; Bishop Ford Central Catholic HS; Brooklyn, NY; (Y); Cmnty Wkr; Science Clb; Service Clb; Pres Sr Cls; High Hon Roll; Hon Roll; Spec Educ.

WALRATH, TIMOTHY; Indian River Central HS; Oxbow, NY; (Y); Am Leg Boys St; Computer Clb; 4-H; Key Clb; School Play; Pres Soph Cls; Stu Cncl; Crs Cntry; Wt Lftg; Wrstlng; Ntl HS Math Cntst 85; Delhi U; Comp Drftsmn.

WALROD, RENEE F; T R Proctor HS; Utica, NY; (Y); Dance Clb; Pep Clb; Spanish Clb; Yrbk Stf; Stu Cncl; Var Cheerleading; Math.

WALSH, ANDREA; John Jay HS; Hpwl Junc, NY; (S); Sec DECA; Nwsp Rptr; JV Var Fld Hcky; Var Swmmng; Dancing Jazz Ballet 81-85; E Fishkill Grls Sftbl Leag 80-85; Fash Sales Cnsltnt 85; Red Cross Lifeguard; Glassboro ST Coll; Pol Sci.

WALSH, ANDREW; Central Islip HS; Central Islip, NY; (Y); 12/391; Aud/Vis; Computer Clb; Intnl Clb; Math Clb; Spanish Clb; Yrbk Rptr; Yrbk Stf; Lit Mag; Tennis; Hon Roll; NEDT Biograph Stry Outstndng Acadmc Engl 85; AMA Awd Outstndng Devotion Yrbk 84-85; SUNY; Bus.

WALSH, BRENDEN; Eastchester HS; Eastchester, NY; (Y); Teachers Aide; Jazz Band; Mrchg Band; JV Var Bsbl; JV Var Bsktbl; JV Var Ftbl; Cit Awd; NHS; Prfct Atten Awd; Ftbl & Bsktbl-Hnrb Mntn-All Leag; Bsbl-All Leag.

WALSH, CATHLEEN M; Whitesboro SR HS; Whitesboro, NY; (Y); 1/330; GAA; School Musical; Yrbk Ed-Chief; Capt Powder Puff Ftbl; Capt Tennis; Trk; High Hon Roll; Jr NHS; Sec NHS; Opt Clb Awd; Gannett Nwsppr Carrier Schlrshp Wnnr 85; Century III Ldrs Schlrshp Wnnr NY ST 85; Cornell U; Telecmmnctns.

WALSH, CHRISTINE; Connetguot HS; Ronkonkoma, NY; (Y); 137/694; Cmnty Wkr; Dance Clb; Teachers Aide; Band; Color Guard; Mrchg Band; Nwsp Ed-Chief; Nwsp Stf; Rep Jr Cls; Pres Stu Cncl; Perf Atten Awds 75-84; Stu Rep Bd Ed 85.

WALSH, ERIN P; Niagara Falls HS; Niagara Falls, NY; (Y); 21/257; Church Yth Grp; Pres French Clb; Key Clb; Nwsp Stf; Yrbk Stf; Rep Sr Cls; JV Sftbl; Hon Roll; NHS; NY ST Regents Schlrshp 85; SUNY At Geneseo; Forgn Languag.

WALSH, FRANK T; La Salle Inst; Averill Park, NY; (Y); 30/90; Am Leg Boys St; CAP; Drama Clb; Mgr ROTC; Ski Clb; Color Guard; Drill Tm; Stu Cncl; High Hon Roll; NHS; Civil Air Patrol Squadron Cadet Of The Yr 83; Lawyer.

WALSH, JAMES J; Cardinal Hayes HS; Bronx, NY; (Y); 19/267; Cmnty Wkr; Library Aide; Office Aide; Teachers Aide; Wt Lftg; High Hon Roll; Hon Roll; Prfct Atten Awd.

WALSH, JOHN; Iowa Prep; Rye, NY; (Y); Boy Scts; Computer Clb; Bowling; JV Crs Cntry; JV Lcrss; Wt Lftg; Prfct Atten Awd; Stu Consrvtn Assoc-Slctd As Smmr Vlntr For Olympc Pk 85; Rye Consrvtn Soc 85; Sci Dntstry.

WALSH, JOHN T; Cardinal Spellman HS; Bronx, NY; (Y); Key Clb; Ftbl; Hon Roll; NY ST Regents Schlrshp 85; SUNY At Brockport; Biology.

WALSH, JOSEPHINE B; Resurrection Acad; Rye, NY; (Y); GAA; Chorus; Swmmng; Mst Imprvd Swmmr 84-85; Bus Mngmnt.

WALSH, KATHLEEN; New Hyde Park Memorial HS; New Hyde Park, NY; (S); 43/269; DECA; FBLA; Girl Scts; Orch; High Hon Roll; Hon Roll; 5th Pl Data Proc FBLA Dist Comp 83; 4th Pl Data Proc FBLA Dist Comp 84; Pace U; Comp Sci.

WALSH, KATHLEEN M; Ward Melville HS; Stony Brook, NY; (Y); Cmnty Wkr; GAA; Ski Clb; Var JV Fld Hcky; JV Mgr(s); Var Sftbl; York Coll; Nrsng.

WALSH, KATHRYN GAETANA; Freeport HS; Freeport, NY; (Y); Sec Church Yth Grp; German Clb; Key Clb; Science Clb; Ski Clb; Band; School Musical; Capt Gym; Lcrss; Tennis; Long Island Bus Ed Cntst 85; NYSMA NY ST Music Assn 83-84; Vrsty Ltr Gymn & Tnns 83-85; Pace U; Bus Mgmt.

WALSH, KATY; Kenmore East HS; Tonawanda, NY; (Y); Boy Scts; Church Yth Grp; GAA; Pep Clb; PAVAS; Mrchg Band; Orch; Nwsp Rptr; JV Tennis; High Hon Roll; Credit Am Hist Adv Plcmnt 85; Gold Silver Medal Town Tennis Comptn 84.

WALSH, KERRI A; New Hyde Park Memorial HS; New Hyde Park, NY; (Y); 17/279; VP Girl Scts; Mathletes; Band; Nwsp Stf; Yrbk Stf; Var Sftbl; JV Capt Vllybl; Jr NHS; NHS; Church Yth Grp.

WALSH, KIM; Victor Central SR HS; Victor, NY; (Y); 107/250; 4-H; Teachers Aide; Capt Color Guard; Drm Mjr(t); Var Bowling; 4-H Awd; Pittsburg Inst; Fshn Mrchndsng.

WALSH, KRISTEN; Fontbonne Hall Acad; Staten Island, NY; (Y); 2/130; French Clb; Library Aide; Teachers Aide; Yrbk Stf; Var Swmmng; Im Vllybl; High Hon Roll; NHS; NEDT Awd; Prfct Atten Awd; Acad Schlrshp 82-84; Hnrs Sci, Math, Eng, Hist & Lang 83-85; Summa Cum Laude Gld Mdl Natl Latin Lst 85; Cmnctns.

WALSH, MATTHEW; Paul V Moore HS; Brewerton, NY; (Y); Boy Scts; Pres Band; Concert Band; Jazz Band; Mrchg Band; Pep Band; School Musical; Var JV Socr; High Hon Roll; Hon Roll; Mst Imprvd Soph In Band 84; Sci.

WALSH, MICHAEL; La Salle Academy HS; Brooklyn, NY; (S); 59/237; Im Bsktbl; Ntl Merit SF; St Johns U; Athletic Admin.

WALSH, MICHAEL P; Holy Cross HS; Whitestone, NY; (Y); 12/285; Am Leg Boys St; Spanish Clb; Nwsp Stf; Yrbk Stf; Coach Actv; Im JV Ftbl; JV Var Tennis; High Hon Roll; NHS; Duke U; Polit Sci.

WALSH, MONICA; Guilderland Central HS; Albany, NY; (Y); Art Clb; Cmnty Wkr; 4-H; Band; Chorus; Church Choir; Concert Band; Pep Band; Symp Band; Gym; Exclince Studio Art 83-84; Cmrcl Art.

WALSH, PATRICIA; Niagara Wheatfield HS; Niagara Falls, NY; (Y); Pep Clb; Ski Clb; Acpl Chr; Cheerleading; Niagara U; Nrsg.

WALSH, PATRICIA M; Sidney HS; Sidney, NY; (Y); 14/114; Am Leg Aux Girls St; Church Yth Grp; French Clb; GAA; Girl Scts; Speech Tm; Yrbk Ed-Chief; Trs Jr Cls; Pres Stu Cncl; Dnfth Awd; NYS Regents Schlrshp 85; St Marys Collfsclgy.

WALSH, PATRICK J; R Pojis HS; Douglaston, NY; (Y); Chess Clb; Lit Mag; Rep Frsh Cls; Rep Stu Cncl; Var Crs Cntry; Var Trk; Hon Roll; Ntl Merit Ltr; Brown U; Intl Rel.

WALSH, SHAWN; Southside HS; Elmira, NY; (Y); 11/375; Chess Clb; Spanish Clb; Varsity Clb; Jazz Band; Mrchg Band; Symp Band; JV Tennis; High Hon Roll; NHS; Ntl Merit SF; Bucknell Schlrshp 85-86; NYS Regents Schlrshp 85; Bruce Beauty Schlrshp-Music 85; Bucknell U; Math.

WALSH, TODD E; Berlin American HS; Apo New York, NY; (S); Boy Scts; Debate Tm; Model UN; Varsity Clb; Rep Soph Cls; Rep Jr Cls; Var Capt Swmmng; High Hon Roll; Hon Roll; NHS; Eagle Scout 83; Berlin Cmmty Dist Svc Awd 83; Chrtr Mbr Berlin Cmmty Teen Cncl 84-85; Engr.

WALSH, TONYA A; West Genesee SR HS; Camillus, NY; (Y); Exploring; Math Tm; Yrbk Stf; High Hon Roll; NHS; Acctg.

WALTER, CINDY; Albion HS; Albion, NY; (S); 4/178; Sec Church Yth Grp; Rep Spanish Clb; Color Guard; Sec Frsh Cls; Sec Stu Cncl; JV Socr; High Hon Roll; Jr NHS; NHS; Sociolgy.

WALTER, JANET; St Johns Prep; Jackson Hts, NY; (Y); 21/415; Dance Clb; Teachers Aide; Chorus; School Musical; Ed Yrbk Stf; High Hon Roll; NHS; Wood Schl Schlrshp 85; Svrl Shlrshps; Wood Schl; Sctrl Sci.

WALTER, MARK; E L Vandermuelen HS; Mt Sinai, NY; (Y); 1/275; Church Yth Grp; Mathletes; Varsity Clb; Nwsp Ed-Chief; Lit Mag; JV Var Socr; Var Tennis; High Hon Roll; NHS; Computer Clb; Lng Isld H S Acad Intl Stud 85.

WALTER, PATRICIA; Saint Edmund HS; Brooklyn, NY; (S); 13/190; Drama Clb; Hosp Aide; Science Clb; Rep Yrbk Stf; VP Jr Cls; Rep Stu Cncl; JV Capt Cheerleading; Hon Roll; NHS; Prin List Hnrs; Sci.

WALTER, PATRICK M; Savevoit Valley Central HS; New Hartford, NY; (Y); Am Leg Boys St; Church Yth Grp; Varsity Clb; Im Bsktbl; Var Capt Ftbl; Var Trk; NHS; Rotary Awd; Chem Engr.

WALTER, SCOTT; Miller Place HS; Miller Pl, NY; (Y); 25/200; JV Var Ftbl; Hon Roll; Vrsty Ltr & Spnsh Awd 84-85; Acctng.

WALTER, TODD; Fonda-Fultonville Central Schl; Fultonville, NY; (Y); Math Tm; High Hon Roll; Hon Roll; NHS; Mech Drwg Awd 84; Arch Engrng.

WALTER JR, WILLIAM; Archbishop Molloy HS; Jackson Heights, NY; (Y); 14/409; Computer Clb; German Clb; Math Clb; Math Tm; Var Crs Cntry; Var Trk; Actuary.

WALTERICH, BRIAN; Depew HS; Depew, NY; (Y); 74/254; School Musical; Bsbl; Vllybl.

WALTERS, AMY; Mynderse Acad; Seneca Falls, NY; (S); 48/132; Hon Roll.

WALTERS JR, CHARLES A; Rome Catholic HS; Rome, NY; (Y); 4/75; Nwsp Rptr; VP Frsh Cls; Pres Soph Cls; Pres Jr Cls; Pres Sr Cls; Var L Ftbl; Im Wt Lftg; Hon Roll; NHS; KC Schlrshp; Pre Med.

WALTERS, DONALD J; Kenmore East HS; Tonawanda, NY; (Y); Boy Scts; German Clb; Im Bsktbl; High Hon Roll; Hon Roll; Eagle Scout; Engrng.

WALTERS, JOHN S; Pittsford Mendon HS; Pittsford, NY; (Y); Math Clb; Model UN; Quiz Bowl; Ski Clb; Chorus; Var Crs Cntry; JV Trk; Hon Roll; NHS; Im Bsbl; German Lang Bowl 83-84; Outstndg Achvt German 84-85; Merit Music 82-83.

WALTERS, LISA BETH; Irandequoit HS; Rochester, NY; (Y); 14/391; Church Yth Grp; Hosp Aide; Band; Chorus; Church Choir; Concert Band; Mrchg Band; Pep Band; High Hon Roll; Hon Roll; Cornell U; Psychlgy.

WALTERS, MICHAEL SCOTT; Watkins Glen Central HS; Watkins Glen, NY; (S); 7/120; Am Leg Boys St; Church Yth Grp; Band; Jazz Band; French Hon Soc; Hon Roll; NHS; Acadmc All Amer 85; Colgate U; Physcs.

WALTERS, NATALIE; West Genesee SR HS; Syracuse, NY; (Y); Key Clb; Chorus; Jazz Band; Mrchg Band; School Musical; School Play; Symp Band; Variety Show; L Sftbl; Hon Roll; Outstndg Undrclssmn Brass-Trumpt 85; Outstdng Voclst 83; All-Cnty Hnrs 83-85; Music.

WALTHER, EVELYN A; Dominican Commercial HS; Glendale, NY; (Y); Teachers Aide; Im Sftbl; Var Swmmng; Timer; Hon Roll; Prfct Atten Awd; St Catherine Sienna Awd; JA AAHPERD; NY Tech U; Hotl Mgmt.

WALTHER, JOANNE; Catholic Central HS; Troy, NY; (Y); Math Clb; Chorus; Variety Show; Yrbk Stf; High Hon Roll; Hon Roll; Hudson Valley CC; Mrktg.

WALTHER, MIKE; Fairport HS; Fairport, NY; (Y); JV Var Bsktbl; Var L Ftbl; Hon Roll; NHS; Acad All-Amer 85; Med.

WALTKE, STEPHANI F; Wallkill SR HS; Wallkill, NY; (Y); 3/209; Church Yth Grp; Drama Clb; Band; Church Choir; Mrchg Band; School Play; High Hon Roll; NHS; Sci & Eng Awd; Oral Roberts U; Pre-Med.

WALTON, ADAM; Valley Central HS; Walden, NY; (Y); JV Var Bsbl; JV Var Ftbl; Hon Roll; Pace U; Accntng.

WALTON, DARREN; Niagara Falls HS; Niagara Falls, NY; (Y); Boy Scts; Pres Church Yth Grp; Library Aide; Nwsp Stf; Yrbk Stf; Trs Jr NHS; Bus Admin.

WALTON, GLENDINE V; Clara Barton HS; Brooklyn, NY; (Y); 32/469; Church Yth Grp; Debate Tm; 4-H; Church Choir; Yrbk Stf; Lit Mag; JV Tennis; Hon Roll; NHS; Prfct Atten Awd; NY ST Regents Schlrshp 85; NY ST Senate Achvt Awd 85; Long Island U; Pre-Med.

WALTON, JUDY; Skaneateles HS; Skaneateles, NY; (S); VP Frsh Cls; VP Soph Cls; VP Jr Cls; Stu Cncl; Var VP Bsktbl; Var L Socr; Var L Trk; High Hon Roll; Jr NHS; NHS; Bus Mngmnt.

WALTON, SANDY; Valley Central HS; Montgomery, NY; (Y); Hosp Aide; Band; Concert Band; Hon Roll; Little League All Stars 82; Vet.

WALTS, CHERYL; Mount Markham HS; W Winfield, NY; (Y); 7/111; Church Yth Grp; English Clb; Intnl Clb; Library Aide; Model UN; Yrbk Ed-Chief; Stu Cncl; NHS; Prfct Atten Awd; Clark Schlrshp 85; Top Englsh II Stu 85; Wells Coll; Bio.

WALTS, TABETHA; Indian River Central HS; Theresa, NY; (Y); 18/120; Hst Key Clb; Latin Clb; Chorus; Var Tennis; Var Timer; Var Trk; Excel Schrshp Awd 84-85; V Trk Tennis Awd 84-85; Jefferson CC; Med Tech.

WALTZ, JOE; Hoosick Falls Central HS; Hoosick Falls, NY; (Y); 2/118; Drama Clb; French Clb; Band; Stu Cncl; L Bsbl; Stat Bsktbl; Mgr Ftbl; High Hon Roll; NHS; Prncpl Schlrshp Awd 83 & 84; Kiwanis Awd 83; Pharm.

WALZ, ANN MARIE; Franklin D Roosevelt HS; Brooklyn, NY; (Y); Sftbl; NYS Regents Schlrshp 85; Brooklyn Coll.

WALZ, JEANETTE; Villa Mario Acad; Depew, NY; (Y); Computer Clb; Hosp Aide; Spanish Clb; Rep Frsh Cls; Rep Jr Cls; NHS; Cmnty Wkr; High Hon Roll; Jr NHS; Med.

WALZER, ERIC; E J Wilson HS; Spencerport, NY; (Y); 1/290; Ski Clb; Varsity Clb; VP Stu Cncl; Var Capt Bsktbl; Var Capt Socr; NHS; Ski Clb; Varsity Clb; Bsbl; Hon Roll; Bus Law Achv Awd 85; U S Marine Corps Distngshd Athlt Awd 85; Engrng.

WAN, STEVEN; High School Of Art & Design; Brooklyn, NY; (S); 3/417; Computer Clb; Library Aide; Math Clb; Math Tm; High Hon Roll; Hon Roll; NHS; Prfct Atten Awd; Haney Medal Awd 84; Daily News Art Excell Awd 3rd Pl 84; Dyker Hts Civic Assoc Awd 84.

WANAMAKER, TRACY; Nyack HS; Upr Nyack, NY; (Y); 80/277; Ski Clb; Variety Show; Ed Yrbk Stf; Lit Mag; Rep Stu Cncl; Var Capt Fld Hcky; Var Sftbl; Var Trk; Achvt Art SR Cls 85; Stu Of Wk Achvt Advncd Govt 85; Geneseo; Libl Arts.

WANDELL, DONNA; Maine Endwell SR HS; Endwell, NY; (Y); 37/252; Hosp Aide; Orch; JV Stat Bsktbl; JV Stat Sftbl; High Hon Roll; NHS; Regents Scholar 85; Natl Hnr Roll 84; SUNY Buffalo; Biochem.

WANDELL, JILL; Keveny Memorial Acad; Cohoes, NY; (Y); Dance Clb; Color Guard; Score Keeper; Vllybl; High Hon Roll; Hon Roll; Typg Awd 83-85; Austin Bty Schl; Csmtlgy.

WANDERLING, AMY; Washingtonville HS; Washingtonville, NY; (Y); French Clb; Band; Concert Band; Symp Band; Bsktbl; Capt Var Tennis; High Hon Roll; NHS; Law.

WANEK, SANDRA M; Oswego HS; Oswego, NY; (Y); French Clb; German Clb; Math Clb; Science Clb; Ski Clb; Varsity Clb; Crs Cntry; Powder Puff Ftbl; Socr; Trk; U Of MI; Med.

WANG, BOBBY; Ellenville HS; Phillipsport, NY; (Y); Computer Clb; Yrbk Stf; Var L Socr; Var L Tennis; High Hon Roll; NHS; Biology.

WANG, EARL C; Williamsville South HS; Williamsville, NY; (Y); 2/245; Math Clb; Orch; High Hon Roll; NHS; Sal; Church Yth Grp; Computer Clb; Ski Clb; Yrbk Stf; Trk; NY ST Regnts Schlrshp 85; Ntl Awd Piano 81; Cornell U; Med.

WANG, GEORGE L Y; Bronx High School Of Science; Elmhurst, NY; (Y); Art Clb; Science Clb; Lit Mag; Off Sr Cls; Stu Cncl; Tennis; Gov Hon Prg Awd; High Hon Roll; 1st Pl Physics In Intl Sci Fair 85; 1st Pl Navy & Air Frc In ISEF 85; MA Inst Of Tech; Elec Engrng.

WANG, HUA; La Guardia H S Of Music And The Arts; Brooklyn, NY; (Y); 167/590; Teachers Aide; Yrbk Stf; Schlrshp Minneapolis MN Art Instruc Schls 81; Art Instruc Schls Annl Art Comp 82; Artst.

WANG, JACK; The Bronx High School Of Science; Flushing, NY; (Y); Yrbk Phtg; SUNY Binghamton; Engrng.

WANG, JANET; United Nations International Schl; Jamaica, NY; (Y); Chorus; Lit Mag; Rep Frsh Cls; Rep Jr Cls; Rep Sr Cls; Rep Stu Cncl; Sftbl; Trk; UCLA; Elec Engrng.

WANG, WEN; Jamaica HS; Jamaica, NY; (Y); 12/534; Computer Clb; French Clb; Math Tm; Office Aide; Band; Concert Band; School Musical; Variety Show; Yrbk Stf; Hon Roll; Westinghouse SF 85; Trustee Schlrshp NYU 85; Creative Arts Soc Awd 85; NY U.

WANGERIN, ANN; Albion HS; Albion, NY; (Y); Computer Clb; Library Aide; Bryant & Stratton; Comp Sci.

WAPPMAN, ROBERT; Frontier Central HS; Hamburg, NY; (Y); 200/500; French Clb; Political Wkr; VP Varsity Clb; Band; JV Bsbl; JV Bsktbl; Var Ftbl; Var Trk; Prfct Atten Awd; Pol Sci.

WARCHOCKI, TIMOTHY; West Seneca East SR HS; W Seneca, NY; (Y); Art Clb; Stage Crew; Yrbk Stf; Lit Mag; JC Awd; Comm Dsgn.

WARCHOL, LAURA; Saranac Lake HS; Paul Smiths, NY; (Y); Powder Puff Ftbl; Timer; Trk; Hon Roll; Barbizon Schl Of Modeling 85; Varsty Lttr Trck 83; Hnrbl Mntn Awd-Pottery In Art 85; NCCC; Modeling.

WARD, ANDREA; Roosevelt JR SR HS; Roosevelt, NY; (Y); 15/190; Church Yth Grp; FBLA; Hosp Aide; Chorus; Color Guard; Variety Show; Yrbk Stf; Hon Roll; Howard U; Phy Thrpy.

WARD, ANGELA; Academy Of Mt St Ursula; Bronx, NY; (Y); Cmnty Wkr; Computer Clb; Drama Clb; Library Aide; Office Aide; Teachers Aide; Yrbk Stf; Stu Cncl; Bus.

WARD, BARBARA; Granville Central HS; Granville, NY; (Y); 18/122; AFS; Math Tm; Band; Concert Band; Mrchg Band; JV Fld Hcky; Hon Roll; Prfct Atten Awd; SUNY; Sec Ed.

WARD, CARA; Bishop Maginn HS; Albany, NY; (Y); Red Cross Aide; School Play; Yrbk Stf; Hon Roll; Fnlst Natl Teen Pgnt 83; Albany ST U.

WARD, CHARLIE D; Bayport-Blue Point HS; Blue Point, NY; (Y); 24/213; Am Leg Boys St; Key Clb; Scholastic Bowl; Rep Frsh Cls; Rep Soph Cls; JV Bsbl; JV Ftbl; JV Var Wrstlng; Hon Roll; NHS; Busnss.

WARD, EDWARD S; Hartford Central Schl; Fort Ann, NY; (Y); 3/47; Math Clb; Yrbk Phtg; Rep Soph Cls; VP Jr Cls; Bsbl; JV Socr; High Hon Roll; Hon Roll; NHS; NY ST Regents Schlrshp 85; Engr.

WARD, JENNIFER; Ossining HS; Ossining, NY; (Y); VP JA; Chorus; Church Choir; Color Guard; School Musical; Var L Fld Hcky; Im Lcrss; Var L Trk; Trs NHS; Hon Roll; All Leag Fld Hcky 84; Phy Ed.

WARD, JENNIFER K; Moravia Central HS; Auburn, NY; (Y); 2/100; Chorus; Concert Band; Jazz Band; Mrchg Band; Yrbk Stf; VP Soph Cls; VP Sr Cls; High Hon Roll; Ntl Merit Ltr; Sal; Cayuga County Comm; Comptr Sci.

WARD, JOHN; Allegany Central Schl; Allegany, NY; (Y); Ski Clb; Trk; High Hon Roll; Hon Roll; Paint.

WARD, KEVIN; W C Mepham HS; Bellmore, NY; (Y); PAVAS; Nwsp Phtg; Yrbk Phtg; Var Lcrss; NASSAU CC; Bus Admn.

WARD, KRIS; Canastota HS; Canastota, NY; (S); #4 In Class; GAA; Intnl Clb; Var L Bsktbl; Var L Fld Hcky; L Capt Sftbl; High Hon Roll; NHS; Church Yth Grp; Mgr(s); Mst Imprvd Fld Hockey Plyr 82-83; 2nd Tm All Stars Fld Hockey 82-83; Mst Outstndg Fld Hoc Plyr 84-85; Clarkson; Acctg.

WARD, LISA; Salamanca Central HS; Salamanca, NY; (S); 8/130; FCA; Trs Frsh Cls; Trs Soph Cls; Trs Jr Cls; Trs Sr Cls; Trs Stu Cncl; Var Capt Cheerleading; Trs French Hon Soc; High Hon Roll; NHS; Cortland.

WARD, LYNETTE S; Harrisville Central HS; Harrisville, NY; (Y); Art Clb; Chorus; Yrbk Sprt Ed; Nrthrn NY Art Show Wnnr; Art Recog, Tlnt Srch Wnnr; Munson Williams; Art Tchr.

WARD, MARCELLA T; Holland Patent HS; Barneveld, NY; (Y); Trs AFS; French Clb; GAA; Mgr Stage Crew; Variety Show; Var Fld Hcky; Var Capt Trk; Hon Roll; AFS Exchng Stu Norway Smmr 84; JR Olymps X-Cnty Skng 85; Downhl Ski Rcng Tm Cptn 81-85; NY ST Mt; Paul Smith Coll; Htl Mgmt.

WARD, MICHAEL; Connetquot HS; Ronkonkoma, NY; (Y); 44/700; Art Clb; Teachers Aide; Drm Mjr(t); School Musical; School Play; Yrbk Stf; Rep Frsh Cls; Hst Soph Cls; Trk; Hon Roll; Hugh O Brien Yth Fndtn Awd-Outstndng Stu 83-84; John Pearl Awd 82-83; Outstndng Art Awd 82-83; Art.

WARD, MICHAEL; Liverpool HS; Liverpool, NY; (S); 57/792; Capt Bowling; Hon Roll; Jr NHS; NHS; MVP Bowling Team 82-83; Oswego Coll.

WARD, MICHAEL; Thomas A Edison HS; Elmira Hts, NY; (Y); Drama Clb; Band; Chorus; Concert Band; Mrchg Band; School Play; Var Trk; Hon Roll; Arch Tech.

WARD, NANCY; Weedsport Central HS; Weedsport, NY; (Y); Art Clb; Band; Chorus; Church Choir; Concert Band; Yrbk Stf; Bsktbl; Bowling; Crs Cntry; Trk; Auburn CC; Bus.

WARD, REBEKAH; Rochester Christian Acad HS; Rochester, NY; (S); Church Yth Grp; Computer Clb; Debate Tm; Drama Clb; FTA; Library Aide; Ski Clb; Teachers Aide; Chorus; Church Choir; Accmpnmnt Schlrshp 84-85; Music Schlrshp 85-86; Music Hnrs 81-2; Houghton Coll; Music.

WARD, ROBERT D; The Allendale Columbia Schl; Rochester, NY; (Y); 1/47; Church Yth Grp; Math Tm; Band; Chorus; Nwsp Rptr; JV Bsbl; Var Bsktbl; JV Socr; High Hon Roll; Ntl Merit SF; Law.

WARD, TERESA; Webster HS; Webster, NY; (Y); 27/563; Church Yth Grp; Cmnty Wkr; Ski Clb; Ed Yrbk Stf; Rep Stu Cncl; NHS; Ntl Merit Ltr; French Clb; Office Aide; Teachers Aide; Intl Arabian Hrs Assn Yth Achvt High Point Awd 84; Svrl Awds For Horse Show Chmpnshp 83-84; Cornell U; Research.

WARD, THERESA; Minisink Valley HS; Port Jervis, NY; (Y); Church Yth Grp; Chorus; High Hon Roll; Hon Roll; Psych.

WARD, TIMOTHY P; Fayetteville-Manlius HS; Manlius, NY; (Y); 5/345; Model UN; Speech Tm; Band; Concert Band; Mrchg Band; Orch; Pep Band; Bausch & Lomb Sci Awd; High Hon Roll; NHS; Bauch & Lomb Sci Schlrshp 85; Northwestern U; Physics.

WARD, WILLIAM W; Fort Ann Central HS; Fort Ann, NY; (Y); French Clb; Math Clb; Hon Roll; NHS; St Schlr; Air Force Acad; Pilot.

WARDEN, BRIAN; Cicero HS; Clay, NY; (S); 85/711; Ski Clb; Var Gym; Hon Roll.

WARDROP, LARA; Williamsville South HS; Williamsville, NY; (Y); 51/245; Drama Clb; Pep Clb; Ski Clb; Yrbk Stf; Cheerleading; Powder Puff Ftbl; Hon Roll; Regnts Schlrshp 85; MI ST U.

WARDROP, MATTHEW; Briarcliff HS; Briarcliff Manor, NY; (Y); Boy Scts; Church Yth Grp; Band; School Play; Yrbk Stf; Sec Frsh Cls; JV Socr; 1st Sci Fair 83; Engrng.

WARHOL, NANCY; Mount Mercy Acad; Buffalo, NY; (Y); Cmnty Wkr; Science Clb; Service Clb; Chorus; Coach Actv; Hon Roll; Bus.

WARMAN, JENNIFER; Freeport HS; Freeport, NY; (Y); 20/450; Hosp Aide; Political Wkr; Chorus; Orch; Ed Nwsp Rptr; High Hon Roll; NHS; NYS Regents Schlrshp 85; LI String Fest ; All-Cnty Orch & Chorus; NY U; Mus.

WARMAN, JOSEPH; Colonie Central HS; Schenectady, NY; (Y); Boy Scts; JV Var Vllybl; IN Inst Of Tech.

WARMUTH, ERIC; Whitesboro Central Schl; Marcy, NY; (Y); Cmnty Wkr; Science Clb; Varsity Clb; Var L Socr; Var L Trk; High Hon Roll; Hon Roll; NHS; Engrng.

WARNER, ALLISON; Fairport HS; Fairport, NY; (Y); 78/610; JA; Ski Clb; Stage Crew; Nwsp Rptr; Rep Stu Cncl; Var L Vllybl; Hon Roll; Vet.

WARNER, ANN M; Riverhead SR HS; Calverton, NY; (Y); 1/250; Drama Clb; Latin Clb; Concert Band; School Play; High Hon Roll; NHS; NHS; Rotary Awd; Val; NY Regents Schlrshp 85; Syracuse U; Brdcst Jrnlsm.

WARNER, BRIAN; Alden HS; Alden, NY; (Y); French Clb; Var Bsbl; Var Bsktbl; Var Ftbl; Hon Roll; Rochester Inst Tech; Engrng.

WARNER, CATHERINE; Newburgh Free Acad; Newburgh, NY; (Y); 29/720; Key Clb; Capt Math Tm; Acpl Chr; Madrigals; Orch; Nwsp Stf; Yrbk Stf; Sec Soph Cls; Rep Stu Cncl; High Hon Roll; Orange Cty Music Ed Schlrshp 85; Music Unl Schlrshp 85; U PA.

WARNER, JAMES C; Riverhead HS; Calverton, NY; (Y); Pres Church Yth Grp; Drama Clb; JCL; Latin Clb; Band; Chorus; Jazz Band; Orch; VP Soph Cls; Pres Stu Cncl; Lions All-ST Bnd 82-85; Long Islnd Yth Orchstr Tour 84; N Fork Music Festvl 82-85; Duke U.

WARNER, KIRSTIN; Harry S Truman HS; Bronx, NY; (Y); Sec Church Yth Grp; French Clb; Y-Teens; Church Choir; French Hon Soc; High Hon Roll; NHS; Prfct Atten Awd; Math Tutor Awd 85; Outstndng Achvt Frnch Awd 84; Sci.

WARNER, LAURIE; Franklin Acad; Malone, NY; (Y); Hosp Aide; Travl/Toursm.

WARNER, MICHAEL; Oakfield-Alabama HS; Oakfield, NY; (Y); 14/80; French Clb; Crs Cntry; Trk; Bus Mgmt.

WARNER, TRESA; Vestal Central SR HS; Vestal, NY; (Y); French Clb; Acctng.

WARNICK, MICHAEL; Kenmore West HS; Kenmore, NY; (Y); Political Wkr; VP Varsity Clb; Im JV Bsbl; JV Capt Ftbl; Capt Var Wrstlng; High Hon Roll; Hon Roll; Jr NHS; Cert Of Recog Twn Tonawanda Repblcns 84-85; Engrng.

WARNICK, SPENCER K; Canajoharie HS; Canajoharie, NY; (Y); 2/90; Aud/Vis; Pres Ski Clb; Varsity Clb; Yrbk Ed-Chief; Mgr Var Crs Cntry; L Var Trk; High Hon Roll; Jr NHS; NHS; Union Coll; Engr.

WARNOCK, GLENN W; Warwick Valley HS; Warwick, NY; (Y); Aud/Vis; Rep Frsh Cls; Rep Soph Cls; Rep Jr Cls; Rep Sr Cls; JV Var Bsktbl; JV Var Socr; Hon Roll; Enrichment Pgm Gifted HS Snrs 85; SAT Schlrshp NYS 85; Accntng.

WARREN, BRIDGET; Granville HS; Hampton, NY; (S); 17/158; Rep Frsh Cls; Rep Stu Cncl; JV Var Bsktbl; JV Var Fld Hcky; JV Var Vllybl; High Hon Roll; Hon Roll; Mst Outstndng Record Keeping 84; Prfct Attndnce 84; MIP Vllybl 85; Green Mountain Coll; Accntng.

WARREN, COLLEEN M; Newburgh Free Acad; Newburgh, NY; (Y); 30/800; Acpl Chr; Chorus; Var Capt Swmmng; Var Timer; High Hon Roll; Jr NHS; Ntl Merit SF; Spanish NHS; Natl Hnr Roll 85; Amer HS Amth Exam 84-85; Bus.

WARREN, CONNIE; Kendall Central HS; Kent, NY; (Y); 16/87; Concert Band; Mrchg Band; Var Capt Bsktbl; Var Capt Sftbl; Var Vllybl; High Hon Roll; Lion Awd; NHS; 4-H; Pep Clb; MVP On Var Bsktbl 85; All-Tourn Tm Var Bsktbl 85; Bst Hitter Var Sftbl 85; SUNY Ag & Tech Delhi; Vet Sci.

WARREN, DEBORAH; West Seneca East SR HS; West Seneca, NY; (Y); Camp Fr Inc; Cmnty Wkr; GAA; Spanish Clb; Chorus; Yrbk Stf; Swmmng; High Hon Roll; Jr NHS; NHS; Bkstr Mngr; Intrmrl Flr Hcky; Grls Chorus.

WARREN, ELIZABETH A; Holy Trinity Dhs; North Bellmore, NY; (S); 15/362; Red Cross Aide; Spanish Clb; Teachers Aide; Variety Show; Yrbk Stf; Rep Frsh Cls; Stu Cncl; Twrlr; Hon Roll; NHS; Hofstra U; Bus Admin.

WARREN, JAMES; York Central HS; Caledonia, NY; (Y); Ski Clb; Sec Frsh Cls; High Hon Roll; Clsrm Hnrs Bio Pysics 84-85; U Tampa; Oceangrphy.

WARREN, KARIN; Minisink Valley HS; Middletown, NY; (Y); 4/200; Sec Key Clb; Band; Concert Band; Mrchg Band; High Hon Roll; Kiwanis Awd; NHS; Ntl Merit Ltr; NYSSMA Music Medals; Flute Sctn Ldr 85-86; Outstndng JR Musician 84-85.

WARREN, KIM; Bay Ridge HS; Brooklyn, NY; (Y); 32/266; Teachers Aide; Chorus; Nwsp Stf; Hon Roll; Prfct Atten Awd; Envrnmntl Awarens & Ldrshp Awd 84-85; Good Ctznshp, Outstndng Chrctr Cert Of Awd 85; Walk Amer Rcgntn; Munter Coll; Comp Sci.

WARREN, KIM; Christopher Columbus HS; Bronx, NY; (Y); 139/792; Coach Actv; PEAK 82-85; Acctg.

WARREN, PETER; Goshen Central HS; Goshen, NY; (Y); Quiz Bowl; Var Crs Cntry; Var Trk; Hon Roll; NHS; Ntl Merit Ltr; NEDT Awd; Hon Awd Coll Skills Cls 84-85; Psych.

WARREN, SARAH; L C Obourn HS; East Rochester, NY; (Y); 2/113; Capt Math Tm; Varsity Clb; Chorus; Concert Band; Capt Var Gym; Var L Sftbl; Capt Var Tennis; NHS; Ntl Merit Schol; Sal; Yale U.

WARREN, WILBERT R; Hempstead HS; Hempstead, NY; (Y); 1/333; Church Yth Grp; Cmnty Wkr; Model UN; Church Choir; Im Bsktbl; JV Trk; High Hon Roll; NHS; Val; Library Aide; Comm For Ntl Achvt Schlrshp 84; Geo Wash Medal 84-85; Cert Achvt 84-85; Cardiologist.

WARRICK, MARGARET; Forestville Central HS; Forestville, NY; (Y); FBLA; Office Aide; Spanish Clb; Teachers Aide; Yrbk Stf; Cit Awd; Hugh O Brian Yth Fndtn Ldrshp Smnr 83-84; Spain Schlrshp 84-85; Fredonia ST U; Soc Wrk.

WARRINGTON, LORI; Hudson Falls Central Schl; Hudson Fall, NY; (Y); Exploring; 4-H; Cheerleading; Area Coca-Cola Bwlng Tourn 85,2nd Pl ST Regnl 85; Nrs.

WARSHAW, STEVEN; Hebrew Academy Of Nassau Co; Oceanside, NY; (S); 10/75; Aud/Vis; Boy Scts; Computer Clb; Math Clb; Math Tm; Orch; Nwsp Stf; Vllybl; Hon Roll; 1st Pl Israel Invntrs Comp 83; Columbia U; Engr.

WARSHAWSKY, CRAIG; South Shore HS; Brooklyn, NY; (Y); Kingsborough Coll; Bus.

WART, MELISSA; Altmar Parish Williamstown HS; Parish, NY; (Y); Church Yth Grp; French Clb; Varsity Clb; Band; Concert Band; Mrchg Band; Pep Band; Var Vllybl; High Hon Roll; Hon Roll; Potsdam Coll; Elem Educ.

WARTER, LAURA L; Monticello HS; White Lake, NY; (Y); NFL; Service Clb; Capt Speech Tm; Band; School Musical; Ed Yrbk Stf; Var L Socr; High Hon Roll; Jr NHS; NHS; Outstndng Spkr Tourn; Ind Mgmt.

WARWICK, COLLEEN; Liverpool HS; Liverpool, NY; (S); 50/775; Church Yth Grp; DECA; French Clb; Pep Clb; Rep Stu Cncl; Capt Cheerleading; Hon Roll; Jr NHS; NHS; Intrntl Rltns.

WARWICK, MICHAEL J; Rome Catholic HS; Rome, NY; (Y); 10/80; Drama Clb; School Musical; Nwsp Rptr; Nwsp Sprt Ed; Yrbk Rptr; Yrbk Stf; Hon Roll; NHS; NEDT Awd; Utica Coll; Jrnlsm.

WASHBOURNE, DAVID M; Beekmantown Central Schl; Plattsburgh, NY; (Y); Boy Scts; Church Yth Grp; VP Exploring; Library Aide; High Hon Roll; Clarkson U; Engrng.

WASHBOURNE, JOHN K; Beekmantown Central Schl; Plattsburgh, NY; (Y); Boy Scts; Model UN; Band; Jazz Band; NHS; Ntl Merit Ltr; Voice Dem Awd; Church Yth Grp; Pres Exploring; French Clb; U Schlr St Lawrence U 85; St Lawrence U; Govt.

WASHBURN, HEIDI; Lakeland HS; Putnam Valley, NY; (Y); FBLA; German Clb; Girl Scts; Pep Clb; Band; Color Guard; Concert Band; Drill Tm; Mrchg Band; Yrbk Stf; Awd Putnam Vly Wmns Clb Crfts Shw 85; Secy.

WASHBURN, KEITH G; Letchworth Central HS; Castile, NY; (Y); Am Leg Boys St; Drama Clb; Varsity Clb; School Play; Im Bsbl; JV Var Ftbl; Im Socr; L Trk; Im Vllybl; High Hon Roll; Elec Engrng.

WASHBURN, RUSSELL; Susquehanna Valley HS; Binghamton, NY; (Y); Computer Clb; French Clb; Mathletes; Quiz Bowl; Crs Cntry; Trk; High Hon Roll; NHS; Ntl Merit Ltr; Prfct Atten Awd; SUNY Buffalo; Engrng.

WASHBURN, SHARON; Marathon Central Schl; Marathon, NY; (Y); Library Aide; Chorus; Stu Mnth 83-84.

WASHBURN, TABATHA; Letchworth HS; Bliss, NY; (S); 23/83; DECA; FFA; Library Aide; Chorus; Church Choir; 4-H Awd; Hon Roll; 1st Pl DECA Food Marktng Region 10 85; Olean Bus Inst; Bus.

WASHBURN, TIMOTHY A; Cambridge Central HS; Cambridge, NY; (Y); 13/88; Yrbk Bus Mgr; Rep Frsh Cls; Rep Soph Cls; Rep Jr Cls; Rep Sr Cls; Rep Stu Cncl; Im Bsktbl; Im Vllybl; Cit Awd; DAR Awd; Cambridge Vly Vol Rescue Squad 85; Regents Schlrshp Awd; Plattsburgh ST U; Comp Sci.

WASHBURN, VALERIE; Berne-Knox-Westerlo HS; Berne, NY; (Y); 1/86; VP Sec 4-H; Band; Chorus; Capt Color Guard; School Musical; Lit Mag; Bausch & Lomb Sci Awd; High Hon Roll; NHS; Val; Union Coll; Psychlgy.

WASHBURN, WENDY S; Wilson Central Schl; Newfane, NY; (Y); 9/140; Aud/Vis; VP Chorus; School Musical; Variety Show; Yrbk Stf; Var L Crs Cntry; Powder Puff Ftbl; Var L Trk; High Hon Roll; Sec NHS; NY ST Regents Schlrshp 85; Math Achvt Awd 85; PTA Schlrshp 85; SUNY; Engrng.

WASHINGTON, ADRIENA; Herbert H Lehman HS; Bronx, NY; (Y); 109/730; Dance Clb; Hosp Aide; Chorus; Nwsp Stf; Trk; Hon Roll; Prfct Atten Awd; Cert Achvt Psych 85; Cert Excll Sci 84; Cert Excll Music 83; CPA.

WASHINGTON, CHRISTOPHER; Cardinal Hayes HS; Bronx, NY; (Y); 35/264; Var L Bsbl; JV Bsktbl; JV Socr; Var L Sftbl; Math.

WASHINGTON, ELIZABETH; East Islip HS; East Islip, NY; (Y); Band; Church Choir; Concert Band; Jazz Band; Mrchg Band; Orch; School Musical; Symp Band; Var Trk; High Hon Roll; All Cnty Music Fstvl 79-80 & 83; Bst Wdwnd Awd 82-83; Camp Merrovista Awd 85; Psych.

WASHINGTON, HABIBA A; Bronx High School Of Science; New York City, NY; (Y); Library Aide; Office Aide; Chorus; Nwsp Rptr; Yrbk Phtg; Yrbk Stf; Secy Of Black Organization For Sci Stu 84-85; Humanities.

WASHINGTON, M RUSSELL; Colonie Central HS; Albany, NY; (Y); Boys Clb Am; Boy Scts; Church Yth Grp; JV Bsktbl; Im Ftbl; Im Sftbl; Im Wt Lftg; High Hon Roll; Hon Roll; NHS; Natl Comnty Ldrhp & Svc Awd 84; Engrng.

WASHINGTON, MICHELE; Cathedral HS; Ny, NY; (Y); 159/298; Church Yth Grp; Drama Clb; Library Aide; Church Choir; Socl Wrk.

WASHINGTON, ROBIN; Clara Barton HS; Brooklyn, NY; (Y); Girl Scts; Office Aide; Sec Chorus; Orch; Variety Show; Rep Soph Cls; Stat Vllybl; Cit Awd; Hon Roll; Prfct Atten Awd; NY U; Comp Sci.

WASHINGTON, STEPHANIE; Queen Of The Rosary Acad; Wyandanch, NY; (S); Church Yth Grp; Hosp Aide; Math Clb; Rep Frsh Cls; Pres Jr Cls; Stu Cncl; JV Capt Bsktbl; Hon Roll; NHS; Ntl Hnr Soc 83-84; B Hnr Roll 82-84; Med Dctr.

WASHINGTON, TANEDRA; Farmingdale HS; Amityville, NY; (Y); Girl Scts; Spanish Clb; Chorus; School Play; Cheerleading; FIT; Fshn Buyer.

WASHKO, CHRISTINE; Lake George HS; Lake George, NY; (Y); Hon Roll; Stu Of Mtn 86; Bus.

WASICKO, JOHN; South New Berlin Central Schl; South New Berlin, NY; (Y); 4/37; Concert Band; Drm Mjr(t); Mrchg Band; Pres Frsh Cls; Pres Jr Cls; Pres Trs Stu Cncl; High Hon Roll; NHS; Math Tm; Band; Mock Trial Tm; Acad All Amer; Lehigh U; Bus Mngmnt.

WASIELEWSKI, NANCY; Hennnger HS; Syracuse, NY; (Y); 10/400; Math Clb; Math Tm; Pep Clb; Rep Jr Cls; Rep Sr Cls; Var Capt Tennis; High Hon Roll; NHS; Pres Scholar Cortland ST 85; Excllnce Sci Awd 85; Cortland ST; Mth Tchr.

WASIERSKI, DAVID; Cardinal O Hara HS; Cheektowaga, NY; (Y); 22/130; 4-H; Bowling; Hon Roll; Canisius Coll; Law.

WASMUND, KOLLEEN; Gowanda Central JR-SR HS; Gowanda, NY; (Y); 51/120; French Clb; Ski Clb; Band; Color Guard; Concert Band; Mrchg Band; Pep Band; JV Var Cheerleading; Var Sftbl; Hon Roll; Med.

WASSEF, SUZY; St Vincent Ferrer HS; New York, NY; (S); 13/102; Drama Clb; Math Clb; Q&S; Madrigals; School Musical; Ed Nwsp Stf; Ed Yrbk Stf; Tennis; Hon Roll; NHS; Guitar Club Awd 82-85; Ntl Sci Olympiad Awd 84; Engr.

WASSERMAN, DEBRA; Commack High Schl South; Dix Hills, NY; (Y); Cmnty Wkr; French Clb; Ed Nwsp Stf; Yrbk Ed-Chief; VP Frsh Cls; VP Soph Cls; Pres Jr Cls; Tennis; High Hon Roll; NHS; Stu Recog Day-Ldrshp Cmnty Svc 83-86; Stu Fclty Cmmttee 83-86; Prod Mgr Drama & Muscl-Publcty 83-85; Polit Sci.

WASSERMAN, ROBERT JOSEPH; Newfield HS; Coram, NY; (Y); Computer Clb; Drama Clb; Political Wkr; VP Temple Yth Grp; Nwsp Stf; Lit Mag; Rep Stu Cncl; Hon Roll; Ntl Merit Ltr; Art Clb; Ntl Art Hnr Soc 84-85; 2nd Pl Frnch Ptry Cntst 85; Dist HS Of Prfrmng Arts 85-86; Grphc Arts.

WASSINGER, CAROL; Alden Central HS; Alden, NY; (Y); 52/198; Church Yth Grp; Pres Science Clb; Rep Spanish Clb; Band; Chorus; Mrchg Band; Pep Band; School Play; Swing Chorus; Soc Wrk.

WATERHOUSE, LORI A; Dansville SR HS; Dansville, NY; (Y); 7/145; Cmnty Wkr; Pres FTA; Teachers Aide; Band; Chorus; Yrbk Stf; Hon Roll; NHS; Ntl Merit Ltr; Regnts Schlrshp 85; Scrpt D Awd 82-85; SUNY Geneseo; Engl.

WATERMAN, BARBARA L; Marcellus SR HS; Marcellus, NY; (Y); 13/167; Band; VP Concert Band; Orch; School Musical; Var L Tennis; Var L Trk; High Hon Roll; NHS; Drama Clb; Ski Clb; Regnts Schlrshp 85; Golub Schlrshp Fnlst 85; Yth Bureau 84-85; SUNY Albany; Vet.

WATERMAN, ELIZABETH C; Panama Central Schl; Ashville, NY; (Y); 2/75; Drama Clb; Pep Clb; Trs Spanish Clb; Sec Sr Cls; Cheerleading; Gym; Sftbl; Swmmng; Hon Roll; NHS; NYS Regnts Schlrshp 85; Jamestown CC; Humnts.

WATERMAN, SHELLEY; Sandy Creek Central HS; Sandy Creek, NY; (Y); 4/90; Church Yth Grp; Drama Clb; JCL; Teachers Aide; Band; SUNY; Pre Vet.

WATERS, DAN; Lyndonville HS; Waterport, NY; (S); 5/61; Church Yth Grp; Church Choir; Trk; Hon Roll; NHS; Prfct Atten Awd; Art Awd 82; Cnsrvtnst.

WATERS, DANIEL; Lyndonville HS; Waterport, NY; (Y); Church Yth Grp; Church Choir; Trk; High Hon Roll; Hon Roll; Varsity Clb; Prfct Atten Awd.

WATERS, JOHN; Onteora Central HS; Woodstock, NY; (Y); 102/245; Church Yth Grp; Cmnty Wkr; Band; Mrchg Band; Yrbk Stf; JV Socr; Var Trk; Regnts Schlrshp Wnnr 85; SUNY Albany; Math.

WATERS, MONICA K; W C Mepham HS; North Bellmore, NY; (Y); Math Clb; Yrbk Stf; Lit Mag; JV Crs Cntry; JV Trk; French Hon Soc; Hon Roll; NHS; Bus.

WATERS, NATALIE JEAN; Lansingburgh HS; Troy, NY; (Y); 4-H; JA; School Musical; Nwsp Ed-Chief; Var L Trk; High Hon Roll; Jr NHS; NHS; Prfct Atten Awd; Drama Clb; Suny Delhi.

WATKINS, MICHELLE; Andrew Jackson HS; Hollis, NY; (Y); Cmnty Wkr; Office Aide; Service Clb; Chorus; Church Choir; School Musical; Nwsp Stf; Yrbk Stf; Prfct Atten Awd; Fstvl Of The Arts Awd 85; Cert Fo Mrt Awd 85; 105th Precnct Civilian Cert Awd 85; Jrnlsm.

WATKINS, SUE; Dryden HS; Dryden, NY; (Y); Church Yth Grp; Drama Clb; Library Aide; Spanish Clb; School Musical; School Play; Stage Crew; Rep Stu Cncl; L Trk; Hon Roll; Schltc Achvt Awd Acad Achvt Soc Stud 83; Soc Stud.

WATROUS, KAREN M; Schalmont HS; Schenectady, NY; (Y); 5/200; Math Tm; Yrbk Phtg; Yrbk Stf; Stat Score Keeper; Stat Timer; Stat Trk; High Hon Roll; Hon Roll; William & Mary; Archlgy.

WATS JR, BRUCE; Auburn HS; Auburn, NY; (Y); Intnl Clb; Yrbk Phtg; High Hon Roll; Hon Roll; NHS; Pace U; Pre-Med.

WATSO, CHRISTINE; Westfield Acad And Central; Westfield, NY; (S); Trs AFS; Key Clb; Band; Chorus; Mrchg Band; L Cheerleading; High Hon Roll; NHS; Ntl Merit Ltr; NY Regents Schlrshp 85.

WATSON, ANDREA DENISE; Martin Luther HS; Flushing, NY; (Y); 13/104; Pres Frsh Cls; Pres Soph Cls; Pres Jr Cls; Pres Sr Cls; Capt Cheerleading; High Hon Roll; Prfct Atten Awd; Am Leg Aux Girls St; Trs German Clb; Office Aide; African Chrstn Tchrs Awd 85; Congrssnl Medal Rcgntn 85; Jeanne Dale Katz Music Awd 85; St Johns U; Pharm.

WATSON, BADREYAH; Springfield Gardens HS; Jamcia, NY; (Y); 106/443; FBLA; Hosp Aide; Chorus; Sal; Prfct Atten Awd; Baruch Coll; Bus Adm.

WATSON, DAVID JOHN; Troy HS; Troy, NY; (Y); 293/423; German Clb; Nwsp Rptr; Soph Cls; Jr Cls; Stu Cncl; High Hon Roll; Hon Roll; Chorus; Nwsp Stf; Frsh Cls; Regents Schlrshp 85; Troy Teachers Assn 85; James Lemke Memorial 85; St Rose; Pre Law.

WATSON, DAWN; Adlai E Stevenson HS; Bronx, NY; (Y); Church Yth Grp; Cmnty Wkr; Pep Clb; Service Clb; Teachers Aide; Stat Vllybl; Cit Awd; Prfct Atten Awd; Accpt Lgl Educ Career Org Prog 84-85; St Augustines Coll; Psych.

WATSON, GREG; Perry Central HS; Perry, NY; (Y); Letterman Clb; Varsity Clb; Band; Concert Band; Jazz Band; Mrchg Band; Bsktbl; Socr; Tennis; Hon Roll; Jeff Barry Mem Bsktbl Awd 85; Wstrn NY Athlt Of Week 85; Bus.

WATSON, JENNIFER; Haldane HS; Cold Spring, NY; (S); 6/70; Ski Clb; Chorus; School Play; Rep Stu Cncl; Var Tennis; High Hon Roll; Hon Roll; NHS; Math.

WATSON, JILL; Pulaski JR-SR HS; Pulaski, NY; (S); 3/96; Church Yth Grp; Drama Clb; Pres GAA; Math Clb; Band; Chorus; Yrbk Sprt Ed; Var Capt Bsktbl; Var Capt Sftbl; Pres NHS; Boston Coll; Educ.

WATSON, JOSEPH; Cardinal Hayes HS; Bronx, NY; (Y); 85/264; Aud/Vis; Camera Clb; Chess Clb; Computer Clb; Varsity Clb; Nwsp Rptr; Nwsp Stf; VP Frsh Cls; Sec Soph Cls; VP Jr Cls; Schl Ltr Bsktbl, Bsbl 83 & 84; U Of S CA; Acctnt.

WATSON, LINDA; Beacon HS; Beacon, NY; (Y); 53/206; Church Yth Grp; Var Score Keeper; Stat L Vllybl; Hon Roll; NY Inst Of Techngly; Elec Engr.

WATSON, MARY BETH; Albertus Magnus HS; New City, NY; (Y); Drama Clb; Latin Clb; PAVAS; School Musical; School Play; Stage Crew; Yrbk Ed-Chief; Hon Roll; Band; Yrbk Stf; Ny Cty Fire Dept Cmnty Srv Awd 82; Ltn Clb 84; Cmnctns.

WATSON, MICHELLE; August Martin HS; Queens, NY; (Y); 18/385; Church Choir; Nwsp Rptr; Trk; Hon Roll; Prfct Atten Awd; 1st Yr Accntng Awd 85; Physcs Clb NY Awd 85; Outstndng Achv Chem 85; Baruch Coll; Accntng.

WATSON, NICOLE H; Holy Trinity Diocesan HS; Roosevelt, NY; (Y); Sec Church Yth Grp; Dance Clb; Drama Clb; Girl Scts; Service Clb; School Musical; School Play; Nwsp Stf; Yrbk Stf; Var Trk; Assn Adv Retarded Childrn 83; 3rd Pl Art Awd; Dickinson Coll Scholar; Katherine Gibbs Coll Scholar; Dickinson Coll; Bus Mngmnt.

WATSON, SEAN; Hoosick Falls Central HS; Hoosick Falls, NY; (Y); 80/115; Boy Scts; Church Yth Grp; Varsity Clb; Var L Ftbl; Wt Lftg; Var L Wrstlng; Co-Capt Ftbl Tm 85-86; Capt Wrstlng Tm 85-86; Greco-Rmn Wrstlng Tm, Empire ST Gams 84; Cochng.

WATSON, TARINE; Ossining HS; Ossining, NY; (Y); Church Yth Grp; Cmnty Wkr; Dance Clb; Girl Scts; Temple Yth Grp; Church Choir; Color Guard; Mrchg Band; Variety Show; Vllybl; Russel Sage Coll; Bus Adm.

WATSON, TRISHA; Bethpage HS; Bethpage, NY; (Y); 60/257; Off Drama Clb; Thesps; Chorus; School Musical; School Play; Capt Cheerleading; Tennis; High Hon Roll; Hon Roll; C W Post U; Jrnlsm.

WATSON, VERONICA M; Roosevelt HS; Yonkers, NY; (Y); Bus Admn.

WATSON, WILLIAM J; Lockport SR HS; Lockport, NY; (Y); Latin Clb; Var L Bsbl; Var L Ice Hcky; Capt L Socr; Hon Roll; NHS; High Hon Roll; Jr NHS; Law.

WATTENBERG, JERRY; Tappan Zee HS; Tappan, NY; (Y); 37/300; JA; Ski Clb; Concert Band; Jazz Band; Yrbk Ed-Chief; NHS; NY U Schlr 85; Regents Schlrshp 85; Natl Hnr Roll 85; NY U; Bus.

WATTS, E DAVID; Northeastern Clinton Central Schl; Mooers, NY; (Y); Model UN; Jazz Band; Mrchg Band; Symp Band; Var Crs Cntry; Hon Roll; Boy Scts; Church Yth Grp; Band; Orch; Schlrs Dllrs 84-86; Military Svc; Law.

WATTS, LIA; Mount Vernon HS; Mount Vernon, NY; (Y); Church Yth Grp; Civic Clb; Dance Clb; Pep Clb; Spanish Clb; Chorus; Mrchg Band; School Musical; School Play; Rep Jr Cls; Htl Mgt.

WATTS, MICHAEL; City Honors HS; Buffalo, NY; (Y); 22/97; Nwsp Rptr; Rep Stu Cncl; Var Bsktbl; Var Capt Tennis; Hon Roll; Prfct Atten Awd; SAR Awd; Bus Mgmt.

WATTS, MICHELLE; Walton HS; Bronx, NY; (Y); 34/675; Office Aide; Swmmng; Tennis; Vllybl; Hon Roll; NHS; Ntl Merit Schol; Regnts Schlrshp 85; Cert Merit Spnsh, Engl, Hstry, Math & Psych 82; SUNY New Paltz; Engrng.

WATTSMAN, TERRI-ANN; Keveny Menorial Acad; Troy, NY; (S); Girl Scts; JV Var Bsktbl; Crs Cntry; Var Sftbl; High Hon Roll; Math Clb.

WATZ, CHRISTOPHER; Grand Island HS; Gr Island, NY; (Y); Church Yth Grp; Drama Clb; Ski Clb; Band; Chorus; Madrigals; School Musical; School Play; Stage Crew; L Socr; Engrng.

WAUGH II, CHARLES J; Waterloo SR HS; Waterloo, NY; (Y); Am Leg Boys St; Drama Clb; Pep Clb; Chorus; School Musical; Rep Soph Cls; Hon Roll; Prfct Atten Awd; Soph & JR Hmecmng Flts Chrprsn 82-84; JR Prom Chrprsn 85; Bus Admin.

WAWROWSKI, MICHELLE; Lancaster Central HS; Lancaster, NY; (S); Boys Clb Am; DECA; GAA; Flag Corp; Variety Show; Hon Roll; Boys Clb Outstndng Membr Yr, Spec Partcp Awd 84; Best Catgry NY ST Ceramic 84; Erie CC; Physcolgy.

WAWRZYNEK, WALTER L; Cardinal O Hara HS; N Tonawanda, NY; (Y); Computer Clb; French Clb; JA; Stage Crew; Bowling; Socr; NCCC; Law.

WAXMAN, BARI R; Midwood HS; Brooklyn, NY; (Y); 51/605; Dance Clb; Math Tm; Model UN; Teachers Aide; Variety Show; Nwsp Bus Mgr; Nwsp Rptr; Yrbk Stf; High Hon Roll; Jr NHS; NYS Regents Schlrshp 85; Intntl Bus.

WAY, CHRISTY L; Susquehanna Valley HS; Kirkwood, NY; (Y); 6/177; Spanish Clb; Band; JV Vllybl; High Hon Roll; Hon Roll; Jr NHS; NHS; Prfct Atten Awd; Regents Schlrshp 85; Moreau Schlrshp 85; Kings Coll; Accntnt.

WAY, SANDRA; Beacon HS; Beacon, NY; (Y); Library Aide; Office Aide; Chorus; Kissler Bus Ins; Sec.

WAYMAN, STEVEN; Schoharie Central HS; Schoharie, NY; (S); Boy Scts; Band; Crs Cntry; Trk; Hon Roll; Order Of The Arrow 81; Eagle Scout 85; Air Force; Pilot.

WAYNE, LISA; Tottenville HS; Staten Island, NY; (Y); 26/400; VP Debate Tm; Drill Tm; Cheerleading; Kiwanis Awd; NHS; Rotary Awd; VP Key Clb; NYC Mayoral Svc Awd 85; Vassar; Pol Sci.

WAYSON, MARGIE; St John Villa Acad; Staten Is, NY; (Y); GAA; Math Tm; Pep Clb; Color Guard; Stu Cncl; Bsktbl; Trk; Rep Frsh Cls; MVP Bsktbl 83-84; Sci Olympd 82-83; Hnrs Trig 84-85; Mt St Vincent Coll; Nrsng.

WAZ, TARRYN; Columbia HS; Troy, NY; (Y); 33/400; Debate Tm; German Clb; Ski Clb; Nwsp Rptr; Nwsp Stf; Yrbk Stf; Socr; Hon Roll; Jr NHS; NHS; Otto Von Guenther Scholar 84-85; Pres Acad Ftns Awd 84-85; Coll St Rose; Advrtsng.

WEAKLAND, PATRICK WAYNE; Hamburg SR HS; Hamburg, NY; (Y); Crmnlgy.

WEATHERWAX, PAMELA; Commack H S North; E Northport, NY; (Y); MMM; Pres Sec Orch; Off Frsh Cls; Off Soph Cls; Off Jr Cls; Off Stu Cncl; JV Timer; Var Trk; High Hon Roll; Educ.

WEAVER, DAVID S; Pittsford Mendon HS; Pittsford, NY; (Y); Var L Bsbl; Var Capt Bsktbl; JV Im Socr; Im Tennis; All Cnty Bsktbl 85; Bates Coll.

WEAVER, ERIKA; Schoharie Central HS; Gallupville, NY; (S); 19/90; Pres Varsity Clb; Yrbk Stf; Sec Jr Cls; VP Sr Cls; Capt Bsktbl; Capt Socr; Var Trk; Hon Roll; Schlrc Cnty All Str Tm Sccr 83 & 84; All Str Sccr Tm Sec 2 84; MIP Bsktbl 83-84; Syracuse U; Engrng.

WEAVER, KARL; Marion JR SR HS; Marion, NY; (Y); Math Tm; Band; Chorus; Pep Band; School Musical; School Play; Yrbk Stf; Rep Stu Cncl; Im Bowling; JV Crs Cntry; NY ST Rgnts Schrlshp 85; Fredonia ST; Poltcl Sci.

WEAVER, KELLY; Remsen Central HS; Remsen, NY; (Y); Church Yth Grp; Cmnty Wkr; Library Aide; Band; Concert Band; Mrchg Band; Frsh Cls; Soph Cls; Trs Jr Cls; Sr Cls; :RN.

WEAVER, MARTY; Lockport HS; Lockport, NY; (Y); 183/454; Computer Clb; Latin Clb; Math Clb; Varsity Clb; Var Capt Bowling; 2nd Pl Niagara Frontier League Bwlng Champ 84; Engr.

WEAVER, MICHELE; Oneida SR HS; Oneida, NY; (S); 1/225; Church Yth Grp; Exploring; Intnl Clb; Spanish Clb; VP Frsh Cls; Pres Stu Cncl; Var Capt Bowling; Cit Awd; DAR Awd; High Hon Roll; Intl Fllwshp Schlrshp 83; Georgetown U; Intl Rltns.

WEAVER, TAMMY; G Ray Bodley HS; Fulton, NY; (Y); High Hon Roll; Hon Roll; Shrthnd Awd 83-84; Yng Vlntrs In Actn 84; Sec.

WEAVER, TONYA; Fort Ann Central Schl; Ft Ann, NY; (Y); 12/51; Band; Concert Band; Mrchg Band; Yrbk Ed-Chief; Yrbk Phtg; Yrbk Rptr; Score Keeper; Vllybl; High Hon Roll; 4-H; 1st Pl St Nrsng Comp 84-85; Doctor.

WEBB, CAROL; Williamsville East HS; Williamsville, NY; (Y); 91/302; 4-H; German Clb; Ski Clb; Capt Var Crs Cntry; Var L Trk; JV Vllybl; High Hon Roll; Prfct Atten Awd; Archit.

WEBB, DONAVAN; South Shore HS; Brooklyn, NY; (Y); Aud/Vis; Teachers Aide; Varsity Clb; Var Bsbl; NY Inst Tech; Electrnc Tech.

WEBB, JANE E; Seton Catholic Central HS; Vestal, NY; (Y); 5/150; Church Yth Grp; Spanish Clb; Band; Mrchg Band; Yrbk Stf; High Hon Roll; Hon Roll; NHS; Spanish NHS; Spnsh Hnr Socty Awd Specl Hlp; ST U Of NY; Acctng.

WEBBER, CHRISTINA; Paul V Moore HS; Constantia, NY; (Y); Exploring; GAA; Math Tm; Sec Science Clb; Stu Cncl; Var JV Socr; JV Trk; JV Vllybl; High Hon Roll; Hon Roll; Grace Awd Indoor Sccr 84-85; Bst Dfndr Awd Indoor Sccr 84-85; SUNY Oswego; Bio Sci.

WEBBER, KEVIN D; St Francis HS; Orchard Park, NY; (Y); 12/146; Pres Church Yth Grp; Quiz Bowl; Ski Clb; Yrbk Stf; JV Bsbl; JV Ice Hcky; Hon Roll; NHS; Knights Of The Alter Awd 82; NY ST Regents Schlrshp 85; U Of Detroit; Chem Engrng.

WEBBER, STEPHEN; Gloversville HS; Gloversville, NY; (Y); Pres Exploring; French Clb; Pres Key Clb; Pep Clb; VP Science Clb; Band; Jazz Band; Pep Band; Stage Crew; Bus.

WEBER, A REGINA; Holy Trinity Diocesan HS; Jericho, NY; (S); 5/390; Math Clb; Stage Crew; Yrbk Stf; Stu Cncl; Red Cross Aide; ROTC; Mu Alp Tht; NHS; NEDT Awd; Soc Distngshd H S Stu Awd 84; Princeton Bk Clb Semi-Fnlst 83-84; Georgetown; Bus.

WEBER, ANNE L; Williamsville North HS; Williamsville, NY; (Y); 1/311; Band; Orch; Pep Band; School Musical; Yrbk Stf; High Hon Roll; Jr NHS; NHS; Ntl Merit Ltr; Val; Outstndng Chem Stu 83; Harvard Book Awd 84; Rgnts Schlrshp 85; Cornell U; Math & Sci.

WEBER, ARON; Clarkston H S North; New City, NY; (Y); Pres Spanish Clb; VP Temple Yth Grp; Swmmng; Hon Roll; Mu Alp Tht; NHS; Pre-Med.

WEBER, C BRITTEN; Sweet Home SR HS; Tonawanda, NY; (Y); 29/425; Yrbk Phtg; Yrbk Stf; JV Lcrss; Hon Roll; NHS; Pres Acadmc Fit Awd 85; Regnts Schlrshp 85; Syracuse U; Bus.

WEBER, CHARLES R; Oneonta HS; Oneonta, NY; (Y); 54/162; Boys Clb Am; Ski Clb; Varsity Clb; Rep Stu Cncl; JV Bowling; L Ftbl; L Trk; JV Wrstlng; St Schlr; NY ST Regents Schlrshp 85; U Of Buffalo; Elec Engr.

WEBER, DANIEL; Olean HS; Olean, NY; (Y); Im Bsktbl; L Capt Ftbl; Im Wt Lftg; Comp.

WEBER, JANICE; Long Island Lutheran HS; W Babylon, NY; (S); 5/105; Band; Chorus; Jazz Band; School Musical; Sec Stu Cncl; JV Var Sftbl; JV Var Vllybl; High Hon Roll; NHS; Socty Distngshd Amer H S Stdnts 85; Music.

WEBER, KAREN; Clarence Central SR HS; Williamsville, NY; (Y); 2/264; Church Yth Grp; Lib Concert Band; Mrchg Band; Pep Band; Nwsp Stf; Bausch & Lomb Sci Awd; High Hon Roll; NHS; Pres Schlr; Sal; Regents Schlrshp 85; Outstndng Phys Stu Yr 85; Dr Joseph Stern Math Awd 85; SUNY Buffalo; Pharm.

WEBER, KARIN; Irondequoit HS; Rochester, NY; (Y); 36/400; Ski Clb; Yrbk Phtg; Ed Yrbk Stf; Rep Frsh Cls; Rep Soph Cls; Rep Jr Cls; Rep Sr Cls; Hon Roll; Latin Clb; Stage Crew; Phtogrphy Schltc Art Shw Key Awd 85; Sprts Phtogrphs Pblshd Lcl Nwsp 85; Phtogrphy.

WEBER, KATHLEEN; F D Roosevelt HS; Staatsburg, NY; (Y); Hosp Aide; Office Aide; Pride Committee 85; Legal Sec.

WEBER, MARIANNE; Columbia HS; Troy, NY; (Y); Ski Clb; Yrbk Stf; Rep Sr Cls; JV Capt Cheerleading; Capt Powder Puff Ftbl; Score Keeper; JV Trk; Springfield Coll; Phy Therapy.

WEBER, MARYBETH; Belmont Central HS; Belmont, NY; (Y); 1/31; Trs Spanish Clb; Trs Band; Chorus; Mrchg Band; Yrbk Ed-Chief; VP Soph Cls; Var Cheerleading; Var Tennis; High Hon Roll; NHS; Comp Sci.

WEBER, MATTHEW J; Kington HS; Woodstock, NY; (Y); 6/520; Sec Band; Orch; Pep Band; Yrbk Sprt Ed; Var Capt Crs Cntry; French Hon Soc; High Hon Roll; NHS; Ntl Merit Ltr; All-ST Wind Ensmbl 84; All-Estrn Cncrt Band 85; IBM Watson Schlrshp 84-85; U Of MI; Mech Engrng.

WEBLEY, KEVIN C; August Martin HS; Jamaica, NY; (Y); Cmnty Wkr; FBLA; Office Aide; Teachers Aide; Varsity Clb; Ftbl; Trk; Wt Lftg.

WEBSTER, COLLEEN; Notre Dame HS; Horseheads, NY; (Y); Cmnty Wkr; French Clb; Political Wkr; Lit Mag; Sftbl; Hon Roll; NHS; Corning CC; Erly Chldhd Educ.

WEBSTER, MARIE L; James I Oneill HS; Highland Falls, NY; (Y); 12/118; Computer Clb; Pres German Clb; Office Aide; Teachers Aide; Chorus; Lit Mag; Pres Bowling; JV Var Socr; High Hon Roll; Jr NHS; West Pt Hosp Altar & Guild Schlrshp 85; Rgnts Schlrshp 85; Mt St Marys Schlrshp 85; Mt St Marys Coll; Nrsng.

WEBSTER, MICHAEL B; Sherburne-Earlville JR SR HS; Smyrna, NY; (Y); Swmmng; Am Leg Boys St; Boy Scts; Drama Clb; Quiz Bowl; Band; Concert Band; Jazz Band; Pep Band; School Musical; Sprts Physcn.

WEBSTER, SHEILA A; Cardinal Spellman HS; Bronx, NY; (Y); Church Yth Grp; Variety Show; Rep Stu Cncl; Im Bsktbl; Var Bowling; Var Trk; Im Vllybl; Hon Roll; Mt St Vincent Coll; Nrs.

WEBSTER, SYLVIA; Hudson HS; Hudson, NY; (Y); AFS; Boys Clb Am; Church Yth Grp; Library Aide; Radio Clb; Spanish Clb; Church Choir; Nwsp Stf; Cheerleading; Trk; Womens Progsv Clb Schlrshp 85; Mohawk Vly Comm; Human Svcs.

WEBSTER, WENDY; Longwood HS; Ridge, NY; (Y); 72/488; Orch; Var Bowling; Var Sftbl; Hon Roll; Peer Ldrshp; Psych.

WECHSLER, DEIRDRE; John Bowne HS; Bayside, NY; (Y); Aud/Vis; Cmnty Wkr; Office Aide; Teachers Aide; Temple Yth Grp; School Play; Off Soph Cls; Off Jr Cls; Rep Stu Cncl; Hon Roll; Supr Yth 84; Pride Of Yankees Awd 84; SUNY; Bus Admin.

WECKER, NICOLE R; Canarsie HS; Brooklyn, NY; (Y); 149/564; Aud/Vis; Drama Clb; PAVAS; Concert Band; Orch; School Musical; NY ST Regents Schlrshp 85; Brooklyn Coll; Psychology.

WEEKES, DONELLE G; Hillcrest HS; New York, NY; (Y); 153/793; Church Yth Grp; Dance Clb; Hosp Aide; JA; Office Aide; Church Choir; Orch; School Musical; Stage Crew; Off Sr Cls; Howard U; Lib Arts.

WEEKS, CHRIS; Ithaca HS; Newfield, NY; (Y); Am Leg Boys St; Church Yth Grp; Jazz Band; Trs Sr Cls; JV Capt Bsbl; Var Capt Bsktbl; Stat Ftbl; Var Capt Golf; NHS; Prfct Atten Awd; Cornell U.

WEEKS, JOHN; Weedsport HS; Weedsport, NY; (Y); 17/90; Yrbk Stf; Sec Frsh Cls; VP Soph Cls; VP Jr Cls; VP Sr Cls; Var JV Diving; Var JV Ftbl; Var JV Swmmng; Hon Roll; Jr NHS; Pre-Med.

WEEMAN, MICHAEL; Cardinal O Hara HS; Grand Island, NY; (Y); 5/150; Chess Clb; Spanish Clb; Drm & Bgl; Var Crs Cntry; Var Trk; High Hon Roll; Hon Roll; Drum & Bugle Corps Treas 83; RIT; Comp Sci.

WEESE, DEBORAH A; Frontier Central HS; Hamburg, NY; (Y); 5/500; Sec Drama Clb; Chorus; School Musical; Sec Nwsp Stf; Rep Sr Cls; High Hon Roll; Sec NHS; Sec JA; Latin Clb; Thesps; Outstndg SR Awd 85; Fredonia Hillman Schlrshp 85; NYSSMA Mixed Chorus 84; Niagara U; Comm.

WEGNER, FRANK; Cathedral Prep; Glendale, NY; (Y); German Clb; Varsity Clb; Bsbl; Bsktbl; Accntnt.

WEGNER, MARCUS C; Kingston HS; Rifton, NY; (Y); 160/600; Church Yth Grp; Drama Clb; Church Choir; School Play; Nwsp Stf; Hon Roll; NYS Rgnts Schlrshp 85; Art.

WEHRLE, BETTINA; Saint John The Baptist HS; Lindenhurst, NY; (Y); 26/556; Church Yth Grp; Debate Tm; Hosp Aide; Color Guard; Swmmng; French Hon Soc; High Hon Roll; Hon Roll; Stage Crew; Nwsp Stf; Pre-Med.

WEHRLE, MICHELLE; Sauquoit Valley Central HS; Sauguoit, NY; (Y); Chorus; Yrbk Stf; Hon Roll.

WEI, LUCY; Fontbonne Hall HS; Brooklyn, NY; (Y); Teachers Aide; Church Choir; Trs Jr Cls; Pres Sr Cls; Tennis; Hon Roll; Prfct Atten Awd; Bus.

WEIBEL, BRIAN; Frontier HS; Blasdell, NY; (S); 20/500; German Clb; Math Clb; Math Tm; Var L Mgr(s); Var L Trk; Hon Roll; NHS; Ntl Merit Ltr; NEDT Awd; Engr.

WEICHERT, WILLIAM; William Nottingham HS; Syracuse, NY; (Y); French Clb; Latin Clb; Nwsp Stf; High Hon Roll; Hon Roll; NHS; Cornell Clb Of Cntrl NY 85; Slvr Mdlst Empire ST Gms Fgr Sktng 84; Estrn Sctnl Qlfr Fgr Sktng 84; Harvard; Sclgy.

WEICK, KEVIN; Kenmore East HS; Tonawanda, NY; (Y); Boy Scts; Church Yth Grp; Church Choir; Stage Crew; Hon Roll; Sci Hnrs Awd 82; U Buffalo; Sci.

WEIDEL, ERIC; Coxsackie-Athens HS; Coxsackie, NY; (Y); German Clb; Ski Clb; Bsbl; Socr; High Hon Roll; Hon Roll.

WEIDEMANN, MICHELLE S; Half Hollow Hills H S East; Melville, NY; (Y); 26/586; French Clb; Hosp Aide; Mrchg Band; Orch; School Musical; Symp Band; High Hon Roll; NHS; Ntl Merit Ltr; Union U; Med.

WEIDEN, ELIZABETH C; Franciscan HS; Yorktown Hts, NY; (Y); Church Yth Grp; Spanish Clb; Church Choir; School Musical; Nwsp Rptr; Yrbk Stf; JV Vllybl; Hon Roll; NHS; Spanish NHS; Manhattan Coll; Pol Sci.

WEIDENFELD, YARDEN F; East JR SR HS; Rochester, NY; (Y); 3/267; Am Leg Boys St; Math Tm; Model UN; Temple Yth Grp; Rep Stu Cncl; Var L Crs Cntry; NHS; Ntl Merit Ltr; Science Clb; Rep Sr Cls; Harvard Bk Awd 84; Frank Garnett Nwspr Carrier Schlrshp 85; Mission To Poland 85; Harvard U.

WEIGEL, DOUGLAS; E Aurora HS; East Aurora, NY; (S); 13/182; Boys Clb Am; Drama Clb; Key Clb; Letterman Clb; Varsity Clb; Stu Cncl; Var Capt Golf; Hon Roll; NHS; School Play; ECIC Sec VI Golf Champ 84; NYS Regents Schlrshp 85; U Of Rochester; Bus Admin.

WEIGEL, JOYCE; Kenmore East HS; Tonawanda, NY; (Y); GAA; Pep Clb; Varsity Clb; JV Var Vllybl; Cnaisius Coll; Sectrl Stds.

WEIGHTMAN, SCOTT; Saranac Central HS; Plattsburgh, NY; (S); Capt Var Bsbl; JV Bsktbl; Var JV Ftbl; Hon Roll; Crim Sci.

WEIL, IVY; John H Glenn HS; E Northport, NY; (Y); Drama Clb; Library Aide; MMM; Spanish Clb; Temple Yth Grp; Chorus; School Musical; School Play; Stage Crew; High Hon Roll; NYSSMA 82 84 85; Music.

WEILACHER, BONNIE; Frewsburg Central HS; Frewsburg, NY; (Y); Rep Band; Chorus; Concert Band; Jazz Band; Mrchg Band; VP Frsh Cls; Pres Soph Cls; Off Stu Cncl; JV Var Cheerleading; NHS; Sci.

WEILAND, PENELOPE; Potsdam Central Schl; Norwood, NY; (Y); AFS; Dance Clb; Math Tm; School Musical; Socr; VP NHS; Ntl Merit SF; St Lawrence U Talentd JRS 83-84; NY ST Regents Scholar 85; Clarkson U; Jrnlsm.

WEILBACHER, DIANE; North Babylon SR HS; Babylon, NY; (Y); French Clb; Intnl Clb; Chorus; Madrigals; School Musical; Swing Chorus; Mgr(s); French Hon Soc; High Hon Roll; NHS; Diane Weilbacher; Vet.

WEILL, STEVEN; Clarkstown HS North; New City, NY; (Y); VP Spanish Clb; School Play; Yrbk Stf; VP Soph Cls; VP Jr Cls; Pres Sr Cls; JV Tennis; JV Trk; Hon Roll; Jr NHS; Phy Fit Awd 84; Hnr Being Stdnt Exch Prog Itly 85; Bus.

WEIMAR, JEANNINE; Fontbonne Hall Acad; Booklyn, NY; (Y); 12/123; Church Yth Grp; Cmnty Wkr; Drama Clb; French Clb; Red Cross Aide; Chorus; Nwsp Stf; Var Capt Swmmng; High Hon Roll; NHS; Hugh O Brian Intl Yth Ldrshp Fndtn 84-85; Dvlpmnt Humn Potntl/Peer Ldrshp 85; Pre-Med.

WEIMER, GERALD; Warsaw Central Schl; Warsaw, NY; (S); 13/93; Church Yth Grp; Cmnty Wkr; Trs JA; Mathletes; Soroptimist; Spanish Clb; Speech Tm; Church Choir; High Hon Roll; NHS; Potsdam Coll; Comp Prgm.

WEIMER, MICHAEL D; Miller Place HS; Miller Place, NY; (Y); Debate Tm; Jazz Band; Mrchg Band; Pep Band; Symp Band; Nwsp Stf; Rep Jr Cls; Ftbl; Hon Roll; St Schlr; Regents Schlrshp 85; Dentistry.

WEINBAUM, ELLEN; Ossining HS; Ossining, NY; (Y); Latin Clb; Model UN; Pep Clb; Teachers Aide; Temple Yth Grp; School Play; Nwsp Rptr; Yrbk Ed-Chief; Yrbk Stf; Stu Cncl; Excllnce In Latin 83-84; Citibnk Essay Cont Fnlst 82-83; HS Essay Cont 1st Pl 82-83; Tchng.

WEINBERG, DONNA; Jericho HS; Westbury, NY; (Y); Art Clb; Computer Clb; Key Clb; Political Wkr; Temple Yth Grp; Chorus; Stage Crew; Mgr(s); Natl Art Hnr Soc 85; FIT; Fshn Merch.

WEINBERG, JEFFREY; Kew-Forest HS; Jamaica, NY; (Y); 1/30; Science Clb; VP Temple Yth Grp; Nwsp Ed-Chief; VP Sftbl; Ntl Merit SF; Val; Qns Coll Pres Awd 83-84; Schl Biol Cup 83; Schl Chem Cup 84; Columbia Coll; Med.

WEINBERG, RICHARD A; Amityville Memorial HS; Amityville, NY; (Y); Am Leg Boys St; Church Yth Grp; Political Wkr; Ski Clb; Varsity Clb; Var Bsbl; Var Ftbl; Boys ST City Cnclmn; Boys ST Squad Ldr; Stockbroker.

WEINBERG, STUART; Farmingdale HS; Farmingdale, NY; (Y); Computer Clb; Debate Tm; Temple Yth Grp; Chorus; Stage Crew; Hon Roll; NHS; Genetics.

WEINBRECHT, LAURA; Longwood HS; N Shirley, NY; (Y); 171/487; Band; Concert Band; Mrchg Band; Hon Roll; NY ST Stu Music Assn 84 & 85; Cert Red Cross Lfgrd 84; Marine Bilgst.

WEINDORF, PAMELA L; Malverne HS; Malverne, NY; (Y); 12/158; Band; Chorus; Church Choir; Flag Corp; Cheerleading; Sftbl; High Hon Roll; NHS; Pres Schlr; Varsity Clb; Math & Sci Tchr Schlrshp 85; Kings Clg; Math.

WEINER, ELAINE; Niskayuna HS; Schdy, NY; (Y); AFS; French Clb; Hosp Aide; Key Clb; Mrchg Band; Orch; School Musical; Symp Band; Cmnty Wkr; 4-H; Stu Writer Wk 85; Cert Achvt Candystrpng,Vol 84.

WEINER, JAY; Susan E Wagner HS; Staten Island, NY; (Y); Chorus; School Play; Stage Crew; Stu Cncl; Cit Awd; High Hon Roll; Hon Roll; Jr NHS; NHS; Law.

WEINER, KAREN; Ithaca HS; Ithaca, NY; (Y); Trs French Clb; VP Intnl Clb; Model UN; Ski Clb; Temple Yth Grp; Chorus; Jazz Band; Mrchg Band; Var JV Cheerleading; VP NHS; Brown U.

WEINHEIMER, LORNA; New Lebanon Central HS; Old Chatham, NY; (Y); 1/55; Church Yth Grp; French Clb; Math Tm; Yrbk Phtg; Yrbk Stf; Stu Cncl; Var Crs Cntry; Var Swmmng; Var Trk; High Hon Roll; Math,Sci Awd 85; Williams Coll Bk Awd 85; Womens Clb Dist Art Awd 85; Med.

WEINHOLTZ, BETH A; Niagara Wheatfield SR HS; N Tonawanda, NY; (Y); 18/313; French Clb; PAVAS; Concert Band; Mrchg Band; Nwsp Ed-Chief; Nwsp Rptr; NHS; Pep Clb; Band; Orch; Niagara U Prsdntl Schlrshp,Acad Schlrshp 85; NY ST Rgnts Schlrshp 85; Niagara U; Bus Mgmt.

WEINICK, ROBIN; John F Kennedy HS; Plainview, NY; (Y); 4/275; VP Intnl Clb; Model UN; Pres Service Clb; Nwsp Stf; Yrbk Stf; High Hon Roll; NHS; Ntl Merit Ltr; U Of Rochester; Doctor.

WEINMANN, LAURA; South Kortright Central HS; Hobart, NY; (Y); 1/23; GAA; Varsity Clb; Band; Concert Band; Mrchg Band; Yrbk Stf; Trs Jr Cls; Var Bsktbl; Var Socr; Var Capt Sftbl; Excllnce Fr I, Hghst Avg Alg 82-83; Excllnce Biol, Hghst Avg Yr 83-84; Excllnce Eng, Hghst Avg 84-85.

WEINSTEIN, BARBARA; Blind Brook HS; Rye Brook, NY; (Y); Math Tm; Ski Clb; Spanish Clb; Acpl Chr; Chorus; School Musical; School Play; Nwsp Stf; Yrbk Stf; Lit Mag; Mrksmnsp 83.

WEINSTEIN, ERIC A; Susan E Wagner HS; Staten Island, NY; (Y); Key Clb; Band; School Musical; School Play; Rep Frsh Cls; Rep Jr Cls; Rep Sr Cls; VP Stu Cncl; High Hon Roll; NHS; NYS Regnts Schlrshp 85; NY U; Intl Affrs.

WEINSTEIN, JONATHAN; Wantagh HS; Wantagh, NY; (Y); 56/289; Jazz Band; Lit Mag; Pres Frsh Cls; Pres Soph Cls; Trs Sr Cls; VP Cmnty Wkr; NHS; Pres Ldrshp Skills Clb 83-85; NY St Rep Hugh O Brian Yth Found; Intl Ldrshp Sem 83; Dickinson Coll.

WEINSTEIN, NANCY ALICIA; Irondequoit HS; Rochester, NY; (Y); 70/340; Cmnty Wkr; Temple Yth Grp; Band; Orch; Pep Band; Nwsp Ed-Chief; Nwsp Rptr; Yrbk Stf; Hon Roll; Gannett Yth Awd 84; Pres Acad Ftnss Awd 84-85; Syracuse U; Brdcst Jrnlsm.

WEINSTEIN, STACY; Sheepshead Bay HS; Brooklyn, NY; (Y); Band; School Musical; Bowling; Arista Mbr 85; Archon Mbr 85; Battle Of The Bands-Winner 85; Brooklyn Coll; Music.

WEINSTEIN, STEVEN M; The Wheatley Schl; Roslyn Hts, NY; (Y); 2/132; Cmnty Wkr; Hosp Aide; Quiz Bowl; Temple Yth Grp; Nwsp Ed-Chief; Lit Mag; Bowling; Cit Awd; NHS; Ntl Merit Ltr; LI Math Fair Gold 84,Brnze 85; Hofstra U Frnch Poetry Cont 2nd Pl 84; Mock Trial Team 2nd Pl Cnty 85; Cornell U; Bio.

WEINSTOCK, DAVID; Jericho HS; Jericho, NY; (Y); Aud/Vis; PAVAS; Concert Band; Jazz Band; Mrchg Band; School Play; Nwsp Sprt Ed; Var Bowling; Var Socr; Var Trk; Law.

WEINTHAL, ERIKA S; Brighton HS; Rochester, NY; (Y); Exploring; German Clb; Model UN; Political Wkr; Radio Clb; Ski Clb; Nwsp Stf; JV Var Socr; JV Sftbl; Rep Soph Cls; NE Conf Awd Russian Lang 85; Oberlin Coll; Pol Sci.

WEINTRAUB, JARETT; Elmont Memorial HS; Elmont, NY; (Y); Computer Clb; Mathletes; Sec Trs Math Tm; Model UN; Science Clb; Pres VP Temple Yth Grp; JV Var Ftbl; JV Var Trk; Ntl Merit SF; Comp Sci.

WEINTRAUB, STACI; Shulamith HS; New York, NY; (S); 4/32; Cmnty Wkr; Math Clb; Temple Yth Grp; School Play; Nwsp Stf; Yrbk Bus Mgr; Rep Jr Cls; Hon Roll; NHS; Queens Coll; Math.

WEIR, COLLEEN; Niagara Falls HS; Niagara Falls, NY; (Y); 39/257; Aud/Vis; Computer Clb; Office Aide; Hon Roll; Jr NHS; NHS; Associated Schls Inc; Trvl.

WEISBERG, DOMINICK; John Dewey HS; Brooklyn, NY; (Y); Computer Clb; Teachers Aide; Band; Concert Band; Jazz Band; Orch; Comp Prgrmmr.

WEISBERGER, MICHAEL J; Ward Melville HS; Setauket, NY; (Y); 3/760; Computer Clb; Math Tm; Concert Band; Jazz Band; Orch; NHS; Ntl Merit SF; Mathletes; Band; Socr; NFAA Mc Donalds Tri ST Jazz Ensmbl 84-85; Intl Art Jazz Stu Scholar Awd 84.

WEISE, MARY; Tri-Valley Central HS; Claryville, NY; (Y); 2/75; Drama Clb; Band; Chorus; Pep Band; School Musical; School Play; Yrbk Stf; Var Socr; High Hon Roll; NHS; Bio Sci.

WEISENFELD, ANDREW; John H Glenn HS; Greenlawn, NY; (Y); 8/260; French Clb; Nwsp Sprt Ed; Pres Frsh Cls; Rep Soph Cls; Rep Jr Cls; Ice Hcky; French Hon Soc; Jr NHS; VP NHS; Ntl Merit Ltr; Rgnts Schlrshp 85; Predntl Acadmc Ftns Awd 85; Cornell U; Biolgcl Sci.

WEISENSALE, ANGELA; Fillmore Central HS; Portageville, NY; (S); Church Yth Grp; Chorus; Nwsp Stf; Sec Soph Cls; Sftbl; High Hon Roll; Hon Roll; NHS; Prfct Atten Awd; Bus.

WEISERBS, KERA F; Midwood H S At Brooklyn College; Brooklyn, NY; (Y); 107/635; Intnl Clb; Math Tm; Lit Mag; Var Swmmng; Semi Fnlst Westinghouse Sci Srch 85; NY JR Acad Sci Cert Merit 85; Grtr NY Metro Math Fair 84; Math.

WEISKERGER, RENEE; Frontier Central HS; Hamburg, NY; (Y); 9/554; JA; Latin Clb; Math Clb; Spanish Clb; Yrbk Stf; Jr NHS; Ntl Merit Ltr; NEDT Awd; Pres Schlr; Natl Merit Schlrshp Ltr Cmmndtn 84; NYS Regnts Schlrshp 85; Duquesne U Schlrshp 85; Duquesne U; Acctg.

WEISMAN, CARLA J; Rye Country Day Schl; Scarsdale, NY; (Y); AFS; Cmnty Wkr; French Clb; Model UN; Band; Orch; School Play; Stage Crew; Nwsp Ed-Chief; Var Cheerleading; Al-ST Band & Orchstr 83-85; Ntl Sci Olympd Bio 83-85; Ntl Frnch Cntst 83 & 84; Psychobio.

WEISS, ANDREW; United Nations International Schl; New York, NY; (Y); Ski Clb; Temple Yth Grp; Lit Mag; Trk; Hist.

WEISS, DAVID; Lansingburgh HS; Troy, NY; (Y); Church Yth Grp; German Clb; Letterman Clb; Varsity Clb; Var Bsbl; Var L Bsktbl; Var L Socr; High Hon Roll; Hon Roll; Lois M Brown Schlrshps, Mstr Sprts Awd 85; Hudson Valley CC; Cvl Engrng.

WEISS, DAVID C; Baldwin SR HS; Baldwin, NY; (Y); Exploring; Key Clb; Mathletes; Trs Temple Yth Grp; Var L Tennis; Cit Awd; High Hon Roll; Hon Roll; NY ST Rgnts Schlrshp 84-85; Brandeis U; Law.

WEISS, ERICK A; Valley Stream Central HS; Valley Stream, NY; (Y); Church Yth Grp; Band; Concert Band; Jazz Band; Mrchg Band; Orch; Ftbl; Wt Lftg.

WEISS, HEIDI; East Meadow HS; East Meadow, NY; (S); 77/414; Debate Tm; FBLA; Temple Yth Grp; Band; Mrchg Band; Symp Band; Yrbk Stf; Tennis.

WEISS, MARK; Edgemont HS; Scarsdale, NY; (S); Capt Debate Tm; Model UN; School Musical; Nwsp Ed-Chief; Rep Frsh Cls; Rep Soph Cls; Cum Larde Soc,Secnd Pl Inter Div Of NY ST Debate Finls,Outstndng Debater Awd Edgemont 84; Amherst College; Economics.

WEISS, MICHAEL J; The Bronx High Schl Of Science; Bronx, NY; (Y); JA; Yrbk Stf; Ntl Merit SF; Arista.

WEISS, MICHELE; Lansingburgh HS; Troy, NY; (Y); French Clb; Chorus; High Hon Roll; Hon Roll; Jr NHS; NHS; Magna Cum Laude 85; Pres Acad Fit Awd 85; Hudson Vly CC; Bus Admin.

WEISS, RICHARD; East Meadow HS; East Meadow, NY; (S); 44/444; Drama Clb; FBLA; Key Clb; School Play; Nwsp Stf; Yrbk Stf; Var Bsbl; JV Ftbl; Var Wt Lftg; Hon Roll; Regents Scholar 85; Spn Awd 83; Albany; Comp Sci.

WEISS, STEPHANIE I; Kings Park HS; Kings Park, NY; (Y); 65/473; Band; Concert Band; Mrchg Band; Fld Hcky; Sftbl; Vllybl; High Hon Roll; Hon Roll; NHS; ST U Albany; Pre-Law.

WEISSBERG, AMY; Long Beach HS; Long Beach, NY; (S); 31/350; Cmnty Wkr; Hosp Aide; Chorus; High Hon Roll; Hon Roll; NHS; Intern Sponsor Pgm 84-85; Future Physicians Clb 82-85; SUNY; Vet Med.

WEISSBERG, ANDREW; Commack HS North; Commack, NY; (Y); Boy Scts; Temple Yth Grp; Y-Teens; Acpl Chr; Chorus; Madrigals; Swing Chorus; Nwsp Rptr; High Hon Roll; Hon Roll; Comms.

WEISSER, WILLIAM J; Woodmere Acad; Far Rockaway, NY; (Y); 1/50; Chess Clb; Concert Band; Nwsp Rptr; Off Sr Cls; Sec Stu Cncl; JV Bsbl; Val; Var Mgr(s); High Hon Roll; Ntl Merit Ltr; Cum Laude Hnr Sco 84; Harvard Alumni Bk Awd 84; Princeton U; Chem.

WEIT, LYNN; East Meadow HS; E Meadow, NY; (S); Debate Tm; FBLA; Key Clb; Band.

WEKLAR, PATRICK; Bishop Maginn HS; Albany, NY; (Y); Art Clb; Variety Show; High Hon Roll; Hon Roll; Phil Schl Of Art; Comm Art.

WEKSLER, LISA; Susan E Wagner HS; Staten Island, NY; (Y); Teachers Aide; School Musical; Yrbk Stf; JV Tennis; Natl Hnr Soc 83-85; Hgh Hnr Rll 83-85; Pedtrcn.

WELCH, ALICIA; Buffalo Academy Of The Sacred Heart; Williamsville, NY; (Y); Hosp Aide; Science Clb; Ski Clb; Spanish Clb; Stage Crew; Nwsp Rptr; Nwsp Stf; Sec Jr Cls; JV Vllybl; Arch.

WELCH, APRIL; East Aurora HS; E Aurora, NY; (Y); 45/182; Boys Clb Am; Church Yth Grp; 4-H; Key Clb; Varsity Clb; Band; Chorus; Church Choir; Concert Band; Jazz Band; All ST Mxd Choir 84; All Star Swm Hnrs 84; Ldng Rle Schl Muscl 85; Alfred U; Comm Art.

WELCH, CHRIS; Union Endicott HS; Endicott, NY; (S); 20/460; Church Yth Grp; JV Bsbl; JV Var Computer Clb; High Hon Roll; Hon Roll; Med.

WELCH, DANIEL; Roosevelt SR HS; Hyde Park, NY; (Y); Cmnty Wkr; Y-Teens; Var L Bsbl; Bus Admin.

WELCH, DIANA; Fairport HS; Fairport, NY; (Y); Cornell U; Vet.

WELCH, GAVIN W; Averill Park HS; E Greenbush, NY; (Y); 4-H; 4-H Awd; Hon Roll; Ntl Merit Ltr; Regents Schlrshp 85; U ME Orono; Micro-Bio.

WELCH, LYNN; Tri Valley HS; Woodbourne, NY; (Y); 14/85; Church Yth Grp; Teachers Aide; Varsity Clb; Band; Yrbk Stf; Sr Cls; Socr; Sftbl; High Hon Roll; NHS.

WELCH, MARC; Victor Central Schl; Victor, NY; (Y); Ski Clb; Varsity Clb; Yrbk Stf; VP Jr Cls; Trs Sr Cls; JV Var Socr; Swmmng; Trk; Hon Roll; RIT; Art.

WELCH, MARK; Avon Central HS; Avon, NY; (Y); 20/102; Church Yth Grp; Ski Clb; Var JV Bsbl; Var JV Bsktbl; Var JV Ftbl; High Hon Roll; Hon Roll; Jr NHS; NHS; JR Athl Cup 85.

WELCH, SHERRY; Hannibal Central Schl; Hannibal, NY; (Y); Church Yth Grp; 4-H; French Clb; Pres Key Clb; JV Socr; High Hon Roll; Hon Roll; Bus.

WELCH, WILLIAM P; Cazenovia Ceantral Schl; Cazenovia, NY; (Y); 24/150; Hon Roll; NY ST Regents Schlrshp 85; Pres Acdmc Fitness Awd 85.

WELCOME, ALTON D; August Martin HS; New York, NY; (Y); John Jay Coll; Lwyr.

WELD, ROGER K; Hamburg HS; Hamburg, NY; (Y); 60/400; Pres Chorus; Var Crs Cntry; U Buffalo; Elect Engrng.

WELGOSS, WILLIAM; Kenmore East HS; Tonawanda, NY; (Y); 23/330; Varsity Clb; Variety Show; Lit Mag; Var Capt Bsbl; Var Capt Socr; High Hon Roll; NHS; St Schlr; Boys Clb Am; Var Bsktbl; Deans Awd 85; Regent Schlrshp 85; OH Northern U; Eng.

WELKER, DAN; West Irondequoit HS; Rochester, NY; (Y); 4/388; Var Varsity Clb; Var L Bsktbl; Var L Ftbl; High Hon Roll; Hon Roll; NHS; Ftbl Monroe Cty E All Star 84; Elect Engrng.

WELLER, KENNETH; Sherburne-Earlville JR SR HS; Earlville, NY; (Y); 53/142; Drama Clb; Ski Clb; St Schlr.

WELLER, MICHAEL; Lake George HS; Lake George, NY; (Y); Aud/Vis; Boy Scts; Computer Clb; Band; Chorus; Mrchg Band; Ice Hcky; JV Var Socr; Hon Roll; NHS; MVP JV Socr Tm 83; Life Sct 85; Comp Sci.

WELLINGTON, INEZ M; Harry S Truman HS; Bronx, NY; (Y); Cmnty Wkr; English Clb; Chorus; Lit Mag; Jrnslsm.

WELLMAN, JOHNNA; Springville Griffith Inst; Springville, NY; (Y); 7/201; Cmnty Wkr; 4-H; Spanish Clb; Chorus; School Play; Rep Jr Cls; Powder Puff Ftbl; Swmmng; Trk; DAR Awd; Syracuse U; Indstrl Desgn.

WELLMAN, SANDRA J; Elmira Free Acad; Elmira, NY; (Y); Sec German Clb; Pep Clb; Color Guard; Trk; High Hon Roll; NHS; NY ST Regents Schlrshp 85; Arnot-Ogden Schl Radiology.

WELLS, COLLINS; Bishop Scully HS; Amsterdam, NY; (Y); Civic Clb; JA; High Hon Roll; Hon Roll; NHS; Spch Pathlgy.

WELLS, DEBORAH L; Living Word Academy; Manlius, NY; (Y); 2/12; Drama Clb; Chorus; School Play; Nwsp Stf; Pres Sr Cls; Var Capt Socr; Var Capt Vllybl; High Hon Roll; Hon Roll; Sal; Cazenovia Coll Alum Schlrshp & Vlybl Schlrshp 85-86; Cngrssnl Cert Merit Awd & Medl 85; Cazenovia Coll; Lbrl Arts.

WELLS, DONALD J; Greenville Central HS; Greenville, NY; (Y); 2/84; Am Leg Boys St; Boy Scts; Spanish Clb; Band; Concert Band; Jazz Band; Mrchg Band; Orch; Pep Band; School Musical; Cmmndr Sons Of Am Leg; MVP Crss Cntry Tm; Miltry.

WELLS, GARY; Christian Brothers Acad; Minoa, NY; (Y); 10/96; Cmnty Wkr; FCA; Pres JA; Nwsp Stf; Var L Bsbl; Var L Ftbl; Im Wt Lftg; Cit Awd; Hon Roll; NHS; Onondaga Comm Schlr 84; Pres Yr Cntrl NY JA 85; Delg Natl JA Conf 84-85; Geo Washington U; Accntnt.

WELLS, JACQUELINE J; Union Endicott HS; Endicott, NY; (Y); 152/435; Dance Clb; Girl Scts; Key Clb; Rep Sr Cls; Var Cheerleading; Var Trk; Hon Roll; Jr NHS; NAACP Outstndg Ldrshp 85; SUNY Coll Buffalo; Elem Educ.

WELLS, KELDA; J C Birdlebough HS; Phoenix, NY; (Y); 10/190; Pres Church Yth Grp; Drama Clb; Band; Church Choir; Concert Band; Mrchg Band; Orch; School Musical; School Play; Stage Crew; U Of Toronto; Moleclr Genetics.

WELLS, LISA; Corinth Central HS; Porter Corners, NY; (Y); Spanish Clb; Variety Show; JV Bsktbl; JV Crs Cntry; Hon Roll; Bus.

WELLS, MARY; Jamesville De Witt HS; Dewitt, NY; (Y); 30/260; Church Yth Grp; VP German Clb; Hosp Aide; Political Wkr; Yrbk Stf; JV Bsktbl; JV Var Socr; JV Var Sftbl; High Hon Roll; Hon Roll; Bus.

WELLS, SHARI; Letchworth Central Schl; Castile, NY; (Y); Drama Clb; 4-H; Math Tm; Spanish Clb; Varsity Clb; Chorus; Color Guard; School Musical; Score Keeper; Swmmng; Natl Hnr Soc 85.

WELLS, VICTORIA; Manlius Pebble Hill HS; Fayetteville, NY; (Y); VP Frsh Cls; Pres Soph Cls; Pres Jr Cls; VP Sr Cls; Pres Stu Cncl; Capt Socr; Capt Tennis; Capt Vllybl; Dnfth Awd; DAR Awd; Best Female Athlete 83-85; MVP Tennis 84-85; Sophie Newcomb.

WELLS, WARREN; Whitesboro SR HS; Whitesboro, NY; (Y); French Clb; Chorus; Yrbk Stf; Lit Mag; Hon Roll; Bus Mgmt.

WELPE, JANICE SUE; Camden HS; Taberg, NY; (Y); 32/194; Am Leg Aux Girls St; Church Yth Grp; Hosp Aide; Ski Clb; Teachers Aide; Var L Crs Cntry; Var Trk; High Hon Roll; Hon Roll; NHS; Spec Olympics Aide 85.

WELSH, CAITLYN; Ballston Spa HS; Ballston Spa, NY; (Y); 3/240; Trs French Clb; Varsity Clb; Trs Frsh Cls; Trs Soph Cls; Sec Jr Cls; Sec Sr Cls; Stu Cncl; Cheerleading; Trk; Cit Awd; Gasson Schlrshp Boston Coll 85-86; Boston Coll; Engl.

WELSH, CATHY; Milford Central HS; Portlandville, NY; (S); Am Leg Aux Girls St; French Clb; Chorus; Nwsp Ed-Chief; Pres Jr Cls; Var Bsktbl; Var Socr; Var Trk; Hon Roll; NHS; Hugh O Brian Yth Ldrshp Sem 84; Liberty Bell Awd 85; Ldrshp Wrkshp Hunt Union Suco Oneonta 85; Engl.

WELSH, KEVIN; Alexandria Central HS; Alexandria, NY; (Y); Am Leg Boys St; Var L Ftbl; Var L Golf; Var JV Ice Hcky; Hon Roll; NHS; Hcky-Sprtsmnshp Awd 82-83; All Lge Hnrb Mntn-Ftbl Grd & Lnbkr 84-85; Golf-MVP 884-85; Comp Sci.

WELSH, NANCY ANNE; Mc Graw Central HS; Mc Graw, NY; (Y); 21/60; Am Leg Aux Girls St; Church Yth Grp; French Clb; Hosp Aide; Varsity Clb; Chorus; Concert Band; Mrchg Band; Trs Yrbk Stf; Pres Sr Cls; Ntl Schlr/Athl Awd 84-85; Stu Cncl Schlrshp 84-85; Sprtsmnshp Awd 84-85; Oswego ST; Educ.

WELSH, ROBT; Alexandra Central HS; Alexandria By, NY; (Y); Aud/Vis; Chess Clb; Yrbk Stf; Sec Frsh Cls; Trs Church Yth Grp; Bsbl; Ftbl; Golf; Ice Hcky; Hon Roll; Schlrshp Pin 85; Law.

WELZEL, ELIZABETH A; Mac Arthur HS; Seaford, NY; (Y); 89/360; Camera Clb; Cmnty Wkr; Science Clb; Hon Roll; NHS; Prsdntl Hlth Ftnss Awd 85; Nassau CC; Bio.

WEMMERUS, NANCY; Roy C Ketcham HS; Wappingers Falls, NY; (S); Pres AFS; Drama Clb; School Musical; School Play; Yrbk Ed-Chief; Trs Frsh Cls; VP Soph Cls; Stu Cncl; Var Tennis; Hst Jr NHS; Lynn Davis Mem Awd 83; Ntl Stu Cncl Assn Awd 84; Grnd Prz Rgnl Sci Fair 83; Cornell; Pol Sci.

WENCK, SHEILA A; Fayetteville-Manlius HS; Fayetteville, NY; (Y); 28/335; Chorus; Lit Mag; Var Swmmng; High Hon Roll; Hon Roll; Sec NHS; Ntl Merit Ltr; Pres Schlr; Church Yth Grp; Cmnty Wkr; Ntl Ltn Exam Magna Cum Laude 82-84; Rgnts Schlrshp 85; U Of Rochester; Pre Med.

WENDEL, AMY; Royalton-Hartland Central HS; Lockport, NY; (Y); 17/100; Spanish Clb; Varsity Clb; VP Frsh Cls; Pres Soph Cls; Rep Stu Cncl; Var Cheerleading; Dnfth Awd; Hon Roll; NHS; Trk; Art Stu Mnth 83-85; Adv.

WENDEL, KELLY; Tonawanda JR SR HS; Tonawanda, NY; (Y); Cornel; Accntng.

WENDELEWSKI, STANLEY J; St Anthonys HS; Smithtown, NY; (Y); Camera Clb; Ski Clb; Yrbk Phtg; Lcrss; High Hon Roll; Hon Roll; Acad Awd Sci, Soc Stud, Eng 82-83; Sci.

WENDLAND, GEORGINA; Lindenhurst HS; Lindenhurst, NY; (Y); 12/600; CAP; Drm Mjr(t); Mrchg Band; School Musical; Nwsp Stf; Yrbk Stf; High Hon Roll; NHS; Church Yth Grp; Drama Clb; Drum Majr 84; Med.

WENDLER, JUAN; St Agnes HS; New York, NY; (Y); 4/100; Hon Roll; NHS; John F Kennedy Chptr Natl Hnr Soc 84; Vet.

WENDLING, JULENE; Villa Maria Acad; Buffalo, NY; (Y); Church Yth Grp; Variety Show; Gym; Swmmng; Comp Sci.

WENGENACK, LISA; Fort Plain Central HS; Nelliston, NY; (S); 3/78; Teachers Aide; Band; Chorus; Concert Band; Jazz Band; Mrchg Band; Pep Band; High Hon Roll; NHS; 4-H; NY ST Regents Schrlshp 84-85; Mayflower Society Awd 83-84; NY ST U; Mus Ed.

WENGER, JODI; Bronx High School Of Science; Flushing, NY; (Y); Cmnty Wkr; Cit Awd; Drama Clb; Nwsp Rptr; Hon Roll; NHS; Jr Acad NY Acad Sci 85; Alpha Kappa Alpha Schrlshp 85; Pres Acad Ftns Awd 85; Wesleyan U; Chem.

WENGEWICZ, SANDRA J; Griffith Int; Springville, NY; (Y); 47/200; French Clb; Pep Clb; Concert Band; Mrchg Band; High Hon Roll; NHS; Pres Schlr; Drama Clb; Nwsp Rptr; Mgr(s); Buffalo U; Comp Sci.

WENNER, ELAINE M; Mercy HS; Fly Creek, NY; (Y); 4/100; Math Clb; Rep Frsh Cls; Rep Soph Cls; Var L Trk; High Hon Roll; Hon Roll; NHS; Dietetics.

WENTKA, DARLENE; Whitesboro SR HS; Yorkville, NY; (Y); GAA; Intnl Clb; Mathletes; Yrbk Stf; Lit Mag; JV Var Fld Hcky; Var Trk; JV Var Vllybl; Jr NHS; NHS.

WENTWORTH, HEATHER; Berlin Central Schl; Stephentown, NY; (Y); 4/57; Band; Chorus; Yrbk Stf; VP Frsh Cls; Trs Jr Cls; Trs Sr Cls; Bsktbl; Sftbl; Vllybl; Hon Roll; Lewis Memrl Schlrshp 85; Fredonia SUNY; Art.

WENTWORTH, MARY ANN; Gloversville HS; Gloversville, NY; (Y); Intnl Clb; Hon Roll; SADD Secy 84-85; Felicita Clb 83-84; Bus.

WENTZ, JONATHAN A; Canandaigua SR Acad; Canandaigua, NY; (Y); 53/277; Art Clb; Drama Clb; Key Clb; Ski Clb; Pres Spanish Clb; Sec Acpl Chr; Sec Chorus; Madrigals; School Musical; Sec Swing Chorus; Prncpls Art Awd 83; NYS Regnts Schlrshp 85; Rochester Inst Tech; Grph Dsgn.

WENZEL, BRIAN R; Pittsford Mendon HS; Pittsford, NY; (Y); 4/273; Var Tennis; High Hon Roll; NHS; Ntl Merit Ltr; Church Yth Grp; Latin Clb; Band; Variety Show; Yrbk Stf; Im Socr; Navy ROTC Schlrshp 83; Air Force ROTC Schlrshp 83; Regents Schlrshp 85; Notre Dam Schlr Awd 85; U Of Notre Dame; Pre-Law.

WENZEL, SHERYL; Allegany Central Schl; Allegany, NY; (Y); Chorus; Stat Var Bsbl; JV Var Cheerleading; Stat Score Keeper; Hon Roll.

WERBEN, DONNA L; Garden City HS; Garden City, NY; (Y); 23/320; Exploring; French Clb; Mathletes; Nwsp Stf; Yrbk Ed-Chief; Lit Mag; Mgr Wrstlng; Sec Jr NHS; 2nd Pl Hofstra U Frnch Ptry Cntst 84; Boston U; Spec Ed.

WERELEY, MICHELLE; New Berlin Central HS; New Berlin, NY; (Y); 23/48; Church Yth Grp; FBLA; Teachers Aide; Yrbk Phtg; Yrbk Stf; Lit Mag; Var Cheerleading; Var Pom Pon; Var Trk; Hon Roll; Busnss Admin; Accntnt.

WERNER, ERNEST; North Babylon SR HS; North Babylon, NY; (Y); Chorus; Stage Crew; JV Ftbl; Embry Riddle; Pilot.

WERNER, JULIET S; Vestal SR HS; Binghamton, NY; (Y); 144/450; Ski Clb; Temple Yth Grp; School Play; Nwsp Stf; Yrbk Stf; Rep Soph Cls; JV Bsktbl; Regnts Schlrshp 85; Hobart.

WERT, KATHY; Union Springs Acad; Middletown, PA; (Y); Ski Clb; Band; Concert Band; Sr Cls; Sthrn Coll TN; Exec Sec.

WERTH, DOREEN; Niagara Wheatfield SR HS; North Tonawanda, NY; (Y); Am Leg Aux Girls St; Sec Church Yth Grp; German Clb; Chorus; Church Choir; Hon Roll; NHS; Niagara Cnty Legsltv Intern 85.

WERTHEIM, SUZANNE; Commack HS; Commack, NY; (Y); 4-H; MMM; Acpl Chr; School Musical; Swing Chorus; Variety Show; Nwsp Rptr; French Hon Soc; High Hon Roll; NHS.

WERTMAN, LOU-ANN; Ogdensburg Free Acad; Ogdensburg, NY; (Y); 34/200; FBLA; Flag Corp; Yrbk Stf; Cheerleading; Ogdensburg Police Benevolnt Assoc Awd 85; Beverly Prosser Johnson Mem 85; Canton; Adm Assist.

WERTS, MELISSA; Anthony A Henninger HS; Syracuse, NY; (Y); Pres Sec Church Yth Grp; Office Aide; Chorus; Sec Church Choir; School Musical; Variety Show; Nwsp Stf; High Hon Roll; Hon Roll; Alpha Kappa Alpha Awd Acad Excllnce 85; General Motors Minority Asstnce Scholar 85; Northeastern U; Indstrl Engrng.

WERTYSCHYN, VALENTINA; Thomas J Corcoran HS; Syracuse, NY; (Y); Art Clb; Spanish Clb; Band; Concert Band; Mrchg Band; Var Tennis; High Hon Roll; NHS; Amer Music Fndtn Band Hnrs 83; Syracuse Cncl Svc Clubs 85; Syracuse U; Music Perf.

WESCOTT, JEFF; Werst Genesee SR HS; Camillus, NY; (Y); Chess Clb; Concert Band; Jazz Band; Nwsp Rptr; Bsbl; Trk; High Hon Roll; Hon Roll; NHS; Math Sympsm Awd 81-83; Long Island U; Cmnctns.

WESCOTT, KATHY; Oakfield-Alabama Central HS; Batavia, NY; (Y); 20/90; Pres AFS; Drama Clb; Office Aide; Teachers Aide; Chorus; Color Guard; School Musical; School Play; High Hon Roll; Hon Roll; Elem Educ.

WESELY, DIANE; Longwood HS; Coram, NY; (Y); 96/500; Key Clb; Church Choir; Yrbk Stf; JV Var Cheerleading; Var Pom Pon; Sftbl; Var Vllybl; Hon Roll.

WESGATE, JODY A; Eastridge HS; Rochester, NY; (Y); 24/204; Pres Spanish Clb; Mrchg Band; Yrbk Bus Mgr; Yrbk Stf; NHS; Church Yth Grp; Cmnty Wkr; Exploring; Girl Scts; Model UN; 1st Pl Genesee Regnl Ceramic Assoc 84; Hofstra U; Intl Bus.

WESLEY, MICHAEL; Hormell HS; Hornell, NY; (Y); 30/200; Band; JV Var Bsktbl; Var Golf; Hon Roll; Prfct Atten Awd; Englsh Achvt Awd 83-84.

WESLINE, SHARON; Nazareth Acad; Rochester, NY; (Y); Trs Exploring; Library Aide; Spanish Clb; School Musical; Yrbk Stf; Rep Stu Cncl; Hon Roll; NHS; Schlrshp 1st Yr Nazareth Acad 82-83; Psych.

WESLING, MOLLY; Bennett HS; Buffalo, NY; (Y); 1/219; Pres AFS; Hosp Aide; Political Wkr; Trs Spanish Clb; Variety Show; Nwsp Ed-Chief; VP Sr Cls; NHS; St Schlr; Val; DECA Region 12 1st 85; ST U NY Buffalo; Bus Admin.

WESOLOWSKY, LUBA; St George Acad; New York, NY; (Y); 1/23; Art Clb; Girl Scts; School Play; High Hon Roll; Hon Roll; NHS; Pace U; Genl Bus.

WESS, BRIAN; Kenmore East SR HS; Kenmore, NY; (Y); 94/330; Drama Clb; Lib Chorus; Concert Band; Jazz Band; Mrchg Band; Orch; School Musical; Trs Swing Chorus; Nwsp Rptr; Nwsp Stf; NY ST Schl Music Anns-Vcl Solo Grd-A 85; 1st 4 Yr Chr Stu KESH Hstry 85; U Of Buffalo Hnrs Chral 84; U S Army; Musicn.

WESS, SANDRA J; Fairport HS; Fairport, NY; (Y); Camp Fr Inc; Chorus; Swmmng; Hon Roll; St Schlr; Goyette Swim Awd 85; Red Raider Swim Awd 85; Var Clb Sec 85; Ball ST U; Bus.

WESSELY, MARY; St Francis Prep; Bayside, NY; (S); 9/690; Cmnty Wkr; VP JA; Library Aide; Capt Color Guard; Var L Sftbl; High Hon Roll; NHS; Rgnts Schlrshp 85; PSAT Cmmndtn; Bus.

WEST, BARBARA; East Aurora HS; East Aurora, NY; (S); 5/182; Trs Boys Clb Am; Yrbk Sprt Ed; L Capt Bsktbl; Var L Sftbl; L Capt Tennis; L Capt Trk; L Capt Vllybl; Hon Roll; NHS; Ntl Merit Ltr; Gftd & Talented Prog E Aurora HS 83-85; Colgate U.

WEST, BRENT V; Johnsburg Central Schl; North Creek, NY; (Y); 4/43; Trs Frsh Cls; VP Jr Cls; Var Capt Bsbl; Var Capt Bsktbl; Var Socr; High Hon Roll; NHS; Clss D ST Champ Sccr Tm 83; Plattsburgh ST; Acctng.

WEST, CHARLES; Cardinal Hayes HS; New York, NY; (Y); 21/264; Boy Scts; Debate Tm; Speech Tm; JV Swmmng; Hon Roll; Cmnty Wkr; Library Aide; Service Clb; Im JV Bsktbl; Cit Awd; U Of CT; Bus Admin.

WEST, CURTIS; Greenville Central HS; Medusa, NY; (Y); Chess Clb; Bsktbl; Golf.

WEST, EDWARD; Plattsb Urgh HS; Plattsburgh, NY; (Y); Aud/Vis; Radio Clb; Ski Clb; Varsity Clb; Stage Crew; Ftbl; Vllybl; Hon Roll; NY ST Regents Schlrshp 85; Clarkson U; Mech Engnrng.

WEST, JOELLE I; Campbell Central Schl; Campbell, NY; (Y); 3/46; French Clb; Trs Varsity Clb; School Musical; Capt Cheerleading; Sftbl; High Hon Roll; NHS; Chorus; NYS Regnts Schlrshp Wnnr 85; Elizabethtown Coll; Bus Adm.

WEST, JOHN TODD; Plattsburgh HS; Plattsburgh, NY; (Y); 3/160; Am Leg Boys St; Computer Clb; Ski Clb; JV Bsbl; JV Ftbl; Ice Hcky; Wt Lftg; High Hon Roll; Var Crs Cntry; CAP; Hnr Rl 82-85; Acad Achvt Awd Eng,Tri 83-84; USAF Acad; Comp Sci.

WEST, JUDITH; Frontier Central HS; Hamburg, NY; (S); 15/600; Exploring; 4-H; French Clb; GAA; Science Clb; Ski Clb; Varsity Clb; Drill Tm; Yrbk Stf; Var Crs Cntry; Awd Crsty Crss Cntry 84; Wnnr 4-H Dog Shw Cnty, ST Fair 84, ST Hrse Bwl 83; Vet Sci.

WEST, KATHRYN A; Marcellus HS; Marcellus, NY; (Y); AFS; Model UN; Ski Clb; School Musical; Symp Band; Nwsp Ed-Chief; Var Crs Cntry; Var Trk; Im Vllybl; 4-H; NY Regnts & E B Morgan Schlrshp; Wells Coll.

WEST, MARC; Westmoreland Central HS; Rome, NY; (Y); Boy Scts; Comp Oprtr.

WEST, SUSAN; Le Roy Central HS; Pavilion, NY; (Y); Am Leg Aux Girls St; Math Tm; Chorus; School Musical; Yrbk Ed-Chief; Var L Cheerleading; High Hon Roll; NHS; Pres AFS; Ski Clb; RPI Mth & Sci Awd 85; Sci.

WESTER, DONALD B; Vernon-Verona-Sherrill Central HS; Vernon Ctr, NY; (Y); 28/249; Am Leg Boys St; Math Clb; Var JV Wrstlng; High Hon Roll; Kiwanis Awd; AFS; Church Yth Grp; Trs Exploring; Mathletes; Var Ftbl; Eagle, NYS Rgnts, VVS Dllrs Schlrs Awds 85; Le Moyne Coll; Comp Sci.

WESTER, GEORGIA; Sauquoit Valley Central HS; Sauquoit, NY; (Y); Sec Drama Clb; Pres Chorus; School Musical; School Play; High Hon Roll; Hon Roll; NHS; Interact Clb 84-85; NYSSMA Area-Al ST Choir 84; Music Perfrmnc.

WESTERLING, STEPHEN C; Taconic Hills Central HS; Hudson, NY; (Y); 6/136; Am Leg Boys St; CAP; Computer Clb; DECA; Political Wkr; Varsity Clb; Band; Concert Band; Mrchg Band; Variety Show; Top Bus Stu 82-85; Math Awds; Military Acad; Law.

WESTFALL, LISA; Midlakes HS; Phelps, NY; (Y); 23/155; Am Leg Aux Girls St; GAA; VP Service Clb; Thesps; Band; Mrchg Band; School Musical; School Play; Yrbk Sprt Ed; Var Capt Fld Hcky; Mohawk Vly CC; Ret Bus Mgmt.

WESTFALL, ROBERT H; Guilderland Central HS; Schenectady, NY; (Y); 98/369; Ski Clb; VP Varsity Clb; Var Capt Bsktbl; Hon Roll; NHS; Regents Schlrshp 84-85; SUNY-ONEONTA; Engr.

WESTFALL, VICKI; Dryden JR SR HS; Etna, NY; (Y); 11/150; Pres Spanish Clb; Stu Cncl; High Hon Roll; Hon Roll; NHS; Acadmc Achvt Awd 84-85; Alfred U; Art.

WESTGATE, ELIZABETH; Ossining HS; Ossining, NY; (Y); Boy Scts; Spanish Clb; High Hon Roll.

WESTHAUSER, LISE; New Hyde Park Memorial HS; New Hyde Park, NY; (Y); Orch; High Hon Roll; Jr NHS; Ntl Merit Ltr; Rensselaer Medal Math,Sci 85; George Washington U Medal Math,Sci 85; SR H All Nassau Cty Orch 84-85; Music.

WESTHOFF, MARYBETH; Dominican Commercial HS; Glendale, NY; (Y); Hosp Aide; Red Cross Aide; Teachers Aide; Hon Roll; NHS.

WESTLAKE, SUE; Frontier Central HS; Lakeview, NY; (Y); FBLA; Hosp Aide; Spanish Clb; Chorus; Church Choir; Hon Roll; Buffalo ST; Bus Mgt.

WESTLEY, SEAN E; St Francis Prep; Jamaica, NY; (Y); Church Yth Grp; Band; JV Var Crs Cntry; JV Var Tennis.

WESTMACOTT, ANDY; Saranac Lake HS; Saranac Lk, NY; (Y); Golf; Hon Roll; Aerontcl Engrng.

WESTON, DONNA; De Sales HS; Waterloo, NY; (Y); Church Yth Grp; Yrbk Ed-Chief; Sec Frsh Cls; JV Socr; High Hon Roll; Hon Roll; Frnch & Englsh Awd 82-83; Accntng Awd 84-85; Nazaraeth Coll; Englsh Tchr.

WESTON, ELGIN; Cardinal Hayes HS; New York, NY; (Y); 94/264; Trk; Hon Roll; Syracuse U; Archit.

WESTON, THOMAS M; A G Berner HS; Massapequa Park, NY; (Y); 30/436; Drama Clb; School Play; Variety Show; Nwsp Bus Mgr; Trs Nwsp Stf; Trs Stu Cncl; Var Lcrss; Var Socr; NHS; Ntl Merit Ltr; T J Watson Mem Schlrshp 85; NYS Regnts Schlrshp 85; Harvard U; Psychlgy.

WESTPFAHL, RICHARD; Mayville Central HS; Mayville, NY; (S); 4/50; Computer Clb; French Clb; JV Bsktbl; L Bowling; Im Fld Hcky; L Tennis; Im Wrstlng; High Hon Roll; Jr NHS; NHS; Schlrshp Jamestown CC 85; Pres Ftnss Awd 84-85; Hnr Stu 85; Jamestown CC; Accntg.

WESTPHAL, DAVID; St Josephs Collegiate Inst; N Tonawanda, NY; (Y); 1/195; Math Tm; Science Clb; Yrbk Rptr; Bowling; High Hon Roll; NHS; Ntl Merit Ltr; Val; Natl Merit Sci Awd; Physcn.

WESTPHAL, GREG; Liverpool HS; Liverpool, NY; (S); 88/791; JV Bsbl; JV Bsktbl; Im Bowling; Im Golf; Im Vllybl; Im Wt Lftg; Hon Roll; Jr NHS; NROTC Fnlst 85; Comp Sci.

WETMORE, BRIAN T; Westhill HS; Syracuse, NY; (Y); JV Ftbl; JV Trk; Lemoyne; Business.

WETMORE, STEVE; Harpursville HS; Nineveh, NY; (Y); 7/100; AFS; Boy Scts; 4-H; French Clb; Varsity Clb; Nwsp Ed-Chief; Nwsp Phtg; Nwsp Rptr; Nwsp Sprt Ed; Nwsp Stf; Wrstlng Most Sprtd Trphy 85; Actvty Awd Trphy 85; Wrstlng 6th Pl Sec IV Fnls 85; Art.

WETTLAUFER, INGE; Skaneateles HS; Skaneateles, NY; (S); Cmnty Wkr; Jr Cls; JV Tennis; High Hon Roll; NHS; Math.

WETZEL, DANIEL; Rush-Henrietta Sperry HS; Rochester, NY; (Y); VP German Clb; ROTC; Varsity Clb; VP Jr Cls; Pres Sr Cls; Var Capt Ftbl; Var Capt Lcrss; Hon Roll; Boys ST 85-86; Navy.

WETZEL, LAURA A; Smithtown High Schl West; Smithtown, NY; (Y); Exploring; German Clb; Concert Band; Mrchg Band; Var L Bsktbl; Hon Roll; NYS Rgnts Schlrshp 85; Pres Acad Fitnss Awd 85; SUNY Binghamton.

WEXLER, SCOTT; Lakeland HS; Yorktown Hts, NY; (Y); FBLA; Temple Yth Grp; Stage Crew; Rep Soph Cls; Rep Jr Cls; Rep Sr Cls; Stu Cncl; Hon Roll; Bus.

WEYBRECHT, SCOTT; Union-Endicott HS; Endicott, NY; (S); 64/432; Boys Clb Am; Boy Scts; Ski Clb; Varsity Clb; Ftbl; Vllybl; Wt Lftg; Hon Roll; Engr.

WEYER, JEANETTE; Seton Catholic Central HS; Endwell, NY; (Y); Art Clb; Cmnty Wkr; French Clb; Key Clb; High Hon Roll; NHS.

WEYRAUTHER, TERI; Preston HS; Bronx, NY; (Y); Art Clb; FNA; Pep Clb; Service Clb; Trs Frsh Cls; Soph Cls; Sec Jr Cls; High Hon Roll; NHS; Hofstra U; Nrs.

WHALEN, ANDREW F; Pavilion Central Schl; Pavilion, NY; (Y); 10/80; Am Leg Boys St; Spanish Clb; Stage Crew; Rep Frsh Cls; Trs Jr Cls; JV Bsbl; Im JV Bsktbl; Var Golf; JV Var Socr; Jr NHS.

WHALEN, BRIAN R; West Seneca W SR HS; West Seneca, NY; (Y); 164/548; Boy Scts; Church Yth Grp; School Musical; JV Crs Cntry; JV Wrstlng; NY ST Regents Schlrshp 84-85; Frank & Helen Cholewka Schlrshp 81-82; Math.

WHALEN, DANIEL A; Christian Brothers Acad; Albany, NY; (Y); Am Leg Boys St; Church Yth Grp; Rep Jr Cls; Stu Cncl; Capt Crs Cntry; Capt Trk; Hon Roll; NEDT Awd; Acctng.

WHALEN, LISA M; Pavilion Central HS; E Bethany, NY; (Y); 4/69; Am Leg Aux Girls St; School Play; Sec Trs Yrbk Bus Mgr; Rep Sr Cls; Pres Stu Cncl; Var Capt Bsktbl; Var Capt Socr; Var Capt Vllybl; High Hon Roll; NHS; Regents Schlrshp Winner 85; Genesee Cnty JR Miss 85; Scholar Athlete Awd 85; Geneseo U; Business Admin.

WHALEN, MAURA; Bishop Maginn HS; Albany, NY; (Y); Debate Tm; Ski Clb; Chorus; School Musical; School Play; VP Church Yth Grp; VP Jr Cls; VP Sr Cls; Bsktbl; Tennis.

WHALEN, MICHAEL R; Paul V Moore HS; Central Sq, NY; (Y); 2/300; AFS; Computer Clb; Math Tm; Radio Clb; Var JV Bsbl; Var Capt Socr; High Hon Roll; VP Jr NHS; VP NHS; Sal; Lcl Hnr Scty Sci; All Leag Hnrbl Ment Sccr; Pres Acad Ftns Awd; U Of Rochester; Optcl Engr.

WHALEY, VERONICA L; Paul V Moore HS; Brewerton, NY; (Y); 10/297; AFS; German Clb; Math Tm; Science Clb; Nwsp Rptr; JV Crs Cntry; Capt Trk; High Hon Roll; Hon Roll; NHS; Regents Schlrshp Wnnr 85; Natl Hnr Socty 84-85; Oneonta Coll.

WHARTON, SCOTT; East Meadow HS; East Meadow, NY; (S); Computer Clb; Debate Tm; FBLA; Chorus; Nwsp Stf; Capt Var Crs Cntry; Var Tennis; Var Capt Trk; High Hon Roll; NHS; 4th Pl Econ Tst NY ST FBLA Cnvntn 85; Battered Boot Awd 83; ST Qualifer For NY ST Crs Cntry; Econ.

WHATMAN, CHRISTINE; Groton JR SR HS; Groton, NY; (Y); Art Clb; FHA; Chorus; Color Guard; Mrchg Band; Hon Roll; Binghamton Art Shw Gold Key Blue Rbbn 85; Tompkins Cnty Daisy Prncss 84-85; Bus.

WHEAT, DONNA; Washingtonville HS; New Windsor, NY; (Y); Art Clb; Cmnty Wkr; Hon Roll; Marist Coll.

WHEATLEY, MARK; Edison Tech & Ind HS; Rochester, NY; (Y); JV Im Bsktbl; Hon Roll; NHS; Childrens Mem Scholar Fund 84-86; Elec Engrng.

WHEATON, TODD; Kenmore East HS; Kenmore, NY; (Y); Mathletes; Math Clb; Math Tm; Gym; Wt Lftg; Wrstlng; Hon Roll; Engrng.

WHEELER, ANDREW; Corning-Painted Post West HS; Corning, NY; (Y); 114/254; Boy Scts; Cmnty Wkr; Thesps; Madrigals; School Play; Variety Show; JA; PAVAS; Acpl Chr; Chorus; Medcl Explr Pst 82-85; Sci Cls Svc Awd 85; Big Brother 82-84.

WHEELER, BETHANY GENE; William Nottingham HS; Syracuse, NY; (Y); 6/230; Latin Clb; Nwsp Ed-Chief; JV Capt Socr; High Hon Roll; Hon Roll; NHS; Pres Schlr; Chorus; Lit Mag; JV Sftbl; Cornell Bk Awd Outstndng Acadmcs/Extrcurrclrs 84; Utstndng Sci Stu 85; S Theiner Memrl Fnd Schlrshp 85; Brown U; Bio.

WHEELER, BETHANY R; Faith Heritage Schl; Vestal, NY; (Y); 2/22; Band; Chorus; Trs Sr Cls; Rep Stu Cncl; Score Keeper; High Hon Roll; NHS; Sal; Church Yth Grp; Church Choir; Distngshd Chrstn H S Stdnts 84; Houghton Coll.

WHEELER, CINDY; Galway HS; Galway, NY; (Y); 7/86; Dance Clb; Trs Drama Clb; Varsity Clb; Sec Chorus; Church Choir; Variety Show; Hst Soph Cls; Sec Trs Cheerleading; JV Trk; High Hon Roll; Acad Awds 83-84; Acad Exclnce By Skidmore 84; Math.

WHEELER, ELLEN; Fort Plain Central HS; Ft Plain, NY; (Y); 7/55; Am Leg Aux Girls St; Sec French Clb; Varsity Clb; Yrbk Sprt Ed; Pres Frsh Cls; Rep VP Stu Cncl; Var Bsktbl; Var Crs Cntry; Var Sftbl; Pres NHS; Most Outstndng Underclsswmn-Athltcs 83-85; All Tri-Vly Leag Selctn-Bsktbl, Sftbl, X-Cntry, Sccr 84-85; Pre-Med.

WHEELER, EMILY; Hoosick Falls Central Schl; Hoosick Falls, NY; (Y); French Clb; Pep Clb; Pres Frsh Cls; Stu Cncl; Hon Roll; NHS; Hnr Awd 83 & 84; Merit Awd 85.

WHEELER, JANICE; Dryden HS; Freeville, NY; (Y); Drama Clb; Spanish Clb; School Musical; School Play; VP Jr Cls; VP Sr Cls; Rep Stu Cncl; Swmmng; Trk; NHS; Spn Schltc Achvt Hon Awd 85; AZ ST U; Psych.

WHEELER, KAREN; Union Springs Acad; Brewerton, NY; (Y); 25/52; Church Yth Grp; Chorus; Church Choir; School Musical; School Play; Variety Show; Yrbk Stf; Im Bsbl; Im Bsktbl; Var Score Keeper; Most Caring SR Awd 84-85; Deans List Hnr 84-85; Most Outstndng Resdnt Of Sunset Hall 84-85; Onondaga CC; Dentl Hygn.

WHEELER, KURTIS P; Cazenovia Central HS; New Woodstock, NY; (Y); 7/153; VP Aud/Vis; Yrbk Bus Mgr; Pres Jr Cls; Pres Stu Cncl; Co-Capt Ftbl; Co-Capt Trk; Ntl Merit SF; Marine ROTC Schlrshp 85; Cngrssmns Medal Of Merit 85; U S Army Rsrv Ntl Schlr/Athlt Awd 85; Harvard U; Intl Reltns.

WHEELER, LORIANN; Fairport HS; Fairport, NY; (Y); Church Yth Grp; Hosp Aide; Red Cross Aide; Yrbk Stf; Hon Roll.

WHEELER, MARY B; St Marys HS; E Aurora, NY; (S); 30/197; Trs 4-H; Hosp Aide; Varsity Clb; Var Badmtn; Var Capt Bsktbl; Var Capt Sftbl; Var Capt Vllybl; DAR Awd; 4-H Awd; NHS; Canisus Coll; Mktng.

WHEELER, MICHAEL; West Genesee HS; Syracuse, NY; (Y); Chess Clb; Var Golf; Elks Awd; High Hon Roll; NHS; Outstndng Achvt Awd AHSME Exam 1st Pl 85; Natl Sci Olympd Awd Chem 85; Chem.

WHEELER JR, NORMAN E; Lansing HS; Lansing, NY; (Y); Am Leg Boys St; Boy Scts; Cmnty Wkr; ROTC; Varsity Clb; High Hon Roll; NHS; Pres Schlr; Val; Tompkins Cnty CC; Hotel Mgmt.

WHEELER, SCOTT M; Williamsville North HS; Schenectady, NY; (Y); 10/315; Church Yth Grp; Cmnty Wkr; Var Capt Bsktbl; Ftbl; Var Capt Vllybl; High Hon Roll; NHS; Clarkson U; Chem Engr.

WHEELER, WENDY; Kenmore West SR HS; Kenmore, NY; (Y); 101/435; Library Aide; Variety Show; Yrbk Sprt Ed; Trs Soph Cls; Var Capt Vllybl; NHS; Pres Acadmc Fit Awd 85; SUNY Geneseo; Elem Ed.

WHELAN, ANNE-MARIE; Scarsdale HS; Scarsdale, NY; (Y); Pres AFS; Church Yth Grp; Cmnty Wkr; Office Aide; Teachers Aide; Frsh Cls; Soph Cls; Yth In Actn Awds 83-84; Regnts Schlrshp 85; Bucknell U; Chld Psych.

WHELAN, BRENDAN; Bishop Grimes HS; N Syracuse, NY; (Y); Boy Scts; Exploring; Var Ftbl; Var Golf; High Hon Roll; NHS; Le Moyne Coll Smmr Schlr 85; Engrng.

WHELAN, COLEEN; St Joseph By The Sea; Staten Island, NY; (Y); 45/241; Yrbk Ed-Chief; Var Bsktbl; Var Sftbl; Hon Roll.

WHELAN, JEFFREY C; Scotia-Glenville HS; Schenectady, NY; (Y); Boy Scts; Cmnty Wkr; Band; Concert Band; Jazz Band; Mrchg Band; Orch; Var L Ftbl; Good Sprtsmnshp Awd Babe Ruth Bsbl 83; Archit.

WHELEHAN, SCOTT; Cold Spring Harbor HS; Huntington, NY; (Y); 7/129; Intnl Clb; School Musical; School Play; Nwsp Sprt Ed; Lit Mag; Ftbl; Ice Hcky; High Hon Roll; NHS; Sal.

WHELTON, KATHRYN A; LaGUARDIA Arts; New York, NY; (Y); Art Clb; Camera Clb; Chess Clb; Cmnty Wkr; Quiz Bowl; Scholastic Bowl; Teachers Aide; Concert Band; Orch; Symp Band; Alfred U; Fine Arts.

WHIPPLE, DIANE; Manhasset HS; Manhasset, NY; (Y); Lcrss; Socr; Nrs.

WHIPPLE, MICHELE; Canastota HS; Canastota, NY; (Y); Camera Clb; Dance Clb; Hosp Aide; Ski Clb; Yrbk Phtg; Gym; Trk; Jrnlsm.

WHIPPLE, WENDY M; Dryden HS; Harford, NY; (Y); Trs Spanish Clb; School Musical; Trs Jr Cls; Rep Stu Cncl; L Scrkpr Bsktbl; L Sftbl; L Swmmng; L High Hon Roll; Hon Roll; NHS; Schl Recrd Swmmng 84-85; Physcl Ed.

WHISPELL, TRACEY R; Trott Vocational HS; Niagara Falls, NY; (Y); Sec Jr Cls; Stat Ftbl; Cit Awd; Arch.

WHITAKER, MICHAEL H; John A Coleman HS; Kingston, NY; (S); 9/78; Drama Clb; Trs Key Clb; Off Ski Clb; Varsity Clb; School Play; Stage Crew; Off Frsh Cls; Off Soph Cls; Off Sr Cls; Var Golf; Ltr Of Cmmndtn Ntl Sci Olympiad 83-84.

WHITAKER, SCOTT; Brighton HS; Rochester, NY; (Y); 1/315; Church Yth Grp; Radio Clb; Ski Clb; Varsity Clb; Rep Soph Cls; Var Capt Bsbl; Var JV Ftbl; Dea Teammate Awd Bsbl 85; Air Force; Biomed Tech.

WHITBECK, HOLLIE; Duanesburg JR SR HS; Delanson, NY; (Y); Church Yth Grp; Girl Scts; Office Aide; Teachers Aide; Band; Chorus; Church Choir; Concert Band; Mrchg Band; Hon Roll; Sec.

WHITCOMB, CHRISTINE; Queensbury HS; Glens Falls, NY; (Y); 15/226; Church Yth Grp; Exploring; Library Aide; Chorus; Church Choir; Concert Band; Var Crs Cntry; VP Capt Trk; High Hon Roll; NHS; Jenkins Mem, Regnts Schlrshps 85; ST U Geneseo; Spec Ed.

WHITCOMB, KIMBERLY; North Rose-Wolcott HS; Wolcott, NY; (Y); FBLA; FFA; Varsity Clb; JV Var Cheerleading; JV Var Socr; Var Trk; Cit Awd; Hon Roll; Intr Dcrtng.

WHITE, ANNIK; Roy C Ketcham HS; Wapp Fls, NY; (Y); Dance Clb; Drama Clb; Hosp Aide; Mathletes; School Musical; Symp Band; Mgr(s); High Hon Roll; Jr NHS; NHS.

WHITE, AUDREY; Troupsburg Central HS; Woodhull, NY; (S); 2/24; Aud/Vis; Sec Church Yth Grp; Computer Clb; Band; Church Choir; Yrbk Bus Mgr; VP Frsh Cls; High Hon Roll; NHS; Sal; Math.

WHITE, BARRY; Mount Vernon HS; Mount Vernon, NY; (Y); 57/580; Church Yth Grp; Computer Clb; FBLA; Lit Mag; Im Mgr Bsbl; Im Mgr Ftbl; CC Awd; High Hon Roll; Rochester Inst Of Tech; Accntng.

WHITE, BETH A; Ravena-Coeymans-Selkirk SR HS; Selkirk, NY; (Y); 4/190; Sec FTA; VP Key Clb; Sr Cls; Rep Stu Cncl; Var Capt Bsktbl; Var Capt Socr; Var Capt Trk; Var Capt Vllybl; High Hon Roll; Sec NHS; NY ST Regents Schlrshp 85; Hartwick Col Oyaron Schlrshp 85; St John Fisher Pres Schlrshp 85; Hartwick Coll; Psychlgy.

WHITE, BLANCA; Midwood HS; Brooklyn, NY; (Y); 212/638; Drama Clb; Band; Sec Chorus; Madrigals; Med.

WHITE, CAROL; Cicero-N Syracuse HS; Clay, NY; (S); 67/711; Rep Jr Cls; JV Var Vllybl; NHS; LeMOYNE Coll; Pre Med.

WHITE, CHRISTINA; Delaware Valley Central Schl; Callicoon, NY; (Y); 6/35; Quiz Bowl; Band; Chorus; Sec Sr Cls; Cheerleading; NHS; Church Yth Grp; Drama Clb; School Musical; Best Schlstc Athlt Awd 85; Music Unlmtd Schlrshp 85; Yng Vlntrs In Actn Awd 85; Syracuse U; Art.

WHITE, CHRISTINE; Commack H S North; Commack, NY; (Y); Exploring; Teachers Aide; Band; Chorus; Nwsp Rptr; Nwsp Stf; Off Frsh Cls; Off Soph Cls; Off Jr Cls; Off Sr Cls; Pre-Med.

WHITE, DAVID; Valley Central HS; Montgomery, NY; (Y); 10/250; Boy Scts; Church Yth Grp; Debate Tm; Library Aide; Natl Beta Clb; Spanish Clb; Hon Roll; NHS; Prfct Atten Awd; Spanish NHS; Rochester Inst Of Tech; Chem.

WHITE, DAWN M; Liverpool HS; Liverpool, NY; (Y); 114/800; Aud/Vis; Church Yth Grp; Computer Clb; JA; Church Choir; Swmmng; Ntl Merit SF; Natl USS Swmmng Offcl 85; Regents Schlrshp 85; NY ST U-Albany; Chem.

WHITE, DIANNE M; Aviation HS; Rego Park, NY; (Y); 7/509; Math Tm; Nwsp Ed-Chief; Trk; JA; Rep Stu Cncl; NHS; Prfct Atten Awd; Copper Union; Engrng.

WHITE, DONNA; Holy Angels Acad; North Tonawanda, NY; (Y); 15/36; Pres Sec Church Yth Grp; Math Clb; Service Clb; Spanish Clb; Chorus; Nwsp Stf; Trs Frsh Cls; Sec Jr Cls; Sec Sr Cls; All Amer Awd 85; Pre-Law.

WHITE, DUANE; Cardinal Hayes HS; Bronx, NY; (Y); 5/264; Computer Clb; Yrbk Ed-Chief; High Hon Roll; Hon Roll; Prfct Atten Awd; Discpln Awd Lat, Engl, Math, Sci, Spnsh; MA Inst Tech; Comp Sci.

WHITE, ELITA; Freeport HS; Freeport, NY; (Y); Church Yth Grp; 4-H; Church Choir; Mgr(s); Score Keeper; Stat Vllybl; 4-H Awd; Hon Roll; Bus Mgmnt.

WHITE, EVAMARIA; Eva Maria White HS; St Albons, NY; (Y); Art Clb; Dance Clb; GAA; Chorus; Variety Show; Im Trk; Hon Roll; Psych.

WHITE, EVERETT B; Buffalo Traditional Schl; Buffalo, NY; (S); 19/116; Boy Scts; Debate Tm; Intnl Clb; Band; Var Bowling; Hon Roll; Concert Band; Mrchg Band; Prfct Atten Awd.

WHITE, GREGORY; Bronx High Schl Of Science; Flushing, NY; (Y); Church Yth Grp; Service Clb; Teachers Aide; Chorus; Lit Mag; Rep Stu Cncl; Hon Roll; NCTE Awd; NHS; Grad Soc Stud, Engl Awds 85; Columbia Coll.

WHITE, HEATHER K; Wheatland-Chli HS; Scottsville, NY; (Y); Am Leg Aux Girls St; Exploring; Ski Clb; Chorus; Jazz Band; Pres Jr Cls; High Hon Roll; NHS; Church Yth Grp; Drama Clb; Rep Intl Mdl UN In The Hague 85; Awd Hghst Avg & Cls Ldr 85; Psych.

WHITE, JACQUELINE; Bronx HS; New York, NY; (Y); Cmnty Wkr; PAVAS; Chorus; Lit Mag; Hon Roll; Borough Pres Cert Excellence 83; NY Assoc Of Assistant Prncpls Language Arts 83; Engineering.

WHITE, JEANINE; Gates-Chili SR HS; Rochester, NY; (S); 21/463; Dance Clb; Drama Clb; School Musical; School Play; Band; Off Jr Cls; VP Sr Cls; Cheerleading; High Hon Roll; NHS; Fdtn Gld Cup Awd Piano Hnr 82; Solo Dnce Cmptn Awd 1st 82-83; Ithaca Coll; Comm.

WHITE, JEFF A; Springfield Central Schl; Cooperstown, NY; (Y); 4/20; 4-H; Var Golf; Hon Roll; NHS; Comp.

WHITE, JOSYANE E; Rhinebeck HS; Clinton Corners, NY; (Y); Pres Band; Pres Chorus; AFS; Ski Clb; School Musical; Yrbk Stf; Vllybl; High Hon Roll; JP Sousa Awd; Area All ST Bnd/Orch 81-84; All ST Bnd 84; ARTS Cmpttr 84; Music.

WHITE, KEVIN; Northeastern Acad; Bronx, NY; (S); Yrbk Phtg; Off Soph Cls; Trs Sr Cls; Capt Vllybl; Hon Roll; Ntl Sci Olymd 84; NY Inst Techngy; Comp Sci.

WHITE, KIM; Niagara Falls HS; Niagara Falls, NY; (Y); Spanish Clb; Chorus; Yrbk Stf; Cheerleading; Swmmng; Perf Atten 82-83; Bus Mgmt.

WHITE, KIMBERLY; Dryden HS; Brooktondale, NY; (Y); Debate Tm; Spanish Clb; Yrbk Stf; Var L Swmmng; Var L Trk; High Hon Roll; JC Awd; Hnr-Moot Ct Comp-Gftd Prgm 84-85; Pre-Law.

WHITE, KIMBERLY; Hutchinson Central Tech HS; Buffalo, NY; (Y); Drill Tm; Bowling; Niagara U; Phy Thrpst.

WHITE, LISA; Christ The King Regional HS; Springfield Grd, NY; (Y); 114/395; Speech Tm; Chorus; Yrbk Stf; Off Sr Cls; 2nd Hnrs 85; Pace U; Bus Mgmt.

WHITE, LISA; Jamesville De Witt HS; Manlius, NY; (Y); JV Sftbl; JV Vllybl; Hon Roll; Chld Dev.

WHITE, MARK; Aviation HS; Bronx, NY; (Y); 74/417; JA; Band; Concert Band; Jazz Band; Cit Awd; Hon Roll; Prfct Atten Awd; Wings Awd 85; Big Big Buddy Awd 85.

WHITE, MARK; Knox Memorial Central HS; Russell, NY; (S); French Clb; Mrchg Band; Yrbk Sprt Ed; Stu Cncl; Bsbl; Bsktbl; Socr; High Hon Roll; NHS; MVP JV Soccer 83; Honerable Mention Basketball 85; Marietta OH; Engineering.

WHITE, MARY; Cleveland Hill HS; Cheektowaga, NY; (Y); 1/130; GAA; Yrbk Stf; Sec Stu Cncl; Score Keeper; High Hon Roll; Pres NHS; Law.

WHITE, MARY; Haverling Central HS; Bath, NY; (Y); 17/150; French Clb; Ed Nwsp Ed-Chief; Yrbk Stf; Rep Jr Cls; Rep Sr Cls; Var Cheerleading; Var Trk; High Hon Roll; Math Clb; Band; Rgnts Schlrshp 85; Cole & Latham Bus Law Awd 85; SUNY Binghamton; Frnch.

WHITE, MATTHEW W; Pleasantville HS; Pleasantville, NY; (Y); 8/91; AFS; Aud/Vis; Intnl Clb; Red Cross Aide; Spanish Clb; Band; Concert Band; Mrchg Band; School Musical; Ed Yrbk Phtg; Intl Ambssdr 84; Outstndg Svc Stu Govrnmnt 83-84; U Of MI-ANN Arbor.

WHITE, MEURETTE; Andrew Jackson HS; Jamaica, NY; (Y); Church Yth Grp; Cmnty Wkr; Letterman Clb; Library Aide; MMM; Office Aide; PAVAS; Political Wkr; Band; Concert Band; Band Pin,Concert Band Pin; Concrt Marchng Band Awd 82-85; John Jay; Law.

WHITE, MICHELLE; Newfane SR HS; Lockport, NY; (Y); VP Varsity Clb; Var L Bsktbl; Var Capt Fld Hcky; Var L Sftbl; Var L Trk; Hon Roll; Trs NHS; Church Yth Grp; Girl Scts; Nwsp Rptr; Empire ST W Region Schlstc Field Hockey 84; Lutheran Schlr Awd 85-86; Aid Assoc-Luth Schlrshp 85-86; Wittenberg U; Bio.

WHITE, OLIVIA; Bishop Loughlin M HS; Brooklyn, NY; (S); Nwsp Stf; Rep Frsh Cls; Rep Soph Cls; Rep Stu Cncl; High Hon Roll; NHS; Hugh O Bryan Awd Ldrshp 84; Bishop Loughlin Hnr Awd 83.

WHITE, OTHA; Amityville Memorial HS; Amityville, NY; (Y); 73/230; Church Yth Grp; Drama Clb; Chorus; Church Choir; Concert Band; Drm Mjr(t); Orch; School Play; Sftbl; Hon Roll; All ST Chorus, All Cnty Chorus 84; Wnr Of Act-So Cmptn & Music Lovers Clb Schlrshp 84 & 85; Temple U; Music.

WHITE, PAT; St Francis Prep; Whitestone, NY; (Y); Drama Clb; Acpl Chr; Chorus; School Musical; Spanish NHS; Dir Awd Music; Hofstra U; Musician.

WHITE, PAULA; West Hempstead HS; W Hempstead, NY; (Y); Rep Frsh Cls; Rep Soph Cls; Rep Jr Cls; Var Trk; Mst Imprvd Trk 84; Bus Mgmt.

WHITE, REGINALD; Brooklyn Technical HS; Brooklyn, NY; (Y); JA; Math Clb; Science Clb; Band; Wt Lftg; Bio-Med.

WHITE, RHONDA; Salmon River Central HS; Rooseveltown, NY; (S); 3/97; Concert Band; Jazz Band; VP Frsh Cls; Pres Soph Cls; Pres Jr Cls; Stat Bsktbl; Var Capt Socr; Hon Roll; NHS; N Cntry Schlr 84; Engrng.

WHITE, RICK; East Hampton HS; Montauk, NY; (Y); Am Leg Boys St; Pres Stu Cncl; Var JV Bsbl; Var JV Ftbl; Cit Awd; High Hon Roll; VFW Awd; Church Yth Grp; Variety Show; Wt Lftg; Stu Ldr 82-85; Suffolk Cnty Ftbl Coaches-Leag Hnrb Mntn 84; Interact 83-85.

WHITE, RODNEY; Seneca Vocatiional HS; Buffalo, NY; (Y); 25/180; Boy Scts; Church Yth Grp; Varsity Clb; JV Var Bsktbl; Var Trk; Hon Roll; Prfct Atten Awd; Bus Monitr 84-85; Ethnc Hstry Clb 84-85; Roadshw Tm Motley Crue 84-85; U Of Buffalo; Acctg.

WHITE, RONALD; Kenmore East SR HS; Tonawanda, NY; (Y); Hosp Aide; JV Var Bsbl; High Hon Roll; Hon Roll; Pre-Med.

WHITE, SCOTT G; Xavier HS; Brooklyn, NY; (Y); 8/227; Drama Clb; Stage Crew; NHS; NEDT Awd; Ntl Latn Cntst Hgh Hnrs 81-85; Boston Coll; Bio.

WHITE, SHERRY L; Massena Central HS; Norfolk, NY; (Y); Cmnty Wkr; Teachers Aide; Rep Frsh Cls; Rep Soph Cls; Rep Jr Cls; JV Crs Cntry; Hon Roll; Secry.

WHITE, STEPHANIE ROSS; Stuyvesant HS; New York, NY; (Y); Dance Clb; Debate Tm; French Clb; Science Clb; School Musical; Gym; French Hon Soc; High Hon Roll; Ntl Merit Ltr; Cert Achvt Hist & Engl 85; Most Dedicated Gymnst Awd 81-82; Dance.

WHITE, SUE; Webster HS; Webster, NY; (Y); 18/540; Office Aide; Cit Awd; High Hon Roll; Hon Roll; Jr NHS; Prfct Atten Awd; Library Aide; Sapnsh Achvt Awd 83; Hist Achvt Awd 83-84.

WHITE, SUSANNA; Canastota HS; Canastota, NY; (Y); 4/130; Trs GAA; Science Clb; Yrbk Ed-Chief; JV Bsktbl; Var Fld Hcky; Var Golf; Var Sftbl; High Hon Roll; NHS; Moose Lodge Schlrshp 85; 3 Yr Sci Schlrshp-Initiatv & Effrt 85; Crtv Wrtng-Hgh Orgnlty 84; U Of CA; Phrmclgy.

WHITE, THOMAS R; Williamson SR HS; Williamson, NY; (Y); 23/115; Am Leg Boys St; Church Yth Grp; Band; Concert Band; Jazz Band; Mrchg Band; Stage Crew; Var Bsbl; JV Bsktbl; Var Capt Socr; Soccer Schlrshp-Houghton Coll 85; Honrbl Mentn-Bsbll All-Star Team 85; Houghton Coll; Electrcl Engrng.

WHITE, TIMOTHY; Rome Free Acad; Rome, NY; (Y); Chess Clb; Intnl Clb; Pep Clb; Science Clb; Rep Stu Cncl; Ftbl; Socr; Wt Lftg; Hon Roll; Jr NHS; Lawyer.

WHITE, TIMOTHY H; Wellsville HS; Wellsville, NY; (Y); 2/130; Aud/Vis; Mrchg Band; School Musical; School Play; Stage Crew; Nwsp Stf; Var Trk; Bausch & Lomb Sci Awd; Hon Roll; NHS; NYS Regents Schlrshp 85; Sthrn Schlrshp 85; Rochester Inst Tech; Comp Pgrmr.

WHITE, TODD EVERETT; Williamsville East HS; Williamsville, NY; (Y); 36/276; Sec Civic Clb; Var L Ftbl; High Hon Roll; NHS; Ntl Merit Ltr; Concert Band; Trk; Outstndng Math Ability Awd 83; Ntl Achvt Semi-Fnlst 84; Vrsty Ftbl Spec Coaches Awd 84; Biophysics.

WHITE, TRACY; Argyle Central HS; Argyle, NY; (Y); 20/65; Church Yth Grp; Pres FHA; GAA; Girl Scts; Chorus; Yrbk Stf; Sec Stu Cncl; Var Cheerleading; Var Pom Pon; Score Keeper; Qn Wintrbll 82-84; Miss TEEN NY Pagnt 85; RN.

WHITE, WENDY; West Genesee HS; Camillus, NY; (Y); Nwsp Stf; Rep Jr Cls; Rep Stu Cncl; Socr; High Hon Roll; NHS; Rep Frsh Cls; Rep Soph Cls; Sftbl; Nrs.

WHITE, WILLIAM; Longwood HS; Shirley, NY; (S); Band; Lit Mag; Hon Roll; SUNY Frmngdl; Vet Tech.

WHITEHOUSE, ERIC B; Lakeland HS; Shrub Oak, NY; (Y); 55/360; Radio Clb; Ski Clb; Var Lcrss; Var Socr; Hon Roll; NHS; NW ST Regnts Schlrshp 85; NY ST U Albany; Bus Adm.

WHITESIDE, OCIE; Seneca Voc HS; Buffalo, NY; (Y); 33/179; Aud/Vis; Camera Clb; Radio Clb; Stage Crew; Nwsp Rptr; Sr Cls; Stu Cncl; Bowling; Prfct Atten Awd; Yth Cmnty Schlrshp 84-85; Bryant & Stratton; Elec Tech.

WHITFIELD, PHYLLIS; Hempstead HS; Hempstead, NY; (Y); 5/333; Cmnty Wkr; Science Clb; Band; Orch; Yrbk Stf; Var Badmtn; High Hon Roll; Hon Roll; VP NHS; Rutgers U; Biochem.

WHITFORD, BRAD; Cuba Central Schl; Cuba, NY; (Y); Ski Clb; Chorus; Stu Cncl; Ftbl; Hon Roll; Civil Engrng.

WHITING, JENNIFER; Auburn HS; Auburn, NY; (Y); ROTC; Chorus; Hon Roll.

WHITING, MELANIE; Olean HS; Olean, NY; (Y); AFS; Church Yth Grp; Science Clb; Ski Clb; Sec Varsity Clb; Band; Chorus; Color Guard; Concert Band; School Musical; SW MO ST U; Trvl.

WHITING, ROCK S; Odessa Montour Central HS; Montour Falls, NY; (Y); 10/80; Am Leg Boys St; Pres Church Yth Grp; Drama Clb; Pres Ski Clb; VP Band; Chorus; Jazz Band; Mrchg Band; School Musical; Church Choir; Ithaca Coll Music Comp Fr HS Stu 1st Pl Orgn 84; Oberlin Conservatory; Orgn.

WHITING, WILLIAM F; Watkins Glen Central HS; Watkins Glen, NY; (Y); Am Leg Boys St; Computer Clb; French Clb; Math Clb; Nwsp Stf; Bausch & Lomb Sci Awd; French Hon Soc; High Hon Roll; NCTE Awd; NHS; SR Yt Corning CC 84-85; Northrp Awd High Score SAT 85; Almuni Assoc Hist Awd 85; U Of R; Sci.

WHITMAN, BONNIE; Northville Central HS; Northville, NY; (Y); 5/43; 4-H; Library Aide; Yrbk Stf; Off Stu Cncl; Mgr(s); Hon Roll; U S Pony Clbs Inc Achvd 4th Lvl Ratg 83; Psych.

WHITMAN, DIANE; Twin Tiers Baptist HS; Horseheads, NY; (S); 3/23; Church Yth Grp; Drama Clb; School Play; Var Bsktbl; Var Socr; High Hon Roll; Ntl Merit Ltr; Quiz Team Capt; Tchr Youth Grp; 1st ST Sci Fair; Baptist Bible Coll; Missionary.

WHITMAN, KAREN; Liverpool HS; Liverpool, NY; (S); 237/760; DECA; Nwsp Ed-Chief; Powder Puff Ftbl; Hon Roll; 2nd Pl Outstndng Chptr Awd NY ST DECA 84; 4th Pl Gen Merch Regnl Lvl DECA 85; Bryant Stratton Powellson; Bus.

WHITMAN, SANDRA; Moriah Central HS; Mineville, NY; (Y); French Clb; GAA; Rep Jr Cls; Stu Cncl; Var Cheerleading; Hon Roll; Bus.

WHITMAN, TIMOTHY; Mayfield JR SR HS; Mayfield, NY; (Y); 7/75; Boy Scts; Church Yth Grp; Library Aide; Nwsp Ed-Chief; Nwsp Rptr; Nwsp Stf.

WHITMER, CARMALETTA MORLOCK; Ellicottville Central Schl; Ellicottville, NY; (Y); 15/42; AFS; Am Leg Aux Girls St; Trs FNA; Spanish Clb; Band; Chorus; Concert Band; Mrchg Band; Var JV Cheerleading; Var JV Sftbl; Prfct Atten Awd; Comp Sci.

WHITMIRE, JENNIFER E; Cambridge HS; Shushan, NY; (Y); 16/82; Church Yth Grp; Band; Chorus; Church Choir; Concert Band; Mrchg Band; Yrbk Ed-Chief; JV Fld Hcky; Hon Roll; NY Rgnts, R Cook Hnrs Schlrshp 85; The Kings Coll; Music.

WHITMORE, WILLIAM; Niagara Wheatfield HS; Niagara Falls, NY; (Y); Church Yth Grp; Latin Clb; Ski Clb; Varsity Clb; High Hon Roll; Hon Roll; NHS; Prfct Atten Awd; Var Swmmng; JV Trk; Houghton Coll; Sci.

WHITNEY, CHRIS R; Portville Central Schl; Portville, NY; (Y); 21/120; FFA; Ski Clb; Bsktbl; Hon Roll; USA Schlrshp 85; Tuition Asst Pgm 85; Jamestown CC; Bus Admin.

WHITNEY, DAVID; Valley Central HS; Montgomery, NY; (Y); 10/260; Spanish Clb; Ed Lit Mag; Var Crs Cntry; Var Trk; Hon Roll; NHS; Spanish NHS; Psych.

WHITNEY, DEBORAH; Granville HS; Whitehall, NY; (Y); AFS; Art Clb; French Clb; Girl Scts; OEA; Yrbk Stf; JV Co-Capt Cheerleading; Score Keeper; Hon Roll; Ntl Merit Ltr; Fash Dsgn.

WHITNEY, LISA M; Chenango Valley HS; Port Crane, NY; (Y); 3/186; Church Yth Grp; 4-H; French Clb; FHA; Key Clb; Library Aide; Teachers Aide; 4-H Awd; Jr NHS; NHS; NY ST Regents Schlrshp 85; Broome CC; Accntng.

WHITNEY, LYNN ANN; Valley Central HS; Montgomery, NY; (Y); Hon Roll.

WHITNEY, SUSAN J; Fairport HS; Fairport, NY; (Y); 35/600; Church Yth Grp; Intnl Clb; Concert Band; Yrbk Bus Mgr; Yrbk Ed-Chief; Hon Roll; Trs NHS; Ntl Merit Ltr; Pres Schlr; Spanish NHS; All NY St Band 82; NY St Orch 83; Wellesley Coll; French.

WHITTAKER, JEFFREY L; Canton Central; Canton, NY; (Y); Crs Cntry; Trk; Hon Roll; Ntl Merit SF; Carnegie Mellon U; Comp Sci.

WHITTAKER, LISA E; Charlotte Valley Central Schl; E Meredith, NY; (Y); FBLA; Key Clb; Latin Clb; Office Aide; Yrbk Stf; Vllybl; Delhi Ag & Tech Coll; Nrsng.

WHITTAKER, SAMANTHA; Springfield Garden HS; Springfield, NY; (Y); 2/750; Church Yth Grp; Service Clb; Church Choir; Crs Cntry; Trk; Hlth Ed.

WHITTIER, KELLIE; Albion HS; Albion, NY; (S); Teachers Aide; Chorus; Swing Chorus; Sec Pres Stu Cncl; Bsbl; Cit Awd; NHS; FNA; Genesee CC; Humn Svcs.

WHITTINGTON, SUSAN; Griffith Inst & Central Schls; West Falls, NY; (Y); Sec Spanish Clb; Band; Concert Band; Mrchg Band; Symp Band; Im Powder Puff Ftbl; Im Vllybl; High Hon Roll; Hon Roll; Trs NHS; Cert Hon NY ST Bar Assoc Mock Trial Trnmnt 85; Htl Mngmnt.

WHITTLETON, PAM; L A Webber HS; Lyndonvl, NY; (Y); 13/53; Church Yth Grp; Varsity Clb; Band; Chorus; Church Choir; Mrchg Band; School Musical; Capt JV Bsktbl; JV Var Socr; Hon Roll; Bus.

WHITTON, MICHAEL A; Gouverneur Central HS; Gouverneur, NY; (Y); Am Leg Boys St; Acpl Chr; School Play; Trs Sr Cls; Rep Stu Cncl; Trs NHS; Regents Scholar 85; Hnrs Grp 85; Potsdam ST U; Secndry Ed.

WHITTON, PAMELA; Hermmo-Dekalb Central HS; Richville, NY; (S); Church Yth Grp; Drama Clb; French Clb; GAA; Band; Chorus; School Play; Stage Crew; Nwsp Stf; Yrbk Bus Mgr; Pre-Law.

WHOLIHAN, SUSAN; St Peters HS For Girls; Staten Island, NY; (Y); FNA; Library Aide; Chorus; School Play; Yrbk Stf; Hon Roll; Pres NHS; Acctg.

WHOLLEY, PAUL S; Pleasantville HS; Pleasantville, NY; (Y); 11/91; Science Clb; Spanish Clb; Lit Mag; Var Ftbl; Var Trk; Capt Wrstlng; High Hon Roll; NHS; Regents Schlrshp 85; Con Edison Awd Wnr 84-85; Team Spirit & Ldrshp For Wrstlng & Ftbl 84-85; Colgate U; Law.

WHYTE, AMELIOUS; Sheepshead Bay HS; Brooklyn, NY; (Y); Hosp Aide; Ski Clb; Yrbk Stf; Stu Cncl; Cit Awd; NHS; Prfct Atten Awd; Library Aide; Office Aide; Rep Jr Cls; JR Svc Awd 84; Pride Of The Yankees-Supr Yth 84 & 85; Pblc Admin.

WHYTE, HEATHER; Roy C Ketcham HS; Wappingers Falls, NY; (S); 133/503; Cmnty Wkr; Dance Clb; Drama Clb; Political Wkr; Ski Clb; Variety Show; Lit Mag; Sec Stu Cncl; Socr; Hon Roll; Stdnt Senate 84-85; Goucher; Bus.

WIATROWSKI, JESSICA; Alden Central HS; Alden, NY; (Y); 31/198; Art Clb; Rep French Clb; Rep Letterman Clb; Chorus; School Musical; School Play; Yrbk Phtg; Ed Yrbk Stf; Rep Sr Cls; Stu Cncl; Presdntl Awd 85; Regents Schlrshp 85; Acadmc Lttrs 82-85; Daemen Coll; Physcl Thrpy.

WICELINSKI, VINCENT; St Francis Prep HS; Flushing, NY; (S); 76/697; Computer Clb; Math Tm; Im Ftbl; Im Socr; Im Sftbl; Im Vllybl; Hon Roll; NHS; Pulaski Asso NYPC Schlrshp Merit Awd 82; Grnd Cncl Of Pulaski Assn NY Metro Area Schlrshp 82; Bus Adm.

WICHROWSKI, WILLIAM E; St John The Baptist D HS; Bay Shores, NY; (Y); Computer Clb; Math Tm; Science Clb; Teachers Aide; Crs Cntry; High Hon Roll; NHS; Ntl Merit Ltr; Med.

WICK, ANGELA; Cicero North Syracuse HS; Clay, NY; (S); 71/711; Hosp Aide; Drm Mjr(t); Mrchg Band; VP Soph Cls; Rep Stu Cncl; Bowling; Powder Puff Ftbl; Sftbl; Twrlr; Fnlst Miss Ntl Tngr 84; Miss N Syracuse Pgnt 84; Lemoyne Coll; Lwyr.

WICK, LISA A; Columbia HS; East Greenbush, NY; (Y); 29/353; Church Yth Grp; Ski Clb; Var Capt Tennis; JV Vllybl; High Hon Roll; NHS; St Schlr; Regnts Schlrshp 85; Oneonta ST U; Envr Consrvtn.

WICKHAM, KRISTINE A; Albany HS; Albany, NY; (Y); 46/600; French Clb; Latin Clb; Lit Mag; Stu Cncl; Trk; NYS Regents Scholarship; Engineering.

WICKHAM, MELISSA; Cattaraugus Central HS; Otto, NY; (Y); 1/66; Pep Clb; Spanish Clb; Band; Mrchg Band; Yrbk Stf; Var Bsktbl; Var Trk; Var Vllybl; High Hon Roll; NHS; Air Force; Cmmnctns.

WICKS, KELLY; Liverpool HS; Liverpool, NY; (S); Sec DECA; Stu Cncl; Mktng.

WICKS, LAURIE; Immaculate Heart Central HS; Watertown, NY; (Y); Pres 4-H; 4-H Awd; Northland; Zoology.

WIDA, MICHELE; Elmire Southside HS; Pine City, NY; (Y); French Clb; Pep Clb; Varsity Clb; Chorus; Ed Yrbk Stf; Mat Maids; Var Sftbl; Timer; Var Vllybl; High Hon Roll; WENY Sprts Awd Vlybll 85; Bus.

WIDER, RONALD; Syosset HS; Syosset, NY; (Y); Ski Clb; JV Lcrss; Var Capt Socr; JV Wrstlng; Hon Roll; Law.

WIDOWSKI, LISA; Liverpool HS; Liverpool, NY; (S); Pres Camp Fr Inc; High Hon Roll; Hon Roll; Jr NHS; NHS; NY ST Rgnts, Credence Schlrshp 85; Mdrn Lang.

WIDRICK, KYLE W; South Jefferson Cenral Schl; Adams, NY; (Y); 8/125; Church Yth Grp; FCA; School Musical; JV Bsktbl; High Hon Roll; Hon Roll; Jr NHS; NHS; Amer H S Athl 85; Acadmc Schlrshp Elizabethtown 85; Regnts Schlrsp 85; Elizabeth Coll; Comp Sci.

WIEBKE, WILLIAM; North Babylon HS; North Babylon, NY; (Y); 115/601; Ftbl; 2nd Pl Hcky,N Babyln Yth Serv 85; Capt Sftbl Tm,N Babyln Yth Serv 85; Chiroprctr.

WIEDEMUTH, MARYANN; Smithtown West HS; Smithtown, NY; (Y); Nwsp Rptr; Hon Roll; NHS; Spanish NHS; Academic Fitness Awd 85; Regents Schlrshp 85.

WIEDENBECK, BROOKE; Maryvale HS; Cheektowaga, NY; (Y); DECA; GAA; VP Varsity Clb; Off Stu Cncl; VP Trk; Library Aide; Pep Clb; Spanish Clb; Coach Actv; Var Crs Cntry; Fredonia ST Coll; Acctg.

WIEGAND, DEBBIE; West Seneca West SR HS; W Seneca, NY; (Y); 98/550; Cmnty Wkr; 4-H; French Clb; Office Aide; Pep Clb; Chorus; Rep Soph Cls; Rep Jr Cls; Rep Sr Cls; Rep Stu Cncl; Athlt Schlrshp OH U 86; OH ST U; Pub Rltns.

WIEGERT, CHRISTINA J; Smithtown High School West; Smithtown, NY; (Y); Trs Church Yth Grp; Sec German Clb; Hosp Aide; Church Choir; Orch; School Musical; Symp Band; Hon Roll; NHS; Pres Schlr; German Hnr Society Schlrshp 85; NY ST Regents Schlrshp 85; 400 Hr Candystriper Awd 85; SUNY Binghamton; Nrsng.

WIEGERT, ERIC; Cohoes HS; Cohoes, NY; (Y); Boy Scts.

WIELAND, ANDREA; Saint Marys Acad; Glens Falls, NY; (S); 9/47; Art Clb; Drama Clb; Soph Cls; Jr Cls; Im JV Bsktbl; Var Powder Puff Ftbl; Var Score Keeper; Var Sftbl; High Hon Roll; Math.

WIELAND, ELIZABETH; Newfield HS; Selden, NY; (Y); Church Yth Grp; Cmnty Wkr; Drama Clb; Chorus; School Musical; Nwsp Rptr; Hon Roll; Bus.

WIELAND, STEPHEN G; Starpoint Central Schl; Lockport, NY; (Y); 6/196; Pres Church Yth Grp; 4-H; Math Tm; Ski Clb; Yrbk Stf; Im Bsktbl; JV Crs Cntry; Im Socr; Hon Roll; Jr NHS; Legislative Intern 84 Niagara County,NY ST Legislative 85; Television Schltc Competition 85; Rochester; Electrical Engnrg.

WIELAND, VIKTORIA; St Marys Acad; Glens Falls, NY; (S); 11/43; Drama Clb; FFA; School Musical; Yrbk Stf; VP Sr Cls; JV Capt Bsktbl; Coach Actv; Powder Puff Ftbl; Capt Sftbl; Hon Roll; Rad Tech.

WIELER, JENNIFER; Wantagh HS; Wantagh, NY; (Y); Concert Band; Orch; Nwsp Stf; Yrbk Sprt Ed; Var Badmtn; Var Capt Cheerleading; Twrlr; Hon Roll; MVP Var Chrldng 85; Comm.

WIELING, CINDY; East Islip HS; East Islip, NY; (Y); Art Clb; Color Guard; Flag Corp; Mrchg Band; Orch; School Musical; School Play; Stage Crew; Trk; Prog Gftd & Tlntd 85; NUSMA 81-85; NY Coll; Art.

WIELOSZYNSKI, JOHN; La Salle SR HS; Niagara Falls, NY; (S); 24/278; Computer Clb; Drama Clb; Chorus; School Musical; Nwsp Rptr; Yrbk Phtg; Im Bowling; Hon Roll; NHS; Prfct Atten Awd; Engr.

WIENCEK, JOHN R; Regis HS; Forest Hills, NY; (Y); Boy Scts; Debate Tm; NFL; Science Clb; Nwsp Rptr; Crs Cntry; Trk; Ntl Merit Ltr; NY U; Bus.

WIENER, ABBY; Lawrence HS; Cedarhurst, NY; (Y); 93/297; Drama Clb; Spanish Clb; Pres Temple Yth Grp; School Musical; Ed Yrbk Stf; High Hon Roll; Regents Schlrshp 85; SUNY Binghampton; Law.

WIENER, BETH L; East Islip HS; East Islip, NY; (Y); 57/475; Art Clb; Boy Scts; Teachers Aide; Temple Yth Grp; Band; Concert Band; Mrchg Band; School Musical; Hon Roll; NY ST Rgnts Schlrshp 85; SUNY New Paltz; Speech Thrpy.

WIERZBINSKI, JACLYNN A; Cheektowaga Central HS; Cheektowaga, NY; (Y); 4/204; Trs FTA; Stu Cncl; Hon Roll; Jr NHS; NHS; Voice Dem Awd; Fire Prev Essy Cont 82; Pol Athl Assoc Schlrshp 85; Rgnts Schlrshp 85; Stu Of Mnth Awd 85; Buffalo ST Coll; Dietetics.

WIESMORE, GREGORY W; Cheektowaga Central HS; Cheektowaga, NY; (Y); 39/204; Chess Clb; Ski Clb; Stu Cncl; Bsktbl; Trk; Wt Lftg; Hon Roll; NHS; St Schlr; NY ST Powerlifting Chmpn 84; NY ST U Buffalo; Bus Adm.

WIESNER, HEATHER; Susan E Wagner HS; Staten Island, NY; (Y); School Musical; Vllybl; Hon Roll; NHS; Ntl Merit Ltr; Karate Awds 82; Blackbelt 85; Farmingdale; Bus.

WIEZALIS, JULIE; West Genesee SR HS; Syracuse, NY; (Y); Church Yth Grp; Hosp Aide; Key Clb; Political Wkr; Ski Clb; Varsity Clb; Yrbk Stf; Rep Stu Cncl; High Hon Roll; NHS; Outstndng Stu Awd 82; Publc Svc Awd 85; Cornell; Pre-Law.

WIGFALL, GENEVA; John Dewey HS; Brooklyn, NY; (Y); JA; Rep Jr Cls; Acad Finance 85-86; Acctng.

WIKLACZ, COLETTE M J; John F Kennedy HS; Utica, NY; (Y); 13/150; Office Aide; Ski Clb; Band; Orch; Hon Roll; Jr NHS; NHS; Mohawk Valley Comm Coll; Bus Ad.

WIKOLASKI, DONNA; Pioneer Central HS; Chaffee, NY; (Y); FHA; Key Clb; Latin Clb; VP Library Aide; Chorus; Color Guard; Latin.

WILBER, TANYA R; Pinecrest Christian Schl; Salisbury Center, NY; (S); 1/7; Chess Clb; Office Aide; School Musical; Sec Frsh Cls; Sec Soph Cls; Sec Jr Cls; L Bsktbl; High Hon Roll; Jr NHS; ACSI Distnghsd HS Stu In Acads & Music 84-85; Ntl Piano Plyrs Guild 76-83; Bio.

WILBUR, COLETTE M; Johnstown HS; Johnstown, NY; (Y); Band; Concert Band; Mrchg Band; Pep Band; Symp Band; Timer; Trk; Hon Roll; Rbrt Mcfeely Memrl Schlrshp 85; Fltn Mntgmery CC All Cnty Schlrshp 85; Fulton Montgomery CC; Accntng.

WILBUR, DAWN; Groten Central HS; Groton, NY; (Y); FHA; Girl Scts; Library Aide; Teachers Aide; VICA; Trs Soph Cls; Var Jr Cls; Rep Stu Cncl; JV Var Bsktbl; Stat Score Keeper; Mst Imprvd Plyr Sftbl 83-84.

WILBUR, KIM; Vernon-Verona-Sherrill HS; Sherrill, NY; (Y); Chorus; Off Frsh Cls; Off Soph Cls; Off Jr Cls; Stu Cncl; Trk; High Hon Roll; Hon Roll; NHS; Bus.

WILBUR, PAUL G; Clinton Central HS; Clinton, NY; (Y); 51/146; Key Clb; Jazz Band; Mrchg Band; Orch; School Musical; Symp Band; Nwsp Sprt Ed; Sec Sr Cls; Ftbl; Trk; Lib Arts.

WILBURG, TERRENCE; Christ The King Regional HS; Ozone Park, NY; (Y); 68/385; Fld Hcky; Gym; Socr; Hon Roll; Civil Engr.

WILCOVE, JENNIFER M; Lansingburgh HS; Troy, NY; (Y); JA; Varsity Clb; Yrbk Stf; Bowling; Var Capt Cheerleading; Gym; JV Score Keeper; Sftbl; Hon Roll; Bus.

WILCOX, ANN MARGARET; Walton Central HS; Walton, NY; (Y); 1/110; Am Leg Aux Girls St; Sec Model UN; Varsity Clb; Orch; Var L Bsktbl; Var L Tennis; High Hon Roll; Pres NHS; 4-H; Girl Scts; Walton Bicentennial Logo Desgn Cont Wnnr 85; Royale Oasis Awd 85; Hghst Avg Regents Mth Sequence 84; Envirnmntl Sci.

WILCOX, MATTHEW E; Corning West HS; Corning, NY; (Y); JV Lcrss; JV Wrstlng; Arch.

WILCOX, PHILIP C; Riverhead HS; Riverhead, NY; (Y); 2/237; Drama Clb; JCL; Latin Clb; Math Tm; Band; Chorus; School Play; Crs Cntry; Bausch & Lomb Sci Awd; Sal; NY ST Regents Schlrshp Wnnr 85; Georgetown U; Chem.

WILCOX, SARAH; Little Falls JR SR HS; Little Falls, NY; (S); 6/112; Church Yth Grp; Band; Church Choir; Orch; Trk; Vllybl; NHS; Soc Stdys Awd 84; Stu Advsry Cncl 82-85; Pre-Med.

WILCZEK, RENEE; West Seneca West SR HS; Cheektowaga, NY; (Y); GAA; Church Choir; Color Guard; Orch; School Musical; Var Swmmng; Hon Roll; Prfct Atten Awd; Camp Fr Inc; Church Yth Grp; Bio Awd 84; Spnsh Hnr Awd 84; Med.

WILCZEK, SANDRA JEAN; Newburgh Free Acad; Newburgh, NY; (Y); Hon Roll; Shorthand Speed Test 84-85; Sorng 100 Pct Shorthand Fnl 84; Ct Rep.

WILD, MICHELLE; West Babylon SR HS; W Babylon, NY; (Y); 24/425; AFS; Church Yth Grp; Cmnty Wkr; FBLA; Hosp Aide; Library Aide; Yrbk Stf; Var Tennis; High Hon Roll; Sec NHS; Prncpls Awd-Bus Dept; Elem Educ.

WILDER, BRUCE; Long Beach SR HS; Long Beach, NY; (Y); Aud/Vis; Church Yth Grp; FCA; Varsity Clb; Band; Church Choir; Concert Band; Drill Tm; Mrchg Band; JV Capt Bsktbl; MVP Trk; Psych.

WILDER, NANCY A; Batavia HS; Batavia, NY; (Y); 37/240; Girl Scts; Red Cross Aide; Chorus; School Musical; Nwsp Rptr; Hon Roll; NHS; Apnsh Merit Awd 81-83; Regents Schlrshp 85; Richard Meyer Schlrshp Int Order Rainbow 85; Genesee Comm Coll; Comp Sci.

WILDT, DARREN JOHN; North Tonawanda SR HS; N Tonawanda, NY; (Y); 83/469; Church Yth Grp; Bsbl; Hon Roll; City Leag All-Star Bsbl Tm 80-83; Intrmrl Flr Hcky Chmpnshp Tm-Capt 80-81; Clarkson U; Chemcl Engrng.

WILEN, MARK; Hebrew Academy Of Nassau Cnty; W Hempstead, NY; (S); Debate Tm; Quiz Bowl; High Hon Roll; Hon Roll; Jr NHS; NHS; Art Clb; Computer Clb; Drama Clb; Arch.

WILEY, GREGORY; Beacon HS; Beacon, NY; (Y); 5/167; VP Church Yth Grp; Capt Math Tm; Science Clb; Varsity Clb; Concert Band; Pep Band; Trk; Bausch & Lomb Sci Awd; Elks Awd; NHS; Elzbth Wolf Schlrshp 85; Clrksn U; Elec Engrng.

WILEY, LINDA; Vestal SR HS; Vestal, NY; (Y); Church Yth Grp; 4-H; Office Aide; Ski Clb; Varsity Clb; Var L Socr; JV Sftbl; Var L Trk; Bus Admin.

WILEY JR, STANLEY W; Onondaga Central HS; Syracuse, NY; (S); 10/73; Pres Computer Clb; FBLA; VP Science Clb; Spanish Clb; School Play; Yrbk Stf; Golf; High Hon Roll; Hon Roll; NHS; Clarkson U; Elec.

WILHELM, GREGORY C; Rome Free Acad; Rome, NY; (Y); 74/488; Intnl Clb; High Hon Roll; Hon Roll; NHS; Pres Schlr; Regnts Schlrshp 85; Colgate Sem 84-85; Pre-Med.

WILINSKI, KARIN; Alfred G Berner HS; Massapequa, NY; (Y); 16/426; Nwsp Sprt Ed; Pres Soph Cls; Pres Jr Cls; Pres Sr Cls; Var Capt Bsktbl; Var Capt Sftbl; Var Capt Vllybl; NHS; French Clb; GAA; Stu Adv Comm 81-85; Massapequa Post Colm 82-85; Berner HS Rookie Yr 82; Dartmouth Coll; Adv.

WILK, KAREN MARIE; Hauppauge HS; Hauppauge, NY; (Y); Cmnty Wkr; Hosp Aide; Orch; Nwsp Stf; Yrbk Stf; JV Var Cheerleading; High Hon Roll; NHS; Ntl Merit Ltr; Prfct Atten Awd; Smithtown Hosp Volntr Awd 85; Var Ltr Orch 83-84; Acctng.

WILK, WILLIAM A; Notre Dame HS; Whitesboro, NY; (Y); 43/174; Church Yth Grp; Nwsp Rptr; Ice Hcky; Trk; Hon Roll; Marine Corps Schlrshp Fndtn Awd 85; NY ST Regnts Schlrshp 85; SUNY Geneseo; Speech Comm.

WILKENS, AUDREY; West Islip HS; West Islip, NY; (Y); 126/525; Drama Clb; Exploring; Acpl Chr; Band; Chorus; Church Choir; Concert Band; Jazz Band; Madrigals; Mrchg Band; Mst Musicl, Dramtc & SCMEA Chrs Hnrs Avg SCMEA Chrs & All ST Chrs; Music Theory Awd; Hofstra U; Music Ed.

WILKIE, GEOFFREY; Liverpool HS; Liverpool, NY; (S); 65/790; CAP; Computer Clb; ROTC; Var Trk; Hon Roll; Jr NHS; NHS; Retired Off Assoc Awd 84; ROTC Schlrshp 85; Air Force Acad; Elec Engrng.

WILKIE, JOHN F; Letchworth Central HS; Silver Springs, NY; (Y); Am Leg Boys St; Art Clb; Computer Clb; 4-H; FFA; PAVAS; Varsity Clb; Yrbk Stf; 4-H Awd; High Hon Roll; Varsity Let Soccer; Hnr Soc; David Dodge Athlete Awd; Whisville; Drafting.

WILKINS, RENEE M; Sacred Heart HS; New York, NY; (Y); Drama Clb; Intnl Clb; Library Aide; School Musical; School Play; Stage Crew; Nwsp Rptr; Yrbk Stf; Resp Therapy.

WILKINS, TRACE; Wyandanch Memorial HS; Wyandanch, NY; (Y); Dance Clb; Drama Clb; Key Clb; Band; Nwsp Bus Mgr; Nwsp Rptr; High Hon Roll; Hon Roll; NHS; Engl, Soc Studys & Amer Hstry Acad Achvts 82-85; Brown U; Ec.

WILKINSON, RACHEL; Grand Island SR HS; Grand Isl, NY; (Y); 76/281; Church Yth Grp; Drama Clb; GAA; Ski Clb; Band; Color Guard; Concert Band; Pep Band; School Musical; Stage Crew; Sptlghts Club Awd 85; SUNY-FREDONIA; Polt Sci.

WILKINSON, ROBERT E; H Frank Carey HS; Garden City, NY; (Y); 12/281; Mathletes; Varsity Clb; Ftbl; Trk; High Hon Roll; Jr NHS; NHS; NY St Regents Schlrshp 85; Vrsty Lttrs-Ftbl & Trk 84-85; Ntl Merit Hnr Rll 85; Polytech Inst Of NY; Elec Engr.

WILKINSON, WENDY; Oneida HS; Oneida, NY; (Y); 25/232; 4-H; FBLA; Band; Yrbk Stf; Sec Frsh Cls; Sec Soph Cls; Dnfth Awd; 4-H Awd; High Hon Roll; NHS; R N Whipple, Prof Sectrs Intl Schlrshps, K Miller Awd 85; SUNY; Secrtrl Sci.

WILKOFF, EVAN; John F Kennedy HS; Merrick, NY; (Y); Pres Exploring; Quiz Bowl; Temple Yth Grp; Band; Jazz Band; School Play; Nwsp Stf; Yrbk Stf; NHS; Ntl Merit Ltr; U VA; Engrng.

WILL, BLAIR; James I Oneill HS; Garrison, NY; (Y); Debate Tm; Var L Sftbl; French Clb; Letterman Clb; Political Wkr; Ski Clb; Var L Lcrss; Mst Valuable Skier 85.

WILL, MARK; Oakfield-Alabama Central Schl; Basom, NY; (Y); 2/73; Boy Scts; French Clb; Math Clb; Band; Chorus; Hon Roll; NHS; 2nd Hghst Avg 82-84; Cornell U; Pre-Vet.

WILL, MATHEW; Oakfield-Alabama Central Schl; Basom, NY; (Y); 7/80; Boy Scts; 4-H; Math Tm; Chorus; Jazz Band; Mrchg Band; Swing Chorus; NHS; NY ST Al-T Chors 84; Purdue U; Pre-Vet Med.

WILLACY, GENENE; Brooklyn Technical HS; Bronx, NY; (Y); Hosp Aide; Teachers Aide; Lit Mag; Hon Roll; NHS; Cert Standard First Aid 85; Resrch Apprentc Pgm Smmr Schlr 85; Ed Chief Local Comm Newsltr 85; Med.

WILLARD, NORMA; Heurelton Central Schl; Heuvelton, NY; (Y); 12/48; 4-H; Chorus; Nwsp Rptr; Nwsp Sprt Ed; Nwsp Stf; Yrbk Stf; Lion Awd; NHS; Ogdensburg Patrlmns Benevlnt Assn Awd 85; Heuvelton Vlntr Fire Dept Awd 85; SUNY; Crmnl Justc.

WILLENS, JODI; Commack South HS; Commack, NY; (Y); Dance Clb; GAA; Office Aide; Teachers Aide; Varsity Clb; Mrchg Band; School Musical; Yrbk Stf; Pom Pon; Kickline Captn 82-86.

WILLETT, STACEY R; Greece Olympia HS; Rochester, NY; (Y); 13/316; Sec Drama Clb; Sec JA; Varsity Clb; VP Chorus; Church Choir; Madrigals; School Musical; Capt Tennis; High Hon Roll; NHS; NY ST Teen Talent Cmptn 83; Chrch Child Choir Drctr 82-84; Speakers Bureau 82-85; Messiah Coll; Nrsng.

WILLETTS, DAWN MARIE; Waterford-Halfmoon HS; Waterford, NY; (Y); 1/83; Math Tm; Teachers Aide; Ed Lit Mag; Sec Frsh Cls; High Hon Roll; NHS; Math Clb; Yrbk Stf; Rensselaer Medal Math & Sci 85; Treas SADD Chapt, Stu Dir ASAP 85; Jr Great Bk Discussion Grp; Math.

WILLEY, DANIELLE; Ballston Spa HS; Ballston Spa, NY; (Y); 5/250; Church Yth Grp; Cmnty Wkr; Girl Scts; Chorus; Drill Tm; Stage Crew; Score Keeper; Timer; High Hon Roll; NHS; Spanish Prize 84; Occuptnl Thrpy.

WILLIAM, GOURLAY; Bishop Timon HS; Cheektowaga, NY; (Y); Nwsp Sprt Ed; Yrbk Sprt Ed; Pres Stu Cncl; JV Crs Cntry; Var Socr; Hon Roll; NHS; Awd Otustndng Achvt Am Hist 84-85; Awd Outstndng Ded Schl Newspaper 84-85; Law.

WILLIAMS, ANNE; Stella Maris HS; Brooklyn, NY; (Y); Math Tm; JV Sftbl; Hon Roll; NHS.

WILLIAMS, ANNE MARIE; St Joseph Hill Acad; Staten Island, NY; (Y); 32/103; Art Clb; Drama Clb; Hosp Aide; JA; School Play; Stage Crew; Trs Soph Cls; Crs Cntry; Trk; Hon Roll; Rutgers U; Phrmcy.

WILLIAMS, ANTHONY; Portville Central Schl; Olean, NY; (Y); 9/120; Ski Clb; VP Jr Cls; VP Sr Cls; Hon Roll; NYS Rgnts Schlrshp 85; Grove City Coll; Engrng.

WILLIAMS, BERNARD; Newark Valley HS; Berkshire, NY; (Y); Church Yth Grp; Drama Clb; School Musical; School Play; Stage Crew; Variety Show; High Hon Roll; Hon Roll.

WILLIAMS, BONNIE; Holland Patent HS; Barneveld, NY; (Y); 4-H; Nwsp Rptr; Rep Church Yth Grp; Rep Jr Cls; Capt Bsktbl; Capt Cheerleading; Capt Fld Hcky; Var Sftbl; Hon Roll; Prfct Atten Awd; Chrldr Partner Stunts Awd 85; Cosmetolgst.

WILLIAMS, BRIDGETTE R; North Rose-Wolcott HS; Wolcott, NY; (Y); 4-H; Var Capt Cheerleading; Var Socr; Var Capt Trk; Hon Roll; Hugh O Brian Ldrshp 80-81; Air Force; Bus.

WILLIAMS, CARLENE; William H Taft HS; Bronx, NY; (Y); Drama Clb; Hosp Aide; Science Clb; Teachers Aide; Pres Chorus; Church Choir; School Play; High Hon Roll; Hon Roll; Prfct Atten Awd; Mayor Awd 83; Ctznshp Awd 83; Ldrshp Awd 83; Lwyr.

WILLIAMS, CECILY; Bishop Ford HS; Brooklyn, NY; (Y); Chorus; Cheerleading; First Honrs 85; Pharmcy.

WILLIAMS, CHERYL; Linton HS; Schenectady, NY; (Y); Ski Clb; Rep Soph Cls; Stat Bsktbl; Var JV Socr; Var Sftbl; Hon Roll; Var Girls Sftbl MVP 85; Pre Law.

WILLIAMS, CHRIS; Elmira Southside HS; Pine City, NY; (Y); Am Leg Boys St; Boy Scts; Cmnty Wkr; German Clb; Pep Clb; Spanish Clb; Var Crs Cntry; JV Socr; Var Trk; High Hon Roll; Bus.

WILLIAMS, CHRISTINA; Parshville-Hopkiton Central HS; Colton, NY; (Y); JV Socr; Hon Roll; Bus Mgmt.

WILLIAMS, CHRISTOHPER J; Horace Greeley HS; Millwood, NY; (Y); 89/272; Boy Scts; Jazz Band; School Musical; Variety Show; Ed Nwsp Bus Mgr; Pres Frsh Cls; VP Stu Cncl; Var Bowling; Score Keeper; Trk; Liberal Arts.

WILLIAMS, CONSTANCE; Freeport HS; Freeport, NY; (Y); Hosp Aide; A K Webber Mem Awd 85; Word Proc.

WILLIAMS, CONSTANCE; Grace Hodley Dodge V HS; Bronx, NY; (Y); 94/439; Dance Clb; JA; Teachers Aide; Chorus; Variety Show; Pres Soph Cls; Var Cheerleading; High Hon Roll; Prfct Atten Awd; Wnr Creative Wrtg Comp 84; Bus.

WILLIAMS, CRAIG A; Town Of Webb HS; Woodgate, NY; (Y); Chorus; Nwsp Phtg; Yrbk Ed-Chief; Lit Mag; Rep Stu Cncl; Badmtn; JV Var Socr; Var Tennis; Var Trk; Sec NHS; Elem Ed.

WILLIAMS, DANIELLE; Uniondale HS; Uniondale, NY; (Y); Church Yth Grp; Jr Cls; Stu Cncl; Capt Var Crs Cntry; Var L Trk; High Hon Roll; Hon Roll; NHS; Med.

WILLIAMS, DAVID J; Pine Bush Central HS; Middletown, NY; (Y); Boy Scts; Concert Band; Mrchg Band; JV Socr; Var Wrstlng; Hon Roll; Rep Stu Cncl; NY ST Regents Schlrshp 85; Eagle Scout Awd 85; Clarkson U; Chem Engrng.

WILLIAMS, DAWN; Islip HS; Islip, NY; (Y); Church Yth Grp; FCA; Teachers Aide; Church Choir; Nwsp Rptr; Yrbk Stf; Hon Roll; Psychlgy.

WILLIAMS, DAWN L; Lyndonville Central HS; Waterport, NY; (Y); 12/67; AFS; Church Yth Grp; Debate Tm; Red Cross Aide; Varsity Clb; VICA; Chorus; Color Guard; School Musical; Stage Crew; Regeants Scholarship For Nursing 85; Air Force; Medical.

WILLIAMS, DESIREE M; Bronx High Schl Of Science; Bronx, NY; (Y); Sec Church Yth Grp; Office Aide; Teachers Aide; Band; Biochem.

WILLIAMS, DESMOND; Christopher Columbus HS; Bronx, NY; (Y); 78/792; Teachers Aide; Band; Cit Awd; Hon Roll; Prfct Atten Awd; Trigonomtry I & II 85; Princpls Pride Of Yankees 84; Govt 84; NYU; Acctng.

WILLIAMS, DEXTER E; Uniondale HS; Hempstead, NY; (Y); Aud/Vis; Boy Scts; Letterman Clb; Science Clb; Band; Concert Band; Var Bsktbl; Capt Ftbl; Hon Roll; Prfct Atten Awd; Engrng.

WILLIAMS, DONNA; Jordan-Elbridge HS; Skaneateles Fls, NY; (Y); Band; Concert Band; Mrchg Band; School Musical; Var Cheerleading; JV Sftbl; Jr NHS; NHS.

WILLIAMS, DONNA; Lindenhurst HS; Lindenhurst, NY; (Y); Girl Scts; Spanish Clb; Band; Concert Band; Mrchg Band; School Play; Symp Band; High Hon Roll; Hon Roll; NHS; NYSSMA Silver Awd Flute 83; Comp.

WILLIAMS, DUANE; Northeastern Clinton HS; Alburg, VT; (Y); Church Yth Grp; Model UN; Hon Roll; NHS.

WILLIAMS, EDWARD A; Cardinal Hayes HS; Brooklyn, NY; (Y); 11/249; Stu Cncl; High Hon Roll; Hon Roll; NY St Regents Schlrshp 85; Penn St; Engrng.

WILLIAMS, EILEEN; G Ray Bodley HS; Fulton, NY; (Y); 54/236; VP Ski Clb; Yrbk Stf; Trs Soph Cls; Trs Jr Cls; Rep Stu Cncl; Var Capt Socr; High Hon Roll; Hon Roll; Yrbk Staff Awd; Mst Out Going Class Awd; Ofc Wrkr Awd; Plattsburg ST; Psychlgy.

WILLIAMS, ELAINE; Sandy Creek Cntrl HS; Pulaski, NY; (Y); Drama Clb; French Clb; Teachers Aide; Band; Chorus; Concert Band; Mrchg Band; School Play; JV Mgr(s); NHS; Jefferson CC; RN.

WILLIAMS, ELIZABETH; Andrew Jackson HS; Queens, NY; (Y); Church Yth Grp; Dance Clb; Chorus; School Musical; Cit Awd; Hon Roll; Bus Admin.

WILLIAMS, ELIZABETH; The Stony Brook Schl; E Setauket, NY; (Y); 6/80; Art Clb; Camera Clb; Church Yth Grp; Debate Tm; Drama Clb; Acpl Chr; Chorus; Madrigals; School Musical; School Play; Cum Laude Soc 85; Slvr Medal-Eng 85; Slvr Medal-Bible 85; Eng Lit.

WILLIAMS, ERIC C; Arlington HS; Poughkeepsie, NY; (Y); 80/530; Boy Scts; Chess Clb; Eagl Sct 85; Hnr Key 85; SUNY Alfred; Cermc Engrng.

WILLIAMS, GREGORY D; Mc Quaid Jesuit HS; Fairport, NY; (Y); 40/185; Art Clb; Teachers Aide; Varsity Clb; Chorus; School Musical; Nwsp Rptr; Yrbk Stf; Var Bsktbl; JV Var Ftbl; Var Trk; NYS Rgnts Schlrshp; Sibleys Schlstc Art Cert Merit; U Buffalo; Bio Chem.

WILLIAMS, GWENDOLYN; William Howard Taft HS; Bronx, NY; (Y); Sec Church Yth Grp; Dance Clb; Drama Clb; English Clb; FBLA; Library Aide; Church Choir; School Play; Lit Mag; Hon Roll; Art & Film Awd 85; Cert Of Awd Accntng Acclnc 84; Hnr Stu Awd 85; Herbert Lehman Coll; Accntng.

WILLIAMS, HUGH C; Port Chester HS; Rye Brook, NY; (Y); Band; Chorus; Church Choir; Concert Band; Mrchg Band; Stage Crew; Bsktbl; Ftbl; Bus Admin.

WILLIAMS, IRENE; John C Birdlebough HS; Pennellville, NY; (Y); French Clb; Stat Bsbl; JV Score Keeper; JV Var Vllybl; High Hon Roll; Hon Roll; Air Force; Data Proc.

WILLIAMS, IVETTE; George Washington HS; New York, NY; (Y); 1/315; Dance Clb; Teachers Aide; Yrbk Stf; Gov Hon Prg Awd; High Hon Roll; VP NHS; Prfct Atten Awd; Val; UFT & Rgnt Schlrshps; John Mooney Math Awd & Dance Bronze Mdl 85; Minerva Awd 85; Rensselaer Poly Inst; Engr.

WILLIAMS, JAMESINE; Susquehanna Valley HS; Binghamton, NY; (Y); Church Yth Grp; Ski Clb; Orch; Nwsp Rptr; Yrbk Stf; Lit Mag; Var Tennis; Hon Roll; Jr NHS; Art Clb; Honors Eng 84-85; NYSSMA Music Awds 82-85; Natl Rifle Assn Awd 84-85; Technel Vitlty Advcmnt Pgm 83-84; Howard U; Sci.

WILLIAMS, JANE; Jamesville-De Witt HS; Dewitt, NY; (Y); Church Yth Grp; Pres German Clb; Stat Bsktbl; Var JV Cheerleading; High Hon Roll; Hon Roll; NHS; Schlstc Art Awds Gold Keys, Hnrbl Mntn 81-85; Fclty Ldrshp & Svc Awd 85; Ononduga CC Outstndng Achvt; Biochem Engrng.

WILLIAMS, JOHN; St John The Baptist HS; Brentwood, NY; (Y); Boy Scts; Chess Clb; Computer Clb; Math Clb; Math Tm; Band; Mrchg Band; Stage Crew; Hon Roll; Mu Alp Tht; Comp Engr.

WILLIAMS, JOHN K; Copiague SR HS; Copiague, NY; (Y); 3/349; Computer Clb; French Clb; Math Clb; Math Tm; Spanish Clb; Crs Cntry; Trk; High Hon Roll; NHS; Schlr Athlt Awd 85; Regnts Schlrshp 85; St Lawrence U; Bio.

WILLIAMS, JOSEPH; Columbia Preparatory Schl; New York, NY; (Y); Church Yth Grp; Civic Clb; Cmnty Wkr; Debate Tm; Drama Clb; Political Wkr; Teachers Aide; Church Choir; Orch; School Musical; Vassar Coll; Political Sci.

WILLIAMS, JOYCE; John Dewey HS; Brooklyn, NY; (Y); JA; Library Aide; Chorus; Yrbk Stf; VFW Awd; Mannes Coll Of Music; Music.

WILLIAMS, JUDITH A; Duanesburg Central JR SR HS; Delanson, NY; (Y); 1/65; Yrbk Bus Mgr; Bausch & Lomb Sci Awd; NHS; Pres Schlr; Val; Camera Clb; Math Clb; Office Aide; Chorus; Yrbk Stf; Latin NHS 82-84; Olympics Of Mind 84-85; Summa Cum Laude-Natl Latin Exam 84; Suny Plattsburgh; Span.

WILLIAMS, JULIE; Williamsville East HS; E Amherst, NY; (Y); Cmnty Wkr; Pep Clb; VP Chorus; Stage Crew; Swing Chorus; Rep Jr Cls; Rep Stu Cncl; Var Capt Cheerleading; High Hon Roll; Hon Roll; U Of MI-DEARBORN; Pblc Rltns.

WILLIAMS, KATHY; Clara Barton HS; Brooklyn, NY; (Y); Exploring; Teachers Aide; Hon Roll; Perf Attndc Awd 83-84; Hunter Clg; Nrsg.

WILLIAMS, KATRINA; Victor Central HS; Victor, NY; (Y); 31/248; Spanish Clb; JV Sftbl; High Hon Roll; Hon Roll; Gregg Typng Awd 84-85.

WILLIAMS, KEITH R; Frontier Central SR HS; Blasdell, NY; (S); Aud/Vis; Church Yth Grp; Exploring; Library Aide; Teachers Aide; Jr Cls; Hon Roll; Jr NHS; NHS; Prfct Atten Awd; Natl Hist & Govrnmnt Awd 85; Bus Admin.

WILLIAMS, KELLY L; Tonawanda JR SR HS; Tonawanda, NY; (Y); 30/235; Band; Concert Band; Mrchg Band; Pep Band; School Musical; Stage Crew; Stat Bsktbl; Score Keeper; Var Socr; Var Sftbl; Regnts Schlrshp 85; Qulty Stu Awd 85; NEDT Awd 81; Mediaille Coll; Comms.

WILLIAMS, KIM; Cazenovia Central Schl; Cazenovia, NY; (Y); Drama Clb; Acpl Chr; Chorus; Madrigals; School Musical; Var Capt Diving; Var Golf; Var Score Keeper; Hon Roll; Low Stroke Avg-Golf 85; 5th Pl Sctn III-GOLF 85; 6th Pl Sctn III & IV-GOLF 85; Law.

WILLIAMS, KIRK D; Prattsburg Central HS; Prattsburg, NY; (Y); 2/39; Church Yth Grp; Varsity Clb; School Play; Pres Jr Cls; VP Sr Cls; Var Capt Bsktbl; Var Capt Ftbl; High Hon Roll; Hon Roll; AF-ROTC Schlrshp Fnlst 84-85; Schl Flag Bearer 84-85; Schlrsph U Of Detroit 84-85; Elect Engrng.

WILLIAMS, KRISTINE; Oceanside SR HS; Oceanside, NY; (Y); 93/531; Church Yth Grp; Cmnty Wkr; Dance Clb; Hosp Aide; Key Clb; Letterman Clb; Pep Clb; Spanish Clb; Varsity Clb; Variety Show; Temple Avodah Humanitarn 85; Donna Murray Mem Nrsng Scholar 85; Pace U; Nrsng.

WILLIAMS, LAMWELL; South Shore HS; Brooklyn, NY; (Y); Church Yth Grp; Cmnty Wkr; FCA; FBLA; FTA; Varsity Clb; VICA; Church Choir; Var Bsbl; Trk; Elec Engrng.

WILLIAMS, LAURA; Notre Dame Bishop Gibbons HS; Schenectady, NY; (S); French Clb; Co-Capt Band; Jazz Band; Mrchg Band; School Musical; Variety Show; Yrbk Stf; Hon Roll; Law.

WILLIAMS, LINDA M; Cardinal Spellman HS; New York, NY; (Y); 20/550; Dance Clb; Yrbk Stf; Stu Cncl; Schlrshps Manhattan & City Coll 85; Regnts Nrs Schlrshp 85; City Coll Of NY; Elem Tchr.

WILLIAMS, LISA; Mohawk Central HS; Mohawk, NY; (S); French Clb; Teachers Aide; Concert Band; Mrchg Band; School Play; Rep Stu Cncl; JV Bsktbl; Var L Cheerleading; High Hon Roll; NHS.

WILLIAMS, LORI; Waverly SR HS; Lowman, NY; (Y); Church Yth Grp; Color Guard; Stage Crew; Variety Show; Rep Stu Cncl; NHS; Boyd Schl; Trvl.

WILLIAMS, LYNN; Maple Hill HS; Castleton, NY; (S); 20/85; French Clb; Girl Scts; Chorus; Var Cheerleading; Fld Hcky; Gym; Sftbl; Vllybl; Hon Roll; Prfct Atten Awd; Bus Adm.

WILLIAMS, MARGARET; Port Chester HS; Port Chester, NY; (Y); Yrbk Phtg; Yrbk Stf; Brdcstng.

WILLIAMS, MARIAN KAREN; Prospect Heights HS; Brooklyn, NY; (Y); 28/301; Dance Clb; Chorus; Hunter Coll; Nrs.

WILLIAMS, MARTIN D; North Rose-Wolcott HS; Rose, NY; (Y); Church Yth Grp; Spanish Clb; Band; Concert Band; Mrchg Band; Stu Cncl; Hon Roll; NHS; Mth.

WILLIAMS, MONIQUE; HS Of Fashion Inds; Queens Vlg, NY; (Y); 147/330; U Of Bridgeport; Bus Adm.

WILLIAMS, OTHNIEL; Andrew Jackson HS; Queens, NY; (Y); Boy Scts; Debate Tm; Drama Clb; Key Clb; Math Clb; Science Clb; Chorus; School Musical; School Play; Socr.

WILLIAMS, OVITA; Clara Barton HS; Brooklyn, NY; (Y); Debate Tm; Girl Scts; Color Guard; Ed Nwsp Ed-Chief; Nwsp Rptr; Pres Soph Cls; Cheerleading; Hon Roll; JC Awd; Kiwanis Awd; Ldrshp Awd Hugh O Brien Sop Ldrshp 84; Psych.

WILLIAMS, PETER; Sachem High School North; Farmingville, NY; (Y); Drama Clb; Band; Chorus; Madrigals; School Musical.

WILLIAMS, REBECCA; Marlboro Central HS; Marlboro, NY; (Y); 5/164; Rep Church Yth Grp; Mgr Drama Clb; Band; Trs Chorus; Ed Yrbk Stf; Cit Awd; High Hon Roll; NHS; Girl Scts; Grl Sct Slvr & Gld Awds 83.

WILLIAMS, RHETT L; Skaneateles HS; Auburn, NY; (Y); Boys Clb Am; Church Yth Grp; Red Cross Aide; JV Bsktbl; JV Var Ftbl; God Cntry Awd; Hon Roll; Teachers Aide; Wt Lftg; Aeron Engrng.

WILLIAMS, ROB J; Brewster HS; Brewster, NY; (Y); Art Clb; Church Yth Grp; Cmnty Wkr; Science Clb; Spanish Clb; Ftbl; Tennis; Jr NHS; NHS; Spanish NHS.

WILLIAMS, ROBERT; Oswego HS; Oswego, NY; (Y); 34/371; Chess Clb; VP JA; Science Clb; Spanish Clb; Chorus; School Musical; Variety Show; Rep Stu Cncl; High Hon Roll; Hon Roll; Runner Up VP Marktng Of Yr CNY JR Achvt 83-84; Delegate To Regn One JR Achvt Conf CNY Area 85; USN Nuc Power Elect Tech.

WILLIAMS, ROBERT COYLE; Briarcliff HS; Briarcliff Mnr, NY; (Y); AFS; Am Leg Boys St; JA; Orch; Rptr Nwsp Ed-Chief; Im Bsktbl; Var Capt Crs Cntry; Var Capt Trk; Vllybl; High Hon Roll; All Leag, All Cntry Crss Cntry 84 & 85; Amer Lgn Sch Wnnr Male 85; Thomas J Watson IBM Schlrshp 85; Princeton U.

WILLIAMS, RYHAAN; Westburg HS; Westbury, NY; (Y); 30/258; Debate Tm; FBLA; Sec Model UN; Speech Tm; Stage Crew; Yrbk Stf; Hon Roll; Artcls Pblshd In Lcl Nwsppr 84; Soc Stds Excllnc Awd 83; Yorker Clb-Treas 84-85; Pre-Med Clb VP 84-85; Cinemtgrphy.

WILLIAMS, SABRINA; Satellite Acad; Brooklyn, NY; (Y); Church Yth Grp; Drama Clb; Girl Scts; Teachers Aide; Church Choir; School Play; Gym; High Hon Roll; Hon Roll; Prfct Atten Awd; Outstndg Acad Achvt 85; Bus.

WILLIAMS, SEAN A; Corning East HS; Beaver Dams, NY; (Y); JA; Pres Model UN; Radio Clb; Ed Yrbk Stf; High Hon Roll; NHS; Ntl Merit SF; Boy Scts; French Clb; Rep Stu Cncl; W Point Invit Wrkshp 85; Black Belt Hidy-Oschiai 82; Yth Crt Side Judge 85; Engrng.

WILLIAMS, SHARI; Frewsburg Central HS; Frewsburg, NY; (Y); 13/94; Var Capt Bsktbl; Var Diving; Var Capt Sftbl; Swmmng; Ithaca Coll Scholar 85; Volunteer Exempt Firemens Scholar 85; Pst Jrnl All Str Bsktbl 83, 84 & 85; Ithaca Coll; Spch Path.

WILLIAMS, SHARON; The Franciscan Acad; Liverpool, NY; (Y); 5/24; Cmnty Wkr; FBLA; NFL; Political Wkr; Pres Jr Cls; Cit Awd; Gov Hon Prg Awd; NHS; Cngrssmns Medl Of Hnr 85; Hghst Avg Soc Stud 81-85; Outstndg Negro Amer Stu 84-85; Syracuse U; Law.

WILLIAMS, STACEY; Marcus Whitman JR SR HS; Rushville, NY; (Y); 3/126; Am Leg Aux Girls St; Ski Clb; Varsity Clb; Chorus; Color Guard; Nwsp Rptr; Yrbk Stf; VP Frsh Cls; Sec Soph Cls; Sec Jr Cls; All-Star Tnns Tm 83; Cornell; Htl/Rest Mgmt.

WILLIAMS, STACEY; Olean HS; Olean, NY; (Y); 80/213; GAA; Varsity Clb; Var L Cheerleading; Var L Trk; ST Qualfr Track 85; Schl & ST Comm Track 85; Intl Bkg.

WILLIAMS, TAMARRA S; Midwood HS; Brooklyn, NY; (Y); 75/605; Cmnty Wkr; Office Aide; Service Clb; Concert Band; Orch; Symp Band; Sal; Arista; Archon; Buffalo U; Pharmclgy.

WILLIAMS, TARA L; St Marys Girls HS; Great Neck, NY; (Y); Art Clb; Cmnty Wkr; Drama Clb; Ski Clb; School Play; Trk; Essay Cont Englsh Compstn 85; 2nd Pl Sci Fair 82-83; Fshn Dsgn.

WILLIAMS, TERRI K; Eastern District HS; Brooklyn, NY; (Y); Dance Clb; 4-H; French Clb; Variety Show; Stu Cncl; Cheerleading; Fld Hcky; Trk; French Hon Soc; High Hon Roll; Brdcstg.

WILLIAMS, THOMAS L; Utica Free Acad; Utica, NY; (Y); Am Leg Boys St; Service Clb; JV Bsbl; Var JV Bowling; Var JV Ftbl; Var Trk; Hon Roll; Bessie E Hicks Scholar 85; Mohawk Vly Frontrs Clb Achvt Awd 85; Amer H S Ath Bowling 85; Blackburn Coll; Bus Mngmnt.

WILLIAMS, VALERIE; Murry Bergtraum HS; New York, NY; (Y); VP JA; Office Aide; Church Choir; Variety Show; Stngrphy II Awd 83; Algebra Awd 83; Mrymnt Coll; Comp Sci.

WILLIAMS, VALERIE; Riverside HS; Buffalo, NY; (S); Pres Church Yth Grp; Sec JA; Library Aide; Math Tm; Spanish Clb; Chorus; Church Choir; Color Guard; Cheerleading; Hon Roll; Medaille Coll; Med.

WILLIAMSON, COLLEEN; Brewster HS; Brewster, NY; (S); 18/188; Drama Clb; Intnl Clb; Spanish Clb; Teachers Aide; School Play; Hon Roll; NHS; Spanish NHS; 2 Hon Men Natl Poetry Cont; Syracuse; Playwrght.

WILLIAMSON, DOUGLAS S; Lewiston-Porter HS; Lewiston, NY; (Y); 31/273; Key Clb; Ski Clb; Var L Socr; Var L Trk; Hon Roll; NHS; 1st Tm All Star Var Socr 84; Lamp Learning Awds 84-85; Natl Hon Rl 84; SUNY Buffalo; Chem Engrng.

WILLIAMSON, MIA; Dominican Commercial HS; St Albans, NY; (Y); Church Yth Grp; Girl Scts; Teachers Aide; Church Choir; Hon Roll; Prfct Atten Awd; Peer Grp Counselor 85; Sienna Clb 83; Comm.

WILLIAMSON, SUSAN D; Sanford H Calhoun HS; Merrick, NY; (Y); 12/340; Key Clb; Mathletes; Yrbk Phtg; Sr Cls; Hon Roll; NHS; Hofstra U.

WILLIANOR, REBECCA; Eisenhower S HS; Pt Jefferson, NY; (Y); Church Yth Grp; Cmnty Wkr; Varsity Clb; Trk.

WILLIG, CAROL; Smithtown HS West; Hauppauge, NY; (Y); German Clb; Stu Cncl; Hon Roll; German Hnr Soc 83-85; Bus Admn.

WILLINGHAM, LISA; Newburgh Free Acad; Newburgh, NY; (Y); Church Yth Grp; OEA; Church Choir; Cit Awd; Hon Roll; Computer Clb; High Hon Roll; Prfct Atten Awd; Outstndng Stu Coop Bookkeepng 85; Chamberlayne JC; Bus Admin.

WILLINGHAM, PEGGY; Emma Willard Schl; San Antonio, TX; (Y); Church Yth Grp; Cmnty Wkr; Debate Tm; Drama Clb; JCL; Latin Clb; NFL; Pep Clb; Speech Tm; Acpl Chr; Actress.

WILLIS, BONNY; Maryvale SR HS; Cheektowaga, NY; (Y); German Clb; GAA; Girl Scts; Spanish Clb; Varsity Clb; Mgr Mgr(s); Var Score Keeper; Var Socr; JV Vllybl; Hon Roll; Sec Sci.

WILLIS, CORINNE; Mahopac HS; Mahopac, NY; (Y); 131/423; Library Aide; Band; Color Guard; Concert Band; Mrchg Band; Stage Crew; Symp Band; Hon Roll; Messiah Coll; Bus.

WILLIS, DANIELLE L; Ward Melville HS; Setauket, NY; (Y); #117 In Class; School Play; Lit Mag; Swmmng; Hon Roll; Ntl Merit Ltr; Writer.

WILLIS, JAMES P; Wilson SR HS; Lockport, NY; (Y); 42/134; Church Yth Grp; Computer Clb; School Play; JV Var Bsbl; Hon Roll; St Schlr; Odyssey Mind ST Champs 81-82, 84-85; U Of Buffalo; Elec Engr.

WILLIS, JEANNE; Sacred Heart Acad; Garden City, NY; (S); 11/189; Church Yth Grp; Chorus; Madrigals; Rep Soph Cls; NHS; Ntl Merit Ltr.

WILLIS, LAURI; Lancaster Central HS; Depew, NY; (S); 132/437; Pres DECA; Rep Soph Cls; Rep Jr Cls; Pep Clb; ST DECA Cntst Fd Mktg 84; 1st Pl Regnl Fd Mktg 84; Bryant; Accntng.

WILLMART, RANDY; Colton Pierrepont HS; Colton, NY; (S); VP Soph Cls; VP Jr Cls; Pres Sr Cls; Hon Roll; Ntl Merit Ltr; Acad All Amer 85; Clarkson U; Engr.

WILLOUGHBY, ERIC; Rice HS; New York, NY; (Y); Cmnty Wkr; FCA; Off Sr Cls; Var L Bsktbl; Im Ftbl; Hon Roll; NHS; Hnr Roll 83-85; Natl Hnr Roll 84-85; Bus Mgmt.

WILLSEY, TINA; Cicero-North Syracuse HS; North Syracuse, NY; (S); 53/611; Sec Church Yth Grp; Var Swmmng; Hon Roll.

WILLSON, AMY B; Windsor HS; Kirkwood, NY; (Y); Am Leg Aux Girls St; Church Yth Grp; Spanish Clb; Stu Cncl; Trk; Wt Lftg; Broone Comm Coll; Physclgy.

WILLSON, LUANNE; Camden Central Schl; Camden, NY; (Y); Band; Concert Band; Jazz Band; School Musical; Yrbk Stf; Stu Cncl; Bsktbl; Score Keeper; Tennis; NHS; USAR Lab Tech Trng 85; All ST Band 85; Phys Ther.

WILMOT, ANNETTE; Cuba Central HS; Cuba, NY; (Y); 2/58; VP Spanish Clb; Varsity Clb; Yrbk Stf; Stat Bsktbl; Stat Ftbl; Var Socr; Var Capt Trk; High Hon Roll; NHS; Sal; Cazenovia; Adv.

WILSEY, KELLEY; Unatego JR SR HS; Otego, NY; (Y); 2/80; Drama Clb; Chorus; Concert Band; Jazz Band; School Musical; School Play; High Hon Roll; NHS; Ski Clb; Band; Hghst Acad Avg Amer Hstry & Engl II 84-85; Music Educ.

WILSON, AMY L; Frontier Central HS; Lake View, NY; (Y); 2/500; Church Yth Grp; Sec 4-H; VP Nwsp Stf; Yrbk Ed-Chief; High Hon Roll; NHS; Ntl Merit Ltr; NEDT Awd; Sal; Acad All Amer 84; Stu Of Mnth 84; Natl Hnr Rl 84; U Of MI Ann Arbor; Elem Educ.

WILSON, AMY M; Rome Free Acad; Rome, NY; (Y); Intnl Clb; Mrchg Band; Nwsp Stf; Yrbk Stf; Powder Puff Ftbl; Bus Admin.

WILSON, AYESHA; St Michaels HS; New York, NY; (Y); Cmnty Wkr; Dance Clb; Drama Clb; Band; School Musical; School Play; Stage Crew; Variety Show; Nwsp Phtg; Nwsp Stf; Syracuse U; Perf Arts.

WILSON, CARLENE; Frankfort-Schuyler HS; Frankfort, NY; (S); GAA; Spanish Clb; Trk; High Hon Roll; NHS; Accntnt.

WILSON, CAROL A; Samuel J Tilden HS; Brooklyn, NY; (Y); 1/502; Sec Cmnty Wkr; Library Aide; Sec Teachers Aide; Gov Hon Prg Awd; Val; Chncllrs Rll Hnr 85; Bst Cls Chnnl 7 85; Gvrnrs Cmmtte Schlrshp 85; Adelphi U; Accntng.

WILSON, CHERYL A; Auburn HS; Auburn, NY; (Y); 59/444; Model UN; Pep Clb; Trs Frsh Cls; Coach Actv; High Hon Roll; Regents Schlrshp 85; SUNY Binghamton.

WILSON, CHRISTINA; Oneida HS; Oneida, NY; (S); 7/225; Spanish Clb; Band; Church Choir; Yrbk Phtg; Yrbk Stf; JV Bsktbl; Var Cheerleading; High Hon Roll; NHS; JR & SR Rep Dollars For Scholars 84-85; Syracuse U; Math.

WILSON, COLLEEN; Bishop Scully HS; Amsterdam, NY; (Y); 13/58; Varsity Clb; Sec Jr Cls; Stu Cncl; Var Cheerleading; Var Sftbl; Hon Roll; NHS; JV Vllybl; Law.

WILSON, CRYSTAL L; Sarah J Hale HS; Brooklyn, NY; (Y); 3/268; JA; Math Tm; Teachers Aide; Church Choir; Hon Roll; NHS; Prfct Atten Awd; Ed Nwsp Stf; Gov Cmmttee Schlstc Achvt 82; Hnr From Elizabeth Holtzman 82; Rgnts Schlrshp 85; NY Inst Of Tech; Acctg.

WILSON, CYNDI; Le Roy Central Schl; Leroy, NY; (Y); Varsity Clb; Band; Concert Band; Drm Mjr(t); Mrchg Band; Yrbk Stf; Socr; Sftbl; Trk; Vllybl; Travel & Tourism.

WILSON, DAWN; Malverne HS; West Hempstead, NY; (S); 7/170; Varsity Clb; Church Choir; Variety Show; Nwsp Stf; Yrbk Sprt Ed; Lit Mag; Pres Soph Cls; Capt Trk; High Hon Roll; NHS; Cmmnd Negro Stu PSAT 84; Outstndg Achvt Engl, Frnch III 83; Cert Merit Engl, Phy R 83; Engr.

WILSON, DEBBIE ANN; Fiorello H Laguardia HS; Bronx, NY; (Y); 111/588; Chorus; Church Choir; School Musical; Nwsp Rptr; Rep Stu Cncl; Hon Roll; Pau U NYC; Attrny.

WILSON, DENISE; Mabel Dean Bacon HS; Bronx, NY; (S); 15/299; Dance Clb; French Clb; FBLA; Mathletes; VICA; Church Choir; Stu Cncl; Hon Roll; NHS; Prfct Atten Awd; Bus Adm.

WILSON, DENISE; The Mary Louis Acad; Queens Village, NY; (Y); Art Clb; Spanish Clb; Socr; Math Hnr Rll; Med Svc Awd; St Johns U; Pedtrcn.

WILSON, DONNA; Nyack HS; Nyack, NY; (Y); 9/277; French Clb; Spanish Clb; Band; Concert Band; Mrchg Band; VP Soph Cls; Socr; Trk; DAR Awd; French Hon Soc; Athlte Of Mnth Awd 84-85; Child Psych.

WILSON, GEOFF; Fayetteville Manlius HS; Manlius, NY; (Y); Debate Tm; JCL; Model UN; Stu Cncl; Im Bsktbl; JV Var Socr; Hon Roll; Natl Sci Olympd 83; Natl Ltn Exm 84; Cntrl NY Mdl UN Bst Delg Lgl Cmmttee 83; Engrng.

WILSON, JAMES; Skaneateles HS; Skaneateles, NY; (S); Stage Crew; Var L Ftbl; Var L Tennis; High Hon Roll; NHS; Tlntd & Gftd Prog 81-84; RIT; Comp Sci.

WILSON, JASON; New Rochelle HS; New Rochelle, NY; (Y); Cmnty Wkr; French Clb; Model UN; Political Wkr; Ski Clb; Rep Jr Cls; Var L Trk; French Hon Soc; Hon Roll; NHS; Alt Cancer Rsrch Pgm Roswell Pk Mem Inst 85; Lead Pgm 85; Model Congress Del 84; Pre-Med.

WILSON, JEFFREY; Cicero-North Syracuse HS; North Syracuse, NY; (S); 2/711; Am Leg Boys St; Aud/Vis; Church Yth Grp; Math Tm; Quiz Bowl; Band; Concert Band; Jazz Band; Mrchg Band; Orch; Mock Trial 84 & 85; Yale Coll; Novelist.

WILSON, JENNIFER; Mattituck HS; Mattituck, NY; (Y); 11/123; Am Leg Aux Girls St; German Clb; Quiz Bowl; Ski Clb; Chorus; School Musical; School Play; Variety Show; Pres Frsh Cls; VP Soph Cls; Amer Axllry Grls Ntn Sntr 85; Amer Auxllr Grls ST Lt Gvrnr 85; Advrtsng.

WILSON, JILL; Cardinal Spellman HS; Bronx, NY; (Y); Church Yth Grp; Intnl Clb; Flag Corp; Nwsp Phtg; Rep Stu Cncl; JV Trk; Hon Roll; Ntl Merit Ltr; Pre-Med.

WILSON, KAREN; Northeastern Acad; Laurelton, NY; (Y); 8/40; Chorus; Church Choir; School Musical; Trs Jr Cls; Off Sr Cls; Im Bsktbl; Hon Roll; Ntl Merit Ltr; Vllybl; Oakwd Coll Hnr Stu Schlrshp 85-86; Ntl Merit Found Ntl Hnr Rl 84-85; Samuel H Rashford Achvt Awd 85; Oakwood Coll; Elem Ed.

WILSON, KATHERINE; Lindenhurst SR HS; Lindenhurst, NY; (Y); French Clb; Yrbk Phtg; Yrbk Stf; Im Vllybl; Hon Roll; NHS; Hofstra U; Med.

WILSON, KATHLEEN ANN; Union-Endicott HS; Endicott, NY; (Y); Am Leg Aux Girls St; Church Yth Grp; Cmnty Wkr; Girl Scts; Hosp Aide; Key Clb; Nwsp Stf; Yrbk Stf; Hon Roll; Bus.

WILSON, KATHY; Chenango Forks HS; Binghamton, NY; (Y); Ski Clb; Cheerleading; Hon Roll; Engr.

WILSON, KELLY; Emma Willard Schl; Albany, NY; (Y); Ski Clb; Nwsp Rptr; Nwsp Stf; Socr; Music.

WILSON, KIMBERLY S; Frontier Central HS; Lake View, NY; (Y); 6/495; Concert Band; Jazz Band; School Musical; Yrbk Ed-Chief; Jr NHS; Ntl Merit Ltr; NEDT Awd; Church Yth Grp; Drama Clb; NYS Regents Schlrshp 85; Thomas Walker Kennedy Schlrshp 85; SUNY At Buffalo; Computer Sci.

WILSON, KRISTIN; Gloversville HS; Gloversville, NY; (Y); Drama Clb; Chorus; School Play; Stage Crew; Var Sftbl; SUNY Cortland; Psych.

WILSON, LAURA S; Newfane SR HS; Lockport, NY; (S); Science Clb; JV Fld Hcky; Hon Roll; NHS; Academic Awd Highest Average In Industl Arts 83-84; 2 Yr Prog Harrison Radiator & Lockport 84-86; GMI; Mech Engrng.

WILSON, LAURIE E; Our Lady Of Perpetual Help HS; Brooklyn, NY; (Y); 18/160; Cmnty Wkr; Drama Clb; Hosp Aide; Nwsp Rptr; High Hon Roll; NHS; Intnl Clb; Chorus; School Musical; School Play; Regnts Nrsng, Wagner & Kassenbrock Memrl Schlrshps 85; Howard Golden Achvt Awd 85; Wagner Coll; Nrsng.

WILSON, MATT; Half Hollow Hills High Schl West; Dix Hills, NY; (Y); Trs Concert Band; Jazz Band; Pres Jr Cls; JV Var Bsktbl; Capt Lcrss; JV Socr; DAR Awd; Hon Roll; Jr NHS; NHS; Beneficial Hodson Merit Scholar WA Coll 85; MVP Var Bsktbl 83-84; MVP Var Lcrss 84; WA Coll.

WILSON, MELISSA; Niagara Falls HS; Niagara Falls, NY; (Y); Sec Church Yth Grp; Hosp Aide; Office Aide; Church Choir; Psych.

WILSON, MICHELE; Catholic Central HS; Cohoes, NY; (Y); 5/179; Math Clb; Math Tm; Concert Band; Yrbk Stf; JV Var Bsktbl; JV Sftbl; Var L Tennis; Var L Trk; High Hon Roll; NHS; Empire ST Games Bsktbl 84-85; Holy Crs Book Prz 85; Engrng.

WILSON, MONICA; Shenendehowa Central Schls; Ballston Lake, NY; (Y); Drama Clb; Band; Jazz Band; Orch; School Musical; School Play; Var Trk; High Hon Roll; Hon Roll; All Eastern Orch 85; Asst Prin Cellist All St Orch 85; Hnr Ltr Trk & Fld 85; ST U NY Albany; Psych.

WILSON, PAM; Roxbury Central HS; Roxbury, NY; (Y); 3/32; Church Yth Grp; Drama Clb; GAA; Sec Rep Stu Cncl; Var Capt Bsktbl; Var Capt Socr; Var Sftbl; High Hon Roll; NHS; Computer Clb; Math Excel 81-84; Acctng Awd 83-84; All Star Bsktbl, Sftbl, Sccr 84-85; Ithaca Coll; Explrtry.

WILSON, PAMELA; Roxbury Central Schl; Roxbury, NY; (S); 4/40; Church Yth Grp; Drama Clb; GAA; Band; Rep Stu Cncl; Var Capt Bsktbl; Var Capt Socr; Sftbl; High Hon Roll; NHS; Math Excel Awd 82 & 84; Accntng Achvt Awd 83.

WILSON, PAMELA; Skaneateles Central HS; Skaneateles, NY; (S); Drama Clb; Band; Var Trk; Var Vllybl; Hon Roll; NHS; Bus.

WILSON, PATRICIA L; Corning-Painted Post West HS; Coopers Plains, NY; (Y); 49/254; Sec Trs Church Yth Grp; Exploring; FBLA; Ski Clb; Band; Chorus; School Musical; Capt Bowling; Hon Roll; Prfct Atten Awd; Sr Bowling Awd 85; Natl Ldrshp Org 83-85; Top 15 Slsprsns Sr Sales 84-85; U Of KY; Pre-Med.

WILSON, RANDALL; Linton HS; Schenectady, NY; (Y); 90/230; 4-H; VP Temple Yth Grp; 4-H Awd; Var Crs Cntry; JV Var Trk; Comp Sci.

WILSON JR, ROBERT; New Rochelle HS; New Rochelle, NY; (Y); Band; Hon Roll; Itln Awd, Band Awd 82; Iona Coll; Bus.

WILSON, SANDRA; Bay Shore SR HS; Bay Shore, NY; (Y); 79/425; GAA; Intnl Clb; Var Crs Cntry; Var Trk; Var Wt Lftg; Hon Roll; Prfct Atten Awd; Spnsh Hnr Awd 83; Trck & Fld Awd 85; Hgh Spnsh Hnr Rll 85; OH ST; Chem.

WILSON, SCOTT; Auburn HS; Auburn, NY; (Y); JV Var Ftbl; Acctg.

WILSON, SHARON; Roy C Ketcham SR HS; Wappingers Fls, NY; (Y); Drama Clb; Stage Crew; Yrbk Phtg; Yrbk Stf; Var Cheerleading; High Hon Roll; Hon Roll; Lit Edtr 85-86; HS Yrbk 85-86; Project Adventure 82-83; IBM HS Coop 85-86; ST U NY Albany; Mktg Mgt.

WILSON, STEPHEN C; Shenendehowa HS; Clifton Park, NY; (Y); Chess Clb; Church Yth Grp; Computer Clb; Key Clb; Science Clb; Ski Clb; High Hon Roll; NHS; Acad Achvt Awd Skidmore Coll Saratogian Paper 84; Key Awd Outstndng Stu 85; Engrng.

WILSON, STEPHEN P; E Syracuse Minoa HS; E Syracuse, NY; (Y); 18/338; Exploring; JV Bowling; High Hon Roll; Hon Roll; Jr NHS; NHS; St Schlr; Rutgers Coll Engrng; Engrng.

WILSON, SUZANNE; Norwood-Norfolk Central HS; Norfolk, NY; (Y); 3/114; French Clb; Pres FTA; Key Clb; Yrbk Stf; Lit Mag; JV Bsktbl; JV Vllybl; High Hon Roll; NHS; Drew Memrl Fund Schlrshp Awd 85; St Lawrence Bar Assn Schlrshp Awd 85; Outstndng Frnch Stu Awd 85; Potsdam ST; Elem Eductn.

WILSON, TAMARA A; Schalmont HS; Duanesburg, NY; (Y); 4-H; Chorus; Concert Band; Drill Tm; Jazz Band; JV Var Trk; High Hon Roll; NHS; Ntl Merit Ltr; French Clb; Critcal Issues Conf Delg-St Lawrence U 85; Outstdng Achv Inchem 85; Stu Spectrum 83; Law.

WILSON, TERESA; Highland HS; Highland, NY; (Y); 25/124; Church Yth Grp; Band; Concert Band; Mrchg Band; Var Cheerleading; Var Trk; High Hon Roll; Jr NHS; NHS; Spanish NHS; Sci.

WILSON, TRENT; Springville Griffith Inst; Springville, NY; (Y); Spanish Clb; Rep Frsh Cls; Var JV Bsbl; JV Ftbl; JV Swmmng; Alfred Ag & Tech Coll; Air Cond.

WILTSE, LESLIE; Pioneer Central HS; Machias, NY; (Y); 36/168; Latin Clb; Vet.

WILTSEY, DONNA; Union Endicott HS; Endicott, NY; (Y); Key Clb; Mathletes; Sec Band; Color Guard; Concert Band; Orch; Nwsp Rptr; Yrbk Rptr; High Hon Roll; NHS; Comp Sci.

WILTSHIRE, AVONNIE A; Elmont Memorial HS; Elmont, NY; (Y); 17/247; Church Yth Grp; Band; Church Choir; School Musical; NHS; Cmnty Wkr; Girl Scts; Concert Band; Mrchg Band; Orch; PTSA Rflctns Prjct 82 & 84; PTA Awd For Arts In Edctn 85; Music.

WINCH, JEROME; Sarange Central Schl; Cadyville, NY; (S); 22/126; Var L Bsbl; JV Bsktbl; Var L Ftbl; Hon Roll; Northern Adirondak Cncl Ski Race Tm; Jr Prom Ct; Clarkson; Elec Engrng.

WINCHELL, MARY; Cohoes HS; Cohoes, NY; (Y); Chorus; Bus.

WINCHELL, NANCY LYNN; Hartford Central School; Fort Ann, NY; (Y); Church Yth Grp; 4-H; JA; Band; Chorus; Mrchg Band; Orch; Symp Band; Yrbk Stf; 4-H Awd; 4-H NYC Career Trip 83; Citznshp Wshngton Focus Trip 84; Bus.

WINDERL, LISA MARY; Bishop Ludden HS; Syracuse, NY; (S); Church Yth Grp; JA; Model UN; Var Cheerleading; High Hon Roll; NHS; Frnch II Awd Achvt 84; Engl Awd 82; Schlrshp 82; Bus Mgmt.

WINDSOR, ANGELA; Miller Place HS; Miller Pl, NY; (Y); FBLA; Ski Clb; Varsity Clb; Nwsp Stf; Yrbk Stf; VP Jr Cls; VP Sr Cls; Capt Cheerleading; Cit Awd; High Hon Roll; Math Awd 83-84; Tchr.

WINDSOR, DAWN; Pioneer Central HS; Arcade, NY; (Y); 15/171; FBLA; Hosp Aide; Latin Clb; Mrchg Band; Hon Roll; Med.

WINDSOR, SEAN; Rocky Point JR SR HS; Rocky Pt, NY; (Y); Ski Clb; Varsity Clb; JV Bsktbl; Var Golf; Var Socr; Hon Roll; Bus Mgmt.

WINDSOR, SUZANNE M; Rocky Point JR-SR HS; Rocky Point, NY; (Y); 41/190; GAA; Hosp Aide; Thesps; Chorus; Mrchg Band; JV Var Cheerleading; Var Golf; Var Mgr(s); Stat Socr; Hon Roll; NY ST Regents Scholarship 85; Mt Saint Mary Clg; Nursing.

WINDUS, LISA; Scio Central Schl; Scio, NY; (S); 1/44; Color Guard; Yrbk Stf; Sec Sr Cls; JV Var Bsktbl; Var Sftbl; Var Tennis; Var Vllybl; DAR Awd; High Hon Roll; NHS; Math.

WING, JOHN P; Pulaski JR SR HS; Richland, NY; (S); AFS; Drama Clb; French Clb; Math Clb; Ski Clb; Band; Chorus; Concert Band; Mrchg Band; School Musical; E La Point Instrmntl Awd 85; Mus Ed.

WINGATE, LISA K; Williamsville North HS; Williamsville, NY; (Y); 8/311; VP Pres Latin Clb; Nwsp Stf; Ed Yrbk Stf; JV Vllybl; High Hon Roll; NCTE Awd; NHS; JCL; Library Aide; Model UN; 1st Pl Wrttn Regnl Latin Exam 84; Acadc Schlrshp Nardin Acad 81; Outstndng Bio Stu Awd 83; Pre-Med.

WINGEN, NICOLE; Minisink Valley HS; Westtown, NY; (Y); Church Yth Grp; JA; Library Aide; Office Aide; Ski Clb; Nwsp Stf; Yrbk Stf; Off Sr Cls; Hon Roll; Most Imprvd Stu 85; Coll Boca Raton; Bus Adm.

WINIKOW, SCOTT K; Spring Valley SR HS; Spring Vly, NY; (Y); Cmnty Wkr; Computer Clb; Political Wkr; Hon Roll; NHS; St Schlr; Ramapa Yth Ct 83-85; Meditatn Tm 85; NY ST Senate & NY ST Asmbly Achvt Awds; Law.

WINK JR, WAYNE H; Uniondale HS; Uniondale, NY; (Y); 26/400; Am Leg Boys St; Trs Debate Tm; Pres Drama Clb; Trs Speech Tm; Trs NHS; Ntl Merit Ltr; Aud/Vis; Church Yth Grp; Cmnty Wkr; Best Actor Awd 85; Copy Editor Schl Nwspr 84-85; NY ST Regents Schlrshp 85; Hofstra U; Polt Sci.

WINKELMAN, DENNIS G; Don Bosco Prep; Pearl River, NY; (S); 25/225; Pep Clb; JV Ftbl; Hon Roll; NHS; Pre Med.

WINKELMAN, ELAINE; Westfield Acad & Central; Westfield, NY; (S); 1/76; VP Frsh Cls; VP Jr Cls; Sec Sr Cls; Var JV Bsktbl; Var Tennis; Var JV Vllybl; High Hon Roll; NHS; Amer Chmcl Soc Awd 84; Regnts Schlrshp 85; Daemen Coll; Cmmrcl Art.

WINKELMAN, JENNIFER; Westfield Academy & Central Schl; Westfield, NY; (S); Band; Chorus; Mrchg Band; VP Soph Cls; JV Var Bsktbl; Var Sftbl; JV Var Vllybl; High Hon Roll; Hon Roll; NHS; Phys Ther.

WINKLEY, BETH; Mount Mercy Acad; East Aurora, NY; (Y); Church Yth Grp; French Clb; JA; Trk; Hon Roll; Cmmnctns.

WINNERT, LAURIE; Lancaster SR HS; Depew, NY; (S); 131/437; DECA; VP Pres Pep Clb; Concert Band; Trs Mrchg Band; Sec Sr Cls; Rep Stu Cncl; Capt L Swmmng; Hon Roll; NHS; AFS; Synch Swm Tm Won 12 Rbbns; Alfred U; Cermc Engrng.

WINSCH, HARRY; Ward Melville HS; East Setauket, NY; (Y); 59/760; Aud/Vis; Pres Computer Clb; Mathletes; Math Tm; Lit Mag; High Hon Roll; Jr NHS; NHS; Rensselaer; Comp Sci.

WINSHIP, SONJA; Gowanda Central JR SR HS; Gowanda, NY; (Y); Band; Color Guard; Mrchg Band; Nwsp Stf; Rep Frsh Cls; Rep Soph Cls; Rep Jr Cls; Rep Stu Cncl; JV Var Cheerleading; JV Var Mgr(s); SUNY.

WINSLOW, LISA MARIE; Ilion JR SR HS; Ilion, NY; (Y); Church Yth Grp; Orch; Pres Frsh Cls; Sec Jr Cls; Pres Sec Stu Cncl; Cheerleading; Gym; Cit Awd; High Hon Roll; Jr NHS; Forgn Exch Stdnt Schlrshp 85; Pre-Law.

WINSLOW, MARYELLEN; Our Lady Of Mercy Acad; N Babylon, NY; (Y); Cmnty Wkr; Hosp Aide; Service Clb; Variety Show; Lit Mag; Var JV Cheerleading; Crs Cntry; Trk; Bsktbl Coch N Babyln Athltc Clb 83-85; Syracuse U; Educ.

WINSLOW, MICHAEL; H Frank Carey HS; Franklin Sq, NY; (Y); 28/222; French Clb; VP Key Clb; Mathletes; VP Science Clb; JV Bsbl; High Hon Roll; Hon Roll; Med.

WINSTON, DOUG; Sacred Heart HS; Yonkers, NY; (Y); Var Trk; Var Wt Lftg; Prfct Atten Awd; Fld Of Elect.

WINSTON, SHERYL M; Commack HS; Commack, NY; (Y); 1/374; Cmnty Wkr; Mathletes; Nwsp Rptr; Lit Mag; NHS; Ntl Merit Ltr; Pres Schlr; Val; Exploring; Hosp Aide; Columbia U Sci Hnrs Prog 84-85; Century III Ldr 85; Yale.

WINSTON, WADE; Peekskill HS; Peekskill, NY; (Y); Church Yth Grp; Acpl Chr; Band; Chorus; Pres Church Choir; School Play; Variety Show; Trk; Hon Roll; SR Cls Awd 85; Law.

WINTER, DAWN; Mamaroneck HS; Mamaroneck, NY; (Y); AFS; French Clb; Latin Clb; Ski Clb; Band; Mrchg Band; Yrbk Stf; Swmmng; Trk; Tufts; Intl Bus.

WINTER, ROBERT J; Whitehall Central HS; Whitehall, NY; (Y); 5/76; Church Yth Grp; Cmnty Wkr; Red Cross Aide; Yrbk Rptr; Yrbk Sprt Ed; Yrbk Stf; Stu Cncl; Bsbl; Ftbl; Cit Awd; Rgnsts Schlrshp Recptn 85; MVP Ftbl & Basbl 85; SADD 84-85; Suny; Bus Mgmt.

WINTER, VIKKI LYNNE; East Syracuse-Minoa HS; E Syracuse, NY; (Y); 10/338; Stat Lcrss; Dnfth Awd; NHS; Prfct Atten Awd; Pres Schlr; Church Yth Grp; Concert Band; Regents Scholar 85; Spn 84; Engl, Bio Hlth 83; Elmera Coll; Intl Bus.

WINTERS, BARBARA ANN; St John The Baptist HS; West Islip, NY; (Y); Cmnty Wkr; Dance Clb; Office Aide; Pep Clb; Varsity Clb; Var Pom Pon; Powder Puff Ftbl; Var Trk; Hon Roll; Psych.

WINTERS, MATTHEW; Tupper Lake HS; Tupper Lake, NY; (Y); Church Yth Grp; Drama Clb; French Clb; Concert Band; Pres Jr Cls; Stu Cncl; Ftbl; High Hon Roll; NHS; Science Clb; Schlr Ath Bstkbl; 1st Pl Sci Fair; Elect Engrng.

WINTERS, MICHELLE; Tupper Lake HS; Tupper Lk, NY; (Y); Church Yth Grp; Stu Cncl; Bsktbl; Socr; Vllybl; Hon Roll; Jr NHS; Jr Ntl Hnr Soc 84-85; Sec.

WINTERS, PETER; Clarkstown HS; New City, NY; (Y); Bsbl; JV Bsktbl; Wt Lftg; Indstrl Bsktbl & Sftbl Lgus 82-85; Bus.

WINTON, WILLIAM; Elmira Southside HS; Elmira, NY; (Y); Church Yth Grp; French Clb; German Clb; Spanish Clb; Church Choir.

WINUM, NAT; Valley Central HS; Walden, NY; (Y); 53/387; Church Yth Grp; Ed English Clb; 4-H; Natl Beta Clb; Ed Lit Mag; Off Frsh Cls; Off Soph Cls; Off Jr Cls; 4-H Awd; Hon Roll; Natl 4-H Agricltrl Awd Comptn 84; Cobleskil Ag & Tech; Agricltr.

WINWARD, THOMAS; Rye Neck HS; Mamaroneck, NY; (Y); 8/98; Trs Exploring; Key Clb; School Musical; Variety Show; Pres NHS; Ntl Merit Ltr; Pres Schlr; CIBA-GEIGY H S Sci Awd 85; Am Legn Awd 85; Bard Coll Crtcl Wrtng Awd 85; Alfred U; Crmnl Justc.

WIRT, KIMBERLY; Auburn HS; Auburn, NY; (Y); Pres Church Yth Grp; Hosp Aide; VP Band; Jazz Band; VP Mrchg Band; Pep Band; VP Symp Band; Variety Show; Hon Roll; Bus Mgmt.

WIRTH, ERIKA; Dominican Commercial HS; Ridgewood, NY; (Y); 41/273; Art Clb; Girl Scts; Church Choir; Yrbk Stf; Rep Jr Cls; Hon Roll; Jr NHS; Sienna Clb; JR Ntl Bus Nhr Soc; Pres Acadmc Ftnss Awd; Hunter Coll.

WIRTH, J GLENN; Grand Island HS; Grand Island, NY; (Y); Boy Scts; Church Yth Grp; Model UN; Ski Clb; Capt Varsity Clb; JV Bsktbl; Score Keeper; Var Capt Socr; Var JV Tennis; Im Vllybl; Vtrnrn.

WIRTH, WENDY; Hilton HS; Hilton, NY; (Y); 10/300; Mrchg Band; Variety Show; Sec Frsh Cls; Sec Soph Cls; Sec Jr Cls; Pres Stu Cncl; Var Capt Cheerleading; NHS; Ntl Merit Ltr; Mrchg Band; Acad Merit Schlr 83-85; Western NY St Fire Dept Queen 84-85; Pyscl Thrpy.

WIRTZ, KRISTINA; James Sperry HS; Henrietta, NY; (Y); 4/300; Drama Clb; Thesps; Chorus; Concert Band; Orch; Mgr School Play; French Hon Soc; High Hon Roll; NHS; Cmnty Wkr; Paideia Cert Excllnc Humnties 85; Acadmc & Music Ltr 85; Molly Mulligan Schlrshp 84; Zoolgy.

WISCH, DINA M; West Islip HS; West Islip, NY; (Y); 17/525; Drama Clb; Model UN; School Musical; Ed Nwsp Rptr; Ed Lit Mag; Pres Sr Cls; Cheerleading; Hon Roll; NHS; Ntl Merit Ltr; Regents Schlrshp 85; Cornell U.

WISCHHUSEN, DOREEN; Northport HS; Northport, NY; (Y); Service Clb; Variety Show; Lit Mag; Var L Gym; NHS; High Hon Roll; USGF ST Champ Teams 81 & 82; Natl Yth Ldrshp Conf 84; NYS Rgnts Schlrshp 85; Amer Legion Schlrshp 85; SUNY-BINGHAMTON; Law.

WISE, LORETTA; Mount Markham SR HS; W Winfield, NY; (Y); 28/115; Church Yth Grp; Drama Clb; 4-H; FHA; Chorus; School Musical; Yrbk Stf; Rep Stu Cncl; Cheerleading; Hon Roll; Ctznshp Awd 84; Munsin Williams Procter Inst.

WISEMAN, CARLA; American International Schl Israel; Apo New York, NY; (Y); Chorus; School Play; Pres Frsh Cls; Pres Soph Cls; Pres Stu Cncl; Var Bsktbl; Var Fld Hcky; Capt Var Sftbl; Consecutive Dean List 85; Psych.

WISEMON, CARMI M; Yeshiva Univ HS For Boys; Brooklyn, NY; (Y); Cmnty Wkr; Political Wkr; Teachers Aide; Temple Yth Grp; Nwsp Rptr; Rep Frsh Cls; Rep Stu Cncl; Hatmada Dlgnc Awd 83-84; Dly Nws Faces & Places 85; Yeshiva U; Psych.

WISER, JOAN M; Ellicottville Central Schl; Great Vly, NY; (Y); Office Aide; Chorus; Concert Band; Jazz Band; Mrchg Band; Trs Jr Cls; Vllybl; Olean Bus Inst; Bus.

WISHANSKY, MARC; Sachem North HS; Holbrook, NY; (Y); 19/1500; Science Clb; Ski Clb; VP Spanish Clb; Jr NHS; NHS; Biomed Engrng.

WISHAU, KAREN; Greece Athena HS; Rochester, NY; (Y); 10/281; Ski Clb; Varsity Clb; Socr; Var Trk; Var Capt Vllybl; NHS; Regnts Schlrshp 85; MVP JV Sccr 83; Cochs Awd Vrsty Vllybl 84; Gnrl Motrs Inst; Elec Engrng.

WISHNIE, BETH; Ossining HS; Briarcliff, NY; (Y); 2/297; Am Leg Aux Girls St; Debate Tm; School Musical; Yrbk Stf; Pres Sr Cls; Capt Fld Hcky; Capt Socr; Cit Awd; Pres Schlr; Sal; Achvt Acad Voice & Drama Awd 85; Regnts Schrshp NY ST 85; Frnch Achvt Awd 81-85; Brown U.

WISLER, KENDRA; William Nottingham HS; Syracuse, NY; (Y); Latin Clb; Spanish Clb; Chorus; Concert Band; Pep Band; Symp Band; Yrbk Phtg; Sec Soph Cls; Var JV Socr; Var JV Trk; Bio Sci.

WISNIEWSKI, KAREN; W Seneca East HS; W Seneca, NY; (Y); 4-H; Color Guard; Drill Tm; Drm & Bgl; Flag Corp; Variety Show; Nwsp Stf; Hon Roll; JC Awd; Sec Sci.

WISNIEWSKI, LINDA L; John Jay HS; Katonah, NY; (Y); 8/300; Art Clb; Trs French Clb; German Clb; Intnl Clb; Sec Leo Clb; Math Tm; Scholastic Bowl; Yrbk Stf; Ed Lit Mag; Cit Awd; Williams Coll; Chem.

WISNIEWSKI, NORMAN; West Seneca East SR HS; Buffalo, NY; (Y); Aud/Vis; CAP; Outstndng Achvt Awd Ger 82-84; Cert Of Merit ST Sen Stachowski 85; Military.

WISNIEWSKI, ROBERT; Niagara Wheatfield SR HS; Niagara Falls, NY; (Y); 1/310; Trs German Clb; Mathletes; Pres Math Clb; Math Tm; Varsity Clb; Band; Mrchg Band; Swmmng; High Hon Roll; NHS; Soph Cls Schlr Of Yr 84; Hgh Overll Avg JR Cls 85; Hgh Avg Mth III, Ger III, Soc 11 R8 Engl 11 R 85; Cornell; Engrng Sci.

WISNOCK, MICHAEL D; Newfane SR HS; Newfane, NY; (Y); 13/181; Am Leg Boys St; Drama Clb; Exploring; Scholastic Bowl; Concert Band; School Musical; Stage Crew; Hon Roll; Arch.

WISWELL, ROBYN; Susquehanna Valley HS; Conklin, NY; (Y); Yrbk Stf; Hon Roll; NHS; Equine.

WITHERELL, AARON; Letchworth Central Schl; Bliss, NY; (Y); Computer Clb; JV Var Ftbl; Var Trk; ST U Coll Buffalo; Bus Admn.

WITHERS, BRIAN D; Somers HS; Somers, NY; (Y); 4/213; Boy Scts; Church Yth Grp; Drama Clb; French Clb; Math Clb; Natl Beta Clb; Band; Chorus; Church Choir; Concert Band; Eagle Scout 82; KY All-State Band 84; VA Polytech Inst; Engrng.

WITKIN, B J; The Knox Schl; Smithtown, NY; (S); 4/35; Computer Clb; Drama Clb; Pres Library Aide; Nwsp Ed-Chief; Capt Crs Cntry; Var Socr; Var Tennis; Hon Roll.

WITKOP, LISA; Niagara Wheatfield HS; Sanborn, NY; (Y); Am Leg Aux Girls St; Sec Church Yth Grp; VP Spanish Clb; Varsity Clb; Rep Stu Cncl; Var Bsktbl; Mgr Sftbl; Var Capt Tennis; High Hon Roll; NHS; Cls Schlr 83; Frgn Lang Awd 84; Ldrshp Merit Awd 85; Engrng.

WITKOWSKI, CHRISTINE; Port Jervis HS; Sparrowbush, NY; (Y); Sec Key Clb; Varsity Clb; Yrbk Stf; Rep Stu Cncl; Tennis; High Hon Roll; NHS.

WITKOWSKI, LYNNE; Henninger HS; Syracuse, NY; (Y); 1/500; Church Yth Grp; Red Cross Aide; Chorus; Variety Show; High Hon Roll; Hon Roll.

WITMER, JOELLE; Fairport HS; Fairport, NY; (Y); Church Yth Grp; Dance Clb; Drama Clb; Chorus; Church Choir; School Musical; School Play; Elem Ed.

WITMEYER, RONALD; East Islip HS; East Islip, NY; (S); 48/475; Stu Cncl; Var Capt Bsbl; Var Capt Bsktbl; Socr; Im Vllybl; Hon Roll; Ntl Merit SF; Carl Yastrzemski Awd, Suffolk Cnty MVP Bsbl 83-84; All-Cnty Bsbl 82-84; All-Leag Bskbl 83-84; Acctng.

WITT, DONNA B; Benjamin N Cardozo HS; Bayside, NY; (Y); 3/476; Dance Clb; School Play; Ed Lit Mag; Var Gym; NHS; Ntl Merit SF; Office Aide; Scholastic Bowl; Teachers Aide; Gov Hon Prg Awd; Grtr Metro NY Math Fair 2nd Prz 82; Queens Coll Pres Achvt Awd 81; Queens Borough Sci Fair 1st Prz 81; Pol Sci.

WITTEK, ORIE MARIE; Loyola Schl; New York, NY; (Y); 1/55; Chess Clb; Church Yth Grp; Debate Tm; Capt Math Tm; NFL; Chrmn Political Wkr; Scholastic Bowl; Chorus; Variety Show; Nwsp Rptr; NY Cty Cmmssn On Status Of Wmn Essy Cntst 85; NY ST Schlrs Awd 85; Amer Irish Hstrcl Soc 85; Barnard Coll; MD.

WITTELS, RONNI; Mahopac HS; Carmel, NY; (Y); 3/400; Capt Math Tm; Pres Temple Yth Grp; JV Var Cheerleading; Stat Ftbl; JV Var Socr; Var Tennis; JV Var Vllybl; High Hon Roll; NHS; Ntl Merit SF; Boston Coll; Attrny.

WITTELSONN, NICOLE; Kings Park HS; Ft Salonga, NY; (Y); 170/393; Computer Clb; Drama Clb; Girl Scts; Teachers Aide; Band; Score Keeper; Hon Roll; U Of Cntrl FL; Law.

WITTENBECK, MICHAEL L; Waterville Central Schl; Waterville, NY; (Y); 13/90; Am Leg Boys St; Pres Varsity Clb; Var L Bsbl; Var Capt Bsktbl; Im Coach Actv; Var L Trk; High Hon Roll; Hon Roll; NHS; R Roberts M Sprtsmnshp Trphy, H Roberts Mem Trphy Bsktbl, Humanitrian Schlrshp 85; ST U ; Oswego; Acctng.

WITTINE, HEIDI; St Francis Prep; Glendale, NY; (S); 32/693; German Clb; Chorus; Sftbl; NHS; Principals List 83-84; Optimates List 82-83; Bus Mgmt.

WITTINGHAM, ANNA L; August Martin HS; Springfield Gd, NY; (Y); Church Yth Grp; Office Aide; Hon Roll; NHS; Teachers Aide; Trk; Bus Adm.

WITTLIN, CRAIG S; Williamsville South HS; Williamsville, NY; (S); Trs DECA; Mgr School Play; Nwsp Rptr; Badmtn; Ftbl; Amherst Rotary Outstnddg Bus Stu Awd 85; DECA ST & Natl Fin & Crdt 84-85; NY ST Regents Schlrshp; Syracuse U; Mrktng.

WITTLINE, HEIDI; St Francis Prep; Glendale, NY; (Y); 32/693; German Clb; Teachers Aide; Chorus; NHS; Prncpls Lst 82-83; Optmt Scty 83-84; Acad All-Amer 84-85; Bus Mgmt.

WITTMAN, RICHARD K; The Stony Brook Schl; Stony Brook, NY; (Y); 12/96; Political Wkr; Thesps; Madrigals; Lit Mag; Stu Cncl; Var Crs Cntry; Capt Var Trk; High Hon Roll; Best Actor In Leading Role 83; Engl Speaking Union Schlr 85; Yale U; British Studies.

WITTMEYER, RON; North Collins Central HS; Springville, NY; (Y); 6/75; Socr; Hon Roll; Jr NHS.

WITTREICH, CAROLYN; Mercy HS; Center Moriches, NY; (Y); Drama Clb; Library Aide; Ski Clb; Band; Hon Roll; Bsktbl 82.

WITZ, EDWARD; Cicero-N Syracuse HS; Clay, NY; (S); 6/711; Am Leg Boys St; Pres Church Yth Grp; L Bsbl; Capt Ftbl; L Wrstlng; Hon Roll; NHS; Ntl Merit Ltr; Opt Clb Awd; Physcn.

WITZ, JOHN; Cicero-North Syracuse HS; Clay, NY; (S); 19/627; VP Church Yth Grp; German Clb; Var Mathletes; Var Math Clb; Var Math Tm; JV Bsbl; JV Bsktbl; Var High Hon Roll; Var Hon Roll; Prfct Atten Awd.

WIWCZAR, WENDY J; Smithtown High School West; Smithtown, NY; (Y); Church Yth Grp; School Musical; Symp Band; Rep Jr Cls; Rep Sr Cls; Var Capt Badmtn; Hon Roll; NHS; Pres Schlr; St Schlr; Grove City Coll; Comp Sci.

WOERTER, LINDA; Greene Central Schl; Greene, NY; (Y); Church Yth Grp; Spanish Clb; Band; Chorus; Concert Band; Mrchg Band; Fld Hcky; High Hon Roll; Hon Roll.

WOHLSTETTER, SCOTT; Wantagh HS; Wantagh, NY; (Y); Aud/Vis; Computer Clb; Mathletes; Math Clb; Nwsp Rptr; Nwsp Stf; JV Var Ftbl; JV Lcrss; Wrstlng; Hon Roll.

WOICCAK, ROBERT; Seton Catholic Central HS; Endwell, NY; (S); Chess Clb; JV Golf; Var Trk; High Hon Roll.

WOICHIK, JOHN S; Dover JR SR HS; Wingdale, NY; (Y); Am Leg Boys St; Drama Clb; Chorus; School Play; Rep Stu Cncl; Bsbl; Trk; Pilot.

WOJACK, JOHN A; Hilton Central HS; Hilton, NY; (Y); Church Yth Grp; Exploring; JA; Church Choir; Concert Band; JV Ftbl; High Hon Roll; Hon Roll; Potsdam ST Coll; Comp Engrng.

WOJCIK, DOUGLAS; Bishop Ludden HS; Liverpool, NY; (S); Boy Scts; Church Yth Grp; Computer Clb; Exploring; Spanish Clb; Yrbk Stf; High Hon Roll; NHS; Order Of Arrow Hnry Boy Scout Orgnztn 84; Outstndng Acmplshmnts In Spanish 84; Bio Chemistry.

WOJCIK, GLENN; Kenmore West HS; Tonawanda, NY; (Y); Capt Civic Clb; Cmnty Wkr; Var Bowling; Hon Roll; Ntl Merit Schol; Bsktbl Hotshot Champ 84; Bsktbl Spot Shot 1st,Foul Shot 1st 85; Mgmt.

WOJCIK, TAMMY; Frontier Central HS; Hamburg, NY; (Y); 5/500; Pep Clb; Ski Clb; Cheerleading; Swmmng; High Hon Roll; Hon Roll; NHS; NEDT Awd; Med.

WOJEWODA, NANCY D; Starpoint Central HS; Lockport, NY; (Y); 5/200; Drama Clb; Spanish Clb; Varsity Clb; Chorus; Stu Cncl; Var JV Fld Hcky; Hon Roll; Jr NHS; VP NHS; Alfred U.

WOJEWODZIC, TAMMY; Morian Central Schl; Pt Henry, NY; (Y); 3/87; AFS; Trs Frsh Cls; Trs Soph Cls; Trs Jr Cls; Rep Sec Stu Cncl; High Hon Roll; NHS; Yrbk Phtg; Var Score Keeper; Mth.

WOJICK, MATTHEW; St Josephs Collegiate Inst; Niagara Falls, NY; (Y); Ski Clb; Chorus; Swing Chorus; Nwsp Ed-Chief; Pres Jr Cls; VP Stu Cncl; Bsbl; NHS; Church Yth Grp; NY ST Mock Trial Tourn 85; Engl.

WOJTAK, PAUL; Moore Catholic HS; Staten Island, NY; (Y); Aud/Vis; JV Bsbl.

WOJTOWICZ, JANET; Williamsville East HS; Buffalo, NY; (Y); 54/299; FBLA; Var Capt Bowling; High Hon Roll; Hgh Avg, Hgh Series Bwlng Awds 85; Canisus Coll; Bus Mngmnt.

WOJTOWICZ, JULIE; Northstar Christian Acad; Rochester, NY; (S); Church Yth Grp; Ski Clb; Teachers Aide; Chorus; Church Choir; Rep Stu Cncl; Capt Cheerleading; Monroe CC; Bus Mgmt.

WOLCOTT, JO ANN LEE; Rome Free Acad; Rome, NY; (Y); 31/536; Jr NHS; NHS; Regnts Schrlshp 85; Suce Geneseo; Acctng.

WOLF, DAVID; Haverling Central Schl; Bath, NY; (S); Political Wkr; Pres Band; Church Choir; Concert Band; Jazz Band; Mrchg Band; Pep Band; School Musical; Stage Crew; Yrbk Stf; All St Band 84; All Eastern Band 85; All Cty Area All St Bands 82-84; Music.

WOLF, DEBRA; The Mary Louis Acad; Richmond Hill, NY; (Y); Art Clb; Hon Roll; NEDT Awd; Soc Studys Excel 83-84; Art Cntst Drwng 1st Pl 84; Adv Illstrtn.

WOLF, KAREN; Northshore HS; Glen Head, NY; (Y); Sec AFS; Am Leg Aux Girls St; Church Yth Grp; Dance Clb; Hosp Aide; Rep Stu Cncl; Var Bsktbl; NHS; AAA Awd 85; Eng.

WOLF, PHILLIPS; Fairport HS; Fairport, NY; (Y); Computer Clb; Model UN; Hon Roll; Spanish NHS.

WOLF, SUSAN; Dominican Commercial HS; Jamaica, NY; (Y); 14/273; Church Yth Grp; Drama Clb; Pep Clb; School Musical; School Play; Stage Crew; Variety Show; Cheerleading; Gym; Siena Awd Princpls List; St Johns U; Phrmcy.

WOLF, THERESA; St Marys HS; Depew, NY; (S); 6/204; Church Yth Grp; Science Clb; Var L Trk; Hon Roll; Health Professions Club 84-85; Engl Awd Acad Achvt 84; Intermediat Alg Awd Acad Achvt 84; Canisus Coll; Accntng.

WOLFE, CHRISTOPHER; Cicero-North Syracuse HS; Clay, NY; (S); 27/711; Debate Tm; Drama Clb; Math Tm; Band; Bowling; Crs Cntry; Timer; Hon Roll; Engrng.

WOLFE, ELIZABETH J; Dundee Central HS; Dundee, NY; (Y); VP Church Yth Grp; ROTC; Pres Spanish Clb; Chorus; School Musical; School Play; Variety Show; Cheerleading; Church Choir; 1st Pl Singing Duet & Solo In Spnsh Language Fair 84-85; Estrn Nazarene Coll; Libral Art.

WOLFE, HEATHER; Barker Central HS; Barker, NY; (Y); AFS; French Clb; FBLA; Chorus; School Musical; Trs Frsh Cls; Trs Soph Cls; Capt JV Bsktbl; JV Var Fld Hcky; Score Keeper; Gregg Typing Cert Awd 84-85; Niagara Co Leg Intern Completion Pgm 85; Law.

WOLFE, JAMES; Lancaster Central HS; Bowmansville, NY; (Y); Church Yth Grp; PAVAS; Band; Chorus; Jazz Band; Mrchg Band; Orch; School Musical; Symp Band; Variety Show; Ithaca Coll; Mus.

WOLFE, JANINE; Freeport HS; Freeport, NY; (Y); Church Yth Grp; Hosp Aide; Leo Clb; Radio Clb; Capt Twrlr; Hon Roll.

WOLFE, MARYALICE; St Patricks CC HS; Catskill, NY; (Y); Red Cross Aide; JV Cheerleading; High Hon Roll; Hon Roll.

WOLFE, TERA; Union-Endicott HS; Endicott, NY; (Y); 93/430; Key Clb; Flag Corp; Mrchg Band; Yrbk Ed-Chief; Yrbk Sprt Ed; Yrbk Stf; Off Soph Cls; Off Jr Cls; Score Keeper; Hon Roll; Cls Ring Staff Best Ring Disply 83; Suny; Rest Mgmt.

WOLFE, WAYNE; Webster HS; Ontario, NY; (Y); 80/500; Model UN; Chorus; School Musical; School Play; Swing Chorus; Rep Frsh Cls; Rep Soph Cls; Rep Stu Cncl; High Hon Roll; NHS; Outstndng Art Stdnt 83; Mdl UN 85; Outstndng Choir Stdnt 85.

WOLFF, DEBORAH; Liverpool HS; Liverpool, NY; (Y); 166/874; Church Yth Grp; Exploring; Ski Clb; Teachers Aide; Chorus; Concert Band; Rep Stu Cncl; Powder Puff Ftbl; Var Tennis; Hon Roll; Bio.

WOLFF JR, JAMES F; Cooperstown Central HS; Hartwick, NY; (Y); 13/100; Quiz Bowl; Concert Band; Jazz Band; Stage Crew; Yrbk Phtg; Var Tennis; High Hon Roll; NHS; Ntl Merit Ltr; French Clb; Mensa Mbr 85-86.

WOLFF, SCOTT W; Newfield HS; Selden, NY; (Y); Pres Church Yth Grp; Service Clb; Lit Mag; Trs Sr Cls; Var Capt Crs Cntry; Var Capt Trk; Varsity Clb; Rep Frsh Cls; Rep Soph Cls; All-County Trck Tm 800 Meters 84 & 85; Coaches Awd 84; HS 500 Meter Record 85; Valparaiso U; Sprts Med.

WOLFISCH, LISA; Williamsville East HS; Buffalo, NY; (Y); 58/274; AFS; Cmnty Wkr; Intnl Clb; Latin Clb; Quiz Bowl; Scholastic Bowl; Temple Yth Grp; Yrbk Stf; Hon Roll; NHS; AFS Exch Stu 83; Adelphi U.

WOLFLEY, JAMES; Alexander Central HS; Alexander, NY; (S); 2/88; Capt Math Tm; Pres Spanish Clb; Trs Yrbk Stf; Stu Cncl; Var JV Bsbl; Var Capt Bsktbl; Bausch & Lomb Sci Awd; Lion Awd; NHS; Sal; Engrng.

WOLFRAM, SRINGARA; Whitney Point SR HS; Lisle, NY; (Y); 22/120; Church Yth Grp; French Clb; Science Clb; Band; Chorus; Concert Band; Mrchg Band; Rep Stu Cncl; JV Vllybl; High Hon Roll; Marine Studs Enrichmnt Pgm Cert 84; Broome CC; Sci.

WOLFRUM, AMY F; Columbia HS; Rensselaer, NY; (Y); Key Clb; Latin Clb; Ski Clb; Ed Lit Mag; NHS; Ntl Merit Ltr; St Schlr; St Lawrence U; Lawyer.

WOLFSON, LISA; Roosevelt HS; Scarsdale, NY; (S); Cmnty Wkr; Girl Scts; Temple Yth Grp; Band; Mrchg Band; Yrbk Stf; Rep Frsh Cls; Rep Soph Cls; High Hon Roll; NHS.

WOLFSON, LISA; Roy C Ketcham HS; Wappingers Fls, NY; (Y); Hosp Aide; Ski Clb; Band; Mrchg Band; JV Var Bsktbl; Var L Sftbl; High Hon Roll; Hon Roll; 1st Tm All Div & Hnbl Mntn All Sectnl Sftbl 85.

WOLFSTEIN, DAVID; Plainview-Old Bethpage HS; Plainview, NY; (Y); 19/194; Cmnty Wkr; Var L Crs Cntry; Var L Trk; Hon Roll; NHS; Pres Schlr; Drama Clb; Key Clb; Model UN; Lit Mag; NYS Regnts Schlrshp 85-89; Binghamton SUNY; Med.

WOLFTEICH, CLAIRE; Lawrence HS; Atlantic Beach, NY; (Y); Lib Band; Orch; Nwsp Ed-Chief; Ed Lit Mag; Gym; NHS; Ntl Merit Ltr; Cmnty Wkr; Service Clb; Mrchg Band; NY ST Sci Supvs Awd All Sci 85; Fr 4 Awd 85; SUNY Old Westbury Humnities Cont Deans & 1st Pl Awd 85; Eng.

WOLICKI, ARLENE; Villa Maria Acad; Buffalo, NY; (Y); Im Bowling; Im Vllybl; Hon Roll; Daughters Of American Revolution 82; Sci Awd-Highest Avg 82; Sewing-Highest Avg 82; U Of Buffalo; Accntnt.

WOLIN, ANDREW; Norwich HS; Norwich, NY; (Y); 1/201; Math Tm; Band; Jazz Band; Pres Frsh Cls; Stu Cncl; High Hon Roll; NHS; Phi Mu Alpha Sinfonia Outstndng Male Musicn Awd NY ST Music Camp 83-84; SUNY Buffalo; Physics.

WOLIN, WENDI; Pittsford Mendon HS; Pittsford, NY; (Y); Cmnty Wkr; Pep Clb; Stage Crew; Rep Stu Cncl; Powder Puff Ftbl; JV Socr; Hon Roll; NHS; Latn Awd Natl 83-84; Acctg.

WOLINTZ, ROBYN J; Midwood HS At Brooklyn College; Brooklyn, NY; (Y); 9/626; Hosp Aide; Math Clb; Math Tm; Science Clb; Service Clb; Concert Band; Lit Mag; Spanish NHS; Brooklyn Coll Frshmn Schlr 85; Cert Partcptn Metro NY Math Fair 84-85; Arista Hnr Socty 84-85; Brooklyn Coll; Physcn.

WOLK, KAREN; Our Lady Of Victory Acad; Yonkers, NY; (S); 5/159; Art Clb; Church Yth Grp; Computer Clb; Drama Clb; Science Clb; Service Clb; Spanish Clb; School Musical; School Play; Lit Mag; Wnnr Chem Cntst 84; Westchester Tricentennial Comp 83; Partl Schlrshp Our Lady Of Vic Acad 83-84.

WOLK, ROBERT I; Horace Mann HS; New York, NY; (Y); Pres Debate Tm; VP Intnl Clb; Sec Model UN; Ed Nwsp Stf; Rep Stu Cncl; Var Crs Cntry; Ntl Merit SF; Latin Clb; Math Tm; Political Wkr; Columbia Sci Hnrs Prog; Rep Brd Trust; JR Crnvl Chrmn; Harvard U; Hstry.

WOLLAND, JENNIFER; Westhampton Beach HS; Westhampton Bch, NY; (Y); FBLA; Spanish Clb; Chorus; Stu Cncl; Hon Roll; NHS; Bus.

WOLLMUTH, KAREN; Mynderse Acad; Seneca Falls, NY; (S); 40/140; Church Yth Grp; Drama Clb; Model UN; Ski Clb; Chorus; School Musical; Swing Chorus; Yrbk Ed-Chief; Sec Stu Cncl; Hon Roll.

WOLNEK, JASON; Connetquot HS; Ronkonkoma, NY; (Y); 6/736; Drama Clb; FBLA; Stage Crew; Trk; High Hon Roll; Jr NHS; Prfct Atten Awd; MIT; Aerontcl Eng.

WOLNIEWICZ, SCOTT; Akron Central Schl; Akron, NY; (Y); Boys Clb Am; Boy Scts; Chess Clb; JV Bsbl; Coach Actv; JV Ftbl; Score Keeper; Var Trk; Wt Lftg; JV Var Wrstlng; All-Leag Trck 84-85; Co-Chmpn Wrstlng 84-85; Math.

WOLOS, JASON; Kenmore West HS; Kenmore, NY; (Y); 44/445; Ski Clb; Variety Show; Ed Yrbk Stf; Sec Jr Cls; Pres Sr Cls; Hon Roll; NHS; Art Clb; Rep Frsh Cls; Rep Soph Cls; Outstndng Ctznshp PTA Ctznshp Awd 85; Outstndng Artistic Abilty Awd 85; U NY Buffalo; Bio Sci.

WOLOSZYN, KAREN; Liverpool HS; Clay, NY; (S); Art Clb; JA; School Musical; Stage Crew; Lit Mag; Hon Roll; NHS; Art.

WOLOSZYN, PATRICIA; Villa Maria Acad; Buffalo, NY; (S); Yrbk Stf; Stat Bsktbl; Im Bowling; Hon Roll; Prfct Atten Awd; Regln Awd; Shrthnd Awd; Commcnts.

WOLPERT, MARK R; Bay Shore HS; Brightwaters, NY; (Y); Cmnty Wkr; Math Tm; Rep Stu Cncl; NY ST Rgnts Schlrshp 85; Albany; Bus.

WOLSEY, THOMAS C; C W Baker HS; Baldwinsville, NY; (Y); 37/441; Ski Clb; Band; Jazz Band; Var Diving; Var Gym; Var Swmmng; Var Tennis; NHS; Kraft Inc, NYS Rgnts Schlrshps 85-86; ST U NY Oswego; Pol Sci.

WOLTER, MARTHA JENNIFER; Batavia HS; Batavia, NY; (Y); 20/240; Church Yth Grp; Cmnty Wkr; GAA; Y-Teens; Band; Chorus; Church Choir; Concert Band; Jazz Band; Mrchg Band; Natl Episcopal Yth Event Rep 84; All State Chorus Member 84; Regents Scholarship Winner 85; Cornell U; Social Work.

WOMBLE, ROBERT N; Brockport HS; Spencerport, NY; (Y); Church Yth Grp; Band; Concert Band; Jazz Band; Mrchg Band; Pep Band; Symp Band; Golf; High Hon Roll; Hon Roll; Lrdshp, Regnts Schlrshps 84-85; Rochester Inst Tech; Engr.

WON, SUSAN J; Brooklyn Technichal HS; Far Rockaway, NY; (Y); Church Yth Grp; Cmnty Wkr; Computer Clb; Hosp Aide; Science Clb; Nwsp Rptr; High Hon Roll; Ntl Merit Ltr; Med.

WONG, ALICE; Richmond Hill HS; Richmond Hill, NY; (Y); FBLA; Key Clb; Var Bsktbl; Var Crs Cntry; Var Sftbl; Hon Roll; NHS; Prfct Atten Awd; Spanish NHS; Bus Hnr Scty 83-85; Math Hnr Scty 82-85; Baruch Coll; Bus Adm.

WONG, CHARLYNE S; New Dorp HS; Staten Island, NY; (Y); 47/780; French Clb; Intnl Clb; Office Aide; Orch; Yrbk Stf; French Hon Soc; Hon Roll; NHS; Prfct Atten Awd; Svc Awd; SUNY Stony Brook.

WONG, CINDY Y; Seward Park HS; New York, NY; (Y); 25/30; Aud/Vis; Cmnty Wkr; Hosp Aide; Office Aide; Service Clb; Teachers Aide; Band; Concert Band; Orch; Stage Crew; Cert Awd Schl Svc 84-85; Eng,Art Cert Awd 83; NY U; Bus.

WONG, DENIE; Horseheads HS; Horseheads, NY; (S); 57/407; Art Clb; JCL; Latin Clb; Sec NFL; Spanish Clb; Variety Show; Yrbk Stf; Rep Frsh Cls; Tennis; High Hon Roll; Youth Cnty Won Office 84; Bus Mktg.

WONG, EMILY; Bronx H S Of Science; Woodside, NY; (Y); Key Clb; Office Aide; Teachers Aide; Haney Medl Awd 83; Biochem.

WONG, GRAHAM; Lasalle Acad; Astoria, NY; (Y).

WONG, HELEN; Murry Bergtraum HS; New York, NY; (Y); 37/579; Library Aide; Spanish Clb; Rep Frsh Cls; Hon Roll; Prfct Atten Awd; Hunter Coll; Spanish.

WONG, JOSE N; Linton HS; Schenectady, NY; (Y); 5/279; Art Clb; Intnl Clb; Varsity Clb; Yrbk Phtg; Soph Cls; Jr Cls; Sr Cls; JV Tennis; Var Trk; High Hon Roll; Rgnts Schlrshp; Clarkson; Mech Engr.

WONG, JUDY; Cathedral HS; Ny, NY; (Y); 18/300; Art Clb; Cmnty Wkr; French Clb; FNA; Hosp Aide; Intnl Clb; Library Aide; Nwsp Stf; Hon Roll; Prfct Atten Awd; NY U; Nrsng.

WONG, KAI; Seward Park HS; New York, NY; (Y); Camera Clb; Math Clb; Teachers Aide; Prfct Atten Awd.

WONG, KATE; New Hyde Park Memorial HS; New Hyde Park, NY; (Y); Art Clb; Church Yth Grp; Hosp Aide; Chorus; Yrbk Stf; Lit Mag; Crs Cntry; Fld Hcky; Trk; Hon Roll; Fashion Inst Tech; Art Dsgn.

WONG, KIN C; Brooklyn Technical HS; New York, NY; (Y); 85/1139; Computer Clb; Math Clb; Orch; Hon Roll; Prfct Atten Awd; Regnts Scholar 85; Mth Awd 85; Cooper Union; Mech Engrng.

WONG, MARY ALIN; Vestal Central SR HS; Vestal, NY; (Y); 45/450; Church Yth Grp; Sec French Clb; Girl Scts; Hosp Aide; Ski Clb; Yrbk Stf; Hon Roll; NHS; Penn ST; Vet.

WONG, MAY; Christopher Columbus HS; Bronx, NY; (S); 28/664; Math Tm; Band; Hon Roll; U Stony Brook; Elect Engrng.

WONG, MEI W; Newtown HS; Woodside, NY; (Y); 9/603; French Clb; Math Tm; Office Aide; Teachers Aide; Orch; Lit Mag; Hon Roll; NHS; Prfct Atten Awd; Dly News Super Yth 83-84; JR Engrng Tech Soc 84-85; Baruch Coll.

WONG, PAUL P; Seward Park HS; New York, NY; (Y); Art Clb; Computer Clb; Office Aide; Political Wkr; Teachers Aide; Nwsp Stf; Yrbk Stf; Swmmng; Capt Vllybl; Arch.

WONG, PENNY; Cathedral HS; Lic, NY; (Y); 5/350; Church Yth Grp; Computer Clb; Dance Clb; French Clb; Library Aide; Chorus; Yrbk Stf; Rep Frsh Cls; Rep Stu Cncl; High Hon Roll; Acad All Amer Schlr Awd 85; Syracuse; Med.

WONG, PETER; August Martin HS; Brooklyn, NY; (Y); 144/375; Aud/Vis; CAP; Computer Clb; Library Aide; Office Aide; Service Clb; Teachers Aide; Band; Concert Band; Orch; 1st Pl SEER 85; Untd Fdrtn Tchrs Awd Cert 85; Cedrt Recgntn CMSP 85; U Of Bridgeport; Comp Sci.

WONG, SALLY; John Adams HS; Richmond Hill, NY; (Y); 23/591; Quiz Bowl; Scholastic Bowl; Teachers Aide; Stage Crew; High Hon Roll; Hon Roll; Rgnts Schlrshp 85; NY U; Comp Engrng.

WONG, SHIRLEY; Lafayette HS; Brooklyn, NY; (Y); Intnl Clb; Office Aide; Chorus; Variety Show; Nwsp Stf; Sec Yrbk Stf; Trs Stu Cncl; Var Cheerleading; Sftbl; Jrnlsm.

WONG, SIUMAY; Franklin D Roosevelt HS; Brooklyn, NY; (Y); 55/560; Office Aide; Chorus; Hon Roll; NHS; NYS Regents Schlrshp 85; Fashion Inst Of Tech; Fashion.

WONG, THERESA; Westhampton Beach HS; E Moriches, NY; (Y); 50/250; FBLA; Girl Scts; Ski Clb; Nwsp Stf; Yrbk Stf; Lit Mag; Trs Soph Cls; JV Bsbl; Var Gym; JV Vllybl; C D Aftermath Awd 80; Gym MVP Awd 83; Comp.

WONG, TIN; John Dewey HS; Brooklyn, NY; (Y); English Clb; Math Tm; Office Aide; Teachers Aide; Nwsp Bus Mgr; JV Sftbl; Jr NHS; Prfct Atten Awd; Coll Rep 84-85; Bus.

WONG, TOMMY; Midwood HS At Brooklyn College; Brooklyn, NY; (Y); 262/612; Boy Scts; Chess Clb; Computer Clb; Intnl Clb; Office Aide; Science Clb; Teachers Aide; Regents Coll Schlrshp 85; Coll Staten Island; Comp Sci.

WONG, VINCENT; Bronx HS Sci; Little Neck, NY; (Y); Lit Mag; Tennis; Ntl Merit Ltr; Engrng.

WONG, WAY HSING; Brooklyn Technical HS; Brooklyn, NY; (Y); Teachers Aide; Yrbk Stf; Hon Roll; NHS; Ntl Merit Ltr; All Arnd Stu 80; Achvt Art-Brd Of Ed 83; Merit Art-Dly Nws & Brd Of Ed 83; Aerspc Engrng.

WONG, WENDY; Hillcrest HS; Flushing, NY; (Y); Pep Clb; Yrbk Stf; Hon Roll; Val; Bst Sci Proj 84; Art.

WOO, JOYCE; Eastchester HS; Tuckahoe, NY; (Y); 4/163; Pres Latin Clb; Capt Math Tm; Nwsp Ed-Chief; Var Capt Socr; Var Vllybl; NHS.

WOO, KATRINA G; Beach Channel HS; Belle Harbor, NY; (Y); Debate Tm; Office Aide; Band; Yrbk Stf; Cit Awd; Hon Roll; Jr NHS; NHS; Math Magzn Editor 84-85; Med.

WOO, SABRINA; Saint Michaels Acad; New York, NY; (Y); Cmnty Wkr; Math Clb; Teachers Aide; Yrbk Stf; High Hon Roll; NHS; Prfct Atten Awd; Sci Fair Sci Awd 82; Trustee Schlrshp 85; NY U; Bus.

WOOD, ANN; Franklin Acad; Malone, NY; (Y); #3 In Class; Sec 4-H; Sec Spanish Clb; Chorus; Church Choir; 4-H Awd; Acadmc Al-Amer 83; Potsdam Coll; Elem Ed.

WOOD, BLAIR; Lyons JR SR HS; Lyons, NY; (Y); 2/90; AFS; Am Leg Boys St; Art Clb; Boy Scts; Church Yth Grp; Latin Clb; Library Aide; Pres Science Clb; VP Ski Clb; Varsity Clb; Stndrd Brer 85-86; Hnr Pass Awd 84-85; Lang Bwl Stu 82-83.

WOOD, BONNIE; Granville Central Schl; Pawlet, VT; (S); French Clb; Chorus; High Hon Roll; Hon Roll; Frnch Awd 83; Designing & Adv.

WOOD, BONNIE; Schuylerville Central Schl; Schuylerville, NY; (Y); FBLA; Trk; Hon Roll; Bus.

WOOD, BRENDA; Walton Central Schl; Walton, NY; (Y); #18 In Class; AFS; Church Yth Grp; Cmnty Wkr; 4-H; Key Clb; Red Cross Aide; Teachers Aide; Chorus; Color Guard; Mrchg Band; Walton Tchrs Assn Schlrshp 85; Merritt C Loudon Mem Awd 85; SR Schlrshp Awd 85; Roberts Wesleyan Coll; Elem Ed.

WOOD, CARINA; Elmira Southside HS; Elmira, NY; (Y); Spanish Clb; Hon Roll; 4th Pl Holiday JR Sngls MDA 84; U Of SC; CPA.

WOOD, CHRISTOP S; Harrisville Central HS; Harrisville, NY; (Y); 2/33; French Clb; Quiz Bowl; Varsity Clb; Chorus; School Musical; School Play; Nwsp Rptr; Stu Cncl; JV Var Bsbl; Var Capt Bsktbl; Nrthrn Athletic Cnfrnc Hnrb Mntn 83-84; Acad All-Northern 84-85; Clarkson U; Chem Engrng.

WOOD, ERIC; Tonawanda JR SR HS; Tonawanda, NY; (Y); Church Yth Grp; Band; Chorus; School Musical; Rep Sr Cls; VP Stu Cncl; Bsktbl; Ftbl; Cit Awd; Hon Roll; Comp Engrng.

WOOD, GARY; Newark Central HS; Lyons, NY; (Y); 67/199; Band; Concert Band; Jazz Band; Mrchg Band; Pep Band; School Musical; Stage Crew; Variety Show; JV Ftbl; Hon Roll; NYSSMA Solo Awd; Band All Cnty; NYSSMA Trio-Outstndng Grd; Music Mrchndsng.

WOOD, JULIE M; Academy Of The Holy Names; New Scotland, NY; (Y); Drama Clb; French Clb; Hosp Aide; Chorus; School Play; Yrbk Ed-Chief; Lit Mag; Swmmng; Tennis; French Hon Soc; Regnts Schlrshp 85; Ntl Sci Bio Awd 85; Excl Bio 83; Coll Of Holy Cross.

WOOD, KAREN; Allegany Central Schl; Allegany, NY; (Y); Ski Clb; Varsity Clb; Ed Yrbk Phtg; Pres Frsh Cls; VP Stu Cncl; JV Bsktbl; JV Cheerleading; Var Capt Sftbl; High Hon Roll; Yrbk Stf; Cnty All Star Sftbl Plyr 83-85; Edinboro U; Bus Mgmt.

WOOD, KELLY A; West Seneca West Senior HS; West Seneca, NY; (Y); 4/543; Mathletes; High Hon Roll; JC Awd; Jr NHS; NHS; Prfct Atten Awd; Canisius Coll Deans Schlrshp 85; Regents Schlrshp 85; Erie & Niagara Schlstc Achvt Rec 85; Conisius Coll; Med.

WOOD, KELLY J; De Ruyter Central Schl; De Ruyter, NY; (Y); 24/42; French Clb; Letterman Clb; Office Aide; Red Cross Aide; Varsity Clb; Yrbk Stf; Rep Stu Cncl; Trs Jr Cls; JV Var Cheerleading; Var Mgr(s); Morrisville Ag & Tech; Bus Admin.

WOOD, KEVIN; Northville Central HS; Mayfield, NY; (Y); Ski Clb; Varsity Clb; Yrbk Stf; Trs Soph Cls; Pres Off Jr Cls; Trs Stu Cncl; Var L Bsbl; Var L Bsktbl; Var L Socr; Band; SADD Stu 85; AADD Stu 85; Varsity Clb Sec 85; Comp Sci.

WOOD, KIMBERLY S; Newfane SR HS; Newfane, NY; (S); 10/167; Math Clb; Math Tm; Varsity Clb; Yrbk Stf; VP Crs Cntry; VP Trk; High Hon Roll; Mu Alp Tht; NHS; Track, Cross-Country; Acctng.

WOOD, LISA; Bishop Ford Central Catholic HS; Brooklyn, NY; (Y); 86/441; Aud/Vis; Var Bsktbl; Var JV Mgr(s); Var Score Keeper; Var Trk; Var Vllybl; Spnsh Cert Of Hnr 82-83; Snd Hnrs 82-83; Pres Physcl Ftns Awd 82-83; Pace U; Accntnt.

WOOD, MARJORIE; East Islip SR HS; Islip Ter, NY; (Y); Cmnty Wkr; High Hon Roll; Hon Roll; BOCES Outstndng Achvt Awd 85; Fncng.

WOOD, MICHELLE; West Seneca East SR HS; Cheektowaga, NY; (Y); Am Leg Aux Girls St; Sec German Clb; School Musical; School Play; High Hon Roll; JC Awd; Jr NHS; NHS; Ger Natl Hnr Soc 84; Ger Declar Cont 85; Law.

WOOD, NATALIE; Charles C D Amico HS; Albion, NY; (S); 26/168; English Clb; Yrbk Phtg; VP Stu Cncl; JV Var Coach Actv; Var L Swmmng; NHS; Library Aide; Office Aide; Spanish Clb; Yth Cares Awd Wnnr 84; Ntl Hnr Soc Schlrshp 85; Lynchbur Coll Freshmn Hon Schlrshp 85; Lynchburg Coll; Ed.

WOOD, NOELE; Cicero North Syracuse HS; Bridgeport, NY; (S); 17/711; Hon Roll; NHS; MONY Schlstc Art Awds 83 & 85; Morrisville Suny Coll; Bsns.

WOOD, RANDALL; Massena Central HS; Massena, NY; (Y); Church Yth Grp; JV Bsbl; JV Bsktbl; JV Var Ftbl; Wt Lftg; Mech Engrng.

WOOD, ROBERT; Miller Place HS; Miller Pl, NY; (Y); 23/200; Chess Clb; Computer Clb; FBLA; Mathletes; Math Tm; Nwsp Ed-Chief; Lit Mag; High Hon Roll; NHS; Boy Scts; Outstndng Achvt In Chem & Blgy; Biochmstry.

WOOD II, ROBERT; Eden Central SR HS; Eden, NY; (Y); 16/205; AFS; Varsity Clb; School Musical; Capt Var Crs Cntry; Capt Var Tennis; L Var Wrstlng; NHS; Pres Schlr; Pres Schlrshp St John Fshr Coll 85; Coaches Athlt Awd 85; St John Fshr Coll; CPA.

WOOD, ROY; Highland HS; Highland, NY; (Y); Church Yth Grp; French Clb; Quiz Bowl; Varsity Clb; Yrbk Sprt Ed; Stu Cncl; Bsktbl; Ftbl; French Hon Soc; Hon Roll; Awd Hghst Avg Hstry 83-84; Awd Cmnty Svcs 84-85; Econ.

WOOD, SARAH; Brighton HS; Rochester, NY; (Y); Church Yth Grp; Exploring; Intnl Clb; Chorus; Nwsp Stf; Med.

WOOD, TERENCE J; Mattituck HS; Mattituck, NY; (Y); German Clb; Socr; Trk; Hon Roll; NY ST Regnts Schlrshp 85; U Of KY; Mech Engrng.

WOOD, TERRY; Watkins Glen HS; Watkins Glen, NY; (S); 5/125; Letterman Clb; Math Clb; Quiz Bowl; Rep Frsh Cls; Rep Soph Cls; Rep Jr Cls; Trs Sr Cls; Rep Stu Cncl; Var L Ftbl; Var L Trk; Engrng.

WOODARD, DANNY; Alden Central HS; Alden, NY; (Y); Church Yth Grp; French Clb; Bsktbl; Im Ftbl; Var Golf; Var Tennis; Liberty U; Bus.

WOODARD, SANDRA; South Park HS; Buffalo, NY; (Y); Church Yth Grp; Cmnty Wkr; Office Aide; Political Wkr; Hon Roll; Merit Roll 83-84; U Of Buffalo; Lwyr.

WOODBURY, ELIZABETH M; John Jay HS; Katonah, NY; (Y); 2/270; Art Clb; Boy Scts; Hosp Aide; Lit Mag; JV Lcrss; High Hon Roll; Hon Roll; Ntl Merit Ltr; Regents Schlrshp; Wellesley Coll; Engl.

WOODCOCK, KELLY; Skaneateles Central HS; Skaneateles, NY; (S); 41/167; Church Yth Grp; Drama Clb; Hosp Aide; School Play; Stage Crew; Nwsp Rptr; Nwsp Stf; Yrbk Stf; Var Cheerleading; High Hon Roll; Syracuse U; Frnch.

WOODCOCK, RENE; Wilson Central Schl; Wilson, NY; (Y); Church Yth Grp; Y-Teens; Chorus; Hon Roll; Cosmtlgst.

WOODCOOK, ROBERT; Groton SR HS; Groton, NY; (Y); Hon Roll; Prfct Atten Awd; Auto Mech.

WOODIN, SHANNAN; Dryden HS; Dryden, NY; (Y); Am Leg Aux Girls St; Spanish Clb; School Play; Nwsp Sprt Ed; Yrbk Sprt Ed; Lit Mag; Var Bsktbl; Mgr Sftbl; High Hon Roll; NHS; Blue Rbbn Cortland Cnty Arts Shw 83-84; Govt.

WOODMANCY, CAROL; Mynderse Acad; Seneca Falls, NY; (S); 52/144; Intnl Clb; JA; Model UN; Ski Clb; Yrbk Stf; Rep Stu Cncl; Socr; Sftbl; Vllybl; Hon Roll.

WOODRUFF, DORCINICA; Kensington HS; Buffalo, NY; (Y); Prfct Atten Awd.

WOODRUFF, KEVIN; John H Glenn HS; Greenlawn, NY; (Y); JV Ftbl; Marn Sci.

WOODS, CHRISTOPHER E; Beach Channel HS; Far Rockaway, NY; (Y); 25/500; FFA; Science Clb; Nwsp Stf; Lit Mag; Tennis; High Hon Roll; Hon Roll; NHS; NYS Regents Schlrshp 85; Hgh Grd Certs 83-85; Arista Hnr Soc 84-85; Marine Sci Cmptn 84; Sci Resch Medal; Yale U; Astr Physcs.

WOODS, DEBRA; Union Endicott HS; Endicott, NY; (Y); Pres Church Yth Grp; Mathletes; Church Choir; Concert Band; Mrchg Band; High Hon Roll; Hon Roll; NHS; Wind Ensmble 83-85; Tutorng 82-85; Mth.

WOODS, JAMIE C; Hamburg SR HS; Hamburg, NY; (Y); 36/389; Church Yth Grp; Chorus; Church Choir; School Musical; Hon Roll; NHS; Bryant & Stratton Accntnt Schlrshp 85; NY ST Regents Schlrshp 85; Womens Chrstn Athl Leag Sftbl 83; Brynt-Strttn Bus Inst; Accntnt.

WOODS, LESSIE MICHELLE; Henninger SR HS; Syracuse, NY; (Y); #49 In Class; Church Yth Grp; GAA; JA; Teachers Aide; Rep Jr Cls; Rep Sr Cls; Stat Bsktbl; Var Hst Socr; High Hon Roll; NHS; Lambda Kappa Mu Awd 82-83; Lwyr.

WOODS, LONICE; Mt St Ursula HS; Bronx, NY; (Y); Sec Church Yth Grp; Dance Clb; Intnl Clb; Hon Roll; Syracuse; Accntng.

WOODS, NANCY; Stella Maris HS; Rockaway Beach, NY; (Y); Yrbk Stf; Pres Soph Cls; Rep Stu Cncl; JV Var Sftbl; JV Vllybl; Math.

WOODS, THOMAS W; Newburgh Free Acad; Newburgh, NY; (Y); 118/625; ROTC; High Hon Roll; Hon Roll; Robt Stone Frstry & Cnsrvtn Schlrshp Grnt 85; Cmp Rogers Envrnmntl Educ Cmp 84; Orange Cnty Trpprs; Dutchess Co CC; Frstry.

WOODSIDE, RANDY; Heuvelton Central HS; Heuvelton, NY; (Y); Latin Clb; Band; Concert Band; Mrchg Band; Bsbl; Bsktbl; Socr; Sftbl; Hon Roll; Canton ATC; Adv Auto Mech.

WOODSIDE, ROBERT C; Cathedral Prep; New York, NY; (Y); 4/20; Nwsp Rptr; Nwsp Stf; Yrbk Rptr; Yrbk Stf; Capt Fld Hcky; St Schlr; Baruch Coll Schlrshp; Baruch Coll; Bus.

WOODWARD, RAYMOND; Linton HS; Schenectady, NY; (Y); Boy Scts; 4-H; JCL; Latin Clb; NHS; W TX ST U; Zoolgy.

WOODWORTH, MARTIN; Olean HS; Olean, NY; (Y); 52/225; Varsity Clb; Var Bowling; Hon Roll; JV Bsbl; Mst Outstndng Bowler 84-85; SUNY Oswego; Accntng.

WOODWORTH, STEVEN; Canisteo Central HS; Hornell, NY; (Y); Var Ftbl; Var Trk; Var Wrstlng; Cit Awd; Hon Roll; Wrstlng Chmp 85; Cvl Engrng.

WOODY, CHERYL D; Northport HS; E Northport, NY; (Y); 96/643; Church Yth Grp; Debate Tm; VP Drama Clb; Pres Science Clb; Acpl Chr; Flag Corp; School Musical; Stage Crew; Hon Roll; NHS; Color Grd Awd 85; Mary Washington Coll.

WOOL, MARK; Thomas J Corcoran HS; Syracuse, NY; (Y); 4/220; Key Clb; Red Cross Aide; Science Clb; Ski Clb; VP NHS; Ntl Merit Ltr; Fredom Fndtns Natl Yth Ldrshp Conf 84; Regents Schlrshp 85; NY ST U-Oswego; Metrlgy.

WOOLEVER, CHARLES; Hornell SR HS; Hornell, NY; (Y); Church Yth Grp; Computer Clb; Band; Concert Band; Mrchg Band; Pep Band; Symp Band; High Hon Roll; Hon Roll; Ogden Bio Exm 7th 85; 9th Pl 84; Alfred U; Comp Progrmg.

WOOLLERY, TREVOR; Dewitt Clinton HS; Bronx, NY; (Y); Art Clb; Key Clb; Teachers Aide; Jr Cls; Crs Cntry; Socr; Trk; Vllybl; Hon Roll; NHS; Math 83; Socl Studies, Engl 84.

WOOLLEY, PETER; St Raymonds Boys HS; Bronx, NY; (Y); Stat Bsktbl; Capt L Crs Cntry; Var Score Keeper; Capt L Trk; Hon Roll; NHS; Fordham U; Jrnlsm.

WOOLRIDGE, KIMBERLY; Liverpool HS; Liverpool, NY; (S); 9/792; Varsity Clb; Rep Jr Cls; Rep Sr Cls; Rep Stu Cncl; Var L Socr; Var L Sftbl; Hon Roll; Jr NHS; NHS; Exploring; NYSPHAA Sec Iii Chmpionshp Reg & Sec 84; Natl Merit Schlrshp Commended Schlr 84; Veterinarian.

WOOLSCHLAGER, WAYNE; Jamestown HS; Jamestown, NY; (Y); VP Church Yth Grp; JA; Acpl Chr; Chorus; Rep Frsh Cls; Rep Soph Cls; Bus.

WOOSTER, JULIE; Perry Central HS; Perry, NY; (Y); French Clb; FHA; Varsity Clb; Band; Concert Band; Mrchg Band; Rep Stu Cncl; JV Var Bsktbl; JV Mgr(s); JV Var Score Keeper.

WOOTEN, JAYNE P; South Shore HS; Brooklyn, NY; (Y); Church Yth Grp; Girl Scts; Spanish Clb; Var Socr; Var Vllybl; Brooklyn Coll; Dietcn.

WOOTON, SUSAN; Delaware Valley Central HS; Callicoon, NY; (S); 1/38; Yrbk Stf; JV L Bsktbl; JV L Socr; High Hon Roll; NHS; Ntl Merit Ltr; Val; Bio, Chem, High Avg Awds 83-84; Arch.

WORDEN, AMY; Allegany Central HS; Allegany, NY; (Y); Art Clb; Church Yth Grp; Teachers Aide; Chorus; Church Choir; School Musical; All Cnty Chorus Awd 83; Egls Clb/What My Family Means To Me Awd 79; Art Ed.

WORDEN, VERONICA; Charles Odickerson HS; Trumansburg, NY; (Y); Var Sftbl; Hon Roll; Parent Tchr Awd 84.

WOREN, MICHAEL ADAM; Lincoln HS; Yonkers, NY; (S); 25/306; Computer Clb; Drama Clb; PAVAS; Pres Temple Yth Grp; Capt Band; School Play; Nwsp Ed-Chief; Rep Stu Cncl; High Hon Roll; Aud/Vis; Pres Of Aristeun Hnr Soc 85; Mech Engr.

WORONKA, CHRISTINE; Eastport HS; Eastport, NY; (S); Varsity Clb; Band; Nwsp Rptr; VP Frsh Cls; Var Sftbl; Hon Roll; VP Jr NHS; NHS; Prfct Atten Awd.

WORRALL, JULIAN; Kenmore East SR HS; Tonawanda, NY; (Y); 30/331; Ski Clb; Im Bowling; Im Socr; Im Vllybl; Hon Roll; NHS; Pres Acad Ftns Awd 85; Case Western Reserve U; Chem En.

WORRELL, CHERYL; Aquinas HS; Bronx, NY; (Y); 29/178; Hosp Aide; Chorus; School Musical; School Play; High Hon Roll; Spanish NHS; Outstndng Ath 83; Chem Awd 85; Svc Bar Walking Hungry 85; Graphic Desgn.

WORRELL, CHRISTINE A; Midwood HS; Brooklyn, NY; (Y); 76/605; Church Yth Grp; Cmnty Wkr; Office Aide; School Musical; Yrbk Stf; Lit Mag; Hon Roll; Jr NHS; NHS; Prfct Atten Awd; Bus Admin.

WORRELL, LISA; Sheepshead Bay HS; Brooklyn, NY; (Y); Dance Clb; Library Aide; Office Aide; Red Cross Aide; Service Clb; Chorus; School Play; Nwsp Stf; Yrbk Stf; Rep Stu Cncl; Track, Spnsh & Srv Awds 82; New Paltz; Law.

WORTH, STEVEN W; Catskill HS; Leeds, NY; (Y); Am Leg Boys St; Boy Scts; Church Yth Grp; Band; Concert Band; Jazz Band; Mrchg Band; School Musical; Off Frsh Cls; Stu Cncl; U S Air Force; Aviation.

WORTH, WALTER; Crown Point Central HS; Crown Pt, NY; (S); 2/30; Drama Clb; Varsity Clb; School Play; VP Pres Jr Cls; Pres Sr Cls; Var Capt Bsktbl; Var Capt Socr; Bausch & Lomb Sci Awd; Cit Awd; DAR Awd; Sccr MVP, All-Leag, Scrng Champ 84; Bsktbl MVP, All-Leag, Scrng Champ 84; Brown U; Comp Engr.

WORTMAN, CARRIE; East Meadow HS; East Meadow, NY; (S); FBLA; Key Clb; Spanish Clb; Temple Yth Grp; Yrbk Rptr; Cheerleading; Lcrss; Tennis; Vllybl; High Hon Roll; Spnsh Frgn Lang Awd 84; Ntl Hlth Fair 85; Yth Partcptn Prjct 85; Bus.

WOUTERS, JEFFREY; Liverpool HS; Liverpool, NY; (S); 38/900; Exploring; Mathletes; Math Clb; Math Tm; Ski Clb; Orch; Var Crs Cntry; Var Trk; JV Wrstlng; High Hon Roll; Cert Achvt Math 84; Comp Engr.

WOYTHAL, SUSAN C; Wellsville HS; Wellsville, NY; (Y); 4/130; Ski Clb; Band; Mrchg Band; School Play; Yrbk Ed-Chief; Yrbk Stf; JV Var Cheerleading; Hon Roll; Trs NHS; Schl Nwspr Hall Of Fame 85; Regents Schlrshp Wnnr 85; SUNY Fredonia; Chem Engrng.

WOYTOWICH, LORRAINE M; Franklin Acad; Malone, NY; (Y); 39/253; GAA; Pep Clb; Spanish Clb; Varsity Clb; Cheerleading; Trk; High Hon Roll; Hon Roll; NHS; Spanish NHS; Travel Club 80-85; Plattsburgh ST; Language.

WOZNY, PETER; Bishop Kearney HS; Rochester, NY; (Y); Aud/Vis; Model UN; Ski Clb; School Musical; Rep Soph Cls; Im Bowling; JV Crs Cntry; JV Tennis; Var Trk; Audio Visual Awd 84; Rochester Inst Tech; Mech Engr.

WRAY, DAVID; Thomas Edison HS; Laurelton, NY; (Y); 24/419; Office Aide; ROTC; Varsity Clb; Socr; Trk; Ntl Merit Ltr; Syracuse U; Chem Engrng.

WREN, MYLES; Ramapo SR HS; Monsey, NY; (Y); Church Yth Grp; Cmnty Wkr; Nwsp Rptr; Var Trk; Hon Roll; Ntl Merit Ltr; Brdcst Jrnlsm.

WRIEDE, LISA; Walt Whitman HS; Melville, NY; (Y); 186/540; Hosp Aide; Key Clb; Office Aide; Teachers Aide; Temple Yth Grp; Yrbk Rptr; Yrbk Stf; Hon Roll; SADD VP 84-86; Bus.

WRIGHT, BRIAN; Middletown HS; Middletown, NY; (Y); Computer Clb; Key Clb; Library Aide; Teachers Aide; Varsity Clb; Yrbk Rptr; Rep Frsh Cls; Rep Soph Cls; Rep Jr Cls; Rep Sr Cls; Mst Consistent Awd 79; Outstndng Lang Arts Stu Awd 79.

WRIGHT, BRIAN; Warwick Valley HS; Warwick, NY; (Y); FFA; JV Var Bsbl; JV Var Ftbl; Dairy Mngmnt Awd 84; Sci.

WRIGHT, CALVERT C; John Jay HS; Katonah, NY; (Y); Chorus; Orch; School Musical; School Play; Variety Show; VP Stu Cncl; Var Capt Bsktbl; Var Capt Crs Cntry; High Hon Roll; NHS; NYS Rgnts Schlrshp 85; NY All-State Orch 84-85; Boys Sprts Schlrshp 84; Columbia U; Frgn Svc.

WRIGHT, CASSANDRA; Nyack HS; Nyack, NY; (Y); Drama Clb; Band; Church Choir; Concert Band; Mrchg Band; Rep Jr Cls; Acad Aeronautics.

WRIGHT, CRAIG; G Ray Bodley HS; Fulton, NY; (Y); Bsbl; Bsktbl; Bowling; Golf; Hon Roll.

WRIGHT, DAVE; Skaneateles Senior HS; Skaneateles, NY; (S); Var JV Bsbl; Var Capt Bsktbl; JV Socr; High Hon Roll; Hon Roll; Jr NHS.

WRIGHT II, DAVID; Victor Central SR HS; Macedon, NY; (Y); 1/210; Mgr Aud/Vis; French Clb; Aud/Vis; Quiz Bowl; Science Clb; Mgr Stage Crew; JV Var Tennis; High Hon Roll; NHS; Rensselaer Math & Sci Medal 86; Jr Achvt Achiever Awd 83; Regnl Sci Olympcs 83; Biochem.

WRIGHT, DOUGLAS E; De Sales Catholic HS; Lockport, NY; (Y); Am Leg Boys St; Political Wkr; VP Sr Cls; VP Stu Cncl; Bsktbl; Capt Ftbl; Hon Roll; Ntl Merit Ltr; Crmnl Justc.

WRIGHT, ERIC; Onteora HS; West Hurley, NY; (S); 4-H; Quiz Bowl; Rep Frsh Cls; Rep Soph Cls; Rep Jr Cls; Rep Sr Cls; Rep Stu Cncl; Var Tennis; High Hon Roll; NHS; Cert Of Excel 84; Ldrshp Trnng Prog 85; Chmcl Engrng.

WRIGHT, EUGENIA MARIA; North Babylon SR HS; North Babylon, NY; (Y); Church Yth Grp; Civic Clb; Cmnty Wkr; Girl Scts; Spanish Clb; Band; Chorus; JV Cheerleading; Swmmng; Cit Awd; Hntngtn Chrstn Schl 1st Pl Sci Fair Awd 81; 3rd Pl Wnnr Alpha Kappa Alpha Cltn Schlrshp 84; Svc Schlrp; Hampton U; Bus.

WRIGHT, GARTH; Ravena-Coeymans-Selkirk HS; Ravena, NY; (Y); 1/175; FBLA; Math Tm; School Play; VP Frsh Cls; Pres Soph Cls; Pres Jr Cls; Stu Cncl; Var Tennis; NHS; Val; Cultural Exchange Stu France 84; Answers Please Team Member; Rensseber Ply Tech; Indl Engrng.

WRIGHT, JAN KRISTY; Waterville JR SR HS; Waterville, NY; (Y); Capt Var Cheerleading; JV Var Fld Hcky; Capt Var Trk; Prfct Atten Awd; Am Leg Aux Girls St; GAA; Varsity Clb; Concert Band; VP Jr Cls; VP Trs Stu Cncl; Bus Admin.

WRIGHT, JEREMY; Berne-Knox-Westerlo Central HS; Berne, NY; (Y); Aud/Vis; Boy Scts; Church Yth Grp; Debate Tm; Drama Clb; Band; Chorus; Concert Band; Mrchg Band; Pep Band; Bst Supprtng Actor One Act Plays 84; Marine Bio.

WRIGHT, KANDEE L; Dundee Central HS; Dundee, NY; (Y); 2/90; Am Leg Aux Girls St; French Clb; Pres Sec Science Clb; Ski Clb; Teachers Aide; Sec Soph Cls; JV Cheerleading; High Hon Roll; Sec NHS; Church Yth Grp; SADD; Frgn Lang.

WRIGHT, KATHLEEN J; Charlotte HS; Rochester, NY; (Y); 1/93; Pres Church Yth Grp; Band; Ed Yrbk Stf; Sr Cls; Var Sftbl; High Hon Roll; NHS; Val; Office Aide; NY ST Rgnts Schlrshp 85; Schlstc Achvmnt Awd 84; Elmira Key Awd 84; SUNY Geneseo; Bus Admin.

WRIGHT, KELLY; Pittsford Sutherland HS; Pittsford, NY; (Y); Art Clb; Pep Clb; Ski Clb; Yrbk Stf; Bsktbl; Cheerleading; High Hon Roll; Hon Roll; NHS; Prfct Atten Awd; Cert Merit Curr Co 83; Awd Achvt Math 83; Mech Engr.

WRIGHT, KELLY L; Vestal HS; Vestal, NY; (Y); 41/450; French Clb; VP Spanish Clb; School Play; Rep Soph Cls; Rep Jr Cls; Rep Sr Cls; Pres Stu Cncl; Var L Swmmng; NHS; NY ST Rgnts Schlrshp 85; Vassar Clg; Lang.

WRIGHT, KIM V; Camden HS; Camden, NY; (Y); 3/200; Mathletes; Nwsp Stf; Rep Stu Cncl; High Hon Roll; Pres NHS; Ntl Merit Ltr; NYS Rgnts Coll Schlrshp 85; Cornell U; Engrng.

WRIGHT, KRISTIN; West Seneca East SR HS; West Seneca, NY; (Y); English Clb; Hosp Aide; Library Aide; Ski Clb; Spanish Clb; Teachers Aide; Rep Soph Cls; Rep Jr Cls; Rep Sr Cls; Rep Stu Cncl; Natl Frgn Lang Awd Latin 82-83; Diploma Merit Prof Spnsh 82-85; Cert Awd Schl Radio Stn 84-85.

WRIGHT, MAUREEN; Kenmore East HS; Buffalo, NY; (Y); Chorus; Color Guard; Flag Corp; Mrchg Band; High Hon Roll; NHS; Ntl Merit SF; Prfct Atten Awd.

WRIGHT, PAMELIA; John Jay HS; Brooklyn, NY; (Y); 32/537; Boys Clb Am; Drama Clb; Sec Church Choir; School Play; Wt Lftg; French Hon Soc; Govt Hon Cert 84; Amer Hstry Hon Cert 84; Art Cert 84; Princeton; Lwyr.

WRIGHT, PATRICIA; Evander Childs HS; Bronx, NY; (Y); Cmnty Wkr; FNA; Hosp Aide; PAVAS; School Play; Stage Crew; Hon Roll; Prfct Atten Awd; Vlntr Awd; NY City Techncl Coll; Nrsng.

WRIGHT, PETER; Bradford Central HS; Campbell, NY; (Y); 7/30; Stage Crew; Socr; ST U NY Brockport; Cmmnctns.

WRIGHT, SHARON; Orcadia HS; Rochester, NY; (Y); 59/292; Pres JA; Sec Soph Cls; Sec Jr Cls; Sec Sr Cls; JV Tennis; Hon Roll; Pres Schlr; Achvt Awd 84-85; U Of NC Greensboro; Cmmnctns.

WRIGHT, SHEILA; Ripley Central HS; Ripley, NY; (S); 4/28; Church Yth Grp; Girl Scts; Pres Library Aide; Scholastic Bowl; Teachers Aide; Chorus; School Musical; Hon Roll; NHS; ST U NY; Teaching.

WRIGHT, TARA-ANNE; Bishop Kearney HS; Brooklyn, NY; (Y); Art Clb; High Hon Roll; Hon Roll; Rgnts Schlrshp 85; Hunter Coll Mrt Awd 85; Hunter Coll; Libl Arts.

WRIGHT, TERRY; Grand Island HS; Gr Island, NY; (Y); Church Yth Grp; Dance Clb; Teachers Aide; Variety Show; Powder Puff Ftbl; Swmmng; Wt Lftg; Niagara U; Social Wrk.

WRIGHT, WENDY J; Cherry Valley Central Schl; Cherry Valley, NY; (Y); 2/40; Sec Drama Clb; Sec French Clb; Jazz Band; Trs Jr Cls; Trs Sr Cls; Sec Stu Cncl; Sec NHS; Sal; NYS Regents Schlrshp 85; Clark Fndtn Schlrshp 85.

WROBEL, MARK; West Genesee HS; Syracuse, NY; (Y); 30/600; Var L Bsbl; Im Coach Actv; Var L Ftbl; Im Wt Lftg; High Hon Roll; Hon Roll; NHS; Prfct Atten Awd; Boy Scts; Cmnty Wkr; All County Hnrb Mntn Var Bsbl 85; All Stars Var Bsbl 85; Comp Sci.

WROTNY, TIMOTHY; Maryvale SR HS; Cheektowaga, NY; (Y); Chorus; School Musical; Var L Tennis; Hon Roll; NHS; Cmmrcl Art.

WTORKOWSKI, JAMES; Hillcrest HS; Ridgewood, NY; (Y); 147/799; Aud/Vis; Church Yth Grp; Cmnty Wkr; Ski Clb; Band; Awd Recgntn Rsrch Sci 84; Awd Hnr Comm Svc 83-84; Elec Engr.

WU, ALAN; Norman Thomas HS; New York, NY; (S); 65/671; Chess Clb; Band; Wt Lftg; Prfct Atten Awd; Comp Prog.

WU, ALAN CHUNG CHIU; Brooklyn Tehcnical HS; Queens, NY; (Y); Hosp Aide; Office Aide; Red Cross Aide; Science Clb; Teachers Aide; High Hon Roll; Hon Roll; NHS; Prfct Atten Awd; Otto P Burgdorf Awd Biol Sci 85; Hnr Certs 82 & 84; Regnts Scholar 85; Cornell U; Med.

WU, CHUNG; F D R HS; Brooklyn, NY; (Y); 109/530; FCA; Chorus; Church Choir; Swmmng; SUNY; Engr.

WU, FRANK; Franklin D Roosevelt HS; Brooklyn, NY; (Y); 12/719; Church Yth Grp; Church Choir; Tennis; Hon Roll; NHS; Cornell U; Biology.

WU, FRANKLIN; South Shore HS; Brooklyn, NY; (Y); Art Clb; Orch; Nwsp Stf; Sr Cls; Badmtn; Bsktbl; Bowling; Hnr Achvt Arts,Sports,Acad 85; Bus.

WU, JAMES K; Benjamin N Cardozo HS; Flushing, NY; (Y); 46/470; Camera Clb; Math Clb; Pres Science Clb; Lit Mag; Im Bsktbl; Im Sftbl; Im Tennis; Hon Roll; NHS; Prfct Atten Awd; U Of Chicago; Bio-Physics.

WU, JUSTINA C; Vestal Central HS; Binghamton, NY; (Y); 4/450; Church Yth Grp; French Clb; Mathletes; Ski Clb; Orch; School Musical; Nwsp Rptr; NHS; Ntl Merit SF; NYS Minority Scholastic Achvt Awd 84; Bio.

WU, LINDA ANN; Northport HS; Northport, NY; (Y); 7/663; Cmnty Wkr; Trs Spanish Clb; Color Guard; High Hon Roll; NHS; Ntl Merit Ltr; Prfct Atten Awd; SAR Awd; Outstndg Bus Awd Berkley Schl; Suffolk Cnty Bus Tchrs Awd; Engl Writing Awd; SUNY Binghamton; Acct.

WU, NANCY M; Port Richmond HS; Staten Island, NY; (Y); 1/581; Boy Scts; Intnl Clb; School Musical; Rptr Nwsp Ed-Chief; NHS; Val; Office Aide; Chorus; High Hon Roll; Young Muscns Comp 83; Edith In Chief Math Magazine 84; Sec Of Belle Brummesl Soc Club 84-85; Yale; Pianist.

WU, RICHARD; La Salle Academy; New York, NY; (S); Art Clb; Math Clb; Math Tm; Yrbk Stf; Bowling; Trk; Hon Roll.

WU, SUSIE; Allegany Central HS; Allegany, NY; (Y); Art Clb; Ski Clb; Trs Stu Cncl; Var L Cheerleading; Var L Tennis; Var L Trk; High Hon Roll; Jr NHS; Gym; Schlrshp Soc Pin 83-84; Outstndng Chrldr 85; JR Attndnt 85; Arch.

WUDEL, ELIZABETH; Massena Central HS; Massena, NY; (Y); Nwsp Rptr; Nwsp Stf; JV L Cheerleading; Im Powder Puff Ftbl; Var Timer; Hon Roll; U Of AZ; Comm.

WULF, KASEY; Cattaraugus Central Schl; Cattaraugus, NY; (Y); 11/57; Pep Clb; Band; Concert Band; Jazz Band; Mrchg Band; Yrbk Stf; Stat Bsbl; Hon Roll; Psych.

WULFF, CHRISTINE; St Dominic HS; E Norwich, NY; (Y); 1/119; Q&S; Quiz Bowl; Nwsp Ed-Chief; Ntl Merit Schol; Val; 4-H; Yrbk Stf; Rep Stu Cncl; Var Bsktbl; NHS; Cornell U; Bio Sci.

WUNDER, JOHN; Marion JR SR HS; Marion, NY; (Y); French Clb; Varsity Clb; Band; Concert Band; Mrchg Band; Yrbk Sprt Ed; JV Var Bsbl; JV Var Bsktbl; JV Var Socr; Alfred ST Coll; Comp Sci.

WUNSCH, SCOTT; Newfield HS; Centereach, NY; (Y); Band; Stage Crew; Im Crs Cntry; Im Trk; Im Wrstlng; Hon Roll; Stony Brook U-NY; Engrng.

WURST, JENNIFER; Maryvale SR HS; Cheektowaga, NY; (Y); Aud/Vis; Church Yth Grp; German Clb; GAA; Library Aide; Nwsp Stf; Hon Roll; NHS; Htl/Restrnt Mngmnt.

WURTH, GRETCHEN; Valley Central HS; Maybrook, NY; (Y); Church Yth Grp; French Clb; Band; Church Choir; Color Guard; Concert Band; Mrchg Band; DAR Awd; French Hon Soc; Hon Roll; Frng Lang.

WYANT, MATTHEW; Beacon HS; M D Beacon, NY; (S); Math Clb; Math Tm; Varsity Clb; Socr; High Hon Roll; Jr NHS; NHS; Ntl Merit Ltr; Sal; Excllnc Awds Math, Sci 84; Hnr Soc Outstndng Stu 84; Comp Sci.

WYANT, MICHELLE D; Starpoint Central HS; N Tonawanda, NY; (Y); 7/196; Math Tm; Varsity Clb; VP Band; Mrchg Band; Pep Band; Var L Golf; JV Tennis; Hon Roll; Jr NHS; NHS; NYS Rgnts Schlrshp 85; Chrch Secy Bd 85; Chrch Sftbll Tm 82-85; NY ST U Buffalo; Phrmcy.

WYCOFF, ANN M; Stoney Brook Prep Schl; Northport, NY; (Y); 30/97; Camera Clb; Exploring; GAA; JA; Library Aide; Varsity Clb; Nwsp Rptr; Capt Swmmng; Trk; Jr NHS; West Point Schlrshp; Swmmng Comptns; YWCA Schlrshp 85; West Point; Intl Law.

WYDYSH, BARBARA L; Hamburg SR HS; Hamburg, NY; (Y); 14/408; Spanish Clb; Acpl Chr; Chorus; Madrigals; School Musical; School Play; Rep Jr Cls; Rep Stu Cncl; Cheerleading; Hon Roll; Theatre Arts.

WYDYSH, JENNIFER L; Sandy Creek Central HS; Lacona, NY; (Y); 6/60; Computer Clb; Intnl Clb; VP Clb; Band; Jazz Band; Yrbk Sprt Ed; Pres Sr Cls; Var JV Bsktbl; JV Socr; JV Sftbl; Natl Latn Exm Magna Cum Laude 83; Regnts Schlrshp 85; Frshmn Acadmc Schlrshp 85; Houghton Coll; Psych.

WYLER, LAUREN; Rye HS; Rye, NY; (Y); Cmnty Wkr; Variety Show; Lit Mag; Rep Stu Cncl; Lcrss; Var Tennis; High Hon Roll; Hon Roll; Pre Law.

WYLIE, MARY; Albertus Magnus HS; Valley Cottage, NY; (Y); 56/190; Phy Thrpy.

WYLLIE, AARON T; Nazareth Regional HS; Brooklyn, NY; (Y); 85/272; Computer Clb; Teachers Aide; Hon Roll; Comp Sci Mdl 85; Hrsbck Rdng Awds 83-85; Math Awd-Alg 83; Comp Engrng.

WYMAN, ARCHIE R; Automotive HS; Brooklyn, NY; (Y); 3/149; Var L FCA; Var L Trk; New York Regents Scholarship.

WYNKOOP, HOPE P; Henninger HS; Syracuse, NY; (Y); 1/400; Math Clb; Trs Soph Cls; Trs Jr Cls; Rep Sr Cls; Trs Stu Cncl; Var Crs Cntry; Var Trk; Bausch & Lomb Sci Awd; CC Awd; Val; NY ST Regents Schlrshp 85; Female Athlete Of Year 85; Harvard Book Clb Awd 84; Brown U; Engrng.

WYNN, ROXANNE; Sheepshead Bay HS; Brooklyn, NY; (Y); Church Yth Grp; Hosp Aide; Math Tm; Service Clb; Nwsp Rptr; Sec Stu Cncl; NCTE Awd; Daily News Pride Yankees Awd 84-85; NY Daily News Acad Olymp Awd 85; Arista 85; Jrnlsm.

WYNNE, MICHAEL J; Marcellus Central HS; Marcellus, NY; (Y); 9/170; Am Leg Boys St; Debate Tm; Model UN; Ski Clb; School Musical; Pres Stu Cncl; NHS; Pres Schlr; Exploring; Political Wkr; Congrssnl Mdl Merit 85; Drivr Memrl Schlrshp 85; WA Wrkshps 85; Bucknell U; Law.

WYNNE, THOMAS M; St Joseph Coll Inst; Orchard Park, NY; (Y); 102/220; Camera Clb; Church Yth Grp; Mathletes; Ski Clb; Nwsp Phtg; Yrbk Ed-Chief; Yrbk Phtg; Yrbk Stf; Swmmng; Hon Roll; SUNY-MARATINE; Engrng.

WYSZKOWSKI, JOY; Tonawanda SR HS; Tonawanda, NY; (Y); Aud/Vis; Church Yth Grp; Science Clb; Band; Chorus; Church Choir; Concert Band; Mrchg Band; Pep Band; School Musical; RN.

YACCARINO, OLIVIA L; Cincinnatus Central Schl; Pitcher, NY; (Y); 6/40; Band; Chorus; Nwsp Ed-Chief; High Hon Roll; Hon Roll; JC Awd; JP Sousa Awd; NHS; Pres Schlr; St Schlr; Police Benevolent Schlrshp 85; Cinnatus Cntrl Educ Schlrshp 85; Albany ST U; Pre-Law.

YACOUB, JOHN P; Archbishop Stepinac HS; White Plains, NY; (Y); 58/206; Computer Clb; French Clb; Nwsp Rptr; Ed Lit Mag; Hon Roll; Ntl Merit Ltr; Rgnts Schlrshp 85; Block S Awd Ltr 85; SUNY Binghamton; Pol Sci.

YACOVELLI, MARIA; West Hempstead HS; Island Pk, NY; (Y); Church Yth Grp; Spanish Clb; Teachers Aide; Var Capt Cheerleading; Coach Actv; Score Keeper; Hon Roll; NHS.

YAECKEL, BETH; Bishop Kearney HS; Webster, NY; (Y); Church Yth Grp; Cmnty Wkr; JA; NFL; Chorus; School Musical; School Play; Stage Crew; Nwsp Stf; Yrbk Stf; St Ritas Bishop Kearney Schlrshp 82; Comm.

YAHN, MELISSA; Bishop Grimes HS; Fayetteville, NY; (Y); Cmnty Wkr; School Musical; Bowling; Powder Puff Ftbl; Hon Roll; NHS; Ntl Hnr Rll 85; Ntl Engl Merit Awd 85; Biochem.

YAHYA, HEATHER; South Shore HS; Brooklyn, NY; (Y); Cmnty Wkr; Science Clb; School Play; Yrbk Stf; Tennis.

YAKABOSKI, MATTHEW; Riverhead HS; Calverton, NY; (Y); 4/225; JCL; Latin Clb; Letterman Clb; Science Clb; Ski Clb; L Socr; L Tennis; L Wrstlng; High Hon Roll; NHS; Chem Engrng.

YAMAJI, ALAN; Westbury SR HS; Westbury, NY; (Y); 13/260; Computer Clb; Mathletes; Nwsp Phtg; Nwsp Rptr; Nwsp Sprt Ed; Nwsp Stf; Yrbk Phtg; Im Bsktbl; Capt Crs Cntry; Im Ftbl; Regents Schlrshp 85.

YAMONICO, MIKE; Longwood HS; Ridge, NY; (Y); 132/488; Hon Roll; Comptrs.

YAN, ALBERT C; John H Glenn HS; E Northport, NY; (Y); 3/260; Chess Clb; Pres Debate Tm; Exploring; Pres French Clb; Pres Mathletes; Science Clb; Pres French Hon Soc; NHS; Ntl Merit SF; Roswell Pk Mem Inst Smr Resrch Part 84; Med.

YANCEY, JENNIFER; Newark SR HS; Newark, NY; (Y); 32/180; Sec Trs French Clb; Ski Clb; VP Frsh Cls; Sec Pres Stu Cncl; Var Swmmng; French Hon Soc; Hon Roll; VP NHS; Political Wkr; JV Trk; Stu Of Mnth 83; Mst Imprvd Swmmr 83.

YANDO, CATHY; Spackenkill HS; Poughkeepsie, NY; (Y); 46/170; Thesps; Stage Crew; Nwsp Stf; Rep Stu Cncl; Var Tennis; Fshn Merch.

YANDO, LISA; Smithtown West HS; Smithtown, NY; (Y); Exploring; Band; Concert Band; Mrchg Band; JV Socr; Vllybl; French Hon Soc; Hon Roll; Won Phil Esposito Fndtn Essay Cntst 84.

YANDON, EDMOND; Saranac Lake HS; Saranac Lk, NY; (Y); 9/128; Computer Clb; JV Golf; Var L Socr; JV Trk; High Hon Roll; Hon Roll; NHS; Stu Cncl Outstndng Athlt Ski 85; Physcs.

YANG, CHARLEEN; St Francis Prep; Flushing, NY; (S); 137/700; Math Clb; Drm & Bgl; Mrchg Band; Pep Band; Opt Clb Awd.

YANG, SEUNG PIL PHILLIP; Bronx High School Of Schienc; Flushing, NY; (Y); Cmnty Wkr; Math Tm; Rep Frsh Cls; Pres Soph Cls; Pres Jr Cls; Pres Stu Cncl; Im Capt Bsktbl; Hon Roll; Nwsp Rptr; Im Vllybl; Pride Of Yankees Awd 85; NY Math Fair Semi-Final 85.

YANKOSKY, THOMAS J; East Islip HS; East Islip, NY; (Y); 59/475; Stu Cncl; Var Capt Lcrss; Hon Roll; Hobart Coll; Law.

YANNONE, SUZANNE; Pierson HS; Sag Harbor, NY; (Y); Office Aide; Band; Mrchg Band; Nwsp Stf; Yrbk Ed-Chief; Yrbk Stf; Rep Frsh Cls; Sec Soph Cls; Sec Jr Cls; Pres Sr Cls; Yr Bk Staff Awd 85; Awd For Svc Girls Athletic Dept 85; Guidance Ofc Asst Awd 85; Awd-Svc Stu Cncl 85; Stony Brook; Emergency Med Tech.

YANOW, MICHELE B; Alfred G Berner HS; Massapequa Park, NY; (Y); 1/426; Drama Clb; Quiz Bowl; Acpl Chr; Variety Show; Nwsp Stf; NHS; Ntl Merit SF; Val; NY ST Smmr Sch Visual Arts 84; NYSSSA Sch Choral Studies 84; Art.

YANOWIAK, TINA; Elmira Southside HS; Elmira, NY; (Y); Chess Clb; Cmnty Wkr; French Clb; Ski Clb; Ed Yrbk Stf; Sec Soph Cls; Sec Jr Cls; Rep Sr Cls; Rep Stu Cncl; L Trk; Michelle Keete Mem Awd 85; Art Inst Pittsburgh; Advrtsng.

YARCEL, DIANE M; Bethpage HS; Bethpage, NY; (Y); 102/280; Dance Clb; Girl Scts; Intnl Clb; Drill Tm; School Musical; JV Var Pom Pon; Var Tennis; Italn Schlrshp 85; SUNY Farmingdale; Bus Admin.

YARDLEY, CRAIG; East Hampton HS; Amagansett, NY; (Y); Am Leg Boys St; Civic Clb; Intnl Clb; Pep Clb; Rep Stu Cncl; JV Var Bsktbl; JV Var Ftbl; Var Golf; High Hon Roll; Hon Roll; Math Awd 82-83; Stu Ldrs Mbr 84-85; Pol Sci.

YASMENT, LEE; Saranac Central HS; Saranac, NY; (S); 11/104; French Clb; Office Aide; Teachers Aide; Band; Concert Band; Jazz Band; Mrchg Band; School Musical; Cheerleading; Hon Roll.

YASUS, JAMES; Herricks SR HS; Williston Park, NY; (S); 101/306; Trs DECA; JV Bsbl; Voice Dem Awd; Nassau CC; Comm.

YATES, AMY M; East Hampton HS; East Hampton, NY; (Y); 21/165; Teachers Aide; School Musical; Yrbk Stf; JV Bsktbl; JV Fld Hcky; Hon Roll; Chorus; Jr Hnrs 81-82; NY St Regents Schlrshp 85; Frgn Exc Stu Denmark 83-84; Kutz Town U; Elem Ed.

YATES JR, CARL DUBOISE; De Witt Clinton HS; Bronx, NY; (Y); Debate Tm; Math Tm; Lit Mag; Cit Awd; Gov Hon Prg Awd; Jr NHS; NHS; Prfct Atten Awd; Office Aide; Teachers Aide; Acadmc Olympcs Membr Daily Nws 85; Pre Engrng Prog H S Stdnts CUNY 85; Cert Svc CUNY 85.

YATES, DAVID; Anteora HS; Shokan, NY; (S); Boy Scts; Math Tm; Chorus; School Musical; Tennis; Hon Roll; NHS; Ntl Hnr Soc 85; Ntl Merit Fndtn 85; Math.

YATES, ROTREASE S; Patchoque-Medford HS; Valley Cottage, NY; (Y); 57/748; Leo Clb; School Musical; School Play; Yrbk Ed-Chief; JV Var Fld Hcky; Var Trk; Hon Roll; NYS Regnts Nrsng Schlrshp 85; PA ST U; Nrs.

YATTAW, JAMES; Waterford-Halfmoon HS; Waterford, NY; (Y); 13/80; Cmnty Wkr; Chorus; Madrigals; Swing Chorus; Yrbk Stf; Pres Frsh Cls; Pres Soph Cls; Pres Jr Cls; Pres Sr Cls; Var Capt Bsktbl; Hgh Hnr Rll; Spc.

YATTEAU, JENNIFER; Our Lady Of Mercy HS; Rochester, NY; (Y); Ski Clb; Bowling; Hon Roll; Monroe CC; Bus.

YAU, PO LAI; Fort Hamilton HS; Brooklyn, NY; (Y); 2/532; Math Tm; Teachers Aide; Var Hon Roll; NHS; Prfct Atten Awd; Sal; ACS Exam Cert 84; Sec Chinese Cultr Clb 83-85; NY U; Engr.

YAUN, LAURA; Onteora HS; West Hurley, NY; (S); Church Yth Grp; Band; Concert Band; Mrchg Band; Variety Show; Nwsp Rptr; Rep Stu Cncl; Vllybl; Hon Roll; NHS.

YAVORNITZKI, LISA; Oneida SR HS; Oneida, NY; (Y); Church Yth Grp; Drama Clb; French Clb; Chorus; School Musical; Yrbk Phtg; Rep Stu Cncl; Z Clb VP Brnch Zonta Clb 85-86; Locl Govt Prog 84-85; JR Prom Qn 85; Elem Ed.

YAW, JIM; Mount Markham HS; W Winfield, NY; (Y); Aud/Vis; Drama Clb; Chorus; Drm & Bgl; School Musical; School Play; Stage Crew; Trk; Hon Roll; Prfct Atten Awd; Herkimer County CC; Radio.

YAW, KARI; Northstar Christian Acad; Rochester, NY; (S); 14/28; Drama Clb; Chorus; Church Choir; Stage Crew; Yrbk Stf; Trs Frsh Cls; Pres Stu Cncl; Var Cheerleading; High Hon Roll; Bsns.

YAW, TAMMY; Ticonderoga HS; Hague, NY; (Y); 22/105; French Clb; Key Clb; Mgr(s); Var L Socr; Var L Trk; High Hon Roll; Hon Roll; Prfct Atten Awd; Albany ST Coll; Comp Sci.

YAWNEY, KELLY; Jordan-Elbridge Central HS; Jordan, NY; (Y); 4-H; Girl Scts; Ski Clb; Spanish Clb; Teachers Aide; Church Choir; Powder Puff Ftbl; CCBI; Law.

YAZBACK, MICHELLE; Our Lady Of Mercy; Webster, NY; (Y); 80/200; Cmnty Wkr; French Clb; JA; Ski Clb; Rep Frsh Cls; Coach Actv; Gym; Var Socr; U Of Dayton; Bus.

YEAGER III, CHARLES J; Middletown HS; Middletown, NY; (Y); 18/400; Natl Beta Clb; Scholastic Bowl; Hon Roll; NHS; Math Awd; Regnts Schlrshp; MI Tech U; Physics.

YEAGER, PETER; John H Glenn HS; Greenlawn, NY; (Y); Var Bsbl; Var Ftbl; Var Wt Lftg; Hon Roll.

YEARSLEY, JOHN; Maple Hill HS; Castleton, NY; (S); French Clb; Stu Cncl; Var Socr; Trk; Hon Roll; Kiwanis Awd; NHS; Pharm.

YEARWOOD, DENISE; Evandet Childs HS; Bronx, NY; (Y); FCA; Acpl Chr; Chorus; Church Choir; School Play; Badmtn; Fld Hcky; Tennis; Prfct Atten Awd; Bio.

YEBERNETSKY, MICHELLE L; H C Technical HS; Buffalo, NY; (Y); JA; Nwsp Stf; Yrbk Stf; Hon Roll; Pres Acad Ftns Awd 85; Hnr Scty 82-85; Buffalo ST Coll; Ism.

YEE, COLEEN; Garden City SR HS; Garden City, NY; (Y); 67/319; Pep Clb; Color Guard; Yrbk Stf; Var Socr; Var High Hon Roll; Var Jr NHS; Kickline 83-85; Itln Clb 84-85; NYS Rgnts Schrlshp, Comm Stdnt; Bus.

YEE, ELISA; Performing Arts HS; New York, NY; (Y); 86/588; School Play; Variety Show; Nwsp Phtg; Nwsp Rptr; Nwsp Stf; French Hon Soc; Hon Roll; ARTS Pgm Hnry Mntn 85; Law.

YEE, EMILY; Norman Thomas HS; New York, NY; (S); 12/671; FBLA; Intnl Clb; Cit Awd; Hon Roll; NHS; Prfct Atten Awd; Acad All Amer 85; NY ST Regents Schlrshp 85; NY U; Comp Pgmr.

YEE, FUNG MAY; Stuyvesant HS; New York, NY; (Y); Teachers Aide; Lit Mag; Cit Awd; Chancellors Rll Hnr 85; Cert SEER Corp Awd 84; U N Cert Merit Creatv Contrbtn 81; Comp Sci.

YEE, HELEN; La Guardia HS Music And The Arts; New York, NY; (Y); Church Yth Grp; Capt FCA; Service Clb; Teachers Aide; Varsity Clb; Chorus; Church Choir; Vllybl; Hon Roll; Prfct Atten Awd; Cert Of Merit Prfmnc 82; Music & Art Mdl 85; Hunter Coll; Human Svcs.

YEE, JUDITH; Seward Park HS; New York, NY; (Y); Computer Clb; Office Aide; Service Clb; Teachers Aide; Concert Band; Rep Stu Cncl; High Hon Roll; Prfct Atten Awd; Kochs Spr Yth Awd Acdmc Achvt 85; Syracuse U; Pblc Adm.

YEE, MAY; Brooklyn Technical HS; Brooklyn, NY; (Y); 27/1139; Math Tm; Office Aide; Science Clb; Ed Yrbk Stf; Hon Roll; Chrmn NHS; Sal; Untd Fed Tchrs Schlrshp 85-86; Regnts Schlrshp 85-86; Cornell U; Ec.

YEE, MICHAEL; Msgr Mc Clancy HS; Jackson Hgts, NY; (Y); Mth.

YEE, SANDY; Hillcrest HS; Briarwood, NY; (Y); Office Aide; Teachers Aide; Nwsp Stf; Med.

YEE, SUSAN R; Newtown HS; Corona, NY; (Y); Key Clb; Math Tm; Office Aide; Service Clb; Nwsp Stf; Yrbk Stf; NY Nath League Awd 84; Regents Schlrshp 85; NY U; Comp Sci.

YEGHIKIAN, GERALDINE; St Francis Prep; Bayside, NY; (S); 141/690; Aud/Vis; Church Yth Grp; Intnl Clb; Yrbk Stf; Hon Roll; NHS; Regents Schlr 85; Excllnce Italian Awd 82; Retreat Ldr 83-85; NY U; Communcatns.

YEHLING, MICHELLE; Churchville-Chili HS; Rochester, NY; (Y); Trs GAA; Concert Band; Pep Band; Yrbk Stf; Stat Bsktbl; JV Var Swmmng; JV Var Vllybl; High Hon Roll; NHS; Mar Bio.

YELLEN, JONATHAN H; Williamsville South HS; Amherst, NY; (Y); 5/250; Trs Math Clb; Pep Clb; Quiz Bowl; Ski Clb; Temple Yth Grp; Acpl Chr; Yrbk Bus Mgr; Rep Stu Cncl; NHS; Ntl Merit Schol; Harvard; Law.

YELLEN, LAURA; Garden City HS; Garden City, NY; (Y); 119/320; Drama Clb; Hosp Aide; Stage Crew; Yrbk Stf; Rep Soph Cls; Mgr(s); Hon Roll; Chorus; Ntl Merit Schlrshp Commnded Stu 84-85; NY ST Regnts Schlrshp 85; Franklin & Marshall Coll; Bus.

YEMAN, JOY; Oneida HS; Oneida, NY; (S); 9/225; Pres 4-H; Teachers Aide; Band; Mrchg Band; Yrbk Stf; 4-H Awd; High Hon Roll; Hon Roll; NHS; Sch Hgh Scr Engl II Rgnts 84; 2nd ST Ornmntl Hortcltr 84; Colgate U Smnr Pgrm 84; Comm.

YENCER, DEBBIE; Alden HS; Alden, NY; (Y); VP French Clb; VP GAA; Letterman Clb; Yrbk Stf; Rep Frsh Cls; Rep Soph Cls; Rep Jr Cls; Pres Stu Cncl; Var Tennis; Var Trk.

YENCER, JAMES; Perry Central HS; Perry, NY; (Y); Boy Scts; Band; Mrchg Band; Tennis; Math.

YENNELLA, MICHELE; Curtis HS; Staten Island, NY; (Y); 24/281; Art Clb; Key Clb; Sec Math Clb; Office Aide; Red Cross Aide; Science Clb; Teachers Aide; Chorus; School Musical; Yrbk Stf; Skidmore Schlrshp 85; Skidmore Coll; Biochemst.

YERGENS, LISA A; Randolph Central Schl; Randolph, NY; (Y); 4/96; Drama Clb; Ski Clb; Sec Spanish Clb; Lit Mag; VP Frsh Cls; JV Var Cheerleading; Var Crs Cntry; Trk; Hon Roll; Trs NHS; St Qual Cross Cty 84; Jamestown Comm Coll; Travel Age.

YERMAK, YELENA; James Madison HS; Brooklyn, NY; (Y); 24/812; JA; Office Aide; Quiz Bowl; Science Clb; Nwsp Ed-Chief; Nwsp Rptr; High Hon Roll; Prfct Atten Awd; Wstnghs Hnrs Grp Wnr 85; Chnclrs Roll Of Hnr 85; Sophie Davis Schl Med; Md.

YESSENOW, KARLA; Brighton HS; Rochester, NY; (Y); 60/315; German Clb; Spanish Clb; Temple Yth Grp; Chorus; Nwsp Rptr; Intl Exch Pgm Schlrshp 85; Outstndng Stdnt Awd, Crtv Svc Awd 84; Frgn Lang.

YETMAN, CHRIS; Immaculate Heart Central HS; Watertown, NY; (Y); Boy Scts; Cmnty Wkr; Intnl Clb; Political Wkr; Ski Clb; Spanish Clb; Varsity Clb; Color Guard; School Play; Var Ftbl; SUNY Oswego; Blgcl Scntst.

YETTO, PATTY; Lansingburgh HS; Troy, NY; (Y); Office Aide; Church Choir; JV Trk; High Hon Roll; Hon Roll; Jr NHS; PN.

YIP, FRANK; La Salle Acad; Brooklyn, NY; (Y); Cmnty Wkr; Rep Frsh Cls; Rep Stu Cncl; JV L Crs Cntry; Im Fld Hcky; Im Ftbl; Stat Score Keeper; Im Socr; Im Sftbl; Stat Timer; Crdnl Hayes Hnrs Scty 83; Ntl Hnr Scty 85; NY Inst Of Tech; Archtctr.

YOCHIM II, BARRIE; Clymer Central Schl; Sherman, NY; (Y); Var L Bsbl; JV Var Bsktbl; JV Var Ftbl; Hon Roll; Brdcstng.

YOERG, NANCY; Turner/Carrol HS; Buffalo, NY; (Y); Hosp Aide; Nwsp Stf; Var L Bsktbl; Var Sftbl; High Hon Roll; Hon Roll; NHS; Schlrshp For Prtl Tuition 82; Buffalo ST Coll; Jrnlsm.

YOKEMICK, CRAIG; Copiague HS; Copiague, NY; (Y); Letterman Clb; Var Bsbl; Var Bsktbl; All Lg Bsbl 85; Var Ltr Bsbl & Bsktbl 85; Engrng.

YOLES, AYELET; Bronx HS Of Science; New York, NY; (Y); NHS.

YOM, UOONG HYUN; Flushing HS; Flushing, NY; (Y); Library Aide; Service Clb; Band; Off Jr Cls; JA; PAVAS; Concert Band; Im Badmtn; Im Bowling; Im Vllybl; Polytechnic; Mech Engr.

YON, MIRACLE; Indian River Central HS; Theresa, NY; (Y); French Clb; Office Aide; School Play; Yrbk Stf; Sec Jr Cls; Sec Sr Cls; Trk; Girl Scts; Chorus; Orch; Proj Charlie 83; Potsdam Coll; Bus.

YONATY, STEPHEN L; Binghamton HS; Binghamton, NY; (Y); Cmnty Wkr; Pres Debate Tm; Key Clb; Ski Clb; Off Jr Cls; Rep Stu Cncl; Golf; Tennis; High Hon Roll; Pres NHS; Cornell; Finc.

YOO, BILLY; Brooklyn Technical HS; Staten Isld, NY; (Y); Debate Tm; Intnl Clb; Office Aide; Speech Tm; Coach Actv; Timer; Wt Lftg.

YOO, POEHYUN R; Flushing HS; Flushing, NY; (Y); #11 In Class; Art Clb; Chess Clb; Cmnty Wkr; Debate Tm; Office Aide; Ski Clb; Teachers Aide; Chorus; Orch; School Musical; Pace U; Bus.

YOON, HYUNSUK; Bronx High School Of Science; Flushing, NY; (Y); Mathletes; Math Tm; Lit Mag; Ntl Merit Ltr; 47th Schl Sci Fair 1st Pl Boroughwide 85; NY Metropltn Math Fair Gld Mdlst 85; Natl Cncl Tchrs/Mth Bk; Phy Sci.

YOON, JUNG AE; Flushing HS; Flushing, NY; (Y); Band; Stage Crew; Yrbk Phtg; Yrbk Stf; Sec Stu Cncl; Mgr Bsktbl; Var Socr; Var Sftbl; Var Vllybl; Kiwanis Awd; ARISTA 82; Pre-Med.

YOOS, JAMES; Geneseo Central HS; Geneseo, NY; (Y); 8/89; Boy Scts; Church Yth Grp; JV Capt Bsbl; Var L Ice Hcky; Var L Socr; High Hon Roll; Jr NHS; NHS; Natl Scl Stds Olympiad/Amer Hist 85; US Coast Guard Acad; Chem Engr.

YORK, ERIK J; Onteora Central Schl; Woodstock, NY; (Y); 80/245; Ski Clb; Yrbk Sprt Ed; Vrsty Ltr Ski Tm; Comp.

YORK, JAMES P; Letchworth Central HS; Castile, NY; (Y); Math Tm; Ski Clb; Varsity Clb; Pres Band; Chorus; Jazz Band; Var L Bsktbl; Var L Socr; High Hon Roll; NHS; Ofrd Pres Schlrshp Alfred U 85-86; All Str Tm SR Vrsty Sccr & Bsktbl 84-85; NYS Regnts Schlrshp Wnnr; Rochester Inst Tech; Mech Engrg.

YORK, KIMBERLY S; North Rose-Wolcott HS; Wolcott, NY; (Y); FBLA; Rep Frsh Cls; Rep Soph Cls; Rep Stu Cncl; Var Capt Cheerleading; Mgr(s); Var Trk; Var Vllybl; High Hon Roll; Hon Roll; NYS Regnts Nrs Schlrshp 85; Oral Roberts U Tulsa OK; Nrs.

YORK, LISA; South Lewis Central HS; Turin, NY; (Y); Ski Clb; JV Var Socr; Var Sftbl; Hon Roll; Data Procssng.

YORK, SUE; Dundee Central Schl; Rock Stm, NY; (Y); 6/66; Varsity Clb; Band; Concert Band; Drill Tm; Mrchg Band; Yrbk Stf; Tennis; High Hon Roll; Score Keeper; Elmira Coll Key Awd 84; Elmira Coll; Ed.

YOST, ANTHONY M; Rome Free Acad; Rome, NY; (Y); Boy Scts; Exploring; Band; Concert Band; Drm & Bgl; Mrchg Band; Orch; Lcrss; Vllybl; Wt Lftg; Morrisvlle Agr/Tech; Elect Engr.

YOUKER, ALAN; Pulaski JR SR HS; Pulaski, NY; (Y); French Clb; Math Clb; Ski Clb; Varsity Clb; Band; Concert Band; Mrchg Band; Var L Bsbl; Var L Ftbl; Hon Roll; John Ben Snow Incentv Awd 85; NY Math Leag 1st Pl 85; Engrng.

YOUNG, ABBY J; Rye HS; Rye, NY; (Y); 29/187; VP Concert Band; VP Mrchg Band; Hon Roll; NHS; Regents Schlrshp 85; Lehigh.

YOUNG, AMY; Mynderse Acad; Seneca Falls, NY; (Y); 28/130; Am Leg Aux Girls St; Drama Clb; Concert Band; Mrchg Band; School Musical; School Play; Yrbk Stf; Trs Stu Cncl; Var Trk; Hon Roll; Communctns.

YOUNG, AMY M; Cardinal Mooney HS; Rochester, NY; (Y); 7/327; Pres Exploring; Yrbk Ed-Chief; Fld Hcky; NHS; Ntl Merit SF; Pres Schlr; Spanish NHS; Church Yth Grp; Off Soph Cls; Off Jr Cls; NYS Regents Schlrshp 85; Spnsh Awd 82 & 84; CYO Chrldng Capt 85; U Of Buffalo; Phy Thrpy.

YOUNG, ANDREW; Guilderland Center HS; Schenectady, NY; (Y); Ski Clb; JV Var Crs Cntry; High Hon Roll; Hon Roll; Dist Ind Arts Asoc 84-85; Guilerlnd Pump & Sales 1st 85; Engrng.

YOUNG, CHRISTA M; Hawthorne Valley HS; Philmont, NY; (Y); Chorus; Orch; School Musical; School Play; Yrbk Stf; Pres Frsh Cls; Sec Sr Cls; Stu Cncl; Var Capt Bsktbl; Var Crs Cntry; Friends World Coll; Psych.

YOUNG, CHRISTIE L; Horace Greeley HS; Mt Kisco, NY; (Y); 60/272; Church Yth Grp; Band; Orch; Var Sftbl; Regents Schlrshp 84-85; PA ST; Comp Sci.

YOUNG, DANIEL J; Harrison HS; Harrison, NY; (Y); #13 In Class; AFS; Boy Scts; Civic Clb; Cmnty Wkr; French Clb; JA; Ski Clb; Sec Temple Yth Grp; Band; Chorus; Mock Trial 85; Nat Merit Comm 85; Hghst Latin Avrg 84-85; U Of PA; Law.

YOUNG, DAWN; Riverside HS; Buffalo, NY; (Y); Cmnty Wkr; Hosp Aide; Key Clb; Library Aide; Tennis; DAR Awd; Reg Nrse.

YOUNG, DENNIS; North Collins Central HS; N Collins, NY; (Y); Pres Soph Cls; JV Socr; Comp Engr.

YOUNG, DIANE; Wilson Central HS; Wilson, NY; (Y); 22/140; Library Aide; Office Aide; Teachers Aide; Band; Nwsp Stf; Yrbk Stf; Fld Hcky; CC Awd; Hon Roll; Bryant & Stratton Schlrshp-Crt Rptng 85; Bryant & Stratton; Lwyrs Asst.

YOUNG, ELIZA A; La Guardia HS; New York, NY; (Y); 5/588; Civic Clb; Drama Clb; Math Tm; Yrbk Stf; Lit Mag; Gov Hon Prg Awd; High Hon Roll; NHS; Art Clb; Art Honor League 84-85; Transit Art Cont-2nd Pl 84; Stud Art Cont, Chan 13 84; History.

YOUNG, ELLEN; Mt St Ursula HS; Bronx, NY; (Y); Drama Clb; Science Clb; VP Church Choir; Yrbk Stf; Off Frsh Cls; High Hon Roll; Hon Roll; Cert Merit 82; NY U.

YOUNG, ERIC W; St Francis HS; Orchard Park, NY; (Y); 3/143; Hosp Aide; Quiz Bowl; Ski Clb; Teachers Aide; Nwsp Rptr; Yrbk Stf; Rep Stu Cncl; Var Capt Socr; NHS; Natl Piano-Playing Auditions 82-84; Geo Washington U.

YOUNG, HENRIETTA; Wyandanch Memorial HS; Wyandanch, NY; (Y); 12/150; Art Clb; Hosp Aide; JA; Pres Spanish Clb; Mrchg Band; Nwsp Sprt Ed; VP Frsh Cls; Stu Cncl; Hon Roll; Ntl Merit Ltr; Art Awd 83 & 84; Stoneybrook U; RN.

YOUNG, JAMES; Forest Hills HS; Forest Hills, NY; (Y); 51/881; Chess Clb; VP Church Yth Grp; Yrbk Stf; High Hon Roll; NHS; Hnbl Mntn 3rd Pl Queens Borough Sci Fair 84; Perf Attndnc Awd 82-84; Elctrc Engrng.

YOUNG, JERRY; Mexico HS; Mexico, NY; (Y); Ski Clb; Var Golf; JV Var Socr; Var Tennis; Hon Roll; Acad & Athltc Achvt 82; Canton ATC; Refrgrtn.

YOUNG, JILL; St Joesephs By The Sea; Staten Island, NY; (Y); Civic Clb; Cmnty Wkr; Dance Clb; Drama Clb; JA; Chorus; School Musical; School Play; JR Achvt Geo; Psych.

YOUNG, JOHN; Dryden HS; Dryden, NY; (Y); Am Leg Boys St; Spanish Clb; Band; Jazz Band; Yrbk Ed-Chief; Pres Frsh Cls; Pres Soph Cls; Var Trk; High Hon Roll; NHS.

YOUNG, JULIA M; Immaculata Acad; Potomac, MD; (Y); 2/74; Yrbk Stf; Sec Soph Cls; Sec Jr Cls; JV Bsktbl; Var Sftbl; Hon Roll; Sec NHS; Sal; West Publshg Co Schlrshp 85-86; George Washington U; Elem Educ.

YOUNG, KAREN M; Whitney Point Central HS; Whitney Point, NY; (Y); 52/135; Church Yth Grp; French Clb; Rep Stu Cncl; Var Cheerleading; Hon Roll; Frch.

YOUNG, KARI ANN; Medina SR HS; Medina, NY; (Y); 1/165; AFS; Concert Band; Mrchg Band; Orch; Nwsp Stf; Yrbk Stf; Lit Mag; Im Badmtn; Im Bowling; Stat Swmmng; FMC Top Chem Stu 85; 1st Pl Orleans Cnty Mock Trl Comptn 84; Honorati 83-85; Jrnlsm.

YOUNG, KAROHN J; Greater New York Acad; Brooklyn, NY; (Y); Drill Tm; Nwsp Phtg; Yrbk Ed-Chief; VP Stu Cncl; Capt Vllybl; Dnfth Awd; Ntl Merit Schol; Aud/Vis; Acadmc All Amer 85; Achvt Awd-Piano Technique 84; Andrews U; Health Psych.

YOUNG, MADELEINE; The Bronx High Schl Science; Hillcrest, NY; (Y); Sec Camera Clb; Office Aide; Science Clb; Teachers Aide; Chorus; Hon Roll; Biochem.

YOUNG, MARLENE D; Valley Stream Central HS; Valley Stream, NY; (Y); AFS; Cmnty Wkr; Drama Clb; Mathletes; Ski Clb; Y-Teens; Band; Chorus; Concert Band; School Musical; Psych.

YOUNG, MARVIN B; Hunter College HS; Queens Village, NY; (Y); Office Aide; Var Bsbl; Var Trk; Jr NHS; Ntl Merit Schol; Bus Admin.

YOUNG, MATTHEW G; Hamburg SR HS; Hamburg, NY; (Y); 14/389; Im Wt Lftg; High Hon Roll; Regents Schlrshp 85; Karr Parker Schlrshp 85; Jr League Bowlng Awds 81-83; SUNY-BUFFALO; Elec Engr.

YOUNG, MICHAEL; Trinity-Pawling HS; Bronx, NY; (Y); Spanish Clb; Varsity Clb; Yrbk Stf; Capt Var Bsbl; Var Ftbl; Capt Var Ice Hcky; Var Socr; Hon Roll; Psychology.

YOUNG, REBECCA; Kenmore West HS; Kenmore, NY; (Y); Girl Scts; Hosp Aide; Math Tm; Stage Crew; Socr; Trk; Cit Awd; Slvr Awd 83; Genesseo ST; Chld Psych.

YOUNG, SANDY; Bronx High Schl Science; Woodside, NY; (Y); Church Yth Grp; Cmnty Wkr; Hosp Aide; Teachers Aide; Yrbk Stf; Lit Mag; Trk; Prfct Atten Awd; Cert Merit Concours Natl De Francais 83-84; PSAL Outdr Trck Mt 5th Pl 400 Mtrs Hrdls 85; Comp Sci.

YOUNG, SCOTT D; Queensbury HS; Glens Falls, NY; (Y); 4/227; Key Clb; Yrbk Phtg; JV Ftbl; Var Capt Swmmng; Var Trk; High Hon Roll; NHS; Rensellaer Polytech Inst Mdlln Math & Sci 83-84; Pres Schlr St Lawrence 85; Regents Schlrshp 85; St Lawrence; Bio.

YOUNG, TAMMY; Fort Plain Central Schl; Fort Plain, NY; (S); Drama Clb; Girl Scts; Library Aide; Office Aide; Varsity Clb; Color Guard; Yrbk Stf; JV Var Socr; JV Var Vllybl; High Hon Roll.

YOUNG, THOMAS; Christian Brothers Acad; Liverpool, NY; (Y); 14/96; NFL; Red Cross Aide; Speech Tm; Chorus; Nwsp Ed-Chief; Yrbk Bus Mgr; Rep Stu Cncl; High Hon Roll; JC Awd; NHS; NY St Regents 85; Brd Of Trustees/Acadmc Schlrshp-Le Moyne Coll 85; Le Moyne Coll-Syracuse NY-BIO.

YOUNG, VANESSA; Riverside HS; Buffalo, NY; (S); 14/206; Cheerleading; Hon Roll; NHS; Studs Reltns Comm 81; Legal Secy.

YOUNG, WAYNE XAVIER; Wyandanch Memorial HS; Wyandanch, NY; (Y); 3/129; Art Clb; Band; Concert Band; Jazz Band; Mrchg Band; Pep Band; High Hon Roll; Hon Roll; Prfct Atten Awd; Rnkd #1 Cls For 2 Yrs 83-84; Awd For Prtcptng In NYIT Erly Start & Brkhvn Labs Engrng Pgms 82-85; NY Inst Of Tech; Chmcl Engrng.

YOUNGHESE, MICHELE; St Johns Preparatory HS; Middle Vlg, NY; (Y); Nwsp Stf; High Hon Roll; Hon Roll; NHS; Bus.

YOUNGS, AMY; Oxford Acad HS; Oxford, NY; (Y); French Clb; Chorus; Yrbk Stf; High Hon Roll; Hon Roll; Prfct Atten Awd; Stu Quarter Awd 85; Merit Awd 85; Spec Recgntn Awd 85; Rhema Bible Coll; Ministry.

YOUNGS, DAWN; Valley Central HS; Montgomery, NY; (Y); Dance Clb; Office Aide; Service Clb; Acpl Chr; Chorus; Capt Color Guard; Drill Tm; School Play; Stage Crew; Tennis; Stu Government Assn Svc Awd 84-85; US Air Force; Law.

YOUREE, DAPHNE; The Knox Schl; St James, NY; (S); 5/32; Art Clb; Church Yth Grp; Drama Clb; Hosp Aide; Math Clb; Spanish Clb; School Musical; School Play; Pres Soph Cls; JV Var Bsktbl; Mst Actv Stu Cncl 83-84; Mst Imprvd Plyr Bsktbll 82-83.

YOVINO, JEANINE; Hauppauge HS; Hauppauge, NY; (Y); Church Yth Grp; Band; Mrchg Band; Orch; School Musical; Stage Crew; Symp Band; High Hon Roll; Hon Roll; NE All-ST Band 84; SCMEA All-Cnty Band 83-84; LI Trng Orch 84-85; Mus.

YOW, ELAINE; Columbia HS; Rensselaer, NY; (Y); Art Clb; Tennis; NHS; Intr Dsgn.

YOX, ROBERT D; Lakeland HS; Yorktown, NY; (Y); 9/300; Rep Soph Cls; Rep Jr Cls; Bsktbl; Var L Socr; Var L Tennis; Ntl Merit Ltr; U VA; Engrng.

YOXALL, THOMAS; Rome Catholic HS; Whitesboro, NY; (Y); 10/80; Cmnty Wkr; Rep Frsh Cls; JV Ftbl; L Var Ice Hcky; JV Lcrss; Im Wt Lftg; High Hon Roll; NEDT Awd; MVP Ice Hockey 83-84; Wnng Goal ST Champnshps Hockey 84-85; Sectn III Titles 81-85, ST Champ 83-85; Phrmcy.

YU, CHARLES; Brooklyn Tech; Elmhurst, NY; (Y); #40 In Class; Computer Clb; JA; Math Clb; Science Clb; Service Clb; Yrbk Rptr; Lit Mag; Jr Cls; Sftbl; High Hon Roll; Cornell U; Cmpt.

YU, JAN H; John F Kennedy HS; New York, NY; (Y); 13/982; Art Clb; Church Yth Grp; Cmnty Wkr; Math Clb; Office Aide; Science Clb; Service Clb; Teachers Aide; Band; Chorus; Acad All-Amer Awd 85; Regents Schlrshp 85; Natl Merit Sci Awd 85; Pre-Med.

YU, LENA W; Kingston HS; Kingston, NY; (Y); 1/520; AFS; Hosp Aide; Trs Science Clb; Orch; Cheerleading; Bausch & Lomb Sci Awd; High Hon Roll; NHS; Harvard Bkk Awd 84; Rensselaer Medl 84.

YU, RANDOLPH; Shenendehowa HS; Clifton Park, NY; (Y); 6/650; NHS; Ntl Merit Ltr; Prfct Atten Awd; Suprior Hnr Roll 82-85; Peer Faciltatr 83-85; Comp Sci.

YU, SHEUNG FUNG; Newtown HS; Elmhurst, NY; (Y); 57/778; Math Tm; Office Aide; Orch; School Play; Nwsp Stf; Yrbk Stf; Hon Roll; Prfct Atten Awd; Nrsng.

YU, TOMMY; Commack H S North; E Northport, NY; (Y); Nwsp Stf; Off Frsh Cls; Off Soph Cls; Off Jr Cls; JV Bsbl; Var Gym; JV Wrstlng; High Hon Roll; VP NHS; Med.

YUAN, ERHMEI; Commack H S South; Commack, NY; (Y); Art Clb; Church Yth Grp; Math Tm; Church Choir; Ed Nwsp Stf; Ed Lit Mag; Var Badmtn; High Hon Roll; NHS; Ntl Art Hnr Scty 85.

YUEN, JUDITH B; Farmingdale HS; Farmingdale, NY; (Y); Science Clb; Church Choir; Yrbk Stf; High Hon Roll; Jr NHS; NHS; Ntl Merit Ltr.

YUN, ANNE; Cold Spring Harbor HS; Laurel Hollow, NY; (Y); 5/136; Exploring; Mathletes; Red Cross Aide; Orch; Yrbk Stf; Var Capt Vllybl; High Hon Roll; Jr NHS; NHS; Prfct Atten Awd; All State Orch 84; Rotry Stu Of Mnth 84; All Conf, Div Vllybl 83; Econ.

YUNG, NANCY; Norman Thomas HS; New York, NY; (S); 8/672; FBLA; NHS; Hon Roll; Prfct Atten Awd; Dynsty Clb; NYU; Comp Sci.

YUNKER, ANNE MARIE; Oakfield-Alabama Central HS; Oakfield, NY; (Y); 1/98; VP AFS; Am Leg Aux Girls St; Sec Drama Clb; Math Clb; Math Tm; Band; Concert Band; Pep Band; NHS; Church Yth Grp; Rep NY John Philip Sousa Ntl 85; U Of R Paidea Awd 85; Cornell; Pre-Med.

YUNKER, TODD; Gates-Chili SR HS; Rochester, NY; (Y); 50/463; Boy Scts; Service Clb; Var Socr; Var Capt Swmmng; Trk; NHS; Dale Mc Mahon Mem Outstndng Ath Awd 85; Monroe Cnty Exec Cmnty Awd 85; Geneseo ST.

YURMAN, JOANNE; Our Lady Of Perpetual Help HS; Brooklyn, NY; (Y); Dance Clb; Gym; High Hon Roll; Scty.

YUSHIMITO, RAMON; Msgr Mc Clancy HS; New York, NY; (Y); 41/214; Art Clb; Library Aide; Office Aide; Pep Clb; Service Clb; Teachers Aide; Varsity Clb; School Play; Var Crs Cntry; Var Trk.

YUSHINSKY, ANDREA; Horseheads HS; Horseheads, NY; (S); 11/407; Church Yth Grp; French Clb; VP JA; JCL; Latin Clb; Chorus; Orch; Hon Roll; NHS; Ntl Merit Ltr; Exch Stu 84; Cum Laude Ntl Latin Exm 82-83; Pre-Law.

YUSTER, DAWN; Bronx High School Of Science; Bayside, NY; (Y); Dance Clb; JA; Office Aide; Teachers Aide; Temple Yth Grp; Band; Var Capt Socr; Var Capt Vllybl; MVP Awd U Santa Clara Vlybl Camp 83; Med.

YUSTER, KEITH L; Hunter College HS; Bayside, NY; (Y); Church Yth Grp; Library Aide; Temple Yth Grp; Y-Teens; Nwsp Rptr; Lit Mag; Var L Bsktbl; L Tennis; Mu Alp Tht; Bsktbl 83-84; Team Sportsmanshp Awd; NY ST Regents Schlrshp 84-85; Valedictorian Bay Terr Jewish Cntr; Rensselaer Polytech:Comp Sci.

YUVIENCO, NICOLE S; Smithtown High School East; Nesconset, NY; (Y); Exploring; Hosp Aide; Off Frsh Cls; Off Soph Cls; Off Jr Cls; High Hon Roll; Hon Roll; NHS; Spanish NHS; Cmnty Wkr; Awd-200 Hrs Hosp Volntr Wrk 85; Med.

YZAGUIRRE, CHARLES R; Mount Saint Michael HS; Bronx, NY; (Y); 20/308; Im Bsktbl; Var L Bowling; L Crs Cntry; Im Sftbl; Hon Roll; NHS; Spanish NHS; Hi-Series Bowling Cty Chmpnshps 84-85; Bus Acctng.

ZABAWA, KIM; Springville-Griffith Inst; Springville, NY; (Y); Church Yth Grp; Hosp Aide; Key Clb; Library Aide; Spanish Clb; Teachers Aide; Chorus; Color Guard; Church Choir; Var Powder Puff Ftbl; Shorthand Awds 84; Outstndng Stu Awd 85; Travel.

ZABEL, C MICHAEL; Canisius HS; Williamsville, NY; (Y); Hosp Aide; VP JA; Model UN; Ski Clb; School Musical; School Play; Yrbk Bus Mgr; Var L Crs Cntry; Var L Trk; Pres Schlr; NY ST Regents Schlrshp 85; Hugh O Brien Ldrshp Awd Semi-Fin 82; Fordham U; Bus.

ZABEL, FREDERICK W; Wilson Central HS; Wilson, NY; (Y); Church Yth Grp; Ski Clb; JV Bsbl; Var Bsktbl; Var Capt Golf; High Hon Roll; Hon Roll; Mech Engrng.

ZABELNY, LISA; Nazareth Acad; Rochester, NY; (S); Hosp Aide; Ski Clb; Chorus; School Musical; Soph Cls; Jr Cls; JV Var Socr; High Hon Roll; Hon Roll; NHS; Magna Cum Laude Awd, Natl Ltn Exm 84.

ZABLE, ILYSE A; Vestal HS; Vestal, NY; (Y); 21/450; Trs Temple Yth Grp; Nwsp Rptr; Nwsp Stf; Rep Frsh Cls; JV Var Bsktbl; High Hon Roll; Hon Roll; NHS; Cmnty Wkr; Ski Clb; Trvl To Israel Smmr Schlrshp 83; Journlsm Awd 85; Cornell U.

ZABLONSKI, MONICA; Immaculate Acad; Hamburg, NY; (Y); Yrbk Stf; Sftbl; Hon Roll; Acctg I Cert Merit 84; Acctg.

ZABRONI, PETER JAMES; St Johns Prep; Brooklyn, NY; (Y); 39/415; Boys Clb Am; Boy Scts; Church Yth Grp; Computer Clb; Library Aide; Bsbl; Bsktbl; Fld Hcky; Ftbl; Score Keeper; St Johns U; Math.

ZACCARDI, ANNMARIE; St Johns Prep; Astoria, NY; (Y); Chorus; School Musical; Stage Crew; Rep Soph Cls; Rep Jr Cls; Rep Stu Cncl; Hon Roll; B Hnr Roll 82; St Johns U; Psychlgy.

ZACCARDO, FILOMENA; Carmel HS; Carmel, NY; (Y); 1/370; Yrbk Stf; Var Capt Socr; Bausch & Lomb Sci Awd; High Hon Roll; NHS; Val; Regetns Schrlshp 85; Rensselaer Polytechnic Inst; Sc.

ZACCARIO, JOHN; Iona Prep; Mamaroneck, NY; (Y); 13/198; Yrbk Stf; Rep Frsh Cls; Rep Stu Cncl; Var Crs Cntry; Ftbl; Capt Trk; High Hon Roll; Hon Roll; Jr NHS; NHS.

ZACEK JR, BRADLEY P; Rome Free Acad; Rome, NY; (Y); Church Yth Grp; Cmnty Wkr; 4-H; Office Aide; Band; Church Choir; 4-H Awd; Hon Roll; Vet.

ZACHARIADIS, CALLY; Bronx High School Of Science; Astoria, NY; (S); Church Yth Grp; Cmnty Wkr; Office Aide; Teachers Aide; Bsktbl; Cheerleading; Tennis; Vllybl; Hon Roll; Prfct Atten Awd; Coll; Teacher.

ZACHER JR, JOHN J; La Salle SR HS; Niagara Falls, NY; (Y); 2/275; Capt Math Tm; Nwsp Ed-Chief; Yrbk Stf; Rep Stu Cncl; Var Bsbl; Var Bsktbl; Var Capt Golf; Pres NHS; Ntl Merit Ltr; Sal.

ZACHER, LAWRENCE; Honeoye HS; Conesus, NY; (S); 4/65; Yrbk Sprt Ed; Pres Frsh Cls; Var Bsbl; Capt Bsktbl; Hon Roll; NHS; Elec Engr.

ZACHMANN, ADRIENE; Shenendehowa HS; Clifton Pk, NY; (Y); Church Yth Grp; Varsity Clb; Band; Orch; Stat Bsktbl; JV Var Fld Hcky; Mgr(s); Score Keeper; JV Var Sftbl; JV Var Vllybl; Phys Educ.

ZACK, DONNA; Amsterdam HS; Amsterdam, NY; (Y); Cmnty Wkr; FBLA; GAA; Political Wkr; Sec Sr Cls; Rep Stu Cncl; Vllybl; Hon Roll; All Cnty Schlrshp 85; Fulton-Montgomery CC; Data Pro.

ZACK, DONNA; Queensbury HS; Glens Falls, NY; (Y); Drama Clb; Key Clb; Band; Chorus; Mrchg Band; School Musical; Yrbk Stf; Stu Cncl; High Hon Roll; Church Yth Grp; Regents Schlrshp 85; SUNY Plattsburg; Nrsg.

ZACK, JUSTIN ROBERT; La Salle Military Acad; Albertson, NY; (Y); 9/92; Computer Clb; Radio Clb; ROTC; Yrbk Phtg; Yrbk Stf; Var Crs Cntry; Wt Lftg; Var High Hon Roll; Jr NHS; NHS; Shooting Awd 82-83; Phys Ftnss Awd 84-85; U AR; Med.

ZACK, SUSAN; Frontier Central HS; Blasdell, NY; (S); 50/600; Drama Clb; French Clb; Quiz Bowl; Ski Clb; Orch; School Musical; Ed Yrbk Phtg; Rep Stu Cncl; Var Mgr(s); Hon Roll; Gold Mdl NYS Sci Fair 82; Polish Clb Treas 83-85; Home Ec Clb VP 82; Syracuse U; Sprts Jrnlsm.

ZADRIMA, LILANA; Aquinas HS; Bronx, NY; (Y); Cmnty Wkr; Exploring; Science Clb; Chorus; School Musical; School Play; Hon Roll; Am Hist Awdd 85; Nrsng.

ZADZILKA, EUGENE W; Lackawanna SR HS; Lackawanna, NY; (Y); 2/270; Am Leg Boys St; Stage Crew; Rep Stu Cncl; NHS; Sal; Letterman Clb; Ski Clb; Spanish Clb; Varsity Clb; School Play; Annl H S Math Exam Awd 85; Schls Awd For Excell In Physcs 85; Elec Engrng.

ZAFFARANO, VICTORIA; Frankfort-Schuyler HS; Frankfort, NY; (S); FBLA; Rep Frsh Cls; Rep Jr Cls; Rep Stu Cncl; JV Var Cheerleading; Vllybl; High Hon Roll; NHS; Suny Oswego; Comp Prog.

ZAFFRANN, RACHEL; Cardinal Mooney HS; Rochester, NY; (Y); Ski Clb; JV Socr; Hon Roll; Pre-Law.

ZAFONTE, BARBARA; G W Hewlett HS; Valley Stream, NY; (Y); 1/400; Church Yth Grp; Cmnty Wkr; Scholastic Bowl; Nwsp Stf; Yrbk Stf; Trk; Hon Roll; NHS; Prfct Atten Awd; Acadmc Bwl 85; Natl Asterean Awd Hnr Socty 85; Gentcs.

ZAGAJESKI II, THOMAS A; Hicksville SR HS; Hicksville, NY; (Y); Computer Clb; Bsbl; NHS; Spanish NHS; Am Leg Boys St; Band; Nwsp Rptr; Yrbk Stf; Trk; Boston Coll; Physcl Thrpst.

ZAGARA, WENDY; Maryvale HS; Chktg, NY; (S); 103/333; Sec DECA; JA; Band; Chorus; Mrchg Band; Stu Cncl; Cheerleading; Hon Roll; DECNY ST Ofcr 84-85; DECA 2nd NYS 85; U NY Buffalo; Bus Admn.

ZAGARELLA, DONNA; Dominican Commercial HS; Cambria Hts, NY; (Y); 109/250; Yrbk Stf; Pres Sr Cls; Rep Stu Cncl; Coach Actv; Sftbl; Vllybl; Hon Roll; MVP Vllybl 84; MVP Vllybl St Marys Trnmnt 83; Sienna Clb; Socl Wrk.

ZAH, GREGORY; Churchille-Chili SR HS; Rochester, NY; (Y); Church Yth Grp; JCL; Latin Clb; Ski Clb; Socr; Hon Roll; Libl Arts.

ZAHLER, MARJORIE; Prishville-Hopkinton Central Schl; Hopkinton, NY; (Y); Yrbk Phtg; Yrbk Stf; Rep Frsh Cls; Pres Soph Cls; Rep Jr Cls; Trs Sr Cls; Var Gym; Var Socr; JV Sftbl; Var Vllybl; Hrbl Mntn In Soccer 83 & 84; Elem Ed.

ZAIDEL, ELIZABETH; C-Pp East HS; Corning, NY; (Y); 32/213; French Clb; Ski Clb; Varsity Clb; Yrbk Sprt Ed; Pres Frsh Cls; Sec Soph Cls; Sec Jr Cls; Sec Sr Cls; Var Capt Swmmng; High Hon Roll; Mst Imprvd Swmmr Awd 82; Bio.

ZAJESKY, JAMES S; Troy HS; Troy, NY; (Y); 84/450; Church Yth Grp; Varsity Clb; Var L Crs Cntry; Var L Trk; High Hon Roll; Hon Roll; NHS; Regnts Schlrshp 84-85; Iona Coll New Rochelle; Engl.

ZAJKOWSKI, RENATA; St Michaels HS; Woodside, NY; (Y); 2/129; Art Clb; Church Yth Grp; Cmnty Wkr; Church Choir; Hon Roll; NHS; NYS Rgnts, Trusteeshp Schlrshps 85-86; NY U; Bus.

ZAK, JENNIFER; Mt Mercy Acad; Buffalo, NY; (Y); Spanish Clb; Church Choir; Yrbk Stf; Sec Sr Cls; JV Swmmng; Hon Roll; NHS; NY Brd Of Rgnts Cert Of Rcgntn 84; 3rd Pl Empire ST Gms Rgnls 83; Notre Dame.

ZAK, JENNIFER NOELLE; Holley Central JR SR HS; Clarendon, NY; (Y); 12/106; Am Leg Aux Girls St; Pres Model UN; School Play; Nwsp Rptr; Yrbk Stf; High Hon Roll; NHS; Rotary Awd; Trs Church Yth Grp; 4-H; NYS Ed-In-Chf, Yth & Govt 83-85; Holley Yth & Govt Clb Pres 83-85; U Prof Lit.

ZAK, KRISTEN; Port Jervis HS; Montague, NJ; (Y); 4/185; Hosp Aide; Varsity Clb; Chorus; Yrbk Stf; Var Trk; High Hon Roll; Trs NHS; Key Clb; Cert Of Merit Spnsh I 82-84; Cert Of Merit Frnch IV 84-85.

ZAKI, CHAHINAZ; Forest Hills HS; Forest Hills, NY; (Y); Aud/Vis; Dance Clb; Debate Tm; Drama Clb; English Clb; Office Aide; Radio Clb; School Musical; School Play; Lit Mag; Yale U; Law.

ZALAT, MARK; Churchville-Chili HS; Rochester, NY; (Y); Math Tm; Model UN; Ski Clb; Band; JV Bsktbl; Var Socr; High Hon Roll; Hon Roll; NHS; Draftng.

ZALBLOCKI, LAURIE ANN; Roy C Ketcham HS; Wappingers Falls, NY; (Y); Cmnty Wkr; Drama Clb; Hosp Aide; Chorus; School Musical; School Play; High Hon Roll; Hon Roll; Prfct Atten Awd; Socl Wrkr.

ZALENSKI, JENNIFER; St Marys HS; Cheektowaga, NY; (S); Church Yth Grp; Science Clb; Rep Soph Cls; Rep Jr Cls; JV Tennis; Gov Hon Prg Awd; High Hon Roll; Jr NHS; NHS; Prfct Atten Awd; Hghst Avg Scl Studies Awd 84; Law.

ZALESAK, MARIANNE G; St Joseph Hill Acad; Staten Island, NY; (Y); 7/103; Cmnty Wkr; Drama Clb; French Clb; Hosp Aide; Teachers Aide; French Hon Soc; High Hon Roll; NHS; Ntl Merit Ltr; NEDT Awd; Comptv & Schlstc Schlrshp Awds St Johns Univ 85-86; St Johns U; Bus Adm.

ZALESKI, JONATHAN; Newfied HS; Selden, NY; (Y); VP Chess Clb; VP Computer Clb; Science Clb; Lit Mag; Lit Merti Awd 85; NYS Rgnts Schlrshp 86; SUNY Albany; Acctng.

ZALEWSKI, BECKY; Immaculata Acad; E Aurora, NY; (Y); Cmnty Wkr; GAA; Political Wkr; Nwsp Rptr; Rep Stu Cncl; Var Bsktbl; Var Sftbl; Var Vllybl; Hon Roll; NEDT Awd; All Star Vllybl Plyr,Stbl Plyr 83-84; Law.

ZALEWSKI, ELIZABETHANN M; Kenmore West SR HS; Tonawanda, NY; (Y); Pres Church Yth Grp; Girl Scts; Band; Concert Band; Mrchg Band; Hon Roll; Scl Wrk.

ZALKIN, GARY S; Spring Valley HS; Spring Valley, NY; (Y); 22/435; Pres Computer Clb; Debate Tm; Letterman Clb; Math Tm; Capt Quiz Bowl; Capt Scholastic Bowl; Nwsp Stf; Var L Trk; French Hon Soc; High Hon Roll; Brandeis U; Law.

ZALKIN, JODY; Liberty Central HS; Liberty, NY; (Y); 8/100; Debate Tm; NFL; Speech Tm; Temple Yth Grp; Nwsp Phtg; Nwsp Rptr; Rep Sr Cls; Var L Tennis; High Hon Roll; Jr NHS; Schlrshp Awd For Jrnlsm 85; NY ST Natl Jrnlsm Wnnr 85; Top 10 In Natl Jrnlsm Cont 85; Acad Awd 84-85; Skidmore Coll; Pre-Med.

ZALMA, ALYSA; Baldwin HS; Baldwin, NY; (S); 9/503; Chorus; Concert Band; Orch; School Musical; Nwsp Stf; High Hon Roll; NHS; Cmnty Wkr; Drama Clb; Library Aide; Schlrshp Bernard Goldberg Flute Wrkshp 84; Gold Mdlst Long Isl Math Fair 83; NY ST All-ST Band 83; Tufts U; Psych.

ZAMAN, FAZIA; W H Taft HS; New York, NY; (Y); Cnsmr Advct Internshp 84; Aristia Soc 83; Mentee At Broux Leganou Hosp 84; Med.

ZAMITES, CAROLLYNN; Our Lady Of Mercy HS; Rochester, NY; (Y); Church Yth Grp; Cmnty Wkr; Hon Roll; Rochester Inst Of Tech; Busnss.

ZAMMATARO, JOHN; Comsewogue HS; Prt Jefferson Sta, NY; (Y); Var Capt Crs Cntry; Var Lcrss; Var Capt Trk; Cvl Engrng.

ZAMMIELLO, LOUIE; John F Kennedy HS; Utica, NY; (Y); Key Clb; Var Capt Bsbl; Var Capt Ftbl; Hon Roll; MVP JV Bsbl 83; Engr.

ZAMMIELLO, ROBERT; Liverpool HS; Liverpool, NY; (S); 204/791; Art Clb; Drama Clb; Chorus; Jazz Band; School Musical; School Play; Swing Chorus; Nwsp Rptr; Rep Stu Cncl; Var Capt Gym; Psych.

ZAMOR, SHEILA; Catherine Mc Auley HS; Brooklyn, NY; (Y); 1/95; French Clb; Nwsp Sprt Ed; Pres Stu Cncl; Capt Bsktbl; Capt Sftbl; Capt Vllybl; Dnfth Awd; Hon Roll; NHS; All Amer Stu Awd 84; Most Valbl Plyr Vllybl 83; Rookie Of The Yr Sftbll 83; NY U; Languages.

ZAMOYTA, RUTH; Saranac Lake HS; Saranac Lake, NY; (Y); 1/134; AFS; Drama Clb; School Play; Lit Mag; Pres Stu Cncl; Var L Bsktbl; Var L Sftbl; Elks Awd; NHS; Val; Regents Schlrshp 85; Womens Civic Chamber Awd 85; Red Letter Awd 85; St Johns U.

ZANCHELLI, MICHAEL T; Clarkstown South HS; Bardonia, NY; (Y); Drama Clb; School Play; Bowling; NYS Rgnts Schlrshp 85; Wake Forest U; Pre Med.

ZANDER, INGRID; St Francis Prep; Jamaica, NY; (Y); 170/700; Church Yth Grp; Cmnty Wkr; Drama Clb; German Clb; Library Aide; Chorus; School Play; Im Sftbl; Ltr Aerbcs Clb 83-84; Fshn Buyer.

ZANDIEH, PEYMAN; St Francis Prep; Whitestone, NY; (S); 26/693; Sec Science Clb; Band; Concert Band; Jazz Band; Mrchg Band; School Musical; Vllybl; High Hon Roll; NHS; All Amer Awd 84-85; Med.

ZANFARDINO, FRED; Woodlands HS; Hartsdale, NY; (Y); Church Yth Grp; Computer Clb; FBLA; Band; Chorus; Hon Roll; Pace U; Accntng.

ZANG, STEVEN C; Arlington HS; Hopewell Junction, NY; (Y); Am Leg Boys St; Var Capt Tennis; High Hon Roll; Natl Tenns Champs 83-85; Rotry Yth Ldrshp Conf 84; Wrtng Awd 85; Brown U; Chem.

ZANINO, MARIA; Fairport HS; Fairport, NY; (Y); Chorus; Im Bsktbl; Im Socr; Im Sftbl; Im Tennis; Im Vllybl; Hon Roll; Librl Arts.

ZANONI, CHRISTOPHER; Sachem HS; Ronkonkuma, NY; (Y); 53/1386; Math Tm; Lit Mag; Hon Roll; Prfct Atten Awd; Engrng.

ZAPATA, LAUREL; St Raymond Acad; Bronx, NY; (Y); #15 In Class; Office Aide; Band; Capt Pom Pon; Hon Roll; Dent.

ZAPATA, RICARDO; Central Ilsip SR HS; Central Islip, NY; (Y); JV Var Socr; High Hon Roll; Hon Roll.

ZAPPA, MARY; Sacred Heart Acad; Malverne, NY; (S); 6/196; FHA; Library Aide; Math Clb; Stage Crew; Rptr Lit Mag; Capt Bowling; Hon Roll; NHS; Office Aide; Pres Christn Life Comm 83-85.

ZAPPALA, ROSANNA; Bishop Grimes HS; N Syracuse, NY; (Y); FBLA; Sec Sr Cls; Bsktbl; Var Socr; JV Trk; NHS; AHSA Amer H S Ath 85; Hmrm Rep 82-85; Hmcmng Queen 82-83; Lencoyne Coll; Acctng.

ZAPPALA, ROSE; Henninger HS; Syracuse, NY; (Y); 49/350; Church Yth Grp; Intnl Clb; JA; Pep Clb; Rep Jr Cls; Trs Sr Cls; Hon Roll; Jr NHS; NHS; Le Moyne; CPA.

ZAPPULLA, GINA; St Peters Girls HS; Staten Isl, NY; (Y); Drama Clb; Hosp Aide; Math Clb; Spanish Clb; Church Choir; Yrbk Stf; Pres Frsh Cls; VP Jr Cls; Cheerleading; Hon Roll; FL ST; Optmtry.

ZARELLI, SUE; Gloversville HS; Gloversville, NY; (Y); 75/226; Rep Stu Cncl; Stat Bsktbl; Stat Ftbl; Powder Puff Ftbl; Im Trk; Hudson Vly Comm Coll; Bus.

ZARETSKY, ADAM; Onteora Central Schl; West Hurley, NY; (S); 28/218; Art Clb; Math Tm; School Play; Hon Roll; NHS; NYS Math League Cert Of Merit 83.

ZARIN, GLENN; East Meadow HS; East Meadow, NY; (S); Computer Clb; Hosp Aide; Library Aide; Nwsp Stf; Ed Lit Mag; Trk; Hon Roll; NHS; Ntl Merit Ltr; Med.

ZARINSKY, VALERIA; F D R M S HS; Brooklyn, NY; (Y); Computer Clb; Dance Clb; English Clb; Math Clb; Var Jr Cls; Var Badmtn; Swmmng; JETS Awd; NYU; Comp.

ZARITSKY, DAVID; Middletown HS; Middletown, NY; (Y); Ski Clb; Pres Temple Yth Grp; Band; School Musical; School Play; Nwsp Ed-Chief; Nwsp Rptr; Yrbk Phtg; Lit Mag; Wt Lftg; Bus Mgmt.

ZARZYNSKI, ROB; Union Endicott HS; Endicott, NY; (S); 7/430; Boys Clb Am; Varsity Clb; Var L Ftbl; Engr.

ZASADA, JOHN R; Chittenango Central HS; Bridgeport, NY; (Y); 31/200; Am Leg Boys St; French Clb; Varsity Clb; Band; Concert Band; Jazz Band; Orch; School Musical; Rep Frsh Cls; Rep Soph Cls; Oneida Daily Disptch Athlt Of Wk Tennis 84-85; Tri-Vly Lgu & All Star & Champ 85; RIT; Bus.

ZASTAWRNY, CHRIS; Greece Athena SR HS; Rochester, NY; (Y); 8/281; JA; Math Clb; Science Clb; Var L Bsbl; High Hon Roll; Hon Roll; NHS; St Schlr; RIT Alumni Schlrshp; Rochester Inst Tech; Chrprctr.

ZASTAWRNY, CHRISTOPHER P; Greece Athena HS; Rochester, NY; (Y); 8/280; JA; Math Tm; Science Clb; Var Bsbl; NHS; Pres Schlr; St Schlr; Rochester Inst Tech; Sci.

ZASTROW, LAUREL; Fredonia Central HS; Fredonia, NY; (Y); Church Yth Grp; Cmnty Wkr; FTA; Hosp Aide; Service Clb; Spanish Clb; Teachers Aide; Nwsp Rptr; Yrbk Stf; High Hon Roll; YES Plaque 83; Socl Wrk.

ZATLUKAL, ELLEN M; Mount Mercy Acad; West Seneca, NY; (Y); 1/200; Trs Church Yth Grp; Computer Clb; JCL; Model UN; Quiz Bowl; Scholastic Bowl; High Hon Roll; NHS; Pres Schlr; Val; Amer H S Math Exam Awd 84; Clsscl Assn W NY Latn II 2nd 83; Canisuis Acdmc Merit Schlr; Canisius Coll.

ZAVA, MARY; Nazareth Acad; Rochester, NY; (Y); Yrbk Stf; JV Bsktbl; Vllybl; Hon Roll; NHS; Schlrshp Nazarth Acad 82-83; Itln Clb Offcr 84-85; Sci.

ZAVAGNIN, ANNMARIE; Kings Park SR HS; Ft Salonga, NY; (Y); 120/393; Office Aide; Hon Roll; Readng Fundmntl 85.

ZAWALSKI, GAVIN W; Oriskany Central HS; Oriskany, NY; (Y); 2/90; Drama Clb; Mathletes; Model UN; Band; Yrbk Ed-Chief; Bausch & Lomb Sci Awd; High Hon Roll; Trs Jr NHS; VP NHS; Sal; Clarkson; Engrng.

ZAWTOCKI, PAM; Little Falls JR SR HS; Little Falls, NY; (Y); 42/119; FBLA; FHA; Girl Scts; Spanish Clb; Band; Concert Band; Flag Corp; Mrchg Band; School Play; Hon Roll; Bryant & Stratton; Bus Adm.

ZAYAC, KELLY; Binghamton HS; Binghamton, NY; (Y); 51/487; Am Leg Aux Girls St; Cmnty Wkr; Key Clb; Ski Clb; Acpl Chr; Chorus; School Musical; Lit Mag; Sec Jr Cls; Sec Sr Cls; Elmira Coll Key Awd 84; U Of VT; Intl Med.

ZAYAS, KATHERINE; Msgr Scanlan HS; Bronx, NY; (Y); Church Yth Grp; Cmnty Wkr; French Clb; Political Wkr; Church Choir; School Play; Nwsp Rptr; VP Jr Cls; French Hon Soc; Prfct Atten Awd; Frnch Hnrs 82; Attndnc-Punctlty 82; Badmntn Gym 84; Berkeley Schls; Bus Adm.

ZAYATZ, PAUL D; North Tonawanda HS; N Tonawanda, NY; (Y); Am Leg Boys St; Cmnty Wkr; Varsity Clb; Var L Bsbl; Coach Actv; High Hon Roll; NHS; Jr NHS; All Leag Bsbl 85; Marine Physcl Ftns Awd 84; Jesse Owens Games Sprint Fnlst 83; Aviatn.

ZAZYCKI, THERESE; Immaculata Acad; Irving, NY; (Y); 28/76; 4-H; French Clb; Hosp Aide; Nwsp Stf; Yrbk Stf; Hon Roll; Mst Crtv Wrtr JR Cls 84; Merits Engl & Frnch; SUNY Geneseo; Comm.

ZAZZERI, CHRISTINE; Newfield HS; Seldne, NY; (Y); Band; Chorus; Concert Band; Mrchg Band; Orch; Pep Band; School Musical; Hon Roll; Jr NHS; Prfct Atten Awd; Marywood Coll; Music Thrpy.

ZDIMAL, MICHELLE; Binghamton HS; Binghamton, NY; (Y); VP Church Yth Grp; Key Clb; Ski Clb; Band; VP Stu Cncl; Mgr(s); JV Var Socr; JV Var Vllybl; High Hon Roll; NHS; Salute Yth 85; Phy Thrpst.

ZDRAHAL, KATERINA; Shenendehowa HS; Rexford, NY; (Y); 19/650; English Clb; Ski Clb; Concert Band; High Hon Roll; Prncpls Awd For Hnr Stu; Certs Of Schltc Achvt.

ZDUNCZYK, CHERYL M; Columbia HS; Castleton, NY; (Y); 95/355; Church Yth Grp; Dance Clb; Debate Tm; Fld Hcky; Trk; Hon Roll; NY ST Regents Schlrshp 85; SUNY Coll Brockport.

ZEAFLA, DOREEN L; Pioneer HS; Yorkshire, NY; (Y); 1/100; Church Yth Grp; Hst FBLA; Rep Frsh Cls; Rep Soph Cls; Rep Jr Cls; Bsktbl; Hon Roll; Bus Admin.

ZECCA, ANTONELLA; St Francis Prep; Flushing, NY; (S); 54/693; Hon Roll; Opt Clb Awd; Accntng.

ZEHNER, CAROLYN; Greenport HS; Greenport, NY; (Y); 1/51; Math Clb; Spanish Clb; School Musical; Nwsp Ed-Chief; Tennis; Vllybl; High Hon Roll; NHS; Ntl Merit Ltr; Val; MA Inst Tech.

ZEHR, DENISE R; Beaver Rivr Central Schl; Castorland, NY; (Y); 8/90; Church Yth Grp; High Hon Roll; Pres NHS; GAA; Girl Scts; Acpl Chr; Chorus; School Musical; Swing Chorus; Mgr(s); Gftd & Tlntd Prog 83-84; Suny Upstate Med Ctr; Rad Tech.

ZEILER, KAREN J; Mahopac HS; Mahopac, NY; (Y); 8/386; Church Yth Grp; Math Tm; Band; Orch; High Hon Roll; Lion Awd; NHS; Concert Band; Mrchg Band; Sound Of Amer Hnr Bnd European Tour 84; NYS Area-All ST Bnd 83-84; Assem Of God Teen Tlnt NE Reg Wn; Suny Potsdam Crane Schl Of Msc.

ZEITLER, ALEXANDRA; Seaford HS; Seaford, NY; (Y); 9/246; Band; Concert Band; Mrchg Band; Nwsp Stf; Yrbk Stf; Var Cheerleading; Coach Actv; Capt Twrlr; High Hon Roll; Sec NHS; Regents Schlrshp 85; Marine Corps Schrlshp 85; Colagte U; Lawyer.

ZELASKO, KATHY; Mount Mercy Acad; Buffalo, NY; (Y); Science Clb; Church Choir; Yrbk Stf; Rep Sr Cls; Im Bowling; Hon Roll; Brnt & Strttn Bus Schl; Secy.

ZELAZNY, LINDA; Walt Whitman HS; Huntington Stat, NY; (Y); 4-H; JV Fld Hcky; PTA Awd Outstdng Acad Imprvmnt 84-85; Awds For Hrs Bck Rdng; C W Post; Bus Mgmt.

ZELICOF, AUDREY; Stuyvesant HS; Forest Hills, NY; (Y); Cmnty Wkr; Computer Clb; French Clb; German Clb; Hosp Aide; Latin Clb; Library Aide; Math Clb; Math Tm; Science Clb; Westnghse Sci Tlnt Srch Wnnr 85; Foundr Publctn Anml Welf 84-85; JR Acad Sci Comp Wnnr 85; Harvard; Med.

ZELL, DEBBIE; Coloniel Central HS; Albany, NY; (Y); Ski Clb; Chorus; Color Guard; Mrchg Band; Orch; Hon Roll; Schenectady CC; Comp Acctng.

ZELLAR, RONALD S; James E Sperry HS; Henrietta, NY; (Y); 42/327; Am Leg Boys St; Boy Scts; Political Wkr; Thesps; Chorus; Crs Cntry; Trk; Hon Roll; Jr NHS; Regnts Schlrshp 85.

ZELLER, CYNTHIA M; Vernon-Verona-Sherrill Central HS; Verona, NY; (Y); 28/240; Church Yth Grp; Dance Clb; Sec Trs 4-H; Quiz Bowl; 4-H Awd; High Hon Roll; Hon Roll; NHS; Oneida Natl Bankers Calf Awd 83; Royson N Whipple Scholar 85; Dollars For Schlrs Scholar 85; Morrisville Ag & Tech; Dairy.

ZELLER, ROBERT; Augsburgh American HS; A P O New York, NY; (Y); 4/63; Cmnty Wkr; VP Letterman Clb; Trs Stu Cncl; VP Ftbl; VP Capt Socr; High Hon Roll; NHS; Church Yth Grp; Drama Clb; Chorus; Pres Schlr 85; Natl Hispnc Schlr 85; Vrsty All-Conf Sccr; Ftbl Off & Def; Georgetown U; Gov.

ZELLNER, DOROTHY; Walter Panas HS; Peekskill, NY; (Y); Cmnty Wkr; Drama Clb; Teachers Aide; Chorus; School Musical; School Play; Stage Crew; Stu Cncl; High Hon Roll; NHS; Albany SUNY; Soc Svcs.

ZELLO, GARY; Waverly JR SR HS; Waverly, NY; (Y); Boy Scts; Church Yth Grp; Cmnty Wkr; Computer Clb; Exploring; Math Clb; Band; Concert Band; Jazz Band; Mrchg Band; Nuc Pwr.

ZELTMANN, CAROL; General Brown HS; Dexter, NY; (Y); 45/133; JCL; Chorus; Stage Crew; Variety Show; Yrbk Stf; Stat Bsktbl; Var Socr; JV Sftbl; Hmnts Schlrshp 85; Ntl Ltn Exam Cum Laude Awd 84; D Youville; Creative Wrtng.

ZEMANEK, LAURA; Johnstown HS; Johnstown, NY; (Y); Drama Clb; Band; Chorus; Jazz Band; School Musical; School Play; Variety Show; Tennis; High Hon Roll; Hon Roll; Perf Arts.

ZENTNER, KAREN; John A Coleman HS; Stone Ridge, NY; (Y); French Clb; Key Clb; JV Bsktbl; JV Vllybl; Engl.

ZENTZ, LISETTE; Oakfield-Alabama HS; Basom, NY; (Y); Art Clb; Dance Clb; Teachers Aide; Color Guard; Cheerleading; Hon Roll; Human Svcs.

ZERAFA, ANDREA; Cardinal Spellman HS; Bronx, NY; (Y); Church Yth Grp; Cmnty Wkr; 2nd Hnrs; Acctg.

ZERBARINI, LYNN-MARIE N; Manhasset JR-SR HS; Manhasset, NY; (Y); 40/200; Church Yth Grp; Service Clb; Chorus; Church Choir; Orch; School Musical; School Play; Lit Mag; High Hon Roll; Dance Clb; Wnnr Span Essay Cntst Hofstra U 85; Barnard Coll; Spanish.

ZERBE, DANIEL; Unatego Central HS; Otego, NY; (Y); 2/89; Am Leg Boys St; Band; Church Choir; VP Sr Cls; Var Ftbl; Var Wrstlng; High Hon Roll; NHS; Dr Sutton Awd, Hghst Stndng Comb Rgnts Kellogg Prz, Unatego Tchrs Assn Schlrshp Awd 85; Houghton Coll; Pre Med.

ZERBE, TAMARA; Unatego JR SR HS; Otego, NY; (Y); Church Yth Grp; Cmnty Wkr; Hosp Aide; Ski Clb; Church Choir; Concert Band; Orch; JV Vllybl; High Hon Roll; NHS; Spec Ed.

ZERBO, MICHAEL; Ossining HS; Ossining, NY; (Y); JV Var Bsbl; JV Var Ftbl; Var Mgr(s); JV Var Wt Lftg; High Hon Roll; Hon Roll; Navy Boot Cmp 85; Nvl ROTC; US Nvl Aviator.

ZERBY, DANAE; Frontier Central HS; Hamburg, NY; (Y); Sec Aud/Vis; Boy Scts; Exploring; French Clb; Pres Girl Scts; Hosp Aide; Red Cross Aide; Color Guard; Stu Cncl; Mgr(s); Var Lttr For Rfl Mgr 85; Nrsng.

ZERRAHN, KAREN; George W Fowler HS; Syracuse, NY; (S); #1 In Class; Nwsp Rptr; Yrbk Stf; Bausch & Lomb Sci Awd; High Hon Roll; NHS; Val; Chem Awd 84; Earth Sci Awd 82; Engr.

ZERVOPOULOS, ALEXANDRA; Nazareth Regional HS; Brooklyn, NY; (Y); Church Yth Grp; Girl Scts; Math Tm; Yrbk Sprt Ed; Yrbk Stf; Hon Roll; NHS; Regents Schlrshp 85; WSUC Schlrshp 85; NYU Schl Of Arts & Sci; Bus.

ZESCHKE, DEBRA; W Irondequoit HS; Rochester, NY; (Y); 80/395; French Clb; Intnl Clb; Ski Clb; Varsity Clb; School Musical; Rep Frsh Cls; Rep Soph Cls; Rep Jr Cls; Rep Sr Cls; Var L Gym; PSYCH.

ZGALJIC, MILICA; Long Island City HS; Astoria, NY; (Y); 8/579; Church Yth Grp; School Play; Nwsp Rptr; Trs Sr Cls; Var Tennis; High Hon Roll; Teachers Aide; Church Choir; Cit Awd; NHS; Regents Schlrshp 85; Hunter Coll Schlrshp 85; Italian Tchrs Awd 82-84; Hunter Coll; Comm.

ZHAO, HONG LEUNG; Newtown HS; Flushing, NY; (Y); 37/772; Computer Clb; English Clb; FBLA; JA; JCL; Math Clb; Quiz Bowl; Science Clb; Service Clb; Teachers Aide; Cert Of Awd Schlrshp 84-85; Cert Of Merit Outstndng Schlrshp Keybrdg 85; NY U; Acctg.

ZIAKAS, HELEN; Eastridge HS; Rochester, NY; (Y); 2/226; Pres Red Cross Aide; Color Guard; Concert Band; Pres Yrbk Stf; Fld Hcky; Vllybl; High Hon Roll; NHS; Sal; Church Yth Grp; Paideia Awd 85; Hghst Scr MAA Exam 85.

ZIBBON, LISA; Alden SR HS; Alden, NY; (Y); 36/198; FTA; Science Clb; Spanish Clb; Chorus; Church Choir; School Play; Yrbk Stf; Socr; High Hon Roll; NHS; Liberty U; Elem Educ.

ZIC, MARIA; St Johns Prep; Astoria, NY; (Y); Trk; Hunter Coll; Hstry.

ZICARI, MARGARET; Nazareth Acad; Rochester, NY; (Y); 13/114; Chorus; School Musical; Trs Soph Cls; VP Rep Stu Cncl; DAR Awd; High Hon Roll; NHS; VFW Awd; Presdntl Acadmc Ftnss Awd 85; Monroe Cty Exec Cmnty Awd 85; Siena Coll; Math.

ZIEBARTH, PAUL; Commack High School North; E Northport, NY; (Y); Sec Church Yth Grp; MMM; Chorus; School Musical; Swing Chorus; Ftbl; High Hon Roll; Hon Roll; All Cnty Chorus 84; Pre-Law.

ZIEG, DAVID; Roy C Ketcham HS; Poughkeepsie, NY; (Y); VP Church Yth Grp; Capt Ftbl; High Hon Roll; Jr NHS; NHS; Landscape Arch.

ZIEGER, PAUL; St Marys Boys HS; New Hyde Park, NY; (S); 9/134; Math Tm; Rep Frsh Cls; Rep Soph Cls; Var Capt Bsbl; JV Var Bsktbl; Coach Actv; Var Capt Socr; High Hon Roll; Jr NHS; NHS; MVP Bsbl 84; Deacon Awd 84.

ZIEGLER, CHRISTINA; Delaware Valley Central HS; Callicoon, NY; (S); 6/38; Drama Clb; Chorus; School Play; Yrbk Stf; Rep Frsh Cls; Pres Soph Cls; Pres Jr Cls; Pres Sr Cls; Stu Cncl; Cheerleading; Awd Outstndng Sophmore 82; Awd Outstndng Jr 83; Phys Therapist.

ZIEGLER, KRISTINE M; Rome Free Acad; Rome, NY; (Y); 102/536; Hosp Aide; Band; Mrchg Band; Pep Band; Nwsp Rptr; Rep Frsh Cls; JV Fld Hcky; Hon Roll; Jr NHS; NHS; Rome Free Acad Cert Svc 85; Cortland ST; Pre-Med.

ZIELINSKI, PATRICIA; East Meadow HS; East Meadow, NY; (S); 38/414; Pres Science Clb; Pres Chorus; Yrbk Phtg; Ed Yrbk Stf; Exploring; FBLA; School Musical; All Cnty Chrs 82; Oswego; Zoolgy.

ZIEMBA, KENNETH S; Lakeland HS; Yorktown, NY; (Y); Exploring; JA; Chorus; Yrbk Stf; Pres Jr Cls; Capt Bsktbl; Capt Ftbl; Capt Lcrss; Capt Socr; Hon Roll.

ZIEMER, LAURA L; West Seneca West SR HS; Cheektowaga, NY; (Y); #16 In Class; Cmnty Wkr; English Clb; Girl Scts; Service Clb; Teachers Aide; Hon Roll; JC Awd; Regents Schlrshp 85; D Youville Coll; Specl Ed.

ZIEMS, FREDERICK; Earl L Vandermeulen HS; Mt Sinai, NY; (Y); French Clb; FBLA; Ski Clb; Varsity Clb; Chorus; Yrbk Stf; Var Crs Cntry; Ftbl; Var Trk; Wrstlng; 5th Pl-Trck Intermed Hurdls 84; Pre Law.

ZIENTARA, DAVID; Cardinal Mooney HS; Rochester, NY; (Y); 7/317; Church Yth Grp; Cmnty Wkr; Band; Concert Band; School Musical; Variety Show; High Hon Roll; Hon Roll; NHS; Lat Hnr Soc 82-84; Rock Band 84-85.

ZIESE, SHARON; Newfield HS; Selden, NY; (Y); Aud/Vis; Computer Clb; Girl Scts; Hosp Aide; Library Aide; Office Aide; High Hon Roll; Hon Roll; Attndnce Awd 83-85; Psych.

ZIFF, LORI; Oyster Bay HS; Oyster Bay, NY; (Y); Drama Clb; Letterman Clb; Model UN; Spanish Clb; Temple Yth Grp; Band; Concert Band; Mrchg Band; Pep Band; School Musical; Bus.

ZIGON, MARIANNE; Central Islip SR HS; Central Islip, NY; (Y); Office Aide; Chorus; Nwsp Stf; Ed Yrbk Stf; VP Frsh Cls; VP Soph Cls; Trs Jr Cls; Stu Cncl; JV Tennis; Hon Roll; Rcgnzd For Outstndng Achvt In Tolerton & Hood Essay Comp 85; SUNY-ALBANY; CPA.

ZIMBARDI, VINCENT; Cattaravgus Central HS; Gowanda, NY; (Y); Boy Scts; Ski Clb; Varsity Clb; Band; Mrchg Band; JV Bsktbl; Var Ftbl; Var Trk; SUNY; Bus Admin.

ZIMBER, SCOTT P; Leroy Central HS; Leroy, NY; (Y); 40/144; Letterman Clb; Ski Clb; Varsity Clb; Yrbk Phtg; Stu Cncl; Var L Ftbl; Var L Wrstlng; High Hon Roll; Monroe CC; Elec Engrng.

ZIMBRICH, URSULA; Greece Athena HS; Rochester, NY; (Y); 32/260; German Clb; Math Tm; Ski Clb; Chorus; High Hon Roll; Hon Roll; NHS; Secndry Ed.

ZIMMER, CAROL E; Webster SR HS; Webster, NY; (Y); Pres Church Yth Grp; Pres Drama Clb; FBLA; Office Aide; Pres Thesps; Pres Acpl Chr; Chorus; Church Choir; Madrigals; Orch; Outstndng Stu Awds In Music & Drama; Music.

ZIMMER, KENNETH J; Amherst Central HS; Amherst, NY; (Y); 40/320; Model UN; Pep Clb; Quiz Bowl; Chorus; Madrigals; School Musical; Stu Cncl; VP Capt Socr; Trk; Hon Roll; Soccer All-Div 84-85; Soccer Mc Donalds Plyr Of Wk 84-85; S M Flickinger Benevolent Fund Schlrshp 85; Holy Cross; Pol Sci.

ZIMMER, LISA A; Kenmore West SR HS; Kenmore, NY; (Y); Church Yth Grp; Dance Clb; Girl Scts; PAVAS; Ski Clb; Variety Show; Cheerleading; Gym; Trk; Vllybl.

ZIMMER JR, PETER A; Bishop Timon HS; Buffalo, NY; (Y); Nwsp Rptr; Nwsp Stf; Yrbk Bus Mgr; Yrbk Ed-Chief; Rep Stu Cncl; Hon Roll; NHS; Recvd Schlrshp Bishop Timon H S 82-86; Cmmnctns.

ZIMMER, TODD J; John H Glenn HS; East Northport, NY; (Y); Science Clb; Nwsp Stf; Lit Mag; Bus Mgt.

ZIMMER, VALERIE; Schoharie Central HS; West Berne, NY; (S); 7/94; Sec Computer Clb; Ski Clb; School Musical; VP Pres Stu Cncl; Var Socr; Var Trk; High Hon Roll; NHS; Engr.

ZIMMERMAN, CORY; The Bronx High School Of Science; Floral Park, NY; (S); Pres Cmnty Wkr; Teachers Aide; Temple Yth Grp; Band; Rep Sr Cls; Capt L Bsbl; NHS; 3rd Prz NY Cty Assoc Tchrs Of Engl Essay Cntst 82; Outstndng Acad Achvt Awd 84; NY Cty Math Fair 82.

ZIMMERMAN, DAVE; Niagara Falls HS; Niagara Falls, NY; (Y); Nwsp Phtg; Capt Ice Hcky; Socr; Brockport ST; Pilot.

ZIMMERMAN, DEBORAH ANN; Ward Melville HS; Stony Brook, NY; (Y); 43/760; Drama Clb; French Clb; GAA; Ski Clb; Spanish Clb; School Play; Nwsp Rptr; Var Swmmng; High Hon Roll; NHS; Am Assn Of Frnch Tchrs Ntl Cntst-Long Island Top 10 81-84; NY St Schl Music Assn-Excllnt Rtng 84; IN U; Bus.

ZIMMERMAN, HEIDI; Martin Van Buren HS; Queens, NY; (Y); 83/579; JA; Key Clb; Library Aide; School Musical; Stage Crew; Var Bowling; Socr; Hon Roll; NHS; Prfct Atten Awd; Frstry Mgmt.

ZIMMERMAN, RONNIE; Our Lady Of Victory HS; Tappan, NY; (S); 14/159; Church Yth Grp; NHS; Spanish NHS; NEDT Cert 84; Teachg.

ZIMMERMAN, TODD; Royalton-Hartland HS; Gasport, NY; (Y); 15/130; Am Leg Boys St; Varsity Clb; Pres Band; Chorus; Concert Band; Drill Tm; Drm & Bgl; Jazz Band; Mrchg Band; Pep Band; Natl Merit Fndtn 85; U Buffalo; Law.

ZIMMERMAN, UZI; East Meadow HS; East Meadow, NY; (S); Debate Tm; Mathletes; Jazz Band; Mrchg Band; Symp Band; Bsbl; Crs Cntry; Tennis; NHS; Mc Donalds Tri-ST Jazz Ensmbl Alt 85; Hugh O Brien Yth Fndtn 84; NYSSMA All ST 85.

ZIMMERMANN, BEATRIZ; Academy Of Mt St Ursula; Bronx, NY; (Y); Nwsp Stf; Spanish NHS; Spnsh Lang Advncd Plcmnt Exam 84-85; Spnsh Lit Adv Plcmnt Exam 84-85; Annl Frgn Lang Cont 83-84; Comm Art.

ZIMMERMANN, JOHN; Tonawanda SR HS; Tonawanda, NY; (Y); Boy Scts; Var Ftbl; Finance.

ZINCONE, CHRISTOPHER E; Lynbrook HS; Lynbrook, NY; (Y); Speech Tm; VP Band; Stat Concert Band; Jazz Band; Mrchg Band; Orch; Pep Band; School Musical; Lit Mag; Hon Roll; Arion Awd Excl Bnd 86; All County Bnd 1st Alto 2nd Alto Sax 82 & 83; Law.

ZINGA, SUZANNE; Liverpool HS; Liverpool, NY; (Y); Var Trk; Ntl Merit Ltr; Psych.

ZINGARO, LINDA; Liverpool HS; Liverpool, NY; (Y); Church Yth Grp; Exploring; Im Powder Puff Ftbl; Hon Roll; Jr NHS; Acctng.

ZINGEL, GABRIELA; Dewitt Clinton HS; Bronx, NY; (Y); Church Yth Grp; Cmnty Wkr; Service Clb; Teachers Aide; Concert Band; Nwsp Ed-Chief; Nwsp Phtg; Hon Roll; NHS; Prfct Atten Awd; City Coll; Med.

ZINK, KARL; Ralph Mc Kee HS; Staten Is, NY; (Y); 130/280; JV Var Ftbl; JV Trk; Wrstlng; Cit Awd; Atndnc Awd 83-85.

ZINK, REBECCA; Greenwich Central HS; Greenwich, NY; (Y); 4-H; Band; Jazz Band; Yrbk Stf; Rep Cmnty Wkr; JV Fld Hcky; Var Trk; High Hon Roll; NHS; School Musical; Hugh O Brian NY N Ldrshp Smnr 84.

ZINO, THERESA; St Francis Prep; Howard Beach, NY; (Y); 359/693; Stage Crew; Nwsp Stf; Alvernian Drama Society Awd 84-85; Spanish Hnrs 84-85; Bus Comm.

ZINSERLING, CRAIG; Liverpool HS; Liverpool, NY; (S); Church Yth Grp; Jazz Band; Mrchg Band; Orch; School Musical; Symp Band; Bsktbl; High Hon Roll; Jr NHS; NHS; Bus Adm.

ZIOLKO, DEBORAH A; Lackawanna SR HS; Lackawanna, NY; (Y); #4 In Class; VP French Clb; GAA; Office Aide; Ski Clb; Stu Cncl; Socr; Sftbl; High Hon Roll; NHS; NYS Rgnts Schlrshp 85; SUNY Buffalo; Phy Thrpy.

ZIOLKOWSKI, DON; St Marys HS; S Cheektowaga, NY; (S); 27/202; Computer Clb; Exploring; Model UN; Quiz Bowl; Science Clb; Varsity Clb; Nwsp Rptr; Nwsp Stf; Lit Mag; Var L Crs Cntry; MVP, MIP Trck & Crss Cntry; MI ST U; Mech Engr.

ZIPNICK, DEBORAH; Newfield HS; Selden, NY; (Y); Camera Clb; Dance Clb; Drama Clb; Temple Yth Grp; Chorus; School Musical; JV Cheerleading; Jr NHS; VP NHS; Spanish NHS; Presdntl Physcl Fitnss Awd 85; Gftd/Tlntd Pgm 82-85; UCLA; TV Brdcstng.

ZIPPRICH, DIANE M; Arlington HS; Hopewell Junction, NY; (Y); 6/620; Orch; Ntl Merit SF; ACTR Gold Mdlst 84; Mary Lou Gotsch Mem Sprtsmnshp Awd 83; Natl High Sch Slavic Hnr Soc 84; Pre Med.

ZIRKEL, TIMOTHY Z; Holy Trinity HS; Hicksville, NY; (S); Exploring; Math Clb; Math Tm; Teachers Aide; Stu Cncl; JV Ftbl; Hon Roll; Hofstra; Comp.

ZIRPOLI, ROSE MARIA; Mt Mercy Acad; Buffalo, NY; (Y); Stage Crew; Cheerleading; Comp Pgmmg.

ZISELAMN, CYNTHIA; Springfield Gardens HS; Rosedale, NY; (Y); 54/443; Teachers Aide; Temple Yth Grp; Nwsp Rptr; Nwsp Stf; Prfct Atten Awd; NYC Super Yth 85; Jrnlsm.

ZISHOLTZ, IAN; Long Beach HS; Long Beach, NY; (S); 17/320; Computer Clb; Drama Clb; School Musical; School Play; High Hon Roll; Hon Roll; NHS; Awds Sci Rsrch 82; 3rd Pl Sci Cngrs 82; 3rd Pl Sci Fair 82; NY U; Prfrmng Arts.

ZISKIN, MARY BETH; Amsterdam HS; Amsterdam, NY; (S); Band; Concert Band; Orch; Symp Band; High Hon Roll; Music.

ZITO, WENDY L; La Salle SR HS; Niagara Fls, NY; (Y); 76/320; Drama Clb; Office Aide; Thesps; Pres Chorus; School Musical; School Play; Sec Stu Cncl; Var Bsktbl; Vllybl; Hon Roll; Troubadour Awd 85; Outstndng Charctrztn Awd; Geraldine J Mann Schrlshp 85; Niagara U; Theatre.

ZITTEL, LARA W; Ralph J Davis HS; Conesus, NY; (Y); Band; Chorus; Concert Band; Mrchg Band; School Musical; Yrbk Bus Mgr; Stu Cncl; Dr D Woodruff Dntl Awd Schlrshp; Monroe CC; Bio.

ZIVANCEV, MELANIE; Christopher Columbus HS; Brooklyn, NY; (S); 6/676; Dance Clb; Drama Clb; Scholastic Bowl; Teachers Aide; Cit Awd; Hon Roll; NCTE Awd; NHS; Prfct Atten Awd; Sarah Lawrence Coll; Comm.

ZIZZI, PERRY V; Orishany Central HS; Oriskany, NY; (Y); 1/89; Drama Clb; Model UN; Political Wkr; Band; Nwsp Ed-Chief; Yrbk Ed-Chief; Sec Stu Cncl; Pres Jr NHS; Val; Key Clb; Leopold Schepp Fndtn Schlrshp; Chch St Stephen Womns Guild Awd; Georgetown U; Govt.

ZMOLIL, DIANE; Midwood HS; Brooklyn, NY; (Y); Girl Scts; Teachers Aide; Color Guard; Twrlr; Wood Schl; Bus.

ZOBRIST, TAMMY LYNN; Kensington HS; Buffalo, NY; (Y); Computer Clb; Trs FNA; Science Clb; Yrbk Stf; Stu Cncl; Hon Roll; Red Cross Aide; ST Modern Miss Philosophy Pgnt 85; Cornell U; Pre-Med.

ZOCCHI, STEFANIE; Maria Regina HS; Yonkers, NY; (Y); 56/127; Dance Clb; Girl Scts; Y-Teens; Hon Roll; Elizabeth Seton Coll; Dsgnr.

ZODIKOFF, MICHELE A; Homer Central HS; Homer, NY; (Y); 43/207; French Clb; Temple Yth Grp; Stage Crew; JV Tennis, JV Vllybl; High Hon Roll; Hon Roll; Regents Coll Schlrshp 85; SUNY Cortland; Psychology.

ZOERB, CHARLES; Frontier Central HS; Hamburg, NY; (Y); Boy Scts; Church Yth Grp; Latin Clb; Comp Sci.

ZOGBY, SUSAN A; Utica Free Acad; Utica, NY; (Y); 5/330; Pres French Clb; Yrbk Ed-Chief; Var Bsktbl; Var Sftbl; Var Capt Vllybl; High Hon Roll; NHS; Opt Clb Awd; Prfct Atten Awd; Rotary Awd; Nazareth Rochester; Soc Wrk.

ZOLESKI, THERESA; Our Lady Of Lourdes HS; Beacon, NY; (Y); 15/150; Varsity Clb; Bsktbl; Var Cheerleading; Ftbl; Hon Roll; Jr NHS; NHS; Mt St Marys Coll; Acctg.

ZOLI, CORRINNE; Glens Falls HS; Glen Falls, NY; (Y); Syracuse U.

ZOLLER, MATTHEW; Fort Plain HS; Ft Plain, NY; (Y); Math Clb; Varsity Clb; L Socr; L Wrstlng; High Hon Roll; Hon Roll; NHS; Prfct Atten Awd; Mst Imprvmnt Sci 83, Hstry 84, Mth 85.

ZOLLO, RICHARD; Germantown Central HS; Germantown, NY; (Y); 1/44; Computer Clb; Band; Chorus; Socr; Vllybl; NHS; Comp Sci.

ZOLNOWSKI, CHERYL; Alden Central HS; Alden, NY; (Y); 50/198; Church Yth Grp; Science Clb; Spanish Clb; Varsity Clb; Nwsp Ed-Chief; Trs Frsh Cls; Pres Soph Cls; Capt Var Cheerleading; Hon Roll; Pres Schlr; Stu Fclty Forum Schlrshp; Acad Awd; Coaches Awd Chrldng; Accntng.

ZOLNOWSKI, RONI SUE; Depew HS; Depew, NY; (Y); 87/254; Church Yth Grp; DECA; French Clb; Office Aide; Rep Stu Cncl; Hon Roll; Stdnt Senate Awd 85; 1st Pl Awd On Genrl Merch Suprvsry DECA; Erie CC; Bus Adm.

ZONIN, JENNIFER; Walt Whitman HS; Huntington Sta, NY; (Y); French Clb; GAA; Key Clb; Office Aide; Teachers Aide; Band; Capt Cheerleading; French Hon Soc; Hon Roll; Pres Jr NHS; Stu Of Mnth Awd,Frech Awd 82-83; Linguist.

ZONNEVILLE, NORMAN; Edison Tech; Rochester, NY; (Y); Library Aide; Stage Crew; JV Bsbl; Prfct Atten Awd; Auto Mechnc.

ZOOK, JOHN M; Corning-Painted Post West HS; Painted Post, NY; (Y); Church Yth Grp; Varsity Clb; JV Bsktbl; Var L Trk; High Hon Roll; NHS; Rensselaer Medal Mth & Sci 85; Elec Engrng.

ZOOTA, HERB; Commack High Schl South; Commack, NY; (Y); Boy Scts; Exploring; Math Tm; High Hon Roll; NHS.

ZORN, JENNIFER; Churchville Chili HS; Churchville, NY; (Y); GAA; Stat Bsktbl; JV Var Socr; JV Var Vllybl; Hon Roll; NHS; 1st Tm All Cty Vlybl 84; Eng Studies.

ZOU, JENNIFER QING; Fort Hamilton HS; Brooklyn, NY; (Y); Cmnty Wkr; Dance Clb; Math Clb; Office Aide; Teachers Aide; Bowling; Accntnt.

ZOULAS, CHRISTINA; Mont Pleasant HS; Schenectady, NY; (Y); Chorus; Color Guard; Mrchg Band; Key Clb; Pep Clb; Spanish Clb; Yrbk Stf; Off Soph Cls; Off Jr Cls; Off Sr Cls; Spec Educ.

ZOVISTOSKI, PAMELA; Saratoga Central Catholic Schl; Schuylerville, NY; (S); Drama Clb; 4-H; Church Choir; School Play; Yrbk Stf; Stat Ftbl; Hon Roll; Achvt Awd, Highest Aver Wrld Hist 83; Achvt Awd, Highest Aver Inter Algebra 84; Lake Erie Coll; Equestrian.

ZUBER, CHRISTINA; Farmingdale HS; Massapequa Park, NY; (Y); 7/643; Band; Concert Band; Mrchg Band; Symp Band; High Hon Roll; Hon Roll; NHS; Hofstra U; Math.

ZUBER, SARAH B; New Hartford HS; Washington Mills, NY; (Y); 16/264; Pres Church Yth Grp; MMM; Jazz Band; School Musical; Symp Band; Nwsp Rptr; Yrbk Stf; High Hon Roll; NHS; Pres Schlr; Most Musical 85; Regents Schlrshp 85; Area All ST Orch 85; St Lawrence U.

ZUCAL, VIRGINIA; Manhasset HS; Manhasset, NY; (Y); Cmnty Wkr; Dance Clb; GAA; Hosp Aide; Spanish Clb; Varsity Clb; Chorus; Drill Tm; Ed Nwsp Stf; Cheerleading; SCA Smmr Study Awd 85; Gentc Engr.

ZUCHOWSKI, LYNN; Fredonia HS; Fredonia, NY; (Y); 1/166; Sec Church Yth Grp; VP 4-H; Science Clb; Spanish Clb; School Musical; Var Capt Cheerleading; High Hon Roll; Key Clb; Chorus; JV Bsktbl; Spnsh Excel Awds 84-85; 1st Spnsh Essay 85; Cum GPA Awd 84.

ZUCHOWSKI, PAUL S; Fredonia Central HS; Fredonia, NY; (Y); 4/187; Sec Am Leg Boys St; Pres VP 4-H; Ski Clb; VP Stu Cncl; Crs Cntry; Bausch & Lomb Sci Awd; Dnfth Awd; Elks Awd; JC Awd; St Schlr; Clarkson U; Elec Engrng.

ZUCKERBERG, AMY; Beach Channel HS; Belle Harbor, NY; (Y); Temple Yth Grp; Concert Band; Yrbk Stf; Tennis; Hon Roll; English Medal 83; Arista 83-85.

ZUGAC, DEBBIE; Cazinovia Central HS; Chittenango, NY; (Y); Pres 4-H; 4-H Awd; Tutrg Frnch Awd 84; Utica; Vet.

ZUHLKE, ROBERT ALAN; Vestal SR HS; Vestal, NY; (Y); 251/457; Prfct Atten Awd; Spkr 85 Vestal Grad 85; Prfct Attndnc Awd 4 Yrs 81-85; US Navy; Elec Engr.

ZUIDEMA, JUDITH; Lansing HS; Lansing, NY; (Y); Spanish Clb; Orch; School Musical; Trs Jr Cls; Trs Sr Cls; Var JV Cheerleading; Var Diving; High Hon Roll; NHS; Acad Music Awd 84-85; Lbrl Arts.

ZUKOWSKI, MARK J; Hutchinson Central Technical HS; Buffalo, NY; (Y); 17/262; Chess Clb; Capt Ice Hcky; Capt Socr; Hon Roll; NHS; Prfct Atten Awd; NY ST Regents Schlrshp 85; Alfred U Pres Schlrshp 85; Buffalo ST Coll; Info Sys Mgmt.

ZULINSKA, AGNES; Our Lady Of Perpetual Help; Brooklyn, NY; (Y); 22/160; Church Yth Grp; Drama Clb; Hosp Aide; Intnl Clb; School Play; Pres Frsh Cls; NHS; Regents Schlrshp 85; Brooklyn; Engr.

ZULLO, DEANNA; Sacred Heart Acad; Malverne, NY; (Y); 55/185; Church Yth Grp; Library Aide; Office Aide; Teachers Aide; Bowling; Hon Roll; NHS; St Johns U.

ZULLO, NINA; Liverpool HS; Liverpool, NY; (S); 27/792; Ski Clb; Stu Cncl; Var Cheerleading; Powder Puff Ftbl; High Hon Roll; Hon Roll; Jr NHS; NHS; Liverpool Annl Acadmc Awds Bkkpng, Acctng I 84; Oswego Forgn Lang Comptn Frnch I 3rd Pl 81; Acctng.

ZUPAN, KEITH; Vernon-Verona-Sherrill HS; Verona, NY; (Y); Rep Soph Cls; Rep Stu Cncl; Im Var Bsktbl; Im Var Ftbl; JV Golf; Im Trk; High Hon Roll; Hon Roll; Bus Admin.

ZURIS, SCOTT; Fairport HS; Fairport, NY; (Y); Computer Clb; Chorus; Comp Sci.

ZURLO, JEFFREY; Glen Falls HS; Glen Falls, NY; (Y); 15/240; Math Tm; Band; Chorus; Yrbk Ed-Chief; Var L Swmmng; High Hon Roll; Jr NHS; NHS; Ntl Merit Ltr; Prfct Atten Awd; Wake Forest U; Chmstry.

ZURLO, MICHAEL; Saratoga Central Catholic HS; Mechanicville, NY; (S); 5/45; Varsity Clb; Ftbl; High Hon Roll; Hon Roll; Math Achvt Awd; Acad All Am; Ntl Hnr Rl.

ZUSIN, TATYANA; Packer Collegiate Inst; Brooklyn, NY; (Y); Cmnty Wkr; Hosp Aide; Teachers Aide; JV Sftbl; Hon Roll; Packer Schlr Awd 83; VA Finkell Peirce Schlrshp Awd/Math 84; Margaret Dennign Spanish Awd 84; Biology.

ZUSTOVICH, CLAUDIA; Sayville HS; Sayville, NY; (Y); 102/375; Cmnty Wkr; Dance Clb; Yrbk Stf; Girl Scts; High Hon Roll; Hon Roll; Prfct Atten Awd; Hampshire Coll MA; Parlegl.

ZVENYATSKY, OLGA; Christopher Columbus HS; Bronx, NY; (S); 1/700; Debate Tm; Math Tm; Office Aide; Temple Yth Grp; Trs Jr Cls; Cit Awd; High Hon Roll; NHS; Prfct Atten Awd; Val; Comp Sci.

ZWART, GAIL; Valley Central HS; Montgomery, NY; (Y); 19/267; Band; Rep Jr Cls; Rep Stu Cncl; Stat Bsbl; Capt Cheerleading; Vllybl; Hon Roll; NHS; Prfct Atten Awd; Spanish NHS; NY ST Schltc Music Assn Medls 83 & 85; OCCC; Actg.

ZWEIFEL, DAPHNE; The Stony Brook Schl; Stony Brook, NY; (Y); 17/84; JV Bsktbl; Var Cheerleading; Var Sftbl; Var Tennis; High Hon Roll; Hon Roll; Silver Mdl Bio 84; Piano Schl Schlrshp/Natl Guild Wnnr 84-85; Ceramics King Awd 84-85; Gold Mdl Spanish; Duke U; Intl Bus Admin.

ZWICK, MICHAEL; Liverpool HS; Liverpool, NY; (S); 21/791; Am Leg Boys St; Concert Band; Jazz Band; Mrchg Band; Orch; Symp Band; High Hon Roll; Jr NHS; NHS; Ntl Merit Ltr; Cornell U; Genetics Rsrch.

ZWIERZYNSKA, DANUTA; Our Lady Of Perpetual Help HS; Brooklyn, NY; (Y); Design.

ZYBERT, STACEY L; Springville-Griffith Inst; Colden, NY; (Y); FBLA; Red Cross Aide; Spanish Clb; Yrbk Stf; Var Bsktbl; Var Crs Cntry; Var Vllybl; CC Awd; Hon Roll; Prfct Atten Awd; Typing 1st In Dist, 5th ST Comp 85; Sch Awds Typing, Shrthnd 110 Wpm 85; Bryant & Stratton; Bus.

ZYDEL, JENNIFER; Bishop Kearney HS; Rochester, NY; (Y); JV Var Cheerleading; Mary Parnell Schrlshp Awd 82-83.

ZYMANEK, MATTHEW; Williamsville South HS; Williamsville, NY; (Y); DECA; JV Var Socr; Var L Trk; High Hon Roll; Hon Roll; ESF Syracuse; Bio.

ZYNDA, ELIZABETH; Arts Acad; Buffalo, NY; (Y); 16/100; Art Clb; Church Yth Grp; Computer Clb; PAVAS; Church Choir; Hon Roll; Bus Mngmnt.

ZYNDA, MARJORIE; Springville Griffith Inst; Lawtons, NY; (Y); 29/197; FBLA; High Hon Roll; Pres Schlr; Cordelian Clb Sprngvle Typng Awd 85; Gregg Shorthand Awds 83; Erie Comm Coll; Sec.

ZYNDA, RONALD; Springville Griffith Inst; Lawtons, NY; (S); 1/250; Debate Tm; 4-H; FFA; High Hon Roll; 1st Pl ST Ag Mech Cntst 84; Beef Prod Awd & Ag Elictrfctn Awd 83; Mech.

ZYSK, CHERYL; La Salle SR HS; Niagara Falls, NY; (Y); Capt Color Guard; Pres Frsh Cls; High Hon Roll; Boy Scts; French Clb; Hosp Aide; Co-Capt Pom Pon; Hon Roll; Jr NHS; Bronze Pin Hnr Rl 83-84; Silver Pin Hnr Rl 84-85; Bryant & Stratton; Bus Mgmt.

ZYSKOWSKI, SHERRY A; John F Kennedy HS; Utica, NY; (Y); 15/120; Exploring; Library Aide; Math Clb; Pep Clb; Yrbk Bus Mgr; Yrbk Stf; Stu Cncl; Hon Roll; Sec Trs NHS; Cngrsmn Mdl Of Merit; Rchstr Inst Of Tech; Med Tch.

PUERTO RICO

ACOSTA, LARISSA; Robinson HS; Miramar, PR; (S); 8/48; Speech Tm; Nwsp Rptr; Yrbk Phtg; Rep Stu Cncl; JV Bsktbl; Var Sftbl; Var Tennis; Var Vllybl; Hon Roll; I E Austin Kelly Essy Wrtng Contst-Hnrb Mntn 84; Achvt Awd-Wrld Hstry I Adv 82; Spn Medal 85; Richmond Coll; Poltcl Sci.

ALEJANDRO, GERMAN; Eloisa Pascual Bairoa III HS; Caguas, PR; (Y); Church Yth Grp; Debate Tm; English Clb; FBLA; Capt Vllybl; U Of The Sacred Heart.

ALFONSO, EDWIN; San Antonio HS; Quebradillas, PR; (Y); 2/32; Camera Clb; Drama Clb; Exploring; Math Tm; Science Clb; Spanish Clb; Off Sr Cls; Trk; Vllybl; Bausch & Lomb Sci Awd; Wnnr Sci Tlnt Srch 85; Grnd Prz ST Sci Fr 84; Wnnr In UPR Cngrss 85; Cornell U; Astrphyscst.

ALI, ALEXIS R; Colegio San Antonio HS; Toa Baja, PR; (S); 13/85; Debate Tm; Math Tm; Trs NFL; Church Choir; Orch; VP Soph Cls; VP Jr Cls; Trk; Pres NHS; Pres Clsrm Yng Am 85; Navy & AF ROTC Schlrshp 85; Ntl Hnr Soc Most Distngushd 84; USAF Acad; Aero Engrng.

ALVAREZ, DOROTHY; Colegio Ponceno HS; Ponce, PR; (S); Dance Clb; Library Aide; Math Clb; Sec Stu Cncl; NHS; Stu Cncl 82; Literary Cntst 82-83; 2nd Hghst Avrg Prize 82; Med.

APONTE TOSTE, BRENDA; Academia Sagrado Corazan HS; Carolina, PR; (S); 2/52; Church Yth Grp; Red Cross Aide; Science Clb; Speech Tm; Chorus; Church Choir; Sec Stu Cncl; Cit Awd; Jr NHS; NHS; CRC Pres Chem 84; UPR; Med Tech.

ARIZMENDI, SYLVIA; Acadamia San Jose; Guaynabo, PR; (Y); 5/112; Church Yth Grp; Science Clb; Chorus; Stage Crew; Nwsp Rptr; Trs Soph Cls; Rep Stu Cncl; Cheerleading; Vllybl; Hon Roll; Sociology Awd 84; Phy Ed Awds 82-83; Sci.

ARROYO, LOURDES LOPEZ; Jose De Diego HS; Aguadilla, PR; (S); Pres Church Yth Grp; FHA; L Vllybl; High Hon Roll; CAAM; Med.

ATKINSON, LESLIE; Robinson Preparatory Schl; Dorado, PR; (S); 5/48; Drama Clb; Hosp Aide; Math Clb; Rep NFL; Variety Show; Yrbk Stf; Pres Sec Stu Cncl; Var JV Cheerleading; NHS; Church Yth Grp; Presdntl Clsrm For Yng Amer 84; Mu Alpha Theta 84; Mst Outstndng Engl Awd 83; U Of CT.

AYOROA, LENA; Colegio Ponceno HS; Ponce, PR; (S); Pres Soph Cls; Pres Jr Cls; Capt Bsktbl; Capt Vllybl; Nwsp Phtg; Nwsp Rptr; Nwsp Stf; Yrbk Phtg; Yrbk Rptr; Yrbk Stf; MVP Vllybl 81-82 & Bsktbl 83; Hghst Avg 83; Pub Com.

BALASQUIDE, MARIA; Colegio Ponceno HS; Ponce, PR; (S); 30/85; Art Clb; Library Aide; Math Tm; Cheerleading; Hon Roll; Good Ave In Clss 82-84; Sagrado Corazon U; Odontlgy.

BAREA, JULIO; Caribbean Schl; Ponce, PR; (S); Pres Chorus; Nwsp Ed-Chief; Trs Yrbk Stf; Ntl Merit SF; NEDT Awd; Drama Clb; Jazz Band; School Musical; School Play; Trs Frsh Cls; Ntl Hispanic Schlr 84-85; Navy Rotc Schlrshp 84-85; Music.

BARRETO, KENNETH; Colegio San Ignacio HS; Rio Piedras, PR; (Y); Boy Scts; Chess Clb; Cmnty Wkr; NFL; Nwsp Ed-Chief; Nwsp Rptr; Nwsp Stf; Score Keeper; Hon Roll; Semi Fnlst Ntl Hspncs Schlrshp Comptn 84-85; 1st Pstr Mkng Cntsts Puerto Rico Wk CSI 82-83; Advrtsng.

BENITEZ, CARLOS H; Colegio Marista HS; Guaynabo, PR; (Y); 8/88; Aud/Vis; Pres Camera Clb; Drama Clb; Pep Clb; Stage Crew; Nwsp Ed-Chief; Nwsp Phtg; Nwsp Stf; Yrbk Ed-Chief; Yrbk Phtg; Most Distgushed Stu Awd 85; Fin.

BON, SAMUEL E; Jose Gautier Benitez HS; Caguas, PR; (Y); Chess Clb; Sec Trs Science Clb; Nwsp Stf; Yrbk Stf; VP Frsh Cls; NHS; US Merit Awd 83; ISEF Fnlst 85; Zoolgy.

BONNIN, MAGDA; Academia Maria Reina; Rio Piedras, PR; (Y); 7/61; Cmnty Wkr; Debate Tm; Math Clb; Math Tm; Science Clb; Yrbk Rptr; Yrbk Stf; Off Sr Cls; Jr NHS; Ntl Merit SF; GA Inst Of Tech; Aero Engr.

BOONE, JOHN; Southwestern Educational Society; Mayaguez, PR; (S); 1/2; Boy Scts; Chess Clb; Church Yth Grp; 4-H; Math Tm; Model UN; Variety Show; Nwsp Rptr; Yrbk Stf; Pres Sr Cls; U CA San Diego.

BUITRAGO, VIVIAN MARIE; Manuela Toro HS; Caguas, PR; (Y); Art Clb; Drama Clb; Girl Scts; Acpl Chr; Band; Orch; School Play; Nwsp Rptr; Yrbk Rptr; VP Stu Cncl; Natl Hispanic Schlr Awd $1500 Schlrshp 85; Zonta Clb Awd 85; Doctor In Med.

CALDERON, MANUEL; Colegio Marista HS; Guaynabo, PR; (Y); 1/88; Boy Scts; Sec Church Yth Grp; Cmnty Wkr; Math Clb; Math Tm; Stage Crew; Nwsp Rptr; Yrbk Stf; JV Var Socr; NHS; MA Inst Of Tech; Chem Engrng.

CALERO, CALIXTO JAVIER; Colegio San Antonio HS; Isabela, PR; (S); 2/29; Cmnty Wkr; Pres English Clb; Math Clb; Science Clb; Service Clb; Spanish Clb; Pres Frsh Cls; Pres Soph Cls; Pres Jr Cls; Pres Sr Cls; Distgshd Yng Ldrshp Awd 84-85; 1st Wrkshp Of Ldrshp 83; U Of PR; Sci.

CALZADA, RAMON L; Academia Sagrado Corazon HS; Bayamon, PR; (S); 2/82; Hosp Aide; JA; Red Cross Aide; Spanish Clb; Nwsp Rptr; Off Jr Cls; Stu Cncl; Var Vllybl; High Hon Roll; Hon Roll; ASC Lit Contst 1st Prz Drama 84; Physcn.

CAPO, RAFAEL; Colegio Ponceno HS; Ponce, PR; (S); 1/81; Math Clb; School Play; Nwsp Ed-Chief; Pres Frsh Cls; Pres Soph Cls; Trs Stu Cncl; High Hon Roll; NHS; Val; Aud/Vis; Spelling Bee Wnnr 80; 1st Pl Ltrary Schl Cntst 82-83; Ldrshp Awd 82; Harvard U; Med.

CHANG, RICHARD; Robinson HS; Hato Rey, PR; (S); 1/38; Math Clb; Lit Mag; High Hon Roll; NHS; NEDT Awd; Most Outstndg Stu; Alg II Awd; Bio Awd; Biochem.

CINTRON, ARIEL; Colegio Ponceno Inc; Ponce, PR; (S); Math Clb; Science Clb; Rep Frsh Cls; NHS; Prfct Atten Awd; Aeronautical Engrng.

COLLAZO, AGNES; Colegio Ponceno HS; Ponce, PR; (S); Dance Clb; Girl Scts; Variety Show; Yrbk Stf; Sec Soph Cls; Rep Jr Cls; NHS.

COLLAZO, REBECCA; Colegio Ponceno HS; Ponce, PR; (S); 3/83; Variety Show; NHS; High Hnrs 82-84; Brdcst Comm.

COLLAZO, SANDRA; Colegio Ponceno HS; Ponce, PR; (S); 5/83; Nwsp Ed-Chief; Yrbk Rptr; Yrbk Stf; NHS; Pharmacy.

COLON, HECTOR; Manuela Toro HS; Caguas, PR; (Y); Church Yth Grp; CAP; Cmnty Wkr; Hosp Aide; Office Aide; Red Cross Aide; Orch; Capt Bsktbl; Gym; Wt Lftg; U Of PR; Gynclgy.

COLON, LUCIA M; Colegio Ponceno HS; Ponce, PR; (S); Dance Clb; Library Aide; Stage Crew; Sec Jr Cls; Hon Roll; Rep NHS; Jacksonville U; Med.

COLON-POMALES, KIM; Colegio Nuestra Senora Del Pila; Guaynabo, PR; (Y); 1/171; Chess Clb; Debate Tm; Drama Clb; VP Math Clb; Math Tm; Model UN; Science Clb; Nwsp Rptr; Hon Roll; Sec NHS; Ntl Hispanic Schlr Awds 84-85; MA Inst Of Tech; Biomedical.

CONCEPCION, GLORIMAR; Colegio San Antonio HS; Hato Rey, PR; (S); 8/101; Cmnty Wkr; Chorus; Church Choir; High Hon Roll; Acad Prog Awd 84-85; Acad Excel Cert 84; Merit Cert For Cooprtn 84; Fshn Dsgn.

CRUZ, DISRAELI; Madre Cabrini HS; Rio Piedras, PR; (S); 3/54; Drama Clb; Library Aide; Stu Cncl; NHS; Merit Awds-Lit Cntst, Phy Ed, Craft, Hghst Av, Faith, Span, & Art; 1st Sci Fair; NHS; VP Stu Cnl.

CRUZ, JOSE; Col San Ignacio De Loyola HS; Rio Piedras, PR; (Y); Math Clb; Crs Cntry; Trk; Rookie Yr Crss Cntry Awd 84; Vrsty & JV Lttrs Track Awds 82 & 84; Pre-Med.

CRUZ, YANIA; Antilles HS; Rio Piedras, PR; (Y); 1/119; Sec Keywanettes; Math Clb; Capt Drill Tm; School Musical; Yrbk Stf; Rep Soph Cls; Powder Puff Ftbl; High Hon Roll; Pres NHS; Rep Frsh Cls; Acad All Amer 85; Aerontcl Engrng.

CUCURELLA, LUCY J; Jose Gautier Benitez HS; Caguas, PR; (Y); Pep Clb; Teachers Aide; School Play; Nwsp Rptr; Stu Cncl; Cheerleading; Hon Roll; Val; U Of Puerto Rico; Comp.

CURBELO, SONGIE; Colegio San Antonio HS; Quebradillas, PR; (S); 1/28; Pres Drama Clb; VP English Clb; 4-H; Pres Leo Clb; Math Clb; Math Tm; Science Clb; Spanish Clb; Chorus; VP Frsh Cls; Good Cndct Awd 80-85; Sci Awd 83-84; Spnsh Lit Cmptn 2nd Pl 84; U Of PR; Chmstry Engr.

DANTE, MARIA M; Wesleyan Acad; Rio Piedras, PR; (Y); 10/26; Teachers Aide; Chorus; Yrbk Bus Mgr; Yrbk Stf; VP Frsh Cls; VP Soph Cls; VP Sr Cls; Var Capt Cheerleading; Hon Roll; NHS; Eagle Mnth Awd; Exch Stu Pgm; UPR; Intr Dsgn.

DAVILA, MELISA; Notre Dame HS; Juncos, PR; (Y); 1/166; Math Clb; Math Tm; Pres Science Clb; Jr NHS; NHS; Prfct Atten Awd; Pres Schlr; Spanish NHS; Hstry Clb Medal & Awd 84 & 85; Suma Cum Laude Coll Bnd Medal & Hnr Mdls 85; Jhn Carroll U OH; Chm Engrng.

DEL ROSARIO, RUBEN; Colegio Ponceno HS; Ponce, PR; (S); 17/83; Mathletes; VP Math Clb; Math Tm; Nwsp Stf; Yrbk Stf; Rep Soph Cls; Rep Jr Cls; VP Stu Cncl; Score Keeper; Comite Organizador Ano Internacional; Intramrl Vllybl Tourn; RUM; Engrng.

DEL VALLE, IGNACIO; Our Lady Of Pilar HS; Rio Piedras, PR; (Y); 19/170; Math Clb; Science Clb; Variety Show; Ed Nwsp Stf; Yrbk Phtg; Yrbk Stf; Im Bsbl; Im Bsktbl; Jr NHS; NHS; Alg II Awd 82-83; GA Tech; Engr.

DEL VALLE, IRMA M; Colegio Ponceno HS; Ponce, PR; (S); Dance Clb; Chorus; Jr Cls; High Hon Roll; Hon Roll; 1st Pz Drama Play 84; 2nd Pz Modern Jazz Dance 84; Med.

DENT, JILL; Antilles HS; Guaynabo, PR; (Y); 14/120; French Clb; Keywanettes; Drill Tm; Yrbk Stf; JV Crs Cntry; Var Mgr(s); Var Powder Puff Ftbl; Var Trk; High Hon Roll; NHS; Recinto U; Phys Educ.

DIAZ, LINDA; Colegio Mandre Cabrini HS; Rio Piedras, PR; (S); Drama Clb; Sec Soph Cls; Jr NHS; NHS; UPR; Indstrl Rltns.

DIAZ, LIZETTE; San Antonio Abad HS; Humacao, PR; (Y); JV Cheerleading; JV Gym; Var L Swmmng; Swmmng Trophy & Ltr 85; Swimming Medal Schl Field Day 85; 1st Pl Tlnt Show 83; Regis Coll; Psych.

DIAZ, SUSAN T; Jose Gauthier Benitez HS; Caguas, PR; (Y); Pres Church Yth Grp; Dance Clb; English Clb; Variety Show; Nwsp Stf; High Hon Roll; Trs NHS; Trs Frsh Cls; Rep Jr Cls; Milestones Freedom Awd 83; Sci Fair 1st 2nd Prz 85; Rep J Gautier Benites Close Up Pgm 85; Comp Engr.

DOMINGUEZ, LOURDES; Academia Sagrado Corozon HS; Santuree, PR; (S); 5/51; Computer Clb; Red Cross Aide; Teachers Aide; Nwsp Stf; NHS; Pope John XXIII Awd 80; Good Manner Awd 80; Comp Sci.

DUFFER, MARTHA; Wesleyan Acad; Guaynabo, PR; (Y); 5/26; Pres Church Yth Grp; Chorus; Nwsp Stf; Yrbk Stf; Rep Stu Cncl; L Var Cheerleading; High Hon Roll; Pres NHS; Ntl Merit SF; Ntl Hspnc Schlr 85; Baylor U; Pschlgy.

DUFFY, CHRISTINA; Baldwin Schl; Rio Piedras, PR; (S); Scholastic Bowl; School Musical; Yrbk Stf; Sec Jr Cls; Cit Awd; High Hon Roll; Jr NHS; NHS; Ntl Merit Ltr; NEDT Awd.

ERAZO, ELIAH; Colegio Santa Rita HS; Bayamon, PR; (Y); 5/72; Dance Clb; NFL; Variety Show; Nwsp Rptr; Yrbk Stf; Rep Sr Cls; Bsktbl; Var Trk; Var Vllybl; High Hon Roll; Perfect Attnd 84-85; Colegio De Mayaguez; Indus Engr.

ERTUR, ELKA; Wesleyan Acad; Bayamon, PR; (Y); 2/26; Yrbk Sprt Ed; Yrbk Stf; Trs Jr Cls; Trs Sr Cls; Var L Bsktbl; Var L Trk; L Var Vllybl; Bausch & Lomb Sci Awd; High Hon Roll; NHS; Pres Phy Ftnss Awd 84; U Of Rochester; Engrng.

FABERY, MARIA PILAR; San Antonio Abad; Humacao, PR; (Y); Nwsp Stf; Yrbk Stf; Sec Frsh Cls; Pres Soph Cls; Pres Sr Cls; Stu Cncl; NHS; Puerto Rico U; Pol Sci.

FARINACCI, PEDRO; Colegio Ponceno HS; Ponce, PR; (S); Camera Clb; Drama Clb; Math Clb; Spanish Clb; School Play; Nwsp Phtg; VP Jr Cls; Bsktbl; Swmmng; Trk; Med.

FELICIANO, SOL; Colegio Ponceno HS; Ponce, PR; (S); Church Yth Grp; Dance Clb; Med.

FERNANDEZ, MARIA E; Colegio Ponceno HS; Ponce, PR; (S); Art Clb; Debate Tm; GAA; Girl Scts; Library Aide; Math Clb; Math Tm; Varsity Clb; School Play; Variety Show; Vllybl, Trck & Fld, Crss Cntry Awd 81-84; Pharm.

FIGUEROA, AGNES; Immaculate Conception Acad; Mayaguez, PR; (S); Camera Clb; Church Yth Grp; Debate Tm; GAA; Girl Scts; Office Aide; Service Clb; Chorus; Church Choir; Nwsp Phtg; Svc Awd 83; Chllngr Of Yr 84; Miss Immaculate Conception Acad 84; U Of Sacred Hrt; Cmmnctns.

FIGUEROA, GEORGE ALEXANDER; Bellas Artes Central HS; Carolina, PR; (Y); Drama Clb; Red Cross Aide; Spanish Clb; Speech Tm; School Play; Stage Crew; Yrbk Stf; Hnrb Mntn Bidimnsnl Sclptr Schl Expo 82; 1st Prz Kinetic Sclptr Schl Expo 84; ARTS Pgm Hnrb Mntn 85; Fshn Dsgnr.

FISCHBACH, KEVIN; Southwestern Educational Soc HS; Mayaguez, PR; (S); Leo Clb; Science Clb; Spanish Clb; School Play; Variety Show; Pres Soph Cls; JV Var Bsktbl; Stat Timer; Sal; 2nd Pl Wnr Forn Comp 84; 1st Pl Wnr Forn Comp Drama 84; Merit Awd 84; U Of PR; Med.

GARCIA, HECTOR; Colegio Ponceno HS; Ponce, PR; (S); 17/83; Cmnty Wkr; Hosp Aide; Yrbk Rptr; Rep Stu Cncl; Acts Of Benefcnce 84; U Of Puerto Rico; Sci.

GIAMELLARO, DAVID P; Antilles HS; Rio Hondo, PR; (Y); 12/89; Church Yth Grp; Pres French Clb; Library Aide; Q&S; Band; School Musical; Lit Mag; Mgr Swmmng; High Hon Roll; NHS; Medl Exc Libry Media Wrk 85; Naval Acad 84-85; Schls Peach Corps Schlrshp 85; SUNY; Bio.

GIERBOLINI, LUIS; Colegio Madre Cabrini HS; Rio Piedras, PR; (S); 3/52; Church Yth Grp; Drama Clb; Capt Math Tm; VP Science Clb; Yrbk Ed-Chief; JV Bsktbl; Score Keeper; Trs NHS; 1st Pl Sci Cont 84; Treas Natl Hnr Scty 84-85; Staff Insular Natl Hnr Scty 84-85; Colegio De Mayaguez; Arntcl Eng.

GIULIANI, MARIA T; Sagrado Corazon Acad; Santurce, PR; (S); 5/51; Red Cross Aide; Nwsp Stf; Pres Frsh Cls; Rep Soph Cls; Pres Stu Cncl; NHS; U Of PR; Cmmrcl Art.

GONZALEZ, FRANCISCO; Colegio San Ignacio De Loyola HS; San Juan, PR; (Y); Cmnty Wkr; French Clb; Math Clb; Pres Model UN; Ed Nwsp Ed-Chief; Rep Frsh Cls; Sec Soph Cls; VP Jr Cls; High Hon Roll; Ntl Merit Schol; Holy Crs Bk Awd 84; Math Assoc Of Amer Awd 84; 1st Pl Math Olympd 85; Harvard U; Econ.

GONZALEZ, LILLIAN; Jose Gautier Benitez; Caguas, PR; (Y); Pres Church Yth Grp; Sec FHA; Girl Scts; Color Guard; School Play; Trs Yrbk Stf; Pres Frsh Cls; Pres Soph Cls; Rep Jr Cls; Rep Sr Cls; Cuerpo De Investgtrs Cienti Ficos Aux 83; Maestros Y Estdnts Pro Art 84; Coll U De Cayey.

GONZALEZ, MARELISA; Col Utra Sra Del Pilar HS; Rio Piedras, PR; (Y); 21/172; Aud/Vis; Church Yth Grp; Drama Clb; NFL; Pres Service Clb; School Play; Variety Show; Nwsp Rptr; Hon Roll; Jr NHS; 1st Prz Tlnt Show Drama 83-85; U De Puerto Rico; Bus Admin.

GONZALEZ RIVERA, HENRY; Colegio Santa Rita HS; Dorado, PR; (S); Church Yth Grp; French Clb; Leo Clb; Math Clb; Chorus; Bsktbl; Lion Awd; NHS; Med.

GUTIERREZ TORRES, ALEX; Yauco HS; Yauco, PR; (S); Church Yth Grp; CAP; Drama Clb; Acpl Chr; Chorus; Color Guard; Pres Jr Cls; Sftbl; Vllybl; Billy Mitchell Awd 83; Amelia Earhart Awd 84; Interamerican U; Sci.

HAYES, NORA CHRISTINE; San Antonio HS; Rio Piedras, PR; (S); 1/85; Computer Clb; Debate Tm; Exploring; 4-H; Mathletes; Math Clb; Math Tm; Science Clb; Yrbk Stf; 4-H Awd.

HERNANDEZ, ADOLFO M; Colegio Ponceno HS; Ponce, PR; (S); JV Bsktbl; Hon Roll; Jr NHS; Hlf Schlrshp 84-85; Engrng.

HERNANDEZ, PATRICIA; Academia San Jorge HS; San Juan, PR; (Y); 10/53; Exploring; Pres French Clb; Chorus; VP Soph Cls; Pres Jr Cls; Stu Cncl; Sftbl; Hon Roll; NHS; U US Mainland; Lang.

HERNANDEZ, RUBEN A; Dr Efrain Sanehez Hidalgo HS; Moca, PR; (Y); CAP; Band; Billy Mitchell Awd CAP 84; Cdt Sqdn Cadet Of Yr 85; CAP Cdt Sqdn Comm Awd 85; U Of PR; Med.

HUNT, JULIANNE; Southwestern Educational Socty HS; Mayaguez, PR; (S); 1/15; Drama Clb; JA; Math Tm; Model UN; Science Clb; Nwsp Rptr; Ed Nwsp Stf; VP Stu Cncl; High Hon Roll; NFL; Sci Fair Reg Awds 80-84; Math Olmpi Reg.

IFARRAGUERRI, AGUSTIN; Colegio San Ignacio HS; Guaynabo, PR; (Y); 6/108.

IRIZARRY, ROSA; Santa Rita College; Bayamon, PR; (Y); 14/72; Church Yth Grp; Dance Clb; Math Clb; Church Choir; Nwsp Rptr; Rep Sr Cls; Hon Roll; NHS; U Of Sacred Heart; Comm.

IRIZARRY ROSARIO, MYRA; Dr Sarltiago Veve Calzada HS; Fajardo, PR; (S); Church Yth Grp; Library Aide; Spanish Clb; Off Sr Cls; High Hon Roll; Hon Roll; Catholic U; B A Sci.

ISERN, SHARON; Antilles HS; Dorado, PR; (Y); 1/88; Trs Sec Keywanettes; Pres Math Clb; Yrbk Stf; Sec Soph Cls; Rep Stu Cncl; Tennis; High Hon Roll; NHS; Presdnts Achvt Awd-TX A & M Univ Cllg Stn ; Equal Opprtnty Engrng Schlrshp-U Of TX.

JACOBSTHAL, SUSAN; Robinson HS; Rio Piedras, PR; (S); 8/48; Computer Clb; Intnl Clb; Math Clb; Yrbk Rptr; VP Jr Cls; Rep Sr Cls; Hon Roll; NHS; Bus Adm.

JIMENEZ, WALTER A; Jose Gautier Benitez HS; Caguas, PR; (Y); Church Yth Grp; Church Choir; Drill Tm; Sci Fair 2nd Pl 85; Engl Fest Spcl Rcgntn Drama 85; El Mundo Nwspr 1st Fnlst Yr Sls Cont 83; CAAM; Elec Engr.

JOHNSON, KIRK; Colegio San Ignacio E Loyola HS; Guaynabo, PR; (Y); VP Computer Clb; Drama Clb; Pres Speech Tm; Teachers Aide; School Play; Nwsp Stf; NEDT Awd; 1st Pl Islnd Fornsc Comptn 85; 2nd Pl Jesuit 1 Act Ply Comptn 84; 3rd Pl Awd Sci Fir 83; Mc Master U; Indstrl Engrng.

LABORDA, ANNETTE M; Colegio Madre Cabrini HS; San Juan, PR; (S); 1/54; Drama Clb; JA; Math Tm; Science Clb; Nwsp Rptr; Ed Yrbk Rptr; Sec Jr Cls; Bowling; Cheerleading; Gym; Sci Fair Prz 84; Math Olympcs 85; Forensic Comp 83; GA Tech; Mech Engr.

LABORDE, MARIA J; Academia San Jose; Guaynabo, PR; (Y); 6/117; Church Yth Grp; Drama Clb; French Clb; Sec Girl Scts; Science Clb; Speech Tm; Nwsp Stf; Yrbk Phtg; Yrbk Stf; Rep Stu Cncl; Schl Rep Pres Clsrm Young Amer 85; Natl Hispanic Schlrs Awd Semi-Fin 85; Harvard U; Pre-Med.

LAGO, LORRAINE; Carribean Schl; Ponce, PR; (S); 1/17; Drama Clb; Math Clb; Math Tm; School Play; Pres Soph Cls; Stu Cncl; Bsktbl; Sec NHS; NEDT Awd; Biomed Engr.

LARSON, CHRISTINA; Robinson Schl; Rio Piedras, PR; (S); 7/48; Computer Clb; Hosp Aide; Math Clb; Pep Clb; Nwsp Rptr; Nwsp Stf; Yrbk Stf; Hon Roll; Span Awd 83; Psych.

LAZARUS, MICHAEL; Southwestern Community Schl; Mayaguez, PR; (S); Drama Clb; Model UN; NFL; Speech Tm; Band; Jazz Band; School Play; Variety Show; Yrbk Bus Mgr; Yrbk Stf; Spnsh Cont 3rd Pl 84; Hnry Ment Wstrn Reg Sci Fair 84; Sci Fair Botany 1st Pl 84.

LLIVINA, ELENA; Academia Maria Reina HS; Levittown, PR; (Y); 1/65; Cmnty Wkr; Math Clb; Pres NFL; Pres Science Clb; Ed Nwsp Stf; French Hon Soc; High Hon Roll; NHS; NEDT Awd; Mensa Ltd 84; Engl Forensic Leag Wnnr 84; Math Awd Mdl 85; Johns Hopkins U; Med.

LOPEZ, LESBY W; Eloiza Paseual HS; Cagaas, PR; (S); DECA; FHA; Church Choir; U Of PR; Commerce Adm.

LOPEZ, MARICARMEN; Colegio San Antonio HS; Rio Piedras, PR; (S); 11/85; Church Yth Grp; Debate Tm; Pres NFL; Red Cross Aide; Band; Chorus; Nwsp Stf; Yrbk Phtg; Hon Roll; Hst NHS; Marquette U Hnr Schlrshp 85; Pres Clsrm Yng Am 85; Syracuse U; Biomed.

LOPEZ, WANDA; Dr Efrain Sanchz Hidalgo HS; Moca, PR; (Y); Church Choir; Vllybl; Hon Roll; Engl Cls Distnctn Cert 85; CORA; Med Tech.

LUGO, LIZA; Academia Sagrado Corazon HS; Isla Verde, PR; (S); Drama Clb; Hosp Aide; JA; NFL; Red Cross Aide; Chorus; Nwsp Rptr; Rep Jr Cls; Hon Roll; Soph Yr First Hnr 83-84; Comm.

LYNCH, PAMELA; St Croix Seventh-Day Adventist HS; Mattapan, MA; (Y); 2/28; Church Yth Grp; Office Aide; Nwsp Rptr; Im Bsbl; Im Socr; Im Sftbl; Im Tennis; Im Vllybl; High Hon Roll; School Musical; Yearbook Staff 85; Pharmacist.

MALAK, RICHARD; Robinson HS; Dorado, PR; (S); Computer Clb; Math Clb; Trs Stu Cncl; Var Bsbl; Var Fld Hcky; Var Socr; High Hon Roll; Hon Roll; Jr NHS; NHS; Law.

MARIN, EDWIN; Colegio San Ignacio HS; Bayamon, PR; (Y); Cmnty Wkr; French Clb; VP Math Clb; Math Tm; Trs Varsity Clb; Capt Var Vllybl; Natl Hispnc Schlrs Awds 84-85; MVP Vlybl 84; MA Inst Tech; Elec Engr.

MARRERO, ARLENE; Colegio San Antonio HS; Rio Piedras, PR; (S); 5/101; Church Yth Grp; English Clb; Sec NFL; Church Choir; Nwsp Ed-Chief; Yrbk Stf; High Hon Roll; NHS; Spch Awd 83; Good Writng Awd 82; Schlrshp Awd 83; U Pureto Rico; Acctng.

MARRERO, IVETTE; Colegio San Antonio HS; Rio Piedras, PR; (S); 14/101; Drama Clb; Nwsp Rptr; Nwsp Stf; Hon Roll; Jr NHS; NHS; Good Wrtng Awd Spnsh; Bus Admin.

MARTINEZ, EDITH; Colegio Ponceno HS; Ponce, PR; (S); Girl Scts; JA; Rep Frsh Cls; Rep Soph Cls; Rep Jr Cls; Rep Stu Cncl; Cheerleading; Swmmng; Trk; High Hon Roll; Intl Stdies.

MARTINEZ, GRETCHEN C; Academia Del Perpetuo Socorro; San Juan, PR; (Y); Drama Clb; French Clb; Natl Beta Clb; NFL; School Play; Stage Crew; Lit Mag; Gov Hon Prg Awd; Pres Schlr; Hon Roll; Natl Hispnc Schlr Awd 85; Engl Frnsc Leag Awd 84; Tbrandeis U; Med.

MARTINEZ-SOTO, JORGE ANTONIO; Colegie San Antonio HS; San Juan, PR; (S); 13/85; Aud/Vis; Hosp Aide; Library Aide; Model UN; Red Cross Aide; Science Clb; Var Wrstlng; Ntl Merit Schol; Acad Prog Awd 84-85; Library Aide Awd 84-85; Spnsh, Engl, Hstry, Math & Sci Awds 82-83; U Of Dayton; Orthodntst.

MATOS, BRENDA E; Colegio San Antonio; Rio Piedras, PR; (S); Church Yth Grp; Debate Tm; Hosp Aide; Math Tm; Model UN; Chorus; Church Choir; Rep Stu Cncl; Jr NHS; NHS; Sci, Relgn, Spnsh, Engl, Hstry, Hm Ec Awds 83-84; Natrl Sci.

MATTA, MARCOS A; Stgo Veve Calzada HS; Luquillo, PR; (S); Camera Clb; Civic Clb; Cmnty Wkr; Debate Tm; English Clb; 4-H; FFA; Library Aide; Math Tm; Office Aide; Hnr Mntn Sci Fair 84; Ntl Cngrss 4-H ST Wnnr 84-85; ST Wnnr Anml Judg & Hnr Rll 85; MI ST U; Pre-Vet.

MAYMI, FERNANDO; Santa Monica Acad; Santurce, PR; (Y); 5/45; Cmnty Wkr; Exploring; Speech Tm; School Play; Trs VP Stu Cncl; Hon Roll; NHS; Schl Outstndg Stu, 100 Best Scrs SAT Coll Brd, Placemnt US Army Acad West Point 85; US Acad; Elect Engr.

MEDINA, BETSY-ANN; Colegio San Antonio HS; Ramey, PR; (S); Office Aide; Pres Soph Cls; Rep Jr Cls; High Hon Roll; NHS; 1st Prz Microbio Prjct Schl & Rgnl Sci Fair 85; 3rd Prz For States Scientific Fair; U Of Puerto Rico; Law.

MELENDEZ, PETER A; Colegio San Antonio HS; Isabela, PR; (S); 1/33; Boy Scts; Debate Tm; English Clb; Pres Science Clb; VP Spanish Clb; VP Jr Cls; Bsktbl; Cit Awd; VP NHS; Nobel Price Ceremonies PR 84; ISEF 3rd Pl 83; ISEF 84; UPR; Biochem.

MICLAU, MICHAEL; Robinson Schl; Punta Las Marias, PR; (S); Computer Clb; Hosp Aide; Library Aide; Math Clb; Math Tm; Scholastic Bowl; Yrbk Stf; Rep Frsh Cls; Rep Soph Cls; Var Bsbl; Bio, Comp, NEDT & Spnsh Awds; Bio.

MITCHELL, CRAIG; Robinson Schl; Dorado, PR; (S); 1/48; Yrbk Phtg; Pres Frsh Cls; Pres Soph Cls; VP Rep Stu Cncl; Var Golf; Tennis; VP NHS; Ntl Merit SF; Math Clb; Math Tm; Mu Alpha Theta; Most Outstndg Stu; Math Awd, Spnsh Awd, Hstry Awd; Bus.

MONSANTO, VIVIAN; Colegio Ponceno HS; Ponce, PR; (S); 1/79; Bsktbl; High Hon Roll; Highest Avg Cls 83 & 84; Med.

MONTANER, LUIS JAVIER; Colegio San Ignacio HS; Santurce, PR; (Y); VP Camera Clb; Cmnty Wkr; Pres Drama Clb; English Clb; French Clb; Spanish Clb; VP Speech Tm; School Play; Yrbk Stf; Lit Mag; Rotary Clb Cert Of Gratitude 82; Best Actor Awd 83 & 85; Cert Of Spnsh & Engl Forenscics 85; KS ST; Vet.

MONTEVERDE, DINABEL; Eugenio M De Hostos HS; Bronx, NY; (Y); Dance Clb; Drama Clb; FBLA; FHA; School Play; Variety Show; Prfct Atten Awd; Hunter Coll; Exec Secy.

MORALES, GUSTAVO; Colegio Madre Cabrini HS; Rio Piedras, PR; (S); Church Yth Grp; Library Aide; Office Aide; Spanish Clb; Flag Corp; VP Soph Cls; NHS; Pedtrcs.

MORALES, JOSE A; Colegio San Antonio HS; Rio Piedras, PR; (S); 10/101; Church Yth Grp; Science Clb; Chorus; Cit Awd; NHS; Bio.

MORALES, LINA; Colegio Ponceno HS; Ponce, PR; (S); Math Clb; Yrbk Stf; Pres Frsh Cls; Rep Soph Cls; Rep Jr Cls; Sec Stu Cncl; Crs Cntry; Trk; Vllybl; High Hon Roll; Cristoforos Committee Secretary; Pres Committee Of Decoration Of Stu Council.

MORALES SANTIAGO, JUAN A; Colegio Santa Rita HS; Toa Baja, PR; (S); Church Yth Grp; Pres Jr Cls; Stu Cncl; NHS.

MORELL, JEANNINE; St Johns Schl; Santurce, PR; (Y); 10/42; Yrbk Ed-Chief; Yrbk Sprt Ed; Yrbk Stf; Lit Mag; Trs Soph Cls; Var Capt Bsktbl; Var Capt Sftbl; Hon Roll; Varsity Clb; Var Trk; Ntl Hispanic Schlr Awd Prgrm Semi Fnlst 85; All-Arnd Athlete 83-85; Political Sci.

MORENO, MIGUEL; Colegio Ponceno; Santa Isabel, PR; (S); 6/83; Church Yth Grp; Math Clb; Math Tm; Tennis; Prfct Atten Awd; Sal; Val; Engr.

NEGRON, DIANA; Baldwin Schl; Guaynabo, PR; (S); Hosp Aide; Science Clb; Pres Jr Cls; Bsktbl; Sftbl; Vllybl; Cit Awd; High Hon Roll; NHS; NEDT Awd; Biochmstry.

NEMES, SUSANNE; Caribbean Schl; Ponce, PR; (S); 1/16; Library Aide; VP Math Clb; Nwsp Ed-Chief; Pres Frsh Cls; Pres Soph Cls; Var Capt Bsktbl; Var Capt Vllybl; High Hon Roll; Pres Trs NHS; Val; Outstndng Phy Ed Stud 82; Ntl Schlr Athl Awd 84; Mst Potntl Bsktbl Plyr 82; Math.

NIKITINE, VADIM; Robinson Schl; Santurce, PR; (S); 3/48; Math Tm; Yrbk Ed-Chief; Yrbk Phtg; Trs VP Cmnty Wkr; Var Capt Bsktbl; Var Co-Capt Socr; Var Capt Tennis; Hon Roll; Pres NHS; Bus Admin.

OJEDA, DAWN; Caribbean Schl; Ponce, PR; (S); 4/15; Office Aide; Nwsp Ed-Chief; Sec Soph Cls; Sec Jr Cls; VP Sr Cls; Cheerleading; Hon Roll; NHS; Ntl Merit SF; NEDT Awd; Engl 10 Merit Awd 83; Modrn Europn Hstry Merit Awd 83; Natl Ed Develpmt Tst Awd 81-82.

OLIVERA, CARLOS; Colegio Ponceno HS; Guayanilla, PR; (S); 10/84; Rptr Science Clb; Church Choir; Nwsp Rptr; Vllybl; High Hon Roll; Hon Roll; English Clb; 1st Pl Sci Fair Immac Concp Clg 80-81; Bst Avg 82; Bst Sci Projct 80; U Of Houston; Pre-Med.

ORTIZ-BLANES, MARIANA; Saint Johns Schl; Guaynabo, PR; (Y); 3/42; French Clb; Math Tm; Pres Model UN; Capt Scholastic Bowl; Pres Service Clb; Chrmn Chorus; Stage Crew; Nwsp Ed-Chief; Yrbk Phtg; Ed Yrbk Stf; Natl Hisp Schlrs Awd Fnlst 84-85; Concours Natl De Francais 82-83fawds Engl, A P Span, Hist 83-84; Harvard U; Govt.

PACHECO MALDONADO, LUIS M; Dr Santiago Veve Calzada HS; Luguillo, PR; (S); Art Clb; Camera Clb; Church Yth Grp; Civic Clb; Cmnty Wkr; Debate Tm; DECA; Drama Clb; Hosp Aide; JCL; Sci Fair 3rd Pl 83; Church Yth Grp Prz 84; Drawng Prz 82; MI ST U; Comptr Sci Engr.

PADILLA, MARTA LUZ; Colegio Ponceno HS; Guayanilla, PR; (S); Office Aide; Band; Concert Band; Jazz Band; Mrchg Band; School Musical; Stu Cncl; High Hon Roll; Hon Roll; Sec Of Cncl Clb 85; Running Tm 85; U Of P R; Med Tech.

PAGAN, NEFTALI; Colegio Ponceno HS; Guayanilla, PR; (S); 2/85; Boy Scts; Pres Chess Clb; Capt Debate Tm; Library Aide; Capt Mathletes; Pres Math Clb; Capt Math Tm; Office Aide; Capt Scholastic Bowl; Pres Science Clb; Jrnlsm Club Pres; Hnrs Math Comp 83-85; US Nvl Acad; Engrng.

PAGAN-ECHEVARRIA, NEFTALI; Colegio Ponceno HS; Guayanilla, PR; (Y); 3/89; Pres Math Clb; Capt Math Tm; Nwsp Rptr; Var Stat Vllybl; High Hon Roll; NHS; Var Score Keeper; Chess Clb; Computer Clb; Capt Debate Tm; U S Naval Acad; Aero Engr.

PAUNETO TIRADO, MADELINE; Manuela Toro Morice HS; Caguas, PR; (S); Church Yth Grp; Debate Tm; Drama Clb; Hosp Aide; JA; Library Aide; Band; Church Choir; Variety Show; VP NHS.

PEDROSA, YVETTE; Ac Sagrado Corazon HS; Santurce, PR; (S); Drama Clb; Hosp Aide; VP JA; Pres NFL; Red Cross Aide; Nwsp Stf; Stu Cncl; Hon Roll; NHS; Forensics Trophy Wnnr No 1, No 2 83-84; U Syracuse; Advertising.

PEREIRA, OMAR; Colegio San Ignaci De Loyola HS; San Juan, PR; (Y); Aud/Vis; Pres VP Computer Clb; Drama Clb; French Clb; Model UN; School Play; Stage Crew; Nwsp Stf; Natl Hispnc Schlr Semi Fnlst 85; Rensselaer Polytechnic Inst.

PEREYO, NEVILLE G; Colegio Ponceno HS; Ponce, PR; (S); Cmnty Wkr; Math Clb; Math Tm; Science Clb; Varsity Clb; Bsbl; Bsktbl; Tennis; Vllybl; High Hon Roll; Math Schlrshp Awd 82; Hghst Avg Stu 82-83; Emory U; Med.

PEREZ, ASTRID A; Colegio San Antonio HS; Rio Piedras, PR; (S); 7/102; Church Yth Grp; Cmnty Wkr; Variety Show; Trk; Jr NHS; NHS; Tercer Honor 83; Medicine.

PEREZ, HERNANDEZ NELIDA; Efrain Sanchez Hidelgo HS; Moca, PR; (Y); 3/44; Computer Clb; FHA; GAA; Trk; Vllybl; Inter Amer U.

PEREZ, ILIA; Colegio Ponceno HS; Guyanilla, PR; (S); 4-H; Math Clb; Rep Frsh Cls; Rep Soph Cls; Sec Jr Cls; Bsktbl; Var JV Trk; Var JV Vllybl; High Hon Roll; NHS; U Of PR; Engrng.

PEREZ, MARIA ISABEL; Caribbean Schl; Ponce, PR; (S); 2/15; Sec Math Clb; Pres Jr Cls; Var Bsktbl; Var Crs Cntry; Var Trk; Var JV Vllybl; High Hon Roll; Jr NHS; NHS; Val; Math.

PEREZ OYOLA, JOHANA; Manuela Toro Morice HS; Caguas, PR; (S); Girl Scts; NHS; U Of PR; Mgmnt.

PINERO, REENE AURIE; Academia Sagrado Corazon; Rio Piedras, PR; (S); 1/82; Dance Clb; Drama Clb; NFL; Red Cross Aide; Drill Tm; School Play; Lit Mag; Stu Cncl; NHS; U Of PR; Phys Thrpy.

PONCE DE LEON, GLORIA; Colegio Ponceno HS; Ponce, PR; (S); Cmnty Wkr; Dance Clb; Vllybl; Hon Roll; Honor 82-84; U PR; Phrmcy.

POTTER, CYNTHIA A; Southwestern Educationl Socty; San German, PR; (S); Art Clb; Dance Clb; Drama Clb; Model UN; Speech Tm; School Play; Ed Nwsp Stf; Ed Yrbk Stf; Pres Sr Cls; VP Stu Cncl; Sci Fair Hnbl Mntn 82; Cert Merit Dept Natrl Resrcs 82; Cert Merit Spnsh Oratory 83; Illstr.

PROSSER, JEFFREY SCOTT; Baldwin Schl; Yabucoa, PR; (S); 1/22; Pres Soph Cls; Pres Sr Cls; Var Bsbl; Var Capt Bsktbl; Var Socr; NHS; Val; Athltc Of Yr 85; All Allnc Tm Bsebl & Scr 85; All Allnc Tm Bsbl & Bsktbl 84; U Of FL.

PUJOLS, ETHEL; Colegio Santa Rita HS; Bayamon, PR; (S); 1/74; Math Clb; Science Clb; Service Clb; Church Choir; Yrbk Phtg; Yrbk Stf; Cheerleading; NHS; Prfct Atten Awd; Sal; Geo Awd 83-84; Hstry Awd 83-84; UPR; Med Technlgst.

QUILES, ZULMA VANESSA; Elasa Pascual Bairoa III HS; Caguas, PR; (S); DECA; FHA; Nwsp Stf; Hnr JR HS 82; U Of Puerto Rico; Natrl Sci.

QUINONES, HILDA; Wesleyan Acad; Rio Piedras, PR; (Y); Church Yth Grp; Chorus; Yrbk Ed-Chief; Yrbk Phtg; Pres Stu Cncl; Stat Socr; High Hon Roll; NEDT Awd; Scholastic Bowl; Semi Finalist National Hispanic Schlrs Awd 85; Houghton College; Chemistry.

QUINONES, ROSSELYN; Colegio Ponceno Inc; Ponce, PR; (S); Math Clb; Science Clb; Sec Band; Concert Band; Mrchg Band; Trs Frsh Cls; Trs Soph Cls; NHS; Hgh Hnr Roll Fresh Cls 83; Hgh Hnr Roll Soph 84.

QUIROS, MARVIN SAMUEL; University HS; Rio Piedras, PR; (Y); Church Yth Grp; Computer Clb; Library Aide; Political Wkr; Yrbk Phtg; Off Sr Cls; Var Bsbl; Golf; Splng Bee Schl Chmpn 82; Ntl Hspnc Schlrshp Awd Prog 84-85; Engl Awd Litry Cntst 81 & 83; U Of Puerto Rico; Comp System.

RAFOLS III, EDWIN; Colegio San Antonio HS; Isabela, PR; (S); 5/38; English Clb; Math Clb; Math Tm; Science Clb; Spanish Clb; Bsbl; Bsktbl; Diving; NHS; 2nd Prize Scntfc Fair Sbjct Marine Sci 84; Special Prize Marine Technlgy Soc US Naval Inst; U Of PR; Arch.

RAMIREZ, JOSE R; Colegio San Antonio HS; Isabela, PR; (S); Church Yth Grp; Computer Clb; Drama Clb; Math Clb; Science Clb; Spanish Clb; Variety Show; VP Jr Cls; Bsbl; Socr; RUM.

RAMIREZ, NECTAR; Colegio San Antonio HS; Rio Piedras, PR; (S); 5/85; Dance Clb; Debate Tm; Hosp Aide; JA; VP Model UN; Band; Pres Jr Cls; Hon Roll; NHS; Pres Clssrm Awd 85; Stu Of Mnth Awd Leo Clb 84; Myrs Forum Prog Awd 84; Purdue U; Chem Engrng.

RAMOS RODRIGUEZ, CALIX; Colegio Santa Rita HS; Bayamon, PR; (S); 1/115; Church Yth Grp; French Clb; Math Clb; Pres Soph Cls; Pres Jr Cls; High Hon Roll; NHS; Pres Schlr; Lit Awd 84; Volunteer Svc 84; UPR; Med.

RAMPOLLA, PEDRO; Colegio San Ignacio De Loyola HS; Guaynabo, PR; (Y); Pres Aud/Vis; Camera Clb; Stage Crew; Yrbk Phtg; Yrbk Stf; Rep Jr Cls; Yrbk Photo Editor; Video Clb Mdl; Ntl Hspnc Semi Fnlst; Biomedcl Engrng.

RICH, TIMOTHY; Antilles HS; FPO Miami, FL; (Y); 5/110; Church Yth Grp; JA; Sec JCL; Sec Latin Clb; Trk; High Hon Roll; JETS Awd; Trs NHS; ST Latin Forum,Pnthln Test 1st Pl 84; Wrld Hist Awd 84; Natl Latin Exam Silver Medal 84; Aerosp Engr.

RIVERA, EDGARDO; Colegio Ponceno HS; Guayama, PR; (S); Boy Scts; High Hon Roll; Engrng.

RIVERA, GREGORY; Menonita Acad; Bayamon, PR; (Y); 2/26; Computer Clb; Trs Frsh Cls; Trs Soph Cls; Trs Jr Cls; Trs Sr Cls; Sal; Natl Hisp Awd SF 85; Sci Bowl 85; Pres Clsrm 85; Elect Engrng.

RIVERA, MILTON A; Immaculate Conception Acad; Mayaguez, PR; (S); 135/148; Boy Scts; Drama Clb; English Clb; Pres VP JA; Science Clb; Service Clb; Spanish Clb; Off Jr Cls; Stu Cncl; Swmmng; 1st Pl V P Fin Jr Achvt & 3rd Pl Sci Fair Microbio 83-84; 3rd Pl Sci Fr Biophy & Jr Achvt Pres 84-85; U Of PR Mayaguez; Bus Admin.

RIVERA, NELSON; Baldwin School Of PR; Humacao, PR; (S); Computer Clb; Math Clb; Math Tm; Science Clb; Yrbk Stf; Trs Stu Cncl; Cit Awd; High Hon Roll; Hon Roll; Trs NHS; 1st Pl Spnsh Spelling Cntst 82; U Of CA Berkely; Engrng.

RIVERA, NURIA; Robinson HS; Bayamon, PR; (Y); 3/47; Spanish Clb; School Play; Nwsp Ed-Chief; Yrbk Bus Mgr; Lit Mag; Pres Sr Cls; Var Bsktbl; Hon Roll; Ntl Merit SF; Journlsm Schlrshp Urban Journ Wrkshp NJ 84; English.

RIVERA MILLAN, AGALEE T; Colegio San Antonio HS; Rio Piedras, PR; (S); 10/101; Church Yth Grp; Church Choir; Hon Roll; NHS; Schlrshp Awd 83; U Of FL; Med.

RIVERA VAZQUEZ, ADRIA M; Jose Gautier Benitez HS; Caguas, PR; (Y); Am Leg Aux Girls St; Church Yth Grp.

ROBERT, LISA; Cupeyville Schl; Rio Piedras, PR; (Y); Cmnty Wkr; VP Key Clb; Sec Model UN; Political Wkr; Variety Show; Rep Soph Cls; VP Jr Cls; Rep Stu Cncl; Var Vllybl; Ntl Merit SF; Ntl Ldrshp Trainng 83; Outstndng Ldr 85; La Salle U; Accntng.

ROCAFORT, VANESSA LOPEZ; Colegio San Antonio HS; Rio Piedras, PR; (S); 2/101; Debate Tm; FCA; Math Tm; NFL; Trs Stu Cncl; JV Var Trk; Capt Vllybl; VP Jr NHS; NHS; First Hrn, Hist & Phys Ed Hnrs 83; Ophtalmology.

RODRIGUEZ, AYMAR; Colegio San Antonio HS; Isabela, PR; (S); Art Clb; Drama Clb; English Clb; Math Clb; Science Clb; Spanish Clb; Chorus; High Hon Roll; Hon Roll; NHS; CAAM Mayaguez; Med.

RODRIGUEZ, LARISSA; Academia Maria Reina HS; Guaynabo, PR; (Y); 3/74; Cmnty Wkr; Dance Clb; Pres Math Clb; Math Tm; VP Science Clb; Lit Mag; Crs Cntry; Trk; NHS; Literary Cont 83; MA Inst Of Tech; Engr.

RODRIGUEZ, MARISOL; Eloisa Pascual HS; Caquas, PR; (S); DECA; FHA; GAA; Cheerleading; Swmmng; Vllybl; Inter Amer U; Bus Admin.

RODRIGUEZ CASTRO, ABNEL; Escuela Superior De Yauco HS; Yauco, PR; (S); Library Aide; Math Tm; School Musical; Ntl Hspnc Schlr Awd 85; Acadmc All-Amer 85; Universidad De Puerto Rico; Med.

ROMAGUERA, RITA; Immaculate Conception Acad; Mayaguez, PR; (Y); 1/74; Debate Tm; JA; Model UN; Yrbk Stf; VP Sec Stu Cncl; Bausch & Lomb Sci Awd; NHS; Val; English Clb; Otstndng Stu Yr 85; U Of Puerto Rico; Pre-Med.

ROMAN, AMAYRIS; Santa Rosa HS; Bayamon, PR; (Y); Church Yth Grp; JA; Political Wkr; Pres Service Clb; Teachers Aide; VP Chorus; Cheerleading; Gym; Baymon Tech U Coll; Lng Tchr.

ROMAN, ANTONIO; Colegio Ponceno HS; Ponce, PR; (S); 13/83; Boy Scts; Pres Soph Cls; VP Jr Cls; Rep Stu Cncl; JV Trk; High Hon Roll; Hon Roll; Jr NHS; Pres NHS; Tae Kwon Do 79-83; Jrnlsm, Math, Guidnc Clbs 84-85; Tufts U; Pre-Med.

ROMAN, LOURDES; Colegio Ponceno HS; Ponce, PR; (S); 10/83; Sec Frsh Cls; Sec Soph Cls; Sec Jr Cls; Pres Sr Cls; Sec Stu Cncl; JV Chess Clb; JV Crs Cntry; JV Trk; High Hon Roll; Hon Roll; MA Coll Of Pharmacy; Pharmcy.

ROSA, ANGELES; Rio Piedras Heights HS; Rio Piedras, PR; (Y); Church Yth Grp; Civic Clb; Dance Clb; Drama Clb; FTA; Girl Scts; PAVAS; Varsity Clb; Color Guard; Variety Show; FL U; Dance Educ.

ROSARIO, EILEEN; Academia Sagrado Corazon; Pto Nuevo, PR; (S); 12/57; Pres Church Yth Grp; Pres English Clb; JA; Red Cross Aide; Science Clb; Church Choir; Rep Frsh Cls; Rep Soph Cls; NHS; Recinto Mayaguez; Engrng.

ROSSELLO, ADOLFO; Colegio Ponceno HS; Ponce, PR; (S); Nwsp Rptr; Nwsp Stf; Yrbk Rptr; Yrbk Stf; Trs Jr Cls; Trs Sr Cls; Rep Stu Cncl; Bsktbl; Coach Actv; Timer; Rep Yr Stu Cncl 83; Mjr Hnr 82-84; Elec Eng.

RUIZ, CARMEN M; Colegio San Antonio De Isabela HS; Quebradillas, PR; (S); Art Clb; Church Yth Grp; Cmnty Wkr; Science Clb; Church Choir; Bsktbl; 4-H Awd; Cert Cprtn/Gd Cndct Spnsh 82; Prfct Attnd, Spnsh, Rlgn, Avg Btr, Hgh Hnr Mdls 83; Grateful Appr Awd 81; Med.

RUIZ, MARITZA; Colegio San Antonio HS; Isabela, PR; (S); Church Yth Grp; English Clb; Math Clb; Science Clb; Spanish Clb; Rep Sr Cls; NHS; Scientfc Fair Awd 4th & 3rd Pl 83-84; Essay Awd 83; Universidad De Puerto Rico; Bio.

RUIZ, SARAI; Academia Sagrado Corazon HS; Carolina, PR; (S); 4/82; Hosp Aide; Library Aide; Red Cross Aide; Drill Tm; Nwsp Stf; High Hon Roll; NCTE Awd; Exclncy Wrld Hstry, Hm Ec 84; Achvt Awd Bio 84; U Of PR; Bio Tchr.

RULLAN, ANA; Liceo Ponceno HS; Ponce, PR; (Y); 1/16; School Play; Nwsp Stf; Pres Frsh Cls; Trs Soph Cls; Sec Trs Stu Cncl; Pres NHS; Val; Spnsh Awd, Engl Awd, Sci Awd, Hstry Awd 85; 1st Prize Schl & Dstrcts Sci Fair 84; Purdue U; Sci.

RUSSE, ANTONIO; Academia Sagrado Corazon; Bayamon, PR; (S); 11/60; English Clb; Math Clb; Math Tm; Science Clb; Nwsp Stf; Yrbk Stf; Stu Cncl; Swmmng; NHS; Spnsh & Math 83-84; Spllng Bee Awd 84; Recinto U; Mech Engrng.

RUSSE, ZAHYRA; Academia Sagrado Corazon; Bayamon, PR; (S); JA; Nwsp Stf; Swmmng; Jr NHS; Lion Awd; Sec NHS; CISC Wnnr 84; Achvt Awds In Bio, Alg I & II, Spnsh & Typng 82-84; U Of Puerto Rico; Med.

SAFIRSTEIN, JUDITH; Robinson HS; Santurce, PR; (S); 2/50; Teachers Aide; High Hon Roll; Ntl Span Exam 1st Prz 84; Chem, Span Rlgn, Geom Awd 84; Arts.

SAN MILLAN, MINNKA; Robinson HS; Santurce, PR; (S); Math Clb; Math Tm; Nwsp Stf; Var Bsktbl; Var Crs Cntry; JV Trk; Hon Roll; NHS; Bronze Medal Trck 83-84; 1st Pl Ntl Spanish Ex 83-84; Sci.

SANABRIA CARLO, DAVID; Colegio Santa Rita; Bayamon, PR; (S); 6/118; Math Tm; Temple Yth Grp; Yrbk Phtg; Off Jr Cls; VP Stu Cncl; Im Trk; NHS; Spanish NHS; Elec Engr.

SANABRIA FLORES, OMAR; Jose De Diego HS; Aguadilla, PR; (S); DECA; JA; Trs Sr Cls; Mrktng.

SANCHEZ, FEDERICO; Colegio San Ignacio HS; Rio Piedras, PR; (Y); Cmnty Wkr; Pep Clb; Science Clb; Varsity Clb; Socr; PR Schlstc Sci Fr 3rd Pl Chem & Microbio 83-85; Smmr Progs At Choate, Phillips Acad & Cornell 82-84; Coll Of The Holy Cross; Vet Med.

SANCHEZ, ROBERTO; U P R Secondary Schl; Hato Rey, PR; (Y); 2/73; Art Clb; Computer Clb; Math Clb; Math Tm; Science Clb; Band; NHS; MA Inst Of Tech; Comp Sci.

SANCHEZ, SEGI GONZALEZ; Manvela Toro Morice HS; Caguas, PR; (Y); Band; School Musical; Clegio Universitario De Mayagu.

SANTA, COLETTE; Colegio Ponceno HS; Ponce, PR; (S); Girl Scts; Library Aide; Math Clb; Teachers Aide; Nwsp Rptr; Pres Jr Cls; High Hon Roll; Hgh Hnr Diplomat; Lit Cert; Emmanuel Coll; Pre-Dent.

SANTIAGO, MARIADEL C; Manuela Toro Horice HS; Caguas, PR; (Y); 4/305; Church Yth Grp; Sec Hosp Aide; Sec Library Aide; Office Aide; Science Clb; Temple Yth Grp; Pres Frsh Cls; Sec Jr Cls; High Hon Roll; Trs NHS; Sci Awd 82; Spnsh Awd 82-85; Hgh Hnr Awd 82-85; Hlth Clss Hgh Hnr Awd 85; U CT Storrs; Rssn.

SANTOS, ERICK; Colegio San Jose HS; Rio Piedras, PR; (Y); 1/92; Chess Clb; Church Yth Grp; Pres Math Clb; Capt Math Tm; VP Model UN; Science Clb; Rep Stu Cncl; Im Ftbl; JV L Wrstlng; Cit Awd; Pres Schlr 85; Ntl Hspnc Schlr Awds Semifnlst 85; Bio Engrng.

SEDA, ERICK; Immaculate Conception Acad; Hormigueros, PR; (S); Boy Scts; Church Yth Grp; Drama Clb; JA; Library Aide; Science Clb; Spanish Clb; Chorus; School Musical; Nwsp Stf; Stu Cncl Outstndng Awd 83-84; Oratory Cntst 3r Prz 82-83; Commnctns.

SEMIDEY, JUAN PABLO; Colegio San Ignacio De Loyola HS; Guaynabo, PR; (Y); Math Clb; Math Tm; Sec Trs Model UN; Speech Tm; Nwsp Bus Mgr; High Hon Roll; NEDT Awd; Pres Schlr; Cmnty Wkr; Computer Clb; Ntl Hispanic Schlrshp 85; Ntl Soc Of Prfssnl Engrs Schlrshp 85; MA Inst Of Tech; Elec Engrng.

SERRANO, EDGARDO MORALES; Madre Cabrini HS; Guaynabo, PR; (S); Hosp Aide; Bsktbl; Spanish NHS; Pharmacist.

SMITH, CHAD; Cupeyville Schl; Caguas, PR; (Y); 2/55; Church Yth Grp; Trs Math Clb; Math Tm; Office Aide; Speech Tm; Concert Band; Variety Show; NHS; Ntl Merit Ltr; Engrng.

SOLER, JOAQUIN; Colegio San Antonio Abad HS; Humacao, PR; (Y); Camera Clb; Chess Clb; Math Clb; Math Tm; Science Clb; Nwsp Sprt Ed; Yrbk Sprt Ed; Rep Sr Cls; Var Bsktbl; Var Crs Cntry; GA Tech; Mech Engr.

SOSA, EDWIN ALFONSO; Colegio San Antonio HS; Quebradillas, PR; (Y); 2/28; Aud/Vis; Camera Clb; Drama Clb; Exploring; VP Science Clb; Math Tm; School Play; Variety Show; Timer; Vllybl; ST Sci Fair 1st Pl & Grnd Prz 84; OH ST Bausch & Lomb 1st Awd 84; SPSE 3rd Awd 84; Sci Tlnt Srch; Caam U; Physics.

SOSA, SALVATORE; Central Bellas Artes HS; J Caparr Bay, PR; (Y); 12/60; CAP; Red Cross Aide; Acpl Chr; Chorus; Madrigals; Orch; School Musical; UNICEF Clndr 83; Govnrs Merit Awd 84; ARTS 84-85; Columbus Schl Dsgn; Illstrtn.

SOSTRE BOU, HECTOR; Colegio Sata Rita HS; Bayamon, PR; (S); 1/115; French Clb; Math Clb; VP Frsh Cls; VP Jr Cls; Hon Roll; Jr NHS; NHS; Prfct Atten Awd; Med.

STANWOOD, ARTHUR; Roosevelt Roads HS; Ceiba, PR; (Y); Office Aide; Band; Ftbl; Socr; Trk; High Hon Roll; Hon Roll; Srgnt Miltary Schl 84-85; U VA; Bus.

SUAREZ, ANA; Academia Maria Reina HS; Aguirre, PR; (Y); 8/71; Drama Clb; French Clb; Hosp Aide; Math Clb; Math Tm; Office Aide; Science Clb; Yrbk Ed-Chief; Sftbl; Hon Roll; GA Tech MITE 84; Georgetown U; Med.

SUED, NADYA ELIZA; Notre Dame HS; Cayey, PR; (Y); 67/168; Art Clb; Chess Clb; Church Yth Grp; Computer Clb; Dance Clb; Drama Clb; 4-H; Girl Scts; Hosp Aide; Intnl Clb; Mst Actv Stdnt Math Clb 83-85; Cacigve Awd 82; Math Recog 82; Coll Of St Benedict; Bio.

TARONJI, LUIS; Colegio San Ignacio De Loyola; San Juan, PR; (Y); Computer Clb; Nwsp Stf; Cert Of Merit 85; Gold Mdl-Bst Tutor Of Math Tutrl Staff 85; U Of PR; Bus Adm.

TERRASSA, LUIS; Colegio Marista HS; Guaynabo, PR; (Y); Aud/Vis; Camera Clb; Yrbk Stf; High Hon Roll; Pres JETS Awd; Pres Jr NHS; NHS; GA Inst Of Vo Tech; Ind Engrg.

TIRADO, WILFREDO; Colegio San Ignacio De Loyola; Rio Piedras, PR; (Y); Boy Scts; Cmnty Wkr; Computer Clb; Im Bsktbl; Im Vllybl; Natl Hspnc Schlr Awd Semi-Fin 85; U Of MA Amhurst; Comp Engrng.

TORRECH, SHELMA; Colegio Santa Rosa HS; Levittown, PR; (Y); 20/97; Art Clb; Church Yth Grp; Dance Clb; Drama Clb; English Clb; FHA; Library Aide; Chorus; School Play; Frsh Cls; Airline Course Diplma 85; U Of PR; Drama.

TORRES, EDWIN; Colegio Madre Cabrini HS; Rio Piedras, PR; (S); Boy Scts; Math Clb; Science Clb; Sr Cls; Bsbl; Bsktbl; Vllybl; NHS; Cert Of Merit Spn Eng Sci Math Hstry & Relign 81-84; U Of PR; Pre-Med.

TORRES, SANDRA; Colegio San Antonio HS; Carolina, PR; (S); 4/101; Dance Clb; Math Tm; Chorus; Variety Show; Nwsp Ed-Chief; Sec Frsh Cls; Capt Cheerleading; High Hon Roll; NHS; Prfct Atten Awd; Accntnt.

TORRES FERRER, JESUS R; Col San Ignacio De Loyola HS; Rio Piedras, PR; (Y); JA; Model UN; Nwsp Rptr; Im Socr; Jr NHS; GA Inst Of Tech; Elec Engr.

VALENTIN VELEZ, WANDA I; Jose De Diego HS; Aguadilla, PR; (S); Church Yth Grp; DECA; JA; Hon Roll.

VARELA RIOS, HECTOR M; Colegio San Ignacio HS; San Juan, PR; (Y); Church Yth Grp; Computer Clb; French Clb; Science Clb; School Play; Yrbk Stf; Rep Sr Cls; Im Bsktbl; Hon Roll; Ntl Merit SF; U Of Puerto Rico; Mech Engr.

VARGAS, CYNTHIA E; San Antonio Acad; Aguirre, PR; (Y); 2/31; Dance Clb; Library Aide; Math Tm; Science Clb; Teachers Aide; Rep Soph Cls; Rep Jr Cls; Rep Sr Cls; Trk; Vllybl; S K & F Lab Co Schlrshp 82; Lit Essy Cntst Merit Awd 84; Purdu U; Dntl Med.

VARGAS, OLGA M; Notre Dame HS; Caguas, PR; (Y); 21/167; Art Clb; Church Yth Grp; Computer Clb; Science Clb; Nwsp Ed-Chief; Nwsp Rptr; Nwsp Stf; Stu Cncl; NHS; 1st Grnd Prz-Litrry Cntst 84 & 85; Soc Stds Medal 85; Hood Coll; Advrtsng.

VASSOS, IRENE; Academia San Jose HS; Rio Piedras, PR; (Y); Trs Art Clb; Camera Clb; FBLA; Pres Science Clb; Hon Roll; NHS; Ntl Merit SF; NEDT Awd; Chem Awd; Comp Sci.

VASWANI, ROSEMARY; Episcopal Cathedral Schl; Santurce, PR; (Y); 7/14; Pres Drama Clb; Pres NFL; School Play; Stage Crew; Variety Show; Nwsp Rptr; Nwsp Stf; Yrbk Ed-Chief; Sec Soph Cls; Sec Jr Cls; Cert Merit Engl 81; Theater Arts.

VAZGUEZ, MARY ANNETTE; Colegio Madre Cabrini HS; Caparra Heights, PR; (Y); 4/65; Pres Science Clb; VP Soph Cls; Stu Cncl; Swmmng; Hon Roll; Pres NHS; JV Bsktbl; 1st Prx Sci Fair 82; Army Cert Achvt 82; Cert Achvt Am Spck Lang Hearng Assoc 82; U Rochester; Med.

VAZQUEZ, MARY A; Madre Cabrini HS; Caparra Heights, PR; (S); 2/63; Hosp Aide; Math Tm; Pres Science Clb; Yrbk Stf; Rep Stu Cncl; JV Bsktbl; Hon Roll; Pres NHS; Church Yth Grp; Computer Clb; 1st Pz Sci Fair 83; USA Army Cert Achvt 83; Soc Sci Awd 82; Med.

VEGA, HECTOR E; Dr Carlos Gonzalez HS; Aguada, PR; (Y); 21/280; Dance Clb; English Clb; Teachers Aide; School Play; Stage Crew; Variety Show; Yrbk Rptr; Yrbk Stf; Sec Sr Cls; Sci Awd 82; Governor Awd Dance 84; Hon Men Foundatn Advncmnt In Arts 85; Fine Arts.

VEGA, NESTOR RIVERA; Commonwealth HS; Dorado, PR; (Y); Math Tm; Band; School Play; Yrbk Ed-Chief; Yrbk Phtg; Golf; Ntl Merit SF; GA Inst Of Technology; Mech En.

VEGA BATISTA, FERNANDO; Colegio Santa Rita HS; Bayamon, PR; (S); 5/81; FCA; Varsity Clb; Bsktbl; Vllybl; NHS; Prfct Atten Awd; UPR; Pharmacy.

VELEZ, FRANCISCO; Colegio San Antonio HS; Isabela, PR; (S); 5/28; Computer Clb; English Clb; Science Clb; Service Clb; VP Sr Cls; Im Bsbl; Im Bsktbl; Im Sftbl; Im Trk; Hon Roll; U Of PR; Dntstry.

VELEZ, GISELA; Perpetuo Socorro Acad; Santurce, PR; (Y); 1/75; Hosp Aide; Math Clb; Math Tm; Pres NFL; Science Clb; Pres Chorus; School Musical; Pres NHS; NEDT Awd; 1st & 2nd Pl Oratory Spanish & Eng Forensic League 84-85; 2nd Pl Poetry Frnch Forensic League 84; Pre-Med.

VELEZ, ROBERTO RUIZ; Yauco HS; Yauco, PR; (Y); ROTC; Hon Roll; Hgh Hnr 82; Cientefia Awd 82; Catholic U-PR; Aerosp Engnrng.

VILELLA, CRISTINA; Antilles HS; Rio Piedras, PR; (Y); 1/89; Q&S; Pres Band; Capt Drill Tm; Drm Mjr(t); Stu Cncl; Capt Tennis; Vllybl; VP NHS; Val; Math Clb; MITES 84; MA Inst Of Tech; Chmcl Engrng.

VILLANUEVA, LISSETTE HERNANDEZ; Jose De Diego HS; Aguadilla, PR; (S); 12/40; Church Yth Grp; Debate Tm; JA; Red Cross Aide; Chorus; School Musical; School Play; Off Sr Cls; High Hon Roll; Hon Roll; Merit Cert 80-85; High Hnr Medal 79 & 82; Colegio De Mayaguez; Ind Mgr.

WILLMORE, MARIA T; Academia Del Perpetuo Secorro HS; Santurce, PR; (Y); 15/75; Ntl Hispnc Schlr 84; Finance.

WRIGHT, JAMES; Baldwin School Of Puerto Rico; Yabucoa, PR; (S); 2/22; Scholastic Bowl; Var L Bsbl; Var L Bsktbl; Var L Socr; Cit Awd; High Hon Roll; NHS; Sal; Pres Frsh Cls; VP Soph Cls; Mst Outstndng Stu 84-85; US Army Rsrve Schlr-Athlete Awd 84-85; U Of FL-GAINESVILLE; Phrmcy.

YANG, WEI-LI; Robinson Schl; Isla Verde, PR; (S); Computer Clb; Mathletes; Math Clb; Math Tm; Spanish Clb; Variety Show; Pom Pon; Hon Roll; Spnsh Awd 83-84; Comp Engrng.

ZAYAS, JUAN C; Manuela Toro Morice HS; Caguas, PR; (Y); Camera Clb; Band; School Musical; Off Sr Cls; NHS; U Of PR; Comp.

RHODE ISLAND

ABBRUZZI, ELENA; Johnston HS; Johnston, RI; (S); 23/237; VP DECA; Capt Drm Mjr(t); Hon Roll; NHS; JV Powder Puff Ftbl; Stat Socr; U Of RI; Bus.

ABELA, STEPHANIE; Prout Memorial HS; E Greenwich, RI; (Y); 13/85; Color Guard; School Musical; Nwsp Rptr; Sec Frsh Cls; Sec Soph Cls; Sec Jr Cls; Sec Sr Cls; JV Bsktbl; Hon Roll; NHS; Nutrtn.

ACCETTA, STEPHANIE; Cranston West HS; Cranston, RI; (Y); GAA; Latin Clb; Political Wkr; Ski Clb; Sec Frsh Cls; Rep Jr Cls; Off Stu Cncl; Var Cheerleading; Var Tennis; Hon Roll; Outstndng HS Wrtr 85; Supt Advsry Bd.

ACETO, RICHARD; North Providence HS; North Providence, RI; (Y); Boy Scts; VP Church Yth Grp; Quiz Bowl; Scholastic Bowl; Band; Concert Band; Mrchg Band; Orch; Stage Crew; Rep Soph Cls; U RI; Pre-Med.

ACKROYD, ALAN; Chariho Regional HS; West Kingston, RI; (S); VP Church Yth Grp; Letterman Clb; Varsity Clb; Rep Sr Cls; Rep Stu Cncl; Coach Actv; Mgr(s); Var L Socr; Hon Roll; Rotary Awd; World Affairs Seminar 84; Accntng.

ADAMS, ANNE MARIE; Woonsocket SR HS; Woonsocket, RI; (Y); Church Yth Grp; Math Tm; Nwsp Rptr; High Hon Roll; Prfct Atten Awd; Holy Crs Bk Awd 85; Germaine B Tougas Awd Excllnce Fr 83; Gld Mdl Natl Lat Exam Summa Cum Laude 83; Archit.

ADAMS, LEAH; East Providence HS; East Providence, RI; (Y); 143/440; 4-H; French Clb; JA; Var L Crs Cntry; Var L Trk; Hon Roll; Harrier Awd Cross Cnty 84; Mst Vlbl Rnnr Outdr Track 85; Wheaton Coll; Bio.

AGNEW, KAREN; Johnston SR HS; Johnston, RI; (Y); 30/254; JA; Hon Roll; RI Coll; Comp Sci.

AHEARN, KELLY; Warren HS; Warren, RI; (Y); 13/130; Yrbk Stf; Stat Score Keeper; JV Vllybl; Hon Roll; NHS; Natl Hon Soc Sec; RI Hon Soc; Newport Schl; Nursing.

AIDALA, RICHARD; Mt St Charles HS; Chepachet, RI; (Y); 10/147; Math Tm; Rep Jr Cls; Im Ice Hcky; Var Tennis; High Hon Roll; NHS; Natl Secdry Ed Acadmc All Amer 85.

ALBANESE, GREGORY; Classical HS; Providence, RI; (Y); Var Bsbl; Var Ice Hcky; Hon Roll; Italian Hnr Soc Natl 85; Providence Coll; Comp Sci.

ALDERMAN, TANYA; Mount St Charles Acad; W Warwick, RI; (Y); 39/164; Church Yth Grp; 4-H; Service Clb; Gym; Swmmng; 4-H Awd; Hon Roll; Provdnc Coll Smmr Sci Prog 84; Marshall U; Med.

ALDRICH, DEBORAH; Scituate JR SR HS; N Scituate, RI; (S); 20/118; Church Yth Grp; Hosp Aide; Yrbk Bus Mgr; Rep Soph Cls; Rep Stu Cncl; Stat Bsktbl; Hon Roll; PWA Of Rnbw 84; Quinnipiac Coll; Phys Thrpy.

ALDRICH, KARI; Coventry HS; Coventry, RI; (Y); Sec Church Yth Grp; Q&S; Spanish Clb; Nwsp Ed-Chief; Nwsp Rptr; Nwsp Stf; Trk; Voice Dem Awd; All Amer Jrnlsm Stdnt 85; Paralegal.

ALESSANDRINI, LISA; Johnston SR HS; Johnston, RI; (S); 8/238; Nwsp Stf; NHS; RI Hnr Scty 85; RI Tchrs Italian Cert Merit 84; Bryant Coll; Bus Admin.

ALEXANDER, WILLIAM; Portsmouth HS; Portsmouth, RI; (Y); Boy Scts; High Hon Roll; Hon Roll; NHS; Comp Sci.

ALGIERE, PATRICK; Chariho Regional HS; Bradford, RI; (Y); 17/302; Aud/Vis; Library Aide; Var Crs Cntry; Var Trk; High Hon Roll; Hon Roll; Pratt Inst; Marin Technlgy.

ALLEN, MELISSA J; Mount St Charles Acad; Franklin, MA; (Y); High Hon Roll; Bio.

ALLEN, SCOTT; Pilgrim HS; Warwick, RI; (Y); Hosp Aide; Math Tm; Ski Clb; Band; Concert Band; Jazz Band; Mrchg Band; Orch; School Musical; Nwsp Rptr; Med.

ALLINSON, ROBERT; Chariho Regional HS; Ashaway, RI; (S); Chess Clb; Drama Clb; Math Tm; Band; Concert Band; Jazz Band; School Play; High Hon Roll; Rotary Awd; RI Hugh O Brian Yth Ldrshp Fdn Amb 84; Math.

ALLSTROM, KRISTINE; Toll Gate HS; Warwick, RI; (Y); 3/393; German Clb; Jazz Band; Nwsp Stf; Yrbk Stf; Trs Soph Cls; Pres Jr Cls; Pres Sr Cls; Var Vllybl; DAR Awd; NHS; Sec Of ST Ldrshp Awd 85; Arion Music Awd 85; U Of PA; Bio.

ALMEIDA, CANDACE M; Saint Raphael Acad; Providence, RI; (Y); 11/172; Drama Clb; French Clb; School Musical; School Play; Vllybl; Hon Roll; NHS; Ntl Negro Schlrshp Semi-Fnlst 84; Ntl Merit Cmmnd Stu 84; RI Coll.

ALMEIDA, PAUL; Birstol HS; Bristol, RI; (S); Boy Scts; Church Yth Grp; JV Bsbl; JV Bsktbl; High Hon Roll; Hon Roll; NHS; RI Tchrs Italian Hnr Roll 83-84; Elec Engr.

ALMEIDA, RICHARD M; Bristol HS; Bristol, RI; (Y); 20/235; Church Yth Grp; Drama Clb; English Clb; ROTC; Yrbk Stf; Stu Cncl; JV Bsktbl; Elks Awd; High Hon Roll; Hon Roll; Elks Ldrshp Awd 85; Engl Awd 85; Fernand St Gemain Cngrssmns Mdl Of Merit 85; US Mrchnt Marine Acad; Engrng.

ALVAREZ, IVAN; Central Falls JR SR HS; Central Falls, RI; (Y); Am Leg Boys St; Chess Clb; Rep Stu Cncl; JV Var Bsktbl; Hon Roll; Jr NHS; NHS; Prfct Atten Awd; Mech Engr.

ALVAREZ, JUAN; Central Falls HS; Central Falls, RI; (Y); 24/136; Boys Clb Am; Church Yth Grp; Drama Clb; JA; School Play; Stage Crew; Yrbk Phtg; Rep Sr Cls; JV Bsktbl; Prfct Atten Awd; Jr Achvt Awds 82-83; CCRI; Accntng.

ALVES, FATIMA; Our Lady Of Fatima HS; Bristol, RI; (Y); 7/36; Sec Frsh Cls; Sec Soph Cls; Sec Jr Cls; Sec Sr Cls; Sec Stu Cncl; Sftbl; Hon Roll; Mc Donalds Crew Person Yr 84; RI Coll.

AMARAL, DIAHANN; Barrington HS; Barrington, RI; (Y); Girl Scts; Red Cross Aide; Yrbk Stf; Cheerleading; JV Mgr(s); Score Keeper; Timer; Var Trk; Hnrbl Mntn In ST For Hurdles 85; Svrl Awds For Hurdles 83-85; Nrthestrn U; Crmnl Lawyer.

AMARAL, RICK; Bristol HS; Bristol, RI; (Y); Debate Tm; Math Clb; Math Tm; Ski Clb; Aeronutc Engr.

AMBROSE, JAMES; Mt St Charles Acad; Norfolk, MA; (S); 11/165; Exploring; ROTC; School Play; Nwsp Ed-Chief; Nwsp Rptr; Nwsp Stf; Lit Mag; Pres Frsh Cls; Pres Sr Cls; JV Ice Hcky; Holy Cross Bk Awd; Ntl Stu Cncl Soc; US Air Force Acad; Aviation.

ANDERES, CECILE; North Kingstown HS; Saunderstown, RI; (Y); 40/375; Varsity Clb; Nwsp Stf; Yrbk Stf; Stu Cncl; Var Fld Hcky; Capt Vllybl; Hon Roll; U RI.

ANDERSON, TANIA; Middletown HS; Middletown, RI; (S); 30/252; Church Yth Grp; Drama Clb; Pres French Clb; Ski Clb; Stage Crew; Yrbk Stf; Lit Mag; Sec Sr Cls; Rep Stu Cncl; Im Crs Cntry; RI Acad Decathln 83; Intnl Bus.

ANDRE, WENDY M; West Warwick HS; W Warwick, RI; (Y); 19/257; Cmnty Wkr; JA; Library Aide; Chorus; School Musical; Nwsp Stf; Yrbk Rptr; Yrbk Sprt Ed; Yrbk Stf; Stu Cncl; Challeng Schlstc Awrd 82-83; Josephine Barber Schlrshp 84-85; U RI; Fash Merch.

ANDREW, KAREN; Pilgrim HS; Warwick, RI; (Y); Sec French Clb; GAA; Red Cross Aide; Band; Mrchg Band; Variety Show; Yrbk Stf; Capt Bsktbl; Capt Vllybl; VP French Hon Soc; Vllybll & Bsktbll All Div 85; Bus.

ANGELL, SUSAN; St Mary Academy Bayview; Providence, RI; (Y); 25/196; Debate Tm; Hosp Aide; Pep Clb; Yrbk Stf; Rep Frsh Cls; Rep Soph Cls; Rep Jr Cls; Rep Stu Cncl; Hon Roll; NHS; Poli Sci.

ANTONUCCI, CARL A; Classical HS; Providence, RI; (Y); 45/287; Boys Clb Am; Cmnty Wkr; Hon Roll; Presdntl Acadmc Achv Awd 85; Italn Hnr Soc 85; RI Tchrs Itln Cert Mert 85; Providnc Coll; Rom Cath Priest.

ANTONUCCIO, KELLY A; Johnston SR HS; Johnston, RI; (Y); Drama Clb; Chorus; School Musical; School Play; Stage Crew; Variety Show; Hon Roll; RI Coll; Actg.

AQUIAR, KEVIN; Portsmouth HS; Portsmouth, RI; (Y); Var Bsbl; SMU; Mech Engrng.

ARANYOS, SHEILA; Portsmouth HS; Portsmouth, RI; (Y); 15/214; French Clb; FBLA; Spanish Clb; School Musical; School Play; Stage Crew; Nwsp Stf; Var Trk; High Hon Roll; Hon Roll.

ARCAND, ANGELA M; Lincoln HS; Manville, RI; (Y); 38/190; Church Yth Grp; Office Aide; Sec Trs Band; Trs Chorus; Sec Trs Concert Band; Sec Trs Mrchg Band; Rep Stu Cncl; Hon Roll; RI Coll; Accntng.

ARCAND, HELENE; Bay View Acad; Coventry, RI; (Y); 10/216; Exploring; French Clb; Church Choir; Orch; School Musical; French Hon Soc; Hon Roll; NHS; Math Clb; Schl Music Awd 84; Solo Perf Excell Awds 83-85.

AREIA, PAULA; Our Lady Of Fatima HS; Bristol, RI; (Y); Church Yth Grp; Political Wkr; Ski Clb; Im Swmmng; Var Trk; Hon Roll; Cert Of Awd In Sci 84; Pre-Law.

ARONSON, ROBIN; Classical HS; Providence, RI; (Y); Cmnty Wkr; VP French Clb; Teachers Aide; School Play; Yrbk Ed-Chief; Yrbk Phtg; Yrbk Stf; Hon Roll; Ntl Merit Ltr; Joel H Zaiman Schlr Awd 85; Lib Art.

ARPAIA, KIMBERLY; Bristol HS; Bristol, RI; (S); 54/220; GAA; Yrbk Stf; Off Soph Cls; Off Jr Cls; Off Sr Cls; Hon Roll; Jr NHS; NHS; Sawyer Schl; Med Sec Asst.

ASTON, GRETCHEN; North Kingstown HS; Jamestown, RI; (Y); 51/371; French Clb; Intnl Clb; Yrbk Stf; Hon Roll; URI; Medcl.

ATKINS, PATRICIA; Middletown HS; Middletown, RI; (S); 28/252; Exploring; Spanish Clb; Bsktbl; Crs Cntry; Powder Puff Ftbl; Trk; Hon Roll; NHS; Spanish NHS; Outdr Receatn.

ATKINS, SCOTT; Portsmouth HS; Portsmouth, RI; (Y); Am Leg Boys St; Boy Scts; Computer Clb; Ski Clb; Band; Var JV Socr; Hon Roll; NHS; Aerontcl Engr.

AUBIN, LINDA D; Lincoln JR SR HS; Manville, RI; (Y); 17/233; Rep Sr Cls; Stu Cncl; Capt Cheerleading; Capt Gym; Vllybl; High Hon Roll; NHS; St James Schlrshp Fund 84; Nrtheastrn U; Chem.

AUBUT, DIANE; Mt St Charles Acad; Franklin, MA; (Y); 19/140; Var Capt Gym; High Hon Roll; Hon Roll; NHS; All Div Tm Gym 83-84; USGF Cls I ST Champ 84-85; USGF Eastern Natls 84-85.

AUCOIN, JOYCE; Woonsocket HS; Woonsocket, RI; (Y); Church Yth Grp; Cmnty Wkr; Dance Clb; Office Aide; Variety Show; Bsktbl; Capt Sftbl; Hon Roll; Prfct Atten Awd; Secy.

AUGER, ANNE; East Providence SR HS; Rumford, RI; (Y); VP Church Yth Grp; Chorus; Rep Soph Cls; Rep Jr Cls; Rep Stu Cncl; Var Cheerleading; Var Gym; Var Sftbl; Var Tennis; Cls Of 1974 Awd Outstndng Ath 85; U CT; Phys Thrpy.

AUGER, ERIC; Mount St Charles Acad; Woonsocket, RI; (Y); 70/150; Trs Church Yth Grp; Drama Clb; Quiz Bowl; Ski Clb; Concert Band; Mrchg Band; Pep Band; Lbrl Arts.

AYARS, KATHY; Portsmouth HS; Portsmouth, RI; (Y); 1/220; Yrbk Stf; Var Bsktbl; Var Socr; Var Tennis; Var Trk; High Hon Roll; Hon Roll; NHS; Savgs Bnds & Mdls Outstndng Grds 80; Sccr Achvt 85; Vet.

AYLSWORTH, WENDY S; Coventry HS; Greene, RI; (S); Church Yth Grp; French Clb; Library Aide; Science Clb; Chorus; Hon Roll; RI JR Grange Princess 82-83; Arch.

BABCOCK, KATHI; Coventry HS; Coventry, RI; (Y); 1/450; Church Yth Grp; Dance Clb; French Clb; Hosp Aide; Variety Show; Yrbk Ed-Chief; Sec Stu Cncl; JV Capt Cheerleading; High Hon Roll; NHS; Brown U Bk Awd 84-85; Outstndng Latin Stu 84-85; Outstndng JR Stu Cncl 84-85; Pre-Med.

BABLENIS, KAREN; Cranston High Schl West; Cranston, RI; (Y); Sec Trs Church Yth Grp; Ski Clb; Spanish Clb; Lit Mag; URI; Bus.

BAILEY, ROBERT; North Kingstown HS; Jamestown, RI; (Y); 32/350; Cmnty Wkr; ROTC; High Hon Roll; Hon Roll; Cadet Of Mth 84; Coast Guard Acad; Marine Arch.

BAK, KERRI; North Providence HS; N Providence, RI; (Y); Church Yth Grp; GAA; Capt JV Bsktbl; JV Sftbl; Hon Roll; Kathrine Gibbs; Med Sec.

BAKER, KAREN; Chariho Regional JR-SR HS; Wyoming, RI; (S); Chorus; Rep Jr Cls; VP Cheerleading; High Hon Roll; Hon Roll; Ntl Chrldng Assoc Spirit Awd 84; Psych.

BAKER, KIMBERLEY; Chariho Regional HS; Wyoming, RI; (Y); 2/347; NHS; Music Dept Schlrshp 84-88; Wad Abusamra Schlrshp 84-85; U RI; Music.

BALCOM, THOS; La Salle Acad; Smithfield, RI; (Y); 39/204; Letterman Clb; Nwsp Stf; Capt Socr; Hon Roll; St Schlr; Ntl Soccer Cachs Assoc; MVP Soccer Awd; Salve Regina Coll; Crimnl Justc.

BALLING, EMILY; Portsmouth HS; Fort Douglas, UT; (Y); Pres Church Yth Grp; Band; Jazz Band; Mrchg Band; Pep Band; Symp Band; Hon Roll; Young Wmnhd Recog Awd 85; Band Sqd Of Yr 83; All ST Rgnl Band 83; Nrsng.

BANKAUSKAS, KAREN; Toll Gate HS; Warwick, RI; (S); Dance Clb; Spanish Clb; Band; Jr Cls; Var JV Cheerleading; Var JV Trk; Prfct Atten Awd; Bryant; Bus Admin.

BARBER, KRISTYN; Chariho Regional HS; Carolina, RI; (Y); Off Stu Cncl; Cpa.

BARBER, LYNDA J; Tolman SR HS; Pawtucket, RI; (Y); French Clb; JA; Hon Roll; Nrsng.

BARBOZA, WENDY; St Mary Acad Bay View; Bristol, RI; (Y); 1/216; French Clb; Math Clb; Orch; JV Sftbl; JV Var Timer; High Hon Roll; Hon Roll; Pres NHS; Prfct Atten Awd; ST Sci Fair 1st; US Naval Acad Smmr Sem; Engrng.

BARIL, ELIZABETH; West Warwick SR HS; W Warwick, RI; (Y); 2/200; Math Clb; Pep Clb; Variety Show; Yrbk Stf; Rep Stu Cncl; Var Cheerleading; High Hon Roll; Prfct Atten Awd; URI Alumni Assn Bk Awd; Hghst Acad Avg; MIT; Engrng.

BARNES, ERIC W; Cranston East HS; Cranston, RI; (Y); 16/405; Church Yth Grp; FCA; Acpl Chr; Pep Band; Variety Show; Rep Stu Cncl; Capt Bsbl; High Hon Roll; NHS; Pres Schlr; Mst Humerous Boy 81; U Of RI; Elec Engrng.

BARRETT, KIMBERLY; Warwick Veterans Memorial HS; Warwick, RI; (S); 16/323; Var Capt Cheerleading; Sftbl; High Hon Roll; Hon Roll; NHS; Mgmt.

BARRETTE, CHRISTINE; Mt St Charles Acad; Woonsocket, RI; (Y); 16/162; Church Yth Grp; Cmnty Wkr; Hosp Aide; Rep Stu Cncl; High Hon Roll; Hon Roll; NHS; RI ST Schlrshp 85; U Of RI; Nrsng.

BARRINGTON, BRYAN A; South Kingstown HS; Peace Dale, RI; (Y); 70/174; Debate Tm; Varsity Clb; Variety Show; Stu Cncl; Bsktbl; Bowling; Ftbl; Vllybl; Hon Roll; Amer Athlt 84-85; Achv Awd Review Math 84-85; New England Tech; Drftng.

BARROS, ROBERT S; Bristol HS; Bristol, RI; (Y); Drama Clb; JA; School Play; Stu Cncl; High Hon Roll; NHS; APSL Natl Lat Hnr Soc 85; Natl Itln Hnr Soc 82-84; Compete Eng Comp 85.

BASILE, BETH A; Prout Memorial HS; North Kingstown, RI; (S); 26/79; Off Church Yth Grp; Red Cross Aide; Off Band; Jazz Band; School Musical; Nwsp Stf; Sec Frsh Cls; Sec Soph Cls; Sec VP Stu Cncl; NHS; Bio Chem.

BATASTINI III, ARMANDO E; Classical HS; Providence, RI; (Y); 40/300; Am Leg Boys St; Pres Church Yth Grp; JCL; VP Latin Clb; Nwsp Stf; Var L Bsktbl; Var L Ftbl; Hon Roll; Ntl Merit Ltr; Summa Cum Laude Gldm Mdlst Latn III 84; U S Naval Acad; Intl Rel.

BATEMAN, SANDRA L; Lincoln JR SR HS; Smithfield, RI; (Y); 62/220; Church Yth Grp; JCL; Band; Var Fld Hcky; Hon Roll; Prfct Atten Awd; 2nd Grnt Schl Sci Fair 83; Hnrbl Mntn Schl Sci Fair 84; 2nd Grnt Sci Fair, Hnrbl Mntn Al-ST Hcky 85; RI Coll; Phy Thrpy.

BATES, RANDALL; Rogers HS; Newport, RI; (S); Am Leg Boys St; Church Yth Grp; Lit Mag; Pres Sr Cls; Var Capt Socr; Tennis; NHS; SAR Awd; Pol Sci.

BAUER, AMY; Our Lady Of Fatima HS; Bristol, RI; (S); Church Yth Grp; Cmnty Wkr; Chorus; Rep Stu Cncl; Var Bsktbl; JV Crs Cntry; Var Sftbl; High Hon Roll; Hon Roll.

BAVER, AMY; Our Lady Of Fatima HS; Bristol, RI; (Y); 2/55; Church Yth Grp; Cmnty Wkr; Chorus; Yrbk Stf; Rep Stu Cncl; Var Bsktbl; JV Crs Cntry; VP Sftbl; High Hon Roll; NHS; MV Vol Awd Wrkng Retard Child 84; Math,Eng Awd 84-85.

BEADE, ERICA N; Charles Shea HS; Pawtucket, RI; (Y); 1/240; Math Tm; Yrbk Stf; High Hon Roll; Hon Roll; NHS; Ntl Merit Ltr; Pres Schlr; Val; Brown U Bk Awd 84; Intl Frgn Lang Awd 85; Frnch Awd Excelnce 85; Wesleyan U; Stdio Art.

BEAUDET, KRISTINE; N Smithfield JR SR HS; N Smithfield, RI; (Y); Hst French Clb; Letterman Clb; Yrbk Stf; JV Var Bsktbl; Var L Cheerleading; JV Var Vllybl; Hon Roll; Sec Frsh Cls; Sec Soph Cls; Sec Jr Cls; Tchr.

BEAUDETTE, LAURINE; Bishop Keough Reginal HS; Central Falls, RI; (S); Church Yth Grp; High Hon Roll; Jr NHS; French & Algebra Awds 84; Bsns.

BECHAZ, LUCINDA; Mount Pleasant HS; Providence, RI; (Y); Dance Clb; Hosp Aide; Office Aide; Varsity Clb; Drm Mjr(t); School Play; Jr Cls; Stu Cncl; Cit Awd; Choir, Ctznshp Awds 84; Typng Awd 80; Essay For Poetry Awd 85; Law.

BEDARD, KATHY; St Marys Academy- Bay View; Coventry, RI; (Y); 26/195; Lit Mag; Rep Frsh Cls; Rep Soph Cls; Rep Jr Cls; Rep Sr Cls; Rep Stu Cncl; Capt Cheerleading; Trk; Dnfth Awd; NHS; URI Merit Schlrshp 85-89; Phy Ftns Awds 82-85; U Of RI; Nrsng.

BEDARD, RICHARD; Burrillville HS; Mapleville, RI; (Y); 10/179; Am Leg Boys St; Church Yth Grp; Band; Concert Band; Jazz Band; Mrchg Band; Pep Band; School Play; Nwsp Stf; Bsktbl; Susan L Farmer Ldrshp Awd 85; RI Hnr Soc 85; Jrnl Essy Cntst 85; SE MA U; Illstrn.

BEHRINGER, RACHEL; North Kingstown HS; N Kingstown, RI; (Y); 48/375; Church Yth Grp; Orch; Rep Jr Cls; Rep Sr Cls; Stu Cncl; Gym; Gov Hon Prg Awd; High Hon Roll; Hon Roll; NHS; N Kngstwn Stu Cncl Schlrshp; Updike Essay Cont Awd; RI Yth Philhrmnc Part Awd; U Of RI.

BEJIAN, SHARON; Warwick Veterans Memorial HS; Warwick, RI; (S); 5/326; Exploring; Yrbk Ed-Chief; Rep Sr Cls; Var L Fld Hcky; Hon Roll; NHS; Spanish NHS; Pharm.

BELANGER, CHRISTOPHER J; Rocky Hill Schl; East Greenwich, RI; (Y); 4/29; School Play; Ed Yrbk Ed-Chief; Ed Lit Mag; Sec Sr Cls; Var Lcrss; Var JV Socr; Ntl Merit SF; Chess Clb; Church Yth Grp; Computer Clb; 4 Yr Schlrshp HS 81; Harvard Bk Awd 84; Brown Bk Awd 84; Century III Sch Ldr 84; Engrng.

BELANGER, DAVID; North Smithfield HS; N Smithfield, RI; (Y); French Clb; Letterman Clb; Stu Cncl; Var L Bsbl; Var L Bsktbl; Capt Ftbl; Hon Roll; Ftbl Unsung Hero 84.

BELANGER, DIANE; Central Falls JR SR HS; Central Falls, RI; (Y); 11/130; Girl Scts; Stage Crew; Capt L Bsktbl; Var Crs Cntry; Capt L Sftbl; Hon Roll; Jr NHS; Prfct Atten Awd; Ice Hockey Schlrshp 79-85; Girl Of Mnth 84-85; RI Hnr Soc 85; Ice Hockey Capt; Providence Coll; Accntng.

BELANGER, KRISTEN; N Smithfield JR SR HS; N Smithfield, RI; (Y); Sec Letterman Clb; Band; Yrbk Stf; Co-Capt Tennis; Hon Roll; NHS; Mst Imprvd Plyr Ten 82-83; MVP Ten 84-85; Cls B ST Ten Champ 82; Clark U.

BELL, KERRI; Lincoln JR HS; Lincoln, RI; (Y); 11/190; Variety Show; Yrbk Sprt Ed; Rep Frsh Cls; Rep Soph Cls; Rep Jr Cls; Rep Stu Cncl; Var Cheerleading; Var Gym; High Hon Roll; Jr NHS; Sports Med.

BELL, MARK R; East Providence SR HS; E Providence, RI; (Y); 4/520; VP JA; Pres Sr Cls; Rep Stu Cncl; Var Crs Cntry; Capt Wrstlng; NHS; Harvard Bk Awd 84; Hugh O Brian Yth Ldrshp Awd 83; RI Hnr Soc 85; Boston U; Bio Med.

BELL, WENDY; Coventry HS; Greene, RI; (Y); French Clb; JCL; Letterman Clb; Ski Clb; Variety Show; Yrbk Stf; Stu Cncl; Score Keeper; High Hon Roll; NHS; Elem Educ.

BELLAFIORE, VITA; St M,Arys Acad-Bay View; E Greenwich, RI; (Y); 33/194; Church Yth Grp; Exploring; Yrbk Stf; Stu Cncl; Crs Cntry; Trk; Hon Roll; NHS; Providence Coll; Poltcl Sci.

BELMORE, RENEE; Bristol HS; Bristol, RI; (S); VP GAA; JCL; Latin Clb; Yrbk Stf; Rep Frsh Cls; Rep Soph Cls; Rep Jr Cls; Rep Sr Cls; High Hon Roll; Hon Roll; Intl Forgn Lang Awd 84; U Of RI Almn Assn Awd 84; Cert Hnrb Merit Cum Laude 84.

BENNETT, CRAIG E; La Salle Acad; Esmond, RI; (Y); 58/298; Pres Church Yth Grp; Pres Exploring; VP JA; Rep Frsh Cls; Rep Soph Cls; Rep Jr Cls; Rep Sr Cls; Capt Swmmng; 2nd Tm All ST Swmmg RI 85; RI Hnr Socty 85; Bryant Coll; Mgmt.

BENNETT, KELLIE; Chariho HS; Carolina, RI; (Y); 3/305; Science Clb; Chorus; Mgr(s); Jr NHS; Allianc Francs Hnrbl Mntn 85; Dr.

BENOIT, PAULA; Warwick Veterans Memorial HS; Warwick, RI; (S); 70/350; Drama Clb; Sec Pres FBLA; Hon Roll; Pblc Spkng, Accntng & FBLA Awds; Johnson & Wales; Lgl Sec.

BENSON, LYNNE; Mt Pleasant HS; Providence, RI; (Y); Hon Roll; Prfct Atten Awd; Accntg, Italn Awds.

BERARD, JEAN; Warwick Veterans Memorial HS; Warwick, RI; (S); Church Yth Grp; JA; Cheerleading; Crs Cntry; Hon Roll; Jr NHS; Spanish NHS.

BERARD, JOEL; Mount Saint Charles Acad; Woonsocket, RI; (Y); Var Ice Hcky; Engrng.

BESSETTE, PAULA; East Providence SR HS; Riverside, RI; (Y); Chorus; Nwsp Stf; Yrbk Stf; Rep Jr Cls; Stu Cncl; Capt Cheerleading; High Hon Roll; NHS; Little Leag Stfbl All Star 84; Boston U; Pre-Dntl.

BETTENCOURT, STEVEN; Warren HS; Warren, RI; (Y); #80 In Class; Church Yth Grp; School Play; Stage Crew; Variety Show; Yrbk Stf; TN Temple U; Bus.

BIBER, MAUREEN; Barrington HS; Barrington, RI; (Y); Dance Clb; Intnl Clb; Trk; High Hon Roll; Hon Roll; Cert Apprctn 82-84; Svc Awd 84-85; Cmmnctns.

BIELAWSKI, KARLA; Johnston SR HS; N Scituate, RI; (S); 13/237; Pres Stu Cncl; Powder Puff Ftbl; Hon Roll; NHS; Stat Ftbl; Pol Sci.

BIERMAN, DAVID; Portsmouth HS; Portsmouth, RI; (Y); 25/250; Am Leg Boys St; FBLA; Library Aide; Nwsp Stf; Capt Crs Cntry; Im Ice Hcky; Im Socr; Var Trk; Hon Roll; NHS.

BIGALKE, ERIK; Rogers HS; Newport, RI; (Y); ROTC; Hon Roll; Hotel Mgmt.

BISBANO, BRUCE; Bristol HS; Bristol, RI; (Y); Band; Concert Band; Jazz Band; Mrchg Band; School Play; Stage Crew; Yrbk Stf; Bsktbl; Golf; High Hon Roll; RI Tchrs Italn Cert Merit 85; Littl Rhody Boys ST Cert Partcptn 85; Arch.

BISCI, SHARON; North Providence HS; N Providence, RI; (Y); Office Aide; Political Wkr; Quiz Bowl; Concert Band; Orch; Nwsp Ed-Chief; Yrbk Bus Mgr; Yrbk Stf; High Hon Roll; Jr NHS.

BISCOE, CHARLES; Barrington HS; Barrington, RI; (Y); Church Yth Grp; Computer Clb; Intnl Clb; Math Tm; Im Bsktbl; Im Sftbl; JV Tennis; High Hon Roll; Hon Roll; St Schlr; Engrng.

BLACK, VICKI; Coventry HS; Coventry, RI; (Y); 14/450; Camp Fr Inc; Drama Clb; French Clb; Latin Clb; Letterman Clb; Varsity Clb; Yrbk Stf; Sec Frsh Cls; Stu Cncl; Stat Bsktbl; Hugh O Brian Awd 84; Coorpt Law.

BLACKSON, TANYA P; Rogers HS; Newport, RI; (Y); Dance Clb; Hon Roll; Vllybl; Afro Exprnc Clb 84-86; Barbizons Schl Of Mdlng 82-83; Young Life; Johnson & Wales; Fshn Mdse.

BLANCHETTE, SUE; Coventry HS; Coventry, RI; (Y); Church Yth Grp; FNA; Hosp Aide; Spanish Clb; Socr; Hon Roll; U RI; Nrsng.

BLENNERHASSETT, ANN; North Providence HS; N Providence, RI; (Y); Yrbk Stf; Twrlr; High Hon Roll; Hon Roll; Jr NHS; NHS; Bus.

BLESSING, GEORGE P; South Kinstown HS; Wakefield, RI; (Y); 19/237; Ski Clb; School Play; Yrbk Stf; Var L Bsbl; Var L Bsktbl; Var L Ftbl; Im Wt Lftg; High Hon Roll; Hon Roll; NHS; All South County & All Div Southern Lge Bsbll 85; U RI; Engnrng.

BLOOMER JR, PERRY H; Bristol HS; Bristol, RI; (S); 33/220; Camera Clb; Pres Church Yth Grp; Pres DECA; Yrbk Bus Mgr; Yrbk Phtg; High Hon Roll; NHS; RI Coll; Elem Ed.

BOFFI, ANGELA; Prout Memorial HS; Warwick, RI; (S); 2/81; Spanish Clb; Chorus; Color Guard; Jazz Band; School Musical; Rep Stu Cncl; High Hon Roll; Hon Roll; All-State Solo/Ensmbl Fstvl 82 & 83; Acad Achvmnt Awds In Spnsh & Bio 82.

BOGAN, JENNIFER; Woonsocket SR HS; Woonsocket, RI; (Y); Band; Concert Band; Mrchg Band; School Play; French Hon Soc; High Hon Roll; Hon Roll; RI Brnze Mdlst All Arnd Comp USGF ST Gym Champ 84; USGF Regnl Comp Bronze Mdlst Bal Bm 84.

BOGOSIAN, DAVID; North Providence HS; N Providence, RI; (Y); Church Yth Grp; Golf; Hon Roll; Jr NHS; NHS; N Providence Babe Ruth All Strs 84 & 82; Rally Pt Racqt Clb Mens Sngl Div C Chmp 84; Bryant Coll; Acctg.

BOLDUC, LISA; Saint Raphael Acad; Pawtucket, RI; (Y); Red Cross Aide; Cheerleading; Camp Fr Inc; Church Yth Grp; Varsity Clb; High Hon Roll; Hon Roll; U Of RI; Chld Psych.

BONIN, RONALD LUCIEN; Woonsocket HS; Woonsocket, RI; (Y); 29/490; VICA; Y-Teens; High Hon Roll; Hon Roll; RI Hnr Soc 85; Math Schlrshp 85; U Of RI; Pre Law.

BOOTIER, JOSEPH R; Chariho Regional HS; Ashaway, RI; (Y); VICA.

BORAGINE, BECKY; St Raphael Acad; Cumberland, RI; (Y); Drama Clb; Girl Scts; Library Aide; School Play; Stage Crew; Var Tennis; Hon Roll.

BORGES, EDMUND; Chariho Regional HS; Ashaway, RI; (S); 5/275; Boy Scts; Math Tm; VICA; Ed Yrbk Stf; Trs Sr Cls; Var Tennis; Gov Hon Prg Awd; High Hon Roll; Ntl Merit Ltr; Stu Of Month 84; ST VICA Basic Pgmmng Cntst 3rd Pl 8 4; Chariho Acad Decath Tm 84-85; Elec Engrng.

BORRELLI, SHERYL; Cranston West HS; Cranston, RI; (Y); Art Clb; PAVAS; Gold Key Natl Schlstc Art Awd 83 & 85; Fleet Natl Bk Art Awd 1st Pl 84; RI Coll; Psych.

BOSSDORF, TRACEY; Pilgrim HS; Warwick, RI; (Y); Yrbk Bus Mgr; High Hon Roll; Hon Roll; Northeaster; Retail.

BOTELHO, FLORA; East Providence SR HS; E Providence, RI; (Y); Cmnty Wkr; JA; VICA; Chorus; Variety Show; Hon Roll; Jr NHS; NHS; Bus Mgt.

BOTELHO, PAUL; East Providence SR HS; E Providence, RI; (Y); Computer Clb; Comp Pgm.

BOUDREAU, KELLY; West Warwick HS; W Warwick, RI; (Y); Art Clb; Variety Show; Yrbk Ed-Chief; Yrbk Phtg; Var Tennis; High Hon Roll; Hon Roll; Gen Art Awd 82-83; Schl Art Awd 84-85; Fashn Desgnr.

BOUFFARD, KATHLEEN; St Raphael Acad; Pawtucket, RI; (Y); 4/269; Drama Clb; Exploring; French Clb; Stage Crew; Yrbk Stf; Var Tennis; High Hon Roll; VP NHS; Varsity Clb; Jr NHS; Providence Coll Awd; Schl & ST Sci Fair Awds; Tufts U; Med.

BOUMENOT, MICHAEL S; Chariho Regional JR SR HS; Ashaway, RI; (Y); VICA; Var Socr; Hnrb Mntn All South Cnty Soccer Tm 83-84; Mech Drftng.

BOURESSA, LISA; Prout Memorial HS; Coventry, RI; (Y); 17/88; Trs French Clb; Hosp Aide; Chorus; Hon Roll; Cert Candy Striper 84; Pre-Med.

BOUVIER, DONNA; Burrillville JR SR HS; Woonsocket, RI; (Y); Am Leg Aux Girls St; Church Yth Grp; FBLA; Office Aide; School Musical; School Play; Nwsp Rptr; Rep Frsh Cls; Hon Roll; Rep Soph Cls; Schl Beauty Pagnt 83; Kathrine Gibbs; Exec Secy.

BOWERS, DARCI; Tiverton HS; Tiverton, RI; (Y); Church Yth Grp; Cmnty Wkr; Girl Scts; ROTC; VP Band; Chorus; Church Choir; Concert Band; Drm Mjr(t); Jazz Band; Excllnc Awds-Clarinet, Flute & Singng 82-85; All Regnl & All ST Band 82-85; Anna Maria Coll; Music Teachr.

BOYCE, DENISE; Warwick Veterans Memorial HS; Warwick, RI; (S); Gym; High Hon Roll; Jr NHS.

BOYD, TINA; Coventry HS; Coventry, RI; (Y); 10/420; Spanish Clb; Rep Frsh Cls; Sec Trs Stu Cncl; Stat Bsktbl; High Hon Roll; NHS; Acccntnt.

BRADY, DAVID T; East Prov SR HS; Rumford, RI; (Y); 28/496; Var Swmmng; Hon Roll; Pres Schlr; James E Driscoll Schlrshp 85; Provdnc Jrnl Blltn Schlstc Awd 85; Pell Medl US Hstry 85; Nrthestrn U; Elec Engrng.

BRAGA, ELIZABETH; Our Ldy Of Fatima HS; Middletown, RI; (S); Am Leg Aux Girls St; Drama Clb; Yrbk Stf; Bsktbl; Chorus; Law.

BREAULT, KATHLEEN; Warwick Veterans Memorial HS; Warwick, RI; (S); 26/300; French Clb; Ed Yrbk Stf; Rep Jr Cls; Rep Sr Cls; French Hon Soc; Hon Roll; Jr NHS; NHS; Math Clb; Chorus; Schl Sci Fair 1st Pl 84; RI Expo Sci Fair Hnrb Mntn 84; RI Coll; Elem Educ.

BREEN, PATRICK D; Barrington HS; Barrington, RI; (Y); 1/249; Computer Clb; Capt Math Tm; Science Clb; Rep Stu Cncl; Bausch & Lomb Sci Awd; High Hon Roll; NHS; Ntl Merit Ltr; Pres Schlr; AF ROTC Scholar 85; RPI Mth/Sci Awd 84; MIT; Aerontcl Engrng.

BREHIO, NANCY; Lincoln JR SR HS; Lincoln, RI; (Y); 16/220; Chrmn Church Yth Grp; Pres Drama Clb; Exploring; JCL; Mathletes; Math Clb; Math Tm; Chorus; School Play; Nwsp Rptr; A T Cross Co Schlrshp 85-86; 2nd ST Sci Fair 85; 2nd Tm All-Div Crs-Cntry 84; Boston Coll; Pre-Med.

BRENIZE, DIANA; Coventry HS; Coventry, RI; (Y); Dance Clb; Band; Concert Band; Mrchg Band; Pep Band; JV Cheerleading; Cert Atten Band 83; Hnrb Mntn Dance & Chrldng 83 & 85; Inter Decrtng.

BRENNAN, KATHLEEN; Saint Raphael Acad; Prov, RI; (Y); 35/195; Cmnty Wkr; Trs Dance Clb; Drama Clb; Stage Crew; Variety Show; Yrbk Bus Mgr; Yrbk Stf; Hon Roll; NHS; Educ Tchr.

BRENNAN, KEVIN; La Salle Acad; Barrington, RI; (Y); 14/257; Letterman Clb; Math Clb; Math Tm; Varsity Clb; Nwsp Rptr; Rep Soph Cls; Var L Socr; Var L Swmmng; High Hon Roll; NHS; Engrng.

BRENNAN, MARJORIE; Charino Regional HS; Rockville, RI; (Y); 26/302; Am Leg Aux Girls St; Sec Girl Scts; Library Aide; Science Clb; Chorus; French Hon Soc; Hon Roll; Jr NHS; Girl Scout Slvr Awd 85; RI Acad Decathln Silver Mdl In Englsh Brnz In Fine Arts 85; Schl Rep RI Modl; Intl Rel.

BRICKEL, LYNDA; East Providence HS; Fairgrove, MO; (Y); 99/520; Hosp Aide; VICA; Cit Awd; Hon Roll; ST VICA Winner Medical Lab Tech 85; Mary Auger Nrsng Schlrshp 85; Cert Merit Sci Fair 82; SW MO ST U; Med.

BRIERLEY, DAVID RYAN; North Smithfield JR SR HS; Woonsocket, RI; (Y); Boy Scts; VP Debate Tm; Sec Exploring; Co-Capt Mathletes; Hon Roll; NHS; Ntl Merit Ltr; Pres Schlr; St Schlr; French Clb; Marjorie Sells Carter Schlrshp; Ntl Eagle Sct Assn; Northeastern U; Chem.

BRIGGS, ELIZABETH; Mt St Charles HS; Smithfield, RI; (Y); 33/141; Church Yth Grp; Tennis; Hon Roll; NHS; Mary Mount Clg; Bus.

BRITLAND, MICHAEL; Tiverton HS; Tiverton, RI; (Y); Am Leg Boys St; ROTC; Drill Tm; Nwsp Ed-Chief; Nwsp Stf; Hon Roll; S E MA U Sptlgt Pgm 84 & 85; Navy Leag Awd 83 & 84; Retd Ofcrs Assn TROA ROTC Medl 85; Physics.

BROCHU, KEITH; Chariho Regional HS; Carolina, RI; (S); Church Yth Grp; Chorus; Off Jr Cls; Stu Cncl; Stat Bsktbl; Var Crs Cntry; Var Trk; Var Hon Roll.

BROOKS, JULIANNE G; Classical HS; Providence, RI; (Y); 62/287; Church Yth Grp; Drm Mjr(t); Italian Clb Secy 84-85; Pres Acad Ftnss Awd; U Of RI; Phrmcy.

BROOKS, STEPHEN E; Cranston H S East; Cranston, RI; (Y); 23/454; Church Yth Grp; Yrbk Stf; JV Ftbl; God Cntry Awd; Hon Roll; Jr NHS; NHS; U RI; Engrng.

BROTHERS, MATTHEW; Mount St Charles Acad; N Smithfield, RI; (Y); 15/150; Cmnty Wkr; Math Tm; Ski Clb; High Hon Roll; NHS; Ntl Merit Ltr.

BROUILLETTE, MICHELE; Prout Memorial HS; Coventry, RI; (S); 15/75; French Clb; Hosp Aide; Math Clb; Math Tm; Ski Clb; Varsity Clb; Color Guard; JV Var Vllybl; Hon Roll; Concert Band; ST Artistic Recognition 84; Sci.

BROUSSEAU, DAVID; Chariho Regional HS; Wyoming, RI; (Y); 47/260; Cmnty Wkr; Im Bsbl; High Hon Roll; Hon Roll; U RI; Bus Admn.

BROWN, ANNA LEE; Central Business HS; Providence, RI; (Y); Cmnty Wkr; Cit Awd; Hon Roll; Prfct Atten Awd; Bus.

BROWN, DEBORAH; Cranston H S West; Cranston, RI; (Y); VP GAA; Intnl Clb; Spanish Clb; Var Im Bsktbl; Var Fld Hcky; Var Sftbl; Var Trk; Var Im Vllybl; Hon Roll; JETS Awd.

BROWN, DIANA; Portsmouth HS; Portsmouth, RI; (Y); Office Aide; Band; Concert Band; Flag Corp; Mrchg Band; Yrbk Stf; JV Capt Bsktbl; Crs Cntry; Powder Puff Ftbl; Socr.

BROWN, ELISE; South Kingstown HS; Wakefield, RI; (Y); 55/250; Drama Clb; Model UN; Chorus; Church Choir; Drm Mjr(t); School Musical; School Play; Stage Crew; Swing Chorus; Variety Show; Princpls Trphy Schl Spirit 85; All ST Solo/Ensmbl Fest Gld Mdl 85; Music.

BROWN, ERIC M; West Warwick SR HS; W Warwick, RI; (Y); 62/225; Var L Ice Hcky; Var L Socr; Hon Roll; Brian Messier Annl Sprts Schlrshp 85; Hawthorne Merit & Athl Schsrshps 85; Hawthorne Coll; Accntng.

BROWN, KRISTEN; Johnston SR HS; Johnston, RI; (Y); Dance Clb; DECA; Yrbk Stf; Rep Soph Cls; Off Stu Cncl; French Hon Soc; Hon Roll; RI Coll; Pre-Schl Tchng.

BROWN, MARK S; La Salle Acad; Coventry, RI; (Y); 26/209; Trs Pres Church Yth Grp; Intnl Clb; Math Tm; Church Choir; Hon Roll; Certificat De Merite En Francais 83-84; French.

BROWN, SEAN; Woonsocket SR HS; Woonsocket, RI; (Y); Drama Clb; French Clb; Math Tm; Model UN; Political Wkr; Quiz Bowl; Science Clb; Teachers Aide; Pres Frsh Cls; Pres Soph Cls; Tech Engrng.

BROWN, TERRIANN; Toll Gate HS; Warwick, RI; (S); 153/393; Hosp Aide; Letterman Clb; VICA; Flag Corp; Yrbk Stf; Frsh Cls; Capt Cheerleading; Trk; All Cty Chrldr 83-84; All Am Fin Chrldng NCA 84; CCRI; Comp Sci.

BRUCKNER, JON; Lincoln HS; Lincoln, RI; (Y); 33/190; Church Yth Grp; Rep Frsh Cls; Rep Soph Cls; Rep Jr Cls; Var Bsktbl; Mgr(s); Score Keeper; Sftbl; Trk; Hon Roll; URI; Elem Educ.

BRUNO, SUZANNE; Cumberland HS; Cumberland, RI; (S); DECA; Chorus; Stage Crew; Nwsp Stf; Lit Mag; Ntl Merit Schol; St Deca Conf Awds 84; VP Deca Clb 84-85; Gen Mgr Deca 84-85; Mgmt.

BRYCE, KARIN; St Raphael Acad; Prov, RI; (Y); Pres Church Yth Grp; Cmny Wkr; Hosp Aide; Church Choir; Sec Sr Cls; Var Sftbl; Vllybl; Hon Roll; Bryant; Bus.

BUCCI, CYNTHIA D; Johnston SR HS; Johnston, RI; (S); 19/250; DECA; Nwsp Rptr; Nwsp Stf; Yrbk Stf; VP Frsh Cls; Capt Cheerleading; Hon Roll; RI Hnr Soc 84-85; Providence Coll; Bus Adm.

BUCCI, JUDI; Tollgate HS; Warwick, RI; (S); Letterman Clb; Pep Clb; Q&S; Chorus; Off Frsh Cls; Stu Cncl; Cheerleading; Mgr(s); Hon Roll; CCRI; Bus.

BUCKI, CAROLYNN; Mt Pleasant HS; Providence, RI; (Y); Art Clb; JA; Hon Roll; NHS; Ski Clb; Teachers Aide; Chorus; School Musical; Yrbk Stf; Stu Cncl; Schlstc Art Awd 85; Art-Paintng Awd 85; Swain Schl Dsgn; Art.

BUFFI, JOANNE M; Johnston SR HS; Johnston, RI; (Y); DECA; Var Cheerleading; Hon Roll; Sec Wrk.

BURDICK, JEAN; Warwick Vetrans Memorial HS; Warwick, RI; (Y); 25/270; Yrbk Stf; Off Soph Cls; Off Jr Cls; Stu Cncl; High Hon Roll; Hon Roll; Spanish NHS.

BURKE, KELLY; Middletown HS; Middletown, RI; (S); 17/252; Church Yth Grp; Church Choir; Yrbk Phtg; Rep Frsh Cls; Rep Soph Cls; VP Jr Cls; VP Sr Cls; JV Var Cheerleading; French Hon Soc.

BURKE, LISA; Rogers HS; Newport, RI; (Y); Church Yth Grp; 4-H; Hosp Aide; Intnl Clb; Spanish Clb; Speech Tm; Band; Chorus; Concert Band; Mrchg Band; 4-H Queen Eastern RI 84; Labo Exch Stu Japan 81; Ctznshp Awd Wash DC 83; Drama.

BURKINSHAW, MATTHEW; Woonsocket HS; Woonsocket, RI; (Y); Boy Scts; Church Yth Grp; Band; Concert Band; Mrchg Band; L Crs Cntry; L Trk; High Hon Roll; Hon Roll; Ntl Merit Ltr; Eagle Scout 82; All ST Outdoor Trk 84; All ST Crs Cntry 84; Law.

BURNETT, JAMES; Woonsocket HS; Woonsocket, RI; (Y); Mrchg Band; High Hon Roll; Hon Roll; US Marine Corps; Avionics.

BURTON, MARY; Portsmouth HS; Portsmouth, RI; (Y); Pres FBLA; Band; Concert Band; Mrchg Band; Nwsp Stf; Capt L Crs Cntry; Trk; Hon Roll; Bus Mgmt.

BUSALD, MARGE; St Raphael Acad; Pawtucket, RI; (Y); Drama Clb; Stage Crew; Tennis; Timer; Trk; 3rd Hnrs; Mke-Up Awd; Pre-Med.

BUTLER, ZINA; East Providence SR HS; Rumford, RI; (Y); Aud/Vis; Acpl Chr; Chorus; Color Guard; Flag Corp; Sec Jr Cls; Stu Cncl; JV Vllybl; NHS; Jr NHS; Cmmnctns.

BUTMARC, ANN; Johnston SR HS; Johnston, RI; (Y); French Clb; Sec Frsh Cls; Powder Puff Ftbl; Hon Roll; Model Leg Page 83; Frnch Awd Of Part 83-84; RI Coll; Psych.

BUTTERFIELD, LISA M; Barrington HS; Barrington, RI; (Y); 50/250; Thesps; Band; Chorus; Concert Band; Mrchg Band; School Play; Variety Show; Yrbk Stf; Var L Cheerleading; Var L Sftbl; RI Hnr Socty; Boston U; Schl Mgmt.

CABRAL, TRACI; Tiverton HS; Tiverton, RI; (Y); Hon Roll; Accntng.

CAFFERTY, COLLEEN; Warwick Veterans HS; Warwick, RI; (Y); French Clb; JA; Pep Clb; Science Clb; Off Jr Cls; Crs Cntry; French Hon Soc; Good Citznshp Awd 82; Frnch Hnr Soc 83-84; URI; Nrsg.

CAHILL, NANCY E; N Smithfeild JR SR HS; Slaterville, RI; (Y); 7/161; French Clb; JA; Band; Church Choir; Concert Band; Yrbk Stf; Sec Frsh Cls; Sr Cls; Stu Cncl; Hon Roll; Pres Acad Ftns Awd 85; R I Hnr Soc 85; R I All St Band 85; Bentley Coll; Bus Adm.

CALABRESE, JILL; Johnston SR HS; Johnston, RI; (S); 9/237; Church Yth Grp; Cmnty Wkr; Dance Clb; Political Wkr; Yrbk Ed-Chief; Pres Soph Cls; Stu Cncl; Var Capt Bsktbl; Var Capt Sftbl; Gov Hon Prg Awd; Comp Sci.

CALISE, LORA; North Providence HS; N Providence, RI; (Y); 6/235; Drm Mjr(t); Twrlr; Gov Hon Prg Awd; High Hon Roll; Hon Roll; NHS; Pres Schlr; St Schlr; RI Franco Am Awd 85; Spnsh Awd; Boosters Schlshp; RI Coll; Tchng.

CALITRI, VINCENT F; La Salle Acad; Johnston, RI; (Y); Church Yth Grp; Computer Clb; Letterman Clb; Capt Quiz Bowl; Var L Wrstlng; Phys Ftns Awd; Northeastern; Comp Engrng Tech.

CAPARCO, ANGELA; Cranston H S West; Cranston, RI; (Y); Spanish Clb; School Musical; Bryant Coll; Acctg.

CAPPALLI, DEBRA; Mt Saint Charles Acad; Harrisville, RI; (Y); Church Yth Grp; Cmnty Wkr; Library Aide; Office Aide; Political Wkr; Ski Clb; High Hon Roll; Hon Roll; NHS; Brown U Enrchmnt Pgm 84; Providence Coll; Law.

CARAGIANIS, CHRISTINE; Portsmouth HS; Portsmouth, RI; (Y); #1 In Class; Rptr FBLA; Ski Clb; Nwsp Ed-Chief; Var L Tennis; High Hon Roll; NHS; Spanish NHS; Val; Voice Dem Awd; Math Tm; HOBY Ldrshp Awd 83; Military Ord Of Wrld War Ldrshp Awd 84; URI Alumni Merit Schlrshp 85; URI; Engrng.

CARBONE, LISA; Mount Saint Charles HS; Woonsocket, RI; (S); 42/165; Trs 4-H; Political Wkr; Service Clb; Stage Crew; Yrbk Stf; Lit Mag; Trs Frsh Cls; Chrmn Stu Cncl; Hon Roll; NHS; US Stu Cncl Awd 83-84; Harvard Bk Awd 84; Century 222 Ldrshp Awd 84; Corp Law.

CARDELLO, ANTHONY; N Smithfield JR/SR HS; Slatersville, RI; (Y); Boy Scts; Church Yth Grp; Exploring; JA; Ftbl; Ice Hcky; Socr; Hon Roll; Ftbl, Ice Hcky & Scer-Town Spnsrd; U S Air Frc; Navagtion.

CARDIN, SHARON; North Smith Field HS; N Smithfield, RI; (Y); 30/146; Pres 4-H; JA; Band; Mrchg Band; Yrbk Stf; Hon Roll; Drama Clb; Office Aide; Quiz Bowl; Pep Band; ST Illustrd Talks Wnnr 1st 4-H 85; Ntl Horse Bowl In PA 84; RI Delg E ST Expo 81-83; Bus Mgmt.

CARDOSO, ANTONIO; Charles E Shea HS; Pawtucket, RI; (Y); Boys Clb Am; Computer Clb; Var Crs Cntry; Var Trk; Honor Role 83-85; Providence Coll; Comp Sci.

CARIGNAN, EUGENE; Coventry HS; Coventry, RI; (Y); Boy Scts; Chess Clb; French Clb; Math Clb; Math Tm; Science Clb; Varsity Clb; Yrbk Phtg; Yrbk Stf; Var Ftbl; RI ST Wrstlg Champ 84-85; Merit Achvt Awd 85; Med.

CARMODY, KELLY; Narragansett HS; Narragansett, RI; (Y); 2/125; Hosp Aide; Model UN; Variety Show; Var Gym; Var Sftbl; Var Capt Tennis; High Hon Roll; NHS; Pres Schlr; Sal; Athltc Boosters Clb Schlrshp 85; PTO Awd 85; U PA; Bio.

CARNEVALE, JOYCE; Johnston SR HS; Johnston, RI; (Y); 33/237; Sec Church Yth Grp; Drama Clb; Yrbk Stf; Sec Soph Cls; VP Jr Cls; Var Cheerleading; Hon Roll; Lion Awd; Johnston Fed Tchrs 4 Yr Scholar 85-89; Lasr Fare LTD Scholar 85; RI Coll; Nrsg.

CARNEY, MICHAEL JAMES; Bishop Hendricken HS; Warwick, RI; (Y); 100/251; Chess Clb; French Clb; Ski Clb; Yrbk Stf; Socr; Sftbl; Swmmng; Hon Roll; NHS; URI; Elec Engrng.

CARNEY, ROBERT; Shea HS; Pawtucket, RI; (Y); Cmnty Wkr; Nwsp Rptr; Ed Nwsp Stf; Rep Soph Cls; Trs Jr Cls; Trs Sr Cls; Hon Roll; Nwsp Staff Awd 83; Alg Awd 83; RI Coll.

CARPENTER JR, KENNETH; Pilgrim HS; Warwick, RI; (Y); 11/308; Math Tm; ROTC; Band; Orch; Yrbk Bus Mgr; High Hon Roll; Hon Roll; NHS; Woncester Polytech; Elec Engr.

CARPETIS, PAUL; Cranston High HS; Cranston, RI; (Y); U RI; Acctnt.

CARR, COURTNEY; Rogers HS; Newport, RI; (Y); Cmnty Wkr; Red Cross Aide; Drill Tm; Flag Corp; Yrbk Stf; Pom Pon; Hon Roll; OK ST U; Acctg.

CARREIRO, RICHARD; Cranston HS; Cranston, RI; (Y); 2/360; Capt Computer Clb; Math Tm; Science Clb; Nwsp Ed-Chief; Bausch & Lomb Sci Awd; NHS; Ntl Merit Schol; Sal; Stat Bsktbl; Stat Ftbl; Sngl RI Rep US Suprcomp Hnrs Pgm 85; Rensselaer Awd Excllnc Math & Sci 84; Untd Italo-Amer Schlrshp; MA Inst Tech; Comp Sci.

CARUSO, JOANNE; Toll Gate HS; Warwick, RI; (Y); 44/398; Church Yth Grp; Spanish Clb; Varsity Clb; Chorus; Yrbk Stf; Off Frsh Cls; Off Soph Cls; Off Jr Cls; Off Sr Cls; Bsktbl; RI Hnr Scty 85; Ntl JR Hnr Scty 82; RI Coll; Pre-Law.

CARVISIGLIA, DIANE; Prout Memorial HS; North Kingstown, RI; (S); 9/87; Cmnty Wkr; GAA; Hosp Aide; Chorus; Jazz Band; School Musical; Variety Show; Rep Stu Cncl; DAR Awd; Hon Roll; Wellesley Coll; Liberal Arts.

CASCALHEIRA, ROSA; Tolman HS; Pawtucket, RI; (Y); 21/283; Drama Clb; French Clb; Hosp Aide; Office Aide; School Play; Yrbk Stf; VP Jr Cls; VP Sr Cls; Rep Stu Cncl; Im Bowling; Flora S Curtis Awd 82; Troph 3rd Natl Frnch Ex Top Scor Schl 83; URI; Phsycns.

CASEY, ANDREA; Cranston High School East; Cranston, RI; (Y); 6/470; Church Yth Grp; Cmnty Wkr; GAA; Q&S; Sec Spanish Clb; Chorus; Color Guard; Ed Nwsp Stf; Yrbk Bus Mgr; Yrbk Ed-Chief; Hugh O Brien Yth Ambssdr 84; Wellesley Coll Bk Awd 85; Outstndng Cumultv Acadmc Achvt 83; Bus.

CASEY, CELIA; Middletown HS; Middletown, RI; (S); 13/252; Drama Clb; Hosp Aide; Color Guard; Orch; School Play; Yrbk Ed-Chief; Lit Mag; French Hon Soc; NHS; Voice Dem Awd; RI Acad Decthln Gold Mdl Engl 83.

CASEY, KARA; St Raphael Acad; Cumberland, RI; (Y); 13/190; Church Yth Grp; Exploring; French Clb; Model UN; Yrbk Ed-Chief; Stu Cncl; Var Bsktbl; Hon Roll; NHS.

CASEY, NOREEN; Narragansett SR HS; Narragansett, RI; (Y); Girl Scts; Hosp Aide; Hon Roll; Prfct Atten Awd; Law.

CASPER, LEISA MARIE; Cranston HS East; Cranston, RI; (Y); #25 In Class; Cmnty Wkr; Hosp Aide; Library Aide; Teachers Aide; Mgr Lit Mag; High Hon Roll; Hon Roll; Jr NHS; Hon Soc 82-83; U Of RI; Law.

CASSAVAUGH, HEIDI L; North Kingstown HS; N Kingstown, RI; (Y); 35/375; High Hon Roll; Hon Roll; NHS; RI Hnr Soc 84-85; Outstndng Bus Stu 84-85; Sawyer School; Trvl.

CASTON, JANEL; Portsmouth HS; Portsmouth, RI; (Y); Sec FBLA; Band; Concert Band; Mrchg Band; Hon Roll; Elect Engr.

CASTRIOTTA, GINA; Smithfield HS; Smithfield, RI; (Y); Nwsp Rptr; Jr Cls; Rep Sr Cls; Chrmn Stu Cncl; Hon Roll; NHS; Cert Of Outstndng Achvt In Sclptrng 85; Outstndng Stu Cert Of Sclptrng 85.

CASTRO, PATRICIA; Our Lady Of Fatima HS; Bristol, RI; (S); Dance Clb; Drama Clb; Stage Crew; Yrbk Bus Mgr; Hon Roll; Prfct Atten Awd; U Of RI; Pharmacy.

CASWELL, ELOISE; Scituate HS; North Scituate, RI; (S); 1/117; Hosp Aide; Yrbk Ed-Chief; Trs Soph Cls; Var Trk; Jr NHS; Val.

CATALDO, ROBERT M; Davies Vo-Tech HS; Pawtucket, RI; (Y); Cmnty Wkr; Political Wkr; Service Clb; VICA; Stu Cncl; Wt Lftg; Wrstlng; RI Trade Shops Schl; Bus.

CAVALIERI, TRISHA; Our Lady Of Fatima HS; Bristol, RI; (S); Church Yth Grp; Dance Clb; Mgr Drama Clb; Mgr Stage Crew; Variety Show; Yrbk Stf; Rep Jr Cls; Stu Cncl; L Sftbl; Hon Roll; H S Sci Fair 81-82; RI ST Sci Fair 3rd 82-83; H S Sci Fair 2nd 82-83; Med Tech.

CAZEAULT, LOUISE; Scituate JR SR HS; N Scituate, RI; (S); 18/117; Girl Scts; Chorus; Rep Soph Cls; Rep Stu Cncl; Hon Roll; Jr NHS; R I Hnr Soc 85; New Englnd Inst Tech; Adm Med A.

CERESA, BRIAN; Chariho HS; Hope Valley, RI; (S); Math Tm; Band; School Musical; Var Crs Cntry; Var Trk; High Hon Roll; Hon Roll; Best Soph, Chariho, Natl Math Test 83-84; RI Music Educ Assn Awds 83-84; All-S Cnty Crss Cntry 84-85.

CERRITO, DANA; Cranston H S West; Cranston, RI; (Y); 21/443; Computer Clb; Exploring; GAA; Ski Clb; Variety Show; Rep Sr Cls; JV Crs Cntry; Var Capt Fld Hcky; Var Sftbl; Jr NHS; Italn Awd 82-85; U PA.

CESANA JR, DENNIS M; Mount Saint Charles Acad; N Providence, RI; (Y); 20/160; Var Ice Hcky; High Hon Roll; Hon Roll; NHS; RI All Star Yankee Conf Hockey 85; Midget Elite Camp Hockey 85; Natl Champs Schlby Hockey 85; Engrng.

CHACE, LORA J; Riverton HS; Tiverton, RI; (Y); 19/217; ROTC; Drill Tm; Nwsp Ed-Chief; Nwsp Rptr; Nwsp Stf; Var Socr; DAR Awd; Hon Roll; NHS; Mltry Ordr Of Wrld Wars 83; Retrd Offcrs Assn 84; Nrotc Schlrshp 85; Army; Nrsng.

CHADWICK, PATRICIA L; Lincoln SR HS; Pawtucket, RI; (Y); 44/220; Girl Scts; JCL; Variety Show; Yrbk Stf; Hon Roll; Pres Schlr; RIC; Psych.

CHAIGNOT, MICHAEL J; Coventry HS; Coventry, RI; (Y); 15/420; Chess Clb; French Clb; Im Wrstlng; French Hon Soc; High Hon Roll; Jr NHS; NHS; Intl Bus.

CHAMBERLAND, RACHELLE; Pilgrim HS; Warwick, RI; (Y); 16/250; Chess Clb; Dance Clb; Stage Crew; Off Frsh Cls; Stu Cncl; Badmtn; Tennis; Hon Roll; NHS 83; Advrtsmnt.

CHAMORRO, CECILIA; St Raphael Acad; Central Falls, RI; (Y); Church Yth Grp; Drama Clb; Vllybl; NHS; 2nd Hnrs 83-85; Psych.

CHAMPAGNE, ELISE; St Mary Acad-Bay View; W Warwick, RI; (Y); 4/210; Math Clb; Nwsp Stf; Yrbk Stf; JV Var Cheerleading; Hon Roll; Jr NHS; NEDT Awd; Bay View Hnr Soc 85; 2nd Grnt Sci Fair 83; Bay View Schlrshp 82-86; Engrng.

CHAPUT, RACHEL; Mount St Charles Acad; Harrisville, RI; (Y); Band; Hon Roll; Ntl Merit Ltr; Rochester Inst Of Tech; Engrng.

CHARELLO, SHERI; North Providence HS; N Providence, RI; (Y); Church Yth Grp; Quiz Bowl; Nwsp Stf; Yrbk Stf; Lit Mag; Cheerleading; Pom Pon; Hon Roll; Jr NHS; NHS; U VT; Bio-Chem.

CHARRON, CHRISTINE; Smithfield HS; Greenville, RI; (Y); 16/180; Computer Clb; Yrbk Stf; Var Capt Bsktbl; Var Capt Crs Cntry; Var Capt Trk; Elks Awd; High Hon Roll; Hon Roll; JC Awd; NHS; Typing II Awd 84; Accntng II Awd 84; All Dist High Jump, All Tourney Tm Bsktbl 85; Bryant Coll; Accntng.

CHARRON, SUSAN; Coventry HS; Coventry, RI; (Y); Church Yth Grp; French Clb; Hosp Aide; Quiz Bowl; Band; Concert Band; Mrchg Band; Stage Crew; Variety Show; Rep Stu Cncl; Acad All-Amer; Nrs.

CHARTRAND, BOB; Woonsocket HS; Woonsocket, RI; (Y); Exploring; VICA; Church Choir; Variety Show; Var Ice Hcky; Wt Lftg; High Hon Roll; NHS; Outstndng Awd Elec Tech 85; CC Of RI; Elec Engrng.

CHARVES, GRETA R; East Providence SR HS; East Providence, RI; (S); 12/520; Trs French Clb; Trs Spanish Clb; NHS; Wellesley Book Awd 84; Bryant Coll; Accntng.

CHECK, JON; Pilgrim HS; Warwick, RI; (Y); Church Yth Grp; Math Tm; Stu Cncl; Hon Roll; URI; Comp.

CHEESMAN, WENDY; Barrington Christian Acad; Barrington, RI; (Y); 1/11; Church Yth Grp; Capt Debate Tm; Teachers Aide; Yrbk Ed-Chief; Rep Stu Cncl; Co-Capt Bsktbl; Ntl Merit Ltr; Val; Messiah Coll Deans Schlrshp 85-86; Messiah Coll; Sprts Med.

CHEN, ALICE; No Smithfield HS; N Smithfield, RI; (Y); 1/150; Church Yth Grp; French Clb; Letterman Clb; Math Tm; Yrbk Stf; Stu Cncl; Var L Tennis; Var L Vllybl; High Hon Roll; Engr.

CHEVIAN, LINDA L; Warwick Veterans Memorial HS; Warwick, RI; (Y); 51/320; Nwsp Rptr; Rep Frsh Cls; Rep Soph Cls; Rep Jr Cls; Rep Sr Cls; French Hon Soc; Hon Roll; Jr NHS; U RI; Jrnlsm.

CHLEBEK, DAWN MARIE; Central Falls JR SR HS; Central Falls, RI; (Y); 7/131; Cmnty Wkr; Hosp Aide; JA; Yrbk Stf; Rep Jr Cls; Rep Sr Cls; Stu Cncl; Hon Roll; Pres Schlr; RI Hon Soc 84-85; Excllnc Bus Awd 84-85; Bryant Coll; Acctg.

CHRISTIAN, ELLEN T; Classical HS; Providence, RI; (Y); Church Yth Grp; Dance Clb; Drama Clb; PAVAS; Thesps; School Musical; School Play; Nwsp Stf; Im Gym; Hon Roll; Cert Of Recgntn Advncmnt & Dedctn Of Perfrmng Arts 83; Wellesley; Cmmnctns.

CHRISTY, TINA; Warwick Veterans Memorial HS; Warwick, RI; (Y); Yrbk Sprt Ed; Yrbk Stf; Off Frsh Cls; Off Soph Cls; Off Jr Cls; Off Sr Cls; Var Capt Cheerleading; Hon Roll; Pre-Law.

CICCONE, LISA; South Kingstown HS; Wakefield, RI; (Y); Chorus; Church Choir; Mgr Fld Hcky; High Hon Roll; Hon Roll; NHS; Cert Excll Frnch Fed Allncs Franc USA 85; Cert Hnr Outstndng Excll, Achvt Chem 84; Sci.

CICILLINE, LISA; Mt St Charles HS; Greenville, RI; (Y); Service Clb; Co-Capt Cheerleading; Hon Roll.

CIFELLI, CYNTHIA S; Warwick Veterans Memorial HS; Warwick, RI; (Y); Spanish Clb; Band; Concert Band; Mrchg Band; Tennis; Hon Roll; Spanish NHS; Sol-Ensmbl Awds 83-84; Al-ST Bnd 83; Bnd Cncl Scty, VP 84 & 85; Quinnipiac Coll; Hlth/Nutrtn.

CIMINI, SUSAN; Bayview Acad; N Providenc, RI; (Y); 38/216; French Clb; Stage Crew; Nwsp Rptr; Nwsp Stf; VP Tennis; Hon Roll; Cmnctns.

CINAMI, DINA; La Salle Acad; Foster, RI; (Y); 20/256; Church Yth Grp; Library Aide; High Hon Roll; Hon Roll; Awds Hghst Hnrs Algbr Cmmnctn Arts & Intro Phy Sci & Recog Achvt Engl; Hghst Achvt Awd Engl; Elem Ed.

CISHEK, DAWN; Mt St Charles HS; Greenville, RI; (S); 17/108; JA; Model UN; Speech Tm; Drill Tm; Chrmn Stu Cncl; Var Cheerleading; Var Swmmng; Im Vllybl; High Hon Roll; Diver Of Yr 82; MVP JV Sftbl 83; Lake Forest Coll; Chem.

CLARK, AMY; Narragansett HS; Narragansett, RI; (Y); 13/145; Camp Fr Inc; Nwsp Ed-Chief; Off Frsh Cls; Off Soph Cls; Off Jr Cls; Off Sr Cls; Off Stu Cncl; JV Sftbl; Hon Roll; NHS; Model Legislature, Page, Lbbyst, Alt Rep 82-85; Italian Clb 84-85; Close-Up 85; Pre-Law.

CLARK, BETH ANN; Narragansett HS; Narragansett, RI; (Y); 7/144; Office Aide; Nwsp Sprt Ed; Jr Cls; Sr Cls; Stu Cncl; Socr; Sftbl; High Hon Roll; Hon Roll; NHS; Blu Rbbn Sci Fair; Bus Adm.

CLARK, CYNTHIA; Warwick Veterans Memorial HS; Warwick, RI; (Y); Church Yth Grp; French Clb; Letterman Clb; Rep Jr Cls; Rep Sr Cls; Sec Stu Cncl; Var Cheerleading; French Hon Soc; High Hon Roll; Hon Roll.

CLARKE, WHITNEY; North Kingstown HS; Jamestown, RI; (Y); Church Yth Grp; Intnl Clb; Library Aide; Mgr(s); JV L Tennis; Hon Roll; Occuptnl Thrpy.

CLEMENT, SCOTT J; Bishop Hendricken HS; N Kingstown, RI; (Y); 3/254; Pres Church Yth Grp; Pres French Clb; Yrbk Ed-Chief; French Hon Soc; High Hon Roll; NHS; Ntl Merit SF; Yrbk Stf; Im Bowling; Crs Cntry; Dartmouty Bk Clb Awd 84; CYO Yth Yr Awd 84; Ntl Frnch Awd 82; Rsrch Sci.

CLEMENT, WILLIAM; Shea HS; Pawtucket, RI; (Y); Aud/Vis; VICA; Band; Concert Band; Jazz Band; Stage Crew; High Hon Roll; Hon Roll; Berklee Coll Mus; Bass Guitar.

COHEN, LAWRENCE; Rogers HS; Newport, RI; (Y); 5/300; Aud/Vis; Computer Clb; Band; Concert Band; Jazz Band; Mrchg Band; Pep Band; Coach Actv; Mat Maids; Sftbl; Abraham G Smith Awd 83-84; All ST Band Awd 82-84; Band Awds 82-84; Doctor.

COLBY, ELIZABETH A; Classical HS; Providence, RI; (Y); 83/272; French Clb; Hosp Aide; Hon Roll; Cert Of Hnr For Acdmc Achvt From Gvnr Of RI 84-85; Hofstra U; Jrnlsm.

COLEMAN, LISA L; Chassicah HS; Providence, RI; (Y); Church Yth Grp; Dance Clb; Drama Clb; Girl Scts; Hosp Aide; JA; Church Choir; Variety Show; Rep Frsh Cls; Hon Roll; Silvr Mdl Natl Latn Exm 83; Magna Cum Laude Natl Latn Exm 85; LSU; Pre Med.

COLEY, STEVEN M; Mount Saint Charles HS; Bellingham, MA; (Y); 55/184; Math Clb; JV Bsktbl; Var Capt Crs Cntry; Hon Roll; Ntl Merit SF; William R Larkin Memrl Schlrshp 84; Syracuse U; Comp Progrmng.

COLLETTE, MICHELLE M; St Raphael Acad; N Providence, RI; (Y); 11/180; Church Yth Grp; Dance Clb; Rep Soph Cls; Rep Stu Cncl; High Hon Roll; Hon Roll; NHS; RI Coll; Secon Educ.

COLLINGS, CHERYL; Cariho Regional HS; Ashaway, RI; (S); 1/286; Yrbk Stf; Var Fld Hcky; Var Trk; High Hon Roll; NHS; Val; Harvard Bk Awd 84; Brown U Bk Awd 84.

COLLINS, CHRIS; Central Falls HS; Central Falls, RI; (Y); 14/160; JV Wrstlng; Hon Roll; RI Hnr Socty; U Of RI; Elctrcl Engrng.

COLLINS, SHARON; Warwick Veterans Memorial HS; Warwick, RI; (Y); 22/323; Am Leg Aux Girls St; Dance Clb; Band; Chorus; Mrchg Band; Orch; High Hon Roll; Jr NHS; Ntl Merit Ltr; Spanish NHS; Rhode Island Coll; Pre-Law.

COLOZZI, YVONNE; Chariho HS; Hope Valley, RI; (S); Chorus; Jr Cls; Stu Cncl; Capt Cheerleading; Mgr(s); Score Keeper; Hon Roll; Comp Pgrmr.

COLUZZI, MARK; Tiverton HS; Tiverton, RI; (S); 6/218; Aud/Vis; Trs VP Church Yth Grp; Quiz Bowl; Stage Crew; Pres JV Bsktbl; High Hon Roll; Hon Roll; NHS; Chrstn Sprtsmnshp Awd 83-84; Ntl Hnr Soc 84; Elec Engr.

CONLON, LESLIE; St Marys Acad; Warwick, RI; (Y); 7/210; French Clb; Math Tm; Capt Quiz Bowl; Teachers Aide; School Play; NHS; NEDT Awd; Boys Clb Am; Cmnty Wkr; Drama Clb; Gold Medl Engl ST Acad Decathln 85; Brown U Bk Awd Engl 85; 2nd Grant ST Sci Fair 83 & 84; Brown U; Spcl Educ.

CONNOLLY, MELISSA; North Kingstown HS; Orlando, FL; (Y); 29/375; Drama Clb; Varsity Clb; School Play; Var Capt Cheerleading; High Hon Roll; Hon Roll; NHS; Outstndng Achvt Engl & Spnsh 85; RI Hnr Soc 85; Intl Fine Arts Coll; Fshn.

CONNORS, JOHN; Burrillville SR HS; Glendale, RI; (Y); 77/200; Camera Clb; Church Yth Grp; Letterman Clb; Varsity Clb; Yrbk Stf; Stu Cncl; Socr; Tennis; Wt Lftg; Wrstlng; CCRI; Lib Arts.

CONTI, MICHELLE; Warwick Veterans HS; Providence, RI; (Y); Trs FBLA; 2nd Typng 85.

COOK, STEVEN; Mount Saint Charles Acad; Millville, MA; (Y); Cmnty Wkr; JV Bsbl; JV Ice Hcky; Church Yth Grp; Quiz Bowl; Y-Teens; Im Bsktbl; Im Tennis; JR All Star Ice Hockey Tms 82 & 83; Young Bike Racer 84 & 85; Med Tech.

COOK, SUE ANN; Narragansett HS; North Kingstown, RI; (Y); JA; Library Aide; Office Aide; Drm & Bgl; Variety Show; Yrbk Phtg; Off Jr Cls; Off Sr Cls; Bsktbl; Trk; Off Aide Awd; Lib Aide Awd; Sport Awd Ltrs; Johnson Wales Coll; Fash Merch.

COOKE, PAMELA; Bishop Keough Regional HS; Providence, RI; (Y); Church Yth Grp; Cmnty Wkr; Church Choir; Drm & Bgl; Variety Show; Pres Sr Cls; Hon Roll; Natl Piano Playing Audtns 80-84; Miss USA Teen RI Wnnr 85-86; Pedtrc Nrsng.

COOPER, YVETTE; Hope HS; Providence, RI; (Y); Am Leg Aux Girls St; Cmnty Wkr; Drama Clb; 4-H; Hosp Aide; Office Aide; Acpl Chr; School Play; Martin Luther Ing Awd Outstndng Soc Studies 85; Pre-Med.

CORDEIRO, ANTHONY; Bristol HS; Bristol, RI; (Y); Boy Scts; Camera Clb; Band; Color Guard; Concert Band; Drm & Bgl; Flag Corp; Jazz Band; Mrchg Band; Golf; Engrng.

CORGAN, KATH; Rogers HS; Newport, RI; (Y); Drama Clb; Leo Clb; Natl Beta Clb; Ski Clb; Var Sftbl; Var Tennis; JV Trk; High Hon Roll; Hon Roll; Myrs Trphy Outstndng Semnshp 83; Citatn Prtcptn Newprt Yth Hcky 84; Gudnc Advsry Brd 83-85; Grphc Comm.

CORNEAU, DAVID P; Our Lady Of Providence HS; Pawtucket, RI; (Y); 16/116; Boys Clb Am; Boy Scts; Church Yth Grp; Math Tm; JV Bsbl; Swmmng; High Hon Roll; U RI; Mech Engrng.

CORNELIUS, GRETCHEN; Rogers HS; Newport, RI; (Y); French Clb; Nwsp Rptr; Rep Stu Cncl; Mgr(s); French Hon Soc; High Hon Roll; NHS; Ntl Hnr Soc, RI Hnr Soc 85; Coll Holy Cross; Poli Sci.

COROA, KIMBERLY; Our Lady Of Fatima HS; Fall River, MA; (Y); Hosp Aide; Chorus; Yrbk Phtg; Cheerleading; Hon Roll; Sci Fair 83 & 84; Chld Care.

CORP, KIM J; Coventry HS; Coventry, RI; (S); 60/385; Church Yth Grp; Chorus; Madrigals; Variety Show; Hon Roll.

CORRENTE, JEFF; Barrington HS; Barrington, RI; (Y); 30/235; Drama Clb; Political Wkr; School Play; Stage Crew; Im Bsktbl; Var Tennis; High Hon Roll; French Clb; Im Badmtn; Var Hon Roll; 3rd Grant RI Expo Sci Fair 85; Hnrs Thomas Edison Max Mc Graw Found 85; Rep US Army JR Sci Symp 85; Bus.

CORRENTE, LORI; Warwick Vets HS; Warwick, RI; (S); Rep DECA; FBLA; Nwsp Rptr; Stu Cncl; Hon Roll; Fshn Inst Tech; Fshn Mrch.

CORRIGAN, FRANCIS V; East Providence HS; East Providence, RI; (S); #16 In Class; Church Yth Grp; Sec JA; Stu Cncl; Var Capt Crs Cntry; Var L Trk; Hon Roll; NHS; Holy Cross Bk Awd 84; Harrier Awd 83; All-Star SR Leag Bsbl 83.

COSTA, DAVID; Bristol HS; Bristol, RI; (Y); DECA; Office Aide; Teachers Aide; Yrbk Stf; Lit Mag; High Hon Roll; NHS; Bus Ed Cert Hnr 85; Bryant Coll; Acctng.

COSTA, ROBERT; Tiverton HS; Tiverton, RI; (Y); Computer Clb; Hon Roll; Comp Engrng.

COSTA, ROBERT; Warren HS; Warren, RI; (Y); 18/136; Cmnty Wkr; Math Tm; Spanish Clb; Band; School Play; Yrbk Ed-Chief; Yrbk Stf; High Hon Roll; Hon Roll; 1st & 2nd Pl Annual Ancnt Hstry Bee 83 & 85; 3rd Pl Ntl Math Cnfrnc Exam 85; Rhode Islnd Coll; Cardiology.

COSTELLO, LAURA; Tollgate HS; West Greenwich, RI; (Y); Church Yth Grp; French Clb; Stu Cncl; Cheerleading; Gym; French Hon Soc; Hon Roll; Prtl Schlrshp To St Mary Acad 82-83; 2nd Pl Schl Sci Fair 82-83; Rep Ntl Assn Of Stu Cncls 83-84; Pre-Med.

COSTELLO, LINDA; Smithfield HS; Greenville, RI; (Y); 9/186; Drama Clb; Band; Off Frsh Cls; Off Soph Cls; Rep Jr Cls; Off Sr Cls; Rep Stu Cncl; NHS; Pres Schlr; U Hartford; Educ.

COTE, MICHAEL R; N Smithfield JR/SR HS; N Smithfield, RI; (Y); French Clb; Trs JA; Band; Hon Roll; 1st Pl Frnch III Reading Comprehnsn Cont 85; Bus.

COTNOIR, EUGENE; Woon HS; Woonsocket, RI; (Y); Church Yth Grp; VICA; Hon Roll.

COTTA, KRISTIN; Portsmouth HS; Portsmouth, RI; (Y); Band; Concert Band; Mrchg Band; Var Sftbl; Johnson & Wales; Bus.

COTTER III, EDWARD; St Raphael Acad; Rumford, RI; (Y); 8/190; Red Cross Aide; Teachers Aide; High Hon Roll; Hon Roll; NHS; Ntl Merit Ltr; Bruzzi-Smith Awd; Providence Coll; Bio.

COUTU, DAVID; Coventry HS; Coventry, RI; (Y); 21/400; Chess Clb; French Clb; Band; Yrbk Stf; Stu Cncl; High Hon Roll; Hon Roll; Jr NHS; Elect Engr.

COUTURE, WALTER; Mount Saint Charles Acad; Bellingham, MA; (Y); Church Yth Grp; Service Clb; Band; Concert Band; Jazz Band; Mrchg Band; Pep Band; School Musical; Var L Crs Cntry; Berkley Coll Music; Music.

COWAN, MICHAEL; Smithfield SR HS; Greenville, RI; (Y); Math Tm; Var Capt Bsktbl; Hon Roll.

COWARD-EDWARD, KRISTEN; Smithfield HS; Smithfield, RI; (Y); Cmnty Wkr; French Clb; Hosp Aide; School Play; Off Frsh Cls; Off Soph Cls; Off Jr Cls; Rep Sr Cls; Off Stu Cncl; Bryant Coll; Bus Mgmt.

CRANE, MARY; Chariho Reginal HS; Ashaway, RI; (S); Drama Clb; Math Tm; VP Science Clb; Band; Chorus; Rep Stu Cncl; Stat Bsktbl; Var Crs Cntry; Var Trk; 1st Grnts Reg Sci Fair 83-84; 3rd 2nd Grnts ST Sci Fair 83-84; Sthrn Reg Chorus 83; Chem Engr.

CRANSTON, KATHRYN; North Kingstown HS; N Kingstown, RI; (Y); 119/375; Church Yth Grp; Hosp Aide; Chorus; Church Choir; JV Swmmng; Hon Roll; Lyndon ST Coll; Therptc Rcrtn.

CRESWICK, BETHANY; Warwick Veterans Memorial HS; Warwick, RI; (Y); 31/297; Chorus; Nwsp Rptr; Nwsp Stf; Rep Jr Cls; Rep Sr Cls; Score Keeper; High Hon Roll; Hon Roll; St Schlr; RI Coll; Nrsng.

CRIBB, RICHARD; Mt St Charles Acad; Smithfield, RI; (Y); 1/148; Teachers Aide; Stage Crew; Im Bsktbl; Crs Cntry; Swmmng; High Hon Roll; NHS; Acad All Amer 85; Provdnce Jrnl Bulltn Scholar 85; Pre-Med.

CRISAFULLI, MARC; Mount St Charles HS; Pawtucket, RI; (S); 22/147; JA; Math Tm; Trs Soph Cls; Chrmn Stu Cncl; Hon Roll; Mst Spirted Stu 83-84; Acad All Amer 83-84; Wntr Crnvl Ct 83-84; Brown U; Med.

CRONIN JR, CHARLES L; Portsmouth HS; Portsmouth, RI; (Y); FBLA; JA; Ski Clb; Variety Show; Im Bsbl; Im Bsktbl; Im Fld Hcky; Im Wt Lftg; High Hon Roll; Hon Roll; Outstndng Ldrshp Schlrshp 85; U RI; Elec Engrng.

CRUZ, ANTONIO; Charles E Shea HS; Pawtucket, RI; (Y); Socr; Trk; Vllybl; Hon Roll; Prfct Atten Awd; Engrng.

CUMMANDO, D MELISSA; West Warwick HS; W Warwick, RI; (Y); 5/225; French Clb; Math Clb; Band; Concert Band; Jazz Band; Mrchg Band; Ed Yrbk Stf; Var Vllybl; NHS; Voice Dem Awd; Brown U Bk Awd-Eng 84; U Of RI; Poltcl Sci.

CURE, MARTIN; St Raphael Acad; Cent Falls, RI; (Y); 88/188; Cmnty Wkr; French Clb; Ski Clb; JV Ftbl; Var Trk; Hon Roll; Boston U; Engrng.

CURRAN, JANICE; North Smithfield JR SR HS; North Smithfield, RI; (Y); 28/161; Church Yth Grp; French Clb; Chorus; Yrbk Stf; Trs Stu Cncl; Hon Roll; NHS; Pres Schlr; CYO Drama Achvt Awd 84; RI Hnr Soc 8 5; Ntl Soc Dghtrs Of Amer Rvltn Schlrshp 85; Quinnipiac Coll; Physcl Thrpy.

CURTIS, MARK; Scituate JR SR HS; North Scituate, RI; (S); 4/130; Art Clb; Chess Clb; Church Yth Grp; Varsity Clb; Concert Band; Jazz Band; Ftbl; Trk; High Hon Roll; NHS; U S Natl Band Awds 85; CEBA-GIBY Sci Awd 85; Coll Brown; Chem.

CYR, JACKIE M; Johnston SR HS; Johnston, RI; (Y); DECA; Red Cross Aide; Nwsp Rptr; Hon Roll; Distrbtv Ed Clbs Of Amer 84-85; Newspr Rptr 83-84; Hrn Roll 82-85; Culmary Arts.

CYR, JODI-LYNN; Woonsocket SR HS; Woonsocket, RI; (Y); Church Yth Grp; Math Clb; Math Tm; JV Trk; Hon Roll; Yth Serv Awd 84; Chrstn Sprtsmanship Awd 84.

D ABATE, KEVIN; Classical HS; Providence, RI; (Y); 104/296; Camera Clb; Dance Clb; Drama Clb; PAVAS; Stage Crew; Hon Roll; Di Luglio Awd Mst Round Stu; Emerson Coll; Tech Thetr.

D ABATE, WENDY S; S Kingstown HS; Wakefield, RI; (Y); 17/210; Cmnty Wkr; Model UN; Yrbk Stf; Sec Stu Cncl; Hon Roll; NHS; Prov Jrnl Stock Mrkt Cntst 84-85; Bus.

D AGOSTINO, CRISTINA L; South Kingstown HS; Wakefield, RI; (Y); 19/175; Drama Clb; Chorus; Variety Show; Yrbk Stf; Sec Frsh Cls; Stu Cncl; Capt Cheerleading; High Hon Roll; Hon Roll; NHS; All New Englnd Concrt Festvl; 2nd Rnnr-Up RI JR Miss; Schlrshp Prog; U Of VT; Bus.

D ANTUONO, ROBERT; Cranston H S West; Cranston, RI; (Y); 10/443; Variety Show; JV Bsbl; Var L Bsktbl; Hon Roll; NHS; CIBA-GEIGY HS Sci Awd 84-85; RI Tchrs Itln Hnr Soc; U Of RI; Engrng.

DA SILVA, ARMANDO; Central Falls HS; Central Falls, RI; (Y); Boys Clb Am; French Clb; Letterman Clb; Quiz Bowl; Variety Show; Rep Soph Cls; Rep Jr Cls; Rep Stu Cncl; Im Bsktbl; JV Var Socr; RI Hon Soc 85; Embry Riddle Aerontcl U; Pilot.

DACUMOS, CLESSIE; Rogers HS; Newport, RI; (Y); Math Tm; Spanish Clb; Off Stu Cncl; High Hon Roll; Hon Roll; Jr NHS; Spanish NHS; Wellesley Coll Bk Awd 85; Ntl Hnr Rll Yrbk 85; Math.

DALY, KATHRYN; Prout Memorial HS; Kingston, RI; (S); 12/79; French Clb; Math Tm; Acpl Chr; School Musical; Yrbk Ed-Chief; Lit Mag; Hon Roll; NHS; Teachers Aide; Band; ST Sci Fair 82; RI Acad Decthln Tm 84-85; U Of RI; Elec Engrng.

DAME, DOUGLAS; Lincoln HS; Lincoln, RI; (Y); JA; RI Schl Elec; Elec Tech.

DAMORE, KELLEY; Mount St Charles Acad; Uxbridge, MA; (Y); 15/170; Church Yth Grp; Hosp Aide; Model UN; Stu Cncl; Cheerleading; Crs Cntry; High Hon Roll; Hon Roll; NHS; Ntl Merit Ldrshp Awd 85; Exclsr Nhr Roll 82-85; Coll Of Holy Cross; Pre Med.

DANDENEAU, CHRISTOPHER; North Providence HS; N Providence, RI; (Y); Ski Clb; Band; Concert Band; Jazz Band; Orch; Pep Band; School Musical; Symp Band; Var Bsbl; Var Capt Bsktbl; Most Vlbl Bsktbll Plyr 84-85; Pre Law.

DANGELOS, WILLIAM; Warwick Veterins HS; Warwick, RI; (Y); Church Yth Grp; Yrbk Stf; Im Bsbl; JV Bsktbl; Var Capt Golf; Hon Roll; All Cty Golf Tm 85.

DAPONTE, DENISE; Pilgrim HS; Warwick, RI; (Y); 33/315; Band; Concert Band; Jazz Band; Mrchg Band; Orch; Pep Band; Hon Roll; NHS; Conductors Awd 85; URI; Pre-Med.

DAREZZO, DAWN; Warwick Veterans Memorial HS; Warwick, RI; (Y); High Hon Roll; Hon Roll; RI JC; Humn Svcs.

DARIGAN, JOHN; Classical HS; Providence, RI; (Y); Church Yth Grp; Y-Teens; Hon Roll; Hstry.

DARVEAU, DIANE; Woonsocket HS; Woonsocket, RI; (Y); Pres Church Yth Grp; JA; Quiz Bowl; High Hon Roll; Hon Roll.

DASILUN, MARIO; Centnal Falls HS; Central Falls, RI; (Y); 10/125; Aud/Vis; Camera Clb; Computer Clb; JA; PAVAS; Varsity Clb; Nwsp Phtg; Yrbk Phtg; Bsbl; Bowling; E S L Effrt 81-82; Var Lttr 83-85; Comp Engr.

DAUPHINAIS, TINA; Cranston High School East; Cranston, RI; (Y); Library Aide; School Play; Pres Stu Cncl; Hon Roll; Spanish NHS; Hnbl Mntn Wrld Poetry 85; Acting.

DAVENPORT, LISA; Lincoln JR SR HS; Lincoln, RI; (Y); JA; Trs Frsh Cls; Trs Soph Cls; Trs Jr Cls; Trs Sr Cls; Trs Stu Cncl; JV Var Cheerleading; Vllybl; RI Coll; Elem Ed.

DAVIS, HEIDI; Prout Memorial HS; E Greenwich, RI; (Y); 26/80; Drama Clb; Flag Corp; School Play; Variety Show; Aud/Vis; Church Yth Grp; PAVAS; Chorus; Nwsp Rptr; Nwsp Stf; Psych.

DAVIS, PAM; North Kingstown HS; N Kingstown, RI; (Y); 102/371; Camera Clb; Cmnty Wkr; Exploring; French Clb; GAA; Varsity Clb; Chorus; Nwsp Stf; Yrbk Ed-Chief; Yrbk Stf.

DAY, STEPHEN; Chariho Regional HS; Ashaway, RI; (S); 11/239; Boy Scts; Church Yth Grp; Computer Clb; Science Clb; Yrbk Stf; High Hon Roll; Jr NHS; Ntl Merit Ltr; NEMA 83-84; Proj Closeup 83-85; Model Legistltre 84-85; Elec Engrng.

DE ANDRADE, ALYSSA BETH; Lincoln HS; Lincoln, RI; (Y); 15/220; JA; Variety Show; Yrbk Ed-Chief; High Hon Roll; Hon Roll; Jr NHS; NHS; Prfct Atten Awd; Pres Schlr; ST Hnr Soc RI 85; RIC; Law.

DE CESARE, BRENDA; St Marys Academy Bay View; Warwick, RI; (Y); Exploring; JA; Hon Roll; U Of RI; Med.

DE COMO, PETER R; Rogers HS; Newport, RI; (Y); Var Bsbl; Var Bsktbl; Var Ftbl; French Hon Soc; High Hon Roll; NHS; Baum Sci Schlrshp 85; US Army Rsv Mdl Acadmc Excllnc 85; Booster Clb Schlrshp 85; RI U; Engrng.

DE GENOVA, KAREN; Pilgrim HS; Warwick, RI; (Y); Dance Clb; Quiz Bowl; Ski Clb; School Play; Capt Cheerleading; Sftbl; High Hon Roll; Italian Hnr Scty 85; Wellesley Alumni Bk Awd 85; Italian Clb Pres 83-85; Frgn Lang.

DE LA CRUZ, MAHLI; Central HS; Providence, RI; (Y); JA; Orch; Nwsp Stf; Lit Mag; Swmmng; Vllybl; Prfct Atten Awd; Johnson & Wales Coll; Bus Mngmn.

DE MATOS, DIANE; Our Lady Of Fatima HS; Bristol, RI; (S); 5/36; Cmnty Wkr; GAA; Varsity Clb; Pres Stu Cncl; Var Bsktbl; Var Bowling; JV Crs Cntry; Var Sftbl; Hon Roll; Hugh O Brien Ldrshp Awd; Spec Ed.

DE MAY, SUSAN; Portsmouth HS; Portsmouth, RI; (Y); 25/220; FBLA; Chorus; Mrchg Band; Soph Cls; Im Ice Hcky; Im Powder Puff Ftbl; Im Socr; Var L Sftbl; Var L Tennis; Hon Roll; Jr Clss Rep-Ctzns Schlrshp Fndtn 84-85; 2nd Tm All Div Tennis & Sftbl 82-85; All-Star Goalie 83-85; Orthpdc Surgeon.

DE ROSA, CARLA; Johnston HS; Johnston, RI; (S); 14/237; High Hon Roll; Hon Roll; NHS; Sci Fair Awd 83; Hist Day Awd 83; New Eng Inst Tech; Comp Pgrmr.

DE SPIRITO III, ANTONIO; Barrington HS; Barrington, RI; (Y); Boy Scts; Church Yth Grp; Cmnty Wkr; Computer Clb; Debate Tm; Library Aide; Math Tm; NFL; Band; NHS; Holy Crss Coll Bk Awd 85; Ad Altare Dei Awd 82; Egl Sct 85; Ec.

DE STEFANO, JEFFREY; Scituate JR SR HS; North Scituate, RI; (S); 2/115; School Musical; Yrbk Stf; Rep Sr Cls; Capt Bsbl; Var Bsktbl; Capt Ftbl; High Hon Roll; Jr NHS; Ntl Merit Ltr; Sal; West Point; Elec Engr.

DEANE, MICHELLE; Our Lady Of Fatima HS; Bristol, RI; (Y); Dance Clb; Drama Clb; School Play; Variety Show; Trk; Hon Roll; Dance Awd 85; Comp.

DEANGELIS, AMY; Johnston SR HS; Johnston, RI; (Y); Girl Scts; Yrbk Stf; Trs Sr Cls; Sftbl; Hon Roll; Jrnlst.

DEERING, NANCY; Warwick Veterans Memorial HS; Warwick, RI; (Y); Camp Fr Inc; Church Yth Grp; Girl Scts; Letterman Clb; Math Tm; Teachers Aide; Chorus; Church Choir; Variety Show; Gym; Psych.

DEFREITAS, CARLOS; St Raphael Acad; Pawtucket, RI; (Y); 21/180; Boys Clb Am; Boy Scts; Exploring; Yrbk Phtg; Rep Stu Cncl; Stat Ice Hcky; Score Keeper; Im Vllybl; Hon Roll; Pres NHS; Bio.

DEGRE, RHONDA; William M Davies Vo-Tech HS; Pawtucket, RI; (Y); VICA; Yrbk Stf; Bowling; Capt Gym; Hon Roll; Shop Vica VP 84-85; Piano Clb 82-83; Culinary Inst Of Am; Culnry Art.

DEITZ, APRIL; Smithfield HS; Greenville, RI; (Y); Am Leg Aux Girls St; Drama Clb; Math Tm; School Play; Stage Crew; Lit Mag; Rep Stu Cncl; Hon Roll; Computer Clb, French Clb.

DEL BUONO, BRENDA; Cranston H S West; Cranston, RI; (Y); VICA; Chorus; Lit Mag; High Hon Roll; Hon Roll; NHS; NEDT Awd; Ldrshp Awd-Future Secys 85; 1st In St, 2nd In Schl VICA Awds-Offc Practice 85; Exec Secy.

DELGADO, JOHN JOSEPH; Hope HS; Providence, RI; (S); Trs Sr Cls; Pres Stu Cncl; Var Bsbl; Var Ftbl; Hon Roll; Prfct Atten Awd; DECA; FBLA; Office Aide; Score Keeper; Schlrshp Prov Jrnl Blntn 85; Cert Of Merit RI & Pro Plntns 82; Bryant Coll; Accntnt.

DELLA CIOPPA, JULIE; Warwick Veterans Memorial HS; Warwick, RI; (S); 8/330; Dance Clb; Yrbk Stf; Pres Frsh Cls; Pres Soph Cls; Pres Jr Cls; Pres Sr Cls; Stu Cncl; Var Cheerleading; High Hon Roll; JC Awd; Brown U Bk Awd; Hugh O Brin Outstndg Soph; Frgn Lagn Spllng Bee Wnnr.

DELPHOS, PAUL; Mount St Charles Acad; Franklin, MA; (Y); 45/150; Cmnty Wkr; Band; Concert Band; Mrchg Band; Var L Bsktbl; Coach Actv; Var L Golf; Var L Socr; Hon Roll; Lion Awd; Civil Engr.

DENIS, DONNA L; Tolman HS; Pawucket, RI; (Y); Camp Fr Inc; Church Yth Grp; Drama Clb; Library Aide.

DENNEN, PAMELA; Warwick Veterans Memorial HS; Providence, RI; (Y); CAP; Computer Clb; Radio Clb; Teachers Aide; Stu Cncl; Hon Roll; Hlth Clb; Exec Committee; Salve Regina; Psych.

DEPALMA, PAUL; North Providence HS; N Providence, RI; (Y); Aud/Vis; JV Var Bsbl; Var Bsktbl; Comp.

DEPASQUALE, PETER; Portsmouth HS; Portsmouth, RI; (Y); VP FBLA; Concert Band; Mrchg Band; Pep Band; Nwsp Sprt Ed; L Crs Cntry; L Golf; Socr; NHS; 3rd Pl ST Comp Litrcy Comp 85; All ST Band 83 & 85; Elec Engr.

DEPAULT, TIMITHY; North Smithfield JR SR HS; No Smithfield, RI; (Y); 40/140; French Clb; Letterman Clb; Var Capt Socr; All Div Socr 84; All Div All Star Play-Off Tm 84; St Anselm Coll; Ed.

DESCHENEAUX, ROGER; Mt St Charles Acad; Blackstone, MA; (Y); 7/147; Boy Scts; High Hon Roll; NHS; Comp Progmmng.

DESCOTEAUX, KENNETH G; Cumberland HS; Cumberland, RI; (Y); 1/436; Boy Scts; Capt Math Tm; Concert Band; Mrchg Band; High Hon Roll; Hon Roll; NHS; Ntl Merit SF; Val; Comp Engr.

DESJARDINS, DIANNE; St Raphael Acad; Pawtucket, RI; (Y); 4/170; French Clb; High Hon Roll; NHS; Var L Cheerleading; RI Coll; Elem Schl Tchr.

DESLAURIERS, LISA; St Mary Academy Bay View; Cranston, RI; (Y); 10/206; Exploring; Hosp Aide; Math Tm; Teachers Aide; Nwsp Stf; Sec Soph Cls; Stu Cncl; Hon Roll; NHS; Ntl Merit Ltr; NEDT Awd 83; Vol Cont Awd 84; Ntl Merit Pgm 85; Phrmcy.

DESLAURIES, DONALD; Woonsocket HS; Woonsocket, RI; (Y); Boy Scts; Church Yth Grp; Drama Clb; French Clb; School Play; Nwsp Ed-Chief; Ftbl; Socr; French Hon Soc; Hon Roll; Frnch Newspaper Ed Cheif 81-82; Ntl Ftns Awd 81-85; Johnson Wales; Rest.

DESMARAIS, JACQUELINE; Woonsocket SR HS; Woonsocket, RI; (Y); French Clb; Sec Jr Cls; Rep Stu Cncl; Var Cheerleading; High Hon Roll; Hon Roll; 2nd Pl RI Holocaust Essay 82.

DESORCY, SHARON; Charles E Shea HS; Pawtucket, RI; (Y); Computer Clb; Library Aide; Office Aide; Hon Roll; Prfct Atten Awd.

DESPLAINES, MICHAEL; St Raphael Acad; Pawtucket, RI; (Y); Cmnty Wkr; Drama Clb; French Clb; Political Wkr; Chorus; School Musical; School Play; Stage Crew; Hon Roll; Boy Scts; Cert Of Merit Vlntr Wrk Audubon Socty RI 85; U Of RI; Plnt Sci.

DESROCHERS, ALAN G; Tiverton HS; Tiverton, RI; (Y); Bristol CC; Acctng.

DESROCHERS, ROLAND; St Ra Phaels Acad; Riverside, RI; (Y); 3/190; Var Ftbl; Capt Trk; High Hon Roll; Hon Roll; NHS; Holy Cross Book Prize 85; Annual HS Math Exam 85; Engnrng.

DESROCHES, GREGORY; Smithfield HS; Esmond, RI; (Y); 85/200; Boys Clb Am; Computer Clb; DECA; French Clb; Math Clb; Math Tm; Science Clb; Prfct Atten Awd; R I New Eng Math Leag 84-85; Outstndng Mrktng Stu 84-85; Johnson & Wales Coll; Arts.

DETHORN, JOHN R; Rogers HS; Newport, RI; (S); Am Leg Boys St; 4-H; FBLA; Nwsp Phtg; Yrbk Stf; Bsbl; Var L Ftbl; Var L Socr; Var Tennis; 9th LA ST Soccr Team 82-84; Boys ST 85; 11th Pl 2nd Team All Dist Soccr 85; U Of CO; Bus Admin.

DI BIASIO, GINA; Coventry HS; Coventry, RI; (Y); Hon Roll; Jr NHS; NHS; Spanish NHS; Psych.

DI CENZO, LISA; North Providence HS; N Providence, RI; (Y); Girl Scts; Bsktbl; Cheerleading; High Hon Roll; Eng Hghst Stu Hnr Awd Lit 81; RI Coll; Psych.

DI MARZIO, DENISE; North Providence HS; N Providence, RI; (Y); Church Yth Grp; Cmnty Wkr; Nwsp Sprt Ed; Nwsp Stf; Yrbk Stf; Lit Mag; High Hon Roll; Hon Roll; Jr NHS; NHS; Order Sons Italy Amer Schlrshp 85; RI Tchrs Itln Cert Merit 84; RI Tchrs Itln Cert Merit 85; Emerson; Adv.

DI MASE, DONNA; Lincoln HS; Lincoln, RI; (Y); 9/209; Church Yth Grp; Nwsp Ed-Chief; Yrbk Stf; Rep Jr Cls; Rep Sr Cls; Rep Stu Cncl; Var Tennis; High Hon Roll; Hon Roll; NHS; Wright Fmly Scholar 85; Boston Coll Scholar 85; Hghr Ed Grant 85; Boston Coll; Polit Sci.

DI NUNZIO, JOSEPH; N Smithfield HS; N Smithfield, RI; (Y); JCL; Band; Chorus; Concert Band; Jazz Band; Mrchg Band; JV Bsktbl; Golf; Hon Roll; All ST Band; 83-85; All ST Jazz Band 84-85; Natl Latin Hnr Soc 84-85; Mc Donalds Band Outcomt Nom 85; Providence Coll.

DI PIPPO, PETER; Middletown HS; Middletown, RI; (S); 1/256; Drama Clb; French Clb; Math Tm; Band; Concert Band; Mrchg Band; Pep Band; School Play; Stage Crew.

DI RUZZO, ANISSA ANN; North Providence HS; N Providence, RI; (Y); 1/233; Ski Clb; Yrbk Stf; Var Capt Cheerleading; Var Gym; High Hon Roll; NHS; Rotary Awd; Val; RI Model Legsltr Stu Rep; Ciba-Geigy H S Sci Awd; Herbert E Hopkins Eng Awd; U Of PA; Bio.

DICK, MARISSA; Warwick Veterans Memorial HS; Warwick, RI; (S); Church Yth Grp; Hosp Aide; Church Choir; Mrchg Band; Jr Cls; Var Cheerleading; High Hon Roll; Jr NHS; Spanish NHS; Library Aide; Solo Ensmble Msc Awd 80-83.

DIETZ, KRISTEN; Cranston High School East; Cranston, RI; (Y); Trs Church Yth Grp; Girl Scts; Library Aide; Office Aide; Sec Lit Mag; Hon Roll; Sci & Soc Studys Fair Awds 83; Bradford Coll; Librl Arts.

DIGIOVANNI, DOLORES; North Providence HS; N Providence, RI; (Y); Girl Scts; Hosp Aide; Church Choir; Crs Cntry; Trk; Decathalon Tm 85; U Of RI; Law.

DITUSA, LISA; Coventry HS; Coventry, RI; (Y); Rep Spanish Clb; Q&S; Nwsp Rptr; Nwsp Stf; Yrbk Stf; Score Keeper; JV Vllybl; Hon Roll; NHS; Acad All-Amer Schlr Prog 84; Natl Ldrshp & Svc Awd 83 & 85.

DO COUTO, KATHLEEN; Tiverton HS; Tiverton, RI; (Y); Cmnty Wkr; Drama Clb; Girl Scts; School Play; Yrbk Stf; Rep Stu Cncl; High Hon Roll; Hon Roll; Girl Scout Silvr Awd 83; Miss RI Natl Teen Ager Pgnt 85; Cmmnctn.

DOD, MARYPATRICIA; Our Lady Of Fatima HS; Barrington, RI; (S); Church Yth Grp; Drama Clb; Chorus; School Play; Stage Crew; Sec Soph Cls; VP Jr Cls; Hon Roll; RI ST Sci Fair 3rd Grnt 82; Schl Sci Fair 1st Cert 82; Schl Sci Fair 4th Cert 83; U Of RI; Marine Bio.

DODD, THOMAS; N Kingstown HS; N Kingstown, RI; (Y); JV Wrstlng; High Hon Roll; Hon Roll; JV Wrstly Hnr Roll Athl 83; Natl Hnr Scty 83; Arch.

DOLAN, KRISTEN; Smithfield HS; Greenville, RI; (Y); 12/196; French Clb; Rep Frsh Cls; Rep Soph Cls; Rep Jr Cls; Sr Cls; Rep Stu Cncl; JV Var Cheerleading; Var Tennis; High Hon Roll; Hon Roll; VP Ec 85; Mass Media Cmmnctns Awd 85; Bentley Coll; Mrktng.

DONNELLY, MICHELLE CHRISTINE; Portsmouth HS; Portsmouth, RI; (Y); 42/209; French Clb; FBLA; Stu Cncl; Cheerleading; Powder Puff Ftbl; Socr; Hon Roll; U RI; Acctg.

DONNELLY, WENDY; Coventry HS; Coventry, RI; (Y); Church Yth Grp; Dance Clb; Radio Clb; Yrbk Stf; Stu Cncl; Var VP Cheerleading; High Hon Roll; Hon Roll; NHS; Diplma Mert Spnsh 84-85; Cnslr Of Wk Awd 85; Elem/Spec Ed Tchr.

DOUGLAS, WILLIAM; Portsmouth HS; Portsmouth, RI; (Y); Civic Clb; FBLA; Concert Band; Mrchg Band; Nwsp Stf; Yrbk Stf; Pres Jr Cls; Rep Stu Cncl; Mgr(s); Cit Awd.

DRAKE, LYNDA; Pilgrim HS; Warwick, RI; (Y); Math Clb; Pep Clb; Spanish Clb; Band; Yrbk Rptr; Cheerleading; JV Capt Fld Hcky; Gym; Mgr Socr; Hon Roll; U Of RI; Pre Dntl.

DRENNAN, ELIZABETH A; South Kingstown HS; Wakefield, RI; (Y); 30/206; Pres Drama Clb; School Musical; School Play; Stage Crew; Variety Show; Socr; High Hon Roll; Hon Roll; St Schlr; RI Hnr Socty 84-85; Drama Schlrshp 84-85; U Of RI; Theatr.

DROTH, KEVIN E; Central Vo Tech; Providence, RI; (Y); Boy Scts; Rep Jr Cls; Hll Inst; Graphc Arts.

DRURY, SHANE; North Providence HS; N Providence, RI; (Y); 29/213; Church Yth Grp; Cmnty Wkr; Letterman Clb; Political Wkr; Bsktbl; Crs Cntry; Golf; Ice Hcky; Trk; High Hon Roll; Bus Mgmt.

DUARTE, SUSAN; Bristol HS; Bristol, RI; (S); 30/220; Teachers Aide; Capt Band; Concert Band; Mrchg Band; Rep Frsh Cls; Capt Cheerleading; Sftbl; High Hon Roll; NHS; Katharine Gibbs Schl; Sec.

DUBOIS, DAVID; Mount St Charles Acad; Woonsocket, RI; (S); 1/143; Boy Scts; Math Tm; Ski Clb; Band; Mrchg Band; Chrmn Stu Cncl; Im Bsktbl; High Hon Roll; NHS; Chem.

DUBOIS, DENISE; St Marys Academy Bay View; Providence, RI; (Y); Drama Clb; Exploring; Thesps; Chorus; School Musical; School Play; Rep Jr Cls; Var Cheerleading; Hon Roll; Church Yth Grp; Italian Clb; Poetry Cntst Awd; Scouting For Spec Olympics Awd; Salve Reogina Coll; Theatre.

DUFFY, CHRISTOPHER O NEILL; Portsmouth HS; Portsmouth, RI; (Y); Boy Scts; Band; Jazz Band; Orch; Pep Band; NHS; Spanish NHS; Eagle Scout; Drum Mjr; MA Yth Wind Ensmble Ger Tour 85; Babson Coll; Bus.

DUFFY, KEVIN; Cranston HS; Cranston, RI; (Y); Am Leg Boys St; Debate Tm; VP Intnl Clb; Political Wkr; Scholastic Bowl; Ski Clb; Off Jr Cls; Off Stu Cncl; Ice Hcky; Trk; Spkr House RI Model Legsltr 84-85; Intl Ambssdr HOBY Fndtn 83; US Senate Yth Pgm 84-85; George Washington U; Intl Affrs.

DUFFY, THOMAS; West Warwick SR HS; W Warwick, RI; (Y); Ftbl.

DUGAS, SCOTT; La Salle HS; Johnston, RI; (Y); 49/259; Boy Scts; Math Tm; JV Wrstlng; Hon Roll; Ntl Yth Physcl Ftns Prog 85; Bryant; Actural Sci.

DUGGAN, TIM P; Middletown HS; Adamsville, RI; (Y); Avtn.

DUHAMEL, MARCEL C; N Smithfield JR SR HS; Forestdale, RI; (Y); 4/154; VP Church Yth Grp; Debate Tm; French Clb; Political Wkr; Pres Jr Cls; Rep Stu Cncl; High Hon Roll; Am Leg Boys St; Boy Scts; Am Leg Boys Ntn 875; Eagle Scout 84; Pol Sci.

DUMAS, BETSY LEE; Cumberland HS; Pawtucket, RI; (Y); Church Yth Grp; Chorus; Church Choir; Mgr(s); Epscpl Diocse Of RI Schlrshp 85; Bay Path JC; Legl Asst.

DUMAS, MONIQUE; Mt St Charles HS; Cumberland, RI; (Y); 20/147; French Clb; JCL; Ski Clb; Var Cheerleading; Hon Roll; NHS; Ec.

DUNBAR, KRISTA; Middletown HS; Little Compton, RI; (Y); Chorus; Spanish NHS; Nrsg.

DUSSAULT, JOANNE; Bishop Keough Regional HS; Pawtucket, RI; (S); Drama Clb; Ski Clb; School Play; Nwsp Stf; Yrbk Ed-Chief; Rep Stu Cncl; Score Keeper; High Hon Roll; Jr NHS; NHS; Biology I 81-82; Chem 83-84; Geom 83-84; U Of RI; Biology.

DWYER, TIMOTHY; St Raphael Acad; Pawtucket, RI; (Y); 27/185; JA; Political Wkr; Pres Jr Cls; Var Bsbl; JV Bsktbl; Var Capt Ftbl; Im Wt Lftg; Dnfth Awd; Hon Roll; NHS; Engrng.

DYER, DAPHNE; Chariho Regional HS; Kenyon, RI; (Y); Art Clb; Drama Clb; Speech Tm; Chorus; Stu Cncl; Crs Cntry; Trk; Hon Roll; Crss Cntry All S Cnty Tm 81; Fshn Dsgn.

EAGAN III, OWEN L; Tiverton HS; Tiverton, RI; (Y); VP Church Yth Grp; Ski Clb; Band; Jazz Band; Orch; School Musical; Variety Show; Socr; Elks Awd; Hon Roll; Selctd All ST Band 83; Selctd All Trnmnt Socr Tm 84; U Of ME Orono; Libl Arts.

EATON, LYNN; N Smithfield JR SR HS; N Smithfield, RI; (Y); Church Yth Grp; Rep Soph Cls; Rep Jr Cls; Rep Sr Cls; Hon Roll; Semi Queen 82-83; Desgn.

EBERT, TRACY; Bishop Keough Regional HS; Greenville, RI; (Y); Debate Tm; Drama Clb; Girl Scts; Trs Frsh Cls; Sftbl; Tennis; High Hon Roll; Hon Roll; Delaware Valley Coll; Anml Husb.

EDWARDO, STEPHANIE; St Raphael Acad; N Prov, RI; (Y); Church Yth Grp; Exploring; Girl Scts; Library Aide; Nwsp Stf; Yrbk Stf; Pres Sr Cls; Bsktbl; Nrsng.

EGAN, KELLY; Chariho Regional HS; Hope Valley, RI; (Y); 35/300; Cmnty Wkr; Yrbk Stf; Rep Jr Cls; JV Bsktbl; Score Keeper; Stat Socr; Hon Roll; Jr NHS; Ed.

EGAN, MARY; St Raphael Acad; Prov, RI; (Y); Church Yth Grp; Dance Clb; Hosp Aide; Science Clb; Yrbk Stf; Sec Stu Cncl; JV Capt Cheerleading; Hon Roll; NHS; U Of RI Bk Awd 85; JR Prom Ct 85; Bus.

ELIAS, ELIZABETH; North Smithfield JR SR HS; N Smithfield, RI; (Y); Drama Clb; Library Aide; School Play; Stage Crew; Yrbk Bus Mgr; Yrbk Stf; Stu Cncl.

ERCOLANO, DONNA; Toll Gate HS; Warwick, RI; (S); 20/498; Pep Clb; Varsity Clb; Cheerleading; High Hon Roll; Hon Roll; Jr NHS; NHS; Psychrst.

ERINAKES, JAMES; La Salle Acad; Coventry, RI; (Y); 3/257; Cmnty Wkr; Math Tm; Model UN; Spanish Clb; Im Bowling; High Hon Roll; NHS; Excllnc Spnsh Awds 83-85; Outstndng Tutr Spnsh Awd 84; Fnlst Jrnl Bulltn Schlrshp 1 Of 10 84; Engr.

ERNST, LAURA; Prout Memorial HS; Block Island, RI; (Y); 15/87; Am Leg Aux Girls St; Church Yth Grp; Cmnty Wkr; Computer Clb; Dance Clb; Debate Tm; Drama Clb; Exploring; French Clb; Political Wkr; WINE News Gme Yth Ldrshp 84; Frdms Found Vly Frge Frdm & Ldrshp 85; Pres Phys Ftnss Awd 83; West Point; Law.

ESPOSITO, TINA; N Smithfield HS; N Smithfield, RI; (Y); 26/164; Drama Clb; Color Guard; Off Stu Cncl; Hon Roll; NHS; Pres Schlr; RI Hnr Soc 85; RI Coll; Comp Sci.

EVA, MICHELE; N Scituate JR-SR Hs; North Scituate, RI; (S); 6/118; French Clb; PAVAS; Band; Chorus; Orch; School Musical; Hon Roll; NHS; NEDT Awd; Colby Coll Bk Awd; All-ST Orch; RI Coll Orch; Intl Reltns.

EVANS, ANN; North Kingstown HS; North Kingstown, RI; (Y); Varsity Clb; Cheerleading.

FAGUNDES, JULIE; East Providence SR HS; East Providence, RI; (S); 4/520; Chorus; Pres Jr Cls; Sec Stu Cncl; Var L Diving; Var Capt Swmmng; Var L Vllybl; High Hon Roll; NHS; Ntl Merit Ltr; Teachers Aide; Dartmouth Clb Bk Awd 84; Bio.

FALCO, SUSAN; Bristol HS; Bristol, RI; (Y); Yrbk Stf; Mrktng.

FALCONE, ELENA; Cranston West HS; Cranston, RI; (Y); Church Yth Grp; Ski Clb; Chorus; Concert Band; Mrchg Band; Lit Mag; Rep Stu Cncl; Hon Roll; NEDT Awd; Outstndng Band Awd 84.

FANTOZZI, KRISTIN; Cranston West HS; Cranston, RI; (Y); Art Clb; Church Yth Grp; Flag Corp; Stage Crew; Variety Show; Stat Bsbl; Var Cheerleading; Mgr(s); Score Keeper; Twrlr; Most Athl Chrldr 83; Ed.

FARIA, MARY L; Our Lady Of Fattma HS; Bristol, RI; (S); Drama Clb; Hosp Aide; School Play; Stage Crew; Yrbk Stf; Hon Roll; Jr NHS; Acad All-Amer 85; Newport Coll; Med.

FARIA, NELIA; Our Lady Of Fatima HS; Warren, RI; (Y); Yrbk Stf; Var Bsktbl; Hon Roll; Bus.

FARLEY, SARA; Saint Raphael Acad; Pawtucket, RI; (Y); 4/180; Exploring; Science Clb; High Hon Roll; NHS; Vet Med.

FARRELL, KELLY; Cranston HS West; Cranston, RI; (Y); Art Clb; Church Yth Grp; French Clb; Latin Clb; Ski Clb; Concert Band; Drm Mjr(t); Mrchg Band; Pep Band; Var Stu Cncl; Fleet Natl Bank Art Awd 85; PCA; Art.

FARRELL, LISA; Saint Raphael Acad; Lincoln, RI; (Y); 16/195; Cmnty Wkr; Exploring; Teachers Aide; Varsity Clb; Yrbk Stf; Stu Cncl; Var Capt Cheerleading; High Hon Roll; Hon Roll; NHS; Roger Williams Coll; Paralegal.

FEALEY, PATRICK W; North Kingstown SR HS; Jamestown, RI; (Y); 37/370; Pres Band; Pres Concert Band; Pres Jazz Band; Pres Mrchg Band; Pep Band; School Musical; Stage Crew; Pres Symp Band; Variety Show; Gov Hon Prg Awd; 3 Cert Mscnshp Berklee Coll Music 83-85 ; Schlrshp Berklee Coll Music 84; Ntl Social Studies Olympid; U Of RI; Pre-Med.

FECTEAU, SEAN P; La Salle Acad; Seekonk, MA; (Y); 37/257; Letterman Clb; Varsity Clb; Var Crs Cntry; Var Golf; Var Ice Hcky; Hon Roll; Math.

FECTEAU JR, THOMAS B; La Salle Acad; Seekonk, MA; (Y); 40/198; Letterman Clb; Varsity Clb; Var Bsbl; Var Golf; Var Capt Ice Hcky; Hon Roll; RI Hnr Socty 85; All ST Hcky Tm 85; New Hampton Prep Schl; Comp.

FEELEY, PATRICIA; East Providence HS; Riverside, RI; (Y); Church Yth Grp; Chorus; Nwsp Stf; Yrbk Stf; Stu Cncl; Cheerleading; Hon Roll; NHS; Chld Care.

FELBER, STEVEN; Lincoln HS; Lincoln, RI; (Y); 13/190; High Hon Roll; Hon Roll; Jr NHS; NHS; Prfct Atten Awd; New England Inst Tech; Eletrncs.

FERMINO, FRANK; Saint Raphael Acad; E Prov, RI; (Y); Var Stat Bsktbl; Score Keeper; Hon Roll; NHS; Tutrl Svcs Rcgntn 83-85; 3rd Hghst Pts BMX Rcng 84; Aerontcl Tech.

FERNSTROM, DIANNE L; East Providence SR HS; Riverside, RI; (Y); 148/500; French Clb; PAVAS; Nwsp Rptr; Yrbk Stf; Gym; OCRI; Int Dsgn.

FERRANTE, DAWN; Central HS; Providence, RI; (Y); FBLA; VP Jr Cls; Hon Roll; Acctng.

FERRARO, CARY; North Kingstown HS; North Kingstown, RI; (Y); 164/375; Varsity Clb; JV Var Cheerleading; Hon Roll; All Am Chrldr 84; CCRI; Nrsng.

FERREIRA, RENEE; Our Lady Of Fatima HS; Bristol, RI; (S); 11/46; Pep Clb; Pres Jr Cls; Var Bsktbl; Var Trk; High Hon Roll; Hon Roll; Sci Fair Certif 82-83; Fnlst Miss RI Natl Teenager Pgnt 84; Natl Awd Wnnr Ldrshp & Svc 84; RIC; Med.

FERREIRA, SILVIA; Cranston HS East; Cranston, RI; (Y); Hosp Aide; Library Aide; Nwsp Stf; Hon Roll; NHS; Katharine Gibbs Schl Awd Futr Secys Wnnr 85; Katharine Gibbs Schl; Bus Adm.

FERRY, ANN; St Marys Academy Bay View; Cranston, RI; (Y); Church Yth Grp; Cmnty Wkr; Exploring; Hosp Aide; Spanish Clb; Yrbk Stf; Rep Frsh Cls; Hon Roll; Fleet Natl Bank Awd Desgn & Cnstrctng Fmly Hme 84; Modl Legsltr 84; Engrng.

FILIBERTO, THOMAS; Chariho Regional HS; Charlestown, RI; (Y); 45/302; Science Clb; Hon Roll; Crs Cntry; Prfct Atten Awd; Grnd Prze Clss Fundraiser 85; Cert Attnmnt Amateur Athl Union USA 85; US Naval Acad; Elec Engr.

FINLEY, KATHLEEN ANN; E Greenwich HS; E Greenwich, RI; (Y); 16/197; Drama Clb; Q&S; Nwsp Ed-Chief; Yrbk Stf; Lit Mag; Var Capt Crs Cntry; Var Capt Trk; Hon Roll; NHS; Boosters Clb, Bostich Ldrshp Awd Schlrshp 85; Bus Mgr Lit Mag 84-85; Tres Hnr Soc Jrnlsm 84-85; Villanova U; Jrnlsm.

FINNERTY, CHRISTINE; Warwick Veterans Mem HS; Warwick, RI; (Y); #83 In Class; Pres DECA; Stu Cncl; High Hon Roll; Hon Roll; Dist Ed Stdnt Yr 85; Outstndng Bus Stdnts 85; RI Hnr Socty 85; Johnson & Waites; Htl Mgmt.

FITZGERALD, GARRETT S; Classical HS; Providence, RI; (Y); 5/295; Math Tm; High Hon Roll; Hon Roll; Ntl Merit SF; St Schlr; MAA Hnr Roll 83-84; Am Assoc Tchrs Italian Comp Hnrble Mention 83; Brown U & Oberlin Coll Cnsrvtry 84; Comp Sci.

FITZGERALD, MICHELE; South Kingstown HS; Wakefield, RI; (Y); 50/250; Art Clb; Band; Concert Band; Mrchg Band; Pep Band; School Play; Var L Socr; L Var Trk; Var Vllybl; Hon Roll; Hnr Excll Art 84; Aerosp Engnr.

FITZGERALD, WENDY; Johnston HS; Johnston, RI; (Y); Art Clb; Office Aide; Chorus; Variety Show; Cheerleading; Hon Roll; Cert Of Achvt-Natl Hstry Day 83-85; RI Coll.

FITZPATRICK, DEBRA JEAN; Mount St Charles Acad; Smithfield, RI; (Y); Sec Frsh Cls; Sec Soph Cls; Var L Bsktbl; Var L Tennis; High Hon Roll; Hon Roll; NHS; Hugh O Brian Yth Ldrshp Awd; Dennis B Mc Creadie Christian Serv Awd; 1st Tm All-Div Tnns; Boston Coll.

FLAD, JENNIFER; Portsmouth HS; Portsmouth, RI; (Y); 33/240; Varsity Clb; Band; Concert Band; Nwsp Phtg; Bsktbl; Crs Cntry; Gym; Powder Puff Ftbl; Socr; Sftbl; Ltr Cross Cty,Gym,Sftbl 82-83; Bus Adm.

FLANAGAN, TIMOTHY; La Salle Acad; Cumberland, RI; (Y); 33/257; Church Yth Grp; Math Tm; Pep Clb; Band; Concert Band; Mrchg Band; Nwsp Rptr; Hon Roll; Aerospc Engrng.

FLAXMAN, CYNTHIA E; The Wheeler Schl; Seekonk, MA; (Y); Drama Clb; Madrigals; School Musical; Nwsp Rptr; Ed Lit Mag; Rep Frsh Cls; Rep Soph Cls; Pres Jr Cls; Rep Sr Cls; Rep Stu Cncl; Cum Laude 84; Lillian Berger Rubenstein Awd Achvt Jewish Music 83; Wellesley Coll Bk Awd 84; Yale U.

FLEMING, MICHAEL; Rogers HS; Newport, RI; (Y); Band; Mrchg Band; Stu Cncl; Socr; Trk; Hon Roll; NEDT Awd; Ntl Spnsh 1st Pl 83, 3rd 85; Astrntcl Engrng.

FLOOD, CATHERINE; Portsmouth HS; Portsmouth, RI; (Y); 10/207; Band; Mrchg Band; Sec Frsh Cls; Pres Stu Cncl; Var L Golf; Var L Socr; High Hon Roll; Hon Roll; NHS; Voice Dem Awd; Democratic Ledrshp Schlrshp 85; Teachers Outstndng Stu Awd 85; Town & Cnty Ledrshp Awd 85; Bryant Coll; Actuarial Math.

FLOOD, KAREN L; Tolman HS; Pawtucket, RI; (Y); Am Leg Aux Girls St; Drama Clb; French Clb; Chorus; School Play; Yrbk Stf; Stu Cncl; Sftbl; High Hon Roll; Outstndg Acad Achvt Awd 83; Outstndg Type Stu 83; Best Frnch Stu Awd 83; Hofstra; Phy.

FLORES, TINA; Woonsocket HS; Woonsocket, RI; (Y); Pres Church Yth Grp; Math Tm; Hon Roll; MINISTRY.

FLYNN, KATIE; St Marys Academy-Bay View; E Greenwich, RI; (Y); 50/210; Boys Clb Am; Debate Tm; Exploring; Yrbk Stf; VP Soph Cls; VP Stu Cncl; Var Tennis; Var Swmmng; Ski Clb; Sftbl 2nd Tm All Div 85; U S Yth Senat Prog ST SF 84; Lwyr.

FLYNN, MICHAEL; La Salle Acad; Smithfield, RI; (Y); 11/256; Debate Tm; Letterman Clb; Math Tm; Political Wkr; Band; Nwsp Stf; Var L Crs Cntry; Var L Trk; High Hon Roll; NHS; 2nd Team All Class Track-Field 86; Law.

FOGERTY, JOHN; Pilgrim HS; Warwick, RI; (Y); U Of RI; Elctrcl Engrng.

FOLEY, GEORGE DANIEL; Smithfield HS; Greenville, RI; (Y); 42/190; Nwsp Stf; Rep Jr Cls; Chrmn Sr Cls; Capt Socr; Capt Trk; Hon Roll; NHS; Pres Schlr; St Schlr; JR Jrnlsm Awd 84; George Washington U; Jrnlsm.

FOLEY, MICHELLE; Narragansett HS; Narragansett, RI; (Y); German Clb; Nwsp Rptr; Off Soph Cls; Stu Cncl; French Hon Soc; High Hon Roll; NHS; Spanish NHS; St Schlr; Russn Clb 84-85; RI Acadmc Decath 84; Forgn Lang.

FOLLIARD, ANNE; Rogers HS; Newport, RI; (Y); Pres VP Church Yth Grp; Quiz Bowl; Chrmn School Play; Variety Show; Yrbk Stf; Chrmn Sr Cls; Stu Cncl; Im Bsktbl; Im Powder Puff Ftbl; Im JV Sftbl; Comm.

FONTENAULT, SHERRY; La Salle Acad; Reboboth, MA; (Y); 68/257; Church Yth Grp; Library Aide; Pep Clb; Band; Rep Frsh Cls; Stat Bsktbl; Sftbl; High Hon Roll; Hon Roll; St Marys Of The Vstn Schlrshp 82; Tchr.

FORTES, ALAN J; Classical HS; Providence, RI; (Y); Boys Clb Am; JA; Spanish Clb; Band; Mrchg Band; Var Capt Bsktbl; Var L Ftbl; Var Trk; Ntl Merit Ltr; Psych.

FORTES, ANTONIO; Hope HS; Providence, RI; (Y); Cit Awd; High Hon Roll; Hon Roll; Capt Crs Cntry; JV Var Socr; Var Trk.

FORTIER, GEO; North Smithfield HS; Woonsocket, RI; (Y); 7/150; Church Yth Grp; French Clb; VP JA; Yrbk Ed-Chief; Pres Frsh Cls; Var L Socr; Hon Roll; 1st Pl Awd Frnch Spllg & 2nd Pl Awd Frnch Pronunctn 83-84.

FORTIN, KATHLEEN; North Smithfield JR/SR HS; Slatersville, RI; (Y); 6/164; Mrchg Band; Yrbk Stf; Var Capt Bsktbl; Var Capt Sftbl; High Hon Roll; Hon Roll; NHS; Church Yth Grp; Quiz Bowl; Yng Comm Ldrs Of Amer 85; RI Hnr Soc 85; Marymount Coll; Bio.

FORTIN, LOUISE; Saint Rapheal Acad; Pawtucket, RI; (Y); Cmnty Wkr; Drama Clb; School Musical; School Play; Stage Crew; Hon Roll; Drama Clb Theatrical Awd 84; Grphc Art.

FORTIN, ROBIN; St Raphael Acad; Pawtucket, RI; (Y); #1 In Class; Cmnty Wkr; Off Stu Cncl; Cheerleading; High Hon Roll; Hon Roll; NHS; Brown Book Awd 84-85.

FOX, CHRISTINE; St Mary Academy-Bay View; Seekonk, MA; (Y); Church Yth Grp; Drama Clb; Pres Exploring; French Clb; Girl Scts; Hosp Aide; Math Clb; Chorus; School Musical; NHS.

FRAIOLI, SHARON; Bishop Keough HS; Providence, RI; (S); Church Yth Grp; Stu Cncl; High Hon Roll; Hon Roll; NHS; Brown U; Biology.

HARRIS, KIEN; East Providence HS; Rumford, RI; (Y); Hosp Aide; JA; Spanish Clb; VICA; Nwsp Rptr; Nwsp Stf; Var Sftbl; Hon Roll; NHS; Astrnmy.

HARRIS, SUPORIA; St Raphael Acad; Providence, RI; (Y); Church Yth Grp; Drama Clb; Exploring; Hosp Aide; Chorus; Church Choir; School Play; Stage Crew; Yrbk Stf; Hon Roll; NC Central U; Bus.

HARTLEY, ROBIN; Coventry HS; West Warwick, RI; (Y); High Hon Roll; Hon Roll; Katherine Gibbs Bus Schl; Bus.

HARTMAN, JENNIFER; Pilgrim HS; Warwick, RI; (Y); Camp Fr Inc; 4-H; GAA; Girl Scts; Letterman Clb; Spanish Clb; Varsity Clb; Chorus; Variety Show; Yrbk Sprt Ed; Cand For Sohp Clss Pres 83-84; URI; Tchng.

HARTNETT, ERYN; Mt St Charles Acad; Woonsocket, RI; (S); 24/165; Pres Jr Cls; Rep Stu Cncl; L Var Bsktbl; L Var Sftbl; High Hon Roll; Hon Roll; NHS; Providence Coll Book Awd 83-84; SYS Anal.

HAUG, DARRIN; Mt St Charles Acad; Bellingham, MA; (Y); 30/150; Cmnty Wkr; Hosp Aide; Mathletes; Ski Clb; Teachers Aide; Band; Concert Band; Mrchg Band; Hon Roll; Cathlc H S Math Lg Top Stdnt Awd 84-85; Worcester Polytechnic Inst.

HAY, WILLIAM ANTHONY; N Kingstown HS; N Kingstown, RI; (Y); Am Leg Boys St; Drama Clb; ROTC; Sec Jr Cls; School Musical; School Play; Rep Soph Cls; JV Trk; NHS; Sen Yth Awd Hearst Fndtn 85; Pell Mdl US Hist 85; Cert Merit Educ Theatre Assn RI 85; Hist.

HAYDEN JR, PHILIP; Cranston West HS; Cranston, RI; (Y); 14/425; Letterman Clb; Ski Clb; Spanish Clb; Var Capt Bsbl; Var Capt Ice Hcky; Hon Roll; NHS; Spanish NHS; RI Hon Soc 85; U PA; Bus.

HAYS, WENDY; Barrington HS; Barrington, RI; (Y); Church Yth Grp; Drama Clb; GAA; Library Aide; Varsity Clb; School Play; Stage Crew; Variety Show; Yrbk Phtg; Yrbk Stf; Fine Arts.

HEINES, RICHARD; Chariho HS; Wood River Jct, RI; (S); Boy Scts; Computer Clb; Math Tm; Band; Concert Band; Jazz Band; Mrchg Band; High Hon Roll; Hon Roll; U Of RI; Engrng.

HELLENDRUNG, MARK; East Providence HS; Rumford, RI; (Y); Yrbk Sprt Ed; Var Capt Bsbl; Var Ftbl; High Hon Roll; NHS; Outstndng Boy 83; Dartmouth Bk Awd 85.

HEMINGWAY, KERRY A; Mount Saint Charles Acad; Greenville, RI; (Y); 5/170; Church Yth Grp; Math Tm; Model UN; Rep Stu Cncl; Var Cheerleading; High Hon Roll; NCTE Awd; NHS; Sportsmanship Awd 83-84; U Notre Dame; Engrng.

HENAULT, DAVID; N Smithfield HS; N Smithfield, RI; (Y); French Clb; Letterman Clb; Varsity Clb; Band; Bsktbl; Golf; Corp Lawyer.

HENNEN, MARTHA; North Providence HS; N Providence, RI; (Y); Nwsp Stf; JV Var Bsktbl; Hon Roll; Jr NHS; Ntl Merit Ltr; Clairborne Pell Amer Hstry Awd 85; Law.

HENRIQUES, GREGORY P; Bishop Hendricken HS; Warwick, RI; (Y); 75/252; Drama Clb; Math Tm; Service Clb; Ski Clb; Nwsp Stf; Yrbk Stf; JV Socr; High Hon Roll; Hon Roll; Jr NHS; Warwick Arts Found Cont-1st Pl 81; Raqtbl Tm ST Champ; Comp Sci.

HEPBURN, STEPHANIE J; Coventry HS; Coventry, RI; (S); 80/480; French Clb; Ski Clb; Stu Cncl; Pom Pon; French Hon Soc; High Hon Roll; Hon Roll; RI Coll; Nrs.

HERMAN, DAVID; Classical HS; Providence, RI; (Y); 29/287; Camera Clb; Temple Yth Grp; Trs Pres Varsity Clb; Nwsp Phtg; Ed Yrbk Phtg; Hon Roll; NHS; Ntl Merit Ltr; U PA.

HERMAN, SANDRA; Coventry HS; Coventry, RI; (Y); Dance Clb; DECA; Radio Clb; Ski Clb; Stu Cncl; Hon Roll; 2nd Pl Gen Mktng DECA ST Comptn 85; Cmmnctns.

HERNANDEZ, ELISA; Central Falls JR SR HS; Central Fls, RI; (Y); Spanish Clb; Crs Cntry; Hon Roll; NHS; RI Coll; Soc Wrkr.

HERRICK, AMY D; St Georges School; Osterville, MA; (Y); Civic Clb; French Clb; Library Aide; Lit Mag; Bsktbl; Var Fld Hcky; Var Lcrss; Ntl Merit SF; Pell Mdl Amer Hist 82; St Georges Top Ftftn 82; Bus.

HERSEY, MICHAEL; Warwick Veterans Memorial HS; Warwick, RI; (Y); Varsity Clb; Yrbk Stf; Rep Soph Cls; Rep Jr Cls; Rep Sr Cls; Socr; Hon Roll.

HIGGINBOTHAM, JULIE; Prout Memorial HS; Jamestown, RI; (S); 8/125; Aud/Vis; Church Yth Grp; Hosp Aide; Band; Concert Band; Stage Crew; Spanish Awd 83-84; 2 Music Awds 82-84; Hnr Roll 82-84; Salve Regina Coll; Law.

HILL, CINDY; Warwick Veterans Memorial HS; Warwick, RI; (S); 56/323; Church Yth Grp; FBLA; Hon Roll; Jr NHS; ST Secy FBLA 84-85; Reprtr Lcl FBLA Chptr 84-85; VP CYO 83-84; Johnson & Wales Coll; Exec Secy.

HILL, DAVID; La Salle Acad; Warwick, RI; (Y); Debate Tm; Band; Nwsp Rptr; Yrbk Rptr; Rep Jr Cls; Crs Cntry; Hon Roll; Library Aide; Pep Clb; Ski Clb; Hnrb Mntn Sci Fr Awd 83; Knight Tmprl Awd 84; Boston U-Yale; Bus.

HILL, JENNIFER L; Portsmouth HS; Portsmouth, RI; (Y); 12/225; Church Yth Grp; Concert Band; Mrchg Band; Nwsp Rptr; Yrbk Stf; VP Stu Cncl; Powder Puff Ftbl; Hon Roll; NHS; Cert Achvmnt Stu Cncl 84; Cert Hnr RI Hghr Ed Assist Athrty 85; Stu Cncl Awd Prtcptn As Vp 85; Randolph-Macon Wmns Coll; Prof.

HILLIKER, KATHLEEN; Woonsocket SR HS; Woonsocket, RI; (Y); Church Yth Grp; Drama Clb; JA; School Play; Cheerleading; High Hon Roll; Dartmouth Coll Awd For Humanities 85; WINE Current Events Awd 83; Sci.

HINCH, KATHERINE; Toll Gate HS; Warwick, RI; (S); 13/393; Pres Letterman Clb; Pres Pep Clb; Q&S; Nwsp Stf; Yrbk Stf; Rep Jr Cls; Rep Sr Cls; Stu Cncl; Capt Cheerleading; High Hon Roll; Pre-Law.

HINES, JAMES; Tiverton HS; Tiverton, RI; (Y); Trs Church Yth Grp; Quiz Bowl; L Bsbl; Im Bsktbl; Im Coach Actv; JV Socr; Im Tennis; Im Vllybl; Law.

HISCOX, CHERYL; Chariho Regional JR SR HS; Charleston, RI; (S); 98/307; Chorus; Madrigals; Yrbk Stf; Chrmn Sr Cls; VP Stu Cncl; Capt Cheerleading; Var Mgr(s); Capt Twrlr; Hon Roll; VP Frsh Cls; Stu Of The Month-Oct 84; Occupational Ther.

HOBIN, KARA M; West Warwick HS; W Warwick, RI; (Y); Cmnty Wkr; French Clb; Fld Hcky; Gym; High Hon Roll; Hon Roll; Hnrs Awds 85; Salve Regina Coll Newport; RN.

HODSON, DIANE LYNN; Smithfield HS; Smithfield, RI; (Y); Church Yth Grp; Yrbk Stf; Elks Awd; Hon Roll; NHS; Pres Schlr; Steubenville U Acad Schlrsh 85; Explrng Hmn Ntr Awd 83-84; Career Educ Awd 83-84; U Of Steubenville; Cnslr.

HOFFMAN, ROBERT J; West Warwick HS; W Warwick, RI; (Y); 2/238; Am Leg Boys St; VP JA; Pep Clb; Variety Show; Yrbk Ed-Chief; Rep Sr Cls; Rep Stu Cncl; Var Trk; Elks Awd; High Hon Roll; Esterline Acad Schlrshp; RI Hnr Soc; U Of Hartford; Comp Engr.

HOLIHEN, TERRENCE; Lasalle Acad; Cranston, RI; (Y); 3/257; Am Leg Boys St; Boys Clb Am; Boy Scts; Church Yth Grp; Cmnty Wkr; Letterman Clb; Math Clb; Math Tm; Political Wkr; Nwsp Rptr; Math.

HOLMAN, ELIZABETH; Barringto/N HS; Barrington, RI; (Y); 71/200; Art Clb; Sec Church Yth Grp; French Clb; Chorus; Church Choir; School Play; Yrbk Stf; Hon Roll; Poetry Awd 85; Cmnctns.

HOLMAN, PAMELA; Chariho HS; Bradford, RI; (S); Aud/Vis; Library Aide; Math Tm; Band; Chorus; Nwsp Stf; High Hon Roll; Hon Roll; Church Yth Grp; Girl Scts; 1st Grd Prz South Cnty Sci Fair 83; 3rd Grd Prz RI Sci Fair 83; Navy Sci Awd Hon Men Sci Fair 83; Premed.

HOLT, CURTIS; North Smithfield JR SR HS; N Smithfield, RI; (Y); Church Yth Grp; JA; Marine Bio.

HOLTMANN, PATRICIA; Johnston HS; Johnston, RI; (Y); Computer Clb; French Clb; Drm Mjr(t); Nwsp Stf; Yrbk Stf; Twrlr; High Hon Roll; Hon Roll; NHS; Bryant Coll; Comp Prog.

HONG, KIL; Shea HS; Pawtucket, RI; (Y); 11th USA TKD Champnshp 2nd Pl 85; Tae Kwon Do Instrctr.

HOPKINS, BENJAMIN I; Ponaganset HS; N Scituate, RI; (Y); 2/169; Art Clb; Camera Clb; Church Yth Grp; Dance Clb; French Clb; Science Clb; Band; Concert Band; Jazz Band; Mrchg Band; Hugh Obrian Outstnand Soph Awd 82-83; Bsktbl All St 84-85; Wean Radio Plyr Of Wk 83-84; Dartmouth Coll; Musical.

HOPKINS, PAMELA S; Coventry HS; Coventry, RI; (S); 26/390; Latin Clb; Sec Science Clb; Band; Concert Band; Mrchg Band; High Hon Roll; Jr NHS; NHS; AATF Frnch Awds 83-84; Outstndng Soph 83; U Of Rhode Island; Lingstcs.

HOPKINS, PETER; Woonsocket SR HS; Woonsocket, RI; (Y); Boy Scts; Church Yth Grp; Cmnty Wkr; Debate Tm; Exploring; Quiz Bowl; Ski Clb; Spanish Clb; Tennis; Hon Roll; Stonehill Coll; Liberal Arts.

HOPKINS, TINA M; Chariho Regional JR SR HS; Wyoming, RI; (Y); 20/301; Var Crs Cntry; JV Trk; High Hon Roll; Hon Roll; Jr NHS; Educ.

HORAN, KIM; Wm Davies Vo-Tech; Lincoln, RI; (Y); Hosp Aide; Pres VP VICA; Rep Soph Cls; Stu Cncl; JV Bsktbl; Im Bowling; High Hon Roll; Hon Roll; Medcl Lab Tech.

HORNER, MELISSA; Lincoln SR HS; Lincoln, RI; (Y); 27/190; Varsity Clb; JV Var Cheerleading; High Hon Roll; Hon Roll; NHS; Sci.

HORRIDGE, KELI; Prout Memorial HS; N Kingstown, RI; (Y); 1/73; Church Yth Grp; Math Tm; Ski Clb; Yrbk Bus Mgr; Trs Frsh Cls; Rep Stu Cncl; High Hon Roll; NHS; St Schlr; Val; St Bernards Schlrshp 85; Boston U; Engrng.

HOWE, HOLLY; Warwick Vetrens HS; Warwick, RI; (Y); Letterman Clb; School Play; Yrbk Rptr; Yrbk Stf; Cheerleading; Hon Roll; Spanish NHS; Dental Hygnst.

HOWES, JONATHAN; Barrington HS; Barrington, RI; (Y); 26/231; Computer Clb; Math Clb; Bsbl; Hon Roll; NHS; Ntl Merit Ltr; Math.

HOYLE, JOHN; Lincoln SR HS; Lincoln, RI; (Y); CAP; School Musical; Variety Show; Yrbk Stf; Pres Sr Cls; Pres Crs Cntry; Ice Hcky; Trk; Cit Awd; Hon Roll; Lincoln Town Rep RI Govrns Ingrtn 85; Northeastern U; Arch.

HUGHES, SUE; Warwick Veterans Memorial HS; Warwick, RI; (S); Dance Clb; DECA; JA; Ski Clb; Rep Frsh Cls; Rep Soph Cls; Rep Jr Cls; Rep Sr Cls; Rep Stu Cncl; Bsbl; U Of RI; Fashion Merch.

HUNT, PAMELA; St Marys Bayview HS; W Greenwich, RI; (Y); Cmnty Wkr; GAA; Yrbk Phtg; Spanish Clb; Crs Cntry; Trk; Hon Roll; All ST Cross Cntry Titles 82-84; All ST Trck Title 84-85; Schlstc Art Awd 1st Pl Hnr Dsgn 82-85; Grphc Dsgn.

HUNT, TRACIE; Narragansett HS; Saunderstown, RI; (Y); 19/127; Cmnty Wkr; Office Aide; Chorus; Variety Show; Rep Frsh Cls; Rep Soph Cls; Rep Jr Cls; Rep Sr Cls; Rep Stu Cncl; Var Bsktbl; RI Hon Soc 85; U Of RI; Psych.

HURTEAU, KEVIN; Woonsocket SR HS; Woonsocket, RI; (Y); VP JA; Var Bsbl; Var Ftbl; Hon Roll; RI Coll; Comp Sci.

HURWITZ, JODI; Shea HS; Pawtucket, RI; (Y); French Clb; Hosp Aide; Pres Temple Yth Grp; Chorus; Nwsp Ed-Chief; Yrbk Ed-Chief; Twrlr; Bureau Jewish Ed Israel Schlrshp 85.

HYSON, CHRISTOPHER; Lincln HS; Lincoln, RI; (Y); 52/190; Church Yth Grp; Cmnty Wkr; Rep Frsh Cls; Rep Jr Cls; Var Capt Bsktbl; Hon Roll; Div B-1 1st Tm All Call All Blackstone Vlly 85; Div B-1 2nd Tm 84; Liberal Arts.

IERVOLINO, ADAM; Bristol HS; Bristol, RI; (S); Golf; NHS; Itln Hnr Soc 83; Roger Williams Coll; Arch.

IMPROTA, CHRISTINE; Pilgrim HS; Warwick, RI; (Y); Pep Clb; Soroptimist; Nwsp Ed-Chief; Nwsp Stf; Rep Jr Cls; Var Cheerleading; High Hon Roll; Wrthy Advsr E Greenwich Asmbly Intl Ordr Rainbow Girls 85; Wnr Ctywde Spllng Bee Fr Lvl 2 83; Nrsg.

INCERA, CHRISTINE; Classical HS; Providence, RI; (Y); Trs Church Yth Grp; Dance Clb; Girl Scts; Ski Clb; Spanish Clb; Spanish NHS; 1st Pl Ntl Spnsh Awd Lvl 2 Spcl 83-84; 2nd Pl Ntl Spnsh Awd Lvl 4 84-85; Providence Coll; Ed.

INGALL, MARJORIE B; Classical HS; Providence, RI; (Y); Drama Clb; School Musical; School Play; Nwsp Rptr; JV Vllybl; Hon Roll; NCTE Awd; Ntl Merit Ltr; Seventeen Magazine Sounding Bd 84; Yng Plywrts Fest, Semi-Fnlsts 84; Engl.

INMAN, DAYNA; Rogers HS; Portsmouth, RI; (Y); Pep Clb; Teachers Aide; Temple Yth Grp; Yrbk Phtg; Yrbk Stf; Vllybl; Doris Morris Awd 83; U BYU; Psychlgst.

ISA, JOSEPH; East Providence SR HS; E Providence, RI; (Y); Boys Clb Am; Boy Scts; Pres Church Yth Grp; Cmnty Wkr; FCA; French Clb; Var L Bsktbl; Var L Trk; Hon Roll; Prfct Atten Awd; Providence Coll; Pre-Med.

ISABELLA, RENEE; North Providence HS; North Providence, RI; (Y); 9/234; Church Yth Grp; Ski Clb; Ed Yrbk Stf; Stat Bsktbl; Score Keeper; Jr NHS; NHS; Pres Schlr; Hon Roll; N Provdnc Alumni Assn Schlrhsp 85; RI Hnr Scty 84-85; U Of VT; Bio.

IZZO, LORI; Warwick Veterans HS; Warwick, RI; (Y); Rep Frsh Cls; Rep Soph Cls; Rep Jr Cls; Rep Stu Cncl; Hon Roll; Crss Age Tutrg 83-85; Italn Hnr Socty 84-85; Law.

JACKSON, BRENDAN; N Smithfield JR SR HS; N Smithfield, RI; (Y); Boy Scts; Church Yth Grp; Letterman Clb; Chorus; Rep Stu Cncl; Var Bsktbl; Var Golf; Var Socr; Providence Coll; Park Serv.

JACKSON, MICHAEL; Middletown HS; Middletown, RI; (S); 3/250; Boy Scts; Math Clb; Math Tm; Science Clb; Var Capt Ftbl; Var L Trk; Var L Wrstlng; High Hon Roll; NHS; Ntl Merit Ltr; RI ST Math Tm 83; Wrstlng 82-83; Eagle Scout 84; Renesslaer Poly Inst; Chem Engr.

JACKSON, RUSSELL; Rogers HS; Newport, RI; (S); VP Church Yth Grp; Variety Show; Trs Sr Cls; Bsktbl; Ftbl; Hon Roll; St Schlr; ELKS Yth Cty Govt Day Mayr 85; American U; Pol Sci.

JACKSON, TASEY F; Classical HS; Providence, RI; (Y); Cmnty Wkr; French Clb; Letterman Clb; Science Clb; Coach Actv; Socr; Tennis; Hon Roll; Bio.

JACOBS, CHERYL; Our Lady Of Fatima HS; Bristol, RI; (S); Drama Clb; Yrbk Phtg; Pres Frsh Cls; Rep Sr Cls; Rep Stu Cncl; Var Bsktbl; Var Capt Crs Cntry; Var Trk; Hon Roll; Pre-Med.

JACOVONI, LISA; First Baptist HS; Lincoln, RI; (Y); 2/14; Church Yth Grp; Pres Pep Clb; Chorus; Pres Soph Cls; Trs Jr Cls; Pres Sr Cls; Var Cheerleading; Hon Roll; Sal; Liberty U; Elem Educ.

JALBERT, WADE J; Woonsocket HS; Woonsocket, RI; (Y); JA; High Hon Roll; Prfct Atten Awd; New England Inst Tech; Elec Eng.

JENKINS, DEBRA; Warren HS; Warren, RI; (Y); 23/100; Band; School Play; Variety Show; Yrbk Stf; Rep Frsh Cls; Rep Soph Cls; Trk; Nrs.

JENKINS, DONNA F; East Providence SR HS; East Providence, RI; (S); 20/520; JA; Band; Stu Cncl; Trk; Hon Roll; NHS; Hosp Aide; Yrbk Stf; U Of RI; Socl Wrk.

JOHN, MICHAEL; Pilgrim HS; Warwick, RI; (Y); Church Yth Grp; Math Tm; Quiz Bowl; Scholastic Bowl; JV Bsktbl; JV Crs Cntry; Var Tennis; High Hon Roll; Jr NHS; Rensselaer Mdl 85; 3rd Ovrall In RI Math Lge Plyoffs 85; Math.

JOHNSON, ALTHEA; Hope HS; Providence, RI; (Y); Dance Clb; Drama Clb; Office Aide; School Play; Variety Show; Cit Awd; Hon Roll; Prfct Atten Awd; URI; Dnce.

JOHNSON, BRADLEY; Barrington HS; Barrington, RI; (Y); Computer Clb; Drama Clb; Math Tm; MMM; Band; Concert Band; Mrchg Band; Stage Crew; High Hon Roll; Hon Roll; Tuffs U; Engrng.

JOHNSON, DIANE K; Pilgrim HS; Warwick, RI; (Y); Church Yth Grp; Intnl Clb; Band; Concert Band; Mrchg Band; Orch; Nwsp Rptr; Rep Sec Soph Cls; Score Keeper; Hon Roll; Elem Tchr.

JOHNSON, FELICIA P; Saint Georges School; Newport, RI; (Y); Debate Tm; Drama Clb; Math Tm; Spanish Clb; Church Choir; Nwsp Rptr; Ed Lit Mag; Capt Fld Hcky; Capt Trk; Hon Roll; Wellesley Coll; Bio.

JOHNSON, KIMBERLY K; Community Christian Schl; Pascoag, RI; (S); 2/53; Church Yth Grp; Bsktbl; Hon Roll; Life Bible Inst.

JOHNSON, RONALD E; Coventry HS; Coventry, RI; (S); 6/400; Boy Scts; Pres Chess Clb; Computer Clb; Band; Rep Stu Cncl; Var Trk; NHS; Ntl Merit Ltr; Pres Church Yth Grp; Acadmc All Amer 85; MIT; Comp Sci.

JOHNSON, TONINE; Hope HS; Providence, RI; (Y); Camera Clb; Dance Clb; Drama Clb; French Clb; Orch; Sr Cls; Cheerleading; Gym; Cit Awd; Arts Rcgntn/Tlnt Srch 84; Urban League Schlrshp 85; NC Schl Of The Arts; Dance.

JONES, CHRIS; Rogers HS; Newport, RI; (Y); Hon Roll; U S Hstry Awd Rogers Soc Studs Dept 85.

JONES, CHRISTINE; Johnston SR HS; Johnston, RI; (S); 4/237; Cmnty Wkr; High Hon Roll; Hon Roll; NHS; Prfct Atten Awd; RI Hnr Soc 85; Travl Agnt.

JONES, CHRISTOPHER; Rogers HS; Newport, RI; (Y); Hon Roll; HS Socl Studies Dept Awd 85.

JONES, KAREN; Central HS; Providence, RI; (Y); High Hon Roll; Johnston & Wates; CPA.

JORDAN, TRACY; Warwick Veterans Memorial HS; Warwick, RI; (Y); Acpl Chr; Chorus; Theatr Art.

JOSLIN, LISA; Chareho HS; Ashaway, RI; (Y); VICA; High Hon Roll; Hon Roll; NHS; RI Hon Soc 85; Acad Achvt Awd 85; Costins Hairdrssng Sch; Csmtlgy.

JOYAL, MICHELLE J; W Warwick SR HS; W Warwick, RI; (Y); Exploring; French Clb; Chorus; Vllybl; Hon Roll; Physcl Thrpy.

JUTRAS, THOMAS; Smithfield HS; Smithfield, RI; (Y); 7/209; Computer Clb; Im Capt Vllybl; High Hon Roll; Drama Clb; Math Clb; Rep Frsh Cls; Rep Soph Cls; Stu Cncl; Hon Roll; Prfct Atten Awd; MA Inst Of Tech; Robtcs Engr.

KALA, LORRIE; East Providense HS; Riverside, RI; (Y); Spanish Clb; Yrbk Stf; Swmmng; Hon Roll; RI Coll; RN.

KARCZ, DIANE; Warren HS; Warren, RI; (Y); Office Aide; Band; Variety Show; Yrbk Stf; Stu Cncl; Hon Roll; NHS.

KATZ, MICHELLE; Cranston High School East; Cranston, RI; (Y); Capt Debate Tm; GAA; Chorus; School Musical; School Play; Tennis; Vllybl; Hon Roll; Jr NHS; Exploring; Welsly Bk Awd 85; Cmmnctns.

KAULL, ELIZABETH; Portsmouth HS; Portsmouth, RI; (Y); 53/260; Dance Clb; Pep Clb; Ski Clb; Band; Concert Band; Cheerleading; Pom Pon; Powder Puff Ftbl; Hon Roll; Elem Educ.

KAYE, LISA; Cranston West HS; Cranston, RI; (Y); Art Clb; Dance Clb; Intnl Clb; Color Guard; Stage Crew; Variety Show; Rep Jr Cls; Pom Pon; Hon Roll; Dance.

KEANEY, KERRI; Warwick Veterans Memorial HS; Warwick, RI; (Y); 12/323; French Clb; Yrbk Stf; Rep Frsh Cls; Rep Soph Cls; Rep Jr Cls; Rep Sr Cls; French Hon Soc; High Hon Roll; Hon Roll; Jr NHS; RI Hnr Soc 85; URI; Bus.

KEENAN, CHRISTINE J; Rogers HS; Newport, RI; (Y); Church Yth Grp; Dance Clb; Library Aide; Ski Clb; Band; Church Choir; Concert Band; Mrchg Band; School Musical; Stu Cncl; Zoolgy.

KEILUHN, JON; St Andrews Schl; Barrington, RI; (S); 1/18; VP Computer Clb; Nwsp Rptr; Yrbk Ed-Chief; Vllybl; High Hon Roll; Hon Roll; NHS; Spanish NHS; Deans List 83-84; Bus.

KELLEY, ERIN; Saint Raphael Acad; Smithfield, RI; (Y); 51/200; Church Yth Grp; Hosp Aide; Yrbk Stf; Hon Roll; U RI; Engrng.

KELLEY, PAULA; Coventry HS; Coventry, RI; (Y); Spanish Clb; Off Stu Cncl; Trk; High Hon Roll; Hon Roll; NHS; St Schlr; Dentsty.

KENNEDY, MAUREEN; St Raphael Acad; Pawtucket, RI; (Y); Drama Clb; School Musical; School Play; Stage Crew; Variety Show; Hon Roll; Church Yth Grp; Cmnty Wkr; Hosp Aide; Library Aide; URI; Med.

KENNEDY, SUSAN J; East Providence SR HS; East Providence, RI; (S); 25/520; Exploring; Band; Concert Band; Pep Band; Nwsp Stf; Stu Cncl; Hon Roll; Ntl Merit Ltr; Psych.

KENNY, SEAN; Mount St Charles HS; North Scituate, RI; (S); Sec Am Leg Boys St; Chrmn Stu Cncl; JV Var Bsbl; Wt Lftg; Hon Roll; Notre Dame Bk Awd 84; Bus.

KENYON, DEBORAH; Chariho Regional JR-SR HS; Ashaway, RI; (S); #28 In Class; Var Capt Bsktbl; JV Sftbl; L Trk; Var Capt Vllybl; Hon Roll; Nutr Sci.

KEOUGH, KERRI; St Mary Bay View Acad; N Providence, RI; (Y); 16/200; Am Leg Aux Girls St; Church Yth Grp; Cmnty Wkr; Exploring; Spanish Clb; Orch; Rep Stu Cncl; Cheerleading; NHS; Ntl Merit SF; Natl Merit Fin 85; Brown U Book Awd 84; RI JR Miss 85; Holy Cross Coll; Banking.

KEOUGH, STACY; Central Falls JR SR HS; Central Fls, RI; (Y); 3/127; Church Yth Grp; Capt Var Cheerleading; Im Coach Actv; High Hon Roll; Jr NHS; Prfct Atten Awd; Outstndng Jr 85; Hnrs 84-85; Acctnt.

KERESZTESSY, FREDERICK; Coventry HS; Coventry, RI; (Y); Boys Clb Am; JV Socr; Hon Roll.

KERRIGAN, TERENCE; Mount Pleasant HS; Providence, RI; (Y); Chess Clb; Ski Clb; Stu Cncl; Hon Roll; L Bsbl; Socr; Swmmng; Tennis; Wt Lftg; Pepperdine U CA; Athl.

KETTLE, KATHY; Chariho Regional HS; W Kingston, RI; (Y); 4-H; Girl Scts; Quiz Bowl; VICA; 4-H Awd; Hon Roll; Stu Of Yr 84-85; Comp Prgmg.

KICIA, KENNETH; Coventry HS; Coventry, RI; (Y); 9/403; Boy Scts; Trs Chess Clb; Computer Clb; Math Tm; Pres Science Clb; Var Socr; Var Trk; High Hon Roll; NHS; Spanish NHS; Eagle Scout 84; 4th Nation Am Compu Sci 85; St Chess Medalin 85; Worcester Poly Tech Inst; Engr.

KIDD, BRANDON; Bishop Hendricken HS; East Greenwich, RI; (Y); 80/242; Boy Scts; Band; Concert Band; Mrchg Band; Hon Roll; Ecolgst.

KILMARTIN, KELLY ERIN; Mount St Charles Acad; Glocester, RI; (Y); Hosp Aide; Ski Clb; Church Choir; School Musical; Var Tennis; High Hon Roll; Hon Roll; Dance Clb; Pres 4-H; Band; Mbr Alter Guild; Chrch Acolyte; Irish Way Prgm 85; Lawyer.

KIM, MI; Portsmouth HS; Portsmouth, RI; (Y); 21/220; Dance Clb; Math Clb; Ski Clb; Flag Corp; Cheerleading; Powder Puff Ftbl; Socr; Trk; Hon Roll; NHS; U Of Rochester; Bio Sci.

KING, KERRI; Coventry HS; Coventry, RI; (Y); 31/400; Dance Clb; Hosp Aide; Spanish Clb; Church Choir; Variety Show; Stu Cncl; Var Capt Cheerleading; High Hon Roll; Hon Roll; NHS; Travel.

KING, MICHAEL; La Salle Academy; E Providence, RI; (Y); 10/257; Church Yth Grp; Cmnty Wkr; Letterman Clb; Math Clb; Pep Clb; Nwsp Stf; Var Chrmn Crs Cntry; Var L Trk; High Hon Roll; NHS; Frank J Cosentino Awd 83; Outstndg Fresh Trckmn 83; Yale Bk Awd 85; Excell Achvt X-Tra Curr Actvts 85; US Air Force Acad; Air Sci.

KINGSBURY, LISA; Shea HS; Pawtucket, RI; (Y); Hosp Aide; Rep Stu Cncl; Im Badmtn; Var Bsktbl; Var Crs Cntry; JV Swmmng; Hon Roll; Nrsng.

KIRWIN, EDWARD; Middletown HS; Middletown, RI; (S); 5/255; Drama Clb; Math Tm; Yrbk Ed-Chief; French Hon Soc; NHS; Ntl Merit Ltr; French Clb; Ski Clb; School Play; Model Legislature 83-85; Stanford U; Chem Engr.

KISTLER, J STEVEN; Community Christian Schl; Mapleville, RI; (S); 1/7; Chorus; Stage Crew; Nwsp Rptr; Nwsp Stf; Yrbk Stf; Var Bsbl; Var Bsktbl; Var Ftbl; High Hon Roll; Hon Roll; Acadmc Schlrshp To Liberty U Lynchburgh VA 85; Liberty U Lynchburg; Pol Sci.

KLAWANSKY, PAUL J; West Warwick HS; W Warwick, RI; (Y); 12/225; Boy Scts; JA; Temple Yth Grp; Tennis; High Hon Roll; Hon Roll; RI Hnr Soc 85; Cntrvl Svgs Bk & WWS Schlrshp Fund Schlrshp 85; U Of RI; Phrmcy.

KNAPMAN, DEBORAH; Bristol HS; Bristol, RI; (S); 6/220; Drama Clb; Pres French Clb; JCL; School Musical; Sec Frsh Cls; Sec Stu Cncl; Cheerleading; Co-Capt Gym; High Hon Roll; Hon Roll; Brown U Bk Awd 84; Ntl Latn Exam 83; Ntl Latn Hnr Soc 83.

KNUST, WENDY; Warwick Veterans Memorial HS; Warwick, RI; (Y); Drama Clb; German Clb; Pep Clb; Spanish Clb; Pom Pon; High Hon Roll; Hon Roll; Jr NHS; Spanish NHS; URI; Acting.

KOBRIN, JANET S; Lincoln Schl; Providence, RI; (Y); AFS; Drama Clb; Pres French Clb; Acpl Chr; Chorus; School Musical; School Play; Lit Mag; Rep Stu Cncl; Ntl Merit SF; Amey Wilson Hart Schlr Gen Acad Excllnc; Frances E Wheeler Schlr Gen Acad Excllnc.

KORZENIOWSKI, KELLY A; Prout Memorial HS; Cranston, RI; (S); 8/79; Debate Tm; Rep Frsh Cls; Hon Roll; NHS; Hugh O Brian Yth Ldrshp Awd; US Hstry Pell Medal; U Of RI; Comp Electrncs Engrng.

KOUNAVIS, ANGELA; Bishop Francis P Keough HS; Pawtucket, RI; (S); Nwsp Stf; Yrbk Stf; Var Sftbl; High Hon Roll; Hon Roll; NHS; Engl Awd 84; Sftbl Allstar Tm Awd 83-84; Biology.

KRAAIJVANGER, PAULUS G; Narragansett HS; Saunderstown, RI; (Y); 2/127; Off Sr Cls; Stu Cncl; Capt Swmmng; High Hon Roll; Hon Roll; NHS; Val; Harvard Prz Bk 84; Century III Ldrs HS Wnnr 84; Natl Hnr Roll 84; Econ.

KRIKORION, DAVID; Lincoln JR SR HS; Lincoln, RI; (Y); 63/190; Am Leg Boys St; Church Yth Grp; Band; Concert Band; Mrchg Band; JV Bsbl; Im Bsktbl; Var Ftbl; Bus.

KULACZ, AUDREY; Charles E Shea HS; Pawtucket, RI; (Y); Yrbk Ed-Chief; Cheerleading; Swmmng; Vllybl; High Hon Roll; Hon Roll; Jr NHS; Trs Frsh Cls; Pres Soph Cls; Rep Jr Cls; Flora Curtis Acad Awd $25 83; RI Coll; Nrsn.

KUNKEL, ELIZABETH H; St Georges HS; Mechanicsburg, PA; (Y); Civic Clb; Debate Tm; Model UN; Lit Mag; Var Bsktbl; Var Socr; Var Sftbl; Aud/Vis; Latin Clb; School Play; Ply Sci.

KUNSTMANN, KEVIN; Cranston East HS; Cranston, RI; (Y); Cmnty Wkr; Political Wkr; JV Bsbl; VP L Wrstlng; High Hon Roll; NHS; Irving J Fay Mem Awd 84; ST Wrstlng Chmpnshps 84; Aero Engrg.

KURECK, JOHN; Lincon JR SR HS; Lincoln, RI; (Y); Church Yth Grp; Nwsp Phtg; Nwsp Stf; Swmmng; Syracuse U; Arch.

KUROS, KRIS M; Bristol HS; Bristol, RI; (Y); Yrbk Sprt Ed; Sec Soph Cls; VP Jr Cls; VP Sr Cls; Rep Stu Cncl; JV Var Cheerleading; Var Powder Puff Ftbl; JV Var Sftbl; High Hon Roll; Trs NHS; RI CC; Rad Tech.

L ESPERANCE, CINDY; Woonsocket HS; Woonsocket, RI; (Y); Art Clb; High Hon Roll; U Of RI; Music Educ.

LA ROCHE, LESLIE; North Providence HS; N Providence, RI; (Y); Church Yth Grp; Hosp Aide; Office Aide; Drm Mjr(t); Nwsp Rptr; High Hon Roll; Jr NHS; Fin Local Rotry Schlrshp; Bio.

LA SCOLA, TODD; St Rapheal Acad; Pawtucket, RI; (Y); 20/200; Boys Clb Am; Nwsp Sprt Ed; JV Bsbl; JV Capt Ftbl; High Hon Roll; Hon Roll; NHS; Hugh O Brien Yth Fndtn 84; Gentc Engrng.

LA TULIPPE, LOUIS; Tiverton HS; Tiverton, RI; (Y); Boy Scts; Church Yth Grp; French Clb; Ski Clb; High Hon Roll; Hon Roll; NHS; VP Soph Cls; JV Bsktbl; Var Golf; Hugh O Brian Yth Ldrshp Awd 84; Orthdntst.

LACHANCE, MARIE; Woonsocket SR HS; Woonsocket, RI; (Y); Drama Clb; Q&S; VICA; School Musical; School Play; Stage Crew; Yrbk Rptr; Yrbk Stf; Army Resrvs.

LACHAPELLE, PAULA; Burrillville JR SR HS; Harrisville, RI; (Y); Church Yth Grp; Band; Concert Band; Mrchg Band; Im Bsktbl; Hon Roll; Comp Engnr.

LACOUTURE, KATIE; North Kingstown HS; Exeter, RI; (Y); 13/375; Varsity Clb; Var Capt Cheerleading; Hon Roll; NHS; R I Hnr Scty 85; Yale U.

LAFOND, CHRISTINE; Woonsocket HS; Woonsocket, RI; (Y); Hon Roll; Early Jan Grad 85; Phrmcy Tech.

LAFOND, DOROTHY; Toll Gate HS; Warwick, RI; (S); 14/393; Drama Clb; Letterman Clb; School Play; Var L Cheerleading; High Hon Roll; Hon Roll; Jr NHS; NHS; Ntl Merit Ltr; Church Yth Grp; Warwick Public Schls French Spelling Bee Level I Winner 82; Theater Arts.

LALIBERTE, DANIEL; Saint Raphael Acad; Pawtucket, RI; (Y); Computer Clb; Comp Pgmr.

LALLIER, CHRISTINE A; Ponaganset HS; North Scituate, RI; (Y); 12/164; Trs Computer Clb; Dance Clb; VP FBLA; Hosp Aide; Teachers Aide; Varsity Clb; School Musical; Nwsp Rptr; Nwsp Sprt Ed; Nwsp Stf; FBLA Typng I & Acctng II Awds 83-85; FBLA Cert Of Merit; Bryant Coll; Accntng.

LAMBERT, KERRI; Warren HS; Warren, RI; (Y); Church Yth Grp; 4-H; Math Clb; JV L Crs Cntry; Var L Trk; 4-H Awd; Hon Roll; RI St Expo-Sci Fair, Grant & R I Dntl Assoc Awd 83; Read Dig Natl 4-H Ldrshp Schlrshp 84; Dental Hygienist.

LANGANKE, STEVEN W; Chariho Regional HS; Ashaway, RI; (Y); 9/320; Church Yth Grp; Var JV Bsktbl; Trk; High Hon Roll; Hon Roll; Cert Merit Fr 84-85; URI; Bus Adm.

LAPERLE, HOLLY; Woonsocket SR HS; Woonsocket, RI; (Y); Computer Clb; JA; Office Aide; Varsity Clb; VICA; Band; Yrbk Stf; JV Bsktbl; Var Fld Hcky; Var Vllybl; Comp Pgmr.

LAPRE, DIANE; Cranston High School East; Cranston, RI; (Y); Church Yth Grp; Library Aide; Acpl Chr; Chorus; School Play; Lit Mag; Rep Frsh Cls; Marine Bio.

LAURIA, DAVID J; Barrington HS; Barrington, RI; (Y); Computer Clb; Drama Clb; Math Tm; MMM; Chorus; Church Choir; School Musical; Variety Show; Nwsp Rptr; Trk; RI U; Comp Engr.

LAWRENCE, CHRISTOPHER R; Johnston SR HS; Johnston, RI; (S); 10/237; Hon Roll; Ntl Hstry Day 83; RI Ntl Hnr Soc 85; U RI; Elec Comp Engr.

LAWRENCE, KELLY; Toll Gate HS; Warwick, RI; (Y); 74/398; Church Yth Grp; VICA; Chorus; JV Bsktbl; Mgr(s); JV Sftbl; Stat Vllybl; Hon Roll; Jr NHS; RI Hnr Soc 85; Sci Fair 81; ST Schlrshp 85; U Of RI; Engrng.

LAWRENCE, KIM; Burrillville HS; Pascoag, RI; (Y); Church Yth Grp; Hosp Aide; Office Aide; Pep Clb; Quiz Bowl; Lit Mag; Rep Stu Cncl; High Hon Roll; Hon Roll; Lion Awd; RI Hnr Soc 85; Presdntl Acadmc Ftns Awd 85; Exclnc In Soclgy 84; Bryant Coll; Bus Cmnctns.

LAWRENCE, LEONARD A; Coventry HS; Coventry, RI; (Y); 5/404; Boy Scts; Chess Clb; Computer Clb; Math Tm; VP Science Clb; Spanish Clb; Stu Cncl; Var L Socr; Var Trk; NHS; 1st Overall Schl Sci Fair & 2nd St 84; St Champ Chess Tm 85; Comp Tm 6th Natl 85; Woocester Polytech; Elec Engr.

LAWSON, ERICA; South Kingstown HS; Kingston, RI; (Y); 1/176; Girl Scts; Capt Math Tm; VP Band; JV Crs Cntry; NHS; Pres Schlr; Val; Drama Clb; German Clb; Jazz Band; Am Mus Assn Awds; Slvr Awd; Frst Cls Awd; Dartmouth Coll; Math Educ.

LAWSON, VICKY; Portsmouth HS; S Hamilton, MA; (Y); JA; Spanish Clb; Yrbk Stf; Hon Roll; Spnsh Hnr Soc Awd 85; Bus.

LE CROY, CLAUDETTE; Middletown HS; Middletown, RI; (S); 2/252; Civic Clb; French Clb; Math Clb; Math Tm; Political Wkr; Science Clb; French Hon Soc; Hon Roll; NHS; Runner-Up H S Century III Competition 84; RI ST Math Team 83; Chem Engrng.

LEATHERS, AUDRA; North Kingstown SR HS; Saunderstown, RI; (Y); 1/375; DAR Awd; Hon Roll; NHS; Val; RI Hnr Soc 84-85; Engl Dept Awd 84-85; Mth Dept Awd 83-84; U RI; Chem Engrng.

LEAVENE, ELIZABETH; North Kingstown HS; N Kingstown, RI; (Y); 64/371; Drama Clb; Intnl Clb; School Play; Stage Crew; Nwsp Rptr; Nwsp Stf; Yrbk Rptr; Yrbk Stf; Hon Roll; Ntl Hnr Soc 84-85; Lit.

LEDOUX, PATRICIA; Shea SR HS; Pawtucket, RI; (Y); Debate Tm; Yrbk Ed-Chief; Yrbk Stf; Off Frsh Cls; Stu Cncl; Hon Roll; NCTE Awd; Lesley Coll; Fmly Cnslr.

LEE, BELINDA; Hope HS; Providence, RI; (Y).

LEE, DEBBIE; Cranston East HS; Cranston, RI; (Y); 14/380; Spanish Clb; Sec Lit Mag; Rep Sr Cls; Rep Stu Cncl; Mgr(s); Var Tennis; Hon Roll; Jr NHS; NHS; Prfct Atten Awd; Spanish NHS; Med.

LEFEBVRE, DONNA; Woonsocket SR HS; Woonsocket, RI; (Y); Church Yth Grp; Library Aide; Pep Clb; Hon Roll; Bus Clb 85; Johnson & Wales Coll; Secy.

LEIGHTON, MICHAEL; Warwick Veterans Memorial HS; Warwick, RI; (S); 19/323; Am Leg Boys St; Civic Clb; Varsity Clb; Yrbk Sprt Ed; Var L Socr; French Hon Soc; High Hon Roll; Hon Roll; Jr NHS; NHS; Charminade U Honolulu; Bus.

LEJA, DEBBIE; North Smithfield HS; N Smithfield, RI; (Y); Church Yth Grp; Cmnty Wkr; French Clb; JA; Stu Cncl; Frnch Clb Svc Awd 83-84; Accntng.

LELAND, MARK ALLEN; East Providence SR HS; Riverside, RI; (Y); Boy Scts; VICA; Hon Roll; Sec Of ST Leadrshp Awd 85; Warren A Geraghty Memrl Awd 85; E Providence Rec Dept Ctr Stu Of Yr Awd 85; CC Of RI; Machine Procssng.

LEMIEUX, DANIEL; Davies Vocational Technical HS; Central Falls, RI; (Y); Boys Clb Am; VICA; High Hon Roll; Hon Roll; New England Tech; Elect.

LEMOS, JAMES; Bristol HS; Bristol, RI; (Y); JV Bsktbl; Var L Ftbl; U Of RI; Acctg.

LEONARDO, DIANA; Scituate HS; N Scitutate, RI; (S); 13/117; Chorus; Hon Roll; Jr NHS; NHS; CC Rhode Island; Legl Secy.

LEPORE, GARY; Barrington HS; Barrington, RI; (Y); Art Clb; Cmnty Wkr; Boy Scts; Swmmng; Bonington Ctzns Schlrshp 85; Peer Ed Awd 85; RI Schl Of Dsgn; Inerior Dsgn.

LESSARD, STEPHEN; Mt St Charles Acad; Woonsocket, RI; (Y); 1/150; Band; Concert Band; Mrchg Band; Orch; Pep Band; Stage Crew; Symp Band; High Hon Roll; NHS; Ntl Merit Ltr; Sci.

LETENDRE, KIM; Burrillville JR SR HS; Pascoag, RI; (Y); Band; Concert Band; Mrchg Band; Stu Cncl; High Hon Roll; CC Of RI.

LETIECQ, DAVID; Portsmouth HS; Portsmouth, RI; (Y); French Clb; Band; Concert Band; Mrchg Band; Variety Show; Nwsp Stf; NHS; Nacel Cltrl Exc Prgm 85; Nrthestrn U; Intl Bus.

LETIECQ, NICOLE; Portsmouth HS; Portsmouth, RI; (Y); FBLA; Band; Concert Band; Mrchg Band; Var L Bsktbl; Im Powder Puff Ftbl; Var L Socr; JV Trk; High Hon Roll; Hon Roll; Intl Bus.

LEVIN, SARA E; Classical HS; Providence, RI; (Y); Cmnty Wkr; French Clb; Hosp Aide; Nwsp Rptr; Nwsp Stf; Yrbk Stf; Socr; JV Trk; Hon Roll; Med.

LEVREAULT, RAYMOND G; Lincoln JR SR HS; Manville, RI; (Y); 135/214; Church Yth Grp; Cmnty Wkr; Office Aide; Church Choir; Relgn.

LEWANDOWSKI, NANCY; Rogers HS; Newport, RI; (Y); Yrbk Stf; Lit Mag; Off Jr Cls; Var Cheerleading; JV Gym; Hon Roll; Kiwanis Awd; Kiwans Clb Schlrshp 85; RI Schlrshp 85; Emerson Coll; Jrnlsm.

LEWIS, ELIZABETH BETSY; North Kingstown HS; N Kingstown, RI; (Y); 5/371; AFS; Drama Clb; Math Tm; Ski Clb; Color Guard; Crs Cntry; Mgr(s); Trk; High Hon Roll; NHS; Alt Confrss-Bundestag Schlrshp 85; Most Impvd Rnnr X-Cntry 84; Med Doctr.

LEWIS, TAMMY J; East Providence SR HS; E Providence, RI; (Y); Rep Church Yth Grp; Quiz Bowl; VICA; Chorus; High Hon Roll; Hon Roll; New England Inst; Word Proc.

LIEDER, KERRY; St Mary Acad Bay View; Cranston, RI; (Y); Cmnty Wkr; Spanish Clb; Gym; Career Awrnss Sec 82-84; Serv Awds 83-85; Providenct Coll.

LIESE, LINDA; Pilgrim HS; Warwick, RI; (S); 50/347; Cmnty Wkr; Band; Concert Band; Drm Mjr(t); Jazz Band; Mrchg Band; Orch; Stage Crew; Capt Cheerleading; Hon Roll.

LIM, JEANNIE; Cranston H S East; Cranston, RI; (Y); 5/449; Pres Dance Clb; Sec Trs Q&S; Band; Nwsp Stf; Yrbk Stf; Sec Jr Cls; VP Stu Cncl; Capt Twrlr; High Hon Roll; VP NHS; Wellesley Coll.

LIMA, CHERYL; West Warwick HS; W Warwick, RI; (Y); 16/236; Yrbk Stf; Var Crs Cntry; Var Vllybl; High Hon Roll; Hon Roll; W Warwick Schlrshp 85; Ntl Engl Merit Awd 84; Typng Awd; U Of Hartford; Art.

LIMA, ELIZABETH; Middletown HS; Middletown, RI; (S); 20/252; Pres Church Yth Grp; Hosp Aide; JV Vllybl; French Hon Soc; Hon Roll; NHS; Mgr Exploring; Mgr Quiz Bowl; Mgr Lit Mag; RI Modern Miss 84; Boston U; Pediatrics.

LIMOGES, MICHELE M; Warwick Veterans Memorial HS; Warwick, RI; (Y); Boy Scts; Exploring; French Clb; Teachers Aide; Off Soph Cls; Off Jr Cls; Stu Cncl; French Hon Soc; High Hon Roll; Hon Roll; RI Coll; Humn Svcs.

LINCOURT, ROBERT CURTIS; Cranston High School East; Cranston, RI; (Y); Trs Church Yth Grp; Band; Drm & Bgl; Var Crs Cntry; Hon Roll; U Of RI; Miltry.

LISI, CHRISTOPHER; North Providence HS; N Providence, RI; (Y); Ski Clb; JV Var Bsbl; Bsktbl; Var L Crs Cntry; Score Keeper; Trk; Hon Roll; 13th St Cross 83; Country Meet; X-Country All-Class B 1st Tm 83; Bryant Coll; Bus Admin.

LLAMAS, CRISTINA; Lincoln Schl; Manville, RI; (Y); AFS; Sec Trs Church Yth Grp; French Clb; JCL; Acpl Chr; Church Choir; Stage Crew; Nwsp Stf; Lit Mag; Amy Wilson Hart Schlrshp Awd 83; Francis E Wheeler Awd 84; RI Music Edc 83-84.

LOFFREDO, JOE; Johnston HS; Johnston, RI; (Y); JA; JV Ftbl; Im Vllybl; Hon Roll; Itln Ntl Hnr Soc 83-85; Bryant Coll; Bus Mngmnt.

LOGHRY, HEATHER; Community Christian Schl; N Scituate, RI; (S); Church Yth Grp; Church Choir; School Play; Sec Sr Cls; Hon Roll; Christian Charctr Awd 84; Music Awd 84; Liberty U; Church Music.

LOIGNON, BRENDA; Prout Memorial HS; West Warwick, RI; (S); 3/75; Debate Tm; Math Tm; Pres Jr Cls; Pres Sr Cls; Stat Bsktbl; Var L Crs Cntry; Var L Sftbl; High Hon Roll; NHS; Ntl Merit Ltr; Century III Ldrshp Awd For Schl 84; Biomedical.

LOMBARDI JR, ANTHONY J; Lasalle Acad; North Providence, RI; (Y); 1/280; CAP; Cmnty Wkr; Capt Math Tm; Political Wkr; Scholastic Bowl; Ed Nwsp Stf; Yrbk Stf; Gov Hon Prg Awd; NHS; Ntl Merit SF; Biology.

LOMBARDI, REBECCA; St Raphael Acad; N Prov, RI; (Y); Church Yth Grp; French Clb; VP Stu Cncl; Bsktbl; Sftbl; Hon Roll; Jr NHS; NHS; Lwyr.

LOMBARDI, STEPHANIE; Mount St Charles Acad; N Smithfield, RI; (Y); Chrmn Church Yth Grp; Cmnty Wkr; French Clb; Quiz Bowl; Church Choir; Stage Crew; Yrbk Phtg; Yrbk Stf; Var Tennis; Hon Roll; Natl Hnr Socty 84-85; Frnch Clb 84-85; Vrsty Tennis Tm 83-84; Psych.

LOMBARDI, VALERIE; Bishop Keough HS; N Providence, RI; (Y); School Play; Yrbk Stf; VP Stu Cncl; High Hon Roll; USAA Natl Awd 85; Soc Wrkr.

LONG, MATTHEW W; Saint Raphael Acad; Barrington, RI; (Y); 3/172; Chess Clb; Church Yth Grp; French Clb; JA; Math Clb; Math Tm; High Hon Roll; JETS Awd; NHS; Ntl Merit SF.

LOPES, WILLIAM; Portsmouth HS; Portsmouth, RI; (Y); 30/220; Concert Band; Mrchg Band; Pep Band; Frsh Cls; Soph Cls; Jr Cls; Sr Cls; JV Bsktbl; High Hon Roll; Hon Roll; Engrng.

LORANGE, RICHARD; Woonsocket HS; Woonsocket, RI; (Y); VICA; Chorus; Stage Crew; Hon Roll; Paramdcs.

LOVELACE, TINA; Johnston HS; Johnston, RI; (Y); DECA; Drama Clb; FBLA; Hosp Aide; High Hon Roll; Hon Roll; Church Yth Grp; Library Aide; Chorus; School Musical; Catherine Gibbs Coll; Lgl Secy.

LOW, JENNIFER; Prout Memorial HS; N Kingstown, RI; (S); 16/79; Letterman Clb; Ski Clb; Varsity Clb; Yrbk Stf; Rep Stu Cncl; Var L Bsktbl; Var L Sftbl; DAR Awd; Hon Roll; NHS; Tm Svc Awd-Varsity Bsktbl 82.

LUCAS, ALBERT E; St Georges Schl; Queens Village, NY; (Y); Pres Spanish Clb; Nwsp Bus Mgr; Nwsp Rptr; Nwsp Stf; Var Bsktbl; Var Ftbl; Var Trk; Cmnty Wkr; Library Aide; Political Wkr; VP Scty 84-85; Pres Eclgy Clb & Libry Assoc 84-85; VP Print Shop 83-85; Crmnl Psych.

LUCIAN, DIANNE; Prout Memorial HS; Wakefield, RI; (S); 1/81; Exploring; Math Tm; Sec Chorus; Madrigals; School Musical; Nwsp Rptr; High Hon Roll.

LUNARDELLI, MICHAEL; Warwick Veterans Memorial HS; Warwick, RI; (S); 16/323; Letterman Clb; Var L Bsbl; High Hon Roll; NHS.

LYNCH, DANIEL; St Raphael Acad; Esmond, RI; (Y); Drama Clb; Exploring; School Play; Stage Crew; JV Bsktbl; Hon Roll; Jr NHS; NHS; Bus.

LYTLE, ROBERT; Rogers HS; Chambersburg, PA; (Y); Am Leg Boys St; Boy Scts; Trs Key Clb; JV Crs Cntry; JV Socr; Var L Trk; Elks Awd; High Hon Roll; Hon Roll; Hstry Awd 85; URI Alum Awd 85; Princeton; Oprtns Rsrch.

MAC DOUGALL, DENISE; Warren HS; Warren, RI; (Y); 3/125; Am Leg Aux Girls St; Yrbk Ed-Chief; VP Frsh Cls; VP Soph Cls; Pres Jr Cls; Pres Sr Cls; Rep Stu Cncl; JV Vllybl; JV Hon Roll; NHS; Rhode Island U Book Awd Wnnr 85; Accntng.

MAC PHEE, WENDY M; Lincoln HS; Lincoln, RI; (Y); 12/220; FBLA; JA; Variety Show; Yrbk Bus Mgr; High Hon Roll; NHS; Prfct Atten Awd; Outstndng Accntng Stu 84-85; 1st Pl Accntng II Cmptn FBLA 84-85; Bryant Coll; Accntng.

MAC QUEEN, ANDREA; Lincoln JR-SR HS; Lincoln, RI; (Y); 31/190; Hosp Aide; Library Aide; Nwsp Rptr; Yrbk Stf; Hon Roll; NHS; Usher SR Awds Nght & Grad 85; Cls Fndraisr Comm 84 & 85; Med.

MACKTAZ, JOSHUA; Mount St Charles HS; Woonsocket, RI; (Y); 36/147; Church Yth Grp; JA; Model UN; Ski Clb; Im Bsktbl; Im Vllybl; Hon Roll; NHS; Synagog By Yr 83-84 & 84-85; Bus Mgmt.

MADERA, ELBA I; Central Falls HS; Central Falls, RI; (Y); Church Yth Grp; Psych.

MAGLIONE, CHARLES; Mount St Charles Acad; N Smithfield, RI; (Y); 8/147; Cmnty Wkr; Math Tm; Model UN; Ski Clb; Socr; High Hon Roll; NHS; Boston Coll; Polit Sci.

MAGLIONE, JANINE; North Providence HS; North Providence, RI; (Y); Art Clb; Teachers Aide; Yrbk Stf; Pres Frsh Cls; Pres Soph Cls; VP Jr Cls; Rep Stu Cncl; Var Twrlr; Hon Roll; Jr NHS; Claudine Sneiders Artist Discovry Comptn 85; Acctng.

MAGUIRE, JOHN; La Salle Acad; Smithfield, RI; (Y); 70/200; Church Yth Grp; Letterman Clb; Pep Clb; Varsity Clb; Nwsp Rptr; Off Soph Cls; Coach Actv; Crs Cntry; Trk; Hon Roll; Natl JR Olympc Crs Cntry Champ 83; Capt Trk Tm 85; U RI; Secndry Ed.

MAGUIRE, STEPHEN; La Salle Acad; Smithfield, RI; (Y); Church Yth Grp; Letterman Clb; Bsbl; Crs Cntry; High Hon Roll; Hon Roll; Boston Coll; Bio Engrng.

MAITLAND, THOMAS P; Warren HS; Warren, RI; (Y); Church Yth Grp; Computer Clb; VP 4-H; Chorus; Church Choir; School Play; Yrbk Stf; Vllybl; 4-H Awd; Cert Achvt 81-82; Yth Grp Awd 84-85; Mnstry.

MAK, SOLIDA; Mount Pleasant HS; Providence, RI; (Y); 2/162; Exploring; Hosp Aide; Intnl Clb; Library Aide; Math Clb; Red Cross Aide; Science Clb; Nwsp Rptr; Swmmng; Vllybl; Cert Awd Phys Smmr Prog 84; Cert Awd Englsh 84; Outstndng Math 85; Boston Coll; Pre-Med.

MAKI, TINA; Chariho Reg JR SR HS; Kenyon, RI; (S); Band; Mgr(s); High Hon Roll; Hon Roll; Acctng.

MALIK, ATTIYA; N Providence HS; Woonsocket, RI; (Y); 65/267; Hosp Aide; Intnl Clb; Ski Clb; Nwsp Stf; Yrbk Stf; Lit Mag; JV Badmtn; JV Trk; Hon Roll; NHS; U MA-AMHERST; Pre-Med.

MALIK, FARHANA; Woonsocket HS; Woonsocket, RI; (Y); Art Clb; Ski Clb; School Play; Yrbk Stf; Stu Cncl; Badmtn; Bsktbl; Gym; Sftbl; Trk; Trophy-Badmntn Chmnshp 83; Awd Stu Cncl, Sprts, Hon Roll & Yrbk 83; Boston Coll; Law.

MALIK, RAJI S; South Kingstown HS; Kingston, RI; (Y); 15/215; Am Leg Boys St; Model UN; Band; Variety Show; Stu Cncl; Var Bsktbl; Var Crs Cntry; Var Ftbl; Var Trk; NHS; Citatn Outstndng Parcptn RI Modl Leg 85; Excllnc Spnsh II-III 84-85; URI Bk Awd 85; Doc.

MALO, ANN; Lincoln JR SR HS; Lincoln, RI; (Y); 54/220; Church Yth Grp; Lib Arts.

MALO, RONNY; Davies Vo Tech; Pawtucket, RI; (Y); Cmnty Wkr; VICA; High Hon Roll; Crpntry.

MALONEY, COURTNEY; Middletown HS; Little Compton, RI; (S); 33/252; Hrzn Bnd Canoeng & Bckpckng Exped 84; MHS Acad Decthln Team 85; Boston U; Pol Sci.

MALTAIS, SHARON E; Ponaganset HS; Harmony, RI; (Y); 11/155; Varsity Clb; Concert Band; Nwsp Ed-Chief; Nwsp Sprt Ed; Yrbk Stf; Var Capt Crs Cntry; Var Capt Trk; High Hon Roll; NHS; RI Hnrs Scty 85; Sprtsmnshp Awd 83; U Of RI; Anml Sci.

MANCIERI, NICHOLAS; Bristol HS; Bristol, RI; (S); 9/225; Var Bsktbl; Ftbl; Powder Puff Ftbl; High Hon Roll; Hon Roll; VP NHS; Elec Engr.

MANDEVILLE, MICHELLE; North Smithfield JR SR HS; N Smithfield, RI; (Y); Letterman Clb; Var L Sftbl; High Hon Roll; Hon Roll; Bryant; Acctng.

MANGIANTE, RICHARD; Johnston HS; Johnston, RI; (Y); Aud/Vis; Nwsp Sprt Ed; JV Var Ftbl; Hon Roll; Providence Coll; Law.

MANGUM, ANDREA; St Raphael Acad; Prov, RI; (Y); Pres Boys Clb Am; Cmnty Wkr; Exploring; Hosp Aide; Var Capt Bsktbl; Elks Awd; Hon Roll; 1st Tm All Div Bsktbll 3 Yrs; 1000 Pt Mrk JR Yr 85; Brk Schl Pt Rcrd 40 Pts Was 34th SR Stdnt 85; Acctnt.

MANNING, DANDY; Portsmouth HS; Portsmouth, RI; (Y); 30/210; Band; School Play; Var L Tennis; Cit Awd; Hon Roll; Kiwanis Awd; Intnl Clb; Pep Clb; Ski Clb; Mrchg Band; RI Hnr Soc 84-85; RI JR Miss Part 85; Rotary Exchng Stu To Belguim 83-84; Amer U; Intl Affrs.

MARCOUX, PAULA; Mount St Charles Acad; Bellingham, MA; (Y); Cmnty Wkr; Sftbl; Yrbk Stf; Sftbl; Hon Roll; NHS; Providence Coll; Pre-Law.

MARGOLIS, JAY; Barrington HS; Barrington, RI; (Y); Computer Clb; Trs VP MMM; Band; School Musical; Crs Cntry; Trk; NHS; Louis Armstrong Jazz Awd 85; Tri-M Music Hnr Soc Awd 85; Carnegie-Mellon U; Appld Math.

MARKHAM, MELISSA; Narragansett HS; Narragansett, RI; (Y); Church Yth Grp; Drama Clb; FHA; Band; Chorus; Concert Band; Mrchg Band; School Play; Stage Crew; Cit Awd; U RI.

MARNANE, DANA; Middletown HS; Middletown, RI; (Y); Pres Spanish Clb; Concert Band; Mrchg Band; Pep Band; Spanish NHS; Multiple Solo & Ensmble Mdls 81-85; Pol Sci.

MARS, CHRYSTAL; Chariho Regional HS; Kenyon, RI; (Y); Church Yth Grp; Church Choir; Hon Roll; Bus Sec.

MARSDEN, MICHELLE; Coventry HS; Coventry, RI; (Y); U Of RI; Phrmcy.

MARTENSON, ERIC; Johnston HS; N Scituate, RI; (Y); JV Ftbl; JV Ice Hcky; Trk; Hon Roll; Bryant Coll; Bus Mgt.

MARTI, JANET; Pilgrim HS; Warwick, RI; (S); 55/333; Church Yth Grp; Concert Band; Orch; Yrbk Bus Mgr; Stu Cncl; Var L Tennis; High Hon Roll; Hon Roll; NHS; Allst Mus Comp 81; 1st Pl Sci Awd 78-80; Silver Mdl Art Comp 81; U MA; Intl Law.

MARTIN, ANITA R; Roger HS; Newport, RI; (Y); Church Choir; Scrtry.

MARTIN, EILEEN; Cranston East HS; Cranston, RI; (Y); Library Aide; Spanish Clb; Chorus; Yrbk Stf; Off Sr Cls; High Hon Roll; Hon Roll; Spanish NHS; Ldrshp Awd Cntst For Future Sec Hon Mntn 85; Shrthnd Schl Awd 85; Bus Mngmnt.

MARTIN, KIMBERLY J; North Kingstown HS; Exeter, RI; (Y); 22/355; Church Yth Grp; Cmnty Wkr; Drama Clb; Trs French Clb; Band; Concert Band; Mrchg Band; Orch; Pep Band; School Musical; U RI Merit Schlrshp 85; All-ST Band, Orch 85; Proj Close-Up 84; U RI; Mus.

MARTIN, SUSAN; St Mary Acad Bay View; N Kingstown, RI; (Y); 4-H; Vet.

MARTINO, GINA M; Tolman SR HS; Pawtucket, RI; (Y); Art Clb; DECA; Girl Scts; Hosp Aide; Office Aide; Chorus; Stu Cncl; Badmtn; Bowling; Gym; 1st Pl Awd Publc Spkng 85; Sawyer; Airline Stewrdss.

MARTUFI JR, ROBERT A; Mount St Charles Acad; Johnston, RI; (Y); Bsbl; JV Var Ice Hcky; Im Wt Lftg; High Hon Roll; Hon Roll; St Schlr; MVP RI Summr Hockey Lg 82; JR C Div ST Champs Edgewood RI 85; U Of Lowell; Chem Engrng.

MASON, ELIZABETH; East Providence HS; Riverside, RI; (Y); 19/444; French Clb; Band; Concert Band; Mrchg Band; Soph Cls; Jr Cls; Cit Awd; Hon Roll; Masonic Awd; Pres Schlr; Salve Regina; Med Tech.

MASON, MARY JO; Mount Saint Charles Acad; Franklin, MA; (Y); 35/150; Pres Church Yth Grp; Church Choir; School Musical; Nwsp Stf; Var Tennis; Hon Roll; Schlstc Achvt Awds 83 & 85; Lcl Prodctns Starrng Sevrl Roles 81-85; Pre Law.

MASSE, SHERRY; Woonsocket SR HS; Woonsocket, RI; (Y); Church Yth Grp; Cmnty Wkr; Drama Clb; JA; Teachers Aide; School Musical; School Play; Variety Show; High Hon Roll; Hon Roll; Melville Corp Schlrshp 85; Tchng.

MASSEY, DOUGLAS; St Andrews HS; Hempstead, NY; (S); Church Yth Grp; Band; Mrchg Band; Pep Band; Yrbk Stf; VP Stu Cncl; Var Capt Bsktbl; Var Crs Cntry; JV Lcrss; Var Capt Socr; Amer HS Athl 84; Barrington Womens Clb Schlrshp 84; Army & Coll Svc Sccr MVP 85; Bus Admin.

MASTANTUONO, LORI; Prout Memorial HS; Cranston, RI; (Y); 22/70; Church Yth Grp; Computer Clb; PAVAS; Ski Clb; Stage Crew; Jr Cls; Sftbl; Hon Roll; Providence Coll; Med.

MASTROSTEFANO, RACHEL; East Providence SR HS; Rumford, RI; (S); 11/520; Church Yth Grp; Color Guard; Flag Corp; Score Keeper; Hon Roll; Jr NHS; NHS; Com Sci.

MATAIS, MARIE T; Rogers HS; Newport, RI; (S); Camp Fr Inc; Spanish Clb; Chorus; Nwsp Stf; Yrbk Phtg; Lit Mag; Pres Stu Cncl; Hon Roll; NHS; Spanish NHS; Wellsley Awd 84; Goucher Coll; Intl Bus.

MATARESE, KIMBERLY; Cranston H S East; Cranston, RI; (Y); GAA; Library Aide; Spanish Clb; Band; Color Guard; Nwsp Stf; Yrbk Stf; Stu Cncl; Tennis; Jr NHS; RI Hnr Soc 85; Sci.

MATHIEU, MICHELE; Portsmouth HS; Portsmouth, RI; (Y); 1/210; Mrchg Band; Var Capt Gym; Var L Socr; Var Capt Sftbl; Bausch & Lomb Sci Awd; Elks Awd; Pres NHS; Val; Band; Concert Band; RPI Math,Sci Awd 84; Rtry Athlt Schlr Awd 85; Holy Cross; Med.

MATTHEW, LEAH; Rogers HS; Durango, CO; (Y); Church Yth Grp; Ski Clb; School Play; Hon Roll; San Diego U; Physcl Thrpst.

MATTIS, SARA; St Mary Acad Bay View; Cranston, RI; (Y); 1/200; Math Clb; Orch; Trs Frsh Cls; Trs Soph Cls; Trs Pres Stu Cncl; High Hon Roll; Hon Roll; NHS; Elec Music.

MAXWELL, DIANE; Bishop Keough HS; Pawt, RI; (Y); Art Clb; Church Yth Grp; Cmnty Wkr; Drama Clb; Nwsp Stf; Hon Roll; Stu Cncl Scholar Awd 83; Salva Regina; Human Svcs.

MAYER, PAULA; N Smithfield JR SR HS; N Smithfield, RI; (Y); Trs French Clb; JA; Letterman Clb; Pres Frsh Cls; Capt Cheerleading; Coach Actv; Co-Capt Gym; Mgr(s); Hon Roll; Chorus; Springfield Coll; Sports Med.

MAYNARD, SUZANNE; Toll Gate HS; Warwick, RI; (S); 15/393; Sec Church Yth Grp; Drama Clb; Q&S; Science Clb; Nwsp Stf; Ed Lit Mag; Capt Cheerleading; French Hon Soc; High Hon Roll; Trs NHS; RI Medical Society; Pharmaceutical Awd; State Science Fair 1st Pl.

MAYNE, NANCY; Chariho Regional SR HS; Bradford, RI; (S); Church Yth Grp; Girl Scts; Acpl Chr; Mgr Band; Chorus; Church Choir; High Hon Roll; Hon Roll; U Of RI; Actg.

MC CARTHY, COLLEEN; Saint Raphael Acad; Rumford, RI; (Y); 20/212; VP Church Yth Grp; Exploring; French Clb; Hosp Aide; Math Tm; Yrbk Stf; Stu Cncl; DAR Awd; High Hon Roll; NHS; Insite 84; Close Up 85.

MC CARTHY, GARY; Rogers HS; Newport, RI; (Y); Bsbl; Socr; Hon Roll; Pace U; Bus Admin.

MC CLAIN, TINA; Saint Raphael Acad; Providence, RI; (Y); Cmnty Wkr; Exploring; Hosp Aide; Red Cross Aide; Swmmng; Hon Roll; Mst Imprvd Cls A Grl Swmmr 85; Acadmc Hnrs; Psych.

MC CORMACK, KEVIN; North Kingstown HS; N Kingstown, RI; (Y); 92/371; Drama Clb; School Musical; School Play; Stage Crew; Yrbk Phtg; Yrbk Stf; High Hon Roll; Hon Roll; U Of RI; Jrnlsm.

MC DEVITT, KERRIE; Barrington HS; Barrington, RI; (Y); 8/233; GAA; VP Pres Intnl Clb; Yrbk Stf; Trs Soph Cls; Trs Jr Cls; Trs Sr Cls; JV Var Fld Hcky; JV Sftbl; High Hon Roll; Sec NHS; Lbrl Arts.

MC DONALD, KATHLEEN; Bishop Keough HS; Providence, RI; (S); Drama Clb; Pres Ski Clb; Speech Tm; Yrbk Phtg; Stu Cncl; Sftbl; Tennis; Hon Roll; Voice Dem Awd; Outstndng Irish-Am Stu Schlrshp 83; Rlgn Awd 84; Outstndng Cath Stu 84; U Of RI; Engl.

MC ELROY, TIMOTHY; La Salle Acad; Riverside, RI; (Y); 40/300; Church Yth Grp; Cmnty Wkr; Drama Clb; JA; Math Clb; Math Tm; Pep Clb; Quiz Bowl; Crs Cntry; Trk; Psych.

MC GAIR, JULIE A; South Kingstown HS; Wakefield, RI; (Y); Model UN; Variety Show; Rep Stu Cncl; Hon Roll; U Of RI.

MC GINN, KRISTEN; Bristol HS; Bristol, RI; (Y); French Clb; Hosp Aide; Ski Clb; Yrbk Sprt Ed; Hon Roll; Nrsng.

MC GIVNEY, MARK; Classical HS; Providence, RI; (Y); 35/287; Ski Clb; Varsity Clb; Yrbk Stf; Var L Ice Hcky; Hon Roll; Pres Schlr; Providence Coll; Accntng.

MC GRATH, COLLEEN; Rogers HS; Newport, RI; (Y); German Clb; Yrbk Bus Mgr; Yrbk Stf; Rep Jr Cls; Powder Puff Ftbl; Hon Roll; Grmn Ntl Hnr Scty; Bus.

MC GRATH, MICHAEL A; Lincoln JR SR HS; Lincoln, RI; (Y); 68/224; Boys Clb Am; Nwsp Stf; Yrbk Stf; Var Capt Swmmng; 3rd ST Swim Meet Champ 83-85; U Of RI; Accntng.

MC GRATH, SUZANNE; Rogers HS; Newport, RI; (Y); 3/250; Powder Puff Ftbl; French Hon Soc; Hon Roll; Frgn Lang.

MC GUIRE, BRENDAN; Smithfield HS; Greenville, RI; (Y); Am Leg Boys St; Church Yth Grp; Pres Frsh Cls; Off Jr Cls; Rep Sr Cls; Rep Stu Cncl; Var L Golf; JV Socr; Hon Roll; Acad Decathalon 85.

MC KENNA, KELLY M; Mount St Charles Acad; Cumberland, RI; (Y); Hosp Aide; Nwsp Rptr; Nwsp Stf; Lit Mag; High Hon Roll; Hon Roll; Emerson & Suffolk Schlrshp 85; Assumption Coll; Jrnlsm.

MC KENNEY, KIM C; East Greenwich HS; E Greenwich, RI; (Y); 34/165; Intnl Clb; Rep Frsh Cls; Var L Bsktbl; Var L Fld Hcky; Var L Sftbl; Hon Roll; Church Yth Grp; Cmnty Wkr; GAA; Variety Show; Hmcmng Qn 83; Princpls Awd Acadmc Excllnc 83-84; Sprtsmnshp Awd Vrsty Sftbl 85; U AZ; Spnsh.

MC KITCHEN, ERIN M; Tolman SR HS; Pawtucket, RI; (Y); Hosp Aide; Chorus; Badmtn; Var Bsktbl; Gym; Sftbl; Swmmng; Var Tennis; Trk; Var Vllybl; Outstndng Bsktbl Plyr Awd 83; All Vly Vlybl Plyr Hnrbl Ment 85; Athl Trnr.

MC LAIN, SCOTT; Tiverton HS; Tiverton, RI; (S); 8/218; High Hon Roll; NHS; Ntl Merit Ltr; U Of RI; Comp Engrng.

MC LINDEN, JOHN; St Raphael Acad; Pawtucket, RI; (Y); Cmnty Wkr; Political Wkr; Band; Orch; Pres Soph Cls; JV Trk; Hon Roll; Jr NHS; Hlth Care Prof.

MC LOUGHLIN, HEATHER; Prout Memorial HS; Peace Dale, RI; (S); 4/81; Math Clb; Aud/Vis; School Musical; Nwsp Phtg; Nwsp Rptr; JV Bsktbl; Hon Roll; Mdl Legslture Rep 84-85; Mrktng.

MC LOUGHLIN, MARY E; Prout Memorial HS; Peacedale, RI; (S); Sec Church Yth Grp; JCL; Political Wkr; Var Color Guard; Madrigals; Mrchg Band; School Play; Hon Roll; Pol Sci.

MC LOUGHLIN, TARA; Prout Memorial HS; Peace Dale, RI; (S); 22/79; Sec Church Yth Grp; JCL; Political Wkr; Acpl Chr; Chorus; Capt Flag Corp; School Musical; Hon Roll; NHS; Mdl Legslture; Acad Decthln; Intl Rel.

MC VEIGH, ALISON; Mt Pleasant HS; Providence, RI; (Y); OEA; Drm & Bgl; Hon Roll; Prfct Atten Awd; Hmn Srvs.

MDGRATH, SUZANNE; Rogers HS; Newport, RI; (Y); 3/250; Powder Puff Ftbl; French Hon Soc; Hon Roll; Frgn Lang.

MEAGHER, THOMAS; Our Lady Of Providence Prep Seminary; Providence, RI; (Y); 29/108; Church Yth Grp; Cmnty Wkr; FBLA; PAVAS; Spanish Clb; Church Choir; Hon Roll; RI Coll; Accntng.

MEANS, MARIE; Middletown HS; Middletown, RI; (S); 10/252; Girl Scts; Teachers Aide; Yrbk Stf; VP Frsh Cls; Var JV Cheerleading; Powder Puff Ftbl; French Hon Soc; Hon Roll; NHS; Boston U; Biomdcl Engrng.

MEDEIROS, DEBRA ANN; Portsmouth HS; Portsmouth, RI; (Y); 40/214; Cmnty Wkr; Band; Concert Band; Mrchg Band; Pep Band; Var Cheerleading; Var Gym; Hon Roll; St Schlr; VFW Awd; MVP Gymstcs 85; 2nd Tm All ST Gymstcs 85; Gymstcs Team Captn 85; George Washington U; Mrktng.

MEDEIROS, EUGENE; Bristol HS; Bristol, RI; (S); 21/230; Church Yth Grp; JCL; Latin Clb; Rep Stu Cncl; Var Bsbl; Var Capt Bsktbl; Hon Roll; NHS; Gold Mdl Ntl Latin Test 82-83; Pre-Law.

MEDEIROS, GEORGE; Smithfield HS; Esmond, RI; (Y); Crs Cntry; Johnson & Wales; Arts.

MEDEIROS, HELDER; Charles E Shea HS; Pawtucket, RI; (Y); Yrbk Sprt Ed; JV Socr; Hon Roll; Prfct Atten Awd; URI; Bus.

MEDEIROS, JAMES; Our Lady Of Providence HS; Pawtucket, RI; (Y); Pres Church Yth Grp; Math Tm; Yrbk Bus Mgr; Rep Frsh Cls; Rep Soph Cls; High Hon Roll; NHS; U Of RI; Bus.

MEINERTZ, GREGORY; Scituate JR SR HS; N Scitutate, RI; (S); 14/118; Varsity Clb; Var L Bsbl; Var L Socr; Hon Roll; Jr NHS; Indpndnt Order Of Odd Fllws Schlrshp 85; Rotry Clb Schlrshp 85; All Div Sccr Hnr 85; U Of RI; Engrng.

MELILLO, LORI; Bishop Keough HS; N Providence, RI; (S); Office Aide; Swmmng; Tennis; High Hon Roll; Jr NHS; NHS; 3rd Pl Sci Fair 82; Span & Biol I Awd 82; Algbr II Awd 83; Providence Coll:Med.

MELLO, CHRISTOPHER J; East Providence HS; East Providence, RI; (S); 21/520; Church Yth Grp; Teachers Aide; Band; Mrchg Band; L Var Bsbl; L Var Bsktbl; Var L Ftbl; High Hon Roll; Northeastern U; Mech Engr.

MELLO, JULIE; Bristol HS; Bristol, RI; (S); Am Leg Aux Girls St; French Clb; JCL; Latin Clb; VP Frsh Cls; VP Soph Cls; VP Jr Cls; VP Sr Cls; Trs Pres Stu Cncl; Capt Cheerleading; Hugh O Brien Yth Fndtn; Holy Cross Bk Awd; Cum Laude Latin Exam Natl.

MELLO, PATRICIA; Bristol HS; Bristol, RI; (Y); 42/222; Sec Latin Clb; Off Frsh Cls; Off Soph Cls; Off Jr Cls; Off Sr Cls; Var Capt Gym; Var Capt Sftbl; Hon Roll; Magna Cum Laude-Natl Ltn Exam 82-83; Awd-RI Dntl Assoc At RI Sci Fair & 2nd Grnt At Sci Fair 85; U Of RI; Dent Hygn.

MELLOTT JR, JACK; North Kingstown HS; N Kingstown, RI; (Y); 98/371; Boy Scts; Band; Concert Band; Mrchg Band; Hnr Band Soloist; Mech Engr.

MELONE, MELANIE; St Marys Bayview HS; Johnston, RI; (Y); Exploring; Math Clb; Spanish Clb; Trs Frsh Cls; Hon Roll; NHS; 2nd Pl Rgnl Comp RIFSC 82; Advrtsng.

MEN, MAKNA; Central HS; Providence, RI; (Y); 5/247; Cmnty Wkr; Hon Roll; NHS; Pres Schlr; St Schlr; Rhode Island Coll; Pol Sci.

MENARD, MARIE; Burrillville JR SR HS; Glendale, RI; (Y); 24/179; Yrbk Stf; Stu Cncl; Hon Roll; Pres Acdmc Ftns Awd 85; Bryant Coll; Htl Mngmnt.

MENDES, GAIL L; Tolman SR HS; Pawtucket, RI; (Y); Cmnty Wkr; Office Aide; Nwsp Ed-Chief; Rep Frsh Cls; Rep Soph Cls; Trs Jr Cls; Rep Sr Cls; Rep Stu Cncl; Stat Ftbl; High Hon Roll; Anthrplgy.

MENDES, PAUL; Charles E Shea HS; Pawtucket, RI; (Y); Church Yth Grp; Dance Clb; Debate Tm; Ski Clb; VP Stu Cncl; Var Bsbl; Im Bsktbl; Var Ftbl; Hon Roll; URI; Bus Mgmt.

MENDOZA, BRENDA; Central Falls JR SR HS; Central Fls, RI; (Y); Boys Clb Am; Church Yth Grp; Cmnty Wkr; Office Aide; Flag Corp; Yrbk Phtg; Var Vllybl; Johnson & Wales Coll; Plt.

MENEZES, JAY; Portsmouth HS; Portsmouth, RI; (Y); Aud/Vis; FBLA; Variety Show; Socr; Comp Progmng.

MENEZES, MONICA; Portsmouth HS; Portsmouth, RI; (Y); 27/215; Church Yth Grp; Math Tm; Pep Clb; Band; Chorus; Mrchg Band; Pep Band; Hon Roll; Math.

MENG, CHARIS; Portsmouth HS; Portsmouth, RI; (Y); 1/250; Dance Clb; Nwsp Stf; High Hon Roll; NHS; Spanish NHS; 1st Pl SR Piano Div 85; Srvd 3 Yrs Natl Rll 84; Wrote 3 Przwnng Artcls Providence Journal 84; Brown; Med.

MENZIES, MARION; Pilgrim HS; Warwick, RI; (Y); Church Yth Grp; French Clb; Hosp Aide; French Hon Soc; Hon Roll; Jr NHS; 3 Yr Svc Awd Candy Striper Prgm Kent Cnty Hosp 85; Awd Cap In Nrsng Vlntr Prgm-Kent Cnty Hosp 84; U Of RI; Nrsng.

MERANDI, WILLIAM; East Providence SR HS; East Providence, RI; (S); 14/522; Cmnty Wkr; MMM; Band; Concert Band; Jazz Band; School Musical; School Play; Wt Lftg; JV Wrstlng; Hon Roll; Baldwin ST Keybrd Wnnr 82; ST Solo/Ensmbl Wnnr 79-83; All ST Selection 80-81; Accntnt.

MERCURIO, MICHAEL J; Warwick Veterans Memorial HS; Warwick, RI; (Y); 128/315; Letterman Clb; Yrbk Sprt Ed; Yrbk Stf; VP Frsh Cls; VP Sr Cls; Capt Crs Cntry; Trk; Health Clb; CPR Instrctr; Blood Drv Coordntr; U Of RI; Medcl Tech.

MERRILL, DAVID; Classical HS; Providence, RI; (Y); Hon Roll; Prfct Atten Awd; U Of RI; Bus.

MESOLELLA, SUZANNE; Mt St Charles HS; N Providence, RI; (Y); 42/165; Cmnty Wkr; Political Wkr; Service Clb; Var L Sftbl; Hon Roll; Ntl Merit Ltr; N Providence Schlrshp Fnd 85; St Thomas; Bio.

MESSIER JR, DAVID J; West Warwick HS; W Warwick, RI; (Y); 17/235; French Clb; High Hon Roll; Hon Roll; RI Hnr Soc 85; U Of RI; Phrmcy.

METAKOS, DESPINA; Prout Memorial H S For Girls; Westerly, RI; (Y); 38/77; VP Church Yth Grp; Exploring; French Clb; VP Intnl Clb; Political Wkr; Ski Clb; Color Guard; Variety Show; Var Capt Vllybl; Hon Roll; Hnr Rll 84; U Of RI; Pharmcst.

METCALF, SHARON; East Providence SR HS; Riverside, RI; (Y); GAA; Library Aide; Ski Clb; Spanish Clb; Var Vllybl; Fash Merch.

METIVIER, DIANE; Tiverton HS; Tiverton, RI; (Y); Cmnty Wkr; Drama Clb; French Clb; Yrbk Stf; High Hon Roll; Hon Roll; NHS.

MEZZANOTTE, THOMAS; Pilgrim HS; Warwick, RI; (Y); Nwsp Rptr; Nwsp Sprt Ed; Var L Bsbl; Var L Bsktbl; Var L Ftbl; High Hon Roll; Ntl Merit Ltr; Spanish NHS; Voice Dem Awd; Church Yth Grp; Hugh O Brian Awd 84; Harvard Bk Awd 85; Med.

MICHAELS, MICHELLE; Tiverton HS; Tiverton, RI; (Y); Girl Scts; Yrbk Stf; Hon Roll; Accntng.

MICHAUD, CHRIS; St Raphael Acad; Pawtucket, RI; (Y); Art Clb; Office Aide; Vllybl; Hon Roll; Wentworth Inst Tech; Int Dsgn.

MICHEL, KAREN E; Tiverton HS; Tiverton, RI; (Y); 16/213; Sec Drama Clb; Yrbk Sprt Ed; Trs Frsh Cls; Trs Soph Cls; Trs Jr Cls; Trs Sr Cls; Rep Stu Cncl; Hon Roll; NHS; Pres Schlr; U RI Bk Awd 84; Irene Nolan Awd 85; Bst Actrss Awd 85; Outstndng Phy Ed Stu 85; U Of RI; Oceangrphy.

MICHELETTI JR, JOHN; Mt St Charles Acad; Johnston, RI; (Y); Math Tm; Stu Cncl; JV Bsktbl; Hon Roll; NHS; Prom Comm Pscl Recgnt Awd; Soc Distngushd Stu; Pub Comm; Boston Coll; Fin.

MIGNANELLI, ROBERT A; Narragansett HS; Narragansett, RI; (Y); 30/140; Boy Scts; Ski Clb; Variety Show; VP Frsh Cls; VP Jr Cls; Var Bsbl; Var Ftbl; Hon Roll.

MILLER, SCOTT; La Salle Acad; N Providence, RI; (Y); 5/360; Aud/Vis; Cmnty Wkr; Capt Debate Tm; Math Tm; Model UN; NFL; Political Wkr; Nwsp Stf; Rep Soph Cls; Trs Jr Cls; 1st Pl Cstl Rsrc Essay; 1st Pl Schl Sci Fair; Brown U; Med.

MINER III, JOHN F; Coventry HS; Coventry, RI; (Y); 28/400; Boy Scts; Chess Clb; Computer Clb; Math Clb; Science Clb; Spanish Clb; Band; Concert Band; Mrchg Band; Hon Roll; U Of RI.

MIRANDA, GORDON; Lincoln HS; Lincoln, RI; (Y); 51/250; Variety Show; Nwsp Stf; Yrbk Phtg; VP Stu Cncl; Var Ftbl; JV Ice Hcky; Pres Schlr; 5 Superltvs-Mst Poplr, Mst Sprtd, Friendlst, Ideal SR & Done Mst For The Clss 85; R I Hnr Scty 85; U Of Central FL; Med Tech.

MIRANDA, MICHAEL; Lincoln SR HS; Lincoln, RI; (Y); 27/190; Pres Stu Cncl; Var Ftbl; Var Ice Hcky; Var Trk; Hon Roll; Ntl Hnr Soc 83-84; Pharmcy.

MITCHELL, STEPHEN; Johnston HS; Johnston, RI; (S); 11/250; JV Ftbl; High Hon Roll; NHS; U Of RI; Chem Engr.

MOFFATT, JACKIE; Rogers HS; Newport, RI; (Y); Church Yth Grp; Dance Clb; Cheerleading; Gym; Powder Puff Ftbl; Trk; NHS; Miss RI Untd Teengr 82; Harry Vaugh Awd Perfrmng Arts 85; U Of RI; Hlth.

MOIO, STEPHANIE; Prout Memorial HS; Cranston, RI; (S); 19/79; Pres Church Yth Grp; Quiz Bowl; Ski Clb; Variety Show; Nwsp Sprt Ed; Sec Jr Cls; Sec Sr Cls; Stat Bsktbl; Var Crs Cntry; Var Vllybl; Hnrb Mntn Crss Cntry 84; MVP Crss Cntry Awd 81; Pre-Law.

MOLLOY, SUZANNE; Mount St Charles Acad; Bellingham, MA; (Y); Pres Church Yth Grp; Hosp Aide; Political Wkr; Ski Clb; Var Capt Gym; Hon Roll; NHS; All Star Gymnstcs Tm 84-85; Gymstcs 2nd Tm All ST, 1st Tm Northern Div 84-85; MVP Vrsty Gymnstcs; Law.

MOLSON, LESLIE MATUKO; The Wheeler Schl; Providence, RI; (Y); Debate Tm; Chorus; School Play; Ed Lit Mag; AFS; Drama Clb; PAVAS; Variety Show; Nwsp Rptr; Yrbk Phtg; Gold Medal Essay; RI Acad Decathlon 84; Outstndng Negro Stu Schlrshp 84; ST Champ Humrs Interprtn 84; Creative Writing.

MONAGHAN, GREGORY F; East Providence HS; Riverside, RI; (S); 6/250; Capt Chess Clb; Computer Clb; High Hon Roll; NHS; U Of RI; Comp Sci.

MONIZ, DENISE; Portsmouth HS; Portsmouth, RI; (Y); 21/210; Band; Concert Band; Mrchg Band; JV Cheerleading; Var Tennis; Hon Roll; High Hon Roll; NHS; URI; Bus.

MONIZ, MICHAEL J; Portsmouth HS; Portsmouth, RI; (Y); 69/250; Ski Clb; Concert Band; Mrchg Band; Pep Band; Variety Show; Socr; Trk; Hon Roll; Providence Coll; Real Est Apprs.

MONTAQUILA, TAMMY; La Salle Acad; Johnston, RI; (Y); 30/257; Rep Frsh Cls; Rep Stu Cncl; Hon Roll; Cert Of Athltc Accomplshmnts 85; Cert Of Recgntn-Algebra I 83; Lawyer.

MONTI, DAVID; Barrington HS; Barrington, RI; (Y); Var Golf; Bus.

MOORE, MELISSA; Charino Reg HS; Ashaway, RI; (S); Church Yth Grp; Drama Clb; Science Clb; Chorus; Rep Jr Cls; Pres Stu Cncl; Cheerleading; Trk; WA Cty Fair Princess 83-US Stu Cncl Awd 84; Fin Miss RI Ntl Teen Ager Pag 83; Psych.

MORA, BASSEM N; Barrington HS; East Providence, RI; (Y); Computer Clb; Debate Tm; French Clb; Intnl Clb; Math Clb; Math Tm; Science Clb; Swmmng; Tennis; NHS; American Chemcl Soc Achvt Awd 84; USAF Cert 84; CA Inst Of Tech; Comptr Sci.

MOREIRA, WENDY; Our Lady Of Fatima HS; Bristol, RI; (Y); Girl Scts; Teachers Aide; Chorus; Church Choir; Stage Crew; Swing Chorus; Variety Show; Yrbk Bus Mgr; Yrbk Stf; Hon Roll; 2nd Pl RI ST Sci Fair 83-84; 2nd Pl H S Sci Fair 83-84; 4th Pl Sci Fair 82-83; Boston U; Psych.

MORIARTY, KAREN; Pilgrim HS; Warwick, RI; (Y); Hosp Aide; Ski Clb; Band; Yrbk Ed-Chief; Yrbk Phtg; Hon Roll; U RI; Educ.

MORIN, MELANIE; West Warwick HS; W Warwick, RI; (Y); Hon Roll.

MORISSEAU, CHRISTINE; North Smithfield JR SR HS; N Smithfield, RI; (Y); French Clb; Letterman Clb; Band; Concert Band; Mrchg Band; JV Var Cheerleading; Med Assist.

MORRIS, MAUREEN A; St Mary Acad Bay View; Swansea, MA; (Y); 20/200; Drama Clb; Exploring; French Clb; Girl Scts; Hosp Aide; Math Clb; Math Tm; Red Cross Aide; Chorus; School Musical; Ind Prz ST Sci Fair; 1st Pl Sunfish Slng Chmpnshps; Bay View Srv Awd; Bus Exec.

MORRISSEAU, SHARON; Woonsocket HS; Woonsocket, RI; (Y); FCA; VP Stu Cncl; Var Capt Bsktbl; Var Capt Tennis; Var Capt Vllybl; High Hon Roll; Hon Roll; NCTE Awd; NHS; Pres Schlr; Prep All Amer Ath 85; Bst Female Stu Ath RI 85; MVP ST Vllybl Trnmnt 84; Wheaton Coll; Biol.

MORROW, JOANNE; Tiverton HS; Tiverton, RI; (S); 4/218; Ski Clb; Capt L Fld Hcky; L Var Trk; High Hon Roll; NHS.

MOSCA, MINDY; Cranston H S West; Cranston, RI; (S); Pres DECA; Nwsp Phtg; Nwsp Rptr; Off Jr Cls; VP Stu Cncl; Capt Cheerleading; Church Yth Grp; GAA; Political Wkr; Ski Clb; Stu Cncl Excllnce Awd 82-83; 2nd Pl Sci Fair 82-84; 1st Pl Entreprenrshp, 2nd Free Entrps Indvdl 84-85; Law.

MOSCARELLI, DAVID C; Johnston HS; Johnston, RI; (Y); Aud/Vis; High Hon Roll; Hon Roll.

MOSKOL, SCOTT; Cranston H S West; Cranston, RI; (Y); 4/408; Am Leg Boys St; Capt Debate Tm; Math Tm; NFL; Political Wkr; Pres VP Temple Yth Grp; Nwsp Stf; Yrbk Stf; Stu Cncl; JV Swmmng; Bst All Arnd Stdnt & Suprntndt Awd 85; Harvard Bk Awd 85; Brown; Med.

MOSS, JACQUELYN K; West Warwick SR HS; W Warwick, RI; (Y); Spanish Clb; Chorus; Variety Show; JV Bsktbl; Var L Sftbl; U RI; Intrprtr.

MOTTA, JOHN; Bristol HS; Bristol, RI; (S); 32/220; Boy Scts; Drama Clb; Ski Clb; School Play; Ftbl; Hon Roll; URI; Engrng.

MOTTA III, JOSEPH; Bristol HS; Bristol, RI; (S); Boy Scts; Cmnty Wkr; FBLA; Teachers Aide; Var Ftbl; Var Wrstlng; High Hon Roll; Hon Roll; NHS; Exploring; St Bronze Mtl In Wrestling 82-83; URI; Business.

MOTTA, KRISTINE; Tiverton HS; Tiverton, RI; (Y); Hst Drama Clb; French Clb; School Play; Yrbk Stf; Hon Roll; Congrs-Bundestag Stu Frgn Exchng Prog 85.

MOUSSEAU JR, ALBERT; Johnston SR HS; Johnston, RI; (Y); Nwsp Stf; Rep Frsh Cls; Rep Jr Cls; Rep Sr Cls; VP Stu Cncl; Bsbl; JV Bsktbl; Hon Roll; Natl Ldrshp & Svc Awds; Rotry Clb Scholar Fnlst; Hstry Day Proj Dist, ST Natl Awd; URI Alumni Hnr; Princeton; Aero Engr.

MOVILLA, GRACIELA; Bishop Keough Regional HS; N Providence, RI; (S); Drama Clb; School Play; High Hon Roll; Hon Roll; NHS; Engl, Religion & Biol Awd; Bryant Coll; Inst Mgmnt.

MOY, COLLEEN; Middletown HS; Newport, RI; (Y); Boys Clb Am; Church Yth Grp; Cmnty Wkr; Dance Clb; Drama Clb; Letterman Clb; Pep Clb; Varsity Clb; Band; Church Choir; Social Work.

MOYER, JOELLE; North Kingstown HS; N Kingstown, RI; (Y); 9/400; Varsity Clb; Stu Cncl; Cheerleading; Gym; Trk; High Hon Roll; Hon Roll; Lion Awd; NHS; Prfct Atten Awd; Nepera Chemcl Awd Basd SAT, Cls Rnk 85; SUNG Binghamton; Comp Sci.

MULCAHY, KERIN; North Smithfield JR SR HS; Slatersville, RI; (Y); French Clb; Yrbk Stf; Cheerleading; High Hon Roll; Hon Roll; Nrsg.

MULLIN, MARYANN; St Raphael Acad; Rumford, RI; (Y); 33/181; Church Yth Grp; Drama Clb; Hosp Aide; Red Cross Aide; Church Choir; School Musical; Hon Roll; NHS; Sisters Of Isabella 82-85; Boston Coll; Bus Mngmt.

MURPHY, MONICA; Classical HS; Providence, RI; (Y); Sec Church Yth Grp; Hosp Aide; JCL; Political Wkr; Nwsp Rptr; Nwsp Stf; Hon Roll; Maxima Cum Laude In JR Clscl League Latin Cntst 83-85; Pltcl Sci.

MURRAY, EILEEN; Veterans Memorial HS; Warwick, RI; (S); Church Yth Grp; DECA; Girl Scts; Ski Clb; Hon Roll; DECA Schlrshp 85; Johnson & Wates:Advrtsng.

MURRAY, JOHN; Warwick Veterans Memorial HS; Warwick, RI; (S); 3/323; Church Yth Grp; Computer Clb; JA; Math Tm; Quiz Bowl; JV Crs Cntry; JV Trk; High Hon Roll; NHS; Ntl Merit Ltr; Resselaer Polytechnic Inst Awd 84; Sons Of Italy Awd 84; Rhode Island Century 3 Simi-Finalist 84; Providence Coll; History.

MURRAY, SANDRA A; Coventry HS; Coventry, RI; (Y); 1/406; Math Tm; VP Science Clb; Spanish Clb; High Hon Roll; NHS; Ntl Merit SF; Val; Outstndng Math, Sci Stu 85; MA Inst Tech; Chem Engrng.

NADAL, ORLANDO; Mt Pleasant HS; Providence, RI; (Y); Church Yth Grp; Computer Clb; Drama Clb; French Clb; Chorus; Church Choir; Lit Mag; Wrstlng; Cit Awd; High Hon Roll; JR Cmmndr Rnk Royl Rngrs SE 84; Spnsh Acadmc Awd PR Hse 85; Upwrd Bnd RI Coll Compltn Awd 85; Naval Acad; Comp Engrng.

NADEAU, SCOTT R; Cumberland HS; Cumberland, RI; (Y); Math Tm; High Hon Roll; Hon Roll; JETS Awd; St Schlr; RI All-St Math Tm; Chem Lab Aide Mad Scientists Clb; Rensselaer Polytech Inst; Engr.

NADEAU, TIMOTHY; North Smithfield HS; N Smithfield, RI; (Y); 54/165; Letterman Clb; Pres Sr Cls; Var L Bsbl; Var Wt Lftg; Hon Roll; New Englnd Inst Of Tech; Robtcs.

NARDI, MARIA; Classical HS; Providence, RI; (Y); Church Yth Grp; Drm Mjr(t); Rep Jr Cls; Capt Twrlr; High Hon Roll; Jr NHS; Cum Laude Soc,Italian Hnr Scoc 85; Med.

NAYSNERSKI, WENDY; Narragansett HS; Narragansett, RI; (Y); #3 In Class; Cmnty Wkr; Hosp Aide; Office Aide; Teachers Aide; Variety Show; Jr Cls; Swmmng; High Hon Roll; NHS; Spanish NHS; Harvard Bk Awd 85; Excel Spnsh Awd 84; Law.

NEHRA, RASHMI; Warwick Veterans HS; Warwick, RI; (S); 14/323; Debate Tm; Speech Tm; Nwsp Stf; Var L Tennis; French Hon Soc; NHS; Mdl Legislature Lbbyst & Rep; Pol Sci.

NEHRING, LYNNEA; North Kingstown HS; Saunderstown, RI; (Y); 107/375; GAA; Letterman Clb; Varsity Clb; Rep Soph Cls; Rep Stu Cncl; Var Capt Bsktbl; JV Crs Cntry; JV Sftbl; Var L Trk; Hon Roll; Physcns Asst.

NELSON, NICK; North Kingstown HS; N Kingstown, RI; (Y); German Clb; VP JA; Math Clb; ROTC; Nrsg.

NERNEY, JOSEPH; Cranston East HS; Cranston, RI; (Y); Variety Show; VP Soph Cls; VP Jr Cls; VP Sr Cls; Var Bsbl; Var Bsktbl; U RI; Pol Sci.

NESBITT, RUPERT; Rogers HS; Newport, RI; (Y); Drama Clb; German Clb; School Play; Lit Mag; Rep Stu Cncl; Hon Roll; JETS Awd; King Mdl Schlrshp 82; Darmouth Alumni Awd Schlrshp For Ldrshp & Achvt 85; Fine Arts.

NEWTON, JENNIFER J; Smithfield HS; Smithfield, RI; (Y); 4/200; Drama Clb; JA; Math Tm; Chorus; School Musical; Stu Cncl; Fld Hcky; Elks Awd; Ntl Merit SF; Gold Mdl RI Solo-Ensemble Comp Voice 84; All-St Soprano Chorus 84.

NEWTON, LIANA; North Kingstown HS; W Greenwich, RI; (Y); Hon Roll; Vet Med.

NICHOLAS, KATHLEEN; Pilgrim HS; Warwick, RI; (Y); Hon Roll; Wrwck Plb Schl Spnsh Spelling Bee 83-84; Chmstry.

NICHOLS, KATHERINE; Woonsocket SR HS; Woonsocket, RI; (Y); Church Yth Grp; French Clb; Math Tm; Quiz Bowl; Scholastic Bowl; High Hon Roll; Ntl Merit SF; Wellesley Coll Bk Awd 85; Excllnce Fr Awd 80-83; Comp Sci.

NICHOLS, STEVEN A; E Providence SR HS; East Providence, RI; (S); 7/530; JV Bsktbl; NHS; Townie Awd 82; U Of RI; Comp Sci.

NIHILL, KAREN; Warren HS; Warren, RI; (Y); 9/97; Concert Band; School Play; Yrbk Stf; Rep Soph Cls; Rep Jr Cls; Off Sr Cls; Rep Stu Cncl; Cheerleading; Gym; Hon Roll; Stu Cncl Awd 85; Bus Mgmt.

NISBET, DEBBIE; Tollgate HS; Warwick, RI; (S); 57/393; Civic Clb; Hosp Aide; Letterman Clb; Var Capt Cheerleading; Hon Roll; Jr NHS; All-Str Chrldng Awd 83-84; Bio.

NOBLE, SARAH; Lincoln JR SR HS; Lincoln, RI; (Y); 1/228; Nwsp Ed-Chief; Rep Stu Cncl; Var L Tennis; L Trk; High Hon Roll; NCTE Awd; NHS; Math Tm; Jr NHS; 1st, 2nd Grant Sci Fair; Harvard Bk Prz; Pell Awd; Med.

NOBLE, SUSAN; Lincoln HS; Lincoln, RI; (Y); 47/190; Nwsp Stf; Yrbk Stf; Tennis; Hon Roll; Lbrl Arts.

NOEL, CHERYL; Woonsocket SR HS; Woonsocket, RI; (Y); Trs Church Yth Grp; Math Clb; Quiz Bowl; Church Choir; Concert Band; Off Sr Cls; JV Bsktbl; Var Capt Crs Cntry; High Hon Roll; Hon Roll; C40 Dram Awd & Family Of The Year; Social Work.

NOLAN, TIMOTHY R; La Salle Acad; Barrington, RI; (Y); #49 In Class; Boy Scts; Church Yth Grp; Pep Clb; School Play; Rep Soph Cls; Swmmng; Hon Roll; St Schlr; St Anselms Coll; Bus.

NOON, AMY; Warwick Vetrans Memorial HS; Warwick, RI; (Y); French Clb; Off Soph Cls; Off Jr Cls; French Hon Soc; High Hon Roll; Hon Roll; Bus.

NOONAN, EILEEN; Wm M Davies Vo Tech; Pawtucket, RI; (Y); Library Aide; Office Aide; Pep Clb; Teachers Aide; Chorus; Color Guard; School Musical; High Hon Roll; Hon Roll; Prfct Atten Awd; Nrsng.

NORATO, NANCY; Cranston H S West; Cranston, RI; (S); 76/443; Pres DECA; Intnl Clb; Ski Clb; Rep Stu Cncl; Cheerleading; Hon Roll; Awd Outstndng Cheerleader 82; Awd For Excllnc Stu Cncl 82; 1st Pl Finance & Credit DECA 83; Bus.

NOREAU, JENNIFER; Johnston HS; Johnston, RI; (S); 11/237; Girl Scts; Mrchg Band; High Hon Roll; NHS; IFLA Awd 84-85; ST Hnr Soc 84-85; Math.

NORMANDIE, MARIE; Coventry HS; Coventry, RI; (Y); CAP; ROTC; Variety Show; Stu Cncl; JV Crs Cntry; JV Trk; DAR Awd; Hon Roll; Billy Mitchel Awd 84; Solo Pilot Flght Wings 85; Outstndng Cadet 85; Northern VA CC; Comp Sci.

NORMANDIN, RICHARD; Woonsocket HS; Woonsocket, RI; (Y); 100/500; Church Yth Grp; Band; Concert Band; Mrchg Band; JV Ftbl; Hon Roll; Clara W Pond Art Schrlshp 85; Schlstc Art Awds 85; Rhode Island All St Band 84-85; Art Inst Boston; Graphic Desgn.

NOTARANTONIO, JULIE; Woonsocket SR HS; Woonsocket, RI; (Y); Debate Tm; Exploring; Hosp Aide; Math Tm; Model UN; NFL; Rep Stu Cncl; High Hon Roll; NHS; Bus.

NOTARIANNI, MICHELE; Cranston High School West; Cranston, RI; (Y); Sec GAA; Math Tm; Var Capt Crs Cntry; Var Capt Trk; High Hon Roll; NHS; NEDT Awd; Intnl Clb; Letterman Clb; School Play; Harvard Bk Awd 85; Rensselaer Medal/Schlrshp 85; 1st Tm All Div-Crss Cntry 84.

NUNES, KENNETH; Davies Vo Tech; Central Falls, RI; (Y); VICA; Hon Roll.

NUNES, MARK C; Rogers HS; Newport, RI; (Y); 310/350; Church Yth Grp; Drama Clb; French Clb; School Play; Variety Show; Nwsp Stf; Yrbk Stf; Trs Jr Cls; Bsktbl; Mgr(s); U Of Rhode Island Bk Awd; Fairfield; Lib Arts.

NUNEZ, ERIC; Central Falls JR SR HS; Central Falls, RI; (Y); 33/157; FCA; Varsity Clb; Stage Crew; Bsktbl; Coach Actv; Ftbl; Score Keeper; Timer; Wt Lftg; Hon Roll; Bst SR Drftsmn 85; New England Tech Bk Awd Drftg & Schlrshp 85; New England Tech; Mech Drftg.

NUTE, CHRISTOPHER; Rogers HS; Fairfax, VA; (Y); Boy Scts; German Clb; VP JA; ROTC; Var Crs Cntry; Var Capt Swmmng; Var L Swmmng; Var L Trk; Hon Roll; Eagle Sct 82; Exrcs & Ftnss.

NYGAARD, ERIK; Bristol HS; Bristol, RI; (S); 23/220; L Var Ftbl; NHS; Ntl Ltn Exmntn Awd 83; U Of AZ; Phrmcy.

O BRIEN, MARY ANN; Mount St Charles Acad; Forestdale, RI; (S); 17/165; Cmnty Wkr; Sec Sr Cls; Stu Cncl; Var L Cheerleading; Var L Tennis; High Hon Roll; NHS; Church Yth Grp; Hosp Aide; Model UN; Ntl Guild Piano Tchrs 84.

O CONNOR, MARILYN; Cumberland HS; Cumberland, RI; (S); Mgr DECA; Chorus; Mgr(s); Score Keeper; Smkng Cncl 83-84; RI CC; Rdlgy.

O CONNOR, SARA; St Raphael Acad; Pawtucket, RI; (Y); 23/178; Cmnty Wkr; Dance Clb; Pep Clb; Pep Band; Yrbk Stf; Frsh Cls; Soph Cls; Jr Cls; Sr Cls; JV Cheerleading; Mosignor Thomas V Cassidy Schlrshp 82; Ntl Hnr Scty 85; UVM.

O DONNELL, KATHLEEN P; Classical HS; Providence, RI; (Y); Church Yth Grp; Cmnty Wkr; Political Wkr; Hon Roll; Boston Coll; Nrs.

O DOWD, CHRISTINE; Narragansett HS; Narragansett, RI; (Y); 6/144; Variety Show; Off Jr Cls; Off Sr Cls; VP Stu Cncl; Cheerleading; Gym; High Hon Roll; Hon Roll; NHS; Spanish NHS.

O GARA, CAROLYN; Woonsocket SR HS; Narragansett, RI; (Y); 14/490; Math Tm; Sec Sr Cls; Rep Stu Cncl; Var L Bsktbl; High Hon Roll; NHS; Pres Schlr; Congrsmn Fernand J St Germain Mdl Fo Merit 85; Coll Of Holy Cross.

O GARA, PATRICIA; East Providence HS; Riverside, RI; (Y); PAVAS; Chorus; Church Choir; School Musical; Variety Show; Cheerleading; Cit Awd; High Hon Roll; Hon Roll; NHS; Hicks Awd 83; Govs Essay Cont 1st Pl 83; Talent Amer 1st Pl 83-85; Music.

O HARA III, PATRICK V; North Smithfield HS; N Smithfield, RI; (Y); Church Yth Grp; Drama Clb; French Clb; Letterman Clb; Variety Show; Yrbk Phtg; Off Frsh Cls; Pres Soph Cls; Var Ice Hcky; CAP; Hugh O Brien Yth Ledrshp Awd 83-84; Northeastern U; Pharmacy.

O LEARY, JOANNE P; Classical HS; Providence, RI; (Y); Church Yth Grp; Dance Clb; Drama Clb; Chorus; Variety Show; French Hon Soc; Hon Roll; Ntl Merit SF; JCL; Cmnty Theatre; JR Alliance Francaise; Theatre.

O NEILL, MAUREEN; Portsmouth HS; Portsmouth, RI; (Y); 4-H; FBLA; Chorus; Crs Cntry; Socr; Chess Clb; NHS; Brown U Bk Awd 85; Psych.

O NEILL, MELISSA; South Kingstown HS; Peace Dale, RI; (Y); Band; Nwsp Sprt Ed; Nwsp Stf; Stu Cncl; Crs Cntry; Var L Gym; Tennis; Hon Roll.

O ROURKE, JAY; Lincoln HS; Lincoln, RI; (Y); Variety Show; Var Bsbl; JV Bsktbl; JV Crs Cntry; JV Ftbl; Var Mgr(s); Im Tennis; ROTC; Comp Engrng.

O ROURKE, SEAN; Cranston High Schl East; Cranston, RI; (Y); 39/367; Boy Scts; Computer Clb; German Clb; Yrbk Stf; Rep Sr Cls; JV Bsbl; JV Bsktbl; Var L Socr; Swmmng; Hon Roll; MVP Soccer 84-85; All Div 1st Team In Soccer 84-85; Outstndng SR Dfnsman In Soccer 84-85; Rensselaer Poly Inst.

O SHEA, CAROLINE; Middletown HS; Middletown, RI; (S); 18/254; Pep Clb; Band; Concert Band; Mrchg Band; Pep Band; Cit Awd; High Hon Roll; Hon Roll; Med.

OCONNOR, MARILYN; Cumberland HS; Cumberland, RI; (S); DECA; Chorus; Stat Bsbl; Stat Bsktbl; Mgr(s); Score Keeper; Hon Roll; 1st Pl ST Cmptn DECA 85; CC Of RI; Bus Admin.

OLIVERA, JOHN; Tiverton HS; Tiverton, RI; (Y); Church Yth Grp; Band; Comp Sci.

OLSON, TODD; Lincoln JR SR HS; Lonsdale, RI; (Y); Boy Scts; FHA; Yrbk Stf; Var Bsbl; JV Ftbl; L Tennis; RIC; Marine Bio.

ONEIL, CHERI; Portsmouth HS; Portsmouth, RI; (Y); FBLA; FFA; Girl Scts; Score Keeper; Vllybl; Anml Sci.

ORABONA, LORI; Mt St Charles Acad; Johnston, RI; (Y); 96/147; Church Yth Grp; JV Bsktbl; Schl Psych.

OSWALD, ALLAN; Portsmouth HS; Portsmouth, RI; (Y); Church Yth Grp; Band; Chorus; Drm Mjr(t); Pep Band; Var L Swmmng; Hon Roll; All ST Band Roch,Chorus 82-85.

OWENS, ADRIAN; Narragansett HS; Narragansett, RI; (Y); 4/114; Boy Scts; Exploring; Spanish Clb; Concert Band; Jazz Band; Variety Show; Crs Cntry; NHS; Ntl Merit Ltr; Chess Clb; 3rd Grnt ST Sci Fair; Bst In Spnsh II & III; Engrng.

OWENS, JONATHAN; Narragansett HS; Narragansett, RI; (Y); 3/116; Boy Scts; Concert Band; Jazz Band; French Hon Soc; High Hon Roll; NHS; Ntl Merit Ltr; Debate Tm; Band; Variety Show; Outstndg Achvt Soc Stud 85; 3rd Grnt RI Expo-Sci Fair 85; Cert Recog RI Acad Decath 85; Engrng.

OWRE, KRISTIN; N Smithfield JR SR HS; N Smithfield, RI; (Y); 78/746; Drama Clb; Letterman Clb; Varsity Clb; Band; Yrbk Rptr; Stu Cncl; JV Var Cheerleading; JV Var Gym; High Hon Roll; Hon Roll; Jr Prom Queen 85; Mdlst NE Rgnl Gymnastic Meet 84; St Gymnastic Champ Tm 82-85; Psych.

OZBEK, ERTURK; Scituate HS; N Scitutate, RI; (S); Am Leg Boys St; Model UN; Scholastic Bowl; Concert Band; Jazz Band; School Play; Yrbk Phtg; Rep Sr Cls; L Ftbl; NEDT Awd; All State Band; Boston U; Intl Reltns.

PACHECO, CATHY; Our Lady Of Fatima HS; Bristol, RI; (Y); Drama Clb; School Play; Yrbk Ed-Chief; Rep Frsh Cls; VP Soph Cls; Rep Jr Cls; VP Stu Cncl; JV Sftbl; Poltcl Sci.

PACHECO, MARLENE; Tiverton HS; Tiverton, RI; (Y); Drama Clb; French Clb; Yrbk Stf; High Hon Roll; Herbert & Claiborne Pell Medl Hist 85.

PACHEW, CATHY; Our Lady Of Fatima HS; Bristol, RI; (Y); Drama Clb; School Play; Yrbk Ed-Chief; VP Soph Cls; Rep Jr Cls; VP Stu Cncl; Sftbl; Hon Roll; Sci Fair Hnrbl Mntn; Providence Coll; Poltcl Sci.

PACI, LISA; Classical HS; Providence, RI; (Y); 33/287; Spanish Clb; Yrbk Ed-Chief; Yrbk Stf; Var Capt Bsktbl; Var Vllybl; High Hon Roll; Pres Schlr; All Cty Bsktbl Team; U Of RI; Pre Med.

PADGETT, MICHELLE D; Classical HS; Providence, RI; (Y); Library Aide; Chorus; Madrigals; High Hon Roll; Hon Roll; CPA.

PAGANO, SUSAN L; Warwick Veterans Memorial HS; Webster, MA; (Y); 12/327; Hosp Aide; Acpl Chr; Chorus; High Hon Roll; NHS; Spanish NHS; Trs Church Yth Grp; Church Choir; Hon Roll; Chris Kampper Mem Schlrshp Awd 85; Nal HS Choral Awd 84-85; Eastrn Nazarene Coll; Pedtrcn.

PAGLIARO, PATTY A; Classical HS; Providence, RI; (Y); Math Clb; PAVAS; Science Clb; School Play; Church Yth Grp; Dance Clb; JA; Office Aide; JV Var Twrlr; Hon Roll; Boston U; Pre Med.

PAIVA, INES; Cranston High School East; Cranston, RI; (Y); French Clb; Rep VICA; Ed Lit Mag; Stu Cncl; French Hon Soc; Hon Roll; ST VICA Comp Silver Medal 84; U MA Amherst; Secndry Educ.

PALARDY, LEAH; Tollgate HS; Warwick, RI; (S); Church Yth Grp; Letterman Clb; Chorus; Stu Cncl; JV Bsktbl; Capt Cheerleading; Hon Roll; Figure Skating Awds 81; Equestrian Awds 81-83; Sci Fair Project 81; Bio.

PALIOTTO, THERESA; Pilgrim HS; Warwick, RI; (Y); Camp Fr Inc; Church Yth Grp; Church Choir; Im Bsktbl; Hon Roll; RI Teachers Of Italian-Certificato Al Merito 84 & 85; Frgn Language Hnrs-Italian 85; Marian Awd 82; RI Coll; Radiolgy.

PALLANTE, DEBORAH; W Warwick SR HS; W Warwick, RI; (Y); Drama Clb; Socr; JV L Trk; Hon Roll; Hnr Rl & Brnze Hnrs 82-83; Typwrtng Prof Cert 83-84; CPA.

PALMER, ANN; Tiverton HS; Tiverton, RI; (Y); Ski Clb; Cheerleading; Hon Roll; Southeastern Mass U; Bus.

PALMIERI, KRISTEN; Warren HS; Kissimmee, FL; (Y); Church Yth Grp; Cmnty Wkr; Girl Scts; Band; Church Choir; Concert Band; Rep Frsh Cls; Rep Soph Cls; Rep Stu Cncl; Var JV Vllybl; Embry Riddle Aerontcl U; Comp.

PALMISCIANO, LYNNE; St Mary Academy Bay View; E Greenwich, RI; (Y); 1/215; Camera Clb; Church Yth Grp; Cmnty Wkr; Exploring; French Clb; Girl Scts; Mathletes; Math Clb; Pep Clb; Quiz Bowl; Harvard Bk Awd 85; RI Acad Decath Slvr Awd Math Hnrs 85; Gld Awd GSA 85; Pre-Med.

PANNONE, DAVID T; Johnston HS; Johnston, RI; (Y); Am Leg Boys St; Cmnty Wkr; Variety Show; JV Var Bsbl; JV Var Ftbl; Citatn Coaches Clss A All Leag Ftbl Tm 85; Sprts Med.

PANZICA, ANN; Narragansett HS; Narragansett, RI; (Y); 1/135; Hosp Aide; Yrbk Stf; Off Soph Cls; Off Jr Cls; High Hon Roll; Hon Roll; NHS; JV Socr; JV Sftbl; Coll De Las Cazes Montpellier France 82-83; Model Legsltr 83-85; Acad Decthln 84-85; MIT; Engrng.

PARENT, MICHELLE A; Bristol HS; Bristol, RI; (S); Dance Clb; Sec GAA; Pres JCL; Math Tm; Yrbk Ed-Chief; Rep Soph Cls; Rep Jr Cls; Rep Sr Cls; Rep Stu Cncl; Stat Vllybl; Ntl Lat Exam Slvr Mdl 83; RI ST Sci Fair 2nd Grnt 84; Ntl Lat Hnr Soc 81-84; Med.

PARI, SANDRA; North Providence HS; N Providence, RI; (Y); 2/250; Church Yth Grp; Ski Clb; Lit Mag; High Hon Roll; Hon Roll; Jr NHS; Comp Sci.

PARKER, DONNA; William M Davies JR Tech HS; Pawtucket, RI; (Y); Church Yth Grp; Pres Pep Clb; VICA; Band; Cheerleading; High Hon Roll; Ntl Merit SF; Art Throphy 80; Modern Miss Cert Achvt 85; RI Design; Fshn Dsgn.

PARKER II, EDWARD F; Tolman SR HS; Pawtucket, RI; (Y); Math Tm; Ski Clb; Golf; Ice Hcky; Hon Roll; Brown Belt 3rd Dgre 85; Crmnlgy.

PARKER, STEPHEN F; North Kingstown HS; N Kingstown, RI; (Y); 114/375; Rep Frsh Cls; Rep Soph Cls; Rep Jr Cls; Rep Sr Cls; Schlstc Art Awd; Museum Fine Arts Schl; Illstrtr.

PARMAN, JENNIFER; Chariho Regional HS; Hope Valley, RI; (Y); 53/302; Trs Exploring; JV Var Bsktbl; U Of RI; Psych.

PARREIRA, ANTONIO R; Charles E Shea HS; Pawtucket, RI; (Y); Boys Clb Am; Aud/Vis; Band; Yrbk Stf; Ftbl; Socr; Hon Roll; RI Coll; Med.

PARRILLO, MAUREEN; St Francis Xavier Acad; Providence, RI; (Y); #5 In Class; Cmnty Wkr; Drama Clb; School Musical; Yrbk Sprt Ed; Rep Jr Cls; Rep Sr Cls; Stu Cncl; Cheerleading; High Hon Roll; Hon Roll; Natl Merit Hnr Roll 84; Salve Regina Coll; Psych.

PARRILLO, SHERRI; Johnsotn SR HS; Johnston, RI; (Y); DECA; Ski Clb; Drm Mjr(t); Powder Puff Ftbl; Twrlr; Hon Roll; Lawyer.

PASION, ROCIO; Central Falls JR SR HS; Central Falls, RI; (Y); 1/120; Crs Cntry; Gov Hon Prg Awd; High Hon Roll; Hon Roll; Jr NHS; Prfct Atten Awd; Pres Phys Ftns & Typwrtng Awds 83; Pell Mdl US Hstry 85.

PATTERSON, KAREN A; Tiverton HS; Tiverton, RI; (Y); 40/218; Ski Clb; Band; Variety Show; Yrbk Phtg; Pres Stu Cncl; Var Fld Hcky; Capt Var Vllybl; Stu Cncl Achvt Awd 85; Hugh O Brian Yth Found Ldrshp Awd 83; Ruth Rocha Awd Outstndng Vlybl Plyr 85; U RI; Bus Adm.

PATTERSON, THERESA M; Warren HS; Warren, RI; (Y); 2/133; School Play; Yrbk Phtg; Yrbk Stf; VP Soph Cls; Stu Cncl; Cheerleading; Bausch & Lomb Sci Awd; DAR Awd; NHS; Sal; Yth Undrstndng Schlrshp To Japan 84; URI Bk Awd 84; Ntl Advnmnt For Arts 84-85; Thtr.

PATTON, ANNE MARIE L; Chariho Regional HS; Bradford, RI; (Y); 89/302; Church Yth Grp; Hon Roll; U RI; Psych.

PAUL, DEBRA; Bistol HS; Bristol, RI; (S); Yrbk Sprt Ed; Off Jr Cls; Off Sr Cls; Bsktbl; Var L Sftbl; High Hon Roll; NHS; Drama Clb; Teachers Aide; School Play; Latin Hnr Scty 82-83; 2nd Team All Div Sftbl 83; Magna Cum Laude Awd Natl Latin Exam 83; U Of NH; Math.

PAYNE, ALICIA H; North Kingstown SR HS; N Kingstown, RI; (Y); 76/375; Art Clb; Hon Roll; Schlstc Art Awd 81-82; CCRI; Cmmrcl Art.

PEAREARA, JOANN; Classical HS; Providence, RI; (Y); French Clb; Hosp Aide; Chorus; Drm Mjr(t); Hon Roll; Bay Path JC; Lang.

PENCARSKI, ROBERT; Lincoln SR HS; Lincoln, RI; (Y); Boy Scts; Computer Clb; VP Frsh Cls; Tennis; Elec Engr.

PENZA, LORRAINE M; Mount St Charles Acad; Johnston, RI; (Y); 41/165; Cmnty Wkr; Drama Clb; Chorus; Variety Show; High Hon Roll; Hon Roll; NHS; Math Tm; Office Aide; Knights Columbus Scholar; Engl Tutor; Providence Coll; Psych.

PERALTA, MARIANELA; St Marys Academy Bayview; Providence, RI; (Y); 15/200; Sec Exploring; French Clb; VP Sec JA; Chorus; Yrbk Stf; Im Gym; Sec Trs NHS; Cmnty Wkr; Debate Tm; Math Clb; Minrty Schlrshp 82-86; 4th Pl Wnr RI Blck Hertge Essy Cntst 85; VP Prsnl Corp Sec Of Yr JA; Syracuse U; Intl Rel.

PERKINS, DEBI; Portsmouth HS; Portsmouth, RI; (Y); 11/220; Pres 4-H; Quiz Bowl; Spanish Clb; L Gym; 4-H Awd; High Hon Roll; Hon Roll; NHS; Spanish NHS; Rep RI Eastern ST Expo 85; Bus.

PERRAS, CATHY A; Coventry HS; Coventry, RI; (Y); 26/394; Pres Letterman Clb; Sr Cls; Var L Bsktbl; Var L Tennis; Var L Trk; Var L Vllybl; NHS; French Clb; Yrbk Stf; Sec Soph Cls; Army Reserve Schlr/Ath Awd; Bst Female Ath Awd; U Of RI; Phys Ed.

PERRIN III, WILLIAM G; Barrington Christian Acad; Rumford, RI; (Y); 2/10; Drama Clb; FCA; School Play; Yrbk Ed-Chief; Pres Stu Cncl; Var Capt Bsktbl; Var Capt Socr; Hon Roll; Sal; MVP Sccxr 84; 2nd Mvp Bsktbll 84; Phillips Acad; Pol Sci.

PERRON, STACEY; North Smithfield JR SR HS; N Smithfield, RI; (Y); Trs Church Yth Grp; French Clb; JA; Letterman Clb; Yrbk Stf; Var L Bsktbl; Var L Gym; Var L Sftbl; Hon Roll; Mst Imprvd-Bsktbl 85; 2nd Tm All Stars-Sftbl 84; Accntng.

PERRY, JAMES M; Coventry HS; Coventry, RI; (Y); Boy Scts; Chess Clb; Church Yth Grp; Math Clb; Math Tm; Quiz Bowl; Stage Crew; Stu Cncl; Eagle Scut 85-86; Math.

PERRY, PAMELA; North Ki/Ngstown HS; N Kingstown, RI; (Y); 145/370; Church Yth Grp; Cmnty Wkr; Band; Hon Roll; New England Coll; Pre-Law.

PERRY, STEPHANIE ANN; Coventry HS; Coventry, RI; (Y); 20/400; Trs Church Yth Grp; 4-H; French Clb; Stage Crew; Yrbk Stf; Stu Cncl; High Hon Roll; Jr NHS; NHS; Intl Stu Ldrshp Pgm 84; Clncl Psy.

PERTAIN, SARAH; Lincoln HS; Lincoln, RI; (Y); Church Yth Grp; Girl Scts; Ski Clb; Yrbk Stf; Stu Cncl; Var L Bsktbl; Var L Fld Hcky; Var L Trk; 4-H Awd; Hon Roll; Physcl Thrpy.

PETERS, KURT; La Salle Acad; Smithfield, RI; (Y); 7/257; Chess Clb; Pres Computer Clb; Math Tm; Nwsp Rptr; Lcrss; Socr; High Hon Roll; NHS; Rensselaer Bk Awd For Math & Sci 85; Engrng.

PETERSON, DEBBY; Tiverton HS; Tiverton, RI; (Y); Church Yth Grp; Band; Concert Band; Mrchg Band; JV Vllybl; Hon Roll; URI; Comp Sci.

PETERSON, MARY; South Kingstown HS; Kingston, RI; (Y); Spanish Clb; Sftbl; Tennis; Hon Roll; Spnsh Stu Exchng 83-84; Spn & Afrca Trp 85.

PETRIN, MARC; North Smithfield JR SR HS; N Smithfield, RI; (Y); Letterman Clb; Varsity Clb; L Bsbl; Var Bsktbl; Stat Ice Hcky; High Hon Roll; Hon Roll; Comp Sci.

PETRONE, MELISSA A; Warwick Veterans Memorial HS; Warwick, RI; (Y); Teachers Aide; Yrbk Stf; Off Jr Cls; Stu Cncl; French Hon Soc; High Hon Roll; Hon Roll; NHS; RI Coll; Bus.

PETRUCCI, LAUREN; Coventry HS; W Greenwich, RI; (Y); Latin Clb; Spanish Clb; Variety Show; Yrbk Stf; Stu Cncl; Hon Roll; Voice Dem Awd.

PETTIGREW, MARK; Cranston High Schl West; Cranston, RI; (Y); Am Leg Boys St; Chess Clb; Trs Church Yth Grp; Computer Clb; Hon Roll; Jr NHS; NHS; NEDT Awd; Outstndng Achvt Chss 83; Comp Engr.

PETTIT, KAREN; Middletown HS; Middletown, RI; (S); 35/252; Band; Concert Band; Mrchg Band; Pep Band; Yrbk Sprt Ed; Yrbk Stf; Powder Puff Ftbl; Vllybl; Hon Roll; Bus Mgmt.

PHANEUF, JANET; Warwick Veterans Mem HS; Warwick, RI; (Y); 15/297; Yrbk Stf; Rep Sr Cls; L Tennis; High Hon Roll; Hon Roll; Jr NHS; NHS; RIC Alumni Hnrs Schlrshp 85; Gorham Textron Schlrshp 85; Rhode Island Coll; Chem.

PHANEUF, ROXANN; Coventry HS; Coventry, RI; (Y); 11/393; Church Yth Grp; Letterman Clb; Varsity Clb; Variety Show; Trs Soph Cls; Trs Jr Cls; Trs Sr Cls; Sftbl; High Hon Roll; NHS; CYO Bsktbl All Star 84 & 85; Marist Coll; Psych.

PHELPS, KRISTIN; Portsmouth HS; Portsmouth, RI; (Y); 9/243; Intnl Clb; Ski Clb; Sec Frsh Cls; Powder Puff Ftbl; High Hon Roll; Hon Roll; NHS; Spanish NHS; Engr.

PHILLIPS, MICHELLE; Our Lady Of Fatima HS; Bristol, RI; (Y); Church Yth Grp; Yrbk Bus Mgr; Yrbk Stf; Sec Frsh Cls; Var Bsktbl; Var Cheerleading; Var Trk; Hon Roll; Johnson & Wales Scholar 84-85; Fin Miss RI Natl Teen Pag 84-85; Acad Awd Scholar Johnson & Wales 85; Johnson & Wales Coll; Comp Pgm.

PHILLIPS, STEPHANIE; Woonsocket SR HS; Woonsokcet, RI; (Y); Math Tm; L JV Crs Cntry; L Trk; High Hon Roll; Biol.

PHIVILAY, PANEKHAM; Mount Pleasant HS; Providence, RI; (Y); 2/162; JV Vllybl; High Hon Roll; Hon Roll; St Schlr; Outstdng Math Awd At Mt Pleasant H S 85; RI Hnr Soc From Mt Pleasant H S 85; ESL Acad Achv Awd 84; U Of RI; Elec Engrng.

PHOU, HONG MENG; William E Tolman HS; Pawtucket, RI; (Y); 36/283; Computer Clb; Math Tm; Badmtn; Socr; Vllybl; High Hon Roll; Hon Roll; Jr NHS; NHS; RI Hnr Soc 85; U Of RI; Comp Electrncs Engrng.

PICARD, CATHY; Mount Saint Charles Acad; Woonsocket, RI; (Y); Sec VP Church Yth Grp; Cmnty Wkr; Drama Clb; Quiz Bowl; Flag Corp; School Musical; Variety Show; Rep Stu Cncl; Hon Roll; CYO Spirit Alive Awd 84; Drama.

PICCOLI, STACY; Narragansett HS; Narragansett, RI; (Y); 22/147; Cmnty Wkr; Hosp Aide; Office Aide; Variety Show; Off Frsh Cls; Off Soph Cls; Jr Cls; Sr Cls; VP Pres Stu Cncl; Capt Cheerleading; 2nd Pl Awd Sci Fair 83; 2nd Pl Awd Sci Fair & Spec Awd In Dnstry 84; Nrsng.

PICERNO JR, CARL A; Classical HS; Providence, RI; (Y); 97/293; Church Yth Grp; Cmnty Wkr; Yrbk Sprt Ed; Rep Jr Cls; JV Bsktbl; Hon Roll; Lion Awd; NHS; Italian Clb 84; URI; Law.

PICH, RALL; Mount Pleasant HS; Providence, RI; (Y); Hon Roll; U Of RI; Elec Engr.

PIMENTAL, DANIEL; Tiverton HS; Tiverton, RI; (Y); Art Clb; Var Bsbl; Var Score Keeper; Hon Roll; Prfct Atten Awd; Tivertn Mdl Schl 8th Grd Fgn Lang 82; Comp Pgm.

PIMENTAL, MICHAEL; Coventry SR HS; Coventry, RI; (Y); Boy Scts; Ski Clb; JV Bsbl; Var Ftbl; Var Ice Hcky; Var Trk; JV Wrstlng; Arch Engr.

PINE, MICHELLE; Cranston HS East; Cranston, RI; (Y); Church Yth Grp; Sec Debate Tm; Library Aide; Political Wkr; Spanish Clb; Rep Jr Cls; Stat Ftbl; Stat Ice Hcky; Stat Mgr(s); Var Sftbl; Brown U Enrchmnt Prog 83-84; Wheelock Coll; Elem Ed.

PINE, SHARON; Cranston High School East; Cranston, RI; (Y); Church Yth Grp; German Clb; Science Clb; Nwsp Stf; Stat Ice Hcky; Var Sftbl; JV Tennis; Hon Roll; 3rd Grnt St Sci Fair 82-83; Speech Thrpy.

PINHEIRO, ELIZABETH; Charles E Shea HS; Pawtucket, RI; (Y); 44/289; Yrbk Stf; High Hon Roll; Hon Roll; NHS; RI Hnr Soc 85; Outstndng-Achvt Intern Pgm & Hm Eco Stu 85; CC Of RI.

PISATURO, LAURA; Classical HS; Providence, RI; (Y); 92/285; Pres Church Yth Grp; Cmnty Wkr; Drama Clb; Pres Exploring; Capt Quiz Bowl; School Musical; School Play; Pres Jr Cls; JV Bsktbl; Var Sftbl; Clsscl HS Thtre Co Awd 85; Cathlc Yth Orgnztn Chrstn Sprtsmnshp Awd 84; ACTS 29 Yth Mnstry.

PLANTE, MICHELE; St Raphael Acad; Pawtucket, RI; (Y); Church Yth Grp; Dance Clb; French Clb; Y-Teens; Rep Frsh Cls; Rep Soph Cls; Rep Jr Cls; Hon Roll; Prfct Atten Awd; Chld Care.

PLANTE, RICHARD; William M Daries Jr Vo Tech; Pawtucket, RI; (Y); 12/151; Computer Clb; VICA; 2nd VICA ST Small Engine Repair Contest 84-85.

PLOURDE, MELISSA; Portsmouth HS; Portsmouth, RI; (Y); 23/210; Church Yth Grp; Band; Mrchg Band; Nwsp Stf; Var Crs Cntry; Capt Var Socr; Var Sftbl; Var Trk; Hon Roll; NHS; Knights Of Col Schlrshp 85; Dixon Ind Schlrshp 85; J P Martin Meml Sprtsmnshp Awd 85; Northeastern U; Phy Ther.

POCCIA, ELENA MARIE; Cranston High West; Cranston, RI; (Y); Church Yth Grp; Dance Clb; Debate Tm; Ski Clb; School Musical; Variety Show; Rep Frsh Cls; Rep Soph Cls; Rep Jr Cls; Capt Cheerleading; Schl Svc Awd 83; Chem.

POIRIER, ANNETTE; Woonsocket SR HS; Woonsocket, RI; (Y); JA; Yrbk Stf; Hon Roll; RI Islnd Hnr Soc 85; Roger Williams Coll; Bus.

POIRIER, JEN; North Kingstown HS; N Kingstown, RI; (Y); 93/371; Church Yth Grp; Cmnty Wkr; Hosp Aide; Band; Concert Band; Yrbk Rptr; Yrbk Stf; Hon Roll; NLSA Awd Cmmnty Serv 85; URI; Bus Mngmnt.

POLLARD, DANIEL L; Classical HS; Providence, RI; (Y); Civic Clb; Computer Clb; JCL; Capt Math Tm; Q&S; Nwsp Ed-Chief; Var L Tennis; High Hon Roll; JETS Awd; Ntl Merit SF; Harvard Book Awd 84; RI All ST Math Team 84; Ntl Cum Laude Soc 84.

PONA, KIMBERLY R; Classical HS; Providence, RI; (Y); Am Leg Aux Girls St; Exploring; VP JA; Capt Drill Tm; Var L Cheerleading; Hon Roll; Natl Achvmnt Schlrshp Program For Outstndng Negro Stu 84; Law.

PONTRBRIAND, JOANNE ELIZABETH; Lincoln JR SR HS; Lincoln, RI; (Y); 60/235; Varsity Clb; Stage Crew; Variety Show; Nwsp Phtg; Jr Cls; JV Bsktbl; Var Fld Hcky; Var Vllybl; Northeastern U; Bus.

PONTON, MICHELLE; St Raphael Acad; Pawtucket, RI; (Y); 23/150; Church Yth Grp; GAA; Hosp Aide; Cheerleading; Sftbl; High Hon Roll; Hon Roll; Jr NHS; NHS.

POON, PETER N; South Kingstown HS; Peace Dale, RI; (Y); 1/180; Church Yth Grp; Drama Clb; Math Tm; Jazz Band; School Musical; School Play; Variety Show; High Hon Roll; Lion Awd; Pres NHS; MTNA Bldwin Jr Kybrd Achvt ST Wnnr 81; Cert Muscnshp Berklee Jaz Ensmbl 84; Brown U Bk Awd 84; Brown U; Med.

POTTER, KAREN; Coventry HS; Coventry, RI; (Y); 7/385; Trs French Clb; JCL; Variety Show; Yrbk Ed-Chief; JV Cheerleading; NHS; Ntl Merit Ltr; St Schlr; French Hon Soc; High Hon Roll; 2nd Pl Statewd Frnch Exm 82; Presdntl Academc Ftnss Awd 85; Cvntry Tchrs Allnce Grnt 85; Brandeis U; Pol Sci.

POUDRIER, ANGELA; North Smithfield HS; Slatersville, RI; (Y); French Clb; FNA; Hosp Aide; Library Aide; RIC; Nrsng.

POWERS, KATHLEEN; Prout Memorial HS; Cranston, RI; (S); 9/75; Band; Concert Band; Jazz Band; Pres Soph Cls; Var Capt Bsktbl; Var Sftbl; Var Vllybl; Hon Roll; JP Sousa Awd; NHS; URI Bok Awd 83-84; Zaugrilli Schlrshp 82-83; Lwyr.

PRADO, INDIRA J; Mount Pleasant HS; Providence, RI; (Y); Rep Jr Cls; High Hon Roll; Hon Roll; Spanish NHS; Spn Acad Awd 85; Boston Coll; Bus Admin.

PRECOPIO, THOMAS; St Rapheal Acad; Eprov, RI; (Y); Aud/Vis; Boy Scts; Church Yth Grp; Cmnty Wkr; School Play; Stage Crew; Stu Cncl; Var Ftbl; Capt Trk; Hon Roll; Pre-Med.

PREVITY, SCOTT; Pilgrim HS; Warwick, RI; (Y); 8/330; Band; Mrchg Band; Orch; Stage Crew; Yrbk Stf; High Hon Roll; Hon Roll; Pres Schlr; RI Coll; Comp Sci.

PREW, MICHAEL; East Providence HS; Providence, RI; (Y); 26/500; Var L Bsbl; Var Capt Ftbl; Var L Trk; Var L Wrstlng; Hon Roll; All ST Ftbl 85; All ST Wrstlng, 4th New Englnd 85; SR Stu/Athl Awd 85; U Of RI; Pol Sci.

PRIM, LINDA; Narragansett HS; Narragansett, RI; (Y); 8/128; French Clb; Library Aide; Nwsp Rptr; Yrbk Ed-Chief; Cheerleading; Gym; Powder Puff Ftbl; Socr; French Hon Soc; Hon Roll; Natl Frnch Cont 85; 2nd Pl Sci Fair 84; Georgetown U; Law.

PRINCE, JOSHUA; Hope HS; Providence, RI; (Y); Boys Clb Am; Hon Roll; URI; Elec Engrng.

PRINCIPE, DONNA; Johnston HS; Johnston, RI; (Y); JA; Rep Frsh Cls; Rep Soph Cls; Stu Cncl; Powder Puff Ftbl; Hon Roll; Social Wrk.

PROULX, CHRISTINE MARIE; North Providence HS; No Providence, RI; (Y); Church Yth Grp; Cmnty Wkr; Cheerleading; High Hon Roll; Hon Roll; Jr NHS; NHS; Katherine Gibbs Schl Schlrshp 85; Katherine Gibbs Schl; Lgl Secy.

PROULX, JACLYN; West Warwick HS; W Warwick, RI; (Y); 52/240; Art Clb; GAA; Varsity Clb; Variety Show; Yrbk Stf; Crs Cntry; Trk; High Hon Roll; Hon Roll; Awd Exclnce Art 85; Fshn Inst Tech; Illustration.

PROVENCAL JR, MICHAEL; Our Lady Of Providence HS; Coventry, RI; (Y); Camera Clb; Yrbk Stf; Trk; Hon Roll; NHS; U Of RI; Comp Sci.

PROVOST, HEATHER; Mount St Charles Acad; Blackstone, MA; (Y); Cmnty Wkr; Math Tm; Red Cross Aide; Ski Clb; Drm Mjr(t); School Play; Sec Soph Cls; Sec Jr Cls; Var Cheerleading; Var Crs Cntry; Phy Thrpst.

PUNSKA, CARRIE; Chariho Regional HS; Hope Valley, RI; (S); Sec Church Yth Grp; Chorus; Madrigals; Rep Frsh Cls; Sec Soph Cls; Rep Jr Cls; Sec Stu Cncl; Var Capt Cheerleading; Vllybl; Hon Roll; Acad All Amer 84; Law.

PURNELL, DAVID; South Kingstown HS; Kingston, RI; (Y); 38/211; Church Yth Grp; Hosp Aide; Im Tennis; Hon Roll; Engr.

QUINTERO, JOSE; Lincoln JR HS; Lincoln, RI; (Y); Boys Clb Am; Dance Clb; Spanish Clb; Variety Show; Bsktbl; Ftbl; Trk; Wt Lftg; Wrstlng; Spanish NHS; US Navy; Modern Lang Teachr.

RALLIS, KRISTEN; North Kingstown HS; Jamestown, RI; (Y); 99/371; Church Yth Grp; Cmnty Wkr; Exploring; GAA; Letterman Clb; Red Cross Aide; Teachers Aide; Sftbl; Hon Roll; FL U; Math.

RAMPONE, ROBT; North Providence HS; N Providence, RI; (Y); Computer Clb; Debate Tm; Math Clb; Office Aide; Radio Clb; Ski Clb; Teachers Aide; Hon Roll; JETS Awd; NHS; U RI; Engrng.

RAPA, DAWN; Classical HS; Providence, RI; (Y); 2/250; Rep Soph Cls; Hon Roll; Itln Hon Soc 84 & 85; Cornell U; Pre Law.

RAPOSA, CYNTHIA; Portsmouth HS; Portsmouth, RI; (Y); 40/221; Church Yth Grp; Hosp Aide; Ski Clb; Band; Concert Band; Flag Corp; Mrchg Band; JV Bsktbl; Im Powder Puff Ftbl; JV Tennis; Acctng.

RASO, KRISTIN; Warren HS; Warren, RI; (Y); Church Yth Grp; Spanish Clb; Teachers Aide; School Play.

RASPALLO, THOMAS S; Cranston HS; Cranston, RI; (Y); Exploring; Letterman Clb; Varsity Clb; Soph Cls; Jr Cls; Sr Cls; Bsbl; Bsktbl; Socr; Hon Roll; Providence Coll; ROTC.

RAWLINGS, KENNETH; North Smith Field JR SR HS; N Smithfield, RI; (Y); Exploring; Letterman Clb; JV Bsbl; Var Bsktbl; Var Crs Cntry; Hon Roll; Engrng.

RAY, KIM S; North Kingstown HS; Exeter, RI; (Y); 80/375; Off Frsh Cls; Off Soph Cls; Off Jr Cls; Off Sr Cls; Stu Cncl; Cheerleading; U RI; Nrsng.

RAY, STEVEN; Pilgrim HS; Warwick, RI; (Y); Art Clb; RI Coll; Cmmrcl Art.

REED, LESLIE A; East Providence SR HS; Riverside, RI; (S); 15/520; JA; Chorus; Rep Sr Cls; Stu Cncl; Var L Swmmng; Var L Trk; Hon Roll; Church Yth Grp; Girl Scts; Library Aide; 2nd Tm All ST Girls Trk 84; 2nd Tm All Div Grls Trk 84; AIIE Chap 110 Awd 84; Math.

REID, DONALD E; West Warwick HS; W Warwick, RI; (Y); 26/225; Boy Scts; Hon Roll; St Schlr; RI Hnr Soc 85; U Of RI; Elec.

REILLY, CHRISTOPHER B; North Smithfield HS; NS Woonsocket, RI; (Y); 1/165; Band; Concert Band; Jazz Band; Mrchg Band; Pep Band; Symp Band; Tennis; High Hon Roll; Hon Roll; NHS; Harvard Bk Awd 85; Pres Acad Ftns Awd 85; Boston U; Bio-Med.

REILLY, ERYN; Charles E Shea HS; Pawtucket, RI; (Y); Computer Clb; Dance Clb; Drama Clb; School Play; Stu Cncl; Accnt Exec.

REILLY, MARY E; Prout Memorial HS; North Kingstown, RI; (S); 4/79; Debate Tm; Chorus; Yrbk Rptr; Yrbk Stf; JV Crs Cntry; High Hon Roll; Hon Roll; Jr NHS; NHS; Church Yth Grp; Brown U Bk Awd 84; Decathln Team 84-85; Engl.

REINIKKA, JOHN E; No Providence HS; N Providence, RI; (Y); 128/250; L Var Ftbl; L Var Wrstlng; Bst Prsnlty Sr Cls 85; U RI; Rsrce Dev.

REIS, CHRISTINE M; East Providence SR HS; East Providence, RI; (S); 22/520; Girl Scts; Rep Soph Cls; JV Bsktbl; Hon Roll; NHS; Portuguese Clb Treas; Acctng.

REMILLARD, NANCY; N Smithfield HS; N Smithfield, RI; (Y); Church Yth Grp; Cmnty Wkr; French Clb; Hosp Aide; Sec JA; Letterman Clb; Office Aide; Teachers Aide; Sec Band; Church Choir; Nrsng.

RENSEHAUSEN, WARREN; Bristol HS; Bristol, RI; (Y); 68/220; Cmnty Wkr; Political Wkr; JV Var Bsktbl; RI Coll; Pol Sci.

RENZI, RENEE; Johnston SR HS; Johnston, RI; (Y); DECA; Hosp Aide; Sec Soph Cls; Rep Jr Cls; Rep Stu Cncl; Capt Powder Puff Ftbl; High Hon Roll; Hon Roll; Hstry Day Awd 82-83; Rhode Island Coll; Med.

REYNOLDS, CHRISTOPHER; North Providence HS; North Providence, RI; (Y); Boys Clb Am; Model UN; Ski Clb; Nwsp Rptr; Nwsp Stf; Yrbk Stf; Lit Mag; Var Ftbl; Var Trk; Law.

REYNOLDS, SUSAN; Coventry HS; Coventry, RI; (Y); Spanish Clb; Trs Soph Cls; Pres Jr Cls; Stu Cncl; Hon Roll; Hugh O Brien Awd 83-84; Jr Prom Queen 85; Cert Apprctn Ntl Assoc Stu Cncl 84; Lib Arts.

REYNOLDS, SUZANNE; Smithfield HS; Greenville, RI; (Y); French Clb; Nwsp Rptr; Yrbk Stf; Trs Sr Cls; Rep Stu Cncl; Var Bsktbl; Var Fld Hcky; Var Sftbl; JV Trk; Hon Roll; Jrnlsm.

RICCI, RHONDA; Cranston H S West; Cranston, RI; (Y); Aud/Vis; Debate Tm; Intnl Clb; JA; Stu Cncl; JV Badmtn; JV Sftbl; JV Vllybl; Hon Roll; Jr NHS; NHS 85; Cert Merit Lang Italian 84 & 85; Providence Coll; Corp Law.

RICH, PAUL A; Bishop Hendricken HS; Warwick, RI; (Y); 8/254; VP Church Yth Grp; Service Clb; High Hon Roll; NHS; Ntl Merit SF.

RICHARDSON, MICHELLE; Mt Pleasant HS; Providence, RI; (Y); 48/164; Library Aide; Sec Temple Yth Grp; Hon Roll; NAACD Outstndng Acadmc Awd 84; Black Hertg Essy Fnlst 85; Hnr Vlntrng Publc Lib 85; U Of RI; Pre Med.

RICHMOND, MARK; Chariho Reg JR SR HS; Shannock, RI; (S); High Hon Roll; Hon Roll; Chem Team 83; Chem.

RIORDAN, JULIE; Bayview Acad; Providence, RI; (Y); French Clb; Orch; Yrbk Stf; Hon Roll; Jr NHS; NHS; Part Schlrshp To Summer Sci Pgm 85; 3 Music Metals-Music Festvl 84-85; 2 Grants In Sci Fair 82-83; Syracuse; Bio.

RITACCO, SHELLY; Narragansett JR SR HS; Narragansett, RI; (Y); Drama Clb; Chorus; Variety Show; Yrbk Phtg; Yrbk Stf; Solo Ensmbl; Lang.

RITAROSSI, GINA; Coventry HS; W Greenwich, RI; (Y); Spanish Clb; JV Cheerleading; Hon Roll; Comp Sci.

RITCHIE, SHARA; Classical HS; Providence, RI; (Y); Concert Band; Jazz Band; Orch; School Musical; Symp Band; Lit Mag; Hon Roll; Music Thrpst.

ROBBINS, MIRIAM; Alternate Learning Program HS; Providence, RI; (S); 5/40; Dance Clb; Drama Clb; Lit Mag; Mac Alester Coll; Anthroplgst.

ROBERTS, CHRISTOPHER; Mt St Charles Acad; Forestdale, RI; (Y); 39/163; Aud/Vis; Band; Jazz Band; Mrchg Band; Pep Band; Stage Crew; Nwsp Stf; Bsbl; Bsktbl; Hon Roll; Mst Vlbl Plyr-Bsbl 85; Jrnlsm.

ROBERTS, DAWN; N Smithfield JR SR HS; N Smithfield, RI; (Y); Chorus; Var Capt Cheerleading; MVP Bsktbl Chrldr 85; Flagler Coll; Bus Mgmt.

ROBERTS, THERESE; Bishop Keough HS; Barrington, RI; (S); Girl Scts; Speech Tm; Church Choir; Nwsp Rptr; Yrbk Stf; Sec Frsh Cls; Rep Stu Cncl; Sftbl; Tennis; Hon Roll; Sci Fair 1st Pl 83; URI Alumni Awd 84; U Of RI; Nrsng.

ROBINSON, KYLE; Rogers HS; Newport, RI; (S); 2/330; Pres Band; Mrchg Band; Orch; Capt Crs Cntry; Trk; High Hon Roll; NHS; Ntl Merit Ltr; Spanish NHS; Harvard Bk Prz 84; Mc Donalds All Am HS Band 84; MA Inst Of Technology; Engr.

ROBINSON, MICHELLE; Portsmouth HS; Portsmouth, RI; (Y); 16/220; Var Capt Bsktbl; Var Capt Jr Cls; Var Capt Trk; Hon Roll; NHS; Hugh O Brien Yth Ldrshp Awd 84; Mil Ordr Wrld Wars Awd 85; All Div 2nd Tm X-Cntry 82-84; Arch.

RODIL, DANIEL A; Bishop Hendricken HS; Warwick, RI; (Y); Boy Scts; VP Debate Tm; Nwsp Rptr; Nwsp Stf; Yrbk Sprt Ed; Yrbk Stf; VP Swmmng; High Hon Roll; NHS; Ntl Merit SF; Intl Relations.

RODINE, KIRSTEN; North Smithfield JR SR HS; N Smithfield, RI; (Y); 5/164; Debate Tm; French Clb; Math Tm; Chorus; Church Choir; Orch; Yrbk Stf; NHS; Ntl Merit SF; Rhode Isl Coll Hnrs Pgm 84-85; All-State Orch 81-84.

ROEVER, PAUL; Charilo Regional HS; Ashaway, RI; (Y); 38/250; Computer Clb; Bsktbl; U RI; Bus Mgmt.

ROGAN, BERNARD; North Kingstown HS; N Kingstown, RI; (Y); Church Yth Grp; Cmnty Wkr; French Clb; Letterman Clb; Ski Clb; Teachers Aide; Varsity Clb; Color Guard; Drill Tm; Orch; Norwich U Northfield; Intl Stds.

ROGERS, THOMAS; North Smithfield HS; N Smithfield, RI; (Y); Letterman Clb; Trs Soph Cls; Trs Jr Cls; Stu Cncl; Var Bsbl; Var Ice Hcky; Var Socr; Bus Mngmnt.

RONCI, ROBERTA; Pilgrim HS; Warwick, RI; (Y); Pep Clb; Variety Show; Cheerleading; Gym; Hon Roll; Jr NHS; Church Yth Grp; Dance Clb; Girl Scts; Letterman Clb; Italian Club 82-85; Italian Natl Hon Soc 82-85; Crmnl Psych.

ROONEY, DAVID; Middletown HS; Middletown, RI; (S); 12/252; French Clb; Math Clb; Math Tm; French Hon Soc; Hon Roll; Comp Engr.

ROSS, KRISTEN; St Raphael Acad; Pawtucket, RI; (Y); 15/180; Drama Clb; French Clb; Stage Crew; Stu Cncl; Vllybl; High Hon Roll; Hon Roll; NHS; Engr.

ROSSI, CHRISTINA; Mount Saint Charles HS; North Smithfield, RI; (S); 10/162; Hosp Aide; Math Clb; Varsity Clb; Pres Soph Cls; Trs Sr Cls; Stu Cncl; Var Tennis; Hon Roll; NHS; Stu Cncl Most Sprtd SR Awd 84; Polt Sci.

ROTH, WILLIAM; Barrington HS; Barrington, RI; (Y); Church Yth Grp; Latin Clb; Ski Clb; Rep Soph Cls; Rep Stu Cncl; Socr; Trk; Latn Awd; U Of NH; Arch.

ROTHFUSS, CRISTIN; Coventry HS; Coventry, RI; (Y); 18/403; French Clb; JCL; Stu Cncl: Var L Bsktbl; Var L Crs Cntry; Var L Sftbl; Var L Trk; High Hon Roll; Jr NHS; NHS; Hugh O Brien Outstndng Soph Stu 83; RIASP Essy Wnnr 84; Pre Law.

ROY, COLLEEN A; North Providence HS; N Providence, RI; (Y); 25/233; Quiz Bowl; Ski Clb; Concert Band; Sftbl; Jr NHS; NHS; Pres Schlr; Vincent Mesolella JR Schlrshp 85; Attndnc Awd 85; RI Coll; Lbrl Arts.

ROYAL, MATTHEW E; Scituate JR SR HS; N Scituate, RI; (Y); 3/117; Art Clb; Boy Scts; School Musical; Stage Crew; High Hon Roll; Jr NHS; Ntl Merit SF; Chess Clb; Brown U Book Awd 84; Carnegie-Mellon U; Mech Engrng.

ROYES, KEVIN MICHAEL; North Smithfield HS; N Smithfield, RI; (Y); 14/146; Pres Church Yth Grp; French Clb; Letterman Clb; Stu Cncl; Ice Hcky; Elks Awd; Hon Roll; RI Suburban Div Hockey Rnn Up 83-84; Div Hockey Champs 84-85; Athltc Recgntn RI Snt 85; Aviatn.

RUEST, DAVID G; East Providence SR HS; East Providence, RI; (S); 13/490; Aud/Vis; Sec Camera Clb; Chess Clb; Pres Computer Clb; Crs Cntry; Trk; NHS; Syracuse U; Comp Sci.

RUGGIERI, PAUL; Cranston High School West; Cranston, RI; (Y); Var Bsbl; Hon Roll; Jr NHS; NHS; Engrng.

RUGGIERO, RICHARD; Johnston HS; Johnston, RI; (S); 19/237; Ski Clb; Trs Sr Cls; JV Bsbl; JV Bsktbl; Var Golf; Im Vllybl; Hon Roll; NHS; Italian Awd; Bryant Coll; Bus Mgmt.

RUSSELL, COLLEEN JEAN; Mount Pleasant HS; Providence, RI; (Y); 1/125; Hosp Aide; Pep Clb; Dnfth Awd; High Hon Roll; Harvard Bk Prz 85; U Of RI Alumni Assn Bk Awd 85; Outstndng Achvt Frgn Lang Itln Bk Awd 85; Bio.

RUSSO, MARGHERITA A; Mount Pleasant HS; Providence, RI; (Y); 3/240; Church Yth Grp; Varsity Clb; Drm Mjr(t); Yrbk Phtg; Yrbk Rptr; Yrbk Stf; Stu Cncl; High Hon Roll; Hon Roll; Outstndg Achiev Foreign Lang, Drug & Alcohol Educ, Italian Hnr Society 85; RI Coll; Bus Adm.

RUZZO, MICHAEL; Coventry HS; Coventry, RI; (Y); Spanish Clb; JV Bsktbl; Var Ftbl; Vllybl; Hon Roll; Vet Sci.

SACCOCCIO, CHERIE MAY; Cranstoen H S West; Hope, RI; (Y); Nwsp Rptr; Nwsp Stf; Yrbk Ed-Chief; Yrbk Stf; Hon Roll; RI Tchrs Itln Cert Merit 84; Cmmnctns.

SACCOCCIO, GINA; Tollgate HS; Warwick, RI; (S); Church Yth Grp; Dance Clb; Letterman Clb; Pep Clb; Chorus; Church Choir; Frsh Cls; Soph Cls; Stu Cncl; Cheerleading; Pre-Law.

SACCOCCIO, LISA; Bishop Francis P Keough HS; North Providence, RI; (S); Cheerleading; High Hon Roll; Jr NHS; NHS; Prfct Atten Awd; Religion, Engl & Pfct Attend Awds 82-83; Bio, Engl & Pfct Attend Awds 83-84.

SADOWSKI, MIKE; Central Falls JR SR HS; Central Fls, RI; (Y); Church Yth Grp; Cmnty Wkr; Rep Soph Cls; Var JV Bsbl; Var JV Bsktbl; JV Ftbl; Cit Awd; High Hon Roll; Hon Roll; Jr NHS; Awd Hnrs 4 Qtrs 83 & 85; Hnbl Mntn All Area Bsbl Sqd 85; Accntng.

SAGAMANG, DALE; Middletown HS; Middletown, RI; (S); 24/250; Computer Clb; Drama Clb; Concert Band; Lit Mag; VP Soph Cls; Var Capt Crs Cntry; Var Trk; Wrstlng; NHS; Ntl Merit Ltr; Boston U; Comp Sci.

SALVADOR, TONI LYN; Portsmouth HS; Portsmouth, RI; (Y); Rep Band; Mrchg Band; Pep Band; Yrbk Rptr; Trs Soph Cls; Trs Jr Cls; Trs Sr Cls; Rep Stu Cncl; Var JV Cheerleading; Var Crs Cntry; Pre-Law.

SAMMONS, DEANNA; Rogers HS; Newport, RI; (Y); GAA; Hosp Aide; Hon Roll; Hospitlty Clb; Steno Awd; Typg Awd; Roger Williams Coll; Law.

SAN SOUCI, JOY; North Smithfield HS; N Smithfield, RI; (Y); Church Yth Grp; French Clb; JA; Office Aide; Chorus; Variety Show; Rep Frsh Cls; Sec Stu Cncl; Miss Fire Prevention 85; Bus Admin.

SANDS, RICHARD; Warwick Veterns Memorial HS; Warwick, RI; (S); Boys Clb Am; Chess Clb; Political Wkr; Drm & Bgl; Pres Stu Cncl; Var Bsbl; Var Trk; Hon Roll; Jr NHS; Masonic Awd; RI ST Chaplain, Intl Order Demolay 84-85; UCLA; Pol Sci.

SANTILLI, JULIE; Tollgate HS; Warwick, RI; (S); Capt Var Cheerleading; Hon Roll; Jr NHS; Princpl Viola RI Philharmonic Sr Yth Orch 84-85; Italian Hnr Soc 84; Phys Thrpy.

SANTORO, PETER; Cumberland HS; Cumberland, RI; (S); Boys Clb Am; DECA; Yrbk Phtg; Yrbk Stf; JV Wrstlng; Hon Roll; Communications.

SANTOS, BRENDA; Bristol HS; Bristol, RI; (Y); Chorus; Drm Mjr(t); Stu Cncl; Gym; Score Keeper; Hon Roll; VP Soph Cls; Pres Jr Cls; Ri All St Chorus 81 & 83; RI Chamber Chorus 83; URI; Engl.

SANTOS, MANUEL; Shea HS; Pawtucket, RI; (Y); Boys Clb Am; Var Socr; Hon Roll; Bus Mngmnt.

SANTOS, STEPHEN; St Raphael Acad; Pawtucket, RI; (Y); 42/191; Boys Clb Am; Var Bsbl; Var Score Keeper; High Hon Roll; Hon Roll; NHS; Boston U; CPA.

SASSI, MICHAEL; St Raphael Acad; Pawtucket, RI; (Y); 52/192; Nwsp Ed-Chief; Rep Frsh Cls; Trs Jr Cls; Trs Sr Cls; Var Capt Ftbl; Hon Roll; Pol Sci.

SAVARD, ROBT; No Smithfield HS; N Smithfield, RI; (Y); CAP; JA; Hon Roll; U RI; Elect Engr.

SAVARIA, MONIQUE; Mount Saint Charles Acad; Woonsocket, RI; (Y); 30/150; French Clb; Yrbk Stf; Cheerleading; Hon Roll; NHS; Johnson & Wales Coll; Fash Merc.

SAVASTANO, KIM; Bishop Francis Keough HS; N Providence, RI; (Y); Cmnty Wkr; Dance Clb; Girl Scts; Hosp Aide; Ski Clb; Yrbk Stf; Pres Soph Cls; Rep Stu Cncl; Var Cheerleading; Hon Roll; Roger Wllms Coll; Frst Pl In Schl Sci Fair 82-83; Fin In Miss Natl Teen-Ager Pgnt 85-86; U S Hstry Awd In Schl 85-86; P C; Psych.

SAVOIE, GARY; Woonsocket HS; Woonsocket, RI; (Y); Boy Scts; Exploring; JV Bsbl; JV Bsktbl; Var L Ftbl; Var L Trk.

FRANCIS, CHRISTOPHER; Bristol HS; Bristol, RI; (Y); JV Ftbl; Hon Roll; Leonardo Da Vinci Schlrshp 85; Salve Regina; Bio Med Tech.

FRANCIS, FRANK; Bristol HS; Bristol, RI; (Y); French Hon Soc; High Hon Roll; NHS; Prfct Atten Awd; JV Ftbl; JV Wrstlng; Cert Of Merit RI Tchrs 84-85; Cert Of Regntn Acad Decthln 85; Cert Of Achvt Army Ntl Guard 85; Robtcs.

FRAVEL, LAURA; Portsmouth HS; Portsmouth, RI; (Y); 60/220; Church Yth Grp; FBLA; Ski Clb; Powder Puff Ftbl; Socr; Sftbl; Hon Roll; 1st Pl Schl Sci Fair 85.

FRAWLEY, MARY; Prout Memorial HS; Cranston, RI; (Y); 10/77; Computer Clb; English Clb; JA; High Hon Roll; Hon Roll; Hghst Grade Soc Stud 85; Hghst Grade Spn III, Am Hstry 85; URI Bk Awd 85; Eng.

FREITAS, PAMELA A; Our Lady Of Fatima HS; Warren, RI; (Y), 2/36; Church Yth Grp; Cmnty Wkr; Teachers Aide; Yrbk Ed-Chief; VP Jr Cls; Pres Sr Cls; Rep Stu Cncl; JV Bsktbl; Elks Awd; High Hon Roll; Providence Coll; Math.

FRISELLA, MARY E; South Kingstown HS; Wakefield, RI; (Y); 14/225; Exploring; Hosp Aide; Model UN; Varsity Clb; Variety Show; Yrbk Stf; Var Bsktbl; Var Fld Hcky; Sftbl; High Hon Roll; Bio Awd 84; Adv Math Awd 85; 1st Tm All Div, All Co Sftbl 86; Sci.

FROST, MEGHAN M; St Marys Acad Bay View; Cranston, RI; (Y); 4/193; Pres Am Leg Aux Girls St; Debate Tm; Pres Sec Exploring; Key Clb; Math Tm; German Clb; Service Clb; Ski Clb; Pres Spanish Clb; Yrbk Stf; Senator Pell Awd-U S Hstry 85; Cranstons Finest Awd 85; Model Legsltr-Sentr 85; U Of PA; Intl Reltns.

GABRIEL, KATHLEEN; Cranston High School East; Cranston, RI; (Y); Church Yth Grp; FHA; NFL; Church Choir; Sec.

GADDES, GAIL; Scituate JR SR HS; N Scituate, RI; (S); 20/115; Church Yth Grp; Red Cross Aide; Acpl Chr; Chorus; Church Choir; School Musical; Variety Show; Nwsp Rptr; Sec Soph Cls; Sec Jr Cls; Hugh O Brian Yth Ldrshp Awd 83; Ntl Hnr Sco 85; Outstndng Chorus Mbr 85; I Dare You Awd 85; U Of VT; Ed.

GAFFETT, KERRI M; Block Island Schl; Block Island, RI; (Y); 1/10; Art Clb; Camera Clb; Church Yth Grp; Girl Scts; Library Aide; Church Choir; Yrbk Ed-Chief; VP Sr Cls; Var Socr; Var Sftbl; Brown U.

GAGNE, SUSAN; Saint Raphael Acad; Pawtucket, RI; (Y); Cmnty Wkr; Drama Clb; School Play; Stage Crew; Rep Stu Cncl; Var Cheerleading; Var Im Sftbl; Hon Roll; Silver R Clb 84-85; Nrsng.

GAGNON, CLAUDINE; Warwick Veterans Memorial HS; Warwick, RI; (Y); 5/300; Letterman Clb; Var Tennis; Var Vllybl; French Hon Soc; High Hon Roll; VP NHS; JV Sftbl; Harvard Bk Awd 85.

GALHARDO, LISA; Tiverton HS; Tiverton, RI; (Y); Rep Jr Cls; Rep Sr Cls; Rep Stu Cncl; Score Keeper; High Hon Roll; Hon Roll; Bus.

GALLAGHER, MELISSA; Burrillville JR SR HS; Harrisville, RI; (Y); Church Yth Grp; FBLA; Chorus; Church Choir; Yrbk Stf; Stu Cncl; Vllybl; Hon Roll; Ldrshp Awd For Future Sctrys-Kthrn Gibbs 84-85; Katherine Gibbs; Exec Sctry.

GALLONE, ANTHONY M; La Salle Acad; N Providence, RI; (Y); 15/257; Church Yth Grp; Letterman Clb; Political Wkr; Varsity Clb; Var Crs Cntry; Trk; French Hon Soc; High Hon Roll; NHS; Frnch Cert Of Merit 81-85; Ltr Outdr Trck 85; Pre-Law.

GAMACHE, JAMES; North Smithfield HS; N Smithfield, RI; (Y); Boy Scts; French Clb; Yrbk Sprt Ed; Stu Cncl; JV Bsbl; High Hon Roll; Hon Roll; SADD 84-85; Pol Sci.

GAMBARDELLA, LAURA; Tolman HS; Pawtucket, RI; (Y); Rep Jr Cls; Im Vllybl; Hon Roll; Comp Lit Goff Jur H; Vlybl Goff Jr H; Bowlng Darlingtn Plns Yth Org; Genetics Res.

GAMELIN, SUZANNE; Coventry HS; Coventry, RI; (Y); Am Leg Aux Girls St; Letterman Clb; Q&S; Variety Show; Nwsp Rptr; Yrbk Sprt Ed; Rep Soph Cls; Rep Jr Cls; Stat Bsktbl; Ntl Merit Ltr; Awd Of Merit From Hugh O Brian Fndtn 84; Awd Of Merit For Frnch Cntst; U Of NH; Chld Psychlgy.

GARCIA, ANGEL; Central HS; Providence, RI; (Y); Chess Clb; Church Yth Grp; Hon Roll; Engrng.

GARCIA, JOSEPH; East Providence SR HS; E Providence, RI; (Y); Art Clb; Drama Clb; Sec French Clb; Band; School Musical; School Play; Nwsp Rptr.

GARDNER, SHERI; Smithfield HS; Smithfield, RI; (Y); High Hon Roll; Hon Roll; Outstndng Achvt Awd Algbr I 83; Outstndng Achvt Awd Acctg I 84; Outstndng Achvt Awd Shrthd I 85; Katherine Gibbs Schl; Exec Secy.

GARZA, TRACY ANN; Mount Pleasant HS; Providence, RI; (Y); Drill Tm; School Play; Yrbk Ed-Chief; Hst Frsh Cls; Rep Soph Cls; Rep Jr Cls; Rep Stu Cncl; Capt Cheerleading; JV Scrkpr Gym; Hon Roll; ST Spnsh Awd 83-84; Drg & Alchl Prgm 84-85; JR Co-Ed Trvl Clb Pres 84-85; North Eastern U; Crmnl Jstce.

GASPARIAN, SONYA; Cranston East HS; Johnston, RI; (Y); 43/460; Church Yth Grp; Dance Clb; Debate Tm; French Clb; Library Aide; JV Bsktbl; Stat Socr; JV Tennis; Jr NHS; Pres Schlr; RI Hnr Scty 85; George Washington U; Pol Sci.

GATES, WILLIAM M; South Kingstown HS; Wakefield, RI; (Y); 45/240; Boy Scts; German Clb; Variety Show; Sec Jr Cls; Rep Stu Cncl; JV Var Socr; Var Trk; Hon Roll; Cultrl Exchng Student-France 85; Frnch.

GAULIN, JACQUELINE A; Cranston HS East; Cranston, RI; (Y); Debate Tm; German Clb; Pres Q&S; Nwsp Phtg; Ed Lit Mag; Var Bsktbl; Var Capt Crs Cntry; Var Capt Trk; All-St Cross-Cntry Hnrs 83-85; William Kenney Mem Schlrshp 85; Maude Scott Mem Awd-Athltc Achvt 81-82; Wheaton Coll; Poltcl Sci.

GEARY, PHYLLIS; Cranston H S East; Cranston, RI; (Y); Church Yth Grp; Drama Clb; Teachers Aide; School Play; Stage Crew; Nwsp Stf; Mgr(s); Score Keeper; Jr NHS; NHS; RI ST Drama Fest 85; RI Regnl Drama Fes 85; RI Coll; Psych.

GEER, GREGORY; Middletown HS; Middletown, RI; (S); 11/252; Drama Clb; Math Tm; Drm Mjr(t); Mrchg Band; School Play; Symp Band; Pres Soph Cls; Trs Sr Cls; Dnfth Awd; Ntl Merit SF; RI Acad Decthln Fine Arts 83; Comp Sci.

GEISSER, BARBARA J; North Providence HS; N Providence, RI; (Y); Church Yth Grp; JV Sftbl; Hon Roll; Premed.

GEMSKI, CANDICE; Cumberland HS; Cumberland, RI; (Y); 71/435; Sec Church Yth Grp; French Clb; Hosp Aide; Ski Clb; Var Vllybl; Hon Roll; Ukrainian Ntl Assn Schlrshp 85; Clark Alumni & Friends Schlrshp 85; Clark U; Gov & Intl Rltns.

GENDREAU, MARY ELLEN; Tiverton HS; Tiverton, RI; (Y); Pres Band; Concert Band; Mrchg Band; Trs Jr Cls; Im Coach Actv; Var Capt Fld Hcky; JV Var Sftbl; High Hon Roll; ROTC; Brwn U Book Awd 85; CPA.

GENNARI, KAREN; East Providence HS; E Providence, RI; (Y); Cmnty Wkr; Dance Clb; Band; Concert Band; Variety Show; Nwsp Rptr; Nwsp Stf; Hon Roll; NHS; Church Yth Grp.

GERMANY, MARGARET S; St Georges Schl; Newport, RI; (Y); PAVAS; Acpl Chr; Chorus; School Musical; Var VP Sftbl; Dance Clb; Debate Tm; Church Choir; JV Tennis; Hon Roll; Choirmastr Awd Vocl Excllnc 83; Lead Role Muscl 85.

GERVAIS, KAREN; Hope HS; Providence, RI; (Y); Yrbk Stf; Off Sr Cls; Hon Roll; Ctznshp 85; Sci Spirit 85; Awd Various Subjects 85; Johnson & Wabs Coll; Travel.

GESSMAN, RICHARD; Cranston High School West; Cranston, RI; (Y); 1/450; Aud/Vis; Letterman Clb; Math Tm; Temple Yth Grp; Pres Band; Concert Band; Jazz Band; Mrchg Band; Pep Band; Yrbk Ed-Chief; RI Hnr Soc 85-86; Brown Book Awd 84-85.

GIBSON, MICHAEL; Portsmouth HS; Portsmouth, RI; (Y); Church Yth Grp; Band; Var Ftbl; Powder Puff Ftbl; JV Wt Lftg; Hon Roll; Ftbll Lttr 84-85.

GIGLIO, GINA; St Raphael Acad; Pawtucket, RI; (Y); 9/192; Drama Clb; French Clb; Nwsp Ed-Chief; Yrbk Stf; Hon Roll; NHS; Concours De Francais 84 & 85; Bus.

GILLIS, GREGORY; Central Falls JR SR HS; Central Falls, RI; (Y); 19/123; Drama Clb; School Musical; Var Capt Bsbl; Var Capt Ftbl; Var Capt Wrstlng; Cit Awd; Hon Roll; Boy Scts; Variety Show; Yrbk Stf; Max Lebida Trphy 85; RI Hnr Scty 85; Army/Natl Schlr Athl Awd 85; U Of RI; Accntnt.

GIORGIANNI, CATHERINE; Bishop Francis P Keough HS; Providence, RI; (S); Tennis; High Hon Roll; NHS; Frnch Awd 82-83; Hist Awd 82-84; ; RI; Mgmnt.

GIRARD, CHRISTINE; North Smithfield JR SR HS; N Smithfield, RI; (Y); 44/164; Church Yth Grp; French Clb; Library Aide; Lib Band; Yrbk Stf; Stu Cncl; Bsktbl; Ntl Merit Ltr; SADD Pres 84-85; Keene ST Coll; Athlc Trng.

GIROUARD, LINDA ANNE; St Raphael Acad; Pawtucket, RI; (S); 5/173; Sec Chess Clb; Drama Clb; French Clb; Hosp Aide; Science Clb; Stage Crew; Stu Cncl; Hon Roll; NHS; R I Med Soc Awd, Amer Soc Mrcbio Awd 83; URI Bk Awd, Amer HS Math Sch Awd 84; Ida Jackson Mem Awd; Providence Coll; Microbio.

GIULIANO, PETER; Narragansett HS; Narragansett, RI; (Y); 6/130; Boy Scts; Computer Clb; Ski Clb; Spanish Clb; Variety Show; Var L Trk; High Hon Roll; NHS; Ntl Merit SF; Spanish NHS; Bus Mngmt.

GIZZARELLI, TRACY L; Warwick Veterans Memorial HS; Warwick, RI; (Y); 68/290; Letterman Clb; Cheerleading; Fld Hcky; Gym; Hon Roll; Jr NHS; Jrnl Bltn All ST Gymnastc Tm 84-85; Gymnstcs Citn From Mayor 82; All City & Div Gymnstc Tm 82-85; RI U.

GLAVIN, TABATHA L; Warren HS; Warren, RI; (Y); Drama Clb; Political Wkr; Speech Tm; Concert Band; School Play; Yrbk Phtg; Yrbk Stf; VP Jr Cls; VP Sr Cls; Rep VP Stu Cncl; Police Officer.

GLEASON, DEBORAH; Prout Memorial HS; North Kingstown, RI; (S); 17/81; Color Guard; Concert Band; School Musical; Hon Roll.

GLUCKSMAN, RICHARD; Pilgrim HS; Warwick, RI; (Y); Cmnty Wkr; Math Tm; Ski Clb; Band; Orch; Nwsp Rptr; VP Soph Cls; Off Jr Cls; Off Sr Cls; Var Tennis; Law.

GODDARD, JOSEPH M; Chariho Regional HS; Charlestown, RI; (Y); Computer Clb; French Clb; Band; Crs Cntry; Trk; French Hon Soc; Hon Roll; U Of RI; Comp Prgmg.

GODFREY, CORNELIA; Alteanate Learning Project; Providence, RI; (S); Art Clb; Library Aide; Spanish Clb; Nwsp Rptr; Nwsp Stf; Yrbk Stf; Off Frsh Cls; Off Soph Cls; Off Jr Cls; Ice Hcky; DECA Awd 83-84; U Of RI; Marine Biol.

GOING, MARTIN; Rogers HS; Newport, RI; (Y); Boy Scts; Church Yth Grp; Cmnty Wkr; Sec Trs Science Clb; School Play; Stu Cncl; Hon Roll; NEDT Awd; Med.

GOLANSKI, CANDACE; Prout Memorial HS; N Kingstown, RI; (Y); 19/77; Church Yth Grp; Chorus; Color Guard; School Play; Stage Crew; Nwsp Rptr; Nwsp Stf; Hon Roll; Ntl Merit Ltr; Pre-Law.

GOLDBERG, BRIAN; Warren HS; Warren, RI; (Y); 13/108; Math Tm; Band; School Play; Bsbl; Hon Roll; Voc Dmcrcy-Fnlst 85.

GOLDBERG, ELAINE; Middletown HS; Middletown, RI; (S); 19/252; Drama Clb; Temple Yth Grp; Mrchg Band; Yrbk Stf; French Hon Soc; Hon Roll; NHS; Ntl Merit Ltr; French Clb; Middletown Pub Schls Excllnce Awd 84; Psychb.

GOLDEN, ERIC; Pilgram HS; Warwick, RI; (Y); Boy Scts; Math Clb; Math Tm; Bsktbl; JV Tennis; Var Trk; Hon Roll; Math.

GOLDSTEIN, JENNIFER; S Kingstown HS; Peace Dale, RI; (Y); Hosp Aide; Nwsp Rptr; JV Var Crs Cntry; JV Trk; CC Awd; Hon Roll; NHS; Exclnce Chem,Spansh II 84-85.

GOMEZ, JOHANN; Central HS; Providence, RI; (Y); JA; VICA; Var Ftbl; Hon Roll; Sci Fair 2nd Grant 85; MAA Anual Math Exam-1st 85; Arch Engr.

GOMEZ, PETER M; Middletown HS; Middletown, RI; (Y); Boy Scts; Drama Clb; Band; Concert Band; Mrchg Band; Pep Band; School Play; Stage Crew; Ed Yrbk Phtg; JV Trk; John Clarke Trst Schlrshp 85; Hofstra U; Comp Sci.

GOOCH, KATHY J; Rogers HS; Newport, RI; (Y); Cmnty Wkr; Chorus; Crs Cntry; Jr NHS; Spch Audlgst.

GORDON, MICHAEL; East Providence SR HS; Riverside, RI; (Y); Art Clb; Drm & Bgl; Pratt Inst; Fshn Dsgn.

GORMAN, JOSEPH; Central HS; Providence, RI; (Y); Boys Clb Am; Church Yth Grp; Trs JA; Political Wkr; L JV Bsbl; Var Crs Cntry; JV Trk; Bsebl Trphys All Stars, Lttle Leag,Big Leag & ST Chmpnshp 82 & 85; Johnson & Wales; Clnry Arts.

GORMLEY, JOS; Coventry HS; Coventry, RI; (Y); 70/400; Sec Spanish Clb; Trs Stu Cncl; JV Wrstlng; Hon Roll; JV Bsbl; Delg 49th Natl Stdnt Cncl Conf 85; Co Chrprsn Stdnt Svc 48th Natl Stdnt Cncl Conf 84; Embry-Riddle Aeronautical U.

GOUGH, MARGARET; Prout Memorial HS; W Warwick, RI; (Y); 33/77; Church Yth Grp; Drama Clb; Girl Scts; Math Tm; VP Acpl Chr; VP Chorus; Church Choir; Flag Corp; School Play; Hon Roll; Gov Pgm Sci & Mth 85; Resp Thrpy.

GOUGH, SHERRY; Coventry HS; Coventry, RI; (Y); Spanish Clb; VP Frsh Cls; VP Soph Cls; Chrmn Jr Cls; Stat Ftbl; Capt Var Sftbl; Hon Roll; Lwyr.

GOUVEIA, CHRYSTAL; Central Falls JR SR HS; Central Fls, RI; (Y); Rep Soph Cls; Rep Jr Cls; Cheerleading.

GOUVEIA, COLLEEN; Toll Gate HS; Warwick, RI; (S); 71/400; Dance Clb; Hosp Aide; Letterman Clb; Chorus; Capt Var Cheerleading; Hon Roll; Jr NHS; All-City Chrldr 84; Hlth Sci.

GOYETTE, PATRICIA; Davies Vocational Tech; Pawtucket, RI; (Y); Girl Scts; VICA; Band; Yrbk Phtg; Var Cheerleading; Var Swmmng; Var Vllybl; Hon Roll; Prfct Atten Awd; Girl Scout Marian Awd 83; Bryant Coll; Acctng.

GRAEVE, THORSTEN; Ponaganset HS; N Scituate, RI; (Y); Computer Clb; Dance Clb; Nwsp Rptr; Nwsp Stf; Var L Crs Cntry; JV Swmmng; Var L Trk; High Hon Roll; NHS; Timer; Capt Schl Comp Pgmmng Cntst Tm; RI Hnr Soc; Rensselaer Polytech Inst Troy.

GRAMMAS, JAMES; Northe Providence HS; N Providence, RI; (Y); Boys Clb Am; Pres Church Yth Grp; Var Wrstlng; VP & Pres Grk Orthdx Yth Assn 84-86; AHEPA Ntl Yth Fndtn Educ Trip Greece 85; Bus.

GRASING, JEAN M; Middletown HS; Middletown, RI; (S); 9/255; Girl Scts; Math Tm; Concert Band; Mrchg Band; Yrbk Ed-Chief; Var Bsktbl; Var Vllybl; French Hon Soc; Hon Roll; NHS; Girls Scout 1st Cls Awd 82; IL Inst Of Tech; Comp Engr.

GRAY, KAREN; South Kingston HS; West Kingston, RI; (Y); 21/215; Art Clb; Math Tm; Hon Roll; NHS; Sewng Excllnc Awd 84; Mc Donalds Crwmembr/Mnth 85; U Of MA; Pre-Med.

GRAY, NICOLA; Mount St Charles Acad; Millville, MA; (Y); 2/160; French Clb; Hosp Aide; Pres Leo Clb; Math Tm; Var Fld Hcky; High Hon Roll; NHS; Ntl Merit Ltr; Med.

GREENLAW, PAUL; Classical HS; Providence, RI; (Y); Debate Tm; French Clb; Science Clb; Varsity Clb; Var Socr; Var Trk; Hon Roll; Jrnlsm.

GRENON, RENEE; Woonsocket SR HS; Woonsocket, RI; (Y); 10/600; Church Yth Grp; Cmnty Wkr; Exploring; FCA; French Clb; JA; Math Clb; Math Tm; Quiz Bowl; Science Clb; Vlntr Srv Achvt-Miss TEEN 81; Dstngshd Srv Awd Cathlc Yth Org 81-84; Brown U; Bio-Engrng.

GRIEVE, KERRIE; Charles E Shea SR HS; Pawtucket, RI; (Y); Chorus; Church Choir; School Play; Yrbk Stf; Trs Frsh Cls; Rep Jr Cls; VP Stu Cncl; High Hon Roll; Hon Roll; Dntl Hygn.

GRILLS, DINA; Chariho Regional HS; Ashaway, RI; (S); Chorus; Nwsp Rptr; Rep Frsh Cls; Rep Soph Cls; Rep Jr Cls; Pres Sr Cls; Cheerleading; Hon Roll; Hmcmng Ct; JR Prom Ct; Jrnlsm.

GROSSI, JOSEPH; Classical HS; Providence, RI; (Y); Church Yth Grp; Science Clb; Lit Mag; Hon Roll; NHS; Itln Clb 83-86; Exclnc In Itln 84-85; Providence Coll.

GRUSLIN, JOSEPH A; Tolman SR HS; Pawtucket, RI; (Y); DECA; Concert Band; JV Ftbl; Prfct Atten Awd; Flight Engr.

GUAY, BRUCE; Mount St Charles HS; North Smithfield, RI; (S); 7/140; Cmnty Wkr; Latin Clb; Political Wkr; Pres Jr Cls; Rep Stu Cncl; Var Ice Hcky; JV Socr; High Hon Roll; NHS; Johns Hopkins U; Med.

GUAY, TOM G; North Kingstown SR HS; Saunderstown, RI; (Y); 66/375; Art Clb; Band; Nwsp Stf; Hon Roll; NHS; Schlstc Art Awds-2 Gold Keys ST & Hnrbl Mntn Natl 85; Parsons Schl Of Dsgn; Illstrtn.

GUERRA, ANA; St Raphael Acad; Cumberland, RI; (Y); Church Yth Grp; JV Var Cheerleading; NHS; Optmtry.

GUERRA, LISA; Our Lady Of Fatima HS; Bristol, RI; (S); Dance Clb; Trs Jr Cls; High Hon Roll; Top Stu Prtugse 81-84; Achvt Cert Engl H Stry Bio Phy Sci Prtugse I II 82-84; Med.

GUILBEAULT, JUDY; Smithfield HS; Smithfield, RI; (Y); Church Yth Grp; Girl Scts; Rep Frsh Cls; Rep Soph Cls; Rep Jr Cls; Rep Stu Cncl; Var Sftbl; High Hon Roll; Hon Roll; Prfct Atten Awd; Sci.

HAGGIS, KIMBERLY; Rogers HS; Newport, RI; (S); Church Yth Grp; Drama Clb; French Clb; Model UN; Service Clb; Church Choir; Yrbk Stf; Tennis; High Hon Roll; NHS; Fr Ntl Hnr Soc 83; Elks Yth Cty Gov Day Awd 84; SR Cls Plays; Fairfield U; Chem.

HAGUE, LISA; Cranston West HS; Cranston, RI; (Y); 7/443; JA; Math Tm; Ed Lit Mag; French Hon Soc; Gov Hon Prg Awd; Hon Roll; Jr NHS; NHS; Ntl Merit Ltr; NEDT Awd; Cornell U; Engrng.

HAINS, THOMAS L; North Kingstown HS; N Kingstown, RI; (Y); Exploring; Ski Clb; Mgr Crs Cntry; Var Trk; New England Inst; Arch Drftng.

HALE, ELIZABETH; Coventry HS; Coventry, RI; (Y); 21/400; Dance Clb; French Clb; Latin Clb; Variety Show; Rep Frsh Cls; Rep Soph Cls; Rep Jr Cls; Trs Stu Cncl; Stat Bsktbl; Trs NHS; Hugh O Brian ILS 84; Pol Sci.

HALLORAN, SUSAN; Lincoln HS; Lincoln, RI; (Y); 49/190; Library Aide; Nwsp Rptr; Nwsp Stf; Crs Cntry; Prfct Atten Awd.

HAMRICK, MILES; Central HS; Providence, RI; (Y); Boy Scts; Drama Clb; JA; Church Choir; Color Guard; Drill Tm; School Play; Lit Mag; Stu Cncl; Cit Awd; Cul Art.

HANDY, STEVEN P; Veterans Memorial HS; Warwick, RI; (Y); Letterman Clb; Varsity Clb; Var Capt Ice Hcky; JV Socr; JV Var Tennis; Hon Roll; Jr NHS; RI Hon Soc 85; U RI; Bus.

HANLEY, MICHAEL; Lincoln HS; Lincoln, RI; (Y); 12/190; Var Capt Bsktbl; Hon Roll; Jr NHS; Prfct Atten Awd.

HANLEY, SALLY; Warwick Veterans Memorial HS; Warwick, RI; (S); 16/340; Yrbk Rptr; Yrbk Stf; Off Sr Cls; French Hon Soc; High Hon Roll; Hon Roll; Northeastern U; Law.

HARDY, RICHARD; East Providence SR HS; Jamestown, RI; (S); 17/520; JV Socr; NHS; U Of RI; Chem Engrng.

HARNOIS, DENISE; Woonsocket SR HS; Woonsocket, RI; (Y); Church Yth Grp; JA; High Hon Roll; Hon Roll; Frnch Spllng B Cntst Wnnr 82; Cnsllr.

HARRINGTON, CRAIG; Chariho Regional HS; West Kingston, RI; (Y); Nwsp Rptr; JV Trk; Outstndng Achvt-Jnlsm 85; U Of RI; Accntng.

HARRIS, JEFF; North Smithfield HS; N Smithfield, RI; (Y); Drama Clb; French Clb; JA; Letterman Clb; JV Bsbl; JV Var Ftbl; Hon Roll.

HARRIS, JULIE; Charles E Shea SR HS; Pawtucket, RI; (Y); 43/250; Church Yth Grp; Cmnty Wkr; FBLA; Office Aide; Quiz Bowl; Nwsp Stf; Yrbk Stf; Hon Roll; NHS; Pres Schlr; RI Bus Inst; Law.

SAWYER, LINDA; Chariho Reg JR SR HS; Wyoming, RI; (S); 4/238; Am Leg Aux Girls St; Church Yth Grp; Yrbk Sprt Ed; Pres Frsh Cls; Pres Soph Cls; Capt Bsktbl; Capt Vllybl; Hon Roll; Model Leg Rep 84-85; Frontiers Of Applied Sci At Yale 83-84; U Of RI; Pharmacy.

SAYLES, KRISTEN; North Smithfield JR SR HS; North Smithfield, RI; (Y); 32/176; Pres Church Yth Grp; Dance Clb; Hosp Aide; Quiz Bowl; Yrbk Rptr; Sr Cls; Ntl Merit Ltr; Debate Tm; French Clb; Hon Roll; Yth Of Yr 84; Otstndg Perfmnc Drma Fest 83-84; Diocesan Senator 84-85; Engl.

SAYLES, MELISSA; North Smithfield HS; N Smithfield, RI; (Y); Sec Church Yth Grp; French Clb; Hosp Aide; Color Guard; Yrbk Ed-Chief; Ed Yrbk Stf; CYO Vlybll MIP 84; Hnrbl Ment, 3rd Oil Pntng Art Fstvls 83; Acctng.

SCANLAN, ROBERT; East Providence HS; E Providence, RI; (Y); Church Yth Grp; Var L Bsktbl; Var L Ftbl; High Hon Roll; NHS; Harvard Bk Awd 85; Lib Arts.

SCANLON, MARY; Rogers HS; Omaha, NE; (Y); Am Leg Aux Girls St; Concert Band; Jazz Band; Mrchg Band; DAR Awd; NHS; St Schlr; Church Yth Grp; Keywanettes; ROTC; Newport Nvl Ofcrs Wvs Clb, Band Boosters, Peoples Cred Un ROTC Acad Schlrshps 85; U OK; Pol Sci.

SCANLON, MICHAEL ANDREW; Rogers HS; Omaha, NE; (Y); Church Yth Grp; Im Bsktbl; Im Socr; Hon Roll; WLNE Awd Cert Crrnt Evnts 85; Sci Fair Awd 83; Work Study Prog 83-84; U OK; Bus.

SCANTLEBURY, ERIC; Chariho HS; Wyoming, RI; (S); Computer Clb; Band; Concert Band; Jazz Band; Mrchg Band; School Musical; Stu Cncl; Crs Cntry; Trk; Prfct Atten Awd; RI Coll Solo & Ensmbl Awd 84; U Of RI; Comp Sci.

SCHMIDIG, BRIAN; Charles E Shea HS; East Rutherford, NJ; (Y); Spanish Clb; Band; Stage Crew; Hon Roll; Proj Bus-Cert Accompl 82; Essay Cont-RIASP-FNLST 82; Med.

SCHNEIDER, ELEONORE E; South Kingstown HS; W Kingston, RI; (Y); 11/175; Am Leg Aux Girls St; Drama Clb; Band; Off Stu Cncl; Fld Hcky; Mgr(s); Trk; High Hon Roll; NHS; Ntl Merit Ltr; Outstndng Achvt In Latin 84; Prfct Atndnc Awd 83.

SCHUMACHER, JULIE; Cranston West HS; Cranston, RI; (Y); Dance Clb; Sec DECA; Ski Clb; Drm Mjr(t); Variety Show; Rep Stu Cncl; Var Trk; JV Var Vllybl; Hon Roll; Jr NHS; Schl Serv Awd 83; 1st Pl Finance Credit 85; A Letter C 500 GAA Points 85; URI; Bus.

SCHWEYER, JOSEPH; Portsmouth HS; Portsmouth, RI; (Y); Boy Scts; Ski Clb; Bsktbl; Coach Actv; Ftbl; Wt Lftg; Hon Roll; Librl Arts.

SCIACCA, IVANA; Johnston SR HS; Johnston, RI; (Y); High Hon Roll; Hon Roll; RI Tchrs Of Itln 84-85; Exec Sec.

SCOTT, KRISTY; Chariho Regional HS; Ashaway, RI; (S); Church Yth Grp; Nwsp Rptr; Nwsp Stf; Sec Frsh Cls; Sec Soph Cls; Sec Jr Cls; Sec Sr Cls; Rep Stu Cncl; L Var Cheerleading; Score Keeper; Prom Court 83-84; U Of RI; Preschl Ed.

SCOTT, LAURIE; Cranston H S East; Cranston, RI; (Y); Art Clb; Var Capt Cheerleading; JV Fld Hcky; JV Gym; Var Trk; Art Cls RI Schl Desgn; RI Schl Desgn; Comm Art.

SCOTT, PAUL; Charles A Shea SR HS; Pawtucket, RI; (Y); 61/257; Pres Drama Clb; Math Tm; School Play; JV Bsbl; Var Ftbl; Booster Clb Schlrshp; Fairlawn Crdnls Ftbl Schlrshp; Art Excllnc; Cmbrlnd Co-Prfrmng Arts; Hofstra U; Drama.

SCOTTI, ANN; Johnston SR HS; Johnston, RI; (S); #50 In Class; DECA; Drama Clb; Chorus; School Play; Variety Show; Crs Cntry; Powder Puff Ftbl; Trk; Hon Roll; Mst Vlbl Plyr Awd Trck 82-83; Chld Care.

SCOTTO, DINA; Johnston SR HS; Johnston, RI; (S); 5/237; Orch; Nwsp Rptr; Ed Yrbk Stf; Crs Cntry; Sftbl; Gov Hon Prg Awd; High Hon Roll; NHS; Prfct Atten Awd; CIBA GEIGY Sci Awd 85; Music Awds 80-85; 4-H Awds For Art 80-83; Vet Med.

SCUNGIO, TONI; Johnston HS; Johnston, RI; (S); 16/237; DECA; Yrbk Stf; Badmtn; Var Capt Cheerleading; Hon Roll; NHS; RI Yth Cncl On Smkng; RI Hnr Soc; Prom Qn Ct; RI Coll.

SEABURY, RHONDA; North Kingstown HS; N Kingstown, RI; (Y); 49/371; High Hon Roll; Hon Roll; CCRI; Acctg.

SEARLE, TAMMY LYNNE; East Providence SR HS; E Providence, RI; (Y); Camp Fr Inc; Church Yth Grp; Girl Scts; Band; Chorus; Church Choir; Concert Band; Jazz Band; Mrchg Band; Off Soph Cls; Intntnl Order Rainbow Girls 4 Yrs; Invlvd In SADD; Rep Sch TV Prog On The Rocks & Svrl Cmmrcls; Nrs.

SEARS, LORI; Portsmouth HS; Portsmouth, RI; (Y); Cmnty Wkr; French Clb; FBLA; Hosp Aide; JA; Varsity Clb; Nwsp Phtg; Nwsp Stf; Yrbk Stf; Var Gym; Engrng.

SEARS, MARK BENEDICT PATRICK; Lincoln HS; Lincoln, RI; (Y); 35/220; Boy Scts; Church Yth Grp; Cmnty Wkr; Political Wkr; Nwsp Rptr; Nwsp Stf; Rep Frsh Cls; Stu Cncl; Tennis; Hon Roll; Ad Altare Dei Awd, Wrld Consrvtn Awd, Pell Awd Hist 84; Catholic U; Law.

SECHIO, DINA; North Providence HS; N Providence, RI; (Y); 2/235; Pres Church Yth Grp; Yrbk Stf; Stu Cncl; High Hon Roll; Hon Roll; Jr NHS; NHS; Sal; Ed.

SEDLOCK, ANNE; St Mary Acad Bayview; E Greenwich, RI; (Y); Church Yth Grp; French Clb; Math Clb; Yrbk Stf; Lit Mag; Hon Roll; NHS; NEDT Awd; St Schlr; ST Sci Fair 2nd Grnt Awd 83; PSAT Commndtn; 2 Schl Svc Awds; Mth.

SEERU, KAREN; Chariho Regional HS; Woodriver, RI; (S); 10/260; Am Leg Aux Girls St; VICA; Band; Chorus; Yrbk Ed-Chief; Stu Cncl; High Hon Roll; Hon Roll; Ntl Merit Ltr; Schlrshp To NE Inst Of Tech VICA Gld Mdl In Data Procsng 84; Bryant Coll; Comp Sci.

SEPTELKA, CINDY; Cumberland HS; Cumberland, RI; (S); Church Yth Grp; DECA; Hosp Aide; JA; Hon Roll; Fin.

SHAPARD, TRACY; Rogers HS; Newport, RI; (Y); FBLA; German Clb; Pep Clb; Drill Tm; Nwsp Rptr; Pres Jr Cls; Var L Cheerleading; Hon Roll; NHS; Camp Fr Inc; Mayfair Prncs; Girls Clb; WA ST U; Nrs.

SHAUGHNESSY, ANNE MARIE; Cranston West HS; Cranston, RI; (Y); GAA; Spanish Clb; Var L Bsktbl; Var Capt Crs Cntry; Var L Tennis; Var Trk; Var Capt Vllybl; Hon Roll; NHS; NEDT Awd; Presndtl Physcl Ftns Awds; RI U; Math.

SHEAHAN, MICHAEL; Mount St Charles HS; North Smithfield, RI; (S); 18/147; VP Jr Cls; JV Socr; VP Tennis; High Hon Roll; NHS; US Naval Acad.

SHEARER, ANNE E; Classical HS; Providence, RI; (Y); Chorus; Hon Roll; Ntl Merit SF; AATF Exam Cont 3rd ST 6th Regn 84; Travlng Theatr Co Good Wrks Theatr 82-84; Photo Clb Pres 83-84; Biol.

SHEEHAN, CAROLE; Rogers HS; Newport, RI; (Y); Pres Church Yth Grp; Cmnty Wkr; French Clb; Quiz Bowl; Service Clb; Chorus; Variety Show; Lit Mag; Stu Cncl; French Hon Soc; Dentstry.

SHEEHAN, KELLY ANNE; Mount Saint Charles Acad; N Smithfield, RI; (Y); 42/162; JV Bsktbl; Var L Sftbl; High Hon Roll; NHS; U Rhode Island; Phrmcy.

SHELHART, JOHN CHRISTOPHER; Bristol HS; Bristol, RI; (Y); 35/220; Am Leg Boys St; Church Yth Grp; Pres Sr Cls; Var L Bsbl; Bsktbl; Hon Roll; Boy Of Yr 82; MVP 82; Sprtsmnshp Awd 83; U Of RI; Intl Bus.

SHERIDAN, COLLEEN; St Marys Acad-Bay View; Warwick, RI; (Y); Drama Clb; Exploring; Office Aide; Pep Clb; Cheerleading; Hon Roll; Jr NHS; Serv Awd 85; Katherine Gibbs Hon Mntn Schlrshp Ldrshp 85; Psych.

SHIMIZU, KEN; South Kingstown HS; Kingston, RI; (Y); 13/215; Art Clb; Debate Tm; Math Tm; Model UN; Var Tennis; High Hon Roll; NHS; Church Choir; Variety Show; Hon Roll; Brown U Bk Awd 85; Mst Outstdng Stu In Acclrtd Chem 85; Excell In Geo 83.

SHOOT, JERILYN A; Pilgrim HS; Warwick, RI; (Y); 21/333; Spanish Clb; Capt Cheerleading; Elks Awd; High Hon Roll; Hon Roll; Jr NHS; Spanish NHS; Letterman Clb; Pep Clb; Variety Show; RI Hnr Soc; Spnsh Intl Frgn Lang Awd; Quonset Pt Mgt Assn Schlrshp; RI Coll; Engl.

SHOPPELL, SHARON; Middletown HS; Middletown, RI; (S); 7/252; Church Yth Grp; Drama Clb; Math Tm; Band; Concert Band; Mrchg Band; Pep Band; Var Sftbl; French Hon Soc; Ntl Merit Ltr; Chem Engrng.

SHORTEN, GREG S; South Kingstown HS; Kingston, RI; (Y); Spanish Clb; VP Soph Cls; Pres Jr Cls; Pres Sr Cls; Rep Stu Cncl; JV Ftbl; JV Socr; Im Vllybl; Hon Roll; Corp Law.

SHURTLEFF, ROBIN; West Warwick HS; W Warwick, RI; (Y); Stu Cncl; Psych.

SICKSCH, LISA; Bishop Keough Regional HS; Providence, RI; (Y); Hosp Aide; Ski Clb; Teachers Aide; Yrbk Rptr; Yrbk Stf; VP Frsh Cls; Hon Roll; NHS; UCLA; Med.

SILVA, DAVID P; Chariho HS; Ashaway, RI; (Y); Church Yth Grp; Letterman Clb; Quiz Bowl; Varsity Clb; Var Capt Bsktbl; L Socr; Var L Trk; Trk 3 Star Awd 83-84 & 84-85; Northeastern; Phys Thrpy.

SILVA, JOHN; Bristol HS; Bristol, RI; (S); 7/237; Math Clb; Math Tm; High Hon Roll; NHS; Rensselear Awd 84; Comp Sci.

SILVA, KIMBERLY A; Our Lady Of Fatima; Seekonk, MA; (Y); Drama Clb; Chorus; Johnson & Wales; Travel.

SILVA, TRACY; East Providence HS; Riverside, RI; (Y); Library Aide; Band; Chorus; Capt Color Guard; Capt Flag Corp; Flag Corp; School Musical; Bsktbl; Trk.

SILVEIRA, LINDA; Bishop Keough Regional HS; Pawtucket, RI; (S); Ski Clb; Yrbk Ed-Chief; Sec Church Yth Grp; Sec Jr Cls; Sec Sr Cls; Rep Stu Cncl; Sftbl; NHS; Pell Grant Hstry Awd 84; Engl Awd 84; French III Awd 84; Bentley Coll; Finance.

SILVIA, ELEANOR; Classical HS; Providence, RI; (Y); Hon Roll.

SILVIA, GARY; Tiverton HS; Tiverton, RI; (Y); Band; Concert Band; Drm & Bgl; Jazz Band; Mrchg Band; Orch; Pep Band; Symp Band; Variety Show; JV Ftbl; Military; Comp.

SIMARD, SUSAN; Tiverton HS; Tiverton, RI; (Y); Drama Clb; Yrbk Stf; Socl Sci.

SIMMONS, ALLISON; Bishop Connolly HS; Newport, RI; (Y); 75/200; Church Yth Grp; Cmnty Wkr; Drama Clb; Ski Clb; Stage Crew; Nwsp Rptr; Rep Sr Cls; High Hon Roll; Hon Roll; Comm.

SIMMONS, GLEN; North Smithfield HS; N Smithfield, RI; (Y); Boy Scts; Yrbk Stf; Rep Stu Cncl; Hon Roll; Span Achvmnt Awd; RI Coll; Educ.

SIMOES, ANA; North Providence HS; N Providence, RI; (Y); Boy Scts; Exploring; French Clb; Variety Show; Var Cheerleading; Var Pom Pon; High Hon Roll; Jr NHS; NHS; Prfct Atten Awd; Bus.

SISSON, LAURIE; St Raphael Acad; Pawtucket, RI; (Y); 49/200; Computer Clb; Drama Clb; Ski Clb; Yrbk Rptr; Off Jr Cls; Cheerleading; Swmmng; Trk; Vllybl; Hon Roll; U Of RI; Comp Fld.

SKOUTAS, STEPHEN T; Smithfield HS; Smithfield, RI; (Y); 32/130; Art Clb; Computer Clb; Rptr DECA; Math Tm; Elks Awd; Hon Roll; Distrbtv Ed Awd 1st ST RI 4 Awds 85; Natl Hnr Socty 85; Pres Acadmc Fit Awd 85; Bryant Coll; Comp Inf Sys.

SLATTERY, STEPHEN; Lincoln HS; Lincoln, RI; (Y); Church Yth Grp; Rep Soph Cls; Rep Jr Cls; Rep Sr Cls; Var Capt Jr Cls; Var Capt Trk; Hon Roll; Marine Corp Dstngshd Athlte 85; Providence Coll; Hstry.

SLOANE, PENNY S; Charles E Shea SR HS; Pawtucket, RI; (Y); 4/249; Temple Yth Grp; Concert Band; Jazz Band; Orch; Pep Band; Yrbk Sprt Ed; Swmmng; DAR Awd; Hon Roll; NHS; Centry III Ldrs Prog Awd 85; U RI Bk Awd 84; Intl Forgn Lang Awd 85; U RI; Music.

SMEDBERG, KAREN; East Providence SR HS; Riverside, RI; (Y); Pres VP Girl Scts; Band; Chorus; Concert Band; Mrchg Band; Score Keeper; Var Vllybl; High Hon Roll; Hon Roll; NHS; RI U; Engr.

SMITH, ANNEE; No Kingstown HS; N Kingstown, RI; (Y); 17/371; Chorus; JV Fld Hcky; High Hon Roll; Hon Roll; NHS; Cert Of Excllnc Frnch I, II & III 83-85; Cert Of Excllnc De Francais 85.

SMITH, ERIC; South Kingstown HS; Peace Dale, RI; (Y); Art Clb; Boy Scts; Political Wkr; Stage Crew; Variety Show; Hon Roll; Tchng.

SMITH, FRANCES; Lincoln SR HS; Lincoln, RI; (Y); 22/220; Chrmn FBLA; Trs JA; Nwsp Stf; Trs Stu Cncl; Capt Bsktbl; Capt Fld Hcky; Capt Sftbl; High Hon Roll; NHS; Voice Dem Awd; 1st Tm All ST Field Hockey Plyr/Def 85; 1st Tm All Div Field Hockey Plyr/Def 85; Bentley Coll; Bus Mngmnt.

SMITH, KAREN; Johnston SR HS; Johnston, RI; (S); 1/237; Am Leg Aux Girls St; Political Wkr; Nwsp Rptr; Sec Frsh Cls; High Hon Roll; NHS; Rotary Awd; Val; Woonasquatucket Vly Rotary Schlrshp 84; Educ.

SMITH, KATHLEEN; Chariho Regional HS; Ashaway, RI; (Y); 22/299; Am Leg Aux Girls St; Cmnty Wkr; Acpl Chr; Band; Chorus; Church Choir; Mrchg Band; Trk; Hon Roll; Model Leg 85-86; SCAT Stop Child Abuse Today VP 85-86; Psych.

SMITH, LAURIE A; Toll Gate HS; Warwick, RI; (Y); 22/393; Math Tm; Spanish Clb; Chorus; Yrbk Stf; High Hon Roll; Hon Roll; Jr NHS; NHS; Ntl Merit SF; Spanish NHS; Educ.

SMITH, MARSHA ELAINE; Central HS; Providence, RI; (Y); JA; Nwsp Stf; Hon Roll; Katherine Gibbs; Acctnt.

SMITH, NANCY A; Barrington HS; Barrington, RI; (Y); Cmnty Wkr; GAA; Yrbk Stf; Lit Mag; Off Soph Cls; JV Capt Fld Hcky; Var Tennis; Hon Roll; Stat Bsbl; Mgr(s); Sentr Modl Legsltr 84-85; Bates Coll ME; Lwyr.

SMITH, RISA; Narragansett HS; Narragansett, RI; (Y); #11 In Class; Cmnty Wkr; Hosp Aide; Office Aide; Variety Show; JV Gym; Powder Puff Ftbl; JV Socr; Hon Roll; NHS; Natl Italn Hon Soc 83-85; RI Italn Hon Soc 83-85.

SMOLAN, ERIC A; Lincoln HS; Lincoln, RI; (Y); #23 In Class; VP Bsbl; JV Bsktbl; Ftbl; Var Ice Hcky; Pres Acadmc Ftns Awd 85; Clarkson U; Engrng.

SNOW, RICHARD; Smithfield HS; Smithfield, RI; (Y); 13/220; Church Yth Grp; Science Clb; Band; Hon Roll.

SOARES, DAVID; North Providence HS; N Providence, RI; (Y); Computer Clb; JV Bsbl; JV Bsktbl; Hnr Roll 82; Elec Engr.

SOBCZYNSKI, MARJORIE; Prout Memorial HS; Warwick, RI; (Y); 21/97; Church Yth Grp; Cmnty Wkr; Hosp Aide; Chorus; Jazz Band; School Musical; School Play; Variety Show; Hon Roll; Med.

SOBRINO, JAIME; North Kingstown HS; Jamestown, RI; (Y); Hon Roll; Hnry Diploma 85; Spnsh Exchng Stu 84-85; U Of Industrial Eng-Madrid Spn.

SOMERS, JENNY R; Mt St Charles Acad; Bellingham, MA; (Y); Cmnty Wkr; Hosp Aide; Red Cross Aide; Ski Clb; JV Bsktbl; Var L Cheerleading; Im Coach Actv; Var Twrlr; High Hon Roll; NHS; U Of New England; Phy Thrpy.

SORRELL, TRACY; Pilgrim HS; Warwick, RI; (Y); Church Yth Grp; JA; Rep Model UN; Science Clb; Spanish Clb; Church Choir; High Hon Roll; Hon Roll; Jr NHS; Spanish NHS; Comp Sci.

SOSCIA, SUSAN; Cranston West HS; Cranston, RI; (Y); 23/420; Ski Clb; Color Guard; Mrchg Band; Variety Show; Trs Soph Cls; VP Pres Stu Cncl; Crs Cntry; Gym; Jr NHS; URI Bk Awd 85; Prncpls Awd 83; Hnr Soc 83-85.

SOUCI, JOY SAN; North Smithfield HS; N Smithfield, RI; (Y); French Clb; JA; Chorus; Sec Stu Cncl; Miss Fire Prev 85; Bus Adm.

SOUSA, ELIZABETH; Bristol HS; Bristol, RI; (S); Sec Church Yth Grp; Drama Clb; GAA; VP JCL; Yrbk Ed-Chief; Rep Sr Cls; VP Stu Cncl; Stat Ftbl; Trs NHS; Pell Awd 84; Century III Ldrshp Awd 84; Mus Awds 83; Med.

SOUZA, LISA; Portsmouth HS; Portsmouth, RI; (Y); 90/200; FBLA; Ski Clb; Spanish NHS; U Of RI; Nursng.

SPAZIANO, LISA; Cranston HS; Cranston, RI; (Y); Art Clb; Church Yth Grp; Computer Clb; Girl Scts; Spanish Clb; Varsity Clb; Variety Show; Yrbk Stf; Var Cheerleading; Hon Roll; Recgntn Chrldng 83-84; Point Awd V Chrldng 84-85; Hnr Rl Pin 82-83; RI Coll; Comp.

SPEAR, MICHELLE; Warreu HS; Warren, RI; (Y); FHA; School Play; Yrbk Stf; Var Bsktbl; Score Keeper; Hon Roll; Comm Coll Of RI; Mgmt.

SPECHT, GREGORY H; Charles E Shea HS; Pawtucket, RI; (Y); 24/250; Boys Clb Am; Boy Scts; Computer Clb; Ski Clb; Nwsp Stf; Rep Frsh Cls; Rep Soph Cls; Rep Jr Cls; Rep Sr Cls; Rep Stu Cncl; Charles E Shea Schlrshp Excell Acad 85; German Club Schlrshp 85; Pawtucket Emblem Club Schlrshp 85; NE U; Phy Thrpy.

SPENCER, WENDY; Johnston HS; Johnston, RI; (S); 42/236; Mgr(s); Hon Roll; NHS; St Schlr; DECA; Sec Soph Cls; Sec Jr Cls; Sec Sr Cls; CCRI; Med Asst.

SPICUZZA, KIM; Mount Pleasant HS; Providence, RI; (Y); 2/150; Debate Tm; Office Aide; Dnfth Awd; High Hon Roll; Hon Roll; NHS; Hugh O Brien Yth Found 84; R J Govnrs Summr Prog Math & Sci 85; Itln Hnr Soc 85; Tchg.

SPINELLA, ELIZABETH; Mount Saint Charles Acad; Woonsocket, RI; (Y); 44/150; Sec Church Yth Grp; Chorus; Flag Corp; Capt Cheerleading; Hon Roll; NHS; Bio Chmstry.

SQUATRITO, ANNE; Bristol HS; Bristol, RI; (S); JCL; Ski Clb; Yrbk Stf; Trs Sr Cls; Sec Stu Cncl; Capt Cheerleading; Var Gym; High Hon Roll; NHS; Rotary Awd; Wheelock Bk Awd 84; Summa Cum Laude Ntl Latin Ex 83; Hmcmng Queen 84; Boston U; Bio Chem.

SQUIZZERO, LINDA; Cranston HS West; Cranston, RI; (Y); 47/443; Exploring; Ski Clb; Acpl Chr; Chorus; Rep Jr Cls; Rep Sr Cls; Rep Stu Cncl; Var Bsktbl; Var Capt Sftbl; Hon Roll; Jr Prom Queen 84; Pres Acdmc Ftnss Awd 85; RI Hnr Scty 85; Tchrs Italian Cert 83; Yth Ftnss Achvmnt Awd; Bryant Coll; Accntng.

ST ANGELO, ANTHONY; North Providence HS; North Providence, RI; (Y); Am Leg Boys St; Aud/Vis; Ski Clb; Nwsp Sprt Ed; Nwsp Stf; Yrbk Sprt Ed; Yrbk Stf; Trs Sr Cls; Trs Stu Cncl; Bsbl; CCRI; Hmn Svcs.

ST LAURENT, ARTHUR; North Smithfield JR SR HS; N Smithfield, RI; (Y); Hon Roll; Engrng.

ST LAURENT, CLAUDINE; Tiverton HS; Tiverton, RI; (Y); Computer Clb; Drama Clb; MMM; Political Wkr; Chorus; School Musical; School Play; Stage Crew; Swing Chorus; Yrbk Stf; Cert Fr Sptlght Pgms Of Prjcts Fr Hgh Lrnng Ptntl SE MA U-N Dartmouth; Elem Tchng.

ST MICHEL, CAROLYN; Tiverton HS; Tiverton, RI; (Y); Yrbk Stf; Pres Frsh Cls; VP Jr Cls; VP Sr Cls; Sec VP Stu Cncl; Vllybl; Hon Roll; Band; Concert Band; Mrchg Band; Accntnt.

ST PIERRE, LAURIE; Coventry HS; Coventry, RI; (Y); 13/415; Sec French Clb; JCL; VP Band; Concert Band; Mrchg Band; Pep Band; Stage Crew; Variety Show; Yrbk Stf; Rep Frsh Cls; Outstndng Band; Radlgy.

ST PIERRE, MARY ELLEN; Coventry HS; Coventry, RI; (S); 75/422; Sec Band; Chorus; Sec Concert Band; Sec Mrchg Band; Variety Show; Pres Stu Cncl; Var Sftbl; Hon Roll; Rep Frsh Cls; Rep Soph Cls; Mst Outstndng Frshmn, Mst Talkative 80-81; Mst Outstndng Soph, Mst Friendly 81-83; U Of CT; Elem Ed.

STANLEY, BRIAN P; Charino HS; Carolina, RI; (Y); 30/300; Boy Scts; Ski Clb; Trk; High Hon Roll; Hon Roll; Northeastern U; Bus Adm.

STATKIEWICZ, TODD; Mount St Charles Acad; Woonsocket, RI; (Y); Band; Var Crs Cntry; Var Trk; Hon Roll; Schltc Art Awd 84; Berkley Schl Of Music; Muscian.

STAVELEY, RICK S; Classical HS; Providence, RI; (Y); Aud/Vis; Hon Roll; Acctnt.

STEINER, CRAIG; Portsmouth HS; Portsmouth, RI; (Y); 1/250; Boy Scts; FBLA; Science Clb; Var Bsbl; Var Bsktbl; Var Swmmng; NHS; Engnr.

STEVENS, DONALD; Chariho Reg JR-SR HS; Carolina, RI; (Y); 25/300; Camera Clb; Computer Clb; Math Tm; Yrbk Ed-Chief; Yrbk Phtg; JV Trk; High Hon Roll; Hon Roll; Jr NHS; Ntl Merit Ltr; MIT; Comp Sci.

STEWART, TRACEY; Smithfield HS; Smithfield, RI; (Y); 24/200; Art Clb; French Clb; Variety Show; Nwsp Stf; Off Frsh Cls; Off Stu Cncl; Bsktbl; Sftbl; Hon Roll; Engrng.

STINSON, JOHN; Johnston HS; Johnston, RI; (S); 7/237; Trk; Wrstlng; Bausch & Lomb Sci Awd; High Hon Roll; NHS; U Of RI; Rbts.

STOKELL, PAUL; North Kingstown HS; N Kingstown, RI; (Y); Chess Clb; Political Wkr; ROTC; Var Trk; Hon Roll; Mech Eng.

STORMONT, BRIAN; Warwick Veterans Memorial HS; Warwick, RI; (S); 5/300; Church Yth Grp; Computer Clb; Math Tm; High Hon Roll; NHS; Comp Sci Awd 84; Elec Engr.

STRONG, CHERYL J; Barrington Christian Acad; Rehoboth, MA; (Y); 4/10; Pres Church Yth Grp; Computer Clb; Drama Clb; Teachers Aide; Yrbk Stf; Rep Jr Cls; Stu Cncl; Var Co-Capt Bsktbl; Var Co-Capt Fld Hcky; Gordon Coll; Elem Ed.

STUDLEY, KATHLEEN ANN; East Providence SR HS; E Providence, RI; (Y); 76/444; VP French Clb; Chorus; Concert Band; Mrchg Band; Orch; School Musical; Variety Show; Prfct Atten Awd; RI Hnr Soc 84-85; RI Coll; Acctng.

SULEWSKI, MARY J; Alternate Learning Project HS; Providence, RI; (S); Church Yth Grp; Church Choir; School Play; Hon Roll; NHS; Katherine Gibbs; Bus.

SULLIVAN, ELLEN; Rogers HS; Portsmouth, RI; (Y); JA; Concert Band; Mrchg Band; Pep Band; Ntl Merit Schol; French Clb; Band; Hon Roll.

SULLIVAN, KATHLEEN; Lincoln HS; Lincoln, RI; (Y); 66/190; Varsity Clb; Swmmng.

SUMNER, PATRICIA; Narragansett HS; Narragansett, RI; (Y); 21/125; Hosp Aide; Variety Show; Jr Cls; Sr Cls; Var Capt Bsktbl; Var Socr; Var Sftbl; Hon Roll; Soph Cls; Prfct Atten Awd; St Sci Fair Winner 84; All St Bsktbll 85; Italian Clb 85; Human Phys.

SUNDSTROM, JAMES; Coventry HS; Coventry, RI; (Y); 23/300; Radio Clb; Stage Crew; NHS; Comm.

SURPRENANT, TINA; Burrillville JR-SR HS; Harrisville, RI; (Y); Math Tm; School Play; Yrbk Stf; Trs Stu Cncl; Var L Fld Hcky; High Hon Roll; NHS; Sec Soph Cls; Stat Bsktbl; Im Sftbl; RI Clg Almn Assn Awd 85; ST RI Citn Oustndng Modl Leg Svc 85; Outstndng Clg Prep JR Math, Engl Awd; Pre-Med.

SUZAWA, VALERIE M; Classical HS; Providence, RI; (Y); Hosp Aide; Math Tm; Orch; French Hon Soc; Gov Hon Prg Awd; High Hon Roll; Ntl Merit SF; Cum Laude Soc; Rensselaer Math, Sci Awd; Med.

SWAIN, KRISTINE; Rogers HS; Newport, RI; (Y); Key Clb; Varsity Clb; Yrbk Stf; Pres Soph Cls; Sec Stu Cncl; JV Var Cheerleading; Gym; Var Tennis; Cit Awd; High Hon Roll; Bus Mgmt.

SWANSON, ERIC; Warren HS; Warren, RI; (Y); 41/128; Church Yth Grp; Ski Clb; Chorus; School Play; Var Ftbl; Ice Hcky; Hon Roll; New Hampshire Coll; Culnry Arts.

SWEET, KAREN; Johnston SR HS; Johnston, RI; (S); 2/237; Am Leg Aux Girls St; Drm Mjr(t); Ed Yrbk Stf; Pres Frsh Cls; Pres Jr Cls; Pres Sr Cls; Stu Cncl; Stat Bsktbl; Stat Ftbl; Capt Powder Puff Ftbl; Hugh O Brian Yth Ldrshp Awd 83; Cntry III Ldrshp ST Fnlst 85; Brdcst Jrnlsm.

SWEET, LISA; Warwick Vetrans Memorial HS; Warwick, RI; (Y); Girl Scts; Varsity Clb; Yrbk Stf; Var Bsktbl; Var Capt Crs Cntry; Var Capt Vllybl; Hon Roll; Spanish NHS; All Div Vlybll 85; All St Hon Men Vlybll 85; All City Vlybll 85.

SWIST, DAVID; Warren HS; Warren, RI; (Y); 1/125; Am Leg Boys St; Math Tm; Quiz Bowl; Band; Yrbk Stf; Rep Frsh Cls; Rep Soph Cls; Rep Jr Cls; High Hon Roll; NHS; Chem Tm; Worcester Poly Inst; Chem.

SYLVIA, MONIQUE; Tiverton HS; Tiverton, RI; (Y); Aud/Vis; Church Yth Grp; Band; Concert Band; Mrchg Band; Stu Cncl; JV Bsktbl; Ftbl; Score Keeper; Trk.

TAGUE, LAURA; Central Falls HS; Central Falls, RI; (Y); 10/130; Am Leg Aux Girls St; Civic Clb; Cmnty Wkr; Drama Clb; Political Wkr; School Musical; School Play; Stage Crew; Ed Nwsp Ed-Chief; Nwsp Rptr; Presdnts Acadmc Ftns Awd 85; All Stake Cast Awd 84; RI Hnr Soc 85; RI Coll; Ed.

TAN, NETH; Tolman HS; Providence, RI; (Y); Math Clb; Math Tm; OEA; Nwsp Phtg; Badmtn; Vllybl; High Hon Roll; Hon Roll; Acadmc Excllnc Awd 83; Hghst Hnrs Awd 83; Boston Coll.

TANG, MICHAEL; Cranston H S East; Cranston, RI; (Y); 12/454; Camera Clb; Debate Tm; French Clb; Science Clb; Nwsp Stf; Yrbk Bus Mgr; Lit Mag; Elks Awd; High Hon Roll; Jr NHS; Rale U; Intl Rltns.

TARDIE, MICHELLE; Tiverton HS; Tiverton, RI; (Y); 57/214; Rep Stu Cncl; Hon Roll; Father Josph Boehr Cncl Knights Columbus Scholar Awd 85; U Of RI; Cmmnctns.

TARDIF, PETER; Woonsocket SR HS; Woonsocket, RI; (Y); Church Yth Grp; French Clb; Rep Jr Cls; JV Bsbl; JV Bsktbl; Var Trk; Hon Roll; Engl Achvt Awd 83; St Joseph Parish CYO Coachs Recog Awd JR Boys Bsktbl 83-85; Pre-Law.

TARRO, PAM; Tollgate HS; Warwick, RI; (S); 19/387; Letterman Clb; Math Clb; Yrbk Stf; Jr Cls; Sr Cls; JV Var Cheerleading; High Hon Roll; Jr NHS; NHS; Intnl Clb; Itln Hnr Scty; Med.

TATE, ALISON A; North Providence HS; North Providence, RI; (Y); Church Yth Grp; Cmnty Wkr; Pep Clb; Political Wkr; Teachers Aide; Band; Concert Band; Jazz Band; Mrchg Band; Nwsp Ed-Chief; Hstry.

TATEN, RICHARD B; Portsmouth HS; Portsmouth, RI; (Y); 6/210; Am Leg Boys St; Science Clb; Nwsp Stf; Var Capt Socr; Var Capt Tennis; High Hon Roll; Jr NHS; NHS; Pres Schlr; Voice Dem Awd; Rotry Schlr Ath Awd; VA Polytech Inst; Engrng.

TAVARES, ANNABELLA; Charles E Shea SR HS; Pawtucket, RI; (Y); Boys Clb Am; Exploring; French Clb; Nwsp Ed-Chief; Ed Yrbk Stf; Off Jr Cls; Hon Roll; Bio.

TAVARES, EUNICE B; Charles E Shea SR HS; Pawtucket, RI; (Y); Church Yth Grp; High Hon Roll; Hon Roll; Cert Awd Excllnce Engl Math & Lang Ar Ts, Social Stds 83; Trophy Acadmc Achvmnt 80-81; Gordon Coll; French.

TAVERNESE, YVETTE; Middletown HS; Middletown, RI; (S); 6/252; JA; Science Clb; Drm Mjr(t); Mrchg Band; Pep Band; Rep Soph Cls; French Hon Soc; NHS; Solo Ensmbl Music Fest Awd 83; Excell Instr Music Awd 82-83; RI ST Frnch Cont 82; Brown U; Biochem.

TAYLOR, GREGORY; Tiverton HS; Tiverton, RI; (Y); 66/214; Church Yth Grp; Mrchg Band; Orch; Variety Show; JV Bsbl; JV Var Bsktbl; JV High Hon Roll; Tiverton Eductrs Assn Schlrshp 85; Anna M M Gottwald Schlrshp 85; Southeastern MA U; Bus Mngmnt.

TAYLOR, JANET; Barrington HS; Barrington, RI; (Y); 51/233; Varsity Clb; JV Bsktbl; JV Fld Hcky; JV Socr; Sftbl; Var L Trk; Hon Roll.

TEIXEIRA, KRISTY; Barrington HS; Barrington, RI; (Y); AFS; Hosp Aide; Intnl Clb; Office Aide; Ed Yrbk Phtg; Yrbk Stf; Rep Stu Cncl; JV Crs Cntry; Im Powder Puff Ftbl; Var Trk; Fin.

TEOLIS, LISA; North Providence HS; N Providence, RI; (Y); Art Clb; Boys Clb Am; Dance Clb; Drama Clb; Yrbk Stf; Cheerleading; Gym; Vllybl; NHS; Ntl Merit Ltr; 2nd Hnrs 83-85; Rick Coll; Nrsng.

THEROUX, DAVID; Lincoln HS; Lincoln, RI; (Y); 62/190; Im Bsktbl; Hon Roll; Optmtry.

THIBEAULT, DENISE; Smithfield SR HS; Greenville, RI; (Y); 47/188; JA; Rep Sr Cls; Rep Stu Cncl; Var L Bsktbl; Im Bowling; Im Sftbl; Im Vllybl; Hon Roll; Outstndng Art Stu 82; Psychlgy.

THIFAULT, CARRIE L; North Smithfield JR SR HS; North Smithfield, RI; (Y); 3/164; Yrbk Stf; High Hon Roll; NHS; Pres Schlr; St Schlr; Holy Cross Bk Awd 84; Carl & Ruby Christiansen Schlrshp 85; VP N Smithfield Hon Soc 85; Bryant Coll; Acctg.

THOMAS, THERESA; Bishop Francis P Keough Rgnl HS; Pawtucket, RI; (S); Rep Stu Cncl; High Hon Roll; Hon Roll; Relg Awd 84; Engl.

THORPE, STEVEN; Mt St Charles HS; Woonsocket, RI; (Y); 8/165; Church Yth Grp; Band; Concert Band; Mrchg Band; Pep Band; Socr; High Hon Roll; Hon Roll; NHS; URI; Comp Engrng.

TIERNEY, JULIE; St Marys Academy-Bay View; East Providence, RI; (Y); 1/193; Latin Clb; Math Clb; Rep Model UN; Chorus; School Musical; Yrbk Stf; Sec Sr Cls; Var Cheerleading; Kiwanis Awd; NHS; Gld Medl & Summa Cum Laude Cert Natl Latn Exm 84; Obtnd Hghst Chem Ave Schl 83; Boston Coll; Bus.

TINER, JAMES; North Providence HS; N Providence, RI; (Y); Boys Clb Am; Chess Clb; Computer Clb; Nwsp Rptr; Hon Roll; Jr NHS; U RI; Med.

TOLBERT, JENNIFER; Portsmouth HS; Springfield, VA; (Y); 1/235; Church Yth Grp; FBLA; Flag Corp; JV Bsktbl; Var L Crs Cntry; Im Powder Puff Ftbl; Var L Socr; JV Trk; High Hon Roll; Hon Roll; RPI Medal Mst Outstndng Stu Math & Sci 85; FBLA Medal, 3rd RI Math Comp 85; Awd Part RI Acad Dec; Chem Engrng.

TOLLEY, KIMBERLY; Tiverton HS; Tiverton, RI; (Y); Church Yth Grp; Dance Clb; Drama Clb; Band; Concert Band; Mrchg Band; Pep Band; School Play; Yrbk Stf; Hon Roll; Gld Music Awd 85; Solo & Ensmbl Awds 82; Phscl Thrpst.

TOOLE, JANE; Lincoln JR/SR HS; Lincoln, RI; (Y); 25/220; Church Yth Grp; Cmnty Wkr; JA; Sec Trs JCL; Latin Clb; Stage Crew; Nwsp Sprt Ed; Nwsp Stf; Rep Soph Cls; Rep Jr Cls; No 1 Feml Golfr Natl H S Athl Coachs Assn 85; Citatn RI Genl Assmbly Recog Dghtrs Amer Revltn Awd 85; Coll Of Holy Cross; Engl.

TOOLE, MICHAEL; La Salle Acad; Seekonk, MA; (Y); 18/257; Church Yth Grp; Letterman Clb; Varsity Clb; Nwsp Rptr; Var L Crs Cntry; Var L Ice Hcky; Var L Trk; High Hon Roll; Brdcst Jrnlsm.

TORKOMIAN, LESA; Middletown HS; Middletown, RI; (S); 22/257; French Clb; Ski Clb; Pres Band; Concert Band; Mrchg Band; Pep Band; Var Capt Bsktbl; Powder Puff Ftbl; Var Sftbl; French Hon Soc; Pre-Med.

TORRES, MIRIAM; Central HS; Providence, RI; (Y); 2/29; Pres Church Yth Grp; Hosp Aide; Spanish Clb; Speech Tm; Lit Mag; Hon Roll; Upward Bound Awds; Daniel Webster Coll; Mgmt.

TOUPIN, DARLENE; Mount Saint Charles Acad; Woonsocket, RI; (Y); 10/147; Cmnty Wkr; Var Capt Cheerleading; High Hon Roll; NHS; Pre Med.

TOW, KEVIN; Classical HS; Providence, RI; (Y); 2/287; Pres Church Yth Grp; Math Tm; Var Capt Trk; High Hon Roll; Sal; Spanish NHS; St Schlr; Boy Scts; Science Clb; Nwsp Stf; Pres Acad Fitnss Awd 85; John Skeffington Memrl Spkr Of Hse Awd 85; Cum Laude Soc 85; MA Inst Of Tech; Engrng.

TRAINOR, KAREN; Warwick Veterans Memorial HS; Warwick, RI; (S); 54/330; Ed Yrbk Stf; Off Frsh Cls; Off Soph Cls; Off Jr Cls; Off Sr Cls.

TRAINOR, TIMOTHY; St Raphael Acad; Providence, RI; (Y); Church Yth Grp; Hosp Aide; JA; Stu Cncl; Bsktbl; Ftbl; Trk; Wt Lftg; MI ST U; Law.

TREANOR, PATRICK; St Raphael Acad; Cumberland, RI; (Y); Ski Clb; High Hon Roll; Htl Mgmnt.

TRENHOLME, CORI L; Tiverton HS; Tiverton, RI; (Y); Ski Clb; Band; Concert Band; Flag Corp; Mrchg Band; Yrbk Stf; Rep Stu Cncl; JV Bsktbl; Cheerleading; Var Socr; Sprts Med.

TRENHOLME, KAREN; Tiverton HS; Tiverton, RI; (S); 1/218; Church Yth Grp; Band; Mrchg Band; Yrbk Stf; VP Soph Cls; Rep Jr Cls; JV Var Cheerleading; High Hon Roll; NHS; Val; Flute Solo & Duet Awds 82; Pell Medl Outstndg US Hist 84; Chem.

TRINQUE, SUSAN; Woonsocket SR HS; Woonsocket, RI; (Y); Yrbk Stf; High Hon Roll; Hon Roll; St Schlr; Katharine Gibbs Schl; Exec Sec.

TROIA, JULIE; Cranston H S West; Cranston, RI; (S); Church Yth Grp; DECA; Yrbk Ed-Chief; Yrbk Stf; Hon Roll; Italina Clb 83-84; Asst Mgr Schl Store 85-86; Top 5 Wnnr Ntl Drnk Drvng Cntst 84-85; Brynat Coll; Bus.

TROIA, LISA; Crantson High School West; Cranston, RI; (S); 163/443; DECA; JA; Ski Clb; Yrbk Ed-Chief; Yrbk Stf; Sr Cls; Pres Stu Cncl; Stu Yr DECA 2nd Pl 85; 1st Pl Fd Mrktng Wnnr DECA 85, 1st Pl ST Lvl; Fshn Inst Tech; Adv.

TSAKONAS, DEMETRIOS; St Raphael Acad; Prov, RI; (Y); 12/177; Boys Clb Am; Exploring; Quiz Bowl; Rep Stu Cncl; JV Socr; Hon Roll; NHS; Chmpshp Quzbwl 85; Med.

TURLO, RALPH; Central HS; Providence, RI; (Y); Hst FBLA; Scholastic Bowl; Rep Stu Cncl; Gov Hon Prg Awd; Hon Roll; Pres Schlr; Dr P A Rizzi Schlrshp, Outstndng Bus Stu Awd Cntrl 85; Bryant Coll; Acctng.

TURPIN, KAREN; Prout Memorial HS; North Kingstown, RI; (S); 12/88; JA; Color Guard; Flag Corp; Hon Roll; Color Guard Flag Capt 84-85; VP Finance JR Achvt 84-85; Sub Religious Educ Tchr 84-85; Accntnt.

UDVARDY, AARON; Bristol HS; Bristol, RI; (Y); Ski Clb; Var Diving; JV Lcrss; Var Swmmng; Var Tennis; Arch.

UNDERHILL, LYNN; Toll Gate HS; Warwick, RI; (S); 2/393; Math Tm; Jazz Band; Nwsp Rptr; Yrbk Ed-Chief; Var Cheerleading; Var Vllybl; NHS; Sal; Harvard Bk Awd & Rensselaer Mdl; Law.

UPERTI, LISA A; Portsmouth HS; Portsmouth, RI; (Y); 16/215; Church Yth Grp; French Clb; Ski Clb; Chorus; High Hon Roll; Hon Roll; NHS; U Of RI; Elem Ed.

UPHAM, LEONARD; Cranston East HS; Cranston, RI; (Y); Church Yth Grp; Var Ftbl; Wt Lftg; Hon Roll; Jr NHS; Exclnc In Frnch 83; Sci Fair Grant 83; Won RI Tana Trnmnt 83.

VACCHI, STEVEN; Portsmouth HS; Portsmouth, RI; (Y); 7/221; L Band; Concert Band; Jazz Band; Mrchg Band; Orch; Pep Band; School Musical; Variety Show; High Hon Roll; NHS; Phi Mu Alpha Siaforria Music Frat 84; Tanglewood Smmr Music Inst 85; Greater Boston Yth Symphony 85; Eastman Schl Of Music; Litertr.

VACHON, JODIE ANN; Johnston SR HS; Johnston, RI; (Y); DECA; Band; Drm & Bgl; School Musical; Yrbk Stf; Twrlr; French Hon Soc; Hon Roll; Frnch Awds For Scrng Hgh Cont & Hnrs 83-85; Music Awd For Part 83; Hnrs Hstry & Englsh 83-85; Nrsng.

VAILLANCOURT, ROGER J; East Providence SR HS; Rumford, RI; (Y); Rhode Isl Schlr 85; Rhode Island Coll; Film Studies.

VALCOURT, VAUGHN; Johnston HS; Johnston, RI; (Y); Boy Scts; Cmnty Wkr; Nwsp Stf; Socr; Wrstlng; High Hon Roll; Ntl Merit Ltr; Bst ST Entry Amer Hstry Day 83; Awd Of Excel In Itln 85.

VALE, AMY; Bishop Keough HS; N Providence, RI; (S); Drama Clb; Ski Clb; School Play; Yrbk Stf; Pres Frsh Cls; Pres Soph Cls; Pres Sr Cls; Rep Stu Cncl; Sftbl; Hon Roll; Religion Awd; Prncpl Adv Board Awd; Stud Cncl Awd; Bryant Coll; Mktg.

VALENCIA, PIEDAD; Central Falls JR/SR HS; Central Fls, RI; (Y); 6/120; Am Leg Aux Girls St; Church Yth Grp; Cmnty Wkr; GAA; Pep Clb; Political Wkr; Off Jr Cls; Off Sr Cls; Stu Cncl; Var Bsktbl; Upward Bnd Pep Awd 83-85; Mdl Leg 85; SADD 85; Med.

VARNUM, BARBARA; Scituate JR SR HS; N Scituate, RI; (S); 16/115; Cmnty Wkr; VP Jr Cls; VP Sr Cls; Capt Var Cheerleading; Var Capt Tennis; DAR Awd; Hon Roll; Jr NHS; NHS; Natl Athl Acad Schlrshp Awd 84-85; U Of CT; Med.

VASCONCELOS, IVONE; Davies Voc Tech; Pawtucket, RI; (Y); Dance Clb; Pep Clb; Varsity Clb; VICA; Chorus; Yrbk Ed-Chief; Bsktbl; Cheerleading; High Hon Roll; Hon Roll; RI U; Law.

VAUGHT, JULIE; Rogers HS; Loring AFB, ME; (Y); Church Yth Grp; VP JA; L Mrchg Band; L Symp Band; JV Cheerleading; French Hon Soc; NHS; Ruth B Franklin Awd 85; Charles B King Schlrshp Awd 85; Pres Acadmc Fit Awd 85; Purdue U; Astron Engrng.

VERGE, JUSTIN; South Kingstown HS; Wakefield, RI; (Y); 25/226; Band; Concert Band; Jazz Band; Mrchg Band; Im Bsktbl; JV Crs Cntry; Var L Ftbl; JV Trk; Im Wt Lftg; Cit Awd.

VIEIRA, LISA M; Johnston SR HS; Johnston, RI; (Y); DECA; Nwsp Stf; NEH Yth Projcts Grant Ntl Histry Day 85; Crmnl Justc.

VIENS, MICHELLE; Lincoln JR SR HS; Manville, RI; (Y); 37/190; Band; Concert Band; Mrchg Band; Hon Roll; NHS; Johnson & Wales Coll; Clnry Art.

VIERA, MARGARET; Bristol HS; Bristol, RI; (S); Church Yth Grp; Drama Clb; JCL; Latin Clb; Teachers Aide; Band; Chorus; Concert Band; Mrchg Band; Pep Band; R I Honor Soc 83-85; Providence Coll RI; Teach Deaf.

VILKER, LEE; Cranston High School West; Cranston, RI; (Y); Exploring; Quiz Bowl; Scholastic Bowl; Spanish Clb; Trs Temple Yth Grp; Yrbk Rptr; Hon Roll; Jr NHS; Ntl Merit Ltr; Spanish NHS; Lttl Rhody Bys ST 85; Smmr Sci Trning Pgrm At PC 85; Bio.

VILLELLA, LYNN; N Providence HS; N Providence, RI; (Y); Church Yth Grp; Cmnty Wkr; Dance Clb; Hosp Aide; Red Cross Aide; Hon Roll; Johnson & Wales Coll; Clnry Art.

VISCIONE, STEPHEN JAY; Bristol HS; Bristol, RI; (Y); 63/226; Boy Scts; Church Yth Grp; Ski Clb; Band; Concert Band; Mrchg Band; Orch; Stu Cncl; Wrstlng; Hon Roll; Bristol Comm Coll; Comp Sci.

VITO, DARREN; St Raphael Acad; Pawtucket, RI; (Y); Hon Roll; 2nd Hnr Awd 84-85; URI; Engrng.

VITO, KRISTEN; Mt St Charles Acad; Woonsocket, RI; (Y); Camera Clb; Cmnty Wkr; Teachers Aide; Yrbk Phtg; Hon Roll; Early Childhd Eductn.

VITULLO, SHERI; Our Lady Of Fatima HS; Warren, RI; (S); Trs Soph Cls; Var Bsktbl; Var Sftbl; Var Trk; Hon Roll; Physcl Therpy.

VIVEIROS, JANICE M; Tiverton HS; Tiverton, RI; (S); 2/218; Yrbk Ed-Chief; Yrbk Stf; Rep Frsh Cls; Rep Pres Soph Cls; Stat Var Bsktbl; Var L Tennis; Elks Awd; High Hon Roll; NHS; Ntl Merit Ltr; Pblc Reltns.

VIVEIROS, PAUL; Bristol HS; Bristol, RI; (S); VP Computer Clb; Math Clb; Math Tm; Teachers Aide; Off Frsh Cls; Off Soph Cls; High Hon Roll; NHS; 2nd Pl Sr Div Reginal Problem Sovling Contest; High Score Math Team Regnl Test; Comp Sci.

VIVEIROS, SHERRI; Tiverton HS; Tiverton, RI; (Y); Ski Clb; Yrbk Stf; Sec Jr Cls; Sec Sr Cls; VP Pres Stu Cncl; Var Cheerleading; High Hon Roll; Hon Roll; Recpnt U RI Bk Awd 85; Fash Design.

VOGEL, PATRICIA; St Mary Acad; Hope, RI; (Y); Church Yth Grp; Cmnty Wkr; Drama Clb; Exploring; French Clb; Intnl Clb; Library Aide; Chorus; Im Bsktbl; Im Sftbl; Sci Fair Awd 1st & 2nd 81-82; 1st Runner Up Regnl Snowball Queen 82-83; Sociology.

VOTTA, CAROL; Johnston HS; Johnston, RI; (S); 28/297; Hosp Aide; DECA; Drm Mjr(t); Hon Roll; NHS; Italian Honor Society 82; RI Honor Society 85; RI College; Nursing.

WALDMAN, SHARON L; Classical HS; Pawtucket, RI; (Y); 24/290; Computer Clb; Dance Clb; Drama Clb; French Clb; JCL; Latin Clb; Science Clb; School Play; Yrbk Stf; Lit Mag; Presdntl Acadm Ftns Awd; Magna Cum Laude; U Of MA Amherst.

WALKER, TRACIE A; Lincoln JR SR HS; Lincoln, RI; (Y); 53/220; Church Yth Grp; Yrbk Stf; Hon Roll; RI Clg; Elem Educ.

WALLACE, DIANE; Tiverton HS; Tiverton, RI; (S); 5/218; Mrchg Band; Orch; Yrbk Stf; Rep Frsh Cls; Rep Soph Cls; JV Var Cheerleading; High Hon Roll; Music Awds 82-83; Elec Engrng.

WALLACE, KIMBERLY; Barrington HS; Barrington, RI; (Y); Frsh Cls; Soph Cls; Jr Cls; St Lukes Schl Hnrs 81-82; RI U; Sci.

WALSH, STEPHONIE ANNE; Portsmouth HS; Portsmouth, RI; (Y); Church Yth Grp; FBLA; Pep Clb; Band; Concert Band; Mrchg Band; Pep Band; Crs Cntry; Powder Puff Ftbl; Trk; Smmr Scientfc Air Forc Acad 85; Futr Bus Ldrs Amer Ntl Ldrshp Conf 85; Bio.

WARDLOW, DAVID; Rogers HS; Newport, RI; (Y); ROTC; Color Guard; Yrbk Phtg; Yrbk Stf; Hon Roll; Aud/Vis; Spanish Clb; Drill Tm; Stage Crew; Nwsp Phtg; Superior Cadet Awd 82; Bus.

WARE, RONNY; Johnston HS; Johnston, RI; (Y); FBLA; ROTC; VP Frsh Cls; JV Bsbl; JV Bsktbl; Wt Lftg; Bus Mngmnt.

WARRENER, BRIAN; Johnston SR HS; Johnston, RI; (S); 1/237; Pres JA; Nwsp Ed-Chief; Sec Trs Stu Cncl; Capt L Ftbl; Capt L Ice Hcky; Capt L Trk; NHS; Ntl Merit Ltr; Val; Brown U Bk Awd 84; 1st Tm All ST Ftbl 84-85; All Dic Hocky 83-84; Pre Law.

WATERMAN, MELANIE; Johnston SR HS; Johnston, RI; (S); 25/237; DECA; Nwsp Stf; Yrbk Stf; Sec Stu Cncl; Score Keeper; Hon Roll; NHS; RI CC; Bkkpng.

WATKINS, CHRISTINE; Alternate Learning Project; Providence, RI; (S); DECA; Yrbk Stf; Hon Roll.

WEAVER, BRIAN; North Kingstown HS; N Kingstown, RI; (Y); Boy Scts; Letterman Clb; Band; Concert Band; Jazz Band; Mrchg Band; Pep Band; Symp Band; Rep Stu Cncl; JV Bsbl; All Div Wrstlng Champ; Music.

WEAVILL, ANDREW; Lincoln JR SR HS; Lincoln, RI; (Y); 34/250; Chess Clb; JCL; Rep Stu Cncl; Im Bsktbl; Jr NHS; RI Higher Ed Assist Authrty 85; Cum Laude Latin 83; 2nd Grant Sci Fair; Bentley Coll; Comp.

WEBB, LISA BETH; Mount St Charles HS; Bellingham, MA; (Y); Church Yth Grp; Dance Clb; High Hon Roll; Hon Roll; NHS; Framingham ST Coll; Media Comm.

WEBBER, RENEE; Portsmouth HS; Portsmouth, RI; (Y); 63/206; Church Yth Grp; Dance Clb; Drama Clb; FBLA; Library Aide; Quiz Bowl; Thesps; School Play; Variety Show; Yrbk Stf; Am Hrt Assoc Cert Of Apprctn 84; Cert Of Apprctn Eastr Sls 83 & 84.

WEEKS, COLLEEN; Narragansett HS; Narragansett, RI; (Y); 20/124; Church Yth Grp; Drama Clb; Letterman Clb; Band; Chorus; Yrbk Stf; VP Frsh Cls; Soph Cls; Jr Cls; Sr Cls; South Cnty Jr Wmns Clb Schlrshp 85; South Cnty Office Park Schlrshp 85; RI Hnr Soc 85; Hofstra U; Poltcl Sci.

WEIGOLD, SABRA; St Mary Academy Bay View; Cranston, RI; (Y); Art Clb; VP Church Yth Grp; Exploring; JCL; Latin Clb; Math Clb; Gold Medal In JR Classical Leag Latin Exam 85; Drawing Schltc Art Awd Compttn 83; Engnrng.

WELCH, KATHY; Warwick Vetrans Memorial HS; Warwick, RI; (Y); Church Yth Grp; Ski Clb; Hon Roll; URI; Phtgrphy.

WELLS, THOMAS J; Warwick Veterans Memorial HS; East Greenwich, RI; (Y); 23/317; Cmnty Wkr; Lit Mag; Hon Roll; Jr NHS; Ntl Merit SF; Spanish NHS; U Of RI; Vet.

WESTCOTT, JEANNETTE; East Greenwich HS; E Greenwich, RI; (Y); VP Drama Clb; Hosp Aide; Chorus; School Musical; Mgr Stage Crew; Hon Roll; Schl Schlr 85; Ed.

WHEELER, LORI A; Classical HS; Providence, RI; (Y); Church Yth Grp; Hon Roll; Vet Sci.

WHITE, JEANNE; Warwick Veterans Memorial HS; Warwick, RI; (S); 107/323; Pres Church Yth Grp; Dance Clb; DECA; JA; Quiz Bowl; Variety Show; Hon Roll; 2nd Pl DECA ST Comp Food Mktng 84; Trophy In Bowlng 83; Letters Of Recog Mktng &de Teacher 84; Johnson & Wales Clg; Fashion.

WHITFORD, JONA; Prout Memorial HS; Exeter, RI; (S); Debate Tm; French Clb; School Musical; Trs Soph Cls; Trs Jr Cls; Hon Roll; Pre-Law.

WILBER, ELLEN; Portsmouth HS; Portsmouth, RI; (Y); Political Wkr; Band; Mrchg Band; Pres Frsh Cls; Rep Trs Stu Cncl; Var Capt Cheerleading; Crs Cntry; High Hon Roll; Hon Roll; NHS; U GA; Ag Econ.

WILBUR, KYLE; Bristol HS; Bristol, RI; (Y); Var Capt Ftbl; Var Capt Ice Hcky; Var Capt Tennis; Hon Roll; Eric W Dober Ftbl Schlrshp 85; Providence Jrnl Hnr Roll Awd 85; All Cls B Div II Deg Lnebckr 84-85; U Of RI.

WILDENHAIN, ANNMARIE; Wm Davies Technical Vo Tech; Pawtucket, RI; (Y); VICA; Camera Clb; Girl Scts; Teachers Aide; Chorus; Pep Band; School Musical; Variety Show; Yrbk Stf; Trs Soph Cls; IFSEA Awd 85; :VICA Cmrcl Fds Cntst Helper 85.

WILKINSON, MARK; Burrillville JR SR HS; Pascoag, RI; (Y); 13/190; Boy Scts; Church Yth Grp; Math Tm; Ski Clb; School Play; Nwsp Rptr; Nwsp Stf; Im Golf; High Hon Roll; Jr NHS; RI ST Awd 85; U RI; Elec Engrng.

WILLIAMS III, HOWARD; Rogers HS; Newport, RI; (Y); Hon Roll; Prfct Atten Awd; R I Cstl Rescs Mgmt Cncl,Essay Cntst 83; CC RI,Comtrs.

WILLIAMS, RONDA; Johnston SR HS; Johnston, RI; (S); 6/238; Church Yth Grp; JA; Ski Clb; Nwsp Rptr; Nwsp Stf; High Hon Roll; NHS; St Schlr; RI Hnr Soc 84-85.

WILMOUTH, RODNEY; Coventry HS; Coventry, RI; (Y); 38/306; ROTC; Varsity Clb; JV L Bsbl; Var L Ftbl; JV L Wrstlng; Hon Roll; 4th Pl RI JV Wrstlng ST Chmpn 85; Bus Mngmnt.

WOJCIK, SHERRI; Middletown HS; Middletown, RI; (S); 23/252; Church Yth Grp; Drama Clb; Chorus; Church Choir; School Play; Lit Mag; High Hon Roll; Hon Roll; Music Awd; Day Care.

WOOD, DANIEL E; Wheeler Schl; Hope Valley, RI; (Y); Pres Exploring; Math Tm; School Musical; School Play; Nwsp Phtg; Rep Jr Cls; Rep Stu Cncl; Var L Lcrss; Var L Socr; Ntl Merit SF.

WOOD, DAVID; Central Falls HS; Central Falls, RI; (Y); 18/136; Pres Art Clb; Cmnty Wkr; Drama Clb; Science Clb; School Musical; School Play; Stage Crew; Yrbk Stf; Var L Bsktbl; Var L Ftbl; Providence Coll; Comp Sci.

WOOD, KEVIN; Portsmouth HS; Portsmouth, RI; (Y); Band; Church Choir; Concert Band; Mrchg Band; Pep Band; Hon Roll; NHS; Rhode Isl Music Ed Assoc All St Band 83-85; U RI; Marine Bio.

WOODCOCK, KIMBERLY; Charles E Shea SR HS; Pawtucket, RI; (Y); Yrbk Stf; Sec Frsh Cls; Sec Soph Cls; Sec Jr Cls; Sec Sr Cls; Off Stu Cncl; Score Keeper; Hon Roll.

WOODS, KELLY ANN; Portsmouth HS; Portsmouth, RI; (Y); Drama Clb; FBLA; Band; School Play; Variety Show; VP Frsh Cls; VP Jr Cls; VP Sr Cls; Rep Stu Cncl; 12 Yrs Stage Dancing 85; Dance.

WOTTON, BROOKE; Portsmouth HS; Portsmouth, RI; (Y); 63/217; FBLA; Stu Cncl; Gym; Powder Puff Ftbl; Tennis; Bus Awd-Outstndng Achvt In Bus 82-83; Boston U; Phy Thrpy.

WRIGHT, SHERI; Prout Memorial HS; E Greenwich, RI; (S); 3/86; Sec Frsh Cls; Pres Soph Cls; Pres Jr Cls; JV VP Bsktbl; VP Crs Cntry; VP Sftbl; Ski Clb; Teachers Aide; High Hon Roll; Hghst Achvmnt Cert Frnch I II 81-84; Hghst Achvmnt Cert Anatomy 82-83; Hghst Achvmnt Geo 82-83; Fin.

YATES, JENNIFER; Cumberland HS; Cumberland, RI; (S); DECA; Drama Clb; Chorus; Color Guard; Drill Tm; School Musical; School Play; Stage Crew; Yrbk Stf; Masonic Awd.

YEOMANS, THOMAS; Rogers HS; Newport, RI; (Y); School Musical; School Play; Stage Crew; JV Bsbl; JV Var Ftbl; JV Trk; Hon Roll; Elec Engrng.

YOUNG, DEREK; Johnston SR HS; Johnston, RI; (Y); Var Capt Ice Hcky.

YOUNG, TRACY; Charino Regional HS; W Kingston, RI; (S); 7/328; Trs 4-H; VP Soph Cls; VP Jr Cls; Var Capt Cheerleading; Var JV Fld Hcky; Trk; 4-H Awd; High Hon Roll; Jr NHS; Prfct Atten Awd; RI Horsemnshp Awd 83; Hmcmng Queen 84; 4-H; Psych.

ZAGAROLI, ALFREDO; Classical HS; Providence, RI; (Y); 27/187; Church Yth Grp; Drama Clb; Science Clb; Band; Drm & Bgl; School Musical; Hon Roll; Pres Schlr; Magna Cum Laude 85; URI; Engrng.

ZANNI, JULIE; St Mary Acad-Bay View; Johnston, RI; (Y); Sec Church Yth Grp; Cmnty Wkr; Exploring; Quiz Bowl; Chorus; Church Choir; Hon Roll; NHS; Seltd Ntnwde Yth Sing Praise 83-85; Itln Clb 84-85; U Of RI; Bio.

ZARRELLA, GINA; St Mayrs Bay View HS; Johnston, RI; (Y); 15/210; Drama Clb; Exploring; Math Clb; Spanish Clb; School Play; Hon Roll; NHS; Cert Educ Dev Natl 83; Cert Merit Serv 85; Vet Med.

ZEMA, JOANNE; Warwick Veterans Memorial HS; Warwick, RI; (Y); VP Acpl Chr; VP Chorus; Yrbk Stf; Rep Frsh Cls; Rep Soph Cls; Rep Jr Cls; High Hon Roll; Hon Roll; Comp Sci.

ZIEGLER, NAOMI AILEEN; Portsmouth HS; Portsmouth, RI; (Y); 6/225; Church Yth Grp; Pres Civic Clb; Band; Mrchg Band; Pep Band; Cit Awd; High Hon Roll; Hon Roll; Jr NHS; NHS.

ZIENOWICZ, DAVID; Bishop Hendricken HS; Cranston, RI; (Y); 11/248; Ski Clb; Jazz Band; JV Ice Hcky; High Hon Roll; NHS; Biomed Engrng.

ZIFCAK, MONICA; Burrillville JR SR HS; Pascoag, RI; (Y); 8/165; Math Tm; VP Soph Cls; Sec Stu Cncl; Var L Fld Hcky; Var L Gym; Var L Sftbl; Hon Roll; NHS; Letterman Clb; School Play; Vrsty Gym MVP 84-85; Vrsty Gm Sprtsmnshp 83-85; Vrsty Fld Hcky 2nd Tm All Div 84; Biol.

ZITO, STEPHANIE; Narragansett HS; Narragansett, RI; (Y); 14/130; Intnl Clb; Variety Show; Rep Jr Cls; Var Tennis; Var Vllybl; Hon Roll; NHS; Ntl Itln Hnr Soc 85; Itln Clb VP 85; RI Tchrs Itln Hnr Soc; Italn.

ZOHLEN, PETER; Rogers HS; Newport, RI; (S); 7/563; Math Clb; Math Tm; Church Choir; Orch; Socr; Swmmng; Trk; High Hon Roll; Hon Roll; NHS; GA Inst Tech; Elec Engrng.

ZUCKER, GEORGE; South Kingstown HS; Kingston, RI; (Y); 2/250; Am Leg Boys St; Art Clb; Church Yth Grp; Pres Computer Clb; Math Clb; High Hon Roll; NHS; Ntl Merit Ltr; Boys Nation 86; Hnbl Mntn RI Clg Wrtg Cntst 86; Jrnlsm.

ZULETA, CESAR A; Central Falls JR HS; Central Fls, RI; (Y); 5/100; High Hon Roll; Hon Roll; Bryant Coll; Bus.

VERMONT

ABATIELL, AUDRA; Mt St Joseph Acad; Rutland, VT; (Y); Church Yth Grp; Dance Clb; Drama Clb; Pres 4-H; Trs Key Clb; Ski Clb; Band; Chorus; Concert Band; Jazz Band; Pres 4-H Cnty Cncl 85; Chf Of Polc Elks Clb Youth Day 85; U VT JR Conf 85; Vet.

ACCIAVATTI, MICHAEL; Colchester HS; Colchester, VT; (Y); Exploring; Political Wkr; Chorus; Nwsp Stf; Lit Mag; Trk; Hon Roll; Dendrolgy.

ADDLEMAN, JEFFREY; Colchester HS; Colchester, VT; (Y); 22/219; Debate Tm; Math Tm; School Play; Capt L Bsbl; Var L Socr; Hon Roll; Jr NHS; NHS; Pres Schlr; Hnrb Mntn-Bsbl 84; U Of VT Digtl Math Exm Awd 85; Cochs Awd-Bsbl 84; U Of VT; Elec Engrng.

ADOLFSSON, TINA; Mount Saint Joseph Acad; Pittsford, VT; (Y); 8/99; Computer Clb; Sec 4-H; Science Clb; Varsity Clb; Yrbk Stf; Var L Cheerleading; Tennis; High Hon Roll; Var L Socr; Hon Roll; VT Grls ST Rep 85; Sec Green Mtn Appaloosa Yth Clb 84; Vet.

AGALLIANOS, H PENELOPE; Putney Schl; Brattleboro, VT; (Y); Trs Church Yth Grp; Cmnty Wkr; Church Choir; Madrigals; School Play; Yrbk Phtg; Yrbk Stf; Lit Mag; Ntl Merit SF; Library Aide; Stnd A Jdcry/Discplnry Commtt 84; Humanities.

ALDRICH, BOBBY; Harwood Union HS; Waterbury Ctr, VT; (Y); JV Bsbl; JV Bsktbl; JV Ftbl; JV Ice Hcky; JV Socr.

ALEXANDER, JO; Richford HS; Enosburg Falls, VT; (Y); Am Leg Aux Girls St; Band; Model UN; Natl Beta Clb; Mrchg Band; School Musical; VP Stu Cncl; Var Bsktbl; Capt Var Socr; Trs NHS; U VT; Med.

ALLARD, BRIAN; Burlington HS; Burlington, VT; (Y); Latin Clb; Var Bsbl; Hon Roll; Coaches Awd JV Bsebl 84; Engr.

ALNASRAWI, LEYLA; Champion Valley Union HS; Shelburne, VT; (Y); Church Yth Grp; Sec JA; Band; Concert Band; Mrchg Band; Orch; School Musical; JV Fld Hcky; High Hon Roll; NHS; U Of VT; Pediatrcn.

ALTRUI, JODI; Mount St Joseph Acad; Rutland, VT; (Y); 9/99; Art Clb; Chorus; Church Choir; Yrbk Stf; Cheerleading; Pom Pon; Hon Roll.

ALVAREZ, NATALIE E; Harwood Union HS; Waterbury, VT; (Y); Camera Clb; Drama Clb; Intnl Clb; Model UN; Chorus; School Musical; School Play; Stage Crew; Hon Roll; Med.

AMEDEN, LISA MARIE; Leland And Gray Union HS; Jamaica, VT; (Y); Band; Mrchg Band; Pep Band; School Play; Pres Frsh Cls; Pres Soph Cls; Pres Jr Cls; Pres Sr Cls; Pres Stu Cncl; Hon Roll.

AMES, JENNIFER; North Country Union HS; Newport, VT; (Y); Am Leg Aux Girls St; Drama Clb; Ski Clb; Band; Chorus; School Musical; School Play; Rep Jr Cls; Cheerleading; Fld Hcky; Govrnr Inst Arts 83; Theatr Arts.

AMYOT, CAROL; Sacred Heart HS; Barton, VT; (Y); Chorus; School Play; Yrbk Stf; Sec Frsh Cls; Socr; Psych.

ANCLIFFE, REBECCA; Chelsea HS; Corinth, VT; (Y); Art Clb; Drama Clb; 4-H; FBLA; NFL; Ski Clb; School Play; Yrbk Phtg; Hon Roll; NHS; VT JA Conf 85; Photo.

ANDERSON, CHRISTINE M; Brattleboro Union HS; Brattleboro, VT; (Y); 3/216; Cmnty Wkr; DECA; Latin Clb; Model UN; Red Cross Aide; Yrbk Phtg; Rep Stu Cncl; Elks Awd; High Hon Roll; Stu Cncl Svc Awd 85; George Broutsas Awd Schlrshp 85; Outstndg SR Portfolio Awd 85; Wheaton; Econ.

ANTON, DAVID; Spaulding HS; Barre, VT; (Y); Am Leg Boys St; Church Yth Grp; Key Clb; Rep Stu Cncl; Var L Golf; Hon Roll; V T Jr PGA Northern St Champ 83.

ARBUCKLE, JENNIFER R; Bellows Falls Union HS; Bellows Falls, VT; (Y); 3/100; Am Leg Aux Girls St; Art Clb; Cmnty Wkr; VP Intnl Clb; Math Tm; Scholastic Bowl; VP Stu Cncl; High Hon Roll; NHS; Ntl Merit SF; JR Conf 84; JR Prom Commtt 84; Fresh Recptn Commtt 84; Arch.

ASHLEY, CYNTHIA M; Essex Jct Educational Center; Westford, VT; (Y); 14/320; VICA; Var L Socr; Im Vllybl; High Hon Roll; NHS; MIP Awd Sccr 81-82; 1st Pl ST VICA Bakg Cntst 83-84; U Of VT; Anml Sci.

ASHLINE, LISA M; Hartford HS; Hartland, VT; (Y); Office Aide; Teachers Aide; Capt Im Bsktbl; Im Sftbl; 4-H Awd; Hon Roll.

ATHERTON, AMY; Burr & Burton Seminary; Bondville, VT; (Y); Church Yth Grp; French Clb; Var Cheerleading; High Hon Roll; Hon Roll; Drama Clb; Chorus; VT JR Conf 85; Bus.

AUDET, ALAN JOSEPH; Peoples Acad; Morrisville, VT; (Y); 15/78; Drama Clb; Mrchg Band; Sec Soph Cls; JV Var Bsktbl; NHS; U Of VT; Bus Admin.

AYERS, LAURIE B; Mount Anthony Union HS; Bennington, VT; (Y); Church Yth Grp; Dance Clb; FBLA; Spanish Clb; Variety Show; Stat Bsktbl; Fld Hcky; Trk; Vllybl; Hon Roll; Outstndng Work Engl 83-84.

BAILEY, CRAIG C; Union-32 HS; Barre, VT; (Y); 1/180; Drama Clb; Band; Jazz Band; School Musical; School Play; High Hon Roll; Val; Outstndng Contrbtn Perfrmng Arts & Band 84-85; VT Hnr Schlrshp 84-85; Ithaca Coll; Cmmnctns.

BAIRD, THOMAS; Hartford HS; White River Jct, VT; (Y); 1/110; Am Leg Boys St; Church Yth Grp; Debate Tm; Math Tm; Bsbl; Ftbl; Wt Lftg; High Hon Roll; Jr NHS; NHS.

BAKER, ARTHUR R; Burlington HS; Burlington, VT; (Y); German Clb; Band; Mrchg Band; Pep Band; Symp Band; Rep Frsh Cls; JV Var Ftbl; Var Tennis; Hon Roll; NHS.

BAKER, CHARITY; Harwood Union HS; Waterbury Centr, VT; (Y); Church Yth Grp; Band; Chorus; School Musical; Rep Stu Cncl; High Hon Roll; Trs NHS; Pres Schlr; Rotary Awd; Church Choir; Cert Of Merit UVM Math Comp 85; Mount Holyoke Coll.

BALLOU, COLETTE P; Middleburg Union HS; Chapel Hill, NC; (Y); 14/196; Drama Clb; Nwsp Rptr; Off Sr Cls; Off Stu Cncl; Var Tennis; Hon Roll; NHS; AFS; Church Yth Grp; School Musical; UNC Chapel Hill; Jrnlsm.

BAMBARA JR, A PAUL; Burr & Burton Seminary; Dorset, VT; (Y); AFS; Am Leg Boys St; 4-H; Model UN; Band; Mrchg Band; Stu Cncl; Tennis; Hon Roll; VP Frsh Cls; Hugh Obrien Rep 84; U Of VT; Law.

BARBOUR, TIMOTHY; Windsor HS; Hartland, VT; (Y); 15/68; Am Leg Boys St; Varsity Clb; School Play; Var L Ftbl; Var Trk; Var Ski Tm Ltrmn 84-85; Hnrs Engl Coll Course 85; Pol Sci.

BARTLEY, BRENDA; Brattleboro Union HS; Putney, VT; (Y); Pres FBLA; Pres FFA; Model UN; Chorus; Yrbk Stf; Lit Mag; Hon Roll; 1st Rnr-Up Mdrn Ms Schlrshp Pgnt 85; Outstndng Data Prcsng Stu 85; New Hampshire Coll; Adm Asstnt.

BAXTER, CINDY; Mount Anthony HS; N Bennington, VT; (Y); Pres Church Yth Grp; Dance Clb; Drama Clb; French Clb; Pep Clb; Ski Clb; Chorus; School Musical; School Play; Lit Mag; Excell Englsh; Muscl Thtr.

BEACH, KELLY; Vergennes Union HS; Vergennes, VT; (Y); 2/127; German Clb; Yrbk Stf; High Hon Roll; Hon Roll; Masonic Awd; NHS; Pres Schlr; Sal; Outstndng Jr Conf; Acctng Comptn; Castleton ST Coll; Sec Ed.

BEAN, ANTHONY; Burlington HS; Burlington, VT; (Y); Am Leg Boys St; Pres Band; Concert Band; Pep Band; Symp Band; Stat Bsbl; Bsktbl; Stat Ftbl; Hon Roll; NHS; Infrmtn Dirctr; Jrnlsm.

BECKER, RACHEL; Mt Mansfield Union HS; Cambridge, VT; (Y); 26/165; Band; Orch; School Musical; School Play; High Hon Roll; Hon Roll; NHS; Concert Band; Mrchg Band; Pep Band; Pro Merito Awd 85; Lucius Jackson Mem Schlrshp 85; Clarkson U; Chem Engrng.

BEGNOCHE, DAVID; Burlington HS; Burlington, VT; (Y); Trk; VT Tech Coll; Elec Engr.

BELKNAP, TERI LEE; Harwood Union HS; Moretown, VT; (Y); Church Yth Grp; Girl Scts; Model UN; Ski Clb; Nwsp Rptr; Nwsp Stf; Yrbk Stf; Var Capt Bsktbl; Var Fld Hcky; Var Capt Sftbl; Boosters Clb Schlrshp 85; Chmplain Coll; Bus Mngmnt.

BELL, SHERRY; Maint Anthony Union HS; Bennington, VT; (Y); 30/250; 4-H; Pep Clb; Hon Roll; NHS; Excllnce Eng 85; Sci.

BELL, TINA; Rutland HS; Rutland, VT; (Y); Accntng.

BENJAMIN, KAREN; Essex Junction Educational Center; Essex Jct, VT; (Y); 22/310; Church Yth Grp; Computer Clb; 4-H; Mrchg Band; Pep Band; Yrbk Ed-Chief; High Hon Roll; Hon Roll; Jr NHS; NHS; U Of VT; Animal Sci.

BENOIT, ROXANNE; Enosburg Falls HS; Richford, VT; (Y); FBLA; FHA; Teachers Aide; Rep Jr Cls; Rep Stu Cncl; High Hon Roll; Hon Roll; Prfct Atten Awd; Pres Awd Phys Ftnss; Hrdst Wrkr Geog; Comp Engnr.

BERGERON, KIM; Colchester HS; Colchester, VT; (S); Am Leg Aux Girls St; Capt Var Bsktbl; JV Var Socr; Capt Var Sftbl; Hon Roll; NHS.

BERGERON, SHARON; Burlington HS; Burlington, VT; (Y); Drama Clb; Girl Scts; Chorus; School Musical; School Play; U VT.

BERGEVIN, MIKE A; Middlebury Union HS; Middlebury, VT; (Y); Band; Concert Band; Jazz Band; Mrchg Band; Var L Ftbl; Hon Roll; NHS; Cnstrctn Mgr.

BERGSTEIN, LAURA; Colchester HS; Colchester, VT; (Y); Drama Clb; Variety Show; Rep Jr Cls; Off Stu Cncl; Stat Bsbl; Stat Socr; Tour Europ Danc Grp; Trvl Agnt.

BERNASCONI, PAUL; Burr & Burton Seminary; Peru, VT; (Y); 6/100; Am Leg Boys St; Boy Scts; Drama Clb; German Clb; School Play; Ed Yrbk Stf; Var L Tennis; Cit Awd; High Hon Roll; NHS; U Of S FL; Engrng.

BERRY, KEVIN; Hartford HS; White River Jct, VT; (Y); 21/140; Band; Concert Band; Jazz Band; Mrchg Band; Pep Band; Bsktbl; Capt Crs Cntry; Lcrss; Hon Roll; JP Sousa Awd; Cmnctns.

BETTIS, WENDY A; Hartford HS; White Rvr Jct, VT; (Y); 16/107; GAA; Pep Clb; Teachers Aide; Yrbk Stf; Var Sftbl; Hon Roll; VT Tech Coll; Vet.

BIANCARDI, JEANA; North Country U HS; Newport, VT; (Y); Debate Tm; French Clb; GAA; School Musical; Yrbk Stf; Stat Bsktbl; JV Fld Hcky; JV Sftbl; URI; Phrmcy.

BICKNELL, PAUL; Vergennes Union HS; Ferrisburg, VT; (Y); 12/152; Am Leg Boys St; VP Frsh Cls; VP Soph Cls; VP Jr Cls; VP Sr Cls; Var Bsktbl; Var Socr; Hon Roll; NHS.

BILOWITH, KAREN; Colchester HS; Colchester, VT; (S); 7/220; Am Leg Aux Girls St; Cheerleading; Fld Hcky; High Hon Roll; Hon Roll; NHS; Frnch, Spnsh Achvt Awds 82-83; Earth Sci Hgh Avg Awd 82; Boston Coll; Pre-Law.

BLACKMER, MELISSA; Rutland HS; N Clarendon, VT; (Y); Trs Church Yth Grp; Math Clb; Science Clb; Hon Roll; Ntl Merit Ltr; Write Sci Fictn.

BLAKE, BAMBI; Leland-Gray Union HS; S Londonderry, VT; (Y); Trs FBLA; Office Aide; Hon Roll; NHS; Top Cls Awd Econ, Alg I, Frnch I; Law.

BLAKE, COURTLAND; Spaulding HS; Barre, VT; (Y); Am Leg Boys St; Key Clb; Ice Hcky; Var Socr; Var Tennis; High Hon Roll; Hon Roll.

BLANCHARD, MICHAEL; Canaan Memorial HS; Canaan, VT; (S); 2/25; Am Leg Boys St; Ski Clb; Band; Yrbk Stf; Var Bsbl; Var Bsktbl; Var Socr; High Hon Roll; Hon Roll; VP NHS; Elec Engrng

BLANEY, SCOTT; Richford HS; Enosburg Falls, VT; (Y); Church Yth Grp; Drama Clb; Model UN; Band; Chorus; School Play; Stage Crew; Variety Show; Var L Bsbl; Var L Bsktbl; Amer Lgn Pittsburg Cadet Trng 85; Norwich Bsktbl Schl 85; Castleton; Law Engrcmnt.

BLISS, KRISTEN; U-32 HS; Barre, VT; (Y); Dance Clb; Teachers Aide; Sr Cls; JV Cheerleading; JV Crs Cntry; JV Var Sftbl; Hon Roll.

BLISS, MICHELE; U-32 HS; E Montpelier, VT; (Y); Church Yth Grp; Rptr Nwsp Stf; Yrbk Bus Mgr; Rep Sr Cls; Hon Roll; Interntl Camp Rep 84; Teen Talnt Speech Div 85; Bus.

BLONDIN, TASSIE; Colchester HS; Colchester, VT; (S); 18/219; Band; School Play; VP Frsh Cls; Rep Soph Cls; Rep Jr Cls; Sec Sr Cls; Rep Stu Cncl; Var L Socr; Hon Roll; VP NHS; Hugh O Brien Yth Ldrshp Fndtn 83; Coachs Awd 83-84; U VT; Bus Admin.

BLOOM, CARRIE; Leland & Gray Union HS; Townshend, VT; (Y); 4-H; Var Bsktbl; Var Socr; Sftbl; Hon Roll; All-Marble Vlly Leag Tm Grls Sccr 84; Top Of Clss Ceramics & Cooking 84-85; Collof The Atlantic; Botany.

BLUMEN, DEBRA; Champlain Valley Union HS; Shelburne, VT; (Y); 2/235; Band; Var L Bsktbl; Capt Bowling; Var L Fld Hcky; Var L Sftbl; High Hon Roll; NHS; Mrchg Band; Earth Sci Awd 82-83; Soc Studies Awd 83-84; French Awd 84-85; Sec Ed.

BODAKY, JIM; Colchester HS; Colchester, VT; (S); 14/220; Am Leg Boys St; CAP; Drama Clb; Nwsp Rptr; Lit Mag; Bausch & Lomb Sci Awd; Gov Hon Prg Awd; High Hon Roll; Hon Roll; NHS; De Forge Ed Awd Scholar 85; U VT; Chem.

BONIN, AUDREY; North Country Union HS; N Troy, VT; (Y); Office Aide; Hon Roll; Engl Dept Awd 84; ST Prmtn VT Tech Coll 83; Bk Knowledge Awd 83-85; Champlain Coll; Legal Secy.

BONNELL, ATHENA; North County Union HS; Newport, VT; (Y); Church Yth Grp; Model UN; Office Aide; Chorus; Church Choir; Hon Roll; Bk Knwldgr Pin 85; Sci Awd 83; Johnson ST Coll; Wrtng.

BOOTH, SUZETTE; Lake Region Union HS; West Glover, VT; (Y); Debate Tm; Pep Clb; Chorus; School Musical; Bsktbl; Fld Hcky; Socr; Sftbl; Trk; Hon Roll; Cnslng.

BORT, SUSAN; Burr & Burton Seminary; Arlington, VT; (Y); Church Yth Grp; CAP; 4-H; French Clb; German Clb; Girl Scts; Ski Clb; Concert Band; Mrchg Band; Var JV Bsktbl.

BOSLEY, PATRICIA; Colchester HS; Colchester, VT; (S); Hon Roll; NHS.

BOTTIGGI, TOM J; Williamstown HS; Williamstown, VT; (Y); 7/50; Computer Clb; French Clb; Yrbk Bus Mgr; JV Bsktbl; JV Socr; Sftbl; Vllybl; High Hon Roll; Hon Roll; VT Boys Bsktbl Coaches Assn All St Tm 84-85; Schl Athlt Of Yr 84-85; Outstndng Stu Awd-Comptrs 84-85; Comp.

BOVIA, KARYN A; Essex Jct HS; Essex Jct, VT; (Y); Intnl Clb; Sr Cls; Stu Cncl; JV Var Tennis; Hon Roll; U Of VT.

BOWEN, SHELLY; Mount Saint Joseph Acad; Mendon, VT; (Y); Psych.

BRADLEY, KARI; U-32 HS; Calais, VT; (Y); Band; Concert Band; Var Ice Hcky; Var Socr; High Hon Roll; Dartmuth JR Bk Awd 85; Boys ST 85; Pholosophy.

BRAMAN, LANCE O; St Johnsbury Acad; St Johnsbury, VT; (Y); 48/132; Aud/Vis; Computer Clb; Stage Crew; Hon Roll; Ntl Merit SF; US Marine Corps.

BRATCHER, DARREN; Mt Anthony Union HS; Pownal, VT; (Y); Am Leg Boys St; Church Yth Grp; Spanish Clb; Vllybl; High Hon Roll; Hon Roll; Bus Admin.

BREAULT, JOAN; North Country Union HS; Newport Center, VT; (Y); Girl Scts; Latin Clb; Office Aide; Chorus; School Play; Yrbk Stf; Hon Roll; Castleton; Nrsng.

BRESSETTE, CHRISTOPHER W; Bellows Free Acad; St Albans, VT; (Y); 24/212; Am Leg Boys St; JV Var Bsbl; JV Var Bsktbl; High Hon Roll; Hon Roll; NHS; Dr Loftus Mem Schlrshp 85; U VT; Engrng.

BRICKELL, JOCELYN; Burr & Burton Seminary HS; Dorset, VT; (Y); Ski Clb; JV Capt Fld Hcky; Hon Roll; JV Sftbl; Im Vllybl; Close Up Clb 85.

BRIERE, ALANA M; Fair Haven Union HS; Castleton, VT; (Y); 5/108; Yrbk Bus Mgr; Var Capt Bsktbl; Var L Socr; Var L Trk; High Hon Roll; Lion Awd; NHS; Am Leg Aux Girls St; Church Yth Grp; Chorus; Fhuhs Alumni Assoc Schlrshp 85; Big Sister Pgm 85; Keynotes 82-85; Springfield Coll; Athl Trng.

BRIGGS, THOMAS; Concord HS; North Concord, VT; (S); 3/19; Am Leg Boys St; Cmnty Wkr; Drama Clb; Radio Clb; School Play; Yrbk Stf; Pres Frsh Cls; Rep Soph Cls; Rep Jr Cls; Rep Sr Cls; Honorable Mention In Soccer 84; Class Marshal 84; Lyndon ST Colg:Business Mgmt.

BRISSON, GAIL; Rutland HS; Rutland, VT; (Y); 10/180; Drama Clb; Nwsp Ed-Chief; Nwsp Rptr; Nwsp Stf; Yrbk Bus Mgr; Yrbk Stf; High Hon Roll; Hon Roll; NHS; Ntl Merit Ltr; Voice Demcrcy Rgnl Wnnr 84; U VT; Eng.

BROPHY, JULIE; Burr & Burton Seminary; E Dorset, VT; (Y); Sec Frsh Cls; L Var Fld Hcky; High Hon Roll; NHS; Stat Bsktbl; Var L Mgr(s); Hon Roll; Acdmc All-Amer 85; Accntng.

BROUGHTON, MICHELLE M; Middlebury Union HS; Bridport, VT; (Y); Church Yth Grp; VICA; Flag Corp; Nwsp Stf; Var JV Bsktbl; Var Socr; Hon Roll; Outstndng JR Draftsprsn Yr 85; Engrng.

BROWE, LORI; Mount Mansfield Union HS; Jericho, VT; (Y); Varsity Clb; Band; Concert Band; Mrchg Band; Yrbk Stf; Stu Cncl; Var Cheerleading; JV Fld Hcky; JV Var Trk; Hon Roll; U Southern ME; Psych.

BROWN, AUDREY; U-32 HS; N Montpelier, VT; (Y); Dance Clb; Hosp Aide; Band; Var Gym; High Hon Roll; Hon Roll.

BROWN, HEIDI; North Country Union HS; Newport, VT; (Y); Chorus; Var Crs Cntry; Hon Roll; Bk Of Knwldge Awd 85; JR Cls Rep 85.

BROWN, STACIE; Mount Anthony U HS; Bennington, VT; (Y); Pres Art Clb; Debate Tm; Office Aide; Nwsp Stf; Yrbk Stf; Prfct Atten Awd; U Bridgeport; Art.

BROWNELL, CHRIS; Mount Anthony Union HS; N Pownal, VT; (Y); 47/300; Am Leg Aux Girls St; Spanish Clb; Yrbk Ed-Chief; Yrbk Stf; High Hon Roll; Hon Roll; Excllnc Engl 84-85; RPI; Psych.

BROWNELL, CHRISTINE L; Mt Anthony Union HS; N Pownal, VT; (Y); 47/300; Am Leg Aux Girls St; Spanish Clb; Yrbk Ed-Chief; Yrbk Stf; High Hon Roll; Hon Roll; Excell Engl; RPI; Psych.

BRUNELLE, MELINDA; Winooski HS; Winooski, VT; (Y); Am Leg Aux Girls St; Scholastic Bowl; Band; Jazz Band; Sec Soph Cls; Pres Jr Cls; Rep Stu Cncl; JV Var Sftbl; Hon Roll; Concert Band; Typng I & Bus Ed Awds; Accntng.

BRYANT, JEFF; Union 32 HS; E Montpelier, VT; (Y); Boy Scts; Debate Tm; Library Aide; Teachers Aide; Concert Band; Mrchg Band; Ntl Merit SF; Rochester Tech Inst; Comp.

BRYCE, ERICKA; Enosburg Falls HS; E Fairfield, VT; (Y); FBLA; Var Capt Cheerleading; High Hon Roll; Hon Roll; Bus Math Awd Coaches Awd Chrldg; Life Sci Awd; Hsng Awd; Engl Awd; Hesser Coll; Legal Sec.

BULLARD, AMY; Chelsea HS; Chelsea, VT; (S); JV Debate Tm; Drama Clb; VP NFL; Band; School Musical; Var Fld Hcky; NHS; Trs Frsh Cls; Trs Soph Cls; VP Stu Cncl; Hugh O Brian Youth Foundation; Biology.

BURDETTE, CHRISTINE; Vermont Acad; Hooksett, NH; (Y); Church Yth Grp; Pres Soph Cls; JV Capt Lcrss; JV Var Socr; Var Trk; Hon Roll; NHS; Hosp Aide; MVP Cross Cnty Ski Tm 82-84; 3rd Pl Cross Cnty Skng Prep Schl Champ 85; Proctor Of Dormitory 85.

BURGE, KATHY; Chelsea HS; Corinth, VT; (S); 1/25; Church Yth Grp; Pres Debate Tm; Pres NFL; Yrbk Ed-Chief; Trs Sr Cls; Bausch & Lomb Sci Awd; Pres NHS; Ntl Merit Ltr; Val; Speech Tm; U S Senate Yth Prog Delg 85; Numers Debt Fornscs Awds 81-85; Dartmouth Coll; Pol Sci.

BURGESS, BONNIE; Mount Anthony Union HS; N Bennington, VT; (Y); FBLA; Ski Clb; Rep Stu Cncl; JV Var Fld Hcky; Southern VT Coll; Accntng.

BURKE, DAVID D; Otter Valley Union HS; Brandon, VT; (Y); 2/94; Quiz Bowl; Yrbk Stf; Var Capt Bsktbl; Var L Golf; Var Capt Socr; Elks Awd; High Hon Roll; Pres NHS; Sal; Hrmn Bore Mem Schlrshp 85; Vrmnt Hnr Schlrshp 85; Drtmth Coll; Engrng.

BUSDEN, SCOTT; Leland And Gay Union HS; Newfane, VT; (Y); Rep Am Leg Boys St; Cmnty Wkr; Dance Clb; Drama Clb; FBLA; Latin Clb; Chorus; Im Var Bsktbl; Im Socr; Var Tennis; Bus.

BUSH, MICHELE; Leland And Gray Union HS; Newfane, VT; (Y); Var Cheerleading; Var Socr; Var Capt Sftbl; Dnfth Awd; High Hon Roll; Hon Roll; NHS; Prom Comm 84-85; Cls Mrshll 85; Bus Mgmnt.

BUSHEY, BRENDA; Bellows Free Acad; St Albans, VT; (Y); Cmnty Wkr; 4-H; Mgr(s); JV Socr; JV Sftbl; 4-H Awd; Castleton; Detectve.

BUSHEY, GARY; Enosburg Falls JR SR HS; Enosburg Falls, VT; (Y); 3/80; Am Leg Boys St; Church Yth Grp; VP Computer Clb; FBLA; Office Aide; Science Clb; Yrbk Stf; Var Socr; High Hon Roll; Pres NHS; USAF; Comp Sci.

BUSHEY, JOCELYN M; Middlebury Union HS; Bridport, VT; (Y); AFS; Camera Clb; JV Fld Hcky; JV Tennis; Hon Roll; Meritrs Svc-Peer Cnslr 84-85; Psych.

BUSKEY, EMILY E; Middlebury Union HS; Middlebury, VT; (Y); Sec Band; Concert Band; Jazz Band; Mrchg Band; Orch; Pep Band; Symp Band; Var Trk; Med.

BUZEMAN, ANDREA; Vergennes Union HS; Vergennes, VT; (Y); 4-H; German Clb; VP Chorus; Church Choir; School Musical; Variety Show; JV Bsktbl; Hon Roll; VT All St Chr 84; Comp Sci.

BUZZELL, PAUL; North Country Union HS; Newport, VT; (Y); French Clb; Key Clb; School Musical; Bsktbl; Tennis; Natl Math Exam 3rd Pl 84; Frnch Exch 85; Frnch Dept Awd 84-85; Bio.

CAMERON, JEFFREY; Otter Valley Union HS; Pittsfield, VT; (Y); French Clb; Teachers Aide; Var Bsbl; Var Socr; Hon Roll; MVL All Star Sccr Tm 83; U VT JR Conf 85; Sprts Psych.

CAMPION, CHRISTOPHER; Winooski HS; Winooski, VT; (Y); Am Leg Boys St; French Clb; Math Tm; Scholastic Bowl; Band; Chorus; Concert Band; Jazz Band; Variety Show; JV Bsbl; All ST Chrs 83; Accptd Mensa 84; Crmnl Jstc.

CAPRIOLA, PAUL; Mt Anthony Union HS; Sarasota, FL; (Y); 65/287; Yrbk Bus Mgr; Yrbk Stf; Altr Servr; Manatee CC; Secndry Educ.

CARBINE, LESLIE; Rutland HS; Rutland, VT; (Y); Drama Clb; Chorus; School Play; Variety Show; JV Capt Cheerleading; Powder Puff Ftbl; JV Var Tennis; Var Twrlr; Hon Roll; Rutlands Cotillion Queen 84; Skidmore Coll; Dance.

CAREY, JOHN; Rice Memorial HS; Shelburne, VT; (Y); Am Leg Boys St; Church Yth Grp; Letterman Clb; Pep Clb; VP Frsh Cls; Stu Cncl; Var Bsktbl; Vllybl; Elks Awd; MVP Div I St Bsktbl Champ Tm 84-85; All St Bsktbl; Bus Admin.

CAREY, SHANNON; Brattleboro Union HS; Brattleboro, VT; (Y); 17/225; FBLA; Intnl Clb; Model UN; VP Band; VP Mrchg Band; School Musical; Rptr Nwsp Ed-Chief; Stu Cncl; Hon Roll; NHS; Windham Found Awd 85; Vermont Stu Assit Corp 85; Northeastern U; Bus Adm.

CARLING, OLIVER; Burlington HS; Burlington, VT; (Y); AFS; Drama Clb; Intnl Clb; Spanish Clb; Band; School Musical; Yrbk Rptr; Tennis; Hon Roll; NHS; Frnch Awd 83; Spnsh Awd 85; Forgn Lang.

CARPENTER, KEVIN; Websterville Baptist Christian Schl; Websterville, VT; (Y); 1/10; Church Yth Grp; Chorus; Church Choir; School Play; Yrbk Ed-Chief; Yrbk Phtg; Pres Sr Cls; Var L Bsktbl; Var L Crs Cntry; Var L Socr; Amer Chrst Hnr Scty 85; Cedarville Coll.

CARPENTER, SCOTT; Webstervle Baptist Christian Schl; Barre, VT; (Y); 2/10; Church Yth Grp; School Play; Stage Crew; Yrbk Sprt Ed; Trs Sr Cls; L Bsktbl; L Socr; High Hon Roll; Hon Roll; Natl Christian Hnr Soc; De Vry Inst Tech; Comp Info Sys.

CARPENTER, WILLIAM H; Burlington HS; Burlington, VT; (Y); Church Yth Grp; Band; Mrchg Band; Stu Cncl; Crs Cntry; Trk; Athlt Mth VT Sprt Castrs, Sprts Wrtrs Assn 84; Nrthrn VT Athltc Conf Al-Star Tm Assn 82-84; Comp Sci.

CARR, DANIEL; Bellows Free Acad; Bakersfield, VT; (Y); 53/208; Sec Church Yth Grp; Computer Clb; 4-H; Math Clb; High Hon Roll; Hon Roll; Brnze Pin 12 Smstrs A 85; Math Awd 85; Eastern Nazerene Coll; Physics.

CARRIER, NANCY; Canaan Memorial HS; Canaan, VT; (S); Am Leg Aux Girls St; Band; Chorus; Pres Jr Cls; Capt Var Bsktbl; Capt Var Socr; High Hon Roll; Drama Clb; Office Aide; Teachers Aide; Med.

CARTER, ELIZABETH; Windsor HS; Windsor, VT; (Y); #1 In Class; Am Leg Aux Girls St; Pep Clb; Mrchg Band; Yrbk Stf; Pres Stu Cncl; Fld Hcky; High Hon Roll; NHS; French Clb; GAA; Chem,Bio,Spch Balfour Awd 84-85; Sci.

CARTER, JENIFER; Fairhaven Union HS; Castleton, VT; (Y); 13/118; Am Leg Aux Girls St; Drama Clb; Pres French Clb; Hosp Aide; Ski Clb; Chorus; School Play; Hon Roll; NHS; Hugh O Brein Yth Ldrshp Sem 84; Coach Area Spec Olympics Pgm 83, 84 & 85; Lib Arts.

CASAGRANDE, ROBYN; Otter Valley Union HS; Pittsford, VT; (Y); French Clb; JA; Concert Band; Mrchg Band; Pep Band; Mgr(s); High Hon Roll; NHS; L Band; Orch; Japan U S Sen Schlrshp Smi-Fnlst 85; Outstndng Awds Frnch II & III, Advncd Am Stds & Geomtry 84-85; Chld Psych.

CASSELLA, RENEE; Burr And Burton HS; S Londonderry, VT; (Y); French Clb; Nwsp Rptr; Yrbk Stf; Cheerleading; Sftbl; Tennis; Hon Roll; Htl/Rest Mngmnt.

CASSESE, CATHERINE; Mount St Joseph Acad; Rutland, VT; (Y); 12/99; Church Yth Grp; Drama Clb; School Play; Stage Crew; Yrbk Ed-Chief; Yrbk Rptr; Yrbk Stf; High Hon Roll; Hon Roll; NHS; Bus.

CECOT, JILL; Otter Valley Union HS; Brandon, VT; (Y); Pres Sec 4-H; Teachers Aide; Yrbk Stf; Ed Lit Mag; Var Cheerleading; JV Mgr(s); 4-H Awd; Hon Roll; VT Rep Natl 4-H Round-Up 83; Eastern St Del Rep VT 83-85; Var Chrldr Mst Dedicated Plyr 84; Psych.

CHAFFEE, KELLY A; Lake Region Union HS; Albany, VT; (Y); Trs FFA; Rep Jr Cls; JV Sftbl; Hon Roll; NHS; Social Wrk.

CHAMPOUX, AMY; Colchester HS; Colchester, VT; (S); 16/220; Var Capt Fld Hcky; Var Capt Tennis; High Hon Roll; Hon Roll; NHS; U Of VT; Med Tech.

CHAPMAN, PAUL; Vergennes HS; Vergennes, VT; (Y); Computer Clb; Var Crs Cntry; Swmmng; Hon Roll; Gvrnrs Inst/Sci & Tech 85; U Of VT; Engr.

CHAPPELL, MARK; Mt Anthony Union HS; Bennington, VT; (Y); Cmnty Wkr; Math Clb; Band; Hon Roll; NHS; Rep Frsh Cls; Rep Soph Cls; Rep Jr Cls; Rep Stu Cncl; JV Socr; Indust Arts Awd 84; RPI; Aero Engr.

CHARRON, JOY; Spaulding HS; Barre, VT; (Y); 16/250; French Clb; Office Aide; Lit Mag; Crs Cntry; Trk; High Hon Roll; Frnch Awd Cert Merit 83; SHS Splng Cntst 1st Pl 84; APSL Ntl Latin Hnr Soc; Pre-Med.

CHARTIER, SCOTT; Otter Valley Union HS; Florence, VT; (Y); Am Leg Boys St; Quiz Bowl; Teachers Aide; Var Bsbl; Var Bsktbl; Var Crs Cntry; NHS; Science Clb; Varsity Clb; Hon Roll; Frnch,Eng,Sci Awd 83-85; Math.

CHAWLA, ANJULIKA; Vermont Acad; Chester, VT; (S); Dance Clb; Key Clb; Math Tm; Bsktbl; Capt Tennis; Hon Roll; Aud/Vis; Debate Tm; Drama Clb; Girl Scts; Rensselaers Medl Excllnce Mth & Sci 84; Astrophyscs.

CHENEY, CHRISTINA; North Country Union HS; Newport, VT; (Y); Hosp Aide; Lib Band; Yrbk Phtg; VP Jr Cls; Rep Stu Cncl; JV Var Fld Hcky; High Hon Roll; NHS; Ski Clb; Chorus; Gov Inst Sci 83; Div I Select Tm Fld Hcky 83 & 84; Dept Hnrs Sci & Soc Stu 83 & 85; Pol Sci.

CHESAUX, MATTHIEU; U-32 HS; Calais, VT; (Y); Church Yth Grp; High Hon Roll; Ambassador Coll; Arch.

CHESLEY, ELIZABETH; Chelsea HS; Chelsea, VT; (Y); FBLA; Library Aide; Teachers Aide; Sftbl; High Hon Roll; NHS; Western Bus Coll; Acctng.

CHIOFFI, ROBIN; Woodstock Union HS; Woodstock, VT; (S); 2/90; Am Leg Aux Girls St; Math Tm; Yrbk Sprt Ed; Sec Soph Cls; Sec Jr Cls; Sec Sr Cls; Var Bsktbl; Var Capt Fld Hcky; Var Tennis; Pres NHS; Hugh Obrian Ldrshp Fndtn 83; Nacel Cltrl Exchang Smmr Pgm Frnce 84; Field Hcky VT ST All-Str Tm 84.

CHIRIATTI, AMY; Mount Mansfield Union HS; Richmond, VT; (Y); Stage Crew; Capt Var Crs Cntry; Score Keeper; Var Trk; Vrsty Ski Capt 83-85.

CHOQUETTE, JACK; North Country Union HS; Newport Center, VT; (Y); Am Leg Boys St; Computer Clb; Debate Tm; French Clb; NFL; Speech Tm; Var JV Wrstlng; High Hon Roll; NHS; Sci Awd 84-85; Green Mtn Boys ST Model Tm; Chem.

CHOQUETTE, ROSE; Sacred Heart SR HS; Newport Ctr, VT; (Y); 7/29; Am Leg Aux Girls St; Cmnty Wkr; Debate Tm; NFL; Church Choir; Madrigals; School Play; Coach Actv; Crs Cntry; Vt Miss Teen 84; 10 Pl Fnsh Ntl Miss Teenpagnt 84; St Rnnrs Up Debate 84-85; Mt Holyoke; Chem.

CHRISTINO, CARA; North Country Union HS; Derby Line, VT; (Y); Church Yth Grp; Cmnty Wkr; Girl Scts; Office Aide; Red Cross Aide; Spanish Clb; Chorus; JV Bsktbl; JV Fld Hcky; Golf; Religous Awd Girl Scout 83; Silver Awd 2nd Highest Girl Scout 83; Galludet Coll; Teach.

CICCOTELLI, LISA; Mount St Joseph Acad; Rutland, VT; (Y); 7/110; Stu Cncl; JV Var Cheerleading; High Hon Roll; Hon Roll; Sec NHS; Pblctn Lit Wrk The Mountain Review 85; Coll Holy Cross; Law.

CIOFFI, ROBERT; Bellows Free Acad; St Albans, VT; (Y); 12/225; Am Leg Boys St; Quiz Bowl; Scholastic Bowl; Yrbk Ed-Chief; JV Bsbl; JV Var Bsktbl; JV Ftbl; High Hon Roll; NHS; Boys Ntn Amer Legn 85; Lwyr.

CIONGOLI, ADAM; Burlington HS; Burlington, VT; (Y); Am Leg Boys St; Drama Clb; Pres Latin Clb; JV Bsktbl; Hon Roll; NHS; Ntl Merit Ltr; Model UN; Chorus; School Play; Cls Rep Hugh O Brien Yth Ledrshp Smnr; Rep To Torary Clb Critical Issues Conf; Natl Writers Cntst; U Of PA; Politics.

CLARK, CAROLYN; Mt Mansfield Union HS; Underhill, VT; (Y); 26/185; Drama Clb; Exploring; Band; Orch; School Musical; High Hon Roll; Masonic Awd; NHS; Church Yth Grp; Chorus; 3rd Natl Hist Day Histrcl Paper 84; VT Histrcl Soc Hstrcl Wrtng 83; Wrk Pblshd ST HS Lit Mag 84/85; Oberlin Coll; Mus.

CLARK, KELLI ANN; Mount St Joseph Acad; Proctor, VT; (Y); Drama Clb; Key Clb; Band; Chorus; School Play; Swing Chorus; Yrbk Phtg; JV Bsktbl; JV Var Cheerleading; Govnr Inst Of Arts 85.

COBURN, CARRIE; Teland & Gray Union HS; W Wardsboro, VT; (Y); FFA; VICA; Yrbk Phtg; Yrbk Stf; Sftbl; Hon Roll; Karen Dauche Art Awd; Brattleboro Grdn Club Schlrshp Awd; Cblskll Ag & Tech; Flrlcltr.

COLLINS, MARY; Mt Anthony Union HS; Bennington, VT; (Y); Ski Clb; Rep Frsh Cls; Rep Soph Cls; Sec Jr Cls; Rep Stu Cncl; JV Fld Hcky; Tchg.

COMPTON, ADRIANNE M; Lake Region U HS; Barton, VT; (Y); Drama Clb; Hosp Aide; Intnl Clb; Pep Clb; School Play; Yrbk Stf; Pres & Founded SADD 83-84; Air Force; Med.

CONSTANTINE JR, EDWIN H; Otter Valley Union HS; Brndon, VT; (Y); Teachers Aide; Hon Roll; NHS; Prfct Atten Awd; Engrng.

COPP, LISA; Concord HS; N Concord, VT; (S); 2/25; 4-H; Math Tm; Scholastic Bowl; Trs Jr Cls; Var Cheerleading; Var Mgr(s); 4-H Awd; High Hon Roll; Hon Roll; NHS.

CORBITT, ROY; St Johnsbury Acad; St Johnsbury, VT; (Y); Intnl Clb; Red Cross Aide; Ski Clb; Crs Cntry; Hon Roll; Engr.

COTE, DANIELLE; North County Union HS; Beebe Plain, VT; (Y); Am Leg Aux Girls St; Drama Clb; French Clb; Madrigals; School Musical; Variety Show; Stu Cncl; Var L Fld Hcky; Hon Roll; Acpl Chr; Dstrct, All State & All Estrn New Englnd Music Fstvls Music Letters 83-85; U Of VT; Psychlgy.

COURCELLE, MICHAEL; Mt St Joseph Acad; Rutland, VT; (Y); Art Clb; Hon Roll; Pol Officer.

COUTURE, MICHELLE; Peoples Acad; Morrisville, VT; (Y); Sec Church Yth Grp; Dance Clb; Teachers Aide; Nwsp Rptr; Nwsp Stf; Yrbk Stf; Cheerleading; Diving; Hon Roll; Champlain Coll; Legal Secr.

COYNE, ALLISON J; Colchester HS; Colchester, VT; (Y); Sec Church Yth Grp; Girl Scts; Band; Chorus; Church Choir; Orch; Hon Roll; Art Clb; Spanish Clb; Concert Band; Music Dept Awd 85; Slvr Awd Grl Scts 84; Gld Ldrshp Awd Grl Scts 85; Music Educ.

CRANE, JENNIFER; Leland & Gray Union HS; W Wardsboro, VT; (Y); Intnl Clb; School Play; Hon Roll; Lcl Wnnr VT Hnrs Comp Exclnce Writing 85; Lang Awd 85; Frnch III & IV Awd 85; Eng Ltr Awd 85; Marlboro Coll; Wrtng.

CREGO, ROBIN L; Mt Anthony Union HS; Bennington, VT; (Y); 48/250; GAA; Var L Bsktbl; Var L Socr; Var L Sftbl; Im Vllybl; Hon Roll; Prfct Atten Awd; JV Bsktbl Ldng Assts 82-83; MVP Sftbl 84-85.

CROSS, DWIGHT A; Northfield JR SR HS; Northfield Fls, VT; (Y); Am Leg Boys St; Boy Scts; Quiz Bowl; Jazz Band; Orch; School Play; Trs Sr Cls; Rep Stu Cncl; Var Capt Ice Hcky; Hon Roll; James Cross Schlrshp 85; Norwich U Schlrshp 85; Hstry Clb Pres-Enrchmnt Pgm; Norwich U; Hstry.

CROSSLEY, KIMBERLY J; Thetford Acad; Thetford Center, VT; (Y); 1/38; Rptr 4-H; Chorus; School Musical; Elks Awd; 4-H Awd; High Hon Roll; NHS; Val; Quiz Bowl; Yrbk Stf; Vermont Schlrs Schlrshp 85; VT 4-H Hrse Jdgng Team 84; VT Delg Estrn ST 4-H Hrse Show 84; U Of VT; Vet Med.

CROWLEY, KATHLEEN; Mount Saint Joseph Acad; Mendon, VT; (Y); 3/95; Rep Am Leg Aux Girls St; Rep Soph Cls; Rep Jr Cls; VP Stu Cncl; L Var Socr; L Var Tennis; L Var Wrstlng; Var High Hon Roll; NHS; VT ST, Marble Vly Leag All Star Sccr Tm 84; ST Champ Sking Tm 82-85.

CUMMING, DOUGLAS; Spaulding HS; Barre, VT; (Y); Am Leg Boys St; Church Yth Grp; Computer Clb; Drama Clb; Nwsp Ed-Chief; Nwsp Phtg; Nwsp Stf; Yrbk Phtg; Yrbk Stf; Hon Roll; Comp Eng.

CURLIN, MARCEL E; Champlin Valley Union HS; Charlotte, VT; (Y); 14/240; German Clb; Latin Clb; Math Tm; Socr; JV Trk; High Hon Roll; Hon Roll; Ntl Merit SF; Attnd New England JR Symposium 83-84 On Sci & Humanities; Hist Awd 83-84; Amhearst Coll; Sci.

CZAPLINSKI, ANNE; Montpelier HS; Montpelier, VT; (Y); 1/107; Am Leg Aux Girls St; French Clb; Hosp Aide; Capt Ski Clb; Varsity Clb; Var Fld Hcky; Var L Trk; High Hon Roll; Sec NHS; Ntl Merit SF; Bio.

D AGOSTINO, EDWARD; Oxbow HS; E Corinth, VT; (Y); 20/90; VP Jr Cls; Pres Stu Cncl; NHS; Drama Clb; French Clb; JV Trk; Hon Roll; Bst Eng Stu 84 & 85; Syracuse U; Pol Sci.

DAGESSE, CINDY; Canaan Memorial HS; Beecher Falls, VT; (S); Drama Clb; Teachers Aide; Chorus; Church Choir; School Musical; Nwsp Rptr; Socr; High Hon Roll; NHS.

DAM, JOANIE; Vergennes Union HS; Vergennes, VT; (Y); 4/105; Camera Clb; Church Yth Grp; FHA; GAA; JA; Varsity Clb; School Play; Bsktbl; Socr; High Hon Roll; Calvin Coll; Bus Admin.

DARROW, JULIE A; Marwood Union HS; Waitsfield, VT; (Y); Band; Chorus; JV Var Cheerleading; High Hon Roll; Hon Roll; Acctg.

DAVIDSON, MARJORIE; Windsor HS; Windsor, VT; (Y); #4 In Class; Am Leg Aux Girls St; Cmnty Wkr; Band; Concert Band; Mrchg Band; Stu Cncl; Fld Hcky; Pom Pon; Sftbl; Swmmng; Balfour Awd Wrtng 84-85.

DAVIS, CARMELLA J; Randolph Union HS; Randolph, VT; (Y); 4/90; Church Yth Grp; Acpl Chr; Church Choir; Concert Band; Madrigals; Mrchg Band; Yrbk Bus Mgr; Sr Cls; High Hon Roll; NHS; VT Bus Ed Scholar 85-86; Castleton ST Coll; Bus Ed.

DAVIS, DEANNE; Lake Region Union HS; Barton, VT; (Y); 7/98; Chorus; Concert Band; School Musical; Rep Jr Cls; Rep Sr Cls; Rep Stu Cncl; Twrlr; High Hon Roll; NHS; Pres Schlr; Eola Johnson Weeks Schlrshp 85; Lee Emerson Schlrshp 85; Amer Aux Barton Past 76 Schlrshp 85; U Of VT; Fshn Merch.

DAVIS, MICHAEL; Whitcomb HS; Bethel, VT; (Y); Church Yth Grp; French Clb; Concert Band; Jazz Band; Mrchg Band; JV Var Crs Cntry; Hon Roll; Prfct Atten Awd.

DAVIS, PARKER ARNOLD; Burr & Burton Seminary HS; Manchester, VT; (Y); 4/100; Band; Jazz Band; VP Jr Cls; Tennis; NHS; Dance Clb; German Clb; Model UN; Ski Clb; Mrchg Band; Close Up Clb 83-84; Southern VT Jazz Fest-1T Sax Soloist 84-85; Stu Cncl 84-85; Ger Exchng Stu 84-85.

DAWSON, MICHELLE E; Champlain Valley Union HS; Charlotte, VT; (Y); Drama Clb; 4-H; Acpl Chr; Chorus; Madrigals; School Musical; School Play; Stage Crew; Variety Show; JR Miss Schlrshp 85; All St Music Festival Schlrshp 84; Mozart Festival Music Schlrshp 83-84; Musical Theatre.

DE FORGE, DAVID; Mt Anthony Union HS; Bennington, VT; (Y); FFA; Teachers Aide; Variety Show; Stu Cncl; Hon Roll; Prfct Atten Awd; Brdcstg.

DE LA BRUERE, MARIE; Sacred Heart HS; Westfield, VT; (S); 5/29; Am Leg Aux Girls St; VP Church Yth Grp; Band; Chorus; Church Choir; Madrigals; Sec Jr Cls; Sec Sr Cls; Capt Socr; VP NHS; Educ.

DECELLES, PATRICK; Sacred Heart HS; Irasburg, VT; (S); 1/29; Co-Capt FCA; Math Tm; Chorus; School Play; Yrbk Stf; Pres Frsh Cls; Pres Soph Cls; Pres Jr Cls; Pres Sr Cls; Var Bsbl; St Michaels Coll.

DENSMORE, JIM; Peoples Acad; Morrisville, VT; (Y); Var Bsbl; Prfct Atten Awd.

DEO, DARCI J; Colchester HS; Grand Isle, VT; (Y); 4-H; 4-H Awd; High Hon Roll; Hon Roll; Hnr Awd 3.0 Av 4 Yrs 85.

DEPOLLO, DIANA; Mt Anthony Union HS; Bennington, VT; (Y); 21/287; Church Yth Grp; Latin Clb; Office Aide; Pep Clb; Science Clb; Yrbk Bus Mgr; Yrbk Phtg; Yrbk Rptr; Yrbk Sprt Ed; Yrbk Stf; Latin Hnr Soc 82-84; Bus Adm.

DERBY, RICH; Colchester HS; Colchester, VT; (S); 3/219; Latin Clb; Red Cross Aide; Thesps; Band; Gym; Tennis; Wrstlng; Elks Awd; Masonic Awd; NHS; Fr Dupont Awd 85; Coachs Awd Wrstlng 84; Wrstlng Lttr 84; St Michaels Coll; Bio.

DESAUTELS, JULIE; Richford HS; Richford, VT; (Y); Drama Clb; Natl Beta Clb; Band; Chorus; School Musical; Yrbk Stf; VP Soph Cls; Mgr(s); Hon Roll; NHS; Champlain Coll; Acctng.

DIETZ, BRIDGET; Woodstock Union HS; Taftsville, VT; (Y); 3/90; Sec Camp Fr Inc; Madrigals; School Musical; Yrbk Stf; Stu Cncl; JV Capt Fld Hcky; Var Capt Trk; High Hon Roll; Hon Roll; Lion Awd; Rnnr Up Am Leg Oratcl Cont 84-85; Am Leg Roy Campbell Schlrshp 85; K Of C Schlrshp 85; U Dallas; Phlsphy.

DIKE, TRACY; Vergennes Union HS; N Ferrisburg, VT; (Y); 1/105; Am Leg Aux Girls St; Scholastic Bowl; School Musical; Pres Jr Cls; Pres Stu Cncl; Var Capt Socr; DAR Awd; Pres NHS; Val; Drama Clb; Century III Ldr Awd 85; Twin ST Sccr Team 85; Ddartmouth Coll; Comp Sci.

DILLOWAY, RIA; Burlington HS; Burlington, VT; (Y); Art Clb; Church Yth Grp; Dance Clb; French Clb; Pep Clb; Spanish Clb; Teachers Aide; Church Choir; Variety Show; Im Fld Hcky; Peer Tutor Svc 84; Ath Commendtn 84; Spec Ed Tchr.

DION, LIZABETH; Winooski HS; Winooski, VT; (Y); Am Leg Aux Girls St; Drama Clb; School Musical; School Play; VP Jr Cls; Rep Stu Cncl; JV Var Bsktbl; Capt Var Fld Hcky; JV Var Sftbl; Im Vllybl.

DOBBINS, SARITA; Oxbow HS; Bradford, VT; (Y); #10 In Class; Band; Jr Cls; Var Bsktbl; Var Fld Hcky; Var Sftbl; Hon Roll; NHS; Prfct Atten Awd; AFS; Church Yth Grp; Home Ec Awd 84; Winooski Msc Fstvl Honr 85; Dent Hygne.

DOBOS, JENNIFER; Stowe HS; Stowe, VT; (Y); 3/48; Chorus; Concert Band; School Musical; School Play; Nwsp Ed-Chief; Yrbk Ed-Chief; Rep Frsh Cls; Sec Jr Cls; High Hon Roll; Hon Roll; 1st Pl Baldwin ST Piano Cmptn 83; Ntl Hstry Day, Hstrcl Paper 1st Pl In ST 85; Middlebury Coll; Jrnlsm.

DORWART, RICH; Burlington HS; Burlington, VT; (Y); Var Trk; NHS; Hosted Frnch Exch Stu Bergerac 84 & 85.

DOUBLEDAY, MICHAEL; Woodstock Union HS; Woodstock, VT; (Y); Am Leg Boys St; Letterman Clb; Teachers Aide; Nwsp Bus Mgr; Pres Sr Cls; VP Stu Cncl; Ftbl; Latin Clb; School Musical; Variety Show; VT Conf 85; Stu Cncl Rep 83-85; US Math Awd 83; Citzns Awd 84; Hstry Awd 85; Williams; Engl.

DOUGLAS, KIMBERLY; Burlington HS; Burlington, VT; (Y); Exploring; Teachers Aide; Im Score Keeper; Im Timer; Hon Roll; Erly Chldhd Educ.

DREHER, STEVE; North Country Union HS; Newport Center, VT; (Y); Rep Am Leg Boys St; German Clb; Key Clb; Ski Clb; Chorus; Madrigals; School Musical; Rep Jr Cls; Var L Fld Hcky; NHS; Bio.

DRIVER, LADON; North Country Union HS; Jay, VT; (Y); Church Yth Grp; DECA; Office Aide; Yrbk Phtg; Yrbk Stf; Var Capt Cheerleading; Mgr(s); Score Keeper; Distrbtv Ed Clbs Amer; Scrtry 84-85; VT Coll Of Cosmtlgy; Cosmtlgy.

DRUKE, THOMAS; Leland & Gray Union HS; Newfane, VT; (Y); 2/65; Variety Show; Yrbk Stf; VP Sr Cls; Bsktbl; Hon Roll; Pres NHS; Sal; Arlo Monroe Awd 85; Dartmouth Coll; Pre Med.

DUARTE, CARLA; Burlingotn HS; Burlington, VT; (Y); Pres Spanish Clb; JV Trk; High Hon Roll; Hon Roll; NHS; Ntl Merit SF; Spnsh Awd-Spnsh Ii & Iii 83-85; Bus Admin.

DUCHARME, JOHN; Windsor HS; Windsor, VT; (Y); Band; Concert Band; Jazz Band; Mrchg Band; School Play; Symp Band; Variety Show; Var Bsbl; Var Bsktbl; Var Ftbl; Dist Jazz Band 85; Outstndg Offns & Defns Awds Ftbl 84.

DUCHARME, LISA; Spaulding HS; Barre, VT; (Y); VP French Clb; Hon Roll; Natl Latin Hnr Soc 85; Pre-Optometry.

DUCHARME, TRACIE; Windsor HS; Windsor, VT; (Y); 8/70; Chorus; Concert Band; Jazz Band; Mrchg Band; School Play; Yrbk Stf; Bsktbl; Fld Hcky; Sftbl; NHS; Balfour Music Awd 85; Am Lgn Schlrshp 85; U Of VT; Educ.

DUDLEY, B DANE; Woodstock Union HS; Woodstock, VT; (Y); 1/89; Pres Church Yth Grp; Jazz Band; Yrbk Ed-Chief; Trs Stu Cncl; High Hon Roll; Trs NHS; Val; Math Tm; Quiz Bowl; Thesps; VT All ST Soccer & Bsktbl Teams 84-85; Amer Legn Boys Ntn Rep 84; Williams Coll; Pre Med.

DUFF, LUCIE; Colchester HS; Colchester, VT; (S); Var Tennis; High Hon Roll; NHS.

DUFRESNE, KAREN E; Twinfield Union HS; Marshfield, VT; (Y); 1/36; Am Leg Aux Girls St; Church Yth Grp; French Clb; Library Aide; Key Clb; Pres Jr Cls; VP Sr Cls; Sftbl; Elks Awd; High Hon Roll; Cntrl VT Medcl Cntr Aux Schlrshp 84-85; New Engld Math Leag Awd 83-85; Norwich U Math/Sci Awd 84-85; VT Coll; Med Tech.

DUKAS, THOMAS; Bellows Freo Acad; St Albans, VT; (Y); Am Leg Boys St; Varsity Clb; Pres Soph Cls; Im Coach Actv; Var Ice Hcky; Var Socr; Im Swmmng; JV Trk; Cit Awd; Hon Roll; Bentley Coll MA; Bus Adm.

DUKE, HOLLY; Williamstown JR-SR HS; Williamstown, VT; (Y); 2/52; Pres Band; Chorus; School Play; Yrbk Stf; Capt Cheerleading; Socr; Sftbl; NHS; Sal; Trs Soph Cls; Intrptr.

DUMONT, MONIQUE; North Country Union HS; N Troy, VT; (Y); Am Leg Aux Girls St; Church Yth Grp; FHA; Ski Clb; Tennis; High Hon Roll; NHS; St Michaels; Art.

DUPONT, TERESA; Concord HS; Lunenburg, VT; (S); 1/21; Drama Clb; Pres French Clb; Ed Yrbk Ed-Chief; Pres Soph Cls; Pres Jr Cls; Pres Sr Cls; Var Mgr(s); Var Score Keeper; Hon Roll; NHS; Lyndon ST Coll; Bus Admin.

DUSTIN, EDWARD; North Country Union HS; Newport, VT; (Y); Chorus; School Musical; JV Var Ftbl; Danial Webster; Pilot.

EARDENSOHN, KRIS; Montpelier HS; Montpelier, VT; (Y); 3/107; Am Leg Aux Girls St; French Clb; Pep Clb; Var Capt Ski Clb; Varsity Clb; Var Capt Crs Cntry; Var Trk; Elks Awd; Trs NHS; Val; New Englnd JR Sci Sympsm At UNH; Silver M & Pres Acadmc Ftnss Awds; St Lawrence U; Bio.

EARLE, KIM; Rutland HS; Rutland, VT; (Y); Am Leg Aux Girls St; Color Guard; Drm & Bgl; Flag Corp; Yrbk Stf; St Joseph Coll; Vet.

EDQUID, FRED; Winooski HS; Winooski, VT; (Y); 1/63; Am Leg Boys St; Math Tm; Scholastic Bowl; Band; School Play; Yrbk Stf; Var Bsbl; Var Bsktbl; Var Ftbl; High Hon Roll; Engrng.

EGGLESTON, MICHELLE; Mount St Joseph HS; Rutland, VT; (Y); Varsity Clb; L Bsktbl; L Sftbl; Hon Roll; NHS.

ELLIG, EILEEN; Rutland HS; Rutland, VT; (Y); 16/180; Capt L Crs Cntry; Capt L Trk; High Hon Roll; Hon Roll; Jr NHS; NHS; Amer Lgn Stu Of Yr Awd 85; Hertz I Awd; ST Athlt Of Yr 84; TX U; Comm.

ELLIS, HEIDI; North Country Union HS; Newport, VT; (Y); Chorus; School Play; Var Cheerleading; Var Socr; Im Sftbl; JV Trk; Im Vllybl; Bk Of Knwldg 85; Awd In Phy Ed 85; Champlain Coll; Med Sec.

ELLISON, KIMBERLY JAY; Rutland HS; Rutland, VT; (Y); CAP; Band; School Play; Nwsp Rptr; Nwsp Stf; Hon Roll; Castleton ST Coll; Comm.

ELWOOD, TONYA; North Country Union HS; Lowell, VT; (Y); DECA; FHA; Teachers Aide; Chorus; CC Vermont; Social Wrkr.

ELZINGA, TENA; Vergennes Union HS; Vergennes, VT; (Y); 7/100; German Clb; Var L Bsktbl; High Hon Roll; Hon Roll.

EMERSON, CINDY; U-32 HS; Montpelier, VT; (Y); Church Yth Grp; Drama Clb; Chorus; Hon Roll; Bio.

ERTLE, STEVE; Oxbow HS; Newbury, VT; (Y); 28/104; Church Yth Grp; Ski Clb; Yrbk Phtg; Trk; Hon Roll; Prfct Atten Awd; Drama Clb; 4-H; Computer Clb; School Musical; Sls & Mrktng.

EVANOIKA, LAURA A; Fair Haven Union HS; Bomoseen, VT; (Y); 4/119; Am Leg Aux Girls St; Chorus; VP Jr Cls; VP Sr Cls; Capt Bowling; Capt Cheerleading; High Hon Roll; Hon Roll; NHS; JR Conf U VT 84-85; Bentley Coll; Acctg.

EVANS, MISSY; Burr & Burton Seminary; Manchester, VT; (Y); Church Yth Grp; Variety Show; Sec Soph Cls; Sec Jr Cls; Var L Bsktbl; Var L Fld Hcky; Var L Sftbl; Hon Roll; Pres NHS; Vet Med.

FACTO, ALTHEA; Mount Anthony Union HS; Bennington, VT; (Y).

FAIR, CANDY; Union 32 HS; E Calais, VT; (Y); Dance Clb; Teachers Aide; Chorus; School Musical; Variety Show; Frsh Cls; Stu Cncl; Var Cheerleading; JV Sftbl; High Hon Roll; Acad Exclnce Am Hist 84-85; Awd Bus Educ 83-84; U Southern CA; Accntng.

FAIVRE, SAMUEL; Otter Valley Union HS; Brandon, VT; (Y); 16/110; Am Leg Boys St; Church Yth Grp; Rep Stu Cncl; Var Capt Crs Cntry; Var L Trk; Hon Roll; Stu Wk 84; VT Div II X-Cntry St Champ 84.

FEIFEL, KAREN; Leland & Gray Union HS; Williamsville, VT; (Y); Church Yth Grp; Yrbk Stf; Sec Soph Cls; Var Cheerleading; JV Sftbl; Hon Roll; Travl.

FIELDER, KELLEY; U-32 HS; Montpelier, VT; (Y); 3/103; Sec 4-H; Hosp Aide; Chorus; Sec Frsh Cls; Off Soph Cls; Off Jr Cls; Sec Sr Cls; Capt Fld Hcky; Capt Trk; Rotary Awd; Plaque-Top 20 In SR Clss 85; U Of VT; Dntl Hygn.

FISHER, HEIDI; Burlington HS; Burlington, VT; (Y); Church Yth Grp; JV Cheerleading; Var Gym; JV Sftbl; Hon Roll; Coachs Awd 84-85; Typng Awd 83-84; Champlain Coll; Data Procssng.

FISHER, TODD; Peoples Acad; Elmore, VT; (Y); 2/84; French Clb; Variety Show; Sec Frsh Cls; Capt Bsbl; JV Bsktbl; Mgr(s); Im Vllybl; Hon Roll; Ltrd Hnrs; U Of VT; Bus Adm.

FITZGERALD, THOMAS J; U-32 HS; E Montpelier, VT; (Y); Am Leg Boys St; Church Yth Grp; Cmnty Wkr; Teachers Aide; Hon Roll; French Clb; Ski Clb; Varsity Clb; Socr; Trk; VT Tech Coll; Comp Sci.

FITZPATRICK, KEITH; Vergennes Union HS; Vergennes, VT; (Y); 2/110; Am Leg Boys St; Pres Leo Clb; Math Tm; Model UN; Scholastic Bowl; Rep Frsh Cls; Pres Soph Cls; Rep Jr Cls; Var Capt Bsktbl; Var Crs Cntry; Schl Wnnr Am Legn Ortcl Cont 85; Gov Inst Arts 83; Law.

FLANDERS, MONICA; Rutland HS; Rutland, VT; (Y); Chorus; Color Guard; Drm & Bgl; Flag Corp; Hon Roll; Fanny Allen; Nrsg.

FLOWER, EMILY L; Middlebury Union HS; Middlebury, VT; (Y); 60/220; AFS; Dance Clb; Drama Clb; Pres 4-H; Band; Chorus; Concert Band; Mrchg Band; Orch; School Musical; Lake Forest Coll; Bio.

FLUR, AMY S; Burlington HS; Burlington, VT; (Y); Am Leg Aux Girls St; Dance Clb; Drama Clb; Acpl Chr; School Musical; Yrbk Stf; Stu Cncl; Var L Tennis; AFS; Church Yth Grp; Tulane U; Psych.

FLYNN, KATHLEEN; Winooski HS; Winooski, VT; (Y); Church Yth Grp; Drama Clb; FCA; FHA; Band; Chorus; Concert Band; Jazz Band; Mrchg Band; School Musical; Champlane UVM.

FOURNIER, LISA; Sacred Heart HS; Newport, VT; (S); 4/29; Am Leg Aux Girls St; Girl Scts; Band; Chorus; Madrigals; VP Stu Cncl; Capt L Bsktbl; Capt L Socr; High Hon Roll; Pres NHS; Sprtmnshp Awd 84; Bkstbl Cchs Awd 84; Mus Fstvls; SUNY Potsdam; Elem Ed.

FRANKEL, STEVEN A; Burlington HS; Burlington, VT; (Y); 5/230; Boy Scts; Drama Clb; Latin Clb; Scholastic Bowl; Temple Yth Grp; Band; Concert Band; Mrchg Band; School Play; Socr; Natl Councl Tchrs Engl Awd Excllnce Writing 84; Awd Excllnce Hstry 82-84; Tufts U.

FRANKENHOFF, JERI LYNNE; Leland & Gray Union HS; Newfane, VT; (Y); 25/60; Debate Tm; NFL; Variety Show; Yrbk Bus Mgr; Yrbk Stf; Sec Jr Cls; Sec Sr Cls; Var Capt Cheerleading; Im Vllybl; Hon Roll; Windham Fndtn Schlrshp 85; Sprtsmnshp Awd 85; Johnson Wales Clg; Fash Merch.

FRENCH, STEPHEN; Ruthland HS; Rutland, VT; (Y); 4/182; Yrbk Ed-Chief; JV Var Bsktbl; Var L Trk; DAR Awd; Jr NHS; Lion Awd; Sec Trs NHS; Pres Schlr; Nwsp Stf; Ftbl; Stu Yr 81-82; City Rutland Schrlshp 85; U Vermont.

FREY, KEVIN; Mount St Joseph Acad; Rutland, VT; (Y); 59/101; FBLA; Band; Jazz Band; Mrchg Band; JV Var Bsbl; Var Im Bsktbl; Bus Mgmt.

FREY, MICHAEL A; Mill River Union HS; Shrewsbury, VT; (Y); 1/180; Am Leg Boys St; Drama Clb; Thesps; Chorus; Madrigals; School Play; Hon Roll; NHS; Ntl Merit SF; Val; Bus Law.

FROST, ERIC B; Lake Region Union HS; W Glover, VT; (Y); Am Leg Boys St; Cmnty Wkr; French Clb; Intnl Clb; Math Tm; Yrbk Stf; High Hon Roll; Hon Roll; NHS; Var Crs Cntry Skng; Top 10 Pcnt ST UVM Mth Cont; Aerontcl Engrng.

FURST, MIKE; Colchester HS; Colchester, VT; (S); 11/220; Boy Scts; Church Yth Grp; Math Tm; Band; Variety Show; JV Socr; L Trk; Hon Roll; NHS; ROTC 4 Yr Coll Schlrshp 85; Clarkson U; Elect Engrng.

GAGE, GEORGE; Burr And Burton Seminary HS; Manchester Center, VT; (Y); Ski Clb; Spanish Clb; Crs Cntry; Trk; Vllybl; High Hon Roll; Hon Roll; NHS; Awd Excllnc Spnsh 83-84; Spnsh Awd Grad 84-85; U Of VT; Bus.

GAGNE, GLENN D; Spaulding HS; Graniteville, VT; (Y); Am Leg Boys St; Pres Chess Clb; Band; Concert Band; Mrchg Band; Nwsp Rptr; Socr; Trk; Hon Roll; Ntl Resrcs Cncl; Govnrs Inst Intl Affrs; Poltcl Sci.

GALLAGHER, HELEN; Mount Saint Joseph Acad; Rutland, VT; (Y); Cmnty Wkr; Hosp Aide; Pep Clb; Drm Mjr(t); Mrchg Band; Twrlr; Conzedovia Coll; Soc Wrkr.

GARCIA, CHRISTOPHER S; Montpelier HS; Montpelier, VT; (Y); 12/104; Am Leg Boys St; Church Yth Grp; VP Pres French Clb; Varsity Clb; JV Bsbl; JV Bsktbl; JV VP Ftbl; JV Trk; High Hon Roll; NHS; Clarkson U; Mech Engrng.

GARDINER, CLAIRE; Burlington HS; S Burlington, VT; (Y); Drama Clb; Intnl Clb; Latin Clb; Model UN; School Musical; School Play; Trk; High Hon Roll; Hon Roll; NHS.

GARDNER, RENEE B; Colchester HS; S Hero, VT; (Y); 21/220; Cmnty Wkr; School Play; Rep Sr Cls; Mgr Stat Bsktbl; JV Var Fld Hcky; Mgr(s); High Hon Roll; Hon Roll; NHS; Pres Schlr; Ntl Hnr Soc,Chmplain Cbl Corp & H P Rssll Schlrshps 85; U Of VT; Elem Educ.

GARRISON, CHARLENE A; Essex Jct Educational Ctr; Essex Jct, VT; (Y); Drama Clb; Chorus; Stage Crew; Yrbk Stf; Hon Roll; Peter Hagadorn Schlrshp 85; Thomas Fay Mem Schlrshp 85; Pro Merito Awd 85; U VT; Math.

GARROW, LESLIE; Richford JR SR HS; Enosburg Falls, VT; (Y); Am Leg Aux Girls St; Cmnty Wkr; Natl Beta Clb; Band; Chorus; Mrchg Band; Pres Jr Cls; Rep Stu Cncl; JV Var Bsktbl; NHS; Miss VT Teen USA Pgnt; VT Stu Asst Corp; Math Tchr.

GAUDETTE, NICOLE D; Burlington HS; Burlington, VT; (Y); Cmnty Wkr; Dance Clb; French Clb; German Clb; Girl Scts; Rep Jr Cls; Stu Cncl; Champlain Coll; Fshn Mdse.

GAWRYS, BRENDA; Mill River Union HS; Clarendon, VT; (Y); Church Yth Grp; JA; JV Golf; Var Sftbl; Swmmng; Tennis; Hon Roll; Jr NHS; Acad Awd Strght A Yr 80; Vrsty Sftbl Awd 84; Golf Awd 85; Art.

GAY, JAMES M; Colchester HS; Colchester, VT; (Y); VP Church Yth Grp; Var Letterman Clb; Bsktbl; Var JV Socr; JV Var Trk; Hon Roll; Mst Imprvd Bsktbl 83; Mst Imprvd JV Sccr 84; Bio Tm Andros Islnd Bahamas; Bio.

GEARWAR, KELLY; Otter Valley Union HS; Brandon, VT; (Y); Am Leg Aux Girls St; French Clb; Varsity Clb; Lit Mag; Pres Frsh Cls; Pres Soph Cls; Off Jr Cls; Pres Sr Cls; Pres Stu Cncl; Bsktbl; Hugh O Brian Yth Fndtn 84; U Of NH; Vtrnrn.

GECHA, BRIAN; Rutland HS; Ctr Rutland, VT; (Y); Cmnty Wkr; Hon Roll; Jr NHS; VT Tech Coll; Arch.

GEISLER, WILL; U-32 HS; Plainfield, VT; (Y); 30/104; AFS; Dance Clb; Drama Clb; PAVAS; Jazz Band; School Musical; School Play; Stage Crew; Off Soph Cls; Rep Jr Cls; Phy Ed Awd; Dirctrs Awd Prfrmng Arts; U Of Vermont; Theater.

GERIAK, KAREN; Burr & Burton Seminary HS; Manchester Ctr, VT; (Y); 47/94; French Clb; Girl Scts; Leo Clb; Ski Clb; Varsity Clb; Bsktbl; Crs Cntry; Fld Hcky; Sftbl; Stephen Carman Schlrshp 85; Hood Coll.

GERVAIS, SUSAN; Enosburg Falls HS; Enosburg Falls, VT; (Y); Church Yth Grp; FFA; FHA; Varsity Clb; JV Var Socr; JV Var Sftbl; Hon Roll; Prfct Atten Awd; Cmnty Wkr; JV Var Bsktbl; Exclnce Foods & Typing II 84-85; Med Secry.

GILARDE, TERRI ANN; Mount Anthony Union HS; Bennington, VT; (Y); #20 In Class; Cmnty Wkr; Ski Clb; Band; Church Choir; Mrchg Band; Stu Cncl; Fld Hcky; Sftbl; High Hon Roll; NHS; Physcl Thrpy.

GILBERT, CHERYL; Cabot HS; Cabot, VT; (Y); 3/12; Drama Clb; French Clb; VP Varsity Clb; Yrbk Ed-Chief; VP Sr Cls; Bsktbl; Socr; Sftbl; Camera Clb; Model UN; Sportsprsn Yr 85; Army Socr Achvt Awd 85; Socr All Lg All ST & Twin ST 85; U VT; Envrnmntl Sci.

GILBERT, LAURIE; Winooski HS; S Burlington, VT; (Y); 20/65; Am Leg Aux Girls St; Drama Clb; French Clb; Scholastic Bowl; School Play; Nwsp Ed-Chief; Lit Mag; Sec Stu Cncl; Var Capt Fld Hcky; Trk.

GILLIS, SANDRA LEE; Spaulding HS; Barre, VT; (Y); 7/250; Church Yth Grp; Pres Varsity Clb; Trs Jr Cls; Trs Sr Cls; Stu Cncl; Var Capt Cheerleading; Var JV Trk; Hon Roll; Sec NHS; Rotary Awd; U Of VT Wrtng Cntst-1st Pl Wnnr 84-85; Robin Lord Memorial Schlrshp 85; Bob Camire Sprtmnshp Schlrshp; U Of NH; Occptnl Thrpy.

GOLDHABER, DAN; Burlington HS; Burlington, VT; (Y); Math Clb; Math Tm; Temple Yth Grp; Tennis; Hon Roll; Jr NHS; Western Civilztn Histry Awd 83-84; Busnss.

GOODROW, HOWARD J; Woodstock Union HS; Woodstock, VT; (Y); Am Leg Boys St; School Musical; Variety Show; Yrbk Sprt Ed; Rep Stu Cncl; Var L Bsbl; Var Capt Bsktbl; Var Capt Ftbl; Var L Golf; Var L Tennis; All ST Ftbl QB, All Star Ftbl & Bsktbl 84-85.

GORHAM, CHERI; Lyndon Inst; Lyndonville, VT; (Y); Church Yth Grp; 4-H; Pres Spanish Clb; Var Fld Hcky; JV Trk; 4-H Awd; High Hon Roll; Hon Roll; Rsrt Mgmt.

GOULD, LORI; Windsor HS; Windsor, VT; (Y); 7/60; Color Guard; Stu Cncl; JV Var Fld Hcky; JV Var Sftbl; Hon Roll; NHS; Pep Clb; Ski Clb; Varsity Clb; Flag Corp.

GRAHAM, JEAN; Canaan Memorial HS; Norton, VT; (S); 3/25; Library Aide; Teachers Aide; Nwsp Rptr; Yrbk Stf; Lit Mag; Pres Stu Cncl; High Hon Roll; Hon Roll; Sec NHS; Anthrplgy.

GRANT, CHERYL; Mt Abraham Union HS; Bristol, VT; (Y); 3/113; Am Leg Aux Girls St; Church Yth Grp; Varsity Clb; Band; Mrchg Band; Pep Band; Pres Frsh Cls; Trs Sr Cls; L Capt Bsktbl; L Capt Fld Hcky; Frshmn Acadmc & Lt Douglas Orvis Schlrshps 85; Amer Legn 85; Bentley Coll; Acctg.

GRAVES, SUE; North County Union HS; Newport, VT; (Y); 12/260; Band; Chorus; Church Choir; Color Guard; Trs Concert Band; Drill Tm; Drm & Bgl; Drm Mjr(t); Flag Corp; Jazz Band; Frnch Awds 82-85; Bk Of Knwldge Pin 82-85; JR All Amer Hall Of Fame Band Hnr 83-84; Naval Acad; Navy Offcr.

GRAY, CHERYL; North Country Union HS; Newport, VT; (S); DECA; Crs Cntry; JV Socr; JV Trk; Hon Roll; NHS; DECA Awd 1st Mktg 85; 3rd Pl Free Enterprs Cont 85; 3rd Pl Team Ope Disply 85; Acctnt.

GRENIER, DAWN; Bellows Free Acad; St Albans, VT; (Y); 1/220; Hosp Aide; Math Tm; Spanish Clb; High Hon Roll; Hon Roll; NHS; Val; Acdmc Bronze Pin 83; Acdmc Slvr Pin 84; Acdmc Gold Pin 85.

GRIMM, REBECCA; Essex Jct Educational Ctr; South Hero, VT; (Y); 13/320; Pres VP Church Yth Grp; Drama Clb; Intnl Clb; Acpl Chr; Chorus; Church Choir; School Musical; Yrbk Stf; Hon Roll; NHS; Worcester Polytech; Biomed Engr.

GRUNDY, JIM; U-32 HS; E Montpelier, VT; (Y); Church Yth Grp; Church Choir; Concert Band; Stage Crew; Nwsp Rptr; Nwsp Stf; Sec Frsh Cls; VP Soph Cls; Trs Jr Cls; Golf; Music Str Ownr.

HADLEY, JESSICA L; Chelsea HS; Chelsea, VT; (S); 1/39; Pres Church Yth Grp; Drama Clb; Sec NFL; School Musical; School Play; Ed Lit Mag; Sec Stu Cncl; Jr NHS; NHS; Voice Dem Awd; ST Frncs Mt 1st Prose Div 85; U VT JR Conf 85; Co Fndr Mother Wrld 85; Earlham Coll; Eclgy.

HALPIN, JOANNE; Mt St Joseph Acad; Rutland, VT; (Y); Am Leg Aux Girls St; Drama Clb; Pep Clb; School Play; Sec Stu Cncl; Var Socr; Var Mgr Sftbl; High Hon Roll; Hon Roll; Trs NHS; Spllng Team; Comm.

HALVERSON, AMY F; Burlington HS; Burlington, VT; (Y); Trs Am Leg Aux Girls St; Latin Clb; Band; Concert Band; Mrchg Band; Orch; Pep Band; School Musical; Symp Band; Yrbk Stf; Pre-Law.

HAMILTON, ANDREW J; Middlebury Union HS; Middlebury, VT; (Y); Am Leg Boys St; Ed Nwsp Stf; Ed Lit Mag; JV Socr; Var Trk; Hon Roll; NHS; Ntl Merit Ltr; Engl.

HAMM, ROBIN L; Bratteboro Union HS; Brattleboro, VT; (Y); 4/200; Intnl Clb; Concert Band; Mrchg Band; Nwsp Stf; Hon Roll; NHS; Pres Schlr; Rotary Awd; Church Yth Grp; Pep Band; Windham Fndtn Schlrshp 85; Frnch Merit Awd 82-83 & 85; Austine Prz 85; Lyndon ST Coll; Cmmnctns.

HAMMOND, RICKY J; Sacred Heart HS; Newport Ctr, VT; (Y); Math Tm; Band; Concert Band; Mrchg Band; School Play; Stage Crew; Bsbl; Bsktbl; Crs Cntry; Socr; Sacred Hrt Alumni Schlrshp 85; Amer Lgn Pst 21 Schlrshp 85; Arthur L Yeaw Mem Schlrshp 85; Drby Almni; Champlain Coll; Elect Engrng.

HANCE, ANDREA; Rutland HS; Rutland, VT; (Y); 32/215; Chorus; Drill Tm; Nwsp Stf; Yrbk Stf; Hon Roll; NHS; U Of VT; Lbrl Arts.

HANCOCK, CYNTHIA; North County Union HS; Newport, VT; (Y); German Clb; Band; Chorus; Mrchg Band; Pep Band; Bsktbl; Score Keeper; Sftbl; Hon Roll; NHS; Schlrshp Ltr 83; Bk Of Knwldge Pin 84; Schlrshp Pin 85; Acctnt.

HARBOUR, JEFF; Mount Anthony Union HS; Bennington, VT; (Y); 41/354; Am Leg Boys St; Band; School Play; Var Bsbl; JV Bsktbl; Var Ftbl; Hon Roll; JR All Amer Hall Fame Band Hnrs 83-84 & 84-85; Bus.

HARDER, SHERRY; Woodstock Union HS; Bridgewater, VT; (Y); FBLA; FFA; Hosp Aide; Office Aide; Political Wkr; Chorus; School Musical; Stage Crew; Stu Cncl; Sftbl.

HARDY, CHRISTOPHER; North Country Union HS; Newport, VT; (Y); Computer Clb; Band; Chorus; Concert Band; Mrchg Band; Stage Crew; Elec.

HARRINGTON, STAR; Mount Anthony Union HS; N Bennington, VT; (Y); 126/260; Rep Stu Cncl; Fld Hcky; JV Sftbl.

HART, CHIP; Burlington HS; Burlington, VT; (Y); Boy Scts; Cmnty Wkr; Computer Clb; French Clb; Latin Clb; Teachers Aide; Nwsp Rptr; Var L Crs Cntry; Var L Tennis; French Hon Soc; Mth.

HAVILAND, CHRISTOPHER; Oxbow HS; W Newbury, VT; (Y); 19/90; Ski Clb; Band; Concert Band; Jazz Band; Mrchg Band; Pep Band; Var Crs Cntry; Var Trk; Hon Roll; NHS; Aviatn.

HAWKINS, BUFFY; U-32 HS; E Calais, VT; (Y); Teachers Aide; Sec Trs Varsity Clb; Off Frsh Cls; Off Soph Cls; Off Jr Cls; Var Bsktbl; Bowling; Var Fld Hcky; Var Sftbl; Hon Roll; St Michaels Coll; Psychlgy.

HAYES, ANGEL; Arlington Memorial HS; Arlington, VT; (Y); Office Aide; Teachers Aide; Yrbk Stf; Hon Roll; Bus.

HEATH, JOANN; North Country Union HS; Island Pond, VT; (Y); Girl Scts; Library Aide; Model UN; Penn ST; Jrnlst.

HEATH, KAREN; Rutland HS; Rutland, VT; (Y); 180/345; Varsity Clb; Var Fld Hcky; Bus.

HEBERT, KYLE P; U-32 HS; Montpelier, VT; (Y); 11/115; Am Leg Boys St; Trs Soph Cls; Off Jr Cls; Off Sr Cls; Capt Ice Hcky; Socr; Tennis; Trk; Hon Roll; U Of VT; Bio.

HECHT, CHRISTOPH; Mt Anthony Union HS; Bennington, VT; (Y); Boy Scts; German Clb; Socr; Trk; UVM Mth Exam 1st Schl 5th ST 85; MAA Exam 1st Schl 85.

HECHT, DEBORA; Rice Memorial HS; Winooski, VT; (Y); FHA; Pep Clb; Pres Science Clb; Spanish Clb; Teachers Aide; Stat Bsktbl; Stat Ftbl; Var L Trk; JV Vllybl; High Hon Roll; Bus Adm.

HEDRICK, DARCY A; Mount Anthony Union HS; Dayton, NJ; (Y); 28/286; Am Leg Aux Girls St; Cmnty Wkr; Rep Stu Cncl; Var L Cheerleading; Var L Golf; High Hon Roll; NHS; Pres Schlr; FCA; Key Clb; Miss VT Teen USA 84; Carls Drug Scholar 85; Fin Chem Fab Scholar 85; Stetson V Deland FL; Bus.

HEISE, CHAD A; Harwood Union HS; Waterbury, VT; (Y); Chorus; Var Crs Cntry; Var Ice Hcky; Var Trk; Hon Roll; NHS.

HENRY, GUY; Colchester HS; Colchester, VT; (S); 10/250; Ski Clb; Var Capt Bsbl; JV Bsktbl; Var Capt Socr; High Hon Roll; Hon Roll; NHS; Elec Engrng.

HEPBURN, LU ANNE; Williamstown JR SR HS; Williamstown, VT; (Y); Cmnty Wkr; Pres Computer Clb; English Clb; French Clb; VP Ski Clb; Teachers Aide; VICA; JV Fld Hcky; High Hon Roll; Hon Roll; Sftbl Rec Ctr MA 83-84; Comp.

HERMAN, WENDY; Canaan Memorial HS; Canaan, VT; (S); 1/25; Am Leg Aux Girls St; Ski Clb; Teachers Aide; Band; Bsktbl; Capt Cheerleading; Fld Hcky; Capt Sftbl; High Hon Roll; Pres NHS; VT JR Conf 84; Child Psych.

HERRICK, KAREN; West Rutland HS; West Rutland, VT; (Y); Drama Clb; Stage Crew; JV Fld Hcky; JV Sftbl; High Hon Roll; Hon Roll; Flrst.

HERRLICH, KATHY; Colchester HS; Colchester, VT; (S); Art Clb; Math Tm; Band; Pep Band; School Play; Trk; High Hon Roll; NHS; U Of VT.

HIGGINS, CORIN; Chelsea HS; Tunbridge, VT; (S); 3/28; Debate Tm; Drama Clb; Pres 4-H; French Clb; GAA; Girl Scts; NFL; Teachers Aide; Varsity Clb; Chorus; Hotel Admin.

HILL, HEATHER L; Lyndon Inst; Lyndonville, VT; (Y); Drama Clb; Latin Clb; NFL; School Play; Nwsp Ed-Chief; Yrbk Bus Mgr; Yrbk Ed-Chief; JV Fld Hcky; JV Trk; High Hon Roll; Attended Governors Inst On Arts 84; Attended Int On Intl Affairs 84; Engl.

HILL, ROBERT; Rutland HS; Pittsford, VT; (Y); 30/225; Am Leg Boys St; Rep Jr Cls; Rep Stu Cncl; JV Bsbl; JV Var Ftbl; JV Trk; Hon Roll; Lawyer.

HILL, TEDDY; Peoples Acad; Wolcott, VT; (Y); High Hon Roll; Hon Roll; Prfct Atten Awd; Mike Randal Woodrkng Awd 84-85; Prfct Attnd 84-85; George & Nettie Merit Awd 84-85; Johnson ST Coll; Bus.

HILLIARD, KIM; Lyndon Inst; Lyndon, VT; (Y); Church Yth Grp; Girl Scts; JV Capt Fld Hcky; High Hon Roll; Hon Roll; Prfct Atten Awd; Champlain Coll; Bus.

HILLIKER, SCOTT; North Country Union HS; Newport, VT; (Y); Var Crs Cntry; Var Trk; U Of VT; Elec Engr.

HIXSON, PETER E; Vermont Acad; Lake Placid, NY; (S); 13/85; Rep Frsh Cls; Rep Frsh Cls; Var Capt Crs Cntry; Var Capt Golf; Var Socr; Var Capt Tennis; Middlebury Coll; Bio.

HOARD, THERESA; Mount Anthony Union HS; Bennington, VT; (Y); Band; Concert Band; Drm Mjr(t); Mrchg Band; Pep Band; JV Var Cheerleading; Hon Roll; Prfct Atten Awd; Flght Atten.

HODGDON, CYNTHIA; Hartford HS; White River Jct, VT; (Y); DECA; FBLA; Pep Clb; Hon Roll; DECA Awd 1st Pl 85; DECA St Hnr Awd 85; Outstndng Perfrmnce-Bus Mgt; O Briens Coll; Csmtlgy.

HOFFMAN, REID G; The Putney Schl; Berkeley, CA; (Y); Art Clb; Camera Clb; Chess Clb; Cmnty Wkr; Computer Clb; Lit Mag; Trs Jr Cls; Var Capt Socr; Vllybl; Ntl Merit SF.

HOLLAND, EARLE; Whitingham HS; Jacksonville, VT; (S); 14/22; Am Leg Boys St; Drama Clb; Trs 4-H; Band; Chorus; Church Choir; Color Guard; Concert Band; Drm Mjr(t); Mrchg Band; U S Navy; Comp.

HOLT, STEVE; Woodstock Union HS; Woodstock, VT; (Y); Latin Clb; Yrbk Stf; Var Ftbl; Swmmng; Var Trk; Bethany; Bus.

HOMMEL, RICK C; Lake Region Union HS; Orleans, VT; (Y); 96/110; DECA; Drama Clb; JA; Concert Band; Jazz Band; School Musical; Var L Bsktbl; Var L Golf; Hon Roll; NHS; Bus Mngmnt.

HOOKS, AMY; Mt Anthony Union HS; Bennington, VT; (Y); Model UN; Spanish Clb; Frsh Cls; Soph Cls; JV Fld Hcky; Hon Roll; Engl Awd 84; G C Hooks Memrl Schlrshp 85; U Of VT; Bus Admin.

HOPE, MICHELLE; Missisquoi Valley Union HS; Swanton, VT; (Y); Cmnty Wkr; Library Aide; Chorus; Variety Show; JV Mgr(s); Hon Roll; Comm.

HOPKINS, SCOTT; Vergennes Union HS; Vergennes, VT; (Y); Boy Scts; Drama Clb; French Clb; School Musical; School Play; Wrstlng.

HORGAN, DOUGLAS; Ruthland HS; Rutland, VT; (Y); Am Leg Boys St; Pres JA; Co-Capt Scholastic Bowl; Pres Sr Cls; Off Stu Cncl; L Socr; L Trk; NHS; Ntl Merit Schol; Hugh O Brian Yth Smnr Ambssdr 83; Swarthmore Coll.

HORNER, JEANNIE; Hanwood Union HS; Burlington, VT; (Y); 6/94; Camera Clb; Ski Clb; Acpl Chr; Chorus; Nwsp Rptr; Yrbk Stf; Pres Frsh Cls; JV Fld Hcky; Swmmng; Rotary Awd; Acctng Stu Yr 85; U VT; Bio.

HOVER, CAPRICE; Fair Haven Union HS; Castleton, VT; (Y); 22/118; Capt Hosp Aide; Teachers Aide; Trk; Rotary Awd; Mgr Drama Clb; Varsity Clb; Acpl Chr; Band; Church Choir; Gym; Rainbw Awd Memrztn 84; U Of S CA; Phy Ed.

HOVEY, GREGORY; Concord HS; N Concord, VT; (S); 5/23; Math Clb; Math Tm; Model UN; Scholastic Bowl; Pres Frsh Cls; Pres Soph Cls; Var Bsbl; Var Bsktbl; Hon Roll; NHS; Indstrl Arts Awd 81-82; Wildlife Bio.

HOWLAND, ANGELA; Hartford HS; West Hartford, VT; (Y); 3/125; AFS; Am Leg Aux Girls St; Hosp Aide; Teachers Aide; Rep Frsh Cls; Bsktbl; High Hon Roll; Hon Roll; Outstndg Eng Stu Awd 82; 2nd Pl Regnl Frgn Lang Comp Spn 85; UVM JR Conf 85; Tchr.

HOWLETT, JENNIFER J; Middlebury Union HS; Bridport, VT; (Y); Church Yth Grp; GAA; Church Choir; Fld Hcky; Tennis; 4-H Awd; Peer Cnslng Awd 83-85.

HUDSON, JENNIFER; Otter Valley Union HS; Pittsford, VT; (Y); Church Yth Grp; Pres French Clb; Scholastic Bowl; School Play; Yrbk Stf; Rep Stu Cncl; Fld Hcky; Golf; Hon Roll; Foundng Mbr Altrntvs Teens 83-86.

HUDSON, MICHELE; U-32 HS; East Calais, VT; (Y); #24 In Class; Cmnty Wkr; Dance Clb; Drama Clb; PAVAS; Teachers Aide; Thesps; Chorus; School Play; Stage Crew; Yrbk Stf; E Calais Wmns Clb Schlrshp 85; Champlain Coll; Travel.

HUFFMAN, JACOB; Burlington HS; Burlington, VT; (Y); Art Clb; Model UN; Ski Clb; Varsity Clb; Var Trk; Gov Hon Prg Awd; Hon Roll; Govnrs Inst Of Arts 85; 1st Pl Cngrssnl Arts Caucus 85; Merit VT Fed Wmns Clbs Art Cont 85; RIS; Vis Art.

HUGO, CHARLES B; Colchester HS; Colchester, VT; (Y); Band; Jazz Band; U VT; Comp Sci.

HUNT, MICHAEL J; Lake Region Union HS; Barton, VT; (Y); 6/90; Church Yth Grp; Intnl Clb; Math Tm; Pep Clb; JV Var Bsbl; Var Crs Cntry; JV Socr; Hon Roll; NHS.

HUNT, TAMMY; Bellows Free Acad; Fairfield, VT; (Y); Church Yth Grp; Office Aide; Rep Stu Cncl; JV L Bsktbl; Var L Cheerleading; JV L Sftbl; Var L Trk; Cit Awd; High Hon Roll; French Clb; 12 Semstr GPA Brnz Pin 85; Medcl Lab Techncn.

HUTCHINS, MARK; Mount Anthony Union HS; Pownal, VT; (Y); 5/300; Drama Clb; German Clb; Mathletes; Math Clb; Capt Math Tm; Science Clb; High Hon Roll; NHS; Pres Schlr; RPI Medal Recipient 83-84; VT ST ARML Mth Tm 84-85; Brown U; Appl Mthmtcs.

HUYNH, PHONG; Mount Anthony Union HS; Bennington, VT; (Y); Hon Roll; NHS; Math.

HYZER, GARY; Mill River Union HS; Wallingford, VT; (Y); 2/135; Am Leg Boys St; Drama Clb; Chorus; Concert Band; Jazz Band; Hon Roll; NHS; Thesps; Band; Mrchg Band; Natl HS Music Inst 84; All New England Band 85; All ST Band 84-85; Music.

IBEY, ANDY C; Twinfield HS; Plainfield, VT; (Y); Var Capt Bsktbl; Hon Roll; Centrl VT Leag All Str 83-85; Div III All ST Tm 84-85; Castleton Coll; Bus.

IZZO, ALAN; Hartford HS; Quechee, VT; (Y); 28/151; Pep Clb; Varsity Clb; Yrbk Stf; Var L Ftbl; Im Lcrss; Var L Tennis; Im Wt Lftg; High Hon Roll; Hon Roll; Rotary Awd; Acadmc All-Amer 85; U San Diego; Comp Sci.

JACOBS, PAMELA; Richford JR SR HS; Richford, VT; (Y); Church Yth Grp; Drama Clb; Girl Scts; Band; Chorus; Church Choir; Mrchg Band; School Play; Nwsp Phtg; Var Socr; Legsltv Art Awd 85; VT ST; Csmtlgy.

JALBERT, PIERRE D; South Burlington HS; S Burlington, VT; (Y); Am Leg Boys St; Jazz Band; Symp Band; Pres NHS; Band; Concert Band; Orch; School Musical; Hon Roll; Muics Tchrs Ntl Assn Compstn Cntst Wnnr 82; Sue Boyer Cnrt Cmpttn Wnnr 84; VT All ST Piano Prfmnc 84; Music.

JAMIESON, JONATHAN; Harwood Union HS; Waitsfield, VT; (Y); Boy Scts; Trs Sr Cls; Var L Crs Cntry; JV Var Trk; Hon Roll.

JERMAN, ERIC; Burr & Burton Seminary; Arlington, VT; (Y); Am Leg Boys St; Debate Tm; VP Soph Cls; Var L Socr; Var L Tennis; High Hon Roll; Hon Roll; VP NHS; Exclnce JR Coll Prep Eng 85.

JILLSON, LISA; Whitingham HS; Readsboro, VT; (S); 7/22; Am Leg Aux Girls St; Office Aide; Spanish Clb; Teachers Aide; Chorus; Flag Corp; School Play; Nwsp Stf; Rep Sr Cls; Stu Cncl; Acctng.

JODOIN, STEPHANIE; Burlington HS; Burlington, VT; (Y); JV Var Bsktbl; JV Sftbl; Var Trk; Hon Roll; NHS; Champlain Coll; Acctng.

JOHNSON, ELIZABETH A; Ruthland HS; Rutland, VT; (Y); 22/180; Library Aide; Hon Roll; Jr NHS; Pres Schlrshp Castleton ST Coll 85; Castleton ST Coll; Accntng.

JOHNSON, JENNIFER; Champlain Valley Union HS; Williston, VT; (Y); Sec AFS; Am Leg Aux Girls St; Band; Orch; Off Soph Cls; Off Jr Cls; Off Sr Cls; High Hon Roll; Hon Roll; NHS; Colby Coll; Human Dev.

JOHNSON, KATHY M; Lake Region Union HS; Orleans, VT; (Y); Church Yth Grp; English Clb; Band; Rep Soph Cls; Rep Jr Cls; High Hon Roll; NHS; Nrs.

JOHNSON, SHELLEY; Spaulding HS; Barre, VT; (Y); 54/255; Pres Sec Spanish Clb; Nwsp Stf; Yrbk Stf; Lit Mag; Stu Cncl; JV Cheerleading; Powder Puff Ftbl; JV Sftbl; Hon Roll; Interact Clb; U Of RI; Phrmcy.

JONES, AMY; Stowe HS; Wolcott, VT; (Y); Drama Clb; Chorus; School Musical; School Play; Nwsp Ed-Chief; Yrbk Stf; Var Crs Cntry; NHS; Church Yth Grp; Hosp Aide; Schl Frnc Prjct; Gvnrs Inst On Fn Arts; Prm Cmmttee; Fordham U; Clsscs.

JOSEPH, CINDY; North Country Union HS; Derby Line, VT; (Y); Am Leg Aux Girls St; Sec Band; Chorus; Concert Band; Pep Band; School Musical; Crs Cntry; Trk; High Hon Roll; NHS; 3rd N Cntry Ntl Math 83-84; Phrmcy.

JOSLIN, CHRISTINA; Concord HS; N Concord, VT; (S); Drama Clb; Girl Scts; Math Clb; Math Tm; Model UN; Band; School Play; VP Frsh Cls; Off Soph Cls; Off Jr Cls; Schlrs Bowl 84.

KALINEN, MELISSA; South Royalton HS; Bethel, VT; (Y); Church Yth Grp; FBLA; Hosp Aide; Varsity Clb; Band; Chorus; Trs Frsh Cls; Sec Soph Cls; Cheerleading; Hon Roll; Modern Miss Acad Awd 85; Champlain; Bus.

KAUFMAN, DANIEL; Burlington HS; Burlington, VT; (Y); Church Yth Grp; Latin Clb; Math Tm; Temple Yth Grp; JV Socr; Var Tennis; Hon Roll; NHS; Williams Coll Bk Awd 85; Rensselaer Math & Sci Medal Wnnr 85.

KEENE, KATHY; Chelsea Public HS; Chelsea, VT; (Y); Pres FBLA; Varsity Clb; Chorus; School Play; Rep Frsh Cls; Rep Soph Cls; Pres Jr Cls; Trs Stu Cncl; Var Bsktbl; High Hon Roll; Bst Actress 82; Mst Imprvd Awd Bsktbl 85; Champlain Coll; Spec Ed.

KEEP, CYNDEE; Hartford HS; Quechee, VT; (Y); Church Yth Grp; Teachers Aide; Hon Roll; Acadmc All Amer Schlr Awd 84-85; 2nd Pl H S Levl U Of VT Wrtg Cntst 84-85; 1st Pl Adv Lvl Frnch 84-85; UVM; Tchg.

KENISON, LYNN; Hartford HS; Sharon, VT; (Y); Am Leg Aux Girls St; FBLA; GAA; Math Tm; Bsktbl; Sftbl; Hon Roll.

KENYON, AMY; Mt Anthony Union HS; N Bennington, VT; (Y); Church Yth Grp; Chorus; Stage Crew; Nwsp Stf; Yrbk Bus Mgr; High Hon Roll; Hon Roll; Acctng.

KENYON, KEITH; Otter Valley Union HS; Brandon, VT; (Y); Bsbl; Crs Cntry; Trk; High Hon Roll; Hon Roll; NHS; U Miami; Law.

KENYON, KRISTI L; South Burlington HS; South Burlington, VT; (Y); Drama Clb; French Clb; Speech Tm; Nwsp Rptr; Nwsp Stf; Yrbk Rptr; Yrbk Stf; Gym; Hon Roll; Achvt Awd Frnscs Spch Team 85; Eckard; Thtre.

KESNER, KARMA J; Twinfield Union HS; Plainfield, VT; (Y); 3/35; French Clb; Hosp Aide; NFL; Chorus; Yrbk Stf; Var Capt Cheerleading; Score Keeper; High Hon Roll; Hon Roll; Sec NHS; U VT; Med Tech.

KIM, MEGAN; Essex Jct Ed Center HS; Essex Jct, VT; (Y); French Clb; Var Capt Tennis; Hon Roll; Coachs Awd Tenns 84; Cert Natl Latin Exam 85; William Smith Clg.

KIMBALL, TONYA; U-32 HS; Montpelier, VT; (Y); Camera Clb; Church Yth Grp; Girl Scts; Hosp Aide; School Play; JV Var Cheerleading; JV Fld Hcky; Var Mgr(s); Var Score Keeper; Hon Roll; Cert Apprctn Centrl VT Medcl Ctr 85; Cert Partcptn Chrldg Fld Hcky 83-85; U Of VT; Med.

KINNEY, JILL; Richford HS; W Berkshire, VT; (Y); FHA; Teachers Aide; Chorus; Drm Mjr(t); Camp Fr Inc; Sec Jr Cls; Var Socr; Var Sftbl; Burlington Coll; Nrsng.

KINNEY, MELISSA J; Colchester HS; S Hero, VT; (Y); Pres Sec Church Yth Grp; Band; Concert Band; Rep Stu Cncl; JV Capt Bsktbl; JV Sftbl; Hon Roll.

KIPP III, EARL; Mount Anthony Union HS; Bennington, VT; (Y); 36/307; Letterman Clb; Im Bsktbl; Var L Ftbl; Im Vllybl; Wt Lftg; Hon Roll; Close Up Fndtn Grp 84-85; Paul Smiths Coll; Forestry.

KIRBY, MICHAEL; Colchester HS; Colchester, VT; (Y); Am Leg Boys St; JA; Math Tm; VP Frsh Cls; Rep Soph Cls; Pres Stu Cncl; Var L Bsbl; JV Bsktbl; Im Bowling; Im Wrstlng; Jr Achvt Sales Awd 84-85; U Of VT; Teacher.

KIRBY, SHAUN K; Essex Junction Educational Center; Essex Junction, VT; (Y); 1/314; Pres Sec Church Yth Grp; Pres VP Exploring; Math Tm; Scholastic Bowl; Speech Tm; Acpl Chr; Chorus; NHS; Ntl Merit SF; Voice Dem Awd; Amer Lgn Schlrshp 84; Essay Cntst ST Wnnr 84; Amer Clg Muscns, Pianist 83-84; Math.

KLITTICH, DEBORAH; Champlain Valley Union HS; Shelb0rne, VT; (Y); 24/236; Am Leg Aux Girls St; VP Church Yth Grp; Red Cross Aide; Chorus; Church Choir; Var Capt Crs Cntry; Var L Trk; High Hon Roll; Hon Roll; Kiwanis Awd; Comm.

KOMOROWSKI, MICHELE; Peoples Acad; St Louis, MO; (Y); 3/89; Church Yth Grp; Drama Clb; French Clb; Band; Chorus; Church Choir; Sec Trs Yrbk Stf; Sec Stu Cncl; Var Church Yth Grp; Hon Roll; Govnrs Inst Arts; Semi Fnlst Miss Schlrshp Pgnt; James Camley Hist Awd; WA U; Intrntl Law.

KONIUTO, LISA; Mount Mansfield Union HS; Underhill, VT; (Y); Church Yth Grp; Band; Chorus; Drm & Bgl; Orch; School Musical; Var L Fld Hcky; L Trk; High Hon Roll; NHS; Natl Piano Audtns 82-84; 2 Yr Bnd Mbrshp Awd 84; U Of Selaware; Educ.

KRAMER, DOUGLAS; Rutland HS; Rutland, VT; (Y); 6/223; Boy Scts; Church Yth Grp; Debate Tm; Pres Science Clb; Teachers Aide; Rep Stu Cncl; High Hon Roll; Hon Roll; NHS; Excllnc Engl Awd 83; Comp Sci.

KUZMIK, KAY; U-32 HS; Barre, VT; (Y); 38/110; Church Yth Grp; Library Aide; Office Aide; Chorus; Church Choir; JV Var Cheerleading; JV Sftbl; Hon Roll; Mst Valuable Chrldr 82-83; Hon Rl 84-85; Scholar 84-85; Champlain Coll; Legal Sec.

LA BOUNTY, TERRI; St Johnsbury Acad; St Johnsbury, VT; (Y); 26/165; Am Leg Aux Girls St; Sec Church Yth Grp; Chorus; School Musical; Sec Sr Cls; Sec Stu Cncl; Var Capt Cheerleading; Trk; Hon Roll; VP Drama Clb; DAR St John Decreacous Chptr Awd 84; Miss Teen VT 84-85; Psych.

LA POINT, CRISTINA; Woodstock Union HS; Woodstock, VT; (Y); Dance Clb; Thesps; Acpl Chr; Chorus; School Musical; Yrbk Stf; Off Jr Cls; Cheerleading; Lcrss; Hon Roll; Chorl Music Schlrshp 84; Bells & Baux Chrs 85; Mst Sprtd, Vlubl & Dedctd Chrldr 83-85; Danc Awd 85; Csmtlgy.

LA PORTE, KAREN L; Colchester HS; Colchester, VT; (Y); 63/200; Dance Clb; Debate Tm; Pres Frsh Cls; Pres Soph Cls; Pres Jr Cls; Co-Capt Cheerleading; Sftbl; HOBY Ldrs Sem 83; Rochester Inst Tech; Ind Engrng.

LABANOWSKI, KURT; Mt Anthony Union HS; Bennington, VT; (Y); German Clb; Ski Clb; L Ftbl; L Trk; Wt Lftg; S UT All Str Ftbl Sqd; 5th VT ST Shot Put 1st Dist; Bus.

LABERGE, CARMEN; Essex Jct Educational Ctr; Essex Junction, VT; (Y); Girl Scts; JA; Key Clb; Library Aide; Var L Sftbl; High Avg Awd 85; Champlain Coll; Data Proc.

LAFERRIERE, MEG; Harwood Union HS; Waitsfield, VT; (Y); Teachers Aide; Varsity Clb; Chorus; Sec Jr Cls; Sec Sr Cls; JV Bsktbl; Capt JV Fld Hcky; JV Mgr(s); Var Capt Trk; High Hon Roll; U Of VT.

LAGASSE, SHELLY; North Country Union HS; Derby Line, VT; (Y); GAA; Latin Clb; Varsity Clb; School Play; Variety Show; Var Capt Bsktbl; JV Var Socr; JV Var Sftbl.

LALIME, PHILIP; Rice Memoiral HS; Burlington, VT; (Y); JV Bsbl; Var Crs Cntry.

LAMBERT, BRUCE; Rice Memorial HS; Burling, VT; (Y); Varsity Clb; Variety Show; JV Var Bsbl; JV Coach Actv; Capt Ftbl; Var Wt Lftg; Norfield Mt Hermen Prep Schl.

LAMELL, ROBERT; Peoples Acad; Morrisville, VT; (Y); 2/55; Scholastic Bowl; Trs Jr Cls; Sec Stu Cncl; Var Bsbl; Var Bsktbl; Var Val; High Hon Roll; Trs NHS; U Of VT; Engrng.

LAMOREY JR, EDWARD A; Spaulding HS; Barre, VT; (Y); 20/265; Key Clb; Varsity Clb; Stu Cncl; Var JV Bsbl; Var Ice Hcky; JV Socr; Hon Roll; Kiwanis Awd; NEDT Awd; Top 10 Pct U VT Math Exm 84-85; Cum Laude Natl Latn Exm 82; U Of VT; Comp Sci.

LANDON, CHRISTINE; Champlain Valley Union HS; Shelburne, VT; (Y); 1/203; Am Leg Aux Girls St; Sec Church Yth Grp; Girl Scts; Key Clb; Model UN; Off Jr Cls; Off Sr Cls; Var Socr; Var Sftbl; Trk; James Fitzpatrick Englsh Awd 83; James Fitzpatrick Frnch IV Awd 84; Tufts U; Bio-Chem.

LANDON, DEBORAH; Champlain Valley Union HS; Shelburne, VT; (Y); 10/235; Am Leg Aux Girls St; Key Clb; Model UN; Chorus; Rep Stu Cncl; Var Capt Gym; Var L Trk; High Hon Roll; Hon Roll; NHS; Math.

LANG, DEANNA; U 32 HS; Worcester, VT; (Y); Church Yth Grp; Dance Clb; Drama Clb; Chorus; School Musical; Lit Mag; High Hon Roll; Hon Roll; Bus.

LANGELLO, MARIANNE; Black River HS; Ludlow, VT; (S); 7/45; AFS; Am Leg Aux Girls St; FHA; Pep Clb; Band; Chorus; Concert Band; Jazz Band; Mrchg Band; Orch; Keene ST Coll; Music.

LANGLEY, ANAIS; Burlington HS; Burlington, VT; (Y); AFS; Model UN; Sec VP Temple Yth Grp; Varsity Clb; Chorus; Rep Jr Cls; Var L Fld Hcky; Mgr(s); JV Trk; Excll VT Hstry Awd 84-85; Frnch Awd 84-85; Grnd Distctn Frnch Awed 82-83; Eng.

LARAMIE, CHARLOTTE; Vergennes Union HS; Vergennes, VT; (Y); Drama Clb; German Clb; Girl Scts; Library Aide; School Musical; School Play; Stage Crew; Yrbk Rptr; Yrbk Stf; Hon Roll; UVM; Engl.

LAROSE, NICOLE; Richford HS; Richford, VT; (Y); 2/46; Am Leg Aux Girls St; Drama Clb; Mrchg Band; Yrbk Ed-Chief; Var JV Bsktbl; Bausch & Lomb Sci Awd; Hon Roll; NHS; Pres Schlr; Sal; Trinitys Jeans Garvin Presdntl Schlrshp 85; Knights Of Columbus Schlrshp 85; VT Rural Lttr Crrs Assoc; Trinity Coll Of VT; Comp Sci.

LARSON, CAROLINE; Oxbos HS; Fairlee, VT; (Y); 3/88; Math Tm; Band; School Play; Trs Jr Cls; Fld Hcky; Trk; High Hon Roll; NHS; Geo Awd 82-83; French II,Alg II,Bio Awds 83-84; Chem Awd Achvt Awd 84-85; U VT; Pre-Med.

LASHWAY, MATTHEW S; Essex Junction Educational Ctr; St Albans, VT; (Y); 45/320; Q&S; JV Var Bsktbl; Trk; Douglas Mac Arthur Awd Ldrshp AFJROTC 84; Appntmnt-US Merchant Marine Acad 85; U Of Vermont; Civil Engrng.

LAVIGNE, KEVIN A; Colchester HS; Colchester, VT; (Y); 18/220; Art Clb; Var Gym; Trk; Wt Lftg; High Hon Roll; NHS; Bdybldng; Plymouth ST Coll; Athl Trner.

LAW, CHRISTY; Whitingham HS; Whitingham, VT; (S); 1/28; Rptr 4-H; French Clb; Spanish Clb; Band; Chorus; Mrchg Band; School Musical; Yrbk Stf; Rep Frsh Cls; Stat Sftbl; VT Inst Of Intl Affrs 84; Spnsh Awd 84; Hghst Hnr Roll 83-84; Liberal Arts.

LAWLOR, BILL; Woodstock Union HS; Woodstock, VT; (Y); Computer Clb; Dance Clb; Service Clb; Stage Crew; Yrbk Stf; JV Bsktbl; Stat Ftbl; Var L Tennis; Hon Roll; Mst Imprvd Tnns Plyr 82-83; U Of Vermont; Bus Mngmt.

LAWRENCE, NANCY J; Colchester HS; S Hero, VT; (Y); 39/213; Breadloaf Yng Wrtrs Confrnce 85; New Englnd Coll; Comm.

LAWREY, MARY; Vergennes Union HS; Vergennes, VT; (Y); 15/120; Stu Cncl; Bsktbl; Cheerleading; Crs Cntry; Fld Hcky; Gym; Sftbl; High Hon Roll; Hon Roll; Pre-Med.

LAWSON, KELLY; Mt Anthony Union HS; Pownal, VT; (Y); 11/254; Am Leg Aux Girls St; Spanish Clb; Yrbk Stf; Stu Cncl; Mgr Socr; High Hon Roll; NHS; Prfct Atten Awd; Peer Cnclr 85; Pre-Law.

LE BARON, AUDRA; Colchester HS; North Hero, VT; (S); 1/220; Church Yth Grp; Drama Clb; 4-H; Sec French Clb; Chorus; Church Choir; School Musical; School Play; Gym; Socr; Japan US Senate Schlrshp 84; Oustndng Sci & Forgn Lang Achvt Troph 84; Harvard-Radcliffe U; Forgn Lang.

LE BEAU, ELOY JR; Burlington HS; Burlington, VT; (Y); Teachers Aide; Yrbk Stf; Hon Roll; Champlian Coll; Bus Mgmt.

LE BEL, TRAVIS G; Bellows Free Acad; St Albans, VT; (S); Church Yth Grp; DECA; Political Wkr; JV Mgr Bsbl; DECA Outstndg Sr Awd 85; Bus Admin.

LE BRUN, BARBARA; Black River HS; Mt Holly, VT; (Y); Band; Chorus; Mrchg Band; JV Var Bsktbl; Var Capt Socr; Var Sftbl; Hon Roll; U S Army Rsrve Natl Schlr/Ath Awd 85; U S Army MVP 85; Natl Socr Coachs Assn Amer 85; P P Pullinen Hnr; Johnson ST Coll; Bus Mgmt.

LE CLAIR, CORINNE; Burlington HS; Burlington, VT; (Y); Hosp Aide; Office Aide; Hon Roll; NHS; Champlain Coll; Bus Adm.

LEBLANC, KIMBERLEE; Sacred Heart HS; N Tory, VT; (Y); Band; Chorus; Church Choir; Concert Band; Jazz Band; Madrigals; Mrchg Band; School Play; Var Bsktbl; Var Socr; 1 Rating All New England Fest 83-85; Solo New England Fest 84-85; U Of VT; Music Teacher.

LELAND, JOY; Oxbow HS; Newbury, VT; (Y); 6/92; Pres Church Yth Grp; Drama Clb; Pres French Clb; Ski Clb; Band; Concert Band; Pep Band; School Play; Var Fld Hcky; Var Sftbl; Frnch Awd 83-85; Selctd Govrnr Inst Arts 84; Visl Arts.

LENO, ANNE MARIE; Mt St Joseph Acad; Rutland, VT; (Y); 12/100; Drm Mjr(t); Nwsp Rptr; Bsktbl; Twrlr; High Hon Roll; Hon Roll; Social Work.

LENZINI, SUSAN; Moutn Anthony Union HS; Bennington, VT; (Y); Cmnty Wkr; Hosp Aide; Nwsp Rptr; Gym; High Hon Roll; Hon Roll; NHS; Prfct Atten Awd; U MN; Pre-Med.

LESAGE, ELIZABETH M; Colchester HS; Colchester, VT; (Y); Pres Sec Art Clb; Sec Church Yth Grp; Rep Frsh Cls; Hon Roll; Art Clb Most Invlvd 82-85; Ed.

LESEM, KRISTINA; Burlington HS; Burlington, VT; (Y); AFS; French Clb; German Clb; Latin Clb; Political Wkr; Chorus; Orch; School Musical; Rep Frsh Cls; Stu Cncl; All ST All New England Music Festvls; All Eastern Music Festvl; Ntl Latin Ex Cum Lauda.

LESEM, TINA; Burlington HS; Burlington, VT; (Y); AFS; French Clb; Latin Clb; Political Wkr; Chorus; Orch; School Musical; Rep Stu Cncl; Var Socr; Var Tennis; All-ST & New England Music Fstvls; All Eastern Music Fstvl; Natl Latin Exam Cum Laude.

LEVY, ERIK B; Vermont Acad; Brookline, MA; (S); Ski Clb; Var Capt Lcrss; JV Var Socr; Dormitory Sr Proctor 85-86; Lib Arts.

LEWONSKI, SHARON; Rice Memorial HS; Colchester, VT; (Y); Hosp Aide; Variety Show; Var Crs Cntry; JV Trk; Hon Roll; Freshman Orientatn Ldr 84-85; Pre-Law.

LIBBY, KRISTIE; Stowe HS; Stowe, VT; (Y); 7/41; Cmnty Wkr; Girl Scts; Red Cross Aide; Ski Clb; Stage Crew; Yrbk Sprt Ed; Sec Frsh Cls; Var JV Bsktbl; Var L Fld Hcky; Var L Sftbl; Stowe Booster Clb Sportsmnshp Awd 85; Cert Adv Lifesavng & CPR Amer Red Crs 84 & 85; Radio Cmmnctns.

LIGHT, ROBYN V; Twinfield HS; Plainfield, VT; (Y); 11/40; Pres French Clb; Hosp Aide; Teachers Aide; Yrbk Ed-Chief; VP Frsh Cls; VP Soph Cls; Trs Jr Cls; Cheerleading; Capt Fld Hcky; Hon Roll; Dip Plus 85; Quinnipiac Coll; Bus.

LONEY, JOCELYN POPPY; Middlebury Union HS; Middlebury, VT; (Y); AFS; Church Yth Grp; Pres Drama Clb; PAVAS; Acpl Chr; Chorus; Madrigals; School Musical; School Play; Stage Crew; Ldrshp Citation Drama Clb 84; Founded Drama Clb-Clb Of The Arts 83; MVHS Musicianship & Achvmnt 83; Vassar Coll; Music.

LONGE, RONALD; Enosburg Falls HS; Sheldon Spgs, VT; (Y); Drama Clb; Teachers Aide; Nwsp Ed-Chief; Nwsp Stf; VP Soph Cls; High Hon Roll; Trs NHS; Stu Of The Mnth 83-85; Hugh O Brian Yth Fndtn 84; Rep To The VT JR Conf 85; St Michaels Coll; Bus Adm.

LORD, MICHAEL JAY; Fair Haven Union HS; Bomoseen, VT; (Y); 1/100; Am Leg Boys St; French Clb; Yrbk Bus Mgr; JV Bsktbl; Coach Actv; Socr; Var L Trk; High Hon Roll; NHS; Prfct Atten Awd; Gov Inst Sci; Jr Conf; U VT; Comp Sci.

LOSO, PAM; Union 32 HS; E Montpelier, VT; (Y); 24/118; Teachers Aide; VICA; Chorus; Swing Chorus; Variety Show; Lit Mag; JV Var Sftbl; Hon Roll; Most Spirtd Sftbl 84; Math.

LOTANE, KRISTIN; Rice Memorial HS; S Burlington, VT; (Y); 18/100; Church Yth Grp; Drama Clb; Chorus; School Musical; School Play; Variety Show; High Hon Roll; Drama Tech Intrnshp 84; Wrtrs Clb 84-85; Comms.

LOVE, SCOTT C; Vermont Acad; Englewood, CO; (S); Camera Clb; Drama Clb; Chorus; Yrbk Ed-Chief; Lit Mag; JV Lcrss; Var Trk; Hon Roll; NHS; Ntl Merit Ltr; Hnrs Engl Wrtng 84-85; Hnrs Art Partcptn 83-85; Wrtr.

LUCIER, MICHELLE; Vergennes Union HS; N Ferrisburg, VT; (Y); 3/113; Am Leg Aux Girls St; Girl Scts; Yrbk Stf; Var Socr; Var Sftbl; High Hon Roll; Hon Roll; NHS; Dartmouth Club Bk Awd 85; U Of VT; Nrs.

LYSTER, PETER; North County Union HS; Belgium; (Y); Am Leg Boys St; Boy Scts; Church Yth Grp; Off Soph Cls; Bsbl; Socr; Hon Roll; NHS; Bk Of Knwldge Pin 83; Schlrshp Ltr,Pin 84-85; Ivy Lge; Math.

MACE, JOHN; Vergennes Union HS; Ferrisburgh, VT; (Y); 8/110; Am Leg Boys St; Golf; Cit Awd; High Hon Roll; NHS; Sec Jr Cls; Sec Sr Cls; Bus Admin.

MACKE, TIM; U-32 HS; Calais, VT; (Y); Band; Jazz Band; School Musical; Stage Crew; Variety Show; Lit Mag; Mgr(s); Hon Roll; Graphic Arts.

MAHAR, KATE; Mt Anthony Union HS; Bennington, VT; (Y); Ski Clb; Stu Cncl; Fld Hcky; Vllybl; Advertsng.

MAHONEY, BILLY; Burlington HS; Burlington, VT; (Y); Cmnty Wkr; French Clb; Letterman Clb; Pep Clb; Red Cross Aide; Teachers Aide; Varsity Clb; Var Bsbl; JV Bsktbl; Var Ftbl; MVP Ftbl 84-85; Hstl Awd-Bsbl 84-85; Coachs Awd-MVP-FRSHMN Bsbl 81-82; Vermont Tech Coll; Adm Asst Pgm.

MAILLET, DIANE M; Essex Jct Educational Ctr; Essex Jct, VT; (Y); Off ROTC; Band; Stage Crew; Yrbk Stf; JV Bsktbl; Var Crs Cntry; DAR Awd; Hon Roll; NHS; Amer Lgn Schlstc Excllnc ROTC Medal 85; EJHS Secrty Dept Schlrshp 85; Dist Band 81-85; Oral Roberts U; Bio Engr.

MALLABAR, JIM; Colchester HS; Colchester, VT; (S); 12/220; Boy Scts; VP Church Yth Grp; Math Tm; Chorus; Church Choir; Bsktbl; Crs Cntry; Trk; NHS; Ntl Merit Ltr; Chrl Fstvls 84-85; T J Watson Mem Schlrshp 85; Clarkson U; Elec Engr.

MANCINI, LISA; Rutland HS; Rutland, VT; (Y); Am Leg Aux Girls St; Debate Tm; Teachers Aide; Nwsp Bus Mgr; Nwsp Rptr; Yrbk Bus Mgr; Yrbk Rptr; Hon Roll; NHS; Ntl Merit Ltr; Stu Of Mnth 83; U Of VT; Jrnlsm.

MARSH, MICHELLE; Black River HS; Ludlow, VT; (S); 3/45; AFS; Library Aide; Band; Chorus; Concert Band; Jazz Band; Mrchg Band; School Musical; Im Badmtn; JV Bsktbl; Colby-Sawyer Coll; Liberal Arts.

MARSHALL, SUSAN M; Harwood Union HS; Waterbury, VT; (Y); Band; Nwsp Rptr; High Hon Roll; Hon Roll; Pres Schlr; Champlain Coll; Acctng.

MARTEL, KANDY; St Johnsbury Acad; St Johnsbury, VT; (Y); Church Yth Grp; French Clb; Band; Chorus; Concert Band; Mrchg Band; JV Bsktbl; Var L Fld Hcky; Var L Sftbl; Hon Roll; Law.

MARTIN, ANDREW; Champlain Valley Union HS; Hinesburg, VT; (Y); Boy Scts; Var JV Bsbl; Var JV Bsktbl; Var JV Crs Cntry; VT Tech Coll; Elec Engrng.

MARTIN, MICHELLE; Otter Valley Union HS; Brandon, VT; (Y); French Clb; Concert Band; School Play; Var Crs Cntry; High Hon Roll; Hon Roll; NHS; FHA; Band; Mrchg Band; New Engl Yng Wrtrs Conf 85; Frnch Awd 85; Trig Adv Alg Awd 85.

MATTE, JOSEPH ALDERIC; Mt Anthony Union HS; N Bennington, VT; (Y); 8/307; Camera Clb; Model UN; Q&S; Pres Science Clb; Nwsp Phtg; Nwsp Rptr; Nwsp Stf; High Hon Roll; Hon Roll; NHS; Ec Excel 85; 3rd Pl MAA Math Exam 84; Pres Schlrshp Marietta Coll 85; Marietta Coll; Poetry.

MATTHEWS, TIM; Colchester HS; Colchester, VT; (S); Am Leg Boys St; Quiz Bowl; Band; Rep Stu Cncl; JV Var Bsbl; Bsktbl; JV Var Socr; Var Wrstlng; NHS.

MAURAIS, MARC; Canaan Memorial HS; Canaan, VT; (S); 4/25; Am Leg Boys St; Church Yth Grp; Variety Show; Nwsp Sprt Ed; Yrbk Stf; DAR Awd; Hon Roll; Pres Jr Cls; Pres Sr Cls; VP Stu Cncl; Bsktbl & Bsbl MVP Awd 83-84.

MAYNARD, BRENDA; Enosburg Falls HS; Bakersfield, VT; (Y); Cmnty Wkr; Sec FBLA; FFA; Off Frsh Cls; Off Soph Cls; Trs Jr Cls; JV Capt Cheerleading; Church Yth Grp; Score Keeper; Alterntv Girl St 84-85; Green Mountain Teen Inst Repres 85; Champlain; Sec.

MC CRAE, LISA; Concord HS; Concord, VT; (S); Church Yth Grp; Drama Clb; 4-H; Math Clb; Model UN; Quiz Bowl; Teachers Aide; Chorus; School Play; Sec Jr Cls.

MC GINN, MICHAEL; Bellows Free Acad; St Albans, VT; (Y); 45/210; Am Leg Boys St; Stage Crew; Yrbk Rptr; Trs Sr Cls; Var Bsbl; Var Ftbl; Capt Var Ice Hcky; Hon Roll; Ftbl All Star 84-85; Shrnrs All Str Ftbl Tm 85; Worcester Acad; Accntng.

MC KEARNAN, COLIN J; Vermont Acad; Brooklyn, NY; (S); Key Clb; Lit Mag; Rep Jr Cls; Var Socr; JV Tennis; Var Capt Wrstlng; Hon Roll; U Of VT Hnrs, Excellence In Wrtng 85.

MC KENNA, JENNIFER; Burlington HS; Burlington, VT; (Y); Hon Roll; Champlain Coll; Acctng.

MC KENZIE, JOHN; Rice Memorial HS; Burlington, VT; (Y); Am Leg Boys St; Church Yth Grp; FCA; Letterman Clb; Varsity Clb; Rep Stu Cncl; Var Capt Bsktbl; Trk; Hon Roll.

MC KINSTRY, LISA; Colchester HS; Colchester, VT; (Y); Art Clb; Church Yth Grp; 4-H; Girl Scts; JA; Math Tm; Spanish Clb; Band; Chorus; Concert Band; Gov Inst Arts VT 85; Painting Awdd 85; U Of VT; Bus Mgmt.

MC LAURIN, CAROLYN E; Burlington HS; Burlington, VT; (Y); Varsity Clb; Yrbk Stf; Var JV Bsktbl; Var JV Fld Hcky; Var Chess Clb; Hon Roll; NHS; Fld Hcky All-Star Tm 84-85; AFS Clb 84-85; Arch.

MC MILLAN, KEVIN; Bellows Free Acad; St Albans, VT; (Y); 45/218; Church Yth Grp; Teachers Aide; Var L Bsbl; Bowling; Hon Roll; Prfct Atten Awd; 1st Squad Sel, All Star Tm 85; Western Carolina U; Bsbl.

MC NALLY, DARCY L; Colchester HS; Colchester, VT; (Y); 48/220; French Clb; Hon Roll; U VT; Bus Adm.

MEAD, DAVID; Champlain Valley Union HS; Shelburne, VT; (Y); Am Leg Boys St; Boy Scts; Church Yth Grp; Band; Pep Band; Rep Soph Cls; Rep Jr Cls; Var Capt Crs Cntry; Var Trk.

MEAKER, ALICE; Harwood Union HS; Waterbury, VT; (Y); French Clb; Model UN; Chorus; School Musical; Stage Crew; Symp Band; Rep Stu Cncl; Hon Roll; NHS; VP Ntl Hnr Scty 85-86.

MERCIER, JEFFERSON; Burr & Burton Seminary; Manchester Ctr, VT; (Y); CAP; German Clb; Ski Clb; Teachers Aide; Pres Soph Cls; Rep Stu Cncl; Var Crs Cntry; JV Socr; Var Tennis; Var Trk; U Of VT.

MERRIAM, LISA; Harwood Union HS; Waterbury, VT; (Y); Drama Clb; Ski Clb; Chorus; School Musical; School Play; Tennis; High Hon Roll; Church Yth Grp; Debate Tm; Spanish Clb; Chmstry.

MESH, ELIZABETH; Chelsea HS; Chelsea, VT; (S); English Clb; NFL; Varsity Clb; Chorus; Yrbk Phtg; Sec Soph Cls; Var Bsktbl; Var Fld Hcky; Hon Roll; NHS; Stu Of Mnth 84 & 85; Grls Bsktbl Cntrl VT Lge 85.

METEVIER, AUDREY LEE; Peoples Acad; Greensboro Bend, VT; (Y); Library Aide; Ski Clb; Crs Cntry; Culenary Arts.

MICHALENOICK, JOY; Windsor HS; Windsor, VT; (Y); Model UN; Pep Clb; Yrbk Stf; NHS; Balfour Awd Driver Ed 85; Prom Comm 84; AIFS Trip France 84; Newbury JC; Travel/Trsm Mngmnt.

MICHAUD, SCOTT J; Colchester HS; Colchester, VT; (Y); Red Cross Aide; Rep Jr Cls; Sec Sr Cls; Sec Stu Cncl; Host Hnr Bnqt 85; 1st Alt Boys St 85; Hnr Eng Cls 85; U VT; Bus Mktg.

MILES, ROBERT; Burlington HS; Burlington, VT; (Y); JV Bsbl; JV Bsktbl; Hon Roll.

MILLER III, SUTHERLAND; Burlington HS; Burlington, VT; (Y); Cmnty Wkr; Drama Clb; Latin Clb; Model UN; Chorus; School Musical; School Play; Stage Crew; Variety Show; Nwsp Phtg; 3rd St Poetry Cntst 85; St & Rgnl Wnnr Genl Svc Admin Essay Cntst 85; Criticla Issues Conf Rotary Clb; Columbia U; Wrtng.

MITCHELL, DEBORAH; Burr And Burton Seminary HS; Manchester Ctr, VT; (Y); 3/100; Am Leg Aux Girls St; Pres 4-H; German Clb; Yrbk Phtg; Rep Jr Cls; Stu Cncl; Var Fld Hcky; High Hon Roll; NHS; Dartmouth Coll Bk Awd 85; Outstndg Achvt Germn Awd 83-85; Exclnc Advncd Plcmnt Engl Awd 84; Intl Econ.

MOERSCH, LISA; Otter Valley HS; Pittsford, VT; (Y); 4-H; French Clb; Hosp Aide; Band; Yrbk Stf; Sec Soph Cls; Pres Jr Cls; Stu Cncl; Cheerleading; Fld Hcky; Fornsc Pathlgst.

MONFETTE, MICHELLE; North Country Union HS; Newport, VT; (Y); Band; Chorus; Concert Band; Jazz Band; Mrchg Band; Pep Band; Rep Stu Cncl; Trk; High Hon Roll; NHS; Schlrshp Ltr 84; Schlrshp Pin 85; Music Ltr Pin 84-85; U VT; Music.

MONTCALM, CHRISTIE; Bellows Free Acad; St Albans, VT; (Y); 20/202; Am Leg Aux Girls St; Nwsp Ed-Chief; Nwsp Rptr; Yrbk Ed-Chief; Yrbk Stf; Sec Jr Cls; Stu Cncl; Capt L Cheerleading; Coach Actv; Var L Tennis; VT Chfs Of Police 85; U Of VT; Pre-Law.

MOON, PATRICIA; Mill River Union HS; Wallingford, VT; (Y); 12/123; Church Yth Grp; Drama Clb; Girl Scts; Hosp Aide; Chorus; Rep Stu Cncl; NHS; Cmnty Wkr; Library Aide; Stage Crew; Grl Sct Silver Awd 84; Silver Mdls VT Sci Fair 84 & 85; UVM Essay Cont Wnnr 84; Engrng.

MOORE, COLLEEN; North Country Union HS; Morgan, VT; (Y); Acpl Chr; Chorus; Madrigals; School Musical; Yrbk Ed-Chief; Pres Jr Cls; Var Bsktbl; JV Socr; High Hon Roll; NHS; Jrnlsm.

MOORS, DONNA; Mt Anthony Union HS; Bennington, VT; (S); 36/251; Hosp Aide; Band; Jazz Band; Mrchg Band; Pep Band; School Musical; School Play; JV Var Bsktbl; Score Keeper; NHS; Lesley Coll; Early Educ.

MOREAU II, BRADFORD J; Vermont Acad; Belchertown, MA; (S); Latin Clb; Library Aide; Ski Clb; Stage Crew; Lit Mag; Var Capt Bsbl; Bsktbl; Crs Cntry; Ftbl; Im Golf; Orange Key; Alter Boy; Flr Proctor; Lib Arts.

MORIN, CHRISTINE; North Country Union HS; W Charleston, VT; (Y); French Clb; Chorus; School Musical; School Play; Variety Show; Yrbk Stf; Mgr(s); Score Keeper; JV Trk; Hon Roll; Psych.

MORIN, ERIC; Richford HS; Richford, VT; (Y); 1/38; Am Leg Boys St; Model UN; JV Bsktbl; Var Socr; Hon Roll; NHS; Prfct Atten Awd; Val; Comp Sci.

MORSE, CHERYL; Woodstock Union HS; Woodstock, VT; (Y); 8/110; Fld Hcky; Lcrss; Dnfth Awd; DAR Awd; Hon Roll; NHS; French Clb; Scholastic Bowl; Yrbk Stf; Colgate U; Intl Stds.

MOULTON, JANA; North Country Union HS; W Charleston, VT; (Y); Lyndon ST Coll; Ed.

MOUNT, STEPHEN J J; Burlington HS; Burlington, VT; (Y); Church Yth Grp; Drama Clb; French Clb; School Musical; Ed Nwsp Stf; Stu Cncl; Var L Ftbl; Var Trk; U VT; Pol Sci.

MUNGER, VIKKI; Fair Haven Union HS; Benson, VT; (Y); 7/118; French Clb; Band; Chorus; Rep Soph Cls; Rep Jr Cls; Fld Hcky; Sftbl; High Hon Roll; Hon Roll; NHS; Alt Girls ST 85; Bryant; Bus Admin.

MURPHY, LINDA M; Colchester HS; Colchester, VT; (Y); Variety Show; Var L Tennis; Hon Roll; U VT; Med Assist.

MYERS, JENNIE; Mt Anthony Union HS; Bennington, VT; (S); Church Yth Grp; Band; Concert Band; Mrchg Band; Pep Band; Rep Frsh Cls; Sec Soph Cls; Sec Jr Cls; Off Stu Cncl; Fld Hcky; Nrsng.

NADEAU, SUZANNE; Mount Anthony Union HS; Shaftsbury, VT; (Y); French Clb; JA; Ski Clb; Yrbk Stf; Stu Cncl; JV Var Bsktbl; JV Var Fld Hcky; JV Sftbl; JV Var Vllybl; Mgr JV Wrstlng; Wrstlng Mgr Awds 83-85; Yrbk Staff Awd 84-85; Field Hockey Awds 83-85; Fashn Desgn.

NAPOLITANO, ANTHONY; Mount Anthony Union HS; Bennington, VT; (Y); 6/350; Church Yth Grp; Cmnty Wkr; English Clb; Spanish Clb; Var Socr; Var Trk; NHS; NEDT Awd; Prfct Atten Awd; Spanish NHS; Hugh O Brian Yth Ldrshp 83-84; Optmtry.

NATIVI, LISA; Spaulding HS; Barre, VT; (Y); 1/250; Am Leg Aux Girls St; Varsity Clb; Rep Stu Cncl; Var JV Bsktbl; Var JV Fld Hcky; Powder Puff Ftbl; Var JV Sftbl; High Hon Roll; NEDT Awd; Rensselaer Medal 86; Doctor.

NEAL, MICKEY; Peoples Acad; Elmore, VT; (Y); Church Yth Grp; Chorus; School Musical; Sec Jr Cls; Rep Stu Cncl; Var Bsbl; Var Bsktbl; Var Socr; High Hon Roll; Prfct Atten Awd; AIC Champlain; Bus.

NEILY, JESSICA; Windsor HS; Windsor, VT; (Y); 2/75; Am Leg Aux Girls St; Pres Sr Cls; Sec Stu Cncl; Capt Fld Hcky; Capt Sftbl; High Hon Roll; NHS; French Clb; Math Tm; Pep Clb; Balfour Awds Pre-Cal, Bio, Spch; Pre-Med.

NEPVEU, DENIS; Peoples Acad; Morrisville, VT; (Y); 3/54; Capt Scholastic Bowl; Stage Crew; Yrbk Phtg; Yrbk Stf; Rep Sr Cls; Var L Socr; Hon Roll; NHS.

NEUSCHAFER, DOUGLAS L; Mount Anthony Union HS; Bennington, VT; (Y); 20/283; German Clb; Latin Clb; Math Clb; Rep Stu Cncl; JV Socr; High Hon Roll; Hon Roll; NHS; Ntl Merit Ltr; NEDT Awd; George Washington U; Law.

NICHOLS, KIMBERLY J; Springfield HS; Springfield, VT; (Y); 14/185; French Clb; Latin Clb; Band; Mgr Nwsp Stf; Mgr Yrbk Stf; Rep Stu Cncl; Elks Awd; High Hon Roll; Hon Roll; Pres Acadmc Fit Awd 85; Clark U.

NICHOLS, LARS; Woodstock Union HS; Woodstock, VT; (S); 28/98; English Clb; Latin Clb; Science Clb; Stage Crew; Mgr Ice Hcky; Var Lcrss; Var JV Socr; Hon Roll; Boy Scts; Drama Clb; Outstndng Latin II Stdnt 84; Cornell; Vet Sci.

NICHOLS, SARAH; Burr & Burton Seminary; Danby, VT; (Y); Church Yth Grp; Drama Clb; German Clb; School Play; Hon Roll; VFW Awd; Voice Dem Awd; Library Aide; Stage Crew; Yrbk Stf; Grmn Exch Pgm 85-86; U VT; Lang.

NILES, CHRISTOPHER H; Peoples Acad; Morrisville, VT; (Y); 1/83; Drama Clb; French Clb; Quiz Bowl; Band; Chorus; Var Socr; Bausch & Lomb Sci Awd; Pres NHS; Ntl Merit SF; Val; Engrng.

NOBLE, AARON S; Colchester HS; Colchester, VT; (Y); Letterman Clb; Varsity Clb; JV Capt Bsbl; JV Capt Bsktbl; JV Capt Socr; U VT; Phys Ed.

NONEMACHER, CHRISTOPHER; Randolph Union HS; Randolph, VT; (S); Church Yth Grp; Pres FFA; JV Bsktbl; High Hon Roll; Hon Roll; NHS; Prfct Atten Awd; Buildngour Am Comm Wnnr 85; Tractor Drvng Cont 84; Vermont Tech Coll; Ag.

NORTON, LAURA; Mount Saint Joseph HS; Rutland, VT; (Y); 10/130; Computer Clb; Varsity Clb; Yrbk Stf; VP Frsh Cls; Stu Cncl; Var Socr; Var Tennis; Hon Roll; Psych.

NOVEMBRINO, LUCY; Mount Mansfield Union HS; Underhill, VT; (Y); Church Yth Grp; Cmnty Wkr; 4-H; Band; Church Choir; Orch; Pep Band; School Musical; HS Band-MIP 84; 25 Mile Cmptitv Trl Ride-Hgh Pt Grd Trphy 84; Cmpltn Cthlc Yth Orgnztn Ldrshp Pgm 83; U Of VT.

O BRIEN, TOM; Mill River Union HS; N Clarendon, VT; (Y); 14/132; Am Leg Boys St; Drama Clb; Chorus; Madrigals; School Play; Stage Crew; Yrbk Stf; Rep Stu Cncl; JV Bsbl; JV Bsktbl; Natl HS Inst Theatre Arts 85; All New Engl Cast 85; All-ST Cast 85.

O DANIEL, JAMES; Vergennes Union HS; Vergennes, VT; (Y); 5/99; Jazz Band; School Musical; Symp Band; Var L Golf; Var L Socr; Var L Swmmng; High Hon Roll; Air Force Smmr Sci Smnr; Cornell U; Elec Engr.

O DONNELL, MAUREEN A; Montpilier HS; Montpelier, VT; (Y); 14/102; GAA; Latin Clb; Model UN; Spanish Clb; Variety Show; JV Var Bsktbl; JV Var Fld Hcky; High Hon Roll; Church Yth Grp; Intnl Clb; Pres Acad Fit Awd 85; Slvr M Awd 85; Bentley Coll; Comp Info Sys.

O HALLORAN, JAMES F; Burlington HS; Burlington, VT; (Y); AFS; Am Leg Boys St; Church Yth Grp; Drama Clb; Latin Clb; Model UN; Pep Clb; Chorus; Church Choir; Madrigals.

O NEILL, PATRICK; Windsor HS; Windsor, VT; (Y); 16/65; Am Leg Boys St; Boy Scts; Church Yth Grp; Acpl Chr; Band; Chorus; Concert Band; Jazz Band; Madrigals; Mrchg Band; Louis Armstron Jazz Awd 85; Hugh O Brian Yth Ldrshp Smnr 84; Chrl Awd; Ithaca ST Coll; Music.

OAKLEY, JULIA; Burr & Burton Seminary; Manchester, VT; (Y); French Clb; JV Bsktbl; Var Crs Cntry; Trk; Vllybl; Hon Roll; Exclince In Frnch Awd 82-85; Exclince In Phy Ed 83-84; Frnch.

OLBERG, LORI; Burlington HS; Burlington, VT; (Y); German Clb; Teachers Aide; Chorus; Yrbk Stf; Var Tennis; Hon Roll; Bus Awd; UVM; Bus.

OLINICK, ELI V; Middlebury Union HS; Middlebury, VT; (Y); 7/180; VP AFS; Am Leg Boys St; Co-Capt Math Tm; Ed Nwsp Ed-Chief; Var L Socr; L Var Trk; NHS; Ntl Merit SF; Rickover Sci Inst 84; UVM/Digital Math Awd 83; Math.

OLSSON, KAREN; Woodstock Union HS; Woodstock, VT; (Y); Church Yth Grp; Band; Chorus; Church Choir; Concert Band; Mrchg Band; Orch; Pep Band; School Musical; Yrbk Stf; Bus Mgmnt.

OMARA, CATHY; Mt Anthony HS; N Bennington, VT; (Y); Dance Clb; Drama Clb; Library Aide; PAVAS; Chorus; Madrigals; Variety Show; Prfct Atten Awd; Harcum Coll; Equine.

OSGOOD, JOE; Oxbow HS; Bradford, VT; (Y); 4-H; Math Tm; VICA; Coach Actv; Capt Wt Lftg; Hon Roll; Bst Grd Math 84-85; Carpntr.

OSTER, KIMBERLY M; Champlain Valley Union HS; Charlotte, VT; (Y); 9/203; AFS; German Clb; Math Tm; Model UN; Ski Clb; Nwsp Rptr; JV Var Fld Hcky; High Hon Roll; NHS; Ntl Merit SF; ST Mth Exam Awd 83-84; Eng Achvt Awd 83; Ger Achvt Awd 83; Geol.

OSTRANDER, JIM; Mt Anthony Union HS; Shaftsbury, VT; (Y); 186/350; High Hon Roll.

OVITT, JENNIFER; Enosburg Falls HS; Enosburg Falls, VT; (Y); Church Yth Grp; 4-H; FFA; Teachers Aide; Variety Show; High Hon Roll; Hon Roll; Excel Typng II,Eng,Rec Keepng 83-85; Champlain Coll; Bus Mgmt.

PACK, PAMELA H; Middlebury Union HS; Middlebury, VT; (Y); 1/194; Dance Clb; Nwsp Stf; Ed Lit Mag; High Hon Roll; NCTE Awd; NHS; Arts Recgntn & Tlnt Srch 85; Yale U; Engl.

PALLINI, LISA; Mt Anthony Union HS; Pownal, VT; (Y); Drama Clb; Office Aide; School Play; Crs Cntry; Socr; Trk; Wt Lftg; Hon Roll; ASU Tempe AZ; Clncl Psychlgst.

PALLMAN, TRECIA; Mount Anthony Union HS; Shaftsbury, VT; (Y); 4/250; Drama Clb; Pep Clb; Band; Chorus; Church Choir; Mrchg Band; School Musical; Yrbk Rptr; High Hon Roll; NHS; Acadmc All Am 85; All ST Chrs 85; Yale Schl Of Physcians; Pre Med.

PALLMERINE, DENNIS; Hartford HS; White River Jct, VT; (Y); 5/107; Am Leg Boys St; Church Yth Grp; Varsity Clb; Band; Concert Band; Jazz Band; Mrchg Band; Socr; Hon Roll; Hesser Coll; Elec Engr.

PALMER, ROLAND; Champlain Valley Union HS; Richmond, VT; (Y); Church Yth Grp; Math Clb; Chorus; Pres Bowling; High Hon Roll; Hon Roll; NHS; Exclnce Eng Achvt Awd 83; Exclnce Math Achvt Awd 83; U VT; Bus Admin.

PARADIS, LISA; Enosburg Falls HS; Enosburg Falls, VT; (Y); FBLA; Library Aide; Flag Corp; Variety Show; Socr; NHS; Prfct Atten Awd; Hghst Hnrs 84-85; Achvt Eng 9 Amer Lit 11 82-83 & 84-85; Excl Bus Math, Bkkpng I, Comp Acctng 82-85; Daniel Webster; Avtn.

PARENT, MARTHA; Sacred Heart HS; Enosburg Falls, VT; (Y); Band; Concert Band; Jazz Band; Mrchg Band; School Play; Var Socr; Var Sftbl; Var Trk; French Hon Soc; High Hon Roll; VSAC Poster Cont Scholar 85; 4 Yr Prfct Atten Awd 81-85; Type I Awd 85; Rivier Coll; Comm Art.

PARKER, JIM; Brattleboro Union HS; Brattleboro, VT; (Y); 18/200; FBLA; Socr; Clark Schlrshp 84-85; Accntng.

PARKER, KELLY; West Rutland HS; Middletown Spgs, VT; (Y); Am Leg Aux Girls St; Teachers Aide; Yrbk Ed-Chief; Yrbk Stf; Sec Soph Cls; Pres Jr Cls; Sec Stu Cncl; High Hon Roll; NHS; Stu Councl Schlrshp 85; Amer Lgn Schlrshp 85; U Of RI; Phrmcy.

PARKER, LISA; Rutland SR HS; Rutland, VT; (Y); Church Yth Grp; Dance Clb; Band; Yrbk Stf; Rep Frsh Cls; Rep Soph Cls; Rep Jr Cls; Rep Stu Cncl; Pom Pon; Hon Roll; Odad Schlrshp 85; Schlrshp Green Mtn Inst 85; Humn Serv.

PARKINSON, JEFFREY; Vegennes Union HS; Vergennes, VT; (Y); 8/100; Am Leg Boys St; Church Yth Grp; Math Tm; Scholastic Bowl; Band; Mrchg Band; Crs Cntry; Hon Roll; NHS; Ntl Merit Schol; VT U; Engr.

PARRY, LAURA; Montpelier HS; Montpelier, VT; (Y); 25/109; Hosp Aide; Yrbk Stf; Mgr(s); Trk; U VT; Med Tech.

PATTERSON, KRISTINA L; Hartford HS; White Rvr Jct, VT; (Y); Church Yth Grp; Pep Clb; Band; Rep Frsh Cls; Bsktbl; JV Cheerleading; JV Var Mgr(s); JV Tennis; Hon Roll; Outstdng Stu Of Yr Bus 85; Sec.

PAYNE, BILLY; Burlington HS; Burlington, VT; (Y); Var Bsbl; Var Bsktbl; Var Ftbl; Bus.

PAYRITS, CINDY; Mill River Union HS; North Clarendon, VT; (Y); Office Aide; Teachers Aide; Chorus; Drm & Bgl; Flag Corp; School Musical; High Hon Roll; Hon Roll; Hosp Aide; Color Guard; Guild Piano Auditions Dist Wnnr 84 & 85; UMTA Non-Comp & Spring Fest Lvl 3 & 4 84-85; Bay Path JC; Exec Secry.

PECK V, THEODORE G; Vermont Acad; Stone Ridge, NY; (S); Math Tm; Ski Clb; Var L Bsbl; Capt L Crs Cntry; Hon Roll; Ussa Jr Olympic Ski Tm 82; N Am Biathlon Champshp 3rd 85; Dartmouth; Sci.

PELTON, LESLIE J; Vermont Acad; Putney, VT; (S); 4-H; French Clb; Band; Chorus; School Musical; Yrbk Rptr; JV Cheerleading; JV Var Socr; JV Tennis; Capt Trk; Headmasters List 84; Orng Key Ldrshp Clb 85-86; Coll.

PENDERGRAST, BLAKE; Stowe JR SR HS; Stowe, VT; (Y); 1/38; AFS; School Musical; Pres Frsh Cls; Trs Soph Cls; Jr Cls; Var Fld Hcky; Dance Clb; Drama Clb; English Clb; Teachers Aide; Govnrs Inst Sci 83; HOBY 84; All New Englnd Music Fstvl 83-85; Biol.

PEPIN, SUSAN; Colchester HS; Colchester, VT; (S); 15/220; Pres Church Yth Grp; Teachers Aide; Ed Lit Mag; Sec Jr Cls; Var Cheerleading; Var Capt Sftbl; High Hon Roll; Hon Roll; Sec NHS; Pres Schlr; Colchester Homemakers Awd/Scholar 85; Knights Columbus Scholar 85; Joseph Mazza Scholar 85; U VT; Bio-Med Engrng.

PERCY, MICHAEL; St Johnsburg Acad; St Johnsbury, VT; (Y); Bsbl; Ftbl; Wt Lftg; Nichols Coll; Bus.

PERKINS, M; Hartford HS; White River Jct, VT; (Y); 12/107; FBLA; Sec Intnl Clb; Teachers Aide; Twrlr; Hon Roll; Prfct Atten Awd; Comp Sci.

PERKINS, MERILEE; Hartford HS; Wilder, VT; (Y); Church Yth Grp; Debate Tm; GAA; Office Aide; Chorus; Var Capt Cheerleading; Mgr(s); Trk; Hon Roll; Outstndng Stu Yr Voctnl Awd-Offc Occptns 85; Secy.

PERKINS, NANCY; Vergenes Union HS; Vergennes, VT; (Y); 5/105; Church Yth Grp; German Clb; Band; Concert Band; Mrchg Band; School Musical; School Play; Pom Pon; High Hon Roll; Hon Roll; Simmonds Precsn Schlrshp 85; Alyson Mace Awd & Schlrshp 85; U Of VT; Librl Arts.

PERL, ERICA S; Burlington HS; Burlington, VT; (Y); Am Leg Aux Girls St; Drama Clb; Scholastic Bowl; Pres Temple Yth Grp; Ed Lit Mag; L Trk; NCTE Awd; Model UN; Chorus; School Musical; Awd Exc Writing 85; Attend New England Young Writers Wrkshp 85; Close Up Pgm 84; Creative Writng.

PERRY, ANDREW; Lake Region Union HS; Irasburg, VT; (S); Boy Scts; Pres DECA; Stage Crew; Hon Roll; CDC ST Pres Awd 85; Acad Achvt Awd 85; Champlain; Bus Admin.

PERRY, LOUISE; Lake Region Union HS; Orleans, VT; (Y); Camera Clb; Church Yth Grp; Math Clb; Math Tm; Science Clb; Ski Clb; Teachers Aide; Yrbk Phtg; Yrbk Stf; Crs Cntry; Roger Barton Mem Schlrshp 85; UVM; Microbio.

PETERS, RACHAEL E; Vermont Acad; Saxtons River, VT; (S); 1/84; Dance Clb; Math Tm; Teachers Aide; Chorus; School Musical; Rep Frsh Cls; L Crs Cntry; JV Fld Hcky; Capt Lcrss; L Socr; Cum Laude Hnry Soc 84; Clss Of 92 Bk Prz 84; Harvard Bk Prz 84.

PETERS, STEPHANNIE; Mount Anthony Union HS; Shaftsbury, VT; (Y); Concert Band; Mrchg Band; Pep Band; Hon Roll; NHS; Goethe-Inst Of Boston Excllnce 84.

PHELPS, GARY; North Country Union HS; Westfield, VT; (Y); Hon Roll; Dept Awd In Frnch II,Blgy,Soc Stds 83-85 Cnsqtvly; Med.

PHILION, VALERIE B; Middlebury Union HS; Shoreham, VT; (Y); AFS; Am Leg Aux Girls St; Off Frsh Cls; JV Var Bsktbl; Var Capt Fld Hcky; JV Sftbl; Hon Roll; Field Hcky Jim Jette Tiger Awd 84; JR Marshal 85; VT U.

PHILIPPON, SKIP; Mount Mansfield Union HS; Jericho, VT; (Y); Var Bsbl; JV Bsktbl; Var Capt Crs Cntry; High Hon Roll; Hon Roll; Engrng.

PHILLIPS, CHAD; North Country Union HS; Island Pond, VT; (Y); U VT Math Test Top 4 Schl, Top 10 Pct St 85; VT Excllnce Wrtng Cntst, N Cnty Jr Cls Wnnr 85; Engrng.

PIERCE, CRAIG L; Colchester HS; Colchester, VT; (Y); Cmnty Wkr; Red Cross Aide; School Play; Yrbk Phtg; Yrbk Stf; VP Jr Cls; Pres Sr Cls; Stu Cncl; Var Golf; Vermont Hnrs Cmptn Excel Wrtng 85; Spirit Awd 84-85; Vermont Boys St Altn 83-84; St Michaels Coll; Engrng.

PIGEON, SUSAN; North Country Union HS; N Troy, VT; (Y); French Clb; Var L Bsktbl; Var L Socr; Var L Sftbl; Hon Roll; Frnch Exch Pgm 85; Bk Knwldge Schlrshp Pin 85; Phys Ther.

PIKE, DEBORAH; Rutland HS; Rutland, VT; (Y); 14/169; Am Leg Aux Girls St; Red Cross Aide; Chorus; Madrigals; Nwsp Rptr; Rep Stu Cncl; Var Capt Fld Hcky; Trk; Hon Roll; NHS; Comm Svc Awd 81-82; All State Music Fstvl 84-85; All New England Music Fstvl 84-85; St Lawrence U.

PIKE, HEATHER; Mount Saint Joseph Acad; Rutland, VT; (Y); Drama Clb; Chorus; School Play; VP Jr Cls; Var Stat Bsktbl; Jrnlsm.

PINETTE, HEATHER; Cabot HS; Cabot, VT; (Y); 1/14; Am Leg Aux Girls St; French Clb; Model UN; Teachers Aide; Varsity Clb; Band; Chorus; School Play; Pres Frsh Cls; Pres Soph Cls; Lesley Coll; Elem Ed.

PION, SALLY; Sacred Heart HS; Derby Line, VT; (Y); Church Yth Grp; Cmnty Wkr; Library Aide; Chorus; Church Choir; Yrbk Bus Mgr; Frsh Cls; Coach Actv; Var Socr; Swmmng; 3rd Pl Vrmnt Hstry Day Essay Cntst 83; 3 Awds Exc In US Hstry 83-85; Rivier Coll; Para Lgl Stds.

PIRIE, CHRISTINE M; Spaulding HS; Barre, VT; (Y); 37/245; Church Yth Grp; Scholastic Bowl; Varsity Clb; Band; Jazz Band; Pep Band; Nwsp Ed-Chief; Nwsp Rptr; Lit Mag; Capt Sftbl; Winooski Vly Music Festvl; Cum Laud Awd-Ntl Latin Exam; Barre Ed Assn Schlrshp Recipnt; U Of VT; Biogcl Sci.

PLANT, HEIDI; Winooski HS; Winooski, VT; (Y); Am Leg Aux Girls St; Church Yth Grp; Cmnty Wkr; FCA; Pres FHA; Teachers Aide; Thesps; Chorus; Hon Roll; NHS; Excllnc Engl II; Trinity Coll; Specl Educ.

PLOOF, CHERYL; Richford HS; East Berkshire, VT; (Y); Drama Clb; FHA; Band; Chorus; Concert Band; Jazz Band; Mrchg Band; School Musical; School Play; Comm Awd 84; Bus Mgr.

POMAINVILLE III, EDWARD J; Otter Valley Union HS; Brandon, VT; (Y); Cmnty Wkr; French Clb; Var Capt Bsktbl; Coach Actv; Var L Socr; Quiz Bowl; Yrbk Stf; VT Sel Socr Tm 85; Psych.

POQUETTE, PHELICIA; Bellows Free Acad; St Albans, VT; (Y); 3/220; Trs Am Leg Aux Girls St; VP Soph Cls; VP Jr Cls; VP Sr Cls; Rep Stu Cncl; Var Capt Bsktbl; Var Socr; Var Sftbl; High Hon Roll; Trs NHS; Stranahan Mem, Aseltine, JR Miss Schlstc Achvt Schlrshps 85; Bryant Coll; Actury Math.

POTTER, BETH; Enosburg Falls HS; E Berkshire, VT; (Y); 2/55; Drama Clb; FHA; JV Bsktbl; Var Mgr(s); High Hon Roll; Hon Roll; VP NHS; Stu Mnth 82; Lcl Wnnr UVM Wrtng Cntst 85; 1st Pl Pblc Spkng Cntst 83; Jrnlsm.

POTTER, SARA B; Harwood Union HS; Waterbury Ctr, VT; (Y); Am Leg Aux Girls St; Drama Clb; Scholastic Bowl; School Musical; Yrbk Stf; Rep Stu Cncl; Var Cheerleading; High Hon Roll; Pres NHS; UVM Contest St Hnbl Mntn 85; Presidential Fitness Award; Allegheny Coll; Cmnctns Law.

POTWIN, ROBIN; Woodstock Union HS; S Pomfret, VT; (Y); 39/90; FHA; Stage Crew; JV Bsktbl; JV Sftbl; Hon Roll; Mitch Hager Art Schlrshp 85; Avis Keith Fnd Schlrshp 85; Cmmrcl Art.

POULIN, SHAWNA; Twinfield Union HS; E Montpelier, VT; (Y); Hosp Aide; Sec Soph Cls; Sec Jr Cls; Pres Sr Cls; Var Bsktbl; Var Fld Hcky; Var Sftbl; High Hon Roll; NHS; Pres Schlrshp Lyndon ST Coll 85; Pres Acadmc Fit Awd 85; Centrl VT North All Str Bsktbl Tm 85; Lyndon ST Coll; Erly Chldhd Ed.

POULIOT, CAROLE; North Country Union HS; Newport, VT; (S); DECA; Chorus; JV Crs Cntry; JV Socr; JV Trk; Hon Roll; Typng I Plaque & Dept Awd 84; VT ST DECA Math Test 2nd Pl 84; DECCA Dept Awd 85; Hesser Coll; Bus Admin.

POWELL, SUSAN; Woodstock Union HS; Woodstock, VT; (Y); Church Yth Grp; Band; Concert Band; Mrchg Band; Pep Band; School Musical; Yrbk Stf; Hon Roll; Prfct Atten Awd.

POWERS, CHRISTOPHER; Burr & Burton Seminary; Manchester Ctr, VT; (Y); 16/93; Band; Church Choir; Jazz Band; Var L Crs Cntry; Var L Socr; Var L Tennis; Hon Roll; Voice Dem Awd; Sci.

PUTTLITZ, ERIK A; Mount Mansfield Union HS; Underhill, VT; (Y); Boy Scts; JA; Orch; School Musical; Var L Tennis; High Hon Roll; Hon Roll; NHS; Dartmouth Bk Club Awd 85; VT JR Conf 85; VT All-ST Music Fest 84-85; Engr.

PUTVAIN, TAMARA; Peoples Acad; Wolcott, VT; (Y); 5/70; French Clb; Hosp Aide; Scholastic Bowl; Variety Show; Pres Frsh Cls; Pres Jr Cls; Rep Stu Cncl; JV Bsktbl; JV Cheerleading; Var Socr; Med.

RABOIN, ALICE; Sacred Heart HS; Newport Ctr, VT; (Y); 5/29; Am Leg Aux Girls St; Office Aide; Chorus; Drill Tm; Madrigals; Yrbk Stf; Trs Stu Cncl; JV Crs Cntry; High Hon Roll; NHS; Kiwanis Voct Schlrshp 85; Hesser Coll; Med Asst.

RAMSEY, MARK; Union High School No 32; Calais, VT; (Y); Am Leg Boys St; Pres French Clb; Ski Clb; Chorus; Var Golf; Var Socr; High Hon Roll; Intl Reltns.

RANNEY, ANNETTE; St Johnsbury Acad; St Johnsbury, VT; (Y); 4-H; Office Aide; Var L Bsktbl; Var L Fld Hcky; Var L Sftbl; High Hon Roll; Hon Roll; Sunday Schl Tchr 81-85; Erly Chldhd Ed.

RECZEK, LYNN; Mount Saint Joseph Acad; Center Rutland, VT; (Y); 11/99; Hosp Aide; Spanish Clb; Varsity Clb; Yrbk Stf; Off Jr Cls; Bsktbl; Sftbl; Hon Roll; U Of VT; Pre-Med.

REED, BETH; W Rutland HS; West Rutland, VT; (Y); 7/43; Band; Yrbk Stf; VP Soph Cls; Sec Stu Cncl; Capt Fld Hcky; High Hon Roll; NHS; NEDT Awd; Prse Acad Fit Awd 85; Mth Prz Exam Awd 85; Scholar W Rutland Leg Aux 85; U Of VT; Psych.

REEDY, SHANNON; Vergennes Union HS; N Ferrisburg, VT; (Y); 6/125; AFS; Chorus; Church Choir; School Musical; High Hon Roll; Hon Roll; Lion Awd; NHS; Alumni Assn Schlrshp 85; Castleton ST Coll; Nrsng.

REID, SU; Colchester HS; Colchester, VT; (S); 2/219; VP Church Yth Grp; Sec Drama Clb; French Clb; Chorus; School Musical; School Play; High Hon Roll; Trs NHS; Ntl Merit Ltr; Sal; Chittenden Cnty Fll Tuitn Schlrshp 85; St Michaels Coll; Theatr.

REID, SUSAN Y; Colchester HS; Colchester, VT; (Y); 2/219; VP Church Yth Grp; Sec Drama Clb; Chorus; Trs NHS; Ntl Merit Ltr; Pres Schlr; Sal; French Clb; Church Choir; School Musical; Am Chrl Awd 85; All St, Dist, All-New Eng Mus Fest 84-85; St Drama Comp 83; St Michaels Coll; Drama.

REIL, MARYELLEN; Williamstown HS; Williamstown, VT; (Y); Mgr(s); Var Socr; JV Sftbl; High Hon Roll; Hon Roll; Thetford Acad Schlrshp 82; VTC; Vet Asst.

REILLY, CATHERINE; Windsor HS; Hartland, VT; (Y); 5/69; Band; Pep Band; VP Frsh Cls; VP Jr Cls; VP Sr Cls; Var Cheerleading; Hon Roll; NHS; NEDT Awd; U ME; Spec Ed.

RHODES, STEPHANIE; North Country Union HS; Newport, VT; (Y); Church Yth Grp; 4-H; French Clb; GAA; JCL; Model UN; Scholastic Bowl; Varsity Clb; JV Var Fld Hcky; JV Trk; Hlth Dept Awd 84; Drivers Ed Dept Awd; Pres Ftns Awd 83-84; Schlstc Ltr 84-85; UVM; Bus Adm.

RICHER, GRETCHEN; Harwood Union HS; Waterbury, VT; (Y); Band; School Musical; Lit Mag; NHS; Prfct Atten Awd; Pres Schlr; U Of VT; Wldlf Bio.

RICHMOND, DANIEL; Mount Anthony Union HS; Bennington, VT; (Y); Am Leg Boys St; Exploring; Model UN; Ski Clb; Spanish Clb; Varsity Clb; Rep Stu Cncl; Socr; Var Tennis; Vllybl; Excel Engl, Frshm Sccr 82-83; Vrsty Tn, JV Sccr 83-84; Vrsty Ten 84-85; Lib Arts.

RIPLEY, SARA; Harwood Union HS; Waterburyctr, VT; (Y); French Clb; ROTC; Varsity Clb; JV Var Bsktbl; Mgr(s); Score Keeper; JV Var Trk; Hon Roll; Jr NHS; NHS; Norwich U; Aerontcl Engrng.

RIVERS, JOSEPH; Vergennes HS; Vergennes, VT; (Y); 14/113; Pres 4-H; Var Capt Wrstlng; Hon Roll; Vet.

ROBILLARD, ROBERT; Sacred Heart HS; Irasburg, VT; (Y); Trs 4-H; Band; Concert Band; Jazz Band; Var Socr; 4-H Awd; Hon Roll; Accntnt.

ROBINSON, REBECCA; North Country OHS; Orleans, VT; (Y); Church Yth Grp; German Clb; Hosp Aide; Band; Chorus; Crs Cntry; Trk; Hon Roll; Maniatty Sprts Awd Crs Cntry 83-85; Phys Ther.

ROORDA, TRIXIE; Otter Valley Union HS; Whiting, VT; (Y); Church Yth Grp; 4-H; Library Aide; Teachers Aide; Varsity Clb; Yrbk Phtg; Yrbk Stf; JV Var Bsktbl; Var Sftbl; Hon Roll; MIP Sftbl 84-85; Tchr.

ROUILLARD, DARCY M; Hartford HS; White River Jct, VT; (Y); 22/151; GAA; Rep Frsh Cls; Rep Soph Cls; Capt Stu Cncl; JV Bsktbl; Var Fld Hcky; Hon Roll; Scty Woman Engrs Cert Merit 85; U Of VT; Bio.

ROVNAK, CAROLYN R; Burr & Burton Seminary; Manchester, VT; (Y); 6/98; Concert Band; Jazz Band; Var JV Bsktbl; Var Sftbl; Cit Awd; High Hon Roll; Hon Roll; NHS; 4-H; Spanish Clb; CVGAL-ALL League Awd-Softbll 84-85; Prof Horse Trainer.

ROWE, JOHN; Rutland Senior HS; Rutland, VT; (Y); 76/180; Am Leg Boys St; Rep Church Yth Grp; Cmnty Wkr; Teachers Aide; Nwsp Rptr; Yrbk Stf; Rep Jr Cls; Rep Sr Cls; Var L Socr; L Trk; 1st Ntl Stores Frndly Awd 84; Comm Arts.

ROY, RENE; North Country Union HS; West Charleston, VT; (S); Church Yth Grp; Drama Clb; FFA; School Musical; School Play; Rep Stu Cncl; Gym; Vllybl; Hon Roll; NHS; Star Greenhand FFA 84-85; U V M; Ag.

ROY, SUSAN; Mount Anthony Union HS; Bennington, VT; (Y); 24/300; Am Leg Aux Girls St; Band; Mrchg Band; L Bsktbl; L Fld Hcky; L Var Sftbl; Vllybl; Hon Roll; NHS; Ntl Merit Ltr; Pre-Med.

ROYA, MELISSA; Bellows Free Acad; Fairfax, VT; (Y); 6/62; DECA; Drama Clb; French Clb; Yrbk Ed-Chief; Rep Soph Cls; Var Capt Fld Hcky; L Var Sftbl; NHS; Pres Schlr; JV Bsktbl; U VT; Child Psych.

RUSSELL, ANDREW W; Mount Anthony Union HS; Bennington, VT; (Y); 29/288; Am Leg Boys St; Church Yth Grp; Drama Clb; Ski Clb; Chorus; VP Jr Cls; Rep Stu Cncl; Bsktbl; NHS; Cngrssmn Yr Awd 85; Lwyr.

RUSSELL, LINDA; Windsor HS; Windsor, VT; (Y); 2/72; Color Guard; Mrchg Band; School Play; Yrbk Ed-Chief; Trk; High Hon Roll; NHS; Sal; Math Tm; 6 Balfour Awds; Salvation Army Schlrshp Awd; Air Force; Psych.

RYEA, ALAN; Richford HS; Richford, VT; (Y); 2/38; Am Leg Boys St; Model UN; Natl Beta Clb; JV Var Bsktbl; High Hon Roll; Pres NHS; Prfct Atten Awd; Drama Clb; Stage Crew; Sec Soph Cls; Potsdam Bsktbl Cmp 83 & 85; U N Pilgrimage Yth 85; JR Conf U Of VT 85; Dartmouth; Mth.

SAIA, SCOTT; Colchester HS; Colchester, VT; (Y); Church Yth Grp; Ski Clb; Varsity Clb; Jazz Band; Rep Soph Cls; Rep Jr Cls; JV Bsbl; JV Var Socr; Hon Roll; Band; Rep ST VT Alpine Olympcs 82; Engrng.

SALEM, SANDY F; Mount Anthony Union HS; Bennington, VT; (Y); Am Leg Aux Girls St; French Clb; GAA; JA; Latin Clb; Model UN; Pep Clb; Ski Clb; Varsity Clb; Variety Show; Female Athlt 84-85; MVP Fld Hcky & Tnns 84-85; U Of VT; Pre-Med.

SANVILLE, SANDRA; North Country Union HS; Newport, VT; (Y); DECA; Hosp Aide; VICA; Chorus; Var Capt Cheerleading; Sftbl; Hon Roll; Prfct Atten Awd; AF.

SARGENT, BLYTHE; Mount Mansfield Union HS; Underhill, VT; (Y); Church Yth Grp; Latin Clb; Quiz Bowl; Chorus; Drm & Bgl; Cheerleading; Crs Cntry; Trk; High Hon Roll; NHS; Math.

SARGENT, BRENDA; Mill River Union HS; Danby, VT; (Y); 4-H; Teachers Aide; Lit Mag; Hon Roll; Hnr Rl 85.

SARGENT, CARA LIA; Northfield JR SR HS; Northfield Falls, VT; (Y); 1/65; Church Yth Grp; Teachers Aide; Band; Concert Band; Mrchg Band; Orch; School Play; Stage Crew; Pres Frsh Cls; Rep Stu Cncl; Brown U Bk Awd 84; Dartmth Clb JR Bk Awd 84; Robert F Pierce Memorial Awd 85; Boston U; Anthrplgy.

SARGENT, GREG; Colchester HS; Colchester, VT; (Y); 35/222; Math Tm; Hon Roll; 5th Intl Comp Prblm Slvng 85; U VT; Comp Sci.

SAUSVILLE JR, DAVID J; Mt Anthony Union HS; Bennington, VT; (Y); 19/307; Var Ftbl; Trk; Vllybl; Hon Roll; NHS; Prfct Atten Awd; Thomas Hall Godo Sportsmnshp Awd 85fsouthern VT Ftbl All Star Tm 84; Berkshire Leag Ftbl All Star Tm; U VT; Wildlfe.

SAVIGNI, SARAH; Williamstown JR SR HS; Williamstown, VT; (Y); 1/45; VP Frsh Cls; Pres Soph Cls; VP Jr Cls; Var Bsktbl; Var Socr; Var Sftbl; High Hon Roll; NHS; Am Leg Aux Girls St; Church Yth Grp; SR H Mathmtcl; Spnsh Awd; Soc Sci Awd; FL Inst Tech; Marine Bio.

SAYAH, SHEILA; Harwood Union HS; Waterbury Ctr, VT; (Y); Cmnty Wkr; Trs Girl Scts; Teachers Aide; Chorus; Stage Crew; Yrbk Stf; Sftbl; High Hon Roll; Hon Roll; Grl Scout Slvr Awd 84 & Gld Awd 86; Nrs.

SCHAWRTZ, PAUL; Sacred Heart HS; Derby Line, VT; (Y); 1/30; Debate Tm; Drama Clb; Band; Chorus; High Hon Roll; Pres NHS; Bio.

SCHLEEDE, LYNNE; Burlington HS; Burlington, VT; (Y); Church Yth Grp; Drama Clb; Latin Clb; Chorus; Church Choir; School Musical; Stage Crew; Kiwanis Awd; NHS; Bio.

SCHOMODY, JANNA E; Burlington HS; Burlington, VT; (Y); Sec AFS; Drama Clb; Model UN; Pep Clb; Band; Chorus; Concert Band; Madrigals; Mrchg Band; Orch; Gov Inst Arts 83; Smmr Pgm AFS Germany 84; Rotary Outstndng Stu 85; VT Hnr Schlrshp VT Stu Asst Corp; U VT.

SCOTT, MARY JANE; West Rutland HS; West Rutland, VT; (Y); 2/43; Rep Am Leg Aux Girls St; Varsity Clb; Band; Chorus; Trs Rep Stu Cncl; Var Bsktbl; Var Fld Hcky; Sec NHS; Sal; Dist Chorus 82; PTO Army Amer Lgn Schlrshps 85; U VT; Dntl Hygne.

SEARS, PAULA; Rutland HS; Rutland, VT; (Y); 69/250; Yrbk Stf; Fld Hcky; Hon Roll; Bay Path; Legl Secy.

SEEMANN, KRISTIN L; South Burlington HS; S Burlington, VT; (Y); 4/202; Band; Ed Yrbk Stf; Var L Socr; Var L Trk; Hon Roll; NHS; Ntl Merit SF; Crs Cntry Ski Team Vrsty, Lttr, Asst Capt; 2nd Pl VT ST X-C Ski Meet 84; 7th Estrn HS Chmpnshps 84; Bio.

SEITZ, KRISTIN; Woodstock Union HS; S Woodstock, VT; (Y); 14/94; Drama Clb; Latin Clb; Spanish Clb; Yrbk Phtg; Fld Hcky; Lcrss; Swmmng; Hon Roll; U VT.

SENDAK, MICHELLE; Colchester HS; Colchester, VT; (S); High Hon Roll; Hon Roll; Jr NHS; NHS; Math.

SHARP, DEBBIE; Mill River Union HS; Wallingford, VT; (Y); Chorus; Trs Soph Cls; VP Jr Cls; Var L Cheerleading; JV Fld Hcky; Hon Roll; VT ST Sci Fair Supr Rtng 84; Grn Mntn Teenage Inst On Drgs & Alchl Schlrshp 85; U Of VT.

SHEA, CHRISTOPHER R; Burlington HS; Burlington, VT; (Y); Church Yth Grp; Drama Clb; Chorus; Nwsp Rptr; Stu Cncl; Hon Roll; NHS; Ntl Merit SF; U Of VT; Studio Art.

SHEA, JEANNE; Bellows Free Acad; Fairfax, VT; (Y); 1/60; Am Leg Aux Girls St; Pres Drama Clb; VP 4-H; Thesps; Elks Awd; NHS; Val; Church Yth Grp; French Clb; Intnl Clb; Gov Inst Arts 84; Jostens Ldrshp Schlrshp 85; VT Hon Schlrshp 85; Dartmouth Coll.

SHEDD, HEATHER; Bellows Free Acad; Fairfax, VT; (Y); 5/61; VP Drama Clb; Sec French Clb; Thesps; Chorus; School Musical; School Play; Rep Stu Cncl; Stat Bsktbl; 4-H Awd; High Hon Roll; Russell Sage Coll; Elem Eductn.

SHELTON, GWENDOLYN; Mt Mansfied Union HS; Underhill, VT; (Y); 2/175; Band; Chorus; Concert Band; Drm & Bgl; Mrchg Band; Orch; Pep Band; School Musical; School Play; Stage Crew.

SHELTRA, CINDY; Lake Region Union HS; Orleans, VT; (S); Church Yth Grp; Trs Bsktbl; Office Aide; Pep Clb; Rep Frsh Cls; Rep Soph Cls; Rep Jr Cls; Rep Sr Cls; Rep Stu Cncl; Var Socr; Trvl & Trsm.

SHEPARD, CHRISTINE A; Colchester HS; Colchester, VT; (Y); AFS; Am Leg Aux Girls St; Cmnty Wkr; Hosp Aide; Letterman Clb; Teachers Aide; Chorus; Color Guard; Pres Jr Cls; JV Var Sftbl; Amer Lgn Axlry Natl Convtn JR Dlgt 85; U Of VT; Chem.

SHEPHARD, JONATHAN C; Burlington HS; Burlington, VT; (Y); Madrigals; School Play; Stage Crew; Pres Church Yth Grp; Drama Clb; Math Tm; Model UN; Political Wkr; Red Cross Aide; Band; 2nd Pl Vcl Schlrshp Mus Fstvl 83; Pres Of SADD 85; Close Up Prgm At WA 85; Carnegie-Mellon U; Drama.

SHEPHERD, ELIZABETH; Rice Memorial HS; Burling, VT; (Y); 22/108; Camera Clb; Church Yth Grp; Chorus; Variety Show; Yrbk Stf; JV Fld Hcky; High Hon Roll; Hon Roll; NHS; VT Sst Pres-Chldrn Of Amer Revltn 84; Honry VT ST Pres-Chldrn Of Amer Rev 85; Hstry.

SHERMAN, DARLENE; Mount Anthony Union HS; Bennington, VT; (Y); 25/307; Church Yth Grp; 4-H; Band; Concert Band; Jazz Band; DAR Awd; Elks Awd; Hon Roll; Lion Awd; Rotary Awd; Bio Sci.

SHERMAN, JAMES; Mount St Joseph Acad; Rutland, VT; (Y); Stu Cncl; Capt Bsbl; Bsktbl; Ftbl; Wt Lftg; Hugh O Brian Yth Ldrshp Alumni VP 85; Atten JR Conf UVM 85; Hugh O Brian Yth Ldrshp Ambsdr 84; Jrnlsm.

SHERMAN, ROBIN; Burr & Burton HS; Dorset, VT; (Y); JV Bsktbl; Var Fld Hcky; JV Sftbl; Var Tennis; Im Vllybl; Hon Roll; Excllnc In Spanish Awd 83-85.

SHONIO, MELODY; Milton HS; Milton, VT; (Y); 5/130; Church Yth Grp; Cmnty Wkr; Office Aide; Stu Cncl; Cheerleading; Socr; DAR Awd; High Hon Roll; NHS; Prfct Atten Awd; Pro Merito; U Of VT; Economics.

SILVER, JAMES; Stowe HS; Stowe, VT; (Y); Boy Scts; Computer Clb; Latin Clb; Ski Clb; School Musical; School Play; Socr; U Of VT; Comp Tech.

SIPLEY, LISA; Vergennes Union HS; Vergennes, VT; (Y); 14/102; Trs Church Yth Grp; 4-H; FBLA; German Clb; Teachers Aide; Church Choir; Off Sr Cls; JV Bsktbl; 4-H Awd; Hon Roll; Accntng.

SKAPOF, JESSICA; Burr & Burton Seminary; Manchester Ctr, VT; (Y); 1/100; French Clb; Spanish Clb; Nwsp Stf; Yrbk Stf; Var Tennis; Im Vllybl; US-JPNSE Senate Schlrshp 85; AP Engl Hnr Awd 85; Alg Awd 83.

SMALL, WINFORD; Stowe HS; Stowe, VT; (Y); Yrbk Stf; Bowling.

SMITH, ANDREA; Harwood Union HS; Moretown, VT; (Y); Am Leg Aux Girls St; Var Capt Ski Clb; Pres Frsh Cls; Sec Stu Cncl; Var L Crs Cntry; Var Capt Trk; Trs NHS; Model UN; Chorus; Concert Band; Dartmth Bk Awd 85; Hugh O Brien Yth Ldrshp Smnrs 84; Gvrnrs Inst Of Arts 85; Lbrl Arts.

SMITH, HEIDI A; Middlebury Union HS; Middlebury, VT; (Y); Sec AFS; Off Soph Cls; Off Jr Cls; Off Sr Cls; Sec Stu Cncl; JV Var Fld Hcky; JV Sftbl; Psych.

SMITH, KRISTIN E; Burlington HS; Burlington, VT; (Y); French Clb; Varsity Clb; Stu Cncl; Var Capt Gym; Var Capt Socr; Var L Tennis; Var L Trk; Hon Roll; Girl Scts; Intnl Clb; UVM.

SMITH, NILS; Mount Mansfield Union HS; Huntington, VT; (Y); Am Leg Boys St; Model UN; Ski Clb; Gov Hon Prg Awd; Bodoin Coll; Lbrl Arts.

SNAITH, SCOTT; Hartford HS; Wht River Jct, VT; (Y); Pep Clb; Varsity Clb; Nwsp Rptr; Yrbk Sprt Ed; Rep Frsh Cls; Capt Ftbl; Capt Ice Hcky; JV Lcrss; Hon Roll; Drftg.

SNIDER, JANE; Richford JR SR HS; Richford, VT; (Y); Drama Clb; Natl Beta Clb; Band; Chorus; School Play; VP Jr Cls; Hon Roll; NHS; Church Yth Grp; Church Choir; Champlain; Secy.

SOKOLOSKI ROLLSON, LORI; Mt Anthony Union HS; N Bennington, VT; (Y); Pep Clb; Cheerleading; Mgr(s); Vllybl; High Hon Roll; Hon Roll; Church Yth Grp; Socr; John James Jr Inpostrl Arts Schlrshp 85; Drftg Awd 82 & 83; Dollrs For Schlrs 85; VT Tech Coll; Arch.

SOUTHWICK, PATRICIA C; Middlebury Union HS; Middlebury, VT; (Y); Chorus; JV Gym; Hon Roll; Prfct Atten Awd; Outstndng Stu Awd 85; Sec.

SPAFFORD, JENNIFER W; Burlington HS; Burlington, VT; (Y); Am Leg Aux Girls St; Drama Clb; Latin Clb; Band; Chorus; Concert Band; Pres Stu Cncl; Capt Crs Cntry; Fld Hcky; NHS; Crs Cntry Ski Coaches Awd 85; Phys Ther.

SPAHN, JOHN; Vergennes Union HS; Ferrisburgh, VT; (Y); 7/110; Math Tm; Red Cross Aide; Rep Stu Cncl; JV Var Bsktbl; JV Var Crs Cntry; Var Capt Golf; Elks Awd; High Hon Roll; Hon Roll; NHS; Bus.

SPOONER, STEPHANIE; Woodstock Union HS; S Pomfret, VT; (Y); Drama Clb; Band; Concert Band; Mrchg Band; Pep Band; School Musical; Sftbl; Hon Roll; Travel.

SPRAFKE, GRETCHEN A; Vermont Academy; Waterford, CT; (S); Key Clb; Ski Clb; Lit Mag; Rep Frsh Cls; Rep Soph Cls; Rep Jr Cls; Rep Stu Cncl; Socr; Tennis; Hon Roll.

SPROUT, LESLIE; Burlington HS; Burlington, VT; (Y); Trs Church Yth Grp; Latin Clb; Math Tm; Orch; High Hon Roll; NHS; Ntl Merit Ltr; AFS; Drama Clb; Model UN; Ntl Latin Exam 85; All ST Music Fest Orch 83-85; All New Engind Music Fest Orch 84-85; Archlgy.

ST ONGE, STEPHEN; North Country Union HS; Newport, VT; (Y); Am Leg Boys St; Debate Tm; Key Clb; NFL; Tennis; High Hon Roll; Hon Roll; NHS; Sr Cls; Schlrshp Lttr 85; Frnch & Hlth Dept Awds 84; Vrsty Debate Lttr & Pin 84 & 85; Oceanstdy Pgm 84; Chem.

STARORYPINSKI, LAURA; Leland & Gray UHS; Williamsville, VT; (Y); Band; Concert Band; Jazz Band; Mrchg Band; Pep Band; VP Soph Cls; VP Jr Cls; VP Sr Cls; VP Stu Cncl; NHS; SADD Secr 84-85; Hugh O Brien Yuth, Music Dir Awd 83-84; U VT; Med.

STARR, JENNIFER; Champlain Valley Union HS; Hinesburg, VT; (Y); Var Bsktbl; Var Socr; Sftbl; All St Catcher Sftbl; All St Goalie Sccr; Acdmc Exclince Span; U VT; Law Enfrcmnt.

STEADMAN, DRUE; Hartford HS; White River Jct, VT; (Y); 6/120; Am Leg Boys St; Varsity Clb; Var L Crs Cntry; Mgr Ice Hcky; Lcrss; JV Socr; High Hon Roll; Comp Engrng.

STEELE, KIMBERLY; Otter Valley Union HS; Sudbury, VT; (Y); Rptr VP 4-H; JV Capt Cheerleading; JV Var Fld Hcky; JV Capt Sftbl; Hrsmnshp Awds & Other Hrs Org Awds 82-84; 4-H Yrly Pin Awds & Hrs 82-84; Wrkng W/Pblc.

STEINER, IRENE E; Essex Jct Ed Ctr; Essex Jct, VT; (Y); 27/330; VP Sec Intnl Clb; Ski Clb; VP Spanish Clb; Sec Soph Cls; Rep Jr Cls; Rep Sr Cls; Tennis; High Hon Roll; Hon Roll; NHS; 3 Yr Vrsty Tnns Awd 85; VT U; Bus.

STEPHANY, DAVID J; Burlington HS; Burlington, VT; (Y); French Clb; Latin Clb; Political Wkr; Yrbk Sprt Ed; Var L Socr; Var L Tennis; Excel Western Civilztn 83; Clascl Assoc Cntst 84; U Vermont.

STEPHANY, KATIE; Burlington HS; Burlington, VT; (Y); AFS; Am Leg Aux Girls St; Model UN; Political Wkr; Varsity Clb; Chorus; Orch; Socr; Tennis; NHS; Wstrn Civ Awd; Vovrnrs Inst Intl Affairs Part; Vrsty Tennis Team MVP; Intl Rltns.

STODDARD, WENDY; Mount Anthony Union HS; Bennington, VT; (Y); Trs Church Yth Grp; Sec 4-H; French Clb; Girl Scts; Ski Clb; Band; Stu Cncl; Var Cheerleading; JV Trk; Hon Roll; FL U; Child Psychlgy.

STOKES, REBECCA; Vergennes Union HS; Ferrisburg, VT; (Y); Church Yth Grp; Cmnty Wkr; 4-H; Teachers Aide; Chorus; Church Choir; Mrchg Band; Variety Show; Var Capt Cheerleading; JV Socr; VT Schl Csmtlgy; Csmtlgy.

STONE, JILL; Windsor HS; Windsor, VT; (Y); Church Yth Grp; Drama Clb; 4-H; Math Tm; Pep Clb; Band; Concert Band; Mrchg Band; School Play; Sec Frsh Cls; NH Coll; Accntng.

STONE, KAREN; Enosburg Falls HS; E Fairfield, VT; (Y); FBLA; Chorus; Var JV Cheerleading; High Hon Roll; Hon Roll; Mst Imprvd Awd JV Chrldr 82-83; Merit Awd Typng FBLA 83-84; Cert Good Grades Typng Cls 83-84; Sec.

STOVER JR, JAMES; Rice Memorial HS; Brlington, VT; (Y); Boy Scts; Ski Clb; Variety Show; Yrbk Stf; JV Bsktbl; Crs Cntry; Trk; High Hon Roll; Hon Roll; Bus Adm.

STRONG, JILL; Rutland SR HS; Rutland, VT; (Y); Church Yth Grp; 4-H; Hosp Aide; Church Choir; Drm & Bgl; Trk; Art Awd 82-83; Hosp Vol 82-83; Stu Mnth 82-83; U VT; Physcl Thrpy.

STUART, CYNTHIA L; Concord HS; Concord, VT; (S); 3/22; Am Leg Aux Girls St; Drama Clb; Math Clb; Model UN; Sec Frsh Cls; Sec Soph Cls; Pres Jr Cls; Bsktbl; Socr; Sftbl; Hugh O Brien Yth Foundation 84; Law.

STUDER, LORETTA; North Country Union HS; W Charleston, VT; (Y); German Clb; Hosp Aide; Band; Chorus; Concert Band; Mrchg Band; School Musical; School Play; Bsktbl; Socr.

SULLIVAN, GAIL; Rutland SR HS; Rutland, VT; (Y); 49/227; Pres Church Yth Grp; Band; Drm & Bgl; Flag Corp; Hon Roll.

SULLIVAN, WINIFRED; Mount Mansfield Union HS; Underhill, VT; (Y); Cmnty Wkr; Latin Clb; Teachers Aide; Nwsp Stf; Bsktbl; Socr; Sftbl; High Hon Roll; Hon Roll.

SUSSLIN, NANA; Bellows Free Acad; St Albans, VT; (Y); 17/224; Band; Chorus; Concert Band; Jazz Band; Mrchg Band; Pep Band; Rep Stu Cncl; Var Tennis; St Albans Cty Ed Assn Schlrshp 85; U Of VT; Psych.

SWANSON, J R; Essex Jct Educational Ctr; Westford, VT; (Y); 51/326; US Pony Clb Natl Knowdown Champ 82; Cmnctns.

SWEENEY, AMY; Montpelier HS; Montpelier, VT; (Y); 27/109; 4-H; French Clb; Church Choir; JV Bsktbl; 4-H Awd; High Hon Roll; VT Coll; Comp.

SWEENEY, JOHN; Brattleboro Union HS; Brattleboro, VT; (Y); 3/216; Am Leg Boys St; Yrbk Sprt Ed; Rep Sr Cls; JV Var Bsbl; JV Var Ftbl; NHS; Model UN; Hon Roll; Elks Natl Mst Valuable Stu Schlrshp 85; Govnrs Wrtng Awd 84; Marlboro Coll Wrtng Awd 84; Worcester Polytech Inst; Engrng.

SWEENEY, TAMMY; North Country Union HS; Newport, VT; (Y); Drama Clb; Model UN; Chorus; School Musical; Yrbk Ed-Chief; VP Sr Cls; NHS; Ntl Merit Ltr; Wells Coll.

SWIATEK, JEFF C; Burlington HS; Burlington, VT; (Y); Boy Scts; German Clb; Math Tm; JV Bsktbl; Var Crs Cntry; Capt Tennis; French Hon Soc; High Hon Roll; Jr NHS; NHS; John Carpenter Awd Tnns 83; Amer Regn Math Lgu 85; Vrsty Athltc Cncl 85; Germn Awd 83-85 Frnch Awd 84; Comp Sci.

SYEDA, HUMERA; Montpelier HS; Montpelier, VT; (Y); Ed Yrbk Stf; High Hon Roll; NHS; Northern New England Jr Sci Humanties Symposium U NH 85; Pre-Med.

TALMAGE, KIRSTEN J; Middlebury Union HS; Ripton, VT; (Y); 7/188; AFS; Math Tm; Teachers Aide; Lit Mag; Hon Roll; Ntl Merit SF; Swarthmore; Astro.

TANNER, STEPHANIE; Concord HS; Lunenburg, VT; (S); 1/18; Model UN; Teachers Aide; Yrbk Ed-Chief; Sec Frsh Cls; Sec Soph Cls; Trs Jr Cls; Trs Sr Cls; Hon Roll; NHS; Gen Bus Awd 82; Accntng Awd 83; Notre Dame; Art.

TARDY, MONICA; Harwood Union HS; Waitsfield, VT; (Y); Cmnty Wkr; Hosp Aide; Model UN; Varsity Clb; Yrbk Stf; Fld Hcky; Score Keeper; High Hon Roll; Prfct Atten Awd; Church Yth Grp; All Star Fld Hcky Tm Cntrl VT Mntn Div 84 & 85; Congrssnl Art Awd ST Vt 85; Champlain Coll; Trvl.

TARTE, PAUL; Vergennes Union HS; Vergennes, VT; (Y); German Clb; JV Var Bsbl; JV Bsktbl; JV Var Socr; Champlain Coll; Bus Mgmt.

TAYLOR, BETH; Spaulding HS; Barre, VT; (Y); 20/250; Am Leg Aux Girls St; Varsity Clb; Yrbk Stf; Lit Mag; Sec Frsh Cls; Sec Soph Cls; Sec Jr Cls; Rep Stu Cncl; JV Var Cheerleading; Hon Roll; Delg To Giftd & Talntd Camp; Latin Hnr Soc; Delg To Stu Gvnmt Day; Librl Arts Coll.

TAYLOR, PAM; Essex Jct Educational Ctr; Essex Ctr, VT; (Y); Church Yth Grp; Drama Clb; Latin Clb; Chorus; Stage Crew; Variety Show; Nwsp Stf; Yrbk Stf; JV Mgr(s); JV Sftbl; Drama & Fine Arts Awd 85; U Of VT; Scndry Ed In Bio.

TAYLOR, SHAWN FRANK; Whitingham HS; Jacksonville, VT; (S); 3/30; Intnl Clb; Letterman Clb; Spanish Clb; Band; Chorus; School Musical; Rep Frsh Cls; Var Bsbl; Var Bsktbl; Im Gym; AAU Fitness Tst 1st Schl Rnk; Army; Law Enfrcmnt.

TEDD, KIM; Mt Anthony Union HS; Goshen, NY; (Y); 12/307; Chorus; Yrbk Stf; JV Var Cheerleading; Var Fld Hcky; High Hon Roll; Jr NHS; NHS; Pres Acadmc Ftns Awd 85; Exclnce In Math 85; Drew U; Pre Med.

TEILLON, SUSAN; Peoples Acad; Morrisville, VT; (Y); 14/54; Church Yth Grp; French Clb; Teachers Aide; Yrbk Stf; JV Var Bsktbl; JV Var Socr; NHS; Ntl Merit Ltr; Psych.

TENNEY, LAUREN; Champlain Valley Union HS; Shelbourne, VT; (Y); AFS; Pres Church Yth Grp; Chorus; School Musical; School Play; Stage Crew; Variety Show; Hon Roll; New England Yth Cncl 84-86; Parish Cncl 84-85; Close-Up 84-85; U Of VT; Math Tchr.

TESSIER, KATHLEEN M; Bellows Free Acad; St Albans, VT; (Y); Band; Chorus; Church Choir; Concert Band; Mrchg Band; School Musical; Rep Stu Cncl; Var Cheerleading; U VT; Arts.

TETREAULT, LYNNE; Bellows Free Acad; Fairfield, VT; (Y); Am Leg Aux Girls St; Trs French Clb; Stage Crew; VP Jr Cls; Pres Rep Stu Cncl; High Hon Roll; NHS; Pres SADD 85; Giftd & Tlntd Pgm 84-85; Med.

THAYER, LINDA M; Peoples Acad; Morrisville, VT; (Y); Aud/Vis; Drama Clb; Chorus; Drm Mjr(t); Bsktbl; Cheerleading; Socr; Sftbl; Hon Roll; French Clb; Castleton ST Coll; Scrtrl Sci.

THIBAULT, DEBBIE; Colchester HS; Colchester, VT; (S); 1/200; JA; Pres Soph Cls; Var JV Bsktbl; Var Mgr(s); Var Capt Socr; High Hon Roll; NHS; Colchester H S Englsh Awd 84-85.

THOMPSON, BETH; Mt Anthony Union HS; Pownal, VT; (Y); 20/280; Nwsp Bus Mgr; High Hon Roll; NHS; Berkshire CC; Sec Sci.

THOMPSON, ERIC S; Black River HS; Ludlow, VT; (Y); 11/48; Drama Clb; School Musical; School Play; Stage Crew; Variety Show; Yrbk Stf; Trs Frsh Cls; JV Bsbl; Var Capt Bsktbl; Var Golf; Bsktbl All Tournmnt Tm 83-85; Western Nw Englnd Coll; Comp.

THOMPSON, JOHN; Paulding HS; Barre, VT; (Y); 18/256; Boy Scts; Key Clb; Sec VICA; Capt Bsktbl; Capt Socr; Trk; NCTE Awd; Thurman W Dix Mem Schlrshp 85; Pro Merito 85; Vermont Tech Coll; Mech Engrng.

THORNTON, RICHARD; Essex Junction Educational Center; Essex Junction, VT; (Y); Church Yth Grp; Stat Bsktbl; Im Lcrss; JV Tennis; Brdcstng.

TILLEY, PATRICIA; Colchester HS; Colchester, VT; (S); Var Crs Cntry; JV Socr; Var Trk; Hon Roll; NHS.

TILLOTSON, SCOTT D; Mount Mansfield Union HS; Jericho, VT; (Y); Var Bsbl; Var Capt Bsktbl; Var JV Socr; High Hon Roll; Hon Roll; NHS; Elec Engrng.

TINKER, EDWARD A; Lake Region Union HS; Orleans, VT; (Y); VP Intnl Clb; Science Clb; Band; Jazz Band; School Musical; Yrbk Stf; Pres Jr Cls; Var Crs Cntry; Hon Roll; NHS.

TOMPKINS, HEIDI A; Middlebury Union HS; Shoreham, VT; (Y); 9/200; School Play; Nwsp Ed-Chief; Nwsp Rptr; Bsktbl; JV Tennis; Hon Roll; NHS; Ntl Merit SF; Voice Dem Awd; AFS; VT USDA Apprntc 84; Brdcst Jrnlsm.

TOWNE, SARAH; Harwood Union HS; Waterbury Ctr, VT; (Y); Band; Concert Band; Orch; School Musical; Lit Mag; JV Bsktbl; High Hon Roll; Hon Roll; NHS; Prfct Atten Awd; Gen Bio Sci Awd 82-83; Frnch 1 Awd 81-82; Champlain Coll; Med Sec Studies.

TRAFTON, SARAH; Mt Mansfield Union HS; S Portland, ME; (Y); English Clb; FHA; Latin Clb; Speech Tm; Teachers Aide; School Play; Nwsp Phtg; Sec Frsh Cls; Trs Soph Cls; Var Coach Actv; Spec Educ Tchr.

TREAT, STEPHEN; Burr And Burton Seminary HS; Manchester Ctr, VT; (Y); 1/100; Boy Scts; VP Sr Cls; Capt Bsktbl; Capt Socr; Bausch & Lomb Sci Awd; DAR Awd; High Hon Roll; Pres NHS; Val; German Clb; VT Hnr Schlrs 85; Burr & Burton Boosters Clb Schlrshp 85; US Hist & Math Awds 85; U Of NC Chapel Hill; Sci.

TREMBLAY, MATTHEW P; Lake Region V HS; Irasburg, VT; (Y); Am Leg Boys St; Pres FFA; Math Tm; Pep Clb; Ski Clb; Yrbk Stf; Rep Jr Cls; Bsbl; Socr; Hon Roll; VT Dairy Indstry Assn Dairy Prodcts Judgng 4th 84-85; Foresty Mngmnt Proficncy Awd 85; Nuclr Power.

TREPANIER, SUSAN; West Rutland HS; West Rutland, VT; (Y); 3/43; Am Leg Aux Girls St; Varsity Clb; Yrbk Stf; Pres Sr Cls; Capt Cheerleading; Capt Fld Hcky; NHS; Pres Schlr; St Schlr; Half Tuitn Scholar Quinnipiac Coll 85; Stu Cncl Scholar 85; Alumni Scholar 85; Quinnipiac Coll; Polit Sci.

TRIPLETT, LORI; Montpelier HS; Montpelier, VT; (Y); 47/109; Drama Clb; Latin Clb; Chorus; School Musical; School Play; Ntl Piano Tchrs Guild Audtn Awd Of Accmplshmnt 85; Music.

TROMBLEY, SALVNN; Peoples Acad; Morrisville, VT; (Y); 6/60; School Musical; Yrbk Sprt Ed; Rep VP Soph Cls; Rep Jr Cls; Rep Sr Cls; Sec Stu Cncl; Bsktbl; Golf; Socr; Hon Roll.

TRUAX, J; Hartford HS; Wilder, VT; (Y); Am Leg Aux Girls St; GAA; Model UN; Pep Clb; Teachers Aide; Rep Jr Cls; Rep Sr Cls; Rep Stu Cncl; Bsktbl; Var Fld Hcky; UVM; Bus.

TRUDEAU, DONALD J; Mt Anthony Union HS; Pownal, VT; (Y); 4/250; Am Leg Boys St; Church Yth Grp; French Clb; Lit Mag; Stu Cncl; JV Ftbl; JV Socr; Var Tennis; NHS; Ntl Merit Ltr; Ntl Ltn Hnr Soc 85; Engrng.

TRUE, KATHERINE; Champlain Valley Union HS; Charlotte, VT; (Y); 16/220; Political Wkr; Nwsp Ed-Chief; Rep Frsh Cls; Rep Soph Cls; Rep Jr Cls; Rep Sr Cls; Rep Stu Cncl; Pres NHS; Ntl Merit SF; Outstndg Essayist Awd 85; Principals Awd Hstry, Eng, Art 83; Govnrs Inst Of Art 83; Wesleyan U; Art.

TRUEMAN, DAVID; Vergennes Union HS; N Ferrisburg, VT; (Y); 12/101; Church Yth Grp; German Clb; Band; Concert Band; Jazz Band; Mrchg Band; Pep Band; School Musical; Symp Band; JV Var Golf; All-ST Music Fstvl Concrt Bnd 83-85; All-New Englnd Music Fstvl Bnd 85; Boston U Tanglewood Inst 85; Bio.

TUCKER, TAMMY; Vergennes Union HS; Vergennes, VT; (Y); 17/110; Am Leg Aux Girls St; French Clb; Teachers Aide; Band; Drm Mjr(t); Mrchg Band; School Musical; Sec Sr Cls; Rep Stu Cncl; JV Var Bsktbl; Vergennes Alumni Assn 85; U VT; Early Childhd Ed.

TUFTS, SUSAN; Whitcomb HS; Bethel, VT; (Y); Church Yth Grp; Drama Clb; School Play; Var Cheerleading; Var Sftbl; Hon Roll; French Clb; Stage Crew; New Englnd Yng Wrtrs Cnfrnc 85; Close Up In VT & Wshngtn DC 84; Hnrb Mntn In Wrld Poetry 85; Brghm Yng U; Psychlgy.

TURGEON, RITA; North Country Union HS; Newport, VT; (Y); School Play; Yrbk Stf; Cheerleading; Mgr(s); Trk; Bk Knwldg Pin 85; Pratt; Art.

TURNER, CHARLENE; Rutland HS; Rutland, VT; (Y); Color Guard; Drm & Bgl; Flag Corp; Yrbk Stf; Hon Roll; Bus.

TUTTLE, CHRISTOPHER A; Chelsea HS; Tunbridge, VT; (S); 2/28; Am Leg Boys St; Debate Tm; Drama Clb; NFL; Band; School Musical; Nwsp Ed-Chief; NHS; Sal; Boston U.

TYLER, ANGELA; Montpelier HS; Montpelier, VT; (Y); 39/109; Pres Debate Tm; Drama Clb; Pres VP 4-H; French Clb; Band; Concert Band; Mrchg Band; Yrbk Stf; Mgr(s); 4-H Awd; 4-H Citznshp Prog Wash DC 85; VT U; Psychlgy.

VAILLANCOURT, PHILIP; Bellows Free Acad; Enosburg Falls, VT; (Y); 35/216; Hon Roll; VT Tech Coll; Elect Engr.

VAILLANT, ANNE L; Putney Schl; Putney, VT; (Y); Art Clb; Drama Clb; Exploring; PAVAS; Political Wkr; Ski Clb; School Play; Lit Mag; Stu Cncl; JV Crs Cntry; Brown U; Psychlgst.

VALCOUR, NICOLE; Peoples Acad; Morrisville, VT; (Y); #4 In Class; Pres Church Yth Grp; Chorus; Concert Band; Jazz Band; Yrbk Phtg; Pres Soph Cls; Var Pres Jr Cls; JV Var Bsktbl; Var Pres NHS; Drama Clb; Madge Churchill Awd Mst Imprvd Athl 85; Theology.

VALLEY, MARK A; Milton JR-SR HS; Milton, VT; (Y); 3/150; Am Leg Boys St; Computer Clb; Band; Var Bsktbl; High Hon Roll; Hon Roll; Ntl Merit SF; U Of VT Math Awd 84; U Of VT JR Conf 83; Comp Engrng.

VANDENBURGH, DOUGLAS L; Mill River Union HS; N Clarendon, VT; (Y); 9/150; Stage Crew; Yrbk Phtg; Yrbk Stf; Bausch & Lomb Sci Awd; Hon Roll; NHS; Ntl Merit SF.

VANDEWEERT, JEAN; Vergennes Union HS; Ferrisburg, VT; (Y); 19/101; Church Yth Grp; 4-H; German Clb; Yrbk Stf; Var JV Bsktbl; Hon Roll; 2nd Pl Shrthnd I Comp Oxbow 85; Accntng.

VEILLEUX, MICHELE; North Country Union HS; N Troy, VT; (Y); Church Yth Grp; French Clb; Acpl Chr; Band; Chorus; Church Choir; Var Fld Hcky; New Engl Music Fest 85; All ST Music Fest 84-85; NE Music Fest 83-85; Nrs.

VERCHEREAU, JOAN; U-32 HS; Montpelier, VT; (Y); Church Yth Grp; Varsity Clb; Nwsp Rptr; Nwsp Stf; Off Soph Cls; Off Jr Cls; Off Sr Cls; Bsktbl; Fld Hcky; Sftbl; Bus.

VERSWEYVELD, MATTHEW; Vergennes Union HS; Vergennes, VT; (Y); 5/96; Computer Clb; Drama Clb; School Play; Stage Crew; Var Crs Cntry; DAR Awd; High Hon Roll; Hon Roll; NHS; VT ST 1-Act Chmpnshp 84; Comp Progmng.

VIENS, CARMEN; Enosburg Falls HS; Enosburg Falls, VT; (Y); FHA; Varsity Clb; Church Choir; Variety Show; Nwsp Sprt Ed; Yrbk Stf; Trs Frsh Cls; Trs Soph Cls; VP Jr Cls; Var Bsktbl; Pres FHA 84-85; Amblnce 1st Aide Vol 83-84; Stu Advsry Bd 83-84; Tourism.

VILLANTI, JON E; Colchester HS; Colchester, VT; (Y); Bsktbl; Crs Cntry; Trk; Hon Roll; Ntl Merit Ltr; Hghst Avg Spnsh I 84-85; U Of Vermont; Bus Adm.

VIVIAN, LORI; Windsor HS; Ascutney, VT; (Y); Pep Clb; Color Guard; Mrchg Band; Stage Crew; Cheerleading; Sftbl; Hon Roll; Trphy Colrgd Sumr Camp 84; Band Awd 85; Bus Mgmt.

VON MOLTKE, DOROTHEA; Hanover HS; Norwich, VT; (Y); Dance Clb; Drama Clb; Intnl Clb; Chorus; School Play; Nwsp Stf; Off Frsh Cls; Off Soph Cls; Vllybl; High Hon Roll; Adv Frnch Recitatn Cont 1st Pl 85; Frnch Grand Concours 3rd Pl 85; Brown U; Theatre Dir.

VOSS, BARRY; Rice Memorial HS; Shelburne, VT; (Y); 9/108; Trs Church Yth Grp; Ski Clb; Band; Chorus; School Play; Rep Frsh Cls; Rep Soph Cls; Off Stu Cncl; Var L Crs Cntry; Capt Socr; Dartmouth Bk Awd 85; Elec Engrng.

VOWLES, STEPHEN C; Bellows Free Acad; Fairfield, VT; (Y); 4/68; Am Leg Boys St; Boy Scts; Drama Clb; 4-H; French Clb; Thesps; Band; NHS; Ntl Merit Ltr; Teachers Aide; Mc Donald All Amer Band 84; Music.

WALLER, LYNN; Champlain Valley Union HS; Charlotte, VT; (Y); AFS; Am Leg Aux Girls St; Church Yth Grp; Cmnty Wkr; Drama Clb; Political Wkr; Acpl Chr; Chorus; Church Choir; Madrigals; Govt.

WARD, WENDI; Montpelier HS; Montpelier, VT; (Y); French Clb; Concert Band; Drill Tm; Powder Puff Ftbl; High Hon Roll; Burlington Schl; Lang.

WARNER, ALAN; Bellows Free Acad; St Albans, VT; (Y); French Clb; Math Tm; Capt Scholastic Bowl; Yrbk Bus Mgr; JV Crs Cntry; JV Tennis; NHS; Top 10 Pct UVM Prz Math Exm 84; Amer Legn Boys ST Altrnt 85; Bus.

WARREN, KAREN; Harwood Union HS; Waterbury, VT; (Y); JV Var Cheerleading; High Hon Roll; Hon Roll; Yr Lng Sci Awd-Genl Bio 83-84; Bus Engl Awd 84-85; Champlain; Bus.

WASHBURN, LISA; Peoples Acad; Morrisville, VT; (Y); Sec Church Yth Grp; Drama Clb; French Clb; Band; Chorus; Jazz Band; School Musical; Yrbk Stf; Hon Roll; NHS; Elem Educ.

WATERMAN, ROGER L; Middlebury Union HS; Vergennes, VT; (Y); Am Leg Boys St; 4-H; School Play; JV Bsktbl; Hon Roll.

WATSON, JILL; North Country Union HS; Derby, VT; (Y); French Clb; Latin Clb; Ski Clb; Varsity Clb; School Play; Nwsp Rptr; Jr Cls; Socr; Trk; Jrnlsm.

WEEKS, BARBARA; Mt Anthony Union HS; Bennington, VT; (Y); 21/263; Dance Clb; High Hon Roll; NHS; Englsh Excell Awd 84; 3rd Rnnr-Up In Teen Pgnt 85; Englsh Commdtns Awd 85; Bennington Coll; Bus Adm.

WEITZ, PAUL; Middlebury Union HS; Salisbury, VT; (Y); 58/230; Am Leg Boys St; Band; Ftbl; Wt Lftg; Whittier Coll.

WELLS, AMY LYNNE; Essex Junction Educational Cntr; Essex Jct, VT; (Y); Rep Am Leg Aux Girls St; Church Yth Grp; Intnl Clb; Ski Clb; JV Bsktbl; Var Capt Socr; Var Capt Tennis; Vllybl; Ten Ltr 85; U VT; Ed.

WELLS, TRICIA; Union 32 HS; Calais, VT; (Y); Dance Clb; Drama Clb; School Musical; School Play; Pres Frsh Cls; Pres Soph Cls; Rep Jr Cls; Rep Stu Cncl; JV Bsktbl; Var Cheerleading; Selectd Jap Govt Spnd Summr Japan 85.

WERLING, TIMOTHY; Vergennes Union HS; Vergennes, VT; (Y); 15/101; Am Leg Boys St; Sec Church Yth Grp; Computer Clb; Concert Band; Mrchg Band; Pep Band; Nwsp Rptr; Var Crs Cntry; Var Wrstlng; Trs NHS; Marie Crovat Schlrshp 85; Comodore Booster Clb Schlrshp 85; U Of VT Mrt In Math 85; Purdue U; Elec Engrng.

WERNECKE, JENNIFER; U-32 HS; Northfield, VT; (Y); 2/110; Am Leg Aux Girls St; Church Yth Grp; French Clb; Band; Var Gym; JV Sftbl; Var Trk; High Hon Roll; U VT Jr Conf 84-85; Pre-Law.

WERNINGER JR, CHARLES F; Essex Jct Educational Ctr; Dallas, TX; (Y); Boy Scts; CAP; ROTC; Ski Clb; Color Guard; Var L Crs Cntry; Var L Tennis; Outstdng Cadet 83; Supr Perf 84-85; Hnr Unit 84-85; Boston U; Aerosp Engnrg.

WESTNEY, CRAIG; Windsor HS; Windsor, VT; (Y); 9/65; Am Leg Boys St; French Clb; Ski Clb; Rep Stu Cncl; Var VP Ftbl; Hon Roll; NHS; Engrng.

WESTOVER, JOHN; Sacred Heart HS; Newport Center, VT; (Y); 3/29; FCA; Concert Band; Jazz Band; School Play; Bsbl; Crs Cntry; Socr; Elks Awd; French Hon Soc; NHS; U Of VT; Prelaw.

WHEELER, BRENDA M; Lake Region Union HS; Albany, VT; (Y); DECA; Pep Clb; Yrbk Stf; VP Soph Cls; Trs Jr Cls; Var Cheerleading; Hon Roll; Champlain Coll.

WHEELER, ROBERT; Burlington HS; Burlington, VT; (Y); Church Yth Grp; Pep Clb; Band; Sec Frsh Cls; JV Var Bsbl; JV Bsktbl; JV Var Ftbl; Hon Roll; Concert Band; Mrchg Band; Var Bsbl Rookie Of The Yr 85; JV Bsbl Outstdng Ptchr 84; Mrktng.

WHEELER, SARAH BILLINGS; Rutland HS; Rutland, VT; (Y); 2/180; Am Leg Aux Girls St; Pres Stu Cncl; Trk; Hon Roll; NHS; Pres Schlr; Sal; Chorus; Cheerleading; Jr NHS; Drtmth Clb Bk Awd 84; I Durkee Frnch Awd, 2nd Pl Oratorical 85; Barnard Coll.

WHITCOMB, KIMBERLY; Spaulding HS; E Barre, VT; (Y); Am Leg Aux Girls St; Sec Church Yth Grp; French Clb; Trs VICA; Var Stat Fld Hcky; Trk; High Hon Roll; Hon Roll; NEDT Awd; 4-H; Spcl Olymp Booster Clb; Proj Excel; Sci Sem; Chem Engr.

WHITE, SHERYL; Bellows Free Acad; Sheldon, VT; (Y); 23/220; Elks Awd; High Hon Roll; Hon Roll; Bronze Pin 85; Fairfield Schlrshp 85; Pro-Merito 85; Champlain Coll; Bus Mgmt.

WHITNEY, KATIE; Montpelier HS; Montpelier, VT; (Y); 15/109; Am Leg Aux Girls St; Sec Spanish Clb; Var L Bsktbl; Var L Crs Cntry; Var L Fld Hcky; Im Powder Puff Ftbl; JV Socr; JV Var Sftbl; High Hon Roll; Bio.

WIEGAND, MICHAEL; Hartford HS; White River Jct, VT; (Y); 37/158; Am Leg Boys St; 4-H; Math Tm; Band; Jazz Band; Pep Band; School Play; Golf; Hon Roll; Ntl Merit Ltr; VT Soc Prfssnl Engrs Fnlst 85; St Anns Clb Schlrshp 85; Carnegie Mellon U; Engrng.

WILKINSON, KAREN; Concord HS; Lunenburg, VT; (S); 3/18; Am Leg Aux Girls St; 4-H; French Clb; Girl Scts; Model UN; Office Aide; Pep Clb; Teachers Aide; Varsity Clb; Yrbk Ed-Chief; Lyndon ST Coll; Elem Ed.

WILLETTE, DIANE MARIE; Spaulding HS; Graniteville, VT; (Y); 8/252; Drama Clb; Band; Chorus; Concert Band; Mrchg Band; Pep Band; School Musical; School Play; High Hon Roll; Hon Roll; Schlrshps 85; U NH; Occup Thrpy.

WILLIAMS, ANNE MARIE; Otter Valley Union HS; Brandon, VT; (Y); Sec Latin Clb; Band; Church Choir; Concert Band; Jazz Band; Mrchg Band; Orch; NHS; Outstndng Achvt Lat II 83; Vrsty Ltr Band/Music 84; Summa Cum Laude Lat 85; Music.

WILLIAMS, DANIEL; Northfield JR SR HS; Northfield, VT; (Y); 11/60; Boy Scts; Scholastic Bowl; Varsity Clb; Band; Jazz Band; School Musical; School Play; Nwsp Ed-Chief; Yrbk Stf; Var Ice Hcky; Top Instrmntlst 84-85; Semper Fidelis Awd Musicl Excllnc 85; John Lockhart Mem Schlrshp Music 85; U Of Hartford; Music Mgmnt.

WILSON, FLETCHER; Mt St Joseph Acad; Rutland, VT; (Y); 15/97; Varsity Clb; Pres Frsh Cls; Capt Ftbl; Ice Hcky; Tennis; Trk; Hon Roll; NHS; Bus.

WING, ROBERT; North Country Union HS; Island Pond, VT; (Y); Am Leg Boys St; Boy Scts; Church Yth Grp; Drama Clb; German Clb; School Play; Nwsp Ed-Chief; Lit Mag; JV Var Tennis; Var L Vllybl; Wrtg.

WOOD, CYNTHIA M; Rutland HS; Rutland, VT; (Y); Church Yth Grp; Chorus; Church Choir; Nwsp Rptr; Rep Frsh Cls; High Hon Roll; Hon Roll; Natl Hnr Rll 84-85; Liberty Baptist Coll; Music.

WOODARD, CHRISTINA; North Country Union HS; Newport Center, VT; (Y); High Hon Roll; Hon Roll; Bk Of Knwldg Awd 84-85; Bus Admin.

WOOTTON, CHARLES; Burr & Burton Seminary; Manchester, VT; (Y); Am Leg Boys St; Computer Clb; Var Bsbl; Var Bsktbl; Mgr(s); Score Keeper; JV Socr; Var Vllybl; High Hon Roll; Hon Roll; U Vermont; Elect Engrng.

WRIGHT, DEAN; Enosburg Falls HS; Enosburg Falls, VT; (Y); Pres VP 4-H; Pres Trs FFA; Quiz Bowl; Varsity Clb; Band; Stu Cncl; Bsktbl; 4-H Awd; Hon Roll; Ag Coll; Ag Bus.

WRIGHT, PRISCILLA; Vergennes Union HS; Underhill, VT; (Y); 5/101; Art Clb; Church Yth Grp; German Clb; Chorus; School Musical; Variety Show; Rep Frsh Cls; High Hon Roll; Hon Roll; NHS; USAF; Elect.

WRIGHT, TINA; North Country Union HS; Newport, VT; (Y); Camera Clb; High Hon Roll; Hon Roll; Pres Schlr; Book Of Knwldg Pin; Russel Sage; Psych.

WULFF, WARREN; Essex Junction HS; Essex Jct, VT; (Y); Church Yth Grp; French Clb; Intnl Clb; Math Clb; Yrbk Stf; Var Golf; Hon Roll; Cornell U; Engrng.

YATES, JOSEPH; Mt Anthony Union HS; Bennington, VT; (Y); Crs Cntry; Trk; Hon Roll; Englsh Commdtn; Crss Cntry Awd; Navy; Elec Tech.

YOUNG, ANDREA; Lake Region Union HS; Craftsbury Common, VT; (S); DECA; Math Tm; Pep Clb; VP Jr Cls; Rep Stu Cncl; Bsktbl; Socr; VT ST DECA Ofc Stu Cnsl Treas 85-86; Hesser Coll; Travel.

YOUNG, BRAD; Twinfield HS; Plainfield, VT; (Y); Church Yth Grp; Drama Clb; FFA; Chorus; Church Choir; Madrigals; Ftbl; Hon Roll.

YOUNG, CATHERINE M; Champlain Valley Union HS; Richmond, VT; (Y); Aud/Vis; Camera Clb; Church Yth Grp; Drama Clb; Ski Clb; Stage Crew; Var Mgr(s); Stat Var Socr; Cit Awd; Hon Roll; Engrng.

YOUNG, STEPHANIE; Enosburg Falls HS; Enosburg Falls, VT; (Y); Am Leg Aux Girls St; Sec VP FHA; Teachers Aide; Stage Crew; Variety Show; Trs Stu Cncl; Bsktbl; Socr; Hon Roll; Chorus; Stu Of Mnth 85; Trvl.

ZAHLER, REUBEN; Champlain Valley Union HS; Charlotte, VT; (Y); AFS; Drama Clb; Model UN; Var L Wrstlng; High Hon Roll; Hon Roll; NHS; Engl Awd 83; Spnsh Awd 85; Psych.

ZARATE, ARIANNA I; Burlington HS; Burlington, VT; (Y); French Clb; Latin Clb; Model UN; Yrbk Stf; Rep Stu Cncl; Socr; Hon Roll; U VT; Intl Bus.

ZENO, MICHELE; Mount Abraham U HS; Bristol, VT; (Y); 19/113; Chorus; Yrbk Stf; Fld Hcky; Mgr(s); NHS; Exc Writing 85; Warner Endwmnt Schlrshp 85; Marie Crovat Schlrshp 85; Champlain Col; Travel.

VIRGIN ISLANDS

ALLEN, CYNTHIA; Charlotte Amalie HS; St Thomas, VI; (S); 22/394; FHA; Girl Scts; Office Aide; VICA; Church Choir; Stage Crew; Cit Awd; High Hon Roll; Art Stu Charlotte Amalie HS 84-85; Virgin Is Ind Arts Archt Drftng Stu 84-85; FHA Virgin Isl Trea; Pratt Inst; Archt Engrn.

BERG, TRENT; Charlotte Amalie HS; St Thomas, VI; (S); 23/475; Chorus; Church Choir; Stage Crew; Rep Jr Cls; Trs Sr Cls; Pres Stu Cncl; Ftbl; Cit Awd; Dnfth Awd; Stu Of Yr 84-85; Oakwood Coll; Lab Tech.

CHOUCOUTOU, MITCHELL; Charlotte Amalie HS; St Thomas, VI; (S); 5/475; Computer Clb; JA; Spanish Clb; Teachers Aide; Tennis; High Hon Roll; Hon Roll; NHS; Spanish NHS; FL Inst Tech; Aviation Mgt.

DAVIDSON, FREDDIA G; Antilles Schl; St Thomas, VI; (Y); Chess Clb; Church Yth Grp; Civic Clb; Cmnty Wkr; Computer Clb; Dance Clb; Drama Clb; French Clb; Girl Scts; Intnl Clb; Natl Hnr Roll 83-84; Emory U; Pre Law.

DE GRASSE, ALISON; Charlotte Amalie HS; St Thomas, VI; (Y); FNA; Hosp Aide; Pep Clb; VICA; Chorus; Drm Mjr(t); Variety Show; Bsbl; Cheerleading; High Hon Roll; Schlrshp For FL Mem 85-86; Awd For Outstndng Stu-Nrsng 84-85; Awd For Outstndng Vol Worker 84-85; FL Mem Coll; Nrsng.

GRIFFITH, JAMES; Charlotte Amalie HS; St Thomas, VI; (S); Church Yth Grp; Debate Tm; Political Wkr; Quiz Bowl; Radio Clb; Scholastic Bowl; Band; Concert Band; Stage Crew; Vllybl; U Of Southern CA; Pre-Med.

HODGE, SHAWN; Charlotte Amalie HS; St Thomas, VI; (S); 21/474; VP Church Yth Grp; Computer Clb; Trs FBLA; Office Aide; Variety Show; Yrbk Stf; Cit Awd; High Hon Roll; Hon Roll; NHS; Stu Of Yr 85; VI FBLA 1st Pl Acctg II 85; Most Lkly To Sccd 85; US Army; Acctg.

MICHAEL, JASON J; Charlotte Amalie HS; St Thomas, VI; (S); 12/350; Quiz Bowl; Lit Mag; French Hon Soc; High Hon Roll; Hon Roll; NHS; Ntl Merit SF; Spanish NHS; Howard U; Physcs.

PARRIS, AGNES; Charlotte Amalie HS; St Thomas, VI; (S); 1/475; Girl Scts; Capt Quiz Bowl; Sec Spanish Clb; Teachers Aide; Color Guard; Off NHS; Ntl Merit Ltr; Pres Spanish NHS; Val; Science Clb; Ldrshp Today & Tomorrow Awd 85; Distngshd Stu Awd 85; Citznshp Awd 85; U Of Pace; Intl Law.

PETTY, CANDACE; Charlotte Amalie HS; St Thomas, VI; (S); 2/475; French Clb; Sec Concert Band; Pres Frsh Cls; Rep Sr Cls; Rep Stu Cncl; High Hon Roll; VP Jr NHS; Pres NHS; Duquesne U; Pre-Med.

SANTANA, INOCENCIA; St Croix Central HS; St Croix, VI; (Y); 1/450; Church Yth Grp; Cmnty Wkr; Capt Quiz Bowl; Yrbk Ed-Chief; Pres NHS; Spanish NHS; Val; Drama Clb; Church Choir; Natl Hispanic Schlrs Awd Pgm 85; Pres Clsrm Rep 84; PREP Pgm 85; MA Inst Tech; Biomed Engr.

SIMEON, ZOZINE A; Sts Peter & Paul HS; St Thomas, VI; (Y); Art Clb; Girl Scts; Library Aide; PAVAS; Red Cross Aide; Teachers Aide; Pres Band; Variety Show; Pres Yrbk Stf; Var Sftbl; Blck Hist, Alchol, Drugs, Poster Cntst 84; Dept Hlth Paintng Cntst 85; Daniel Webster Coll; Trvl Mgmnt.

THOMAS JR, EDWARD; Charlotte Amalie HS; St Thomas, VI; (S); 3/450; Debate Tm; Quiz Bowl; Science Clb; High Hon Roll; NHS; Ntl Merit Ltr; Spanish NHS; FL Inst Of Tech; Phys.

THOMAS, VANLEER; Charlotte Amalie HS; St Thomas, VI; (S); 20/475; Library Aide; Stu Cncl; High Hon Roll; NHS; Spanish NHS; Prncpls Ldrshp Awd 85; SR Hmrm Pres 85; Ntl Sci Mrt Awd Physcs 85; Jackson ST U; Math.

ZAKERS, DERICK; Charlotte Amalie HS; St Thomas, VI; (S); 4/475; Drill Tm; Hon Roll; NHS; Spanish NHS; Acad All-Amer Awd 85; Ntl Sci Merit Awd 85; U Of Tampa; Bio.

FOREIGN COUNTRIES

AGNE, MARIA FATIMA D; Simon A Sanchez HS; Guam; (S); Computer Clb; FNA; Church Choir; Yrbk Stf; Off Sr Cls; Rep Stu Cncl; Bowling; Hon Roll; NHS; Prfct Atten Awd; Acctnt.

AGUON, IVY ROSE; Hanau HS; APO, NY; (Y); FTA; Sec Math Clb; Natl Beta Clb; Spanish Clb; Pres Jr Cls; Rep Stu Cncl; Hon Roll; NHS; Nwsp Rptr; Jr NHS; Miss JR 85; Geom Outstndng 83.

ALBEA, JOHN; Torrejon HS; Apo New York, NY; (Y); 2/100; Chess Clb; Hosp Aide; ROTC; Crs Cntry; NHS; Tulane; Med Doctr.

ALLARD, MICHAEL; Balboa HS; APO Miami, FL; (Y); Chess Clb; Drama Clb; School Play; Crs Cntry; Socr; Trk; Wrstlng; Hon Roll; OK U; Bus Admin.

ALLEGRO, FRANK; Uruguayan American Schl; Apo Miami, FL; (Y); Nwsp Stf; JV Bsktbl; Var L Socr; Var Swmmng; JV Trk; Hon Roll; Comp Sci.

ALLEN, JOHN J; Yokota HS; Apo San Fran, CA; (Y); 1/80; Computer Clb; Math Clb; Quiz Bowl; Teachers Aide; Yrbk Ed-Chief; Stu Cncl; Var Capt Socr; Bausch & Lomb Sci Awd; Pres NHS; Pres Schlr; Army Rserv Natl Acadmc & Athl Excllnc Awd 85; Harvard Bk Clb Boston Awd 84; MA Inst Tech; Engrng.

ALLEN, PETE; Memorial Composite HS; Alberta Canada; (Y); Church Yth Grp; Drama Clb; FFA; School Musical; School Play; Yrbk Phtg; Wrstlng; High Hon Roll; Ntl Merit Ltr; Hstry.

AMEND, JENNIFER; Bluefield SR HS; Canada; (Y); Church Yth Grp; Hosp Aide; Intnl Clb; Office Aide; Pep Clb; PAVAS; Spanish Clb; Band; Chorus; Mrchg Band; Dalhousie U; Spch Pathlgy.

ASHKENASI, DANNY F; John F Kennedy Schl; W Germany; (Y); Chorus; School Musical; School Play; Stage Crew; Swing Chorus; Nwsp Rptr; Swmmng; Wrstlng; 12 J F K Particpatn Awds 10 Plays & 10 Musicals 82-84; Film Dirctr.

BERNATH, ELIZABETH A; Torrejon American HS; Hill AFB, UT; (Y); Red Cross Aide; ROTC; Band; Chorus; School Musical; Sec Stu Cncl; Capt Bowling; High Hon Roll; VP NHS; SAR Awd; Ntl Sojrnrs Mdl 83; Mrs Elzbth Shoemkr Awd For Excllnc Music 85; Pres Acadmc Ftns Awd 85; U S Air Force.

BLALOCK, LAURA; General H H Arnold HS; Apo, NY; (Y); FBLA; Pep Clb; Spanish Clb; Chorus; Mrchg Band; Yrbk Stf; JV Cheerleading; JV Var Vllybl; High Hon Roll; NHS; Pres Acad Ftns Awd 85; Gen H H Arnold Educ Schlrshp 85; Lab Tech.

BLALOCK, SANDRA D; General H H Arnold HS; APO, NY; (Y); Keywanettes; Pep Clb; Spanish Clb; Chorus; Mrchg Band; Yrbk Stf; High Hon Roll; Hon Roll; NHS; Pres Acad Ftns Awd 85; Gen H H Arnold Educ Schlrshp 85; Bus Mgmt.

BOWMAN, JULI; Giessen American HS; APO, NY; (Y); 38/500; Aud/Vis; Cmnty Wkr; FHA; Girl Scts; Teachers Aide; Chorus; High Hon Roll; Prfct Atten Awd; U TX El Paso; Nrsg.

BOWMAN, PAUL; Evangelical Cristian Acad; Waterman, IL; (Y); 1/7; Church Yth Grp; Office Aide; Chorus; Church Choir; School Musical; School Play; Socr; Hon Roll; Pres NHS; Quiz Bowl; Distngshd JR & SR Assn Chrstn Schls Intl 84-85; U Of Madrid; Forgn Mssns.

BRANDT, ERIK A; Cairo American Coll; Egypt; (Y); 13/112; Art Clb; Debate Tm; Drama Clb; Model UN; Speech Tm; Thesps; Band; Chorus; Jazz Band; School Musical; Best Western Civiliation Stu Awd; Poli Sci.

BRANDT, WINIFRED LYNN; Stuttgart American HS; Apo New York, NY; (Y); 25/137; FBLA; Chrmn Model UN; Political Wkr; Lit Mag; Off Sr Cls; Rep Stu Cncl; Var Socr; Key Clb; Pep Clb; Sec Soph Cls; Outstndng Fml Stu, Scl Stds Stu & Senate Stu Of Yr 85; Trinity U; Pltcl Sci.

BRANNAMAN, CINDY A; Greengates HS; Middletown, OH; (Y); Art Clb; Drama Clb; Spanish Clb; Teachers Aide; Band; Concert Band; Mrchg Band; Pep Band; Stage Crew; Socr; Bio.

BROMINSKI, E DIANE; Heidelberg HS; A P O New York, NY; (Y); Cmnty Wkr; Computer Clb; Library Aide; Office Aide; Spanish Clb; Drill Tm; Var Mgr(s); Swmmng; Hon Roll; Pep Clb; U Maryland; Psych.

BRONNER, DAVID E; Stuttgart American HS; Apo New York, NY; (Y); Am Leg Boys St; Political Wkr; Ski Clb; Var Jr Cls; Crs Cntry; Golf.

CADWELL, ANGELA M; American School Of Madrid HS; Madrid; (Y); 12/43; Church Yth Grp; GAA; Spanish Clb; Var Bsktbl; Coach Actv; Var Sftbl; Var Vllybl; Hon Roll; NEDT Awd; NHS; Cornelia Connelly Partl Schlrshp 82; MVP Vllybl/Am Sch Of Madrid 85; Advcd Plcmnt Spnsh Lagn Exm 85; U Of San Diego; Engrng.

CAVANAUGH, BETH; American School Of The Hague; Netherlands; (Y); Sec Model UN; VP Pep Clb; Nwsp Rptr; VP Frsh Cls; Pres Soph Cls; Cheerleading; Capt Tennis; Capt Vllybl; Hon Roll; NHS; Hugh O Brian Yth Ldrshp Awd 84; Tennis Tm Awd Winner 85; Vllybl Tm Awd Winner 85; Bus Adm.

CAVAZOS, DEE M; Balboa HS; Apo Miami, FL; (Y); Church Yth Grp; Spanish Clb; Concert Band; Jazz Band; Mrchg Band; Symp Band; Yrbk Stf; VP Frsh Cls; CC Awd; Blk Hstry Week Essay Cont Wnr 84; Mass Comm.

CHIARINI, MONICA; Carol Morgan HS; Dom Rep; (Y); French Clb; Science Clb; Crs Cntry; Trk; French Hon Soc; High Hon Roll; FL U; Bio Med.

CISNEROS, MARC; Frankfurt American HS; A P O New York, NY; (Y); 21/320; Chess Clb; Pres Church Yth Grp; Letterman Clb; VP Model UN; Scholastic Bowl; Stu Cncl; Ftbl; Var Capt Socr; Hon Roll; NHS; European Jr Sci & Humanities Symp Finlst 84; Wnr Parliamntry Proc FBLA Conf 85; Semi-Fin Hspnc Schlr; Willamette U; Chem Engrng.

CLARK, JOAN; Shape HS; Boulder, CO; (Y); 21/63; Model UN; Ski Clb; Spanish Clb; Band; Color Guard; Drill Tm; Mrchg Band; Hon Roll; American Coll-Paris; Marine Bio.

CONTRERAS, LOURDES MARIA; College Beau Soleil HS; Coral Gables, FL; (Y); 1/12; Cmnty Wkr; French Clb; Pep Clb; Ski Clb; School Play; Variety Show; JV Cheerleading; Hon Roll; Tulane U; Pre-Law.

COPPEDGE, LORRI; Hitra Videregandi Skole HS; Malta, MT; (Y); Sec Frsh Cls; Exchng Stu Dorway 84-85; E MT Clg; Econ.

COSPER, LISA MARIE; Kadena HS; Belton, TX; (Y); 8/89; Church Yth Grp; Teachers Aide; Acpl Chr; Church Choir; Concert Band; Jazz Band; Madrigals; Mrchg Band; Hon Roll; NHS; Bus Mgmt.

COTTRILL, EDWARD A; Berlin American HS; Apo New York, NY; (Y); Church Yth Grp; ROTC; Spanish Clb; Chorus; VP Frsh Cls; Var Crs Cntry; Var L Socr; Var L Sftbl; High Hon Roll; Hon Roll; Acadmc Ltr 84-85; Mary Washington Coll; Comp Sci.

CRUZ, CHRISTOPHER A; John F Kennedy Schl; W Germany; (Y); 22/84; Drama Clb; Acpl Chr; Chorus; School Musical; School Play; Swing Chorus; Variety Show; Rep Stu Cncl; Gym; Boy Scts; Intl Schools Awd Theatre Associations Traveling Troupe 84-85; U Of Southern CA; Acting.

DARR, DANA; Albert Einstein Gymnasium HS; Westville, IN; (Y); Drama Clb; German Clb; Pres JA; Speech Tm; Mrchg Band; Orch; School Play; Hon Roll; NCTE Awd; Rotary Awd; IN U; Osteopath.

DAVIS, MARTHA; Hanau American HS; Apo, NY; (Y); 7/132; Church Yth Grp; German Clb; VP Powder Puff Ftbl; JV Tennis; JV Vllybl; Hon Roll; Masonic Awd; NHS; JR Beta Clb 81-82; Govrnr Sci Awd 82-83; Germn Amer Prtnrshp Prog 82-84; U Of SC; Bus.

DE LIZ, THERESE; General H H Arnold HS; West Germany; (Y); French Clb; German Clb; School Play; Nwsp Rptr; Nwsp Stf; Sec Soph Cls; JV Var Cheerleading; Church Choir; JV Tennis; Cnsrvtn Essy Cont 1st Pl Schl & Dist 81-82; 2nd Pl Esrra Essy Cont 82-83; 1st Pl Yng Wmns Scty Art Awd; Med.

DEMING, MIKE; Kaiserslautern American HS; APO, NY; (Y); Letterman Clb; Var Bsktbl; Var Ftbl; Var Trk; Hon Roll; Prfct Atten Awd; Hmcmng Page 83; U MD.

DOLAN, JEFFERSON; International School Of Kenya; Long Beach, CA; (Y); 7/48; Chess Clb; Scholastic Bowl; Varsity Clb; School Musical; School Play; Stage Crew; Var Bsktbl; High Hon Roll; NHS; Ntl Merit Ltr; Citi-Bank Athltc & Acadmc Achvt Awd 85; Outstndng Athlete Awd 84; UC-BERKELEY; Engrng.

EATON, LISA; Ramstein HS; Orlando, FL; (Y); 21/220; Pep Clb; Church Choir; School Musical; Nwsp Ed-Chief; Yrbk Ed-Chief; VP Stu Cncl; Var Bowling; Sftbl; High Hon Roll; NHS; Combined Schlrshp Fund 85; U FL; Pre-Med.

EMPLAINCOURT, MARY; St Johns International Schl; Tusaloosa, AL; (Y); French Clb; JCL; Latin Clb; Var Crs Cntry; Mgr(s); Var Swmmng; Hon Roll; NHS; Outstndng Latin II Stu 82-83; Prfct Paper Natl Latin II Exam 82-83; Hghst Natl Frnch Exam 83-84; U Of AL; Marine Bio.

EMPLAINCOURT, SHANE; St Johns International HS; Tuscaloosa, AL; (Y); French Clb; JCL; Latin Clb; Hon Roll; Jr NHS; NHS; Latin Natl Hnr Scty 84; Mbr Of St Johns Intl Cycling Tm 84-85; 2 Gold Mdl On Natl Latin Exams 81 & 83; U Of AL; Premed.

ESCHRICH, BONNIE; Berlin American HS; Apo New York, NY; (S); Church Yth Grp; German Clb; School Play; Sec Jr Cls; Rep Stu Cncl; Socr; Swmmng; High Hon Roll; Hon Roll; NHS; Swim Team Capt 84-85; Powder Puff Ftbl 84-85; Sftbl 82-84; U Of WY.

EYTCHISON, GREGORY; Naples American HS; FPO New York, NY; (Y); 8/80; Boy Scts; Church Yth Grp; FCA; Math Tm; Nwsp Rptr; JV Bsbl; JV Var Ftbl; Var Socr; Hon Roll; NHS; Cert Achvt VA AAA ST Ftbl Champs 83; DODDS Meditrrnean Ldrsh Conf Livorno Italy; Engrng.

FERGUSON, BETHANY; New Tribes Mission Schl; Battle Creek, MI; (Y); Chorus; School Play; Yrbk Stf; L Bsktbl; Capt Coach Actv; Socr; Swmmng; Vllybl; Hon Roll; Grand Rapids Bapt Coll.

FLATEN, ARNE R; American Intl School In Isreal; A P O New York, NY; (Y); 3/40; Chorus; Yrbk Stf; Pres Sr Cls; JV Capt Bsktbl; JV Capt Socr; High Hon Roll; NHS; Aud/Vis; Quiz Bowl; Band; Engl, Art Exclnc Awds 84; Eastern Mediterranaen Athltc All-Star Soccr Conf 84; St Olaf; Art.

FLEMING, LAURA ANN; Kingsmead HS; Cathedral City, CA; (Y); AFS; Church Yth Grp; Computer Clb; Drama Clb; Library Aide; Spanish Clb; Teachers Aide; Church Choir; School Play; Trs Frsh Cls; All-Str Sccr & Sftbl; UCLA; Bus Exec.

GLAYSHER, ROBIN; Torrejon American HS; APO, NY; (Y); 5/85; Aud/Vis; Red Cross Aide; Band; School Musical; Pres Jr Cls; Pres Sr Cls; Crs Cntry; Trk; NHS; Church Yth Grp; TASCO Schlrshp 85; Queens Coll Schlrshp 85; All Tourn Bsktbl 85; Queens Coll; Intl Bus.

GORDON, STEPHEN; Prairie HS; Wolf Point, MT; (Y); Church Yth Grp; Drama Clb; Math Tm; Band; School Play; JV Crs Cntry; Var Trk; High Hon Roll; Hon Roll; NHS; Vol Evnglsm; Comp Sci.

GOUSLIN, BARBARA; Nile C Kennick HS; Newport, RI; (Y); 20/56; Letterman Clb; Service Clb; Teachers Aide; Varsity Clb; Capt L Crs Cntry; Powder Puff Ftbl; Capt L Trk; Hon Roll; U Of WA; Psych.

GREGORY, CHAUVONNA Y; Frankfurt American HS; Apo New York, NY; (Y); FBLA; U Of MD; Accntg.

HAINES, KIMBERLY J; American International Schl; A P O New York, NY; (Y); Church Yth Grp; Orch; Symp Band; Yrbk Ed-Chief; Var Bsktbl; Var Cheerleading; Co-Capt Fld Hcky; High Hon Roll; NHS; Acadmc Exclnc In Socl Sci 83; St Olaf Coll; Music.

HARDING, KAREN E; Rift Valley Acad; N Kingstown, RI; (Y); Church Yth Grp; Letterman Clb; Acpl Chr; Chorus; Var JV Bsktbl; JV Capt Fld Hcky; Var Vllybl; Hon Roll; NHS; Phila Coll Bible; Elem Ed.

HARRIS, ANGEL D; Frankfurt American HS; APO, NY; (Y); Cmnty Wkr; Dance Clb; Girl Scts; Hosp Aide; Library Aide; Red Cross Aide; Teachers Aide; Varsity Clb; Y-Teens; Drill Tm; Homecmng Queen Amer Yth Actvts 83; MVP Sftbl 81; Usareur Sftbl Chmps 83-85.

HEAPY, TODD; Neuernberg American HS; Annandale, VA; (Y); Art Clb; FCA; German Clb; Key Clb; Teachers Aide; Yrbk Phtg; JV Var Socr; Hon Roll; Cal Poly CA ST; Auto Desgn.

HICKS, LEAH; Stuttgart American HS; West Germany; (Y); 3/141; French Clb; Model UN; Q&S; Nwsp Stf; Lit Mag; Off Sr Cls; Mgr(s); Hon Roll; NHS; Pres Schlr; Georgetown U; Bio.

HINKLE, JONATHAN; Grand Bahama Catholic HS; Patrick AFB, FL; (Y); 5/80; Church Yth Grp; Band; Concert Band; Jazz Band; Mrchg Band; Hon Roll; High Hnrs Math,Hist & Bio 85; Orange Coast Clg; Sales/Mktg.

HOCHHALTER, BRENDA; Interamerican Acad; Great Falls, MT; (Y); Church Yth Grp; Drama Clb; Hosp Aide; Nwsp Rptr; Yrbk Stf; Pres Frsh Cls; Rep Stu Cncl; Sftbl; Swmmng; Timer; U MT; Elem Ed.

HOLT, DIANE; Nurnberg Am HS; Ft Bliss, TX; (Y); 5/114; Concert Band; Mrchg Band; Pres Rep Jr Cls; VP Rep Sr Cls; Hst Stu Cncl; Var Powder Puff Ftbl; Var L Vllybl; Hon Roll; Trs NHS; Sec Exploring; Bst All Arnd Plyr-Vrsty Vllybl 83-84; Hghst Achvt In Chmstry & Electrncs 83-84; Allegheny; Bio.

HOODENPYLE, SHERI; Heidelberg American HS; A P O New York, NY; (Y); Office Aide; Varsity Clb; Variety Show; Stu Cncl; Capt Var Socr; Capt Var Vllybl; Im Powder Puff Ftbl; Army Resv Natl Schlr-Athl Awd 85; All-Conf Soccer 85; All-Conf Vlybl 84; Bowling Green ST U; Bus Adm.

HOWE, JULIE; International Schl Of Brussels; Dallas, TX; (Y); Var L Bsktbl; Var Capt Sftbl; Var Capt Vllybl; Hon Roll; Debate Tm; TX ST All Star Vllybll Tm 84; Vllybll 1st Tm All Dist Mst Outstndng Httr 84; Bsktbll & Sftbl Tour 85; U KS; Lib Arts.

INMAN, CIRSTEN; Kaiserslautern American HS; Apo New York, NY; (Y); 15/191; Nwsp Ed-Chief; Yrbk Ed-Chief; Rep Stu Cncl; High Hon Roll; Sec Jr NHS; NHS; Pres Schlr; Church Yth Grp; Dance Clb; Drama Clb; Exclince Art II 82; Acdmc Exclince Jrnlsm 84; Acdmc Exclince Yrbr 84; Helen Pietrullas Schl Csmtlgy.

ISE, SABRINA J; Nile C Kinnick HS; FPO Seattle, WA; (Y); 1/70; Service Clb; Sec Trs Stu Cncl; Var Capt Cheerleading; Var Crs Cntry; High Hon Roll; Var Pres NHS; Pres Schlr; Val; Voice Dem Awd; Church Yth Grp; Schlrshp Jpn-Amer Assn 85; U C Davis; Bio Sci.

JENKINS, JENNIFER A; London Central HS; Boone, NC; (Y); 8/114; Church Yth Grp; Trs Natl Beta Clb; Concert Band; Drm Mjr(t); Mrchg Band; School Musical; Symp Band; Nwsp Stf; Rep Stu Cncl; Cheerleading; Most Outstndg Fresh 81-82; All ST Band 81-83; Intl Hnr Band 84-85; Musicnshp Awd 84-85; Hmcmng Queen 85; Appalachian ST U; Music Ed.

JOHNSTON, JEANENE; Morrison Christian Acad; Taiwan; (Y); Church Yth Grp; Pep Clb; Chorus; Church Choir; School Musical; Stage Crew; Tennis; Vllybl; NHS; Ozark Christian Coll; Acctnt.

KENDALL, MARIBETH CROPPER; Heidelberg HS; Leavenworth, KS; (Y); Red Cross Aide; ROTC; Hon Roll; Jr NHS; NHS; Top Hstry Stu 79; Accntng.

KIM, LORRIE; Seoul International Schl; Korea; (Y); Debate Tm; Drama Clb; Quiz Bowl; Nwsp Rptr; Ed Lit Mag; Rep Soph Cls; Sec Jr Cls; Sec Stu Cncl; High Hon Roll; Ntl Merit SF; Project Day 83-84; Litr.

KOENIG, KIM; H H Arnold HS; APO, NY; (Y); Teachers Aide; Pres Frsh Cls; Rep Soph Cls; Rep Jr Cls; Stat Bsbl; Var Cheerleading; Var Golf; JV Mgr(s); Hon Roll; Jr NHS; U Of CA; Acctng.

KOLKO, BETH; The American School In Japan; Poughkeepsie, NY; (Y); Speech Tm; Thesps; School Musical; School Play; Stage Crew; Nwsp Ed-Chief; Nwsp Rptr; Rep Stu Cncl; High Hon Roll; NHS; Outstndng SR Engl Awd 85; Thomas J Watson Memrl Schlrshp 85; Rotry Schlrshp Study Abrd 82-83; Oberlin Coll; Crtve Wrtng.

LEWELLYN, BARBARA; Steven Decatur HS; Pensacola, FL; (Y); 1/24; Church Yth Grp; JCL; Keywanettes; Socr; Cit Awd; Hon Roll; Theias Optimist Clb 83-85; FL ST U; Gentcs.

LOFLIN, NINA; Hanav American HS; A P O New York, NY; (Y); 8/150; Church Yth Grp; Cmnty Wkr; German Clb; Co-Capt Band; Co-Capt Concert Band; Co-Capt Pep Band; Powder Puff Ftbl; JV Tennis; Jr NHS; NHS; Outstndng Musicianshp-Advncd Band 85; Psych.

MAHOOD, DIANA L; American Community Schl; Endicott, NY; (Y); 1/25; Mathletes; Model UN; Symp Band; Yrbk Ed-Chief; Var Crs Cntry; JV Tennis; Var Wt Lftg; High Hon Roll; NHS; Ntl Merit SF; Amer Cmmnty Schl Awds Mst Outstndng Stu Awd 83-84; Physcs, Engl, Comp Sci, Spnsh 83; U S Hstry, Eng 84; Math.

MANNING, JODY; Frankfurt American HS; Omaha, NE; (Y); 3/380; Pres Church Yth Grp; Trs Sec Concert Band; Trs Sec Mrchg Band; School Play; Stu Cncl; Hon Roll; NHS; Ntl Merit Ltr; Drama Clb; Yrbk Stf; Grankfurth Amer HS Eagle Acad Awd 85; Model NATO Clb 85; US Hstry Excptnl Achv Awd; U Of VA-RICHMOND; Accntng.

MARTIN, KARIN; San Jose La Salle HS; A P O Miami, FL; (Y); Art Clb; Drama Clb; English Clb; 4-H; Spanish Clb; Acpl Chr; Nwsp Rptr; Rep Stu Cncl; Im Socr; Church Yth Grp; Engl Awd 84; 1st Pl Sci Fair 84; Pub Rel.

MARTINDALE, RACHAEL; Torrejon American HS; Pensacola, FL; (Y); Aud/Vis; Church Yth Grp; Girl Scts; Office Aide; Red Cross Aide; Band; Chorus; Church Choir; Concert Band; Drm Mjr(t); Mst Tlntd SR Clss 85; Elizabeth Shoemaker Mem Awd For Mst Outstdng Music Stu 85; Hgh Acad Hnr 84-85; Pensacola JR Coll; Music.

MAY, SANDRA; Ramstein HS; APO New York, NY; (Y); 4/220; French Clb; Math Clb; Variety Show; Rep Jr Cls; Rep Sr Cls; Stu Cncl; Bsktbl; Socr; Sftbl; NHS; Cmbnd Schlrshp Fund Schlrshp 85; Acad All-Amer 84; US Achv Acad-Stu Cncl, Math, Sci, Ldrshp 84-85; U Of MD; Comp Sci.

MC CARTHY, KATHAN B; Ramstein HS; APO, NY; (Y); VP French Clb; Hosp Aide; Keywanettes; Band; Nwsp Stf; Lit Mag; VA Tech; Elem Educ.

MC GEHEE, SHANNON; London Central HS; England; (Y); 1/106; Red Cross Aide; Pres Varsity Clb; Drill Tm; School Musical; Rep Stu Cncl; Var L Bsktbl; Var L Vllybl; NHS; Pres Schlr; Val; Greenhand Common Ofcrs Wives Clb Schlrshp 85; Don T Burrows Awd Schl/Athl Awd 85; Outstndng Dormie Awd; TX A&M U; Bio-Engrng.

MC KINNIS, DARIN N; Canadian Acad; Troy, MI; (Y); 3/56; Computer Clb; Chorus; School Play; Symp Band; Var Bsbl; Var Socr; Wrstlng; High Hon Roll; Sci Awd 85; Mst Outstndng SR Awd 85; MI U; Aerspc Engr.

MIAZGA, PETER G; Ridley College; Remsen, NY; (Y); Boy Scts; CAP; Mathletes; ROTC; Drill Tm; Var Badmtn; Var Crs Cntry; JV Socr; Im Tennis; Hon Roll; Albany Schl Phrmcy; Phrmcy.

MIDDLETON, KAREN; American Schl In Aberdeen; Scotland; (Y); 1/31; Aud/Vis; Natl Beta Clb; Quiz Bowl; School Musical; High Hon Roll; NHS; Prfct Atten Awd; Val; Voice Dem Awd; Embry-Riddle Aeronaut U; Aviatn.

MILLER, MICHELLE K; International School Of Choueifa; United Arab Emeri; (Y); 2/7; French Clb; Speech Tm; School Musical; Yrbk Stf; Hon Roll; Med.

MINSHALL, SUZY; Aulendorf Gymnasim; Inkom, ID; (Y); Art Clb; Church Yth Grp; FHA; GAA; Concert Band; Pep Band; Trk; Hon Roll; Jr NHS; NHS; Cngrss-Bundestag Exch Pgm Scholar 84-85; Summr Hnrs Pgm ID ST U 84; Earlham Coll Merit Scholar 85; Earlham Coll IN; Politcs.

MORROW, LESLEE; Woodbridge American HS; Biloxi, MS; (Y); Church Yth Grp; Drama Clb; FCA; Natl Beta Clb; Teachers Aide; Varsity Clb; Church Choir; Yrbk Stf; Trs Frsh Cls; Var L Bsktbl; TX A&M; Acctng.

MULLIGAN, STEVEN J; Stuttgart AM HS; Apo New York, NY; (Y); 7/150; Debate Tm; German Clb; Key Clb; NFL; Ski Clb; Teachers Aide; Tennis; High Hon Roll; Hon Roll; NHS; Chllnge 84 Madrid Spain 84; Germ Am Sem Germ Govt 84; Most Outstndng Plyr Tens 85; Purdue; Engrng.

NESMITH, TRAVIS; American School In London; England; (Y); Church Yth Grp; Quiz Bowl; Spanish Clb; Var Bsktbl; JV Socr; Var Tennis; Var Vllybl; High Hon Roll; Hon Roll; Ntl Merit SF; Lbrl Arts.

NICHOLS, THEODORE H; Korea Christian Acad; Korea; (Y); Boy Scts; Church Yth Grp; Q&S; Band; Chorus; Church Choir; School Musical; School Play; Nwsp Rptr; L Bsktbl; Auburn U; Physics.

NOWLIN, ZACHARY; Frankfurt Am HS; Apo New York, NY; (Y); 5/360; Model UN; Nwsp Ed-Chief; Nwsp Rptr; Rep Sr Cls; Rep Stu Cncl; JV Tennis; High Hon Roll; Rep NHS; Pres Schlr; Delta Epsilon Phi Deutsche Ehrenverbindung 85; Pres Schlrshp 85; Outstdng Achv In Wrld Hstry Geo 83; Duke U; Librl Arts.

OLLIE, RUSSELL D; Wagner HS; APO San Francsco, CA; (Y); Pres Q&S; Boy Scts; VP Computer Clb; French Clb; Nwsp Stf; Lit Mag; Rep Soph Cls; Hon Roll; Prfct Atten Awd; Rep Frsh Cls; PVOT Stu Of Sem 84-85; Aerontcl Engrg.

PAPERA, KATHERINE; Kadena HS; APO San Fran, CA; (Y); French Clb; Teachers Aide; Nwsp Stf; Yrbk Stf; Pres Stu Cncl; JV Var Bsktbl; Var Powder Puff Ftbl; JV Trk; Cit Awd; NHS; MD U; Bus Mgmt.

PARRA, MARGOT; College Du Leman HS; Switzerland; (Y); Math Clb; Natl Beta Clb; Hon Roll; NHS; 96th Pcntl Verbal NMSQ Tst, 90th Mth NMSQ Tst 84-85; Stanford; Sci.

PELLERIN, DENISE; Louis J Robichaud HS; Canada; (Y); 3/31; Art Clb; Chess Clb; Church Yth Grp; Computer Clb; Awd Volntr Tutrng Proj 84; Hm Ec Certfd Babystr 82; Mt St Vincent U; Physiothrpy.

RAY, MELISSA A; Heidelberg American HS; A P O, NY; (Y); 36/140; Model UN; Varsity Clb; Yrbk Stf; Rep Stu Cncl; Capt Var Crs Cntry; Pom Pon; L Var Socr; L Var Trk; Crs Cntry Mst Val Rnr 83; Trk Mst Points Scrd 85; Crs Cntry Mst Competitive 84; U AZ; Gen.

RAYOS, MARIBEL; Nile C Kinnick HS; FPO Seattle, WA; (Y); Church Yth Grp; Rptr FBLA; Natl Beta Clb; Service Clb; Spanish Clb; High Hon Roll; Jr NHS; NHS; Spanish NHS; Computer Clb; Achvt Awd Acctng 84-85; Anchor Clb 83-85; FL ST; Comp Engr.

ROBINSON, MICHELLE L; Yokota HS; APO San Fran, CA; (Y); Church Yth Grp; Math Clb; Pep Clb; Teachers Aide; Yrbk Phtg; Var L Bsktbl; JV Cheerleading; Coach Actv; Var L Diving; Powder Puff Ftbl; Auburn U; Busnss.

ROGERS, ROBERT; General H H Arnold HS; APO, NY; (Y); Boy Scts; Church Yth Grp; Drama Clb; French Clb; ROTC; School Play; Stage Crew; Egl Sct 84; Educ Asstnce Assn Schlrshp 85; PA ST; Elec Engrng.

ROSENFELD, ALIZAH; The International Schl Of Geneva; Switzerland; (Y); Cmnty Wkr; Temple Yth Grp; Yrbk Stf; Mgr(s); Socr; Tennis; Hon Roll; Prfct Atten Awd; 1st Pl ST Hstry Prjct 85; Math.

SAMPSON, DANIELLE; W T Sampson HS; FBPO Norfolk, VA; (Y); Office Aide; Chorus; Lit Mag; Powder Puff Ftbl; High Hon Roll; Hon Roll; NHS; Spindrift Lit Magazine Awd 85; Bus.

SCHMIDT, KURT; Osterholz American HS; New York, NY; (Y); Boy Scts; Church Yth Grp; French Clb; Var Ftbl; Var Socr; TX A&M; Archit.

SCHREYER, STUART; J R Robson HS; Moffat, CO; (Y); Ski Clb; Rep Frsh Cls; Rep Soph Cls; Rep Jr Cls; Rep Sr Cls; VP Stu Cncl; L Bsktbl; L Ftbl; Ice Hcky; Hon Roll; Top Math Stu 84; Am Hist,Comp Sci Awd 84; U Southern CO; Comp Sci.

SCHUCHARD, BARBARA; St Albert HS; Bellflower, CA; (Y); JV Bsktbl; Acadmc Achvt Awd 83-84; Bldg.

SHELLABARGER, DOUGLAS; Kaiserslautern American HS; APO New York, NY; (Y); Varsity Clb; Socr; Hon Roll; FL ST U; Bus.

SHIPMAN, AMY; American Community Schl; Papillion, NE; (Y); Church Yth Grp; French Clb; Pep Clb; Chorus; Concert Band; Mrchg Band; Pep Band; Symp Band; Yrbk Stf; Var Cheerleading; FL ST U.

SNIDER, MELISA M; Taegu American Schl; APO San Fran, CA; (Y); 1/25; Nwsp Rptr; Sec Soph Cls; VP Jr Cls; Pres Stu Cncl; JV Var Cheerleading; Hon Roll; Jr NHS; NHS; Ntl Merit SF; FCA; T Awd Outstndng Schltc Ability; Outstndng Engl Stu Awd; Outstndng Sci Stu Awd; Elem Ed.

SOBALLE, THERESE; Kadena HS; FPO Seattle, WA; (Y); Church Yth Grp; Computer Clb; French Clb; Model UN; Concert Band; Yrbk Stf; Var Swmmng; High Hon Roll; Art Clb; Church Choir; Hnr Schlrshp 84-85; Hnrs Diplma 85; Rockford Coll; Pre-Med.

SPEARS, KIMBERLY A; Augsburg American HS; Apo, NY; (Y); 6/58; Church Yth Grp; Cmnty Wkr; Office Aide; Radio Clb; Red Cross Aide; ROTC; Drill Tm; Nwsp Rptr; High Hon Roll; Hon Roll; Outstndng AE-I Cadet AFJROTC 81-82; Sr Suprltve Mst Likely Succeed 84-85; Blue & Slvr Hnr Awd 84-85; City Coll Chicago; Eng HS Tchr.

SPRAY, ELLA K; Bitburg America HS; A P O, NY; (Y); 1/130; Pres Model UN; Pres Q&S; Concert Band; Yrbk Ed-Chief; Yrbk Phtg; Yrbk Stf; Lit Mag; Hon Roll; Jr NHS; Pres NHS; Lang.

STOUT, JOHNIE DENISE; W T Sampson HS; Bristol, VA; (Y); 4/35; Model UN; Spanish Clb; Rep Frsh Cls; Rep Soph Cls; Pres Jr Cls; Powder Puff Ftbl; L Sftbl; L Vllybl; Hon Roll; Jr NHS; Outstndng Bus Stu Of Yr 83-84; VA Intermnt Coll; Englsh.

SULLIVAN, DAVID J; Wagoner HS; APO San Fran, CA; (Y); 3/300; Church Yth Grp; Scholastic Bowl; Teachers Aide; Rep Frsh Cls; Rep Soph Cls; Pres Stu Cncl; Var JV Golf; Var JV Tennis; French Hon Soc; High Hon Roll; Pre-Med.

THOMAS, ANDRE; Wurzburg American HS; Hampton, VA; (Y); Church Yth Grp; JA; Model UN; Trs Spanish Clb; Hon Roll; Jr NHS; Ntl Merit Ltr; Sci Fair Hnrbl Mntn Chem 82; Spc Rec TAG Smmr Sci Enrchmnt 82; Div Spprt Comm 3rd Inf 84; Howard U; Chem.

TURNEY, MARK; Faith Acad; Manila; (Y); Church Yth Grp; Office Aide; Teachers Aide; Church Choir; Orch; School Musical; Im Sftbl; Var Wt Lftg; Var Wrstlng; High Hon Roll; 3rd Pl Champnshp Wrstlng 84-85; SW MO ST U; Ed.

VAN BRAMER, JOHN; American Interntl Schl Of The Hauge; The Netherlands; (Y); Boy Scts; Church Yth Grp; French Clb; Quiz Bowl; Scholastic Bowl; Var L Bsbl; Var L Bsktbl; Var L Ftbl; Hon Roll; OH St U; Elect Engrng.

VEENSTRA, ALEXANDER A OLLIE; Justice Von Libilung Gymnasium HS; Brooklyn, NY; (Y); Boy Scts; Church Yth Grp; JA; Band; Mrchg Band; Orch; Symp Band; JV Ftbl; JV Wrstlng; Hon Roll; Sci.

VENEGAS, ADRIANA E; American HS; Edo De Mexico; (Y); 43/100; Spanish Clb; Nwsp Stf; Hon Roll; NHS; Prfct Atten Awd; Hardin Simmons; Hstry.

VOLLERO, LISA D; Vicenza American HS; Apo New York, NY; (Y); 3/54; Pres Drama Clb; VP Thesps; Ed Lit Mag; Rep Stu Cncl; L Trk; Stat Wrstlng; Bausch & Lomb Sci Awd; High Hon Roll; NHS; Pres Schlr; 4 Yr Army ROTC Scholar 85; Locl Awd 85; Rensselaer Polytech; Engrng.

WALDEN, ANGELA; American Community Schl; Houston, TX; (Y); 78/220; Dance Clb; FBLA; Pep Clb; Thesps; Band; Chorus; Concert Band; Swing Chorus; Cheerleading; Hon Roll; Miss JR Ebone 1st Pl 84; 1st Pl In Creatv Wrtng Shrt Stry For 2nd Grdrs 85; 1st Pl In Sci Fair 82; U Of Houston; Psych.

WALL, KARLA AMY; Balboa HS; Rep Of Panama; (Y); Girl Scts; Thesps; Chorus; Variety Show; Sec Stu Cncl; Med.

WALSH, FRANCIS PAUL; Woodbridge American HS; A P O New York, NY; (Y); 3/50.

WATSON, JEFF; Stavanger American Schl; Norway; (Y); Church Yth Grp; Natl Beta Clb; Church Choir; Concert Band; Trs Soph Cls; Trs Stu Cncl; Var L Ftbl; Var L Trk; NEDT Awd; Opt Clb Awd; Sprts Med.

WEEDER, TAMI; William T Sampson JR-SR HS; Fbpo Norfolk, VA; (Y); 1/32; Scholastic Bowl; Band; School Play; Stage Crew; Variety Show; Rep Jr Cls; Var Powder Puff Ftbl; High Hon Roll; Sec NHS; Rep Stu Cncl; Brigham Young U Smmr Schlrs Acad Partcpnt 83; Pres Clssrm Yng Amer 85; Math & Sci Hnr Stdnt Ed Trp 85.

WING, DAN; Frankfurt American HS; Apo New York, NY; (Y); Trs FBLA; Computer Clb; Teachers Aide; Nwsp Stf; Natl Ski Ptrl 85; Comp Sci.

WRIGHT, CYNDI; Stavanger American Schl; Stavanger Norway; (Y); Chorus; Stage Crew; Variety Show; Nwsp Stf; Yrbk Stf; Var Cheerleading; Var Gym; Hon Roll; Pep Clb; Nwsp Rptr; 3rd Pl Sci Fair Awds 82-83; Top 2 Per-Cent On NEDT 83; Bus.

CONNECTICUT

Aafedt, Daniel R
Windsor HS
Windsor, CT

Abbott, Sheryl
Daniel HS
Madison, CT

Accurso, Ann Marie
Saint Mary HS
Greenwich, CT

Adam, Lisa
Trumbull HS
Trumbull, CT

Adamo, M Liss
Saint Bernard HS
Westerly, RI

Adams, Cindy
Farmington HS
Unionville, CT

Adelberg, Marc E
Enfield HS
Enfield, CT

Akoury, Lisa
Masuk HS
Monroe, CT

Algiere, Michele
St Bernard HS
Bradford, RI

Allen, Julie M
Terryville HS
Plymouth, CT

Alpert, Lauren
Amity Regional SR
Woodbridge, CT

Amaker, Karen
Richard C Lee HS
New Haven, CT

Amaral, Craig
Notre Dame
Catholic HS
Bpt, CT

Ambrusco, John
Notre Dame HS
W Haven, CT

Amendola, Scott
Danbury HS
Danbury, CT

Amodei, Victor
North Haven HS
N Haven, CT

Anderson, Erik
East Lyme HS
East Lyme, CT

Anderson, Kellie
Litchfield HS
Litchfield, CT

Annunziata,
Christina M
Cheshire Acad
Cheshire, CT

Ansaldo, James
Guilford HS
Guilford, CT

Anzivine, Deanna
Crosby HS
Waterbury, CT

Archambault,
Danielle
St Bernard HS
Lisbon, CT

Archambault,
Marianne
Tourtellotte
Memorial HS
N Grosvenordale

Armstrong,
Jacqueline
Staples HS
Westport, CT

Asbjornsen, Heidi
Pomperaug HS
Southbury, CT

Ashby, Karen
The Masters Schl
West Hartford, CT

Ashe, Lorraine
Holy Cross HS
Waterbury, CT

Avery, Robert
Central Catholic HS
Norwalk, CT

Baboff, Amy
Amity Regional SR
Bethany, CT

Bailey, Susan L
Southington HS
Southington, CT

Baldo, Renee
North Haven HS
N Haven, CT

Baldwin, Sheree
Lenore
Stratford HS
Stratford, CT

Baldwin, Steven
Robert E Fitch SR
Groton, CT

Barbee, Jr Donald C
Brien Mc Mahon
Norwalk, CT

Barber, Diane
Manchester HS
Manchester, CT

Barber, Scott
Westhill HS
Stamford, CT

Barker, John
Tourtellotte
Memorial HS
Thompson, CT

Barrett, Debbie
Thomaston HS
Thomaston, CT

Bartolotta, Lisa
St Joseph HS
Ansonia, CT

Bassett, Todd
North Haven HS
N Haven, CT

Bastrzycki, Stephan
Northwestern
Reginal No 7
Collinsville, CT

Bates, Susan M
Lyman Hall HS
Wallingford, CT

Battaglino, Annette
C
Shelton HS
Shelton, CT

Baum, Jr Henry T
Daniel Hand HS
Madison, CT

Becher, Thomas
Greenwich HS
Greenwich, CT

Beckenstein,
Michele
Guilford HS
Guilford, CT

Bedard, Donna
East Catholic HS
E Hartford, CT

Beesley, Jr Neil
Notre Dame HS
W Haven, CT

Beezel, Charles M
Shelton HS
Huntington, CT

Begg, Michael
Holy Cross HS
Waterbury, CT

Belcher, Dana
Norwalk HS
Norwalk, CT

Belcher, Liama
Thomas Snell
Weaver HS
Hartford, CT

Bell, Kenneth
Southington HS
Plantsville, CT

Bellitto, Robert
Fairfield College
Prep School
Fairfield, CT

Belsito, Karin
Tolland HS
Tolland, CT

Bender, Shelly
North Haven HS
N Haven, CT

Benoit, Kenneth
Warren F Kaynor
Regnl Voc Tec
Watertown, CT

Benson, Heather
Staples HS
Westport, CT

Bequary, Christine
Litchfield HS
Northfield, CT

Berg, Scott M
Southington HS
Southington, CT

Bernard, David
Fairfield College
Prep Schl
Bridgeport, CT

Bernard, Marcel
Weaver HS
Hartford, CT

Berry, Dawn Marie
St Bernard HS
Norwich, CT

Bianchi, Mark
Amity Regional SR
Woodbridge, CT

Bibeau, Paula
Windham
Regional-Voc Tech
Willimantic, CT

Binder, Darren
Todd
Avon HS
Avon, CT

Blake, Robert
Westhill HS
Stamford, CT

Blount, Robert
Notre Dame HS
New Haven, CT

Blundo, Scott
Holy Cross HS
Woodbury, CT

Body, Stephen
Holy Cross HS
Oakville, CT

Bogues, Sharon
Danbury HS
Danbury, CT

Bohannon, Bobby
New Canaan HS
New Canaan, CT

Boiano, Daniel
Holy Cross HS
Waterbury, CT

Bolduc, Joel
Windham HS
Willimantic, CT

Bolduc, John
Windham HS
Willimantic, CT

Boles, Matthew
Trumbull HS
Trumbull, CT

Bosak, Anne
Sacred Heart Acad
Stamford, CT

Bowen, Melissa
Seymour HS
Seymour, CT

Bowers, Ray
Derby HS
Derby, CT

Bowler, Jacqueline
St Marys HS
W Haven, CT

Bradley, Mark
Central HS
Bridgeport, CT

Bradley, Trish
Danbury HS
Danbury, CT

Braga, Kerry
Ellington HS
Ellington, CT

Breading, Sandra
Naugatuck HS
Naugatuck, CT

Breault, David
Putham HS
Putnam, CT

Breton, Steven
St Paul Catholic HS
Bristol, CT

Bright, Renee
The Cheshire Acad
Cheshire, CT

Brody, Bridget
Thomaston HS
Thomaston, CT

Broesch, Kathryn
Andrew Warde HS
Fairfield, CT

Broughton, Jacquelyn
Francis T Maloney
Meriden, CT

Brovero, Michael
Griswold HS
Norwich, CT

Brown, Kim
Rockville HS
Manchester, CT

Brown, Matthew H
Loomis Chaffee Schl
West Hartford, CT

Brown, Michael
Trumball HS
Trumbull, CT

Bruchac, Tori
Joel Barlow HS
W Redding, CT

Bryan, Amy E
Wilton HS
Wilton, CT

Bryk, Barbara
St Bernard HS
Uncasville, CT

Buck, Kathleen S
The Morgan HS
Clinton, CT

Buckley, Patrick
Berlin HS
Kensington, CT

Buismato, Lisa Michelle
Nonnewaug HS
Woodbury, CT

Butkiewicz, Kristin
West Haven HS
W Haven, CT

Cacace, Christina
East Catholic HS
Coventry, CT

Caiaze, Robert
Plainville HS
Plainville, CT

Cain, Monique Renee
James Hillhouse HS
New Haven, CT

Campagna, Joseph
Berlin HS
Kensington, CT

Campoli, Debbie
Amity SR HS
Woodbridge, CT

Campos, Jose
Naugatuck HS
Naugatuck, CT

Canal, Janeen
Tolland HS
Tolland, CT

Capasso, Maria
St Marys HS
New Haven, CT

Capitani, Dina R
Old Saybrook HS
Old Saybrook, CT

Capobianco, Thomas
Plainfield HS
Sterling, CT

Carbone, Mario
Windham HS
Willimantic, CT

Cardone, Kellie
Notre Dame Acad
Bethlehem, CT

Carmon, Sheila
Wilbur Cross HS
New Haven, CT

Carreras, Ismael E
William H Hall HS
W Hartford, CT

Carroll, Sean
Stratford HS
Stratford, CT

Carrozzo, Chris
Northwestern Regional No 7 HS
Winsted, CT

Carter, Stephen
Jonathan Law HS
Milford, CT

Castellano, Lisa
Norwalk HS
Norwalk, CT

Castonguay, Lisa
New Milford HS
New Milford, CT

Cavallaro, Mark
Notre Dame HS
West Haven, CT

Cenkus, Tara
Cheshire HS
Cheshire, CT

Cerino, Scott
Trumbull HS
Trumbull, CT

Chakmakjian, Carmen
Notre Dame Catholic HS
Bridgeport, CT

Chambers, Deirdre
Weaver HS
Hartford, CT

Chambers, Kelly Ann
J M Writht Technical HS
Stamford, CT

Chamblin, Beth
East Lyme HS
E Lyme, CT

Chapman, Kenneth D
Simsbury HS
W Sims, CT

Chapman, Roger L
Guilford HS
Guilford, CT

Chary, Kasthury
Stamford HS
Stamford, CT

Cherian, Beena
Sacred Heart Acad
Old Greenwich, CT

Chevalier, Judith A
Hamden HS
Hamden, CT

Chiappinelli, John P
Central Catholic HS
S Norwalk, CT

Chiat, Jonathan
Trumbull HS
Trumbull, CT

Chicoine, Denise
East Catholic HS
E Hartford, CT

Chin, Camille A
The Gunnery HS
Brooklyn, NY

Chmielecki, Sandra
St Bernard HS
Taftville, CT

Christian, Melissa
T Orrington HS
Torrington, CT

Christie, Jeffrey
Holy Cross HS
Watertown, CT

Chupka, Lee
Torrington HS
Torrington, CT

Chupka, Wendy
Torrington HS
Torrington, CT

Cipriano, Melissa
Crosby HS
Waterbury, CT

Clark, Kristen Leigh
St Bernard HS
Ledyard, CT

Clark, Todd
Putnam HS
Putnam, CT

Cleary, Annie
Trumbull HS
Trumbull, CT

Close, Glen S
Guilford HS
Guilford, CT

Cobbol, Suzanne
Westover Schl
Naugatuck, CT

Cody, Alisa
Farmington HS
Farmington, CT

Colburn, Kristyn
Branford HS
Branford, CT

Collings, Abigail
Trumbull HS
Trumbull, CT

Collins, Amanda C
Saint Mary HS
Greenwich, CT

Colucci, Anthony R
St Joseph HS
Ansonia, CT

Commander, Jane
Old Saybrook SR
Old Saybrook, CT

Conant, Eileen
Sacred Heart Acad
Stamford, CT

Conelli, Francine
Sacred Heart Acad
Branford, CT

Connell, Kim O
Trumbull HS
Trumbull, CT

Coratola, John A
Lewis S Mills HS
Harwinton, CT

Corcoran, Jeffrey M
New Fairfield HS
New Fairfield, CT

Cordone, Laura
Notre Dame Acad
Wolcott, CT

Cosgriff, Catherine
A
Daniel Hand HS
Madison, CT

Costello, Eric
Choate Rosemary
Hall HS
Old Saybrook, CT

Costello, Gregory
Southington HS
Plantsville, CT

Coutts, Cynthia
Shelton HS
Shelton, CT

Coutu, Bonnie
Windham HS
Willimantic, CT

Cox, Catherine Mary
Daniel Hand HS
Madison, CT

Coyne, David
The Morgan Schl
Clinton, CT

Coyne, Kerry
Norwalk HS
E Norwalk, CT

Craig, Joseph
Bethel HS
Bethel, CT

Culmone, Jeffrey
Notre Dame HS
Milford, CT

Currie, Mary
Granby Memorial
W Granby, CT

Cusanelli, Diane
Lynn
West Haven HS
W Haven, CT

D Agostini, Lisa
Stamford HS
Stamford, CT

D Amaro, Michael
Shelton HS
Shelton, CT

Damamian, Beth M
The Morgan Schl
Clinton, CT

Dang, Loan Phuong
Kinswood-Oxford
E Hartford, CT

Darcy, Carey-Anne
Cheshire HS
Cheshire, CT

Dauphinais, Debby
Killingly HS
Brooklyn, CT

Davidson, Susanne
A
Northwest Catholic
Hartford, CT

Davidson, III
William F
Fairfield Prep
Stratford, CT

Davis, Carla Ann
Sacred Heart Acad
New Haven, CT

Davis, Kimberly
Weaver HS
Hartford, CT

Davis, Mary-Beth
Bulkeley HS
Hartford, CT

De Bonee, Jeffrey
Avon Old Farms
Hampden, MA

De Brigita, Rhonda
St Marys HS
W Haven, CT

De Capua, Sarah
Shelton HS
Shelton, CT

De Gasperis,
Christine M
Berlin HS
Kensington, CT

De Maio, Theodore
A
Wilbur L Cross HS
New Haven, CT

Debernardo, Caren
Trumball HS
Trumbull, CT

Debo, Sylvia
Mary Immaculate
New Britain, CT

Decaprio, Mary
Evelyn
Sacred Heart Acad
Hamden, CT

Defeo, Renee
Windham HS
W Willington, CT

Delio, Karla
Central Catholic HS
Norwalk, CT

Deluca, Susie
Sacred Heart Acad
Stamford, CT

Demjan, Tabitha
Notre Dame
Catholic HS
Bridgeprort, CT

Denis, Karen
Joseph A Foran HS
Milford, CT

Dennis, Ronald
Central HS
Bridgeport, CT

Dervin, Karen
Pomperaug HS
Southbury, CT

Dery, Lisa
Putnam HS
Putnam, CT

Desrosiers, Jeanette
Naugatuck HS
Naugatuck, CT

Devaney, Kathleen
Guilford HS
Guilford, CT

Devino, Sara
Holy Cross HS
Oxford, CT

Devivo, Joseph M
King Schl
Wilton, CT

Di Buccio, Anthony
V
Notre Dame HS
Branford, CT

Di Elsi, Dawn Marie
St Marys HS
New Haven, CT

Di Mauro, Vanessa
Justine
South Catholic HS
Rocky Hill, CT

Dinenno, Denise
Sacred Heart Acad
West Haven, CT

Dinho, Alan
Danbury HS
Danbury, CT

Dione, Michelle
The Morgan Schl
Clinton, CT

Diorio, Geri A
Notre Dame
Catholic HS
Bridgeport, CT

Divittis, Jennie
Holy Cross HS
Wolcott, CT

Dizigan, Mark
St Bernard HS
Waterford, CT

Dobkins, David
Watertown HS
Oakville, CT

Doering, Brett
Portland HS
Portland, CT

Dolan, Walter
North Haven SR HS
North Haven, CT

Dollak, Melissa
Wm H Hall HS
W Hartford, CT

Dolyak, Daniel
Shelton HS
Shelton, CT

Donovan, Kelley
North Branford HS
North Branford, CT

Donovan, Lauren Anne
Our Lady Of The Angels Acad
Somers, CT

Dooley, Patrick J
Shelton HS
Shelton, CT

Dorsey, Jennifer
Sacred Heart Acad
New Haven, CT

Doughty, Bonnie
Plainville HS
Plainville, CT

Douglas, Kathy
Westhill HS
Stamford, CT

Doukas, David
Mark T Sheehan HS
Wallingford, CT

Dowd, David
Enrico Fermi HS
Enfield, CT

Doyle, Sean
Notre Dame HS
N Haven, CT

Driscoll, Kevin
Danbury HS
Danbury, CT

Drugan, Danielle Elizabeth
Lyme Old Lyme HS
Old Lyme, CT

Du Bac, Bryan David
Trumbull HS
Trumbull, CT

Dube, Jennifer
Tolland HS
Tolland, CT

Dubik, Anna Lesia
New Britain HS
New Britain, CT

Ducharme, Lori
Marianapolis Prep
Douglas, MA

Duda, Wendy
Notre Dame Catholic HS
Easton, CT

Duer, Kelly
Holy Cross HS
Wolcott, CT

Durkin, Ian
Brookfield HS
Brookfield, CT

Durwin, Karen
Trumbull HS
Trumbull, CT

Dutertre, Albert
Stamford HS
Stamford, CT

Dutko, Jill
Lyman Hall HS
Wallingford, CT

Dykema, Erik P
New Canaan HS
New Canaan, CT

Eckbreth, Kelly Anne
Glastonbury HS
Glastonbury, CT

Edwards, Jenine
Hillhouse HS
New Haven, CT

Eisman, Hannah
West Haven HS
W Haven, CT

Elkow, Christopher
Ridgefield HS
Ridgefield, CT

Ellington, David
Saint Bernard HS
Stonington, CT

English, Susan
Bethel HS
Bethel, CT

Erickson, Troy
Wethersfield HS
Wethersfield, CT

Erlenheim, Judith
Trumbull HS
Trumbull, CT

Espinoza, Sheila Jeanette
New Britain HS
New Britain, CT

Esposito, Lisa
Trumbull HS
Trumbull, CT

Esposito, Michele
North Branford HS
Northford, CT

Estelle, Diane
St Bernard HS
Groton Long Point, CT

Evans, Brett
Guilford HS
Guilford, CT

Eveland, Jeffrey
Greenwich HS
Riverside, CT

Fagan, Dawn
Jonathan Law HS
Milford, CT

Fallis, Barbara
Southington HS
Southington, CT

Faulkner, Prescott
Simsbury HS
W Simsbury, CT

Fedak, Kimberly
Stamford Catholic
Stamford, CT

Feeney, Joseph
St Bernard HS
New London, CT

Ferguson, Brian
St Mary HS
Greenwich, CT

Ferrara, Michelle
Brookfield HS
Brookfield Ctr, CT

Ferraro, Rosanna
St Mary HS
New Haven, CT

Filingeri, Deborah-Lee
St Joseph HS
Huntington, CT

Fillion, Michael R
St Bernard HS
Noank, CT

Finnemore, Michelle
Plainfield HS
Dayville, CT

Flanagan, Clare
St Bernard HS
Norwich, CT

Flathers, Scott
Guilford HS
Guilford, CT

Foellmer, Oliver
Guilford HS
Guilford, CT

Fogelberg, Camilla
Notre Dame Central
Bridgeport, CT

Foley, Jennifer
Mancheter HS
Manchester, CT

Foley, John B
St Thomas More HS
Plan Dome, NY

Foley, Sean T
New Fairfield HS
New Fairfield, CT

Fonicello, Susan P
Guilford HS
Guilford, CT

Fonovic, Lisa
Masuk HS
Monroe, CT

Foreman, Lesa
Bethel HS
Bethel, CT

Forte, Francis
Notre Dame HS
Hamden, CT

Fowler, Kimberly
Southington HS
Plantsville, CT

Franceschet, John
North Haven HS
N Haven, CT

Frankes, Deborah E
Amity Regional HS
Woodbridge, CT

Fratarcangeli, Kenneth
Jonathan Law HS
Milford, CT

Frattarola, Mark W
Greenwich HS
Greenwich, CT

Fritsche, Wayne R
Danbury HS
Danbury, CT

Fritz, Chuck
The Morgan Schl
Clinton, CT

Froliger, Jo Ann
Naugatuck HS
Naugatuck, CT

Fuller, Katrina
Bassick HS
Bridgeport, CT

Furbert, Traci A
Wilbur Cross HS
New Haven, CT

Fusco, John
George J Penney HS
E Hartford, CT

Futtner, Jeff
East Hartford HS
E Hartford, CT

Gagliardi, Gerard
Notre Dame HS
Hamden, CT

Gagne, Bernadette
Jonathan Law HS
Milford, CT

Gallagher, Adrienne C
Greenwich HS
Cos Cob, CT

Gambardella, Lynn
Hamden HS
Hamden, CT

Gannon, Patrick M
Danbury HS
Danbury, CT

Gans, Jennifer
Weston HS
Weston, CT

Garcia, Graciella
Saint Marys HS
Hamden, CT

Garden, Caroline
Miss Porters Schl
Lexington, KY

Gaudio, Craig T
Stamford HS
Stamford, CT

Gauss, Michael H
The Robert Fitch
Gales Ferry, CT

Gay, Susan
Norwalk HS
Norwalk, CT

Gazdik, Ronald J
Joel Barlow HS
Redding, CT

Gedansky, Beth
Amity Regional HS
Woodbridge, CT

Gemma, Michelle
Robert E Fitch SR
Groton, CT

Geoghegan, Noreen
Northwest Catholic
West Hartford, CT

Gesseck, Stefanie Lynn
Saint Margarets-Mc Ternan HS
Cheshire, CT

Gettles, Shannon
Wilby HS
Waterbury, CT

Giaimo, Jr Edward M
North Haven HS
North Haven, CT

Gibbons, Kristine
Immaculate HS
Brookfield, CT

Gilbert, II Gregory
Greenwich HS
Old Greenwich, CT

Gillis, La Chale
New London HS
New London, CT

Gilloren, Kimberly
St Marys HS
Derby, CT

Ginch, Barry
Bethel HS
Bethel, CT

Ginsburg, Mitchell
Bloomfield HS
Bloomfield, CT

Glenn, Lindsay
Norwalk HS
Norwalk, CT

Glenn, Lisa
Holy Cross HS
Waterbury, CT

Gluch, Anna
South Catholic HS
Hartford, CT

Golba, Cathleen
John F Kennedy HS
Waterbury, CT

Golub, Neil
Norwalk HS
Norwalk, CT

Goodman, Lori
New Fairfield HS
New Fairfld, CT

Gordon, Julie
Bethel HS
Bethel, CT

Gornish, Alanna E
William Hall HS
W Hartford, CT

Goshgarian, Mark
Danbury HS
Danbury, CT

Gouthier, Jonathan J
The Gilbert Schl
Winsted, CT

Graboski, Paul
Oliver Wolcott Technical Schl
Torrington, CT

Granskog, Cindy
Stamford HS
Stamford, CT

Grant, Cassandra
New Britain SR HS
New Britain, CT

Gray, Christopher E
Cheshire HS
Cheshire, CT

Greco, Jay
Notre Dame HS
New Haven, CT

Greene, Belinda
Bassick HS
Bridgeport, CT

Greenia, Laurie
Amity Regional HS
New Haven, CT

Grote, Walter E
Simsbury HS
Simsbury, CT

Guiner, Stephanie
Sacred Heart Acad
E Norwalk, CT

Haase, Donna
Windsor HS
Windsor, CT

Hackett, Ellen
Sacred Heart Acad
West Haven, CT

Hall, Susan E
Andrew Warde HS
Fairfield, CT

Halpin, Elizabeth
Greenwich HS
Greenwich, CT

Haman, Lynn
Southington HS
Southington, CT

Hamann, James B
Hatchkiss Schl
Hummelstown, PA

Hamelin, Wendy
Kaynor Regional Vo-Tech HS
Wolcott, CT

Hamilton, Dennis
Avon Old Farms
New Britain, CT

Hammie, Sheila
Wilbur Cross HS
New Haven, CT

Handrinos, Peter
Fairfield College Prep Schl
Norwalk, CT

Hanna, John
Staples HS
Westport, CT

Hanratty, Mark G
Greenwich HS
Greenwich, CT

Hansen, Mark
Shelton HS
Shelton, CT

Hanson, Edward
Jonathan Law HS
Milford, CT

Hargreaves, Beth
Trumbull HS
Trumbull, CT

Harmon, Warren
Manchester HS
Manchester, CT

Harris, Andrew
New Canaan HS
New Canaan, CT

Harris, Ericka
James Hillhouse HS
New Haven, CT

Harris, Tia
Suffield HS
West Suffield, CT

Hartung, Nancy
Notre Dame Catholic HS
Trumbull, CT

Hartwell, Robert
Plainfield HS
Sterling, CT

Hathaway, John
Windham Reg
Vo-Tec Schl
Lebanon, CT

Hattier, Tom
Masuk HS
Monroe, CT

Hatzinikolas, Christina
East Hartford HS
E Hartford, CT

Havourd, Victoria L
Shelton HS
Shelton, CT

Havrilko, Johanna
Shelton HS
Shelton, CT

Haynos, Judith Ellen
Newtown HS
Newtown, CT

Heap, Shannon Michael
New London HS
New London, CT

Hebert, Dennis
Norwich Free Acad
Norwich, CT

Helt, David
New Fairfield HS
New Fairfield, CT

Henderson, Amelia
Richard C Lee HS
New Haven, CT

Henry, Susan
East Hartford HS
E Hartford, CT

Herman, Marianne C
Trumbull HS
Trumbull, CT

Herring, Lorri
Platt HS
Meriden, CT

Hickcox, Katharine J
William H Hall HS
W Hartford, CT

Hildreth, Scott
Ste Bernard HS
Norwich, CT

Hoffman, Christine
Kingswood-Oxford
Bloomfield, CT

Holness, Christopher
Daniel Hand HS
Madison, CT

Holt, John
Hotchkiss Schl
St Albans, VT

Horensavitz, Tammy Anne
West Haven HS
Hamden, CT

Hoyt, Sheri
Norwalk HS
Norwalk, CT

Hribko, Richard A
Notre Dame HS
East Haven, CT

Hristov, Jr Peter
Notre Dame Catholic HS
Bridgeport, CT

Huerta, Anna
Stamford HS
Stamford, CT

Hughes, Andrea
Sacred Heart Acad
Derby, CT

Hull, Harold
Plainfield HS
Moosup, CT

Hunt, Iris
Kolbe Cathedral HS
Bridgeport, CT

Hunter, Maureen
R H A M HS
Amston, CT

Hunter, Yolanda
Hillhouse HS
Hamden, CT

Hurlbert, Daniel
Coginchaug Regional
Durham, CT

Hurst, IV Victor W
Amity Regional HS
Woodbridge, CT

Hussey, III Richard
Trumbull HS
Trumbull, CT

Hwang, Helen
Glastonbury HS
Glastonbury, CT

Iannucci, Sherry
Sacred Heart Acad
W Haven, CT

Inger, Marc
Lewis S Mills HS
Harwinton, CT

Iovanne, Richard
Notre Dame HS
New Haven, CT

Isaac, Paul
Shelton HS
Huntington, CT

Isaacs, Meredith
Trumbull HS
Trumbull, CT

Jachimiec, Halina
Bulkeley HS
Hartford, CT

Jankowski, Christa
East Catholic HS
Bristol, CT

Jansen, John M
Joseph A Foran HS
Milford, CT

Jaronczyk, Jennifer
Holy Cross HS
Ansonia, CT

Jeannin, Jeffrey
Warren F Kaynor
Oakville, CT

Jenacaro, Diana
Shelton HS
Shelton, CT

Jenkins, Gail
Pomperaug Regional
Southbury, CT

Jennings, Angela
Thomas Snell Weaver HS
Hartford, CT

Johnson, Erik
The Hotchkiss Schl
Madison, WI

Johnson, Jennifer
St Bernard HS
Groton, CT

Johnson, Mark
Stamford HS
Stamford, CT

Jones, John
Danbury HS
Danbury, CT

Jones, John
East Haven HS
E Haven, CT

Jones, Kimberly F
South Windsor HS
S Windsor, CT

Jones, Michele D
Choate Rosemary Hall HS
Queens Village, NY

Juhasz, Susan
Sacred Heart Acad
N Haven, CT

Juleson, Raymond
Manchester HS
Manchester, CT

Jung, Marlene Doris
Granby Memorial
Granby, CT

Karagiannis, Ourania
East Hartford HS
East Hartford, CT

Karas, Judith Anne
Westhill HS
Stamford, CT

Karcher, Beth
Trumbull HS
Trumbull, CT

Karcher, Colleen
Shelton HS
Shelton, CT

Katan, Joshua
Lyme-Oldlyme HS
South Lyme, CT

Katz, Rachel A
Avon HS
Avon, CT

Keefe, Kelley Marie
Glastonbury HS
Glastonbury, CT

Keene, Gretchen M
Trumbull HS
Trumbull, CT

Keeshan, Ralph Timothy
The Forman Schl
Litchfield, CT

Keilhauer, Catalina
Miss Porters Schl
Hingham, MA

Keish, Brian F
Glastonbury HS
Glastonbury, CT

Keiss, Aija
Manchester HS
Manchester, CT

Kellett, Mary Jane
Shelton HS
Shelton, CT

Kelley, Edward
Ridgefield HS
Ridgefield, CT

Kelley, Tim
East Catholic HS
Manchester, CT

Kennedy, Dennis
Killingly HS
Wauregan, CT

Kennedy, Robert H
Danbury HS
Danbury, CT

Kenney, Jr Thomas J
Holy Cross HS
Waterbury, CT

Kerrigan, Richard K
Montville HS
Chicago, IL

Kertesz, Lynn
Ridgefield HS
Ridgefield, CT

Khan, Tara E
Staples HS
Westport, CT

Kiczyinski, Matt
Branford HS
Branford, CT

Killeen, Mary Elizabeth
Holy Cross HS
Waterbury, CT

Kimbleton, Kern
Trumbull HS
Trumbull, CT

Kinsella, Leanne
Brookfield HS
Brookfield, CT

Kirby, Carolyn
Conard HS
W Hartford, CT

Kirch, Susan Ann
Stafford HS
Stafford Sprgs, CT

Klimek, Christine
Central Catholic HS
Norwalk, CT

Kluess, Courtney R
Ridgefield HS
Ridgefield, CT

Knox, Daren
Oliver Wolcott Reg
Torrington, CT

Kohl, Michelle
Manchester HS
Manchester, CT

Kohli, Anuj
Danbury HS
Danbury, CT

Komarowska, Agnes
Norwalk HS
Norwalk, CT

Koperwhats, Kathy
Stratford HS
Stratford, CT

Kordys, Cynthia
Southington HS
Southington, CT

Koren, Edna
Ledyard HS
Ledyard, CT

Kramer, Marc
Andrew Warde HS
Fairfield, CT

Kriz, John E
Trumbull HS
Trumbull, CT

Krupnikoff, Henry
Avon Old Farms
W Hartford, CT

Kubis, John
Stafford HS
Stafford Springs, CT

Kuhn, Susan
Rockville HS
Vernon, CT

L Heureux, Kimberly
Southington HS
Southington, CT

La Barre, Brenda Jean
Griswold HS
Jewett City, CT

La France, Cassandra Joyce
Terryville HS
Terryville, CT

La Vecchia, Antoinette
Darien HS
Darien, CT

Lamar, Rodney
Weaver HS
Hartford, CT

Lambert, Elizabeth
Waterford HS
Waterford, CT

Lamy, David
East Catholic HS
Vernon, CT

Lang, Marcia
St Bernard HS
Lebanon, CT

Lange, Scott
Danbury HS
Danbury, CT

Lange, Shelley
Cheshire Acad
Wallingford, CT

Lanza, John
East Lyme HS
Niantic, CT

Larese, Jack P
Mark T Sheehan HS
Wallingford, CT

Larkham, Robert
Norwich Free Acad
Baltic, CT

Larkin, Holly
Notre Dame Acad
Oakville, CT

Lathrop, Pamela
Saint Bernard HS
Bozrah, CT

Lavanga, Daniel A
New Fairfield HS
New Fairfield, CT

Lawlor, IV James R
Holy Cross HS
Waterbury, CT

Layton, Christine
Newington HS
Newington, CT

Le, Trang
Central HS
Bridgeport, CT

Le Clerc, Marjorie S
Stamford HS
Stamford, CT

Le Fort, James D
Southington HS
Southington, CT

Leahan, John J M
Suffield HS
Suffield, CT

Lee, Jerome Peter Haddam
Killingworth HS
Killingworth, CT

Lee, Suyin
Amity Regional SR
Orange, CT

Lefebvre, Timothy
Oliver Wolcott
Winsted, CT

Lehmann, Steven
Oliver Wolcott Tech
Winsted, CT

Lengyel, Lisa
Saint Marys HS
E Haven, CT

Leuteritz, Eric
Simsbury HS
Simsbury, CT

Levin, David M
William Hall HS
W Hartford, CT

Lewis, Jennifer
Mark T Sheehan HS
Wallingford, CT

Lewis, Kimberly
Baptist Bible Acad
Waterford, CT

Libano, Celeste Ann
Coginchaug Regional
Durham, CT

Lieb, James R
Fairfield College
Huntington, CT

Ligouri, Tina
Masuk HS
Monroe, CT

Lillis, Geraldine
St Marys HS
Hamden, CT

Limbacher, Jr Richard B
Greenwich HS
Greenwich, CT

Ljungaren, Deborah
St Marys HS
N Haven, CT

Locker, Michael C
Westhill HS
Stamford, CT

Loum, Jeannine
Seymour HS
Seymour, CT

Lovejoy, Todd
Danbury HS
Danbury, CT

Lowney, Mark
Amity Regional HS
Orange, CT

Lozada, Stephanie
Central HS
Bridgeport, CT

Lubas, Mark
Wethersfield HS
Wethersfield, CT

Lucasiewicz, Amy
Wamogo Regional
Morris, CT

Ludwig, Deborah A
Brien Mc Mahon
Norwalk, CT

Luning, Jonathon T
New Milford HS
Sherman, CT

Lussier, Christine
Newington HS
Newington, CT

Lyon, Rebecca
Staples HS
Westport, CT

Lyons, Karen
Central Catholic HS
East Norwalk, CT

Mac Donald, Sarah
William H Hall HS
W Hartford, CT

Mac Dowell, Melissa
Southington HS
Southington, CT

Mac Leod, Kristin
East Lyme HS
Niantic, CT

Macauley, Jr Arthur P
St Bernard HS
Westerly, RI

Maccio, Stephanie
Southington HS
Southington, CT

Mack, Joseph
Rockville HS
Vernon, CT

Mackay, Bryan
Holy Cross HS
Waterbury, CT

Madden, Kevin
East Catholic HS
Vernon, CT

Maggi, Lea
Shelton HS
Shelton, CT

Magno, Cathryn
Bloomfield HS
Bloomfield, CT

Maiorano, Rachel A
North Branford HS
N Branford, CT

Mallane, Darren
Naugatuck HS
Naugatuck, CT

Manchuck, Amy Marie
Sacred Heart Acad
Stamford, CT

Mancini, Tony
Warren F Kaynor Regional Vo Tech
Watertown, CT

Mancuso, Michael
Masuk HS
Monroe, CT

Mangiagli, Susan Ann
Southington HS
Southington, CT

Mansfield, Christopher S
Hopkins Grammar Day Prosp Hill Schl
New Haven, CT

March, Scott
Danbury HS
Danbury, CT

Marchesseault, Donald
South Windsor HS
S Windsor, CT

Marcotte, Andrea
Trumbull HS
Trumbull, CT

Marcucci, Jennifer
St Marys HS
E Haven, CT

Margelot, Gary
Watertown HS
Watertown, CT

Markham, Robert
Pomperaug HS
Southbury, CT

Marone, Matthew J
St Bernard HS
N Franklin, CT

Marshall, John
Rockville HS
Vernon, CT

Martin, Bonnie
Danbury HS
Danbury, CT

Martin, Kimberly
Central Catholic HS
Wesport, CT

Martin, Sharon
Wilbur Cross HS
New Haven, CT

Martindale, Charles
Notre Dame HS
New Haven, CT

Martinez, Jose Rene
St Bernard HS
New London, CT

Maschio, Karen
Sacred Heart Acad
Wallingford, CT

Massey, Mike
Norwalk HS
Norwalk, CT

Massi, Maria
St Thomas Aquinas
New Britain, CT

Massicotte, Michael
Northwest Catholic
W Simsbury, CT

Mastroianni, Michael
Pomperaug HS
Middlebury, CT

Matic, Janette
Westhill HS
Stamford, CT

MautteIII, Sidney Douglas
West Woods Christian Acad
Meriden, CT

Mc Bride, Shelley
Saint Bernard HS
Lisbon, CT

Mc Carley, Kristie
Danbury HS
Danbury, CT

Mc Carthy, Susan M
Convent Of The Sacred Heart
Stamford, CT

Mc Closkey, Sean
Killingly HS
Danielson, CT

Mc Cullagh, Jeanne
Stamford Catholic
Stamford, CT

Mc Govern, George
Masuk HS
Monroe, CT

Mc Kaige, Wendy
Sacred Heart Acad
Stamford, CT

Mc Kenna, III Joseph
Windsor Locks HS
Windsor Locks, CT

Mc Knight, Whitney
Glastonbury HS
Apalachin, NY

Mc Laughlin, Sue
Wilton HS
Wilton, CT

Mc Lellan, Delisa
Westhill HS
Stamford, CT

Mc Queen, Wendy
Tolland HS
Tolland, CT

Mc Williams, William A
New Fairfield HS
New Fairfield, CT

Meaddough, Erika L
Amity Regional SR
Bethany, CT

Melvin, Michael
Avon Old Farms
Avon, CT

Mendoza, Paula
Brien Mc Mahon
Norwalk, CT

Merrill, Jean Marie Ella T
Graso-Southeaster
New London, CT

Messier, Robert
Bristol Central HS
Bristol, CT

Messinger, Richard A
William H Hall HS
W Hartford, CT

Michalak, Lisa
Berlin HS
Kensington, CT

Michaud, Liz A
Lyme-Old Lyme HS
Old Lyme, CT

Michaud, Louise
Manchester HS
Manchester, CT

Michaud, Paula
Enfield HS
Enfield, CT

Middleton, Jeanine
West Haven HS
W Haven, CT

Mihalek, Michael
Mark T Sheehan HS
Wallingford, CT

Mihaly, Matthew
Trumbull HS
Trumbull, CT

Milewski, Yvonne
Stamford Catholic
Stamford, CT

Miller, Jr Daniel J Ellington HS Ellington, CT	Miller, Stacey Manchester HS Hartford, CT	Minar, Mark New London HS New London, CT	Miner, Lori Trumbull HS Trumbull, CT	Minnick, Beth East Hartford HS E Hartford, CT	Mirando, Richard H C Wilcox Technical Schl Plantsville, CT	Mirmina, Steven A Jonathan Law HS Milford, CT	Mitchell, Carole D Bloomfield HS Bloomfield, CT	Mizeski, Suzanne Naugatuck HS Union City, CT	Modugno, Marcy Holy Cross HS Seymour, CT

Modzelewski, Francis Mark Naugatuck HS Naugatuck, CT	Monarchie, Chris Norwalk HS Norwalk, CT	Montgomery, Jason Heritage Christian Cheshire, CT	Monti, Jr David A Southington HS Plantsville, CT	Moore, III Alexander Fairfield Prep Redding, CT	Moore, Elizabeth Amity Regional HS Bethany, CT	Moquin, Karen Jonathan Law HS Milford, CT	Mora, Joseph Berlin HS Berlin, CT	Morabito, Brian Bethel HS Bethel, CT	Morea, Jennifer Holy Cross HS Waterbury, CT

Morgan, Edward Canterbury Schl Huntington, NY	Morgan, Michelle The Morgan Schl Clinton, CT	Morin, Robin Tolland HS Tolland, CT	Morris, II Freddie Windsor HS Windsor, CT	Morrison, Alwyn Ray Kolbe Cathedral HS Bridgeport, CT	Moy, Wayne Danbury HS Danbury, CT	Mueller, Maria Bristol Central HS Bristol, CT	Mulhall, Bill Trumbull HS Trumbull, CT	Murkett, Jeffrey St Bernard HS Norwich, CT	Murkett, Timothy St Bernard HS Norwich, CT

Murphy, Elizabeth East Catholic HS Ellington, CT	Musacchio, Jacqueline M Bethel HS Bethel, CT	Nagle, Martin St Bernard HS East Lyme, CT	Napoli, Michael Guilford HS Guilford, CT	Narang, Priya Staples HS Westport, CT	Naughton, Thomas Suffield HS Suffield, CT	Navickas, John RHAM HS Marlborough, CT	Neary, Darlene East Lyme HS Niantic, CT	Nemetz, David Brookfield HS Brookfield, CT	Nesson, Eric Amity Regional HS Bethany, CT

Nguyen, Tuan Windham HS Willimantic, CT	Nichols, Sue Pomperaug HS Southbury, CT	Nigam, Vivek Southington HS Southington, CT	Nirmal, Mary Mark T Sheehan HS Wallingford, CT	Noome, Mark Staples HS Westport, CT	Noonan, Mark Old Saybrook SR Old Saybrook, CT	Norris, Amy Academy Of The Holy Family Norwich, CT	Nosal, Michael Westhill HS Stamford, CT	Notarino, Connie A East Haven HS E Haven, CT	O Brien, Colleen Guilford SR HS Guilford, CT

O Connor, Laura A Stamford Catholic Stamford, CT	O Connor, Mairead Glastonbury HS S Glastonbury, CT	O Connor, Philip X Wilbur L Cross HS New Haven, CT	Owens, Douglas Oliver Wolcott Technical Schl Torrington, CT	Pace, Michael North Haven HS N Haven, CT	Palicki, Lisa Manchester HS Manchester, CT	Palmer, Nancy I Greenwich HS Cos Cob, CT	Palmer, Shawn Rocky Hill HS Rocky Hill, CT	Palmieri, Kim Tracy Southington HS Plantsville, CT	Papp, Jennifer E Plainfield HS Moosup, CT

Parham, Deania Masuk HS Monroe, CT	Parillo, Audrey North Haven HS N Haven, CT	Park, John Choate Rosemary Hall HS Vienna, VA	Patacca, Jr Angelo M Glastonbury HS Glastonbury, CT	Paternostro, Patrick Watertown HS Watertown, CT	Payne, Lariayn Low Heywood Thomas Schl Stamford, CT	Pearce, Kerry A Traumbull HS Trumbull, CT	Pearlman, Lawrence Hotchkiss HS Cambridge, MA	Pegeas, George Buckeley HS Hartford, CT	Pelchat, Sherri Simsbury HS Simsbury, CT

Pellei, David D
Fairfield College
Preparatory Schl
Trumbull, CT

Pensiero, Frank
Notre Dame
Catholic HS
Bridgeport, CT

Pepe, Mara D
Danbury HS
Danbury, CT

Perlot, David
Southington HS
Southington, CT

Perna, Richard
St Mary HS
Cos Cob, CT

Perrott, Stephanie
Nonnewaug HS
Seymour, CT

Peterson, II B
Douglas
Fairfield College
Prepatory Schl
Shelton, CT

Peterson, Jonathan
New London HS
New London, CT

Petit, Lou-Anne E
Northwestern
Regional #7 HS
New Hartford, CT

Petrasy, Elaine
Pomperaug HS
Southbury, CT

Petrillo, Jennifer
Arlene
North Haven HS
North Haven, CT

Petrokaitis,
Elizabeth
Holy Cross HS
Waterbury, CT

Petruzzi, Donald
Kennedy HS
Waterbury, CT

Pfahler, Kristin
Berlin HS
Kensington, CT

Phillips, Deidre
Sacred Heart Acad
Seymour, CT

Phillips, Jedan
Pomfret HS
Queens, NY

Phillips, Karen
Pomperaug HS
Southbury, CT

Pimer, Laura
Platt Regional
West Haven, CT

Pinto, Kim
Stamford HS
Stamford, CT

Pirigyi, Jr Albert J
Windsor HS
Windsor, CT

Piver, Jon
Stonington HS
Stonington, CT

Pizzi, Lauren A
Sacred Heart Acad
Ansonia, CT

Plasky, Ronald C
Naugatuck HS
Naugatuck, CT

Pleasent-Roman,
Gerardo O
South Catholic HS
E Hartford, CT

Poirier, Ryan
Killingly HS
Brooklyn, CT

Polidoro, Daniel
Granby Memorial
Granby, CT

Pope, Christopher
Charles
Ridgefield HS
Ridgefield, CT

Porricelli, Michael
St Mary HS
Old Greenwich, CT

Porydzy, Laura
Southington HS
Southington, CT

Powell, Nadine
Stratford HS
Stratford, CT

Powell, Simone
Weaver HS
Hartford, CT

Prajer, Stephen
Seymour HS
Oxford, CT

Pratt, John
Watkinson Schl
Glastonbury, CT

Prendergast, Lynn
Ames
Daniel Hand HS
Madison, CT

Press, Randi
Amity Regional HS
Orange, CT

Preston, Elizabeth
St Bernards HS
Charlestown, RI

Prior, Dawn
Southington HS
Southington, CT

Prodan, Angela Jean
Shelton HS
Shelton, CT

Proulx, John Daniel
Mark T Sheehan HS
Wallingford, CT

Przybylski, Bruno
Southington HS
Plantsville, CT

Purdy, Christine
Masuk HS
Monroe, CT

Quinn, Lori
North Branford HS
Northford, CT

Quinn, Pamela
Michele
Ridgefield HS
Ridgefield, CT

Rabenold, Christa
Brien Mc Mahon
Darien, CT

Rabin, Bradford
Choate Rosemary
Hall HS
Short Hills, NJ

Rabitaille, Andrea
New London HS
New London, CT

Raffone, IV Eugene
Notre Dame HS
Orange, CT

Ragozzino, Michelle
West Haven HS
W Haven, CT

Rak, Robert
New Britain HS
New Britain, CT

Rametta, Frances
Rita
S Catholic HS
Hartford, CT

Ramos, Edward
Simsbury HS
Jersey City, NJ

Rashba, Gary
Amity Regional SR
Orange, CT

Ray, Jr Paul W
East Catholic HS
Tolland, CT

Read, Karen
St Bernard HS
Stonington, CT

Recce, Jean
Shelton HS
Shelton, CT

Redden, Denise N
Naugatick HS
Naugatuck, CT

Redinger, Paula
Rockville HS
Vernon, CT

Reece, Paula
Jonathan Lw HS
Milford, CT

Reed, April
Trumbull HS
Trumbull, CT

Rees, Elizabeth
Brien Mcmahon HS
Norwalk, CT

Regal, Joseph
Fairfield Prep
Fairfield, CT

Reiling, Mark
The Hotchkiss Schl
Litchfield, CT

Reilly, Stacey
Canton HS
Canton, CT

Rek, Laura
Naugatuck HS
Naugatuck, CT

Renda, Craig
Danburg HS
Danbury, CT

Renda, Jr Frank
Wilcox Tech HS
Wallingford, CT

Reynolds, Jennifer
Bethel HS
Bethel, CT

Reynolds, Karen
Canton HS
Collinsville, CT

Ricci, Melissa E
Sacred Heart Acad
New Haven, CT

Richardson, Larry
Darnell
Central HS
Bridgeport, CT

Riley, Mary
Christine
Miss Porters Schl
Larchmont, NY

Rish, Michelle
Amity Regional HS
Woodbridge, CT

Rishi, Arthur
Amity Regional HS
Woodbridge, CT

Ritch, Wendy
Greenwich HS
Cos Cob, CT

Ritter, Karen A
Amity Regional SR
Woodbridge, CT

Robbins, Tara E
Lyman Hall HS
Wallingford, CT

Robinson, Brett S
Norwich Free Acad
Lisbon, CT

Robinson, George
Hillhouse HS
New Haven, CT

Robinson, Michael
Bassick HS
Bridgeport, CT

Robinson, Opal
Bassick HS
Bridgeport, CT

Robinson, Putrina
Wilbur Cross HS
New Haven, CT

Robinson, Stacy
Haddam-Killingwort
h HS
Killingworth, CT

Rocheleau, Tom
Newington HS
Newington, CT

Rodick, Kiraly
Lauralton Hall HS
Milfort, CT

Rodrigue, Susan
George J Penney HS
E Hartford, CT

Rogozinski, Keith
St Thomas More HS
Thomaston, CT

Rolfe, John J
Torrington HS
Torrington, CT

Romaniello, Susan
Crosby HS
Waterbury, CT

Rose, Steven
Branford HS
Branford, CT

Rosefsky, Douglas
The Taft Schl
Binghamton, NY

Rosenblatt, Sarah
William Hall HS
W Hartford, CT

Ross, Betsy
Danbury HS
Danbury, CT

Ross, Jr Jonathan
Woodman
Daniel Hand HS
Madison, CT

Rousseau, Michael
Lewis S Mills HS
Burlington, CT

Rowland, Wendy
Bethel HS
Southbury, CT

Ruran, Dani N
William H Ahll HS
West Hartford, CT

Russell, Kevin
Danbury HS
Danbury, CT

Russo, Gina
St Bernards HS
Franklin, CT

Russo, Jon M
Tolland HS
Tolland, CT

Russo, Michele
Sacred Heart Acad
Hamden, CT

Ryan, Andrea
East Catholic HS
Manchester, CT

Ryan, Denise
Cheshire HS
Cheshire, CT

Sabia, Heather
Stamford HS
Stamford, CT

Sabin, Heidi
Acad Of The Holy
Taftville, CT

Sacchi, Cheryl
John F Kennedy HS
Waterbury, CT

Salvin, Amy
The Morgan HS
Clinton, CT

Sanders, Brian T
Hopkins Grammar
West Haven, CT

Santangelo, Melissa
Sacred Heart Acad
Ansonia, CT

Santarsiero, Gina
Holy Cross HS
Waterbury, CT

Santino, Michele
West Haven HS
W Haven, CT

Sarno, Marino
Rosario
Brien Mc Mahon
Norwalk, CT

Savage, Anne M
Greenwich HS
Old Greenwich, CT

Savage, Mark
Bristol Eastern HS
Unionville, CT

Savulak, Susan T
St Paul Catholic HS
Unionville, CT

Savvaides, Andy
Norwalk HS
Norwalk, CT

Scebelo, Steve
Newfairfield HS
New Fairfield, CT

Schick, Kim
Ellington HS
Ellington, CT

Schlaefer, David
East Catholic HS
Bolton, CT

Schneider, Kurt
Canterbury HS
Sea Girt, NJ

Schweighofer, Peter
Ridgefield HS
Ridgefield, CT

Scicchitano,
Caterina L
Stamford HS
Stamford, CT

Sciortino, Michael J
Trumbull HS
Trumbull, CT

Scully, Janice
Frank Scott Bunnell
Stratford, CT

Searles, Debra
Naugatuck HS
Naugatuck, CT

Seaver, Shannon
Bristol Eastern HS
Bristol, CT

Segretario, Kristen
Bristol Central HS
Bristol, CT

Sementini, Nancy
Stamford HS
Stamford, CT

Semon, Suzanne
Saint Josephs HS
Ansonia, CT

Senesac, Robert J
St Paul Catholic HS
Bristol, CT

Serrambana, Jr
Victor
East Catholic HS
Vernon, CT

Sesto, Vincenzo
Bristol Central HS
Bristol, CT

Sharp, Christopher
Westhill HS
Stamford, CT

Sheftel, Stephen
O H Platt HS
Meriden, CT

Shek, Karen E
Academy Of Our
Lady Of Mercy HS
Milford, CT

Shelton, Dana
Notre Dame Acad
Waterbury, CT

Sherman, Mia E
William H Hall HS
West Hartford, CT

Shinn, Wendy
Hartford Christian
Ellington, CT

Short, Ingrid
Northwestern
Regional #7 HS
New Hartford, CT

Sibilla, Angela
Stamford HS
Stamford, CT

Sickler, Stacey
Daniel Hand HS
Madison, CT

Sikorski, Patrick
Norwich Regional
Norwich, CT

Silkoff, Shari
James Hillhouse HS
New Haven, CT

Silva, Dayle
Danbury HS
Danbury, CT

Silva, Jessica
Ansonia HS
Ansonia, CT

Silvester, III
Theodore
Avon Old Farms
Rye, NH

Simione, III William
J
Notre Dame HS
Orange, CT

Sirowich, Michael
Seymour HS
Oxford, CT

Sisk, Brian
East Hartford HS
E Hartford, CT

Sivjee, Khalil
Rham HS
Andover, CT

Skelly, Suzanne
South Catholic HS
Wethersfield, CT

Slay, Tonia
Guilford HS
Guilford, CT

Smallwood,
Bradford
Simsbury HS
W Simsbury, CT

Smilancsky, Diane
Brien Mc Mahon
S Norwalk, CT

Smith, Chris W
Naugatuck HS
Naugatuck, CT

Smith, Daryl R
Greenwich HS
Old Greenwich, CT

Smith, Djuana
Wilbur Cross HS
New Haven, CT

Smith, Lisa Yvette
James Hillhouse HS
New Haven, CT

Smith, Michael
Suffield HS
Suffield, CT

Smith, Monica
James Hillhouse HS
New Haven, CT

Smith, Sharon
East Hartford HS
E Hartford, CT

Smith, Teryl Ann
North Branford HS
Northford, CT

Smuts, Maria
Old Saybrook HS
Old Saybrook, CT

Snyder, Andrew
Amity Regional SR
Woodbridge, CT

Sodlosky, Lee-Ann
Sacred Heart Acad
West Haven, CT

Sohn, Robert
Newington HS
Newington, CT

Solla, Melissa
Bulkeley HS
Hartford, CT

Sorensen, Holly
Shelton HS
Shelton, CT

Sousa, Norman
Robert E Fitch SR
Groton, CT

Spagnoletti, Joseph
J
Watertown HS
Oakville, CT

Spence, Carline
Bassick HS
Bridgeport, CT

Speziali, Christine
St Bernard HS
Stonington, CT

Spies, Stacy
Weston HS
Weston, CT

Spillane, Erin
Bethel HS
Bethel, CT

Stabile, Denise M
Danbury HS
Danbury, CT

Starkey, Jim
Holy Cross HS
Ansonia, CT

Starziski, Janice
Naugatuck HS
Naugatuck, CT

Stasiuk, Christina
Southington HS
Southington, CT

Stearns, David L
Xavier HS
Wallingford, CT

Steffanci, Tom
Southington HS
Plantsville, CT

Stella, Louise
Southington HS
Southington, CT

Stephenson, Georgia
Westhill HS
Stamford, CT

Sterling, Marie
East Hartford HS
E Hartford, CT

Stewart, John
Torrington HS
Torrington, CT

Stewart, William M
Northwestern
Regional #7 HS
Gloucester, MA

Stockey, Andrew
Simsbury HS
W Simsbury, CT

Stolfi, Stephen M
Crosby HS
Waterbury, CT

Stone, Ilene
Cheshire HS
Cheshire, CT

Strang, John
Ansonia HS
Ansonia, CT

Strange, Gerald
Bristol Central HS
Bristol, CT

Strelow, Tiffany
Weston HS
Weston, CT

Stringer, IV Edward
F
Middletown HS
Middletown, CT

Sullivan, John M
Notre Dame HS
N Branford, CT

Sunseri, Mark
Danbury HS
Danbury, CT

Surowiec, Cindy
Berlin HS
Berlin, CT

Sutton, Frank
Southeastern Tech
Lyme, CT

Swagerty, Mark R
Newington HS
Newington, CT

Swanson, Kerry D
Naugatuck HS
Naugatuck, CT

Sweeney, Patrick T
Southington HS
Southington, CT

Swindle, Honey
New London HS
New London, CT

Symanski, Tracy
Jonathan Law HS
Milford, CT

Szatkowski, Paul
Manchester HS
Manchester, CT

Szatkowski, Susan
Bethel HS
Bethel, CT

Szymborski,
Alexandra
Greenwich HS
Old Greenwich, CT

Tar, Eva Marie
Valley Regional HS
Chester, CT

Tartaglia, Donna
Masuk HS
Monroe, CT

Tauber, Dan
Westhill HS
Stamford, CT

Taylor, Michael
Manchester HS
Manchester, CT

Terkelsen, Sandra
Greenwich HS
Greenwich, CT

Thalberg, Debra A
Amity SR HS
Woodbridge, CT

Thayer, Rebekah
Holy Cross HS
Propect, CT

Thibodrow, Lisa A
East Hartford HS
E Hartford, CT

Thomas, Aglaeezahira
Bloomfield HS
Bloomfield, CT

Thompson, Dushawn
Stratford HS
Stratford, CT

Thompson, Kim
North Bradford HS
Northford, CT

Thompson, Michael
Crosby HS
Waterbury, CT

Thompson, Michelle
Guilford SR HS
Guilford, CT

Thompson, Michelle A
Danbury HS
Danbury, CT

Thompson, Tammy L
Crosby HS
Waterbury, CT

Tiberio, Roger
Stratford HS
Stratford, CT

Tiemann, Jennifer
Danbury HS
Westlake Village, CA

Tiernan, Edward
St Thomas More
Brentwood, NY

Tillson, Karen
Trumbull HS
Solon, OH

Tobin, Debra Sarah
Trumbull HS
Trumbull, CT

Tolomeo, Concettina
East Haven HS
North Haven, CT

Toman, Lori L
Enrico Fermi HS
Enfield, CT

Tomolonis, Paul
East Windsor HS
Broad Brook, CT

Tornillo, Penni Diane
Stratford HS
Stratford, CT

Toth, Cheryl Ann
New Britain HS
New Britain, CT

Townsend, Steve
Kaynor RVTS HS
Waterbury, CT

Trailor, Suzanne
St Bernard HS
Norwich, CT

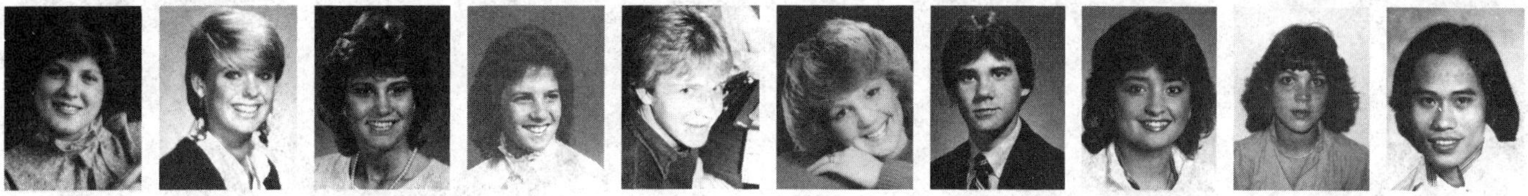

Traisci, Leigh
New Fairfield HS
New Fairfield, CT

Trojan, Heather
Low Heywood Thomas HS
Rowayton, CT

Trojanowski, Lori
Southington HS
Southington, CT

Trudel, Christine
Danbury HS
Danbury, CT

Tubridy, Bob
East Lyme HS
Niantic, CT

Turko, Michelle
St Joseph HS
Monroe, CT

Tyranski, Chad
Newtown HS
Newtown, CT

Valinho, Suzanne
Naugatuck HS
Naugatuck, CT

Van Dine, Heather
East Catholic HS
Bolton, CT

Van Nguyen, Tam
Richard C Lee HS
New Haven, CT

Vardon, Kelly
Naugatuck HS
Naugatuck, CT

Varvisiotis, Toula
Sacred Heart Acad
Stamford, CT

Vegiard, Roland Lee
East Catholic HS
E Hartford, CT

Vella, Andrea
Bethel HS
Bethel, CT

Veltri, Louie
St Joseph HS
Trumbull, CT

Venditto, Dee Ann
East Haven HS
E Haven, CT

Vendola, Arthur R
St Pual HS
Farmington, CT

Venice, Robert
Emmett O Brien
Ansonia, CT

Ventresca, Paula M
St Paul Catholic HS
Thomaston, CT

Verdone, Cheryl
Granby Memorial
Granby, CT

Vetro, Donna
Hamden HS
Hamden, CT

Virelli, Jason
Jonathan Law HS
Milford, CT

Vitelli, William
Joseph A Foran HS
Milford, CT

Voisine, Janice L
St Paul Catholic HS
Bristol, CT

Von Jako, Christopher Richard
Avon Old Farms
Melrose, MA

Wade, Ladora
Sacred Heart Acad
Hamden, CT

Wagnblas, Adam
Notre Dame HS
Ffld, CT

Wagner, Michele
Cheshire HS
Cheshire, CT

Wakeley, Aaron Jakab
Milford Acad
Huntington, CT

Waldron, Dale
St Bernard HS
Preston, CT

Walenda, Grace
Newtown HS
Sandy Hook, CT

Walker, Evan Hudson
Hopkins HS
Hamden, CT

Walker, Tiffany
Weaver HS
Hartford, CT

Wallin, Eva Kristina
Bethel HS
Bethel, CT

Walsh, Erin
Sacred Heart Acad
Stamford, CT

Wankerl, Thomas
Newington HS
Newington, CT

Warne, Kate
Notre Dame C H S
Fairfield, CT

Waterman, Janel
James Hillhouse HS
New Haven, CT

Weeks, Stephanie
St Bernard HS
Waterford, CT

Weiland, James
Wilton HS
Wilton, CT

Wells, Allison
Shelton HS
Shelton, CT

Werkheiser, Lora
Shelton HS
Shelton, CT

West, Lisa
Branford HS
Garland, TX

Westby, Stephanie
Trumbull HS
Trumbull, CT

Weyant, II James
Mark T Sheehan HS
Wallingford, CT

Wheeler, Jr Frederick W
Jonathan Law HS
Milford, CT

White, Brian
Vinal Regional Tech/Voch HS
Middletown, CT

Whyte, Jeffrey R
East Hartford HS
E Hartford, CT

Williams, Janice
Sacred Heart Acad
New Haven, CT

Williams, Tonya
Wilbur Cross HS
New Haven, CT

Wilmot, Brian Norwalk HS Norwalk, CT	Wilson, Karen Jonathan Law HS Milford, CT	Wilson, Kimberly A C Westhill HS Stamford, CT	Wilson, Margaret Yvette Brien Mc Mahon Norwalk, CT	Wilson, Samuel Vincent Notre Dame HS W Haven, CT	Wishart, Daniel L St Paul Catholic HS Bristol, CT	Wolinski, Robert Norwich Reg Vo Tech Schl Norwich, CT	Woodard, Paulette R Thomas Snell Weaver HS Hartford, CT	Woodberry, Roger Avon Old Farms HS Reading, MA	Woodman, David North Branford HS North Branford, CT

Wosleger, Jeff Stamford Catholic Stamford, CT	Wynn, Charles Windham HS Colmbia, CT	Yamamoto, Marie A East Hartford HS E Hartford, CT	Yepes, Diana Brien Mc Mahon Rowayton, CT	Yerxa, Daniel Joseph A Foran HS Milford, CT	Youngs, Jill Tolland HS Tolland, CT	Yum, David O H Platt HS Meriden, CT	Zack, Henry J St Joseph HS Trumbull, CT	Zak, Rebecca Southington HS Southington, CT	Zars, Erik Bloomfield HS Bloomfield, CT

Zawacki, Karen Marie Danbury HS Danbury, CT	Zawilinski, Brian Vinal Reg Voc Tech Middletown, CT	Zelinski, Christine Seymour HS Seymour, CT	Ziehl, Matthew Greens Farms Acad Greens Farms, CT	Zigmond, Gary Norwalk HS Norwalk, CT	Zingo, Gina Masuk HS Monroe, CT	Zinych, Mark Amity Regional SR Bethany, CT	Zisterer, Ute Lyman HS West Germany	Zitnay, Jeffrey S Shelton HS Shelton, CT	Zolla, Phillip Notre Dame HS Ansonia, CT

MAINE

Zymba, Paul F Enfield HS Enfield, CT	Alberi, Michele Oxford Hils HS S Paris, ME	Allen, Susan Robert W Traip Kittery, ME	Alward, Jeanne Caribou HS New Sweden, ME	Andrews, Jean Vinalhaven HS Vinalhaven, ME	Anthoine, Scott Lewiston HS Lewiston, ME	Atkinson, Ida Bonny Eagle HS Hollis, ME	Azevedo, Cheryle Oak Hill HS Sabattus, ME	Bachelder, Brent Alan Telstar Regional HS Newry, ME

Bachelder, Carolyn Leavitt Area HS Leeds, ME	Bailey, Dale Biddeford HS Biddeford, ME	Baker, Milton Valley HS Bingham, ME	Ball, Christopher Lake Region HS North Bridgton, ME	Bantos, Melissa A Edward Little HS Auburn, ME	Bard, Ryan Van Buren Dist Secondary Schl Van Buren, ME	Barker, Angela M Massabesic HS Waterboro, ME	Beal, Chrisopher Jonesport-Beals HS Beals, ME	Beal, Glenace Jonesport-Beals HS Beals, ME	Beal, Jr Lewis Jonesport-Beals HS Beals, ME

Bennett, Richard Presque Isle HS Presque Isle, ME	Black, Valerie L Winslow HS Winslow, ME	Blease, Kimberlee Orono HS Orono, ME	Blier, Beverly Fort Kent Community HS Ft Kent, ME	Boardman, Stephanie Lawrence HS Fairfield, ME	Boston, Jr Robert C Wells HS Wells, ME	Bouchard, Jennifer Edward Little HS Auburn, ME	Brilton, Michelle Rene South Portland HS South Portland, ME	Brown, Jodie L Wells HS Wells, ME	Buckley, Julie Lewiston HS Lewiston, ME

Burnham, Jeff Oxford Hills HS Norway, ME	Cairnie, Melissa Lawrence HS Waterville, ME	Caron, April Fort Kent Comm Fort Kent Mills, ME	Caron, Marty Washburn District Washburn, ME	Caron, Ronald Community HS Ft Kent, ME	Carver, Jean Denise Narraguagus HS Addison, ME	Castner, Shawn Leavitt Area HS Greene, ME	Chandler, Susan Fryeburg Acad Fryeburg, ME	Chase, Linda M Lincon Acad Pemaquid Beach, ME	Cialini-Charles, Melissa Windham HS S Windham, ME

Clark, Tom
Cony HS
Gardiner, ME

Clarke, Ellen
Edward Little HS
Auburn, ME

Cloutier, Kevin
Portland HS
Portland, ME

Cobb, Janet S
Greenville HS
Greenville, ME

Corbin, David
Cony HS
Augusta, ME

Cornelio, Ann
Jay HS
Jay, ME

Courant, Jay
Leavitt Area HS
Greene, ME

Cristina, Scott
Jay HS
Jay, ME

Cropley, II Roger L
Mattanawcook Acad
Lincoln, ME

Currier, Kristin
Mount Blue HS
Farmington, ME

Cushman, Daphne
Hodgdon HS
Houlton, ME

De Giosafatto, Joann
Ellsworth HS
Ellsworth, ME

Delmonaco, John P
Calais HS
Calais, ME

Dinsmore, Lisa
Tralp Acad
Kittery, ME

Dorrego, Ana
Winslow HS
Spain

Dunn, Mary
Houlton HS
Houlton, ME

Dunton, Randall
Gorham HS
Gorham, ME

Durgin, Wendy
Windham HS
S Casco, ME

Elliott, Lori
Bangor HS
Bangor, ME

Ellsmore, Tracy C
Machias Memorial
Machias, ME

Erickson, Kirsten
Lisbon Falls Christian Acad
Lisbon Falls, ME

Favreau, Deborah
Morse HS
Bath, ME

Fecteau, Christopher M
Bangor HS
Bangor, ME

Felton, Rita C
Robert W Traip
Kittery, ME

Flewelling, Brent
Easton HS
Easton, ME

Flood, Stacy
Nokomis Regional
Hartland, ME

Foster, Kaye L
Skowhegan Area HS
Skowhegan, ME

Fowley, Lissa
Windham HS
Poland Spg, ME

Fraser, Sue
Telstar Regional HS
Bethel, ME

Gagnon, Gregory
Lewiston HS
Lewiston, ME

Gannon, Anne Arlene
Falmouth HS
Falmouth, ME

Garris, Janie B
Cony HS
Augusta, ME

Garrison, Michelle
Cony HS
Augusta, ME

Giguere, Steven
Lewiston HS
Lewiston, ME

Giroux, Frederick P
Kennebec Valley Christian HS
Fairfield, ME

Goodwin, Theresa Lynn
Deering HS
Portland, ME

Gosselin, Denise P
Lewiston HS
Lewiston, ME

Gould, William T
Edward Little HS
Minot, ME

Greenleaf, Michele
Gardiner Area HS
Gardiner, ME

Grenier, Martin
Forest Hills HS
Jackman, ME

Hall, Wanda N
Leavitt Area HS
Greene, ME

Hanna, Sarah
Westbrook HS
Westbrook, ME

Hawksley, Thomas W
Bangor HS
Bangor, ME

Hayden, Michelle Rae
Mt Blue HS
Dryden, ME

Hennin, Raoul
Morse HS
Woolwich, ME

Hilbinger, Carol Lee
Deering HS
Portland, ME

Hodgdon, Tammy
Belfast Area HS
Belfast, ME

Hodgson, Karyn
Fryeburg Acad
Fryeburg, ME

Howe, Stephen
Cony HS
Augusta, ME

Hunter, Connie
Lawrence HS
Fairfield, ME

Huntress, Wendy Lee
Massabesic HS
Springvale, ME

Jackson, Brian
Deering HS
Portland, ME

Jacobs, Shawn M
Mexico HS
Mexico, ME

Jacques, Richard
Livermore Falls HS
Livermore Falls, ME

Jamison, Nathalie Lynn
Gardiner Area HS
Randolph, ME

Jandreau, Kevin Niles
Ashland Community
Portage, ME

Jean, Ellen
Freeport HS
Freeport, ME

Johnson, Jennifer J
Caribou HS
Stockholm, ME

Jones, Robert
York HS
York, ME

Jordan, Lisa
Telstar Regional HS
Locke Mills, ME

Jordan, Rhonda J
Leavitt Area HS
Turner, ME

Karkos, Kern
Mt Blue HS
Wilton, ME

Kearns, Brenda
Hampden Acad
Hampden Highland, ME

Keaten, James
Skowhegan Area HS
Skowhegan, ME

King, Debora A
Mattanawcook Acad
Lincoln Ctr, ME

King, Mya Lisa
Hampden Acad
Hampden, ME

Knapton, Jeff
Westbrook HS
Westbrook, ME

Knowlton, Nancy J
Hampden Acad
Hampden, ME

Kreie, Joyce L
Wells HS
Ogunquit, ME

La Porte, Renee M
Skowhegan Area HS
Skowhegan, ME

Lachance, Debbie
St Dominic Regional
Lewiston, ME

Lahaie, Derek A
St Dominics
Regional HS
Lewiston, ME

Laney, Kandi L
Skowhegan Area HS
Skowhegan, ME

Laplante, Cindy
Lewiston HS
Lewiston, ME

Layne, Jennifer
Fryeburg Acad
N Fryeburg, ME

Lenfestey, Sally
Jonesport-Beals HS
Beals, ME

Libby, Deborah L
Portland HS
Portland, ME

Littlefield, Barbara
Sanford HS
Sanford, ME

Lounsbury, Jr Dan
T
Morse HS
Bath, ME

Mahler, Timothy W
Gorham HS
Gorham, ME

Mann, Thomas
Bucksport HS
Bucksport, ME

Marsanskis, Michael
Belfast Area HS
Belfast, ME

Martell, Tammy
Bonny Eagle HS
Limerick, ME

Martin, Thomas
Fort Kent Com HS
Fort Kent, ME

Mazerolle, Paula A
Caribau HS
Caribou, ME

Mc Auslin, Judy
Gardiner Area HS
Gardiner, ME

Mc Clure, Linden H
Mt Abram HS
Kingfield, ME

Mc Divitt, Suzette
Presque Isle HS
Presque Isle, ME

Mc Dowell, Ruth
Woodland HS
Princeton, ME

Mc Pherson, Teresa
Houlton HS
Houlton, ME

Michaud, Cathie
Lewiston HS
Lewiston, ME

Miller, Tabitha
Kennebunk HS
Kennebunk Port,
ME

Milsop, Jennifer
Windham HS
Westbrook, ME

Miranda, Gina
Madawaska HS
Madawaska, ME

Monahan, Jr John
M
Oxford Hills HS .
Oxford, ME

Moore, Joanne
Belfast Area HS
Belfast, ME

Morang, Stacy C
Gardiner Area HS
Gardiner, ME

Mullen, Bridget
Lincoln HS
Vinalhaven, ME

Murphy, Sean E
Caribou HS
Caribou, ME

Myatt, Maryann
Oak Hill HS
Litchfield, ME

Nadeau, Christopher
Leavitt Area HS
Leeds, ME

Nicholas, Laurie
Westbrook HS
Westbrook, ME

Norris, Lee Ann
Rumford HS
Rumford, ME

Norton, Paula F
Washington Acad
Jonesboro, ME

O Bryan, Bridget
Ann Patricia
Lincoln Acad
Damariscotta, ME

Ordway, George
Katahdin HS
Sherman Mills, ME

Page, Shallee T
Ellsworth HS
Ellsworth, ME

Parr, Donna
Belfast Area HS
Boca Raton, FL

Pearl, Jennifer
Westbrok HS
Raymond, ME

Pelletier, Elaine
Fort Kent
Community HS
Fort Kent, ME

Pelletier, Tricia
Allyson
Deering HS
Portland, ME

Perry, Maureen A
Lewiston HS
Lewiston, ME

Pineo, Stephanie J
Washington Acad
Jonesboro, ME

Pio, Gina
Deering HS
Portland, ME

Pittman, Tammy
Madawaska HS
Madawaska, ME

Porath, Brett
Cony HS
Augusta, ME

Poulin, Larry
Lewiston HS
Lewiston, ME

Powers, Michelle
Westbrook HS
Westbrook, ME

Ranger, Ann
Westbrook HS
Westbrook, ME

Ray, Jr Donald
Gray New
Gloucester HS
New Gloucester, ME

Rice, Nancy
Stearns HS
Millinocket, ME

Riley, Deborah
Windham HS
Raymond, ME

Roberts, Christopher
C
Wells HS
Wells, ME

Robillard, Randall
Marshwood HS
Eliot, ME

Rolfe, Stephen
Westbrook HS
Westbrook, ME

Romanet, Amy B
Massabesic HS
Limerick, ME

Romero, Linda
Woodland HS
Woodland, ME

Rose, Richard
Cheverus HS
Portland, ME

Rublee, Vikki
Penquis Valley HS
Milo, ME

Rudy, Edwina
Kippy
South Portland HS
South Portland, ME

Saban, Kathy
Arskine Academy
Palermo, ME

Sadler, Kathy
Woodland HS
Woodland, ME

Sawyer, Dawn E
Sacopee Valley HS
E Baldwin, ME

Schmitt, Cynthia
Livermore Falls HS
Livermore Falls, ME

Scigliano, Lisa
York HS
York, ME

Shackley, Deborah
Westbrook HS
Westbrook, ME

Shaw, Michael
Oxford Hills HS
South Paris, ME

Smith, Jennifer Joy
Open Bible Baptist
Christian Schl
New Vineyard, ME

Smith, Tiffany
Piscataquis Comm
Abbot Village, ME

Sprague, Michele
Bangor HS
Bangor, ME

Stairs, Darrin B
Freeport HS
Freeport, ME

Stoutamyer, Adam
Madison HS
Madison, ME

Strait, John Chip
Wells HS
Wells, ME

Stratton, Bradley J
Winthrop HS
Winthrop, ME

Struven, Christopher
Fryeburg Acad
Fryeburg, ME

Talon, Tracy
Hampden Academy
Hampden, ME

Tanguay, Denise
Michele
Mt Ararat HS
S Harpswell, ME

Tardiff, Julie Ann
Winthrop HS
Winthrop, ME

Targett, Jill Alma
Gray New
Gloucester HS
Gray, ME

Tetu, Dawn
Marshwood HS
S Berwick, ME

Theriault, Myscha
MSAD No 70
Hodgdon HS
N Amity, ME

Thompson, Kirk B
Freeport HS
Freeport, ME

Todd, Heidi
Caribou HS
Caribou, ME

Todd, Sheri L
York HS
Cape Neddick, ME

Treiber, John
Morse HS
West Bath, ME

Vane, Kathlyn
Machias Memorial
Machias, ME

Vo, An
Portland HS
Portland, ME

Waite, Brian D
Calais HS
Calais, ME

Waite, Elizabeth M
Mexico HS
Mexico, ME

Ward, Richard P
Lewiston HS
Lewiston, ME

Ward, Russell
Fryeburg Acad
Wareham, MA

Warsky, Stephanie
Wiscasset HS
Wiscasset, ME

Watkins, Melissa
Lake Region HS
Casco, ME

Webster, Kelly
Medomak Valley HS
Waldoboro, ME

Weigelt, Earl
Forest Hills HS
Jackman, ME

Wheeler, David L
Waterville Schls
Waterville, ME

White, Michelle
Sanford HS
Sanford, ME

White, Stacey
Caribou HS
Caribou, ME

Whitney, June
Windham HS
N Windham, ME

Wilson, Kristine
Westbrook HS
Westbrook, ME

Wolff, Kathleen P
Lake Region HS
Bridgton, ME

Wood, Travis
Messalonskee HS
Oakland, ME

Woodard, Michelle
Valley HS
Bingham, ME

Worthley, Carol
Rumford HS
W Peru, ME

Zimmerman, Steve
Robert W Traip
Kittery, ME

MASSA-CHUSETTS

Abgrab, Russell J
Westport HS
Westport, MA

Abney, Audrey
Bridgewater
Raynham Regiona
Raynham, MA

Abraham, Robert
Westbridge HS
Concord, MA

Abromovitch,
Christine
Haverhill HS
Haverhill, MA

Acciardo, Pamela C
Coyle And Cassidy
Selkirk, NY

Adamik, Dawn L
North Middlesex
Regional HS
W Townsend, MA

Adams, Cynthia
Taunton HS
Taunton, MA

Adderley, Jr
Thomas John
Ayer HS
Ft Devens, MA

Addis, Craig E
Northampton HS
Florence, MA

Adiletto, Daniel
Franklin HS
Franklin, MA

Adkins, Kimberly
N Andover HS
N Andover, MA

Albertelli, Christine
Melrose HS
Boston, MA

Aletto, Mary Jo
Presentation Of
Mary Acad
Salem, NH

Allen, Irving V
Somerville HS
Somerville, MA

Alley, Robin K
St Louis Acad
Lowell, MA

Alosi, Timothy B
Sacred Heart HS
Plymouth, MA

Alukonis, Karen
Lynn Classical HS
Lynn, MA

Alves, Mark D
Dartmouth HS
South Dartmouth,
MA

Alves, Susan
Madison Park HS
Boston, MA

Alwardt, Anita L
Bay Path Reg
North Oxford, MA

Ambach, Karen
Leslie
North Brookfield
North Brookfield,
MA

Amiott, William
Southbridge HS
Southbridge, MA

Amsden, David
Kendrick
St Johns HS
Holden, MA

Amstein, Jill
Mohawk Trail
Regional HS
Shelburne, MA

Anderson, Carrie
Ann
Methuen HS
Methuen, MA

Anderson, Cheri
New Bedford HS
New Bedfore, MA

Andrade,
Christopher
B M C Durfee HS
Fall River, MA

Andry, Natasha
Boston Technical
Boston, MA

Anton, Mary
Bishop Feehan HS
Mansfield, MA

Anton, Peter
Phillips Acad
Lawrence, MA

Antonian, Kim
Marie
Auburn HS
Auburn, MA

Antonio, James P
Bishop Fenwick HS
Peabody, MA

Antonucci, Maria
St Barnards C C HS
Leominster, MA

Apazidis, John
Boston Latin Schl
Boston, MA

Arangio, Alana M
Saugus HS
Saugus, MA

Arangio, Jennifer C
Saugus HS
Saugus, MA

Arbit, Lori
Stoughton HS
Stoughton, MA

Arieta, Michael
Silver Lake Regional
Kingston, MA

Armstrong, Carolyn A
Plymouth-Carver Regional SR HS
S Londonderry, VT

Armstrong, Patricia
Salem HS
Salem, MA

Arnold, III William P
Longmeadow HS
Springfield, MA

Arsenault, Theodore
Beverly HS
Beverly, MA

Artioli, Michelle
High School Of Springfield
Springfield, MA

Augeri, Maria-Rose
Presentation Of Mary Acad
Methuen, MA

Austin, Sheila Jo
Malden HS
Malden, MA

Axt, Jr Louis A
Drury SR HS
North Adams, MA

Bachand, Linda
Oxford HS
Oxford, MA

Baglione, Michele
Methuen HS
Methuen, MA

Baier, Cathy L
Dartmouth HS
S Dartmouth, MA

Bailey, Celia
Barnstable HS
Osterville, MA

Baker, Christine
Stoughton HS
Stoughton, MA

Baldwin, Aaron E
Marthas Vineyard Regional HS
Vineyard Haven, MA

Balester, Wendy
Randolph HS
Randolph, MA

Bambury, Jim C
Saugus HS
Saugus, MA

Banks, Cheryl
Fitchburg HS
Fitchburg, MA

Barbosa, Luis
Cathedral HS
Boston, MA

Barker, Jane
Andover HS
Andover, MA

Barletta, Bonnie
Matignon HS
Medford, MA

Barrette, Michael
Belmont HS
Belmont, MA

Barros, Luis
Tounton HS
Taunton, MA

Barros, Mary
Dartmouth HS
S Dartmouth, MA

Barry, John Joseph
Andover HS
Andover, MA

Barry, Judy
Revere HS
Revere, MA

Barry, Susan
King Philip Regional HS
Norfolk, MA

Barsam, Julie Roxanne
Belmont HS
Belmont, MA

Bartel, Wendy
Billerica Memorial
Pinehurst, MA

Basler, William Joseph
Burlington HS
Burlington, MA

Battista, Lisa
Holy Name Central Catholic HS
Auburn, MA

Beal, Todd N
Marblehead HS
Marblehead, MA

Beatrice, Jonathan L
Tri-Country Vocational Schl
Franklin, MA

Beck, George C
Xaverian Brothers
Wellesley, MA

Beland, Stephen
Central Catholic HS
Lowell, MA

Belavitch, David
Central Catholic HS
Salem, NH

Bell, Marlene
Dracut SR HS
Dracut, MA

Belletete, Michelle
St Bernards Central Catholic HS
Winchendon, MA

Bembenck, Debbie
Bartlett HS
Webster, MA

Bendel, Paula
Clinton HS
Clinton, MA

Bentley, Rhonda M
Berkshire Schl
New York, NY

Bentley, Tonia
Mission Church HS
Jamaica Plain, MA

Berger, Mark R
Plymouth-Carver
Plymouth, MA

Bergeron, Judith
Southbridge HS
Southridge, MA

Bernat, Jennifer
Hoosac Valley Regional HS
Cheshire, MA

Bernier, Anne Marie
Bartlett HS
Webster, MA

Berrios, Javier Palevi
HS Of Commerce
Springfield, MA

Berube, James
Salem HS
Salem, MA

Bialy, Beth
Bartlett HS
Webster, MA

Bier, Karen
Westwood HS
Westwood, MA

Bikales, Thomas J
Belmont HS
Lincoln, MA

Bishop, Rachell
Bedford HS
Bedford, MA

Bishop, Steven
Wachusett Regional
Holden, MA

Bistany, Marie
Cushing Acad
Ashburnham, MA

Bixby, Barbara
Westport HS
Westport, MA

Blacker, Dina
Sharon HS
Sharon, MA

Blake, Caryn L
Holyoke HS
Holyoke, MA

Blanchard, Michael
New Bedford HS
New Bedford, MA

Blaser, Christopher J
Lunenburg HS
Lunenburg, MA

Bloniarz, Todd Michael
Gateway Regional
Blandford, MA

Bodio, Lisa A
Milford HS
Milford, MA

Boger, Robert E
Mansfield HS
Mansfield, MA

Boisvert, Scott W
Drury SR HS
North Adams, MA

Bonczyk, Lori A
Holy Name CC HS
Worcester, MA

Bonner, Mary
Notre Dame Acad
Braintree, MA

Boothroyd, Renee
Newburyport HS
Newburyport, MA

Bordieri, Paula
Reading Memorial
Reading, MA

Botolino, Lisa J
Arlington HS
Arlington, MA

Bouchard, Sandra
B M C Durfee HS
Fall River, MA

Boudreau, Donna
Arlington SR HS
Arlington, MA

Boudreau, Marilyn Ann
Notre Dame
Worcester, MA

Boudrot, Pamela A
Dedham HS
Dedham, MA

Boulanger, Danielle
N Andover HS
North Andover, MA

Bourgeois, Cheryl
Matignon HS
Waltham, MA

Bowden, Karen
Whitman Hanson Regional HS
Whitman, MA

Bowen, Jr Joseph
Melrose HS
Melrose, MA

Bower, Colin
Manchester JR SR
Manchester, MA

Bowes, Sherylene
King Philip Regional HS
Plainville, MA

Boyer, Lawrence
Smith Acad
Hatfield, MA

Bracken, Michael E
Boston College HS
Braintree, MA

Bradford, Lauren D
Reading Memorial
Reading, MA

Braga, Charles
Bishop Connolly HS
Fall River, MA

Braithwaite, David
Falmouth HS
Falmouth, MA

Brennan, Jennifer
Hingham HS
Hingham, MA

Bresnahan, Cassandra
Bishop Stang HS
New Bedford, MA

Brideau, Michelle
Fitchburg HS
Fitchburg, MA

Brigham, David G
Sheppard Hill Regional HS
Charlton, MA

Brigham, Sharon Ann
Weymouth North
Weymouth, MA

Brodie, Heather
St Bernards HS
Ashby, MA

Bromberg, Robin
Revere HS
Revere, MA

Brooks, Lisa
Academy Of Notre
Westford, MA

Brown, Dahiel S
Milton Acad
Chicago, IL

Brown, David M
Plymouth-Carver
Plymouth, MA

Brown, Erica I
Natick HS
Natick, MA

Brown, Jennifer Ann
North Broouf ield
N Brookfield, MA

Brown, Lori A
Gloucester HS
Gloucester, MA

Brown, Robyn C
Brockton HS
Brockton, MA

Bruno, Roberta
Presentation Of Mary Acad
N Salem, NH

Buchalter, Stephen S
Algonquin Regional
Northboro, MA

Buchanan, Stephen S
Weston HS
Weston, MA

Buck, Jason P
Athol HS
Athol, MA

Buddenhagen, Kelly
Bishop Stang HS
Newport, RI

Budding, Anthony D
Lexington HS
Lexington, MA

Buggiero, Donna
Fontbonne Acad
Readville, MA

Buoniconti, Corinna
Agawam HS
Agawam, MA

Burke, Ann Marie
Bishop Stano HS
S Dartmouth, MA

Burke, Annmarie
Gardner HS
Gardner, MA

Burke, Jr James E
Brockton HS
Brockton, MA

Burnett, John
Turners Falls HS
Erving, MA

Burnham, Anne
Brimmer And May
Chestnut Hill, MA

Busa, Gina
Tewksbury Memorial HS
Tewksbury, MA

Bush, Brett M
Gardner HS
Gardner, MA

Butler, John A
Cogle & Cassidy HS
Taunton, MA

Cabral, Douglas
New Bedford HS
New Bedford, MA

Caggiano, Mark A
Dennis Yarmouth R
S Yarmouth, MA

Cairns, Theresa
Presentation Of Mary Acad
Hampstead, NH

Caitlin-Ahern, Jeanmarie
Bishop Feehan HS
Sharon, MA

Caldon, Maureen F
Cathedral HS
Hampden, MA

Call, Kristine M
Bellingham Memorial HS
Bellingham, MA

Callaghan, Patricia
Reading Memorial
Reading, MA

Callahan, Kerry
Leominster HS
Leominster, MA

Callahan, Susan
Easthampton HS
Easthampton, MA

Camarata, Anna
Boston Latin HS
Boston, MA

Cameron, Cheryl Ann
Trinton Regional
Rowley, MA

Cameron, Christine
Notre Dame Acad
S Weymouth, MA

Camp, Mark
North Middlesex Regional HS
Pepperell, MA

Campanale, Michael J
Arlington HS
Arlington, MA

Campbell, Roberta
Holy Name C C HS
Uxbridge, MA

Candido, Lisa
Dartmouth HS
N Dartmouth, MA

Cannatelli, Denise M
Malden HS
Malden, MA

Caparelliotis, David
Marian HS
Framingham, MA

Cappuccio, Carolyn
Norwood SR HS
Norwood, MA

Carbone, Matthew
Haverhill HS
Bradford, MA

Carchio, Donna
King Philip Regional HS
Wrentham, MA

Cardarelli, Cheryl
Malden HS
Malden, MA

Cardello, Joseph
Matignon HS
Medford, MA

Carnes, Gretchen
Shawsheen Valley
Tewksbury, MA

Caron, Cynthia
St Bernards C C HS
Fitchburg, MA

Caron, Lisa
Agawam HS
Feeding Hls, MA

Caron, Rosemary
Billerica Memorial
Billerica, MA

Carpenter, Kevin
Technical HS
Springfield, MA

Carr, Andrew E
Burlington HS
Burlington, MA

Carroll, Lesa
Old Rochester
Regional HS
Mattapoisett, MA

Carter, Donald
Dartmouth HS
N Dartmouth, MA

Caruso, Stephen M
Sacred Heart HS
N Weymouth, MA

Casavant, Lisa
Murdock HS
Winchendon, MA

Cass, Lisa
Abington HS
Abington, MA

Cassidy, Laura
Mansfield HS
Mansfield, MA

Castrucci, Karen
Milford HS
Milford, MA

Catalano, Joseph
Methuen HS
Methuen, MA

Cavanaugh, Lisa
Billerica Memorial
Billerica, MA

Cederholm, Laura
Marlboro HS
Marlboro, MA

Cerrone, Christina
M
Revere HS
Revere, MA

Cerrone, Jr
Salvatore C
Saint Dominic Savio
E Boston, MA

Chaff, Diane
Haverhill HS
Haverhill, MA

Chagaris, Keith E
Norwood HS
Norwood, MA

Chamnan, Phat
South Boston HS
Brighton, MA

Champoux, Noelle
Revere HS
Revere, MA

Chan, Hon Kee
Cushing Acad
Brookline, MA

Chandler, Charles
Boston Tech HS
Boston, MA

Charette, Catherine
A
Palmer HS
Three Rivers, MA

Chase, Edward
North Quincy HS
Quincy, MA

Chase, William
Central Catholic HS
Haverhill, MA

Cherrington, Colette
A
Milford HS
Hopedale, MA

Cheseborough,
Lynnette
West Roxbury HS
Dorchester, MA

Chesna, James
Revere HS
Revere, MA

Chesnicka, Daniel J
Westfield HS
Westfield, MA

Chester, Kellyann
Uxbridge HS
Uxbridge, MA

Chevaire, Nicole
Westford Acad
Westford, MA

Chiarenza, Joseph
Medford HS
Medford, MA

Chiavaras, Mary
Lunenburg HS
Lunenburg, MA

Chiavettone, Gerald
Heath
Joseph Case HS
Seekonk, MA

Chisholm, Donald P
Reading Memorial
Reading, MA

Choquette, Joseph R
Silver Lake Regional
Halifax, MA

Chow, Mat
Berkshire Schl
Hong Kong

Ciarcia, Christopher
J
Catholic Memorial
Dorchester, MA

Cimino, Daniela
Marian HS
Milford, MA

Clark, Amy
Lee HS
Otis, MA

Clark, Kino
Blackstone Vly
Regnl Vo-Tech HS
Milford, MA

Clark, Melanie
Bishop Feehan HS
N Attleboro, MA

Clark, Paul E
West Springfield HS
W Springfield, MA

Clark, Stephanie
Norwell HS
Norwell, MA

Clarkson, David C
Newburyport HS
Newburyport, MA

Cleary, John
St Johns HS
Grafton, MA

Cleary, Nancy
Westford Acad
Westford, MA

Clemons, Tracey
The High School Of
Springfield, MA

Clerc, Marc
Apponequet HS
Lakeville, MA

Cloutier, Rosella
Agawam HS
Agawam, MA

Co-Wallis, Gwen
Marie
Silver Lake Regional
Halifax, MA

Coe, Wayne R
Murdock HS
Winchendon, MA

Cogliano, Mike A
Billerica Memorial
Billerica, MA

Cohen, Rebecca
Winthrop HS
Winthrop, MA

Cole, Cynthia
Norwell HS
Norwell, MA

Collier, Karen
Sacred Heart HS
S Weymouth, MA

Collins, Andrew M
Millis HS
Millis, MA

Collins, Christopher
H
Millis HS
Millis, MA

Collins, Gregory M
Boston College HS
Quincy, MA

Collins, Melissa
Plymouth-Carver
Plymouth, MA

Collins, Michelle
Smilford HS
Milford, MA

Collins, Mike
Chicopee HS
Chicopee, MA

Collins, Roslinde M
Westford Acad
Westford, MA

Comeau, Marsha A
Dracut HS
Dracut, MA

Comeau, Noreen
Haverhill HS
Haverhill, MA

Conboy, Thomas L
Central Catholic HS
Salem, NH

Condit, Daniel
Maynard HS
Maynard, MA

Condon, Mark
Bishop Connolly HS
Westport, MA

Connell, John
Don Boco HS
Brighton, MA

Connell, Mary
Academy Of Notre
Westford, MA

Connolly, Emily
Fontbonne Acad
Dorchester, MA

Conrad, Robert C
Walpole HS
Walpole, MA

Conry, Christopher
Scott
Don Bosco
Technical HS
Chestnut Hill, MA

Cook, Jr Harland L
Walpole HS
Walpole, MA

Coons, Christine M
Monument
Mountain Regiona
Housatonic, MA

Coppola, Joseph P
Berkshire Schl
W Springfield, MA

Cora, Amarilys
Chelsea HS
Boston, MA

Coraccio, Carol
Billerica Memorial
Billerica, MA

Corcoran, Holly
Bedford HS
Bedford, MA

Cornelius, Douglas
Brockton HS
Brockton, MA

Correira, Jon Paul
Coyle-Cassidy HS
Taunton, MA

Corrigan, Kerry
Ursuline Acad
Norwood, MA

Corriveau, Tracy
Wachusett Regional
Auburn, MA

Cosentini, Michela
Classical HS
Springfield, MA

Cossaboom, Brian J
Middleboro HS
Middleboro, MA

Costa, Christopher
New Bedford HS
New Bedford, MA

Cote, Heather A
Silver Lake Reg HS
Halifax, MA

Cotton, Stacey
Norton HS
Norton, MA

Coughlin, Kathleen
Arliington Catholic
Arlington, MA

Cowden, Wendie
Auburn HS
Auburn, MA

Craig, Lee A
Easthampton HS
Easthampton, MA

Crance, Gina-Lyn
Southbridge HS
Southbridge, MA

Cravenho, Christine
A
Sacred Heart HS
Kingston, MA

Crevecoeur, Jean
Edward
Boston English HS
Dorchester, MA

Cridge, Patti
Westford Acad
Westford, MA

Crochetiere, Ronald
South Hadley HS
South Hadley, MA

Crowell, Jerelyn J
Woburn HS
Woburn, MA

Crowley, Christine
Silver Lake Regional
Kingston, MA

Cullinane, Carey
Marian HS
Sudbury, MA

Cunningham,
Caroline
Miss Halls Schl
Lagrangeville, NY

Cunningham,
Charles
Silver Lake Regional
Halifax, MA

Cunningham, John
Saugus HS
Saugus, MA

Currie, Jennifer
Fontbonne Acad
Plymouth, MA

Currier, Greg
Nauset Reg HS
N Truro, MA

Cutter, Stephanie
Bridgewater-Raynha
m Regional HS
Raynham, MA

Cutting, Stephanie
A
Belmont HS
Belmont, MA

Da Silva, Alice
Lowell HS
Lowell, MA

Daley, Joyce A
Hyde Park Acad
Hyde Park, MA

Dalimonte, Kim
Bartlett HS
Webster, MA

Dalpe, Mary T
Hudson Catholic HS
Marlboro, MA

Dalterio, John
St Johns HS
Hyannisport, MA

Daly, Joanne
Holy Name Central
Catholic HS
Worcester, MA

Dambrosio, Gennaro
St Dominic Savio
Revere, MA

Dandy, Michele S
West Springfield HS
W Springfield, MA

Daniels, Todd
Smith Acad
Hatfield, MA

Danielson, Serena
Arlington HS
Arlington, MA

Daron, Michael
Groton-Dustnable
Regional HS
Groton, MA

Dauphinais, Kevin
Braintree HS
Braintree, MA

Dauphinais, Wendy
Lunenburg HS
Lunenburg, MA

David, Lynn Emily
Murdock HS
Winchendon, MA

Davidson, Bridgette
Our Lady Of
Nazareth Acad
Lynnfield, MA

Davies, Christopher
Nelson
Chatham HS
N Chatham, MA

Davis, Bridgette
Nauset Regional HS
Eastham, MA

Dawson, Michael
New Bedford HS
New Bedford, MA

De Cristofaro,
Daniel
Silver Lake Regional
Kingston, MA

De Fusco, Andrea
Presentation Of
Mary Acad
Methuen, MA

De Leo, Kerri
Mohawk Trail
Regional HS
Buckland, MA

De Loria, Daniel G
Chicopee
Comprehensive HS
Chicopee, MA

De Luca, Michelle
St Mary HS
Lawrence, MA

De Lucia, Janice
Presentation Of
Mary Acad
Methuen, MA

De Mase, II Delia
Bishop Feehan HS
Franklin, MA

De Paulis, Cathy
Greater Lowel
Regional Vo Tech
Lowell, MA

De Simone, Michael
F
Burlington HS
Burlington, MA

De Voir, Michelle
Suzanne
Andover HS
Andover, MA

Decker, Tim
Bartlett HS
Webster, MA

Degaetano, Kelli
Bishop Connolly HS
Westport, MA

Deignan, Deidre M
Uxbridge HS
Uxbridge, MA

Del Negro, Philip C
Cathedral HS
Springfield, MA

Del Vecchio,
Michele A
Quincy HS
Quincy, MA

Delaney, Mary
St Bernards CC HS
Fitchburg, MA

Delfino, Lisa M
Attleboro HS
Attleboro, MA

Dellorfano, Anthony
Xaverian Bros HS
Cohasset, MA

Dellovo, Debbie
Burlington HS
Burlington, MA

Delorey, Christine M
Dennis-Yarmouth Regional HS
Yarmouth Port, MA

Deminski, Caroline
Presentation Of Mary Acad
Methuen, MA

Dempsey, Dianna
Monument Mountain Regiona
Gt Barrington, MA

Deneen, Michele
Arlington Catholic
Waltham, MA

Dennis, Colleen M
Cathedral HS
Enfield, CT

Depina, Maria
Madison Park HS
Boston, MA

Desmond, Jr Edward A
St Johns Prep Schl
Beverly, MA

Deveau, Charles
Don Bosco Tech HS
Roslindale, MA

Devine, Julie
Notre Dame Acad
Scituate, MA

Di Carlo, Jill
Marian HS
Framingham, MA

Di Cresce, Laurie A
Marian HS
Sudbury, MA

Di Fiore, Rose Maria
Presentation Of Mary Acad
Methuen, MA

Di Giacomo, Julie
Medford HS
Medford, MA

Di Palma, Hope G
Shawsheen Valley
Tewksbury, MA

Di Pilato, Vincent H
Tahanto Regional
Boylston, MA

Di Sabatino, Denise
Malden HS
Malden, MA

Diamond, Pamela
W Springfield HS
W Springfield, MA

Diaz, David
Drury SR HS
North Adams, MA

Dickson, Shannon
Drury SR HS
Clarksburg, MA

Digiovanni, Arthur
Central Catholic HS
Lowell, MA

Dimuzio, Angela
Rockland HS
Rockland, MA

Dion, Cheryl M
BMC Durfee HS
Fall River, MA

Dion, David
Montachusett Regional Vo Tec
Fitchburg, MA

Dion, Michelle
St Peter-Marian Cc
Sterling Junction, MA

Dirsa, Peter
Haverhill HS
Haverhill, MA

Dodge, Everlyn
Whitman Hanson Regional HS
Whitman, MA

Dodson, Donna
Algonquin Regional
Northboro, MA

Doherty, Jim P
Burlington HS
Burlington, MA

Dorr, Kim
Franklin HS
Franklin, MA

Dorr, Michael King
Newton Catholic HS
Newton, MA

Dorrington, Michael
Franklin HS
Franklin, MA

Doucette, Christine
North Shore Regional Voc HS
Beverly, MA

Dougan, Marianne
Randolph HS
Randolph, MA

Douglas, Janet
Smith Acad
Hatfield, MA

Downer, Michael E
Trinton Regional
Salisbury, MA

Downes, Katharine A
Milton Acad
Brookline, MA

Downie, Martin
Classical HS
Springfield, MA

Downing, Kimberly
Agawam HS
Agawam, MA

Doyle, Beth
Archbishop Williams
Weymouth, MA

Doyle, Craig M
Waltham SR HS
Waltham, MA

Doyle, Jr Kenneth J
Waltham SR HS
Waltham, MA

Doyle, Samantha
Bartlett HS
Webster, MA

Drake, John
Andover HS
Andover, MA

Drumm, Gerald
Lynn English HS
Lynn, MA

Duby, Carolyn
Bishop Connolly HS
Adamsville, RI

Dufault, Daniel
Central Catholic HS
Pelham, NH

Duffy, Mary Kate
Marian HS
Natick, MA

Duggan, Ann
North Quincy HS
Quincy, MA

Dulong, Susan
Apponequet Regional HS
East Freetown, MA

Dunn, Charles
Chelmsford HS
Chelmsford, MA

Dunn, Diane
St Bernards Cc HS
Fitch, MA

Dunn, Kathryn Lee
Dennis-Yarmouth Regional HS
West Yarmouth, MA

Dworman, Scott
Chapel Hill Chauncy Hall HS
Framingham, MA

Dwyer, Kimberly
Bellingham Mem
Bellingham, MA

Dye, Michael
Brokcton HS
Brockton, MA

Dyer, Karen
Braintree HS
Braintree, MA

Dzigas, Jay J
Marlboro HS
Marlboro, MA

Early, Jill M
St Louis Acad
Lowell, MA

Eaton, Nancy L
Bellingham Memorial JR SR HS
Bellingham, MA

Edry, Mark J
Acton Boxborough Regional HS
Acton, MA

Edson, Kimberley
Chatham JR SR HS
W Chatham, MA

Edson, Michael R
Athol HS
Athol, MA

Edwards, Sandra
Shepherd Hill Regioanl HS
Dudley, MA

Ela, Holly
Ayer HS
Ayer, MA

Elguezabal, Luis
Marian HS
Framingham, MA

Elias, Karen
Methuen HS
Methuen, MA

Ellis, Jenepher
Mauset Regional HS
S Orleans, MA

Ellis, Michael G
Nowell HS
Norwell, MA

Elster, Michael
St Johns HS
Shrewsbury, MA

Enxuga, Rose
N B HS
New Bedford, MA

Erickson, Harley A
Harwich HS
N Harwich, MA

Erickson, Julie
Stoughton HS
Stoughton, MA

Esper, Kristin Ann
Leominster HS
Leominster, MA

Estabrook, Timothy
Chicopee
Comprehensive HS
Chicopee, MA

Evans, Darold
Sandwich HS
Forestdale, MA

Fabbri, Judith F
Saint Rose HS
Chelsea, MA

Fair, Michael J
Natick HS
Natick, MA

Faria, Lisa
Coyle & Cassidy HS
Taunton, MA

Farina, Wendy A
Southwick HS
Southwick, MA

Farooq, Nabil M
Milford HS
Milford, MA

Farrell, Louis
Methuen HS
Methuen, MA

Farrell, Stephen
Holy Name Central
Catholic HS
North Grafton, MA

Faust, Michael John
Hingham HS
Poway, CA

Favazza, Mary
Gloucester HS
Gloucester, MA

Fearing, Shari
Hudson HS
Hudson, MA

Federico, Lisa
Haverhill HS
Haverhill, MA

Ferguson, Douglas E
Central Catholic HS
Salem, NH

Ferlez, Jennifer A
Leominster HS
Leominster, MA

Fernandes, John
New Bedford HS
New Bedford, MA

Ferrara, Tonia
Hudson HS
Hudson, MA

Ffrench, Sherdon
Malhai
Medford HS
Medford, MA

Fijal, Sherry L
Classical HS
Springfield, MA

Filiault, Michelle A
Moosac Valley HS
N Adams, MA

Filleti, Carmen
Don Bosco Tech
Hyde Park, MA

Fink, Katherine
Westfield HS
Westfield, MA

Finn, Christy
Acad Of Notre
Dunstable, MA

Fiore, Lisa Marie
Fontbonne Acad
Hyde Park, MA

Fitch, Brian
Plymouth Carver
Plymouth, MA

Fitch, Michelle
Taconic HS
Pittsfield, MA

Fitzgibbons,
Stephen
Holyoke HS
Holvoke. MA

Fitzpatrick, Jr Earl
W
Malden Catholic HS
Malden, MA

Fitzpatrick, Michael
F J
Catholic Memorial
Dedham, MA

Fitzsimmons, Maura
Matighon HS
Melrose, MA

Flanigan, Annmarie
Bridgewater-Raynha
m Regional HS
Bridgewater, MA

Flavin, Edward J
Quincy HS
Quincy, MA

Flores, Rebecca
Academy Of Notre
Concord, NH

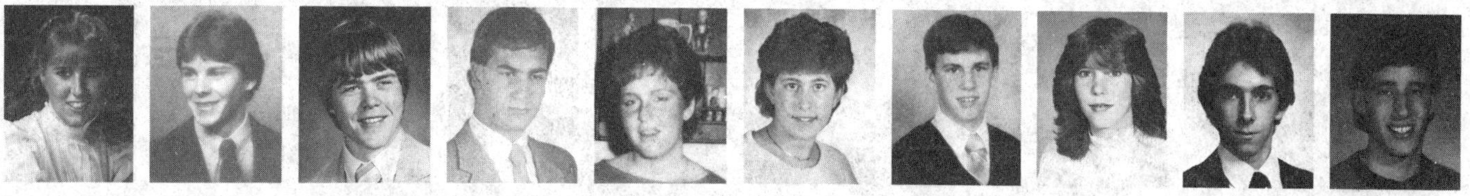

Flynn, Melissa J
Oakmont Regional
Westminster, MA

Flynn, Paul
Bishop Feehan HS
Walpole, MA

Folan, Karl M
Lynn Vocational
Technical Inst
Lynn, MA

Foley, Brian
Cathedral HS
Springfield, MA

Foley, Christine
Marie
Wachusett Regional
Rutland, MA

Fonner, Suzanne
Cathedral HS
Springfield, MA

Forbes, Michael
Whitman Hanson
Regional HS
Whitman, MA

Ford, Kathryn
Lexington HS
Lexington, MA

Forkey, Joseph N
Lunenburg HS
Lunenburg, MA

Forman, Brian
Randolph HS
Randolph, MA

Forster, Lisa
St Bernards Central
Catholic HS
Leominster, MA

Fortin, Wendy D
Holyoke HS
Holyoke, MA

Forziati, Christine
Easthampton HS
Easthampton, MA

Foster, Jr James H
Boston Technical
Jamaica Plain, MA

Foster, Jane
Hingham HS
Hingham, MA

Fowler, Heather J
East Bridgewater
E Bridgewater, MA

Fox, Debra
Marblehead HS
Marblehead, MA

Fox, Steven
Malden HS
Malden, MA

Franciose, Stephanie
Beverly HS
Beverly, MA

Francis, John
Central Catholic HS
Bradford, MA

Francis, Scott
Holy Name Central
Catholic HS
Worcester, MA

Frederick, Ronald A
Chicopee HS
Chicopee, MA

Freeman, Jill
Holliston HS
Holliston, MA

French, W Scot
Mt Everett Reg HS
Sheffield, MA

Friel, Kerri A
Andover HS
Andover, MA

Fuchs, Julius A
St Joseph Central
Pittsfield, MA

Fuller, Stephen D
Braintree HS
Braintree, MA

Fullerton, Charlotte
L
Saint Mary HS
Haverhill, MA

Furtado, Bernadette
Biship Stang HS
New Bedford, MA

Fusco, Jr Anthony
Central Catholic HS
Methuen, MA

Fushpanski, Suzanne
Triton Regional HS
Salisbury, MA

Gagnon, Lynette M
Westfield HS
Westfield, MA

Gagnon, Mary Beth
Bishop Connolly HS
Fall River, MA

Gallagher, Elizabeth
Fontbonne Acad
Stoughton, MA

Gallien, Sandra
David Prouty HS
E Brookfield, MA

Games, Debbi S
Georgetown HS
Georgetown, MA

Gatzke, Robin
Lexington HS
Lexington, MA

Gaudet, Heidi
High School Of
Springfield, MA

Gavoni, Beth
Silver Lake Regional
Kingston, MA

Gavron, David
Masconomet
Regional HS
W Boxford, MA

Gaynor, Ann
Randolph HS
Randolph, MA

Gelgut, Jacqueline
Westfield HS
Westfield, MA

Gelinas, Mark
St Bernards CC HS
Fitchburg, MA

Gentile, Susan E
Mount St Joseph
Newton Highlands, MA

Gentili, Gina
Mansfield HS
Mansfield, MA

Getchell, Stefanie Adams
Newburyport HS
Newburyport, MA

Getson, Debbie
Framingham South
Framingham, MA

Giaramita, Karrie
Bishop Fenwick HS
Saugus, MA

Giardina, Michele
Woburn HS
Woburn, MA

Gilligan, Lawrence
Malden HS
Malden, MA

Gillman, Michael
Easthampton HS
Easthampton, MA

Gilmartin, Brian
St Johns HS
Auburn, MA

Girr, Catherine
Longmeadow HS
Longmeadow, MA

Gladstone, Pamela
Methuen HS
Methuen, MA

Glavickas, Catherine
Easthampton HS
Easthampton, MA

Glushik, John
Westfield HS
Westfield, MA

Goddeau, Scott
Cathedral HS
Somers, CT

Godek, Jr Thomas G
Hull HS
Hull, MA

Godes, Arlene
Randolph HS
Randolph, MA

Goldberg, Paula
Governor Dummer
Andover, MA

Golden, Christopher
Marian HS
Framingham, MA

Gomes, David
New Bedford HS
New Bedford, MA

Goodreau, Tricia J
Westfield HS
Westfield, MA

Gordon, Kimberly
Leicester HS
Roddale, MA

Gosselin, Amy
Lawrence HS
Lawrence, MA

Gosselin, Michelle
Bishop Stang HS
Westport, MA

Gould, Kenneth
Central Catholic HS
Lawrence, MA

Goulston, Kenneth
Newton North HS
Newtonville, MA

Govoni, James M
Plymouth Carver
Plymouth, MA

Gracia, Matthew D
New Bedford HS
New Bedford, MA

Grant, Heather Lee
David Prouty
Regional HS
E Brookfield, MA

Grant, Kimberly
Attleboro HS
Attleboro, MA

Gray, Peter L
Malden HS
Malden, MA

Greaves, Sheila
Medway HS
Medway, MA

Greelish, Jeffrey
Holy Home HS
W Brookfield, MA

Greelish, Maureen
Holy Name C C HS
Fiskdale, MA

Green, Pamela
Archbishop Williams
Weymouth, MA

Greenberg, Myles D
Andover HS
Andover, MA

Greene, Pamela
Bishop Feehan HS
Cumberland, RI

Gregory, Lisa
Wareham HS
Wareham, MA

Griffin, Jeanne M
Archbishop Williams
Randolph, MA

Griffin, Michael J
Westfield Vocational
Westfield, MA

Grinnell, Gary M
Foxborough HS
Foxboro, MA

Grugnale, Stacy
Classical HS
Lynn, MA

Guarino, Daniel
St Dominic Savio
Revere, MA

Guerin, Donna
Greater Lowell Voke
Lowell, MA

Guertin, Lisa
St Bernards C C HS
Winchendon, MA

Gulliver, Karen A
Leominster HS
Leominster, MA

Gulluni, Maria
Cathedral HS
Springfield, MA

Gustowski, Dianne H
St Marys HS
Worcester, MA

Gutowski, Richard G
West Springfield HS
W Springfield, MA

Guyer, Eric
Masconomet
Regional HS
Middleton, MA

Haber, Veronica
North Middlesex
Regional HS
Ft Devens, MA

Haddon, Richard J
Blackstone Valley
Vo Tech HS
E Douglas, MA

Hagglund, John
St Johns HS
Sutton, MA

Hagopian, Gregory S
Belmont HS
Belmont, MA

Hague, Marc
Northbridge JR SR
Whitinsville, MA

Haley, Tracy
Northbridge JR SR
Northbridge, MA

Hall, Julie
Monument
Mountain Regiona
W Stockbridge, MA

Hall, La Rhetta
HS Of Commerce
Sprinffield, MA

Hallisey, Martha
Fontbonne Acad
Avon, MA

Halpin, Jacqueline D
Archbishop Williams
Weymouth, MA

Hammond, Sandra
Wellesley SR HS
Wellesley, MA

Hancock, Dwayne
Westport HS
Westport, MA

Handren, Mark
Coyle & Cassidy HS
Taunton, MA

Hannabury, John
Malden Catholic HS
Malden, MA

Hanry, Herman
Technical HS
Springfield, MA

Harcovitz, Katherine
King Philip Regional HS
Norfolk, MA

Harding, Jennifer A
Georgetown HS
Georgeotwn, MA

Harper, Gary
Northbridge JR-SR
Whitinsville, MA

Harrington, Brian
Cathedral HS
Springfield, MA

Harrop, Pamela M
Bishop Feehan HS
N Attleboro, MA

Hart, Joseph
West Roxbury HS
Boston, MA

Hartmann, Donald A
Tahanto Regional
Boylston, MA

Hatcher, Jeffrey L
Mosconomet Regional HS
Boxford, MA

Hayes, Tanja
Bishop Connolly HS
Fall River, MA

Hayter, Royce
Joseph Case HS
Seekonk, MA

Healy, Suzette
Tahanto Regional
Boylston, MA

Healy, Thomas
Tri-County Reg
Franklin, MA

Hebert, Jeffrey M
Grafton Memorial SR HS
S Grafton, MA

Heinegg, Ayo P
Phillips Acad
Saudi Arabia

Henault, Christine
Medway JR SR HS
Medway, MA

Henderson, Mark
Bridgewater Raynham Regiona
Bridgewater, MA

Hennemuth, Gary
Falmouth HS
N Falmouth, MA

Herbert, Jr Roger G
Barnstable HS
Centerville, MA

Hermenau, Wayne
Brockton HS
Brockton, MA

Hewson, Sheri
Stoughton HS
Stoughton, MA

Higgins, Cindy
Barnstable HS
Hyannis, MA

Hill, Michael
Chicopee HS
Chicopee, MA

Hilliard, Catherine
Hopedale JR SR HS
Hopedale, MA

Hinds, Dawn
Jeremiah E Burke
Dorchester, MA

Hines, David
Lynn English HS
Lynn, MA

Hines, Kathleen B
Randolph HS
Randolph, MA

Hingston, James Christopher
Columbus HS
Boston, MA

Hoag, Michael R
Bishop Feehan HS
Attleboro, MA

Hoffmeister, Mitchell
Franklin HS
Franklin, MA

Hogan, Melissa A
Dartmoth HS
S Darmouth, MA

Holbrook, Keith M
Bishop Stang HS
Wareham, MA

Holloway, Marie
St Peter-Marian C C
Worcester, MA

Holmes, Kirsten Erica
Holy Name Central Catholic HS
Auburn, MA

Holton, Jeffrey M
West Bridgewater
West Bridgewatr, MA

Holway, III Lowell H
Natick HS
S Natick, MA

Hopkinson, Mary B
Milford HS
Milford, MA

Horgan, Kevin P
Ayer HS
Ayer, MA

Horgan, Timothy J
Woburn SR HS
Woburn, MA

Howard, Brendan
St Bernards C C HS
Leominster, MA

Hubbard, Karen Lee
Wakefield HS
Wakefield, MA

Hudlin, Melissa Anne
Ayer HS
Ayer, MA

Hudson, Holly
Mohawk Trail Regional HS
Rowe, MA

Huff, Susan A
Girls Catholic HS
Everett, MA

Hultin, Stephen O
Rockport HS
Rockport, MA

Humason, Larry
Lee HS
Monterey, MA

Hunte, Pamela L
Academy Of Notre Dame HS
Mason, NH

Hurley, Brian C
Doherty Memorial
Worcester, MA

Hurley, Thomas M
Coyle And Cassidy
South Easton, MA

Hutner, Edward L
Westborough HS
Westboro, MA

Huuskonen, Sonene
Salem HS
Salem, MA

Hyppolite, Karla L
Boston Latin Schl
Dorchester, MA

Imbrescia, Philip
Everett HS
Everett, MA

Isaksen, Mark
Fairhaven HS
Fairhaven, MA

Isserlis, Debra J
Somerset HS
Somerset, MA

Jackson, Timango
High School Of
Springfield, MA

Jankius, Brian C
Quaboag Regional
W Brookfield, MA

Janski, Todd E
Gardner HS
Gardner, MA

Joerres, Christine
Dartmouth HS
N Dartmouth, MA

Johnson, Courtney
Burncoat SR HS
Worcester, MA

Johnson, Elizabeth B
Mount Saint Joseph
Watertown, MA

Johnson, Ian P
Westboro HS
Westboro, MA

Johnson, Jeffrey
Smith Acad
N Hatfield, MA

Johnson, Kathryn
King Philip Regional HS
Norfolk, MA

Johnson, Maureen
Weymouth North
Weymouth, MA

Johnson, Susan A
King Philip
Regional HS
Plainville, MA

Jones, Amybeth
Wakefield Memorial
Wakefield, MA

Jones, Paul F
Westfield HS
Westfield, MA

Joyce, William
Boston College HS
Medford, MA

Judson, Jerilyn
Burlington HS
Burlington, MA

Jump, Kerri-Lynn
Acad Of Notre
Lowell, MA

Justinski, Donna
North Attleboro HS
N Attleboro, MA

Kaczmarek, Stephen
Berkshire HS
River Hills, WI

Kadilis, Alexia A
Bishop Connolly HS
Middletown, RI

Kaiser, Robert D
Winthrop HS
Winthrop, MA

Kam, Paul Vang
Burlington HS
Burlington, MA

Kampfer, Faith
Marlboro HS
Marlboro, MA

Kamrowski, Michael
Wareham HS
Buzzards Bay, MA

Kane, Nancy M
St Clare HS
Hyde Park, MA

Kapsambelis, Niki D
Norwell HS
Norwell, MA

Karadizian, Richard
Z
Watertown HS
Watertown, MA

Karalekas,
Christopher
New Bedford HS
New Bedford, MA

Karkutt, Karen
St Bernards HS
Fitchburg, MA

Katsos, George E
Arlington HS
Arlington, MA

Katz, Jessyca L
Andover HS
Andover, MA

Kawa, Shirley
Whitman-Hanson
Regional HS
Whitman, MA

Keddy, Carolyn
Fontbonne Acad
Quincy, MA

Keefe, Jr Kevin
Michael
Boston College HS
Winchester, MA

Kehoe, Dean
Revere HS
Revere, MA

Keiran, Kathleen M
Cardinal Spellman
N Falmouth, MA

Keith, James
Faith Baptist
Christian Acad HS
W Springfield, MA

Kelleher, Heather
Notre Dame Acad
Norwell, MA

Kelley, Therese
Coyle And Cassidy
Taunton, MA

Kelliher, Brendan
Norwood SR HS
Norwood, MA

Kelly, Edward
Westford Acad
Westford, MA

Kessinger, Laurie
Hull HS
Hull, MA

Khambaty, Murriam
J
Gloucester HS
Gloucester, MA

Khozozian, John
Watertown HS
Watertown, MA

Kiley, Jr William P
Triton Reg HS
Rowley, MA

Kilgore, Lisa B
Braintree HS
Braintree, MA

Killion, Paula
Blue Hills Regional
Holbrook, MA

Kim, Andrew
Malden Catholic HS
Medford, MA

King, Christopher
Holy Name Central
Catholic HS
Spencer, MA

King, John A
No Middlesex Reg
W Townsend, MA

King, Renese E
South Lancaster
South Lancaster,
MA

King, Sheryl
Monson HS
Monson, MA

King, William R
Frontier Regional
So Deerfield, MA

Kingman, Eamon R
East Bridgewater
East Bridgewater,
MA

Kingsbury, Dale A
Newburyport HS
Newburyport, MA

Kingsley, Pamela
Joseph Case HS
Swansea, MA

Kirwin, Laura
Braintree HS
Braintree, MA

Kitka, Jr Frederick
Bartlett HS
Webster, MA

Knightly, Johnna
Metheun HS
Methuen, MA

Knox, John Anthony
Weymouth
Vocational Technica
E Weymouth, MA

Kohli, Neeraj
Holliston HS
Holliston, MA

Kosak, Carolyn
Arlington HS
Arlington, MA

Koss, Dana
Needham HS
Needham, MA

Kourepenis, Kerry S
Watertown HS
Watertown, MA

Kozlowski, Debra
Bartlett HS
Webster, MA

Kratz, David F
Central Catholic HS
N Andover, MA

Krause, Tonya
North Brookfield
N Brookfield, MA

Kreitzberg, Tina
Stoughton HS
Stoughton, MA

Kress, Walter P
East Hampton HS
Easthampton, MA

Krigest, Mitchell
Milton HS
Milton, MA

Kritzas, Athena
Haverhill HS
Bradford, MA

Kroll, Dana
Southbridge HS
Southbridge, MA

Kupiec, Yael
Bedford HS
Bedford, MA

Kurto, Peter M
Deerfield Acad &
Saratoga Spgs HS
Saratoga Springs,
NY

La Belle, Jr David A
Turners Falls HS
Millers Falls, MA

La Brunerie,
Rebecca
Dana Hall HS
Columbia, MO

La Court, Lori Ann
Everett HS
Everett, MA

La Scola, Eric
Newton North HS
Newton, MA

Ladetto, Stephen J
Bourne HS
Sagamore, MA

Ladurantaye, Renee
Taunton HS
Taunton, MA

Lafferty, Dawn
Diman Regional Voc Tech HS
Fall River, MA

Lafrenais, Kerry
Southbridge HS
Southbridge, MA

Lagace, Michael
Bridgewater-Raynham Reg HS
Raynham, MA

Lague, Susan
Milford HS
Milford, MA

Lake, Luellen
Madison Park HS
Boston, MA

Lambert, Brian M
Central Catholic HS
El Paso, TX

Lanciani, Mike
Monachusett Regional HS
Sterling, MA

Langlais, Catherine
Bishop Connolly HS
Fall River, MA

Langord, Laura L
Algonquin Regional
Southborough, MA

Lariviere, Susan
Bartlett HS
Webster, MA

Larkin, Christopher
Hopedale JR SR HS
Hopedale, MA

Larson, Geoffrey Owen
Mohawk Trail Regional HS
Colrain, MA

Larson, Mark
Marian HS
Framingham, MA

Latham, Edward A
Sandwich HS
Sandwich, MA

Lattin, Jeffrey J
Whitman-Hanson Regional HS
Whitman, MA

Latulippe, Michelle
St Marys HS
Westfield, MA

Laura, Richard
Matignon HS
Somerville, MA

Laurino, Paul P
Boston Latin Schl
Roslindale, MA

Lawrence, Maria A
Notre Dame
Worcester, MA

Lawson, Lisa
Southwick HS
Springfield, MA

Lawton, Alisha O
Framingham North
Hyde Park, MA

Lazo, Michael L
Boston College HS
W Roxbury, MA

Le Brun, James K
Milford HS
Milford, MA

Le Tourneau, Paul
Taunton HS
Berkley, MA

Leary, Betty Ann
Holy Names Christian HS
Worcester, MA

Leavitt, John R R
Northfield Mt Hermon Schl
Southborough, MA

Leclerc, Jay
St Peter Marian HS
Worcester, MA

Leclerc, Scott
St Peter-Marion CC
Worcester, MA

Ledgister, Floyd
Randolph HS
Randolph, MA

Leduc, Pamela
Southbridge HS
Southbridge, MA

Lee, David Chun Young
Cushing Acad
Hong Kong

Legere, Michelle L
English HS
Lynn, MA

Leistritz, Michael
Holy Name Central Catholic HS
Worcester, MA

Lemay, Michael P
Oakmont Regional
Westminster, MA

Lenart, Peter C
Cathedral HS
Chicopee, MA

Lentini, Andrea
Woburn SR HS
Woburn, MA

Leonardo, Lisa A
Somerset HS
Somerset, MA

Leroy, Emmlynn L
North Cambridge Catholic HS
Somerville, MA

Lescarbeau, Kim
Drury SR HS
N Adams, MA

Leslie, Cheryl
Northbridge JR & SR HS
Whitinsville, MA

Letizio, Gina
Presentation Of Mary Acad
Lawrence, MA

Letourneau, Michelle
Presentation Of Mary Acad
Chester, NH

Lever, Joann
Methuen HS
Methuen, MA

Levine, Rachel A
Newton North HS
Newton, MA

Lifrak, Joseph
Bishop Connolly HS
Fall River, MA

Lima, James
Salem HS
Salem, MA

Linger, Dave
Holliston HS
Holliston, MA

Linscott, Julie
Newburyport HS
Newburyport, MA

Litchfield, Richard J
Brockton HS
Brockton, MA

Livingstone, Lisa
North Quincy HS
Quincy, MA

Llewelyn, Daniel P
Pioneer Valley Regional HS
Northfield, MA

Lobo, Jason M
Southwick HS
Southwick, MA

Lodish, Heidi
The Brimmer And May Schl
Brookline, MA

Lombard, Theresa
Norton HS
Norton, MA

Lombardi, John
Holy Name HS
Worcester, MA

Lombardozzi, Lisa A
Malden HS
Malden, MA

Lopes, Dulce
Brockton HS
Central Falls, RI

Lopes, Paul R
Fairhaven HS
Fairhaven, MA

Lord, Kenneth Ronald
Westport HS
Westport, MA

Lorden, Diana
Groton-Dunstable
Groton, MA

Lovato, Cheryl
Plymouth-Carver
Carver, MA

Loverro, Jodi
Clinton HS
Clinton, MA

Lucchetti, Mary
Fontbonne Acad
Milton, MA

Luccio, Darlene
Ursuline Acad
Dedham, MA

Lucey, Joanne
Holy Name CCHS
Worcester, MA

Lukowski, Doreen
Masconemet Regional HS
Topsfield, MA

Luter, Kelley L
Bedford HS
Bedford, MA

Luz, Troy
Diman Regional Voke HS
Fall River, MA

Lydon, Jr James F
St Dominic Savio
Chelsea, MA

Lynch, Jennie
Fontbonne Acad
Stoughton, MA

Lynch, Jerome F
Cathedral HS
Springfeld, MA

Lynch, Kimberley
Middleboro HS
Middleboro, MA

Lyons, Jean
Milton HS
Milton, MA

Lyons, Susan
Boston Latin HS
Boston, MA

Mac Donald, Robin
Bridgewater-Raynham Regional HS
Raynham, MA

Mac Donald, Stephen J
St Patricks HS
Waltham, MA

Mac Kinnon, Corinne
Taunton HS
Taunton, MA

Mac Kizer, Richard
St Johns HS
W Boylston, MA

Mac Nevin, Colin
Newton North HS
Newton Lower Fls, MA

Machnik, Michael C
Central Catholic HS
Salem, NH

Maguire, Jr Dennis F
Bishop Fenwick HS
Lynn, MA

Mahanor, Elizabeth
Fontbonne Acad
Milton, MA

Mahoney, Gerald J
Cardinal Spellman
Brockton, MA

Majkut, Tracey
Bridgewater-Raynham Regional HS
Raynham, MA

Malandrinos, Paul
Chicopee HS
Chicopee, MA

Maldonado, Luis A
Holyoke HS
Holyoke, MA

Malkasian, Matthew H
Northbridge JR SR
Whitinsville, MA

Mallloux, Diane
Fitchburg HS
Fitchburg, MA

Manheim, Francesca
Falmouth HS
Falmouth, MA

Mankodi, Sonal
Peabody Veterans Memorial HS
Peabody, MA

Manning, Sharon A
Tyngsboro JR-SR
Tyngsboro, MA

Mara, Joseph D
Grafton HS
South Grafton, MA

Marciano, Sue
Woburn Senior HS
Woburn, MA

Marcus, Greta
Randolph HS
Randolph, MA

Marino, Chris
Malden Catholic HS
Malden, MA

Markella, Jay D
Abington HS
Abington, MA

Marley, Brenda M
St Mary HS
Lawrence, MA

Marmer, Mark
Andover HS
Andover, MA

Marquis, Charles
English HS
Lynn, MA

Marquis, Sheila
Presentation Of Mary Acad
Lawrence, MA

Marsolais, Denise
Triton Regional HS
Salisbury, MA

Martin, Doug
New Bedford HS
New Bedford, MA

Martone, II Dino J
Andover HS
Andover, MA

Maryea, Minnah
High School Of Springfield, MA

Matarazzo, Roseann
Christopher Columbus HS
Boston, MA

Matthews, Christopher
English HS
Boston, MA

Mattress, Mary
Holy Name CC HS
Worcester, MA

Matula, Carolyn Ann
Somerset HS
Somerset, MA

Maurello, Anthony J
St Johns HS
Shrewsbury, MA

Mayall, Robin
Durfee HS
Fall River, MA

Mayer, Holly
Mount Alvernia HS
W Roxbury, MA

Mayo, Michaela
East Bridgewater
E Bridgewater, MA

Mazza, Tara
Mohwak Trail Regional HS
Plainfield, MA

Mc Auley, Jr Daniel
Medford HS
Medford, MA

Mc Bride, Barbara E
Burlington HS
Burlington, MA

Mc Cann, Kimberly M
Westfield HS
Westfield, MA

Mc Carthy, Jennie
Academy Of Notre
Tewksbury, MA

Mc Carthy, Joanna M
Duxbury HS
Duxbury, MA

Mc Carthy, Kelly A
Cathedral HS
Indian Orchard, MA

Mc Carthy, Sean
Catholic Memorial
W Roxbury, MA

Mc Clellan, Mark D
Marblehead HS
Marblehead, MA

Mc Collem, Carolyn
Bedford HS
Bedford, MA

Mc Cormack, Amy C
Scituate HS
Scituate, MA

Mc Donald, Megan E
Cathedral HS
Springfield, MA

Mc Donough, Kathleen V
Dedham HS
Dedham, MA

Mc Eachern, John H
Gloucester HS
Gloucester, MA

Mc Eleney, Patrick
Arlington Catholic
Arlington, MA

Mc Elligott, Jr David
Arlington Catholic
Arlington, MA

Mc Ganty, Chris
Nashoba Regional
Bolton, MA

Mc Gilvray, Heather
Bedford Public HS
Bedford, MA

Mc Gonagle, Michael D
Sandwich JR SR HS
Sandwich, MA

Mc Gonagle, Paul C
Burlington HS
Burlington, MA

Mc Gough, Karen
Arlington Catholic
Arlington, MA

Mc Kay, Kathy
Joseph Case HS
Swansea, MA

Mc Kenna, Maureen
Silver Lake Regional
Halifax, MA

Mc Keown, Denise M
Andover HS
Andover, MA

Mc Laughlin, Julie
Lowell HS
Lowell, MA

Mc Laughlin, Mary Ellen
Ursuline Acad
W Roxbury, MA

Mc Lean, Adam J
Chicopee Comprehensive HS
Chicopee, MA

Mc Lellan, Helenanne
Marian HS
Hopkinton, MA

Mc Nally, Peter R
N Quincy HS
Quincy, MA

Mc Naught, James A
Xaverian Brothers
Walpole, MA

Mc Phelim, Lisa
Concord-Carlisle HS
Concord, MA

Mc Quade, Kathryn
Presentation Of Mary Acad
Hampstead, NH

Medeiros, Lisa
Wilmington HS
Wilmington, MA

Medeiros, Maryellen
Bishop Connolly HS
Fall River, MA

Medeiros, Nelson
New Bedford HS
New Bedford, MA

Melanson, Lisa
St Bernards Central Catholic HS
Fitchburg, MA

Melanson, Norita
St Gregory HS
Dorchester, MA

Melia, Mary
Beverly HS
Beverly, MA

Mercer, Robert
Malden HS
Malden, MA

Merchant, Lorraine
Fontbonne Acad
Canton, MA

Mercurio, Joseph
Arlington Catholic
Billerica, MA

Meringer, Brian E
Rockport HS
Rockport, MA

Michaeles, Christopher
St Johns HS
Sturbridge, MA

Michalewich, Richard
Bishop Connolly HS
Somerset, MA

Miga, Theodore
Holyoke HS
Holyoke, MA

Miles, Shannon Megan
Holyoke HS
Holyoke, MA

Miller, Brian D
Wareham HS
Wareham, MA

Miller, Debra S
Randolph HS
Randolph, MA

Minkwitz, III Russell E
Walpole HS
Walpole, MA

Mirovich, Stephanie
St Bernards Central Catholic HS
Fitchburg, MA

Mitri, Ramzi
Holbrook JR SR HS
Holbrook, MA

Moccio, Anthony
Agawam HS
Agawam, MA

Mokrzycki, Kerry J
West Springfield HS
W Springfield, MA

Monast, Robert
BMC Durfee HS
Fall River, MA

Monchamp, Lisa
Holyoke Catholic
Holyoke, MA

Mooney, Christine
Beverly HS
Beverly, MA

Mooney, Jay F
Quaboag Reg HS
Warren, MA

Moore, Jessica M
Nipmuc Regional
Hopedale, MA

Mooy, Bruce E
Ayer HS
El Paso, TX

Morando, Laurie
Maiden HS
Malden, MA

Moriarty, Patricia M
Fontbonne Acad HS
Milton, MA

Morin, Pamela
St Bernards CC HS
Leominster, MA

Morris, Michael
Brockton HS
Brockton, MA

Mosman, Deborah
Holy Name Central Catholic HS
Grofton, MA

Mousley, Jeffrey R
R C Mahar Regional
Orange, MA

Muckian, Kristen
Classical HS
Lynn, MA

Muksuris, Stelyio
Matignon HS
Cambridge, MA

Mulcahy, Kathleen E
Doherty Memorial
Worcester, MA

Mulch, Theodore
North Quincy HS
Quincy, MA

Mullaney, Stephen
St Bernards Central Catholic HS
Leominster, MA

Munroe, Daniel John
David Prouty HS
East Brookfield, MA

Murad, Elaine
Saint Clare HS
Roslindale, MA

Murphy, Carolyn
Holyoke HS
Holyoke, MA

Murphy, Geraldine
North Quincy HS
Quincy, MA

Murphy, Patricia A
Belmont HS
Belmont, MA

Murray, John
Williston-Northampton HS
Atlanta, GA

Murray, Lisa
Hingham HS
Hingham, MA

Murray, Patrick J
Beverly HS
Beverly Farms, MA

Nadeau, Jr Elliott L
Shrewsbury SR HS
Shrewsbury, MA

Naggiar, Edoardo R
Bishop Connolly HS
Fall River, MA

Nambiar, Sunitha N
Lincoln-Sudbury Regional HS
Sudbury, MA

Nash, Kerry
North Quincy HS
Quincy, MA

Nason, Daniel F
St Bernards Central Catholic HS
Westminster, MA

Nault, Patricia
Presentation Of Mary Acad
Lawrence, MA

Naze, James M
Marlboro HS
Marlboro, MA

Nedder, Joseph A
Xaverian Brothers
Dedham, MA

Nelson, Debbie
Holy Name Central Catholic HS
Worcester, MA

Nelson, Eric
St Johns Preparatory Schl
Boxford, MA

Nemet, Irene
Weymouth North
E Weymouth, MA

Neret, Tracey A
Milton HS
Milton, MA

Nichols, William
Marian HS
Hopkinton, MA

Nicholson, Gary J
Xaverian Brothers
Abington, MA

Nielsen, Carl Daniel
Tantasqua Regional
Brookfield, MA

Niestepski, Chris
Barstable HS
Centerville, MA

Nilsen, Susan
Silverlake Regional
Kingston, MA

Nitkin, Deborah
Randolph HS
Randolph, MA

Nivala, Eric
Gardner HS
Gardner, MA

Nogueira, Paula
Classical HS
Springfield, MA

Noonan, Jeanne-Marie
Fontbonne Acad
Brockton, MA

Noyes, Douglas Evan
Tewksbury Memorial HS
Tewksbury, MA

Nunna, Padmini
Marian HS
Framingham, MA

O Brien, Christine
Holy Name C C HS
Worcester, MA

O Brien, John P
Needham HS
Needham, MA

O Connell, David E
Sacred Heart HS
Plympton, MA

O Leary, Kelly Ann
St Bernards C C HS
Fitchburg, MA

O Shaughnessy, John P
Minnechaug R HS
Wilbraham, MA

O Sullivan, Colleen
Catherkal HS
Springfield, MA

O Toole, Austin A
Uxbridge HS
Uxbridge, MA

Obrien, Tara
Fontbonne Academy
Milton, MA

Omeara, Patricia
Randolph HS
Randolph, MA

Oncay, William
Medway HS
Medway, MA

Orlandi, Lisa A
Westfield HS
Westfield, MA

Ortyl, Kevin
Holyoke Catholic
Easthampton, MA

Orzechowski, Darren E
Palmer HS
Palmer, MA

Ouellette, Robert
Bishop Connolly HS
Westport, MA

Paine, Jr Richard S
Narragansett Regional HS
Baldwinville, MA

Palermo, Richard
Central Catholic HS
Plaiston, NH

Panico, Daniel
Saugus HS
Saugus, MA

Pappas, Christos J
North Quincy HS
Quincy, MA

Paquin, Marc J
Tewksbury Memorial HS
Tewksbury, MA

Parent, Albert
New Bedford HS
New Bedford, MA

Parent, Mark
New Bedford HS
New Bedford, MA

Parisi, Scott P
Gloucester HS
Gloucester, MA

Parker, Amy
Matignon HS
Lexington, MA

Parker, Debra
Nipmuc Regional
Upton, MA

Parker, Lois A
Ralph C Mahar Regional HS
Athol, MA

Parker, Shannon L
Middlesex Schl
Bedford, MA

Parsa, Parwane S
Lexington HS
Lexington, MA

Pascal, Lisa
Methuen HS
Methuen, MA

Pasciuto, Susan
Auburn HS
Auburn, MA

Pasquini, Cynthia M
Ludlow HS
Ludlow, MA

Patel, Priti
Woburn HS
Woburn, MA

Patterson, Jeffrey
Concord-Carlisle HS
Concord, MA

Patti, Eleanor R
St Rose HS
East Boston, MA

Paul, Joseph
Chatham JR-SR HS
Chatham, MA

Peck, Ronald J
Central Catholic HS
Andover, MA

Peck, Stephen
Norton HS
Norton, MA

Peczka, Stephanie T
Revere HS
Revere, MA

Pelletier, Gary
Taunton HS
Taunton, MA

Pelletier, Kathleen
Hudson HS
Hudson, MA

Peloquin, Jill
Easthampton HS
Easthampton, MA

Peloquin, Tina
Easthampton HS
Easthampton, MA

Pemberton, Shawna
Fairhae HS
Fairhaven, MA

Penta, Pasquale
Medford HS
Medford, MA

Pepin, David
Hocyoke Catholic
Chicopee, MA

Pepper, Steven
Cathedral HS
Springfield, MA

Perakslis, Mark S
Silver Lake Regional
Pembroke, MA

Pereira, Darlene
Bishop Connolly HS
Fall River, MA

Pereira, Patricia Jane F M
Bishop Connolly HS
Fall River, MA

Perrone, Kimberly E
Pittsfield HS
Pittsfield, MA

Perry, Brian K
New Bedford HS
Acushnet, MA

Perry, Christine M
New Bedford HS
New Bedford, MA

Perry, Lisa
Lenox Memorial HS
Lenox, MA

Petcen, Melissa
Smith Acad
Hatfield, MA

Peterson, Julie
New Bedford HS
Acushnet, MA

Peterson, Thomas A
Shrewsbury SR HS
Shrewsbury, MA

Petrakos, Stephanie
Nroth Quincy HS
Quincy, MA

Petrie, Maria T
West Bridgewater
W Bridgewater, MA

Phillips, Brian J
Joseph Case HS
Swansea, MA

Phillips, Christopher
Diman Reginal Vocational HS
Swansea, MA

Phillips, Denise
Saugus HS
Saugus, MA

Phillips, Melanie
Falmouth HS
E Falmouth, MA

Phillips, Sheila
Greenfield HS
Arden, NC

Piazza, Joanne
Methuen HS
Methuen, MA

Picard, Mary Ann
Bishop Feehan HS
Cumberland, RI

Picroski, Fred
Classical HS
Springfield, MA

Pieri, Andrea
Agawan HS
Feeding Hls, MA

Pietrusiak, Jr William J
Xaverian Brothers
Medfield, MA

Plasse, Lisa
Bartlett HS
Webster, MA

Plunkett, Mary
Wellesley HS
Wellesley, MA

Poirier, Jonathan A
Hampshire Regional
Williamsburg, MA

Ponte, Marlene
Bishop Connolly HS
Fall River, MA

Postera, Brian
Mohawk Trail
Regional HS
Charlemont, MA

Potter, John B
Malden Catholic HS
Lynn, MA

Potvin, Andrew F
Drury SR HS
North Adams, MA

Powell, Pamela
Natick HS
S Natick, MA

Powers, Michele
St Peter Marian C C
Shrewsbury, MA

Powers, Thomas G
Natick HS
Natick, MA

Preston, David J
Belchertown HS
Belchertown, MA

Previte, Gail
Matignon HS
Lexington, MA

Priestley, Andrew
St Peter Marian C C
Boylston, MA

Pugh, Mary
Hopedale JR/SR HS
Hopedale, MA

Puri, Nita
Wilbraham Monson
Wilbraham, MA

Puryear, Monique
Medford HS
W Medford, MA

Pustinger, Melinda
Southwick HS
Tolland, MA

Puzniak, Laura
Presentation Of
Mary Acad
Methuen, MA

Puzyn, Lori
Matignon HS
Cambridge, MA

Pysczynski, Linda
Bedford HS
Bedford, MA

Quagan, Jennifer
Reading Memorial
Reading, MA

Quinlan, John V
Plymouth-Carver
Plymouth, MA

Quinlan, Shannon
Notre Dame Acad
Duxbury, MA

Rahman, Farzana
Lunenburg HS
Lunenburg, MA

Ramirez, Patricia
Southbridge HS
Southbridge, MA

Ramos, Monica
BMC Durfee HS
Fall River, MA

Raneri, Leo A
Catholic Memorial
Dedham, MA

Raphel, Bruce S
Brockton HS
Brockton, MA

Rarick, Timothy
Wilbraham &
Monson Acad
Canaan, NY

Ratta, Saverio
Newton North HS
W Newton, MA

Ravida, Jerald
Joseph
Boston Latin HS
E Boston, MA

Reardon, Noreen
Girls Catholic HS
Medford, MA

Reedy, Christine
Marian HS
Framingham, MA

Regan, Tina
Fontbonne Acad
Stoughton, MA

Regulus, Michelle L
Phillips Acad
Aurora, IL

Reid, Mary
Turners Falls HS
Turners Falls, MA

Reidy, Mary V
Arlington HS
Arlington, MA

Renner, Sheila
Arlington Catholic
Concord, MA

Resendes, Robert
Bishop Connolly HS
Tiverton, RI

Resnick, Joanne
Hull HS
Hull, MA

Reusch, Martha J
Lawrence HS
Lawrence, MA

Reynolds, Tracy A
Mount St Joseph
Brighton, MA

Ricciuti, Maria
St Bernards CC HS
Fitchburg, MA

Richards, Linda
Reading Memorial
Reading, MA

Richards, Steven B
Beverly HS
Beverly, MA

Richards, Tamara L
Franklin HS
Franklin, MA

Richardson, Jr
Nehemiah E
Ayer HS
Shirley, MA

Rickley, Carol
Methuen HS
Methuen, MA

Riggs, Glenn R
Tantasqua Regional
Brookfield, MA

Rinaldi, John M
Acton-Boxborough
Regional HS
Boxborough, MA

Rinaldo, Maria
Holy Wamc Central
Catholic HS
Worcester, MA

Rittenberg, Sheri R
Burlington HS
Burlington, MA

Ritucci, Donald M
Brockton HS
Brockton, MA

Rizzo, Joseph
Everett HS
Everett, MA

Rizzo, Ralph
Christopher
Columbus HS
Charlestown, MA

Rizzotto, Kerri
Randolph HS
Randolph, MA

Roberts, Doug M
Quaboag Regional
Warren, MA

Roberts, Lisa
Boston Latin Schl
Brighton, MA

Roberts, Margo
Bourne HS
Otis AFB, MA

Robinson, Heather
Medway JR-SR HS
Medway, MA

Robinson, Lisa
Ursuline Acad
West Roxbury, MA

Roda, Ana Lucia
New Bedford HS
New Bedford, MA

Rodericks, Ron
Brockton HS
Brockton, MA

Rodrigues,
Marcelina
Madison Park HS
Boston, MA

Rodriguez, Carlos
Newton North HS
Newton, MA

Roeser, Stefan
Marblehead HS
Marblehead, MA

Roffman, Denise
Randolph HS
Randolph, MA

Rogalski, April
Dawne
Saugus HS
Saugus, MA

Rogers, Paul V
Somerset HS
Somerset, MA

Rogowski, April
Marie
Greenfield HS
Greenfield, MA

Ronan, Edward
North Andover HS
North Andover, MA

Rosenthal, Jamie
Randolph HS
Randolph, MA

Ross, David M
Nantucket HS
Nantucket, MA

Rossiter, Renee
Easthampton HS
Easthampton, MA

Rotondi, Ellen L
Bishop Fenwick HS
Wakefield, MA

Rotondo, Lisa M
Reading Memorial
Reading, MA

Rottenberg, Linda
Newton South HS
Newton, MA

Rousseau, Neal
Bishop Feehan HS
Attleboro, MA

Roy, Celeste
Saint Louis Acad
Lowell, MA

Rozman, Mark
St Johns Prep
Haverhill, MA

Rubin, Doug W
Natick HS
Natick, MA

Rudd, Susan
Our Lady Of
Nazareth Acad
Arlington, MA

Rummo, Paul
Marian HS
Milford, MA

Russell, Sharon
Cathedral HS
Springfield, MA

Russo, Cristina M
Melrose HS
Melrose, MA

Ryan, Dawn
Bay Path Regional
Vocational HS
Charlton, MA

Ryan, John C
Plymouth-Carver
Carver, MA

Salm, Susan
Archbishop Williams
Holbrook, MA

Salomao, Joao
Hudson HS
Hudson, MA

Salomao, Maria L
Hudson HS
Hudson, MA

Salzman, Eric
Newton North HS
Newton, MA

Samar, Lisa
Monson JR SR HS
Palmer, MA

Sampson, Elizabeth
St Bernards Central
Catholic HS
Leominster, MA

Sanders, Karen M
Bridgewater-Raynha
m Regional HS
Raynham, MA

Sanpakit, Tony T
Berkshire Schl
Glenmont, NY

Santiago, Robin
New Bedford HS
New Bedford, MA

Santos, Joseph
Melrose HS
Melrose, MA

Saraceno, Scott
Central Catholic HS
N Andover, MA

Sarkis, Anthony M
Drury SR HS
North Adams, MA

Sarmaniote, Janyce
Ursuline Acad
Boston, MA

Sarno, Doreen
Arlington Catholic
Medford, MA

Sasen, Cindy D
Bellingham JR SR
Bellingham, MA

Saulnier, Michael S
North Attleboro HS
North Attleboro,
MA

Sauvan, Mike C
Newburyport HS
Newburyport, MA

Savoie, Craig A
Lowell HS
Lowell, MA

Scaletti, Tony R
Newburyport HS
Newburyport, MA

Scalzo, Silvio
Malden Catholic HS
Lexington, MA

Scheer, Debbie
Ludlow HS
Ludlow, MA

Schmiz, Jennifer
Somerville HS
Somerville, MA

Schultz, Richard
Barnstable HS
Hyannis, MA

Schumaker, John
Melrose HS
Boston, MA

Schwartz, Neil D
Newton South HS
Newton, MA

Scott, Andrew
Reading Memorial
Reading, MA

Seaman, Jr John T
Dennis-Yarmouth
Regional HS
East Dennis, MA

Sears, Stacey
Georgetown JR SR
Georgetown, MA

Seidler, Cippy
Nantucket HS
Nantucket, MA

Sepuka, Lisa
Holy Name C C HS
Auburn, MA

Sergel, Theresa C
Bartlett HS
Webster, MA

Sexton, Laura
Ursuline Acad
Dedham, MA

Seymourian, Deanna
Woodward Schl
Milton, MA

Shao, Katherine
Winchester HS
Winchester, MA

Shea, Kevin
Winthrop HS
Winthrop, MA

Shea, Kristen
Taunton HS
E Taunton, MA

Sheahan, Kelly
Durfee HS
Fall River, MA

Sheldon, Deborah
Leominster HS
Leominster, MA

Shellito, Julie
Pioneer Valley
Regional Schl
Northfield, MA

Shellito, Michael
Pioneer Valley
Regional Schl
Northfield, MA

Shields, Jr Michael
T
Dennis-Yarmouth
Regional HS
South Yarmouth

Shikrallah, William
L
Georgetown JR SR
Georgetown, MA

Shine, Dennis F
Holy Name CC HS
Worcester, MA

Shriver, Holly
Chicopee
Comprehensive HS
Chicopee, MA

Shurtluff, Kevin
North Quincy HS
Quincy, MA

Sideri, Maria
Presentation Of
Mary Acad
Methuen, MA

Siemer, Shirley
Anne
Nauset Regional HS
Wellfleet, MA

Silveira, Victor
New Bedford HS
New Bedford, MA

Simard, Michele
Presentation Of
Mary Acad
Salem, NH

Simas, Jose
New Bedford HS
New Bedford, MA

Simmler,
Christopher R
Xaverian Brothers
Franklin, MA

Sims, Heather
Eugenia
Natick HS
West Natick, MA

Sirois, Dave
Bishop Fenwick HS
Salem, MA

Skantzaris, Maria
Burlington HS
Burlington, MA

Skouras, Thomas
Lynn English HS
Lynn, MA

Slattery, Thomas J
Catholic Memorial
Boston, MA

Slayter, Stephen R
Hyde Park Acad
Roslindale, MA

Slein, Juliana
Coyle & Cassidy HS
S Easton, MA

Slomski, Jeffrey J
Marian HS
Sudbury, MA

Slysz, Lisa
Smith Acad HS
Hatfield, MA

Smack, James W
Westborough HS
Westborough, MA

Smarz, Laurie
Smith Acad
Hatfield, MA

Smigielski, Thomas
Lynn Classical HS
Lynn, MA

Smith, David W B
Dover-Sherborn HS
Dover, MA

Smith, John
Lenox Memorial HS
Lenox, MA

Smith, Kathleen
Haverhill HS
Haverhill, MA

Smith, Kimberly
Taunton HS
Taunton, MA

Smith, Robin
Bishop Connolly HS
Westport, MA

Smith, Sara
Norton HS
Norton, MA

Smith, Timothy R
Xaverian Brothers
Medfield, MA

Smith, Tina
Aqawam HS
Agawam, MA

Soccorso, Andrea
Melrose HS
Melrose, MA

Solano, Michael
St Dominic Savio
Saugus, MA

Solis, Michelle
Greater Boston
Stoneham, MA

Solomonides, John
Bedford HS
Bedford, MA

Souden, Stephanie L
Falmouth HS
E Falmouth, MA

Sousa, Kimberly
Acad Of Notre
Westford, MA

Sousa, Lawrence W
Brockton HS
Brockton, MA

Sparks, Sharon
Hopedale JR SR HS
Hopedale, MA

Spaulding, Gary B
Tahanto Regional
Berlin, MA

Speliotes, Elizabeth
K
Newton North HS
W Newton, MA

Spellman, Maryellen
St Clare HS
W Roxbury, MA

St Cyr, Andrea
Notre Dame Acad
Brockton, MA

St Germain,
Jennifer
Mohawk Trail
Regional HS
Charlemont, MA

St Pierre, James F
Attleboro HS
South Attleboro,
MA

Staley, II James R
Newton No HS
Auburndale, MA

Stamoulis, Evan
Natick HS
Natick, MA

Start, Natalie
Barnstable HS
Cotait, MA

Stechenfinger,
William A
Hamilton-Wenham
Regional HS
S Hamilton, MA

Stein, Brenda
St Clare HS
Roslindale, MA

Stephens, Carrie
Lynne
Wareham HS
Buzzards Bay, MA

Sterczala, Beth
Bartlett HS
Webster, MA

Stewart, Christopher
Medway SR SR HS
Medway, MA

Stewart, Donna L
Salem HS
Salem, MA

Stewart, Jill
Lunenburg HS
Lunenburg, MA

Stockton, Philip L
Newton North HS
Auburndale, MA

Struski, Barry P
Plymouth Carver
Carver, MA

Stuart, Kaplan
Wellesley SR HS
Wellesley, MA

Suchodolski,
Gretchen K
Andover HS
Andover, MA

Sullivan, Amy Marie
Pittsfield HS
Pittsfield, MA

Sullivan, Cassandra
Hingham HS
Hingham, MA

Sullivan, Daniel
Weymouth North
Weymouth, MA

Sullivan, John
Andover HS
Andover, MA

Sullivan, Michael P
Palmer HS
Three Rivers, MA

Sullivan, Scott
Edward
Quincy Vo Tech
Weymouth, MA

Summers, Jennifer
Chatham JR SR HS
N Chatham, MA

Surette, Shaun
St Bernards HS
Fitchburg, MA

Swardstrom, Mark
W
Bourne HS
Bourne, MA

Sweeney, Julie E
Dedham HS
Dedham, MA

Sweet, Stuart
Haverhill HS
Haverhill, MA

Sweezey, Ken
Archbishop Williams
Abington, MA

Swistak, Dawn
Marie
Hoosac Valley HS
Adams, MA

Sylvia, Edward
Middleboro HS
Middleboro, MA

Sylvia, Lori
New Bedford HS
New Bedford, MA

Sylvian, Patrick
Camb-Rindge And
Latin HS
Cambridge, MA

Szlyk, Laura
Shepherd Hill
Regional HS
Dudley, MA

Tamagini, Lisa A
Lexington Christian
Wakefield, MA

Tanagni, Paul
Milford HS
Milford, MA

Tardanico, Christine
M
Stoughton HS
Stoughton, MA

Tatro, Gordon F
Westfield HS
Westfield, MA

Tattrie, Kevin
Franklin HS
Franklin, MA

Tavares, Patricia
Westport HS
Westport, MA

Tavares, Pauline
New Bedford HS
New Bedford, MA

Taylor, Rick
Burlington HS
Burlington, MA

Teague, Andrea
Beverly HS
Beverly, MA

Terenzi, Dolores
Pope John XXIII
Central HS
East Boston, MA

Tetreau, Terese
Douglas Memorial
E Douglas, MA

Teverovsky, Vadim
Concord-Carlisle HS
Concord, MA

Theroux, Cheryl
Chicopee
Comprehensive HS
Chicopee, MA

Theroux, Denise M
Belingham Memorial
JR/SR HS
Dellingham, MA

Thirumalaisamy,
Pillan K
Newton South HS
Newton, MA

Thomas, Andrew
Bishop Stang HS
New Bedford, MA

Thomas, Gregory
Scott
Technical HS
Indian Orchard, MA

Thomas, Janine
Norfolk County
Agricutural HS
South Weymouth,
MA

Thomas, Richard E
Springfield
Technical HS
Springfield, MA

Thompson, Chris
Westwood HS
Westwood, MA

Thompson,
Christopher P
Marblehead HS
Marblehead, MA

Thomson, Jeffrey M
Lynn English HS
Lynn, MA

Thong, Julie
Rockland HS
Rockland, MA

Tilghman, Jennifer
F
Andover HS
Andover, MA

Tillotson, Lisa E
Grafton HS
Grafton, MA

Tilman, Teressa
Bedford HS
Boston, MA

Tobin, Alana A
Billerica Memorial
Billerica, MA

Todres, Jonathan
Dennis Yarmouth
Regional HS
South Yarmouth,
MA

Toloczko, Joseph
St Peter Marian C C
Worcester, MA

Tougas, Colette J
Duxbury HS
Greenharbor, MA

Toussaint, Jason R
Beverly HS
Beverly, MA

Towne, Michelle
Ayer HS
Shirley, MA

Towne, Sherrie L
Classical HS
Springfield, MA

Traficante, Daniel
Central Catholic HS
Methuen, MA

Tran, Khiem T
Clinton HS
Clinton, MA

Trask, Michael A
Xaverian Brothers
Randolph, MA

Trauber, Robert S
Dover-Sherborn
Regional HS
Brookline, MA

Travis, Mark W
Norwell HS
Norwell, MA

Treadup, Anne
Marie
Bishop Stang HS
New Bedford, MA

Tremblay, David A
Old Rochester
Regional HS
Marion, MA

Tremblay, Michelle
Montachusett RVTS
Fitchburg, MA

Tremblay, Traci
Hamilton-Wenham
Regional HS
S Hamilton, MA

Trionfi, Angela
Revere HS
Revere, MA

Tripoli, Maria
Bishop Fenwick HS
Peabody, MA

Tsirigotis, Petros
Bishop Guertin HS
Lowell, MA

Tuffin, Amalie
Acton Boxborough
Regional HS
Acton, MA

Turcotte, Jayne
Attleboro HS
Attleboro, MA

Turner, Clem
Deerfield Acad
Queens Village, NY

Tuttle, Anne
Norwell HS
Norwell, MA

Twigg, Michele
Wellesley HS
Wellesley, MA

Ulrich, Jennifer
Lenox Memorial HS
Lenox, MA

Underwood, Lynn
Ann
Chicopee HS
Chicopee, MA

Urbano, Maria
Medway JR SR HS
Medway, MA

Vadala, Marie
Gloucester HS
Gloucester, MA

Vagos, Virginia
New Bedford HS
New Bedford, MA

Valcourt, Dawn
Westport HS
Westport, MA

Valencourt, Michelle
North Brookfield
N Brookfield, MA

Vaughan, Alice
Methuen HS
Methuen, MA

Ventura, Edythan
Cushing Acad
Wakefield, MA

Vieira, Jr Frank J
Salem HS
Salem, MA

Vincent, Luke
Bishop Connolly HS
Fall River, MA

Vinocour, Daniel S
Chicopee HS
Chicopee, MA

Vinson, Yvette
Cushing Acad
Depew, NY

Viveiros, John
Old Rochester
Regional HS
Rochester, MA

Voyer, Kevin
Agawam HS
Feeding Hls, MA

Vyravanadan,
Kaushalya
Somerville HS
Somerville, MA

Wadsworth, Tracy
Bishop Fenwick HS
Gloucester, MA

Walenty, Margaret
Uxbridge HS
Uxbridge, MA

Walker, Darlene L
Rockland HS
Rockland, MA

Walker, David
Somerset HS
Somerset, MA

Wall, Philip
Mansfield HS
Mansfield, MA

Wallace, Karyn
St Mary HS
Newton, NH

Wallen, Robert
Nipmuc Regional
West Upton, MA

Wallenmaier, Lisa
Bridgewater
Raynham Reg HS
Raynham, MA

Walsh, Brian K
Boston Latin Acad
Brighton, MA

Walsh, Chris
Medway JR SR HS
Medway, MA

Walsh, David M
Matignon HS
Somerville, MA

Walsh, Susanne
Wellesley HS
Wellesley, MA

Waltman, Fay E
Malden HS
Malden, MA

Wanat, Kari
Easthampton HS
Easthampton, MA

Wareing, Richard F
Bishop Stang HS
New Bedford, MA

Washer, Glenn A
Mohawk Trl Reg HS
Shelburne Falls, MA

Washington, Charles B
Madison Park HS
Dorchester, MA

Wassmann, Julie M
Grafton SR HS
North Grafton, MA

Watson, Heidi
Hingham HS
Hingham, MA

Waugh, Scott
Hingham HS
Hingham, MA

Weiss, Thomas P
Xaverian Brothers
Norwood, MA

Weissman, Brian
B M C Durfee HS
Fall River, MA

Welch, Veronica
Bedford HS
Bedford, MA

Welles, Stephen M
Dennis Yarmouth Regional HS
West Dennis, MA

Wells, Lisa
Chicopee Comprehensive HS
Easthampton, MA

Wells, Suzanne
Natick HS
Natick, MA

Wenstrom, Tricia
Norwood HS
Norwood, MA

West, Jr Charles M
Brockton HS
Brockton, MA

Whalen, Eleanor
Arlington Catholic
Medford, MA

White, Ellen P
Frontier Reg HS
Whately, MA

White, John
Classical HS
Springfield, MA

Whiteside, Kevin
Wellesley HS
Wellesley, MA

Whitney, Kevin B
Oakmont Regional
Ashburnham, MA

Whitten, Russell
Marblehead HS
Mablehead, MA

Wiedl, Craig J
Middleborough HS
Middleboro, MA

Wilkinson, Rebecca E
Walpole HS
Walpole, MA

Williams, May L
Norton HS
Norton, MA

Williams, Melody
New Bedford HS
New Bedford, MA

Williams, Tanya J
Boston Latin Acad
Dorchester, MA

Willie, James T
Concord-Carlisle HS
Concord, MA

Wilson, Amanda Lynn
Ayer SR HS
Ayer, MA

Wilson, Elizabeth
Commerce HS
Springfield, MA

Wing, Gary W
Burlington HS
Burlington, MA

Winkler, Alfred C
Groton Schl
Jamaica, NY

Wissell, Matthew
St Peter-Marian HS
Rochdale, MA

Witover, Julie
Andover HS
Andover, MA

Wolrich, Elyse
Randolph HS
Randolph, MA

Wong, Diana S
Randolph HS
Randolph, MA

Wong, Fred J
Xaverian Brothers
Brockton, MA

Wood, Darleen
Holy Name HS
Auburn, MA

Woods, Joseph
Chicopee Comprehensive HS
Chicopee, MA

Workman, Kerri Lynne
Somerset HS
Somerset, MA

Wrenn, Kathryn
Doherty Memorial
Worcester, MA

Wysocki, Mark
Cathedral HS
Springfield, MA

Yon, Kerri
Franklin HS
Franklin, MA

Young, Sean D
Xaverian Br HS
Foxboro, MA

Zarinetchi, Farisa
Brookline HS
Brookline, MA

Zarle, Stig
Lexington HS
Lexington, MA

Zawislak, Linda
Bartlett HS
Webster, MA

Zdrojewski, Mike
Woburn SR HS
Woburn, MA

Zdziarski, Julie Ann
Monument Mountain HS
Great Barrington, MA

Zgrodnik, Kimberly
Hopkins Academy
Hadley, MA

Zokowski, Margaret
Smith Acad
Hatfield, MA

Zurzolo, Gabriela
Ursuline Acad
Stoughton, MA

Zwicker, James L
St Peter-Marian HS
Worcester, MA

NEW HAMPSHIRE

Adkins, Wendy
Franklin HS
Franklin, NH

Aldrich, Ken
Spaulding HS
Rochester, NH

Allen, Bonnie
Newport HS
Newport, NH

Allen, Vicki
Concord HS
Concord, NH

Andrews, Peter J
Keene HS
Keene, NH

Annis, Karen
Merrimack HS
Merrimack, NH

Aronson, John
Laconia HS
Laconia, NH

Augustinowicz, Walter
Stevens HS
Venice, FL

Austen, Scott
Milford Area SR HS
Amherst, NH

Ayotte, Scott
Berlin HS
Berlin, NH

Bacon, Rebecca
Fall Mountain Regional HS
Alstead, NH

Bailey, Brenda J
Pembroke Acad
Chichester, NH

Bakanec, Bradley S
Londonderry HS
Londonderry, NH

Baron, Jonathan E
Manchester High School Central
Manchester, NH

Bascom, Kimberley
Salem HS
Salem, NH

Beaubien, Suzanne
Milford Area SR HS
Milford, NH

Beauchesne, Robin
Alvirne HS
Hudson, NH

Beaudet, Marc
Salem HS
Salem, NH

Bechard, Kathi
Londonderry HS
Londonderry, NH

Belanger, Laura L
Manchester West
Bedford, NH

Bergeron, Tammy
Memorial HS
Manchester, NH

Bibbins, Judith
Pembroue Acad
Concord, NH

Bickford, Chris C
Concord HS
Concord, NH

Birch, Peter
Bishop Guertin HS
Westford, MA

Bishop, Ron
Goffstown HS
New Boston, NH

Blanchette, Kim Renee
Keene HS
Keene, NH

Boisvert, Denise M
Pembroke Acad
Suncook, NH

Boisvert, Paul
Alvirne HS
Hudson, NH

Boland, Stephen J
Bishop Guertin HS
Nashua, NH

Bowler, Gregg
Concord HS
Concord, NH

Brawn, James
Portsmouth HS
Newington, NH

Brockney, Richard
Spauldine HS
Rochester, NH

Brooks, David
Portsmouth HS
Greenland, NH

Brouillette, Diane
Spaulding HS
Rochester, NH

Browall, Scott
Salem HS
Salem, NH

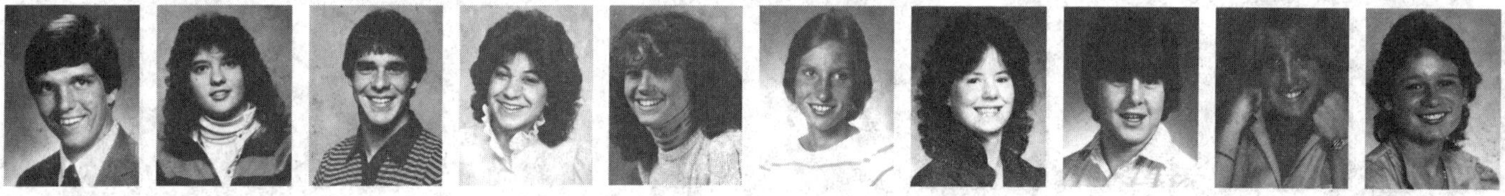

Brown, David P
Concord HS
Concord, NH

Brown, Wendy
Belmont HS
Laconia, NH

Brusseau, William
Littleton HS
Littleton, NH

Buco, Andrea
Salem HS
Salem, NH

Burbank, Barbara
Spaulding HS
Rochester, NH

Burney, Sheryl K
Somersworth HS
Somersworth, NH

Buttrick, Melanie
Concord HS
Bow, NH

Cabral, Scott
Gorham HS
Berlin, NH

Cariello, Wendy
Moulton Borough
Center Hrbr, NH

Carignan, Anne Marie
Spaulding HS
Rochester, NH

Carlow, Tami A
Trinity HS
Manchester, NH

Carmody, Bernadette Therese
Merrimack Valley
Penacook, NH

Carter, Kevin
Christian Fellowship
Laconia, NH

Cartier, Daniel
Saint Thomas Aquinas HS
Dover, NH

Casselberry, Diane
Spaulding HS
Rochester, NH

Cea, Stephen
Salem HS
Salem, NH

Chapin, Greg
Winnisquam Regional HS
Northfield, NH

Chase, Heather M
Phillips Exeter Acad
Muncie, IN

Chiasson, Allan
Nute HS
Milton Mills, NH

Child, Mary E
Manchester Central
Manchester, NH

Chin, Winnie Y
Coffstown HS
Manchester, NH

Chinchar, Chris Ann
Portsmouth HS
Rye, NH

Cleary, Laura
Moultonborough
Center Hrbr, NH

Clermont, Nicole
Lin-Wood HS
N Woodstock, NH

Closson, Tom
Bishop Guertin HS
Nashua, NH

Cocchiaro, Lisa
Salem HS
Salem, NH

Cole, Montgomery
Salem HS
Salem, NH

Coleman, Thomas
Spaulding HS
Rochester, NH

Collins, Greg
Spaulding HS
Rochester, NH

Conklin, Heather
Oyster River HS
Madbury, NH

Conner, W Sean
Trinity HS
Bedford, NH

Connolly, Richard
Dover HS
Dover, NH

Connors, Bryce
Manchester Memorial HS
Manchester, NH

Cooke, Deborah
Fall Mountain Regional HS
Charlestown, NH

Costello, Angela
Central HS
Manchester, NH

Cotter, John
Bishop Guertin HS
Nashua, NH

Couture, Lisa
Spaulding HS
Rochester, NH

Coyne, Robert
Bishop Guertin HS
Hollis, NH

Crisp, Stephen
Bishop Guertin HS
Hollis, NH

Cronin, Jon Andrew
Portsmouth HS
Rye, NH

Cross, Dianne
Salem HS
Salem, NH

Crowley, Sherry
Pembroke Acad
Concord, NH

D Auteuil, Monica
Salem HS
Salem, NH

Dahl, Nicholas H
Bishop Guertin HS
Nashua, NH

Davis, Todd
Milford Area SR HS
Amherst, NH

Dearborn, Leigh Ann
Franklin JR SR HS
Hill, NH

Decost, Richard
Spaulding HS
Rochester, NH

Del Giudice, Kerry L
Central HS
Manchester, NH

Delage, Gregory S
Nashua HS
Nashua, NH

Desrochers, Michael R
Goffstown HS
Manchester, NH

Dexter, David
Spaulding HS
Gonic, NH

Di Prizio, Peter
Spaulding HS
Rochester, NH

Dickey, David
Central Catholic HS
Salem, NH

Dikeman, Glenn W
Phillips Exeter Acad
Joplin, MO

Dodd, Barbra
Inter-Lakes HS
Ctr Sandwich, NH

Dolan, Timothy S
Central Catholic HS
Pelham, NH

Donnelly, Michael P
Mascoma Valley
Regional HS
Grafton, NH

Doubek, Christopher
Winnacunnet HS
Hampton, NH

Doward, Joan
Manchester HS
Allenstown, NH

Dresser, Scott G
Milford Area SR HS
Amherst, NH

Duffy, Patrick
Pinkerton Acad
Windham, NH

Dunbar, Amy
Hollis Area HS
Hollis, NH

Dupuis, Ann Marie
Trinity HS
Manchester, NH

Dupuis, Joel
Woodsville HS
Woodsville, NH

Dupuis, Mark
Spaulding HS
Rochester, NH

Dustin, Scott Allen
Hillsboro-Deering
Hillsboro, NH

Duval, Michael
Bishop Guertin HS
Nashua, NH

Dwyer, David
Manchester
Memorial HS
Manchester, NH

Edwards, William R
Winnacunnet HS
Hampton, NH

Ellis, Jon
Spaulding HS
E Rochester, NH

Errera, Jr Leonard J
Mascenic Regional
New Ipswich, NH

Esenwine, Matthew
Weare HS
Weare, NH

Faford, Michelle
Londonderry HS
Londonderry, NH

Farar, Deborah
Alvirne HS
Hudson, NH

Farmer, Teresa
Winnisquam
Regional HS
Tilton, NH

Faulhaber, Sherry
Spaulding HS
Rochester, NH

Fauteux, Lucy
Presentation Of
Mary HS
Nashua, NH

Fecteau, Richard
Franklin JR-SR HS
Franklin, NH

Fillio, Christopher P
Exeter Area HS
East Kingston, NH

Flanders, David
Keene HS
Keene, NH

Flanders, Douglas P
Keene HS
Keene, NH

Fontaine, II Arthur
Franklin JR SR HS
W Franklin, NH

Foret, Gretchen
Merrimack HS
Merrimack, NH

Freitas, Steven
Salem HS
Salem, NH

Gaimari, Stephen
Bishop Guertin HS
Nashua, NH

Garvey, James
Alvirne HS
Hudson, NH

Gaudreau, Brenda
Concord HS
Concord, NH

Gilbert, Colleen
Marie
Timberlane Reg HS
Plaistow, NH

Gilchrist, Michele S
St Pauls Schl
Columbus, OH

Girard, Diane Jean
Memorial HS
Manchester, NH

Girard, Michelle
Am Goffstown HS
Manchester, NH

Girouard, Kelly
Concord HS
Concord, NH

Glidden, Bobbie-Jo
Farmington HS
Farmington, NH

Glidden, Janet
Spaulding HS
E Wakefield, NH

Goldthwaite,
Jae-Ann D
Alvirne HS
Hudson, NH

Gorski, John M
Exeter Area HS
Exeter, NH

Goudreault, Cynthia
E
Timberlane Regional
Plaistow, NH

Gourdeau, Raymond
L
Timberlane Regionel
Atkinson, NH

Grieco, Lynda S
Salem HS
Salem, NH

Griffin, Glenna
Presentation Of
Mary Acad
Nahsua, NH

Griffin, Michael
Concord HS
Concord, NH

Griffin, Peter
Raymond
Raymond HS
Raymond, NH

Grumbling,
Kimberley
Dublin Schl
Newmarket, NH

Guerin, Richard E
Laconia HS
Laconia, NH

Guilmett, Brenda
Laconia HS
Laconia, NH

Halbedel, Rhonda
Mascenic Regional
Greenville, NH

Hamilton, Jill M
Portsmouth SR HS
Greenland, NH

Hammond, Kristine
Marie
Concord HS
Bow, NH

Hanson, Wendy Jo
Woodsville HS
Haverhill, NH

Harmon, Tammy
Concord HS
Manchester, NH

Haynes, Jeffrey
Lynn
Stevens HS
Claremont, NH

Hayward, Jeanette
Dover HS
Dover, NH

Heffernan, Elaine
Nashua HS
Nashua, NH

Heim, David
Saint Thomas
Aquinas HS
Exeter, NH

Higgins, Stephen
Coe-Brown
Northwood Acad
Barrington, NH

Holbrook, Marcia J
Memorial HS
Manchester, NH

Hopkins, Penny
Fall Mountain
Regional HS
Claremont, NH

Horymski, David
Concord HS
Concord, NH

Hovatter, Gina
Manchester High
School West
Manchester, NH

Howard, Clint
Spaulding HS
Rochester, NH

Howard, Timothy
Plymouth Area HS
Plymouth, NH

Huff, Melissa Leigh
Somersworth HS
Somersworth, NH

Ireland, Kelly L
Alvirne HS
Hudson, NH

Jano, Lonnie
Portsmouth HS
Portsmouth, NH

Jennings, Timothy
Bishop Guertin HS
Merrimack, NH

Jennison, Sheri
Rochester Spaulding
Barrington, NH

Johnson, Keri Ann
Newport HS
Goshen, NH

Johnson, Kristin A
Pinkerton Acad
Derry, NH

Johnson, Susan
Concord HS
Bow, NH

Johnson, Walter
Bishop Guertin HS
Nashua, NH

Kaiser, Dee
Woodsville HS
Woodsville, NH

Kealey, Joleen M
Salem HS
Salem, NH

Keenan, Lori
Epping HS
Epping, NH

Kelsey, Kristine
Spaulding HS
Rochester, NH

King, Karen J
Somersworth HS
Somersworth, NH

Kitchen, Amy
Jennifer
Milford Area SR HS
Amherst, NH

Klamka, Peter
Bishop Guertin HS
Nashua, NH

Klena, Kali
Portsmouth HS
Portsmouth, NH

Klotz, Emily
Portsmouth HS
New Castle, NH

Kobilarcsik, M
Gregory
Trinity HS
Windham, NH

Kolok, Kurtiss
Christian Fellowship
Laconia, NH

La Plante, Troy
Franklin JR SR HS
Franklin, NH

La Rose, Lisa
Laconia HS
Weirs Beach, NH

Lacasse, Nicholas
Lebanon SR HS
W Lebanon, NH

Laferte, Denise
Spaulding HS
Barrington, NH

Lamb, Kim
Salem HS
Salem, NH

Lambert, Debra
Manchester Central
Manchester, NH

Lamy, Angela M
Manchester H S
Manchester, NH

Landry, Cindy
Salem HS
Salem, NH

Langelier, Kym E
Mount Saint Mary
Nashua, NH

Langs, Debbie
Dover HS
Dover, NH

Lapierre, Chantal
Colebrook Acad
N Stratford, NH

Lassey, Karen
Concord HS
Bow, NH

Lataille, Michael R
Alvirine HS
Hudson, NH

Le Duc, Karen E
Pinkerton Acad
East Hampstead,
NH

Leaor, Kimberly
Milford Area SR HS
Milford, NH

Leduc, Nicole
Presentation Of
Mary Acad
Pelham, NH

Lee, Bernard
Pinkerton Acad
Manchester, NH

Lemieux, Maurene
Alvirne HS
Hudson, NH

Leone, Wendy
Timberlane Regional
Atkinson, NH

Levine, Sharyn
Goffstown Area HS
Goffstown, NH

Lindsay, Christine
Mary
Oyster River HS
Durham, NH

Little, Caylene
Pembroke Acad
Pembroke, NH

Lombardi, Vince
Milford Area SR HS
Amherst, NH

Loomis, Mike
Concord HS
Concord, NH

Macri, Lisa
Alvirne HS
Hudson, NH

Magnell, Laureen M
Mascoma Valley
Regional HS
Enfield, NH

Mahoney, Tim
Goffstown Area JR/
SR HS
Goffstown, NH

Marsh, Shawn
Spaulding HS
Rochester, NH

Mason, Michelle
Orford HS
Orford, NH

Mayhew, Karen
Milford Area SR HS
Amherst, NH

Mc Cabe, Brian S
Laconia HS
Laconia, NH

Mc Cormick, Shawn
Salem HS
Salem, NH

Melanson, Lisa
Timberlane Regional
Sandown, NH

Mercer, Greg
Oyster River HS
Madbury, NH

Merrihew, Michael
Spaulding HS
Rochester, NH

Miller, Kevin David
Salem HS
Salem, NH

Minton, Nora
Kennett HS
Jackson, NH

Morgan, Maureen
Molly
Spaulding SR HS
Rochester, NH

Morin, Marc
Gilford HS
Gilford, NH

Morin, Scott
Memorial HS
Manchester, NH

Morneau, Roland
Joe
Farmington HS
Farmington, NH

Morse, Donald E
Memorial HS
Manchester, NH

Morse, Karen
Pembroke Acad
Concord, NH

Mueller, Scott A
Salem HS
Salem, NH

Mullen, Donald
Concord HS
Concord, NH

Musial, Melissa
Manchester
Memorial HS
Manchester, NH

Nadeau, Courtney
Lynne
Portsmouth HS
Portsmouth, NH

Nealey, Pamela Jean
Salem HS
Salem, NH

Newcomb, Ross J
Conval Regional HS
Hancock, NH

Newell, III Ronald
Pembroke Acad
Suncook, NH

Noble, Jeff
Franklin HS
Franklin, NH

Norwood, Heather
Spaulding HS
Rochester, NH

Nutile, Christopher A
Bishop Guertin HS
Nashua, NH

O Connor, Patricia Anne
Salem HS
Salem, NH

O Rourke, II Gerard P
Alton Central HS
Laconia, NH

O Shea, Kevin M
St Thomas Aquinas
Madbury, NH

Olivier, Bryan M
Dover HS
Dover, NH

Omberg, Peter D
Aloirne HS
Hudson, NH

Ouellette, Maureen
Conant HS
Jaffrey, NH

Oxford, Allison Lea
Milford Area SR HS
Milford, NH

Paddock, Jr Robert E
Littleton HS
Littleton, NH

Paini, Cindy J
Memorial HS
Manchester, NH

Palardis, Tina
Salem HS
Salem, NH

Pangraze, Melissa
Memorial HS
Auburn, NH

Paradise, Debra
Milford Area SR HS
Amherst, NH

Parsons, Mary
Fall Mt Reg HS
Charlestown, NH

Paul, Charlene
Hopkinton HS
Concord, NH

Peacock, Chris
Kennett HS
Silver Lk, NH

Pearson, Michael
Colebrook Acad
Dixville Notch, NH

Pelletier, Scott
Dover HS
Dover, NH

Pepin, Michelle
Spaulding HS
Rochester, NH

Perron, Susan R
Pelham HS
Pelham, NH

Pesula, Jeffrey
Bishop Guertin HS
Litchfield, NH

Phillips, Kimberly
St Thomas Aquinas
Rye, NH

Pichette, James
S E New Hampshire Christian Acad
Berwick, ME

Plaisted, Mark
Moultonborough
Moultonboro, NH

Poirier, Judith M
Manchester West
Manchester, NH

Porter, Gerri
Belmont HS
Belmont, NH

Preston, Michael S
Alvirne HS
Hudson, NH

Przygrodzki, Robert
Trinity HS
Manchester, NH

Rafferty, Lauriann
Winnacunnet HS
Hampton Beach, NH

Ramsden, Catherine
Pinkerton Acad
Windham, NH

Rawnsley, Ross
Merrimack HS
Merrimack, NH

Rees, Carla
Manchester West
Manchester, NH

Riel, Lurene M
Pittsfield HS
Pittsfield, NH

Robbins, Carl W
Nashua SR HS
Nashua, NH

Robidoux, Scot J
Pelham HS
Pelham, NH

Robinson, Lynn
Salem HS
Salem, NH

Rogers, Tracy
Concord HS
Bow, NH

Rollins, Jonathan J
Ashland HS
Ashland, NH

Rose, Todd J
Berlin HS
Dummer, NH

Rowe, Diane
Thayer HS
Winchester, NH

Rowe, Jennifer
Portsmouth SR HS
Rye, NH

Sage, Jeffery
Winnisquam Regional HS
Tilton, NH

Samsel, J Patrick
Bishop Guertin HS
Nashua, NH

Samson, Elaine
Pinkerton Acad
Auburn, NH

Samson, Richard C
Colebrook Acad
W Stewartstown, NH

Sanborn, Carrie L
Plymouth Area HS
Wentworth, NH

Sanphy, Rebecca A
Kennett HS
Glen, NH

Santaniello, Chris
Gilford HS
Gilford, NH

Saucier, Linda
Pembroke Acad
Suncook, NH

Scouras, Greg
Portsmouth SR HS
Portsmouth, NH

Senecabaugh, Terri A
Plymouth Area HS
Plymouth, NH

Shaughnessy, Jeanne
Ashland HS
Plymouth, NH

Sheridan, Chris
Gilford Middle HS
Gilford, NH

Signorello, Robert
Bishop Guertin HS
Nashua, NH

Sisti, Robyn
St Thomas Aquinas
Smithfield, RI

Smith, Alexis E
Conant HS
Rindge, NH

Smith, Daniel
Bishop Guertin HS
Lowell, MA

Smith, Jason
A Crosby Kennett
Ctr Conway, NH

Smith, Kelly
Portsmouth HS
Rye, NH

Soczewinski, Richard
Franklin HS
Franklin, NH

Solosko, Thomas A
Nashua SR HS
Nashua, NH

Spaulding, Richard
Kearsarge Regional
New London, NH

Spencer, Steven M
Nashua SR HS
Nashua, NH

Stallings, Carlton
Alvirne HS
Hudson, NH

Stevens, Michelle
Dover HS
Dover, NH

Stotz, Laura C
Milfrod Area SR HS
Milford, NH

Stpierre, Eric
Concord HS
Concord, NH

Street, Tavia
Holderness Schl
Meredith, NH

Sullivan, Debra
Trinity HS
Manchester, NH

Sullivan, James
Bishop Guertin HS
Lowell, MA

Talbot, Michelle
Presentation Of
Mary HS
Pelham, NH

Tardif, Gerard P
Bishop Guertin HS
Nashua, NH

Taylor, Donald
Berlin HS
Berlin, NH

Taylor, Tracy
Portsmouth HS
Pease Afb, NH

Theriault, Kim
Spaulding HS
Rochester, NH

Therrien, Donna
Dover HS
Dover, NH

Thibault, Carrie J
Franklin JR SR HS
Franklin, NH

Thibault, Jodie
Mascenic Regional
Greenville, NH

Titus, Michelle
Salem HS
Salem, NH

Tonnesen, Gregory
Milford Area SR HS
Amherst, NH

Treen, Karl
Derryfields Schl
Merrimack, NH

Turgeon, Kristine
Concord HS
Concord, NH

Twombley, Scott
Spaulding HS
Sanbornville, NH

Van Vliet, Miller J
Concord HS
Bow, NH

Vanhooser, John O
The Derryfield Schl
Amherst, NH

Violette, Andrew
Concord HS
Bow, NH

Violette, Lisa
Belmont HS
Laconia, NH

Wade, Jr Michael D
Bishop Guertin HS
Salem, NH

Walker, Peter
Bishop Brady HS
Tilton, NH

Wallace, Susan
Franklin HS
Franklin, NH

Wallent, Karen
Nashua HS
Nashua, NH

Walters, Jean
Elizabeth
Alvirne HS
Hudson, NH

Werderman, John
Peter
Hollis Area HS
Hollis, NH

Wheeler, Michael
Kennett HS
Conway, NH

White, Carolyn
Trinity HS
Manchester, NH

White, Matthew
Coe-Brown
Northwood Acad
Barrington, NH

Williams, Michael
Concord HS
Concord, NH

Williamson, Craig
Bishop Guertin HS
Amherst, NH

Wilson, Cassie
Stevens HS
Claremont, NH

Winiecki, Jessica A
Milford Area SR HS
Amherst, NH

Wishnefsky, Lisa
Lebanon HS
Lebanon, NH

Woodward, Mark A
Kearsarge Regional
New London, NH

Wyatt, III Clarence
Nute HS
Milton, NH

Zannini, Jill M
Salem HS
Salem, NH

NEW YORK

Aaron, Timothy S
Brockport HS
Hamlin, NY

Abadir, Esther H
Union Springs Acad
Lancaster, NY

Abbate, Kathleen
Curtis HS
Staten Island, NY

Abbatiello, Michael
A G Berner HS
Massapequa Park,
NY

Abel, Jr L David
Oneida ST HS
Oneida, NY

Abeles, Gwen D
Jericho HS
Jericho, NY

Aber, Jeffrey C
Port Jervis HS
Middletown, NY

Abraham, Suzanne
M
Liverpool HS
Liverpool, NY

Abramowitz, David
N
Stuyvesant HS
Jamaica, NY

Abrams, Lawrence
Manhattan Ctr For
Science Math
Bronx, NY

Acampora, Kenneth
Sachem HS
Lk Ronkonkoma,
NY

Acevedo, Margarita
Cathedral HS
Ny, NY

PHOTO
NOT
AVAILABLE

Achenbach, Linda M
Starpoint Central
North Tonawanda,
NY

Achury, Angela
St Johns
Preparatory HS
Jackson Heights,
NY

Ackerbauer, Michael
Lakeland HS
Mohegan Lake, NY

Ackerman, Brian M
Curtis HS
Staten Island, NY

Ackerman, Naomi
West Hempstead
Island Park, NY

Ackerman, Wendi A
Paul V Moore HS
Constantia, NY

Acluche, Pierre Max
Springfield Gardens
Rosedale, NY

Acosta, Angelo
All Hallows HS
New York, NY

Adam, Lauren
Mount Mercy Acad
Lackawanna, NY

Adamcyk, Valerie
Manhasset HS
Manhasset, NY

Adamowicz, Gerald
K
Chatham HS
East Chatham, NY

Adams, Gregory
Fayetteville-Manlius
Fayetteville, NY

Adams, Mark
Manhatton Center
For Science & Math
New York, NY

Adams, Michelle L
The Mary Louis
Queens Village, NY

Adelmann, Charlene
West Seneca West
SR HS
W Seneca, NY

Adle, Kelly
Oneida HS
Oneida, NY

Adler, Andrew F
Horace Mann
Barnard Schl
Holliswood, NY

Adler, David
New Rochelle HS
New Rochelle, NY

Adler, Leonard
Bronx High School
Of Science
New York, NY

Adler, Peter
Franklin K Lane HS
Glendale, NY

Africa, David
Liverpool HS
Syracuse, NY

Aggrippino, Jeanne
Hudson HS
Hudson, NY

Agosta, Annmarie
Fontbonne Hall
Brooklyn, NY

Aguirre, Joseph M
Archbishop Molloy
New Hyde Pk, NY

Ahart, Lori L
Watkins Glen
Central HS
Watkins Glen, NY

Aiello, Debra
Saint Gabriels HS
New Rochelle, NY

Aiello, John F
Julia Richman HS
New York, NY

Ailloni-Charas, Orrin
Blind Brook HS
Rye Brook, NY

Aladin, Marie-Alan
The Bronx High
Schl Of Science
Cambria Hts, NY

Alaimo, Mark A
Cardinal Mooney
Hilton, NY

Alban, Jorge
Rocky Point HS
Rocky Point, NY

Alban, Philip
So Kortright Central
Bloomville, NY

Albanese, Lisa Marie
Academy Of St
Smithtown, NY

Albano, Matthew
Walter Panas HS
Peekskill, NY

Alberga, Kristofer A
Mont Pleasant HS
Schenectady, NY

Alberry, Monique
Gouverneur HS
Gouverneur, NY

Albertelli, Omar
United Nations
International Schl
New York, NY

Albrecht, Eric
Union-Endicott HS
Endicott, NY

Albrecht, Lisa
Villa Maria Acad
Cheektowaga, NY

Alcorn, Stephanie
Cortland JR SR HS
Cortland, NY

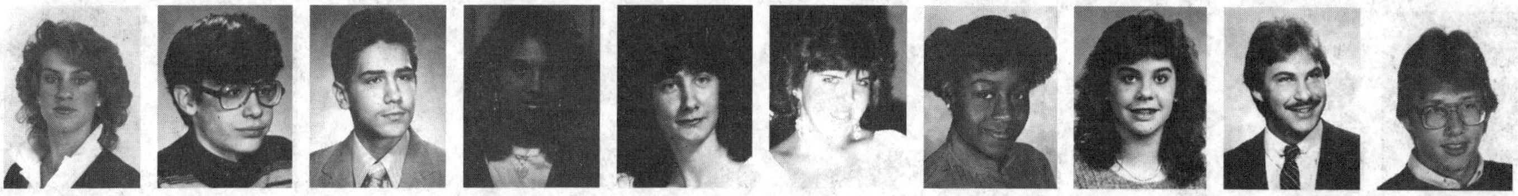

Aldrich, Lisa
Manlius Pebble Hill
Cazenovia, NY

Aldrich, Mark
Spackenkill HS
Poughkeepsie, NY

Aleman, Alejandro J
Glen Cove HS
Glen Cove, NY

Alfano, Michele A
Riverdale Country
Bronx, NY

Alfarano, April M
Maria Regina HS
Yonkers, NY

Alfieri, Renee
Richmond Hill HS
Richmond Hill, NY

Alford, Nicole
Brooklyn Technical
Brooklyn, NY

Alia, Phyllis
Halfhollow Hills H
S West HS
Dix Hills, NY

Alicastro, Glenn T
Commack South HS
Commack, NY

Alkinburgh, Scott
Broadalbin Central
Johnstown, NY

Allen, Crystal
Riverhead HS
Riverhead, NY

Allen, Eric
St Peters Boys HS
Staten Isld, NY

Allen, Mark
S Glens Falls SR HS
S Glens Falls, NY

Allen, Mary
Notre Dame
Academy HS
Staten Island, NY

Allen, Michael
East Syracuse
Minoa HS
Minoa, NY

Allen, Nadine M
Northport HS
Northport, NY

Allen, Theodore Anthony
Half Hollow Hills H
S East
Wheatley Heights

Alpert, Kelly
Commack H S
E Northport, NY

Alsop, Janis
Riverside HS
Buffalo, NY

Alston, Kelvin E
Benjamin Franklin
Rochester, NY

Alvarado, Leslie
St Francis Prep Schl
Flushing, NY

Alvarado, Margarett
Rocky Point JR SR
Rocky Pt, NY

Alvarado, Zaray
St Pius V HS
Bronx, NY

Alvarenga, Silvia
Yonkers HS
Yonkers, NY

Alversa, Joanne
The Mary Louis
S Ozone Park, NY

Alyse, Feder
East Meadow HS
E Meadow, NY

Ambroise, Arielle
West Hempstead
W Hempstead, NY

Ambrose, Anna Marie
Eden SR HS
Eden, NY

Ambrose, Christopher K
John A Coleman HS
Kingston, NY

Ameno, Charles
Lancaster Central
Lancaster, NY

Amitrano, Ralph
Bishop Ford Central
Catholic HS
Brooklyn, NY

Ammirato, Anthony
Mineola HS
Mineola, NY

Amodio, Michelle
Pulaski JR & SR
Pulaski, NY

Amoia, Nancy
Bishop Kearney HS
Brooklyn, NY

Amoretti, Martha
La Salle SR HS
Niagara Falls, NY

Amos, Guy
John Jay HS
Hopewell Junction, NY

Ampuero, George
Msgr Mc Clancy
Mem HS
Flushing, NY

Amster, Robert
Locust Valley HS
Bayville, NY

Amyot, Todd
Athena HS
Rochester, NY

Anable, Angela
Coxsackie-Athens
Coxsackie, NY

Photo
Not
Available

Anand, Savinder
Richmond Hill HS
Richmond Hill, NY

Ancewicz, Lorelei A
St Dominic HS
Westbury, NY

Anctil, Elizabeth
Northeastern
Clinton Central HS
Rouses Pt, NY

Anderlik, Joelle
Cicero-North
Syracuse HS
Clay, NY

Andersen, Lori
Centereach HS
Centereach, NY

Anderson, Daren
Westhampton Beach
Westhampton Bch, NY

Anderson, Donnyle
Letchworth Crntral
Castile, NY

Anderson, Jade
Dominican
Commercial HS
Jamaica, NY

Anderson, Jeffrey T
Manhatte Center
For Science & Math
New York City, NY

Anderson, Karen L
Uniondale HS
Uniondale, NY

Anderson, Michael
Mynderse Acad
Seneca Falls, NY

Anderson, Ruth A
Sachem HS North
Farmingville, NY

Anderson, Steven B
Berne-Knox-Westerl
o Central HS
East Berne, NY

Anderson, Valerie G
Maple Grove HS
Bemus Point, NY

Andre, Mirlene
Mabel Dean Bacon
Vocational HS
Miami, FL

Andresen, Lisa
Salmon River HS
Brasher Falls, NY

Andrews, Amy B
Holland Patent
Central HS
North Western, NY

Andriano, Clare
St Francis Prep
College Point, NY

Andrus, Gregory
Paul V Moore HS
Hastings, NY

Andrus, Wendy
Granville Central
Granville, NY

Andryshak, Coleen
Lynn
S S Seward Inst
Goshen, NY

Anello, Angelo
La Salle SR HS
Niagara Falls, NY

Anello, Jane
Manhasset HS
Manhasset, NY

Angeles, Maria
Southwestern
Central HS
Lakewood, NY

Angerhofer,
Timothy E
Pittsford-Mendon
Pittsford, NY

Angililli, Jean M
York Central HS
Mt Morris, NY

Angione, Chris
Commack South HS
Commack, NY

Anglisano, Toni Ann
Lindenhurst HS
Lindenhurst, NY

Angrum, Anita
Saint Pius V HS
Bronx, NY

Angus, Gabrielle M
Hammondsport
Central HS
Hammondsport, NY

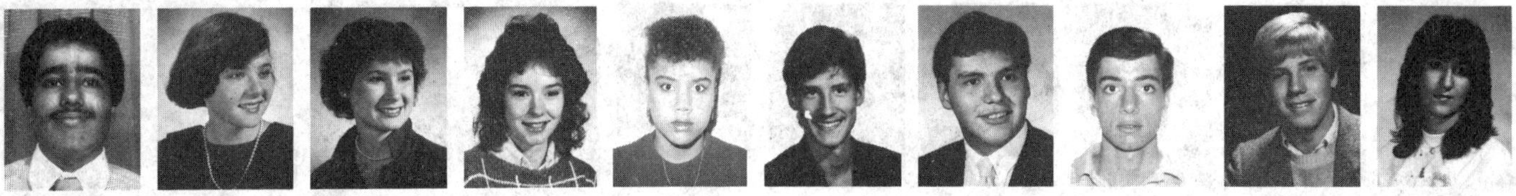

Annabi, Amged
Sacred Heart HS
Yonkers, NY

Anslow, Anne
Bishop Ludden HS
Baldwinsville, NY

Anstett, Bernadette
St Marys HS
Lancaster, NY

Anthony, Anne
Marie
Aquinas Inst
Rochester, NY

Anthony, Martha S
Midwood HS
Brooklyn, NY

Antonovich, David
Union Springs Acad
Woodside, NY

Aparicio, Ruben
View Rochelle HS
New Rochelle, NY

Aponte, Juan
Regis HS
Astoria, NY

Appel, James
Woodmere Acad
Atlantic Beach, NY

Appel, Sherri
Commack North HS
Commack, NY

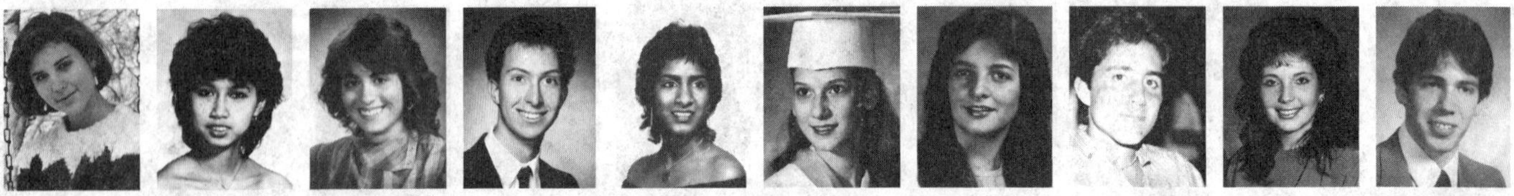

Aptman, Suzanne
Horace Greeley HS
Chappaqua, NY

Apun, Sheena C
Hillcrest HS
Elmhurst, NY

Aquino, Theresa P
Shaker HS
Latham, NY

Arbore, Mario
Bethpage HS
Plainview, NY

Archer, Jasme I
Richmond Hill HS
Richmond Hill, NY

Arcieri, Elizabeth
Bishop Kearney HS
Brooklyn, NY

Arciold, Christine
Grover Cleveland
Ridgewood, NY

Ardito, Joseph
Archbishop Molloy
W Hempstead, NY

Arena, Jo Ann
St John Villa Acad
Staten Island, NY

Arena, Mark A
G Ray Bodley HS
Fulton, NY

Ariano, Anthony K
Canarsie HS
Brooklyn, NY

Arias, Francisco
The Bronx HS Of
New York, NY

Arias, Leslie D
St Johns Prep
Queens, NY

Arico, Francine
St Raymond Acad
Bronx, NY

Arki, Cindy
Riverside HS
Buffalo, NY

Arnell, Jr Malcolm
M
Baro Hall Acad
Brooklyn, NY

Arney, Doreen M
Nanuet SR HS
Nanuet, NY

Aronov, Irina
Forest Hills HS
Forest Hills, NY

Arrieux, Roger G
Holy Trinity HS
Freeport, NY

Arrillaga, Jorge
New Rochelle HS
New Rochelle, NY

Arrington, Betty
A Philip Randolph
New York, NY

Artl, Michelle
Fairport HS
Fairport, NY

Arzonetti, Tina M
Pine Bush HS
Middletown, NY

Aschoff, Kelly
Port Jervis HS
Port Jervis, NY

Ashburn, Jr John B
Roy C Ketcham HS
Wappingers Fall,
NY

Ashe, David B
Bethlehem Central
Delmar, NY

Assimakopoulos,
Nicolle
John F Kennedy HS
New York, NY

Asvazadourian,
Corrine
Our Lady Of Victory
Pleasantville, NY

Atchie, Megan
Haverling Central
Bath, NY

Athanassiades, John
Bronx High School
Of Sci
Bayside, NY

Atkins, Kristin
Lindenhurst SR HS
Lindenhurst, NY

Atkinson, Erin
Far Rockaway HS
Far Rockaway, NY

Auckland, Wendy
Annette
Arkport Central
Arkport, NY

Augustinos, Elena
Liverpool HS
Liverpool, NY

Auletta, Roseann
Herbert H Lehman
Bronx, NY

Auriemma, Maria
Antonietta
Mineola HS
Mineola, NY

Austin, Bucky
Cohocton Central
Cohocton, NY

Austin, Diana D
White Plains HS
White Plains, NY

Austin, Heather
Lake George JR SR
Pilot Knob, NY

Austin, Velma
New Rochelle HS
New Rochelle, NY

Avant, Kristen
Churchville-Chili SR
Churchville, NY

Avery, Brian
Skaneateles HS
Auburn, NY

Avery, Julia L
F H Laguardia H S
Of The Musi
Bronx, NY

Avery, Laura
Mickey
Fonda-Fultonville
Central HS

Awobuluyi, Marcia
Kehinde
Hillcrest HS
Cambria Hts, NY

Ayos, Amelia A
Susan E Wagner HS
Staten Island, NY

Ayres, Cynthia
Newfield HS
Coram, NY

Azinaro, Susan
Preston HS
Bronx, NY

Babcock, Barbra
Granviille JR & SR
Granville, NY

Babcock, Kimberly
Hornell SR HS
Hornell, NY

Babilot, Michael
Weedsport JR SR
Weedsport, NY

Babington, Tobie
Shenendehowa HS
Clifton Pk, NY

Bacchus, Paul
South Shore HS
Brooklyn, NY

Back, Ronald
Valhalla HS
White Plains, NY

Badalament,
Racquel
Commack H S
Commack, NY

Baggia, Catherine
Hunter College HS
Forest Hills, NY

Baglio, Beth Ann
Springville Griffith
Springville, NY

Bahamonde, Pedro
Cardinal Hayes HS
Bronx, NY

Bailey, David A
Mohonasen SR HS
Schenectady, NY

Bailey, III Jack S
Jamesville-De Witt
Dewitt, NY

Bailey, Jane
W C Mepham HS
Bellmore, NY

Bailey, Kimberly A
Lansingburgh HS
Troy, NY

Bailey, II Michael J
Whitesboro SR HS
Whitesboro, NY

Bailey, Michelle
Nazareth Acad
Rochester, NY

Bains, David F
Gananda Central
School District
Macedon, NY

Baird, Andre G
Mount Saint
Michael Acad
Bronx, NY

Baires, Ana
Dominican
Commercial HS
Jamaica, NY

Bak, Greg
Niagara Catholic HS
Niagara Falls, NY

Baker, Amy
East Aurora HS
West Falls, NY

Baker, Russ
Tonawanda JR SR
Tonawanda, NY

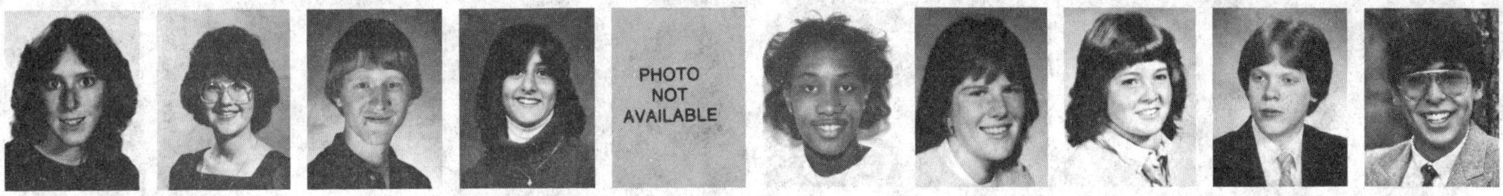

Baker, Sharon
Connetquot HS
Bohemia, NY

Bakker, Karen A
Newburgh Free
Newburgh, NY

Balch, Allen
Waterloo SR HS
Waterloo, NY

Balducci, Jeannine
Marie
Irvington HS
Irvington, NY

Ball, Terri
Wilson Central HS
Ransomville, NY

Ballard, Anita T
Midwood HS
Brooklyn, NY

Ballard, Doreen
Milford Central HS
Milford, NY

Ballinger, Teena
Corning Painted
Post West HS
Corning, NY

Ballou, James
Cicero North
Syracuse HS
Bridgeport, NY

Baltierra, David
Soesterberg
American HS
A P O, NY

Baltz, Stacey
Long Island
Lutheran HS
Massapequa, NY

Baltzer, David A
Watkins Glen
Central HS
Watkins Glen, NY

Balzano, Silvio
Cardinal Spellman
Bronx, NY

Ban, Wannie
Bronx H S Of
New York, NY

Banach, Denise
Liverpool HS
Liverpool, NY

Bannan, Lisa
Kenmore East
Senior HS
Tonawanda, NY

Bannister, Cleveland
Bishop Louglin HS
Brooklyn, NY

Baran, Ron
Weedsport Central
Auburn, NY

Barbatauly, Denise
West Hempstead
W Hempstead, NY

Barben, Lora Lee
Gerneral Brown HS
Watertown, NY

Barber, Malinda D
Ellicottville Central
Salamanca, NY

Barber, Sam
Bishop Grimes HS
Syracuse, NY

Barbera, Lisa
Central Islip HS
Central Islip, NY

Bard, Christopher
Seaford HS
Seaford, NY

Bard, Kerrian
Seaford HS
Seaford, NY

Barden, Carole
Catham Central HS
Chatham, NY

Bari, Samina
Notre Dame
Academy HS
Staten Island, NY

Barkley, James
Archbishop Stepinac
Pleasantville, NY

Barnes, Jr Garry E
Marlboro HS
Marlboro, NY

Barnes, Holly
Ticonderoga HS
Ticonderoga, NY

Barnes, Joseph H
Roy C Ketcham HS
Poughkeepsie, NY

Barnes, Melanie
St Gabriel HS
New Rochelle, NY

Barnes, Melissa
Bishop Loughlin HS
Brooklyn, NY

Barnes, Michelle A
Bay Shore HS
Bay Shore, NY

Barnes, Veda D
Poughkeepsie HS
Poughkeepsie, NY

Barnwell, Michele R
Notre Dame Schl
New York, NY

Baron, Lisa
Riverside HS
Buffalo, NY

Barone, Amy
Batavia Ssr HS
Batavia, NY

Barone, Lisa
West Genesee SR
Camillus, NY

Baroulette, Lorna
Dominican
Commercial HS
Queens Vlge, NY

Barous, Maria
St Johns Prep HS
Astoria, NY

Barrigar, Beth
Odessa-Montour
Central HS
Odessa, NY

Barron, Sheila M
Shaker HS
Loudonville, NY

Barrow, Arlette
Brooklyn Technical
Brooklyn, NY

Barsky, Victoria
F D Roosevelt HS
Brooklyn, NY

Bartholomew, Diana
J
Berlin American HS
Apo New York, NY

Bartlett, Deborah
Liverpool HS
Liverpool, NY

Bartlett, Denise
Sheepshead Bay HS
Brooklyn, NY

Barton, Daniel
F D Roosevelt HS
Hyde Park, NY

Barton, Robert
St Marys Acad
Johnsonville, NY

Barvian, Mark
Attica SR HS
Strykersville, NY

Basello, Julie A
The Mary Louis
Flushing, NY

Bashaw, Michelle
Anna-Lisa
Elizabethtown-Lewis
Central Schl
Lewis, NY

Basic, Antonella
St Johns Prep
Queens, NY

Basil, Lisa
Horseheads HS
Horseheads, NY

Basile, Rita M
Vestal SR HS
Apalachin, NY

Bassarath, Jr C
Sheldon
L I Lutheran HS
Westbury, NY

Basty, Cheryl Ann
Hamburg SR HS
Hamburg, NY

Basuino, Leonard C
Xaverian HS
Brooklyn, NY

Bates, Jr Dennis G
Royalton-Hartland
Central Schl
Middleport, NY

Bates, John
Thousand Islands
Clayton, NY

Battey, Erik
Cardinal Spellman
Bronx, NY

Battige, Jr C
Kenneth
Christian Brothers
Latham, NY

Bauer, Beth Ann
Washingtonville SR
Monroe, NY

Bauer, Robert
Frontier Central HS
Hamburg, NY

Baumach, Barbara
Sachem H S North
Lk Ronkonkoma,
NY

Bauman, Eric S
Mahopac HS
Mahopac, NY

Bauter, Stacy
General Brown HS
Dexter, NY

Baxter, Lillian
Monsignor Scanlan
Bronx, NY

Bayer, Raymond
Moore Catholic HS
Staten Island, NY

Beard, Jennifer May
Henninger HS
Syracuse, NY

Beasley, Johnita
Hutchinson Central
Technical HS
Buffalo, NY

Beattie, Rachel H
Hunter College HS
Flushing, NY

Beaty, Terri
Corning-Painted
Post West HS
Painted Post, NY

Beaudin, Chrissy
Glens Falls HS
Glens Falls, NY

Bechard, Lisa
Liverpool HS
Liverpool, NY

Bechtel, Randy
Hamburg SR HS
Hamburg, NY

Beck, Pamela J
Long Island
Lutheran HS
E Meadow, NY

Beck, Paul
Raymond
New Hartford HS
New Hartford, NY

Becker, Sanford
Ballston Spa HS
Ballston Spa, NY

Beckman, Heidi A
Bay Shore HS
Bay Shore, NY

Beckner, Stephanie
Jordan-Elbridge HS
Elbridge, NY

Bednarz, Marianne
M
Glen Cove HS
Glen Cove, NY

Bedortha, Mary
Eileen
Bishop Grimes HS
Fayetteville, NY

Beebe, Michelle
Shenendehowa HS
Clifton Park, NY

Beecher, James
Elmira Free Acad
Elmira, NY

Begany, Alison
Sacred Heart HS
Yonkers, NY

Behari, Jr Joseph
Savona Central Schl
Savona, NY

Behr, Darrin J
Performin Arts At
La Guardia HS
New York, NY

Beirne, Andrew
Ossining HS
Scarborough, NY

Beirne, Andrew E
Newtown HS
Elmhurst, NY

Belen, Kendrick E
La Salle Acad
New York, NY

Bell, Anthony
Joseph
East Rockaway HS
E Rockaway, NY

Bell, Casey L
Laguardia H S Of
Music & The Arts
Bronx, NY

Bell, Cynthia
Sachem High School
Lk Ronkonkoma,
NY

Bell, Debi
Centereach HS
Centereach, NY

Bell, Jennifer A
Norman Thomas HS
Bronx, NY

Bell, Joseph W
Greece Arcadia HS
Rochester, NY

Bellavia, Regina
Rocky Point JR SR
Rocky Point, NY

Belle, Germaine A
Midwood HS
Brooklyn, NY

Bellizzi, Maria
Cardinal Spellman
Bronx, NY

Bello, John
South Shore HS
Brooklyn, NY

Bellos, Maria
Mahopac HS
Mahopac Falls, NY

Bellum, Karoline
Cooperstown Central
Cooperstown, NY

Belmont, Debbie
Frankfort-Schuyler
Central HS
Frankfort, NY

Belt, Katherine
Northport HS
Northport, NY

Benbow, Curin
The Knox Schl
East Setauket, NY

Benedict, Jill
Fairport HS
Fairport, NY

Benjamin, Keli S
Franklin Acad
Malone, NY

Benjamin, Lisa
North Babylon SR
Wheatley Heights,
NY

Benjamin, Mary L
Mt Markham HS
Cassville, NY

Benjamin, Steve
Hendrick Hudson
Peekskill, NY

Bennear, Elisabeth Ruth
Jamesville Dewitt
Dewitt, NY

Bennett, Jeffrey
West Canada Valley Central HS
Poland, NY

Bennett, Robert
De Witt Clinton HS
Bronx, NY

Bennett, Victoria A
Saratoga Springs SR
Saratoga Springs, NY

Benson, Eric Gerard
Mahopac HS
Mahopac, NY

Benson, Kim
Rocky Point JR SR
Rocky Point, NY

Benson, Jr Van Ness
Dover JR-SR HS
Wingdale, NY

Berger, Denise
North Babylon SR
N Babylon, NY

Bergman, Meredith
Mamaroneck HS
Mamaroneck, NY

Bergmann, Andrew
Huntington HS
Huntington, NY

Berkoff, Melissa K
Smithtown East HS
Nesconset, NY

Berkowitz, Ellen
Washingtonville HS
Monroe, NY

Bermejo, Wanda
Cardinal Spellman
Bronx, NY

Bernard, Andrew
Sheepshead Bay HS
Brooklyn, NY

Bernard, Dina
Acad Mt Saint
Bronx, NY

Bernas, Michelle
Mount St Mary
N Tonawanda, NY

Bernstein, Cheryl
Jamesville De Witt
Fayetteville, NY

Bernstein, Jordana Simone
John H Glenn HS
Huntington, NY

Bernstein, Wendy
Commack High Schl
East Northport, NY

Berrafati, Joseph F
Irvington HS
Ardsley On Hudson, NY

Berry, Courtney A
The Mary Louis
Flushing, NY

Berry, Jr John F
Mephan HS
North Bellmore, NY

Berstein, Bradford
Wheatley HS
Old Westbery, NY

Besanson, Ellen A
Paul V Moore HS
Central Square, NY

Besch, Rose Ann
Cleveland Hill HS
Cheektowaga, NY

Besdansky, Barbara A
W T Clarke HS
Westbury, NY

Besse, Karl
Queensbury HS
Glens Falls, NY

Bessette, Jr Warren D
Hugh C Williams
Canton, NY

Betances, Yolanda
Bishop Kearney HS
Brooklyn, NY

Betancourt, Alex
MSGR Mc Clancy
Jackson Hgts, NY

Bettino, Rita
Westlake HS
Valhalla, NY

Betz, Lisa
Central HS
Valley Stream, NY

Bezman, Steven A
Elmont Memorial
Elmont, NY

Bhatia, Vivek
John Jay HS
Wappingers Fall, NY

Bhatt, Jay
Pittsford Mendon
Pittsford, NY

Bibawy, Nermin
Haverling Central
Bath, NY

Bier, Elizabeth M
Bishop Ludden HS
Syracuse, NY

Biggs, William
St Nicholas Of Tolentine HS
New York, NY

Bikowsky, Daniel M
Rocky Point JR SR
Rocky Point, NY

Billotti, Dena
Hilton Central HS
Hilton, NY

Binder, Terry
Brewster HS
Brewster, NY

Bingham, Nikki
Salmon River Central HS
Ft Covington, NY

Bini, Jacqueline
Commack H S
Dix Hills, NY

Biondi, Lisa R A
Kenmore West SR
Kenmore, NY

Bischel, Julie
Fayetteville-Manlius
Manlius, NY

Bish, Connie Jo
Frontier Central Senior HS
Hamburg, NY

Bish, Rebecca
Kenmore West SR
Tonawanda, NY

Bishop, Ann
Roy C Ketcham HS
Poughkeepsie, NY

Bishop, Lou J
Union Endicott HS
Endwell, NY

Bishop, Michael J
Auburn HS
Auburn, NY

Bivetto, Fred
St Johns Prep
Howard Bch, NY

Black, Carol
John Jay HS
Hopewell Jct, NY

Black, Karen
Smithtown East HS
Nesconset, NY

Black, Paula C
De Witt Clinton HS
New York, NY

Blackman, Kirk R
Francis Lewis HS
Laurelton, NY

Blackman, Wade
Waverly JR SR HS
Waverly, NY

Blahowicz, James
West Seneca West SR HS
West Seneca, NY

Blair, Barbara
Webster HS
Webster, NY

Blair, Charmine M
Northeastern Acad
Bronx, NY

Blais, Kristin A
Southold HS
Peconic, NY

Blake, Monica
Professional Childrens Schl
Edison, NJ

Blam, Holly
East Islip SR HS
Great River, NY

Blanchard, Carrie
Roy C Ketcham SR
Poughkeepsie, NY

Blanco, Robert
Archbishop Molloy
Flushing, NY

Blaney, Karen E
St Marys Girls HS
Manhasset, NY

Blasi, Valerie
Southside HS
Rockville Ctr, NY

Blassberg, Adrienne
Spring Valley SR
Spring Vly, NY

Blatteis, Michelle
Mineola HS
Roslyn Heights, NY

Blewett, Brandee
Berlin American HS
Apo New York, NY

Blinn, Laurie
Lake Placid HS
Lake Placid, NY

Bliss, Dianne M
Kendall JR SR HS
Hamlin, NY

Blitz, Erica
Carmel HS
Carmel, NY

Bliziotis, William
The High School Of
Art & Design
Flushing, NY

Blom, Kirsten
Port Richmond HS
Staten Isld, NY

Blood, Colleen
Jamestown HS
Jamestown, NY

Blood, John J
Alfred G Berner HS
Massapequa, NY

Blowe, Josephine
East Hampton HS
E Hampton, NY

Blum, Tracy Ann
Charles H Roth HS
Rochester, NY

Bluman, Eric M
Jamesville-Dewitt
Jamesville, NY

Blumenkranz, Adam
East Meadow HS
East Meadow, NY

Blumreich, Janna
Barker Central HS
Barker, NY

Bly, Jennifer
Southside SR HS
Pine City, NY

Boardway, Kristine
Gloversville HS
Gloversville, NY

Bobe, Rosalia
Cathedral HS
Bkly, NY

Boccone, Steve
East Meadow HS
E Meadow, NY

Boddie, Michele L
Cardinal Spellman
Brooklyn, NY

Boder, Robert
Newfield HS
Selden, NY

Bodnar, Jacqueline
St Catharines HS
Bronx, NY

Bogardus, Michael
Harverling Central
Bath, NY

Bohan, Michael
Olean HS
Olean, NY

Boice, Heath P
Cambridge Central
Cambridge, NY

Boink, Jr James N
Liverpool HS
Liverpool, NY

Bolanos, Carolina
Springfield Gardens
Hollis, NY

Bold, Kristen
Victor Central HS
Victor, NY

Bolden, Vernie
James E Sperry HS
Rochester, NY

Bolebruch, Mark R
Mayfield HS
Gloversville, NY

Bolger, Michelle
James I O Neill HS
Apo New York, NY

Bolowsky, Daniel P
Lake Shore HS
Derby, NY

Boncaro, David
Colonie Central HS
Albany, NY

Bonesky, Susan
Niagara Wheatfield
SR HS
North Tonawanda,
NY

Bongiorno, Joseph
St John The Baptist
D HS
East Islip, NY

Bongiovi, Carolee H
Seaford HS
Seaford, NY

Bonilla, Cecilia
Yonkers HS
Yonkers, NY

Bonina, Andrea E
St Saviour HS
Brooklyn, NY

Bonner, Madelyn
Manhasset HS
Manhasset, NY

Bookman, Tom R
Mac Arthur HS
Levittown, NY

Boothe, Nicola
Spring Valley SR
Spring Vly, NY

Borchert, Anne
Marlboro Central
Marlboro, NY

Boreali, Lawrence F
Cobleskill Central
Howes Cave, NY

Borland, Renee
J C Birdlebough HS
Pennellville, NY

Bornheimer, John
Lyons HS
Lyons, NY

Bornholdt, Elizabeth
A
Schreiber HS
Port Washington,
NY

Bornstein, Daniel
Tuxedo HS
Tuxedo Park, NY

Boroski, Christopher
D
Pittsford-Mendon
Pittsford, NY

Bortkiewicz, Anna
Saunders Trades &
Technical HS
Yonkers, NY

Bott, Harold J
Mount Saint
Michael Acad
Bronx, NY

Boucher, Jeff
Hartford Central HS
Hartford, NY

Boucher, Michelle L
Cardinal Spellman
New York, NY

Bouchereau, Tanya
Bishop Loughlin
Memorial HS
Brooklyn, NY

Bounaugurio, John
E J
Wislon-Spencerpor
Rochester, NY

Bourdeau, Penny
Plattsburgh HS
Plattsburgh, NY

Bourgault, Brian
Tamarac HS
Troy, NY

Bourgeois, Trampess
Camden Central HS
Cleveland, NY

Bourquin, Ramona
Saranac Lake HS
Bloomingdale, NY

Boutis, Harry
Herricks HS
New Hyde Pk, NY

Bowden, Tracy
Martin Luther King
JR HS
Bklyn, NY

Bowen, Kimberly A
Fort Ann Central
W Fort Ann, NY

Bowen, Melissa L
Lockport SR HS
Lockport, NY

Bowers, Dawn Marie
Cardinal Spellman
New York, NY

Bowles, Rodney
North Babylon SR
North Babylon, NY

Bowman, Laurie A
Union Springs
Central Schl
Cayuga, NY

Bowman, Lynne
Linton HS
Schenectady, NY

Bowman, Sherrilyn
Batavia HS
Batavia, NY

Boycheck, Ann
Marie
Henninger HS
Syracuse, NY

Boyd, Tim
Beacon HS
Beacon, NY

Boyko, Susan Marie
Oneida HS
Verona Bch, NY

Boynton, Kari
Mynderse Acad
Seneca Falls, NY

Bozan, Erik
Cardinal Hayes HS
New York, NY

Brachman, Jay
Martin Van Buren
Hollis Hls, NY

Bracy, Theda
Murry Bergtraum
Woodside, NY

Bradshaw, Mary M
East HS
Rochester, NY

Bradt, Barbara
Johnstown HS
Johnstown, NY

Brady, Michael
Earl L
Vandermeulen HS
Mt Sinai, NY

Braider, John W
St Anthonys HS
St James, NY

Brandt, Thomas A
Johnstown HS
Fort Plain, NY

Braney, R
Christopher
Fayetteville-Manlius
Manlius, NY

Brass, Stacey
Lawrence HS
N Woodmere, NY

Brathwaite,
Jacqueline
Cathedral HS
New York, NY

Brault, Teresa
Hornell SR HS
Ft Lauderdale, FL

Brazill, Christine
Vestal SR HS
Vestal, NY

Breen, John Patrick
West Hempstead
Island Park, NY

Breen, Riobart E
Lansingburgh HS
Troy, NY

Brehm, Douglas
E L Vandermeulen
Mt Sinai, NY

Bremer, Celine M
Christ Community
Church HS
Brockport, NY

Brennan, Alicia
Manhasset HS
Manhasset, NY

Brennan, Brenda
Cohoes HS
Cohoes, NY

Brenner, Joel S
Williamsville North
Williamsville, NY

Brescia, Jacqueline
A
Utica Free Acad
Utica, NY

Bresky, Stacey D
Fallsburg Central
South Fallsburg, NY

Breslin, Mary Claire
Vestal SR HS
Vestal, NY

Brewer, Jennifer
Elmira Southside
Elmira, NY

Brewster, Michelle
Thomas A Edison
Elmira, NY

Bridge, Bonita
Oakfield-Alabama
Central HS
Oakfield, NY

Briggins, Vivian
Acad Of Mt St
Bronx, NY

Bright, Sedonia
Grace H Dodge V
New York, NY

Brignol, Sheila M
St Johns Prep
Brooklyn, NY

Brink, Carey
Saranac Lake HS
Saranac Lake, NY

Brink, Timothy
East Meadow HS
East Meadow, NY

Brinton, Scott
Longwood HS
Medford, NY

Brittis, Nicole
The Masters Schl
Yonkers, NY

Brockhum, Connie L
Gloversville HS
Gloversville, NY

Brockor, Douglas J
Romo Frog Acad
Ava, NY

Brodlieb, Wendy B
Lawrence HS
Lawrence, NY

Brodsky, Stephen
Commack HS
Commack, NY

Bromirski, Timothy
Hoosick Falls
Central HS
Hoosick Falls, NY

Brooks, Paul T
Bishop Ludden HS
Syracuse, NY

Brosch, Eric
Amsterdam HS
Amsterdam, NY

Broushet, Angelique
E
Jamaica HS
Flushing, NY

Brown, Audrey
Our Savior Lutheran
Bronx, NY

Brown, Colleen
Bishop Kearney HS
Brooklyn, NY

Brown, Dionne
Mt Vernon HS
Mount Vernon, NY

Brown, Elyda
Clifton-Fine Central
Harrisville, NY

Brown, Kenneth E
Msgr Farrell HS
Staten Island, NY

Brown, Luanne
C W Baker HS
Baldwinsville, NY

Brown, Monica
Villa Maria Acad
Buffalo, NY

Brown, Paul F
B N Cardozo HS
Little Neck, NY

Brown, Rebecca
Groton Central HS
Groton, NY

Brown, Sheryll
Springfield Gardens
Rosedale, NY

Brown, Sophie
William Howard
Taft HS
Bronx, NY

Brown, Stephania
The Masters Schl
Ardsley, NY

Brown, Timothy
Longwood HS
Middle Island, NY

Browne, Kevin
La Salle Acad
New York, NY

Brucculeri,
Josephine
St Johns Prep
Jackson Hts, NY

Bruce, Patricia L
Gloversville HS
Gloversville, NY

Bruck, Michael L
G W Hewlett HS
N Woodmere, NY

Brumbaugh, Mark
G Ray Bodley HS
Fulton, NY

Brunett, Sandra
Bishop Kearney HS
Webster, NY

Brunhofer, Kristen
Bethlehem Central
Glenmont, NY

Bruns, Laura Dawn
Holland Patent HS
Barneveld, NY

Bruzzese,
Jean-Marie
John Dewey HS
Brooklyn, NY

Bryan, Chevarlo
Frt Hamilton HS
Brooklyn, NY

Bryant, Diana
Greene Central HS
Greene, NY

Bryant, Leanne
Heidelberg
American HS
Apo New York, NY

Bryant, Noel L
Stissing Mt JR SR
Ancramdale, NY

Buchler, Robert
Union-Endicott HS
Owego, NY

Buckland, Sandra M
Mt St Mary Acad
N Tonawanda, NY

Buckley, Kimberly
Freeport HS
Freeport, NY

Buckowski, Paul
Saranac Lake HS
Saranac Lake, NY

Budd, Jodi
Middletown HS
Middletown, NY

Buddington, Winton
Potsdam HS
Potsdam, NY

Budries, Lauren L
Mahopac HS
Carmel, NY

Bueford, Sean
Rice HS
New York, NY

Bugaj, Greg M
Hamburg SR HS
Hamburg, NY

Buhl, Ann L
Saugerties SR HS
Saugerties, NY

Buhrer, Donelle
Vernon-Verona-Sherrill HS
Vernon, NY

Bukovsky, Anne Marie
Sacred Heart HS
Yonkers, NY

Bulger, Judy
Moore Catholic HS
Staten Island, NY

Bulger, Marcy E
Notre Dame Bishop Gibbons HS
Schenectady, NY

Bull, Marcia
Far Rockaway HS
Hempstead, NY

Bullock, Kimberly
Dominican Commercial HS
Jamaica, NY

Bulterman, Dara Anne
Thousand Islands
Clayton, NY

Bundy, Kelly
Liverpool HS
Liverpool, NY

Bunt, Wray C
Johnson City HS
Johnson City, NY

Buonagurio, Joseph
Connetquot Central
Ronkonkoma, NY

Burch, David M
Martin Van Buren
Queens Village, NY

Burg, Patricia
Grand Island HS
Grand Island, NY

Burg, Rebecca
Grand Island HS
Grand Is, NY

Burgess, Brian
Union Springs Acad
Elmira, NY

Burghart, Kelley
Unatago JR-SR HS
Otego, NY

Burgos, Bienvenido
Thomas A Edison
Brooklyn, NY

Burkart, Kimberly
Bethlehem Central
Delmar, NY

Burke, Cathleen P
H Frank Carey HS
Garden City So, NY

Burke, Charles T
Notre Dame HS
Elmira, NY

Burke, Jennifer
Saratoga Springs HS
Greenfield Ctr, NY

Burke, Kevin
Bethpage HS
Bethpage, NY

Burke, Kimberly L
Hempstead HS
Hempstead, NY

Burke, Maurita B
Notre Dame HS
Elmira, NY

Burke, Timothy
Glens Falls SR HS
Glens Falls, NY

Burkhardt, William A
Friends Acad
Old Brookville, NY

Burnett, Corey
Cicero North Syracuse HS
North Syracuse, NY

Burnett, David T
John Jay HS
Hopewell Jct, NY

Burns, Karen
Knox Memorial Central HS
Russell, NY

Burns, Kelley C
Westhill HS
Syracuse, NY

Burns, Lisa
Sachem HS
Holtsville, NY

Burr, Melissa
West Genesee HS
Camillus, NY

Burton, Kristen M
Fairport HS
Fairport, NY

Burton, Sherry A
Westmoreland Central Schl
Rome, NY

Buscemi, Richard
St Josephs Collegiate Inst
Kenmore, NY

Busch, Dolores
Taconic Hills HS
Hillsdale, NY

Bush, Jack
Canisteo Central
Canisteo, NY

Bush, Phyllis
Homer Central HS
Homer, NY

Bushnell, Jr Timothy
Victor Central HS
Victor, NY

Busmire, Tina
Kendall JR SR HS
Kendall, NY

Busseno, William
Amsterdam HS
Amsterdam, NY

Bussi, Doreen C
Kenmore East HS
Tonawanda, NY

Butler, Antwann
Manlius Pebble Hill
Syracuse, NY

Butterfield, Dave
South Glenns Falls Central HS
S Glens Falls, NY

Buzzelli, Robert
La Salle SR HS
Niagara Falls, NY

Byous, Stacy
Carthage Centra HS
W Carthage, NY

Byrnes, Christian
Bethpage HS
Bethpage, NY

Caccamise, Dina
Notre Dame HS
Le Roy, NY

Cadre, Gianni
Cardinal Spellman
Bronx, NY

Cady, Karen
Holland Patent Central Schl
Holland Patent, NY

Cady, Kimberly
Thomas A Edison
Elmira Heights, NY

Cafiero, Victoria
Bishop Kearney HS
Brooklyn, NY

Cahill, Heather Ann
Maria Regina HS
Bronx, NY

Cahill, Kenneth A
Island Trees SR HS
Levittown, NY

Cain, Bob
Schobarie HS
Schoharie, NY

Calabrese, Anthony M
Island Trees HS
Bethpage, NY

Calabrese, Regina Ann
St Edmund HS
Brooklyn, NY

Calabro, Diane
Westhampton Beach
E Quogue, NY

Calamari, Robert
Fordham Preparatory Schl
Bronx, NY

Calderon, Wendy
John Dewey HS
Brooklyn, NY

Calderone, Shirley
Bishop Cunningham
Oswego, NY

Caldovino, Denise
St Edmund HS
Brooklyn, NY

Caldwell, Steven M
Seaford HS
Seaford, NY

Calkins, Anne
Bishop Grimes HS
Syracuse, NY

Call, Andrew
Carmel HS
Carmel, NY

Callahan, Gerard
John Jay SR HS
Wappingers Fall, NY

Callahan, Shawn R
Watkins Glen Central HS
Watkins Glen, NY

Callery, Jr Patrick
Biship Kearney HS
Rochester, NY

Calli, William S
New Hartford SR
Utica, NY

Camacho, Jr Ramon
St Johns Preparatory HS
Brooklyn, NY

Cambi, Michael G
Yorktown HS
Yorktown Heights, NY

Cambio, Elena M
Notre Dame HS
Elmira, NY

Cameron, Christina Jean
Longwood HS
Coram, NY

Cameron, Richard R
Shenendehowa HS
Ballston Lake, NY

Cameron, Scott
Farmingdale HS
Farmingdale, NY

Caminito, Marie
Deer Park HS
Deer Park, NY

Campanella, Peter
Smithtown High Schl East
Nesconset, NY

Campbell, James P
Paul V Moore HS
Bernhards Bay, NY

Campbell, Randy
Midwood HS
Brooklyn, NY

Campbell, Sandra
Sherburne-Earlville
Sherburne, NY

Campolo, III Philip A
Bishop Grimes HS
E Syracuse, NY

Canaguier, Michele
Sauquoit Valley Central HS
Clayville, NY

Canales Acevedo, Haydee E
St Pius V HS
Bronx, NY

Canales Acevedo, Vilma Maria
St Pius V HS
Bronx, NY

Candy, Matthew E
North Tonawanda SR HS
N Tonawanda, NY

Cannavo, Thomas J
St Josephs Collegiate Inst
Kenmore, NY

Cannon, Joan-Marie
Fontbonne Hall
Brooklyn, NY

Cantone, Michael S
Roy C Ketcham SR
Poughkeepsie, NY

Capano, Allison
Seaford HS
Seaford, NY

Capocci, Gina
Academy Of The
Pt Chester, NY

Capodanno, Andrea T
Acad Of The
Larchmont, NY

Capone, Michael
Fowler HS
Syracuse, NY

Caputo, James R
Arlington HS
Poughkeepsie, NY

Caputo, Johanna
West Seneca East SR HS
West Seneca, NY

Caracci, Diana L
Gates-Chili HS
Rochester, NY

Caragine, Joseph M
Walter Panas HS
Peekskill, NY

Carbino, Burton John
L I Luthern JR/SR
Massapequa, NY

Carbonaro, Michael J
Kings Park SR HS
Northport, NY

Carbone, Christine
John Jay HS
Hopewell Jct, NY

Carbone, Janelle M
Adlai E Stevenson
Bronx, NY

Carbone, Trina
Rochester Christian
Penfield, NY

Carboni, Chris
Hutch-Tech HS
Buffalo, NY

Cardinali, Angela
Jericho SR HS
Syosset, NY

Carillion, Diane C
Baldwin SR HS
Baldwin, NY

Carino, Diane L
Lakeland HS
Mohegan Lake, NY

Carl, Susan
Liverpool HS
Liverpool, NY

Carlos, Robert M
Lakeland HS
Yorktown Heights, NY

Carlson, Debra
South Park HS
Buffalo, NY

Carlucci, Karen
St Saviour HS
Brooklyn, NY

Carmody, Jill
Delaware Acad
Treadwell, NY

Carmona, Lisa Maria
Saint Joseph HS
Brooklyn, NY

Carney, James
Kenmore East HS
Tonawanda, NY

Carniello, Glenn
N Babylon HS
North Babylon, NY

Caroleo, Christine
St Catharine Acad
Bronx, NY

Carollo, James P
Uniondale HS
Uniondale, NY

Carosa, Mary Lee
Gates-Chili HS
Henrietta, NY

Carpenter, Robert D
West Islip HS
W Islip, NY

Carpenter, Vanessa
St Hildas HS
New York, NY

Carr, Kathleen
Liverpool HS
Liverpool, NY

Carr, Jr Lester W
Clyde-Savannah HS
Clyde, NY

Carr, Tracey
Union Springs
Attica, NY

Carrasquillo, Ezra U
The Packer Collegiate Inst
Brooklyn, NY

Carreno, Carmen Maria
Schalmont HS
Schenectady, NY

Carroll, John
St Francis Prep
Jamaica, NY

Carroll, Scott A
Liverpool HS
Liverpool, NY

Carson, Mary
New Rochelle HS
New Rochelle, NY

Carter, Debbie
Hendrick Hudson
Montrose, NY

Carter, Kimberly A
Holy Trinity HS
Levittown, NY

Carty, Jacqueline
Newfield HS
Selden, NY

Caruso, Marie
St John Villa Acad
Brooklyn, NY

Caruso, Mike
Mc Kee V & T HS
Staten Is, NY

Caruso, Teri Ann
John H Glenn HS
E Northport, NY

Carvallo, Susan
Long Island City HS
Astoria, NY

Carver, Danielle F
Scarsdale HS
Scarsdale, NY

Casa, Douglas
Newfield HS
Selden, NY

Casado, Christine
Norman Thomas
Commercial HS
New York, NY

Casadonte, Kelly
Mohawk Central
Mohawk, NY

Casale, Christine
Newwburgh Free
New Windsor, NY

Casamento,
Theodore
Niagara Wheatfield
SR HS
Niagara Falls, NY

Cascone, Karen
Mahopac HS
Mahopac, NY

Case, Melinda
Smithtown HS West
Smithtown, NY

Casella, Jacquelyn A
Union Endicott HS
Endwell, NY

Casey, Brian
Bishop Kearney HS
Rochester, NY

Casey, Jennifer
West Islip HS
West Islip, NY

Casey, Maureen E
Sayville HS
West Sayville, NY

Casillo, Michelle
Depew HS
Depew, NY

Casler, Christine
Canastota JR SR
Canastota, NY

Caso, Lourdes
Bishop Kearney HS
Brooklyn, NY

Casolare, Stephanie
Canastota HS
Canastota, NY

Cassera, Lisa
Linton HS
Schenectady, NY

Castellan, Ritza
Clara Barton HS
Brooklyn, NY

Castellano, Frank X
Bellport SR HS
Ballport, NY

Castillo, Teresa
Cathedral HS
Bx, NY

Castine, Todd
Northeastern
Clinton Central HS
Chazy, NY

Castoe, Brenda
Arlington High
Wapp Falls, NY

Castro, Raphael
Angel
Cardinal Hayes HS
New York, NY

Castrogiovanni,
Chris
North Babylon SR
N Babylon, NY

Cataldo, William
Washingtonville HS
Chester, NY

Catone, Joseph D
Aquinas Inst
Rochester, NY

Cattaneo, Maryanne
Newfield HS
Coram, NY

Catuosco, Ann
Marie
West Islip HS
W Islip, NY

Cavalier, Linda
Campbell Central
Campbell, NY

Cavalieri, Lisa
Williamsville East
Williamsville, NY

Cavallaro, Kathy A
Coming-Painted
Post East HS
Corning, NY

Cavic, Paris
Richfield Springs
Central HS
Richfield Spgs, NY

Cebula, Michael D
Amsterdam HS
Hagaman, NY

Ceder, Amy
Kenmore West SR
Kenmore, NY

Celestine, James
Andrew Jackson HS
Jamaica, NY

Cerbone, Edward J
St Anthonys HS
Ronkonkoma, NY

Cermak, Denise
St John The Baptist
Smithtown, NY

Cerpa, Desiree
Herbert H Lehman
Bronx, NY

Chadderdon,
Laureen H
Cairo-Durham JR &
SR HS
Acra, NY

Chagas, Maria
New Rochelle HS
New Rochelle, NY

Chaifetz, Francine
Commack North HS
Commack, NY

Chamberlain, Dave
Gloversville HS
Gloversville, NY

Chamberlain, Laura
Elmira Southside
Elmira, NY

Chamson, Amy R
The New Lincoln
New York, NY

Chandler, Karla A
Newark SR HS
Newark, NY

Chandler, Richard
Cairo-Durham HS
Acra, NY

Chang, Lisa
James I O Neill HS
West Point, NY

Chang, Noel L
Hunter College HS
New York, NY

Chao, Roberta
Spackenkill HS
Poughkeepsie, NY

Chapin, Steven H
North Babylon SR
North Babylon, NY

Chapman, Gail
Lindenhurst HS
Lindenhurst, NY

Chapman, Robert
Susquehanna Valley
Conklin, NY

Charlap, Richard R
St Francis HS
Hamburg, NY

Chase, Catherine
Spackenkill HS
Poughkeepsie, NY

Chase, Kimberly
Pioneer Central HS
Machias, NY

Chase, Nelson
Hudson Falls SR
Hudson Falls, NY

Chasen, Michael
Hewlett HS
Hewlett Harbor, NY

Chasney, Wayne
Franklin Acad
Malone, NY

Chatterton, Andrew
Saranac Lake HS
Saranac Lk, NY

Chayban, Jenny
Riverside HS
Buffalo, NY

Chen, Catherine A
Geneseo Central HS
Geneseo, NY

Chen, Chai T
North Shore HS
Glen Head, NY

Chen, Humphrey
Bronx HS Of
New York, NY

Chen, Jerry C
Shaker HS
Loudonville, NY

Chenaille, Jeanette
Massena Central HS
Massena, NY

Cheng, Delton
Midwood HS
Brooklyn, NY

Chenouda, Dina
Lawrence HS
N Woodmere, NY

Chianca, Peter
Carmel HS
Carmel, NY

Chiaramonte,
Deirdre
Emma Willard Schl
Staatsburg, NY

Childers, Pamela J
Paul V Moore HS
Brewerton, NY

Childs, Bryan
Franklin Acad
Bangor, NY

Childs, Rebecca
Indian River Central
Philadelphia, NY

PHOTO
NOT
AVAILABLE

Childs, Robin L
New Paltz Central
New Paltz, NY

Childs, William H
East Islip HS
East Islip, NY

Chille, Ralph
Niagara Falls HS
Niagara Falls, NY

Chiriatti, Robin
Poughkeepsie HS
Poughkeepsie, NY

Chirico, Lisa
Notre Dame HS
Utica, NY

Chiu, Lisa
Murry Bergstraum
New York, NY

Cho, Baek Y
Brooklyn Tech HS
Queens, NY

Choi, Mark
Bronx H S Of
Bronx, NY

Chokshi, Parag
New Rochelle HS
New Rochelle, NY

Chorazak, Jennifer
Frontier Central HS
Blasdell, NY

Chotkowski, Steven
C
Scotia Glenville HS
Scotia, NY

Chou, Albert E
Williamsville South
Buffalo, NY

Chovan, Joe R
Cicero North
Syracuse HS
N Syracuse, NY

Chrisley, Christina
Byron-Bergen
Central Schl
S Byron, NY

Chriss, Neil A
Whtie Plains HS
White Plains, NY

Christensen, Kirk W
Shenendehowa
Central Schl
Ballston Lake, NY

Christian, San Jay
F D Roosevelt HS
Brooklyn, NY

Christiana, Jr
Joseph W
John F Kennedy HS
Waccabuc, NY

Christie, Otis
August Martin HS
Jamaica, NY

Christmann, Tammy
B
Wallkill HS
Clintondale, NY

Christon, Lorrie
Narrowsburg
Central Schl
Narrowsburg, NY

Chu, Cavy
Bishop Kearney HS
Brooklyn, NY

Chudoba, Donna
Mount Mercy HS
Buffalo, NY

Chuhta, Steven
Tamarac HS
Troy, NY

Ciano, Mike D
Sachem HS North
Holtsville, NY

Ciardullo, John
Valley Central HS
Walden, NY

Cicci, Joseph
Fayetteville-Manlius
Fayetteville, NY

Cichanowicz, Sara
Mattituck HS
Cutchogue, NY

Ciciola, Dawn M
Maria Regina HS
Bronx, NY

Ciechanowicz, Lisa S
Walt Whitman HS
South Huntington,
NY

Cifuentes, Patricia
Smithtown H S
Smithtown, NY

Cilento, Ben
The Knox Schl
Miami Bch, FL

Ciluffo, Dianne
Nazareth Acad
Rochester, NY

Cimino, Vincent
Washingtonville HS
Monroe, NY

Cintron, Norma Y
Jane Addams
Vocational HS
Bronx, NY

Cioch, Loretta
Frankfort-Schuyler
Frankfort, NY

Cioffi, Teresa Marie
Bishop Kearney HS
Brooklyn, NY

Ciperley, Jamie
Lynn
Columbia HS
Castleton, NY

Cipolla, Kim
Union-Endicott HS
Endicott, NY

Cipriano, Gina
East Syracuse
Minoa HS
Minoa, NY

Cirando, Lisa
Bishop Grimes HS
Syracuse, NY

Cirillo, Christine
Cicero-North HS
Clay, NY

Cirillo, Deron
Mount St Michael
Bronx, NY

Cirillo, Donna
Cardinal Spellman
Bronx, NY

Cirrito, Cheryl
Tonawanda HS
Tonawanda, NY

Cisek, Julius
Carmel HS
Carmel, NY

Clancy, Debbie J
East Meadow HS
East Meadow, NY

Clancy, Geraldine
John Jay HS
Katonah, NY

Clancy, William M
Salesian HS
Bronx, NY

Clark, Andrea
Palmyra-Macedon
Walworth, NY

Clark, Christine
Our Lady Of Mercy
Northport, NY

Clark, Elaine
Avon Central School
Avon, NY

Clark, Jennifer
Broadalhin Central
Broadalbin, NY

Clark, Kathleen
North Shore HS
Glen Head, NY

Clark, Kimberly
Pulaski JR SR HS
Pulaski, NY

Clark, Patrick J
Wayne Central HS
Macedon, NY

Clark, Rick
Vestal SR HS
Vestal, NY

Clark, Theresa
Gloversville HS
Johnstown, NY

Clark, Tia
Wantagh HS
Seaford, NY

Clarke, Christina
Springfield Gardens
Springfield Gds, NY

Clarke, Scott
Andover Central
Andover, NY

Clarman, Cruz
James Monroe HS
Bronx, NY

Clavell, Carlos M
Samuel Gompers
Vocational Tech HS
Bronx, NY

Claveria, Mary Ann
F
The Mary Louis
Jamaica, NY

Cleary, Linda
The Mary Louis
Bayside, NY

Cleland, Tara
Notre Dame/Bishop
Gibbons HS
Schenectady, NY

Clemens, Mike P
Copiaque HS
Copiague, NY

Clina, Matthew J
Millbrook HS
Pleasant Valley, NY

Clum, Scott
Solvay HS
Syracuse, NY

Coates, Carriann
Ellenville HS
Ellenville, NY

Coates, Diane
Churchville-Chili SR
Churchville, NY

Coats, Jennifer
Randolph Central
E Randolph, NY

Cobb, Caroline B
Eldred Central Schl
Eldred, NY

Coelho, Amy
Minisink Valley HS
Port Jervis, NY

Coffey, Michael W
St John The Baptist D HS
Bay Shore, NY

Cohen, Alan J
Seaford HS
Seaford, NY

Cohen, Amy R
G W Hewlett HS
Woodmere, NY

Cohen, Bradley J
Lafayette HS
Brooklyn, NY

Cohen, Charles C
Amgerst Central HS
North Tonawanda, NY

Cohen, Scott M
North Babylon HS
N Babylon, NY

Cohen, Stacey B
Lawrence HS
Woodmere, NY

Cohen, Vivian
Manhattan Center For Science & Math
New York, NY

Cohn, Jody L
Lawrence HS
Inwood, NY

Colaiuti, Caryn
Sewanhaka HS
Stewart Manor, NY

Cole, Amy
Gouverneur JR SR
Gouverneur, NY

Cole, David M
Bronx H S Of
Flushing, NY

Cole, Peter D
Stuyvesant HS
Flushing, NY

Cole, Robert E
Oneida SR HS
Oneida Castle, NY

Colella, Helen
South Shore HS
Brooklyn, NY

Coleman, Kristine
Albertus Magnus
New City, NY

Collette, Timothy
Queensbury Central
Glens Falls, NY

Collins, Andrew
Long Beach HS
Long Beach, NY

Collins, Anne
Chester HS
Chester, NY

Collins, Carrie
James I O Neill HS
West Point, NY

Collins, Jennifer
E L Vandermeuten
Pt Jefferson, NY

Collins, Kimberly A
Louis D Brandeis
Corona, NY

Collins, Timothy
Susquehanna Valley
Binghamton, NY

Collymore, Kathy
Far Rockaway HS
Far Rockaway, NY

Coloma, Ralph
Sacred Heart HS
Yonkers, NY

Colomara, Christine
Notre Dame Acad
Staten Island, NY

Colombo, Josephine
Our Lady Of Perpetual Help
Brooklyn, NY

Colon, Herminio
E J Wilson HS
Spencerport, NY

Colon, Miriam E
High School Of Fashion Industri
Bronx, NY

Colyer, Amy
Schoharie Central
Schoharie, NY

Comito, Vincent
Seaford HS
Seaford, NY

Condello, Mary
Glen Cove HS
Glen Cove, NY

Condos, Panayota
H S Of Art &
Long Island City, NY

Cone, Elizabeth A
Smithtown HS West
Smithtown, NY

Coniglario, Carol Teresa
Commack High School South
Commack, NY

Conigliaro, Charles Peter
St Pauls Schl
Westbury, NY

Conklin, Michele
Oneida Senior HS
Munnsville, NY

Conley, Kelly
Frankfort Schuyler Central HS
Frankfort, NY

Conlon, Edward
Bethpage HS
Bethpage, NY

Connelly, Carolyn
Garden City SR HS
Stewart Manor, NY

Conners, Kim
Hendrick Hudson
Montrose, NY

Connolly, Kristen
Brentwood HS Ross
Brentwood, NY

Connolly, Sean T
John F Kennedy HS
Bedford, NY

Connolly, Shane
John C Birdlebough
Phoenix, NY

Connor, Brian O
Msgr Scanlan HS
Flushing, NY

Conquet, Lisa
Jamaica HS
Jamaica, NY

Conrad, Pamela
Faith Bible Acad
Fort Plain, NY

Conrod, Tracey Lynn
Farmingdale SR HS
Massapequa Park, NY

Conti, Lisamarie
Amsterdam HS
Amsterdam, NY

Contino, Nancy
South Shore HS
Brooklyn, NY

Contratti, David
Roy C Ketcham HS
Poughkeepsie, NY

Convery, Susan K
Fox Lane HS
Mount Kisco, NY

Conway, Jacqueline A
Cardinal Spellman
Bronx, NY

Cook, Jennifer
Midwood HS
Brooklyn, NY

Cook, Mary B
Hoosick Falls Central HS
Eagle Bridge, NY

Cook, Matthew
Hendrick Hudson
Peekskill, NY

Cook, Tracy
Saugerties HS
Saugerties, NY

Cooper, Stacy
Tottenville HS
Staten Island, NY

Cooper, Theresa A
Hillcrest HS
S Ozone Pk, NY

Cooperman, Todd
Oceanside SR HS
Oceanside, NY

Coppeto, Thomas J
Mt Vernon HS
Mount Vernon, NY

Corbi, Caroline
Cardinal Spellman
Bronx, NY

Corcoran, Pamela
Bishop Grimes HS
Liverpool, NY

Corkery, Todd E
Jamestown HS
Jamestown, NY

Corman, Aaron
Bethlehem Central
Glenmont, NY

Cornacchio, Sallyann
Moore Catholic HS
Staten Island, NY

Cornell, Deborah
Newfield HS
Selden, NY

Cornell, Rebecca J
Pawling HS
Pawling, NY

Cornish, Anne
Town Of Webb HS
Old Forge, NY

Cornnell, Richard
Holland Patent
Central HS
Holland Patent, NY

Cornute, Antoinette R
Saratoga Springs HS
Saratoga Springs, NY

Corona, Nicholas
St Francis Prep
Queens Village, NY

Corradino, Michelle
Sachem North HS
Holbrook, NY

Correa, Ana Maria
St Johns Prep
Elmhurst, NY

Correa, Jr Antonio
Cardinal Hayes HS
Bronx, NY

Correa, Lynda
Grover Cleveland
Maspeth, NY

Correia, Derek L
Northport HS
Northport, NY

Corrigan, Jeannine
The Mary Louis
Jackson Heights, NY

Corroon, Courtney T
Garden City SR HS
Garden City, NY

Corson, Michelle
Elmira Southside
Elmira, NY

Cort, Sharon
Freeport HS
Freeport, NY

Coscia, Dawn K
John F Kennedy HS
Bronx, NY

Cosentino, Peter F
Fordham
Preparatory Schl
Bronx, NY

Costa, Peter R
John F Kennedy HS
Yorktown Heights, NY

Costello, Julie A
Sauquoit Valley
Central HS
Frankfort, NY

Costello, Thomas E
St Anthonys HS
Dix Hills, NY

Cote, Joanne E
Middletown HS
Middletown, NY

Cothran, Traci
Onondaga Central
Nedrow, NY

Cottone, Michelle
Victor Central Schl
Victor, NY

Cottrell, James
Hutchinson Central
Buffalo, NY

Cotugno, Joanne
East Meadow HS
E Meadow, NY

Couloumbis, Nikki D
Fallsburg Central
Woodbourne, NY

Cousins, Andrea
Bethlehem Central
Glenmont, NY

Covi, Renee
Rocky Point JR/SR
Rocky Point, NY

Covington, Edith J
John Bowne HS
Rego Park, NY

Cowan, Kimberly
John Jay SR HS
Hopewell Juncti, NY

Cox, Carrie
Albion HS
Albion, NY

Cox, Geoffrey
Nyack HS
Nyack, NY

Cox, Jessica
Lynbrook HS
Lynbrook, NY

Cox, Kim
Remsen Central
Remsen, NY

Coyle, Edward S
Glen Cove HS
Glen Cove, NY

Craft, Jr Kenneth D
Northport HS
Northport, NY

Craiglow, Lisa Anne
Williamsville East
East Amherst, NY

Cramer, Teresa
Corning Painted
Post West HS
Lindley, NY

Crandall, Amy
Camden HS
Blossvale, NY

Craney, Brenda
Tamarac Britton
Kill Cent
Troy, NY

Cranston, Lynn
Springville Griffith
Springville, NY

Craparo, Joseph Charles
Seton Catholic
Central HS
Binghamton, NY

Cratsley, Cynthia Rae
Odessa Montour
Central Schl
Odessa, NY

Crawford, Kim Marie
St John The Baptist
Deer Pk, NY

Creech, Richard L
Liverpool HS
Liverpool, NY

Crespo, Daisy
Norman Thomas HS
Brooklyn, NY

Cristal, Julieta F
Harrison HS
New Rochelle, NY

Crobar, Steven L
Liverpool HS
Liverpool, NY

Cromas, Faith
St Edmunds HS
Brooklyn, NY

Cromer, Francoise
Mt Vernon HS
Mount Vernon, NY

Cronin, James
Msgr Mc Clancy HS
Sunnyside, NY

Cronin, Michelle
Lafayette HS
Nedrow, NY

Cronk, Edward
Liverpool HS
Liverpool, NY

Cronk, II Ronald L
East
Syracuse-Minoa Cen
Minoa, NY

Crounse, David A
Shaker HS
Albany, NY

Crowley, Kerri J
Prattsburg Central
Branchport, NY

Cruz, Franklin
Christ The King
Regional HS
Howard Beach, NY

Cruz, Jeanne M
St John Villa Acad
Staten Island, NY

Csaki, Michele
Colonie Central HS
Schenectady, NY

Cubas, Jr Edilberto Martin
Cardinal Hayes HS
New York, NY

Cucchiara, Peter
H Frank Carey HS
Franklin Sq, NY

Cuevas, Nelson
St Agnes HS
New York, NY

Cuffaro, Catherine
Union-Endicott HS
Endicott, NY

Cuffe, James F
Fox Lane HS
Mt Kisco, NY

Cullen, Susan
De Sales Catholic
Gasport, NY

Cummings, Debra
Susquehanna Valley
Binghamton, NY

Cummings, Gizzelle
De Witt Clinton HS
Bronx, NY

Cummings, Mary
Oxford Acad HS
Oxford, NY

Cummings, Mich L
Caior-Durham HS
Acra, NY

Cummings, Michael J
Pelham Memorial
Pelham, NY

Cummings, Scott D
Vestal SR HS
Vestal, NY

Cunningham, Leslie
Salmon River
Central HS
Constable, NY

Cura, Monica
Msgr Scanlan HS
Elmhurst, NY

Curcio, Stephanie A
Newfield HS
Selden, NY

Curley, Michael D
Shenendehowa HS
Clifton Park, NY

Curran, Andrew B
John Jay HS
Katonah, NY

Curran, Christopher
Saranac Lake
Central HS
Saranac Lk, NY

Curran, Patricia A
Garden City HS
Garden City, NY

Curren, Timothy
Voorheesville HS
Altamont, NY

Curtin, II R C Kelly
Orchard Park HS
Hamburg, NY

Curtis, Timothy
Watertown HS
Watertown, NY

Cusato, Kristen
Pine Bush HS
Pine Bush, NY

Cushman, Howard
North Rose-Wolcott
Red Creek, NY

Cutignola, Diane
Commack North HS
E Northport, NY

Cutting, Hope Anne
T
Curtis HS
Staten Island, NY

Cybriwsky, Kristan
Connetquot HS
Oakdale, NY

Cybulski, Dinamarie
Villa Maria Acad
Buffalo, NY

Cyrus, Tonya
St Raymonds
Academy For Girls
Bronx, NY

Czapla, Dawn M
Lancaster HS
Lancaster, NY

D Addario, John
Cardinal Spellman
Bronx, NY

D Angelo, Frank
Mc Kee Technical
Staten Island, NY

D Angelo, Kimberly
La Guardia HS Of
Music & Art
Bayside, NY

D Annunzio,
Margaret Mary E
Tho Loyola Schl
Brooklyn, NY

D Erasmo, Frances
Mahopac HS
Mahopac, NY

Daby, Donna
Lake Placid Central
Lake Placid, NY

Daddario, Darren M
St Johns Preparatory
Astoria, NY

Dailey, Joy
Newark SR HS
Lyons, NY

Daka, Jimmy Gzim
Mount Saint
Michael Acad
New York, NY

Dakin, Brian
Richard
Fox Lane HS
Mt Kisco, NY

Dalesandro, Mark
Lasalle HS
Niagara Falls, NY

Daley, Daniel V
Msgr Mc Clancy HS
Brooklyn, NY

Daley, Erin M
St Francis Prep HS
Woodhaven, NY

Dallura, Russ
St John The Baptist
Centereach, NY

Dalrymple,
Nicole-Yanique
Erasmus Hall HS
Brooklyn, NY

Daly, Alison
Hendrick Hudson
Montrose, NY

Daly, Laura K
Amherst Central HS
Amherst, NY

Daly, Margaret A
Carle Place HS
Carle Place, NY

Daly, Michael W
New Hyde Park
Memorial HS
New Hyde Park, NY

Damas, Margarette
Washington Irving
Brooklyn, NY

Damico, James C
Nazareth Regional
Brooklyn, NY

PHOTO
NOT
AVAILABLE

Danas, Vasilios
Fort Hamilton HS
Brooklyn, NY

Daniels, Sandra E
Averill Park HS
Averill Park, NY

Danisi, Tina
Newfield HS
Selden, NY

Dannewitz, Kenneth
R
Hampton Bays HS
Hampton Bays, NY

Darch, Lynn
Buffalo Academy Of
The Sacred Heart
E Amherst, NY

Darguste, Elizabeth
Bishop Kearney HS
Brooklyn, NY

Darling, Brian
Jordan-Elbridge HS
Jordan, NY

Darling, Kelly
South Lewis JR SR
Brantingham, NY

Darling, Ray L
Gloversville HS
Gloversville, NY

Das, Surjya P
Guilderland Central
Guilderland, NY

Dasilva, Teresa
Dominican
Commercial HS
Jamaica, NY

Dattilo, Theresa
Monsignor Scanlan
Bronx, NY

Davern, Connie
Commack North HS
Commack, NY

David, Amy
Bishop Grimes HS
E Syracuse, NY

David, Lafleur
Sheepshead Bay HS
Brooklyn, NY

Davide, Salvatore J
Monsignor Farrell
Staten Island, NY

Davidson, Jennifer
L
Delaware Acad
Delhi, NY

Davie, Kelly
Port Richmond HS
Staten Isld, NY

Davis, Dale E
Cortland SR HS
Cortland, NY

Davis, Denice Y
Dominican
Commercial HS
Jamaica Queens, NY

Davis, Georgia
Lynne
Rome Free Acad
Blossvale, NY

Davis, Greg R
Horace Mann School
New York, NY

Davis, H Christian
Dundee Central HS
Lakemont, NY

Davis, Lashan
Newburgh Free
New Windsor, NY

Davis, Melissa Anne
Newark SR HS
Newark, NY

Davis, Sandra
Bishop Kearney HS
Brooklyn, NY

Davis, Scott
Corning-Painted
Post West HS
Painted Post, NY

Davis, Suzette
Queen Of The
Rosary Acad
Westbury, NY

Davis, Todd
Oneida HS
Canastota, NY

Davis, Vicki
Perry Central HS
Perry, NY

Davison, Donna Kay
Liverpool HS
Liverpool, NY

Davison, Wayne K
Cicero-North
Syracuse HS
Clay, NY

Dawson, Steven
Allen
W T Sampson HS
Bevier, MO

De Angelis, Jr
Edward
Saugerties HS
Saugert Ies, NY

De Aveiro, Robert
Lafayette HS
Brooklyn, NY

De Bernardo, Gail
Christopher
Columbus HS
Bronx, NY

De Betta, Josephine
St John Villa Acad
Staten Is, NY

De Blasis, Maria R
Cardinal Mooney
Rochester, NY

De Caro, Adria
Commack HS North
Commack, NY

De Fanti, Lucy
Preston HS
Bronx, NY

De Fazio, Christian
Lockport SR HS
Lockport, NY

De Filippo,
Elizabeth
John Jay SR HS
Hopewell Junction,
NY

De Forest, Eric
Tupper Lake HS
Tupper Lk, NY

De Frees, Jr Bruce
D
Rome Free Acad
Lee Center, NY

De La Osa Cruz,
Steven Marco
Thomas A Edison
Elmira Hts, NY

De La Torre,
Geraldine
Spring Valley SR
Monsey, NY

De Lacerda, Jr
Alberto G
North Babylon SR
North Babylon, NY

De Lamarter,
Michelle
Waterloo SR HS
Waterloo, NY

De Luca, Michael
The Kew-Forest
Forest Hills, NY

De Maille, Gregory
St John The Baptist
W Babylon, NY

De Marchi, Jason
West Genesee SR
Camillus, NY

De Orazio, Diana
Seton Catholic
Central HS
Binghamton, NY

De Palma, Peter M
Pittsford Mendon
Pittsford, NY

De Roberts, Lynn
Cicero
North-Syracuse HS
Brewerton, NY

De Rosa, Karen M
Smithtown High
School West
Smithtown, NY

De Rycke, Kim
Fairport HS
Fairport, NY

De Santis, Lori
St Joseph By The
Sea HS
Staten Island, NY

De Silva, Judith
New Dorp HS
Staten Island, NY

De Sousa, Christine
Mineola HS
Mineola, NY

De Sousa, Patricia
Acad Of St Joseph
Kings Park, NY

De Stefano,
Christopher A
Deer Park HS
Deer Park, NY

De Touche, Amelia
C
Dominican
Commercial HS
Jamaica, NY

De Vaul, Virginia
East
Syracuse-Minoa Cen
Kirkville, NY

De Vito, Damon
La Salle Institute Of
Troy HS
Troy, NY

De Vito, Sina
Bishop Kearney HS
Brooklyn, NY

De Wysocki,
Jacqueline
Fox Lane HS
Pound Ridge, NY

Dean, Dawn M
Naples Central Schl
Naples, NY

Dean, Nadia
Norman Thomas HS
Bronx, NY

Decicco, Vincent L
Rocky Point HS
Rocky Point, NY

Decker, James M
Eldred Central Schl
Barryville, NY

Decker, Sandra
Sherburne-Earlville
North Norwich, NY

Deegan, Stacey L
Huntington HS
Huntington, NY

Deeks, Kimberly A
West Senca West
SR HS
West Seneca, NY

Deely, Gregory
Clarkstown South
New City, NY

Deere, Kelly
Brentwood
Sonderling HS
Brentwood, NY

Defillipo, Natalie
West Hempstead
W Hempstead, NY

Degutis, Christopher
Amsterdam HS
Amsterdam, NY

Del Duco, Steven J
Somers Central HS
Yorktown Heights,
NY

Del Monte, Jr
Edward J
Port Chester SR HS
Port Chester, NY

Del Negro, Christine
M
John Joy HS
Pound Ridge, NY

Del Signore, Cindy
Cicero-North
Syracuse HS
N Syracuse, NY

Del Valle, Alexandra
Aqinas HS
New York, NY

Delancey, Herbert E
Bishop Ford Central
Catholic HS
Newyork, NY

Delevan, Kelly
Fredonia HS
Fredonia, NY

Delia, Carmela
Christ The King HS
Glendale, NY

Dell, Kristi A
Bellport HS
East Patchogue, NY

Dellamore, Leslie
Liverpool HS
Liverpool, NY

Delwo, Kristi
Herkimer HS
Herkimer, NY

Demaio, Christine G
Fontbonne Hall
Brooklyn, NY

Dembeck, Jennifer
Washingtonvile HS
Rock Tavern, NY

Demetriades, Ritsa
Archbishop Iakovos
Bayside, NY

Demicoli, Mark
St John The Baptist
Massapequa, NY

Demmin, Darlene A
Wilson Central JR
SR HS
Wilson, NY

Dempsey, James W
St Anthonys HS
Kings Park, NY

Dempster, Zaria M
Flushing HS
Flushing, NY

Denicourt, Scott
Potsdam HS
Potsdam, NY

Dennis, Jodie Ann
Roy C Ketcham HS
Poughkeepsie, NY

Dent, Peter
H S Of Fashion
Brooklyn, NY

Denton, Susan E
Copiague HS
Lindenhurst, NY

Deonarine, Marina
M
Norman Thomas HS
Hollis, NY

Derella, Michael
Mohawk Central
Mohawk, NY

Derosa, Robert J
Patchoque-Medrod
E Patchogue, NY

Desanctis, David A
St Marys Boys HS
Manhasset, NY

Desiderio, Ricio I
Kings Park SR HS
Smithtown, NY

Desjardins, Maurice
West Seneca East
SR HS
Cheektowaga, NY

Deslaurier, Colleen
M
Tottenville HS
Staten Island, NY

Desmoine, Luz
Cathedral HS
Ny, NY

Desormeaux,
Michelle
Berlin Central Schl
Stephentown, NY

Desso, Alyson L
Marcellus SR HS
Marcellus, NY

Devin, Erin
Mount Mercy Acad
Orchard Pk, NY

Devoe, III Robert W
East Islip HS
E Islip, NY

Dewitt, Marcia J
Cairo-Durham HS
Leeds, NY

Di Bella, Lori A
H Frank Carey HS
Franklin Square,
NY

Di Cesare, Nicole
Valley Central HS
Newburgh, NY

Di Cuffa, Jr Aldo
Utica Free Acad
Utica, NY

Di Fusco, Thomas
Long Beach HS
Long Beach, NY

Di Liberto, Laura
St Joseph Hill Acad
Staten Island, NY

Di Mare, Joseph G
Regis HS
Staten Island, NY

Di Napoli, Gina
Anne
Monsignor Scanlan
Bronx, NY

Di Scioscia,
Stephanie
Gloversville HS
Gloversville, NY

Dia Paul, Joseph
Niagara Wheatfield
SR HS
Sanborn, NY

Dicerbo, Cheri
Manhasset HS
Manhasset, NY

Dickerson, Crystal L
Mt Vernon HS
Mt Vernon, NY

Dickinson, Darlene
L
Harpursville Central
Harpursville, NY

Dickinson, Donna
Cicero HS
Kirkville, NY

Dickman, Gloria I
Vestal SR HS
Binghamton, NY

Dickson, Julie
Thousand Islands
Clayton, NY

Dicruttalo, III
Albert
Gloversville HS
Gloversville, NY

Diefendorf, Donald
S
Cazenovia HS
Cazenovia, NY

Diehl, Julie
Mt Mercy Acad
Buffalo, NY

Dietzman, Brian
Delaware Acad
Delhi, NY

Diez, Lisa
Oceanside SR HS
Oceanside, NY

Digiorgi, Nicole
Lakeland SR HS
Yorktown Hts, NY

Dignam, Lynn
St John The Baptist
W Babylon, NY

Dilgard, Angela
Dominican Acad
Queens Village, NY

Dill, Kathleen A
Millbrook Schl
Verbank, NY

Dillard, Lay Foya
August Martin HS
Jamaica, NY

Dillon, Kathleen M
The Mary Louis
Richmond Hill, NY

Dimaculangan, Lisa
M
St Jean Baptiste HS
New York, NY

Dimitrov, Barbara
Bishop Kearney HS
Rochester, NY

Dimon, R Thomas
Gouverneur HS
Gouverneur, NY

Dinapoli, Mia
Commack H S
Dix Hills, NY

Dineen, Patrick
Mt St Michael Acad
Yonkers, NY

Dingle, Jeffrey Mark
West Hempstead
W Hempstead, NY

Dingle, Kevin
Bronx H S Of
New York, NY

Diolallevi, Anna Lisa
Christ The King
Regional HS
Elmhurst, NY

Dionisio, Marcy
Miller Place HS
Miller Pl, NY

Diveronica, Steve
Canastota HS
Canastota, NY

Divirgilio, Sarah
St Johns Prep
Astoria, NY

Dixey, Patricia
John Jay SR HS
Hopewell Jct, NY

Dixon, Amy
Kenmore West SR
Kenmore, NY

Dixon, Marsha H
Midwood HS
Brooklyn, NY

Dizon, Marie
Deanna E
St Peters HS For
Staten Isl, NY

Dizon, Rowena
Francesca I
Sachem HS
Holbrook, NY

Dmytrenko, Adrian
R
New Hyde Park
Memorial HS
New Hyde Park, NY

Docherty, Marilyn
Cardinal Spellman
Bronx, NY

Dodds, Penny L
Taconic Hills
Central HS
Hillsdale, NY

Dodge, Linda M
Canastota HS
Canastota, NY

Doherty, Erin Anne
East Meadow HS
E Meadow, NY

Dohrenwend, Terri
A
Centereach HS
Centereach, NY

Doht, Robert C
North Babylon HS
N Babylon, NY

Dolan, Paul T
Mc Quaid Jesuit HS
Pittsford, NY

Dolata, Carole
Commack High Schl
Commack, NY

Dolph, Larry
Bishop Cunningham
Oswego, NY

Dombrow, Russell
W
Bishop Ludden HS
Syracuse, NY

Dombrowski, Jill M
West Seneca East
SR HS
West Seneca, NY

Dombrowski, Lori
Alden HS
Elma, NY

Dominelli, Richard
A
Clarkstown South
Nyack, NY

Dominguez, Julio
Cesar
Cardinal Hayes HS
New York, NY

Dominguez, Rodolfo
Eastern District HS
Brooklyn, NY

Donegan, Colleen
Academy Of St
Coram, NY

Donohue, Catherine
Anne
Smithtown High
School East
Smithtown, NY

Donohue, Eileen
Saratoga Centera
Catholic HS
Bronx, NY

Donohue, Patricia A
Smithtown HS
Smithtown, NY

Donovan, Kristen H
Ardsley HS
Ardsley, NY

Donovan, Mark P
Fayetteville-Manlius
Manlius, NY

Doolittle, Jr Mark A
Johnson City HS
Johnson City, NY

Dore, Catherine
Joanne
Holy Trinity HS
Bethpage, NY

Doremus, Constance
Ann
Riverhead HS
Riverhead, NY

Dorn, Tina
Vernon-Verona-Sher
rill HS
Vernon Ctr, NY

Dorsey, Bryan
Chester HS
Goshen, NY

Dorval, Carlene
Port Jervis HS
Huguenot, NY

Doscher, Susan
Spackenkill HS
Poughkeepsie, NY

Doss, Cheryl
Ohondaga Central
Syracuse, NY

Doty, Valerie
Glens Falls SR HS
Glen Falls, NY

Dougherty, Tricia
East Islip HS
East Islip, NY

Douglas, Courtney
Mt Vernon HS
Mount Vernon, NY

Douglas, Tanya
Marie
Cardinal Spellman
Bronx, NY

Dounias, George J
Smithtown H S
Smithtown, NY

Dourdis, Kikie
Poughkeepsie HS
Poughkeepsie, NY

Dowd, Patrick H
Johnstown HS
Johnstown, NY

Dowley, Jeff A
F D Roosevelt HS
Staatsburg, NY

Dowling, John W
John F Kennedy HS
Carmel, NY

Downing, Robin
Corning-Painted
Post West HS
Corning, NY

Doyen, Kurt C
Red Jacket Central
Palmyra, NY

Doyle, Julie A
Auburn HS
Auburn, NY

Doyle, William
Sachem HS
Lk Ronkonkoma,
NY

Drabinski, Diane
Webster HS
Webster, NY

Drake, Jennifer A
Elmira Southside
Pine City, NY

Drazen, Bradford
Binghamton HS
Binghamton, NY

Drejas, Doreen J
Villa Maria Acad
Cheektowaga, NY

Drews, II Leslie H O
Byron-Bergen
Central Schl
Byron, NY

Driggs, David T
Vestal SR HS
Vestal, NY

Driscoll, Dawn
Francis HS
Staten Island, NY

Driscoll, John
Sholy Trinity HS
East Meadow, NY

Drury, Colleen M
Bishop Ludden HS
Syracuse, NY

Du Bois, Karen E
Orchard Park HS
Orchard Park, NY

Dubey, Ajay K
George W Hewlett
Hewlett, NY

Ducatte, Melissa
Saranac Central HS
Cadyville, NY

Duclos, Antoine
Andrew Jackson HS
Queens Village, NY

Dudash, Sheila
Bishop Ludden HS
Liverpool, NY

Duddleston, Nancy
Central HS
Valley Stream, NY

Duffy, Janine
St Francis Prep
Astoria, NY

Duffy, Nancy A
James I O Neill HS
Highland Falls, NY

Dulaney, Deborah
Cornwall Central HS
Cornwall, NY

Dumbleton, Ellen
Dominican
Commercial HS
Glendale, NY

Dume, Adelina
Hunter College HS
Woodside, NY

Dundon, Colleen
Mahopac HS
Mahopac, NY

Dunford, Beth
United Nations
International Schl
New York, NY

Dungie, Chris D
Mount Saint
Michael Acad
Bronx, NY

Dunker, Patricia
Ann
Our Lady Of
Perpetual Hilp HS
Brooklyn, NY

Dunn, Cindy
La Webber JR SR
Lyndonville, NY

Dunn, David
Haverling Central
Bath, NY

Dunn, Glorious
De Witt Clinton HS
Bronx, NY

Dunn, Michael
St John The Baptist
Gt River, NY

Dunne, Charles G
Garden City SR HS
Garden City, NY

Duprey, Charmain
Crown Point Central
Crown Pt, NY

Durand, Marcella C
Hunter College HS
New York, NY

Durniak, Karen J
Arlington HS
Hopewell Jct, NY

Dursi, Cynthia
Fox Lane HS
Bedford, NY

Durso, Anthony P
Rome Free Acad
Rome, NY

Duryea, Scott
New Rochelle HS
New Rochelle, NY

Duvilaire, Nadia
Martin Luther King
Jr HS
Brooklyn, NY

Dvorak, Michelle G
West Seneca E SR
West Seneca, NY

Dwaileebe, Jenny
Olean HS
Olean, NY

Dwyer, Dawn M
Pawling HS
Pawling, NY

Dwyer, Michael
Mount Vernon HS
Mount Vernon, NY

Dye, Annette
Frankfort-Schuyler
Utica, NY

Dyer, Anne
Our Lady Of Victory
Bronx, NY

Dyer, Bernadette L
Springfield Gardens
Springfield Gdns,
NY

Dyer, Michael
Lake Placid Central
Lake Placid, NY

Dyett, Michelle
Wingate HS
Brooklyn, NY

Dysard, Barb
Albion HS
Albion, NY

Dzaak, Dwayne
Bishop Timon HS
West Seneca, NY

Dziadiw, Stenia
Acad Of The Holy
Slingerlands, NY

Eames, Wendy
Amsterdam HS
Amsterdam, NY

Earle, Tammy
Hannibal Central
Hannibal, NY

Eastman, Kari
Greenwich Central
Greenwich, NY

Eastwood,
Lorna-Marie
Commack High Schl
Commack, NY

Eaton, Timothy J
New Hyde Park
Memorial JR SR HS
New Hyde Park, NY

Ebanks, Karen
Andrew Jackson HS
Queens Village, NY

Ebert, Michelle L
Brockport HS
Brockport, NY

Echols, Eugenia
Buffalo Acad Of
The Sacred Heart
Buffalo, NY

Eckard, Robert T
G Ray Bodley HS
Fulton, NY

Eckert, Todd
Sunnyside Christian
N Rose, NY

Eddy, Mark
Clifton-Fine Central
Newton Falls, NY

Edelman, Peri
Valley Stream S HS
Lynbrook, NY

Edgar, Deborah S
Earl L
Vandermeulen HS
Pt Jefferson, NY

Edge, Wendy L
La Guardia HS
Springfield Gdn, NY

Edick, Anthony W
Westmoreland
Central HS
Clinton, NY

Edinger, Henry F
Corcoran HS
Syracuse, NY

Edmiston, Dawn M
John F Kennedy HS
Utica, NY

Edmond, Yanique M
Cathedral HS
New York, NY

Edmunds, Sunja E
Ward Melville HS
Stony Brook, NY

Edwards, Dale
Silver Creek Central
Silver Creek, NY

Edwards, David
New Rochelle HS
New Rochelle, NY

Edwards, David Lee
Silver Creek Central
Silver Creek, NY

Edwards, Kristin M
Shenendehowa HS
Clifton Park, NY

Egan, Kimberly A
Sacred Heart HS
Bronx, NY

Egan, Michael
Mineola HS
Mineola, NY

Egelston, Mikki
Oakfield-Alabama
Central HS
Oakfield, NY

Egle, Jeffrey D
Arkport Central
Arkport, NY

Ehmann, Christine
E
Our Lady Of Mercy
Rochester, NY

Eiche, Carolyn J
St Francis
Preparatory Schl
Glendale, NY

Eichwald, Kenneth
B
Harrison HS
Harrison, NY

Eidenweil, John C
Wantagh HS
Wantagh, NY

Eisenberg, Heidi
G W Hewlett HS
Hewlett, NY

Eisenhauer, John
Immaculate Heart
Central HS
Watertown, NY

Eklund, Joshua
Smithtown High
School East
St James, NY

Elia, James M
East Meadow HS
East Meadow, NY

Elliott, Ginalyn
Sachem North HS
Holtsville, NY

Ellis, Janet
Cohoes HS
Cohoes, NY

Ellis, John Mitchell
Midwood HS
Brooklyn, NY

Ellis, Kimberly
Glens Falls HS
Glens Falls, NY

Ellison, Tessa
Stuyvesant HS
Brooklyn, NY

Elmore, Jr Matthew
White Plains HS
White Plains, NY

Embler, Jill
Valley Central HS
Walden, NY

Emerson, Jill
Geneva HS
Penn Yan, NY

Emery, Joel
Salmon River
Crntral School
Bombay, NY

Emmi, Christine
Canastota Central
Canastota, NY

Encalada, Carlos F
Cardinal Spellman
Bronx, NY

Engel, Chris
Jamestown HS
Jamestown, NY

Engle, Carl S
Elba Central Schl
Elba, NY

Engle, Marcella
Kenmore West SR
Bowling Green, KY

Englesberg, Bari Sue
Newfield HS
Coram, NY

Enright, Beth
Acad Of The
New Rochelle, NY

Episcopio, Leonard
G
Lafayette HS
Brooklyn, NY

Eppel, Becky
Union Springs
Scipio Center, NY

Eppel, Dieter
Union Springs Acad
Scipio Center, NY

Erickson, Kathryn
Vernon-Verona-Sher
rill Central HS
Vernon, NY

Ernst, Patricia
Saratoga Central
Catholic HS
Gansevoort, NY

Ervin, Anthony
Williamsville North
Williamsville, NY

Erway, Victor M
Cherry Valley HS
Cherry Valley, NY

Eskedal, Sandra
Patricia
Scotia-Glenville HS
Scotia, NY

Esperto, George
East Meadow HS
East Meadow, NY

Esposito, Gina
Newfield HS
Selden, NY

Estenoz, Maria
Grand Island HS
Grand Island, NY

Estrada, Fred
Island Trees HS
Levittown, NY

Estrella, Claribel
Edward R Murrow
Brooklyn, NY

Evangelista, Susan
A
Sachem North HS
Lake Ronkonkoma,
NY

Evans, Camille
Holy Trinity HS
Uniondale, NY

Everett, Korrie
Smithtown H S
Hauppauge, NY

Ewanow, Rob
Eastridge HS
Rochester, NY

Ewing, Jeff
Shenendehowa HS
Ballston Lake, NY

Fabery, Micheal
Cicero North
Syracuse HS
N Syracuse, NY

Fabish, David Z
F D Roosevelt HS
Staatsburg, NY

Facey, Erika
Long Island
Lutheran HS
Freeport, NY

Fair, Jocelyn
Hendrick Hudson
Buchanan, NY

Fairbanks, John
Daniel
Union Springs Acad
Jamestown, NY

Fairbanks, Rebecca
Union Springs Acad
Jamestown, NY

Falabella, Carol
Notre Dame
Academy HS
Staten Island, NY

Falinski, Natalia K
Thomas R Proctor
Utica, NY

Falis, Neil D
Clarkstown H S
New City, NY

Falkowski, Agatha
Ichabod Crane HS
Valatie, NY

Fancher, Barb
Portville HS
Portville, NY

Fancher, Mark
Nottingham HS
Syracuse, NY

Farage, Regina
Bishop Kearney HS
Brooklyn, NY

Farinha, Nigel I
Xavier HS
Hollis Queens, NY

Farnella, Hilary J
Jamestown HS
Jamestown, NY

Farney, Peter W
South Lewis Central
Lyons Falls, NY

Farr, Samara
Horseheads HS
Big Flats, NY

Farrell, Tracy Lynn
Division Avenue HS
Levittown, NY

Farrington, Abby A
Covent Of The
Sacred Heart HS
Sea Bright, NJ

Farrington, Robert
M
La Salle Acad
New York, NY

Farthing, Jennifer A
Chenango Valley HS
Binghamton, NY

Farzan, David J
Williamsville South
Williamsville, NY

Fasanelle, Joan
Marie
Fontbonne Hall
Brooklyn, NY

Fasciglione, Joseph
Mount St Michael
Bronx, NY

Fasoldt, Jeffrey C
Liverpool HS
Liverpool, NY

Fassnacht, Tina
Valley Central HS
Montgomery, NY

Faucher, Kimberlie
F
Cicero-North
Syracuse HS
Brewerton, NY

Faulkner, Denise
Clymer Central Schl
Clymer, NY

Faulkner, Gary
Shenendehowa HS
Waterford, NY

Fauls, Brian
Smithtown H S
Smithtown, NY

Fay, Margaret
Liverpool HS
North Syracuse, NY

Fay, Sean
Mynderse Acad
Seneca Falls, NY

Feagles, Judy
St Johnsville
Central Schl
St Johnsville, NY

Feathers, Neil
New Pebanon
Central HS
Hancock, MA

Featherston, Paul
Poughkeepsie HS
Queens Village, NY

Fedele, Elizabeth
Nazareth Acad
Rochester, NY

Feduniec, Denys A
Sachem HS North
Lake Grove, NY

Feeney, Mary
St Patricks Central
Catholic HS
Coxsackie, NY

Feeny, Sharon
Saratoga Central
Catholic HS
Saratoga Springs,
NY

Fegan, Andrew
Wilson Magnet HS
Rochester, NY

Feinson, Andrea
Long Beach HS
Long Beach, NY

Feist, Nicole F
Hunter College HS
New York, NY

Felberbaum, Nancy
John F Kennedy HS
Riverdale, NY

Feldman, Alan
Bronx HS Of
Bronx, NY

Feldman, Lynn R
Harrison HS
Harrison, NY

Feldman, Nicole
Broadalbin Central
Johnstown, NY

Feldman, Wendy
South Shore HS
Brooklyn, NY

Felicetti, Laura
Saint John The
Baptist HS
Lindenhurst, NY

Feliciano, Felix
Aviation HS
Bronx, NY

Feller, Lynne Carol
Churchville-Chili SR
Rochester, NY

Fenster, David
Francis HS
Staten Island, NY

Fenton, Zanita
Union Endicott HS
Endicott, NY

Ferchen, Richard A
Niagara Wheatfield
Sanborn, NY

Ferguson, Lettie
Ann
Union Springs Acad
Middletown, NY

Ferguson, Shannon
L
Bishop Ford Central
Brooklyn, NY

Fermo, Carolyn
Academy Of St
Kings Pk, NY

Fernandes, Donna
Brewster HS
Brewster, NY

Fernandes, Jr
Manuel D
Iona Prep HS
Yonkers, NY

Fernandez, Christine
L
Claybon A Bouron
JR SR HS
Voorheesville, NY

Fernandez, Francine
High School Of Art
& Design
Astoria, NY

Fernandez, Vicky
St Francis Prep
College Point, NY

Ferrara, Michael C
Pittsford Mendon
Pittsford, NY

Ferreira, Antonio M
Mohawk Central
Mohawk, NY

Ferretti, Theresa
Shenendehowa HS
Clifton Park, NY

Ferris, Deborah
Winddon Ashland
Jewett HS
Ashland, NY

Ferris, Theresa L
G Ray Bodley HS
Fulton, NY

Ferruzza, Jeffrey
Aquinas Inst
Rochester, NY

Fidler, Philip
Walter Panas HS
Peekskill, NY

Fiello, Jeffrey
West Genesee SR
Syracuse, NY

Fiero, Suzanne
General Douglas
Mac Arthur HS
Levittown, NY

Fierro, Doreen L
Academy Of The
Resurrection HS
Port Chester, NY

Figueroa, Adam
Manhattan Ctr For
Science & Math
New York, NY

Figueroa, Camille
Manhattan Center
For Science & Math
New York, NY

Figueroa, Mary
Christ The King
RHS HS
Maspeth, NY

Filasky, Julie
Rocky Point JR SR
Rocky Point, NY

Filingeri, Andrea
Frankfort-Schuyler
Central HS
Frankfort, NY

Filipowski, Kathlee
Ann
Minisink Valley HS
Middletown, NY

Filipski, Dorie
Springville Griffith
Colden, NY

Filosa, Jennifer
Anne
Sachem North HS
Farmingville, NY

Filpo, Lizette
Hillcrest HS
Corona, NY

Filsaime, Arnelle
Fashion Industries
Brooklyn, NY

Finch, Janice
Murry Bergtraum
Bronx, NY

Finch, Marc
Camden HS
Camden, NY

Finger, Andrea
Monsignor Seanlan
Bronx, NY

Fingerling,
Maryellen
Academy Of St
Northport, NY

Finguerra, Mark
St Pauls Schl
Westbury, NY

Fink, Tracy A
Amherst Central HS
Amherst, NY

Finkbeiner, Paul G
Jamestown HS
Jamestown, NY

Finnerty, II Gary H
Altmar-Parish-Willi
amstown Ctl HS
Williamstown, NY

Fiodeliso, James J
Cardinal Mooney
Rochester, NY

Fioravanti, Clayton
L
Ithaca HS
Ithaca, NY

Fiore, Pat
John D Kennedy HS
Utica, NY

Fiorentino, Annette
Lakeland HS
Putnam Valley, NY

Fischer, Kelly E
Auburn HS
Auburn, NY

Fisher, Elizabeth
Little Falls JR SR
Little Falls, NY

Fisher, Kimberly
Amsterdam HS
Amsterdam, NY

Fisher, Tammy
Franklin Acad
Malone, NY

Fisher, William
Scott
Lyndonville Central
Waterport, NY

Fitch, Allicia
Mont Pleasant HS
Schenectady, NY

Fitch, Doris T
Rome Free Acad
Rome, NY

Fitts, Landon T
Saunders Trades &
Tech HS
Yonkers, NY

Fitz-Gordon,
Heather
St Francis Prep
Queens Village, NY

Fitzgerald,
Bernadette T
Homer Central HS
Cortland, NY

Fitzgerald, Patricia
H
St Barnabas HS
Yonkers, NY

Fitzgerald, Regina
St Edmund HS
Brooklyn, NY

Fitzgerald, Theresa
Holy Trinity HS
West Hempstead,
NY

Fitzsimmons, Diana
Washingtonville HS
Washingtonville, NY

Flanders, T Patrick
Canajoharie Central
Canajoharie, NY

Flanigan, Ann
Hudson Falls SR
Hudson Falls, NY

Fleary, Nocole B
James Madison HS
Brooklyn, NY

Fletcher, Jeff
Naples Central HS
Naples, NY

Flick, Vicki L
La Fargeville
Central HS
Clayton, NY

Flood, Brian
St Marys Boys HS
Muttontown, NY

Flores, Diana
Christopher
Columbus HS
Bronx, NY

Flynn, Deborah
Newark Valley HS
Owego, NY

Flynn, Patricia
Smithtown High
School East
Smithtown, NY

Fodrowski,
Elizabeth A
Smithtown West HS
Smithtown, NY

Fogle, Troy
Corning-Painted
Post West HS
Corning, NY

Foley, Kevin
Washingtonville HS
Blooming Grove, NY

Foley, Maureen
General Douglas
Mac Arthur HS
Levittown, NY

Fonseca, Patricia
Saratoga Springs HS
Greenfield Center,
NY

Fontana, David
Hauppauge HS
Smithtown, NY

Forbes, Carl A
Yonkers HS
Yonkers, NY

Ford, Courtney
City Honors Schl
Buffalo, NY

Ford, Maria
Hillcrest HS
Cambria Hts, NY

Ford, Sean Crispin
Archbishop Walsh
Olean, NY

Forster, Latisha
H S Fashions
New York, NY

Forti, Rene
St Johns Prep
Astoria, NY

Fortunate, Robert
Iona Preparatory
White Plains, NY

Fortunato, Jay
Farmingdale SR HS
Farmingdale, NY

Foss, Denise M
Holland Central
South Wales, NY

Foster, Lori R
Cuba Central Schl
Cuba, NY

Foster, Thomas
Amsterdam HS
Amsterdam, NY

Fowler, John K
Wilson Central Schl
Wilson, NY

Foxworth, Hope
La Salle SR HS
Niagara Falls, NY

Fradenburg, Sean
Oneida HS
Oneida, NY

Fraioli, Chris
Iona Prep
Larchmont, NY

Francia, Joanne
G W Hewlett HS
Valley Stream, NY

Franciamore, Sergio
New Rochelle HS
Scarsdale, NY

Francis, Jr Anthony D
John F Kennedy HS
New York, NY

Francis, Avemaria M
Bishop Ford Central Catholic HS
Brooklyn, NY

Francis, Scott J
Paul V Moore HS
Brewerton, NY

Francois, Daniah Jean
Dominican Commercial HS
Elmhurst, NY

Frangos, Stephanie
The Norman Howard Schl
Rochester, NY

Frank, Jeff
Mayfield JR SR HS
Mayfield, NY

Frank, Robin
Hilton Central HS
Hilton, NY

Frankel, Lawrence M
Lawrence HS
Woodmere, NY

Frankel, Serena
JLM Great Neck North SR HS
Great Neck, NY

Frankino, Nancy
St Marys HS
Buffalo, NY

Franqui, Alicia
Aquinas HS
Bronx, NY

Franzen, Keith M
Whitesboro Central
Whitesboro, NY

Franzitta, Donna
Valley Stream Central HS
Valley Stream, NY

Fras, Andrew I
Binghamton HS
Binghamton, NY

Frasca, Danielle
Riverhead HS
Manorville, NY

Fraser, Daniel
Liberty HS
Ferndale, NY

Fraser, Stuart
Eden Central HS
Eden, NY

Frasier, Gary
Gloversville HS
Gloversville, NY

Free, Robert A
Hamburg SR HS
Boston, NY

Free, Thomas A
Hamburg SR HS
Boston, NY

Freedberg, Douglas B
Middletown HS
Middletown, NY

French, Matthew
Sherburne-Earlville Central HS
Sherburne, NY

French, Mechelle
Hudson Falls HS
Hudson Falls, NY

Frevele, Terry
St John The Baptist
Ronkonkoma, NY

Frey, Evelyn
Dominican Commercial HS
Brooklyn, NY

Frey, Sue
Vestal SR HS
Vestal, NY

Friedle, David
James I O Neill HS
Highland Fls, NY

Friedman, Lee Ann
William Floyd HS
Mastic, NY

Friedman, Vicki
John F Kennedy HS
Bronx, NY

Friends, II Richard L
Hornell SR HS
Hornell, NY

Fritton, Jr Joseph E
Trott Vocational HS
Niagara Falls, NY

Fritton, Rhonda A
Newfane SR HS
Lockport, NY

Fritzen, Katrina
Duanesburg Central
Quaker St, NY

Frlan, Karmen
Washington Irving
Astoria, NY

Froelich, Laura J
The Spence Schl
New York, NY

Fronczak, Mark
Niagara Wheatfield
Niagara Falls, NY

Frouxides, Vivian
Farmingdale HS
Farmingdale, NY

Fuca, Gloria
Christopher Columbus HS
Bronx, NY

Fuhrman, Jason K
Ardsley HS
Dobbs Ferry, NY

Fuhst, Jr Robert F
Mt St Michael Acad
Bronx, NY

Fuller, Barbara
Gouverneur HS
Gouverneur, NY

Fuller, Donna Faye
Mt Vernon HS
Mount Vernon, NY

Fuller, Hugh L
Edison Tech & Occupational Ctr
Spencerport, NY

Fuller, Steve
Mt St Joseph HS
Buffalo, NY

Fuller, William L
Homer Central HS
Homer, NY

Fulton, Marlon
Long Beach SR HS
Long Beach, NY

Furst, Michael
Oceanside HS
Oceanside, NY

Gabel, Carolee R
Wallkill SR HS
Wallkill, NY

Gabel, Lisa A
Gowanda JR SR HS
Gowanda, NY

Gabel, Michael P
Northport HS
Northport, NY

Gabriel, Beverley E
Sarah J Hale HS
Brooklyn, NY

Gabriel, Jr Michael J
Huntington HS
Huntington Sta, NY

Gabrielli, Andrea L
Huntington HS
Huntington, NY

Gage, Jennifer
Bishop Scully HS
Fultonville, NY

Gage, Kelly
John Jay HS
Hopewell Juncti, NY

Gagliano, Christina
Curtis HS
Staten Island, NY

Gaglio, Paula Marie
Moore Catholic HS
Staten Island, NY

Galante, David Nguyen
Eastmeadow HS
Eastmeadow, NY

Galas, Tammy
Tonawanda SR HS
Tonawanda, NY

Galasso, Mary Lauren
Acad Of St Joseph
Greenlawn, NY

Galbi, Dwight E
Maine-Endwell SR
Endwell, NY

Galbraith, Diane
Dryden Central HS
Freeville, NY

Galeano, Ana Maria
Roy C Ketcham HS
Poughkeepsie, NY

Gallacchi, Brian
Albany HS
Albany, NY

Gallagher, Amanda
Pelham Memorial
Pelham Manor, NY

Gallagher, John
Archbishop Molloy
Whitestone, NY

Gallant, Candace
Cardinal O Hara HS
Buffalo, NY

Gallo, Frances
Mahopac HS
Mahopac, NY

Galloway, Tonya
Mt Vernon HS
Mount Vernon, NY

Galluccio, Kenneth
Lindenhurst HS
Lindenhurst, NY

Galluzzo, Dianne M
Plainview Old
Bethpage HS
Plainview, NY

Galunas, Cynthia
East Hampton HS
E Hampton, NY

Galunas, Laurie
East Hamptonm HS
E Hampton, NY

Galvin, Jeffrey M B
Westhill HS
Syracuse, NY

Gamache, Valerie
Glens Falls HS
Glen Falls, NY

Gambino, Anthony
Nazareth Regional
Brooklyn, NY

Gamble, Michelle
Marie
Honeoye Falls-Lima
Honeoye Falls, NY

Gamerman, Ellen
Mamaroneck HS
Larchmont, NY

Ganey, Christine
Frontier Central HS
Hamburg, NY

Gannon, Lisa A
Suffern HS
Sloatsburg, NY

Ganott, Gail D
Chazy Central Rural
Chazy, NY

Garbarino, John
Michael
Regis HS
Scarsdale, NY

Garcia, Janet
Bishop Loughlin HS
Brooklyn, NY

Garczynski, Judith
Farmingdale HS
Farmingdale, NY

Gardinier, Timothy
Amsterdam HS
Amsterdam, NY

Gardinier, William
Little Falls JR SR
Little Falls, NY

Gardner, Larry
North Rose-Wolcott
Wolcott, NY

Gardner, Thomas H
Loneisland Lutheran
Garden City, NY

PHOTO NOT AVAILABLE
Garnett, Beth M
Lawrence HS
Atlantic Beach, NY

Garofalo, Shari
Cicero-North
Syracuse HS
Clay, NY

Garofolo, Lisa
Nazareth Acad
Rochester, NY

Garrison, Blake
St Patricks Cc HS
Palenville, NY

Garrison, Naomi
Penn Yan Acad
Penn Yan, NY

Garrity, David G
Corning-Painted
Post W HS
Painted Post, NY

Gartani, Camille
Roy C Ketcham SR
Poughkeepsie, NY

Gary, Kevin
Catholic Central HS
Troy, NY

Gassler, John P
Pelham Memorial
Pelham, NY

Gates, Kathryn
Horseheads SR HS
Horseheads, NY

Gates, Ken
Mt Markham
Central HS
W Winfield, NY

Gatt, Sandra
Newfield SR HS
Selden, NY

Gau, Elizabeth
Bishop Kearney HS
Rochester, NY

Gaudette, Anna
Marie
Canastota JR SR
Canastota, NY

Gehrmann, Robin
Midwood HS
Brooklyn, NY

Geisler, Traci
Stockbridge Valley
Central HS
Munnsville, NY

Gelfand, Boris Y
Bronx H S Of
New York, NY

Gelfuso, Tom
Frankfort Schuyler
Central HS
Frankfort, NY

Gelin, John C
Bishop Ford Central
Catholic HS
Brooklyn, NY

Geller, Amy
Yeshiva University
HS For Girls
Flushing, NY

Geloso, Antionette
Fonda Fultonville
Central S HS
Fonda, NY

Generous, Donna
John C Birdlebough
Phoenix, NY

Genge, II Clifton K
Corning Fainted
Post West HS
Painted Post, NY

Gengler, Matthew G
Shoreham Wading
River HS
Shoreham, NY

Genna, Carl
Somers HS
Katonah, NY

Gentile, Jr Joseph B
Oswego HS
Oswego, NY

Gentile, Wendy
Roosevelt HS
Yonkers, NY

Genung, Scott
South New Berlin
Central HS
Norwich, NY

George, Patricia
Notre Dame HS
Batavia, NY

George, Richelle
Lincon HS
Yonkers, NY

Geppi, Jr Thomas A
La Salle Inst
Watervliet, NY

Gerace, Joseph S
Frontier Central HS
Hamburg, NY

Gerard, Sandra R
Greece Arcadia HS
Rochester, NY

Geraty, Alicia L
East HS
Rochester, NY

Gerazounis, Peter
Holy Cross HS
Woodside, NY

Gerentine, Jr Joe
Beacon HS
Beacon, NY

Germiller, Janice M
Arlington Senior HS
Poughkeepsie, NY

Germiller, John A
Arlington HS
Poughkeepsie, NY

Gers, Lia
Barker Central Schl
Barker, NY

Gersch, Alan M
Ramaz Schl
New York, NY

Gersh, Michael
Smithtown High
Schl East
Nesconset, NY

Gervase, Lorel
Batavia HS
Batavia, NY

Gesselli, Teresa
Mahopac HS
Mahopac, NY

Ghent, Gina
St Joseph By The
Sea HS
Staten Island, NY

Ghezzi, Roxanne M
Solvay HS
Solvay, NY

Ghostlaw, Paul
Salmon River
Central HS
Fort Covington, NY

Giacobbi, James
Christian Brothers
Fayetteville, NY

Giambalvo, Gina
Bishop Kearney HS
Brooklyn, NY

Giammattei, Andrea
Marlboro HS
Marlboro, NY

Giannakis, Anna
Archbishop Iakovos
Bayside, NY

Giannetta, Matthew J
Archbishop Stepinac
Yonkers, NY

Giannico, Denise
Valley Stream Central HS
Valley Stream, NY

Giannino, Anthony R
St Anthony HS
East Northport, NY

Giatzikis, Vicky
Our Lady Of Perpetual Help HS
Brooklyn, NY

Gibbons, Susan A
Middletown HS
Middletown, NY

Gibbs, Evelyn T
Richmond Hills HS
Jamaica, NY

Gibbs, Lisa
Murry Bergtraum
Brooklyn, NY

Gibson, Jeanette
Hempstead HS
Hempstead, NY

Giddings, Anne M
Paul V Moore HS
Central Square, NY

Giff, Alice P
Elmont Memorial
Weston, CT

Gigliotti, Jenni
Gates Chili HS
Rochester, NY

Gilady, Elizabeth I
Francis Lewis HS
Flushing, NY

Gilbert, Catherine H
Ellicottville Central
E Otto, NY

Gilbert, Kevin
G Ray Bodley HS
Fulton, NY

Gilbert, Vicki
Canaseraga Central
Canaseraga, NY

Gilchick, Stacey
North Babylon Sr
North Babylon, NY

Gillen, Patricia A
Stella Maris HS
Brooklyn, NY

Gillett, Dorothy
Midwood HS
Brooklyn, NY

Gillett, Glenn
Beach Channel HS
Glendale, NY

Gillett, Teresa Ann
North Rose-Wolcott
Wolcott, NY

Gills, Karen
Bishop Loughlin Memorial HS
Brooklyn, NY

Gilman, Cathy
Mount Assumption
Plattsburgh, NY

Gilman, Kurt
South Glens Falls SR HS
S Glens Falls, NY

Gilmore, Jr Louis D
Oswego HS
Oswego, NY

Gilpin, Laurice
Cathedral HS
New York, NY

Gilroy, Jennifer M
St Francis Preparatory Schl
Glendale, NY

Gimpel, Kathleen
Earl L Vandermeulen HS
Pt Jefferson, NY

Ginquitti, Donna
Valley Central HS
Maybrook, NY

Giorlandino, Carmelo
Abraham Lincoln
Brooklyn, NY

Gipple, Michelle
Williamsville South
Williamsville, NY

Giraldez, Denise
Minisink Valley HS
Westtown, NY

Girard, David
Mexico HS
Oswego, NY

Girardi, Joseph
Mineola HS
Mineola, NY

Girrbach, Bonnie
Jeffersonvle-Youngsvle Cntrl HS
Kenoza Lake, NY

Girsky, Jeff O
Half Hollow Hills HS East
Dix Hills, NY

Girven, Kenneth
Lincoln HS
Yonkers, NY

Giunta, Joanne
Marlboro Central
Marlboro, NY

Glasco, Casaundra
Edison Vo Tech
Rochester, NY

Glass, Allison
Centereach HS
Centereach, NY

Glazier, Daniel
Sandy Creek Central
Lacona, NY

Glazier, Laura
Franklin Acad
Malone, NY

Gleason, II Charles F
Oneonta SR HS
Oneonta, NY

Glogowski, Kimberly A
Hamburg Senior
Hamburg, NY

Glow, Kathleen
Morrisville-Eaton Central Schl
Morrisville, NY

Gluck, Lori
Jericho HS
Syosset, NY

Goble, Patricia Anne
Middletown HS
Middletown, NY

Gocha, Anthony S
Riverhead HS
Riverhead, NY

Godfrey, Richard
Francis Lewis HS
Northport, FL

Gohil, Penelope
John Dewey HS
Brooklyn, NY

Golbois, Vivyan L
Lawrence HS
N Woodmere, NY

Goldberg, Beth
Hebrew Academy Of Nassau County
Great Neck, NY

Goldberg, Melinda L
Saunders Trades & Technical HS
Yonkers, NY

Golden, Allison S
Saugerties HS
Saugerties, NY

Golden, James
North Babylon HS
North Babylon, NY

Golden, Michael
Geneva HS
Geneva, NY

Goldman, Marc
Farmingdale HS
S Farmingdale, NY

Goldstein, Avram F
Yeshiva University
Flushing, NY

Goldstein, Cynthia M
Sachem High School
Lk Ronkonkoma, NY

Goldstein, Howard J
Newburgh Free
New Windsor, NY

Goldstein, Joanne
Onteora HS
Shandaken, NY

Goldstein, Karen
Half Hollow Hills High Schl East
Melville, NY

Gongora, Geraldine
Attica SR HS
Attica, NY

Gonzales, Gene Vincent
Cicero North Syracuse HS
Clay, NY

Gonzalez, Flavio A
Hillcrest HS
Briarwood, NY

Gonzalez, Gabriela
St Johns Prep
Astoria, NY

Gonzalez, Gina
Niagara Catholic HS
Niagara Falls, NY

Goodacre, Dawn M
St Agnes Acad
College Point, NY

Goodberry, Andrea
La Salle SR HS
Niagara Falls, NY

Gooden, Ilale
Baldwin SR HS
Baldwin, NY

Goodnight, Thomas
Wilson Central HS
Wilson, NY

Goodnough, Catherine A
St Barnabas HS
Bronx, NY

Gopal, Sunil
Half Hollow Hills High Schl East
Dix Hills, NY

Gordon, Scott A
Franklin Acad
Malone, NY

Gorman, Cynthia J
Grand Island SR HS
Grand Isl, NY

Gorman, Douglas M
Starpoint Central
Sanborn, NY

Gorman, Kelli
Horseheads HS
Horseheads, NY

Gorman, Lisa
Nazareth Acad
Rochester, NY

Gorman, Sharon E
Smithtown East HS
Nesconset, NY

Gotlieb, Brian Lance
Midwood HS At Brooklyn Coll
Brooklyn, NY

Gottbetter, Adam S
Irvington HS
Irvington, NY

Gottefeld, Jon
Port Richmond HS
Staten Isld, NY

Goult, Lisa
Bishop Ludden HS
Syracuse, NY

Gowan, Barbara Jo
Saranac Lake HS
Saranac Lake, NY

Grabiec, John M
Islip HS
Islip, NY

Grabow, Douglas E
Babylon HS
Babylon, NY

Grace, Amanda J
Franklin Delano Roosevelt HS
Hyde Park, NY

Grady, Debra
Man-Center For Sci & Math
Bronx, NY

Grady, Suzanne R
Buffalo Acad Of The Sacred Heart
Port Clinton, OH

Graham, Deanna
Hartford Central HS
Hartford, NY

Graham, Sonia
Bishop Grimes HS
Syracuse, NY

Grakowsky, Michael
Charles H Roth HS
W Henrietta, NY

Grande, Hallie E C
The Buffalo
Orchard Pk, NY

Granger, Allan J
Twin Tiers Baptist
Elmira, NY

Grant, Jacqualine
Bishop Kearney HS
Rochester, NY

Grant, Jodi
Oyster Bay HS
Oyster Bay, NY

Grant, Marc
Cardinal Spellman
Bronx, NY

Grant, Margaret
Caledonia-Mumford
Caledonia, NY

Grassmann, Robert J
Cicero North Syracuse HS
Clay, NY

Graue, Mary Lou
The Mary Louis
S Ozone Park, NY

Graumenz, Cathy
Paul V Moore HS
Bernhards Bay, NY

Gray, Charmaine
Holy Trinity HS
Hempstead, NY

Gray, Michelle
Immaculata HS
New York, NY

Gray, Robert
Lake George Central
Lake George, NY

Gray, Sharon
Whitesboro SR HS
Whitesboro, NY

Grayson, Adam
Onteora HS
West Hurley, NY

Greco, Vito J
Rome Free Acad
Rome, NY

Green, Cheryl
Amsterdam HS
Amsterdam, NY

Green, Donald
Bishop Kearney HS
Rochester, NY

Green, Jennifer
Marlboro HS
Milton, NY

Green, Kristine
Liverpool HS
Clay, NY

Green, Pamela
Ft Ann Central HS
Ft Ann, NY

Green, Wendy
John C Birdlebough
Phoenix, NY

Greenaway, Andrea
Northeastern Acad
Jamaica, NY

Greenberg, Julie E
Laguardia HS Of Music & Arts
New York, NY

Greenberg, Sharon B
John F Kennedy HS
Bronx, NY

Greene, Maria
North Babylon SR
N Babylon, NY

Greenebaum, Wendy M
Marlboro Central
Marlboro, NY

Greenfield, Barak J
Hebrew Academy Of Nassau County
Great Neck, NY

Greenfield, Eric
Delaware Academy And Central Schl
Delhi, NY

Greenleaf, Kimberly
Whitesboro SR HS
Utica, NY

Greenwich, Grace
Mount Vernon HS
Mount Vernon, NY

Gregg, Lataji
Susan E Wagner HS
Staten Island, NY

Gregor, Eric C
Kenmore East SR
Tonawanda, NY

Gregory, Joyce
Cathedral HS
Brkn, NY

Gresalfi, Charles R
Lynbrook HS
E Rockaway, NY

Greubel, Kirk
Stamford H Calhoun
Merrick, NY

Grier, Jr David E
E L Vandermeulen
Mt Sinai, NY

Griffin, Andre
John Dewey HS
Brooklyn, NY

Griffin, Charles
Freeport HS
Freeport, NY

Griffin, Mike
Manlius Pebble Hill
Cazenovia, NY

Griffith, Paul
Amsterdam HS
Ft Johnson, NY

Grigoli, John
Oneonta SR HS
Oneonta, NY

Grillo, Dominick J
Tottenville HS
Staten Island, NY

Grine, Mary Eileen
Nordin Acad
Kenmore, NY

Grinnell, Steve M
Corning East HS
Corning, NY

Grinnell, Teresa
Tully Central HS
Tully, NY

Grippe, Chandra Michaele
Middletown HS
Middletown, NY

Grist, Lori
Cicero North Syracuse HS
Clay, NY

Grobman, William
Herricks HS
New Hyde Park, NY

Groening, Bruce
Jamesville-Dewitt
Dewitt, NY

Grogan, Elizabeth
Bishop Kearney HS
Brooklyn, NY

Gross, Matthew
Ellsworth J Wilson
Spencerport, NY

Grosse, Carla J
Stuyvesant HS
Brooklyn, NY

Grossfeld, Scott
Commack H S
Commack, NY

Grossman, Sheri
Oceanside HS
Oceanside, NY

Grossc, Francine
Liverpool HS
Syracuse, NY

Groth, Mike
Jamesville-De Witt
Jamesville, NY

Gruber, Michael
Spring Valley HS
Spring Valley, NY

Grund, Ellen M
Clarisstown So HS
New City, NY

Gruzzon, Cesar A
All Hallows Inst
Bronx, NY

Grzankowski, Susan
Villa Maria Acad
Buffalo, NY

Gualtieri, Eugene
Anthony A
Henninger HS
Syracuse, NY

Gualtieri, Thomas P
Fayetteville-Manlius
Manlius, NY

Guanu, Seth R
Cherry Valley
Central HS
Cherry Valley, NY

Guardado, Edwin
Freeport HS
Freeport, NY

Guastella, Angela
Bishop Kearney HS
Brooklyn, NY

Gubbins, Dawn
Notre Dame HS
Whitesboro, NY

Gudas, Timothy
Horseheads HS
Horseheads, NY

Guerin, James
Valley Stream
Central HS
Valley Stream, NY

Guernelli, Gianileia
F
Cardinal Spellman
New York, NY

Guernsey, Joey
Mc Graw HS
Mcgraw, NY

Guerra, Louis J
Locust Valley HS
Bayville, NY

Guerry, Amy
Horseheads HS
Horseheads, NY

Gugluizza, Joseph E
Cortland JR SR HS
Cortland, NY

Guilbert, Rebecca
Magr Scanlan HS
Bronx, NY

Guile, Daniel
Jamesville-Dewitt
Jamesville, NY

Guillen, Jr Josue
Pericles
Hunter College
Campus Schl
New York, NY

Guinti, John A
Tottenville HS
Staten Island, NY

Guinyard, Melanie
Queen Of The
Rosary Acad
Roosevelt, NY

Gulisano, June
Eastridge HS
Rochester, NY

Gullo, Christina
West Seneca East
SR HS
Buffalo, NY

Gullo, Joseph
Lafayette HS
Brooklyn, NY

Gupta, Neena
Vestal SR HS
Binghamton, NY

Gusakov, Scott
East Aurora HS
East Aurora, NY

Guyer, Jolynn
Mexico HS
Fulton, NY

Guzik, Patrick R
Berlin American HS
Apo, NY

Guzman, Claribel
Mabel Dean Baron
New York, NY

Guzman, Lyn
Buffalo Academy Of
Sacred Heart
Williamsville, NY

Guzman, Maria
Norman Thomas HS
New York, NY

Guzski, Denise
John F Kennedy HS
Utica, NY

Gwydir, Craig
L I Lutheran HS
Huntington, NY

Haber, Michael I
Ramaz Upper Schl
New York, NY

Hackett, Laurie
Plattsburgh HS
Plattsburgh, NY

Haddleton, Cindy
Gates-Chili SR HS
Rochester, NY

Hadlock, Judy
South New Berlin
Central HS
Norwich, NY

Haeffner, Kimberly
Rocky Point HS
Rocky Point, NY

Hafele, Robert W
Downsville Central
Downsville, NY

Hagerty, Marjorie T
Lakeland HS
Yorktown Heights,
NY

Haggerty, Maura
Pelham Memorial
Pelham, NY

Hago, John R
La Salle Acad
Woodside, NY

Haigh, Jr Richard
Lakeland HS
Putnam Vly, NY

Halamandaris,
Annette
Curtis HS
Staten Island, NY

Hall, Colleen M
Johnson City SR HS
Johnson City, NY

Hall, David
Hannibal Central
Hannibal, NY

Hall, Gabriela Y
Saint Barnabas HS
Bronx, NY

Hall, Larry J
Hadley Luzerne HS
Hadley, NY

Hall, Wendy Lynn
Canastota HS
Canastota, NY

Halladay, Cheryl
Groton Central Schl
Groton, NY

Hallett, Nancy
Candor Central HS
Willseyville, NY

Hallock, John
Pittsford Sutherland
Pittsford, NY

Hallowell, Lisa
Liperpool HS
Liverpool, NY

Halse, Richard E
Troy HS
Troy, NY

Hamaludin,
Alisande
Hillcrest HS
Brooklyn, NY

Hamilton, David B
Gouverneur Central
Gouverneur, NY

Hamilton, Montrese
Niagara Falls HS
Niagara Falls, NY

Hamlin, Lisa
Hudson Falls HS
Hudson Falls, NY

Hammond, Timothy
J
New Hartford SR
New Hartford, NY

Han, William
La Salle Acad
New York, NY

Hanchuk, Walter
Regis HS
Astoria, NY

Handley, James
Patchague-Medford
Patchogue, NY

Handley, Richard
Arlington
High-North Campus
Poughkeepsie, NY

Haneke, Mark D
Cairo-Durham HS
Oak Hill, NY

Hankin, Laura K
Hackley Schl
Purchase, NY

Hannay, Douglas C
Greenville Central
Westerlo, NY

Hannis, Eric R
Chenango Valley HS
Binghamton, NY

Hanrahan, Joseph G
Roxbury Central HS
Roxbury, NY

Hanrahan, Julie
Anne
Smithtown H S East
St James, NY

Hans, Jr Peter D
Cortland HS
Cortland, NY

Hansen, Robt
Alden Central HS
Marilla, NY

Hanson, Cindy
Potsdam HS
Potsdam, NY

Hantman, Patti Lisa
Bethpage HS
Bethpage, NY

Harbert, Terence
Nottingham HS
Syracuse, NY

Hardenstine,
Tammy
Rome Free Acad
Rome, NY

Hargett, Candy
South Glens Falls
Gansevoort, NY

Hargrove, Tina C
Half Hollow Hills
Melville, NY

Harkavy, Elliot G
Midwood HS
Brooklyn, NY

Harkenrider,
Christine M
Hornell SR HS
Hornell, NY

Harley, Nicole
Cardinal Spellman
New York, NY

Harmer, Terry
Spackenkill HS
Poughkeepsie, NY

Harmon, David J
Saratoga Springs HS
Ballston Spa, NY

Harnes, Deborah
Naples American
FPO, NY

Harper, Tammy
Newfield Central
Newfield, NY

Harper, Virginia
St John The Baptist
Lindenhurst, NY

Harrell, Laurie
Amsterdam HS
Amsterdam, NY

Harrigan, Noreen C
Newfield HS
Selden, NY

Harrington, Jr
Bruce E
Canastota HS
Canastota, NY

Harrington, Dawn
Bishop Ludden HS
Bridgeport, NY

Harris, Cheryl
St Michael Acad
New York, NY

Harris, Clifton F
Malverne HS
W Hempstead, NY

Harris, George
Liverpool HS
Liverpool, NY

Harris, Ian J
Baldwin SR HS
S Hempstead, NY

Harris, Rich
Saugerties HS
Saugerties, NY

Harris, Susan
Maryvale HS
Cheektowaga, NY

Harrison, Kevin
Warwick Valley HS
Warwick, NY

Hart, Christopher W
Horace Mann HS
Englewood, NJ

Hart, Raymond L
Peekskill HS
Peekskill, NY

Harter, Glen
Brockport Central
Brockport, NY

Hartman, Daniel L
Westmoreland
Central Schl
Rome, NY

Hartman, Patrick
Thomas
Aquinas Inst
Rochester, NY

Hartrich, Laura A
Buff Acad Of The
Sacred Heart
Tonawanda, NY

Harvey, Deanie
Lynn
Bradford Central
Beaver Dams, NY

Harvey, Dennis
Herbert H Lehman
Bronx, NY

Haseley, Laurie
Niagara Wheatfield
Sanborn, NY

Hasell, Sandra
Danita
Mabel Dean Bacon
Brooklyn, NY

Haskins, Kimberly
Y
The Mary Louis
Laurelton, NY

Haskins, Pamela
Gail
Portledge Schl
Oyster Bay, NY

Haslauer, Christine
Whitesboro SR HS
Utica, NY

Hasty, Kevin
Wyandanch
Memorial HS
Wyandanch, NY

Haury, Madalyn
Paul V Moore HS
W Monroe, NY

Hausman, Alicia T
John F Kennedy HS
Plainview, NY

Hawkins, Craig
Vestal SR HS
Vestal, NY

Hayes, Tracey A
Canandaigua Acad
Canandaigua, NY

Haymon, Kris
Lehman HS
Bronx, NY

Hayner, Brian P
Tamarac HS
Troy, NY

Hazlehurst, Tanya
Aquinas HS
Bronx, NY

Head, Anne
Notre Dame HS
Utica, NY

Healy, Patrick
Seaford HS
Seaford, NY

Heaney, Mark D
Garden City HS
Garden City, NY

Hearn, Leah T
E Syracuse Minoa
Kirkville, NY

Hearty, Patrick
Bethpage HS
Bethpage, NY

Hearty, Timothy
Bethpage HS
Bethpage, NY

Heath, Carole
Oyster Bay HS
Oyster Bay, NY

Hebert, Kristin
Acad Of The Holy
Troy, NY

Hebert, Richard B
Schalmont HS
Duanesburg, NY

Heck, Robert E
Union-Endicott HS
Endicott, NY

Heffelfinger, Syrena
Hornell SR HS
Hornell, NY

Hegener, Kara
Roy C Ketcham HS
Wappingers Fall,
NY

Heiges, Andrew C
Lasalle Military
Academy HS
East Islip, NY

Heil, Christopher
Bainbridge-Guilford
Bainbridge, NY

Helenbrook, Robert S
Grand Island SR HS
Grand Is, NY

Helldorfer, Susan
Our Lady Of Mercy
Bethpage, NY

Heller, Matthew
Hauppauge HS
Hauppauge, NY

Heller, Valerie A
Pittsford Sutherland
Pittsford, NY

Helmer, Robert
Newfield HS
Centereach, NY

Heltman, Kristin
East Aurora HS
East Aurora, NY

Hemmer, Kenneth A
Susan E Wagner HS
Staten Island, NY

Hemmerick, Christine
St John The Baptist
E Islip, NY

Hendricks, Darian Christopher
Cardinal Spellman
Bronx, NY

Hendricks, Simone Clair
St Catharine Acad
Bronx, NY

Hendrickson, Linda
Plainedge HS
Massapogua, NY

Henesey, Maura M
G W Fowler HS
Syracuse, NY

Henriquez, Wills S
St Anthonys HS
Massapequa, NY

Henry, Kevin A
Westbury SR HS
E Norwich, NY

Hensen, Cheryl
Liverpool HS
Liverpool, NY

Hensinger, Robin Anne
Half Hollow Hills East HS
Wheatley Hts, NY

Herd, Victoria L
Miller Place HS
Miller Pl, NY

Heredia, Tina
Franklin Acad
Burke, NY

Herl, Lynne
Lockport SR HS
Lockport, NY

Herlihy, Margaret
Centereach HS
Centereach, NY

Herlihy, Maureen B
Sayville HS
Bayport, NY

Hernandez, Vanessa
Washington Irving
Brooklyn, NY

Herndon, Rodney
Mount Vernon HS
Mount Vernon, NY

Herr, Cindy
Long Island Lutheran HS
E Northport, NY

Herron, David M
Owen O Young HS
Mohawk, NY

Hersch, Jonathan
Commack H S
Commack, NY

Hertel, Mark
Mount Saint Michael Acad
Bronx, NY

Hertz, Eugene Steven
S H Calhoun HS
Merrick, NY

Herubin, Colleen
John F Kennedy HS
Utica, NY

Herzig, Bryin
Cazenovia Central
Cazenovia, NY

Hesse, Anita K
Grover Cleveland
Middle Village, NY

Hester, Peter W
Garden City HS
Garden City, NY

Hettenbach, James F
St Anthonys HS
Centerport, NY

Hewes, Gina
Charles O Dickerson
Trumansburg, NY

Hewlett, Ursela
Academy Of Mt St
Bronx, NY

Hickey, Kevin D
Oneonta HS
Oneonta, NY

Hickey, Michael P
Webster HS
Penfield, NY

Hickok, Jr Roy Keith
Massena Central HS
Massena, NY

Hicks, Stephen
Longwood HS
Coram, NY

Hidalgo, Jules
Mountainside Christian Acad
Schroon Lake, NY

Hidalgo, Michelle
Mountainside Christian Acad
Schroon Lake, NY

Higgins, James F
Rome Free Acad
Rome, NY

Highsmith, David Earl
Blessed Sacrament
Mt Vernon, NY

Hightower, Felice
John Dewey HS
Brooklyn, NY

Hile, Mary Michelle
Newburgh Free
Newburgh, NY

Hill, Cassandra
Hempstead HS
Hempstead, NY

Hill, Daniel
Frewsburg Central
Frewsburg, NY

Hill, Nathan
Liverpool HS
N Syracuse, NY

Hill, Randolph A
Cardinal Hayes HS
Bronx, NY

Hill, Robert E
Suffern HS
Suffern, NY

Hillabush, Tamara
Byron-Bergen Central HS
Byron, NY

Hilpl, Kimberly
Alexandria Central
Alexandria Bay, NY

Hilts, Barbara
Morrisville-Eaton Central HS
Eaton, NY

Hinchman, John
Marlboro HS
Marlboro, NY

Hinckson, Corane
Acad Of Mt St
New York, NY

Hinds, Chellyanne
John Dewey HS
Brooklyn, NY

Hine, Wendy
Fredonia HS
Fredonia, NY

Hines, Brian
Hamburg SR HS
Hamburg, NY

Hinkley, Jodi
Susquehanna Valley
Kirkwood, NY

Hirsch, Mitchell
Freeport HS
Freeport, NY

Hirsch, Susan
Nazareth Acad
Rochester, NY

Hirschberg, Robert
Sheepshead Bay HS
Brooklyn, NY

Hirschl, Ann R
The Masters Schl
Washington, MO

Hirth, Rebecca
Hendrick Hudson
Peekskill, NY

Hitchcock, Celina
Mt Merry Acad
Buffalo, NY

Hitchcock, Stacey L
Pulaski Acadamy & Central Schl
Pulaski, NY

Hoagland, Jason C
Whitehall JR SR
Whitehall, NY

Hoagland, Kim
Kenmore West HS
Kenmore, NY

Hobaica, II Joseph B
T R Proctor HS
Utica, NY

Hobbs, Lisa
Far Rockaway HS
Brooklyn, NY

Hoch, Heidi A
Greece Athena HS
Rochester, NY

Hochfeld, Eric
Oceanside HS
Oceanside, NY

Hocker, Nancy J
Southold HS
Southold, NY

Hodapp, Patricia M
Mria Regina HS
White Plains, NY

Hodge, Andrea M
Paul V Moore HS
Brewerton, NY

Hodges, Eric
Greece Athena HS
Rochester, NY

Hodgson, Melissa
Nazareth Regional
Brooklyn, NY

Hodnett, Calvin
Rice HS
New York, NY

Hoeffner, Steve
Hornell SR HS
Hornell, NY

Hoeflich, Lauren A
Woodmere Acad
Woodmere, NY

Hoepelman, William J
Newtown HS
New York City, NY

Hoffman, John P
Marcus Whitman
Central HS
Gorham, NY

Hoffman, Philip S
Fairport HS
Fairport, NY

Hoffman, Jr Robert
Northville Central
Speculator, NY

Hoffmann, Kenneth A
La Salle Military
Stony Brook, NY

Hogan, Jr John F
Mt St Michael Acad
Bronx, NY

Hogan, Suzanne M
C W Baker HS
Baldwinsville, NY

Hogrewe, Kyle
Crand Island HS
Gr Island, NY

Hokenson, Heidi
Farmingdale HS
Farmingdale, NY

Holder, Francine
South Shore HS
Brooklyn, NY

Holder, Rochelle
Kenmore East SR
Tonawanda, NY

Holdsworth, George M
The Stony Brook
Mt Sinai, NY

Holloway, Sybil
Our Lady Of Mercy
Westbury, NY

Holloway, Victoria
Woodlands HS
White Plains, NY

Holm, Vanessa
Torreton American
Oildale, CA

Holman, Eric
Jordan-Elbridge HS
Jordan, NY

Holmes, Keshia R
St Francis Prep
Brooklyn, NY

Holmes, Laura M
Smithtown H S
Smithtown, NY

Holmes, Tonia Victoria
Norman Thomas HS
Brooklyn, NY

Holstein, Rich
Jamesville De Witt
Syracuse, NY

Holt, Kerrie A
Catskill SR HS
Catskill, NY

Holt, Raymond R
G Ray Bodley HS
Fulton, NY

Holton, Denise E
Valley Steam
Central HS
Valley Stream, NY

Holvik, Sharon
Huntington HS
Huntington Sta, NY

Holz, Larry
Commack High
School South
Dix Hills, NY

Holzweiss, Robert
Franciscan HS
Peekskill, NY

Hom, Xenia B
Hillcrest HS
Jamaica, NY

Homer, Christopher M
Cortland JR SR HS
Cortland, NY

Hong, Hien C
Edison Vo Tech
Rochester, NY

Honigmann, Gloria Marie
Bethpage HS
Bethpage, NY

Hood, Erica
Granville HS
Granville, NY

Hope, Robin
G Ray Bodley HS
Fulton, NY

Hopkins, Aaron
Bishop Cunningham
Oswego, NY

Hopkins, Christopher
Cazenovia Central
Cazenovia, NY

Hopkins, Jeanette
Preston HS
Bronx, NY

Hopkins, Jonathan
Bishop Cunningham
Oswego, NY

Hoplight, Lisa Marie
Niagara Wheatfield
Niagara Fls, NY

Hoppenthaler, Sandra
Coxsackie Athens
JR SR HS
W Coxsackie, NY

Hopseker, Vicki
Watertown HS
Watertown, NY

Horan, Donald
Andover Central
Andover, NY

Horan, Erin
Edward R Murrow
Brooklyn, NY

Horan, Grace E
Walt Whitman HS
Huntington, NY

Horioglu, Roger
The Bronx H S Of
Flushing, NY

Hormann, Barbra A
Fontbonne Hall
Brooklyn, NY

Horn, John G
City Honors HS
Buffalo, NY

Horn, Travis
Union Endicott HS
Endicott, NY

Hornauer, Michele Lee
Sharon Springs
Central Schl
Sharon Springs, NY

Horoszewski, Deborah
Bainbridge-Guilford
Bainbridge, NY

Horvath, Kristy M
Rye Country Day
Ryebrook, NY

Horvath, Wade R
Mattituck HS
Cutchogue, NY

Hosier, Wende
Webutuck Central
Amenia, NY

Hotchkiss, Peter R
Cicero-North
Syracuse HS
N Syracuse, NY

Houpt, Kristen
Niagara Wheatfield
Niagara Falls, NY

Howard, Debra
Roslyn HS
Roslyn, NY

Howard, Eric M
Prattsburg Central
Prattsburg, NY

Howard, Tina D
Wyandanch
Memorial HS
Wyandanch, NY

Howell, Sandra Jeanne
Samuel T Tilden
Brooklyn, NY

Hoyt, Laurence E
Smithtown High
School West
Smithtown, NY

Hoyt, Shelly
Ripley Central HS
Ripley, NY

Hoyt, Wendy
Columbia HS
Castleton, NY

Hu, Chiming
Newtown HS
Elmhurst, NY

Hu, Lisa P
John Jay HS
Hopewell Jct, NY

Hubbard, Julia
Walton Central Schl
Walton, NY

Hubbard, Stacey
Horseheads SR HS
Elmira, NY

Hubell, Dina
Saddle River Day
Spring Valley, NY

Hubert, Laura
Delaware Valley
Central Schl
Fremont Cntr, NY

Hug, Vickie
Monroe Woodbury
SR HS
Monroe, NY

Hughes, Patrick
Christian Brothers
Liverpool, NY

Hulbert, Todd
Minisink Valley HS
Middletown, NY

Hull, Cathy
Saugerties HS
Malden, NY

Hulse, Lori
Riverhead HS
Calverton, NY

Hulse, Terri
Whitney Point C S
Maine, NY

Humbert, Sheri
North Rose-Wolcott
Clyde, NY

Hunsinger, Charles
Newfield Central
Newfield, NY

Hunt, Dawn A
Dover JR SR HS
Dover Plains, NY

Hunt, Eric
Lafayette HS
Brooklyn, NY

Hunt, Erika J
Patchogue-Medford
Patchogue, NY

Hunt, Holly L
Walter Panas HS
Crompond, NY

Huntley, Nadia
Dominican
Commercial HS
Jamaica, NY

Hurley, Colleen
Alden Central HS
Alden, NY

Hurley, Ken
Carmel HS
Carmel, NY

Hurley, Michael J
Lake Placid Central
Lake Placid, NY

Hurtubise, Christine
Monsignor Scanlan
Flushing, NY

Hussey, Kathleen
Monticello HS
Monticello, NY

Hutchinson, Shane
Chenango Forks
Central HS
Binghamton, NY

Hutchinson, Wendy
Fairport HS
Fairport, NY

Hutton, Clifford
Union Endicott HS
Endicott, NY

Hwang, Victor
Hauppauge HS
Smithtown, NY

Hynes, Christopher
S
Greenville JR SR
Greenville, NY

Hynes, Tina M
Our Lady Of Mercy
Fairport, NY

Iacobelli, Carol M
Mt St Marys Acad
Tonawanda, NY

Iacovetta, Ana
Cardinal Spellman
Bronx, NY

Iadicicco, Augie J
Niagara-Wheatfield
SR HS
Niagara Falls, NY

Ibanez, Elinor Rose
Dominican
Commercial HS
Brooklyn, NY

Icochea, Helen
St Peters HS For
Staten Island, NY

Idiculla, Saji
Geneseo Central
Geneseo, NY

Imhof, Meg
Portledge HS
Bayville, NY

Imiolo, Deborah
Ann
Maryvale SR HS
Cheektowaga, NY

Indelicato, Gina
Monsignor Scanlan
Bayside, NY

Infante, Bridgid
John S Burke
Catholic HS
New Windsor, NY

Infante, Cindy
Islip HS
Islip, NY

Ingher, Stacy
Commack High
School South
Commack, NY

Inglese, Steven
Nazareth Regional
Brooklyn, NY

Ingrassia, III John R
Monsignor Farrell
Staten Island, NY

Ingravallo,
Katherine
Fontbonne Hall
Brooklyn, NY

Inneo, Joan
Williamsville East
Williamsville, NY

Innis, Niger R
Brooklyn Tech
New York, NY

Irizarry, Gilbert
Patchogue Medford
Medford, NY

Irizarry, Jr
Raymond
Sheepshead Bay HS
Brooklyn, NY

Irons, Michael
Lake George HS
Pilot Knob, NY

Israel, Lee A
Half Hollow Hills
High School East
Dix Hills, NY

Itoh, Miki
Academy Of The
Larchmont, NY

Izen, Beth
John H Glenn HS
E Northport, NY

Izydorczak, Jerry
Alden Central HS
Alden, NY

Izzi, Patti
Hicksville Senior HS
Hicksville, NY

Jablon, Kyle S
Lawrence HS
Cedarhurst, NY

Jabs, Stacey
Saugerties HS
Saugerties, NY

Jackemuk, Gary
West Genesee SR
Camillus, NY

Jackino, Jennifer
Pelham Memorial
Pelham Manor, NY

Jackowski, Charles
Franklin Delano
Roosevelt HS
Hyde Park, NY

Jackson, Anthony M
Cardinal Spellman
Bronx, NY

Jackson, Dave L
Mount Vewrnon HS
Mount Vernon, NY

Jackson, Dianne E
C A Bouton JR SR
Voorheesville, NY

Jackson, Howard
Far Rockaway HS
Far Rockaway, NY

Jackson, Jeuanita
South Park HS
Buffalo, NY

Jackson, Kristine
Marie
Johnstown HS
Johnstown, NY

Jackson, Lee Anna
Curtis HS
Staten Island, NY

Jackson, Matthew
Pelham Memorial
Pelham, NY

Jackson, Michael J
Albany HS
Albany, NY

Jackson, Pamela
Elizabeth
Music & Art HS
New York, NY

Jackson, Shez
Mount Vernon HS
Mt Vernon, NY

Jackson, Valerie E
St Lawrence Central
Winthrop, NY

Jacob, John J
Tonawanda JR SR
Tonawanda, NY

Jacobs, Mark
Pelham Memorial
Pelham, NY

Jacobus, Lynette
Addison Central HS
Addison, NY

Jacques, Susan B
Homer SR HS
Homer, NY

Jaeger, Barbara J
Baldwin SR HS
Baldwin, NY

Jaffee, Dara
Bethpage HS
Plainview, NY

Jager, Erik
Queensbury HS
Glens Falls, NY

Jagodzinski, Andrew J
Brockport SR HS
Hamlin, NY

Jakuc, Christina Lynn
Shenendehowa Central HS
Clifton Park, NY

James, Claudia
Saranac Central HS
Morrisonville, NY

James, Faith A
Midwood High
Brooklyn, NY

James, Ian R
James I O Neill HS
West Point, NY

James, Jocklin
Copiague SR HS
Amityville, NY

James, Stephanie
Copiague SR HS
Copiague, NY

Jamison, Michele A
Pittsford Mendon
Pittsford, NY

Jangro, Rhonda
Schoharie Central
Schoharie, NY

Janne, Pasi A
United Nations International Schl
New York, NY

Jansen, Lori
Chenango Valley HS
Binghamton, NY

Jantson, Andrea
Glens Falls HS
Glens Falls, NY

Jarmacz, Judi-Lynne
East Syracuse-Minoa HS
Minoa, NY

Jarrett, Jean
Newtown HS
East Elmhurst, NY

Jarvela, Jennifer A
Roy C Ketcham SR
Wappinger Fls, NY

Jarvis, Kevin
Massena Central HS
Massena, NY

Jarvis, Tammy L
Massena Central HS
Massena, NY

Jaskolkowski, Lori Ann
Lincoln HS
Yonkers, NY

Jasper, Mary
Niagara Wheatfield SR HS
Niagara Falls, NY

Jastremski, Kimberly
Fayetteville-Manlius
Chittenango, NY

Javeline, Barry J
Comsewogue SR HS
Prt Jefferson Stn, NY

Jaycard, Martin
Hicksville HS
Hicksville, NY

Jellinek, Mark
Rockland Country Day HS
Palisades, NY

Jemetz, Bohdan
West Genesee SR
Warners, NY

Jenal, William L
New Hyde Park Memorial HS
New Hyde Park, NY

Jendras, Douglas
Mahopac HS
Mahopac, NY

Jenkins, Michael
Maple Hill HS
Castleton, NY

Jennings, Melissa
Cicero-North Syracuse HS
Brewerton, NY

Jennings, Jr Stanley
Chenango Forks Central Schl
Binghamton, NY

Jerge, Jon
Grand Island HS
Grand Is, NY

Jerry, Rhonda
Saranac Central HS
Cadyville, NY

Jha, Bhuvdutt Bunty
John Bowne HS
Yonkers, NY

Jimenez, Jr Rafael
Cardinal Hayes HS
New York, NY

Jimenez, Richard A
Cardinal Hayes HS
New York, NY

Jimenez, Wyona
Immaculata HS
New York, NY

Jiranek, Kathryn
Miller Place HS
Miller Pl, NY

Jock, Chris
Salmon River Central HS
Bombay, NY

John, Paul
Yonkers HS
Yonkers, NY

John, Susan
Long Island City HS
Long Island City, NY

Johnson, Ann
Byron-Bergen Central Schl
Bergen, NY

Johnson, Anna
Washington Irving
New York, NY

Johnson, Joseph
Lewiston Porter HS
Youngstown, NY

Johnson, Kim
Dundee Central HS
Penn Yan, NY

Johnson, Lynn
Jamestown HS
Jamestown, NY

Johnson, Marv
Rome Free Acad
Rome, NY

Johnson, Jr Melvin
Roosevelt JR SR HS
Roosevelt, NY

Johnson, Michael C
North Babylon HS
North Babylon, NY

Johnson, Phyllis
Dundee Central HS
Himrod, NY

Johnson, Ronald E
Mount St Michael
Yonkers, NY

Johnson, Jr Russell D
Rome Free Acad
Rome, NY

Johnson, Shara
Jamesville-De Witt
Syracuse, NY

Johnson, Tracy Lea
Arlington HS
Poughkeepsie, NY

Johnson, Wayne W
Cicero-North Syracuse HS
Syracuse, NY

Johnston, Michael F
Elmira Notre Dame
Elmira, NY

Jones, Carol A
Norman Thomas HS
Brooklyn, NY

Jones, Christine
Albion HS
Albion, NY

Jones, Eric
Saratoga Central Catholic HS
Ballston Spa, NY

Jones, III Frank L
Nottingham HS
Syracuse, NY

Jones, Frederick
Hempstead HS
Hempstead, NY

Jones, Gregory Scott
Pine Valley Central
South Dayton, NY

Jones, Julie
South Lewis Central
Boonville, NY

Jones, Karen
Bishop Kearney HS
Brooklyn, NY

Jones, Kendrick
Hempstead HS
Hempstead, NY

Jones, Kim
Woodlands HS
White Plains, NY

Jones, Matthew
Scotia-Glenville HS
Scotia, NY

Jones, Sandra
Frankfort-Schuyler
Frankfort, NY

Jones, Scott A
Archbishop Stepinac
White Plains, NY

Jones, Tara
Cardinal Spellman
Bronx, NY

Jones, Warren
Cardinal Hayes HS
Bronx, NY

Jordan, Catherine
Dover JR SR HS
Wingdale, NY

Jordan, Kimberly
Liverpool HS
Liverpool, NY

Jordan, Sonya
Saratoga Springs SR
Porter Corners, NY

Jordan, Yvette
A Philip Randolph
Brook, NY

Jou, Peter
St Agnes HS
New York, NY

Jouben, Lisa
Richfield Springs
Central HS
Richfield Spgs, NY

Joyce, Steven
Newark HS
Newark, NY

Joyner, Robin
Altmar-Parish-Willi
amstown HS
Williamstown, NY

Joyner, Shirell
Central Islip SR HS
Central Islip, NY

Jozwick, Tammy
Dover JR SR HS
Wingdale, NY

Jubin, Annoica
Sidney SR HS
Unadilla, NY

Judge, Diane E
Baldwin SR HS
Baldwin, NY

Judge, Sheryl
Dominican
Commercial HS
Far Rockaway, NY

Judon, La Neshia R
Lakenheath
American HS
APO, NY

Judski, Kathy-Joy
Seton Catholic HS
Binghamton, NY

Juengerkes, Wendy
East Islip HS
E Islip, NY

Julch, Paul
Spring Valley HS
Monsey, NY

Jules, Michele
St Edmund HS
Brooklyn, NY

Juliano, Virginia M
Christ The King HS
Brooklyn, NY

Jurman, Laurence
Half Hollow Hills
High Schl West
Dix Hills, NY

Ka Koyiannis,
Theodore M
Garden City HS
Garden City, NY

Kabatchnik, Edan
Horseheads HS
Elmira, NY

Kacer, Robert
New Hyde Park
Memorial HS
New Hyde Park, NY

Kaczmarczyk,
Christine
Schenectady
Christian Schl
Burnt Hills, NY

Kaczorowski, Julie L
West Seneca East
Cheektowaga, NY

Kaczorowski, Kevin
West Seneca East
SR HS
Buffalo, NY

Kagan, Erran
Herricks SR HS
Searingtown, NY

Kahler, Christopher
Smithtown High
School East
Nesconset, NY

Kahn, Cynthia
Music And Art
Riverdale, NY

Kahn, Deborah N
Great Neck North
SR HS
Great Neck, NY

Kahn, Lisa
Earl L
Vandermeulen HS
Mt Sinai, NY

Kahne, Bruce
Abraham Lincoln
Brooklyn, NY

Kalafarski, Carol
G Ray Bodley HS
Fulton, NY

Kalafarski, Edward
M
G Ray Bodley HS
Fulton, NY

Kalfa, Paul
Long Island City HS
Astoria, NY

Kalik, Noreen S
James Madison HS
Brooklyn, NY

Kallfelz, Kristen
Bishop Ludden HS
Syracuse, NY

Kalten, Suzanne M
Plainedge HS
Seaford, NY

Kalweit, Kimberly A
West Irondequoit
Rochester, NY

Kampf, Robyn
Commack North HS
E Northport, NY

Kandall, Marlene H
Professional
Childrens Schl
New York, NY

Kandilakis, Dean
Ossining HS
Ossining, NY

Kane, Ryan
Rome Catholic HS
Rome, NY

Kantha, Shivanthi
Smithtown East HS
Nesconset, NY

Kaplan, Audrey H
East Islip HS
Islip Terrace, NY

Karafanda, Diane M
Shaker HS
Latham, NY

Karchner, Keith
Monticelo HS
Monticello, NY

Karpeles, Christine
St Peters HS For
Staten Isl, NY

Karpinos, Tracy
Half Hollow Hills
East HS
Dix Hills, NY

Karukakalam,
Matthew
Hicksville HS
Westbury, NY

Kaseguma, Rick
Unatego HS
Unadilla, NY

Kashmer, Kimberly
Horseheads HS
Horseheads, NY

Kassin, Myles S
Clarkstown High
School North
New City, NY

Kastner, Diana L
Alfred G Berner HS
Massapequa Park,
NY

Kataskas, Erik M
North Rose-Wolcott
N Rose, NY

Katz, Debra A
Walt Whitman HS
Hunt Sta, NY

Katz, Lilach
H Frank Carey HS
West Hempstead,
NY

Katz, Melissa
Commack High
School North
E Northport, NY

Kaufman, Jeff S
Shenendehowa
Central HS
Clifton Park, NY

Kaufman, Suzanne
Roy C Ketcham HS
Wappingers Falls,
NY

Kaup, Lisa
Pual D Schreiber
Pt Washington, NY

Kavan, Bill
Westhampton Beach
Westhampton Bea,
NY

Kavan, Jr H Richard
Hauppauge HS
Hauppauge, NY

Kay, Cindy
Smithtown High School West
Smithtown, NY

Kay, Elysia M
H Frank Carey HS
Garden City, NY

Kazenoff, Suzanne
Rocky Point JR SR
Rocky Point, NY

Keane, Patricia Marie
Orchard Park HS
Orchard Park, NY

Keenan, Brian
Bishop Kearney HS
Rochester, NY

Keenan, Kathryn
Oneida HS
Oneida, NY

Keeney, Cani
Batavia HS
Batavia, NY

Keitel, Vanessa
Guilderland Central
Albany, NY

Kekke, Tomoko
Paul D Schreiber
Port Washington, NY

Keller, David B
Fairport HS
Fairport, NY

Keller, Kathleen M
St Catharine Acad
Bronx, NY

Keller, Melanie
Groton Central HS
Groton, NY

Kelley, Chris
Alden Central HS
Alden, NY

Kelley, Cynthia
Lowville Acad & Central Schl
Lowville, NY

Kelley, Lisa
Saugerties HS
Saugerties, NY

Kelly, Delynn
West Irondequoit
Rochester, NY

Kelly, Douglas A
Bronx High School Of Science
Bronx, NY

Kelly, Eileen
North Rockland HS
Garnerville, NY

Kelly, Kim
Wellsville HS
Genesee, PA

Kelly, Patrick J
Dansville Central
Dansville, NY

Kelly, Patti J
Onteora HS
Pine Hill, NY

Kelly, Sharon
Nazareth Acad
Rochester, NY

Kelly, Wasson
Monroe HS
Rochester, NY

Kelly, William
St Marys Boys HS
Williston Park, NY

Kelsch, Robert D
Plainedge HS
N Massapequa, NY

Kemmerer, Richard
Victor SR HS
Victor, NY

Kendall, Alan
Potsdam Central HS
Hannawa Falls, NY

Kendall, Douglas J
Vestal HS
Binghamton, NY

Kennedy, Dennis E
Tullyu Central Schl
Tully, NY

Kennedy, Rusell L
North Salem HS
Purdys, NY

Kennedy, Theresa
Horseheads HS
Horseheads, NY

Kennedy, William
Archbishop Stepinac
Yorktown Heights, NY

PHOTO NOT AVAILABLE

Kennelly, Patrick
Iona Prep
Larchmont, NY

Kenny, Stephen
Grand Island HS
Grand Island, NY

Keolamphu, Joseph
Pelham Memorial
Pelham, NY

Kernaghan, Donna
Deer Park HS
Deer Park, NY

Kerr, Carla
Springfield Gardens
Springfield Grdns, NY

Kerr, Jennifer M
Chittenango HS
Bridgeport, NY

Kervin, Susan M
Scio Central Schl
Allentown, NY

Kester, Kevin T
Pittsford Mendon
Pittsford, NY

Ketcham, Yvonne M
Canandaigua Acad
Canandaigua, NY

Ketchmere, Michael E
Gates-Chili HS
Rochester, NY

Keyes, Sheila
Seton Catholic Central HS
Binghamton, NY

Kien, Thai-Bao H
Southampton HS
Southampton, NY

Kiernan, Lisa
Beacon HS
Beacon, NY

Kilcommons, Geraldine A
Wantagh HS
Wantagh, NY

Kilkenny, Tom
Smithtown High Schl East
Saint James, NY

Kim, Lisa
Franklin D Roosevelt HS
Brooklyn, NY

Kim, Raymond J
Onteora Central JR SR HS
Woodstock, NY

Kimball, Angela
Sandy Creek Central
Sandy Creek, NY

Kimber, Thomas W
Geneseo Central
Geneseo, NY

Kimmel, John D
Newfane SR HS
Lockport, NY

Kimmel, Michael
Wayland Central HS
Wayland, NY

Kinch, Stacy
Walton Central HS
Walton, NY

King, Betsy M
Hoosick Falls Central Schl
Hoosick Fls, NY

King, Bill
Bishop Ludden HS
Syracuse, NY

King, Linda
Berlin Central HS
Cropseyville, NY

Kinlen, William G
Lehman HS
Bronx, NY

Kinne, Laura
Vernon-Verona-Sherrill HS
Blossvale, NY

Kinney, Darlene
Midlakes HS
Clifton Springs, NY

Kinney, Robert B
Pittsford Mendon
Pittsford, NY

Kinoshita, Althea
Somes HS
Katohah, NY

Kinsella, Jeanne
Sacred Heart Acad
New Hyde Park, NY

Kintner, Laura
Scio Central Schl
Scio, NY

Kirby, Joseph
Cardinal Spellman
Bronx, NY

Kirby, Tina
Edison Tech HS
Rochester, NY

Kirimca, Irfan
Lafayette HS
Brooklyn, NY

Kirk, Robert J
Greenwick Central
Greenwich, NY

Kirkwood, Richard T
Saint Francis HS
Lackawanna, NY

Kleefield, Jacqueline B
Riverdale Country
New York City, NY

Kleiman, Tammy A
Cicero-North
Syracuse HS
N Syracuse, NY

Klein, Corey
Long Beach HS
Long Beach, NY

Klein, Eric A
Cicero-North
Syracuse Central HS
N Syracuse, NY

Klein, Erik
Berlin Central HS
Berlin, NY

Klein, Karen
St Marys HS
Williamsville, NY

Klein, Keith
Sachem North HS
Centerach, NY

Klein, Robert
James E Sperry HS
Pittsford, NY

Kleinclaus, Holly
Kenmore East HS
Buffalo, NY

Klemenko, Kim
New York Military
Stony Brook, NY

Klement, Orna
White Plains HS
White Plains, NY

Klempa, Veronica
Minisink Valley HS
New Hampton, NY

Klick, Susanne
South Glens Falls SR HS
S Glens Falls, NY

Klindt, Debra L
Sidney HS
Sidney Center, NY

Kling, Walter
Pulaski JR SR HS
Pulaski, NY

Klinkowize, Laura
Pelham Meemorial
Pelham, NY

Klisiwecz, Walter P
Hamilton Central
Hubbardsville, NY

Klock, Brian
Grand Island HS
Gr Island, NY

Kluepfel, David F
Connetquot HS
Ronkonkoma, NY

Knapik, Raylene A
Amsterdam HS
Amsterdam, NY

Knapp, Mary
Elmira Southside
Wellsburg, NY

Knapp, Paula
F D Roosevelt HS
Hyde Park, NY

Knechtel, Judith Anne
Liverpool HS
Liverpool, NY

Knight, George
Aviation HS
Flushing, NY

Knights, Melissa
Medina SR HS
Medina, NY

Knipple, Robert
Union Springs Acad
Jamestown, NY

Knott, Kathleen A
New Hyde Park Memorial HS
New Hyde Park, NY

Knox, Jacqueline J
Aquinas HS
Bronx, NY

Knudsen, Randy
Lindenhurst HS
Lindenhurst, NY

Ko, John
Stuyvesant HS
Elmhurst, NY

Kochem, Heather E
Schalmont HS
Schenectady, NY

Kocher, Mininder S
Mcquaid Jesuit HS
Penfield, NY

Koenig, Jaclyn J
Williamsville South
Williamsville, NY

Koenig, Jon Gregory
Fairport HS
Fairport, NY

Koenig, Lyle
Newfield HS
Coram, NY

Koenig, Mark
Carmel HS
Carmel, NY

Koerper, Kathleen
Churchville-Chili
Rochester, NY

Kogon, S Marny
Columbia HS
Castleton, NY

Kohler, Heather
Patchohue-Medford
N Patchogue, NY

Kohnberg, Stewart Jason
Martin Van Buren
Bayside, NY

Kokesch, Anna L
St Marys Acad
Ft Edward, NY

Kokocinski, Mike
Dunkirk SR HS
Dunkirk, NY

Kolacki, Elizabeth
Broadalbin Central
Broadalbin, NY

Kolch, Kimberly
Rome Free Acad
Rome, NY

Komorowski, Stefanie
Unatego JR SR HS
Unadilla, NY

Konieczny, Eileen
Broadalbin HS
Broadalbin, NY

Kontrabecki, Amy
Hambrurg Central
Hamburg, NY

Koonz, II William
Colonie Central HS
Schenectady, NY

Koopmann, Rebecca
Middleburgh Central Schl
Fultonham, NY

Kopacz, Susan
West Seneca West SR HS
West Seneca, NY

Kordyjak, Michele
Amsterdam HS
Amsterdam, NY

Koreman, Donna
Bishop Maginn HS
Albany, NY

Kornacki, Florence
West Valley Central
W Valley, NY

Kosara, Cathy
Warwick Valley HS
Warwick, NY

Kosloski, Jr James J
Floral Park Memorial HS
Floral Park, NY

Koszalka, Joan
Copiague HS
Lindenhurst, NY

Kot, Raymond
Grand Island HS
Gr Island, NY

Kovacs, Eva
Ellsworth J Wilson
Rochester, NY

Koval, Marie
Mayfield Central
Mayfield, NY

Kovarick, Paul
Union Endicott HS
Endicott, NY

Kowal, Julie
Warwick Valley HS
Goshen, NY

Kowalczyk, Barbara
Gloversville HS
Gloversville, NY

Kowalewski, John
Vestal SR HS
Apalachin, NY

Kowalowski, Laura
Northern Adirondack Centra
Ellenburg Depot, NY

Kowalski, Thomas P
Solvay HS
Syracuse, NY

Kozlowski, Fred
Union Endicott HS
Endwell, NY

Kozlowski, Laura K
Dunkirk HS
Dunkirk, NY

Kozodoy, Julia A
St Francis Prep
Woodhaven, NY

Kozower, Max J
Williamsville North
Getzville, NY

Kraft, Heidi Marie
Bishop Kearney HS
Rochester, NY

Kramer, Dennis J
Springville-Griffith
Boston, NY

Kramer, Michael
Farmingdale HS
N Massapequa, NY

Kranbuhl, Michael
Vernon-Verona-Sher
ill HS
Blossvale, NY

Kratz, John A
C W Baker HS
Baldwinsville, NY

Kraus, Cathy L
Plainedge HS
Bethpage, NY

Krause, Jody L
Palmyra Macedon
Palmyra, NY

Krause, Karl E
Deposit Central HS
Deposit, NY

Krauss, Deborah J
Blind Brook HS
Rye Brook, NY

Kreger, Lori
Oneonta SR HS
Oneonta, NY

Kriesel, Laura
Lierpool HS
Liverpool, NY

Krishnappa,
Nandini
Shenendehowa HS
Clifton Park, NY

Kromer, Susan M
A G Berner HS
Massapequa, NY

Kron, Eric J
Susquehanna Valley
SR HS
Binghamton, NY

Krone, Stacey J
Glen Cove HS
Glen Cove, NY

Kroner, Jill
Eastridge HS
Rochester, NY

Kroog, John
Lindenhurst HS
Lindenhurst, NY

Kroslow, Michele
The Stoney Brook
Stony Brook, NY

Kruft, David
Floral Park
Memorial HS
Floral Park, NY

Kruk, Jackie
Mont Pleasnat HS
Schenectady, NY

Krupkin, Ilona
Ezra Acad Of
College Point, NY

Krupski, James
Mattituck HS
Peconic, NY

Kryman, Lori
Notre Dame HS
Batavia, NY

Kubera, Michael T
Dunkirk HS
Dunkirk, NY

Kubes, Anissa
Mohonasen HS
Schenectady, NY

Kubik, Anthony S
Johnson City SR HS
Binghamton, NY

Kuebler, Karen E
Lake Shore Central
Derby, NY

Kuhl, Joe
St John The Baptist
D HS
Lindenhurst, NY

Kuhn, Janice M
Wayne Central HS
Macedon, NY

Kulers, Laura
Mahopac HS
Mahopac, NY

Kulinowski, Karen
West Seneca East
SR HS
W Seneca, NY

Kumbatovic,
Nicholas
Msgr Mcclancy HS
Astoria, NY

Kummer, Michael J
Archbishop Molloy
Middle Village, NY

Kuo, Hsiao
Newtown HS
Elmhurst, NY

Kurdziel, Kevin
Emerson Vocational
Buffalo, NY

Kurek, Teresa
Niagara Catholic HS
Niagara Falls, NY

Kurylo, Natalie
Spackenkill HS
Poughkeepsie, NY

Kusmierz, Dawn
Mount Mercy Acad
Buffalo, NY

Kuzmicki, John W
Monsignor Farrell
Staten Island, NY

Kwan, Susan M
Elmont Memorial
Elmont, NY

La Barge, Dennis
Northern
Adirondack HS
Altona, NY

La Buz, Tammy
John F Kennedy HS
Utica, NY

La Farnara, Kim
Oakfield-Alabama
Central HS
Oakfield, NY

La Greca, Steven T
Plainedge HS
N Massapequa, NY

La Londe,
Jacqueline
Charles H Roth HS
Honeoye Falls, NY

La Morte, Debbie
Washingtonville HS
Campbell Hall, NY

La Placa, Andrew
Bishop Kearney HS
Rochester, NY

La Porte, Kenna
Northeastern
Clinton Central HS
Mooers, NY

La Quay, Lisa
Pine Valley Central
South Dayton, NY

La Venia, Deborah
Bishop Kearney HS
Brooklyn, NY

Labash, Paul
Eastridge HS
Rochester, NY

Labossiere, Chantal
J
Francis Lewis HS
Bayside, NY

Labrousse, Soraya
Dominican
Commercial HS
Queens Vlge, NY

Lackey, Stephen
Glens Falls SR HS
Glens Falls, NY

Lacourse, Lisa
Massena Central HS
Massena, NY

Lafleur, Ronald
Jordan-Elbridge HS
Memphis, NY

Lafountain, Jeffrey
J
Newfane SR HS
Newfane, NY

Lageraaen, Paul
Farmingdale HS
Farmingdale, NY

Lagua, Belinda T
Jamesville-De Witt
Jamesville, NY

Laguzza, Jennifer L
Arlington HS
Pleasant Valley, NY

Lai, William
Fort Hamilton HS
Brooklyn, NY

Laieta, Christine
Academy Of St
Holbrook, NY

Lakhan, Gillian
Brooklyn Technical
Brooklyn, NY

Lallier, Debra
Seaford HS
Seaford, NY

Lamb, Patricia
Mexico HS
Mexico, NY

Lamitie, Lynn
Franklin Acad
Malone, NY

Lamoureux, Edward
Horseheads HS
Horseheads, NY

Lamparella, Susan
Vestal HS
Vestal, NY

Lampuri, Anthony
Christian Brothers
Liverpool, NY

Lanci, Vincent
St Marys Boys HS
Roslyn, NY

Lancton, Jeff
Mahopac HS
Mahopac, NY

Landers, Kim
Royalton-Hartland
Gasport, NY

Landrio, Mark
Notre Dame-Bishop
Gibbons HS
Delanson, NY

Lane, David
Woodmere Acad
Hewlett, NY

Lane, Tracey
Waterloo SR HS
Waterloo, NY

Lang, Barbara
Schoharie Cendral
Sloansville, NY

Lang, Christine M
Frontier Central HS
Hamburg, NY

Langdon, Karen E
Batavia HS
Batavia, NY

Langelotti, Kimberly
Greece Athena HS
Rochester, NY

Langer, Loretta J
Mineola HS
Mineola, NY

Lanning, Jr David C
Spencer-Van Etten
Central Schl
Spencer, NY

Lanphere, Tammy
Ripley Central Schl
Ripley, NY

Lansing, Brian C
Connetquot HS
Sayville, NY

Lanzendorf, Donna
L
Mohonasen SR HS
Schenectady, NY

Lanzisera, Dominick
Locust Valley HS
Bayville, NY

Lanzisera, Joseph
Roy C Ketcham HS
Poughkeepsie, NY

Laperuta, Nancy T
Stissing Mountain
Stafordsville, NY

Lapesa, Anna
Bishop Frd C C H
Brooklyn, NY

Lapine, Carmen
Beacon HS
Beacon, NY

Laragy, Molly
Bishop Kearney HS
Rochester, NY

Laramie, Mark
Northeastern
Clinton Central Schl
Champlain, NY

Laraway, Wesley D
Middleburgh
Central HS
Middleburgh, NY

Larkin, Greta C
Notre Dame HS
Utica, NY

Larrea, Giovanni
St Franics Prep
Jamaica, NY

Larrier, Carrie
Sheepshead Bay HS
Brooklyn, NY

Larsen, Bob
Westmoreland
Central HS
Rome, NY

Lasher, Christine A
Fairport HS
Fairport, NY

Lasher, Evan H
Valley Stream South
Valley Stream, NY

Lasher, Michele
Dolgeville Central
Dolgeville, NY

Laskin, Hyunja F
The Bronx High
School Of Science
New York, NY

Lassen, Diane
New Dorp HS
Staten Island, NY

Later, Kristine E
Penfield HS
Rochester, NY

Latham, William H
Garden City SR HS
Garden City, NY

Latimer, Steve
Fredonia HS
Fredonia, NY

Latorre, Mary
Catherine
Marymount Schl Of
Woodside, NY

Lau, Kin Hung
Bronx High Schl Of
New York, NY

Lau, Kitty Kit-Yee
H S Of Fashion
Brooklyn, NY

Lauffer, Jennifer D
Niagara Wheatfield
SR HS
N Tona, NY

Laughney, George K
Union-Endicott HS
Endicott, NY

Lavalley, Roberta
Lansingburgh HS
Troy, NY

Lavery, Beth
Springville Griffith
Springville, NY

Law, Denise
Cortland JR SR HS
Cortland, NY

Law, James P
Saranac Lake HS
Saranac Lake, NY

Law, Julie
South Lewis HS
Lyons Fls, NY

Law, Leslie
Parishville
Hopkinton HS
Colton, NY

Law, Melissa
Stissing Mountain
JR SR HS
Pine Plains, NY

Lawler, Sean
Auburn HS
Auburn, NY

Lawrence, Charise
Abraham Lincoln
Brooklyn, NY

Lawton, Debbie
Gloversville HS
Gloversville, NY

Lawton, Edwin D
Springville Griffith
Collins, NY

Lawton, Lynnore S
La Guardia Hs Of
Musci & The Arts
Brooklyn, NY

Lazar, Ellyn H
Spring Valley SR
New City, NY

Lazzaro, Randall C
Xavier HS
Brooklyn, NY

Le, Long
Union-Endicott HS
Endwell, NY

Le Bar, Denise Anne
Gowanda Central
Gowanda, NY

Le Blanc, Gess
Mount Saint
Michael Acad
Bronx, NY

Le Blanc, Rona
Cardinal Spellman
Bronx, NY

Le Clair, Amanda
Northern
Adirondark Centra
Ellenburg Depot,
NY

Le Doux, Paula Jean
Kingston HS
Tillson, NY

Le May, Scott
Canastota HS
Canastota, NY

Le Roy, Marie
Jeffersonville-Young
sville HS
Jeffersonville, NY

Le Styne, Sandra
Mona Lisa
Lehman HS
Bronx, NY

Leach, Patricia
Sodus Central HS
Alton, NY

Leach, Sean
Alden Central HS
Alden, NY

Leach, Troy
Grand Island SR HS
Grand Isl, NY

Leatbers, Suzanne
Greece Athena HS
Rochester, NY

Leatherland,
Tammy Lee
Massena Central HS
Massena, NY

Leben, Jennifer
Sheepshead Bay HS
Brooklyn, NY

Leclair, Kerry
Moriah Central HS
Pt Henry, NY

Lecraw, Josephine
Pelham Memorial
Pelham, NY

Lee, Andrea
F D Roosevelt HS
Staatsburg, NY

Lee, Katherine
Flushing HS
Flushing, NY

Lee, Nancy A
Queensbury HS
Glens Falls, NY

Lee, Noele
Gorton HS
Yonkers, NY

Lee, Stephen
Archbishop Molloy
Howard Beach, NY

Lee, Wai-Fong
Norman Thomas HS
New York, NY

Leehr, John N
Curtis HS
Staten Island, NY

Leeper, Jonathan
Jamestown HS
Jamestown, NY

Legas, Helene
St Francis Prep
Jackson Heights, NY

Lehmann, Kristina M
Byron-Bergen HS
Byron, NY

Lehner, Kenneth R
Canisius HS
Buffalo, NY

Lehnert, Kim Lynn
North Babylon HS
North Babylon, NY

Leidich, Raymond
Union Springs Acad
Middletown, NY

Leining, Christine
Hoosic Valley Central HS
Schagticoke, NY

Leirey, James E
Kingston HS
Kingston, NY

Lelis, Ausra T
Cardinal Mooney
Rochester, NY

Lenczewski, Vincent
Archbishop Molloy
Middle Vlg, NY

Lener, Ed
Charles O Dickerson
Ithaca, NY

Lonihan, Kathleen
Dominican Commercial HS
Middle Vlge, NY

Lennane, Tracy
Port Jervis HS
Port Jervis, NY

Lennox, Brian
Caledonia-Mumford
Caledonia, NY

Leo, Kim
Islip HS
Islip, NY

Leon, Rachel
Mont Pleasant HS
Schenectady, NY

Leonard, Patricia M
Whitney Point Central HS
Endwell, NY

Leone, Robert
Sachen High School
Holtsville, NY

Lepitsch, Barbara
Smithtown High School West
Smithtown, NY

Lerch, Brian
Lockport SR HS
Lockport, NY

Leroux, Paula
Salmon River Central HS
Ft Covington, NY

Leshkowich, Ann Marie
Garden City SR HS
Garden City, NY

Lesser, Jane
Smithtown West HS
Smithtown, NY

Lester, Carl A
Rice HS
New York, NY

Letteriello, Dina
Bishop Kearney HS
Brooklyn, NY

Lettko, Kevin X
Troy HS
Troy, NY

Letton, Sarina R
Saugerties HS
Saugerties, NY

Levesque, Lisa
Mercy HS
Riverhead, NY

Levin, Lisa A
Newburgh Free
Newburgh, NY

Levine, Brian Earl L
Vandermeulen HS
Mt Sinai, NY

Levine, Kimberly A
General Douglas Mac Arthur HS
Wantagh, NY

Levy, Jonathan
The Gow Schl
Pt Washington, NY

Levy, Kirk
Plainedge HS
N Massapequa, NY

Levy, Stella
Mt Vernon HS
Mount Vernon, NY

Lewandowski, Danette R
Mount Mercy Acad
Buffalo, NY

Lewandowski, Gerald
St Marys HS
Depew, NY

Lewis, Jeff
Cornwall Central HS
Highland Mls, NY

Lewis, Terence
Roosevelt HS
Roosevelt, NY

Lewis, Timothy A
Hunter College HS
New York, NY

Lewis, Vincent C
Mount Saint Michael Acad
Bronx, NY

Lezcano, Karina D
Msgr Scanlan HS
Jackson Heights, NY

Li, Bonnie P
Newtown HS
Elmhurst, NY

Libby, Bonnie L
New Covenant Christian Schl
Rochester, NY

Libertino, Stacy
Academy Of The Resurrection HS
New Rochelle, NY

Licata, Christopher
Bishop Timo HS
W Seneca, NY

Lichorwic, Doug
VVS HS
Vernon, NY

Liddle, Heather R
Lyon JR & SR HS
Newark, NY

Liddle, Melanie A
Naples Central HS
Naples, NY

Lieb, David J
Albany HS
Albany, NY

Lifton, Judie B
Friends Acad
Old Westbury, NY

Lin, Eugene
Archbishop Holloy
Elmhurst, NY

Linares, Marialisa
Saint Pius V HS
Bronx, NY

Lincoln, Brenda
Newfield Central
Newfield, NY

Lindahl, William C
Seaford SR HS
Seaford, NY

Lindberg, Laura
Nottingham HS
Syracuse, NY

Lindsay, David
Riverhead HS
Riverhead, NY

Link, Gail Ann
Bishop Kearney HS
Webster, NY

Linker, Kerrie L
Arlington HS
Poughkeepsie, NY

Lino, Josette
Margaretville Central HS
Arkville, NY

Lippoth, Jeanne
Acad Of The Rsrctn
New Rochelle, NY

Lipscomb, Karla Anthony A
Henninger HS
Syracuse, NY

Liscum, Kristen
Hugh C Williams
Canton, NY

Little, Jr Edward
Long Island Lutheran JR SR HS
W Hempstead, NY

Littlebear, Michael
Midwood HS
Brooklyn, NY

Litvin, Stan
James Madison HS
Brooklyn, NY

Liu, Maria
Hillcrest HS
Brooklyn, NY

Liuba, Arabella J
Hackley Schl
Scarsdale, NY

Livingston, Cheryl
Liverpool HS
Liverpool, NY

Lizewski, John Joseph
Mattituck-Cutchogue HS
Cutchoque, NY

Llaguno, Monica A
St Saviour HS
Brooklyn, NY

Lloreda, Linda
Saranac Lake Central HS
Saranac Lk, NY

Lloyd, Richard
Northern Adirondack Central
Plattsburgh, NY

Lloyd, Sharon
C A Bouton JR SR
Voorheesville, NY

Lo Cascio, Keith W
Commack High School South
Commack, NY

Lo Macchio, Lisa
Liverpool HS
Liverpool, NY

Lo Vullo, Steven
Kenmore West SR
Tonawanda, NY

Loatman, Lewis
Riverhea SR HS
Riverhead, NY

Lobo, Paul A
The Loyola Schl
New York, NY

Locaputo, David
Solvay HS
Syracuse, NY

Locke, Heidi K
Saratoga Springs HS
Saratoga Springs, NY

Locke, Renee H
Brockport Central
Spencerport, NY

Lockwood, Robert M
New Rochelle HS
New Rochelle, NY

Lockyer, Mary Jo
Fox Lane HS
Bedford Vlg, NY

Loderer, Kirsten
St Francis Preparatory HS
Middle Village, NY

Loew, David H
Fonda-Fultonville Central HS
Fonda, NY

Logan, Erica
James Sperry HS
Pittsford, NY

Logan, Khalda D
La Guardia Music & The Arts HS
Queens New York, NY

Logiudice, Michael
Arlington HS
Poughheepsie, NY

Logsdon, Scott
Notre Dame HS
Pavilion, NY

Lohman, Jon
Irvington HS
Irvington, NY

Lois, Jennifer
Hendrick Hudson
Peekskill, NY

Lombardi, Celeste
Ramapo HS
Pomona, NY

Lombardi, Filomena
Saschem HS
Ronkonkoma, NY

Lombardi, Jennifer
Walt Whitman HS
Melville, NY

Lombardo, John
Newfield HS
Selden, NY

Long, Gina
Bishop Grimes HS
Liverpool, NY

Long, Jeri Lynn
Longwood HS
Middle Island, NY

Long, Patrick J
The Nichols Schl
Buffalo, NY

Looker, Suzanne
Indian River Central
Calcium, NY

Loomis, Craig R
Gowanda Central
Perrysburg, NY

Lopater, Steven J
Great Neck South
Glen Cove, NY

Lopez, Alex
Newtown HS
Elmhurst, NY

Lopez, Daniel
Fort Hamilton HS
Brooklyn, NY

Lopez, Lawrence A
St Anthonys HS
Holbrook, NY

Lopez, Mauricio
Lindenhurst HS
Lindenhurst, NY

Lopez, Noelle Denise
Adlai E Stevenson
Bronx, NY

Lopez, Robert
Sheepshead Bay HS
Brooklyn, NY

Lopitz, Amanda
Canastota HS
Canastota, NY

Lord, Michelle
Camden HS
Cleveland, NY

Loren, Heather
New Rochelle HS
New Rochelle, NY

Lorenz, Karen
Franciscan HS
Garrison, NY

Lorie, Craig
East Meadow HS
E Meadow, NY

Losito, John
Elmira Free Acad
Elmira, NY

Lotito, Christopher J
Edward R Murrow
Brooklyn, NY

Lougheed, Michael S
Stissing Mt HS
Pine Plains, NY

Louie, Kerry
Xaverian HS
Brooklyn, NY

Louis, Jimmy
The Bronx High School Of Science
Bronx, NY

Louison, Carolyn L
Midwood HS
Brooklyn, NY

Love, Tracie
Haverling Central
Bath, NY

Low, Robert C
High School Of The Performing Arts
New York City, NY

Luba, Louis J
St Francis HS
Blasdell, NY

Lucarelli, Leonard
Commack High School South

Lucarelli, Steve
Lackawanna SR HS
Lackawanna, NY

Lucas, Elizabeth Noreen
Stella Maris HS
Ozone Park, NY

Lucas, Kathleen
Fredonia HS
Fredonia, NY

Luce, III Dominick
Walter Panas HS
Peekskill, NY

Lucena, Amy C
Academy Of Saint
Brentwood, NY

Luciano, John J
East Hampton HS
E Hampton, NY

Luckman, James
Barker Central HS
Gasport, NY

Luczak, Lynn
Frontier Central HS
Hamburg, NY

Ludden, Theresa
Welsville HS
Wellsville, NY

Ludlam, Joyce M
Johnson City HS
Johnson City, NY

Lugbauer, John P
East Islip HS
East Islip, NY

Luisa, Edward M
Franciscan HS
Yorktown Hts, NY

Lukasiewicz, Timothy
West Seneca West
Buffalo, NY

Lukawski, Jolanta E
St Joseph Hill Acad
Brooklyn, NY

Luna, Zulma
Manhattan Center For Math & Science
New York, NY

Lundy, Kathy
Liverpool HS
Liverpool, NY

Lupkin, Jonathan Benjamin N
Cardozo HS
Bayside, NY

Lupo, Dawn
Commack H S
Commack, NY

Lupo, Thomas
Richmond Hill HS
Richmond Hill, NY

Lusaka, Patrick J
Roosevelt HS
Scarsdale, NY

Lusk, Yvonne D
Marathon Central
Marathon, NY

Luvera, William
Copiague SR HS
Amity Harbor, NY

Ly, Long V
Newtown HS
Elmhurst, NY

Lynam, John Luke
Cicero North Syracuse HS
N Syracuse, NY

Lynch, James
All Hallows HS
Bronx, NY

Lynch, Jr Robert H
Clarkstown South SR HS
W Nyack, NY

Lynk, John
J C Birdlebough HS
Phoenix, NY

Lynk, Michael
J C Bridglebough
Phoenix, NY

Mac Intyre, Kimberley
Delaware Academy And Central Schl
Delhi, NY

Mac Lennan, C James
Wilson Magnet HS
Clyde, NY

Mac Mullin, Christopher W
Wallkill SR HS
Wallkill, NY

Mac Pherson, Kelly
Cardinal Mooney
Rochester, NY

Macchia, Michele L
Maria Regina HS
Scarsdale, NY

Maccone, Janet
Sachem High School North Campus
Holtsville, NY

Machabee, Charles
Franklin Acad
Malone, NY

Maciag, Robert
Notre Dame/Bishop Gibbons HS
Schenectady, NY

Macintyre, Kelly
Patchoque-Medford
Medford, NY

Mack, Catherine R
Mary Louis Acad
Flushing, NY

Mackie, Andrew J
Carmel HS
Stormville, NY

Mackie, Jane
Sacred Heart Acad
East Meadow, NY

Mackintosh, Elizabeth
Murry Bergtraum
Staten Island, NY

Macomber, Edward H
Honeoye Falls-Lima SR HS
Honeoye Falls, NY

Macrone, Tracy
Smithtown H S
Smithtown, NY

Maddock, Thomas More
Bishop Ludden HS
Camillus, NY

Madison, Andrea
Corinth Central HS
Corinth, NY

Madison, Arthur E
Cicero N Syracuse
Clay, NY

Madissoo, Andres
Jamesville-De Witt
Fayetteville, NY

Madrigal, Elma Cheryl Sarreal
Albertus Magnus
Orangeburg, NY

Madsen, Kristen
Liverpool HS
Liverpool, NY

Magahis, Pacifico A
Regis HS
Staten Island, NY

Magardino, Tommy
Edgemont HS
Scarsdale, NY

Maggiore, Rosa
Bishop Kearney HS
Brooklyn, NY

Maggs, Lori Anne
Islip HS
Islip, NY

Magrich, Paul B
Lasalle SR HS
Niagara Falls, NY

Maguire, Jr Robert E
Canajoharie HS
Canajoharie, NY

Magyar, Beverly Louise
Taconic Hills HS
Hillsdale, NY

Mahanna, Ellen
Holland Patent Central Schl
Barneveld, NY

Mahar, Deborah A
Solvay HS
Syracuse, NY

Mahar, Kathleen
Spackenkill HS
Poughkeepsie, NY

Maher, Edward
Longwood HS
Coram, NY

Mahoney, Donna
Bethpage HS
Plainview, NY

Mahoney, Karen
Deer Park HS
Deer Park, NY

Maida, Janet
Mt Saint Joseph
Buffalo, NY

Maignan, Sabine
Queen Of The Rosary Acad
Massapequa, NY

Mainelli, Benji
Bronx H S Of
New York, NY

Majeed, Shahzad
Cardinal Hayes HS
New York, NY

Majors, Shawn
Hilton HS
Hilton, NY

Makinen, Mika
Smithtown HS West
Smithtown, NY

Malark, Valerie
Saranac Central HS
Dannemora, NY

Malcho, Karyn
Fairport HS
Fairport, NY

Malcolm, Larell G
Erasmus Hall
Brooklyn, NY

Maleady, Anne
St Peters H S For
Staten Island, NY

Malkoff, Jason A
Spring Valley SR Rt 59 HS
Spring Valley, NY

Malley, Wendy
Valley Central HS
Montgomery, NY

Mallory, Michael L
Paul V Moore HS
Central Sq, NY

Malmquist, Karen
Vestal Central SR
Vestal, NY

Maloney, Jane A
Ossining HS
Briarcliff, NY

Maloney, Patrick
Fordham Prep
Mamaroneck, NY

Maloney, William J
Archbishop Stepinac
Harrison, NY

Maluenda, Annette
Domincan Acad
Elmhurst, NY

Manalastas, Carmen
Jamaica HS
Hollis, NY

Mancuso, Noel
Churchville-Chili
Rochester, NY

Mandaro, Richard
St John The Baptist
Deer Park, NY

Mandava, Suresh
Arlington HS
Poughkeepsie, NY

Mandel, Alicia
Wilson Central HS
Ransomville, NY

Mandel, Peter J
Francis Lewis HS
Queens Village, NY

Mandera, Cindy
John H Glenn HS
E Northport, NY

Mandzyk, Christine
Mount Saint Mary
Buffalo, NY

Manginelli, Cheryl
Newfield HS
Seldne, NY

Mannino, Peter
V S Central HS
Valley Stream, NY

Mannion, John
Bishop Ludden HS
Syracuse, NY

Mannix, Daniel
Garden City HS
Garden City, NY

Manoli, Victor R
Cairo-Durham HS
Acra, NY

Manor, Tamara L
Northeaster Clinton
Central HS
Rouses Point, NY

Mansfield, Dave
Alden Central HS
E Aurora, NY

Mansouri, Richard
Horseheads HS
Horseheads, NY

Mantani, Anna
Lynn
St Peters Girls HS
Staten Island, NY

Manthey, Jeffrey
Peekskill HS
Peekskill, NY

Manzo, Kenneth
V S Central HS
Valley Stream, NY

Mapp, Lea
John Dewey HS
Brooklyn, NY

Maragioglio, Karen
East Islip HS
Islip Ter, NY

Marano, Anna E
St Johns Prep HS
Middle Village, NY

Marcantonio,
Raffaella
Grand Island HS
Grand Is, NY

Marcario, Danielle
Marie
Clarkstown North
New City, NY

Marchona, Paul
New Rochelle HS
New Rochelle, NY

Marcus, Jillian M
New Rochelle HS
New Rochelle, NY

Margeson, Roxanne
M
Churchville-Chili
Central Schl
Churchville, NY

Margolies, Sharon
Woodmere Acad
Baldwin Harbor, NY

Marhamati, Darius
Valley Central HS
Maybrook, NY

Marincic, Kathleen
Hudson Falls
Central HS
Glens Falls, NY

Marinello, Mark J
Beach Channel HS
Belle Harbor, NY

Marino, Frank
John F Kennedy HS
Utica, NY

Marion, Kimberly M
Notre Dame Acad
Staten Island, NY

Markham, Gerald G
Washington Acad
Salem Central
Salem, NY

Markham, Steve J
Ellicottville Central
Great Vly, NY

Markiewicz, James
Sherburne-Earlville
Earlville, NY

Markovich, Gail L
Kensington HS
Buffalo, NY

Marks, Jill M
De Sales HS
Waterloo, NY

Marotte, Joseph
Susan Wagner HS
Staten Isld, NY

Marrero, Lisa A
Polytechnic Prep
Country Day Schl
Brooklyn, NY

Marro, Laura
St Joseph By The
Staten Island, NY

Marsanico, Vincent
Holy Cross HS
Flushing, NY

Marsch, Peter M
Liverpool HS
Liverpool, NY

Marsh, Jack
Letchworth Central
Bliss, NY

Marsh, Julie A
Corning East HS
Corning, NY

Marsh, Suzanne C
Rlington HS
Poughkeepsie, NY

Marshall, Julie
De Ruyter Central
Sheds, NY

Marshall, Kevin
Starpoint Central
Lockport, NY

Marshall, Krista
Lansing HS
Lansing, NY

Marshall, Michelle L
Abraham Lincoln
Brooklyn, NY

Marsillo, Anthony
Washingtonville SR
Campbell Hall, NY

Marte, Steven
Bishop Grimes HS
E Syracuse, NY

Martelli, Shari
La Salle SR HS
Niagara Falls, NY

Martin, Betsy
Franklin Acad
Malone, NY

Martin, Chris
Niskayuna HS
Schdy, NY

Martin, Clevette R
Webster HS
Webster, NY

Martin, Dale
Webster HS
Webster, NY

Martin, Dolores
St Francis Prep
Ozone Pk, NY

Martin, Heather
Gowanda Central
Perrysburg, NY

Martin, Jeff
Saugerties HS
Saugerties, NY

Martin, John
Deer Park HS
Deer Pk, NY

Martin, Jonathan
Garden City HS
Garden City, NY

Martin, Joseph C
Newfield HS
Selden, NY

Martin, Joyce
New Hyde Park
Memorial HS
New Hyde Park, NY

Martin, Keith
Msgr Scanlan HS
Bronx, NY

Martin, Kimberly A
Hunter College HS
Whitestone, NY

Martin, Maureen
Liverpool HS
Liverpool, NY

Martin, Monique
Walton HS
Bronx, NY

Martin, Randy
Greene Central Schl
Chenanago Forks,
NY

Martin, Travis L
South New Berlin
Central Schl
New Berlin, NY

Martin, William
Windham-Ashland-J
ewett-Central HS
Hensonville, NY

Martinez, Juan
Lasalle Acad
New York, NY

Martinez, Marlen
Monsignor Scanlan
Bronx, NY

Martinez, Melissa
Roger B Chaffee HS
FPO New York, NY

Martini,
Mary-Antoinette
Norman Thomas HS
Astoria, NY

Martini, Robert T
Xaverian HS
Brooklyn, NY

Martizez, Marlene
Cathedral HS
New York, NY

Martuscello, Renee
Amsterdam HS
Amsterdam, NY

Mascola, Susanne
Clarkstown South
West Nyack, NY

Masercola, Mary Jo
John F Kennedy HS
Utica, NY

Maslona, Peter J
West Seneca East
SR HS
West Seneca, NY

Mason, Dawn
Hoosick Falls
Central Schl
Eagle Bridge, NY

Massac, Alexander
D
Cardinal Spellman
Bronx, NY

Massaro, Maria
Niagara Falls HS
Niagara Falls, NY

Massey, Kathy M
Roy C Ketchem HS
Wappinger Fls, NY

Masterov, Michael
Bronx H S Of
Tenafly, NJ

Masters, Mike
The Wheatley HS
East Williston, NY

Mastranadi, Michele
Union-Endicott HS
Endicott, NY

Mastrandrea, Lynn
Saint Edmund HS
Brooklyn, NY

Masuicca,
Christopher
Pulaski JR & SR
Pulaski, NY

Masullo, Gina M
John Jay HS
Wappingers Fall,
NY

Mateo, Felix
South Side SR HS
Rockville Ctr, NY

Mathieu, Nancy
Nazareth Regional
Brooklyn, NY

Matias, Moses
Manhattan Center
New York, NY

Matis, Sheri-Lynn B
Little Falls HS
St Johnsville, NY

Mattes, William
Earl L
Vandermeulen HS
Mt Sinai, NY

Matteson, Melanie
Franklin Acad
Malone, NY

Matthews, Kenneth
Rice HS
Brooklyn, NY

Matthews, Nancy
Lee
Grand Island HS
Grand Island, NY

Matthews, Suzanne
M
Grand Island HS
Grand Island, NE

Mattis, Jacqueline S
Our Savior Lutheran
Bronx, NY

Mattu, Eunice
St Peters HS For
Staten Isl, NY

Maxfield, Derek D
Dundee Central HS
Dundee, NY

Maxfield, Jay
Saranac Lake HS
Saranac Lake, NY

May, Paul
Lindenhurst HS
Lindenhurst, NY

May-Beard,
Nathaniel J
High School Of
Fashion Indstrs
Brooklyn, NY

Mayes, Chris
Union Endicott HS
Endicott, NY

Mayette, Rodney
Dover JR SR HS
Dover Plains, NY

Mayfield, Michael
Liverpool HS
Liverpool, NY

Mays, Paul
Valley Central HS
Wallkill, NY

Mazourek, Roberta
Newfield Central
Newfield, NY

Mazur, Cynthia
Horseheads SR HS
Horseheads, NY

Mazzaferro,
Christine
Greenport HS
Greenport, NY

Mazzella, Annmarie
Cardinal Spellman
Bronx, NY

Mazzeo, Carla
Marlboro HS
Newburgh, NY

Mazzocchi, Lisa
Anne
Northport HS
E Northport, NY

Mc Allister, B
Buckley
Trinity Schl
New York, NY

Mc Ateer, Lynn
Tuxedo HS
Sterling Forest, NY

Mc Bride, Edward
Mechanicville HS
Mechanicville, NY

Mc Bride, Mariellen
Academy Of The
Tuckahoe, NY

Mc Carthy, Patricia
Pearl River HS
Pearl River, NY

Mc Carty, Skip
Odessa-Montour
Central Schl
Montour Falls, NY

Mc Clernan,
Rita-Louise
Saugerties Central
Saugerties, NY

Mc Connell, Donald
W
Arkport Central
Arkport, NY

Mc Connon, Sheila
Staten Island Acad
Staten Island, NY

Mc Cormick,
Michelle
C W Baker HS
Baldwinsville, NY

Mc Coy, Meegan
Holland Patent
Central Schl
Rome, NY

Mc Cue, Charles
Washingtonville SR
Washingtonville, NY

Mc Cue, Gregory S
Newburgh Free
New Windsor, NY

Mc Cullagh, Margo
Anne
Farmingdale HS
N Massapequa, NY

Mc Cumber,
Stephanie L
Bainbridge-Guilford
JR-SR HS
Bainbridge, NY

Mc Donald, Steven
A
Xavier HS
Cambria Hts, NY

Mc Dougal, Michael
Copiague SR HS
Copiague, NY

Mc Dowall, John
Monticello HS
Harris, NY

Mc Elroy, George
Jeffersonville
Youngsville C HS
Kenoza Lk, NY

Mc Elroye, Amy L
Edison Technical &
Occupatnl Center
Rochester, NY

Mc Erlean, Michael
M
St John The
Baptist-Diocesan HS
Selden, NY

Mc Fall, Jonathan
Hornell HS
Hornell, NY

Mc Farland, Karen
Manlius Pebble Hill
Syracuse, NY

Mc Garry, Tara A
Maria Regina HS
Crestwood, NY

Mc Gee, Tracy
Candor HS
Candor, NY

Mc Ghee, Sheila B
Hempstead HS
Hempstead, NY

Mc Gorry, Jennifer
St Francis Prep
Bayside, NY

Mc Graw, Shaun
Liverpool HS
Liverpool, NY

Mc Graw, Tim
Grand Island SR HS
Grand Island, NY

Mc Guinness, Bridget
Unatego JR SR HS
Otego, NY

Mc Guire, Lisa
West Seneca West SR HS
West Seneca, NY

Mc Guire, Marcie
Lowville Academy & Central Schl
Lowville, NY

Mc Hugh, Christine
Valley Stream Central HS
Valley Stream, NY

Mc Hugh, Matthew
Rocky Point JR SR
Rocky Pt, NY

Mc Inerney, William G
St Anthonys HS
Setauket, NY

Mc Intosh, Donald
Commack HS South
Commack, NY

Mc Intosh, Morris
Pulaski HS
Pulaski, NY

Mc Intyre, Sharlene E
Charles H Roth HS
W Henrietta, NY

Mc Kain, Mari
Miller Place HS
Miller Pl, NY

Mc Keithen, Kyomi Yoshiko
Bishop Loughlin Memorial HS
Brooklyn, NY

Mc Kenna, Christopher
Peekskill HS
Peekskill, NY

Mc Kenna, Patricia
Preston HS
Bronx, NY

Mc Kenney, David R
West Seneca Christian Schl
W Seneca, NY

Mc Kenzie, Deborah
The Franciscan
Syracuse, NY

Mc Kenzie, Michael P
Tolly JR SR HS
Lafayette, NY

Mc Koy, Sheila
Hempstead HS
Hempstead, NY

Mc Lain, Lareesa V
Beach Channell HS
Rock Bch, NY

Mc Lain, Jr Stanley Eugene
Oneida SR HS
Oneida, NY

Mc Laughlin, Michelle
Marlboro HS
Marlboro, NY

Mc Laurin, Anissa
Mount Vernon HS
Mt Vernon, NY

Mc Lean, Jarred T
New Rochelle HS
New Rochelle, NY

Mc Lellan, Lisa M
Camden Central HS
Camden, NY

Mc Lellan, Sonia
E J Wilson HS
Spencerport, NY

Mc Lendon, Sandi M
Holy Trinity D HS
Roosevelt, NY

Mc Loughlin, Ann M
Ichabod Crane HS
Schodack Landing, NY

Mc Mahon, Yvette M
Penfield HS
Penfield, NY

Mc Neill, Martin
Walt Whitman HS
Huntington Stat, NY

Mc Nelis, Patrick
Commack H S
East Northport, NY

Mc Nerney, Michael
Cathedral Prep
Rockaway Beach, NY

Mc Nish, Gladys
F D Roosevelt HS
Brooklyn, NY

Mc Nulty, Sharon
The Mary Louis
Forest Hills, NY

Mc Quade, Patrick
Union Endicott HS
Endicott, NY

Mc Rae, Denise
John Dewey HS
Brooklyn, NY

Mc Rae, Rozela
Saint Catharine
Bronx, NY

Meakens, Karen D
Bronx HS Of Sci
New Rochelle, NY

Means, Linda
Union Endicott HS
Endicott, NY

Mecca, Michele
Bethlehem Central
Delmar, NY

Meci, Sean G
Newfield HS
Selden, NY

Medico, Cosmo
Cicero-North-Syracuse HS
Mattydale, NY

Medina, Roseanne
Saint John The Baptist D HS
Brentwood, NY

Mednick, Rhonda
Ramapo SR HS
Suffern, NY

Meehan, Austin
St Marys HS
Glen Cove, NY

Meeks, Jr Reginald
Mynderse Acad
Seneca Falls, NY

Meghji, Shabnam
Hillcrest HS
Elmhurst, NY

Mehta, Indira
Forest Hills HS
Forest Hills, NY

Mehta, Parastu S
Jamesville-De Witt
De Witt, NY

Mei, Fen
Cararsie HS
Brooklyn, NY

Meier, Elise
Frontier Central HS
Hamburg, NY

Meilinger, Christop S
Northville Central
Northville, NY

Meissner, Elizabeth
Buffalo Traditional
Buffalo, NY

Meister, Jeffrey
Buffalo Traditional
Buffalo, NY

Melendez, Gina Lynn
Doughkeepsie HS
Poughkeepsie, NY

Melendez, Samuel
Richmond HS
Hollis, NY

Melfi, Patrick
Bishop Cunningham
Oswego, NY

Mellen, Andrew
Thousand Islands
Chaumont, NY

Mellon, Jr Wayne H
Cicero-North Syracuse HS
North Syracuse, NY

Meltzer, Marna
Jamesville De Witt
Dewitt, NY

Mendoza, Zoraida
Eli Whitney Voc HS
Brooklyn, NY

Menech, Darcy
Bishop Scully HS
Amsterdam, NY

Menihan, David M
Cardinal Spellman
Bronx, NY

Menninger, Sandra
Springville Griffith
Colden, NY

Mentekidis, Dimitrios James
Dobbs Ferry HS
Irvington, NY

Mentuck, Michelle M
Holy Trinity HS
N Massapequa, NY

Mera, Alex
United Nations International Schl
New York, NY

Mercado, Margarita
John F Kennedy HS
Bronx, NY

Merchant, Erik J
Cattaraugus Central
Cattaraugus, NY

Merisca, Rolande
John Jay HS
Brooklyn, NY

Merkling, Cliff
Christian Brothers
Syracuse, NY

Merlino, Mario J
Msgr Farrell HS
Staten Island, NY

Merritt, Patricia
Cicero-North
Syracuse HS
North Syracuse, NY

Merza, Maria
Saint Peters H S
For Girls
Staten Isl, NY

Messina, David
Notre Dame HS
Batavia, NY

Messina, Maria
Maryvale SR HS
Chktg, NY

Messina, Shelley
Notre Dame HS
Batavia, NY

Messineo,
Alessandra M
John Jay HS
Hopewell Jct, NY

Metera, Wm
Binghamton HS
Binghamton, NY

Meteyer, Brian
Bishop Kearney HS
Rochester, NY

Metzger, Jocelyn M
Brighton HS
New York, NY

Metzler, Kurt
Douglas
Dover JR SR HS
Dover Plains, NY

Meury, Joseph
St John The Baptist
Amityville, NY

Meury, William
St John Th Baptist
Amityville, NY

Meyer, Andrew
Hillcrest HS
Jamaica, NY

Meyer, Christopher
H
Pine Bush HS
Bloomingburg, NY

Meyer, Cynthia
St Barnabas HS
Yonkers, NY

Meyer, Cynthia L
Nortre Dame Acad
Staten Island, NY

Meyer, Jenny
Williamsville East
East Amherst, NY

Meyer, Leone F
Amherst Central SR
Amherst, NY

Meyers, Elisabeth
Connetquot SR HS
Ronkonkoma, NY

Meyers, Gregg
Smithtown High
School West
Smithtown, NY

Meyers, William
Buddy J
Saugerties JR-SR
Saugerties, NY

Michael, Frederico
Scotia Glenville HS
Scotia, NY

Michaels, Valentina
Academy Of St
Joseph HS
E Patchogue, NY

Michalek, Anthony
A
Chatham Central
Canaan, NY

Michie, Chinita
Saint Pius V HS
Bronx, NY

Micilcavage, Debra
Union-Endicott HS
Endicott, NY

Mickle, Donna
John A Coleman HS
Kingston, NY

Micros, Matthew A
The Allendale
Columbia Schl
Pittsford, NY

Middleton,
Christopher L
Garden City HS
Garden City, NY

Miett, Anne E
Bishop Grimes HS
E Syracuse, NY

Miett, Catherine
Bishop Grimes HS
E Syracuse, NY

Migdalia, Dejesus
John Jay HS
Brooklyn, NY

Mikels, Sue
Union-Endicott HS
Endicott, NY

Mikowski, Karen A
Cheektowaga
Central HS
Cheektowaga, NY

Mikulko, Lydia
Hillcrest HS
Kew Gardens, NY

Mikus, Jay
Cicero-North
Syracuse HS
Clay, NY

Milanes, Max R
Bronx Science HS
New York, NY

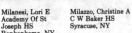

Milanesi, Lori E
Academy Of St
Joseph HS
Ronkonkoma, NY

Milazzo, Christine A
C W Baker HS
Syracuse, NY

Milborrow, Michele
Greece Athena HS
Rochester, NY

Milin, Gregory S
Mt St Michael Acad
Bronx, NY

Miliotto, Lynne
Mount Saint Mary
Tonawanda, NY

Miller, Adrianne J
Lake Shore Central
Angola, NY

Miller, Christine
Lasalle SR HS
Niagara Falls, NY

Miller, Christine
Ann
Garden City SR HS
Garden City, NY

Miller, Clinton
Bishop Loughlin M
Booklyn, NY

Miller, David
Farmingdale HS
Farmingdale, NY

Miller, Deanna Lynn
James E Sperry HS
Rochester, NY

Miller, Eduardo
Cardinal Spellman
Bronx, NY

Miller, Jacquelyn
Lisa
East Meadow HS
E Meadow, NY

Miller, James D
Hammondsport
Central HS
Hammondsport, NY

Miller, Jeffrey D
Vestal SR HS
Vestal, NY

Miller, Jill M
Union-Endicott HS
Simi Valley, CA

Miller, Lisa Anne
Jamesville-Dewitt
Manlius, NY

Miller, Peter K
Mount St Michael
Yonkers, NY

Miller, Rogena
Webster SR HS
Penfield, NY

Miller, Steve
Gowanda Central
Collins, NY

Miller, Teresa
Mayville Central
Dewittville, NY

Milligan, Valerie L
Taconic Hills HS
Ghent, NY

Mills, Jacki
Walton JR SR HS
Walton, NY

Mills, Stacy
Tottneville HS
Staten Island, NY

Milord, Fabiola
Washington Irving
Jackson Hts, NY

Milton, Mary Ann
Mercy HS
Hampton Bays, NY

Mims, Maronda Lisa
Saint Catharine
Bronx, NY

Mineo, Joseph
Seaford HS
Seaford, NY

Miner, Todd
Horseheads HS
Horseheads, NY

Minikel, Stephen
Msgr Mc Clancy HS
Woodside, NY

Minnolera, Michael E
Iroquois HS
Lancaster, NY

Miranda, Melinda
Waterford-Halfmoon
Waterford, NY

Mirsky, Mark
Ossining HS
Ossining, NY

Misantonis, Dimitrios
Albertus Magnus
Garnerville, NY

Misita, Jr Robert M
East Islip HS
East Islip, NY

Mitchell, Denise L
Pulaski JR-SR HS
Pulaski, NY

Mitchell, Joanne
Tottenville HS
Staten Island, NY

Moday, Kristin
Pelham HS
Pelham, NY

Modell, Daniel A
John F Kennedy HS
Bronx, NY

Modesti, Phillip B
Jamesville-De Witt
Fayetteville, NY

PHOTO
NOT
AVAILABLE

Moffit, Michelle
Pine Valley Central
Cattaraugus, NY

Mohr, Chris
Washingtonville SR
Washingtonville, NY

Mohr, Kimberlee I
W Seneca East SR
Cheektowaga, NY

Moldenhauer, Christina R
Fairport HS
Fairport, NY

Molloy, Christine Earl L
Vandermuelen HS
Pt Jefferson Sta, NY

Molloy, Kristen L
Westhampton Bch
Westhampton Bch, NY

Molner, Nancy A
Seaford Trinity HS
Seaford, NY

Monaco, Kelli
Mount Mercy Acad
Buffalo, NY

Monaco, Lisa
Immaculata Acad
Orchard Park, NY

Monahan, Patricia
St Barnabas HS
Yonkers, NY

Monahan, Patricia A
Fayetteville Manlius
Manlius, NY

Moncayo, Magaly
Clara Barton HS
Brooklyn, NY

Mondesir, Elizenda
South Side HS
Hempstead, NY

Mone, Michelle
Fontbonne Hall
Brooklyn, NY

Monette, Amy S
Franklin Acad
Malone, NY

Monette, Brian
Franklin Acad HS
Malone, NY

Mongelluzzo, Donna
John H Glenn HS
Huntington, NY

Monroe, Dorie
Schuylerville Central
Gansevoort, NY

Monroe, Jeffrey
Cardinal Hayes HS
New York, NY

Monroe, Ken
Greenwich Central
Salem, NY

Monroe, Lynne M
Mc Greaw Central
E Freetown, NY

Montanaro, Lucy
John C Birdlebough
Pennellville, NY

Montanaro, Mary
John C Birdlebough
Pennellvl, NY

Montgomery, Letasha
Lafayette HS
Buffalo, NY

Montoute, Valerie
Bishop Loughlin M
Brooklyn, NY

Montplaisir, David
Liverpool HS
Liverpool, NY

Moonen, Peter
Vernon-Verona-Sherrill HS
Verona, NY

Mooney, Robert
Harborfields HS
Huntington, NY

Moore, Andrew D
John Jay SR HS
Cross River, NY

Moore, Cindy
Wellsville HS
Wellsville, NY

Moore, El-Melek Alleyne
John Dewey HS
Brooklyn, NY

Moore, James E
Jamesville De Witt
Dewitt, NY

Moore, Kathleen R
Naples Central HS
Naples, NY

Moore, Kathryn
Homer Central HS
Preble, NY

Moore, Mari Beth
York Central HS
Leicester, NY

Moore, Michael D
Schenectady Christian Schl
Alplaus, NY

Moore, S Gordon
Roy C Ketcham HS
Wappingers Fall, NY

Moore, Tracy
Byron-Bergen Central HS
Byron, NY

Moragne, Tamu Amani
John Dewey HS
Silver Spring, MD

Morais, Amandio
Aviation HS
Jamaica, NY

Morales, Audrey
Walton HS
Bronx, NY

Morales, Milagros
Dominican Commercial HS
Brooklyn, NY

Morales, Ramona G
Westbury SR HS
Westbury, NY

Moran, Corinne
Whitesboro SR HS
Whitesboro, NY

Moran, Patricia
West Seneca West SR HS
Cheektg, NY

Moran, Robert
Haldane HS
Cold Spring, NY

Morand, Edward
Moore Catholic HS
Staten Isl, NY

Morasco, Genevieve
The Mary Louis
Jamaica Estates, NY

Moravec, Sharon Marie
Vicenza American
Apo New York, NY

Morehouse, Michael D
Massena Central HS
Massena, NY

Morell, Deanna
Palmyra Macedon
Palmyra, NY

Moreno, James
Bishopo Loughlin M
Brooklyn, NY

Morgan, Brenda
John Dewey HS
Brooklyn, NY

Morgan, Eileen M
Commack South HS
Commack, NY

Morgan, Stephen
La Fayette Central
La Fayette, NY

Morgan, Suzanne J
De Sales HS
Waterloo, NY

Morgan, Tasha
Harry S Truman HS
Bronx, NY

Morgenthaler, Karen M
Port Byron Central
Auburn, NY

Morreale, Maria J
John F Kennedy HS
Katonah, NY

Morrin, Renee
Romulus Central
Waterloo, NY

Morris, Paul R
Taconic Hills HS
Philmont, NY

Morris, Sharon
South Shore HS
Brooklyn, NY

Morris, Sophia
John Dewey HS
Peekskill, NY

Morris, William J
Hendrick Hudson
Montrose, NY

Morrison, Debra A
Arlington HS
La Grangeville, NY

Morrison, G Scott
North Shore HS
Glen Head, NY

Morrison, Meg A
West HS
Painted Post, NY

Morrison, Michael R
John F Kennedy HS
Brewster, NY

Morrison, Susan L
Paul V Moore HS
Brewerton, NY

Morrissey, Patricia J
Rocky Point JR-SR
Miller Place, NY

Morrow, Jill
Churchville-Chili SR
Rochester, NY

Morschauser, Dana
John Glenn HS
Greenlawn, NY

Morton, III Glenn R
Batavia SR HS
Batavia, NY

Morvay, Daniel P
Clymer Central HS
Clymer, NY

Mosca, Anne Marie
Farmingdale HS
Farmingdale, NY

Mosher, Amy
Cicero-North
Syracuse HS
Clay, NY

Mosher, Deborah
Brockport Central
Hamlin, NY

Mosher, Louann
Watertown HS
Watertown, NY

Mosher, Susan
Corinth Central HS
Corinth, NY

Mosier, Carmen
La Salle SR HS
Niagara Falls, NY

Motley, Derrick W
Pine Bush HS
Middletown, NY

Motley, Rohana
The Stonybrook
Bronx, NY

Mott, Elizabeth
Jordan-Elbridge
Central HS
Elbdidge, NY

Moulton, Sheri
Parishville-Hopkinto
n Central HS
Potsdam, NY

Mousaw, Karen
Colton Pierrepont
Central Schl
Colton, NY

Moustopoulos, Fotis
C
Flushing HS
Flushing, NY

Moy, Tsui Gnee
Beach Channel HS
Rockaway Park, NY

Moyal, Douglas D
Benjamin Cardozo
Little Neck, NY

Moyer, Michelle
John C Birdlebough
Pheonix, NY

Muccini, Laura L
St Marys Girls HS
Douglaston, NY

Mullen, Christopher
P
MSGR Mc Clancy
Memorial HS
Astoria, NY

Mullen, Jonelle
Eastport HS
Manorville, NY

Muller, Diane
Commack HS North
East Northport, NY

Muller, Ellen
Batavia HS
Batavia, NY

Muller, Stephen E
St Anthonys HS
Smithtown, NY

Mullin, Daniel R
South Jefferson
Central HS
Adams Center, NY

Mullins, Margaret
Brooklyn Technical
Roosevelt Isl, NY

Mulvehill, Brian
Xavier HS
Brooklyn, NY

Mulvey, Lisa L
Westhampton Beach
E Quogue, NY

Mulyca, Mark D
Schalmont HS
Schenectady, NY

Muma, Robert W
St John The Baptist
Brentwood, NY

Mundle, Verneta
New Rochelle HS
New Rochelle, NY

Muniz, Yolanda
Maria Regina HS
Yorktown Hghts,
NY

Munroe, Giselle
Clara Barton HS
Brooklyn, NY

Murarka, Amal
Shenendehowa HS
Clifton Pk, NY

Murmer, Mark
Auburn HS
Auburn, NY

Murphy, Anita M
Our Lady Of Victory
Bronx, NY

Murphy, Ann
Colonie Central HS
Loudonville, NY

Murphy, Celeste
Michele
Freeport HS
Freeport, NY

Murphy, Charles
Columbia HS
Rensselar, NY

Murphy, Edward D
Newfane HS
Burt, NY

Murphy, John M
Mount St Michael
Bronx, NY

Murphy, Rosanne
St Peters H S For
Staten Isl, NY

Murphy, Stacey M
Bishop Kearney HS
Brooklyn, NY

Murphy, Tasha M
The Mary Louis
Jamaica, NY

Murphy, Veronica
St John The Baptist
Diocesan HS
Central Islip, NY

Murray, Bernice
Morrisville-Eaton
Peterboro, NY

Murray, Karen
Sacred Heart Acad
Mineola, NY

Murray, Karyn
Pulaski JR-SR HS
Pulaski, NY

Murray, Kristen
Vestal SR HS
Apalachin, NY

Murray, Meredith A
Baldwin SR HS
Baldwin, NY

Murray, Patti J
Red Jacket Central
Clifton Springs, NY

Murray, Robert
New Covenant
Christian Schl
Webster, NY

Murray, Robert W
Guilderland Central
Guilderland, NY

Murrer, Patricia
Greece Arcadia HS
Rochester, NY

Musa, John
Archbishop Molloy
Brooklyn, NY

Muscarella, Anthony
Marc
York Central HS
Mount Morris, NY

Muscianesi, Dana
St Joseph By The
Sea HS
Staten Island, NY

Mustafa, Syed
Ahmed
Corning Painted
Post East HS
Corning, NY

Mykula, Tania
Roosevelt HS
Yonkers, NY

Nackley, II James J
New Hartford HS
New Hartford, NY

Nadel, Fredric D
New Rochelle HS
New Rochelle, NY

Nadell, Martha J
Poly Prep CDS HS
Brooklyn, NY

Nadjadi, Clifford
Havelring Central
Bath, NY

Naegele, Steven M
Herkimer SR HS
Herkimer, NY

Nagel, Joseph
Turner/Carroll HS
Buffalo, NY

Naidu, Bablu
Roy C Ketcham HS
Wapp Fls, NY

Naisby, Jr James H
G
East Islip HS
Great River, NY

Nakatsugawa,
Jun-Ya
Jamesville Dewitt
Syracuse, NY

Namdar, Benjamin
Ezra Acad
Forest Hills, NY

Nanavati, Nilesh
Monroe HS
Rochester, NY

Nance, Demetrius
Enrico
New Rochelle HS
New Rochelle, NY

Nanno, Edward
Christian Brothers
Syracuse, NY

Napolitano, Phyllis
Anne V
Bishop Kearney HS
Brooklyn, NY

Naraine, Raymond S
La Salle Acad
New York, NY

Narlis, Maria E
Port Chester HS
Rye Brook, NY

Nash, Chantell
Bethlehem Central
Delmar, NY

Nash, Valerie
Washington Irving
New York, NY

Naso, Mark W
Highland HS
Highland, NY

Naso, Vincenza
St Peters High Schl
For Girls
Staten Isl, NY

Nass, Rachael
Lafayette HS
Brooklyn, NY

Nassau, Michelle E
G W Hewlett HS
N Woodmere, NY

Natali, Michele
Paul V Moore HS
Brewerton, NY

Natalie, Lawrence J
Bay Shore HS
Bay Shore, NY

Navarra, Joan
Albion HS
Albion, NY

Nawrocki, John K
New Hyde Park
Memorial HS
New Hyde Park, NY

Neal, Victoria
J C Birdlebough HS
Phoenix, NY

Neary, Coleen
Nazareth Acad
Rochester, NY

Nee, Samantha
St Vincent Ferrer
Jackson Heights,
NY

Negbaur, Gary L
Trinity Schl
New York, NY

Negrin, Barry
Roosevelt HS
Yonkers, NY

Negrin, Bruce K
New Rochelle HS
New Rochelle, NY

Negron, Michelle I
Aquinas HS
Bronx, NY

Nehring, Lawrence
Eden Central HS
Eden, NY

Neils, Collette
Bronx H S Of
New York, NY

Neller, David
Middletown HS
Middletown, NY

Nelsen, David A
Northport HS
East Northport, NY

Nelson, Carmen
Pine Valley Central
Cherry Creek, NY

Nelson, Diane
Windham-Ashland-J
ewett Central Schl
Hensonville, NY

Nelson, Donna L
Comsewogue SR HS
Port Jeff Sta, NY

Nelson, Mark
Lake George HS
Kattskill Bay, NY

Nelson, Shaunte
Mt Vernon HS
Mt Veron, NY

Nelson, Stephanie A
Cardinal Mooney
Rochester, NY

Nemec, Richard S
Miller Place HS
Miller Place, NY

Nentwich, Kevin
Sachem HS
Holbrook, NY

Nester, Georgia
Sauquoit Valley
Central HS
Sauquoit, NY

Neto, Marilene
Dominican
Commercial HS
Richmond Hill, NY

Neumann, Robert
Irondequoit HS
Rochester, NY

Neveloff, Daniel I
Tottenville HS
Staten Island, NY

Nevins, David
Haverling HS
Bath, NY

Nevins, Grace
Onteora Central HS
Boiceville, NY

Newborn, Joanne
Bishop Kearney HS
Brooklyn, NY

Newell, Hope
Greenville JR SR
Greenville, NY

Newell, Pauline
Harry S Truman HS
Bronx, NY

Newman, Betina
Rose
George W Fawler
Syracuse, NY

Newton, John
Andrew Jackson HS
Cambria Heights,
NY

Ng, Diana
Brooklyn Technical
New York, NY

Ng, Frank
Aviation HS
Woodside, NY

Ngo, Anh
New Burgh Free
Newburgh, NY

Nguyen, John Hanh
Peekskill HS
Peekskill, NY

Nguyen, Judy
Phuong-Minhle
Gates-Chili HS
Rochester, NY

Nguyen, Mary
Seton Catholic
Central HS
Johnson City, NY

Nguyen, Quoc
Tottenville HS
Staten Island, NY

Nicastro, Joanne
Waterloo SR HS
Waterloo, NY

Nichol, Judene
Liverpool HS
Liverpool, NY

Nicholls, Renee
St Joseph HS
Brooklyn, NY

Nichols, Susan
Cazenovia HS
Cazenovia, NY

Nickel, Jeffrey
Bethlehem Central
Delmar, NY

Nicolellis, Deborah
L
Longwood HS
Yaphank, NY

Niese, Kelly A
Fayetteville-Manlius
Manlius, NY

Nieves, Firgia
Sarah J Hale HS
Brooklyn, NY

Nieves, Nancy M
John Jay SR HS
Fishkill, NY

Nikolits, Stephen A
Hackley Schl
Pleasantville, NY

Nikstenas, Joseph E
Amsterdam HS
Amsterdam, NY

Niles, Sharleen
Mc Graw Central
Mc Graw, NY

Nir, Dror N
Ramaz Upper Schl
Flushing, NY

Nisanian, Anahid
Jaquelline
Forest Hills HS
Sunnyside, NY

Nobbs, Tobi
Southwestern
Central Schl
Jamestown, NY

Noble, Jennifer
Mineola HS
Mineola, NY

Nocilla, Charles
Martin Van Buren
Bayside, NY

Noeller, Thomas
Frontier Central HS
Hamburg, NY

Nolan, Courtney
Notre Dame HS
New York, NY

Nolan, Thomas J
La Salle Acad
New York, NY

Nolander, Eric E
Holland Patent HS
Rome, NY

Noll, Nancy
Jamesville-Dewitt
Fayetteville, NY

Noll, Stephen
South HS
Valley Stream, NY

Noonan, Rachel E
Brockport HS
Brockport, NY

Norden, Kelli Ann
Mercy HS
Centereach, NY

Norman, Claudia
Mount Vernon HS
Mount Vernon, NY

Normand, John E
Monsignor Farrell
Staten Island, NY

Normandin, Joelle
Glens Falls SR HS
Glens Falls, NY

Notaroberto, Lisa
Sacred Heart Acad
E Meadow, NY

Nour, Magda
Hunter College HS
New York, NY

Novak, Cindy Lynn
Roxbury Central
Roxbury, NY

Novakovic, Diana
Greater New York
Woodside, NY

Nozell, Lori J
L C Obourn HS
E Rochester, NY

Nugent, Kimberly
Rocky Point JR SR
Rocky Point, NY

Nurse, Althea
Edward R Murrow
Queens, NY

Nutter, Heidi
Bainbridge-Guilford
Bainbridge, NY

Nyahay, Denise A
John F Kennedy HS
Carmel, NY

O Brien, Bridget
Glen Falls HS
Glens Falls, NY

O Brien, James
Patrick Michael
Seton Catholic
Central HS
Binghamton, NY

O Connell, J
Michael
Saratoga Spgs HS
Saratoga Spgs, NY

O Dell, Scott
Walton Central HS
Walton, NY

O Donnell, Brian
Saugerties HS
Rochester Hills, MI

O Donnell, John
Ossing HS
Ossining, NY

O Donnell, Noreen
M
Sheepshead Bay HS
Brooklyn, NY

O Donnell, Phyllis
M
Saint Joseph
By-The-Sea HS
Staten Island, NY

O Farrell, James F
Cardinal Spellman
Bronx, NY

O Halloran, Kevin
Camden HS
Taberg, NY

O Hanlon, Denise
New Dorp HS
Staten Island, NY

O Hanlon, Michael
St John The Baptist
Copiague, NY

O Hara, Patrick J
Williamsville East
Williamsville, NY

O Hare, Kelly L
West Seneca E HS
West Seneca, NY

O Herron, Elizabeth
H
Elmira Southside
Elmira, NY

O Kane, John
St Ohn The Baptist
Islip, NY

O Leary, Jean Marie
White Plains HS
White Plains, NY

O Leary, Kelly
Whitesboro SR HS
Whitesboro, NY

O Malley, Kerri-Ann
Connetgout HS
Bohemia, NY

O Malley, Kirsten
John Dewey HS
Brooklyn, NY

O Neil, Christina S
Sachem HS
Lake Ronkonkoma,
NY

O Neil, Leigh E
Greene HS
Greene, NY

O Neill, Lucien
Nazareth Regional
Brooklyn, NY

O Neill, Terri
Port Jervis HS
Westbrookville, NY

O Shea, Danny
Mount Saint
Michaels Acad
New York, NY

O Shea, Janet M
Yorktown HS
Yorktown Hts, NY

O Shea, Lorraine A
Riverdale Country
Bronx, NY

O Toole, Stacy Ann
The Ursuline Schl
New Rochelle, NY

Oakes, Julie A
Massena Central HS
Massena, NY

Oakes, Oliver David
Corning-Painted
Post West HS
Corning, NY

Oakley, Robert
North Tonawanda
N Tonawanda, NY

Obas, Remy
The Kew-Forest
Holliswood, NY

Occhipinti, Frank
Lakeland SR HS
Peekskill, NY

Occhiuzzo, Kelly A
Lawrence HS
Cedarhurst, NY

Occhiuzzo, Tara
Lawrence HS
Cedarhurst, NY

Ocke, Darrin T
Wayne Central SR
Ontario, NY

Oconnell, Robert
Tappan Zee HS
Blauvelt, NY

Oconnor, Christine
Far Rockaway HS
Far Rockaway, NY

Oddo, Samantha
Lake George Central
Lake George, NY

Oddy, Carol Janet
Nottingham HS
Syracuse, NY

Odebralski, John J
Dunkirk SR HS
Dunkirk, NY

Odwyer, Jeffrey S
Pittsford Mendon
Pittsford, NY

Ofori-Mankata, Juliet
Unite Nations International Schl
Teaneck, NJ

Okrent, Deborah A
Beacon HS
Beacon, NY

Olberding, Deborah A
Cardinal Spellman
Bronx, NY

Olden, Stacey
Clara Barton HS
Brooklyn, NY

Oleary, Jennifer
Maria Regina HS
Yonkers, NY

Olin, Craig H
South Side HS
Rockville Ctr, NY

Oliver, Amena
Northwest Acad
Jamaica, NY

Oliver, Jr Stephen W
Ravena Coeymans
Selkirk SR HS
Selkirk, NY

Olivera, Audrey
Cardinal Spellman
Bronx, NY

Oliveri, Sheryl Ann
Dundee Central HS
Rock Stream, NY

Olivieri, Joseph A
Liverpool HS
Liverpool, NY

Olsen, Elizabeth S
Elba Central Schl
Elba, NY

Olsen, Paul M
Clarkstown North
New City, NY

Olsen, Walter
Riverhead HS
Riverhead, NY

Olson, Ann M
The Brearley Schl
New York, NY

Ongjoco, Roxanne C S
Perry Central Schl
Perry, NY

Onsi, Douglas E
Jamesville-De Witt
De Witt, NY

Onyeije, Uzoma C
Liverpool HS
Liverpool, NY

Oquendo, Vivian Lee
Cathedral HS
Woodside, NY

Oranges, Joann
Roy C Ketcham HS
Wappinger Fls, NY

Orff, Edward J
Garden City HS
Garden City, NY

Organisciak, Mark
Frankfort-Schuyler Central HS
Frankfort, NY

Orlando, Karen A
Plainview Old Bethpage HS
Plainview, NY

Orlando, Jr Stephen P
Solvay HS
Syracuse, NY

Ormiston, Matt
Maple Hill HS
Castleton, NY

Ornt, Tina
Churchville-Chili
Rochester, NY

Ortega, Jr Jose
Bishop Ford C C HS
Brooklyn, NY

Ortega, Lourdes
Norman Thomas HS
Brooklyn, NY

Ortega, Wladimir
St Johns Prep
Woodside, NY

Ortiz, Grisel
St Raymond Acad
Bronx, NY

Ortiz, Jeannette F
HS Of Art & Design
Bronx, NY

Ortiz, Ramona
Mt St Joseph Acad
Buffalo, NY

Ortiz, Virginia
Norman Thomas HS
New York, NY

Ortmann, Erik
Islip HS
Bayshore, NY

Osborn, Lisa
Watkins Glen HS
Rock Stream, NY

Oscar, Corliss
Clara Barton HS
Brooklyn, NY

Oshatz, Daniel T
Scarsdale HS
Scarsdale, NY

Oshea, Anne M
Old Westbury Schl Of The Holy Child
Point Lookout, NY

Osinski, Susan M
Mount St Mary
Grand Island, NY

Oslansky, Audra L
Sachem SR HS
Holtsville, NY

Ossenberg, Michele
Nottingham HS
Syracuse, NY

Ost, George
Aviation HS
Long Isl City, NY

Ostermeier, Earl
Grand Island HS
Gr Island, NY

Oswald, Annette
Roy C Ketcham HS
Wappingers Falls, NY

Oswald, Stephanie
Saugerties HS
Saugerties, NY

Oswalt, Edward F
Royalton Hartland Central HS
Lockport, NY

Otte, John
Mohonasen SR HS
Schenectady, NY

Otto, David H
Scarsdale HS
Scarsdale, NY

Otto, Paula J
Newburgh Free
Newburgh, NY

Overweg, Elizabeth
Bronx Science HS
Riverdale, NY

Owens, John
St Marys Boys HS
E Williston, NY

Ozimkowski, Edward
Bethpage HS
Bethpage, NY

Paccione, Lucille
St Johns Prep
Astoria, NY

Pacheco, Celia
Norman Thomas HS
Bronx, NY

Pachetti, Josephine
Buffalo Alternative
Buffalo, NY

Pacific, Alex D
Immaculate Heart Central HS
Watertown, NY

Padilla, Cristina A
Bishop Kearney HS
Jackson Heights, NY

Pagano, Daniel L
Kings Park SR HS
Kings Park, NY

Pagano, Marisa
Susan E Wagner HS
Staten Island, NY

Paganuzzi, Barbara M
Pelham Memorial
Pelham, NY

Page, Kathryn
Catholic Central HS
Troy, NY

Page, Kim
Albion HS
Albion, NY

Page, Robert
Gates Chili SR HS
Rochester, NY

Page, Thomas
Frontier Central HS
Blasdell, NY

Paglia, Joanne
Mercy HS
Moriches, NY

Pais, Salvatore
Brooklyn Technical
Jackson Heights, NY

Pajak, Arthur
Xavier HS
Brooklyn, NY

Palaski, Tamara
Notre Dame HS
Whitesboro, NY

Paldino, Laurie Jane
Mamaroneck HS
Mamaroneck, NY

Palermo, Catherine
Webster HS
Webster, NY

Palmatier, Cynthia
Wellsville HS
Alma, NY

Palmatier, Thomas
Bishop Scully HS
Amsterdam, NY

Palmer, Douglas D
Hartford Central
Granville, NY

Palmer, Rocco J
T R Proctor HS
Utica, NY

Palozzi, Christopher M
Greece Olympia HS
Rochester, NY

Palumbo, David
East Meadow HS
East Meadow, NY

Pam, Aaron
Sleepy Hollow HS
North Tarrytown, NY

Panagakos, Peter
Archbishop Iakovos
Jamaica, NY

Panczner, Gregory
Mont Pleasant HS
Pattersonville, NY

Panczyk, Richard
Cheektowaga Central HS
Tucson, AZ

Panessa, Mary B
Arlington HS
Poughkeepsie, NY

Panetta, Joseph R
Notre Dame HS
Oriskany, NY

Pannetta, Kerry
St Peters H S For
Staten Isl, NY

Pannone, Anthony
St Joseph By The
Staten Island, NY

Pantano, Lynne M
Nardin Acad
Buffalo, NY

Pantazi, Gina
St Johns Preparatory Schl
L I C, NY

Paoloni, Christina
Long Island City HS
Astoria, NY

Papaiakovou, Stacey
John Dewey HS
Brooklyn, NY

Pappas, Christin P
Midwood HS
Brooklyn, NY

Paradis, Jr Vinicio
All Hallows Inst
New York, NY

Paraskeva, Helen
Center Moriches HS
Ctr Moriches, NY

Pardo, Gissella
Bishop Ford C C HS
Brooklyn, NY

Pardo, Rosa M
The Mary Louis
South Ozone Park, NY

Paris, Jessica
Medina SR HS
Medina, NY

Parisi, Michelle
The Mary Louis
Flushing, NY

Park, Yosop
Sheepshead Bay HS
New York, NY

Parker, Kathy
Bayside HS
Bayside, NY

Parker, Stacy Omar
Long Island Lutheran HS
Westbury, NY

Parker, Thomas
Valley Central HS
Newburgh, NY

Parks, Kristy
Nazareth Acad
Rochester, NY

Parlo, Kimberly A
Northport HS
E Northport, NY

Parr, Ronald
Smithtown High Schl East
Saint James, NY

Parr, Scott Kenneth
Kenmore East SR
Tonawanda, NY

Parraga, Audrey
The Mary Louis
Kew Gardens, NY

Parrinelli, Nicholas
Floral Park Memorial HS
Floral Park, NY

Parrinello, Michael C
Copiague HS
Copiague, NY

Parrish, Laura Michelle
Cicero North Syracuse HS
Clay, NY

Parrott, Janice L
Hudson Falls HS
Hudson Falls, NY

Parsons, Daniel J
Fairport HS
Fairport, NY

Parsons, David
Sharon Springs Central HS
Sharon Springs, NY

Parsons, Gwendolyn M
Troy HS
Wynantskill, NY

Parsons, Mike
Webster HS
Webster, NY

Parsons, Steven
Nazareth Regional
Brooklyn, NY

Parzuchowski, Michael J
The Fox Lane HS
Pound Ridge, NY

Pascal, Tammy
Cornwall Central HS
Newburgh, NY

Pascarella, Maribeth
Liverpool HS
Liverpool, NY

Pasciak, Pamela
North Tonawanda SR HS
No Tonawanda, NY

Pascocello, Christopher
Central HS
Valley Stream, NY

Paslawsky, Natalie
Villa Maria Acad
Buffalo, NY

Passmore, Kathleen
Ellenville Central
Ellenville, NY

Pastorino, Stacey
Onteora HS
Woodstock, NY

Pata, Cynthia M
Hilton HS
Hilton, NY

Patane, Sebastian
George W Fowler
Syracuse, NY

Patanzo, Lisa
Newark HS
Newark, NY

Patchen, Jason
Bethlehem Central
Delmar, NY

Patel, Kushal A
Roosevelt HS
Bayside, NY

Pateras, Katherine
Archbishop Iakovos
Jamaica, NY

Pathammavong, Somphane
Batavia HS
Batavia, NY

Patnaude, Jr Frank W
Chazy Central Rural
Chazy, NY

Patric, La Quita
Nazareth Acad
Rochester, NY

Patricca, Thomas L
Linton HS
Schenectady, NY

Patrick, Shawn
Linton HS
Schenectady, NY

Patrignani, Anthony
Waterford Halfmoon
Waterford, NY

Pattengill, Vikki
South New Berlin Central Schl
S New Berlin, NY

Patti, Michele L
Averill Park HS
Troy, NY

Paul, Beth Ann
Gates-Chili HS
Rochester, NY

Paul, Camille
Springfield Gardens
Rosedale, NY

Paul, Leonard
Northeastern Acad
Brooklyn, NY

Paul, Louis C
Baldwin SR HS
Baldwin, NY

Paul, Nirva
Acad Of Mt St
Bronx, NY

Pauiinski, Christine
Wells Central Schl
Piseco, NY

Pawlak, James
Holland Central
Holland, NY

Payne, Andre
John F Kennedy HS
Bronx, NY

Payne, Bertram
Friends Acad
Roosevelt, NY

Payne, Debra J
Paul V Moore HS
Hastings, NY

Payne, Tyrone
Hempstead HS
Hempstead, NY

Payton, Lisa
Michelle
Bishop Ford Central
Catholic HS
Brooklyn, NY

Paz, Michael
Long Beach HS
Lido Beach, NY

Pazda, Kimberly J
Lancaster Central
Depew, NY

Peace, Sondra
Portville Central
Portville, NY

Pearce, Christopher
J
Beach Channel HS
Ozone Pk, NY

Pearson, Michele M
Fontbonne Hall
Brooklyn, NY

Pebworth, Russell
W
Hendrick Hudson
Croton-On-Hudson,
NY

Peck, Barbara E
Mineola HS
Williston Park, NY

Peck, Benjamin W
Fayetteville-Manlius
Fayetteville, NY

Pederson, Neil
G Ray Bodley HS
Fulton, NY

Pedrico, Elena
Shaun
Ripley Central Schl
Ripley, NY

Pekarik, Edward
Monsignor Mc
Clancy HS
Glendale, NY

Pelczynski, Darleen
Villa Maria Acad
Buffalo, NY

Pelissier, Cassandra
Dominican
Commercial HS
Queens Vlge, NY

Pellegrini, Christine
Half Hollow Hills
High School East
Dix Hills, NY

Pellegrino, Michelle
Lindenhurst HS
Lindenhurst, NY

Pellet, Jennifer A
Caridnal Spellman
New York, NY

Pellini, Lynn Ann
John Jay SR HS
Katonah, NY

Pena, Angela
John Dewey HS
Brooklyn, NY

Pendell, Mary Lou
Crown Point Central
Crown Pt, NY

Pendergast, Michelle
Cicero-North
Syracuse HS
N Syracuse, NY

Penn, Phillip J
Regis HS
Yonkers, NY

Penner, Judy
Sherburne-Earlville
Sherburne, NY

Penning,
Christopher
South Glens Falls
SR HS
S Glens Falls, NY

Pennington, Russ
Vestal HS
Vestal, NY

Pennisi, Joseph M
Troy High
Troy, NY

Perciavalle, Peter
Thomas Edison HS
Richmond Hill, NY

Pereira, Eddie
Saint Francis Prep
Corona, NY

Perez, Aimee
Sacred Heart HS
Yonkers, NY

Perez, Angelica
Norman Thomas HS
New York, NY

Perez, Elsa
Aquinas HS
New York, NY

Perez, Sofia
Hunter College HS
Astoria, NY

Perez, Jr Thomas
Xaverian HS
Brooklyn, NY

Perkins, Eunice
Aquinas HS
Bronx, NY

Perkins, Julie M
Camden Central HS
N Bay, NY

Perkins, Matthew
Columbia HS
E Greenbush, NY

Perna, Diane
Greece Arcadia HS
Rochester, NY

Perraud, Carolyn
Preston HS
Bronx, NY

Perreca, Louise M
Sachem HS
Farmingville, NY

Perrin, Jacqueline J
Notre Dame Acad
Staten Island, NY

Perrotta, Pasquale
Archbishop Stepinac
Mt Vernon, NY

Perry, Denise
Uniondale HS
Uniondale, NY

Perry, Donald C
Erasmus Hall HS
Brooklyn, NY

Perry, Julie E
Red Creek JR SR
Red Creek, NY

Perry, Michael L
Hillcrest HS
Jamaica, NY

Perschbach, Penny
Newfield HS
Selden, NY

Persche, Michael
Farmingdale HS
Farmingdale, NY

Persico, Jerilyn
St Francis Prep
Bellerose, NY

Pesce, Laura F
St John Villa Acad
Staten Island, NY

Peta, Jr Joseph
Liverpool HS
Liverpool, NY

Peters, Sharon
Smithtown H S East
Smithtown, NY

Petersen, Denise
Holy Trinity HS
Hicksville, NY

Peterson, Barbara
Central Islip HS
Central Islip, NY

Peterson, Ginger
Southampton HS
Southampton, NY

Peterson, Kim
Hornell SR HS
Hornell, NY

Peterson, Sharon
Vestal Central HS
Endicott, NY

Peterson, Tammy
Westmoreland
Central HS
Westmoreland, NY

Petit, Marie
Northeastern Acad
Brooklyn, NY

Petkus, Annmarie A
Division Avenue HS
Levittown, NY

Petragnani, Darren
Bishop Grimes HS
Syracuse, NY

Petri, Elizabeth M
Sachem HS
Holbrook, NY

Petrillo, Richard
Mt Vernon HS
Scarsdale, NY

Pettersen, Donna
St Peters H S For
Staten Island, NY

Pettit, Kenneth F
Minisink Valley
Central HS
Middletown, NY

Pettit, Mark
Johnstown HS
Johnstown, NY

Pettus, Jr Richard S
New Dorp HS
New York, NY

Peyton, Donna M
Far Rockaway HS
Far Rockaway, NY

Pfeuffer, Wendy
Marie
Rome Free Acad
Rome, NY

Pfuntner, Kimberley
Pfuntner
Geneseo Central HS
Geneseo, NY

Phifer, Lisa
Ossining HS
Ossining, NY

Philips, Allison
Central Islip HS
Islip Terrace, NY

Phillips, Graham V
John Jay HS
Katonah, NY

Phillips, Renee
Frontier HS
Hamburg, NY

Phillips, Robert
Springville-Griffith
Inst & C S
Colden, NY

Piagneri, Paul A
St Johns Prep HS
Astoria, NY

Pianella, Maria L
Driskany Central
Rome, NY

Picard, Nancy
Dominican
Commercial HS
Queens Vlge, NY

Picardi, Christina
Paul D Schreiber
Port Washington,
NY

Pickering, Roy
Cardinal Spellman
Bronx, NY

Pierce, Crystal A
G Ray Bodley HS
Fulton, NY

Pierce, David A
Lewiston-Porter HS
Lewiston, NY

Pierce, Jacqueline
Pulaski JR SR HS
Pulaski, NY

Pierce, Paula
Minisink Valley
Central HS
New Hampton, NY

Pierleoni, Maria
Virginia
Greece Arcadia HS
Rochester, NY

Pierre, Sandra
Manhattan Center
For Science & Math
Brooklyn, NY

Pierson, Kristen S
Pine Bush HS
Pine Bush, NY

Pierson, Michael
Newfield HS
Coram, NY

Pierson, Paul
Newfield HS
Coram, NY

Pietrowicz, Michele
Fowler HS
Syracuse, NY

Pietrowicz, Theresa
Cicero-North
Syracuse HS
Clay, NY

Pietz, Cheryl Lynn
West Seneca East
SR HS
W Seneca, NY

Pike, Christopher
Onteora HS
Woodstock, NY

Pike, Wendy
Frontier Central HS
Hamburg, NY

Pillo, Deidre Ann
Notre Dame HS
Batavia, NY

Pinckney, Leslie J
Murry Bergtraum
Bronx, NY

Pincus, Miriam B
Francis Lewis HS
Fresh Meadows, NY

Pinder, Michelle M
Newburgh Free
New Windsor, NY

Pineda, Iris
St Pius V HS
Bronx, NY

Pingryn, Michael
Auburn HS
Auburn, NY

Pintro, Harry
Harry S Truman HS
Bronx, NY

Pinzas, Jessica
Windsor Central HS
Conklin, NY

Pinzon, Gabrielle
The Mary Louis
Jamaica, NY

Pirozzolo, Susan
Horseheads HS
Horseheads, NY

Pisciarino, Denise
Liverpool HS
Liverpool, NY

Piskorz, Jeff A
Cheektowaga
Central HS
Cheektowaga, NY

Piston, Edward J
Liverpool HS
Liverpool, NY

Pitkin, Darrin
General Brown HS
Dexter, NY

Pitman, Keith D
Marathon Central
Marathon, NY

Pittari, Paul
Archbishop Molloy
Middle Village, NY

Pittman, Carlane
Harry S Truman HS
Bronx, NY

Pittman, Zoe L
Williamsville East
Buffalo, NY

Pitts, Jerrod
N Babylon SR HS
N Babylon, NY

Pizzola, Nicholas A
Homer Central HS
Cortland, NY

Place, Suzanne
Vestral SR HS
Vestal, NY

Plata, Lissel
Bronx H S Of
New York, NY

Plopper, Steve
Hilton Central HS
Hilton, NY

Pluff, Michael
Altmar-Parish
Williamstown HS
Parish, NY

Podadera, Jose Luis
Set Agnes HS
Jackson Hts, NY

Pokowicz, Stephen
Walt Whitman HS
Huntington, NY

Pollack, Darren
Hudson HS
Hudson, NY

Pollicino, Debra A
Bishop Kearney HS
Brooklyn, NY

Pollina, Stacy L
Sacchem HS North
Holbrook, NY

Pollock, Christopher
Walt Whitman HS
Huntington, NY

Poole, Beth Ann
Ithaca HS
Ithaca, NY

Popoli, Tina
Mount Vernon HS
Mount Vernon, NY

Porter, Jeannette
Hill
Hunter College HS
Bronx, NY

Postullo, Donna
Jericho SR HS
Jericho, NY

Potchinsky, Stuart
Binghamton HS
Binghamton, NY

Potter, Carl W
Liverpool HS
Liverpool, NY

Powch, Oksana
Eldred Central Schl
Glen Spey, NY

Powell, Darius
Saint Francis Prep
Maspeth, NY

Powell, Suzanne M
Scotia-Glenville HS
Scotia, NY

Powers, Dawn
Hudson Falls HS
Hudson Falls, NY

Powlis, III Volney A
North Babylon SR
North Babylon, NY

Prashaw, Bettina
Tupper Lake HS
Tupper Lk, NY

Pratt, Steven B
Holland Patent
Central HS
Holland Patent, NY

Prentice, Todd
Highland HS
Highland, NY

Preston, James
Archbishop Molloy
Bayside, NY

Preston, Sandra
Acad Of The Holy
Albany, NY

Pretorius, Peter
The Knox Schl
E Northport, NY

Prettitore, Gina
St Francis Prep Schl
Flushing, NY

Pribis, Douglas
Ichabod Crane HS
Valatie, NY

Price, Craig
Port Jervis HS
Sparrowbush, NY

Price, Terri
Falconer Central
Kennedy, NY

Prince, Sharon
Cardinal Spellman
Bronx, NY

Principal, Sauveta
Samuel J Tilden HS
Brooklyn, NY

Pringle, Charlene L
Hillcrest HS
Jamaica, NY

Prinzi, Mark
Avon Central HS
Avon, NY

Priola, Karin
Seaford HS
Seaford, NY

Pritchard, Denise M
Frankfort Schuyler
Frankfort, NY

Privitar, Donna M
St Barnabas HS
Bronx, NY

Prock, Christina
Catholic Central HS
Wynantskill, NY

Procopio, Linda
Nottingham HS
Cazenovia, NY

Profeta, Adrianne
Maria Regina HS
Yonkers, NY

Profeta, Lisa M
St Johns Prep
Astoria, NY

Proios, John
Hicksville SR HS
Hicksville, NY

Proskin, Lisa A
Shalcer HS
Menands, NY

Protass, Josh M
Rye Country Day
New Rochelle, NY

Prozny, Penelope L
Williamsville South
Williamsville, NY

Prunoske, Pam
Hornell SR HS
Hornell, NY

Pryzgoda, Dennis
Sacred Heart HS
Yonkers, NY

Pugh, Timothy
Onondaga HS
Nedrow, NY

Puleo, Paul
Frankfort-Schuyler
Central HS
Frankfort, NY

Pullins, Paige
Fayetteville-Manius
Fayetteville, NY

Pullo, Dominic
Niagara Falls HS
Niagara Falls, NY

Pullo, Scott
St Josephs
Collegiate Inst
N Tonawanda, NY

Pulver, Joseph W
Ichabod Crane HS
Kinderhook, NY

Pulvirenti, Patricia
St
Joseph-By-The-Se
Staten Island, NY

Pumford, Brian
Falconer Central HS
Jamestown, NY

Pumford, Ken
Falconer Central HS
Jamestown, NY

Purdy, III Gordon L
Wells Central Schl
Speculator, NY

Purdy, Jr William
Cicero North
Syracuse HS
Clay, NY

Puretas, Cynthia
St Pius V HS
Bronx, NY

Purner, Matthew
Queensbury HS
Glens Falls, NY

Purtell, Julie
Horseheads HS
Horseheads, NY

Pushkarsh, Vanessa
Saint Patricks Ctl
Catholic HS
Durham, NY

Putnam, James
Hannibal Central
Sterling, NY

Pysher, Paul A
Catskill HS
Cementon, NY

Quackenbush, Jr
Edward
Westport Central
Westport, NY

Quackenbush,
Melissa
Liverpool HS
Liverpool, NY

Quadagno, Michael
Archbishop Stepinac
Harrison, NY

Quagliana, Paul M
Amherst Central SR
Snyder, NY

Quain, Kathleen M
Johnson City HS
Johnson City, NY

Quellhorst, Eric
Arlington HS
Poughkeepsie, NY

Quenneville, Michael
Massena Central HS
Massena, NY

Quinn, Christine M
Manhasset HS
Manhasset, NY

Quinn, Eric
Weedsport JR SR
Sennett, NY

Quinn, Leo
Saratoga Central
Catholic HS
Ballston Spa, NY

Quist, Nicola A
Midwood HS
Brooklyn, NY

Rabb, Latifah A
F H La Guardia H S
Of Music & Arts
New York City, NY

Racchumi, Evelyn
Cathedral HS
New York, NY

Race, Jolene
Hudson HS
Hudson, NY

Racitano, Roxanne
Jamestown HS
Jamestown, NY

Racquet, John C
Columbia HS
Castleton, NY

Radesi, Jr Felix
John
York Central HS
Leicester, NY

Radice, Elizabeth
Saint John The
Baptist HS
Massapequa, NY

Radliff, Bryan
Shenendehowa HS
Clifton Park, NY

Rafalski, Dawn
Fillmore Central HS
Houghton, NY

Raffaele, Alice
Brooklyn Acad
Brooklyn, NY

Ragona, Joanie
South Side HS
Rockville Centr, NY

Raguso, Laura
Aquinas HS
Bronx, NY

Raible, Lisa
Rhinebeck HS
Rhinebeck, NY

Rainbow, Jodi
Liverpool HS
Liverpool, NY

Raiti, Adam
Liverpool HS
Liverpool, NY

Ralston, Larraine
Massena Central HS
Massena, NY

Rambadt, Michael P
Carmel HS
Patterson, NY

Ramin, Janet R
Sewanhaka HS
Floral Park, NY

Ramirez, David
St Fransis
Preporatory Schl
Elmhurst, NY

Ramlogan, Kushmawattie
Flushing HS
Flushing, NY

Ramos, Jacqueline
Theodore Roosevelt
New York, NY

Ramsey, Stephen M
St Anthonys HS
Smithtown, NY

Randall, James C
Whitesboro SR HS
Whitesboro, NY

Randall, Theresa
Groton Central HS
Groton, NY

Randolph, Davina
Monroe School Of The Arts
Rochester, NY

Ranger, Nadine
Bay Ridge HS
Brooklyn, NY

Ransom, Renee
Mohonasen HS
Schenectady, NY

Rao, Anjali
Jericho HS
Syosset, NY

Rapaglia, Eric D
Tottenville HS
Staten Island, NY

Rapkin, Mitzi
Brighton HS
Rochester, NY

Rappa, Lisa
South Shore HS
Brooklyn, NY

Raptis, Thomas
New Rochelle HS
New Rochelle, NY

Rasmussen, Jill
Bethlehem Central
Delmar, NY

Rasmussen, Tina
Clayton A Bouton JR SR HS
Slidell, LA

Ratajack, Bill
Brewster HS
Brewster, NY

Ratajczak, Cindy
St Marys HS
Cheektowaga, NY

Rater, Marty
Clymer Central Schl
Clymer, NY

Rauer, Scott J
Rocky Point JR SR
Rocky Point, NY

Rawson, Karen
Mexico HS
Mexico, NY

Ray, Gordon K
Utica Free Acad
Utica, NY

Rayeski, Elizabeth A
Corning-Painted Post West HS
Corning, NY

Raymond, Stacey
Moriah Central HS
Mineville, NY

Raymond, Tona R
Izmir American HS
Ft Leonard Wood, MO

Reali, Dean A
Brockport HS
Spencerport, NY

Reardon, Matt
Spacken HS
Poughkeepsie, NY

Reardon, Rita E
Glens Falls SR HS
Glens Falls, NY

Rearson, Darryl M
Fairport HS
Fairport, NY

Reaves, Nancy M
Ellsworth J Wilson
Rochester, NY

Redding, Susan M
Jamesville-Dewitt
Dewitt, NY

Redler, Kenneth Sean
Suffern HS
Suffern, NY

Reece, Sophia Allison
Mt Vernon HS
Mt Vernon, NY

Reed, Andy
James O Neil HS
West Point, NY

Reed, Kristi A
New Berlin Central
New Berlin, NY

Reed, Lonnita
Riverside HS
Buffalo, NY

Reese, Denise
Wantagh HS
Wantagh, NY

Reese, James F
Reed Creek JR SR
Red Creek, NY

Reese, Jonathan P
West Babylm HS
W Babylon, NY

Reeth, Janice
Smithtown H S East
Nissequoque, NY

Regina, Joyce
Dominican Commercial HS
Flushing, NY

Reich, Christopher
Minisink Valley HS
Westtown, NY

Reichert, Paul
Hamburg SR HS
Hamburg, NY

Reilly, Irene
Queen Of The Rosary Acad
Ptlookout, NY

Reilly, Michael
Stuyvesant HS
New York, NY

Reimann, Lori-Ann
Port Chester HS
Port Chester, NY

Reimer, Ross
South Western Central HS
Bemus Point, NY

Reinhardt, Christopher S
Connetquot SR HS
Oakdale, NY

Reino, Christopher V
Sachem HS
Holtsville, NY

Reinwald, Andrea
Scarsdale HS
Scarsdale, NY

Reiter, Larry
Oceanside HS
Oceanside, NY

Reiter, Scott W
Clinton Central HS
Clinton, NY

Relyea, Mary E
Canastota HS
Canastota, NY

Rendeiro, Danielle M
St Joseph By The Sea HS
Staten Island, NY

Renta, Kenneth
Wallkill SR HS
Plattekill, NY

Renz, Lisa D
Mohonasen HS
Schenectady, NY

Reres, Anthony
Monsignor Mc Clancy Memoria
Maspeth, NY

Restieri, Lawrence
Cold Spring Harbor
Cold Spring Har, NY

Restino, Stephen J
Fayetteville-Manlius
Manlius, NY

Retz, Susan
Union Springs Acad
Chittenango, NY

Reutlinger, Leah E
East Syracuse-Minoa
E Syracuse, NY

Revette, Renee T
Paul V Moore HS
Central Square, NY

Reyes, Ann Marie
Academy Of St
Central Islip, NY

Reyes, Myrna
Aquinas HS
Bronx, NY

Reynolds, Michael
Pelham Memorial
Pelham, NY

Reynolds, Samuel F
Kensington HS
Buffalo, NY

Rhee, Phillip
Uniondale HS
Uniondale, NY

Ricardo, Henry
Regis HS
Tappan, NY

Riccardelli, Silvestro
St John The Baptist
Oakdale, NY

Riccardi, Tiziana
St Peters High
School For Girls
Staten Isl, NY

Riccelli, Shari
West Genesee HS
Camillus, NY

Ricchiuti, Michael
W Islip HS
W Islip, NY

Rice, Brenda
G Ray Bodley HS
Fulton, NY

Rice, Jr David
Rice HS
New York, NY

Rice, Jenifer C
Hutchinson Central
Tech HS
Buffalo, NY

Rice, Robert
Albion HS
Albion, NY

Rice, Sharlet
Sachen North HS
Holbrook, NY

Rice, Theresa
Smithtown High
Schl West
Smithtown, NY

Rich, Jo Ann
Chittenango HS
Chittenango, NY

Richards, Martu J
St Raymond Acad
Bronx, NY

Richards, Todd
Salmon River
Central HS
Ft Covington, NY

Richardson, Carla
Springfields Gardens
Queens, NY

Richer, Dennis
Liverpool HS
Liverpool, NY

Richer, Harold J
Elmira Free Acad
Elmira, NY

Richman, Scott A
Jericho JR SR HS
Jericho, NY

Richter, Pamela K
Benjamin N Cardoza
Bayside, NY

Rickard, Debra M
Horseheads HS
Horseheads, NY

Rico, Sergio A
Bronx Science HS
Forest Hills, NY

Rider, Samantha
Highland HS
Highland, NY

Riegl, Edward
South Side HS
S Hempstead, NY

Riehl, Diane Susan
Central Islip HS
Central Islip, NY

Rifenburgh,
Christine
Lindenhurst HS
Lindenhurst, NY

Riffkin, Jodi B
New Rochelle HS
Scarsdale, NY

Rifflard, Tammy
Washingtonville HS
Washingtonville, NY

Riker, Becky A
Westhampton Beach
Westhampton, NY

Riley, Dora
Charlotte JR-SR HS
Rochester, NY

Rinaldi, John
Saint John The
Baptist HS
Deer Park, NY

Rink, Cheryl
Homell SR HS
Hornell, NY

Rios, Jose
John Dewey HS
Brooklyn, NY

Risolo, John
Bishop Kearney HS
Rochester, NY

Rivaldo, Christina
Bishop Kearney HS
Rochester, NY

Rivellini, Tom P
Gouverneur Central
Gouverneur, NY

Rivera, Annlysette
Midwood HS
Brooklyn, NY

Rivera, Gina
La Guardia HS Of
Music & The Arts
New York, NY

Rivera, Joanna
De Witt Clinton HS
Bronx, NY

Rivera, John
Frontier Central HS
Hamburg, NY

Rivieccio, Lucia
Commack High
School North
Commack, NY

Rizzo, David
Iona Preparatory
Eastchester, NY

Rizzo, John C
Bishop Cunningham
Oswego, NY

Rizzo, Karen Marie
Falconer Central HS
Jamestown, NY

Roach, Keith J
Ilion SR HS
Ilion, NY

Roark, Sheri
Whitesboro SR HS
Utica, NY

Robbins, Mary
Therese
Suffern HS
Monsey, NY

Roberti, Susan
Cardinal Spellman
Bronx, NY

Roberto, Donna
Union Endicott HS
Endicott, NY

Roberts, David P
Baldwin SR HS
Baldwin, NY

Roberts, Kenneth
Yonkers HS
Yonkers, NY

Roberts, Kevin
Bishop Loughlin
Memorial HS
Brooklyn, NY

Roberts, Mark T
Oneida SR HS
Oneida, NY

Roberts, Renee
Horseheads HS
Big Flats, NY

Roberts, Robyn
St Hildas And St
Hughs HS
Bronx, NY

Roberts, Sharon
Colonie Central HS
Loudonville, NY

Robertson, Jeffrey
Caledonia-Mumford
Central Schl
Caledonia, NY

Robertson, William
Eastridge HS
Rochester, NY

Robertson, Zhakoor
Boys & Girls HS
Brooklyn, NY

Robinson, Chris P
Glen Falls HS
Glens Falls, NY

Robinson, Joseph A
St Anthonys HS
Huntington Sta, NY

Robinson, Sandra
Wilson Magnet HS
Rochester, NY

Robinson, Suzanne
Lindenhurst SR HS
Lindenhurst, NY

Robinson, Traci
Ellen
New Rochelle HS
New Rochelle, NY

Robison, Matthew
T R Proctor HS
Utica, NY

Roby, Mary
Warwick Valley HS
Warwick, NY

Rocci, Chuck A
T R Proctor HS
Utica, NY

Rocco, Tom
Half Hollow Hills
East HS
Dix Hills, NY

Roche, Yvette
Cardinal Spellman
Bronx, NY

Rodden, Christine
St Vincent Ferrer
New York, NY

Rodgers, John
Jeaford HS
Seaford, NY

Rodgers, Wm
Long Island
Lutherman HS
Hicksville, NY

Rodriguez, Angel
Mount St Michael
Bronx, NY

Rodriguez, George
Thomas
The Bronx H S Of
Queens, NY

Rodriguez, Grace
Longwood HS
Coram, NY

Rodriguez, Isaura
Herbert H Lehman
Bronx, NY

Rodriguez, Ivette
Lehman HS
Bronx, NY

Rodriguez, Joanne
Aquinas HS
New York, NY

Rodriguez, Marina C
George Washington
New York, NY

Rodriguez, Maritza
Aquinas HS
New York, NY

Rodriguez, Miguel
Oyster Bay HS
E Norwich, NY

Rodriguez, Oscar
Peekskill HS
White Plains, NY

Rodriquez, Barbara
D
St Nicholas Of
Tolentine HS
Bronx, NY

Rogers, Colleen
East Islip HS
East Islip, NY

Rogers, Kim
Riverhead HS
Riverhead, NY

Rogers, William
Brewster HS
Brewster, NY

Rogozinski, Deborah
Mattituck HS
Mattituck, NY

Rohan, Brian
Msgr Mc Clancy HS
Forest Hills, NY

Rohan, Patrick
East Meadow HS
East Meadow, NY

Rohl, Jeff
Amherst Central HS
Eggertsville, NY

Rojas, Eugenia
John Jay HS
Brooklyn, NY

Rojas, Gina M
Notre Dame Schl
Rosedale, NY

Roll, Krista L
Galwag Central HS
Galway, NY

Roller, Karen G
Valley Stream South
Valley Stream, NY

Roller, Michele
Garden City SR HS
Garden City, NY

Rollins, Diana
St Francis Prep
Bayside, NY

Romaine, James R
Valley Central HS
Walden, NY

Romaine, Joan
Valley Central HS
Walden, NY

Roman, Francis M
The Loyola Schl
Woodside, NY

Roman, John
Rocky Point Jr Sr
Rocky Point, NY

Roman, Mari Pat
Oriskany Central
Rome, NY

Romaneo, Jeffrey
East Aurora HS
East Aurora, NY

Romano, Wayne
Aquinas Inst
Spencerport, NY

Romanow, Jeffrey E
John F Kennedy HS
Plainview, NY

Romanowski, Craig
Royalton-Hartland
Gasport, NY

Romero, Judith B
Hillcrest HS
Jackson Hts, NY

Roosa, Leigh
Marlboro Central
Newburgh, NY

Roque, Donna
John Adams HS
S Ozone Pk, NY

Rose, David
Cicero-North
Syracuse HS
North Syracuse, NY

Rose, Dona A
Oneida Senior HS
Oneida, NY

Roseboom, Valerie
Mont Pleasant HS
Schenectady, NY

Rosen, Jodi S
G W Hewlett HS
Hewlett, NY

Rosen, Lisa
Oceanside HS
Oceanside, NY

Rosenbaum, Morris
Forest Hills HS
Forest Hills, NY

Rosenberg, Sheryl
Valley Central HS
Walden, NY

Rosenfeld, John J
Horseheads HS
Horseheads, NY

Rosenstein, Shari L
Washingtonville HS
Blooming Grove, NY

Rosenthal, Brenda
Brighton HS
Rochester, NY

Rosenthal, Diane
Syosset HS
Woodbury, NY

Roskos, Robert
Sachem High School
Holbrook, NY

Rosner, Cheray
Yeshiva University
High Schl Girls
Passaic, NJ

Ross, Dianne
Christopher
Columbus HS
Bronx, NY

Rossetti, Timothy S
Greece Athena HS
Rochester, NY

Rossi, Eric S
Commack H S
Commack, NY

Rossi, Janet
Lynbrook HS
Lynbrook, NY

Roters, Stephanie
Cathedral HS
Astoria, NY

Rothaug, Tina
Middleburgh
Central HS
Middleburgh, NY

Rothfarb, Lilly A
Walt Whitman HS
Huntington, NY

Rothman, Jonathan
H
New Rochelle HS
New Rochelle, NY

Rothman, Robert
Commack North HS
Commack, NY

Rounsaville, Betty
De Ruyter Central
De Ruyter, NY

Rourke, Bridget
Academy Of The
Holy Names
Albany, NY

Rouse, Jennifer
Waterloo SR HS
Waterloo, NY

Roy, Melissa L
Nyack SR HS
Vly Cottage, NY

Rozanski, Andrea
Perry Central HS
Perry, NY

Rozycki, Jennifer
Gloversville HS
Gloversville, NY

Rubin, Alexande S
Horace Greeley HS
Chappaqua, NY

Rubin, Mark
Commack H S
Commack, NY

Rubin, Sydelle
Commack H S
Smithtown, NY

Rubio, Sharih
Hornell HS
Hornell, NY

Ruchandani, Nandita
Union-Endicott HS
Endicott, NY

Rudd, Alexis H
Columbia Grammar & Prep
New York, NY

Rudd, Melisa
Oakfield Alabama
Basom, NY

Rudolph, Edna A
Freeport HS
Freeport, NY

Rudolph, Maureen
Stella Maris HS
Breezy Point, NY

Ruff, Sherry
Holy Angels Acad
Buffalo, NY

Ruffino, Gina
Gatavia SR HS
Batavia, NY

Ruggiero, Linda
East Meadow HS
E Meadow, NY

Ruhmel, II Joseph F
Notre Dame HS
Horseheads, NY

Ruhmel, Rhonda
Southside HS
Elmira, NY

Ruiz, Jose
Cardinal Spellman
Bronx, NY

Ruiz, Ralph
Central Islip HS
Central Islip, NY

Rulison, Rebecca
Broadalbin Central
Broadalbin, NY

Rumsey, David
Horseheads SR HS
Millport, NY

Rurey, Bryan
Pulaski JR SR HS
Pulaski, NY

Rush, Patricia A
Amsterdam HS
Amsterdam, NY

Rush, Steven
New Amsterdam HS
Amsterdam, NY

Russell, Kelley Suzanne
Eden SR HS
Eden, NY

Russell, Roxanne
Clara Barton HS
New York, NY

Russo, Chris
Hendrick Hudson
Verplanck, NY

Russo, Jennifer
Valley Stream North
Elmont, NY

Russo, Nancy
Academy Of The Pt Chester, NY

Russo, Peter E
Ross Brentwood HS
Brentwood, NY

Rust, Tammie K
Saratoga Springs SR
Gansevoort, NY

Rustia, Rosalie Payawal
Stella Maris HS
Howard Beach, NY

Ruvolo, Kristina Marie
Our Lady Of Perpetual Help
Brooklyn, NY

Ryan, Eileen Marie
Saugerties HS
Saugerties, NY

Ryan, Lisa Lynn
Cortland JR SR HS
Cortland, NY

Ryan, Michael W
Cicero North Syracuse HS
Clay, NY

Ryan, Monica J
The Mary Louis
Jackson Heights, NY

Ryan, Winter Brook
Northport HS
E Northport, NY

Ryerson, Caryn
Port Jervis HS
Pt Jervis, NY

Ryngwalski, Andrea
Villa Maria Acad
Buffalo, NY

Sabater, Lucia A
Scarsdale HS
Scarsdale, NY

Sabatino, Jerome E
Regis HS
Corona, NY

Sabia, Christopher
Commack High School South
Commack, NY

Sabo, Christie
Mount Mercy Acad
W Seneca, NY

Sacco, Theresa
Waverly JR SR HS
Waverly, NY

Sada, Tony
Liverpool HS
Liverpool, NY

Sadeghian, Scott
East Aurora HS
East Aurora, NY

Sadlon, Barbara
Little Falls JR SR
Little Falls, NY

Safis, Kenneth N
La Salle SR HS
Niagara Falls, NY

Sahner, Kelly Paige
Half Hollow Hills H S East
Dix Hills, NY

Salamido, Pat
Union-Endicott HS
Endicott, NY

Salat, Michael
John H Glenn HS
E Northport, NY

Salem, Molly
Bishop Grimes HS
E Syracuse, NY

Salerno, David
Minisink Valley HS
Port Jervis, NY

Salerno, Stephen M
Rome Free Acad
Rome, NY

Salmon, Nadine
Northeastern Acad
Bronx, NY

Salva, Laura
Franciscan HS
Mohegan Lake, NY

Samala, George
Nyack HS
Nyack, NY

Sammons, Stephanie
York Central HS
Leicester, NY

Sampson, Anne
Greene Central HS
Greene, NY

Sampson, Elizabeth
Roy C Ketcham SR
Wappingers Fls, NY

Samson, Rosanne
Emma Willard Schl
Loudonville, NY

Samuel, Alice
Valley Central HS
Montgomery, NY

Samuel, Roslyn
Saugerties HS
Saugerties, NY

Samuels, Dionne
Gorton HS
Yonkers, NY

Sanchez, Glenn
Smithtown High School West
Smithtown, NY

Sanchez, Jay
William Floyd HS
Shirley, NY

Sanchez, Maria Earl L
Vandermeulen HS
Mt Sinai, NY

Sanchez, Sophia
Cairo Durham HS
Round Top, NY

Sanchez, Yvette
The Mary Louis
Floral Park, NY

Sander, Henry
Delaware Academy & Central HS
Delhi, NY

Sanfilippo, Lisa S
Seton Catholic Central HS
Binghamton, NY

Sangen, Monica A
Floral Park Memorial HS
Floral Pk, NY

Sanguedolce, Joanne
Nazareth Acad
Spencerport, NY

Sanon, Edison
Nazareth Regional
Brooklyn, NY

Santangelo, Pasquale V
Bishop Ford C C HS
Brooklyn, NY

Santiago, Edward
Park West HS
Brooklyn, NY

Santiago, Elizabeth
Clara Barton HS
Brooklyn, NY

Santiago, Maria
Cathedral HS
Ny, NY

Santini, Betsy Marie
John F Kennedy HS
Bronx, NY

Santon, Douglas
Bishop Scully HS
Amsterdam, NY

Santoro, Joseph
Rocky Point JR SR
Rocky Point, NY

Santos, Gracelyn
Fernandez
St Peters High
School For Girls
Staten Island, NY

Santos, Jose
Alexandre
St Joseph By The
Sea HS
Staten Island, NY

Santos, Kelly
Walt Whitman HS
Huntington Stat,
NY

Santucci, Beverly
Yorktown HS
Mt Kisco, NY

Sappelsa, Laura
H Frank Carey HS
Franklin Sq, NY

Sarrett, Jeffrey
Oceanside HS
Oceanside, NY

Saunders, Michael
La Salle Military
Queens, NY

Sauter, Andrea
The Franciscan
N Syracuse, NY

Savage, Suzanne V
Glens Falls SR HS
Hudson Falls, NY

Savich, Diane M
Johnson City SR HS
Johnson City, NY

Savino, Tracey Anne
East Islip SR HS
Islip Terrace, NY

Sawkiw, Michael
Cohoes HS
Cohoes, NY

Sawtelle, Scott
Millbrook HS
Millbrook, NY

Sayegh, Michael
Sacred Heart HS
Yonkers, NY

Scalcione, Kerry
St John The Baptist
Massapequa, NY

Scalise, Arthur M
Babylon HS
Babylon, NY

Scalzo, David
Jamesville-De Witt
Dewitt, NY

Scanlan, Gerard A
Clarkstown High
Schl South
New City, NY

Scardino, Richard
St Francis Prep
Ozone Park, NY

Scarlotta, Frank
Granville HS
Granville, NY

Scattaglia, Christina
Saint John Villa
Staten Island, NY

Scelzo, William A
Baldwin SR HS
Baldwin, NY

Schabel, Joy E
Walt Whitman HS
Melville, NY

Schacht, Christa
Maria
St Francis Prep
Forest Hills, NY

Schaefer, Catherine
M
Villa Maria Acad
Sloan, NY

Schaffel, Jonathan
Elmont Memorial
Elmont, NY

Schalk, Nadine
Royalton-Hartland
Central HS
Middleport, NY

Schantz, Jr Robert
E
Fairport HS
Fairport, NY

Scharning, Kamila
East Islip HS
E Islip, NY

Scheideler, Kathy
Hauppauge HS
Smithtown, NY

Scheifla, Jr Albert
Hutch Tech
Buffalo, NY

Scheltz, Lisa
Mynderse Acad
Seneca Falls, NY

Schenck, William
Aquinas Inst
Rochester, NY

Schenkman, Mark
E L Vander Meulen
Mt Sinai, NY

Scherhaufer, Scott
Chenango Forks HS
Castle Creek, NY

Scherrer, Andrew M
Skaneateles Central
Skaneateles, NY

Schiavone, Paul M
Moore Catholic HS
Staten Island, NY

Schiff, Jeffrey C
Binghamton HS
Binghamton, NY

Schillawski, David
Holland Patent HS
Holland Patent, NY

Schilling, Margaret
E
John Jay HS
Katonah, NY

Schiltz, Gregg
Holland Central HS
Holland, NY

Schimenti, Michelle
Williamsville North
Getzville, NY

Schimmoller, Brian
Shenendehowa
Central HS
Bow, NH

Schirtzer, Rosanne
M
Woodlands HS
Hartsdale, NY

Schleith, Helmut
Hicksville HS
Hicksville, NY

Schley, Jaishree
Bronx High Schl Of
Bronx, NY

Schlinger, Stephen
Chester HS
Chester, NY

Schmackenberg,
Heidi L
Hudson HS
Claverack, NY

Schmidt, David
Bronx High School
Of Science
Hollis Hills, NY

Schmidt, Frank
Mahopac HS
Mahopac, NY

Schmidt, Julianne
Stella Maris HS
Woodhaven, NY

Schmidt, Justine
Cleveland Hill HS
Cheektowaga, NY

Schnabel, Peter A
Francis Lewis HS
Bayside, NY

Schneider, Bradley
M
Beach Channel HS
Belle Harb, NY

Schneider, Robert J
Francis Lewis HS
Flushing, NY

Schneller, Eddie
Walter Panas HS
Peekskill, NY

Schnoes, Cynthia D
Walter Panas HS
Peekskill, NY

Schnurbusch, Tamie
James E Sperry HS
Rochester, NY

Schoepflin, Monty L
Springville-Griffith
Springville, NY

Scholten, Heidi
Cold Spring Harbor
Huntington, NY

Schoonover, Charles
J
York Central HS
Piffard, NY

Schosger, Lauralynn
Corning-Painted
Post HS
Painted Post, NY

Schott, Lara
Brockport HS
Brockport, NY

Schrager, Norman
Roosevelt HS
Yonkers, NY

Schreiber, Markus
Sheepshead Bay HS
Brooklyn, NY

Schreivogl, Stacy
Berne-Knox-Westerl
o Central HS
East Berne, NY

Schroder, Renee
Riverhead HS
Jamesport, NY

Schrot, Lisa
Walter Panas HS
Peekskill, NY

Schuebler, Peter
Archbishop Molloy
Ridgewood, NY

Schukal, Kristen J
John Jay SR HS
Hopewell Jct, NY

Schuler, Greta A
Ticonderoga HS
Ticonderoga, NY

Schulman, Steven F
Smithtown East HS
Smithtown, NY

Schult, Heidi
Clarkstown North
New City, NY

Schultz, Cindy
Coxsackie-Athens
W Coxsackie, NY

Schumann, Kari R
East HS
Rochester, NY

Schwab, Alexandra
Pelham Memorial
Pelham Manor, NY

Schwabl, Jill
Mount Mercy Acad
Buffalo, NY

Schwaller, John
Cucning-Painted
Post West HS
Painted Post, NY

Schwaller, Peter J
Somers HS
Somers, NY

Schwartz, Brian P
Camden HS
Blossvale, NY

Schwartz, David
Massapequa HS
Massapequa, NY

Schwartz, David D
Ramapo SR HS
Suffern, NY

Schwartz, Jodi
South Shore HS
Brooklyn, NY

Schwartz, Mark
Churchville-Chili
Churchville, NY

Schweiger, Robert F
N Tonawanda SR
N Tonawanda, NY

Schweizer, Lisa
Moore Catholic HS
Staten Island, NY

Sciabarra, Geraldine
Bishop Karney HS
Brooklyn, NY

Scialdone, Vincent
Utica Free Acad
Utica. NY

Scicutella, Angela
John Adams HS
Richmond Hl, NY

Scirocco, Michele
Scotia-Glenville HS
Scotia, NY

Sciulli, Alisa J
Irvington HS
Irvington, NY

Sclafani, Frank
Archbishop Stepinac
Port Chester, NY

Sclamo, Louisa M
Jefferson HS
Rochester, NY

Scocchera, Richard
Frontier SR HS
Hamburg, NY

Scolnik, Meryl
Earl L
Vandermeulen HS
Port Jefferson, NY

Scordo, Cheryl A
Bishop Grimes HS
E Syracuse, NY

Scott, Andrea
Rome Catholic HS
Rome, NY

Scott, Andrea L
Gates-Chili SR HS
Rochester, NY

Scott, Jr Bernard
Bishop Loughlin
Memorial HS
Brooklyn, NY

Scott, Bradley C
Haverling JR SR
Savona, NY

Scott, Catherine
Oneonta SR HS
Oneonta, NY

Scott, Gary
Pelham Memorial
Pelham, NY

Scott, Jr James
Joseph
St Johns
Preparatory Schl
Astoria, NY

Scott, Julie
Trott Vocational HS
Alden, NY

Scott, Marion
Northeastern Acad
Bronx, NY

Scott, III Thomas P
Oneill HS
Ft Montgomery, NY

Scott, Wayne
North Babylon SR
N Babylon, NY

Scott, Wendy A
Whitesboro SR HS
Whitesboro, NY

Scrimale, Richard
Solvay HS
Solvay, NY

Scuderi, Thomas
Sheepshead Bay HS
Brooklyn, NY

Scullion, Kathryn
Jeffersonville-Young
sville Cen Schl
North Branch, NY

Seaman, Kevin
Susan E Wagner HS
Staten Isld, NY

Searles, Tina
Adessa Montour
Central Schl
Alpine, NY

Sebastiano, Anna M
Half Hollow Hills
East HS
Titusville, FL

Seekings, Carrie
Cassadaga Valley
Cassadaga, NY

Seeley, Jodi L
East Aurora HS
E Aurora, NY

Seepersad, Dookran
Norman Thomas HS
Queens, NY

Seider, David F
Hudson HS
Hudson, NY

Seidman, Cynthia
Half Hollow Hills
East HS
Dix Hills, NY

Seiferth, April Holly
Mamaroneck HS
Larchmont, NY

Seiler, Stephanie H
John L Miller Great
Neck N SR HS
Great Neck, NY

Selca, George
Christopher
Columbus HS
Bronx, NY

Selditch, April Y
Centereach HS
Centereach, NY

Selee, Bryan
Camden SR HS
Camden, NY

Seligman, Jason
United Nations
International Schl
New York, NY

Seller, Stuart
Williamsville North
SR HS
Williamsville, NY

Semc Ken, Adam
Farmingdale HS
Farmingdale, NY

Semel, Michael A
Hanppauge HS
Smithtown, NY

Senior, Kelly
Newfield HS
Selden, NY

Sephton, Amy
Westhampton Beach
Mastic, NY

Sergeant, Kristi
Our Lady Of Mercy
Sodus, NY

Serrano, Richard
Regis HS
Bronx, NY

Serrano, Robert
A F Stevenson HS
Bronx, NY

Serratore, Elizabeth
Nyack SR HS
Vly Cottage, NY

Serviss, Tracy
Webster HS
Penfield, NY

Sethi, Gail
The Mary Louis
Flushing, NY

Seul, Michael
St Anthonys HS
Centereach, NY

Seward, Sandra J
Byron-Bergen
Central HS
Byron, NY

Sfiligoi, Daniel
St John The Baptist
D HS
Lindenhurst, NY

Sgarlata, Danielle
Clarkstown High
School South
W Nyack, NY

Sgobbo, Angelo
Harrison HS
E White Plains, NY

Sgro, Maria
Churchville-Chili SR
Rochester, NY

Sgroi, Patrick
East SR HS
West Seneca, NY

Sguera, Maria
Earl L
Vandermeulen HS
Mt Sinai, NY

Shackelton, Geoffrey
S
Walton Central Schl
Walton, NY

Shah, Dipti
Hillcrest HS
Corona, NY

Shampanier, Judy
Commack H S
Commack, NY

Shamroth, Janet
New Field HS
Selden, NY

Shand, Natalie A
Curtis HS
Staten Island, NY

Shapiro, Michael
Monticello HS
Kauneonga Lake,
NY

Shapiro, Sidra Lee
Pittsford Mendon
Pittsford, NY

Sharpe, Terrilyn
Liverpool HS
Liverpool, NY

Shatz, Stephanie M
St John The Baptist
Bayshore, NY

Shaughnessy, James
St Francis Prep
Holliswood, NY

Shaughnessy,
Yvonne
Cicero-N Syracuse
N Syracuse, NY

Shaver, Christopher
St Marys Acad
Fort Edward, NY

Shaw, Ida
St Raymond
Academy For Girls
New York, NY

Shaw, Kristin
Yorktown HS
Yorktown Hts, NY

Shaw, Lynda Anne
Gates-Chili HS
Rochester, NY

Shaw, Rebecca M
Gowanda Central
Collins, NY

Shebroe, David
Connetquot HS
Lk Ronkonkoma,
NY

Shedlin, Robin D
Scarsdale HS
Scarsdale, NY

Sheehan, Joseph R
Wheatland Chili HS
Scottsville, NY

Sheehan, Maura D
Rocky Point HS
Rocky Point, NY

Sheehan, Robin J
Scotia-Glenville HS
Scotia, NY

Sheehy, Sharlene
Fairport HS
Fairport, NY

Sheff, Daniel
Frontier Central SR
Hamburg, NY

Sheffield, Jr
Frederick M
Oswego HS
Oswego, NY

Sheffield, Scott
Randolph Central
Randolph, NY

Sheils, Daniel
Saugerties HS
Saugerties, NY

Shelanskey, Tami
Corning-Painted
Post West HS
Painted Post, NY

Sheldon, Jennifer
Hoosick Falls
Central HS
Petersburg, NY

Shelton, Colleen
Lindenhurst SR HS
Lindenhurst, NY

Shepard, Lori
Earl Vandermeulen
Mt Sinai, NY

Shepardson, Nancy
Elizabeth
Auburn HS
Auburn, NY

Shephard, Shannon
Akron Central HS
Akron, NY

Shepherd, Kelly
High School Of
Fashion Indust
Brooklyn, NY

Sheridan, Robert A
A G Berner HS
Massapequa Park,
NY

Sherwin, Carol
Manhasset HS
Floral Pk, NY

Sherwood, David
Southampton HS
Southampton, NY

Sherwood, Jason
Tate
Oneonta HS
Otego, NY

Shields, Kevin M
La Salle Military
Manhasset, NY

Shimkin,
Christopher
Mamaroneck HS
Larchmont, NY

Shimmel, Jennifer
Brushton-Moira
Central HS
Moira, NY

Shindelman, Andrea
L
Tottenville HS
Staten Island, NY

Shirazi, Sherin
Grand Island HS
Grand Island, NY

Shubert, Traci L
Grand Island SR HS
Grand Island, NY

Shulman, Alissa M
Williamsville North
North Tonawanda,
NY

Shults, Dale
Carnajoharie Central
Canajoharie, NY

Siciliano, Carl
Lindehurst HS
Lindenhurst, NY

Siegel, Audra
Commack High
School South
Commack, NY

Siegel, Jill
Commack HS North
E Northport, NY

Siegel, Paul
Half Hollow Hills
East HS
Dix Hills, NY

Siegle, Elizabeth
Union Endicott HS
Endicott, NY

Sifert, Robin
Michael
Saratoga Central
Catholic HS
Schuylerville, NY

Sigmone, Harry
Holy Cross HS
Flushing, NY

Sikora, Jr Robert A
Mercy HS
Aquebogue, NY

Silberbusch, Julie M
Patchogue-Medford
Patchogue, NY

Silcox, Mindy
Westhampton Beach
E Quogue, NY

Silich, Robert C
Regis HS
Staten Island, NY

Sills, Kimberly
Medina SR HS
Knowlesville, NY

Silverio, Arlene B
Franklin Delano
Roosevelt HS
Poughkeepsie, NY

Silverman, Cindy
Seaford HS
Seaford, NY

Silvermintz, Daniel
Lynbrook HS
E Rockaway, NY

Silvestri, Dawn
Glen Cove HS
Glen Cove, NY

Simmons, Kevin
Williamsville East
East Amherst, NY

Simner, Janni Lee
Oceanside HS
Oceanside, NY

Simon, Richard
Roy C Ketcham HS
Poughkeepsie, NY

Simon, Thomas
Frontier Central HS
Hamburg, NY

Simoncic, Michael F
Sayville HS
Sayville, NY

Simons, Ivette
Cardinal Spellman
Bronx, NY

Simons, Sonya L
Uniondale HS
Uniondale, NY

Sinclair, Judith
Prospect Heights
Brooklyn, NY

Singer, Rena L
Tottenville HS
Staten Island, NY

Sinicropi, Michael
Amsterdam HS
Amsterdam, NY

Sinigaglia, Joanne M
St Agnes Academic
Flushing, NY

Sink, Jennifer
Royalton Hartland
Gasport, NY

Sinkler, Michele
Nazareth Academy
Rochester, NY

Siragusa, Paul R
Baldwin HS
Baldwin, NY

Sisto, John
Bishop Grimes HS
Syracuse, NY

Sklar, Wendy
Roosevelt HS
Yonkers, NY

Skolnik, Brett
Spring Valley SR
Spring Vly, NY

Skorupa, Thomas A
Pelham Memorial
Pelham, NY

Skrupa, Susan
West Genesee HS
Camillus, NY

Skyer, Nicole A
Midwood HS
Belle Harbor, NY

Slade, Trina
Cardinal Spellman
Bronx, NY

Slanetz, Carolyn
Abigail
Portledge HS
Locust Valley, NY

Slater, Jennifer
Lynn
Our Lady Of Victory
New York, NY

Slaven, Shawn
Le Roy Central HS
Leroy, NY

Slaver, Art
Keveny Memorial
Cohoes, NY

Slavik, Jacqueline M
Kingston HS
Lake Katrine, NY

Slayton, Melissa
Avaca Central Schl
Avoca, NY

Slingerland, Amy
Minisink Valley HS
Westown, NY

Slottje, Josh
Vestal SR HS
Vestal, NY

Slywka, Mark
St Marys Acad
Diamond Point, NY

Smatlak,
Anne-Marie
St John The Baptist
P HS
Brightwaters, NY

Smedley, Pamela
Bainbridge-Guilford
Bainbridge, NY

Smeragliuolo,
Michelle
Jamestown SR HS
Jamestown, NY

Smith, Bill
Franklin Acad
N Bangor, NY

Smith, Brandon
John
Hadley-Luzerne
Central Schl
Lake Luzerne, NY

Smith, Catherine
Harry S Truman HS
Bronx, NY

Smith, Christopher
J
Johnson City SR HS
Johnson City, NY

Smith, Daniel
Columbia HS
E Greenbush, NY

Smith, David M
Whitesboro SR HS
Marcy, NY

Smith, Dawn
Mayfield JR SR HS
Gloversville, NY

Smith, December
Louann
Sigonella American
FPO, NY

Smith, Derek S
Roslyn HS
Roslyn, NY

Smith, Edna
Susquehanna Valley
Conklin, NY

Smith, Horace
Mc Kee Vocational
& Tech
Staten Is, NY

Smith, Jeffrey W
Johnstown HS
Johnstown, NY

Smith, Josie A M
Ogdensburg Free
Ogdensburg, NY

Smith, Karen
Rome Free Acad
Rome, NY

Smith, Kent
Mercy HS
Shoreham, NY

Smith, Kimberleigh
Horseheads HS
Horseheads, NY

Smith, Kwaw D
Mt Vernon HS
Mt Vernon, NY

Smith, Lawrence M
Newfield HS
Selden, NY

Smith, Linda A
Shaker HS
Latham, NY

Smith, Patricia
Ichabod Crane HS
Valatie, NY

Smith, Paula Marie
Faith Heritage HS
Pulaski, NY

Smith, Rebecca
Mohonasen HS
Schenectady, NY

Smith, Rodger
Niagara Falls HS
Niagara Falls, NY

Smith, Shawn
Newfield HS
Selden, NY

Smith, Shelley G
Notre Dame-Bishop
Gibbons HS
Schenechacy, NY

Smith, Susanne
Cold Spring Harbor
Huntington, NY

Smith, Tara Ann
Herricks SR HS
New Hyde Park, NY

Smith, Tracie
Wellsville Central
Wellsville, NY

Smith, Victoria L
Our Lady Of
Lourdes HS
Verbank, NY

Smith, Wendy
Potsdam Central HS
Potsdam, NY

Smith, Wendy Anne
Minerva Central
Minerva, NY

Smukall, Carl
Ahica Central HS
Darien Ctr, NY

Snare, David
Mont Pleasant HS
Schenectady, NY

Snell, Martha
Victor Central HS
Victor, NY

Snellinger, Lucy
Port Jervis HS
Port Jervis, NY

Snogles, Jeffrey
Cicero-North
Syracuse HS
N Syracuse, NY

Snowberger, Debra
Union Endicott HS
Endicott, NY

Snyder, Cheri
Cicero North
Syracuse HS
Clay, NY

Snyder, Christina
Rensselaer JR SR
Rensselaer, NY

Snyder, Eric
Lindenhurst HS
Lindenhurst, NY

Snyder, Randi
Susan E Wagner HS
East Stroudsburg, PA

Snyder, Robert
Riverside HS
Buffalo, NY

Snyder, William A
Saratoga Springs HS
Saratoga, NY

Sober, Melissa
Lansingburgh HS
Troy, NY

Sokolowski, William
Liverpool HS
North Syracuse, NY

Solin, Allison
New Rochelle HS
New Rochelle, NY

Sollitto, Donna
Valley Stream
Central HS
Valley Stream, NY

Solomon, Irene
Stuyvesant HS
New York, NY

Solomon, Ronaldo
Whitney Point HS
Castle Creek, NY

Sonkin, Michael
East Islip HS
East Islip, NY

Sonnenblick, Amy
Hebrew Academy Of
Nassau County
Manhasset Hills, NY

Sorbero, Richard J
Amsterdam HS
Amsterdam, NY

Sorensen, Carol
Ossining HS
Ossining, NY

Sorensen, Steven A
Waverly JR SR HS
Waverly, NY

Soriano, Maria
Julita
St Johns Prep
Elmhurst, NY

Soriano, Salvatore A
Archbishop Molloy
Rosedale, NY

Soto, Christopher
Mount Saint
Micheal Acad
Mt Vernon, NY

Soto, Rafael
St Agnes HS
New York, NY

Sotolongo, Frank
John Dewey HS
Brooklyn, NY

Spada, Joe
John A Coleman HS
Stone Ridge, NY

Spadone, John
Lackwanna SR HS
Lackawanna, NY

Spagnolo, Anthony
Spring Valley SR
Spring Vly, NY

Spanakos, Helen
Garden City SR HS
Garden City, NY

Spear, Sydney B
Bayshore HS
Bayshore, NY

Specht, Adam
Hebrew Academy Of
Nassau County
Bethpage, NY

Spencer, Cynthia
East Aurora HS
East Aurora, NY

Speres, Constantine A
Garden City HS
Garden City, NY

Sperling, Linnae R
Binghamton HS
Binghamton, NY

Spero, Jr Richard B
East Hampton HS
Amagansett, NY

Speroni, John V
Division Avenue HS
Levittown, NY

Speros, George E
Cardinal Spellman
Bronx, NY

Spetter, Victoria C
Gen D Mac Arthur
Wantagh, NY

Spicer, Alisa
James Madison HS
Brooklyn, NY

Spicer, Deidre K
Walt Whitman HS
Huntington, NY

Spicer, Velvet
Oakfield-Alabama
Oakfield, NY

Spiess, Kelli
Liverpool HS
Liverpool, NY

Spivey, Scott
Sacred Heart HS
Yonkers, NY

Spolarich, Michael J
New Hyde Park
Memorial HS
New Hyde Park, NY

Spradlin, Tina
Waterloo HS
Waterloo, NY

Sprague, Dean
Falconer Central HS
Falconer, NY

Sprague, Jo
Horseheads HS
Horseheads, NY

Sprik, Grace
Aquinas Inst
Penfield, NY

Sprow, Laura
Potsdam HS
Hannawa Falls, NY

Squier, Denise
Lakeland SR HS
Mahopac, NY

Squillace, Linda
Linton HS
Schenectady, NY

Srinivasan, Ravi
Gloversville HS
Gloversville, NY

Sriubas, Andy R
Carmel HS
Carmel, NY

St Germain, Leo
Heuvelton Central
Heuvelton, NY

St John, Jennifer
Brewster HS
Patterson, NY

Stabile, Theresa J
Garden City HS
Garden City, NY

Stachowicz, Timothy
North Rose-Wolcott
Red Crk, NY

Stackelhouse, Stacey J
Bitburg American
Apple Valley, CA

Stadler, Dawn M
Lake Shore HS
Angola, NY

Stahel, Laura
Garden City HS
Garden City, NY

Stahura, Mary
Frontier SR HS
Blasdell, NY

Staley, Patricia
Dominican
Commercial HS
St Albans, NY

Stallings, Danyan
Roosevelt HS
Yonkers, NY

Stallsworth, Darrell
Aviation HS
E Elmhurst, NY

Stalmack, Tammy
Central Islip HS
Central Islip, NY

Stamm, Anna
Vestal SR HS
Vestal, NY

Stamos, Nicholas D
Westhill HS
Syracuse, NY

Stanchfield, Helen
Rome Free Acad
Taberg, NY

Staniszewski, Diane
N Babylon HS
North Babylon, NY

Stanley, George
Nottingham HS
Syracuse, NY

Stark, Joanne
Potsdam Central HS
Potsdam, NY

Starling, Rebecca
East Aurora HS
East Aurora, NY

PHOTO
NOT
AVAILABLE

Starowitz, Jr Leo
Byron Bergen
Central Schl
Elba, NY

Staub, Scott
Susquehanna Valley
Conklin, NY

Stauss, Carolyn L
Academy Of Saint
Joseph HS
E Northport, NY

Stebbins, Tammy
Waterloo SR HS
Waterloo, NY

Steeb, Kristine
Greece Athena HS
Rochester, NY

Stefanelli, Michael
W C Mepham HS
North Bellmore, NY

Stein, Sharon
Rye Neck HS
Mamaroneck, NY

Steinas, Stephanie
Nozareth Acad
Rochester, NY

Steinberg, Judi
Christopher
Columbus HS
Bronx, NY

Steiness, Susan
Northport HS
Northport, NY

Steinschaden, Heidi
Vienna
Sachem HS
Holbrook, NY

Steitler, Jason
Newark Central HS
Newark, NY

Stephens, Lorraine
Martin Van Buren
Jamaica, NY

Stepnowsky,
Cynthia
Mattituck HS
Cutchogue, NY

Steuerwald, Beverly
Center Moriches HS
Manorville, NY

Stevens, Carey
Westhampton Beach
Westhamptn Bch,
NY

Stevens, Sheri L
Wilson Central HS
Lockport, NY

Stewart, Owen
Springfield Gardens
New York, NY

Sticca, Patricia
W Seneca East SR
W Seneca, NY

Stinson, Dexter
Cardinal Hayes HS
Bronx, NY

Stiverson, Shelli
Fairport HS
Fairport, NY

Stock, Pamela
Cleveland Hill HS
Cheektowaga, NY

Stockman, Kevin
Queensbury HS
Glens Falls, NY

Stoio, Angela
Whitesboro SR HS
Whitesboro, NY

Stone, Stephen S
Holy Trinity HS
Syosset, NY

Storm, Gretchen
Voorheesville HS
Slingerlands, NY

Stott, Della
New Rockelle HS
New Rochelle, NY

Stovall, III David
Cardinal Spellman
Bronx, NY

Stover, Jr Richard
Amherst Central HS
Amherst, NY

Strachan, Tracy
Far Rockaway HS
Jamaica, NY

Stracher, David
Long Beach HS
Lido Beach, NY

Strahs, Rachel S
Bronx High School
Of Science HS
Flushing, NY

Straight, Darryl
Troy HS
Troy, NY

Strail, Barbara J
Camden Central HS
Camden, NY

Strange, Deborah
Harrison HS
White Plains, NY

Strange, Rodney J
Southside HS
Elmira, NY

Strassburg, II
William L
Tonawanda JR SR
Tonawanda, NY

Stratmann, Jennifer
Avon JR SR HS
Avon, NY

Strauss, Nicholas
Oneida SR HS
Oneida, NY

Streb, Thomas
Avon JR-SR HS
Avon, NY

Streit, Peter N
Pittsford Mendon
Rochester, NY

Strong, Jr William
H
Madison Central HS
Oriskany Falls, NY

Strothman,
Elizabeth
Richmond Hill HS
Richmond Hill, NY

Strowbridge, Laura
Bethpage HS
Plainview, NY

Strozewski, Kristen
M
Nardin Acad
Alden, NY

Struwing, Scott T
Paul V Moore HS
Central Square, NY

Stura, Diane
Rocky Point HS
Long Island, NY

Stuzin, Michelle
Nancy
Bethpage HS
Plainview, NY

Styles, Auria O
Shenendehowa HS
Clifton Park, NY

Suarez, Noreen
St Catherine Acad
Bronx, NY

Suarez, Pedro J
Nazareth Regional
Brooklyn, NY

Suazo, Karen
Cardinal Spellman
Bronx, NY

Sucato, James
Joseph
Our Lady Of
Lourdes HS
Poughkeepsie, NY

Sullivan, Bernadette
Newfield HS
Selden, NY

Sullivan, Colleen
Liverpool HS
Liverpool, NY

Sullivan, Kelly
Bayport-Bluepoint
Bayport, NY

Sullivan, Michael
Bishop Kearney HS
Rochester, NY

Sullivan, Shannon
Stissing Mt JR SR
Red Hook, NY

Summers, Theodore
V
Sutherland HS
Pittsford, NY

Summers, Todd
The Norman
Howard HS
Rochester, NY

Summerville, Darcie
Gray Bodley HS
Fulton, NY

Summit, Joshua
Southampton HS
Water Mill, NY

Supon, Jr Donald
La Salle SR HS
Niagara Falls, NY

Susman, Christine
Liverpool HS
Liverpool, NY

Sutton, Stanley R
Jasper Central Schl
Jasper, NY

Sutton, Susan
Broadalbin HS
Broadalbin, NY

Svarplaitis, Terri
Dover JR SR HS
Wingdale, NY

Sweeney, Joseph C
Monsignor Farrell
Staten Island, NY

Sweeney, William
Amsterdam HS
Hagaman, NY

Swenson, Constance
Longwood HS
Coram, NY

Swetz, Tracy
Aquinas Inst
Rochester, NY

Sybert, Christopher
Victor Central HS
Victor, NY

Sydney, Richard
Victor Central HS
Victor, NY

Symonds, Michelle
Troupsburg Central
Troupsburg, NY

Symonds, Toby
Spackenkill HS
Poughkeepsie, NY

Symula, Derek
Palmyrs-Macedon
Macedon, NY

Syposs, Rachel
Mount Saint Mary
Sanborn, NY

Szabo, Christie L
South Side HS
S Hempstead, NY

Szabo, Gregg
Columbus HS
New York, NY

Szatanek, Jeffery
Liverpool HS
Liverpool, NY

Szatanek, Michelle
Liverpool HS
Liverpool, NY

Szczech, Lynda
Anne Marie
Vestial SR HS
Binghamton, NY

Szeflinski, Stacey
Richfield Spring
Central HS
Richfield Spgs, NY

Tabora, Kathy
Colonie Central HS
Albany, NY

Tackentien, Lori
Ann
Cattaraugus Central
Cattaraugus, NY

Taft, Jeffrey
J C Birdlebough HS
Fulton, NY

Taft, Sherry
Churchville-Chili
Churchville, NY

Tafuri, Lena
Oceanside HS
Oceanside, NY

Tait, Heather
Walton HS
Bronx, NY

Takac, Kristen
Orchard Park HS
Buffalo, NY

Takach, Monica
Maryvale SR HS
Chktg, NY

Takats, Paul
Centereach HS
Centereach, NY

Talamo, Teresa
Lafayette HS
Brooklyn, NY

Tallie, Patrina C
Newburgh Free
Newburgh, NY

Tallman, Michael L
Ithaca HS
Ithaca, NY

Talty, Meg
Mt Mercy Acad
Buffalo, NY

Tamburrino, Frank
Msgr Mc Clancy HS
Astoria, NY

Tanner, Amy
Hudson HS
Hudson, NY

Tannin, Betty Y
Horace Greeley HS
Chappaqua, NY

Tanon, Robert
St Francis
Preparatory HS
Flushing, NY

Tansey, Debbie
Central Islip HS
Central Islip, NY

Tanzi, John A
Kings Park HS
Kings Park, NY

Tarcha, Nicholas A
Johnson City HS
Binghamton, NY

Tardy, Cassandra L
Byron-Bergen
Central Schl
Bergen, NY

Tarre, Shari J
Horace Greeley HS
Chappaqua, NY

Tarsia, Liliana
Central HS
Valley Stream, NY

Tavarez, Noralin
A E Stevenson HS
Bronx, NY

Tavernia, Tammy
Franklin Acad
Malone, NY

Tavlarides,
Mnostula A
Fayetteville-Manlius
Fayetteville, NY

Tavolilla, Carmela
Academy Of The
Tuckahoe, NY

Taylor, Amy
Chenango Valley HS
Binghamton, NY

Taylor, Daryl Ann
Colonie Central HS
Albany, NY

Taylor, Kim
Norman Thomas HS
New York, NY

Taylor, Lynore
N Babylon SR HS
N Babylon, NY

Taylor, Malik E
Rice HS
New York, NY

Taylor, Olivia
August Martin HS
Jamica, NY

Taylor, Shunda M
St Anthonys HS
Deer Park, NY

Teale, Michele
Gloversville HS
Gloversville, NY

Tedesco, Julie
Depew HS
Depew, NY

Tehan, Patricia
Frankfort-Schuyler
Frankfort, NY

Teitelbaum, Jennifer
Island Trees HS
Levittown, NY

Teitter, John E
Saugerties JR SR
Saugerties, NY

Telesca, Pamela
Acad Ressurrection
Rye Brook, NY

Telgheder, David
Minisink Valley HS
Slate Hill, NY

Telgheder, Nancy
Minisink Valley HS
Slate Hill, NY

Temple, Donna
Murray Bergtraum
Bronx, NY

Ten, Aida E
Tottenville HS
Staten Island, NY

Teng, Eric
Herricks SR HS
New Hyde Park, NY

Tenison, Ruth E
Amsterdam HS
Amsterdam, NY

Tenshaw, Linda
Liverpool HS
Liverpool, NY

Tepper, Bonnie E
Sachem North HS
Holbrook, NY

Terrell, Daniel A
The Stony Brook
Smithtown, NY

Territo, William
Frewsburg Central
Frewsburg, NY

Terry, Amy
Westhampton Beach
Westhampton, NY

Terzian, Peter E
Shaker HS
Latham, NY

Tesiero, Kelly
Columbia HS
Rensselaer, NY

Testa, Stephen H
Garden City SR HS
Garden City, NY

Testman, Samantha
Walton HS
Bronx, NY

Texidor, Jose
Walton HS
Bronx, NY

Thai, Senh
New Utrecht HS
Brooklyn, NY

Thakur, Sanjiv K
Dansville SR HS
Dansville, NY

Theodore, Sophia
Potsdam Central HS
Potsdam, NY

Therency, Marie
Magdala
Cathedral HS
Brklyn, NY

Theriault, Brian
Gouverneur HS
Gouverneur, NY

Thero, Daniel P
La Salle Inst
Latham, NY

Thibaut, Michele B
Hilton Central HS
Hilton, NY

Thier, Krista D
Hahn HS
Apo New York, NY

Thomann, David J
Webster HS
Webster, NY

Thomas, John
Yonkers HS
Yonkers, NY

Thomas, John T
Caledonia-Mumford
Central Schl
Caledonia, NY

Thomas, Kathleen
John C Birdlebough
Phoenix, NY

Thomas, Kelly M
Whitesboro SR HS
Utica, NY

Thomas, Leontyne A
Hunter College HS
Laurelton, NY

Thomas, Michael B
Hackley Schl
Yonkers, NY

Thomas, Sarah
Geneva HS
Geneva, NY

Thomas, Sharon
John F Kennedy HS
Utica, NY

Thompson, Anne
Notre Dame Acad
Staten Island, NY

Thompson, Brenda
Far Rockaway HS
Far Rockaway, NY

Thompson,
Christopher Harlow
St Josephs By The
Sea HS
Staten Island, NY

Thompson, Penny
York Central Schl
Leicester, NY

Thompson, Sundae
J
Charlotte JR SR HS
Rochester, NY

Thompson, Teresa
Albion Central HS
Albion, NY

Thorne, Dyon
Christopher
Columbus HS
Bronx, NY

Thornhill, Selena M
Loguardia H S Of
Music & The Arts
Jackson Heights,
NY

Thornton, Jean M
Lakeland SR HS
Putnam Valley, NY

Thurnherr, Michael
West Sensca East
SR HS
Cheektowaga, NY

Tiedemann, Robert
H Frank Carey HS
Franklin Square,
NY

Tiernan, Christin M
Notre Dame Acad
Brooklyn, NY

Tiffany, Teresa
Victor Central Schl
Victor, NY

Tighe, Michael S
Cobleskill Central
Howes Cave, NY

Tilison, Dawn
Scotia-Glenville HS
Scotia, NY

Tirone, Lisa
Cardinal O Hara HS
Tonawanda, NY

Tiso, Marcello
Clarkstown South
Nanuet, NY

Tite, Cynthia L
Tully Central HS
Tully, NY

Titus, Albert H
Sauquoit Valley
Central Schl
Sauquoit, NY

Titus, Dan
Horseheads HS
Horseheads, NY

To, Edward Ha
Brooklyn Technical
Elmhurst, NY

To, Quy
Herbert Holehman
Bronx, NY

Toback, Karen Ellen
Deer Park HS
Deer Park, NY

Tobin, Ellen R
Our Lady Of Mercy
Rochester, NY

Tobin, Erica
Midwood
Hs-Medical Scienc
Brooklyn, NY

Tobin, Kelly
Eldred Central HS
Pond Eddy, NY

Todaro, Phyllis
Letchworth Central
Silver Spgs, NY

Toeller, Susan
East Hampton HS
E Hampton, NY

Tom, Connie
Bayside HS
Bayside, NY

Tomaine, Cathleen
Union Endicott HS
Endicott, NY

Tomanek, Margaret
R
Johnson City HS
Binghamton, NY

Tompkins, Amy
G Ray Bodley HS
Fulton, NY

Tompkins, Christine
L
Cherry Valley
Central Schl
Cherry Valley, NY

Toomin, Amy
Clarkstown H S
New City, NY

Toppin, Stephanie
Liverpool HS
Liverpool, NY

Toppin, Susan
Osterholz American
APO New York, NY

Torizo, Judy Ann
St Edmund HS
Brooklyn, NY

Torre, Donna M
Bishop Kearney HS
Brooklyn, NY

Torres, Alissa
Friedman
The Mary Louis
Flushing, NY

Torres, Angela
Cardinal Spellman
Bronx, NY

Torres, Janet
Hillcrest HS
Jamaica, NY

Toscano, Joseph
Aquinas Instit
Rochester, NY

Toscano, Maria
Narrowsburg
Central HS
Lk Huntington, NY

Tostanoski, Tina M
Corning-Painted
Post West HS
Corning, NY

Tota, Paulette
Mount Saint Mary
Williamsville, NY

Toussaint, Mary
Brooklyn Technical
Brooklyn, NY

Tow, Michael H
Great Neck South
Great Neck, NY

Tracey, Sheila
Arlington HS
Poughkeepsie, NY

Tracy, Robin
Waverly JR-SR HS
Waverly, NY

Tracy, Sandi
Millbrook HS
Millbrook, NY

Trad, Michael
Bishop Ford Central
Catholic HS
Brooklyn, NY

Trainor, Tricia
St John The Baptist
S Hauppauge, NY

Traub, Joanne
West Genesee SR
Syracuse, NY

Traubel, Barbara
Carthage Central
Philadelphia, PA

Traviss, Nora M
Maria Rfegina HS
White Plains, NY

Treanor, William P
Cardinal Spellman
Bronx, NY

Trefzer, Sharon A
St Agnes Academic
Whitestone, NY

Trennert, Jason
Hauppauge HS
Smithtown, NY

Tretola, Michael
James
Bethpage HS
Hicksville, NY

Treubert, Elizabeth
Acad Of Saint
Joseph HS
Centereach, NY

Trezza, Marie Janis
Lindenhurst HS
Lindenhurst, NY

Trichilo, Angelo
Christian Brothers
Albany, NY

Trilly, Jonathan
S H Calhoun HS
Merrick, NY

Trim, Rebecca
Saranacc Lake HS
Saranac Lake, NY

Trimbur, Cynthia
Cicero North
Syracuse HS
East Syracuse, NY

Tripp, Barbara A
Johnson City HS
Johnson City, NY

Trombley, Jr
Arlington J
Franklin Acad
Malone, NY

Trotta, Mark
Port Jervis HS
Port Jervis, NY

Trowbridge, Kristine
G
Pittsford Mendon
Pittsford, NY

Truax, Jackie L
Le Roy Central HS
Le Roy, NY

Trudeaux, Lyle
Union Endicott HS
Endicott, NY

Truex, Shelley
Susquehanna Valley
Binghamton, NY

Truex, Vicki
Susquehanna Valley
Binghamton, NY

Truocchio, Ralph
Longwood HS
Middle Island, NY

Truong, Myphuong
Curtis HS
Staten Island, NY

Tsang, Anna
Midwood HS
Brooklyn, NY

Tsz Mei Cho, Susan
Seward Park HS
New York, NY

Tucker, Josephine
Curtis HS
Staten Island, NY

Tully, Brian Patrick
St Marys Boys High
New Hyde Park, NY

Tully, Tracey
Liverpool HS
Liverpool, NY

Tummiolo, Rosa
Bishop Kearney HS
Brooklyn, NY

Tung, Tsuyoshi M
Edgemont HS
Scarsdale, NY

Turer, Joleen Georgi
New Rochelle HS
New Rochelle, NY

Turker, Bilgin
High School Of
Fashion Ind
Flushing, NY

Turkovich, Michael
R
Archbishop Stepinac
Yonkers, NY

Turnbull, Natalie
Southside HS
South Hempstead,
NY

Turner, Deborah
Martin Luther King
Ny, NY

Turner, Jill E
Madrid Waddington
Waddington, NY

Turner, Stephenie
Auburn HS
Auburn, NY

Turner, Teresa M
John Jay HS
Warrenton, VA

Turpin, Donna
Riverhead HS
Riverhead, NY

Tuttle, Brian D
Waterville Central
Waterville, NY

Tutty, Christopher
Aquinas Inst
Rochester, NY

Tyler, Edward K
Westhill HS
Syracuse, NY

Tyndell, Jennifer
Corning West HS
Beaver Dams, NY

Udle, Kellie
Connetquot HS
Ronkonkoma, NY

Urban, Elizabeth
Holy Trinity
Diosesan HS
Levittown, NY

Urena, Betty
Dominican
Commercial HS
Jamaica, NY

Vaile, Mara
Sachem HS
Holbrook, NY

Valazquez, Monique
T
Hunter College HS
New York, NY

Valceanu, John G
Baldwin SR HS
Baldwin, NY

Valdmanis, Marita
Hastings HS
Hastings-On-Hudsn,
NY

Valerio, Peter
Amsterdam HS
Amsterdam, NY

Vallone, Paul J
Penfield HS
Penfield, NY

Van Aller, Glenn
Middleburgh
Central HS
Middleburgh, NY

Van Brunt, James
Sherburne-Earlville
JR SR HS
Sherburne, NY

Van Dusen, Scott
Romulus Central
Geneva, NY

Van Ord, Amy
Chautauqua Central
Sherman, NY

Van Sickle, Susan
Mynderse Acad
Seneca Falls, NY

Van Winkle, Doris
Altmar-Parish-Willi
amstown HS
Williamstown, NY

Van Woert, James
Scott
Harpursville HS
Harpursville, NY

Van Zandt, Adam F
Seton Catholic
Central HS
Binghamton, NY

Vance, Russell
Longwood HS
Coram, NY

Vanderlinde,
Kristen
Clarkstown South
West Nyack, NY

Vandersteur, Derek
Oakfield Alabama
Central HS
Oakfield, NY

Vanleuven, Anne
Minisink Valley
Central HS
Middletown, NY

Vanvalkenburg, Lisa
Chenango Forks HS
Binghamton, NY

Vanwie, Rebecca
Fonda-Fultonville
Central HS
Fonda, NY

Vargas, Martina
De Witt Clinton HS
Bronx, NY

Vargas, Viviana
Yonkers HS
Yonkers, NY

Varshavchik,
Semyon
Bay Shore HS
Bay Shore, NY

Vasquez, Lissette
Curtis HS
Staten Island, NY

Vasse, Mary B
New Paltz HS
New Paltz, NY

Vazquez, Javier E
John Dewey HS
Brooklyn, NY

Vazquez, Nancy
Norman Thomas HS
Jamaica, NY

Vea, Marie
Notre Dame HS
Horseheads, NY

Veciana, Hiram
Regis HS
New York, NY

Vedder, Michelle
Duanesburg Central
Delanson, NY

Vega, Fernando A
Eastern District HS
Brooklyn, NY

Vela, Enrique
St Francis Prep
Elmhurst, NY

Velasquez, Diana
Adlai E Stevenson
Bronx, NY

Velasquez, Lillian
Franklin Delano
Roosevelt HS
Brooklyn, NY

Velez, Luz
St Pius V HS
Bronx, NY

Venia, Nicholas
James
Pelham Memorial
Pelham Manor, NY

Vennochi, Leslie
New Rochelle HS
New Rochelle, NY

Ventimiglia, Paula
M
Uniondale HS
Uniondale, NY

Ventre, Edna R
Franklin K Lane HS
Glendale, NY

Ventura, Cara Della
Notre Dame Acad
Staten Island, NY

Verbridge, Wendy
Marion JR SR HS
Marion, NY

Verdile, Tina M
Bay Shore HS
Brightwaters, NY

Vereen, Audrey
Lynn
Norman Thomas HS
New York, NY

Verni, Scott A
Mt St Michael Acad
Bronx, NY

Verrico, James A
Amherst Central HS
Amherst, NY

Verrigni, Lori
Guilderland HS
Schenectady, NY

Vescio, Paul A
Nyack SR HS
Valley Cottage, NY

Viceconte, Robert
Central HS
Valley Stream, NY

Vilchez, Caroline
The Mary Louis
Flushing, NY

Villanueva, Richard
J
Tappan Zee HS
Orangeburg, NY

Villareal, Joyce
Christ The King
Reg HS
S Ozone Park, NY

Vinals, Antonio
Garden City SR HS
Garden City, NY

Vincze, Judith M
St Francis Prep
Bayside Hills, NY

Vine, Lisa D
Falconer Central HS
Kennedy, NY

Virga, Michael
Longwood HS
Coram, NY

Virginia, Elizabeth
Notre Dame Acad
Staten Island, NY

Viruet, Sean
Cardinal Hayes HS
Bronx, NY

Vitagliano, Anna
Cardinal Spellman
Bronx, NY

Vitarbo, Gregory M
North Rockland HS
Thiells, NY

Vitere, Cynthia
Lynn
Pelham Memorial
Pelham, NY

Vittorio, Melodie
Liverpool HS
Liverpool, NY

Vladyka, Sharon A
Whitehall Central
Whitehall, NY

Voce, Daniel A
Whitesboro SR HS
Whitesboro, NY

Vogt, Colleen
Eastridge HS
Rochester, NY

Volkert, Carol D
Christian Central
Tonawanda, NY

Vollerthun, Willy T
West Hempstead
West Hempstead,
NY

Vollmer, David L
Watkins Glen HS
Tyrone, NY

Voloshen, Cheryl
Susquehanna Valley
Conklin, NY

Von Ahnen, William
H
Delaware Valley
Central HS
Callicoon, NY

Voorhees, Seth
Cato-Meridian HS
Cato, NY

Vorce, Cynthia
Whitesboro Central
Marcy, NY

Vosburg, III John F
Galamanca HS
Salamanca, NY

Voyias, Lisa
Francis Lewis HS
Flushing, NY

Vrejan, Sandra
Bethpage HS
Plainview, NY

Vunk, Michael P
Patchogue-Medford
Patchogue, NY

Wade, Paul
Mt St Michael Acad
Bronx, NY

Wadkins, Tracey
St1ttgart American
Apo New York, NY

Waechter, Rob
Lakeland HS
Yorktown Hts, NY

Wagar, Murene
Gloversville HS
Gloversville, NY

Wagner, Christine
Auburn HS
Auburn, NY

Wagner, Elizabeth
Cardinal O Hara HS
Tonawanda, NY

Wainio, Lisa
Liverpool HS
Liverpool, NY

Waite, Kathleen
Comsewogue HS
Terryville, NY

Waldbaum, Brian
Ward Melville HS
Centereach, NY

Waldman, David
East Islip HS
Islip Terrace, NY

Waldman, Robert
East Islip SR HS
Islip Terrace, NY

Waldmann, John
Glens Falls HS
Glens Falls, NY

Waldmiller, Brian
Aquinas Inst
Rochester, NY

Walker, Angela
Michelle
Hutchinson-Central
Technical HS
Buffalo, NY

Walker, Anthony B
Cardinal Hayes HS
New York, NY

Walker, Deborah
Westport Central
Westport, NY

Walker, Errica
Mc Kinley HS
Buffalo, NY

Walker, Keith
Archbishop Stepinac
Yonkers, NY

Walker, Marybeth
Ossing HS
Ossining, NY

Walker, William
Amityville Memorial
Amityville, NY

Wall, Stephanie
Bishop Kearney HS
Brooklyn, NY

Wallace, Sandy
G Ray Bodley HS
Fulton, NY

Waller, Brian
Lakeland HS
Yorktown Hts, NY

Walsh, Andrea
John Jay HS
Hpwl Junc, NY

Walsh, Frank T
La Salle Inst
Averill Park, NY

Walsh, John T
Cardinal Spellman
Bronx, NY

Walsh, Kerri A
New Hyde Park
Memorial HS
New Hyde Park, NY

Walsh, Todd E
Berlin American HS
Apo New York, NY

Walters, Amy
Mynderse Acad
Seneca Falls, NY

Walters, Jr Charles A
Rome Catholic HS
Rome, NY

Walther, Evelyn A
Dominican
Commercial HS
Glendale, NY

Walther, Mike
Fairport HS
Fairport, NY

Walton, Adam
Valley Central HS
Walden, NY

Wanek, Sandra M
Oswego HS
Oswego, NY

Wang, Hua
La Guardia H S Of
Music And The Arts
Brooklyn, NY

Wappman, Robert
Frontier Central HS
Hamburg, NY

Ward, Jennifer
Ossining HS
Ossining, NY

Ward, Kris
Canastota HS
Canastota, NY

Ward, Michael
Connetquot HS
Ronkonkoma, NY

Ward, Michael
Liverpool HS
Liverpool, NY

Ward, Teresa
Webster HS
Webster, NY

Wardrop, Matthew
Briarcliff HS
Briarcliff Manor, NY

Warner, Kirstin
Harry S Truman HS
Bronx, NY

Warren, Wilbert R
Hempstead HS
Hempstead, NY

Warrick, Margaret
Forestville Central
Forestville, NY

Warshawsky, Craig
South Shore HS
Brooklyn, NY

Warwick, Colleen
Liverpool HS
Liverpool, NY

Warwick, Michael J
Rome Catholic HS
Rome, NY

Washburn, Heidi
Lakeland HS
Putnam Valley, NY

Washburn, Keith G
Letchworth Central
Castile, NY

Washburn, Tabatha
Letchworth HS
Bliss, NY

Washburn, Timothy A
Cambridge Central
Cambridge, NY

Washburn, Valerie
Berne-Knox-Westerlo HS
Berne, NY

Washington, Stephanie
Queen Of The Rosary Acad
Wyandanch, NY

Wasserman, Robert Joseph
Newfield HS
Coram, NY

Watson, David John
Troy HS
Troy, NY

Watson, Jill
Pulaski JR-SR HS
Pulaski, NY

Watson, Sean
Hoosick Falls Central HS
Hoosick Falls, NY

Waugh, II Charles J
Waterloo SR HS
Waterloo, NY

Wawrzynek, Walter L
Cardinal O Hara HS
N Tonawanda, NY

Waxman, Bari R
Midwood HS
Brooklyn, NY

Weaver, Karl
Marion JR SR HS
Marion, NY

Webber, Christina
Paul V Moore HS
Constantia, NY

Weber, Anne L
Williamsville North
Williamsville, NY

Weber, Charles R
Oneonta HS
Oneonta, NY

Weber, Marianne
Columbia HS
Troy, NY

Webster, Marie L
James I Oneill HS
Highland Falls, NY

Wecker, Nicole R
Canarsie HS
Brooklyn, NY

Weilbacher, Diane
North Babylon SR
Babylon, NY

Weinberg, Jeffrey
Kew-Forest HS
Jamaica, NY

Weinberg, Richard A
Amityville Memorial
Amityville, NY

Weiner, Jay
Susan E Wagner HS
Staten Island, NY

Weinholtz, Beth A
Niagara Wheatfield SR HS
N Tonawanda, NY

Weinick, Robin
John F Kennedy HS
Plainview, NY

Weinmann, Laura
South Kortright Central HS
Hobart, NY

Weinstein, Eric A
Susan E Wagner HS
Staten Island, NY

Weintraub, Jarett
Elmont Memorial
Elmont, NY

Weisensale, Angela
Fillmore Central HS
Portageville, NY

Weiss, David C
Baldwin SR HS
Baldwin, NY

Weissberg, Amy
Long Beach HS
Long Beach, NY

Welch, April
East Aurora HS
E Aurora, NY

Weller, Kenneth
Sherburne-Earlville JR SR HS
Earlville, NY

Wellman, Sandra J
Elmira Free Acad
Elmira, NY

Wells, Collins
Bishop Scully HS
Amsterdam, NY

Wells, Deborah L
Living Word
Manlius, NY

Wells, Donald J
Greenville Central
Greenville, NY

Wells, Gary
Christian Brothers
Minoa, NY

Wells, Jacqueline J
Union Endicott HS
Endicott, NY

Welsh, Kevin
Alexandria Central
Alexandria, NY

Wendel, Amy
Royalton-Hartland Central HS
Lockport, NY

Wentworth, Mary Ann
Gloversville HS
Gloversville, NY

Wenzel, Brian R
Pittsford Mendon
Pittsford, NY

Wenzel, Sheryl
Allegany Central
Allegany, NY

Werts, Melissa
Anthony A
Henninger HS
Syracuse, NY

Wescott, Kathy
Oakfield-Alabama
Central HS
Batavia, NY

West, Joelle I
Campbell Central
Campbell, NY

West, John Todd
Plattsburgh HS
Plattsburgh, NY

Westerling, Stephen
C
Taconic Hills
Central HS
Hudson, NY

Weston, Elgin
Cardinal Hayes HS
New York, NY

Wetzel, Laura A
Smithtown High
Schl West
Smithtown, NY

Weyrauther, Teri
Preston HS
Bronx, NY

Whalen, Andrew F
Pavilion Central
Pavilion, NY

Whalen, Brian R
West Seneca W SR
West Seneca, NY

Wheat, Donna
Washingtonville HS
New Windsor, NY

Wheeler, Cindy
Galway HS
Galway, NY

Wheeler, Loriann
Fairport HS
Fairport, NY

Wheeler, Mary B
St Marys HS
E Aurora, NY

Wheeler, Michael
West Genesee HS
Syracuse, NY

Wheeler, Scott M
Williamsville North
Schenectady, NY

Whelan, Anne-Marie
Scarsdale HS
Scarsdale, NY

Whipple, Diane
Manhasset HS
Manhasset, NY

Whipple, Michele
Canastota HS
Canastota, NY

Whipple, Wendy M
Dryden HS
Harford, NY

White, Barry
Mount Vernon HS
Mount Vernon, NY

White, Dawn M
Liverpool HS
Liverpool, NY

White, Duane
Cardinal Hayes HS
Bronx, NY

White, Everett B
Buffalo Traditional
Buffalo, NY

White, Josyane E
Rhinebeck HS
Clinton Corners, NY

White, Lisa
Christ The King
Regional HS

White, Michelle
Newfane SR HS
Lockport, NY

White, Olivia
Bishop Loughlin M
Brooklyn, NY

White, Rick
East Hampton HS
Montauk, NY

White, Rodney
Seneca Vocatiional
Buffalo, NY

White, Scott G
Xavier HS
Brooklyn, NY

White, Thomas R
Williamson SR HS
Williamson, NY

White, Timothy H
Wellsville HS
Wellsville, NY

White, Todd Everett
Williamsville East
Williamsville, NY

Whiting, Rock S
Odessa Montour
Central HS
Montour Falls, NY

Whiting, William F
Watkins Glen
Central HS
Watkins Glen, NY

Whitney, Lisa M
Chenango Valley HS
Port Crane, NY

Whittaker,
Samantha
Springfield Garden
Springfield, NY

Whittleton, Pam
L A Webber HS
Lyndonvl, NY

Whitton, Michael A
Gouverneur Central
Gouverneur, NY

Wholley, Paul S
Pleasantville HS
Pleasantville, NY

Wiatrowski, Jessica
Alden Central HS
Alden, NY

Wick, Angela
Cicero North
Syracuse HS
Clay, NY

Wick, Lisa A
Columbia HS
East Greenbush, NY

Wiener, Beth L
East Islip HS
East Islip, NY

Wiesmore, Gregory
W
Cheektowaga
Central HS
Cheektowaga, NY

Wiesner, Heather
Susan E Wagner HS
Staten Island, NY

Wiklacz, Colette M
J
John F Kennedy HS
Utica, NY

Wilber, Tanya R
Pinecrest Christian
Salisbury Center,
NY

Wilcove, Jennifer M
Lansingburgh HS
Troy, NY

Wilcox, Matthew E
Corning West HS
Corning, NY

Wilcox, Philip C
Riverhead HS
Riverhead, NY

Wilcox, Sarah
Little Falls JR SR
Little Falls, NY

Wilder, Nancy A
Batavia HS
Batavia, NY

Wildt, Darren John
North Tonawanda
SR HS
N Tonawanda, NY

Wiley, Jr Stanley W
Onondaga Central
Syracuse, NY

Wilk, William A
Notre Dame HS
Whitesboro, NY

Wilkens, Audrey
West Islip HS
West Islip, NY

Wilkie, Geoffrey
Liverpool HS
Liverpool, NY

Wilkinson, Robert E
H Frank Carey HS
Garden City, NY

Willacy, Genene
Brooklyn Technical
Bronx, NY

Williams, Anthony
Portville Central
Olean, NY

Williams, Bernard
Newark Valley HS
Berkshire, NY

Williams, Bonnie
Holland Patent HS
Barneveld, NY

Williams, Constance
Grace Hodley Dodge
V HS
Bronx, NY

Williams, David J
Pine Bush Central
Middletown, NY

Williams, Desiree M
Bronx High Schl Of
Bronx, NY

Williams, Edward A
Cardinal Hayes HS
Brooklyn, NY

Williams, Gwendolyn
William Howard Taft HS
Bronx, NY

Williams, Hugh C
Port Chester HS
Rye Brook, NY

Williams, Jamesine
Susquehanna Valley
Binghamton, NY

Williams, Joseph
Columbia Preparatory Schl
New York, NY

Williams, Lamwell
South Shore HS
Brooklyn, NY

Williams, Rebecca
Marlboro Central
Marlboro, NY

Williams, Ryhaan
Westburg HS
Westbury, NY

Williams, Sean A
Corning East HS
Beaver Dams, NY

Williams, Terri K
Eastern District HS
Brooklyn, NY

Williams, Thomas L
Utica Free Acad
Utica, NY

Williams, Valerie
Riverside HS
Buffalo, NY

Williamson, Douglas S
Lewiston-Porter HS
Lewiston, NY

Williamson, Mia
Dominican Commercial HS
St Albans, NY

Willingham, Peggy
Emma Willard Schl
San Antonio, TX

Willis, Danielle L
Ward Melville HS
Setauket, NY

Willis, Lauri
Lancaster Central
Depew, NY

Willsey, Tina
Cicero-North Syracuse HS
North Syracuse, NY

Wilson, Carol A
Samuel J Tilden HS
Brooklyn, NY

Wilson, Crystal L
Sarah J Hale HS
Brooklyn, NY

Wilson, Debbie Ann
Fiorello H Laguardia HS
Bronx, NY

Wilson, Denise
The Mary Louis
Queens Village, NY

Wilson, Jill
Cardinal Spellman
Bronx, NY

Wilson, Laurie E
Our Lady Of Perpetual Help HS
Brooklyn, NY

Wilson, Patricia L
Corning-Painted Post West HS
Coopers Plains, NY

Wiltsey, Donna
Union Endicott HS
Endicott, NY

Winchell, Nancy Lynn
Hartford Central
Fort Ann, NY

Windsor, Dawn
Pioneer Central HS
Arcade, NY

Wingate, Lisa K
Williamsville North
Williamsville, NY

Wink, Jr Wayne H
Uniondale HS
Uniondale, NY

Winkelman, Elaine
Westfield Acad & Westfield, NY

Winkelman, Jennifer
Westfield Academy & Central Schl
Westfield, NY

Winkley, Beth
Mount Mercy Acad
East Aurora, NY

Winnert, Laurie
Lancaster SR HS
Depew, NY

Winslow, Maryellen
Our Lady Of Mercy
N Babylon, NY

Winters, Barbara Ann
St John The Baptist
West Islip, NY

Winward, Thomas
Rye Neck HS
Mamaroneck, NY

Wischhusen, Doreen
Northport HS
Northport, NY

Wishnie, Beth
Ossining HS
Briarcliff, NY

Wisniewski, Robert
Niagara Wheatfield SR HS
Niagara Falls, NY

Wisnock, Michael D
Newfane SR HS
Newfane, NY

Withers, Brian D
Somers HS
Somers, NY

Witkowski, Christine
Port Jervis HS
Sparrowbush, NY

Wittek, Orie Marie
Loyola Schl
New York, NY

Witz, John
Cicero-North Syracuse HS
Clay, NY

Wojack, John A
Hilton Central HS
Hilton, NY

Wojick, Matthew
St Josephs Collegiate Inst
Niagara Falls, NY

Wolfe, Elizabeth J
Dundee Central HS
Dundee, NY

Wolff, Deborah
Liverpool HS
Liverpool, NY

Wolk, Robert I
Horace Mann HS
New York, NY

Wolland, Jennifer
Westhampton Beach
Westhampton Bch, NY

Wolniewicz, Scott
Akron Central Schl
Akron, NY

Wolpert, Mark R
Bay Shore HS
Brightwaters, NY

Wong, Denie
Horseheads HS
Horseheads, NY

Wong, Mei W
Newtown HS
Woodside, NY

Wong, Penny
Cathedral HS
Lic, NY

Wong, Peter
August Martin HS
Brooklyn, NY

Wood, Bonnie
Granville Central
Pawlet, VT

Wood, Kevin
Northville Central
Mayfield, NY

Woodard, Danny
Alden Central HS
Alden, NY

Woodard, Sandra
South Park HS
Buffalo, NY

Woods, Christopher E
Beach Channel HS
Far Rockaway, NY

Woods, Debra
Union Endicott HS
Endicott, NY

Woods, Thomas W
Newburgh Free
Newburgh, NY

Woodside, Robert C
Cathedral Prep
New York, NY

Woodward, Raymond
Linton HS
Schenectady, NY

Woren, Michael Adam
Lincoln HS
Yonkers, NY

Worrall, Julian
Kenmore East SR
Tonawanda, NY

Worrell, Christine A
Midwood HS
Brooklyn, NY

Worrell, Lisa
Sheepshead Bay HS
Brooklyn, NY

Worth, Steven W
Catskill HS
Leeds, NY

Worth, Walter
Crown Point Central
Crown Pt, NY

Wray, David
Thomas Edison HS
Laurelton, NY

Wright, Eric
Onteora HS
West Hurley, NY

Wright, Eugenia
Maria
North Babylon SR
North Babylon, NY

Wright, Sharon
Orcadia HS
Rochester, NY

Wright, Tara-Anne
Bishop Kearney HS
Brooklyn, NY

Wu, Nancy M
Port Richmond HS
Staten Island, NY

Wyllie, Aaron T
Nazareth Regional
Brooklyn, NY

Wynne, Michael J
Marcellus Central
Marcellus, NY

Wyszkowski, Joy
Tonawanda SR HS
Tonawanda, NY

Yacoub, John P
Archbishop Stepinac
White Plains, NY

Yamaji, Alan
Westbury SR HS
Westbury, NY

Yang, Seung Pil
Phillip
Bronx High School
Of Schienc
Flushing, NY

Yannone, Suzanne
Pierson HS
Sag Harbor, NY

Yanow, Michele B
Alfred G Berner HS
Massapequa Park,
NY

Yardley, Craig
East Hampton HS
Amagansett, NY

Yates, Amy M
East Hampton HS
East Hampton, NY

Yates, David
Anteora HS
Shokan, NY

Yattaw, James
Waterford-Halfmoon
Waterford, NY

Yau, Po Lai
Fort Hamilton HS
Brooklyn, NY

Yaw, Tammy
Ticonderoga HS
Hague, NY

Yearwood, Denise
Evandet Childs HS
Bronx, NY

Yee, Elisa
Performing Arts HS
New York, NY

Yellen, Laura
Garden City HS
Garden City, NY

Yeman, Joy
Oneida HS
Oneida, NY

Yencer, James
Perry Central HS
Perry, NY

Yennella, Michele
Curtis HS
Staten Island, NY

Yermak, Yelena
James Madison HS
Brooklyn, NY

Yom, Uoong Hyun
Flushing HS
Flushing, NY

York, Kimberly S
North Rose-Wolcott
Wolcott, NY

Young, Amy M
Cardinal Mooney
Rochester, NY

Young, Eliza A
La Guardia HS
New York, NY

Young, Henrietta
Wyandanch
Memorial HS
Wyandanch, NY

Young, Matthew G
Hamburg SR HS
Hamburg, NY

Young, Michael
Trinity-Pawling HS
Bronx, NY

Young, Thomas
Christian Brothers
Liverpool, NY

Youngs, Dawn
Valley Central HS
Montgomery, NY

Yovino, Jeanine
Hauppauge HS
Hauppauge, NY

Yu, Jan H
John F Kennedy HS
New York, NY

Yu, Randolph
Shenendehowa HS
Clifton Park, NY

Yuan, Erhmei
Commack H S
Commack, NY

Zachariadis, Cally
Bronx High School
Of Science
Astoria, NY

Zack, Donna
Queensbury HS
Glens Falls, NY

Zagajeski, II Thomas
A
Hicksville SR HS
Hicksville, NY

Zagara, Wendy
Maryvale HS
Chktg, NY

Zaki, Chahinaz
Forest Hills HS
Forest Hills, NY

Zalat, Mark
Churchville-Chili
Rochester, NY

Zalesak, Marianne G
St Joseph Hill Acad
Staten Island, NY

Zalewski,
Elizabethann M
Kenmore West SR
Tonawanda, NY

Zamites, Carollynn
Our Lady Of Mercy
Rochester, NY

Zammiello, Louie
John F Kennedy HS
Utica, NY

Zanchelli, Michael T
Clarkstown South
Bardonia, NY

Zapata, Laurel
St Raymond Acad
Bronx, NY

Zappala, Rosanna
Bishop Grimes HS
N Syracuse, NY

Zasada, John R
Chittenango Central
Bridgeport, NY

Zayac, Kelly
Binghamton HS
Binghamton, NY

Zayas, Katherine
Msgr Scanlan HS
Bronx, NY

Zdunczyk, Cheryl M
Columbia HS
Castleton, NY

Zeiler, Karen J
Mahopac HS
Mahopac, NY

Zeller, Cynthia M
Vernon-Verona-Sher
rill Central HS
Verona, NY

Zeller, Robert
Augsburgh American
A P O New York,
NY

Zello, Gary
Waverly JR SR HS
Waverly, NY

Zemanek, Laura
Johnstown HS
Johnstown, NY

Zervopoulos,
Alexandra
Nazareth Regional
Brooklyn, NY

Zgaljic, Milica
Long Island City HS
Astoria, NY

Zhao, Hong Leung
Newtown HS
Flushing, NY

Ziff, Lori
Oyster Bay HS
Oyster Bay, NY

Zimmer, Kenneth J
Amherst Central HS
Amherst, NY

Zimmerman, Cory
The Bronx High
School Of Science
Floral Park, NY

Zinserling, Craig
Liverpool HS
Liverpool, NY

Zipnick, Deborah
Newfield HS
Selden, NY

Zipprich, Diane M
Arlington HS
Hopewell Junction, NY

Zisholtz, Ian
Long Beach HS
Long Beach, NY

Zivancev, Melanie Christopher
Columbus HS
Brooklyn, NY

Zobrist, Tammy Lynn
Kensington HS
Buffalo, NY

Zodikoff, Michele A
Homer Central HS
Homer, NY

Zook, John M
Corning-Painted Post West HS
Painted Post, NY

Zoota, Herb
Commack High Schl
Commack, NY

Zou, Jennifer Qing
Fort Hamilton HS
Brooklyn, NY

Zuber, Christina
Farmingdale HS
Massapequa Park, NY

Zurlo, Jeffrey
Glen Falls HS
Glen Falls, NY

Zybert, Stacey L
Springville-Griffith
Colden, NY

Zydel, Jennifer
Bishop Kearney HS
Rochester, NY

PUERTO RICO

Alfonso, Edwin
San Antonio HS
Quebradillas, PR

Ali, Alexis R
Colegio San Antonio
Toa Baja, PR

Alvarez, Dorothy
Colegio Ponceno HS
Ponce, PR

Arroyo, Lourdes Lopez
Jose De Diego HS
Aguadilla, PR

Ayoroa, Lena
Colegio Ponceno HS
Ponce, PR

Barea, Julio
Caribbean Schl
Ponce, PR

Barreto, Kenneth
Colegio San Ignacio
Rio Piedras, PR

Benitez, Carlos H
Colegio Marista HS
Guaynabo, PR

Buitrago, Vivian Marie
Manuela Toro HS
Caguas, PR

Calderon, Manuel
Colegio Marista HS
Guaynabo, PR

Calero, Calixto Javier
Colegio San Antonio
Isabela, PR

Calzada, Ramon L
Academia Sagrado Corazon HS
Bayamon, PR

Capo, Rafael
Colegio Ponceno HS
Ponce, PR

Cintron, Ariel
Colegio Ponceno Inc
Ponce, PR

Collazo, Agnes
Colegio Ponceno HS
Ponce, PR

Collazo, Rebecca
Colegio Ponceno HS
Ponce, PR

Collazo, Sandra
Colegio Ponceno HS
Ponce, PR

Colon, Lucia M
Colegio Ponceno HS
Ponce, PR

Colon-Pomales, Kim
Colegio Nuestra Senora Del Pila
Guaynabo, PR

Concepcion, Glorimar
Colegio San Antonio
Hato Rey, PR

Cucurella, Lucy J
Jose Gautier Benitez
Caguas, PR

Dante, Maria M
Wesleyan Acad
Rio Piedras, PR

Del Rosario, Ruben
Colegio Ponceno HS
Ponce, PR

Del Valle, Irma M
Colegio Ponceno HS
Ponce, PR

Diaz, Susan T
Jose Gauthier Benitez HS
Caguas, PR

Duffer, Martha
Wesleyan Acad
Guaynabo, PR

Fernandez, Maria E
Colegio Ponceno HS
Ponce, PR

Figueroa, George Alexander
Bellas Artes Central
Carolina, PR

Fischbach, Kevin
Southwestern Educational Soc HS
Mayaguez, PR

Garcia, Hector
Colegio Ponceno HS
Ponce, PR

Giamellaro, David P
Antilles HS
Rio Hondo, PR

Gonzalez, Francisco
Colegio San Ignacio De Loyola HS
San Juan, PR

Gonzalez, Marelisa
Col Utra Sra Del Pilar HS
Rio Piedras, PR

Gonzalez Rivera, Henry
Colegio Santa Rita
Dorado, PR

Hayes, Nora Christine
San Antonio HS
Rio Piedras, PR

Hernandez, Adolfo M
Colegio Ponceno HS
Ponce, PR

Hernandez, Patricia
Academia San Jorge
San Juan, PR

Irizarry Rosario, Myra
Dr Sarltiago Veve Calzada HS
Fajardo, PR

Isern, Sharon
Antilles HS
Dorado, PR

Jimenez, Walter A
Jose Gautier Benitez
Caguas, PR

Johnson, Kirk
Colegio San Ignacio E Loyola HS
Guaynabo, PR

Laborda, Annette M
Colegio Madre Cabrini HS
San Juan, PR

Laborde, Maria J
Academia San Jose
Guaynabo, PR

Lago, Lorraine
Carribean Schl
Ponce, PR

Larson, Christina
Robinson Schl
Rio Piedras, PR

Llivina, Elena
Academia Maria Reina HS
Levittown, PR

Lopez, Lesby W
Eloiza Paseual HS
Cagaas, PR

Lopez, Maricarmen
Clegio San Antonio
Rio Piedras, PR

Lugo, Liza
Academia Sagrado Corazon HS
Isla Verde, PR

Lynch, Pamela
St Croix Seventh-Day Advent
Mattapan, MA

Martinez, Edith
Colegio Ponceno HS
Ponce, PR

Martinez-Soto, Jorge Antonio
Colegie San Antonio
San Juan, PR

Matos, Brenda E
Colegio San Antonio
Rio Piedras, PR

Maymi, Fernando
Santa Monica Acad
Santurce, PR

Medina, Betsy-Ann
Colegio San Antonio
Ramey, PR

Melendez, Peter A
Colegio San Antonio
Isabela, PR

Miclau, Michael
Robinson Schl
Punta Las Marias, PR

Monsanto, Vivian
Colegio Ponceno HS
Ponce, PR

Montaner, Luis Javier
Colegio San Ignacio
Santurce, PR

Monteverde, Dinabel
Eugenio M De Hostos HS
Bronx, NY

Morales, Lina
Colegio Ponceno HS
Ponce, PR

Negron, Diana
Baldwin Schl
Guaynabo, PR

Nemes, Susanne
Caribbean Schl
Ponce, PR

Ojeda, Dawn
Caribbean Schl
Ponce, PR

Ortiz-Blanes, Mariana
Saint Johns Schl
Guaynabo, PR

Pagan-Echevarria, Neftali
Colegio Ponceno HS
Guayanilla, PR

Pauneto Tirado, Madeline
Manuela Toro Morice HS
Caguas, PR

Pereyo, Neville G
Colegio Ponceno HS
Ponce, PR

Perez, Maria Isabel
Caribbean Schl
Ponce, PR

Perez Oyola, Johana
Manuela Toro Morice HS
Caguas, PR

Prosser, Jeffrey Scott
Baldwin Schl
Yabucoa, PR

Quiles, Zulma Vanessa
Elasa Pascual Bairoa III HS
Caguas, PR

Quinones, Rosselyn
Colegio Ponceno Inc
Ponce, PR

Quiros, Marvin Samuel
University HS
Rio Piedras, PR

Rafols, III Edwin
Colegio San Antonio
Isabela, PR

Ramirez, Nectar
Colegio San Antonio
Rio Piedras, PR

Ramos Rodriguez, Calix
Colegio Santa Rita
Bayamon, PR

Rampolla, Pedro
Colegio San Ignacio De Loyola HS
Guaynabo, PR

Rivera, Gregory
Menonita Acad
Bayamon, PR

Rivera, Milton A
Immaculate Conception Acad
Mayaguez, PR

Rivera, Nuria
Robinson HS
Bayamon, PR

Rivera Millan, Agalee T
Colegio San Antonio
Rio Piedras, PR

Robert, Lisa
Cupeyville Schl
Rio Piedras, PR

Romaguera, Rita
Immaculate Conception Acad
Mayaguez, PR

Roman, Antonio
Colegio Ponceno HS
Ponce, PR

Roman, Lourdes
Colegio Ponceno HS
Ponce, PR

Rosa, Angeles
Rio Piedras Heights
Rio Piedras, PR

Rossello, Adolfo
Colegio Ponceno HS
Ponce, PR

Ruiz, Carmen M
Colegio San Antonio De Isabela HS
Quebradillas, PR

Ruiz, Maritza
Colegio San Antonio
Isabela, PR

Sanabria Carlo, David
Colegio Santa Rita
Bayamon, PR

Sanchez, Federico
Colegio San Ignacio
Rio Piedras, PR

Semidey, Juan Pablo
Colegio San Ignacio De Loyola HS
Guaynabo, PR

Serrano, Edgardo Morales
Madre Cabrini HS
Guaynabo, PR

Smith, Chad
Cupeyville Schl
Caguas, PR

Sostre Bou, Hector
Colegio Sata Rita
Bayamon, PR

Sued, Nadya Eliza
Notre Dame HS
Cayey, PR

Terrassa, Luis
Colegio Marista HS
Guaynabo, PR

Torrech, Shelma
Colegio Santa Rosa
Levittown, PR

Torres, Edwin
Colegio Madre Cabrini HS
Rio Piedras, PR

Torres Ferrer, Jesus R
Col San Ignacio De Loyola HS
Rio Piedras, PR

Valentin Velez, Wanda I
Jose De Diego HS
Aguadilla, PR

Varela Rios, Hector M
Colegio San Ignacio
San Juan, PR

Vargas, Olga M
Notre Dame HS
Caguas, PR

Vaswani, Rosemary
Episcopal Cathedral
Santurce, PR

Vazquez, Mary A
Madre Cabrini HS
Caparra Heights, PR

Vega Batista, Fernando
Colegio Santa Rita
Bayamon, PR

Velez, Francisco
Colegio San Antonio
Isabela, PR

Vilella, Cristina
Antilles HS
Rio Piedras, PR

Wright, James
Baldwin School Of Puerto Rico
Yabucoa, PR

RHODE ISLAND

Albanese, Gregory
Classical HS
Providence, RI

Allen, Scott
Pilgrim HS
Warwick, RI

Almeida, Paul
Birstol HS
Bristol, RI

Areia, Paula
Our Lady Of Fatima
Bristol, RI

Babcock, Kathi
Coventry HS
Coventry, RI

Balling, Emily
Portsmouth HS
Fort Douglas, UT

Baril, Elizabeth
West Warwick SR
W Warwick, RI

Barnes, Eric W
Cranston East HS
Cranston, RI

Bedard, Richard
Burrillville HS
Mapleville, RI

Bell, Kerri
Lincoln JR HS
Lincoln, RI

Belmore, Renee
Bristol HS
Bristol, RI

Blackson, Tanya P
Rogers HS
Newport, RI

Boffi, Angela
Prout Memorial HS
Warwick, RI

Bonin, Ronald Lucien
Woonsocket HS
Woonsocket, RI

Bossdorf, Tracey
Pilgrim HS
Warwick, RI

Boudreau, Kelly
West Warwick HS
W Warwick, RI

Boumenot, Michael S
Chariho Regional JR SR HS
Ashaway, RI

Bouvier, Donna
Burrillville JR SR
Woonsocket, RI

Bowers, Darci
Tiverton HS
Tiverton, RI

Brierley, David Ryan
North Smithfield JR SR HS
Woonsocket, RI

Briggs, Elizabeth
Mt St Charles HS
Smithfield, RI

Brouillette, Michele
Prout Memorial HS
Coventry, RI

Brown, Mark S
La Salle Acad
Coventry, RI

Brown, Terriann
Toll Gate HS
Warwick, RI

Bucci, Cynthia D
Johnston SR HS
Johnston, RI

Bucci, Judi
Tollgate HS
Warwick, RI

Burke, Lisa
Rogers HS
Newport, RI

Carpenter, Jr Kenneth
Pilgrim HS
Warwick, RI

Carr, Courtney
Rogers HS
Newport, RI

Caruso, Joanne
Toll Gate HS
Warwick, RI

Cascalheira, Rosa
Tolman HS
Pawtucket, RI

Castriotta, Gina
Smithfield HS
Smithfield, RI

Cavalieri, Trisha
Our Lady Of Fatima
Bristol, RI

Cesana, Jr Dennis M
Mount Saint Charles
N Providence, RI

Charron, Christine
Smithfield HS
Greenville, RI

Chartrand, Bob
Woonsocket HS
Woonsocket, RI

Chlebek, Dawn Marie
Central Falls JR SR
Central Falls, RI

Christy, Tina
Warwick Veterans Memorial HS
Warwick, RI

Cifelli, Cynthia S
Warwick Veterans Memorial HS
Warwick, RI

Coleman, Lisa L
Chassicah HS
Providence, RI

Collins, Sharon
Warwick Veterans Memorial HS
Warwick, RI

Conlon, Leslie
St Marys Acad
Warwick, RI

Cordeiro, Anthony
Bristol HS
Bristol, RI

Corp, Kim J
Coventry HS
Coventry, RI

Corrigan, Francis V
East Providence HS
East Providence, RI

Costa, Robert
Warren HS
Warren, RI

Creswick, Bethany
Warwick Veterans Memorial HS
Warwick, RI

Crisafulli, Marc
Mount St Charles
Pawtucket, RI

Cure, Martin
St Raphael Acad
Cent Falls, RI

Curran, Janice
North Smithfield JR SR HS
North Smithfield, RI

D Abate, Kevin
Classical HS
Providence, RI

Daly, Kathryn
Prout Memorial HS
Kingston, RI

Dandeneau, Christopher
North Providence
N Providence, RI

Darveau, Diane
Woonsocket HS
Woonsocket, RI

Davis, Pam
North Kingstown
N Kingstown, RI

De Andrade, Alyssa Beth
Lincoln HS
Lincoln, RI

De Matos, Diane
Our Lady Of Fatima
Bristol, RI

De Spirito, III Antonio
Barrington HS
Barrington, RI

Delgado, John Joseph
Hope HS
Providence, RI

Dennen, Pamela
Warwick Veterans Memorial HS
Providence, RI

Dethorn, John R
Rogers HS
Newport, RI

Dick, Marissa
Warwick Veterans Memorial HS
Warwick, RI

Ditusa, Lisa
Coventry HS
Coventry, RI

Do Couto, Kathleen
Tiverton HS
Tiverton, RI

Donnelly, Michelle Christine
Portsmouth HS
Portsmouth, RI

Dwyer, Timothy
St Raphael Acad
Pawtucket, RI

Eagan, III Owen L
Tiverton HS
Tiverton, RI

Fagundes, Julie
East Providence SR
East Providence, RI

Fecteau, Sean P
La Salle Acad
Seekonk, MA

Fecteau, Jr Thomas B
La Salle Acad
Seekonk, MA

Finley, Kathleen Ann
E Greenwich HS
E Greenwich, RI

Fitzgerald, Garrett S
Classical HS
Providence, RI

Fleming, Michael
Rogers HS
Newport, RI

Flood, Karen L
Tolman HS
Pawtucket, RI

Fortier, Geo
North Smithfield SR HS
Woonsocket, RI

Frisella, Mary E
South Kingstown
Wakefield, RI

Gaddes, Gail
Scituate JR SR HS
N Scituate, RI

Gagnon, Claudine
Warwick Veterans Memorial HS
Warwick, RI

Garza, Tracy Ann
Mount Pleasant HS
Providence, RI

Gasparian, Sonya
Cranston East HS
Johnston, RI

Gaulin, Jacqueline A
Cranston HS East
Cranston, RI

Geer, Gregory
Middletown HS
Middletown, RI

Gennari, Karen
East Providence HS
E Providence, RI

Gillis, Gregory
Central Falls JR SR
Central Falls, RI

Gleason, Deborah
Prout Memorial HS
North Kingstown, RI

Goldberg, Brian
Warren HS
Warren, RI

Gorman, Joseph
Central HS
Providence, RI

Gray, Karen
South Kingston HS
West Kingston, RI

Gray, Nicola
Mount St Charles
Millville, MA

Hague, Lisa
Cranston West HS
Cranston, RI

Higginbotham, Julie
Prout Memorial HS
Jamestown, RI

Johnson, Diane K
Pilgrim HS
Warwick, RI

Johnson, Kimberly K
Community Christian Schl
Pascoag, RI

Johnson, Ronald E
Coventry HS
Coventry, RI

Jones, Christine
Johnston SR HS
Johnston, RI

Jordan, Tracy
Warwick Veterans Memorial HS
Warwick, RI

Jutras, Thomas
Smithfield HS
Smithfield, RI

Kennedy, Susan J
East Providence SR
East Providence, RI

Kobrin, Janet S
Lincoln Schl
Providence, RI

Korzeniowski, Kelly A
Prout Memorial HS
Cranston, RI

Lambert, Kerri
Warren HS
Warren, RI

Langanke, Steven W
Chariho Regional
Ashaway, RI

Lauria, David J
Barrington HS
Barrington, RI

Lawson, Erica
South Kingstown
Kingston, RI

Leavene, Elizabeth
North Kingstown
N Kingstown, RI

Leighton, Michael
Warwick Veterans Memorial HS
Warwick, RI

Lepore, Gary
Barrington HS
Barrington, RI

Lewis, Elizabeth Betsy
North Kingstown
N Kingstown, RI

Lima, Cheryl
West Warwick HS
W Warwick, RI

Lima, Elizabeth
Middletown HS
Middletown, RI

Llamas, Cristina
Lincoln Schl
Manville, RI

Lombardi, Jr Anthony J
Lasalle Acad
North Providence, RI

Lombardi, Stephanie
Mount St Charles
N Smithfield, RI

Long, Matthew W
Saint Raphael Acad
Barrington, RI

Low, Jennifer
Prout Memorial HS
N Kingstown, RI

Lucas, Albert E
St Georges Schl
Queens Village, NY

Malo, Ann
Lincoln JR SR HS
Lincoln, RI

Martino, Gina M
Tolman SR HS
Pawtucket, RI

Martufi, Jr Robert A
Mount St Charles
Johnston, RI

Matais, Marie T
Rogers HS
Newport, RI

Mc Kenney, Kim C
East Greenwich HS
E Greenwich, RI

Mc Loughlin, Mary E
Prout Memorial HS
Peacedale, RI

Mc Loughlin, Tara
Prout Memorial HS
Peace Dale, RI

Meagher, Thomas
Our Lady Of Providence Pre
Providence, RI

Mellott, Jr Jack
North Kingstown
N Kingstown, RI

Melone, Melanie
St Marys Bayview
Johnston, RI

Mignanelli, Robert A
Narragansett HS
Narragansett, RI

Molloy, Suzanne
Mount St Charles
Bellingham, MA

Morris, Maureen A
St Mary Acad
Swansea, MA

Moss, Jacquelyn K
West Warwick SR
W Warwick, RI

Motta, John
Bristol HS
Bristol, RI

Motta, III Joseph
Bristol HS
Bristol, RI

Murphy, Monica
Classical HS
Providence, RI

Murray, Sandra A
Coventry HS
Coventry, RI

Nadeau, Scott R
Cumberland HS
Cumberland, RI

Nicholas, Kathleen
Pilgrim HS
Warwick, RI

Noble, Sarah
Lincoln JR SR HS
Lincoln, RI

Noon, Amy
Warwick Veterans Memorial HS
Warwick, RI

Norato, Nancy
Cranston H S West
Cranston, RI

Noreau, Jennifer
Johnston HS
Johnston, RI

Normandin, Richard
Woonsocket HS
Woonsocket, RI

Nutc, Christopher
Rogers HS
Fairfax, VA

O Leary, Joanne P
Classical HS
Providence, RI

O Shea, Caroline
Middletown HS
Middletown, RI

Palardy, Leah
Tollgate HS
Warwick, RI

Paliotto, Theresa
Pilgrim HS
Warwick, RI

Patterson, Karen A
Tiverton HS
Tiverton, RI

Peareara, Joann
Classical HS
Providence, RI

Penza, Lorraine M
Mount St Charles
Johnston, RI

Perkins, Debi
Portsmouth HS
Portsmouth, RI

Perry, James M
Coventry HS
Coventry, RI

Perry, Stephanie Ann
Coventry HS
Coventry, RI

Petrone, Melissa A
Warwick Vetrans Memorial HS
Warwick, RI

Pettit, Karen
Middletown HS
Middletown, RI

Phillips, Stephanie
Woonsocket SR HS
Woonsokcet, RI

Pimental, Michael
Coventry SR HS
Coventry, RI

Plante, Richard
William M Daries Jr
Pawtucket, RI

Pona, Kimberly R
Classical HS
Providence, RI

Punska, Carrie
Chariho Regional
Hope Valley, RI

Quintero, Jose
Lincoln JR HS
Lincoln, RI

Reed, Leslie A
East Providence SR
Riverside, RI

Reilly, Eryn
Charles E Shea HS
Pawtucket, RI

Reilly, Mary E
Prout Memorial HS
North Kingstown, RI

Rensehausen, Warren
Bristol HS
Bristol, RI

Ricci, Rhonda
Cranston H S West
Cranston, RI

Robinson, Kyle
Rogers HS
Newport, RI

Royal, Matthew E
Scituate JR SR HS
N Scituate, RI

Ruggiero, Richard
Johnston HS
Johnston, RI

Sammons, Deanna
Rogers HS
Newport, RI

Sands, Richard
Warwick Veterns Memorial HS
Warwick, RI

Sayles, Kristen
North Smithfield JR SR HS
North Smithfield, RI

Schmidig, Brian
Charles E Shea HS
East Rutherford, NJ

Schneider, Eleonore E
South Kingstown
W Kingston, RI

Scott, Paul
Charles A Shea SR
Pawtucket, RI

Scotto, Dina
Johnston SR HS
Johnston, RI

Searle, Tammy Lynne
East Providence SR
E Providence, RI

Sears, Lori
Portsmouth HS
Portsmouth, RI

Sears, Mark
Benedict Patrick
Lincoln HS
Lincoln, RI

Sechio, Dina
North Providence
N Providence, RI

Seeru, Karen
Chariho Regional
Woodriver, RI

Shoot, Jerilyn A
Pilgrim HS
Warwick, RI

Slattery, Stephen
Lincoln HS
Lincoln, RI

Smith, Eric
South Kingstown
Peace Dale, RI

Spinella, Elizabeth
Mount Saint Charles
Woonsocket, RI

Squizzero, Linda
Cranston HS West
Cranston, RI

Studley, Kathleen Ann
East Providence SR
E Providence, RI

Tardie, Michelle
Tiverton HS
Tiverton, RI

Tardif, Peter
Woonsocket SR HS
Woonsocket, RI

Tate, Alison A
North Providence
North Providence, RI

Tavares, Eunice B
Charles E Shea SR
Pawtucket, RI

Tavernese, Yvette
Middletown HS
Middletown, RI

Tierney, Julie
St Marys Academy-Bay View
East Providence, RI

Toole, Jane
Lincoln JR/SR HS
Lincoln, RI

Toole, Michael
La Salle Acad
Seekonk, MA

Troia, Julie
Cranston H S West
Cranston, RI

Troia, Lisa
Crantson High School West
Cranston, RI

Turpin, Karen
Prout Memorial HS
North Kingstown, RI

Udvardy, Aaron
Bristol HS
Bristol, RI

Vitullo, Sheri
Our Lady Of Fatima
Warren, RI

Viveiros, Sherri
Tiverton HS
Tiverton, RI

Vogel, Patricia
St Mary Acad
Hope, RI

Wallace, Kimberly
Barrington HS
Barrington, RI

Walsh, Stephonie Anne
Portsmouth HS
Portsmouth, RI

Wardlow, David
Rogers HS
Newport, RI

Warrener, Brian
Johnston SR HS
Johnston, RI

Webber, Renee
Portsmouth HS
Portsmouth, RI

White, Jeanne
Warwick Veterans Memorial HS
Warwick, RI

Wilbur, Kyle
Bristol HS
Bristol, RI

Wright, Sheri
Prout Memorial HS
E Greenwich, RI

Young, Tracy
Charino Regional
W Kingston, RI

Zanni, Julie
St Mary Acad-Bay
Johnston, RI

Zienowicz, David
Bishop Hendricken
Cranston, RI

Zuleta, Cesar A
Central Falls JR HS
Central Fls, RI

VERMONT

Abatiell, Audra
Mt St Joseph Acad
Rutland, VT

Adolfsson, Tina
Mount Saint Joseph
Pittsford, VT

Alexander, Jo
Richford HS
Enosburg Falls, VT

Allard, Brian
Burlington HS
Burlington, VT

Alvarez, Natalie E
Harwood Union HS
Waterbury, VT

Ameden, Lisa Marie
Leland And Gray Union HS
Jamaica, VT

Arbuckle, Jennifer R
Bellows Falls Union
Bellows Falls, VT

Barbour, Timothy
Windsor HS
Hartland, VT

Bean, Anthony
Burlington HS
Burlington, VT

Blanchard, Michael
Canaan Memorial
Canaan, VT

Bliss, Kristen
U-32 HS
Barre, VT

Blumen, Debra
Champlain Valley
Union HS
Shelburne, VT

Bort, Susan
Burr & Burton
Arlington, VT

Bovia, Karyn A
Essex Jct HS
Essex Jct, VT

Braman, Lance O
St Johnsbury Acad
St Johnsbury, VT

Bressette,
Christopher W
Bellows Free Acad
St Albans, VT

Briere, Alana M
Fair Haven Union
Castleton, VT

Brophy, Julie
Burr & Burton
E Dorset, VT

Busden, Scott
Leland And Gay
Union HS
Newfane, VT

Bush, Michele
Leland And Gray
Union HS
Newfane, VT

Carpenter, Kevin
Websterville Baptist
Christian Schl
Websterville, VT

Casagrande, Robyn
Otter Valley Union
Pittsford, VT

Cecot, Jill
Otter Valley Union
Brandon, VT

Charron, Joy
Spaulding HS
Barre, VT

Cote, Danielle
North County Union
Beebe Plain, VT

Coyne, Allison J
Colchester HS
Colchester, VT

Czaplinski, Anne
Montpelier HS
Montpelier, VT

Davidson, Marjorie
Windsor HS
Windsor, VT

Davis, Carmella J
Randolph Union HS
Randolph, VT

Davis, Deanne
Lake Region Union
Barton, VT

Davis, Parker
Arnold
Burr & Burton
Seminary HS
Manchester, VT

Derby, Rich
Colchester HS
Colchester, VT

Dike, Tracy
Vergennes Union
N Ferrisburg, VT

Douglas, Kimberly
Burlington HS
Burlington, VT

Eardensohn, Kris
Montpelier HS
Montpelier, VT

Ellig, Eileen
Rutland HS
Rutland, VT

Ertle, Steve
Oxbow HS
Newbury, VT

Evans, Missy
Burr & Burton
Manchester, VT

Garrow, Leslie
Richford JR SR HS
Enosburg Falls, VT

Gawrys, Brenda
Mill River Union
Clarendon, VT

Gilarde, Terri Ann
Mount Anthony
Union HS
Bennington, VT

Gilbert, Cheryl
Cabot HS
Cabot, VT

Gilbert, Laurie
Winooski HS
S Burlington, VT

Hamm, Robin L
Bratteboro Union
Brattleboro, VT

Harbour, Jeff
Mount Anthony
Union HS
Bennington, VT

Herman, Wendy
Canaan Memorial
Canaan, VT

Hill, Heather L
Lyndon Inst
Lyndonville, VT

Hill, Teddy
Peoples Acad
Wolcott, VT

Hovey, Gregory
Concord HS
N Concord, VT

Howland, Angela
Hartford HS
West Hartford, VT

Jalbert, Pierre D
South Burlington
S Burlington, VT

Jerman, Eric
Burr & Burton
Arlington, VT

Keene, Kathy
Chelsea Public HS
Chelsea, VT

Kenyon, Keith
Otter Valley Union
Brandon, VT

Kirby, Shaun K
Essex Junction
Educational Center
Essex Junction, VT

Klittich, Deborah
Champlain Valley
Union HS
Shelb0rne, VT

Komorowski,
Michele
Peoples Acad
St Louis, MO

La Bounty, Terri
St Johnsbury Acad
St Johnsbury, VT

Lamorey, Jr Edward
A
Spaulding HS
Barre, VT

Landon, Christine
Champlain Valley
Union HS
Shelburne, VT

Larose, Nicole
Richford HS
Richford, VT

Lashway, Matthew S
Essex Junction
Educational Ctr
St Albans, VT

Le Bel, Travis G
Bellows Free Acad
St Albans, VT

Leblanc, Kimberlee
Sacred Heart HS
N Tory, VT

Leland, Joy
Oxbow HS
Newbury, VT

Longe, Ronald
Enosburg Falls HS
Sheldon Spgs, VT

Maurais, Marc
Canaan Memorial
Canaan, VT

Mc Ginn, Michael
Bellows Free Acad
St Albans, VT

Michalenoick, Joy
Windsor HS
Windsor, VT

Mitchell, Deborah
Burr And Burton
Seminary HS
Manchester Ctr, VT

Montcalm, Christie
Bellows Free Acad
St Albans, VT

Morin, Christine
North Country
Union HS
W Charleston, VT

Munger, Vikki
Fair Haven Union
Benson, VT

Nativi, Lisa
Spaulding HS
Barre, VT

Nichols, Lars
Woodstock Union
Woodstock, VT

Nonemacher,
Christopher
Randolph Union HS
Randolph, VT

Oster, Kimberly M
Champlain Valley
Union HS
Charlotte, VT

Ostrander, Jim
Mt Anthony Union
Shaftsbury, VT

Ovitt, Jennifer
Enosburg Falls HS
Enosburg Falls, VT

Pallini, Lisa
Mt Anthony Union
Pownal, VT

Pallman, Trecia
Mount Anthony
Union HS
Shaftsbury, VT

Parker, Jim
Brattleboro Union
Brattleboro, VT

Payrits, Cindy
Mill River Union
North Clarendon, VT

Pelton, Leslie J
Vermont Acad
Putney, VT

Perkins, Merilee
Hartford HS
Wilder, VT

Perl, Erica S
Burlington HS
Burlington, VT

Perry, Andrew
Lake Region Union
Irasburg, VT

Pirie, Christine M
Spaulding HS
Barre, VT

Pomainville, III
Edward J
Otter Valley Union
Brandon, VT

Roy, Rene
North Country
Union HS
West Charleston, VT

Russell, Andrew W
Mount Anthony
Union HS
Bennington, VT

Savigni, Sarah
Williamstown JR SR
Williamstown, VT

Sayah, Sheila
Harwood Union HS
Waterbury Ctr, VT

Shelton, Gwendolyn
Mt Mansfied Union
Underhill, VT

Sherman, James
Mount St Joseph
Rutland, VT

Spahn, John
Vergennes Union
Ferrisburgh, VT

Studer, Loretta
North Country
Union HS
W Charleston, VT

Tarte, Paul
Vergennes Union
Vergennes, VT

Taylor, Beth
Spaulding HS
Barre, VT

Tetreault, Lynne
Bellows Free Acad
Fairfield, VT

Thompson, John
Paulding HS
Barre, VT

Tillotson, Scott D
Mount Mansfield
Union HS
Jericho, VT

Tompkins, Heidi A
Middlebury Union
Shoreham, VT

Tucker, Tammy
Vergennes Union
Vergennes, VT

Veilleux, Michele
North Country
Union HS
N Troy, VT

Vowles, Stephen C
Bellows Free Acad
Fairfield, VT

Watson, Jill
North Country
Union HS
Derby, VT

Williams, Daniel
Northfield JR SR
Northfield, VT

VIRGIN ISLANDS

Allen, Cynthia
Charlotte Amalie
St Thomas, VI

Berg, Trent
Charlotte Amalie
St Thomas, VI

PHOTO NOT AVAILABLE

Griffith, James
Charlotte Amalie
St Thomas, VI

Hodge, Shawn
Charlotte Amalie
St Thomas, VI

Santana, Inocencia
St Croix Central HS
St Croix, VI

Simeon, Zozine A
Sts Peter & Paul HS
St Thomas, VI

Thomas, Jr Edward
Charlotte Amalie
St Thomas, VI

Thomas, Vanleer
Charlotte Amalie
St Thomas, VI

Zakers, Derick
Charlotte Amalie
St Thomas, VI

FOREIGN COUNTRIES

Agne, Maria Fatima D
Simon A Sanchez
Guam

Allegro, Frank
Uruguayan
American Schl
Apo Miami, FL

Allen, John J
Yokota HS
Apo San Fran, CA

Allen, Pete
Memorial Composite
Alberta Canada

Blalock, Laura
General H H Arnold
Apo, NY

Blalock, Sandra D
General H H Arnold
APO, NY

Bowman, Paul
Evangelical Cristian
Waterman, IL

Brandt, Erik A
Cairo American Coll
Egypt

Brandt, Winifred
Lynn
Stuttgart American
Apo New York, NY

Brominski, E Diane
Heidelberg HS
A P O New York, NY

Cadwell, Angela M
American School Of
Madrid HS
Madrid

Cavanaugh, Beth
American School Of
The Hague
Netherlands

Chiarini, Monica
Carol Morgan HS
Dom Rep

Cisneros, Marc
Frankfurt American
A P O New York, NY

Cottrill, Edward A
Berlin American HS
Apo New York, NY

Davis, Martha
Hanau American HS
Apo, NY

Deming, Mike
Kaiserslautern
American HS
APO, NY

Eaton, Lisa
Ramstein HS
Orlando, FL

Eschrich, Bonnie
Berlin American HS
Apo New York, NY

Eytchison, Gregory
Naples American
FPO New York, NY

Gordon, Stephen
Prairie HS
Wolf Point, MT

Harris, Angel D
Frankfurt American
APO, NY

Hoodenpyle, Sheri
Heidelberg
American HS
A P O New York, NY

Inman, Cirsten
Kaiserslautern
American HS
Apo New York, NY

Jenkins, Jennifer A
London Central HS
Boone, NC

Kim, Lorrie
Seoul International
Korea

Koenig, Kim
H H Arnold HS
APO, NY

Mahood, Diana L
American
Community Schl
Endicott, NY

Martindale, Rachael
Torrejon American
Pensacola, FL

Mc Kinnis, Darin N
Ccnadian Acad
Troy, MI

Mulligan, Steven J
Stuttgart AM HS
Apo New York, NY

Nowlin, Zachary
Frankfurt Am HS
Apo New York, NY

Ollie, Russell D
Wagner HS
APO San Francsco,
CA

Ray, Melissa A
Heidelberg
American HS
A P O, NY

Shipman, Amy
American
Community Schl
Papillion, NE

Snider, Melisa M
Taegu American
APO San Fran, CA

Sullivan, David J
Wagoner HS
APO San Fran, CA

Thomas, Andre
Wurzburg American
Hampton, VA

Turney, Mark
Faith Acad
Manila

Veenstra, Alexander
A Ollie
Justice Von Libilung
Gymnasium HS
Brooklyn, NY

Walden, Angela
American
Community Schl
Houston, TX

Wall, Karla Amy
Balboa HS
Rep Of Panama

Watson, Jeff
Stavanger American
Norway

Wright, Cyndi
Stavanger American
Stavanger Norway